Bowmar's

Adventures In Music Listening

by DR. LEON BURTON, DR. CHARLES HOFFER
and DR. WILLIAM HUGHES

LEVEL 1

Student Activity Book

Editor: Debbie Cavalier
Consulting Editor: Sandy Feldstein
Illustrations: Jeannette Aquino
Layout: Debbie Lipton

Contents

Ohihi Owo Ti Ka Huhahi?

African Folk Song

. **Color the instruments you heard in "Ohihi Owo Ti Ka Huhahi?"**

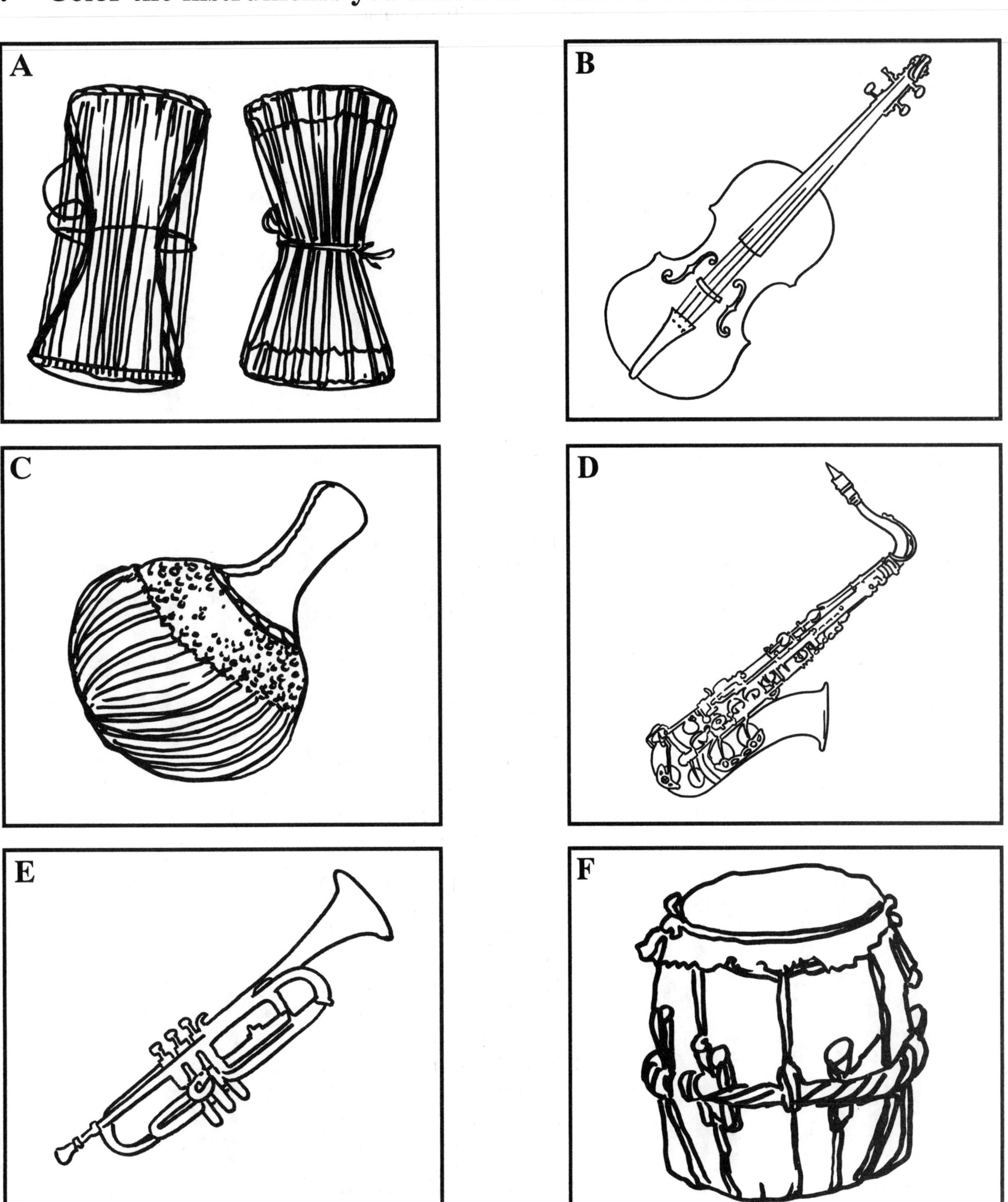

Ohihi Owo Ti Ka Huhahi?

African Folk Song

2. Color the picture that looks most like the music your heard.

A

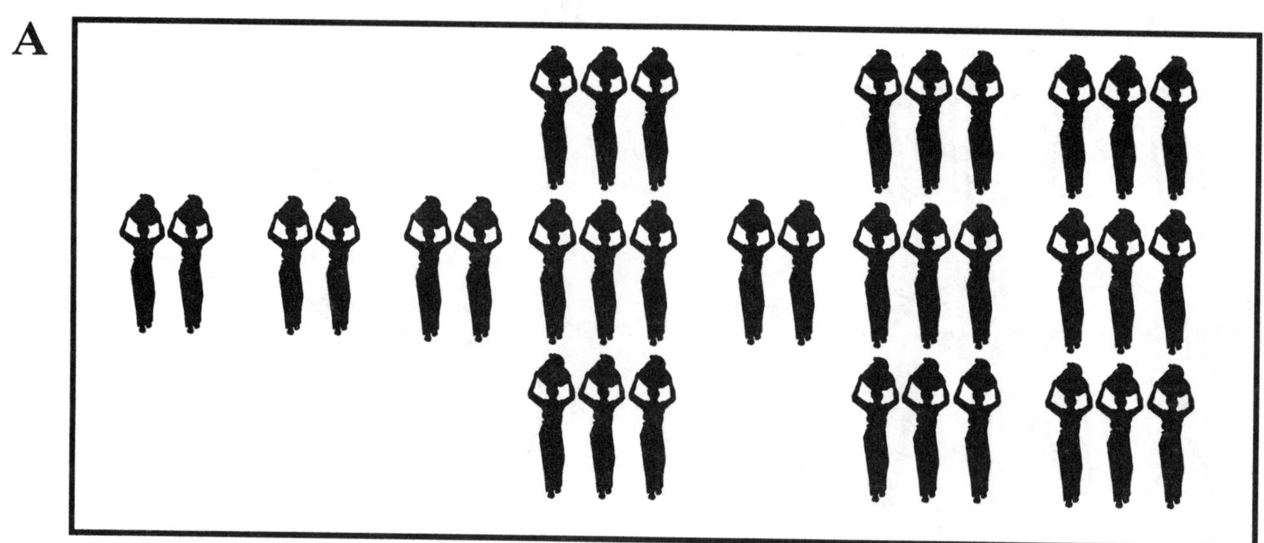

B

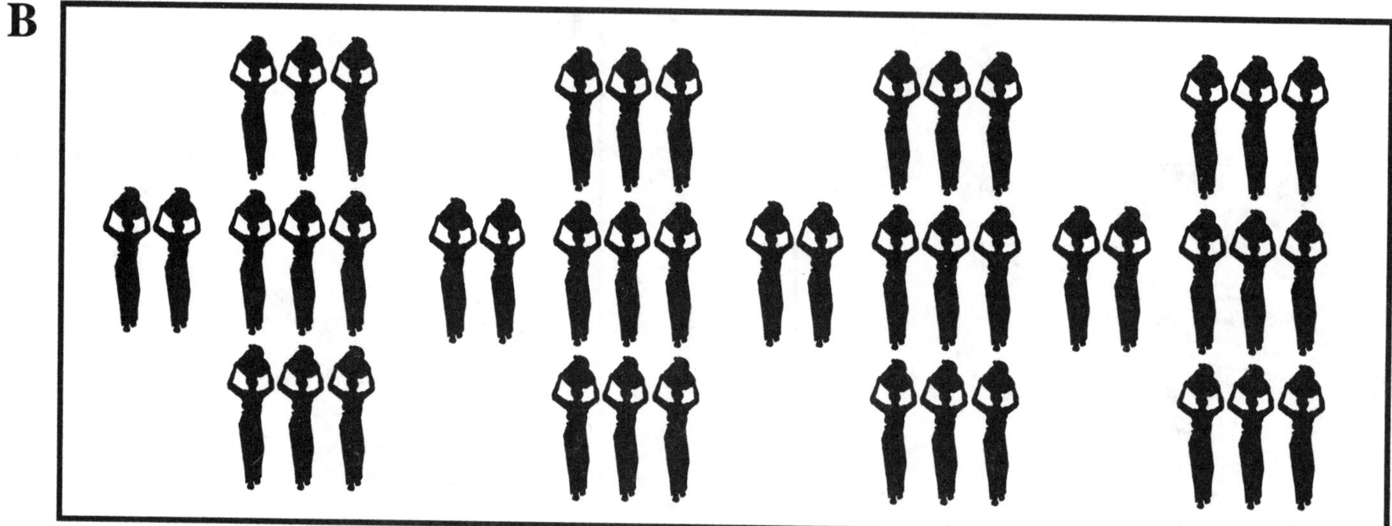

C

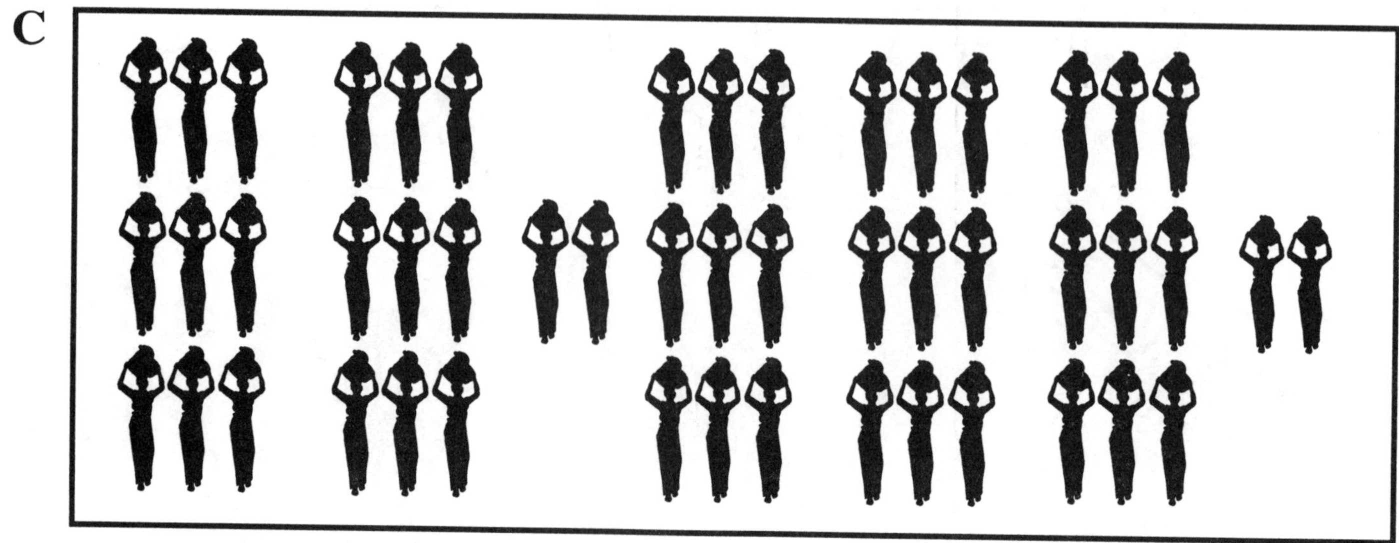

Simple Gifts

American Shaker Song

1. Color the chair that looks most like a simple Shaker chair.

2. Color the instrument you heard playing with the singers.

Teasing

Bartok

1. **Color the pictures of the instruments that are in a woodwind quintet.**
2. **Number them in the sequence they were played.**

March, Trumpet, and Drum

Bizet

1. **Color the picture of the drum.**

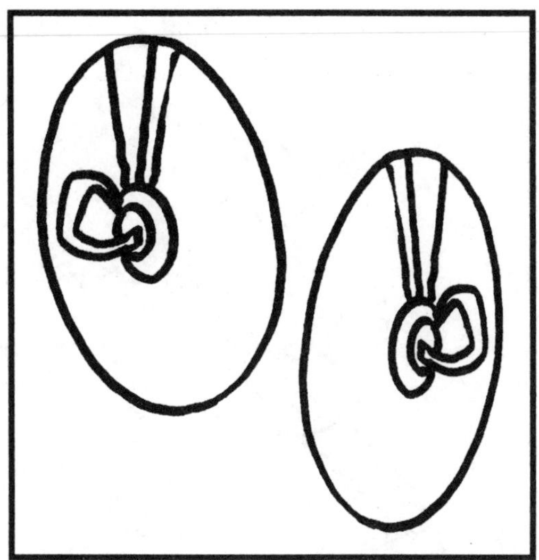

2. **Color the picture of the trumpet.**

3. **Color the picture that looks most like the music sounded.**

Gigue

Corelli

1. Color the picture that looks most like skipping.

2. Color the picture that looks most like the three sections of "Gigue."

Golliwogg's Cakewalk
Claude Debussy

. Color the boxes in the picture that look like the beats you heard in the music.

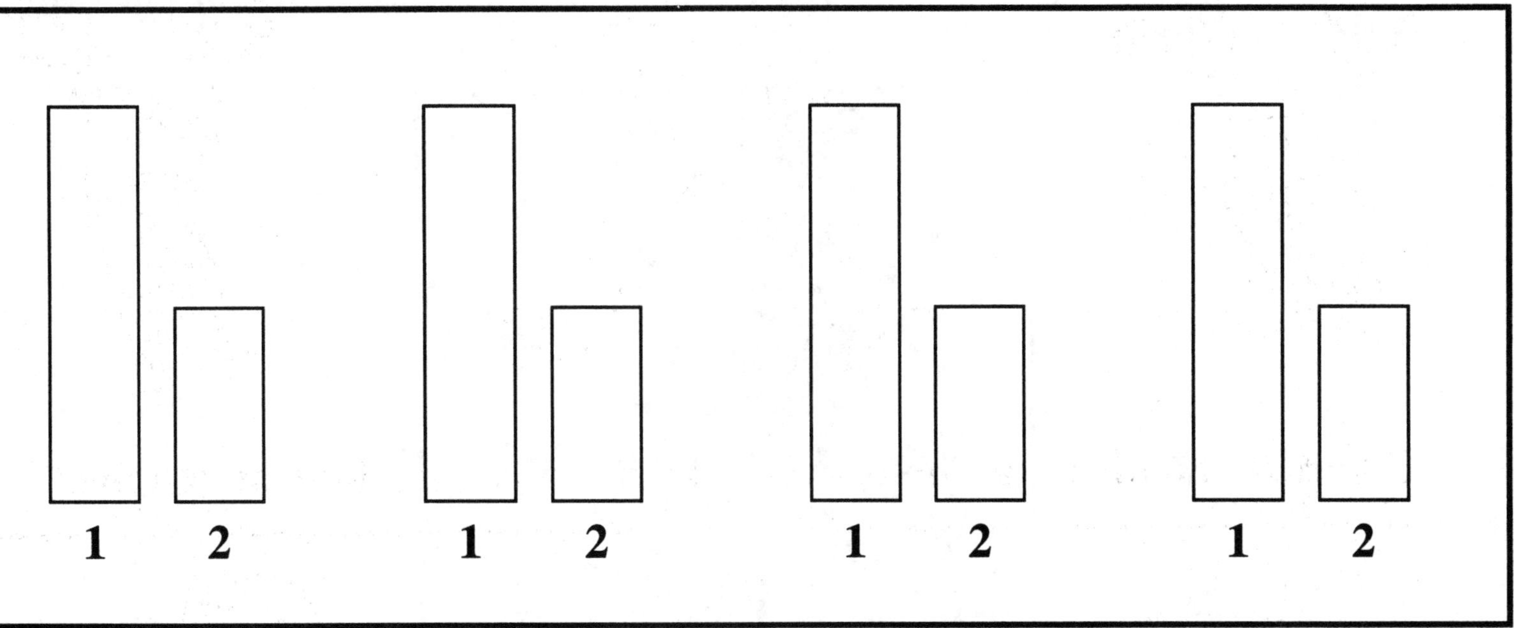

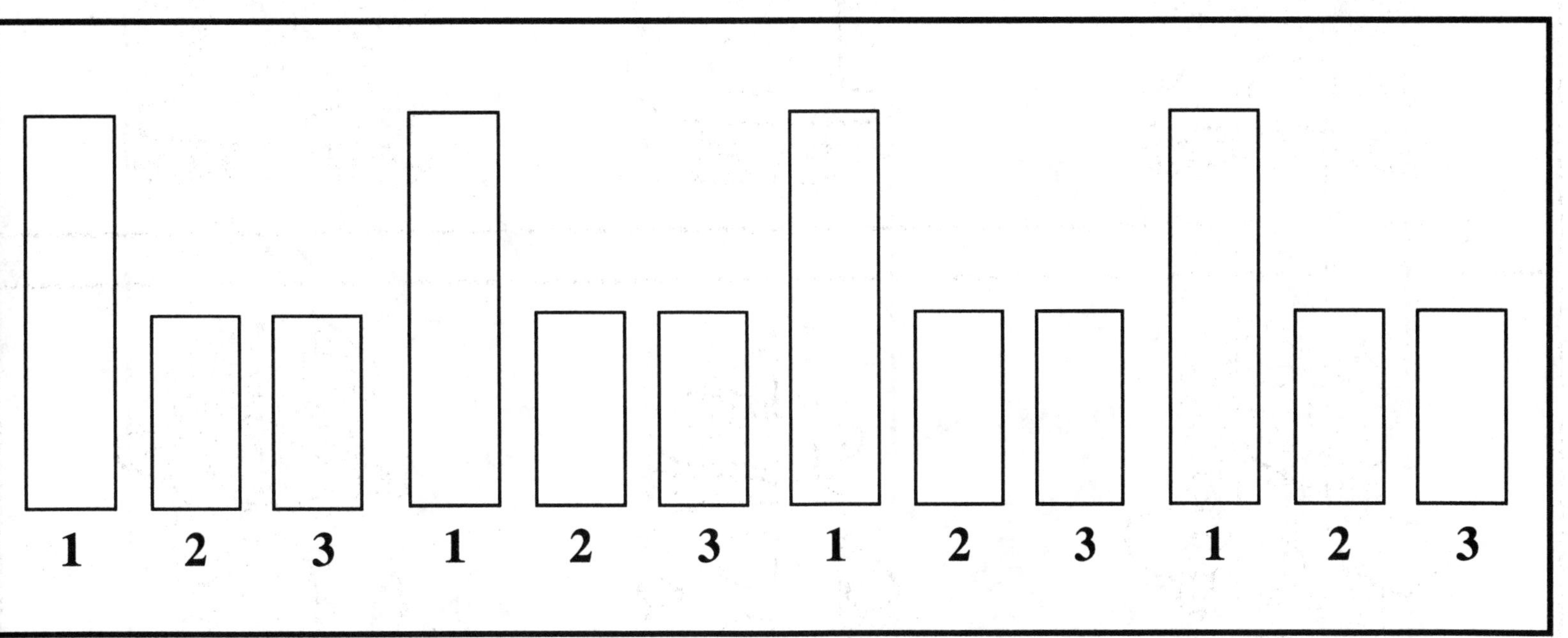

Marching Band, Acrobats and Juggler

Donaldson

1. Use green to color the picture of the circus performer that matches the music you hear.
2. Use yellow to color the picture of the circus performer that matches the music you hear.
3. Use red to color the picture of the circus performer that matches the music you hear.

Dance Of The Merry Dwarfs

Elwell

1. **Color the A person red.**

2. **Color the B person yellow.**

3. **Color the C person green.**

Dance Of The Merry Dwarfs
Elwell

4. Color the picture that looks like the order of the melodies in "Dance of the Merry Dwarfs."

Funeral March of a Marionette

Gounod

. **Color the picture that looks like the order of the melodies you heard in the music.**

Morning

Grieg

1. **Color the picture of the instrument you heard playing the melody when the music started.**

2. **Color the picture that looks most like the music sounds.**

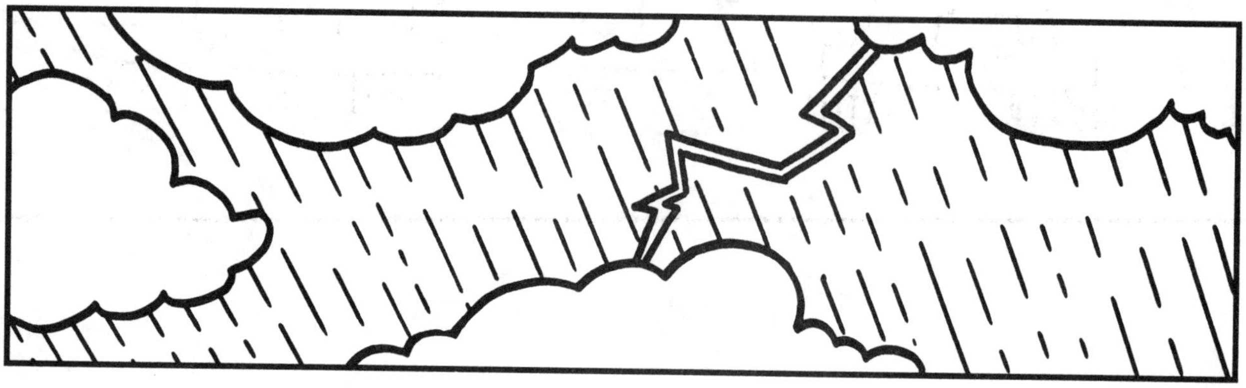

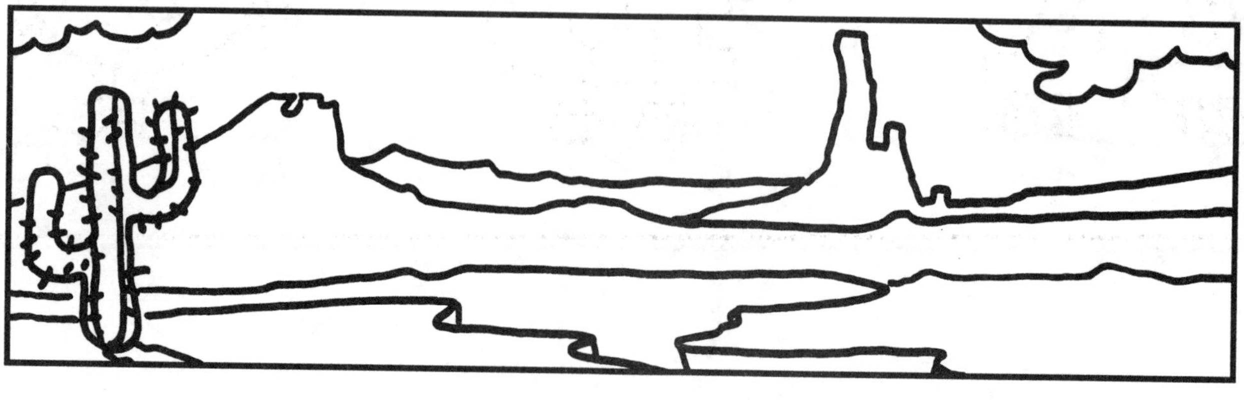

Bourrée

Handel

1. Color the picture with the letter people that best describes the sections of "Bourrée."

Bourrée

Handel

2. Color the pictures of the two families of instruments that played the music in "Bourrée."

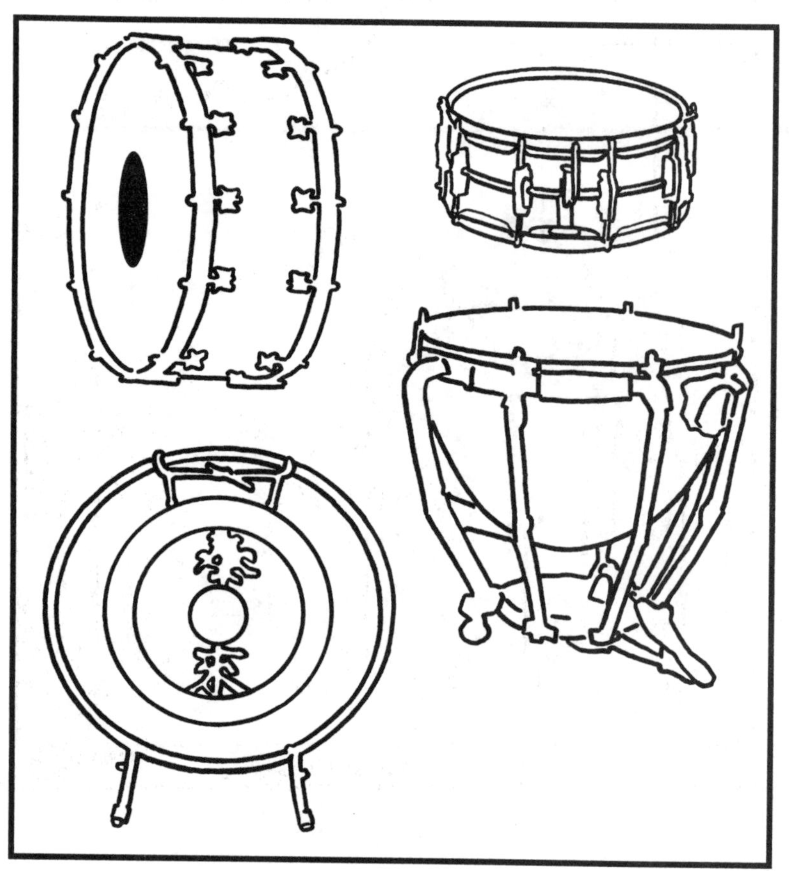

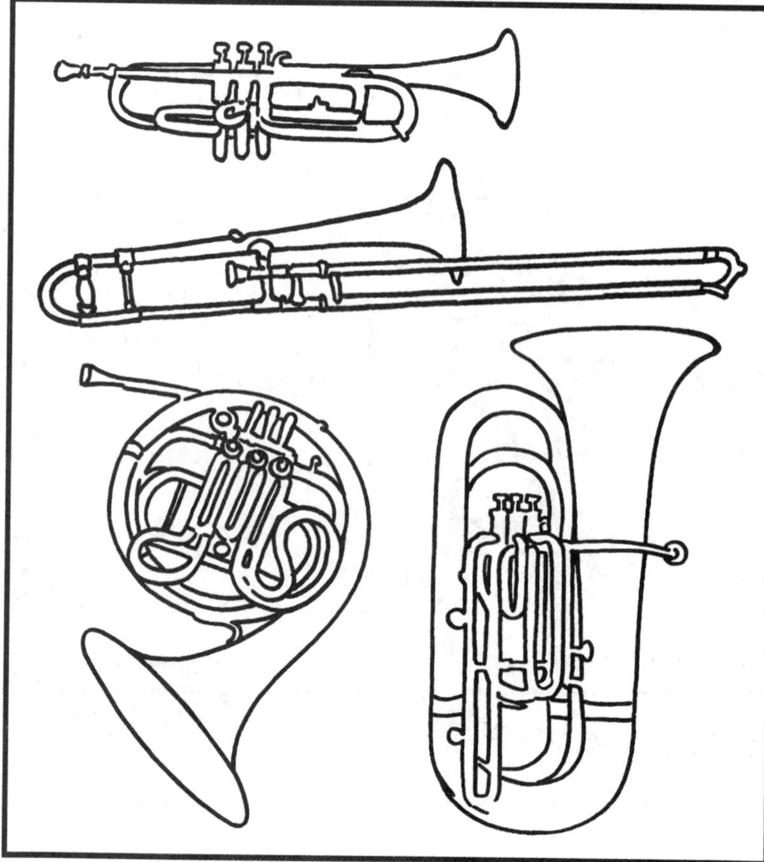

Viennese Musical Clock

Kodály

1. Color the picture that looks most like the music sounds in "Viennese Musical Clock."

La Bamba

Latin American

1. **Color the picture of the rhythm sticks yellow.**
2. **Color the picture of the maracas blue.**
3. **Color the picture of the bongo drums brown.**
4. **Color the picture of the clavés black.**
5. **Color the picture of the guiro orange.**

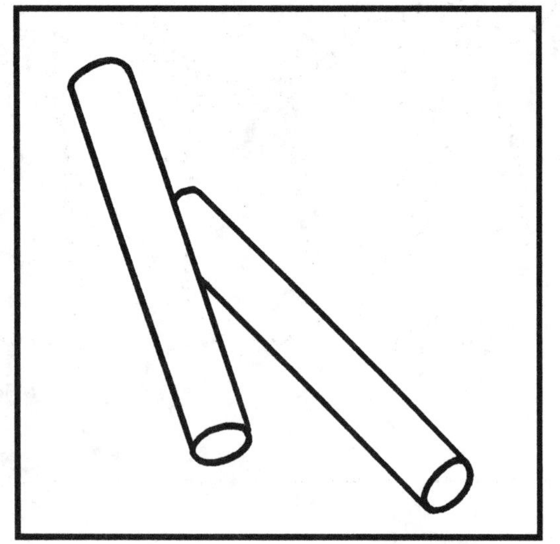

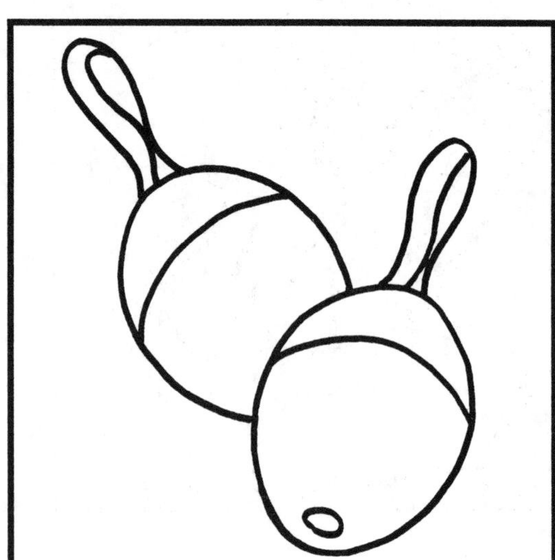

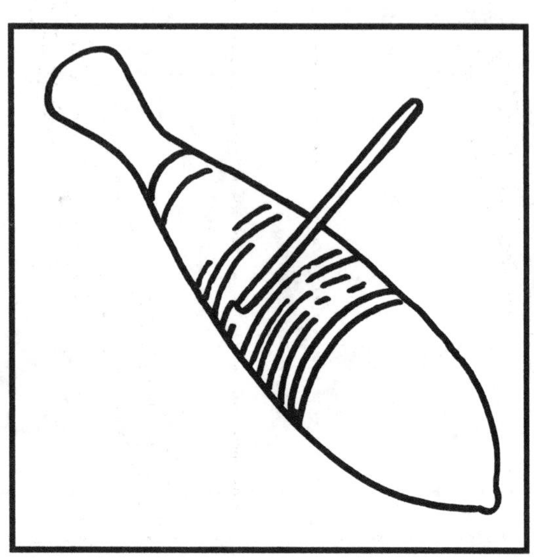

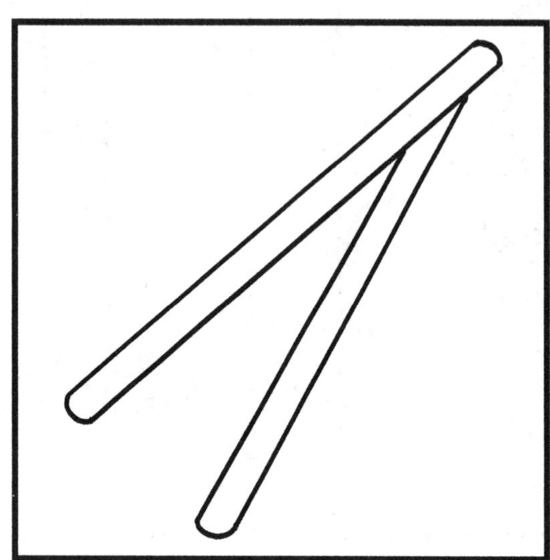

Dance of the Shepherds

Menotti

1. **These two pictures represent the two sections of music in "Dance of the Shepherd's." Color the picture that represents the section of music that was louder and faster.**

2. **Color the picture of the oboe.**

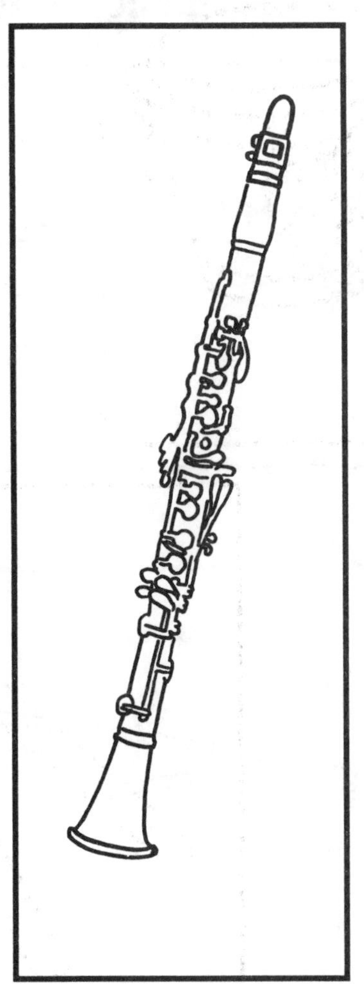

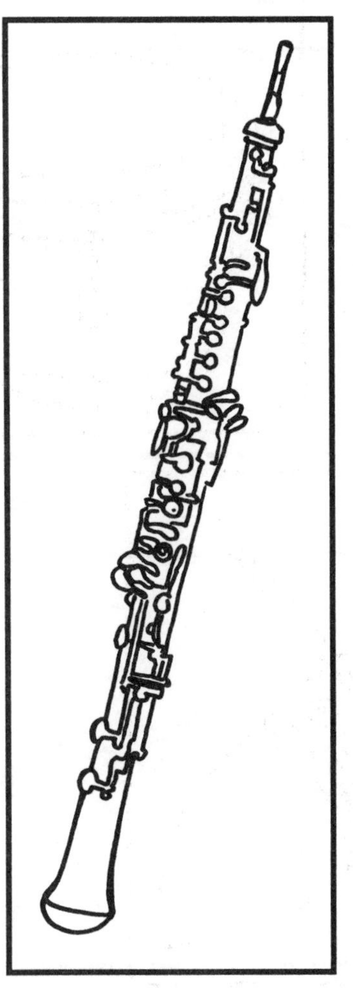

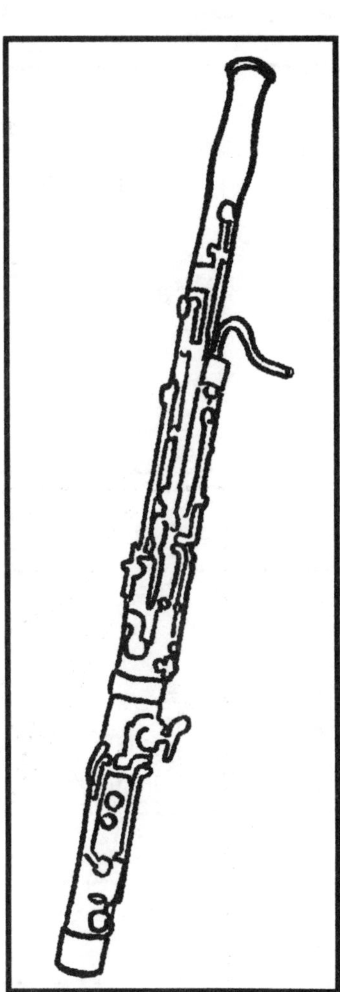

Bydlo

Mussorgsky

1. **Color the picture of the instrument that plays the melody in "Bydlo."**

2. **Color the picture that looks most like the music sounded in "Bydlo."**

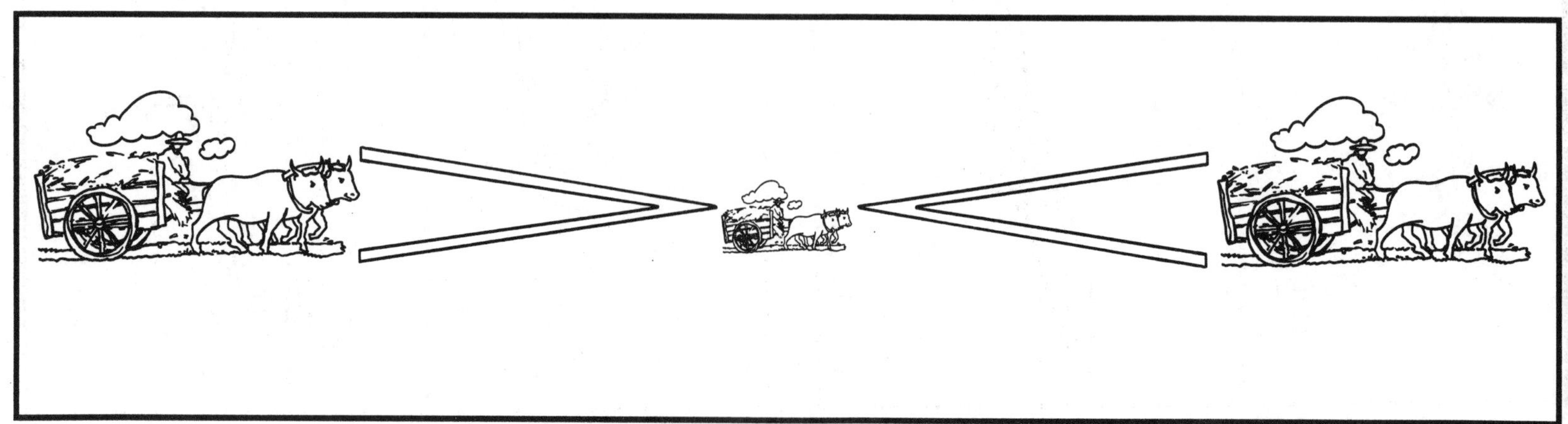

Ballet of Chicks in Their Shells

Mussorgsky

3. **Color the picture of the family of instruments that plays the "Ballet of Chicks in Their Shells."**

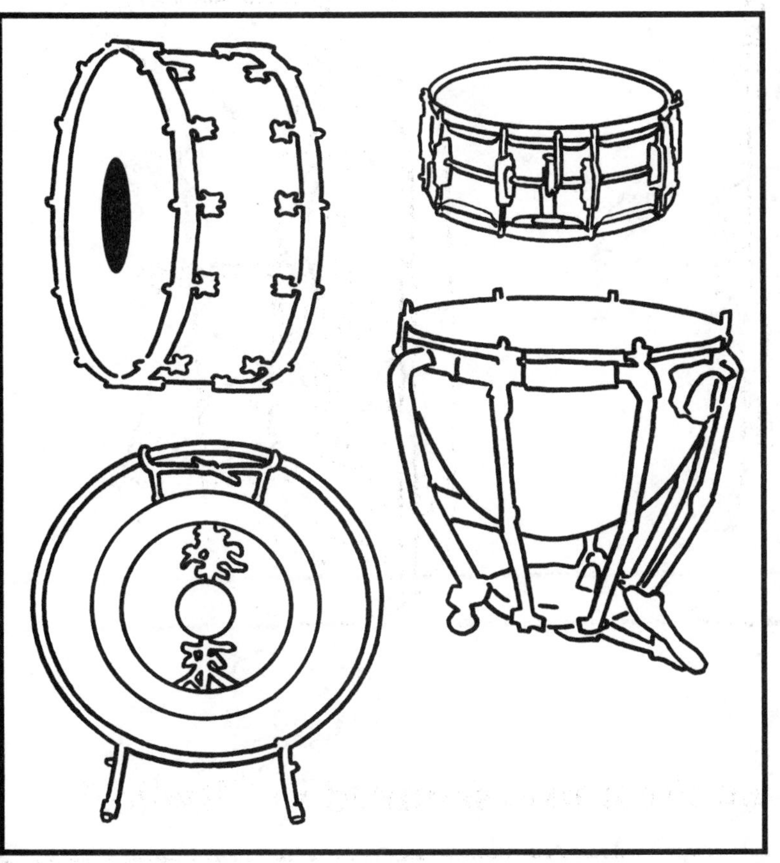

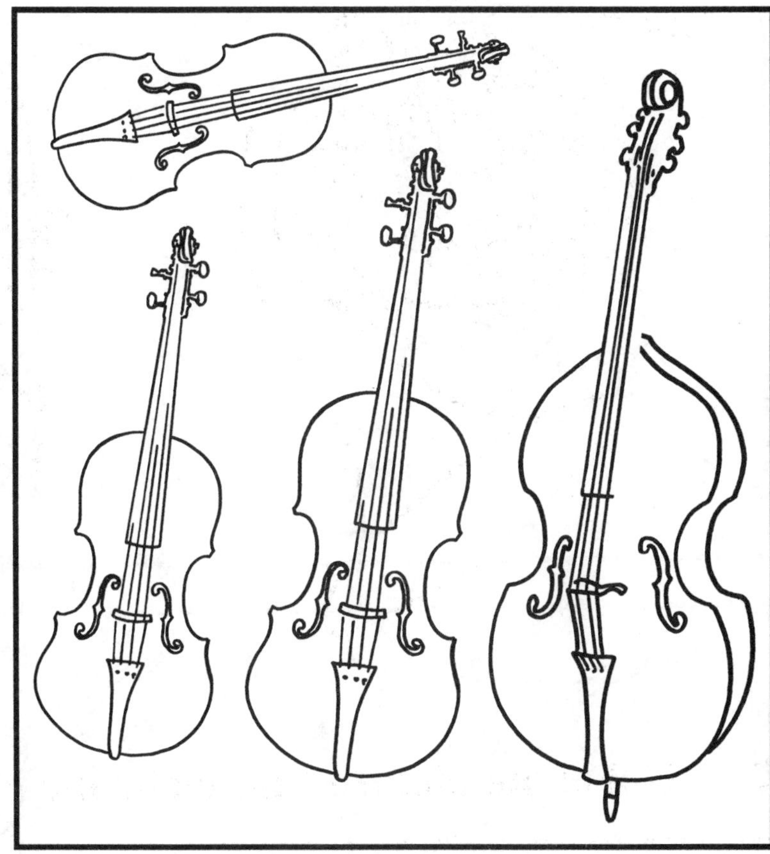

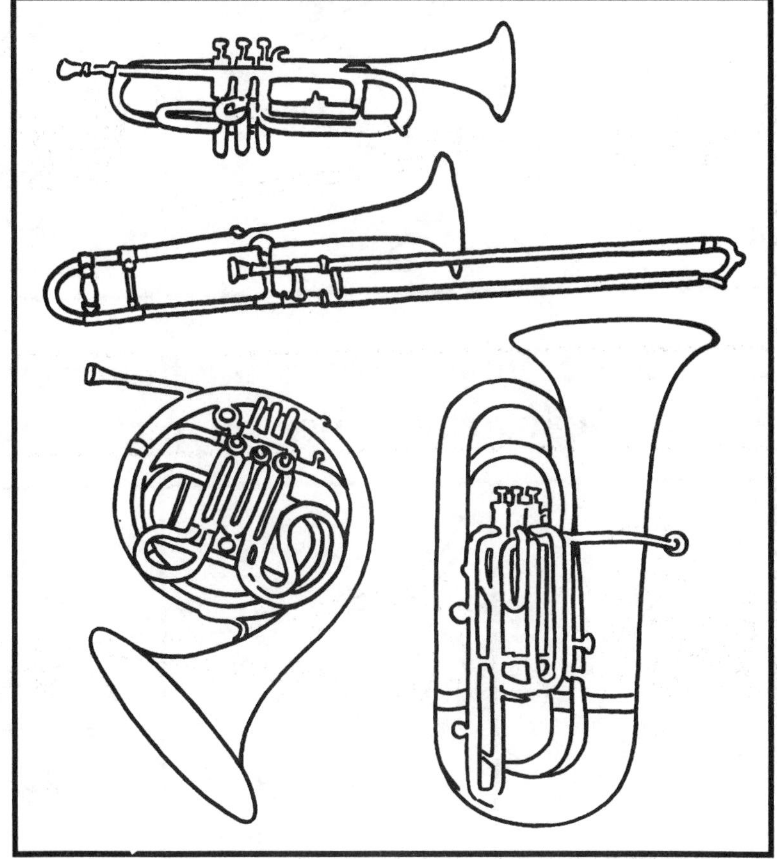

Run, Run

Pinto

1. **Color the picture that looks most like the music you heard in "Run, Run."**

2. **Color the picture of the finger cymbals gold. Color the picture of the triangle gray. Color the picture of the rhythm sticks brown.**

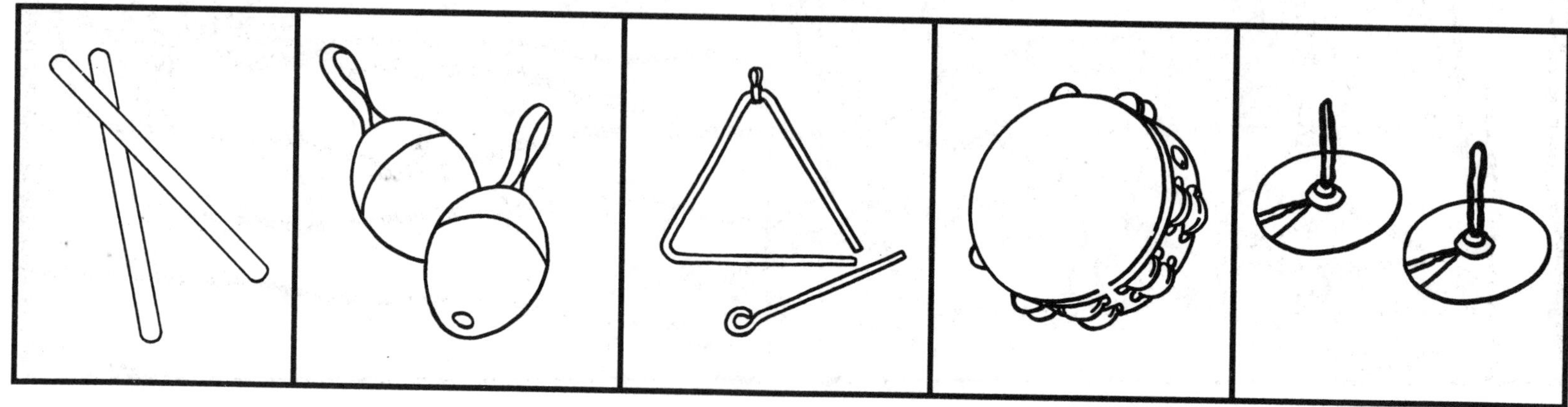

Troika
Prokofiev

1. **Color the picture that looks most like the music of "Troika" sounds.**

Troika
Prokofiev

2. Color the pictures of the instruments that were used to accompany the music of "Troika."

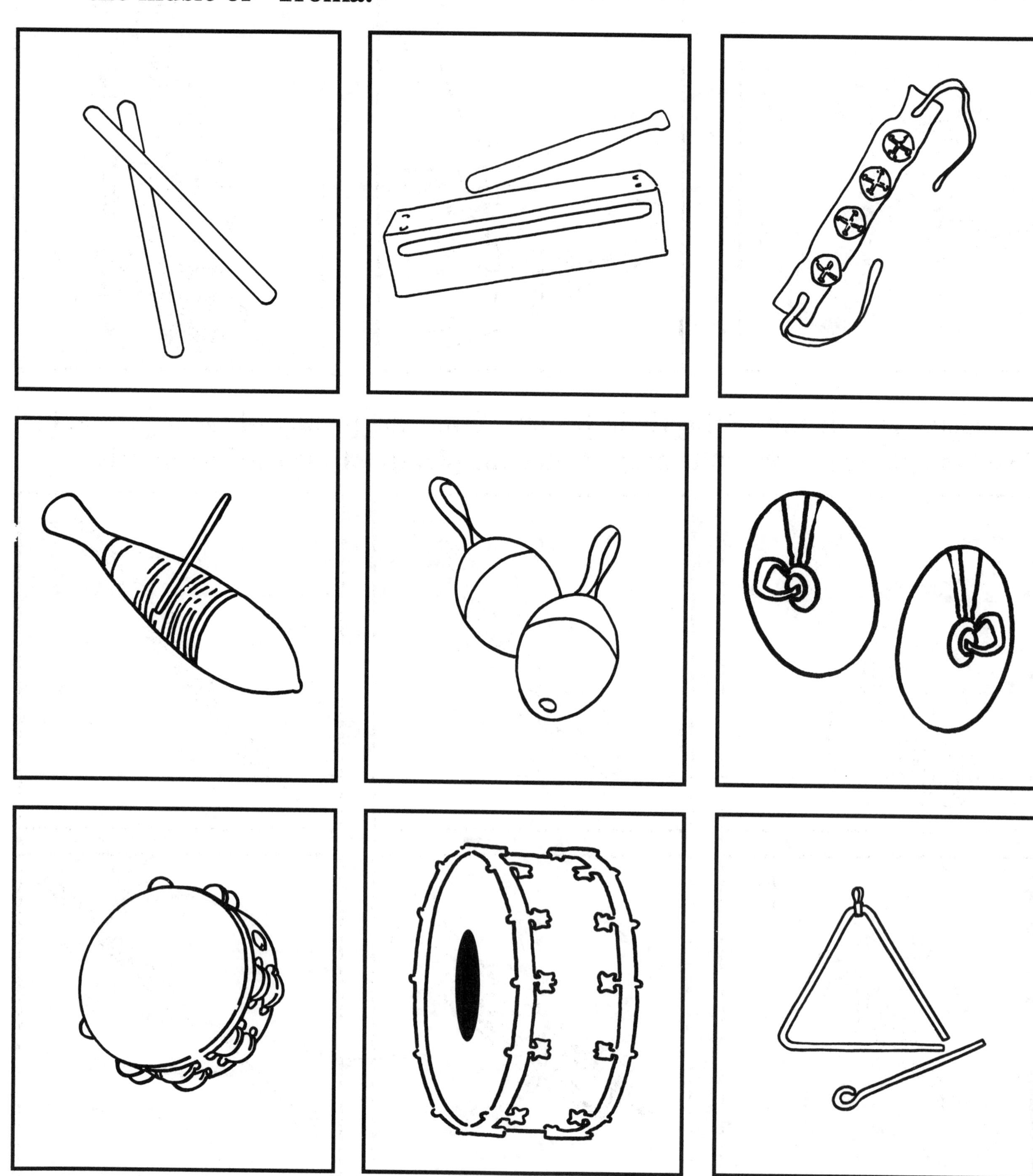

Hop O' My Thumb

Ravel

1. **Color the picture that looks like a child who is lost.**

2. **Color the picture of the violin brown. Color the picture of the oboe black. Color the picture of the flute gray. Color the picture of the clarinet purple.**

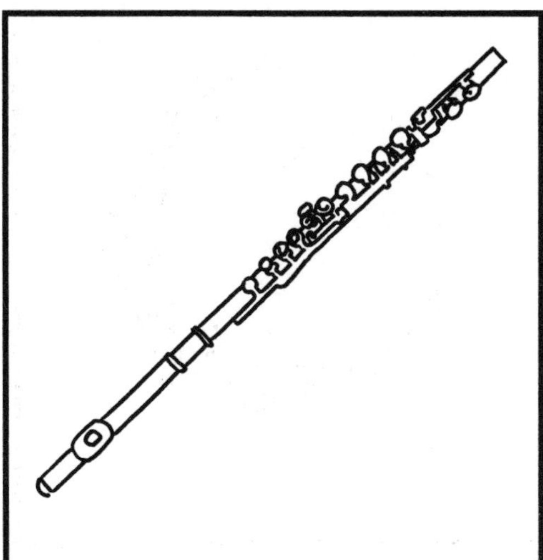

Flight of the Bumble Bee

Rimsky-Korsakov

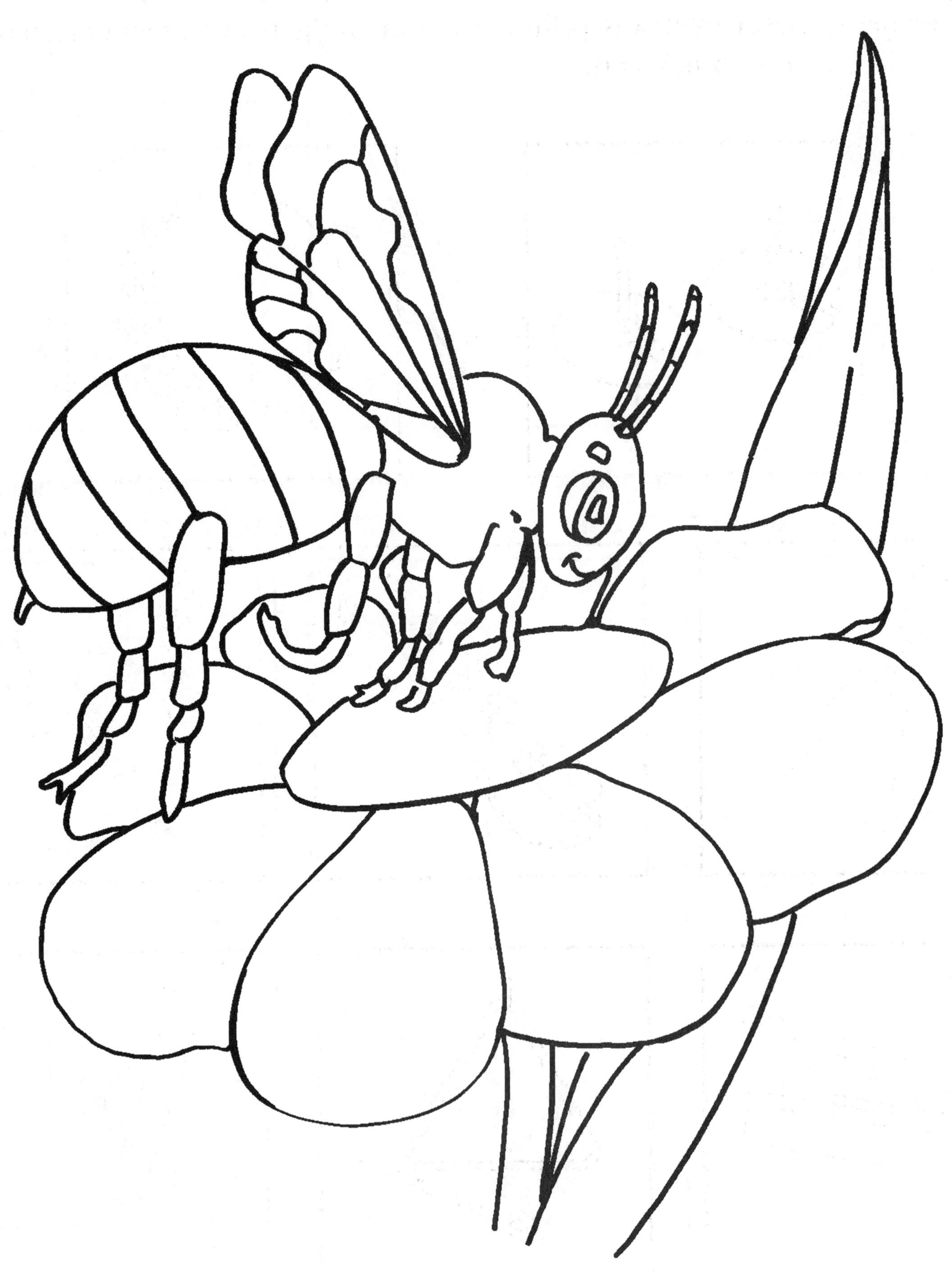

March of the Siamese Children

Rodgers

1. Color the picture of the tambourine orange; jingle bells purple, triangle silver or gray, finger cymbals yellow, rhythm sticks brown, claves green, maracas blue, wood block red.

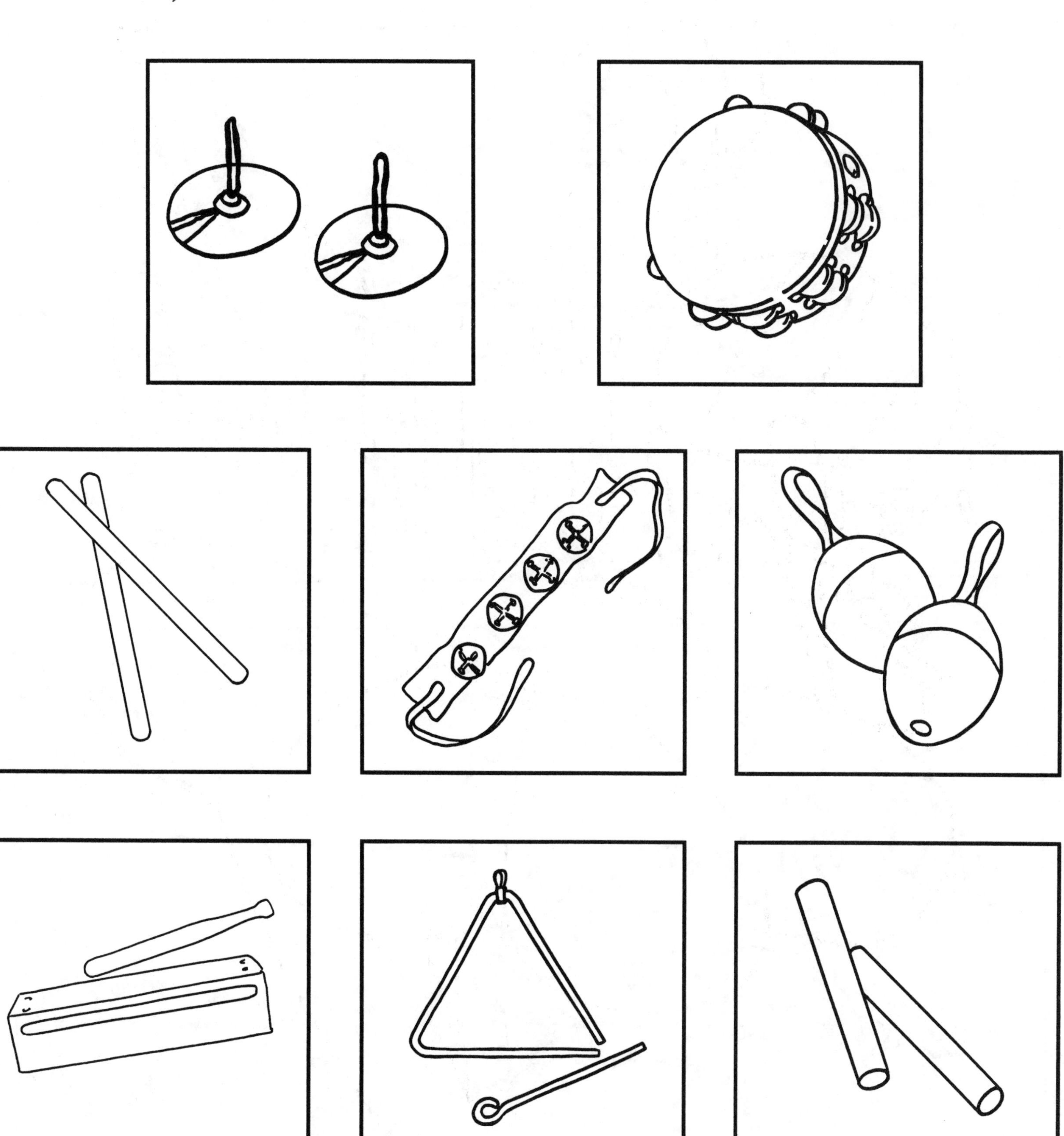

William Tell

Rossini

1. Color the picture that looks most like the music of "Overture To William Tell" sounds. Tell why the picture you selected looks like the music sounded.

William Tell
Rossini

Pizzicato

Rossini-Respighi

. **Color the picture with the letter people that best describes the sections of "Pizzicato."**

Waltz

Rossini-Respighi

2. **Color the picture of the violin brown. Color the picture of the clarinet green.**

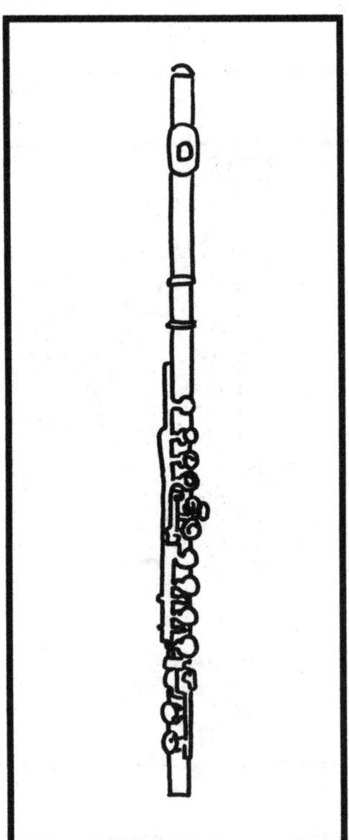

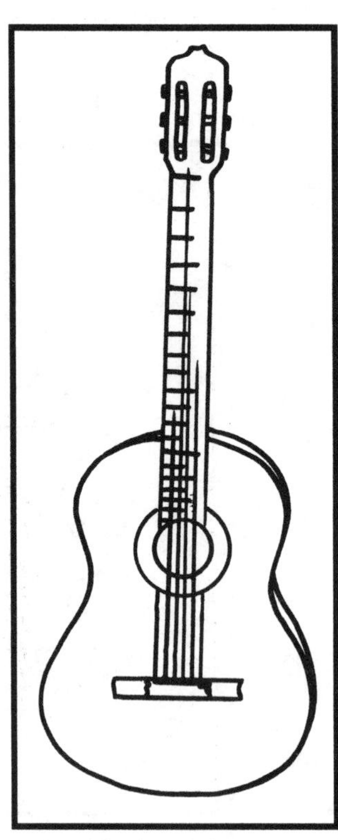
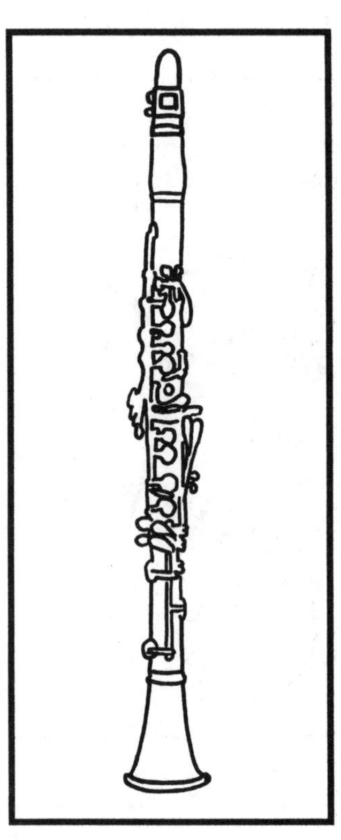

3. **Color the picture of the instrument that played the melody in the A sections of the music brown. Color the picture of the instrument that played the melody in the B section of the music green.**

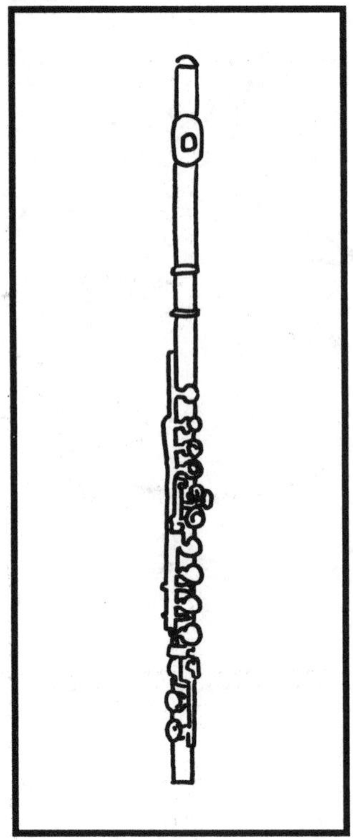
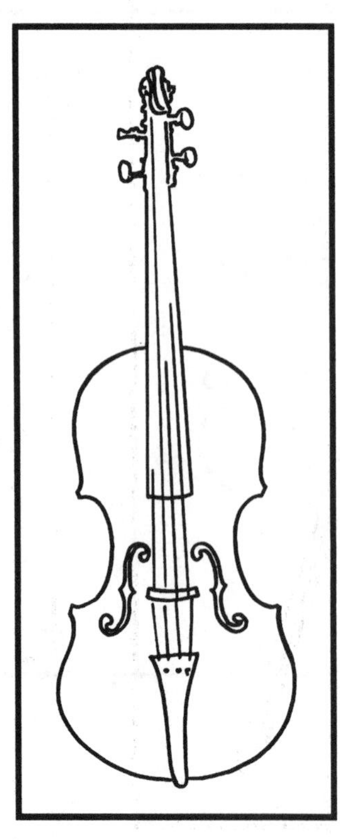
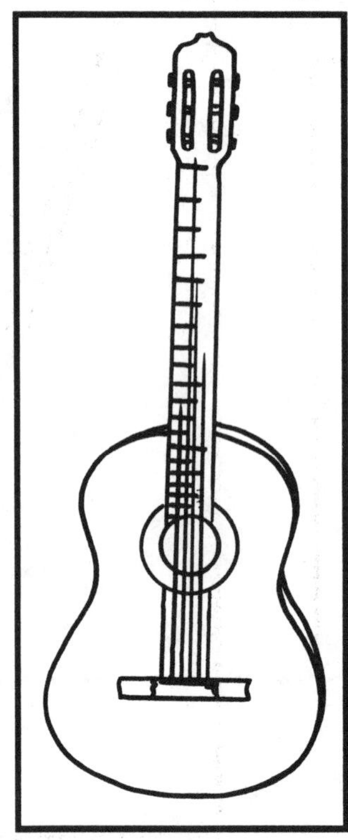
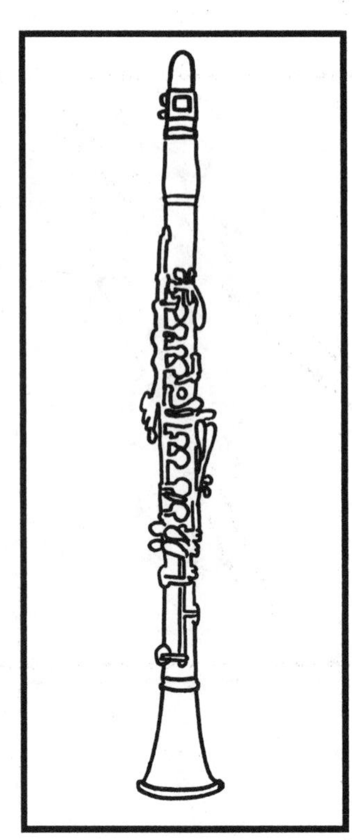

Dark Eyes
Russian Folk Song

1. Color the picture of the acoustic guitar.

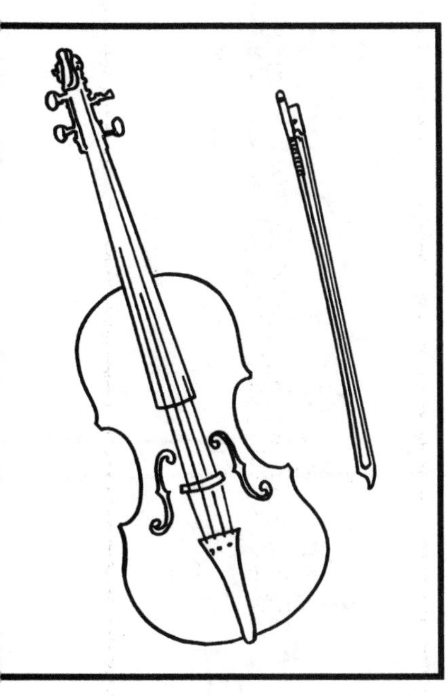

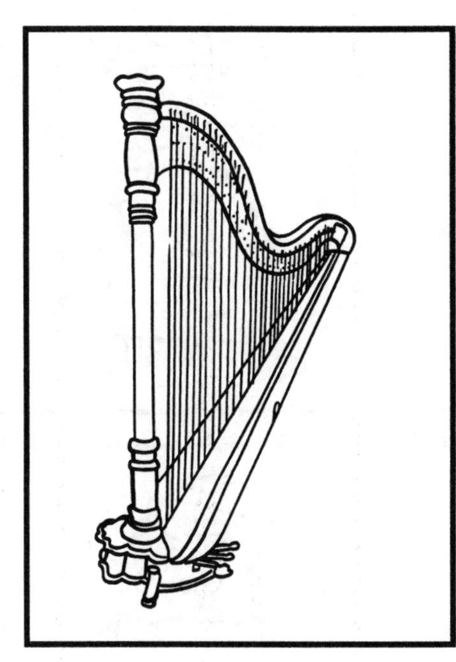

2. Color the picture that shows what is used to play the guitar.

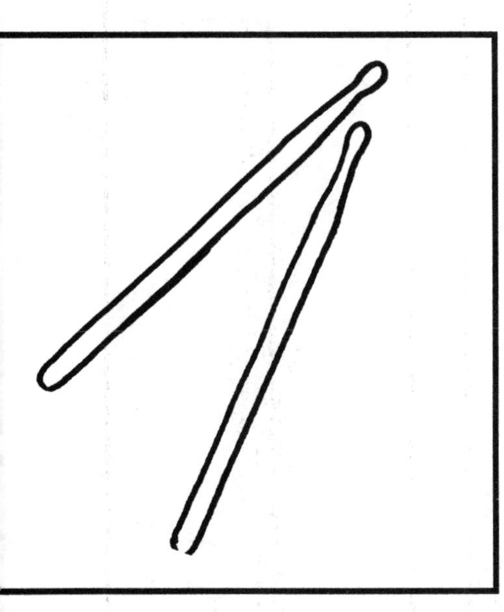

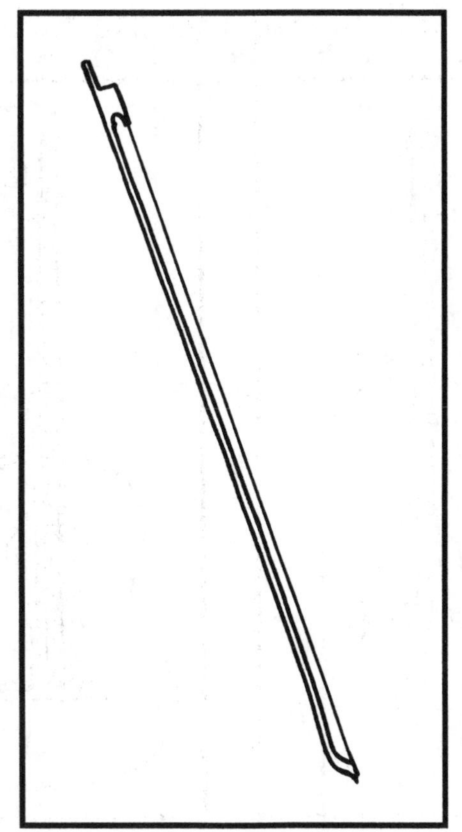

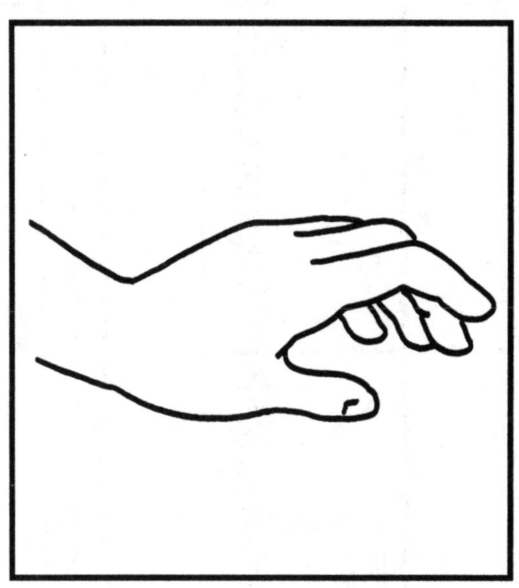

The Elephant

Saint - Saëns

1. **Color the picture with the letter people that best describes the sections of "The Elephant."**

2. **Color the picture of the instrument used as the elephant in the music.**

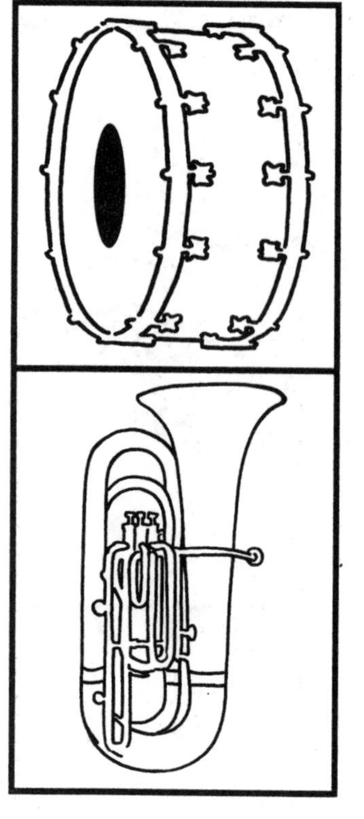

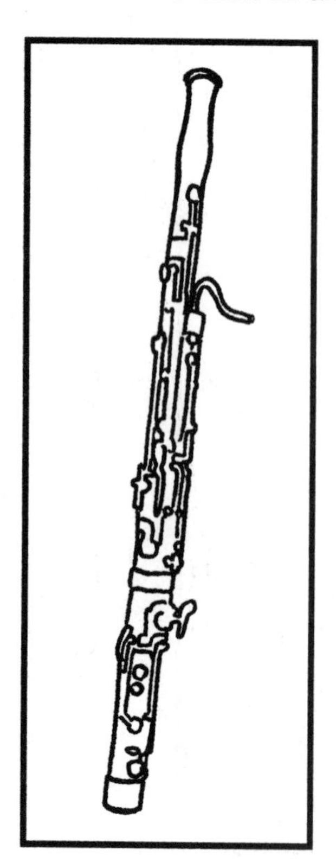

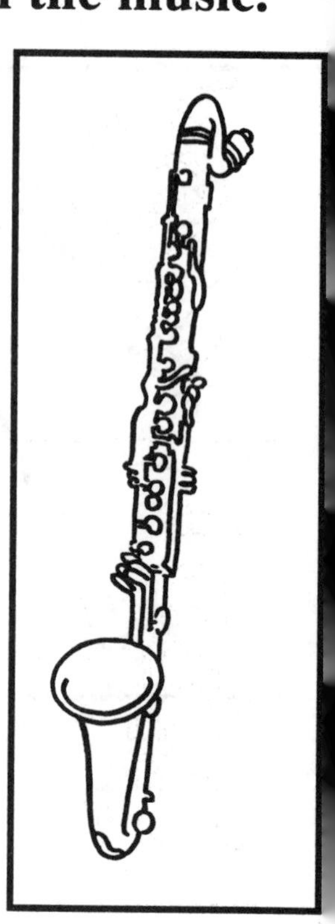

The Swan

Saint - Saëns

1. **Color the picture that looks most like the music in "The Swan" sounds.**

2. **Color the picture of the instrument that represented the swan in the music.**

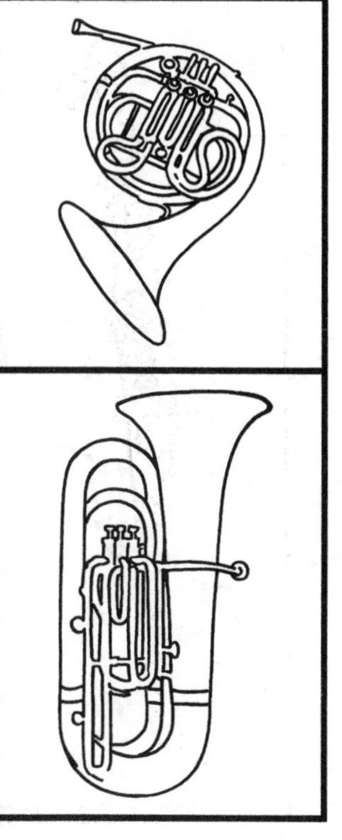

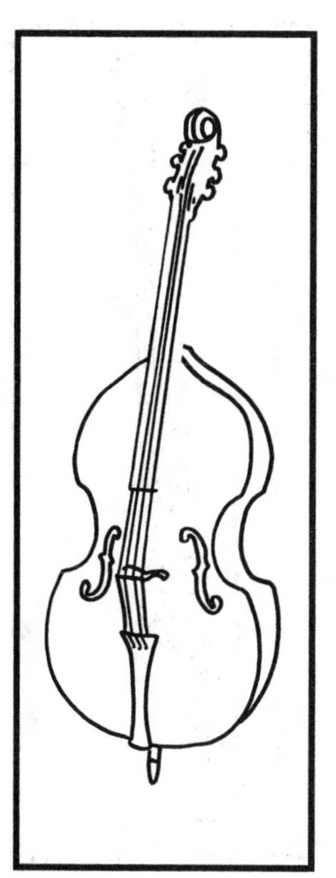
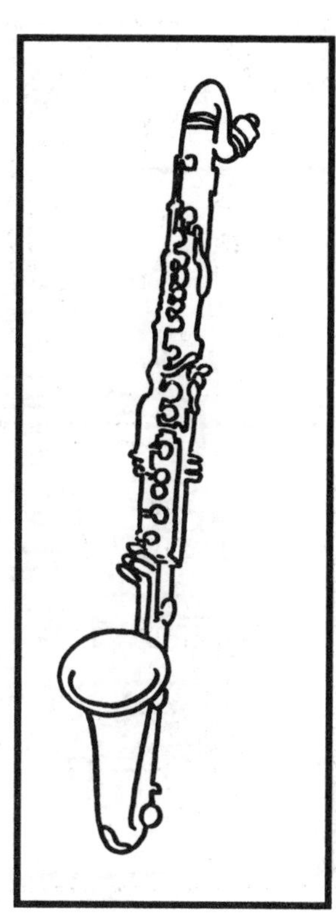

The Happy Farmer
Schumann

1. **Color the picture that looks like the music sounds.**

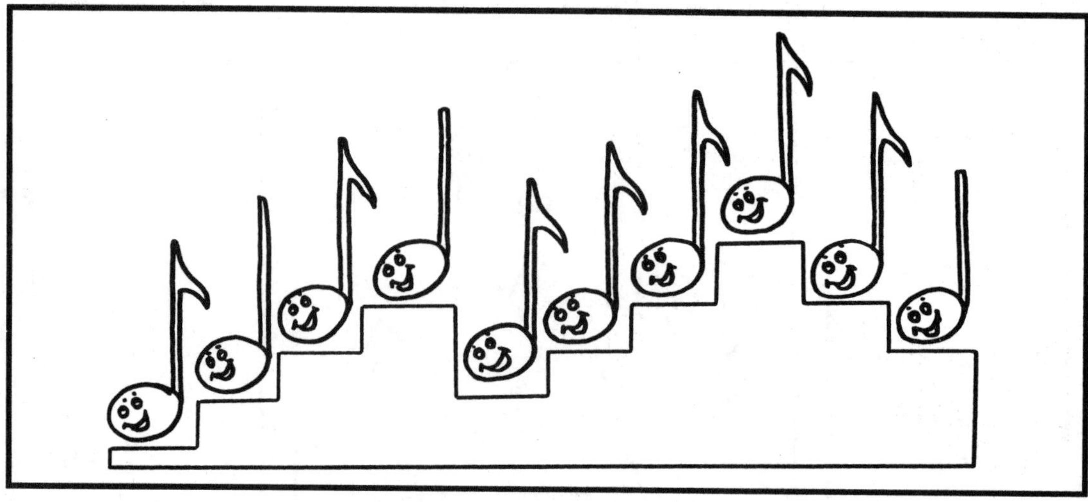

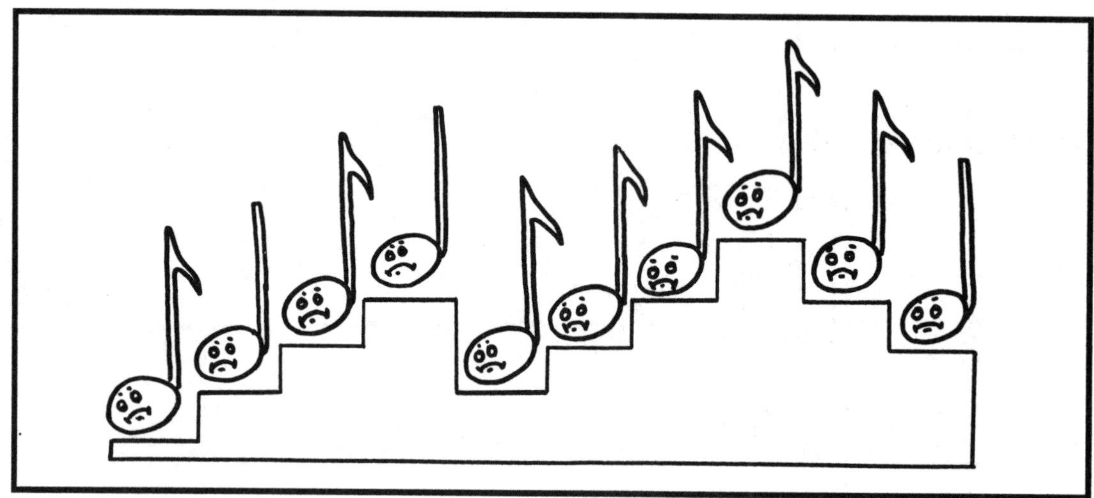

2. **Color the picture of the instrument the music was written for.**

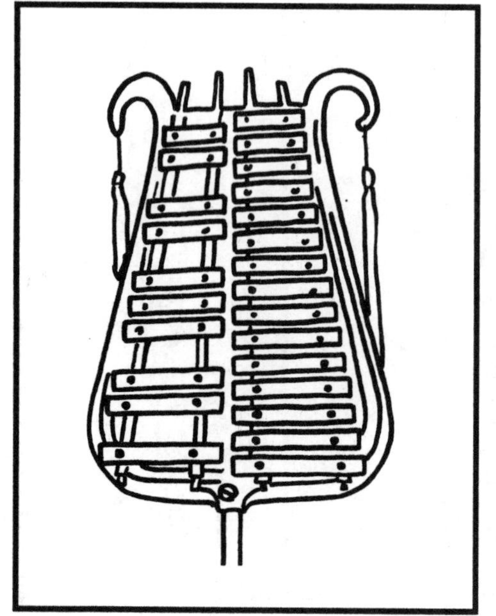

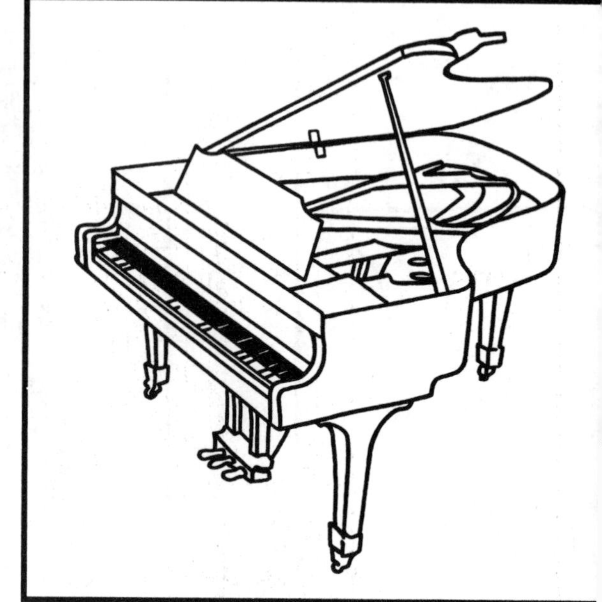

Tritsch Tratsch Polka

Strauss

1. **Look at the pictures of crescendos and accents. Color the crescendos green. Color the accents blue.**

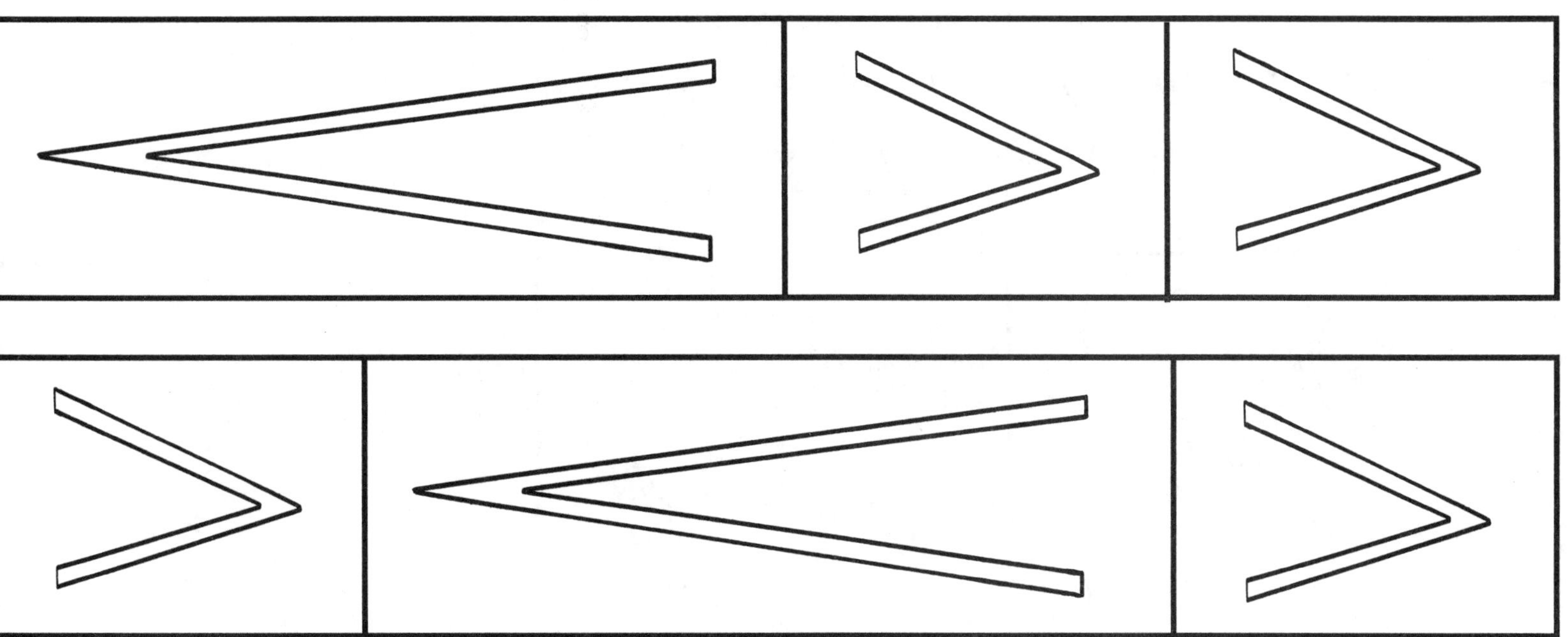

2. **Color the picture that looks most like people dancing the polka.**

Circus Polka

Stravinsky

1. **Color the picture of the clarinet black.**
2. **Color the picture of the trombone green.**
3. **Color the picture of the violin brown.**
4. **Color the picture of the French horn gold.**
5. **Color the picture of the timpani orange.**

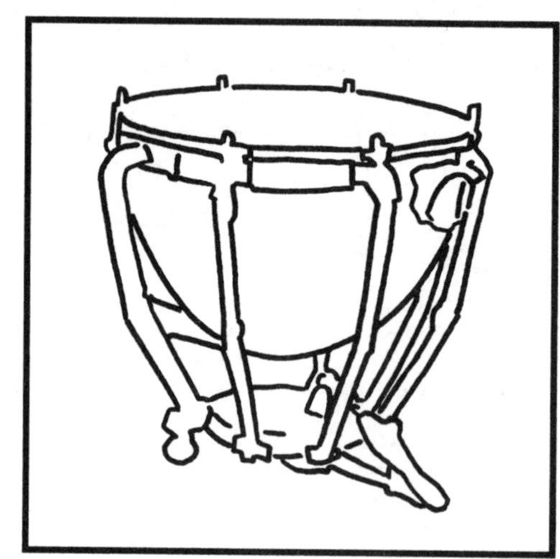

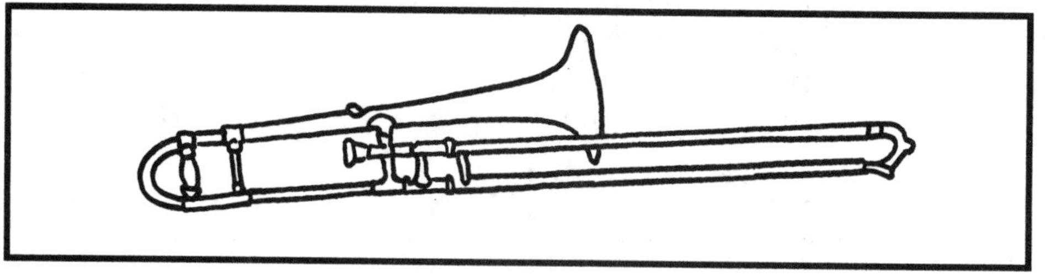
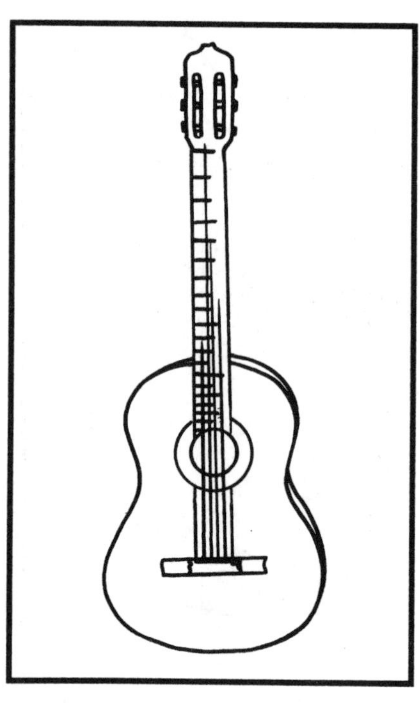
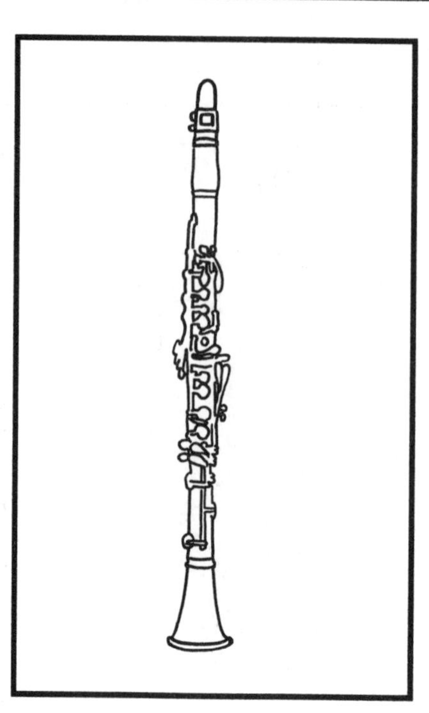
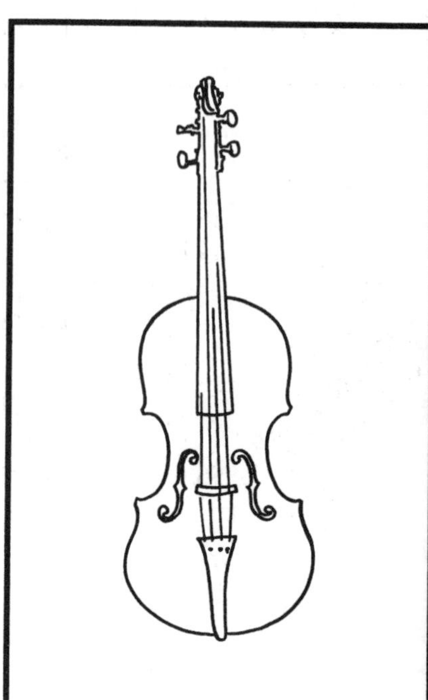

Dance Of The Sugarplum Fairy

Tchaikovsky

. **Color the pictures of the instruments that belong to the percussion family.**

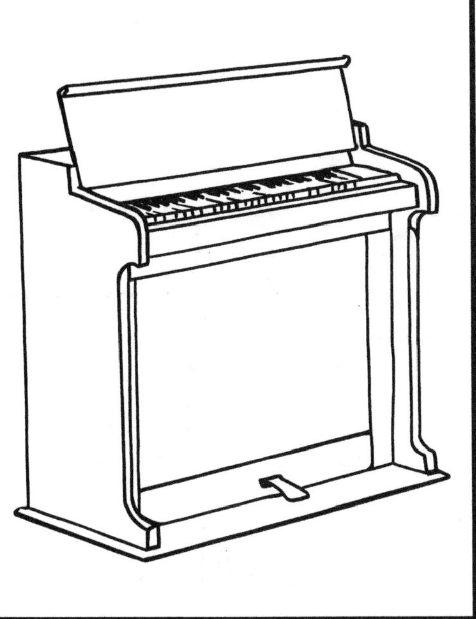

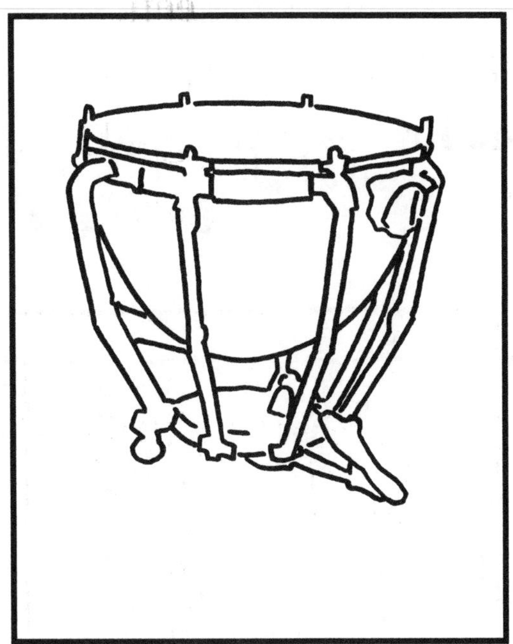

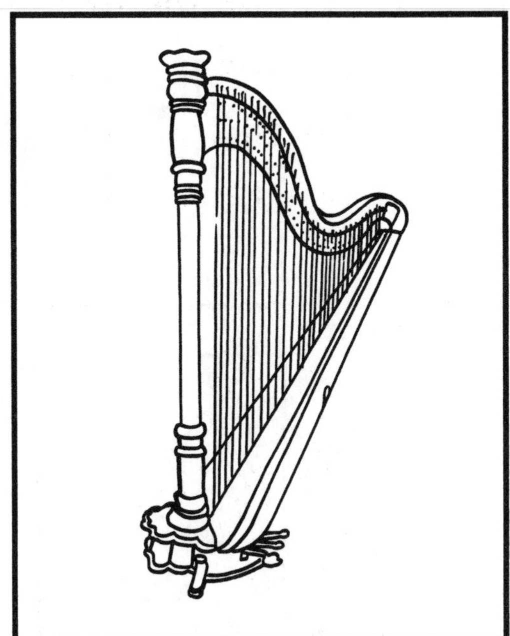

. **Color the picture of the celesta.**

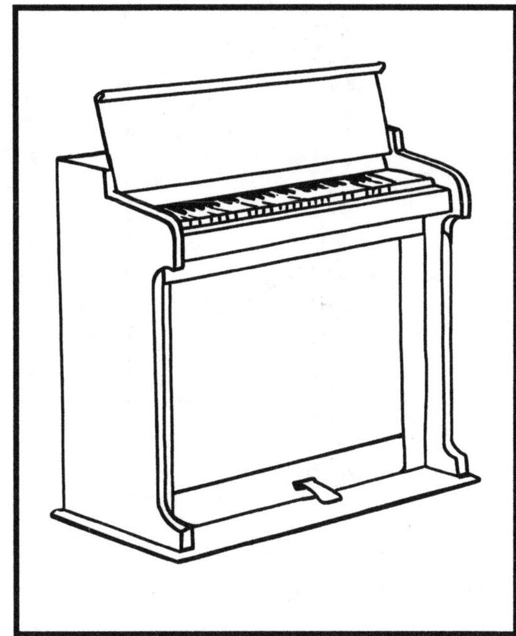

Let's Run Across The Hill

Villa-Lobos

1. Color the picture that looks most like the music sounds.

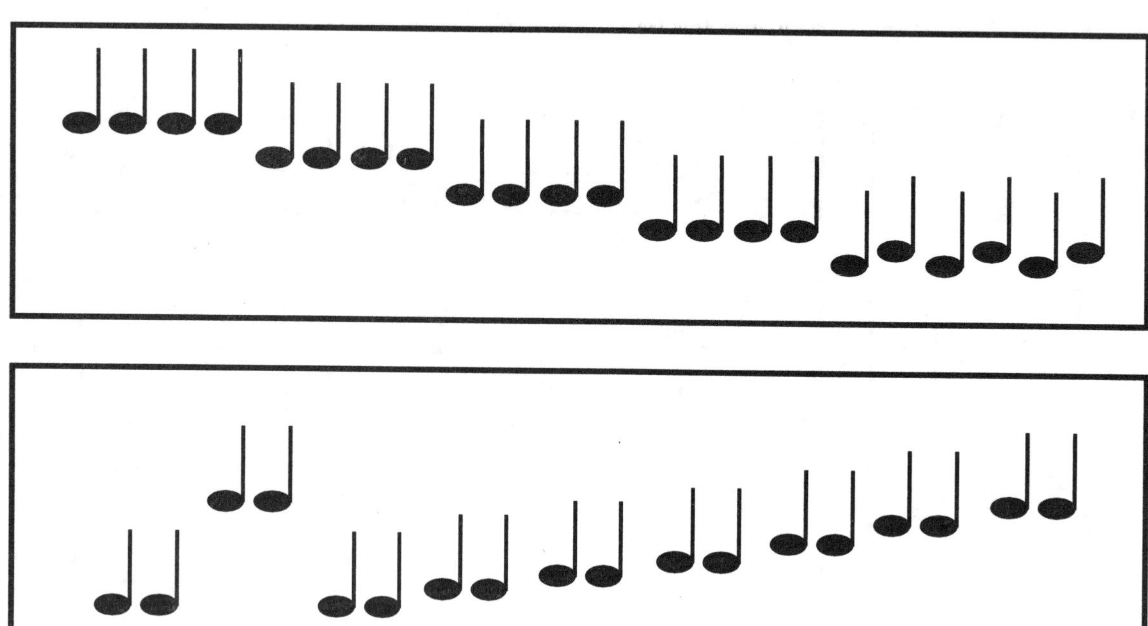

2. Color the picture that includes the instruments in a woodwind quintet.

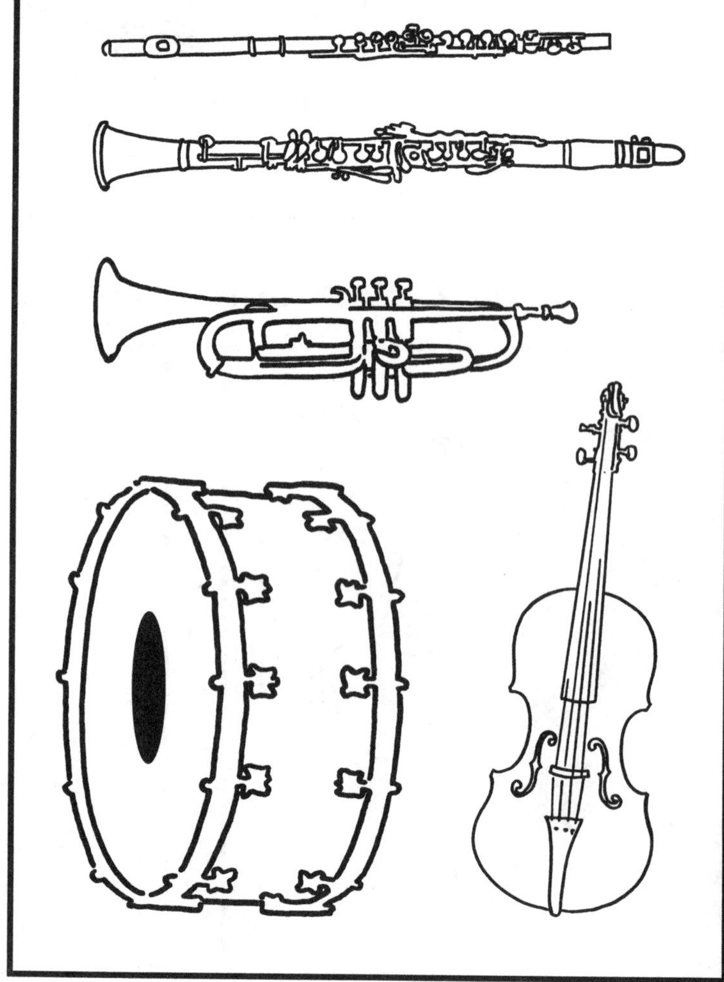

Kongo Ndongo

In 1994, Odeneho Nana Oduro Numapau II,
President of the Ghana National House of Chiefs,
initiated ceremonies in Africa and the Americas
to beg forgiveness of African Americans
for his ancestors' involvement in the slave trade.
In recognition of this extraordinary event,
this book is dedicated
to him.

FRONT COVER: This figurine is probably an idealized portrait of the first ancestor, or founder, of a Kongo clan. He is seated on a chest containing the ancestor's bones, with another casket for relics on the belly.

African Kingdoms of the Past

Kongo Ndongo

West Central Africa

Kenny Mann

Dillon Press • Parsippany, New Jersey

ACKNOWLEDGMENTS

The author wishes to acknowledge the interest, patience, and expertise of the following consultants: Clarence G. Seckel, Jr., Curriculum Coordinator of Social Studies, School District 189, East Saint Louis, IL; Edna J. Whitfield, Social Studies Supervisor (retired), St. Louis Public Schools, St. Louis, MO; and Dr. John K. Thornton, Associate Professor of History, Millersville University, Millersville, PA.

CREDITS

Design and Illustration: Maryann Zanconato
Picture Research: Kenny Mann and Valerie Vogel

PHOTO CREDITS

All photographs by Silver Burdett Ginn (SBG) unless otherwise noted.
Front Cover: © Hughes Dubois Photographie, Brussels.
José Pessoa/Museu e Laboratorio Anthropologico Coimbra/Courtesy, Arquivo Nacional de Fotografia: 35. José Pessoa/Museu Nacional de Etnologia/Courtesy, Arquivo Nacional de Fotografia: 41, 67. © Hughes Dubois Photographie, Brussels: 69. E.T. Archive: 57. Mary Evans Picture Library: 17, 55, 62–63, 90–91. The Granger Collection, New York: 56. The Hutchison Library: 24, 24–25, 70, 94, 95, 96; © B. Gerard: Title page, 93. Instituto Português dos Museus Arquivo Nacional de Fotografia: 86. Museo Naval, Madrid: 58. Mirabella Ricciardi: 37. Private Collection. Photo by Peter Terrail: 53. Courtesy, John Thornton: 66. W. Schneider Schütz/Staatliche Museen Preußischer Kulturbesitz, Museum für Völkerkunde, Berlin: 87. Maps, Ortelius Design: 6, 23, 26.

Library of Congress Cataloging-in-Publication Data

Mann, Kenny.
Kongo, Ndongo: West Central Africa / Kenny Mann. — 1st ed.
p. cm. — (African kingdoms of the past)
Includes bibliographical references and index.
ISBN 0-87518-658-0 (LSB). — ISBN 0-382-39298-1 (pbk.)
1. Kongo (African people)—History—Juvenile literature. 2. Kongo (African people)—Folklore—Juvenile literature. 3. Ndongo (African people)—History—Juvenile literature. 4. Ndongo (African people)—Folklore—Juvenile literature. 5. Oral tradition—Angola—Juvenile literature. 6. Slave-trade—Angola—History—Juvenile literature. 7. Portugal—Colonies—Africa—Juvenile literature. 8. Angola—History—Juvenile literature. I Title. II. Series.
DT560.K66M35 1996 95-31307
966'.004963931—dc20

Summary: A survey of the oral traditions and history of the African kingdoms of Kongo and Ndongo, which once occupied the region of west central Africa that is now the nation of Angola. This study also offers insight into the kingdoms' relationship with Portugal and participation in the slave trade.

Published by Dillon Press,
A Division of Simon & Schuster,
299 Jefferson Road, Parsippany, New Jersey 07054

First edition
Printed in the United States of America
10 9 8 7 6 5 4 3 2 1

Table of Contents

African Kingdoms

Note: Dates marked with an * are approximate.

50,000	B.C.	A.D.	500	1200	1400

Date	Event
***50,000 B.C.**	Early peoples living in what is now Angola
***2000 B.C.**	Western Stream of Bantu people settles in central Africa
***500 B.C.**	Bantu settle in northern Angola
***350 B.C.**	Bantu learn to make iron tools and weapons
***300 B.C.**	Mayan calendar invented
214 B.C.	Great Wall of China built
A.D. 200	Kingdom of Ghana established in western Sudan
711	North African Muslims (Moors) conquer Spain
1143	Portugal becomes independent from Spain
1180s	Kingdom of Kongo founded
1270	Eighth and last Crusade sets out; Aztecs are at height of power
1419	Prince Henry the Navigator begins financing expeditions down African coast
1434	Portuguese captain Gil Eames rounds Cape Bojador
1442	First West African slaves taken to Lisbon
1450s	Age of exploration begins
1453	Turks capture Constantinople; seek new routes to the East
1483	Diogo Cão arrives at mouth of Zaire River, takes four African hostages to Europe
1485	Cão returns to Kongo with hostages
1491	Portuguese fleet arrives at mouth of the Zaire; *mwene Soyo* and *mwene Kongo* baptized
1492	Christopher Columbus arrives in the Americas
1498	Vasco da Gama rounds the Cape of Good Hope on his way to India
1506	Dom Afonso I crowned king of Kongo
1520s	São Tomé becomes one of the world's leading sugar producers
1526	Afonso writes to king of Portugal complaining about slave trade
1543	King Afonso I dies
1550s	Ndongo founded
1568	Imbangala invade Kongo
1591	Filippo Pigafetta writes an account of the Kingdom of Kongo

time

1600 1700 2000

1600 Slavery introduced to Americas

1622 Njinga of Ndongo signs peace treaty with Portuguese governor Correia de Souza

1624–1655 Njinga fights Ngola Hari and Portuguese over succession to Ndongo throne

1630s Province of Soyo breaks away from kingdom of Kongo

1641 Dutch arrive in Luanda

1647–1648 Njinga and the Dutch join forces against the Portuguese

1648 Portuguese fleet from Brazil arrives in Luanda; Dutch surrender and depart

1656 Peace treaty with the Portuguese signed; boundaries of Mbundu kingdom defined

1656 Witchcraft trials held in Salem, Massachusetts

1658 Father Antonio Gaeta da Napoli records Njinga's life history

1663 Queen Njinga dies

1665 Battle of Mbwila; civil war breaks out in Kongo

1686 Beatriz Kimpa Vita born

1704 Beatriz Kimpa Vita possessed by Saint Anthony

1706 Beatriz Kimpa Vita burned at the stake

1776 American colonies declare independence from Great Britain

1791 Slaves from Kongo and Ndongo help to overthrow French government in Haiti

1920s Portuguese immigrants settle in Angola

1955 King Pedro VII, last king of Kongo, dies

1956 Popular Movement for the Liberation of Angola (MPLA) formed

1961 Front for the Liberation of Angola (FNLA) formed

1965 National Union for the Total Independence of Angola (UNITA) formed; rival rebel groups battle for power

1975 Portugal withdraws from Angola

1992 Election held in Angola; MPLA wins, but rival factions continue fighting

1994 Angolans sign truce

Introduction

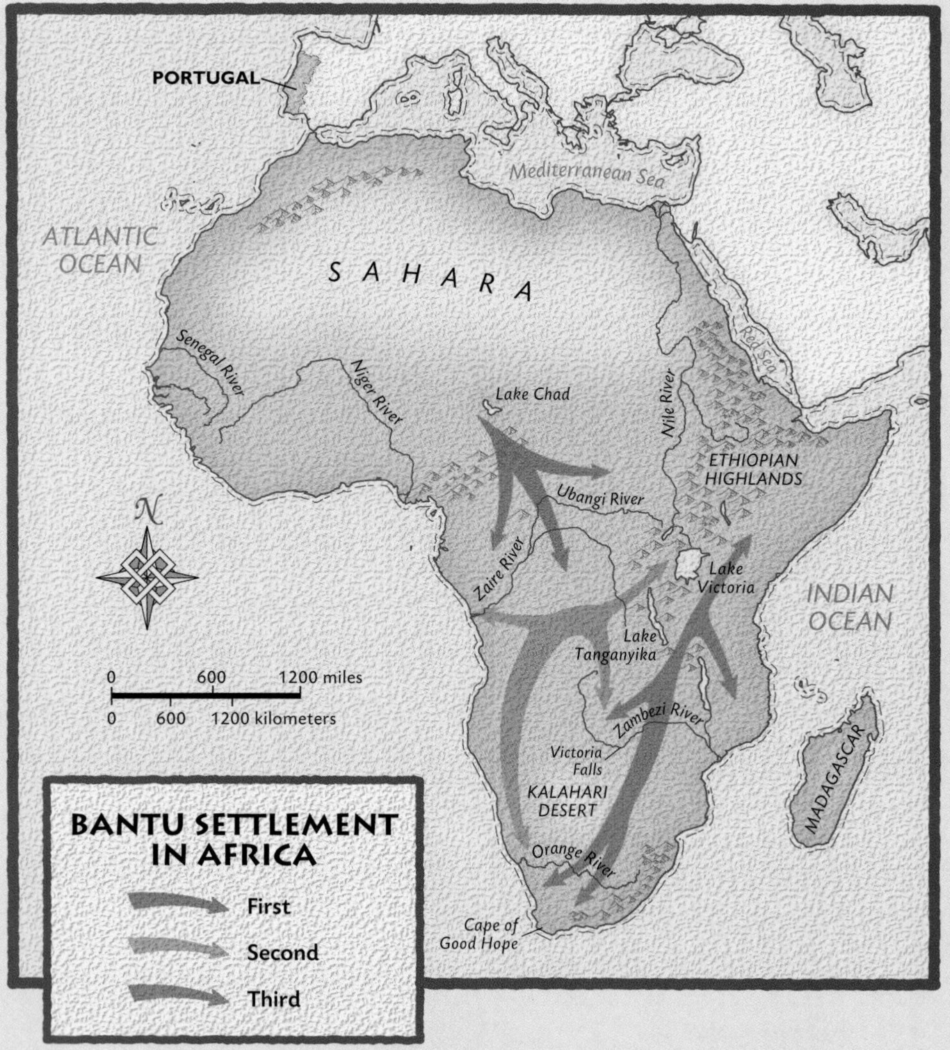

▲ Between 500 B.C. and A.D. 1500, the Bantu migrated from Central Cameroon, a region south of the Sahara, to the central, western, eastern, and southern regions of the continent.

For nearly 500 years, from the late fifteenth century to the late twentieth century, the region of west central Africa now called Angola had close and mostly unhappy relations with the European nation of Portugal. During its time as a Portuguese colony, Angola was torn by war and conquest, and its people lived in poverty and experienced much suffering.

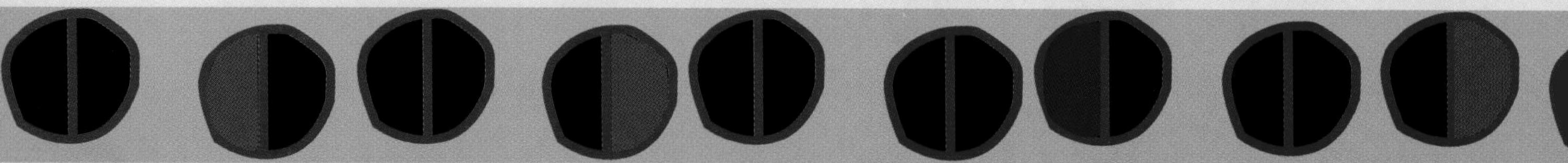

Before the colonial period, however, despite much local warfare, the region had been divided into flourishing kingdoms. People there raised crops and tended animals. They lived out their lives within the framework of a belief system that helped them to respect and understand their environment. Their kings and queens ruled with an iron hand. There was little other than the kingdoms' own internal stresses and strains to disturb them.

Who were these people? Where did they come from? How were they able to thrive in an environment that was deadly to most of the early Europeans who tried to live there?

There are clues to these questions all over Angola. Evidence of human habitation in the region thousands of years ago has been found in many places. Marks on rocks, massive stone pillars, and prehistoric tools are just a few of the signs that people have lived in Angola since about 50,000 B.C., perhaps even much earlier.

The visible signs tell one story. The invisible signs revealed by carbon dating and other modern techniques tell another. A link between the visible and the invisible has been provided by the study of language.

Languages change as groups of people move from one area to another, adapt to their surroundings, and intermarry with other groups. By observing language changes over time and distance, historians can track the movements of related groups of people from one location to another.

Scholars of African history have divided the African people into various language groups. One of these is the Bantu group. The word *ntu* (N too)*, common to over 400 languages in this language family, means "person." *Ba-ntu* is simply the plural form, meaning "people."

The oral traditions of the Bantu people generally place them in their current locations only about 500 years ago. But modern historians have learned that the Bantu were already on the move and had reached their present locations much earlier. The original Bantu language seems to have evolved in the region of present-day Cameroon. From there, it spread eastward and southward

> The word for "bird" in Kiswaheli, which is spoken all over eastern Africa, is *ndege* (n-DE-ge). In Angola, however, the word is *ndele* (n-DE-le). The two words have the same Bantu root, but have altered slightly over time and in different regions.

* Words that may be difficult to pronounce have been spelled phonetically in parentheses. A pronunciation key appears on page 98.

The origin of the name *Kongo* is lost in time. In the Kikongo language, *ku-ngo* (kuh-n-goh) means "the land of the leopard." The word for "hunter" is *nkongo*, while that for a "hurled weapon" is *kongo* or *kong*. The word *kongo* also refers to a powerful, high-born individual—someone likely to become a king or noble. The name for the kingdom could have arisen from any or all of these sources, especially since all these words refer to symbols of power.

as the Bantu spread out over the continent. The Bantu did not migrate in large numbers, as was originally thought. Rather, small traveling groups gradually infiltrated new areas and intermarried with the hunter-gatherers and farmers native to those places.

By about 2000 B.C., Bantu of the so-called Western Stream had settled in the deep forests of central Africa. Here, they learned to plant yams and other root crops and to tend the trees that bore fruit, oil, palm nuts, bark, and other useful products. They kept goats and cleared the forest with simple stone axes.

The stone tools of these early Bantu people limited their hunting and farming techniques. Imagine the labor required to cut down a giant tree with only stone axes! It was easier for these early peoples to cultivate land and hunt in the open savannah, which they found beyond the Zaire (zeye EER) River, in what is now northern Angola. They settled there around 500 B.C. By 350 B.C., these Bantu had learned how to make tools and weapons out of iron.

It is not clear whether knowledge of ironworking was carried south to Angola from the ancient Nile City of Meroë (ME roh), which flourished as an iron-making center, or whether it came from East Africa, where people were smelting iron ore as early as the seventh century B.C. It could be that the early Bantu actually discovered the technique themselves. No one knows for certain, but ironworking definitely lifted the Bantu out of the Stone Age. Now they could make tools and weapons that were sharper, more practical, and more durable than those made of stone, bone, or wood. They became better hunters, better farmers, and better warriors, truly adapted to life in their newfound environments.

Once the Western Stream Bantu had settled in the region, they were able to develop the rich culture and political system that have fascinated historians ever since the first Portuguese arrived at the mouth of the Zaire River in 1483. The great kingdom of Kongo (not to be confused with the modern nation of Congo) had been founded in what is now northern Angola some 300 years earlier, when Europe still floundered in the Dark Ages.

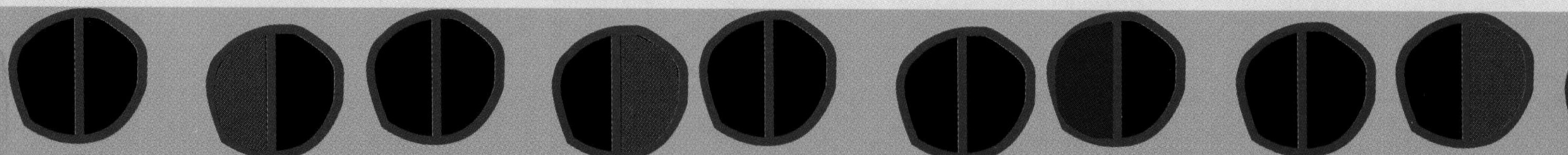

In the early years after the arrival of the Portuguese, the Kongo kings welcomed the newcomers as profitable new trading partners. The kings wanted the benefits of European technology and the skills of reading and writing. The Portuguese, for their part, had come as traders, not conquerors, and naturally hoped for profitable business relations. They had also come with the fervent desire to introduce Christianity to Africa, and were amazed when the Kongo nobility seemed more than willing to embrace the Catholic faith.

Having developed in different places thousands of miles apart, the two cultures were very different from each other. Yet they were also similar in some respects.

Portugal had separated from Spain and established itself as an independent kingdom in the mid-twelfth century, just as Kongo was on the rise. Around the same time, the Portuguese expelled the Moors, who had invaded the region from North Africa several centuries earlier. The Moorish influence in Portuguese life and culture remained strong, however, and after several centuries of intermarriage with the Moors, the Portuguese had developed "brotherly" attitudes toward other dark-skinned peoples. In Angola and other African territories, they easily intermarried with Africans and absorbed some of their culture.

Portugal was divided into two very distinct classes: the peasant class and the ruling class. The peasants had little to do with the ruling class and cared little for the nobility's ideas of expansion and empire. They preferred to continue their traditional occupations of farming, small trading, and shopkeeping.

Kongo society was similarly divided. Legends recall that the ruling class were "strangers" who had come from "the north" to conquer the local people. The ruling class lived in the towns, and the peasants occupied small villages. The ruling class also had grand ideas of expanding the kingdom. Once the Portuguese arrived, the ruling class became deeply involved in international trade, while the peasants merely provided trade goods—especially the raffia cloth for which Kongo became famous.

Anthropologists have recently coined the term *Bakongo* to describe speakers of the Kikongo language. Kikongo-speakers inhabit a region much larger than the original kingdom of Kongo. The inhabitants of the kingdom itself called themselves *Esikongo*, or "citizens of the kingdom of Kongo." No other people, although they spoke the same language, would have used the term *Esikongo*.

Both nations were also intensely nationalistic, although in different ways. The Portuguese were determined that their tiny country be recognized as a mighty world power. Threatened by the superior power of Spain, Portugal had developed something of an inferiority complex. It had no choice but to look outward, beyond its own borders. By the early fifteenth century, the Portuguese had begun their brief period of glory. For a hundred years, they were the world leaders in navigation, exploration, conquest, and trade on three continents.

The Kongo leaders also wanted their kingdom to be the greatest and most powerful in the region. Unlike the Portuguese, though, they were not threatened by a superior power. Indeed, many European visitors noted that the Esikongo—the inhabitants of the kingdom—believed themselves to be the best, the happiest, and the most fortunate people on earth! It had

Kongo Men

Many Europeans were impressed by the Esikongo. These illustrations of Esikongo men and women were probably drawn by an artist who had read a report written by Duarte Lopes, a Portuguese sailor who visited Kongo in 1578. ▶

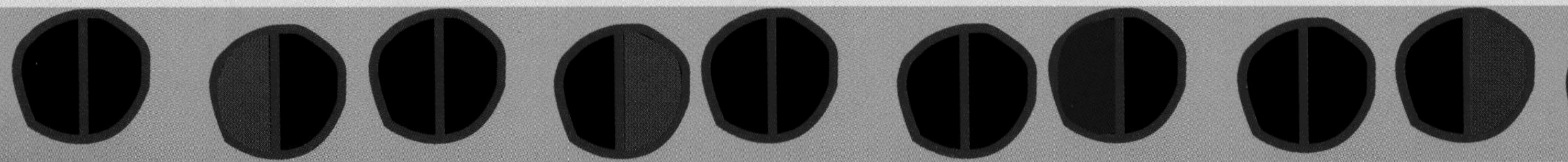

never entered their heads that the day might come when they too might be conquered.

Trade, Christianity, and peaceful brotherhood were the hallmarks of the new relationship between the Kongo nation and Portugal. During the first years of the Kongo-Portuguese alliance, it seemed that the cooperative experiment between the two nations might actually succeed. Sadly, this was not to be. Christianity was soon absorbed into age-old Kongo beliefs. The climate and tropical diseases proved deadly to the Portuguese. The peaceful trade of cloth, ivory, and other local goods soon gave way to the abominations of the slave trade. And civil war finally brought about the kingdom's downfall. The great experiment failed.

What had happened in the kingdom of Kongo influenced the state of Ndongo (DON goh), farther south. Some Kongo kings claimed that Ndongo was a vassal state under Kongo's control. In fact, Kongo and Ndongo had always been rivals, but Ndongo was unable to establish itself as a kingdom until the late sixteenth century, when it profited handsomely from the slave trade.

Both Kongo and Ndongo were eventually absorbed into the Portuguese colony of Angola. How might these kingdoms have developed without European intervention? Would they have continued in the age-old ways? Or would other factors have led to their downfall? These are questions that occupy historians of the region.

> "The climate here [in Kongo] is so unhealthy for the foreigner that of all those who go there, few fail to sicken, and of those who sicken, few fail to die, and those who survive are obliged to withstand the intense heat of the torrid zone, suffering hunger, thirst, and many other miseries for which there is no relief save patience, of which much is needed . . . to tolerate the discomforts of such a wretched place."
> — *A sixteenth-century report*

Kongo Women

KONGO

Kongo—The Founding Stories

Nimi A Lukeni: Crossing the Zaire River

A long, long time ago, in the province of Corimba, near the great Zaire River, there lived a woman named Ne Lukeni (ne loo KAY nee) [Lady Lukeni]. She was married, and, in time, she bore her husband a son, named Nimi a Lukeni (Nimi, son of Lukeni). The boy grew to be a strong, healthy youth, defiant in nature and eager for power.

One day, Ne Lukeni wished to cross the great river to reach a market on the other side. The ferryman there kept her waiting, and Ne Lukeni became impatient. She berated the man and badgered him endlessly. She was pregnant, she shouted. She should cross immediately!

It did not pay to annoy the ferryman. After all, he was master of these waters, and no one could cross the great river without his services.

"Perhaps you are a queen," he sneered, "or at least the mother of a king, that you cannot wait patiently like everyone else. When the other passengers have crossed, then you, too, may cross the river."

Ne Lukeni was furious. How dare this lowly ferryman treat her so insolently!

KONGO

Ne Lukeni returned home and told her son, Nimi a Lukeni, what had happened. Now the young man saw at once his chance to seize the power for which he yearned.

"Console yourself, Mother," her son said, "for this I promise you. You shall indeed be the mother of a king. And I, Nimi a Lukeni, shall be that king. But first, I must have a kingdom."

From then on, Nimi a Lukeni had only one aim. He would cross the Zaire and conquer the rich and fertile lands to the south of the great river.

Nimi a Lukeni recruited many people, luring them with promises of land and great riches. In time, he departed from his homeland with all his followers, his father, mother, and sister, and set out to make his promise come true.

With the cunning of a jackal, Nimi a Lukeni entrenched himself in an area of impregnable mountain crags. This spot lay near the ancient trade routes reaching from the sea coast deep into the interior, and from the north to the south. Many people traveled these paths, carrying with them salt and valuable shell money, cloth, ivory, foodstuffs, and other precious items of trade. From his rocky fortress, Nimi a Lukeni and his armed followers were able to ambush the travelers. They took their goods and forced them to pay heavy tolls in order to pass.

Nimi a Lukeni also conducted fierce raids into the land surrounding his outpost. He found criminals, outcasts, adventurers, and men of greed to join his forces. Before long, he had become known as a single-minded and unyielding leader, and his followers proclaimed him their king. From then on, he was addressed as *mwene* (MWE ne) *Kongo*—king of Kongo.

When he judged the time to be right, King Nimi invaded the lands across the Zaire. He fought and conquered as he marched, driving local lords from their ancestral lands. At length, King Nimi and his people reached a mountain known as Vumba. It was here that, with great foresight, the *mwene Kongo* chose to build his capital city.

At the top of the mountain, King Nimi found a wide, flat plain, in the center of which was a lake. He commanded his people to fill in the lake with earth. When this was done, they built houses and roads, and for their king, a palace.

The city came to be known as Mbanza (m BAHN zah) [city] Kongo. The site was truly chosen with great wisdom. It lay near the crossroads of trade, and for miles in all directions one could look far out over the land. The earth was rich and fertile. The sun shone, the rain fell, and the people prospered.

After his military triumphs, King Nimi proved to be a prudent and wise king. He laid down the first laws, which were just and true. In time, through strength and valor, he conquered other areas, and his capital was eventually surrounded by a vast territory consisting of many provinces.

One day, King Nimi assembled at his palace enclosure those relatives, companions, and slaves whom he deemed worthy. The *mwene Kongo* entered his dwelling and returned with the sacred knife that symbolized his dignity, his royalty, and his laws. Then he took also a buffalo tail, the other symbol of his royalty, and his people knelt before him. King Nimi raised his right hand, and all were silent.

King Nimi was indeed a wise man. To each of his selected people, he entrusted the governorship of a province. Each was to go forth for a period of not less than three years, governing wisely and bringing prosperity to his province, and thus to the kingdom.

"For two reasons the earliest lords of the country placed this territory on the said summit; first, because it lies in almost the very middle of the kingdom, whence subsidies could be quickly sent to every part; and then, because the natural elevation gives good air, a secure position, and one not to be taken by force. . . . There is no lack of water springs on this high plain . . . to which the people descend . . . and carry the water into the city in vessels of wood and terra cotta, and also in gourds on the shoulders of slaves."
—Filippo Pigafetta, a description of Mbanza Kongo from A Report of the Kingdom of Kongo, *1591*

In this way was the kingdom of Kongo formed, and it became the largest and most powerful of those lands along the western coast of central Africa. And in this way did Nimi a Lukeni keep his promise to his mother, Ne Lukeni, who did indeed become the mother of a king.

Truth and Myth

The story of Nimi a Lukeni has been handed down among the people of Kongo—the Esikongo—for many centuries. There are also other founding stories, quite different from the one told here. Which one is true? The answer varies, depending on who is telling the story and when.

The earliest known story, recorded in the 1580s, describes how several provinces simply joined together to form a kingdom, with one strong leader as king.

Later stories that resemble the one in this book were traditional during the seventeenth and early eighteenth centuries. They describe how Nimi a Lukeni conquered various provinces to become an all-powerful king. In one version, Nimi a Lukeni is the ferryman, wielding his power at the river crossing. In this story, the pregnant woman who wished to cross the river was his aunt, not his mother. It is said that Nimi a Lukeni killed her. Instead of treating him as a criminal, the people admired his hard-heartedness and proclaimed him their king, or *mwene Kongo*. He elected individuals — usually members of the royal family—as governors of the provinces and, relying on their loyalty, thus forged a new kingdom. This story of Nimi a Lukeni reflects the existing political structure at the time, since during the seventeenth and eighteenth centuries, the kings did in fact have absolute power.

After 1700 the stories claim that the founding king was a blacksmith, the inventor of the art of the forge. He provided his people with the iron tools of agriculture and the weapons of war. These were far superior to the implements of bone, wood, stone, and copper used by neighboring peoples. The blacksmith's people were thus able to produce more food and win more battles than their rivals. He naturally became a leader, and metalwork became the privilege of the Kongo nobility.

In Esikongo tradition, a blacksmith is a fair and just man. In these stories the king attained his power through his reputation for the wise and skillful judgment of disputes. Again, the blacksmith tradition is close to the real situation in Kongo during the eighteenth century. At that time, attempts were made to reduce the

In Kikongo the king was called the *mwene Kongo*. The Portuguese corrupted this to *mani Kongo*.

king's authority and redistribute power more equitably among the various provinces of the kingdom.

After 1850 the story changes yet again! At this time, local clans were more powerful and important than before. Thus it was natural for each clan to claim in its version of the story that it had founded and organized the kingdom.

Interpreting the Stories

Since the first Portuguese landed on the shores of Kongo in 1483, the history of the area has been extensively studied and documented. European officials, traders, and missionaries left behind a wealth of material in the form of books, diaries, letters, official records, and dictionaries. Although their paintings and drawings often reflect European tasks and values, they remain useful sources of information on Kongo life. While the Esikongo had previously relied on oral histories, they very soon became literate in the Portuguese language, and later in the

◀ In Africa south of the Sahara, this short-handled hoe with an iron blade replaced the digging stick after the introduction of iron.

Kikongo language. Since 1491, they too have produced thousands of letters, documents, and scholarly works recording and analyzing the history of their own country.

All these chroniclers agree that Nimi a Lukeni, or the "founding father," and his clan came from a place "north of the Zaire" sometime during the mid-fourteenth century. Until the eighteenth century, the Esikongo regarded this ruling class as "foreigners" or "strangers."

Was the first *mwene Kongo* really a blacksmith? It is certainly possible.

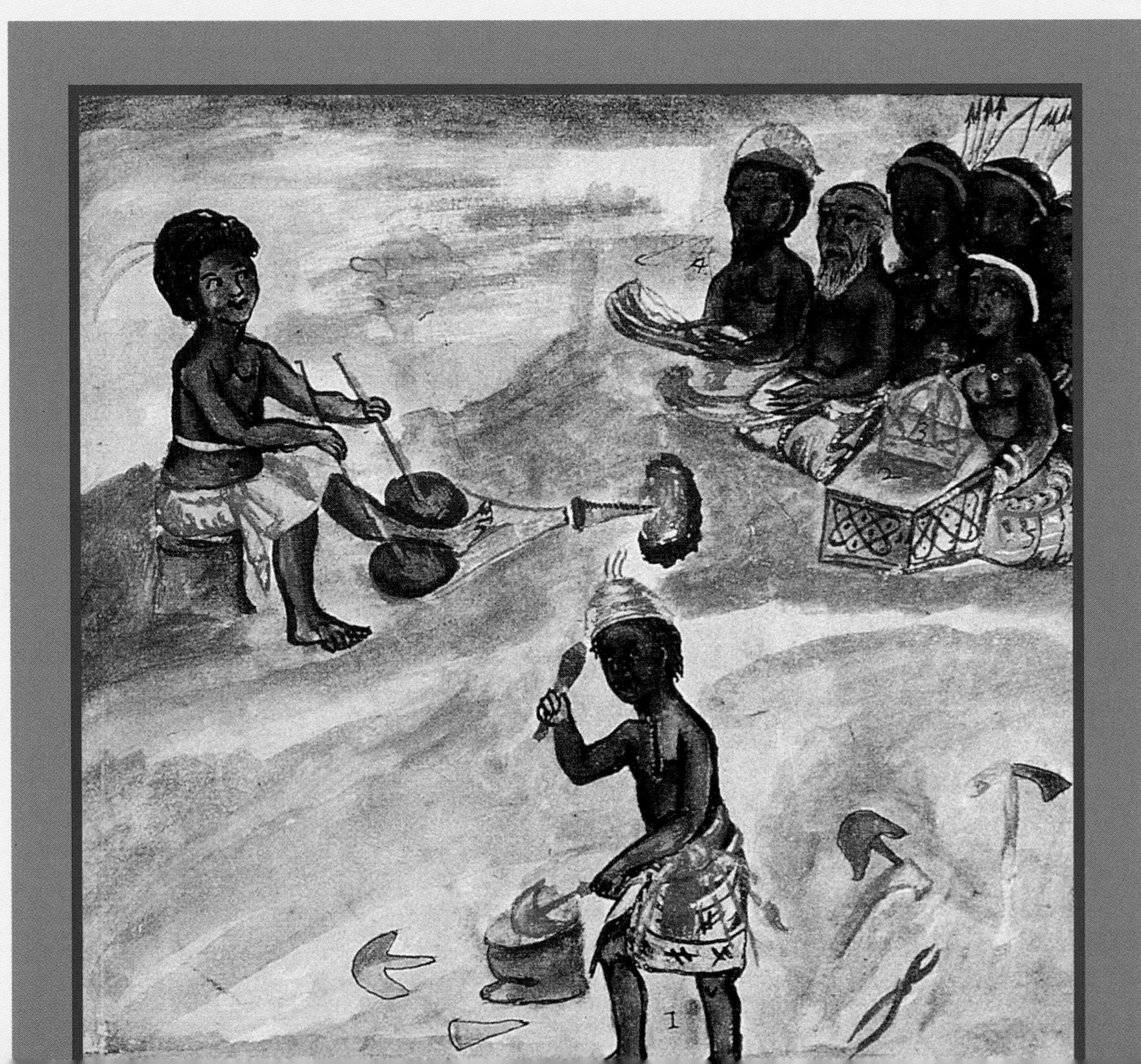

Historians guess that many blacksmiths were also traders, seeking new markets for the copper that was mined in the regions north of the Zaire River. Different groups or clans had to cooperate with one another to create safe trade routes and a uniform system of taxation. They probably chose one man—perhaps Nimi a Lukeni—to be their leader. To represent them all, he would have had to break with his own clan.

It is possible that this leader took his clan farther south, conquering as he went and creating a new trade route in the process. The place where this route crossed an older east-west route leading inland from the coast may have proved the ideal place for the capital city. It is also possible that a chiefdom already existed where the trade routes crossed. Its leader may have seized the opportunity for greater power and built a capital city around a convenient marketplace. Either way, the kingdom was expanded through trade, conquest, and careful marriages with neighboring peoples.

There is probably some truth in each version of the founding story. It is also possible that the different versions are meant as allegories. They may be interpreted symbolically, much like ancient Greek myths and tales, or like "Cinderella" and "Jack the Giant Killer."

For example, Nimi a Lukeni could represent a character who had to be a ruthless outcast to earn the power he sought. He had to break the bonds with his clan by "killing" his relative. This would explain why he was revered rather than despised for his actions. Later he is said to have been "prudent and wise." In other words, a great leader must be both brutal and loving, both ruthless and just.

The fine details of the founding story may never be discovered. It is clear, however, that the first *mwene Kongo* and his followers were highly skilled, resourceful people. They forged a huge kingdom that knitted the Esikongo people together for 300 years. That kingdom is gone, and while the Esikongo still inhabit their homelands, it may not be long before their stories, too, are gone.

◀ **A blacksmith uses bellows to create enough heat to smelt iron ore so that it can be shaped using the hammer and anvil. This painting was done in the seventeenth century by the Italian missionary, Antonio Cavazzi, who faithfully recorded all that he saw.**

The Kingdom Flourishes

When Portuguese merchants arrived off the coast of West Africa in the 1470s, they were astonished to find a series of highly civilized kingdoms—Mali, Benin, Calabar, and others. The magnificently dressed rulers of these kingdoms wielded godly power; their royal households boasted untold wealth in gold, ivory, and slaves; and some of their cities rivaled those of Europe in size and splendor.

When the Portuguese arrived in the kingdom of Kongo in 1483, they found a very different but equally dazzling civilization, described as "the most powerful and magnificent country in all Guinea." They were to remain deeply involved in the region for almost 500 years.

The Kongo Region

The kingdom of Kongo was never clearly defined by boundaries. Several kings claimed a region stretching far north of the Zaire River and east to the Kwango River. Perhaps a kingdom of this size once existed, but kings were in the habit of claiming more territory than they actually controlled. In the sixteenth century, the kingdom was probably roughly bound to the north by the Zaire River, to the west by the Atlantic Ocean, to the east by the Nkisi (n KEE see) River, about 970 km (600 mi) inland, and from there in a southwesterly line to the island of Luanda on the coast. Historians estimate the population then at about 350,000 people. Today the area corresponds to the northwestern section of Angola and the eastern wedge of Zaire.

How did the kingdom rise to power? What did Nimi a Lukeni, or the first *mwene Kongo*, find that enabled him to forge many small provinces into an empire of over 250,000 sq. km (100,000 sq. mi)? More than anything else, historians believe, Nimi a Lukeni was lucky! He found a region abundant in water and rich in plant, animal, and mineral resources. He found local people with a language similar to his own. They knew their environment

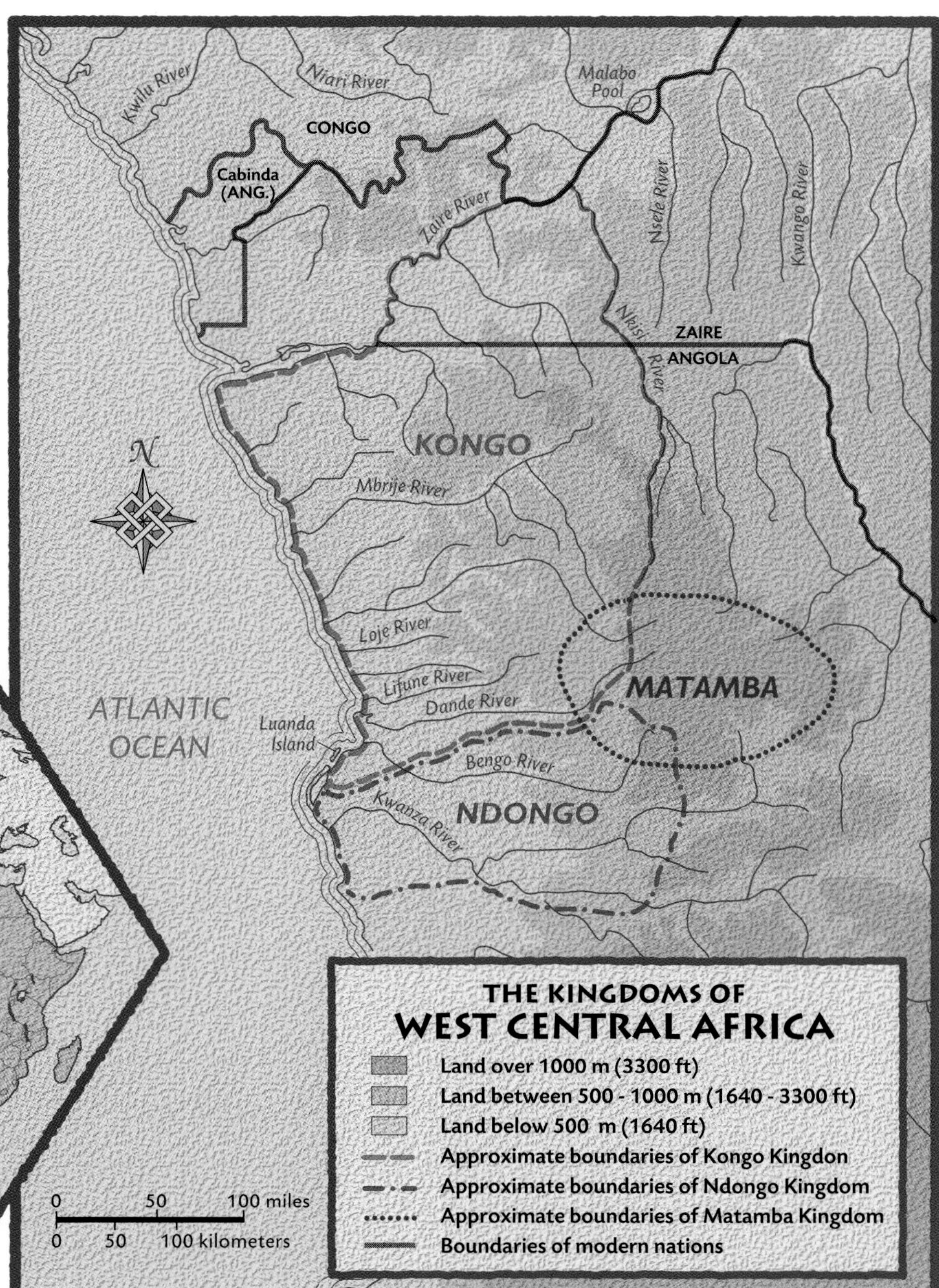

Before the sixteenth century, the kingdom of Kongo may have been much larger, stretching north beyond the Zaire River as well as much farther south. Kongo kings often claimed part of the kingdom of Ndongo, to the south, as their own. ▶

This view looks out from the craggy heights of the eastern mountains over the flatter central zone. ▶

The landscape in southern Angola, near Luanda, is dry and unwelcoming. ▼

intimately and were superb agriculturists. As a conqueror, Nimi a Lukeni had moved into a prime area, ripe for expansion and growth. He was greatly helped by the natural ecology of the region.

South of the Zaire River, there are three distinct ecological regions: the coastal zone, the central zone, and the plateau zone. Each runs roughly parallel to the coast.

The plateau zone, draining from the hills of the central zone into the Kwango River, is arid and inhospitable. Great ridges, barren and stony, traverse the land from north to south and are dissected by wooded river valleys. These supported only a few inhabitants, who raised cereal crops like sorghum and millet. The valleys are surrounded by flat-topped mountains

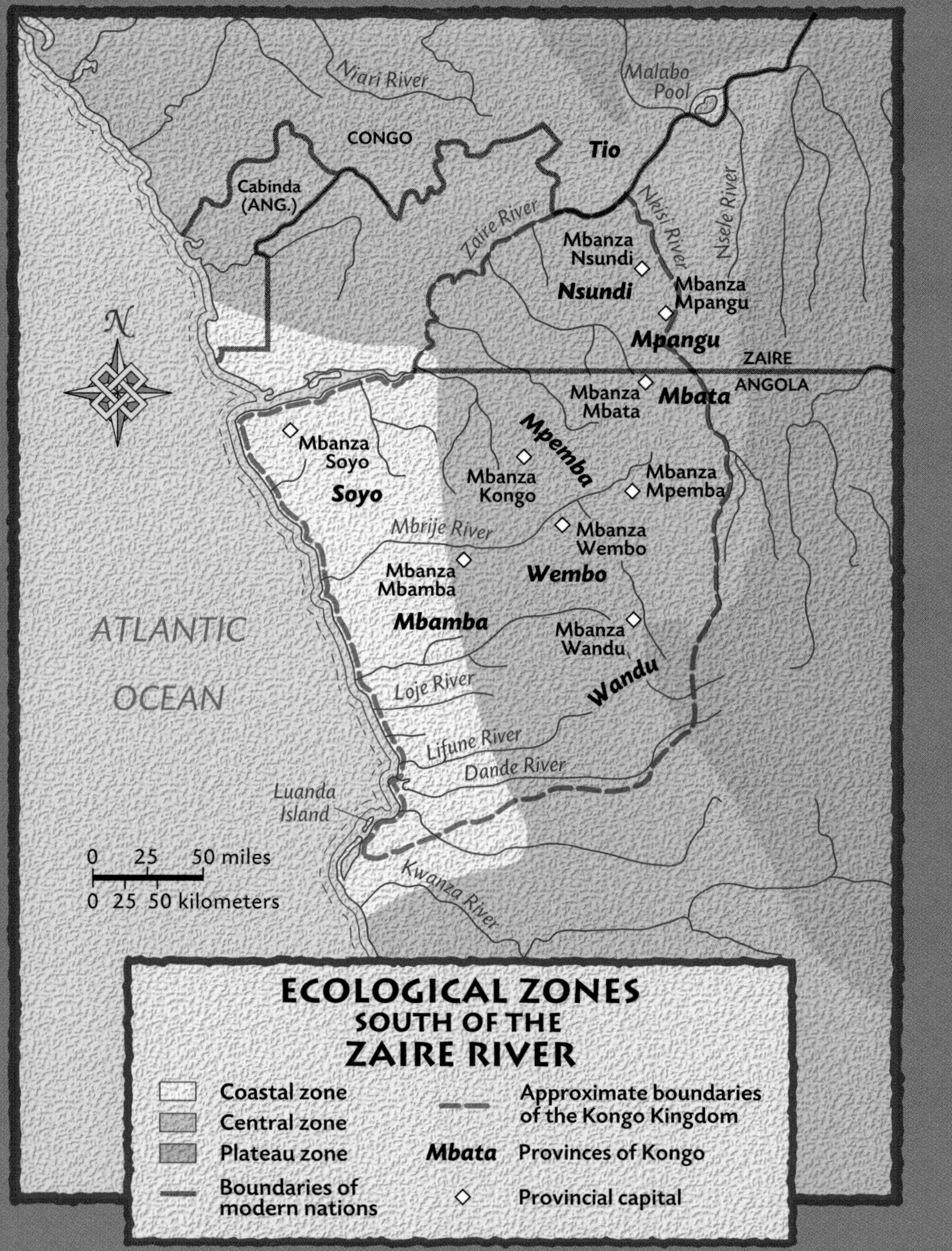

that look like fortresses and form natural barriers to invasion.

The backbone of the central zone is formed by a ridge of mountains, up to 1,200 m (3,600 ft) high, stretching south from the Zaire River. To the east they flatten out to form the plateau zone. To the west they drop gradually to the plains of the coastal zone.

Five hundred years ago, the vegetation ranged from savannah in the lower southwest to rain forest in the mountains, with intense cultivation in between. Because of its high rainfall and fertile soils, the central zone was, and still is, the most densely populated of the three.

▲ The central zone was always densely populated, as evidenced by the large number of provincial capitals located there. In the fifteenth and sixteenth centuries, there were eight major provinces in Kongo. Mbata and Mpangu, in the Nkisi River valley, produced raffia cloth. Nsundi, to the north, had access to the copper trade north of the Zaire River. Mbamba oversaw the collection of *nzimbu* shells from Luanda. Wembo controlled the copper mines farther east. Mpemba province was the location of the kingdom's capital, Mbanza Kongo. Soyo, to the west, was one of the strongest provinces. Its capital, Mbanza Soyo, later rivaled Mbanza Kongo in power and wealth. The southeastern province of Wandu eventually became the stronghold of Queen Njinga of Ndongo.

Nimi a Lukeni's capital city, Mbanza Kongo—later renamed São (sou) Salvador—stands in ruins today, 240 km (150 mi) east of the coast and 130 km (80 mi) south of the Zaire River. Located in the northern part of the central zone, it lies on a broad plateau, about 16 km (10 mi) in circumference and some 600 m (1,800 ft) above sea level. For about 32 km (20 mi) around the capital, the land was densely populated and heavily cultivated. Sixteenth-century observers estimated that the area supported between 60,000 and 100,000 inhabitants.

A great variety of crops and plants was cultivated in the central zone. Along the fertile valleys of the Nkisi River, for instance, at least eight types of palm flourished. The leaves of the raffia palm provided fibers that were woven into exquisite cloths of various sizes and quality that could be worn only by the king and his nobles. The Europeans compared them to the best and most costly silks, velvets, and taffetas. Their value was determined by their weight, place of origin, and weaving style, and they were frequently used as a form of currency.

Other palms throughout the central zone provided palm oil, wine, vinegar, fruits, and bread, all derived from various parts of the tree. The Esikongo even made a salad dressing of the white milk that oozed out of a hole bored in the top of the tree. Palm tree leaves and trunks were used in buildings, game traps, fishing snares, clothing, cosmetics, and medicines.

The cola nut—fruit of the cola tree—was another major crop. It was used as a food, a thirst quencher, and a mild stimulant. The Esikongo also cultivated a wide variety of fruit unknown to Europeans. Later, their orchards produced guavas, lemons, and oranges, which were imported from Portugal.

The central zone was also rich in various grains, cultivated beans, peas, yams, bananas, and plantains. Imported peanuts, sugar cane, and pineapples also flourished. The Esikongo were also masters at collecting the "free" fruits of the wild—edible roots and tubers, leaves, berries, and over 20 species of mushrooms.

> "It must be remembered that gold, silver and other metals . . . are not used as money in these countries. And so it happens that with gold and silver in abundance, either in mass or in coin, yet nothing can be bought except with shells."
> — *Filippo Pigafetta, 1591*

The coastal zone, dropping down gradually from the high central plateau, was much less fertile. It suffered from low rainfall and loose, sandy soils. Most people lived along the Zaire estuary, where higher rainfall allowed the cultivation of rice in the muddy mangrove swamps. Near the southern coast, the sandy, acidic soils supported little more than grasses, thorn trees, and palms. Farther inland, the coast gave way to a rocky desert.

Along the beaches, women manufactured salt by boiling sea water. They also dove for special shells called *nzimbu* (n ZIHM boo), which were used as currency throughout the kingdom. The best shells were thin, shiny, and black and came from the island of Luanda, now part of the capital city of Angola. The men of the coastal zone produced a rough bark cloth by unrolling and pounding the bark of palm trees.

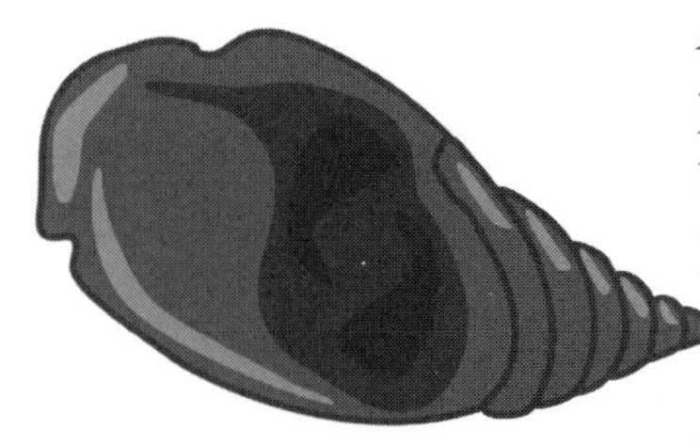

▲ *Nzimbu* shells were used as currency.

More than enough food was produced in all three zones for trade, although crops were sometimes devastated by drought, floods, swarms of locusts, or, in the central zone, elephants.

Wildlife was abundant everywhere. "Small game"—snakes, lizards, rats, and even insects and worms—was eaten. Larger game such as elephant, antelope, leopard, and buffalo was also consumed. Hunters had to go through elaborate rituals to protect themselves and honor the beasts they ate. Fish were also plentiful in the various rivers and lakes.

Rain fell in deluges from September to May. A Florentine priest traveling in the region in 1665 described walking for days in waist-high water, plagued by swarms of mosquitoes. Floods and mud slides were common. Crops and buildings were often ruined.

The dry season from May to September was a welcome respite. This was the time when people traded, visited relatives, enjoyed various social occasions, or went to war. Quite frequently, however, the dry season turned into disastrous drought. Crops failed, animals and people starved, and tensions ran high. Then people turned to the rainmaker, or *nganga* (n GAHN guh)—a person with magical powers. Understandably, the *nganga* played an extremely important role in Kongo society.

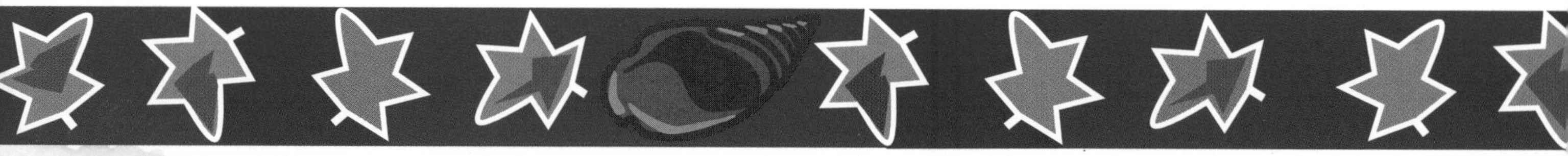

Men, Women, and Work

Labor was strictly divided between men and women. The women were fairly skilled potters. They worked the land, sowing, tending, and harvesting the many crops. They also did all the collecting of wild berries, roots, and other edible plants. Women cooked and took care of children and domestic animals and participated in many of the sacred Esikongo rituals.

The men cleared the forests and scrub. They harvested many tree crops, such as palm oil, palm wine, and fruit, and made medicines from plant and animal products. They built houses out of branches and thatch and also hunted, fished, and traded.

▲ In this painting by Cavazzi, a seated nobleman examines raffia cloth displayed by a trader.

Some men were artisans, with the blacksmiths holding the highest positions. Knowledge of metalworking may have spread west from East Africa some time during the four-

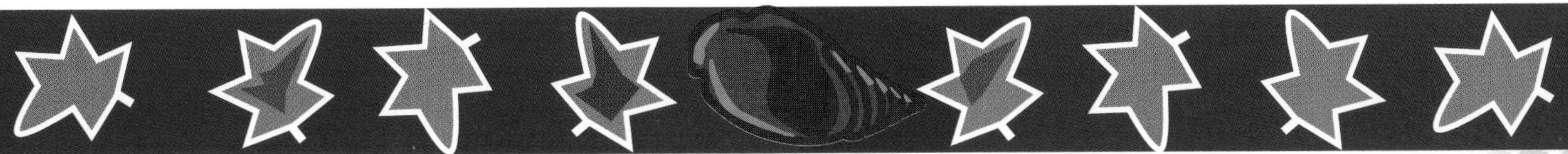

teenth century—just when historians pinpoint the founding of the kingdom.

Iron ore was commonly found in the rocks of the Kongo region, and the blacksmiths were experts at their art. They also knew how to melt lead and to forge copper and tin. Recent evidence has shown that they were aware of lead poisoning and had an effective cure for it: massive doses of mashed papaya doused in palm oil.

Limited amounts of copper were found within the kingdom, but there were rich deposits north of the Zaire River. The copper deposits may have played a role in the formation of the kingdom, as explained in Chapter 1. Copper would continue to influence Kongo's history for several centuries.

Copper was used for ceremonial and religious objects. Men and women wore as many elaborate bracelets and armbands as possible. People were

A Kongo woman cultivates her field using an iron hoe, while another woman carries wares in her basket for sale at market. Behind the women stands a thatched granary. ▶

reported wearing up to 12 kg (25 lbs) of copper at one time! Perhaps this show was merely decorative, but it may have been meant to indicate wealth and status.

Woodworkers were highly revered and made figurines for ritual, magic, or protective use. They also made drums, which were played at celebrations and in times of war. In addition, woodworkers produced simple furniture and household items. Civet (a species of wildcat) and otter skins were reserved for the nobility. Expert basket makers used local wicker to make containers and fishing nets. And many European visitors were amazed at the men's skill at weaving the famed raffia cloth and other textiles, which rivaled European textiles in their texture and beauty.

Cult, Status, and Society

The Esikongo saw a natural hierarchy, or ranking, in plant, animal, and human life. Thus the work that men and women did and the natural materials they used defined their positions in society. Men who wove the raffia cloth, for example, enjoyed a higher status than those who made the rougher bark cloth.

The Esikongo had a rich oral tradition. Their lives were enriched by poems, ritual songs and phrases, prayers, speeches, love songs, eulogies, praises, stories, proverbs, riddles, and other forms of verbal expression. To them, words were the source of good and evil. Words formed messages to the ancestors and gave individuals the power to act. Words praised the king at the magnificent ceremonies, and thus reinforced the greatness of the kingdom. The praises were intoned by heralds to a solemn accompaniment of lutes and drums.

Members of this secret society in Kongo were photographed in 1914. They covered their bodies with pipe clay and wore grass skirts held up by ceremonial belts. ▼

Blacksmiths were considered superior to woodworkers. A leopard skin was more "noble" than that of a civet. And the palm tree was the noblest tree of all.

A cult can be defined as a system of religious belief and ritual.

Esikongo society had many other divisions. The *kitome* (kih TOH me) were individuals responsible for maintaining harmony between people and the natural world by praying to important ancestors and dieties. They were believed to bring or withhold rain. They blessed the seed, gave permission for the harvest, and received its first fruits. They were responsible for the fertility of people, plants, and animals. The *kitome* usually performed their rituals near sacred bodies of water, which were believed to form the boundary between this world and the next. The *kitome* beloned to a class of priests called *nganga*.

Several secret and powerful cults also ruled Esikongo society. The most influential of these was the *kimpasi* (kihm-PAH see). The *kimpasi* cult had to do with suffering. Members of this cult believed that they had "died" and were then reborn, their bodies possessed by an ancestor spirit. Another cult was connected with water and earth spirits. The *mwene Kongo* also headed a cult, which was concerned with the graves of former kings. Yet another cult centered around the powers of destruction and protection, as symbolized by whirlwinds and other forces of nature.

When the Portuguese arrived, bringing Christianity with them, the Esikongo leaders adopted the religion as another cult—one that would eventually influence the entire region.

The Tribute System

Mountains effectively separated the people of the three zones, so that they even spoke different dialects of their common language, Kikongo. In addition, each zone produced different commodities. The products of the coastal zone had low value there, but high value farther east. Similarly, products of the east were highly valued in the west.

This fact allowed the Esikongo to devise a clever system of enforced tribute and tax that linked the three zones economically and politically, making each dependent on the

KIKONGO WORDS

Esikongo	the people of Kongo
Mukongo	an individual
kanda	a social group sharing a common interest
kitome	a spiritual leader of a particular cult
mwene	Lord or king
nzimbu	shell money

other. This practice may have existed in regions north of the Zaire River and as far south as Luanda long before the kingdom was founded.

Key to the system were powerful groups of people known as *kanda*. A *kanda* could be any social group that shared a common interest, and each town, village, and province usually had several *kanda*. The *kanda* organized markets in different locations at different times during the four-day Kongo week. They were probably also responsible for collecting taxes and tribute and passing them on to the king.

Historians believe that the earliest *kanda* were absorbed into Kongo. Their leaders became the governors of their own districts within their own provinces, which had become part of the Kongo kingdom. The governors set up their capitals in the most fertile regions of each province. This arrangement concentrated their power in the larger towns, while the rest of the populace was scattered throughout the countryside. It also allowed the king to exploit the resources of the three zones directly instead of merely taxing passing trade.

The kingdom was divided into many units called *rendas*. Each *renda* was

The *mwene Kongo* appointed the provincial governors for a period of three years. They had many fiscal, military, and administrative duties. For example, the governors had to accompany the *mwene Kongo* to war. They brought their own vassals and soldiers and enforced the same obligation on the lower chiefs. In this way the king could mobilize an army of 80,000 men. The governors had to prove their allegiance by visiting Mbanza Kongo once every three years or whenever summoned. Failure to do so was considered out-and-out rebellion.

charged a tax. The amount depended on the number of people living in the *renda*, and it could be paid in money, labor, or goods. A royal official was granted the *renda* collection for a three-year term. He kept some for himself and passed some on to the king at the capital. The taxes financed the king's household, the army, and other government expenses.

The king also collected tribute. Local people produced foodstuffs and other products from the resources available to them. Their *kanda* demanded a portion of this as tribute in return for their work. In turn, the governors of each province demanded tribute from the local *kanda*. The governors sent a portion of it to the capital, keeping some for themselves. The king sent the governors valuable gifts of products from a different zone of the kingdom. The governors maintained their regional power by distributing some of these coveted products to the local *kanda*. The king was expected to reallocate the tribute he received from the outlying provinces to the powerful *kanda* of the central province.

The governors of the coastal zone sent salt and shells as tribute to the capital. The governors in the central zone sent raffia cloth, while those of the southern, northern, and eastern areas sent copper. The system worked because people wanted the goods they could not get in their own provinces, and these goods were luxuries that most people could not afford to buy. The system also kept the entire power structure beholden to the king.

The luxury items—mainly salt and raffia cloth—were thus much in demand, and their production was encouraged. Sometimes the king even tried to control the production centers and the collection and distribution of *nzimba* shells himself.

As these items moved up the line of tribute, they became concentrated in the hands of the wealthy ruling class. Domestic animals also moved up the chain. Rural people raised chickens, goats, pigs, and sometimes cattle, but they seldom got to enjoy these foods themselves. They were given to the *kanda* and passed on through the governors to the king and other nobles, who all lived at the capital. The most valuable products of all three zones were thus to be found at the lively marketplace in Mbanza Kongo.

The ruling class benefited from this

system. They justified their gains through the economic, political, and spiritual obligations they undertook. The peasants unfortunately had no such chances. Several European visitors reported that they lived in "miserable poverty," similar to conditions in some parts of Europe at the time.

This, then, was the complex world into which the Portuguese stepped. After their arrival it was never to be the same again.

Some historians believe that the kingdom of Kongo was not divided into regions and markets controlled by the various *kanda*. They suggest that the government was extremely centralized. Most provinces, they say, (except for Soyo and Mbata, which were formed before the kingdom was founded), were ruled by nobles appointed by the king. The *mwene Kongo* could install or remove these officials at will. They were most often members of the king's extended royal family, which ensured their loyalty. By frequently rotating the available positions, the king ensured that no one remained in power long enough to challenge the throne. When a new king came to power, he had to diplomatically replace disloyal or threatening provincial governors with his own officials. Often, rival candidates had large followings, and dispute over the valued government positions could lead to war.

There were no donkeys, horses, or camels in the region. Merchants rode oxen along the trade routes. In this carving, the ox is mounted on the backs of two birds, and its pipe-smoking rider is protected by two magical figurines. ▶

The Esikongo Meet the Portuguese

In his book *Heart of Darkness*, written in 1890, Joseph Conrad described the Zaire River (or Congo, as it was then known) as follows: "Going up that river was like traveling back to the beginnings of the world, when vegetation rioted on the earth and the big trees were kings. An empty stream, a great silence, an impenetrable forest."

Four hundred years earlier, in 1483, the Portuguese sailor Diogo Cão (dee OH go kou) was the first European to see the Zaire. How must he have felt as his caravel, or small sailing ship, carefully negotiated the wide, muddy waters of the great river? And what were the feelings of the African people who emerged from the forest to watch this strange apparition float upstream?

Diogo Cão and the Esikongo

Cão anchored his ship at Mpinda (m PIHN duh), in the Zaire estuary, in the province of Soyo. Perhaps the Esikongo believed that Cão and his crew were returning ancestors. After all, they came from the sea, which was regarded as the barrier between this life and the next. The Europeans were white, just as spirits were supposed to be. They spoke a strange language, and they brought with them marvelous gifts from "another world"—one that the Esikongo

▲ Villagers emerge from the depths of the forest along the Zaire River.

Diogo Cão

▲ Diogo Cão made these inscriptions on rocks in the Zaire estuary in 1483. They were discovered 400 years later.

had never encountered. Perhaps, however, the Esikongo simply recognized these white strangers as "foreigners," who had come for peaceful trade.

Whatever their feelings, the Esikongo came on board the caravel and traded ivory for cloth. Through sign language, the Europeans learned that the river was called Zaire and that it ran through a kingdom called Kongo. The king, the Esikongo indicated, lived several days' journey away.

Cão asked the African scouts to guide a Portuguese delegation to the king, and to bring them back at a specified time. Meanwhile, he stayed near the ship and erected a *padrao* (pah DRAH oh),

a stone pillar brought all the way from Lisbon, to commemorate his arrival.

Weeks later, after sailing another 1,100 km (700 mi) farther south, Cão returned to Mpinda, but there was still no sign of his men. Seizing four African hostages, Cão sent word to the king that these men would be returned on his next voyage if his men came back safe and sound. Cão then sailed on to Portugal.

"In the year . . .of 1482 since the birth of our Lord Jesus Christ, the most serene, most excellent, and potent prince, King D. Joao of Portugal, did order this land to be discovered and these *padraos* to be set up by D. Cão, an esquire of his household."

— *Inscription on the* padrao *erected by Cão at the mouth of the Zaire River.*

In Lisbon the hostages were treated kindly. They met the king of Portugal, were entertained by the nobility, and eventually converted to Christianity. These men now wore rich European clothing and spoke some Portuguese. After two years in Portugal, they had changed a great deal from when they first traded on board Cão's caravel.

In 1485, Diogo Cão returned to the Zaire, found his men, and released his hostages. The former hostages were now personal witnesses to the wonders of the "other world" and functioned as able interpreters. They impressed the king with their reports. In keeping with tradition, the *mwene kongo* sent gifts of ivory and raffia cloth to Diogo Cão. He hoped to include the newcomers in the ancient system of tribute.

Cão died on the return journey to Portugal, but the *mwene Kongo*'s diplomacy was not ignored. The Portuguese king, seeing a great opportunity for trade, ordered a mass assault on Kongo. It was not to be achieved with weapons, but with trade goods, technology, and, above all, the Catholic faith.

Christianity for the Esikongo

In March 1491, a fleet of Portuguese ships arrived at the mouth of the Zaire. This time, it brought priests, missionaries, carpenters, masons, tools, instruments, horses, clothes, ornaments, and religious items—everything the Portuguese needed to infiltrate the Kongo culture with their own. They even brought women, who were directed to teach the Esikongo the arts of Portuguese housekeeping!

The ships anchored again at Mpinda, and the captain presented the district governor, or *mwene Soyo*, with gifts. The *mwene Soyo* greeted the Europeans by touching both hands to the ground and putting them to his head—a sacred gesture of the *mbumba* cult. Then he organized a great festival of singing, drumming, and dancing. The Portuguese fired their muskets in a show of power. Finally the *mwene Soyo* and his son were baptized.

The scene was repeated at Mbanza Kongo, the capital, a week's march from Mpinda. The Portuguese were

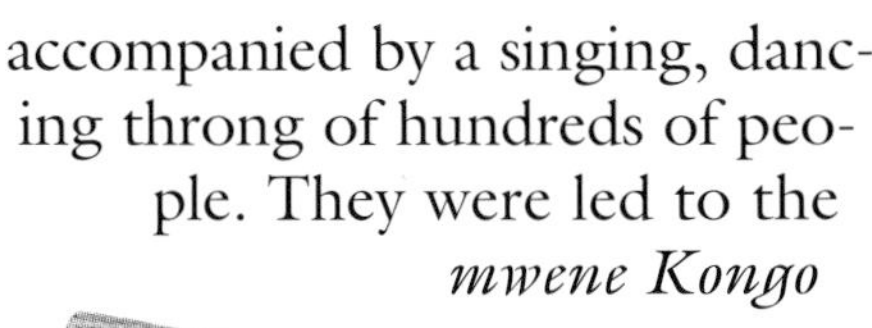

accompanied by a singing, dancing throng of hundreds of people. They were led to the *mwene Kongo* himself, Nzinga a Nkuwu (n ZIHN guh ah n KOO woo). He sat on a throne inlaid with ivory and raised on a great platform. He wore a loincloth, a royal cap, and copper bracelets. A zebra tail— the badge of kingship—hung from his left shoulder.

The Portuguese presented the king with brocades, velvet and silk fabrics, horsetails mounted in silver, gold and silver trinkets, magnificent garments, and a cage of red pigeons. The king greeted the Portuguese with ritual *mbumba* cult gestures. Then he asked to be baptized.

The Portuguese priests—who, after all, had come thousands of miles for just this purpose—could not believe their luck. In West Africa, their missions had met with little success. But here was an African culture that seemed to welcome Christianity with open arms!

On May 3, 1491, the *mwene Kongo*, most of his court, and hundreds of commoners were baptized. The nobles took Portuguese names and titles. Nzinga a

◀ Once Christianity took hold in Kongo, many crucifixes like this one were made, in which Christ was depicted as an African, and often as a woman.

Chiefly Protocol

The most important of the dignitaries grasps his own right wrist in his left hand, places the index finger of his right hand on the ground, carries it to his temples three times, opens the hand, presses the tips of his fingers to the ground, and then with closed fists beats the hands together rhythmically. This last gesture is repeated by every person present.

◀The *nwene Kongo* is baptized.

The Esikongo believed in a supreme god, the creator, called *Nzambi a Mpugu.* But since he was invisible and inaccessible, he could not be worshipped or even represented in any form. Christianity strengthened this belief in a divine being. A host of lesser gods and spirits of deceased ancestors governed the individual's life. People wore many idols and fetishes. Some also worshipped the sun, moon, or stars. Most people consulted an oracle before making decisions or embarking on a journey.

Nkuwu became King Joao (jou) [John] I, after the Portuguese king. His son, the governor of the province of Nsundi, was now called Afonso—a name that, as one chronicler noted, "he was to make glorious." Immediately after the ceremony, building began on a stone church.

The Portuguese believed they had accomplished their mission, but the Esikongo actually had their own reasons for accepting Christianity. Some historians believe that they saw baptism into Christianity as an initiation into another cult headed by the Portuguese king. In this light, baptism would not have seemed strange to the Esikongo at all.

In addition, the *mwene Kongo* was very interested in trade. Indeed, he controlled all trade in the kingdom and was eager to impress the Portuguese with Kongo's suitability as a trading partner. What better way to achieve this than by "taking on" the strangers' religion?

The *mwene Kongo* was also about to help his son Afonso put down a rebellion in the Nsundi province. He wanted to enlist Portuguese aid in this matter and knew that once he was baptized, it would be hard for the Portuguese to refuse him.

Aid From the Portuguese

King Joao was right. The Portuguese felt obliged to help a brother in Christ. Thus a black army, aided by a few white soldiers, marched to battle under the Christian banner. The Portuguese soldiers wore armor, used crossbows, and were immensely skillful at sword fighting. The Esikongo warriors, also skilled swordsmen, carried buffalo-hide shields. They opened the battle with volleys of arrows, followed by a charge into hand-to-hand combat. The Portuguese also helped by drawing their ship up river, near to the island where the battle was raging. From there, they launched their ship's artillery at the enemy.

Not surprisingly, the *mwene Kongo* returned to the capital in triumph. In gratitude, he settled the Portuguese in their own section of town, near his palace. For a time, peace and friendship ruled. Doors were left open, it was said, with no need for guards. The 500-year association between the Esikongo and the Portuguese had begun.

Europeans reported that Kongo soldiers often practiced military drills and remained stationed near their lords' enclosures, ready to march at a moment's notice. During battle, valiant men fired up the soldiers' courage by beating with sticks on wooden bells. Ranks of archers advanced, dodging and darting in all directions until their captain signaled a retreat, and a second rank of archers came forward. Generals and lesser captains signaled precise commands with drums, horns, and other instruments.

In the late fifteenth century, the gun was still a very primitive weapon. A few Portuguese soldiers in Kongo might have had matchlock muskets. These were deadly but took a long time to reload and had a short range. They were probably not of much use in African warfare. European soldiers relied on arrows and pikes until the 1680s, when the flintlock musket was developed. Only then did the gun became the main weapon in Africa.

Tribute and Trade— A Delicate Balance

Afonso: The True Believer

When King Joao I died, his wife, baptized Eleanor, kept his death secret, for she was a good Christian, and she wished her Christian son, Afonso, to become king. In truth, his brother Mpanzu claimed the throne, and Mpanzu despised the Christian faith.

Thus, for three days following Joao's death, Eleanor allowed no one near the king's chambers. In great haste, she sent runners to the province of Nsundi, where Afonso was governor. And each ran his distance, passing on his message to the next, until word of his father's death reached Afonso. And in one day and two nights, he accomplished with marvelous speed, being carried by porters, the great distance and suddenly appeared in the city.

Now, together with the death of King Joao, was announced the succession to the throne of Dom Afonso. But his rival Mpanzu had many followers. They hated the Christians and believed that they had brought ill upon the land. How could their *kanda* compete with the wondrous gifts brought by the white strangers, which only the king could buy? Not only this, but these Christians ruled that a man might have only one wife! For this reason, the

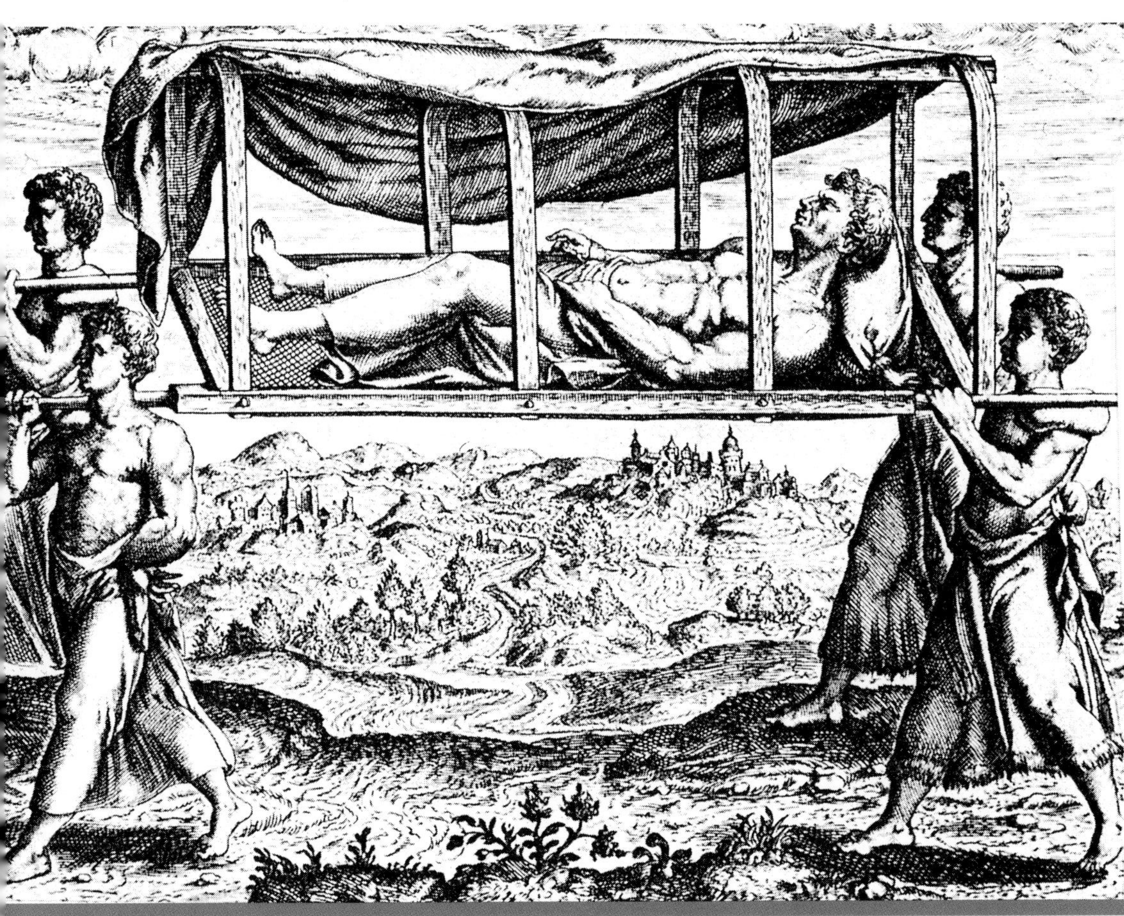

◀ In Kongo, the king or wealthy nobles often traveled in a litter, carried by four slaves. For long distances, a relay system was organized. One team would cover a certain distance, and then another team would take over. In this way, King Afonso was able to cover the great distance from Mbanza Nsundi to Mbanza Kongo in only one day and two nights to claim the throne.

Christians supported Afonso, who was baptized and who was the son of Eleanor, the king's principal wife.

Mpanzu and his followers were outraged. How could a man build his family and become prosperous with only one wife? Indeed, with their new ideas these

In this sixteenth century drawing a Portuguese captain kneels before King Afonso, whose African subjects prostrate themselves on the ground. Afonso is shown wearing European clothing, which he often did, especially on ceremonial occasions. The crown may be the artist's addition. ▶

strangers from foreign shores were undermining the very foundations of the ancient Kongo cults and traditions. Mpanzu vowed to seize the throne and rid the land of these troublesome people.

He then collected a great force, to the number of nearly 200,000 men, and came armed against Afonso. Dom Afonso awaited him in the royal city with those few friends—some 10,000—who had agreed to defend the place. But

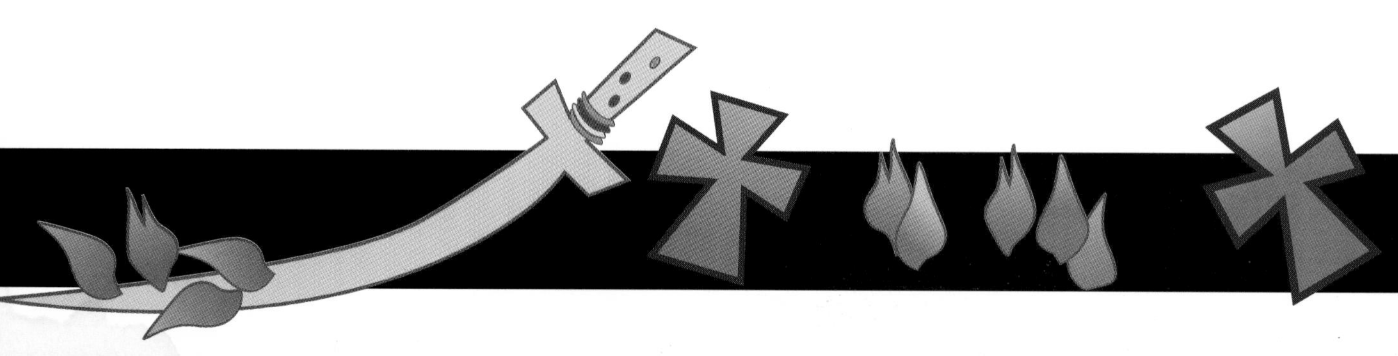

they proved doubtful and timid on account of the great army Mpanzu had brought with him.

Afonso was resolute. Those who wished to surrender should do so, he cried. He would fight in the name of God, who would protect him and his followers! And they received further encouragement from the aged lord of Soyo. “Behold, my age is now 100 years,” he said, “and yet I take arms, being zealous for the religion that I have adopted. And do you, who are in the flower of your age, show timidity, and so little loyalty to your lawful sovereign?”

At this moment came a heavenly vision in the form of a bright and beautiful light. At the sight of this, Afonso fell on his knees in tears, lifting his eyes and hands to heaven, in a state of rapture from what he saw. All present did the same and were blinded for a time by the brightness of the light. Then, by degrees, lifting their eyes to heaven, they saw five flaming swords that remained transfixed in a circle for the space of an hour.

This vision greatly strengthened the minds of the citizens, even while it struck terror into the hearts of the opposing army. Notwithstanding, Mpanzu ordered his army to block the only passage from the royal city. On this path there was a shallow marsh, and here Mpanzu’s soldiers drove sharp stakes, covering them with water, so that the enemy might suddenly be ensnared by them and perish.

In the early morning, Mpanzu led the assault with furious energy on the north side of the city, where the great plain forms an open battleground. Here, Dom Afonso and his handful of men were ranged against the pagans. But before they could fight, Mpanzu’s men launched their arrows and fled!

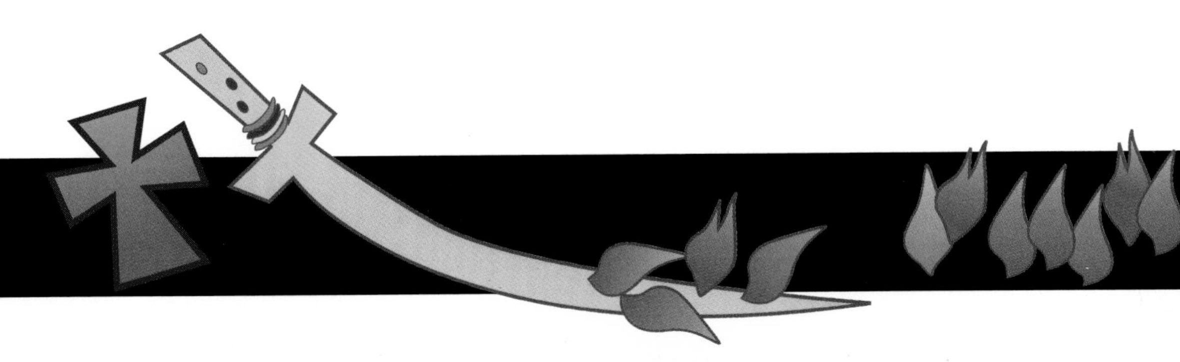

The next day, Mpanzu returned to the assault in the same place and again—at the moment of attack—seemed to flee in fear!

Afonso was amazed. What cowards were these? Why had he been so easily granted this victory? Afonso's men had captured some enemy soldiers. From them, they learned that Afonso's victory was the result of a miracle. At first, the enemy had been confused and blinded by the dazzling vision of a lady in white. Then they had been put to flight by a knight riding a great white steed and bearing a red cross on his breast.

On hearing this, Dom Afonso sent word to Mpanzu that these visions were the Virgin Mary, the Mother of God, and Saint James, who were sent from God to his aid. If Mpanzu would become a Christian, said Afonso's message, he too could receive similar favors.

Mpanzu would not in any way consent to this. He spent the night arranging for the conquest of the city from two positions. Part of his army he sent to the narrow pass where he had placed stakes in the marshes. With the other, led by himself, he attempted to reach the city by way of the river, where there were no guards. He made his first onslaught but was easily routed. Hoping to push on to the other side of the city, while his enemies were defending the pass, Mpanzu fell into a trap, for those who were in the city, hearing from their scouts that Mpanzu was coming their way, hastened there to repulse him. They fought with such fury against him that, being overcome by fright, he rushed headlong into the marshy ambush covered with stakes that he himself had prepared. And there, almost maddened with pain, the points of the stakes being poisoned and penetrating his flesh, Mpanzu's life ended.

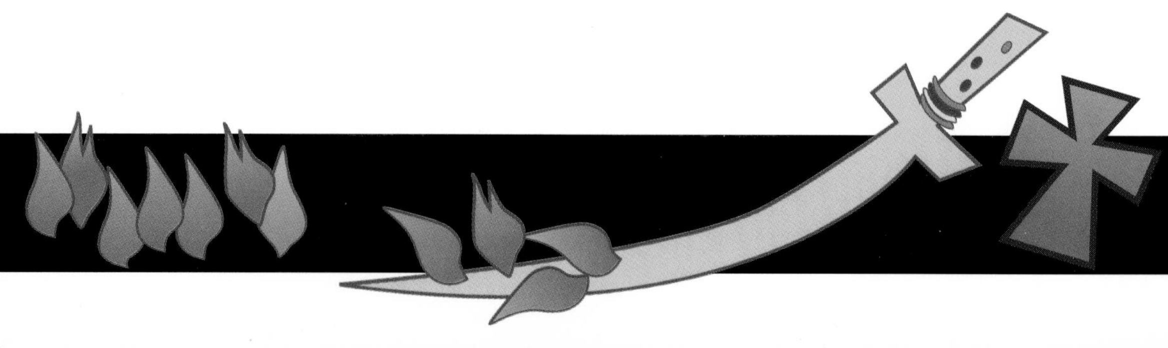

With this victory and the death of his rival, King Afonso was freed from further opposition. At once, he set about building the Church of the Holy Cross, so called after the flaming swords seen in the sky. To set an example for his people, he was the first to carry stones on his shoulders for the foundation. The building was quickly raised, and a great number of nobles asked for baptism.

Besides this, King Afonso assembled the governors from the different provinces. He told them publicly that whoever possessed idols contrary to the Christian religion must give them up or be burned and receive no pardon. Thus in less than a month were brought to the court all the sorcery books, magic writings, and idols that had been worshipped as gods. Truly, great numbers of these things were collected—winged dragons, serpents of horrible shape, large goats, tigers, and various monstrous animals. The more they were ugly and deformed, the more they had been held in honor.

Now the king commanded that to the same place where he had conquered Mpanzu every person should bring a piece of wood. A great pile was raised, and there the idols were cast in and burned. Then Afonso assembled all the people and gave them crosses and images of the saints, which he had received from the Portuguese. He commanded each of his lords to build a church and to erect crosses in the cities of the provinces that they ruled.

In this manner, in process of time, the Catholic faith took root in those regions. And when King Afonso was near death, he spoke of the Christian religion with great love and trust. He left no doubt that the cross and the true faith were forever imprinted on his heart.

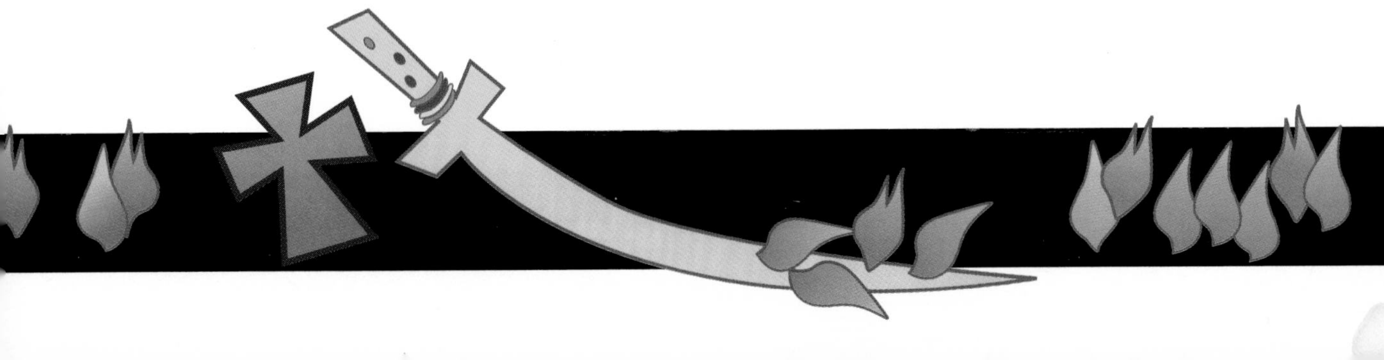

In 1791, Daniel Defoe (author of *Robinson Crusoe)* wrote a popular book called *Travels of Captain Singleton.* His book astonished nineteenth-century readers because it seemed to have foreseen the discoveries made then in the Congo by the explorer Henry Morton Stanley. In fact, Defoe carries his hero, Captain Singleton, through exactly the same scenes and events that Duarte Lopes experienced when he visited Kongo in 1578, and which were translated by Filippo Pigafetta in 1591. Clearly, Defoe had read this important historical work.

The Historical Record

This account of Afonso's rise to power in 1506 is adapted from a book written by Filippo Pigafetta in 1591 and translated into English in 1597. Pigafetta's work was, in turn, drawn from the accounts of Duarte (dwart) Lopes, (loh-PEZ) a sailor who voyaged to Luanda in 1578. Lopes spent 12 years in the kingdom of Kongo. He was knighted there and served as Kongo's ambassador to Rome. His account gave historians one of the fullest and most accurate records of the region at that time.

King Afonso I remains one of the most fascinating figures of the kingdom's turbulent history. In fact, a missionary, writing in 1889, claimed that "a Negro from the Kongo knows the names of only three kings—that of the reigning monarch, that of his predecessor, and that of Dom Afonso I."

What kind of a man was Afonso? Why did he so eagerly accept the Christian faith, and what kind of kingdom did he envision? Rui d'Aguiar (rwee dah-GWAHR), a Catholic priest in the Kongo, provides some insight into these questions in a letter he wrote to the king of Portugal in 1516.

May your Highness be informed that Afonso's Christian life is such that he appears to me not as a man but as an angel. . . . For I assure your Highness that it is he who instructs us; better than we, he knows the Prophets and the Gospel of Our Lord Jesus Christ and all the lives of the saints. . . . I must say, Lord, that he does nothing but study and that many times he falls asleep over his books. . . . When he gives audience or when he dispenses justice, his words are inspired by God . . .

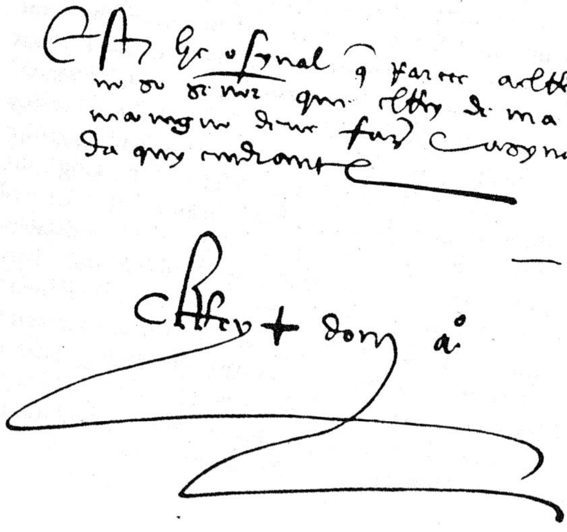

▲ Afonso dictated many letters to the king of Portugal. Shown here are the last lines of a letter with his official signature.

As Pigafetta relates, Afonso began his reign by destroying the traditional idols and replacing them with sacred objects of the Catholic faith. He also built several churches in Mbanza Kongo.

Afonso was a progressive man for his time. He developed an education policy for the children of nobles. By 1516, more than a thousand boys attended school in Mbanza Kongo, where they learned reading, writing, and the articles of the Catholic faith. One of the king's sisters also directed schools for girls—a truly innovative program.

Afonso learned to speak and write Portuguese. He wore Portuguese clothing and modeled his court on the court in Lisbon. (By the sixteenth century, Kongo nobles had adopted Portuguese titles, such as "principes, duques, marquezes" [princes, dukes, marquises].) Afonso kept up an endless stream of letters to "his brother" the king, demanding more priests and, especially, more teachers for his schools.

Afonso sent many young men to Portugal to be educated. One of them became the principal of a college in Lisbon. Another—Afonso's own son Henrique—became a bishop and returned to the kingdom to perform his religious duties there.

A Balancing Act

Afonso inherited a situation that had begun with his father, King Joao I. Joao had defined the Christian religion as a new cult—one that fit in very well with the existing Kongo traditions. But most of the nobles were also baptized and therefore belonged to the same cult. King Joao failed to make the new cult his exclusive realm, and so had to share his status and power with his titleholders.

In addition, King Joao had very little to offer the Portuguese. They came looking for gold, and the best he could offer was ivory and palm cloth. So the Portuguese reduced the value of their own gifts, which in turn reduced the king's status at the peak of the tribute system.

Many of King Joao's chief titleholders—those important men and

Afonso's educational policy paid off. Members of the Esikongo ruling class were able to write letters in Portuguese, using either paper (which was very expensive) or banana leaves. Court testimonies, records of inquests, certificates of office, and church proceedings were recorded. Literacy made better and faster communications possible to the interior of the kingdom and also directly to Europe. Kongo schools were so good that Miguel de Castro, a seventeenth-century nobleman educated there, could hold his own in Europe as a recognized author of Latin poetry.

In 1495, King Joao I of Kongo threw the Christians–led by his own son, Afonso–out of Mbanza Kongo. Afonso became governor of Nsundi. Many Portuguese followed this Christian prince and became his supporters when he was king and moved to the capital, where he revived the Christian faith. Most Esikongo were baptized and actively sought the sacrament. They took saints' names, learned Christian songs and prayers, and celebrated Christian holidays. At the same time, they continued to believe that their ancestors could affect their lives. To them, the Christian saints they worshipped were much like the "spirits" they had worshipped before the arrival of Christianity.

women of the *kanda* and *kitome* groups and the lords of the various provinces—were completely opposed to the Christians. After all, the Catholic priests threatened the status of the *kitome*, who were spiritual leaders or "priests" in their own right. And when the Catholic priests demanded that the king keep only his principal wife, the Kongo officials saw their own security crumbling, for the king's lesser wives were almost always related to the titleholders and created their bond to the royal house.

It was thus easy for Afonso's brother Mpanzu to gain followers and build his huge army. Even though Mpanzu was defeated by Afonso, his followers formed a discontented, bristling group that continually threatened the king's power.

Afonso, however, was in a stronger position than his father had been. For several years, he had been governor of the province of Nsundi, northeast of the capital. From there, he controlled the trade route to the mining region north of the Zaire River, where copper was collected. When he became

Copper was sold in the form of arm rings. Between 1506 and 1511, Afonso exported 5,200 such arm rings.

king, Afonso was able to offer the Portuguese this copper, which was highly valued in Europe. In return, their gifts to him increased in value. Afonso distributed these gifts among the governors of the provinces, thus gradually winning their support.

▲ Copper arm rings similar to this one were a valuable form of currency in Kongo.

Afonso personally manipulated the trade of the kingdom. He not only controlled the copper route but also held the monopoly on the valuable *nzimbu* shells collected at Luanda. With the copper, the shells, and ivory, palm cloth, skins, and honey collected through the tribute system, he could purchase more goods from the Portuguese traders than anyone else.

Afonso's power thus hung delicately in the balance. As long as he could supply the Portuguese with valuable trade goods, he could maintain his authority as king. As soon as that position was threatened, he would tumble.

Black Gold

As in many other parts of Africa, slavery was common in the kingdom of Kongo. Slaves were usually war captives, criminals, or other undesirables. Sometimes, people would pawn themselves or a relative into slavery to pay off a debt. Slaves usually worked as soldiers, laborers, or domestic servants. In many cases, because they were politically neutral and had lost their tribal ties, slaves were useful in government and could attain highly responsible positions. In Kongo, they might be messengers, nobles, and trusted merchants, trading for their masters.

Slaves in Africa were usually not far removed from their homelands. They were largely familiar with the culture that had enslaved them. Their labor benefited the local African economy, and they could marry, own property, and often buy or otherwise earn their freedom. This was a very different system from the type of slavery established by the Portuguese soon after their explorations of the west African coast had begun.

The Beginnings

In 1415, Prince Henry of Portugal, known as Henry the Navigator, had been a Crusader in the North African Muslim port city of Ceuta (say-OO-tah). There he saw camel caravans arrive, heavily laden with gold. Where did the gold come from? the prince inquired. From the fabulously wealthy kingdom of Mali, south of the Sahara, he was told. Prince Henry determined to find the source of this African gold by sailing down the west coast of the continent.

At this time, the Europeans had also developed a taste for sugar, which had fetched top prices ever since Crusaders in the Middle East tasted it for the first time. So the Portuguese were also searching for tropical islands like Madeira (mah DEE ruh), far off the western coast of present-day Morocco, where sugar cane could be grown.

In the Middle Ages, the European economy had been mostly based on spices and other rare goods obtained from the Far East. The trade routes passed over land and by sea from China and Malaysia via India, converging on the city of Constantinople (Istanbul). In 1453, the city—the vital link between Europe and the east—fell to the Turks. The trade routes were closed to European merchants and the prices of goods skyrocketed. Now, Europeans searched not only for gold and new lands suitable for planting sugar cane, but also for new routes to the East. These factors were the cata-

In this eighteenth-century drawing of Kongo life, an African slave carries a parasol of woven grass for his African master. ▶

"The noble spirit of this Prince was ever urging him . . . to carry out very great deeds. . . . He had also a wish to know the land that lay beyond the isles of Canary and that cape called Bojador, for up to his time, neither by writings, nor by the memory of man, was known with certainty the nature of the land beyond that Cape."
—*Gomes Eannes de Anzurara,* Discovery and Conquest of Guinea, *1453*

lysts that triggered the explosive age of exploration.

The Italian explorer Christopher Columbus thought he could reach the East by sailing west. But the Portuguese believed that they might reach the East by sailing around Africa to India. The journey around Africa had never before been attempted. How big was Africa? How long would the voyage take? No one knew. But the lure of gold, new sugar plantations, and great profits to be made from trade with India and China was irresistible.

Starting around 1419, Prince Henry financed one voyage after another. By 1433, he had sent 15 expeditions down Africa's northwestern coast, but each turned back at the infamous Cape Bojador (boh hah DOR). They were afraid to continue, for, it was said, ". . . beyond this cape there is no race of men nor place of inhabitants . . . while the currents

Courtesy of the Granger Collection

▲ In this fifteenth-century painting, Prince Henry of Portugal leads troops against the Muslim city of Ceuta, on Africa's northern shore. As a Crusader, Henry received much geographical and historical information about Africa from the Moors. When his campaigns were over, he set up a map-making institute and a center of worldwide exploration. Prince Henry financed several voyages of exploration down the west coast of Africa.

The Portuguese made their way down the west coast of Africa in ships like this sixteenth-century caravel. ▶

are so terrible that no ship having once passed . . . will ever be able to return."

At last, in 1434, a captain named Gil Eannes (zheel ahnsh) rounded the cape and landed on the African coast. The spell was broken, and now each new voyage ventured farther south.

In 1442, a few West Africans were captured as "souvenirs" and taken to Lisbon. It soon became fashionable for middle- and upper-class Europeans to own black servants, and over the next 60 years, the slow trickle of slaves from West Africa to Europe became a flood. By 1550, African slaves made up at least 10 percent of the population of Lisbon.

While the Portuguese had not come to Africa in search of slaves, they were familiar with the practice of slavery. In fact, European merchants used slaves from North Africa and Russia to work sugar plantations on various Mediterranean islands. The uninhabited islands of Principe (PREEN see pay) and São Tomé (sou toh-MAY), off the central west

◀ This Portuguese map, drawn in 1502, shows extensive knowledge of West Africa. The kingdom of Kongo is marked south of the Zaire River.

By 1731, when this French map was drawn, Europeans had gained greater knowledge of the kingdom of Kongo or "Royaume de Congo" in French. ▼

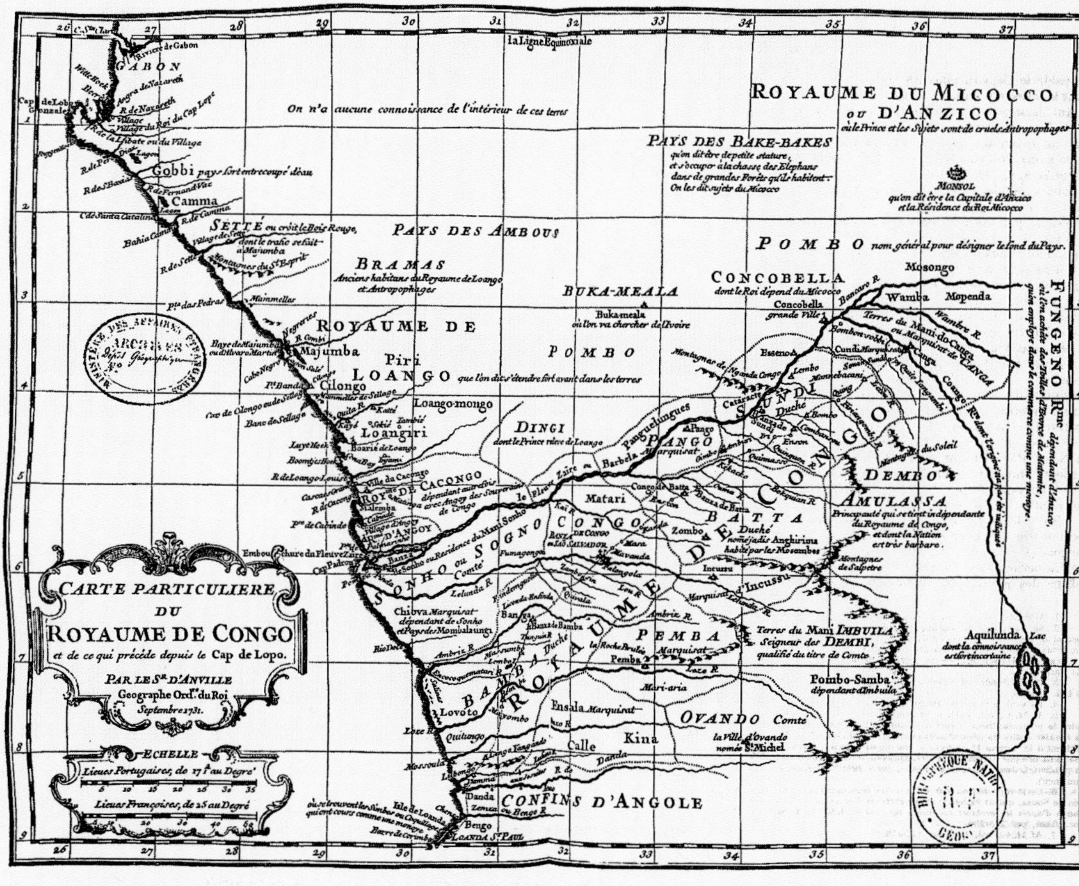

African coast, turned out to be perfect for growing sugar cane. To the Portuguese, it was logical to use slaves captured from the mainland to work these new plantations. And once Columbus had reached the Americas in 1492, it was a further logical step to establish the Portuguese plantation system in the "New World."

By 1482, gold and slaves were being exported from the Portuguese trading fort of El Mina on the Gold Coast (Ghana). By 1483, Diogo Cão had reached the mouth of the Zaire River. Only five years later, Bartholomeu Dias reached the Cape of Good Hope. And in 1498, Vasco da Gama rounded the Cape and sailed for Calicutt in India. The Portuguese had found their African gold. They had found islands for their sugar plantations, and they had found their trade route to the East. On the way, they had discovered a trade that was to prove more lucrative than gold, sugar, or spices—the slave trade, so profitable that its human cargo came to be called "black gold."

Afonso's Monopoly Threatened

The economy of the kingdom of Kongo was based mainly on the tribute system, in which war captives and goods such as cloth, ivory, skins, domestic animals, and foodstuffs were exchanged. The king received enough revenue from these

MONEY, MONEY, MONEY

Standard-size vessels contained specific numbers of *nzimbu* shells, ranging from 40 to 20,000. Large shells were ten times more valuable than small shells.

Values in the mid-seventeenth century were the following (dollar amounts are based on silver values in January 1995).

1 *funda* = 1,000 big shells = 100 *reis* = 58 grams of silver = $113
1 *lukufu* = 10,000 big shells = 1,000 *reis* = 580 grams of silver = $226
1 *kofo* = 20,000 big shells = 2,000 *reis* = 1160 grams of silver = $452

Afonso I paid a stonemason as much as one *kofo* per day! A *reis* (rays) was a silver coin used not for purchasing goods but as a way of keeping accounts. The value of goods was convverted to *reis* so that a trader knew the exact value of his holdings in stock without actually having the goods.

goods and from trade tolls and taxes to maintain his authority. He also monopolized the *nzimbu* shell money collected at Luanga.

The Portuguese brought goods with them that upset the carefully balanced give-and-take of the tribute system. Red parasols, gilt mirrors, brass hairpins, and other trinkets soon became hot items among the Esikongo. In exchange, the Portuguese accepted ivory, copper, cloth, skins, and slaves. From the start of the Kongo-Portuguese relationship, Kongo had exported slaves to the sugar plantations on the island of São Tomé, which had become one of the leading sugar producers in the world. As the demand for sugar in Europe escalated, the plantations on the island and in the Portuguese colony of Brazil grew in size and number. Managers could not get enough slaves to do the work, and those they bought usually died after three to five years. Thus there was a constant need to replace them. By 1516, Kongo was already exporting 4,000 slaves a year, and that number was to rise continuously.

Touch and Go

Afonso must have been very disappointed in the Portuguese. He cer-

São Tomé—Capital of Portuguese West Africa

Portuguese sailors reached the uninhabited island of São Tomé in 1472, and official settlement began in 1473. The climate there was deadly to Europeans. The earliest settlement consisted of 600 exiled Jewish children, sent to settle or die. Those who did survive intermarried with Africans and Portuguese. Soon a mixed plantation colony developed that became the seat of Portuguese government in the Gulf of Guinea. Its authority stretched from the fort of El Mina (in Ghana) to the colony of Angola, south of Kongo, which included the kingdom of Ndongo and which the Portuguese founded in 1571. The Tomistas, as the inhabitants of São Tomé were called, were extremely active in all the Portuguese ventures in Africa. On São Tomé, a common creole language was spoken. This mixture of Portuguese and African languages was spoken in trading communities throughout the Gulf region. In the nineteenth century, it was gradually replaced by Pidgin English, still spoken today. Pidgin English contains many Portuguese words, reflecting its origins on São Tomé.

tainly desired trade contacts with them. He was also a truly devout Christian and sincerely believed that the Portuguese and Esikongo cultures could flourish side by side, each benefiting from the other. Yet he complained in his letters to the Portuguese king that the Portuguese soldiers did not fight well, or carry out their assignments. In other words, they were of little use to him in his various wars. In a letter written in 1526, Afonso also complained bitterly that the provincial governors and chiefs were becoming richer in European goods than he. Now, having no need of the king, they refused tribute and rebelled.

Afonso could only maintain his position as *mwene Kongo* through the tribute system. He had to contend with the mounting Portuguese pressure for more and more slaves in exchange for the goods he needed to keep his titleholders in allegiance and for the priests, artisans, and teachers he badly needed and so often requested.

By Kongo law, only war captives could be sold into slavery, and there were very few available. Afonso raided a nearby region for slaves, but he had no guns and no standing

army. Certain Kongo individuals were kidnapping Kongo's own people for sale and dealing directly with the Portuguese. Meanwhile the Portuguese themselves were raiding the interior. Even the Portuguese priests, whom Afonso had so admired, were heavily involved in the slave trade.

Afonso now turned to his old contacts in the Nsundi region, where he had been governor. They had kept the copper route from the Tio (TEE oh) region north of Nsundi to the coast open for years. Now they were able to supply slaves along this route, which passed through Afonso's capital at Mbanza Kongo. By supplying the Portuguese with slaves, Afonso was able to maintain his power at the top of the tribute system. In addition, the Tio people demanded *nzimbu* shell money for their slaves. Afonso held the monopoly on the shells, which prevented the Portuguese from direct purchase with the Tio.

◀ Traders known as *pombeiros*, who were usually Afro-Portuguese of mixed blood, traveled far into the interior to buy slaves from African traders. Such journeys could last two years or more. The captives—men, women, and children—wore heavy yokes to prevent escape. Many Africans died before they ever reached the Portuguese ships at the coast.

In 1526, Afonso wrote to the king of Portugal about the slave trade: "We cannot estimate how great the damage is, because the merchants capture daily our own subjects, sons of our noblemen, vassals, and relatives . . . and cause them to be sold. . . . It is our will that in these kingdoms there should not be any trade in slaves or market for slaves." Some historians believe Afonso was writing about Kongo. Others suggest that he was referring to Ndongo, Kongo's rival in trade. He would have wanted the slave trade in Ndongo to cease in order to benefit his own kingdom.

There are no definite statistics on the number of slaves exported from Kongo, but rough estimates suggest that about 350,000 people were taken between 1500 and 1600. In all, 2 million or more Angolans were bought or captured by Portuguese, French, British, Brazilian, and Dutch merchants.

Afonso was at times threatened by attempts to seize the throne. He even narrowly escaped assassination in 1540. His position in Kongo had been threatened by the Portuguese and the slave trade. Yet he strengthened his power and used it effectively, ensuring the loyalty of his titleholders. He ignored the Christian rule on monogamy and placed his sons in important government positions. Through tribute, he drew in many new regions, expanding the kingdom to almost double its size. He established Christianity throughout the region, and developed a highly literate upper class through his education system.

When Afonso died in 1543, he is said to have been forgotten by the king in Portugal. It is ironic that Afonso has gone down in history as Kongo's greatest king—the one who is remembered to this day above all others. In fact, some historians call the reign of Dom Afonso I the "Golden Age" of Kongo.

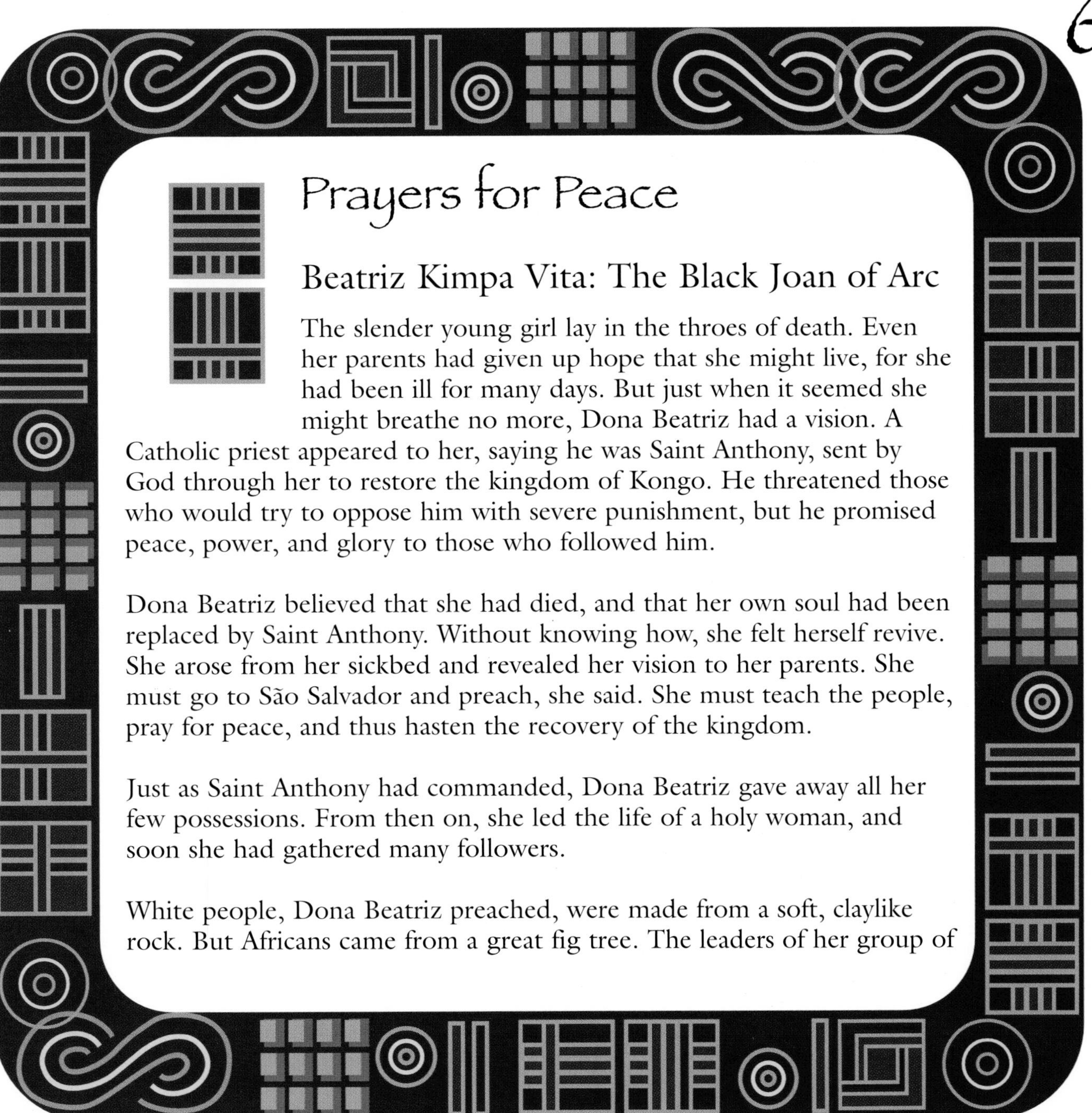

Prayers for Peace

Beatriz Kimpa Vita: The Black Joan of Arc

The slender young girl lay in the throes of death. Even her parents had given up hope that she might live, for she had been ill for many days. But just when it seemed she might breathe no more, Dona Beatriz had a vision. A Catholic priest appeared to her, saying he was Saint Anthony, sent by God through her to restore the kingdom of Kongo. He threatened those who would try to oppose him with severe punishment, but he promised peace, power, and glory to those who followed him.

Dona Beatriz believed that she had died, and that her own soul had been replaced by Saint Anthony. Without knowing how, she felt herself revive. She arose from her sickbed and revealed her vision to her parents. She must go to São Salvador and preach, she said. She must teach the people, pray for peace, and thus hasten the recovery of the kingdom.

Just as Saint Anthony had commanded, Dona Beatriz gave away all her few possessions. From then on, she led the life of a holy woman, and soon she had gathered many followers.

White people, Dona Beatriz preached, were made from a soft, claylike rock. But Africans came from a great fig tree. The leaders of her group of followers proudly wore crowns of the braided fibers of this tree, which they saw as the emblem of their faith. The Kongo, Dona Beatriz taught, was the true Holy Land, and the founders of Christianity were Negroes. Christ had been born in São Salvador and baptized in Nsundi. The Virgin Mary had been born of an African slave woman.

Dona Beatriz predicted a golden age. She would reoccupy Mbanza Kongo—now called São Salvador—which had been destroyed by enemy invasions. The roots of fallen trees would transform themselves into gold and silver. The ruins of the city would reveal treasure troves of precious stones and metals. And all the rich products of the whites would come to those who followed this new faith and worked to rebuild the kingdom. Kongo would revive in all its former glory!

Wherever Dona Beatriz went, her women disciples cleared her path. And when she walked these paths, it was said that twisted trees suddenly grew straight. People wished to touch her and to receive her blessed touch in return. They gave her their cloaks to cover her head and fought over food and drink that she had touched.

Every Friday, Dona Beatriz imitated the death of Christ. She claimed that she "died and went to heaven," where she dined with God and pleaded the cause of the Negroes, especially the restoration of the

◀ Father Barnardo da Gallo painted this portrait of Beatriz Kimpa Vita. "This young woman was about twenty-two years old. She was rather slender and fine-featured. Externally she appeared very devout. She spoke with gravity, and seemed to weigh each word. She foretold the future and predicted, among other things, that the day of Judgement was near."
—Father Lorenzo da Lucca, 1706

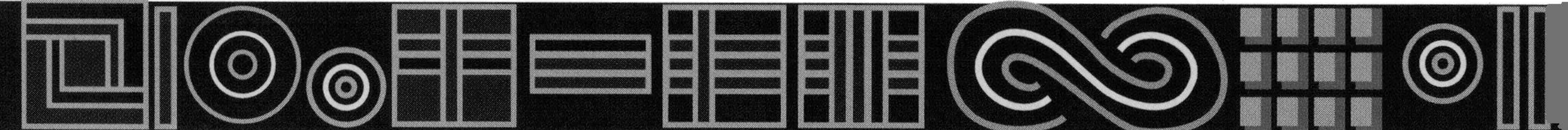

kingdom. On Saturdays, she was "born again," returning to earth to bring God's messages to her people. Dona Beatriz also wished to imitate the Virgin Mary and to have a son who would become a savior. A son was indeed born to her, a son whom she claimed came from heaven.

The Esikongo believed that their prayers had been answered. After years of pain and suffering, God had at last cast his benevolent eye upon them. Dona Beatriz was His messenger, and the kingdom would find salvation through her.

Dona Beatriz prepared to reoccupy the abandoned city of São Salvador. She commanded the nobles to follow her there and to recognize her as their spiritual leader. From their numbers, she said, she would choose one to be the *mwene Kongo*.

And thus it happened that São Salvador was soon repopulated. Some went there to worship Dona Beatriz, the saint; others to see the rebuilt capital. Some merely went to watch, while others believed they could miraculously recover their health. Some came with political ambitions, and some were returning home.

◀ This nineteenth-century wooden image from Kongo idealizes feminine beauty as a mother tenderly cradles her infant's head in her hands. The figure was believed to have healing powers for gynecological illnesses.

In São Salvador, Dona Beatriz Kimpa Vita pronounced herself the spiritual leader of the kingdom. Already present in the capital city was a man named Pedro Constantinho da Silva. He was a noble of high position who was making preparations for King Pedro IV to leave his island of refuge and reenter the city. Seeing here a chance for his own advancement, da Silva too joined Dona Beatriz's movement and converted to her beliefs. In return, she crowned him the "true" king of Kongo.

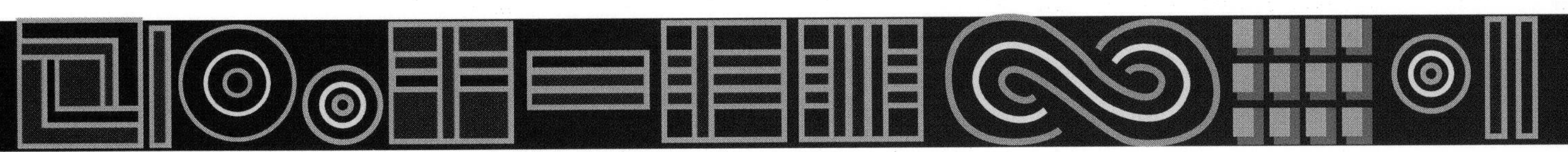

While many Esikongo were thus enthralled with their Saint Anthony, there were those who opposed Beatriz. The ruler of the southern province of Mbamba wished to rid his domain of her doctrine. With holy zeal, he took up a great cross and traveled with it throughout the huge region, rounding up the devils incarnate and purging the people of their unholy beliefs.

The Catholic priests in the kingdom also became increasingly outraged. Fathers Bernardo da Gallo and Lorenzo da Lucca, both missionaries of the Italian Capuchin order, charged that this “Saint Anthony” was undermining their teachings. Dona Beatriz is a fraud! they claimed. She had changed the words of sacred Catholic hymns to suit her own purposes. And what kind of a heretic was she, who claimed to be Saint Anthony—a man—yet also claimed the virgin birth of her own son?

The missionaries demanded that King Pedro take action against Dona Beatriz. At first, Pedro held back, for he did not wish to alienate the people who believed in her. But in the end, the Capuchin friars prevailed. On July 2, 1706, Bernardo da Gallo and Lorenzo da Lucca were witnesses as Dona Beatriz, her “Angel Guardian” (a disciple named Barros), and her newborn son were brought to trial.

The royal messengers stood in the center of the great multitude of people and gave a signal with bells that they carried in each hand. At once, the people fell back, and in the space appeared the judge. He was clad from head to foot in a black mantle and wore a black hat. The culprits were led before him. The young woman, who carried her child in her arms, was filled with fear and dread. She sat on the bare ground before the crowd, her head lowered.

In solemn tones, as befitted the occasion, the judge began to speak. First he eulogized the king. Then he spoke at length, giving proof of his own worthiness as a judge.

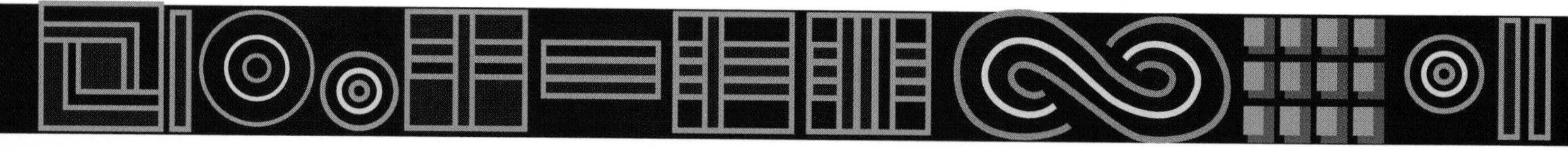

The crowd remained deadly silent. The judge paused. Now, at last, the sentence would be pronounced upon the culprits.

Under the false name of Saint Anthony, the judge proclaimed, this woman—Dona Beatriz Kimpa Vita—had deceived the people with her heresies and falsehoods. Consequently the king, her lord, and the royal councils condemned her to be burned at the stake, together with her child and her disciple, Barros, known as Saint John. Father da Lucca found this too great a cruelty and persuaded the king to let the baby live.

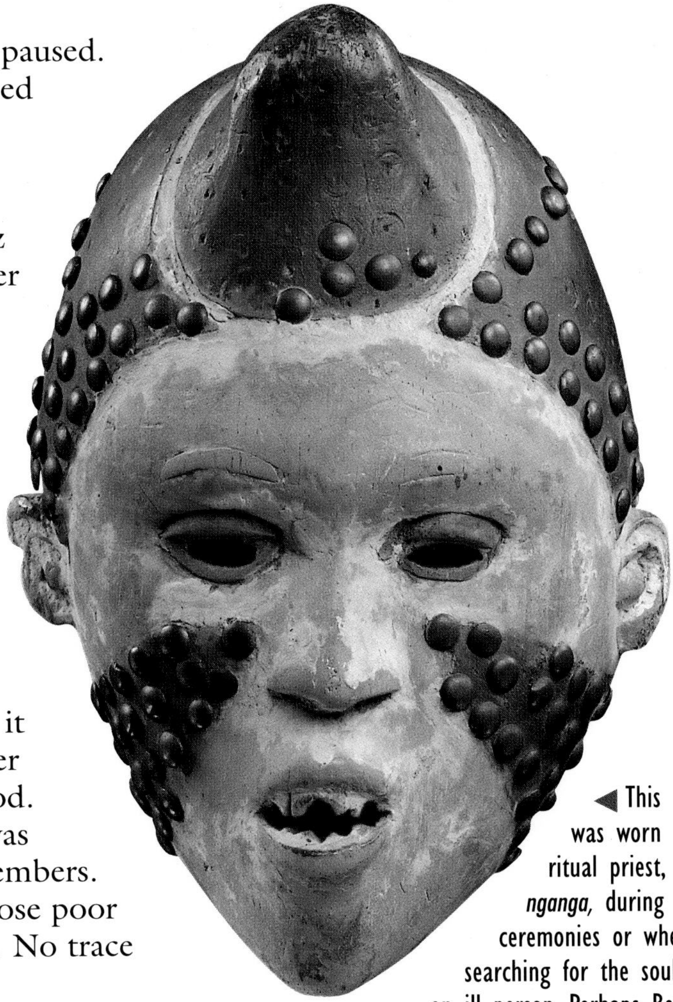

Amid the great tumult of the crowd, Dona Beatriz and Barros were led to the stake. She cried out her willingness to recant, to take back the words that had led her thus far, but it was too late. With the name of Jesus upon her lips, she was thrown upon a great pile of wood. Torches set the pyre alight, and soon there was nothing left of Dona Beatriz but bones and embers. The next day, men came and burned even those poor bones yet again, reducing them to fine ashes. No trace whatsoever of Dona Beatriz should remain.

◀ This mask was worn by the ritual priest, or *nganga,* during official ceremonies or when searching for the soul of an ill person. Perhaps Beatriz wore such a mask in her role as an *nganga.* The white color is associated with death.

Poor Saint Anthony, who was in the habit of dying and rising again, this time died but did not rise again. Thus did Father Bernardo da Gallo comment upon the tragic death of Beatriz Kimpa Vita, which he had helped to bring about.

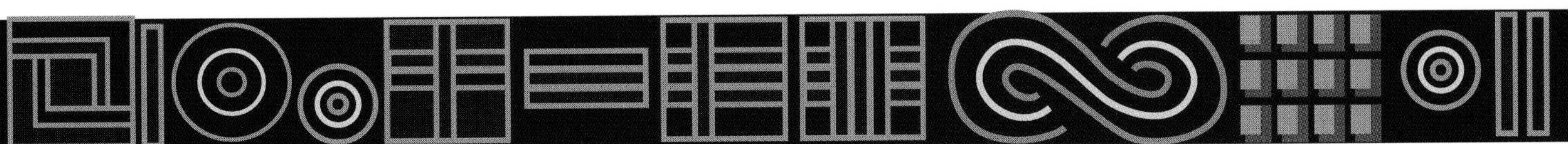

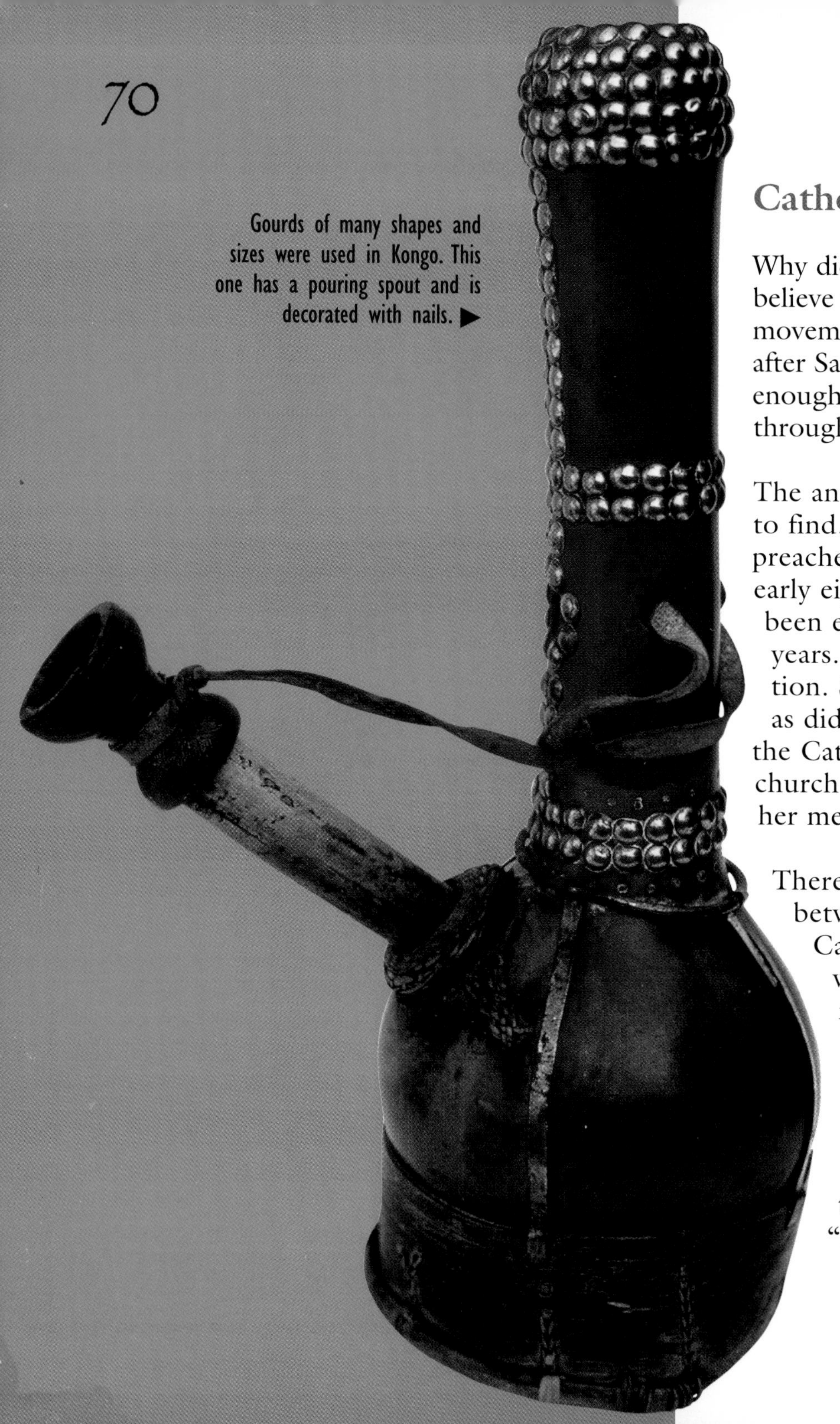

Gourds of many shapes and sizes were used in Kongo. This one has a pouring spout and is decorated with nails. ▶

Catholicism and Kongo Cults

Why did the Esikongo peasants so fully believe in Beatriz Kimpa Vita's religious movement, which historians call Antonianism, after Saint Anthony? Did they not have strong enough beliefs of their own to carry them through the dark ages of Kongo?

The answers to these questions are not hard to find. After all, Beatriz accepted and preached many Christian ideas, and by the early eighteenth century, the Esikongo had been exposed to Christianity for over 200 years. Beatriz was against vice and superstition. She generally abhorred the same sins as did the Catholic fathers. And just like the Catholics, she established her own church and sent out missionaries to preach her message.

There were, however, major differences between Beatriz and the European Catholics. She told her people not to worship the cross, because it was responsible for Christ's death. She rejected Catholic baptism, confession, and prayer, and she made polygamy (several wives to one man) legal. She opposed the white missionaries in Kongo and accused them of preventing the work of her "black saints."

Scholars of Kongo culture have placed Beatriz firmly within the framework of the *kimpasi* cult. Before being possessed by Saint Anthony, she had been an *nganga marinda*—a spiritual *kimpasi* leader who had the power to communicate directly with ancestors and other spirits. In this cult, it was normal for members to symbolically "die" and be possessed by spirits who then inhabited their bodies. It was perfectly acceptable, then, for her to be possessed by Saint Anthony in the same way.

In Esikongo ideals of justice, people's intentions were as a important as their actions. A man who killed another might be pardoned if it was felt that his intentions were for the good of the community and not for himself. Dona Beatriz argued that the Catholic sacraments of marriage, baptism, and confession served no purpose. God would know the believer's intentions without needing to hear formal vows. In this vein, she criticized not only the European Catholics but also the Kongo rulers. She charged that they were fighting their wars for personal gain and not for the public good. Not one of them was fit to be king.

Beatriz burned not only the old fetishes but also the Christian cross. She believed in direct communication with God and with the other world, as she had practiced as an *nganga marinda*, and she had no need of any special objects of worship, including the cross.

In Beatriz's time, the oral traditions in the kingdom revered Afonso as the bringer of Christianity to Kongo. So Beatriz's claim that Christ had been born in São Salvador (where Afonso had reigned and built the first churches) and baptized in Nsundi (where Afonso had been governor) simply conformed to the oral traditions already in place.

In these ways, Beatriz invented an ideology that took the best of both worlds and appealed to many Esikongo—especially the peasants. Unfortunately, she found herself in a position that could not be tolerated by either the Capuchin missionaries or the Kongo ruling class.

The Old Kingdom Dies

Beatriz was born around 1686 and possessed by Saint Anthony in 1704. Why did she appear when she did? Why not earlier in Kongo's history, or later?

Beatriz's story is similar to that of Joan of Arc—a fifteenth-century French peasant whose religious visions and courage enabled her to lead an army to victory. She too was burned at the stake as a heretic. In southeast Africa, in the mid-nineteenth century, a young Xhosa (KOH suh) maiden named Nonquase also had deeply religious visions. Unfortunately her visions led her people to commit suicide by killing off most of their cattle, their main source of food. In each of these cases, a spiritual leader arose when radically different cultures came into conflict and a nation had been in turmoil for a long period.

So it was in Kongo. At first, and for a whole century after Afonso's death in 1543, the kingdom experienced a period of great expansion. This growth was fueled partly by the slave trade, but mostly by the cloth trade with the colony of Angola, farther to the south. In fact, by 1610, Kongo was exporting 100,000 m (110,000 yd) of cloth a year to Angola—an extraordinary amount for the time.

There were minor setbacks to this expansion. In 1568, for example, the kingdom was invaded by the ferocious Imbangala—a warrior people from the east who were known to be cannibals. With Portuguese help, they were eventually driven back.

The critical event that led to the kingdom's ruin occurred in the 1630s, when the large and powerful province of Soyo broke away from Kongo. Soyo harbored rival branches of the royal *kanda*, with members who were candidates for the throne. On October 29, 1665, the Portuguese fought Kongo in an insignificant battle over a small territory called Mbwila. Yet the battle proved to be the turning point in Kongo's history. During the fray the reigning king was killed. With no designated successor to the throne, the country erupted into civil war as the royal rivals fought bitterly over the throne.

In Kongo, there had never been strict provisions for the succession to the throne. It was not an ancestral position, but one for which members of the royal family competed. Often, after a king died, war broke out between rival claimants until one or other of them won. The fighting provided the Esikongo leaders with many war captives, who later were sold as slaves to the Europeans.

▲ The warrior Imbangala were fierce cannibals living in the remote regions east of Kongo. Severe drought possibly drove them to invade the kingdom.

At the end of the eighteenth century, a priest visited São Salvador. He wrote that he found nothing more than a few untidy huts behind a palisade. The great Catholic cathedral and churches had "passed away like the torrential rains which simply moisten the surface and leave the subsoil dry and sterile." In the 1880s, Baptist missionaries and Portuguese officials tore down what was left of Mbanza Kongo/São Salvador and used the materials to build their churches and government buildings.

In the process, the old city of Mbanza Kongo, which had been renamed São Salvador, was destroyed and abandoned. Without a capital, the rival branches of the royal family seized various provinces and waged war continually over who would repopulate and control the capital. The civil war provided hundreds of thousands of captives, who were sold into slavery.

Life in the kingdom became impossible. Peasants could not grow their crops or continue their daily lives. They were in constant danger, either from cross-fire or from slavers. Thousands abandoned their villages and took refuge from the endless wars in far-off mountain regions. The entire system of trade, tribute, and power was upset. By 1700 a generation of Esikongo had grown up never knowing a period of peace.

It is not so surprising, then, that when Beatriz arose as a powerful leader, she found many followers. It is also not surprising that she was seen as a major threat, not only to the Catholic establishment but also to the political hierarchy of the kingdom. When she proclaimed herself Kongo's spiritual leader, for example, she immediately antagonized the *kitome* chiefs, who saw themselves as the nation's spiritual leaders. When Beatriz crowned Pedro Constantinho da Silva as king, she removed that authority from others who claimed that office. Although Beatriz's very ashes were burned so that no "holy relics" might remain, the Antonian movement did not die out immediately. Like a lingering flame, there was hope that the kingdom might revive. But slavery, greed, and war had done their damage.

By the end of the eighteenth century, São Salvador was a pitiful collection of huts. In the 1950s, a British traveler named Clement Egerton visited the site and interviewed a 70-year-old man who claimed to be Dom Pedro VII, last king of the Kongo.

The old man lived in a modest house. His walls were hung with pictures of Portuguese royalty. He received a small stipend from the Portuguese authorities and grew a little coffee and rice.

Egerton was shown the royal regalia. There was "a royal robe trimmed with white fur, which looked more like rabbit than ermine, and a silver crown, a scepter, and miscellaneous utensils."

In 1955 the old man died. He was the last descendent of the Kongo kings.

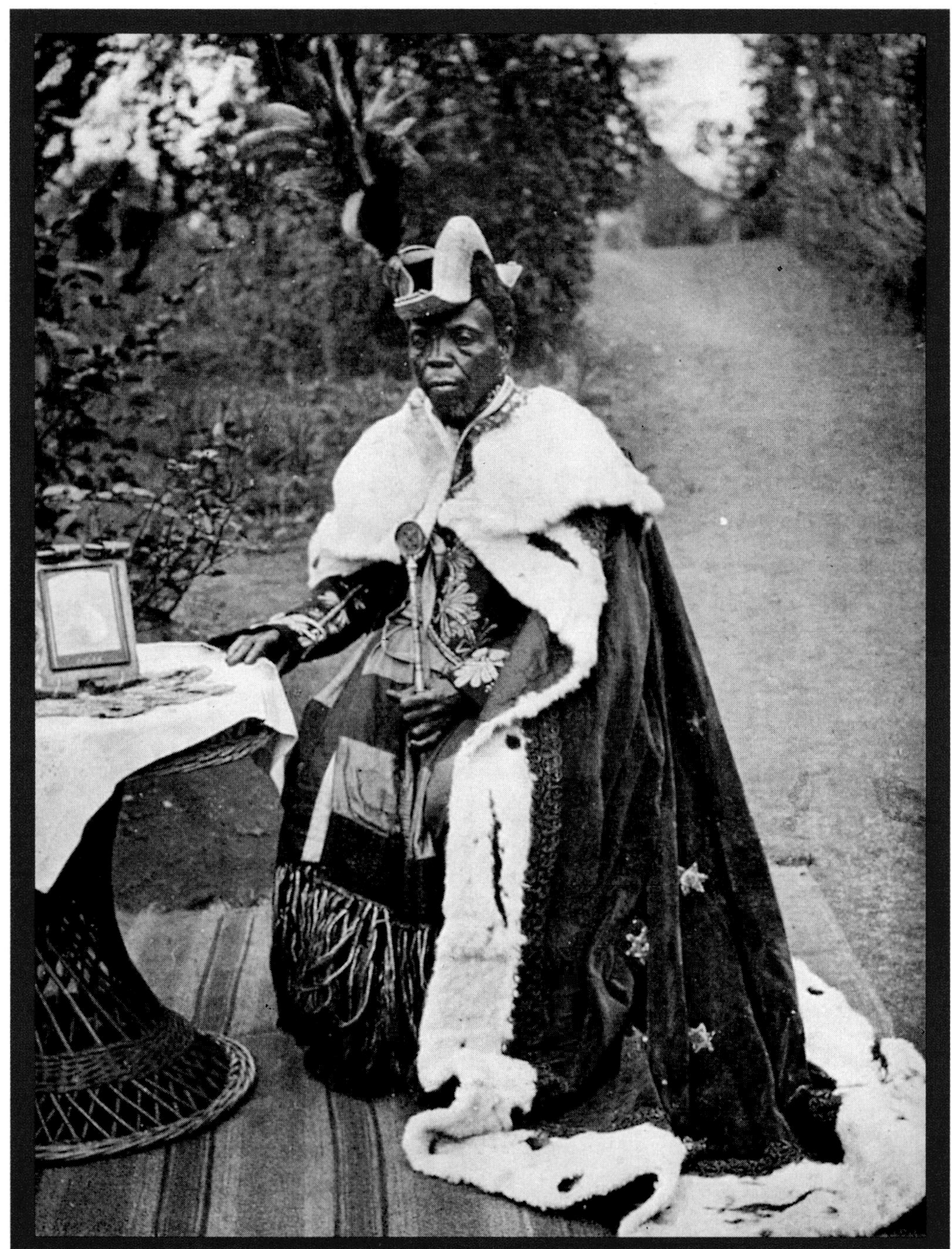

◀ In 1914 the British missionary John Weeks photographed Mbembe, King Pedro VI of Kongo. The robes and the silver scepter were a present from the king of Portugal in 1888. They were state property and passed from the king to his successor. When Clement Egerton visited São Salvador in the 1950s, he saw the last remaining relics of the royal regalia.

Ndongo

Ndongo—From Ngola to Angola

Njinga: The Warrior Queen

I am an old woman now, with few years to live. As we sit here, Father Giovanni, I will tell you my stories, and you will write them down. Thus may future generations know the story of Queen Njinga (JIHN guh)!

I have suffered much. I fought for my power. But in my youth, I watched while my brother Mbandi tottered on the throne. What right had this cowardly weakling to become king? By mere virtue of being our father's son, did he seize the throne and the title of Ngola. But there was no merit to him.

Ah, what sorrow did Ngola Mbandi cause me! First he took my first-born son and sent him to the Kingdom of Heaven—murdered, so that he should never oppose my brother. Then he took the throne but could not lead his people. Instead we Mbundu have been persecuted, killed, our lands plundered, our people captured into slavery. I myself, dear Father, lost my own husband in battle.

And you, Father, soon will administer the last rites to this poor body. And what will you write of me, Njinga? Will you write of my great battles, as I

Ndongo

led my people, fearlessly, my arrows speeding true and fast? Will you write that my banners flew high and proud and that Portuguese soldiers quivered before them?

Perhaps, Father Giovanni, you will write of the evil the Portuguese have done to our lands. In my youth I had hope. Surely, I believed, there must be some good in these men who came from afar. But each new governor proved worse than the last. Greedy are they, Father Giovanni. Greedy, proud, and stupid, for they say they come in peace, yet do they wage unceasing war.

I learned patience, Father Giovanni. All around me there was nothing but suffering. I vowed that one day I would avenge my brother for the death of my son. And I would avenge the Portuguese for the death of my country.

Ah, those Portuguese are cunning jackals! What promises they made us! I recall Louis Mendes de Vasconcellos, that new governor of Luanda. What pledges of friendship he made, and of peaceful trade! We should become Christians, he said. He showed us royal decrees sent by his king, ordering his people to help us, the people of Mbundu. What need have we, who have lived for so long in these realms, of outside help? Perhaps in your wisdom, Father Giovanni, you have an answer to this question.

What sweet words Vasconcellos used! But we watched from afar and awaited the treachery we knew would come.

Vasconcellos demanded tribute from my brother Ngola Mbandi, king of Ndongo. As though Ndongo were a vassal state of the Portuguese! We refused, and his revenge was swift, for he destroyed our capital at Kabasa by fire. We fled before him, taking hostages whom we hid on an island in

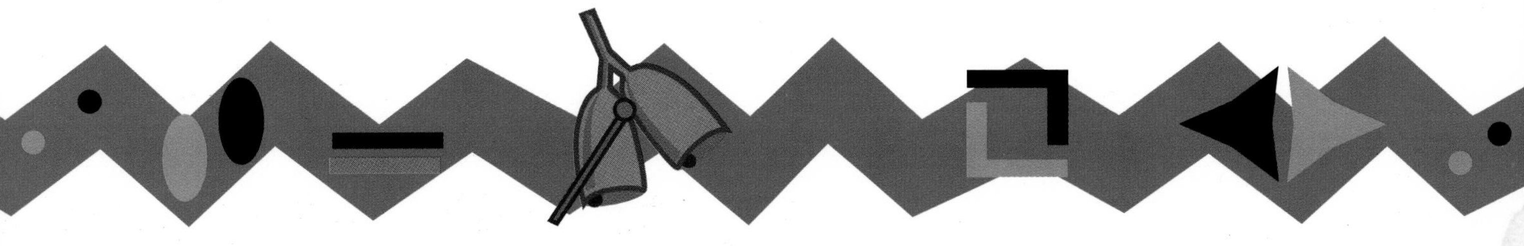

the river. Vasconcellos's rage knew no bounds. Oh, Father Giovanni, nothing can measure our grief when we learned that he had executed our Mbundu chieftains.

What were we now but a land of refugees with a king who hid himself in fear on an island? Now we faced also the Imbangala—those warriors from the east. They joined the Portuguese and hounded us like dogs in the bush. They captured our people and sold them to the *pombeiros*—those cursed men of mixed blood, who have made it their work to sell our people to their masters.

Truly, Father Giovanni, our great kingdom lay in ruins. Our people were starving, and our children had never known peace. My brother, the king, dared not even leave his island refuge! How we yearned for a truce! But now we heard that a new governor had arrived in Luanda. Word filtered back to us that this man, named Jaoa Correia de Souza, wished to sign a peace treaty. He had lost too many men to our arrows and to sickness. He had lost too much trade.

You may think me proud and stubborn, Father Giovanni. But it was at this time in my life that I decided to take matters into my own hands. Perhaps I could persuade this de Souza to help us rid our land of the Imbangala. Thus, I went to Luanda as Ngola Mbandi's ambassador. I made the journey with a hard heart and a strong will. I would not give in to these usurpers! The treaty should be fair and of benefit to both sides, or I would not sign it.

Thus did I come face to face with this Correia de Souza, in the great rooms of his mansion in Luanda. But I was cunning, Father Giovanni. Do you think I wished to appear as some flighty maiden, to beg on her knees before this

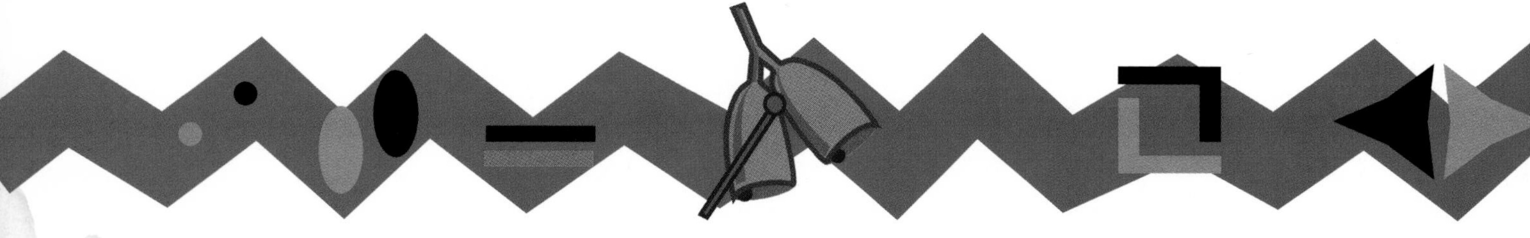

arrogant stranger? No! I came with my women, my guard of honor. And when we entered the reception room, my women went forward first, splendidly clad, as a phalanx fit to greet a governor and to guard an ambassador.

The room was filled with people whom the governor had commanded to attend, and great was their astonishment when they beheld me! Oh, Father Giovanni, this was a proud moment! I saw soldiers with gleaming helmets, and ladies stiff with skirts and jewels. I saw gentlemen, powdered and ruffed, with plumed hats and great swords. I saw many of your priests, darkly clad against the richness of the scene.

There sat de Souza, in a great carved chair on a raised dais. For me there was but a carpet, strewn with cushions. Did they think that I, Njinga, would deign

In 1622, Njinga met with the Portuguese governor, Joao Correia de Souza, in Luanda.

to sit on the floor while this arrogant foreigner looked down upon me from his throne? Never! I gave no hint of my thoughts but clapped my hands for my maid. She understood at once and knelt before me on all fours. I sat upon her back, and a better throne I have never had!

Father Giovanni, I smile today when I recall that scene. How shocked were the guests! What murmurs and whispers fled about the great hall! But de Souza was a man of mettle. He too showed not by a muscle his true feelings but made me welcome in the name of his sovereign, King Felipe IV of Portugal.

Now do you write this down, Father Giovanni, for this is how I wish to be remembered.

I allowed the governor to speak first. He told of his regret for events of the past, of the bloodshed, death, and ill will that had so long plagued our nations. I waited. “We wish to live in peace with the Mbundu,” he said. “We wish to trade so that both nations may benefit. And we wish to bring you the word of our Savior, Jesus Christ, so that your people may enter the Kingdom of Heaven.”

I had no interest in these words, for we had heard them before. Patiently, I waited for the conditions of the treaty.

“If your king, Ngola Mbandi, will release those soldiers and traders he now holds hostage, I offer him a treaty of friendship.”

I would not make things easy for Governor Correia de Souza. “We too yearn to see our people returned and unharmed,” I replied. “You have taken our brothers and sisters, our fathers and uncles. May we not expect their return, also?”

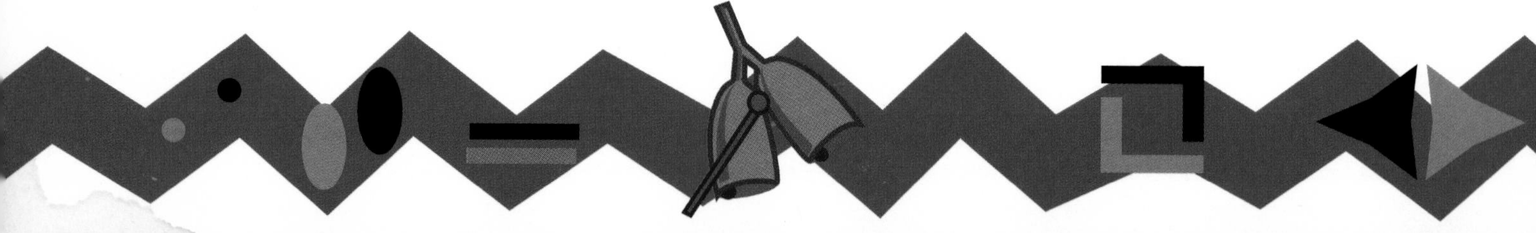

Again, the guests rustled and whispered. Did I dare oppose their governor? I did!

"If you meet our conditions," the governor continued, "I am prepared to accept the right of Ndongo to exist as an independent kingdom, with Ngola Mbandi on the throne."

My heart quivered in anger, but still I showed nothing. What were these foolish words? Was Ndongo not already an independent kingdom, ruled by our kings for centuries past! But de Souza had said he would accept my brother as king. This was joyful news, for until then the Portuguese had claimed their puppet, that traitor Ngola Hari, as the king of Ndongo and would accept no other.

Now I asked the governor what returns he required in exchange for these concessions. The audience hushed, eager to hear his words.

"If Ndongo is to be recognized as a kingdom," he smiled, "we will expect an annual tribute, to be discussed at a later date."

Scorn filled my being. "Ngola Mbandi has no need to pay tribute!" I replied. "If the governor wishes to live in peace, he has only to withdraw his troops from our lands. You have destroyed Ndongo and caused our people to suffer great hunger and sorrow. But we are not conquered. Tribute, O governor, can be demanded only from a conquered people!"

I had my strength, Father Giovanni. I knew I must not for a moment show weakness or guile. And in de Souza's eyes I saw that he recognized me as an equal. Now we began the work of building the treaty, piece by piece, as one builds a house. And after many hours we came to agree. I promised that we would return the Portuguese hostages. We would also

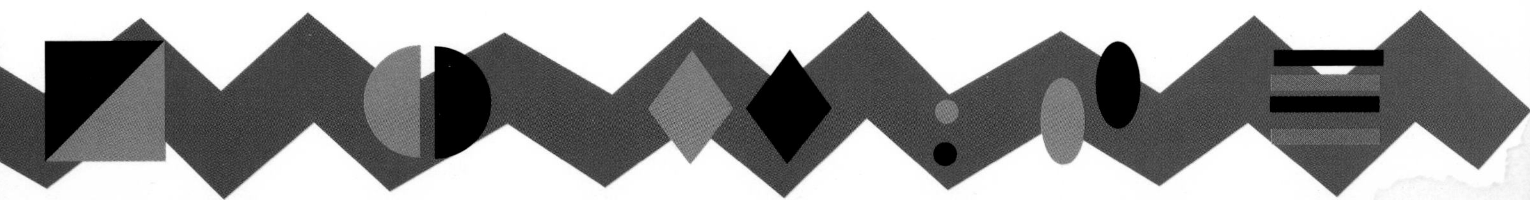

gather up those fugitive slaves who had sought refuge in our lands and deliver them to the governor. On his part, he would withdraw his people from our towns, and he would help us to expel the Imbangala from Ndongo.

These were but the details, Father Giovanni. But the true glory came at the moment when we signed the treaty, for we signed not as conqueror and vassal, but as equals, as brothers in peace, as representatives of two independent nations. Of this, Father Giovanni, I am most proud.

As I prepare to join my ancestors, Father Giovanni, I am at peace. I have given my life for my people. I have taken another name, Dona Anna de Souza, that I might join your faith. When I am gone, I beg you to clothe me in your Capuchin habit, that my people may see me in the true faith. And I ask you to bury me in my royal robes, and to lay my bow and arrow upon my breast. And may these tales that I have related to you forever guard the true spirit of Anna de Souza, Queen Njinga of Ndongo and Matamba.

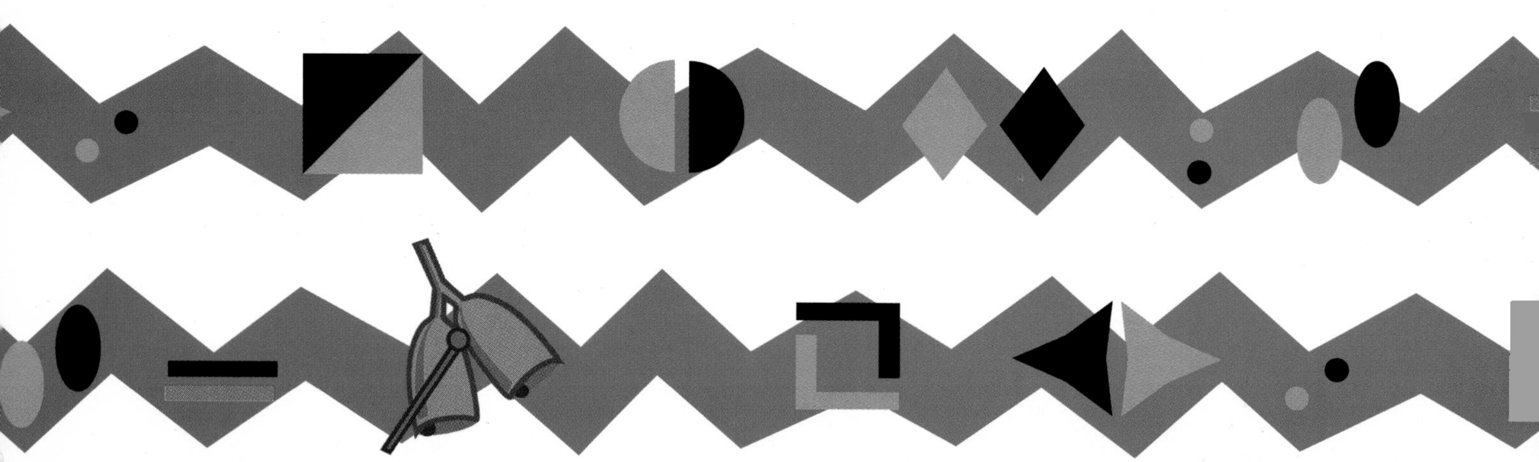

◀ Father Giovanni Antonio Cavazzi heard Njinga's stories from the queen herself and made many drawings and paintings recording her life. He depicted himself here with African chapel boys.

Fact and Fiction

Njinga of Ndongo—or Queen Njinga of Matamba, as she later came to be known—has gone down in history as a quite remarkable woman. However, there is much controversy surrounding her story.

To begin with, the historic meeting with Correia de Souza was never actually recorded at the time! The story—and most of the rest of Njinga's colorful life history—was first written down in 1658 by the Capuchin missionary Giovanni Antonio Gaeta da Napoli. In 1687, Giovanni Antonio Cavazzi published his version of Njinga's story, but there were many other eyewitness reports written during her lifetime.

Father Giovanni attended Njinga during her final years, when she had become a devout Catholic, and

Governor Vasconcellos had good intentions when he arrived in Luanda in the early 1600s. He denounced the traders and conquistadores who had ruined the land. But after only four years in Luanda, he had become a very rich man through the slave trade. He completely altered his views about Angola: "It is only through severity and fear that we can hold our own against these indomitable heathens." These were his words of advice to his successor, Governor Correia de Souza.

administered the last rites to her when she lay dying. He took the information for his chronicles from Njinga herself. She undoubtedly wished to die a heroine and probably tailored her story to her own advantage.

Njinga may have done this because she had alienated the Mbundu people, whom she claimed as her followers. First, they expressly forbade women to hold positions of power. Although some supported her as a candidate to the throne by descent, they automatically disqualified her because she was a woman. Second, there were those who questioned her lineage. They said that she was descended from a different mother than Ngola Mbandi, and could therefore not be considered kin at all. Others said that her father was a slave at the royal court, a man with no lineage to speak of. It was also not known whether Njinga was really Ngola Mbandi's "ambassador." It is quite possible that she simply took this role upon herself, turning it to her best advantage.

Njinga signed the treaty with Correia de Souza in 1622. She remained at Luanda for several months, receiving instruction from the Jesuit priests in preparation for

▲ Njinga was baptized in 1622. She used the Catholic name of Dona Anna de Souza, in honor of the governor.

her baptism. For Njinga knew that if she was to get anywhere with the Portuguese, she would have to accept their faith, even if only in name. The Portuguese hoped that Njinga herself would help spread Catholicism in Ndongo.

The baptism was a grand ceremony attended by all of Luanda society. In honor of Governor de Souza, Njinga renamed herself Dona Anna de Souza.

Immediately afterwards, she departed for the island camp of the king, Ngola Mbandi.

For the next 40 years Njinga played a very important role in the politics of Angola. In Portugal, Njinga is still regularly featured in school textbooks. And in Brazil, popular plays called *congoadas* (con goh AH duhz) feature Queen Njinga exchanging embassies with the king of Kongo.

After the Treaty

The Portuguese knew they had to gain control over Angola's interior if they were to profit from trade. They were also the allies of the puppet king, Angola Hari, who had agreed to become their vassal. The war waged from 1624 to 1655 was over who would rule Ndongo: the Portuguese, with Ngola Hari on the throne; Njinga's half-brother Ngola Mbandi; or Njinga herself.

Angola was the name the Portuguese originally used for the territory of Ndongo. This was a corruption of the Mbundu word *ngola* which was probably a royal title or the name of an iron emblem of authority.

◀ Photographed in 1975, this Mbundu chief wears a headdress similar to those depicted by Cavazzi in 1687, which were worn by the kings and queens of Angola and Matamba.

In keeping with the terms of the treaty, Ngola Mbandi released his Portuguese hostages. But his spies reported that the Portuguese were not withdrawing. Instead they were fortifying their strongholds in Ndongo. Eventually, Mbandi learned that Governor de Souza had been recalled to Lisbon. The new governor ignored the peace treaty.

At this point, Njinga sought the help of Kaza, leader of a group of Imbangala. These people were mercenary warriors who hired themselves out to anyone who would pay them. Apparently Kaza accepted Njinga's authority, for he agreed to form an alliance with her. Meanwhile, Njinga's half brother Ngola Mbandi committed suicide. It is said that Njinga murdered his young son, who would have been the next king.

Njinga's alliance grew to include several Mbundu chieftains. They closed off all trade routes and confined the Portuguese to the coast. This was the final straw. The Portuguese called for aid from Lisbon, and when it came, they declared all-out war against Njinga.

The aging queen used clever tactics to keep her army intact. She was driven ever farther east, away from the grassy plains of Ndongo. But she did not give up. Instead, she led her people on a long and dreadful march even farther east, to the ancient kingdom of Matamba. Here, Njinga captured the reigning queen, had her branded as a slave, and took the throne of Matamba herself.

For the next ten years, Queen Njinga held fast in Matamba. With Kaza and

> "When the Queen comes on a scene, everyone falls on his knees, kisses the ground and claps his hands. If women are present, they express their delight by beating their open mouths with the palms of their hands as they utter a series of short cries of 'ah! ah! ah!'"
>
> —*A seventeenth-century observer*

his Imbangala people among her soldiers, she had to tolerate their cannibal rites. She deliberately kept all her movements secret and often allowed false rumors of her actions to reach the Portuguese. When Kaza abandoned Njinga in 1628, she lacked manpower, but outdid the Portuguese in cunning.

In 1639, the new governor of Luanda tried to make peace with Njinga. He sent ambassadors, a priest, and a nobleman fluent in the Mbundu language. But they returned empty-handed.

Meanwhile, the Dutch—who were as thirsty for trade as the Portuguese—had arrived near the Zaire River and were trading with the kingdom of Kongo. The Protestant Dutch and the Catholic Portuguese were dire enemies. They had clashed in Europe, in Brazil, on the west coast of Africa, and in the Far East. It was to be no different in Ndongo.

In 1641, Dutch ships came south and anchored near Luanda. They had vastly superior forces and gun power to the Portuguese, who sensibly withdrew to their farms inland, leaving the Dutch to occupy Luanda.

◀ This sculpture from central Angola is an effigy of a nineteenth-century king. The upturned hairstyle and huge hands and feet reflect the king's power and strength.

There followed a series of tremendous wars. In 1647–1648, Njinga's army besieged Massangano, the Portuguese stronghold. Had the city fallen, Njinga would have conquered Portuguese Angola. But the city held. Meanwhile, in Lisbon, King Joao IV had decided to regain Angola at all costs. In May 1648, a well-equipped armada led by Salvador de Saa set sail from Rio de Janeiro in Brazil, arriving in Luanda a few weeks later. By this time, the Dutch had become less interested in Angola and more interested in regions farther south on the continent. To everyone's surprise, they surrendered to de Saa without a fight and departed.

Once again, the Portuguese were determined to gain control of Angola, and of Kongo to the north, where trade relations had also deteriorated. Njinga's alliance of African chiefs had begun to crumble, and it was now to her advantage to negotiate again with the Portuguese.

In fact, both sides recognized a stalemate, and a peace treaty was signed in 1656. This time, the Mbundu territory was clearly defined. The Matamba kingdom, which Njinga occupied, was bound by the Lukala River on the west, the Kwango on the east, the Kwanza on the south, and the kingdom of Kongo to the north. Njinga opened Matamba to the slave traders but retained a monopoly over slave exports. She agreed to send an annual tribute of slaves to Luanda. Both sides agreed to get rid of the troublesome Imbangala.

During a battle before the peace, one of Njinga's warriors had found a crucifix. Njinga regarded this as a sign that she must renew her Christian faith. Consultation with a captured Catholic priest and with her own spirit mediums encouraged her reconversion. She agreed to renounce the Imbangala practices of cannibalism and human sacrifice that she had taken up while using their warriors. She built several churches in Matamba and, at the age of 75, even married one of her followers.

Queen Njinga of Matamba will always be an enigmatic figure. She was a woman of extraordinary intelligence, courage, and skill. Yet she was also cruel, violent, and cunning. She died in 1663, aged 81, attended by the good Father Antonio Giovanni Cavazzi.

Epilogue

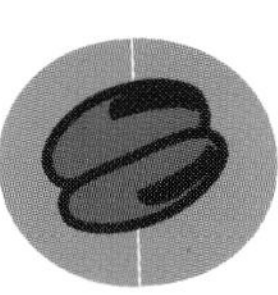

The Portuguese colony of Angola eventually grew to include Kongo, Ndongo, and a number of lesser states. Despite war, deadly tropical diseases, and all the discomforts of life below the equator, the Portuguese persisted in Kongo and Ndongo into the late twentieth century.

But the Portuguese did not take control easily. Their efforts spanned several centuries, and there was strong resistance from different sections of the African population. King Afonso, Beatriz Kimpa Vita, Queen Njinga—these are the heroes and heroines of a resistance movement that persists in Angola to the present day.

In Kongo the authority of the kings declined as the demand for slaves increased. Mbanza Kongo, the capital, had been the main center of trade and the traditional residence of the king for centuries. But as the Portuguese settled along the coast, they developed new trade routes into the interior, bypassing the capital and thus the king's control.

These routes brought slaves and other goods to the important province of Soyo at the mouth of the Zaire River, which then surpassed Mbanza Kongo as a slave trading center. Soyo had always been a fairly independent province that appointed its own rulers and was influential in electing new kings. The province profited so greatly from the slave trade that it was no longer economically tied to Mbanza Kongo.

When the Dutch arrived on the Kongo coast in the seventeenth century, the competition for slaves increased. In the early eighteenth century, the English became major slave traders. The civil wars in Kongo at this time provided traders with thousands of captives, who were exported through ports just north of the Zaire River along the Loanga coast. In fact, at least a fifth of all Africans sent to the Americas came from Kongo and traveled through these ports.

By the end of the eighteenth century, the French had become major exporters of African slaves. In fact, about half of the population of the then French colony of Haiti came from Kongo. They played an important role in the Haitian revolution of 1791, when slaves overthrew the French government of the island. One of

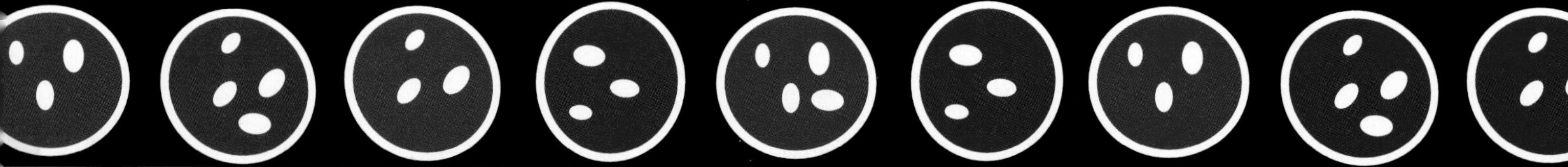

their revolutionary leaders, named Macaya, claimed that he had served the king of Kongo.

Kongo was eventually reunited in the eighteenth century under Dom Pedro IV. But civil wars had brought about drastic changes, and the new "kingdom" was more of an old memory than an actual fact.

The same was true of Ndongo. With the growth of the slave trade, the island of São Tomé had developed into the main export center of slaves to the Portuguese colony of Brazil. Eventually, the São Tomé traders set up another major export center at Luanda. From there they purchased slaves from the king, or *ngola* of Ndongo. This increased his power enormously; he was able to expand his kingdom westward, toward the coast, just as the Portuguese were attempting to penetrate the interior. By the mid-eighteenth century,

◀ These slaves wait to be placed on board a ship to Brazil. They are guarded by an African trader. Historians calculate that about 20 percent of slaves in North America and 60 percent of the slaves on Haiti originally came from Angola.

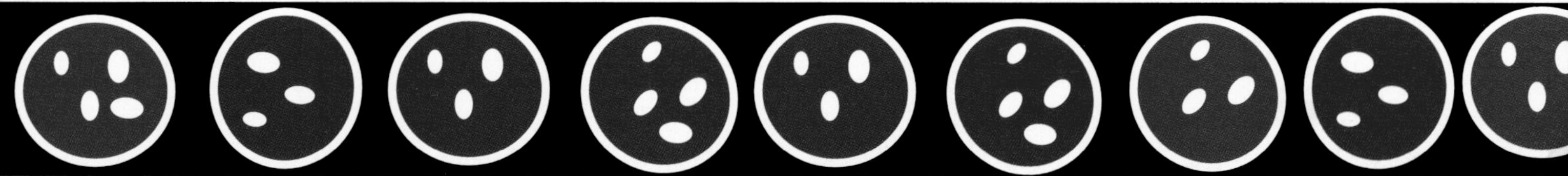

Luanda was exporting over 10,000 slaves a year, more than any other place on the African coast.

With the slave trade came missionaries. Many were heavily involved in the slave trade, and their hypocrisy was well noted by the African people. First came the Portuguese Catholics and then the Dutch Protestants and later came Baptists, Anglicans, Methodists, and representatives of other religions. All of them tried to influence the Angolans by putting down their native belief systems. Amazingly enough, the old beliefs survived and are still practiced by about half of the 10 million people living in the region today.

OLD LUANDA AND NEW LUANDA

Luanda grew from a small town in the fifteenth century (as shown above) to a large city in the twentieth century. ▶

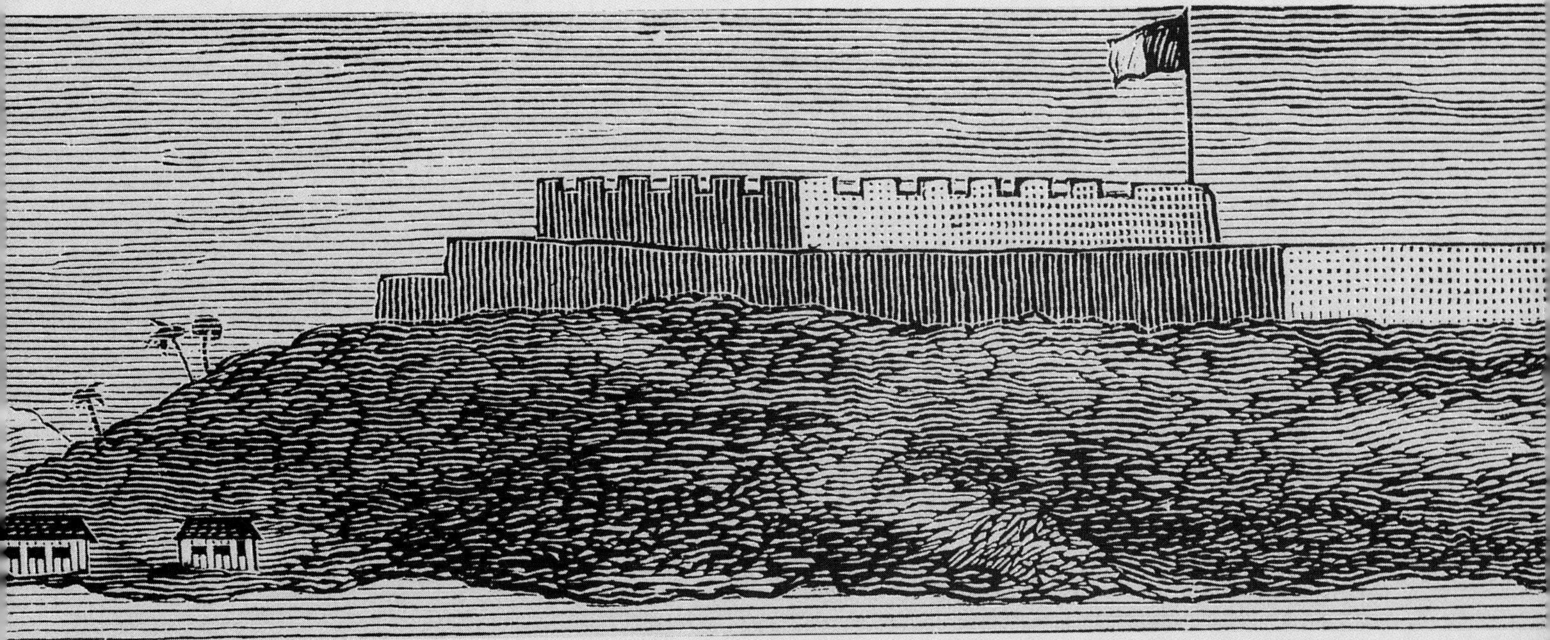

The slave trade declined during the 1800s, but its impact on African economic development was far-reaching. In exchange for captives, traders had imported guns, Indian cottons, and cheap Brazilian rum. No investment was made in African crafts and industry. Instead, the Portuguese developed coffee and cocoa plantations alongside their sugar cane and tobacco farms in the central highlands in Angola. In the late 1920s the Portuguese government decided to improve the region's economy. Soon afterwards, thousands of Portuguese immigrants flooded into Angola to set up businesses or farms. New industries, such as fishing and mining for diamonds and iron ore, were developed. Railways and roads were built. Luanda became a major seaport. Mbanza Kongo and Soyo became important centers of oil production.

Even today, however, Angola's economy is still based in agriculture. Seventy-five percent of its people are farmers or herders, living in rural areas. The Mbundu and the Bakongo are still among the largest ethnic groups there

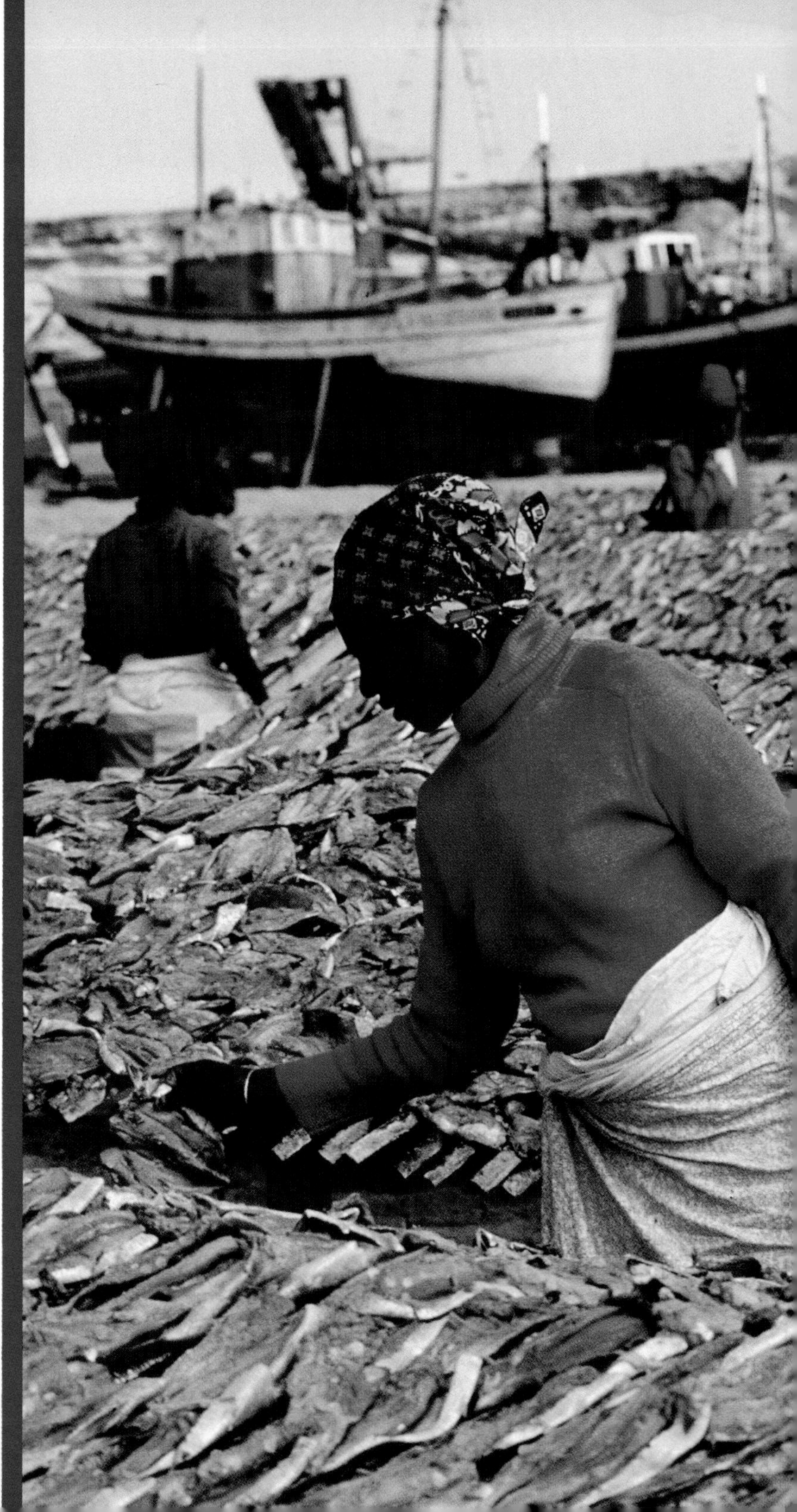

A woman dries fish for export from Luanda. ▶

and still speak their Bantu languages. Europeans, educated Africans, and mestizos—people of mixed blood—speak Portuguese.

By the 1950s the Angolans had been under Portuguese authority for almost 500 years. The coffee industry had taken over large tracts of native farmland, and Portuguese immigrants crowded Angolan towns. The government had neglected to educate the Angolan people, who were tired of their inferior position in their own country. At this time, many other African nations were seeking and

▲ Young Angolan girls wearing beaded headdresses and brightly colored skirts perform a traditional dance.

winning their independence from the colonial powers. Angola would not be left out, although its struggle would take some time.

In 1956 the Popular Movement for the Liberation of Angola (MPLA) was formed. In 1961, northern rebels formed the Front for the Liberation of Angola (FNLA) and sparked a revolt that spread throughout the nation. The FNLA was based on a faction of the Kongo royal *kanda*. Four years later, southern rebels formed the National Union for Total Independence of Angola (UNITA). To quell the fighting and regain control over its colony, Portugal mobilized an army of 60,000 soldiers. For the next 13 years, Angola was consumed by civil war as rival groups battled for power.

In 1975, Portugal withdrew from Angola and its other colonies in Africa, leaving the nation open to exploitation

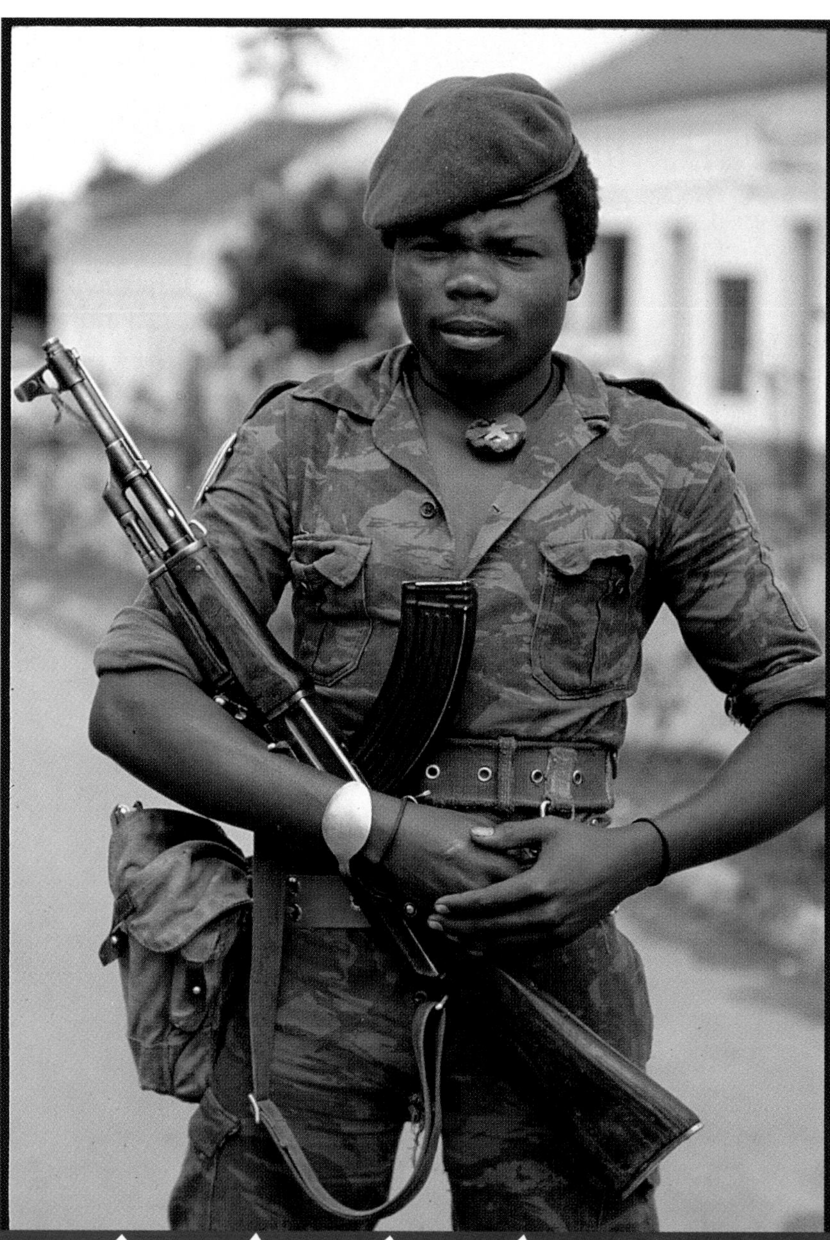

This young Mbundu man is a soldier for the MPLA. He carries a Soviet gun. ▶

Today the people of Angola have no voice in their government. The Popular Movement for the Liberation of Angola is the only political party in the country. Much like the old kings of Kongo and Ndongo, the party leader serves as the nation's president, head of state, and commander in chief of the armed forces.

by other powers, each with its own goals. Zaire supported the FNLA. South Africa supported UNITA. And the Communist nations of Cuba and the former Soviet Union supported the MPLA. France, Britain, and the United States all became involved in support of one group or another.

Just as in Kongo during the seventeenth century, and for much the same reasons, the civil war continued with unabated fury. The war broke down transportation systems and disrupted food production. Most Europeans fled the country. Business, agriculture, fishing, mining—all came to a virtual standstill. After several attempted cease-fires, an election was held in 1992. The MPLA won, but rival groups would not accept the results, and fighting broke out again. By this time, some 2 million Angolans—about a fifth of the total population—were refugees, totally dependent on outside aid from various organizations for food and shelter.

In 1994 a new truce was signed. This time, perhaps, it will hold, allowing Angola finally to renew its ties to the past and to build toward a peaceful future.

Pronunciation Key

Some words in this book may be new to you or difficult to pronounce. Those words have been spelled phonetically in parentheses. The syllable that receives stress in a word is shown in small capital letters. The following pronunciation key shows how letters are used to show different sounds.

a	after	(AF tur)
ah	father	(FAH thur)
ai	care	(kair)
aw	dog	(dawg)
ay	paper	(PAY pur)
e	letter	(LET ur)
ee	eat	(eet)
ih	trip	(trihp)
eye	idea	(eye DEE uh)
y	hide	(hyd)
ye	lie	(lye)
oh	flow	(floh)
oi	boy	(boi)
oo	rule	(rool)
or	horse	(hors)
ou	cow	(kou)
yoo	few	(fyoo)
u	taken	(TAY kun)
	matter	(MAT ur)
uh	ago	(uh goh)
ch	chicken	(CHIHK un)
g	game	(gaym)
ing	coming	(KUM ing)
j	job	(jahb)
k	came	(kaym)
ng	long	(lawng)
s	city	(SIH tee)
sh	ship	(shihp)
th	thin	(thihn)
thh	feather	(FETHH ur)
y	yard	(yahrd)
z	size	(syz)
zh	division	(duh VIHZH un)

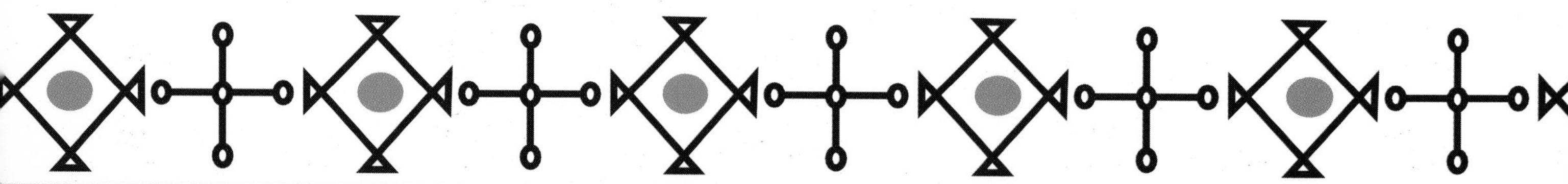

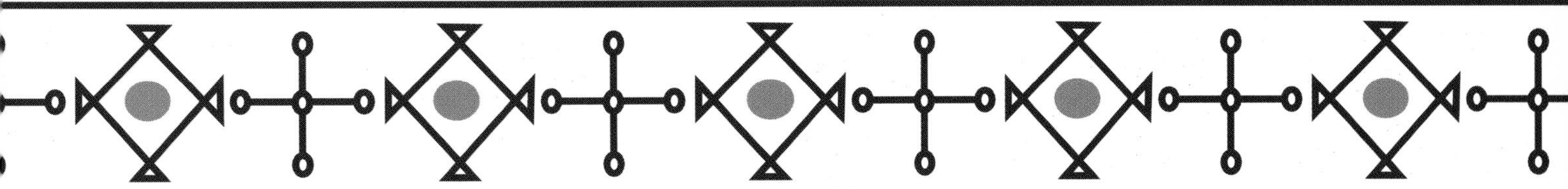

For Further Reading

(* = recommended for younger readers)

Balandier, Georges. *Daily Life in the Kingdom of Kongo.* New York: Pantheon Books, 1968.

Boyd, Herb. *African History for Beginners.* New York: Writers and Readers Publishing, 1991.*

Davidson, Basil. *Africa in History.* New York: Macmillan, 1991.

———. *African Kingdoms.* New York: Time-Life Books, 1966.

———. *A Guide to African History.* New York: Doubleday, Zenith Books, 1965.

———. *The Lost Cities of Africa.* Boston: Little, Brown 1970.

DeGraft-Johnson, J. C. *African Glory.* New York: Walker, 1954.

Delgado, Ralph. *Historia de Angola* (A History of Angola). 2 vols. Lisbon: Edicao de Banco de Angola.

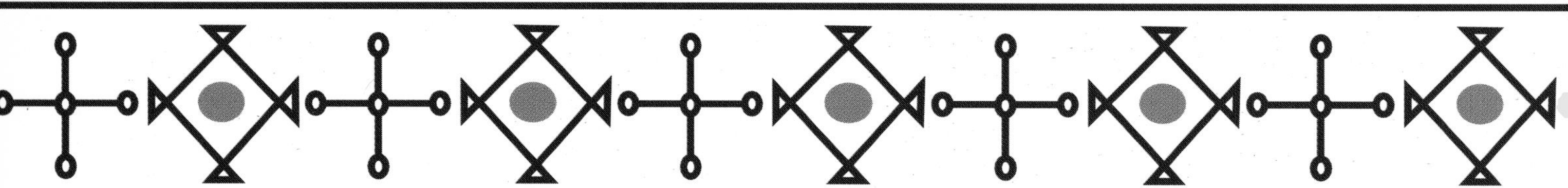

Dobler, Lavinia. *Great Kingdoms of the African Past.* New York: Doubleday, Zenith Books, 1965.*

Harris, Joseph E. *African Kingdoms and Their History.* New York: New American Library, 1987.

Hilton, Anne. *The Kingdom of Kongo.* New York: Oxford University Press, 1985.

Ki-Zerbo, Joseph. *Die Geschichte Schwarz-Afrikas* (The History of Black Africa). Wuppertal: Peter Hammer, 1979.

Kwamena-Poh, Michael. *African History in Maps.* London: Longman, 1982.

McEvedy, Collin. *The Penguin Atlas of African History.* London: Penguin Books, 1980.*

Miller, Joseph. "Nzinga of Matamba in a New Perspective." *Journal of African History* 16. 2 (1975): 202–16.

Murray, Jocelyn. *Cultural Atlas of Africa.* New York: Facts on File, 1989.*

Oliver, Ronald. *The African Experience.* New York: HarperCollins, 1991.

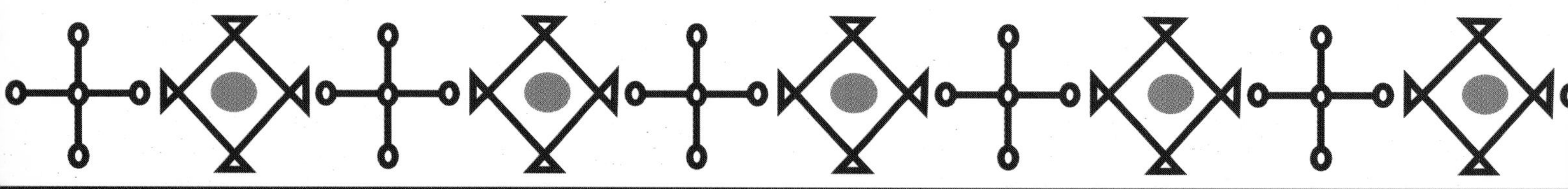

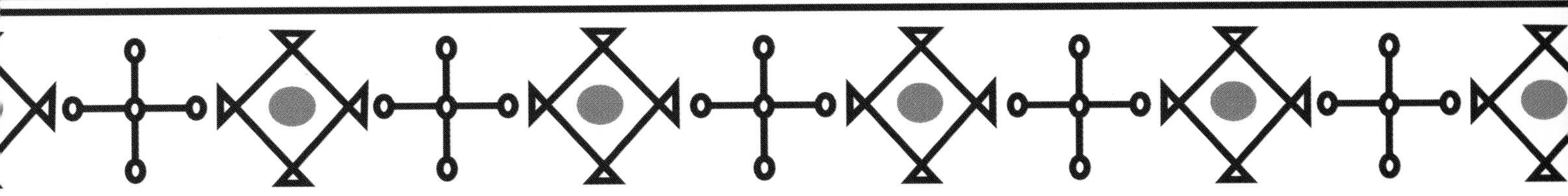

———. *The Dawn of African History.* London: Oxford University Press, 1968.

Oliver, Roland, and J. D. Fage. *A Short History of Africa.* 6th ed. London: Penguin Books, 1988.

Pigafetta, Filippo. *A Report of the Kingdom of Kongo.* London: John Murray, 1881. Reprint. London: Frank Cass, 1970.

Polatnick, Florence, and B. Saletan. *Shapers of Africa.* New York: J. Messner, 1969.

Schachtzabel, Alfred. *Im Hochland von Angola* (In the Highlands of Angola). Deutsche Buchwerkstatten, 1923.

Scholefield, A. *The Dark Kingdoms.* New York: William Morrow, 1975.

Stacey, Tom. *Peoples of the Earth.* Tom Stacey and Europa Verlag, 1972.*

Thornton, John K. *The Kingdom of Kongo: Civil War and Transition, 1641–1718.* Madison: University of Wisconsin Press, 1983.

Weeks, John H. *Among the Primitive Bakongo.* London: Seely, Service, 1914.

Wheeler, Douglas L., and R. Pelissier. *Angola.* London: Pall Mall Press,

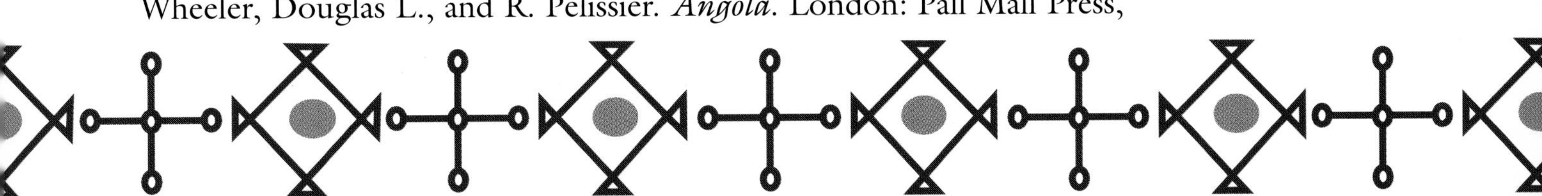

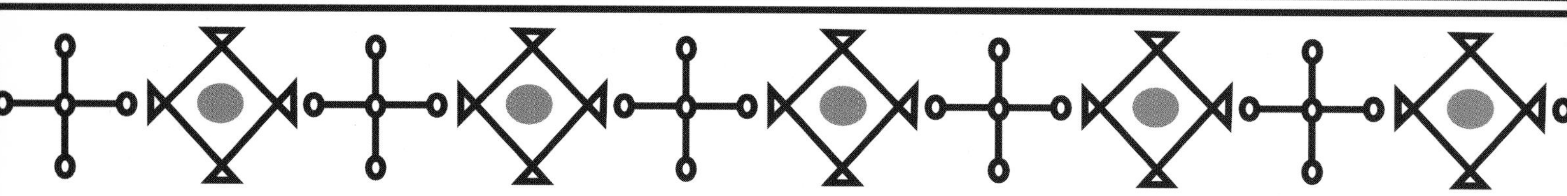

Index

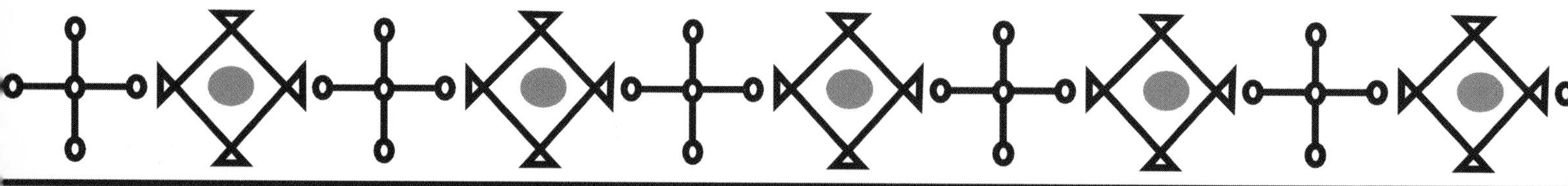

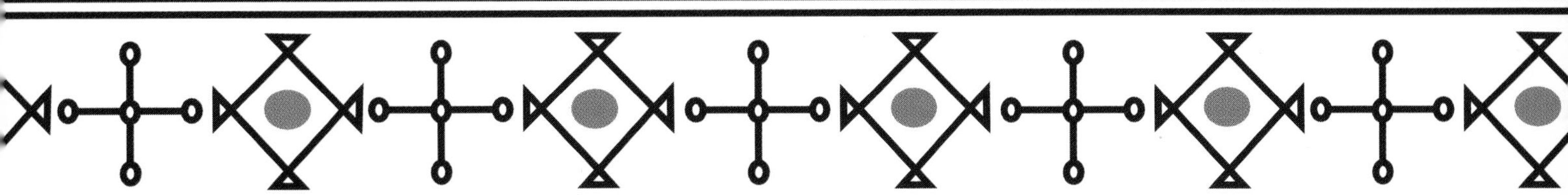

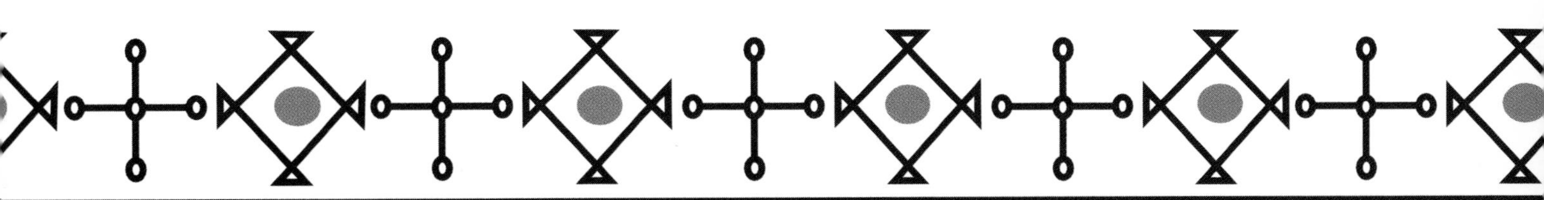

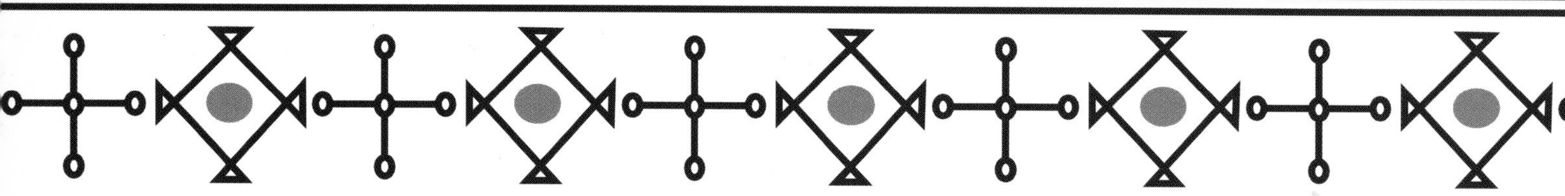

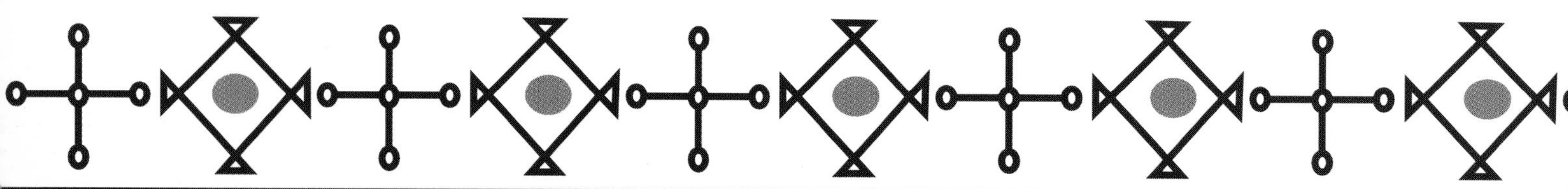

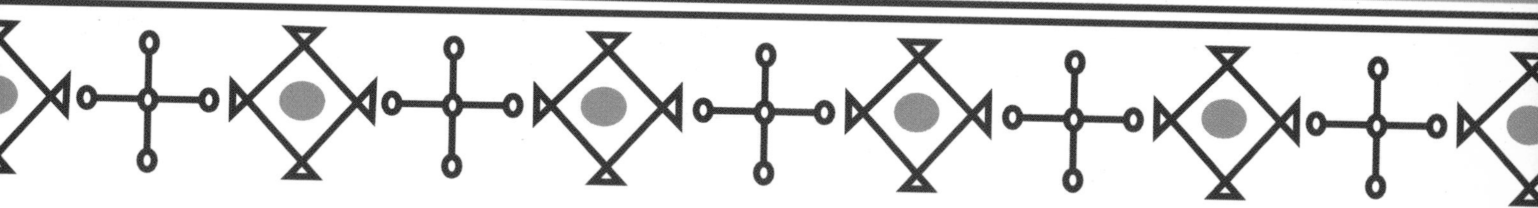

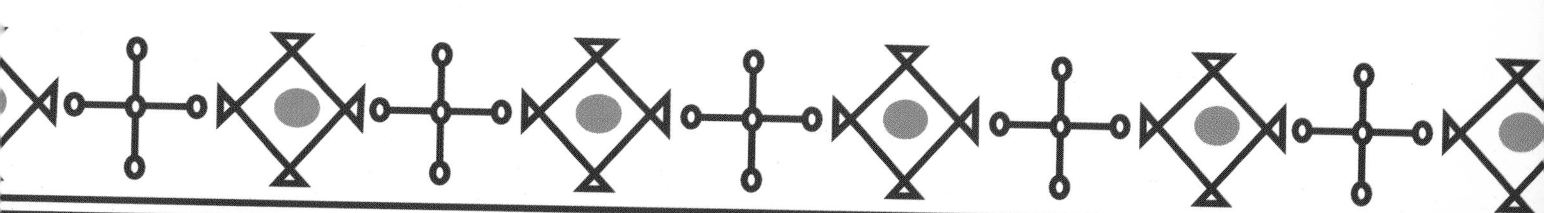

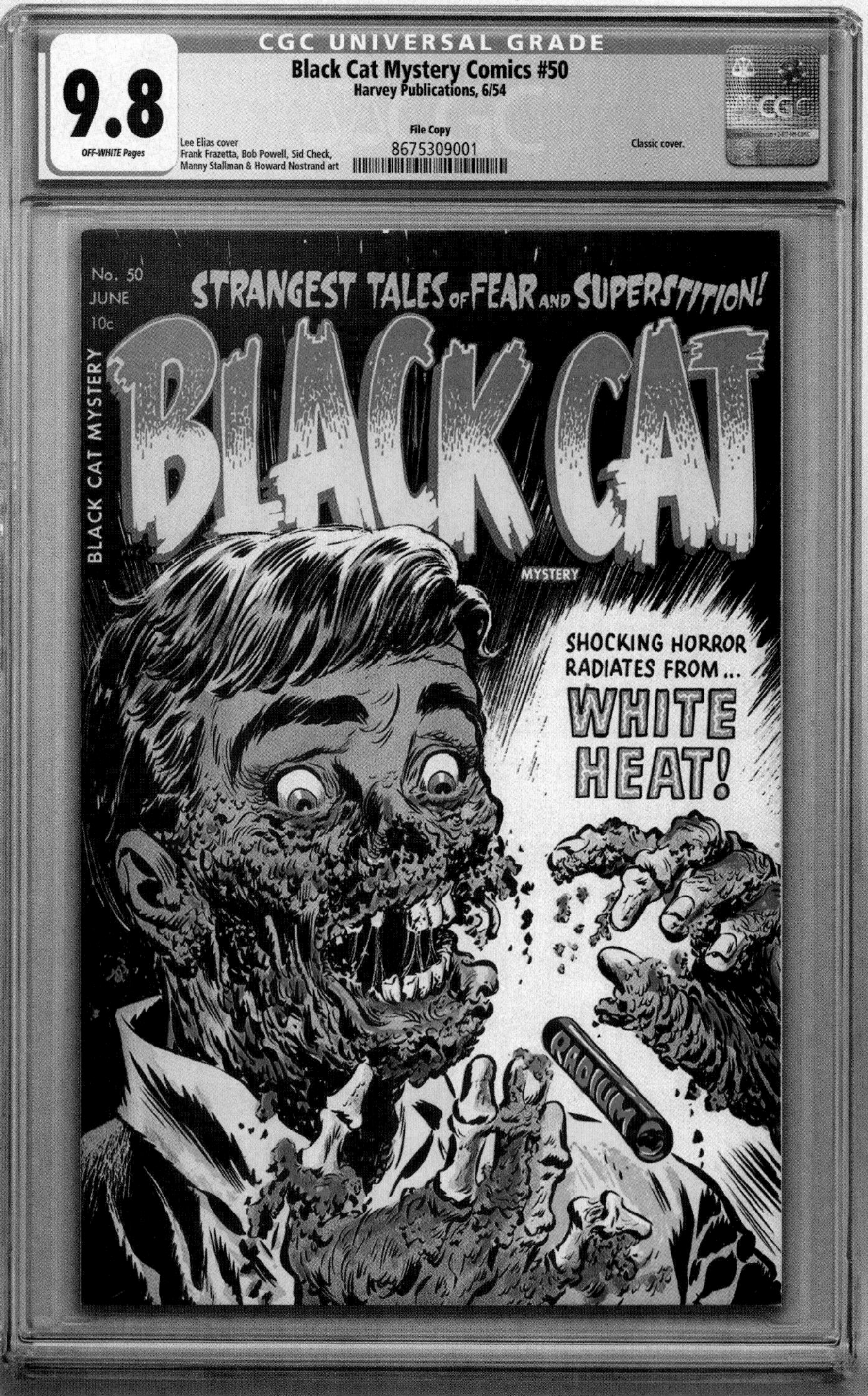

THE OVERSTREET COMIC BOOK PRICE GUIDE

48TH EDITION

COMICS FROM THE 1500s–PRESENT INCLUDED
FULLY ILLUSTRATED CATALOGUE
& EVALUATION GUIDE

by ROBERT M. OVERSTREET

GEMSTONE PUBLISHING

Stephen A. Geppi, President & Chief Executive Officer
J.C. Vaughn, Vice-President of Publishing
Mark Huesman, Creative Director
Amanda Sheriff, Associate Editor
Carrie Wood, Assistant Editor
Braelynn Bowersox, Staff Writer
Mike Wilbur, Warehouse Operations
Tom Garey, Kathy Weaver, Brett Canby, Angela Phillips-Mills, Accounting Services

SPECIAL CONTRIBUTORS TO THIS EDITION

Robert L. Beerbohm • Dr. Arnold T. Blumberg • Gene Gonzales • Terry Hoknes • Paul Levitz • Tom Mason
Charles S. Novinskie • Richard D. Olson, Ph.D. • Amanda Sheriff • J.C. Vaughn • Carrie Wood

SPECIAL ADVISORS TO THIS EDITION

Darren Adams • Grant Adey • Bill Alexander • David T. Alexander • Tyler Alexander • Lon Allen • Dave Anderson
David J. Anderson, DDS • Matt Ballesteros • L.E. Becker • Jim Berry • Tim Bildhauser • Peter Bilelis • Steve Borock
Scott Braden • Richard M. Brown • Shawn Caffrey • Charles Cerrito • Jeff Cerrito • John Chruscinski
Paul Clairmont • Art Cloos • Bill Cole • Ashley Cotter-Cairns • Jesse James Criscione • Frank Cwiklik
Brock Dickinson • Gary Dolgoff • John Dolmayan • Walter Durajlija • Ken Dyber • Daniel Ertle
D'Arcy Farrell • Bill Fidyk • Paul M. Figura • Joseph Fiore • Stephen Fishler • Dan Fogel • John Foster
Dan Gallo • Stephen Gentner • Steve Geppi • Douglas Gillock • Sean Goodrich • Tom Gordon III
Andy Greenham • Eric J. Groves • Jay Halstead • Terry Hoknes • Steven Houston • Jeff Itkin • Dr. Steven Kahn
Nick Katradis • Ivan Kocmarek • Robert Krause • Ben Labonog • Ben Lichtenstein • Stephen Lipson • Paul Litch
Doug Mabry • Brian Marcus • Jon McClure • Todd McDevitt • Mike McKenzie • Steve Mortensen • Marc Nathan
Josh Nathanson • Tom Nelson • Jamie Newbold • Terry O'Neill • Michael Pavlic • Bill Ponseti • Mick Rabin
Yolanda Ramirez • Alex Reece • Greg Reece • Rob Reynolds • Steve Ricketts • Ben Samuels • Barry Sandoval
Phil Schlaefer • Dylan Schwartz • Alika Seki • Todd Sheffer • Frank Simmons • Marc Sims • Lauren Sisselman
Tony Starks • West Stephan • Al Stoltz • Doug Sulipa • Michael Tierney • Ted VanLiew
Frank Verzyl • John Verzyl • Rose Verzyl • Rick Whitelock • Mike Wilbur • Harley Yee • Vincent Zurzolo, Jr.

See a full list of Overstreet Advisors on pages 1216-1220

NOTICE: Values for items pictured in this book are based on author's experience, consultations with a network of advisors including collectors specializing in various categories, and actual prices realized for specific items sold through private sales and auctions. The values offered in this book are approximations influenced by many factors including condition, rarity and demand, and they should serve as only guidelines, presenting an average range of what one might expect to pay for the items. In the marketplace, knowledge and opinions held by both sellers and buyers determine prices asked and prices paid. This is not a price list of items for sale or items wanted by the author or publisher. The author and the publisher shall not be held responsible for losses that may occur in the purchase, sale or other transaction of property because of information contained herein. Efforts have been made to present accurate information, but the possibility of error exists. Readers who believe that have discovered an error are invited to mail corrective information to the author, Robert M. Overstreet, at Gemstone Publishing, 10150 York Rd., Suite 300, Hunt Valley, MD 21030. Verified corrections will be incorporated into future editions of this book.

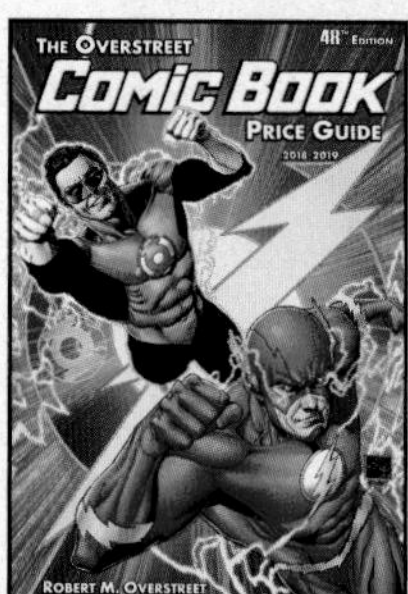

Flash and Green Lantern Hardcover Edition ISBN: 978-1-60360-220-4
Flash and Green Lantern Soft Cover Edition ISBN: 978-1-60360-221-1

Planet of the Apes Hardcover Edition ISBN: 978-1-60360-222-8
Planet of the Apes Soft Cover Edition ISBN: 978-1-60360-223-5

American Flagg Hardcover Edition ISBN: 978-1-60360-224-2
American Flagg Soft Cover Edition ISBN: 978-1-60360-225-9

Thanos - Hero Initiative Hardcover Edition ISBN: 978-1-60360-226-6

Printed in the United States of America

10 9 8 7 6 5 4 3 2 1

Forty-Eighth Edition: July 2018

TABLE OF CONTENTS

ACKNOWLEDGEMENTS

Ethan Van Sciver kicked off our 48th annual edition with his terrific cover featuring The Flash and Green Lantern. Ryan Sook took up the challenge and delivered his stunning *Planet of the Apes* anniversary cover. Not to be outdone, Howard Chaykin, colorist Wil Quintana and lettering wizard Ken Bruzenak brought us the 35th anniversary of Chaykin's *American Flagg!* Joe Jusko picked up the (Infinity) gauntlet and delivered a mind-blowing Thanos cover for the Hero Initiative edition. And Georges Jeanty, inker Karl Story and colorist Dan Jackson offered up our first *Buffy The Vampire Slayer* cover on the *Big, Big* edition.

Special thanks to Gemstone's own Mark Huesman, J.C. Vaughn, Amanda Sheriff, Mike Wilbur, Carrie Wood and Braelynn Bowersox.

Special Thanks to the Overstreet Advisors who contributed to this edition, including Darren Adams, Grant Adey, Bill Alexander, David T. Alexander, Tyler Alexander, Lon Allen, Dave Anderson, David J. Anderson, DDS, Matt Ballesteros, L.E. Becker, Robert L. Beerbohm, Jim Berry, Tim Bildhauser, Peter Bilelis, Dr. Arnold T. Blumberg, Steve Borock, Scott Braden, Richard M. Brown, Shawn Caffrey, Charles & Jeff Cerrito, John Chruscinski, Paul Clairmont, Art Cloos, Bill Cole, Jack Copley, Ashley Cotter-Cairns, Jesse James Criscione, Frank Cwiklik, Brock Dickinson, Gary Dolgoff, John Dolmayan, Walter Durajlija, Ken Dyber, Daniel Ertle, D'Arcy Farrell, Bill Fidyk, Paul M. Figura, Joseph Fiore, Stephen Fishler, Dan Fogel, John Foster, Dan Gallo, Stephen Gentner, Steve Geppi, Douglas Gillock, Sean Goodrich, Tom Gordon III, Andy Greenham, Eric J. Groves, Jim Halperin, Jay Halstead, Rick Hirsch, Terry Hoknes, Steven Houston, Jeff Itkin, Dr. Steven Kahn, Nick Katradis, Ivan Kocmarek, Robert Krause, Ben Labonog, Ben Lichtenstein, Stephen Lipson, Paul Litch, Doug Mabry, Brian Marcus, Jon McClure, Todd McDevitt, Mike McKenzie, Steve Mortensen, Marc Nathan, Josh Nathanson, Tom Nelson, Jamie Newbold, Terry O'Neill, Michael Pavlic, Bill Ponseti, Mick Rabin, Yolanda Ramirez, Alex Reece, Greg Reece, Rob Reynolds, Steve Ricketts, Ben Samuels, Barry Sandoval, Phil Schlaefer, Dylan Schwartz, Alika Seki, Todd Sheffer, Frank Simmons, Marc Sims, Lauren Sisselman, Tony Starks, West Stephan, Al Stoltz, Doug Sulipa, Michael Tierney, Ted VanLiew, Frank Verzyl, John Verzyl, Rose Verzyl, Eddie Wendt, Rick Whitelock, Mike Wilbur, Harley Yee, Vincent Zurzolo, Jr., as well as to our additional contributors, including Stephen Baer, Ron Ballard, Jonathan Bennett, Mike Bromberg, Dr. Jonathan Calure, Ledge King, Rod Matlack, John Mlachnik, Bill Parker, Kevin Poling, Eric Stucki, and Hermann Urbanek. Without their active participation, this project would not have been possible.

Additionally, I would like to personally extend my thanks to all of those who encouraged and supported first the creation of and then subsequently the expansion of the Guide over the past four decades. While it's impossible in this brief space to individually acknowledge every individual, mention is certainly due to Lon Allen (Golden Age data), Mark Arnold (Harvey data), Larry Bigman (Frazetta-Williamson data), Bill Blackbeard (Platinum Age cover photos), Steve Borock and Mark Haspel (Grading), Glenn Bray (Kurtzman data), Gary M. Carter (DC data), J. B. Clifford Jr. (EC data), Gary Coddington (Superman data), Gary Colabuono (Golden Age ashcan data), Wilt Conine (Fawcett data), Chris Cormier (Miracleman data), Dr. S. M. Davidson (Cupples & Leon data), Al Dellinges (Kubert data), Stephen Fishler (10-Point Grading system), Chris Friesen (Glossary additions), David Gerstein (Walt Disney Comics data), Kevin Hancer (Tarzan data), Charles Heffelfinger and Jim Ivey (March of Comics listing), R. C. Holland and Ron Pussell (*Seduction* and *Parade of Pleasure* data), Grant Irwin (Quality data), Richard Kravitz (Kelly data), Phil Levine (giveaway data), Paul Litch (Copper & Modern Age data), Dan Malan & Charles Heffelfinger (Classic Comics data), Jon McClure (Whitman data), Fred Nardelli (Frazetta data), Michelle Nolan (Love comics), Mike Nolan (MLJ, Timely, Nedor data), George Olshevsky (Timely data), Dr. Richard Olson (Grading and Yellow Kid info), Chris Pedrin (DC War data), Scott Pell ('50s data), Greg Robertson (National data), Don Rosa (Late 1940s to 1950s data), Matt Schiffman (Bronze Age data), Frank Scigliano (Little Lulu data), Gene Seger (Buck Rogers data), Rick Sloane (Archie data), David R. Smith, Archivist, Walt Disney Productions (Disney data), Bill Spicer and Zetta DeVoe (Western Publishing Co. data), Tony Starks (Silver and Bronze Age data), Al Stoltz (Golden Age & Promo data), Doug Sulipa (Bronze Age data), Don and Maggie Thompson (Four Color listing), Mike Tiefenbacher & Jerry Sinkovec (Atlas and National data), Raymond True & Philip J. Gaudino (Classic Comics data), Jim Vadeboncoeur Jr. (Williamson and Atlas data), Richard Samuel West (Victorian Age and Platinum Age data), Kim Weston (Disney and Barks data), Cat Yronwode (Spirit data), Andrew Zerbe and Gary Behymer (M. E. data).

A special thanks, as always, to my wife Caroline, for her encouragement and support on such a tremendous project, and to all who placed ads in this edition.

CGC AND NON-CGC GOLDEN AGE, SILVER AGE AND BRONZE AGE. ALL GENRES

• SOLID GRADING, SOLID REPUTATION, COMPETITIVE PRICING •

ALL THAT SERVICE FOR ONLY 10%!!
Take Advantage Now!... 'Dat Fee is Way Too Low to Last!

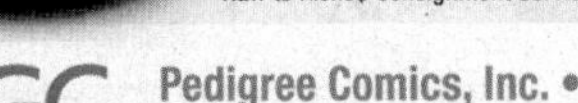

PedigreeComics.com®

CGC
Comics Guaranty, LLC
Charter Member Dealer

Sales Reporting Partner
GPAnalysis

The Apex
of Elegance
and Class
Alex
Raymond

FIRST
COMICS NEWS
FIRST COMICS NEWS STAF
COLUMNISTS
Alex
Bob A
Dærick Grö
Migue
Tany
Tim Ch
CONTRIBUTORS
Alex Sin
Mike B
Buzz
Holly Go
Howard C
Mark
Marwan El N
Naif Al-M
Scott Mck
Trevor Von
PODCASTERS
Art
Chris Ma
Colt C
Jamie
REPORTERS
Chris S
Franc
Grant Offenb
Martin
Phil
REVIEWERS
Alexander Ray
Calvin D
Giovan
Ric C
Wayn
EDITORIAL STAFF
Jez Ibelle ♦ ED
Matthew Szewczyk ♦ MANAGING ED
Reinhardt Schäfer ♦ BUREAU CHIE
Richard Vasseur ♦ BUREAU CHIEF CA
Rik Offenberger ♦ EDITOR-IN-C
CLASSIC HEROES
TRADMARK ™ & COPYRIGHT © 2018 MARVEL COMICS
INDIE HEROES
TRADMARK ™ & COPYRIGHT © 2018 ARCHIE COMICS
MOVIE HEROES
TRADMARK ™ & COPYRIGHT © 2018 DC COMICS
TV HEROES
TRADMARK ™ & COPYRIGHT © 2018 MARVEL COMICS

THE WORLD'S MOST EXCITING, BELOVED, COMICAL, FRIGHTENING, AND RECOGNIZABLE LICENSED PROPERTIES.
IN ALL-NEW COMICS.
AND ALL UNDER ONE BANNER.
ZORRO
FUNNY BOOKS
UNDERDOG AND PALS
THE FRIENDLY GHOST
Casper's CAPERS
PINK PANTHER
Surfside SPECIAL
The THREE STOOGES
ADAM GREEN'S
HATCHET
CARSON OF VENUS
AMERICAN MYTHOLOGY
PRODUCTIONS

TOP COW PRODUCTIONS, INC.
image
IMAGECOMICS.COM // TOPCOW.CO
CYBER FORCE IS TM & © 2018 TOP C
PRODUCTIONS INC., IMAGE COMICS® AND
LOGOS ARE REGISTERED TRADEMARKS
IMAGE COMICS, INC. ALL RIGHTS RESERV
"CYBER FORCE
brilliant reimagining
Silvestri's landmark serie
- Comicsve
SILVESTRI • HAWKINS • HILL • ROJO
CYBER FORCE
AVAILABLE NOW

THE LEAGUE OF EXTRAORDINARY GENTLEMEN'S SPECTACULAR FOURTH AND FINAL VOLUME,
The TEMPEST
COMING SUMMER 2018!
The LEAGUE of EXTRAORDINARY GENTLEMEN
ILLUSTRATED Masterpieces
Featuring Stories by the World's Gravest Authors
THE TEMPEST
ALAN MOORE • KEVIN O'NEILL
No. 1 OF SIX
GREAT BRITAIN
WELCOME TO THE STORY TO END ALL STORIES.
O'Neill
ALAN MOORE
KEVIN O'NEILL
Top Shelf PRODUCTIONS
FULL COLOR • 32 PAGES • $4.99
© Alan Moore & Kevin O'Neill. Co-published by Top Shelf Productions and Knockabout Comics

comic artfans

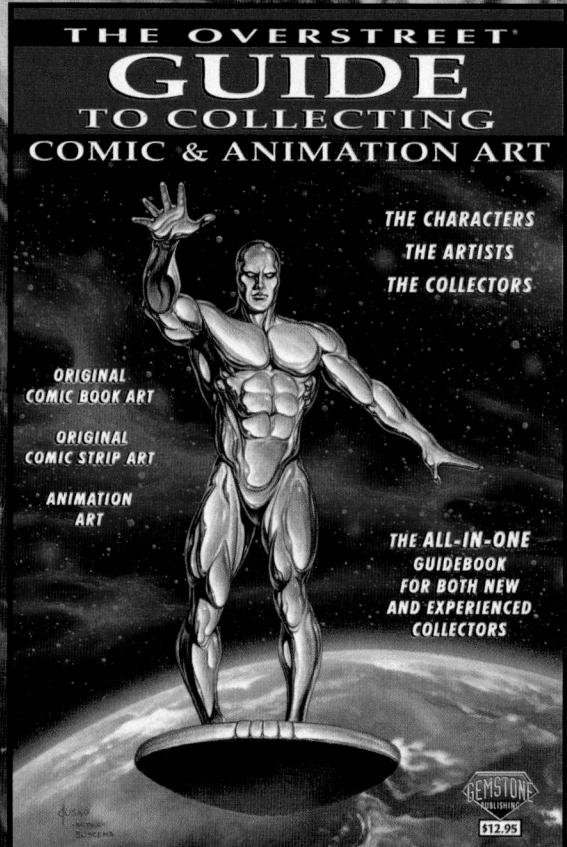

In Memoriam

John Verzyl

Comic Book Collector
Comic Book Dealer
Our Dear Friend
And so much more...

February 14, 1961 – March 10, 2018

TORPEDO COMICS
TORPEDO

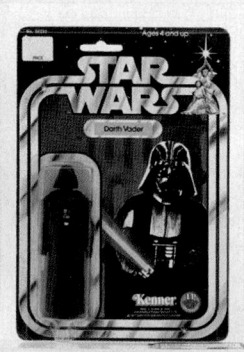

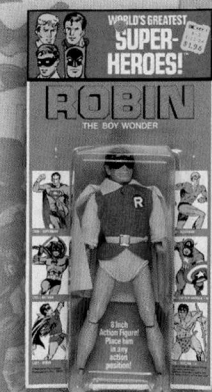

HAS THERE EVER BEEN A BETTER TIME TO BE A COMIC BOOK FAN?
WITH COMIC BOOK-INSPIRED MOVIES, TV SHOWS AND VIDEO GAMES, MORE PEOPLE THAN EVER ARE DISCOVERING THE CHARACTERS AND STORIES WE LOVE!

THAT'S COOL BECAUSE AS GREAT AS MANY OF THE OTHER INCARNATIONS HAVE BEEN, COMICS STILL DO IT BEST!

"BUT CHANCES ARE THAT IF YOU'RE READING THIS BOOK, YOU ALREADY LOVE COMICS OR KNOW SOMEONE WHO DOES."
"IN JUST A MOMENT, WE'LL GET DOWN TO BASICS..."

WE HOPE YOU'LL FIND THIS BOOK TO BE A SUPERB REFERENCE, NO MATTER WHAT TYPE OF COMICS YOU LIKE.

OUR MARKET REPORTS START ON PAGE 89, AND THEY OFFER THE INSIGHT OF THE OVERSTREET ADVISORS ABOUT BACK ISSUE SALES...
AND WE HAVE TONS OF PRICING DATA, TOP COMICS, GRADING TIPS, AND MORE!

THE OVERSTREET
48TH EDITION
COMIC BOOK
PRICE GUIDE
2018-2019
ROBERT M. OVERSTREET
IT MIGHT BE HARD TO BELIEVE, BUT THIS IS THE 48TH EDITION OF *THE OVERSTREET COMIC BOOK PRICE GUIDE!*
ABOUT THIS BOOK
BY J.C. VAUGHN
ILLUSTRATED BY GENE GONZALES

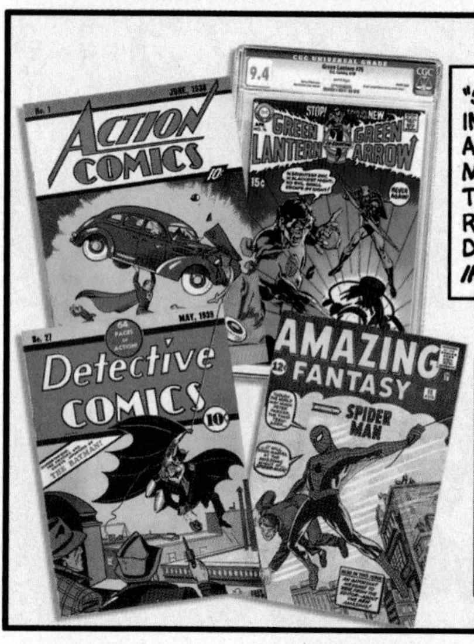
ACTION COMICS
GREEN LANTERN GREEN ARROW
DETECTIVE COMICS
AMAZING FANTASY
SPIDER MAN

"SINCE THE *GUIDE*'S DEBUT IN 1970, THERE HAVE BEEN A LOT OF CHANGES IN THE MARKETPLACE. FOR INSTANCE, THERE HAVE ALWAYS BEEN RECORD PRICES, BUT THESE DAYS THEY CAN MAKE *INTERNATIONAL NEWS...*"

"WHEN YOU KEEP UP WITH *RECORD PRICES*, WHAT'S *SELLING*, WHAT'S *NOT* SELLING, AND WHAT'S SUDDENLY *IN DEMAND*, IT HELPS YOU KNOW WHAT YOU SHOULD BE WILLING TO PAY OR WHEN TO SELL."

Buffy
A MARVEL COMICS LIMITED SERIES
WOLVERINE
THE TRANSFORMERS
Comico
Primer
GRENDEL

AND THERE HAVE BEEN LOTS OF OTHER CHANGES, TOO. WE'VE BEEN STUDYING THIS FOR *FOUR DECADES* NOW AND ONE THING IS REALLY CLEAR...

THE MORE YOU *KNOW* ABOUT COMICS, THE MORE YOU *WANT* TO KNOW. AND WE'VE BEEN HAPPY TO HELP PEOPLE LEARN FOR *48 YEARS*.

ONE OF THE COOL THINGS ABOUT COMIC BOOKS IS THAT THERE ARE LOTS OF NEW ONES TO DISCOVER...

AND THERE ARE LITERALLY HUNDREDS OF THOUSANDS OF DIFFERENT BACK ISSUES, TOO!

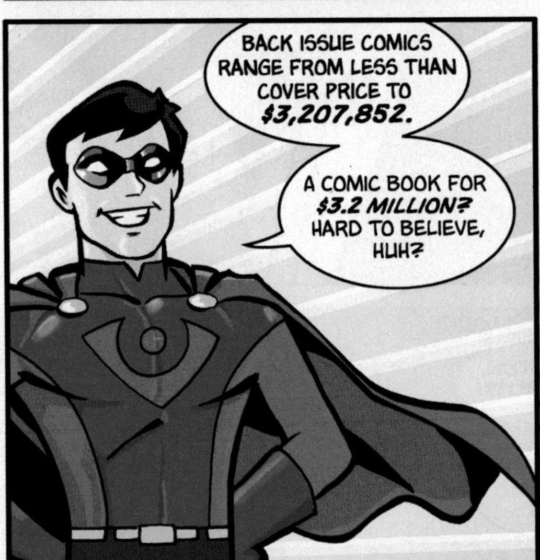
BACK ISSUE COMICS RANGE FROM LESS THAN COVER PRICE TO ***$3,207,852.***
A COMIC BOOK FOR ***$3.2 MILLION?*** HARD TO BELIEVE, HUH?

THE FIRST COMIC TO HIT $1 MILLION WAS ***ACTION COMICS*** #1, THE FIRST APPEARANCE OF ***SUPERMAN***.
THE SECOND, JUST A FEW DAYS LATER, WAS ***DETECTIVE COMICS*** #27, THE FIRST APPEARANCE OF ***BATMAN***.
ANOTHER ACTION #1 SOLD FOR ***$1.5 MILLION*** JUST A SHORT WHILE AFTER THAT.

MANY OTHERS HAVE SOLD FOR RECORD PRICES IN THE LAST FEW YEARS, EVEN WITH THE TOUGH ECONOMY NATIONALLY.

THE GRADE AND SCARCITY OF THE ISSUES HAVE A LOT TO DO WITH THAT. WE'LL GET INTO THAT IN JUST A BIT...

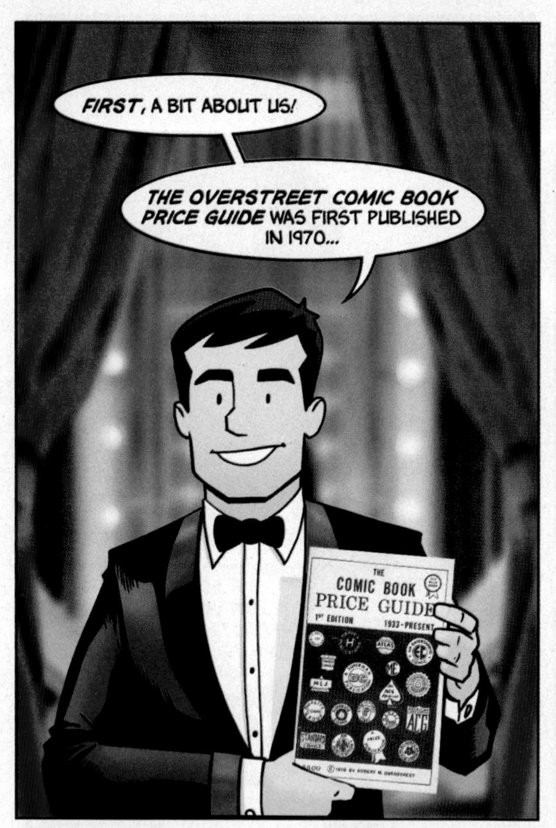

FIRST, A BIT ABOUT US!
THE OVERSTREET COMIC BOOK PRICE GUIDE WAS FIRST PUBLISHED IN 1970...
THE COMIC BOOK PRICE GUIDE
1ST EDITION 1933-PRESENT

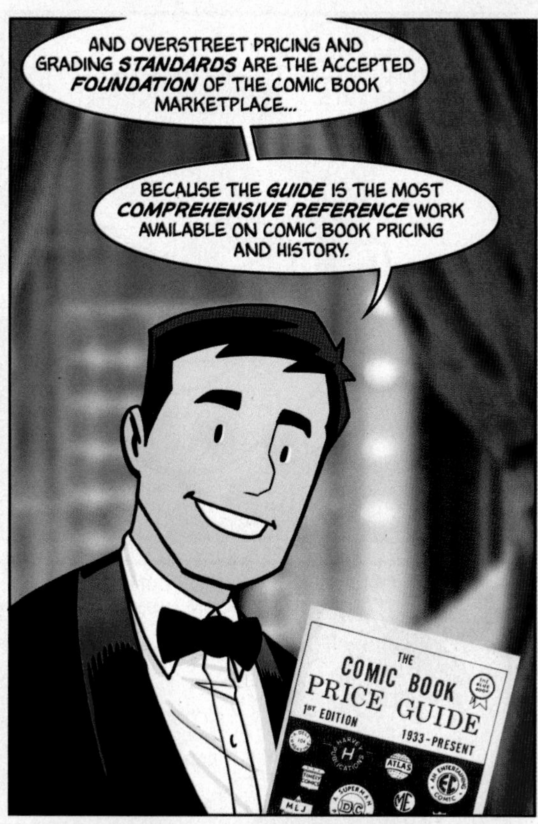

AND OVERSTREET PRICING AND GRADING STANDARDS ARE THE ACCEPTED FOUNDATION OF THE COMIC BOOK MARKETPLACE...
BECAUSE THE GUIDE IS THE MOST COMPREHENSIVE REFERENCE WORK AVAILABLE ON COMIC BOOK PRICING AND HISTORY.
THE COMIC BOOK PRICE GUIDE
1ST EDITION 1933-PRESENT

COMICS ARE LISTED *ALPHABETICALLY BY TITLE,* REGARDLESS OF PUBLISHER...

THE MAIN PRICING SECTION FEATURES COMICS FROM 1934 TO PRESENT.

THIS BOOK ALSO INCLUDES...

Big Little Books
Promotional Comics
Pioneer Age Comics
Victorian Age Comics
Platinum Age Comics

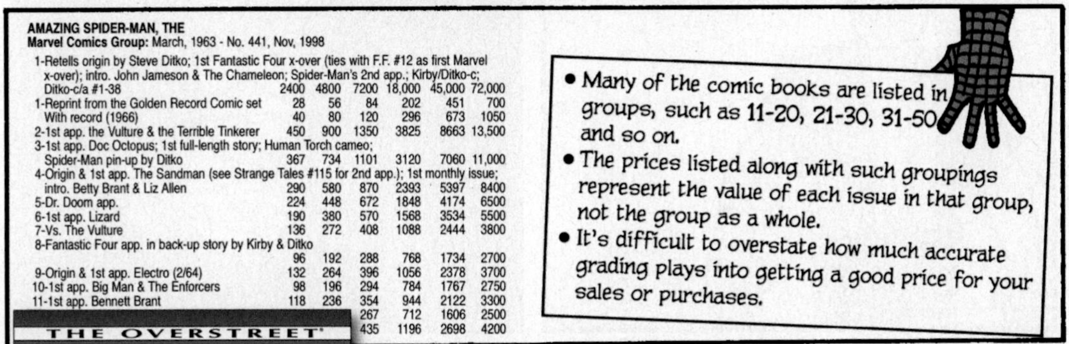

9.2
9.0
8.5
8.0
7.5
7.0
6.5
6.0
5.5
5.0
4.5
4.0
3.5
3.0
2.5
2.0

PRICES ARE LISTED IN SIX GRADES, RANGING FROM 2.0 TO 9.2 ON A 10.0 SCALE.

THERE ARE MORE GRADES THAN THE SIX WE HAVE LISTED, BUT THESE WILL GIVE YOU THE KEYS TO UNDERSTANDING THE MARKET.

WHILE PRICES BELOW 9.2 ARE FAIRLY STEADY, IT'S IMPORTANT TO NOTE THAT PRICES ABOVE 9.2 ARE FREQUENTLY CONSIDERED EXTREMELY VOLATILE.

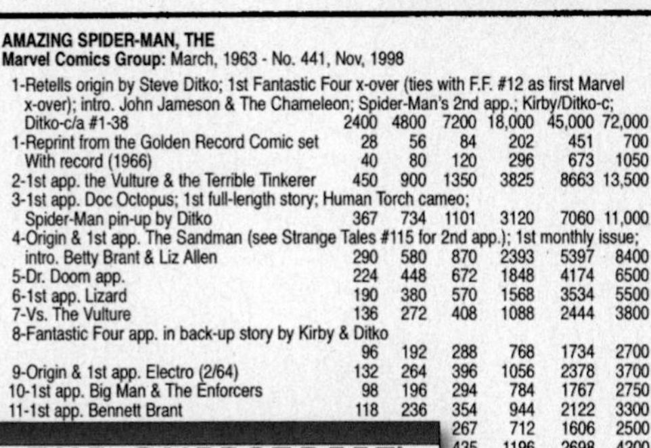

AMAZING SPIDER-MAN, THE
Marvel Comics Group: March, 1963 - No. 441, Nov, 1998

1-Retells origin by Steve Ditko; 1st Fantastic Four x-over (ties with F.F. #12 as first Marvel x-over); intro. John Jameson & The Chameleon; Spider-Man's 2nd app.; Kirby/Ditko-c; Ditko-c/a #1-38	2400	4800	7200	18,000	45,000	72,000
1-Reprint from the Golden Record Comic set	28	56	84	202	451	700
With record (1966)	40	80	120	296	673	1050
2-1st app. the Vulture & the Terrible Tinkerer	450	900	1350	3825	8663	13,500
3-1st app. Doc Octopus; 1st full-length story; Human Torch cameo; Spider-Man pin-up by Ditko	367	734	1101	3120	7060	11,000
4-Origin & 1st app. The Sandman (see Strange Tales #115 for 2nd app.); 1st monthly issue; intro. Betty Brant & Liz Allen	290	580	870	2393	5397	8400
5-Dr. Doom app.	224	448	672	1848	4174	6500
6-1st app. Lizard	190	380	570	1568	3534	5500
7-Vs. The Vulture	136	272	408	1088	2444	3800
8-Fantastic Four app. in back-up story by Kirby & Ditko	96	192	288	768	1734	2700
9-Origin & 1st app. Electro (2/64)	132	264	396	1056	2378	3700
10-1st app. Big Man & The Enforcers	98	196	294	784	1767	2750
11-1st app. Bennett Brant	118	236	354	944	2122	3300
			267	712	1606	2500
			435	1196	2698	4200

- Many of the comic books are listed in groups, such as 11-20, 21-30, 31-50 and so on.
- The prices listed along with such groupings represent the value of each issue in that group, not the group as a whole.
- It's difficult to overstate how much accurate grading plays into getting a good price for your sales or purchases.

THE BEST PART IS THERE ARE MANY DIFFERENT WAYS TO COLLECT.

YOU CAN CHOOSE TO FOLLOW INDIVIDUAL PUBLISHERS, WRITERS, ARTISTS, CHARACTERS...

YOU CAN COLLECT SUPERHEROES, WAR COMICS, WESTERNS, ROMANCE OR WHATEVER YOU LIKE...

YOU CAN CHOOSE #1 ISSUES, FIRST APPEARANCES, CROSSOVERS, OR MANY OTHER VARIATIONS.

THE BEST THING TO COLLECT IS WHAT YOU LIKE, NOT WHAT SOMEONE ELSE LIKES.

WHETHER IT'S SPIDER-MAN OR EVERY COMIC THAT CAME OUT THE MONTH YOU WERE BORN, IT'S BEST TO DO IT WITH A PLAN.

THE BEST WAY TO HAVE A GOOD PLAN IS TO FIRST GET INFORMED.

THE BEST WAY TO GET INFORMED IS TO GO TO THE EXPERTS!
CAN'T I SAY "OR ELSE!" AFTER THAT?

LEARN THE INS AND OUTS OF COLLECTING, INCLUDING HOW TO TAKE CARE OF YOUR COLLECTION!

Learn how to grade your comics and why the grades make a difference!

LEARN WHAT TO EXPECT AT CONVENTIONS OR WHEN BUYING AND SELLING COMICS.
AND MAYBE HOW TO FIGHT ZOMBIES...

IT'S ALSO IMPORTANT TO REMEMBER THAT THIS BOOK IS A GUIDE, NOT A DEALER'S PRICE LIST. THE MARKET SETS THE PRICES.

WITH INPUT FROM A NETWORK OF EXPERIENCED ADVISORS INCLUDING WELL ESTABLISHED COLLECTORS, DEALERS AND HISTORIANS OF POPULAR CULTURE, WE HAVE UNDERTAKEN SIGNIFICANT EFFORT TO ASSEMBLE THIS PRICING INFORMATION.

THE RESULTING LISTINGS COME THROUGH THE OBSERVATION AND DOCUMENTATION OF PRICES REALIZED THROUGH HOBBY AND TRADE SHOWS, CATALOG SALES, RETAIL SALES, AND INTERNET, LIVE AND MAIL-IN AUCTIONS. DOCUMENTED PERSONAL SALES MAY ALSO BE INCLUDED.

WE HAVE EARNED OUR REPUTATION FOR OUR CAUTIOUS, CONSERVATIVE APPROACH TO PRICING.

WE ACTIVELY ENCOURAGE READERS WHO BELIEVE THEY HAVE DISCOVERED AN ERROR TO MAIL RELATED INFORMATION TO THE AUTHOR.
WRITE TO: ROBERT M. OVERSTREET GEMSTONE PUBLISHING, INC. 10150 YORK RD., SUITE 300 HUNT VALLEY, MD 21030
OR EMAIL FEEDBACK@GEMSTONEPUB.COM
VERIFIED CORRECTIONS WILL BE INCORPORATED INTO FUTURE EDITIONS OF THIS BOOK.
Editor's note: For more updates, visit *Scoop* at http://scoop.PreviewsWorld.com.

OVERSTREET MARKET REPORT 2018

TOP KEY BOOKS IN ALL GRADES SOLD WELL AT RECORD PRICES THROUGHOUT THE YEAR

by Robert M. Overstreet

A few noteworthy sales: ***All Star Comics*** *#8, CGC 9.4 for $936,223,* ***Fantastic Comics*** *#3 in CGC 9.4 Mile High for $243,000,* ***Marvel Comics*** *#1 in CGC 6.0 for $215,000, and* ***Superman*** *#1 in CGC 5.5 for $507,500.*

Although few of the top key books sold last year were in high grade, there were many keys in the lower grades that sold for record prices. Dave Anderson, DDS said, "Sales were strong across the board particularly so with key issues both in the Silver Age and the Golden Age. Demand is so high for key issues that multi-million dollar comic auctions are commonplace." A "Key Issue" can be the first appearance of a major character or a classic cover. Eric Groves pointed out, "A great cover can sell a book today just as it did 65 years ago when it first went up on the rack. Any World War II cover, especially those depicting Hitler, Mussolini or Tojo, or all three, is highly desirable. The more imaginative the better."

All comic book auctions utilize the internet increasing bidding exponentially. Eric Groves agreed, "The internet has enabled commerce in comic books to extend world-wide. This international exposure of books for sale, particularly at auction, drives values upward."

Heritage Auctions reported that more than 53.7% of total revenues came from the internet, a 26% surge over 2016. Online sales at Heritage came to $438,298,484 in 2017, a 26% increase over the previous record of $348,107,079 in 2016. Of the total, vintage comic books and comic art hit a record $44.3 million in 2017. They also last year surpassed 1 million online bidder members covering all data catagories that they auction.

Josh Nathanson of ComicLink reported, "2017 was the biggest year we've ever seen for our auction division. Aggressive buyers added many thousands of examples of certified books and comic related artwork to their collections, setting many new sales records for the hobby."

Rob Reynolds of ComicConnnect wrote, "2017 was, by far, the biggest year in ComicConnect's history. Our consignors sold more comics, for more money, than ever before while thousands of new bidders joined and placed millions of dollars in bids. The usual suspects dominated the year's top ten lists with owners of Golden Age Keys, Joker covers, and the almighty *Amazing Fantasy* #15 enjoying incredible growth. ComicConnect offered several single owner collections including some of the rarest and most sought-after comics in the world."

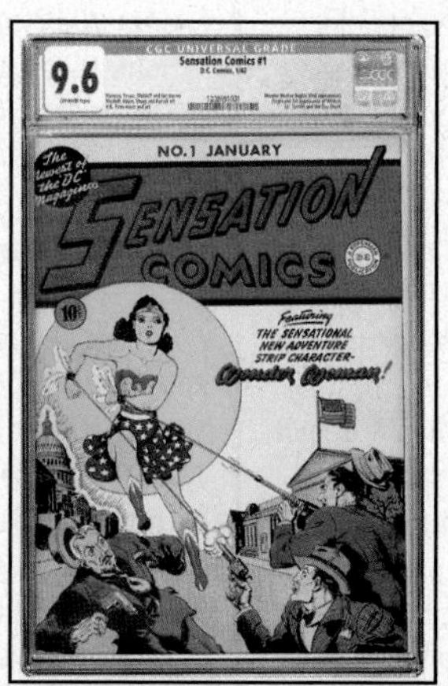

Sensation Comics ***#1,*** *CGC 9.6, Mile High copy sold for $399,100!*

ComicConnect sold the extensive comic and art collection of life-time fan, Jon Berk, the auction taking place in June 2017. The collection, heavy in Golden and Silver Age books realized over $7 million! Rob Reynolds pointed out, "The Jon Berk Collection was the most-asked-about, written-about, talked-about auction in our history. The collection was packed with comics and original comic art that have not been on the market for years, if not decades." A few highlights included: *Action Comics* #1, CGC 5.5-conserved $393,000, #7 CGC 5.5 $188,000, *Detective Comics* #27, CGC 6.5-rest. $313,000, *Fantastic Comics* #1 CGC 9.8 Mile High $66,000, #3 CGC 9.4 Mile High $243,000, #22, CGC 9.4 Mile High $26,609, *Mystery Men Comics* #1 CGC 9.0 Mile High $41,000, #2 CGC 9.6 Mile High $38,500, #3 CGC 9.6 Mile High $57,000, *Silver Streak* #16 CGC 8.5 $21,000, *Whiz Comics* #2(#1) CGC 6.5-rest. $36,500, *Wonder Comics* #1 CGC 9.4 $68,000, *Wonderworld* #3 CGC 9.4 Mile High $51,000, #7 CGC 9.6 Mile High $66,000, and #8 CGC 9.4 Mile High $33,000.

Golden Age: Peter Bilelis, Esq. reported, "The year of the Woman: The 2017 film's titanic success helped catapult Wonder Woman's popularity as her fan base continues to grow. The film helped *All Star Comics* #8, her first appearance, move into a more apropos position for a Golden Age key. Reported sale prices of this GA Key repeatedly set new record highs throughout 2017." Art Cloos agreed, "The success of the Wonder Woman movie early on pushed up the price of her keys with *All Star* #8 prices moving up a significant amount, and the same is true for *Sensation* and *Wonder Woman* comics."

Ken Dyber (Cloud 9 Comics) wrote, "Good Girl books in particular are very hot at the moment, with classic covers and Matt Baker covers selling for nosebleed prices." Frank Simmons (Coast to Coast Comics) reported, "There has been a strong revival of the Golden Age comic market. Golden Age comics are selling currently as strong as I have seen in comics! Timely and pre-Code Horror have made a big comeback this year regarding sales." West Stephan (CBCS) agreed, "We find ourselves in a very bullish comic book marketplace. Blue chip keys, classic covers and mainline Golden Age books are in very high demand. World War II covers from all publishers are very sought after. Schomburg is the king here, but if you have a 1940s cover WWII, it will sell at or above *Guide* levels. Risque covers are also in high demand due to their racy cover content. "

Tony Starks reported, "EC comics seem to be on a lot more collectors want list than they were a few years ago. Any issue that we get in quickly sells. Riding along with the increase in demand for ECs is pre-Code Horror in general, especially books with classic (that is lurid, gruesome and/or titilating covers). Classic Good Girl covers are much sought after as well."

Beckett Media purchased Comic Book Certification Service, LLC (CBCS) in October 2017. Beckett, the most trusted brand in collectibles, long known for their baseball card price guides, grading services and authentication services have now moved into comic book certification. Steve Borock, CBCS co-founder and president, said Beckett's infrastructure and global reach provides the grading company with unprecendented opportunity for growth. Borock, CEO Michael Bornstein and other key staff members will continue to serve collectors from CBCS's new offices in Dallas, Texas.

Golden Age Sales:

Action Comics #1 CGC 8.0 $461,555, #2 CBCS 9.2 Rest $16,800, #3 CGC 7.0 $55,009, #6 CGC 7.0 $24,500, #7 CGC 5.5 $188,000, CGC 1.0 $44,500, NC, pm CBCS 0.1 $1,250, #12 CBCS 0.5 $1,400, #13 CGC 1.5 $26,509, #15 CGC 3.0 $7,607, CGC 2.0 $4,900, #19 CGC 6.0 $7,917, #21 CGC 8.5 $22,566, #23 CGC 5.0 $15,200, CGC 4.5 $17,138, #35 CGC 9.0 $6,500, #63 CGC 8.5 $3,200, #64 CGC 9.4 $12,000.

Adventure Comics #40, CGC 7.0 $27,600.

All American Comics #16 CGC 6.5 $215,100, CGC 3.5 $66,000.

All Negro #1 CGC 7.5 $14,340.

All Star Comics #3 CGC 7.0 $40,000, CGC 6.5 $32,000, CGC 1.5 $7,400, #8 CGC 9.4 $936,223, CGC 2.0 $23,900.

Amazing Mystery Funnies V2/7 CGC 8.5 $3,766.

Amazing Man #23 CGC 9.4 Mile High $5,550.

America's Best #1 CGC 6.5 $1,050.

Archie Comics #1 CGC 4.0 $24,500, #50 CGC 7.5 $6,274.

Arrow #3 CGC 5.0 $1,775.

Astonishing #4 CGC 8.0 $4,100.

Banner Comics #3 CGC 9.6 Mile High $11,250.

Batman #1 CGC 7.0 $334,600, CBCS 7.0 $34,057 Rest, CBCS 0.1 $1,605, #49 CBCS 9.2 $9,600, $65 CGC 9.0 $8,000, $121 CGC 8.5 $18,200.

Big 3 #3 CGC 8.5 $2,700.

Blue Beetle #9 CGC 9.0 Mile High $4,770.

Blue Bolt Weird #115 CGC 9.6 $16,730.

Blue Ribbon Comics #10 CGC 7.0 Larson $2,249, #14 CGC 9.4 San Fran, $4,150.

Boy Comics #3 CGC 8.5 Mile High $6,572.

Brenda Starr #14 CGC 9.4 Mile High $45,750.

Captain America Comics #1 CGC NG $9,556, #46 CGC 85 $43,020, CGC 5.0 $9,350.

Captain Battle #5, CGC 8.5 $3,000.

Captain Courageous #6 CGC 9.4 $8,100.

Captain Marvel Advs.#1 CGC 0.5 $4,901.

Casper the Friendly Ghost #1 St. John CGC 7.0 $4,650.

Catman #1 CGC 9.0 $16,667, #3 CGC 7.0 $6,200, #19 CGC 8.0 $7,200

Century of Comics #1 CGC 6.5 $5,700.

Champ Comics #11 CGC 9.4 Mile High $4,900, #17 CGC 9.8 Mile High $6,422.

Champion Comics #10 CGC 9.2 Mile High $11,600.

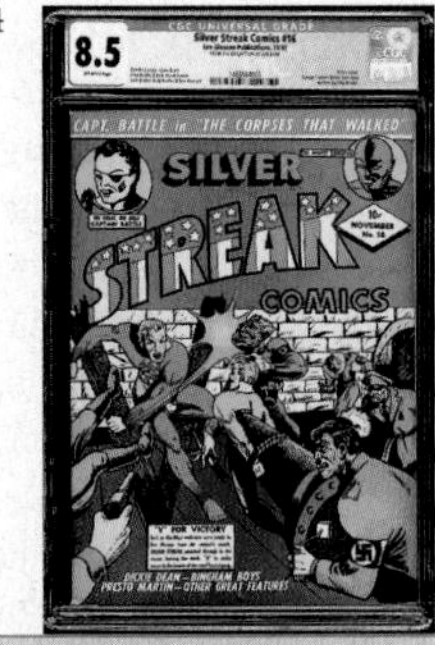

Silver Streak Comics *#16, CGC 8.5 sold for $21,000.*

Crash Comics #1 CGC 9.0 Mile High $9,960, #4 CGC 9.6 Mile High $23,000, #5 CGC 9.4 Mile High $14,601.

Crime Does Not Pay #26 CGC 9.4 Mile High $4,302.

Crime SuspenStories #1 CGC 9.8 Gaines $7,100.

Daredevil Battles Hitler #1 CGC 8.5 $12,200, #6 CGC 8.0 $1,227, #11 CGC 8.0 $6,100.

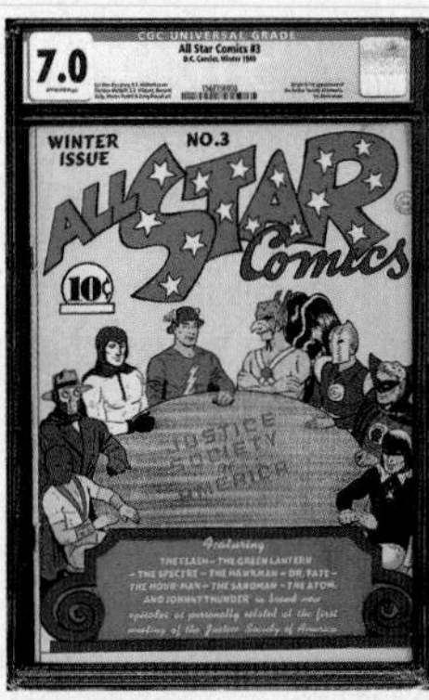

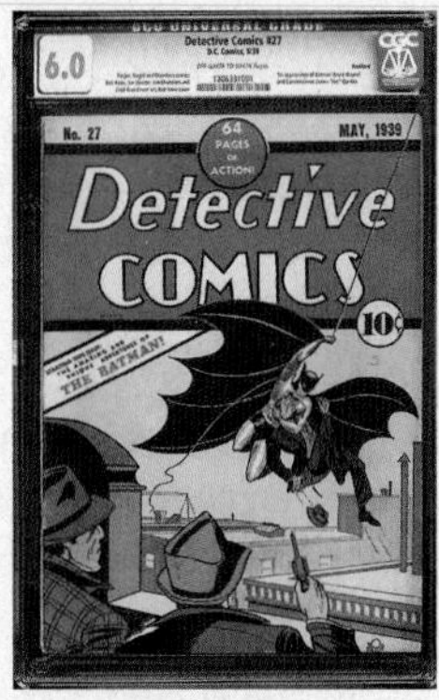

A few more noteworthy sales: ***All-American Comics*** *#16, CGC 6.5 for $215,100,* ***All Star Comics*** *#3, CGC 7.0 for $40,000,* ***Batman*** *#1, CGC 7.0 for $334,600, and* ***Detective Comics*** *#27, CGC 6.0 for $732,000.*

Detective Comics #1 CGC 3.5 $29,000, #4 CGC 6.0 $8,200, #27 CGC 6.5 Rest $313,000, CGC 2.5 $450,000, $280,000, NC $37,045, #29 CGC 3.0 $66,199, #31 CGC 5.0 $131,450, CGC 1.0 $44,000, #33 CGC 8.0 $167,300, #35 CBCS 9.8 Rest. $18,800, #36 CGC 6.0 $44,000, #38 CGC 4.0 $40,630, CGC 3.0 $54,010, #49 CBCS 9.2 $9,600,#62 CGC 9.4 $77,101, #69 CGC 6.5 $29,500, #79 CGC 9.4 $66,000, #122 CGC 8.0 $8,351, #140 CGC 7.5 $14,751.

Detective Picture Stories #3, CGC 7.0 $4,900.

Diary Secrets #21 CGC 6.0 $2,868.

Dime Comics #1 CGC 5.5 $851.

Donald Duck 4-Color #29 CGC 8.5 $17,925.

Exciting Comics #25 CGC 9.0 Mile High $7,219.

Famous Funnies A Carnival of Comics nn CGC 6.0 $3,100.

Fantastic Comics #1 CGC 9.8 Mile High $66,000, #3 CGC 9.4 Mile High $243,000, CGC 0.5 $7,266, #22 CGC 9.4 Mile HIgh $25,509.

Fantoman #2 CGC 7.5 $2,550.

Farmer's Daughter #3, CGC 7.5 $2,868.

Fight Against Crime #20 CGC 4.5 $2,300.

Flame #6, CGC 9.2 Mile High $7,901, #9 CGC 9.4 Mile High $5,800.

Flash Comics #1 (DC) CGC 2.5 #62,599.

Flash Comics #1 (Faw) CGC 4.5 $19,756.

Four Favorites #10 CGC 9.0 Mile High $14,017.

Frankenstein #26 CGC 7.5 $300.

Funnies On Parade nn CGC 7.5 $7,700.

Funny Pages #40 CGC 7.0 $6,400, #42 CGC 5.5 $3,099.

Funny Picture Stories #1 CGC 7.0 $2,459.

Gay Comics #18 CGC 8.5 $3,200.

Georgie #25 CGC 9.2 $2,868.

Gulf Funny Weekly #1 FN $1,950.

Hangman #3 CGC 4.0 $2,600.

Haunted Thrills #5 CGC 6.5 $1,661.

Headline #8 GCC 2.0 $3,851.

Human Torch #12 CGC 7.5 $11,200.

Hyper Mystery #2 CGC 4.5 $1,555.

Incredible Science Fiction #33, CGC 9.6 Gaines $3,122.

Jackpot #4 CGC 2.0 $4,505, #7 CGC 8.0 $2,306.

Jumbo Comics #9 CGC 7.5 $13,656.

Keen Detective Funnies #20, CGC 7.5 $4,600.

Keen Komics V2/#1 CGC 2.0 $4,000.

Krazy Komics #9 CGC 7.0 $3,434.

Lightning V2/#3 CGC 9.6 Mile High $8,800.

Marvel Comics #1 CGC 6.0 $215,000, CGC 2.5 $87,252.

Marvel Tales #95 CGC 3.0 $675.

Master Comics #1 NM -Denver $11,950, $21 CGC 8.5 $9,400.

Miracle Comics #2 CGC 6.5 $1,311.

More Fun #53 CGC 0.5 $2,250, #61 CGC 9.4 $16,250.

Motion Picture Funnies Weekly #1 CGC 3.5 $27,500.

My Girl Pearl #1 CGC 8.5 $4,100.

Mystery Men #1 CGC 9.0 Mile High $41,000, #3 CGC 9.6 Mile High $57,000, #30 CGC 9.4 Mile High $15,000, CGC 3.0 $2,629.

Mystic Comics #8 CGC 9.2 $21,076.

New Fun #1 FN $11,200.

Our Army at War #81 CGC 8.5 $5,736.

Out of the Shadows #8 CGC 7.0 $3,200.

Patsy Walker #1 Mile High $28,680, #5 CGC 9.4 Mile High $3,585.

Peanuts #1 CGC 8.5 $22,705, CGC 4.5 $3,679.

Pep Comics #16 CGC 8.5 $11,200, #20 CGC 4.5 $3,312, #22 CGC 8.0 $252,100, #23 CGC 1.8 $3,700, #34 CGC 5.0 $15,200, #41 CGC 6.5 $3,433.

Phantom Feature Book #20 CGC 8.5 Mile High $13,145.

Phantom Lady #17, CGC 7.0 $11,350, #23 CGC 6.5 $4,500.

Planet Comics #1 CGC 8.0 $20,315, #15 CGC 6.0 $10,755.

Prize Comics #20 CGC 8.0 $8,275.

Punch Comics #1 CGC 8.5 Denver $3,800, #12 CGC 6.5 $22,500.

Real Life #3 CGC 9.0 $20,018.

Red Dragon #7 CGC 8.0 $5,840.

Red Raven #1 CGC 6.0 Larson $15,200.

Samson #1 CGC 9.4 Mile High $7,767.

Science Comics #3, CGC 9.4 Larson $17,977.

Sensation Comics #1 CGC 9.6 $399,100.

Seven Seas #6, CGC 9.4 $25,000.

Sherry the Showgirl #1, CGC 4.5 $2,509.

Shield-Wizard #8, CGC 7.5 $3,500.

Silver Streak #1 CGC 8.5 $15,200, #3 CGC 8.5 $8,800, #4

CGC 9.6 $6,200, #6 CGC 7.0 $22,501, #8 CGC 80 $8,400, #16 CGC 8.5 $21,000, #23 CGC 8.5 $1,300.
Smash Comics #1 CGC 9.0 $8,200.
Space Western #44 CGC 9.2 $2,255.
Speed Comics #42 CBCS 9.8 $1,777, #11 CGC 8.5 $1,777, #18 CGC 4.5 $2,988.
Spirit #22 CGC 8.5 $2,900.
Spook #1 CGC 8.0 $775.
Startling Comics #49 CGC 8.0 $13,001.
Startling Terror Tales #11 CGC 6.0 $1,851.
Sub-Mariner Comics #1 CGC 7.5 $35,850, #6 CGC 6.5 $1,546, #11 CGC 9.4 $30,100.
Sun Girl #1 CGC 9.0 $5,400.
Super Rabbit #1 CGC 7.5 $1,777.
Superboy #68 CGC 8.0 $10,250.
Superman #1 CBCS 9.4 rest. $100,000, CGC 5.5 $507,500, CGC 1.0 $110,000, $64,600, NC $14,200.
Super Mystery V6/#3 CGC 5.0 $2,750.
Suspense Comics #3 CBCS 9.2 Mile High $262,900.
Target Comics #4 CGC 8.5 $2,629.
Teen Age Romances #25 CGC 6.0 $3,585.
Terry & the Pirates Feature Book #2 CGC 9.6 Mile High $6,572.
Terry Toons #38 CGC 9.0 $3,824.
Thing #12 CBCS 7.5 $41,040.
Thrill Comics #1 (Faw) CGC 9.0 $41,040.
Thrilling Comics #1 CGC 7.5 $3,433, #19 CGC 9.6 $6,200.
Thrilling Crime Cases #49 CGC 5.5 $611.
Tomb of Terror #15, CGC 8.5 $2,577.
Top Notch #9 CGC 8.0 $3,710.
U.S. Jones #1 CGC 6.5 $5,200, #2 CGC 8.0 $13,800.
United States Marines #2 CGC 7.0 $785.
USA Comics #1 CGC 8.5 $10,456, #8 CGC 2.0 $3,306, #10 CGC 6.5 $4,355.
V Comics #1 CGC 6.5 $1,500, #2 CGC 9.2 $5,700.
Venus #11 CGC 6.5 $705, #19 CGC 6.0 $7,311.
Victory Comics #1 CGC 3.5 $940, #3 CGC 8.0 $1,450, 4 CGC 8.0 $1,060,
War Comics #1 CGC 8.0 $925.
Weird Comics #1 CGC 9.0 $6,209, #18 CGC 7.0 $4,850, #19 CGC 7.0 $2,427, #20 CGC 4.5 $8,822.
Wham Comics #1 CGC 9.2 $2,473, #2 CGC 8.0 $1,326.
Whirlwind Comics #1 CGC 9.2 $4,900, CGC 4.5 $1,850, #3 CGC 8.0 $1,650.
Whiz Comics #2(#1) CGC 6.5 Rest $36,500, #4 CGC 8.5 $7,200.
Witness #1 CGC 9.0 $2,506.
Wonder Comics #1 CGC 9.4 $68,000, #2 CGC 9.2 $19,200.
Wonder Woman #1 CGC 1.0 $12,000, $10,285.
Wonderworld Comics #3 CGC 9.6 $51,000, #7 CGC 9.6 Mile High $66,000, #11 CGC 9.6 Mile High $19,000, #30 CGC 9.4 Mile High $6,200.
Yankee Comics #1 CGC 5.0 $605.
Yellow Claw #1 CGC 6.5 $858.
Zip Comics #1 CGC 6.5 $3,544, #34 CGC 8.0 $6,800.

Silver Age: The Silver Age is over 60 years old and the vast majority of books bought and sold are from this period. Key books continue to set records, even in the lower grades.

Josh Nathanson (ComicLink) reported, "Demand for Silver Age comics is as strong as it has ever been. As usual, major Marvel and DC Keys led the way in 2017 with exceptional results for several premiere and "1st appearance" issues achieved. Many tradional keys sold for impressive amounts including *Amazing Fantasy* #15, *Journey Into Mystery* #83, *Amazing Spider-Man* #1, etc."

Steven Houston reported, "The Silver Age era of comics is still the most in demand from collectors and speculators. The leader of the Silver Age market is still Marvel Comics. Key Marvel Silver Age books are still exploding in demand and price. Covering all grades, be it CGC, or raw, the blazing heat of collector activity upon this era of comics has not abated."

Eric Groves wrote, "Several books from this era have achieved astronomical prices, namely *Amazing Fantasy* #15, when in high grade. Yet there is one key point to keep in mind about this period. For all but the earliest issues (*Showcase* #4 and the like) there are a multitude of copies out there. We think established values may be here to stay." He continued, "Condition is everything with comics from this age. Many collectors are buying only key Silver Age issues, that is, first appearances and origins."

The Mile High copy of ***Suspense Comics #3****, 9.2 sold for $262,900*

Ken Dyber (Cloud 9 Comics) reported, "Silver Age has been selling quite strong this past year. I am the lowest, inventory wise, I've ever been on not only key issues, but also filling/run issues. I'm slowly restocking, but I've had several customers clear me out of many good titles."

Silver Age through Modern Age Sales:
Action Comics #242 CBCS 7.5 $19,120, #252 CGC 9.0 $30,037, CBCS 7.5 $6,400, CGC 6.5 $4,182, CGC 5.5 $2,412, CGC 5.0 $2,300, CGC 4.0 $1,461.
Adventure Comics #210 CGC 7.0 $6,316, #247 CGC 6.5 $8,365, CGC 3.0 $1,016.
Adventures of the Fly #2 CGC 9.2 $1,158, #6 CGC 9.4 $572, #7 CGC 9.2 $827.
Amazing Fantasy #15 CGC 9.2 $460,000, CGC 9.0 $395,000, CGC 7.0 $125,000, $95,600, CGC 6.5 $54,970, CGC 6.0 $45,410, CGC 5.5 $38,240, CGC 5.0 $40,630, $32,500, CBCS 2.5 $14,251, $13,700, CGC 1.5 $1,255, CGC 0.5 $6,106.
Amazing Spider-Man #1 CGC 9.4 $131,450, CGC 8.0 $32,111, CBCS 8.5 $29,975, CGC 7.0 $17,149, CGC 5.0 $6,819, CBCS 3.0 $4,300, CGC 0.5 $1,411, #2 CGC 9.0 $19,007, #3 CGC 9.6 $47,800, #14 CGC 9.6 $22,250, #129 CGC 9.4 $1,966 CGC 9.2 $2,049.
Aquaman #1 CGC 9.6 $28,250, #3 CBCS 9.0 $2,200.
Archie's Madhouse #22 CBCS 6.5 $956.
Avengers #1 CBCS 9.4 $65,725, CGC 8.5 $ 22,001, $16,075, CGC 5.5 $3,600, CBCS 5.0 $2,450, #4 CGC 9.6 $27,485, CGC 9.2 $8,100, CGC 8.0 $3,200, CGC 4.0 $857.
Batman #121 CGC 8.5 $18,200, #139 CGC 1.8 $133, #155 CGC 7.5 $526, 171 CGC 5.5 $326, 181 CGC 9.4 $6,700, CGC

9.2 $5,250, CGC 9.0 $4,000, #411 CGC 9.4 $2,525.
Brave & the Bold #28 CGC 9.0 $77,675, CGC 9.0 $72,559, CGC 7.0 $10,000, CGC 60 $6,450, CGC 5.5 $5,655, #53 CGC 9.0 $1,650, #54 CGC 9.8 $30,055.
Captain Atom #83 CGC 7.5 $477.
Daredevil #1 CGC 9.4 $24,251, CGC 8.5 $6,500, $5,800, CGC 7.5 $3,450, CBCS 4.5 $1,151.
Detective Comics #225 CGC 4.5 $3,855, #298 CGC 7.5 $700, #359 CGC 8.0 $2,300, CGC 7.0.
Doctor Solar #1 CGC 7.5 $340.
Doctor Strange #169 CGC 9.2 $1,104.
Fantastic Four #1 CGC 9.0 $161,325, CGC 7.0 $25,000, CBCS 6.5 $15,100, #4 CGC 9.4 $26,290, #5 CGC 9.0 $29,916, CGC 7.0 $3,915, #12 CGC 7.0 $1,850, #48 CGC 9.8 $21,000, CGC 9.0 $1.800, CGC 6.0 $595, #50, CGC 9.2 $1,525, Annual #1 CGC 9.6 $5,622.
Giant Size X-Men #1 CGC 9.4 $2,376.
Green Lantern #1 CGC 8.0 $3,733, CGC 6.5 $1,700, #65 CGC 9.0 $1,475.
House of Secrets #92 CGC 9.6 $14,501, CGC 9.4 $8,200, CGC 9.0 $2,400, CBCS 3.5 $400.
Incredible Hulk #1 CBCS 8.5 $141,011, CGC 7.0 $57,555, CGC 6.5 $34,655, CGC 6.0 $26,502, CBCS 3.0 $7,527, $4,106, CGC 1.5 $5,471, #2 CGC 9.0 $12,001, CGC 7.5 $2,800, #5, CGC 9.0 $4,500, #181 CGC 9.6 $8,600, CGC 9.2 $5,211, CGC 9.0 $3,325, CBCS 2.5 $706, #194 CGC 9.4 $4,916.
Iron Fist #14 CGC 9.6 $10,250.
Iron Man #1 CGC 9.4 $2,500, CGC 9.2 $1,525, CGC 2.0 $165.
Journey Into Mystery #83 CGC 9.4 $191,200, CBCS 9.4 Rest. $6,300, CGC 8.0 $30,555, #85 CGC 9.4 $28,680.
Justice League #1 CGC 7.5 $7,800, CGCC 6.5 $2,700, CGC 5.5 $2,800.
Magnus Robot Fighter #1 CGC 8.0 #615.
Metal Men #6 CGC 9.2 $450.
Night Nurse #4 CGC 9.2 $275.
Our Army At War #81 CGC 8.5 $5,736.
Sergeant Fury #1 CGC 8.0 $4,063, CBCS 6.0 $1,338.
Showcase #1 CGC 6.0 $2,250, #4 CGC 8.5 $155,350, CGC 3.5 $13,861, CBCS 2.0 $9,560, CBCS 1.8 $5,488, #22 CGC 9.2 $149,375, CGC 6.0 $7,200, CGC 4.0 $2,650, CGC 2.5 $1,400, #23 CGC 9.0 $8,962, #30 CGC 9.2 $8,066, #37 CGC 9.0 $3,755.
Silver Surfer #1 CGC 9.8 $27,000, CBCS 9.8 $19,120.
Star Trek #1 CBCS 9.4 $3,346.
Strange Tales #110 CBCS 9.2 $23,302, CGC 8.5 $8,166, #114, CGC 9.0 $10,234.
Tales of Suspense #39 CGC 9.6 $276,000, CBCS 9.6 $155,350, CGC 7.0 $11,805, CGC 6.5 $6,900, CGC 2.5 $2,800.
Tales To Astonish #27 CGC 7.0 $4,600, CBCS 6.5 $3,301, #35 CGC 7.5 $1,938, #44 CGC 8.5 $565.
Teenage Mutant Ninja Turtles #1 CGC 8.0 $4,700.
Walking Dead #1 CGC 9.9 $14,601.
Werewolf by Night #32 CGC 9.2 $1.800.
X-Men #1 CGC 9.0 $43,337, CGC 8.5 $23.302, CGC 5.0 $5,877, CGC 3.5 $2,506, CGC 1.8 $1,301.

Bronze Age: Dan Gallo reported, "The Bronze Age is a mixed bag. The sheer quantities available have kept many books flat or trending down. There are exceptions though. *Incredible Hulk* #181, *Amazing Spider-Man* #129, and *House of Secrets* #92 are stronger than ever. When buying Bronze Age books it is very important to get the highest grade possible even if you have to buy fewer books to do so."

Ben Labonog wrote, "Although there is tremendous supply, there seems to be relentless interest and demand for *Hulk* #181. This book is now $500 minimum to get into the door with a complete copy. *X-Men* #101 has been asked for a lot this year since the Phoenix movie was announced. Jim Starlin Thanos/Capt. Marvel covers have also been in strong demand."

Josh Nathanson (ComicLink) reported, "Comic books from the 1970s continue to be one of the most popular collecting eras with prices for keys and many non keys in high grade reaching levels that would have seemed unachievable not that many years ago."

****

The following market reports were submitted from some of our many advisors and are published here for your information. They will provide important insights into the thinking of many key players in the marketplace. The opinions in these reports belong to each contributor and do not necessarily reflect the views of the publisher or the staff of *The Overstreet Comic Book Price Guide* or Gemstone Publishing.

See you next year.

Bob

Robert M. Overstreet

Amazing Fantasy *#15 CGC 9.0 sold for $415,000,* ***Amazing Spider-Man*** *# 1 CGC 9.4 sold for $131,450,* ***Journey Into Mystery*** *#83 in CGC 9.4 sold for $191,200,* ***Showcase*** *#4 in CGC 8.5 sold for $155,350 and* ***Tales of Suspense*** *#39 in CGC 9.6 for $276,000.*

THE JOHN VERZYL OVERSTREET® ADVISOR AWARD

We are pleased to announce the formation of The John Verzyl Overstreet Advisor Award in honor of our friend and longtime contributor John Verzyl, and as a tribute to the many ways he added to our understanding, our love of comics, and our lives.

The John Verzyl Overstreet Advisor Award will be presented annually to the Overstreet Advisor or Advisors whose knowledge, contributions, ethics, and reputation are held in the highest esteem by his or her peers.

John Verzyl, center, with friends
Mark Haspel (left) and Steve Borock (right) on the occasion
of certifying his copy of *All-American Comics* #16.

Nominations may be made by any Overstreet Advisor in good standing.

Nominations should include the nominee's name and a description of why he or she best represents the positive attributes that John embodied for our hobby.

Selections from those nominations will be made by a committee including John's longtime friends, colleagues, and the Overstreet staff.

The first recipient or recipients will be announced in *The Overstreet Comic Book Price Guide* #49.

Nominations will be accepted until March 29, 2019.

To make a nomination, email Gemstone Publishing's Mark Huesman at humark@gemstonepub.com.

OVERSTREET COVER SUBJECTS
FIRST APPEARANCES

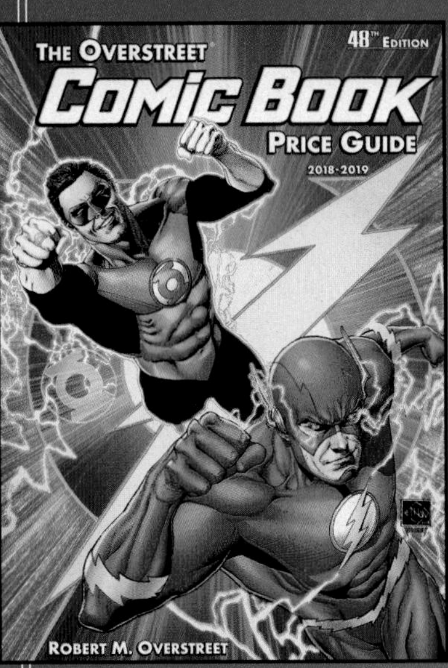

GREEN LANTERN
Showcase #22
September-October 1959
2018 NM- PRICE: $45,000

THE FLASH
Showcase #4
September-October 1956
2018 NM- PRICE: $150,000

PLANET OF THE APES
Movie Comics - Beneath the Planet of the Apes
December 1970
2018 NM- PRICE: $150

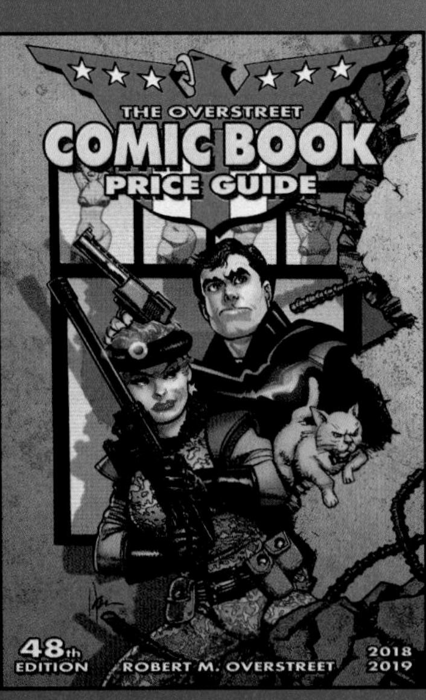

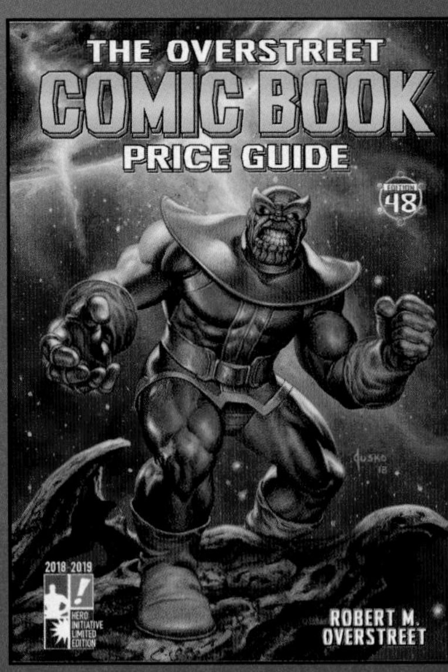

REUBEN FLAGG
American Flagg! #1
October 1983
2018 NM- PRICE: $4

THANOS
Iron Man #55
February 1973
2018 NM- PRICE: $1500

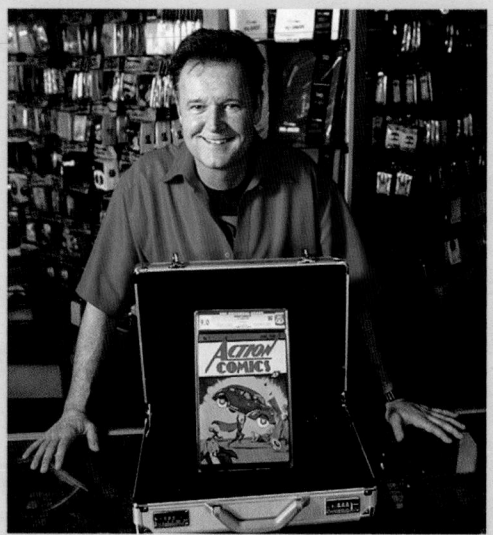

Grant Adey
Halo Certification Pty Ltd. - Australia

First up, the new direction Australian Comic Cons are taking. Promotors have gone to considerable lengths and capital expenditure to put "comics" back into comic cons. I'm not at liberty to roll out their forecasted plans for 2018, but I can describe what has already started. Johnny Huynh for Oz Con (Reed Pop) has created a comics central district, very smart. Halo attended and what I observed was the beginning of the road to recovery. Great interest and demand for original art covers, signed variants, movie and TV star signed comics.

Keys, it's all about keys, which leads me to Supanova. Dan Zachariou produced the greatest magic act since Houdini. One month out of Brisbane's Supanova he announced Stan Lee, a euphoric atmosphere of positive energy swept the nation. Thousands of fans and people who knew little of comics were drawn into this orgy of collecting comics. For Halo it meant selecting top gear, only one month prep, and our monthly expenditure got thrown out the window. Through the good graces of Dan Zachariou and Max Anderson of Stan Lee Collectables, I asked Halo Designer Brett Nolan to produce the Halo Stan Lee collectibles autograph label. In very short time Brett had worked his black magic and came up with a design approved by Supanova & Stan Lee Collectibles. Preparation was moving along nicely. Local comic book shops went into hyper drive ordering books for the event. A smart move by Norm Bardell of Fats Comics was to offer signed books to people unable to attend. His stock comics or people could supply their own. The Australian people positively charged with enthusiasm seized the moment. One announcement of one man had sent the Australian comic economy to crazed record breaking levels. The wealth creation within the Australian industry certainly travelled into the U.S via Diamond, Lone Star (sorry, My Comic Shop), etc. Then 2 weeks later, right on the heels of Supanova Brisbane convention, Dan Zachariou pulls another rabbit from the hat announcing Stan Lee for his Adelaide convention. I sat back in my chair thinking this is a masterful stroke of business and promotion. Creating opportunity for all.

So this is what I'm writing about, the new direction lead by the top, creating a positive environment for wealth creation & opportunity.

South East Asia came alive, with comic conventions in Manila, Singapore, Hong Kong, and Kuala Lumpur. I visited a Singapore comic store inside a major shopping centre. Mind blowing to say the least, the entrance to the shop was straight out of a modern sci-fi movie, ordering done through floor mounted kiosk type pedestals, touch screen credit card activated, place your order. No comics, TPB, statues, toys on display. All on screen. So place your order, take a walk through an air lock displaying most products behind softly lit glass, and at the end pick up your order boxed ready to go. Very slick. I know you're saying this won't work in western shops. Well, if your customers are 50+ you're probably right, but if they're 18 to 35, this is right up their alley. Retail on the whole has become impersonal, Freddy's advice is no longer needed or wanted, and the kids have the world in their pocket.

For the last 2 years Halo has seen wagon loads of comics for grading carrying the My Comic Shop sticker. I would say MCS had 80% of the south Pacific market. In the last 6 months MCS still holds the lion's share of back issue grading, new books is a different matter. The Asian shops have taken about 30% of what we see come in. New issues, variants boarded and bagged just as nice as MCS's books. For the Oceania region, shipping is faster and less expensive, and also the currency exchange is softer. Artists in the Asia region are very talented, fast learners, fast workers. They work at very reasonable rates. It would not surprise me if the top US publishers kept a small creative team of artists then sent page work to the South Pacific.

Diamonds are forever, restoration is not. Recently restored books have been resubmitted for grading. Moderate to extensively professionally restored books for example, books graded 9.2 restored are no longer 9.2. Encapsulated 12 years ago, the paint has faded at a different rate to the ink, tear seals have opened up, pieces have come away, bleached pages have turned tan/brittle so on. So at the time of inspection the book was 9.2, but 12 years down the track things have changed. Climate and display methods play a major role, but this also goes for non-restored books. Shop-displayed books under bright lights will fade if exposed for long durations. With pressing, we've seen an alarming number of cooked books. Steam pressing has been around for 20 years plus, and recently with the giddy up in prices steam pressing has gone nuts.

Again 9.8 at the time of inspection sure, but 12 months later white covers look toasted around the edges, pages gone to tan edges with off white centres.

Some examples encapsulated we've seen rusty staples with migration. There's no way any grading company passed the book 9.8 with rusty staples. At the time of inspection all was ok, but 10 years later the book is a GD/GD+. At Halo, we cold press, no foreign materials are introduced. Down side it's a slow process and would never work on a commercial scale. During the Stan Lee tour of Australia we cracked hundreds of slabs for autographing. The tour brought in a lot of people unfamiliar with comics or certification. People picked up the general idea very quickly with many returning to have other books certified.

For the U.S. market Halo continues to bump along with slow growth, mainly servicing the collector market. Minimum orders of 10 books or more are required and at \$45 it's expensive. Taking one or two books \$45-\$90, costs more than that in administration. Let's say the average modern slab price is \$20 and the company charges exact shipping costs. For a one book customer it goes something like this: P.O. box (annual fee) to unpacking (staff + disposal costs) to admin. (logged into the system, calls, email etc.) to billing and accounts (clearing, sorting mistakes) to holding (a system is required for safety, factory floor space) to grading (staff & requirements) to encapsulation (staff, case cost, inner well, label) to despatch (staff, packing supplies). For $20?. This is just a glossary of what is required. The CEO has monthly budgets, insurance, federal and state taxes, payroll, company improvements, and promotion and so on. Companies that expand too quickly with many small customers will soon feel the weight of admin. and service. Bigger does not always mean more profit, it can also have a negative effect. CEOs need balance, consideration for people and all company matters. Remember that of the seven deadly sins, deadliest of all is pride.

For discussion purposes I'd like to suggest a Roll of Honour be introduced to the long standing Overstreet publications. This being for Advisors who have passed away. Great advisors who contributed so much to the industry. Rather than they just disappear from the pages. I'd like Bruce Ellsworth stated, friend and mentor for too short a time. Maybe a short mention of their pedigrees or landmark achievements.

Anyhow this is Slim signing off from the furthest outpost.

Bill Alexander
Collector

Hi everyone from Central California.

The comic book market presently appears to have never looked stronger. Record breaking high end sales just keep on occurring with comic books from all ages.

Two amazing Marvel cover price variant sales in 2017 were Type 1A Marvel *New Mutants* #98 CGC 6.5 FN+(1st appearance of Deadpool) $1.50 Australian cover price variant that sold for $1,800.00 on eBay and Type 1 Marvel *Flintstones* #1 CGC 1.0 FR 35¢ cover price variant that sold for $1,000.00 on eBay. Type 1A cover price variant awareness is increasing at an accelerated rate in the hobby. Speaking of Type 1A cover price variants, one can check out rarecomics.wordpress.com to view the free on line 2018 Type 1A cover price variant price guide for Marvel & DC 1980s comic books.

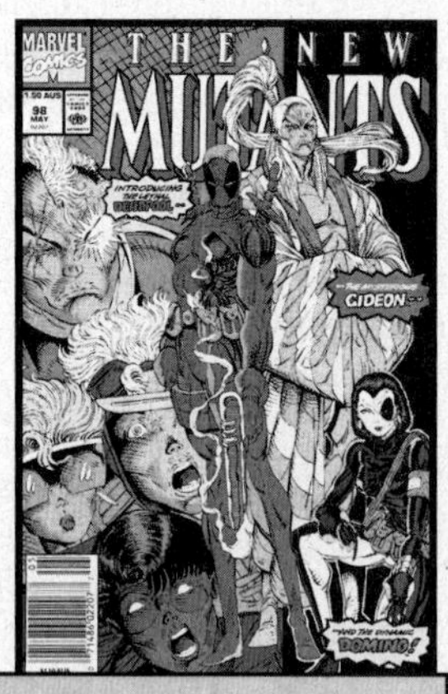

This Australian cover variant of **New Mutants #98** sold for $1800.

A few notable comic sales of 2017, *Archie's Madhouse* #22 CGC 2.0(restored) $260.00, CGC 4.5 $495.00, *Star Wars* #3 CGC 9.2(Type 1 35¢ variant) $2,700.00, *Kid Colt* #205 VG+ (Type 1 30¢ price variant) $306.00, *Amazing Spider-Man* #238 CGC 9.6 (Type 1A 75¢ price variant) $712.99 eBay, #252 PGX 9.8 (Type 1A 75¢ price variant) $555.00, *Detective Comics* #524 9.2 (Type 1A 75¢ price variant) $143.50 eBay, *Detective Comics* #525 9.2 (Type 1A 75¢ price variant) $152.50 eBay, *Detective Comics* #529 9.6 (Type 1A 75¢ price variant) $380.00 eBay, *Detective Comics* #531 9.6 (Type 1A 75¢ price variant) $355.00 eBay. With the top ten Bronze Age comics listed in last year's *Overstreet Guide* #47, FIVE of the books listed were Type 1 Marvel 35¢ cover price variants. Happy collecting to everyone.

David T. Alexander, Tyler Alexander and Edward Wendt DTAcollectibles.com Culture and Thrills, Inc.

Three trends have been prominent in the collecting field in 2017.

1) The popular comic book related TV programs and movies have brought many new people into the hobby. Some of these people were casual readers before the media push and many others were not even aware that comic books still existed. Now people think it is cool to read and collect comics but the question is, how many of these new fans will stay in the hobby for the long term? I do know that once you get started it is easy to get hooked on comic books. That is what happened to me in the early 1950s and I still have not been able to shake the habit. For this reason I predict that many new collectors will be long term members of the collecting community.

2) The convention fever is at an all-time high. In the early 1970s, the 6-8 major conventions that took place during the summer made it easy to spend 2-3 months on the road, crossing the country and successfully buying and selling old funny books. This was an exhilarating experience that went on into the early 1980s. By then most large cities had a convention or two, gas prices and travel expenses increased and there was less incentive to spend months on the road. As conventions grew, costs to attend also escalated. The internet caught on by the end of the ‹90s and conventions were not so popular. Collectors could buy books from all corners of the country without travel costs. While the internet is a useful tool, it does not provide the personal contact that is such an important aspect of the convention experience. Major conventions have been taking place in every major city for the last decade. They have grown to become media events pushing comic book collection to a secondary level of their activities. The costs to set up at these events have forced many comic sellers to stop participating. We all are aware that the costs for a promoter to run a weekend event at a big city convention center are huge and that the majority of attendees might only be interested in obtaining an autograph of a current TV star. These events have led to a rebirth of the 1970s type comic conventions. Local events have popped up all over the country and feature comic books being bought and sold by collectors. Many of these are like the old days when cons were held in hotel ballrooms. It is a luxury to stay in the hotel and take the elevator down to the dealers room instead of being at a hotel a mile or two away from a convention center and taking a cab daily or getting stuck for a $15 parking fee. If you can go to a comic show where the table fee is reasonable enough to allow a collector to sell his own books you are returning back to the early days. I have been to many of these smaller events over the last couple of years and they have been fantastic. I was in California at the beginning of 2018 and was able to attend three of these comic oriented events and got loads of books at each. If you get to Los Angeles, I would recommend the Los Angeles Comic Book and Science Fiction Con. It has been going on for four decades and has never changed its focus. It is still like an old time comic show and takes place several times a year. Two other recommendations that might be of interest are the Oklahoma Alliance of Fandom event in October of each year and the Daytona Beach Comic Con that takes place twice a year. These are all top notch events for hard core comic collectors. I have nothing to do with any of these but attend them whenever I can and want to make other collectors aware of these opportunities.

3) Many old timers are cashing in their chips. I'm talking about guys that were in the hobby before I even knew it existed. These were guys that had some of the rarest Golden-Age books. Many of them were no longer active in the hobby but held on to their books. When they are gone the family disposes of the collection and suddenly there are many extremely elusive issues on the market. In the last year I have picked up a ton of super rare books that were buried in dormant collections. Stay on the lookout for more rare books to surface in the next year.

What was popular in 2017?: Very simple! Anything with a ten cent cover price. The mainstream Golden Age titles and publishers are like blue chip stocks. They might have slight price fluctuations but they will always be in high demand. All ten cent and many twelve cent cover price comics are historic American artifacts and iconic pieces of past popular culture. What was once a child's plaything now commands a King's ransom.

Some of our most requested issues during 2017 were:

- *Moon Girl* - the short run EC super hero series,
- *Sunset Carson* - the B-Western film star comics published by Charlton,
- Timely Captain America appearances,
- All pre-Code issues with Bill Ward and Matt Baker art,
- *Rangers* #6-26,
- Joker appearances in *Batman* and *Detective* issues,
- Hitler covers and appearances,
- American flag, motorcycle, snake, golf and ice cream covers,
- Popeye comics from the 1930s,
- Any comics that feature African American characters,
- Frank Frazetta art in funny animal issues,
- WW II and Korean War comics depicting extrem e violence to enemy soldiers,
- Issues with stories about and references to marijuana and drug use,
- Golden Age comics that have an art style or thematic influence on the 1960s Underground Comix movement, issues that have a format transition aspect, short run and one-shot issues published by Avon Comics in the early 1950s,
- EC & *Classics Illustrated* Canadian variants,
- Foreign comics,
- Comic stories in non-traditional formats such as paperback books, pulp magazines, sports programs-general magazines,
- Undocumented extreme violence in pre-Code Horror and Crime comics, and magazines or movie posters with cover art by comic book artists,
- and as always, anything with Spider-Man.

The Silver Age of comics introduced many of the characters that are still celebrated today. This period saw the return of the superhero as the centerpiece for most publishers' catalogs. As big time first appearances in the Golden Age keep rising in value, it is boxing out most collectors from ever owning a true "key" book from this time period. Therefore many collectors who focus on quality over quantity have gravitated towards the Silver Age in order to own a big first appearance book. Books like *Amazing Fantasy* #15, *Tales of Suspense* #39, *Hulk* #1, *Showcase* #4, etc. still command record prices but are more available than their Golden Age counterparts. We think over the next decade we will see these books continue to rise in value and likely create a smaller base of potential buyers. We believe this makes the "second-tier" Silver Age keys like *Amazing Spider-Man* #1, *Avengers* #1, *Avengers* #4, *JLA* #1, etc. great values for collectors looking to obtain an important first appearance/first issue book. One fun aspect to collecting that has taken hold in the last few years is the rediscovery of lesser known characters from the Silver and Bronze Ages. With movies and TV shows using more and more characters in their projects it is a lot of fun to hunt for first appearances of more obscure characters as their potential roles are announced or hinted at in media. This assures that there will always be books to hunt for online, in stores or at conventions, and as we all know too well, the thrill of the hunt is often the most fun part of collecting.

Outside of the superhero realm we have seen some interesting trends in the last year. Romance comics from the Silver and Bronze Ages continue to sell briskly. Risqué or symbolic covers and stories command premiums. Issues that feature panels that inspired the art of Roy Lichtenstein sell almost immediately at well over *Guide* prices. Marvel, DC and Charlton horror and fantasy from the late '50s through the '70s have really picked up as collectors have recognized some of the great art and stories of this once neglected genre.

The marketplace for Bronze Age of comics continued to be a strong and rising area of collector interest. The key issues, especially in high grades, were hard to keep in stock. *House of Secrets* #92 was the leader of the pack in interest and sales, and *Incredible Hulk* #180 and #181 were turned over almost immediately. *Marvel Spotlight* #5, *Strange Adventures* #205, and *Iron Man* #55 were the top requested issues at shows. Many collectors are focusing on completing their runs and focusing on minor character first appearances. With the ubiquity of comic characters across pop culture, they are expecting the price points to continue to rise.

It was not just the key issues that were in demand. DC and Marvel Romance comics were particularly good sellers with enticing art, retro fashions and cultural themes bringing new fans to the genre. Issues with racially diverse characters are starting to become a niche market. Similarly themed Charlton and Archie issues are also becoming of interest to collectors. Comic magazines and treasury-sized issues were popular this year. They remain difficult to find in high grade but the mid-grade examples started to see more interest in the market.

We hope collectors find this information interesting and useful. If you want more details or in-depth info you can contact us at any time. If you see us at any of the conventions don't hesitate to stop and ask us questions!

Dave Anderson, DDS
Collector

As another year winds down, I can report that 2017 was another healthy year for the comic book market. Sales were strong across the board particularly so with key issues both in the Silver Age and the Golden Age. Demand is so high for key issues that multi-million dollar comic auctions are commonplace. Rising confidence in the economy in general contributed to investors pouring large sums of money into comics all while the stock market set new record highs nearly every day. Although many believe the stock market is due for a correction at some point, I don't see the value of comics taking a dramatic downturn in the forseeable future. There's simply too much passion in the comic world for collectors to suddenly divest themselves of their collections. Even if we knew some sort of correction is coming, I just don't see mass panic and sell offs occuring in the comic market. Certainly this is a testament to the strength of the market both as a hobby and an investment vehicle.

Lauren Becker
Comic*Pop Collectibles

DC Comics: Rebirth was a shot in the arm for DC, as the New 52 became tiresome and unwelcomed. Not every Rebirth title was a winner (*Blue Beetle*, *Hellblazer*, to name a few), but others gained a great bump with better stories with great art (Greg Rucka and Liam Sharpe on *Wonder Woman*), and a sense of "old fashioned" characters made new again (Superman). One of the big winners, even though it was totally expected, was *Batman*. What many believed to be an impossible task to follow Scott Snyder on such an acclaimed run, Tom King showed his chops, and has (in my opinion) outdone Snyder in the writing department of the Dark Knight. Asked for at EVERY convention is *Batman* #24 (the "marry me" issue), where 1st prints are going for $15.00. Almost every issue after has been selling out with very high demand. Case in point was *Batman Annual* #2 with a Batman/Catwoman story (by King and Lee Weeks). The issue sold out from the distributor TWO WEEKS before release! Prices had shot up to $25.00 before settling around the $12.00 mark.

The new *Dark Nights: Metal* mini-series is on fire, with #1's 1st print METALLIC (I have to stress this) covers fetching $10.00 minimum. The one-shot off-shoots have also been dominating the back issue sales as *Batman: The Red Death* (Flash) was heavily underordered and has seen prices between $10-15.00! *Dark Nights: The Batman Who Laughs* one-shot sold out immediately and is also a $10.00 book. As a side note, *Teen Titans* #12, which features this insane Batman version has been selling for $15.00 to $30.00. You better believe that DC is making a mandate to keep this character alive for future stories.

DC had two inter-company crossovers within Warner Brothers. The first was a series of DC/Hanna Barbera one shots. They did moderately well, although we were surprised that they did not take off. *Green Lantern/Space Ghost*, which was very well written and penciled, only gained slight recognition. The DC/Looney Tunes crossovers, however, SOLD OUT very quickly, with the stand out being *Batman/Elmer Fudd*! Written by Tom King (that guy AGAIN) this was perhaps the BEST Batman story to be written for 2017! Imagine Elmer Fudd (and the other Looney Tunes) ala *Sin City*, and you get a small example of how the story is laid out. One of the most requested comics at NYCC, we sold out at $30.00 for 1st prints and $10.00 for 2nd prints.

How do you make a low selling title hot? Put a cover artist on it that exemplifies the character (even though the stories and art work are less than stellar). *Supergirl* #12 has the first cover done by Stanley "Artgerm" Lau. It was an "order all you want" variant and dealers STILL didnt order enough. A solid $10! *Harley Quinn* has "order all you want" variants by Frank Cho and they are constantly selling for $5-10.

Batman/TMNT II #1 has just arrived, and the demand is almost as high as the original mini-series, proving that sometimes you can still go back to the well.

Which leads into *Doomsday Clock* #1, an ambitious 12-issue mini-series that connects the DCU with Alan Moore's *Watchmen*. The *Watchmen* universe continues on after 30 years and people are genuinely excited over it. The 1st issue had four covers (regular, Superman variant, 11:57 B&W release, and a very awesome Rorschach lenticular using old Dave Gibbons art), with all of them selling out within hours from the distributor. The most popular cover being the Gary Frank Superman variant, prices have been closing at $10-12. As a side note, the "button" mini series, that links to *Doomsday Clock*, that ran in *Batman* #21,22 and *Flash* #21,22 has also been exceptionally popular. *Batman* #21 lenticular and *Flash* #21 lenticular are the front runners as each have sold for $15.00 each (just an FYI, *Flash* #21 features the reappearance of the Golden Age Flash).

It seems like DC can do very little wrong...

Marvel Comics: And then there's Marvel. Great movies, great Netflix streaming shows, subpar comics.

Civil War II was a swing and a miss with a convoluted story that no one seemed to care about. I include it in the 2017 report because it finally ended in early 2017 (I think. The story was so tedious that it seemed to run forever).

Secret Empire did SLIGHTLY better, mainly because of the "phone it in" J. Scott Campbell 1:50 variant covers, but this was a story that might have looked good on paper, but the outcome was a muddled mess. The artwork was all over the place and did not seem cohesive to any sort of order. Our orders were relatively low on both series, and we are thankful for that.

Not to say that Marvel didnt have a few hits. The *Totally Awesome Hulk/Weapon X* storyline did well, especially with *Totally Awesome Hulk* #22 introducing the hybrid character Weapon H (soon to have his own series). That particular issue is $30-50.

However, not even that can turn the tide for Marvel. Trying to compete with DC's Rebirth series, Marvel tried to implement "Legacy." A soft restart using "legacy" numbering for the titles (ie...with all the *Venom* titles that have been published, the legacy numbering starts at #150). Marvel has also gone back to old fashion times with 3-tier house ads inside the comics (ala the 1970s) and even a fresh version of the "Mighty Marvel Value Stamps", with stores receiving actual stamp books, so people can collect.

But what REALLY made this a "must have" were the lenticular covers that Marvel tried on each title...at least, they TRIED to make this a must have. Instead of making these special covers an open order, and letting retailers order all that they wanted, they made them orderable based on a ratio of previous ordered titles. So, for example, if you wanted the lenticular cover variant to *Mighty Thor* #700, you had to order 175% or more REGULAR COVERS than you did of *Mighty Thor* #19 in order to qualify for the lenticular covers. So as an example, if you ordered 100 copies of *Mighty Thor* #19, you had to order a MINIMUM of 175 copies of the regular cover before you could order any of the lenticulars. What started out as an exciting promotion, instantly failed, as many retailers did not qualify, nor did not WANT to qualify as, realistically, what would they do with those extra copies? Also, add to the abysmal effects of the covers (images did not match up, and it looked like the homage image was eaten by the original image), and the whole experiment went south.

It has now broken that Disney will be acquiring Fox Entertainment for $52 billion! What will that mean to the comics industry? Maybe a new *Fantastic Four* series, and PERHAPS, a *Predator vs. Wolverine* or *The Runaways Meets The Simpsons* mini-series, but outside of the impending Fox/Marvel movies merging, it's nothing of great importance to the actual comic PRINT industry (in my opinion, at least).

Image Comics: Many titles have come out of Image with great fanfare, as new #1s come hot right out of the gate, and then afterwards, merely mediocre sales. *God Country* #1 was hot hot hot with prices realizing $40-50.00 for 1st prints...and then it died. *Redneck* #1 was the same, with 1st prints selling as high as $15.00 but unfortunately couldn't keep future issues popular enough to keep the demand high. Even the almighty *Walking Dead* has been experiencing a slow down in sales. However, don't count them out yet as many new titles are coming out of the gate. Mark Millar just signed a deal with Netflix for the Millar Universe and guess who the publisher is? A new version of *Kick-Ass* is coming, and many people seem excited!

Independents: The newest company making wave is AfterShock comics. They seem to have a grasp of what the audience is looking for and how to keep the retailers happy. Their biggest seller is *Babyteeth* (written by Donny Cates), and has been consistent with the sales. Black Mask is another publisher that seems to have the finger on the pulse of the industry with such innovative titles as *Black* and *4 Kids Walk Into A Bank*.

Oni Press has a big hit with ***Rick and Morty****.*
(#1 shown)

Oni Press has a hit with *Rick and Morty*! Issue #1 1st prints sell for $200.00 in RAW NM/MT condition. The 1:50 variant has seen sale prices as high as $1500.00 UNGRADED! When an animated show can make a major fast food chain (McDonald's) bring back an item that has not been produced in over 20 years, you might have a cultural phenomenon on your hands. As a side note, the series on TV is perhaps THE smartest written dialogued show produced in awhile. Dark, smart, and often times hilarious. A HIGHLY recommended series.

BOOM! Studios has a great "first look" deal with Fox and have been coming out with some great titles (*Fence*, *Giant Days*, *Klaus*), but with the new Disney deal, will Boom! be pushed to the wayside? Time will tell.

Recent Sales: CGC comics are still sought after either at shows or on-line. Some recent examples: *Green Lantern* #76 CGC 9.4 Sig. Series Neal Adams for $5100.00, *Amazing Spider-Man* #25 (1:1000 Gil Kane Remastered Variant) CGC 9.8 for $2000.00, *Venom* #150 (1:1000 McFarlane Remastered Variant) CGC 9.8 for $1200.00, *New Mutants* #98 CGC 9.8 for $800.00, *Amazing Spider-Man* #129 CGC 9.2 for $1500.00, *Incredible Hulk* #181 CGC 8.0...$2100.00, *Strange Adventures* #169 CGC 8.5 for $200.00, *Marvel Spotlight* #5 CGC 3.0 SS Roy Thomas for $300.00, *Amazing Spider-Man* #300 CGC 9.6 for $400.00 and *Iron Fist* #14 CGC 9.6 for $800.00.

It seems that the trend for key Silver is continuing to rise, no matter WHAT grade. We recently just sold an *Amazing Spider-Man* #1 with a xeroxed back cover and a partially xeroxed front cover for $1500.00!!! It seems that even in such a wrecked condition, it was still highly desired! As the prices become more and more expensive, it doesn't matter what the condition is as long as it can still be attained for a collection.

Golden Age is now considered a bargain compared to what Silver Age is now bringing in. What many considered as out of reach, are now being snapped up at a furious rate. A good example was a copy of *All-American Comics* #25 (1st Dr. Mid-Nite) we received. It was sold within 3 weeks for $2500.00 in about a Good condition. The 1st appearance of Wolverine (*Hulk* #181) in the same grade goes for ALMOST 1/2 that price and is approximately 30 years newer. How long until the prices for Golden Age start catching up?

There has also been, as I see it, a game with dealers trying to "one-up" each other on getting the most esoteric comics in their collection/inventory, titles outside the normal Timelys/DC/EC companies. For example, we had a copy of *Zip-Jet Comics* #1 in Good condition that lasted, at best, an hour, as dealers were coming out of the woodwork wanting to purchase it. Not a particularly key comic, but the rarity of the book was hard to deny, and it went for 2-1/2 times *Guide*. The same with a copy of Lev Gleason's *Daredevil* #27 with a bondage/torture cover. Double *Guide* very quickly to another dealer. Expect many of these low tier Golden Age titles to become snapped up very quickly by the average collector soon.

Jim Berry
Collector

Hello. I am a long-time collector and part-time eBay dealer (jb233) with a small online store featuring high-grade raw comics from the 1940s-1980s. I specialize in Golden and Silver Age gems with a particular fondness for pre-Code horror comics, science fiction, crime, WWII era comics, anything old, unusual, rare or featuring art/covers by L.B. Cole, Alex Schomburg, Steve Ditko, Bernard Baily, Matt Fox, Basil Wolverton, Feldstein, Frazetta, and a host of others. I also read newer stuff by the great creators of today, Warren Ellis, Daniel Clowes, Garth Ennis, Ed Brubaker, Jeff Lemire, anything Jodorowsky and Moebius.

As I've mentioned in previous reports, the world of comic collecting has become quite crowded with dealers of all stripes, particularly professional Craig-listers scrapping to make a living hunting garage sales and flipping whatever they can get their hands on to make a profit. Frankly, those folks are hungrier than me and their appetite includes anything and everything so long as there's a buck to be made. I get it and, frankly, I wish I had the ambition to expand my universe and make more money – but, for me, it starts and stops with comics.

Along with my eBay and convention acquisitions, I've managed to find two collections this year of note. And both collections brought larger collecting questions to the fore that I hadn't considered.

The first collection was a small box of Silver and Bronze keys featuring a run of *X-Men* from #94 up. It was a broad collection but the one book that really stood out was the copy of *X-Men* #94. Even though it was only a VG copy with a cover crease in the lower right corner, as soon as I opened it, I felt a jolt of electricity (Had Storm shocked me?!) – The book had a double cover.

I've always been fascinated with double cover comics and I've never quite swallowed the notion that they're only as valuable as the highest grade of the two covers. I follow double covers on eBay and they usually do a little better than *Guide* – but for a hobby that now rewards 9.8 copies exponentially more than 9.4 copies, I think double cover comics are horribly undervalued.

I appreciate that this may seem like a 'trumped' up comment given that I am now the owner of a double cover *X-Men* #94 – but this book got me to thinking because it was, suddenly, in front of my face and I said, "Wow" – after 40 years of collecting and trading and dealing, I have not seen that many double covers, let alone a double cover key. Really, it's just about the rarity and how the hobby values 9.8 copies of a given book versus double covers.

To expand on this example and, submitted for your approval from the CGC census, there are 5360 registered copies of *X-Men* #94. 32 of them are 9.8. Are any of them double covers? No. Does anyone care for now? I don't think so . . . maybe just a few goofballs like me. But I think they are one of the cool secrets remaining in the hobby and I think double cover comics are one of them. I would love to correspond with anyone regarding the actual rarity and printing process that produces double cover comics. Maybe there's a place to do an article for next year's *Guide*?

The second collection of note came to me through a friend. There were over 4000 books that had been collected by a woman who worked for the government and spent a lot of time in the U.K., teaching on a military base. So, a lot of her books were United Kingdom variants, which I've never really thought twice about. But it was a nice collection so I did some research and found this great article online:

http://www.wymann.info/comics/060-PencePriceVariants.html

Check it out if you're so interested. The bottom line for those old UK copies is that they're far more rare than US copies and, aside from the price indica, they are identical and should not be discounted. If anything, they should be treated as rare variant copies. I also read that the UK copies were published first, before the US copies, so the inks were fresher and denser and the color is more saturated lending a deeper, richer color to the covers. And you can really see this if you have a stack of UK books against the US books. It's a small difference but it's interesting.

I mentioned this a few years ago – but anyone interested in the history of old comic collections should check out the key site for pedigree collections. It's a great read for the stories of some of the great comic collections: http://comicpedigrees.com

Enjoy the hobby – there's so much out there between the movies and the massive wave of new creators now that it's hard to keep track of all the cool stuff!

If you're in Washington, you can't miss the chance to go to Hills of Comics in Auburn. It's the biggest shop west of Mile High (I think) and the owner is a Prince among men, John Hill! Tell him Jim sent you and he'll give you 10% off!

Here's a list of prices realized in 2017 that I had something to do with: *Mystic* #19 VG $291; *Marvel Mystery* #92 VG $622; *Crime Does Not Pay* #43 VG/FN $372; *Startling* #35 (CGC 8.5) $1457; *Spook* #26 VG $324; *Mr. Mystery* #13 $577; *Daredevil* (1941) #11 GD+ $980; *Silver Streak* #14 VG+ $1413; *USA Comics* #5 GD+ $811; *Captain America Comics* #77 VG $761; and *Mystery Tales* #1 VG $244.

Thank you, Mr. Overstreet and your crew for your neverending efforts!

Good luck to you all in 2018.

Tim Bildhauser
CBCS - Foreign Comic Specialist
Associate Editor Foreign Comic Collector Magazine

Wow… what a year 2017 has been in the foreign comic book market! Not only have sales been higher than ever, both in price and volume, but there have been books that have surfaced that the existence of could only be speculated on being that no one had been able to produce a copy. The most notable of which, I would say, is a Filipino (Goodwill Bookstore) copy of *Superman* #233. For several years now it was somewhat assumed that this book existed based on the fact that it appeared in house ads within the Goodwill Bookstore editions, but until early December of 2017 no one in the foreign collecting community had actually seen a copy. That all changed when a collector contacted me through my website (www.myforeigncomics.webs.com) to discuss a few books he had acquired through a dealer on the West Coast.

Sales this year have been up over last year and some of the most notable ones that I saw and were reported to me are as follows. I'll list the books by their corresponding American title and issue number so it's easier for those unfamiliar with these books to understand what the significance of each book is.

From Mexico:
Action Comics #252 (slabbed 3.0) - $512.32
Amazing Spider-Man #14 - $102.50
Amazing Spider-Man #129 (1st edition) - $102.50
Amazing Spider-Man #129 (2nd edition) - $109.50
Amazing Spider-Man #194 - $33
Avengers #1 (1st edition, 2 copies) - $700 & $660
Avengers #57 (2nd edition) - $41.76
Batman #121 - $430
Batman #189 - $26.76
Batman #227 - $255
Batman #232 (2 copies) - $138 & $79
Conan the Barbarian #1 - $111.50
Daredevil #1 (2 copies) - $216.20 & $199.99
Detective Comics #194 (*Batman* #1 in Mexico) - $3,384.45
Dr. Strange #169 - $14.99
Fantastic Four #5 - $2,000
Fantastic Four #48 - $239.50
House of Secrets #92 (private sale) - $1,000
Incredible Hulk #102 (2nd edition) - $26
Kamandi #1 - $16.50
Our Love Story #1 - $26
Sgt. Fury and His Howling Commandos #1 - $138.50
Superman #73 (*Superman* #1 in Mexico) - $1,991
X-Men #12 - $50
X-Men #14 - $34.33

From Italy:
Amazing Spider-Man #194 - $24.50
Conan the Barbarian #1 (7.5 signed by Roy Thomas) - $125
Ghost Rider #1 - $26

French Canadian:
Amazing Spider-Man #129 - $89
Amazing Spider-Man #238 - $70
Amazing Spider-Man #252 - $45
Giant-Size X-Men #1 - $60
Incredible Hulk #180 - $17.21
Iron Man #128 - $22
Kamandi #1 - $15.50
X-Men #141/142 - $35

From Greece:
Amazing Spider-Man #1 (1st edition) - $36.76
Amazing Spider-Man #194 - $28.76
Conan the Barbarian #1 - $31
Iron Man #3 (cover is *Iron Man* #55) - $80
X-Men #94 - $34

From Australia:
Amazing Spider-Man #194 - $49

Avengers #1 - $56
Batman #227 - $225.38
Conan the Barbarian #1 (Yaffa) - $56
Conan the Barbarian #1 (Newton) - $51
Incredible Hulk #1 - $66.22
New Mutants #100 (2 copies) - $62 & $31
Showcase #22 - $77
Superman #233 - $52
X-Men #1 - $64

From Germany:
Amazing Spider-Man #194 (1st edition) - $26.55
Amazing Spider-Man #194 (2nd edition) - $20.50
Avengers #57 - $39
Fantastic Four #48 - $41
Fantastic Four #49 - $44
Fantastic Four #52 - $110.50
Green Lantern #76 - $40

From the U.K.:
Amazing Spider-Man #194 - $19.50
Batman Adventures #12 - $147
Conan the Barbarian #1 (2nd edition) - $51
Incredible Hulk #181 - $378.33

From Spain:
Amazing Spider-Man #194 - $24.50
Conan the Barbarian #1 (1st edition) - $56
Conan the Barbarian #1 (2nd edition) - $52
Hero For Hire #1 - $17.50

Other notable sales include:
Amazing Spider-Man #1 India - $26.76
Amazing Spider-Man #194 Netherlands - $29.76
Amazing Spider-Man #252 Slovakia - $41
Batman #227 Lebanon - $122.50
France - $110.50
Brazil - $217.50
Brazil (altered cover art, #227 story not inside) $27.76
Batman #251 Lebanon - $88
Batman Adventures #12 Argentina - $125
Conan the Barbarian #1 Finland - $52.07
Portugal - $29.76
Fantastic Four #48 Denmark - $17.50
Incredible Hulk #1 Israel - $330
Secret Wars #8 Netherlands - $24.49

I think it's long past due that American collectors and dealers start to realize that there's, literally, a whole world of comics out there beyond what they're familiar with and that just because they might not know anything about those books it doesn't mean they don't hold value. Even outside their country of origin. I've been watching and studying the market for foreign editions for nearly a decade now and every year have noted a steady increase in both prices and the number of people collecting them. That being the case I think it's a positive sign that the hobby is healthy and still has room to grow and thrive for years to come.

Peter Bilelis, Esq.
Collector

Hello everyone and welcome to my Market Report for 2017-2018. Writing this a week before Christmas 2017, after a year full of great comic book conventions, auctions, films, and other hobby-related events, and I think this past year in the hobby can best be described as "The Year of ..."

The Year of the Golden Anniversary: I can't believe this year marks the 50th anniversary for so many landmark books, including *Iron Man* #1, *Captain America* #100, *Hulk* #102, and *Silver Surfer* #1. Funny how time flies.

The Year of the Woman: Of course, I'm referring to Wonder Woman. Yes, there has always been a quiet but consistent fan-following that collects titles featuring this hero. But the 2017 film's titanic success helped catapult Wonder Woman's popularity as her fan-base continues to grow. This is great news as this character has always had so much potential. The film also helped *All Star Comics* #8, her first appearance, move into a more apropos position for a key Golden Age (GA) first appearance of a superhero that's arguably as well-known and as much a part of pop culture as Superman and Batman. Reported sale prices of this GA key repeatedly set new record highs throughout 2017 and it seems to be still heating up! Titles like *All Star*, *Sensation*, and *Wonder Woman* all benefited in upward sales and higher prices, as did other titles in both the GA and Silver Age (SA) in which she appears. If you're looking for a very undervalued key piece of the Wonder Woman mythos (and can't afford *All Star* #8, *Sensation* #1, or *Wonder Woman*#1, which I think are all still very undervalued), then I think *WW* #98-99, *All Star* #12, and *JLA* #56 are books worth considering.

The Year of the Spider: The blockbuster film *Spider-Man: Homecoming* helped propel this character's vintage comic book sales to new heights. Before the film was announced, *Amazing Fantasy* #15 (Spidey's origin and first appearance) was continuing to slowly creep up in value. Approximately 6 months before the film debut, however, reported sale prices started jumping. I did some quick math on copies I tracked in grade VG+ (4.5) and the average reported sale price was around $16,500 in 2016, but jumped to $27,000 in 2017. That's more than a 60% increase! I tracked copies in 4.5 as I think this grade is more representative of average value movement than say the highest graded copy or similar. While many think the prices at which this book is currently selling are unsustainable, I'm not so sure I agree. Why? Well, this might be blasphemy, but I think Spider-Man (and the Fantastic Four and X-Men) actually did more for the SA than *Showcase* #4 and #22. While it's true that DCs The Flash and Green Lantern were the creative spark that ushered the dawn of the SA, I think the blaze that followed was largely cemented by the Marvel Age soap opera style of story-telling. And, despite the number of existing *Amazing Fantasy* #15 copies, I still believe *Amazing Fantasy* #15 is the *Action Comics* #1 of the SA. Finally, I think Spidey has a huge and growing following in and out of the hobby. For these reasons, I think *Amazing Fantasy* #15 today is a little like *Action Comics* #1 at the point when most folks couldn't imagine it ever hitting $1 Million. And, I think *Amazing Spider-Man* #1 is another book to grab while you can, along with all the major first appearances, including the Goblins, Shocker, Kingpin, Venom, and Carnage.

The Year of the Speculator: I may sound like a broken record, but what's up with all the tourists in the hobby? I attended a bunch of shows this year including San Diego Comic-Con and NYCC and a common theme continues to be people that clearly have little-to-no interest in the actual material trying to find deals on books that they plan to flip for profits "as soon as the film comes out." Yes, hobbyists have always bought books that are trending up but that was in addition to what they collected and read. The amount of non-dealer speculation buying seems to be growing. I know this dynamic is helping to push prices higher and higher, but is it actually doing anything good for the health of the hobby? I wonder…

Other Thoughts: If Comic-Con and NYCC are any indicator, the hobby is alive and well. People from 8 - 88 were there all in search of back issues. More importantly, many of these people were looking for raw books, which is the best news. I say this because, as much as the slab is a sort of necessary evil for selling, it does zero to support the fundamental building blocks of the hobby's roots - people wanting to buy back issues in order to read stories and enjoy artwork of their favorite characters. Having said that, I was a little disappointed with the GA aspect of the convention circuit because of something I'm going to call the "museum" effect. So many sellers seem to revere their GA books more than anyone else. If you look at their GA wall books, most are common run books in mid-grade but have very aggressive pricing. And, if they have a low or mid-grade restored lesser key (e.g. *Adventure* #40), jump back! The price often rivals that of the most recent unrestored VF copy's sale. And, many sellers will not negotiate on price for these books, claiming the given book (doesn't matter which one it might be) is one of the seller's favorites and he/she would be happy to hold onto it (excuse me, but are you a curator or a seller?). Anyway, I call this the "museum" effect because the books appear to be for sale, but based on the factors described above, will do nothing but sit on walls for your viewing pleasure. Not sure I know who benefits from this arrangement.

eBay is a great buying/selling venue and there are still some good deals to be found. But, I'm also amazed at some of the opportunistic buy-it-now pricing for hot books. For instance, there is a constant rotation of *Amazing Fantasy* #15s on eBay with buy-it-nows that vary from around $40k for 4.0s to $100 - 110k for 6.5s. Looking at completed sales, however, confirms that these BINs are nowhere near market. As I write this, the Heritage Signature Auction recently ended, as did an eBay auction style sale, and 6.0s are actually selling for high $40s. And a 6.5 that was sold through Heritage yielded $55k. Regardless of where you purchase, if you want solid advice, talk to folks like Terry O'Neill at Terry's Comics, Al Stoltz at Basement Comics, Joe Vereneault at JHV Associates, and Barry Sandoval at Heritage Auctions.

These are some books I think have a lot of growth potential: GA *More Funs* featuring the Spectre - classic GA noir (well, up until Percival Popp showed up) and sooner or later the DC film machine is going to realize that a murdered city cop that now haunts the earth doling out macabre vengeance to baddies is *prima facie* material for its dark and gritty view of film-making. *Master Comics* #21-48, *Capt. Marvel Jr.* #4, 10, 13, *Adventure* #79, *Fighting Yank* WWII cover books, and *National* #7 - these books have some of the best WWII covers, yet do not command the prices of other WWII cover books. *Jackpot* featuring Archie. All the JSA/JLA cross-over books, but especially *Flash* #110, 123, *JLA* #21, 22, 29, 30, 56. SA Marvel keys in addition to *Amazing Fantasy* #15, like (especially) *X-Men* #1, *Fantastic Four* #1, *Tales of Suspense* #39, and *Incredible Hulk* #1. *Showcase* #55 is another book I think is a sleeper. I can't think of any other book that has more origins and first appearances than this one, and with its dark cover can be tough to find in very high grade. I also remain on the hunt for high grade copies of *Action* #242, 252, and *Adventure* #247. I think they are very uncommon in grades over 6.5 and if you have any of these (or any other books like those I've mentioned), I'd love to hear from you at pbilelis@yahoo.com. Finally, *Silver Surfer* #1-18 contain some of the absolute best story-telling and artwork from the era, but this character suffered a set-back with the awful on-screen portrayal. I hope he gets added to the MCU and rebooted, as his story has such depth and potential. Finally, a special shout out to Craig, Dorian, and Christi who helped with the research for this Market Report.

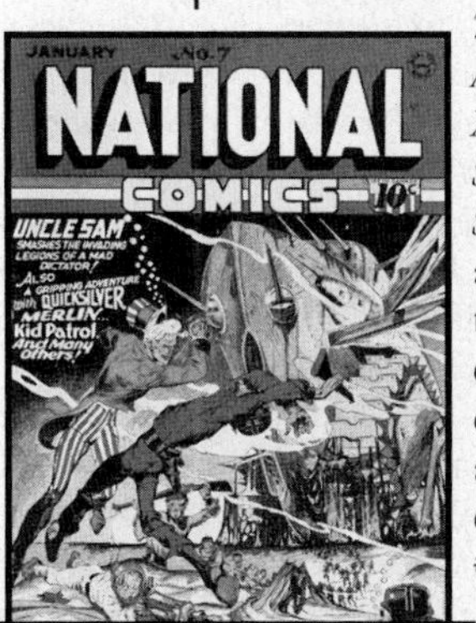

World War II covers (like **National Comics #7**) have growth potential.

Good luck hunting in 2018…

Steve Borock
CBCS
President and Primary Grader

To start off, as every year, I would like to thank Bob Overstreet for steering our hobby correctly, and most importantly, impartially for 48 years! Bob changed our hobby so many years ago with pricing and grading standards, and shaped generations of collectors and sellers alike. He might be the hardest working man in our hobby! Behind the scenes are J.C. Vaughn and Mark Huesman, two guys who get very little credit and work too many hours on making this *Guide* as great as it is. Thanks, as well, to Steve Geppi for keeping the *Guide* going.

I will not be talking about pricing because as a grader I need to stay impartial and treat a modern comic with the same care and grading as I would, say, an *Action Comics* #1. I can't care what a comic is worth while grading it; I just have to get the grade correct, check for restoration, and get it to encapsulation. It's a fine line to walk, but I work hard at it every day.

I can tell you what has been submitted for grading that seems to us at CBCS to be "hot" for submitters: Golden Age and early Silver Age of all genres and grades, Silver Age and Bronze Age keys, Modern keys, and signed comics. As I am sure this will also be mentioned in many of the market reports you will read here, every time a TV show or movie about a character or team gets mentioned, we see a flood of issues with those characters for speculation resale.

Our Verified Signature Program (VSP), which verifies signatures that have not been witnessed, has seen so many cool vintage books with creator signatures such as Frank Frazetta, Bob Kane, Jack Kirby, Stan Lee, Alex Schomberg, Al Feldstein and many others, as well as Modern Age comics signed by creators such as J. Scott Campbell, Adam Hughes, Mark Brooks, Todd McFarlane, and many others. Certifying and authenticating unwitnessed signatures has really taken off!

While 2017 was phenomenal for CBCS and 2018 has started out to be a fantastic year as well, it would be a huge mistake to not mention the overwhelming loss our hobby suffered this year with the unexpected passing of John Verzyl.

To those that knew him, John was a giant among giants. You probably have seen his Comic Heaven ads in the *Guide* year after year, but you might be unaware of the incredible impact he had on the hobby, on the *Guide*, and on those who called him "friend."

John was the epitome of a hobbyist and a mentor to me. He, with the help of his photographic memory, worked endlessly on helping with pricing and history for so many years of the *Guide*. He loved collecting Edgar Church/Mile High Collection issues ("They are so cherry!"). As enthusiastic as he was about great comic books, he was also very humble about the amazing collection he owned personally, one of which most of us could only dream of owning a tenth.

He spent time with new collectors, gladly helping them understand the ins and out of collecting (including me!). Surprisingly enough, he also taught the "giants" of our hobby many things they did not know. Though John's passing is tragic, his children, Rose and John, Jr., will keep Comic Heaven going and I know that John would have loved this great news. He was so proud of his children (a prouder father would be damn hard to find)! Good-bye dear friend; you will always be remembered, and remembered fondly, with much love.

As I mentioned, this has been a fantastic year for CBCS. Not just in terms of the amazing amount of books we have been flooded with (and really are flooded with books!), but here is the big news:

In October 2017, CBCS became a member of Beckett Media team, joining the Beckett line of collectible services and products. The name Beckett is one of the most recognizable names in the sports card world and with the acquisition of CBCS, Beckett's goal is to become a true, one-stop shop for all collector needs. This includes cards, comics, and autograph authentication (including autographed comics). With the help of Beckett, CBCS will continue to provide the best customer service, the best turnaround times in the industry, attend more shows/events, with the most knowledgeable graders and staff in the comic book hobby. I cannot tell you how amazing this has been for CBCS as well as for me personally!

As always, I want to give a shout out to our hobby's greatest charity, The Hero Initiative. Hero gives back to those in need who created or worked on the wonderful characters we all enjoy with food, medical, housing and other help that is needed. Please check them out at www.heroinitiative.org. This marks the 9th year that there is a Hero Initiative limited edition of *The Overstreet Comic Book Price Guide*. All of the proceeds go directly to the charity. I hope this is the copy you are reading right now!

I will end my market report the same way I do every year. This is for the "newer" collectors in our great hobby, as I would hope that the more seasoned collectors already know this information. Even though I really believe in this hobby, this market and its future and have so since I was a kid (I am 55), there is no such thing as a "free lunch." If you are going to "invest" in comic books, you had better love what you buy. If the economy ever goes "really bad," just like stocks, precious metals, real estate, or anything else considered an "investment," you will not be able to sell them for a really high price very quickly and you can certainly not use comic books to feed, house or take care of your family.

The best advice I can give you is this: "Buy what you like and can afford." It's really that simple, which is why it's been my war cry for so many years.

Just enjoy collecting and reading comic books, enjoy the amazing friendships we make in this wonderful hobby. Look around and enjoy all the cool stuff this hobby has to offer from original comic art and comic books, to the movies and TV shows based on the characters we all love so much, to comic memorabilia, going to the conventions and so on. It will all seem worth it in the end.

I hope to see and talk with many of you at the conventions that CBCS and I will be attending this coming year! Thank you for taking the time to read this and, as always, HAPPY COLLECTING!

Richard M. Brown
Collector

Reportedly, almost half of comic store visitors are women. We know the "Warrior Princess" Wonder Woman is driving DC. Harley Quinn hasn't lost any of her recent popularity. Black Widow in the movies and Supergirl and Black Canary on television reinforce that appeal.

Prices on the Rise: Guardians of the Galaxy and related characters, thanks to the movies. *All Star Comics* #8 and other early Wonder Woman appearances. Watch for *Whiz Comics* and Black Adam appearances to grow in prominence. And always keep and eye on Archie in *Pep* #22.

Jeff and Charles Cerrito
HotFlips.com

Jeff Cerrito - In the past few years I have given a report on all the conventions I have done during the year. This year I am going to change it a little bit and focus on some shows (or promoters) that have done excellent work in bringing in the fans.

This past year has seen record turnouts for established comic book conventions. Reed Exhibitions continues to put on mind-boggling events for fans. Just when you thought a show could reach its capacity, they continue to bring in more and more attendees. Take their flagship show, New York Comic Con. This past year they drew over 200,000 fans. TWO HUNDRED THOUSAND FANS!! I remember when a show would draw 15,000 fans and that was a must-do show. They continue to evolve with new things to do at the show, better talent as far as artists, creators and media guests as well. It's not just New York though. Their C2E2 show in Chicago and Emerald City Comic Con show in Seattle all had upticks to their attendance. Again, this is due to their devotion to bringing quality to the fans. As long as there is room to hold the fans, I see these shows growing and growing. Looking forward to their startup convention this coming year in Philadelphia, Keystone Comic Con, as well seeing how their shows over the pond in the UK fare. I'm sure they will all be must see events.

Another company that has put on incredible shows for the fans are the guys over at Fan Expo Headquarters. The shows that I exhibited at - Dallas, MegaCon, Boston, and Toronto all had guest lists that were downright amazing. They had top notch celebrities, artists, creators, and even their cosplay guest list was second to none. There was truly a guest or guests for everyone who attended. They also had record setting attendance numbers as well.

Of course there is San Diego. San Diego is San Diego and while not everyone can get into the show, the fortunate enough ones are bound to have a good time. What I like about it is that it engulfs the entire city. You are literally living in Nerd Heaven for a week.

The last show I'll talk about in any kind of depth is the London Super Comic Con. This year was great. It was in a new venue (that venue could use some work) but it was a great show. It was centrally located in London this year as opposed to over by the docks. You had restaurants, pubs, nightlife, everything you wanted right outside. This is more geared to the comic enthusiast. This year had tons of artists and creators. The guys who run this show are comic book fans, so they know what comic fans want.

There are some conventions, without mentioning any names, that have work to do. A few of them have potential, and time will tell if they pan out or not. There are some, which used to be, well established conventions, that seem to have made a 180 and are on a downward spiral. Some of these I have done for almost 20 years, when we were just comic book dealers and before we got into the supply business. Makes you scratch your head.

If I could give advice or if any promoter is reading this I would say to them: Listen to your fans. Listen to the dealers. Dealers want conventions to make money, as in turn, the dealer will make money. So it is really in the best interests for all promoters to listen. Some promoters get it, like the few I listed above.

Last year was amazing as far as conventions are concerned and I cant wait for this year!!

Charles Cerrito - HotFlips.com - As far as the comic book market goes, the market is stronger than ever, really no change to last year's titles, like *Star Wars*, *Avengers*, *Deadpool* and *Harley Quinn* are still going strong. Again it is due to the hype and movies that are being released every year and that is what brings the value up even more.

The biggest surprise was DC's Wonder Woman, It was great all around, it captured a young female audience and gave a role model to look up to. That was not all though, as *Star Wars* gave that as well. This past year was the rise of Girl Power and Super Heroines and is a nice addition to the industry where everyone of all ages, male or female, can go to a convention and just have a blast.

As long as they keep making great movies and hit TV shows, This industry will be around for generations to come. More fans equals more potential collectors.

Paul Clairmont
PNJ Comics

Overview of the Market: I wrote last year about how the market seemed to be settling in 2016 and while we moved into 2017 that trend continued with some weeks even flatlining. It feels like the gold rush days of feverishly scooping up keys doesn't have that same sense of urgency. Comic books are a form of entertainment looking to survive in a modern pop culture world. With so much available to keep people entertained, the level of interest weens from time to time. The attention span begins to shift much more quickly than ever before. Holding that interest for collectors and the public as a whole is becoming much tougher for publishers in the digital age. With the internet comes other avenues for people to spend their money and for dealers to earn their share of the collector's disposable spending. The demand is still very strong for quality books of all eras and books for investors to speculate on, but they are not as willing to spend so blindly on the next speculative rumor.

We have now completed over five years of operations in 2017 and there is never a shortage of projects that kept us busy. One of these projects was the privilege to work with some very passionate folks on an inaugural price guide of Canadian Price Variants spear-headed by Benjamin Noble. It was fun and informative to collaborate with Ben, Doug, Jon, Bill and Angelo on this guide which is available for free on-line at our website or from Gemstone's site *Scoop* at this address: http://scoop.previewsworld.com

It is a living document that works well as a checklist too. It will continue to be upgraded and updated but it helps establish a foundation for this niche and growing market. I'll reintroduce my section on Canadian Price Variants in this market report to shed some of my insights for this area that I've advocated for years in previous reports.

For the 1st time in our five years of operations, PNJ Comics sold more Modern era comics than any other genre. The Modern Age sales were closely followed by Copper Age with Bronze and Silver Age almost even and Golden Age nearly non-existent in our sales. There are many reasons for this shift. I think the main reason is that speculators/investors turned to Modern books such as *Amazing Spider-Man* #361, *Harbinger* #1 and so on because the price points haven't reached the stratosphere yet so they are comfortable acquiring these keys in lower triple and double-digit price points for uncertified high grade and even under $10.00 for a potential sleeper key. That lower cost means lower risk and higher return on investment with larger margins. Compare that to Bronze and Silver Age keys that are often already too pricey in mid/high to high grade such as *Incredible Hulk* #181, which has exploded in price in recent years. That is one book that defies logic as there is simply way too much supply in essentially any grade that it should satisfy the highest demand peaks.

The problem with a lot of these Modern keys is that it is unexplored territory so it is truly a gamble spending some higher dollars on books of this genre and hoping they continue to appreciate. Usually the trend observed in the market is a short and dramatic spike in price as the market hasn't been flooded with quality high grade examples and a small sector of the speculators buy in quickly and as more copies surface, the price continues to drop. What is apparent is that the life span of the peak is much shorter as there is always something to replace the latest rumors with a new rumor the following week. In the long term, many of these books often rebound again and climb in price as the rumors do come to fruition.

There is something to be said about a title. Early in 2017 when it was announced that the latest *Star Wars* movie to be released in December would have the name "The Last Jedi ", it wasn't long for people to take notice of *Star Wars* #49 by Marvel Comics with its title "The Last Jedi" embedded on the cover with Luke holding a light saber. This immediately caused a stir, and not wanting to sit on any of our copies, we promptly sent out 25 issues for grading that all received 9.8 – White pages. These copies all sold within a month of having them graded for anywhere between $150.00 to $250.00. I was ecstatic to sell those issues as they are books that would normally sit on a shelf collecting dust if it wasn't for a boost from the movie industry. Collectors should take note that this issue has absolutely nothing to do with the story of the upcoming movie besides sharing the same title. I mention this example because it is a perfect commentary to how the comic market has changed so much. With the internet, people need to be savvy and not react to everything released with such impulse.

Anyone else starting to get the sense that the entertainment world is starting to churn out quantity over quality? The onslaught of shows such as *Iron Fist* and *Defenders* have people changing the channel for any number of reasons that the viewers might have. For me, they were a real let down compared to stuff being produced even four years earlier. *The Walking Dead* might be an indication that people's interests are weaning as it falls into a repetitive theme. How many times do humans continue to just fight other human camps? Is there a point!?!? When will they discover the bigger picture? People want substance once in a while, not campy ultra-violence mixed with melodramatic ramblings, and it shows as the series is seeing some of its lowest viewer turnout in nearly 5 years. *Preacher* is also having trouble finding its groove with viewers.

We have been seeing a rise in interest and sales for high grade "Newsstand" and "Canadian Price Variants." I repeat, high grade as there seems to be a lot of confusion surrounding this niche group. That is to say that not all copies of Newsstand and Canadian Price Variants are in demand but it's the true high-grade copies that are very sought after. Keys are even tougher to find in high grade. A quick glance at eBay will illustrate that point. Search a book like *Jonah Hex* #92 or *G.I. Joe* #21 and *Amazing Spider-Man* #252 and see how many Canadian Price Variants come up, if any. If a copy is available, just look at the condition. It will likely be very beaten up or over-graded by the seller.

We decided to hold off on buying many private collections this year. Our main reason for doing so was that we still have so many quality high grade books that we've accumulated over the past five years that we decided to focus our attention on trying to process our own books and bring them to market. The other reason we slowed our buying was the lack of worthwhile collections that surfaced this year.

That's not to say that the well has run dry and there won't be opportunities in the coming years. These types of things happen and it takes time to unearth some good material. We did have our opportunities to see some great books such as *Amazing Fantasy* #15 and *Incredible Hulk* #1 this year but we've noticed that when the material is truly earth shattering, the owner is reluctant to sell as they are looking to maximize profit on the books. I can't fault them for looking out for their best interests and moving cautiously. We've always dealt with people in a no-pressure and straight forward manner so they don't feel like they're being taken advantage of. We believe to treat someone any different is poor business. We still have so much inventory that we want to get to market that we don't want the burden of buying entire collections where 98% of the material is common and usually unsellable only to get 2% that is sellable in a reasonable time frame and then find the time to process any new material while we already have so many projects on the go.

Notable Sales of Uncertified copies (USD): *Amazing Spider-Man* #344 (Mark Jewelers Variant) NM- = $70.00, *Black Lightning* #1 NM+ = $145.00, *Marvel Premiere* #19 NM- = $120.00, *Star Wars* #49 NM+ = $60.00, *Detective Comics* #532 (Canadian Price Variant) NM = $60.00, *Detective Comics* #577 (Canadian Price Variant) NM = $70.00, *Amazing Spider-Man* #119 NM = $150.00, *Amazing Spider-Man* #120 NM = $200.00, *Detective Comics* #359 VF- (Signed by Adam West, Burt Ward & Yvonne Craig) = $2,000.00, *Batman* #357 (Canadian Price Variant) VF = $100.00, *Crisis on Infinite Earths* #7 (Canadian Price Variant) NM = $87.00, *Thor* #225 VF = $95.00, *Secret Wars* #8 (Canadian Price Variant) NM+ to NM/MT = $338.00, *Marvel Team-Up* #141 (Canadian Price Variant) NM = $102.00, *Strange Adventures* #205 F/VF = $350.00, *Wonder Woman* #160 FN- = $170.00 and *Justice League of America* #179 (Whitman Variant) FN+ = $265.00.

Notable Sales of Certified (CGC) copies (USD): *Vampirella* #16 CGC 9.8 = $630.00, *Spectacular Spider-Man* #64 CGC 9.8 = $570.00, *New Mutants Annual* #2 CGC 9.8 = $370.00, *NYX* #3 CGC 9.6 = $570.00, *NYX* #5 CGC 9.8 = $215.00, *Frankenstein* #1 CGC 9.6 = $315.00, *Frankenstein* #17 CGC 9.8 = $305.00, *X-Men* #121 CGC 9.8 = $340.00, *Star Wars* #49 CGC 9.8 = $250.00, *Star Wars* #49 CGC 9.6 = $150.00, *Wolverine Origins* #10 (3rd Claw Variant) CGC 9.6 = $615.00, *Amazing Spider-Man* #134 CGC 9.6 = $350.00, *Foom* #2 (2 copies) CGC 9.8 = $750.00 & $670.00, *Catwoman* #51 CGC 9.8 = $215.00, *Catwoman* #74 CGC 9.8 = $180.00, *Marvel Graphic Novel* #4 CGC 9.6 = $360.00, *Venom* #1 (Dell'Otto Variant) CGC 9.8 = $390.00, *Amazing Spider-Man* #678 (Venom Variant) CGC 9.4 = $1,840.00, *Batman* #635 CGC 9.8 = $240.00, *Supernatural Thrillers* #5 CGC 9.8 = $310.00, *Amazing Spider-Man* #300 CGC 9.4 = $500.00, *Superman/Batman* #7 (French Dell' Otto Variant) CGC 9.8 = $1,320.00, *Wolverine: The Best There Is* #1 CGC 9.8 = $330.00, *Red Sonja* #1 CGC 9.8 = $170.00, *Henchgirl* #1 CGC 9.8 = $362.00, *Tomb Raider* #33 CGC 9.6 = $170.00, *Archie Comics Digest* #1 CGC 9.4 = $530.00, *Weird Mystery Tales* #21 CGC 9.2 = $170.00, *Tomb of Dracula* #13 CGC 9.6 = $419.00 and *Marvel Premiere* #28 CGC 9.6 = $470.00

*Spider-Man titles (like **Amazing Spider-Man** #300) are popular for Certified sales.*

Canadian Price Variants: It appears that after years of discussing this niche market of the hobby, it is beginning to stick more and more as other dealers/advisors/collectors are sharing observations. Publishers such as Marvel and DC Comics started distinguishing a separate single Canadian Price for books beginning in October 1982 as there was a widening gap in the USD to CDN currency rates. This practice continued well into the late 1980s until publishers began simply placing both USD and CDN prices in the price box together. Canadian Price Variants are exact copies published at the exact same time and on the exact same presses as their direct edition and newsstand counterparts. The indicia, ad pages, covers and content are exactly the same. The only exception is the UPC box and the price box which will display only a single price. The most common and recognized are the 75¢ and 95¢ for Marvel and 95¢ and $1.00 for DC. Other publishers such as Gold Key, Whitman and Archie also published Canadian Price Variants, but for my report I'll only be discussing Marvel and DC. Therefore, they should not be considered Canadian Editions as so many Golden Age comics are identified with different publishers and different advertising content. The grading companies label these as "Canadian Edition" but they are truly variants for the reason explained above.

These books are scarce and even more scarce in any grade above VF (8.0). Here is a simple and very common-sense approach to understand the Canadian Price Variants scarcity. As mentioned, these books were part of the total amount published of a particular title. Take for example, *Batman* #357 to #402 which had approximately 75,303 to 97,741 copies per month of each issue. For this example, let's assume half that published amount would be Newsstand distribution and the other half would be Direct Market distribution. The Canadian Market was 1/10th the size of the U.S market based on population statistics. Therefore, we can assume that publishers would match distribution closely as it wouldn't make good business sense to make the Canadian Price Variant published more than 1/10th. So, 1/10th of the Newsstand distribution would be approximately 3,765 to 4,887 Canadian Price Variants of each issue between *Batman* #357 to #402. Canadian Price Variants weren't heavily collected by savvy collectors as they were distributed to places such as grocery stores, convenience stores and drug stores. This left the Canadian Price Variants to be fanned through and beaten up by the general public, not coveted in high grade by savvy collectors who were buying from specialty stores and comic shops that were receiving Direct Editions. So, of those 3,765 to 4,887 Canadian Price Variants, let's be generous and say that 1/5th survived in VF (8.0) or better. That would mean that there were only 753 to 977 issues that survived in better than Very Fine (8.0). That assumes that the entire published run was a 100% sell through, which it was not, as the unsold copies were returned and destroyed. In reality, there are even fewer copies available and it is possible that only 10% of that number are in true NM- (9.2) condition or better. Realistically, there would be 60 to 80 copies of each issue in 9.2 or better if we assume 20% were returned by the stores to the distributor to be destroyed. That makes for a very small supply of these niche comics to fill demand. They may be in larger supply throughout certain areas of Canada, but using the example above, it will be very tough to find them in true high grade and when they are in high grade they will bring premiums above the regular counterparts and when they are key issues the prices soar even higher.

It would be great to see this niche market grow even more as there are plenty of opportunities to find some very tough books in the wild. Many issues have not even been found in high grade, especially when it comes to Marvel's spin-off line, Star Comics which focused on the younger collectors with titles such as *Care Bears*, *Strawberry Shortcake* and *Droids* to name a few. For years we have garnered some record prices for key Canadian Price Variants and in 2017 we noticed that regular issues in high grade are also smashing record prices too. This will be an area where you won't see a flood of high grade books come to market and dilute demand as there just aren't enough examples in high grade. I guess the best comparison I can think of is the lack of high grade 35¢ price variants from the mid '70s that were used in the 6 test markets around the U.S. I do foresee a strong demand for these books in high grade in the years to come.

Silver Age: As was the case in 2016, we saw relatively little in the way of Silver Age sales. Again, mainly due to the lack of quality books coming out of private collections. Condition is also key, as many of these books are easily acquired in low grade and are slow movers as people only seem to want keys, so we didn't want to bury ourselves with listing a lot of that type of material. Unique and key books certainly sell. We had a beautiful raw copy of *Detective Comics* #359 featuring the 1st appearance of Batgirl. Additionally, we had this particular copy autographed back in 2012 by Adam West, Burt Ward and Yvonne Craig who were of course Batman, Robin and Batgirl in the ABC TV show in the 1960s. It presented a unique opportunity as all three characters grace the cover of this issue. We sold that copy as an uncertified raw copy to a collector for $2,000.00 USD. Not more than a week after the sale, Adam West passed away and the seller's remorse set in.

Bronze Age: We finally started processing some very high-grade books from a collection we acquired about three years ago from New York. We had many of these books certified and they yielded the 1st CGC 9.8 copies from the *Daredevil* run in that collection. We've advocated for nearly six years that being "First to Market" has helped drive our success and with this collection it rings true again. We had a copy of *Daredevil* #102 in CGC 9.8 sell for $750.00 USD because it was the 1st 9.8 copy to come to market. We're really excited as we finally started focusing more on this collection in the last quarter of 2017, after allowing it to sit dormant for so many years, and look forward to bringing many more single highest graded copies to market from this amazing group of books.

House of Secrets #92 was trending upwards very quickly. There were some incredible sales of both certified and uncertified copies setting some incredible record prices. A CGC 9.6 sold for $16,000.00 USD (not our sale) with raw copies on eBay exceeding four-digit prices for solid looking copies in the Very Fine (8.0) range. This book was always extremely popular and it is very difficult to acquire in high grade due to the dark cover leaving it susceptible to glaring flaws if not handled carefully. With the passing of comic book legend Bernie Wrightson, this book is rocketing to one of the most important books of the Bronze Age.

Copper Age: In 2016 we mentioned that we saw a levelling off of the upward trend in prices for books in this era. It appears the market was just catching its breath then it decided to explode again with the resurgence of interest in books such as *Web of Spider-Man* #18, *Amazing Spider-Man* #299, #300, *Amazing Spider-Man* #361 and any other Venom related books as confirmation of a Venom movie was being released in the near future. CGC 9.8 copies of *Amazing Spider-Man* #300 surged beyond $2,000 USD. All Venom related books are seeing huge spikes in realized prices. This also spilled over to characters such as Carnage as the rumor is that he may appear in the movie too.

More 1st appearances keep popping up and it's providing a steady climb in prices as the untapped Copper Age just keeps amazing us with new and obscure events that were overlooked for the past 30 years. *Web of Spider-Man* #36 with Tombstone's 1st appearance and *Spectacular Spider-Man* #107 with Sin Eater's 1st appearance have been picking up in interest and prices.

The landmark mini-series, *Watchmen*, has also seen a little increase as they are optioned for a HBO series in a few years and are being woven into the DC universe.

The oddest phenomenon has to be Stan Lee related comic covers. Stan has been represented on comic book covers and within stories and there is a surge in demand and prices for anything related to Stan. I can only theorize that this has to do with his age and people are wanting to have his autograph before he is no longer doing the con circuit. For example, a book such as *Marvel Age* #41 released in 1986 and boasting a Stan Lee photo cover have copies achieving prices that boggle the mind. CGC 9.8 copies were hitting nearly $500.00 USD, and we even sold a raw copy for $405.00 USD. There are other books with Stan Lee on them but this one seems to be the one to get people excited.

Modern Age: The usual suspects remain consistent sellers such as *Amazing Spider-Man* #344, #361 and *Batman Adventures* #12 to name a few. Obscure variants are soaring in prices. We sold a copy of *Amazing Spider-Man* #678 variant with Mary Jane as Venom on the cover in CGC 9.4 for $1,800.00 USD and as of this writing, raw copies are going north of $2,000.00 USD. Other monster variants are books such as the Del Otto variant of *Amazing Spider-Man* #667 with CGC 9.8 copies clearing $5,000.00 USD. In our opinion it is interesting to see some of these realized prices but we question long term sustainability since it is very obscure and only seems to relish in the spotlight with a few niche group of collectors who share the like interest for the book. The collecting community in large are not so focused on these variants and with prices so high it is not worth the time or effort to pay the high prices and try to resell them. You would be better off putting that kind of money into books with more mass appeal if you are looking to resell as a retailer.

Venom related books are picking up with the upcoming movie. Ones to watch out for are *Venom: Lethal Protector* #1 as this is Venom's first solo book. *Venom: Sinner Takes All* #3 which features the first Lady Venom. *Venom Lethal Protector* #4 also has good potential as it boasts the 1st female Symbiote. The real sleeper Venom books that have been under most speculators' radar are *Spider-Man Adventures* #8, 9 and 10. This series was based on the mid-1990s animated series and these 3 issues in particular boast the first animated Venom. It has a very small print run and is extremely tough for collectors and speculators to find, let alone find in high grade or even try finding the newsstand editions of these three books.

We were introduced to Weapon H this year. A mash up of Hulk and Wolverine with the 1st full appearance in *Totally Awesome Hulk* #22. Seems to be a popular premise so hopefully the story telling holds up and it continues to have an audience. CGC 9.8 copies sell very well in the $150.00 to $200.00 USD range at this time.

People have even started to hunt down newsstand copies in this era as a way to enhance their treasure hunting. There is a premium being paid for Image newsstand books such as *Spawn* #1. What makes this area interesting is that it is relatively new so there is no exact checklist of what was distributed in newsstand format. You can bet the numbers are low so finding them in high grade out in the wild on your adventures might be like spotting Sasquatch. Most dealers don't make the distinction between newsstand and direct of this era so they are mostly populating the $1.00 and $2.00 bins at this time. Likely, that is where many will remain as its another niche area but *Spawn* #1 is a fine example of an issue that certainly garners higher premiums.

I don't think I can recall an era where collecting a book because of its cover is the most significant factor in purchasing decisions. Publishers have caught onto this and are certainly working this angle to its fullest extreme now. It seems that every issue that is published weekly has a variant cover, 2nd print cover and so on. I'm not sure if its too much for the average collector but there certainly is no shortage of choice for the consumer if they collect Modern Age comics.

I mentioned earlier that we sold more Moderns this year than any other , and it was the fact that realized margins are the largest when it comes to graded copies. Hence, more emphasis was placed on projects revolved around processing and having graded copies available to the market place. It makes the most economic sense to grade Modern Age comics as compared to the other eras such as Silver and Bronze Age because certified copies in 9.2 barely realize the listed NM- prices in the *Guide* and usually sell for under the Near Mint minus listed prices. Therefore, taking a Modern book that guides for $5.00 USD and having it graded and then selling it for even $75.00 USD yields a profit margin greater then 100%. The inventory pool is never ending when it comes to Modern age books as well. It is easier to keep them readily stocked in high grade as compared to Bronze and Silver Age books.

There are certainly a lot of opportunities for collectors with the ever-shifting interest of different eras of books as some see renewed interest and some get pushed out of the spotlight. Things are very cyclical with comic books and magazines so what is popular now may not be the following year or two as other areas gain recognition again. I sure would love to see more appreciation for books such as early to mid-Bronze Age books. These are so much tougher to find in high grade then today's Modern variants but in the past 5 years we have seen the evolution of the hobby interest move to what receives attention on comic book sites on the internet. The thing to do is not get so caught up with the rumors but collect what truly interests you. If you are a speculator and trying to hustle to beat the crowds, best of luck… it's a daily grind and takes a lot of hard work.

There you have it! We look forward to a promising 2018 and are excited to complete a few more goals and projects. My love and appreciation to my wife and son, Nicole and Jack. To my Pops, without you there would never be the memories of collecting comics that I cherish. Once again, a big thank you to my close friends, Doug & Cathy. Your friendship, mentorship and long chats have meant the world to us. Happy collecting to all in 2018!

Art Cloos
Collector

It's December 5th as I write this and another year comes to an end. Both dealers and collectors remain optimistic about the health of the collector market and the world of comic fandom seems to be present in so many areas from TV to the movies and from toys to video games. It does appear that the comic world has quite a hold on the broader world of pop culture. In some ways, superheroes have become part of the modern American mythos. The geeks are having their day and we are all loving it.

This year the hobby has seen an ever increasing number of both new toy and comic shows and it seems that not a week goes by without one or more cons vying for one's attention and dollars. Indeed it is becoming more and more difficult to keep track of what's out there, let alone finding the time to go to them. This year we will have gone to close to 40 shows by the end of December and in thinking back, the contrasts can be interesting. Most small comic shows such as John Paul's NJ ones are really comic focused and not much into cosplay or media guests. Both the attendees and the dealers are true comic people, and books that are out of the main stream of the Big Two are sold and discussed at them. By contrast the bigger shows want and attract cosplayers, media guests and artists and the more limited focus for comic people is on the big ticket books of the Big Two. Even the larger vintage toy shows now have comic dealers setting up with a ToyConNJ Nov show comic dealer selling an *All Star Comics* #33 (8.0) for $2,400.

Speculators are buying up early Wonder Wonder appearances like **Sensation Comics #1**.

The cost of setting up and selling at a show has long been a frequent concern for dealers and this past year it's an issue that has resulted in multiple comic dealers I know who are cutting back their set ups at some of the larger shows because the cost does not leave them much in terms of net profit after sales. This is due to the shows greater focus on media guests and content and the resultant higher costs to run the show that are passed on to dealers and attendees. They are turning to other venues such as online auctions and auction houses instead. Selling comics, both old and new, has been both a part of comic cons and one (but not all of course) of the reasons for their existence from that first one in July 1964 in New York City. There is a feeling that now that comic selling seems to be increasingly marginalized at a lot of the larger shows and it really should be addressed by promoters because the larger shows still are comic cons and it would be a great loss if more comic dealers leave as well.

Something to keep in mind is that market reports depend on several factors. One is location. Something that is hot in one area may not be in another and this will be reflected in what is sold at most regional shows. This does not apply to the big mega cons which draw a national audience rather then a regional one. Different sellers have different customer bases. Some might not sell nationally, others might. Other factors apply too and all this is obvious of course but sometimes I think people don't get it and have to be reminded. Reduced dealer attendance at the bigger shows will also have an impact if it continues. This applies to my report too as well here on the east coast so take it as you will.

We (meaning my better half and I) have specific comic areas we collect in and we tend to focus on them and I approach my reports from that perspective. But looking at the broader market sales of Gold, Silver and Bronze books set new records every year (as I say below for *All Star Comics* #8). In the areas we focus on meaning for me the Batman titles, *Detective* and *Batman* just always sell well as do the Silver age Marvel and DCs I also collect. For my better half it's the Wonder Woman books meaning *Sensation* and *Wonder Woman* which are her comics that are the hot ones right now because it's not just comic collectors buying them but Wonder Woman advocates who won't read any comics that she is not in. It's also *Comic Cavalcade* and *All Star* (beyond the #8) for her which are starting to show signs of rising prices too.

DC Silver Age keys of course sell well and are hard to find. Paper quality was not great for a lot of them and they can be impossible to find with off white or white paper. Low grades will sell at *Guide* or better at times, and high grades will sell way above *Guide* if you can find them. The same is true of Marvel Keys. Collections always come to market of course but it's telling that a lot of them don't contain early Silver Age keys.

To zero in on one specific area for this report that we collect in, let's look at Wonder Woman. The success of the *Wonder Woman* movie early on pushed up the price of her keys with *All Star* #8 prices moving up a significant amount, and the same is true for *Sensation* and *Wonder Woman* comics. A *Sensation* #1 CGC 0.5 recently sold for $5,750. An *All Star* #8 CGC 9.4 sold for a record $936,223.00. The seller of the *All Star* had two other Wonder Woman keys which closed with new record highs as well. *Sensation Comics* #1 CGC 9.6 for $399,100.00, which is a new record for this issue, and *Wonder Woman* #1 CGC 9.0 a 'Solicitation Copy' for $226,877.77. However the prices asked for *Wonder Woman* #1 overall seem to be outdistancing *Sensation* #1 in all grades and it is the title collectors key on which I find interesting. Early on the focus was on the keys but now later issues are beginning to movie steadily up and higher grade copies are coming into the market with correspondingly higher asking prices. Vintage Wonder Woman comic collectors that we know are finding it more and more difficult to buy the missing numbers in their runs with one telling me she should have bought her missing keys 10 years ago instead of waiting. One Golden Age title that is still affordable that she appears in is *Comic Cavalcade* where she appears in solo stories and this might be an area to focus on for collectors. Will this trend continue? Only time will tell but given her status as one of the DC trinity, it seems that prices are finally beginning to reflect her status in the history of comics.

To finish with the Wonder Woman focus, as I type this the *Justice League* movie is still in movie theaters. With its mediocre reception by both viewers and critics, will it affect the value of the Justice League titles? Well at this time there are 28 copies of *Brave and the Bold* #28 up for auction or sale, and there are 27 GPA confirmed sales for 2017 as of this morning. Overall a fair amount of activity for a key from 1960 that has not shown up all that often in the past. In terms of *Justice League* #1, twenty eight copies are also up for auction currently on eBay and this has been not atypical for the last year. With Wonder Woman being a charter member, Wonder Woman collectors have long been buying the title because of her and I suspect this will continue. GPA shows that over the last 12 months only one copy has sold reaching the 9.0 grade, again not atypical for DC/NPP books from this time as they are very hard to find in high grade. Most copies coming to market during that time were lower grades often in the 4.5 range and 27 total sales for the year are reported to date. Asking prices in the different grades have been pushed up some but not a lot. Again only time will tell how these two books will shake out in terms of demand and price. Also, only time will tell how it will affect the value of the books of other characters in it, but I don't think either Superman or Batman comic fans have anything to worry about as pertains to the value of their books.

A few niches to keep in mind. The comic art collecting community continues to generate sales but it's the Wild West of collecting as there is no price guide to refer to and there is a lot to learn about it before beginning to buy pieces. It is not an area to just dive into. We both collect comic art but confine it to art for Batman and Wonder Woman (obviously). Foreign comics (yes only Batman and Wonder Woman for us) are a fascinating area that we both have discovered but again one needs to learn the ins and outs of it as the language barrier can cause problems in knowing what exactly one is buying. Finally, collecting vintage comic fanzines is a great way to discover the history of fandom and I recommend them to anyone who wants to learn about the 57 year history of comic fandom.

Confirmed sales for 2017 are: *Adventure Comics* #254 FN+ $200; *Action Comics* #276 FN+ $90; *All Star Comics* #19 VG $400, #33 (8.0) $2,400; *Batman Annual* First Series #7 FN/VF (7.0) $50; *Giant Superman Annual* FN+(6.5) $52; *Green Lantern* #2, VF $275, #16 (4.0) #$180, $18 (6.0) $65; *Mystery into Space* #53, (7.5) $1,400, #77 FN (6.0) $40; *Sea Devils* #4 VF $75; *Sensation Comics* #1 (0.5) $5,750, #9 GD(2.0) $400, #14 GD/VG (3.0) $275, #26 GD(2.0) $125, #30 GD/VG(3.0) $408, #36 VG/FN (5.0) $363, #55 GD/VG (3.0) $79, #62 VG/FN (5.0) $180, #104 GD (2.0) $75; *Showcase* #8 FN- $1,600, #20 (7.0) $1,500, #29 FN $75, #41 FN+ $52, #42 VF+ $190, # 48 VF $54 and *Wonder Woman* #214 VF $67.

As you read this in the summer of 2018, I hope the new year is bringing you new and exciting additions to your collections and I will see you in 2019.

Ashley Cotter-Cairns & Sean Goodrich SellMyComicBooks.com

***Amazing Fantasy* #15 vs Bitcoin:** As I sit down to write this market report in December, the snow has begun to fall on Quebec, Bitcoin has broken the $18,000 barrier, and I'm looking for a way to piece this all together with our year of comic book buying and selling.

I'll start by saying that *Amazing Fantasy* #15 is the Bitcoin of the comic book world. Just when you think it can't get any hotter, prices keep breaking out. Especially in the VG range, which seems to be the sweet spot of RELATIVE affordability, combined with decent eye appeal and probable return on investment. The most recent sale of $25,000 seems about normal, for now, at least.

I shudder when I think of the price we let a CGC 4.5 Signature Series (Stan Lee, of course) go for early in the year. Now it would be worth a significantly greater amount. But that's hindsight for you. If only we'd bought Bitcoin with the proceeds...

One exception to the good news for *Amazing Fantasy* #15 fans is that CGC 0.5 and 1.0 copies have barely appreciated at all. The entry level a year ago was about $5K for a 0.5, and that hasn't changed. Spider-Fans have standards, it seems.

Incredible Hulk #181 is not far behind in the hot comics stakes. The price of a CGC 9.8, which had got sort of sticky around the early teens last year, has now powered up to almost $20,000. Signature Series 9.8s will just about break $20K.

All the upward pressure means a decent VG copy will now set you back about $1,000. Who knows what the price will be by the time you're reading this in the summer of 2018?

Two big-ish movies hit the Silver Screen this Fall: *Thor: Ragnarok* and *Justice League*. I went to see both on opening night. *Thor* got more laughs, but I felt Marvel Studios might have over-done the comedy a bit; *Justice League* was a bit of a mess, but still enjoyable.

Not a lot happened to prices of *Journey into Mystery* #83 or *Incredible Hulk* #1, but prices of *Brave and the Bold* #28 and to a lesser extent, *Justice League of America* #1 were bullish all year. Lots of low-grade examples came our way, but these DC keys are still miles away, price-wise, from their Marvel counterparts.

Talking of Marvel keys, the price of *Fantastic Four* #1 has finally woken up. Investors and collectors have realized that this book was under-valued. Given that it's from 1961, and tough to find with nice eye appeal, especially above VG-FN, the book has shown strong gains in all grades, with FN+ copies approaching $20K. I expect this upward trend to continue, because *Fantastic Four* #1 is still relatively cheap.

Notable Collections in 2017: The year began with a bang! We had been chasing a collection in Australia for a few months. Finally we agreed on $30,000. Shipping took forever, but our patience was rewarded. We had fun unpacking long runs of Golden Age Hero, funny books and Horror. Highlights included early *Wonder Woman* (with a decent #98 – very tough book) and *Sensation Comics*, *Detective* and *Batman*, including the hard-to-find issues *Batman* #47 (first detailed origin) and #49 (first Mad Hatter and Vicki Vale). The Aussie collection also included a *Venus* #1, two copies of *Phantom Stranger* #1 (another tough book!) and hundreds more, stretching right into the Bronze Age.

Literally the same day, we agreed to buy a collection of Archies from California. These were SUPER-nice, spanning mid-1940s to late-1950s. The average grade was about 7.0 – how often do you see a single 1940s Archie in that shape, let alone a few hundred? Many of the books became the single highest graded in the CGC census, and plenty snuck their way into Sean Goodrich's personal Archie collection.

Perhaps the most satisfying collection for me personally came through a Facebook message. A young man living near Quebec City here in Canada was offering a collection on behalf of his mother. It was almost exclusively DC Silver Age. A quick glance at the list showed the usual *JLA*, *Green Lantern*, *Flash* and other runs.

I always ask for pics of *JLA* #28-30, because you never know… and sure enough, it turned out to be *Brave and the Bold*. I made a trip to meet them, struck a price and drove back home with about 1,500 books. Many had some water damage, but the collection included *Showcase* #8 and #22, *JLA* #1, *Flash* #110 and #139 and many more keys.

The ones which escaped the water graded in the 7.5 to 9.0 range — many were heartbreakers, including the *Brave and the Bold* #28, which looked like a 9.0 from the front but ended up getting a 5.0 – it's the nicest 5.0 you'll ever see, with staining and some creases, all on the back cover. Now part of my growing collection of key issues.

One of my favorite finds of the year was a Bronze Age Marvel collection with keys like *Hulk* #181, with the Marvel Value Stamps cut out – but still kept with the comics! Sean taped the MVS back into the *Hulk* and submitted it to CGC. I was bitterly disappointed to see that they didn't put a special note on the label. "MVS reattached by tape" would have been totally appropriate, don't you think? It would have been a fascinating price experiment, as missing MVS copies sell for about one-third the price of complete books in the same grade. But it got the usual qualified label.

Ten Books to Watch in 2018: Without tipping our hand too strongly (after all, we publish an annual 100 Hot Comics list – see below), here are ten books you should keep an eye on in the next 12 months. For fun, I've noted a recent CGC sale alongside each book.

Action Comics #242 (1st Brainiac, rare and under-valued) CGC 3.5 $1,313

Adventure Comics #247 (1st Legion of Super-Heroes, vastly under-rated and rare Silver Age key) CGC 6.5 $8,365

Amazing Spider-Man #20 (1st Scorpion, tipped for a future appearance in post-credit scene of *Spider-Man: Homecoming*) CGC 9.2 $2,629

Aquaman #1 (1st solo book, under-valued and has been slumbering for years) CGC 8.0 $2,250

Archie's Madhouse #22 (1st Sabrina the Teenage Witch, very scarce book) CGC 4.5 $495

Batman #121 (1st Mr. Zero / Mr. Freeze, ironically super-hot!) CGC 5.0 $2,200

Batman #181 (1st Poison Ivy, relentlessly increasing in value) CGC 8.0 $1,850

Detective Comics #140 (1st Riddler, tough tough book) CGC 6.5 $11,500

House of Secrets #92 (1st Swamp Thing, price has broken out) CGC 9.4 $7,595

Strange Adventures #205 (1st Deadman, still cheap-ish!) CGC 9.0 $1,125

What's New at Sell My Comic Books?: Business is brisk and keeping Sean and me happy and busy. We opened our first office space in October 2016, and our own "Justice League" of staff – Sean (Moran), Scott and Jamie – are doing a fantastic job of keeping the books moving out the door. (We're hiring again to keep up with demand!)

We've begun a tradition of unboxing collections on camera and uploading the videos to YouTube (YouTube.com/SellMyComicBooks). I've also begun sharing my thoughts about comic book collecting and investing with with the world: my favorite so far is called The Amazing Spider-MATH — demonstrating how it makes sense financially to buy *Amazing Spider-Man* #1 before you start putting the rest of the run together.

As ever, our 100 Hot Comics list is the most popular section of our website, trying to predict which books will be good investments within the next 12 months. This year, we've added lots more "Top List" pages, including Romance, Horror, and 100 most valuable Variant Comics. This modern phenomenon can no longer be ignored, with the sale of the Dell'otto variant of *Amazing Spider-Man* #667 for $10,000 cementing the reputation of variant covers as big business.

By the time you read this, PressMyComicBooks.com will have launched. We're soft-launching our service to our eBay customers, before rolling it out to the general public (or dealers, of course). Our pricing structure is markedly different to other companies offering pressing, and if you want to do it yourself, you can stream our video course on how to press comics.

Here's to Another Great Year! As ever, Sean and I are very happy to be Overstreet advisors, and contribute our experience and excitement at being a small part of this fun industry. Thanks for the opportunity. To any of our fellow dealers reading this who are considering retirement, please get in touch, and let's talk about how we might acquire your inventory at a price which suits everybody.

Happy collecting, investing and dealing everybody!

Jesse James Criscione
Jesse James Comics

There was a simple theme in the comic book industry in 2017: "Brand". Branding was a HUGE factor in a lot of publishers making bigger names for themselves.

Through visuals, displays, and swag, customers have become extremely loyal to Brands (Image came to be the #1 fan based driven publishers) that they felt have strong partnerships with their local comic shop (LCS). We saw a huge communication increase with presidents, team members, and creators. All asking "What can we do to help you sell more books?" We saw a increase of openness to match our brand to their brand in stronger partnerships to increase our sales and customer retention for that brand and future sales.

Brands like Aftershock, Valiant, Black Mask, Boom and etc.. also took to Facebook, Twitter and Instagram to keep the customers informed almost daily. We saw a huge increase in the quality of their webpages and customer loyal groups. Cool packages were highlighted as the reason to follow these publishers. Coffin Comic's Brian Pulido took it to a whole new level of mastering Kickstarter and creating one of the most loyal fanbases on the planet. Every fan was part of the Coffin Comics family.

We saw in 2017 a slew of creators also sign exclusive deals with publishers and letting the public know that they were happy to represent these brands at all forums. There was also the 7 Image Founders + 1 who seemed to own every aspect of media in 2017. Their fans base rallied big time around these '90s stars and made them more relevant today then ever, even from back then. This has meant bigger sales for the LCS that knew how to piggy back and market around them and attract those fans and sell them some cool Founder goods. Creator Rob Liefeld led the way in 2017. His love for the industry was only second to his fanbase. There wasn't one day where he was wasn't engaging with them on Facebook or Twitter.

We also saw a ton of closures of comic book stores across the nation in 2017. The theme of almost all of them was the lack of Online Sales. E-commerce will be the biggest key to making it through 2018. Without online sales in 2018, or at least establishing it, 2019 is a maybe for the business to move on.

eBay has made a strong push to make comic books one of their top selling catagories. In 2017 they had their own Exclusives, partnering up with LCS (My Comic Shop and Jesse James Comics), to bring a very cost effective collectible comic book to people across the world. The "Buy online, pick up at store" sales almost tripled in 2017. More customers like the ideal that the item is reserved and will be there when they arrive, at their convenience, to pick up their awesome books. Plus, they also shop while in the store for more items during their visit. Amazon still remains a low point for comic books and hopefully in 2018 they realize its time to get involved and help awareness with their huge brand.

Customer service remains to be a huge focus for all stores. The customers experience outweighs everything else. They want to be heard and they want to be served. They don't want headaches when it comes to a exchange or return. They don't want to hear about a distributor not sending their books. They just want them. Their voice matters. In 2017 a lot of stores found out the hard way, the customers has a ton of chooses and they will choose wisely based on how they are treated.

Movies and TV shows has almost zero traction in the modern day LCS. Yeah, some books spiked, but overall the lack of the movie industry teaming up with the LCS obviously is embarrassing. Until, we can brand together with the movie or Tv industry, it's not something we can rely on for future sales.

The greatest thing about 2017 though, was the rise of the Independent Publisher. All pie charts, reports and other measure showed one thing. For Independents, sales as a whole stayed between 30% to 32% each quarter. Plainly meaning, 1 out 3 books that left a store were a Independent book. These publishers continue to change the market and introduce new fans organically through the LCS or their own webpages. In 2018, I foresee Independent publisher adding 1% to 2 % more in market share. Image and Boom continue to push the levers on increasing their readership.

We have a very bright 2018 ahead in the comic book industry. The customer base is looking for relevant brands, the ease of shopping online or in the stores, local comic shops that listen to their concerns, great books at a great price, and the most important thing they want is the best service possible.

Brock Dickinson
Collector

2017 has been a year of change and transition. On the personal side I've changed jobs (hello University of Waterloo!), on the collecting side my local comic shop has a new owner (Hello Norm at Mostly Comics in St. Catharines!), while in the industry as a whole, upheaval and transition seem to be the order of the day. From DC Rebirth to Marvel Legacy and beyond, the industry's old order seems to be shifting, and it's a little unclear what will emerge when the dust settles.

As always, I'll do my best in this report to read the tea leaves around these changes, and try to identify some key trends and patterns that drove the market in 2017 and may continue into 2018 and beyond. And, as with previous years, I'll focus my comments on the Bronze to Modern period (say, 1975 to the present), the area of the market I understand best.

First, it's important to acknowledge that much of the market for this era is driven by current activity. In other words, what are new comics, TV shows or movies doing to shape people's perceptions and desires right now, and how is that driving the market? First, it's probably fair to say that Marvel Comics is struggling in the new comic market, and its haphazard attempts to right the ship have created confusion and apathy in the marketplace. This has caused a marked retreat in some Marvel prices, and the cooling off of some previously hot characters (such as Deadpool). Marvel's hugely successful movies and buzzworthy TV shows have not driven new readers to the comics. Meanwhile, DC Comics appears to have had a very successful year, building on its "Rebirth" initiative of 2016, and ramping up interest with projects including *Metal* and *Doomsday Clock*. However, it's increasingly clear that a healthy market requires both big companies to be performing well, and with Marvel's struggles, big question marks hang over the hobby. This uncertainty has made for a relatively quiet year in terms of back issue price increases.

Having said that, there were some bright spots. Mainstay characters continued to be popular, and although Deadpool may be slumping, popular characters including Spider-Man and Harley Quinn appeared to be holding their ground. Perhaps the hottest character of the year, however, was Batman. A substantial number of Batman appearances and issues sold out and went through multiple printings, with some capturing solid prices on the aftermarket (including *Batman* #24 at $10-$12, *Batman Annual* #2 at $12-$15, *Batman Who Laughs* #1 at $10-$15, and *Teen Titans* #12 at $20-$30). Batman titles were generally solid sellers on the back issue market, with the exception of New 52 issues, which cooled significantly.

A few other characters also seemed to attract attention. There were modest upticks in interest around some second tier characters including Moon Knight and Lobo and their Copper Age appearances. The growing popularity of female characters, a strongly noticeable trend in recent years, also continued. Interest in Spider-Gwen remained high, and her first appearance in *Edge of Spider-Verse* #2 ($100) continues to climb in price. X-23, the female Wolverine spin-off, also remained hot, and her first appearance in *NYX* #3 ($400) is now a genuine (and high-priced) key. Over at DC, *Power Girl* (including #27 at $80) and *Gotham City Sirens* issues made modest gains, while *Zatanna* issues continued to soar (including #16 at $75). With rumours circulating that high profile DC writing recruit Brian Michael Bendis may write a new *Zatanna* series, this may continue to be a series to watch.

For a number of years now, movies and TV shows have been the primary drivers of the recent back issue market, but this trend also slowed somewhat in 2017. On the Marvel side of things, the release of *Guardians of the Galaxy 2* earlier in the year sparked some brief interest in Guardians-related appearances, but this retreated fairly quickly after the movie, while the *Thor: Ragnarok* movie seemed to have only minimal impacts on the market. The one exception to this is early appearances of Adam Warlock – and particularly those appearances written or pencilled by Jim Starlin – which attracted a lot of movie-driven attention throughout year. This interest also spilled over into a general interest in the Infinity stones and the Infinity Gauntlet, as Marvel builds towards their central role in upcoming *Avengers* movies.

On the DC movie side, *Wonder Woman* back issues did see some strongly renewed interest this year, with some issues undergoing substantial price increases (e.g. *Wonder Woman* (1942 series) #204 with the first appearance of Nubia approaching $200). Also attracting a lot of interest were the Adam Hughes covers from the 1987 *Wonder Woman* series. While last year's *Guide* broke out prices for Hughes' *Catwoman* and *Zatanna* books, the *Wonder Woman* books need to follow suit. Of particular interest is #184, which now routinely sells in the $100 range. Contrary to this *Wonder Woman* trend, however, the *Justice League* movie later in the year did little to drive back issue sales.

A few other characters seemed to have renewed interest sparked by movie or TV projects. Key issues of *New Mutants* were up strongly, while Hellboy, Venom and Punisher key appearances also experienced some additional attention. By and large, though, the impact of TV and movie announcements was both smaller in size and shorter in duration this year than in the past, while some previously-hot properties (such as *The Walking Dead*) appeared largely unchanged in the market. The shift to more obscure and team-based movie projects also made it difficult for the market to focus on specific books. For example, DC announced an upcoming *Gotham City Sirens* films featuring the popular female characters Harley Quinn, Poison Ivy and Catwoman. However, collectors seeking the first appearance of this team of villains were split between those chasing *Gotham City Sirens* #1 ($60), those focused on that issue's prelude in *Detective Comics* #850 ($30), and an early team-up of the same characters in *Catwoman* (1993 series) #89 ($20).

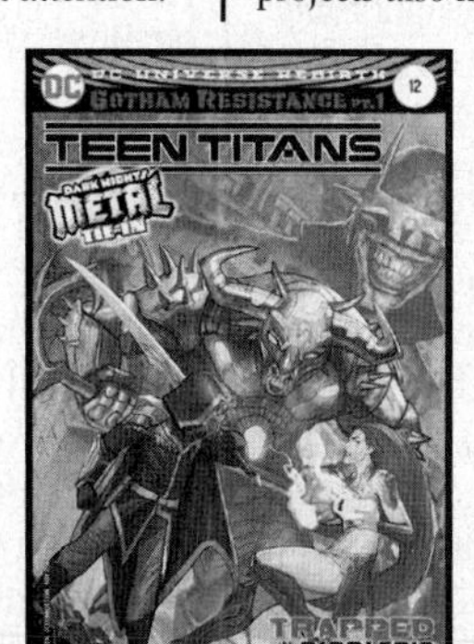

The Batman Who Laughs made **Teen Titans #12** a hot seller.

While multimedia productions perhaps declined as a driver of the market in 2017, there was an increased focus on previously unremarked variants. While the 35¢ Marvel test price variants of the 1970s have been well-known for many years, there is an increasing fascination with other price and distribution variants in some portions of the marketplace. The 35¢ variants remain very hot, and the earlier 30¢ Marvel price variants also gathered steam this year. At the same time, a number of other variants began to gain increased attention, and experienced some substantial price increases. This trend was probably led by Canadian cover price variants, which can credibly be argued (though actual data is scant) to represent about 2% of total print runs for some Copper Age books. This makes these books elusive (especially in high grade), and in NM- or better these books will often command 200% to 1000% of current *Guide* prices.

There was also strengthened interest in early direct market books, late newsstand editions, Whitman variants, and UK pence price variants, all from the 1970s and 1980s, and Marvel Pressman and DC Universe cover logo variants from the 1990s. Many of these books are extremely scarce, but so little is known about supply and distribution that prices can still vary widely. Nonetheless, there is a clear market trend to increased value for these books, and the 35¢ *Star Wars* #1 variant is a clear indication of how far these trends can go over time.

A number of other wide trends could be observed within the industry this year. One surprise was that Treasury Edition comics from the 1970s and 1980s began to take off, particularly in high grade. Treasuries have always been the "ugly stepchild" of the comic world, hard to store and difficult to find in high grade – but there is an increasing recognition that they contain some key stories and events, as well as art from favourite artists, and sometimes reprints of key issues that have become incredibly pricey. It also helped that CBCS began grading (though not slabbing) Treasuries this past year. *Superman Vs. The Amazing Spider-Man* probably has the highest interest levels, but high grade copies were in demand across the board. This is also an area of the market where there are many poorly-researched variants with odd distribution, so new books continue to be found. Big gainers included *All-New Collector's Edition*, *Famous First Edition*, *Limited Collector's Edition*, *Marvel Treasury Edition*, and a host of Marvel one-shots and movie specials.

Comics from the Copper Age (about 1982 to 1992, though as always, the dates are fuzzy around the edges) continued to secure their place as collectibles with rising prices. There are still many undiscovered gems from this era, but also an increasing recognition of the period's key issues. Regular readers of my Market Report will know that every year, I go online to the CGC message boards for some assistance in "crowdsourcing" a list of the Top 50 Key Copper Age books. Here's what emerged from the discussion as this year's Top 50:

- *Albedo* #2
- *Amazing Spider-Man* #238, #252, #298, #300, #316
- *Archie's Girls, Betty and Veronica* #320
- *Batman* #357, #404, #428
- *Batman: The Dark Knight Returns* #1
- *Batman: The Killing Joke*
- *Bone* #1
- *Caliber Presents* #1
- *Comico Primer* #2
- *Crisis on Infinite Earths* #7
- *The Crow* #1
- *Daredevil* #181
- *DC Comics Presents* #47
- *Evil Ernie* #1
- *G.I. Joe: A Real American Hero* #1, #21
- *Harbinger* #1
- *Incredible Hulk* #271, #340
- *Marvel Graphic Novel* #4
- *Marvel Super Heroes Secret Wars* #8
- *Miracleman* #15
- *New Mutants* #87, #98
- *Punisher* (limited series) #1
- *Sandman* #1, #8
- *Spectacular Spider-Man* #64
- *Silver Surfer* #34
- *Spawn* #1
- *Suicide Squad* #1
- *Superman* #75
- *Swamp Thing* #21, #37
- *Tales of the New Teen Titans* #44
- *Thor* #337
- *Transformers* #1
- *Teenage Mutant Ninja Turtles* #1
- *Uncanny X-Men* #221, #266
- *Warrior* (UK Magazine) #1
- *Watchmen* #1
- *Wolverine* (limited series) #1
- *X-Factor* #6

Copper Age interest continues to grow in a range of "indie" characters, as this is increasingly seen as an era of high creativity. Early appearances of characters including The Crow, Hellboy, Spawn, and the Teenage Mutant Ninja Turtles were all strong. The substantial price increases of *Scooby Doo* issues in the late Silver/early Bronze period were also driving prices for later Bronze and Copper issues, which are often hard to find, and especially difficult in high grade.

Another emerging Copper trend is an increased interest in "promotional" publications. While an early Spawn appearance in *Malibu Sun* #13 ($125) has long commanded solid prices, there was a big spike this year in issues of *Marvel Age*. This is a book that should probably be added to the *Overstreet Guide* – in addition to news and promotional articles, it often included comic stories themselves, sometimes in the form of four-page previews, but sometimes in the form of original book-length comic stories. This year, *Marvel Age* #41 (featuring a cover photo of Stan Lee) took off. Although prices varied widely, it was not unusual to see prices for high grade copies in excess of $200. Many other issues, featuring early appearances of characters such as Rocket Raccoon, the Infinity Gauntlet, the Guardians of the Galaxy, Spider-Man's black costume, etc. have also experienced substantial price increases. Just as issues of Marvel's 1970s in-house magazine *FOOM* have increased in recent years, *Marvel Age* is now following suit.

There also appeared to be an uptick in interest in Jack Kirby's DC work this year. Perhaps the combination of a *Kamandi* revival, the appearance of villain Steppenwolf in the *Justice League* movie, and Kirby's 100th birthday helped spur this along, but prices around these classic but sometimes weak sellers definitely firmed up.

Finally, the impact of slabbed and graded comics continues to reshape the hobby. Cover art and cover artists continue to rise in importance, partly because of the encapsulated nature of third party graded books, which make the story content inaccessible. Modern artists at the forefront of this trend continue to include Adam Hughes, Todd McFarlane, Gabriele Dell'Otto, J. Scott Campbell, and Frank Cho. However, there was increased interest this year in the work of Francesco Mattina, Stanley "Artgerm" Lau, Joshua Middleton, Siya Oum, and Jenny Frison.

Once again, I appreciate the opportunity to be a part of *Overstreet*'s Market Reports. *The Guide* is an incredible achievement, and its annual publication is a huge and continuing benefit to our hobby. I look forward to reading the reports of all my fellow advisors, and hope that my modest contributions aid in understanding where our hobby goes next!

Gary Dolgoff
Gary Dolgoff Comics

Ah, the ever-shifting "cosmos of comics" and of comics collecting. As of late, I've noticed a trend. Two things are simultaneously occurring in the comics industry:

1) A number of long-time collectors are reaching an older age wherein they are seriously considering (and in some cases, acting on) selling their long-time collections, or at least part of it, though many of the ol' timers are electing to keep their books, and that's cool too.

Tales to Astonish #27 is the prize of many collections.

2) Many, many collectors are still into collecting and I think they, as well as I, will continue to do the "Collecting thang" for many years to come.

Many of the folks who are selling their collections understandably don't want a potential buyer to cherry pick the best, or the oldest, parts of their collection and leave them the comics that would be "tougher to move on out" on their own. The seller then has to deal with all the leftovers.

I love to buy it all. I have a burgeoning staff, highly competent cool to work with, and I have the space (5000 square feet, with aisles of 8-foot metal shelving) to deal with it all. This makes it easier for me to buy it all. Between me and my "warehouse enthusiastic bunch," we are learning more and more about comics from the last 30 years or so that are worth over *Guide* so I can take that into account when evaluating a collection to potentially purchase.

Thus, it all can be taken into account when I and my travelling assistants assess a collection. I have a couple of folks here at Gary Dolgoff Comics who enjoy travelling with me to look at these "far and wide" collections.

Even after 48+ years in comics, it's still an enthusiastic adventure for me and for my crew. Some have been with me 3-5 years, some since the early 2000s, and in one case since 1998. (A personal/business note: My wife works with me and the crew part-time, and that is good.)

Let's now take a look at some real world examples from the ground floor of the comic book marketplace: the personal comic book collection for sale. Here are some notable market-moments from last year from my perspective.

Major Key-Issues Continue To Shine Despite Condition: An affable 80-year old gent came to my warehouse and sold me a few "preferred early Silver Age" (*Showcase* #1, 7, 8, etc.) plus a small batch of 10-cent cover Archie-title comics (I ended up getting around 30% over *Guide* for the Fine+ Showcase #8.) During his warehouse visit, he mentioned his collection that he had at home in Chicopee, Massachusetts (about 15-20 minutes from me!).

He said he has stacks of early to mid-Silver Age, and asks if I would like to come over to check them out. You bet! The prize was *Tales To Astonish* #27 (1st Ant-Man) and he also had a few small piles of post-code 10-cent DCs and lots of late 10-cent cover-price Archies. He was quite pleased that I could pay almost $1000 for the *TTA* #27, even with a large tear on the back cover. Apparently he didn't know the significance of that issue, owing in part to Ant-Man not being in costume on the cover.

The *TTA* #27, I offered about 60-70 percent of value to pay. He also had a number of post-code 10-cent cover DCs, so I paid him 50-60 percent of *Guide* for these GD/VG to VG *Batman* and *Detective* comics; 40-50 percent of *Guide*, for those late 10¢ cover Superman (various titles) - as I often must discount them 20% or so to sell. I paid him for the comics (several thousand dollars) and all parties were happy. He told me that I paid more than he thought he'd get, which was all right with me.

The Collection from Wausau, WI: This good fellow had been buying comics since the 1960s (into the 1970s, right through the present), collecting and saving them, and keeping them in pretty nice shape! I was particularly impressed, because when I first read comics in the Silver Age, the comics were read and then came to be in "beat shape" very soon after. However, this fellow treated his comics well! They were mostly in GD/VG to FN shape.

I went up there with my main "travelling warehouse fella" Patrick, and together we figured out his collection, over a day and a half, approximately. We graded a bunch of oldies, crunched numbers, including the later-era newer stuff, which not every dealer will take into account, but like I say, every book has a value. I figured on paying 50% average on his '60s Marvels (they were actually 1964 to 1971); and I figured somewhat more than 50% on, say, the *Amazing Spideys* and *Avengers;* somewhat less than 50%, on, for instance, the *Strange Tales* and *Tales To Astonish* issues. We ended up getting the collection, and to make the deal more memorable than it already was - we loaded up the comics through the beginning of a classic Mid-West blizzard!

Later, we were honored to receive this glowing review online from the seller:

"...after a few phone calls and emails, he and his man Patrick came to my house in Wausau, Wisconsin. For 12 hours they expertly and efficiently graded and evaluated my comics. The next day they returned and Gary made me a generous offer, which I accepted, and they got to the massive job of moving 250 boxes from my basement to their truck. My wife and I thoroughly enjoyed their visit, and I give Galactic Gary and Peerless Patrick 5 stars each." The seller and his wife were very pleasant to meet. Part of the joy of dealing and buying comics is the people.

A Local *Walking Dead* Collection: The seller had #1 thru #165 - very simple. I evaluated the books and pointed out that color-breaking creases on the spine and other small flaws reduce them from perfect "9.4 & better" shape. The #1, for instance, had some small color-breaks in the spine (otherwise, it was pretty sharp), so I rated it an 8.0 for the market. *Walking Dead* #1 is somewhat of an exception to the rule - where even very low-grade copies sell for good money. That being said, once you get into some of the more-moderate Modern Age keys, then low-grade copies can be essentially worthless where their VF/NM to MT counterparts could be worth hundreds, or more!

A Manhattan, NY - Upper West Side Collection: The guy didn't want to sell everything, but he was willing to sell enough that it was well worth a "buying ride." Going to his Upper West Side apartment, I enjoyed looking at the comics and I bought them. I must tell you that many of the oldies were very tattered, and a number of the books were brittle. But "what the hey", the group had a stack of low-grade (some even coverless) ECs (which I love), *Walt Disney's Comics and Stories* #31 thru #371, and much much more. They were fun books, including a copy of a "World War 3" comic. I evaluated paying 50% for much of the comics on average - as the ECs I knew would sell for *Guide*, even in PR condition, and I would have to discount many of the *WDC&S* comics 20% or more (except for the very early Barks issues which I would get *Guide* for.)

A Milfort, CT Collection: I had talked with the owner of this collection a few years ago, but she wasn't ready to sell her late father's collection yet. We built up a good rapport over our time of discussing the collection and life in general - and a few years later, she was ready to have me come over, for a return look.

There was a beautiful *Incredible Hulk* #181 (1st Wolverine), an awesome *Strange Tales* #101, a restored *Tales of Suspense* #39, and best of all, a beautiful 1940s *Captain America* #61(with the Red Skull), which I kept for myself.

Not every book was great, for sure, but it's always nice to get some early Keys as well as "keepsies" in a collection. For the '60s Superman titles, for instance, I had to pay less than 50%, because unless they're in sharp condition, they must be sold for 25% to 40% off of *Guide* to have a chance of selling.

I paid her a nice price, taking into account both the over-*Guide* books, and the more "regular-run" stuff and she was happy to get room on her shelf for some murals she wanted to put up. Everybody has their "thing" that they're into. With me, it's comic books, amongst other things.

A Comic Book Magazines Collection From Brooklyn, NY: This good fella and I had (and always have had) a really good rapport. What he'd have me do is pick up a group of stuff from his home in Brooklyn, then evaluate it at the Warehouse and offer him what I can do for each group. Then I'd simply mail him my GDC check. It's always worked out, as it did for this 1960s through early 1980s magazine collection containing over 30 Magazine boxes with runs of *Creepy*, *Eerie*, *Savage Sword*, *Kung-Fu*, etc., and best of all, those cool 1970s Horror reprints with those trashy, bloody covers - what fun! The *Creepy*, *Eerie*, and other Warren mags I may have to sell for an average of 20% off of *Guide*, but on the other hand, those "primitive" '70s mags (*Tales From The Tomb*, *Witches Tales*, etc.) I'll probably get an average of 20% over *Guide*, though they're in GD/VG to VG shape on average.

A Moose Jaw, Canada Collection!: I had never been in Moose Jaw before, so when I got offered a 1960s Marvel collection (issues #1s through around 1968 of *Fantastic Four*, *Spidey*, *X-Men*, *Avengers*, *Sgt. Fury*, etc.) how could I say no? I brought my manager Rob with me so he could get the buying experience with me, and we had a great time as well The good fellow selling me the books was extra happy to have me there as he was craving "Comic book conversations" living in a place that had a particularly small comic book community. I figured on paying 50 percent of *Guide*, average, for the 1964 to 1968 Marvels, 60% for the earlier Marvels, and 70% for the early '60s #1s (though they were GD to VG- mostly.)

Interestingly enough, while we were there (a small, fairly remote city in south-central Saskatchewan) I was contacted by another Moose Javian selling off some of his collection. This was entirely unrelated in any way to the first seller! Rob and I had a great time doing a late-night deal there too. Also of note: we found our way to a very unique local attraction, Tunnels of Moose Jaw. Look it up. It's quite the memorable experience and I'm glad we did that.

These are just a sampling of the deals I've bought - and continue to buy, year after year, decade after decade. We have 800,000+ comics and comic mags, and I don't use a want-list when I purchase, as my general comic book philosophy is "every comic, in every grade, has a use, and a place, in the GD Warehouse." The market is generally fertile, and with my able assistants, each day of "biz" is a joy indeed.

The Golden Age

DC Comics: Generally, any superhero DC will sell, and

pretty quickly in all grades, poor to mint! I find *More Fun Comics*, with The Spectre (#52 thru 107) to be tougher to get, as the years go by, and many of the early '40s covers of this title are amongst the most captivating of all '40s comics. I own *More Fun* #61 in nice shape amongst my "keepsies" comics. I love that book, with the simple, yet striking, Dr. Fate cover. It looks almost 3-D.

Wonder Woman has always been a real solid seller, but lately (especially after the fantastic *Wonder Woman* movie) has moved up to be a top-tier title. I own almost all of the 1st 100 issues - and no, they're not for sale. I dig 'em' too much. I will, however, sell the doubles I get in from various collections. Most of these older *Wonder Woman* issues go for somewhat over *Guide* and certain issues, most notably #7 (with the outstanding "1000 years in the future - Wonder Woman for President" cover) sells for at least 5x *Guide*. Issue #1 has also gone up in value by more than 5x in the last several years.

Early *Action* and *Detective* comics go for well over *Guide*, and *Action* #7 - the 2nd Superman cover - goes for double *Guide*, or more. I know that if I want a shot at getting these "early Goldies" plus those 1940s through '50s *Wonder Woman* comics, I must really "pony up" the paying price, and I will.

Timely Comics (which are, essentially, Golden Age Marvels): They have always, personally, fascinated me, especially the World War II and earlier issues. I myself collect Timelys, and I own well over 100 of them. Some of my favorites are the *USA Comics* with the spectacular Captain America covers. They're worth well over *Guide*. Whenever I get a Golden Age collection, I pay a premium, in general, for Timelys - and then keep just about all of them, except if I already have that particular issue...(and I love those Red Skull covers).

Disney Comics: They sell ok, but in general, not as fast as the superhero comics. I particularly like to get the 1st 50 (or so) issues of *Walt Disney's Comics & Stories* plus the rare issues. *Four Color* #4, 9, 29, 62 - the earliest Donald Duck *Four Colors* - always move on out, and are fun to own.

Fawcett Comics: Many of them don't sell as fast as their counterparts from DC or Timely, but they are still just cool to have, particularly the earlier Mac Raboy *Master Comics* issues #21 thru 40. What great, dramatic, striking covers those are!

Other Golden Age Companies: Centaurs (late '30s/ early '40s) sell great, are rare, and go for over *Guide*. MLJs (again, mostly early '40s) sell well and are tougher to get these days than in the past, especially the fabled 8-issue run of *Hangman Comics*.

Early appearances of Archie, Betty and Veronica, etc. are now highly desirable, and go for over *Guide*, sometimes very significantly. *Pep* #22 is Archie's first appearance, worth well over *Guide*, and very tough to find. Years ago, when I bought a 500-box collection in southern California (and on my Birthday), the only Archie title the seller avidly collected was *Jughead*.As a result, I now own *Jughead* #1-up.

Pre-Code Horror Comics: They sell well across the board and for a number of them, I must pay a premium, as these issues can go for 150- 200% of *Guide*, sometimes more. For instance, this year I sold a 9.0 copy of *Black Cat* #50 (burning away face cover) worth $4550 in *Guide* for $9000. A couple of years ago, I got a 90%+ complete collection of pre-Code Horror comics, and boy did I have fun looking at all those covers and gleefully showing them to my interested warehouse crew. I kept a few handfuls of these for myself.

EC Comics: To me, they are, overall, the "best comics ever." I just love to check out the Horror, Sci-Fi (which are sooo intelligently written, way ahead of their time, and fascinating), Crime (gripping'). My favorite is the 18-issue run of *Shock Suspenstories* - the first number of issues had one story each (4 total) of Crime, Horror, Sci-Fi, and one "human interest" story often tackling "taboo in comics" subjects, such as racism, violent patriotism, etc. Talk about "way ahead of its time."

The Silver Age

Marvel Comics: These continue to be the "Belles of The Ball." I love to buy Silver Age collections, but I especially "dig" when they have a generous amount of Marvels as they are continuous sellers. They're the main "brick 'n mortar" of the Dolgoff warehouse. I still remember buying my 1st issue of *Amazing Spider-Man* (#4) on the stands. Many of us related very much to the emotions and frailties that the characters and the alter-egos (especially Peter Parker/Spidey) felt. Being a native New Yorker, it was really cool that so many superhero Marvel '60s battles took place in the Big Apple.

The early 1960s Marvels continue to sell blazingly in all grades. Number 1 issues and first appearances all sell. Regardless of whether they are sharp, ok, or beat-up, weathered, "primitively restored" etc., they move quite well! Consequently I must pay extra-high prices for these "babies." These are the premier comics that set comicdom ablaze and ignited a world of comic book lovers!

Amazing Fantasy #15 (1st Spider-Man) continues, more than ever, to lead the pack. Every year it increases in value; and even a British edition, in Good to Very Good, sells very well. All the other keys: *Amazing Spider-Man* #1, *Fantastic Four* #1, *Journey Into Mystery* #83 (1st app Thor), *Tales Of Suspense* #39 (1st app Iron Man), *Tales To Astonish* #27 (1st Ant-Man and the issue #1s of *Avengers*, *X-Men*, *Daredevil*, *Sgt. Fury* are top sellers, no matter what the shape of the book.

Early issues (that are not #1s) sell well at *Guide* (some a bit above, some a bit below) again, in all conditions (especially *Amazing Spider-Man* and early Iron Man appearances in *Tales Of Suspense* #40 through #50) just continue to sell better and better.

For Marvels 1965 through 1971, I mostly get *Guide* in Fair to Fine, and over *Guide* if they're 9.4 to 9.8. The 1968 #1s/premiere issues go for somewhat over *Guide* in most grades.

DC Comics: *Showcase* #4 is like the *Amazing Fantasy* #15 of the DC set. They go for well over *Guide* and the value keeps on increasing. *Showcase* #22 is also very popular (I sold a brittle copy of #22 for over $800!) The other early '60s DC #1s and 1st appearances all sell well at *Guide*, and often above *Guide*. I enjoy buying DC collections as well.

Many of the DC books, were, and are, wonderful reading, with very imaginative stories. I used to subscribe in the sixties to *JLA*, and to *Adventure* (when the Legion of Super-Heroes was in it - I loved those stories!) and a good part of the memories that many of us older comics fans have is sitting back and reading those time-honored Silver Age DCs.

Batman issues sell so well that I dub them, sales-wise, "honorary Marvels." *Detective*, *Flash* and *Green Lantern* all sell solidly (and when Neal Adams did his late '60s GL/GA issues of *Green Lantern*, I must say I was enthralled with the art as well as Denny O'Neill's story-telling. Those titles sell well enough, with *Flash* sales gaining momentum lately.

Superman titles (post-Code) sales are slow, and I find that I must sell them at well below *Guide* (unless they are high grade, then that is a different story.) I still like having them in stock as we pride ourselves at gdcomics of having a broad-based "everything" stock.

Miscellaneous Silver Age: I enjoy having and being able to offer up runs of everything from *Captain Atom*, *Blue Beetle*, and *Thunder Agents*, to *Archie*, *Strange Suspense Stories*, and *Donald Duck*. They generally don't fly outta here, but they are in my mind, essential to a well-rounded and cool stock of comics.

<u>The Bronze Age (1970s thru about 1981)</u>

Bronze Age comics are increasingly popular as more and more folks who read them as they grew up have "come of age." 1970s books have so much good and interesting reading, from *Warlock* by Jim Starlin to those heady *Man-Thing* comics, to the Neal Adams *Batman* and *Detective*, and those "fun 'n funky" *Prez* mini-series, as well as *Rima the Jungle Girl* and those Fourth World Kirby books (*Forever People*, *New Gods*, etc.!) Although I have (estimated) over 100,000 Bronze Age books, I still like obtaining collections of those, as they fill in runs, various conditions of comics, etc.

Bronze Keys: Leading the pack is *Incredible Hulk* #181 (1st full app Wolverine.) I sold a CGC 9.2 for $4250. Then there's *Amazing Spider-Man* #129 (1st app Punisher), a CGC 9.2 of which I sold for $2100. Also "burning up the airwaves" with desirability are: *Iron Man* #55 (1st Thanos), *Batman* #232 (1st Ra's al Ghul), *Batman* #251 (that great Joker cover!), *Werewolf By Night* #32 (1st Moon Knight), *Green Lantern* #87 (1st John Stewart GL), *Hero For Hire* #1 (1st Luke Cage) and much, much more.

I always am very pleased to see a collection with these Bronze Age keys. They definitely make a collection one that I'm quite enthusiastic to assess, and to potentially purchase.

Bronze Non-keys: Just like with the '60s comics, many of the long term characters sell well (especially *Amazing Spider-Man*, *Batman*, and *X-Men* #94 thru 143. Those books always fly! Many of the discontinued titles (e.g. *Man-Thing*, *Shadow*, *Nova*, *Stalker*, etc.) sell more slowly than I'd like, but again, they are an essential part of the GDC well-rounded inventory.

<u>The Modern Comics (1980s thru the 2000's)</u>

I am into stocking the newer comics, as yet another part of my "u-can buy it at gdcomics" inventory/idea. I have enthusiastic, younger crew members at The Warehouse who know and keep up with these comics. Someday, I'll have to read them as I hear so many good things. When I purchase a collection, of course I take these "higher value" recent comics into account. For example, *New Mutants* #87 (1st Cable), *New Mutants* #98 (1st Deadpool); *Batman Adventures* #12 (1st Harley Quinn); *Saga* #1; *Walking Dead* #1 through #10 and #19; *Swamp Thing* #37 (1st Hellblazer); *Amazing Spider-Man* #361 (1st Venom); #252 and #300; *Rachel Rising* #1; *NYX* #3; *Before Watchmen: Dr. Manhattan* #4; *X-Men* #266 (1st Gambit); and much, much more. I take into account even the non-expensive "recents" when I purchase a collection.

Original Art: This year (2017), I've gotten in more of it than I have in a long time, and the variety I got in is "something else" and cool. Some examples:

- Over 300 '80s-'90s original covers
- *Captain Action* pages by Gil Kane
- Early (1930s) Thimble Theatre Popeye - 2 dailies
- A number of 1950s Dell original covers (including Walt Kelly Pogo)
- '60s & '70s signed Kirby pages (Kamandi, Thor, etc.)
- Recent *Defenders* pages

I enjoy purchasing all kinds of art - from Krazy Kat 1930s to Archie 1990s, from Ditko and Kirby '60s and '70s pages, to *Prince Valiant* 1940s Sundays. And I have a modest, but "into it" art collection.

Well, "that's all folks" for now. Comics Forever!!

Walter Durajlija and Jay Halstead Big B Comics/International Comic Exchange (ICE)

I'm so excited to be contributing to the 48th *Overstreet Comic Book Price Guide*. The 48th issue! That's a lot of *Guides*! I hope you take the time to learn from and enjoy this year's edition. *The Guide* remains an indispensable resource for all comic book collectors. Your local comic book shop remains the best place to go snag one so hurry on in. I'd like to thank all the advisors for sharing their views and insights in these very useful Market Reports. A special thank you to the stellar Overstreet team on yet another great edition of *The Guide*.

This year I'd like to introduce Jay Halstead, the General Manager of the International Comic Exchange (ICE), as a contributor to this Market Report. (2nd half of this report).

Please visit the ICE website www.icomicexchange.com and the Big B Comics website www.bigbcomics.com to learn more about our businesses. We hope you'll find both sites inviting and informative and we would appreciate any feedback!

New comic sales were down in 2017. There seemed to be a general malaise in the publishing side of the hobby. Customer reaction to Marvel's wholesale changing of their characters was not received well and that was reflected in our shops with too many cancelled subscriptions. Marvel's Legacy initiative has the potential to reverse some of the damage done. In the end it will come down to consistent quality storytelling delivered on time at price points that are a fair value to the customers. DC fared better in 2017 with all things Batman ruling the roost. It's incredible how many great stories keep springing from the Batman character, as he's an inexhaustible source of great stories and great villains too!

Our 2 retail stores, one in Hamilton, Ontario and one in Niagara Falls Ontario, have both had to make adjustments to deal with the decrease in new comic and graphic novel sales. At this stage it would be easy to retreat and order only what we know will sell but we all know that would be a mistake and lead to even more sales drops. We continue to order and support a wide variety of titles and we position ourselves with good back stock of titles that we can promote and get behind, titles that deliver quality to our customers. In both shops we've also put extra focus on our back issue selection. The secondary market for comics continues to show strength at our shops.

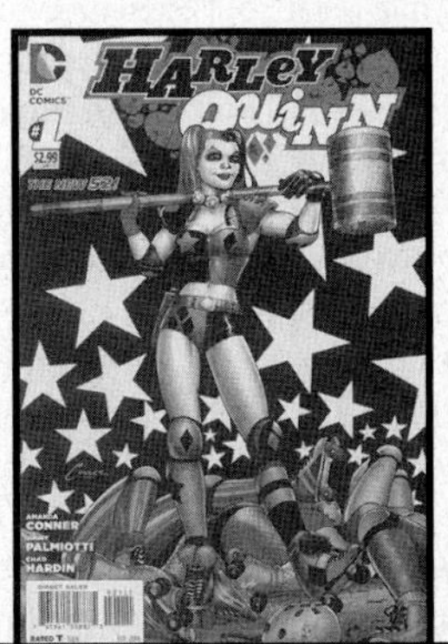

Key issues of ***Harley Quinn*** *sell well from the "Hot Wall of Comics".*

The Big B Comics shops are home to a very active back issue collecting community. One of the more popular features at our shops is the "Hot Wall of Comics". This is a place where we'll throw up ungraded copies of comics like *Amazing Spider-Man* #300, #361, *New Mutants* #87, #98, J. Scott Campbell covers, key Harley Quinn issues etc. We price these reasonably at or very close to current market and most of the books don't last more than a few days before selling. There has been insatiable demand for books like *ASM* #300 throughout all of 2017 especially in the affordable mid grades. For us the bestselling back issue titles continue to be *Amazing Spider-Man* and *Batman*.

We've seen a drop off in large collections being offered to us. I'm not sure if it was just an off year or whether the Bell Curve has moved though on people with old collections or whether it's that most people choose to sell their own stuff through the multiple social media platforms available. Let's hope it's the first of these scenarios and that we'll see some nice collections start coming in.

The best collection that walked into our shop in 2017 had some nice high grade late Silver Age and early Bronze Age. The highlights included a VF+ *House of Secrets* #92 and a VF *Amazing Spider-Man* #50. Other notable non-graded pick-ups included high grade copies of *The Spirit* #22 (CDN Edition) and *Brenda Starr* #14 both of which were very hot books in 2017.

Here are some raw ungraded books we sold over 2017 (USD$):

House of Secrets #92 VF+ - $1,600
Amazing Spider-Man #50 VF - $850
Amazing Spider-Man #300 FN/VF - 175
Batman #171 FN- $225
Strange Tales #110 VG+ - $1,500
Incredible Hulk #181 VG/FN but with coupon out - $525

I think the bargain grades for 2018 will be the mid grades. Over the past few years we're seen prices run up in the low end copies (just have to own an issue) and the high end "bragging rights" copies. This has left solid VG- to FN+ copies seem like relative bargains. I'm calling on these grades of most of the heavily traded key issues to see some appreciation.

"Canadian Whites" continues to be a passion of mine but I'll send you to read the excellent reports submitted by Ivan Kocmarek and Stephen Lipson. I can say that supply, or more correctly the lack of supply, continues to be the main stumbling block to building a wider collecting base for the Whites.

I continue to blog on the comic book fan website www.comicbookdaily.com (CBD). My *Undervalued Spotlight* is still an exercise I enjoy doing every week. Comic Book Daily's other contributors, Scott VanDerploeg, Mike Huddleston, Dennis DePues and Ivan Kocmarek all make the site well worth some regular visits. These guys all bring supreme knowledge of our hobby and some great insights.

This is where I'll turn things over to Jay Halstead who runs the International Comic Exchange (ICE).

Greetings! My name is Jay and I'm one of the new guys on the block taking over as general manager of the International Comic Exchange in January of 2017. I've got lots to talk about regarding sales and what's of interest this year but first I'll start with a little about me.

I started collecting comics in the mid 1980s when I was about 11. I remember fondly collecting all 3 Spidey titles at the time, and of course Batman. I remember it was years before I ever found a copy of *Web of Spider-Man* #7 (Hulk cover)-- Ah the days before the internet and even realizing there were, gasp, pull lists??? At the age of 15 I set up at my first flea market, by my late teens I was a regular and I was hooked. We've all come a long way since then but we still have so much further to go. I absolutely look forward to the challenges and opportunities to come in 2018 and beyond!

Another year has come and gone and some things just never change. The New England Patriots are still good, my Montreal Canadians still suck and *Amazing Fantasy* #15 is still the book most collectors/investors drool over! Over at ICE, we set numerous records on *Amazing Fantasy* #15 (I believe we sold 4 copies) and quite honestly, we could have sold many more copies if we had them. Personally I don't think we'll ever see another Marvel Key with this type of demand, and what really amounts to this type of love—people young and old, absolutely love Spidey! Even with the horrific Andrew Garfield pulling the mighty Spidey into the depths of, well, you know where, Spidey is still the king of the hill and seems impervious to bad reviews and bad publicity. *Amazing Fantasy* #15 is basically the #1 Holy Grail in comicdom by default because the only 2 books that "out Grail" it, *Action Comics* #1 and *Detective Comics* #27, are simply unattainable to almost all of us. *Amazing Fantasy* #15 thus becomes the best book still in play.

Even though Spidey seems impervious to lackluster representations in other media I can't say the same for everyone else. I've noticed some relevant books spiked after Disney announced their takeover of Fox, these runs on *Fantastic Four* and *X-Men* issues were natural market reactions to the optimism that Disney's future efforts on the properties bring to the table. I've also notices the opposite market reactions when once expected future projects don't get realized (Inhumans). These happenings tell me that media news still plays a very important speculative role in determining value. The unanswerable question is how good/or bad these future projects will be and what lasting effect they will have on value. My advice is to tread carefully and don't knee jerk react to the latest news because that is what everybody else is doing.

So what's hot and what's not? I'll start with the not-hot. How's about Silver Age and Bronze Age Marvel run books? Yikes! We get those from consignors and have to explain that yes, GPA says this, but most are trending lower and if you want to move them we have to price them lower. These are great books, parts of storylines that went on for decades (before the new Marvel today that has almost no connection to the '60s-'70s-'80s stuff). But as each calendar year passes, more and more collectors/investors continue to search for unique Golden Age and Silver/Bronze/Copper Age keys instead. So many books from this amazing hobby of ours go ignored, and sadly I don't think this is going to change in the near future. People coming into the hobby today (just take a few minutes to go up and down Facebook or Instagram) are buying one big book, not a run of say, *Avengers* from #65-99. There will always be core collectors, but it continues to shrink every year.

The demand and desire to own the best of the best has never been greater. Important key issues continue to set records every time there is an auction. Also, books that haven't been seen for a while go quickly when priced with a reasonable (although record), buy it now prices. Great books priced well will sell, and they'll sell all day long. People email me or drop in daily wanting advice on how to invest in comics. These are the same people that used to invest with their banks and brokers. I don't want to tell you that buying a comic is a better investment than something you can get from the bank, but I've seen more and more people adding comics to their investing portfolios. The year-over-year gains on high end, quality older material has been phenomenal. Who would have thought that you'd have to spend $50,000 just for a super low grade *Detective Comics* #31 say, 10 years ago? How about the continual up-tick on books like *Spirit* #22, *Brenda Starr* #14 and *Pep* #34? I can go on and on about books that so many of us believed had hit their high, and then they go on to shatter that high the next go-around. These are books that at one point were barely worth more than their surrounding issues, and it's with these types of books that opportunities abound.

Here are some of International Comics Exchange (ICE) highlight sales for 2017:

- *Amazing Fantasy* CBCS 2.0 $11,000
- *X-Men* #1 CGC 9.0 $37, 500
- *X-Men* #94 CGC 9.8 $14,000
- *Adventure Comics* #247 CGC 6.5 $6,100
- *Flash Comics* #86 CGC 8.5 $24,000
- *Lobo* (DELL, 1965) #1 CGC 9.8 $7,000

That *Lobo* sale is especially a good one, as this goes right with what I've been saying! This is an under-rated, under-appreciated book with phenomenal upside, as it's the first African American to headline his own comic book wherein he plays the hero! What's mainly ignored is that it came out nearly a year before *Fantastic Four* #52 hit the stands (first Black Panther). We actually have sold 4 copies of *Lobo* #1 in 2017, but that 9.8 was an eye opener!

Lastly, I know it's been over-stated in these reports year after year, but you can never go wrong buying what you truly love and have that desire to own. I've known a good many friends who have lived by this rule and they are now sitting on substantial collections.

Well there you have Jay's first market report, drop him a line to talk some comics.

I'd like to take this opportunity to thank all the people I work with at Big B Comics, we have the best team in the business!

Ken Dyber
Cloud 9 Comics

Hello friends, readers and collectors. I'm the owner and founder of Cloud 9 Comics. Cloud 9 Comics has a brick & mortar store in Portland, OR which is open 7 days a week from 11am – 7pm, a website with thousands of vintage comics for sale, an eBay store (eBay ID: cloudninecomics), as well as a national presence at conventions around the country. We sell Golden – Modern/Renaissance Age comics back issues, new comics, graphic novels/TPBs, Funko POPs and Magic/Pokémon cards in our store. At conventions and on our website we specialize in selling key issues/1st appearances, as well as the occasional slab or two (although most of our sales are raw comics). Come by and visit our store sometime at 2621 SE Clinton St. Portland, OR 97202. You can also follow us via social media at: Facebook: cloudninecomics or Twitter at: cloud9_comics. You can also contact me directly at: ken@cloudninecomics.com.

Golden Age: Overall selling was very strong this past year. My Golden Age section is almost wiped out at present. Good Girl books in particular are very hot at the moment, with classic covers and Matt Baker covers selling for nosebleed prices. Some Good Girl books need major adjustments upwards in pricing in the *Guide*. *Nellie The Nurse* #1 is only $900 in NM- in *Guide*. I think this book needs to move upwards 400% across all grades to just get it started. It's a very tough book to find in any grade with the CGC Census at only 14 graded copies. Three recent GPA reported sales of $699 in 5.5, $309 in 3.5 & $275 in 3.0 all are 4x *Guide* or better % wise. Also, Heritage just auctioned off the *Patsy Walker* #1 Mile High copy, and... this sale kind of blew my mind, as it's not even her 1st appearance (which is *Miss America Comics* #2 and almost impossible to find). It went for a whopping $28,680!! Yes, I know it's the Mile High, and a tough black cover, but this was one of the more jaw-dropping sales I've seen in a while, especially for a Good Girl book. There are 17 books on the CGC Census for this one, so a tad bit more, but still very scare book. A recent CGC 4.0 went for $1643 and a CGC 3.5 for $1047. These sales are like 8x *Guide*, with NM- only being at $1500. I know the *Guide* tends to be conservative, but this is just absolutely ridiculous, and frankly insulting to the comic community that the NM- listing is less than what 4.0's are going for. I'd conservatively say this one needs to go up 6x *Guide* in all grades to get it remotely close to present market. Both of these books are from 1945 too, so they're very early Good Girl books, as most of them tend to be from the later '40s, not mid 1940s.

I think part of this feeding frenzy may also be due to how crazy some of the Horror books have been selling, and it's making the classic GGA covers look dirt cheap in comparison. *Phantom Lady* #17 has taken a large leap forward with very strong sales such as: CGC 8.0 for $15,535, CGC 7.5 for $14,340 and a CGC 6.0 for a whopping $9750! The *Guide* should increase 100% in 2.0-6.0 grades and at least 50% for 8.0 & higher. One title to keep your eye out for that's still a bit under the radar is *Junie Prom*, a 7-issue series. Issues #1 and #6 seem to be the most sought after covers, but there are a couple other pretty saucy covers in the short run. The entire run in *Guide* needs to increase 400% for all books in all grades with a large % increase for these 2 issues. *Junior Comics* continues to be one of the toughest GGA runs to put together with every cover being pretty awesome. Some of these stories are just outrageous with GGA throughout every issue. The entire run needs at least a 50% increase in all grades for all issues.

Joker Comics from 1942 needs price increases across the board. I suggested a 25-50% increase in all prices for all the GGA covers as these are very tough to find and always sell well above Guide. *Joker Comics* #2 is a major sleeper key issue being the 1st Tessie The Typist. This book needs a 200-300% increase in *Guide* in all grades! *Cindy* #37 is selling for huge prices, usually 3-4x *Guide*, so *Guide* prices should increase in all grade by 200% to get close to accurate. Also, *Georgie* #25 is a great painted cover with the Marvel circular logo on it, and is the cherry in that run. *Guide* is still very low/incorrect on this book. A 6.5 sold via a Herritage auction for around $1000 I believe. *Guide* is like $150. How about a 500% increase in all grades in *Guide* on that book just to start as this is a book I see even less then *Cindy* #37.

Sun Girl #1 is a sleeper key issue that isn't per se a traditional GGA type book, but certainly appeals to those collectors. Her 1st appearance is *Sun Gir*l #1, and the *Guide* needs to say as much as CGC and CBCS labels do. The Jon Berk sale of *Sun Girl* #1 CGC 9.0 for $5400 was at a price that many didn't see coming. That's over double *Guide* and the latest CGC 7.0 sale for $2500 is 150% above *Guide*. So, I think this book needs a fairly large upward movement. I recommend a 50% increase in all grades.

Rusty Comics (Timely) is an undervalued series in *Guide*, and should double in all grades in *Guide*. Issue #14 (Beach cover) seems to be the cover most in demand, with a CGC 3.0 selling in Sept. for $298! *Guide* value for a 3.0 is $39 (that's 7x *Guide* ladies & gentlemen!). I think *Overstreet* might want to make an adjustment upward on this book in all grades quite substantially more then my 100% across the board mark up for this title on this particular book. Just a suggestion.

Tales of Suspense #1, *Tales To Astonish* #1 and *Journey Into Mystery* #1 are all selling quite strong and need to move upwards in *Guide* considerably. I recommend a 50% increase in pricing across the board to make the *Guide* more in line with the present market.

The Phantom Stranger #1 (from 1952 – 1st appearance) needs a dramatic price increase in *Guide*. I suggest 100% increase in all grades. All issues in this scarce run need 50% increases with this issue doubling just to get it close to what sales are going for.

Silver Age: Has been selling quite strong this past year. I am the lowest inventory wise I've ever been on not only key issues, but also filling/run issues. I'm slowly restocking, but I've had several customers clear me out of many good titles. There was a point this past year where I was sold out of *Amazing Spider-Man* issues #1-30 (all copies, any grade). That's never happened to me before.

A few books of note that need adjustments in *Guide* are *Strange Adventures* #180 & #187. Both issues have really taken off and need major adjustments upwards in the *Guide*. Issue #180 (1st Animal Man) should go up at least 50% in all grades with a suggested NM- price of $1200. Also, issue

#187 (1st Enchantress) needs its own line listing, and needs a dramatic increase in pricing across the board with a suggested NM- price of $1600 (It's currently $95, which is rather embarrassing that the *Guide* is off by 1800%!?. Last reported GPA sale was in 2015 for $1750, so $1600 seems conservative to me).

Bronze Age: *Ms. Marvel* #9 (1st Deathbird) needs its own line listing with a NM- suggested price of $35. She's a great character, and if you haven't read Brubaker "Rise and Fall of the Shi'ar Empire" in which she's an integral part, I high suggest checking it out. *Hero For Hire* #10 is the 1st appearance of Mr. Death and should be noted so in the *Guide* with a separate line listing of $50 for NM- (or $5 greater than the books around it). *Power Man* #19 is the 1st appearance of Cotton-Mouth and should be noted in *Guide* with a suggested line listing of $60 in NM-.

Shade The Changing Man #1 (his 1st appearance) seems like a good buy at only $20 in NM- in *Guide*. This price should go up however, and I'd recommend $35 for NM-.

Captain America issues across the board need to be raised in *Guide* here, especially when you consider their pricing in regards to other Marvel titles. *Captain America* #149 (not a key issue) as an example is $25 in NM-, where as *Avengers* #86 (also not a key issue) is $90 in NM-, both issues are out within the same 12 month period. I suggest a 40% increase in NM- with appropriate raises in the coinciding lower grade ranges. *Incredible Hulk* issues also from this time period (early Bronze Age) should also go up in *Guide* across the board. I suggest a 25% increase here in NM-.

Copper Age: *Uncanny X-Men* #148 is the 1st appearance of Caliban and needs to have the *Guide* say this. It should get its own line listing with a NM- suggested price of $22. The *Marvel Graphic Novels* from the 1982 series all need to go up in *Guide*. I suggest a 25% increase across the board for all of them in NM-, with a few exceptions needing to go up further. *MGN* #1 Death of Captain Marvel should be $100 in NM- & #4 (1st New Mutants) should be $175 in NM-. Also, #17 Revenge of the Living Monolith should get its own line listing as it's the very 1st brief appearance of Apocalypse. I suggest $35 for NM- to start with. *New Mutants* #26 (1st Legion needs an upward adjustment in *Guide* with the TV on). I suggest a NM- of $35. Also, *New Mutants* #87 (1st Cable) has started selling well again, and needs an upward adjustment in *Guide* to at least $150 if not $175 for NM-. *Primer* #2 (1st Grendel) has picked up considerable interest. I had 3 copies in this year, and all 3 sold VERY quickly at above *Guide* prices. Slabbed 9.2s are selling for around $300 (*Guide* is currently $190), with 8.5s even going for around $200. Raw copies are selling for close to these #'s for me. I suggested *Guide* moving this book up to $275 in *Guide* in NM-, as it hasn't had any significant increase in *Guide* for years, and there are now proven sales that would agree with this price suggestion.

Amazing Spider-Man is hot (again)! The Venom movie staring Tom Hardy has a lot of people excited. *ASM* #300 needs a dramatic jump in *Guide* (really for the 1st time, as it's always been going up fairly steadily). I suggest $475 for NM- with CGC 9.8s selling for just under $2000 at the time of this writing. *ASM* #316 is a classic cover from the Copper Age, and arguably the coolest Venom cover ever. This one should also go up in *Guide*. Also, Carnage has been announced as the villain in the movie, and thus, *ASM* #361s are hot. This book needs a major jump in *Guide*, as NM- copies are selling for just under $100, with graded 9.8s going around $350. I suggest $100 for NM- in *Guide*, and for #344 (1st Cletus Kassady - who becomes Carnage) a price of $50 for NM-. A couple other Spidey key issues that need their own line listing in *Guide* are #210 1st Madame Web. I regularly sell out of this issue, sometimes almost as soon as I put it out for sale. I recommend a NM-/9.2 price of $30. Also, issue #212 1st Hydro-Man, is another book that I am constantly sold out of. I recommend a NM-/9.2 price of $25.

Booster Gold #1 continues to sell briskly when I get them in. *Guide* is currently $22 in NM- and needs to come up a good bit with CGC 9.2s selling around $80 and 9.8s going for $200. I suggest a new NM- listing of $50. Also, #6 his origin issue should get its own line listing of $10 in NM-.

Watchmen comics continue to sell well. I keep finding myself out of all issues with it harder to restock high grade issues in particular. *Guide* currently has #1 at $60 for NM-, which I think is a good price and should stay the same, however, issues 2-12 are at $18 for NM-, which is quite low compared with #1, and they all sell well. I suggest an increase of 2-12 to $35 for NM- to reduce the spread, as high grade copies continue to sell above *Guide* for me.

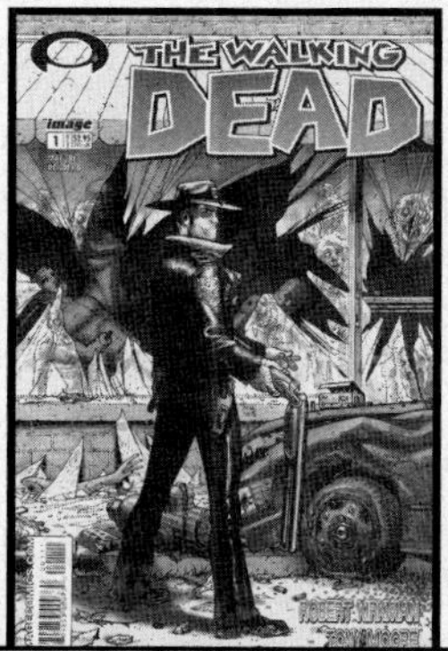

Modern Age: *Bone* #1 continues to be one of the hardest comics to find in any grade from this time period. Beat up copies raw are going for $200-$500 (which seems to be the entry point for this book). I just bought a collection that had a raw VG- copy, and I kept it for myself, as it's the 1st copy I've ever had offered to me. I suggest a NM- price of $900, which should probably go up sooner than later.

The Walking Dead #1 could be considered the start of a period we could call The Renaissance Age.

Renaissance Age: For those of you who haven't read previous markets reports I've done, I now feel we are finished with the Modern Age of comics and into a new time period, one, which I call the Renaissance Age. I feel this new time period started with the release of *Walking Dead* #1, and shows a major pivot in the buying patterns of comic readers into more non-superhero comics. This point will be further proven a bit farther in my market report when I discuss my stores best-selling trades.

A key issue I think could have a lot of potential is *Invincible Iron Man* #9 the 1st full appearance of Riri Williams (the new female Iron Man). I suggest a NM- price listing in *Guide* of $20, but this is one to keep your eye on. If anyone out there has a chance to get their hands on a *Zombie Tramp* #1 hold on to it, as it's jumping into my Modern/Renaissance Age Top 25 at #7 at a suggested NM- line listing of $1000, with #2 suggested at $500 & #3 suggested at $350. This is a 3 issue self-published series on SR Distro from 2010 by Dan Medoza (now being released by Action Lab). These 3 books need to be added to the *Overstreet Price Guide*, as they are not even listed in it.

Saga #1 on Image continues to sell almost as fast as I can get it in stock. Raw NM- copies are selling for around $250 for me, but almost any copy sells for $175 - $200 in worn condition. This is my #1 selling TPB in my store (by a lot). Our store has a Top 50 best-selling TPB/Graphic Novel section. We only include the 1st volume here if it's a multi volume series (as per se a one off), otherwise, *Saga* #2-7 would all be in the Top 50 as well most likely.

Here's our store's top 20 selling TPBs (again only Vol. 1s if multi volumes): 1. *Saga*. 2. *Paper Girls*. 3. *Rick & Morty*. 4. *Lumberjanes*. 5. *Deadly Class*. 6. *Monstress*. 7. *Bitch Planet*. 8. *Preacher*. 9. *The Flintstones*. 10. *Low*. 11. *Y The Last Man*. 12. *Sandman*. 13. *Darth Vader*. 14. *Pretty Deadly*. 15. *Wicked + The Divine*. 16. *Adventure Time*. 17. *East of West*. 18. *Ms. Marvel*. 19. *Black Science*. 20. *Rat Queens*. That breaks down to 11 on Image, 1 on Oni, 2 on Boom, 4 on DC/Vertigo and 2 on Marvel. Yes, it does help that Image is based in Portland, and has a large amount of their creators based here, but then again, Dark Horse is also based here, and they have none on our top 20 (Heck, half of their *Hellboy* series aren't even in print! Which just boggles my mind considering there have been very successful *Hellboy* movies, and there is a reboot in the works with the actor that plays Sheriff Hopper on *Stranger Things* to be the new Hellboy).

Marvel just doesn't seem to care about new comics anymore, as they can't market them correctly, some are just horribly done, and they seem to reboot titles too frequently. *Ms. Marvel* is the only Marvel super hero title on this list, she's literally just barely there at #20. Of DC's 4 titles listed here, none are super hero related, and the only relatively new one is *The Flintstones* (which really is brilliant and should have become an ongoing series instead of just a 12 issue mini-series). Now, I only have one store (and a relatively new one at that, having just finished the 3rd year being open), and Portland is definitely not a typical U.S. city for a variety of reasons, so I don't know if what sells in my shop is selling the same in other stores, but I think many of us who have stores can agree, that we really need Marvel to start caring about new comics again. Yes, new comics do not create billions of dollars like the movies do, but comic book stores are the origin place for most people who get into comics, and, eventually spend their hard earned dollars on movies, toys, cards, games, and other swag. Marvel, please stop raising your comic prices ($5 for new comics is too much). If they are $3, go to $3.25, if they are $4, go to $4.25.

OK, nuff about that, lastly, for those of you that have read my reports in the part, you know that I'm pushing for Overstreet to include in the front of the *Guide* a Copper/Modern/Renaissance Age Top 25 as this is what a majority of people buy/sell/collect. As I've previously stated, I'm not including a majority of the variants that get offered annually, as many go way up, then way down over time, so the only ones that are listed here are ones that have held strong at current prices for years.

1. *Gobbledygook* #1: $6800
2. *Teenage Mutant Ninja Turtles* #1: $5400
3. *Gobbledygook* #2: $4000
4. *Walking Dead* #1: $1700
5. *Rick & Morty* #1 1 in 50 Variant: $1500
6. *Albedo* #2: $1200
7. *Miracleman* #1 Gold Edition: $1100
8. *Zombie Tramp* #1 $1000
9. *Bone* #1: $900
10. *Batman* #608 Retailer Incentive Edition: $800
11. *Batman Adventures* #12: $500
12. *Vampirella* #113: $500
13. *Zombie Tramp* #2: $500
14. *Amazing Spider-Man* #300: $475
15. *Miracleman* #1 Blue Edition: $450
16. *Venom Lethal Protector* #1 Black Cover Printing Error: $400
17. *Walking Dead* #2: $400
18. *Zombie Tramp* #3: $350
19. *New Mutants* #98: $325
20. *Primer* #2: $275
21. *Walking Dead* #19: $260
22. *Chew* #1: $250
23. *Y: The Last Man* #1: $250
24. *Peter Panzerfaust* #1: $230
25. *Saga* #1: $225
26. *Walking Dead* #3: $225
27. *Knights of the Dinner Table* #1: $200
28. *Walking Dead* #27: $200
29. *Spawn* #1 Black and White Edition: $200
30. *Invincible* #1: $200
31. *Grendel* #1: $175
32. *Cry For Dawn* #1: $175

Thanks to everyone who came to our booth at a con, our new store in Portland, as well as our website in 2017.

Daniel Ertle
CBCS - Modern Expert

As I have said the last few years, I have somewhat of a unique perspective on the happenings in the world of modern comics. As the modern expert at CBCS I can see the trends reflected in what comes across my desk that ranges from 1975 to present. This last year seemed a little different than the previous year with movies having less of an affect on submissions, at least in terms of moderns, with the exception of *Star Wars* books. We are still receiving a bevy of variant titles and, in what seems like a resurgence of '90s gimmicks, most of them are foil or chrome. Of course we still see books that have become staples of modern comics being sent in at a pretty standard rate.

Last year we had movies like *Batman V Superman* and *Civil War* which had a noticeable effect on the submissions. This year however, movies like *Justice League* and *Guardians of the Galaxy Vol. 2* did not foster the same number in submission increase; we did see a minimal increase of books containing the original Guardians team. We also got a short uptick in Punisher books coming in, this I presume to be from the television series that was released recently. As mentioned previously, one franchise not suffering from consumer fatigue is *Star Wars*. With new movies coming out yearly, we are still getting heaps of *Star Wars* related books from all eras of *Star Wars* comics. And of course the Infinity Gauntlet series has always been a very popular submission but it does seem to be ramping up a bit as we get closer to the release of the *Avengers: Infinity War* movie. As for the future effect of movie and TV releases on modern comic grading submissions, who knows what will happen with news of a possible Disney buy out of FOX on the horizon. If the buyout occurs, this would allow Marvel Studios the rights to use the X-Men and other franchises. At any rate, if there is a buyout and I do notice higher submission rates, I'll be sure to mention it in the next market report.

The most popular submissions this year in terms of moderns do seem to be variants. Almost every book now has a few variant covers to accompany it on Wednesday plus even more variants for specific conventions. This has been a popular concept for a while now, but what makes this year seem different is the amount of gimmick covers that are coming out. Chrome and foil has made a comeback this year in a big way and I can't leave out Lenticulars making their return this year as well. We see this a lot from Counterpoint Comics. They are already notorious for their cover swipes on books like Dead Pooh, Hardlee Thin, and Notti & Nyce but on top of having a ton of cover swipes, they also get chromium editions. DC seems to have doubled down on their chromium covers this year as well. While they are very popular and get submitted a lot, they are unfortunately easy to damage and display fingerprints very well. In the case of Marvel, it's their Lenticular covers that have come out recently. These are always sturdy covers that tend to grade well. With as '90s as this all sounds, it will soon be culminated in Valiant's *Quantum and Woody* Most Variant Cover of All Time. This book seems to feature as many gimmicks as they could fit on the one book including genuine '90s foil. This is going to be a joy to input when we undoubtedly get some submitted to us.

We of course still get submitted to us books that are staples of modern comic collecting. Plenty of *Wolverine* limited series, *X-Men* and *Spider-Man* of all types. Also, books like *Walking Dead* and *Spawn* never seem to go out of fashion. I did report last year that we were seeing less of *Deadpool* and more of *Harley*. While this is still true, I am starting to see a downturn in *Batman Adventures* #12 submissions. This isn't to say that few are being submitted, but rather that so many were being submitted previously that it seems to have leveled out a bit. That being said it still remains one of our most popular modern submissions. One thing that we have changed at CBCS that affects these "staples" is that we now list whether a book is a Newsstand or Direct Edition on books from 1977-2000. This change affects a huge portion of books that are submitted to us and is something that people have been asking for for a long time. Some people are so excited about this change that they are sending their books in for a reholder so they can have Newsstand or Direct Edition listed on their label. This change mostly applies to Marvel, DC, Archie and some Image books but a few other publishers were making this distinction at the time as well.

Overall this was another solid year for moderns at CBCS. I get to see a variety of comics and I also get to see the trends happening in real time. We will all see if next year brings back the movie influence on comic collecting in moderns and how Disney/Marvel handles the X-Men and other series they might acquire. Another thing to look at in the upcoming year is if publishers continue to produce covers featuring gimmicks that were once popular in the '90s and how fans react to them if they do. Will we see the continued growth in gimmicks and will it reach '90s levels? Or will it fade away in replacement of some new variant fad? With all that said, I hope everyone continues to enjoy collecting comics and I hope to see a growth in readership all around. Happy hunting.

D'Arcy Farrell
Pendragon Comics

Modern Back Issue Sales: Marvel's Legacy started people thinking of the past 30 years. Marvel just moved on from its bad MARVEL NOW storylines and second *Secret Wars* (also bad), to its recent reincarnation, LEGACY. This is an ok thing, IF Marvel just sticks with it and makes ok stories. Numbering its whole universe as if none of the inbetween volumes ever restarted at #1 is a good move. This has affected back issue sales somewhat as collectors of recent history, now have a reason to connect it all. Lets hope Marvel can be original with its stories and stop chasing DC.

Marvels movies continue box office success, and this also helps grow the fanbase. What Marvel lacks in comic stories, connecting storylines (DC's greatest strength) and originality, their movies are all geared towards a future Infinity/Thanos epic conclusion.

DC is having trouble with its movies. Not that they are

bad. But audiences are craving less serious, more comical styles. DC movies are not for the same fanbase as Marvel.

In relating this to comic sales, DC's back issues are strong nonetheless. *Teen Titans* in the 1980s, *Deathstroke*, early Vertigo runs, anything Wonder Woman and Batman have been strong all year long.

Indy's biggest sales are Dark Horse *Star Wars* everything. So many first appearances that will eventually payoff. Valiant is also strong, great writing in 1990s just cant be ignored.

Bronze-Copper Age Sales: DC always wins this, as this is where the market's most undervalued, low printed items lay. Marvel at this time was topdog, but so was its printruns. Always in the limelight and in demand, Marvel values on back issues are rarely undervalued.

What shocked me this year, was the rise in demand for funnies and Archies. Anything made by companies Harvey, Archie, Whitman, and Gold Key. The demand of these companies are also in Silver Age, as many are still so cheap.

Silver Age Sales: Supergirl, Wonder Woman, Zatanna, Batgirl. These DC gals beat all in sales with the exception of Batman. DC super heroines/villainesses of all names have huge demand.

Catwoman is getting more deserved attention due to the Bat-date in recent new comics. Zatanna is so under-appreciated, but people have been taking notice of this mystic wonder. Any key, early, or important issues are being scooped up. *JLA* tapered off from last year's high, but its still so important a title, and undervalued, it still should be invested in.

Marvel sales are always good as it was Marvel's only time of originality and its beginnings. Thank you Steve Ditko and Jack "King" Kirby for all your creations of Marvel. Very little editing, if any, was ever needed for these geniuses.

New Comic Releases Of 2017: DC ended the year on high high sales of *Batman: White Knight*, Batman Metal series and all its one-shots, especially *Man Who Laughs*. *Mister Miracle* and the other Kirby revivals were a nice surprise. Totally unexpected, *Mister Miracle* sold very high by year's end. Batman's date with Catwoman was huge as well.

Biggest 2017 summer sale was DC's Push the Button! The long series, *Doomsday Clock*, about to come out will most likely be the top 2018 seller, in mid run as you read this.

Marvel fell pretty flat. Spinning out of a bad 2016 of *Secret Wars* and Marvel Now, it started to turn around once Legacy started. Logan being alive in *Marvel Legacy* one-shot is being unravelled now as I write this. Once this is printed, we will all know how he is back. Let's hope Marvel doesnt do the typical bad rebirth it's famous for.

Indies.... what shone to me? These companies are on an upswing: Titan, Boom!, Joe Books, Aftershock and Valiant. Titan keeps making interesting mature comics with short runs. Sometimes novel or TV/movie based, or Horror, Sci-fi etc. Much like what Dark Horse used to be, but even better. Titan constantly acquires new licenses for new product.

Boom! and Boom! Kids had decent sales and improved overall. Joe Books keeps putting out comics for younger fans like 3-8 year olds whereas most companies totally ignore them (DC has some decent kid books like *Teen Titans Go!* and the DC Super Hero Girl trades). Aftershock has nice cutting edge horror. Valiant constantly puts out a great product, give it a chance.

Sales decreased for me in Dynamite, Dark Horse and Avatar. It's either repetitious or less titles being made.

Image sales for the most part only exist as everyone is buying #1s hoping to score the next *Walking Dead*. So many titles are short lived, most never read, a bit of a glut.

This can be proven simply by looking at comparing issue #1 with #2,3,4,5 – a good title doesn't decrease much if at all. *Batman: White Knight* and the DC Metals are an example where the #2,3,4s have higher numbers than the #1.

Trades and Hardcovers To Read: Best value for the money are the DC collections of Golden Age Superman, Wonder Woman and the like. Also *From Hell* and anything written by Jeff Lemire. If you want serious, non-hero stuff, try anything done by Vertigo like *Swamp Thing*, *Sandman*, *Y: the Last Man*, and *Preacher*. The top indie trade to buy must be *Saga* Vol. 1 and it is very affordable at $9.99.

The best trade for younger audiences is the *DC Super Hero Girls*, which has 5 volumes. Great for younger and even older audiences. For boys I'd suggest *Batman/TMNT*.

Marvel has some ok trades, the best would be *Old Man Logan* Vol. 1, Frank Miller's *Daredevil*, *Punisher Max*, *Infinity Gauntlet*, Miller's *Wolverine*, *Kraven's Last Hunt*, and *Maximum Carnage*.

The best DC super hero trades are near endless, but I'll limit it to a top 10: *Kingdom Come*, *Batman: Hush*, *Dark Knight Returns*, *Watchmen*, *Blackest Night*, Azzarello's *Joker*, *Superman: Red Son*, *Green Lantern: Rebirth*, Morrison's *Arkham Asylum*, and the trilogy of *Crisis on Infinite Earths*, *Infinite Crisis*, and *Final Crisis* (and add *Identity Crisis* as well).

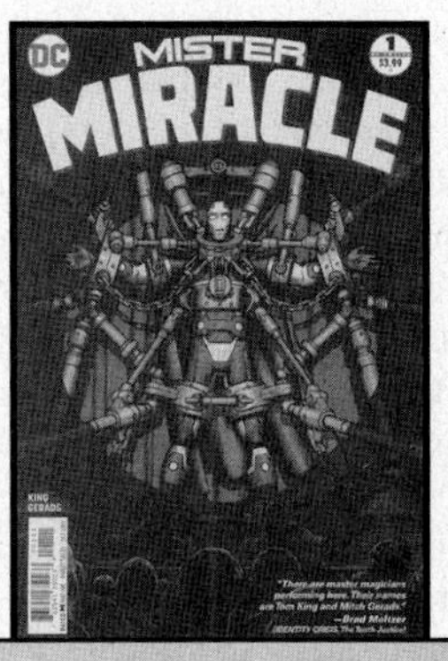

The success of the new ***Mister Miracle*** *series was an unexpected surprise.*

Bill Fidyk
Collector

It has been an interesting year for magazine back issues due to increased interest from collectors – primarily for Horror magazines. Comparatively, the magazine back issue market is vastly different from the regular comic market and this is mainly due to the fact that the mindset of collector is different. Many comic collectors dismiss comic magazines due to their oversized format while many other comic book collectors who chase key books or the speculator hot book of the month ignore magazines altogether due to their lack of key investment issues. While it is true that there are not many true key books in the magazine back issue market, there seemed to be a short list of magazine keys that collectors scooped up when they hit the market which resulted in strong prices. The two magazines that showed high desire and price were *Vampirella* #1 and *Savage Tales* #1 (1st Man-Thing). In high grade (9.0 or higher), these magazines demanded strong prices and did not last long when put up for sale; in addition, few copies in high grade came up for sale this past year. Both books feature first appearances of still popular characters as well which certainly helps their future collectability and I only see these books slowly increasing in value in the future. On the opposite end of the sales spectrum, *Marvel Preview* #4 and #7 have cooled off a bit and I don't see these magazines hitting the sales peaks they did when the first *Guardians of the Galaxy* movie came out. While they can still be considered key books and they certainly won't plummet back to the prices they once were (many of these could have been had for $10-$15 in high grade pre Marvel movie era), I predict that high grade copies (9.4 or higher) will remain steady in price but won't increase very much. *Marvel Preview* #2 on the other hand is still relatively undervalued and has a lot of room for growth and potential.

Another factor that sets the magazine back issue market apart from the comic book market is the fact that the majority of magazine collectors are run collectors vs. key book collectors. Most collectors who are pursuing a run of *Creepy* magazine are also after *Vampirella* and *Eerie* runs as well. Same goes for Skywald. I don't know a single collector who only wants a run of *Scream*; instead, they are after *Nightmare* and *Psycho* as well. High grade runs of these books are worth pursing due to great art and stories and many collectors (many Bronze Horror as well as pre-Code collectors) are finally catching on to this fact and are now starting their runs. Simply put, these books won't stay cheap forever. In addition, there are fewer truly high grade copies of these magazines due to their oversized format—they were harder to store and keep in nice shape as compared to their comic counterparts. Many collectors and dealers still seem to have a mindset that many of the Warrens are plentiful in high grade because there were so many warehouse copies that were purchased in the early to mid-eighties. Many of these copies have been sold since and are now locked away in private collections. The supply is finally starting to dwindle for high grade copies and there are several issues from each of the three main titles (*Creepy*, *Eerie*, *Vampirella*) that cannot be found on dealer sites or even eBay at all in any grade. This wasn't the case five to ten years ago. If you are on the fence about collecting these titles—don't wait much longer.

Paul Figura
CBCS - Modern and Vintage Grader

First off, I have to give out a big apology to everyone. I do so that the gracious and hardworking people at *Overstreet* do not catch any backlash for my error. I mistakenly stated in the 47th Edition of the *Overstreet Comic Book Price Guide* that the 1st appearance of Speedy and the retelling of his origin was in *Adventure Comics* #209 and #262. Speedy's (Roy Harper) 1st appearance was actually in *More Fun Comics* #73, November 1941. While those *Adventure* issues did deal with his origin story, they definitely were not his 1st appearance. So once again, a big "I'm sorry" for throwing out that misinformation! Now let us get back to the business at hand, comics!

I am spending more time in grading as a modern and vintage grader at CBCS. The number of books we see coming into our facility is still staggering, and it is nice to see our hobby still growing and flourishing like it is! That is all due to you, the collector. Thanks to you, we all can continue to work and enjoy what we are doing year after year here at CBCS.

So let's talk about collecting comic books. First and foremost, as a collector, you have to know your limitations. Buy what you can afford. I cannot stress this enough, buy what you like! Many people speculate on what will be the next big thing, or which movie or television series is coming out. While that certainly is one way to go, sadly enough that doesn't always work out. Some comics that you invested in, hoping they would explode on the market are now just sitting in a stack collecting dust. As with most things, and certainly, with the popularity of the movies and television shows, you will see certain comics skyrocket in popularity and price. The comic book market is like any other, it has its ups and downs. It is best to keep things simple. Is that one prized book you want now out of reach? Just keep an eye on it, you never know when its popularity could run its course and it just might become more affordable. Watch, read, and pay attention to how the book is doing, invest wisely, and have fun. Other alternatives could be to look at a lower grade copy. Some copies could be a complete disaster, but with modern technology and the advancement in the restoration processes, some of those old books can put on some modern brilliance. Restoration, when done correctly, is not as frowned upon as it once was. The stigma of owning a restored book is more appealing now compared to the past. Just know that if you do decide to get a comic restored or conserved, there are people out there that pass themselves off as "comic restoration experts." Make sure you see their work before submitting your treasures to them to be worked on.

Another technique collectors and dealers are using is pressing. Pressing is a technique used to flatten, and get wrinkles and some blemishes out of a book to give it a better overall appearance. On higher grade books that have just a few problems, a good press can boost the grade a few points, and possibly get you to that 9.8 you desire. What pressing will not do is cover up serious defects, creasing and tears. While it is possible to flatten out a crease, the color loss will still be there if the color was broken to begin with. Tears and holes, well that is just something one has to learn to live with, short of restoring the book pressing will not help there. While a good press can squeeze a few extra points out of your book in the hopes that your grade might be bumped a bit higher, a bad press can do exactly the opposite and drop your grade a bit. Noticeable pebbling, added staining, indents pressed into the book, anything one can see, will affect the grade. Also, if the book is already a disaster, no amount of pressing is going to help it. Review your choices when picking books to press and grade, as some books are just not worth the extra money put into pressing them.

One more way you can afford a Silver Age classic is through the Foreign Market. For example, the early issues of *Amazing Spider-Man*, or *Avengers*, which go for a premium price here, are very much undervalued for a U.K. Edition. It is pretty much the same comic from the U.S. with just a change in the pricing. Instead of the 12 cent price, it will have a pence price. The foreign market is catching up, but there is still time to grab an early issue of something like *Amazing Spider-Man* #1 for a lot cheaper than you would pay for it in the U.S. If you would like to see some examples, our Foreign Comics Advisor, Tim Bildhouser, runs a website that discusses the market surrounding foreign comic books. You can see this information at: www.foreigncomics.web.com, as well as his online magazine www.foreigncomiccollector.webs.com. They definitely are worth a look, and they might save you a few bucks. Foreign comics are becoming big collectible items. Foreign comics such as the Australian copy of the *Avengers* #1, which features a cover with a very different look to it than the American version, would be a welcome add to any collection, as well as becoming a prized piece to show off! Not to mention increasing the value of your collection.

So, what's hot right now? I can only speak as to what I am seeing come across my desk here at CBCS. Batman titles sporting covers and/or art by the great Neal Adams! The ever-popular *Batman* #200, highlighting nine popular Batman comic covers in the background. *Batman* #227, which swipes the *Detective Comics* #31 cover by Bob Kane. *Batman* #232 featuring the 1st appearance of Ra's al Ghul, and the 2nd appearance of Talia, a follow up to *Detective Comics* #411 which featured her 1st appearance just a month before. The 1st appearance of Two-Face since the Golden Age, in *Batman* #234. *Batman* #244, another Ra's al Ghul appearance and classic cover, and finally *Batman* #251, the modern day return of the Joker! Usually when we see these book they have a Neal Adams signature on them, and a few more with a Denny O'Neil signature. A great comic team-up and a great addition to any collection. A final mention to the Batman family would be *Batman Adventures* #12, the 1st comic book appearance of Harley Quinn from September, 1993. That book is usually seen around here on a daily basis, and with all the reprints and convention exclusives one could have a nice collection with this book alone!

Making a quick switch to Marvel, *New Mutants* #98 from February, 1991, featuring the 1st appearance of Deadpool. There are multiple copies submitted to us almost daily, followed closely by *New Mutants* #87 from March, 1990, the 1st appearance of Cable, and *Uncanny X-Men* #266, Late August, 1990, featuring the 1st appearance of Gambit in X-Men continuity. Jumping over to the *Incredible Hulk*, #180, #181 and #182. Those books are always on peoples want lists, with issue #181 leading the way as the 1st full appearance of Wolverine. Issues 180 and 182 have cameo appearances of him as well. Having all three is a must for all those completests out there!

Looking into the Silver Age, the more popular sighting from Marvel are early runs of *Amazing Spider-Man*, *Fantastic Four* and *X-Men*, with a minor nod to *Tales to Astonish* issues showcasing the early Hulk and Namor appearances in Marvel. We are also noticing a bit more Marvel horror coming in to CBCS to be graded. Those early pre-superhero *Tales of Suspense*, *Tales to Astonish*, *Journey into Mystery* and *Strange Tales* are more popular than ever. Those titles go right along with the 1950s EC that are always a welcome sight! Popular DC's Silver Age submissions are, as of late, the few early appearances of the Teen Titans. With the announcement of the Titans TV show, those early appearances in *Showcase* #59 dated November-December, 1965, and in the *Brave and the Bold Comics* # 54 from June-July, 1964 and #60 cover dated June-July, 1965. Those issues feature the first three appearances of the Teen Titans, as well as the first appearance of Wonder Girl (Donna Troy). Interest in those books seem to be increasing and I am sure we will see more copies here in the CBCS grading room as the release date for the show draws near. Other recurrent *Showcase* issues that I have noticed more of feature the Flash, Aquaman and the Atom. Surprisingly enough, while we did see a few more issues of the *Brave and the Bold* #28, #29 and 30, the 1st three appearances of the Justice League of America, as well as a few early *Justice League of America* comics, there were not as many as I would have imagined. This reaffirms my previous statement about speculating. Collectors were waiting to see the results of the *Justice League* movie before taking a chance on purchasing.

Over the last few years, as I have mentioned in previous reports the increase in *Shazam* #1 from February, 1973, and #28 dated March-April, 1977, the 1st Bronze Age appearance of Black Adam. Those comics started appearing more frequently with the announcement of the casting of Black Adam and the forth-coming *Shazam* movie. I have not noticed any increase in Fawcett's *Captain Marvel Adventures*, *Whiz Comics* or any of the Marvel Family comics outside of the occasional *Marvel Family* #1 from December, 1945. This issue features the 1st appearance of Black Adam, and his only Golden Age appearance until his 2nd appearance 32 years later. Movies and TV aside, if you like it, and it interests you, take a chance, investigate first and collect what you like!

That's it for this year! 2018 is here with more comic related movies that will thrill us all! They will offer readers and collectors more comics to search for as we all try and complete those collections. So once again, until my next report, Happy Hunting!

Joseph Fiore
ComicWiz.com

What a year in comics! I will most look back at 2017 as the year I was able to watch our hobby market thrive, and in some cases, reach new heights. On the latter point, more notably with the continuing trend of movies playing a huge part in price surges and collector demand, and on the heels of Wonder Woman celebrating 75 years in comics, let's kick things off with what was arguably one of the best superhero movies of the year - *Wonder Woman*.

It truly made a statement not only because of Gal Gadot's amazing screen presence, or that it has the potential to draw in new female comic fans, but on the merits of it being a female-led and directed superhero movie. Director Patty Jenkins did a superb job representing the character that William Marston (with co-creators Elizabeth Holloway and Olive Byrne) envisioned. Yes, there is certainly controversy in the Marston-era, and with 1/4 of every book featuring bondage, "spanking parties", or some sexually provocative theme, so it's truly amazing that any of these comics ever got published. It is however an era that also first introduced the female heroine, as well as segments like "Wonder Women of History" which acted to empower young female readers. With the success this film has enjoyed, look for demand and interest to continue to rise for Marston-era Wonder Woman issues. The success of movies at the box office continued to translate to sustained and/or newly forming interests in character origins, first appearances, and new comic releases.

Movies like *Logan*, *Thor: Ragnarok*, *Spider-Man: Homecoming* and *Guardians of the Galaxy Vol 2* cemented the success Marvel has enjoyed with its characters in major motion pictures. Conversely, DC's *Justice League* was beleaguered with fan criticism right from go, and after having watched it, I didn't think it was nearly as bad as critics claimed. Interestingly, while superheroes in movies have had a big influence on which comics get hot, what I hadn't noticed with any degree of granularity is how heavily fan criticisms and reactions to the movie's weigh on collectors perceptions. Within days of *Justice League* being released, Facebook groups were buzzing, with many discussions negatively focusing on Rotten Tomatoes critic reviews and audience scores. People who had watched *Justice League* were convinced the movie review site had it wrong, or that there might have been some terrible miscalculation at work. At that time, I hadn't really put much weight on these suggestions, and resigned to the thought that critics don't always get things right. However it wasn't until *The Last Jedi* was released in December that divisive talk reemerged similar to what had happened with *Justice League*. This time it centered around what was being described as "burner accounts" being used by reviewers to deliberately bring down the score of *The Last Jedi* film. It certainly caught my attention because up until that point, I could see how box office success often translated to a stronger character driven comic market, so this notion that perceptions toward a movies success could be skewed or subverted raised the questions not only of HOW this could be possible, but WHY anyone would do such a thing?

My participation in Facebook (FB) groups centered around my hobby interests and pursuits has continued to evolve, and the more memorable experiences for me are those moments where you can see the influence licensing and merchandising, particularly toy advertising in comic books, have had on collectors from my generation.

Perhaps my favourite post was seeing one of the children used in packaging photography for the Stretch Armstrong line of toys reappear in one of the biggest vintage toy groups. Now in his 40s, Mike Seta posted an updated photo of himself, using the same facial expression, holding the same Stretch toy he did as a young boy. It was the coolest thing in the history of coolest things! And what a thrill it was to be able to reconnect to one of my favourite childhood toys, and recalling how that Stretch ad in comics got me hooked on the toy in the first place! These groups continue to be great environments for collectors to congregate, buy, sell or trade and wax nostalgic. As with any online buying, selling or trading, it's becoming more important to exercise precaution.

Beyond the mess raffles (a cross between gambling and "chase" scheme) are causing in FB comic groups, one of the more concerning aspects of using FB is its continued commitment to allowing closed collecting groups and communities, and with it, a tendency to produce reputational blind spots for collectors. One notable example that comes to mind is an auctioneer in Pennsylvania who allegedly vanished with consignors money, leaving a trail of nearly 100 victims, and losses totaling somewhere between $100,000 to $500,000. The story takes an unusual turn when one of the victims claims (through a bankruptcy objection filing) that he had consigned a CGC 1.5 *All Star Comics* #8 (first appearance of Wonder Woman) which hammered for $24,000. The victim alleges the auctioneer vanished with the money, and a short time after, had used the allegedly stolen money to fund a toy grading company. The matter is currently in bankruptcy court, with little to no prospect victims will ever see a cent. Those who might see some form of redress will see only a fraction of their losses returned to them, and will possibly need to wait anywhere from 3-5 years to be paid. I draw on this example not only for the outrageousness that someone could use bankruptcy as a shield, and seemingly come up with capital to fund a new venture a short time after telling his consignors his accounts were frozen, but because most of the promoting/marketing with his new grading company venture is happening in a closed Facebook group, which is coincidentally run by one of his business partners. Strangely enough, the web-based evidence on this individual and the auction company, and his past businesses can all be found with a quick Google search, but somehow it is being overlooked by members of the FB group who continue to use and actively recommend the services of his grading company. There are incredible enterprising aspects to our hobby, and certainly a record sale of $936,223.00 for a CGC 9.4 *All Star Comics* #8 in August may be enough for people to dust off their copies and sell. These occurrences, while rare, still call for a need for people to make sure they are doing their due diligence, and to ensure at the very minimum it involves a Google search on the name of the individual, the company and its principles or partners. The amount of money being thrown around by grown adults on memories and nostalgia now more than ever calls for these precautions and steps to be taken.

I've always tried to use a "make lemonade when you're given lemons" outlook in life. Unfortunately, as with any thriving market, there are moments where things falter, and when these situations occur, we must try as best we can to make them learning moments. In the last year I've seen far too many high scale collection thefts occur. The most notable theft being the Rancho Obi Wan (the "Smithsonian of 'Star Wars') which was said to have totalled $200,000 in stolen collectibles. The theft was not immediately noticed - in fact, it took several months before people began noticing some of the rarer items from the collection reappear for sale. The perpetrator chose to use a broker who he knew preferred using a third-party grader, as a method to perhaps make them less distinguishable when they reappeared for sale. The perpetrator also was a close friend of the collection owner. He eventually plead guilty to one count of felony grand theft, and was sentenced in December to one year in prison. I have provided several post-loss appraisals in the last year as well, and I can't emphasize enough the importance of insuring your collection. One of the questions I keep seeing brought up on the CGC forums relates to appraising collections, and it is always advisable to use an accredited appraiser in your area. The rise in peril losses due to inclement weather, hurricanes and wildfires - in all, the disasters that hit the US in 2017 have taken a heavy toll as well, and while immediate concern should undoubtedly be for human safety, the toll it has taken on collections has already been made noticeable with online shares and the amount of post-loss appraisals being requested. In light of these events, there is no better time to catalogue your collections, take as many photos as possible, and store this information somewhere safe. While insurance can be cold comfort for any collection loss situation, especially with items of great sentimental or nostalgic value, a spreadsheet with good, clear photographs or scans can help ensure there is no room for doubt on ownership or claimed values. Whether it be theft or peril loss, if there is any advice that should be heeded from this market report, it's to take the necessary measures and steps to safeguard it.

This year also marked a return to tried and true methods in terms of my participation and setting-up at local shows. Beginning with the tradition (6th year now) of setting-up at the 4-day annual outdoor show called Kempenfest in the late July, early August long-weekend, and it's continued to be a great way to interface with collectors, to buy and sell comics, and more notably one of the better collection acquisitions from this year came from a lead from that show. I also really enjoyed participating in our local libraries second annual "Comic-Con" - a great time was had by all. Which reminds me of the recent judgement favouring Comic-Con International (CCI), the nonprofit that has run San Diego Comic-Con (SDCC) for almost 50 years. The court ruling means any shows using the word "Comic Con" would potentially need to obtain license from CCI to use the term, or else be forced to rename their events. Online discussion around this has been ongoing, and I can see both sides of the debate. Being a trademark owner myself, I can understand "the defend it or lose it" argument, and the reasons why CCI/SDCC did what they did. I also see how this decision could make things more difficult for shows to be able to contend and maintain a foothold in an increasingly cutthroat industry. It will certainly be interesting to see how this will impact the overall comic convention scene in the future.

In the last week of October, one of the bigger comic news stories involved Beckett Media acquiring Comic Book Certification Service (CBCS). The service which I began writing about in my 2014 market report, and in my estimation, the best thing to happen to the comic book certification market, is now a part of the Beckett family. Collectors should only expect great things from this acquisition. I recently was involved in a debate over competition in comic grading with someone who insisted CGC "fetched more", and one of the examples I reflected on was how I was quietly hoping for there to be some value disparity when CBCS first opened its doors. I remember drawing up a list of Silver Age keys, with grades and expected prices using CGC past sales data, and challenged myself to buy anything that popped-up in a CBCS slab that sold below CGC value. I was never able to buy a single copy from that list. Nearly every CBCS slab from that list which appeared for sale not only commanded too nearly CGC values, but some went over fair market value. It was an unprecedented thing to witness so soon after CBCS opened its doors, and I've always felt that it was primarily to do with people buying into Steve Borock's reputation, and I'm sure that's what informed Beckett's decision as well. I couldn't be happier for the comic hobby as I see this acquisition as an important milestone in the evolution of competition in comic book certification.

What's on the horizon is possibly the most exciting - a *Black Panther* movie, and the *Avengers: Infinity War*. These two movies have caused such a stir that every copy of *Fantastic Four* #52 sold faster than I could get them in. There is no doubt in my mind that T'Challa will be one of the hottest characters in upcoming years, and while we should be talking about another example of superhero movies ushering in diversity, I'm also excited about what this will mean for his key appearances. I used to write about missing the boat on *Our Army at War* #83 before it shot up to the stratosphere, I anticipate copies of *Fantastic Four* #52 will very quickly emulate a similar upward value trajectory. It's uncertain what effect *Avengers: Infinity War* will have on the original *Infinity War* and *Infinity Gauntlet* comic series, as more recent reports appear to indicate they aren't adapting the comic story in the movie. Although it's expected that *Iron Man* #55 will experience a value bump from Thanos playing the major villain role.

I've also been noticing Canadian Price Variants (CPV's) have been heating up, although it seems to be too early to tell whether there will be enough of a sustained interest for this market segment to enjoy the growth it really deserves.

The one trend I have noticed which is of some concern are requests seeking not only key issues, such as the 75¢ price variant of *Amazing Spider-Man* #236 (first Hobgoblin), but a request for unheard of high grade examples only. I think I've received over a dozen inquiries for a CGC 9.6 copy, but this is a CPV that too infrequently shows up in 9.6, and you're always holding some hope the Tattooz haven't been removed regardless of grade. I think CPV's overlooked history might lend to a growing and sustained interest if enough people spend time to understand why they exist, their production numbers compared to US newsstand and direct editions, and if they don't get too hung up with having a "best copy." I also see the growing trend of collectors seeking US newsstand issues working to reinforce the aspects that have drawn collectors to CPV's. Foreign edition key focus collectors are also entering into the mix looking for key CPV issues, but are seemingly more reasonably content finding 5.0 to 8.5 copies or "budget" copies. Overall, I've been most pleased being able to continue to add to my personal collection. Some pieces have slipped through my fingers, but I've also managed to acquire some "goal" pieces in the area of original comic art, and Star Wars toy collecting.

I made one of my top 3 "in the wild" finds using a tracking software I built, and I feel technology will continue to be an enabler in discovering new finds, and discovering them early enough to cut out the competition. On the technology point, one of the best projects to emerge this past year from the comic art collecting community is ComicArtTracker.com. While I am not involved with the project, I can say I have used it and find that the user interface is clean, and the search reach is one of the aspects I found to be particularly impressive. A word of warning - while technology is in my mind an enabler to finding those pieces you may not have noticed or would otherwise miss, it's also going to put a dent in your wallet! In sum, the year that went by has shown a strong market health, where diversity in superhero movies has seemingly been more well received and able to attain sustained levels of box office success that hasn't yet found a way to emulate as well or without adversity in hobby conversation or in comic panels. Keeping a pulse on the market calls for the same approaches in weeding out bad operators in our hobby pursuits, and safeguarding what we've already spent years assembling. As I sign off, I'd like to wish you all a better year than the last, and happy collecting everyone!

Dan Fogel
Hippy Comix

Although I contributed info as always, I skipped a formal essay last year in lieu of my modest contributions to the essential reference *The Overstreet Guide To Collecting Concert Posters*. I'm back with a short but sweet market report to celebrate my 40th year as a comic book dealer and my 31st year as an Overstreet Special Advisor! In addition to being one of Unca Bob's Junior Woodchucks, my main gig is writing & publishing *Fogel's Underground Price & Grading Guide*, and as such most of what I sell these days are Alternative, Indy, Small Press, and Underground Comix. But I always keep my oars in the Mainstream of comic books by occasionally buying and selling cool collections of all genres.

Most of my knowledge of the current Mainstream market comes from a better friend than I deserve, the legendary Tim Kupin of Koop's Comics. He's been selling funnybooks longer than I have, and buys and sells many many longboxes across the country. The following info comes from Koop himself, and is a tiny fraction of what he sold last year but is meant to highlight greater trends and noteworthy sales.

CBCS Graded Sales: *House of Mystery* #79 7.0 $100 and *House of Secrets* #11 7.0 $150 (both Jack Kirby, not listed as such in the *Guide*!), *Infinity Gauntlet* #1 9.6 $130, *Shocking Mystery Cases* #51 6.0 $190 (L.B. Cole), *Superman* #199 6.0 $240 (1st Superman/Flash race).

CGC Graded Sales: *Marvel Graphic Novel* #1 9.8 $300 (Death of Captain Marvel), *Marvel Graphic Novel* #4 9.8 $350 (1st New Mutants; cracked holder).

Over *Guide* Raw Sales: *Amazing Spider-Man* #298 VF/NM $75 (1st Todd McFarlane & Eddie Brock), *Amazing Spider-Man* #300 VF/NM $250, *Amazing Spider-Man* #301 VF/NM $55, *Crack Comics* #51 GD+ $50 (Reed Crandall), *Epic Illustrated* #3 NM- $100 (1st Dreadstar), *Hero For Hire* #2 VG- $50 (1st Claire Temple), *Last Avengers Story* (2 issue set) NM- $30, *Marvel Special Edition Featuring Star Wars* #3 (Treasury) 2 copies, both NM-, 1 for $55 & 1 for $60, *Vampirella* #1 GD- $125.

Raw Sales: *Creepy* #1 VF $80, *FOOM* #1 FN $25, *Marvel Premiere* #15 FN/VF $100 (1st Iron Fist), *Marvel Spotlight* #5 FN+ $150 (1st Ghost Rider), *Saga* #19 (Diamond Summit Retailer Variant) 2 copies, both VF/NM 1 for $35 & 1 for $45, *Sandman* (1989) #1 NM $100, *Silver Surfer* #14 VF $75, *Star Wars* #107 VF+ $45, *Strange Tales Annual* #1 GD+ $100.

As always, I must thank Bob Overstreet, Steve Geppi, J.C. Vaughn, Mark Huesman, Amanda Sheriff, and all the fine folks at Gemstone Publishing for allowing me to contribute to the *Overstreet Comic Book Price Guide*. And a huge special thank you to Koop for providing me with this sales data and the great benefit of his knowledge and support!

John Foster
South Philly Comics

Greetings everyone, this is John Foster reporting from sunny Philadelphia! This will be my last time reporting from South Philly Comics since we decided to close down our brick and mortar store late this year. Now I'll be hustling comics on my own, online and at shows. As much as we loved cultivating a wonderful comic community in South Philadelphia the fatigue of operating a physical shop was just too much. However, next year I'll be reporting from Ontario Street Comics, which might be familiar to those of you who have seen the movie *Unbreakable*.

In addition to selling them our entire back issue section (around 100 long boxes), they also got me in the deal! It was a fantastic learning experience operating my own shop for 6 years but it feels great to get back to doing what I love the most - being a back issue guy. Just a man, an *Overstreet*, O.W.L. card, proper lighting, and an endless stacks of funny books to inspect and price. Going from a shop with around a hundred long boxes of comics, to a shop with hundreds, is absolutely fantastic for a guy like me. But enough about me - on to the comics!

Descender *is one of the top selling Image comics.*

Let's start with monthly comic sales: continuing from last year, our Marvel readership has been slowly ebbing with a few exceptions. *Unbeatable Squirrel Girl* remained strong, as has *Thanos*, *Thor*, and *Doctor Strange*. Despite our generally low *Inhumans* numbers, we sold a ton of the new *Black Bolt* solo series by novelist Saladin Ahmed and artist Christian James Ward, which delivered a compelling story and mind-blowing art. *X-Men: Gold* and *X-Men: Blue* debuted strong but we saw readership dwindle a bit and eventually plateau (which honestly is to be expected with so any X-titles out there). The 1st printing of *X-Men: Gold* #1, however, was a whole different story. Due to the controversial art fiasco with artist Ardian Syaf, that book was hot for a minute, selling for around $30 each, but has cooled down by now to little over cover price.

Speaking of controversial Marvel comics this year, we actually had only a few people complain about the *Secret Empire* event, which was kinda shocking considering the media backlash. To be honest, it seemed that most of the people complaining were people who don't even read comics. The complaints I did hear were mostly about empty character deaths and story pacing. The *Marvel Legacy* one-shot was easily Marvel's biggest hit this year and a step in the right direction.

With DC Comics, we continued to see growth from last year's Rebirth change up. *All-Star Batman*, *Batman*, *Batwoman*, *Flash*, *Superman*, and *Wonder Woman* sales remained solid. We did see a drop in our Young Animal readership which started out strong. *Doom Patrol* alone remained a big seller for us despite its constant lateness. The *Batman / Flash* "The Button" crossover definitely topped our DC Comics sales this year! The combination of the two comics being popular titles on their own, combined with a Watchmen bump with fun Lenticular covers that only lasted for 4 issues in 2 months was incredible. It really resulted in extra sales from folks who don't usually collect single issues anymore, with the issues coming out in the perfect amount of time to hold their attention. The *Dark Nights: Metal* event is also pretty successful - people really can't get enough Batman. Even the One-Shots are selling well, with both *Batman: The Red Death*, and *The Batman Who Laughs* remaining on top. The *Batman/Elmer Fudd* one-shot was also a huge success out of nowhere, even earning a 2nd printing. The 1st printing is still going for around $10-$20. The media coverage of Batman's marriage proposal to Catwoman in *Batman* #24 made that book hot as well; it is still selling for over cover price.

At Image Comics our usual suspects were still on top: *Saga*, *Walking Dead*, *Descender*, *East of West*, and *Paper Girls*. *God Country* was also a big hit for writer Donny Cates, who is having a heck of a year (*Redneck*, *Doctor Strange*, and *Thanos*.) This year was Image Comics' 25 year anniversary and they decided to go big on the celebration by offering exactly 1,992 blind boxes to retailers for $125 a pop with major allocations. Each Blind box features an assortment of 25 polybagged limited edition variants of 17 new Image series, plus the possibility of a *Walking Dead: Here's Negan* #1 which is itself limited to 500 copies. It was an interesting gamble deciding on how to exactly sell them. I was only able to get one box and decided to open all the bags and sell them individually. My box was honestly pretty lame - I still made a good profit, but I had to work for it!

Now, on to back issues sales and acquisitions: Unlike our monthly comics, our back issue sales were greatly affected by Movie/TV media hype. *New Mutants* #87 1st Cable (1st print), and especially *New Mutants* #98 1st Deadpool, flew out the door in any shape above *Guide* value.

New Teen Titans #2 1st Deathstroke, already on the upswing, became even more desirable with the news that the character will appear in the next Batman movie. With the success of R-rated comic movies like *Deadpool* and *Logan*, I've noticed prices and interest going up for fan favorite character Lobo's 1st appearance in *Omega Men* #3. The best movie hype sales bump this year easily goes to *Darkhawk* #1. Rumors spread that Darkhawk would appear in *Guardians of the Galaxy 2*, which turned a common dollar bin book into a $50+ book. The best part about it was that Darkhawk never even appeared in the movie! Prices have since chilled, with the exception of high grade slabbed copies.

This year we had great success picking up and moving lots of interesting Silver Age books like *Captain America* #117 1st Falcon, *Marvel Super-Heroes* #18 1st Guardians of the Galaxy, and *Strange Tales Annual* #2 1st Spidey crossover and 4th appearance. We also did quite well selling any and all wacky *Superman* and *Superman's Girlfriend Lois Lane* books just for the zany covers! More than any other single title it was our *Flash* section that got hit the hardest this year. Regardless of the issue or its condition, I had no shortage of people happy to buy them up. As usual, I couldn't keep up with the demand for *Amazing Spider-Man* from this era, but it was fun to try.

As far as our Bronze Age sales went this year, it was Kirby's DC work, anything with Bernie Wrightson art, and Marvel Comics in general that were the breadwinners. We were fortunate enough to grab a few complete runs of Kirby's *New Gods* and *Forever People*, as well as a bunch of his *Superman's Pal Jimmy Olsen* issues, including issue #134 the 1st appearance of Darkseid! That issue and the early Darkseid appearances sold immediately, and over *Guide* prices. Same goes for *Forever People* #1, his 1st full appearance. The "non-key" issues also sold quickly, because, come on, it's the King of Comics we're talking about here! Nothing really special to report about our Copper Age sales this year. Just a lot of fun cheap reads, and people filling in holes in their collections. *Amazing Spider-Man* #298- #300 (Venom brief and 1st appearances) and *TMNT* were our most requested issues from this era.

That's it from South Philly Comics -- thanks for reading! For what it's worth, here's some advice for shop owners: treat customers with respect! I can't tell you the amount of stories I hear about elitist clerks turning people off, or women getting harassed or being spoken down to. Not a good business model to make people uncomfortable in your store. Remember that you are an Ambassador of the hobby, and if the hobby is to continue, it needs new readers and collectors.

Lastly, here's the best thing I've heard to sum up the comic retail experience, from comic guru Joe Ferrara of Atlantis Fantasyworld Comics, in Santa Cruz, CA: "It's easy to sell comics, but how do you make a profit?" With Diamond discounts what they are, plus the cost of shipping and general business expenses, figuring out how to turn a profit can be a real challenge. I look forward to more comic adventures and to report next year from Ontario Street Comics. Thank you J.C Vaughn, Mark Huesman, and the whole *Overstreet* gang for putting this fine book together and letting me contribute. Cheers everyone!

Dan Gallo
Dealer

This hobby is insane. Money is pouring into prime material at unprecedented levels. First it was "Big Gold" and then it was high grade "Big Silver." Now mid-grade "Big Silver" is being pulled up on the heels of the higher graded realizations. It's like a 6.0 is the new 8.0. Because there is so much money in it right now it is nearly impossible to stay ahead of the curve. Paying what something is "worth" is a bargain in itself. And don't even get me started on original art!

The fun in the hobby comes from buying and selling. Holding is no fun. Is there a greater feeling that comes from being fresh off the kill? Maybe you just sold something and realized a great price or maybe you made a quick flip and made a couple of bucks. Maybe you won something at a great price at auction, (And I mean "won," not "buy." Anyone can "buy." The goal is to win!). How about the feeling when that package arrives with your latest score? Tell me that's not fun.

Let's talk books. I promise to not bore you with pages upon pages of outdated sales data. Instead I will offer a short, concise report with some market insight and observations focused more on the future instead of the past. Here we go:

Golden Age: I define "Big Gold" as the top 20 or so best Golden Age books to have as derived from a combination of both value and desirability. All can be found listed in *Overstreet*'s Top 100 GA Comics, but not necessarily in order. There are plenty of high priced books that no one cares about plus ones that are living on past glory. Studs like *More Fun Comics* #73, *Wonder Woman* #1 and *Sensation Comics* #1 inexplicitly haven't yet cracked the top 25. Remember, it is not solely about the price; people have to care.

In last year's report I wrote that *Journey into Mystery* #83 had been flat for a while but was due for a bump. Turns out that happened. This year I feel the same way about Captain Marvel. *Whiz Comics* #2 (#1) is a monster, extremely scarce and extremely pricey. Most people are already priced out of that market. Books like *Marvel Family* #1 (1st Black Adam), and *Captain Marvel Adventures* #18 (1st Mary Marvel) are both relatively affordable and possess potential upside. Keep an eye on them. If you have deeper pockets, books like *Whiz Comics* #2 (#1), *Flash Comics* #1, *Marvel Comics* #1 and *More Fun Comics* #73 should all be at the top of your list.

Silver Age: I define "Big Silver" in a similar fashion but I don't factor in top census books. It's all about where they trade in available grades, say 5.0 – 8.0. Just because there is one in 9.6 that got stupid money, I wouldn't put it on my list if it wasn't going to be there already.

If you have read any of my previous reports then you already know how much I love *Fantastic Four* #4, the 1st Namor. Realized prices have begun to firm up but they still have a ways to go. Another pet book of mine is *Tales to Astonish* #13, the 1st Groot. It is ridiculously scarce and should be worth a heck of a lot more. *Silver Surfer* #3, the 1st Mephisto, and *Journey into Mystery* #85, the 1st Loki, are also head scratchers, (way too tough to be this cheap). My "obvious" pick this year is *Showcase* #22, the 1st SA Green Lantern. I put it ahead of the *Brave and the Bold* #28 and the 2nd best DC Silver Age book behind *Showcase* #4. This book is undervalued in every grade and on last year's list *Overstreet* had it behind *Brave and the Bold* #28, *Tales To Astonish* #27, *X-Men* #1, and *Avengers* #1. Wrong. It's better.

Bronze Age: The Bronze Age is a mixed bag. The sheer quantities available have kept many books…good books, flat or trending down. There are exceptions though. *Incredible Hulk* #181, *Amazing Spider-Man* #129, and *House of Secrets* #92 are stronger than ever. *Werewolf by Night* #32 is still popular. I love *Batman* #232. *Tomb of Dracula* #10 and *Marvel Spotlight* #5 I still like a lot. What I am down on is *Amazing Spider-Man* #121 & #122, *Hero for Hire* #1, *X-Men* #94, *Marvel Premiere* #15, (although last year this one was looking good). I wouldn't necessarily recommend dumping but rather exercise some caution in that space. Also, when buying Bronze Age books it is very important to get the highest grade possible even if you have to buy fewer books to do so.

Modern Age: Except for the *Venom* #1 black error copy, which is very scarce, stick to 9.8s. Even if instead of buying 2-3 books in 9.6 you can only afford one in 9.8, get the 9.8. The spread is going to get wider and wider. Two of my favorite books from this era are *Punisher* Limited Series #1 and *Amazing Spider-Man* #252. Solid books that won't break the bank.

Original Comic Book Art: Have you bought your first piece of art yet?? If you haven't, I think it's time. Get your feet wet at a comfortable price point, ease your way in and build from there. You will be glad you did.

Conclusion: As a dealer I don't deal in bulk or miscellaneous issues, only graded books with significance. I like to say I have the meat but no potatoes. I grow my inventory high but not wide. If you tilt towards the investment side then that is the way to go. Buy the very best and at the highest grade you can afford. I would rather have one big book as opposed to multiple smaller ones. Less is more. If you tilt towards the collector side then just buy what you like. You don't need me, or anyone else, telling you how to collect.

With the hobby on such a bull run it is often difficult to acquire prime material at the price you want. You always feel like you are paying a little more than you want to. That's fine. It's OK to overpay a bit. It's not OK to get slammed. There is a fine line between being aggressive and just plain crazy.

Stephen Gentner
Golden Age Specialist

Greetings! 2017 has been a very productive collecting year for me. Not just after the usual suspects, but also an awakening to more of the varied prism of art and creators in our hobby. I will lead off with a creator who was taken from us too early. Whose artistic style was award winning, and whose story telling was tantalizing. I speak of Darwyn Cooke. With all the success of Wonder Woman in her movie, and all the hype before its release, Princess Diana has re-introduced her magnificence to the hobby and public at large. She never really left, but my focus here goes directly to Cooke's magnum opus, *DC: The New Frontier*. (A first rate cartoon movie of *New Frontier* ala Darwyn Cooke is quite true to the book and his art.) There is so much history described, with The Justice League and other DC characters woven heroically into the narrative. Wonder Woman figures prominently in the story. I had never read the book, and was turned on to it by new Chris Simons of "I Like Comics". This slice of Wonder Woman is so true to her strength, independence, courage, and mental toughness. Cooke's interpretation of her is wonderful, at once approachable, but if you look deeper into his art, strength, and depth of character shine forth. Here is an original piece he produced in the New Frontier time frame:

Having found this piece, I sought all the Darwyn Cooke covers I could find. Collectors will find his work with little stress, as most are still around and not terribly dear. His cover work on the myriad of titles he graced is so very distinctive to the eye. Wonderfully strange perspectives and proportions abound. Not every piece is a gem, but so very many are! For me, discovering his fun, approachable, and imaginative renderings was a breath of fresh ink!

I am referred to as a Golden Age Specialist. I guess it comes from my deep appreciation for Golden Age artists such as Schomburg, Baker, Kamen, Burnley, Kirby, Ray, Robinson, etc. The Golden Age was so fresh, imaginative, and dangerously brutal at stereotyping cultures, and ethnicities in a completely unabashed way. Not politically correct at ALL. Most especially the propaganda covers of

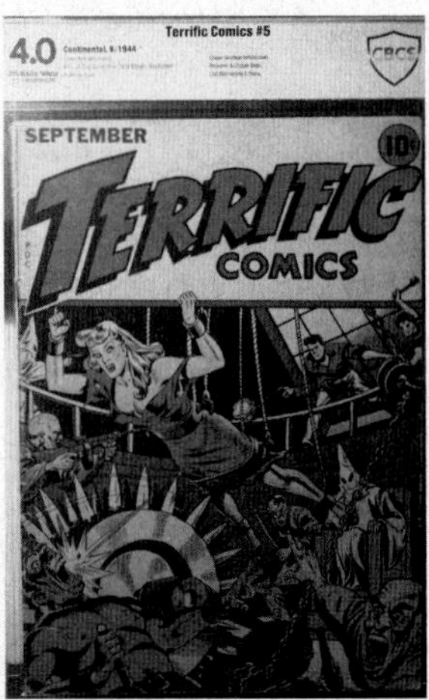

World War Two. I love them for it! There are so many Timely Schomburg pieces which boggle the mind. His thick necked Nazis, and optically and dentally challenged Japanese villains! I recently had an exemplary, and rare example of this wartime Schomburg genre *Terrific Comics* #5 slabbed. I was thrilled to get a copy:

Thematically, this cover has it all...the atrocity committing skunks about to harm a "good girl" damsel in distress. The perspective bending mastery of Alex Schomburg's art. His tiny vignettes in every corner of the cover. He is at the absolute top of this gruesome idiom. But along with the bravery of our heroes, the good girl type of comics were beginning here. The Internet has most all the cover images one can think of. But....you still have to know what to ask for. The *Gerber Photo Journal* changed my world when I got it so many years ago. Just riffle slowly through the pages, and damn near every comic cover of note can be found... and you don't have to know what title to look for. Just keep turning pages. Following the good girl genre, from 1946 until the Comic Book Code was installed, a plethora of great covers and interiors exist. It is also one of my favorite types of cover. Obscure, unseen, unremembered racy covers abound. Even I was caught flat footed with that "grey-tone" covered *Cindy* #37. I had to scramble to pay through the nose for one:

The fact being, good girl covers and interior art exist in some of the most unexpected places. Once exposed, the race goes full sprint. Along with the propaganda and girlie books, graphic crime covers arrived as well. Gerber laid his photos out by his perception of importance. Bigger images for "bigger" books. So you have to look carefully into the smaller images, and some of them are so very wrong!!! But Golden Age comic boundaries were limitless then. A propaganda cover I discovered a few years ago was one that Gerber's image wasn't big enough to catch me. Only after seeing the book in person could I appreciate the surreal, coloring perfection, and graphic stereotyping the artist achieved. I have never seen another cover so perfectly bizarre in this time frame. *Air Ace* Volume #2 from 1945:

My thrust this year in this genre has been to seek out and secure Golden Age and Atomic Age material with off beat covers. Earlier Victor Fox books have it all. In almost every way you could delineate pulchritude, violence, and crime, Fox delivered. Companies like Ziff Davis, Superior, Fiction House, Avon and others are where I am also looking. Have you bought a *Gerber Photo Journal*?

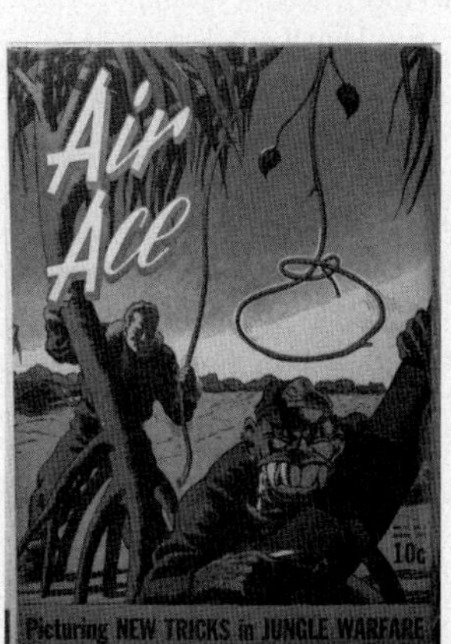

Another area I have explored is funny animal books, along with Harvey, Dell, and Gold Key offerings. I secured a high grade run of all the early *Rocky and Bullwinkle* books. They are so incredibly colorful, and tie in so nicely with their classic animated adventures. A smattering of high grade Harvey titles like *Little Lotta*, *Little Dot*, *Spooky*, *Hot Stuff*, *Casper*, *Wendy*...etc. I was drawn to them because they were pristine copies. I had never seen those kid books in anything but poor condition. You want to talk about attrition! The charm and innocence of them takes me back to long summers in the late 1950s and early '60s.

Lastly, something new. I have a handful of nice old Archie Comics. We all read them. We all enjoyed them. The new *Afterlife With Archie* series is truly amazing. Explosive and unexpected. Along with *The Chilling Adventures of Sabrina*, conventional Archie plot lines are twisted into horror. For all the Archie stuff I read as a kid, both series really moved me. The *Afterlife With Archie* series has many excellent variant covers. Some naughty, some nice, some gruesome! Very limited print runs on these. With Sabrina supposedly getting a TV series coming out of *Riverdale*, things are popping! After all the standard Marvel, and DC fare in Gold, Silver, and Bronze...the flavor of these different areas I have described really deserve your attention. Grinding after icon cover Marvels and DCs is fine. Gee, hardly anyone is chasing those books, anyway. The off beat stuff is not as white bread to your palette of comic fare. I find them more fun...which is why we're here! Good hunting!

Eric J. Groves
The Comic Art Foundation

Our beloved hobby finds itself in a brave new world. If comics are not at the center of American popular culture, they are very close to it. Comics have inspired countless movies and television shows, some of them superbly crafted. Graphic novels are now established as literature. The Internet has enabled commerce in comic books to extend worldwide. This international exposure of books for sale, particularly at auction, drives values upward. Certification of books in very high grades, as everyone knows, inspires buyer confidence and earns results in above *Guide* prices. High grade key comics have become investments for the wealthy. For good or for ill, this is how we live now.

Books in Demand: We base our comments about sought-after issues on want lists we receive, available auction results and our experience at conventions. We are all well aware of the most coveted books, so we do not recite them here. Instead, we report on collectors sniffing out comics not merely because of scarcity or investment potential, but for other more aesthetic reasons.

A great cover can sell a book today just as it did 65 years ago when it first went up on the rack. Any World War II cover, especially those depicting Hitler, Mussolini or Tojo, or all three, is highly desirable. The more imaginative the better, see, i.e. *Air Fighters* #8 (Japanese with swastika eyes).

A multitude of outstanding covers emerged from the Atomic Age. Requested examples include *Dynamic* #12 (chess cover); *Space Action* #2 (visor cover); *Red Seal* #2 (bondage, skull and hypodermic needle all in one); *Tomb of Terror* #15 (exploding head). People want any cover by Matt Baker, especially the most suggestive ones, found in titles like *Romantic Marriage*, *Pictorial Romance*, *Teen-Age Romances*, *True Love Pictorial* and the like.

We hear frequent requests for low number Archie comics, *Cat-Man* (any), *Space Western* (any), Atlas titles like *Yellow Claw* and *Black Knight*, and just about any pre-Code horror comic. The quest for some issues might be surprising. Try to find a copy of *Casper* #1 (St. John) in grade; it's a tough book and will sell at a premium. Fans are hunting for low number *Little Lulu* comics (under number 50) especially in condition, and will pay full book for them.

We recognize the pent-up desire for Golden Age titles traditionally considered second-tier comics. When such books come up for sale at auction, the bidding is brisk. Examples include, without limitation, titles such as *Amazing Mystery Funnies* (Centaur), *Champion* (Harvey), *Crash Comics* (Holyoke), *Bang-Up* (Progressive), *Black Cobra* (Ajax), *Blue Ribbon* (MLJ), *Lightning Comics* (Ace), *Funny Picture Stories* (Centaur), *Hyper-Mystery* (Hypo), *Miracl*e (Hillman), *Rocket Comics* (Hillman), *Spotlight* (Chesler), *Star Ranger* (Centaur) and *Wonderworld* (Fox). Individual issues of these titles can be very scarce indeed. The point is: interest in Golden Age comics is broadening, not narrowing.

Era by Era: Platinum Age books are regarded as of limited interest and notoriously slow movers. Yet, we do sell them, usually at a discount. Certain of them have excellent eye appeal, such as *Winnie Winkle*, and are fun to read, the contents never reprinted elsewhere. Check out *Barney Google and Spark Plug*. And keep in mind: some Platinum Age books are nearly a century old! They set the stage for things to come.

Of the Golden Age, what can be said? Our experience is that almost all G.A. books sell, sooner or later, often sooner, in all grades. We perceive some sticker shock for Timelys these days, but they remain the caviar of comics. Generation-skipping DC titles are as marketable as ever, especially Batman. Pre-Robin *Detective* comics are now pretty much beyond the reach of most collectors. *Wonder Woman* is hot, of course, as are *Sensation* issues of the same time frame, particularly with covers by H.G. Peter. Other fast sellers for us include *Flash*, *All-American*, *Green Lantern*, *Superman*, *Adventure* and low-number *World's Finest*. *Star-Spangled*, not so much, despite excellent artwork by Simon and Kirby.

As to the others, intensity of interest varies from title to title, often dependent on the artist. Quality comics do all right, but demand is strongest for those with early art by Eisner, Reed Crandall and Jack Cole. Low number *Hit Comics* with their exquisite covers are highly desirable, but try to find them. Fawcett books do not sell at a fast pace unless they include Raboy art. They are bargains, by our lights, and fun to read. Lev Gleason titles like *Boy* and *Daredevil* have picked up, with the early WWII issues hotter than ever. The covers were often sensational, see, for example, *Daredevil* #11 featuring Quasimodo bondage. MLJ titles do better than before, particularly those with WWII covers, see *Hangman* and early *Pep* issues. The reason for this, we think, is scarcity. MLJs simply do not turn up as they once did. Finally, interest has increased in some reprint comics such as *Popular*, *Famous Funnies* and *Sparkler* chiefly because, in our opinion, early issues included costumed hero stories not reprinted from newspapers.

With respect to the Atomic Age (1946-1956), we have for years touted this era as perhaps the most innovative and entertaining time in comic history. After the war, publishers had an expansive audience and the freedom to try whatever they had the nerve to try. They invented entirely new genres: crime, romance, war and horror. They expanded the teenager genre beyond Archie. They exploited movies, radio, and, yes, television. During this era, Bill Gaines took his father's fledgling company, E.C., and by hiring the finest bullpen ever, produced some of the best comic art in history.

There are too many desirable Atomic Age titles to mention here, so we will strive to be concise. First: remember there were superhero titles published and sold during the Atomic Age, some of them very well crafted. However, the superheroes faced serious competition during this period and there were only so many dimes to go around. Second: there are many scarce issues from this age and values have been increasing as a result. Third: quite a few titles have proven to be solid investments and have a bright future. This is especially true as to high grade copies. Perhaps from an investment standpoint, the most solid Atomic Age company to collect other than E.C. is Atlas, the successor to Timely and the precursor to Marvel. Atlas was active in all genres and did well even after adoption of the Comics Code Authority. Good girl art, by the way, hit its zenith during this time. Check out the Feldstein covers on *Junior* or *Meet Corliss Archer*, to say nothing of *Phantom Lady* or *Torchy*.

Ah, the Silver Age. Several books from this era have achieved astronomical prices, namely *Amazing Fantasy* #15, when in high grade. Yet there is one key point to keep in mind about this period. For all but the earliest issues (*Showcase* #4 and the like) there are a multitude of copies out there. Comic readers, as fandom came to life in the early 1960s, began accumulating books, not disposing of them. Nonetheless, we think established values may be here to stay, with the following important caveats. First: condition is everything with comics from this age. Second: keep in mind that many collectors are buying only key Silver Age issues, that is, first appearances and origins. If collectors are not trying to complete runs of certain titles, then we should question the stability of values assigned to non-key issues.

That said, we observe that fans are collecting entire runs of *Amazing Spider-Man*, *Fantastic Four* and a few other Marvel titles. Batman collectors generally want every issue, so do Superman fans, for the most part. We must ponder whether there is much of a future for titles like *Hawkman*, *Rip Hunter*, *Metal Men*, etc.—except for key issues, that is.

Trends and Conclusions: Commerce in old comic books is laissez-faire, that is, unregulated, free from government interference. Only two unofficial regulators exist which can influence the price of a comic. First is the condition assigned to it by professional graders at CGC or CBCS. Second is the value assigned to it by the *Overstreet Comic Book Price Guide*. Otherwise, it is strictly a matter of supply and demand. Books can be physically secured and insured. But their future value in the marketplace is not guaranteed. So if you are buying strictly for investment purposes, choose wisely.

Of conventions: these days, it appears there is something for everyone. Big shows such as WizardWorld offer a platform for cosplayers but not necessarily a serious marketplace for old comics. San Diego is all about movies. But there are regional conventions which bring buyers and sellers together so real business can be done, such as in Baltimore. Among these smaller cons is the annual show in Norman, Oklahoma, put on in October by the Oklahoma Alliance of Fandom, known locally as OAF, under the direction of Bart Bush. He can be contacted at bbush3@cox.net. Real comics, real people, reasonable prices. You are cordially invited.

In conclusion, we see the market for comic books to be as vibrant as it has ever been. The auction houses are bringing to market genuinely scarce books, such as those in the Jon Berk collection sold by ComicConnect. The fan base appears to be expansive with a broader range of interests. Music and television shows generate interest in characters, old and new. Nonetheless, we still remain wary of an excess of "irrational exuberance," which can drive prices to the point where they bear no relationship to the intrinsic value of the book. We should love the art, not the object. Happy hunting!

STEVEN HOUSTON & JOHN DOLMAYAN TORPEDO COMICS

STEVEN HOUSTON

Welcome to another market report from Torpedo Comics based here in Las Vegas. This report breaks with tradition, instead of beginning with the usual sales reports, I have decided to begin with perhaps the most divisive and controversial aspect of the industry from 2016-17 – the fall of Marvel Comics. I agree that it is not the usual way to start a fact-driven report, but due to the unusual circumstances of today's market, I firmly believe its essential to come clean with some truth (no matter how painful it is)

The Market: Opinion – Marvel Comics, A Company In Crisis

This year, the market has seen DC Comics perform the greatest comeback in comics history, from the dregs of a failed New 52 Universe, to the stratospheric highs of 'Rebirth', never in my time as a retailer have I seen such a turnaround. As for DC's main competitor, Marvel Comics, never have I seen such a dismal failure to understand the market (its audience), resulting in plummeting sales and panic within the company. From September 2016 through June 2017, we dropped our Marvel orders at least 30%, actually taking the rather drastic step of only ordering some titles for subscription customers. We are talking about the biggest decline in Marvel sales across the board since those dark days of late 1994. In my opinion, the reason for this drastic sales decline is the result of two marketing campaigns, one concerning the constant search for 'collectors' and the other, perhaps more controversial, the search for new readers. Let's take a look at the search for collectors that Marvel has been on for a few years now. Basically, what I'm referencing is the constant renumbering and rebooting of series with the resulting variant editions in an effort to attract hardcore (used to be called Marvel Zombies) collectors, specifically those who want everything and feel obligated to collect everything. For the last few years, Marvel's marketing team has unleashed a series of blatant 'sales hunting' promotions, showering readers of new product with a host of new number one's, then allowing the new series to continue for twenty or thirty issues before ending said series and beginning a fresh new volume with its huge amount of fresh new variants. Marvel has basically drowned its readership with reboots and restarts until the customers began to lose interest and actually drop titles. After talking with various customers, I am yet to meet any that thinks all these reboots are a good idea – not one.

The second aspect of Marvel's marketing and editorial direction concerned the search for NEW readers. Of course, there is nothing wrong with this publishing method, comic book publishers have been trying to garner new readers, with all sorts of new ideas and promotions, almost since the beginning of the medium, but what made this effort different was the way Marvel seemed to be blatantly pushing established readers away. The most maddening aspect of this new Marvel editorial policy was the fact that Marvel's extremely successful movie franchises exposed numerous Marvel characters to the widest possible audience and then when it came to the publishing division, they decided to ignore the movies. Thus, let's say someone has been watching the *Avengers* and *Iron Man* movies and decides to take a look in a comic store...yes, you've got it, they will NOT find Tony Stark on the new issue rack, only in back-issue bins or older trade paperbacks. The same scenario holds true for the Bruce Banner Hulk, Hawkeye, Wolverine and Thor. They replaced Tony Stark with a teenage girl, the Dr. Banner Hulk with a Korean teenager, Thor with Jane Foster, Wolverine with a teen-age girl, Hawkeye with a woman, among other history-wrecking decisions.

Regarding Thor – perhaps the poster boy of mistreatment, over the last ten years the writers and editors have systematically destroyed the mythos of Asgard, thus any fan of the Thor movies would see NOTHING in which to relate. They would see no Asgard, but Asgardia, no Odin, just three women ruling Asgardia and even worse, the Thor they see in the movies is now 'unworthy' and can't even hold Mjolnir – his mighty hammer! On a personal level (which I'm loath to state, but here goes...) After collecting Thor religiously since 1987 (completing a near full-set) I'm no longer interested in the title – I don't recognize these characters any more, and I wonder how many older fans of Thor are out there, just like me?

One must think hard about this situation for a moment, how could this happen? How could a publishing giant who employs hundreds of super-talented and creative minds suddenly lose all concepts of what makes a Marvel Comic special? The only conclusion one can come to is that the 'powers that be', were under the assumption that something was wrong with the Marvel Universe and it needed to be changed for this new progressive era. With this in mind, writers and editors were hired who were not steeped in Marvel Universe knowledge, but brought something else to the creative process – the ability to ignore established continuity and even worse, the need to tear down what has gone before. The main bone of contention from this new group of editors and writers seems to be that Marvel was suffering from a severe lack of diversity, both ethnic and gender within its universe. Not hard to see, when one considers that Marvel's early days go all the way back to 1939, when such concerns were not even an afterthought. The basic thrust of the idea to bring more diversity to the Marvel Universe is a good one, both socially and financially. There is no downside to bringing more characters of various ethnic heritage or genders to the fore, a marketing technique that could attract NEW readers to the Marvel Universe. The problem was the way in which this 'edict' was implemented, not by creating NEW characters that would be added to the sandbox known as the Marvel Universe, but rather, take the easy way out and simply replace established characters with new ones. We are talking about a serious case of creative bankruptcy here, not the famous 'House of Ideas' from days of yore. Someone working in the upper echelons (highly paid no doubt) of Marvel thought this was a good time for this (insane) publishing strategy and look where we are, dropping sales and perhaps an opportunity lost. In fact, I believe that when the history of comics is written, the absolute failure of Marvel to capitalize on the successes of their blockbuster movies by translating movie fans into readers, will be a cautionary tale, told again and again by creative publishing businesses of HOW TO DESTROY YOUR BASE READERSHIP!

Update – according to Marvel's solicitations for August through November of 2017, they are heavily promoting 'Marvel Legacy', which Marvel exclaims, "Marvel Legacy continues with fresh, exciting stories that define the next chapter in Marvel history while honoring that which came BEFORE!" What can be discerned from the solicitations is Marvel's panic, as it tries to stop the bleeding of its readership, by calling for the return of their ESTABLISHED audience, readers who were pushed away by Marvel's destructive creative decisions, or as they would say, 'bold new editorial policies'. How are they trying to bring readers back into the fold? Well, they are brushing off the tried and true renumbering gig again, giving readers *Thor* #700, *Iron Man* #593, *Incredible Hulk* #709 and so on and so on. The real test for Marvel will be how long they can continue with the older numbering, before the urge to create a host of new number ones overwhelms them. Let's see if Marvel can turn things around for next year's report, I doubt it, but I'm ever hopeful, the industry needs a strong and viable Marvel Comics.

Okay, back to the regularly scheduled reports.... The beginning of my last report in the 47th *Overstreet Guide* began with news of our new store in Las Vegas, so not wanting to break with 'tradition', I'm announcing that our NEW bigger and better store, opened with a massive creator-signing event on May 19th 2017. After encouraging sales from our previous store, John decided to jump into a larger location. Going all-out, not only with the amount of product for sale, but also with the signing at the store. John organized a three-day signing event, featuring Jim Lee on the 19th, Arthur Adams on the 20th and J. Scott Campbell on the 21st. An official from the city gave their blessing to the store, which coincided with a massive advertising campaign, utilizing traditional media such as billboards and radio, as well as going 'viral' on the internet. The signing was a massive success, working in conjunction with the good fellows of CGC, setting the template for future signings. Three more signing events have occurred to date, setting an example to comic fans in Las Vegas, that Torpedo Comics is here to stay and we will be working hard to bring in new customers. We have major plans for 2018, basically entailing that we will undertake a signing event every month of the year! Ambitious yes, but we have a goal – to make Torpedo Comics 'THE' place to go in Las Vegas for the ultimate comic store experience.

The High End Market Report: The Silver Age era of comics is still the most in demand from collectors and speculators as this report is being written. The leader of the Silver Age market is still Marvel Comics. Key Marvel Silver Age books are still exploding in demand and price. Covering all grades, be it CGC or raw, the blazing heat of collector activity upon this era of comics has not abated, in fact, as the price of the higher grades reaches ever higher, demand is falling upon lower grades. The 2016-17 season has been our most successful ever for CGC sales. It seems as if everyone wants to join the Marvel 'key issue' party these days, with lower end collectors stretching their budgets to breaking point to snatch up the 1.8 and 2.0 grades of most Marvel keys. The super-hot book of last year, *Incredible Hulk* #1 has cooled a little, while demand for Spider-Man's first appearance in *Amazing Fantasy* #15 remains strong, especially in 2.0 grades. *Avengers* #1, *Daredevil* #1 and *Tales of Suspense* #39 (first Iron Man) have been selling well, while from out of the shadows, *Fantastic Four* #1 is beginning to make a comeback. In one of the great mysteries of recent years, *Fantastic Four* #1 dipped in collector popularity, an amazing thing to see when one considers the historical significance of this issue. Well, the drought is over, as demand has exploded in the last few months as collectors and speculators have realized this book is underpriced!

Regarding DC's Silver Age keys, demand has been less spectacular, with the usual suspects being *Showcase* #4 (first Flash), *Brave and the Bold* #28 (first Justice League) and *Showcase* #22 (first Green Lantern). The rarity of these issues and the resulting high prices keeps this era of DC collecting within a small niche of high-end collectors, with lower income collectors seemingly giving up on these issues, even in 1.8 or 2.0 conditions. Where DC is shining right now is in the Golden Age market, which has experienced a rather spectacular comeback in recent months. We are not Golden Age specialists, but we have been asked many times for Golden Age *Batman* and *Detective* issues, with special attention being paid to ANY Joker covers.

Silver and Bronze Age Sales: We have sold a tremendous amount of Silver/Bronze material, from *Amazing Spider-Man*, *Batman*, *Captain America*, *Daredevil*, *Detective Comics*, *Fantastic Four*, *Flash*, *Green Lantern*, *Incredible Hulk*, *Justice League*, *Thor* and *X-Men*. The seemingly perfect price point for our customers is $30-50 a book, with nice VF 8.0 copies from the Silver/Bronze era most appreciated by the customers. We have also sold a massive amount of CGC books from our vintage selection. We have also been getting many sales within the $15-25 area, mainly from titles published from 1976-79. Most of the titles published during this era are not valuable enough to take to most shows (due to the high table costs) and so we were able to bring many of these titles out for the first time in the store. Titles like *Amazing Adventures* #18-39, *Astonishing Tales* #26-36, *Captain America* #218-240, *Daredevil* #145-167, *Howard the Duck* #2-31, *Ka-Zar* #1-20, *Marvel Chillers*, *Marvel Team-Up* #20-75, *Marvel Two-in-One* #10-50 and *Thor* #240-280. As for DC Comics, *Batman* and *Detective* from the late 1970s have always sold, but at the store we have been able to sell issues of some of the more odd titles, such as *Black Lightning*, *DC Special Series*, *DC Super Stars*, *First Issue Special*, *Karate Kid*, *Kobra*, *Omac*, *Richard Dragon Kung Fu Fighter* and the *Secret Society of Super-Villains*. I have to admit, I always get a rush when I see titles like this popping up on the sales sheets. The price point and condition level that seems the most attractive to collectors of this material ranges from $10-15 with conditions around the VF, VF+ and especially the VF/NM grade.

As to the 'bread and butter' of 1960s and 1970s back-issue sales, the icon titles such as *Amazing Spider-Man*, *Batman* and *Detective* are still kings. It's rather gratifying to see collectors still attempting to either complete their runs on these long-running titles, or at least upgrade. Here are some examples of Silver Age raw back-issue sales: *Action Comics* #224 VG+ $120, *All Star Comics* #58 FN/VF $75, *Amazing Spider-Man* #19 FN- $150, #21 FN $150, #28 FN- $255, #42 FN- $80, #59 FN- $66, *Atom* #1 VG+ $275, *Avengers* #2 G $125, #181 NM- $175, *Batman* #181 FN- $250, #251 VG- $150, *Captain Marvel* #1 FN/VF $90, #17 VF- $65, #29 VF $50, #33 VG/FN $32, *Conan* #1 VF- $150, *Daredevil* #4 G/VG $80, *DC Special* #29 NM- $95, *Defenders* #2 VF+ $65, *Detective Comics* #405 FN+ $90, *Doctor Strange* #2 VF/NM $72, *Fantastic Four* #45 FN- $300, #112 FN- $85, *Flash* #113 VG- $100, *Green Lantern* #6 FN- $90, *Hawkman* #6 VF- $80, *Iron Fist* #1 FN+ $52, *Logan's Run* #6 VF/NM $90, *Marvel Spotlight* #32 VF- $75, *Star Wars* #1 VF+ $125, *Strange Tales* #123 FN/VF $95, #155 VF $75, *Sub-Mariner* #1 VF $240, *Superman* #252 VF- $65, *Tales of Suspense* #45 VG+ $200, *Tales to Astonish* #41 VG/FN $125, *Thor* #162 VF+ $80, *Warlock* #1 VF- $75, *Weird War Tales* #1 FN/VF $125, *World's Finest* #100 VG $90, and *X-Men* #97 FN/VF $100. The aforementioned issues are only a tiny fraction of our Silver and Bronze Age sales, a success to be sure and proof for us that 'If you build it they will come' – sorry for the blatant analogy, but I couldn't help myself. As for CGCs, here is a selection of sales (in store and on eBay): *Amazing Spider-Man* #1 CGC 7.5 $25,500, #1 CGC 4.0 (restored) Signature Series Stan Lee $3000, #14 (first Green Goblin), CGC 6.0 $1000, #129 (first Punisher) CGC 9.2 $2500, CGC 8.5 $1800, #149 CGC 9.6 $500, #300 (full Venom) CGC 9.8 $2500, *Avengers* #1 CGC 7.5 Signature Series Stan Lee $10,000, #4 (Captain America returns) CGC 9.2 $12,500, 7.5 $4000, #55 (first Ultron) CGC 9.2 $800, #57 (first Vision) CGC 9.0 $1200, #196 (first full Taskmaster) CGC 9.8 $600, *Batman* #49 CGC 4.0 $700, #121(first Mr. Freeze) CGC 4.5 $1750, #232 CGC 7.5 $450, *Daredevil* #1 CGC 8.0 $6000, #7 CGC 8.5 $900, *Detective Comics* #69 (Golden Age Joker cover) CGC 6.0 $21,000, #359 (Batgirl) CGC 6.5 $1050, *Fantastic Four* #4 (Sub-Mariner returns) CGC 6.0 $2500, #5 (first Dr. Doom) CGC 6.0 $3500, #8 CGC 5.0 $500, #48 (first Silver Surfer) CGC 9.6 $9000, #66 CGC 9.2 $900, *Flash* #110 CGC 7.0 $1800, *Hero for Hire* #1 CGC 7.5 $600, *Incredible Hulk* #1 CGC 7.0 $50,000, CGC 2.5 $9500, #2 CGC 4.0 $1200, #181 (first Wolverine) CGC 9.2 Signature Series Stan Lee $6500, #181 CGC 9.6 $9500, *Iron Man* #1 CGC 9.4 $2400, #55 (first Thanos), CGC 8.5 $1500, *Journey into Mystery* #83 (first Thor) CGC 7.5 Signature Series Stan Lee $21,000, CGC 3.5 Signature Series Stan Lee $2000, 3.0 $4000, *Showcase* #10 CGC 6.0 $800, *Silver Surfer* #1 CGC 5.0 $500, *Star Trek* #1 (Gold Key) CGC 8.0 $900, *Star Wars* #1 CGC 9.8 $1500, *Strange Tales* #110 (first Dr. Strange) CGC 6.0 $3500, *Superman* #15 (Golden Age) CGC 5.0 $1000, *Superman's Pal Jimmy Olsen* #135 CGC 8.5 $600, *Tales to Astonish* #27 (first Henry Pym) CGC 7.0 $10,500, *Tales of Suspense* #39 (first Iron Man) CGC 7.5 Signature Series Stan Lee $17,500, *Thor* #165 CGC 8.0 $700, and *X-Men* #1 CGC 7.5 $15,000, #1 CGC 5.5 Signature Series Stan Lee $3800.

Copper and Modern Comic Sales Report: This report is based on some minor convention sales, but most of the information revealed here is from our store. This is the first year where we have had such a large selection of comics from 1980 through 2016 for sale in the same location, seven days a week. Given that caveat, and the fact that we note all sales in meticulous fashion, I'm confident that this report is the most accurate ever given by Torpedo Comics.

Regarding sales from titles published between 1980 and 1989, the usual keys sell well, specifically *Amazing Spider-Man* #300 (the Venom movie!!), *Batman* #404-407 (Year One), *Batman* #426-429 (Death in the Family), *Batman the Dark Knight Returns* #1-4, *DC Comics Presents* #26 (first New Teen Titans), *Marvel Secret Wars* #8 (origin black Spidey costume), *New Teen Titans* #2 (first Deathstroke), *Tales of the New Teen Titans* #44 (first Nightwing), *Thor* #337 (first Beta Ray Bill), *Transformers* #1, *Watchmen* #1-12 and *Wolverine* #1 (1982 series). What has been a surprise is the rather slow sales of the core 1980s icon titles such as *Amazing Spider-Man*, *Captain America*, *Daredevil*, *Fantastic Four*, *Incredible Hulk*, *Iron Man*, *Justice League*, *Legion of Super-Heroes*, *New Teen Titans*, *Thor* and even the *X-Men*. One has to acknowledge that the sheer amount of back-issue inventory from the 1980s is mind-blowing and the added pressure of high-end reprints of material from this era is not helping. Low to medium grade 1980s are practically worthless at this time, with the minimum grade we put in the store being VF (8.0) with VF/NM (9.0) to NM (9.4) being the preferred grade by those collectors seeking out 1980s titles.

As for the 1990s, Spider-Man and Batman rule the sales charts, with interest in Venom peaking right now, due to the news that Tom Hardy has agreed to play Eddie Brock in a Venom movie. Our best non-Marvel or DC title is *Spawn*, which still sells very well – in fact Todd McFarlane's work is still held in high esteem by his fans both old (those that were there in the '90s) and newer fans. The other fan-favorite character to break out in the 1990s, Deadpool is still selling well, especially his first appearance in *New Mutants* #98, the two limited series from 1993 and 1994 and especially the 1997 series #1-12. Other mutant titles are not faring too well, with the lowest X-Men back-issue sales I have ever seen as a retailer. Surprise of the year, must be the explosion in sales of *Infinity War* #1-6, a book that was printed in huge quantities and considered quarter-bin fodder for many years has suddenly become of interest to speculators. Yes, I'm talking about the upcoming *Avengers: Infinity War* blockbuster, a movie that has no relation to the comic of 1992, except the name!

According to our sales reports, DC's sales are dominated by not only *Batman*, but his massive family of related titles, such as *Birds of Prey*, *Catwoman*, *Nightwing* and *Robin*, leaving many titles languishing in the back-issue bins, such as *Legion*, all Superman books and even the *Teen Titans*. *Green Lantern* sales are okay, with the *Flash* selling the best from all non-Batman related titles – a testament to the power of the television series.

As for Marvel, apart from *Deadpool*, *Amazing Spider-Man* and the various Venom limited series, sales have been stunningly cold, caused (in my opinion) by the rather lackluster new product on the new issue racks. In terms of independent titles, we pulled all the classics out, as well as some obscure series, but reaction has been muted, to say the least, a direct result of many of these publishers characters and universes being 'dead' to the modern audience.

As for the 2000s, Batman and his related titles have an even more dominant stranglehold on back-issue sales than either the 1980s or the 1990s. DC has had a successful 2000s in terms of creating huge story arcs, especially with the *Blackest Night* Green Lantern epic, *52*, *Countdown*, *Infinite Crisis*, but Batman and related titles have grown to dominate sales. While DC's New 52 initiative eventually ground to a halt, their answer has turned out to be an outstanding success – 'Rebirth'. Our sales reports show clearly that DC 'Rebirth' titles make up 60% of all back-issue sales over the last year. In fact when the 'Rebirth' back issue sales are taken into account, the period covering 2015-2016 contains more sales than 2000-2014! Other than Marvel the recent back-issue market is very strong, especially if one adds in the thousands of variant editions available to avid collectors.

Comic Sales Related To The Movies: As most dealers already know the real heat for a given back issue after a television series or movie is announced that features said character, is about two years before the actual movie is released. Once the movie is released, prices drop and it's onto the 'next big thing'. As for 2016, the back-issue heat for Doctor Strange cooled off, just as the movie was released and *Strange Tales* #110 (first Doctor Strange) cooled off and then went cold! Most grades under 8.0 have fallen off from 2015 prices, however, interest in other Doctor Strange issues has continued at a higher rate than before 2015. This is especially true for *Doctor Strange* #169, which is holding strong in 8.0 and above, especially in raw ungraded condition. In fact, this book sells far better raw than in CGC. Every copy we have had this year has sold, from 4.0 to 7.0, so for this dealer, *Doctor Strange* #169 was the breakout book for the doctor, not *Strange Tales* #110. Also still selling well are any copies of *Marvel Premiere* #3 and *Doctor Strange* #1 (1974). Both issues have been elevated due to the movies release and so the days of finding these issues for cheap are over. We price raw copies of *Doctor Strange* #169 in 9.0 at $600, *Marvel Premiere* #3 in 9.2 at $250 and *Doctor Strange* #1 in 9.2 at $300.

***Doctor Strange* #169 was more of a breakout book than *Strange Tales* #110.**

Marvel's other blockbuster release this year, *Guardians*

of the Galaxy 2, had little effect on the already well-scouted keys from this franchise: First Drax/Thanos from *Iron Man* #55, first Gamora in *Strange Tales* #180, first Nebula from *Avengers* #256, first Rocket Raccoon from *Marvel Preview* magazine #7 and first Starlord from *Marvel Preview* magazine #4. As for Groot, his first appearance in *Tales to Astonish* #13 (1960) is still hot, with collectors still struggling to find any copies over 2.0, which is not really hard to understand when one considers that to date, only six copies have been graded above 8.0. The current 9.2 *Guide* price is listed at $8000, however, I must admit, I think if the 9.2 copy (purchased in 2012 for $2868) was to come to market, I estimate a price of $20,000 – easy! Apparently there is a 9.4 copy graded that has never been sold, the price for that gem would be astronomical in my opinion. As for the other characters who appeared in the movie, their appearances exploded in price and demand, with Ego's first appearance in *Thor* #132 momentarily disappearing from back-issue bins across the country, however as of writing, prices on this book have stabilized at $250-300 for a 9.2 copy. The first appearance of Mantis in *Avengers* #112 was in much higher demand and then dropped off to lower levels. This book that was once selling for as much as $530 in 9.2 (back in 2015) has now fallen to under $200, a spectacular example of the current level of speculator boom and bust approach to movie and TV characters purloined from the comics. The other character to receive collector and speculator attention from the movie was Ayesha, formally Her and originally Paragon. This one proved to be tough for the speculators, which book was going to be the hot one? Some chose the original appearance of Paragon from *Incredible Hulk Annual* #6 (1977), others decided upon *Marvel Two-in-One* #61 (1980), the first appearance of Her, while a few brave souls chose the first appearance of Ayesha, from *Fantastic Four* #11 (1998). With books of this era (1977-98), high-grade CGC 9.8 copies were the collector's choice and incredible as it may seem, the *Hulk Annual* managed to break the $500 mark (in 9.8), while the *Guide* price for 9.2 copies is currently listed at $12.

Speculator and collector interest with the few key characters of the *Thor: Ragnarok* movie have fans hunting down *Journey Into Mystery* #102 (1st Hela), especially after seeing Hela in her full glory via previews of the movie. Looks like the *Overstreet* entry for *Journey into Mystery* #102 will have to be changed next year, as at this time, the *Guide* makes no reference to Hela's appearance in issue #102. We sold a raw 2.0 for $150 at Comic Con, not bad considering the current *Guide* price is $38! Other Hela appearances have seen a little spike in interest as well, especially *Thor* #150 with its beautiful red cover ($145 in 9.2 in the current *Guide*). The real heat in terms of speculator and collector interest is not with any comic published in the 1960s or the 1970s, but rather, a modern comic – *Incredible Hulk* #92 (2006), which is the first appearance of the 'Planet Hulk' story, the subject of the popular movie preview, where the Hulk and Thor are seen getting ready to battle as 'space gladiators'. Currently this book guides at $5 in 9.2, however a quick perusal of eBay will show a wide range of prices, all emblazoned with the tagline – '*Ragnarok* movie', ranging from $50 for raw NM copies, up to $200 for a CGC 9.8 copy.

Regarding DC/Warner Bros., they released *Wonder Woman* on June 2nd of 2017 to critical and financial success, however the actual impact on the world of comics was negligible at best. *Wonder Woman* back-issue sales have picked up from a few years ago, but with most *Wonder Woman* keys already expensive and out of the price range of most collectors, there have been no discernable price increases on any *Wonder Woman* issues. DC's 'big kahuna' – the *Justice League* movie seems to have had a negligible effect on *JLA* (Silver and Bronze age) back issues as a whole, with the more modern *Flash* issues being more popular than either *Aquaman*, *Superman* or *Wonder Woman*. *Batman* still sells well (from all eras) but that is due to the core Batman fan base and has nothing to do with his appearance in the *Justice League* movie. Opening on July 7th 2017, the latest episode in the Spider-Man movie franchise, *Spider-Man: Homecoming*, opened to some critical praise and surprised many with its box office power, but in terms of comics, nothing came out of this movie for speculators to grab hold off. In fact, in terms of the wider comic market, summer 2016 through the summer of 2017 has seen some slowing down of the movie related speculator boom. This can be said of the various TV and cable shows as well, leading to one conclusion - fans and speculators are in limbo right now, a sort of holding pattern as they consume every movie tip they can get their hands on, looking for the next big thing. In terms of the calendar, the next big movie to hit the theatres is the *Black Panther*, arriving in February of 2018 and then the ultimate super-hero blockbuster: *Avengers Infinity War* (Part One, slated for May 2018). With the major key for the Justice League movie being either *Brave and the Bold* #28 or *Justice League of America* #1, there's no chance of speculators picking up a 'steal' on this book, so demand has been rather calm on these books, with no real heat on any other Justice League books either. Looking past the *Justice League* movie and onto the *Black Panther*, the story could not be more different. *Fantastic Four* #52-53 are still in demand (down from a year ago, but still respectable), with much of the new heat falling on *Jungle Action* #6, the first appearance of Killmonger (to be played by Michael B. Jordan). This book began getting some speculator attention last year, as noted by the $150 *Guide* price in 9.2 in this year's *Guide* (#47) and prices have continued to increase, with raw 9.2 copies currently selling for $250/300 with a CGC 9.8 selling for $1250 in November 2016.

In Conclusion: Some of you who have read my reports in the past may be wondering where my convention report information is – please see John Dolmayan's report regarding any Torpedo Comics insight into conventions. I agree with everything he wrote.

Even though one publisher continually falls upon its

own sword, the industry as a whole is strong, with a vast array of publishers creating cutting edge material for a whole new generation of readers and collectors. DC Comics is going through another Golden Age of creativity, managing to bring readers back into the fold with 'Rebirth', even though many promised never to come back towards the end of the misguided New 52 initiative. They are now in the driver's seat for the entire industry, and it's up to everyone else to catch them.

John Dolmayan - Torpedo Comics

2017 has been a great year for Torpedo Comics. We have moved our store to an amazing location in Las Vegas at 7300 Arroyo Crossing Parkway suite 105 and have achieved a personal goal of creating a comic book store reminiscent of what drew me to the industry in the first place. Interestingly enough, it's a store full of comics ranging in age and price from 1939 to present with an emphasis on back issues, over 200 long boxes at present, with over 1000 CGC and CBCS Comics on hand at any given time. We have filled our 3500 square foot location with high end, investment grade comics and collectibles such as first edition books and high end limited edition statues as well as vintage toys but mostly we have tens of thousands of comic books and original art. Robert Isaac, our store manager and our team have worked incredibly hard to bring a list of guests to our store only rivaled by the biggest comic conventions and we pledge to continue to bring amazingly talented people closer to the fans who love them, with at least one event per month. Come to Torpedo Comics In Las Vegas, you won't be disappointed.

As much as we have tried to build a real comic book store and not just one in name, it seems like the convention industry is doing just the opposite. The prices just keep going up and the real collectors either can't get in or just do not want to go through the bother. We have cut our convention schedule down to just these shows; Emerald City, C2E2, Wondercon, Silicon Valley, San Diego Comic-Con, and Stan Lee's Los Angeles Comic Con (going to the east coast is not an option but we are working on it). We had planned to expand to around 30 shows per year, but it became clear to us that most shows and expos had as much to do with collecting comics as pizza does to yogurt. Some "comic cons" have as little as 3% comic book dealers out of 1000 booths, pathetic. It's understandable that with the popularity of comic book related movies people are attending conventions who know nothing about comics on any level, yet they'll buy something like a Pop! toy or t-shirt but the concept of buying comics is completely alien to them, trust me we tried. The costs go up and our profits go down, couple that with some buyers who think they are experts quoting GPA as the beginning and end of the cost of our goods. Never factoring in rent, employee costs, taxes, convention costs, etc., and that most dealers report no sales to GPA, most shops report no sales, and that as a general rule even if the last sale was $100 why would I sell it for less or even at the same price? When the GPA conversation comes up we suggest the buyer find the nearest GPA store or booth and buy from them and leave us alone. In other words bottom feed off someone else, we know what we have, we know our grading, and we pay top dollar for quality and expect to be paid accordingly for quality. Our customers make profits hand over fist as a general rule because we sell them the best possible books and don't push crap inventory. We have all seen the same clowns who go from booth to booth looking for the dealer who mis-priced a book or doesn't know a book is on fire and like a lion looking for the injured gazelle they will look at every book you have and purchase nothing. These are not collectors who you can spend hours talking comics with, they are scum, and when they are at my booth, I wait with eager anticipation for them to find something to purchase, so that I can tell them it's not for sale and raise the price after they leave. Something has to change, with the tide of rising prices and less real buyers, shows like Terry O'Neill's Yorba Linda one day show are making a real splash and I imagine we will see more of these types of smaller, more comic-centric shows springing up across the country. Who knows, perhaps we will have one of our own one-day shows as well.

Aside from the boobs we all should avoid, there has been a steady stream of fresh collectors and investors coming into the hobby and spending a lot of money on key issues all across the board. *Amazing Fantasy* #15 is skyrocketing and should level off if only momentarily but the books to buy as many copies as you can find are *X-Men* #1, *Fantastic Four* #1-10,12 and #48, in my opinion these books are under-valued and a lot of money will be made on them going forward. As always I recommend to all my investors buy as many copies of the keys as possible and if a great deal is available don't shy away from multiple copies of the keys. We now have a concierge program at Torpedo Comics, we hand-pick great investments for our clients depending on their particular budget and provide full appraisals for insurance purposes. The plan we place in motion is a constant five-year return on investment where the portfolio is turned over every five years, we will happily explain to any new investors who are interested in joining the program. Comics, as always, are great places to invest in something real. A fun way to make money and touch on the spirit and love we all had as youths for these amazing heroes and story lines.

The future looks bright and as usual we look forward to seeing you our friends at conventions and at our store. We wish you all health and happiness and amazing comic book finds!

Jeff Itkin
Elite Comic Source

Yes, another year has gone by, and like many of the previous years it was filled with many positive events in comics. Thankfully, Elite Comic Source is here to break it down for you, but before we get started I'd like to thank everyone responsible for continuing to put all their efforts and time in annually publishing *The Overstreet Comic Book Price Guide*. It truly is a wonderful source of comic illumination that covers a gamut of information. I'd also like to acknowledge and thank our fans and patrons that continue to purchase from us at conventions and online at our new website elitecomicsource.com and the many conventions we attend. Ok, no more acknowledgements and shameless plugs, time to analyze the exciting and soaring value of collectible comic books, the marketplace and superhero movie dominance in cinema.

Then and Now: Prior to 2017 there was a 5-year span in which I witnessed a continued decline in non-key back issue purchases. People stopped buying the filler issues in runs and focused their funds on key books. Collectors and investors were drawn to the excitement and exposure through the larger than life characters of the big screen and the growing comic market. Money has been pouring into first appearances of major characters and classic covers across all time frames and reaching record highs almost monthly every year. But for the first time in almost half a decade I finally witnessed a small resurgence in back issue sales. Collectors may be getting back to the basics of buying for more enjoyment and exploration than investment. I believe this trend should continue, but as usual pricing is still an issue as buyers are hoping for a deal and will shop around if they feel they can get a book elsewhere for less.

There was a good variety of publishers and titles sold across the board. The usual powerhouse of sales came from Marvel with a strong second place showing from DC, who had a large uptick of interest last year and will again this year. I expect another good year in comics as interest and exposure is not slowing down anytime soon.

Golden Age: Comics are awesome to collect but Golden Age is even more amazing. It continues to be my favorite time frame and the most fulfilling in all aspects of collecting for me. Prices continue to soar to heights that appear to have no ceiling at times. The blue chip comics in this time frame are always in demand and coveted, and when one gets out of reach financially the next in its place will shortly follow. If you get a chance to purchase any mega GA key for market you better jump on it. The chance may come around just once and if you hesitate, someone else is not far behind you to purchase it from underneath you.

Some of the hottest books (outside of the already elite issues) I have seen for the GA in 2017 that will continue to grow this year are: Any *Detective Comics* and *Batman* comics with Joker covers and 1st appearances of any major Bat-Villains, *Action Comics* #21(first appearance of Lex Luthor), *Captain America Comics* #46, *Pep Comics* #22 (first appearance of Archie), *All Star Comics* #3(first appearance of Justice Society), *All-American Comics* #61 (first appearance of Solomon Grundy) and many, many more. If jumping into Golden Age you can feel confident in putting your money into first appearances of any top character and feel confident you have something that is going to be in demand and continue to grow in value for a long time to come.

Atomic Age: A strong year for this time frame as just about anything Sci-fi, Horror, Gangster, Romance and Super Hero in grades 7.0 or higher can expect to sell in multiples of *Guide,* if you can find some of these rare issues at all. I find that some of the most dedicated and passionate collectors in our collectible find this to be their age of interest. It is a truly fascinating time frame, filled with important comic history, with highly publicized trials of questionable comic book material, comic codes and a transition of popularity from Superhero comics to Gangster, Romance, Sci-Fi and Horror. It may have also brought us one of the greatest Good Girl Artist ever. His name is Matt Baker, and in my opinion his ability to capture the beauty of his female characters is still unmatched to this day. Any Romance cover with his work is easily multiples of *Guide* in any grade, extremely rare and especially coveted by a steep growing market of collectors. He is also most famous for his work on *Phantom Lady* but my favorite titles of his are *Diary Secrets*, *Teenage Romance*, *Wartime Romance*, and *Cinderella Love*. If you get a chance check out *Cinderella Love* #25, *Teen-Age Romances* #32 and *Diary Secrets* #15,17, and 19.

Silver Age: This era is the king of all eras, as it brings the most attention and recognitions amongst a larger scope of collectors and con attendees. All mainstream Marvel titles continue to stay strong followed by DC's line up of super heroes. Back issues were steady but Key issues still rule the market. There continues to be strong growth in an ever-thriving market. *Amazing Fantasy* #15 continues to dominate this era, as it should. It has the most recognized Marvel Character in the world, an iconic cover, a great story and created by the legendary Stan Lee. With the sharp increased value of this book a ripple effect is echoing across all other mega keys. The aphorism "A rising tide raises all boats" couldn't be any truer. Every mega Silver Age Key has gone up in price and will continue to play catch up through 2018 as I don't see any slowing down of *Amazing Fantasy* #15. Another positive take from 2017 is that DC keys continued to be very strong in the marketplace. Obviously not to the extent of Marvel's more loved and recognized characters, but the DC market has been growing and evolving consistently the past few years. The DC growth should continue for years to come as it still has many great opportunities to invest in and collect at reasonable prices. Especially in comparison to its counterpart. Collectors are quick and savvy, and it won't take long for things to change, so if you are at all thinking about some DC keys to purchase, do it sooner than later.

Bronze and Copper Age: Another year of being the top selling time frame for Elite Comic Source, at least in regard to the number of individual books sold. It is strongly felt that many great characters and artists rule this time frame. It was an influential era of comic innovation, storytelling, dynamic cover and interior page design as well as strong character development. These aspects from this time frame helped seed and give birth to the next generation of readers, collectors and the con attendees who hope to meet some of the industry's greatest artists. Back issues sales of non-key issues were stronger in 2017 than prior years and should continue into this year. The selling strategy has not changed for this time frame as everything other than extremely high grade or key has to be sold at half of *Guide*. This has been a standard practice for us and many others for a decade now.

Chrome Age/Steel Age(1992-2003): Nothing really new and exciting here. Anything with Deadpool, Spawn, Venom, Carnage, Batman, Spider-Man, Valiant, Harley Quinn and Batman were consistent best sellers at all cons. *Batman Adventures* #12 is still a strong sell, but has slowed down greatly from its 2016 demand and *Spawn* #1 black and white is still a consistently strong sell.

Current/Modern Age(2003-Now): I really enjoy this period of comics, a true exploration into innovation. A scramble by every publisher to strike gold with some new character, story line or hot new artist. These business practices have led to an endless sea of reading material with bottomless story arcs across all genres. It can be quite a chore to amass all the issues for a title you have an interest in. But the glory of this era is its solution to this dilemma with Graphic Novels and Trade Paperbacks. For nearly 10+ years the industry has more and more adopted this format as a regular practice for nearly every title published. A patron can now walk into any shop and have a library to choose from with complete story arcs. It really makes a great environment for people to enter a comic store and locate something easy for them to find interest in.

Movies/TV/Cartoons: The representations of comic characters in the many facets of media were very strong in 2017 and will continue through this year and years to come. Regrettably a representation doesn't guarantee a positive experience nor movie success. This year did have some let downs on a few highly anticipated movies. A movie that did not disappoint and exceeded already high expectations was *Wonder Woman*, this was an outstanding movie and seemed to give some life and hope that DC has finally gotten a clue on how to properly make a movie that supports characters outside of just Superman and Batman. Disappointingly it was 4-5 months later when we received *Justice League* and that nasty doubt began to set in again as the movie fell well short of expectations. Fortunately, it had enough interest and eye candy to fool enough people and that is all that will be needed for a launching point and the future of the DC universe in theaters. We were at least able to witness a commitment to DC's larger picture for it's future with the main cast appearances of The Flash, Aquaman and Cyborg.

Marvel continues their dominance in movies and crushed it with *Thor: Ragnorok* and *Spider-Man: Homecoming*. We also got to see the second installment of *Guardians of the Galaxy*, but unfortunately that left me disappointed and wondering what the hell was that. The year ended with *Star Wars* latest installment, *The Last Jedi*, and like all *Star Wars* movies it was highly touted and anticipated. Unfortunately, to me this movie was a massive let down and I have lost any small faith in this title I already had in ever consistently getting back on track to greatness. As for the next installment of Star Wars due in May 2019, I will not be rushing out to see another disappointing movie.

Netflix and Cable TV shows for both Marvel and DC have continued success with their series. I haven't watched everything, but I have definitely seen a lot. DC dominates TV and keeps interest with large multi-show crossover events. Really enjoying *The Flash* as my favorite DC show and love watching *Agents of S.H.I.E.L.D.* Watched *Inhumans* as well but that was a bit of a stinker and hot mess, if not for the acting of Iwan Rheon (Ramsay Bolton from *Game of Thrones*) it would be completely unwatchable. Marvel has a strong presence on Netflix with dark and gritty shows, high budgets, good acting (except for *Iron Fist*, mind numbing painful casting for this character) and solid storytelling. Hard to pick a favorite on Netflix but really enjoying *Daredevil* and *The Punisher*.

Wrap Up: Our site elitecomicsource.com is up and running full steam ahead, and we will be traveling around setting up at conventions and buying collections nationwide. The comic industry was strong in 2017 with large gains in Silver Age and Golden Age Keys and will be again in 2018. Record breaking numbers every year for these books with no slowing down in sight. Comics are fun anyway you can get them, either as a reader, collector, investor or child still trying to figure it out. Have fun and enjoy the collectible. If you are a comic collector and investor, I'll leave you with my mantra, "buy smart, sell smarter."

Dr. Steven Kahn
Inner Child Comics and Collectibles

Subsequent to being named as an Overstreet advisor in last year's edition (something I could have never imagined happening), I sat down and tried to figure out why it happened and how I could make a contribution to the book and hobby. Up until last year, I considered myself just another collector on steroids. The passion and excitement of collecting helped me to create a second act in my life that is exhilarating and satisfying beyond my dreams. After practicing oral surgery for over 40 years, I let it go and opened my store, The Inner Child Comics and Collectibles about 5 years ago, in Kenosha Wisconsin.

Instead of going to work with anxiety and stress of how things might go terribly wrong and the heavy responsibility of the job itself, and acting as a surgeon and an anesthesiologist at the same time, I now go to work every day filled with excitement and anticipation. I never know who may drop in the store or call me with something that I may have never owned, and possibly never even seen. Although significant finds may be few and far between, I, nonetheless feel like a kid on Christmas morning whenever the phone rings or someone pops in the store. It is, and continues to be, intoxicating.

I have been religiously buying this price guide for over the last 30 years. Each summer, I'd find myself getting increasingly excited as the San Diego Comic-Con approached because I knew that the *Guide* was about to be released. Even though we now have the ability to track current comic values in a nearly real time manner through various Apps and the Internet, I discovered that I still need and use the *Guide* as much as I ever have.

It would seem that the *Guide* would have become obsolete. And yet it roars on. While probably 95 per cent of all collectible price guides have disappeared and are no longer available in any form in print or online, *Overstreet* has defied the odds and dominates the collectible industry. It has truly become a behemoth. Clocking in at 1200+ pages, it is a testament to the hard working staff. And for me, none of this would have ever happened if it were not for the encouragement I got from Jeff Vaughn throughout these recent years. His vision has guided me as a colleague and friend. Whenever we speak, our mutual enthusiasm is contagious and I feel excited to be involved in the hobby more than ever. He is a great contributor and motivator.

To better understand the importance of the *Guide*, we need to step back a bit. It is important to remember that there was a time before the Internet. To a large extent, most of us had faint ideas of what anything in the field of comics was worth prior to 1971. There were limited reference resources. The original *Overstreet Guides* were typewritten sheets transferred to book form. *Overstreet* became an oasis for all of us to drink in the knowledge of what our collections were worth and what to pay to fill out our runs. There was nowhere else to get this information. Probably the best analogy I could make would be to compare it to getting a new Beatles album in the 1960s. You would come home, barricade yourself in your room for days on end, and soak it all in. *Overstreet* gave us knowledge and knowledge was power.

The value of *Overstreet* extends beyond the pricing itself. There is so much more to comic collecting and Overstreet has provided a resource that can fill your time literally for for months after you receive a new edition. My favorite part of the *Guide* has always been, and continues to be, the market reports like the one you are reading now. Over the years, I developed a long list of favorites. For example, missing Doug Sulipa's encyclopedic and detailed contributions would probably have left a void in my collecting life. Having never met Doug, I have called him a couple of times and his eager willingness to share his knowledge, time and experience was refreshing and formed a great model to apply to myself. I hope that I can provide and perform a similar service for any readers that might have questions for me. I am generally available 7 days a week, 18 hours a day. Please give me a call.

On the other hand, the hyperbole of some of the reports is something that I learned to process very differently. These reports seemed to be addressed to an audience that does not have the material of which they speak. There are too many reports parroting the same findings which apply to a microscopic fragment of the collecting community. I will address my take on that later in my report.

I would pose this question. How many of my fellow collectors have a long box or two of 9.6-9.8 graded key or semi key Silver or Bronze books? And who of you out there has recently snagged a collection of *Marvel Mystery* or Golden Age *Caps*? They are getting as rare as hen's teeth. Finding important collections is getting harder and harder. While I love to read about how healthy the marketplace is, I suspect that once you skim beneath the surface, a totally different picture appears. I've discovered this when talking to dealers and collectors who are not in that rarefied air and that we read about in these market reports. As the saying goes, the rich get richer. And then there's the rest of us.

We need to also consider that the average collector has limited funds and cannot invest the capital to grade most of his key books. And yet while it need not be repeated, in order to get the maximum return in highly desirable books, grading is the only option.

We therefore need to pick and choose carefully and even today many collectors are unaware of the benefit of utilizing pre-screening options to help control costs. Once a collector gets burned after submitting books that he doesn't realize are mid-grade at best, he will tend to shy away from future submissions. I can't tell you how many CGC graded books I have received over the years from collections where the collector submitted books where the grading cost more than the book was worth.

What To Do When It's Time To Pass On Your Collection: There are important choices that you need to make regarding where your treasures go when the time comes to move away from your collection. whether that decision is due to financial considerations, downsizing, or a variety of other reasons, it is critical to take the time to do a thorough assessment and make the right choice.

For many of you, if you presume that your spouse or children will suddenly give as much care or attention to the dispersion of your collection after you are gone, when they barely tolerated it while you were living with them and it for decades, think again. I have seen it repeat itself time and time again. It is as predictable as death and taxes. When you read about the stories of the great collections that were obtained over the years, many of them were obtained from totally disinterested relatives. (Note the Mile High and others).

The first thing I advise is taking the time for reflection on what it took to build your collection. And pat yourself on the back. With many of you, it took thousands of hours, along with the expense, effort, travel and disappointments along the way. There is usually a powerful emotional component expressing itself as well.

I have seen in many families that a partner, spouse or children have pent up resentment of the time that was directed elsewhere instead of towards the family, and that frequently plays out after the fact.

In addition, many just don't care. I have seen many, many times that a collector invests virtually no time at all in what to do with his or her collection until it's too late. Just remember, none of us will live forever and planning is essential. No one can figure out your wishes better than you when you are no longer there.

You then need to look at the reason you are selling your collection. I had an experience like that when I decided to retire from oral surgery. I wanted to sell my practice as that would help to finance a variety of things moving forward, so I put it on the marketplace. I discovered something that made me very uncomfortable. Not one of the people interested in purchasing the practice seemed to care about my patients. They said all the right things, but I constantly picked up signs of a lack of empathy inside them, and a self serving attitude. Their motivations were based on commerce, not people.

I discovered that, for me, the best way to see the true character of a potential purchaser was to tell them that I was not going to sell to them and then sit back and watch. It was then that all was revealed. The facade disappeared and I was exposed to who I was truly dealing with. Frequently, all the sweet talk was replaced with venom and if that is an important factor to you, you must be prepared for that and act appropriately.

When I realized that all they were interested in was how much money they might eventually drain from my patients, my decision became easy and obvious. I gave it all away. All the equipment and supplies were donated to a variety of free clinics and charities. (Note to any skeptics: donating depreciated equipment has no tax benefits whatsoever.)

You must then decide what you want in the end. if you must sell or merely want to get the best price, your options become easier. Find the best deal. It's as simple as that. But be aware that all deals are not created equal. Buyers of collections must take into account the cost of doing business, including travel, advertising costs, search engine optimization expenses and the like. Many dealers invest hundreds of thousands of dollars per year to find collections. They even brag about it in their ads. Do not be naive enough to think that these factors do not affect the final price they are willing to pay. You can't just hop on a plane and fly coast to coast at a moments notice, without paying a hefty price each time.

Remember that all collections are not created equal. Some collections are very easy to process and sell. If you have an important collection of key Golden Age books, it doesn't matter how you have organized or collated them. You will find a long line of eager buyers queuing up as soon as you put the word out. On the other hand, if you have a couple hundred long boxes of raw, uncollated comics from the '90s or comics that have to be reprocessed and bagged and boarded, and there is a lack of key issues, you must be aware of the time and cost of a third party to do all that work. You may discover that it will be difficult to get a price that is more than it would cost to change the bags and boards.

I've had a couple of observations as I seek more collections. I've noticed that the less interested the seller has in the collection or the less attached he is, the easier the negotiations are. Easy to buy, but I prefer buying a collection from someone who loved what he was doing. Passion loves passion. It is a reward in and of itself.

Next, you need to figure out where you want your collection to go. Unfortunately, in this area, your options become more limited. I am always amazed when I see serious art collections, valued at tens to hundreds of millions of dollars that are donated to renowned art museums. When I look deeper and see the contents of the collection, I realize that probably 90 to 95 per cent of it will never be seen by the public. A small portion might appear at a show, which feels to me like a mere token to satisfy the donor, nothing more. Subsequent to that, the collection disappears into the bowels of the museum, vanishing from the public forever.

If the primary reason for the donation was to create a tax write off, I would understand, but if the donor wanted the collection to be shared by future generations, it seems to be going in the wrong direction. Donating to a University would also appear to be a way to preserve a collection, but again, comics are not a priority in most museums and the probability of the general public ever having access to these collection is very unlikely. Anyone with questions about this, please feel free to contact me at any time.

How a Comic Book or Series Becomes Uncollectible: If you have ever set up at a comic book show, you will soon discover that certain titles are winners and others are losers. As a matter of fact, some titles sit in their boxes for show after show, year after year, only gathering dust. These comics have become uncollectible. They don't sell at any price point.

As a collector, how do you figure all of that out? Believe it or not, there are signs that herald these changes years before they are manifest and with a little research, you can discover what will fall into this category. There is one caveat, however. Even with the uncollectibles, #1 issues in pristine condition will attract interest. But these exceptions are far outweighed by the rules that I will explain. These rules also apply to many areas of collecting beyond comics and there is a lesson in this for all of us. The following list are major inflection points to consider.

1) The average collector is over 60 years old. Above this age, people begin to think of all the issues relating to retiring, downsizing etc. They also need to plan for the time that there will be little or no income and cannot live beyond their means. In addition, when they entered the hobby, price points were totally different and it is difficult for them to feed their habit at escalating prices and advancing years. The

peak time for investing in hobbies generally ranges from the ages of 45-60. At that time retirement is still far off, disposable income is available and collectors want to capture the memories and feelings of their youth.

2) The numbers of power players in the hobby begins to contract. The average collector will not see this one, but those in the upper echelons of collecting understand it well. In virtually every collecting category, a handful of dealers control much of the market movement. They are critical to the survival of the hobby.

3) The titles that are affected no longer sit in your neighborhood comic store or at local shows. When sellers see no activity, they stop offering them at their stores and shows and they get buried in back stock storage. Books cannot sell if they are not offered. And the death spiral begins.

4) Once the steady decline in completed sales begins, it can be very hard to stop. Initially, the decline only affects mid to lower grade books. Historically, key books in higher grade are initially immune. But as the disease spreads, things change. Key books drop in price and begin to be included in larger lots as an enticement to buy. Then even larger lots appear and then they all disappear.

5). The sell through rate on eBay drops below 20 per cent. The reality is that supply outstrips demand in many categories. At some point, a critical saturation point is reached when virtually nothing sells which can lead to a crash of the entire subset or title. As just one example, look at all of the overproduced sportscards boxes and sets from the '90s. Today, you literally cannot give these away.

The Market Today: It would seem that I'm presenting a gloomy picture of comic collecting which is contrary to many of the other reports in the *Guide*. Yet the market seems to be saying it is very healthy. So what is the truth?

From my standpoint, this market has room to absorb as much key Golden Age superhero books as is out there right now. And records will continue to fall. If you are a seller and price your graded, major key books slightly below *Guide*, you will have no trouble selling them. And the same thing applies to the Silver and Bronze keys, especially in high grade.

The popularity of the costumed superheroes continues to dominate our pop culture. And there is something remarkable there. Look no farther than Batman in the movies. Batman has been portrayed by Michael Keaton, George Clooney, Christian Bale, Ben Affleck, Val Kilmer and others. More incredibly, the public has willingly accepted a rotating lineup that would have been unthinkable a short time ago. Imagine a character like Walter White from Breaking Bad or Indiana Jones being played by a different actor with each iteration of the franchise. Unthinkable. The character rules, not the person portraying him. As long as there are good stories to tell, the characters remain strong and new generations of collectors join the hobby. It is what I have constantly told my radio audience as part of our indoctrination about what will hold its value or escalate. New collectors increase demand and demand is the driving engine is virtually every aspect of our hobby.

I'd now like to take that information and apply it to our favorite whipping boy, the Western. The Western is a great model of how entire genres ultimately fail and are unlikely to ever recover. When I was a kid, Westerns were everywhere. In the movies and on TV. There were dozens of Western TV series and almost all of them thrived. Then one day it was just all over. At the time it felt like someone just flipped a switch. Collectors aged and passed away and no one took up the mantle moving forward. In addition, unlike the superheroes, real people played these characters and they got old and passed on as well. No collectors arrived to replace the old. No demand led to no market and before you knew what happened, it was "Bye, bye Western." The only segment that survived were the toys and the guns, which still attract collectors today because of crossover interest from other collectibles. I strongly believe that some day, super heroes will suffer the same fate, but there are reasons that will not be very soon. Keep reading!

The great tonic that has kept comics in the forefront of pop culture collectibles begins with the introduction of multiple new generations of collectors. This initially developed from the mass appeal of the superhero movie. When Disney took over Marvel and bought out George Lucas and Star Wars, the dye was cast. Grown ups were now in charge and a company who knew how to protect a franchise was now in control. Disney has a rotation with its stable of characters and titles, and has figured out how to effectively reintroduce characters or movies in rotation every 10-15 years. New generation, new collectors. New Generation, new collectors. Get it. In addition, if a cartoon is getting stale, they may decide to spice things up and produce it as a live action feature. It's actually a beautiful thing to watch. They also are bringing their audiences to all the associated merchandising. Have you ever looked at a Disney toy or action figure? Look closely and you will see that there are no dates of production. That leaves open the possibility of recycling old stock in the future as new merchandise. Ka Ching!

With Disney taking over Fox, their future was shining even brighter. I expect a quality reboot of the X-Men is coming and save your *Fantastic Four* #48s. I think there is a real chance that we will finally see a quality Fantastic Four movie or better yet an extended television series in a couple of years. Don't worry about any of it with Disney. The mouse has it covered.

What's It All Worth Today: One of the biggest problems in figuring out the real value of your comics is to separate the hyperbole from the truth. Some people want to let everyone know that they and their businesses are the best. This leads to confusion. Remember that commerce at 9.6 to 9.8 may have no relationship to commerce at 6.0. As an example, several years ago *Green Lantern* #76 went up in the *Guide* by 50 per cent at 9.2. Looking at the previous *Guide*, it was noteworthy that there was virtually no movement at in any of the lower grade levels. None. I discovered that translated frequently across the board in other titles and issues, with the exception of the major Gold and Silver keys. The health of the market at the highest levels is frequently not related or is an inaccurate indicator of lower graded copies.

There are large segments in the comic collecting community that are in deep trouble. Many appear to be headed for uncollectible status or extinction, with their only hope at resurrection lying in the corporate boardrooms of the motion picture and television studios. There is no better tonic for a dead franchise than to make a movie or better yet an open ended TV series that may run forever.

And THAT is why so many dealers hang on to hundreds or thousands of long boxes of seemingly worthless comics. It can all change overnight. When the Guardians of the Galaxy was being turned into a movie, I remembered thinking, I'm pretty sure I've got a lot of *Infinity Gauntlet* issues buried somewhere. Organization is not my strong suit, so it took a while, but I found nearly an entire short box of #1's that had never been read or touched by sweaty collectors' hands. That example helps to explain why so many of us keep hanging on to all that back stock.

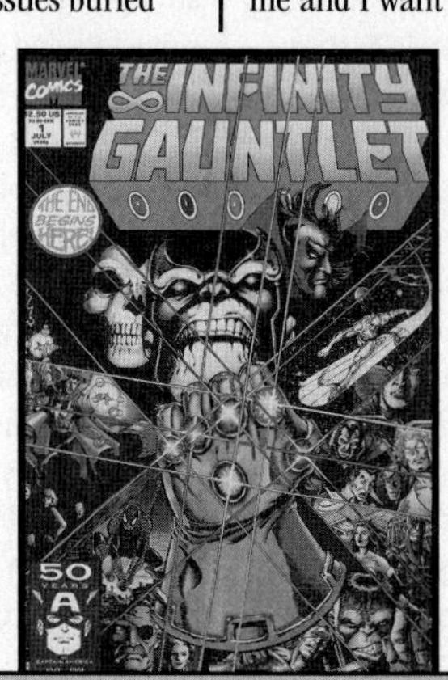

Infinity Gauntlet *issues are a fine example of why dealers hang on to their back stock.*

As our collections grow to the point of threatening marriages, we need to either get more storage or figure out what we need to let go. It's only then that we recall those 30 copies of *Batman Adventures* #12 or *New Mutants* #98 that were just gathering dust for years and we were literally giving them away years before.

Despite the fact that graded comics rule the marketplace, they only represent a very small percent of the books out there. I would like to address ungraded, non-key comics, which cover probably the other 99 percent of what is out there and that is a very different world. Market Reports would be very different if they only reflected non-graded comics.

When I am buying a collection, it is very difficult to work with sellers who don't understand how the collecting business works. When I receive an extensive Excel spreadsheet of their collection, warning flags arise. One of the first things that frequently stands out is an absence of the key books. They then "generously" assess their books at a grade of 8.0 or 9.0 and are willing to let them go at 50% of *Guide*. Look up a title like *Kamandi*, *Kull* or *Master of Kung Fu* or any Western or Charlton or Gold Key funny animal, do the math and try to give an honest response. Unless there are hidden gems, these books will cost more to collate and re-bag than most of them are worth. I face this reality all the time.

I could sell copies of *Iron Man* #1 or #55 all day long. But what about the other 400 plus issues. Record prices correspond to super high graded copies or keys and the rest is not very healthy or reflective of my experience.

I know that it may be a bitter pill for many of us to swallow, but I wish that the *Guide* would finally bite the bullet and reboot values across the board to expose the reality of what we are experiencing in the marketplace. This especially pertains to certain sectors within the comic book universe. As I said earlier, demand for broad areas of comic collecting is not static at all, but continues to deteriorate. I have another axiom that I share with my radio audience that when no new collectors come into any segment for years, that problems for that sector can become irreparable. When demand dies, books become unsellable at almost any price.

The Museum and The Video Game Connection: As I mentioned earlier in the report, I am in this business as an extension of a lifelong passion for collecting. All of this; the comics, the toys, statues and action figures and the like are all examples of artistic expression which continually feeds me and I want it to be appreciated after I am gone. I am hopeful that my family will be involved in managing my personal collection long after I'm gone. A Pop Culture museum remains on the drawing boards. We continue to look for acquiring additional content for the museum, and my older son, Jonathan, may curate that. Any leads to help in that would be greatly appreciated.

My younger son, Deniz is on a somewhat different but parallel journey to the one I have taken. His expertise is in video games and his passion is insatiable. His Nintendo collection of games and displays may be the finest in the country. His experience in the commerce of video games is changing day by day. Nintendo is now about 35 years old and the stars seem to be aligning for an explosion that may rival that comics has had over the past several decades. Collectors are reaching their middle years and many have the means to let loose financially and recreate the nostalgia of their youth. I believe prices will soar and records will fall.

By the time you read this article, his company, WATA, will have been launched and will be accepting games for certification. WATA, I believe, will become the authority in grading video games. Deniz has put together a stellar team to offer reliable third party grading for all video games, whether they be cartridges, complete in box or sealed. The team he has recruited includes Mark Haspel from CGC and a number of other well known experts, many of whom cross over from the comic book industry. His intention and business model hopes to mirror the effects that CGC had on the comic book industry.

When CGC began, they were criticized by the comic collecting community from top to bottom. They were told that grading would never be embraced and discouraged by virtually every comic dealer in the marketplace. But that all changed. To see the effect that grading has had on this industry, go no farther than the pages in this *Guide* and you will see the impact it has had on the hobby. It has driven it to levels that no one could have imagined. I believe the same will be true with video games.

Deniz's mission, however expands beyond grading and collecting. He is intending to create a community of collectors to share their passions and create forums to satisfy that as well and plans to do that through WATA. If you want to read a little more about Deniz, pick up a copy of *The Overstreet Guide to Collecting Video Games*, where he was interviewed.

I never realized how much I wanted to share. Once again, I would like to thank the staff of *Overstreet* for allowing me to join their advisory board and write this report. Remember that collecting is a joy. For me, it fills many missing voids from my childhood and continues to enrich me today, even as I collect Social Security. I feel like a kid again. I would be remiss if I didn't acknowledge and thank one other person. For the last 10-15 years I have never done a show without the help of my friend, Dan Davis. Dan is another passionate collector with encyclopedic knowledge of the hobby and it is a genuine pleasure to man our booth together. Having a caring, reliable and honest person by your side is a treasure. After a hiatus from doing shows, we hope to hit the road again in 2018. If you see us, please stop by and say hello and tell us your story. I will do my best to report back to you at about this time next year.

If you are a dealer, encourage the young ones to collect and try to give them a little break. They are truly the future of the hobby. Enjoy what you have. If you can, share it with others.

While I am eager for more collections, Iam pulling back on my advertising as I have found personal referrals are the most valuable cherished and satisfying. We are actively seeking and buying a whole variety of collections; comics, video games, action figures, toys, statues original comic art, and the list goes on.

Being a relic of the last century, there is only one tried and true way to reach me and I encourage you to use it. Call me 7 days a week, 18 hours a day at 847-971-1223 and I will be delighted to help you in any way I can. I would love to hear from you. Thank to all of you for taking the time to get to know me. I look forward to either talking to you or meeting you soon. And until next year, I'll just say, "Nuff said!"

IVAN KOCMAREK
COLLECTOR

This past year seemed to be a plateau year in terms of the sales achieved by Canadian war-time comics, that is, those comics which I prefer to call WECA (War Exchange Conservation Act – see my article in *OCBPG* #44) comics which were produced in Canada from 1941-46 and which represent the First Age of Canadian comics. Availability and auction results seemed to flatten most over the summer con season but were relatively healthy on auction sites during the spring and fall.

Here is a summary of the top 20 results of online sales of WECA comics for this year:

1	*Super* (Citren) nn	5.5	$13,484
2	*Nelvana* Comp.	5.0	$8,360
3	*Dime* #1	2.5	$3,100
4	*Colossal* (red cover)	5.0	$3,000
5	*Dime* #1	4.5	$3,000
6	*Wow* #26	8.0	$2,322
7	*Better* V1 #4	6.5	$2,100
8	*Triumph* #25	7.0	$2,100
9	*Wow* #16	4.5	$2,100
10	*Triumph* #21	7.5	$1,900
11	*Wow* #3	4.5	$1,655
12	*Rocket* V1 #6	6.5	$1,475
13	*Active* #20	6.5	$1,350
14	*Colossal* (sub cover)	3.0	$1,300
15	*Triumph* #24	6.0	$1,250
16	*Better* V1 #4	3.5	$1,186
17	*Triumph* #23	1.5	$1,136
18	*Super Duper* #3	2.5	$1,101
19	*Triumph* #14	4.5	$976
20	*Rocket* V1 #8	7.0	$975

You can see that the prices for these books are generally holding steady overall and that the WECA comics bubble hasn't burst. You can also see that this top-20 list is made up entirely of Bell Features and Maple Leaf books except for the Citren *Super Comics* (which reprints much of *Pep Comics* #22) and F. E. Howard's *Super Duper Comics*, which was meant largely for distribution in the US and which came out in 1947, making it properly fall just outside the WECA window, but because it contains previously unpublished Bell Features stories including the first full Mr. Monster story, we pull it back into the fold. Anglo-American and Educational Project run books don't seem to produce the same collectible gravity as Bell and Maple Leaf books.

I'm still hoping that American Fawcett collectors will latch onto the fact that the Anglo-American redraws of Captain Marvel, Captain Marvel Jr., Spy Smasher, Ibis, etc. stories are new versions of the Fawcett scripts they are familiar with—new versions with different splash pages and panels. If those collectors woke up to this fact, it could represent a fresh avenue of collectible product and would certainly boost the Anglo-American stock.

In Canada, comic publisher Chapterhouse (best known perhaps as the home of Captain Canuck) has re-tooled the mainstay Anglo-American hero, Freelance, for today, and brought him back in his own comic. Chapterhouse also has plans in the works to reprint as many of the old Canadian war-time comics as it can obtain clearance for, starting with a *Freelance Omnibus*. Chapterhouse already has the *Johnny Canuck Compendium* in its catalogue and will soon publish the Fred Kelly Mr. Monster book that Rachel

Richey has put together.

In September, I had a successful Kickstarter crowdfunding campaign in support of my book *Heroes of the Home Front* which examines the backstories of many of the Bell Features war-time artists and which reproduces over 150 original Bell Features art pages from the holdings of the Library and Archives of Canada. By the time you read this it should be out in the hands of those people who supported the project. Also by the time you read this, the first *WECA Comics Price Guide* should also be out and available in limited numbers. It is the first comprehensive checklist of all the comic books produced in Canada from 1941-46 and has been put together by fellow WECA comics collectors Tony Andrews, Jim Finlay, Walter Durajlija, and myself.

All of these initiatives should help increase the awareness of the existence and collectability of these first Canadian comics and possibly boost their prices in upcoming online auctions.

The 'Big Bang' in this niche collecting area happened about 3-4 years ago when more began to be written about these rare books and they couldn't fly under the radar any longer. A good number of collections started to appear on the auction sites and more people began asking about them at dealers' tables during cons.

From the results we've seen in this year's auctions, collectors appear to have become more selective about purchasing these hard-to-find books. Still, their prices are not going to go down and are only going to increase over the long run. They are still a very rare commodity. Looking at the CGC Census figures on these comics while I write this, I can see that not one of the run of the 770 or so individual comics that came out in Canada from 1941-46 has reached a slabbed census count of ten copies. That issue of *Super Comics* that heads the list in this report has 8 copies in the census, *Wow Comics* #1 and *Grand Slam Comics* #49 have 7 copies each, while *Dime Comics* #1 and F. E. Howard's *Super Comics* Vol. 2 #5 have 6 copies each. The great majority of the census for WECA books is a vacuum dotted with zeroes. In this context, I also have to report that 9 new Signature Series WECA books appeared in the census this year after con appearances by Jack Tremblay in July and Gerald Lazare in September.

These war-time Canadian books are still struggling to find their collecting and value profile in the market but the prognosis is a good one.

Robert Krause
Primo Comics

Greetings from Primo Comics! We operate an online comic book store at primocomics.com as well as an eBay store at primo comics1. It has been a great year in the world of comics with steady demand across most genres. A continued theme I am seeing is a scarcity of back issues available in the marketplace. The continued proliferation of comic book related movies drives interest in demand for the respective characters and exports this demand globally. It simply has become quite difficult to obtain back issues pre-1990 in grade for a reasonable amount of money. Collections that have historically been concentrated domestically are now been scattered across the globe. 40% of our sales are outside the United States with the top counties being Canada, Australia and Great Britain.

Copper Age comics continue to rise in demand and value. I truly see this era as the "new vintage" with great creators and classic story lines. Books from this era command the most value and demand in higher grades, 9.4 or higher. Demand becomes soft in grades under 9.0. Many collectors grew up during this era and want to reacquire books and story lines that rekindle nostalgic memories of their childhoods. Key books with 1st appearances dominate this era of collecting such as the debuts of Spawn, Gambit and Deadpool.

The aforementioned being stated, it begs the question of what is a 1st appearance? Is it the first time the character ever appears on the printed page? Is it the first cameo appearance? Or is it the first full appearance? This has plagued the hobby for some time and much confusion has ensued. I have seen a shift in the hobby of collectors seeking out scarce and obscure true 1st appearance of a character of the first time the character ever appeared in print. For instance, Teenage Mutant Ninja Turtles had their 1st appearance on the back cover of *Goobleygook* #1 and the hobby recognizes this as their 1st appearance but does not recognize *Malibu Sun* #13 as the 1st appearance of Spawn. I have seen the shift beginning to happen. Seek out true 1st appearances of characters that are obscure. The prices of these books is often much less than the current recognized 1st appearance. I believe the gap will collapse over time.

Lastly, the overall market remains strong and I look forward to the new year of collecting!! Happy collecting!!

Ben Labonog
Collector

Overview of the Market: Hello, and thanks for stopping by to read! I trust everyone's collecting experiences have been profitable, memorable, and enjoyable this past year. The major auction houses continued to pump out quality books over and over again, which must be a lot of hustle for them to continue to attract prospective consignors. Just how does one decide whom to consign with? Well, aside from the consignment fees and market exposure, the relationship with the auction house can play a critical role. We witnessed Jon Berk unload his collection through ComicConnect/Metropolis due to outstanding relations over his collecting years. Of course, timing always seems to play a key part in buying/selling/trading of comics. As I type this, a *Captain America Comics* #1 CGC 1.5 just sold at public auction for \$70k. To my knowledge, this is the highest price point for a low-grade copy selling publicly or privately. It was nice to see two unrestored copies of *Marvel Comics* #1 sell at strong prices of $87k (CGC 2.5) and $215k (CGC 6.0 Twilight Copy), respectively. This is a historical comic for the ages and looks like it is rebounding even if the demand is smaller amongst the majority of Golden Age collectors.

The social media market for comics is quite impressive. I have observed weekly LIVE auctions on YouTube and sales on Instagram, Twitter, and Facebook. Most of the social media users appear to be Silver to Modern Age collectors, which is probably a fair representation on a grander scale. Golden Age collectors make up the minority of the collecting base now, despite continued strong sales for Golden Age comics. There are now so many routes online that collectors can utilize to buy, sell, trade, and share comics. Networking is certainly one of the blessings the power of the Internet has provided.

As far as conventions go, the larger shows like SDCC, NYCC, etc. are filled with Hollywood power, cosplay delight, and comics. However, the six figure crowds and travel/admission costs are deterring many collectors from attending. Nothing beats face-to-face deals and picking up books at a con though. I believe the small, one day shows have made a come back! The Berkeley Con put on by Marc Newman (House of Comics) and Tim (wormboy on CGC boards) is a nice little, old school show that has the feel of being in a back room at a Holiday Inn in the mid 1980s. It's only $5 to get in with lots of raw books to flip through. You won't see any big mega GA keys at this show, but there are still plenty of good books and keys to buy.

Golden Age: Golden Age will continue to be the challenge that collectors need to keep themselves going in this hobby. Just finding any copy of a scarce book can be more satisfying than obtaining a book in high grade. If anything, it is important for newer collectors to read up on the history of comics so they can appreciate the roots of the hobby. When I think of books like *Detective* #1, *Action* #1, *Detective* #27, and *Marvel* #1 -- these are the pre-1940 books that are key, historical pillars of the hobby.

Golden Age goodness continues to be in demand whether raw or graded. Avoiding the Hollywood spec and hype are *Human Torch* #2(1) and *Sub-Mariner Comics* #1. These are going relatively cheap these days. I was able to hook up a friend with a copy of *Torch* #2(1) in CGC 3.5 (slight) for a $3,400. That sounds like a bargain considering other what other Golden Age #1s are going for these days. If you are wondering why *Torch* #1 is listed as "#2(1)", it is because *Red Raven Comics* #1 was the first comic in that series. However, since it was considered a failed one-shot comic in 1940, Goodman decided to continue the series with the second issue renaming it *Human Torch Comics*. It was such a confusing time in 1940 for comic book publishers. It is hard to imagine any comic produced by Joe Simon and Jack Kirby could be a failure, but poor sales reflected that. *Subby* #1s have been tucked away for the most part of the year. I was offered one copy in 1.5, but it was missing the staples and was brittle. The owner was asking $5,500, so I passed. Lately, I have seen a few more being offered on eBay at stronger prices. Perhaps some speculation is brewing since DC released Aquaman on the big screen. That has to make the MCU a bit bothered that DC beat them to the punch since the Sub-Mariner was the first Marvel (Timely) superhero that pre-dated Aquaman.

Currently, *Cap* #1 is hitting some all time highs with a CGC 1.5 copy selling for $70K. It has passed *Batman* #1 momentarily, but the Joker will always keep *Batman* #1 in the race. Some project *Cap* #1 will pass *Superman* #1 and become the #3 GA book. I don't see this happening. *Superman* #1 is an earlier book and is scarcer (especially in high grade). Plus, there is something to say about Superman being the first superhero to receive his own comic book title (1939). The *Justice League* film reminded us all just how powerful Superman is! That film was nearly pure Golden Age.

Wonder Woman #7 has been an interesting book to watch. Demand and price points have reached about $1,000/point in low grade. It has a unique and interesting cover to say the least. All Wonder Woman comics have received more demand and interest since Gal Gadot took the role. She is the perfect actress to play Diana Prince, and I am glad to see demand for WW titles go up.

Silver Age: How many of you are picky collectors about having colors being really deep and bold? Try finding these SA comics with deep, DARK greens (listed in order of the tougher challenge from my experience): *Fantastic Four* #1, *X-Men* #1, and *Flash* #105. Finding an *Fantastic Four* #1 with a dark green monster is not easy. Often, the monster is a brighter green than the dark forest green that I prefer. For *X-Men* #1, the side bar box and the horizontal box above the Beast is often difficult to find in dark green (it's often lime green). The same goes for *Flash* #105 with lime green Mirror Master head shots all too often present. Another printing challenge is finding a *Tales of Suspense* #39 with the FULL set of quotes along the front cover's right edge. Those quotes are often miscut. The same goes for *Fantastic Four* #48 and the full quotes, but it is not as difficult to find with the full set of quotes as *Tales of Suspense* #39.

I believe *Fantastic Four* #4 is still an undervalued key. Imagine if/when Sub-Mariner hits movie screens, *Fantastic Four* #4 could be posed for some strong demand. I think we are already feeling some tremors over this year based on some eBay and auction sales, but it's still low compared to other keys. *Fantastic Four* #1 and 5 are gaining some steam, and likely because of the FOX/Disney merger. I still find it amazing how Hollywood has impacted the vintage comic book market. *Amazing Spider-Man* #1 is smoking hot right now, and all because the *Amazing Fantasy* #15 train just won't slow down as it takes about $7k to get a complete copy now. This has bumped up *Amazing Spider-Man* #1 demand tremendously as people are eliminated from the *Amazing Fantasy* #15 low-grade market. *Strange Tales* #110 has slowed tremendously, but still enjoyed a healthy bump.

Daredevil #1, *Avengers* #1, and *X-Men* #1 are bargains compared to *Amazing Fantasy* #15 and *Hulk* #1 prices.

Brave and the Bold #28 is an interesting book. The *Justice League* movie didn't make prices crazy. There was some decent increase and demand over the last two years, but prices were all over the map in lower grade. *Adventure* #247 could be a sleeper book. Is *Flash* #105 overvalued? *Showcase* #6 (1st Challengers by Kirby) is DC's version of the Fantastic Four without powers, and is also undervalued. If you are a Jack Kirby fan, please pick up a raw copy and check out the panels. You will undoubtedly think you are seeing Reed Richards and Ben Grimm in the panels!

Bronze Age: Although there is tremendous supply, there seems to be relentless interest and demand for *Hulk* #181. This book is now $500 minimum to get into the door with a complete copy. I've witnessed copies missing the value stamp, but otherwise look 8.0, still sell for north of $1000. Every now and then, I see a copy with faded colors on eBay. It always catches my eye, because it's different and I get tired of seeing the same brightly colored high-grade copies. *X-Men* #101 has been asked for a lot this year since the Phoenix movie was announced. Jim Starlin Thanos/Capt. Marvel covers have also been in strong demand. I picked up a reader copy of *Avengers Annual* #7 (1977). It's the first time I read that issue and it has the most complete background history of Thanos and the Infinity Gauntlet gems in one comic. I would recommend reading that book before seeing *Avengers: Infinity War*.

Copper Age: This is the era where I bought most of my comics as a kid from 7-11 stores and my LCS. Earlier in this year, I went on a brief run on buying solely newsstand editions of some 1980s keys: *Daredevil* #158/168, *Wolverine* #1-4, *Amazing Spider-Man* #238/252/300, *Hulk* #340, etc. It was fun and a new challenge for someone used to hunting for Timelys. The newsstand editions vs. direct editions peaked my interest, and so I decided to do a random, one time eBay sampling count of some newsstand keys from the early '80s to the early '90s. In most cases, the sample size on eBay was 200+ copies but a few books had sample sizes of 100+ copies. Here is what I found – all %'s represent the percentage of newsstand copies on eBay for that particular book: *Daredevil* #168 (56%, 1981), *Wolverine* #1 (35%, 1982), *ASM* #238 (40%, 1983), *Secret Wars* #8 (16%, 1984), *Hulk* #340 (13%, 1988), *ASM* #300 (20%, 1988), *New Mutants* #87 (10%, 1990), *X-Men* #266 (8%, 1990), *Silver Surfer* #44 (12%, 1990), *New Mutants* #98 (13%, 1990), *Infinity Gauntlet* #1 (8%, 1991). Although the data is small and just a random sampling, it does support the theory that late '80s/early '90s newsstand copies are scarcer than early '80s newsstand copies. This would make sense as local comic shops began appearing in the '70s and '80s. This meant less and less newsstand copies were being printed and distributed to grocery stores, drug stores, gas stations, etc. through the 1990s. The direct edition copies were printed in masses and sold at local comic shops. Newsstand editions are commonly found beat, and much tougher to find in high grade. Direct editions are more commonly found in high grade because customers, who bought them from their LCS, were typically collectors who took very good care of their comics. I have to credit Chris Williamson of Fantastic Comics for his expertise in Copper Age comics and original art. Chris is also a local, renowned expert on Disneyland history and vintage Disney collectibles, but his contribution to this research on Copper newsstand editions was much appreciated!

In conclusion, the thrill is always in the hunt! Whether you collect pre-Code horror Ditko covers, vintage aluminum Christmas trees, or monster trading cards --there is always an itch to find something unique and a great joy to stumble across a rare comic by accident. Read some comics, and don't just collect slabs. We will all be left with reprints one day anyway.

Ben Lichtenstein
Zapp Comics

One word....Insane.

Ok, maybe not insane, but in 2017, the demand for key issues of comic books just roared. I've been calling a peak in back issue pricing and demand for 3 years running and I'm wrong again. Like a train in the distance coming closer, so is the buzz of more and more new money entering our hobby. As of this writing in December, I can say that our back issue sales have never been better and I continue to encounter new customers and new money wanting in on comics. Anecdotally, I'm seeing many buyers with deep pockets from other hobbies, such as stamps/coins/baseball cards joining in on the fun with money to burn. I've even been told by reliable sources of venture capital being deployed into comic books as an asset class. Where this all goes long term, I cannot say, but short term the party will continue as the punch bowl is overflowing.

First, a little info on my operation: Our 2 brick and mortar shops in Wayne and Manalapan are focused on comics books, but also sell gaming cards, trading cards, action figures (new and vintage) and all things related. Back issues is an area that we emphasize and which sets us apart. There are many different types of comic shops and we like to be a store that carries more than just the new releases. I love to buy and sell secondary market stuff, like back issues, single cards, vintage toys, etc. It's more exciting and gives our customers another reason to visit.

This is our 24th year in business and sales on back issues have never been better.

On the new issue front, DC continues to be very fan/retailer-friendly, with tight consistent storytelling that is faithful to the iconic characters. This allowed us to order very heavily with confidence as customers are responding well to most of their offerings.

This year, the Batman Metal storyline has been a smash hit, with multiple printings needed as stores keep selling out. The *Doomsday Clock* series looks excellent and the #1 issue is in our top 3 best sellers this year. The *Justice League* movie arrived, with much anticipation, but mixed reviews. I would prefer if DC would "lighten up" their movies, in a literal sense, as both *Batman V Superman* and *Justice League* suffered from a muddiness that I think has been off-putting. Gal Gadot's Wonder Woman is the most popular star of the DC Cinematic universe. Sales on Wonder Woman comics/merchandise have been brisk, as both male and female customers have hopped on the wagon!

In contrast to DC's publishing success, Marvel continues to disappoint readers and retailers. Sales are at all-time lows due to weak story-telling, gimmicks and character changes that are generally meeting with a thumbs down. I believe that Marvel needs a complete overhaul, similar to DC New 52. This year Marvel made an attempt with their Marvel Legacy reboot. This unfortunately has been a failure for the fans. Also, for us retailers, Legacy was controversial due to onerous ordering requirements. I decided to put my budget on the line and jumped through hoops to receive all the Lenticular covers. As of this writing, I'm looking at lots of unsold Legacy. Ouch,that hurt! The Lenticular covers seemed defective as they didn't function properly (there was an ever-present "shadow" no matter how you held the darn things.) The numbering was a confusing mess. Whereas both DC New 52 and Rebirth were events that I was rewarded handsomely for committing big numbers to, the Marvel Legacy was really disappointing.

I have mentioned that my sales at my shops are strong in spite of Marvel publishing woes. If Marvel's sales were back to normal, wow, what a year 2017 would have been! Happily, as of this writing, Marvel has finally responded to years of poor results and just made a drastic change at the top, bringing in a new editor finally. I'm hopeful that things will turn around in 2018 for the House of Ideas.

There are lots of wonderful independent titles coming out, with a some really high-quality stuff and lots of amateurish or hack level material coming out. So, for every breakout hit like *Saga*, *Outcast*, *Southern Bastards*, *Realm*, *Black Science*, etc., there are tons of unproven titles that are released and result in lost money. So, we do our best to stock a diverse mix without going broke in the process.

Back issue sales of independents continue to be very hard to manage, with extreme volatility and short supply when a title takes off. My approach is to give as many titles a chance as possible, but the most common trend is #1 selling decently and then steep declines on subsequent issues.

Walking Dead has not slowed down at all. We were lucky enough to purchase several complete runs of *Walking Dead* from #1 and up and sales very very strong. #2 is probably my most requested *Walking Dead* at this time. Just red hot and scarce. Although I predict the TV show will wane, it seems that the back issues are unstoppable.

Free Comic Book Day continues to be a winner, with big crowds enjoying our hobby and supporting us. As the online market continues to expand, customers are showing us that they still value getting out of the house and shopping in-person at a local business.

Local Comic Book Shop Day is a new event to promote brick and mortar shops, but has yet to make an impact. I'm feeling that consumers may be feeling "event fatigue".

Social Media continues to be essential in communicating with our customers and marketing our shop. We do almost zero traditional advertising and rely on the wit of my partner Corry Brown and employee Dave Potosnak to light up Facebook, YouTube, Instagram,etc.

In other news, we launched our inaugural Zapp! Comic Con this year and it was a winner. We hold many events at our shop, such as signings/artist appearances, etc, but space is limited. So, we decided to have our own Comic convention at our local Wayne NJ firehouse, with tons of sale merchandise, artists, charity auction, costumed characters, freebies, etc. Our goal with Zapp Comic Con is to have fun, with a low admission of $5 and tons of great deals. We sold out of tickets in advance, and plan on expanding in the future, with a promise of low admission and lots to see and buy. I'm optimistic that it's a great option for our local customers to attend a con without breaking the bank or traveling too far.

Back Issues: There's white-hot demand for Golden Age books in particular Good Girl/bondage/Horror classic cover. We're seeing much more demand now for these books, as many collectors have finished their Silver Age runs and are chasing the much rarer Golden Age stuff. Also, there is a scarcity to some of these titles that makes the hunt a lot more fun. The market for a lot of the Golden rarities is actually quite strong, as sales are infrequent due to scarcity but when certain books are offered, those in the know pounce aggressively.

Many scarcer books sell for 3, 5 or even 10 times *Guide* if there is no prior sales data available. I was happy to pick up a really nice original owner pre-Code collection, all Horror stuff! We sold many classic gory covers at multiples of *Guide*, with interest coming in from around the country. Sales were on fire! I wish I could get more.

Silver Age and Bronze Age continue to sell great with the keys leading the way. I won't bore you with a list of the all the keys that everyone wants. Suffice to say, demand has not ebbed at all. Specific issues that jumped with media tie-ins have cooled somewhat, such as *Fantastic Four* #45 (Inhumans), but that's the exception. Nearly every first appearance or #1 is up this year.

The early issues of all major Marvel titles are showing even stronger pricing and demand, with no end in sight.

Amazing Spider-Man has been picking up quite a bit. *Amazing*s are always a very predictable strong seller, but pricing has jumped on all the early issues from #1-25, and the important keys. We just picked up a complete run of

#1-700 and another run of #5 to #140 and sales are very strong with pricing 20% to 30% higher than last year.

Copper Age stuff, particularly the first appearances and iconic storylines, continue to move very quickly.

I'm also happy to report that we sell lots of those abundant '90s comics. Although I still have tons in stock, it's fun to see demand for 1990s *Spawn*, *Spider-Man*, *X-Men*, *Darkhawk*, etc. Even some of the previously unsalable stuff like *WildCATs* has gotten some interest now. Although the supply is nowhere near drying up, it does help us a lot to be able to actually sell some of these issues at more than just bulk rates.

While relatively slow, we are able to sell Gold Keys and Charltons. Some of these books have beautiful covers, are tough in high grade and contain some characters that live on today. Dells are still really tough to move unless discounted steeply.

We attended several conventions this year. We're doing well at most conventions, with plenty of demand at all price levels, Lots of readers filling in their runs of cheap stuff, lots of middle buyers digging in the bargain books for cheap Silver/Bronze and the usual hordes of key issue buyers.

New York Comic Con is still our biggest convention for us. 5 days of action. Demand was strong for all levels, from $2 comics up to big keys. All the usual stuff, like multiples of *Walking Dead* #1, *Hulk* #181, *Amazing Spider-Man* #129, etc. moved easily.

I will say that interest in back issues is, for us, at an all time high. I've never seen this many new collectors and also new dealers entering the market.

Overall, I've been able to keep the store full of fresh material this year, but it has become markedly more difficult to purchase books. When buying collections or individual keys, competition is fierce, with generally at least 4 or 5 other bidders showing up. So, sellers are getting excellent prices and I've had to really sharpen my pencil when making an offer, with the expectation that inventory will turn very fast, but at thin margin. The afore-mentioned *Amazing Spider-Man* collections were acquired in competition with many other advertisers in this Overstreet and man was it tough. Prices are higher than ever on good material!

I love buying comics and have to keep the customers happy so will offer what it takes.

I must mention that we are always looking for Golden Age up to Modern Age, so if you have a collection or individual key issues, contact me anytime for a fast competitive offer! My success rate on reaching a winning offer on the collections that I want is quite high, so please contact us if you have a large value collection or key for sale.

In closing, I would like to sincerely thank everyone who has bought from or sold to us this year. I'm very lucky to be doing what I love and will continue to ride this crazy rollercoaster of a market!

Stephen Lipson
Collector

Not many people are aware that Canada published their own comics during the Golden Age. These wartime era comics hosted a stable of superheroes that where both analogous and indigenous to Canada. Such iconic heroes as Nelvana of the Northern Lights and her brethren spoke to Canada's role on both the Home front and smashing the Axis abroad.

These comics were published primarily from 1941-1946, as a result of the implementation of the War Exchange Conservation Act, wherein non-essential items were prohibited for import into Canada, including pulp literature. As a result, Canada started its own fledgling comic book industry.

These comics were essentially published with colour covers, with interiors that were published in black and white, in order to defray costly publishing expenses. Hence, these comics are now referred to as "Canadian Whites" by both collectors and historians alike. That said, the very early issues of *Wow Comics* published by Bell Features and the very early issues of *Better Comics* published by Maple Leaf sport colour interiors.

The first publisher was Maple Leaf Publishing books out of Vancouver, BC such as *Better Comics*, *Rocket Comics, Bing Bang Comics* and *Lucky Comics*. The aforementioned Maple Leaf comics introduced the first Canadian superhero in *Better Comics* #1 in March of 1941 (The Iron Man). Maple Leaf comics are deemed to be the scarcest and command a premium when changing hands. Anglo American (Double "A") Publishing in Toronto introduced Freelance and a host of Fawcett derived characters to Canada, including Captain Marvel and Spy Smasher. The next publisher was Bell Features in Toronto with Johnny Canuck, Nelvana, the Penguin and Thunderfist, etc. in such flagship titles as *Dime Comics*, *Triumph Comics*, *Active Comics*, and *Commando Comics.* Finally, Educational Projects out of Montreal, Quebec introduced Canada Jack in its flagship title, *Canadian Heroes*.

It is important to note that these vestiges of Canadian Pop Culture helped create a Canadian identity within their pages. Canada Jack was an athlete that battled the 5th column saboteurs on the Canadian home front in Canadian Heroes comic books. While he was not larger than life and not endowed with super powers, the Canadian youth of the Second World War at home could emulate and subsequently identify with Canada Jack. This sort of homegrown sentiment could also be likened to Johnny Canuck, who while also was not larger than life, helped smash the Axis abroad, including Hitler.

Nelvana was the first superhero with a Canadian national identity, and graced the pages of *Triumph Comics*. In fact, Nelvana pre-dated Wonder Woman by almost four months! She came to aid of the indigenous peoples of the North West Territories in her early appearances, and could fly along the Aurora Borealis.

Sadly, the War Exchange Conservation Act was repealed

in 1946, and subsequently American comic books were allowed to be imported into Canada. Hence, Captain America and Superman and their brethren replaced their Canadian counterparts in full colour for only a dime. This ushered in the demise of the "Canadian Whites", as the floundering industry could no longer complete. The last ditch efforts to produce Canadian homegrown comics in full color just did not stand up against their American predecessors Subsequently, many of the publishing houses in Canada folded, including Anglo-American publishing, Maple Leaf Publishing, and eventually Bell Features.

Notable 2017 Canadian Golden Age Comic Sales via eBay and Auction Houses:

Dime Comics #1 (1st Johnny Canuck) CGC 2.5 $3100.00
Triumph Comics #25 (Nelvana-c) CGC 7.0 $2100.00
Wow Comics #16 (1st Penguin-c) CGC 4.5 $2100.00
Active Comics #20 (Classic Hockey-c) CGC 6.5 $1350.00
Better Comics Vol 1 #4 Uncertified $1200.00

2017 Personal Sales of note:

Canadian Heroes Vol 1 #5 (1st Canada Jack) 2.0 Uncertified $2500.00
Better Comics Vol 1 #8 Uncertified 1.5 $1500.00
Rocket Comics Vol 5 #4 Uncertified 1.5 $750.00
Slam-Bang Comics #7 Uncertified 5.5 $1300.00
Active Comics #29 Uncertified 3.5 $350.00
Space Nomad Vol 1 #1 Uncertified 4.0 $650.00

Canadian Whites are still volatile and command high prices. However, recent ComicLink auction results would suggest that the prices are starting to come down to earth, as opposed to being in another stratosphere. The sheer dearth of these vestiges of pop-culture continue to be nevertheless elusive at best. Collectors of these books tend not to sell any copies entrenched in their collections. It should be interesting to see if more of these books surface in 2018.

Doug Mabry
The Great Escape

Greetings once again from Tennessee and Kentucky! It's been another exciting year to collect comics. Of course, TV and movies continued to influence what collectors were looking for. Unfortunately, though, sales of new comics have taken a hit this year. People just haven't responded to the DC Rebirth books in the same way that they did for the New 52 books. It seems that people are getting "reboot fatigue". Perhaps that's why Marvel has gone back to the old numbering.

Several trends have become apparent over the past couple of years. One is that several whole categories of comics that were once avidly collected have begun to fade away. Genres such as Funny Animal, Western, and Classics have suffered significantly in the last ten years as older collectors have left the market and have not been replaced by younger ones. Younger folks just haven't grown up reading these books and don't feel the nostalgia for them. We have to significantly discount these just to sell them at all, or put them in lots on eBay where we might get a quarter of book value.

Similarly, we've seen a decade long decline in interest in some of the DC Silver Age books, such as *Jimmy Olsen*, *Lois Lane*, *World's Finest*, and *Adventure Comics*. Perhaps it seems a difficult enough task for a Superman fan to collect his main two books, *Superman* and *Action*, and they just don't seem interested in trying to collect everything. We currently have several hundred of these marked at half price in our sale section, and they're still slow movers.

Another trend seems to be partially a product of the Age of Encapsulation in which we find ourselves. We've seen for several years now a move towards collecting what are considered classic covers, especially in the Golden Age market. But with slabbing becoming more and more prevalent I've noticed another change: acceptance of detached covers or centerfolds. This just doesn't seen to be near as important to collectors now as it once was. I can only speculate that if someone is collecting a book primarily for the cover, then the appearance of the cover becomes the overriding consideration. After all, if you're never going to take the book out of the slab would you rather have a comic that appears Fine but the cover is detached at the single staple, or one that has an attached cover but only a Good+ appearance? More and more folks are opting for the nicer looking book. I think maybe it's time to reevaluate the grading standards on this issue.

Now here's what's happening in the different areas:

Golden Age: We've had quite a bit of good Golden Age in this year. The only things I haven't seen are Timelys and MLJs. We did pick up runs of *Big Town*, *Boy Comics*, *Gangbusters*, and *Mr. District Attorney*. We also picked up a nice original owner collection from Michigan that had some nice pre-War books. Some individual sales: *Action Comics* #47, GD, $400, #67, VG+, $400, *All-American Comics* #18, GD, $1225, #24, FR, $180, *Batman* #18, GD, $450, #64, FR, $75, # 67, VG, $205, #105, GD, $148, *Beware Terror Tales* #2, GD, $75, *Black Cat* #21, VG, $44, *Black Terror* #13, VG, $125, *Blazing Comics* #4, VG, $75, *Blue Beetle* #25, GD, $40, *Blue Bolt* #9, GD, $125, *Blue Ribbon* #15, FR, $65, *Captain Marvel Adventures* #6, VG+, $300, #25, GD-, $50, #32, FN, $150, *Daredevil Comics* #16, VG, $160, *Detective Comics* #79, GD, $175, #109, VG, $500, #149, VG, $175, $141, FR,$45, #163, VG, $162, *Feature Comics* #49, VG, $60, *Frontline Combat* #7, VG, $46, *Funnyman* #3, GD, $20, *Harvey Hits* #56, NM, $250, *Heroic Comics* #18, GD/VG, $40, *Ibis* #5, VG+, $125, *Journey Into Fear* #18, VG, $68, *Jumbo Comics* #98, FN, $85, *Jungle Comics*, #68, GD, $28, *Lars of Mars* #10, CBCS 5.0, $260, *Lorna The Jungle Girl* #12, GD/VG, $30, *Mad* #9, PGX 6.5, $200, *Modern Comics* #60, VG, $64, *Nyoka* #3, VG, $72, *Our Fighting Forces* #1, GD-, $100, *Planet Comics* #45, GD, $95, #55, VG, $155, *Plastic Man* #2, VG $360, #24, VG, $82, *Rangers* #34, VF-, $150, *Shadow Comics* #37, GD, $65, *Smash Comics* #28, VG, $60, *Star Spangled Comics* #33, VG/FN, $100, *Steve Canyon* #6, VF/NM, $140, *Supersnipe* #10, VG, $98. *This Magazine Is Haunted* #19, GD, $50, *Walt Disney's*

Comics & Stories #26, VG, $200, #34, VG/FN, $227, *Weird Fantasy* #22, VG, $72, *Weird Horrors* #8, GD, $47, *Weird Science* #16, GD, $44, *Whiz Comics* #54, FN, $90, *Wings* #36, VG, $81, #75, VG, $60, *Wonder Woman* #44, GD, $87, #69, and FR/GD, $80.

Silver/Bronze Age: *All-Star Western* #10, FN, $100, *Amazing Spider-Man* #8, CGC 7.5, $700, #18, VG, $100, #50, GD-, $60, #121, FN+, $185, #121, VG+, $80, #122, GD, $56, *Avengers* #6, VG, $120, #57, VG+, $131, *Captain America* #117, FN, $90, *Daredevil* #1, GD-, $300, *Fantastic Four* #3, VG, $500, #45, GD, $110, #48, GD, $70, #48, VF/NM, $1225, *Forever People* #1, CGC 7.5, $110, *Green Lantern* #40, VG/FN, $120, *Hawkman* #4, GD+, $125, *Incredible Hulk* #102, VG, $50, #181, GD+, $591, #181, GD/VG, $857, *Journey Into Mystery* #103, $100, *Marvel Premiere* #15, FN, $150, *Marvel Spotlight* #28, NM, $100, *Nick Fury* #14, CGC 6.5 (signed by Stan Lee), $60, *Silver Surfer* #1, VG, $130, #1, PGX 5.5, $250, *Strange Tales* #68, FN, $110, #116, VG, $44, *Sub-Mariner* #1, FN, $66, *Tales Of Suspense* #10, VG, $100, #54, VG, $52, *Tales To Astonish* #24, GD, $26, *Werewolf By Night* #32, FN, $423, *Uncanny X-Men* #4, VG, $350, #12, VG+, $125, and *Giant-Size X-Men* #1, FN, $500.

Modern Age: *Amazing Spider-Man* #316, CGC 9.6, $70, *Birds Of Prey* #8, CGC 9.0, $60, *Complete Frank Miller Dark Knight* Hard Cover, NM, $51, *Detective* #414, CGC 7.0 (Signed), $90, *Green Arrow* (Rebirth), #8 Neal Adams Variant, CGC 9.2 (Signed), $30, *Harley Quinn Valentine's Day Special* #1, CGC 9.6, $20, *Marvel Super-Hero Secret Wars* #8, CGC 9.6, $75, *New Mutants* #98, NM, $300, NM-, $325, *Pitt* #1, CGC 9.8, $30, *Savage She-Hulk* #1, CGC 8.5, $35, *Spider-Man* #1 (Silver), CGC 9.6, $45, *Star Wars* #42, VF/NM, $70, *Tales Of the Teen Titans* #44, VF, $50, #44, CGC 9.2, $90, *Teenage Mutant Ninja Turtles* #2 (1st Print), FN, $75, #3, $100, #4, $50, *Venom: Lethal Protector* #1 (Gold Variant), NM, $100, *Walking Dead* #2, VF/NM, $227, and *Wolverine* v.1 #1, CGC 9.4, $75.

Brian Marcus
Cavalier Comics

Greetings from the mountains of Southwest Virginia! It was a banner year for my store since we relocated to a shopping center with a reasonable lease. For the first time ever, I actually have walk in traffic. Sales have been up by about 20% but I hate to say, it's not from new comics. Toys and games have been my biggest sellers the past year since the move.

New comics sales from Marvel have been sluggish. I haven't seen sales like this since the comic bust of the '90s. Way too many event books, changing of characters, poor writing and art have lead to this downturn for me. DC titles have been consistent but my numbers have dropped on those too. But on the upside, I have more people looking to pick up back issues. People just want a good self-contained story to read and I've had so many discovering the older storylines from the '80s and '90s. Independent sales, have been steady with Image leading the way. They still have several solid titles like *Redneck*, *Saga*, *Seven to Eternity*, and *Walking Dead*. The Alterna Press newspaper stock comics have been a surprise hit at $1.50 each, especially *Amazing Age*. Sales of graphic novels have been through the roof since I've moved.

I haven't sold many Silver Age books this past year since my stock is running low and I haven't been able to pick up any older collections. But on the bright side, I'm seeing more Bronze and Copper Age collections coming through and that's what's been moving since they are more affordable

Notable sales this past year include *New Teen Titans* #2 CGC 9.4 $200, *Tales of the Teen Titans* #44 CGC 9.6 $125, *Amazing Spider-Man* #194 CGC 9.2 $175, *New Mutants* #87 (1st Cable) I've sold several copies of this from Fine to Near Mint.

Jon McClure
Collector

Greetings from Portland, Oregon! Sales this year on eBay were decent, and here's a sampling from the last quarter of 2017: *Amazing Adventures* #4 FN $140, *Batman* #156 FN/VF $180, 357 Type 1a Canadian Cover Price Variant VF $150, *Brave And The Bold* #3 GD $70, *Daredevil* #7 FN $175, *Fantastic Four* #48 GD+ $170, *Mad* #13 VG- $40, *Our Army At War* #38 FN $54, *Sparkler* #19 VG/FN $100, *Spellbound* #29 VG+ $68, *Super DC Giant* #21 VG+ $77, *Tales Of Suspense* #19 VG+ $125, *United States Marines* #3 GD/VG $138, *Whiz* #67 VG $60, and a *Wonder Woman* run of #178-207 FN $500.

Low to mid-grade Marvels sold in antique malls at 150% *Guide* or higher. Double *Guide* was not uncommon to receive from speculators and collectors looking for undervalued and overlooked titles. Comics sometimes sell in person that just won't move online, even at a fraction of the cost. DCs were sluggish in general in general except for key issues and large runs. Archies sold well as they have for the last few years. I sold low grade Dells this year except for Western titles in the $5 to $15 range at an average of 100% *Guide*, with Westerns bringing only about 65% *Guide*. Charlton Romance sales were slow again this year, with low to mid-grade copies selling in the $5-8 range. Comic sales in general were slightly up (regardless of publisher) from last year, with TV and movie tie-ins keys impossible to keep in stock.

Marvel Type 1 test market cover price variants continue to break record sales results that are well above the listed values of easy to find Bronze Age key books such as *Incredible Hulk* #181(11/74) listed in *OCBPG* #47 at $3500 in raw 9.2 NM-. Publisher experiments in the 20th century repeatedly birthed Type 1 cover price variants immediately before universal price hikes, such as the shift from 10 to 12 cents per copy that occurred in January 1962, and the 25 cent to 30 cent shift famously embodied by the Marvel variants cover dated 4-8/1976 and from 30 to 35 cents for variants cover dated 6-10/1977. Despite much heckling back in the day from fellow advisors and critics, when I discovered and publicized the existence of the Marvel cover price variants in *Comic Book Marketplace* #51(8/97), such comics have soared in popularity and value. For a history of comic book variants from the Golden Age to the present, as well as a list of known variants and a lexicon of variant types, with examples that continue to evolve and expand, refer to my article from 2010 in the *Overstreet Comic Book Price Guide* #40, "A History of Publisher Experimentation and Variant Comic Books," pages #1010-1038. An updated version is in progress for the 50th Annual *OCBPG*.

Marvel Type 1 test market cover price variants are absolutely the hottest Bronze Age books pursued by collectors and speculators, with some comics realizing prices of 50 or more times than the same non-variant issues, and often double digit multiples of listed *Guide* values! Auction results on Marvel test market variants can fluctuate wildly. Key books listed by the *Guide* in the top 10 Gold, Silver and Bronze Age categories are there due to consistent sales and demand, and currently five of the top 10 Bronze Age comics are 35 cent variants. The ratio of regular 30 cent copies of *Star Wars* #1 in CGC 9.4 NM to 9.8 NM/M (there are over 2000) to the 35 cent variant of #1 is 200 to 1, according to the CGC census. Roughly twenty certified 35 cent copies exist in NM 9.4 or better, of which two certified copies exist in CGC 9.6 NM+ condition to date. The highest graded examples of Marvel variants are bringing truly astronomical prices at auction, especially the Western and Horror titles that had the lowest distribution, as sales were poor for regular editions let alone variants, hence their collective cancellations in 1976-1977.

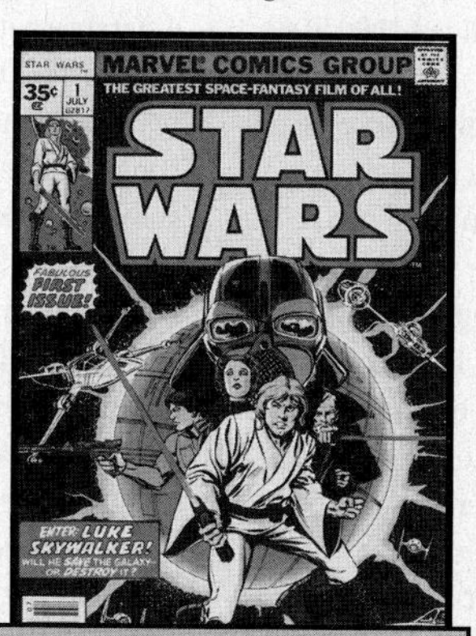

All discussions on Marvel price variants start with the **Star Wars #1 35¢ variant.**

Archie 15 cent Type 1 cover price variants now have over 80% confirmed to exist, so I feel confident that all 112 issues will eventually surface. Doug Sulipa and I estimate that such 15 cent variants are about 500-1000 times scarcer than their 12 cent counterparts. Regular 12 cent sci-fi monster issues from 1961-1962 sold for about 2-4 times *Guide*, so the 15 cent variants of these books should logically be higher in value. It's difficult to nail down actual worth when such items are rarely change hands, and the listings do not appear in the *Guide* yet, although collectors and dealers are well aware. I believe all 15 cent Archie Type 1 cover price variants have enormous investment potential, especially the three super-keys: *Archie's Madhouse* #22(10/62), *Archie's Girls Betty and Veronica* #75(3/62) and *Josie* #1(2/63).

Sixteen different Type 1 Charlton 15 cent test market cover price variants from March 1962 may be out there, but currently *Space War* #15 (3/62) and *Texas Rangers* #32 (3/62) are the only two examples confirmed to exist. Such 15 cent variants are so scarce and unknown to collectors that no sales have ever been reported, and only four total copies are confirmed to exist (three #32s and one #15). No additional 15 cent variants surfaced in the last year, and real value is difficult to judge without any money changing hands. I find such cusp era variants interesting and hope collectors will share acquisitions with me and/or the *Guide* so I can disseminate the information.

Type 1a cover price variants simultaneously published for foreign distribution are increasing in demand according to Doug Sulipa. Bronze and Copper Age Marvel and to a lesser extent DC Type 1a Canadian cover price variants are now routinely selling for 150-400% *Guide*, and select CGC high grade key issues of popular characters have been bringing 400-2000% of *Guide*; such books are at least 10 times scarcer due to low print runs. Canada's population is about 10% of the US population, thus about 10% of all Print Runs are Canadian copies, however roughly 80% of the surviving copies are Direct Editions, bought in comic shops and saved by collectors. Most of the Newsstand editions were bought by non-collecting readers, with a much lower survival rate, and most are well read FR/GD to FN/VF copies. Most VF/NM or better Type 1a Canadian Newsstand Cover Price Variants are 50 to 300 times scarcer than their US Direct Market counterparts in high grade; randomly checking the CGC census will substantiate this for most items. High grade examples from the Silver and Bronze age of Type 1a variants are scarcer still, largely due to damages that occurred in transit, and in particular water damage found on pence editions shipped overseas. Such difficulties predate contemporary standard procedures like simultaneous off-site printing, a reality that renders the concept of origination meaningless, at least for modern books. Marvel collectors dominate about 75% of the Type 1a Canadian cover price and British pence variant market, while DC and the others split the remaining 25%, with non-DC books accounting for less than 10% of total sales, a ratio that steepens when you hit the 1990s, when Type 1a cover price variants that don't say Marvel or at least DC have yet to show any real pulse outside of key issues.

Only five DC pence issues exist from the early Bronze age: *Action* #402 (7/71), *Adventure* #408 (7/71), *Detective* #413 (7/71), *Flash* #208 (8/71), and *Superman's Pal Jimmy Olsen* #139 (7/71). *Action* #402, *Detective* #413, and *Flash* #208 have Neal Adams covers, and the *Flash* issue is a 52 page giant, so such books have attractive qualities beyond just being Type 1a variants, and can bring 500% *Guide* or more than cents editions. Interest is also increasing in DC pence editions published from March 1978 to

September 1981, and such books often bring double *Guide* or more.

Dell Canadian and U.K. Type 1a cover price editions are being collected more, and currently sell at at a modest premium of 125-150% of standard cents editions. Western Publishing's Type 1a Canadian 75 cent cover price variants of 60 cent Whitmans from 1984 sell briskly at 300-400% *Guide* due to extremely low print runs, according to Doug Sulipa, who states that he has a waiting list for any copies in Fine Plus or better condition; it should be noted that alleged copies of 1983 Type 1a 75 cent Whitman variants do not exist. Whitman pre-pack comics dated 8-12/1980 are red hot sellers due to scarcity and bring $100-$500 or more in Very Fine or better condition. Refer to my article, "The Whitman Mystery," in *Comic Book Marketplace* magazine #85-86 (9-10/01) for the strange story behind what caused the scarcity of Gold Key/Whitman comics dated 1980-1984 and their untimely demise.

Type 1A variants are drawing the attention of collectors and investors like never before. I have long argued that Type 1A variants would climb in interest due to scarcity. The scarcity of Canadian newsstand cover price variants versus simultaneously published U.S. direct editions is a chasm of difference, roughly 50 to 1 by comparison! Even "newsstand variants," the newsstand edition of comics extending into the 1990s, have come to bring a premium of up to 1000% or more due to scarcity, as print runs descended year by year. Check out the free new online Price Guide for Type 1A Canadian cover price Marvel and DC comics from the 1980s at rarecomicsblog.com. The Guide contains only Marvel and DC at this juncture, beginning with books cover dated 10/82 and ending with issues cover dated 9/88 for DC and 8/86 for Marvel. Key issues in the top ten include *Batman* #357 (3/83), *Swamp Thing* #37 (6/85) and *Amazing Spider-Man* #238 (3/83), the latter key issue burdened with a confusing insert, an unusual dilemma that I will address.

Amazing Spider-Man #238 is not incomplete without Tattooz. It was printed in a standard, old fashioned way, independent of the Tattooz inserted later just like Mark Jewelers ads from the 1970s were inserted. Should we call *Incredible Hulk* #181(11/74) without a Mark Jewelers insert incomplete? I believe this problem originates from the fact that the comic's cover mentions Tattooz, as does the cover to *Fantastic Four* #252(3/83). Ideally, the Tattooz ARE absent due to the slow degradation of the contents that will eventually effect paper quality inside. *Overstreet* listings are confused, forced to respond to CGC's nonsensical view. Once upon a time, I called Bob Overstreet and told him that the *FF* #252's Tattooz were being used as *Spidey* #238's Tattooz and that the cure was to list them as same value, which he agreed with and subsequently did so. Collectors aren't sure what to believe and that's how the CGC myth is perpetuated, the myth of being incomplete without Tattooz. At some point, although my original note remains in the *Guide* about the switching of Tattooz between books, this was changed back to the original mistaken listing (including the explicit mistaken statement that NO Type 1a Canadian variants exist with Tattooz) with two values, with and without Tattooz. The *FF* #252s are listed in *Overstreet* #47(2017) at $8 with Tattooz and $6 without in NM-, and *ASM* #238 is listed at $150 with and $80 without in NM-, a discrepancy that highlights this dilemma, with Tattooz worth between $2 and $70 for the same item. As no copies of *FF* #252 Type 1A have ever been confirmed to have Tattooz, all copies submitted would automatically be delineated as CGC green label (incomplete) unless Tattooz were inserted, thereby CREATING a variant which is not valid, as home made variants do not a variant make. All CGC would have to do is say "no Tattooz" on the label and have a blue label, leaving it to the collector to decide on the relative importance of its inclusion. There is little if any difference between the mistaken use of the term "Canadian Edition" for Type 1A variants and insisting books without inserts are incomplete. The situation is ridiculous; it is a conceptual failure. Any real NM- or better copy will and should be taken seriously with or without the insert. Tattooz were inserted in *Amazing Spider-Man* #238 and *Fantastic Four* #252 and advertised on the covers; *Captain America* #279 (3/83) and *Star Wars* #69 (3/83) were given Tattooz without advertising on the covers. Because neither of the latter books are considered incomplete without the inserts and would receive CGC blue labels, it stands to reason that *ASM* #238 and *FF* #252 are not incomplete without Tattooz either, as the books are complete, having been printed in a standard way, independent of the Tattooz that were then inserted. The only difference is the ads on the covers, and those are irrelevant as they are part of the printing process of the book itself.

Early Marvel Direct Sale Editions are scarcer and sell for an average of 200-500% of regular newsstand editions according to Doug Sulipa; such books were sometimes erroneously referred to as "Marvel Whitmans" due to their simultaneous distribution in department and drug stores in Whitman bags. Early Marvel Direct Market Editions have a duality of purpose, and thus have the unique honor of being "special market editions" that required a secondary market to help justify the cost of their existence in smaller print runs. The Direct Sales market was in its infancy, and Marvel wanted to monitor retailers' return credits, hence the confusion surrounding the odd but necessary difference in appearance between such books and their newsstand counterparts. Short gaps in production occurred from 2/1977 to 5/1979, as it cost less for Marvel to roll the dice against bogus returns than over-produce books erratically purchased by chain retailers. All early Direct Market Editions were produced except for the cover dates 1-3/1978, 7/1978, and 3-4/1979, and such comics are sought after largely by hardcore Marvel collectors and completists.

The comics industry remains healthy. May it stay that way.

Todd McDevitt
New Dimension Comics

Greetings from Western Pennsylvania! Home of Matt Baker, Steve Ditko, Jack Cole and New Dimension Comics! I've been in this crazy business for 32 years now, have 6 store locations, about 3 million (literally) comic books, and not enough hours in the day. Here are some of my observations of the comic book marketplace from this past year.

Buying. I'm buying more comic collections than ever. I have piles of long boxes stacked taller than me (and I'm a tall guy!), some of which have been sitting for years waiting for me to get to them. So much was coming in that I got a new warehouse and in about a year it has accumulated well over 100 pallets of comics. Yes, I'm measuring my stock in PALLETS now. There are some days I'm measuring deals in TRUCKLOADS! So, I think I will spend a lot of this report on this aspect of the market since it's where I have tons of experience.

So, what do I do with all these comics? Well, I sell them! Big batches get run through a bit of a food chain. I have fought for years to keep back issues relevant in my stores. It's very tempting to decide, as lots of comic shops have done, that they aren't worth the sales floor space. I feel they are part of the identity of a comic shop. Plus, they are heck of a value! With new comics costing $3-4 and some content is a gamble, you can get proven, classic stories from the rich history of publishing for less. And, no waiting! The challenge is keeping up with matching our changing needs with our rapidly incoming selections.

Dollar bins. After a quick pass for things we need, the rest get sent to dollar land. This is another area I focus on with each store having these bargain bins. I try to keep them rotating and fresh, a nice bonus to having 6 locations. At our flagship store in Ellwood City, we have over 500,000 sorted comics in our basement. We pluck from there to restock stores weekly, but also open it up to customers the last Saturday in January and September for $1 each. There is a constant effort to file in new arrivals to keep both of these goals satisfied. In doing this, there is just SO much material we are slogging through that we miss stuff. I sold an *Amazing Spider-Man* #300 for $1. Oops. Plus, we live in a world where new books pop up as hot regularly. *Batman Chronicles* #21 was nothing until Brian Michael Bendis signed with DC (it's his first work there) and today is $15-25. Gems can be found!

Even though I'm aggressive with the bulk volume component of the hobby, I still do a lot with vintage books. After all this time, it's still my favorite part. I often joke that some people have buying addictions to shoes, CDs, etc. I'm addicted to buying comics! I don't have much of a poker face when I'm buying cool old books!

Steve Mortensen
Miracle Comics

In 2017, money continued to pour into the comic book market in all genres. This year, I didn't see any areas of softness – collectors were buying up everything and paying premium prices. The overall U.S. economy has been strong and lots of cash has been flowing.

I believe any major collectibles or fine arts purchase – whether it is a sports card, coin or famous painting – has an impact on the overall collectibles market. On November 15, 2017, a rare Leonardo da Vinci painting sold at auction at Christie's for $450 million – the highest price ever paid for a painting. The previous highest sale was a Picasso for $176 million. The da Vinci painting measures 18 x 25 inches – slightly smaller than the *Mona Lisa* – but it is one of only 20 paintings known to have been painted solely by him. In comparison, a Frank Frazetta oil painting sold at Heritage Auctions for $1 million in August of 2016. I think it shows how much room there is to grow in the comic book and original art market.

All comics saw growth in 2017, but I noticed substantial growth in the low-grade Golden Age books, especially Timelys. As a small example from my personal collection, I purchased a *Sub-Mariner* #41 (Atlas, 1955) in VG+ in November 2017 from Heritage Auctions for $430, which was double the *Guide* value in aggressive bidding. Timely/Atlas, in particular, are in high demand and the lower grades are more affordable to the general collector.

Key books in the Silver Age are bringing strong prices. *Amazing Fantasy* #15 and *Fantastic Four* #1 saw jumps in low-grade. *Amazing Fantasy* #15 sold for $35,000 in CGC 4.0, up from a high of $19,200 in 2016 for a CGC 4.0. *Fantastic Four* #1 sold for $7,768 in CGC 4.0 in 2017 and $5,450 as a high for a CGC 4.0 in 2016. I see that low-grade, Golden/Silver Age books are anchoring the market right now. Many great key books are still "affordable" to the mid-level collector.

Market analysis: Golden Age – Along with the low-grade issues, the market is still dominated by the past sales of expensive comic books. The top copies of *Action Comics* #1 and *Detective Comics* #27 did not change hands in 2017. The closest was a sale of *Detective Comics* #27 in May for $710,000 in CGC 5.0 (blue label). A conserved copy of *Action Comics* #1 sold in CGC 5.5 for $393,000. Funny enough, a single page of *Action Comics* #1 (5th page) which registers NG (No Grade) in an encapsulated CGC holder, sold for $16,000 in November of 2017.

Silver Age – The spread between graded 9.2 copies and 9.8 copies is staggering. Taking a non-descript issue like *Amazing Spider-Man* #10, you can see the difference. A CGC 9.2 copy sold in November of 2017 for $3,107; a CGC 9.4 sold in August of 2017 for $4,400; a CGC 9.6 copy sold in July of 2017 for $6,000; a CGC 9.8 sold for $16,730 in May of 2017.

Bronze Age – I find *Werewolf By Night* #32 (1st app Moon Knight) the most compelling book of this era. CGC

9.8 prices ($14,000+) are coming close to *Incredible Hulk* #181 in CGC 9.8 ($18,000+). The book is very difficult to grade in CGC 9.8 and there have been only 14 copies graded at this level out of 1,873 copies. That represents less than 1% of the census on this issue. At some point, I expect Marvel will introduce the character in the movies and prices may skyrocket. CGC 9.6 copies are easier to find and they sell for around $4,000-5,000 while CGC 9.4 copies sell in the $3,000 range.

Copper Age – Clearly the leader in this group is *Teenage Mutant Ninja Turtles* #1 First Printing. This is another difficult book to find in CGC 9.8. A copy traded hands in May of 2017 in CGC 9.8 for $27,485. In November 2017, a CGC 9.6 sold at Heritage Auctions for $26,290, setting a new precedent for CGC 9.8 copies (the book had been signed on the inside by Eastman and Laird but still received a blue label – not a Signature Series copy). A CGC 9.4 is a very respectable copy of this issue and sells in the $7,500 range. CGC 6.0s sell in the $2,000 range which is great for an entry level collector looking for an investment-quality book.

Modern Age – As with *TMNT* #1, *Walking Dead* #1 represents the banner comic of the modern era – what I call the "Millennial Age" of modern comics (comics published after 2000). It is hard to know how this book will hold its value once the TV series completes. As of now, it is going strong. CGC 9.9s sell for around $15,000 (there are 24 of them out of 2,795 copies graded – less than 1% like *Werewolf By Night* #32 in CGC 9.8). A CGC 9.8 copy will cost you about $2,300. It's difficult to gauge the demand on this book moving forward given the volatility of the Modern market. I do see the book dropping in value once the TV show is over – however, if the comic book series continues after the TV show, the drop may not be that significant.

2018 looks to be another great year for collectibles and comic books. If the world economy continues to grow, I see records being set by many of the key issues and an overall appreciation for all comic books. While it used to be mostly U.S.-based, the comic book market has now expanded globally. I have many customers in Australia, Singapore, Japan and Europe. It is common for many collectors to invest part of their investment portfolio in tangible assets like collectibles and metals. The rise of Bitcoin may prove to also expand the overall comic market as many people still do not have access to U.S. dollars. As technology and government regulations improve, more global collectors could enter the market through Bitcoin. Of course, besides the monetary aspects, how cool is it to own one of your favorite treasures?

Marc Nathan
Cards, Comics and Collectibles
Baltimore Comic-Con

As of November 1, Cards, Comics and Collectibles has moved into a new location that is five times bigger than my previous store. Located right on Main Street in town, my new location was – in the 1930s through the '60s – a movie theater. So, if one can picture how big a movie theater is, that's the size of the retail space my store currently encompasses. And, since we've been able to showcase our wide diversity of products prominently in our larger location, everything seems to be working and every product category seems to be selling well.

My numbers, at the end of the year, are up since I moved into my new store. With that, I may not be the best guy to talk about what isn't working right now; although I do know what isn't working in a lot of places – and that's the bi-weekly/monthly comic book scene dependent just on subscriptions and newsstands. Yes, comic book sales are down for the first time in a decade, but yet, potentially, other things are not. For example, are collectible card games down? I don't think so. Are new and different toys, action figures, and statues down? It doesn't seem like it at my store. Is apparel down? Well, maybe a little bit, but it still sells. You can sell everything from t-shirts to hoodies to bathrobes – whatever kind of apparel you may have. This week, we're getting in Black Panther masks. Big, rubber, Black Panther masks. Are they going to sell? They sure will. It's a cool item that will sell up until the *Black Panther* movie breaks, and probably into *Avengers: Infinity War*. The secret is predicting the next trend, and that's by watching what movies and TV shows are coming up that people are talking about. Whether it's *Star Wars* or *Avengers* or even *Justice League*, you have to be prepared for their popularity.

Talking about popular, Golden Age did exceptionally well during 2017 in terms of mainstream super-heroes. I can't get them fast enough. Supermans, Batmans, and *All Star Comics* are standard DCs that sell and sell. Timelys, when you can get them, sure. Specific great covers always sell, and they always will. No matter what it is, be it a Jungle, be it War, whatever book it is. If it's a great cover, it's a great cover, and these comics will always sell just for their nature. And, there seems to be no price resistance in the Golden Age market, in general. With an early Superman and an early Batman, there is definitely no price resistance. If someone is asking for $2,000 for the book, then they will get $2,000. It just is. Timelys do that, too, when I get them, but I don't get them enough. For that reason, I'm not a Timely expert, but they do sell. However, if I got three or 300 Timelys, they would sell for me, but I can't say that for everyone. Anyway, the Golden Age market is certainly not a declining market in any way, shape, or form.

In terms of Silver Age, Bronze Age, and Modern Age books together, if it's a first appearance of a popular character, a key issue, a great cover, or a number one, there is absolutely zero price resistance. Take whichever key you want to talk about. For example, *Tales of Suspense* #39 (first appearance of Marvel's Iron Man) – no price resistance. *Amazing Spider-Man* #1 – no price resistance.

First appearance of Marvel's Rhino – no price resistance. *Amazing Spider-Man* #50, which is great cover and the first appearance of the Kingpin – no price resistance.

There is also no price resistance to a great Silver Age or Bronze Age cover. And there's no price resistance in key issues. In fact, I'll say there is even less price resistance in Bronze Age or Modern Age keys, because prices are more affordable. To a generation where 1972 isn't that far removed from 1962, an *Amazing Spider-Man* #1 and a *Hero for Hire* #1 (first appearance of Marvel's Luke Cage) are different, but not that different. Sure, one's $3,000 and one's $200. But, $200 could easily lead to $300 with the right collector, and it is happening. It's happening over and over and over. You go to any one-day, two-day, three-day show where there's people looking for comics, and you have a *Hero for Hire* #1 or *Werewolf by Night* #32 (first appearance of Marvel's Moon Knight) or whatever it is, and the folks that see it will buy that first appearance or key, but they will have zero interest in the second and later appearances of the character. They just want that first appearance.

Make no mistake: Folks are investing in Bronze Age and Modern Age books. Just ask yourself: Is there going to be a new TV show starring Marvel's Cloak and Dagger? There sure is. So, how do you think *Spectacular Spider-Man* #64 is doing? It's just the nature of it. It's funny, too, that comic book veterans would invest in Marvel Comics' *Infinity Gauntlet*. However, collectors new to the hobby would instead buy *Infinity War* – because that's the name of the movie. And, that's what they know. And, in that case, you have to take them back slowly and introduce them to the beginning.

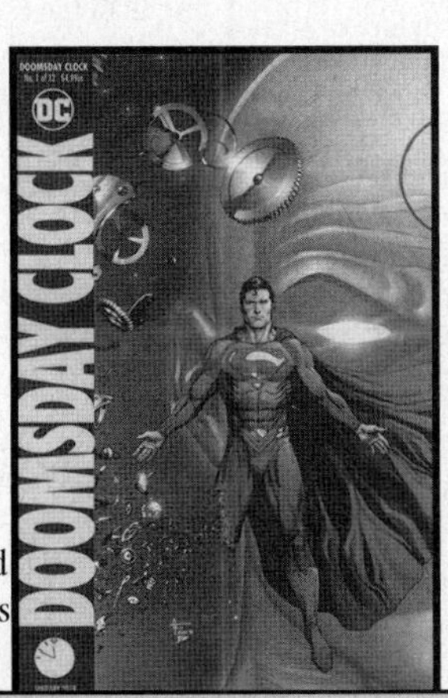

DC's **Doomsday Clock** is selling in great numbers.

As far as new stuff, DC Comics' *Metal* and *Doomsday Clock* are selling in great numbers at my store. In fact, when one of those books ship, we have a really good week. Those books are bringing collectors into the store who end up buying other things like they always do. Batman, a Marvel comic, whatever it is. They are also buying bags, boards, and boxes; they're shopping. When a title that sells to a larger audience ships, the collectors become customers and shop throughout the store. And we put other things in their hands, and hopefully they will learn to appreciate other comics from Boom! or Valiant or Dynamite or anybody else. And, it can happen; it does happen. Everything from the Jim Henson Universe that Boom! is putting out, like the *Labyrinth* books, are selling at larger numbers. It's funny; if you ask fans why *Labyrinth* is selling – is it popular because of the movie or because they miss David Bowie? And the answer that you usually get is both. All the Jim Henson books that Boom! is putting out are just growing. And, you can see why.

Something I'm still learning about is magazines – Marvel and otherwise. I know people want them, and I'm selling them. And, although I haven't brought them to conventions yet, I'm going to start in 2018. Reason one: I have a lot. Reason two: They are not as heavy as I remember them to be in regards to carrying them to shows. The thing about Marvel magazines, for example, is that they are from the 1970s. I mistakenly thought they could be found anywhere, but that's not the case. I've since put more focus on them.

As far as comic book shows go, I made a conscious decision in 2016 that I wanted to do conventions that were one- or two-day shows and my booth money, travel money, and table money was going to a guy or a gal who owns a comic book store, or would spend the money from the show buying more comic books. I'm not saying I'm never going to do a corporately owned show again, but I didn't do it in 2017, I have no plans to do it in 2018, and I have to say that I like what I'm doing much, much more. It's more affordable. I'm still selling the same amount of books since there's no price resistance to keys. I still need books. I still need inventory to sell. I'm still buying books for shows and my store. I'm not doing less shows, I'm only doing conventions that are not corporately owned shows. I'm driving to a place where it's someone like me; someone who owns a store or two and puts on a show in their neighborhood. And I'd rather give that guy my booth money because he lives the way I live. He or she's not faceless – it's someone I can talk to on the phone tomorrow, and I do. We talk all the time and we know who we are.

I did a show for a friend of mine in Virginia who I had not spoken to in a long time. I found out he was doing a little one-day show in the middle of Virginia. Not far, but far enough that I had to get a hotel room to stay the night. I immediately contacted this guy, and found out that his was the first show – which was large enough to almost be called a convention, but it was a one-day show — in about five years that there wasn't a single Funko Pop in the room. There were things other than comics – some toys – but there were no Pops. And, my first thought was, "Oh, crap! I should have brought Pops." But the truth is, I had actually gone somewhere that comics were still the focus. It was really fun, but I didn't get to buy much, though.

When it comes to what I purchase for myself, I still buy what I always buy: vintage Disney, Barks *Four Colors* and earlier *Mickey Mouse Magazines*. Even if I have them already – call me a hoarder, in that regard I don't care! One day, I'll actually sit down and put them in order, deciding which ones are my nicest and grade them. Call me lazy, but I don't even know where all the books are – I just want more. You know, I buy a box and take it home, and it goes with the other box. Occasionally, I'll get something I've never seen before or had before, or I know it's better than the one I had before just by looking at it. I'm also always buying stuff for resale, too, which includes keys and number ones. And, I buy people's collections. Being in my new location, people are treating Cards, Comics and Collectibles like it is a new store, although we've been around for 34 years. But, I'm buying collections all the time for all those interested.

Josh Nathanson, Douglas Gillock & Rick Hirsch
ComicLink

ComicLink is now in its 23rd year serving the collector community on ComicLink.com as a consignment-based firm. Between our Featured and Focused Auctions and The Comic Book Exchange®, we have utilized the power of the Internet since 1996 as a means for sellers to find the right kind of buyer for their valuable vintage comic books online. We also specialize in valuable original comic book and fantasy related artwork. 2017 was the biggest year we've ever seen for our auction division. Aggressive buyers added many thousands of examples of certified comic books and comic related original artwork to their collections, setting many new sales records for the hobby. Like we've seen in the past few years, strength was exhibited across virtually every collecting genre. From Golden Age rarities of the 1930s and early '50s to the Silver and Bronze Age keys and high-grades of the late 1950s through the '70s, and right up through Copper and Modern Age era, the bar was raised on record sales this year. We see this growth trend continuing for years to come. Movies based on comic books continue to be the #1 most popular form of entertainment in the world with the buildup and release of each film capturing massive attention from untold millions of fans. There are more than two dozen live-action TV series adapted from comic books currently airing, including some of the most watched shows on the air. 2018 will be the biggest year yet for Hollywood movies and TV shows devoted to our beloved characters and the attention from the mainstream world will continue to create new collectors for decades to come who will be interested in the vintage appearances of their favorites.

Throughout 2017, many sales records were set by examples from the John G. Fantucchio Pedigree collection sold in various ComicLink auctions. In late 2016, ComicLink introduced the Fantucchio collection, a recent CGC-recognized pedigree that includes most comic books published by Marvel, DC and many other publishers from the inception of the Marvel era through the mid-'70s. The books were collected by artist John Fantucchio and stored in ideal conditions. The result is a collection of beautifully preserved comic books with bright, bold colors and page quality that appears as if it just came off of the newsstands. Examples from the Fantucchio collection will continue to be sold at auction on ComicLink throughout 2018.

Silver Age (1956-1969): Demand for Silver Age comics is as strong as it has ever been. As usual, major Marvel and DC keys led the way in 2017 with exceptional results for several premiere and "1st appearance" issues achieved. Many traditional keys sold for impressive amounts including *Amazing Fantasy* #15 (1st Spider-Man) CGC 9.2 for $460,000 and CGC 8.0 for $261,010 (just two examples of the numerous all-time records in grade that ComicLink sellers have realized for this book in 2017); *Journey Into Mystery* #83 (1st Thor) CGC 9.0 for $62,500; *Amazing Spider-Man* #1 (2nd Spider-Man, 1st Jameson) CGC 9.2 for $99,999 and CGC 8.0 for $33,000; *Brave and the Bold* #54 (1st Teen Titans) CGC 9.8 Fantucchio Pedigree for $39,888 (a new record for a post-1963 DC); *Silver Surfer* #1 (Origin of Surfer) CGC 9.8 Fantucchio Pedigree for $36,009; and *Strange Tales* #110 (1st Doctor Strange) CGC 9.4 for $36,000. Prices for the entire Silver Age *Amazing Spider-Man* run have continued to escalate, with no seemingly no end in sight for the most collected title of the era.

With many thousands of transactions throughout the year, there are way too many examples on ComicLink.com to list all of the exceptional results here, but here are some representative Silver Age examples: *Action Comics* #242 (1st Brainiac) CGC 4.5 for $2,422, #252 (1st Supergirl) CGC 8.5 for $19,750; *Adventure Comics* #252 (1st Legion) CGC 5.0 for $3,100, #300 (Legion series begins) CGC 9.0 for $5,900; *Amazing Fantasy* #15 (1st Spider-Man) CGC 9.2 for $460,000, CGC 8.0 for $261,010 (All-Time Record in Grade), CGC 7.0 for $132,500, CGC 5.0 for $53,001; *Amazing Spider-Man* #1 (2nd Spider-Man, 1st Jameson) CGC 9.2 for $99,999, CGC 8.0 for $33,000, CGC 6.0 Signature Series for $15,000, #2 (1st Vulture) CGC 9.2 for $21,900, CGC 9.0 for $19,007, #3 (1st Dr. Octopus) CGC 9.4 for $18,750, #4 (1st Sandman) CGC 9.2 for $10,250, #5 (early Doctor Doom) for CGC 9.2 for $9,600, #6 (1st Lizard) CGC 9.4 for $7,973, #7 (2nd Vulture) CGC 9.6 for $19,138, CGC 9.4 for $11,255, CGC 9.2 for $3,850, #8 (1st Living Brain) CGC 9.2 for $3,200, CGC 9.0 for $2,607, #9 (1st Electro) CGC 9.2 for $5,100, #10 (1st Enforcers) CGC 9.8 for $13,706, CGC 9.2 for $3,599, #11 (2nd Dr. Octopus) CGC 9.6 for $23,706, #13 (1st Mysterio) CGC 9.6 for $23,245, CGC 9.0 for $3,301, #14 (1st Green Goblin) CGC 9.6 for $22,250, CGC 9.2 for $8,800, CGC 9.0 for $8,355, #15 (1st Kraven) CGC 9.4 for $5,119, CGC 9.2 for $3,850, CGC 9.0 for $3,600, #16 (1st Daredevil crossover) CGC 9.2 for $2,600, #17 (2nd Green Goblin) CGC 9.8 for $17,750, #18 CGC 9.6 for $5,400, #20 (1st Scorpion) CGC 9.8 for $18,750, CGC 9.2 for $4,101, #23 (Early Green Goblin) CGC 9.4 for $3,978, CGC 9.2 for $2,300, #24 CGC 9.4 for $3,234, #28 (1st Molten Man, classic black cover) CGC 9.0 for $4,140, #31 (1st Gwen Stacy & Harry Osborn) CGC 9.4 CVA for $5,988, #39 (1st Romita art, Goblin ID revealed) CGC 9.6 for $6,600, #40 (Origin of Goblin) CGC 9.8 for $18,250, #42 (1st Mary Jane face reveal) CGC 9.8 for $6,305, #45 CGC 9.8 for $3,176, #46 (1st Shocker) CGC 9.8 for $11,800, #50 (1st Kingpin) CGC 9.6 for

$14,518, CGC 9.4 for $8,350, CGC 9.2 $2,911, #51 (1st Kingpin cover) CGC 9.6 for $5,959, #52 CGC 9.8 for $7,170, CGC 9.6 for $3,905, #54 CGC 9.8 for $4,767, #55 CGC 9.8 for $6,100, #56 CGC 9.8 for $5,200, #58 CGC 9.6 for $2,300, #59 (1st MJ cover) CGC 9.8 for $2,857, #60 CGC 9.6 for $5,200, #61 (1st Gwen cover) CGC 9.8 for $4,355, #66 CGC 9.8 for $2,434, #70 CGC 9.8 for $3,556, #71 CGC 9.8 for $3,377, #78 CGC 9.8 for $2,977, *Annual* #1 (1st Sinister Six) CGC 9.4 for $14,052, CGC 9.0 for $3,700, *Annual* #2 CGC 9.4 for $2,250, *Annual* #5 CGC 9.8 for $4,087; *Aquaman* #1 CGC 9.6 for $28,250, #4 CGC 9.6 for $2,307, #5 CGC 9.6 for $2,500, #25 CGC 9.6 for $2,500, #33 (1st Aquagirl) CGC 9.6 Pacific Coast Pedigree for $5,100, #35 (1st Black Manta) CBCS 9.0 for $2,200; *Avengers* #1 (1st Avengers) CGC 8.5 for $23,750, #2 CGC 9.0 for $3,322, #4 (1st SA Captain America) CGC 9.4 for $13,000, #8 (1st Kang) CGC 9.6 for $5,155, #41 CGC 9.8 for $3,665, #54 (1st Ultron appearance--cameo) CGC 9.8 for $2,888, #57 (1st Vision) CGC 9.6 CVA for $4,500, #71 (1st Invaders) CGC 9.8 for $2,155; *Batman* #121 (1st Mr. Freeze as Mr. Zero) CGC 6.0 Fantucchio Pedigree for $3,600, #171 (1st SA Riddler) CGC 9.0 for $2,000, #181 (1st Poison Ivy) CGC 9.4 for $10,250, #210 (Adams Catwoman bondage cover) CGC 9.8 for $4,823; *Blue Beetle* #1 (1st Question) for CGC 9.8 CVA $2,200; *Brave and the Bold* #28 (1st Justice League) CGC 4.0 for $3,900, #54 (1st Teen Titans) CGC 9.8 for $39,888, #85 (1st revamped Green Arrow) CGC 9.6 for $3,133; *Daredevil* #1 (1st Daredevil) CGC 9.4 for $24,251, #2 CGC 9.4 for $3,167, #5 CGC 9.6 for $2,322, #10 CGC 9.8 for $6,600, #24 CGC 9.8 for $4,127, #64 CGC 9.8 for $3,800; *Detective Comics* #275 CGC 9.6 for $5,600, #302 CGC 9.4 for $2,350, #309 CGC 9.6 for $3,640, #356 CGC 9.8 for $3,211, for #359 (1st Batgirl) CGC 9.2 for $7,909; *Fantastic Four* #2 (1st Skrulls) CGC 9.0 CVA for $13,750, #4 (1st SA Sub-Mariner) CGC 9.0 for $9,100, #5 (1st Dr. Doom) CGC 9.0 for $26,916, CGC 7.0 for $4,900, #7 CGC 9.4 for $18,750, #16 (Early Doctor Doom, 1st Ant-Man crossover) CGC 9.2 for $3,000, #23 (Early Doctor Doom) CGC 9.2 Curator Pedigree for $2,000, #25 (1st Thing/Hulk battle) CGC 9.4 for $4,025, #45 (1st Inhumans) CGC 9.0 for $3,100, #46 (1st full Black Bolt) CGC 9.8 for $19,000, CGC 9.6 for $4,955, #48 (1st Silver Surfer & Galactus) CGC 9.6 for $10,555, #49 (1st Silver Surfer cover) CGC 9.6 for $9,755, CGC 9.4 for $4,937, #50 (classic Silver Surfer cover) CGC 9.6 for $14,250, #52 (1st Black Panther) CGC 9.6 for $15,805, CGC 9.2 for $7,623, #67 (1st Him/Warlock) CGC 9.8 for $8,800, *Annua*l #6 (1st Annihilus, birth of Franklin) CGC 9.8 for $5,200; *Flash* #128 (1st Abra-Kadabra) CGC 9.0 for $3,150, #131 CGC 9.6 for $3,087; *Green Lantern* #73 CGC 9.8 Fantucchio Pedigree for $4,600; *Hawkman* #4 (1st Zatanna) CGC 9.4 for $4,212; *House of Mystery* #181 CGC 9.8 for $2,768; *House of Secrets* #61 (1st Eclipso) CGC 9.4 for $4,525, CGC 9.2 for $3,860; *Incredible Hulk* #1 (1st Hulk) CGC 6.5 for $40,001, #2 (1st green Hulk) CGC 8.5 for $8,850; *Iron Man* #1 CGC 9.4 for $2,499; *Journey Into Mystery* #83 (1st Thor) CGC 9.0 for $62,500, CGC 7.5 Fantucchio Pedigree for $17,000, CGC 7.0 for $13,251, #88 CGC 8.5 9.4 Fantucchio Pedigree for $4,767, #103 CGC 9.4 Fantucchio Pedigree for $6,100, #112 CGC 9.4 Fantucchio Pedigree for $5,100; *Justice League of America* #1 CGC 7.5 for $7,800, #5 CGC 9.0 for $2,655, #7 CBCS 9.4 for $7,655, #13 CGC 9.4 for $4,400, #38 CGC 9.8 for $3,944, #39 CGC 9.8 for $7,200, CGC 9.6 for $3,300, #48 CGC 9.8 for $4,877, #49 CGC 9.8 for $9,109, #57 CGC 9.8 for $3,100, #64 (1st SA Red Tornado) CGC 9.8 for $3,688, #67 CGC 9.6 for $3,333, #70 CGC 9.8 for $3,655, #75 (1st Revamped Black Canary) CGC 9.6 for $8,777; *Marvel Tales* #1 (1st reprint of *Amazing Fantasy* #15 and other early Marvel origins) CGC 9.4 for $3,634; *Nick Fury, Agent of SHIELD* #1 CGC 9.8 for $2,600; *Sgt. Fury and His Howling Commandos* #13 (classic Captain America crossover) CGC 9.8 for $13,250; *Showcase #22* CBCS 6.0 Verified Signature for $8,480, #30 (1st solo Aquaman comic book) CGC 9.4 Bethlehem Pedigree for $25,000, #37 (1st Metal Men) CGC 9.0 for $5,100; #75 (1st Hawk & Dove) CGC 9.8 for $6,100; *Silver Surfer* #1 (Origin of Surfer) CGC 9.8 for $36,009 Fantucchio Pedigree, #3 (1st Mephisto) CGC 9.8 for $10,250, #4 (classic Thor battle cover) CGC 9.4 for $5,211; *Star Spangled War Stories* #84 (1st Mademoiselle Marie) CGC 8.0 for $2,600; *Strange Tales* #89 (1st Fin Fang Foom) CGC 5.5 for $2,125, #106 (early FF crossover) CGC 9.6 $4,100, #107 CGC 9.0 Signature Series for $1,744, #110 (1st Doctor Strange) CGC 9.4 for $36,000, CGC 8.5 for $11,250, CGC 6.0 for $2,666, *Annual* #2 (4th Spider-Man, 1st crossover) CGC 9.4 CVA for $20,694, CGC 9.2 for $3,950; *Sub-Mariner* #1 CGC 9.8 for $5,105; Superboy #68 (1st Bizarro) CGC 8.0 for $10,250, CGC 6.5 for $3,088; *Tales of Suspense* #39 CGC 6.0 for $7,111, #48 (1st Red & Gold Iron Man armor) CGC 9.2 for $2,988, #58 (classic Iron Man vs. Captain America battle cover) CGC 9.6 for $16,750, #59 (Captain America solo series begins) CGC 9.8 for $5,200, #75 (1st Sharon Carter) CGC 9.6 for $2,655; *Tales to Astonish* #13 (1st Groot) CGC 5.5 for $3,300, #27 (1st Ant-Man) CGC 8.5 for $20,000, CGC 7.0 for $10,627, #30 CGC 9.0 for $2,050, #44 (1st Wasp) CBCS 9.4 for $8,988, CGC 8.5 $3,855, #93 (Hulk/Silver Surfer crossover) CGC 9.6 for $2,900; *X-Men* #1 (1st X-Men & Magneto) CGC 7.5 for $12,472, #2 CGC 9.6 for $26,500, #4 (1st Quicksilver & Scarlet Witch) CGC 9.4 for $13,805, CBCS 9.2 for $6,657, #6 CGC 9.6 for $4,668, #21 CGC 9.8 for $2,951, #26 CGC 9.8 for $3,091, #28 CGC 9.6 for $2,200, #31 CGC 9.8 for $3,667, #35 (Spider-Man crossover) CGC 9.8 for $6,600, #36 CGC 9.8 for $3,099, #42 (death of Professor X) CGC 9.8 for $7,600, #49 (1st Polaris, Steranko cover) CGC 9.6 CVA for $1,868, #50 (classic Steranko cover) CGC 9.8 for $2,321, #56 (Adams cover) CGC 9.8 for $2,222, #58 (Adams cover) CGC 9.8 for $3,700, #64 (1st Sunfire) CGC 9.8 for $2,799, and #70 CGC 9.8 for $2,456.

Golden Age (1935-1955): The Golden Age remained the primary focus for many of ComicLink's buyers in 2017 and we were thrilled to offer one of the largest selections of quality comic books from this seminal era of collecting both at auction and on The Exchange®, including many high grade and pedigree examples. Some of the top highlights included traditional keys such *Superman* #1 CGC 5.5 for $505,000 (highest known price ever paid for a *Superman* #1); *Detective Comics* #27 (1st Batman) CGC 2.5 for $380,000; *Marvel Comics* #1 (1st Marvel comic, 1st Human Torch, Origin Sub-Mariner) CGC 2.5 for $87,251; *All Star Comics* #8 (1st Wonder Woman) CGC 5.5 for $83,888; *Wonder Woman* #1 CGC 5.5 for $44,515; *All Star Comics* #3 (1st Justice Society) CGC 5.5 for $28,250; *Detective Comics* #38 (1st Robin) CGC 4.5 Slight Restoration for $27,561, and from the very end of the Golden Age, *Detective Comics* #225 (1st Martian Manhunter) CGC 8.0 for $25,001.

Early Batman appearances continued to grow in value, even in the lower and middle grades. Example of 2017 sales include *Detective Comics* #29 (2nd Batman cover) CGC 1.8 Brittle Pages for $22,750, #31 (classic Batman cover) CGC 1.8 Brittle Pages for $25,250, #33 (1st origin of Batman) CGC 0.5 for $9,125, #35 (classic fifth Batman cover) CGC 3.5 for $30,009, and #36 (6th Batman cover) CGC 6.0 for $44,000.

Another hot area has practically any Golden Age appearances of DC villains who remain popular today. Some highlights in this area include *Action Comics* #23 (1st Luthor) CGC 4.5 for $17,138,, *Batman* #11 (1st Joker cover in title) CGC 7.5 for $15,361, #65 (Catwoman cover) CGC 9.0 for $8,000, *Detective Comics* #58 (1st Penguin) CGC 4.5 for $7,150, #62 (classic Robinson Joker cover) CGC 8.0 for $15,850, #67 (1st Penguin cover) CGC 7.0 for $5,500, #71 (classic Robinson Joker cover) CGC 5.5 for $5,200, #122 (1st Catwoman cover in title) CGC 8.0 Hawkeye Pedigree for $8,351, #140 (1st Riddler) CGC 6.5 CVA for $22,250, and #168 (Origin of Joker, 1st Red Hood) CGC 6.0 for $19,027.

"Good Girl Art" examples from the late Golden Age continue to set record prices. 2017 saw the sale of *Brenda Starr* #14 (classic bondage cover) CGC 9.4 Mile High Pedigree for $45,750 and *Phantom Lady* #17 (all-time classic "headlights" cover) CGC 7.0 for $11,350.

Here's a more detailed list of prices achieved for Golden Age books in 2017.

Action Comics #23 (1st Luthor) CGC 4.5 for $17,138, #64 CGC 9.4 $12,250; *Adventure Comics* #93 CGC 9.4 for $3,430; *All Star Comics* #3 (1st Justice Society) CGC 5.5 for $28,250, #8 (1st Wonder Woman) CGC 5.5 for $83,888, CBCS 9.6 Extensive Restoration for $50,000; CGC 2.0 for $27,055; *America's Best Comics* #6 CGC 9.6 for $7,678, #26 CGC 9.0 for $3,150; *Batman* #6 CGC 7.0 for $2,722, #9 CBCS 8.0 for $6,127, #11 (1st Joker cover in title) CGC 7.5 for $15,361, #16 (1st Alfred) CGC 7.5 for $7,600, #37 CGC 5.5 for $2,000, #39 CGC 9.4 for $4,650, #44 CGC 8.5 for $9,600, #47 (origin cover/story) CGC 7.0 for $3,177, #49 CGC 9.2 $9,600, CGC 8.5 for $8,400, #65 (Catwoman cover/story) CGC 9.0 for $8,000; *Better Comics* #4 CGC 6.5 for $2,100; *Beware* #6 CGC 6.0 for $2,000; *Black Terror* #7 CGC 8.5 for $2,000; *Boy Comics* #11 CGC 8.5 for $2,000, #16 CGC 9.6 for $2,300; *Brenda Starr* #14 CGC 9.4 Mile High Pedigree for $45,750; Brick Bradford #6 CGC 8.0 for $2,100; *Captain America Comics*, #2 (2nd Captain America) CGC 7.0 for $16,002, CGC 1.8 for $3,288, #12 CGC 4.5 for $2,300, #26 CGC 4.0 for $2,800, #27 CBCS 6.0 CVA for $3,400, #33 CGC 5.0 for $3,200, #36 CGC 5.5 for $4,910, #37 CGC 5.0 for $7,988, #38 CGC 8.5 for $5,100, #41 CGC 6.5 $2,901, #46 (Holocaust cover) CGC 5.0 for $10,750, #48 CGC 8.5 for $2,916, #60 CGC 8.5 for $2,900, #74 (Red Skull cover) CGC 6.0 for $12,555, 1942 #nn"Annual" CGC 3.0 for $8,325; *Captain Marvel Adventures* #18 (1st Mary Marvel) CGC 5.0 for $3,600; *Captain Science* #6 CGC 9.0 for $7,100; *Catman Comics* #15 CGC 3.5 for $2,600; *Chamber of Chills* #23 CGC 6.0 for $2,400; *Cinderella Love* #26 CGC 8.0 for $2,200; *Colossal Comics* #1 CGC 5.0 for $3,000; *Crime Patrol* #7 (early EC) CGC 9.4 for $2,524; *Detective Comics* #6 CGC 6.5 for $6,600, #27 (1st Batman) CGC 2.5 for $380,000; #29 (2nd Batman cover) CGC 1.8 Brittle Pages for $22,750, #31 (classic Batman cover) CGC 1.8 Brittle Pages for $25,250, #33 (1st origin of Batman) CGC 0.5 for $9,125, #35 (classic Batman cover) CGC 3.5 for $30,009, #36 CGC 6.0 for $44,000, #38 (1st Robin) CGC 4.5 Slight Restoration for $27,561, #39 CGC 5.5 for $4,050, #41 CBCS 9.0 for $6,500, #45 CGC 9.0 for $12,550, #58 (1st Penguin) CGC 4.5 for $7,150, #62 (classic Robinson Joker cover) CGC 8.0 for $15,850, CGC 4.5 for $5,600, #71 (classic Robinson Joker cover) CGC 5.5 for $5,200, #76 (classic Robinson Joker cover) CGC 8.5 for $8,600, CGC 8.0 $7,200, #85 CGC 6.5 for $3,300, #91 CGC 8.0 for $3,500, #118 CGC 8.0 for $3,127, #122 (1st Catwoman cover in title) CGC 8.0 Hawkeye Pedigree for $8,351, #124 CGC 8.5 for $3,117, #140 (1st Riddler) CGC 6.5 CVA for $22,250, #164 CGC 9.2 for $8,300, #168 (Origin of Joker, 1st Red Hood) CGC 6.0 for $19,027, #187 CGC 5.0 for $2,300, #225 (1st Martian Manhunter) CGC 8.0 for $25,001, CGC 5.0 for $4,601; *Dime Comics* #1 CGC 4.5 for $3,000; *Dynamic Comics* #8 (classic cover) CBCS 3.0 for $2,300; *Famous Funnies* #209 (1st Frazetta Buck Rogers cover/art) CGC 9.4 for $3,223; *Fantastic Comics* #4 CGC 8.5 for $5,122; *Feature Book* #22 (Phantom "Hot Poker" cover) CGC 7.0 for $2,500; *Fight Comics* #41 CGC 8.0 for $2,800; *Firehair Comics* #1 CGC 9.6 for $3,133; Flash Comics #86 (1st Black Canary) CGC 5.5 Restored for $4,450; *Funny Pages* #7 CGC 6.0 for $2,500, #35 CGC 8.0 for $3,600, #40 CGC 6.5 for $4,111; *Ghostly Weird Tales* #122 CGC 6.5 for $2,350; *Giant Comics Edition* #15 CGC 5.0 for $4,150; *Green Hornet* #13 CGC 7.0 for $4,050; *Headline Comics* #8 CGC 3.5 for $5,099; *Hit Comics* #17 CGC 6.5 for $3,366; *Human Torch* #11 CGC 8.5 CVA for $7,200; *Jumbo Comics* #16 CBCS for $1,288; *Keen Detective Funnies* #23 (1st Air Man) CGC 6.5 for $2,234; *Mad* #1 CGC 9.2 for $11,372, #3 CGC 9.6 for $4,085; *Marvel Comics* #1 (1st Marvel comic, 1st Human Torch, Origin Sub-Mariner) CGC 2.5 for $87,251; *Marvel Mystery Comics* #4 CGC 2.0 for $6,095, #7 CGC 7.5 for $7,700, #13 CGC 6.0 for $3,233, #15 CGC 8.0 for $5,101, #24 CGC 9.2 for $7,977, CGC 8.0 for $4,351, #28 CGC 8.5 for $10,283, CGC 8.0 for $8,988, #29 CGC 7.5 for $4,151, #39 CGC 7.5 for $3,333, #40 CGC 7.0 for $7,000, #41 CGC 7.5 for $4,455, #50 CGC for $3,765. #55 CGC 8.5 for $3,350, #63 CGC 6.0 for $4,651, #66 CGC 8.5 for $3,600, #71 CGC 9.4 for $6,087, #82 CGC 8.0 for $5,255, CGC

7.5 for $4,950; *Marvel Tales* #95 CGC 9.0 White Mountain Pedigree for $4,277; *Mask Comics* #2 CGC 5.5 for $2,959; *Master Comics* #21 (classic Captain Nazi cover) CGC 8.5 for $9,400; *Men's Adventures* #22 CGC 8.0 for $4,310; *Miss America Comics* #1 CGC 4.0 for $1,900; *Monster* #1 CGC 9.2 for $3,100; *More Fun Comics* #55 (1st Doctor Fate) CGC 8.0 for $18,900, CGC 2.0 for $4,200, #62 CGC 8.5 for $3,852; *Mystic Comics* (Timely Vol. 1) #9 CGC 1.8 for $3,100; *Mystic* (Atlas) #28 CGC 8.0 for $3,602; *New Adventure Comics* #25 CGC 4.5 for $4,300, #28 (Rare) CGC 3.5 for $3,200; *Out of the Shadows* #8 (classic horror cover) CGC 7.0 for $3,200; *Pep Comics* #20 CGC 6.0 for $5,856, CGC 2.5 for $2,600, #26 (1st Veronica in "Archie") CGC 2.0 for $5,365, #34 CGC 8.5 for $17,250, #44 CGC 8.0 for $3,100; *Phantom Lady* #17 (classic "headlights" cover) CGC 7.0 for $11,350, CGC 5.0 for $6,750, #23 CGC 6.5 for $4,500; *Phantom Stranger* #1 (1st Phantom Stranger) CGC 4.5 for $3,652, #2 CGC 7.0 for $2,877, #4 CG 5.5 for $2,501; *Prize Comics* #18 (rare) CGC 7.0 for $3,500; *Rangers Comics* #26 CGC 9.0 for $3,968, *Sensation Comics* #6 (1st Wonder Woman's magic lasso) CGC 3.5 for $4,544, #71 CGC 9.0 for $3,663, #84 CGC 9.4 for $3,444, #103 CGC 9.2 $2,311; *Showcase* #1 CGC 6.0 for $2,250; *Silver Streak Comics* #6 (classic cover) CGC 5.5 for $6,544; *Skeleton Hand* #1 CGC 9.4 for $3,100; *Startling Comics* #49 (Schomburg robot cover) CGC 3.0 for $2,255; *Startling Terror Tales* #11 (classic L.B. Cole cover) CBCS 7.0 for $3,102; *Strange Tales* #28 CGC 5.5 for $2,475, #42 CGC 8.5 for $2,500; *Sun Fun Komiks* #1 CGC 7,5 for $4,544, *Super Comics:* the *Pep Comics* #22 of Canada (1st Archie) #nn CGC 5.5 for $13,484; *Superman* #1 CGC 5.5 for $507,500, CBCS 9.4 Extensive Restoration for $100,000; #46 CGC 9.2 for $3,222, #53 (origin cover/story) CGC 9.0 for $7.200, CGC 8.0 for $3,400, #57 (Lois as Superwoman cover) CGC 9.0 for $3,055; *Super-Mystery Comics* V6 #1 (Gerber "no show") CGC 6.0 for $2,850; *Supersnipe Comics* #9 CGC 8.5 for $3,300; *Tales From the Crypt* #23 CGC 9.2 for $3,888; *Teen-Age Romances* #14 (Baker cover) CGC 6.5 for $4,766; *Thunda* #1 CGC 6.5 for $2,600; *USA Comics* #5 CGC 4.5 for $2,665, #9 CGC 5.0 for $4,968; *Weird Comics* #1 CGC 5.0 for $3,375; *Weird Mysteries* #5 (classic horror tales) CGC 4.5 for $4,001; *Weird Science* #10 CG 9.4 sold for $3,012; *Weird Tales of the Future* #2 CGC 7.5 for $3,475; #25 CGC 6.5 for $3,101; *Wonder Comics* #15 CGC 9.0 for $4,100; *Wonder Woman* #1 CGC 5.5 for $44, 515, CGC 0.5 for $6,363, #2 CGC 7.5 for $7,322, #6 CGC 7.5 for $6,800, #7 CBCS 7.5 for $8,101, #45 CGC 9.0 for $6,511; *Wonderworld Comics* #6 CGC 8.0 CGC 8.0 for $5,700; *World's Finest Comics* #3 (1st Scarecrow) CGC 4.5 for $4,000, #10 CGC 9.2 for $4,200; *Wow Comics* (Canadian) #26 CGC 8.0 for $2,322; *Yellow Claw* #1 CGC 7.0 for $2,102; *Young Allies* #4 (Red Skull cover) CGC 8.0 for $5,050; *Young King Cole* #1 CGC 9.4 for $3,200; *Zip Comics* #18 CGC 5.0 for $2,714, and #35 CGC 8.0 for $2,888.

Bronze Age (1970-1979): Comic books from the 1970s continue to be one of the most popular collecting eras with prices for keys and many non keys in high grade reaching levels that would have seemed unachievable not that many years ago. Long-time collectors may not think of these books as "vintage material", but 1970 was almost 50 years ago now and the majority of higher grade examples from many popular runs have settled into permanent collections, while genre titles that were less popular with collectors "back in the day" such as horror, romance, westerns and humor barely exist in high grade. This leaves the many Bronze Age collectors competing aggressively for the few nice examples that come onto the market, driving up prices. First appearances of characters from this era are red hot led by Wolverine in *Incredible Hulk* #181 CGC 9.8 for $20,750; Sabretooth in *Iron Fist* #14 CGC 9.6 CVA Price Variant for $19,750; Swamp Thing in *House of Secrets* #92 CGC 9.6 for $15,250; the Punisher in *Amazing Spider-Man* #129 CGC 9.8 Mark Jeweler Version for $13,800; Moon Knight in *Werewolf By Night* #32 CGC 9.8 for $19,380; the "New" X-Men in *Giant-Size X-Men* #1 CGC 9.8 for $8,000; Thanos and Drax in *Iron Man* #55 CGC 9.8 for $7,088; Morbius in *Amazing Spider-Man* #101 CGC 9.8 for $6,316 and Phoenix in *X-Men* #101 CGC 9.8 for $2,988. Perhaps even more impressive than the prices on the keys is seeing prices of $1,000, $2000 and up for non-key "run" books from the 1970s on titles such as *Iron Man*, *Captain America*, *Thor* and *X-Men*.

A deeper list of highlights from this era includes *All Star Comics* #58 (1st Power Girl) CGC 9.8 for $1,855; *Amazing Spider-Man* #85 CGC 9.8 for $2,977, #86 (1st Revamped Black Widow) CGC 9.8 for $3,800, #89 CGC 9.8 for $3,000, #90 (Death of Captain Stacy) CGC 9.8 for $3,600, #100 (classic Anniversary cover) CGC 9.8 for $3,600, #101 (1st Morbius) CGC 9.8 for $6,316, CGC 9.4 for $2,237, #102 (2nd Morbius) CGC 9.8 $3,876, #111 CGC 9.8 for $1,900, #129 (1st Punisher) CGC 9.8 for $13,800, CGC 9.4 $2,600, #148 CGC 9.8 for $2,533, *Annual* #7 CGC 9.8 for $4,801; *Avengers* #87 (origin of Black Panther) CGC 9.8 for $1,655; *Batman* #232 (1st Ra's al Ghul) CGC 9.8 for $4,409, #244 (classic Batman vs. Ra's al Ghul Adams cover) CGC 9.8 for $2,567, #251 (classic Adams Joker cover) CGC 9.8 for $6,700; *The Cat* #1 (1st Greer Nelson, the future Tigra) CGC 9.8 for $2,400; *Conan* #1 (1st Conan in comic books) CGC 9.6 for $2,322; *Daredevil* #133 CGC 9.8 Price Variant for $2,600; *Detective Comics* #395 ("Creature of the Night" Batman era begins) CGC 9.6 for $3,600, #400 (1st Man-Bat) CGC 9.6 for $2,001, #411 (1st Talia) CGC 9.4 for $4,300; *Fantastic Four* #110 CGC 9.8 Fantucchio Pedigree for $2,008, #112 (classic Thing vs. Hulk battle cover) CGC 9.8 for $6,300; *Giant-size X-Men* #1 (1st Storm, Colossus, Nightcrawler &

***All Star Comics** #58 is a highlight from the Bronze Age.*

2nd full Wolverine) CGC 9.8 for $8,000, CGC 9.6 for $3,232; *Green Lantern* #76 (classic Adams Green Lantern/Green Arrow series begins) CGC 9.6 for $6,890, #87 (1st John Stewart) CGC 9.8 for $2,800; *Hero for Hire* #1 (1st Luke Cage) CGC 9.4 for $3,791; *House of Secrets* #92 (1st Swamp Thing) CGC 9.6 for $15,250, CGC 9.4 for $8,200; *Incredible Hulk* #181 CGC 9.8 (1st full Wolverine) for $20,750, ; *Iron Fist* #14 (1st Sabretooth) CGC 9.6 CVA Price Variant for $19,750; *Iron Man* #47 (origin retold with Barry Smith art) CGC 9.8 for $3,601, #52 CGC 9.8 for $5,100, #54 (1st Moondragon) CGC 9.8 for $2,101, #55 (1st Thanos and Drax) CGC 9.8 for $7,088; *Marvel Feature* #1 (1st Defenders) CGC 9.8 for $6,201, CGC 9.4 CVA for $1,100; *Marvel Premiere* #1 (Him becomes Warlock) CGC 9.8 for $5,000, #15 (1st Iron Fist) CGC 9.8 for $4,500; *Marvel Spotlight* #5 (1st Ghost Rider) CGC 9.2 for $2,200; *Ms. Marvel* #1 (Carol Danvers becomes Ms. Marvel) CGC 9.8 for $1,901; *New Gods* #1 (1st Orion) CGC 9.8 for $2,075; *Scooby Doo* #1 (1975 Charlton) CGC 9.8 for $3,100; *Star Wars* #1 (1st Star Wars in comics, came out before the movie) CGC 8.5 Price Variant for $7,377; *Sub-Mariner* #34 (Defenders Prelude) CGC 9.8 for $2,100; *Tomb of Dracula* #10 (1st Blade) CGC 9.8 for $6,007; *Werewolf By Night* #32 (1st Moon Knight) CGC 9.8 for $19,380, CGC 9.2 for $2,300; *X-Men* #94 (2nd "New" X-Men, 1st in on-going title) CGC 9.8 for $15,805, #101 (1st Phoenix) CGC 9.8 for $2,988.

Modern Age (Post 1979): The start of the modern age, 1980, now goes back almost 40 years, with untold thousands of comic books published during the era. Although most books from this era are available in large quantities in high grade and have not yet shown significant price growth, there are notable exceptions, especially keys certified at the elite 9.9 and 9.8 grading tiers. Having already adapted the characters from the Silver Age and Bronze Age, Hollywood is now turning to the 1980s, 1990s and beyond to find the next generation of movie and TV shows, which is driving interest in the first appearances of characters like the New Mutants, Venom, Gambit, Cable, Silver Sable and many more. Some of our more notable sales in 2017 included *Amazing Spider-Man* #265 (1st Silver Sable) CGC 9.9 for $2,577, #300 (1st full Venom) CGC 9.8 for $2,100, *#361* (1st full Carnage) CGC 9.9 Sextuple cover for $8,600, *Love and Rockets* #1 (1981) CGC 9.8 for $1,432; *Marvel Graphic Novel* #4 (1st New Mutants) CGC 9.8 for $951; *Miracleman* #15 (death of Kid Miracleman) CGC 9.9 for $3,345; *New Mutants* #87 (1st Cable) CGC 9.9 Signature Series for $10,250; *Teenage Mutant Ninja Turtles* #1 (rare first Print) CGC 9.4 for $7,600, CGC 8.0 for $4,800; *Uncanny X-Men* #266 CGC 9.9 for $5,600, *Walking Dead* #1 (1st Rick Grimes) CGC 9.8 for $3,100, CGC 9.6 for $2,006; and *Walking Dead: Here's Negan Preview* #-1 CGC 9.9 for $5,600.

Original Art: Original Comic Art continues to draw the attention of more and more collectors and this segment of ComicLink's business has been incredibly dynamic in the past few years. Just a few standout 2017 art sales include Jack Kirby *Fantastic Four* #77 cover for $185,555; Frank Frazetta *Tales From the Crypt* Ballantine Book Cover Oil Painting for $130,000; Andy Kubert *Uncanny X-Men* #266 cover for $130,000; Neal Adams *Justice League of America* #92 cover for $47,100; Bernie Wrightson Original Art Illustration Plate Published in *Frankenstein Marvel Illustrated Novel* for $46,440; Jim Starlin *Iron Man* #55 title splash for $44,777; Carl Barks *Donald Duck: Terror of the River* Oil Painting for $44,000; Gil Kane and John Romita *Amazing Spider-Man* #138 cover for $31,000; John Romita *Daredevil* #16 panel page for $30,500; Gene Colan *Daredevil* #64 cover for $27,800; Todd McFarlane *Spider-Man* #14 double page splash for $26,750; George Evans *Haunt of Fear* #15 complete story for $25,250; Graham Ingels *Tales From the Crypt* #46 complete story for $25,250; Stephen Bissette *Saga of the Swamp Thing* #24 cover for $22,694; John Romita *Amazing Spider-Man* #68 panel page for $21,815; Michael Turner *Wizard Millennium Edition* #1 cover for $21,361; Mike Zeck *Marvel Superheroes Secret Wars* #9 cover for $20,461; Dave Cockrum *Marvel Fanfare* #3 wrap-around cover for $20,250; Gil Kane *Marvel Triple Action* #10 cover for $20,250; John Byrne *Man of Steel* #6 splash for $19,750; John Romita *Amazing Spider-Man* #68 panel page for $18,250; Gil Kane *Thor* #216 cover for $18,050; John Romita *Daredevil* #105 cover for $17,362; John Byrne *X-Men* #109 panel page for $17,350; John Romita Jr. *Daredevil The Man Without Fear* #1 cover for $17,201; Gil Kane *Thor* #201 cover for $16,250; *Jim Lee* X-Men: Wolverine and Psylocke Hunting Party Illustration Published in *Wizard: Jim Lee, Millennium Edition* for $16,250; Alex Ross *Avengers* Classic Poster painting for $26,250; Jim Starlin *Iron Man* #55 panel page for $16,035; Todd McFarlane *Amazing Spider-Man* #308 panel page for $16,000; John Byrne *Avengers* #165 panel page for $15,750; Frank Miller *Daredevil* #158 panel page for $15,505; George Tuska *Iron Man* #22 splash for $15,350; Steve Geiger *Incredible Hulk* #337 cover for $15,277; and Frank Frazetta *Death Dealer V* preliminary painting for $15,250.

Conclusion: 2018 will likely generate many more record-breakers on ComicLink.com. With over two decades online serving buyers and sellers in the collecting community, ComicLink is the longest running and most established consignment service in the hobby. If you have material like some of the books or artwork described above and you would like to achieve the types of prices described, come to the web site, view our auction schedule, and give us a call and we will work hand-in-hand with you to optimize the value of your collection utilizing either the auction service, the Comic Book Exchange or both.

In addition to selling certified comic books and original artwork, our team of over a dozen full-time professionals can assist you with with everything from evaluating your comic books for third party grading certification with CGC and CBCS to processing, pricing, marketing and selling them. We do all this work, and offer upfront cash advances, for a very minimal commission rate, with the focus being a high level of service for each of our sellers.

Tom Nelson
Top Notch Comics

Here I am again writing my annual market report during the first week of December 2017. I would say 2017 is finishing with a big increase in sales compared to 2016. Last year being an election year there were to many uncertainties on people's minds and it kept money bottled up. With the job economy improving, more people working, more people getting paid overtime, it's easier for collectors to have disposable income to spend on comic books. The comic book movies continue to play a major role with price increases and overall increase in demand for back issue comic book collecting. The price increases on first appearances are still dominating the back issue comic book marketplace for Silver to Modern Marvel & DC superhero books, and run collectors in common grade are still finding bargains against *Guide* prices.

One of this years biggest movies was Spider-Man, and there was huge demand for *Amazing Spider-Man* back issue comics. The most highest collected series from the Silver Age to present, including his first appearance in *Amazing Fantasy* #15. I would like to give a run down of the most requested and liquid books of the *Amazing Spider-Man* run. Issue #1 first in series, #2 first Vulture, #3 first Doc Octopus, #6 first Lizard, #14 first Green Goblin, #20 first Scorpion, #31 first Gwen Stacy, #41 first Rhino, #50 first Kingpin, #101 first Morbius, the Living Vampire, #121 death of Gwen Stacy, #129 first Punisher, #194 first Black Cat, #238 first Hobgoblin, #252 first black costume, #265 first Silver Sable, #300 first Venom, #361 Carnage, and Annual #1 first Sinister Six.

I'm going to continue my trend of a top ten market report for 1970-1979, 1980-1989, 1990-1999. To qualify for my lists the comic needed to have distribution to the entire United States. This means I'm excluding comics that are price variants, errors, recalled, pre-packs, convention exclusives, mailing away comics, and others that had spotty distribution. There are many valuable and rare books that fall in those categories, but that is a subset of main stream comic book collecting. They are difficult to track and some do not trade on the open market frequently enough to gauge a realistic price. My requirement to qualify for my top ten lists is the book is sold online at least monthly in any type of grade, and is available at most major conventions.

Here we go with the 1970-1979 Top 10 in 9.2 value:

#1 *Incredible Hulk* #181 $4,200
#2 *House of Secrets* #92 $3,500
#3 *Cerebus* #1 $2,500
#4 *Scooby Doo* #1 $2,500
#5 *Amazing Spider-Man* #129 $2,000
#6 *Green Lantern* #76 $2,000
#7 *Iron Man* #55 $1,600
#8 *Giant-Size X-Men* #1 $1600
#9 *Werewolf by Night* #32 $1500
#10 *Marvel Spotlight* #5 $1500

The leader of the pack for Bronze Age is the undisputed king *Incredible Hulk* #181 the first full appearance of Wolverine. *House of Secrets* #92 first Swamp Thing moves into second place, up from third place last year. Low print run Independent *Cerebus* #1 holds onto the third spot. Saturday morning cartoon *Scooby Doo* #1 from 1970 holds the #4 position. #5 is *Amazing Spider-Man* #129 the first Punisher, moving up from #7 last year. #6 is *Green Lantern* #76 who finished down one spot from last year. #7 *Iron Man* #55 first Thanos is up two spots from last year. #8 is *Giant-Size X-Men* #1 keeping last year's position. #9 is *Werewolf by Night* #32, the first Moon Knight moving up one position. #10 breaking in this year is *Marvel Spotlight* #5 the first Ghost Rider. Hero For Hire #1 tumbled from last year's position in #6 to out of the top ten, I guess there is an after-series hangover going on with the declining value of Luke Cage in 2017. Some books which are right on the edge of breaking in the top ten and can command at least one thousand dollars in 9.2 are *X-Men* #94, *Hero For Hire* #1, *Jimmy Olsen* #134, *Detective Comics* #411, *Batman* #232, and *Batman* #227.

Moving on to the Top 10 1980-1989 in 9.2 value:

#1 *Teenage Mutant Ninja Turtles* #1 $5,000
#2 *Albedo* #2 $1500
#3 *Teenage Mutant Ninja Turtles* #1 2nd print $600
#4 *Archie's Girls, Betty and Veronica* #320 $500
#5 *Amazing Spider-Man* #300 $375
#6 *Primer* #2 $300
#7 *Crow* #1 $250
#8 *New Teen Titans* #2 $200
#9 *Daredevil* #168 $200
#10 *Tick Special Edition* #1 $200

There is still nothing close in value to the *Teenage Mutant Ninja Turtles* #1 as they keep the King Crown of the 1980s. Second place is another independent *Albedo* #2, first appearance of Usagi Yojimbo. Third goes to the second printing of *Teenage Mutant Ninja Turtles* #1. Fourth is *Archie's Girls, Betty and Veronica* #320 first Cheryl Blossom. Fifth is one of the hottest most frequently traded books, *Amazing Spider-Man* #300 first Venom, up from last years 7th position. Sixth place is *Primer* #2, first Grendel. Seventh is *The Crow* #1, even though it's not his first appearance, it has a very cool jet black cover. #8 is *New Teen Titans* #2 the first appearance of Deathstroke. Moving down this year to number nine is *Daredevil* #168 the first Elektra. Breaking in at the ten spot of the first appearance of Tick, *Tick Special Edition* #1. Some books on the edge of the top ten are, *DC Comics Presents* #26, *Hulk* #271, *Marvel Graphic Novel* #4, *Caliber Presents* #1, *Amazing Spider-Man* #238, *Batman* #357, *Batman Dark Knight Returns* #1, and *Teenage Mutant Ninja Turtles* #2.

The Top 10 1990-1999 comic books in 9.2

#1 *Bone* #1 $1000
#2 *Batman Adventures* #12 $475
#3 *Marvel Collectible Classics* #1 $450
#4 *Goon* #1 $300
#5 *New Mutants* #98 $300

#6 *Spawn* #1 Black and White edition $300
#7 *Marvel Collectible Classics* #2 $200
#8 *Strangers in Paradise* #1 $200
#9 *New Mutants* #87 $180
#10 *Spider-Man* #1 Platinum $180

Bone #1 stands alone at the top position as the only thousand dollar book from the decade. The #2 spot is *Batman Adventures* #12 the first appearance of Harley Quinn. This comic book has stabilized in price since the release of the movie *Suicide Squad* during 2016, there are more anticipated movies with Harley Quinn in the future and could lead to future spikes. #3 is *Marvel Collectible Classics Spider-Man* #1 from 1998, which is a Chrome reprint of *Amazing Spider-Man* #300. The fourth position is independent *Goon* #1, first app. of the Goon. Fifth place is the very popular *New Mutants* #98 first Deadpool. Sixth place is *Spawn* #1 Black and White edition which was released in 1997. *Spawn* has seen an increase in demand during 2017 and this issue leads the way. Seventh is the second issue of *Marvel Collectible Classics Spider-Man* #2 which has a homage cover of *Spider-Man* 1990 #1. Eighth place is new to the top ten, *Strangers in Paradise* #1. Ninth place is *New Mutants* #87 which breaks into the top ten, this is the first appearance of Cable. The final spot goes to *Spider-Man* #1 1990 Platinum edition. Some comics that are on the edge of breaking in are *San Diego Comic Con* #2, first Hellboy, *Batman Harley Quinn*, *Malibu Sun* #13 early Spawn, *Evil Ernie* #1 Lady Death, and *Incredible Hulk* #377 scarce 3rd printing.

Some of the hot Modern books from 2000 to current that have been high value, high demand movers this year are *Walking Dead* early issues, *NYX* #3 first X-23, *Edge of Spider-Verse* #2 first Spider-Gwen, *Rick and Morty* #1, *Y: The Last Man* #1, *Saga* #1 and *Invincible* #1.

Some notable CGC certified sales we had this year: *Action Comics* #285 8.5 $499.95, *Adventure Comics* #269 8.5 $995.00, *Adventure* #269 7.0 $374.95, *Akira* #1 9.8 $135.00 (3) copies, *All Star Comics* #58 9.4 $300.00, *All Star* #58 9.2 $200.00, *Amazing Spider-Man* #6 7.0 $1049.95, *Amazing Spider-Man* #7 7.0 $675.00, *Amazing Spider-Man* #14 5.0 $799.95, *Amazing Spider-Man* #14 9.0 $6500.00, *Amazing Spider-Man* #15 7.5 $945.00, *Amazing Spider-Man* #20 6.5 $300.00, *Amazing Spider-Man* #31 7.0 $300.00, *Amazing Spider-Man* #39 9.0 $949.95, *Amazing Spider-Man* #50 7.0 499.95, *Amazing Spider-Man* #121 9.6 $1185.00, *Amazing Spider-Man* #129 8.0 $995.00, *Amazing Spider-Man* #194 9.2 $189.95 (3) copies, *Amazing Spider-Man* #238 9.6 $300.00, *Amazing Spider-Man* #252 9.4 $115.00, *Amazing Spider-Man* #256 9.8 285.00 (3) copies, *Amazing Spider-Man* #300 9.8 $2250.00 newsstand edition, 9.4 $499.95, 9.2 $365.00, $375.00, 8.5 $349.95, *Amazing Spider-Man* #316 9.6 $149.95, 9.4 $99.95, 9.2 $65.00, *Amazing Spider-Man* #361 9.8 $300.00, 9.6 $159.95, 9.4 $85.00, 9.2 $99.95, *Aquaman* #7 9.2 $400.00, *Aquaman* #35 7.0 $475.00, *Aquaman* #53 9.4 $170.00, *Batman* #49 3.0 $950.00, *Batman* #66 7.5 $1400.00, *Batman* #155 6.0 $300.00, *Batman* #181 5.5 $400.00, *Batman* #181 4.0 $225.00, *Batman* #181 8.0 $1800.00, *Batman* #232 8.0 $500.00, *Batman* #251 6.0 $275.00, *Batman* #635 9.4 $99.95, *Batman Adventures* #12 9.4 $590.00, *Batman Harley Quinn* 9.0 $125.00, *Batman Dark Knight Returns* #1 9.2 $115.00, *Blackhawk* #133 3.0 $249.95, *Brave and the Bold* #34 7.5 $945.00, *Brave and the Bold* #54 7.5 $800.00, *Captain America* #110 9.2 $250.00, *Captain Marvel* #17 9.2 $175.00, *Catwoman* #51 9.8 $225.00, *Daredevil* #1 2.0 $690.00, *Daredevil* #168 9.2 $190.00, *DC Comics Presents* #26 9.8 $700.00, 9.2 $185.00, *Defenders* #28 9.2 $190.00, *Detective* #114 5.0 $995.00, *Detective* #233 5.0 $3500.00, *Detective* #233 5.0 $2850.00, *Detective* #880 9.8 $440.00, *Doctor Solar* #1 7.5 $475.00, *Doom Patrol* #99 8.0 $524.00, *Evil Ernie* #1 9.0 $140.00, *Fantastic Four* #12 5.0 $675.00, *Fantastic Four* #52 8.0 $1325.00, *Fantastic Four* #52 7.0 $700.00, *Fantastic Four* #52 6.0 $500.00, *Flash* #106 4.0 $500.00, *Flash* #110 4.0 $379.95, *Flash* #113 6.0 $300.00, *Flash* #123 6.0 $1089.95, *Flash* #137 9.0 $500.00, *Forever People* #1 9.4 $445.00, *Four Color* #199 9.0 $1350.00, *Giant-Size Defenders* #3 9.4 $300.00, *Giant-Size X-Men* #1 8.0 $1000.00, *Giant-Size X-Men* #1 6.0 $600.00, *Giant-Size X-Men* #1 4.0 $400.00, *Giant-Size X-Men* #1 9.2 $1600.00, *G.I. Joe* #21 9.8 $500.00, *Green Lama* #1 6.5 $500.00, *Green Lantern* #7 7.0 $500.00, *Green Lantern* #40 8.5 $485.00, *Green Lantern* #87 9.0 $380.00, *Hawkman* #1 8.0 $500.00, *Incredible Hulk* #180 9.0 $550.00, *Incredible Hulk* #181 9.0 $3075.00, *Infinity Gauntlet* #1 9.8 $150.00 (6) copies, *Invincible* #1 9.2 $200.00 (2) copies, *Iron Man* #1 6.0 $400.00, *Iron Man* #54 9.6 $750.00, *Jughead* #1 7.5 $1500.00, *Justice League of America* #1 3.5 $950.00, *Little LuLu* #1 7.0 $350.00, *Marvel Premiere* #1 9.0 $285.00, *Marvel Premiere* #15 9.0 $450.00, *Marvel Preview* #4 9.0 $300.00, *Marvel Spotlight* #5 6.5 $300.00, 9.2 $1500.00, *Marvel Super Heroes* #13 8.5 $700.00, *My Greatest Adventure* #80 $425.00, *Nellie the Nurse* #1 3.5 $300.00, *New Teen Titans* #2 9.8 $600.00, 9.2 $175.00, 9.0 $175.00, 8.5 $150.00, *Night Nurse* #1 9.2 $600.00, *NYX* #3 9.2 $400.00, *Peanuts* #1 1963 9.2 $500.00, *Hero For Hire* #1 8.5 $500.00, *Richie Rich* #1 1.0 $285.00, *Rick and Morty* #1 9.8 $700.00, *Sandman* #8 variant 9.0 $500.00, *Sensation* #100 4.0 $425.00, *Showcase* #37 6.0 $500.00, *Silver Surfer* #4 8.5 $550.00, *Silver Surfer* #44 9.8 $300.00 (3) copies, *Spawn* #1 9.8 $125.00, *Star Trek* #1 7.5 $425.00, *Star Wars* #1 9.2 $175.00, *Superboy* #1 3.0 $1500.00, *Superboy* #5 6.0 $1000.00, *Superboy* #68 4.5 $979.95, *Super Friends* #7 9.4 $150.00, *Lois Lane* #70 8.5 $385.00, *Jimmy Olsen* #134 8.5 $565.00, *Tales of Suspense* #57 8.0 $875.00, *Tales to Astonish* #35 5.0 $600.00, *Teen-Age Romances* #2 5.0 $500.00, *Thor* #165 $425.00, *Tomb of Dracula* #10 9.0 $60.00, *Two-Gun Kid* #60 6.5 $600.00, *X-Men* #1 4.0 $3000.00, *X-Men* #101 9.6 $945.00, *Walking Dead* #1 9.8 $2700.00, *Werewolf by Night* #32 9.0 $1025.00, *Worlds Finest* #71 4.0 $700.00, *Zatanna* #15 9.8 $300.00, and #16 9.8 $300.00.

Jamie Newbold
Southern California Comics

Folks, it feels like I've written this statement before: "New comic book sales were down in the previous year." It's a tiresome phrase born from the quicksand-like turf of our business. New comics can be real bastards to a retail outlet making a living from their sales. For our concerns; I estimate sales collectively dropped a total of 30% since 2012. Back then, Image was enjoying a "Second Coming" and New 52's sales plateau was still generous. I blame Marvel and a clutch of the "variant" crowd for speculating more than they read.

Marvel left many of my readers in the dust as they galloped forward with plots, themes, and even art, all of which my customers chastised. Marvel alluded to a change happening in 2017, purporting to give back to legacy readers the Marvel Universe they/I wanted. When I console my customers over the fate of their favorite versions of their favorite Marvel heroes, they counter with Marvel's $3.99 as a show-stopper. The readers lamenting the days of $2.99 at Marvel are frustrated with their now-standard $3.99 price tag, and the all-too-frequent, ludicrous $4.99 "special issue." These readers don't want to shift to digital, but are left with the feeling Marvel is pushing them that direction, while removing paper editions and comic book stores from the equation. The lack of consistency and continuity of their stories made being a fan of even the *Secret Empire* event maddening, especially when the main title climax shipped after the ancillary issues already blew the conclusion.

Marvel let the "Captain America is Hydra" storyline run its *Hail Hydra* course to an expected conclusion. The fans felt enough was enough, pelting Marvel with "turn-the-clock-back" comments about their favorite heroes. At post-time *Captain America* #695 returned us to a more desirable version of Cap on what appears to be a vision quest. The *Thanos* Legacy storyline felt like old school Jim Starlin storytelling. Some things are returning to normal. I hope future sales reflect it.

I've railed repeatedly against the foolishness of the variant curse. Marvel's cash-cow does not come from comics my customers buy to read on a regular basis (unless they buy freakishly large quantities of the same issue): it comes from the incessant gimmick covers, which too many customers believe in for their own financial gain. I'm jaded, explaining the lack of depth in our variants to window shoppers looking for 1:500 ratio books at some price vastly lower than my competitors or eBay (like that ever happens!) Like so many other savvy stores, I refuse to "chase the dragon" Marvel helped create. At least DC seems to please my customers with their 50/50 ratio covers (DC is poised to either succeed with *Doomsday Clock* or draw ire for an overpriced "add-on" to the *Watchmen* that gets delayed and ends with a fizzle.) And, while I may lose an occasional sale, at least I'm not sitting on tons of unsold *Star Wars/Secret Empire/Edge of Venomverse* commons!

I respect the fact that companies like Image will produce a variant solely for sales use by retailers: a Retailer Appreciation copy. That breeds brand loyalty and satisfaction. Their stories are widely varied with occasional output striking major chords with the fans. With Image Comics you get a box of chocolates: you never know what you are going to get with each new release!

Speaking of variants - the 1990s collectors have commented on their feelings of déjà vu regarding the relentless variant editions being produced. Those buyers will stand toe-to-toe with a variant addict today and broadcast the lesson they learned: Don't get caught up in our past. The enthusiasm wanes when the covers lose interest and sadly decline in value. We are all victims of repetitive marketing.

I have a theory based upon research I gained while writing my upcoming book: *The Forensic Comicologist; a Unique Life in Comics* published by McFarlane Press (shameless plug). One of the ancient, consistent aspects of comic book publishing is the "Five-Year Plan." Back in olden times comic book publishers assumed their readership changed over every five years. Meaning: if DC published a particular Superman story where he turned into a gorilla (and you love it), they might write a slightly altered version of the story five years later for your younger brother. Back in the day the publishers might have considered the age of eight as a "jumping-in" point and age thirteen as a young reader's exit from comics.

The formula was self-perpetuating. The comic book industry followed this engineered theme for decades. I think Marvel and DC's frequent re-design indicates the Five-Year Plan may still be in effect: Infinite Crisis in 2006 upsets the DC Universe...only to be revamped with DC New 52 in 2011...followed by the Rebirth of DC in 2016. DC has always been enthralled with the Five Year Plan: in 2006 Dick Grayson replaces Batman...followed by Batman replacing Dick Grayson in New 52 in (you guessed it) 2011. Do the math.

An even more fascinating example follows the Marvel Implosion of 1957. They lost their distributor and a lot of money. Just under five years later we get *Fantastic Four* #1! The timing may just be a coincidence, but few of us are privy to all editorial thoughts behind the changes made by comic book publishers in the past decades. I have an even more pronounced example: *Giant-Size X-Men* #1. My peers remember the end of Marvel's run of new stories in *X-Men* in March 1970 with issue number sixty-six. Even Neal Adams' artistic infusion could not stop the title from eventual demise. Marvel used the title to re-launch old stories in reprint form. Five years later (August 1975) Marvel released *Giant-Size X-Men* #1 with an almost all-new line-up of mutant X-ers to risk their own lives to protect humans and mutants alike. Five Years.

The point is if comic book readers weren't around to witness a potential disaster the first time; they get another shot a generation later. My older customers do complain the writing seems repetitive with recent comic books. They feel they may not be the target audience for new comics from the Big Two. I emphasize a point with a store tally figuring my customer base at roughly fifty percent being thirty and older. They relate to a growing, younger customer base also turning away from epic story arcs that don't satisfy.

Marvel is not the only publisher I feel needed a self-check in 2017. Archie Comics required a wake-up call. Diamond distributed Halloween ComicFest comics for the annual ritual: an alternative to handing out candy for Halloween. The comics were single representations from several companies willing to offer something for stores to either give away themselves, or furnish to parents to hand out. DC tuned in with a title for little kids and a more mature *Batman* for teens. I looked over the small representation from a handful of companies and was surprised the output was too mature for small kids; often the bulk of trick-or-treaters at my house. I sorted those out, including Archie's *Chilling Adventures of Sabrina Season 2.* I calculated it would fall into the teenage category and handed them out to mostly girls appearing in that age group. What a shock to find out there's a sex panel within! There's also a topless woman in a second panel. What the hell? Did somebody at Archie foul up their choice of contribution? Who was I supposed to hand this out to? This controversial error in judgment even hit the news.

I continue to thrive selling back issues. I'm probably one of less than ten stores statewide having abundance and selections of back issues greater than the remaining 99% of the stores. I've met most of those ten through various California comic conventions. There's always a likelihood back-issue oriented store owners will exhibit at conventions. I've sold at local shows for decades. The shows are as important to me for the sales opportunities as they are for "re-upping" inventory. At least they used to be. My store's reach to acquire comic books regularly stretched into Los Angeles and its surrounding counties starting about seven years ago. Suddenly, we required less effort to buy collections from dealers and attendees at conventions; because the store drew it all in. And the collections just keep getting better.

The large Golden Age collection purchase from a year ago spiked huge sales at the store and into Comic-Con International where sales doubled. The payoff from other Gold and Silver Age acquisitions between the 2016 and 2017 Conventions was reward for all the money spent and effort.

Holding on to a massive Golden Age collection is tough. The price points are often higher than Silver Age equivalents, so turning a profit quickly may be of expediency. For us, the hope was the store could make the sales via internet and walk-in traffic. It did, allowing us time to breathe a little easier, into the 2017 San Diego Con. A couple of the significant sales at the 2017 Con included a *Detective Comics* #31 CBCS 3.0 with a married centerfold. We had it priced at 30K and sold it for $28,000. We finalized the purchase for a *Batman* #1 around that time: a CGC 4.0 with extensive, amateur restoration. Sale price: $27,600. A couple of other noteworthy GA sales: *Wonder Woman* #1 CGC 6.0 with moderate, pro restoration sold for $9,000. A *Detective Comics* #2 CGC 1.0 with some restoration sold for $4,000. That was an interesting book because I originally found it in the bottom of a box of magazines from a collection at our store. The pages were all loose, scrambled around the box bottom. Matt, my store manager, diligently put all the pages together with the mated cover halves. He checked the contents against Grand Comics Database and discovered we owned a complete copy!

We had a flurry of Silver Age sales before, during and after Con: *Incredible Hulk* #1 CGC 6.5 for $28,000 and *Fantastic Four* #1 CGC 5.0 $8,000. Despite my die-hard fanaticism to retain my collection of *Amazing Fantasy* #15s, I did sell a couple: a raw, un-restored 1.0 for $6,900 and a CGC 1.8 Signature Series for $9,500.

And now: The Wonder Woman Story. In 2016, I purchased a copy of *All Star Comics* #8 from the descendants of the original owner. The family anticipated big bucks until I sadly pointed out a missing centerfold (thanks again Grand Comics Database). I paid them an agreeable price for their incomplete copy, eventually sending it off to get slabbed. I wanted it protected and broadcast: restoration-free.

During Comic Con 2017 another *All-Star Comics* 8 showed up: on eBay. It was advertised as coverless, but complete. I inquired about the status of the centerfold. The owner slabbed it sometime ago, so I relied on his memory to gauge the status of the centerfold. He said it was detached, but intact. I bought it; for the centerfold.

***Detective Comics* #31 with a married centerfold was one of the standout sales for the year.**

It came in the mail quickly. I broke it out of its container and opened to the centerfold. Apparently the seller and I envisioned two different opinions of the meaning of "intact." The page I needed had a large shred of paper missing doing me no good with my upgrade intention. If I kept it I needed it cheaper for a profitable upgrade. The seller argued my definition of intact, but Webster's Dictionary made it clear to the seller, so he refunded my money and I sent his book back. He wasn't a fan of discounting or partial refunds, so any efforts at compromise were a waste of time.

The likelihood that I would own two copies of *All Star Comics* 8, albeit briefly; seemed remote before Con. I briefly owned two in 2017. I wanted the centerfold and figured I'd let the incomplete copy lounge around for awhile (Fortunately, I never broke it out of its container.)

I received an e-mail in October of 2017. An old partner of mine from my police officer days knew a guy in Los Angeles with a copy of a comic book he thought was an *All Star Comics* #8. I was put in touch, learning my buddy's friend Mike did own a coverless copy. Mike said his dad only kept one comic book from his youth: this ratty, old copy with the first Wonder Woman story. Mike sent me photos I used to validate his claim. More importantly it was complete with an intact centerfold!

Mike brought the comic down from LA and we sealed the deal. The centerfold was conveniently loose. I removed my copy from its container to fit the replacement centerfold. The staples did not line up with my copy and the page was about 1/8" wider. Still, it would forever be complete. I inserted the page into my copy and sent it off for grading. I like CBCS' Blue Label with the "Married" underscored, over a CGC Qualified label. It came back a 1.8 Married as expected: a solid upgrade from its previous .5 status. Plus, I still owned a second copy; my third in 2017. That's three more copies of *All Star Comics* 8 than the zero copies I've previously owned. More significant: two were original-owner obtained and all in the same year!

Speaking of CGC, CBCS, and comic encapsulation: At the 2017 Comic-Con International, I witnessed a concerning action involving graded containers. Specifically: PGX containers. Ken Dyber from Cloud 9 Comics put on a brief demonstration at his booth. He'd assembled several PGX encapsulated comics, laying them on top of his comic book boxes. We watched as he manipulated the containers so they would pop open without cracking. Next, he removed the inner-well-encased comic book out of that container and switched it with another PGX-encapsulated book. In other words, he literally traded the contents of two PGX comic books without damaging the containers and then refastened them shut as though they'd never been open.

Once removed, the label can be expertly removed and even replaced with another label. I proved this by attacking the only PGX book I have in inventory: An issue of *Batman* #366 signed by Walt Simonson. It wasn't an attack, so much as a pull on the container halves and they popped open in my hands. I pushed the halves back together seemingly tight. The date of the container's utilization was 2015. This act cannot be reproduced using either CGC or CBCS containers. The plastic on those containers cracks and is irreparable leaving signs of tampering. The implications are frightening if buyers believe in the sanctity of all PGX-graded comics. PGX critics and supporters I've spoken with point out the sanctity and security of the inner well. The obvious issue is the inner well can also be tampered with, making it possible to access the PGX label; leaving little evidence of the crime. PGX container owners not particularly observant may never notice any changes to graded comics they own. CGC containers do have a history of tampering against CGC's best intentions. However, the safety designs inherent with both CGC and CBCS containers make tampering more or less obvious.

If a necessary redesign of PGX containers fixed the problem (if any were performed after 2015), we still have to dwell on the dilemma of the older containers. Keeping a short story "evergreen" has its limits. I wrote about this container issue in December 2017. By July 2018 the issue may already be resolved or something else cropped up to plague PGX. I'm only now becoming privy to a conflict involving PGX and CBCS and their certification of original sketch art. Certificates Of Authentification (COA) are dangerous for consumers like a painted crosswalk is dangerous for pedestrians; we tend to put too much trust into protection that's only worth its weight in paper (or paint.) Don't let beguiling COAs trump your better judgment when making a purchase. Signatures may be valid, but a sketch added later may not.

One collection worth noting "began" arriving at our store in late September 2017. I say began because it took the seller five-plus pick-up truckloads to get it all to my shop over a month's time. The collection originated from a store in Los Angeles, closed almost forty years. The left-behind contents ended up in the home of the mother of the original owner. Now, after these forty years, she wanted the boxes of comic books gone. A friend of the original owner, Ray, accepted the challenge of off-loading the comics and chose my store as the benefactor. Although the boxes took up a good portion of two rooms at the woman's home, I consider this collection a warehouse find because it consisted of over 100 boxes of comics, ranging from 1975-1983. The collection of unsold comics were ordered from direct market distribution in large quantities, bagged and stored as inventory. These books never made it to a display shelf or back issue bin. I assume these comics were not meant to be stored for forty years, but they were.

When Ray first contacted me he underplayed the quantity and variety of titles. When the first boxes made their trek southward I realized had no idea of the quantity of comics; thousands of them and almost all unsold from the day they arrived at the now-defunct store. And so many copies of the same books in high grade!

Here's a sampling of the titles: *Ms. Marvel* #1-5, *Spectacular Spider-Man* #1-6, *Marvel Spotlight* #32, *Marvel Spotlight* V2 #1-4, *Iron Fist* #14, *Star Wars* #1-20, *Showcase* #97-100, *Eternals* #1-10, *Machine Man* #1, *Black Panther* #1-3, *Black Goliath* #1, *Super-Friends* #1, *2001, A Space Odyssey* #1-8, *Marvel Feature* #1-7, *Savage She-Hulk* #1, *Spider-Woman* #1, *Dazzler* #1, *Micronauts* #1 and many more in quantities ranging from a handful to stacks. Many untouched copies easily grade from 9.4-9.8. Some were sent off to grading and most will be at Comic Con 2018.

Will we ever see an *Overstreet Price Guide* containing an inaugural 9.4 column? The circulating data can be extrapolated from 9.0-9.2, not graded sales. I'd like to see Gemstone tackle physical changes in the book and the accuracy of their values. Perhaps the demand for raw high-grade Bronze Age to Modern Age comics justifies a stab at shaking up the status quo of the book.

Terry O'Neill
Terry's Comics/CalComicCon/ Nationwide Comics

This report focuses on convention and mail order aspects of comic collecting.

Sales from 2016 to 2017 continue to be very strong.

Golden Age (1938-1945): The Golden Age market is Gold (exceptional), even common issues from Fawcett and Fiction House are selling well. As some newer collectors start to realize that many Silver/Bronze Age are very common they are looking for more challenges in collecting and finding Golden Age a nice area to collect and not as expensive as it is thought to be. We acquired a vast DC collection known as the Jerome Wenker Collection with Graham Crackers. This collection contained every DC comic published from the beginning till September 2016. It was only 22 issues short with only 84 issues incomplete to have every issue published by DC including variants. Quite a few of rare and scarce titles such as Pre-Hero *Adventure, New Adventure, New Comics* and *More Fun Comics* sold extremely well at well above *Guide* prices. Some sales of note: *Green Lantern* #1 CGC VG+ $6,000, *Batman* #1 no cover PR $7,000, *Detective Comics* #32 FR $1350, *Wonder Woman* #1 CGC resto FR/GD $9000, *Sensation Comics* #1 CGC PR resto $6000, *Planet Comics* #1 CBCS VF+ resto $4150, *Captain America Comics* #30 FN+ $2000, and *Uncle Sam Quarterly* #5 CGC FN/VF resto $1200.

Atom Age (1946-1955): One of the most interesting, and my favorite areas for serious collectors. There are so many long and short running titles that have all sorts of content. We have done extremely well selling Teen Humor titles from all publishers, especially short run titles like *Babe, Hickory, Farmer's Daughter* and *Starlet O'Hara.* We also did well with longer running titles like *Buzzy, Date with Judy, Frankie, My Friend Irma* and *Suzie.* Other titles that sold well were *Annie Oakley* (Atlas), *Sugar and Spike, Jann of the Jungle, Dean Martin & Jerry Lewis, Adventures of Bob Hope, Girls' Romances* and *Jackie Gleason*. Some sales of note: *Wartime Romances* #1 FN $340, *Junior* #14 VG- $425, *Thing* #15 FN $550, *Brenda Star* #14 VG $850, *Canteen Kate* #3 VG/FN $225, *Nellie the Nurse* #19 FN+ $212, *Phantom Lady* #14 GD/VG $650, *Girls' Romances* #62 VF- $140, and *Jackie Gleason #2 VG/FN $200.*

Silver Age (1956-1970): Early Keys and 1st appearances are selling fast and at increasing values. Keep in mind many issues that were once hot are now cool, as a TV show or movie has already been released and the interest in a certain character such as Doctor Strange or the Inhumans has been lessened. As always, higher grade, especially DC keys still have the most potential as investments. *Fantastic Four* #1 and *Journey into Mystery* #83 are being sought and put away, especially as the newest *Thor* movie is doing so well. Some still affordable Silver Age are *Challengers of the Unknown* #1 and *Hawkman* #1, they have great art and are fun to read. *Amazing Spider-Man* #14 and #50 sell very fast usually often quite high, also *X-Men* #50 and *Brave and the Bold* #54 are sought after. Some sales of note: *Amazing Fantasy* #15 CBCS GD+ $11,000, *Amazing Spider-Man* #1 PGX VG $5200, *Brave and the Bold* #28 CGC FN- $5850, *Showcase* #4 CBCS GD $10,000, *Tales of Suspense* #39 GD+ $2700, *Fantastic Four* #1 CGC GD $3400, *Incredible Hulk* #1 CBCS GD+ $7000, *Superboy* #68 FN/VF $2400, *X-Men* #1 CGC FN $5800, *Journey into Mystery* #83 CGC GD/VG $3500, and *Action Comics* #242 CBCS FN+ $2600.

Bronze Age (1971-1985): *House of Secrets* #92 is nowhere to be found at shows and sells rapidly whenever one is acquired. *Hero for Hire* and *Iron Fist* have cooled now that the Netflix series are out. There is renewed interest in DC's Jack Kirby's Fourth World comics from this period such as *New Gods, Mister Miracle* and *The Forever People*. Also *Omac, Kamandi, Shazam* and *The Shadow* are being asked for once again. Some sales of note: *Shazam* #1 CGC NM/MT Double cover $1300, *Werewolf By Night* #32 CGC NM $1800, *Incredible Hulk* #181 CGC NM- $3,500, *Giant-Size X-Men* #1 CGC VF $900, *House of Secrets* #92 CGC VF $820, *Iron Man* #55 CGC VF $850, *Amazing Spider-Man #129* CGC NM- $1500, *X-Men* #94 CGC VF/NM $850, and #129 CGC NM/MT $600.

Magazines: Most of our magazine sales are from the catalog, so we will bring magazines to shows when given want lists. An interesting magazine is *1984/1994* by Warren, an attempt to bring Underground (Adult) stories to the mainstream comic world. In my Navy days, I usually read Warren and Marvel magazines as they were written without Comic Code oversight and had wonderful black & white art. Many artists did their best work for these as they did not have the restrictions of comic books. Some sales of note: *Savage Sword of Conan* #7 CGC NM/MT $550, #11 CGC NM+ $143, *Kull and the Barbarians* #3 CGC NM/MT $150, *Vampirella* #33 CGC NM- $200, *Eerie* #17 FN/VF $128, and *Savage Tales #1* CGC VF+ $350.

Modern Age & Independents (1986-Present): As always *Amazing Spider-Man* and *X-Men* are the most collected titles from this era. This era also brought in the first wave of independent publishers with titles like *Captain Victory, Miracleman, Bone, Teenage Mutant Ninja Turtles, American Flagg* and *Elf Quest*. Some comics like *Batman Adventures* #12 and *New Mutants* #98 have gone cool after reaching record high prices before their debut characters appeared in movies. Some sales of note: *Savage Dragon* limited series #1 CGC NM/NT $70, *Spawn* #1 CGC NM/MT $100, *Miracleman* #15 CGC NM/MT $450, *Amazing Spider-Man* #361 PGX NM+ $150, *Batman Adventures* #12 CGC NM+ $725, and *#12 NM $500.*

Graded Books: Selling graded comics on-line has been getting us through the lean time when we are not doing conventions and while working on inventory for our next catalog. The collector of only graded comics seems to seldom shop at comic shows and almost never will buy from our general (un-graded) inventory. All grading companies have both strong and weak points, and it is a great way to keep very nice comics from getting damaged.

Internet Sales: Except for our newest purchases, the vast majority of our entire vintage inventory is on our website: www.TerrysComics.com. We have over 60,000 comics in inventory and it is impossible to have an actual image of them all on our website. We will send scans on request but only for more expensive comics. Buy with confidence from an experienced dealer. All items sold by Terry's Comics can be returned within 30 days as received if not satisfied.

In summary, many hot ticket item collectors that are chasing the latest TV show or movie characters complain about *Overstreet Price Guide* prices. While the *Guide* cannot give daily price adjustments as it is printed and reflect prices from a year or more ago, it has always been a stable pricing tool for most vintage comic books. I use the *Overstreet Price Guide* because it is relevant on virtually all non-key or hot comics. It is still the best reference to vintage comics that exists.

Michael Pavlic
Purple Gorilla Comics

Greetings from southern Alberta! Well, the worst recession in recent memory has sure kicked us around pretty good, but the resilience of the comic stores here is rather impressive. All the stores survived and a new one was added to the mix. So all of us retailers must give a hearty "Thank You!" to our customers for giving us the opportunity to do what we love: sell comics!

And what, pray tell, am I selling?

Marvel Comics: Marvel continues to rule the roost, outselling any other publisher by a huge margin. Popular titles include *Amazing Spider-Man*, *Avengers*, *Captain America*, *Hulk*, *Iron Man*, *Ghost Rider*, *Punisher*, *Transformers*, *Thor*, *Wolverine* and *X-Men*. I'd include *Venom*, *Star Wars* (1st series) and *Deadpool* but I never seem to keep them in stock long enough and with sufficient numbers. And look out for Carnage, that character was super popular before, once he hits the big screen, I can see *Amazing Spider-Man* #361 spiking up like *New Mutants* #98 did (If the movie is GOOD!) For years I've sold *Amazing Spider-Man* #361 at $150, now it starts at $200.

Silver Age Marvels move and move quickly, it doesn't matter the genre, I can sell Romance books almost as fast as the Superhero ones. Same with Westerns and War comics. The occasional Atlas era books that I come across move at double *Guide*. You just don't see them "in the wild" very often up here.

DC Comics: Like Marvel, any Silver Age DC sell quickly, yes, even the Romance books! *Batman* has made a comeback, last year they didn't move, but now the title's back in vogue. I had a bunch of late 1970s- early 1980s *Batman* and *Detective*s and now they are all gone. These comics had a much lower print run than those in the late 1980s, making them relatively hard to find.

Wonder Woman is more popular now than I've ever seen and the 1st series issues go for double *Guide*, the Brian Bolland covers are $10 each. If I had any Adam Hughes covers, they'd be pricey too.

Not much else going on in DC, *Flash*, *Catwoman* and *Supergirl* have a following, *Harley Quinn* has died down (although it is because I have a hard time replacing them). There is a lot of interest in Teen Titans but it seems to be restricted to *Teen Titans Go!* People look at the "regular" TT and wonder why they aren't funny! DC should make *TT Go!* a monthly title.

Independent Publishers: *Spawn*, *Aliens*, *Predator* and *AvP* are the top titles. Any *Spawn* above issue #125 are hard to find, any *Aliens/Predator*, same thing. Oh, and Dark Horse *Star Wars*, super popular. It's hard to replace stock in these titles.

Kids Titles: An under appreciated genre of comics but perhaps the most important. The "entry level" comics of my youth: Archie, Disney, Bugs Bunny *et al* sell for me and I sell a LOT of them. Priced at a comfortable level ($2 each) I've sold hundreds of them in the last year. Same experience with Archie Digests. We need these kids to "graduate" to other comics (or keep reading the stuff they like) if this industry is to survive in the coming decades. We lost a generation in the late 1990s-early 2000s when the industry collapsed, let's not lose this generation too!

For the older collectors of the kids books, *Uncle Scrooge* sells fast, followed by *Donald Duck*, *Mickey Mouse*, *Bugs Bunny* and *Casper*. Demand outstrips supply for 1950s-1960s Dell and Gold Keys.

Westerns & War Comics: They move! Dells, Gold Keys, Marvels and DCs all move quickly. Heck, even Charltons move! I don't know if it's because we live in the prairies and have the Calgary Stampede, but Westerns sell quickly. Same with War books, can't keep them in. The people who buy these are generally not collectors in the sense of "what's it worth in *Overstreet*", rather they are fans of the book and the genre. *Sgt. Rock*, *G.I. Combat*, *Unknown Soldier* and *Sgt. Fury* are the most requested books and those funky Dell *Combat* painted covers always make an easy sale.

Horror: So much demand, so little supply. Any EC reprints are $15 now. Any movie related books are at least double, if not triple *Guide*. Go find the Marvel *Nightmare on Elm Street* magazines, I double dog dare you!! Those are at least $30-$40 books now.

The last few *Nightbreeds* by Epic had print runs of 22,000 approximately (it says so in the final issue). Hard to find. Haven't seen the Epic *Hellraisers* in a long time. Bronze Age Marvel DC and Charlton (especially Tom Sutton covers) go quickly.

Underground Comix: I'm the only game in town when it comes to these comix. There was a flurry of *Fabulous Furry Freak Bros.* sales this year, so much so that I now have none! Doesn't matter what printing it is, doesn't matter the shape. And you never see any issues above #10. Anything by R. Crumb sells, again doesn't matter the printing or shape. *Cherry* is popular as is *Harold Hedd* and *Zap*. If I had any Dan Clowes stuff, it would sell too. There is some interest in *Hate* and *Reid Fleming*. Almost every Underground sells well above the *Fogel Guide*. I truly believe that guide is much too low. Perhaps you folks in the huge Metropolitan cities in the USA are drowning in comix and thus this is reflected in the *Fogel Guide* prices, but dang, they're hard to find here.

Some of you might wonder why I don't talk about key books, slabbed 9.6 books or variant covers and the like. Well, it's because I'm more interested in serving the people who actually read and enjoy their comics as opposed to those who see comics as a commodity. Speculators destroyed the industry in the 1990s and with all the crazy numbers books get because of a movie announcement, I see it happening again. Anyone still getting *Guide* price for *X-Factor* #5 and #6? I sure ain't! Anyone asking for Inhumans now? Not in my world! For the love of Gawd, buy what you like, don't buy what you are told to buy by some guy on a website or because it's going to be made into a TV show or movie.

I want to thank the fine folks at *Overstreet* who once again gave me this platform to communicate with you. I also need to thank Dave at Amazing Fantasy in Red Deer Alberta and Ben and Marty at Phoenix Comics here in Calgary for their support and advice. A heartfelt thank you to my customers this past year, it was a tough one for all of us and I'm nothing without you. Lastly, as is tradition, a thank you to Doyle, this is all your fault!

Bill Ponseti
Fantastic Worlds Comics

Greetings Comic Lovers!

2017 marked our first full year back as a comic book shop retailer. It has been an up and down year, the primary culprit in the down cycles has been the glut of new comics and long story arcs coming out from Marvel and DC. DC performed better on whole than Marvel did for us, which was surprising. I can't remember a time when *Flash* and *Batman* consistently outsold *X-Men* and *Amazing Spider-Man*, but that was certainly the case for us this year.

We continue to enjoy slow, but steady, growth in our new comic sales, which have been bolstered by our young crowd. Seems the large amount of comic book related movies has driven new comic book readers from 6 – 16 for us, and that is a healthy sign for the long-term growth of our hobby. Not only are these kids buying new comics, but trade paperbacks, toys, and most importantly, back issues! We have several youngsters that regularly buy Silver and Bronze Age back issues. Very refreshing.

Speaking of the Silver and Bronze Age markets, we've been fortunate to have come into some very nice original owner collections from these eras this year, and the key issues were scooped up rapidly. Not as many run collectors as I am used to, but I do still see folks with lists coming in from time to time. As it relates to key Bronze issues, I can't keep *Incredible Hulk* #181 or *Werewolf by Night* #32 in stock. We had quite a few higher-grade copies of these comics come into the shop via original owner collections, and they briskly sold for well over GPA prices. For Silver Age Key comics, it's getting tougher for us to replace this inventory, as market conditions no longer offer anything with margin left on the bone at any of the auction sites. So, we are reliant on what walks in the store, and the pickings for these have been relatively slim as of this writing. We get the occasional *Amazing Spider-Man* #1, but mostly we get the later '60s keys in collections, not the early '60s keys. Golden Age has been very slow for us this past year. Even when we were fortunate enough to score some small batches of original owner Golden Age, they have not been fast sellers for us. For more modern keys, I can sell all the Amazing Spider-Man #300s and #361s I can get in stock. Wish I had a case of each.

In the original comic artwork area, we have experienced fantastic growth for our business in this section of the comic collecting world. Silver Age art has gotten so pricey, that when we are able to source some from our honey holes, they don't last long. But again, like their Silver Age counterparts in the comics, the price to re-acquire these on the open market is prohibitive to make a profit. We have landed quite a few Bronze, Copper and Modern Age original art collections that have found happy buyers very quickly. I expect this area of the market to continue to grow, because you can get killer stuff by great artists at a fraction of the Silver Age original art prices. I made a few nice Golden Age art sales this year, but there are still plenty of bargains in this area, and not nearly as many buyers as there should be.

The comic ephemera market for us, vintage toys, cards, games, puzzles, etc. has not been good this year. The ship may have sailed for now on this segment.

I am optimistic about the hobby in general though, and if the new comic publishers can just get out of their own way, it might become profitable again for retailers.

I still get a huge thrill every time a new collection of Bronze or Silver Age comics walks in, and am over the moon when I get some killer original artwork, so clearly the fire of passion for the hobby still burns brightly for me.

Until next time, Happy Collecting!

Greg Reece & Alex Reece
Reece's Rare Comics

Greg Reece - Hello Everyone, 2017 has come and gone and as we gear up for the 2018 season, it's time to reflect on the past year. Despite many reports you will read to the contrary, we noticed a resurgence in the run collector, a very positive sign for the hobby. We saw this at shows but particularly noticed online sales increasing in this area. Many of our customers expressed frustration at wanting an *Avengers*

#12 for example, but they only wanted a VG copy. Those are readily available at shows but if you live hours away from a major trade show you are generally limited to online venues. All of that said, we also saw tremendous growth in high end/key certified material. CGC continues to be the market leader in this area but it was interesting to note the Beckett purchase of CBCS. On a micro level, I think this is good for CBCS in that they have struggled at times implementing processes. But it's even better news on a macro level as it shows that a very large company believes in the certification process for the long term.

As we enter our 10th year (my 23rd overall in the comic business), Reece's Rare Comics is experiencing rapid growth. To that end, by the time you are reading this we will have rolled out reececomics.com version 3.0. This will include a vastly improved, much more user friendly consignment option. We will also have blogs, video from our time on the circuit, and much more.

Disney's acquisition of Fox was a potentially landscape changing event. I'm sure many of my fellow Overstreet advisors will comment as well but needless to say if you haven't locked up a *Fantastic Four* #1 or *X-Men* #1 my advice would be to do it sooner rather than later. I would also be buying *Fantastic Four* #4, #5, #48 and many others in the Fantastic Four universe along wth *X-Men* #12, #14, etc. It really is only a matter of time until these movies are done right and I can envision a multi-year film run for both of these franchises. Aside from *X-Men* #1 and *Fantastic Four* #1, other top picks for 2018 include: *Amazing Spider-Man* #1. I've been beating the drum on this book for a couple of years and it started breaking out in the 2nd half of 2017. It has plenty of room to run as *Amazing Fantasy* #15 sails out of sight (although I expect a correction on this book I don't think it'll be more than 15% or so. It won't crash and burn but the price increases are unsustainable). *Tales Of Suspense* #39 (especially 7.0+ copies) as it's still an early Marvel key, is not especially easy to find in grade, and is still relatively affordable.

Lastly I'd note something I mentioned 5-6 years ago. The market is becoming increasingly sophisticated. Back then I noted you could purchase books with outstanding eye appeal for the same cost as a dull, mis-wrapped copy. Those days are no more. There are 20-25% premiums regularly paid for great looking, bright, well centered copies as it relates to their pedestrian, poor page quality, mis-wrapped brethren. Since this is now a reality and not just speculation, I'd expect the gap to widen. So all of that said, when buying investment grade books, I believe it will pay off in the long term to be extra picky about the copies you purchase.

As always, thanks for all of your business over the years. I love what I do and who I do it with.

Alex Reece - Reece's Rare Comics

Hello again to everyone! As always, with the close of another year comes a new market report, as hard as it may be to believe that the year is over. 2017 was a record breaking year for Reece's Rare Comics, as we shattered multiple sales records, doubled our online inventory, and started taking consignments on a large scale. The market is overall very healthy, and I'll delve into the details in the following paragraphs.

Let's begin with a rundown of the 2017 conventions. We set up at 12 conventions this year with varying degrees of success. Firstly, Reed POP should be commended for continuing to run A+ top tier comic shows. All three of their shows that we did in 2017 (Emerald City Seattle, C2E2 Chicago, and New York Comic Con) were very tightly run, extremely organized, and highly profitable events. They remain committed to comic books at their shows, and in an era where comic vendors are increasingly marginalized and pushed to the side, this is a welcome reprieve. Marc Nathan also ran a top notch Baltimore Comic Con. Fire alarms aside, this continues to be a great comic book focused show, and in spite of all of the comic book vendors, there still is enough money in the room to make it worthwhile. A new show for us in 2017 was Planet Comicon in Kansas City. We did well there, and it is always great to meet customers at a show you have never been to before. Unfortunately, they moved it from April in 2017 to February in 2018, so we will not be returning due to scheduling conflicts. Another first was setting up at the famed San Diego Comic Con. While we have attended in years past, this was our first time setting up a booth, and it was unfortunately rather lackluster in terms of sales. MegaCon in Orlando was great again even though it was on Memorial Day Weekend, and WonderCon in Anaheim was slightly above average.

I will wrap up talking about our show season with the Wizard World shows from 2017. Outside of the Rosemont show, which is just a great comic town, they were quite a disappointment. Our team noticed markedly decreased sales at their shows when compared to 2016, which in and of itself was a down year for Wizard. To anyone who has been attending their shows over the past few years, this comes as no surprise. They have been intent on becoming more of a Pop Culture experience, being a "Comic" Con in name only. It is a shame, as some Wizard shows used to be among our top earners, and while we will still be attending two of their shows in 2018, they will be reevaluated on a yearly basis.

Sales trends at these shows were more of the same seen in years past. Keys and/or high grade books sold extremely well, and at many shows our wall was decimated by clientele hungry for high end books. We also noticed an increasing demand for third party encapsulated books, more so even than in years past. Of the graded material, we did see stronger prices for CGC books as opposed to CBCS books. The reasons for this are numerous and well documented elsewhere, but hopefully with Beckett newly at the helm, prices will begin to rival those of CGC graded books again. Competition in the graded comic book market is a very good thing, so I hope that CBCS is able to continue to provide it.

I also want to quickly mention raw, non-key issues. Many dealers have bemoaned the dearth of run collectors in recent years, citing evidence that most people at shows are only there to buy keys. I would argue that that is merely how the conventions have changed along with the rising prices of key books; people want to make their big purchases at a show so they can see the books in hand. When spending hundreds or even thousands of dollars, this makes sense. When filling in runs however, collectors are much more content to buy online, and that is a trend that we were party to in 2017. With Austin joining for his first full year in 2017, we were able to upload and list many more common or lower grade issues on our website, and sales of those types of books increased accordingly. In short, while keys and high grade still remain safely at the top of the pedestal, run collectors are not dead; they have simply moved to an easier buying experience, namely, the internet.

Finally, let's talk about some of the biggest movers I see for 2018. My top pick goes to *Fantastic Four* #1. For a book from 1961 that establishes Marvel's first Superhero team, I believe it to be criminally undervalued, even though it had a solid year of gains in 2017. With less than 1300 Universal copies on the CGC census in 17 years of grading, I don't think there will be enough copies to satisfy demand when the market finally figures out that this book is too cheap, and there are a few reasons for this. Obviously it's a blue chip key by anybody's standards. It's also extremely difficult in grade, with only 7 copies grading CGC 9.2 or better (compare that with *Amazing Spider-Man* #1, which has 25 copies in the same range). Furthermore, with Disney acquiring the movie rights to the franchise from Fox, we could finally see the long awaited Marvel Cinematic Universe tie in. When that inevitably gets announced, the sky is the limit, and you will want to be on the ride. As always in these situations, buy the highest grade you can afford to see the highest returns, but try to at least get into a 2.0/2.5 to see a solid return on your investment.

***Fantastic Four* #1** *should be one of the biggest movers for 2018.*

On another note, a trend I do not see continuing is the stratospheric rise that *Amazing Fantasy* #15 has been on. While it has been amazing to watch, with prices doubling in two years in many cases, I do believe it is in a bit of a bubble. Much of this frenzy was kicked off by a few record shattering auction results, not a foundational shift in supply or demand. After those initial auctions it spiraled out of control into people paying out seemingly crazy amounts of money for fear of the book rising to a price they would never be able to afford. Fear of missing out can be a powerful motivator, and I think that played at least some part in these recent price increases. While the bubble may not burst and cause prices to fall back to pre-2017 levels, I do believe that the growth of this book will slow tremendously in 2018. To that end, if you are holding onto an *Amazing Fantasy* #15 and are unsure of what to do, it might not be a bad time to either sell it or trade it into another high dollar key or keys. I simply cannot see another time in the near future when an *Amazing Fantasy* #15 will have as much buying power as it does now.

Overall I think the market is quite healthy. We bought and sold tons of books throughout the year, and I don't see any signs of it slowing down. I hope everyone had a great 2017, and I'm looking forward to seeing all of you in 2018 as well. We will be attending 11 trade shows this year, so make sure to stop by and say hello if we're in your town. As always, you can find our full trade show schedule on our website (www.reececomics.com). Feel free to contact Greg, myself, or Austin with any and all of your collecting needs, and have a great 2018!

STEVE RICKETTS
CBCS

Greetings to fellow comic book fans from sunny Florida! For those of you who don't know me; my dear friends Steve Borock, Michael Bornstein, West Stephan, and myself started Comic Book Certification Service (CBCS) from nothing more than an idea. CBCS is now four years old and growing exponentially every year. Over that time, I've filled many roles with the company, from Grading to GM. For the last year, I have been the President of CBCS Pressing.

I have loved comics since I was old enough to hold a book, and this year I have become an Advisor to the *Overstreet Comic Book Price Guide*. I can remember reading the *Guide* when I was a young collector. To say that I was "reading" the *Guide* would be an understatement. I literally destroyed them by studying them. The knowledge they contained was like a drug to me, and I couldn't get enough of it. To have been chosen to join the ranks of an "Advisor" is sincerely an honor for me.

That said, in my first report I literally must say "Thank You" to a few of the people who helped me achieve the dream of working in the world of comic books. My childhood friend, Greg Clark, who made me realize there were people working in the comic book industry, and that I could be one of them one day. My late selling buddies, John Swift and Troy Dudley, whom are both still with me in spirit. Darin Porteen, who has been my foundation, even when everything crumbled around me. Steve Borock and West Stephan, who have taught me more about vintage comics than I ever thought I could possibly learn. Finally, my lovely wife, Anne Marie, who always trusts and believes in me.

As President of CBCS Pressing, please let me say that I am concerned with the number of books we see pass through

CBCS that have been pressed badly. It seems every day a new "garage presser" springs up, mashing books, destroying books, while unknowingly thinking that he (or she) is doing a good job. I've even seen people on social media praising their go-to presser, not realizing that the person they are using is (at best) not doing a good job, or (at worst) destroying comic books. I certainly don't claim to be the only trustworthy presser, but I would like to say that when choosing a presser, cheaper is not better. Nor should your choice be the fastest turnaround time. Turnaround time is 100% dependent on demand. That's the equivalent of choosing a certain a restaurant because there are no cars in the parking lot. I don't understand the thought process behind that.

Now I've said my peace. If you don't use me, please use someone who has been pressing comics for a long time. They are worth the price they charge, and they are definitely worth the wait. I say that as a long-time collector who loves the hobby and respects each comic book as a piece of history. Please help us preserve our comic books properly for the generations to come.

What are people submitting for pressing and grading? Anything with a movie tie-in is hot, hot, HOT! As I write this, I can't tell you how many copies of *Fantastic Four* #52 and *Black Panther* #1 I've pressed in the last several months. Black Panther has risen to levels of popularity beyond anyone's imagination. I liken it to the wave created with the first Iron Man film. It's good to see this much enthusiasm over a previously "second-tier" character.

Also heavily submitted are *New Mutants* #98, *Batman Adventures* #12, and a surprising number of *Incredible Hulk* #181 and *Giant-Size X-Men* #1. *Infinity Gauntlet* #1 is also a heavy-hitter because it seems that almost every submission has at least one or two copies in it. *Walking Dead* #1 is still strong, but I've seen the submission of all other issues of *Walking Dead* all but completely come to a halt.

Newsstand and Direct variants are quickly gaining popularity with the mainstream collectors. CBCS has seized the reins on this niche of the hobby, by being the only grading service to identify Newsstand and Direct Edition copies in the variant field of the label on books from 1977 through 2000. Once the CBCS census goes live, it will be interesting to see the numbers that have been submitted. In the late 1970s, Direct Edition comics were less common than Newsstand Editions. As years progressed, Newsstand copies became more and more scarce, with the Newsstand copies of some comics being incredibly hard to find. The hobby will start to learn more about the scarcity of each issue in the coming years. More information is better for everyone, especially involving something that was hiding right under our very noses.

Golden Age submissions are also strong, and I've seen some extremely nice GA books come through for pressing. Along with the standard Batman and Superman titles, I've seen a big increase in titles containing Wonder Woman, Aquaman, Captain America, Namor, and Human Torch. Lots of Schomburg and Frazetta covers, as well as a surprising number of high grade L.B. Cole horror issues. My job is SO AWESOME!

I do see a healthy number of Silver and Bronze Age comics crossing my desk. Big key issues are not in short supply, with *Amazing Fantasy* #15, *Fantastic Four* #1, *Amazing Spider-Man* #1, *Daredevil* #1, *Incredible Hulk* #1, and *Avengers* #1 being submitted regularly, with many copies in very high grade. I've also noticed a lot of minor keys are being submitted, such as *Defenders* #1, *Nova* #1, *Spider-Woman* #1, *Marvel Spotlight* #32, and the like.

Foreign edition comics are picking up a lot of interest. A once tiny, and very obscure portion of our hobby is growing rapidly. I've seen many foreign comics over the last year, with the numbers growing every month. I love watching these once overlooked niches grow wings and take off.

I can't predict what the next hot comic book will be, but keep an eye on what Hollywood is working on. That seems to almost certainly ignite interest and demand.

And with that, my first *Overstreet Price Guide* Market Report is in the books. I'm glad to be here, and extremely blessed to be involved with an industry I've loved my whole life. Best wishes, and happy collecting, to you all!

Ben Samuels
Golden Age/Foreign Comics Specialist

This has been another very interesting year in the world of comic book collecting.

It doesn't seem so long ago that *Amazing Spider-Man* #300 was the only comic published during or after the late 1980s that was worth any significant amount of money but that is definitely no longer the case. It also doesn't seem so long ago that no distinction was made between newsstand and direct editions but the newsstand editions certainly command a premium now.

I have noticed that movie and TV-related speculation can quickly drive certain comics to command surprisingly high prices. Certain scarcer variants of popular new comics are also often the target of aggressive speculation. But more often than not these radical price rises are simply market bubbles and it is my feeling that this type of speculation in new issues, upcoming movie and TV tie-ins, and "flavor of the month" comics can be very risky.

With regard to Silver Age comics, it should be news to absolutely no one that the prices of high grade superhero keys continue to rise with no sign of stopping or even slowing down. As they say, the rich get richer. Or more precisely, the expensive get even more expensive. But as is often the case, a rising tide lifts all (or most) boats, because even lesser keys from the Bronze, Copper and Modern Age are showing healthy gains.

The only losers I can think of to mention continue to be Golden Age comic strip reprint titles like *Popular Comics*, *Tip Top*, *Sparkler*, and the like. Also the more pedestrian issues of

Four Color Comics and non-key non-Marvel Western comics can be a tough sell. Run-of-the-mill Fawcett and Quality comics also seem to face a very soft market.

I have noticed that the market is very strong for 1950s Horror comics with classic or at least cool-looking cover art. EC comics in general seem to be selling better than they have over the past few years. Some specific sales that I have noted include: *Black Cat Mystery* #50 graded CGC 7.5 sold for $3,825; *Chamber of Chills* #19 sold for CGC 5.5 sold for $2,625; *Crime SuspenStories* #22 graded CGC 4.5 and 5.0 sold for $2,800-$2,900, issues graded CGC 3.5 and 4.0 sold for $1,700-$1,800, and a CGC 2.5 sold for $1,350; *Dark Mysteries* #19 graded CGC 7.0 sold for $3,100; *Lawbreakers Suspense Stories* #11 graded CGC 3.5 sold for $1,850; *Startling Terror Tales* #11 graded CGC 6.0 sold for $1,850 and a copy graded CGC 2.0 sold for $1,025; *Thrilling Crime Cases* #49 graded CGC 8.0 sold for $2,150; and *Weird Mysteries* #5 graded CGC 3.0 sold for $3,125.

Another segment of the market showing extremely strong sales is Good Girl, working girl, and teen-age Humor comics, particularly issues with headlight covers. Fox Comics' *Junior*, *Meet Corliss Archer*, and *Sunny, America's Sweetheart* are in high demand whenever they show up for sale, particularly the issues with art by Al Feldstein. Of course demand for early Archie comics remains very healthy. Recently there seems to be very strong interest in, and appreciation for, Timely/Marvel comics like *Tessie the Typist*, *Millie the Model*, *Nellie the Nurse*, *Georgie*, *Lana*, *Margie*, *My Friend Irma*, *My Girl Pearl*, and other similar titles.

For the most part these comics used to be only collected for interior art by Harvey Kurtzman or Basil Wolverton but issues of these titles are now being sought out for their cover art and scarcity more than their contents. *Cindy* #37 is an interesting example of a comic of this type. It used to be a "nothing" comic, as recently as 2015 it has a price spread of $14 for GD 2.0 to $140 for NM- 9.2 but since I've begun tracking sales of this issue I have documented a copy sold as VG/FN (raw) for $1,600, a VG+ (raw) copy sold for $1,795, and a copy graded CGC 6.0 sold for $2,870. So the demand for this issue is clearly consistent, and surprisingly strong. Of course the beautiful graytone headlight cover (now recognized as "classic") helps to explain the interest.

Some other impressive sales I have noted include: *Annie Oakley* #1 graded CGC 8.0 sold for $1,435; *Gay Comics* #39 (raw) low to mid-grade sold for $2,025; *Gay Comics* #40 (raw) low to mid-grade sold for $575 (*Gay Comics* #39 and #40 are the last two issues of the title, I believe they are scarce.); *G.I. Jane* #6 graded CGC 6.5 sold for $1,135; *Jetta* #7 graded CGC 4.0 sold for $1,300; and *Junior* #12 graded CGC 6.5 sold for $2,270;

It seems like a strange world we live in where a girly humor comic can command prices equal to or greater than a nice Timely super-hero comic!

And here is another fascinating example (to me, at least) of the changing landscape of comic book values. A friend of mine recently bought a copy of *Avengers* #1 graded CGC 5.5 for $3,150. At the very same time, in a well-publicized auction, a copy of *Superman* #4 graded CGC 6.5 sold for $3,100. So a mid-grade Silver Age Marvel key sold for (a little) MORE than a pretty darn nice copy of a historically significant Golden Age superhero comic that featured the second appearance of Lex Luthor! Personally, I find this rather surprising and very interesting.

Another segment of the comic book market that I find fascinating is the growing interest in foreign edition of American comics. Now, before I begin I should note that Canadian Comic collectors exist mostly in a separate "eco-system" from collectors of other foreign comics and I am not going to address Canadian comics in this market report, as other advisers are much more knowledgeable about that branch of collecting.

We live in a big world and collecting comic books from Mexico, South and Central America, Europe, Asia, and Australia come with different, interesting, challenges and opportunities. Many collectors like to choose a single favorite comic and then try to find editions from as many different countries as they can. Beginners who want to test the waters with something fairly familiar can start with UK pence editions of Marvel Silver Age comics, which are virtually identical to the US editions, except for the pence cover price. They were printed at the same time and on the same presses as the US editions but with much smaller print runs. It is not unreasonable to think of them as scarce cover price variants. A UK pence copy of *Amazing Fantasy* #15 graded CGC 6.0 recently sold for $27,485, a significant discount from the US edition but still a healthy chunk of cash. As the relative scarcity of these comics becomes better appreciated I believe it will not be long before UK pence copies achieve price parity with the US editions, and they will eventually command a premium.

There is strong demand for near-contemporaneous foreign editions of Silver Age key issues in English from the UK and Australia, as well as comics in Spanish and Portuguese from publishers like Alan Class and L. Miller & Son (UK), Ebal (Brazil), La Prensa and Editorial Novaro (Spain and Latin America). Gold and Silver Age superhero comics from Scandinavian countries are also popular. Some of these foreign comics can realize prices in the high hundreds, and even four figures. I personally bought a copy of the Mexican edition of *X-Men* #1; La Prensa's *Los Hombres X* #1 graded CBCS 5.5 for $1,500 and have no fear that I will lose money should I ever decide to sell it. Below are a few foreign comics to watch:

UK - published by Alan Class:

Creepy Worlds #32 (corresponds to *Fantastic Four* #1, issues #32-38 all have early *Fantastic Four* covers and stories)
Mystic #54 (corresponds to *Avengers* #1)
Mystic #55 (corresponds to *Avengers* #4)
Out of This World #17 (contains interior of *Amazing Fantasy* #15, but not the cover)

Sinister Tales #23 (corresponds to *Tales of Suspense* #39)
Mexico - published by La Prensa:
Cuentos de Brujas #178 (corresponds to Journey into Mystery #83)
Diabolico #1 (corresponds to Daredevil #1)
El Sorprendente Hombre Arana #1 (corresponds to Amazing Spider-Man #1)
Los Hombres X #1 (corresponds to *X-Men* #1)
Los Vengadores #1 (corresponds to *Avengers* #4)
Published by Editorial Novaro:
Superman #197 (corresponds to *Adventure Comics* #247)

There are some fascinating quirks in the world of foreign comic collecting. For example, the death of Gwen Stacy was very controversial in Mexico so rather than publish an edition of *Amazing Spider-Man* #121 they wrote and drew an all-new story for the Latin American market in which Gwen Stacy lived, making *El Sorprendente Hombre Arana* #128 an unusually desirable issue.

On the other hand, in Brazil editions of *Adventure Comics* featuring the Legion of Super-Heroes had been being published for some time before they got around to producing an edition of *Adventure Comics* #247, Ebal's *Superboy-Bi* #10. Even though it is the Brazilian edition of the first appearance of the Legion, because it is not Brazil's first appearance of the Legion means it is not quite as valuable as it might otherwise be. So it is important to do proper research and perform due diligence when exploring the unfamiliar world of foreign comic collecting.

For people interested in learning more about foreign comics, good resources are the "Foreign Comic Book Collectors" and "Foreign Comic Book Collectors - buy, sell and trade" Facebook groups.

Phil Schlaefer
Champion Comics / Comic-Press.com

I set up at 23 shows in 2017, among them some of the biggest and best: San Diego Comic-Con, Emerald City, Wonder Con, Rose City and the California Comic Convention. The majority had a healthy comic buying community interested in vintage Gold up to the Modern Age. Gaining in popularity were "Signature Series" books. I brought comics in line with the particular guests at each show. The most popular were titles by George Pérez, Todd McFarlane, Rob Liefeld, Dave Gibbons, J. Scott Campbell, and of course... Stan Lee!

Modern variant books still lead the charge for newer collectors. However, they seem to burn quickly and drop in price after a few months with a few exceptions. *Amazing Spider-Man* #700 is still in high demand. *The Walking Dead* #1 is holding strong, but the rest of the series has cooled greatly.

The largest demand and biggest price increase percentage wise goes to the biggie, *Amazing Fantasy* #15. Even coverless copies are achieving record prices and demand!

The next biggest flurries belong to these two Bronze Age books: *House of Secrets* #92 and *Amazing Spider-Man* #129. *House of Secrets* #92 flew by *Green Lantern* #76 as the must-have book of '70s DC. With its gorgeous black cover and Wrightson art, it is quite possibly the toughest Bronze Age book to find in grade. With the advent of the much anticipated *Punisher* TV show on Netflix, *Amazing Spider-Man* #129 is red hot. The show is a smash hit, so that book has staying power on an ever-growing collector's want list in any grade.

Incredible Hulk #181 also made a comeback move, with increases across the board. Honorable mention goes to *Brave and the Bold* #28, *Fantastic Four* #4 and *Amazing Spider-Man* #1.

Dylan Schwartz
Collector

Wow, it has been a year already. At Dylan Universe Comics, we are seeing a large demand for first appearances, cool covers, and classic story lines. This is how the market has been for a while. However, prices have been steady for these first appearances. Movie dependent comics (comics that are abruptly "good" because of a newly announced movie) are unstable long term. Some have been steady, others not so much. *Amazing Spider-Man* #300 is an interesting example. It has always been a desired "key" issue. But it has seen a decent price fluctuation since July. Shortly prior to July, the comic had been rising in value, due to an announcement of Tom Hardy being in Sony's *Venom* movie. The comic has been on the uptrend since. What about the future? After the movie, I predict the comic will either lose value or rise more in value, directly related to the success of the movie. But what about ten years from now? Will traditional superheroes even be the "main" genre of comics?

There is a big push toward Golden Age comics in the current market. They are rising in value. There is more demand. There are more collectors, and the comics are rarer than later ages, such as Bronze Age comics. It would not be surprising if movies were made out of classic Golden Age characters. The market has changed. It is getting better. The market will continue to grow as new television shows and movies are constantly being made. The market is very strong. There are always collectors who want comics, and that is how it will be for a long time.

Alika Seki, P.E.
Maui Comics & Collectibles

It was a big year for Maui Comics! We moved our store to a new, bigger location next to local favorites Sheik's restaurant and Paradise Video (a 30 year old, locally owned video store)! We also had the second ever Maui Comic Con (www.mauicomiccon.com) at its new and permanent home-venue, University of Hawaii – Maui College at the Student Union (Pilina) building. The Maui Comic Con boasted legendary comic creator Stan Sakai as well as

Marvel legends Joe Rubinstein and Mark Texeira, as well as leagues of Hawaii local comic creators, and vendors from all islands. Maui Comics has only been around 3 short years, and in the decade prior there were no comic stores on Maui at all. That being said, comic book and nerd culture in general on our little island has exploded! I'd like to thank, as always, the guys who keep this shop going; Swan Kaho'okele, Travis Shultz, Jason "Phormat" David, Nick Hopkins, Ryan Balberdi and Kaleo Kaina – as well as my co-organizer for the Maui Comic Con, Kenneth Gardner. And I can't go further without remembering my mentor and late partner, Mr. Bruce Ellsworth whom I think about often, especially when finding new collections.

The majority of the collections that we found on island this year were mid to high grade Bronze Age collections. Notable issues include: *Fantastic Four* #52 (the first appearance of Black Panther of course heating up in anticipation of the upcoming Marvel movie) in Fine/Very Fine condition sold for $400, *Marvel Spotlight* #5 (first appearance of Ghost Rider) in Fine condition sold for $350, *Amazing Spider-Man* #129 (first appearance of the Punisher definitely hot in response to the amazing first season of the eponymous Netflix series) in Very Fine condition sold for $700. We sold many other copies of the *ASM* #129s and *FF* #52s, but those are the highest priced ones sold this year. We also sold a lower grade *Giant-Sized X-Men* #1 at the end of 2017 for $350. Those who thought that the popularity of superhero movies and television shows would not impact the collectible comic market are surely eating those words. Low grade Silver Age comics, featuring all stripes of characters are in demand. Not just the titles featuring main (Spidey, FF, X-books etc.) stars, but also lesser known titles. Demand for *Iron Fist* as well as the *Master of Kung Fu* books have increased markedly in the past year.

On the topic of notable collections, I want to take time and acknowledge one of the most impressive Silver Age collection of comics I have seen in a long time, discovered by Howard Rockman whom shares a mutual friend with us in the late Bruce Ellsworth. Howard's newly acquired collection is called the D.N.A. Collection and includes every key issue of the Silver Age, both Marvel and DC as well as a plethora of war and sci-fi books from the Atomic and Silver Ages. Congratulations, Howard!

One last collection of note that we acquired this year, in pieces, was a beautiful example of Underground Comix by a great local Maui hippie, and friend of the store Sleepy John. His collection consisted of about 200-250 comics and cover the best of the underground comix scene of the late '60s and '70s, including titles such as: *Slow Death*, *Grim Wit*, *Bizarre Sex*, *Skull*, *Freak Brothers*, *Mr. Natural*, *Mickey Rat* and all of the classics of the time. I know the *OCBPG* doesn't cover these books, but the collection is worth mentioning – and available for sale at our shop!

The year 2017 also saw our store get into the Original Comic Art market. We went from having no original art, to having 2 binders full. We've since sold pieces by the masters such as Todd McFarlane, John Romita Sr., Bill Sienkiewicz, Art Adams, Bob Layton, Steve Leialoha, Joe Rubinstein, Mike Mignola and so many more.

The Maui Comic Con was a great opportunity to stock up on original art from Joe Rubinstein and Mark Texeira. Stan Sakai also did some great live drawing demos for the crowd, and allowed us to auction the drawings to benefit Maui College student groups. While Stan has never sold any original pages from *Usagi Yojimbo* (an amazing fact that I learned while talking with him), I did get to see him working on his latest issue. Guests of the Maui Comic Con definitely got a treat when they saw Stan working on issue 166 of *Usagi Yojimbo* as he spoiled the beginning of the new story arc eagerly when asked by his fans. If any of you folks out there in comic-land ever visit Maui around Halloween time, please come check out the Maui Comic Con. You'll be happy you did. It is the only free to the public comic convention that focuses on local creators, and seeks to get to the root of what a comic convention is about – celebrating the medium of comics!

As always we need to shout out our local nerd podcast that has been recording live in-store for the past 2 years – the NERDWatch with host Greg "G-Money" Turner, Professor Barry Wurst, Gannon, Jason "Phormat" David, Todd Bernardy, Swan "the comic henchman" Kaho'okele, Bruce Hennesey, Charles "Big C" Yale-Tang and the rotating crew of nerds! Find the podcast on Soundcloud, Audioboom, iTunes and the MAUIWatch app to keep current with the latest nerd and pop culture.

The comic community on Maui continues to grow and the future holds so many surprises! Stay tuned, and always practice Aloha!

Todd Sheffer
Hake's Americana

2017 was another banner year for record prices in all categories of collectibles and the demand for high graded comics continues. The year showed more interest in original comic book art and graded key books as investors and collectors fight to own the best of the best pieces. Confidence remains high in graded books from CGC and CBCS and they continue to bring in higher prices for higher grade comics.

Original art keeps getting attention with covers and key pages from classic artists continuing to show big returns. Look for art to continue to have more interest as newer artists transition to digital format.

Vintage toys and collectibles have been getting much attention, most notably *Star Wars* action figures are bringing record breaking prices with the continued success of the movie franchise.

Golden Age: Early DC superhero titles have renewed interest with the emergence of Wonder Woman and the rest of the Justice League in movie theaters attracting new collectors and driving the already avid collectors to seek out the early appearances of key characters. Pedigree books such as Mile High copies and others bring top dollar when they come to market. Uncertified issues also command high prices with scarce titles and issues getting scooped up by savvy collectors when they come up for sale.

Silver Age: Marvel continues to be the desired choice in Silver Age. *Amazing Fantasy* #15 shows no signs of slowing down in increasing value in any grade. Spider-Man continues to be the hottest character with early issues being highly sought after especially those with first appearances of key villains. Movie and TV involvement also drives prices up on 1960s books. Look for renewed interest in *Fantastic Four* and *X-Men* as these titles get new support from Marvel in the coming year with the Disney-Fox deal.

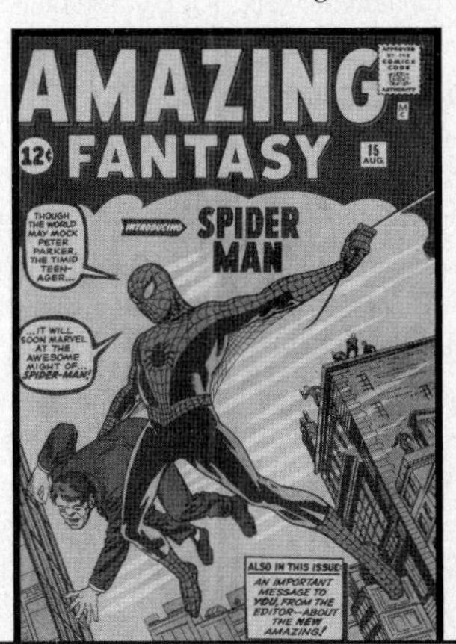

Amazing Fantasy *#15 shows no sign of slowing down*

Copper/Modern Age: Again, TV and movies drive these newer issues forward with Netflix series, AMC, the CW and other networks pulling material from comics. *The Walking Dead*, *The Punisher*, *Defenders*, *Supergirl* and more are getting the attention of viewers weekly with big ratings for most. First appearances of modern characters such as Harley Quinn, Deadpool, Cable, Rocket Raccoon and others keep increasing with each new film sequel.

Notable 2017 Comic Sales at Hakes.com: *Top-Notch Comics* #2 CGC 9.6 Mile High Copy $10,923, *All Star Comics* #7 CGC 9.2 $10,620, *More Fun Comics* #72 CGC 9.6 $9,503, *Journey Into Mystery* #83 CGC 5.0 $4,640, *All Star Comics* #8 CBCS 2.5 $31,925, *TMNT* #1 CGC 9.4 $9,216, *Amazing Fantasy* #15 CGC 7.5 $140,760 (a record price at this time).

Notable 2017 Art Sales at Hakes.com: *Mad Magazine* #121 cover art by Norman Mingo $57,242, *Captain America* #265 cover art by Mike Zeck $18,350, Justice League Of America Licensing Style Guide art by José Luis García-López $12,214, *Black Panther* #5 variant cover art by Greg Hildebrandt $5,900, *The Punisher War Journal* #25 cover art by Michael Golden $3,893, *Fantastic Four* #289 cover by John Byrne $24,727, *Urban Legends* #1 cover by Daniel Clowes $19,801, *Incredible Hulk* #3 original page by Jack Kirby $19,704.

Notable 2017 Merchandise Sales at Hake's: Justice League Of America Tattoo Gum Full Display Box $6,140, Gilbert Nuclear Physics No. U-238 Atomic Energy Lab $8,697 and a second set at $12,980, *Star Wars* Obi-Wan Kenobi (double-telescoping) AFA 80 $76,700, *Star Wars* Luke Skywalker AFA 95 $50,622, Topps *Mars Attacks* SGC graded card set $7,788, and *Star Wars* Tie Fighter AFA 85 $7,139.

Frank Simmons
Coast to Coast Comics

Greetings and salutations to all in this incredible hobby we all love! Please enjoy our opinions of this year's market sales and trends.

If I could provide one piece of valuable advice it would be not to wait to purchase a comic you really, really want. I can not stress this enough. Great Golden Age comics along with Silver Age seem to be snatched up as fast as offered when graded and priced appropriately. he best time to buy that treasured comic you have always wanted is when you see it available or when it is being offered to you. The days of readily available vintage comics has changed in dramatic fashion.

General overview of price increases in the market:

1) Golden Age: There has been a strong revival of the Golden Age comic market. Golden Age comics are selling currently as strong as I have ever seen them sell and at price points we have never seen in comics! Last year we observed caution on extremely high dollar purchases such as *Action* #1, *Detective* #27, *Adventure* #40, etc. This year seems to bear a completely different market. Hard to find comics in this genre along with high grade examples are being snapped up almost as quickly as they are being offered. Timely & pre-Code Horror have made a big come back this years regarding sales. Pre-Code Horror in particular has seen price increases in some cases as much as 400%, a case in point *Mister Mystery* #1! I feel a 10% to 20% increase in book value is appropriate this allows a conservative text value, the actual undeniable value of course is determined by the market and a host of details regarding each comic and sale.

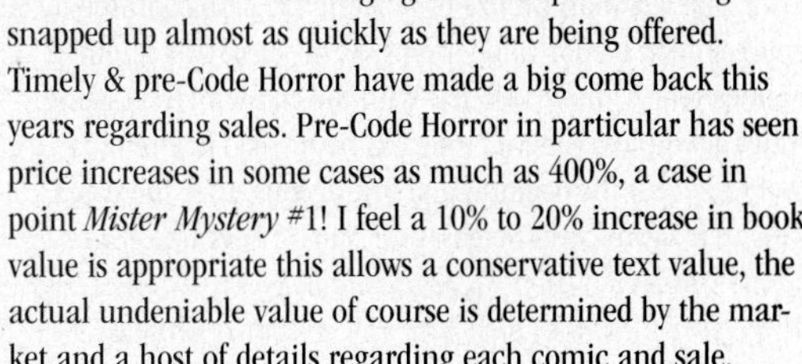

2) Silver Age: This area of the hobby is extremely hot, especially in the area of high grade keys. Marvel & DC keys have seen increases in the 20% to 30% range. With prices at already all new heights this is particularly impressive. In conversations with other dealers and collectors all over the country there seems to be a consensus that investment purchases have skyrocketed! GPA has shown incredible, almost unbelievable, price jumps especially for comics such as *Amazing Fantasy* #15, *Amazing Spider-Man* #1, *X-Men* #1, *Tales of Suspense* #39 and *Fantastic Four* #1 just to mention a few. Silver Age remains the strongest and most viable area of the comic market and should continue with no real end in sight.

3) Bronze Age comics have made a strong rebound from last year's sales in my opinion. Comic book keys are fairly strong and fairly stable as well. Unlike Silver Age or Golden Age, Bronze Age comics prices have seen modest gains most likely because of a higher level of availability. Just about

every Bronze Age key has increased however unlike last year I see slight gains with some rare corrections regarding value. I would say 0% increase is healthy, as for keys, actual sales would determine the value of each independently.

4) Current,variants etc... Not really familiar with this area of the market.

Copper Age/Modern Age: This area of the hobby continues to be fun, dynamic and offer a ton of available inventory to those seeking to indulge. *Batman Adventures* #12, first appearance of Harley Quinn continues to be a dominant comic in this area of the hobby. Harley Quinn makes her very first appearance in a comic book after her iconic TV debut, and thus things will never be the same! Barbara Gordon is attending a costume party, she decides to go dressed as none other than her hero and secret identity, Batgirl! This comic has seen prices nearing 2k for NM MINT 9.8 graded copies. I sold 8 raw ultra high grade (graded by the present owner of the comic not a grading company) copies myself this year with an average sale of almost $1400.00!!! This year has been particularly strong for raw comic sales across the board. In my opinion this has further been fueled by comic buyers wanting to purchase "a book" as opposed to purchasing a "label".

Bronze Age/Silver Age/Golden Age: Golden Age has made a huge push in sales this year, almost on par with Silver Age! I have to clarify here, to be specific based on availability as we all know there is far, far less Golden Age material available compared to Silver Age. I think the same can be said regarding Silver Age available inventory, it will always be less than Bronze or Modern. DC keys continue to appreciate at record value jumps, as this year was another banner year without a doubt. With the comic market being infused with investment money as never seen before, this looks like just the beginning of outrageous price increases. This year saw record increases for Marvel Keys like *Amazing Spider-Man* #1, *X-Men* #1, *Fantastic Four* #1, *Journey Into Mystery* #83, *Tales Of Suspense* #39, *Amazing Fantasy* #15. Just when it seemed like the percentage and dollar increases were maxing out, we watched these mega key type comics increase once again like never before! This year's breakout comic issue in terms of price jump had to be *Amazing Fantasy* #15 with increases of 30%, 40% & even more depending on grade, eye appeal and of course page quality.

Last year I mentioned a "sleeper" on the "most wanted" list among collectors, *House Of Secrets* #92. Well it looks like our predictions were correct as this mega DC key doubled in value this last year! This awesome key 1st appearance of Swamp Thing is illustrated by none other than the "Master Of Macabre" himself Mr. Bernie Wrightson! I had the distinct privilege and pleasure to meet the late great Mr. Bernie Wrightson at a Sacramento comic show this past February, 2017. Bernie Wrightson was truly a gentleman that loved comic books and comic art. Bernie explained that his very distinct style of art was a self taught style. He didn't have a formal training in art like many other artists. He taught himself and perfected his craft over the decades. I think Mr. Wrightson was best known for his Frankenstein work and of course his incredible Swamp Thing art for DC Comics in the early 1970s. For those that are not aware, we lost the great "Master of Macabre" in March of 2017. Rest in peace Mr. Bernie Wrightson, thank you for giving us all so much incredible art to enjoy over the years, truly a champion of comic book lovers everywhere!

The year 2017 was a very strong year for Coast To Coast Comics thanks to the incredible patronage of the very best customers the internet has to offer. We experienced a strong demand for raw high grade keys both Marvel and DC. 2017 seemed to also be a resurgence of the "completest run" collector, as we noticed a lot more collectors looking to put together full runs of comics as opposed to just buying key issues which have dominated the comic market over the past few years. 2018 looks to be another incredible year for Comicdom! For those reading this report, Coast To Coast Comics Comics would like to personally thank you! We also would like to wish all of you in the comic galaxy a healthy and prosperous 2018. This is an amazing hobby that we all love and continue to see evolve in ways that never seemed remotely possible! Please look up our auctions on eBay, as we are proudly celebrating our 19th year on this great venue!

Marc Sims
Big B Comics - Barrie

Hello and welcome to my market report! Here you will find all the exciting happenings that I've experienced in my little corner of the comic market in beautiful Barrie, Ontario and the greater Toronto area.

2017 has been another banner year for my business. We have seen strong gains at my retail store Big B Comics Barrie, at our convention appearances, and through various online outlets. The market continues to be robust and I am feeling cautiously optimistic about the future.

My biggest online platform continues to be eBay. The fees can be high and it does present its own challenges with the user base, but it is hard to match the reach that eBay provides. Particularly when it comes to more casual customers, as opposed to the seasoned veterans that tend to troll the 3 main comic auctions houses, eBay allows me an avenue to sell lower priced items that may not necessarily move as quickly in my local market. Sometimes it's also simply that I've run out of room in my store or I've found something I know I can make money on but doesn't necessarily fit in with what I normally carry. With eBay I basically have a digital store open 24/7 to supplement my physical store, and without any of the headache and cost of tech development or support. I love it. You can find me under the username "slowdowntubby", an ID I've had since I started on eBay in 1999 and just don't have the heart to change!

Instagram is another popular platform where I've had good success selling comics, this time to the younger crowd.

There is a great community aspect to IG that I love. Here you will find people who genuinely love comics (especially Golden Age) and are more interested in sharing photos of their newest prized possessions than they are in cashing in on the latest movie announcement. It is truly refreshing and heartening to see 20-25 year old collectors discovering Matt Baker or EC Comics for the first time! I imagine they get the same feeling scrolling through their feeds as I got the first time I leafed through the pages of the *Gerber Photo Journals*. Meeting some of these newer collectors face to face at conventions and at my store gives me a lot of confidence that this hobby of ours is in very good hands.

In years past I used to set up at numerous conventions all across Canada and the Eastern US. In the early 2000s I did 12-15 shows a year. I am now down to exhibiting at just one show, and that is the Toronto Comic Book Show which happens 4-5 times a year in North York. Comic fans have no shortage of so called comic conventions to choose from in North America. In Ontario there is pretty much a collectible show of one kind or another every weekend and something billing itself as a comic-con twice a month. But there is one thing that joins nearly all of these comic-cons together, and that is the fact they don't really have any comics anymore. It's been happening for a few years now, but I think the evolution is finally complete: the word "Comic-con" now is really code for "Pop Culture Con".

This is a product of the immense popularity of the comic book characters that we see in film adaptations, and the corresponding lack of popularity of the actual comic books they're based on. A movie like *Guardians of the Galaxy 2* grossed over $860 million at the box office. The latest *GotG* comic at the time I'm writing this did just over 23k in unit sales for $92k gross, and that's sell-in to retailers, not sell through to consumers. Even if we factor in other sales of the reading material through graphic novels and digital and whatever else, or the different price of the comic compared to a movie ticket, we are looking at somewhere in the neighborhood of 0.0005% of people who see the movie also reading the comics. *Guardians* is perhaps an extreme example but the numbers are just as brutal for every property.

So you can see it's a natural evolution that comic cons would evolve and change as they have gotten larger and more mainstream. Promoters need to cater to what people buying the tickets want to see. That means more Movie and TV stars, more autograph opportunities and photo ops, more pop culture merchandise, and less space devoted to dusty bins of comics. It also means massive rising costs for both the exhibitor and the consumer. If a visitor to a comic-con is out $500 for passes for him and his family, food, parking, and the couple photo ops he's prepaid for before even coming through the door, it doesn't leave a whole lot of extra cash to spend at my booth.

Now don't get me wrong; I love comic cons and love the enthusiasm that frequent con-goers have for the hobby. With very rare exceptions, I just don't look at them any longer as an opportunity to sell vintage comic books. As I said, I do the Toronto Comic Book Show every couple months. Out of the hundred or so shows I could attend locally, that's the only one that's all about comics and is filled with people who just want to dig through bins. I highly recommend it to all my customers and wish that there were more shows like it in other markets so I could get back on the road and meet more new faces who love vintage comics as much as I do!

Speaking of loving comics, I've operated a brick and mortar comic book since about 2002. I've worked in one since 1996. The crash of the mid to late '90s was my entrance to being a retailer. I never got to experience the boom part of 1988-93 other than as a fan but I do have firsthand knowledge of the bust, mostly in the form of one buyout after another of old store stock from that time. I think 2018 could be a trying time for retail comic book stores. I see too many of the same mistakes of the 1990s being repeated again.

I wrote above about the massive success of comic book movies compared to the paltry sales of new comic books. People love the characters and stories but aren't necessarily enticed to buy the books. Why is that? An inability on the part of publishers to turn those movie goers into comic readers is certainly part of the problem. A lack of progressive stores that are well stocked, well run, and inclusive is certainly also on the list. Then we have cannibalization of sales via digital sales or piracy; general economic malaise; a society that just doesn't read as much as it used to. All these and more can be listed as contributors.

But when we get right down to it I think the real problem comes down to execution from the publishers. If the stories aren't engaging, or in many cases just downright confusing, people don't buy them. It's as simple as that. I think what we have right now in comics is a real dearth of quality material, particularly from the supposed flagship shop in town, Marvel Comics. Legacy numbering, stops and starts, bloated events that go nowhere, artistic changes from issue to issue – it all adds up to a big mess that people have pretty clearly rejected.

My hope is that they can turn it around soon. Marvel has too big a piece of the pie and too many shops depend on a healthy Marvel to be healthy themselves. I think if we see a sustained drop off in sales we will see large scale store closures down the line. I am confident my shop can weather the storm and no doubt come out stronger in the end, but I worry for those who haven't made the effort to diversify yet.

On the positive side, DC has really been on fire with their output all year. I'm sure it's no coincidence that all my DC books are selling gangbusters while Marvel languishes. Sure they are using some '90s era gimmicks like foil covers and lenticular covers, but the stuff under the covers is what has people coming back to my shop and wanting to read more. Quality content always sells.

With new comic sales being relatively flat, this really has been the year of the vintage back issue comic for me. I wrote a couple years back in my market report that I was making a concerted effort to transform my store into more of a back issue store and the results continue to be positive. I have been selling quality back issue books like never before! The only thing that seems to slow us down is lack of supply. Hunting for collections is as competitive as I have ever seen it. Just the other day I made what I thought was an extremely strong offer on a low grade *Incredible Hulk* #181 that presented like a 2.5 but also had half a story page missing and was outbid by another buyer. That book by itself is crazy; it is by far my number one most requested back issue. I also field constant requests for Good Girl, all the most gruesome GA horror books, Timelys, any Nazi cover, key Batmans (all the villain keys are smoking hot), and of course the top 10 Silver Age Marvels. I buy those at full GPA or close to it, sit on them for 6 months or so and decide if I want to sell them then at a profit or not. The way those books appreciate I feel it's short sighted to ever sell for current market price unless you absolutely need the cash that day. *AF* #15, *ASM* #1, *Hulk* #1, *FF* #1, and *TOS* #39 in particular all command premiums over GPA or the *Guide* if you are patient.

DC Golden Age is red hot, particularly anything big logo. Incomplete copies have become the newest trend as people just want to own something or perhaps want to marry several incompletes together in to one franken-comic. I put a *Detective Comics* #35 on Instagram with a photo copied front cover, no back cover, and the entire first wrap missing and had it sold within a few hours for $1500. I think back on that now and the buyer got a steal, considering a 2.0 is about $20,000.

DC Silver Age continues to be an under-discussed section of the market amongst many more casual fans, but long time collectors know to snap them up whenever possible. I think the thing that most new collectors don't grasp right away is that 7.0 is high grade for a DC from Silver Ag1955-1961 or so. To contrast, you can go on the internet right now and buy an entire Silver Age Marvel set in 9.0 and up in probably 6 months. All it takes is money (lots and lots of it, mind you). They are not particularly rare. But try to put together a run of *Brave and the Bold* or *Showcase* in even 8.0. You could be waiting years for the right copies to come up. Never mind a title like *Strange Adventures* or *House of Mystery*. They don't have the glamour or recognition of a title like *Amazing Spider-Man*, but if you like to collect cool old stuff that is pretty rare and also won't necessarily break the bank, dive deep into the early DC Silver Age. They are so cool.

Silver Age titles like **House of Mystery** are very rare in high grade.

Bronze and Copper Age are strong and steady with not a whole lot of fluctuation these days. Pretty well all of the keys have been sussed out and pre-speculated on already. The big guns continue to be very popular, even if not exactly rare. *Hulk* #181, *ASM* #129, *Ghost Rider* #1, *Marvel Spotlight* #5, *House of Secrets* #92, and *G-S X-Men* #1 lead the way. I sold bunches of copies of each throughout the year and end it looking for more. Of the six, *HoS* #92 is by far the toughest to find. *Hulk* #180 is also a book very much on the rise.

ASM #300 was the book of the year in many parts, hitting over $2500 in CGC 9.8 for a newsstand copy. The book jumped over 50% in value in basically all grades after the Venom movie was announced, which to me is amazing as this is certainly a comic with plentiful supply. I know someone who bought 100 copies off the newsstand! Amazingly it continues to hold value in all grades as of right now but to me it's a hot potato. I know Venom is likely this generation's Wolverine, but I still say sell now.

Canadian newsstand variants continue to gain traction in areas outside Canada. I have boxes and boxes of these so they are certainly not rare, but like most other dealers buying comics every day in Canada, I can report that they are rare in NM. True 9.8s command a large premium, but it has to be a title that's already collected. No one (yet) is paying good money for copies of *Power Pack* or similar titles just because they are Canadian.

This year I've also been seeing a huge uptick in demand for Treasury Editions, particularly anything in FN or better. They sell briskly at over *Guide* in FN and heavy multiples in VF/NM or better. *Superman vs Spider-Man*, all the Batmans, and *Superman vs Muhammad Ali* are the most requested. Also high on many people's want lists are the Curtis/Marvel Mags from the '70s. These are a treasure trove of great artists and stories, and contain more than their fair share of first appearances too. Grab them when you see them in NM at *Guide* prices.

I sold more comics than I ever have before this year which means I must have also bought a lot of comics. The biggest and best collection by far was also the most bittersweet. A dear friend and longtime customer died suddenly in July 2017 and for me it was my first experience having to work with the estate of someone I considered a close friend. It was very difficult, but in the end I take solace in knowing that my friend's treasured comic collection is finding its way into the hands of other collectors who I hope will appreciate them as much as he did. This collection was extremely deep in DC Silver Age, containing long runs of every title, slabbed and raw, and more than a few highest graded examples. There were also large quantities of Golden Age, with an emphasis on ECs and Batmans. Some of the highlights included a *Detective* #30 CGC 5.5, #32 CGC 5.5, #73 CGC 8.0, *Superman* #3 6.5, *Batman* #4 CGC 3.5, #5 CGC 6.0, #9 CGC 6.0, *Crime SuspenStories* #22 CGC 7.0, *Flash* #105 CGC 7.5, and nearly every Silver Age key.

Other highlights for purchases from this year include 3 copies of *Amazing Spider-Man* #1 (CGC 2.0, 6.5, and a Pence copy 2.0 – I love Pence copies!), *Amazing Fantasy*

#15 CGC 2.0, *Avengers* #1 CBCS 8.5, *Avengers* #4 CGC 8.0 & 7.0, *Brave & the Bold* #28 CBCS 5.5, CGC 4.0 & 1.5, *Fantastic Four* #1 CGC 3.0, *Flash* #105 CGC 5.5, #123 CGC 8.0, *Giant-Size X-Men* #1 CGC 9.0 & 8.5, *Hulk* #1 CBCS 8.5, *Journey into Mystery* #83 CGC 3.5, 2.5, & 1.5, *Tales to Astonish* #27 CGC 5.0, and a whole lot more that you probably don't want to read about! Suffice to say I spent a lot on comics this year and am always looking to spend more.

More and more I have people coming in to my store asking for advice on what to collect and how to be successful with their collections. I will share with you the same advice I give all of them. Be patient. Whatever you are looking for it will almost always come around again, and sometimes a deal can be too good to be true (especially online). Collect what you are passionate about, and you will always come out ahead in the end. Educate yourself. You probably wouldn't buy a new fridge or car without doing a little bit of research first, so if you are planning on spending significant money on comics, treat them no differently. Most importantly, remember that collecting comics is supposed to be fun. I have fun doing this every day and there's no reason you can't too.

To close out this report I want to thank all of the Big B Comics Barrie customers who have helped make this my best year yet. Your enthusiasm and passion motivate me every day. I also want to thank my staff without whom none of this would be possible: Alice-ann Pilon, Jeremy Moore, Marshall Geddes, and Ian Pitkin – you're the best. And lastly a hearty thanks to Bob Overstreet and Mark Huesman, my fellow advisors, and all the others who help put together this essential tome. I use it every day and I hope you will too.

Lauren Sisselman
Comics Journalist

What a year it's been! We've seen some record breaking sales with *Amazing Fantasy* #15s, Wonder Woman keys have been strong, and even Archie books have continued to climb. But there's one group of books I'd like to talk about today. A niche in our hobby, but these books are very near and dear to my heart.

Dell Four Color Disney Princess comics (Specifically the early princesses): Snow White made her film debut in 1937 and was an instant hit. It was only natural that the first princess would get the comic treatment as well! In 1944 Snow White appeared in *Dell Four Color Comics* #49, which is a pretty under-valued book. With a beautiful Walt Kelly (Pogo) cover, this book deserves to be hotter than it is. I wouldn't say this specific comic is necessarily rare, but not many have come up for sale recently. The last graded sale for one of these books was in 2015, an 8.0 for $345. The highest graded copy (9.2) sold for $1,314.50. Raw copies pop up on eBay here and there, and tend to go for under $150. Snow White also appeared in *Dell Four Color* #382, which is a cheaper option if you're looking for an early Snow White comic. A 9.0 copy sold for $355 in September of 17, and on eBay they are very affordable.

The second princess in the Disney line up is Cinderella, who also saved the company from financial ruin. Copies of *Four Color* #272 featuring Cinderella won't cost you an arm and a leg. Most copies on eBay have sold for under $50. The last graded copy (6.5) sold in November of 2017 for $23. Even the reprint in *Four Color* #786 go for under $50.

Last, we have my personal favorite, Sleeping Beauty. There were a handful of Sleeping Beauty comics that had come out under the Dell line, including *Four Color*, *Giant*, and Gold Key. *Four Color* #973 hasn't had any recent graded sales, and on eBay you can get them for under $20. *Four Color* #984, focusing on the Fairies that cared for Sleeping Beauty, hasn't had any recent GPA updates, and on eBay they are all under $50.

It's fair to say that the Ducks and early Disney books are always hot, but the early Princess books are overlooked. I don't think this will last forever though, as more and more Disney fans are seeking out unusual and early examples of their favorite Princesses. These books have the potential to heat up, but it may take several years to get there.

Tony Starks
Comics Ina Flash!

Another year… And the back issue market continues along similar paths that it has the past several years. More blockbuster movies, more Netflix superhero series, more TV super hero series. For the most part, more interest in those characters first and key appearances. We also see old trends coming back, such as popular relaunches of a title or character (Kamandi and Mister Miracle for example) generating interest in the vintage, original books.

While movies and TV seem to drive first issues and first appearances, year after year we sell lots of average condition run issues of Silver and Bronze Age books. After years of being depressed, the market on this type of material stabilized several years ago. Probably because the huge oversupply of such books has subsided. Starting about 10 years ago, collectors were glutting the market by selling these run books trying to raise money for high grade keys. Many have given up - the really big books in high grade are simply too expensive for the vast majority of collectors. They would have to sell their house and kids - not their comics - to purchase a NM *Amazing Spider-Man* #1 ($90,000+). Many collectors have decided to keep their collections be satisfied with a VG for $4,000 instead. Also worth keeping in mind that this year's "run" book might be next years "must have" do to a movie or TV series. Say like *Black Lightning*, which has shot up in demand and price with the CW TV series debuting in Jan 2018.

Just a few examples of sales of average books: *Avengers* #28 GD @ $20, *Batman* #258 FN- @ $12, *Black Goliath* #5 NM @ $9, *Brave and the Bold* #93 VG+ @ $11, *Champions*

#1 FN @ $10, *Cowgirl Romance* #12 FN/VF @ $55, *DC Comics Presents* #1 NM- @ $30, *Fantastic Four* #111 VF- @ $20, *Fantastic Four Annual* #6 FN/VF @ $75, *Fantasy Masterpieces* #2 VG+ @ $8, *Invaders* #5 FN+ @ $8, *Kid Colt* #124 VG+ @ $8, *Mad House* #96 NM @ $12, *ManBat* #1 FN/VF @ $7, *Rima the Jungle Girl* #1 NM @$15, *Star Trek* #6 VG/FN @ $18, *Tales to Astonish* #61 GD @ $8, *Thor* #150 VF @ $32, *War is Hell* #9 NM- $40, *Wonder Woman* #103 VG- @ $50, and #104 VG @ $55. Taken over a year, sales like this don't set any records but do add up.

But it's not all inexpensive stuff here at Comics Ina Flash! We have some high end and better sales as well, often times professionally graded: *Amazing Spider-Man* #361 2nd Print CBCS 9.8 @ $150, *Archie Comics* #50 CBCS 4.5 @ $886, *Batman* #227 VG+ @ $100, #237 VF+ @ $100, *Black Panther* #8 CGC 9.8 @ $150, *Detective Comics* #151 CGC 6.0 (1st Pow Wow Smith) @ $425, *Detective Comics* #411 VG/FN @ $75, *Fantastic Four* #48 VG @ $200, #48 GD/VG @ $150, *Green Lantern* #17 VF/NM @ $160, *Inhumans* #1VF/NM @ $50, *Justice League of America* #1 coverless @ $90, *Mister Miracle* #1 CGC 9.4 @ $510, *Sensation Comics* #46 CGC 8.5 @ $1100, *Strange Adventures* #216 NM @ $100, *Tales of Suspense* #41 VG @ $150, *Tomb of Dracula* #10 CGC 7.5 @ $300, *Walking Dead* #19 CGC 9.8 @ $541, and *Wonder Woman* #1 (1987) CGC 9.8 @ $125.

Just a few books I see heating up of late. These are not books that no one wanted last year, but demand is notably up. *Amazing Spider-Man* #129, 300 and 361, *The Demon* #1, *House of Secrets* #92, and *Mister Miracle* #1.

EC comics seem to be on a lot more collectors want list than they were a few years ago. Any issue that we get in quickly sells. Riding along with the increase in demand for ECs is pre-Code Horror in general, especially books with classic (that is lurid, gruesome and/or titillating covers. Speaking of titillating covers, classic Good Girl covers are much sought after as well. Golden Age as well continues to show growth. Better Silver Age books now sell at prices that make Golden Age look like a better value to many collectors.

Overall, the market's health seems to continue to improve. It is still very driven by movies and TV, but you see solid interest and sales in other genres as well

WEST STEPHAN
CBCS

Once again we find ourselves in a very bullish comic book marketplace. Blue chip keys, classic covers and mainline Golden Age books are in very high demand. It is a very rare occurrence to see any of these books sell at *Guide*, as they often sell for many multiples of *Guide*! For example, Heritage just sold a *Marvel Mystery Comics* #30 CBCS 7.5 for $5258 (2016 *Overstreet Guide* value is $3154). They also sold a *Detective Comics* #140 CBCS 3.0 for $4063 (2016 *Overstreet Guide* value is $2700).

World War II covers from all publishers are very sought after. Schomburg is the king here, but if you have a 1940s cover WWII cover, it will sell at or above *Guide* levels. Risque covers, such as *Fight Comics* #35, *Sunny* #11 and *Dogface Dooley* #5, are also in high demand due to their racy cover content. Many of these have sold for 5-10 times *Guide* or more. A GD/VG copy of *Sunny* #11 sold for $1000 (2016 *Overstreet Guide* value is $218).

Silver Age keys are always quick sellers. *Brave & the Bold* #28 took a nice jump, with the movie expecting to increase demand. A CBCS 6.0 copy sold for $8365 (2016 *Overstreet Guide* value is $5600). A CBCS 2.0 copy of *Showcase* #4 sold for $9560 (2016 *Overstreet Guide* value is $6000). Someone submitted a *Tales of Suspense* #39 that got a 9.6 with White pages. It's was the nicest, freshest copy I've ever seen! Equally impressive was the CBCS 9.8 copy of *Silver Surfer* #1 we graded, it was virtually flawless!

***Suspense Comics** #3 was an exciting submission for the office of CBCS.*

We also had in influx of obscure comic books being sent in for certification, some of which I have never seen in person. We are also getting a very high volume of foreign comic books. These are hard to decipher some times, but they are very fun to look through! It is very interesting to see how different countries depict American comic books.

By far, the most exciting submission for me personally was the *Suspense Comics* #3 Edgar Church/Mile High copy! I think everyone in the Golden Age collecting community was in shock when it surfaced. For decades, this previously "lost" Mile High was debated as to whether or not it actually existed at all! It is not listed on the original 1977 list made by Chuck Rozanski, founder & original seller of the collection. Many times through the years Chuck was asked if the book existed and he could not remember. That's not surprising, as back in 1977 the *Overstreet* value of the book was about five bucks & hardly worth remembering. After being graded 9.2 with White Pages by CBCS, it sold through Heritage at a record price of $262,900, the highest price ever paid for a non-superhero Golden Age comic book.

In 2018, with more movies, Netflix and TV shows based around comic books, I expect the bullish market to continue. Thank you Mr. Bob Overstreet, J.C. Vaughn, Mark Huesman & all the other contributors who dedicate their time and expertise to create this wonderful tool for collectors, the *Overstreet Price Guide*!

Al Stoltz
Basement Comics

What a long year with many miles on the road again travelling to comic conventions across the country, and it gets tougher every year as I get older. I am not the oldest comic dealer out there at 55 years old, but the seven day a week pace I keep and miles of driving and crappy rest stop food does wear on me more and more these days. I had a chance to set up at C2E2, NYCC, Baltimore Comic Con, Heroes Con, Mega Con and many more shows including my favorite local shows run by Fred Edison's Clandestine Shows and Ricky from First State Comic Cons and lastly Derek Woywood's Philly one day show that seems to have been taking place for centuries now. I attended SDCC this year and it has been at least five years or so since I stepped into that building....what a complete madhouse that is!

Set up is usually with two booth spaces, but every now and then we book just one. Wedging 10 tons of junk into a 5 ton space seems to be getting easier, and those who stop by to chat or buy always like that we overstock the booth with a little of everything. We really find lots of non-comic stuff these days I like and add it to the online stores we maintain on eBay, Amazon and our own Web page Vintagebasementcomics.com. We have purchased some great vintage toys from the 1950s and 1960s that came from a closed out store from long ago and we have great new old-stock character items and other standard toys that are like new. We also fell into a lot of art that was reasonable to buy and I liked it so we just keep posting it online as fast as we buy it. A great Pay Boyette Charlton painting was among one of the newer purchases we made and I am sure it will not last long out there on the market.

Show sales were strong but as you know it's blah, blah, blah.....Keys....secondary keys and anything that can be tied to a movie or hint of a movie coming out. The day traders call us and pour over our eBay store looking for those books while mostly ignoring the zillions of other items because it's not in a movie and would be stupid to slab and sell for more.

We were able to buy many keys and cool things this year but a chance buy with my best friend Jeff Weaver was a winner! It was an original owner Marvel collection with most of the runs complete and stretching to the late 2000s. All the Key issues and high grade books were pressed by me at Basement Comics Pressing and were sold through ComicLink for mostly above GPA listed sale prices. It stuns me as people pay more and more month after month and don't seem to notice that these items pour in regularly as opposed to early 1930s books that almost never show up..... but let's stay with a theme here – they are not in a movie so they are not sought after. We have many books that were bought and just set to the side last year that will eventually all get graded and shipped off mostly to an auction house or given a one shot listing online at what we will feel is market projected price.

Show crowds are generally huge but the amount of true comic buyers at times is a fraction of people wandering around looking at the other offerings at the show. Shows like SDCC and NYCC can be tough to get in and old time comic buyers gave up trying to fight the wave of humanity in the room. After decades of doing shows it just seems like fun to reconnect with dealers you see only occasionally and have stuck it out as long as you have. I can add that I will miss John Verzyl, who recently passed away, wandering around the show floors. His passion for comics and food made him one of my favorite comic dealers and I had maybe one of the funniest dinners of my life while attending C2E2 a few years ago. His loss to the comic world and his depth of knowledge will not be replaced. My third Fanzine that will now be pushed to be released at NYCC 2018 will focus on the great comic legend John Verzyl and hopefully will be a fun comic nostalgia read.

Basement Comics Pressing is now four years old and we have grown into a readily accepted option for pressing needs. We handle more books than ever per month and added even more equipment to keep up and try to stay in the 3 week and out the door mode! We are keeping prices low and turn around times in the 2-4 week range we see to make customers happy! A recent submitter was stunned and pleased with his *Teenage Mutant Ninja Turtles* #1 First Print that received a stunning 9.8 after passing through our shop. This part of the business now keeps me busy and out of the front office nearly all day. It was interesting and odd to add a service component to my company, but it really has worked out and has been a great addition to the Basement Comics business.

We started a Youtube channel called Basement Comics and it consists of interviews I mostly do at shows of the dealers I can convince to let me film them and occasionally some stores I pop into in my travels. We have maybe a dozen interviews up and I liked the idea of doing them in a manner that makes them like an old time Fanzine article.... nostalgia creeps up on me as I age yet again.

Doug Sulipa
Doug Sulipa's Comic World

About seven years ago, I switched my main focus to providing the comics the collectors demanded most, in the time period when they at their peak demand, so once again 2017 continued to be yet another blockbuster year in sales for us. At time of this writing, I am 61 years old, thus Silver Age, Bronze Age and Golden Age comics, along with oddball comics remain my personal favorites, and the main comics I sold from 1971-2010, yet these are no longer what the vast majority of collectors seek out. The continued boom of comics, sci-fi & related movies, TV shows and other media have transformed the marketplace into something new and yet hard to pinpoint. If we assume there are for example about 200,000 collectors actively currently buying back issue comics, I would estimate: (a) less than 1% will buy a comic valued at $1000 or more in 2018, and (b) less than 10% will buy a comic valued at $200 or more in 2018. Yes, everyone likes to dream about owning the Top-100 comics of the Golden, Silver and Bronze Ages. We are all dazzled and amazed by the continued record prices on the most valuable comics. But, then the 90% majority of collectors return to reality and routinely buy comics in the $1.00 to $50.00 price range, and occasionally splurge to buy a comic in the $51 to $200 range. This has made Copper Age and Modern Age comics the new bestsellers in back issue comics. They have overtaken Bronze Age comics which have had a hold on the market for most of the last decade. The current values of Bronze Age comics, especially in higher grades, have pushed the majority of the keys out the weekly budgets of the average collector. Since demand for Copper Age and Modern Age comics have been so much on the rise, I have had 1000's of key issue comics of the era graded by CGC, along with the more affordable Bronze Age keys, which still have a strong following. I have never encountered such huge demand and sales for a select group of comics as I have had for these, in my entire career as a dealer since 1971. Bronze, Copper and Modern sales (CGC and raw) now make up about 85% of my sales. Collectors love to speculate on under-valued and over-looked minor key issues, with *Guide* values in the $3 to $20 range for 9.2 copies, thus they are ready, able and highly motivated to also buy high grade CGC copies of same in the $50 to $200 price range. Check out my notable CGC sales at the end of this article for many samples.

I still sell plenty of Silver Age, Bronze Age comics (raw - non CGC graded) from every known publisher; Marvel and DC always lead the way, but since I have perhaps the world's biggest selection of many of the less collected publishers, I always sell 1000's of comics and oddball format items from 1950s through to about 2010 that other dealers do not bother to carry: ACG, Alternatives, Archie, Atlas/Seaboard, Captain Canuck, Cartoon & Humor comics, *CARtoons & Hot Rod CARtoons* Mags, Charlton, *Classics Illustrated*, Comic Digests, Comic Magazines/Fanzines, Dell, Fawcett, French & Foreign comics, Gold Key, Harvey, Horror, King, Love comics, Parody Mags (*Mad, Cracked, Sick*), Personality, Religious comics, Sci-Fi, Skywald, Teenage comics, Tower, Treasuries, UK British comics, Underground, War Comics, Warren mags, Western Comics, and Whitman. Most of these collectors are NOT looking for high grade investment quality copies. They want mostly presentable copies to fill in their collections, or lower grade cheaper reading copies.

This year I experimented by sending in hundreds of items to get CGC graded, items that most other sellers do not bother with, and many in fact only have a few copies listed in the CGC Census. This included Canadian variants, Atlas/Seaboard, comic magazines, selected Gold Key #1s of the 1960s (mostly in 7.0 to 8.5 grade range), *Star Trek* (Gold Key), *Turok* (Gold Key), Treasuries (CBCS Graded) and Whitman variants of DC Comics. Based on many years of selling raw comics, I expected these would eventually sell, but did not expect immediate success with all these items in the first month. Most buyers bought multiple items at once, as many were just waiting for nice higher graded copies to finally surface.

Canadian Newsstand Cover Price Variants: These Canadian variants (type 1a newsstand edition with single price on cover; printed simultaneously on the same presses as the standard USA editions), have been steadily growing in demand for nearly 20 years.These Variants Include; Archie comics & digests (Giants from late 1950s thru mid 1960s with 35 cent cover prices; and 9/1982-4/1997 with digests to 12/1997), Alternative Comics (many uncharted), Charlton (2/1983-8/1984), *Cracked* magazine (uncharted), DC (all newsstand comics, magazines and digests from 10/1982-9/1988), Dell (6/1956-1-2/1961 = 15 cent variant; back cover variants with strips in place of ads = possibly Canadian; Giants with 30-35 cent cover prices = confirmed Canadian), Gold Key / Whitman (5-8/1968, 3/1972-4/1973, 12/1977-3/1978, 1-7/1984), Harvey (1959-3/1974 Giants with 35 cent cover prices), Hamilton Pub (*Vampirella* #113 from 1988 = USA editions list for $550 in *Overstreet* = highest priced Canadian variant?), *Mad* (some 1964 & 7/1978-7/1979), Marvel; Canadian newsstand variant cover price editions (all newsstand comics, magazines, Treasuries, and digests from 10/1982-08/1986; Marvel Mass Market Paperbacks with Canadian variants, some with the Canadian flag on cover; *Spectacular Spider-Man* #1 magazine from 1968; Marvel 1960s Annuals with blank back cover, blank inside front and blank inside back cover), Modern Publishing (1983 only? = *Voltron* Canadian variants exist); Warren (3/1977-3/1983); Whitman variants of the Gold Key comics (11/1971 thru 4/1980; Canadian newsstand variant cover price issues (4-8/1968 with 15 cent prices, 3/1972-4/1973 with 20 cent prices; 12/1977-3/1978 with reverse 30 cent prices); Canadian variants of Whitman comics (75 cent cover price issues of 1984 Whitman comics that are 60 cents in USA; these are rare in High Grade, with 9.2 copies worth $50 or more each).

Finally, a price guide for variants exists: *The 2018 Price Guide for 1980's Marvel & DC Newsstand Canadian Cover Price Variants (Type 1A)* created by Benjamin Noble, with input from myself, Ben Noble, Jon McClure (writer of the premier and definitive article on variants in *Overstreet Guide* #40), Paul Clairmont (PNJ Comics), Bill Alexander and Angelo Virone. It is free online at our website or from Gemstone's site *Scoop* indirectly through this address http://scoop.previewsworld.com or more directly at: https://rarecomics.wordpress.com/. Perhaps as the market continues to grow, all the other publisher variants can slowly also be added in. This guide was created by a group of dedicated people who want to provide a source of info to go to, fulfilling a bit of a void in the marketplace. About 75% of the 1980s Marvel and DC Canadian variants have an *Overstreet Guide* 9.2 value of $3.00 to $5.00, but are quite scarce in VF/NM or better, thus even the slowest selling titles have a minimum value of $10.00 for a strictly graded 9.2 example. Marvel and DC Canadian variants have an *Overstreet Guide* 9.2 value of $10.00 or higher, and are valued at about 150% on average (as a stable starting point) of the current market value of a standard Direct edition.

Magazines (CGC Graded Sales in 2017): *Bizarre Adventures* #27 X-Men 1981 B&W Marvel Mag Pérez, Gulacy,

Buscema CGC 9.8 = $128.20; *Captain Britain* (1970s UK Marvel) #17,22,25 (Captain America team-up vs Red Skull storyline Low Print CGC NMMT 9.8 = $199.00 each); *Creepy* #144 CGC 9.8 $175.

Deadly Hands Of Kung Fu #1 Starlin, Shang-Chi 1974 Bruce Lee, Neal Adams CGC 9.8 = $600.30; #1 CGC 9.8 = $575.00; #2 first origin Shang-Chi 1974 Adams, Starlin 9.8= $231.35; #3 Shang-Chi 1974 Gulacy, Adams 9.8 = $222.75; #4 David Carradine, Adams Fu Manchu 1974 Shang-Chi 9.6 = $136.75; #5 1st Manchurian 1974 Shang-Chi Gulacy, Kirby 9.6 = $136.75; #7 Bruce Lee 1974 Shang-Chi, Fu Manchu, Pérez NM+ 9.6 = $136.75; #7 9.4 = $102.35; #11 Billy Jack Adams 1975 Shang-Chi Pérez CGC 9.6 = $128.15; #15 Iron Fist 1975 Shang Chi, Cardy, Starlin, Gulacy 9.6 = $128.15; #27 Swordquest 1976 White Tiger Dezuniga 9.8 = $188.35; Annual #1 Fu Manchu 1974 Shang-Chi, Iron Fist 9.8 = $214.15.

Dracula Lives #1 9.0 $149; #5 Bram Stoker adaptation, Colan 1974 CGC 9.6 = $136.75; CGC NM 9.4 = $102.35; #10 1st Lilith solo 1975 Neal Adams, Dezuniga, Giordano CGC 9.6 = $145.35; *Dracula Lives Annual* #1 Marvel B&W Mag Neal Adams, Marcos, Buscema, CGC NM/MT 9.8 = $257.15. *Haunt Of Horror* #1 Marvel Magazine 1974 Werewolf Skull, Disch, Heath, CGC NM+ 9.6 = $159; #1 9.4 = $110.95; *Heavy Metal* #1 Moebius, Druillet, Bode, Corben, Hildebrandt, 1977 Scarce CGC 9.8 = $429.15; *Kull and The Barbarians* #1 Adams, Kane, Wood, Severin, 1975 9.8 = $179; 9.8 = $153.95; #1 9.6 = $93.75; *Legion Of Monsters* #1 Origin 1st Manphibian 1975 Marvel B&W Adams 9.6 = $257.15; #1 9.4 = $171.15; *Marvel Preview* #1 Man-Gods From Beyond 1975 Mag Neal Adams, Alex Nino, CGC NM+ 9.6 $179; #2 1st Origin Punisher, 1st Dominic Fortune 9.6 = $386.15; #2 9.4= $300.15; #8 Legion Of Monsters 1976 Morbius, Blade, Morrow, Ploog 9.8 = $343.15; 9.8 = $310; #8 9.6 =$205.55; #10 Thor The Mighty 1977 Jim Starlin, Barr, Hercules 9.8 = $162.55; #12 Haunt Of Horror, Lilith 1977 Dracula, Kaluta, Pérez 9.8 = $189.

Monsters Unleashed #1 Marvel 1973 Werewolf, Robert Bloch, Solomon Kane 9.6 = $257.15(2); #1 9.4= $153.95; #2 Frankenstein Marvel 1973 Boris, Brunner, Karloff 9.6 = $145.35; #3 Origin Man-Thing 1973 Son of Satan preview, Adams 9.6 = $145.35; #4 CGC 9.8 $239; #4 9.4 = $93.75; #5 Man-Thing, Frankenstein 1974 Werewolf; #5 CGC 9.8 $229; 9.8 = $196.95; #5 9.4 = $93.75; #6 9.6 = $135.75; #7 Werewolf By Night 1974 Frankenstein, Williamson 9.4 = $93.75; #7 9.6 = $135.75; #9 CGC 9.8 $229; #10 Origin 2nd Tigra, Were-Woman, 1975 Frankenstein 9.4 = $129; #11 CGC 9.8 $219; #11 9.4 = $93.75; *Monsters Unleashed Annual* #1 Werewolf, Man-Thing 1975 Neal Adams 9.4 = $102.35.

Pizzazz #1 Marvel Magazine 1977 Star Wars, Tarzan comics, KISS rare CGC NM/MT 9.8 = $299; *Space 1999* #1 Charlton B&W Magazine 1975, Gray Morrow, 9.8 = $214.15; *Spirit Special* #nn Warren, Corben, Eisner, 1975 Mail Only 1500 Printed CGC 9.0 $249.00; *Star Wars Weekly* (UK British Marvel Comic 1977-1978) #1 with rare bonus CGC NM/MT 9.8 = $601.15; #2 with rare bonus CGC NM/MT 9.8 = $343.15.

Tales Of The Zombie #1 1973 Mag, Origin/1st Simon Garth, Boris 9.2 = $153.95; #2 2nd Brother Voodoo & Simon Garth, 1973 Boris #2 CGC 9.8 $239; #2 9.6 = $136.75; #2 9.6 = $145.35; #2 9.4 = $102.35; #3 Simon Garth, 1974 Boris Vallejo 9.8 = $196.95; #3 CGC 9.8 $229; #3 9.6 = $136.75; #4 CGC 9.8 $229; #9 9.8 = $196.95; *Unknown Worlds of Science Fiction Special* #1 Marvel Fred Brown, Nino CGC NM+ 9.6 = $128.15; *Vampire Tales* #1 1973 Origin & 1st Morbius series 9.6 = $300.15; #1 9.4 = $214.15(2 copies); #3 second Satana, 1st Morbius cover, 1974, Maroto, Derleth #3 CGC 9.8 $249; #3 9.6= $162.55; #3 9.4 = $110.95; #4 Morbius true 1st Lilith 4/1974 Boris Vallejo #4 CGC 9.8 $229; #4 9.2 = $85.15; #5 origin Morbius, 1974, Barsac, Robert Bloch, Count Yorga #5 CGC 9.8 $249; #5 9.4 = $102.35; #8 1974 Morbius, 1st Blade solo story 9.6= $193.50; #8 NM 9.4 = $145.35.

Star Trek (Gold Key Comics) CGC Graded Sales: *Star Trek* #29 NM 9.4 = $199; #29 9.2 = $149; #32 9.4 $159; #34 9.2 $109; #35 9.4 = $159; #39 9.4 $159; #40 9.6 $209 (2 copies); #41 9.2 $99; #42 9.6 = $199; #42 9.4 $145; #44 9.4 $140; #45 9.4 $145; #46 9.6 = $199; #50 9.6 = $199; #51 9.6 = $199; #53 9.6 $199; #55 9.4 $145; #58 9.4 $145; #61 NM- 9.2 $99.

Star Wars (1977 Marvel Series; all 1st Prints unless noted) Graded Sales: *Star Wars* #1 1st print CGC 9.6 NM+ $699; #1 reprint 9.4 $109; #2 9.8 $249 (2 copies); #2 9.6 $149; #2 9.4 $109; #3 CGC 9.8 $249; #3 9.6 $149; #3 9.6 $139; #4 9.8 $249; #4 9.6 $149; #6 9.8 $199; #6 9.6 $99; #8 9.8 $193; #9 9.8 $169; #10 9.8 $159; #11 9.8 $112; #49 9.8 $179; #49 9.6 $109; #68 re-intro Boba Fett classic cover story CGC 9.6 = $139 (3 copies); and *Star Wars Annual* #2 9.8 $139.

Treasury-Size Comics Graded by CBCS - Sales in 2017: *All New Collector's Edition* #C-56 Superman Vs. Muhammad Ali 1978 1st Print Neal Adams (CBCS 9.8 $899; 9.6 $625; 9.4 $499); *DC Special Series* #27 Batman Vs. Incredible Hulk 1981 (CBCS 9.6 $249; 9.2 $169); *Famous First Edition* (#F-5 *Batman* #1 1975 CBCS 9.0 = $107) (#F-6 *Wonder Woman* #1 1975 CBCS 9.4 = $170) (#C-30 *Sensation* #1 1974 CBCS 9.2 = $125); *Limited Collector's Edition* #37 Batman CBCS 8.0 $69; *Limited Collectors Edition* #C-51 Talia, Ra's Al Ghul 1977 Neal Adams CBCS 9.6 $179; *Marvel Special Spectacular Spider-Man* #1 Sinister Six 1975 Treasury CBCS 9.8 $299; *Marvel Treasury* #1 Spectacular Spider-Man 1974; CBCS 9.6 $349 = 2 Copies; 9.2 $169)(#4 Conan The Barbarian 1975 Barry Windsor Smith CBCS 9.6 $175; 9.0 $75)(#5 Incredible Hulk 1975 Kirby CBCS 9.4 $119)(#6 Doctor Strange 1975 Baron Mordo, Brunner, Ditko CBCS 9.4 $119; 9.4 $115)(#7 Mighty Avengers 1975 Vision Ultron CBCS 9.4 $119)(#25 Hulk Vs. Spider-Man CBCS 9.6 $149); *Marvel Special Edition Featuring Star Wars* #1 1977 (CBCS 9.6 $179; 9.6 $159 = 2 Copies; 9.2 $89)(#2 1978 CBCS 9.6 $159); *Marvel Treasury Special 2001: A Space Odyssey* #1 Movie Jack Kirby CBCS 9.6 $139; *Special Collector's Edition Featuring Savage Fists Of Kung-Fu* #1 (1975) CBCS 9.6 $129.00; *Superman Vs. The Amazing Spider-Man* #1 1976 Andru, Neal Adams (CBCS

9.8 $799 = 2 Copies; 9.6 $499 = 2 Copies; 9.4 $359; 9.2 $249; 9.2 $225; 8.5 $169).

Whitman Variants of DC Comics - CGC Graded Sales in 2017: *Action Comics* #481 NM 9.4 = $89; #482 NM- 9.2 = $75; #483 VF/NM 9.0 = $59; #490 NM+ 9.6 = $99; #491 CGC 9.6 = $99; #492 9.6 = $99; *Brave and The Bold* #145 NM 9.4 = $79; #146 NM+ 9.6 = $99; #147 NM+ 9.6 = $99; #165 VF/NM 9.0 = $59; *DC Comics Presents* #3 9.0 = $69; *Justice League of America* #176 9.0 = $69; *Legion of Super-Heroes* #266 9.6 = $119; *New Adventures of Superboy* #5 9.4 = $99; *Superboy & The Legion* #244 9.4 = $89; *Superman* #330 9.6 = $99; #331 9.6 = $109; #332 9.6 = $99; and #345 9.2 = $84.

Michael Tierney
Collector's Edition
& The Comic Book Store

A coin dealer considering a change of hobbies recently lamented about how coins were the wrong hobby for investors because so much of the values for Numismatics are based on silver coins. His logic was that comics could never crash in value simply because the price of silver dropped.

Unfortunately, the comic industry is indeed subject to crashes -- especially with new comic sales. I've experienced the black-and-white boom and bust of the Eighties, the speculation boom and bust of the Nineties, and many other crashes that followed a boom.

The crash of 2017 came without a preceding boom. This year had dismal new comics sales as DC pushed firmly to the #1 spot atop the publisher sales chart, steadying their sales with bright spots like Batman's marriage proposal and subsequent engagement to Catwoman, plus a strong performance from the Batman spinoff event of *Dark Nights: Metal*. Meanwhile, Marvel Comics plummeted to a lower line average than I've ever seen. While Marvel is making far more titles per month than they did during my first business year in 1982, the overall average sold per Marvel title dropped so low that it's unprecedented in my experience.

Some odd patterns have manifested across the decades, like the Punisher having averaged over 50 copies per store when it was an All-Ages title and now only selling a combined dozen copies between both stores as a Mature Readers title -- for the peak month of the year. In my particular market, younger and older readers alike seem to prefer their tough as nails heroes without an excess of guts and grit.

But the movement of Marvel's entire line into an Older Teen rating was not the main factor as to why Marvel's Super Hero line has been following a spectacular crash-dive on the sales charts.

The bigger factor cited by customers was Marvel's Social Justice Warriors initiative, which replaced the heart of their most entrenched characters with new characters that combined different ethnicities, sex, and age. Sales dropped steadily throughout the duration of this initiative, and the reason was painfully obvious.

Thirty-Five years of dealing with the public has taught me that you have to be very careful when dealing with the subjects of politics or religion, and no one ever wants to hear about someone else's sexual preferences. Marvel infused all three across their entire core.

It's not that customers are against change.

The latest incarnation of Ms. Marvel as a Middle Eastern Muslim girl performed well as a new character. Because the mantle of Marvel has changed not only publishers, but also feature characters multiple times in the Captain and Ms titles, there is no longer is a single accepted icon.

When the mantle of the Mighty Thor was taken over by a cancer terminal Jane Foster, it benefitted from great art and story -- but also came with a 'temporary caveat' in the question of her impending doom. Customers still wanted Odinson back as Thor, had asked constantly for updates about his return. I told them wait for the next *Thor* movie -- Marvel always returns the characters back to normal by the time of a new movie's release. Then they didn't, which frustrated so many customers who felt that the Jane Foster storyline had already far exceeded the expiration of expectation -- much in the same way that, by the time the Red Hulk's identity was finally revealed after three years, no one cared.

New customers wanted to continue the adventures of the characters they'd discovered in the movies, but couldn't. Captain America was either the Falcon working a part-time job, or an evil incarnation of Steve Rogers. Hawkeye is a woman. Wolverine was either a young girl or an Old Man. Iron Man had two titles, one with the *Infamous Iron Man* role filled by the villain Doctor Doom, and the *Invincible Iron Man* title with a fifteen-year old black girl -- both of which combined to sell less than Tony Stark did alone. The combined sales of the She-Hulk with the She dropped from her title, and the self-congratulatory *Totally Awesome Hulk* featuring Amedeus Cho were far, far less than Bruce Banner's *Hulk*.

The reaction of the shoppers? "You've got to be kidding! You're joking, right?" These were oft repeated quotes.

With their "All New All Different" initiative Marvel certainly tried to do many new and different new things -- which never have a very high rate of success. The problem was that they did it as a replacement for their entire core line. If they had introduced all these new characters in new titles, their success rate would not have been a bad ratio. But by abandoning the core of characters who made the movies so successful, Marvel ensured a downward spiral of failing and flailing sales. The same thing happened a few years back when DC gave readers the Summer of Filler with *Flashpoint*, and even worse was the sales disaster known as *Convergence*.

Like DC once did, Marvel forgot the lesson of giving the customers what they want.

And anyone wanting the Fantastic Four was just flat out of luck as Marvel continued to allow the franchise to lie fallow. The Fantastic Four wasn't even getting cameo appearances in Marvel's crossover event: *Secret Empire*. Marvel did a good job by shipping this event book on schedule, which maintained sales levels throughout the run, but those levels were only a third of the previous year's *Civil War II* event. *Secret Empire* crossovers and spinoffs sold very, very little.

Marvel did finally move away from the constant relaunches and returned to Legacy numbering. But they killed the relaunch by making the variant Lenticular covers available only to retailers who first ordered two to three times their average sales of the regular covers first. Retailers across America, myself included, ignored the incentives. Some called it a boycott, but I had turned in my orders before that. It made no sense to buy an abundance of stock that wouldn't sell -- just to have an opportunity to buy even more excess product which might be allocated.

My cheap bins have enough stock already, which includes the last set of lenticular Future's End covers from DC, despite having ordered low on them. With no one expressing any interest at all in this new Marvel set, it was an easy pass.

The launch with the one-shot *Marvel Legacy* #1, which consisted of previews from the upcoming Legacy books, was best described by one customer who asked: "Didn't they use to give these away as a Free Comic Book Day book?" I ordered really, really light -- and still have unsold copies.

The disconnect between Marvel and retailers was illustrated in reports about how during the Marvel breakfast for retailers at New York ComicCon, an unidentified retailer complained to the Marvel panel about the failure of the Legacy relaunch in his store, and at first received applause from some retailers, but then others booed. Given the spike in failed comic books stores in 2017, I had to wonder if the boos were a reaction similar to when battered wives defend their abusers -- battered retailers syndrome? Either that or there is a distinct schism where their markets are completely different from mine and others. Marvel's reaction? Breakfast was over early. They then announced that the SJW initiative would continue unabated in 2018, with an emphasis on content for the LBGT community.

Speaking strictly for my market, demand continued to decline during and after the Legacy sales initiative in October. Not a single person inquired about the incentive Lenticular covers. No one cared and only a handful of the regular issues sold out. I dodged taking a bath in red ink -- which was especially important after a September which dipped to a seventeen-year low for both locations.

DC's **Dark Nights** crossover was a bright spot for sales.

It would have been a lot worse except the bright spot of DC's *Dark Nights*, a Batman crossover event that started in September and completely dominated the month of October. What made the *Dark Nights* so much more effective than the previous *Flashpoint* or *Convergence* events is that DC did not stop their normal continuity and replace it with short term events. *Dark Nights* ran concurrently with the established continuity, and the end result was that DC widened their sales lead over Marvel to double digits with a 15% margin.

Still, October sales of new comics were my worst since 1990! That shocking statistic indicates how DC's sales bump was the tiniest of molehills when compared to top sellers of years past. The Death of Superman sold 2,000 copies of *Superman* #75, and I'd worried that I might have lost my mind with that order. They all sold within two hours, except for one box that had to be recovered from the delivery driver's home. Many of those copies introduced new readers who still shop with me today.

The fact that Marvel regularly solicits for 1 in 2,000 variants is an example of the schism between retailer demographics that I referenced earlier. Stores in larger metropolitan areas often have more people living in a five mile radius of their store than live in the whole of Arkansas. The metropolitan area of Memphis, Tennessee has more people than the entire state of Arkansas. Plus, the only U.S. territory with lower earnings per capita is the territory of Puerto Rico. So trends that might be obscured in the crowds of bigger markets are immediately distinct in mine.

One of those trends is the certainty that I will never again see a book sell in quantities like *Superman* #75. This is because of the current sales model that publishers follow. With a single distributor, publishers have begun guarding actual information until the actual release and instead feed retailers a steady diet of hyperbole. When Wolverine lost his adamantium, it was hinted that he might get it back in multiple solicitations. Fortunately I didn't bite, because none of those books contained anything special. *Wolverine* Volume 2 #45 is where he finally returned to normal, and was a complete surprise. I ended up missing out on a whole lot of sales and never had a chance to cultivate new readers with that event. Despite the intentionally stunted print run, this issue rarely sells as a back issue.

Another example of similar results from DC was their Death of the Family Batman event. The original Death in the Family featured the death of the Jason Todd Robin, and was a monster seller for DC. The entire four-issue series in *Batman* #426 through #429 has maintained value and demand across the intervening decades. In the more recent Death in the Family, the Damian version of Robin died immediately after the event was over, in issue #8 of the soon to be cancelled *Batman Inc.* spinoff. That was another example of a book that would have sold monster numbers if retailers had a clue. Second printings did ship soon after, but received a lackluster response. Perhaps DC banked on customers instead turning to digital copies, but this is a collectables hobby, and no customer I've ever talked with took that route. And there has never been any back issue demand for that book, either. Yet another example of how frustrating fans can have negative long term results.

Marvel sales free-fall intensified in November, with DC widening the gap to a 40% lead. There have been short spells where DC outsold Marvel in the past, the most recent being last year's DC Rebirth relaunch, but none have been by such wide margins. This was a sea change, where Marvel's ebbing sales lacked only a declaration by James Earl Jones, in his most menacing Darth Vader voice, about how complete their failure was.

Apparently Marvel's publisher heard the echo of Darth Vader's words when it was announced in November that Axel Alonso was out as the Editor-in-Chief, and C. B. Cebulski was in.

Independent comic sales were overall steady, with no major new breakout titles, but a lot of reliable titles pounding out the most effective sales formula of them all: good stories with good art. Unfortunately some independent publishers made the same mistakes that Marvel is making and DC once made.

Magnus, Robot Fighter was reinvented as a woman, and another classic Gold Key character, Turok, was also revamped -- once again. In the mini-series *Sovereigns* Magnus looked like he was still a guy, but had robotic attachments. None of these sold at either store. When Jim Shooter and Valiant relaunched the Gold Key characters back in the Nineties, he stayed faithful to the established formulas and coupled them with solid stories. They sold by the hundreds. When Shooter left, the heroes were morphed into the dysfunctional, anti-hero mold that is so popular with writers today, but not my customers. Sales dropped steadily until there were none.

The mishmashes didn't stop there. Robert E. Howard's Kull the Barbarian was reinvented as a time traveling warrior in yet another example of a complete sales fail. *Kull the Eternal* sold to a single person between both of my stores.

The sad thing about all this is that it used to be Hollywood that always tried to reinvent the comic characters and ended up with epic failures. Nowadays comics are doing well in the movies which stay faithful to the original comics, and the current comics are the ones doing the reinventing. The resulting failures remain the same. Whenever you reinvent the wheel you get a square, and that's hard to roll with. An axel will end up hitting the road (Marvel pun intended).

When customers can't find what they want on the new comics racks, they turn to vintage inventory. Key DC sales showed a lot of influence from the *Justice League* movie. *Aquaman* #1 sold in GD- for $130 and #2 in GD+ for $42. *Atom* #1 for $225 in VG+.

One interesting trend that I've noticed on eBay is how Batman auctions for identical copies increase in bidding as day progresses into night. Like the character, Batman fans come out at night. Batman not only ruled the night and new comics sales in 2017, but back issues sales as well. *Batman* (v1) #56 in GD- for $95; #107 in GD+ for $75; #114 in VG for $125; #117 in VG- for $110; #128 in VG- for $75; #129 (Robin's origin retold) in VG+ for $135; #136 in VG+ for $120; #181 in GD for $50; #189 in VG+ for $65; #200 in FN+ for $50; #208 in VF- for $50; and the Volume 2 #1 in VF/NM for $110 were just a few examples. *Detective Comics* with Batman #297 (last 10 cent issue) in FN for $80. *Famous First Edition* C-26 with *Action Comics* #1 reprint in VF+ for $50. *Flash* (v1) #109 (2nd appearance Mirror Master) in VG- for $150; and #123 (1st mention Earth 2) in GD+ for $250. *Green Lantern* (v1) #2 in Fair for $50 and #8 in VG+ for $80. *Harley Quinn* #1 in VG+ for $38. *Justice League of America* (v1) #2 in GD+ for $125; #4 (Green Arrow joins) in VG- for #125 and a second copy in in GD+ for $95; and #10 in VG+ for $95. *My Greatest Adventure* #82 in VG+ for $42. *Showcase* #34 (1st Silver Age Atom) in Fair for $80; and #79 (1st appearance Dolphin) in VF- for $31. *Superboy* #66 in FN for $90.

Marvel's key sales were also influenced by their movies, but were still the most anemic I've ever seen them.

Amazing Spider-Man (v1) #8 sold for $138 in GD; #26 (4th appearance Green Goblin) went for $110 in FN-; and the series appearance of the black costume in #252 sold for $60 in VF/NM. The 1st appearance of the Collector in *Avengers* (v1) #1 #28 sold in VG+ for $68. *Conan the Barbarian* #1 in VG- for $45. *Defenders* (v1) #1 in FN- for $36. *Fantastic Four* (v1) #53 (origin & 2nd appearance Black Panther) in VG+ for $50. *Fear* #1 in VF- for $52. *Giant-Sized X-Men* #1 (1st appearance Colossus and others) in VF- for $600. *Journey Into Mystery* (Thor) #84 (2nd appearance) in VG+ for $600; #85 (1st Loki & 1st Heimdall) in GD+ for $275; and #108 (early Dr. Strange/Avengers x-over) in FN- for $65. *Kull the Conqueror* (v1) #1 in VF for $35. *Marvel Feature* #1 (1st appearance/origin Defenders) in VG+ for $50. *Marvel Spotlight* #2 (origin/1st appearance Werewolf by Night) in FN for $54. *New Mutants* #98 (1st Deadpool) in VG/NM for $200. *Secret Wars* #8 (origin Venom suit) in VF/NM for $60. *Sgt. Fury* #1 (signed by Stan Lee and Jack Kirby -- uncertified) in FN- for $1000. *Spider-Woman* (v1) #1 in VF/NM for $32. *Star Wars* (v1) #107 (final issue/ low distribution) in VF for $54. *Strange Tales* (v1) #85 in GD+ for $45. *X-Men* (v1) #95 (origin Storm) in GD- for $45. *X-Men Gold* #1 sold half a dozen copies thanks to controversial content that will not be reprinted. Initially these sold in NM for $10, then $15, and eventually $20 *Wolverine Origins* #10 (variant) in NM for $77.

Other publishers filled the void created by Marvel's declining demand. Fawcett's *Captain Marvel Jr.* #69 sold in VG- for $40; #92 in VG- for $45; and #93 in VG- for $45. *Crime Fighters* #13 sold in FN+ for $49. *Dell Giant Comics* #21 with M.G.M.'s Tom and Jerry Picnic Time in VG+ for $25. *Four Color* #690 with The Conqueror movie adaptation and a John Wayne cover sold in VG+ for $23. While they still draw attention, John Wayne covers move more slowly than they did in the past. *Land of the Lost* #7 in GD+ for $30. *Mutt & Jeff* #18 in GD for $16; and #60 in GD+ for $17. *Scooby Doo* (Charlton Comics) #1 in FN+ for $35. *Walking Dead* #6 (Shane killed) in NM for $80; and #92 (intro. Jesus) in NM for $60. *Walking Dead Weekly* #29 (reprints 1st Michonne) in NM for $60.

With many buyers reallocating their weekly new comics

budget into vintage comics, back issues priced below $20 had very strong demand. So while the number of key, high dollar sales were down, the overall volume of lower priced back issues were way up.

TED VANLIEW
SUPERWORLD COMICS

Hey Ladies and Gents, this past year has been our best yet. The market remains consistently strong for good material, be it desirable Golden and Atomic Age books, or Silver and Bronze Age as well. The surprising area to us has been the 1980s through Modern books that have emerged. It seems that every week another book or three jumps in demand! Not complaining. 'Twasn't that long ago that I was convinced that nothing published after 1975 would amount to more than a pile of ash. Wrong I was! And happy to be so. No one could have predicted the proliferation of movies and TV shows that have propelled the popularity of comics and their concepts into the mainstream.

We, of course, are still focused of the older comics, as I've always been convinced that books with intrinsic scarcity will hold their value best. That said, it's amazing to see how different the landscape is from, say, 20 years ago. In the mid-'90s, books like *Batman* #1 and *Captain America Comics* #1 were considered fairly common for Golden Age keys. Look at them now. Who knew? *Action Comics* #1 and *Detective Comics* #27 always led the way, and *All-American Comics* #16, *More Fun Comics* #52 and *Flash Comics* #1 were always scarce. But others like *All Star Comics* #8 and *More Fun Comics* #73, as examples, weren't all that expensive, if they can be found. A lot of Golden Age titles that used to be cheap, even though they were relatively scarce, have been climbing quickly. Earlier issues of *Four Favorites*, *Speed*, *All-New*, *Prize*, *Cat-Man*, *Frankenstein*, and Matt Baker Romance titles have moved into the spotlight. Nedors, considered "Poor Man's Timelys" if you will, remain popular, especially the War covers. Almost any comic with a decent Schomburg, L.B. Cole, or Lou Fine cover will sell well in most grades.

There are lots of oddball books from the Golden Age that are scarce and sought after. For example, *Punch Comics*, *Terrific Comics*, *Headline* #8 and #11, *Great Comics* #3 and others too numerous to mention. Centaur Comics, which were published between 1937 and 1942, are always guaranteed to turn heads. Ditto for many comics published by Fox, especially ones featuring Lou Fine or Reed Crandall art. Fox and Centaurs were sort of an afterthought to collectors decades ago, but have since come to the fore. I think many collectors enjoy the difficulty of the search fo these amazing books.

Timelys remain high on many want lists, although some titles get more love than others. Any *Captain America* that we get sells so fast, I get paper cuts! After that, it depends what's on the cover with the other titles. DCs are mostly desirable, with the Batman titles being great, and the scarcer early titles like *More Fun* being juicy. In recent years, folks have discovered the joys of lesser known or shorter-run titles like *Leading Comics* and *Comic Cavalcade*.

For Silver Age, we start with these words: *Amazing Fantasy* #15. Yikes! This book has been anoited the Golden Boy of the Silver Age. Everybody wants it. Other Marvel #1 issues are tearing the joint up as well, although I feel that *Fantastic Four* #1 is currently undervalued. It is the title that started it all for the Marvel Age of Comics after all. *Fantastic Four* #5 is on the climb, as Doctor Doom is rumored to be getting his own movie. But even if it doesn't happen, we're all still fascinated by the evil doctor.

There seems to be a rotating cycle of "hotness" to various books. *Amazing Spider-Man* #14 is always great, but at times folks are begging for a copy. Same with *Fantastic Four* #48, *Journey Into Mystery* #112, *Tales of Suspense* #57, *Tales to Astonish* #44, *Fantastic Four* #52, *Strange Tales* #135, *Daredevil* #7, *X-Men* #4, 12, 35 and many others lead this category. Almost any issues in high grade will sell pretty quickly. We tend to price lesser grade run books at varied levels of discount, as collectors and readers like to get deals on them. The internet age has transformed the market. It's pretty easy to see which books are plentiful and which are more challenging to pick up. DCs are a more mysterious animal. Some of them fly, and others languish. Batman titles seem to be more widely popular than Superman titles in general. Although the earlier into the Silver Age we get, the scarcer the books are, and the more popular.

Titles from the other publishers are totally hit or miss, and very unpredictable. Harvey, Dell/Gold Key, Archie, Charlton, Tower, and ACG published lots of fun stuff, but are overlooked by the majority of collectors, which is tragic since there are lots of gems to be enjoyed. *Magnus Robot Fighter*, *Doctor Solar*, *Star Trek*, *Little Dot*, *Little Lulu*, *Blast Off* w/3 Rocketeers, *Thunder Agents*, *Dr. Graves* and so many more are just great fun, and some have great art by Wally Wood, Russ Manning and others. A lot of Archies and Duck books are genuinely funny and very entertaining. It doesn't have to be all super-heroes, y'know! And this from someone who's grown up lovin' super-heroes, make no mistake.

The gap between Marvel and DC is more pronounced in the Bronze Age. When I think of good titles and key issues, mostly Marvel books come to mind, although Batman is the standard bearer for DC once again. Any book with a Neal Adams cover is a player. Adams cover AND art, whooee! Marvel expanded greatly during this period, and the early '70s titles they launched have been popular for some time. What's changing is that the mid-'70s to early '80 titles are coming on. *Ms. Marvel*, *Spider-Woman*, *Black Goliath*, *Black Lightning*, *Nova* and many others have been rocketing to prominence. Changing demographics have been a factor as well, with black heroes such as Luke Cage and women such as Captain Marvel finding more favor. This trend has expanded to the '80s to the Modern Age books, although it is very selective. Almost any character or title linked to a TV show or movie has become "hot", and titles whose early issues had limited print runs and then became popular have taken on value. Examples of this are *Cerebus* and especially *Teenage Mutant Ninja Turtles. Turtles* #1 1st print is going for ungodly numbers. Actually, 2nd and 3rd prints of the first few issues ain't cheap neither! Characters like Deadpool, Cable, Venom, Carnage, Gambit, Red Hood, Livewire, Harley Quinn and others have made the leap to stardom.

Alright, (writer's cramp), you'll have to wait 'til next time for more pearls of wisdom.

Best regards to all!

Rick Whitelock
New Force Comics

2017 was quite the year for vintage comic sales. The auction season was highlighted with the sale of the Jon Berk collection. This collection brought to the market many rarely or never before seen treasures. Of particular interest was his complete Centaur Collection that was a rare comic collector's dream. I think having all of these books offered at one time, really created a market interest in the publisher, unlike I have even known. We have long been Centaur afficianados, but had never seen interest in the books from this publisher, like we did leading up to and following the Berk auction. Couple that with his Fox book offerings, and these 2 segments of the vintage market have seen demand (and prices) unlike any I can recall. Naturally, the issue becomes supply (which has been scarce in the market for some time). It will be interesting to see if any major collections or offerings follow up.

Another area we have seen incredible demand for is the "classic" cover requests. Books like *Pep* #34, *Terrific* #5, *Real Life* #3, *Great* #3, *Superman* #14, etc., have long been highly sought after books, but the price levels we saw in 2017 were exponential over any previous offerings we had sold. Finding quality material to offer has been a real challenge.

Silver Age keys seem to be an area that, while always in demand, really moved from a price stand point. About 10 years ago we coined the term "price per point" (relative to CGC graded comics) to help us identify good prices of Silver Age keys, relative to their asking prices. For example, if I knew we could sell a *Hulk* #1 at $X per point (*ie* a CGC 4.0 @12K) then any time I noticed the book being offered at a discount to the PPP (price per point), I knew to pick it up. 2017 saw this market move somewhat exponentially across the majority of SA keys (*Amazing Fantasy* #15, *Amazing Spider-Man* #1, *Fantastic Four* #1, *Journey Into Mystery* #83, etc). It will be interesting to see if the market can sustain some of the auction and subsequent private sale prices that have been realized this past year.

Can't wait to see what 2018 has in store for the vintage comic market.

Harley Yee
Harley Yee Rare Comics

The market in 2017 saw unprecedented growth with many record and eye-popping prices realized. With the stock market at record highs and the influx of more foreign buyers, I see 2018 as another record year.

One of the new trends I see more of is new collectors going straight into Golden Age comics instead of starting in Silver Age or Bronze Age like in the past. With the internet and social media combined it has become so much easier to trade and interact with fellow collectors with similar interests and acquire the knowledge that's harder when dealing in Golden Age.

The old bread and butter Silver Age and Bronze Age also saw some record prices with *Amazing Fantasy* #15 and *Incredible Hulk* #181 leading the way. The demand for these books and other key Silver Age and Bronze Age has not slowed down with me selling a record number of them in 2017.

I expect 2018 to be another record year because with Silver Age and Bronze Age always strong, and with Golden Age hot, you can't ask for anything else.

Vincent Zurzolo, Frank Cwiklik & Rob Reynolds
Metropolis Collectibles
ComicConnect.com

Vincent Zurzolo - Metropolis Collectibles and ComicConnect.com

Before I report on the state of the market I want to thank all of our friends, family, clients, consignors, sellers, and creators past and present for everything you've done to help Metropolis and ComicConnect enjoy the best year we've ever had. Demand for vintage comics, art, memorabilia, and action figures is at an all-time high and looks to only be getting stronger.

Billionaire Marc Lasry's Collection, The Hope Collection, The Jon Berk Collection, The World's Greatest *Walking Dead* Comic & Art Collection, and The Hidden Valley Collection are just several of the major collections we've brought to market over the last year. The excitement that built up around these major events was reflected in the amazing prices realized. Record-breaking sales for *Amazing Fantasy* #15 CGC 9.0 for $395,000, *Action Comics* #1 CGC Conserved 5.5 $393,000, and *Marvel Comics* #1 CGC 6.0 Twilight Copy $215,000 are just three of the many highlights from this last year.

As mentioned just above, our sale of *Amazing Fantasy* #15 CGC 9.0 $395,000 (almost $200,000 over our pre-auction estimate) took an already high demand, pricey book and launched it into the stratosphere. As of this writing it has plateaued but, as it has many times in the past, it will eventually go up again due to more record-breaking sales and increased demand. This is still one of the great books to buy.

Original art like Steve Ditko's *Amazing Spider-Man* #6 pg. 15 for $115,000, and #12 pg. 18 for a record breaking

$136,000, as well as Jack Kirby's *Fantastic Four* #3 pg. 23 for $44,500 and *Incredible Hulk* #4 pg. 10 for $43,500, show that art by the masters, like Ditko and Kirby will continue to soar.

We were also pleasantly surprised by the strong showing of Modern Age powerhouse *The Walking Dead*, issue #1 pg. 2 went for $27,000, the cover for issue #27 hammered at $18,300, and the highest-graded 9.9 Mint copy of *Walking Dead* #1 sold for $14,601, proving that the Modern Age market is alive and well.

This year we brought an incredible action figure/toy collection to market. Captain Action, Aurora Model Scenes, Aurora Glow in the Darks, Marvel Secret Wars, DC Super Powers, all mint in box or on card were gobbled up by a frenzy of bidders. Highlights from this sale include Captain Action Aquaman and Superman sets, Super Powers Cyborg action figure, and the Godzilla Aurora model kit.

The highest-graded copy of ***Walking Dead*** *#1 (9.9 Mint) sold for an amazing $14,601.*

Many of you will recall the Oakland Collection. It was a collection of over 3,500 late Silver to Bronze Age comics in an average of 9.6 condition I found with another dealer in 1998. After almost 20 years, I was contacted by the owner I purchased the collection from. He was coming to New York City and wanted to get together. I was very touched that he even remembered me and eagerly agreed. When we met, I gave him a tour of the gallery and our stock room. I showed him an *Action Comics* #1 and a few other cool books. After looking over the funny books, he told me he had been worried about me all these years and had been following my career. He was relieved to see I had done well. I asked him why he was worried. He told me that I had offered him over double what other dealers offered him for his collection and he was worried that I was too nice a guy (his words not mine, stop laughing) to succeed and would get gobbled up by the sharks. I was really touched by this sentiment and thanked him for his kindness and concern. Later over lunch he told me he wanted to thank me for buying his collection. He wanted me to know that the money he received helped to save his life. I wasn't aware but he was very ill at the time and had no health insurance. The money helped pay for his operation and he has been fine since. I was really blown away hearing this. Tears welled up in my eyes and I thanked him for sharing and told him how happy I was to hear this news. It is not often I get to learn how a purchase I made helped a person. I am not sharing this story with you to get a pat on the back. My motives back then were not altruistic. I bought the collection to make money, which I did. I share this with you because it was really wonderful for me to learn this information. While I am in the comic business, it is nice to know that the dollars and cents sometimes add up to something more than simply dollars and cents. Perhaps, in your life you have experienced something like this as well. I sure hope so. It made my year.

Frank Cwiklik - Metropolis Collectibles

Usually, our Metropolis Gallery in midtown Manhattan hosts art openings, exhibits centered around specific illustrators, like Frank Frazetta or the Hildebrandt brothers, or around themes such as *Star Wars*, *The Walking Dead*, or specific heroes or publishers. This year, we also hosted a very special exhibit displaying art and comics from a collector, Jon Berk, whose passion for comics has made him a legend in the hobby. This event says a lot about how the business has changed and grown in recent years.

While some pedigrees in the past have led curious collectors to research the original buyers, as with the Edgar Church/Mile High pedigree, it's only now that the art and business of comic collecting has reached the level of art collecting, where careful curators amass selections of important work that eventually are displayed in museums and galleries, both to show off the pieces themselves and to highlight the passions and tastes of the collector. Now that this first generation of comic collector/historians is retiring and letting the world share in their carefully constructed mini-museums, so much of the history of the medium is becoming accessible to a wider audience. As more buyers enter the market teased by the success of major hero keys, new enthusiasts naturally broaden their horizons, no longer focusing solely on nostalgia buys or tick-box want list, but instead eagerly seeking out and learning from collectors like Jon Berk, taking note of their particular interests and the books, they hoarded and stored lovingly to preserve the few remaining copies of what was once a heavily saturated and easily found pop culture medium.

The faces that came to the gallery that night ranged from old hands happy to once again swap anecdotes and trivia, and the next generation of buyers, flush and ready to buy, soaking up all the information and history they could glean from the books, the art, and the collectors who preserved them when everyone else considered them junk. The Berk collection itself was heavy with WWII-era comics and art, perfect for the current market which is once again hungry for the simple, clean, dynamic work of the early 1940s, and a healthy selection of pre-Code Horror, also a red-hot market. We were processing books in this collection that we'd only ever seen one copy of in 25+ years of inventory (and more than a few were the copies we'd sold him, making them the sole existing copy we'd ever laid eyes on). It was truly exciting not only to see these rarities but to see the staggering number of new buyers who knew what they were, and wanted to add them to their collection.

In many other hobbies, the interest dies down as a generation taps out and retires to greener pastures (and a significantly less crowded rec room!). We've seen the decline in stamp, coin, and newspaper collecting, along with others, while comic collecting booms and expands annually. It's not only the wild success of Marvel and DC's hero movies, as an appearance by Aquaman in the *Justice League* movie has no bearing whatsoever on the sudden demand for early single-digit issues of *Mad*. Many buyers may enter the market due to hot key issues popping up on their eBay or Amazon feed, but what keeps them coming is the variety and breadth of the market, as each niche field, from EC to Romance comics to bondage covers to high-grade go-go check DC, is its own unique microcosm with its own enthusiasts, rarities, and riches.

Conventions have become more of a PR and buying opportunity for us, as our business model matures into auctions, galleries, and specialized events, making the show-stock, books-on-the-table con model less and less feasible. Transforming our San Diego and New York convention booths into mini-museums, displaying our latest keys and upcoming auction goodies, has both increased our floor traffic and cemented our brand, setting us apart in a healthy way while still boosting the profile and potential buyer's pool for the business as a whole, bringing more money to the table for all the dealers trying to make a go of what can sometimes be a very tough business. We've noticed a significant bump in art sales at conventions, as we've made serious inroads in this very competitive market and found many new clients from displaying our most impressive pieces at shows. Overall, the greater part of our sales still comes from auctions, as buyers want the chance to compete over rare items, and sellers are attracted to the roll of the dice that the auction market offers.

That's not to say we haven't had luck in retail – our eBay sales have been improving, as some buyers wary of the increasingly rough nature of the internet retreat to better-known sites and stay there for all their buying. Sales on our own site have held steady as well, and we've been able to snag some impressive collections this past year, most notably a steady stream of rare 1950s DC, Horror, Humor, and Sci-fi books that have sold well over *Guide* due to their rarity. We're still toiling on our new site, which should now hopefully be unveiled by mid-2018 and will be a complete and total overhaul of the entire Metro infrastructure and buying system, which we're very excited about, but has proven to be a massive undertaking. The wait will be well worth it.

In a time of nearly constant change, it's unsurprising that folks are flocking to history, buying past treasures and little four-color time machines. What's encouraging is the wide range of interests, buyers, and sales avenues that we're seeing steadily working for us and attracting new buyers. Seeing the past, present, and future of the comic collecting business in our gallery on that warm and welcome evening of the Berk Gallery opening was satisfying and encouraging.

Rob Reynolds - ComicConnect.com

2017 was, by far, the biggest year in ComicConnect's history. Our consignors sold more comics, for more money, than ever before while thousands of new bidders joined and placed millions of dollars in bids. The usual suspects dominated the year's top ten lists with owners of Golden Age keys, Joker covers, and the almighty *Amazing Fantasy* #15 enjoying incredible growth. ComicConnect offered several single owner collections including some of the rarest and most sought-after comics in the world.

Marc Lasry, Milwaukee Bucks majority owner and hedge fund billionaire, chose ComicConnect to auction off his collection of vintage comic books. "It was with great enthusiasm that I opened the doors of my own personal Fortress of Collection to my fellow investors," Lasry said.

Event Auction XXIX & The Marc Lasry Collection (December 2016)

Action Comics #7 CGC 7.0 C $40,500
All Star Comics #3 CGC 7.0 $69,000
All Star Comics #8 CGC 4.5 $54,555
Amazing Fantasy #15 CGC 6.5 $36,608
Batman #1 CGC 8.0 Larson Copy $390,000
Batman #1 CGC 6.5 $180,000
Batman #1 CGC 2.0 $79,900
Captain America Comics #1 CGC 7.0 R $35,500
Detective Comics #28 CGC 8.5 Billy Wright $64,000
Detective Comics #29 CGC 3.5 $40,500
Detective Comics #31 CGC 4.5 $96,000
Detective Comics #38 CGC 4.0 $35,000
Incredible Hulk #1 CGC 8.5 $132,000
Incredible Hulk #1 CGC 7.5 $37,500
More Fun Comics #73 CGC 8.0 C $44,355
Tales to Astonish #35 CGC 9.4 White Mountain $51,000
Wonder Woman #1 CGC 5.0 $40,500
X-Men #1 CGC 9.2 $50,050

The Hope Collection made its debut in our first major auction of 2017. The collection was passed down to the owner from a dear friend that wanted to give her some hope for the future. She chose ComicConnect to assist her in the sale of the comics and we were proud to do our very best for her. The *Amazing Fantasy* #15 CGC 9.0 from the collection set a record in the grade that still stands.

Event Auction XXX (March 2017)

All-American Comics #16 CGC 3.5 $66,000
Amazing Fantasy #15 CGC 9.0 $395,000
Amazing Fantasy #15 CGC 5.0 $57,000
Amazing Fantasy #15 CGC 4.5 $37,0003
Batman #1 CGC 7.5 R $39,502
Captain America Comics #1 CGC 7.0 Color Error Copy $74,000
Captain America Comics #1 CBCS 8.5 R $35,000
Daredevil #2 CGC 9.8 Pacific Coast $44,629
Detective Comics #29 CGC 3.0 $66,010
Detective Comics #38 CGC 3.0 $54,010
Fantastic Four #1 CGC 8.0 $35,000
Incredible Hulk #1 CBCS 8.5 $141,011
Incredible Hulk #1 CGC 7.5 $47,500
Jungle Comics #1 CGC 9.6 Church Copy $45,000
More Fun Comics #55 CGC 9.4 Nova Scotia $51,007
More Fun Comics #73 CGC 6.0 $55,222

Superman #1 CGC 1.0 $64,600
Thrill Comics #1 CGC 9.0 $41,040
X-Men #3 CGC 9.8 Pacific Coast $35,505

The Spring Auction was filled with the rarities and high-grade keys that ComicConnect auctions are known for. We offered a host of books that we almost never see, let along auction. Yet again, *Amazing Fantasy* #15 results were record-setting.

2017 Spring Special (May 2017)

Action Comics #2 CGC 7.5 $95,002
Action Comics #7 CGC 4.0 $125,000
Amazing Fantasy #15 CGC 7.5 $102,001
Amazing Fantasy #15 CGC 6.5 $61,000
Batman #1 CGC 6.0 R $44,100
Captain America Comics #1 CGC 8.0 R Simon Sig $42,500
More Fun Comics #56 CGC 9.2 Church Copy $41,500
Superman #1 CBCS 7.0 R $77,200

The Jon Berk Collection was the most-asked-about, written-about, talked-about auction in our history. The collection was packed with comics and original comic art that have not been on the market in years, if not decades, and collectors responded with record numbers. The entire staff of ComicConnect felt honored to have represented the collection at auction. All of the hard work we put in paid off for one of the greatest collectors this hobby has ever known.

Jon Berk Collection Auction (June 2017)

Action Comics #1 CGC 5.5 C $393,000
Action Comics #3 CGC 7.0 $55,009
Action Comics #7 CGC 5.5 Court Case Copy $188,000
Amazing Man Comics #22 CGC 7.0 $38,500
Captain America Comics #1 CGC 7.0 R $35,000
Comics Magazine, The #1 CGC 9.0 $38,000
Detective Comics #27 CGC 6.5 R $313,000
Fantastic Comics #1 CGC 9.8 Church Copy $66,000
Fantastic Comics #3 CGC 9.4 Church Copy $243,000
Mystery Men #1 CGC 9.0 Church Copy $41,000
Mystery Men #2 CGC 9.6 Church Copy $38,500
Mystery Men #3 CGC 9.6 Church Copy $57,000
Whiz Comics #2 (#1) CGC 6.5 R $36,500
Wonder Comics #1 CGC 9.4 Overstreet Copy $68,000
Wonderworld #3 CGC 9.4 Church Copy $51,000
Wonderworld #7 CGC 9.6 $66,000

Jon Berk Collection Original Art:

All New Comics #8 cover by Alex Schomburg $66,000
Amazing Spider-Man #6 page by Steve Ditko $105,000
Cat-Man Comics #25 cover by Rudy Palais $52,897
Daredevil #1 page by Bill Everett $37,500
Fantastic Four #3 page by Jack Kirby $44,500
Fantastic Four #14 page by Jack Kirby $38,500
Incredible Hulk #4 page by Jack Kirby $43,500
Pep Comics #30 cover by Bob Montana $61,777
Planet Comics #1 cover by Lou Fine $146,444

Superman was the star of the fourth Event Auction of the year. ComicConnect offered three copies and each set new records for the condition. We've noticed as *Action Comics* #1 continues to get priced out of the hands of even some of our well-heeled investment collectors, *Superman* #1 has become the book to own and guys are just diving on it. *Wonder Woman* #1 cemented itself as a blue-chip investment book with record prices as well.

Event Auction XXXII (September 2017)

All-American Comics #16 CGC 6.5 R $36,0002
All Star Comics #8 CGC 5.5 $87,000
Amazing Fantasy #15 CGC 5.5 $36,509
Batman #1 CGC 7.5 R $35,500
Detective Comics #31 CGC 1.0 $44,000
Fantastic Comics #3 CGC 5.5 $44,500
Incredible Hulk #1 CGC 7.0 $57,555
Pep Comics #22 CGC 8.0 $252,100
Superman #1 CGC 8.0 R $150,555
Superman #1 CGC 1.0 $110,000
Superman #1 CGC 7.0 R $67,000
Wonder Woman #1 CGC 8.5 $163,000
Wonder Woman #1 CGC 5.0 $43,650
X-Men #1 CGC 9.0 $43,337

The last Event Auction of the year featured The Hidden Valley Collection with an *Action Comics* #1 as well as a copy of *Superman* #1. *Marvel Comics* #1 hit a record price for a CGC 6.0 copy. In addition to nearly 500 pieces of original comic art, the most valuable *Walking Dead* collection in the world was offered including highest graded copies of dozens of comics and an incredible group of art that has never been duplicated.

Event Auction XXXIII (December 2017)

Action Comics #1 CGC 8.0 C $461,555
Action Comics #2 CGC 4.0 $36,000
Action Comics #7 CGC 1.0 Siegel Copy $44,500
All Star Comics #3 CGC 7.0 $40,000
All Star Comics #8 CGC 4.5 $49,388
Amazing Spider-Man #12 page by Steve Ditko $136,000
Captain America Comics #1 CGC 1.5 $70,051
Detective Comics #29 CGC 6.5 C $42,500
Detective Comics #62 CGC 9.4 $77,101
Detective Comics #71 CGC 9.4 Rockford Copy $66,000
Fantastic Four #48 CGC 9.8 $30,000
Flash Comics #1 CGC 2.5 $63,500
Marvel Comics #1 CGC 6.0 Twilight Copy $215,000
Superman #1 CGC 7.0 R $52,000
Walking Dead #1 CGC 9.9 $14,601
Walking Dead #27 CGC 9.9 $4,000
Walking Dead #1 page 2 by Tony Moore $27,000
Walking Dead #27 cover by Charlie Adlard $18,300

With every auction, the market strengthens as prices that were once surprising are reinforced under the auction hammer. Comic books are firmly entrenched in a growth pattern. With new buyers coming to the market in every auction, it's never too late to jump in to the investment collectible market. Thank you to all our bidders (and underbidders) and I wish all of our collectors the very best of luck. Please let me know how I can help you build a world-class collection.

THE WAR REPORT

by Matt Ballesteros & the War Correspondents
(Andy Greenham and Mick Rabin)

We are proud to present the 10th rendition of the War Report. An independent assessment of the war comic market segment researched and developed by avid enthusiasts of the niche. This recurring dispatch has been an accounting of the war segment of the comic book hobby for a decade now, which was created and is maintained for our own edification and hopefully, to your enjoyment.

Thanks to all our returning readers and supporters, your comments and encouragement have been tank fuel to us. For this edition we are revisiting a decade of highlights, discoveries and elucidations. We hope returning readers will appreciate the refresher and newcomers find this compendium of information handy.

A History of War

Although we created this report to do open discovery of the war segment, there was of course hesitation to do so at first. There was an advantageous element to anonymity, in that my cohorts and I could gain from astute purchases on issues that no one had intel on. Nevertheless, we felt it was better for the hobby, and certainly for the growth of our segment, if we openly shared our knowledge and findings.

So, in 2007 and 2008 we embarked on a quest to produce a comprehensive detailing of war comics, their creators, the characters, the art, the stories and the market. This was spurred on by a few factors; momentum originally created by Chris Pedrin's "Big Five" compendium, the creation of the Big Five War Summit, the onset of a frenzy in the war comic after-market not ever seen prior to 2007, and finally, the request by JC Vaughn and the fine crew at Overstreet inviting me to develop a comprehensive list of the top war comics in the hobby.

It was obvious to me that I needed to enlist the help of expert enthusiasts. So, I assembled a team of war comic hobbyists from the US and Canada that I not only hold in the highest esteem, but whom I consider to be better versed in the matter of war comic specifics, lore and history. I have since referred to them fondly as The War Correspondents and they have contributed over the years in various capacities. Thanks Alan Bartholomew, Richard Evans, Andy Greenham, Keith Marlow, Mick Rabin and Brian "Shep" Sheppard! I so appreciate all your selfless contributions throughout these years!

Title Abbreviations of the Big Five
AAMOW – All American Men of War
GIC – G.I. Combat
OAAW – Our Army at War
OFF – Our Fighting Forces
SSWS – Star Spangled War Stories

1st WAR REPORT - 2008

The Campaign: The first thing we did was go through the *Overstreet Price Guide* and record every instance of a title or issue that was either a war comic, or that had war subject matter, or that contained the appearance of a war-related character, etc. We also used resource material outside the *Overstreet Price Guide* to fill in holes or corroborate specific findings. But, after we reached well beyond our 1000th line listing of different war comic titles, with no end in sight, we truly realized what a laborious campaign we had embarked on.

After developing our massive "master list," our second task was to determine what truly constituted a "war comic." So, we set parameters that narrowed the field by characterizing war comics as "stories centered on the military, which is involved in armed conflicts" and, as such, needed to be relegated to those wars "categorized as a major conflict". We were able to easily eliminate a good deal of candidates by employing the notion that "Any war story blended with a superhero is, by definition, a 'fantasy' story and would not be a war story.

We also needed to create a sub-classification within the genre to fine-tune the report. This classification consisted of defining what type of war themes existed; for instance, war battle tales, war adventure, cold war, war propaganda, etc. We quickly ascertained that we needed to put our focus on stories that were predominantly centered on characters engulfed in "battle". Thus, **War Battle Tales** has become our category of choice—a refined list that, still boasts over 700 listings.

Since most of war comics both began and flourished in earlier comic ages, our focus on reporting has been primarily on two of our own comic age classifications; the Golden Age and the Atom/Silver/Bronze Age. However, we do pay heed to what we refer to as the Modern Age of War, as a good number of incredible war comics have been published from the '80s to the present. They just don't typically get as much attention outside our genre.

With all this data in place, each year the War Correspondents and I would vote anonymously on the ranking of the top 30 to 50 war comics in existence. Factors on criteria included elements such as: significance of book, character appearances, art and storyline, rarity, etc. From this we have not only been able to present and maintain a current ranking on key war titles, but to share reasoning for market fluctuations on interest and value.

That was the result of our 1st War Report. Following is a summary of our ensuing decade of reporting.

{2018 comments to our original suppositions are inside brackets such as these}

2nd WAR REPORT - 2009

News from the Front: After the 2007 war comic rush, war comics gained additional momentum spurred on primarily by the avaricious zeal for "DC War". Although the market shifted to an entirely new and higher gear, some of the prices garnered on war comics reflected a "frenzy" mentality that was not necessarily indicative of the market of long-term war comic collectors. It was a matter of supply and demand of course, combined with the fear that no other copy existed in a particular grade or higher. War comics in publishing lines such as Atlas, Charlton, and Dell were also gaining notoriety and achieving value momentum. With Atlas, for instance, who had continuing characters that preceded Rock, the likes of Battle Brady, Combat Kelly, and Combat Casey, all helped the Atlas line gain significance. Charlton introduced Captain Schultz in *Fightin' Army* #76, launching the "Lonely War of Willy Schultz" storyline, as well as *Army War Heroes* #22 which introduced the Iron Corporal. But none of them maintained the continuity that would make DC characters so notable. Thus, although sought after, war comics from these lines remain relatively attainable. Still, these publishers made indelible marks on the genre.

Key Events of 2009: Sgt. Rock turned 50! —Propelling further interest in *OAAW* #83 and all other early Rock issues.

War Comics that were underrated or underappreciated: *OAAW* #90 is first to explain how Rock became Sgt. Rock. So, it's his earliest origin issue (*OAAW* #128 is the first book to recall Sgt. Rock's time in boot camp).

OAAW #109 is the tale of Sgt. Rock's very first battle/skirmish in WWII.

War comics we said to look out for: *Don Winslow* – His early books gain momentum as the character's historic significance grows.

SSWS #84 through #89 – Mlle. Marie. apps. Her importance to the DC War Mythos was starting to come to light.

War comics that we thought were perhaps overrated? *SSWS* #90 Dino storylines. *{Boy, did we ever get that wrong. Apologies to war-dino fans. We are converts!}*

War comics that were easiest to find in 2009: *Weird War Tales* #1 – all the way up to 9.2s. Seem to be all over the place. Also *OAAW* #81 and *GIC* # 87 in low grade.

Key Sales in 2009: *OAAW* #95 (Bulldozer's entry into Easy Co.) CGC 9.0 $4600, *GIC* #83 (the classic cover gem) CGC 9.2 $4000, *OAAW* #109 (Sgt Rock's "first battle") CGC 9.0 $3450, *SSWS* #151 (Unknown Soldier's first solo comic) CGC 9.8 $2629, *Two Fisted Tales* #19 (EC war classic) CGC 9.8 $200, and *GIC* #44 CGC 9.0, *GIC* #68 CGC 7.5, and *OAAW* #1 CGC 8.0—each of which sold for around $3,000.

3rd WAR REPORT - 2010 through 2011

After three solid years of aggressive and heavy gains in the war comic field (2008-2010), the market ostensibly stabilized in 2011. It had little to do with the economic downturn and a great deal to do with availability and supply. The slow economy did not hinder high dollar sales and new record prices (the Heritage auction featuring the Savannah pedigrees is a great example). Interest in war drove more middle and low grade to the market. For instance, on eBay pre-2008, you would only come across a couple thousand war comics at any given time, at whatever grade. By 2010, on-the-spot search for war comics on eBay brought up literally 10,000 or more listings *{and now in 2018 eBay brings up nearly 50,000 line-items}*. War comics maintained a strong collector base however [in 2010]. The threads on the CGC boards remained abuzz with devoted group of enthusiasts. A factor that was non-existent prior to 2000.

Key Events of 2010-2011: *Sgt. Fury* #1 gained a surprising amount of momentum in 2010-2011 (9.4 being highest on census) *{10 years later seven 9.4s have yet to top that}*. Mick Rabin said, "In my opinion, the hottest war book of 2010 was not a DC war book; it was Marvel's *Sgt. Fury* #1. Also *GIC* #87 and the introduction of the infamous Haunted Tank celebrated its 50th anniversary.

Foxhole #1

War Comics that were underrated: *OFF* #49 – 1st Pooch, very tough to find and undervalued. *OAAW* # 218 – First Glanzman USS Stevens – one of the best series ever written. High Grade DC War Keys – there was not a single DC War of our top 20 that topped CGC 9.0 on census.

Notable Comics for us: *Foxhole* #1 – Classic Kirby cover and *OAAW* #100.

Key sales in 2010-2011: 500 CGC war comics from the Andy Greenham collection in a market in short supply of quality war. The Mound City Auction, featuring a slew of Savannah Pedigrees. *Showcase* #45 Savannah CGC 9.6 $6,600. *Sgt. Fury* #1 CGC 9.0 $10,000 (A war comic breaks the five-figure barrier again, a rarity at the time.) *Sgt. Fury* #1 CGC 8.5 $5750. *OAAW* #128 CGC 9.4 Savannah $4500.

OAAW #118 CGC 9.6 Savannah $3350 *{Single highest grade under #121}*. *GIC* #100 CGC 9.4 $3,100. *GIC* #123 CGC 9.4 $2875 (Mlle. Marie app. in Haunted Tank). *OAAW* #83 CGC 6.0 $1600, *OAAW* #83 CGC 5.5 $1100, *OAAW* #83 CGC 4.0 $900 (1st true Sgt. Rock).

What issues do we believe have finest war stories written? *OFF* #40 – "The Silent Ones" by Kubert.

OAAW #79 – "What's the Price of a B-17" Kubert.

OAAW #218 through 1977 – Sam Glanzman's USS Stevens back-up features in numerous issues.

OFF #146 – "Burma Sky" R. Ballard.

4th WAR REPORT - 2011 through 2012

For a second time in five years, Keith Marlow decided to unload his extensive high-grade war collection. Although, Keith recouped a moderate gross return on his war comics overall, individual sales were wildly divergent. There were some amazing prices actualized and there were some downright and surprising disasters. Consequently, war books in auctions and sales in 2012 were spread out among a greater number of collectors, not lumped in concentrated pockets. We believed that it was unlikely that a large mass of high grade war books would hit the market again in the few years following *{We were right. We still haven't seen anything to rival war comic auctions from 2007-2012}*. A good number of individual sales broke every record in 2012 and transcended the values and prices comparable to key superhero books. But, the existing market could not bear the weight of multiple auctions and the sale of such a large collection all at one time. Thus there was a drop in middle and low-grade war comics that we attributed not to lack of interest in the genre, but to the fact that the market was suddenly flooded with a greater supply of low to mid-grade war comics from those hoping to ride the coattails of the high-grade war frenzy.

Key Events of 2011-2012: Clarifying Sgt. Rock's first appearances in the *Price Guide*.

Bob Overstreet invited us to help redefine and illuminate details on Sgt. Rock's first appearance in the succession of books credited with the character's origination. Of course, referring to the shroud of mystery surrounding the first "true" appearance of Sgt. Rock in *GIC* #68, *OAAW* #81, #82 and #83.

We researched and itemized any book credited with a Rock prototype or early appearance (including minor prototypes). We also contemporaneously dug into any historical data that we could get our hands on to ensure we were considering anomalous factors (including articles, interviews with the creators, and published subject matter expert opinions) Here is what we found:

***G.I. Combat* #68 – "The Rock"** (Jan 1959). A character named Jimmy referred to as "The Rock" appears as a sergeant on the cover, but as a private in the story. And although DC later reprints the story in early 1972 (see *OAAW* #242), editors have to modify the reprinted issue to fit DC's needs by editing Jimmy's name out. In brief, *GIC* #68 is definitely a key Sgt. Rock prototype, but undeniably not his first true appearance.

***Our Army at War* #81 – "The Rock of Easy"** (April 1959). Three months after *GIC* #68, *OAAW* #81 features a story with a character named "Sgt. Rocky", who is referred to as "The Rock of Easy". However, Sgt Rocky is a "4th grade rate" sergeant (only has three chevrons/stripes) and not the Master Sergeant we all know the true Sgt. Rock to be. Nevertheless, with the editor's promise of more stories of a "...Rock-like Sergeant", it is clear that the creative team has something in mind, making *OAAW* #81 a significant prototype issue.

***Our Army at War* #82 – "Hold up Easy"** (May 1959). Appearance of a character named Sgt. Rock ... Wait! Appearance of "a" Sgt. Rock?! What does that mean? And why isn't this issue credited with his "first" appearance? Well, in this final Kanigher and Drucker prototype amalgam, we get a character that is still short of the Kanigher and Kubert creation, and who appears in a supporting "motivator" role to the main characters of the story. Moreover, and of particular significance, he appears again only as the prototyped 4th grade rate sergeant (three stripes/chevrons). Nonetheless, it is important to state that the character does actually physically "appear" in the issue, and is not merely appearing "in name only" as widely believed in the industry. With this clarification, his key prototype appearance in six panels in the six-page story "Hold up Easy" should have a considerable impact on the importance of this comic from this point forward.

Our Army at War #83

***Our Army at War* #83 – "The Rock and Wall"** (June 1959). As a demonstratively key determinant, Sgt. Rock is finally introduced as the <u>main character</u> of the title story, and more importantly, as a "Master Sergeant" (six stripes—three chevrons and three rockers) by what is the 1st actual collaboration on Rock between creators Kanigher and Kubert (who are credited as the true progenitors of the defined character). Further, readers are finally given the 1st definitive narration, as compared to all the other previous issues, that unequivocally defines the "Rock of Easy" <u>as</u> Sgt. Rock in the actual storyline. All these key elements combined make *OAAW* #83 the indisputable issue to furnish the 1st "true appearance" of Sgt. Rock.

***Our Army at War* #84 – "Laughter on Snakehead Hill"** (July 1959). Story advances true Sgt. Rock continuity in the 13-page title story featuring Sgt. Rock and Easy Co. And with this being his 2nd true appearance, it is a significant issue.

"The Spoils of War": Starting with the 4th report, we began sharing hypothesis on which war comics may be worthy of acquisition for investment sake. Stating various disclaimers about both our bias and the fact that we were just collectors not investment advisers, we doled out recommendations on which issues to look out for. Here were some recommendations:

<u>Long Term Return</u>

Don Winslow #1 (Dell) – A golden age character and series that has not yet had a chance to blossom to its full potential. It should bring you back a small return in 5+ years. *{So far so good on this prediction.}*

OAAW #100 – We believe the market does not yet reflect nor understand the potential of this comic. We predicted it would gain momentum over 4 to 5 years. *{Correct again, but slow in growth.}*

OAAW #83 – obvious pick. *{Correct.}*

<u>Short Term Return</u>

OAAW #82 – A comic that has been woefully misunderstood, giving it the most potential to climb aggressively. An important and pivotal book, in our opinion, that is greatly undervalued. *{Nope. Still misunderstood. Growth has been very slow and not aggressive. We still strongly believe in it though}*

Losing Ground

OAAW #81. Mainly because the market realigned its core focus onto *OAAW* #83, undermining the value of #81 in the short term. It has great long-term potential. But, it's going to take a few years. *{Correct. It has mostly stabilized, and we see healthy hints of future growth.}*

Key Sales in 2011-2012: *Sgt. Fury* #1 in 9.4 sells for nearly $30K! *OAAW* #83 CGC 8.0 $17,000, *OAAW* #83 CGC 7.5 $9,600, and *Sgt. Fury* #2 and #13 (Captain America crossover) both gained momentum. But mid-grade copies of the entire Sgt. Fury run were available by the veritable truckload. *{Still are}*.

War Comics We Found Underrated: *OFF* #49 – The first Pooch had not gained deserved value *{few sales to measure, and still woefully underappreciated}*

War Books that Are Tough to Find: *Wings* #2 through #20 are incredibly tough to find.

War Stories with Impact: *OFF* #40 – "The Silent ones". *Unknown Soldier* #21 (2010) – An impactful tale from the point of view of an AK47.

5th WAR REPORT - 2012 through 2013

There was no event more significant, and quite frankly more sorrowful, than that of the passing of Joe Kubert in 2012. Here is a quote about Joe from our report that year:

He made such an indelible mark on pop culture and the entire realm of illustrated media that it is difficult to imagine that he is no longer with us. Yet, his contributions have been so monumental, so permanent, and so important, that Joe and his legacy will forever remain here with us. His style and approach converted new admirers into fanatics, his dedication to the craft paved the way for aspiring artists and professionals, and his singular contributions downright launched entire genres. Still, as much of a pillar as he was to many of us, he maintained a noble, warm and friendly demeanor. He will be missed.

Rest in peace Joe.

News of the Market in 2012 – 2013: All quiet on the western front. That is the most prevailing reaction we received from every corner of the market. After five years of aggressive changes, it was apparent that, for most titles and except for high-grade copies, war comics dug in.

Spoils of War 2012 -2013:

Long Term Return

Two-Fisted Tales #18 and *Frontline Combat* #1 (EC) – In our opinion these are not correctly reflecting scarcity, value, and potential. They should bring you a moderate return in 5+ years. *{Correct, although it has experienced fluctuations, but it is gaining in value.}*

OAAW #84 (DC) – We expect a reasonable return in 5+ years on this gem. *{Reasonable forecast, but not perfect. Take advantage of this underappreciated comic.}*

Short Term Return

War Comics #11 (ATLAS) – Originally sought for its flamethrower cover, it is apparent that its scarcity and striking black cover (impossible to locate without wear) is making this comic a preeminent issue. We expect solid returns within one year. *{Correct. But so, so tough to find.}*

Losing Ground

Weird War #1 – Although a Bronze Age must-have, and the first issue of the infamous war-horror theme, it seems to have stalled. *{Correct. But, it's only a matter of time before these become Bronze classics.}*

AAMOW #82 – Hopefully Johnny Cloud can get this up and gaining momentum in the next decade. *{Correct. Still waiting…}*

Key Intel we shared in 2013: In January, 1958, the first twelve-page story was introduced, beginning with "The DI and the Sand Fleas" in *GIC* #56. That issue is already a semi-key because of its searing Kubert cover and significance as a prototype in the genesis of Sgt. Rock. Within a year, this expanded 12 page format gave rise to what are now the classic Big-5 characters: Gunner and Sarge, Sgt. Rock and Easy Company, Mlle. Marie, The War That Time Forgot (Dinosaur-war books), Johnny Cloud, and Haunted Tank, in that order.

Pre-1960 books garner higher prices for truly quality covers. These are not called out in *Overstreet*, but savvy war collectors know which ones you want to have. Covers like early Russ Heath on *SSWS* #38 and *OAAW* #40 and Grandenetti Frogman covers. There are also, interestingly, a string of 'pink' covers (*SSWS* #69) and process blue covers (*OAAW* #65 and #68) that get collectors digging deeper into their wallets for nice examples.

War Books that Are Tough to Find: *SSWS* #154 (much harder that *SSWS* #151), *GIC* #141 and #142 (Very tough 15-centers), *OAAW* #245 (black cover), *OAAW* #250 (Unusually tough book), *OAAW* #256 (Again, possible distribution issue here), *Sgt. Rock* #329 Whitman Variant (ridiculously tough).

Key Atlas books to seek: *War Comics* #11, *War Comics* #23, *War Comics* #26, *Battlefront* #15, *Battlefront* #26, *Battle* #30, *Battlefield* #11, *Combat* #1, *Combat* #5, *War Action* #14, and *Navy Action* #2.

6th WAR REPORT - 2013 through 2014

Although there have been some notable transactions and the unearthing of semi-occasional high-grade war comics in this period, it was a desolate market. We believe that this was a direct result of collectors hanging on to their war comics with fervor *{Which holds true today}*. The niche remained strong overall though and looking at sales throughout 2013 and 2014 we witnessed that nearly all, excepting a few war comics, were retaining their value. Further, if key, continued to appreciate boldly in value.

A case for Rock: We began postulating strongly that *OAAW* #83 (the first true app. of Sgt. Rock) should make Overstreet's Top 20 Silver Age Comics. Sales in 2013; a raw 2.0 went for nearly $700, a CGC 3.0 $1000, a CGC 4.0 $1800 and a CGC 6.0 $4,000.

Key Intel: Fewer still know that *GIC* #87 is in the middle of the longest string of uninterrupted washtone covers in the history of comics—the "Perty-Thirty." Those 30 issues start with *GIC* #75 and continue unabated until *GIC* #104. Even *Sea Devils* can't touch that.

Spoils of War:

Long Term Return

Atlas War – The entire comic line. Especially high grade. Expectations; reasonable returns within 5 years. *{Nope. These are going to require 10+ years. Still, interest is helping these ascend in value}*

Short Term Return

Battle #'s 1-10 (Atlas) – If you can find any of these issues in 8.0 or better. Look at getting a return in one to two years. *{No meaningful data. Assumptions hold that high-grade copies would command stout prices}*

About Face, the Variants of War (Andy Greenham): Many of you are aware of direct edition comics vs. newsstand edition comics. Typically, the newsstand books would have a UPC code on the front cover. The direct edition books also had that box, but no UPC code, thus differentiating the two versions. Among other things, the non-UPC version would have the box filled with either Sgt. Rock's helmet, or an ad for DC comics, or sometimes even just left blank. Here is a short list of the issues that have both variations of variants: *AAMOW* (none), *GIC* (#223-228), *OAAW* (none), *OFF* (none), *Sgt. Rock* (#345-422), *SSWS* (none), *Unknown Soldier* (#250-268), and *Weird War Tales* (#92-124).

7th WAR REPORT - 2014 through 2015

A Medal of Honor: *Our Army at War* #83 has finally earned its place in Overstreet's top 20 Silver Age comics listing! *{which was ranked #18 in Overstreet's top 50 Silver Age Comics list in 2015}*. This is a significant milestone, and this may be the first time that a non-superhero-based comic book has broken into the ranks of the top 20 list. An amazing feat given that it is a comic book that hails from a discontinued series, based specifically on a World War II character and storyline. Key sales of *OAAW* #83 in 2014 included a CGC 7.0 approx. $7400, CGC 4.0's over $2000 each, a CGC 3.0 $1000 and a CGC 1.8 for nearly $800.

Field Report: The market remained calm in 2014-2015. Except for a spike of action here and there, the landscape remained fairly quiet another year. With less war comics released from collections, naturally less were available to be acquired. All the same, some titles were getting action as interest rose on once overlooked or underestimated titles. Two particular runs that appear to have gained stronger interest in the last year are Atlas War titles as a whole, and interestingly, *SSWS* from DC's Big Five omnibus. High grade copies are being picked up instantaneously.

SSWS began getting more attention for primarily two reasons, Dinos AND Mademoiselle Marie! Although based in fantasy, the dinosaur issues that crossed-over into the war genre struck a chord with many a young reader when originally published and then gradually garnered and maintained a perpetual cult following. A CGC 9.0 copy of *SSWS* #90, the first issue in the Dinosaur run (which also features Mlle. Marie) went for about $4200. By the way, it is a true rarity to see an 8.0 copy or better of issues that Mlle. Marie graces, especially *SSWS* #84 through #91 (Mlle. Marie remains an enduring personality in the Big Five war line, not only for her story, but also for the strength of character she represents, the symbolic spirit she characterized in the resistance against tyranny, and more meaningfully, as the notion was largely unsung at the time of these issue's publishing, the important roles that women play in war-based conflicts).

War Comic Spotlight: A war comic to watch carefully, better yet, to acquire is *OAAW* #196. A classic Kubert/Rock cover and a Kubert story inside, its importance to both the war comic genre AND to the entire comic hobby has, in our opinion, yet to be realized. We hope to reveal and discuss its true significance in future reports. In the meantime, snap up a copy... in whatever grade you can find. *{Riveting intelligence still to come...}*

The Spoils of War:

Long Term Return

Combat (Atlas 1952) – With only an 11-issue run, this title still made an impact on the war comic genre *{not enough data exists to determine its trajectory, but still a good bet in our mind}*

Short Term Return

Sgt. Rock #302 – As of 2014 there were only five CGC 9.8 copies on census and you would expect to pay more than $500+ for a copy. We believed it would not take long for this comic to crest $1000 *{Hard to say, mainly because there were no 9.8's sold to record new data.}* This comic however qualifies as a long-term Bronze Age investment. Here's a good example of its scarcity; *Sgt. Rock* #302, published in 1977 (the seminal first issue) has only five 9.8 copies on census. Compare that to *Star Wars* #1 (published the same year) which boasts almost *{575}* 9.8s on census. OK, so there was a larger print run. Still, it doesn't change the fact that war comics in high grade in any era are very, very tough to find.

8th WAR REPORT - 2015 through 2016

The Best Cover on the Battlefield: We were delighted to be a part of the development of a 2000 copy limited run of *Overstreet Comic Book Price Guides* featuring a dedicated Sgt. Rock (and Easy Co.) cover drawn by none other than the great Russ Heath! If you don't have a one of the limited-edition copies of *Overstreet* #46, then here's the finished image: Hope you have one!

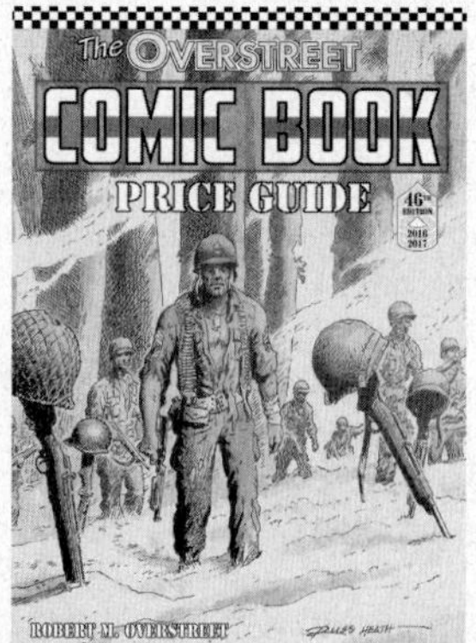

Field Report: After some calm in 2013 and 2014, war comics were seeing action again in late 2015 and 2016! There were consistent sales happening on keys, high grade, and/or low census war comics on almost ANY publishing line or title. Titles that continued to move well included a good swath of DC's Big-5, but they are accompanied by Atlas war titles, EC war in high grade, Fiction House, and Don Winslow issues in various titles. Even so, a great number of mid to low-grade war comics are available that are not only affordable, but continue to experience pretty stagnant growth. Here are highlights:

Don Winslow – Sells in any title, re-emphasizing what an important figure he is to the development of the war (adventure) genre. A Merwil Publishing 1937 *Don Winslow* #1 in CGC 7.5 sold for $2600.

Fiction House – Fans are very aware that *Fight Comics* and *Wings Comics* have been solid Golden Age war comic pillars. The Mile High *Wings* #1 sold for $15,500 in CGC 9.8. A bargain, for the single highest copy of *Wings* #1 (which sits atop our Golden Age War ranking).

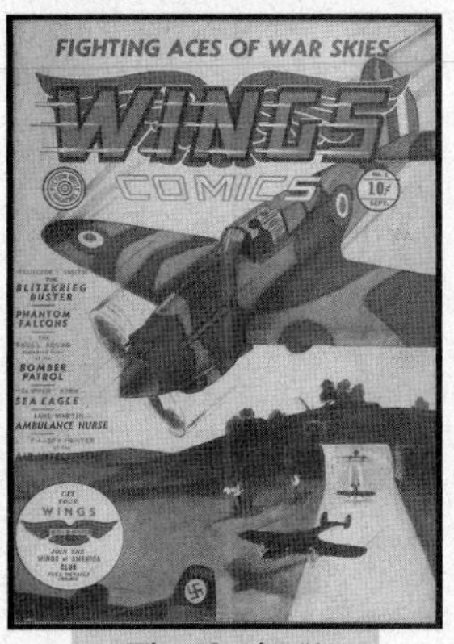

Wings Comics #1

DC's *Showcase* continue to have their day in the sun. Although there are only a few issues dedicated to the war theme, these mid 1960s war comics still stand their ground.

Sgt Fury #1 experienced small value hits to its armor. We're only talking a few percent loss though. We believe that the comic's value and ranking benefitted greatly from the halo effect of the Marvel movie hype. So, perhaps it stands to reason that there should have been a small market adjustment. Sales: *Sgt. Fury* #1 CGC 3.0 $500, CGC 5.0 $800, CBCS 5.5 $950, CGC 6.0 $1700, CGC 7.0 $2600 and CGC 8.5 $5000.

EC War – particularly high-grade. Issues of *Frontline Combat* and *Two-Fisted Tales* above 9.0 have no problems selling, and those coveted 9.6 and 9.8 Gaines File copies that pop up are selling for $2000 or $3000 a copy. Notably, key issue *Two Fisted Tales* #18 in CGC 9.6 went for about $3600.

Atlas War continues to move, particularly the titles *Battle* and *Combat*. Atlas war in general is still very affordable compared to DC war and Fiction House.

OAAW #83—climbs to #15 on Overstreet's Top 50 Silver Age Comics!

Early Rock in *OAAW* continue to sell, whether key or not. Case and point, a CGC copy of issue #108 in 9.0 (25 issues after Rock's first appearance) went for $2800. We understand 1st issues and key issues selling for high dollar…but, non-key comics 25 issues after the 1st appearance? Unusual. Punctuating the fact is that any Rock comic from the early 1960s commands attention.

Battlefield Ops – The Longest Battle (Mick Rabin): I have known only a handful of collectors who ever completed an entire run of DC war comics and two collectors who amassed the even more daunting complete Atlas war collection. Every ONE of these collections was painstakingly assembled piecemeal...no more than a few issues at any one time. The grade range on these piecemeal collections was more expansive than VF, probably because the no-less devoted people who amassed them are more pragmatic than I could ever hope to be. It took me years to finally arrive at a rather nasty conclusion. Essentially, I could go my whole life and likely never complete them all if I was limiting myself to VF or better copies...but I am stubborn and decided long ago that I could live with that reality. A lot of long-time dealers see me at shows, still combing the bins, and express that they're a bit shocked that I'm still looking—decades after I began--but that says something about how truly difficult this quest has been.

Intel from the War Correspondents – The 'Post-War' Era (Brian Sheppard): It's worth looking into what I call the 'Post-War' era of war comics, namely titles that have been published generally since the main DC titles ended their runs. While the quality varies, I think this is territory worth exploring for enthusiasts of the war genre, as war comic fans tend to be content-oriented, actually reading and re-reading the books. Do yourself a favor and get these comics:

The 'Nam, Semper Fi, Sgt. Rock Special #2, *War Idyll, War in Heaven*, *Between Hell and a Hard Place*, *The Losers Crisis Special*, *Swamp Thing* #82 and #83, 2010's *Star Spangled War* one shot, *Viet Nam Journal*, *High Shining Brass*, *Gulf War Journal*, *Savage Tales*, *Battlegroup Peiper*, *Days of Darkness*, *Medal of Honor* and Sam Glanzman's *A Sailor's Story*. So, if you think war comics ended with *Sgt. Rock* #422 in 1998, think again.

The Spoils of War:

<u>Long Term Return</u>

High Grade Bronze Age War – What makes this an exceptional opportunity is that Bronze Age war is incredibly inexpensive compared to other genres of the same era. It's a good time to snap up high grade, yet still cheap copies of *Blitzkrieg*, *Combat Kelly*, *Sgt. Rock*, *Unknown Soldier*, *Weird War* and key issues of the Big-5. Be patient, but we believe these comics will have their time in the spotlight not too long from now. *{Still true}*

<u>Short Term Return</u>

Blazing Combat (Warren) – This politically in-tune comic magazine is a must have for any fan of war comics, Warren magazines, and a slew of hot-shot '60s comic artists. Get your hands on the highest grade of any these that you can… and of course target issue #1. *{Still true}*

<u>Losing Ground</u>

Sgt. Fury #1 was taking a little hit. We are blaming it on post Marvel movie market corrections. Couple that with the {700} copies on census and it makes sense that it was taking a small dip. In this case, we say: take advantage of this!! Consider this if you are doubtful; Disney owns Marvel. This intellectual property is now in their tome of mythos. *{Mid-grade copies are starting to rise*}

<u>Gaining Ground</u>

OAAW #84 is taking its rightful role as Sgt. Rock's true 2nd appearance. It is currently affordable… *{Still true, but warming up.}*

Operation 'Pop Art' (Matt Ballesteros): 54 years after DC published *All American Men of War* #89, and 53 years after Roy Lichtenstein unveiled his Pop art phenomena, Heath creates a Redux of *Whaam!*, a Lichtenstein piece influenced heavily by comic book imagery from Jerry Grandenetti, Irv Novick and, of course, Russ Heath.

There is an enormous amount of controversy about Lichtenstein utilizing the pre-existing art found in comics to compose his pieces. There are both supporters and critics of his adoption of the medium. *Whaam!* is of course considered one of Lichtenstein's most popular pieces and is perhaps one of the most recognizable works of Pop art next to Warhol's Campbell's Soup Cans or his Marilyn Dyptich. It was a rewarding experience to see Heath regenerate the piece.

9th WAR REPORT - 2016 through 2017

Field Report: The latter half of 2016 and first half of 2017 saw war comics holding at relatively the same forward line established over the previous two years. Consequently, it also experienced nearly the same amount of action. High-grade war from any publisher was snapped up almost immediately, commanding gradually better and better prices. Low to mid-grade war comics (4.0 or less) are available at the same modest prices set in the last few years. With scant high-grade copies available, the demand is high and the acquisition is low. Attainment of said specimens is thus a true achievement in the war comic segment—garnering both praise and envy amongst the avid war collecting community. Here are some highlights of the 2016-2017 year:

Andy Greenham reports that the most common request that he has is for *OAAW* #83 (Sgt. Rock), then *GIC* #87 (Haunted Tank), then *SSWS* #84 (Mlle. Marie). After that, it's *SSWS* #151 (Unknown Soldier).

Golden Age War continues to grow in popularity. Existing Fiction House collectors, the heady growth of *Don Winslow* interest, and collectors attempting to complete a *Wings* run, are all collectively placing lesser known Golden Age titles in the spotlight. Good examples of this are *Bill Barnes*, *Boy Commandos*, *Contact Comics*, *U.S. Marines* (and so on). Key sales: *Bill Barnes* #1 CGC 7.0 (1st issue of Air Ace title) – over $550. *Contact Comics* #2 CGC 6.5 – over $450.

Don Winslow is not losing any nautical speed and represents what we believe is the first contiguous war comic character in the hobby, his first appearance in *Popular Comics* #1 dates back to 1936, before Superman. Key sales: *Don Winslow of the Navy* #1 CGC 7.0 (1937, 1st solo book) – over $1300. *Don Winslow of the Navy* #3 (1943) in CGC 9.2 (Mile High) – over $1600.

Wings remains aloft across its entire 124 issue run. Issues in mid or low-grade are downright attainable. Key sales: *Wings* #1 CGC 7.5 – over $1350. *Wings* #3 CGC 7.0 – over $350.

Sgt. Fury is slowly advancing again. There isn't a significant bump in worth yet, but we again recommend that this would be the time to get your hands on this comic. Key sales: *Sgt. Fury* #1 CGC 7.0 – $3100 to $3600. *Sgt. Fury* #5 CGC 9.8 – approx. $4800.

DC War continues to maintain its preeminent status. That said, no extraordinary sales occurred in the last year, other than the expected general and gradual growth of this entire line. Key sales: *GIC* #87 CGC 8.0 (1st app. of Haunted Tank) – approx. $2500. *GIC* #114 CGC 9.4 (origin Haunted Tank) – over $1300.

OAAWs – Key Sgt. Rock issues continue to garner much of the market's attention. Despite that, *OAAW* #81, once considered Sgt. Rock's 1st appearance, has softened a bit for the middle and lower-grade specimens. We don't anticipate the book to fall too hard in lower grades, and we expect market growth in grades 6.0 and above because it is still a pivotal prototype comic, very difficult to acquire, and rare in grades 7.0 and above because of its purple cover. We are, however, scratching our heads a bit, because of the lack of sales to report on *OAAW* #82, as the recent reclassification of #82 has both collectors and speculators potentially puzzled. Nevertheless, this would still make *OAAW* #82 the seminal final Sgt. Rock prototype. The fact that the market doesn't know what to do with it is in your benefit. *OAAW* #83 in a 4.0 grade seven years ago were averaging just under $400, now each command nearly $3000 apiece. We see no slowing on this title in any grade, and with approximately less than 150 "known" copies currently (in all grades combined), you're going to have to fight to get a copy of what is considered the *Action* #1 and/or *Detective* #27 of war comics. Key sales: *OAAW* #81 CGC 7.0 (key Sgt. Rock prototype) – over $2000. *OAAW* #82 CGC 7.0 (last Sgt. Rock prototype) – over $850. *OAAW* #83 CGC 4.0 (1st true Sgt. Rock) – over $2500.

War on an Open Field (By Mick Rabin): The focus of comics collecting has – for better or worse – shifted further away from interior stories and more towards covers in the past decade or so. It probably has a lot to do with widespread use of slabs and chat forums where collectors discuss their acquisitions and the thing getting displayed most often is the cover itself. You'd be hard-pressed to find a DC war comics collector without a "Top-10 Covers" list. But there's something else compelling that I recognized that wasn't apparent before. It's not so much about what IS on the covers as what is NOT on the covers.

GIC #75 is not just the tour-de-force Grandenetti washtone with the greys, blacks, and blues. It's that there ARE NO WORDS ON THE COVER AT ALL The high impact of art, music, and literature is often-times a product of the dynamics between what IS rendered, played, and written AND what is NOT. At some point, Kanigher, Jack Adler, and the war comics crew began piloting the idea of "word-economy." An early example is *SSWS* #39 (Nov. 1955). It has ZERO captions, chapter titles, or word balloons. Slightly later, *AAMOW* #35 (July '56), the second washtone war cover, has NO text box, but just two words in the lower right—"Battle Call."

There are other later standouts like *AAMOW* #62 (Oct. '58) with two words—"No Cover" (again NOT contained in a text box). It's definitely one of the best Big-5 covers ever. *SSWS* #74 (Oct. '58), *GIC* #69—the "one-off" before the deluge of the Perty Thirty starting with *GIC* #75). In short, Big-5 creators clearly knew what they were doing—go for MAXIMUM IMPACT.

10th WAR REPORT - 2017 through 2018

News from the Front: The 2017-2018 period is continuing to hold the line as it has in the past few years. A decade into this report, we are witnessing a clearer separation in action (in any publishing line) between high-grade versus the plenteous low-grade war. With very limited high-grade available there is scant field action to report on in depth. But, we have noticed one-off divergent activity that demonstrates growth and/or focus in deeper niche segments within the war category. Great examples of that are the sales of a high-grade *Sgt. Fury* with a Captain America appearance, *Two Fisted Tales* from the acclaimed EC line, any of the *Wings* comics from Fiction House, a *Real Life Comics* with a classic Hitler cover, etc. Conversely, the higher-grade DC War and key Sgt. Rock issues continue to get their attention. Below are some samples sales of interest.

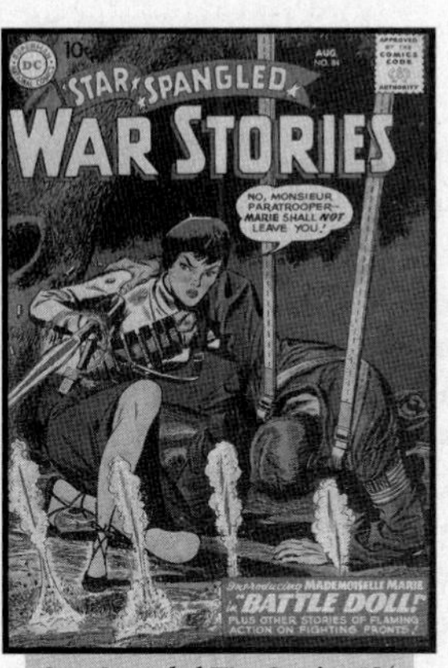

Star Spangled War Stories #84

2017-2018 Sales of note: *Bill Barnes* #7 CGC 5.5 $3,350, *Blazing Combat* #1 CGC 8.0 $1,150, *GIC* #114 CGC 9.6 $1,765, *OAAW* #81 CGC 8.5 $5,750, *OAAW* #83 CGC 3.0 $1,675, *OAAW* #83 CGC 5.5 $4,700, *OFF* #1 CGC 7.5 $1,400, *Rangers Comics* #26 CGC 5.5 $1,150, *Real Life Comics* #3 CGC 9.0 $20,000, *Real Life Comics* #3 CGC 5.5 $5,250, *Sgt. Fury* #1 CGC 8.0 $3,350, *Sgt. Fury* #1 CGC 6.5 $1,725, *Sgt. Fury* #2 CGC 9.4 $2,900, *Sgt. Fury* #13 CGC 9.8 $11,350, *Sgt. Fury* #13 CGC 9.2 $1,300, *SSWS* #90 CGC 6.5 $1,050, *Two-Fisted Tales* #18 CGC 9.8 $6,000, *Two-Fisted Tales* #19 CGC 9.8 $2,050, and *Wings* #1 CGC 8.5 $1,900.

2017-2018 Field Report from Andy Greenham: Hi again, everyone! It's hard to believe, but here we are again with a new Overstreet and War Report. Man, what's with this time thing not slowing down? Quip aside, I want to extend my gratitude to Matt and Mick for allowing me to join them in putting out this annual War Report. I know I'm biased, but I truly feel it is the most interesting and informative report amongst all the market reports. Also, many thanks to Overstreet for allowing this much-needed report to be included in the *Guide* year after year. For this report, I wanted to give my thoughts on the current marketplace on war comics, as well as reflect upon the past War Comic Cover "Survivor Series" contests that I held for many consecutive years on the CGC boards.

Andy's War Comic Marketplace: I usually set up and exhibit at around eight shows a year. When you're a dealer selling books, you will always have folks asking for this or that. While there are still collectors who are putting their runs together and filling in their want lists, the majority of collectors have shifted to a key-oriented mindset. That is, a lot of people now are focusing on 1st appearances and #1 issues. That's not a terrible thing, as these people haven't left the market of comics, but it does make the run collectors quite a bit scarce themselves. Now, war comic book collectors are a different animal. They seem to be more of a full-fledged collector, more of a purist in terms of collecting for the love of the material. I can relate, as I was definitely one of them for a long period of time. It's not like I've stopped loving war books or comics in general, it's just that I've shifted gears and taken off my collector's hat and put my dealer's hat on. Either way, I've got lots to say from both sides of the table!

The non-war collector seems to pay attention to our War Comic Rankings. Any copies of *OAAW* #83 sell immediately, even if they're priced aggressively. The book's demand far out-weighs the supply. *SSWS* #84, the first appearance of Mlle. Marie, is another hot key issue. There don't seem to be any cheap copies around anymore, and the cheapest seem to start at $200. Another war comic that is smoking hot is *SSWS* #90, the first dinosaur issue. Again, not necessarily with just war comic collectors, but also with key collectors. This is another book that starts around $200 and goes up from there. Surprisingly, I've been asked less and less for *GIC* #87, my favorite war comic. It's the first appearance of the Haunted Tank, and it's got one of the most amazing Russ Heath washtone covers that's out there. It's still a great book, but I tend to see it around on other dealer's walls much more frequently that the other keys.

The Best of the War Comic Covers Polls: If you've been following us over the years, you'd know that I have run a contest on the CGC boards with the purpose of determining the best war comic covers out there. I have done this year to year, and sometimes narrowed it to cover categories such as; best DC War, best washtone, best non-washtone, best non-DC, etc. It was always a ton of fun and a great contest overall. Seeing how people voted and listening to their feedback was also interesting, as what determined what was "the best" changed from person to person. Even the fact of how different people's tastes actually didn't change the results that much, which is supported by the fact that certain covers continue to place in the top 3, again and again. Here are seven years of results:

- **Year 1, Best War Cover:** Winner - *GIC* #80, 2nd *AAMOW* #94, 3rd *GIC* #91.
- **Year 2: War Correspondents Candidates:** *OAAW* #112, *OFF* #71 and #20, *GIC* #78, #83 and #87.
- **Year 3: Non-Washtone Covers:** Winner - *Two-Fisted Tales* #30, 2nd *GIC* #46, 3rd *SSWS* #81.
- **Year 4: Joe Kubert Covers:** Winner - *Brave and the Bold* #44, 2nd *SSWS* #138, 3rd *GIC* #78.
- **Year 5: Russ Heath Covers:** Winner - *GIC* #80, 2nd *AAMOW* #94, 3rd *Marvel Tales* #130.
- **Year 6: Weird War Covers:** Winner - *WW* #4, 2nd *WW* #5, 3rd *WW* #80 (all 3 Kubert covers).
- **Year 7: Grandenetti Covers:** Winner - *OFF* #9, 2nd *SSWS* #64, 3rd *OAAW* #70.

GAINING RANK

Here is the 10th edition of the war comic ranking. Each comic book's position in the ranks was based on criteria such as who was on the creative team, key storylines, art, first appearances, popularity, market value, scarcity, etc. For comparison and historical reference, this year we included our original ranking from 2008 (where we only published 20 to 30 issues).

TOP 50 ATOM / SILVER / BRONZE AGE WAR COMICS OF 2018

ISSUE	2018 RANK	2017 RANK	2008 RANK	MERIT
Our Army at War #83	1	1	1	1st true app. of Sgt. Rock (Kanigher/Kubert Master Sgt.)
Sgt. Fury #1	2	2	10	1st app. of Sgt. Fury
G.I. Combat #87	3	3	2	1st app. of Haunted Tank
Our Army at War #81	4-t	4-t	4	Sgt. Rock prototype (Non Kanigher/Kubert "Sgt. Rocky")
Our Army at War #82	4-t	4-t	5	Sgt. Rock prototype (Non Kanigher/Kubert 4th grade rate Sgt.)
G.I. Combat #68	6-t	6	3	Sgt. Rock prototype (Kanigher/Kubert "The Rock" story
Two-Fisted Tales #18	6-t	7-t	7	1st issue to start EC War run
Our Army at War #1	8	7-t	6	1st issue of Big Five war title
Star Spangled War Stories #84	9	11	20	1st app. of Mademoiselle Marie
Our Army at War #90	10	10	9	How Sgt. Rock got his stripes
Frontline Combat #1	11	9	8	1st issue of EC all war title
G.I. Combat #44	12	12	11	1st DC issue of Big Five war Title, early washtone
Our Army at War #84	13	15	25	2nd app. of Sgt Rock
Our Fighting Forces #1	14	13	13	1st issue of Big Five war title
Our Army at War #88	15	14	12	1st Sgt. Rock cover (Kubert)
Star Spangled War Stories #90	16	18	NA	1st Dinosaur "War That Time Forgot" ish
Our Army at War #85	17	16	24	1st app. of Ice Cream Soldier and 2nd Kubert Sgt. Rock
Star Spangled War Stories #131	18	17	17	1st issue of Big Five war title
All American Men of War #127	19	19	18	1st issue of Big Five war title
Our Fighting Forces #45	20	20	14	Gunner & Sarge run begins (Kanigher/Grandenetti, predates OAAW #83)
Our Army at War #112	21	21	23	Classic roster ("Brady Bunch") cover
Our Army at War #151	22	23	19	1st app. of Enemy Ace
G.I. Combat #1	23	24-t	22	1st issue of Quality Comics title
Our Army at War #91	24-t	22	15	1st all Sgt. Rock issue
All American Men of War #67	24-t	24-t	26	1st app. of Gunner & Sarge (predates OAAW #83, not Grandenetti)
Battle #1	26	27	NA	1st issue of Atlas war title
G.I. Combat #91	27-t	26	NA	1st Haunted Tank Cover (washtone)
Combat #1	27-t	29	NA	1st issue of Atlas War title (black cover)
Blazing Combat #1	29	30	28	1st issue of Warren war Magazine
G.I. Combat #75	30	28	NA	1st in "Perty Thirty" washtone run
Our Army at War #100	31	32	NA	Scarce Kubert (black cover)
All American Men of War #28	32	31	16	1st Sgt. Rock prototype (Kubert art)
Star Spangled War Stories #151	33	33	NA	1st solo app. of Unknown Soldier
Our Army at War #196	34	44	NA	Key transitional comic (classic Kubert cover)
Two-Fisted Tales Annual #1	35-t	34	21	Early 132 pg. EC war annual
Foxhole #1	35-t	36	NA	1st ish Mainline title (classic Kirby cover)
Our Army at War #168	37	40	NA	1st app. of the Unknown Soldier
G.I. Combat #80	38	38	NA	Classic washtone cover
Our Army at War #86	39	35	27	Early Sgt. Rock
Fightin' Marines 15 (#1)	40	37	29	1st issue of St. John war Title (Baker art)
G.I. Combat #69	41-t	39	NA	1st in Grandenetti washtone trifecta
Our Army at War #128	41-t	41	NA	Training & origin of Sgt. Rock
Our Fighting Forces #49	43	42-t	NA	1st app. of Pooch
All American Men of War #82	44	42-t	30	1st app. of Johnny Cloud
All American Men of War #89	45	47	NA	Historic issue influenced Lichtenstein pop art paintings

Our Army at War #95	46	45	NA	1st app. of Bulldozer
G.I. Combat #83	47	46	NA	1st Big Al, Little Al & Charlie (2nd cover of washtone trifecta)
Sgt Rock #302	48	49	NA	1st issue of seminal Bronze Age war title
Sgt. Fury #13	49	48	NA	2nd Silver Age solo app. of Captain America
G.I. Combat #114	50	50-t	NA	Origin of Haunted Tank
War Comics #11	NA	NA	NA	Honorable mention

Only 30 war comics were ranked in 2008. Our biggest movers over the last decade include Sgt. Fury #1, OAAW #84 and SSWS #90. Mlle. Marie in SSWS #84 makes our top 10 in 2018. OAAW #196 was the strongest mover this year.

TOP 15 GOLDEN AGE WAR COMICS OF 2018

ISSUE	2018 RANK	2017 RANK	2008 RANK	MERIT
Wings #1	1	1	1	1st issue in long running air war title
War Comics #1	2	2	2	1st comic completely devoted to war content
Don Winslow #1 (1937)	3	3	NA	Very early war adventure title
Real Life #3	4	4	3	Hitler Cover (early 1942 WWII)
Contact Comics #1	5	5	4	1st issue of air battles title
Don Winslow #1 (1939)	6	6	NA	Rare Four Color issue (#2)
Real Life Comics #1	7	7	5	1st issue of adventure title
Rangers Comics #8	8	8	8	US Rangers begin
Wings Comics #2	9	9	6	2nd issue of key air war title
US Marines #2	10	10	NA	Classic Cover (Bailey art)
Bill Barnes Comics #1	11	11	7	1st issue of Air Ace title
Don Winslow of the Navy #1 ('43)	12	12	NA	1st comic of 73 issue series (Captain Marvel on cover)
Rangers Comics #26	13	14	NA	Classic cover
Remember Pearl Harbor (nn)	14	13	9	1942 illustrated story of the battle
American Library nn (#1)	15	15	NA	"Thirty Seconds Over Tokyo" (movie)

Contact Comics #1

TOP 5 ATLAS WAR COMICS OF 2018

ISSUE	2018 RANK	2017 RANK	MERIT
Battle #1	1	1	1st issue of Atlas war title
Combat #1	2	2	1st issue of Atlas War title (black cover)
War Comics #1	3	3	1st issue of Atlas War title
War Comics #11	4	5	Classic flamethrower cover
War Action #1	5	4	1st issue of Atlas War title

Soldier and Marine #11

TOP 5 CHARLTON WAR COMICS OF 2018

ISSUE	2018 RANK	2017 RANK	MERIT
Fightin' Marines 15 (#1)	1	1	1st issue in St. John war title (Baker art)
Attack #54	2	2	1st issue in short war title (100 pgs)
Soldier and Marine #11	3	3	1st ish in short war title (Bob Powell art)
US Air Force #1	4	4	1st issue of Charlton war title
Fightin' Navy #74	5	5	1st issue of Charlton war title (formerly Don Winslow)

Over and Out

Thanks for reading the War Report. A big thank you to those supporters who have stuck by our side and shared excellent thoughts and comments these last 10 years. We so appreciate it. Our hats are off again to the men behind this publication: Bob Overstreet, JC Vaughn, and Mark Huesman.

Thanks to the troops

Thank you, Mick Rabin and Andy Greenham, for your continuous contributions to this dispatch. Without your expertise this report would be woefully lacking.
I salute you both!

KEY SALES FROM 2017-2018

The following lists of sales were reported to Gemstone during the year and represent only a small portion of the total amount of important books that have sold. For other sales information, please see the Overstreet Market Report starting on page 89.

GOLDEN AGE - SALES OF CERTIFIED COMICS

Action Comics #56 CGC 2.5 $450
Adventure Comics #97 CGC 7.0 $472
All-American Comics #60 CGC 9.0 $1,025.42
All Select Comics #3 CGC 6.0 $1,570.58
All Star Comics #14 CGC 5.0 $650
Archie Comics #8 CGC 2.0 $339.84
Archie Comics #16 CGC 1.8 $162.25
Batman #1 CGC 2.0 $75,000
Batman #14 CGC 6.5 $1,817.20
Batman #21 CGC 8.0 $1,298
Batman #22 CGC 8.0 $1,427.80
Batman #23 CGC 1.8 $420
Batman #25 CGC 5.5 $1,200
Batman #26 CGC 5.0 $600
Batman #32 CGC 4.5 $400
Batman #37 CGC 4.0 $1,150
Batman #37 CGC 5.0 $1,815
Batman #37 CGC 7.0 $1,810
Batman #44 CGC 4.0 $805
Batman #52 CGC 5.5 $1,001
Batman #55 CGC 5.0 $706
Batman #56 CGC 8.0 $767
Batman #59 CGC 5.0 $1,338
Batman #66 CGC 4.5 $510
Buck Rogers #1 CGC 6.0 $1,038.40
Buck Rogers #3 CGC 6.5 $413
Buck Rogers #4 CGC 8.0 $737.50
Captain Aero Comics #26 CGC 3.5 $312.70
Captain America Comics #1 CGC 1.8 $62,000
Captain America Comics #34 CGC 6.5 $2,200
Captain America Comics #77 CGC 3.5 $600
Captain Battle Comics #3 CGC 5.0 $250
Captain Marvel Adventures #3 CGC 6.5 $1,070.85
Classic Comics #4 CGC 8.5 $1,256.46
Crack Comics #1 CGC 6.5 $1,557.60
Crack Comics #7 CGC 8.5 $843.70
Crime Does Not Pay #34 CGC 9.4 $1,035.15
Crime Does Not Pay #41 CGC 9.2 $590
Crime SuspenStories #20 CGC 5.0 $200
Detective Comics #62 CGC 5.5 $5,900
Detective Comics #74 CGC 3.0 $389.40
Detective Comics #85 CGC 6.5 $3,300
Detective Comics #91 CGC 7.5 $2,559
Detective Comics #109 CGC 3.0 $816
Detective Comics #109 CGC 4.5 $722
Detective Comics #109 CGC 6.0 $1,206
Detective Comics #109 CGC 6.0 $1,206
Detective Comics #123 CGC 7.5 $392
Detective Comics #124 CGC 6.5 $1,317
Detective Comics #128 CGC 6.5 $1,350
Detective Comics #128 CGC 7.5 $1,068
Detective Comics #128 CGC 8.0 $2,176
Detective Comics #137 CGC 6.0 $1,600
Famous Funnies #145 CGC 9.4 $207.68
Four Color Comics (Series 1) #4 CGC 4.0 $6,425.10
Four Color Comics #29 CGC 4.5 $1,427.80
Funny Pages #38 CBCS 3.5 $2,300
Gene Autry Comics #1 CGC 7.0 $401.20
Green Lama #2 CGC 5.0 $200
Human Torch #2 (#1) CGC 3.5 $3,400 (slight rest.)
Human Torch #12 CGC 7.0 $5,322
Human Torch #35 CGC 2.0 $189.51
King Comics #17 CGC 6.0 $155.76
Large Feature Comic #5 CGC 6.5 $428.34 (restored)
Large Feature Comic #6 CGC 4.5 $118.00
Lash Larue Western #43 CGC 9.6 $272.58
Lone Ranger Comics #1 CGC 4.0 $318.01 (restored)
MAD #22 CGC 9.0 $413
March Of Comics #4 CGC 5.0 $1,622.50
March Of Comics #41 CGC 5.0 $843.70
Marvel Comics #1 CGC 0.5 $39,000
Marvel Mystery Comics #9 CGC 4.0 $6,250 (restored)
Marvel Mystery Comics #15 CGC 7.0 $2,923
Marvel Mystery Comics #19 CGC 7.0 $1,920
Marvel Mystery Comics #20 CGC 7.0 $2,550
Marvel Mystery Comics #23 CGC 6.5 $1,600

Marvel Mystery Comics #25 CGC 6.5 $1,811
Marvel Mystery Comics #33 CGC 7.0 $2,811
Marvel Mystery Comics #39 CGC 5.5 $907
Marvel Mystery Comics #50 CGC 8.0 $3,300
Marvel Mystery Comics #64 CGC 8.5 $254
Sensation Comics #13 CGC 6.0 $2,652
Star Spangled Comics #2 CGC 8.0 $1,180.00
Startling Comics #35 CGC 8.5 $1,457
Startling Comics #49 CGC 9.6 $72,000
Superman #4 CGC 1.0 $928.07
Superman #17 CGC 5.0 $2,500
Superman #23 CGC 6.0 $725
Superman #31 CGC 5.0 $450
Superman #34 CGC 4.5 $350
Superman #36 CGC 5.0 $400
Thrilling Comics #44 CGC 4.5 $911
Tomb of Terror #15 CGC 8.5 $3,400
USA Comics #5 CGC 4.5 $2,665
Wonder Woman #6 CGC 2.5 $3,200
Young Allies Comics #4 CGC 8.0 $5,000

SILVER AGE - SALES OF CERTIFIED COMICS

Action Comics #252 CGC 3.0 $885
Adventure Comics #267 CGC 3.5 $200
Amazing Fantasy #15 CGC 1.0 $7,900
Amazing Fantasy #15 CGC 1.5 $13,200 (Signed Stan Lee)
Amazing Fantasy #15 CGC 2.5 $19,000 (Signed Stan Lee)
Amazing Fantasy #15 CGC 5.0 $49,000
Amazing Fantasy #15 CGC 5.5 $42,000
Amazing Spider-Man #1 CGC 2.5 $3,500
Amazing Spider-Man #1 CGC 9.0 $58,000
Amazing Spider-Man #2 CGC 4.5 $1,200
Amazing Spider-Man #3 CGC 3.0 $650
Amazing Spider-Man #5 CGC 1.5 $250
Amazing Spider-Man #6 CGC 9.0 $4,100
Amazing Spider-Man #9 CGC 7.0 $358.25
Amazing Spider-Man #14 CBCS 9.0 $5,100
Amazing Spider-Man #14 CGC 4.5 $600
Amazing Spider-Man #14 CGC 3.5 $306.98
Amazing Spider-Man #15 CGC 7.5 $778.80
Amazing Spider-Man #28 CGC 3.5 $200
Amazing Spider-Man #39 CGC 5.0 $389.40
Amazing Spider-Man #40 CGC 8.5 $900
Amazing Spider-Man #40 CGC 8.0 $236.00
Amazing Spider-Man #47 CGC 8.5 $300
Amazing Spider-Man #50 CGC 7.5 $1,000
Amazing Spider-Man #50 CGC 9.0 $1,800
Amazing Spider-Man #75 CGC 9.2 $200
America's Best TV Comics #1 CGC 9.6 $298.54
Aquaman #35 CGC 5.0 $216
Avengers #1 PGX 7.5 $6,700
Avengers #1 CGC 3.0 $1,600
Avengers #1 CGC 5.5 $3,000
Avengers #3 CGC 9.6 $17,000
Avengers #4 CBCS 7.5 $2,700
Avengers #12 CGC 9.0 $400
Avengers #55 CGC 6.5 $200
Avengers #57 CGC 9.6 $5,500
Batman #121 CGC 3.5 $1,300
Brave and the Bold #28 CGC 2.5 $2,200
Brave and the Bold #28 CGC 5.0 $4,500
Brave and the Bold #28 CGC 6.5 $1,600 (restored)
Brave and the Bold #28 CGC 7.5 $6,730
Captain America #100 CGC 5.0 $250
Captain America #100 CGC 7.5 $400
Detective Comics #225 CGC 7.5 $22,000
Detective Comics #359 CGC 4.5 $500
Detective Comics #359 CGC 1.8 $184.32
Fantastic Four #4 CGC 3.5 $675 (Sig. series)
Fantastic Four #45 CGC 3.0 $300
Fantastic Four #52 CGC 6.5 $600
Flash #105 CGC 8.0 $11,000
Hawkman #4 CGC 5.5 $265.50
Incredible Hulk #1 CGC 2.0 $6,800
Incredible Hulk #2 CGC 8.5 $8,500
Iron Man #1 CGC 9.8 $12,000 (Pacific Coast)
Journey Into Mystery #112 CGC 9.4 $2,800
Justice League Of America #8 CGC 9.0 $811.25
Justice League Of America #11 CGC 8.5 $244.02
Justice League Of America #16 CGC 9.0 $356.95
Rip Hunter Time Master #3 CGC 9.6 $572.45
Showcase #20 CGC 7.5 $1,109.79
Strange Tales #89 CGC 7.5 $4,500
Strange Tales #110 CGC 3.5 $1,100
Superman's GF Lois Lane #1 CGC 4.0 $800
Tales Of Suspense #2 CGC 7.0 $681.45
Tales of Suspense #58 CGC 7.0 $400
Tales to Astonish #27 CGC 4.0 $2,011
X-Men #1 CBCS 6.5 $5,400
X-Men #1 CGC 3.0 $2,250
X-Men #2 CGC 5.0 $750

BRONZE AGE - SALES OF CERTIFIED COMICS

All-Star Western #10 CGC 9.6 $2,270.50
Amazing Spider-Man #100 CGC 9.0 $300
Amazing Spider-Man #121 CGC 9.8 $3,824
Amazing Spider-Man #121 CGC 9.6 $1,500
Amazing Spider-Man #121 CGC 6.5 $200
Amazing Spider-Man #122 CGC 8.5 $227.15
Amazing Spider-Man #122 CGC 7.5 $200
Amazing Spider-Man #129 CGC 9.2 $2,065
Amazing Spider-Man #129 CGC 9.2 $1,900
Amazing Spider-Man #135 CGC 8.0 $118
American Splendor #1 CGC 9.6 $406.30
Avengers #87 CGC 9.6 $956
Batman #234 CGC 6.5 $250
Beneath the Planet of the Apes CGC 9.6 $478
Conan The Barbarian #1 CGC 9.2 $486.75
Defenders #1 CGC 9.8 $1,792.50
Detective Comics #411 CGC 8.5 $300
Doc Savage #1 CGC 9.8 $776.75
Giant-Size X-Men #1 CGC 9.4 $2,151
Giant-Size X-Men #1 CGC 5.5 $550
Green Lantern #76 CGC 9.2 $2,390
Green Lantern #87 CGC 9.6 $1,553.50
Hero for Hire #1 CGC 7.0 $265
Hero For Hire #1 CGC 7.0 $300
House of Secrets #92 CGC 9.2 $4,780
House of Secrets #92 CGC 9.0 $2,400
House of Secrets #92 CGC 3.0 $300
Incredible Hulk #180 CGC 9.6 $1,912
Incredible Hulk #180 CGC 7.5 $400
Incredible Hulk #181 CGC 7.0 $2,000
Incredible Hulk #181 CGC 5.0 $778.80 (restored)
Incredible Hulk #181 CGC 4.5 $1,150
Incredible Hulk #181 CGC 2.0 $600
Incredible Hulk #271 CGC 9.2 $118
Iron Man #30 CGC 9.8 $15,000
Iron Man #55 CGC 9.6 $3,824
Marvel Premiere #3 CGC 9.8 $717
Marvel Premiere #15 CGC 9.8 $3,346
Marvel Team-Up #1 CGC 9.6 $2,600
Night Nurse #1 CGC 9.6 $2,031.50
Silver Surfer #44 CGC 7.0 $55
Starslayer #2 CGC 9.8 $118
Star Wars #1 CGC 9.6 $366
Star Wars #1 CGC 8.0 $300
Swamp Thing #10 CGC 9.8 $1,195
Tomb of Dracula #10 CGC 9.8 $1,912
Tomb of Dracula #10 CGC 7.0 $200
Werewolf By Night #32 CGC 9.6 $5,019
Wolverine Limited Series #2 CGC 9.8 $118
X-Men #95 CGC 9.8 $896.25
X-Men #101 CGC 9.8 $2,868
X-Men #101 CGC 8.0 $250
X-Men #126 CGC 9.4 $85

COPPER - MODERN AGE - SALES OF CERTIFIED COMICS

Albedo #2 CGC 9.8 $6,871.25
Amazing Spider-Man #300 CGC 9.2 $375
Amazing Spider-Man #300 CGC 9.0 $285.56
Amazing Spider-Man #300 CGC 8.0 $400
Batman Adventures #12 CGC 9.8 $1,673
Batman: Harley Quinn nn CGC 9.6 $157.06
Batman: The Dark Knight Returns #1 CGC 9.8 $717
Batman: The Killing Joke CGC 9.8 $172.76
Crow, The #4 CGC 9.0 $162.25
Daredevil #168 CGC 9.8 $1075.50
Incredible Hulk #340 CGC 6.0 $55
Infinity Gauntlet #1 CGC 9.8 $335
Marvel Graphic Novel #4 CGC 9.8 $717
New Mutants #87 CGC 9.8 $597.50
New Mutants #98 CGC 9.6 $350
New Mutants #98 CGC 7.0 $375
New Mutants #98 CGC 7.0 $200
Spawn #1 CGC 9.8 $196
Teenage Mutant Ninja Turtles #1 CGC 9.8 $38,240
Teenage Mutant Ninja Turtles #1 CGC 9.4 $9,215.80
Teenage Mutant Ninja Turtles #1 CGC 8.5 $197.30
Teenage Mutant Ninja Turtles #4 CGC 9.6 $206.38
Thundercats #1 CGC 9.8 $131.45
Transformers: Dark Cybertron #1 CGC 9.9 $118
Uncle Scrooge #179 (Whitman) CGC 9.2 $726.56
Walking Dead #1 CGC 9.8 $2,900
Wonder Woman V2 #1 CGC 9.8 $259.15
X-Factor #5 CGC 9.8 $155.76
X-Factor #6 CGC 8.5 $118
Y: The Last Man #1 CGC 9.4 $203.15

GOLDEN AGE - ATOM AGE SALES

All Winners Comics #3 VG/FN $2,200
All-Select Comics #2 FN+ $2,500
Batman #47 VG+ $1,350
Batman #56 GD- $95
Batman #66 VG+ $420
Captain America Comics #46 VG $5,900
Captain America Comics #77 VG $761
Captain Marvel Jr. #69 VG- $40
Crime Does Not Pay #43 VG/FN $372
Crime Fighters #13 FN= $49
Daredevil (1941) #11 GD+ $980
Daredevil Comics #11 FN/VF $3,450
Human Torch #12 VG/FN $3,500
Journey Into Mystery #2 VF+ $2,200
Marvel Mystery Comics #92 VG $622
Mutt & Jeff #18 GD $16
Mystery Tales #1 VG $244
Mystic #19 VG $291
Pep Comics #28 FN+ $2,550
Silver Streak Comics #14 VG+ $1,413
Spook #26 VG $324
Terrific Comics #5 GD/VG $4,500
Terrific Comics #5 VG/FN $5,700
USA Comics #5 GD+ $811
USA Comics #11 VG/FN $3,300
Wonder Woman #7 VG $4,400

SILVER AGE SALES

Amazing Spider-Man #1 VG/FN $5,000
Amazing Spider-Man #2 VG/FN $1,500
Amazing Spider-Man #3 FN/VF $2,200
Amazing Spider-Man #5 VG/FN $550
Avengers #4 FN/VF $1,800
Batman #121 GD $600
Brave and the Bold #28 VG- $2,900
Daredevil #1 VF+ $5,000
Daredevil #7 VG+ $150
Detective Comics #225 VG/FN $3,800
Fantastic Four #1 VG- $4,100
Fantastic Four #3 GD/VG $365
Fantastic Four #5 FN $2,700
Fantastic Four #48 FR- $45 (front cover only)
Fantastic Four #62 VG- $20
Fantastic Four #63 VG $20
Incredible Hulk #1 FR $4,000
Incredible Hulk #3 VF+ $3,900
Journey Into Mystery #83 VG $3,500
Superboy #68 VF+ $4,500
Tales of Suspense #39 VG- $3,100
Tales to Astonish #13 VG+ $2,000
Tales to Astonish #27 VG/FN $3,100
X-Men #1 VG/FN $4,200

BRONZE AGE TO MODERN AGE SALES

Amazing Spider-Man #129 NM- $1,800
Amazing Spider-Man #238 FN/VF $80
Captain Marvel #33 GD/VG $20
Conan the Barbarian #1 VG- $45
Daredevil #158 VF- $60
Daredevil #168 FN+ $90
Defenders #1 FN- $36
Famous 1st Edition C-26 (Action #1) VF+ $50
Fear #1 VF- $52
Giant-Size X-Men #1 VF- $600
Giant-Size X-Men #1 VG/FN $450
Harley Quinn #1 VG+ $38
Incredible Hulk #181 NM- $4,600
Incredible Hulk #340 VF/NM $40 (newsstand)
Infinity Gauntlet #1 NM- $30
Infinity Gauntlet #1 NM- $30
Kull the Conqueror #1 VF $35
Marvel Feature #1 VG+ $50
Marvel Premiere #28 VF- $30
Marvel Spotlight #2 FN $54
New Mutants #98 VG/FN $200
Secret Wars #8 VF/NM $60
Secret Wars #8 VF $100 (Canadian Newsstand)
Spider-Woman #1 VF/NM $32
Walking Dead #2 VF/NM $227
Walking Dead #6 NM $80
Walking Dead #92 $60
Walking Dead Weekly #29 NM $60
Wolverine Origins #10 (variant-c) NM $77
X-Men #141 VG/FN $65
X-Men #142 VF- $45
X-Men #266 VF- $50

TOP COMICS

The following tables denote the rate of appreciation of the top Golden Age, Platinum Age, Silver Age and Bronze Age comics, as well as selected genres over the past year. The retail value for a Near Mint- copy of each comic (or VF where a Near Mint- copy is not known to exist) in 2018 is compared to its Near Mint- value in 2017. The rate of return for 2018 over 2017 is given. The place in rank is given for each comic by year, with its corresponding value in highest known grade. These tables can be very useful in forecasting trends in the market place. For instance, the investor might want to know which book is yielding the best dividend from one year to the next, or one might just be interested in seeing how the popularity of books changes from year to year. For instance, *Sensation Comics* #1 was in 30th place in 2017 and has increased to 27th place in 2018. Premium books are also included in these tables and are denoted with an asterisk(*).

The following tables are meant as a guide to the investor. However, it should be pointed out that trends may change at anytime and that some books can meet market resistance with a slowdown in price increases, while others can develop into real comers from a presently dormant state. In the long run, if the investor sticks to the books that are appreciating steadily each year, he shouldn't go very far wrong.

TOP 100 GOLDEN AGE COMICS

TITLE/ISSUE#	2018 RANK	2018 NM- PRICE	2017 RANK	2017 NM- PRICE	$ INCR.	% INCR.
Action Comics #1	1	$3,800,000	1	$3,200,000	$600,000	19%
Detective Comics #27	2	$2,500,000	2	$2,200,000	$300,000	14%
Superman #1	3	$1,300,000	3	$1,200,000	$100,000	8%
All-American Comics #16	4	$800,000	4	$750,000	$50,000	7%
Batman #1	5	$750,000	5	$650,000	$100,000	15%
Marvel Comics #1	6	$680,000	6	$625,000	$55,000	9%
Action Comics #7	7	$480,000	7	$420,000	$60,000	14%
Captain America Comics #1	8	$460,000	8	$400,000	$60,000	15%
Pep Comics #22	9	$350,000	9	$320,000	$30,000	9%
Action Comics #10	10	$300,000	10	$280,000	$20,000	7%
All Star Comics #8	10	$300,000	12	$260,000	$40,000	15%
Detective Comics #31	10	$300,000	11	$270,000	$30,000	11%
Whiz Comics #2 (#1)	13	$270,000	13	$240,000	$30,000	13%
Detective Comics #29	14	$250,000	14	$220,000	$30,000	14%
Flash Comics #1	15	$230,000	15	$210,000	$20,000	10%
Detective Comics #33	16	$210,000	16	$190,000	$20,000	11%
Action Comics #2	17	$200,000	16	$190,000	$10,000	5%
Archie Comics #1	18	$190,000	18	$185,000	$5,000	3%
Detective Comics #35	18	$190,000	20	$170,000	$20,000	12%
More Fun Comics #52	18	$190,000	19	$180,000	$10,000	6%
Action Comics #13	21	$180,000	21	$160,000	$20,000	13%
Adventure Comics #40	22	$170,000	21	$160,000	$10,000	6%
Wonder Woman #1	23	$160,000	26	$125,000	$35,000	28%
Detective Comics #38	24	$145,000	23	$135,000	$10,000	7%
Action Comics #3	25	$143,000	23	$135,000	$8,000	6%
All Star Comics #3	26	$140,000	23	$135,000	$5,000	4%
Sensation Comics #1	27	$125,000	30	$100,000	$25,000	25%
More Fun Comics #73	28	$120,000	27	$115,000	$5,000	4%
Suspense Comics #3	29	$115,000	28	$110,000	$5,000	5%
Marvel Mystery Comics #9	30	$110,000	29	$105,000	$5,000	5%
Detective Comics #28	31	$105,000	30	$100,000	$5,000	5%
Detective Comics #1	32	VF $100,000	30	VF $100,000	$0	0%
Marvel Mystery Comics #2	33	$100,000	33	$95,000	$5,000	5%
Captain Marvel Adventures #1	34	$90,000	35	$80,000	$10,000	13%
Detective Comics #36	34	$90,000	35	$80,000	$10,000	13%
More Fun Comics #53	36	$86,000	34	$84,000	$2,000	2%
Marvel Mystery Comics #5	37	$85,000	35	$80,000	$5,000	6%
Sub-Mariner Comics #1	38	$84,000	35	$80,000	$4,000	5%
Green Lantern #1	39	$74,000	39	$72,000	$2,000	3%
Detective Comics #37	40	$72,000	42	$65,000	$7,000	11%
Human Torch #2 (#1)	40	$72,000	40	$70,000	$2,000	3%

TITLE/ISSUE#	2018 RANK	2018 NM- PRICE	2017 RANK	2017 NM- PRICE	$ INCR.	% INCR.
Superman #2	42	$70,000	41	$67,000	$3,000	4%
Action Comics #4	43	$66,000	43	$62,000	$4,000	6%
Action Comics #5	43	$66,000	43	$62,000	$4,000	6%
Action Comics #6	43	$66,000	43	$62,000	$4,000	6%
Action Comics #23	46	$65,000	50	$56,000	$9,000	16%
Marvel Mystery Comics #4	46	$65,000	47	$60,000	$5,000	8%
Adventure Comics #48	48	$63,000	43	$62,000	$1,000	2%
Captain America Comics #2	49	$62,000	48	$58,000	$4,000	7%
All-American Comics #19	50	$60,000	50	$56,000	$4,000	7%
Marvel Mystery Comics #3	50	$60,000	52	$55,000	$5,000	9%
New Fun Comics #1	52	VF $59,000	48	VF $58,000	$1,000	2%
Batman #2	53	$55,000	54	$50,000	$5,000	10%
Captain America Comics #3	53	$55,000	53	$52,000	$3,000	6%
Daring Mystery Comics #1	55	$52,000	54	$50,000	$2,000	4%
Walt Disney's Comics & Stories #1	55	$52,000	54	$50,000	$2,000	4%
Action Comics #8	57	$50,000	57	$47,000	$3,000	6%
Action Comics #9	57	$50,000	57	$47,000	$3,000	6%
Action Comics #15	57	$50,000	59	$45,000	$5,000	11%
Action Comics #12	60	$48,000	60	$44,000	$4,000	9%
Marvel Mystery Comics 132 pg.	61	VF $44,000	61	VF $43,500	$500	1%
Wonder Comics #1	61	$44,000	63	$42,000	$2,000	5%
Famous Funnies-Series 1	63	VF $43,500	62	VF $43,000	$500	1%
Amazing Man Comics #5	64	$42,000	64	$40,000	$2,000	5%
Four Color Series 1 (Donald Duck) #4	64	$42,000	64	$40,000	$2,000	5%
Motion Picture Funnies Weekly #1	64	$42,000	68	$38,000	$4,000	11%
More Fun Comics #54	67	$41,000	64	$40,000	$1,000	3%
Detective Comics #2	68	VF $40,000	67	VF $39,000	$1,000	3%
Fantastic Comics #3	68	$40,000	74	$36,000	$4,000	11%
More Fun Comics #55	68	$40,000	68	$38,000	$2,000	5%
Red Raven Comics #1	68	$40,000	68	$38,000	$2,000	5%
All-Select Comics #1	72	$39,000	68	$38,000	$1,000	3%
Mystic Comics #1	72	$39,000	68	$38,000	$1,000	3%
Captain America Comics 132 pg.	74	VF $38,000	73	VF $37,000	$1,000	3%
Silver Streak Comics #6	74	$38,000	74	$36,000	$2,000	6%
Superman #3	74	$38,000	74	$36,000	$2,000	6%
All Winners Comics #1	77	$37,000	74	$36,000	$1,000	3%
Marvel Mystery Comics #8	77	$37,000	78	$35,000	$2,000	6%
Captain America Comics #74	79	$36,000	79	$33,000	$3,000	9%
Detective Comics #30	80	$35,000	81	$32,000	$3,000	9%
Detective Comics #40	80	$35,000	84	$30,000	$5,000	17%
Double Action Comics #2	80	$35,000	81	$32,000	$3,000	9%
Jackpot Comics #4	80	$35,000	81	$32,000	$3,000	9%
Terrific Comics #5	80	$35,000	79	$33,000	$2,000	6%
All-American Comics #61	85	$34,000	101	$27,000	$7,000	26%
Action Comics #17	86	$32,000	84	$30,000	$2,000	7%
Jumbo Comics #1	86	VF $32,000	84	VF $30,000	$2,000	7%
Marvel Mystery Comics #10	86	$32,000	84	$30,000	$2,000	7%
Punch Comics #12	86	$32,000	100	$28,000	$4,000	14%
All-American Comics #17	90	$31,000	84	$30,000	$1,000	3%
New York World's Fair 1939	90	VFNM $31,000	84	VFNM $30,000	$1,000	3%
Action Comics #19	92	$30,000	91	$29,000	$1,000	3%
All-American Comics #18	92	$30,000	91	$29,000	$1,000	3%
Archie Comics #2	92	$30,000	91	$29,000	$1,000	3%
Detective Comics #32	92	$30,000	98	$28,000	$2,000	7%
Green Giant Comics #1	92	$30,000	91	$29,000	$1,000	3%
New Book of Comics #1	92	VF $30,000	84	VF $30,000	$0	0%
New Fun Comics #6	92	VF $30,000	91	VF $29,000	$1,000	3%
Action Comics #20	99	$29,000	96	$28,000	$1,000	4%
All-American Comics #25	100	$29,000	97	$28,000	$1,000	4%
Exciting Comics #9	100	$29,000	99	$28,000	$1,000	4%
World's Best Comics #1	100	$29,000	101	$27,000	$2,000	7%

TOP 50 SILVER AGE COMICS

TITLE/ISSUE#	2018 RANK	2018 NM- PRICE	2017 RANK	2017 NM- PRICE	$ INCR.	% INCR.
Amazing Fantasy #15	1	$375,000	1	$350,000	$25,000	7%
Incredible Hulk #1	2	$265,000	2	$240,000	$25,000	10%
Fantastic Four #1	3	$160,000	3	$140,000	$20,000	14%
Showcase #4	4	$150,000	4	$130,000	$20,000	15%
Brave and the Bold #28	5	$88,000	5	$80,000	$8,000	10%
Journey Into Mystery #83	6	$80,000	6	$75,000	$5,000	7%
Amazing Spider-Man #1	7	$72,000	7	$68,000	$4,000	6%
Tales of Suspense #39	8	$50,000	8	$48,000	$2,000	4%
X-Men #1	8	$50,000	8	$48,000	$2,000	4%
Tales to Astonish #27	10	$48,000	10	$45,000	$3,000	7%
Showcase #22	11	$45,000	12	$38,000	$7,000	18%
Avengers #1	12	$42,000	11	$40,000	$2,000	5%
Flash #105	13	$30,000	13	$26,000	$4,000	15%
Justice League of America #1	14	$28,000	13	$26,000	$2,000	8%
Adventure Comics #247	15	$27,000	15	$24,000	$3,000	13%
Our Army at War #83	16	$26,000	15	$24,000	$2,000	8%
Action Comics #242	17	$25,000	19	$20,000	$5,000	25%
Action Comics #252	17	$25,000	17	$22,000	$3,000	14%
Showcase #8	19	$22,000	18	$21,000	$1,000	5%
Fantastic Four #5	20	$20,000	19	$20,000	$0	0%
Strange Tales #110	21	$19,000	21	$18,000	$1,000	6%
Green Lantern #1	22	$17,500	22	$17,000	$500	3%
Fantastic Four #2	23	$15,000	23	$14,000	$1,000	7%
Fantastic Four #4	23	$15,000	23	$14,000	$1,000	7%
Fantastic Four #3	25	$14,000	26	$13,000	$1,000	8%
Showcase #9	25	$14,000	23	$14,000	$0	0%
Amazing Spider-Man #2	27	$13,500	26	$13,000	$500	4%
Fantastic Four #12	28	$13,000	26	$13,000	$0	0%
Sgt. Fury #1	28	$13,000	29	$12,500	$500	4%
Superman's G.F. Lois Lane #1	28	$13,000	29	$12,500	$500	4%
Incredible Hulk #2	31	$12,500	31	$11,500	$1,000	9%
Tales to Astonish #35	32	$11,500	36	$10,000	$1,500	15%
Amazing Spider-Man #3	33	$11,000	33	$10,500	$500	5%
Daredevil #1	33	$11,000	33	$10,500	$500	5%
Showcase #14	33	$11,000	32	$10,800	$200	2%
Our Army at War #81	36	$10,500	36	$10,000	$500	5%
Showcase #6	36	$10,500	36	$10,000	$500	5%
Showcase #13	36	$10,500	35	$10,300	$200	2%
Showcase #17	39	$10,000	39	$9,500	$500	5%
Tales to Astonish #13	39	$10,000	42	$8,000	$2,000	25%
Richie Rich #1	41	$9,500	40	$9,000	$500	6%
Brave and the Bold #25	42	$8,500	42	$8,000	$500	6%
Amazing Spider-Man #4	43	$8,400	41	$8,200	$200	2%
Avengers #4	44	$8,000	44	$7,500	$500	7%
Flash #106	44	$8,000	47	$7,000	$1,000	14%
Journey Into Mystery #84	44	$8,000	44	$7,500	$500	7%
Journey Into Mystery #85	47	$7,500	46	$7,300	$200	3%
Incredible Hulk #3	48	$7,200	47	$7,000	$200	3%
Flash #123	49	$7,000	52	$6,000	$1,000	17%
Brave and the Bold #29	50	$6,800	49	$6,800	$0	0%
Fantastic Four #6	50	$6,800	49	$6,800	$0	0%

TOP 25 BRONZE AGE COMICS

TITLE/ISSUE#	2018 RANK	2018 NM- PRICE	2017 RANK	2017 NM- PRICE	$ INCR.	% INCR.
Star Wars #1 (35¢ price variant)	1	$11,000	1	$10,000	$1,000	10%
Incredible Hulk #181	2	$4,200	3	$3,500	$700	20%
Iron Fist #14 (35¢ price variant)	2	$4,200	2	$4,000	$200	5%
Cerebus #1	4	$2,900	4	$2,800	$100	4%
Green Lantern #76	5	$2,700	5	$2,700	$0	0%
Scooby Doo (1970) #1	6	$2,500	6	$2,000	$500	25%
House of Secrets #92	7	$2,400	7	$1,800	$600	33%
Amazing Spider-Man #129	8	$1,700	10	$1,500	$200	13%
Giant-Size X-Men #1	8	$1,700	8	$1,600	$100	6%
Star Wars #2 (35¢ price variant)	10	$1,600	10	$1,500	$100	7%
Star Wars #3 (35¢ price variant)	10	$1,600	10	$1,500	$100	7%
Star Wars #4 (35¢ price variant)	10	$1,600	10	$1,500	$100	7%
Uncle Scrooge #179 (Whitman)	10	$1,600	8	$1,600	$0	0%
Iron Man #55	14	$1,500	14	$1,400	$100	7%
X-Men #94	15	$1,400	14	$1,400	$0	0%
DC 100 Page Sup. Spec. #5	16	$1,300	16	$1,200	$100	8%
Batman #227	17	$950	17	$900	$50	6%
Batman #251	18	$925	17	$900	$25	3%
All-Star Western #10	19	$850	19	$850	$0	0%
Batman #232	19	$850	20	$800	$50	6%
Vampirella Special HC	21	$740	21	$740	$0	0%
Amazing Spider-Man #121	22	$725	22	$725	$0	0%
Conan the Barbarian #1	23	$600	23	$575	$25	4%
Amazing Spider-Man #122	24	$525	23	$575	-$50	-9%
Vampirella Annual #1	25	$450	25	$450	$0	0%

TOP 25 COPPER AGE COMICS

TITLE/ISSUE#	2018 RANK	2018 NM- PRICE	2017 RANK	2017 NM- PRICE	$ INCR.	% INCR.
Gobbledygook #1	1	$6,200	1	$6,000	$200	3%
Teenage Mutant Ninja Turtles #1	2	$5,200	2	$4,500	$700	16%
Gobbledygook #2	3	$2,400	3	$2,300	$100	4%
Miracleman Gold #1	4	$1,500	4	$1,500	$0	0%
Albedo #2	4	$1,500	5	$1,400	$100	7%
Miracleman Blue #1	6	$850	6	$850	$0	0%
Vampirella #113	7	$550	7	$550	$0	0%
Sandman #8	8	$450	8	$400	$50	13%
Amazing Spider-Man #300	9	$350	10	$250	$100	40%
New Mutants #98	10	$315	9	$310	$5	2%
Spider-Man Gold 2nd UPC #1	11	$210	11	$210	$0	0%
Primer #2	11	$210	13	$190	$20	11%
Cry For Dawn HorrorCon Ed. #3	13	$200	12	$200	$0	0%
Eightball #1	13	$200	38	$65	$135	208%
Spider-Man Platinum #1	15	$195	15	$185	$10	5%
Grendel #1	16	$190	13	$190	$0	0%
Evil Ernie #1	17	$185	16	$175	$10	6%
Crow, The #1	18	$180	17	$160	$20	13%
New Mutants #87	19	$175	17	$160	$15	9%
Caliber Presents #1	19	$175	19	$150	$0	0%
Amazing Spider-Man #238	21	$160	19	$150	$10	7%
Swamp Thing #37	22	$145	21	$140	$5	4%
Batman #357	23	$140	22	$135	$5	4%
Harbinger #1	24	$130	23	$125	$0	0%
Cry For Dawn #1	25	$125	23	$125	$0	0%
Transformers #1	25	$125	23	$125	$0	0%
X-Men (Uncanny) #266	25	$125	23	$125	$0	0%

TOP 20 MODERN AGE COMICS

TITLE/ISSUE#	2018 RANK	2018 NM- PRICE	2017 RANK	2017 NM- PRICE	$ INCR.	% INCR.
Walking Dead #1	1	$1,200	1	$1,150	$50	4%
Bone #1	2	$850	2	$800	$50	6%
Venom Lethal Protector #1 (black-c)	3	$500	4	$400	$100	25%
Batman Adventures #12	4	$475	3	$450	$25	6%
Walking Dead #2	5	$360	5	$350	$10	3%
Goon, The #1	6	$300	6	$275	$25	9%
Invincible #1	7	$250	12	$175	$75	43%
Walking Dead #19	7	$250	7	$250	$0	0%
Preacher #1	9	$225	8	$225	$0	0%
Chew #1	9	$225	8	$225	$0	0%
Spawn #1 (B&W edition)	9	$225	10	$200	$25	13%
Captain Marvel (2012) 2nd printing #17	12	$200	15	$150	$50	33%
Walking Dead #3	13	$185	11	$180	$5	3%
Bone #2	14	$175	15	$150	$25	17%
Strangers in Paradise #1	15	$170	13	$160	$10	6%
Y: The Last Man #1	16	$165	13	$160	$5	3%
Saga #1	17	$150	15	$150	$0	0%
Walking Dead #27	17	$150	15	$150	$0	0%
Superman #75 (Platinum Edition)	19	$100	20	$95	$5	5%
Peter Panzerfaust #1	20	$75	19	$125	-$50	-40%

TOP 10 PLATINUM AGE COMICS

TITLE/ISSUE#	2018 RANK	2018 PRICE	2017 RANK	2017 PRICE	$ INCR.	% INCR.
Yellow Kid in McFadden Flats	1	FN $15,000	1	FN $14,500	$500	3%
Mickey Mouse Book (2nd printing)-variant	2	FN $8,000	2	FN $8,000	$0	0%
Little Sammy Sneeze	2	FN $8,000	3	FN $7,000	$1,000	14%
Little Nemo 1906	4	FN $5,500	4	FN $5,500	$0	0%
Mickey Mouse Book (1st printing)	5	VF $5,300	5	VF $5,300	$0	0%
Little Nemo 1909	6	FN $4,000	6	FN $4,000	$0	0%
Pore Li'l Mose	6	FN $4,000	6	FN $4,000	$0	0%
Yellow Kid #1	8	FN $3,900	8	FN $3,800	$100	3%
Happy Hooligan Book 1	9	VF $3,400	10	VF $3,300	$100	3%
Buster Brown and His Resolutions 1903	10	FN $3,300	9	FN $3,400	-$100	-3%
Mickey Mouse Book (2nd printing)	10	VF $3,300	10	VF $3,300	$0	0%

TOP 10 CRIME COMICS

TITLE/ISSUE#	2018 RANK	2018 NM- PRICE	2017 RANK	2017 NM- PRICE	$ INCR.	% INCR.
Crime Does Not Pay #22	1	$12,500	1	$12,000	$500	4%
Crime Does Not Pay #24	2	$12,000	2	$11,500	$500	4%
Crime Does Not Pay #23	3	$5,600	3	$5,500	$100	2%
True Crime Comics #2	4	$3,700	4	$3,600	$100	3%
Crime Does Not Pay #33	5	$3,400	5	$3,200	$200	6%
True Crime Comics #3	6	$2,600	6	$2,500	$100	4%
The Killers #1	7	$2,300	7	$2,300	$0	0%
Crimes By Women #1	8	$2,000	8	$2,000	$0	0%
The Killers #2	9	$1,900	9	$1,900	$0	0%
Crime Does Not Pay, Best of ('44)	10	$1,800	10	$1,750	$50	3%
True Crime Comics #4	10	$1,800	10	$1,750	$50	3%

TOP 10 HORROR COMICS

TITLE/ISSUE#	2018 RANK	2018 NM- PRICE	2017 RANK	2017 NM- PRICE	$ INCR.	% INCR.
Journey into Mystery #1	1	$16,000	1	$14,000	$2,000	14%
Eerie #1	2	$13,000	2	$12,000	$1,000	8%
Strange Tales #1	3	$12,500	3	$11,000	$1,500	14%
Tales to Astonish #1	3	$12,000	3	$11,000	$1,000	9%
Tales of Terror Annual #1	3	VF $10,800	5	VF $10,400	$400	4%
Vault of Horror #12	4	$10,500	6	$10,000	$500	5%
Crypt of Terror #17	7	$6,000	7	$6,000	$0	0%
Haunt of Fear #15	8	$5,700	8	$5,600	$100	2%
Crime Patrol #15	9	$5,000	9	$4,800	$200	4%
House of Mystery #1	10	$4,500	10	$4,400	$100	2%

TOP 10 ROMANCE COMICS

TITLE/ISSUE#	2018 RANK	2018 NM- PRICE	2017 RANK	2017 NM- PRICE	$ INCR.	% INCR.
Giant Comics Edition #12	1	$14,000	1	$12,000	$2,000	17%
Daring Love #1	2	$4,100	2	$4,000	$100	3%
Negro Romance #1	3	$3,500	3	$3,400	$100	3%
Intimate Confessions #1	4	$3,100	4	$3,000	$100	3%
Giant Comics Edition #15	5	$3,000	5	$2,800	$200	7%
Negro Romance #2	6	$2,900	5	$2,800	$100	4%
Negro Romance #3	6	$2,900	5	$2,800	$100	4%
Giant Comics Edition #9	8	$2,600	8	$2,500	$100	4%
Forbidden Love #1	9	$2,000	9	$1,900	$100	5%
Modern Love #1	10	$1,650	10	$1,600	$50	3%

TOP 10 SCI-FI COMICS

TITLE/ISSUE#	2018 RANK	2018 NM- PRICE	2017 RANK	2017 NM- PRICE	$ INCR.	% INCR.
Showcase #17 (Adam Strange)	1	$10,000	1	$9,500	$500	5%
Mystery In Space #1	2	$7,300	2	$7,200	$100	1%
Strange Adventures #1	3	$5,200	3	$5,200	$0	0%
Weird Science #12 (#1)	4	$5,000	8	$4,000	$1,000	25%
Journey Into Unknown Worlds #36	5	$4,800	4	$4,800	$0	0%
Showcase #15 (Space Ranger)	5	$4,800	4	$4,800	$0	0%
Weird Science-Fantasy Annual 1952	5	$4,800	6	$4,700	$100	2%
Mystery in Space #53	8	$4,500	7	$4,500	$0	0%
Weird Fantasy #13 (#1)	9	$4,000	8	$4,000	$0	0%
Fawcett Movie #15 (Man From Planet X)	10	$3,800	10	$3,800	$0	0%

TOP 10 WESTERN COMICS

TITLE/ISSUE#	2018 RANK	2018 NM- PRICE	2017 RANK	2017 NM- PRICE	$ INCR.	% INCR.
Gene Autry Comics #1	1	$7,500	1	$7,500	$0	0%
Hopalong Cassidy #1	2	$4,600	2	$4,500	$100	2%
Roy Rogers Four Color #38	4	$4,400	4	$4,400	$0	0%
*Lone Ranger Ice Cream 1939 2nd	2	VF $4,000	2	VF $4,500	-$500	-11%
John Wayne Adventure Comics #1	5	$3,900	5	$3,900	$0	0%
Red Ryder Comics #1	6	$3,900	6	$3,800	$100	3%
*Lone Ranger Ice Cream 1939	6	VF $3,800	6	VF $3,800	$0	0%
Western Picture Stories #1	8	$3,800	8	$3,700	$100	3%
*Tom Mix Ralston #1	9	$3,200	9	$3,600	-$400	-11%
*Red Ryder Victory Patrol '42	10	$1,300	10	$1,300	$0	0%

GRADING DEFINITIONS

When grading a comic book, common sense must be employed. The overall eye appeal and beauty of the comic book must be taken into account along with its technical flaws to arrive at the appropriate grade.

10.0 GEM MINT (GM): This is an exceptional example of a given book - the best ever seen. The slightest bindery defects and/or printing flaws may be seen only upon very close inspection. The overall look is "as if it has never been handled or released for purchase." Only the slightest bindery or printing defects are allowed, and these would be imperceptible on first viewing. No bindery tears. Cover is flat with no surface wear. Inks are bright with high reflectivity. Well centered and firmly secured to interior pages. Corners are cut square and sharp. No creases. No dates or stamped markings allowed. No soiling, staining or other discoloration. Spine is tight and flat. No spine roll or split allowed. Staples must be original, centered and clean with no rust. No staple tears or stress lines. Paper is white, supple and fresh. No hint of acidity in the odor of the newsprint. No interior autographs or owner signatures. Centerfold is firmly secure. No interior tears.

9.9 MINT (MT): Near perfect in every way. Only subtle bindery or printing defects are allowed. No bindery tears. Cover is flat with no surface wear. Inks are bright with high reflectivity. Generally well centered and firmly secured to interior pages. Corners are cut square and sharp. No creases. Small, inconspicuous, lightly penciled, stamped or inked arrival dates are acceptable as long as they are in an unobtrusive location. No soiling, staining or other discoloration. Spine is tight and flat. No spine roll or split allowed. Staples must be original, generally centered and clean with no rust. No staple tears or stress lines. Paper is white, supple and fresh. No hint of acidity in the odor of the newsprint. Centerfold is firmly secure. No interior tears.

9.8 NEAR MINT/MINT (NM/MT): Nearly perfect in every way with only minor imperfections that keep it from the next higher grade. Only subtle bindery or printing defects are allowed. No bindery tears. Cover is flat with no surface wear. Inks are bright with high reflectivity. Generally well centered and firmly secured to interior pages. Corners are cut square and sharp. No creases. Small, inconspicuous, lightly penciled, stamped or inked arrival dates are acceptable as long as they are in an unobtrusive location. No soiling, staining or other discoloration. Spine is tight and flat. No spine roll or split allowed. Staples must be original, generally centered and clean with no rust. No staple tears or stress lines. Paper is off-white to white, supple and fresh. No hint of acidity in the odor of the newsprint. Centerfold is firmly secure. Only the slightest interior tears are allowed.

9.6 NEAR MINT+ (NM+): Nearly perfect with a minor additional virtue or virtues that raise it from Near Mint. The overall look is "as if it was just purchased and read once or twice." Only subtle bindery or printing defects are allowed. No bindery tears are allowed, although on Golden Age books bindery tears of up to 1/8" have been noted. Cover is flat with no surface wear. Inks are bright with high reflectivity. Well centered and firmly secured to interior pages. One corner may be almost imperceptibly blunted, but still almost sharp and cut square. Almost imperceptible indentations are permissible, but no creases, bends, or color break. Small, inconspicuous, lightly penciled, stamped or inked arrival dates are acceptable as long as they are in an unobtrusive location. No soiling, staining or other discoloration. Spine is tight and flat. No spine roll or split allowed. Staples must be original, generally centered, with only the slightest discoloration. No staple tears, stress lines, or rust migration. Paper is off-white, supple and fresh. No hint of acidity in the odor of the newsprint. Centerfold is firmly secure. Only the slightest interior tears are allowed.

9.4 NEAR MINT (NM): Nearly perfect with only minor imperfections that keep it from the next higher grade. Minor feathering that does not distract from the overall beauty of an otherwise higher grade copy is acceptable for this grade. The overall look is "as if it was just purchased and read once or twice." Subtle bindery defects are allowed. Bindery tears must be less than 1/16" on Silver Age and later books, although on Golden Age books bindery tears of up to 1/4" have been noted. Cover is flat with no surface wear. Inks are bright with high reflectivity. Generally well centered and secured to interior pages. Corners are cut square and sharp with ever-so-slight blunting permitted. A 1/16" bend is permitted with no color break. No creases. Small, inconspicuous, lightly penciled, stamped or inked arrival dates are acceptable as long as they are in an unobtrusive location. No soiling, staining or other discoloration apart from slight foxing. Spine is tight and flat. No spine roll or split allowed. Staples are generally centered; may have slight discoloration. No staple tears are allowed; almost no stress lines. No rust migration. In rare cases, a comic was not stapled at the bindery and therefore has a missing staple; this is not considered a defect. Any staple can be replaced on books up to Fine, but only vintage staples can be used on books from Very Fine to Near Mint. Mint books must have original staples. Paper is cream to off-white, supple and fresh. No hint of acidity in the odor of the newsprint. Centerfold is secure. Slight interior tears are allowed.

9.2 NEAR MINT- (NM-): Nearly perfect with only

a minor additional defect or defects that keep it from Near Mint. A limited number of minor bindery defects are allowed. A light, barely noticeable water stain or minor foxing that does not distract from the beauty of the book is acceptable for this grade. Cover is flat with no surface wear. Inks are bright with only the slightest dimming of reflectivity. Generally well centered and secured to interior pages. Corners are cut square and sharp with ever-so-slight blunting permitted. A 1/16"-1/8" bend is permitted with no color break. No creases. Small, inconspicuous, lightly penciled, stamped or inked arrival dates are acceptable as long as they are in an unobtrusive location. No soiling, staining or other discoloration apart from slight foxing. Spine is tight and flat. No spine roll or split allowed. Staples may show some discoloration. No staple tears are allowed; almost no stress lines. No rust migration. In rare cases, a comic was not stapled at the bindery and therefore has a missing staple; this is not considered a defect. Any staple can be replaced on books up to Fine, but only vintage staples can be used on books from Very Fine to Near Mint. Mint books must have original staples. Paper is cream to off-white, supple and fresh. No hint of acidity in the odor of the newsprint. Centerfold is secure. Slight interior tears are allowed.

9.0 VERY FINE/NEAR MINT (VF/NM): Nearly perfect with outstanding eye appeal. A limited number of bindery defects are allowed. Almost flat cover with almost imperceptible wear. Inks are bright with slightly diminished reflectivity. An 1/8" bend is allowed if color is not broken. Corners are cut square and sharp with ever-so-slight blunting permitted but no creases. Several lightly penciled, stamped or inked arrival dates are acceptable. No obvious soiling, staining or other discoloration, except for very minor foxing. Spine is tight and flat. No spine roll or split allowed. Staples may show some discoloration. Only the slightest staple tears are allowed. A very minor accumulation of stress lines may be present if they are nearly imperceptible. No rust migration. In rare cases, a comic was not stapled at the bindery and therefore has a missing staple; this is not considered a defect. Any staple can be replaced on books up to Fine, but only vintage staples can be used on books from Very Fine to Near Mint. Mint books must have original staples. Paper is cream to off-white and supple. No hint of acidity in the odor of the newsprint. Centerfold is secure. Very minor interior tears may be present.

8.5 VERY FINE+ (VF+): Fits the criteria for Very Fine but with an additional virtue or small accumulation of virtues that improves the book's appearance by a perceptible amount.

8.0 VERY FINE (VF): An excellent copy with outstanding eye appeal. Sharp, bright and clean with supple pages. A comic book in this grade has the appearance of having been carefully handled. A limited accumulation of minor bindery defects is allowed. Cover is relatively flat with minimal surface wear beginning to show, possibly including some minute wear at corners. Inks are generally bright with moderate to high reflectivity. A 1/4" crease is acceptable if color is not broken. Stamped or inked arrival dates may be present. No obvious soiling, staining or other discoloration, except for minor foxing. Spine is almost flat with no roll. Possible minor color break allowed. Staples may show some discoloration. Very slight staple tears and a few almost very minor to minor stress lines may be present. No rust migration. In rare cases, a comic was not stapled at the bindery and therefore has a missing staple; this is not considered a defect. Any staple can be replaced on books up to Fine, but only vintage staples can be used on books from Very Fine to Near Mint. Mint books must have original staples. Paper is tan to cream and supple. No hint of acidity in the odor of the newsprint. Centerfold is mostly secure. Minor interior tears at the margin may be present.

7.5 VERY FINE– (VF–): Fits the criteria for Very Fine but with an additional defect or small accumulation of defects that detracts from the book's appearance by a perceptible amount.

7.0 FINE/VERY FINE (FN/VF): An above-average copy that shows minor wear but is still relatively flat and clean with outstanding eye appeal. A small accumulation of minor bindery defects is allowed. Minor cover wear beginning to show with interior yellowing or tanning allowed, possibly including minor creases. Corners may be blunted or abraded. Inks are generally bright with a moderate reduction in reflectivity. Stamped or inked arrival dates may be present. No obvious soiling, staining or other discoloration, except for minor foxing. The slightest spine roll may be present, as well as a possible moderate color break. Staples may show some discoloration. Slight staple tears and a slight accumulation of light stress lines may be present. Slight rust migration. In rare cases, a comic was not stapled at the bindery and therefore has a missing staple; this is not considered a defect. Any staple can be replaced on books up to Fine, but only vintage staples can be used on books from Very Fine to Near Mint. Mint books must have original staples. Paper is tan to cream, but not brown. No hint of acidity in the odor of the newsprint. Centerfold is mostly secure. Minor interior tears at the margin may be present.

6.5 FINE+ (FN+): Fits the criteria for Fine but with an additional virtue or small accumulation of virtues that improves the book's appearance by a perceptible amount.

6.0 FINE (FN): An above-average copy that shows minor wear but is still relatively flat and clean with no significant creasing or other serious defects. Eye appeal is somewhat reduced because of slight surface wear and the accumulation of small defects, especially on the spine and edges. A FINE condition comic book appears to have been read a few times and has been handled with moderate care. Some accumulation of minor bindery defects is allowed. Minor cover wear apparent, with minor to moderate creases. Inks show a major reduction in reflectivity. Blunted or abraded corners are more common, as is minor staining, soiling, discoloration, and/or foxing. Stamped or inked arrival dates may be present. A minor spine roll is allowed. There can also be a 1/4" spine split or severe color break. Staples show minor discoloration. Minor staple tears and an accumulation of stress lines may be present, as well as minor rust migration. In rare cases, a comic was not stapled at the bindery and therefore has a missing staple; this is not considered a defect. Any staple can be replaced on books up to Fine, but only vintage staples can be used on books from Very Fine to Near Mint. Mint books must have original staples. Paper is brown to tan and fairly supple with no signs of brittleness. No hint of acidity in the odor of the newsprint. Minor interior tears at the margin may be present. Centerfold may be loose but not detached.

5.5 FINE– (FN–): Fits the criteria for Fine but with an additional defect or small accumulation of defects that detracts from the book's appearance by a perceptible amount.

5.0 VERY GOOD/FINE (VG/FN): An above-average but well-used comic book. A comic in this grade shows some moderate wear; eye appeal is somewhat reduced because of the accumulation of defects. Still a desirable copy that has been handled with some care. An accumulation of bindery defects is allowed. Minor to moderate cover wear apparent, with minor to moderate creases and/or dimples. Inks have major to extreme reduction in reflectivity. Blunted or abraded corners are increasingly common, as is minor to moderate staining, discoloration, and/or foxing. Stamped or inked arrival dates may be present. A minor to moderate spine roll is allowed. A spine split of up to 1/2" may be present. Staples show minor discoloration. A slight accumulation of minor staple tears and an accumulation of minor stress lines may also be present, as well as minor rust migration. In rare cases, a comic was not stapled at the bindery and therefore has a missing staple; this is not considered a defect. Any staple can be replaced on books up to Fine, but only vintage staples can be used on books from Very Fine to Near Mint. Mint books must have original staples. Paper is brown to tan with no signs of brittleness. May have the faintest trace of an acidic odor. Centerfold may be loose but not detached. Minor tears may also be present.

4.5 VERY GOOD+ (VG+): Fits the criteria for Very Good but with an additional virtue or small accumulation of virtues that improves the book's appearance by a perceptible amount.

4.0 VERY GOOD (VG): The average used comic book. A comic in this grade shows some significant moderate wear, but still has not accumulated enough total defects to reduce eye appeal to the point that it is not a desirable copy. Cover shows moderate to significant wear, and may be loose but not completely detached. Moderate to extreme reduction in reflectivity. Can have an accumulation of creases or dimples. Corners may be blunted or abraded. Store stamps, name stamps, arrival dates, initials, etc. have no effect on this grade. Some discoloration, fading, foxing, and even minor soiling is allowed. As much as a 1/4" triangle can be missing out of the corner or edge; a missing 1/8" square is also acceptable. Only minor unobtrusive tape and other amateur repair allowed on otherwise high grade copies. Moderate spine roll may be present and/or a 1" spine split. Staples discolored. Minor to moderate staple tears and stress lines may be present, as well as some rust migration. Paper is brown but not brittle. A minor acidic odor can be detectable. Minor to moderate tears may be present. Centerfold may be loose or detached at one staple.

3.5 VERY GOOD– (VG–): Fits the criteria for Very Good but with an additional defect or small accumulation of defects that detracts from the book's appearance by a perceptible amount.

3.0 GOOD/VERY GOOD (GD/VG): A used comic book showing some substantial wear. Cover shows significant wear, and may be loose or even detached at one staple. Cover reflectivity is very low. Can have a book-length crease and/or dimples. Corners may be blunted or even rounded. Discoloration, fading, foxing, and even minor to moderate soiling is allowed. A triangle from 1/4" to 1/2" can be missing out of the corner or edge; a missing 1/8" to 1/4" square is also acceptable. Tape and other amateur repair may be present. Moderate spine roll likely. May have a spine split of anywhere from 1" to 1-1/2". Staples may be rusted or replaced. Minor to moderate staple tears and moderate stress lines may be present, as well as some rust migration. Paper is brown but not brittle. Centerfold may be loose or detached at one staple. Minor to moderate interior tears may be present.

2.5 GOOD+ (GD+): Fits the criteria for Good but with an additional virtue or small accumulation of virtues that improves the book's appearance by a perceptible amount.

2.0 GOOD (GD): Shows substantial wear; often considered a "reading copy." Cover shows significant wear and may even be detached. Cover reflectivity is low and in some cases completely absent. Book-length creases and dimples may be present. Rounded corners are more common. Moderate soiling, staining, discoloration and foxing may be present. The largest piece allowed missing from the front or back cover is usually a 1/2" triangle or a 1/4" square, although some Silver Age books such as 1960s Marvels have had the price corner box clipped from the top left front cover and may be considered Good if they would otherwise have graded higher. Tape and other forms of amateur repair are common in Silver Age and older books. Spine roll is likely. May have up to a 2" spine split. Staples may be degraded, replaced or missing. Moderate staple tears and stress lines may be present, as well as rust migration. Paper is brown but not brittle. Centerfold may be loose or detached. Moderate interior tears may be present.

1.8 GOOD– (GD–): Fits the criteria for Good but with an

additional defect or small accumulation of defects that detracts from the book's appearance by a perceptible amount.

1.5 FAIR/GOOD (FR/GD): A comic showing substantial to heavy wear. A copy in this grade still has all pages and covers, although there may be pieces missing up to and including missing coupons and/or Marvel Value Stamps that do not impact the story. Books in this grade are commonly creased, scuffed, abraded, soiled, and possibly unattractive, but still generally readable. Cover shows considerable wear and may be detached. Nearly no reflectivity to no reflectivity remaining. Store stamp, name stamp, arrival date and initials are permitted. Book-length creases, tears and folds may be present. Rounded corners are increasingly common. Soiling, staining, discoloration and foxing is generally present. Up to 1/10 of the back cover may be missing. Tape and other forms of amateur repair are increasingly common in Silver Age and older books. Spine roll is common. May have a spine split between 2" and 2/3 the length of the book. Staples may be degraded, replaced or missing. Staple tears and stress lines are common, as well as rust migration. Paper is brown and may show brittleness around the edges. Acidic odor may be present. Centerfold may be loose or detached. Interior tears are common.

1.0 FAIR (FR): A copy in this grade shows heavy wear. Some collectors consider this the lowest collectible grade because comic books in lesser condition are usually incomplete and/or brittle. Comics in this grade are usually soiled, faded, ragged and possibly unattractive. This is the last grade in which a comic remains generally readable. Cover may be detached, and inks have lost all reflectivity. Creases, tears and/or folds are prevalent. Corners are commonly rounded or absent. Soiling and staining is present. Books in this condition generally have all pages and most of the covers, although there may be up to 1/4 of the front cover missing or no back cover, but not both. Tape and other forms of amateur repair are more common. Spine roll is more common; spine split can extend up to 2/3 the length of the book. Staples may be missing or show rust and discoloration. An accumulation of staple tears and stress lines may be present, as well as rust migration. Paper is brown and may show brittleness around the edges but not in the central portion of the pages. Acidic odor may be present. Accumulation of interior tears. Chunks may be missing. The centerfold may be missing if readability is generally preserved (although there may be difficulty). Coupons may be cut.

0.5 POOR (PR): Most comic books in this grade have been sufficiently degraded to the point where there is little or no collector value; they are easily identified by a complete absence of eye appeal. Comics in this grade are brittle almost to the point of turning to dust with a touch, and are usually incomplete. Extreme cover fading may render the cover almost indiscernible. May have extremely severe stains, mildew or heavy cover abrasion to the point that some cover inks are indistinct/absent. Covers may be detached with large chunks missing. Can have extremely ragged edges and extensive creasing. Corners are rounded or virtually absent. Covers may have been defaced with paints, varnishes, glues, oil, indelible markers or dyes, and may have suffered heavy water damage. Can also have extensive amateur repairs such as laminated covers. Extreme spine roll present; can have extremely ragged spines or a complete, book-length split. Staples can be missing or show extreme rust and discoloration. Extensive staple tears and stress lines may be present, as well as extreme rust migration. Paper exhibits moderate to severe brittleness (where the comic book literally falls apart when examined). Extreme acidic odor may be present. Extensive interior tears. Multiple pages, including the centerfold, may be missing that affect readability. Coupons may be cut.

0.3 INCOMPLETE (INC): Books that are coverless, but are otherwise complete, or covers missing their interiors.

0.1 INCOMPLETE (INC): Coverless copies that have incomplete interiors, wraps or single pages will receive a grade of .1 as will just front covers or just back covers.

PUBLISHERS' CODES

The following abbreviations are used with cover reproductions throughout the book for copyright purposes:

ABC-America's Best Comics
AC-AC Comics
ACE-Ace Periodicals
ACG-American Comics Group
AJAX-Ajax-Farrell
ACP-Archie Comic Publications
BP-Better Publications
C & L-Cupples & Leon
CC-Charlton Comics
CEN-Centaur Publications
CCG-Columbia Comics Group
CG-Catechetical Guild
CHES-Harry 'A' Chesler
CM-Comics Magazine
CN-Cartoon Network
CPI-Conan Properties Inc.
DC-DC Comics, Inc.
DELL-Dell Publishing Co.
DH-Dark Horse
DIS-Disney Enterprises, Inc.
DMP-David McKay Publishing
DYN-Dynamite Entertainment
DS-D. S. Publishing Co.
EAS-Eastern Color Printing Co.
EC-E. C. Comics
ECL-Eclipse Comics
ENWIL-Enwil Associates
EP-Elliott Publications
ERB-Edgar Rice Burroughs
FAW-Fawcett Publications
FC-First Comics
FF-Famous Funnies
FH-Fiction House Magazines
FOX-Fox Feature Syndicate
GIL-Gilberton
GK-Gold Key
GP-Great Publications
HARV-Harvey Publications
H-B-Hanna-Barbera
HILL-Hillman Periodicals
HOKE-Holyoke Publishing Co.
IM-Image Comics
KING-King Features Syndicate
LEV-Lev Gleason Publications
MAL-Malibu Comics
MAR-Marvel Characters, Inc.
ME-Magazine Enterprises
MLJ-MLJ Magazines
MS-Mirage Studios
NOVP-Novelty Press
NYNS-New York News Syndicate
PG-Premier Group
PINE-Pines
PMI-Parents' Magazine Institute
PRIZE-Prize Publications
QUA-Quality Comics Group
REAL-Realistic Comics
RH-Rural Home
S & S-Street and Smith Publishers
SKY-Skywald Publications
STAR-Star Publications
STD-Standard Comics
STJ-St. John Publishing Co.
SUPR-Superior Comics
TC-Tower Comics
TM-Trojan Magazines
TMP-Todd McFarlane Prods.
TOBY-Toby Press
TOPS-Tops Comics
UFS-United Features Syndicate
VAL-Valiant
VITL-Vital Publications
WB-Warner Brothers.
WEST-Western Publishing Co.
WHIT-Whitman Publishing Co.
WHW-William H. Wise
WMG-William M. Gaines (E. C.)
WP-Warren Publishing Co.
YM-Youthful Magazines
Z-D-Ziff-Davis Publishing Co.

OVERSTREET ADVISORS

Even before the first edition of *The Overstreet Comic Book Price Guide* was printed, author Robert M. Overstreet solicited pricing data, historical notations, and general information from a variety of sources. What was initially an informal group offering input quickly became an organized field of comic book collectors, dealers and historians whose opinions are actively solicited in advance of each edition of this book. Some of these Overstreet Advisors are specialists who deal in particular niches within the comic book world, while others are generalists who are interested in commenting on the broader marketplace. Each advisor provides information from their respective areas of interest and expertise, spanning the history of American comics.

While some choose to offer pricing and historical information in the form of annotated sales catalogs, auction catalogs, or documented private sales, assistance from others comes in the form of the market reports such as those beginning on page 97 in this book. In addition to those who have served as Overstreet Advisors almost since *The Guide*'s inception, each year new contributors are sought.

With that in mind, we are pleased to present our newest Overstreet Advisors:

THE CLASS OF 2018

KEIF A. FROMM
Collector/Historian

JAY HALSTEAD
International Comic Exchange
Hamilton, ON Canada

STEVE RICKETTS
CBCS Pressing
Dallas, TX

SEAN RUTAN
Hake's Americana
York, PA

MIKE STEVENS
Hake's Americana
York, PA

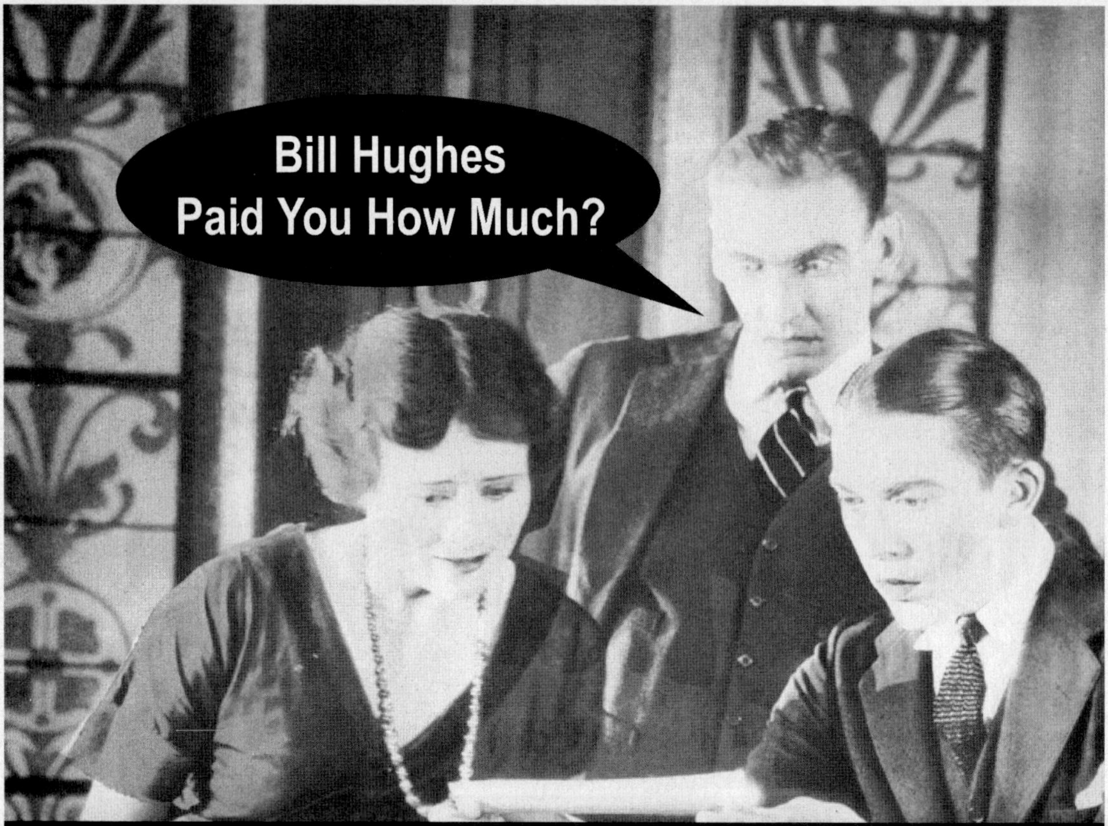

Bill Hughes
Paid You How Much?

972-539-9190

CALL NOW FOR IMMEDIATE PAYMENT!!

ALWAYS SEEKING:

Golden-Age, Silver-Age, & Bronze-Age Comics
Vintage Original Comic & Collector Card Art
Vintage Baseball Cards & Uncut Sheets
Movie Posters & Stills
Western, Sci-Fi, and Comedy Collectibles
Vintage Toys in Original Boxes
Vintage Disneyana & Other Animation
Original Comic Art

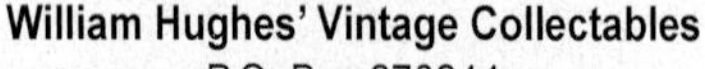

William Hughes' Vintage Collectables
P.O. Box 270244
Flower Mound, Texas 75027
Office: 972-539-9190
Mobile: 973-432-4070

www.VintageCollectables.net
Email: whughes199@yahoo.com
eBay User: comic-warehouse

Senior Advisor Overstreet Price Guide

JUST THE FACTS

THE NATION'S LARGEST COMIC DEALER METROPOLIS

FACT 1: ABSOLUTELY NO OTHER COMIC DEALER BUYS MORE GOLDEN AND SILVER AGE COMICS THAN METROPOLIS.

Although the pages of the price guide are filled with other dealers offering to pay "top dollar," the simple truth is that Metropolis spends more money on more quality comic book collections year in and year out than any other dealers in the country. We have the funds and the expertise to back up our word. The fact is that we have spent nearly 8 million dollars on rare comic books and movie posters over the last year. If you have comic books to sell please call us at 1.800.229.6387. A generous finder's fee will be given if you know of any comic book or movie poster collections that we purchase. All calls will be strictly confidential.

FACT 2: ABSOLUTELY NO OTHER COMIC DEALER SELLS MORE GOLDEN AND SILVER AGE COMICS THAN METROPOLIS.

We simply have the best stock of Golden and Silver Age comic books in the country. The thousands of collectors familiar with our strict grading standards and excellent service can attest to this. Chances are, if you want it, we have it!

METROPOLISCOMICS.COM 36 W 37TH ST, 6TH FL, NEW YORK, NY 10018
PH: 212.260.4147 FX: 212.260.4304 BUYING@METROPOLISCOMICS.COM
TOLL-FREE 1.800.229 M[illegible]O (6387) INTERNATIONAL: 001.212.260.4147

GOLDEN AGE

WANT LIST COMICS

SILVER AGE

WE FILL WANT LISTS

We have a simple question to ask . . . have you

E-MAILED

us your want list yet? Here is what it will cost you . . . 5 to 10 minutes of your time. Here is what you could stand to gain . . . SOME OR ALL OF THE COMIC BOOKS (CGC OR RAW) THAT YOU HAVE BEEN SEARCHING FOR THE LAST FEW YEARS!!!

WHAT ARE YOU WAITING FOR?

"The **Batman #1** you sold me was in the **nicest, unrestored condition** I've ever seen!", **Bob Overstreet, author "The Official Overstreet Comic Book Price Guide."**

"I'm glad that you have a **great selection** of **Golden Age** and **Silver Age** comics in stock. You have been able to constantly find books to fill some very tough missing holes in my collection. I also appreciate your **consistent, tight** grading and **fair** prices!"

Dan Hampton, Las Cruces, NM

These are just two of the **many** satisfied customers that have bought books from us in the past. Over the years, we have developed a **very strong return customer base** because we **ACCURATELY** price, grade, and describe books (in detail) over the phone and through the mail/email. If CGC books are desired, we can definitely fill those needs as well !!! In the past few years, we have acquired nearly **EVERY** major **Golden Age** and **Silver Age** book **more than once** for our many want list clients. These include books like **Action 1, Detective 1, Detective 27, Marvel 1, Superman 1** and more recent gems like **AF 15, FF 1, Hulk 1, Flash 105** and **Showcase 4, 8, 22. OUR SPECIALTY IS GOLD, SILVER, BRONZE, AND COPPER AGE BOOKS (1933 - 1993)**. Please check out our **great selection** of old books! (CGC or Raw).

We don't claim that we can fill every list all the time, but if any company can accomplish this, it **would certainly** be us! We can say this with **much confidence** because our representatives travel to the **majority** of the 50 states and Canada plus attend many of the major comic book conventions (San Diego, Chicago, Detroit, New York, etc.) to uncover books **you would not** have the opportunity to find. When we are not on the road, we spend **MANY** hours on the phone locating books from our **long** list of past and present comic sources we've developed over the **25 years** we have been dealing in comic books. When sending your want list either **E-MAIL** us, or mail us and include a self-addressed stamped envelope (if possible), **your phone number,** and a good time to reach you. We **DON'T** send out catalogs, so **please** ask for **specific** books and **conditions** desired. We will contact you **when** we find the items you've requested. **Phone calls are also welcomed. WE WILL GLADLY SUGGEST AND PERSONALLY PUT TOGETHER COMIC BOOK INVESTMENT PORTFOLIOS FOR BIG AND SMALL INVESTORS. OUR ADVICE IS ALWAYS FREE!**

SAVE YOURSELF ALL THE HASSLE AND LET US DO THE LOOKING FOR YOU!
CALL, FAX, MAIL, OR EMAIL US YOUR WANT LIST!

YOU HAVE NOTHING TO LOSE AND EVERYTHING ON YOUR WANT LIST TO GAIN!

Competitive pricing always. Accurate grading. **MANY CGC BOOKS AVAILABLE.** Friendly, courteous service. **Interest free time payments/layaways possible.** Checks, Money Orders, Visa, Mastercard, Discover and American Express accepted for total payment **OR** down payment on books. 7 day money back guarantee before a sale is considered final on all non-CGC books. No collect calls please.

PayPal payments accepted

Our office/warehouse # is:
1-918-299-0440

Call us anytime between 1 pm and 8 pm, CST
Please ask for our private FAX #

Charter
Member Dealer

WANT LIST COMICS
BOX 701932
TULSA, OK 74170-1932

Senior Advisor to the Overstreet Comic Price Guide
CBG Customer Service Award
References gladly provided!

Please e-mail your want list to wlc777@cox.net

Charter
Member Dealer

$$$ We Spent 12 million dollars on comic books last year! $$$
Best Comics
INTERNATIONAL
EST. 1991
OVERSTREET ADVISOR
WE have all the old comics your mother threw out!
We are paying CASH for old comics 1928 - 2018,
toys, TV/Movie memorabilia & props, old toys
statue collections, and much more!
NEW COMICS EVERY WEDNESDAY!
YOUR NUMBER ONE SOURCE FOR:
Detective COMICS
Action figures
Sideshow Collectibles
Bowen Statues
Neca, Kotobukiya,
Hot Toys
DC Collectibles
bestcomics.com
Golden Age•Silver Age•Modern Age
Comics For Sale!
1300 Jericho Tpke.
New Hyde Park, NY. 11040
Tel: 516-328-1900
Email: tommybest@aol.com
twitter.com/bestcomicsNY
facebook.com/bestcomicsinternational
All characters © 2018 respective Copyright holders. All rights reserved
We Spent 12 million dollars on comic books last year!
We Spent 12 million dollars on comic books last year!
$$$ We Spent 12 million dollars on comics books last year! $$$

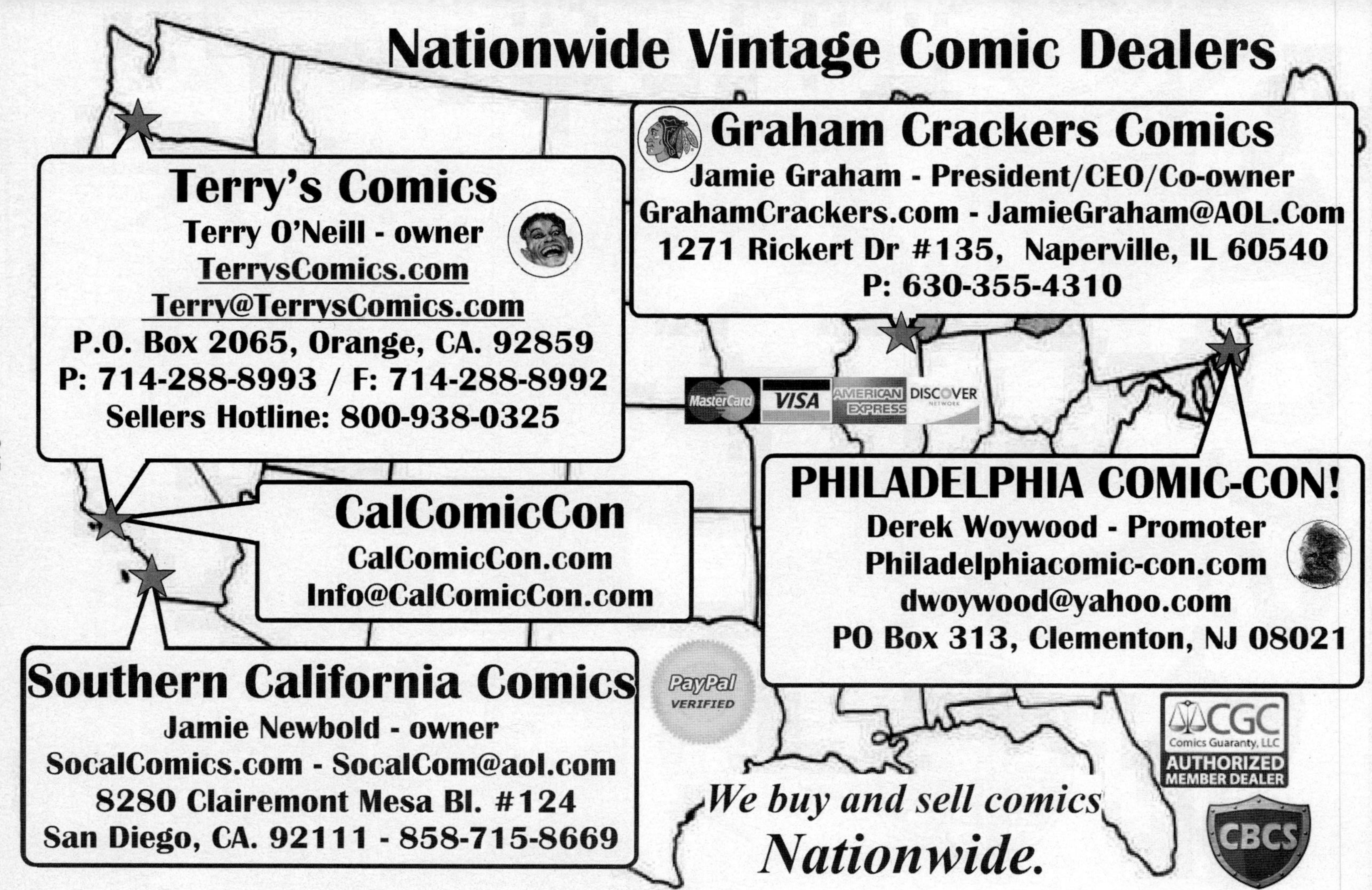

Nationwide Vintage Comic Dealers
Terry's Comics
Terry O'Neill - owner
TerrysComics.com
Terry@TerrysComics.com
P.O. Box 2065, Orange, CA. 92859
P: 714-288-8993 / F: 714-288-8992
Sellers Hotline: 800-938-0325
Graham Crackers Comics
Jamie Graham - President/CEO/Co-owner
GrahamCrackers.com - JamieGraham@AOL.Com
1271 Rickert Dr #135, Naperville, IL 60540
P: 630-355-4310
MasterCard
VISA
AMERICAN EXPRESS
DISCOVER
CalComicCon
CalComicCon.com
Info@CalComicCon.com
PHILADELPHIA COMIC-CON!
Derek Woywood - Promoter
Philadelphiacomic-con.com
dwoywood@yahoo.com
PO Box 313, Clementon, NJ 08021
Southern California Comics
Jamie Newbold - owner
SocalComics.com - SocalCom@aol.com
8280 Clairemont Mesa Bl. #124
San Diego, CA. 92111 - 858-715-8669
PayPal VERIFIED
CGC Comics Guaranty, LLC AUTHORIZED MEMBER DEALER
CBCS
We buy and sell comics
Nationwide.

DISCOVER...
Senior Advisor
Overstreet
Price Guide
MARVEL
MARCH
MYSTERY COMICS
10¢
No. 5
HUMAN TORCH
SUB-MARINER
ELECTRO The Robot
THE ANGEL
KA-ZAR The Great
Plus Other Features
like a flaming comet THE HUMAN TORCH streaked to the rescue!
NITRO CHLORIDE
12¢
the AMAZING SPIDER-MAN
1 MAR.
2 GREAT FEATURE-LENGTH SPIDER-MAN THRILLERS!
THE FANTASTIC FOUR THINK I'M TRAPPED! BUT THEY DON'T SUSPECT MY REAL POWER!
EXTRA ADDED ATTRACTION: SPIDER-MAN MEETS THE FANTASTIC FOUR, A
'the CHAMELEON STRIKES!'

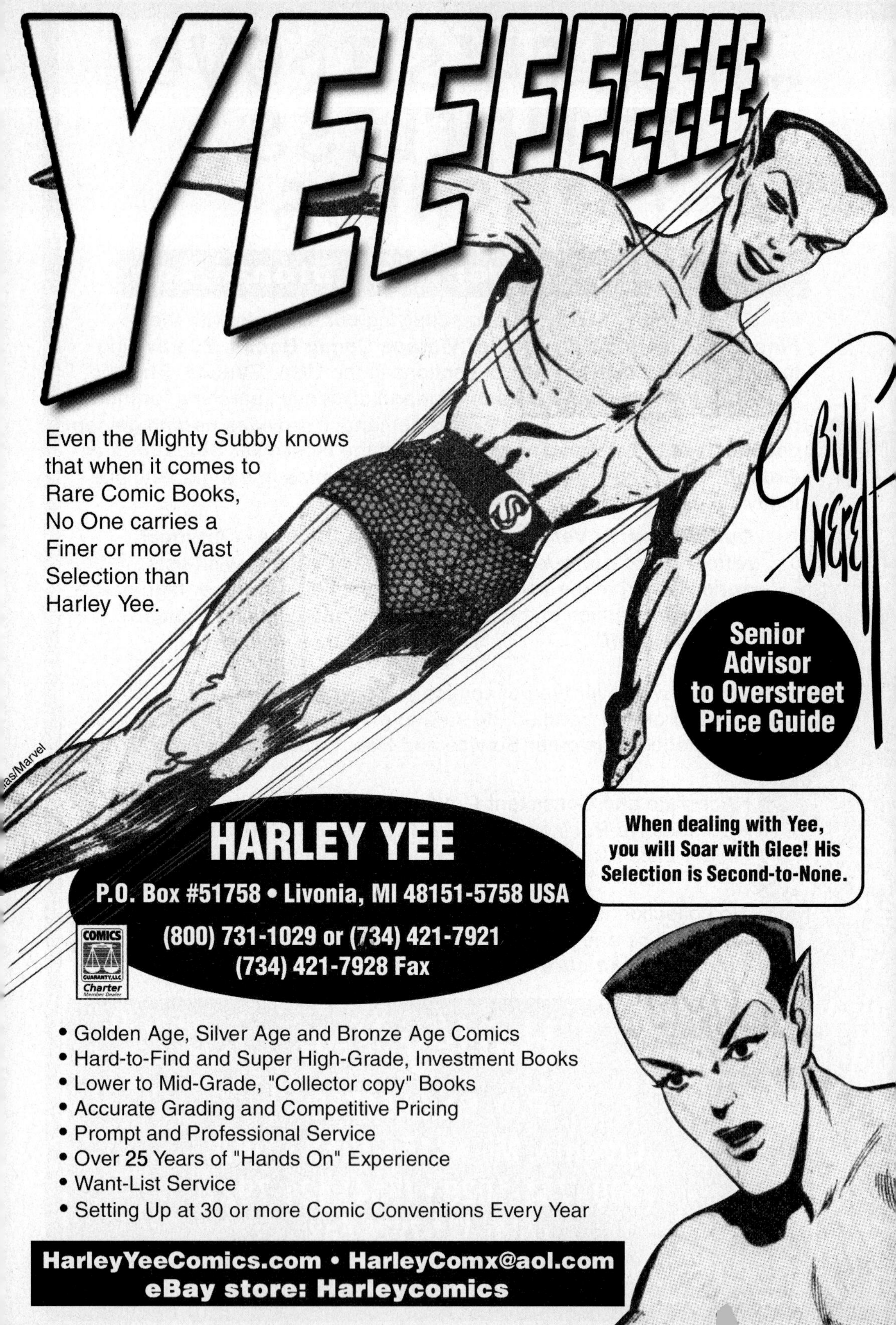
YEEEEEEE
Even the Mighty Subby knows that when it comes to Rare Comic Books, No One carries a Finer or more Vast Selection than Harley Yee.
Bill Everett
Senior Advisor to Overstreet Price Guide
When dealing with Yee, you will Soar with Glee! His Selection is Second-to-None.
HARLEY YEE
P.O. Box #51758 • Livonia, MI 48151-5758 USA
(800) 731-1029 or (734) 421-7921
(734) 421-7928 Fax
COMICS GUARANTY, LLC Charter Member Dealer
• Golden Age, Silver Age and Bronze Age Comics
• Hard-to-Find and Super High-Grade, Investment Books
• Lower to Mid-Grade, "Collector copy" Books
• Accurate Grading and Competitive Pricing
• Prompt and Professional Service
• Over 25 Years of "Hands On" Experience
• Want-List Service
• Setting Up at 30 or more Comic Conventions Every Year
HarleyYeeComics.com • HarleyComx@aol.com
eBay store: Harleycomics

THE SELLER'S GUIDE

Yes, here are the pages you're looking for. These percentages will help you determine the sale value of your collection. If you do not find your title, call with any questions. We have purchased many of the major well-known collections. We are serious about buying your comics and paying you the most for them.

If you have comics or related items for sale call or send your list for a quote. No collection is too large or small. Immediate funds available of 500K and beyond.

These are some of the high prices we will pay. Percentages stated will be paid for any grade unless otherwise noted. All percentages based on this Overstreet Guide.

—*JAMES PAYETTE*

We are paying 100% of Guide for the following:

All Select....1-up
All Winners....6-up
America's Best....1-up
Black Terror....1-25
Captain Aero....3-25
Captain America....11-up
Catman....1-up
Dynamic....2-15
Exciting....3-50
Human Torch....6-35
Marvel Mystery....11-up
Pep....22-45
Prize....2-50
Reform School Girl....1
Speed....10-30
Startling....2-up
Sub-Mariner....3-32
Thrilling....2-52
U.S.A.....6-up
Wonder (Nedor)....1-up

We are paying 75% of Guide for the following:

Action 1-15
Adventure 247
All New 2-13
All Winners 1-5
Amazing Man all
Amazing Mystery Funnies all
Andy Devine
Arrow all
Captain America 1-10
Daredevil (2nd) 1
Detective 2-26
Detective Eye all
Detective Picture Stories all
Fantastic Four 1-2
Four Favorites 3-27
Funny Pages all
Funny Picture Stories all
Hangman all
Jumbo 1-10
Journey into Mystery 83
Keen Detective Funnies all
Marvel Mystery 1-10
Mystery Men all
Showcase 4
Spiderman 1-2
Superman 1
Superman's Pal 1
Tim McCoy all
Wonder (Fox)
Young Allies all

BUYING & SELLING GOLDEN & SILVER AGE COMICS SINCE 1975

the GOBLIN'S DEN
70 Port Street East, Suite 201
Mississauga, ON, Canada
L5G 4V8
Ph# 905-990-2713 Fax# 416-622-0574
email: GOBLINSDEN@rogers.com
ALWAYS
Buying Comics
and Original
Comic Art
Highest prices paid for quality pre-Code crime,
horror and good girl comics and original art.
Top prices paid for art by: A.Adams, N.Adams, D.Ayers, B.Bailey,
M.Baker, B. Breathed, F.Brunner, J.Buscema, J.Byrne, L.B. Cole,
G.Colan, S.Ditko, F.Frazetta, R.Frenz, D.Heck, J.Jones, M.Kaluta,
J.Kamen, G.Kane, J.Kirby, J.Lee, G.Pérez, T.McFarlane, M.Ploog,
K.Pollard, J.Romita Sr., J.Romita Jr., J.Simon, A. Schomburg,
M.Schultz, C.Schulz, B.W.Smith, J.Steranko, A.Vargas, and B.Wrightson.
DAN ORGILL '98.
(AFTER ROMITA)

AMAZING FANTASY
12¢
SPIDER-MAN

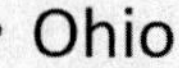

Richie Rich
THE POOR LITTLE RICH BOY
HARVEY COMICS
12¢
Casper

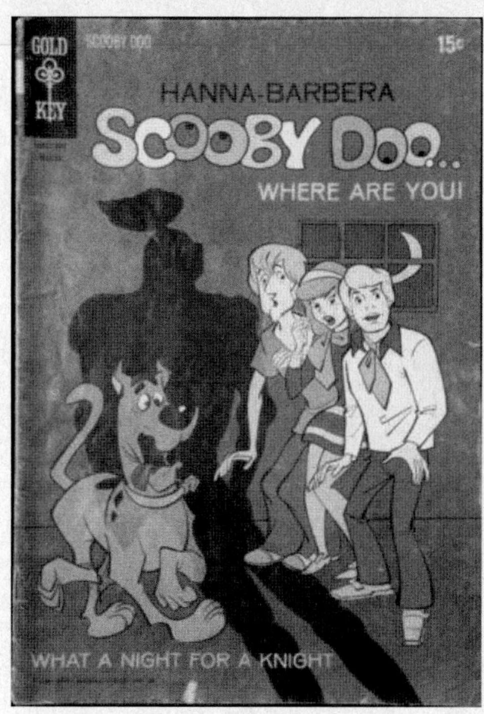
GOLD KEY
15¢
HANNA-BARBERA
SCOOBY DOO...
WHERE ARE YOU!
WHAT A NIGHT FOR A KNIGHT

The Comic Book Price Guide
NO. 5
1875 Edgar Rice Burroughs 1975
NO. 6
The Comic Book Price Guide
The Spirit of '76
$7.50
The Comic Book Price Guide
$9.95
The Comic Book Price Guide
No. 14
$9.95
I'M SITTING ON TOP OF THE WORLD! EVERYBODY'S CALLING TO CONGRATULATE ME FOR BEING ON THE COVER OF THE PRICE GUIDE!
Katy Keene
SEE THE STARS CALLING KATY
The Overstreet Comic Book Price Guide
42ND EDITION 2012-2013
ROBERT M. OVERSTREET
The Overstreet Comic Book Price Guide
48TH EDITION
2018-2019
The Overstreet Comic Book Price Guide
The No. 1 Guide
Robert M. Overstreet

BIG LITTLE BOOKS

INTRODUCTION

In 1932, at the depths of the Great Depression, comic books were not selling despite their successes in the previous two decades. Desperate publishers had already reduced prices to 25¢, but this was still too much for many people to spend on entertainment.

Comic books quickly evolved into two newer formats, the comics magazine and the Big Little Book. Both types retailed for 10¢.

Big Little Books began by reprinting the art (and adapting the stories) from newspaper comics. As their success grew and publishers began commissioning original material, movie adaptations and other entertainment-derived stories became commonplace.

GRADING

Before a Big Little Book's value can be assessed, its condition or state of preservation must be determined. A book in **Near Mint** condition will bring many times the price of the same book in **Poor** condition. Many variables influence the grading of a Big Little Book and all must be considered in the final evaluation. Due to the way they are constructed, damage occurs with very little use - usually to the spine, book edges and binding. More important defects that affect grading are: Split spines, pages missing, page browning or brittleness, writing, crayoning, loose pages, color fading, chunks missing, and rolling or out of square. The following grading guide is given to aid the novice:

9.4 Near Mint: The overall look is as if it was just purchased and maybe opened once; only subtle defects are allowed; paper is cream to off-white, supple and fresh; cover is flat with no surface wear or creases; inks and colors are bright; small penciled or inked arrival dates are acceptable; very slight blunting of corners at top and bottom of spine are common; outside corners are cut square and sharp. Books in this grade could bring prices of guide and a half or more.

9.0 Very Fine/Near Mint: Limited number of defects; full cover gloss with only very slight wear on book corners and edges; very minor foxing; very minor tears allowed, binding still square and tight with no pages missing; paper quality still fresh from cream to off-white. Dates, stamps or initials allowed on cover or inside.

8.0 Very Fine: Most of the cover gloss retained with minor wear appearing at corners and around edges; spine tight with no pages missing; cream/tan paper allowed if still supple; up to 1/4" bend allowed on covers with no color break; cover relatively flat; minor tears allowed.

6.0 Fine: Slight wear beginning to show; cover gloss reduced but still clean, pages tan/brown but still supple (not brittle); up to 1/4" split or color break allowed; minor discoloration and/or foxing allowed.

4.0 Very Good: Obviously a read copy with original printing luster almost gone; some fading and discoloration, but not soiled; some signs of wear such as corner splits and spine rolling; paper can be brown but not brittle; a few pages can be loose but not missing; no chunks missing; blunted corners acceptable.

2.0 Good: An average used copy complete with only minor pieces missing from the spine, which may be partially split; slightly soiled or marked with spine rolling; color flaking and wear around edges, but perfectly sound and legible; could have minor tape repairs but otherwise complete.

1.0 Fair: Very heavily read and soiled with small chunks missing from cover; most or all of spine could be missing; multiple splits in spine and loose pages, but still sound and legible, bringing 50 to 70 percent of good price.

0.5 Poor: Damaged, heavily weathered, soiled or otherwise unsuited for collecting purposes.

IMPORTANT

Most BLBs on the market today will fall in the **Good** to **Fine** grade category. When **Very Fine** to **Near Mint** BLBs are offered for sale, they usually bring premium prices.

A WORD ON PRICING

The prices are given for **Good**, **Fine** and **Very Fine/ Near Mint** condition. A book in **Fair** would be 50-70% of the **Good** price. **Very Good** would be halfway between the **Good** and **Fine** price, and **Very Fine** would be halfway between the **Fine** and **Very Fine/ Near Mint** price. The prices listed were averaged from convention sales, dealers' lists, adzines, auctions, and by special contact with dealers and collectors from coast to coast. The prices and the spreads were determined from sales of copies in available condition or the highest grade known. Since most available copies are in the **Good** to **Fine** range, neither dealers nor collectors should let the **Very Fine/Near Mint** column influence the prices they are willing to charge or pay for books in less than near perfect condition.

The prices listed reflect a six times spread from **Good** to **Very Fine/ Near Mint** (1 - 3 - 6). We feel this spread accurately reflects the current market, especially when you consider the scarcity of books in **Very Fine/Near Mint** condition. When one or both end sheets are missing, the book's value would drop about a half grade.

Books with movie scenes are of double importance due to the high crossover demand by movie collectors.

Abbreviations: a-art; c-cover; nn-no number; p-pages; r-reprint.

Publisher Codes: BRP-Blue Ribbon Press; **ERB**-Edgar Rice Burroughs; **EVW**-Engel van Wiseman; **FAW**-Fawcett Publishing Co.; **Gold**-Goldsmith Publishing Co.; **Lynn**-Lynn Publishing Co.; **McKay**-David McKay Co.; **Whit**-Whitman Publishing Co.; **World**-World Syndicate Publishing Co.

Terminology: *All Pictures Comics*-no text, all drawings; *Fast-Action*-A special series of Dell books highly collected; *Flip Pictures*-upper right corner of interior pages contain drawings that are put into motion when rifled; *Movie Scenes*-book illustrated with scenes from the movie. *Soft Cover*-A thin single sheet of cardboard used in binding most of the giveaway versions.

"Big Little Book" and "Better Little Book" are registered trademarks of Whitman Publishing Co. "Little Big Book" is a registered trademark of the Saalfield Publishing Co.

"Pop-Up" is a registered trademark of Blue Ribbon Press. "Little Big Book" is a registered trademark of the Saalfield Co.

Top 20 Big Little Books and related size books*

Issue#	Rank	Title	Price
731	1	Mickey Mouse the Mail Pilot (variant version of Mickey Mouse #717) (A VG copy sold at auction for $7,170)	
nn	2	Mickey Mouse and Minnie Mouse at Macy's	$2,700
nn	3	Mickey Mouse and Minnie March to Macy's	$2,200
717	4	Mickey Mouse (skinny Mickey on-c)	$2,000
W-707	5	Dick Tracy The Detective	$1,500
725	6	Big Little Mother Goose HC	$1,300
717	7	Mickey Mouse (reg. Mickey on-c)	$1,200
nn	8	Mickey Mouse Silly Symphonies	$1,100
721	9	Big Little Paint Book (336 pg.)	$1,000
nn	10	Mickey Mouse Mail Pilot (Great Big Midget Book)	$925
725	11	Big Little Mother Goose SC	$900
nn	11	Mickey Mouse (Great Big Midget Book)	$900
nn	11	Mickey Mouse and the Magic Carpet	$900
721	14	Big Little Paint Book (320 pg.)	$800
nn	14	Mickey Mouse Sails For Treasure Island (Great Big Midget Book)	$800
4063	16	Popeye Thimble Theater Starring... (2nd printing)	$700
1126	17	Laughing Dragon of Oz	$650
4063	18	Popeye Thimble Theater Starring... (1st printing)	$600
nn	18	Buck Rogers	$600
nn	18	Buck Rogers in the City of Floating Globes	$600

*Includes only the various sized BLBs; no premiums, giveaways or other divergent forms are included.

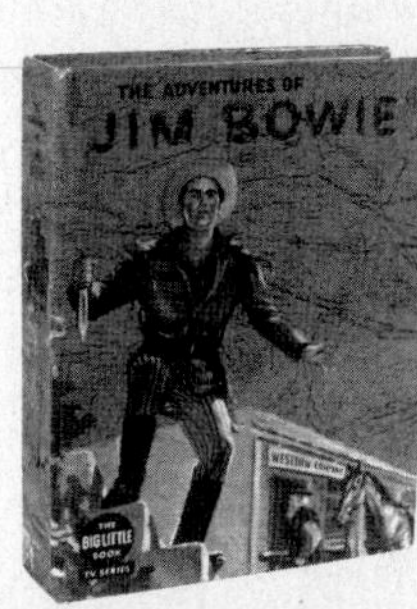

1648 - Adventures of Jim Bowie © WHIT

1497 - Bambi's Children © DIS

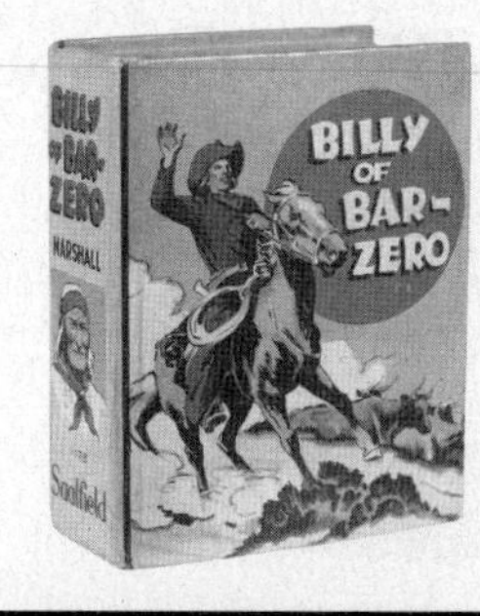

1178 - Billy of Bar-Zero © Saalfield

	GD	FN	VF/NM
1175-0- **Abbie an' Slats**, 1940, Saalfield, 400 pgs.	11.00	27.50	70.00
1182- **Abbie an' Slats-and Becky**, 1940, Saalfield, 400 pgs.	11.00	27.50	70.00
nn- **ABC's To Draw and Color, The**, 1930s, Whitman, 4" x 5 1/4" x 1 1/12" deep, cardboard box contains 320 double-sided sheets to color and a box of crayons	29.00	73.00	200.00
1177- **Ace Drummond**, 1935, Whitman, 432 pgs.	11.00	27.50	70.00
Admiral Byrd (See Paramount Newsreel ...)			
nn- **Adventures of Charlie McCarthy and Edgar Bergen, The**, 1938, Dell, 194 pgs., Fast-Action Story, soft-c	20.00	50.00	140.00
1422- **Adventures of Huckleberry Finn, The**, 1939, Whitman, 432 pgs., Henry E. Vallely-a	10.00	25.00	65.00
1648- **Adventures of Jim Bowie** (TV Series), 1958, Whitman, 280 pgs.	4.00	10.00	26.00
1056- **Adventures of Krazy Kat and Ignatz Mouse in Koko Land**, 1934, Saalfield, 160 pgs., oblong size, hard-c, Herriman-c/a	57.00	143.00	400.00
1306- **Adventures of Krazy Kat and Ignatz Mouse in Koko Land**, 1934, Saalfield, 164 pgs., oblong size, soft-c, Herriman-c/a	64.00	160.00	450.00
1082- **Adventures of Pete the Tramp, The**, 1935, Saalfield, hard-c, by C. D. Russell	10.00	25.00	65.00
1312- **Adventures of Pete the Tramp, The**, 1935, Saalfield, soft-c, by C. D. Russell	10.00	25.00	65.00
1053- **Adventures of Tim Tyler**, 1934, Saalfield, hard-c, oblong size, by Lyman Young	20.00	50.00	140.00
1303- **Adventures of Tim Tyler**, 1934, Saalfield, soft-c, oblong size, by Lyman Young	20.00	50.00	140.00
1058- **Adventures of Tom Sawyer, The**, 1934, Saalfield, 160 pgs., hard-c, Park Sumner-a	10.00	25.00	65.00
1308- **Adventures of Tom Sawyer, The**, 1934, Saalfield, 160 pgs., soft-c, Park Sumner-a	10.00	25.00	65.00
1448- **Air Fighters of America**, 1941, Whitman, 432 pgs., flip picture	11.00	27.50	70.00
Alexander Smart, ESQ. (See Top Line Comics)			
759- **Alice in Wonderland**, 1933, Whitman, 160 pgs., hard-c, photo-c, movie scenes	36.00	90.00	250.00
1481- **Allen Pike of the Parachute Squad U.S.A.**, 1941, Whitman, 432 pgs.	12.00	30.00	75.00
763- **Alley Oop and Dinny**, 1935, Whitman, 384 pgs., V. T. Hamlin-a	17.00	42.50	120.00
1473- **Alley Oop and Dinny in the Jungles of Moo**, 1938, Whitman, 432 pgs., V. T. Hamlin-a	17.00	42.50	120.00
nn- **Alley Oop and the Missing King of Moo**, 1938, Whitman, 36 pgs., 2 1/2" x 3 1/2", Penny Book	10.00	25.00	60.00
nn- **Alley Oop in the Kingdom of Foo**, 1938, Whitman, 68 pgs., 3 1/4" x 3 1/2", Pan-Am premium	23.00	57.50	160.00
nn- **Alley Oop Taming a Dinosaur**, 1938, Whitman, 68 pgs., 3 1/2" x 3 3/4", Pan-Am premium	23.00	57.50	160.00
nn- **"Alley Oop the Invasion of Moo,"** 1935, Whitman, 260 pgs., Cocomalt premium, soft-c; V. T. Hamlin-a	18.00	45.00	125.00
Andy Burnette (See Walt Disney's...)			
Andy Panda (Also see Walter Lantz ...)			
531- **Andy Panda**, 1943, Whitman, 3 3/4x8 3/4", Tall Comic Book, All Pictures Comics	14.00	35.00	100.00
1425- **Andy Panda and Tiny Tom**, 1944, Whitman, All Pictures Comics	10.00	25.00	65.00
1431- **Andy Panda and the Mad Dog Mystery**, 1947, Whitman, 288 pgs., by Walter Lantz	10.00	25.00	65.00
1441- **Andy Panda in the City of Ice**, 1948, Whitman, All Picture Comics, by Walter Lantz	10.00	25.00	65.00
1459- **Andy Panda and the Pirate Ghosts**, 1949, Whitman, 88 pgs., by Walter Lantz	10.00	25.00	65.00
1485- **Andy Panda's Vacation**, 1946, Whitman, All Pictures Comics, by Walter Lantz	10.00	25.00	65.00
15- **Andy Panda (The Adventures of)**, 1942, Dell, Fast-Action Story	14.00	35.00	100.00
707-10 - **Andy Panda and Presto the Pup**, 1949, Whitman	10.00	25.00	65.00
1130- **Apple Mary and Dennie Foil the Swindlers**, 1936, Whitman, 432 pgs. (Forerunner to Mary Worth)	10.00	25.00	65.00

	GD	FN	VF/NM
1403- **Apple Mary and Dennie's Lucky Apples**, 1939, Whitman, 432 pgs.	10.00	25.00	65.00
2017- **(#17)-Aquaman-Scourge of the Sea**, 1968, Whitman, 260 pgs., 39 cents, hard-c, color illos	4.00	10.00	27.00
1192- **Arizona Kid on the Bandit Trail, The**, 1936, Whitman, 432 pgs.	10.00	25.00	60.00
1469- **Bambi** (Walt Disney's), 1942, Whitman, 432 pgs.	18.00	45.00	125.00
1497- **Bambi's Children** (Disney), 1943, Whitman, 432 pgs., Disney Studios-a	18.00	45.00	125.00
1138- **Bandits at Bay**, 1938, Saalfield, 400 pgs.	8.00	20.00	50.00
1459- **Barney Baxter in the Air with the Eagle Squadron**, 1938, Whitman, 432 pgs.	10.00	25.00	65.00
1083- **Barney Google**, 1935, Saalfield, hard-c	16.00	40.00	115.00
1313- **Barney Google**, 1935, Saalfield, soft-c	16.00	40.00	115.00
2031-(#31)- **Batman and Robin in the Cheetah Caper**, 1969, Whitman, 258 pgs.	4.00	10.00	27.00
5771- **Batman and Robin in the Cheetah Caper**, 1974, Whitman, 258 pgs., 49 cents	2.00	5.00	12.00
5771-1- **Batman and Robin in the Cheetah Caper**, 1974, Whitman, 258 pgs., 69 cents	2.00	5.00	12.00
5771-2- **Batman and Robin in the Cheetah Caper**, 1975?, Whitman, 258 pgs.	2.00	5.00	12.00
nn- **Beauty and the Beast**, nd (1930s), np (Whitman), 36 pgs., 3" x 3 1/2" Penny Book	4.00	10.00	22.00
Beep Beep The Road Runner (See Road Runner)			
760- **Believe It or Not!**, 1933, Whitman, 160 pgs., by Ripley (c. 1931)	10.00	25.00	60.00
Betty Bear's Lesson (See Wee Little Books)			
1119- **Betty Boop in Snow White**, 1934, Whitman, 240 pgs., hard-c; adapted from Max Fleischer Paramount Talkartoon	46.00	115.00	325.00
1119- **Betty Boop in Snow White**, 1934, Whitman, 240 pgs., soft-c; same contents as hard-c (Rare)	64.00	160.00	450.00
1158- **Betty Boop in "Miss Gullivers Travels,"** 1935, Whitman, 288 pgs., hard-c (Scarce)	57.00	143.00	400.00
2070- **Big Big Paint Book**, 1936, Whitman, 432 pgs., 8 1/2" x 11 3/8", B&W pages to color	21.00	52.50	150.00
1432- **Big Chief Wahoo and the Lost Pioneers**, 1942, Whitman, 432 pgs., Elmer Woggon-a	11.00	27.50	70.00
1443- **Big Chief Wahoo and the Great Gusto**, 1938, Whitman, 432 pgs., Elmer Woggon-a	11.00	27.50	70.00
1483- **Big Chief Wahoo and the Magic Lamp**, 1940, Whitman, 432 pgs., flip pictures, Woggon-c/a	11.00	27.50	70.00
725- **Big Little Mother Goose, The**, 1934, Whitman, 580 pgs. (Rare) Hardcover	163.00	408.00	1300.00
725- **Big Little Mother Goose, The**, 1934, Whitman, 580 pgs. (Rare) Softcover	123.00	308.00	900.00
1005- **Big Little Nickel Book**, 1935, Whitman, 144 pgs., Blackie Bear stories and Donna the Donkey	8.00	20.00	50.00
1006- **Big Little Nickel Book**, 1935, Whitman, 144 pgs., Blackie Bear stories, folk tales in primer style	8.00	20.00	50.00
1007- **Big Little Nickel Book**, 1935, Whitman, 144 pgs., Peter Rabbit, etc.	8.00	20.00	50.00
1008- **Big Little Nickel Book**, 1935, Whitman, 144 pgs., Wee Wee Woman, etc.	8.00	20.00	50.00
721- **Big Little Paint Book,** The, 1933, Whitman, 320 pgs., 3 3/4" x 8 1/2", for crayoning; first printing has green page ends; second printing has purple page ends (both are rare)	114.00	285.00	800.00
721- **Big Little Paint Book,** The, 1933, Whitman, 336 pgs., 3 3/4" x 8 1/2", for crayoning; first printing has green page ends; second printing has purple page ends (both are rare)	125.00	313.00	1000.00
1178- **Billy of Bar-Zero**, 1940, Saalfield, 400 pgs.	10.00	25.00	60.00
773- **Billy the Kid**, 1935, Whitman, 432 pgs., Hal Arbo-a	10.00	25.00	65.00
1159- **Billy the Kid on Tall Butte**, 1939, Saalfield, 400 pgs.	9.00	22.50	60.00
1174- **Billy the Kid's Pledge**, 1940, Saalfield, 400 pgs.	9.00	22.50	60.00
nn- **Billy the Kid, Western Outlaw**, 1935, Whitman, 260 pgs., Cocomalt premium, Hal Arbo-a, soft-c	12.00	30.00	85.00
1057- **Black Beauty**, 1934, Saalfield, hard-c	8.00	20.00	50.00

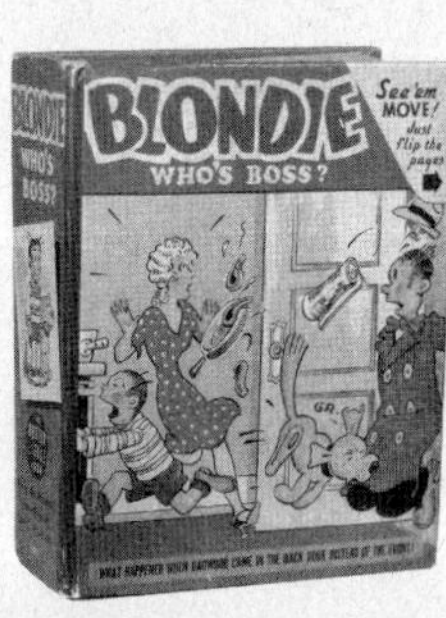

1423 - Blondie Who's Boss © WHIT

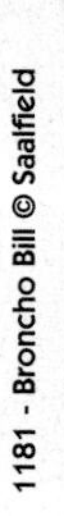
1181 - Broncho Bill © Saalfield

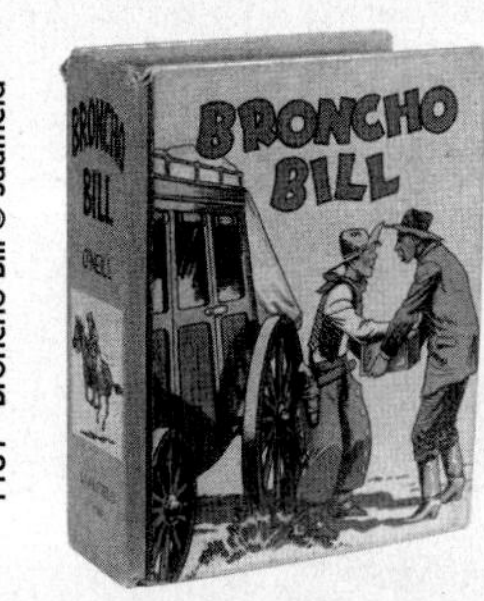

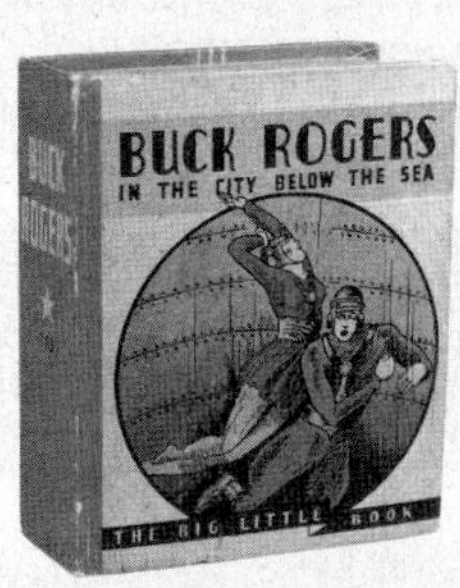

765 - Buck Rogers in the City Below the Sea © KING

	GD	FN	VF/NM
1307- Black Beauty, 1934, Saalfield, soft-c	8.00	20.00	50.00
1414- Black Silver and His Pirate Crew, 1937, Whitman, 300 pgs.	10.00	25.00	65.00
1447- Blaze Brandon with the Foreign Legion, 1938, Whitman, 432 pgs.	10.00	25.00	65.00
1410- Blondie and Dagwood in Hot Water, 1946, Whitman, 352 pgs., by Chic Young	10.00	25.00	60.00
1415- Blondie and Baby Dumpling, 1937, Whitman, 432 pgs., by Chic Young	10.00	25.00	65.00
1419- Oh, Blondie the Bumsteads Carry On, 1941, Whitman, 432 pgs., flip pictures, by Chic Young	10.00	25.00	65.00
1423- Blondie Who's Boss?, 1942, Whitman, 432 pgs., flip pictures, by Chic Young	10.00	25.00	65.00
1429- Blondie with Baby Dumpling and Daisy, 1939, Whitman, 432 pgs., by Chic Young	10.00	25.00	65.00
1430- Blondie Count Cookie in Too!, 1947, Whitman, 288 pgs., by Chic Young	10.00	25.00	60.00
1438- Blondie and Dagwood Everybody's Happy, 1948, Whitman, 288 pgs., by Chic Young	10.00	25.00	60.00
1450- Blondie No Dull Moments, 1948, Whitman, 288 pgs., by Chic Young	10.00	25.00	60.00
1463- Blondie Fun For All, 1949, Whitman, 288 pgs., by Chic Young	10.00	25.00	60.00
1466- Blondie or Life Among the Bumsteads, 1944, Whitman, 352 pgs., by Chic Young	10.00	25.00	65.00
1476- Blondie and Bouncing Baby Dumpling, 1940, Whitman, 432 pgs., by Chic Young	10.00	25.00	65.00
1487- Blondie Baby Dumpling and All!, 1941, Whitman, 432 pgs. flip pictures, by Chic Young	10.00	25.00	65.00
1490- Blondie Papa Knows Best, 1945, Whitman, 352 pgs., by Chic Young	10.00	25.00	60.00
1491- Blondie-Cookie and Daisy's Pups, 1943, Whitman, 1st printing, 432 pgs.	10.00	25.00	65.00
1491- Blondie-Cookie and Daisy's Pups, 1943, Whitman,. 2nd printing with different back-c & 352 pgs.	9.00	22.50	55.00
703-10- Blondie and Dagwood Some Fun!, 1949, Whitman, by Chic Young	8.00	20.00	48.00
21- Blondie and Dagwood, 1936, Lynn, by Chic Young	16.00	40.00	115.00
1108- Bobby Benson on the H-Bar-O Ranch, 1934, Whitman, 300 pgs., based on radio serial	12.00	30.00	75.00
Bobby Thatcher and the Samarang Emerald (See Top-Line Comics)			
1432- Bob Stone the Young Detective, 1937, Whitman, 240 pgs., movie scenes	11.00	27.50	70.00
2002- (#2)-Bonanza-The Bubble Gum Kid, 1967, Whitman, 260 pgs., 39 cents, hard-c, color illos	4.00	10.00	27.00
1139- Border Eagle, The, 1938, Saalfield, 400 pgs.	8.00	20.00	50.00
1153- Boss of the Chisholm Trail, 1939, Saalfield, 400 pgs.	8.00	20.00	50.00
1425- Brad Turner in Transatlantic Flight, 1939, Whitman, 432 pgs.	10.00	25.00	60.00
1058- Brave Little Tailor, The (Disney), 1939, Whitman, 5" x 5 1/2", 68 pgs., hard-c (Mickey Mouse)	12.00	30.00	85.00
1427- Brenda Starr and the Masked Impostor, 1943, Whitman, 352 pgs., Dale Messick-a	12.00	30.00	80.00
1426- Brer Rabbit (Walt Disney's ...), 1947, Whitman, All Picture Comics, from "Song Of The South" movie	18.00	45.00	125.00
704-10- Brer Rabbit, 1949, Whitman	14.00	35.00	100.00
1059- Brick Bradford in the City Beneath the Sea, 1934, Saalfield, hard-c, by William Ritt & Clarence Gray	13.00	32.50	90.00
1309- Brick Bradford in the City Beneath the Sea, 1934, Saalfield, soft-c, by Ritt & Gray	13.00	32.50	90.00
1468- Brick Bradford with Brocco the Modern Buccaneer, 1938, Whitman, 432 pgs., by Wrn. Ritt & Clarence Gray	10.00	25.00	60.00
1133- Bringing Up Father, 1936, Whitman, 432 pgs., by George McManus	12.00	30.00	85.00
1100- Broadway Bill, 1935, Saalfield, photo-c, 4 1/2" x 5 1/4", movie scenes (Columbia Pictures, horse racing)	11.00	27.50	70.00
1580- Broadway Bill, 1935, Saalfield, soft-c, photo-c, movie scenes	11.00	27.50	70.00

	GD	FN	VF/NM
1181- Broncho Bill, 1940, Saalfield, 400 pgs.	10.00	25.00	60.00
nn- Broncho Bill, 1935, Whitman, 148 pgs., 3 1/2" x 4", Tarzan Ice Cream cup lid premium	25.00	62.50	175.00
nn- Broncho Bill in Suicide Canyon (See Top-Line Comics)			
1417- Bronc Peeler the Lone Cowboy, 1937, Whitman, 432 pgs., by Fred Harman, forerunner of Red Ryder (also see Red Death on the Range)	10.00	25.00	60.00
nn- Brownies' Merry Adventures, The, 1993, Barefoot Books, 202 pgs., reprints from Palmer Cox's late 1800s books	3.00	7.50	18.00
1470- Buccaneer, The, 1938, Whitman, 240 pgs., photo-c, movie scenes	12.00	30.00	75.00
1646- Buccaneers, The (TV Series), 1958, Whitman, 4 1/2" x 5 1/4", 280 pgs., Russ Manning-a	4.00	10.00	25.00
1104- Buck Jones in the Fighting Code, 1934, Whitman, 160 pgs., hard-c, movie scenes	14.00	35.00	95.00
1116- Buck Jones in Ride 'Em Cowboy (Universal Presents), 1935, Whitman, 240 pgs., photo-c, movie scenes	14.00	35.00	95.00
1174- Buck Jones in the Roaring West (Universal Presents), 1935, Whitman, 240 pgs., movie scenes	14.00	35.00	95.00
1188- Buck Jones in the Fighting Rangers (Universal Presents), 1936, Whitman, 240 pgs., photo-c, movie scenes	14.00	35.00	95.00
1404- Buck Jones and the Two-Gun Kid, 1937, Whitman, 432 pgs.	10.00	25.00	65.00
1451- Buck Jones and the Killers of Crooked Butte, 1940, Whitman, 432 pgs.	10.00	25.00	65.00
1461- Buck Jones and the Rock Creek Cattle War, 1938, Whitman, 432 pgs.	10.00	25.00	65.00
1486- Buck Jones and the Rough Riders in Forbidden Trails, 1943, Whitman, flip pictures, based on movie; Tim McCoy app.	12.00	30.00	80.00
3- Buck Jones in the Red Rider, 1934, EVW, 160 pgs., movie scenes	21.00	52.50	150.00
8- Buck Jones Cowboy Masquerade, 1938, Whitman, 132 pgs., soft-c, 3 3/4" x 3 1/2", Buddy Book premium	24.00	60.00	170.00
15- Buck Jones in Rocky Rhodes, 1935, EVW, 160 pgs., photo-c, movie scenes	29.00	73.00	200.00
4069- Buck Jones and the Night Riders, 1937, Whitman, 7" x 9", 320 pgs., Big Big Book	39.00	98.00	275.00
nn- Buck Jones on the Six-Gun Trail, 1939, Whitman, 36 pgs., 2 1/2" x 3 1/2", Penny Book	10.00	25.00	60.00
nn- Buck Jones Big Thrill Chewing Gum, 1934, Whitman, 8 pgs., 2 1/2" x 3 1/2" (6 diff.) each...	14.00	35.00	100.00
742- Buck Rogers in the 25th Century A.D., 1933, Whitman, 320 pgs., Dick Calkins-a	43.00	108.00	300.00
nn- Buck Rogers in the 25th Century A.D., 1933, Whitman, 204 pgs.,Cocomalt premium, Calkins-a	29.00	73.00	200.00
765- Buck Rogers in the City Below the Sea, 1934, Whitman, 320 pgs., Dick Calkins-a	32.00	80.00	225.00
765- Buck Rogers in the City Below the Sea, 1934, Whitman, 324 pgs., soft-c, Dick Calkins-c/a (Rare)	57.00	143.00	400.00
1143- Buck Rogers on the Moons of Saturn, 1934, Whitman, 320 pgs., Dick Calkins-a	32.00	80.00	225.00
nn- Buck Rogers on the Moons of Saturn, 1934, Whitman, 324 pgs., premium w/no ads, soft 3-color-c, Dick Calkins-a	50.00	125.00	350.00
1169- Buck Rogers and the Depth Men of Jupiter, 1935, Whitman, 432 pgs., Calkins-a	34.00	85.00	240.00
1178- Buck Rogers and the Doom Comet, 1935, Whitman, 432 pgs., Calkins-a	31.00	78.00	220.00
1197- Buck Rogers and the Planetoid Plot, 1936, Whitman, 432 pgs., Calkins-a	31.00	78.00	220.00
1409- Buck Rogers Vs. the Fiend of Space, 1940, Whitman, 432 pgs., Calkins-a	40.00	100.00	280.00
1437- Buck Rogers in the War with the Planet Venus, 1938, Whitman, 432 pgs., Calkins-a	31.00	78.00	220.00
1474- Buck Rogers and the Overturned World, 1941, Whitman, 432 pgs., flip pictures, Calkins-a	33.00	83.00	230.00
1490- Buck Rogers and the Super-Dwarf of Space, 1943, Whitman, 11 Pictures Comics, Calkins-a	31.00	78.00	220.00
4057- Buck Rogers, The Adventures of, 1934, Whitman, 7" x 9 1/2", 320 pgs., Big Big Book, "The Story of Buck Rogers on the Planet Eros,"			

713 - Buffalo Bill and the Pony Express © WHIT

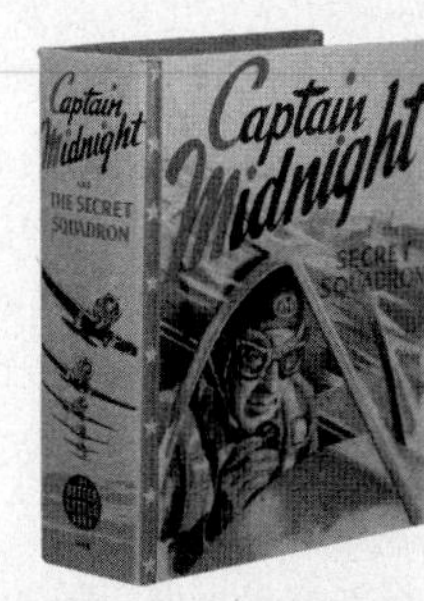

1488 - Captain Midnight and the Secret Squadron © FAW

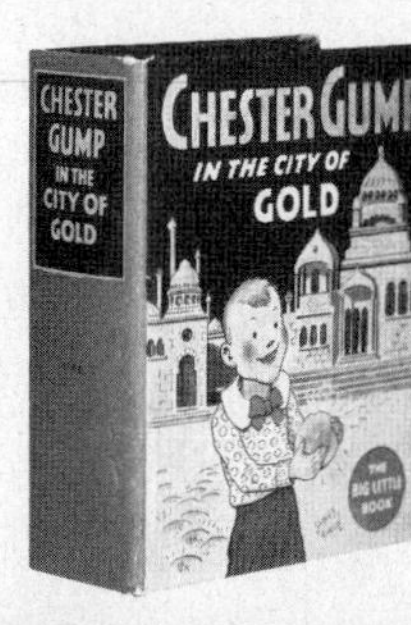

1146 - Chester Gump in the City of Gold © WHIT

	GD	FN	VF/NM
Calkins-c/a	71.00	178.00	500.00
nn- **Buck Rogers**, 1935, Whitman, 4" x 3 1/2", Tarzan Ice Cream cup premium (Rare)	86.00	215.00	600.00
nn- **Buck Rogers in the City of Floating Globes,** 1935, Whitman, 258 pgs., Cocomalt premium, soft-c, Dick Calkins-a	86.00	215.00	600.00
nn- **Buck Rogers Big Thrill Chewing Gum**, 1934, Whitman, 8 pgs., 2 1/2" x 3 " (6 diff.) each...	21.00	52.50	150.00
1135- **Buckskin and Bullets**, 1938, Saalfield, 400 pgs.	8.00	20.00	50.00
Buffalo Bill (See Wild West Adventures of ...)			
nn- **Buffalo Bill**, 1934, World Syndicate, All pictures, by J. Carroll Mansfield	10.00	25.00	60.00
713- **Buffalo Bill and the Pony Express**, 1934, Whitman, hard-c, 384 pgs., Hal Arbo-a	11.00	27.50	70.00
nn- **Buffalo Bill and the Pony Express**, 1934, Whitman, soft-c, 384 pgs., Hal Arbo-a; three-color premium (Rare)	43.00	108.00	300.00
1194- **Buffalo Bill Plays a Lone Hand**, 1936, Whitman, 432 pgs., Hal Arbo-a	10.00	25.00	60.00
530- **Bugs Bunny**, 1943, Whitman, All Pictures Comics, Tall Comic Book, 3 1/4" x 8 1/4", reprints/Looney Tunes 1 & 5	17.00	42.50	120.00
1403- **Bugs Bunny and the Pirate Loot**, 1947, Whitman, All Pictures Comics	11.00	27.50	70.00
1435- **Bugs Bunny**, 1944, Whitman, All Pictures Comics	12.00	30.00	75.00
1440- **Bugs Bunny in Risky Business**, 1948, Whitman, All Pictures & Comics	11.00	27.50	70.00
1455- **Bugs Bunny and Klondike Gold,** 1948, Whitman, 288 pgs.	11.00	27.50	70.00
1465- **Bugs Bunny The Masked Marvel**, 1949, Whitman, 288 pgs.	11.00	27.50	70.00
1496- **Bugs Bunny and His Pals,** 1945, Whitman, All Pictures Comics; r/Four Color Comics #33	11.00	27.50	70.00
13- **Bugs Bunny and the Secret of Storm Island**, 1942, Dell,194 pgs., Fast-Action Story	27.00	68.00	190.00
706-10- **Bugs Bunny and the Giant Brothers,** 1949, Whitman	10.00	25.00	60.00
2007- **(#7)-Bugs Bunny-Double Trouble on Diamond Island**, 1967, Whitman, 260 pgs., 39 cents, hard-c, color illos	5.00	12.50	33.00
2029-**(#29)- Bugs Bunny, Accidental Adventure,** 1969, Whitman, 256 pgs., hard-c, color illos.	4.00	10.00	22.00
2952- **Bugs Bunny's Mistake**, 1949, Whitman, 3 1/4" x 4", 24 pgs., Tiny Tales, full color (5 cents) (1030-5 on back-c)	10.00	25.00	60.00
5757-2- **Bugs Bunny in Double Trouble on Diamond Island**,1967, (1980-reprints #2007), Whitman, 260 pgs., soft-c, 79 cents, B&W	2.00	5.00	14.00
5758- **Bugs Bunny, Accidental Adventure,** 1973, Whitman, 256 pgs., soft-c, B&W illos.	2.00	5.00	14.00
5758-1- **Bugs Bunny, Accidental Adventure,** 1973, Whitman, 256 pgs., soft-c, B&W illos.	2.00	5.00	14.00
5772- **Bugs Bunny the Last Crusader**, 1975, Whitman, 49 cents, flip-it book	2.00	5.00	14.00
5772-2- **Bugs Bunny the Last Crusader**, 1975, Whitman, $1.50, flip-it book	1.00	2.50	6.00
1169- **Bullet Benton**, 1939, Saalfield, 400 pgs.	10.00	25.00	60.00
nn- **Bulletman and the Return of Mr. Murder**, 1941, Fawcett, 196 pgs., Dime Action Book	39.00	98.00	275.00
1142- **Bullets Across the Border** (A Billy The Kid story), 1938, Saalfield, 400 pgs.	10.00	25.00	60.00
Bunky (See Top-Line Comics)			
837- **Bunty** (Punch and Judy), 1935, Whitman, 28 pgs., Magic-Action with 3 pop-ups	12.00	30.00	80.00
1091- **Burn 'Em Up Barnes**, 1935, Saalfield, hard-c, movie scenes	10.00	25.00	60.00
1321- **Burn 'Em Up Barnes**, 1935, Saalfield, soft-c, movie scenes	10.00	25.00	60.00
1415- **Buz Sawyer and Bomber 13**,1946, Whitman, 352 pgs., Roy Crane-a	10.00	25.00	60.00
1412- **Calling W-1-X-Y-Z, Jimmy Kean and the Radio Spies**, 1939, Whitman, 300 pgs.	11.00	27.50	70.00
Call of the Wild (See Jack London's...)			
1107- **Camels are Coming**, 1935, Saalfield, movie scenes	10.00	25.00	60.00
1587- **Camels are Coming**, 1935, Saalfield, movie scenes	10.00	25.00	60.00
nn- **Captain and the Kids, Boys Vill Be Boys, The**, 1938, 68 pgs., Pan-Am Oil premium, soft-c	12.00	30.00	85.00
1128- **Captain Easy Soldier of Fortune**, 1934, Whitman, 432 pgs., Roy Crane-a	11.00	27.50	70.00
nn- **Captain Easy Soldier of Fortune**, 1934, Whitman, 436 pgs., Premium, no ads, soft 3-color-c, Roy Crane-a	20.00	50.00	140.00
1474- **Captain Easy Behind Enemy Lines**, 1943, Whitman, 352 pgs., Roy Crane-a	11.00	27.50	70.00
nn- **Captain Easy and Wash Tubbs**, 1935, 260 pgs., Cocomalt premium, Roy Crane-a	11.00	27.50	70.00
1444- **Captain Frank Hawks Air Ace and the League of Twelve**, 1938, Whitman, 432 pgs.	11.00	27.50	70.00
nn- **Captain Marvel**, 1941, Fawcett, 196 pgs., Dime Action Book	50.00	125.00	350.00
1402- **Captain Midnight and Sheik Jomak Khan**, 1946, Whitman, 352 pgs.	16.00	40.00	115.00
1452- **Captain Midnight and the Moon Woman**, 1943, Whitman, 352 pgs.	18.00	45.00	125.00
1458- **Captain Midnight Vs. The Terror of the Orient**, 1942, Whitman, 432 pgs., flip pictures, Hess-a	18.00	45.00	125.00
1488- **Captain Midnight and the Secret Squadron**, 1941, Whitman, 432 pgs.	18.00	45.00	125.00
Captain Robb of.. (See Dirigible ZR90 ...)			
nn- **Cauliflower Catnip Pearls of Peril**, 1981, Teacup Tales, 290 pgs., Joe Wehrle Jr.-s/a; deliberately printed on aged-looking paper to look like an old BLB	4.00	10.00	27.00
20- **Ceiling Zero,** 1936, Lynn, 128 pgs., 7 1/2" x 5", hard-c, James Cagney, Pat O'Brien photos on-c, movie scenes, Warner Bros. Pictures	11.00	27.50	70.00
1093- **Chandu the Magician**, 1935, Saalfield, 5" x 5 1/4", 160 pgs., hard-c, Bela Lugosi photo-c, movie scenes	13.00	32.50	90.00
1323- **Chandu the Magician**, 1935, Saalfield, 5" x 5 1/4", 160 pgs., soft-c, Bela Lugosi photo-c	14.00	35.00	100.00
Charlie Chan (See Inspector ...)			
1459- **Charlie Chan Solves a New Mystery** (See Inspector..), 1940, Whitman, 432 pgs., Alfred Andriola-a	12.00	30.00	85.00
1478- **Charlie Chan of the Honolulu Police, Inspector**, 1939, Whitman, 432 pgs., Andriola-a	12.00	30.00	85.00
Charlie McCarthy (See Story Of ...)			
734- **Chester Gump at Silver Creek Ranch**, 1933, Whitman, 320 pgs., Sidney Smith-a	13.00	32.50	90.00
nn- **Chester Gump at Silver Creek Ranch**, 1933, Whitman, 204 pgs., Cocomalt premium, soft-c, Sidney Smith-a	14.00	35.00	100.00
nn- **Chester Gump at Silver Creek Ranch**, 1933, Whitman, 52 pgs., 4" x 5 1/2", premium-no ads, soft-c, Sidney Smith-a	21.00	52.50	150.00
766- **Chester Gump Finds the Hidden Treasure**, 1934, Whitman, 320 pgs., Sidney Smith-a	12.00	30.00	85.00
nn- **Chester Gump Finds the Hidden Treasure**, 1934, Whitman, 52 pgs., 3 1/2" x 5 3/4", premium-no ads, soft-c, Sidney Smith-a	21.00	52.50	150.00
nn- **Chester Gump Finds the Hidden Treasure**, 1934, Whitman, 52 pgs., 4" x 5 1/2", premium-no ads, Sidney Smith-a	21.00	52.50	150.00
1146- **Chester Gump in the City Of Gold**, 1935, Whitman, 432 pgs., Sidney Smith-a	12.00	30.00	85.00
nn- **Chester Gump in the City Of Gold**, 1935, Whitman, 436 pgs., premium-no ads, 3-color, soft-c, Sidney Smith-a	24.00	60.00	165.00
1402- **Chester Gump in the Pole to Pole Flight**, 1937, Whitman, 432 pgs.	12.00	30.00	75.00
5- **Chester Gump and His Friends**, 1934, Whitman, 132 pgs., 3 1/2" x 3 1/2", soft-c, Tarzan Ice Cream cup lid premium	23.00	57.50	160.00
nn- **Chester Gump at the North Pole**, 1938, Whitman, 68 pgs. soft-c, 3 3/4" x 3 1/2", Pan-Am giveaway	23.00	57.50	160.00

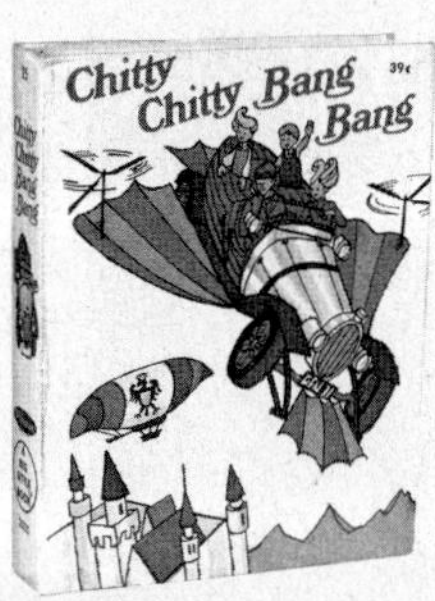

2025 - Chitty Chitty Bang Bang © DIS

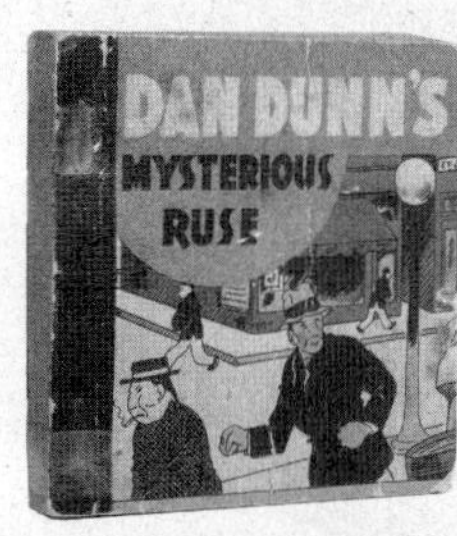

9 - Dan Dunn's Mysterious Ruse © WHIT

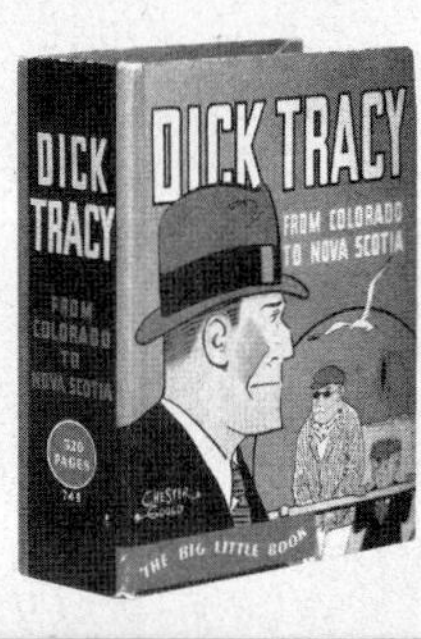

749 - Dick Tracy from Colorado to Nova Scotia © NYNS

GD FN VF/NM

nn- **Chicken Greedy**, nd(1930s), np (Whitman), 36 pgs., 3" x 2 1/2", Penny Book 4.00 10.00 22.00
nn- **Chicken Licken**, nd (1930s), np (Whitman), 36 pgs., 3" x 2 1/2", Penny Book 4.00 10.00 22.00
1101- **Chief of the Rangers**, 1935, Saalfield, hard-c, Tom Mix photo-c, movie scenes from "The Miracle Rider" 13.00 32.50 90.00
1581- **Chief of the Rangers**, 1935, Saalfield, soft-c, Tom Mix photo-c, movie scenes 13.00 32.50 90.00
Child's Garden of Verses (See Wee Little Books)
L14- **Chip Collins' Adventures on Bat Island**, 1935, Lynn, 192 pgs. 11.00 27.50 70.00
2025- **Chitty Chitty Bang Bang**, 1968, Whitman, movie photos 4.00 10.00 27.00
Chubby Little Books, 1935, Whitman, 3" x 2 1/2", 200 pgs.
W803- **Golden Hours Story Book, The** 5.00 12.50 30.00
W803- **Story Hours Story Book, The** 5.00 12.50 30.00
W804- **Gay Book of Little Stories, The** 5.00 12.50 30.00
W804- **Glad Book of Little Stories, The** 5.00 12.50 30.00
W804- **Joy Book of Little Stories, The** 5.00 12.50 30.00
W804- **Sunny Book of Little Stories, The** 5.00 12.50 30.00
1453- **Chuck Malloy Railroad Detective on the Streamliner**, 1938, Whitman, 300 pgs. 8.00 20.00 50.00
Cinderella (See Walt Disney's...)
Clyde Beatty (See The Steel Arena)
1410- **Clyde Beatty Daredevil Lion and Tiger Tamer**, 1939, Whitman, 300 pgs. 12.00 30.00 80.00
1480- **Coach Bernie Bierman's Brick Barton and the Winning Eleven**, 1938, 300 pgs. 10.00 25.00 60.00
1446- **Convoy Patrol** (A Thrilling U.S. Navy Story), 1942, Whitman, 432 pgs., flip pictures 10.00 25.00 60.00
1127- **Corley of the Wilderness Trail**, 1937, Saalfield, hard-c 10.00 25.00 60.00
1607- **Corley of the Wilderness Trail**, 1937, Saalfield, soft-c 10.00 25.00 60.00
1- **Count of Monte Cristo**, 1934, EVW, 160 pgs., (Five Star Library), movie scenes, hard-c (Rare) 20.00 50.00 140.00
1457- **Cowboy Lingo Boys' Book of Western Facts**, 1938, Whitman, 300 pgs., Fred Harman-a 8.00 20.00 50.00
1171- **Cowboy Malloy**, 1940, Saalfield, 400 pgs. 7.00 17.50 40.00
1106- **Cowboy Millionaire**, 1935, Saalfield, movie scenes with George O'Brien, photo-c, hard-c 12.00 30.00 80.00
1586- **Cowboy Millionaire**, 1935, Saalfield, movie scenes with George O'Brien, photo-c, soft-c 12.00 30.00 80.00
724- **Cowboy Stories**, 1933, Whitman, 300 pgs., Hal Arbo-a 10.00 25.00 65.00
nn- **Cowboy Stories**, 1933, Whitman, 52 pgs., soft-c, premium-no ads, 4" x 5 1/2" Hal Arbo-a 12.00 30.00 80.00
1161- **Crimson Cloak, The**, 1939, Saalfield, 400 pgs. 10.00 25.00 60.00
L19- **Curley Harper at Lakespur**, 1935, Lynn, 192 pgs. 10.00 25.00 60.00
5785-2- **Daffy Duck in Twice the Trouble**, 1980, Whitman, 260 pgs., 79 cents soft-c 1.00 2.50 6.00
2018-(#18)-**Daktari-Night of Terror**, 1968, Whitman, 260 pgs., 39 cents, hard-c, color illos 4.00 10.00 27.00
1010- **Dan Dunn And The Gangsters' Frame-Up**, 1937, Whitman, 7 1/4" x 5 1/2", 64 pgs., Nickel Book 29.00 73.00 200.00
1116- **Dan Dunn "Crime Never Pays,"** 1934, Whitman, 320 pgs., by Norman Marsh 8.00 20.00 50.00
1125- **Dan Dunn on the Trail of the Counterfeiters**, 1936, Whitman, 432 pgs., by Norman Marsh 8.00 20.00 50.00
1171- **Dan Dunn and the Crime Master**, 1937, Whitman, 432 pgs., by Norman Marsh 8.00 20.00 50.00
1417- **Dan Dunn and the Underworld Gorillas**, 1941, Whitman, All Pictures Comics, flip pictures, by Norman Marsh 8.00 20.00 50.00
1454- **Dan Dunn on the Trail of Wu Fang**, 1938, Whitman, 432 pgs., by Norman Marsh 10.00 25.00 65.00
1481- **Dan Dunn and the Border Smugglers**, 1938, Whitman, 432 pgs., by Norman Marsh 7.00 17.50 45.00
1492- **Dan Dunn and the Dope Ring**, 1940, Whitman, 432 pgs., by Norman Marsh 7.00 17.50 45.00
nn- **Dan Dunn and the Bank Hold-Up**, 1938, Whitman, 36 pgs., 2 1/2" x 3 1/2", Penny Book 8.00 20.00 50.00
nn- **Dan Dunn and the Zeppelin Of Doom**, 1938, Dell, 196 pgs., Fast-Action Story, soft-c 18.00 45.00 125.00
nn- **Dan Dunn Meets Chang Loo**, 1938, Whitman, 66 pgs., Pan-Am premium, by Norman Marsh 23.00 57.50 160.00
nn- **Dan Dunn Plays a Lone Hand**, 1938, Whitman, 36 pgs., 2 1/2" x 3 1/2", Penny Book 8.00 20.00 50.00
3 3/4" x 3 1/2", Buddy book 24.00 60.00 170.00
6- **Dan Dunn Secret Operative 48 and the Counterfeiter Ring**, 1938, Whitman, 132 pgs., soft-c, 3 3/4" x 3 1/2", Buddy Book premium 24.00 60.00 170.00
9- **Dan Dunn's Mysterious Ruse**, 1936, Whitman, 132 pgs., soft-c, 3 1/2" x 3 1/2", Tarzan Ice Cream cup lid premium 24.00 60.00 170.00
1177- **Danger Trail North**, 1940, Saalfield, 400 pgs. 10.00 25.00 60.00
1151- **Danger Trails in Africa**, 1935, Whitman, 432 pgs. 12.00 30.00 80.00
nn- **Daniel Boone**, 1934, World Syndicate, High Lights of History Series, hard-c, All in Pictures 10.00 25.00 60.00
1160- **Dan of the Lazy L**, 1939, Saalfield, 400 pgs. 10.00 25.00 60.00
1148- **David Copperfield**, 1934, Whitman, hard-c, 160 pgs., photo-c, movie scenes (W. C. Fields) 12.00 30.00 80.00
nn- **David Copperfield**, 1934, Whitman, soft-c, 164 pgs., movie scenes 12.00 30.00 80.00
1151- **Death by Short Wave**, 1938, Saalfield 10.00 25.00 65.00
1156- **Denny the Ace Detective**, 1938, Saalfield, 400 pgs. 10.00 25.00 60.00
1431- **Desert Eagle and the Hidden Fortress, The**, 1941, Whitman, 432 pgs., flip pictures 10.00 25.00 65.00
1458- **Desert Eagle Rides Again, The**, 1939, Whitman, 300 pgs. 10.00 25.00 65.00
1136- **Desert Justice**, 1938, Saalfield, 400 pgs. 10.00 25.00 60.00
1484- **Detective Higgins of the Racket Squad**, 1938, Whitman, 432 pgs. 10.00 25.00 65.00
1124- **Dickie Moore in the Little Red School House**, 1936, Whitman, 240 pgs., photo-c, movie scenes (Chesterfield Motion Picts. Corp) 12.00 30.00 80.00
W-707- **Dick Tracy the Detective, The Adventures of**, 1933, Whitman, 320 pgs. (The 1st Big Little Book), by Chester Gould (Scarce) 188.00 470.00 1500.00
nn- **Dick Tracy Detective, The Adventures of**, 1933, Whitman, 52 pgs., 4" x 5 1/2", premium-no ads, soft-c, by Chester Gould 79.00 198.00 550.00
nn- **Dick Tracy Detective, The Adventures of**, 1933, Whitman, 52 pgs., 4" x 5 1/2", inside back-c & back-c ads for Sundial Shoes, soft-c, by Chester Gould 82.00 205.00 575.00
710- **Dick Tracy and Dick Tracy, Jr.** (The Advs. of ...), 1933, Whitman, 320 pgs., by Chester Gould 57.00 143.00 400.00
nn- **Dick Tracy and Dick Tracy, Jr.** (The Advs. of ...), 1933, Whitman, 52 pgs., premium-no ads, soft-c, 4" x 5 1/2", by Chester Gould 57.00 143.00 400.00
nn- **Dick Tracy the Detective and Dick Tracy, Jr.**, 1933, Whitman, 52 pgs., premium-no ads, 3 1/2"x 5 1/4", soft-c, by Chester Gould 57.00 143.00 400.00
723- **Dick Tracy Out West**, 1933, Whitman, 300 pgs., by Chester Gould 26.00 65.00 185.00
749- **Dick Tracy from Colorado to Nova Scotia**, 1933, Whitman, 320 pgs., by Chester Gould 24.00 60.00 170.00
nn- **Dick Tracy from Colorado to Nova Scotia**, 1933, Whitman, 204 pgs., premium-no ads, soft-c, by Chester Gould 26.00 65.00 185.00
1105- **Dick Tracy and the Stolen Bonds**, 1934, Whitman, 320 pgs., by Chester Gould 14.00 35.00 100.00
1112- **Dick Tracy and the Racketeer Gang**, 1936, Whitman, 432 pgs., by Chester Gould 14.00 35.00 95.00
1137- **Dick Tracy Solves the Penfield Mystery**, 1934, Whitman, 320 pgs., by Chester Gould 14.00 35.00 100.00
nn- **Dick Tracy Solves the Penfield Mystery**, 1934, Whitman, 324 pgs., premium-no ads, 3-color, soft-c, by Chester Gould 36.00 90.00 250.00

1454 - Dick Tracy on the High Seas © NYNS

nn - Dick Tracy and the Maroon Mask Gang © NYNS

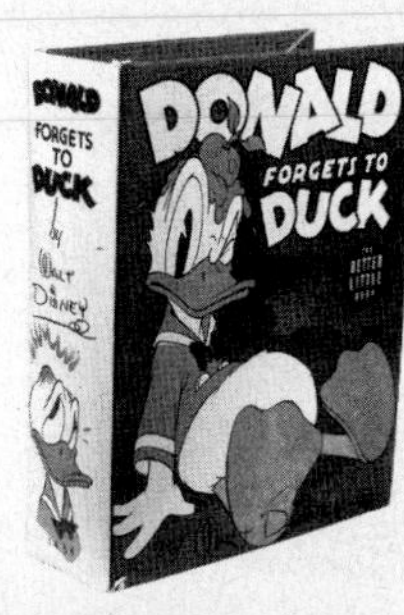
1434 - Donald Duck Forgets to Duck © DIS

GD FN VF/NM

1163- Dick Tracy and the Boris Arson Gang, 1935, Whitman, 432 pgs., by Chester Gould 15.00 37.50 105.00

1170- Dick Tracy on the Trail of Larceny Lu, 1935, Whitman, 432 pgs., by Chester Gould 14.00 35.00 95.00

1185- Dick Tracy in Chains of Crime, 1936, Whitman, 432 pgs., by Chester Gould 15.00 37.50 105.00

1412- Dick Tracy and Yogee Yamma, 1946, Whitman, 352 pgs., by Chester Gould 14.00 35.00 95.00

1420- Dick Tracy and the Hotel Murders, 1937, Whitman, 432 pgs., by Chester Gould 15.00 37.50 105.00

1434- Dick Tracy and the Phantom Ship, 1940, Whitman, 432 pgs., by Chester Gould 15.00 37.50 105.00

1436- Dick Tracy and the Mad Killer, 1947, Whitman, 288 pgs., by Chester Gould 13.00 32.50 90.00

1439- Dick Tracy and His G-Men, 1941, Whitman, 432 pgs., flip pictures, by Chester Gould 15.00 37.50 105.00

1445- Dick Tracy and the Bicycle Gang, 1948, Whitman, 288 pgs., by Chester Gould 13.00 32.50 90.00

1446- Detective Dick Tracy and the Spider Gang, 1937, Whitman, 240 pgs., scenes from "Adventures of Dick Tracy" serial 19.00 47.50 130.00

1449- Dick Tracy Special F.B.I. Operative, 1943, Whitman, 432 pgs. by Chester Gould 15.00 37.50 105.00

1454- Dick Tracy on the High Seas, 1939, Whitman, 432 pgs., by Chester Gould 15.00 37.50 105.00

1460- Dick Tracy and the Tiger Lilly Gang, 1949, Whitman, 288 pgs., by Chester Gould 13.00 32.50 90.00

1478- Dick Tracy on Voodoo Island, 1944, Whitman, 352 pgs., by Chester Gould 13.00 32.50 90.00

1479- Detective Dick Tracy Vs. Crooks in Disguise, 1939, Whitman, 432 pgs., flip pictures, by Chester Gould 15.00 37.50 105.00

1482- Dick Tracy and the Wreath Kidnapping Case, 1945, Whitman, 352 pgs. 14.00 35.00 95.00

1488- Dick Tracy the Super-Detective, 1939, Whitman, 432 pgs., by Chester Gould 15.00 37.50 105.00

1491- Dick Tracy the Man with No Face, 1938, Whitman, 432 pgs. 15.00 37.50 105.00

1495- Dick Tracy Returns, 1939, Whitman, 432 pgs., based on Republic Motion Picture serial, Chester Gould-a 15.00 37.50 105.00

2001- (#1)-Dick Tracy-Encounters Facey, 1967, Whitman, 260 pgs., 39 cents, hard-c, color illos 4.00 10.00 27.00

3912- Dick Tracy Big Little Book Picture Puzzles, 1938, Whitman, 7 1/2" x 10 1/4" box with 2 jigsaw puzzles 50.00 125.00 350.00
Variant set, same cover w/2 puzzles showing Dick Tracy & Jr. in crime lab & Dick Tracy patting down a gangster 50.00 125.00 350.00

4055- Dick Tracy, The Adventures of, 1934, Whitman, 7" x 9 1/2", 320 pgs., Big Big Book, by Chester Gould 57.00 143.00 400.00

4071- Dick Tracy and the Mystery of the Purple Cross, 1938, 7" x 9 1/2", 320 pgs., Big Big Book, by Chester Gould (Scarce) 50.00 125.00 350.00

nn- Dick Tracy and the Invisible Man, 1939, Whitman, 3 1/4" x 3 3/4", 132 pgs., stapled, soft-c, Quaker Oats premium; NBC radio play script, Chester Gould-a 37.00 93.00 260.00

Vol. 2- Dick Tracy's Ghost Ship, 1939, Whitman, 3 1/2" x 3 1/2", 132 pgs., soft-c, stapled, Quaker Oats premium; NBC radio play script episode from actual radio show; Gould-a 37.00 93.00 260.00

3- Dick Tracy Meets a New Gang, 1934, Whitman, 3" x 3 1/2", 132 pgs., soft-c, Tarzan Ice Cream cup lid premium 36.00 90.00 250.00

11- Dick Tracy in Smashing the Famon Racket, 1938, Whitman, 3 3/4" x 3 1/2", Buddy Book-ice cream premium, by Chester Gould 36.00 90.00 250.00

nn- Dick Tracy Gets His Man, 1938, Whitman, 36 pgs., 2 1/2" x 3 1/2", Penny Book 8.00 20.00 50.00

nn- Dick Tracy the Detective, 1938, Whitman, 36 pgs., 2 1/2" x 3 1/2", Penny Book 8.00 20.00 50.00

9- Dick Tracy and the Frozen Bullet Murders, 1941, Dell, 196 pgs., Fast-Action Story, soft-c, by Gould 37.00 93.00 260.00

6833- Dick Tracy Detective and Federal Agent, 1936, Dell, 244 pgs., Cartoon Story Books, hard-c, by Gould 39.00 98.00 275.00

nn- Dick Tracy Detective and Federal Agent, 1936, Dell, 244 pgs., Fast-Action Story, soft-c, by Gould 34.00 85.00 240.00

nn- Dick Tracy and the Blackmailers, 1939, Dell, 196 pgs., Fast-Action Story, soft-c, by Gould 34.00 85.00 240.00

nn- Dick Tracy and the Chain of Evidence, Detective, 1938, Dell, 196 pgs., Fast-Action Story, soft-c, by Chester Gould 34.00 85.00 240.00

nn- Dick Tracy and the Crook Without a Face, 1938, Whitman, 68 pgs., 3 1/4" x 3 1/2", Pan-Am giveaway, Gould-c/a 29.00 73.00 200.00

nn- Dick Tracy and the Maroon Mask Gang, 1938, Dell, 196 pgs., Fast-Action Story, soft-c, by Gould 34.00 85.00 240.00

nn- Dick Tracy Cross-Country Race, 1934, Whitman, 8 pgs., 2 1/2" x 3", Big Thrill chewing gum premium (6 diff.) 12.00 30.00 85.00

nn- Dick Whittington and his Cat, nd(1930s), np(Whitman), 36 pgs., Penny Book 3.00 7.50 20.00

Dinglehoofer und His Dog Adolph (See Top-Line Comics)

Dinky (See Jackie Cooper in ...)

1464- Dirigible ZR90 and the Disappearing Zeppelin (Captain Robb of ...), 1941, Whitman, 300 pgs., Al Lewin-a 14.00 35.00 100.00

1167- Dixie Dugan Among the Cowboys, 1939, Saalfield, 400 pgs. 10.00 25.00 65.00

1188- Dixie Dugan and Cuddles, 1940, Saalfield, 400 pgs., by Striebel & McEvoy 10.00 25.00 65.00

Doctor Doom (See Foreign Spies... & International Spy...)

Dog of Flanders, A (See Frankie Thomas in ...)

1114- Dog Stars of Hollywood, 1936, Saalfield, photo-c, photo-illos 12.00 30.00 75.00

1594- Dog Stars of Hollywood, 1936, Saalfield, photo-c, soft-c, photo-illos 12.00 30.00 75.00

nn- Dolls and Dresses Big Little Set, 1930s, Whitman, box contains 20 dolls on paper, 128 sheets of clothing to color & cut out, includes crayons 36.00 90.00 250.00

Donald Duck (See Silly Symphony... & Walt Disney's ...)

800- Donald Duck in Bringing Up the Boys, 1948, Whitman, hard-c, Story Hour series 10.00 25.00 65.00

1404- Donald Duck (Says Such a Life) (Disney), 1939, Whitman, 432 pgs., Taliaferro-a 19.00 47.50 130.00

1411- Donald Duck and Ghost Morgan's Treasure (Disney), 1946, Whitman, All Pictures Comics, Barks-a; reprints FC #9 24.00 60.00 165.00

1422- Donald Duck Sees Stars (Disney), 1941, Whitman, 432 pgs., flip pictures, Taliaferro-a 18.00 45.00 125.00

1424- Donald Duck Says Such Luck (Disney), 1941, Whitman, 432 pgs., flip pictures, Taliaferro-a 18.00 45.00 125.00

1430- Donald Duck Headed For Trouble (Disney), 1942, Whitman, 432 pgs., flip pictures, Taliaferro-a 18.00 45.00 125.00

1432- Donald Duck and the Green Serpent (Disney), 1947, Whitman, All Pictures Comics, Barks-a; reprints FC #108 20.00 50.00 140.00

1434- Donald Duck Forgets To Duck (Disney), 1939, Whitman, 432 pgs., Taliaferro-a 18.00 45.00 125.00

1438- Donald Duck Off the Beam (Disney), 1943, Whitman, 352 pgs., flip pictures, Taliaferro-a 18.00 45.00 125.00

1438- Donald Duck Off the Beam (Disney), 1943, Whitman, 432 pgs., flip pictures, Taliaferro-a 18.00 45.00 125.00

1449- Donald Duck Lays Down the Law, 1948, Whitman, 288 pgs., Barks-a 18.00 45.00 125.00

1457- Donald Duck in Volcano Valley (Disney), 1949, Whitman, 288 pgs., Barks-a 18.00 45.00 125.00

1462- Donald Duck Gets Fed Up (Disney), 1940, Whitman, 432 pgs.,Taliaferro-a 18.00 45.00 125.00

1478- Donald Duck-Hunting For Trouble (Disney), 1938, Whitman, 432 pgs., Taliaferro-a 18.00 45.00 125.00

1484- Donald Duck is Here Again!, 1944, Whitman, All Pictures Comics, Taliaferro-a 18.00 45.00 125.00

1486- Donald Duck Up in the Air (Disney), 1945, Whitman, 352 pgs., Barks-a 20.00 50.00 140.00

705-10- Donald Duck and the Mystery of the Double X, (Disney), 1949, Whitman, Barks-a 12.00 30.00 80.00

2033-(#33)- Donald Duck, Luck of the Ducks, 1969, Whitman, 256 pgs., hard-c, 39 cents, color illos. 4.00 10.00 22.00

2009-(#9)-Donald Duck-The Fabulous Diamond Fountain, (Walt Disney), 1967, Whitman, 260 pgs., 39 cents, hard-c, color illos 4.00 10.00 27.00

5756- Donald Duck-The Fabulous Diamond Fountain, (Walt Disney), 1973, Whitman, 260 pgs., 79 cents, soft-c, color illos 3.00 7.50 20.00

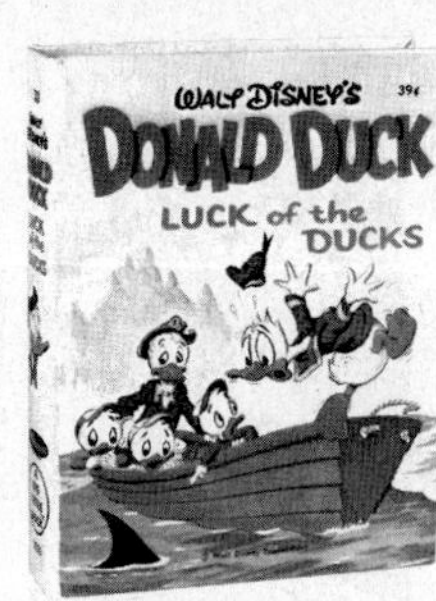

5764 - Donald Duck, Luck of the Ducks © DIS

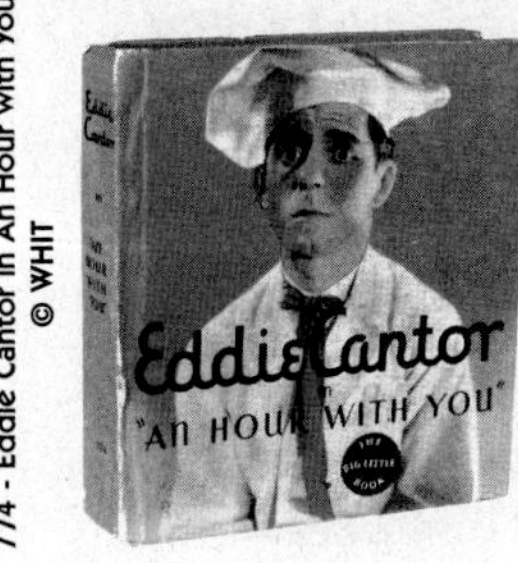

774 - Eddie Cantor in An Hour with You © WHIT

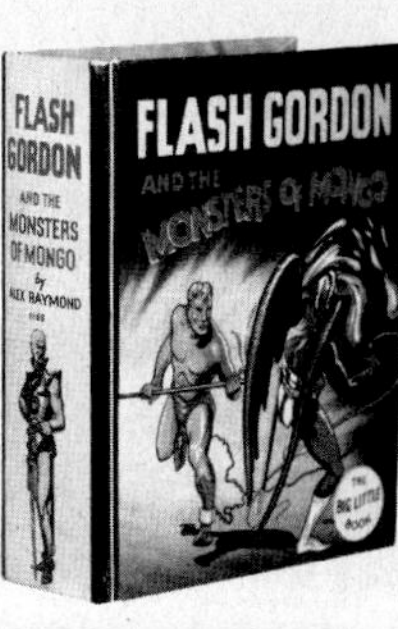

1166 - Flash Gordon and the Monsters of Mongo © KING

	GD	FN	VF/NM
5756-1- Donald Duck-The Fabulous Diamond Fountain, (Walt Disney), 1973, Whitman, 260 pgs., 79 cents, soft-c, color illos	3.00	7.50	20.00
5756-2- Donald Duck-The Fabulous Diamond Fountain, (Walt Disney), 1973, Whitman, 260 pgs., 79 cents, soft-c, color illos	3.00	7.50	20.00
5760- Donald Duck in Volcano Valley (Disney), 1973, Whitman, 39 cents, flip-it book	3.00	7.50	20.00
5760-2- Donald Duck in Volcano Valley (Disney), 1973, Whitman, 79 cents, flip-it book	2.00	5.00	14.00
5764- Donald Duck, Luck of the Ducks, 1969, Whitman, 256 pgs., soft-c, 49 cents, color illos.	3.00	7.50	20.00
5773- Donald Duck - The Lost Jungle City, 1975, Whitman, 49 cents, flip-it book; 6 printings through 1980	2.00	5.00	14.00
nn- Donald Duck and the Ducklings, 1938, Dell, 194 pgs., Fast-Action Story, soft-c, Taliaferro-a	36.00	90.00	250.00
nn- Donald Duck Out of Luck (Disney), 1940, Dell, 196 pgs., Fast-Action Story, has Four Color #4 on back-c, Taliaferro-a	36.00	90.00	250.00
8- Donald Duck Takes It on the Chin (Disney), 1941, Dell, 196 pgs., Fast-Action Story, soft-c, Taliaferro-a	36.00	90.00	250.00
L13- Donnie and the Pirates, 1935, Lynn, 192 pgs.	10.00	25.00	60.00
1438- Don O'Dare Finds War, 1940, Whitman, 432 pgs.	10.00	25.00	60.00
1107- Don Winslow, U.S.N., 1935, Whitman, 432 pgs.	16.00	40.00	110.00
nn- Don Winslow, U.S.N., 1935, Whitman, 436 pgs., premium-no ads, 3-color, soft-c	19.00	47.50	130.00
1408- Don Winslow and the Giant Girl Spy, 1946, Whitman, 352 pgs.	12.00	30.00	75.00
1418- Don Winslow Navy Intelligence Ace, 1942, Whitman, 432 pgs., flip pictures	14.00	35.00	100.00
1419- Don Winslow of the Navy Vs. the Scorpion Gang, 1938, Whitman, 432 pgs.	14.00	35.00	100.00
1453- Don Winslow of the Navy and the Secret Enemy Base, 1943, Whitman, 352 pgs.	14.00	35.00	100.00
1489- Don Winslow of the Navy and the Great War Plot, 1940, Whitman, 432 pgs.	14.00	35.00	100.00
nn- Don Winslow U.S. Navy and the Missing Admiral, 1938, Whitman, 36 pgs., 2 1/2" x 3 1/2", Penny Book	7.00	17.50	40.00
1137- Doomed To Die, 1938, Saalfield, 400 pgs.	10.00	25.00	60.00
1140- Down Cartridge Creek, 1938, Saalfield, 400 pgs.	10.00	25.00	60.00
1416- Draftie of the U.S. Army, 1943, Whitman, All Pictures Comics	10.00	25.00	65.00
1100B- Dreams (Your dreams & what they mean), 1938, Whitman, 36 pgs., 2 1/2" x 3 1/2", Penny Book	3.00	7.50	20.00
24- Dumb Dora and Bing Brown, 1936, Lynn	11.00	27.50	70.00
1400- Dumbo, of the Circus - Only His Ears Grew! (Disney), 1941, Whitman, 432 pgs., based on Disney movie	18.00	45.00	125.00
10- Dumbo the Flying Elephant (Disney), 1944, Dell, 194 pgs., Fast-Action Story, soft-c	29.00	73.00	200.00
nn- East O' the Sun and West O' the Moon, nd (1930s), np (Whitman), 36 pgs., 3" x 2 1/2", Penny Book	3.00	7.50	20.00
774- Eddie Cantor in An Hour with You, 1934, Whitman, 154 pgs., 4 1/4" x 5 1/4", photo-c, movie scenes	12.00	30.00	85.00
nn- Eddie Cantor in Laughland, 1934, Goldsmith, 132 pgs., soft-c, photo-c, Vallely-a	12.00	30.00	85.00
1106- Ella Cinders and the Mysterious House, 1934, Whitman, 432 pgs.	12.00	30.00	75.00
nn- Ella Cinders and the Mysterious House, 1934, Whitman, 52 pgs., premium-no ads, soft-c, 3 1/2" x 5 3/4"	14.00	35.00	100.00
nn- Ella Cinders and the Mysterious House, 1934, Whitman, 52 pgs., Lemix Korlix desserts ad by Perkins Products Co. on back-c, soft-c, 3 1/2" x 5 3/4"	18.00	45.00	125.00
nn- Ella Cinders, 1935, Whitman, 148 pgs., 3 1/4" x 4", Tarzan Ice Cream cup lid premium	24.00	60.00	165.00
nn- Ella Cinders Plays Duchess, 1938, Whitman, 68 pgs., 3 3/4" x 3 1/2", Pan-Am Oil premium	16.00	40.00	115.00
nn- Ella Cinders Solves a Mystery, 1938, Whitman, 68 pgs., Pan-Am Oil premium, soft-c	16.00	40.00	115.00
11- Ella Cinders' Exciting Experience, 1934, Whitman, 3 1/2" x 3 1/2", 132 pgs., Tarzan Ice Cream cup lid giveaway	24.00	60.00	165.00
1406- Ellery Queen the Adventure of the Last Man Club, 1940, Whitman, 432 pgs.	12.00	30.00	80.00
1472- Ellery Queen the Master Detective, 1942, Whitman, 432 pgs., flip pictures	12.00	30.00	80.00
1081- Elmer and his Dog Spot, 1935, Saalfield, hard-c	8.00	20.00	50.00
1311- Elmer and his Dog Spot, 1935, Saalfield, soft-c	8.00	20.00	50.00
722- Erik Noble and the Forty-Niners, 1934, Whitman, 384 pgs.	8.00	20.00	50.00
nn- Erik Noble and the Forty-Niners, 1934, Whitman, 386 pgs., 3-color, soft-c (Rare)	36.00	90.00	250.00
684- Famous Comics (in open box), 1934, Whitman, 48 pgs., 3 3/4" x 8 1/2", (3 books in set): Book 1 - Katzenjammer Kids, Barney Google, & Little Jimmy Book 2 - Polly and Her Pals, Little Jimmy, & Katzenjammer Kids Book 3 - Little Annie Rooney, Katzenjammer Kids, & Polly and Her Pals Complete set	50.00	125.00	350.00
2019-(#19)- Fantastic Four in the House of Horrors, 1968, Whitman, 256 pgs., hard-c, color illos.	4.00	10.00	27.00
5775 - Fantastic Four in the House of Horrors, 1976, Whitman, 256 pgs., soft-c, color illos.	3.00	7.50	20.00
5775-1 - Fantastic Four in the House of Horrors, 1976, Whitman, 256 pgs., soft-c, color illos.	3.00	7.50	20.00
1058- Farmyard Symphony, The (Disney), 1939, 5" X 5 1/2", 68 pgs., hard-c	11.00	27.50	70.00
1129- Felix the Cat, 1936, Whitman, 432 pgs., Messmer-a	24.00	60.00	170.00
1439- Felix the Cat, 1943, Whitman, All Pictures Comics, Messmer-a	21.00	52.50	150.00
1465- Felix the Cat, 1945, Whitman, All Pictures Comics, Messmer-a	18.00	45.00	125.00
nn- Felix (Flip book), 1967, World Retrospective of Animation Cinema, 188 pgs., 2 1/2" x 4" by Otto Messmer	4.00	10.00	27.00
nn- Fighting Cowboy of Nugget Gulch, The, 1939, Whitman, 2 1/2" x 3 1/2", Penny Book	4.00	10.00	25.00
1401- Fighting Heroes Battle for Freedom, 1943, Whitman, All Pictures Comics, from "Heroes of Democracy" strip, by Stookie Allen	8.00	20.00	50.00
6- Fighting President, The, 1934, EVW (Five Star Library), 160 pgs., photo-c, photo ill., F. D. Roosevelt	10.00	25.00	60.00
nn- Fire Chief Ed Wynn and "His Old Fire Horse," 1934, Goldsmith, 132 pgs., H. Vallely-a, photo, soft-c	10.00	25.00	60.00
1464- Flame Boy and the Indians' Secret, 1938, Whitman, 300 pgs., Sekakuku-a (Hopi Indian)	8.00	20.00	50.00
22- Flaming Guns, 1935, EVW, with Tom Mix, movie scenes Hardcover	43.00	108.00	300.00
(Scarce) Softcover	50.00	125.00	350.00
1110- Flash Gordon on the Planet Mongo, 1934, Whitman, 320 pgs., by Alex Raymond	39.00	98.00	275.00
1166- Flash Gordon and the Monsters of Mongo, 1935, Whitman, 432 pgs., by Alex Raymond	37.00	93.00	260.00
nn- Flash Gordon and the Monsters of Mongo, 1935, Whitman, 436 pgs., premium-no ads, 3-color, soft-c, by Raymond	61.00	153.00	430.00
1171- Flash Gordon and the Tournaments of Mongo, 1935, Whitman, 432 pgs., by Alex Raymond	36.00	90.00	250.00
1190- Flash Gordon and the Witch Queen of Mongo, 1936, Whitman, 432 pgs., by Alex Raymond	36.00	90.00	250.00
1407- Flash Gordon in the Water World of Mongo, 1937, Whitman, 432 pgs., by Alex Raymond	31.00	78.00	215.00
1423- Flash Gordon and the Perils of Mongo, 1940, Whitman, 432 pgs., by Alex Raymond	29.00	73.00	200.00
1424- Flash Gordon in the Jungles of Mongo, 1947, Whitman, 352 pgs., by Alex Raymond	23.00	57.50	160.00
1443- Flash Gordon in the Ice World of Mongo, 1942, Whitman, 432 pgs., flip pictures, by Alex Raymond	30.00	75.00	210.00
1447- Flash Gordon and the Fiery Desert of Mongo, 1948, Whitman, 288 pgs., Raymond-a	23.00	57.50	160.00
1469- Flash Gordon and the Power Men of Mongo, 1943,			

nn - Flintstones: It's About Time © H-B

1494 - Gene Autry Cowboy Detective © WHIT

6833 - G-Man on Lightning Island © WHIT

GD FN VF/NM

Whitman, 352 pgs., by Alex Raymond 31.00 78.00 220.00

1479- Flash Gordon and the Red Sword Invaders, 1945, Whitman, 352 pgs., by Alex Raymond 29.00 73.00 200.00

1484- Flash Gordon and the Tyrant of Mongo, 1941, Whitman, 432 pgs., flip pictures, by Alex Raymond 31.00 78.00 220.00

1492- Flash Gordon in the Forest Kingdom of Mongo, 1938, Whitman, 432 pgs., by Alex Raymond 39.00 98.00 270.00

12- Flash Gordon and the Ape Men of Mor, 1942, Dell, 196 pgs., Fast-Action Story, by Alex Raymond 36.00 90.00 250.00

6833- Flash Gordon Vs. the Emperor of Mongo, 1936, Dell, 244 pgs., Cartoon Story Books, hard-c, Raymond-c/a 43.00 108.00 300.00

nn- Flash Gordon Vs. the Emperor of Mongo, 1936, Dell, 244 pgs., Fast-Action Story, soft-c, Alex Raymond-c/a 36.00 90.00 250.00

1467- Flint Roper and the Six-Gun Showdown, 1941, Whitman, 300 pgs. 10.00 25.00 60.00

2014-(#14)- Flintstones-The Case of the Many Missing Things, 1968, Whitman, 260 pgs., 39 cents, hard-c, color illos 4.00 10.00 27.00

nn- Flintstones: A Friend From the Past, 1977, Modern Promotions, 244 pgs., 49 cents, soft-c, flip pictures 2.00 5.00 11.00

nn- Flintstones: It's About Time, 1977, Modern Promotions, 244 pgs., 49 cents, soft-c, flip pictures 2.00 5.00 11.00

nn- Flintstones: Pebbles & Bamm-Bamm Meet Santa Claus, 1977, Modern Promotions, 244 pgs., 49 cents, soft-c, flip pictures 2.00 5.00 11.00

nn- Flintstones: The Great Balloon Race, 1977, Modern Promotions, 244 pgs., 49 cents, soft-c, flip pictures 2.00 5.00 11.00

nn- Flintstones: The Mystery of the Many Missing Things, 1977, Modern Promotions, 244 pgs., 49 cents, soft-c, flip pictures 2.00 5.00 11.00

2003-(#3)- Flipper-Killer Whale Trouble, 1967, Whitman, 260 pgs., hard-c, 39 cents, color illos 3.00 7.50 20.00

2032-(#32)- Flipper, Deep-Sea Photographer, 1969, Whitman, 256 pgs., hard-c, color illos. 3.00 7.50 20.00

1108- Flying the Sky Clipper with Winsie Atkins, 1936, Whitman, 432 pgs. 10.00 25.00 60.00

1460- Foreign Spies Doctor Doom and the Ghost Submarine, 1939, Whitman, 432 pgs., Al McWilliams-a 12.00 30.00 75.00

1100B- Fortune Teller, 1938, Whitman, 36 pgs., 2 1/2" x 3 1/2", Penny Book 3.00 7.50 20.00

1175- Frank Buck Presents Ted Towers Animal Master, 1935, Whitman, 432 pgs. 11.00 27.50 70.00

2015-(#15)-Frankenstein, Jr. - The Menace of the Heartless Monster, 1968, Whitman, 260 pgs., 39 cents, hard-c, color illos.4.00 10.00 27.00

16- Frankie Thomas in A Dog of Flanders, 1935, EVW, movie scenes 12.00 30.00 75.00

1121- Frank Merriwell at Yale, 1935, 432 pgs. 10.00 25.00 60.00

Freckles and His Friends in the North Woods (See Top-Line Comics)

nn- Freckles and His Friends Stage a Play, 1938, Whitman, 36 pgs., 2 1/2" x 3 1/2", Penny Book 10.00 25.00 60.00

1164- Freckles and the Lost Diamond Mine, 1937, Whitman, 432 pgs., Merrill Blosser-a 11.00 27.50 70.00

nn- Freckles and the Mystery Ship, 1935, Whitman, 66 pgs., Pan-Am premium 12.00 30.00 75.00

1100B- Fun, Puzzles, Riddles, 1938, Whitman, 36 pgs., 2 1/2" x 3 1/2", Penny Book 3.00 7.50 20.00

1433- Gang Busters Step In, 1939, Whitman, 432 pgs., Henry E. Vallely-a 11.00 27.50 70.00

1437- Gang Busters Smash Through, 1942, Whitman, 432 pgs. 11.00 27.50 70.00

1451- Gang Busters in Action!, 1938, Whitman, 432 pgs. 11.00 27.50 70.00

nn- Gang Busters and Guns of the Law, 1940, Dell, 4" x 5", 194 pgs., Fast-Action Story, soft-c 27.00 68.00 190.00

nn- Gang Busters and the Radio Clues, 1938, Whitman, 36 pgs., 2 1/2" x 3 1/2", Penny Book 8.00 20.00 50.00

1409- Gene Autry and Raiders of the Range, 1946, Whitman, 352 pgs. 12.00 30.00 80.00

1425- Gene Autry and the Mystery of Paint Rock Canyon, 1947, Whitman, 288 pgs. 12.00 30.00 80.00

1428- Gene Autry Special Ranger, 1941, Whitman, 432 pgs., Erwin Hess-a 16.00 40.00 115.00

GD FN VF/NM

1433- Gene Autry in Public Cowboy No. 1, 1938, Whitman, 240 pgs., photo-c, movie scenes (1st Autry BLB) 29.00 73.00 200.00

1434- Gene Autry and the Gun-Smoke Reckoning, 1943, Whitman, 352 pgs. 16.00 40.00 110.00

1439- Gene Autry and the Land Grab Mystery, 1948, Whitman, 290 pgs. 12.00 30.00 75.00

1456- Gene Autry in Special Ranger Rule, 1945, Whitman, 352 pgs., Henry E. Vallely-a 16.00 40.00 110.00

1461- Gene Autry and the Red Bandit's Ghost, 1949, Whitman, 288 pgs. 11.00 27.50 70.00

1483- Gene Autry in Law of the Range, 1939, Whitman, 432 pgs. 16.00 40.00 110.00

1493- Gene Autry and the Hawk of the Hills, 1942, Whitman, 428 pgs., flip pictures, Vallely-a 16.00 40.00 110.00

1494- Gene Autry Cowboy Detective, 1940, Whitman, 432 pgs., Erwin Hess-a 16.00 40.00 110.00

700-10- Gene Autry and the Bandits of Silver Tip, 1949, Whitman 11.00 27.50 70.00

714-10- Gene Autry and the Range War, 1950, Whitman 11.00 27.50 70.00

nn- Gene Autry in Gun-Smoke, 1938, Dell, 196 pgs., Fast-Action story, soft-c 27.00 68.00 190.00

2035-(#35)- Gentle Ben, Mystery of the Everglades, 1969, Whitman, 256 pgs., hard-c, color illos. 3.00 7.50 20.00

1176- Gentleman Joe Palooka, 1940, Saalfield, 400 pgs. 10.00 25.00 60.00

George O'Brien (See The Cowboy Millionaire)

1101- George O'Brien and the Arizona Badman, 1936?, Whitman 10.00 25.00 60.00

1418- George O'Brien in Gun Law, 1938, Whitman, 240 pgs., photo-c, movie scenes, RKO Radio Pictures 10.00 25.00 60.00

1457- George O'Brien and the Hooded Riders, 1940, Whitman, 432 pgs., Erwin Hess-a 8.00 20.00 50.00

nn- George O'Brien and the Arizona Bad Man, 1939, Whitman, 36 pgs., 2 1/2" x 3 1/2", Penny Book 8.00 20.00 50.00

1462- Ghost Avenger, 1943, Whitman, 432 pgs., flip pictures, Henry Vallely-a 10.00 25.00 60.00

nn- Ghost Gun Gang Meet Their Match, The, 1939. Whitman, 2 1/2" x 3 1/2", Penny Book 8.00 20.00 50.00

nn- Gingerbread Boy, The, nd(1930s), np(Whitman), 36 pgs., Penny Book 2.00 5.00 15.00

1118- G-Man on the Crime Trail, 1936, Whitman, 432 pgs. 11.00 27.50 70.00

1147- G-Man Vs. the Red X, 1936, Whitman, 432 pgs. 12.00 30.00 80.00

1162- G-Man Allen, 1939, Saalfield, 400 pgs. 11.00 27.50 70.00

1173- G-Man in Action, A, 1940, Saalfield, 400 pgs., J.R. White-a 11.00 27.50 70.00

1434- G-Man and the Radio Bank Robberies, 1937, Whitman, 432 pgs. 12.00 30.00 80.00

1469- G-Man and the Gun Runners, The, 1940, Whitman, 432 pgs. 12.00 30.00 80.00

1470- G-Man vs. the Fifth Column, 1941, Whitman, 432 pgs., flip pictures 12.00 30.00 80.00

1493- G-Man Breaking the Gambling Ring, 1938, Whitman, 432 pgs., James Gary-a 12.00 30.00 80.00

nn- G-Man on Lightning Island, 1936, Dell, 244 pgs., Fast-Action Story, soft-c, Henry E. Vallely-a 24.00 60.00 170.00

nn- G-Man, Underworld Chief, 1938, Whitman, Buddy Book premium, 29.00 73.00 200.00

6833- G-Man on Lightning Island, 1936, Dell, 244 pgs., Cartoon Story Book, hard-c, Henry E. Vallely-a 18.00 45.00 125.00

4- G-Men Foil the Kidnappers, 1936, Whitman, 132 pgs., 3 1/2" x 3 1/2", soft-c, Tarzan Ice Cream cup lid premium 24.00 60.00 165.00

1157- G-Men on the Trail, 1938, Saalfield, 400 pgs.10.00 25.00 60.00

1168- G Men on the Job, 1935, Whitman, 432 pgs.12.00 30.00 75.00

nn- G-Men on the Job Again, 1938, Whitman, 36 pgs., 2 1/2" x 3 1/2", Penny Book 10.00 25.00 60.00

nn- G-Men and Kidnap Justice, 1938, Whitman, 68 pgs., Pan-Am premium, soft-c 12.00 30.00 75.00

nn- G-Men and the Missing Clues, 1938, Whitman, 36 pgs., 2 1/2"x 3 1/2",

nn - The Gumps in Radio Land © L&F

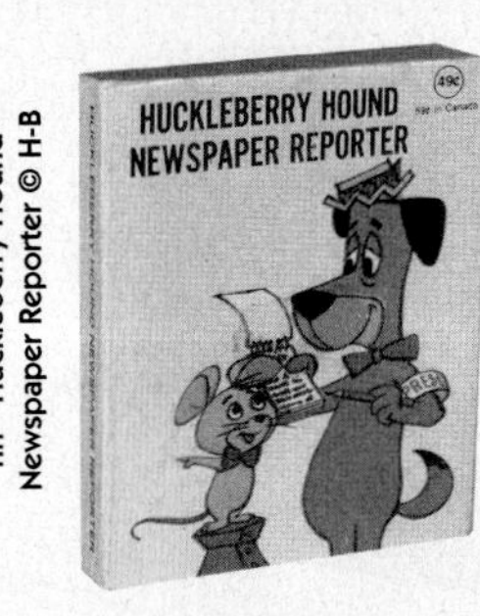

nn - Huckleberry Hound Newspaper Reporter © H-B

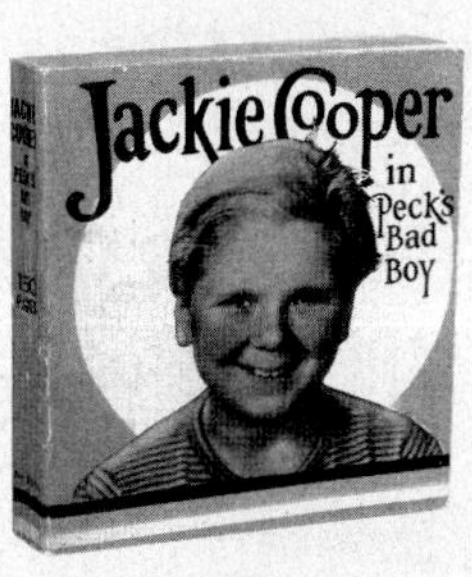

1314 - Jackie Cooper in Peck's Bad Boy © Saalfield

	GD	FN	VF/NM
Penny Book	10.00	25.00	60.00
1097- Go Into Your Dance, 1935, Saalfield, 160 pgs.. photo-c, movie scenes with Al Jolson & Ruby Keeler	13.00	32.50	90.00
1577- Go Into Your Dance, 1935, Saalfield, 160 pgs., photo-c, movie scenes, soft-c	13.00	32.50	90.00
2021- Goofy in Giant Trouble (Walt Disney's ...), 1968, Whitman, hard-c, 260 pgs., 39 cents, color illos.	3.00	7.50	20.00
5751- Goofy in Giant Trouble (Walt Disney's ...), 1968, Whitman, soft-c, 260 pgs., 39 cents, color illos.	3.00	7.50	20.00
5751-2- Goofy in Giant Trouble, 1968 (1980-reprint of '67 version), Whitman, soft-c, 260 pgs., 79 cents, B&W	1.00	2.50	8.00
8- Great Expectations, 1934, EVW, (Five Star Library), 160 pgs., photo-c, movie scenes	14.00	35.00	100.00
1453- Green Hornet Strikes!, The, 1940, Whitman, 432 pgs., Robert Weisman-a	34.00	85.00	240.00
1480- Green Hornet Cracks Down, The, 1942, Whitman, 432 pgs., flip pictures, Henry Vallely-a	31.00	78.00	220.00
1496- Green Hornet Returns, The, 1941, Whitman, 432 pgs., flip pictures	34.00	85.00	240.00
5778- Grimm's Ghost Stories, 1976, Whitman, 256 pgs., Laura French-s adapted from fairy tales; blue spine & back-c	2.00	5.00	13.00
5778-1- Grimm's Ghost Stories, 1976, Whitman, 256 pgs., reprint of #5778; yellow spine & back-c	2.00	5.00	13.00
1172- Gullivers' Travels, 1939, Saalfield, 320 pgs., adapted from Paramount Pict. Cartoons (Rare) Hardcover	26.00	65.00	180.00
(Scarce) Softcover	29.00	73.00	205.00
nn- Gumps In Radio Land, The (Andy Gump and the Chest of Gold), 1937, Lehn & Fink Prod. Corp., 100 pgs., 3 1/4" x 5 1/2", Pebeco Tooth Paste giveaway, by Gus Edson	20.00	50.00	140.00
nn- Gunmen of Rustlers' Gulch, The, 1939, Whitman, 36 pgs., 2 1/2" x 3 1/2", Penny Book	7.00	17.50	40.00
1426- Guns in the Roaring West, 1937, Whitman, 300 pgs.	7.00	17.50	40.00
1647- Gunsmoke (TV Series), 1958, Whitman, 280 pgs., 4 1/2" x 5 3/4"	5.00	12.50	30.00
1101- Hairbreath Harry in Department QT, 1935, Whitman, 384 pgs., by J. M. Alexander	10.00	25.00	65.00
1413- Hal Hardy in the Lost Land of Giants, 1938, Whitman, 300 pgs., "The World 1,000,000 Years Ago"	10.00	25.00	65.00
1159- Hall of Fame of the Air, 1936, Whitman, 432 pgs., by Capt. Eddie Rickenbacker	8.00	20.00	50.00
nn- Hansel and Grethel, The Story of, nd (1930s), no publ., 36 pgs., Penny Book	2.00	5.00	15.00
1145- Hap Lee's Selection of Movie Gags, 1935, Whitman, 160 pgs., photos of stars	13.00	32.50	90.00
Happy Prince, The (See Wee Little Books)			
1111- Hard Rock Harrigan-A Story of Boulder Dam, 1935, Saalfield, hard-c, photo-c, photo illos.	10.00	25.00	60.00
1591- Hard Rock Harrigan-A Story of Boulder Dam, 1935, Saalfield, soft-c, photo-c, photo illos.	10.00	25.00	60.00
1418- Harold Teen Swinging at the Sugar Bowl, 1939, Whitman, 432 pgs., by Carl Ed	10.00	25.00	60.00
nn- Hercules - The Legendary Journeys, 1998, Chronicle Books, 310 pgs., based on TV series, 1-color (brown) illos	1.00	2.50	9.00
1100B- Hobbies, 1938, Whitman, 36 pgs., 2 1/2" x 3 1/2", Penny Book	2.00	5.00	15.00
1125- Hockey Spare, The, 1937, Saalfield, sports book	7.00	17.50	40.00
1605- Hockey Spare, The, 1937, Saalfield, soft-c	7.00	17.50	40.00
728- Homeless Homer, 1934, Whitman, by Dee Dobbin, for young kids	4.00	10.00	25.00
17- Hoosier Schoolmaster, The, 1935, EVW, movie scenes	13.00	32.50	90.00
715- Houdini's Big Little Book of Magic, 1927 (1933), 300 pgs.	14.00	35.00	95.00
nn- Houdini's Big Little Book of Magic, 1927 (1933), 196 pgs., American Oil Co. premium, soft-c	14.00	35.00	95.00
nn- Houdini's Big Little Book of Magic, 1927 (1933), 204 pgs., Cocomalt premium, soft-c	14.00	35.00	95.00
Huckleberry Finn (See The Adventures of...)			
nn- Huckleberry Hound Newspaper Reporter, 1977, Modern Promotions, 244 pgs., 49 cents, soft-c, flip pictures	2.00	5.00	13.00
1644- Hugh O'Brian TV's Wyatt Earp (TV Series), 1958, Whitman, 280 pgs.	5.00	12.50	30.00
5782-2- Incredible Hulk Lost in Time, 1980, 260 pgs., 79¢-c, soft-c, B&W	2.00	5.00	10.00
1424- Inspector Charlie Chan Villainy on the High Seas, 1942, Whitman, 432 pgs., flip pictures	14.00	35.00	95.00
1186- Inspector Wade of Scotland Yard, 1940, Saalfield, 400 pgs.	10.00	25.00	60.00
1194- Inspector Wade and The Feathered Serpent, 1939, Saalfield, 400 pgs.	10.00	25.00	60.00
1448- Inspector Wade Solves the Mystery of the Red Aces, 1937, Whitman, 432 pgs.	10.00	25.00	60.00
1148- International Spy Doctor Doom Faces Death at Dawn, 1937, Whitman, 432 pgs., Arbo-a	12.00	30.00	75.00
1155- In the Name of the Law, 1937, Whitman, 432 pgs., Henry E. Vallely-a	10.00	25.00	60.00
2012-(#12)-Invaders, The-Alien Missile Threat (TV Series), 1967, Whitman, 260 pgs., hard-c, 39 cents, color illos.	4.00	10.00	27.00
1403- Invisible Scarlet O'Neil, 1942, Whitman, All Pictures Comics, flip pictures	12.00	30.00	75.00
1406- Invisible Scarlet O'Neil Versus the King of the Slums, 1946, Whitman, 352 pgs.	10.00	25.00	60.00
1098- It Happened One Night, 1935, Saalfield, 160 pgs., Little Big Book, Clark Gable, Claudette Colbert photo-c, movie scenes from Academy Award winner	14.00	35.00	100.00
1578- It Happened One Night, 1935, Saalfield, 160 pgs., soft-c	14.00	35.00	100.00
Jack and Jill (See Wee Little Books)			
1432- Jack Armstrong and the Mystery of the Iron Key, 1939, Whitman, 432 pgs., Henry E. Vallely-a	12.00	30.00	85.00
1435- Jack Armstrong and the Ivory Treasure, 1937, Whitman, 432 pgs., Henry Vallely-a	12.00	30.00	85.00
Jackie Cooper (See Story Of..)			
1084- Jackie Cooper in Peck's Bad Boy, 1934, Saalfield, 160 pgs., hard, photo-c, movie scenes	15.00	37.50	105.00
1314- Jackie Cooper in Peck's Bad Boy, 1934, Saalfield, 160 pgs., soft, photo-c, movie scenes	15.00	37.50	105.00
1402- Jackie Cooper in "Gangster's Boy," 1939, Whitman, 240 pgs., photo-c, movie scenes	15.00	37.50	105.00
13- Jackie Cooper in Dinky, 1935, EVW, 160 pgs., movie scenes	15.00	37.50	105.00
nn- Jack King of the Secret Service and the Counterfeiters, 1939, Whitman, 36 pgs., 2 1/2" x 3 1/2", Penny Book, by John G. Gray	10.00	25.00	60.00
L11- Jack London's Call of the Wild, 1935, Lynn, 20th Cent. Pic., movie scenes with Clark Gable	12.00	30.00	80.00
nn- Jack Pearl as Detective Baron Munchausen, 1934, Goldsmith, 132 pgs., soft-c	12.00	30.00	85.00
1102- Jack Swift and His Rocket Ship, 1934, Whitman, 320 pgs.	16.00	40.00	110.00
1498- Jane Arden the Vanished Princess, Whitman, 300 pgs.	10.00	25.00	60.00
1179- Jane Withers in This is the Life (20th Century-Fox Presents...), 1935, Whitman, 240 pgs., photo-c, movie scenes	12.00	30.00	80.00
1463- Jane Withers in Keep Smiling, 1938, Whitman, 240 pgs., photo-c, movie scenes	12.00	30.00	80.00
Jaragu of the Jungle (See Rex Beach's ...)			
1447- Jerry Parker Police Reporter and the Candid Camera Clue, 1941, Whitman, 300 pgs.	10.00	25.00	60.00
Jim Bowie (See Adventures of ...)			
nn- Jim Brant of the Highway Patrol and the Mysterious Accident, 1939, Whitman, 36 pgs., 2 1/2" x 3 1/2", Penny Book	9.00	22.50	55.00
1466- Jim Craig State Trooper and the Kidnapped Governor, 1938, Whitman, 432 pgs.	10.00	25.00	60.00
nn- Jim Doyle Private Detective and the Train Hold-Up, 1939, Whitman, 36 pgs., 2 1/2" x 3 1/2", Penny Book	10.00	25.00	65.00
1180- Jim Hardy Ace Reporter, 1940, Saalfield, 400 pgs., Dick Moores-a	10.00	25.00	65.00
1143- Jimmy Allen in the Air Mail Robbery, 1936, Whitman, 432 pgs.			

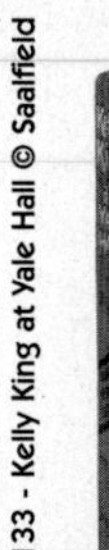

1442 - Junior G-Men © WHIT

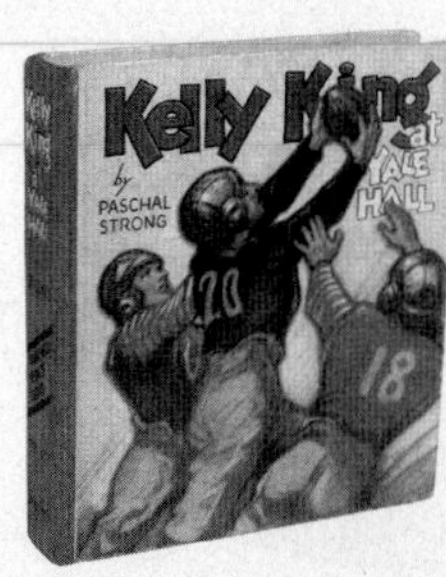

1133 - Kelly King at Yale Hall © Saalfield

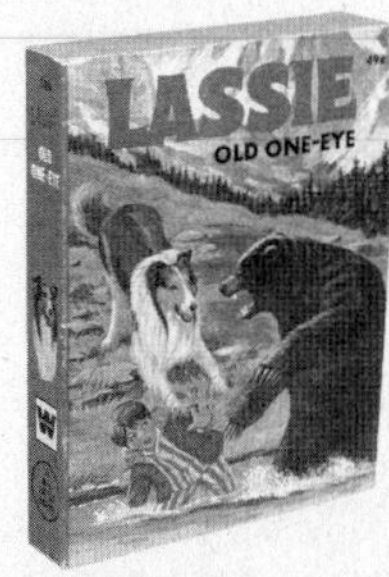

5769 - Lassie, Old One-Eye © WHIT

	GD	FN	VF/NM
	10.00	25.00	65.00
27- Jimmy Allen in The Sky Parade, 1936, Lynn, 130 pgs., 5 x 7 1/2", Paramount Pictures, movie scenes	12.00	30.00	75.00
L15- Jimmy and the Tiger, 1935, Lynn, 192 pgs.	10.00	25.00	65.00
1428- Jim Starr of the Border Patrol, 1937, Whitman, 432 pgs.	10.00	25.00	65.00
Joan of Arc (See Wee Little Books)			
1105- Joe Louis the Brown Bomber, 1936, Whitman, 240 pgs., photo-c, photo-illos.	20.00	50.00	140.00
Joe Palooka (See Gentleman ...)			
1123- Joe Palooka the Heavyweight Boxing Champ, 1934, Whitman, 320 pgs., Ham Fisher-a	18.00	45.00	125.00
1168- Joe Palooka's Great Adventure, 1939, Saalfield	14.00	35.00	100.00
nn- Joe Penner's Duck Farm, 1935, Goldsmith, Henry Vallely-a	11.00	27.50	70.00
1402- John Carter of Mars, 1940, Whitman, 432 pgs., John Coleman Burroughs-a	50.00	125.00	350.00
nn- John Carter of Mars, 1940, Dell, 194 pgs., Fast-Action Story, soft-c	64.00	160.00	450.00
1164- Johnny Forty Five, 1938, Saalfield, 400 pgs.	10.00	25.00	60.00
John Wayne (See Westward Ho!)			
1100B- Jokes (A book of laughs galore), 1938, Whitman, 36 pgs., 2 1/2" x 3 1/2", Penny Book, laughing guy-c	2.00	5.00	15.00
1100B- Jokes (A book of side-splitting funny stories), 1938, Whitman, 36 pgs., 2 1/2" x 3 1/2", Penny Book, clowns on-c	2.00	5.00	15.00
2026-(#26)- Journey to the Center of the Earth, The Fiery Foe, 1968, Whitman	4.00	10.00	27.00
Jungle Jim (See Top-Line Comics)			
1138- Jungle Jim, 1936, Whitman, 432 pgs., Alex Raymond-a	20.00	50.00	140.00
1139- Jungle Jim and the Vampire Woman, 1937, Whitman, 432 pgs., Alex Raymond-a	20.00	50.00	140.00
1442- Junior G-Men, 1937, Whitman, 432 pgs., Henry E. Vallely-a	11.00	27.50	70.00
nn- Junior G-Men Solve a Crime, 1939, Whitman, 36 pgs., 2 1/2" x 3 1/2", Penny Book	11.00	27.50	70.00
1422- Junior Nebb on the Diamond Bar Ranch, 1938, Whitman, 300 pgs., by Sol Hess	11.00	27.50	70.00
1470- Junior Nebb Joins the Circus, 1939, Whitman, 300 pgs. by Sol Hess	11.00	27.50	70.00
nn- Junior Nebb Elephant Trainer, 1939, Whitman, 68 pgs., Pan-Am Oil premium, soft-c	13.00	32.50	90.00
1052- "Just Kids" (Adventures of ...), 1934, Saalfield, oblong size, by Ad Carter	18.00	45.00	125.00
1094- Just Kids and the Mysterious Stranger, 1935, Saalfield, 160 pgs., by Ad Carter	13.00	32.50	90.00
1184- Just Kids and Deep-Sea Dan, 1940, Saalfield, 400 pgs., by Ad Carter	12.00	30.00	75.00
1302- Just Kids, The Adventures of, 1934, Saalfield, oblong size, soft-c, by Ad Carter	20.00	50.00	140.00
1324- Just Kids and the Mysterious Stranger, 1935, Saalfield, 160 pgs., soft-c, by Ad Carter ,	13.00	32.50	90.00
1401- Just Kids, 1937, Whitman, 432 pgs., by Ad Carter	13.00	32.50	90.00
1055- Katzenjammer Kids in the Mountains, 1934, Saalfield, hard-c, oblong, H. H. Knerr-a	16.00	40.00	115.00
1305- Katzenjammer Kids in the Mountains, 1934, Saalfield, soft-c, oblong, H. H. Knerr-a	16.00	40.00	115.00
14- Katzenjammer Kids, The, 1942, Dell, 194 pgs., Fast-Action Story, H. H. Knerr-a	18.00	45.00	125.00
1411- Kay Darcy and the Mystery Hideout, 1937, Whitman, 300 pgs., Charles Mueller-a	12.00	30.00	80.00
1180- Kayo in the Land of Sunshine (With Moon Mullins), 1937, Whitman, 432 pgs., by Willard	13.00	32.50	90.00
1415- Kayo and Moon Mullins and the One Man Gang, 1939, Whitman, 432 pgs., by Frank Willard	11.00	27.50	70.00
7- Kayo and Moon Mullins 'Way Down South, 1938, Whitman, 132 pgs., 3 1/2" x 3 1/2", Buddy Book	21.00	52.50	150.00
1105- Kazan in Revenge of the North (James Oliver Curwood's...), 1937, Whitman, 432 pgs., Henry E. Vallely-a	11.00	25.00	60.00
1471- Kazan, King of the Pack (James Oliver Curwood's...), 1940, Whitman, 432 pgs.	9.00	22.50	55.00
1420- Keep 'Em Flying! U.S.A. for America's Defense, 1943, Whitman, 432 pgs., Henry E. Vallely-a, flip pictures	10.00	25.00	60.00
1133- Kelly King at Yale Hall, 1937, Saalfield	9.00	22.50	55.00
Ken Maynard (See Strawberry Roan & Western Frontier)			
5- Ken Maynard in "Wheels of Destiny," 1934, EVW, 160 pgs., movie scenes (scarce)	20.00	50.00	140.00
776- Ken Maynard in "Gun Justice," 1934, Whitman, 160 pgs., hard-c, movie scenes (Universal Pic.)	14.00	35.00	95.00
776- Ken Maynard in "Gun Justice," 1934, Whitman, 160 pgs., soft-c, movie scenes (Universal Pic.)	14.00	35.00	95.00
1430- Ken Maynard in Western Justice, 1938, Whitman, 432 pgs., Irwin Myers-a	11.00	27.50	70.00
1442- Ken Maynard and the Gun Wolves of the Gila, 1939, Whitman, 432 pgs.	11.00	27.50	70.00
nn- Ken Maynard in Six-Gun Law, 1938, Whitman, 36 pgs., 2 1/2" x 3 1/2", Penny Book	9.00	22.50	55.00
1134- King of Crime, 1938, Saalfield, 400 pgs.	10.00	25.00	60.00
King of the Royal Mounted (See Zane Grey)			
nn- Kit Carson, 1933, World Syndicate, by J. Carroll Mansfield, High Lights Of History Series, hard-c	10.00	25.00	60.00
nn- Kit Carson, 1933, World Syndicate, same as hard-c above but with a black cloth-c	10.00	25.00	60.00
1105- Kit Carson and the Mystery Riders, 1935, Saalfield, hard-c, Johnny Mack Brown photo-c, movie scenes	13.00	32.50	90.00
1585- Kit Carson and the Mystery Riders, 1935, Saalfield, soft-c, Johnny Mack Brown photo-c, movie scenes	13.00	32.50	90.00
Krazy Kat (See Adventures of...)			
2004- (#4)-Lassie-Adventure in Alaska (TV Series), 1967, Whitman, hard-c, 260 pgs., 39 cents, color illos	4.00	10.00	27.00
5754- Lassie-Adventure in Alaska (TV Series), 1973, Whitman, soft-c, 260 pgs., 49 cents, color illos	2.00	5.00	15.00
2027- Lassie and the Shabby Sheik (TV Series), 1968, Whitman, hard-c, 260 pgs., 39 cents	4.00	10.00	25.00
5762- Lassie and the Shabby Sheik (TV Series), 1972, Whitman, soft-c, 260 pgs., 39 cents	2.00	5.00	15.00
5769- Lassie, Old One-Eye (TV Series), 1975, Whitman, soft-c, 260 pgs., 49 cents, three printings	2.00	5.00	15.00
1132- Last Days of Pompeii, The, 1935, Whitman, 5 1/4" x 6 1/4", 260 pgs., photo-c, movie scenes	12.00	30.00	85.00
1128- Last Man Out (Baseball), 1937, Saalfield, hard-c	10.00	25.00	60.00
L30- Last of the Mohicans, The, 1936, Lynn, 192 pgs., movie scenes with Randolph Scott, United Artists Pictures	12.00	30.00	80.00
1126- Laughing Dragon of Oz, The, 1934, Whitman 432 pgs., by Frank Baum (scarce)	86.00	215.00	600.00
1086- Laurel and Hardy, 1934, Saalfield, 160 pgs., hard-c, photo-c, movie scenes	21.00	52.50	145.00
1316- Laurel and Hardy, 1934, Saalfield, 160 pgs. soft-c, photo-c, movie scenes	21.00	52.50	145.00
1092- Law of the Wild, The, 1935, Saalfield, 160 pgs., photo-c, movie scenes of Rex, The Wild Horse & Rin-Tin-Tin Jr.	11.00	27.50	70.00
1322- Law of the Wild, The, 1935, Saalfield, 160 pgs., photo-c, movie scenes, soft-c	11.00	27.50	70.00
1100B- Learn to be a Ventriloquist, 1938, Whitman, 36 pgs. 2 1/2" x 3 1/2", Penny Book	2.00	5.00	15.00
1149- Lee Brady Range Detective, 1938, Saalfield, 400 pgs.	9.00	22.50	55.00
L10- Les Miserables (Victor Hugo's ...), 1935, Lynn, 192 pgs., movie scenes	12.00	30.00	80.00
1441- Lightning Jim U.S. Marshal Brings Law to the West, 1940, Whitman, 432 pgs., based on radio program	10.00	25.00	65.00
nn- Lightning Jim Whipple U.S. Marshal in Indian Territory, 1939, Whitman, 36 pgs., 2 1/2" x 3 1/2", Penny Book	8.00	20.00	50.00
653- Lions and Tigers (With Clyde Beatty), 1934, Whitman, 160 pgs., photo-c movie scenes	12.00	30.00	85.00
1187- Li'l Abner and the Ratfields, 1940, Saalfield, 400 pgs., by Al Capp	14.00	35.00	95.00
1193- Li'l Abner and Sadie Hawkins Day, 1940, Saalfield, 400 pgs., by Al Capp	14.00	35.00	95.00

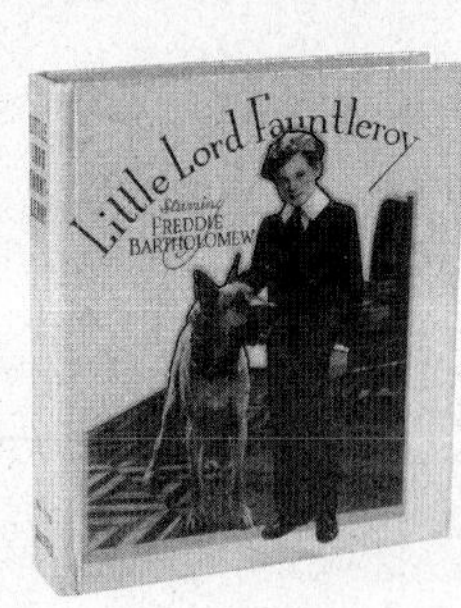
1118 - Little Lord Fauntleroy © Saalfield

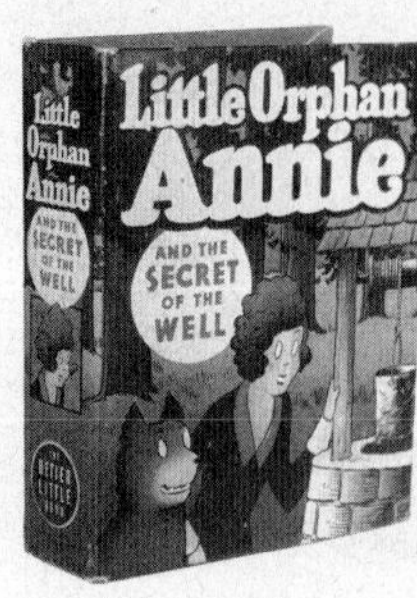
1417 - Little Orphan Annie and the Secret of the Well © WHIT

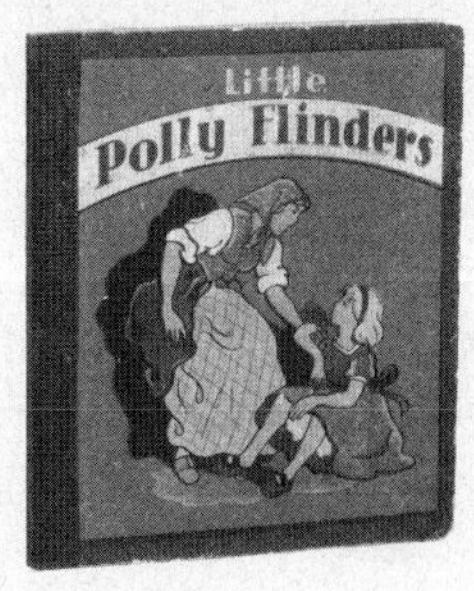
nn - Little Polly Flinders

1198- **Li'l Abner in New York**, 1936, Whitman, 432 pgs., by Al Capp 15.00 37.50 105.00

1401- **Li'l Abner Among the Millionaires**, 1939, Whitman, 432 pgs., by Al Capp 15.00 37.50 105.00

1054- **Little Annie Rooney**, 1934, Saalfield, oblong - 4" x 8", All Pictures Comics, hard-c 14.00 35.00 100.00

1304- **Little Annie Rooney**, 1934, Saalfield, oblong - 4" x 8", All Pictures, soft-c 14.00 35.00 100.00

1117- **Little Annie Rooney and the Orphan House**, 1936, Whitman, 432 pgs. 11.00 27.50 70.00

1406- **Little Annie Rooney on the Highway to Adventure**, 1938, Whitman, 432 pgs. 11.00 27.50 70.00

1149- **Little Big Shot** (With Sybil Jason), 1935, Whitman, 240 pgs., photo-c, movie scenes 12.00 30.00 85.00

nn- **Little Black Sambo**, nd (1930s), np (Whitman), 36 pgs., 3" x 2 1/2", Penny Book 12.00 30.00 75.00

Little Bo-Peep (See Wee Little Books)

Little Colonel, The (See Shirley Temple)

1148- **Little Green Door, The**, 1938, Saalfield, 400 pgs. 10.00 25.00 60.00

1112- **Little Hollywood Stars**, 1935, Saalfield, movie scenes (Little Rascals, etc.), hard-c 12.00 30.00 85.00

1592- **Little Hollywood Stars**, 1935, Saalfield, movie scenes, soft-c 12.00 30.00 85.00

1087- **Little Jimmy's Gold Hunt**, 1935, Saalfield, 160 pgs., hard-c, Little Big Book, by Swinnerton 16.00 40.00 110.00

1317- **Little Jimmy's Gold Hunt**, 1935, Saalfield, 160 pgs., 4 1/4" x 5 3/4", soft-c, by Swinnerton 16.00 40.00 110.00

Little Joe and the City Gangsters (See Top-Line Comics)

Little Joe Otter's Slide (See Wee Little Books)

1118- **Little Lord Fauntleroy**, 1936, Saalfield, movie scenes, photo-c, 4 1/2" x 5 1/4", starring Mickey Rooney & Freddie Bartholomew, hard-c 10.00 25.00 60.00

1598- **Little Lord Fauntleroy**, 1936, Saalfield, photo-c, movie scenes, soft-c 10.00 25.00 60.00

1192- **Little Mary Mixup and the Grocery Robberies**, 1940, Saalfield 10.00 25.00 60.00

8- **Little Mary Mixup Wins A Prize**, 1936, Whitman, 132 pgs., 3 1/2" x 3 1/2", soft-c, Tarzan Ice Cream cup lid premium 24.00 60.00 165.00

1150- **Little Men**, 1934, Whitman, 4 3/4" x 5 1/4", movie scenes (Mascot Prod.), photo-c, hard-c 10.00 25.00 65.00

9- **Little Minister, The**,-Katharine Hepburn, 1935, 160 pgs., 4 1/4" x 5 1/2", EVW (Five Star Library), movie scenes (RKO)14.00 35.00 100.00

1120- **Little Miss Muffet**, 1936, Whitman, 432 pgs., by Fanny Y. Cory 11.00 27.50 70.00

708- **Little Orphan Annie**, 1933, Whitman, 320 pgs., by Harold Gray, the 2nd Big Little Book 43.00 108.00 300.00

nn- **Little Orphan Annie**, 1928('33), Whitman, 52 pgs., 4" x 5 1/2", premium-no ads, soft-c, by Harold Gray 29.00 73.00 200.00

716- **Little Orphan Annie and Sandy**, 1933, Whitman, 320 pgs., by Harold Gray 24.00 60.00 170.00

716- **Little Orphan Annie and Sandy**, 1933, Whitman, 300 pgs., by Harold Gray 20.00 50.00 140.00

nn- **Little Orphan Annie and Sandy**, 1933, Whitman, 52 pgs., premium, no ads, 4" x 5 1/2", soft-c by Harold Gray 29.00 73.00 200.00

748- **Little Orphan Annie and Chizzler**, 1933, Whitman, 320 pgs., by Harold Gray 14.00 35.00 100.00

1010- **Little Orphan Annie and the Big Town Gunmen**, 1937, 7 1/4" x 5 1/2", 64 pgs., Nickel Book 12.00 30.00 85.00

nn- **Little Orphan Annie with the Circus**, 1934, Whitman, 320 pgs., same cover as L.O.A. 708 but with blue background, Ovaltine giveaway stamp inside front-c, by Harold Gray 36.00 90.00 250.00

1103- **Little Orphan Annie with the Circus**, 1934, Whitman, 320 pgs. 14.00 35.00 100.00

1140- **Little Orphan Annie and the Big Train Robbery**, 1934, Whitman, 300 pgs., by Gray 14.00 35.00 100.00

1140- **Little Orphan Annie and the Big Train Robbery**, 1934, Whitman, 300 pgs., premium-no ads, soft-c, by Harold Gray 26.00 65.00 180.00

1154- **Little Orphan Annie and the Ghost Gang**, 1935, Whitman, 432 pgs. by Harold Gray 14.00 35.00 100.00

nn- **Little Orphan Annie and the Ghost Gang**, 1935, Whitman, 436 pgs., premium-no ads, 3-color, soft-c, by Harold Gray 26.00 65.00 180.00

1162- **Little Orphan Annie and Punjab the Wizard**, 1935, Whitman, 432 pgs., by Harold Gray 14.00 35.00 100.00

1186- **Little Orphan Annie and the $1,000,000 Formula**, 1936, Whitman, 432 pgs., by Gray 13.00 32.50 90.00

1414- **Little Orphan Annie and the Ancient Treasure of Am**, 1939, Whitman, 432 pgs., by Gray 12.00 30.00 80.00

1416- **Little Orphan Annie in the Movies**, 1937, Whitman, 432 pgs., by Harold Gray 12.00 30.00 80.00

1417- **Little Orphan Annie and the Secret of the Well**, 1947, Whitman, 352 pgs., by Gray 11.00 27.50 70.00

1435- **Little Orphan Annie and the Gooneyville Mystery**, 1947, Whitman, 288 pgs., by Gray 12.00 30.00 75.00

1446- **Little Orphan Annie in the Thieves' Den**, 1949, Whitman, 288 pgs., by Harold Gray 12.00 30.00 75.00

1449- **Little Orphan Annie and the Mysterious Shoemaker**, 1938, Whitman, 432 pgs., by Harold Gray 12.00 30.00 85.00

1457- **Little Orphan Annie and Her Junior Commandos**, 1943, Whitman, 352 pgs., by H. Gray 10.00 25.00 60.00

1461- **Little Orphan Annie and the Underground Hide-Out**, 1945, Whitman, 352 pgs., by Gray 10.00 25.00 60.00

1468- **Little Orphan Annie and the Ancient Treasure of Am**, 1949 (Misdated 1939), 288 pgs., by Gray 10.00 25.00 60.00

1482- **Little Orphan Annie and the Haunted Mansion**, 1941, Whitman, 432 pgs., flip pictures, by Harold Gray 12.00 30.00 80.00

3048- **Little Orphan Annie and Her Big Little Kit**, 1937, Whitman, 384 pgs., 4 1/2" x 6 1/2" box, includes miniature box of 4 crayons-red, yellow, blue and green 64.00 160.00 450.00

4054- **Little Orphan Annie, The Story of**, 1934, Whitman, 7" x 9 1/2", 320 pgs., Big Big Book, Harold Gray-c/a 30.00 75.00 210.00

nn- **Little Orphan Annie Gets into Trouble**, 1938, Whitman, 36 pgs., 2 1/2" x 3 1/2", Penny Book 9.00 22.50 55.00

nn- **Little Orphan Annie in Hollywood**, 1937, Whitman, 3 1/2" x 3 1/4", Pan-Am premium, soft-c 23.00 57.50 160.00

nn- **Little Orphan Annie in Rags to Riches**, 1939, Dell, 194 pgs., Fast-Action Story, soft-c 26.00 65.00 180.00

nn- **Little Orphan Annie Saves Sandy**, 1938, Whitman, 36 pgs., 2 1/2" x 3 1/2", Penny Book 10.00 25.00 60.00

nn- **Little Orphan Annie Under the Big Top**, 1938, Dell, 194 pgs., Fast-Action Story, soft-c 25.00 62.50 175.00

nn- **Little Orphan Annie Wee Little Books** (In open box) nn, 1934, Whitman, 44 pgs., by H. Gray

L.O.A. And Daddy Warbucks 9.00 22.50 55.00
L.O.A. And Her Dog Sandy 9.00 22.50 55.00
L.O.A. And The Lucky Knife 9.00 22.50 55.00
L.O.A. And The Pinch-Pennys 9.00 22.50 55.00
L.O.A. At Happy Home 9.00 22.50 55.00
L.O.A. Finds Mickey 9.00 22.50 55.00
Complete set with box 57.00 143.00 400.00

nn- **Little Polly Flinders, The Story of**, nd (1930s), no publ., 36 pgs., 2 1/2" x 3", Penny Book 2.00 5.00 15.00

nn- **Little Red Hen, The**, nd(1930s), np(Whitman), 36 pgs., Penny Book 2.00 5.00 15.00

nn- **Little Red Riding Hood**, nd(1930s), np(Whitman), 36 pgs., 3" x 2 1/2", Penny Book 2.00 5.00 15.00

nn- **Little Red Riding Hood and the Big Bad Wolf** (Disney), 1934, McKay, 36 pgs., stiff-c, Disney Studio-a

Sized (7 3/4" x 10") 24.00 60.00 170.00
Different version (6 1/4" x 8 1/2") blue spine 16.00 40.00 115.00

757- **Little Women**, 1934, Whitman, 4 3/4" x 5 1/4", 160 pgs., photo-c, movie scenes, starring Katharine Hepburn 14.00 35.00 100.00

Littlest Rebel, The (See Shirley Temple)

1181- **Lone Ranger and his Horse Silver**, 1935, Whitman, 432 pgs., Hal Arbo-a 20.00 50.00 140.00

1196- **Lone Ranger and the Vanishing Herd**, 1936, Whitman, 432 pgs. 16.00 40.00 110.00

1407- **Lone Ranger and Dead Men's Mine, The**, 1939, Whitman,

1405 - Lone Star Martin of the Texas Rangers © WHIT

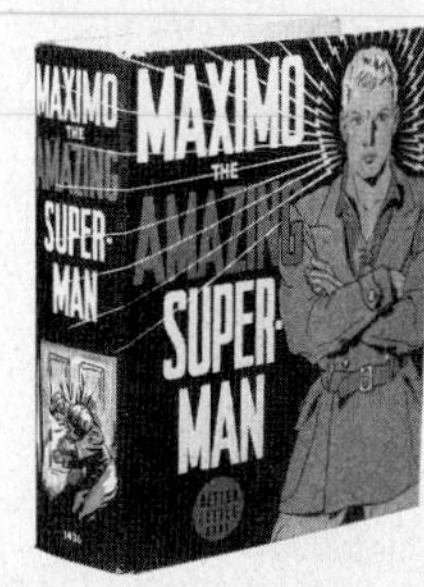

1436 - Maximo the Amazing Superman © WHIT

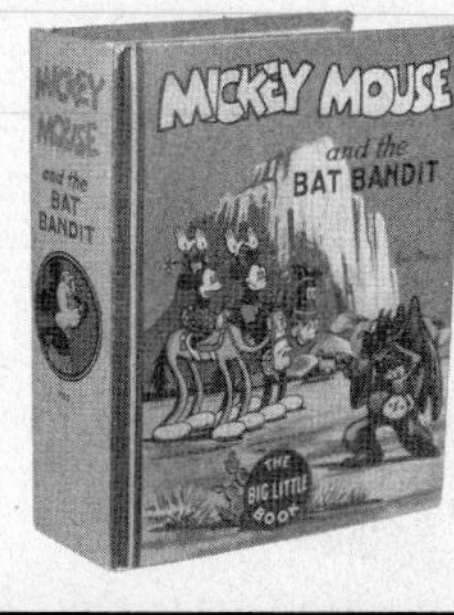

1153 - Mickey Mouse and the Bat Bandit © DIS

	GD	FN	VF/NM
432 pgs.	14.00	35.00	100.00
1421- Lone Ranger on the Barbary Coast, The, 1944, Whitman, 352 pgs., Henry Vallely-a	12.00	30.00	80.00
1428- Lone Ranger and the Secret Weapon, The, 1943, Whitman,	12.00	30.00	80.00
1431- Lone Ranger and the Secret Killer, The, 1937, Whitman 432 pgs., H. Anderson-a	16.00	40.00	110.00
1450- Lone Ranger and the Black Shirt Highwayman, The, 1939, Whitman, 432 pgs.	14.00	35.00	100.00
1465- Lone Ranger and the Menace of Murder Valley, The, 1938, Whitman, 432 pgs., Robert Wiseman-a	13.00	32.50	90.00
1468- Lone Ranger Follows Through, The, 1941, Whitman, 432 pgs., H.E. Vallely-a	13.00	32.50	90.00
1477- Lone Ranger and the Great Western Span, The, 1942, Whitman, 424 pgs., H. E. Vallely-a	12.00	30.00	80.00
1489- Lone Ranger and the Red Renegades, The, 1939, Whitman, 432 pgs.	16.00	40.00	110.00
1498- Lone Ranger and the Silver Bullets, 1946, Whitman, 352 pgs., Henry E. Vallely-a	12.00	30.00	80.00
712-10- Lone Ranger and the Secret of Somber Cavern, The, 1950, Whitman	10.00	25.00	65.00
2013- (#13)-Lone Ranger Outwits Crazy Cougar, The, 1968, Whitman, 260 pgs., 39 cents, hard-c, color illos	4.00	10.00	27.00
5774- Lone Ranger Outwits Crazy Cougar, The, 1976, Whitman, 260 pgs., 49 cents, soft-c, color illos	4.00	10.00	22.00
5774-1- Lone Ranger Outwits Crazy Cougar, The, 1979, Whitman, 260 pgs., 69 cents, soft-c, color illos	4.00	10.00	22.00
nn- Lone Ranger and the Lost Valley, The, 1938, Dell, 196 pgs., Fast-Action Story, soft-c	26.00	65.00	180.00
1405- Lone Star Martin of the Texas Rangers, 1939, Whitman, 432 pgs.	12.00	30.00	85.00
19- Lost City, The, 1935, EVW, movie scenes	12.00	30.00	80.00
1103- Lost Jungle, The (With Clyde Beatty), 1936, Saalfield, movie scenes, hard-c	12.00	30.00	80.00
1583- Lost Jungle, The (With Clyde Beatty), 1936, Saalfield, movie scenes, soft -c	11.00	27.50	70.00
753- Lost Patrol, The, 1934, Whitman, 160 pgs., photo-c, movie scenes with Boris Karloff	12.00	30.00	75.00
nn- Lost World, The - Jurassic Park 2, 1997, Chronicle Books, 312 pgs., adapts movie, 1-color (green) illos	3.00	7.50	20.00
1189- Mac of the Marines in Africa, 1936, Whitman, 432 pgs.	10.00	25.00	60.00
1400- Mac of the Marines in China, 1938, Whitman, 432 pgs.	10.00	25.00	60.00
1100B- Magic Tricks (With explanations), 1938, Whitman, 36 pgs., 2 1/2" x 3 1/2", Penny Book, rabbit in hat-c	2.00	5.00	15.00
1100B- Magic Tricks (How to do them), 1938, Whitman, 36 pgs., 2 1/2" x 3 1/2", Penny Book, genie-c	2.00	5.00	15.00
Major Hoople (See Our Boarding House)			
2022-(#22)- Major Matt Mason, Moon Mission, 1968, Whitman, 256 pgs., hard-c, color illos.	4.00	10.00	27.00
1167- Mandrake the Magician, 1935, Whitman, 432 pgs., by Lee Falk & Phil Davis	16.00	40.00	110.00
1418- Mandrake the Magician and the Flame Pearls, 1946, Whitman, 352 pgs., by Lee Falk & Phil Davis	12.00	30.00	85.00
1431- Mandrake the Magician and the Midnight Monster, 1939, Whitman, 432 pgs., by Lee Falk & Phil Davis	14.00	35.00	95.00
1454- Mandrake the Magician Mighty Solver of Mysteries, 1941, Whitman, 432 pgs., by Lee Falk & Phil Davis, flip pictures	14.00	35.00	95.00
2011-(#11)-Man From U.N.C.L.E., The-The Calcutta Affair (TV Series), 1967, Whitman, 260 pgs., 39¢, hard-c, color illos	4.00	10.00	27.00
1429- Marge's Little Lulu Alvin and Tubby, 1947, Whitman, All Pictures Comics, Stanley-a	27.00	68.00	190.00
1438- Mary Lee and the Mystery of the Indian Beads, 1937, Whitman, 300 pgs.	10.00	25.00	60.00
1165- Masked Man of the Mesa, The, 1939, Saalfield, 400 pgs.	9.00	22.50	55.00
nn- Mask of Zorro, The, 1998, Chronicle Books, 312 pgs., adapts movie, 1-color (yellow-green) illos	1.00	2.50	9.00
1436- Maximo the Amazing Superman, 1940, Whitman, 432 pgs., Henry E. Vallely-a	12.00	30.00	80.00

	GD	FN	VF/NM
1444- Maximo the Amazing Superman and the Crystals of Doom, 1941, Whitman,432 pgs., Henry E. Vallely-a	12.00	30.00	80.00
1445- Maximo the Amazing Superman and the Supermachine, 1941, Whitman, 432 pgs.	12.00	30.00	80.00
755- Men of the Mounted, 1934, Whitman, 320 pgs.	12.00	30.00	80.00
nn- Men of the Mounted, 1933, Whitman, 52 pgs., 3 1/2" x 5 3/4", premium-no ads; other versions with Poll Parrot & Perkins ad; soft-c	14.00	35.00	100.00
nn- Men of the Mounted, 1934, Whitman, Cocomalt premium, soft-c, by Ted McCall	10.00	25.00	60.00
1475- Men With Wings, 1938, Whitman, 240 pgs., photo-c, movie scenes (Paramount Pics.)	12.00	30.00	85.00
1170- Mickey Finn, 1940, Saalfield, 400 pgs., by Frank Leonard	10.00	25.00	865.00
717- Mickey Mouse (Disney), (1st printing) 1933, Whitman, 320 pgs., Gottfredson-a, skinny Mickey on cover	235.00	588.00	2000.00
717- Mickey Mouse (Disney), (2nd printing)1933, Whitman, 320 pgs., Gottfredson-a, regular Mickey on cover	150.00	375.00	1200.00
nn- Mickey Mouse (Disney), 1933, Dean & Son, Great Big Midget Book, 320 pgs.	123.00	308.00	900.00
731- Mickey Mouse the Mail Pilot (Disney), 1933, Whitman, (This is the same book as the 1st Mickey Mouse BLB #717(2nd printing) but with "The Mail Pilot" printed on the front. Lower left of back cover has a small box printed over the existing "No. 717." "No. 731" is printed next to it.) (Sold at auction in 2014 in VG+ condition for $7170, and in FR/GD condition for $2,500)			
726- Mickey Mouse in Blaggard Castle (Disney), 1934, Whitman, 320 pgs., Gottfredson-a	30.00	75.00	210.00
731- Mickey Mouse the Mail Pilot (Disney), 1933, Whitman, 300 pgs., Gottfredson-a	30.00	75.00	210.00
731- Mickey Mouse the Mail Pilot (Disney), 1933, Whitman, 300 pgs., soft cover; Gottfredson-a (Rare)	64.00	160.00	450.00
nn- Mickey Mouse the Mail Pilot (Disney), 1933, Whitman, 292 pgs., American Oil Co. premium, soft-c, Gottfredson-a; another version 3 1/2" x 4 3/4"	30.00	75.00	210.00
nn- Mickey Mouse the Mail Pilot (Disney), 1933, Dean & Son, Great Big Midget Book (Rare)	124.00	310.00	925.00
750- Mickey Mouse Sails for Treasure Island (Disney), 1933, Whitman, 320 pgs., Gottfredson-a	30.00	75.00	210.00
nn- Mickey Mouse Sails for Treasure Island (Disney), 1935, Whitman, 196 pgs., premium-no ads, soft-c, Gottfredson-a (Scarce)	36.00	90.00	250.00
nn- Mickey Mouse Sails for Treasure Island (Disney), 1935, Whitman, 196 pgs., Kolynos Dental Cream premium (Scarce)	36.00	90.00	250.00
nn- Mickey Mouse Sails for Treasure Island (Disney), 1933, Dean & Son, Great Big Midget Book, 320 pgs.	114.00	285.00	800.00
756- Mickey Mouse Presents a Walt Disney Silly Symphony (Disney), 1934, Whitman, 240 pgs., Bucky Bug app.	29.00	73.00	200.00
801- Mickey Mouse's Summer Vacation, 1948, Whitman, hard-c, Story Hour series	12.00	30.00	85.00
1058- Mickey Mouse Box, The (Disney), 1939, Whitman, 10" x 11 1/2" x 1", (set includes 6 books from the 1058 series, all 5" x 5 1/2", 68 pgs. Lid features Mickey & Minnie, Donald Duck, Goofy and Clarabelle Cow. The six books are: The Brave Little Tailor, Mother Pluto, The Ugly Ducklings, The Practical Pig, Timid Elmer, and The Farmyard Symphony (a VF set sold for $5175 in Nov, 2014)			
1111- Mickey Mouse Presents Walt Disney's Silly Symphonies Stories, 1936, Whitman, 432 pgs., Donald Duck app.	29.00	73.00	200.00
1128- Mickey Mouse and Pluto the Racer (Disney), 1936, Whitman, 432 pgs., Gottfredson-a	24.00	60.00	170.00
1139- Mickey Mouse the Detective (Disney), 1934, Whitman, 300 pgs., Gottfredson-a	29.00	73.00	200.00
1139- Mickey Mouse the Detective (Disney), 1934, Whitman, 304 pgs., premium-no ads, soft-c, Gottfredson-a (Scarce)	43.00	108.00	300.00
1153- Mickey Mouse and the Bat Bandit (Disney), 1935, Whitman, 432 pgs., Gottfredson-a	26.00	65.00	180.00
nn- Mickey Mouse and the Bat Bandit (Disney), 1935, Whitman, 436 pgs., premium-no ads, 3-color, soft-c, Gottfredson-a (Scarce)			

1483 - Mickey Mouse Bell Boy Detective © DIS

nn - Minute-Man © FAW

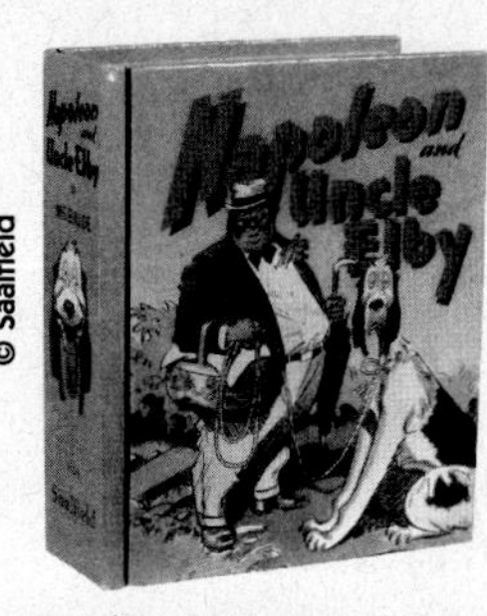

1150 - Napoleon and Uncle Elby © Saalfield

GD FN VF/NM

43.00 108.00 300.00
1160- Mickey Mouse and Bobo the Elephant (Disney), 1935, Whitman, 432 pgs., Gottfredson-a 26.00 65.00 180.00
1187- Mickey Mouse and the Sacred Jewel (Disney), 1936, Whitman, 432 pgs., Gottfredson-a 24.00 60.00 170.00
1401- Mickey Mouse in the Treasure Hunt (Disney), 1941, Whitman, 430 pgs., flip pictures of Pluto, Gottfredson-a 22.00 52.50 155.00
1409- Mickey Mouse Runs His Own Newspaper (Disney), 1937, Whitman, 432 pgs., Gottfredson-a 22.00 52.50 155.00
1413- Mickey Mouse and the 'Lectro Box (Disney), 1946, Whitman, 352 pgs., Gottfredson-a 16.00 40.00 115.00
1417- Mickey Mouse on Sky Island (Disney), 1941, Whitman, 432 pgs., flip pictures, Gottfredson-a; considered by Gottfredson to be his best Mickey story 22.00 52.50 155.00
1428- Mickey Mouse in the Foreign Legion (Disney), 1940, Whitman, 432 pgs., Gottfredson-a 22.00 52.50 155.00
1429- Mickey Mouse and the Magic Lamp (Disney), 1942, Whitman, 432 pgs., flip pictures 22.00 52.50 155.00
1433- Mickey Mouse and the Lazy Daisy Mystery (Disney), 1947, Whitman, 288 pgs. 16.00 40.00 115.00
1444- Mickey Mouse in the World of Tomorrow (Disney), 1948, Whitman, 288 pgs., Gottfredson-a 24.00 60.00 170.00
1451- Mickey Mouse and the Desert Palace (Disney), 1948, Whitman, 288 pgs. 16.00 40.00 115.00
1463- Mickey Mouse and the Pirate Submarine (Disney), 1939, Whitman, 432 pgs., Gottfredson-a 22.00 52.50 155.00
1464- Mickey Mouse and the Stolen Jewels (Disney), 1949, Whitman, 288 pgs. 21.00 52.50 145.00
1471- Mickey Mouse and the Dude Ranch Bandit (Disney), 1943, Whitman, 432 pgs., flip pictures 22.00 52.50 155.00
1475- Mickey Mouse and the 7 Ghosts (Disney), 1940, Whitman, 432 pgs., Gottfredson-a 22.00 52.50 155.00
1476- Mickey Mouse in the Race for Riches (Disney), 1938, Whitman, 432 pgs., Gottfredson-a 22.00 52.50 155.00
1483- Mickey Mouse Bell Boy Detective (Disney), 1945, Whitman, 352 pgs. 21.00 52.50 145.00
1499- Mickey Mouse on the Cave-Man Island (Disney), 1944, Whitman, 352 pgs. 21.00 52.50 145.00
2004- Mickey Mouse With This Big Big Color Set, Here Comes (Disney), 1936, Whitman, (Very Rare), 224 pgs., 12" x 8 1/4" box, with red, yellow and blue crayons, contains 224 loose pages to color, reprinted from early Mickey Mouse related movie and strip reprints. Attached to center of lid is a 5" tall separate die-cut cardboard Mickey Mouse figure (a VF/NM set sold for $1701 in July 2014) 235.00 588.00 2000.00
2020-(#20)- Mickey Mouse, Adventure in Outer Space, 1968, Whitman, 256 pgs.,hard-c, color illos. 4.00 10.00 27.00
3059- Mickey Mouse Big Little Set (Disney), 1936, Whitman, 8 1/4" x 8 1/2", with crayons, box contains a 4" x 5 1/4" soft-c book with 160 pgs. of Mickey to color, reprinted from early Mickey Mouse BLBs, (Rare)
(a copy in NM sold for $1897 in Nov, 2011, a VF copy sold for $1147 in 2013)
5750- Mickey Mouse, Adventure in Outer Space, 1973, Whitman, 256 pgs.,soft-c, 39 cents, color illos. 2.00 5.00 15.00
3049- Mickey Mouse and His Big Little Kit (Disney), 1937, Whitman, 384 pgs., 4 1/2" x 6 1/2" box, includes miniature box of 4 crayons-red, yellow, blue and green (a copy in VF/NM sold for $335 in 2015)
3061- Mickey Mouse to Draw and Color (The Big Little Set), nd (early 1930s), Whitman, with crayons; box contains 320 loose pages to color, reprinted from early Mickey Mouse BLBs 123.00 308.00 880.00
4062- Mickey Mouse, The Story Of, 1935, Whitman, 7" x 9 1/2", 320 pgs., Big Big Book, Gottfredson-a 82.00 205.00 575.00
4062- Mickey Mouse and the Smugglers, The Story Of, 1935, Whitman, (Scarce), 7" x 9 1/2", 320 pgs., Big Big Book, same contents as above version; Gottfredson-a 82.00 205.00 575.00
708-10- Mickey Mouse on the Haunted Island (Disney), 1950, Whitman, Gottfredson-a 12.00 30.00 80.00
nn- Mickey Mouse and Minnie at Macy's, 1934 Whitman, 148 pgs., 3 1/4" x 3 1/2", soft-c, R. H. Macy & Co. Christmas giveaway (Rare, less than 20 known copies) 300.00 750.00 2700.00
nn- Mickey Mouse and Minnie March to Macy's, 1935, Whitman, 148 pgs., 3 1/2" x 3 1/2", soft-c, R. H. Macy & Co. Christmas giveaway (scarce) 259.00 648.00 2200.00
nn- Mickey Mouse and the Magic Carpet, 1935, Whitman, 148 pgs., 3 1/2"x 4", soft-c, giveaway, Gottfredson-a, Donald Duck app. 123.00 308.00 900.00
nn- Mickey Mouse Silly Symphonies, 1934, Dean & Son, Ltd (England), 48 pgs., with 4 pop-ups, Babes In The Woods, King Neptune
With dust jacket 138.00 345.00 1100.00
Without dust jacket 100.00 250.00 700.00
nn- Mickey Mouse the Sheriff of Nugget Gulch (Disney) 1938, Dell, 196 pgs., Fast-Action Story, soft-c, Gottfredson-a 36.00 90.00 250.00
nn- Mickey Mouse Waddle Book, 1934, BRP, 20 pgs., 7 1/2" x 10", forerunner of the Blue Ribbon Pop-Up books; with 4 removable articulated cardboard characters Book Only 100.00 200.00 500.00
(A complete copy in VG/FN w/VF dustjacket sold for $5676 in 2010)
(A complete copy in VF with dustjacket ramp & band sold for $573 in 2014)
nn- Mickey Mouse with Goofy and Mickey's Nephews, 1938, Dell, Fast-Action Story, Gottfredson-a 36.00 90.00 250.00
16- Mickey Mouse and Pluto (Disney), 1942, Dell, 196 pgs., Fast-Action story 36.00 90.00 250.00
512- Mickey Mouse Wee Little Books (In open box), nn, 1934, Whitman, 44 pgs., small size, soft-c
Mickey Mouse and Tanglefoot 13.00 32.50 90.00
Mickey Mouse at the Carnival 13.00 32.50 90.00
Mickey Mouse Will Not Quit! 13.00 32.50 90.00
Mickey Mouse Wins the Race! 13.00 32.50 90.00
Mickey Mouse's Misfortune 13.00 32.50 90.00
Mickey Mouse's Uphill Fight 13.00 32.50 90.00
Complete set with box 96.00 240.00 675.00
1493- Mickey Rooney and Judy Garland and How They Got into the Movies, 1941, Whitman, 432 pgs., photo-c 12.00 30.00 75.00
1427- Mickey Rooney Himself, 1939, Whitman, 240 pgs., photo-c, movie scenes, life story 12.00 30.00 75.00
532- Mickey's Dog Pluto (Disney), 1943, Whitman, All Picture Comics, A Tall Comic Book , 3 3/4" x 8 3/4" 20.00 50.00 140.00
284- Midget Jumbo Coloring Book, 1935, Saalfield 43.00 108.00 300.00
2113- Midget Jumbo Coloring Book, 1935, Saalfield, 240 pgs. 43.00 108.00 300.00
21- Midsummer Night's Dream, 1935, EVW, movie scenes 12.00 30.00 85.00
nn- Minute-Man (Mystery of the Spy Ring), 1941, Fawcett, Dime Action Book 36.00 90.00 250.00
710- Moby Dick the Great White Whale, The Story of, 1934, Whitman, 160 pgs., photo-c, movie scenes from "The Sea Beast" 12.00 30.00 85.00
746- Moon Mullins and Kayo (Kayo and Moon Mullins-inside), 1933, Whitman, 320 pgs., Frank Willard-c/a 12.00 30.00 75.00
nn- Moon Mullins and Kayo, 1933, Whitman, Cocomalt premium, soft-c, by Willard 12.00 30.00 75.00
1134- Moon Mullins and the Plushbottom Twins, 1935, Whitman, 432 pgs., Willard-c/a 12.00 30.00 75.00
nn- Moon Mullins and the Plushbottom Twins, 1935, Whitman, 436 pgs., premium-no ads, 3-color, soft-c, by Willard 18.00 45.00 125.00
1058- Mother Pluto (Disney), 1939, Whitman, 68 pgs., hard-c 11.00 27.50 70.00
1100B- Movie Jokes (From the talkies), 1938, Whitman, 36 pgs., 2 1/2" x 3 1/2", Penny Book 2.00 5.00 15.00
1408- Mr. District Attorney on the Job, 1941, Whitman, 432 pgs., flip pictures 10.00 25.00 65.00
nn- Musicians of Bremen, The, nd (1930s), np (Whitman), 36 pgs., 3" x 2 1/2", Penny Book 2.00 5.00 15.00
1113- Mutt and Jeff, 1936, Whitman, 300 pgs., by Bud Fisher 26.00 65.00 180.00
1116- My Life and Times (By Shirley Temple), 1936, Saalfield, Little Big Book, hard-c, photo-c/illos 12.00 30.00 85.00
1596- My Life and Times (By Shirley Temple), 1936, Saalfield, Little Big Book, soft-c, photo-c/illos 12.00 30.00 85.00
1497- Myra North Special Nurse and Foreign Spies, 1938, Whitman, 432 pgs. 11.00 27.50 70.00
1400- Nancy and Sluggo, 1946, Whitman, All Pictures Comics,

1456 - Our Gang Adventures © WHIT

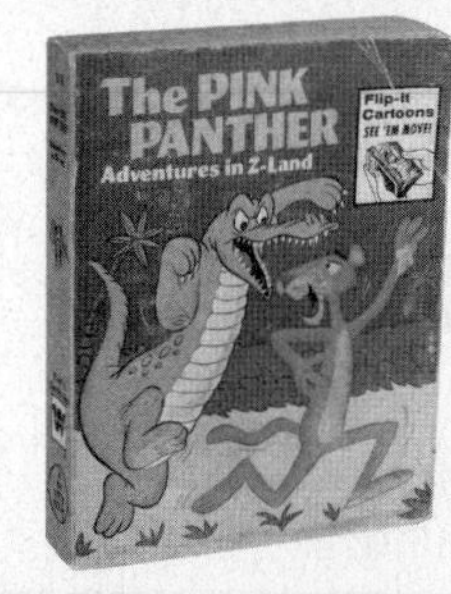

5776 - The Pink Panther Adventures in Z-Land © MGM

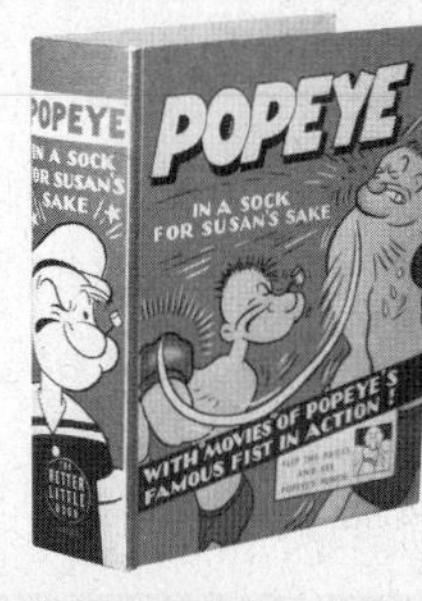

1485 - Popeye in A Sock For Susan's Sake © KING

	GD	FN	VF/NM
Ernie Bushmiller-a	12.00	30.00	75.00
1487- Nancy Has Fun, 1946, Whitman, All Pictures Comics	12.00	30.00	75.00
1150- Napoleon and Uncle Elby, 1938, Saalfield, 400 pgs., by Clifford McBride	11.00	27.50	70.00
1166- Napoleon Uncle Elby And Little Mary, 1939, Saalfield, 400 pgs., by Clifford McBride	11.00	27.50	70.00
1179- Ned Brant Adventure Bound, 1940, Saalfield, 400 pgs.	10.00	25.00	60.00
1146- Nevada Rides The Danger Trail, 1938, Saalfield, 400 pgs., J.R. White-a	10.00	25.00	60.00
1147- Nevada Whalen, Avenger, 1938, Saalfield, 400 pgs.	10.00	25.00	60.00
Nicodemus O'Malley (See Top-Line Comics)			
1115- Og Son of Fire, 1936, Whitman, 432 pgs.	12.00	30.00	85.00
1419- Oh, Blondie the Bumsteads (See Blondie)			
11- Oliver Twist, 1935, EVW (Five Star Library), movie scenes, starring Dickie Moore (Monogram Pictures)	12.00	30.00	80.00
718- Once Upon a Time, 1933, Whitman, 364 pgs., soft-c	12.00	30.00	80.00
712- 100 Fairy Tales for Children, The, 1933, Whitman, 288 pgs., Circle Library	10.00	25.00	60.00
1099- One Night of Love, 1935, Saalfield, 160 pgs., hard-c, photo-c, movie scenes, Columbia Pictures, starring Grace Moore	12.00	30.00	85.00
1579- One Night of Love, 1935, Sat, 160 pgs., soft-c, photo-c, movie scenes, Columbia Pictures, starring Grace Moore	12.00	30.00	85.00
1155- $1000 Reward, 1938, Saalfield, 400 pgs.	10.00	25.00	60.00
Orphan Annie (See Little Orphan ...)			
L17- O'Shaughnessy's Boy, 1935, Lynn, 192 pgs., movie scenes, w/Wallace Beery & Jackie Cooper (Metro-Goldwyn-Mayer)	11.00	27.50	70.00
1109- Oswald the Lucky Rabbit, 1934, Whitman, 288 pgs.	16.00	40.00	115.00
1403- Oswald Rabbit Plays G-Man, 1937, Whitman, 240 pgs., movie scenes by Walter Lantz	18.00	45.00	125.00
1190- Our Boarding House, Major Hoople and his Horse, 1940, Saalfield, 400 pgs.	11.00	27.50	70.00
1085- Our Gang, 1934, Saalfield, 160 pgs., photo-c, movie scenes, hard-c	15.00	37.50	105.00
1315- Our Gang, 1934, Saalfield, 160 pgs., photo-c, movie scenes, soft-c	15.00	37.50	105.00
1451- "Our Gang" on the March, 1942, Whitman, 432 pgs., flip pictures, Vallely-a	15.00	37.50	105.00
1456- Our Gang Adventures, 1948, Whitman, 288 pgs.	12.00	30.00	85.00
nn- Paramount Newsreel Men with Admiral Byrd in Little America, 1934, Whitman, 96 pgs., 6 1/4" x 6 1/4", photo-c, photo ill.	14.00	35.00	100.00
nn- Patch, nd (1930s), np (Whitman), 36 pgs., 3" x 2 1/2", Penny Book	2.00	5.00	15.00
1445- Pat Nelson Ace of Test Pilots, 1937, Whitman, 432 pgs.	10.00	25.00	60.00
1411- Peggy Brown and the Mystery Basket, 1941, Whitman, 432 pgs., flip pictures, Henry E. Vallely-a	10.00	25.00	65.00
1423- Peggy Brown and the Secret Treasure, 1947, Whitman, 288 pgs., Henry E. Vallely-a	10.00	25.00	65.00
1427- Peggy Brown and the Runaway Auto Trailer, 1937, Whitman, 300 pgs., Henry E. Vallely-a	10.00	25.00	65.00
1463- Peggy Brown and the Jewel of Fire, 1943, Whitman, 352 pgs., Henry E. Vallely-a	10.00	25.00	65.00
1491- Peggy Brown in the Big Haunted House, 1940, Whitman, 432 pgs., Vallely-a	10.00	25.00	65.00
1143- Peril Afloat, 1938, Saalfield, 400 pgs.	10.00	25.00	60.00
1199- Perry Winkle and the Rinkeydinks, 1937, Whitman, 432 pgs., by Martin Branner	14.00	35.00	95.00
1487- Perry Winkle and the Rinkeydinks get a Horse, 1938, Whitman, 432 pgs., by Martin Branner	14.00	35.00	95.00
Peter Pan (See Wee Little Books)			
nn- Peter Rabbit, nd(1930s), np(Whitman), 36 pgs., Penny Book, 3" x 2 1/2"	5.00	12.50	33.00
Peter Rabbit's Carrots (See Wee Little Books)			
1100- Phantom, The, 1936, Whitman, 432 pgs., by Lee Falk & Ray Moore	27.00	68.00	190.00
1416- Phantom and the Girl of Mystery, The, 1947, Whitman, 352 pgs. by Falk & Moore	12.00	30.00	80.00
1421- Phantom and Desert Justice, The, 1941, Whitman, 432 pgs., flip pictures, by Falk & Moore	14.00	35.00	100.00
1468- Phantom and the Sky Pirates, The, 1945, Whitman, 352 pgs., by Falk & Moore	13.00	32.50	90.00
1474- Phantom and the Sign of the Skull, The, 1939, Whitman, 432 pgs., by Falk & Moore	16.00	40.00	110.00
1489- Phantom, Return of the..., 1942, Whitman, 432 pgs., flip pictures, by Falk & Moore	14.00	35.00	100.00
1130- Phil Burton, Sleuth (Scout Book), 1937, Saalfield, hard-c	7.00	17.50	40.00
Pied Piper of Hamlin (See Wee Little Books)			
1466- Pilot Pete Dive Bomber, 1941, Whitman, 432 pgs., flip pictures	10.00	25.00	60.00
5776- Pink Panther Adventures in Z-Land, The, 1976, Whitman, 260 pgs., soft-c, 49 cents, B&W	1.00	2.50	8.00
5776-2- Pink Panther Adventures in Z-Land, The, 1980, Whitman, 260 pgs., soft-c, 79 cents, B&W	1.00	2.50	8.00
5783-2- Pink Panther at Castle Kreep, The, 1980, Whitman, 260 pgs., soft-c, 79 cents, B&W	1.00	2.50	8.00
Pinocchio and Jiminy Cricket (See Walt Disney's ...)			
nn- Pioneers of the Wild West (Blue-c), 1933, World Syndicate, High Lights of History Series	7.00	17.50	40.00
With dustjacket	29.00	73.00	200.00
nn- Pioneers of the Wild West (Red-c), 1933, World Syndicate, High Lights of History Series	7.00	17.50	40.00
1123- Plainsman, The, 1936, Whitman, 240 pgs., photo-c, movie scenes with Gary Cooper (Paramount Pics.)	14.00	35.00	100.00
Pluto (See Mickey's Dog ... & Walt Disney's ...)			
2114- Pocket Coloring Book, 1935, Saalfield	27.00	68.00	190.00
1060- Polly and Her Pals on the Farm, 1934, Saalfield, 164 pgs., hard-c, by Cliff Sterrett	12.00	30.00	80.00
1310- Polly and Her Pals on the Farm, 1934, Saalfield, soft-c	12.00	30.00	80.00
1051- Popeye, Adventures of..., 1934, Saalfield, oblong-size, E.C. Segar-a, hard-c	43.00	108.00	300.00
1088- Popeye in Puddleburg, 1934, Saalfield, 160 pgs., hard-c, E. C. Segar-a	18.00	45.00	125.00
1113- Popeye Starring in Choose Your Weppins, 1936, Saalfield, 160 pgs., hard-c, Segar-a	36.00	90.00	250.00
1117- Popeye's Ark, 1936, Saalfield, 4 1/2" x 5 1/2", hard-c, Segar-a	19.00	47.50	135.00
1163- Popeye Sees the Sea, 1936, Whitman, 432 pgs., Segar-a	20.00	50.00	140.00
1301- Popeye, Adventures of..., 1934, Saalfield, oblong-size, Segar-a	43.00	108.00	300.00
1318- Popeye in Puddleburg, 1934, Saalfield, 160 pgs., soft-c, Segar-a	19.00	47.50	135.00
1405- Popeye and the Jeep, 1937, Whitman, 432 pgs., Segar-a	20.00	50.00	140.00
1406- Popeye the Super-Fighter, 1939, Whitman, All Pictures Comics, flip pictures, Segar-a	19.00	47.50	135.00
1422- Popeye the Sailor Man, 1947, Whitman, All Pictures Comics	12.00	30.00	85.00
1450- Popeye in Quest of His Poopdeck Pappy, 1937, Whitman, 432 pgs., Segar-c/a	14.00	35.00	100.00
1458- Popeye and Queen Olive Oyl, 1949, Whitman, 288 pgs., Sagendorf-a	12.00	30.00	85.00
1459- Popeye and the Quest for the Rainbird, 1943, Whitman, Winner & Zaboly-a	14.00	35.00	95.00
1480- Popeye the Spinach Eater, 1945, Whitman, All Pictures Comics	12.00	30.00	85.00
1485- Popeye in a Sock for Susan's Sake, 1940, Whitman, 432 pgs., flip pictures	14.00	35.00	95.00
1497- Popeye and Caster Oyl the Detective, 1941, Whitman,			

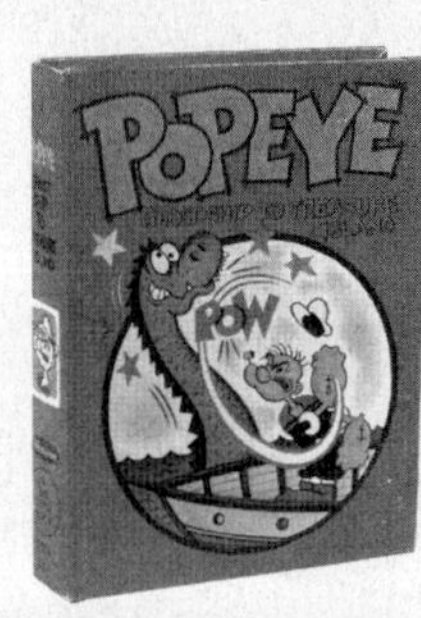

2008 - Popeye-Ghost Ship To Treasure Island © KING

nn - "Pop-Up" Jack The Giant Killer © BRP

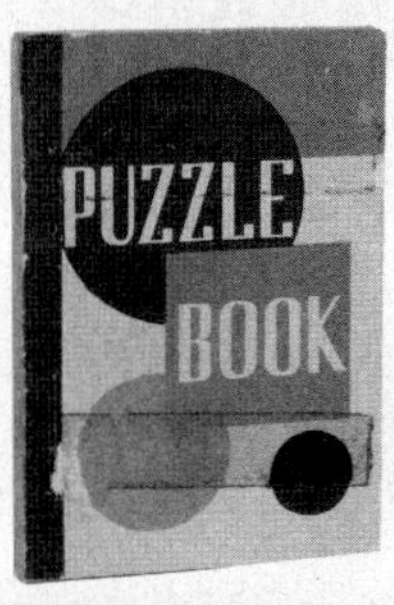

1100B - Puzzle Book © WHIT

GD FN VF/NM

432 pgs. flip pictures, Segar-a 16.00 40.00 115.00
1499- Popeye and the Deep Sea Mystery, 1939, Whitman, 432 pgs., Segar-c/a 16.00 40.00 115.00
1593- Popeye Starring in Choose Your Weppins, 1936, Saalfield, 160 pgs., soft-c, Segar-a 16.00 40.00 115.00
1597- Popeye's Ark, 1936, Saalfield, 4 1/2" x 5 1/2", soft-c, Segar-a 16.00 40.00 115.00
2008-(#8)- Popeye-Ghost Ship to Treasure Island, 1967, Whitman, 260 pgs., 39 cents, hard-c, color illos 4.00 10.00 27.00
5755- Popeye-Ghost Ship to Treasure Island, 1973, Whitman, 260 pgs., soft-c, color illos 2.00 5.00 15.00
2034-(#34)- Popeye, Danger Ahoy!, 1969, Whitman, 256 pgs., hard-c, color illos. 4.00 10.00 25.00
5768- Popeye, Danger Ahoy!, 1975, Whitman, 256 pgs., soft-c, color illos. 2.00 5.00 15.00
4063- Popeye, Thimble Theatre Starring, 1935, Whitman, 7" x 9 1/2", 320 pgs., Big Big Book, Segar-c/a; (Cactus cover w/yellow logo) 86.00 215.00 600.00
4063- Popeye, Thimble Theatre Starring, 1935, Whitman, 7" x 9 1/2", 320 pgs., Big Big Book, Segar-c/a; (Big Balloon-c with red logo), (2nd printing w/same contents as above) 100.00 250.00 700.00
5761- Popeye and Queen Olive Oyl, 1973, 260 pgs., B&W, soft-c 4.00 10.00 27.00
5761-2- Popeye and Queen Olive Oyl, 1973 (1980-reprint of 1973 version), 260 pgs., 79 cents, B&W, soft-c 2.00 5.00 15.00
103- "Pop-Up" Buck Rogers in the Dangerous Mission (with Pop-Up picture), 1934, BRP, 62 pgs., The Midget Pop-Up Book w/Pop-Up in center of book, Calkins-a 121.00 303.00 850.00
206- "Pop-Up" Buck Rogers - Strange Adventures in the Spider Ship, The, 1935, BRP, 24 pgs., 8" x 9", 3 Pop-Ups, hard-c, by Dick Calkins 121.00 303.00 850.00
nn- "Pop-Up" Cinderella, 1933, BRP, 7 1/2" x 9 3/4", 4 Pop-Ups, hard-c
With dustjacket ($2.00) 68.00 170.00 475.00
Without dustjacket 57.00 143.00 400.00
207- "Pop-Up" Dick Tracy-Capture of Boris Arson, 1935, BRP, 24 pgs., 8" x 9", 3 Pop-Ups, hard-c, by Gould 68.00 170.00 475.00
210- "Pop-Up" Flash Gordon Tournament of Death, The, 1935, BRP, 24 pgs., 8" x 9", 3 Pop-Ups, hard-c, by Alex Raymond 114.00 285.00 800.00
202- "Pop-Up" Goldilocks and the Three Bears, The, 1934, BRP, 24 pgs., 8" x 9", 3 Pop-Ups, hard-c 36.00 90.00 250.00
nn- "Pop-Up" Jack and the Beanstalk, 1933, BRP, hard-c (50 cents), 1 Pop-Up 36.00 90.00 250.00
nn- "Pop-Up" Jack the Giant Killer, 1933, BRP, hard-c (50 cents), 1 Pop-Up 36.00 90.00 250.00
nn- "Pop-Up" Jack the Giant Killer, 1933, BRP, 4 Pop-Ups, hard-c
With dustjacket ($2.00) 68.00 170.00 475.00
Without dust jacket 57.00 143.00 400.00
105- "Pop-Up" Little Black Sambo, (with Pop-Up picture), 1934, BRP, 62 pgs., The Midget Pop-Up Book, one Pop-Up in center of book 43.00 108.00 325.00
208- "Pop-Up" Little Orphan Annie and Jumbo the Circus Elephant, 1935, BRP, 24 pgs., 8" x 9 1/2", 3 Pop-Ups, hard-c, by H. Gray 68.00 170.00 475.00
nn- "Pop-Up" Little Red Ridinghood, 1933, BRP, hard-c (50 cents), 1 Pop-Up 43.00 108.00 300.00
nn- "Pop-Up" Mickey Mouse, The, 1933, BRP, 34 pgs., 6 1/2" x 9", 3 Pop-Ups, hard-c, Gottfredson-a (75 cents) 54.00 135.00 375.00
nn- "Pop-Up" Mickey Mouse in King Arthur's Court, The, 1933, BRP, 56 pgs., 7 1/2" x 9 1/4", 4 Pop-Ups, hard-c, Gottfredson-a
With dust jacket ($2.00) 123.00 308.00 900.00
Without dustjacket 93.00 233.00 650.00
101- "Pop-Up" Mickey Mouse in "Ye Olden Days" (with Pop-Up picture), 1934, 62 pgs., BRP, The Midget Pop-Up Book, one Pop-Up in center of book, Gottfredson-a 107.00 268.00 750.00
nn- "Pop-Up" Minnie Mouse, The, 1933, BRP, 36 pgs., 6 1/2" x 9", 3 Pop-Ups, hard-c (75 cents), Gottfredson-a 50.00 125.00 350.00
203- "Pop-Up" Mother Goose, The, 1934, BRP, 24 pgs., 8" x 9 1/4", 3 Pop-Ups, hard-c 43.00 108.00 300.00
nn- "Pop-Up" Mother Goose Rhymes, The, 1933, BRP, 96 pgs., 7 1/2" x 9 1/4", 4 Pop-Ups, hard-c
With dustjacket ($2.00) 46.00 115.00 325.00
Without dustjacket 43.00 108.00 300.00
209- "Pop-Up" New Adventures of Tarzan, 1935, BRP, 24 pgs., 8" x 9", 3 Pop-Ups, hard-c 107.00 268.00 750.00
104- "Pop-Up" Peter Rabbit, The (with Pop-Up picture), 1934, BRP, 62 pgs., The Midget Pop-Up Book, one Pop-Up in center of book 50.00 125.00 350.00
nn- "Pop-Up" Pinocchio, 1933, BRP, 7 1/2" x 9 3/4", 4 Pop-Ups, hard-c
With dustjacket ($2.00) 61.00 153.00 425.00
Without dust jacket 54.00 135.00 375.00
102- "Pop-Up" Popeye among the White Savages (with Pop-Up picture), 1934, BRP, 62 pgs., The Midget Pop-Up Book, one Pop-Up in center of book, E. C. Segar-a 61.00 153.00 425.00
205- "Pop-Up" Popeye with the Hag of the Seven Seas, The, 1935, BRP, 24 pgs., 8" x 9", 3 Pop-Ups, hard-c, Segar-a 68.00 170.00 475.00
201- "Pop-Up" Puss In Boots, The, 1934, BRP, 24 pgs., 3 Pop-Ups, hard-c 37.00 93.00 260.00
nn- "Pop-Up" Silly Symphonies, The (Mickey Mouse Presents His ...), 1933, BRP, 56 pgs., 9 3/4" x 7 1/2", 4 Pop-Ups, hard-c
With dust jacket ($2.00) 107.00 268.00 750.00
Without dust jacket 71.00 178.00 500.00
nn- "Pop-Up" Sleeping Beauty, 1933, BRP, hard-c, (50 cents), 1 Pop-up 41.00 103.00 290.00
212- "Pop-Up" Terry and the Pirates in Shipwrecked, The, 1935, BRP, 24 pgs., 8" x 9", 3 Pop-Ups, hard-c 71.00 178.00 500.00
211- "Pop-Up" Tim Tyler in the Jungle, The, 1935, BRP, 24 pgs., 8" x 9", 3 Pop-Ups, hard-c 46.00 115.00 325.00
1404- Porky Pig and His Gang, 1946, Whitman, All Pictures Comics, Barks-a, reprints Four Color #48 20.00 50.00 140.00
1408- Porky Pig and Petunia, 1942, Whitman, All Pictures Comics, flip pictures, reprints Four Color #16 & Famous Gang Book of Comics 12.00 30.00 85.00
1176- Powder Smoke Range, 1935, Whitman, 240 pgs., photo-c, movie scenes, Hoot Gibson, Harey Carey app. (RKO Radio Pict.) 11.00 27.50 70.00
1058- Practical Pig!, The (Disney), 1939, Whitman, 68 pgs., 5" x 5 1/2", hard-c 11.00 27.50 70.00
758- Prairie Bill and the Covered Wagon, 1934, Whitman, 384 pgs., Hal Arbo-a 10.00 25.00 60.00
nn- Prairie Bill and the Covered Wagon, 1934, Whitman, 390 pgs., premium-no ads, 3-color, soft-c, Hal Arbo-a 12.00 30.00 85.00
1440- Punch Davis of the U.S. Aircraft Carrier, 1945, Whitman, 352 pgs. 9.00 22.50 55.00
nn- Puss in Boots, nd(1930s), np(Whitman), 36 pgs., Penny Book 2.00 5.00 15.00
1100B- Puzzle Book, 1938, Whitman, 36 pgs., 2 1/2" x 3 1/2", Penny Book 3.00 7.50 20.00
1100B- Puzzles, 1938, Whitman, 36 pgs., 2 1/2" x 3 1/2", Penny Book 3.00 7.50 20.00
1100B- Quiz Book, The, 1938, Whitman, 36 pgs., 2 1/2" x 3 1/2", Penny Book 3.00 7.50 20.00
1142- Radio Patrol, 1935, Whitman, 432 pgs., by Eddie Sullivan & Charlie Schmidt (#1) 12.00 30.00 75.00
1173- Radio Patrol Trailing the Safeblowers, 1937, Whitman, 432 pgs. 10.00 25.00 60.00
1496- Radio Patrol Outwitting the Gang Chief, 1939, Whitman, 432 pgs. 10.00 25.00 60.00
1498- Radio Patrol and Big Dan's Mobsters, 1937, Whitman, 432 pgs. 10.00 25.00 60.00
nn- Raiders of the Lost Ark, 1998, Chronicle Books, 304 pgs., adapts movie, 1-color (green) illos 4.00 10.00 22.00
1441- Range Busters, The, 1942, Whitman, 432 pgs., Henry E. Vallely-a 10.00 25.00 60.00
1163- Ranger and the Cowboy, The, 1939, Saalfield, 400 pgs. 10.00 25.00 60.00
1154- Rangers on the Rio Grande, 1938, Saalfield, 400 pgs. 10.00 25.00 60.00
1447- Ray Land of the Tank Corps, U.S.A., 1942, Whitman, 432 pgs., flip pictures, Hess-a 10.00 25.00 60.00
1157- Red Barry Ace-Detective, 1935, Whitman, 432 pgs., by Will Gould 12.00 30.00 85.00

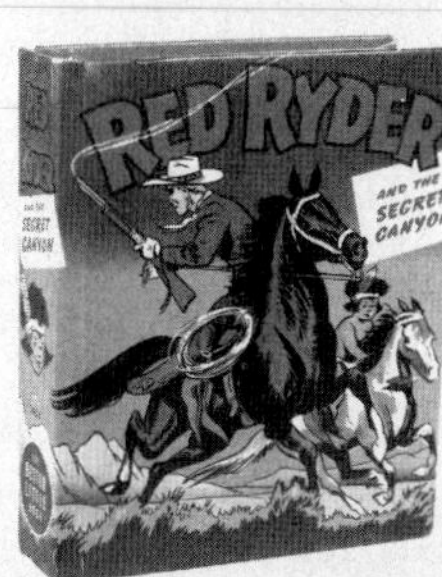

1454 - Red Ryder and the Secret Canyon © WHIT

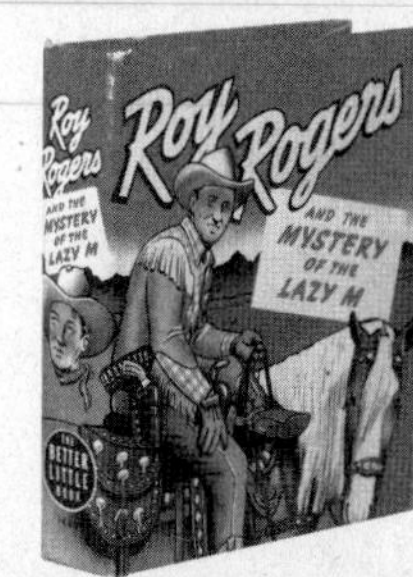

1462 - Roy Rogers and the Mystery of the Lazy M © Roy Rogers

1195 - Shooting Sheriffs of the Wild West © WHIT

	GD	FN	VF/NM

1426- **Red Barry Undercover Man**, 1939, Whitman, 432 pgs., by Will Gould 12.00 30.00 75.00
20- **Red Davis**, 1935, EVW, 160 pgs. 11.00 27.50 70.00
1449- **Red Death on the Range, The**, 1940, Whitman, 432 pgs., Fred Harman-a (Bronc Peeler) 11.00 27.50 70.00
nn- **Red Falcon Adventures, The**, 1937, Seal Right Ice Cream, 8 pgs., set of 50 books, circular in shape
Issue #1 64.00 160.00 450.00
Issue #2-5 43.00 108.00 300.00
Issue #6-10 36.00 90.00 250.00
Issue #11-50 21.00 52.50 150.00
nn- **Red Hen and the Fox, The**, nd(1930s), np(Whitman), 36 pgs., 3" x 2 1/2", Penny Book 3.00 7.50 18.00
1145- **Red-Hot Holsters**, 1938, Saalfield, 400 pgs. 10.00 25.00 60.00
1400- **Red Ryder and Little Beaver on Hoofs of Thunder**, 1939, Whitman, 432 pgs., Harman-c/a 13.00 32.50 90.00
1414- **Red Ryder and the Squaw-Tooth Rustlers**, 1946, Whitman, 352 pgs., Fred Harman-a 12.00 30.00 75.00
1427- **Red Ryder and the Code of the West**, 1941, Whitman, 432 pgs., flip pictures, by Harman 12.00 30.00 80.00
1440- **Red Ryder the Fighting Westerner**, 1940, Whitman, Harman-a 12.00 30.00 80.00
1443- **Red Ryder and the Rimrock Killer**, 1948, Whitman, 288 pgs., Harman-a 11.00 27.50 70.00
1450- **Red Ryder and Western Border Guns**, 1942, Whitman, 432 pgs., flip pictures, by Harman 12.00 30.00 80.00
1454- **Red Ryder and the Secret Canyon**, 1948, Whitman, 288 pgs., Harman-a 11.00 27.50 70.00
1466- **Red Ryder and Circus Luck**, 1947, Whitman, 288 pgs., by Fred Harman 11.00 27.50 70.00
1473- **Red Ryder in War on the Range**, 1945, Whitman, 352 pgs., by Fred Harman 12.00 30.00 75.00
1475- **Red Ryder and the Outlaw of Painted Valley**, 1943, Whitman, 352 pgs., by Harman 11.00 27.50 70.00
702-10- **Red Ryder Acting Sheriff**, 1949, Whitman, by Fred Hannan 10.00 25.00 65.00
nn- **Red Ryder Brings Law to Devil's Hole**, 1939, Dell, 196 pgs., Fast-Action Story, Harman-c/a 29.00 73.00 200.00
nn- **Red Ryder and the Highway Robbers**, 1938, Whitman, 36 pgs., 2 1/2" x 3 1/2", Penny Book 10.00 25.00 65.00
754- **Reg'lar Fellers**, 1933, Whitman, 320 pgs., by Gene Byrnes 11.00 27.50 70.00
nn- **Reg'lar Fellers**, 1933, Whitman, 202 pgs., Cocomalt premium, by Gene Byrnes 11.00 27.50 70.00
1424- **Rex Beach's Jaragu of the Jungle**, 1937, Whitman, 432 pgs. 9.00 22.50 55.00
12- **Rex, King of Wild Horses in "Stampede,"** 1935, EVW, 160 pgs., movie scenes, Columbia Pictures 10.00 25.00 60.00
1100B- **Riddles for Fun**, 1938, Whitman, 36 pgs., 2 1/2" x 3 1/2", Penny Book 3.00 7.50 20.00
1100B- **Riddles to Guess**, 1938, Whitman, 36 pgs., 2 1/2" x 3 1/2", Penny Book 3.00 7.50 20.00
1425- **Riders of Lone Trails**, 1937, Whitman, 300 pgs. 10.00 25.00 65.00
1141- **Rio Raiders** (A Billy The Kid Story), 1938, Saalfield, 400 pgs. 10.00 25.00 65.00
2023-(#23)- **The Road Runner, The Super Beep Catcher,** 1968, Whitman, 256 pgs., hard-c, color illos. 1.00 2.50 9.00
5759- **The Road Runner, The Super Beep Catcher,** 1973, Whitman, 256 pgs., soft-c, 39 cents, B&W illos., and flip pictures 2.00 5.00 12.00
5767-2- **Road Runner, The Lost Road Runner Mine, The,** 1974 (1980), 260 pgs., 79 cents, B&W, soft-c 2.00 5.00 12.00
5784- **The Road Runner and the Unidentified Coyote,** 1974, Whitman, 260 pgs., soft-c, flip pictures 2.00 5.00 12.00
5784-2- **The Road Runner and the Unidentified Coyote,** 1980, Whitman, 260 pgs., soft-c, flip pictures 2.00 5.00 12.00
nn- **Road To Perdition**, 2002, Dreamworks, screenplay from movie, hard-c (Dreamworks and 20th Century Fox) 1.00 2.50 9.00
Robin Hood (See Wee Little Books)
10- **Robin Hood**, 1935, EVW, 160 pgs., movie scenes w/Douglas Fairbanks (United Artists), hard-c 14.00 35.00 100.00

	GD	FN	VF/NM

719- **Robinson Crusoe** (The Story of...), nd (1933), Whitman, 364 pgs., soft-c 12.00 30.00 75.00
1421- **Roy Rogers and the Dwarf-Cattle Ranch**, 1947, Whitman, 352 pgs., Henry E. Vallely-a 12.00 30.00 75.00
1437- **Roy Rogers and the Deadly Treasure**, 1947, Whitman, 288 pgs. 12.00 30.00 75.00
1448- **Roy Rogers and the Mystery of the Howling Mesa**, 1948, Whitman, 288 pgs. 12.00 30.00 75.00
1452- **Roy Rogers in Robbers' Roost**, 1948, Whitman, 288 pgs. 12.00 30.00 75.00
1460- **Roy Rogers Robinhood of the Range**, 1942, Whitman, 432 pgs., Hess-a (1st) 14.00 35.00 100.00
1462- **Roy Rogers and the Mystery of the Lazy M**, 1949, Whitman 10.00 25.00 65.00
1476- **Roy Rogers King of the Cowboys**, 1943, Whitman, 352 pgs., Irwin Myers-a, based on movie 16.00 40.00 110.00
1494- **Roy Rogers at Crossed Feathers Ranch**, 1945, Whitman, 320 pgs., Erwin Hess-a , 3 1/4" x 5 1/2" 12.00 30.00 75.00
701-10- **Roy Rogers and the Snowbound Outlaws**, 1949, 3 1/4" x 5 1/2" 10.00 25.00 60.00
715-10- **Roy Rogers Range Detective**, 1950, Whitman, 2 1/2" x 5" 10.00 25.00 60.00
nn- **Sandy Gregg Federal Agent on Special Assignment**, 1939, Whitman, 36 pgs., 2 1/2" x 3 1/2", Penny Book 9.00 22.50 55.00
Sappo (See Top-Line Comics)
1122- **Scrappy**, 1934, Whitman, 288 pgs. 12.00 30.00 75.00
L12- **Scrappy** (The Adventures of...), 1935, Lynn, 192 pgs., movie scenes 12.00 30.00 75.00
1191- **Secret Agent K-7**,1940, Saalfield, 400 pgs., based on radio show 9.00 22.50 55.00
1144- **Secret Agent X-9**, 1936, Whitman, 432 pgs., Charles Flanders-a 15.00 37.50 105.00
1472- **Secret Agent X-9 and the Mad Assassin**, 1938, Whitman, 432 pgs., Charles Flanders-a 15.00 37.50 105.00
1161- **Sequoia**, 1935, Whitman, 160 pgs., photo-c, movie scenes 12.00 30.00 75.00
1430- **Shadow and the Living Death, The**, 1940, Whitman, 432 pgs., Erwin Hess-a 39.00 98.00 275.00
1443- **Shadow and the Master of Evil, The**, 1941, Whitman, 432 pgs., flip pictures, Hess-a 39.00 98.00 275.00
1495- **Shadow and the Ghost Makers, The**, 1942, Whitman, 432 pgs., John Coleman Burroughs-c 39.00 98.00 275.00
2024- **Shazzan, The Glass Princess**, 1968, Whitman, Hanna-Barbera 3.00 7.50 20.00
Shirley Temple (See My Life and Times & Story of..)
1095- **Shirley Temple and Lionel Barrymore Starring In "The Little Colonel,"** 1935, Saalfield, photo hard-c, movie scenes 18.00 45.00 125.00
1115- **Shirley Temple in "The Littlest Rebel,"** 1935, Saalfield, photo-c, movie scenes, hard-c 18.00 45.00 125.00
1575- **Shirley Temple and Lionel Barrymore Starring In "The Little Colonel,"** 1935, Saalfield, photo soft-c, movie scenes 18.00 45.00 125.00
1595- **Shirley Temple in "The Littlest Rebel,"** 1935, Saalfield, photo-c, movie scenes, soft-c 18.00 45.00 125.00
1195- **Shooting Sheriffs of the Wild West**, 1936, Whitman, 432 pgs. 8.00 20.00 50.00
1169- **Silly Symphony Featuring Donald Duck** (Disney), 1937, Whitman, 432 pgs., Taliaferro-a 25.00 62.50 175.00
1441- **Silly Symphony Featuring Donald Duck and His (MIS) Adventures** (Disney), 1937, Whitman, 432 pgs., Taliaferro-a 25.00 62.50 175.00
1155- **Silver Streak, The**, 1935, Whitman, 160 pgs., photo-c, movie scenes (RKO Radio Pict.) 10.00 25.00 65.00
Simple Simon (See Wee Little Books)
1649- **Sir Lancelot** (TV Series), 1958, Whitman, 280 pgs. 6.00 18.00 35.00
1112- **Skeezix in Africa**, 1934, Whitman, 300 pgs., Frank King-a 8.00 20.00 50.00
1408- **Skeezix at the Military Academy**, 1938, Whitman, 432 pgs., Frank King-a 8.00 20.00 50.00
1414- **Skeezix Goes to War**, 1944, Whitman, 352 pgs., Frank King-a 8.00 20.00 50.00

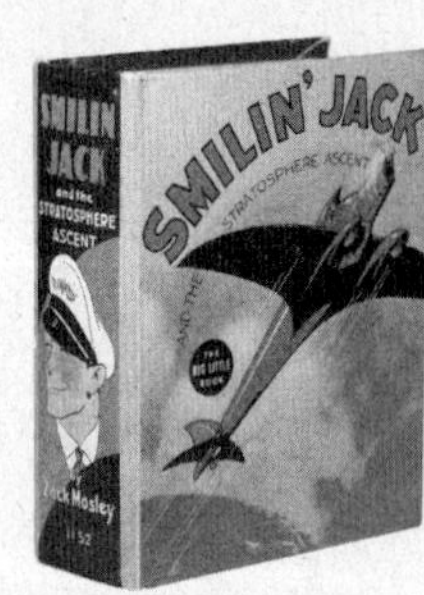

1152 - Smilin' Jack and the Stratosphere Ascent © WHIT

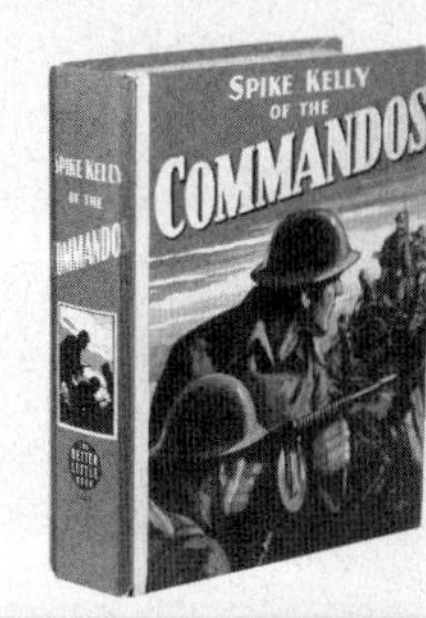

1467 - Spike Kelly of the Commandos © WHIT

1426 - Steve Hunter of the U.S. Coast Guard Under Secret Orders © WHIT

GD FN VF/NM

1419- Skeezix on His Own in the Big City, 1941, Whitman, All Pictures Comics, flip pictures, Frank King-a 8.00 20.00 50.00
761- Skippy, 1934, Whitman, 320 pgs., by Percy Crosby 8.00 20.00 50.00
4056- Skippy, The Story of, 1934, Whitman, 320 pgs., 7" x 9 1/2", Big Big Book, Percy Crosby-a 23.00 57.50 160.00
nn- Skippy, The Story of, 1934, Whitman, Phillips Dental Magnesia premium, soft-c, by Percy Crosby 8.00 20.00 50.00
1127- Skyroads (Hurricane Hawk's name not on cover), 1936, Whitman, 432 pgs., by Lt. Dick Calkins, Russell Keaton-a 11.00 27.50 70.00
1439- Skyroads with Clipper Williams of the Flying Legion, 1938, Whitman, 432 pgs., by Lt. Dick Calkins, Keaton-a 11.00 27.50 70.00
1127- Skyroads with Hurricane Hawk, 1936, Whitman, 432 pgs., by Lt. Dick Calkins, Russell Keaton-a 10.00 25.00 65.00
Smilin' Jack and his Flivver Plane (See Top-Line Comics)
1152- Smilin' Jack and the Stratosphere Ascent, 1937, Whitman, 432 pgs., Zack Mosley-a 12.00 30.00 85.00
1412- Smilin' Jack Flying High with "Downwind," 1942, Whitman, 432 pgs., Zack Mosley-a 12.00 30.00 80.00
1416- Smilin' Jack in Wings over the Pacific, 1939, Whitman, 432 pgs., Zack Mosley-a 12.00 30.00 80.00
1419- Smilin' Jack and the Jungle Pipe Line, 1947, Whitman, 352 pgs., Zack Mosley-a 12.00 30.00 75.00
1445- Smilin' Jack and the Escape from Death Rock, 1943, Whitman, 352 pgs., Mosley-a 12.00 30.00 75.00
1464- Smilin' Jack and the Coral Princess, 1945, Whitman, 352 pgs., Zack Mosley-a 12.00 30.00 75.00
1473- Smilin' Jack Speed Pilot, 1941, Whitman, 432 pgs., Zack Mosley-a 12.00 30.00 80.00
2- Smilin' Jack and his Stratosphere Plane, 1938, Whitman, 132 pgs., Buddy Book, soft-c, Zack Mosley-a 27.00 68.00 190.00
nn- Smilin' Jack Grounded on a Tropical Shore, 1938, Whitman, 36 pgs., 2 1/2" x 3 1/2", Penny Book 1000 25.00 60.00
11- Smilin' Jack and the Border Bandits, 1941, Dell, 196 pgs., Fast-Action Story, soft-c, Zack Mosley-a 24.00 60.00 170.00
745- Smitty Golden Gloves Tournament, 1934, Whitman, 320 pgs., Walter Berndt-a 12.00 30.00 75.00
nn- Smitty Golden Gloves Tournament, 1934, Whitman, 204 pgs., Cocomalt premium, soft-c, Walter Berndt-a 12.00 30.00 85.00
1404- Smitty and Herby Lost Among the Indians, 1941, Whitman, All Pictures Comics 10.00 25.00 60.00
1477- Smitty in Going Native, 1938, Whitman, 300 pgs., Walter Berndt-a 10.00 25.00 60.00
2- Smitty and Herby, 1936, Whitman, 132 pgs., 3 1/2" x 3 1/2", soft-c, Tarzan Ice Cream cup lid premium 24.00 60.00 170.00
9- Smitty's Brother Herby and the Police Horse, 1938, Whitman, 132 pgs., 3 1/4" x 3 1/2", Buddy Book-ice cream premium, by Walter Berndt 24.00 60.00 170.00
1010- Smokey Stover Firefighter of Foo, 1937, Whitman, 7 1/4" x 5 1/2", 64 pgs., Nickel Book, Bill Holman-a 12.00 30.00 85.00
1413- Smokey Stover, 1942, Whitman, All Pictures Comics, flip pictures, Bill Holman-a 12.00 30.00 85.00
1421- Smokey Stover the Foo Fighter, 1938, Whitman, 432 pgs., Bill Holman-a 12.00 30.00 85.00
1481- Smokey Stover the Foolish Foo Fighter, 1942, Whitman, All Pictures Comics 12.00 30.00 85.00
1- Smokey Stover the Fireman of Foo, 1938, Whitman, 3 3/4" x 3 1/2", 132 pgs., Buddy Book-ice cream premium, by Bill Holman 27.00 68.00 190.00
1100A- Smokey Stover, 1938, Whitman, 36 pgs., 2 1/2" x 3 1/2", Penny Book 10.00 25.00 65.00
nn- Smokey Stover and the Fire Chief of Foo, 1938, Whitman, 36 pgs., 2 1/2" x 3 1/2", Penny Book, yellow shirt on-c 10.00 25.00 65.00
nn- Smokey Stover and the Fire Chief of Foo, 1938, Whitman, 36 pgs., Penny Book, green shirt on-c 10.00 25.00 65.00
1460- Snow White and the Seven Dwarfs (The Story of Walt Disney's ...), 1938, Whitman, 288 pgs. 18.00 45.00 125.00
1136- Sombrero Pete, 1936, Whitman, 432 pgs. 10.00 25.00 60.00
1152- Son of Mystery, 1939, Saalfield, 400 pgs. 10.00 25.00 60.00
1191- SOS Coast Guard, 1936, Whitman, 432 pgs., Henry E. Vallely-a 10.00 25.00 65.00

GD FN VF/NM

2016-(#16)-Space Ghost-The Sorceress of Cyba-3 (TV Cartoon), 1968, Whitman, 260 pgs., 39¢-c, hard-c, color illos 10.00 25.00 60.00
1455- Speed Douglas and the Mole Gang-The Great Sabotage Plot, 1941, Whitman, 432 pgs., flip pictures 10.00 25.00 60.00
5779- Spider-Man Zaps Mr. Zodiac, 1976, 260 pgs., soft-c, B&W 1.00 2.50 9.00
5779-2- Spider-Man Zaps Mr. Zodiac, 1980, 260 pgs., 79¢-c, soft-c, B&W 1.00 2.50 6.00
1467- Spike Kelly of the Commandos, 1943, Whitman, 352 pgs. 10.00 25.00 60.00
1144- Spook Riders on the Overland, 1938, Saalfield, 400 pgs. 10.00 25.00 60.00
768- Spy, The, 1936, Whitman, 300 pgs. 12.00 30.00 75.00
nn- Spy Smasher and the Red Death, 1941, Fawcett, 4" x 5 1/2", Dime Action Book 43.00 108.00 300.00
1120- Stan Kent Freshman Fullback, 1936, Saalfield, 148 pgs., hard-c 8.00 20.00 50.00
1132- Stan Kent, Captain, 1937, Saalfield 8.00 20.00 50.00
1600- Stan Kent Freshman Fullback, 1936, Saalfield, 148 pgs., soft-c 8.00 20.00 50.00
1123- Stan Kent Varsity Man, 1936, Saalfield, 160 pgs., hard-c 8.00 20.00 50.00
1603- Stan Kent Varsity Man, 1936, Saalfield, 160 pgs., soft-c 8.00 20.00 50.00
nn- Star Wars - A New Hope, 1997, Chronicle Books, 320 pgs., adapts movie, 1-color (blue) illos 3.00 7.50 20.00
nn- Star Wars - Empire Strikes Back, The, 1997, Chronicle Books, 296 pgs., adapts movie, 1-color (blue) illos 3.00 7.50 20.00
nn- Star Wars - Episode 1 - The Phantom Menace, 1999, Chronicle Books, 344 pgs., adapts movie, 1-color (blue) illos 1.00 2.50 9.00
nn- Star Wars - Episode 2 - Attack of the Clones, 2002, Chronicle Books, 340 pgs., adapts movie, 1-color (blue) illos 1.00 2.50 9.00
nn- Star Wars - Return of the Jedi, 1997, Chronicle Books, 312 pgs., adapts movie, 1-color (blue) illos 3.00 7.50 20.00
1104- Steel Arena, The (With Clyde Beatty), 1936, Saalfield, hard-c, movie scenes adapted from "The Lost Jungle" 12.00 30.00 75.00
1584- Steel Arena, The (With Clyde Beatty), 1936, Saalfield, soft-c, movie scenes 12.00 30.00 75.00
1426- Steve Hunter of the U.S. Coast Guard Under Secret Orders, 1942, Whitman, 432 pgs. 10.00 25.00 60.00
1456- Story of Charlie McCarthy and Edgar Bergen, The, 1938, Whitman, 288 pgs. 10.00 25.00 60.00
Story of Daniel, The (See Wee Little Books)
Story of David, The (See Wee Little Books)
1110- Story of Freddie Bartholomew, The, 1935, Saalfield, 4 1/2" x 5 1/4", hard-c, movie scenes (MGM) 10.00 25.00 60.00
1590- Story of Freddie Bartholomew, The, 1935, Saalfield, 4 1/2" x 5 1/4", soft-c, movie scenes (MGM) 10.00 25.00 60.00
Story of Gideon, The (See Wee Little Books)
W714- Story of Jackie Cooper, The, 1933, Whitman, 240 pgs., photo-c, movie scenes, "Skippy" & "Sooky" movie 12.00 30.00 80.00
Story of Joseph, The (See Wee Little Books)
Story of Moses, The (See Wee Little Books)
Story of Ruth and Naomi (See Wee Little Books)
1089- Story of Shirley Temple, The, 1934, Saalfield, 160 pgs., hard-c, photo-c, movie scenes 11.00 27.50 70.00
1319- Story of Shirley Temple, The, 1934, Saalfield, 160 pgs., soft-c, photo-c, movie scenes 11.00 27.50 70.00
1090- Strawberry-Roan, 1934, Saalfield, 160 pgs., hard-c, Ken Maynard photo-c, movie scenes 11.00 27.50 70.00
1320- Strawberry-Roan, 1934, Saalfield, 160 pgs., soft-c, Ken Maynard photo-c, movie scenes 11.00 27.50 70.00
Streaky and the Football Signals (See Top-Line Comics)
5780-2- Superman in the Phantom Zone Connection, 1980, 260 pgs., 79¢-c, soft-c, B&W 1.00 2.50 9.00
582- "Swap It" Book, The, 1949, Samuel Lowe Co., 260 pgs., 3 1/2" x 4 1/2"
1. Little Tex in the Midst of Trouble 5.00 12.50 30.00
2. Little Tex's Escape 5.00 12.50 30.00
3. Little Tex Comes to the XY Ranch 5.00 12.50 30.00
4. Get Them Cowboy 5.00 12.50 30.00
5. The Mail Must Go Through! A Story of the Pony Express

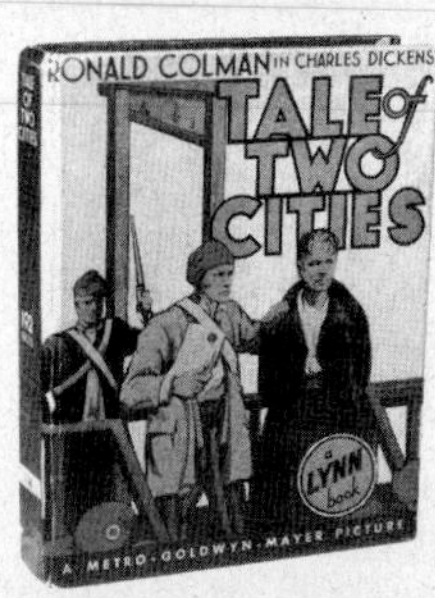

L16 - A Tale of Two Cities © LYNN

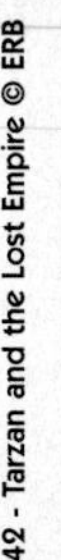
1442 - Tarzan and the Lost Empire © ERB

1446 - Terry and the Pirates and the Giant's Revenge © WHIT

	GD	FN	VF/NM
	5.00	12.50	30.00
6. Nevada Jones, Trouble Shooter	5.00	12.50	30.00
7. Danny Meets the Cowboys	5.00	12.50	30.00
8. Flint Adams and the Stage Coach	5.00	12.50	30.00
9. Bud Shinners and the Oregon Trail	5.00	12.50	30.00
10. The Outlaws' Last Ride	5.00	12.50	30.00
Sybil Jason (See Little Big Shot)			
747- **Tailspin Tommy in the Famous Pay-Roll Mystery**, 1933, Whitman, hard-c, 320 pgs., Hal Forrest-a (# 1)	12.00	30.00	85.00
747- **Tailspin Tommy in the Famous Pay-Roll Mystery**, 1933, Whitman, soft-c, 320 pgs., Hal Forrest-a (# 1)	12.00	30.00	85.00
nn- **Tailspin Tommy the Pay-Roll Mystery**, 1934, Whitman, 52 pgs., 3 1/2" x 5 1/4", premium-no ads, soft-c; another version with Perkins ad, Hal Forrest-a	18.00	45.00	125.00
1110- **Tailspin Tommy and the Island in the Sky,** 1936, Whitman, 432 pgs., Hal Forrest-a	11.00	27.50	70.00
1124- **Tailspin Tommy the Dirigible Flight to the North Pole**, 1934, Whitman, 432 pgs., H. Forrest-a	12.00	30.00	85.00
nn- **Tailspin Tommy the Dirigible Flight to the North Pole**, 1934, Whitman, 436 pgs., 3-color, soft-c, premium-no ads, Hal Forrest-a	29.00	73.00	200.00
1172- **Tailspin Tommy Hunting for Pirate Gold**, 1935, Whitman, 432 pgs., Hal Forrest-a	11.00	27.50	70.00
1183- **Tailspin Tommy Air Racer**, 1940, Saalfield, 400 pgs., hard-c	11.00	27.50	70.00
1184- **Tailspin Tommy in the Great Air Mystery**, 1936, Whitman, 240 pgs., photo-c, movie scenes	12.00	30.00	85.00
1410- **Tailspin Tommy the Weasel and His "Skywaymen,"** 1941, Whitman, All Pictures Comics, flip pictures	10.00	25.00	65.00
1413- **Tailspin Tommy and the Lost Transport**, 1940, Whitman, 432 pgs., Hal Forrest-a	10.00	25.00	65.00
1423- **Tailspin Tommy and the Hooded Flyer**, 1937, Whitman, 432 pgs., Hal Forrest-a	11.00	27.50	70.00
1494- **Tailspin Tommy and the Sky Bandits**, 1938, Whitman 432 pgs., Hal Forrest-a	11.00	27.50	70.00
nn- **Tailspin Tommy and the Airliner Mystery**, 1938, Dell, 196 pgs., Fast-Action Story, soft-c, Hal Forrest-a	43.00	108.00	300.00
nn- **Tailspin Tommy in Flying Aces**, 1938, Dell, 196 pgs., Fast-Action Story, soft-c, Hal Forrest-a	43.00	108.00	300.00
nn- **Tailspin Tommy in Wings Over the Arctic**, 1934, Whitman, Cocomalt premium, Forrest-a	14.00	35.00	100.00
nn- **Tailspin Tommy Big Thrill Chewing Gum**, 1934, Whitman, 8 pgs., 2 1/2" x 3 " (6 diff.) each..	11.00	27.50	70.00
3- **Tailspin Tommy on the Mountain of Human Sacrifice**, 1938, Whitman, soft-c, Buddy Book	29.00	73.00	200.00
7- **Tailspin Tommy's Perilous Adventure**, 1934, Whitman, 132 pgs., 3 1/2" x 3 1/2" soft-c, Tarzan Ice Cream cup premium	29.00	73.00	200.00
nn- **Tailspin Tommy**, 1935, Whitman, 148 pgs., 3 1/2" x 4", Tarzan Ice Cream cup premium	32.00	80.00	225.00
L16- **Tale of Two Cities, A**, 1935, Lynn, movie scenes	12.00	30.00	85.00
744- **Tarzan of the Apes**, 1933, Whitman, 320 pgs., by Edgar Rice Burroughs (1st)	43.00	108.00	300.00
nn- **Tarzan of the Apes**, 1935, Whitman, 52 pgs., 3 1/2" x 5 1/4", soft-c, stapled, premium, no ad; another version with a Perkins ad; reprints panels from Hal Foster's newspaper adaptation	54.00	135.00	375.00
769- **Tarzan the Fearless**, 1934, Whitman, 240 pgs., Buster Crabbe photo-c, movie scenes, ERB	29.00	73.00	200.00
770- **Tarzan Twins, The**, 1934, Whitman, 432 pgs., ERB	82.00	205.00	575.00
770- **Tarzan Twins, The**, 1935, Whitman, 432 pgs., ERB	54.00	135.00	375.00
nn- **Tarzan Twins, The**, 1935, Whitman, 52 pgs., 3 1/2" x 5 3/4", premium-with & without ads, soft-c, ERB	68.00	170.00	475.00
nn- **Tarzan Twins, The**, 1935, Whitman, 436 pgs., 3-color, soft-c, premium-no ads, ERB	71.00	178.00	500.00
778- **Tarzan of the Screen** (The Story of Johnny Weissmuller), 1934, Whitman, 240 pgs., photo-c, movie scenes, ERB	29.00	73.00	200.00
1102- **Tarzan, The Return of**, 1936, Whitman, 432 pgs., Edgar Rice Burroughs	21.00	52.50	150.00
1180- **Tarzan, The New Adventures of**, 1935, Whitman, 160 pgs., Herman Brix photo-c, movie scenes, ERB	24.00	60.00	165.00
1182- **Tarzan Escapes**, 1936, Whitman, 240 pgs., Johnny Weissmuller photo-c, movie scenes, ERB	29.00	73.00	200.00
1407- **Tarzan Lord of the Jungle**, 1946, Whitman, 352 pgs., ERB	14.00	35.00	100.00
1410- **Tarzan, The Beasts of**, 1937, Whitman, 432 pgs., Edgar Rice Burroughs	21.00	52.50	145.00
1442- **Tarzan and the Lost Empire**, 1948, Whitman, 288 pgs., ERB	14.00	35.00	100.00
1444- **Tarzan and the Ant Men**, 1945, Whitman, 352 pgs., ERB	14.00	35.00	100.00
1448- **Tarzan and the Golden Lion**, 1943, Whitman, 432 pgs., ERB	20.00	50.00	140.00
1452- **Tarzan the Untamed**, 1941, Whitman, 432 pgs., flip pictures, ERB	20.00	50.00	140.00
1453- **Tarzan the Terrible**, 1942, Whitman, 432 pgs., flip pictures, ERB	20.00	50.00	140.00
1467- **Tarzan in the Land of the Giant Apes**, 1949, Whitman, ERB	14.00	35.00	100.00
1477- **Tarzan, The Son of**, 1939, Whitman, 432 pgs., ERB	20.00	50.00	140.00
1488- **Tarzan's Revenge**, 1938, Whitman, 432 pgs., ERB	20.00	50.00	140.00
1495- **Tarzan and the Jewels of Opar**, 1940, Whitman, 432 pgs.	20.00	50.00	140.00
4056- **Tarzan and the Tarzan Twins with Jad-Bal-Ja the Golden Lion**, 1936, Whitman, 7" x 9 1/2", 320 pgs., Big Big Book	60.00	150.00	470.00
709-10- **Tarzan and the Journey of Terror**, 1950, Whitman, 2 1/2" x 5", ERB, Marsh-a	10.00	25.00	65.00
2005- **(#5)-Tarzan: The Mark of the Red Hyena**, 1967, Whitman, 260 pgs., 39 cents, hard-c, color illos	4.00	10.00	27.00
nn- **Tarzan**, 1935, Whitman, 148 pgs., soft-c, 3 1/2" x 4", Tarzan Ice Cream cup premium, ERB (scarce)	86.00	215.00	600.00
nn- **Tarzan and a Daring Rescue**, 1938, Whitman, 68 pgs., Pan-Am premium, soft-c, ERB (blank back-c version also exists)	50.00	125.00	350.00
nn- **Tarzan and his Jungle Friends**, 1936, Whitman, 132 pgs., soft-c, 3 1/2" x 3 1/2", Tarzan Ice Cream cup premium, ERB (scarce)	86.00	215.00	600.00
nn- **Tarzan in the Golden City**, 1938, Whitman, 68 pgs., Pan-Am premium, soft-c, 3 1/2" x 3 3/4", ERB	50.00	125.00	350.00
nn- **Tarzan The Avenger**, 1939, Dell, 194 pgs., Fast-Action Story, ERB, soft-c	36.00	90.00	250.00
nn- **Tarzan with the Tarzan Twins in the Jungle**, 1938, Dell, 194 pgs., Fast-Action Story, ERB	36.00	90.00	250.00
1100B- **Tell Your Fortune**, 1938, Whitman, 36 pgs., 2 1/2" x 3 1/2", Penny Book	4.00	10.00	24.00
nn- **Terminator 2: Judgment Day**, 1998, Chronicle Books, 310 pgs., adapts movie, 1-color (blue-gray) illos	1.00	2.50	9.00
1156- **Terry and the Pirates**, 1935, Whitman, 432 pgs., Milton Caniff-a (#1)	14.00	35.00	100.00
nn- **Terry and the Pirates**, 1935, Whitman, 52 pgs., 3 1/2" x 5 1/4", soft-c, premium, Milton Caniff-a; 3 versions: No ad, Sears ad & Perkins ad	29.00	73.00	200.00
1412- **Terry and the Pirates Shipwrecked on a Desert Island**, 1938, Whitman, 432 pgs., Milton Caniff-a	12.00	30.00	85.00
1420- **Terry and War in the Jungle**, 1946, Whitman, 352 pgs., Milton Caniff-a	12.00	30.00	80.00
1436- **Terry and the Pirates The Plantation Mystery**, 1942, Whitman, 432 pgs., flip pictures, Milton Caniff-a	12.00	30.00	85.00
1446- **Terry and the Pirates and the Giant's Vengeance**, 1939, Whitman, 432 pgs., Caniff-a	12.00	30.00	85.00
1499- **Terry and the Pirates in the Mountain Stronghold**, 1941, Whitman, 432 pgs., Caniff-a	12.00	30.00	85.00
4073- **Terry and the Pirates, The Adventures of**, 1938, Whitman, 7" x 9 1/2", 320 pgs., Big Big Book, Milton Caniff-a	39.00	98.00	275.00
4- **Terry and the Pirates Ashore in Singapore**, 1938, Whitman, 132 pgs., 3 1/2" x 3 3/4", soft-c, Buddy Book premium	27.00	68.00	190.00

nn - The Texas Ranger and The Rustler Gang © WHIT

1472 - Tiny Tim in the Big, Big World © WHIT

nn - Tom Mix in The Fighting Cowboy © WHIT

GD FN VF/NM

10- **Terry and the Pirates Meet Again**, 1936, Whitman, 132 pgs., 3 1/2" x 3 1/2", soft-c, Tarzan Ice Cream cup lid premium 39.00 98.00 275.00
nn- **Terry and the Pirates, Adventures of**, 1938, 36 pgs., 2 1/2" x 3 1/2", Penny Book, Caniff-a 10.00 25.00 60.00
nn- **Terry and the Pirates and the Island Rescue**, 1938, Whitman, 68 pgs., 3 1/4" x 3 1/2", Pan-Am premium 21.00 52.50 150.00
nn- **Terry and the Pirates on Their Travels**, 1938, 36 pgs., 2 1/2" x 3 1/2", Penny Book, Caniff-a 10.00 25.00 60.00
nn- **Terry and the Pirates and the Mystery Ship**, 1938, Dell, 194 pgs., Fast-Action Story, soft-c 29.00 73.00 200.00
1492- **Terry Lee Flight Officer U.S.A.**, 1944, Whitman, 352 pgs., Milton Caniff-a 12.00 30.00 75.00
7- **Texas Bad Man, The** (Tom Mix), 1934, EVW, 160 pgs., (Five Star Library), movie scenes 18.00 45.00 125.00
1429- **Texas Kid, The**, 1937, Whitman, 432 pgs. 8.00 20.00 50.00
1135- **Texas Ranger, The**, 1936, Whitman, 432 pgs., Hal Arbo-a 8.00 20.00 50.00
nn- **Texas Ranger, The**, 1935, Whitman, 260 pgs., Cocomalt premium, soft-c, Hal Arbo-a 12.00 30.00 75.00
nn- **Texas Ranger and the Rustler Gang, The**, 1936, Whitman, Pan-Am giveaway 21.00 52.50 150.00
nn- **Texas Ranger in the West, The**, 1938, Whitman, 36 pgs., 2 1/2" x 3 1/2", Penny Book 8.00 20.00 50.00
nn- **Texas Ranger to the Rescue, The**, 1938, Whitman, 36 pgs., 2 1/2" x 3 1/2", Penny Book 8.00 20.00 50.00
12- **Texas Ranger in Rustler Strategy, The**, 1936, Whitman, 132 pgs., 3 1/2" x 3 1/2", soft-c, Tarzan Ice Cream cup lid premium 26.00 65.00 180.00
Tex Thorne (See Zane Grey)
Thimble Theatre (See Popeye)
26- **13 Hours By Air**, 1936, Lynn, 128 pgs., 5" x 7 1/2", photo-c, movie scenes (Paramount Pictures) 12.00 30.00 75.00
nn- **Three Bears, The**, nd (1930s), np (Whitman), 36 pgs., 3" x 2 1/2", Penny Book 3.00 7.50 20.00
1129- **Three Finger Joe** (Baseball), 1937, Saalfield, Robert A. Graef-a 8.00 20.00 50.00
nn- **Three Little Pigs, The**, nd (1930s), np (Whitman), 36 pgs., 3" x 2 1/2", Penny Book 3.00 7.50 20.00
1131- **Three Musketeers**, 1935, Whitman, 182 pgs., 5 1/4" x 6 1/4", photo-c, movie scenes 14.00 35.00 100.00
1409- **Thumper and the Seven Dwarfs** (Disney), 1944, Whitman, All Pictures Comics 21.00 52.50 150.00
1108- **Tiger Lady, The** (The life of Mabel Stark, animal trainer), 1935, Saalfield, photo-c, movie scenes, hard-c 10.00 25.00 60.00
1588- **Tiger Lady, The**, 1935, Saalfield, photo-c, movie scenes, soft-c 10.00 25.00 60.00
1442- **Tillie the Toiler and the Wild Man of Desert Island**, 1941, Whitman, 432 pgs., Russ Westover-a 11.00 27.50 70.00
1058- **"Timid Elmer"** (Disney), 1939, Whitman, 5" x 5 1/2", 68 pgs., hard-c 11.00 27.50 70.00
1152- **Tim McCoy in the Prescott Kid**, 1935, Whitman, 160 pgs., hard-c, photo-c, movie scenes 18.00 45.00 125.00
1193- **Tim McCoy in the Westerner**, 1936, Whitman, 240 pgs., photo-c, movie scenes 1400 35.00 100.00
1436- **Tim McCoy on the Tomahawk Trail**, 1937, Whitman, 432 pgs., Robert Weisman-a 12.00 30.00 75.00
1490- **Tim McCoy and the Sandy Gulch Stampede**, 1939, Whitman, 424 pgs. 10.00 25.00 65.00
2- **Tim McCoy in Beyond the Law**, 1934, EVW, Five Star Library, photo-c, movie scenes (Columbia Pict.) Hardcover 14.00 35.00 100.00
(Rare) Softcover 36.00 90.00 250.00
10- **Tim McCoy in Fighting the Redskins**, 1938, Whitman, 130 pgs., Buddy Book, soft-c 27.00 68.00 190.00
14- **Tim McCoy in Speedwings**, 1935, EVW, Five Star Library, 160 pgs., photo-c, movie scenes (Columbia Pictures) 1900 47.50 135.00
nn- **Tim the Builder**, nd (1930s), np (Whitman), 36 pgs., 3" x 2 1/2", Penny Book 3.00 7.50 20.00
Tim Tyler (Also see Adventures of ...)
1140- **Tim Tyler's Luck Adventures in the Ivory Patrol**, 1937, Whitman, 432 pgs., by Lyman Young 10.00 25.00 65.00
1479- **Tim Tyler's Luck and the Plot of the Exiled King**, 1939, Whitman, 432 pgs., by Lyman Young 10.00 25.00 60.00
767- **Tiny Tim, The Adventures of**, 1935, Whitman, 384 pgs., by Stanley Link 12.00 30.00 85.00
1172- **Tiny Tim and the Mechanical Men**, 1937, Whitman, 432 pgs., by Stanley Link 12.00 30.00 75.00
1472- **Tiny Tim in the Big, Big World**, 1945, Whitman, 352 pgs., by Stanley Link 12.00 30.00 75.00
2006- **(#6)-Tom and Jerry Meet Mr. Fingers**, 1967, Whitman, 39¢-c 260 pgs., hard-c, color illos. 4.00 10.00 27.00
5752- **Tom and Jerry Meet Mr. Fingers**, 1973, Whitman, 39¢-c 260 pgs., soft-c, color illos., 5 printings 2.00 5.00 15.00
2030-**(#30)- Tom and Jerry, The Astro-Nots**, 1969, Whitman, 256 pgs., hard-c, color illos. 3.00 7.50 20.00
5765- **Tom and Jerry, The Astro-Nots**, 1974, Whitman, 256 pgs., soft-c, color illos. 2.00 5.00 15.00
5787-2- **Tom and Jerry Under the Big Top**, 1980, Whitman, 79¢-c, 260 pgs., soft-c, B&W 2.00 5.00 15.00
723- **Tom Beatty Ace of the Service**, 1934, Whitman, 256 pgs., George Taylor-a 12.00 30.00 75.00
nn- **Tom Beatty Ace of the Service**, 1934, Whitman, 260 pgs., soft-c 12.00 30.00 75.00
1165- **Tom Beatty Ace of the Service Scores Again**, 1937, Whitman, 432 pgs., Weisman-a 11.00 27.50 70.00
1420- **Tom Beatty Ace of the Service and the Big Brain Gang**, 1939, Whitman, 432 pgs. 11.00 27.50 70.00
nn- **Tom Beatty Ace Detective and the Gorgon Gang**, 1938?, Whitman, 36 pgs., 2 1/2" x 3 1/2", Penny Book 10.00 25.00 60.00
nn- **Tom Beatty Ace of the Service and the Kidnapers**, 1938?, Whitman, 36 pgs., 2 1/2" x 3 1/2", Penny Book 10.00 25.00 60.00
1102- **Tom Mason on Top**, 1935, Saalfield, 160 pgs., Tom Mix photo-c, from Mascot serial "The Miracle Rider," movie scenes, hard-c 18.00 45.00 125.00
1582- **Tom Mason on Top**, 1935, Saalfield, 160 pgs., Tom Mix photo-c, movie scenes, soft-c 18.00 45.00 125.00
Tom Mix (See Chief of the Rangers, Flaming Guns & Texas Bad Man)
762- **Tom Mix and Tony Jr. in "Terror Trail,"** 1934, Whitman, 160 pgs., movie scenes 18.00 45.00 125.00
1144- **Tom Mix in the Fighting Cowboy**, 1935, Whitman, 432 pgs., Hal Arbo-a 12.00 30.00 85.00
nn- **Tom Mix in the Fighting Cowboy**, 1935, Whitman, 436 pgs., premium-no ads, 3 color, soft-c, Hal Arbo-a 21.00 52.50 150.00
1166- **Tom Mix in the Range War**, 1937, Whitman, 432 pgs., Hal Arbo-a 10.00 25.00 65.00
1173- **Tom Mix Plays a Lone Hand**, 1935, Whitman, 288 pgs., hard-c, Hal Arbo-a 10.00 25.00 65.00
1183- **Tom Mix and the Stranger from the South**, 1936, Whitman, 432 pgs. 10.00 25.00 65.00
1462- **Tom Mix and the Hoard of Montezuma**, 1937, Whitman, H. E. Vallely-a 10.00 25.00 65.00
1482- **Tom Mix and His Circus on the Barbary Coast**, 1940, Whitman, 432 pgs., James Gary-a 10.00 25.00 65.00
3047- **Tom Mix and His Big Little Kit**, 1937, Whitman, 384 pgs., 4 1/2" x 6 1/2" box, includes miniature box of 4 crayons-red, yellow, blue and green 71.00 178.00 500.00
4068- **Tom Mix and the Scourge of Paradise Valley**, 1937, Whitman, 7" x 9 1/2", 320 pgs., Big Big Book, Vallely-a 29.00 73.00 200.00
6833- **Tom Mix in the Riding Avenger**, 1936, Dell, 244 pgs., Cartoon Story Book, hard-c 19.00 47.50 130.00
nn- **Tom Mix Rides to the Rescue**, 1939, 36 pgs., 2 1/2" x 3", Penny Book 10.00 25.00 60.00
nn- **Tom Mix Avenges the Dry Gulched Range King**, 1939, Dell, 196 pgs., Fast-Action Story, soft-c 20.00 50.00 140.00
nn- **Tom Mix in the Riding Avenger**, 1936, Dell, 244 pgs., Fast-Action Story 20.00 50.00 140.00
nn- **Tom Mix the Trail of the Terrible 6**, 1935, Ralston Purina Co., 84 pgs., 3" x 3 1/2", premium 18.00 45.00 125.00
4- **Tom Mix and Tony in the Rider of Death Valley**, 1934, EVW, Five Star Library, 160 pgs., movie scenes (Universal Pictures), hard-c 17.00 42.50 120.00
4- **Tom Mix and Tony in the Rider of Death Valley**,

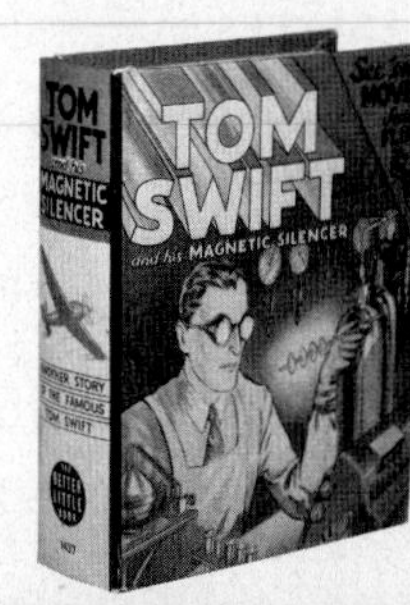

1437 - Tom Swift and His Magnetic Silencer © WHIT

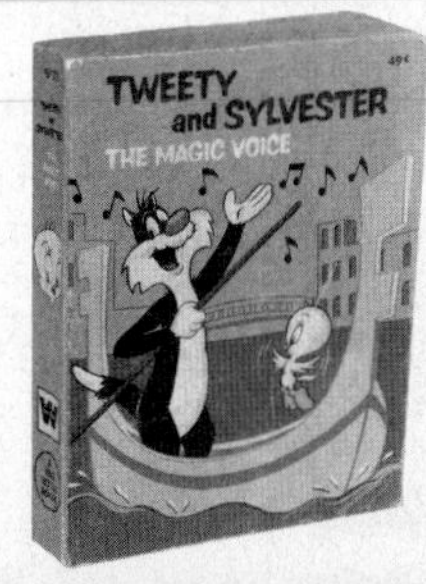

5777 - Tweety and Sylvester, The Magic Voice © WB

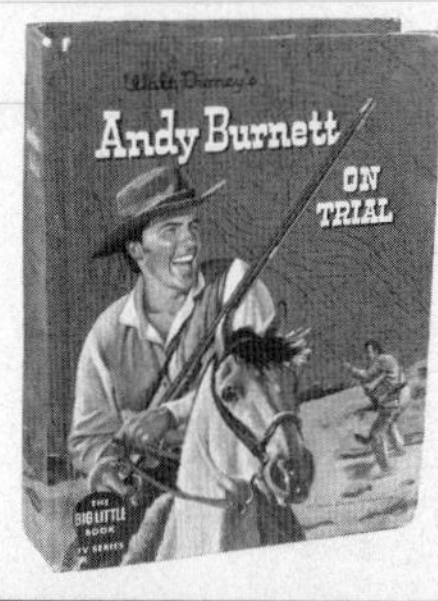

1645 - Walt Disney's Andy Burnett on the Trail © DIS

GD FN VF/NM

1934, EVW, Five Star Library, 160 pgs., movie scenes
(Universal Pictures), soft-c (Rare) 36.00 90.00 250.00
7- Tom Mix in the Texas Bad Man, 1934, EVW, Five Star Library,
160 pgs., movie scenes, hard-c 18.00 45.00 125.00
7- Tom Mix in the Texas Bad Man, 1934, EVW, Five Star Library,
160 pgs., movie scenes; soft-c (Rare) 36.00 90.00 250.00
10- Tom Mix in the Tepee Ranch Mystery, 1938, Whitman,
132 pgs., Buddy Book, soft-c 21.00 52.50 150.00
1126- Tommy of Troop Six (Scout Book), 1937, Saalfield, hard-c
9.00 22.50 55.00
1606- Tommy of Troop Six (Scout Book), 1937, Saalfield, soft-c
9.00 22.50 55.00
Tom Sawyer (See Adventures of ...)
1437- Tom Swift and His Magnetic Silencer, 1941, Whitman,
432 pgs., flip pictures 29.00 73.00 200.00
1485- Tom Swift and His Giant Telescope, 1939, Whitman,
432 pgs., James Gary-a 21.00 52.50 150.00
540- Top-Line Comics (In Open Box), 1935, Whitman, 164 pgs.,
3 1/2" x 3 1/2", 3 books in set, all soft-c:
Bobby Thatcher and the Samarang Emerald 16.00 40.00 110.00
Broncho Bill in Suicide Canyon 16.00 40.00 110.00
Freckles and His Friends in the North Woods 16.00 40.00 110.00
Complete set with box 50.00 125.00 350.00
541- Top-Line Comics (In Open Box), 1935, Whitman, 164 pgs.,
3 1/2" x 3 1/2", 3 books in set; all soft-c:
Little Joe and the City Gangsters 16.00 40.00 110.00
Smilin' Jack and His Flivver Plane 16.00 40.00 110.00
Streaky and the Football Signals 16.00 40.00 110.00
Complete set with box 50.00 125.00 350.00
542- Top-Line Comics (In Open Box), 1935, Whitman, 164 pgs.,
3 1/2" x 3 1/2", 3 books in set; all soft-c:
Dinglehoofer Und His Dog Adolph by Knerr 16.00 40.00 110.00
Jungle Jim by Alex Raymond 18.00 45.00 125.00
Sappo by Segar 18.00 45.00 125.00
Complete set with box 64.00 160.00 450.00
543- Top-Line Comics (In Open Box), 1935, Whitman, 164 pgs.,
3 1/2" x 3 1/2", 3 books in set; all soft-c:
Alexander Smart, ESQ by Winner 16.00 40.00 110.00
Bunky by Billy de Beck 16.00 40.00 110.00
Nicodemus O'Malley by Carter 16.00 40.00 110.00
Complete set with box 50.00 125.00 350.00
1158- Tracked by a G-Man, 1939, Saalfield, 400 pgs.
9.00 22.50 55.00
25- Trail of the Lonesome Pine, The, 1936, Lynn, movie scenes
12.00 30.00 85.00
nn- Trail of the Terrible 6 (See Tom Mix ...)
1185- Trail to Squaw Gulch, The, 1940, Saalfield, 400 pgs.
10.00 25.00 60.00
720- Treasure Island, 1933, Whitman, 362 pgs. 12.00 30.00 85.00
1141- Treasure Island, 1934, Whitman, 164 pgs., hard-c, 4 1/4" x 5 1/4",
Jackie Cooper photo-c, movie scenes 12.00 30.00 85.00
1141- Treasure Island, 1934, Whitman, 164 pgs., soft-c, 4 1/4" x 5 1/4",
Jackie Cooper photo-c, movie scenes 12.00 30.00 85.00
1018- Trick and Puzzle Book, 1939, Whitman, 100 pgs.,
soft-c 3.00 7.50 20.00
1100B- Tricks Easy to Do (Slight of hand & magic), 1938, Whitman,
36 pgs., 2 1/2" x 3 1/2", Penny Book 3.00 7.50 20.00
1100B- Tricks You Can Do, 1938, Whitman, 36 pgs., 2 1/2" x 3 1/2",
Penny Book 3.00 7.50 20.00
5777- Tweety and Sylvester, The Magic Voice, 1976, Whitman, 260 pgs.,
soft-c, flip-it feature; 5 printings 2.00 5.00 11.00
1104- Two-Gun Montana, 1936, Whitman, 432 pgs., Henry E. Vallely-a
10.00 25.00 60.00
nn- Two-Gun Montana Shoots it Out, 1939, Whitman, 36 pgs.,
2 1/2" x 3 1/2", Penny Book 10.00 25.00 60.00
1058- Ugly Duckling, The (Disney), 1939, Whitman, 68 pgs.,
5" x 5 1/2", hard-c 14.00 35.00 95.00
nn- Ugly Duckling, The, nd (1930s), np (Whitman), 36 pgs.,
3" x 2 1/2", Penny Book 4.00 10.00 22.00
Unc' Billy Gets Even (See Wee Little Books)
1114- Uncle Don's Strange Adventures, 1935, Whitman, 300 pgs.,
radio star-Uncle Don Carney 10.00 25.00 65.00
722- Uncle Ray's Story of the United States, 1934, Whitman,
300 pgs. 10.00 25.00 65.00
1461- Uncle Sam's Sky Defenders, 1941, Whitman, 432 pgs., flip pictures
10.00 25.00 60.00
1405- Uncle Wiggily's Adventures, 1946, Whitman, All Pictures Comics
12.00 30.00 85.00
1411- Union Pacific, 1939, Whitman, 240 pgs., photo-c, movie scenes
11.00 27.50 70.00
With Union Pacific letter 36.00 90.00 250.00
1189- Up Dead Horse Canyon, 1940, Saalfield, 400 pgs.
9.00 22.50 55.00
1455- Vic Sands of the U.S. Flying Fortress Bomber Squadron,
1944, Whitman, 352 pgs. 11.00 27.50 70.00
nn- Visit to Santa Claus, 1938?, Whitman, Pan Am premium by
Snow Plane; soft-c (Rare) 29.00 73.00 200.00
1645- Walt Disney's Andy Burnett on the Trail (TV Series),
1958, Whitman, 280 pgs. 4.00 10.00 27.00
803- Walt Disney's Bongo, 1948, Whitman,
hard-c, Story Hour Series 12.00 30.00 75.00
711-10-Walt Disney's Cinderella and the Magic Wand, 1950, Whitman,
2 1/2" x 5", based on Disney movie 10.00 25.00 65.00
845- Walt Disney's Donald Duck and his Cat Troubles (Disney), 1948,
Whitman, 100 pgs., 5" x 5 1/2", hard-c 12.00 30.00 75.00
845- Walt Disney's Donald Duck and the Boys, 1948, Whitman, 100 pgs.,
5" x 5 1/2", hard-c, Barks-a 21.00 52.50 150.00
2952- Walt Disney's Donald Duck in the Great Kite Maker,
1949, Whitman, 24 pgs., 3 1/4" x 4", Tiny Tales, full color (5 cents)
10.00 25.00 60.00
804- Walt Disney's Mickey and the Beanstalk, 1948, Whitman,
hard-c, Story Hour Series 12.00 30.00 75.00
845- Walt Disney's Mickey Mouse and the Boy Thursday,
194 pgs., Whitman, 5" x 5 1/2", 100 pgs. 12.00 30.00 75.00
845- Walt Disney's Mickey Mouse the Miracle Maker,
1948, Whitman, 5" x 5 1/2", 100 pgs. 12.00 30.00 75.00
2952- Walt Disney's Mickey Mouse and the Night Prowlers, Whitman, 1949,
24 pgs., 3 1/4" x 4", Tiny Tales, full color (5 ¢)10.00 25.00 60.00
5770- Walt Disney's Mickey Mouse - Mystery at Disneyland, Whitman, 1975,
260 pgs., four printings 2.00 5.00 13.00
5781-2- Walt Disney's Mickey Mouse - Mystery at Dead Man's Cove, Whitman,
1980, 260 pgs., two printings 2.00 5.00 11.00
845- Walt Disney's Minnie Mouse and the Antique Chair,
1948, Whitman, 5" x 5 1/2", 100 pgs. 12.00 30.00 75.00
1435- Walt Disney's Pinocchio and Jiminy Cricket, 1940,
Whitman, 432 pgs. 25.00 62.50 175.00
nn- Walt Disney's Pinocchio and Jiminy Cricket, Fast Action Story,
1940, Dell, 432 pgs. 36.00 90.00 250.00
845- Walt Disney's Poor Pluto, 1948, Whitman, 5" x 5 1/2",
100 pgs., hard-c 12.00 30.00 75.00
1467- Walt Disney's Pluto the Pup (Disney), 1938, Whitman,
432 pgs., Gottfredson-a 16.00 40.00 110.00
1066- Walt Disney's Story of Clarabelle Cow (Disney),
1938, Whitman, 100 pgs. 12.00 30.00 75.00
66- Walt Disney's Story of Dippy the Goof (Disney),
1938, Whitman, 100 pgs. 12.00 30.00 75.00
1066- Walt Disney's Story of Donald Duck (Disney), 1938,
Whitman, 100 pgs., hard-c, Taliaferro-a 12.00 30.00 75.00
1066- Walt Disney's Story of Goofy (Disney), 1938, Whitman, 100 pgs.,
hard-c 12.00 30.00 75.00
1066- Walt Disney's Story of Mickey Mouse (Disney), 1938, Whitman, 100
pgs., hard-c, Gottfredson-a, Donald Duck app.12.00 30.00 75.00
1066- Walt Disney's Story of Minnie Mouse (Disney),
1938, Whitman, 100 pgs., hard-c 12.00 30.00 75.00
1066- Walt Disney's Story of Pluto the Pup, (Disney),
1938, Whitman, 100 pgs., hard-c 12.00 30.00 75.00
2952- Walter Lantz Presents Andy Panda's Rescue, 1949, Whitman, Tiny
Tales, full color (5 cents) (1030-5 on back-c) 10.00 25.00 60.00
751- Wash Tubbs in Pandemonia, 1934, Whitman, 320 pgs., Roy Crane-a
12.00 30.00 75.00
nn- Wash Tubbs in Pandemonia, 1934, Whitman, 52 pgs., 4" x 5 1/2",
premium-no ads, soft-c, Roy Crane-a 20.00 50.00 140.00

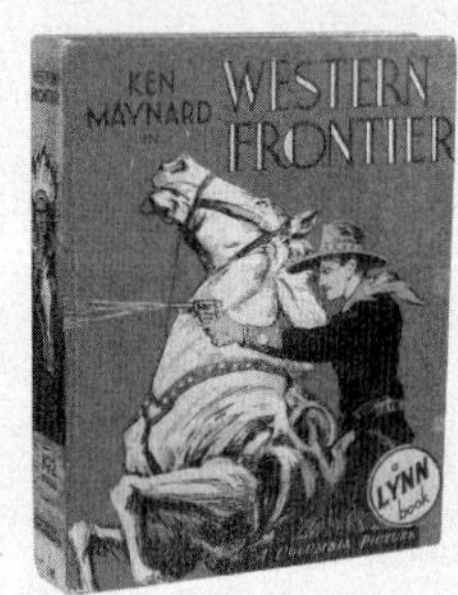

L18 - Western Frontier © LYNN

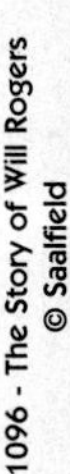

1096 - The Story of Will Rogers © Saalfield

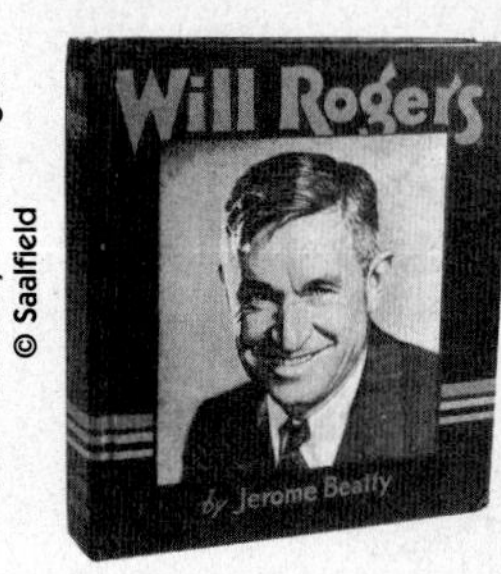

1010 - Zane Grey's King of the Royal Mounted in Arctic Law © WHIT

GD FN VF/NM

1455- Wash Tubbs and Captain Easy Hunting For Whales,
1938, Whitman, 432 pgs., Roy Crane-a 12.00 30.00 75.00

6- Wash Tubbs in Foreign Travel, 1934, Whitman, soft-c, 3 1/2" x 3 1/2",
Tarzan Ice Cream cup premium 29.00 73.00 200.00

513- Wee Little Books (In Open Box), 1934, Whitman, 44 pgs.,
small size, 6 books in set (children's classics)
(Both Red box and Green box editions exist)
Child's Garden of Verses 5.00 12.50 30.00
The Happy Prince (The Story of) 5.00 12.50 30.00
Joan of Arc (The Story of) 5.00 12.50 30.00
Peter Pan (The Story of) 5.00 12.50 30.00
Pied Piper Of Hamlin 5.00 12.50 30.00
Robin Hood (A Story of...) 5.00 12.50 30.00
Complete set with box 31.00 78.00 220.00

514- Wee Little Books (In Open Box), 1934, Whitman, 44 pgs.,
small size, 6 books in set
Jack And Jill 5.00 12.50 30.00
Little Bo-Peep 5.00 12.50 30.00
Little Tommy Tucker 5.00 12.50 30.00
Mother Goose 5.00 12.50 30.00
Old King Cole 5.00 12.50 30.00
Simple Simon 5.00 12.50 30.00
Complete set with box 33.00 83.00 230.00

518- Wee Little Books (In Open Box), 1933, Whitman, 44 pgs.,
small size, 6 books in set, written by Thornton Burgess
Betty Bear's Lesson-1930 5.00 12.50 30.00
Jimmy Skunk's Justice-1933 5.00 12.50 30.00
Little Joe Otter's Slide-1929 5.00 12.50 30.00
Peter Rabbit's Carrots-1933 5.00 12.50 30.00
Unc' Billy Gets Even-1930 5.00 12.50 30.00
Whitefoot's Secret-1933 5.00 12.50 30.00
Complete set with box 33.00 83.00 230.00

519- Wee Little Books (In Open Box) (Bible Stories), 1934, Whitman,
44 pgs., small size, 6 books in set, Helen Janes-a
The Story of David 5.00 12.50 30.00
The Story of Gideon 5.00 12.50 30.00
The Story of Daniel 5.00 12.50 30.00
The Story of Joseph 5.00 12.50 30.00
The Story of Ruth and Naomi 5.00 12.50 30.00
The Story of Moses 5.00 12.50 30.00
Complete set with box 33.00 83.00 230.00

1471- Wells Fargo, 1938, Whitman, 240 pgs., photo-c, movie scenes
12.00 30.00 80.00

L18- Western Frontier, 1935, Lynn, 192 pgs., starring Ken
Maynard, movie scenes 14.00 35.00 100.00

1121- West Pointers on the Gridiron, 1936, Saalfield, 148 pgs., hard-c,
sports book 7.00 17.50 45.00

1601- West Pointers on the Gridiron, 1936, Saalfield, 148 pgs., soft-c,
sports book 7.00 17.50 45.00

1124- West Point Five, The, 1937, Saalfield, 4 3/4" x 5 1/4", sports book,
hard-c 7.00 17.50 45.00

1604- West Point Five, The, 1937, Saalfield, 4 1/4" x 5 1/4", sports
book, soft-c 7.00 17.50 45.00

1164- West Point of the Air, 1935, Whitman, 160 pgs., photo-c,
movie scenes 12.00 30.00 75.00

18- Westward Ho!, 1935, EVW, 160 pgs., movie scenes, starring
John Wayne (Scarce) 57.00 143.00 400.00

1109- We Three, 1935, Saalfield, 160 pgs., photo-c, movie scenes, by
John Barrymore, hard-c 10.00 25.00 60.00

1589- We Three, 1935, Saalfield, 160 pgs., photo-c, movie scenes, by
John Barrymore, soft-c 10.00 25.00 60.00

Whitefoot's Secret (See Wee Little Books)

nn- Who's Afraid of the Big Bad Wolf, "Three Little Pigs" (Disney), 1933,
McKay, 36 pgs., 6" x 8 1/2", stiff-c, Disney studio-a
27.00 68.00 190.00

nn- Wild West Adventures of Buffalo Bill, 1935, Whitman, 260 pgs.,
Cocomalt premium, soft-c, Hal Arbo-a 12.00 30.00 80.00

1096- Will Rogers, The Story of, 1935, Saalfield, photo-hard-c
8.00 20.00 50.00

1576- Will Rogers, The Story of, 1935, Saalfield, photo-soft-c
8.00 20.00 50.00

1458- Wimpy the Hamburger Eater, 1938, Whitman, 432 pgs., E.C. Segar-a
14.00 35.00 100.00

1433- Windy Wayne and His Flying Wing, 1942, Whitman, 432 pgs.,
flip pictures 10.00 25.00 60.00

1131- Winged Four, The, 1937, Saalfield, sports book, hard-c
10.00 25.00 60.00

1407- Wings of the U.S.A., 1940, Whitman, 432 pgs., Thomas Hickey-a
10.00 25.00 60.00

nn- Winning of the Old Northwest, The, 1934, World Syndicate, High
Lights of History Series, full color-c 10.00 25.00 60.00

nn- Winning of the Old Northwest, The, 1934, World Syndicate, High
Lights of History Series; red & silver-c 10.00 25.00 60.00

1122- Winning Point, The, 1936, Saalfield, (Football), hard-c
7.00 17.50 40.00

1602- Winning Point, The, 1936, Saalfield, soft-c 7.00 17.50 40.00

nn- Wizard of Oz Waddle Book, 1934, BRP, 20 pgs., 7 1/2" x 10",
forerunner of the Blue Ribbon Pop-Up books; with 6 removable
articulated cardboard characters. Book only 54.00 135.00 375.00
Dust jacket only61.00 153.00 490.00
Near Mint Complete - $12,500

710-10-Woody Woodpecker Big Game Hunter, 1950, Whitman,
by Walter Lantz 9.00 22.50 55.00

2010-(#10)-Woody Woodpecker-The Meteor Menace, 1967, Whitman,
260 pgs., 39¢-c, hard-c, color illos. 4.00 10.00 27.00

5753- Woody Woodpecker-The Meteor Menace, 1973, Whitman,
260 pgs., no price, soft-c, color illos. 1.00 2.50 6.00

2028- Woody Woodpecker-The Sinister Signal, 1969, Whitman
4.00 10.00 22.00

5763- Woody Woodpecker-The Sinister Signal, 1974, Whitman,
1st printing-no price; 2nd printing-39¢-c 1.00 2.50 6.00

23- World of Monsters, The, 1935, EVW, Five Star Library,
movie scenes 12.00 30.00 85.00

779- World War in Photographs, The, 1934, Whitman, photo-c,
photo illus. 9.00 22.50 55.00

Wyatt Earp (See Hugh O'Brian ...)

nn- Xena - Warrior Princess, 1998, Chronicle Books, 310 pgs.,
based on TV series, 1-color (purple) illos 1.00 2.50 9.00

nn- Yogi Bear Goes Country & Western, 1977, Modern Promotions,
244 pgs., 49 cents, soft-c, flip pictures 2.00 5.00 13.00

nn- Yogi Bear Saves Jellystone Park, 1977, Modern Promotions,
244 pgs., 49 cents, soft-c, flip pictures 2.00 5.00 13.00

nn- Zane Grey's Cowboys of the West, 1935, Whitman, 148 pgs.,
3 3/4" x 4", Tarzan Ice Cream Cup premium, soft-c,
Arbo-a 29.00 73.00 200.00

Zane Grey's King of the Royal Mounted (See Men of the Mounted)

1010- Zane Grey's King of the Royal Mounted in Arctic Law, 1937,
Whitman, 7 1/4" x 5 1/2", 64 pgs., Nickel Book12.00 30.00 75.00

1103- Zane Grey's King of the Royal Mounted, 1936, Whitman,
432 pgs. 10.00 25.00 65.00

nn- Zane Grey's King of the Royal Mounted, 1935, Whitman,
260 pgs., Cocomalt premium, soft-c 12.00 30.00 85.00

**1179- Zane Grey's King of the Royal Mounted and the Northern
Treasure**, 1937, Whitman, 432 pgs. 10.00 25.00 60.00

1405- Zane Grey's King of the Royal Mounted the Long Arm of the Law,
1942, Whitman, All Pictures Comics 10.00 25.00 60.00

1452- Zane Grey's King of the Royal Mounted Gets His Man,
1938, Whitman, 432 pgs. 10.00 25.00 60.00

**1486- Zane Grey's King of the Royal Mounted and the Great Jewel
Mystery**, 1939, Whitman, 432 pgs. 10.00 25.00 60.00

5- Zane Grey's King of the Royal Mounted in the Far North, 1938,
Whitman, 132 pgs., Buddy Book, soft-c (Rare)36.00 90.00 250.00

nn- Zane Grey's King of the Royal Mounted in Law of the North, 1939,
Whitman, 36 pgs., 2 1/2" x 3 1/2", Penny Book7.00 17.50 45.00

nn- Zane Grey's King of the Royal Mounted Policing the Frozen North,
1938, Dell, 196 pgs., Fast-Action Story, soft-c18.00 45.00 125.00

1440- Zane Grey's Tex Thorne Comes Out of the West,
1937, Whitman, 432 pgs. 10.00 25.00 60.00

1465- Zip Saunders King of the Speedway, 1939, 432 pgs.,
Weisman-a 10.00 25.00 60.00

THE MARKETING OF A MEDIUM

by Dr. Arnold T. Blumberg, DCD

with new material and additional research by Sol M. Davidson, PhD, and Robert L. Beerbohm

Everyone wants something for free. It's in our nature to look for the quick fix, the good deal, the complimentary gift. We long to hit the lottery and quit our job, to win the trip around the world, or find that pot of gold at the end of the proverbial rainbow. Collectors in particular are certainly built to appreciate the notion of the "free gift," since it not only means a new item to collect and enjoy, but no risk or obligation in order to acquire it.

Ah, but there's the rub. Because things are not always what they seem, and "free gifts" usually come with a price. As the saying goes, "there's no such thing as a free lunch," so if it seems too good to be true, it probably is. This is the case even in the world of comics, where premiums and giveaways have a familiar agenda hidden behind the bright colors and fanciful stories. But where did it all begin?

Some of the earliest characters that were used as successful tools in promotional comics were Palmer Cox's creation "The Brownies." The illustration shown here showcases them drinking and endorsing Seal Brand Coffee.

EXTRA EXTRA

As we learn more about the early history of the comic book industry through continual investigation and the publishing of articles like those regularly featured in this book, we gain a much greater understanding of the financial and creative forces at work in shaping the medium, but perhaps one of the most intriguing and least recognized factors that influenced the dawn of comics is the concept of the premium or giveaway. (Note: Some of the historical information referenced in this article is derived from material also presented in Robert L. Beerbohm's introductory article to the Platinum Age section.)

The birth of the comic book as we know it today is intimately connected with the development of the comic strip in American newspapers and their use as an advertising and marketing tool for staple products such as bread, milk, and cereal. From the very beginning, comic characters have played several roles in pop culture, entertaining the youth of the country while also (sometimes none too subtly) acting as hucksters for whatever corporation foots the bill. From important staples to frivolous material produced simply to make a buck, these products have utilized the comics medium to sell, sell, sell. And what better way to hook a prospective customer than to give them "something for nothing?"

Starting in the 1850s, comics were being used in free almanacs such as **Elton's**, **Hostetter's** and **Wright's** to lure readers for the little booklets to sell patent medicine, farm products, tobacco, shoe polish, etc. Most of these are exceedingly rare today, hence it is difficult to compile an accurate history. More mention of these early precursors can be found in the Victorian Comics Era essay following this one. But although comic characters themselves were already being aggressively merchandised all around the world by the mid-1890s--as with, for example, Palmer Cox's **The Brownies**--the real starting point for the success of comics as a giveaway marketing mechanism can be traced to the introduction of **The Yellow Kid**, Richard Outcault's now legendary newspaper strip.

Newspaper publishers had already recognized that comic strips could boost circulation as well as please sponsors and advertisers by drawing more eyes to the page, so Sunday "supplements" were introduced to entice fans. Outcault's creation cemented the theory with proof of comic characters' marketing and merchandising power.

This unused cover was designed as the second cover for "Motion Picture Funnies Weekly." While the concept for this promotional comic title never caught on, the inaugural issue did feature the origin and first printed appearance of the Sub-Mariner.

Soon after, Outcault (who had most likely been inspired by Cox's merchandising success with **The Brownies** in the first place) caught lightning in a bottle once more with **Buster Brown**, who has the distinction of being America's first nationally licensed comic strip character. Soon, comic strips proliferated throughout the nation's newspapers as tycoons like Hearst and Pulitzer recognized the drawing power of the new medium and fought circulation wars to capture the pennies of the nouveau readership. They paid exorbitant salaries to comic strip artists such as Rudolph Dirks (**Katzenjammer Kids**), and used the funnies as newspaper supplements and as premiums to attract readers. Corporations soon had the chance to license recognizable personas as their own personal pitchmen (or women or animals...). Comic character merchandise wasn't far behind, resulting in a boom of future collectibles now catalogued in volumes like **Hake's Price Guide to Character Toys**.

TWO BIRTHS FOR THE PRICE OF ONE

Comic books themselves were at the heart of this movement, and giveaway and premium collections of comic strips not only appealed to children and adults alike, but provided the impetus for the birth of the modern comic book format itself. It could be said that without the concept of the giveaway comic or the marketing push behind it, there would be no comic book industry as we have it today. Well-known now is the story of how in spring 1933 Harry Wildenberg of Eastern Color Printing Company convinced Proctor & Gamble to sponsor the first modern comic book, **Funnies on Parade**, as a premium. Its success led to the first continuing comic book, **Famous Funnies**, and the rest, as they say, is history.

In 1935, while working on the printing presses of Eastern Color developing how modern comic books get printed, Juliun J. Proskauer came up with an idea for printing "Comic-Books-For-Industry." In July 1936 he made his first sale through his newly formed William C. Popper & Co. to David M. Davies, then advertising manager for Seagram's Distillers Corp. for three million copies of **Seagram's Merrymakers** in time for the 1936-37 Christmas season. "Thus was a new industry born," wrote **Printing News** in August 1945.

Even a casual perusal of the listings in this section of the Guide will dazzle the reader with the endless variety of purposes that this medium has served. Yes, promos have been used to hawk products from athletic equipment to zithers and zip codes, but comics are too versatile an art form to be confined to a few uses. They've swayed elections in cities (**The O'Dwyer Story**, 1949), in states (**Giant for a Day**: Jacob Javits, 1946) and nationwide (**The Story of Harry Truman**, 1948); solicited for charities (**Donald Duck and the Red Feather**, 1948); addressed health issues (**Blondie**, 1949, mental hygiene); discouraged kids from smoking (**Captain America Meets the Asthma Monster**, 1987); coached youngsters in sports skills (**Circling the Bases**, 1947, A.G. Spaulding); explained scientific complexities (**Adventures in Science**, 1946-61, GE); pleaded for social justice (**Consumer Comics**, 1975); espoused religious causes (**Oral Roberts' True Stories**, 1950s); protected the environment (**Our Spaceship Earth**, 1947); encouraged tourism (**Wyoming, The Cowboy State**, 1954); conveyed a sense of history (**Louisiana Purchase**, 1953); taught about computers (**Superman Radio Shack Giveaway**, 1980); trained employees (**Dial Finance Dialogues**, 1961-70) and executives (**Beneficial Finance System, Managing New Employees**, 1950s); cautioned safety (**Willy Wing Flap**, 1944(?)); announced corporate annual results (**Motorola Annual Report**, 1952); defended free enterprise (**Steve Merritt**, 1949); hammered communism (**How Stalin Hopes to Destroy America**, 1951); fought discrimination (**Mammy Yokum & the Great Dogpatch Mystery**, 1956, B'nai Brith); aided young workers in job-hunting (**The Job Scene**, 1969); battled the scourge of sickle cell anemia (**Where's Herbie**, 1972, U.S. H.E.W.); inspired the overcoming of adversity (**Al Capp by Li'l Abner**, 1946); fostered reading (**Linus Gets a Library Card**, 1960); recruited for the armed forces (**Li'l Abner Joins the Navy**, 1950); beguiled readers into learning languages (**Blondie**, 1949, Philadelphia public schools); and even instructed in such delicate matters as birth control

Every market and product has been on the promotional comic book bandwagon. Freihofer's Baking Company distributed a comic in the 1940s that featured reprinted pages from "All-American Comics."

(**Escape from Fear**, 1950 (revised 1959, etc.), for Planned Parenthood).

READ ALL ABOUT IT

The impact of this new approach to advertising was not lost on the business world. Contrary to modern belief, comic books were hardly discounted by the adults of the time...at least not those who had the marketing savvy to recognize an opportunity - or a threat - when they saw one. In the April 1933 issue of **Fortune** magazine, an article titled "The Funny Papers" trumpeted the arrival of comics as a force to be reckoned with in the world of advertising and business, and what's more, a force to fear as well. At first providing a brief survey of the newspaper comic strip business (which for many of the magazine's readers must have seemed a foreign topic for serious discussion), the article goes on to examine the incredible financial draw of comics and their characters:

"Between 70 and 75 per cent {sic} of the readers of any newspaper follow its comic sections regularly...Even the advertiser has succumbed to the comic, and in 1932 spent well over $1,000,000 for comic-paper space."

"**Comic Weekly** is the comic section of seventeen Hearst Sunday papers...Advertisers who market their wares through balloon-speaking manikins {sic} may enjoy the proximity of Jiggs, Maggie, Barney Google, and other funny Hearst headliners."

Although the article continues to cast the notion of relying on comic strip material to sell product in a negative light, actually suggesting that advertisers who utilize comics are violating unspoken rules of "advertising decorum" and bringing themselves "down to the level" of comics (and since when have advertisers been stalwart preservers of good taste and high moral standards), there is no doubt that they are viewing comics in a new light. The comic characters have arrived by 1933...and they're ready to help sell your merchandise too.

Fortune wasn't the only one to take notice as World War II came and went. In 1948, Louis P. Birk, the head of Brevity, Inc., an important promotional comics publisher said, "Comics are serious business." In an article in **Printers' Ink** magazine, he estimated that more than 80 different "comic booklets" had been produced and more than 45,000,000 million copies distributed in the five years before 1948. But of course, comics were serious business long before businessman/historian Birk noted the fact for posterity.

THE MARCH OF WAR AND BEYOND

Through the relentless currents of time, comic strips, books, and the characters that starred in them became more and more an intrinsic part of American culture. During the turmoil of the Great Depression and World War II, comic characters in print and celluloid form entertained while informing and selling at the same time, and premium and giveaway comics came well and truly into their own, pushing everything from loaves of bread to war bonds.

In the 1950s and '60s, there was a shift in focus as the power of giveaway and premium comics was applied to more altruistic endeavors than simply selling something. Comic book format pamphlets, fully illustrated and often inventively written, taught children about banking, money, the dangers of poison and other household products, and even chronicled moments in American history. The comic book as giveaway was now not only a marketing gimmick--it was a tool for educating as well.

The promotional title "March of Comics" was a prolific comic that ran for 36 years and 488 issues featuring a variety of subjects and characters. (#20 shown)

The 1970s and '80s saw another boom in premium and giveaway comics. Every product imaginable seemed to have a licensing deal with a comic book character, usually one of the prominent flag bearers of the Big Two, Marvel or DC. Spider-Man fought bravely against the Beetle for the benefit of All Detergent; Captain America allied himself with the Campbell Kids; and Superman helped a class of computer students beat a disaster-conjuring foe at his own game with the help of Radio Shack Tandy computers.

Newspapers rediscovered the power of comics, not just with enlarged strip supplements but with actual comic books. Spider-Man, the Hulk, and others turned up as giveaway comic extras in various American newspapers (including Chicago and Dallas publications), while a whole series of public information comics like those produced decades earlier used superheroes to caution children about the dangers of smoking, drugs, and child abuse.

Comics also turned up in a plethora of other toy products as the 1980s introduced kids to the joy of electronic games and action figures. Supplementary comics provided "free" with action figure and video game packages told the backstory about the product, adding depth to the play experience while providing an extra incentive to buy. Comics became an intrinsic part of the Atari line of video cartridges, for example, eventually spawning its own full-blown newsstand series as well.

As the twentieth century gave way to the twenty-first, giveaway comics were still being produced for inclusion in action figure and video game packages, as well as in conjunction with countless consumer items and corporations. It seems that the medium still has a lot to offer for all those companies desperate to make the most of their market share.

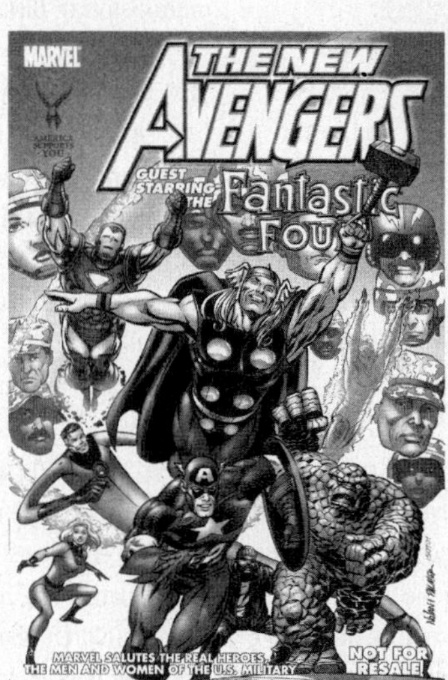

Today, promotional comics continue to be used as a marketing tool to reach both children and adults alike. This 2005 comic was produced by Marvel Comics as a salute to the men and women of the armed forces.

A COMIC BY ANY OTHER NAME

One of the earliest names for promotional comics was "special purpose comics." In their pursuit of superheroes, collectors have allowed promotional comics to lie fallow - underappreciated and uncollected. Without a legitimate name, these products were given sundry other appellations - industrial comics, promos, giveaways, premiums, promics - each accurate but only for a small segment of the unorganized but lusty and lively medium. Perhaps no one name can cover all the variations and purposes of this branch of comic art, but for practical reasons if we accept the general premise that these comics were created to promote an idea, a product or a person, then "Promotional Comics" is probably as convenient a catch-all title as we can come up with.

We used the phrase "for practical reasons" because the word "practical" goes to the heart of promotional comics more than it does for any other comics product. What greater testimony is there to the medium's impact on American culture than to note their use by hard-headed, profit-minded business people and corporations? They invest their money and they expect results.

Today, premium comics continue to thrive and are still utilized as a valuable marketing and promotional tool. "Free" comics are still packaged with action figures and video games, and offered as mail-away premiums from a variety of product manufacturers. The comic industry itself has expanded its use of giveaway comics to self-promote as well, with "ash-can" and other giveaway editions turning up at conventions and comic shops to advertise upcoming series and special events. Many of these function as old-fashioned premiums, with a coupon or other response required from the reader to receive the comic.

As for the supplements and giveaways printed all those years ago, they have spawned a collectible fervor all their own, thanks to their atypical distribution and frequent rarity. For that and the desire to delve deeper into comics history, we hope that by focusing more directly on this genre, we can enhance our understanding of this vital component in the development and history of the modern comic book.

Whether you're a collector or not, we're all motivated by that desire to get something for nothing. For as long as consumers are enticed by the notion of the "free gift," promotional comics will remain a vital marketing component in many business models, but they will also continue to fight the stigma that has long been associated with the industry as a whole. "Respectable" sources like **Fortune** may have taken notice of the power of comic-related advertising 71 years ago, but after all this time comics still fight an uphill battle to establish some measure of dignity for the medium. Perhaps the higher visibility of promotional comics will eventually prove to be a deciding factor in that intellectual war.

See ya in the funny papers.

Action Comics #1 USPS © DC

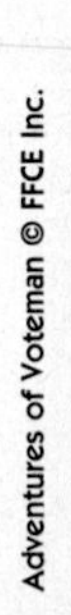

Adventures of Voteman © FFCE Inc.

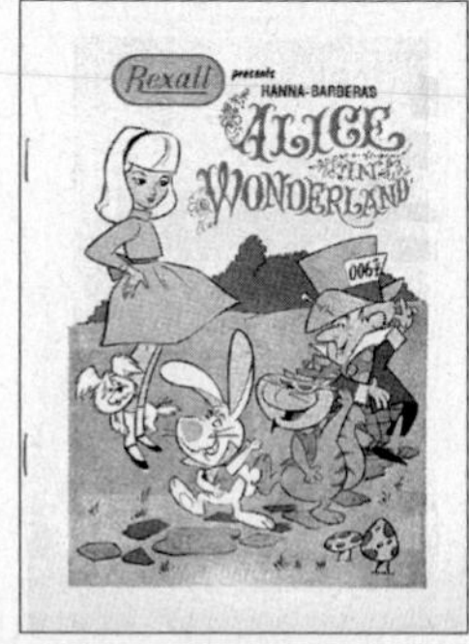

Alice in Wonderland Rexall © H-B

	GD 2.0	VG 4.0	FN 6.0	VF 8.0	VF/NM 9.0	NM- 9.2

ACTION COMICS
DC Comics: 1947 - 1998 (Giveaway)

1 (1976) paper cover w/10¢ price, 16 pgs. in color; reprints complete Superman story from #1 ('38) 4 8 12 27 44 60
1 (1976) Safeguard Giveaway; paper cover w/"free", 16 pgs. in color; reprints complete Superman story from #1 ('38) 4 8 12 27 44 60
1 (1983) paper cover w/10¢ price, 16 pgs. in color; reprints complete Superman story from #1 ('38) 3 6 9 15 22 28
1 (1987 Nestle Quik; 1988, 50¢) 2 4 6 8 10 12
1 (1992)-Came w/Reign of Superman packs 4.00
1 (1998 U.S. Postal Service, $7.95) Reprints entire issue; extra outer half-cover contains First Day Issuance of 32¢ Superman stamp with Sept. 10, 1998 Cleveland, OH postmark 1 2 3 5 6 8
Theater (1947, 32 pgs., 5" x 7", nn)-Vigilante story based on Columbia Vigilante serial; no Superman-c or story 71 142 213 454 777 1100

ACTION ZONE
CBS Television: 1994 (Promotes CBS Saturday morning cartoons)

1-WildC.A.T.s, T.M.N.Turtles, Skeleton Warriors stories; Jim Lee-c 4.00

ADVENTURE COMICS
IGA: No date (early 1940s) (Paper-c, 32 pgs.)

Two diff. issues; Super-Mystery-r from 1941 21 42 63 122 199 275

ADVENTURE IN DISNEYLAND
Walt Disney Productions (Dist. by Richfield Oil): May, 1955 (Giveaway, soft-c., 16 pgs)

nn 11 22 33 60 83 105

ADVENTURES @ EBAY
eBay: 2000 (6 3/4" x 4 1/2", 16 pgs.)

1-Judd Winick-a/Rucka & Van Meter-s; intro to eBay comic buying 2.50

ADVENTURES IN JET POWER
General Electric: 1950

nn 8 16 24 40 50 60

ADVENTURES OF BIG BOY (Also titled Adventures of the Big Boy)
Timely Comics/Webs Adv. Corp./Illus. Features: 1956 - Present (Giveaway) (East & West editions of early issues)

1-Everett-c/a 116 232 348 742 1271 1800
2-Everett-c/a 47 94 141 296 498 700
3-5: 4-Robot-c 20 40 60 118 192 265
6-10: 6-Sci/fic issue 10 20 30 64 132 200
11-20: 11,13-DeCarlo-a 6 12 18 41 76 110
21-30 4 8 12 27 44 60
31-50 3 6 9 17 26 35
51-100 2 4 6 9 13 16
101-150 2 4 6 8 10 12
151-240: 239-Wizard of Oz parody-c 1 2 3 5 7 9
241-265,267-269,271-300: 6.00
266-Superman x-over 3 6 9 17 26 35
270-TV's Buck Rogers-c/s 3 6 9 14 20 25
301-400 4.00
401-500 3.00
1-(2nd series - '76-'84,Paragon Prod.) (...Shoney's Big Boy) 1 3 4 6 8 10
2-20 5.00
21-50 3.00
Summer, 1959 issue, large size 7 14 21 44 82 120

ADVENTURES OF G. I. JOE
1969 (3-1/4x7") (20 & 16 pgs.)

First Series: 1-Danger of the Depths. 2-Perilous Rescue. 3-Secret Mission to Spy Island. 4-Mysterious Explosion. 5-Fantastic Free Fall. 6-Eight Ropes of Danger. 7-Mouth of Doom. 8-Hidden Missile Discovery. 9-Space Walk Mystery. 10-Fight for Survival. 11-The Shark's Surprise.
Second Series: 2-Flying Space Adventure. 4-White Tiger Hunt. 7-Capture of the Pygmy Gorilla. 12-Secret of the Mummy's Tomb.
Third Series: Reprinted surviving titles of First Series. Fourth Series: 13-Adventure Team Headquarters. 14-Search For the Stolen Idol.
each.... 3 6 9 17 26 35

ADVENTURES OF JELL-O MAN AND WOBBLY, THE
Welsh Publishing Group: 1991 ($1.25)

1 4.00

ADVENTURES OF KOOL-AID MAN
Marvel Comics: 1983 - No. 3, 1985 (Mail order giveaway)
Archie Comics: No. 4, 1987 - No. 8, 1989

1-8: 4-8-Dan DeCarlo-a/c 1 2 3 5 7 9

ADVENTURES OF MARGARET O'BRIEN, THE
Bambury Fashions (Clothes): 1947 (20 pgs. in color, slick-c, regular size) (Premium)

In "The Big City" movie adaptation (scarce) 20 40 60 120 195 270

ADVENTURES OF QUIK BUNNY
Nestle's Quik: 1984 (Giveaway, 32 pgs.)

nn-Spider-Man app. 2 4 6 9 13 16

ADVENTURES OF STUBBY, SANTA'S SMALLEST REINDEER, THE
W. T. Grant Co.: nd (early 1940s) (Giveaway, 12 pgs.)

nn 8 16 24 42 54 65

ADVENTURES OF VOTEMAN, THE
Foundation For Citizen Education Inc.: 1968

nn 4 8 12 27 44 60

ADVENTURES WITH SANTA CLAUS
Promotional Publ. Co. (Murphy's Store): No date (early 50's) (9-3/4x 6-3/4", 24 pgs., giveaway, paper-c)

nn-Contains 8 pgs. ads 6 12 18 31 38 45
16 pg. version 7 14 21 35 43 50

AIR POWER (CBS TV & the U.S. Air Force Presents)
Prudential Insurance Co.: 1956 (5-1/4x7-1/4", 32 pgs., giveaway, soft-c)

nn-Toth-a? Based on 'You Are There' TV program by Walter Cronkite 10 20 30 56 76 95

ALASKA BUSH PILOT
Jan Enterprises: 1959 (Paper cover, 10¢)

1-Promotes Bush Pilot Club (A 9.4 sold for $62 in 2014)
NOTE: *A CGC certified 9.9 Mint sold for $632.50 in 2005.*

ALICE IN BLUNDERLAND
Industrial Services: 1952 (Paper cover, 16 pgs. in color)

nn-Facts about government waste and inefficiency 15 30 45 86 133 180

ALICE IN WONDERLAND
Western Printing Company/Whitman Publ. Co.: 1965; 1969; 1982

Meets Santa Claus(1950s), nd, 16 pgs. 6 12 18 28 34 40
Rexall Giveaway(1965, 16 pgs., 5x7-1/4) Western Printing (TV, Hanna-Barbera) 3 6 9 16 23 30
Wonder Bakery Giveaway(1969, 16 pgs, color, nn, nd) (Continental Baking Company) 3 6 9 15 22 28

ALICE IN WONDERLAND MEETS SANTA
No publisher: nd (6-5/8x9-11/16", 16 pgs., giveaway, paper-c)

nn 9 18 27 50 65 80

ALL ABOARD, MR. LINCOLN
Assoc. of American Railroads: Jan, 1959 (16 pgs.)

nn-Abraham Lincoln and the Railroads 6 12 18 28 34 40

ALL NEW COMICS
Harvey Comics: Oct, 1993 (Giveaway, no cover price, 16 pgs.)(Hanna-Barbera)

1-Flintstones, Scooby Doo, Jetsons, Yogi Bear & Wacky Races previews for upcoming Harvey's new Hanna-Barbera line-up 1 2 3 4 5 7
NOTE: *Material previewed in Harvey giveaway was eventually published by Archie.*

AMAZING SPIDER-MAN, THE
Marvel Comics Group

Acme & Dingo Children's Boots (1980)-Spider-Woman app. 2 4 6 11 16 20
Adventures in Reading Starring... (1990,1991) Bogdanove & Romita-c/a 5.00
Aim Toothpaste Giveaway (36 pgs., reg. size)-1 pg. origin recap; Green Goblin-c/story 2 4 6 10 14 18
Aim Toothpaste Giveaway (16 pgs., reg. size)-Dr. Octopus app. 2 4 6 10 14 18
All Detergent Giveaway (1979, 36 pgs.), nn-Origin-r 2 4 6 10 14 18
Amazing Fantasy #15 (8/02) reprint included in Spider-Man DVD Collector's Gift Set 5.00
Amazing Fantasy #15 (2006) News America Marketing newspaper giveaway 4.00
Amazing Spider-Man nn (1990, 6-1/8x9", 28 pgs.)-Shan-Lon giveaway; retells origin of Spider-Man; Bagley-a/Saviuk-c 2 4 6 8 10 12
Amazing Spider-Man nn (1990, 6-1/8x9", 28 pgs.)-Shan-Lon giveaway; reprints Amazing Spider-Man #303 w/McFarlane-c/a 2 4 6 8 10 12

Archie FCBD 2003 © AP

Archie Your Official Store Club Magazine © AP

Atari Force #4 © Atari

	GD 2.0	VG 4.0	FN 6.0	VF 8.0	VF/NM 9.0	NM- 9.2

Amazing Spider-Man #1 Reprint (1990, 4-1/4x6-1/4", 28 pgs.)-Packaged with the book "Start Collecting Comic Books" from Running Press 4.00
Amazing Spider-Man #3 Reprint (2004)-Best Buy/Sony giveaway 2.50
Amazing Spider-Man #50 (Sony Pictures Edition) (8/04)-mini-comic included in Spider-Man 2 movie DVD Collector's Gift Set; r/#50 & various ASM covers with Dr. Octopus 2.50
Amazing Spider-Man #129 (Lion Gate Films) (6/04)-promotional comic given away at movie theaters on opening night for The Punisher 2.50
...& Power Pack (1984, nn)(Nat'l Committee for Prevention of Child Abuse) (two versions, mail offer & store giveaway)-Mooney-a; Byrne-c
Mail offer 2 4 6 9 11 14
Store giveaway 5.00
...& The Hulk (Special Edition)(6/8/80; 20 pgs.)-Supplement to Chicago Tribune 2 4 6 10 14 18
...& The Incredible Hulk (1981, 1982; 36 pgs.)-Sanger Harris or May D&F supplement to Dallas Times, Dallas Herald, Denver Post, Kansas City Star, Tulsa World; Foley's supplement to Houston Chronicle (1982, 16 pgs.)- "Great Rodeo Robbery"; The Jones Store-giveaway (1983, 16 pgs.) 2 4 6 13 18 22
...and the New Mutants Featuring Skids nn (National Committee for Prevention of Child Abuse/K-Mart giveaway)-Williams-c(i) 5.00
... Battles Ignorance (1992)(Sylvan Learning Systems) giveaway; Mad Thinker app. Kupperberg-a 1 2 3 5 7 9
...Captain America, The Incredible Hulk, & Spider-Woman (1981) (7-11 Stores giveaway; 36 pgs.) 2 4 6 11 16 20
...: Christmas in Dallas (1983) (Supplement to Dallas Times Herald) giveaway 2 4 6 11 16 20
...: Danger in Dallas (1983) (Supplement to Dallas Times Herald) giveaway 2 4 6 11 16 20
...: Danger in Denver (1983) (Supplement to Denver Post) giveaway for May D&F stores 2 4 6 11 16 20
..., Fire-Star, And Ice-Man at the Dallas Ballet Nutcracker (1983; supplement to Dallas Times Herald)-Mooney-p 2 4 6 11 16 20
Giveaway-Esquire Magazine (2/69)-Miniature-Still attached (scarce) 12 24 36 83 182 280
Giveaway-Eye Magazine (2/69)-Miniature-Still attached 9 18 27 60 120 180
...: Riot at Robotworld (1991; 16 pgs.)(National Action Council for Minorities in Engineering, Inc.) giveaway; Saviuk-c 1 2 3 5 6 8
..., Storm & Powerman (1982; 20 pgs.)(American Cancer Society) giveaway; also a 1991 2nd printing and a 1994 printing 1 2 3 5 6 8
...Vs. The Hulk (Special Edition; 1979, 20 pgs.)(Supplement to Columbus Dispatch) 2 4 6 13 18 22
...Vs. The Prodigy (Giveaway, 16 pgs. in color (1976, 5x6-1/2")-Sex education; (1 million printed; 35-50¢) 2 4 6 8 10 12
Spidey & The Mini-Marvels Halloween 2003 Ashcan (12/03, 8 1/2"x 5 1/2") Giarusso-s/a; Venom and Green Goblin app. 2.00

AMERICA MENACED!
Vital Publications: 1950 (Paper-c)
nn-Anti-communism 39 78 117 236 388 540

AMERICAN COMICS
Theatre Giveaways (Liberty Theatre, Grand Rapids, Mich. known): 1940's
Many possible combinations. "Golden Age" superhero comics with new cover added and given away at theaters. Following known: Superman #59, Capt. Marvel #20, 21, Capt. Marvel Jr. #5, Action #33, Classics Comics #8, Whiz #39. Value would vary with book and should be 70-80 percent of the original.

AMERICA UNDER SOCIALISM
National Research Bureau: 1950 (Paper-c)
nn-Anti-communism; 16 pages (a VG copy sold for $806 in 2016)

ANDY HARDY COMICS
Western Printing Co.:
...& the New Automatic Gas Clothes Dryer (1952, 5x7-1/4", 16 pgs.) Bendix Giveaway (soft-c) 6 12 18 31 38 45

ANIMANIACS EMERGENCY WORLD
DC Comics: 1995
nn-American Red Cross 5.00

APACHE HUNTER
Creative Pictorials: 1954 (18 pgs. in color) (promo copy) (saddle stitched)
nn-Severin, Heath stories 15 30 45 85 130 175

AQUATEERS MEET THE SUPER FRIENDS
DC Comics: 1979
nn 2 4 6 11 16 20

ARCHIE AND HIS GANG (Zeta Beta Tau Presents...)
Archie Publications: Dec. 1950 (St. Louis National Convention giveaway)
nn-Contains new cover stapled over Archie Comics #47 (11-12/50) on inside; produced for Zeta Beta Tau 27 54 81 160 263 365

ARCHIE COMICS (Also see Sabrina)
Archie Publications
... And Friends and the Shield (10/02, 8 1/2"x 5 1/2") Diamond Comic Dist. 4.00
... And Friends - A Halloween Tale (10/98, 8 1/2"x 5 1/2") Diamond Comic Dist.; Sabrina and Sonic app.; Dan DeCarlo-a 4.00
... And Friends - A Timely Tale (10/01, 8 1/2"x 5 1/2") Diamond Comic Dist. 4.00
... And Friends Monster Bash 2003 (8 1/2"x 5 1/2") Diamond Comic Dist. Halloween 4.00
...And His Friends Help Raise Literacy Awareness In Mississippi nn (3/94) 1 2 3 5 6 8
...And His Friends Vs. The Household Toxic Wastes nn (1993, 16 pgs.) produced for the San Diego Regional Household Hazardous Materials Program 1 2 3 5 6 8
...And His Pals in the Peer Helping Program nn (2/91, 7"x4 1/2") produced by the FBI 1 2 3 5 6 8
...And the History of Electronics nn (5/90, 36 pgs.)-Radio Shack giveaway; Bender-c/a 1 2 3 5 6 8
Fairmont Potato Chips Giveaway-Mini comics 1970 (6 issues-nn's.,6 7/8" x 2 1/4", 8 pgs. each) 3 6 9 18 28 38
Fairmont Potato Chips Giveaway-Mini comics 1971 (4 issues-nn's.,6 7/8" x 5", 8 pgs. each) 3 6 9 18 28 38
Little Archie, The House That Wouldn't Move ('07, 8-1/2" x 5-3/8" Halloween mini-comic) 2.00
...'s Ham Radio Adventure (1997) Morse code instruction; Goldberg-a 6.00
...'s Weird Mysteries (9/99, 8 1/2"x 5 1/2") Diamond Comic Dist. Halloween giveaway 3.00
Tales From Riverdale (2006, 8 1/2"x 5 1/2") Diamond Comic Dist. Halloween giveaway 3.00
...: The Dawn of Time ('10, 8-1/2" x 5-3/8" Halloween mini-comic) 3.00
...: The Mystery of the Museum Sleep-In ('08, 8-1/2" x 5-3/8" Halloween mini-comic) 3.00
... Your Official Store Club Magazine nn (10/48, 9-1/2x6-1/2, 16 pgs.)- "Wolf Whistle" Archie on front-c; B. R. Baker Co. ad on back-c (a CGC 7.5 copy sold for $1912 in Feb. 2013)

ARCHIE SHOE-STORE GIVEAWAY
Archie Publications: 1944-50 (12-15 pgs. of games, puzzles, stories like Superman-Tim books, No nos. - came out monthly)

	GD 2.0	VG 4.0	FN 6.0	VF 8.0	VF/NM 9.0	NM- 9.2
(1944-47)-issues	24	48	72	140	230	320
2/48-Peggy Lee photo-c	24	48	72	140	230	320
3/48-Marylee Robb photo-c	20	40	60	117	189	260
4/48-Gloria De Haven photo-c	24	48	72	140	230	320
5/48, 6/48, 7/48, 10/48	20	40	60	117	189	260
8/48-Story on Shirley Temple	25	50	75	147	241	335
5/49-Kathleen Hughes photo-c	20	40	60	114	182	250
6/49, 7/49, 9/49	18	36	54	103	162	220
8/49-Archie photo-c from radio show	29	58	87	170	278	385
10/49-Gloria Mann photo-c from radio show	21	42	63	126	206	285
11/49, 12/49, 2/50, 3/50	20	40	60	115	185	255

ARCHIE'S JOKE BOOK MAGAZINE (See Joke Book ...)
Archie Publications
Drug Store Giveaway (No. 39 w/new-c) 8 16 24 44 57 70

ARCHIE'S TEN ISSUE COLLECTOR'S SET (Title inside of cover only)
Archie Publications: June, 1997 - No. 10, June, 1997 ($1.50, 20 pgs.)
1-10: 1,7-Archie. 2,8-Betty & Veronica. 3,9-Veronica. 4-Betty. 5-World of Archie. 6-Jughead. 10-Archie and Friends each... 5.00

ASTRO COMICS
American Airlines (Harvey): 1968 - 1979 (Giveaway)(Reprints of Harvey comics)
1968-Richie Rich, Hot Stuff, Casper, Wendy on-c only; Spooky and Nightmare app. inside 3 6 9 19 30 40
1970-Casper, Spooky, Hot Stuff, Stumbo the Giant, Little Audrey, Little Lotta, & Richie Rich reprints. Five different versions 3 6 9 16 23 30
1973,1975,1976: 1973-Three different versions 2 4 6 9 12 15
1977-r/Richie Rich & Casper #20. 1978-r/Richie Rich & Casper #25. 1979-r/Richie Rich & Casper #30 (scarce) 2 4 6 8 10 12

ATARI FORCE (Given away with Atari games)
DC Comics: 1982 - No. 5, 1983
1-3 (1982, 5X7", 52 pgs.) 1 2 3 5 6 8
4,5 (1982-1983, 52 pgs.)(scarcer) 2 4 6 9 12 15

AURORA COMIC SCENES INSTRUCTION BOOKLET (Included with superhero model kits)
Aurora Plastics Co.: 1974 (6-1/4x9-3/4," 8 pgs., slick paper)
181-140-Tarzan; Neal Adams-a 3 6 9 18 27 38
182-140-Spider-Man. 4 8 12 23 37 50
183-140-Tonto(Gil Kane art). 184-140-Hulk. 185-140-Superman. 186-140-Superboy.

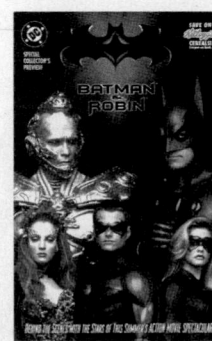

Batman and Robin Movie Preview © DC

Beetle Bailey Cerebral Palsy Assn. V2 #73 © CC

The Blazing Forest © WEST

GD 2.0 VG 4.0 FN 6.0 VF 8.0 VF/NM 9.0 NM- 9.2

187-140-Batman. 188-140-The Lone Ranger(1974-by Gil Kane). 192-140-Captain America(1975). 193-140-Robin 3 6 9 16 23 30

BACK TO THE FUTURE
Harvey Comics
Special nn (1991, 20 pgs.)-Brunner-c; given away at Universal Studios in Florida 6.00

BALTIMORE COLTS
American Visuals Corp.: 1950 (Giveaway)
nn-Eisner-c 42 84 126 265 445 625

BAMBI (Disney)
K. K. Publications (Giveaways): 1941, 1942
1941-Horlick's Malted Milk & various toy stores; text & pictures; most copies mailed out with store stickers on-c 43 86 129 271 461 650
1942-Same as 4-Color #12, but no price (Same as '41 issue?) (Scarce) 97 194 291 621 1061 1500

BATMAN
DC Comics: 1966 - Present
Act II Popcorn mini-comic(1998) 5.00
Batman #121 Toys R Us edition (1997) r/1st Mr. Freeze 5.00
Batman #279 Mini-comic with Monogram Model kit (1995) 5.00
Batman #362 Mervyn's edition (1989) 5.00
Batman #608 New York Post edition (2002) 5.00
Batman Adventures #25 Best Western edition (1997) 5.00
Batman and Other DC Classics 1 (1989, giveaway)-DC Comics/Diamond Comic Distributors; Batman origin-r/Batman #47, Camelot 3000-r, Justice League-r('87), New Teen Titans-r 5.00
Batman and Robin movie preview (1997, 8 pgs.) Kellogg's Cereal promo 3.00
Batman Beyond Six Flags edition 1 2 3 5 6 8
Batman: Canadian Multiculturalism Custom (1992) 5.00
Batman Claritan edition (1999) 3.00
Kellogg's Poptarts comics (1966, Set of 6, 16 pgs.); All were folded and placed in Poptarts boxes. Infantino art on Catwoman and Joker issues.
"The Man in the Iron Mask", "The Penguin's Fowl Play", "The Joker's Happy Victims", "The Catwoman's Catnapping Caper", "The Mad Hatter's Hat Crimes", "The Case of the Batman II" each.... 5 10 15 31 53 75
Mask of the Phantasm (1993) Mini-comic released w/video 1 2 3 5 7 9
Onstar - Auto Show Special Edition (OnStar Corp., 2001, 8 pgs.) Riddler app. 3.00
Pizza Hut giveaway (12/77)-exact-r of #122,123; Joker app. 2 4 6 9 12 15
Prell Shampoo giveaway (1966, 16 pgs.)- "The Joker's Practical Jokes" (6-7/8x3-3/8") 10 20 30 69 147 225
Revell in pack (1995) 4.00
...: The 10-Cent Adventure (3/02, 10¢) intro. to the "Bruce Wayne: Murderer" x-over; Rucka-s/Burchett & Janson-a/Dave Johnson-c; these are alternate copies with special outer half-covers (at least 10 different) promoting comics, toys and games shops 3.00

BATMAN RECORD COMIC
National Periodical Publications: 1966 (one-shot)
1-With record (still sealed) 12 24 36 80 173 265
Comic only 8 16 24 52 99 145

BEETLE BAILEY
Charlton Comics: 1969-1970 (Giveaways)
Armed Forces ('69)-same as regular issue (#68) 2 4 6 10 14 18
Armed Forces ('70) 2 4 6 10 14 18
Bold Detergent ('69)-same as regular issue (#67) 2 4 6 10 14 18
Cerebral Palsy Assn. V2#71('69) - V2#73(#1,1/70) 2.00
Red Cross (1969, 5x7", 16 pgs., paper-c) 2 4 6 10 14 18

BELLAIRE BICYCLE CO.
Bellaire Bicycle Co.: 1940 (promotional comic)(64 pgs.)
nn-Contains Wonderworld #12 w/new-c. Contents can vary w/diff. 1940's books 47 94 141 296 498 700

BEST WESTERN GIVEAWAY
DC Comics: 1999
nn-Best Western hotels 2.50

BETTER LIFE FOR YOU, A
Harvey Publications Inc.: (16 pgs., paper cover)
nn-Better living through higher productivity 3 6 9 15 22 28

BEWARE THE BOOBY TRAP
Malcolm Alter: 1970 (5" x 7")
nn-Deals with drug abuse 4 8 12 23 37 50

GD 2.0 VG 4.0 FN 6.0 VF 8.0 VF/NM 9.0 NM- 9.2

B-FORCE (Milwaukee Brewers and Wisconsin Dental Asso.)
Dark Horse Comics: 2001 (School and stadium giveaway)
nn-Brewers players combat the evils of smokeless tobacco 3.00

BIG BOY (see Adventures of...)

BIG JIM'S P.A.C.K.
Mattel, Inc. (Marvel Comics): No date (1975) (16 pgs.)
nn-Giveaway with Big Jim doll; Buscema/Sinnott-c/a 4 8 12 23 37 50

"BILL AND TED'S EXCELLENT ADVENTURE" MOVIE ADAPTATION
DC Comics: 1989 (No cover price)
nn-Torres-a 4.00

BIONICLE (LEGO robot toys)
DC Comics: Jun, 2001 - No. 27, Nov, 2005 ($2.25/$3.25, 16 pages, available to LEGO club members)
1 1 2 3 5 6 8
2-5 6.00
6-13 4.00
14-27 3.00
The Legend of Bionicle (McDonald's Mini-comic, 4-1/4 x 7") 4.00
Special Edition #0 (Six Heroes...One Destiny) '03 San Diego Comic Con; Ashley Wood-c 6.00

BLACK GOLD
Esso Service Station (Giveaway): 1945? (8 pgs. in color)
nn-Reprints from True Comics 6 12 18 28 34 40

BLADE SINS OF THE FATHER
Marvel Comics: Aug, 1996 (24 pgs. with paper cover)
1-Theatrical preview; possibly limited to 2000 copies (Value will be based on sale)

BLAZING FOREST, THE (See Forest Fire and Smokey Bear)
Western Printing: 1962 (20 pgs., 5x7", slick-c)
nn-Smokey The Bear fire prevention 3 6 9 14 20 26

BLESSED PIUS X
Catechetical Guild (Giveaway): No date (Text/comics, 32 pgs., paper-c)
nn 8 16 24 40 50 60

BLIND JUSTICE (Also see Batman: Blind Justice)
DC Comics/Diamond Comic Distributors: 1989 (Giveaway, squarebound)
nn-Contains Detective #598-600 by Batman movie writer Sam Hamm, w/covers; published same time as originals? 6.00

BLONDIE COMICS
Harvey Publications: 1950-1964
1950 Giveaway 8 16 24 40 50 60
1962,1964 Giveaway 3 6 9 16 23 30
N. Y. State Dept. of Mental Hygiene Giveaway-(1950) Regular size; 16 pgs.; no # 4 8 12 23 37 50
N. Y. State Dept. of Mental Hygiene Giveaway-(1956) Regular size; 16 pgs.; no # 3 6 9 16 24 32
N. Y. State Dept. of Mental Hygiene Giveaway-(1961) Regular size; 16 pgs.; no # 3 6 9 15 22 28

BLOOD IS THE HARVEST
Catechetical Guild: 1950 (32 pgs., paper-c)
(Scarce)-Anti-communism (21 known copies) 252 504 756 1613 2757 3900
Black & white version (5 known copies), saddle stitched 110 220 330 704 1202 1700
Untrimmed version (only one known copy); estimated value - $1000
NOTE: *In 1979 nine copies of the color version surfaced from the old Guild's files plus the five black & white copies.*

BLUE BIRD CHILDREN'S MAGAZINE, THE
Graphic Information Service: V1#2, 1957 - No. 10 1958 (16 pgs., soft-c, regular size)
V1#2-10: Pat, Pete & Blue Bird app. 2 4 6 8 11 14

BLUE BIRD COMICS
Various Shoe Stores: 1947 - 1950 (Giveaway, 36 pgs.)
Charlton Comics: 1959 - 1964 (Giveaway)
nn-(1947-50, not Charlton)(36 pgs.)-Several issues; Human Torch, Sub-Mariner app. in some 20 40 60 114 182 250
1959-(Charlton) Lil Genius, Wild Bill Hickok, Black Fury, Masked Raider, Timmy The Timid Ghost, Freddy (All #1) 3 6 9 14 20 26
1959-(Charlton, same 6 titles; all #2-5) except (#5) Masked Raider #21 3 6 9 14 20 25
1959-(#5) Masked Raider #21 3 6 9 15 22 28
1960-(6 titles, all #6-9) Black Fury, Masked Raider, Freddy, Timmy the Timid Ghost,

Bugs Bunny Fights the Man From Mars
Quaker C-4 © WB

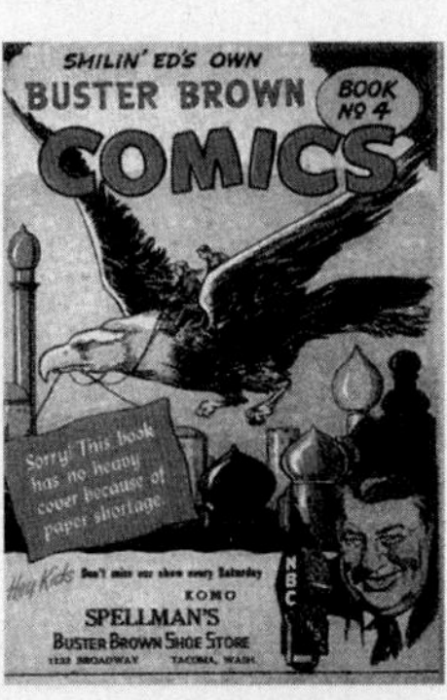

Buster Brown Comics #4
© Brown Shoe Co.

Captain America - Return of the Asthma
Monster © MAR

GD VG FN VF VF/NM NM-
2.0 4.0 6.0 8.0 9.0 9.2

Li'l Genius, Six Gun Heroes 3 6 9 14 19 24
1961-(All #10's) Black Fury, Masked Raider, Freddy, Timmy the Timid Ghost,
Li'l Genius, Six Gun Heroes (Charlton) 2 4 6 13 18 22
1961-(All #11-13) Lil Genius, Wyatt Earp, Black Fury, Timmy the Timid Ghost, Atomic Mouse,
Freddy 2 4 6 13 18 22
1962-(All #14) Lil Genius, Wyatt Earp, Black Fury, Timmy the Timid Ghost, Atomic Mouse,
Freddy 2 4 6 13 18 22
1962-(6 titles, all #15) Lil Genius, Six Gun Heroes, Black Fury, Timmy the Timid Ghost,
Texas Rangers, Freddy 2 4 6 13 18 22
1962-(7 titles, all #16) Lil Genius, Six Gun Heroes, Black Fury, Timmy the Timid Ghost,
Texas Rangers, Wyatt Earp, Atomic Mouse 2 4 6 13 18 22
1963-(All #17) My Little Margie, Lil Genius, Timmy the Timid Ghost, Texas Rangers (Charlton)
2 4 6 9 13 16
1964-(All #18) Mysteries of Unexplored Worlds, Teenage Hotrodders, War Heroes, Wyatt Earp
(Charlton) 2 4 6 9 13 16

NOTE: *Reprints comics of regular issue, with Blue Bird shoe promo on back cover, with upper front cover imprint of various shoe retailers. Printed from 1959 to 1962, with issues 1 thru 16. The 8 different front cover imprints for issues 1 thru 16 are, 1) Blue Bird Shoes, 2) Schiff's Shoes, 3) Big Shoe Store, 4) E.D. Edwards Shoe Store, 5) R & S Shoe store, 6) Federal Shoe Store, 7) Kirby's Shoes, 8) Gallenkamps.*

BOB & BETTY & SANTA'S WISHING WHISTLE (Also see A Christmas Carol, Merry Christmas From Sears Toyland, and Santa's Christmas Comic Variety Show)
Sears Roebuck & Co.: 1941 (Christmas giveaway, 12 pgs., oblong)

nn 21 42 63 126 206 285

BOBBY BENSON'S B-BAR-B RIDERS (Radio)
Magazine Enterprises/AC Comics

...in the Tunnel of Gold-(1936, 5-1/4x8"; 100 pgs.) Radio giveaway by Hecker-H.O. Company
(H.O. Oats); contains 22 color pgs. of comics, rest in novel form
11 22 33 64 90 115
...And The Lost Herd-same as above 11 22 33 64 90 115

BOBBY GETS HEP
Bell Telephone: 1946

nn-Bell Telephone Systems giveaway 5 10 15 24 30 35

BOBBY SHELBY COMICS
Shelby Cycle Co./Harvey Publications: 1949

nn 5 10 14 20 24 28

BOY SCOUT ADVENTURE
Boy Scouts of America: 1954 (16 pgs., paper cover)

nn 5 10 15 22 26 30

BOYS' RANCH
Harvey Publications: 1951

Shoe Store Giveaway #5,6 (Identical to regular issues except Simon & Kirby centerfold
replaced with ad) 14 28 42 76 108 140

BOZO THE CLOWN (TV)
Dell Publishing Co.: 1961

Giveaway-1961, 16 pgs., 3-1/2x7-1/4", Apsco Products
5 10 15 30 50 70

BRER RABBIT IN "ICE CREAM FOR THE PARTY"
American Dairy Association: 1955 (5x7-1/4", 16 pgs., soft-c) (Walt Disney) (Premium)

nn-(Scarce) 39 78 117 231 378 525

BUCK ROGERS (In the 25th Century)
Kelloggs Corn Flakes Giveaway: 1933 (6x8", 36 pgs)

370A-By Phil Nowlan & Dick Calkins; 1st Buck Rogers radio premium & 1st app.
in comics (tells origin) (Reissued in 1995) 54 108 162 400 - -
with envelope 74 148 222 550 - -

BUGS BUNNY (Puffed Rice Giveaway)
Quaker Cereals: 1949 (32 pgs. each, 3-1/8x6-7/8")

A1-Traps the Counterfeiters, A2-Aboard Mystery Submarine, A3- Rocket to the Moon, A4-Lion Tamer, A5-Rescues the Beautiful Princess, B1-Buried Treasure, B2-Outwits the Smugglers, B3-Joins the Marines, B4-Meets the Dwarf Ghost, B5-Finds Aladdin's Lamp, C1-Lost in the Frozen North, C2-Secret Agent, C3-Captured by Cannibals, C4-Fights the Man from Mars, C5-And the Haunted Cave
each.... 8 16 24 40 50 60
Mailing Envelope (has illo of Bugs on front)(Each envelope designates what set it contains,
A,B or C on front) 8 16 24 40 50 60

BUGS BUNNY (3-D)
Cheerios Giveaway: 1953 (Pocket size) (15 titles)

each.... 10 20 30 54 72 90
Mailing Envelope (has Bugs drawn on front) 10 20 30 54 72 90

BUGS BUNNY
DC Comics: May, 1997 ($4.95, 24 pgs., comic-sized)

1-Numbered ed. of 100,000; "1st Day of Issue" stamp cancellation on-c 6.00

BUGS BUNNY POSTAL COMIC
DC Comics: 1997 (64 pgs., 7.5" x 5")

nn -Mail Fan; Daffy Duck app. 4.50

BULLETMAN
Fawcett Publications

Well Known Comics (1942)-Paper-c, glued binding; printed in red
(Bestmaid/Samuel Lowe giveaway) 15 30 45 85 130 175

BULLS-EYE (Cody of The Pony Express No. 8 on)
Charlton: 1955 (Great Scott Shoe Store giveaway)

Reprints #2 with new cover 18 36 54 103 162 220

BUSTER BROWN COMICS (Radio)(Also see My Dog Tige in Promotional sec.)
Brown Shoe Co.: 1945 - No. 43, 1959 (No. 5: paper-c)

nn, nd (#1,scarce)-Featuring Smilin' Ed McConnell & the Buster Brown gang "Midnight" the cat, "Squeaky" the mouse & "Froggy" the Gremlin; covers mention diff. shoe stores.
Contains adventure stories 63 126 189 403 689 975
2 20 40 60 114 182 250
3,5-10 13 26 39 74 105 135
4 (Rare)-Low print run due to paper shortage 18 36 54 107 169 230
11-20 9 18 27 47 61 75
21-24,26-28 6 12 18 31 38 45
25,33-37,40,41-Crandall-a in all 10 20 30 56 76 95
29-32-"Interplanetary Police Vs. the Space Siren" by Crandall (pencils only #29)
10 20 30 58 79 100
38,39,42,43 6 12 18 31 38 45

BUSTER BROWN COMICS (Radio)
Brown Shoe Co: 1950s

...Goes to Mars (2/58-Western Printing), slick-c, 20 pgs., reg. size
14 28 42 80 115 150
...In "Buster Makes the Team!" (1959-Custom Comics)
8 16 24 44 57 70
...In The Jet Age (`50s), slick-c, 20 pgs., 5x7-1/4" 10 20 30 58 79 100
...Of the Safety Patrol ('60-Custom Comics) 3 6 9 17 26 35
...Out of This World ('59-Custom Comics) 7 14 21 35 43 50
...Safety Coloring Book ('58, 16 pgs.)-Slick paper 7 14 21 35 43 50

CALL FROM CHRIST
Catechetical Educational Society: 1952 (Giveaway, 36 pgs.)

nn 7 14 21 35 43 50

CANCELLED COMIC CAVALCADE
DC Comics, Inc.: Summer, 1978 - No. 2, Fall, 1978 (8-1/2x11", B&W)
(Xeroxed pgs. on one side only w/blue cover and taped spine)(Only 35 sets produced)

1-(412 pgs.) Contains xeroxed copies of art for: Black Lightning #12, cover to #13; Claw #13,14; The Deserter #1; Doorway to Nightmare #6; Firestorm #6; The Green Team #2,3.
2-(532 pgs.) Contains xeroxed copies of art for: Kamandi #60 (including Omac), #61; Prez #5; Shade #9 (including The Odd Man); Showcase #105 (Deadman), 106 (The Creeper); Secret Society of Super Villains #16 & 17; The Vixen #1; and covers to Army at War #2, Battle Classics #3, Demand Classics #1 & 2, Dynamic Classics #3, Mr. Miracle #26, Ragman #6, Weird Mystery #25 & 26, & Western Classics #1 & 2.
(A FN set of Number 1 & 2 was sold in 2005 for $3680; a VG set sold in 2007 for $2629)

NOTE: *In June, 1978, DC cancelled several of their titles. For copyright purposes, the unpublished original art for these titles was xeroxed, bound in the above books, published and distributed. Only 35 copies were made. Beware of bootleg copies.*

CAP'N CRUNCH COMICS (See Quaker Oats)
Quaker Oats Co.: 1963; 1965 (16 pgs.; miniature giveaways; 2-1/2x6-1/2")

(1963 titles)- "The Picture Pirates", "The Fountain of Youth", "I'm Dreaming of a Wide Isthmus".
(1965 titles)- "Bewitched, Betwitched, & Betweaked", "Seadog Meets the Witch Doctor",
"A Witch in Time" 5 10 15 31 53 75

CAPTAIN ACTION (Toy)
National Periodical Publications

...& Action Boy('67)-Ideal Toy Co. giveaway (1st app. Captain Action)
10 20 30 68 144 220

CAPTAIN AMERICA
Marvel Comics Group

...& The Campbell Kids (1980, 36pg. giveaway, Campbell's Soup/U.S. Dept. of Energy)
2 4 6 9 13 16
...Goes To War Against Drugs(1990, no #, giveaway)-Distributed to direct sales shops;
2nd printing exists 1 2 3 5 6 8

Captain Marvel and the Lts. of Safety #2 © FAW

Century of Comics © EAS

Cheerios Premium W3 © DIS

	GD 2.0	VG 4.0	FN 6.0	VF 8.0	VF/NM 9.0	NM- 9.2
...Meets The Asthma Monster (1987, no #, giveaway, Your Physician and Glaxo, Inc.)	1	2	3	5	6	8
Return of The Asthma Monster Vol. 1 #2 (1992, giveaway, Your Physician & Allen & Hanbury's)	1	2	3	5	6	8
...Vs. Asthma Monster (1990, no #, giveaway, Your Physician & Allen & Hanbury's)	1	2	3	5	6	8

CAPTAIN AMERICA COMICS
Timely/Marvel Comics: 1954

	GD	VG	FN	VF	VF/NM	NM-
Shoestore Giveaway #77	174	348	522	1114	1907	2700

CAPTAIN ATOM
Nationwide Publishers

	GD	VG	FN	VF	VF/NM	NM-
...- Secret of the Columbian Jungle (16 pgs. in color, paper-c, 3-3/4x5-1/8")- Fireside Marshmallow giveaway	6	12	18	28	34	40

CAPTAIN BEN DIX
Bendix Aviation Corporation: 1943 (Small size)

	GD	VG	FN	VF	VF/NM	NM-
nn	8	16	24	44	57	70

CAPTAIN BEN DIX IN ACTION WITH THE INVISIBLE CREW
Bendix Aviation Corp.: 1940s (nd), (20 pgs, 8-1/4"x11", heavy paper)

	GD	VG	FN	VF	VF/NM	NM-
nn-WWII bomber-c; Japanese app.	7	14	21	37	46	55

CAPTAIN BEN DIX IN SECRETS OF THE INVISIBLE CREW
Bendix Aviation Corp.: 1940s (nd), (32 pgs, soft-c)

	GD	VG	FN	VF	VF/NM	NM-
nn	7	14	21	35	43	50

CAPTAIN FORTUNE PRESENTS
Vital Publications: 1955 - 1959 (Giveaway, 3-1/4x6-7/8", 16 pgs.)

	GD	VG	FN	VF	VF/NM	NM-
"Davy Crockett in Episodes of the Creek War", "Davy Crockett at the Alamo", "In Sherwood Forest Tells Strange Tales of Robin Hood" ('57), "Meets Bolivar the Liberator" ('59), "Tells How Buffalo Bill Fights the Dog Soldiers" ('57), "Young Davy Crockett"	4	7	9	14	17	20

CAPTAIN GALLANT (...of the Foreign Legion) (TV)
Charlton Comics

	GD	VG	FN	VF	VF/NM	NM-
Heinz Foods Premium (#1?)(1955; regular size)-U.S. Pictorial; contains Buster Crabbe photos; Don Heck-a	1	3	4	6	8	10
Mailing Envelope						20.00

CAPTAIN JOLLY ADVENTURES
Johnston and Cushing: 1950's, nd (Post Corn Fetti cereal giveaway) (5-1/4" x 4-1/2")

	GD	VG	FN	VF	VF/NM	NM-
1-3: 1-Captain Jolly Advs. 2-Captain Jolly and His Pirate Crew in Off To Treasure Island. 3-C.J. & His Pirate Crew in The Terror Of The Deep	2	4	5	7	8	10

CAPTAIN MARVEL ADVENTURES
Fawcett Publications

	GD	VG	FN	VF	VF/NM	NM-
Bond Bread Giveaways-(24 pgs.; pocket size-7-1/4x3-1/2"; paper cover): "...& the Stolen City" ('48), "The Boy Who Never Heard of Capt. Marvel", "Meets the Weatherman" (1950) (reprint) each....	22	44	66	128	209	290
...Well Known Comics (1944; 12 pgs.; 8-1/2x10-1/2")-printed in red & in blue; soft-c; glued binding - (Bestmaid/Samuel Lowe Co. giveaway)	15	30	45	94	147	200

CAPTAIN MARVEL ADVENTURES (Also see Flash and Funny Stuff)
Fawcett Publications (Wheaties Giveaway): 1945 (6x8", full color, paper-c)

	GD	VG	FN	VF	VF/NM	NM-
nn- "Captain Marvel & the Threads of Life" plus 2 other stories (32 pgs.)	55	110	275	550	-	-

NOTE: *All copies were taped at each corner to a box of Wheaties and are never found in Fine or Mint condition. Prices listed for each grade include tape. File copy stamped "June 21, 1947".*

CAPTAIN MARVEL AND THE LTS. OF SAFETY
Ebasco Services/Fawcett Publications: 1950 - 1951 (3 issues - no No.'s)

	GD	VG	FN	VF	VF/NM	NM-
nn (#1) "Danger Flies a Kite" ('50, scarce),	39	78	117	240	395	550
nn (#2)"Danger Takes to Climbing" ('50),	26	52	78	154	252	350
nn (#3)"Danger Smashes Street Lights" ('51)	26	52	78	154	252	350

CAPTAIN MARVEL, JR.
Fawcett Publications: (1944; 12 pgs.; 8-1/2x10-1/2")

	GD	VG	FN	VF	VF/NM	NM-
...Well Known Comics (Printed in blue; paper-c, glued binding)-Bestmaid/Samuel Lowe Co. giveaway	14	28	42	76	108	140

CARDINAL MINDSZENTY (The Truth Behind the Trial of...)
Catechetical Guild Education Society: 1949 (24 pgs., paper cover)

	GD	VG	FN	VF	VF/NM	NM-
nn-Anti-communism	12	24	36	69	97	125
Press Proof-(Very Rare)-(Full color, 7-1/2x11-3/4", untrimmed) Only two known copies						300.00
Preview Copy (B&W, stapled), 18 pgs.; contains first 13 pgs. of Cardinal Mindszenty and was sent out as an advance promotion. Only one known copy						300.00 - 400.00

NOTE: *Regular edition also printed in French. There was also a movie released in 1949 called "Guilty of Treason" which is a fact-based account of the trial and imprisonment of Cardinal Mindszenty by the Communist regime in Hungary.*

CARNIVAL OF COMICS
Fleet-Air Shoes: 1954 (Giveaway)

	GD	VG	FN	VF	VF/NM	NM-
nn-Contains a comic bound with new cover; several combinations possible; Charlton's Eh! known	5	10	15	24	30	35

CARTOON NETWORK
DC Comics: 1997 (Giveaway)

	GD	VG	FN	VF	VF/NM	NM-
nn-reprints Cow and Chicken, Scooby-Doo, & Flintstones stories						4.00

CARVEL COMICS (Amazing Advs. of Capt. Carvel)
Carvel Corp. (Ice Cream): 1975 - No. 5, 1976 (25¢; #3-5: 35¢) (#4,5: 3-1/4x5")

	GD	VG	FN	VF	VF/NM	NM-
1-3	1	2	3	5	6	8
4,5(1976)-Baseball theme	2	4	6	8	10	12

CASE OF THE WASTED WATER, THE
Rheem Water Heating: 1972? (Giveaway)

	GD	VG	FN	VF	VF/NM	NM-
nn-Neal Adams-a	4	8	12	27	44	60

CASPER SPECIAL
Target Stores (Harvey): nd (Dec, 1990) (Giveaway with $1.00 cover)

	GD	VG	FN	VF	VF/NM	NM-
Three issues-Given away with Casper video						6.00

CASPER, THE FRIENDLY GHOST (Paramount Picture Star...)(2nd Series)
Harvey Publications

	GD	VG	FN	VF	VF/NM	NM-
American Dental Association (Giveaways):						
...'s Dental Health Activity Book-1977	2	4	6	8	11	14
...Presents Space Age Dentistry-1972	2	4	6	9	13	16
..., His Den, & Their Dentist Fight the Tooth Demons-1974	2	4	6	9	13	16
Casper Rides the School Bus (1960, 7x3.5", 16 pgs.)	2	4	6	9	13	16

CELEBRATE THE CENTURY SUPERHEROES STAMP ALBUM
DC Comics: 1998 - No. 5, 2000 (32 pgs.)

	GD	VG	FN	VF	VF/NM	NM-
1-5: Historical stories hosted by DC heroes						4.00

CENTIPEDE
DC Comics: 1983

	GD	VG	FN	VF	VF/NM	NM-
1-Based on Atari video game	2	4	6	9	13	16

CENTURY OF COMICS
Eastern Color Printing Co.: 1933 (100 pgs.)
Bought by Wheatena, Malt-O-Milk, John Wanamaker, Kinney Shoe Stores, & others to be used as premiums and radio giveaways. No publisher listed.

	GD	VG	FN	VF	VF/NM	NM-
nn-Mutt & Jeff, Joe Palooka, etc. reprints	1867	3734	5601	14,000	-	-

CHEERIOS PREMIUMS (Disney)
Walt Disney Productions: 1947 (16 titles, pocket size, 32 pgs.)

	GD	VG	FN	VF	VF/NM	NM-
Mailing Envelope for each set "W,X,Y & Z" (has Mickey illo on front)(each envelope designates the set it contains on the front)	8	16	24	44	57	70
Set "W"						
W1-Donald Duck & the Pirates	8	16	24	44	57	70
W2-Bucky Bug & the Cannibal King	5	10	15	23	28	32
W3-Pluto Joins the F.B.I.	5	10	15	23	28	32
W4-Mickey Mouse & the Haunted House	5	10	15	24	30	35
Set "X"						
X1-Donald Duck, Counter Spy	8	16	24	44	57	70
X2-Goofy Lost in the Desert	5	10	15	23	28	32
X3-Br'er Rabbit Outwits Br'er Fox	5	10	15	23	28	32
X4-Mickey Mouse at the Rodeo	6	12	18	28	34	40
Set "Y"						
Y1-Donald Duck's Atom Bomb by Carl Barks. Disney has banned reprinting this book	68	136	204	435	743	1050
Y2-Br'er Rabbit's Secret	5	10	15	23	28	32
Y3-Dumbo & the Circus Mystery	5	10	15	23	28	32
Y4-Mickey Mouse Meets the Wizard	6	12	18	28	34	40
Set "Z"						
Z1-Donald Duck Pilots a Jet Plane (not by Barks)	8	16	24	44	57	70
Z2-Pluto Turns Sleuth Hound	5	10	15	23	28	32
Z3-The Seven Dwarfs & the Enchanted Mtn.	6	12	18	28	34	40
Z4-Mickey Mouse's Secret Room	6	12	18	28	34	40

CHEERIOS 3-D GIVEAWAYS (Disney)
Walt Disney Productions: 1954 (24 titles, pocket size) (Glasses came in envelopes)

	GD	VG	FN	VF	VF/NM	NM-
Glasses only...	4	7	10	14	17	20
Mailing Envelope (no art on front)	6	12	18	27	33	38

Cheerios 3-D Giveaways - Donald Duck, Apache Gold © DIS

A Christmas Carol © Sears

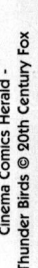

Cinema Comics Herald - Thunder Birds © 20th Century Fox

	GD 2.0	VG 4.0	FN 6.0	VF 8.0	VF/NM 9.0	NM- 9.2
(Set 1)						
1-Donald Duck & Uncle Scrooge, the Firefighters	6	12	18	31	38	45
2-Mickey Mouse & Goofy, Pirate Plunder	6	12	18	31	38	45
3-Donald Duck's Nephews, the Fabulous Inventors	7	14	21	35	43	50
4-Mickey Mouse, Secret of the Ming Vase	6	12	18	27	33	38
5-Donald Duck with Huey, Dewey, & Louie; ...the Seafarers (title on 2nd page)	6	12	18	31	38	45
6-Mickey Mouse, Moaning Mountain	6	12	18	27	33	38
7-Donald Duck, Apache Gold	6	12	18	31	38	45
8-Mickey Mouse, Flight to Nowhere	6	12	18	27	33	38
(Set 2)						
1-Donald Duck, Treasure of Timbuktu	6	12	18	31	38	45
2-Mickey Mouse & Pluto, Operation China	6	12	18	27	33	38
3-Donald Duck and the Magic Cows	6	12	18	31	38	45
4-Mickey Mouse & Goofy, Kid Kokonut	6	12	18	27	33	38
5-Donald Duck, Mystery Ship	6	12	18	31	38	45
6-Mickey Mouse, Phantom Sheriff	6	12	18	27	33	38
7-Donald Duck, Circus Adventures	6	12	18	31	38	45
8-Mickey Mouse, Arctic Explorers	6	12	18	27	33	38
(Set 3)						
1-Donald Duck & Witch Hazel	6	12	18	31	38	45
2-Mickey Mouse in Darkest Africa	6	12	18	27	33	38
3-Donald Duck & Uncle Scrooge, Timber Trouble	6	12	18	31	38	45
4-Mickey Mouse, Rajah's Rescue	6	12	18	27	33	38
5-Donald Duck in Robot Reporter	6	12	18	31	38	45
6-Mickey Mouse, Slumbering Sleuth	6	12	18	27	33	38
7-Donald Duck in the Foreign Legion	6	12	18	31	38	45
8-Mickey Mouse, Airwalking Wonder	6	12	18	27	33	38

CHESTY AND COPTIE (Disney)
Los Angeles Community Chest: 1946 (Giveaway, 4pgs.)

nn-(One known copy) by Floyd Gottfredson (a GD copy sold for $371.65 on 2/12/17)

CHESTY AND HIS HELPERS (Disney)
Los Angeles War Chest: 1943 (Giveaway, 12 pgs., 5-1/2x7-1/4")

nn-Chesty & Coptie	50	100	150	315	533	750

CHOCOLATE THE FLAVOR OF FRIENDSHIP AROUND THE WORLD
The Nestle Company: 1955

nn	6	12	18	28	34	40

CHRISTMAS ADVENTURE, THE
S. Rose (H. L. Green Giveaway): 1963 (16 pgs.)

nn	2	4	6	10	14	18

CHRISTMAS ADVENTURES WITH ELMER THE ELF
1949 (paper-c)

nn	4	7	10	14	17	20

CHRISTMAS AT THE ROTUNDA (Titled Ford Rotunda Christmas Book 1957 on) (Regular size)
Ford Motor Co. (Western Printing): 1954 - 1961 (Given away every Christmas at one location)

1954-56 issues (nn's)	8	16	24	42	54	65
1957-61 issues (nn's)	7	14	21	37	46	55

CHRISTMAS CAROL, A
Sears Roebuck & Co.: No date (1942-43) (Giveaway, 32 pgs., 8-1/4x10-3/4", paper cover)

nn-Comics & coloring book	22	44	66	128	209	290

CHRISTMAS CAROL, A (Also see Bob & Santa's Wishing Whistle, Merry Christmas From Sears Toyland, and Santa's Christmas Comic Variety Show)
Sears Roebuck & Co.: 1940s? (Christmas giveaway, 20 pgs.)

nn-Comic book & animated coloring book	20	40	60	120	195	270

CHRISTMAS CAROLS
Hot Shoppes Giveaway: 1959? (16 pgs.)

nn	4	8	11	16	19	22

CHRISTMAS COLORING FUN
H. Burnside: 1964 (20 pgs., slick-c, B&W)

nn	2	4	6	11	16	20

CHRISTMAS DREAM, A
Promotional Publishing Co.: 1950 (Kinney Shoe Store Giveaway, 16 pgs.)

nn	5	10	15	23	28	32

CHRISTMAS DREAM, A
J. J. Newberry Co.: 1952? (Giveaway, paper cover, 16 pgs.)

nn	5	10	14	20	24	28

CHRISTMAS DREAM, A
Promotional Publ. Co.: 1952 (Giveaway, 16 pgs., paper cover)

nn	5	10	14	20	24	28

CHRISTMAS FUN AROUND THE WORLD
No publisher: No date (early 50's) (16 pgs., paper cover)

nn	5	10	15	23	28	32

CHRISTMAS FUN BOOK
G. C. Murphy Co.: 1950 (Giveaway, paper cover)

nn-Contains paper dolls	6	12	18	29	36	42

CHRISTMAS IS COMING!
No publisher: No date (early 50's?) (Store giveaway, 16 pgs.)

nn-Santa cover	6	12	18	29	36	42

CHRISTMAS JOURNEY THROUGH SPACE
Promotional Publishing Co.: 1960

nn-Reprints 1954 issue Jolly Christmas Book with new slick cover	3	6	9	16	23	30

CHRISTMAS ON THE MOON
W. T. Grant Co.: 1958 (Giveaway, 20 pgs., slick cover)

nn	9	18	27	47	61	75

CHRISTMAS PLAY BOOK
Gould-Stoner Co.: 1946 (Giveaway, 16 pgs., paper cover)

nn	9	18	27	47	61	75

CHRISTMAS ROUNDUP
Promotional Publishing Co.: 1960

nn-Marv Levy-c/a	2	4	6	9	13	16

CHRISTMAS STORY CUT-OUT BOOK, THE
Catechetical Guild: No. 393, 1951 (15¢, 36 pgs.)

393-Half text & half comics	8	16	24	42	54	65

CHRISTMAS USA (Through 300 Years) (Also see Uncle Sam's...)
Promotional Publ. Co.: 1956 (Giveaway)

nn-Marv Levy-c/a	4	7	9	14	16	18

CHRISTMAS WITH SNOW WHITE AND THE SEVEN DWARFS
Kobackers Giftstore of Buffalo, N.Y.: 1953 (16 pgs., paper-c)

nn	8	16	24	42	54	65

CHRISTOPHERS, THE
Catechetical Guild: 1951 (Giveaway, 36 pgs.) (Some copies have 15¢ sticker)

nn-Stalin as Satan in Hell; Hitler & Lincoln app.	26	52	78	154	252	350

CHUCKY JACK'S A-COMIN'
Great Smoky Mountains Historical Assn., Gatlinburg, TN: 1956 (Reg. size)

nn-Life of John Sevier, founder of Tennessee	8	16	24	42	54	65

CINDERELLA IN "FAIREST OF THE FAIR" (Walt Disney)
American Dairy Association (Premium): 1955 (5x7-1/4", 16 pgs., soft-c)

nn	10	20	30	56	76	95

CINEMA COMICS HERALD
Paramount Pictures/Universal/RKO/20th Century Fox/Republic:
1941 - 1943 (4-pg. movie "trailers", paper-c, 7-1/2x10-1/2")(Giveaway)

	GD 2.0	VG 4.0	FN 6.0	VF 8.0	VF/NM 9.0	NM- 9.2
"Mr. Bug Goes to Town" (1941)	17	34	51	98	154	210
"Bedtime Story"	12	24	36	69	97	125
"Lady For A Night", John Wayne, Joan Blondell ('42)	20	40	60	117	189	260
"Reap The Wild Wind" (1942)	14	28	42	76	108	140
"Thunder Birds" (1942)	12	24	36	69	97	125
"They All Kissed the Bride"	12	24	36	69	97	125
"Arabian Nights" (nd)	14	28	42	76	108	140
"Bombardie" (1943)	12	24	36	69	97	125
"Crash Dive" (1943)-Tyrone Power	14	28	42	76	108	140

NOTE: *The 1941-42 issues contain line art with color photos. 1943 issues are line art.*

CLASSICS GIVEAWAYS (Classic Comics reprints)

	GD 2.0	VG 4.0	FN 6.0	VF 8.0	VF/NM 9.0	NM- 9.2
12/41–Walter Theatre Enterprises (Huntington, WV) giveaway containing #2 (orig.) w/new generic-c (only 1 known copy)	97	194	291	621	1061	1500
1942–Double Comics containing CC#1 (orig.) (diff. cover) (not actually a giveaway) (very rare) (also see Double Comics) (only one known copy)	168	336	504	1075	1838	2600
12/42–Saks 34th St. Giveaway containing CC#7 (orig.) (diff. cover) (very rare; only 6 known copies)	343	686	1029	2400	4200	6000

2/43–American Comics containing CC#8 (orig.) (Liberty Theatre giveaway) (different cover)

Classics Giveaways 1956 - Ben Franklin 5-10 Store © GIL

Comic Books - New World © MPC

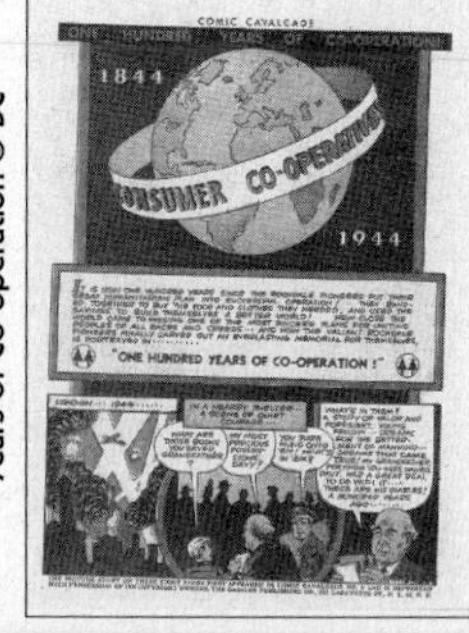

Comic Cavalcade - One Hundred Years of Co-operation © DC

	GD 2.0	VG 4.0	FN 6.0	VF 8.0	VF/NM 9.0	NM- 9.2
(only one known copy) (see American Comics)	123	246	369	787	1344	1900
12/44–Robin Hood Flour Co. Giveaway - #7-CC(R) (diff. cover) (rare) (edition probably 5 [22])	206	412	618	1318	2259	3200

NOTE: How are above editions determined without CC covers? 1942 is dated 1942, and CC#1-first reprint did not come out until 5/43. 12/42 and 2/43 are determined by blue note at bottom of first text page only in original edition. 12/44 is estimated from page width each reprint edition had progressively slightly smaller page width.

	GD	VG	FN	VF	VF/NM	NM-
1951–Shelter Thru the Ages (C.I. Educational Series) (actually Giveaway by the Ruberoid Co.) (16 pgs.) (contains original artwork by H. C. Kiefer) (there are 5 diff. back cover ad variations: "Ranch" house ad, "Igloo" ad, "Doll House" ad, "Tree House" ad & blank) (scarce)	68	136	204	435	743	1050
1952–George Daynor Biography Giveaway (CC logo) (partly comic book/pictures/newspaper articles) (story of man who built Palace Depression out of junkyard swamp in NJ) (64 pgs.) (very rare; only 3 known copies, one missing back-c)	377	754	1131	2639	4620	6600
1953–Westinghouse/Dreams of a Man (C.I. Educational Series) (Westinghousebio./ Westinghouse Co. giveaway) (contains original artwork by H. C. Kiefer) (16 pgs.) (also French/Spanish/Italian versions) (scarce)	52	104	156	328	552	775
NOTE: Reproductions of 1951, 1952, and 1953 exist with color photocopy covers and black & white photocopy interior ("W.C.N. Reprint")	2	4	5	7	8	10
1951-53–Coward Shoe Giveaways (all editions very rare); 2 variations of back-c ad exist: With back-c photo ad: 5 (87), 12 (89), 22 (85), 32 (85), 49 (85), 69 (87), 72 (no HRN), 80 (0), 91 (0), 92 (0), 96 (0), 98 (0), 100 (0), 101 (0), 103-105 (all Os)	30	60	90	177	289	400
With back-c cartoon ad: 106-109 (all 0s), 110 (111), 112 (0)	31	62	93	186	303	420
1956–Ben Franklin 5-10 Store Giveaway (#65-PC with back cover ad) (scarce)	24	48	72	142	234	325
1956–Ben Franklin Insurance Co. Giveaway (#65-PC with diff. back cover ad) (very rare)	48	96	144	302	514	725
11/56–Sealtest Co. Edition - #4 (135) (identical to regular edition except for Sealtest logo printed, not stamped, on front cover) (only two copies known to exist)	28	56	84	165	270	375
1958–Get-Well Giveaway containing #15-CI (new cartoon-type cover) (Pressman Pharmacy) (only one copy known to exist)	28	56	84	165	270	375
1967-68–Twin Circle Giveaway Editions - all HRN 166, with back cover ad for National Catholic Press.						
2(R68), 4(R67), 10(R68), 13(R68)	3	6	9	21	32	42
48(R67), 128(R68), 535(576-R68)	4	8	12	22	34	45
16(R68), 68(R67)	5	10	15	30	48	65
12/69–Christmas Giveaway ("A Christmas Adventure") (reprints Picture Parade #4-1953, new cover) (4 ad variations)						
Stacey's Dept. Store	3	6	9	20	31	42
Anne & Hope Store	5	10	15	30	50	70
Gibson's Dept. Store (rare)	5	10	15	30	50	70
"Merry Christmas" & blank ad space	3	6	9	20	31	42

CLEAR THE TRACK!
Association of American Railroads: 1954 (paper-c, 16 pgs.)

	GD	VG	FN	VF	VF/NM	NM-
nn	5	10	15	24	30	35

CLIFF MERRITT SETS THE RECORD STRAIGHT
Brotherhood of Railroad Trainsmen: Giveaway (2 different issues)

	GD	VG	FN	VF	VF/NM	NM-
...and the Very Candid Candidate by Al Williamson	1	3	4	6	8	10
...Sets the Record Straight by Al Williamson (2 different-c: one by Williamson, the other by McWilliams)	1	3	4	6	8	10

CLYDE BEATTY COMICS (Also see Crackajack Funnies)
Commodore Productions & Artists, Inc.

	GD	VG	FN	VF	VF/NM	NM-
...African Jungle Book('56)-Richfield Oil Co. 16 pg. giveaway, soft-c	11	22	33	62	86	110

C-M-O COMICS
Chicago Mail Order Co.(Centaur): 1942 - No. 2, 1942 (68 pgs., full color)

	GD	VG	FN	VF	VF/NM	NM-
1-Invisible Terror, Super Ann, & Plymo the Rubber Man app. (all Centaur costume heroes)	129	258	387	826	1413	2000
2-Invisible Terror, Super Ann app.	90	180	270	576	988	1400

COCOMALT BIG BOOK OF COMICS
Harry 'A' Chesler (Cocomalt Premium): 1938 (Reg. size, full color, 52 pgs.)

	GD	VG	FN	VF	VF/NM	NM-
1-(Scarce)-Biro-c/a; Little Nemo by Winsor McCay Jr., Dan Hastings; Jack Cole, Guardineer, Gustavson, Bob Wood-a	226	452	678	1446	2473	3500

COLONEL OF TWO WORLDS, THE
DC Comics: 2015 (Kentucky Fried Chicken promotion, no price)

1-Flash, Green Lantern and Colonel Sanders vs. the evil Colonel of Earth-3; Derenick-a 3.00

COMIC BOOK (Also see Comics From Weatherbird)
American Juniors Shoe: 1954 (Giveaway)

Contains a comic rebound with new cover. Several combinations possible. Contents determine price.

COMIC BOOK CONFIDENTIAL
Sphinx Productions: 1988 (Giveaway, 16 pgs.)

1-Tie-in to a documentary about comic creators; creator biographies; Chester Brown-c 5.00

COMIC BOOK MAGAZINE
Chicago Tribune & other newspapers: 1940 - 1943 (Similar to Spirit sections) (7-3/4x10-3/4"; full color; 16-24 pgs. ea.)

	GD	VG	FN	VF	VF/NM	NM-
1940 issues	7	14	21	37	46	55
1941, 1942 issues	6	12	18	28	34	40
1943 issues	5	10	15	24	30	35

NOTE: *Published weekly. Texas Slim, Kit Carson, Spooky, Josie, Nuts & Jolts, Lew Loyal, Brenda Starr, Daniel Boone, Captain Storm, Rocky, Smokey Stover, Tiny Tim, Little Joe, Fu Manchu appear among others. Early issues had photo stories with pictures from the movies; later issues had comic art.*

COMIC BOOKS (Series 1)
Metropolitan Printing Co. (Giveaway): 1950 (16 pgs.; 5-1/4x8-1/2"; full color; bound at top; paper cover)

	GD	VG	FN	VF	VF/NM	NM-
1-Boots and Saddles; intro The Masked Marshal	6	12	18	28	34	40
1-The Green Jet; Green Lama by Raboy	20	40	60	117	189	260
1-My Pal Dizzy (Teen-age)	4	8	12	18	22	25
1-New World; origin Atomaster (costumed hero)	9	18	27	52	69	85
1-Talullah (Teen-age)	4	8	12	18	22	25

COMIC CAVALCADE
All-American/National Periodical Publications

	GD	VG	FN	VF	VF/NM	NM-
Giveaway (1944, 8 pgs., paper-c, in color)-One Hundred Years of Co-operation-r/Comic Cavalcade #9	43	86	129	271	461	650
Giveaway (1945, 16 pgs., paper-c, in color)-Movie "Tomorrow The World" (Nazi theme); r/Comic Cavalcade #10	58	116	174	371	636	900
Giveaway (c. 1944-45; 8 pgs, paper-c, in color)-The Twain Shall Meet-r/Comic Cavalcade #8	43	86	129	271	461	650

COMIC SELECTIONS (Shoe store giveaway)
Parents' Magazine Press: 1944-46 (Reprints from Calling All Girls, True Comics, True Aviation, & Real Heroes)

	GD	VG	FN	VF	VF/NM	NM-
1	5	10	15	22	26	30
2-6	4	8	11	16	19	22

COMICS FROM WEATHER BIRD (Also see Comic Book, Edward's Shoes, Free Comics to You & Weather Bird)
Weather Bird Shoes: 1954 - 1957 (Giveaway)
Contains a comic bound with new cover. Many combinations possible. Contents would determine price. Some issues do not contain complete comics, but only parts of comics. Value equals 40 to 60 percent of contents.

COMICS READING LIBRARIES (Educational Series)
King Features (Charlton Publ.): 1973, 1977, 1979 (36 pgs. in color) (Giveaways)

	GD	VG	FN	VF	VF/NM	NM-
R-01-Tiger, Quincy	2	4	6	8	11	14
R-02-Beetle Bailey, Blondie & Popeye	2	4	6	10	14	18
R-03-Blondie, Beetle Bailey	2	4	6	8	11	14
R-04-Tim Tyler's Luck, Felix the Cat	3	6	9	16	23	30
R-05-Quincy, Henry	2	4	6	8	11	14
R-06-The Phantom, Mandrake	3	6	9	16	23	30
1977 reprint(R-04)	2	4	6	9	13	16
R-07-Popeye, Little King	2	4	6	13	18	22
R-08-Prince Valiant (Foster), Flash Gordon	3	6	9	18	27	36
1977 reprint	2	4	6	11	16	20
R-09-Hagar the Horrible, Boner's Ark	2	4	6	10	14	18
R-10-Redeye, Tiger	2	4	6	8	11	14
R-11-Blondie, Hi & Lois	2	4	6	8	11	14
R-12-Popeye-Swee'pea, Brutus	2	4	6	13	18	22
R-13-Beetle Bailey, Little King	2	4	6	8	11	14
R-14-Quincy-Hamlet	2	4	6	8	11	14
R-15-The Phantom, The Genius	2	4	6	13	18	22
R-16-Flash Gordon, Mandrake	3	6	9	18	27	36
1977 reprint	2	4	6	10	14	18
Other 1977 editions....	2	4	6	8	10	12
1979 editions (68 pgs.)	2	4	6	8	10	12

NOTE: *Above giveaways available with purchase of $45.00 in merchandise. Used as a reading skills aid for small children.*

COMMANDMENTS OF GOD
Catechetical Guild: 1954, 1958

	GD	VG	FN	VF	VF/NM	NM-
300-Same contents in both editions; diff-c	5	10	15	24	29	34

COMPLIMENTARY COMICS
Sales Promotion Publ.: No date (1950's) (Giveaway)

	GD	VG	FN	VF	VF/NM	NM-
1-Strongman by Powell, 3 stories	8	16	24	40	50	60

Craftsman Bolt-On Systems Save the Justice League #1 © DC

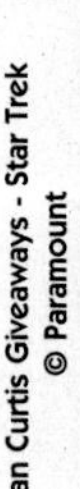
Dan Curtis Giveaways - Star Trek © Paramount

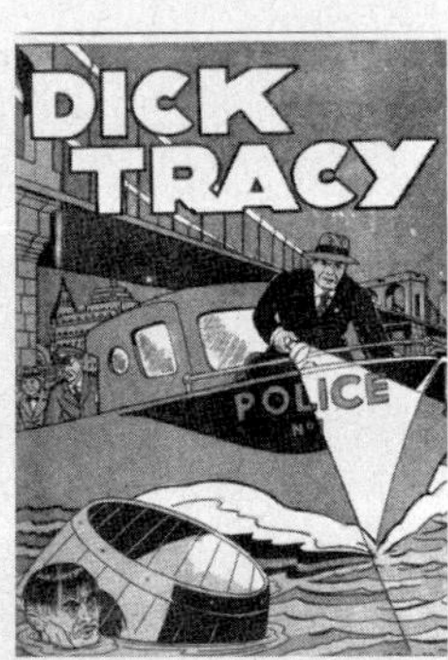

Dick Tracy Popped Wheat Giveaway © Tribune Media Services

	GD 2.0	VG 4.0	FN 6.0	VF 8.0	VF/NM 9.0	NM- 9.2
COPPER - THE OLDEST AND NEWEST METAL						
Commercial Comics: 1959						
nn	3	6	9	14	20	25
CRACKAJACK FUNNIES (Giveaway)						
Malto-Meal: 1937 (Full size, soft-c, full color, 32 pgs.)(Before No. 1?)						
nn-Features Dan Dunn, G-Man, Speed Bolton, Buck Jones, The Nebbs, Clyde Beatty, Freckles, Major Hoople, Wash Tubbs	90	180	270	576	988	1400
CRAFTSMAN BOLT-ON SYSTEMS SAVE THE JUSTICE LEAGUE						
DC Comics: 2012 (Giveaway promo for Craftsman Bolt-On Tool System)						
1-Christian Duce-a/c; New-52 Justice League, The Key and Royal Flush Gang app.						3.00
CRISIS AT THE CARSONS						
Pictorial Media: 1958 (Reg. size)						
nn	5	10	15	24	30	35
CROSLEY'S HOUSE OF FUN (Also see Tee and Vee Crosley...)						
Crosley Div. AVCO Mfg. Corp.: 1950 (Giveaway, paper cover, 32 pgs.)						
nn-Strips revolve around Crosley appliances	5	10	15	22	26	30
DAGWOOD SPLITS THE ATOM (Also see Topix V8#4)						
King Features Syndicate: 1949 (Science comic with King Features characters) (Giveaway)						
nn-Half comic, half text; Popeye, Olive Oyl, Henry, Mandrake, Little King, Katzenjammer Kids app.	6	12	18	31	38	45
DAISY COMICS (Daisy Air Rifles)						
Eastern Color Printing Co.: Dec, 1936 (5-1/4x7-1/2")						
nn-Joe Palooka, Buck Rogers (2 pgs. from Famous Funnies No. 18, 1st full cover app.), Napoleon Flying to Fame, Butty & Fally	35	70	105	208	339	470
DAISY LOW OF THE GIRL SCOUTS						
Girl Scouts of America: 1954, 1965 (16 pgs., paper-c)						
1954-Story of Juliette Gordon Low	5	10	15	22	26	30
1965	2	4	6	9	12	15
DAN CURTIS GIVEAWAYS						
Western Publishing Co.:1974 (3x6", 24 pgs., reprints)						
1-Dark Shadows	2	4	6	9	13	16
2,6-Star Trek	2	4	6	9	13	16
3,4,7-9: 3-The Twilight Zone. 4-Ripley's Believe It or Not! 7-The Occult Files of Dr. Spektor. 8-Dagar the Invincible. 9-Grimm's Ghost Stories	2	4	6	8	10	12
5-Turok, Son of Stone (partial-r/Turok #78)	2	4	6	9	13	16
DANNY AND THE DEMOXICYCLE						
Virginia Highway Safety Division: 1970s (Reg. size, slick-c)						
nn	3	6	9	19	30	40
DANNY KAYE'S BAND FUN BOOK						
H & A Selmer: 1959 (Giveaway)						
nn	7	14	21	35	43	50
DAREDEVIL						
Marvel Comics Group: 1993						
...Vs. Vapora 1 (Engineering Show Giveaway, 16 pg.) - Intro Vapora						6.00
DAVY CROCKETT (TV)						
Dell Publishing Co.						
...Christmas Book (no date, 16 pgs., paper-c)-Sears giveaway	6	12	18	31	38	45
...Safety Trails (1955, 16pgs, 3-1/4x7")-Cities Service giveaway	8	16	24	40	50	60
DAVY CROCKETT						
Charlton Comics						
Hunting With... nn ('55, 16 pgs.)-Ben Franklin Store giveaway (Publ.-S. Rose)	5	10	15	24	30	35
DAVY CROCKETT						
Walt Disney Prod.: (1955, 16 pgs., 5x7-1/4", slick, photo-c)						
...In the Raid at Piney Creek-American Motors giveaway	8	16	24	40	50	60
DC SAMPLER						
DC Comics: nn (#1) 1983 - No. 3, 1984 (36 pgs.; 6 1/2" x 10", giveaway)						
nn(#1) -3: nn-Wraparound-c, previews upcoming issues. 3-Kirby-a	1	2	3	4	5	7
DC SPOTLIGHT						
DC Comics: 1985 (50th anniversary special) (giveaway)						
1-Includes profiles on Batman: The Dark Knight & Watchmen						6.00
DEATH JR. HALLOWEEN SPECIAL						
Image Comics: Oct, 2006 (8-1/2"x 5-1/2", Halloween giveaway)						
nn-Guy Davis-a/Joe Morrisey-s; wraparound-c						2.50
DENNIS THE MENACE						
Hallden (Fawcett)						
...& Dirt ('59)-Soil Conservation giveaway; r-# 36; Wiseman-c/a	3	6	9	14	20	26
...& Dirt ('68)-reprints '59 edition	2	4	6	8	11	14
...Away We Go('70)-Caladryl giveaway	2	4	6	8	10	12
...Coping with Family Stress-giveaway	2	4	6	8	10	12
...Takes a Poke at Poison('61)-Food & Drug Admin. giveaway; Wiseman-c/a	2	4	6	8	10	12
...Takes a Poke at Poison-Revised 1/66, 11/70	1	2	3	5	6	8
...Takes a Poke at Poison-Revised 1972, 1974, 1977, 1981	1	2	3	4	5	7
DESERT DAWN						
E.C./American Museum of Natural History: 1935 (paper-c)						
nn-Johnny Jackrabbit stars. Three known copies: A Fair copy (brittle) sold for $657 in 2007. A GD+ copy (brittle) sold for $2300 in 2005. Another Fair copy (brittle) sold for $690 in 2004						
DETECTIVE COMICS (Also see other Batman titles)						
National Periodical Publications/DC Comics						
27 (1984)-Oreo Cookies giveaway (32 pgs., paper-c) r-/Det. #27,#38 & Batman #1 (1st Joker)	4	8	12	27	44	60
38 (1995) Blockbuster Video edition; reprints 1st Robin app.						3.00
38 (1997) Toys R Us edition						3.00
359 (1997) Toys R Us edition; reprints 1st Batgirl app.						3.00
373 (1997, 6 1/4" x 4") Warner Brothers Home Video						3.00
DICK TRACY GIVEAWAYS						
1939 - 1958; 1990						
Buster Brown Shoes Giveaway (1940s?, 36 pgs. in color); 1938-39-r by Gould	21	42	63	126	206	285
Gillmore Giveaway (See Superbook)						
...Hatful of Fun (No date, 1950-52, 32pgs.; 8-1/2x10")-Dick Tracy hat promotion; Dick Tracy games, magic tricks. Miller Bros. premium	15	30	45	90	140	190
Motorola Giveaway (1953)-Reprints Harvey Comics Library #2; "The Case of the Sparkle Plenty TV Mystery"	6	12	18	28	34	40
Original Dick Tracy by Chester Gould, The (Aug, 1990, 16 pgs., 5-1/2x8-1/2")-Gladstone Publ.; Bread Giveaway	1	3	4	6	8	10
Popped Wheat Giveaway (1947, 16 pgs. in color)-1940-r; Sig Feuchtwanger Publ.; Gould-a	4	8	12	18	22	25
...Presents the Family Fun Book; Tip Top Bread Giveaway, no date or number (1940, Fawcett Publ., 16 pgs. in color)-Spy Smasher, Ibis, Lance O'Casey app.	30	60	90	177	289	400
Same as above but without app. of heroes & Dick Tracy on cover only	14	28	42	82	121	160
Service Station Giveaway (1958, 16 pgs. in color)(regular size, slick cover)-Harvey Info. Press	5	10	14	20	24	28
Shoe Store Giveaway (Weatherbird and Triangle Stores)(1939, 16 pgs.)-Gould-a	14	28	42	80	115	150
DICK TRACY SHEDS LIGHT ON THE MOLE						
Western Printing Co.: 1949 (16 pgs.) (Ray-O-Vac Flashlights giveaway)						
nn-Not by Gould	8	16	24	42	54	65
DICK WINGATE OF THE U.S. NAVY						
Superior Publ./Toby Press: 1951; 1953 (no month)						
nn-U.S. Navy giveaway	5	10	15	24	30	35
1(1953, Toby)-Reprints nn issue? (same-c)	5	10	14	20	24	28
DIG 'EM						
Kellogg's Sugar Smacks Giveaway: 1973 (2-3/8x6", 16 pgs.)						
nn-4 different issues	1	3	4	6	8	10
DISNEY MAGAZINE						
Procter and Gamble giveaway: nn (#1), Sept, 1976 - nn (#4), Jan, 1977						
nn-All have an original Mickey story in color, 12-13 pgs. ea. and info/articles on Disney movies, cartoons. All have partial photo covers of a movie star with 1-2 pg. story. Covers: 1-Bob Hope, 2-Debbie Reynolds, 3-Groucho Marx, 4-Rock Hudson.	2	4	6	10	14	18
DOC CARTER VD COMICS						
Health Publications Institute, Raleigh, N. C. (Giveaway): 1949 (16 pgs. in color) (Paper-c)						

Drummer Boy at Gettysburg © ENP&MA

Eat Right to Work and Win © Swift & Co.

Elsie the Cow Borden Giveaway © DS

GD 2.0 | VG 4.0 | FN 6.0 | VF 8.0 | VF/NM 9.0 | NM- 9.2

nn 26 52 78 154 252 350

DONALD AND MICKEY MERRY CHRISTMAS (Formerly Famous Gang Book Of Comics)
K. K. Publ./Firestone Tire & Rubber Co.: 1943 - 1949 (Giveaway, 20 pgs.)
Put out each Christmas; 1943 issue titled "Firestone Presents Comics" (Disney)

1943-Donald Duck-r/WDC&S #32 by Carl Barks 90 180 270 576 988 1400
1944-Donald Duck-r/WDC&S #35 by Barks 84 168 252 538 919 1300
1945- "Donald Duck's Best Christmas", 8 pgs. Carl Barks; intro. & 1st app. Grandma Duck in comic books 113 226 339 718 1234 1750
1946-Donald Duck in "Santa's Stormy Visit", 8 pgs. Carl Barks 71 142 213 454 777 1100
1947-Donald Duck in "Three Good Little Ducks", 8 pgs. Carl Barks 71 142 213 454 777 1100
1948-Donald Duck in "Toyland", 8 pgs. Carl Barks 71 142 213 454 777 1100
1949-Donald Duck in "New Toys", 8 pgs. Barks 65 130 195 416 708 1000

DONALD DUCK
K. K. Publications: 1944 (Christmas giveaway, paper-c, 16 pgs.)(2 versions)
nn-Kelly cover reprint 113 226 339 718 1234 1750

DONALD DUCK AND THE RED FEATHER
Red Feather Giveaway: 1948 (8-1/2x11", 4 pgs., B&W)
nn 20 40 60 120 195 270

DONALD DUCK IN "THE LITTERBUG"
Keep America Beautiful: 1963 (5x7-1/4", 16 pgs., soft-c) (Disney giveaway)
nn 5 10 15 33 57 80

DONALD DUCK "PLOTTING PICNICKERS" (See Frito-Lay Giveaway)

DONALD DUCK'S SURPRISE PARTY
Walt Disney Productions: 1948 (16 pgs.) (Giveaway for Icy Frost Twins Ice Cream Bars)
nn-(Rare)-Kelly-c/a 226 452 678 1446 2473 3500

DON FORTUNE MAGAZINE
Fawcett Publications: 1940s (Mini-comic)
1-3 (Rare) (A set of 3 in 9.0 sold for $116 in 2016)

DOT AND DASH AND THE LUCKY JINGLE PIGGIE
Sears Roebuck Co.: 1942 (Christmas giveaway, 12 pgs.)
nn-Contains a war stamp album and a punch out Jingle Piggie bank 12 24 36 69 97 125

DOUBLE TALK (Also see Two-Faces)
Feature Publications: No date (1962?) (32 pgs., full color, slick-c)
Christian Anti-Communism Crusade (Giveaway)
nn-Sickle with blood-c 19 38 57 111 176 240

DRUMMER BOY AT GETTYSBURG
Eastern National Park & Monument Association: 1976
nn-Fred Ray-a 3 6 9 15 22 28

DUMBO (Walt Disney's..., The Flying Elephant)
Weatherbird Shoes/Ernest Kern Co.(Detroit)/ Wieboldt's (Chicago): 1941
(K.K. Publ. Giveaway)
nn-16 pgs., 9x10" (Rare) 43 86 129 271 461 650
nn-52 pgs., 5-1/2x8-1/2", slick cover in color; B&W interior; half text, half reprints 4-Color No. 17 (Dept. store) 22 44 66 131 216 300

DUMBO WEEKLY
Walt Disney Prod.: 1942 (Premium supplied by Diamond D-X Gas Stations)(4 pgs. each)
1 30 60 90 177 289 400
2-16 12 24 36 67 94 120
Binder only (linen-like stock) 150
NOTE: *A cover and binder came separate at gas stations. Came with membership card.*

EAT RIGHT TO WORK AND WIN
Swift & Company: 1942 (16 pgs.) (Giveaway)
Blondie, Henry, Flash Gordon by Alex Raymond, Toots & Casper, Thimble Theatre(Popeye), Tillie the Toiler, The Phantom, The Little King, & Bringing up Father - original strips just for this book -(in daily strip form which shows what foods we should eat and why) 28 56 84 168 274 380

EDWARD'S SHOES GIVEAWAY
Edward's Shoe Store: 1954 (Has clown on cover)
Contains comic with new cover. Many combinations possible. Contents determines price, 50-60 percent of original. (Similar to Comics From Weatherbird & Free Comics to You)

EE-YI-EE-YI-OH!
Consumer Power Co.: 1972 (Paper-c)
nn - A barnyard fable about ecology 1 3 4 6 8 10

ELSIE THE COW
D. S. Publishing Co.
Borden's cheese comic picture bk ("40, giveaway) 20 40 60 114 182 250
Borden Milk Giveaway-(16 pgs., nn) (3 ishs, "A Trip Through Space" and 2 others, 1957) 14 28 42 81 118 155
Elsie's Fun Book(1950; Borden Milk) 14 28 42 81 118 155
Everyday Birthday Fun With... (1957; 20 pgs.)(100th Anniversary); Kubert-a 14 28 42 81 118 155

ESCAPE FROM FEAR
Planned Parenthood of America: 1956, 1962, 1969 (Giveaway, 8 pgs., color) (On birth control)
1956 edition 11 22 33 62 86 110
1962 edition 4 8 12 27 44 60
1969 edition 3 6 9 17 26 35

EVEL KNIEVEL
Marvel Comics Group (Ideal Toy Corp.): 1974 (Giveaway, 20 pgs.)
nn-Contains photo on inside back-c 4 8 12 27 44 60

FAMOUS COMICS (Also see Favorite Comics)
Zain-Eppy/United Features Syndicate: No date; Mid 1930's (24 pgs., paper-c)
nn-Reprinted from 1933 & 1934 newspaper strips in color; Joe Palooka, Hairbreadth Harry, Napoleon, The Nebbs, etc. (Many different versions known) 77 154 231 493 847 1200

FAMOUS FAIRY TALES
K. K. Publ. Co.: 1942; 1943 (32 pgs.); 1944 (16 pgs.) (Giveaway, soft-c)
1942-Kelly-a 40 80 120 244 402 560
1943-r-/Fairy Tale Parade No. 2,3; Kelly-a 27 54 81 158 259 360
1944-Kelly-a 24 48 72 140 230 320

FAMOUS FUNNIES - A CARNIVAL OF COMICS
Eastern Color: 1933
36 pgs., no date given, no publisher, no number; contains strip reprints of The Bungle Family, Dixie Dugan, Hairbreadth Harry, Joe Palooka, Keeping Up With the Jones, Mutt & Jeff, Reg'lar Fellers, S'Matter Pop, Strange As It Seems, and others. This book was sold by M. C. Gaines to Wheatena, Malt-O-Milk, John Wanamaker, Kinney Shoe Stores, & others to be given away as premiums and radio giveaways (1933). Originally came with a mailing envelope. 541 1082 1623 3950 6975 10,000

FAMOUS GANG BOOK OF COMICS (Becomes Donald & Mickey Merry Christmas 1943 on)
Firestone Tire & Rubber Co.: Dec, 1942 (Christmas giveaway, 32 pgs., paper-c)
nn-(Rare)-Porky Pig, Bugs Bunny, Mary Jane & Sniffles, Elmer Fudd; r/Looney Tunes 71 142 213 454 777 1100

FANTASTIC FOUR
Marvel Comics
nn (1981, 32 pgs.) Young Model Builders Club 2 4 6 9 13 16
Vol. 3 #60 Baltimore Comic Book Show (10/02, newspaper supplement) 200,000 copies were distributed to Baltimore Sun home subscribers to promote Baltimore Comic Con 4.00

FATHER OF CHARITY
Catechetical Guild Giveaway: No date (32 pgs.; paper cover)
nn 5 10 15 25 31 36

FAVORITE COMICS (Also see Famous Comics)
Grocery Store Giveaway (Diff. Corp.) (detergent): 1934 (36 pgs.)
Book 1-The Nebbs, Strange As It Seems, Napoleon, Joe Palooka, Dixie Dugan, S'Matter Pop, Hairbreadth Harry, etc. reprints 200 400 600 900 - -
Book 2,3 150 300 450 675 - -

FAWCETT MINIATURES (See Mighty Midget)
Fawcett Publications: 1946 (3-3/4x5", 12-24 pgs.) (Wheaties giveaways)
Captain Marvel "And the Horn of Plenty"; Bulletman story 14 28 42 76 108 140
Captain Marvel "& the Raiders From Space"; Golden Arrow story 14 28 42 76 108 140
Captain Marvel Jr. "The Case of the Poison Press!" Bulletman story 14 28 42 76 108 140
Delecta of the Planets; C. C. Beck art; B&W inside; 12 pgs.; 3 printing variations (coloring) exist 20 40 60 114 182 250

FEARLESS FOSDICK
Capp Enterprises Inc.: 1951
...& The Case of The Red Feather 6 12 18 28 34 40

FIFTY WHO MADE DC GREAT
DC Comics: 1985 (Reg. size, slick-c)
nn 1 3 4 6 8 10

FIGHT FOR FREEDOM

Freedom Train nn © CN

Future Cop: L.A.P.D. © EA

HI, KIDS! HERE'S YOUR SET OF 5 GENE AUTRY COMIC BOOKS!

Gene Autry Comics Mailing Envelope © DELL

	GD 2.0	VG 4.0	FN 6.0	VF 8.0	VF/NM 9.0	NM- 9.2

National Assoc. of Mfgrs./General Comics: 1949, 1951 (Giveaway, 16 pgs.)
nn-Dan Barry-c/a; used in **POP**, pg. 102 — 6 12 18 33 41 48

FIRE AND BLAST
National Fire Protection Assoc.: 1952 (Giveaway, 16 pgs., paper-c)
nn-Mart Baily A-Bomb-c; about fire prevention — 16 32 48 94 147 200

FIRE CHIEF AND THE SAFE OL' FIREFLY, THE
National Board of Fire Underwriters: 1952 (16 pgs.) (Safety brochure given away at schools) (produced by American Visuals Corp.)(Eisner)
nn-(Rare) Eisner-c/a — 41 82 123 263 442 620

FLASH, THE
DC Comics
nn-(1990) Brochure for CBS TV series — 4.00
The Flash Comes to a Standstill (1981, General Foods giveaway, 8 pages, 3-1/2 x 6-3/4", oblong) — 2 4 6 11 16 20

FLASH COMICS (Also see Captain Marvel and Funny Stuff)
National Periodical Publications: 1946 (6-1/2x8-1/4", 32 pgs.)(Wheaties Giveaway)
nn-Johnny Thunder, Ghost Patrol, The Flash & Kubert Hawkman app.; Irwin Hasen-c/a — 100 200 700 1000 – –
NOTE: *All known copies were taped to Wheaties boxes and are never found in mint condition. Copies with light tape residue bring the listed prices in all grades*

FLASH FORCE 2000
DC Comics: 1984
1-5 — 6.00

FLASH GORDON
Dell Publishing Co.: 1943 (20 pgs.)
Macy's Giveaway-(Rare); not by Raymond — 58 116 174 371 636 900

FLASH GORDON
Harvey Comics: 1951 (16 pgs. in color, regular size, paper-c) (Gordon Bread giveaway)
1,2: 1-r/strips 10/24/37 - 2/6/38. 2-r/strips 7/14/40 - 10/6/40; Reprints by Raymond each.... — 2 4 6 9 12 15
NOTE: *Most copies have brittle edges.*

FLINTSTONES FUN BOOK, THE
Denny's giveaway: 1990
1-20 — 1 2 3 5 6 8

FLOOD RELIEF
Malibu Comics (Ultraverse): Jan, 1994 (36 pgs.)(Ordered thru mail w/$5.00 to Red Cross)
1-Hardcase, Prime & Prototype app. — 6.00

FOREST FIRE (Also see The Blazing Forest and Smokey Bear)
American Forestry Assn.(Commerical Comics): 1949 (dated-1950) (16 pgs., paper-c)
nn-Intro/1st app. Smokey The Forest Fire Preventing Bear; created by Rudy Wendelein; Wendelein/Sparling-a; 'Carter Oil Co.' on back-c of original — 20 40 60 114 182 250

FOREST RANGER HANDBOOK
Wrather Corp.: 1967 (5x7", 20 pgs., slick-c)
nn-WIth Corey Stuart & Lassie photo-c — 2 4 6 13 18 22

FORGOTTEN STORY BEHIND NORTH BEACH, THE
Catechetical Guild: No date (8 pgs., paper-c)
nn — 5 10 15 24 30 35

FORK IN THE ROAD
U.S. Army Recruiting Service: 1961 (16 pgs., paper-c)
nn — 2 4 6 11 16 20

48 FAMOUS AMERICANS
J. C. Penney Co. (Cpr. Edwin H. Stroh): 1947 (Giveaway) (Half-size in color)
nn - Simon & Kirby-a — 11 22 33 64 90 115

FOXHOLE ON YOUR LAWN
No Publisher: No date
nn-Charles Biro art — 4 7 10 14 17 20

FRANKIE LUER'S SPACE ADVENTURES
Luer Packing Co.: 1955 (5x7", 36 pgs., slick-c)
nn - With Davey Rocket — 4 8 12 17 21 24

FREDDY
Charlton Comics
Schiff's Shoes Presents... #1 (1959)-Giveaway — 4 8 11 16 19 22

FREE COMIC BOOK DAY EDITIONS (Now listed in the regular section)

FREE COMICS TO YOU FROM... (name of shoe store) (Has clown on cover & another with a rabbit) (Like comics from Weather Bird & Edward's Shoes)
Shoe Store Giveaway: Circa 1956, 1960-61
Contains a comic bound with new cover - several combinations possible; some Harvey titles known. Contents determine price.

FREEDOM TRAIN
Street & Smith Publications: 1948 (Giveaway)
nn-Powell-c w/mailer — 16 32 48 94 147 200

FREIHOFER'S COMIC BOOK
All-American Comics: 1940s (7 1/2 x 10 1/4")(Freihofer's Donuts promotional)
2nd edition-(Scarce) Cover features All-American Comics characters Ultra-Man, Hop Harrigan, Red, White and Blue, Scribbly and others (A CGC 4.0 copy sold for $836.50 in May, 2012)

FRIENDLY GHOST, CASPER, THE
Harvey Publications: 1967 (16 pgs.)
American Dental Assoc. giveaway-Small size — 3 6 9 17 25 32

FRITO-LAY GIVEAWAY
Frito-Lay: 1962 (3-1/4x7", soft-c, 16 pgs.) (Disney)
nn-Donald Duck "Plotting Picnickers" — 5 10 15 30 50 70
nn-Ludwig Von Drake "Fish Stampede" — 3 6 9 19 30 40
nn- Mickey Mouse & Goofy "Bicep Bungle" — 3 6 9 21 33 45

FROM GOODWILL INDUSTRIES, A GOOD LIFE
Goodwill Industries: 1950s (regular size)
1 — 8 16 24 40 50 60

FRONTIER DAYS
Robin Hood Shoe Store (Brown Shoe): 1956 (Giveaway)
1 — 4 7 10 14 17 20

FRONTIERS OF FREEDOM
Institute of Life Insurance: 1950 (Giveaway, paper cover)
nn-Dan Barry-a — 9 18 27 47 61 75

FUNNIES ON PARADE (Premium)(See Toy World Funnies)
Eastern Color Printing Co.: 1933 (36 pgs., slick cover)
No date or publisher listed
nn-Contains Sunday page reprints of Mutt & Jeff, Joe Palooka, Hairbreadth Harry, Reg'lar Fellers, Skippy, & others (10,000 print run). This book was printed for Proctor & Gamble to be given away & came out before Famous Funnies or Century of Comics. — 1000 2000 3000 76000 13,800 20,000

FUNNY PICTURE STORIES
Comics Magazine Co./Centaur Publications: 1930s (Giveaway, 16-20 pgs., slick-c)
Promotes diff. laundries; has box on cover where "your Laundry Name" is printed — 41 82 123 256 428 600

FUNNY STUFF (Also see Captain Marvel & Flash Comics)
National Periodical Publications (Wheaties Giveaway): 1946 (6-1/2x8-1/4")
nn-(Scarce)-Dodo & the Frog, Three Mouseketeers, etc.; came taped to Wheaties box; never found in better than fine — 45 90 315 450 – –

FUTURE COP: L.A.P.D. (Electronic Arts video game)
DC Comics (WildStorm): 1998
nn-Ron Lim-a/Dave Johnson-c — 3.00

GABBY HAYES WESTERN (Movie star)
Fawcett Publications
Quaker Oats Giveaway nn's(#1-5, 1951, 2-1/2x7") (Kagran Corp.)-...In Tracks of Guilt, ...In the Fence Post Mystery, ...In the Accidental Sherlock, ...In the Frame-Up, ...In the Double Cross Brand known — 10 20 30 54 72 90
Mailing Envelope (has illo of Gabby on front) — 10 20 30 54 72 90

GARY GIBSON COMICS (Donut club membership)
National Dunking Association: 1950 (Included in donut box with pin and card)
1-Western soft-c, 16 pgs.; folded into the box — 5 10 14 20 24 28

GENE AUTRY COMICS
Dell Publishing Co.
...Adventure Comics And Play-Fun Book ('47)-32 pgs., 8x6-1/2"; games, comics, magic (Pillsbury premium) — 20 40 60 120 196 270
Quaker Oats Giveaway(1950)-2-1/2x6-3/4"; 5 different versions; "Death Card Gang", "Phantoms of the Cave", "Riddle of Laughing Mtn.", "Secret of Lost Valley", "Bond of the Broken Arrow" (came in wrapper) each... — 10 20 30 58 79 100
Mailing Envelope (has illo. of Gene on front) — 10 20 30 58 79 100
3-D Giveaway(1953)-Pocket-size; 5 different — 10 20 30 58 79 100

Gulf Funny Weekly #357 © Gulf Oil

Henry Aldrich Comics nn © DELL

Hoods Up #1 © Fram Corp.

	GD 2.0	VG 4.0	FN 6.0	VF 8.0	VF/NM 9.0	NM- 9.2
Mailing Envelope (no art on front)	8	16	24	44	57	70

GENE AUTRY TIM (Formerly Tim) (Becomes Tim in Space)
Tim Stores: 1950 (Half-size) (B&W Giveaway)
nn-Several issues (All Scarce) 19 38 57 109 172 235

GENERAL FOODS SUPER-HEROES
DC Comics: 1979, 1980
1-4 (1979), 1-4 (1980) each... 12.00

G. I. COMICS (Also see Jeep & Overseas Comics)
Giveaways: 1945 - No. 73?, 1946 (Distributed to U. S. Armed Forces)
1-73-Contains Prince Valiant by Foster, Blondie, Smilin' Jack, Mickey Finn, Terry & the Pirates, Donald Duck, Alley Oop, Moon Mullins & Capt. Easy strip reprints (at least 73 issues known to exist) 8 16 24 42 54 65

GODZILLA VS. MEGALON
Cinema Shares Int.: 1976 (4 pgs. on newsprint) (Movie theater giveaway)
nn-1st. comic app. Godzilla in U.S. 4 8 12 17 21 24

GOLDEN ARROW
Fawcett Publications
...Well Known Comics (1944; 12 pgs.; 8-1/2x10-1/2"; paper-c; glued binding)- Bestmaid/Samuel Lowe giveaway; printed in green 10 20 30 54 72 90

GOLDILOCKS & THE THREE BEARS
K. K. Publications: 1943 (Giveaway)
nn 13 26 39 74 105 135

GREAT PEOPLE OF GENESIS, THE
David C. Cook Publ. Co.: No date (Religious giveaway, 64 pgs.)
nn-Reprint/Sunday Pix Weekly 5 10 15 23 28 32

GREAT SACRAMENT, THE
Catechetical Guild: 1953 (Giveaway, 36 pgs.)
nn 5 10 15 22 26 30

GREEN JET COMICS, THE (See Comic Books, Series 1)

GRENADA
Commercial Comics Co.: 1983 (Giveaway produced by the CIA)
1-Air dropped over Grenada during 1983 invasion 3 6 9 21 33 45

GRIT (YOU'VE GOT TO HAVE...)
GRIT Publishing Co.: 1959
nn-GRIT newspaper sales recruitment comic; Schaffenberger-a. Later version has altered artwork 5 10 15 22 26 30

GROWING UP WITH JUDY
1952
nn-General Electric giveaway 4 8 12 18 22 25

GULF FUNNY WEEKLY (Gulf Comic Weekly No. 1-4)(See Standard Oil Comics)
Gulf Oil Company (Giveaway): 1933 - No. 422, 5/23/41 (in full color; 4 pgs.; tabloid size to 2/3/39; 2/10/39 on, regular comic book size)(early issues undated)

	GD	VG	FN	VF	VF/NM	NM-
1	77	154	231	493	847	1200
2-5	37	74	111	222	361	500
6-30	21	42	63	124	202	280
31-100	15	30	45	86	133	180
101-196	12	24	36	67	94	120
197-Wings Winfair begins(1/29/37); by Fred Meagher beginning in 1938	26	52	78	154	252	350
198-300 (Last tabloid size)	15	30	45	86	133	180
301-350 (Regular size)	10	20	30	54	72	90
351-422	8	16	24	42	54	65

GULLIVER'S TRAVELS
Macy's Department Store: 1939, small size
nn-Christmas giveaway 14 28 42 82 121 160

GUN THAT WON THE WEST, THE
Winchester-Western Division & Olin Mathieson Chemical Corp.: 1956 (Giveaway, 24 pgs.)
nn-Painted-c 5 10 15 24 30 35

HAPPINESS AND HEALING FOR YOU (Also see Oral Roberts'...)
Commercial Comics: 1955 (36 pgs., slick cover) (Oral Roberts Giveaway)
nn 10 20 30 56 76 95
NOTE: *The success of this book prompted Oral Roberts to go into the publishing business himself to produce his own material.*

HAPPI TIME FUN BOOK
Sears, Roebuck & Co.: 1940s - 1950s (32 pgs., soft-c)
nn-Comics, games, puzzles, & magic tricks cut -outs 4 7 10 14 17 20

HAPPY CHAMP, THE (The Story of Joker Osborn)
Western Publ.: 1965
nn-About water-skiing 3 6 9 19 30 40

HAPPY TOOTH
DC Comics: 1996
1 3.00

HARLEM YOUTH REPORT (Also see All-Negro Comics and Negro Romances)
Custom Comics, Inc.: 1964 (Giveaway)(No #1-4)
5-"Youth in the Ghetto" and "The Blueprint For Change"; distr. in Harlem only; has map of central Harlem on back-c (scarce) 57 114 171 456 1028 1600

HAWKMAN - THE SKY'S THE LIMIT
DC Comics: 1981 (General Foods giveaway, 8 pages, 3-1/2 x 6-3/4", oblong)
nn 2 4 6 10 14 18

HAWTHORN-MELODY FARMS DAIRY COMICS
Everybody's Publishing Co.: No date (1950's) (Giveaway)
nn-Cheerie Chick, Tuffy Turtle, Robin Koo Koo, Donald & Longhorn Legends 2 4 6 8 11 14

H-BOMB AND YOU
Commercial Comics: (? date) (small size, slick-c)
nn - H–Bomb explosion-c 16 32 45 94 147 200

HENRY ALDRICH COMICS (TV)
Dell Publishing Co.: 1951 (16 pgs., soft-c)
Giveaway - Capehart radio 3 6 9 19 30 40

HERE IS SANTA CLAUS
Goldsmith Publ. Co. (Kann's in Washington, D.C.): 1930s (16 pgs., 8 in color) (stiff paper covers)
nn 14 28 42 80 115 150

HERE'S HOW AMERICA'S CARTOONISTS HELP TO SELL U.S. SAVINGS BONDS
Harvey Comics: 1950? (16 pgs., giveaway, paper cover)
Contains: Joe Palooka, Donald Duck, Archie, Kerry Drake, Red Ryder, Blondie & Steve Canyon 20 40 60 114 182 250

HISTORY OF GAS
American Gas Assoc.: Mar, 1947 (Giveaway, 16 pgs., soft-c)
nn-Miss Flame narrates 9 18 27 50 65 80

HOME DEPOT, SAFETY HEROES
Marvel Comics.: Oct, 2005 (Giveaway)
nn-Spider-Man and the Fantastic Four on the cover; Olliffe-a/c; Roseman-s 2.50

HONEYBEE BIRDWHISTLE AND HER PET PEPI (Introducing...)
Newspaper Enterprise Assoc.: 1969 (Giveaway, 24 pgs., B&W, slick cover)
nn-Contains Freckles newspaper strips with a short biography of Henry Fornhals (artist) & Fred Fox (writer) of the strip 4 8 12 28 47 65

HOODS UP
Fram Corp.: 1953 (15¢, distributed to service station owners, 16 pgs.)
1-(Very Rare); only 2 known); Eisner-c/a in all (a CGC 9.0 copy sold for $1840 in 2006)
2-6-(Very Rare; only 1 known of #3, 2 known of #2,4) 48 96 144 302 514 725
NOTE: *Convertible Connie gives tips for service stations, selling Fram oil filters.*

HOOKED (Anti-drug comic distributed at NYC methadone clinics)
U.S. Dept. of Health: 1966 (giveaway, oblong)
nn-Distributed between May and July, 1966 4 8 12 23 37 50

HOPALONG CASSIDY
Fawcett Publications

	GD	VG	FN	VF	VF/NM	NM-
Grape Nuts Flakes giveaway (1950,9x6")	14	28	42	78	112	145
...& the Mad Barber (1951 Bond Bread giveaway)-7x5"; used in **SOTI**, pgs. 308,309	18	36	54	103	162	220
...Meets the Brend Brothers Bandits (1951 Bond Bread giveaway, color, paper-c, 16 pgs., 3-1/2x7")- Fawcett Publ.	9	18	27	47	61	75
...Strange Legacy (1951 Bond Bread giveaway)	9	18	27	47	61	75
White Tower Giveaway (1946, 16pgs., paper-c)	9	18	27	52	69	85

HOPPY THE MARVEL BUNNY (WELL KNOWN COMICS)
Fawcett Publications: 1944 (8-1/2x10-1/2", paper-c)
Bestmaid/Samuel Lowe (printed in red or blue) 10 20 30 56 76 95

HOT STUFF, THE LITTLE DEVIL
Harvey Publications (Illustrated Humor):1963

The Iron Giant © WB

It's Fun to Stay Alive © NADA

Joe Palooka Body Building Instruction Book © HARV

GD 2.0 VG 4.0 FN 6.0 VF 8.0 VF/NM 9.0 NM- 9.2

Shoestore Giveaway 3 6 9 21 33 45

HOW KIDS ENJOY NEW YORK
American Airlines: 1966 (Giveaway, 40 pgs., 4x9")
nn-Includes 8 color pages by Bob Kane featuring a tour of New York and his studio (a VG copy sold for $180 and a FN+ sold for $250 in 2004)

HOW STALIN HOPES WE WILL DESTROY AMERICA
Joe Lowe Co. (Pictorial Media): 1951 (Giveaway, 16 pgs.)
nn 39 78 117 240 395 550

HURRICANE KIDS, THE (Also See Magic Morro, The Owl, Popular Comics #45)
R.S. Callender: 1941 (Giveaway, 7-1/2x5-1/4", soft-c)
nn-Will Ely-a. 8 16 24 44 57 70

IF THE DEVIL WOULD TALK
Roman Catholic Catechetical Guild/Impact Publ.: 1950; 1958 (32 pgs.; paper cover; in full color)
nn-(Scarce)-About secularism (20-30 copies known to exist); very low distribution 116 232 348 742 1271 1800
1958 Edition-(Impact Publ.); art & script changed to meet church criticism of earlier edition; 80 plus copies known to exist 33 66 99 194 317 440
Black & White version of nn edition; small size; only 4 known copies exist 36 72 108 211 343 475
NOTE: *The original edition of this book was printed and killed by the Guild's board of directors. It is believed that a very limited number of copies were distributed. The 1958 version was a complete bomb with very limited, if any, circulation. In 1979, 11 original, 4 1958 reprints, and 4 B&W's surfaced from the Guild's old files in St. Paul, Minnesota.*

IN LOVE WITH JESUS
Catechetical Educational Society: 1952 (Giveaway, 36 pgs.)
nn 7 14 21 37 46 55

INTERSTATE THEATRES' FUN CLUB COMICS
Interstate Theatres: Mid 1940's (10¢ on cover) (B&W cover) (Premium)
Cover features MLJ characters looking at a copy of Top-Notch Comics, but contains an early Detective Comic on inside; many combinations 14 28 42 78 112 145

IN THE GOOD HANDS OF THE ROCKEFELLER TEAM
Country Art Studios: No date (paper cover, 8 pgs.)
nn-Joe Simon-a 8 16 24 42 54 65

IRON GIANT
DC Comics: 1999 (4 pages, theater giveaway)
1-Previews movie 3.00

IRON HORSE GOES TO WAR, THE
Association of American Railroads: 1960 (Giveaway, 16 pgs.)
nn-Civil War & railroads 3 6 9 17 26 35

IS THIS TOMORROW?
Catechetical Guild: 1947 (One Shot) (3 editions) (52 pgs.)
1-Theme of communists taking over the USA; (no price on cover) Used in **POP**, pg. 102 36 72 108 211 343 475
1-(10¢ on cover)(Red price on yellow circle) 36 72 108 211 343 475
1-(10¢ on cover)(Yellow price on red circle) 36 72 108 211 343 475
1-(10¢ on cover)(Yellow price on black circle) 36 72 108 211 343 475
1-Has blank circle with no price on cover 36 72 108 211 343 475
Black & White advance copy titled "Confidential" (52 pgs.)-Contains script and art edited out of the color edition, including one page of extreme violence showing mob nailing a Cardinal to a door; (only two known copies). A VF+ sold in 2/08 for $3346. A NM 9.2 sold in 11/16 for $2629.
NOTE: *The original color version first sold for 10 cents. Since sales were good, it was later printed as a giveaway. Approximately four million in total were printed. The two black and white copies listed plus two other versions as well as a full color untrimmed version surfaced in 1979 from the Guild's old files in St. Paul, Minnesota.*

IT'S FUN TO STAY ALIVE
National Automobile Dealers Association: 1948 (Giveaway, 16 pgs., heavy stock paper)
Featuring: Bugs Bunny, The Berrys, Dixie Dugan, Elmer, Henry, Tim Tyler, Bruce Gentry, Abbie & Slats, Joe Jinks, The Toodles, & Cokey; all art copyright 1946-48 drawn especially for this book 15 30 45 84 127 170

IT'S TIME FOR REASON - NOT TREASON
Liberty Lobby: 1967 (Reg. size, soft-c) (Anti-communist)
nn 6 12 18 41 76 110

JACK AND CHUCK LEARN THE HARD WAY
Commercia Comics/Wagner Electric Co.: 1950s (Reg. size, soft-c)
nn-Automotive giveaway 9 18 27 47 61 75

JACK & JILL VISIT TOYTOWN WITH ELMER THE ELF
Butler Brothers (Toytown Stores): 1949 (Giveaway, 16 pgs., paper cover)
nn 5 10 15 22 26 30

JACK ARMSTRONG (Radio)(See True Comics)
Parents' Institute: 1949
12-Premium version (distr. in Chicago only); Free printed on upper right-c; no price (Rare) 18 36 54 107 169 230

JACKIE JOYNER KERSEE IN HIGH HURDLES (Kellogg's Tony's Sports Comics)
DC Comics: 1992 (Sports Illustrated)
nn 5.00

JACKPOT OF FUN COMIC BOOK
DCA Food Ind.: 1957, giveaway (paper cover, regular size)
nn-Features Howdy Doody 12 24 36 67 94 120

JEDLICKA SHOES
DC Comics: 1961 (Funny animal-c)
nn-Contains Superman #142 9 18 27 58 114 170

JEEP COMICS
R. B. Leffingwell & Co.: 1945 - 1946 (16 pgs.)(King Features Syndicate)
1-(Giveaways)-Strip reprints in all issues; Tarzan, Flash Gordon, Blondie, The Nebbs, Little Iodine, Red Ryder, Don Winslow, The Phantom, Johnny Hazard, Katzenjammer Kids; distr. to U.S. Armed Forces from 1945-1946 16 32 48 94 147 200
2-5 14 28 42 80 115 150
6-46 6 12 18 31 38 45

JINGLE BELLS CHRISTMAS BOOK
Montgomery Ward (Giveaway): 1971 (20 pgs., B&W inside, slick-c)
nn 6.00

JOAN OF ARC
Catechetical Guild (Topix) (Giveaway): No date (28 pgs., blank back-c)
nn-Ingrid Bergman photo-c; Addison Burbank-a 13 26 39 72 101 130
NOTE: *Unpublished version exists which came from the Guild's files.*

JOE PALOOKA (2nd Series)
Harvey Publications
...Body Building Instruction Book (1958 B&M Sports Toy giveaway, 16 pgs., 5-1/4x7")-Origin 8 16 24 42 54 65
...Fights His Way Back (1945 Giveaway, 24 pgs.) Family Comics 11 22 33 62 86 110
...in Hi There! (1949 Red Cross giveaway, 12 pgs., 4-3/4x6") 7 14 21 37 46 55
...in It's All in the Family (1945 Red Cross giveaway, 16 pgs., regular size) 8 16 24 40 50 60

JOE THE GENIE OF STEEL (Also see "Return of...")
U.S. Steel Corp., Pittsburgh, PA: 1950 (16 pgs, reg size)
nn-Joe Magarac, the Paul Bunyan of steel 9 18 27 50 65 80

JOHNNY GETS THE WORD
Dept. of Health of New York City: 1963 (small size)
nn - Prevention of venereal diseases 5 10 15 33 57 80
NOTE: *A CGC 9.6 copy sold in 2016 for $263.*

JOHNNY JINGLE'S LUCKY DAY
American Dairy Assoc.: 1956 (16 pgs.; 7-1/4x5-1/8") (Giveaway) (Disney)
nn 5 10 15 24 30 35

JOHNSON MAKES THE TEAM
B.F. Goodrich: 1950 (Reg. size) (Football giveaway)
nn 6 12 18 31 38 45

JO-JOY (The Adventures of...)
W. T. Grant Dept. Stores: 1945 - 1953 (Christmas gift comic, 16 pgs., 7-1/16x10-1/4")
1945-53 issues 7 14 21 37 46 55

JOLLY CHRISTMAS BOOK (See Christmas Journey Through Space)
Promotional Publ. Co.: 1951; 1954; 1955 (36 pgs.; 24 pgs.)
1951-(Woolworth giveaway)-slightly oversized; no slick cover; Marv Levy-c/a 7 14 21 37 46 55
1954-(Hot Shoppes giveaway)-regular size-reprints 1951 issue; slick cover added; 24 pgs.; no ads 6 12 18 31 38 45
1955-(J. M. McDonald Co. giveaway)-reg. size 6 12 18 28 34 40

JOURNEY OF DISCOVERY WITH MARK STEEL (See Mark Steel)

JUMPING JACKS PRESENTS THE WHIZ KIDS
Jumping Jacks Stores giveaway: 1978 (In 3-D) with glasses (4 pgs.)
nn 6.00

Kerry Drake Detective Cases © PS

King James © DC

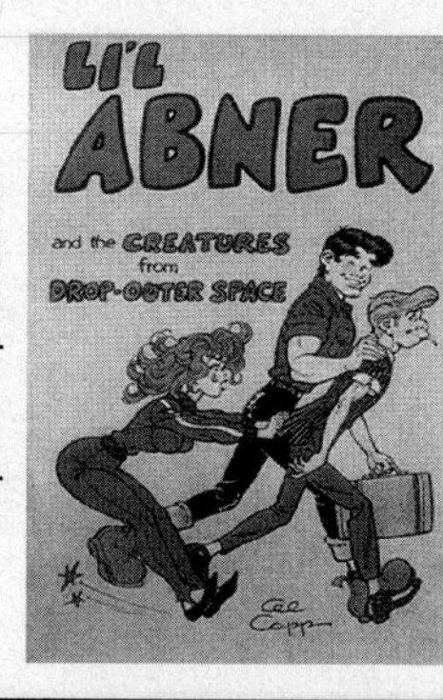

Li'l Abner and the Creatures From Drop-Outer Space © HARV

JUNGLE BOOK FUN BOOK, THE (Disney)
Baskin Robbins: 1978

	GD 2.0	VG 4.0	FN 6.0	VF 8.0	VF/NM 9.0	NM- 9.2
nn-Ice Cream giveaway	2	4	6	9	12	15

JUSTICE LEAGUE OF AMERICA
DC Comics: 1999 (included in Justice League of America Monopoly game)

	GD 2.0	VG 4.0	FN 6.0	VF 8.0	VF/NM 9.0	NM- 9.2
nn - Reprints 1st app. in Brave and the Bold #28						2.50

KASCO KOMICS
Kasko Grainfeed (Giveaway): 1945; No. 2, 1949 (Regular size, paper-c)

	GD 2.0	VG 4.0	FN 6.0	VF 8.0	VF/NM 9.0	NM- 9.2
1(1945)-Similar to Katy Keene; Bill Woggon-a; 28 pgs.; 6-7/8x9-7/8"	20	40	60	120	195	270
2(1949)-Woggon-c/a	15	30	45	84	127	170

KATY AND KEN VISIT SANTA WITH MISTER WISH
S. S. Kresge Co. : 1948 (Giveaway, 16 pgs., paper-c)

	GD 2.0	VG 4.0	FN 6.0	VF 8.0	VF/NM 9.0	NM- 9.2
nn	6	12	18	29	36	42

KELLOGG'S CINNAMON MINI-BUNS SUPER-HEROES
DC Comics: 1993 (4 1/4" x 2 3/4")

	GD 2.0	VG 4.0	FN 6.0	VF 8.0	VF/NM 9.0	NM- 9.2
4 editions: Flash, Justice League America, Superman, Wonder Woman and the Star Riders each.....						4.00

KERRY DRAKE DETECTIVE CASES
Publisher's Syndicate

	GD 2.0	VG 4.0	FN 6.0	VF 8.0	VF/NM 9.0	NM- 9.2
...in the Case of the Sleeping City-(1951)-16 pg. giveaway for armed forces; paper cover	6	12	18	28	34	40

KEY COMICS
Key Clothing Co./Peterson Clothing: 1951 - 1956 (32 pgs.) (Giveaway)
Contains a comic from different publishers bound with new cover. Cover changed each year. Many combinations possible. Distributed in Nebraska, Iowa, & Kansas. Contents would determine price, 40-60 percent of original.

KING JAMES "THE KING OF BASKETBALL"
DC Comics: 2004 (Promo comic for LeBron James and Powerade Flava23 sports drink)

	GD 2.0	VG 4.0	FN 6.0	VF 8.0	VF/NM 9.0	NM- 9.2
nn - Ten different covers by various artists; 4 covers for retail, 4 for mail-in, 1 for military commissaries, and 1 general market; Damion Scott-a/Gary Phillips-s						2.50

KIRBY'S SHOES COMICS
Kirby's Shoes: 1959 - 1961 (8 pgs., soft-c)

	GD 2.0	VG 4.0	FN 6.0	VF 8.0	VF/NM 9.0	NM- 9.2
nn-Features Kirby the Golden Bear	3	5	7	10	12	14

KITE FUN BOOK
Pacific, Gas & Electric/Sou. California Edison/Florida Power & Light/ Missouri Public Service Co.: 1952 - 1998 (16 pgs, 5x7-1/4", soft-c)

	GD 2.0	VG 4.0	FN 6.0	VF 8.0	VF/NM 9.0	NM- 9.2
1952-Having Fun With Kites (P.G.&E.)	10	20	30	54	72	90
1953-Pinocchio Learns About Kites (Disney)	37	74	111	222	361	500
1954-Donald Duck Tells About Kites-Fla. Power, S.C.E. & version with label issues -Barks pencils-8 pgs.; inks-7 pgs. (Rare)	194	388	582	1242	2121	3000
1954-Donald Duck Tells About Kites-P.G.&E. issue -7th page redrawn changing middle 3 panels to show P.G.&E. in story line; (All Barks-a) Scarce	181	362	543	1158	1979	2800
1955-Brer Rabbit in "A Kite Tail" (Disney)	24	48	72	144	237	330
1956-Woody Woodpecker (Lantz)	12	24	36	67	94	120
1957-Ruff and Reddy (exist?)						
1958-Tom And Jerry (M.G.M.)	9	18	27	52	69	85
1959-Bugs Bunny (Warner Bros.)	4	8	12	27	44	60
1960-Porky Pig (Warner Bros.)	4	8	12	28	47	65
1960-Bugs Bunny (Warner Bros.)	4	8	12	28	47	65
1961-Huckleberry Hound (Hanna-Barbera)	5	10	15	31	53	75
1962-Yogi Bear (Hanna-Barbera)	4	8	12	25	40	55
1963-Rocky and Bullwinkle (TV)(Jay Ward)	5	10	15	35	63	90
1963-Top Cat (TV)(Hanna-Barbera)	3	6	9	19	30	40
1964-Magilla Gorilla (TV)(Hanna-Barbera)	3	6	9	17	26	35
1965-Jinks, Pixie and Dixie (TV)(Hanna-Barbera)	3	6	9	15	22	28
1965-Tweety and Sylvester (Warner); S.C.E. version with Reddy Kilowatt app.	2	4	6	9	13	16
1966-Secret Squirrel (Hanna-Barbera); S.C.E. version with Reddy Kilowatt app.	5	10	15	30	50	70
1967-Beep! Beep! The Road Runner (TV)(Warner)	2	4	6	11	16	20
1968-Bugs Bunny (Warner Bros.)	2	4	6	13	18	22
1969-Dastardly and Muttley (TV)(Hanna-Barbera)	3	6	9	19	30	40
1970-Rocky and Bullwinkle (TV)(Jay Ward)	4	8	12	27	44	60
1971-Beep! Beep! The Road Runner (TV)(Warner)	2	4	6	11	16	20
1972-The Pink Panther (TV)	2	4	6	10	14	18
1973-Lassie (TV)	3	6	9	15	22	28
1974-Underdog (TV)	2	4	6	11	16	20
1975-Ben Franklin	2	4	6	8	10	12
1976-The Brady Bunch (TV)	3	6	9	16	23	30
1977-Ben Franklin (exist?)	2	4	6	8	10	12
1977-Popeye	2	4	6	9	13	16
1978-Happy Days (TV)	2	4	6	11	16	20
1979-Eight is Enough (TV)	2	4	6	9	13	16
1980-The Waltons (TV, released in 1981)	2	4	6	9	13	16
1982-Tweety and Sylvester	2	4	6	8	11	14
1984-Smokey Bear	1	3	4	6	8	10
1986-Road Runner	1	2	3	5	6	8
1997-Thomas Edison						4.00
1998-Edison Field (Anaheim Stadium)						3.00

KNOWING'S NOT ENOUGH
Commercial Comics: 1956 (Reg. size, paper-c) (United States Steel safety giveaway)

	GD 2.0	VG 4.0	FN 6.0	VF 8.0	VF/NM 9.0	NM- 9.2
nn	7	14	21	35	43	50

KNOW YOUR MASS
Catechetical Guild: No. 303, 1958 (35¢, 100 Pg. Giant) (Square binding)

	GD 2.0	VG 4.0	FN 6.0	VF 8.0	VF/NM 9.0	NM- 9.2
303-In color	7	14	21	35	43	50

KOLYNOS PRESENTS THE WHITE GUARD
Whitehall Pharmacal Co.: 1949 (paper cover, 8 pgs.)

	GD 2.0	VG 4.0	FN 6.0	VF 8.0	VF/NM 9.0	NM- 9.2
nn	6	12	18	31	38	45

KOLYNOS PRESENTS THE WICKED WITCH
Whitehall Pharmacal Co.: 1951 (paper cover, 8 pgs.)

	GD 2.0	VG 4.0	FN 6.0	VF 8.0	VF/NM 9.0	NM- 9.2
nn-Anti-tooth decay	4	7	10	14	17	20

K. O. PUNCH, THE (Also see Lucky Fights It Through & Sidewalk Romance)
E. C. Comics: 1948 (VD Educational giveaway)

	GD 2.0	VG 4.0	FN 6.0	VF 8.0	VF/NM 9.0	NM- 9.2
nn-Feldstein-splash; Kamen-a	113	226	339	718	1234	1750

KOREA MY HOME (Also see Yalta to Korea)
Johnstone and Cushing: nd (1950s, slick-c, regular size)

	GD 2.0	VG 4.0	FN 6.0	VF 8.0	VF/NM 9.0	NM- 9.2
nn-Anti-communist; Korean War	23	46	69	136	223	310

KRIM-KO KOMICS
Krim-ko Chocolate Drink: 5/18/35 - No. 6, 6/22/35; 1936 - 1939 (weekly)

	GD 2.0	VG 4.0	FN 6.0	VF 8.0	VF/NM 9.0	NM- 9.2
1-(16 pgs., soft-c, Dairy giveaways)-Tom, Mary & Sparky Advs. by Russell Keaton, Jim Hawkins by Dick Moores, Mystery Island! by Rick Yager begin	14	28	42	78	112	145
2-6 (6/22/35)	10	20	30	58	79	100
Lola, Secret Agent; 184 issues, 4 pg. giveaways - all original stories each....	8	16	24	40	50	60

LABOR IS A PARTNER
Catechetical Guild Educational Society: 1949 (32 pgs., paper-c)

	GD 2.0	VG 4.0	FN 6.0	VF 8.0	VF/NM 9.0	NM- 9.2
nn-Anti-communism	41	82	123	256	428	600

Confidential Preview-(8-1/2x11", B&W, saddle stitched)-only one known copy; text varies from color version, advertises next book on secularism (If the Devil Would Talk)
(A VF- copy sold for $2629 in 11/2016 and a VG/FN copy sold for $454 in 1/2017)

LADIES - WOULDN'T IT BE BETTER TO KNOW
American Cancer Society: 1969 (Reg. size)

	GD 2.0	VG 4.0	FN 6.0	VF 8.0	VF/NM 9.0	NM- 9.2
nn	4	8	12	22	35	48

LADY AND THE TRAMP IN "BUTTER LATE THAN NEVER"
American Dairy Assoc. (Premium): 1955 (16 pgs., 5x7-1/4", soft-c) (Disney)

	GD 2.0	VG 4.0	FN 6.0	VF 8.0	VF/NM 9.0	NM- 9.2
nn	9	18	27	47	61	75

LASSIE (TV)
Dell Publ. Co

	GD 2.0	VG 4.0	FN 6.0	VF 8.0	VF/NM 9.0	NM- 9.2
The Adventures of... nn-(Red Heart Dog Food giveaway, 1949)-16 pgs, soft-c; 1st app. Lassie in comics	36	72	108	216	351	485

LIFE OF THE BLESSED VIRGIN
Catechetical Guild (Giveaway): 1950 (68pgs.) (square binding)

	GD 2.0	VG 4.0	FN 6.0	VF 8.0	VF/NM 9.0	NM- 9.2
nn-Contains "The Woman of the Promise" & "Mother of Us All" rebound	9	18	27	50	65	80

LIGHTNING RACERS
DC Comics: 1989

	GD 2.0	VG 4.0	FN 6.0	VF 8.0	VF/NM 9.0	NM- 9.2
1						4.50

LI'L ABNER (Al Capp's) (Also see Natural Disasters!)
Harvey Publ./Toby Press

	GD 2.0	VG 4.0	FN 6.0	VF 8.0	VF/NM 9.0	NM- 9.2
...& the Creatures from Drop-Outer Space-nn (Job Corps giveaway; 36 pgs., in color) (entire book by Frank Frazetta)	21	42	63	124	202	280
...Joins the Navy (1950) (Toby Press Premium)	11	22	33	62	86	110

Al Capp by Li'l Abner (Circa 1946, nd, giveaway) Al Capp bio and his life as an amputee

Lone Ranger Cheerios 1954 © Lone Ranger Inc.

Lucky Fights It Through © EC

March of Comics #36 © KING

	GD 2.0	VG 4.0	FN 6.0	VF 8.0	VF/NM 9.0	NM- 9.2
	11	22	33	62	86	110

LITTLE ALONZO
Macy's Dept. Store: 1938 (B&W, 5-1/2x8-1/2")(Christmas giveaway)
nn-By Ferdinand the Bull's Munro Leaf 9 18 27 50 65 80

LITTLE ARCHIE (See Archie Comics)

LITTLE DOT
Harvey Publications
Shoe store giveaway 2 4 8 12 27 44 60

LITTLE FIR TREE, THE
W. T. Grant Co. : nd (1942) (8-1/2x11") (12 pgs. with cover, color & B&W, heavy paper) (Christmas giveaway)
nn-Story by Hans Christian Anderson; 8 pg. Kelly-r/Santa Claus Funnies (not signed); X-Mas-c
94 188 282 597 1024 1450

LITTLE KLINKER
Little Klinker Ventures: Nov, 1960 (20 pgs.) (slick cover) (Montgomery Ward Giveaway)
nn - Christmas; Santa-c 3 6 9 14 20 25

LITTLE MISS SUNBEAM COMICS
Magazine Enterprises/Quality Bakers of America
Bread Giveaway 1-4(Quality Bakers, 1949-50)-14 pgs. each
6 12 18 31 38 45
Bread Giveaway (1957,61; 16pgs, reg. size) 5 10 15 24 30 35

LITTLE ORPHAN ANNIE
David McKay Publ./Dell Publishing Co.
Junior Commandos Giveaway (same-c as 4-Color #18, K.K. Publ.)(Big Shoe Store); same back cover as '47 Popped Wheat giveaway; 16 pgs; flag-c; r/strips 9/7/42-10/10/42 26 52 78 154 252 350
Popped Wheat Giveaway ('47)-16 pgs. full color; reprints strips from 5/3/40 to 6/20/40
4 8 12 18 22 25
Quaker Sparkies Giveaway (1940) 18 36 54 103 162 220
Quaker Sparkies Giveaway (1941, full color, 20 pgs.); "LOA and the Rescue"; r/strips 4/13/39-6/21/39 & 7/6/39-7/17/39. "LOA and the Kidnappers"; r/strips 11/28/38-1/28/39 15 30 45 94 147 200
Quaker Sparkies Giveaway (1942, full color, 20 pgs.); "LOA and Mr. Gudge"; r/strips 2/13/38-3/21/38 & 4/18/37-5/30/37. "LOA and the Great Am"
15 30 45 88 137 185

LITTLE TREE THAT WASN'T WANTED, THE
W. T. Grant Co. (Giveaway): 1960, (Color, 28 pgs.)
nn-Christmas story, puzzles and games 3 6 9 21 33 45

LOADED (Also see Re-Loaded)
DC Comics: 1995 (Interplay Productions)
1-Garth Ennis-s; promotes video game 4.00

LONE RANGER, THE
Dell Publishing Co.
Cheerios Giveaways (1954, 16 pgs., 2-1/2x7", soft-c) #1- "The Lone Ranger, His Mask & How He Met Tonto". #2- "The Lone Ranger & the Story of Silver"
each.... 12 24 36 69 97 125
Doll Giveaways (Gabriel Ind.)(1973, 3-1/4x5")- "The Story of The Lone Ranger," "The Carson City Bank Robbery" & "The Apache Buffalo Hunt"
2 4 6 12 16 20
How the Lone Ranger Captured Silver Book(1936)-Silvercup Bread giveaway
55 110 165 352 601 850
...In Milk for Big Mike (1955, Dairy Association giveaway), soft-c; 5x7-1/4", 16 pgs. 10 20 30 58 79 100
Legend of The Lone Ranger (1969, 16 pgs., giveaway)-Origin The Lone Ranger
4 8 12 21 33 45
Merita Bread giveaway (1954, 16 pgs., 5x7-1/4")- "How to Be a Lone Ranger Health & Safety Scout" 14 28 42 80 115 150
Merita Bread giveaway (1955, 16 pgs., 5x7-1/4")- "Official Lone Ranger and Tonto Coloring Book" 12 24 36 69 97 125
Merita Bread giveaway (1956, 16 pgs., 5x7-1/4")- "Tells the Story of Branding"
12 24 36 69 97 125

LONE RANGER COMICS, THE
Lone Ranger, Inc. : Book 1, 1939(inside) (shows 1938 on-c) (52 pgs. in color; regular size) (Ice cream mail order)
Book 1-(Scarce)-The first western comic devoted to a single character; not by Vallely 571 1142 1713 4000 - -
2nd version w/large full color promo poster pasted over centerfold & a smaller poster pasted over back cover; includes new additional premiums not originally offered (Rare) 643 1286 1929 4500 - -

LOONEY TUNES
DC Comics: 1991, 1998
Claritin promotional issue (1998); Colgate mini-comic (1998) 3.00
Tyson's 1-10 (1991) 4.00

LUCKY FIGHTS IT THROUGH (Also see The K. O. Punch & Sidewalk Romance)
Educational Comics: 1949 (Giveaway, 16 pgs. in color, paper-c)
nn-(Very Rare)-1st Kurtzman work for E.C.; V.D. prevention
174 348 522 1114 1907 2700
nn-Reprint in color (1977) 7.00
NOTE: *Subtitled "The Story of That Ignorant, Ignorant Cowboy". Prepared for Communications Materials Center, Columbia University.*

LUDWIG VON DRAKE (See Frito-Lay Giveaway)

MACO TOYS COMIC
Maco Toys/Charlton Comics: 1959 (Giveaway, 36 pgs.)
1-All military stories featuring Maco Toys 3 6 9 14 19 24

MAD MAGAZINE
DC Comics: 1997, 1999, 2008
Special Edition (1997, Tang giveaway) 3.00
Stocking Stuffer (1999) 3.00
San Diego Comic-Con Edition (2008) Watchmen parody with Fabry-a; Aragonés cartoons 3.00

MAGAZINELAND USA
DC Comics: 1977
nn-Kubert-c/a 3 6 9 16 22 28

MAGIC MORRO (Also see Super Comics #21, The Owl, & The Hurricane Kids)
K. K. Publications: 1941 (7-1/2 x 5-1/4", giveaway, soft-c)
nn-Ken Ernst-a. 10 20 30 54 72 90

MAGIC OF CHRISTMAS AT NEWBERRYS, THE
E. S. London: 1967 (Giveaway) (B&W, slick-c, 20 pgs.)
nn 1 3 4 6 8 10

MAGIC SHOE ADVENTURE BOOK
Western Publications: 1962 - No. 3, 1963 (Shoe store giveaway, Reg. size)
nn-(1962) 5 10 15 34 60 85
1 (1963)-And the Flaming Threat 4 8 12 28 47 65
2 (1963)-And the Winning Run 4 8 12 28 47 65
3 (1963)-And the Missing Masterpiece Mystery 4 8 12 28 47 65

MAJOR INAPAK THE SPACE ACE
Magazine Enterprises (Inapac Foods): 1951 (20 pgs.) (Giveaway)
1-Bob Powell-c/a 5.00
NOTE: *Many warehouse copies surfaced in 1973.*

MAMMY YOKUM & THE GREAT DOGPATCH MYSTERY
Toby Press: 1951 (Giveaway)
nn-Li'l Abner 15 30 45 88 137 185
nn-Reprint (1956) 5 10 15 22 26 30

MAN NAMED STEVENSON, A
Democratic National Committee: 1952 (20 pgs., 5 1/4 x 7")
nn 9 18 27 47 61 75

MAN OF PEACE, POPE PIUS XII
Catechetical Guild: 1950 (See Pope Pius XII... & To V2#8)
nn-All Powell-a 7 14 21 35 43 50

MAN OF STEEL BEST WESTERN
DC Comics: 1997 (Best Western hotels promo)
3-Reprints Superman's first post-Crisis meeting with Batman 4.00

MAN WHO RUNS INTERFERENCE
General Comics, Inc./Institute of Life Insurance: 1946 (Paper-c)
nn-Football premium 5 10 15 22 26 30

MAN WHO WOULDN'T QUIT, THE
Harvey Publications Inc.: 1952 (16 pgs., paper cover)
nn-The value of voting 4 8 12 18 22 25

MARCH OF COMICS (Boys' and Girls'...#3-353)
K. K. Publications/Western Publishing Co.: 1946 - No. 488, April, 1982 (#1-4 are not numbered) (K.K. Giveaway) (Founded by Sig Feuchtwanger)
Early issues were full size, 32 pages, and were printed with and without an extra cover of slick stock, just for the advertiser. The binding was stapled if the slick cover was added; otherwise, the pages were glued together at the spine. Most 1948 - 1951 issues were full size,24 pages, pulp covers. Starting in 1952 they were half-size (with a few

March of Comics #75 © WB

March of Comics #90 © Gene Autry

March of Comics #151 © Roy Rogers

exceptions) and 32 pages with slick covers.1959 and later issues had only 16 pages plus covers. 1952 -1959 issues read oblong; 1960 and later issues read upright. All have new stories except where noted.

	GD 2.0	VG 4.0	FN 6.0	VF 8.0	VF/NM 9.0	NM- 9.2
nn (#1, 1946)-Goldilocks; Kelly back-c (16 pgs., stapled)	47	94	141	296	498	700
nn (#2, 1946)-How Santa Got His Red Suit; Kelly-a (11 pgs., r/4-Color #61 from 1944) (16pgs., stapled)	30	60	90	177	289	400
nn (#3, 1947)-Our Gang (Walt Kelly)	36	72	108	211	343	475
nn (#4)-Donald Duck by Carl Barks, "Maharajah Donald", 28 pgs.; Kelly-c? (Disney)	757	1514	2271	5526	9763	14,000
5-Andy Panda (Walter Lantz)	17	34	51	100	158	215
6-Popular Fairy Tales; Kelly-c; Noonan-a(2)	18	36	54	105	165	225
7-Oswald the Rabbit	20	40	60	114	182	250
8-Mickey Mouse, 32 pgs. (Disney)	41	82	123	256	428	600
9(nn)-The Story of the Gloomy Bunny	12	24	36	69	97	125
10-Out of Santa's Bag	11	22	33	64	90	115
11-Fun With Santa Claus	10	20	30	58	79	100
12-Santa's Toys	10	20	30	58	79	100
13-Santa's Surprise	10	20	30	58	79	100
14-Santa's Candy Kitchen	10	20	30	58	79	100
15-Hip-It-Ty Hop & the Big Bass Viol	10	20	30	56	76	95
16-Woody Woodpecker (1947)(Walter Lantz)	14	28	42	78	112	145
17-Roy Rogers (1948)	20	40	60	120	195	270
18-Popular Fairy Tales	12	24	36	67	94	120
19-Uncle Wiggily	10	20	30	58	79	100
20-Donald Duck by Carl Barks, "Darkest Africa", 22 pgs.; Kelly-c (Disney)	271	542	813	1734	2967	4200
21-Tom and Jerry	11	22	33	62	86	110
22-Andy Panda (Lantz)	11	22	33	62	86	110
23-Raggedy Ann & Andy; Kerr-a	13	26	39	72	101	130
24-Felix the Cat, 1932 daily strip reprints by Otto Messmer	16	32	48	94	147	200
25-Gene Autry	17	34	51	100	158	215
26-Our Gang; Walt Kelly	16	32	48	96	151	205
27-Mickey Mouse; r/in M. M. #240 (Disney)	29	58	87	172	281	390
28-Gene Autry	17	34	51	98	154	210
29-Easter Bonnet Shop	9	18	27	47	61	75
30-Here Comes Santa	8	16	24	44	57	70
31-Santa's Busy Corner	8	16	24	44	57	70
32-No book produced						
33-A Christmas Carol (12/48)	9	18	27	47	61	75
34-Woody Woodpecker	11	22	33	62	86	110
35-Roy Rogers (1948)	19	38	57	112	179	245
36-Felix the Cat(1949); by Messmer; '34 strip-r	14	28	42	82	121	160
37-Popeye	14	28	42	78	112	145
38-Oswald the Rabbit	8	16	24	44	57	70
39-Gene Autry	16	32	48	94	147	200
40-Andy and Woody	8	16	24	44	57	70
41-Donald Duck by Carl Barks, "Race to the South Seas", 22 pgs.; Kelly-c	245	490	735	1568	2684	3800
42-Porky Pig	9	18	27	47	61	75
43-Henry	8	16	24	42	54	65
44-Bugs Bunny	9	18	27	52	69	85
45-Mickey Mouse (Disney)	20	40	60	120	195	270
46-Tom and Jerry	9	18	27	52	69	85
47-Roy Rogers	15	30	45	90	140	190
48-Greetings from Santa	6	12	18	31	38	45
49-Santa Is Here	6	12	18	31	38	45
50-Santa Claus' Workshop (1949)	6	12	18	31	38	45
51-Felix the Cat (1950) by Messmer	14	28	42	80	115	150
52-Popeye	11	22	33	62	86	110
53-Oswald the Rabbit	8	16	24	40	50	60
54-Gene Autry	15	30	45	84	127	170
55-Andy and Woody	8	16	24	40	50	60
56-Donald Duck; not by Barks; Barks art on back-c (Disney)	20	40	60	114	182	260
57-Porky Pig	8	16	24	40	50	60
58-Henry	7	14	21	35	43	50
59-Bugs Bunny	9	18	27	47	61	75
60-Mickey Mouse (Disney)	20	40	60	120	195	270
61-Tom and Jerry	8	16	24	40	50	60
62-Roy Rogers	15	30	45	90	140	190
63-Welcome Santa (1/2-size, oblong)	6	12	18	31	38	45
64(nn)-Santa's Helpers (1/2-size, oblong)	6	12	18	31	38	45
65(nn)-Jingle Bells (1950) (1/2-size, oblong)	6	12	18	31	38	45
66-Popeye (1951)	12	24	36	67	94	120

	GD 2.0	VG 4.0	FN 6.0	VF 8.0	VF/NM 9.0	NM- 9.2
67-Oswald the Rabbit	7	14	21	35	43	50
68-Roy Rogers	14	28	42	80	115	150
69-Donald Duck; Barks-a on back-c (Disney)	20	40	60	114	182	250
70-Tom and Jerry	8	16	24	40	50	60
71-Porky Pig	8	16	24	42	54	65
72-Krazy Kat	9	18	27	47	61	75
73-Roy Rogers	14	28	42	82	121	160
74-Mickey Mouse (1951)(Disney)	19	38	57	111	176	246
75-Bugs Bunny	9	18	27	47	61	75
76-Andy and Woody	8	16	24	40	50	60
77-Roy Rogers	14	28	42	82	121	160
78-Gene Autry (1951); last regular size issue	14	28	42	80	115	150

Note: All pre #79 issues came with or without a slick protective wrap-around cover over the regular cover which advertised Poll Parrot Shoes, Sears, etc. This outer cover protects the inside pages making them in nicer condition.
Issues with the outer cover are worth 15-25% more

	GD 2.0	VG 4.0	FN 6.0	VF 8.0	VF/NM 9.0	NM- 9.2
79-Andy Panda (1952, 5x7" size)	7	14	21	35	43	50
80-Popeye	8	16	24	40	50	60
81-Oswald the Rabbit	6	12	18	29	36	42
82-Tarzan; Lex Barker photo-c	15	30	45	84	127	170
83-Bugs Bunny	7	14	21	37	46	55
84-Henry	6	12	18	29	36	42
85-Woody Woodpecker	6	12	18	29	36	42
86-Roy Rogers	11	22	33	62	86	110
87-Krazy Kat	8	16	24	44	57	70
88-Tom and Jerry	6	12	18	31	38	45
89-Porky Pig	6	12	18	29	36	42
90-Gene Autry	11	22	33	62	86	110
91-Roy Rogers & Santa	11	22	33	62	86	110
92-Christmas with Santa	5	10	15	24	30	35
93-Woody Woodpecker (1953)	5	10	15	23	28	32
94-Indian Chief	10	20	30	54	72	90
95-Oswald the Rabbit	5	10	15	23	28	32
96-Popeye	10	20	30	54	72	90
97-Bugs Bunny	7	14	21	35	43	50
98-Tarzan; Lex Barker photo-c	14	28	42	82	121	160
99-Porky Pig	5	10	15	23	28	32
100-Roy Rogers	10	20	30	58	79	100
101-Henry	5	10	15	22	26	30
102-Tom Corbett (TV)('53, early app).; painted-c	12	24	36	67	94	120
103-Tom and Jerry	5	10	15	23	28	32
104-Gene Autry	10	20	30	56	76	95
105-Roy Rogers	10	20	30	56	76	95
106-Santa's Helpers	5	10	15	24	30	35
107-Santa's Christmas Book - not published						
108-Fun with Santa (1953)	5	10	15	24	30	35
109-Woody Woodpecker (1954)	5	10	15	24	30	35
110-Indian Chief	6	12	18	31	38	45
111-Oswald the Rabbit	5	10	15	22	26	30
112-Henry	4	9	13	18	22	26
113-Porky Pig	5	10	15	22	26	30
114-Tarzan; Russ Manning-a	14	28	42	82	121	160
115-Bugs Bunny	6	12	18	27	33	38
116-Roy Rogers	10	20	30	56	76	95
117-Popeye	10	20	30	54	72	90
118-Flash Gordon; painted-c	11	22	33	62	86	110
119-Tom and Jerry	5	10	15	22	26	30
120-Gene Autry	10	20	30	58	76	95
121-Roy Rogers	10	20	30	58	76	95
122-Santa's Surprise (1954)	5	10	15	22	26	30
123-Santa's Christmas Book	5	10	15	22	26	30
124-Woody Woodpecker (1955)	4	9	13	18	22	26
125-Tarzan; Lex Barker photo-c	14	28	42	78	112	145
126-Oswald the Rabbit	4	9	13	18	22	26
127-Indian Chief	7	14	21	35	43	50
128-Tom and Jerry	4	9	13	18	22	26
129-Henry	4	8	12	17	21	24
130-Porky Pig	4	9	13	18	22	26
131-Roy Rogers	10	20	30	56	76	95
132-Bugs Bunny	5	10	15	23	28	32
133-Flash Gordon; painted-c	11	22	33	60	83	105
134-Popeye	8	16	24	42	54	65
135-Gene Autry	10	20	30	56	76	95
136-Roy Rogers	10	20	30	56	76	95
137-Gifts from Santa	4	7	10	14	17	20

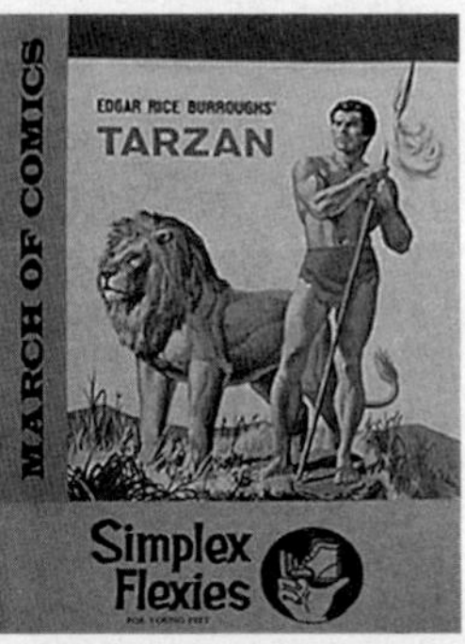

March of Comics #252 © ERB

March of Comics #287 © WB

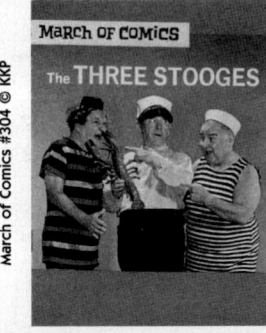

March of Comics #304 © KKP

	GD 2.0	VG 4.0	FN 6.0	VF 8.0	VF/NM 9.0	NM- 9.2
138-Fun at Christmas (1955)	4	7	10	14	17	20
139-Woody Woodpecker (1956)	4	9	13	18	22	26
140-Indian Chief	7	14	21	35	43	50
141-Oswald the Rabbit	4	9	13	18	22	26
142-Flash Gordon	12	24	36	67	94	120
143-Porky Pig	4	9	13	18	22	26
144-Tarzan; Russ Manning-a; painted-c	13	26	39	72	101	130
145-Tom and Jerry	4	9	13	18	22	26
146-Roy Rogers; photo-c	10	20	30	56	76	95
147-Henry	4	8	11	16	19	22
148-Popeye	8	16	24	42	54	65
149-Bugs Bunny	5	10	15	22	26	30
150-Gene Autry	10	20	30	56	76	95
151-Roy Rogers	10	20	30	56	76	95
152-The Night Before Christmas	4	8	11	16	19	22
153-Merry Christmas (1956)	4	9	13	18	22	26
154-Tom and Jerry (1957)	4	9	13	18	22	26
155-Tarzan; photo-c	12	24	36	69	97	125
156-Oswald the Rabbit	4	9	13	18	22	26
157-Popeye	7	14	21	35	43	50
158-Woody Woodpecker	4	9	13	18	22	26
159-Indian Chief	7	14	21	35	43	50
160-Bugs Bunny	5	10	15	22	26	30
161-Roy Rogers	9	18	27	52	69	85
162-Henry	4	8	11	16	19	22
163-Rin Tin Tin (TV)	8	16	24	42	54	65
164-Porky Pig	4	9	13	18	22	26
165-The Lone Ranger	9	18	27	50	65	80
166-Santa and His Reindeer	4	7	10	14	17	20
167-Roy Rogers and Santa	9	18	27	52	69	85
168-Santa Claus' Workshop (1957, full size)	4	8	11	16	19	22
169-Popeye (1958)	7	14	21	35	43	50
170-Indian Chief	7	14	21	35	43	50
171-Oswald the Rabbit	4	8	12	17	21	24
172-Tarzan	11	22	33	60	83	105
173-Tom and Jerry	4	8	12	17	21	24
174-The Lone Ranger	9	18	27	50	65	80
175-Porky Pig	4	8	12	17	21	24
176-Roy Rogers	9	18	27	47	61	75
177-Woody Woodpecker	4	8	12	17	21	24
178-Henry	4	8	11	16	19	22
179-Bugs Bunny	4	8	12	17	21	24
180-Rin Tin Tin (TV)	7	14	21	37	46	55
181-Happy Holiday	4	7	9	14	16	18
182-Happi Tim	4	8	11	16	19	22
183-Welcome Santa (1958, full size)	4	7	9	14	16	18
184-Woody Woodpecker (1959)	4	8	11	16	19	22
185-Tarzan; photo-c	10	20	30	58	79	100
186-Oswald the Rabbit	4	8	11	16	19	22
187-Indian Chief	6	12	18	28	34	40
188-Bugs Bunny	4	8	11	16	19	22
189-Henry	4	7	10	14	17	20
190-Tom and Jerry	4	8	11	16	19	22
191-Roy Rogers	8	16	24	44	57	70
192-Porky Pig	4	8	11	16	19	22
193-The Lone Ranger	9	18	27	47	61	75
194-Popeye	6	12	18	31	38	45
195-Rin Tin Tin (TV)	7	14	21	35	43	50
196-Sears Special - not published						
197-Santa Is Coming	4	7	10	14	17	20
198-Santa's Helpers (1959)	4	7	10	14	17	20
199-Huckleberry Hound (TV)(1960, early app.)	8	16	24	42	54	65
200-Fury (TV)	6	12	18	28	34	40
201-Bugs Bunny	4	8	11	16	19	22
202-Space Explorer	8	16	24	42	54	65
203-Woody Woodpecker	4	7	10	14	17	20
204-Tarzan	9	18	27	52	69	85
205-Mighty Mouse	6	12	18	33	41	48
206-Roy Rogers; photo-c	8	16	24	42	54	65
207-Tom and Jerry	4	7	10	14	17	20
208-The Lone Ranger; Clayton Moore photo-c	10	20	30	54	72	90
209-Porky Pig	4	7	10	14	17	20
210-Lassie (TV)	6	12	18	33	41	48
211-Sears Special - not published						
212-Christmas Eve	4	7	10	14	17	20
213-Here Comes Santa (1960)	4	7	10	14	17	20
214-Huckleberry Hound (TV)(1961)	7	14	21	35	43	50
215-Hi Yo Silver	8	16	24	40	50	60
216-Rocky & His Friends (TV)(1961); predates Rocky and His Fiendish Friends #1 (see Four Color #1128)	9	18	27	52	69	85
217-Lassie (TV)	6	12	18	31	38	45
218-Porky Pig	4	7	10	14	17	20
219-Journey to the Sun	5	10	15	24	30	35
220-Bugs Bunny	4	8	11	16	19	22
221-Roy and Dale; photo-c	8	16	24	42	54	65
222-Woody Woodpecker	4	7	10	14	17	20
223-Tarzan	9	18	27	50	65	80
224-Tom and Jerry	4	7	10	14	17	20
225-The Lone Ranger	8	16	24	40	50	60
226-Christmas Treasury (1961)	4	7	10	14	17	20
227-Letters to Santa (1961)	4	7	10	14	17	20
228-Sears Special - not published?						
229-The Flintstones (TV)(1962); early app.; predates 1st Flintstones Gold Key issue (#7)	10	20	30	54	72	90
230-Lassie (TV)	6	12	18	27	33	38
231-Bugs Bunny	4	8	11	16	19	22
232-The Three Stooges	9	18	27	52	69	85
233-Bullwinkle (TV) (1962, very early app.)	9	18	27	52	69	85
234-Smokey the Bear	5	10	15	23	28	32
235-Huckleberry Hound (TV)	7	14	21	35	43	50
236-Roy and Dale	7	14	21	35	43	50
237-Mighty Mouse	6	12	18	27	33	38
238-The Lone Ranger	8	16	24	40	50	60
239-Woody Woodpecker	4	7	10	14	17	20
240-Tarzan	8	16	24	44	57	70
241-Santa Claus Around the World	4	7	9	14	16	18
242-Santa's Toyland (1962)	4	7	9	14	16	18
243-The Flintstones (TV)(1963)	8	16	24	44	57	70
244-Mister Ed (TV); early app.; photo-c	7	14	21	35	43	50
245-Bugs Bunny	4	8	11	16	19	22
246-Popeye	6	12	18	27	33	38
247-Mighty Mouse	6	12	18	27	33	38
248-The Three Stooges	10	20	30	54	72	90
249-Woody Woodpecker	4	7	10	14	17	20
250-Roy and Dale	7	14	21	35	43	50
251-Little Lulu & Witch Hazel	11	22	33	60	83	105
252-Tarzan; painted-c	8	16	24	42	54	65
253-Yogi Bear (TV)	8	16	24	40	50	60
254-Lassie (TV)	6	12	18	27	33	38
255-Santa's Christmas List	4	7	10	14	17	20
256-Christmas Party (1963)	4	7	10	14	17	20
257-Mighty Mouse	6	12	18	27	33	38
258-The Sword in the Stone (Disney)	8	16	24	42	54	65
259-Bugs Bunny	4	8	11	16	19	22
260-Mister Ed (TV)	6	12	18	31	38	45
261-Woody Woodpecker	4	7	10	14	17	20
262-Tarzan	8	16	24	40	50	60
263-Donald Duck; not by Barks (Disney)	9	18	27	52	69	85
264-Popeye	6	12	18	27	33	38
265-Yogi Bear (TV)	6	12	18	31	38	45
266-Lassie (TV)	5	10	15	23	28	32
267-Little Lulu; Irving Tripp-a	10	20	30	56	76	95
268-The Three Stooges	9	18	27	47	61	75
269-A Jolly Christmas	3	6	8	12	14	16
270-Santa's Little Helpers	3	6	8	12	14	16
271-The Flintstones (TV)(1965)	8	16	24	44	57	70
272-Tarzan	8	16	24	40	50	60
273-Bugs Bunny	4	8	11	16	19	22
274-Popeye	6	12	18	27	33	38
275-Little Lulu; Irving Tripp-a	9	18	27	50	65	80
276-The Jetsons (TV)	12	24	36	67	94	120
277-Daffy Duck	4	8	11	16	19	22
278-Lassie (TV)	5	10	15	23	28	32
279-Yogi Bear (TV)	6	12	18	31	38	45
280-The Three Stooges; photo-c	9	18	27	47	61	75
281-Tom and Jerry	4	7	9	14	16	18
282-Mister Ed (TV)	6	12	18	31	38	45
283-Santa's Visit	4	7	9	14	16	18
284-Christmas Parade (1965)	4	7	9	14	16	18
285-Astro Boy (TV); 2nd app. Astro Boy	26	52	78	154	252	350

March of Comics #306 © DIS

March of Comics #364 © H-B

March of Comics #385 © WEST

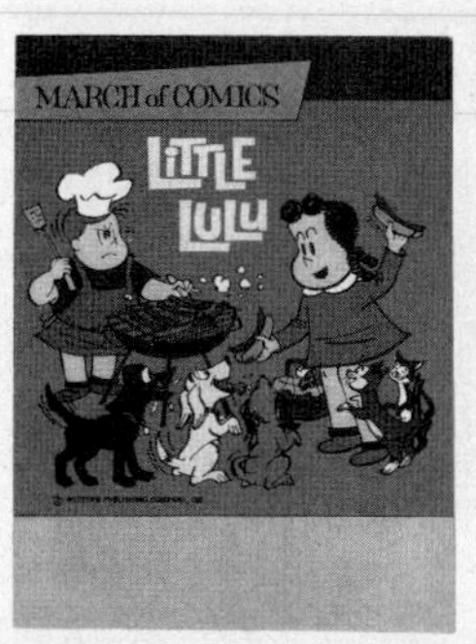

	GD 2.0	VG 4.0	FN 6.0	VF 8.0	VF/NM 9.0	NM- 9.2
286-Tarzan	7	14	21	37	46	55
287-Bugs Bunny	4	8	11	16	19	22
288-Daffy Duck	4	7	10	14	17	20
289-The Flintstones (TV)	8	16	24	44	57	70
290-Mister Ed (TV); photo-c	5	10	15	24	30	35
291-Yogi Bear (TV)	6	12	18	27	33	38
292-The Three Stooges; photo-c	9	18	27	47	61	75
293-Little Lulu; Irving Tripp-a	8	16	24	42	54	65
294-Popeye	5	10	15	24	30	35
295-Tom and Jerry	4	7	9	14	16	18
296-Lassie (TV); photo-c	5	10	15	22	26	30
297-Christmas Bells	3	6	8	12	14	16
298-Santa's Sleigh (1966)	3	6	8	12	14	16
299-The Flintstones (TV)(1967)	8	16	24	44	57	70
300-Tarzan	7	14	21	37	46	55
301-Bugs Bunny	4	7	10	14	17	20
302-Laurel and Hardy (TV); photo-c	6	12	18	28	34	40
303-Daffy Duck	3	6	8	12	14	16
304-The Three Stooges; photo-c	7	14	21	35	43	50
305-Tom and Jerry	3	6	8	12	14	16
306-Daniel Boone (TV); Fess Parker photo-c	7	14	21	35	43	50
307-Little Lulu; Irving Tripp-a	7	14	21	37	46	55
308-Lassie (TV); photo-c	5	10	15	22	26	30
309-Yogi Bear (TV)	5	10	15	24	30	35
310-The Lone Ranger; Clayton Moore photo-c	10	20	30	54	72	90
311-Santa's Show	4	7	9	14	16	18
312-Christmas Album (1967)	4	7	9	14	16	18
313-Daffy Duck (1968)	3	6	8	12	14	16
314-Laurel and Hardy (TV)	6	12	18	27	33	38
315-Bugs Bunny	4	7	10	14	17	20
316-The Three Stooges	8	16	24	40	50	60
317-The Flintstones (TV)	8	16	24	42	54	65
318-Tarzan	7	14	21	35	43	50
319-Yogi Bear (TV)	5	10	15	24	30	35
320-Space Family Robinson (TV); Spiegle-a	11	22	33	62	86	110
321-Tom and Jerry	3	6	8	12	14	16
322-The Lone Ranger	7	14	21	37	46	55
323-Little Lulu; not by Stanley	5	10	15	24	30	35
324-Lassie (TV); photo-c	5	10	15	22	26	30
325-Fun with Santa	4	7	9	14	16	18
326-Christmas Story (1968)	4	7	9	14	16	18
327-The Flintstones (TV)(1969)	8	16	24	42	54	65
328-Space Family Robinson (TV); Spiegle-a	11	22	33	62	86	110
329-Bugs Bunny	4	7	10	14	17	20
330-The Jetsons (TV)	10	20	30	56	76	95
331-Daffy Duck	3	6	8	12	14	16
332-Tarzan	6	12	18	28	34	40
333-Tom and Jerry	3	6	8	12	14	16
334-Lassie (TV)	4	9	13	18	22	26
335-Little Lulu	5	10	15	24	30	35
336-The Three Stooges	8	16	24	40	50	60
337-Yogi Bear (TV)	5	10	15	24	30	35
338-The Lone Ranger	7	14	21	37	46	55
339-(Was not published)						
340-Here Comes Santa (1969)	3	6	8	12	14	16
341-The Flintstones (TV)	8	16	24	42	54	65
342-Tarzan	3	6	9	19	30	40
343-Bugs Bunny	2	4	6	10	14	18
344-Yogi Bear (TV)	3	6	9	16	23	30
345-Tom and Jerry	2	4	6	9	13	16
346-Lassie (TV)	3	6	9	15	21	26
347-Daffy Duck	2	4	6	9	13	16
348-The Jetsons (TV)	5	10	15	34	60	85
349-Little Lulu; not by Stanley	3	6	9	16	23	30
350-The Lone Ranger	3	6	9	17	26	35
351-Beep-Beep, the Road Runner (TV)	2	4	6	11	16	20
352-Space Family Robinson (TV); Spiegle-a	6	12	18	41	76	110
353-Beep-Beep, the Road Runner (1971) (TV)	2	4	6	11	16	20
354-Tarzan (1971)	3	6	9	17	26	35
355-Little Lulu; not by Stanley	3	6	9	16	23	30
356-Scooby Doo, Where Are You? (TV)	6	12	18	37	66	95
357-Daffy Duck & Porky Pig	2	4	6	8	11	14
358-Lassie (TV)	3	6	9	14	19	24
359-Baby Snoots	2	4	6	10	14	18
360-H. R. Pufnstuf (TV); photo-c	6	12	18	37	66	95

	GD 2.0	VG 4.0	FN 6.0	VF 8.0	VF/NM 9.0	NM- 9.2
361-Tom and Jerry	2	4	6	8	11	14
362-Smokey Bear (TV)	2	4	6	8	11	14
363-Bugs Bunny & Yosemite Sam	2	4	6	9	13	16
364-The Banana Splits (TV); photo-c	5	10	15	33	57	80
365-Tom and Jerry (1972)	2	4	6	8	11	14
366-Tarzan	3	6	9	17	26	35
367-Bugs Bunny & Porky Pig	2	4	6	9	13	16
368-Scooby Doo (TV)(4/72)	5	10	15	33	57	80
369-Little Lulu; not by Stanley	3	6	9	14	19	24
370-Lassie (TV); photo-c	3	6	9	14	19	24
371-Baby Snoots	2	4	6	9	13	16
372-Smokey the Bear (TV)	2	4	6	8	11	14
373-The Three Stooges	4	8	12	23	37	50
374-Wacky Witch	2	4	6	8	11	14
375-Beep-Beep & Daffy Duck (TV)	2	4	6	8	11	14
376-The Pink Panther (1972) (TV)	2	4	6	10	14	18
377-Baby Snoots (1973)	2	4	6	9	13	16
378-Turok, Son of Stone; new-a	6	12	18	42	79	115
379-Heckle & Jeckle New Terrytoons (TV)	2	4	6	8	11	14
380-Bugs Bunny & Yosemite Sam	2	4	6	8	11	14
381-Lassie (TV)	2	4	6	11	16	20
382-Scooby Doo, Where Are You? (TV)	5	10	15	30	50	70
383-Smokey the Bear (TV)	2	4	6	8	11	14
384-Pink Panther (TV)	2	4	6	8	11	14
385-Little Lulu	2	4	6	13	18	22
386-Wacky Witch	2	4	6	8	11	14
387-Beep-Beep & Daffy Duck (TV)	2	4	6	8	11	14
388-Tom and Jerry (1973)	2	4	6	8	11	14
389-Little Lulu; not by Stanley	2	4	6	13	18	22
390-Pink Panther (TV)	2	4	6	8	11	14
391-Scooby Doo (TV)	4	8	12	25	40	55
392-Bugs Bunny & Yosemite Sam	2	4	6	8	10	12
393-New Terrytoons (Heckle & Jeckle) (TV)	2	4	6	8	10	12
394-Lassie (TV)	2	4	6	9	13	16
395-Woodsy Owl	2	4	6	8	10	12
396-Baby Snoots	2	4	6	8	11	14
397-Beep-Beep & Daffy Duck (TV)	2	4	6	8	10	12
398-Wacky Witch	2	4	6	8	10	12
399-Turok, Son of Stone; new-a	6	12	18	40	73	105
400-Tom and Jerry	2	4	6	8	10	12
401-Baby Snoots (1975) (r/#371)	2	4	6	8	11	14
402-Daffy Duck (r/#313)	1	3	4	6	8	10
403-Bugs Bunny (r/#343)	2	4	6	8	10	12
404-Space Family Robinson (TV)(r/#328)	5	10	15	35	63	90
405-Cracky	1	3	4	6	8	10
406-Little Lulu (r/#355)	2	4	6	10	14	18
407-Smokey the Bear (TV)(r/#362)	2	4	6	8	10	12
408-Turok, Son of Stone; c-r/Turok #20 w/changes; new-a	5	10	15	35	63	90
409-Pink Panther (TV)	1	3	4	6	8	10
410-Wacky Witch	1	2	3	5	6	8
411-Lassie (TV)(r/#324)	2	4	6	9	13	16
412-New Terrytoons (1975) (TV)	1	2	3	5	6	8
413-Daffy Duck (1976)(r/#331)	1	2	3	5	6	8
414-Space Family Robinson (r/#328)	5	10	15	34	60	85
415-Bugs Bunny (r/#329)	1	2	3	5	6	8
416-Beep-Beep, the Road Runner (r/#353)(TV)	1	2	3	5	6	8
417-Little Lulu (r/#323)	2	4	6	10	14	18
418-Pink Panther (r/#384) (TV)	1	2	3	5	6	8
419-Baby Snoots (r/#377)	1	3	4	6	8	10
420-Woody Woodpecker	1	2	3	5	6	8
421-Tweety & Sylvester	1	2	3	5	6	8
422-Wacky Witch (r/#386)	1	2	3	5	6	8
423-Little Monsters	1	3	4	6	8	10
424-Cracky (12/76)	1	2	3	5	6	8
425-Daffy Duck	1	2	3	5	6	8
426-Underdog (TV)	3	6	9	21	33	45
427-Little Lulu (r/#335)	2	4	6	8	11	14
428-Bugs Bunny	1	2	3	4	5	7
429-The Pink Panther (TV)	1	2	3	4	5	7
430-Beep-Beep, the Road Runner (TV)	1	2	3	4	5	7
431-Baby Snoots	1	2	3	5	6	8
432-Lassie (TV)	2	4	6	8	10	12
433-437: 433-Tweety & Sylvester. 434-Wacky Witch. 435-New Terrytoons (TV). 436-Wacky Advs. of Cracky. 437-Daffy Duck	1	2	3	4	5	7

Martin Luther King and the Montgomery Story © Fellowship Reconciliation

Marvel Collector's Edition: X-Men © MAR

The Matrix © WB

	GD 2.0	VG 4.0	FN 6.0	VF 8.0	VF/NM 9.0	NM- 9.2
438-Underdog (TV)	3	6	9	19	30	40
439-Little Lulu (r/#349)	2	4	6	8	11	14
440-442,444-446: 440-Bugs Bunny. 441-The Pink Panther (TV). 442-Beep-Beep, the Road Runner (TV). 444-Tom and Jerry. 445-Tweety and Sylvester. 446-Wacky Witch	1	2	3	5	6	8
443-Baby Snoots	1	2	3	5	6	8
447-Mighty Mouse	2	4	6	8	10	12
448-455,457,458: 448-Cracky. 449-Pink Panther (TV). 450-Baby Snoots. 451-Tom and Jerry. 452-Bugs Bunny. 453-Popeye. 454-Woody Woodpecker. 455-Beep-Beep, the Road Runner (TV). 457-Tweety & Sylvester. 458-Wacky Witch	1	2	3	5	6	8
456-Little Lulu (r/#369)	2	4	6	8	10	12
459-Mighty Mouse	2	4	6	8	10	12
460-466: 460-Daffy Duck. 461-The Pink Panther (TV). 462-Baby Snoots. 463-Tom and Jerry. 464-Bugs Bunny. 465-Popeye. 466-Woody Woodpecker	1	2	3	5	6	8
467-Underdog (TV)	3	6	9	17	26	35
468-Little Lulu (r/#385)	1	2	3	5	6	8
469-Tweety & Sylvester	1	2	3	5	6	8
470-Wacky Witch	1	2	3	5	6	8
471-Mighty Mouse	1	3	4	6	8	10
472-474,476-478: 472-Heckle & Jeckle(12/80). 473-Pink Panther(1/81)(TV). 474-Baby Snoots. 476-Bugs Bunny. 477-Popeye. 478-Woody Woodpecker	1	2	3	5	6	8
475-Little Lulu (r/#323)	1	3	4	6	8	10
479-Underdog (TV)	3	6	9	16	23	30
480-482: 480-Tom and Jerry. 481-Tweety and Sylvester. 482-Wacky Witch	1	2	3	4	5	8
483-Mighty Mouse	1	3	4	6	8	10
484-487: 484-Heckle & Jeckle. 485-Baby Snoots. 486-The Pink Panther (TV). 487-Bugs Bunny	1	2	3	4	5	8
488-Little Lulu (4/82) (r/#335) (Last issue)	2	4	6	10	14	18

MARCH TO MARKET, THE
Pictorial Media/Swift & Co.: 1948, 1950 (Giveaway)

nn-The story of meat	4	7	9	14	16	18

MARGARET O'BRIEN (See The Adventures of...)

MARK STEEL
American Iron & Steel Institute: 1967, 1968, 1972 (Giveaway) (24 pgs.)

1967,1968- "Journey of Discovery with..."; Neal Adams art	4	8	12	23	37	50
1972- "...Fights Pollution"; N. Adams-a	2	4	6	9	13	15

MARTIN LUTHER KING AND THE MONTGOMERY STORY
Fellowship Reconciliation: 1957 (Giveaway, 16 pgs.) (A Spanish edition also exists)
nn-In color with paper-c (a VF copy sold for $261 in 2013, a FN/VF copy sold for $76 in 2015 and a CGC 8.0 copy sold for $185 in 2017)

MARTIN LUTHER KING AND THE MONTGOMERY STORY
Top Shelf/Fellowship Reconciliation: 2011, 2013 ($5.00, newsprint-c, 16 pgs.)

nn-(2011) Reprint of the 1957 giveaway published by Fellowship Reconciliation; stapled						10.00
nn-(2013) Reprint has glued binding unlike the stapled 2011 version						10.00

MARVEL COLLECTOR'S EDITION: X-MEN
Marvel Comics: 1993 (3-3/4x6-1/2")

1-4-Pizza Hut giveaways						5.00

MARVEL COMICS PRESENTS
Marvel Comics: 1987, 1988 (4 1/4 x 6 1/4, 20 pgs.)
...Mini Comic Giveaway

nn-(1988) Alf	1	2	3	5	6	8
nn-(1987) Captain America r/ #250	1	2	3	4	5	7
nn-(1987) Care Bears (Star Comics...)	1	2	3	4	5	7
nn-(1988) Flintstone Kids	1	2	3	5	6	8
nn-(1987) Heathcliffe (Star Comics...)	1	2	3	4	5	7
nn-(1987) Spider-Man-r/Spect. Spider-Man #21	1	2	3	4	5	7
nn-(1988) Spider-Man-r/Amazing Spider-Man #1	1	2	3	4	5	7
nn-(1988) X-Men-reprints X-Men #53; B. Smith-a	1	2	3	4	5	7

MARVEL GUIDE TO COLLECTING COMICS, THE
Marvel Comics: 1982 (16 pgs., newsprint pages and cover)

1-Simonson-c	1	2	3	4	5	7

MARVEL MINI-BOOKS
Marvel Comics Group: 1966 (50 pgs., B&W; 5/8x7/8") (6 different issues) (Smallest comics ever published) (Marvel Mania Giveaways)

Captain America, Millie the Model, Sgt. Fury, Hulk, Thor each...	2	4	6	11	16	20
Spider-Man	3	6	9	14	20	25

NOTE: *Each came from gum machines in six different color covers, usually one color: Pink, yellow, green, etc.*

MARVEL SUPER-HERO ISLAND ADVENTURES
Marvel Comics: 1999 (Sold at the park polybagged with Captain America V3 #19, one other comic, 5 trading cards and a cloisonn'e pin)

1-Promotes Universal Studios Islands of Adventures theme park						4.00

MARY'S GREATEST APOSTLE (St. Louis Grignion de Montfort)
Catechetical Guild (Topix) (Giveaway): No date (16 pgs.; paper cover)

nn	5	10	15	23	28	32

MASK
DC Comics: 1985

1-3						6.00

MASKED PILOT, THE (See Popular Comics #43)
R.S. Callender: 1939 (7-1/2x5-1/4", 16 pgs., premium, non-slick-c)

nn-Bob Jenney-a	8	16	24	44	57	70

MASTERS OF THE UNIVERSE (He-Man)
DC Comics: 1982 (giveaways with action figures, at least 35 different issues, unnumbered)

nn	2	4	6	8	10	12

MATRIX, THE (1999 movie)
Warner Brothers: 1999 (Recalled by Warner Bros. over questionable content)

nn-Paul Chadwick-s/a (16 pgs.); Geof Darrow-c	1	2	3	5	6	8

McCRORY'S CHRISTMAS BOOK
Western Printing Co: 1955 (36 pgs., slick-c) (McCrory Stores Corp. giveaway)

nn-Painted-c	5	10	15	22	26	30

McCRORY'S TOYLAND BRINGS YOU SANTA'S PRIVATE EYES
Promotional Publ. Co.: 1956 (16 pgs.) (Giveaway)

nn-Has 9 pg. story plus 7 pgs. toy ads	4	8	11	16	19	22

McCRORY'S WONDERFUL CHRISTMAS
Promotional Publ. Co.: 1954 (20 pgs., slick-c) (Giveaway)

nn	4	8	12	18	22	25

McDONALDS COMMANDRONS
DC Comics: 1985

nn-Four editions						5.00

MEDAL FOR BOWZER, A (Giveaway)
American Visuals Corp.: 1966 (8 pgs.)

nn-Eisner-c/script; Bowzer (a dog) survives untried pneumonia cure and earns his medal; (medical experimentation on animals)	16	32	48	111	246	380

MEET HIYA A FRIEND OF SANTA CLAUS
Julian J. Proskauer/Sundial Shoe Stores, etc.: 1949 (18 pgs.?, paper-c)(Giveaway)

nn	6	12	18	33	41	48

MEET THE NEW POST-GAZETTE SUNDAY FUNNIES
Pittsburgh Post Gazette: 3/12/49 (7-1/4x10-1/4", 16 pgs., paper-c)
Commercial Comics (insert in newspaper) (Rare)

Dick Tracy by Gould, Gasoline Alley, Terry & the Pirates, Brenda Starr, Buck Rogers by Yager, The Gumps, Peter Rabbit by Fago, Superman, Funnyman by Siegel & Shuster, The Saint, Archie, & others done especially for this book. A fine copy sold at auction in 1985 for $276.00.	260	520	780	1700	-	-

MEN OF COURAGE
Catechetical Guild: 1949

Bound Topix comics-V7#2,4,6,8,10,16,18,20	6	12	18	33	41	48

MEN WHO MOVE THE NATION
Publisher unknown: (Giveaway) (B&W)

nn-Neal Adams-a	6	12	18	33	41	48

MERRY CHRISTMAS, A
K. K. Publications (Child Life Shoes): 1948 (Giveaway)

nn-Santa cover	8	16	24	44	57	70

MERRY CHRISTMAS
K. K. Publications (Blue Bird Shoes Giveaway): 1956 (7-1/4x5-1/4")

nn-Santa cover	4	8	12	18	22	25

MERRY CHRISTMAS FROM MICKEY MOUSE
K. K. Publications: 1939 (16 pgs.) (Color & B&W) (Shoe store giveaway)

nn-Donald Duck & Pluto app.; text with art (Rare); c-reprint/Mickey Mouse Mag. V3#3 (12/37)(Rare)	245	490	735	1568	2684	3800

Mickey Mouse Magazine Vol. 2 #2 © DIS

Miles the Monster © Dover Speedway

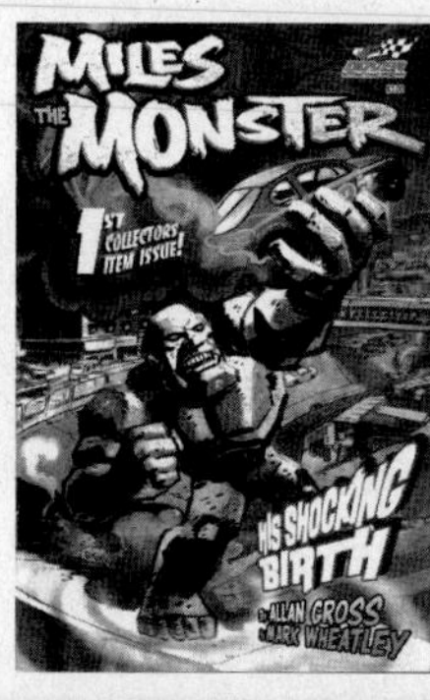

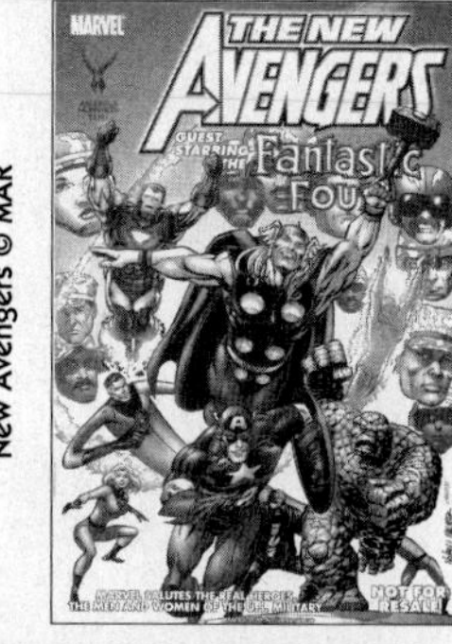
New Avengers © MAR

	GD 2.0	VG 4.0	FN 6.0	VF 8.0	VF/NM 9.0	NM- 9.2

MERRY CHRISTMAS FROM SEARS TOYLAND (See Santa's Christmas Comic, Bob & Betty & Santa's Wishing Whistle, and A Christmas Carol)
Sears Roebuck Giveaway: 1939 (16 pgs.) (Color)(Die-cut)
nn-Dick Tracy, Little Orphan Annie, The Gumps, Terry & the Pirates 103 206 309 659 1130 1600

MICKEY MOUSE (Also see Frito-Lay Giveaway)
Dell Publ. Co
...& Goofy Explore Business(1978) 2 4 6 8 10 12
...& Goofy Explore Energy(1976-1978, 36 pgs.); Exxon giveaway in color; regular size 2 4 6 8 10 12
...& Goofy Explore Energy Conservation(1976-1978)-Exxon 2 4 6 8 10 12
...& Goofy Explore The Universe of Energy(1985, 20 pgs.); Exxon giveaway in color; regular size 1 2 3 5 7 9
The Perils of Mickey nn (1993, 5-1/4x7-1/4", 16 pgs.)-Nabisco giveaway w/ games, Nabisco coupons & 6 pgs. of stories; Phantom Blot app. 6.00

MICKEY MOUSE MAGAZINE
Walt Disney Productions: V1#1, Jan, 1933 - V1#9, Sept, 1933 (5-1/4x7-1/4") No. 1-3 published by Kamen-Blair (Kay Kamen, Inc.)
(Scarce)-Distributed by dairies and leading stores through their local theatres. First few issues had 5¢ listed on cover, later ones had no price.
V1#1 417 834 1668 5000 - -
2-4 150 300 600 1200 - -
5-9 100 200 400 800 - -
NOTE: *A rare V1#1 Hardbound copy with a glassine dust jacket sold in July 2017 for $13,145.*

MICKEY MOUSE MAGAZINE (Digest size)
Walt Disney Productions: V1#1, 11/33 - V2#12, 10/35 (Mills giveaways issued by different dairies)
V1#1 145 290 435 943 1600 -
2-12: 2-X-Mas issue 47 94 141 296 498 700
V2#1 (11/34) Donald Duck in sailor suit pg. 6 (cameo) 39 78 117 240 395 550
V2#2-4,6-12: 2-X-Mas issue. 4-St. Valentine-c 37 74 111 222 361 500
V2#5 (3/35) 1st app. Donald Duck in sailor outfit on-c 100 200 300 635 1093 1550

MICKEY MOUSE MAGAZINE
K.K. Publications: V4#1, Oct, 1938 (Giveaway)
V4#1 41 82 123 256 428 600

MIGHTY ATOM, THE
Whitman
Giveaway (1959, '63, Whitman)-Evans-a 3 6 9 16 23 30
Giveaway ('64r, '65r, '66r, '67r, '68r)-Evans-r? 2 4 6 10 14 18
Giveaway ('73r, '76r) 2 4 6 8 11 14

MILES THE MONSTER (Initially sold only at the Dover Speedway track)
Dover International Speedway, Inc.: 2006 ($3.00)
1,2-Allan Gross & Mark Wheatley-s/Wheatley-a 3.00

MILITARY COURTESY
Harvey Publications: (16 pgs.)
nn-Regulations and saluting instructions 5 10 14 20 24 28

MINUTE MAN
Sovereign Service Station giveaway: No date (16 pgs., B&W, paper-c blue & red)
nn-American history 4 7 9 14 16 18

MINUTE MAN ANSWERS THE CALL, THE
By M. C. Gaines: 1942,1943,1944,1945 (4 pgs.) (Giveaway inserted in Jr. JSA Membership Kit)
nn-Sheldon Moldoff-a 22 44 66 132 216 300

MIRACLE ON BROADWAY
Broadway Comics: Dec, 1995 (Giveaway)
1-Ernie Colon-c/a; Jim Shooter & Co. story; 1st known digitally printed comic book; 1st app. Spire & Knights on Broadway (1150 print run) 20.00
NOTE: *Miracle on Broadway was a limited edition comic given to 1100 VIPs in the entertainment industry for the 1995 Holiday Season.*

MISS SUNBEAM (See Little Miss Sunbeam Comics)

MR. BUG GOES TO TOWN (See Cinema Comics Herald)
K.K. Publications: 1941 (Giveaway, 52 pgs.)
nn-Cartoon movie (scarce) 68 136 204 435 743 1050

MR. PEANUT, THE PERSONAL STORY OF
Planters Nut & Chocolate Co.: 1956
nn 4 8 12 22 35 48

MOTHER OF US ALL
Catechetical Guild Giveaway: 1950? (32 pgs.)
nn 5 10 15 23 28 32

MOTION PICTURE FUNNIES WEEKLY (Amazing Man #5 on?)
First Funnies, Inc.: 1939 (Giveaway)(B&W, 36 pgs.) No month given; last panel in Sub-Mariner story dated 4/39 (Also see Colossus, Green Giant & Invaders No. 20)
1-Origin & 1st printed app. Sub-Mariner by Bill Everett (8 pgs.); Fred Schwab-c; reprinted in Marvel Mystery #1 with color added over the craft tint which was used to shade the black & white version; Spy Ring, American Ace (reprinted in Marvel Mystery #3) app. (Rare)-only eight known copies, one near mint with white pages, the rest with brown pages. 6000 12,000 18,000 30,000 42,000 -
Covers only to #2-4 (set) 800
NOTE: Eight copies (plus one coverless) were discovered in 1974 in the estate of the deceased publisher. Covers only to issues No. 2-4 were also found which evidently were printed in advance along with #1. #1 was to be distributed only through motion picture movie houses. However, it is believed that only advanced copies were sent out and the motion picture houses not going for the idea. Possible distribution at local theaters in Boston suspected. The "pay" copy (graded at 9.0) was discovered after 1974, bringing the total known to nine. The last panel of Sub-Mariner contains a rectangular box with "Continued Next Week" printed in it. When reprinted in Marvel Mystery, the box was left in with lettering omitted.

MY DOG TIGE (Buster Brown's Dog)
Buster Brown Shoes: 1957 (Giveaway)
nn 5 10 15 24 30 35

MY GREATEST THRILLS IN BASEBALL
Mission of California: 1950s? (16 pg. Giveaway)
nn-By Mickey Mantle 50 100 150 315 533 750

MYSTERIOUS ADVENTURES WITH SANTA CLAUS
Lansburgh's: 1948 (paper cover)
nn 13 26 39 72 101 130

NAKED FORCE!
Commercial Comics: 1958 (Small size)
nn 3 6 8 11 13 15

NATURAL DISASTERS!
Graphic Information Service/ Civil Defense: 1956 (16 pgs., soft-c)
nn-Al Capp Li'l Abner-c; Li'l Abner cameo (1 panel); narrated by Mr. Civil Defense 10 20 30 56 76 95

NAVY: HISTORY & TRADITION
Stokes Walesby Co./Dept. of Navy: 1958 - 1961 (nn) (Giveaway)
1772-1778, 1778-1782, 1782-1817, 1817-1865, 1865-1936, 1940-1945:
1772-1778-16 pg. in color 5 10 15 22 26 30
1861: Naval Actions of the Civil War: 1865-36 pg. in color; flag-c 5 10 15 22 26 30

NEW ADVENTURE OF WALT DISNEY'S SNOW WHITE AND THE SEVEN DWARFS, A (See Snow White Bendix Giveaway)

NEW ADVENTURES OF PETER PAN (Disney)
Western Publishing Co.: 1953 (5x7-1/4", 36 pgs.) (Admiral giveaway)
nn 13 26 39 72 101 130

NEW AVENGERS... (Giveaway for U.S Military personnel)
Marvel Comics: 2005 - Present (Distributed by Army & Air Force Exchange Service)
... Guest Starring the Fantastic Four (4/05) Bendis-s/Jurgens-a/c 5.00
...: Pot of Gold (AAFES 110th Anniversary Issue) (10/05) Jenkins-s/Nolan-a/c 5.00
(#3) ...: Avengers & X-Men Time Trouble (4/06) Kirkman-s 5.00
(#4) ...: Letters Home (12/06) Capt. America, Punisher, Silver Surfer, Ghost Rider on-c 5.00
5-The Spirit of America (10/05) Captain America app. 5.00
6-Fireline (8/08) Spider-Man, Iron Man & Hulk app. Richards-a/Dave Ross-c 5.00
7-An Army of One (2009) Frank Cho pin-up on back-c 5.00
8-The Promise (12/09) Captain America (Bucky) app. 5.00

NEW FRONTIERS
Harvey Information Press (United States Steel Corp.) : 1958 (16 pgs., paper-c)
nn-History of barbed wire 4 8 12 18 22 25

NEW TEEN TITANS, THE
DC Comics: Nov. 1983
nn(11/83-Keebler Co. Giveaway)-In cooperation with "The President's Drug Awareness Campaign"; came in Presidential envelope w/letter from White House (Nancy Reagan) 1 2 3 5 6 8
nn-(re-issue of above on Mando paper for direct sales market); American Soft Drink Industry version; I.B.M. Corp. version 5.00

NEW USES FOR GOOD EARTH
Mined Land Conservation: 1960 (paper-c)

On the Air nn © NBC

Oxydol-Dreft #1 © TOBY

Peter Wheat #33 © Bakers Assoc.

	GD 2.0	VG 4.0	FN 6.0	VF 8.0	VF/NM 9.0	NM- 9.2
nn	3	6	9	19	30	40

NOLAN RYAN IN THE WINNING PITCH (Kellogg's Tony's Sports Comics)
DC Comics: 1992 (Sports Illustrated)

	GD 2.0	VG 4.0	FN 6.0	VF 8.0	VF/NM 9.0	NM- 9.2
nn						5.00

OLD GLORY COMICS
Chesapeake & Ohio Railway: 1944 (Giveaway)

	GD 2.0	VG 4.0	FN 6.0	VF 8.0	VF/NM 9.0	NM- 9.2
nn-Capt. Fearless reprint	8	16	24	40	50	60

ON THE AIR
NBC Network Comic: 1947 (Giveaway, paper-c, regular size)

	GD 2.0	VG 4.0	FN 6.0	VF 8.0	VF/NM 9.0	NM- 9.2
nn-(Rare)	18	36	54	107	169	230

OPERATION SURVIVAL!
Graphic Information Service/ Civil Defense: 1957 (16 pgs., soft-c)

	GD 2.0	VG 4.0	FN 6.0	VF 8.0	VF/NM 9.0	NM- 9.2
nn-Al Capp Li'l Abner-c; Li'l Abner cameo (1 panel); narrated by Mr. Civil Defense	10	20	30	56	76	95

OUT OF THE PAST A CLUE TO THE FUTURE
E. C. Comics (Public Affairs Comm.): 1946? (16 pgs.) (paper cover)

	GD 2.0	VG 4.0	FN 6.0	VF 8.0	VF/NM 9.0	NM- 9.2
nn-Based on public affairs pamphlet "What Foreign Trade Means to You"	20	40	60	120	195	270

OUTSTANDING AMERICAN WAR HEROES
The Parents' Institute: 1944 (16 pgs., paper-c)

	GD 2.0	VG 4.0	FN 6.0	VF 8.0	VF/NM 9.0	NM- 9.2
nn-Reprints from True Comics	5	10	15	22	26	30

OVERSEAS COMICS (Also see G.I. Comics & Jeep Comics)
Giveaway (Distributed to U.S. Armed Forces): 1944 - No. 105?, 1946 (7-1/4x10-1/4"; 16 pgs. in color)

	GD 2.0	VG 4.0	FN 6.0	VF 8.0	VF/NM 9.0	NM- 9.2
23-105-Bringing Up Father (by McManus), Popeye, Joe Palooka, Dick Tracy, Superman, Gasoline Alley, Buz Sawyer, Li'l Abner, Blondie, Terry & the Pirates, Out Our Way	7	14	21	35	43	50

OWL, THE (See Crackajack Funnies #25 & Popular Comics #72)(Also see The Hurricane Kids & Magic Morro)
Western Pub. Co./R.S. Callender: 1940 (Giveaway)(7-1/2x5-1/4")(Soft-c, color)

	GD 2.0	VG 4.0	FN 6.0	VF 8.0	VF/NM 9.0	NM- 9.2
nn-Frank Thomas-a	15	30	45	86	133	180

OXYDOL-DREFT
Toby Press:1950 (Set of 6 pocket-size giveaways; distributed through the mail as a set) (Scarce)

	GD 2.0	VG 4.0	FN 6.0	VF 8.0	VF/NM 9.0	NM- 9.2
1-3: 1-Li'l Abner. 2-Daisy Mae. 3-Shmoo	9	18	27	47	61	75
4-John Wayne; Williamson/Frazetta-c from John Wayne #3	12	24	36	67	94	120
5-Archie	11	22	33	62	86	110
6-Terrytoons Mighty Mouse	9	18	27	47	61	75
Mailing Envelope (has All Capp's Shmoo on front)	9	18	27	52	69	85

OZZIE SMITH IN THE KID WHO COULD (Kellogg's Tony's Sports Comics)
DC Comics: 1992 (Sports Illustrated)

	GD 2.0	VG 4.0	FN 6.0	VF 8.0	VF/NM 9.0	NM- 9.2
nn-Ozzie Smith app.						5.00

PADRE OF THE POOR
Catechetical Guild: nd (Giveaway) (16 pgs., paper-c)

	GD 2.0	VG 4.0	FN 6.0	VF 8.0	VF/NM 9.0	NM- 9.2
nn	6	12	18	27	33	38

PAUL TERRY'S HOW TO DRAW FUNNY CARTOONS
Terrytoons, Inc. (Giveaway): 1940's (14 pgs.) (Black & White)

	GD 2.0	VG 4.0	FN 6.0	VF 8.0	VF/NM 9.0	NM- 9.2
nn-Heckle & Jeckle, Mighty Mouse, etc.	13	26	39	72	101	130

PETER PAN (See New Adventures of Peter Pan)

PETER PENNY AND HIS MAGIC DOLLAR
American Bankers Association, N. Y. (Giveaway): 1947 (16 pgs.; paper-c; regular size)

	GD 2.0	VG 4.0	FN 6.0	VF 8.0	VF/NM 9.0	NM- 9.2
nn-(Scarce)-Used in **SOTI**, pg. 310, 311	20	40	60	114	182	250
Diff. version (7-1/4x11")-redrawn, 16 pgs., paper-c	10	20	30	56	76	95

PETER WHEAT (The Adventures of...)
Bakers Associates Giveaway: 1948 - 1957? (16 pgs. in color) (paper covers)

	GD 2.0	VG 4.0	FN 6.0	VF 8.0	VF/NM 9.0	NM- 9.2
nn(No.1)-States on last page, end of 1st Adventure of...; Kelly-a	26	52	78	154	252	350
nn(4 issues)-Kelly-a	14	28	42	82	121	160
6-10-All Kelly-a	10	20	30	54	72	90
11-20-All Kelly-a	9	18	27	50	65	80
21-35-All Kelly-a	8	16	24	40	50	60
36-66	6	12	18	28	34	40
...Artist's Workbook ('54, digest size)	6	12	18	28	34	40
...Four-In-One Fun Pack (Vol. 2, '54), oblong, comics w/puzzles	7	14	21	35	43	50
...Fun Book ('52, 32 pgs., paper-c, B&W & color, 8-1/2x10-3/4")-Contains cut-outs, puzzles, games, magic & pages to color	8	16	24	44	57	70

NOTE: ***Al Hubbard** art #36 on; written by Del Connell.*

PETER WHEAT NEWS
Bakers Associates: 1948 - No. 63, 1953 (4 pgs. in color)

	GD 2.0	VG 4.0	FN 6.0	VF 8.0	VF/NM 9.0	NM- 9.2
Vol. 1-All have 2 pgs. Peter Wheat by Kelly	21	42	63	126	206	285
2-10	13	26	39	72	101	130
11-20	8	16	24	40	50	60
21-30	6	12	18	28	34	40
31-63	4	7	10	14	17	20

NOTE: *Early issues have no date & **Kelly** art.*

PINOCCHIO
Cocomalt/Montgomery Ward Co.: 1940 (10 pgs.; giveaway, linen-like paper)

	GD 2.0	VG 4.0	FN 6.0	VF 8.0	VF/NM 9.0	NM- 9.2
nn-Cocomalt edition	43	86	129	271	456	640
nn-store edition	36	72	108	215	350	485

PIUS XII MAN OF PEACE
Catechetical Guild: No date (12 pgs.; 5-1/2x8-1/2") (B&W)

	GD 2.0	VG 4.0	FN 6.0	VF 8.0	VF/NM 9.0	NM- 9.2
nn-Catechetical Guild Giveaway	6	12	18	33	41	48

PLOT TO STEAL THE WORLD, THE
Work & Unity Group: 1948, 16pgs., paper-c

	GD 2.0	VG 4.0	FN 6.0	VF 8.0	VF/NM 9.0	NM- 9.2
nn-Anti commumism	18	36	54	105	165	225

POCAHONTAS
Pocahontas Fuel Company (Coal): 1941 - No. 2, 1942

	GD 2.0	VG 4.0	FN 6.0	VF 8.0	VF/NM 9.0	NM- 9.2
nn(#1), 2-Feat. life story of Indian princess Pocahontas & facts about Pocahontas coal, Pocahontas, VA.	15	30	45	86	133	180

POLL PARROT
Poll Parrot Shoe Store/International Shoe
K. K. Publications (Giveaway): 1950 - No. 4, 1951; No. 2, 1959 - No. 16, 1962

	GD 2.0	VG 4.0	FN 6.0	VF 8.0	VF/NM 9.0	NM- 9.2
1 ('50)-Howdy Doody; small size	18	36	54	107	169	230
2-4('51)-Howdy Doody	15	30	45	88	137	185
2('59)-16('62): 2-The Secret of Crumbley Castle. 5-Bandit Busters. 6-Fortune Finders. 7-The Make-Believe Mummy. 8-Mixed Up Mission('60). 10-The Frightful Flight. 11-Showdown at Sunup. 12-Maniac at Mubu Island. 13-...and the Runaway Genie. 14-Bully for You. 15-Trapped In Tall Timber. 16-...& the Rajah's Ruby('62)	2	4	6	11	16	20

POPEYE
Whitman

	GD 2.0	VG 4.0	FN 6.0	VF 8.0	VF/NM 9.0	NM- 9.2
Bold Detergent giveaway (Same as regular issue #94)	2	4	6	9	13	16
Quaker Cereal premium (1989, 16pp, small size,4 diff.)(Popeye & the Time Machine, --On Safari, --& Big Foot, --vs. Bluto)	2	4	6	8	10	12

POPEYE
Charlton (King Features) (Giveaway): 1972 - 1974 (36 pgs. in color)

	GD 2.0	VG 4.0	FN 6.0	VF 8.0	VF/NM 9.0	NM- 9.2
E-1 to E-15 (Educational comics)	2	4	6	9	13	16
nn-Popeye Gettin' Better Grades-4 pgs. used as intro. to above giveaways (in color)	2	4	6	9	13	16

POPSICLE PETE FUN BOOK (See All-American Comics #6)
Joe Lowe Corp.: 1947, 1948

	GD 2.0	VG 4.0	FN 6.0	VF 8.0	VF/NM 9.0	NM- 9.2
nn-36 pgs. in color; Sammy 'n' Claras, The King Who Couldn't Sleep & Popsicle Pete stories, games, cut-outs	10	20	30	58	79	100
Adventure Book ('48)-Has Classics ad with checklist to HRN #343 (Great Expectations #43)	9	18	27	52	69	85

PORKY'S BOOK OF TRICKS
K. K. Publications (Giveaway): 1942 (8-1/2x5-1/2", 48 pgs.)

	GD 2.0	VG 4.0	FN 6.0	VF 8.0	VF/NM 9.0	NM- 9.2
nn-7 pg. comic story, text stories, plus games & puzzles	55	110	165	352	601	850

POST GAZETTE (See Meet the New...)

PUNISHER: COUNTDOWN (Movie)
Marvel Comics: 2004 (7 1/4" X 4 3/4" mini-comic packaged with Punisher DVD)

	GD 2.0	VG 4.0	FN 6.0	VF 8.0	VF/NM 9.0	NM- 9.2
nn-Prequel to 2004 movie; Ennis-s/Dillon-a/Bradstreet-c						2.50

PURE OIL COMICS (Also see Salerno Carnival of Comics, 24 Pages of Comics, & Vicks Comics)
Pure Oil Giveaway: Late 1930's (24 pgs., regular size, paper-c)

	GD 2.0	VG 4.0	FN 6.0	VF 8.0	VF/NM 9.0	NM- 9.2
nn-Contains 1-2 pg. strips; i.e., Hairbreadth Harry, Skyroads, Buck Rogers by Calkins & Yager, Olly of the Movies, Napoleon, S'Matter Pop, etc. Also a 16 pg. 1938 giveaway with Buck Rogers	35	70	105	208	339	470

QUAKER OATS (Also see Cap'n Crunch)
Quaker Oats Co.: 1965 (Giveaway) (2-1/2x5-1/2") (16 pgs.)

Reddy Kilowatt #2 © EC

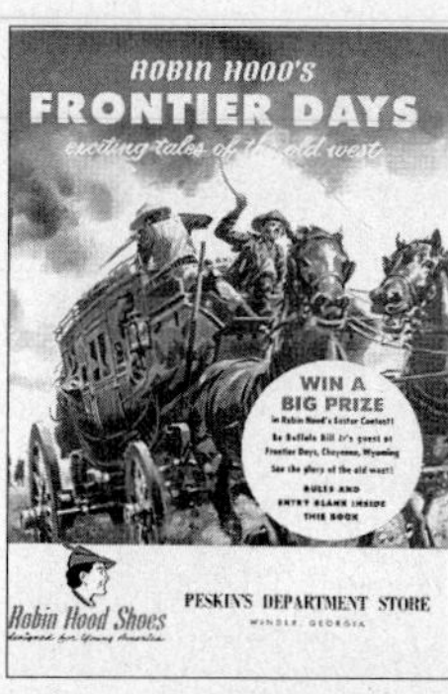

Robin Hood's Frontier Days © Robin Hood Shoes

Roy Rogers Riders Club Comics © Roy Rogers

	GD 2.0	VG 4.0	FN 6.0	VF 8.0	VF/NM 9.0	NM- 9.2

"Plenty of Glutton", starring Quake & Quisp; 3 6 9 14 19 24
"Lava Come-Back", "Kite Tale" 1 3 4 6 8 10

RAILROADS DELIVER THE GOODS!
Assoc. of American Railroads: Dec, 1954; Sept, 1957 (16 pgs., paper-c)
nn-The story of railway freight 6 12 18 28 34 40

RAILS ACROSS AMERICA!
Assoc. of American Railroads: nd (16 pgs.)
nn 6 12 18 28 34 40

READY THEN, READY NOW
Western Publications: 1966 (National Guard military giveaway, regular size)
nn 5 10 15 33 57 80

REAL FUN OF DRIVING!!, THE
Chrysler Corp.: 1965, 1966, 1967 (Regular size, 16 pgs.)
nn-Schaffenberger-a (12 pgs.) 1 2 3 5 6 8

REAL HIT
Fox Feature Publications: 1944 (Savings Bond premium)
1-Blue Beetle-r; Blue Beetle on-c 17 34 51 98 154 210
NOTE: *Two versions exist, with and without covers. The coverless version has the title, No. 1 and price printed at top of splash page.*

RED BALL COMIC BOOK
Parents' Magazine Institute: 1947 (Red Ball Shoes giveaway)
nn-Reprints from True Comics 4 8 12 17 21 24

REDDY GOOSE
International Shoe Co. (Western Printing): No number, 1958?; No. 2, Jan, 1959 - No. 16, July, 1962 (Giveaway)
nn (#1) 4 8 12 23 37 50
2-16 3 6 9 14 20 25

REDDY KILOWATT (5¢) (Also see Story of Edison)
Educational Comics (E. C.): 1946 - No. 2, 1947; 1956 - 1965 (no month) (16 pgs., paper-c)
nn-A Visit With Reddy (1948-1954?) 9 18 27 52 69 85
nn-Reddy Made Magic (1946, 5¢) 13 26 39 74 105 135
nn-Reddy Made Magic (1958) 9 18 27 52 69 85
2-Edison, the Man Who Changed the World (3/4" smaller than #1) (1947, 5¢)
13 26 39 74 105 135
...Comic Book 2 (1954)- "Light's Diamond Jubilee" 10 20 30 56 76 95
...Comic Book 2 (1956, 16 pgs.)- "Wizard of Light" 9 18 27 52 69 85
...Comic Book 2 (1958, 16 pgs.)- "Wizard of Light" 9 18 27 50 65 78
...Comic Book 2 (1965, 16 pgs.)- "Wizard of Light" 4 8 12 28 44 60
...Comic Book 3 (1956, 8 pgs.)- "The Space Kite"; Orlando story; regular size
9 18 27 52 69 85
...Comic Book 3 (1960, 8 pgs.)- "The Space Kite"; Orlando story; regular size
5 10 15 30 50 70
NOTE: *Several copies surfaced in 1979.*

REDDY MADE MAGIC
Educational Comics (E. C.): 1956, 1958 (16 pgs., paper-c)
1-Reddy Kilowatt-r (splash panel changed) 11 22 33 60 83 105
1 (1958 edition) 6 12 18 31 38 45

RED ICEBERG, THE
Impact Publ. (Catechetical Guild): 1960 (10¢, 16 pgs., Communist propaganda)
nn-(Rare)- "We The People" back-c 32 64 96 230 515 800
2nd version- "Impact Press" back-c 25 50 75 175 388 600
3rd version- "Explains comic" back-c 25 50 75 175 388 600
4th version- "Impact Press w/World Wide Secret Heart Program ad"
25 50 75 175 388 600
5th version- "Chicago Inter-Student Catholic Action" back-c
23 46 69 161 356 550
NOTE: *This book was the Guild's last anti-communist propaganda book and had very limited circulation. 3 - 4 copies surfaced in 1979 from the defunct publisher's files. Other copies do turn up.*

RED RYDER COMICS
Dell Publ. Co.
Buster Brown Shoes Giveaway (1941, color, soft-c, 32 pgs.)
18 36 54 107 169 225
Red Ryder Super Book of Comics (1944, paper-c, 32 pgs.; blank back-c)
Magic Morro app. 18 36 54 105 165 225
Red Ryder Victory Patrol-nn(1942, 32 pgs.)(Langendorf bread; includes cut-out membership card and certificate, order blank and "Slide-Up" decoder, and a Super Book of Comics in color (same content as Super Book #4 w/diff. cover
(Pan-Am)) (Rare) 84 168 252 538 919 1300
Red Ryder Victory Patrol-nn(1943, 32 pgs.)(Langendorf bread; includes cut-out "Rodeomatic" radio decoder, order coupon for "Magic V-Badge", cut-out membership card and certificate and a full color Super Book of comics comic book)
(Rare) 58 116 174 371 636 900
Red Ryder Victory Patrol-nn(1944, 32 pgs.)-r-/#43,44; comic has a paper-c & is stapled inside a triple cardboard fold-out-c; contains membership card, decoder, map of R.R. home range, etc. Herky app. (Langendorf Bread giveaway; sub-titled 'Super Book of Comics')
(Rare) 58 116 174 371 636 900
Wells Lamont Corp. giveaway (1950)-16 pgs. in color; regular size; paper-c;
1941-r 14 28 42 76 108 140

RETURN OF JOE THE GENIE OF STEEL (Also see Joe The Genie of Steel)
U. S. Steel Corp., Pittsburgh, PA/Commercial Comics: 1951 (U. S. Steel Corp. giveaway)
nn-Joe Magarac, the Paul Bunyan of steel 4 8 12 28 47 65

REX MORGAN M.D. TALKS ABOUT YOUR UNBORN CHILD
(No publisher) Fetal Alcohol, Tobacco & Firearms giveaway, 1980 (Reg. size, paper-c)
nn 3 6 9 19 30 40

RICHIE RICH, CASPER & WENDY NATIONAL LEAGUE
Harvey Publications: June, 1976 (52 pgs.) (newsstand edition also exists)
1 (Released-3/76 with 6/76 date) 3 6 9 15 22 28
1 (6/76)-2nd version w/San Francisco Giants & KTVU 2 logos; has "Compliments of Giants and Straw Hat Pizza" on-c 3 6 9 15 22 28
1-Variants for other 11 NL teams, similar to Giants version but with different ad on inside front-c 3 6 9 15 22 28

RIDE THE HIGH IRON!
Assoc. of American Railroads: Jan, 1957 (16 pgs.)
nn-The Story of modern passenger trains 5 10 15 24 30 35

RIPLEY'S BELIEVE IT OR NOT!
Harvey Publications
J. C. Penney giveaway (1948) 9 18 27 50 65 80

ROBIN HOOD (New Adventures of...)
Walt Disney Productions: 1952 (Flour giveaways, 5x7-1/4", 36 pgs.)
"New Adventures of Robin Hood", "Ghosts of Waylea Castle", & "The Miller's Ransom" each.... 4 7 10 14 17 20

ROBIN HOOD'S FRONTIER DAYS (...Western Tales, Adventures of... #1)
Shoe Store Giveaway (Robin Hood Stores): 1956 (20 pgs., slick-c)(7 issues?)
nn 6 12 18 31 38 45
nn-Issues with Crandall-a 8 16 24 42 54 65

ROCKETS AND RANGE RIDERS
Richfield Oil Corp.: May, 1957 (Giveaway, 16 pgs., soft-c)
nn-Toth-a 18 36 54 103 162 220

ROUND THE WORLD GIFT
National War Fund (Giveaway): No date (mid 1940's) (4 pgs.)
nn 12 24 36 67 94 120

ROY ROGERS COMICS
Dell Publishing Co.
...& the Man From Dodge City (Dodge giveaway, 16 pgs., 1954)-Frontier, Inc.
(5x7-1/4") 12 24 36 69 97 125
Official Roy Rogers Riders Club Comics (1952; 16 pgs., reg. size, paper-c)
15 30 45 86 133 180

RUDOLPH, THE RED-NOSED REINDEER
Montgomery Ward: 1939 (2,400,000 copies printed); Dec, 1951 (Giveaway)
Paper cover-1st app. in print; written by Robert May; ill. by Denver Gillen
15 30 45 84 127 175
Hardcover version 19 38 57 109 172 235
1951 Edition (Has 1939 date)-36 pgs., slick-c printed in red & brown; pulp interior printed in four mixed-ink colors: red, green, blue & brown 11 22 33 62 86 110
1951 Edition with red-spiral promotional booklet printed on high quality stock, 8-1/2"x11", in red & brown, 25 pages composed of 4 fold outs, single sheets and the Rudolph comic book inserted (rare) 47 94 141 296 498 700

SABRINA THE TEENAGE WITCH AND HER BOOK OF MAGIC
Archie Comic Publications: 1970 (small size giveaway)
2 - (A graded 9.4 copy sold for $121 in 2014)

SAD CASE OF WAITING ROOM WILLIE, THE
American Visuals Corp. (For Baltimore Medical Society): (nd, 1950?)
(14 pgs. in color; paper covers; regular size)
nn-By Will Eisner (Rare) 45 90 135 282 476 670

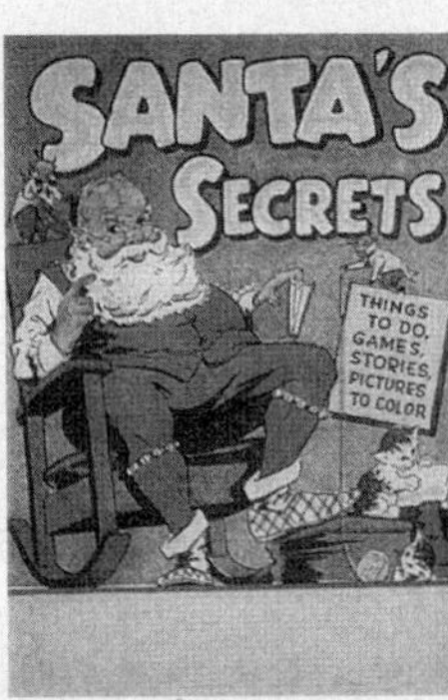

Santa's Secrets © Sam B. Anson

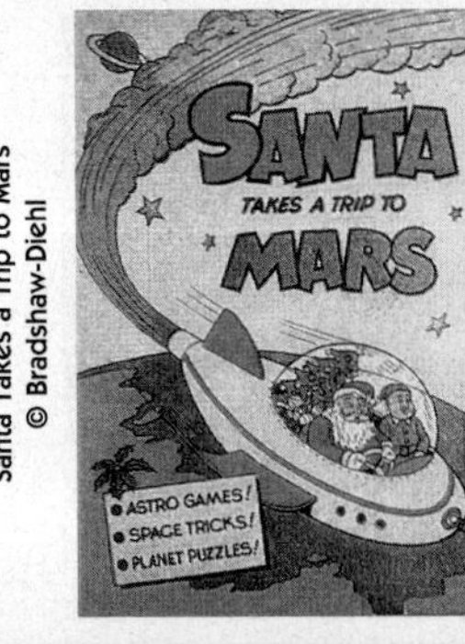

Santa Takes a Trip to Mars © Bradshaw-Diehl

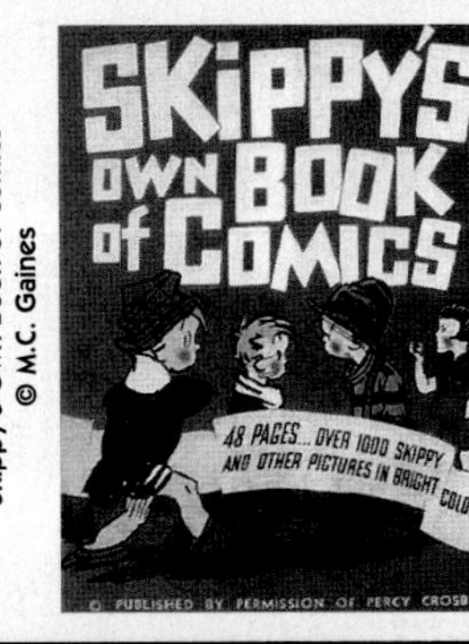

Skippy's Own Book of Comics © M.C. Gaines

	GD 2.0	VG 4.0	FN 6.0	VF 8.0	VF/NM 9.0	NM- 9.2
SAD SACK COMICS						
Harvey Publications: 1957-1962						
Armed Forces Complimentary copies, HD #1-40 (1957-1962)	3	6	9	15	22	28
SALERNO CARNIVAL OF COMICS (Also see Pure Oil Comics, 24 Pages of Comics, & Vicks Comics)						
Salerno Cookie Co.: Late 1930s (Giveaway, 16 pgs, paper-c)						
nn-Color reprints of Calkins' Buck Rogers & Skyroads, plus other strips from Famous Funnies	42	84	126	265	445	625
SALUTE TO THE BOY SCOUTS						
Association of American Railroads: 1960 (16 pgs., paper-c, regular size)						
nn-History of scouting and the railroad	3	6	9	16	23	30
SANTA AND POLLYANNA PLAY THE GLAD GAME						
Western Publ.: Aug, 1960 (16 pgs.) (Disney giveaway)						
nn	3	6	9	14	20	25
SANTA & THE BUCCANEERS						
Promotional Publ. Co.: 1959 (Giveaway, paper-c)						
nn-Reprints 1952 Santa & the Pirates	2	4	6	11	16	20
SANTA & THE CHRISTMAS CHICKADEE						
Murphy's: 1974 (Giveaway, 20 pgs.)						
nn	2	4	6	8	10	12
SANTA & THE PIRATES						
Promotional Publ. Co.: 1952 (Giveaway)						
nn-Marv Levy-c/a	4	8	12	17	21	24
SANTA CLAUS FUNNIES (Also see The Little Fir Tree)						
W. T. Grant Co./Whitman Publishing: nd; 1940 (Giveaway, 8x10"; 12 pgs., color & B&W, heavy paper)						
nn-(2 versions- no date and 1940)	41	82	123	256	428	600
SANTA IS HERE!						
Western Publ. (Giveaway): 1949 (oblong, slick-c)						
nn	6	12	18	33	38	45
SANTA ON THE JOLLY ROGER						
Promotional Publ. Co. (Giveaway): 1965						
nn-Marv Levy-c/a	2	4	6	8	10	12
SANTA! SANTA!						
R. Jackson: 1974 (20 pgs.) (Montgomery Ward giveaway)						
nn	1	3	4	6	8	10
SANTA'S BUNDLE OF FUN						
Gimbels: 1969 (Giveaway, B&W, 20 pgs.)						
nn-Coloring book & games	2	4	6	8	10	12
SANTA'S CHRISTMAS COMIC VARIETY SHOW (See Merry Christmas From Sears Toyland, Bob & Betty & Santa's Wishing Whistle, and A Christmas Carol)						
Sears Roebuck & Co.: 1943 (24 pgs.)						
Contains puzzles & new comics of Dick Tracy, Little Orphan Annie, Moon Mullins, Terry & the Pirates, etc.	54	108	162	343	574	825
SANTA'S CHRISTMAS TIME STORIES						
Premium Sales, Inc.: nd (Late 1940s) (16 pgs., paper-c) (Giveaway)						
nn	6	12	18	33	41	48
SANTA'S CIRCUS						
Promotional Publ. Co.: 1964 (Giveaway, half-size)						
nn-Marv Levy-c/a	2	4	6	9	12	15
SANTA'S FUN BOOK						
Promotional Publ. Co.: 1951, 1952 (Regular size, 16 pgs., paper-c) (Murphy's giveaway)						
nn	6	12	18	27	33	38
SANTA'S GIFT BOOK						
No Publisher: No date (16 pgs.)						
nn-Puzzles, games only	4	8	12	17	21	24
SANTA'S NEW STORY BOOK						
Wallace Hamilton Campbell: 1949 (16 pgs., paper-c) (Giveaway)						
nn	6	12	18	33	41	48
SANTA'S REAL STORY BOOK						
Wallace Hamilton Campbell/W. W. Orris: 1948, 1952 (Giveaway, 16 pgs.)						
nn	6	12	18	33	41	48

	GD 2.0	VG 4.0	FN 6.0	VF 8.0	VF/NM 9.0	NM- 9.2
SANTA'S RIDE						
W. T. Grant Co.: 1959 (Giveaway)						
nn	3	6	9	14	19	24
SANTA'S RODEO						
Promotional Publ. Co.: 1964 (Giveaway, half-size)						
nn-Marv Levy-a	2	4	6	9	12	15
SANTA'S SECRET CAVE						
W.T. Grant Co.: 1960 (Giveaway, half-size)						
nn	2	4	6	11	16	20
SANTA'S SECRETS						
Sam B. Anson Christmas giveaway: 1951, 1952? (16 pgs., paper-c)						
nn-Has games, stories & pictures to color	4	8	12	18	22	25
SANTA'S STORIES						
K. K. Publications (Klines Dept. Store): 1953 (Regular size, paper-c)						
nn-Kelly-a	15	30	45	90	140	190
nn-Another version (1953, glossy-c, half-size, 7-1/4x5-1/4")-Kelly-a	15	30	45	85	130	175
SANTA'S SURPRISE						
K. K. Publications: 1947 (Giveaway, 36 pgs., slick-c)						
nn	8	16	24	42	54	65
SANTA'S TOYTOWN FUN BOOK						
Promotional Publ. Co.: 1953 (Giveaway)						
nn-Marv Levy-c	4	8	11	16	19	22
SANTA TAKES A TRIP TO MARS						
Bradshaw-Diehl Co., Huntington, W.VA.: 1950s (nd) (Giveaway, 16 pgs.)						
nn	4	8	11	16	19	22
SCHWINN BIKE THRILLS						
Schwinn Bicycle Co.: 1959 (Reg. size)						
nn	8	16	24	44	57	70
SCIENCE FAIR STORY OF ELECTRONICS						
Radio Shack/Tandy Corp.: 1975 - 1987 (Giveaway)						
11 different issues (approx. 1 per year) each....						3.00
SECRETS BEHIND THE COMICS						
Famous Enterprises, Inc.: 1947 (Small size; advertised in Timely comics)						
nn - By Stan Lee; profile of Syd Shores (w/4 pgs. of his Blonde Phantom), Mike Sekowsky, Basil Wolverton, Al Jaffee & Martin Goodman; description of Captain America's creation with images	77	154	231	493	847	1200
SEEING WASHINGTON						
Commercial Comics: 1957 (also sold at 25¢)(Slick-c, reg. size)						
nn	6	12	18	28	34	40
SERGEANT PRESTON OF THE YUKON						
Quaker Cereals: 1956 (4 comic booklets) (Soft-c, 16 pgs., 7x2-1/2" & 5x2-1/2") Giveaways						
"How He Found Yukon King", "The Case That Made Him A Sergeant", "How Yukon King Saved Him From The Wolves", "How He Became A Mountie" each...	9	18	27	47	61	75
SHAZAM! (Visits Portland Oregon in 1943)						
DC Comics: 1989 (69¢ cover)						
nn-Promotes Super-Heroes exhibit at Oregon Museum of Science and Industry; reprints Golden Age Captain Marvel story	2	4	6	9	12	15
SHERIFF OF COCHISE, THE (TV)						
Mobil: 1957 (16 pgs.) Giveaway						
nn-Schaffenberger-a	4	9	13	18	22	26
SIDEWALK ROMANCE (Also see The K. O. Punch & Lucky Fights It Through)						
Health Publications: 1950						
nn-VD educational giveaway	47	94	141	296	498	700
SILLY PUTTY MAN						
DC Comics: 1978						
1	2	4	6	11	16	20
SKATING SKILLS						
Custom Comics, Inc./Chicago Roller Skates: 1957 (36 & 12 pgs.; 5x7", two versions) (10¢)						
nn-Resembles old ACG cover plus interior art	4	7	10	14	17	20
SKIPPY'S OWN BOOK OF COMICS (See Popular Comics)						

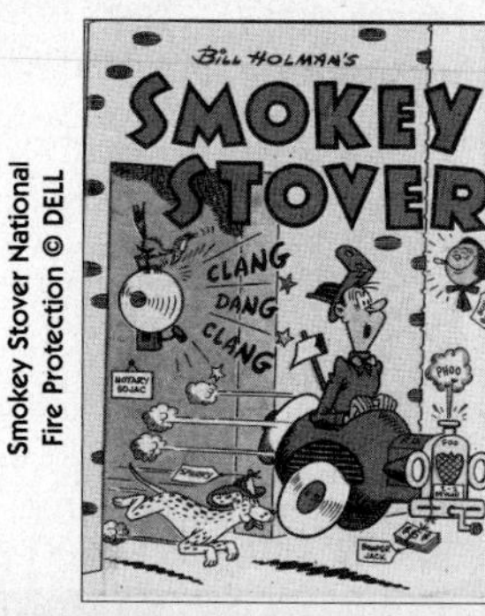

Smokey Stover National Fire Protection © DELL

Special Edition #4 © DC

The Spirit 6/23/40 © Will Eisner

GD 2.0 | VG 4.0 | FN 6.0 | VF 8.0 | VF/NM 9.0 | NM- 9.2

No publisher listed: 1934 (Giveaway, 52 pgs., strip reprints)
nn-(Scarce)-By Percy Crosby 343 686 1029 2400 4200 6000
Published by Max C. Gaines for Phillip's Dental Magnesia to be advertised on the Skippy Radio Show and given away with the purchase of a tube of Phillip's Tooth Paste. This is the first four-color comic book of reprints about one character.

SKY KING "RUNAWAY TRAIN" (TV)
National Biscuit Co.: 1964 (Regular size, 16 pgs.)
nn 5 10 15 35 63 90

SLAM BANG COMICS
Post Cereal Giveaway: No. 9, No date
9-Dynamic Man, Echo, Mr. E, Yankee Boy app. 9 18 27 50 65 80

SMILIN' JACK
Dell Publishing Co.
Popped Wheat Giveaway (1947)-1938 strip reprints; 16 pgs. in full color
2 4 6 8 11 14
Shoe Store Giveaway-1938 strip reprints; 16 pgs. 5 10 15 24 30 35
Sparked Wheat Giveaway (1942)-16 pgs. in full color 5 10 15 24 30 35

SMOKEY BEAR (See Forest Fire for 1st app.)
Dell Publ. Co.: 1959,1960
True Story of..., The -U.S. Forest Service giveaway-Publ. by Western Printing Co.; reprints 1st 16 pgs. of Four Color #932. Inside front-c differs slightly in 1959 & 1960 editions
6 12 18 28 34 40
1964,1969 reprints 2 4 6 11 16 20

SMOKEY STOVER
Dell Publishing Co.
General Motors giveaway (1953) 8 16 24 42 54 65
National Fire Protection giveaway(1953 & 1954)-16 pgs., paper-c
8 16 24 42 54 65

SNOW FOR CHRISTMAS
W. T. Grant Co.: 1957 (16 pgs.) (Giveaway)
nn 4 8 12 18 22 25

SNOW WHITE AND THE SEVEN DWARFS
Bendix Washing Machines: 1952 (32 pgs., 5x7-1/4", soft-c) (Disney)
nn 11 22 33 62 86 110

SNOW WHITE AND THE SEVEN DWARFS
Promotional Publ. Co.: 1957 (Small size)
nn 6 12 18 28 34 40

SNOW WHITE AND THE SEVEN DWARFS
Western Printing Co.: 1958 (16 pgs, 5x7-1/4", soft-c) (Disney premium)
nn- "Mystery of the Missing Magic" 6 12 18 31 38 45

SNOW WHITE AND THE 7 DWARFS IN "MILKY WAY"
American Dairy Assoc.: 1955 (16 pgs., soft-c, 5x7-1/4") (Disney premium)
nn 7 14 21 35 43 50

SOLDIER OF GOD
Conventual Franciscans of Marytown: 1982 ($1.00)
nn-Story of Father Maximilian Kobe, priest in WWII Poland; Ray Chatton-a 5.00

SPACE GHOST COAST TO COAST
Cartoon Network: Apr, 1994 (giveaway to Turner Broadcasting employees)
1-(8 pgs.); origin of Space Ghost 6.00

SPACE PATROL (TV)
Ziff-Davis Publishing Co. (Approved Comics)
...'s Special Mission (8 pgs., B&W, Giveaway) 45 90 135 284 480 675

SPARKY
Fire Protection Association: 1961 (Reg. size, paper-c)
nn 3 6 9 16 24 32

SPECIAL AGENT
Assoc. of American Railroads: Oct, 1959 (16 pgs.)
nn-The Story of the railroad police 6 12 18 28 34 40

SPECIAL DELIVERY
Post Hall Synd.: 1951 (32 pgs.; B&W) (Giveaway)
nn-Origin of Pogo, Swamp, etc.; 2 pg. biog. on Walt Kelly (One copy sold in 1980 for $150.00)

SPECIAL EDITION (U. S. Navy Giveaways)
National Periodical Publs.: 1944 - 1945 (Reg. comic format with wording simplified, 52 pgs.)
1-Action (1944)-Reprints Action #80 77 154 231 493 847 1200

GD 2.0 | VG 4.0 | FN 6.0 | VF 8.0 | VF/NM 9.0 | NM- 9.2

2-Action (1944)-Reprints Action #81 77 154 231 493 847 1200
3-Superman (1944)-Reprints Superman #33 77 154 231 493 847 1200
4-Detective (1944)-Reprints Detective #97 77 154 231 493 847 1200
5-Superman (1945)-Reprints Superman #34 77 154 231 493 847 1200
6-Action (1945)-Reprints Action #84 77 154 231 493 847 1200
NOTE: ***Wayne Boring*** *c-1, 2, 6.* ***Dick Sprang*** *c-4.*

SPIDER-MAN (See Amazing Spider-Man, The)

SPIRIT, THE (Weekly Comic Book)(Distributed through various newspapers & other sources)
Will Eisner: 6/2/40 - 10/5/52 (16 pgs.; 8 pgs.) (no cover) (in color)
NOTE: **Eisner** script, pencils/inks for the most part from 6/2/40-4/26/42; a few stories assisted by Jack Cole, Fine, Powell and Kotsky.

6/2/40(#1)-Origin/1st app. The Spirit; reprinted in Police #11; Lady Luck (Brenda Banks) (1st app.) by Chuck Mazoujian & Mr. Mystic (1st. app.) by S. R. (Bob) Powell begin (rare) 400 800 1200 2800 4900 7000
6/9/40(#2) 77 154 231 493 847 1200
6/16/40(#3)-Black Queen app. in Spirit 41 82 123 256 428 600
6/23/40(#4)-Mr. Mystic receives magical necklace 32 64 96 188 307 425
6/30/40(#5) 32 64 96 188 307 425
7/7/40(#6)-1st app. Spirit carplane; Black Queen app. in Spirit
34 68 102 199 325 450
7/14/40(#7)-8/4/40(#10): 7/21/40-Spirit becomes fugitive wanted for murder
28 56 84 165 270 375
8/11/40-9/22/40: 9/15/40-Racist-c 26 52 78 154 252 350
9/29/40-Ellen drops engagement with Homer Creep 22 44 66 132 216 300
10/6/40-11/3/40 22 44 66 132 216 300
11/10/40-The Black Queen app. 22 44 66 132 216 300
11/17/40, 11/24/40 22 44 66 132 216 300
12/1/40-Ellen spanking by Spirit on cover & inside; Eisner-1st 3 pgs., J. Cole rest
26 52 78 154 252 350
12/8/40-3/9/41 16 32 48 94 147 200
3/16/41-Intro. & 1st app. Silk Satin 20 40 60 118 192 265
3/23/41-6/1/41: 5/11/41-Last Lady Luck by Mazoujian. 5/18/41-Lady Luck by Nick Viscardi begins, ends 2/22/42 15 30 45 90 140 190
6/8/41-2nd app. Satin; Spirit learns Satin is also a British agent
18 36 54 103 162 220
6/15/41-1st app. Twilight 17 34 51 98 154 210
6/22/41-Hitler app. in Spirit 16 32 48 94 147 200
6/29/41-1/25/42,2/8/42 14 28 42 81 118 155
2/1/42-1st app. Duchess 16 32 48 94 147 200
2/15/42-4/26/42-Lady Luck by Klaus Nordling begins 3/1/42
15 30 45 84 127 170
5/3/42-8/16/42-Eisner/Fine/Quality staff assists on Spirit
12 24 36 69 97 125
8/23/42-Satin cover splash; Spirit by Eisner/Fine although signed by Fine
17 34 51 98 154 210
8/30/42,9/27/42-10/11/42,10/25/42-11/8/42-Eisner/Fine/Quality staff assists on Spirit 12 24 36 67 94 120
9/6/42-9/20/42,10/18/42-Fine/Belfi art on Spirit; scripts by Manly Wade Wellman
9 18 27 50 65 80
11/15/42-12/6/42,12/20/42,12/27/42,1/17/43-4/18/43,5/9/43-8/8/43-Wellman/ Woolfolk scripts, Fine pencils, Quality staff inks 9 18 27 50 65 80
12/13/42,1/3/43,1/10/43,4/25/43,5/2/43-Eisner scripts/layouts; Fine pencils, Quality staff inks 10 20 30 54 72 90
8/15/43-Eisner script/layout; pencils/inks by Quality staff; Jack Cole-a
8 16 24 44 57 70
8/22/43-12/12/43-Wellman/Woolfolk scripts, Fine pencils, Quality staff inks; Mr. Mystic by Guardineer-10/10/43-10/24/43 8 16 24 44 57 70
12/19/43-8/13/44-Wellman/Woolfolk/Jack Cole scripts; Cole, Fine & Robin King-a; Last Mr. Mystic-5/14/44 8 16 24 42 54 65
8/20/44-12/16/45-Wellman/Woolfolk scripts; Fine art with unknown staff assists
8 16 24 42 54 65
NOTE: *Scripts/layouts by Eisner, or Eisner/Nordling, Eisner/Mercer or Spranger/Eisner; inks by Eisner or Eisner/Spranger in issues 12/23/45-2/2/47.*
12/23/45-1/6/46: 12/23/45-Christmas-c 9 18 27 52 69 85
1/13/46-Origin Spirit retold 13 26 39 72 101 130
1/20/46-1st postwar Satin app. 11 22 33 64 90 115
1/27/46-3/10/46: 3/3/46-Last Lady Luck by Nordling 9 18 27 52 69 85
3/17/46-Intro. & 1st app. Nylon 11 22 33 64 90 115
3/24/46,3/31/46,4/14/46 9 18 27 52 69 85
4/7/46-2nd app. Nylon 10 20 30 56 76 95
4/21/46-Intro. & 1st app. Mr. Carrion & His Pet Buzzard Julia
13 26 39 72 101 130
4/28/46-5/12/46,5/26/46-6/30/46: Lady Luck by Fred Schwab in issues 5/5/46-11/3/46 9 18 27 52 69 85
5/19/46-2nd app. Mr. Carrion 10 20 30 56 76 95

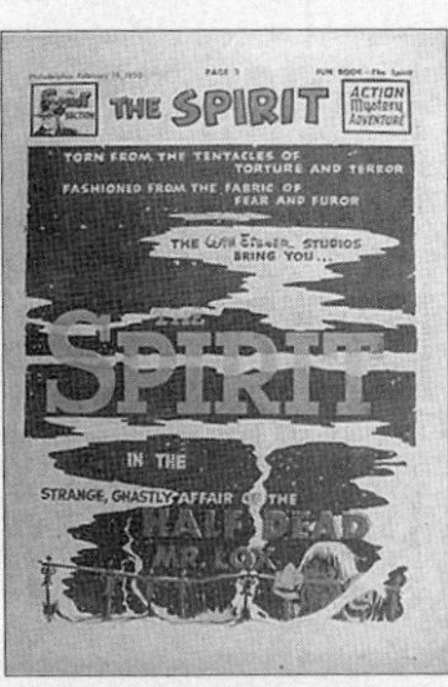

The Spirit 2/19/50 © Will Eisner

The Spirit 8/03/52 © Will Eisner

Standard Oil Comics #5B © Standard Oil

	GD 2.0	VG 4.0	FN 6.0	VF 8.0	VF/NM 9.0	NM- 9.2
7/7/46-Intro. & 1st app. Dulcet Tone & Skinny	11	22	33	64	90	115
7/14/46-9/29/46	9	18	27	52	69	85
10/6/46-Intro. & 1st app. P'Gell	13	26	39	74	105	135
10/13/46-11/3/46,11/16/46-11/24/46	9	18	27	52	69	85
11/10/46-2nd app. P'Gell	11	22	33	62	86	110
12/1/46-3rd app. P'Gell	10	20	30	54	72	90
12/8/46-2/2/47	9	18	27	50	65	80

NOTE: *Scripts, pencils/inks by Eisner except where noted in issues 2/9/47-12/19/48.*

	GD 2.0	VG 4.0	FN 6.0	VF 8.0	VF/NM 9.0	NM- 9.2
2/9/47-7/6/47: 6/8/47-Eisner self satire	9	18	27	50	65	80
7/13/47- "Hansel & Gretel" fairy tales	11	22	33	64	90	115
7/20/47-Li'L Abner, Daddy Warbucks, Dick Tracy, Fearless Fosdick parody; A-Bomb blast-c	13	26	39	72	101	130
7/27/47-9/14/47	9	18	27	50	65	80
9/21/47-Pearl Harbor flashback	10	20	30	56	76	95
9/28/47-1st mention of Flying Saucers in comics-3 months after 1st sighting in Idaho on 6/25/47	18	36	54	103	162	220
10/5/47- "Cinderella" fairy tales	11	22	33	64	90	115
10/12/47-11/30/47	9	18	27	50	65	80
12/7/47-Intro. & 1st app. Powder Pouf	13	26	39	72	101	130
12/14/47-12/28/47	9	18	27	50	65	80
1/4/48-2nd app. Powder Pouf	10	20	30	54	72	90
1/11/48-1st app. Sparrow Fallon; Powder Pouf app.	10	20	30	54	72	90
1/18/48-He-Man ad cover; satire issue	10	20	30	54	72	90
1/25/48-Intro. & 1st app. Castanet	13	26	39	72	101	130
2/1/48-2nd app. Castanet	9	18	27	52	69	85
2/8/48-3/7/48	9	18	27	50	65	80
3/14/48-Only app. Kretchma	9	18	27	52	69	85
3/21/48,3/28/48,4/11/48-4/25/48	9	18	27	50	65	80
4/4/48-Only app. Wild Rice	9	18	27	52	69	85
5/2/48-2nd app. Sparrow	9	18	27	50	65	80
5/9/48-6/27/48,7/11/48,7/18/48: 6/13/48-TV issue	9	18	27	50	65	80
7/4/48-Spirit by Andre Le Blanc	8	16	24	42	54	65
7/25/48-Ambrose Bierce's "The Thing" adaptation classic by Eisner/Grandenetti	15	30	45	90	140	190
8/1/48-8/15/48,8/29/48-9/12/48	9	18	27	50	65	80
8/22/48-Poe's "Fall of the House of Usher" classic by Eisner/Grandenetti	15	30	45	90	140	190
9/19/48-Only app. Lorelei	10	20	30	54	72	90
9/26/48-10/31/48	9	18	27	50	65	80
11/7/48-Only app. Plaster of Paris	11	22	33	64	90	115
11/14/48-12/19/48	9	18	27	50	65	80

NOTE: *Scripts by Eisner or Feiffer or Eisner/Feiffer or Nordling. Art by Eisner with backgrounds by Eisner, Grandenetti, Le Blanc, Stallman, Nordling, Dixon and/or others in issues 12/26/48-4/1/51 except where noted.*

	GD 2.0	VG 4.0	FN 6.0	VF 8.0	VF/NM 9.0	NM- 9.2
12/26/48-Reprints some covers of 1948 with flashbacks	9	18	27	50	65	80
1/2/49-1/16/49	9	18	27	50	65	80
1/23/49,1/30/49-1st & 2nd app. Thorne	10	20	30	54	72	90
2/6/49-8/14/49	9	18	27	50	65	80
8/21/49,8/28/49-1st & 2nd app. Monica Veto	10	20	30	54	72	90
9/4/49,9/11/49	9	18	27	50	65	80
9/18/49-Love comic cover; has gag love comic ads on inside	10	20	30	54	72	90
9/25/49-Only app. Ice	9	18	27	52	69	85
10/2/49,10/9/49-Autumn News appears & dies in 10/9 issue	9	18	27	52	69	85
10/16/49-11/27/49,12/18/49,12/25/49	9	18	27	50	65	80
12/4/49,12/11/49-1st & 2nd app. Flaxen	9	18	27	52	69	85
1/1/50-Flashbacks to all of the Spirit girls-Thorne, Ellen, Satin, & Monica	4	28	42	76	108	140
1/8/50-Intro. & 1st app. Sand Saref	15	30	45	86	133	180
1/15/50-2nd app. Saref	13	26	39	72	101	130
1/22/50-2/5/50	9	18	27	50	65	80
2/12/50-Roller Derby issue	10	20	30	54	72	90
2/19/50-Half Dead Mr. Lox - Classic horror	11	22	33	64	90	115
2/26/50-4/23/50,5/14/50,5/28/50,7/23/50-9/3/50	9	18	27	50	65	80
4/30/50-Script/art by Le Blanc with Eisner framing	8	16	24	40	50	60
5/7/50,6/4/50-7/16/50-Abe Kanegson-a	8	16	24	40	50	60
5/21/50-Script by Feiffer/Eisner, art by Blaisdell, Eisner framing	8	16	24	40	50	60
9/10/50-P'Gell returns	10	20	30	54	72	90
9/17/50-1/7/51	9	18	27	50	65	80
1/14/51-Life Magazine cover; brief biography of Comm. Dolan, Sand Saref, Silk Satin, P'Gell, Sammy & Willum, Darling O'Shea, & Mr. Carrion & His Pet Buzzard Julia, with pin-ups by Eisner	11	22	33	64	90	115
1/21/51,2/4/51-4/1/51	9	18	27	50	65	80
1/28/51- "The Meanest Man in the World" by Eisner	11	22	33	64	90	115
4/8/51-7/29/51,8/12/51-Last Eisner issue	9	18	27	50	65	80
8/5/51,8/19/51-7/20/52-Not Eisner	8	16	24	40	50	60
7/27/52-(Rare)-Denny Colt in Outer Space by Wally Wood; 7 pg. S/F story of E.C. vintage	53	106	159	334	567	800
8/3/52-(Rare)- "Mission...The Moon" by Wood	53	106	159	334	567	800
8/10/52-(Rare)- "A DP On The Moon" by Wood	53	106	159	334	567	800
8/17/52-(Rare)- "Heart" by Wood/Eisner	47	94	141	296	498	700
8/24/52-(Rare)- "Rescue" by Wood	53	106	159	334	567	800
8/31/52-(Rare)- "The Last Man" by Wood	53	106	159	334	567	800
9/7/52-(Rare)- "The Man in The Moon" by Wood	53	106	159	334	567	800
9/14/52-(Rare)-Eisner/Wenzel-a	34	68	102	199	325	450
9/21/52-(Rare)- "Denny Colt, Alias The Spirit/Space Report" by Eisner/Wenzel	36	72	108	211	343	475
9/28/52-(Rare)- "Return From The Moon" by Wood	48	96	144	302	509	715
10/5/52-(Rare)- "The Last Story" by Eisner	30	60	90	177	289	400

Large Tabloid pages from 1946 on (Eisner) - Price 200 percent over listed prices.

NOTE: *Spirit sections came out in both large and small format. Some newspapers went to the 8-pg. format months before others. Some printed the pages so they cannot be folded into a small comic book section; these are worth less. (Also see Three Comics & Spiritman).*

SPY SMASHER
Fawcett Publications

	GD 2.0	VG 4.0	FN 6.0	VF 8.0	VF/NM 9.0	NM- 9.2
Well Known Comics (1944, 12 pgs., 8-1/2x10-1/2"), paper-c, glued binding, printed in green; Bestmaid/Samuel Lowe giveaway	15	30	45	83	124	165

STANDARD OIL COMICS (Also see Gulf Funny Weekly)
Standard Oil Co.: 1932-1934 (Giveaway, tabloid size, 4 pgs. in color)

	GD 2.0	VG 4.0	FN 6.0	VF 8.0	VF/NM 9.0	NM- 9.2
nn (Dec. 1932)	65	130	195	416	708	1000
1-Series has original art	53	106	159	334	567	800
2-5	22	44	66	132	216	300
6-14: 14-Fred Opper strip, 1 pg.	15	30	45	85	130	175
1A (Jan 1933)	53	106	159	334	567	800
2A-14A (1933)	37	74	111	222	361	500
1B (1934)	41	82	123	256	428	600
2B-?B (1934)	37	74	111	222	361	500

NOTE: *Series A contains Frederick Opper's Si & Mirandi; Series B contains Goofus: He's From The Big City; McVittle by Walter O'Ehrle; interior strips include Pesty And His Pop & Smiling Slim by Sid Hicks.*

STAR TEAM
Marvel Comics Group: 1977 (6-1/2x5", 20 pgs.) (Ideal Toy Giveaway)

	GD 2.0	VG 4.0	FN 6.0	VF 8.0	VF/NM 9.0	NM- 9.2
nn	3	6	9	14	19	24

STEVE CANYON COMICS
Harvey Publications

	GD 2.0	VG 4.0	FN 6.0	VF 8.0	VF/NM 9.0	NM- 9.2
Dept. Store giveaway #3(6/48, 36pp)	10	20	30	54	72	90
...'s Secret Mission (1951, 16 pgs., Armed Forces giveaway); Caniff-a	9	18	27	47	61	75
Strictly for the Smart Birds (1951, 16 pgs.)-Information Comics Div. (Harvey) Premium	8	16	24	40	50	60

STORIES OF CHRISTMAS
K. K. Publications: 1942 (Giveaway, 32 pgs., paper cover)

	GD 2.0	VG 4.0	FN 6.0	VF 8.0	VF/NM 9.0	NM- 9.2
nn-Adaptation of "A Christmas Carol"; Kelly story "The Fir Tree"; Infinity-c	50	100	150	315	533	750

STORY HOUR SERIES (Disney)
Whitman Publ. Co.: 1948, 1949; 1951-1953 (36 pgs., paper-c) (4-3/4x6-1/2")
Given away with subscription to Walt Disney's Comics & Stories

	GD 2.0	VG 4.0	FN 6.0	VF 8.0	VF/NM 9.0	NM- 9.2
nn(1948)-Mickey Mouse and the Boy Thursday	12	24	36	67	94	120
nn(1948)-Mickey Mouse the Miracle Master	12	24	36	67	94	120
nn(1948)-Minnie Mouse and Antique Chair	12	24	36	67	94	120
nn(1949)-The Three Orphan Kittens(B&W & color)	9	18	27	47	61	75
nn(1949)-Danny-The Little Black Lamb	9	18	27	47	61	75
800(1948)-Donald Duck in "Bringing Up the Boys"	15	30	45	88	137	185
1953 edition	11	22	33	64	90	115
801(1948)-Mickey Mouse's Summer Vacation	10	20	30	56	76	95
1951, 1952 editions	7	14	21	35	43	50
802(1948)-Bugs Bunny's Adventures	9	18	27	50	65	80
803(1948)-Bongo	8	16	24	40	50	60
804(1948)-Mickey and the Beanstalk	9	18	27	47	61	75
805-15(1949)-Andy Panda and His Friends	8	16	24	40	50	60
806-15(1949)-Tom and Jerry	8	16	24	44	57	70
808-15(1949)-Johnny Appleseed	8	16	24	40	50	60

1948, 1949 Hard Cover Edition of each....30% - 40% more.

STOP AND GO, THE SAFETY TWINS
J.C. Penney: no date (giveaway)

	GD 2.0	VG 4.0	FN 6.0	VF 8.0	VF/NM 9.0	NM- 9.2
nn	5	10	15	24	30	35

STORY OF CHECKS THE
Federal Reserve Bank: 1979 (Reg. size)

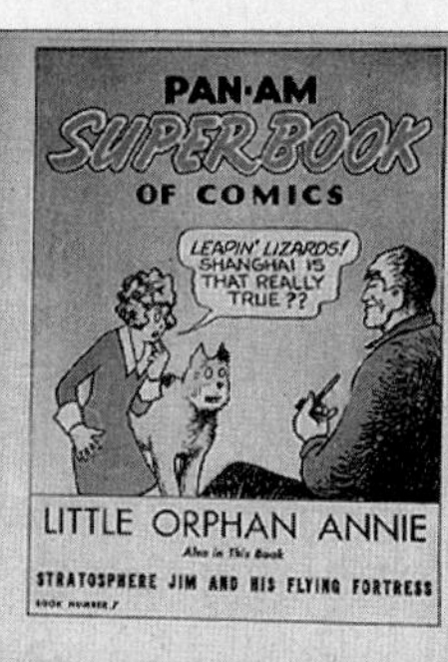

Super Book of Comics #7 © News Syndicate

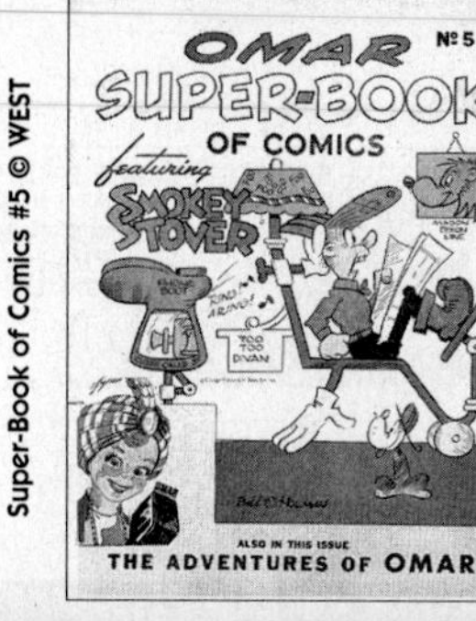

Super-Book of Comics #5 © WEST

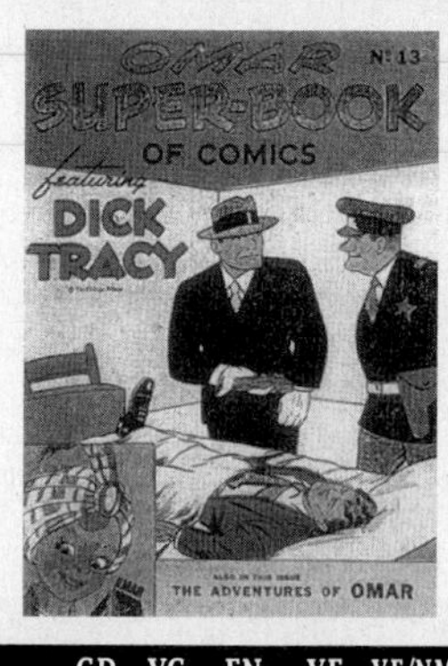

Super-Book of Comics #13 © NYNS

	GD 2.0	VG 4.0	FN 6.0	VF 8.0	VF/NM 9.0	NM- 9.2
nn	1	3	4	6	8	10
STORY OF CHECKS AND ELECTRONIC PAYMENTS						
Federal Reserve Bank: 1983 (Reg size)						
nn	1	2	3	5	6	8
STORY OF CONSUMER CREDIT						
Federal Reserve Bank: 1980 (Reg. size)						
nn	1	2	3	5	6	8
STORY OF EDISON, THE						
Educational Comics: 1956 (16 pgs.) (Reddy Killowatt)						
nn-Reprint of Reddy Kilowatt #2(1947)	7	14	21	37	46	55
STORY OF FOREIGN TRADE AND EXCHANGE						
Federal Reserve Bank: 1985 (Reg. size)						
nn	1	2	3	5	6	8
STORY OF HARRY S. TRUMAN, THE						
Democratic National Committee: 1948 (Giveaway, regular size, soft-c, 16 pg.)						
nn-Gives biography on career of Truman; used in **SOTI**, pg. 311	14	28	42	76	108	140
STORY OF INFLATION, THE						
Federal Reserve Bank: 1980s (Reg size)						
nn	1	3	4	6	8	10
STORY OF MONEY						
William C. Popper: 1962, 1965						
nn-Soft-c	3	6	9	16	23	30
STORY OF MONEY						
Federal Reserve Bank: 1984 (Reg. size)						
nn	1	3	4	6	8	10
STORY OF THE BALLET, THE						
Selva and Sons, Inc.: 1954 (16 pgs., paper cover)						
nn	4	8	11	16	19	22
STRANGE AS IT SEEMS						
McNaught Syndicate: 1936 (B&W, 5" x 7", 24 pgs.)						
nn-Ex-Lax giveaway	8	16	24	44	57	70
SUGAR BEAR						
Post Cereal Giveaway: No date, circa 1975? (2 1/2" x 4 1/2", 16 pgs.)						
"The Almost Take Over of the Post Office", "The Race Across the Atlantic", "The Zoo Goes Wild" each...	1	2	3	5	6	8
SUNDAY WORLD'S EASTER EGG FULL OF EASTER MEAT FOR LITTLE PEOPLE						
Supplement to the New York World: 3/27/1898 (soft-c, 16pg, 4"x8" approx., opens at top, color & B&W)(Giveaway)(shaped like an Easter egg)						
nn-By R.F. Outcault	18	36	54	107	169	230
SUPER BOOK OF COMICS						
Western Publ. Co.: nd (1942-1943?) (Soft-c, 32 pgs.) (Pan-Am/Gilmore Oil/Kelloggs premiums)						
nn-Dick Tracy (Gilmore)-Magic Morro app. (2 versions: Dick Tracy Jr. on cover and a filing cabinet cover)	37	74	111	222	361	500
1-Dick Tracy & The Smuggling Ring; Stratosphere Jim app. (Rare) (Pan-Am)	28	56	84	168	274	380
1-Smilin' Jack, Magic Morro (Pan-Am)	14	28	42	76	108	140
2-Smilin' Jack, Stratosphere Jim (Pan-Am)	14	28	42	76	108	140
2-Smitty, Magic Morro (Pan-Am)	14	28	42	76	108	140
3-Captain Midnight, Magic Morro (Pan-Am)	22	44	66	131	216	300
3-Moon Mullins?	13	26	39	74	105	135
4-Red Ryder, Magic Morro (Pan-Am). Same content as Red Ryder Victory Patrol comic w/diff. cover	15	30	45	85	130	175
4-Smitty, Stratosphere Jim (Pan-Am)	13	26	39	74	105	135
5-Don Winslow, Magic Morro (Gilmore)	15	30	45	85	130	175
5-Don Winslow, Stratosphere Jim (Pan-Am)	15	30	45	85	130	175
5-Terry & the Pirates	17	34	51	98	154	210
6-Don Winslow, Stratosphere Jim (Pan-Am)-McWilliams-a	15	30	45	85	130	175
6-King of the Royal Mounted, Magic Morro (Pan-Am)	15	30	45	85	130	175
7-Dick Tracy, Magic Morro (Pan-Am)	19	38	57	112	179	245
7-Little Orphan Annie	11	22	33	64	90	115
8-Dick Tracy, Stratosphere Jim (Pan-Am)	17	34	51	98	154	210
8-Dan Dunn, Magic Morro (Pan-Am)	11	22	33	64	90	115
9-Terry & the Pirates, Magic Morro (Pan-Am)	17	34	51	98	154	210
10-Red Ryder, Magic Morro (Pan-Am)	15	30	45	85	130	175

	GD 2.0	VG 4.0	FN 6.0	VF 8.0	VF/NM 9.0	NM- 9.2
SUPER-BOOK OF COMICS						
Western Publishing Co.: (Omar Bread & Hancock Oil Co. giveaways) 1944 - No. 30, 1947 (Omar); 1947 - 1948 (Hancock) (16 pgs.)						
NOTE: The Hancock issues are all exact reprints of the earlier Omar issues. The issue numbers were removed in some of the reprints.						
1-Dick Tracy (Omar, 1944)	15	30	45	94	147	200
1-Dick Tracy (Hancock, 1947)	14	28	42	78	112	145
2-Bugs Bunny (Omar, 1944)	8	16	24	40	50	60
2-Bugs Bunny (Hancock, 1947)	6	12	18	32	39	46
3-Terry & the Pirates (Omar, 1944)	11	22	33	60	83	105
3-Terry & the Pirates (Hancock, 1947)	10	20	30	54	72	90
4-Andy Panda (Omar, 1944)	8	16	24	40	50	60
4-Andy Panda (Hancock, 1947)	6	12	18	32	39	46
5-Smokey Stover (Omar, 1945)	6	12	18	32	39	46
5-Smokey Stover (Hancock, 1947)	5	10	15	24	30	35
6-Porky Pig (Omar, 1945)	8	16	24	40	50	60
6-Porky Pig (Hancock, 1947)	6	12	18	32	39	46
7-Smilin' Jack (Omar, 1945)	8	16	24	40	50	60
7-Smilin' Jack (Hancock, 1947)	6	12	18	32	39	46
8-Oswald the Rabbit (Omar, 1945)	6	12	18	32	39	46
8-Oswald the Rabbit (Hancock, 1947)	5	10	15	24	30	35
9-Alley Oop (Omar, 1945)	11	22	33	64	90	115
9-Alley Oop (Hancock, 1947)	11	22	33	60	83	105
10-Elmer Fudd (Omar, 1945)	6	12	18	32	39	46
10-Elmer Fudd (Hancock, 1947)	5	10	15	24	30	35
11-Little Orphan Annie (Omar, 1945)	8	16	24	42	53	64
11-Little Orphan Annie (Hancock, 1947)	7	14	21	36	45	54
12-Woody Woodpecker (Omar, 1945)	6	12	18	32	39	46
12-Woody Woodpecker (Hancock, 1947)	5	10	15	24	30	35
13-Dick Tracy (Omar, 1945)	11	22	33	64	90	115
13-Dick Tracy (Hancock, 1947)	11	22	33	60	83	105
14-Bugs Bunny (Omar, 1945)	6	12	18	32	39	46
14-Bugs Bunny (Hancock, 1947)	5	10	15	24	30	35
15-Andy Panda (Omar, 1945)	6	12	18	28	34	40
15-Andy Panda (Hancock, 1947)	5	10	15	24	30	35
16-Terry & the Pirates (Omar, 1945)	11	22	33	60	83	105
16-Terry & the Pirates (Hancock, 1947)	9	18	27	47	61	75
17-Smokey Stover (Omar, 1946)	6	12	18	32	39	46
17-Smokey Stover (Hancock, 1948?)	5	10	15	24	30	35
18-Porky Pig (Omar, 1946)	6	12	18	28	34	40
18-Porky Pig (Hancock, 1948?)	5	10	15	24	30	35
19-Smilin' Jack (Omar, 1946)	6	12	18	32	39	46
nn-Smilin' Jack (Hancock, 1948)	5	10	15	24	30	35
20-Oswald the Rabbit (Omar, 1946)	6	12	18	28	34	40
nn-Oswald the Rabbit (Hancock, 1948)	5	10	15	24	30	35
21-Gasoline Alley (Omar, 1946)	8	16	24	42	53	64
nn-Gasoline Alley (Hancock, 1948)	7	14	21	36	45	54
22-Elmer Fudd (Omar, 1946)	6	12	18	28	34	40
nn-Elmer Fudd (Hancock, 1948)	5	10	15	24	30	35
23-Little Orphan Annie (Omar, 1946)	8	16	24	40	50	60
nn-Little Orphan Annie (Hancock, 1948)	6	12	18	32	39	46
24-Woody Woodpecker (Omar, 1946)	6	12	18	28	34	40
nn-Woody Woodpecker (Hancock, 1948)	5	10	15	24	30	35
25-Dick Tracy (Omar, 1946)	11	22	33	60	83	105
nn-Dick Tracy (Hancock, 1948)	9	18	27	50	65	80
26-Bugs Bunny (Omar, 1946))	6	12	18	28	34	40
nn-Bugs Bunny (Hancock, 1948)	5	10	15	24	30	35
27-Andy Panda (Omar, 1946)	6	12	18	28	34	40
27-Andy Panda (Hancock, 1948)	5	10	15	24	30	35
28-Terry & the Pirates (Omar, 1946)	11	22	33	60	83	105
28-Terry & the Pirates (Hancock, 1948)	9	18	27	47	61	75
29-Smokey Stover (Omar, 1947)	6	12	18	28	34	40
29-Smokey Stover (Hancock, 1948)	5	10	15	24	30	35
30-Porky Pig (Omar, 1947)	6	12	18	28	34	40
30-Porky Pig (Hancock, 1948)	5	10	15	24	30	35
nn-Bugs Bunny (Hancock, 1948)-Does not match any Omar book	6	12	18	28	34	40
SUPER CIRCUS (TV)						
Cross Publishing Co.						
1-(1951, Weather Bird Shoes giveaway)	8	16	24	40	50	60
SUPER FRIENDS						
DC Comics: 1981 (Giveaway, no ads, no code or price)						
...Special 1 -r/Super Friends #19 & 36	2	4	6	9	13	16
SUPERGEAR COMICS						

Superman #97 - Pizza Hut © DC

Superman (miniature) #1 © DC

Superman-Tim 3/48 © DC

GD VG FN VF VF/NM NM-
2.0 4.0 6.0 8.0 9.0 9.2

GD VG FN VF VF/NM NM-
2.0 4.0 6.0 8.0 9.0 9.2

Jacobs Corp.: 1976 (Giveaway, 4 pgs. in color, slick paper)
nn-(Rare)-Superman, Lois Lane; Steve Lombard app. (500 copies printed, over half destroyed?) 18 36 54 126 281 435

SUPERGIRL
DC Comics: 1984, 1986 (Giveaway, Baxter paper)
nn-(American Honda/U.S. Dept. Transportation) Torres-c/a 2 4 6 8 11 14

SUPER HEROES PUZZLES AND GAMES
General Mills Giveaway (Marvel Comics Group): 1979 (32 pgs., regular size)
nn-Four 2-pg. origin stories of Spider-Man, Captain America, The Hulk, & Spider-Woman 3 6 9 14 20 26

SUPERMAN
National Periodical Publ./DC Comics
72-Giveaway(9-10/51)-(Rare)-Price blackened out; came with banner wrapped around book; without banner 76 152 228 486 831 1175
72-Giveaway with banner 123 246 369 787 1344 1900
Bradman birthday custom (1988)(extremely limited distribution) - a CGC 9.6 copy sold for $2600, a NM copy sold for $1125, and a FN/VF copy sold for $800 in 2011-2012, plus a CGC 9.0 sold for $421 in 12/12 and a CGC 9.6 copy sold for $1314 in 8/15
... For the Animals (2000, Doris Day Animal Foundation, 30 pgs.) polybagged with Gotham Adventures #22, Hourman #12, Impulse #58, Looney Tunes #62, Stars and S.T.R.I.P.E. #8 and Superman Adventures #41 2.50
Kelloggs Giveaway-(2/3 normal size, 1954)-r-two stories/Superman #55 30 60 90 177 289 400
Kenner: Man of Steel (Doomsday is Coming) (1995, 16 pgs.) packaged with set of Superman and Doomsday action figures 4.00
...Meets the Quik Bunny (1987, Nestles Quik premium, 36 pgs.) 1 2 3 5 7 9
Pizza Hut Premiums (12/77)-Exact reprints of 1950s comics except for paid ads (set of 6 exist?); Vol. 1-r#97 (#113-r also known) 2 4 6 8 10 12
Radio Shack Giveaway-36 pgs. (7/80) "The Computers That Saved Metropolis", Starlin/Giordano-a; advertising insert in Action #509, New Advs. of Superboy #7, Legion of Super-Heroes #265, & House of Mystery #282. (All comics were 68 pgs.) Cover of inserts printed on newsprint. Giveaway contains 4 extra pgs. of Radio Shack advertising that inserts do not have 1 2 3 5 7 9
Radio Shack Giveaway-(7/81) "Victory by Computer" 1 2 3 5 7 9
Radio Shack Giveaway-(7/82) "Computer Masters of Metropolis" 1 2 3 5 7 9

SUPERMAN ADVENTURES, THE (TV)
DC Comics: 1996 (Based on animated series)
1-(1996) Preview issue distributed at Warner Bros. stores 4.00
Titus Game Edition (1998) 2.50

SUPERMAN AND THE GREAT CLEVELAND FIRE
National Periodical Publ.: 1948 (Giveaway, 4 pgs., no cover) (Hospital Fund)
nn-In full color 71 142 213 454 777 1100

SUPERMAN AT THE GILBERT HALL OF SCIENCE
National Periodical Publ.: 1948 (Giveaway) (Gilbert Chemistry Sets / A.C. Gilbert Co.)
nn-(8 1/2" x 5 1/2") 39 78 117 240 395 550

SUPERMAN (Miniature)
National Periodical Publ.: 1942; 1955 - 1956 (3 issues, no #'s, 32 pgs.)
The pages are numbered in the 1st issue: 1-32; 2nd: 1A-32A, and 3rd: 1B-32B
No date-Py-Co-Pay Tooth Powder giveaway (8 pgs.; circa 1942)(The Adventures of...) Japanese air battle 39 78 117 240 395 550
1-The Superman Time Capsule (Kellogg's Sugar Smacks)(1955) 21 42 63 122 199 275
1A-Duel in Space (1955) 20 40 60 114 182 250
1B-The Super Show of Metropolis (also #1-32, no B)(1955) 20 40 60 114 182 250

NOTE: *Numbering variations exist. Each title could have any combination-#1, 1A, or 1B.*

SUPERMAN RECORD COMIC
National Periodical Publications: 1966 (Golden Records)
(With record)-Record reads origin of Superman from comic; came with iron-on patch, decoder, membership card & button; comic-r/Superman #125,146 10 20 30 64 132 200
Comic only 5 10 15 30 50 70

SUPERMAN'S BUDDY (Costume Comic)
National Periodical Publs.: 1954 (4 pgs., slick paper-c; one-shot) (Came in box w/costume)
1-With box & costume 123 246 369 787 1344 1900
Comic only 55 110 165 352 601 850
1-(1958 edition)-Printed in 2 colors 17 34 51 98 154 210

SUPERMAN'S CHRISTMAS ADVENTURE
National Periodical Publications: 1940, 1944 (Giveaway, 16 pgs.)
Distributed by Nehi drinks, Bailey Store, Ivey-Keith Co., Kennedy's Boys Shop, Macy's Store, Boston Store
1(1940)-Burnley-a; F. Ray-c/r from Superman #6 (Scarce)-Superman saves Santa Claus. Santa makes real Superman Toys offered in 1940. 1st merchandising story; versions with Royal Crown Cola ad on front-c & Boston Store ad on front-c; cover art on each has the same layout but different art 459 918 1377 3350 5925 8500
nn(1944) w/Santa Claus & X-mas tree-c 100 200 300 635 1093 1550
nn(1944) w/Candy cane & Superman-c 100 200 300 635 1093 1550
nn(1944) w/1940-c (Santa over chimney); Superman image (from Superman #6) on back-c 100 200 300 635 1093 1550

SUPERMAN-TIM (Becomes Tim)
Superman-Tim Stores/National Periodical Publ.: Aug, 1942 - May, 1950 (Half size) (B&W Giveaway w/2 color covers) (Publ. monthly 2/43 on)(All have Superman illos)

	GD 2.0	VG 4.0	FN 6.0	VF 8.0	VF/NM 9.0	NM- 9.2
8/42 (#1)- 2 pg. Superman story	142	284	426	909	1555	2200
9/42 (#2) Superman/Uncle Sam flag-c	55	110	165	352	601	850
12/42-Christmas-c	43	86	129	276	461	650
1/43	42	84	126	265	445	625
2/43, 3/43-Classic flag-c	41	82	123	256	428	600
4/43, 5/43, 6/43, 8/43	37	74	111	222	361	500
7/43-Classic Superman bomb-c	41	82	123	256	428	600
9/43, 10/43, 11/43, 12/43	30	60	90	177	289	400
1/44-12/44	24	48	72	140	230	320
1/45-5/45, 8/45, 10-12/45 (X-mas-c), 1/46-8/46	22	44	66	128	209	290
6/45-Classic Superman-c	23	46	69	138	227	315
7/45-Classic Superman flag-c	23	46	69	138	227	315
9/45-1st stamp album issue	48	96	114	302	509	715
9/46-2nd stamp album issue	41	82	123	256	428	600
10/46-1st Superman story	29	58	87	170	278	385
11/46, 12/46, 1/47-8/47 issues-Superman story in each; 2/47-Infinity-c. All 36 pgs.	29	58	87	170	278	385
9/47-Stamp album issue & Superman story	40	80	120	246	411	575
10/47, 11/47, 12/47-Superman stories (24 pgs.)	29	58	87	170	278	385
1/48-7/48,10/48, 11/48, 12/48, 2/49, 4/49-11/49	23	46	69	138	227	315
8/48-Contains full page ad for Superman-Tim watch giveaway	23	46	69	138	227	315
9/48-Stamp album issue	32	64	96	188	307	425
1/49-Full page Superman bank cut-out	23	46	69	138	227	315
3/49-Full page Superman boxing game cut-out	23	46	69	138	227	315
12/49-3/50, 5/50-Superman stories	25	50	75	150	245	340
4/50-Superman story, baseball stories; photo-c without Superman	29	58	87	170	278	385

NOTE: *All issues have Superman illustrations throughout. The page count varies depending on whether a Superman-Tim comic story is inserted. If it is, the page count is either 36 or 24 pages. Otherwise all issues are 16 pages. Each issue has a special place for inserting a full color Superman stamp. The stamp album issues had spaces for the stamps given away the past year. The books were mailed as a subscription premium. The stamps were given away free (or when you made a purchase) only when you physically came into the store.*

SUPER SEAMAN SLOPPY
Allied Pristine Union Council, Buffalo, NY: 1940s, 8pg., reg. size (Soft-c)
nn 9 18 27 47 61 75

SURVEY
Marvel Comics Group: 1948 (Readership survey for advertisers, reg. size)
nn-Harvey Kurtzman-c/a 87 174 261 553 952 1350

SWAMP FOX, THE
Walt Disney Productions: 1960 (14 pgs, small size) (Canada Dry Premiums)
Titles: (A)-Tory Masquerade, (B)-Turnabout Tactics, (C)-Rindau Rampage; each came in paper sleeve, books 1,2 & 3;
Set with sleeves 5 10 15 31 53 75
Comic only 2 4 6 13 18 22

SWORDQUEST
DC Comics/Atari Pub.: 1982, 52pg., 5"x7" (Giveaway with video games)
1,2-Roy Thomas & Gerry Conway-s; George Pérez & Dick Giordano-c/a in all 2 4 6 10 14 18
3-Low print 3 6 9 15 22 28

SYNDICATE FEATURES (Sci/fi)
Harry A. Chesler Syndicate: V1#3, 11/15/37; V1#5, 12/15/37 (Tabloid size, 3 colors, 4 pgs.) (Editors premium) (Came folded)
V1#3,5-Dan Hastings daily strips-Guardineer-a 155 310 465 992 1696 2400

TAKING A CHANCE
American Cancer Society: no date (giveaway)
nn-Anti-smoking 2 4 6 11 16 20

TASTEE-FREEZ COMICS (Also see Harvey Hits and Richie Rich)
Harvey Comics: 1957 (10¢, 36 pgs.)(6 different issues given away)

Tastee-Freez Comics #5 © HARV

Time of Decision © HARV

Tom Mix Comics #2 © FAW

	GD 2.0	VG 4.0	FN 6.0	VF 8.0	VF/NM 9.0	NM- 9.2

1-Little Dot on cover; Richie Rich "Ride 'Em Cowboy" story published one year prior to being printed in Harvey Hits #9. 8 16 24 51 96 140
2,4,5: 2-Rags Rabbit. 4-Sad Sack. 5-Mazie 2 4 6 8 10 12
3-Casper 2 4 6 11 16 20
6-Dick Tracy 2 4 6 11 16 20
nn-Brings You Space Facts and Fun Book 1 2 3 5 6 8

TAYLOR'S CHRISTMAS TABLOID
Dept. Store Giveaway: Mid 1930s, Cleveland, Ohio (Tabloid size; in color)
nn-(Very Rare)-Among the earliest pro work of Siegel & Shuster; one full color page called "The Battle in the Stratosphere", with a pre-Superman look; Shuster art thoughout. (Only 1 known copy) Estimated value... 4000.00

TAZ'S 40TH BIRTHDAY BLOWOUT
DC Comics: 1994 (K-Mart giveaway, 16 pgs.)
nn-Six pg. story, games and puzzles 4.00

TEE AND VEE CROSLEY IN TELEVISION LAND COMICS (Also see Crosley's House of Fun)
Crosley Division, Avco Mfg. Corp. : 1951 (52 pgs.; 8x11"; paper cover; in color) (Giveaway)
Many stories, puzzles, cut-outs, games, etc. 8 16 24 40 50 60

TEEN-AGE BOOBY TRAP
Commercial Comics: 1970 (Small size)
nn 3 6 9 16 23 30

TENNESSEE JED (Radio)
Fox Syndicate? (Wm. C. Popper & Co.): nd (1945) (16 pgs.; paper-c; reg. size; giveaway)
nn 20 40 60 117 189 260

TENNIS (...For Speed, Stamina, Strength, Skill)
Tennis Educational Foundation: 1956 (16 pgs.; soft cover; 10¢)
Book 1-Endorsed by Gene Tunney, Ralph Kiner, etc. showing how tennis has helped them 6 12 18 28 34 40

TERRY AND THE PIRATES
Dell Publishing Co.: 1939 - 1953 (By Milton Caniff)
Buster Brown Shoes giveaway(1938)-32 pgs.; in color 20 40 60 114 182 250
Canada Dry Premiums-Books #1-3(1953, 36 pgs.; 2x5")-Harvey; #1-Hot Shot Charlie Flies Again; 2-In Forced Landing; 3-Dragon Lady in Distress) 14 28 42 78 112 145
Gambles Giveaway (1938, 16 pgs.) 9 18 27 50 65 80
Gillmore Giveaway (1938, 24 pgs.) 9 18 27 52 69 85
Popped Wheat Giveaway(1938)-Strip reprints in full color; Caniff-a 2 4 6 8 10 12
Shoe Store giveaway (Weatherbird & Poll-Parrot)(1938, 16 pgs., soft-c)(2-diff.) 9 18 27 52 69 85
Sparked Wheat Giveaway(1942, 16 pgs.)-In color 9 18 27 52 69 85

TERRY AND THE PIRATES
Libby's Radio Premium: 1941 (16 pgs.; reg. size)(shipped folded in the mail)
"Adventure of the Ruby of Genghis Khan" - Each pg. is a puzzle that must be completed to read the story 400 800 1200 2600 - -

THAT THE WORLD MAY BELIEVE
Catechetical Guild Giveaway: No date (16 pgs.) (Graymoor Friars distr.)
nn 5 10 14 20 24 28

THREAT TO FREEDOM
1965 (Small size)
nn - Anti-communism pamphlet; hammer & sickle-c 8 16 24 54 102 150

3-D COLOR CLASSICS (Wendy's Kid's Club)
Wendy's Int'l Inc.: 1995 (5 1/2" x 8", comes with 3-D glasses)
The Elephant's Child, Gulliver's Travels, Peter Pan, The Time Machine, 20,000 Leagues Under the Sea: Neal Adams-a in all each.... 3.50

350 YEARS OF AMERICAN DAIRY FOODS
American Dairy Assoc.: 1957 (5x7", 16 pgs.)
nn-History of milk 3 6 8 12 14 16

THUMPER (Disney)
Grosset & Dunlap: 1942 (50¢, 32pgs., hardcover book, 7"x8-1/2" w/dust jacket)
nn-Given away (along with a copy of Bambi) for a $2.00, 2-year subscription to WDC&S in 1942. (Xmas offer). Book only 15 30 45 90 140 190
Dust jacket only 10 20 30 56 76 95

TILLY AND TED-TINKERTOTLAND
W. T. Grant Co.: 1945 (Giveaway, 20 pgs.)
nn-Christmas comic 9 18 27 47 61 75

TIM (Formerly Superman-Tim; becomes Gene Autry-Tim)
Tim Stores: June, 1950 - Oct, 1950 (B&W, half-size)
4 issues; 6/50, 9/50, 10/50 known 17 34 51 98 154 210

TIM AND SALLY'S ADVENTURES AT MARINELAND
Marineland Restaurant & Bar, Marineland, CA: 1957 (5x7", 16 pgs., soft-c)
nn-copyright Oceanarium, Inc. 2 4 6 8 11 14

TIME OF DECISION
Harvey Publications Inc.: (16 pgs., paper cover)
nn-ROTC recruitment 5 10 15 22 26 30

TIM IN SPACE (Formerly Gene Autry Tim; becomes Tim Tomorrow)
Tim Stores: 1950 (1/2 size giveaway) (B&W)
nn 14 28 42 80 115 150

TIM TOMORROW (Formerly Tim In Space)
Tim Stores: 8/51, 9/51, 10/51, Christmas, 1951 (5x7-3/4")
nn-Prof. Fumble & Captain Kit Comet in all 14 28 42 80 115 150

TIM TYLER'S LUCK
Standard Comics (King Feat. Syndicate): 1950s (Reg. size, slick-c)
nn-Felix the at app. 4 7 10 14 17 20

TITANS BEAT (Teen Titans)
DC Comics: Aug, 1996 (16 pgs., paper-c)
1-Intro./preview new Teen Titans members; Pérez-a 4.00

TOM MIX (...Commandos Comics #10-12)
Ralston-Purina Co.: Sept, 1940 - No. 12, Nov, 1942 (36 pgs.); 1983 (one-shot)
Given away for two Ralston box-tops; 1983 came in cereal box
1-Origin (life) Tom Mix; Fred Meagher-a 206 412 618 1318 2259 3200
2 43 86 129 271 461 650
3-9 37 74 111 222 361 500
10-12: 10-Origin Tom Mix Commando Unit; Speed O'Dare begins; Japanese sub-c. 12-Sci/fi-c 30 60 90 177 289 400
1983- "Taking of Grizzly Grebb", Toth-a; 16 pg. miniature 2 4 6 9 12 15

TOM SAWYER COMICS
Giveaway: 1951? (Paper cover)
nn-Contains a coverless Hopalong Cassidy from 1951; other combinations known 3 6 9 14 20 25

TOO MUCH, TOO LITTLE
Federal Reserve Bank: 1989 (Reg. size)
9-13 1 3 4 6 8 10

TOP-NOTCH COMICS
MLJ Magazines/Rex Theater: 1940s (theater giveaway, sepia-c)
1-Black Hood-c; content & covers can vary 57 114 171 362 619 875

TOWN THAT FORGOT SANTA, THE
W. T. Grant Co.: 1961 (Giveaway, 24 pgs.)
nn 3 6 9 16 23 30

TOY LAND FUNNIES (See Funnies On Parade)
Eastern Color Printing Co.: 1934 (32 pgs., Hecht Co. store giveaway)
nn-Reprints Buck Rogers Sunday pages #199-201 from Famous Funnies #5. A rare variation of Funnies On Parade; same format, similar contents, same cover except for large Santa placed in center (value will be based on sale)

TOY WORLD FUNNIES (See Funnies On Parade)
Eastern Color Printing Co.: 1933 (36 pgs., slick cover, Golden Eagle and Wanamaker giveaway)
nn-Contains contents from Funnies On Parade/Century Of Comics. A rare variation of Funnies On Parade; same format, similar contents, same cover except for large Santa placed in center. A GD/VG 3.0 copy sold for $5258 in May 2016.

TRAPPED
Harvey Publications (Columbia Univ. Press): 1951 (Giveaway, soft-c, 16 pgs)
nn-Drug education comic (30,000 printed?) distributed to schools.; mentioned in **SOTI**, pgs. 256,350 2 4 6 8 10 12
NOTE: *Many copies surfaced in 1979 causing a setback in price; beware of trimmed edges, because many copies have a brittle edge.*

TRIPLE-A BASEBALL HEROES
Marvel Comics: 2007 (Minor league baseball stadium giveaway)
1-Special John Watson painted-c for Memphis, Durham and Buffalo; generic cover with team logos for each of the other 27 teams; Spider-Man, Iron Man, FF app. 3.00

TRIP TO OUTER SPACE WITH SANTA
Sales Promotions, Inc/Peoria Dry Goods: 1950s (paper-c)
nn-Comics, games & puzzles 5 10 15 22 26 30

TRIP WITH SANTA ON CHRISTMAS EVE, A
Rockford Dry Goods Co.: No date (Early 1950s) (Giveaway, 16 pgs., paper-c)

Unkept Promise © Legion of Truth

Watch Out For Big Talk © GC

Weather-Bird #1 © WEST

	GD 2.0	VG 4.0	FN 6.0	VF 8.0	VF/NM 9.0	NM- 9.2

nn 5 10 15 22 26 30

TRUTH BEHIND THE TRIAL OF CARDINAL MINDSZENTY, THE (See Cardinal Mindszenty)

24 PAGES OF COMICS (No title) (Also see Pure Oil Comics, Salerno Carnival of Comics, & Vicks Comics)
Giveaway by various outlets including Sears: Late 1930s

nn-Contains strip reprints-Buck Rogers, Napoleon, Sky Roads, War on Crime 31 62 93 186 303 420

TWO FACES OF COMMUNISM (Also see Double Talk)
Christian Anti-Communism Crusade, Houston, Texas: 1961 (Giveaway, paper-c, 36 pgs.)

nn 22 44 66 132 216 300

2001, A SPACE ODYSSEY (Movie)
Marvel Comics Group

Howard Johnson giveaway (1968, 8pp); 6 pg. movie adaptation, 2 pg. games, puzzles; McWilliams-a 2 4 6 9 12 15

UNCLE SAM'S CHRISTMAS STORY
Promotional Publ. Co.: 1958 (Giveaway)

nn-Reprints 1956 Christmas USA 2 4 6 10 13 16

UNCLE WIGGILY COMICS
Herberger's Clothing Store: 1942 (32 pgs., paper cover)

nn-Comic panels with 6 pages of puzzles 14 28 42 80 115 150

UNKEPT PROMISE
Legion of Truth: 1949 (Giveaway, 24 pgs.)

nn-Anti-alcohol 10 20 30 58 79 100

UNTOLD LEGEND OF THE BATMAN, THE
DC Comics: 1989 (28 pgs., 6X9", limited series of cereal premiums)

1-1st & 2nd printings known; Byrne-a 2 4 6 8 10 12
2,3: 1st & 2nd printings known 1 2 3 5 7 9

UNTOUCHABLES, THE (TV)
Leaf Brands, Inc.

Topps Bubblegum premiums produced by Leaf Brands, Inc.-2-1/2x4-1/2", 8 pgs. (3 diff. issues) "The Organization, Jamaica Ginger, The Otto Frick Story (drug), 3000 Suspects, The Antidote, Mexican Stakeout, Little Egypt, Purple Gang, Bugs Moran Story, & Lily Dallas Story" 3 6 9 16 23 30

VICKS COMICS (See Pure Oil Comics, Salerno Carnival of Comics & 24 Pages of Comics)
Eastern Color Printing Co. (Vicks Chemical Co.): nd (circa 1938) (Giveaway, 68 pgs. in color)

nn-Famous Funnies-r (before #40); contains 5 pgs. Buck Rogers (4 pgs. from F.F. #15, & 1 pg. from #16) Joe Palooka, Napoleon, etc. app. 58 116 174 371 636 900
nn-16 loose, untrimmed page giveaway; paper-c; r/Famous Funnies #14; Buck Rogers, Joe Palooka app. Has either "Vicks Comics" printed on cover or only a local store name as the logo. 22 44 66 131 216 300

WALT DISNEY'S COMICS & STORIES
K.K. Publications: 1942-1963 known (7-1/3"x10-1/4", 4 pgs. in color, slick paper) (folded horizontally once or twice as mailers) (Xmas subscription offer)

1942 mailer-r/Kelly cover to WDC&S 25; 2-year subscription + two Grosset & Dunlap hardcover books (32-pages each), of Bambi and of Thumper, offered for $2.00; came in an illustrated C&S envelope with an enclosed postage paid envelope
(Rare) Mailer only 23 46 69 138 227 315
with envelopes 28 56 84 168 274 380
1947,1948 mailer 18 36 54 107 169 230
1949 mailer-A rare Barks item: Same WDC&S cover as 1942 mailer, but with art changed so that nephew is handing teacher Donald a comic book rather than an apple, as originally drawn by Kelly. The tiny, 7/8"x1-1/4" cover shown was a rejected cover by Barks that was intended for C&S 110, but was redrawn by Kelly for C&S 111. The original art has been lost and this is its only app. (Rare) 39 78 117 236 388 540
1950 mailer-P.1 r/Kelly cover to Dell Xmas Parade 1 (without title); p.2 r/Kelly cover to C&S 101 (w/o title), but with the art altered to show Donald reading C&S 122 (by Kelly); hardcover book, "Donald Duck in Bringing Up the Boys" given with a $1.00 one-year subscription; P.4 r/full Kelly Xmas cover to C&S 99 (Rare) 18 36 54 103 162 220
1952 mailer-P1 r/cover WDC&S #88 15 30 45 84 127 170
1953 mailer-P.1 r/cover Dell Xmas Parade 4 (w/o title); insides offer "Donald Duck Full Speed Ahead," a 28-page, color, 5-5/8"x6-5/8" book, not of the Story Hour series; P.4 r/full Barks C&S 148 cover (Rare) 15 30 45 84 127 170
1963 mailer-Pgs. 1,2 & 4 r/GK Xmas art; P.3 r/a 1963 C&S cover (Scarce) 6 12 18 42 79 115

NOTE: *It is assumed a different mailer was printed each Xmas for at least twenty years.*

WALT DISNEY'S COMICS & STORIES
Walt Disney Productions: 1943 (36 pgs.) (Dept. store Xmas giveaway)

nn-X-Mas-c with Donald & the Boys; Donald Duck by Jack Hannah; Thumper by Ken Hultgren 58 116 174 371 636 900

	GD 2.0	VG 4.0	FN 6.0	VF 8.0	VF/NM 9.0	NM- 9.2

WARLORD
DC Comics: (Remco Toy giveaway, 2-3/4x4")

nn 5.00

WATCH OUT FOR BIG TALK
General Comics: 1950

nn-Dan Barry-a; about crooked politicians 7 14 21 37 46 55

WEATHER-BIRD (See Comics From..., Dick Tracy, Free Comics to You..., Super Circus & Terry and the Pirates)
International Shoe Co./Western Printing Co.: 1958 - No. 16, July, 1962 (Shoe store giveaway)

1 4 8 12 24 38 52
2-16 3 6 9 14 19 24

NOTE: *The numbers are located in the lower bottom panel, pg. 1. All feature a character called Weather-Bird.*

WEATHER BIRD COMICS (See Comics From Weather Bird)
Weather Bird Shoes: 1955 - 1958 (Giveaway)

nn-Contains a comic bound with new cover. Several combinations possible; contents determine price (40 - 60 percent of contents).

WEEKLY COMIC MAGAZINE
Fox Publications: May 12, 1940 (16 pgs.) (Others exist w/o super-heroes)

(1st Version)-8 pg. Blue Beetle story, 7 pg. Patty O'Day story; two copies known to exist. (a VF copy sold in 5/07 for $1553)
(2nd Version)-7 two-pg. adventures of Blue Beetle, Patty O'Day, Yarko, Dr. Fung, Green Mask, Spark Stevens, & Rex Dexter (two known copies, a FN sold in 2007 for $1912, other is GD)
(3rd version)-Captain Valor (only one known copy, in VG+; it sold in 2005 for $480) -
Discovered with business papers, letters and exploitation material promoting **Weekly Comic Magazine** for use by newspapers in the same manner of **The Spirit** weeklies. Interesting note: these are dated three weeks before the first Spirit comic. Letters indicate that samples may have been sent to a few newspapers. These sections were actually 15-1/2x22" pages which will fold down to an approximate 8x10" comic booklet. Other various comic sections were found with the above, but were more like the Sunday comic sections in format.

WE HIT THE JACKPOT
General Comics, Inc./American Affairs: 1947 (Promotional comic)(Paper-c)

nn 6 12 18 31 38 45

WHAT DO YOU KNOW ABOUT THIS COMICS SEAL OF APPROVAL?
No publisher listed (DC Comics Giveaway): nd (1955) (4 pgs., slick paper-c)

nn-(Rare) 110 220 330 704 1202 1700

WHAT IF THEY CALL ME "CHICKEN"?
Kiwanis International: 1970 (giveaway)

nn-Educational anti-marijuana comic 4 8 12 23 37 50

WHAT'S BEHIND THESE HEADLINES
William C. Popper Co.: 1948 (16 pgs.)

nn-Comic insert "The Plot to Steal the World" 6 12 18 31 38 45

WHAT'S IN IT FOR YOU?
Harvey Publications Inc.: (16 pgs., paper cover)

nn-National Guard recruitment 4 7 10 14 17 20

WHEATIES (Premiums)
Walt Disney Productions: 1950 & 1951 (32 titles, pocket-size, 32 pgs.)

Mailing Envelope (no art on front)(Designates sets A,B,C or D on front) 7 14 21 37 46 55

(Set A-1 to A-8, 1950)

A-1-Mickey Mouse & the Disappearing Island, A-5-Mickey Mouse, Roving Reporter each... 6 12 18 28 34 40
A-2-Grandma Duck, Homespun Detective, A-6-Li'l Bad Wolf, Forest Ranger, A-7-Goofy, Tightrope Acrobat, A-8-Pluto & the Bogus Money each... 5 10 15 24 30 35
A-3-Donald Duck & the Haunted Jewels, A-4-Donald Duck & the Giant Ape each... 8 16 24 42 54 65

(Set B-1 to B-8, 1950)

B-1-Mickey Mouse & the Pharoah's Curse, B-4-Mickey Mouse & the Mystery Sea Monster each... 6 12 18 31 38 45
B-2-Pluto, Canine Cowpoke, B-5-Li'l Bad Wolf in the Hollow Tree Hideout, B-7-Goofy & the Gangsters each... 5 10 15 24 30 35
B-3-Donald Duck & the Buccaneers, B-6-Donald Duck,Trail Blazer, B-8 Donald Duck, Klondike Kid each... 8 16 24 42 54 65

(Set C-1 to C-8, 1951)

C-1-Donald Duck & the Inca Idol, C-5-Donald Duck in the Lost Lakes, C-8-Donald Duck Deep-Sea Diver each... 8 16 24 42 54 65
C-2-Mickey Mouse & the Magic Mountain, C-6-Mickey Mouse & the Stagecoach Bandits each... 6 12 18 31 38 45
C-3-Li'l Bad Wolf, Fire Fighter, C-4-Gus & Jaq Save the Ship, C-7-Goofy, Big Game Hunter each... 5 10 15 24 30 35

(Set D-1 to D-8, 1951)

Whiz Comics Wheaties Giveaway © FAW

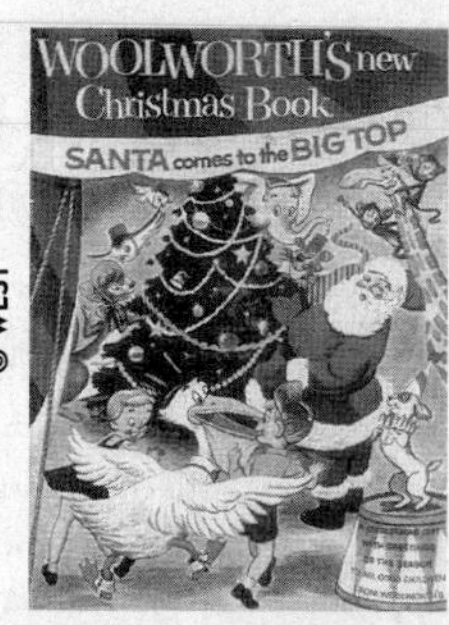

Woolworth's Christmas Story Book © WEST

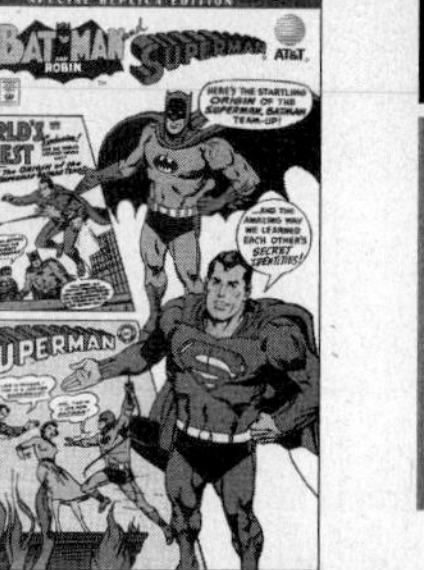

World's Finest Comics #179 (Best Western) © DC

GD 2.0 | VG 4.0 | FN 6.0 | VF 8.0 | VF/NM 9.0 | NM- 9.2

D-1-Donald Duck in Indian Country, D-5-Donald Duck, Mighty Mystic
each... 8 16 24 42 54 65
D-2-Mickey Mouse and the Abandoned Mine, D-6-Mickey Mouse & the Medicine Man
each... 6 12 18 31 38 45
D-3-Pluto & the Mysterious Package, D-4-Bre'r Rabbit's Sunken Treasure,
D-7-Li'l Bad Wolf and the Secret of the Woods, D-8-Minnie Mouse, Girl Explorer
each... 5 10 15 24 30 35
NOTE: *Some copies lack the Wheaties ad.*

WHEEL OF PROGRESS, THE
Assoc. of American Railroads: Oct, 1957 (16 pgs.)
nn-Bill Bunce 6 12 18 28 34 40

WHIZ COMICS (Formerly Flash Comics & Thrill Comics #1)
Fawcett Publications
Wheaties Giveaway(1946, Miniature, 6-1/2x8-1/4", 32 pgs.); all copies were taped at each corner to a box of Wheaties and are never found in very fine or mint condition; "Capt. Marvel & the Water Thieves", plus Golden Arrow, Ibis, Crime Smasher stories
80 160 400 - - -

WILD KINGDOM (TV) (Mutual of Omaha's...)
Western Printing Co.: 1965, 1966 (Giveaway, regular size, slick-c, 16 pgs.)
nn-Front & back-c are different on 1966 edition 2 4 6 9 12 15

WISCO/KLARER COMIC BOOK (Miniature)
Marvel Comics/Vital Publ./Fawcett Publ.: 1948 - 1964 (3-1/2x6-3/4", 24 pgs.)
Given away by Wisco "99" Service Stations, Carnation Malted Milk, Klarer Health Wieners, Fleers Dubble Bubble Gum, Rodeo All-Meat Wieners, Perfect Potato Chips, & others; see ad in Tom Mix #21
Blackstone & the Gold Medal Mystery (1948) 7 14 21 37 46 55
Blackstone "Solves the Sealed Vault Mystery" (1950) 7 14 21 37 46 55
Blaze Carson in "The Sheriff Shoots It Out" (1950) 7 14 21 37 46 55
Captain Marvel & Billy's Big Game (r/Capt. Marvel Adv. #76)
24 48 72 144 237 330
(Prices vary widely on this book)
China Boy in "A Trip to the Zoo" #10 (1948) 4 8 12 18 22 25
Indoors-Outdoors Game Book 3 6 9 11 13 15
Jim Solar Space Sheriff in "Battle for Mars", "Between Two Worlds", "Conquers Outer Space", "The Creatures on the Comet", "Defeats the Moon Missile Men", "Encounter Creatures on Comet", "Meet the Jupiter Jumpers", "Meets the Man From Mars", "On Traffic Duty", "Outlaws of the Spaceways", "Pirates of the Planet X", "Protects Space Lanes", "Raiders From the Sun", "Ring Around Saturn", "Robots of Rhea", "The Sky Ruby", "Spacetts of the Sky", "Spidermen of Venus", "Trouble on Mercury"
6 12 18 28 34 40
Johnny Starboard & the Underseas Pirates (1948) 4 8 12 18 22 25
Kid Colt in "He Lived by His Guns" (1950) 8 16 24 40 50 60
Little Aspirin as the "Crook Catcher" #2 (1950) 3 6 9 11 13 15
Little Aspirin in "Naughty But Nice" #6 (1950) 3 6 9 11 13 15
Return of the Black Phantom (not M.E. character)(Roy Dare)(1948)
5 10 15 24 30 35
Secrets of Magic 4 7 9 14 16 18
Slim Morgan "Brings Justice to Mesa City" #3 4 7 9 14 16 18
Super Rabbit(1950)-Cuts Red Tape, Stops Crime Wave!
8 16 24 44 57 70
Tex Farnum, Frontiersman (1948) 4 8 12 18 22 25
Tex Taylor in "Draw or Die, Cowpoke!" (1950) 6 12 18 28 34 40
Tex Taylor in "An Exciting Adventure at the Gold Mine" (1950)
6 12 18 27 33 38
Wacky Quacky in "All-Aboard" 3 5 7 10 12 14
When School Is Out 3 5 7 10 12 14
Willie in a "Comic-Comic Book Fall" #1 4 7 9 14 16 18
Wonder Duck "An Adventure at the Rodeo of the Fearless Quacker!" (1950)
8 16 24 42 54 65
Rare uncut version of three; includes Capt. Marvel, Tex Farnum, Black Phantom
(A VG copy sold in Sept. 2015 for $147)
Rare uncut version of three; includes China Boy, Blackstone, Johnny Starboard & the Underseas Pirates (A FN/VF copy sold in Sept. 2015 for $137)
Rare uncut version of three; all Jim Solar (A VG copy sold in Sept. 2015 for $79)
Rare uncut version of three; includes Willie in a "Comic-Comic Book Fall", Little Aspirin #2, Slim Morgan Brings Justice to Mesa City (a VF/FN copy sold for $54 in Nov. 2007)

WIZARD OF OZ
MGM: 1967 (small size)
"Dorothy and Friends Visit Oz", "Dorothy Meets the Wizard", "The Tin Woodsman Saves Dorothy" each... 2 4 6 8 10 12

WOLVERINE
Marvel Comics
145-(1999 Nabisco mail-in offer) Sienkiewicz-c 10 20 30 64 132 200
...Son of Canada (4/01, ed. of 65,000) Spider-Man & The Hulk app.; Lim-a 3.00

WOMAN OF THE PROMISE, THE
Catechetical Guild: 1950 (General Distr.) (Paper cover, 32 pgs.)
nn 6 12 18 28 34 40

WONDER BOOK OF RUBBER
B.F. Goodrich: 1947 (Promo giveaway
nn 5 10 15 22 26 30

WONDERFUL WORLD OF DUCKS (See Golden Picture Story Book)
Colgate Palmolive Co.: 1975
1-Mostly-r 1 3 4 6 8 10

WONDER WOMAN
DC Comics: 1977
Pizza Hut Giveaways (12/77)-Reprints #60,62 2 4 6 9 13 16
... - The Minotaur (1981, General Foods giveaway, 8 pages, 3-1/2 x 6-3/4", oblong)
2 4 6 13 18 22

WONDER WORKER OF PERU
Catechetical Guild: No date (5x7", 16 pgs., B&W, giveaway)
nn 6 12 18 28 34 40

WOODY WOODPECKER
Dell Publishing Co.
Clover Stamp-Newspaper Boy Contest('56)-9 pg. story-(Giveaway)
8 16 24 40 50 60
In Chevrolet Wonderland(1954-Giveaway)(Western Publ.)-20 pgs., full story line; Chilly Willy app. 18 36 54 105 165 225
...Meets Scotty MacTape(1953-Scotch Tape giveaway)-16 pgs., full size
18 36 54 105 165 225

WOOLWORTH'S CHRISTMAS STORY BOOK
Promotional Publ. Co.(Western Printing Co.): 1952 - 1954 (16 pgs., paper-c) (See Jolly Christmas Book)
nn: 1952 issue-Marv Levy c/a 7 14 21 35 43 50

WOOLWORTH'S HAPPY TIME CHRISTMAS BOOK
F. W. Woolworth Co. (Western Printing Co.): 1952 (Christmas giveaway)
nn-36 pgs. 6 12 18 31 38 45

WORLD'S FINEST COMICS
National Periodical Publ./DC Comics
Giveaway (c. 1944-45, 8 pgs., in color, paper-c)-Johnny Everyman-r/World's Finest
21 42 63 124 202 280
Giveaway (c. 1949, 8 pgs., in color, paper-c)- "Make Way For Youth" r/World's Finest; based on film of same name 19 38 57 111 176 240
#176, #179- Best Western reprint edition (1997) 3.00

WORLD'S GREATEST SUPER HEROES
DC Comics (Nutra Comics) (Child Vitamins, Inc.): 1977 (Giveaway, 3-3/4x3-3/4", 24 pgs.)
nn-Batman & Robin app.; health tips 2 4 6 10 14 18

WYOMING THE COWBOY STATE
1954 (Giveaway, slick-c)
nn 5 10 15 22 26 30

XMAS FUNNIES
Kinney Shoes: No date (Giveaway, paper cover, 36 pgs.?)
Contains 1933 color strip-r; Mutt & Jeff, etc. 30 60 90 177 289 400

X-MEN THE MOVIE
Marvel Comics/Toys R' Us: 2000
Special Movie Prequel Edition 5.00

X2 PRESENTS THE ULTIMATE X-MEN #2
Marvel Comics/New York Post: July, 2003
Reprint distributed inside issue of the New York Post 2.50

YALTA TO KOREA (Also see Korea My Home)
M. Phillip Corp. (Republican National Committee): 1952 (Giveaway, paper-c)
nn-(8 pgs.)-Anti-communist propaganda book 18 36 54 105 165 225

YOGI BEAR (TV)
Dell Publishing Co.
Giveaway ('84, '86)-City of Los Angeles, "Creative First Aid" & "Earthquake Preparedness for Children" 1 2 3 4 5 7

YOUR TRIP TO NEWSPAPERLAND
Philadelphia Evening Bulletin (Printed by Harvey Press): June, 1955 (14x11-1/2", 12 pgs.)
nn-Joe Palooka takes kids on newspaper tour 6 12 18 27 33 38

YOUR VOTE IS VITAL!
Harvey Publications Inc.: 1952 (5" x 7", 16 pgs., paper cover)
nn-The importance of voting 5 10 14 20 24 28

The American Comic Book: 1500s-1828

For the last few years, we have featured a tremendous article by noted historian and collector Eric C. Caren on the foundations of what we now call "The Pioneer Age" of comics. We look forward to a new article on this significant topic in a future edition of *The Overstreet Comic Book Price Guide*. In the meantime, should you need it, Caren's article may be found in the 35th through 39th editions.

That said, even with the space constraints in this edition of the *Guide*, we could not possibly exclude reference to these incredible, formative works.

German broadsheet, dated 1569.

Why are these illustrations and sequences of illustrations important to the comic books of today?

The Murder of King Henry III (1589).

Quite frankly, because we can see in them the very building blocks of the comic art form.

The shooting of the Italian Concini (1617).

Over the course of just a few hundred years, we the evolution of narration, word balloons, panel-to-panel progression of story, and so much more. If these stories aren't developed first, how would be every have reached the point that that *The Adventures of Mr. Obadiah Oldbuck* could have come along in 1842?

As the investigation of comic book history has blown away the notion that comic books were a 20 century invention, it hasn't been easy to convince some, even with the clear, linear progression of the artful melding of illustration and words.

"Want to avoid an argument in social discourse? Steer clear of politics and religion. In the latter category, the most controversial subject is human evolution. Collectors can become just as squeamish when you start messing with the evolution of a particular collectible," Eric Caren wrote in his article. "In most cases, the origin of a particular comic character will be universally agreed upon, but try tackling the origin of printed comics and you are asking for trouble."

THE BUBBLERS MEDLEY, or a SKETCH of the TIMES Being EUROPES MEMORIAL for the YEAR 1720.

"The Bubblers Medley" (1720).

"Join, or Die" from the Pennsylvania Gazette, *May 9, 1754.*

"Amusement for John Bull..." from The European Magazine *(1783).*

But the evidence is there for any who choose to look. Before the original comics of the Golden Age, there were comic strip reprints collected in comic book form. The practice dated back decades earlier, of course, but coalesced into the current form when the realities of the Great Depression spawned the modern incarnation of the comic book and its immediate cousin, the Big Little Book.

Everything that came later, though, did so because the acceptance of the visual language had already been worked out. Before Spider-Man and the Hulk, before Superman and Batman, before the Yellow Kid, Little Nemo, and the Brownies, cartoonists and editorial illustrators were working out how to tell a story or simply convey their ideas in this new artform.

Without this sort of work, without these pioneers, we simply wouldn't be where we are today.

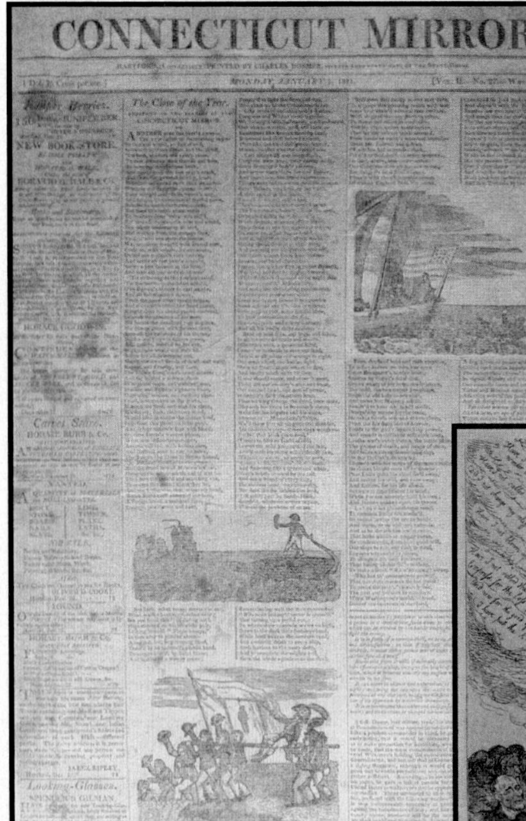
CONNECTICUT MIRROR.

Cartoons satirizing Napoleon on the front page of the Connecticut Mirror, *dated January 7, 1811.*

Another Napoleon cartoon, this time dubbing him "The Corsican Munchausen," from the London Strand, *December 4, 1813.*

"A Consultation at the Medical Board" from The Pasquin or General Satirist *(1821)*.

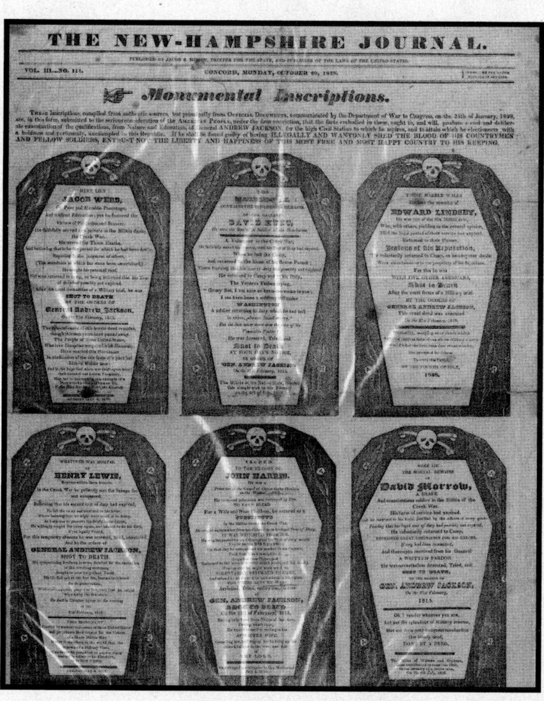

THE NEW-HAMPSHIRE JOURNAL.

VOL. III....NO. 111. CONCORD, MONDAY, OCTOBER 20, 1828.

Monumental Inscriptions.

These Inscriptions, compiled from authentic sources, but principally from OFFICIAL DOCUMENTS, communicated by the Department of War to Congress, on the 25th of January, 1828, are, in this form, submitted to the serious consideration of the AMERICAN PEOPLE, under the firm conviction, that the facts embodied in them, ought to, and will, produce a cool and deliberate examination of the qualifications, from Nature and Education, of General ANDREW JACKSON, for the high Civil Station to which he aspires, and to attain which he electioneers with a boldness and pertinacity, unexampled in this Republic. If he shall be found guilty of having ILLEGALLY AND WANTONLY SHED THE BLOOD OF HIS COUNTRYMEN AND FELLOW SOLDIERS, ENTRUST NOT THE LIBERTY AND HAPPINESS OF THIS MOST FREE AND MOST HAPPY COUNTRY TO HIS KEEPING.

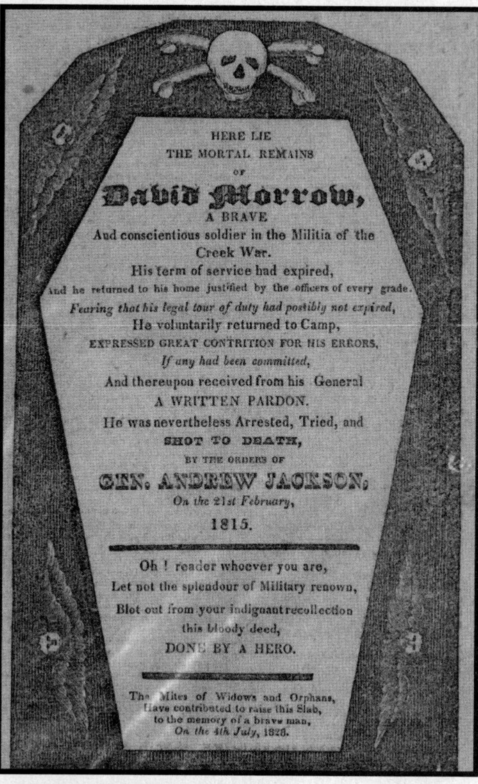

HERE LIE
THE MORTAL REMAINS
OF
David Morrow,
A BRAVE
And conscientious soldier in the Militia of the
Creek War.
His term of service had expired,
and he returned to his home justified by the officers of every grade.
Fearing that his legal tour of duty had possibly not expired,
He voluntarily returned to Camp,
EXPRESSED GREAT CONTRITION FOR HIS ERRORS,
If any had been committed,
And thereupon received from his General
A WRITTEN PARDON.
He was nevertheless Arrested, Tried, and
SHOT TO DEATH,
BY THE ORDERS OF
GEN. ANDREW JACKSON,
On the 21st February,
1815.

Oh! reader whoever you are,
Let not the splendour of Military renown,
Blot out from your indignant recollection
this bloody deed,
DONE BY A HERO.

The Mites of Widows and Orphans,
Have contributed to raise this Slab,
to the memory of a brave man,
On the 4th July, 1828.

Above left, the front page of The New Hampshire Journal, *dated October 20, 1828, with multiple tombstone "panels." To the right is a detail of the bottom right tombstone.*

THE VICTORIAN AGE

Comic Strips and Books: 1646-1900
A Concise History & Price Index Of The Field As Of 2018

ORIGINS OF EARLY AMERICAN COMIC STRIPS BEFORE THE YELLOW KID

by Robert Lee Beerbohm, Richard Samuel West & Richard D. Olson, PhD ©2018

(This article was originally created by Doug Wheeler, Robert Beerbohm and Richard D. Olson, PhD for CBPG #32 and continues to be revised annually by the current authors.) We welcome any and all corrections and additions. Special Thanks This Installment To Leonardo De Sa, Terrence Keegen, Gabriel Laderman and Joe Rainone.

Left: "The Burning of Mr. John Rogers," 1646 is the earliest-known North American cartoon printed on paper printed in the earliest children's primer in America.

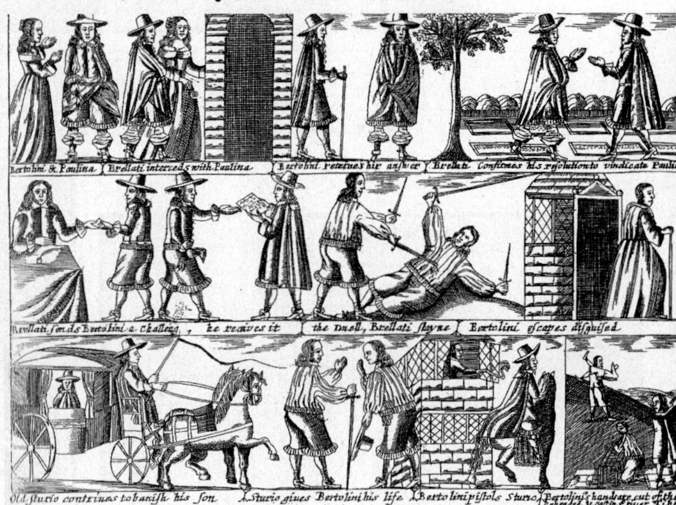

"God's Revenge For Murder" By John Reynolds, unknown artist, 16
Earliest-known sequential comic "panel" strip created in the English langua

Left: From his pamphlet Plain Truth 1747 containing Ben Franklin's earliest-known cartoon titled "Heaven Helps Only Thos Who Help Themselves" depicting ancient "super hero" Hercules in the upper right corner. Middle: "A Warm Place - Hell", one of two images definitely known to be drawn and engraved by Paul Revere, 1768. Word balloons had wide-spread usage in many cartoons in the 1700s. Right: The Tables Turned by James Gillray, 1797 commenting on an "invasion" of England by 1400 French convicts. The use of word balloons was wide spread in many parts of the world long before the Yellow Kid's parrot uttered a few words in 1896.

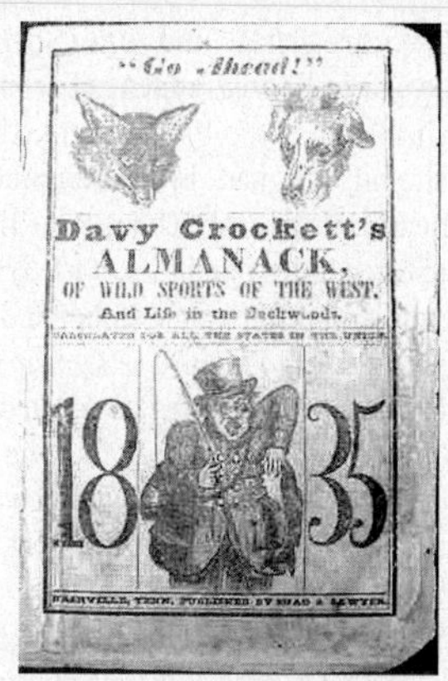

The Comic Almanac(k) debuted in America in 1831 with the earliest-known titles starting heavy with humor and sporting crude woodcut single panel cartoons. Ellm's American Comic Almanac was one of the first. By 1835 Davy Crockett, one of the nation's earliest national folk heroes, began issuing his own version. In the late 1840s the Comic Almanac(k)s began to offer tall-tale sequential comic strips which became somewhat commonplace in the 1850s, fueled by the advent of the California Gold Rush. They were instrumental in the development of the American comic strip and we will be reporting more new finds after further research into American folklore.

We have a lot of new discoveries to share with you again this year as amply evident in the price index which follows this year's history lesson. A quantum leap has finally been achieved in the area of introducing the comic book collecting world to *American Comic Almanac(k)s* as well as a huge multitude of American humor periodicals, many of which contained sequential comic strips.

This Victorian Era section is devoted to comic strips and books published during the years the United States expanded across the North American continent, fought a Civil War, shifted from an agrarian to an industrial society, "welcomed" waves of immigrants, and struggled over race, class, religion, temperance, and suffrage - and all of it depicted and satirized by generations of mostly now long-forgotten cartoonists. The social attitudes, beliefs, and conventions of 19th century America, the good as well as the bad, are to be found in abundance. Perhaps the first question to pop into most readers' minds will be, "What, beyond the happenstance of publication date, are Victorian Era comics?"

There has been a long slow-motion evolution of the comic strip which was not invented in America, contrary to many previous history books on the subject. One must examine many aspects of concurrent popular culture. The main aspect that we believe most distinguishes Victorian Era comic strips from those of later eras was the extremely rare use of word balloons within sequential (multi-picture) comic stories. When word balloons were used, it was nearly always within single-panel cartoons. On the occasions when they appeared inside a strip, with very few exceptions, the ballooned dialogue was inconsequential. Nineteenth-century comics tended to place both narration and dialogue beneath comic panels rather than within the panel's borders as they were thought by many to interfere with the art. Many of these comics are to the word balloon-strewn post-Yellow Kid comics of the 20th Century as silent movies are to the later "talkies." Just as sound changed how stories were structured on film, so too did comic strips change when the words were moved from beneath panels to inside them, and dialogue rather than narration drove the story in conjunction with the pictures.

The Victorian Era of actual comic strip books began on different dates in different nations, depending on when the first publication of a sequential comic book on their soil is known to have occurred. For the U.S. this happened when the American literary periodical *Brother Jonathan* printed the 40-page, 195-panel graphic novel *The Adventures of Mr. Obadiah Oldbuck* as a special extra dated September 14, 1842. Almost six decades later, America's Victorian comics came to their end, replaced by the onslaught of Platinum Age books reprinting newspaper strips from Bennett, Hearst, and Pulitzer Sunday comic sections, among many others.

There is considerable overlap between Victorian Era and Platinum Age comic books and strips. Those publications that continued from one century into the next, such as *Puck*, *Judge*, and *Life*, have their pre-1900 issues listed within the Victorian Age section, while their post-1899 issues can be found inside the Platinum Age. Some non-sequential (i.e., single-panel) American comic items existing prior to 1842 are also listed herein, going back to 1795. These belong to what could tentatively be called the Age of Caricature (1770s through 1830s). This was a fertile period for the art in England, when Gillray and Rowlandson, and, later, Cruikshank, Heath, and Seymour were that nation's top cartoonists. During the same period in the U.S., there were no artists who made their living as caricaturists, though William Charles, printer and engraver, did produce about two dozen spirited cartoon broadsides from 1805 to 1820, the most important ones concerning events of the War of 1812.

In addition, one can trace origins of American comic books to the humorous Comic Almanacs which began in earnest in the early 1830s.

The earliest known cartoon-like woodcut printed on paper in North America was in a Puritan children's book first published in 1646. Titled simply *The Burning of Mr. John Rogers*, it showed in flaming graphic detail what happens to those who stray from the flock and have to be burned at the stake. Dr. Wertham would have had a field day with that one!

Cartoon broadsides and other single panel images, often using word balloons, appeared from pre-Revolution days through the end of the 19th Century. The earliest known attributed cartoon, designed by the ubiquitous Benjamin Franklin, was "Heaven Helps Only Those Who Help Themselves," which first appeared in his pamphlet *Plain Truth* in 1747.

The most popularly remembered 18th-Century American cartoons are likely Franklin's *"Join or Die"* in 1754, representing the American Colonies as severed snake parts, and *"The Bloody Massacre Perpetrated in King Street"* -- Paul Revere's 1770 depiction of the Boston Massacre, which he pirated from the earlier Henry Pelham broadsheet cartoon *"The Fruits of Arbitrary Power."*

In September 1826, John Warner Barber, New Haven, Ct. (1798-1885) designed and self-published the broadside *The Drunkard's Progress, Or The Direct Road to Poverty, Wretchedness and Ruin* showing in four stages sequentially "The Morning Dram" which is "The Beginning of Sorrow, " "The Grog Shop" with its "Bad Company," "The Confirmed Drunkard" in a state of "Beastly Intoxication," and the "Concluding Scene" with the family being driven off to the alms house. It is an interesting set of cuts, faintly reminiscent of Hogarth. Barber began his career in 1819, age 21, engraving on wood. He devoted most of his career to the multitude of art chores associated with book production. As late as 1870 he was issuing *Barber's Temperance Tracts,* which built upon his 1826 original plus four panels showing the positive effects of living without alcohol.

The first American whose fame was based primarily on his cartoons appears to be David Claypoole Johnston (1798-1865). Johnston provided illustrations for various almanacs, books, and periodicals, including the masthead for *Brother Jonathans*. Most notable of Johnston's comics work was his nine-issue series *Scraps*, which he self-published from 1828 to 1849. This series was highly influenced by George Cruikshank's series *Scraps and Sketches*, which first appeared in 1827. Because of the resemblance, Johnston became known in his day as "the American Cruikshank." Each issue of Johnston's *Scraps* consists of four large folio-sized pages, printed on one side, with nine to twelve single-panel cartoons per page, and each page often organized around a theme. Also popular was his comic album Outlines Illustrative of the Journal of F****** A*** K***** (1835), which parodied passages from the journal of recently published observations on America by British actress Fanny Kemble.

Johnston, himself a failed actor, had an interest in the theater his entire career. In addition to producing a number of prints depicting American actors in famous roles, he collaborated with actor Henry J. Finn to produce the 1831 *(American) Comic Annual*, with Finn as Editor and Johnston as artist, published by Richardson, Lord and Holbrook, Boston. It featured almost 30 full-page Johnston-designed copper engravings and woodcuts. Also that year, Finn solo produced *Finn's Comic Sketch Book*, a twelve-page album similar to Johnston's *Scraps* with upwards of half a dozen single-panel cartoons per page. It was published by Peabody and Co, of New York in business from 1831-1843. (Finn died tragically in a steamboat accident Jan. 13, 1840.)

Perhaps Johnston's most interesting contribution to the history of the comic strip in American came in 1837, when he produced the sequential comic broadside, *Illustrations of the Adventures & Achievements of the Renowned Don Quixote & his Doughty Squire Sancho Panza* (27.4 x 30.4 cm). This blank-reverse engraved print was an elaborate twelve-panel satire of the Andrew Jackson-Van Buren administration. It likely sold for 25 cents, seeing distribution in Boston, New York and Philadelphia. Much later, in 1863, Johnston drew another sequential comic broadside, *The House the Jeff Built* (27.5 x 36.7 cm), a bitter indictment of Jefferson Davis and the Southern slavocracy.

In July 1839, Wilson and Company, a newly formed New York printing firm, began publishing a mammoth newspaper by the name of *Brother Jonathan*. The publisher, J. Gregg Wilson had employed the newspaper format for *Brother Jonathan* to circumvent the higher postage rates imposed on magazines, but *Brother Jonathan* was a newspaper in format only -- it contained not a shred of news, instead specializing in serialized fiction, some of it written by Americans but most of it pirated from foreign sources. Despite the cost savings, the mammoth format had its limitations; when opened it measured a whopping three feet by four feet. So, once *Brother Jonathan* was an established success, Wilson and Day began in January 1841 the simultaneous publication of a magazine-sized quarto edition of *Brother Jonathan* that reprinted the contents of the mammoth edition.

Later that same year, to capitalize on the name recognition of their successful twin publications, Wilson and Company started issuing book-length *Brother Jonathan Extras* in the same format as the quarto magazine. These reprints are counted among the earliest paperback books in America. Most of the *Extra* numbers were pirated European novels. For example their eighth extra was the first American printing of a Charles Dickens novel. But for their ninth *Extra*, they did something no American publisher had ever done before -- they pirated a graphic novel, Rodolphe Töpffer's *The Adventures of Mr. Obadiah Oldbuck.* By reformatting *Oldbuck* from its original small oblong strip design to fit *Brother Jonathan's* standard quarto format Wilson and Company inadvertently made this edition (alone) of *Obadiah Oldbuck* resemble a modern comic book. *Oldbuck's* arrival on the shores of the New World would directly inspire a wave of American imitators. [*This first Wilson printing of Oldbuck from 1842 was reprinted in same-size limited edition facsimile by the Naples Comicon in 2003. An English translation by Leonardo De Sá of Töpffer's original draft is at leonardo desa.interdinamica. net/comics/lds/*]

Even though in 1904 (in its September 3 edition), *The New York Times* accurately identified the *Brother Jonathan Extra* as the first American comic book as well as Wilson & Co. utilizing Tilt & Bougue's original printing plates as well as still being in print for sale in New York at such a late date, Töpffer has already been largely forgotten in the New World. It is high time Töpffer received credit long overdue as the inventor of the modern comic strip, laying previously long-held myths to rest.

Töpffer (1799-1846) was a playwright, novelist, artist, and teacher from Geneva, Switzerland, who in 1827 had begun producing what he called "picture novels," sharing them with his friends and students. His earliest editions were self-published via lithography on transfer paper as they use the word "autographie" in their imprints. The earliest printers were J. Freydig, Frutiger (1830s) and Schmidt (1840s). These first sequential comic books, scripted in Töpffer's native French language, found their way to Paris and became an instant hit. According to Gombrich in *Art and Illusion* (1960), "Töpffer recognized that he could rely on the reader to supplement from their own lives what was omitted between the panels. This is crucial in the development of the sequential comic strip."

The demand for his comic books soon outstripped the supply, and pirated editions, redrawn by others, were created by Parisian publisher Aubert to capitalize on this. In a world where international copyright conventions did not exist, this was perfectly legal, if morally questionable. Thus, in 1841, London publisher Tilt and Bogue commissioned George Cruikshank to create an English version of Töpffer's *Les Amours de M. Vieux Bois* by pirating Aubert's pirated edition of the Geneva original.

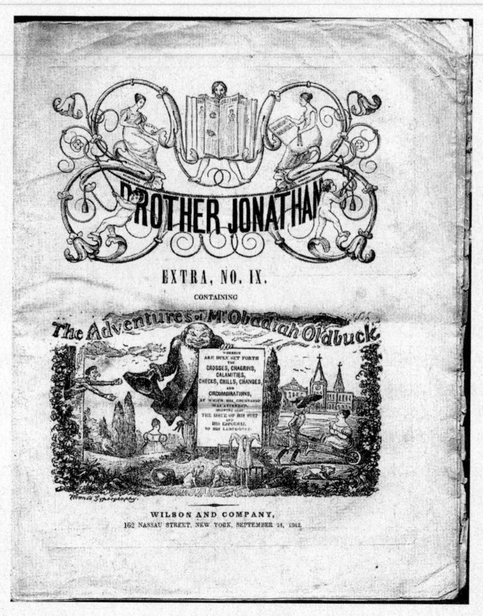

Cover to the subscriber version of the earliest-known sequential comic book published in America, The Adventures of Mr. Obadiah Oldbuck, Sept. 1842, Wilson & Co. New York, originally conceived in 1828 in Geneva Switzerland by creator Rodolphe Töpffer.

This English translation, co-financed by George Cruikshank himself, sported a new cover page by George's brother Robert, based on a montage of Töpffer's scenes. Confirmation of this fact came when George Cruikshank's personal copy surfaced in auction recently with the inscription "Copied from a French book by my Brother Robert" above the title page with the same scene. This is the translation that was reprinted by America's Wilson and Company as *The Adventures of Mr. Obadiah Oldbuck* utilizing the original Tilt and Bogue printing plates.

Tilt and Bogue followed up their success by translating into English two additional stories of Töpffer's seven published graphic novels: *Beau Ogleby*, circa 1843 (originally Histoire de M. Jabot), and *Bachelor Butterfly* two years later (from *Histoire de M. Cryptogame)*. David Bogue also published picture-story strip books by John Leighton using the pseudonym Luke Limner. He wrote and drew beautiful comic books titled *London Out of Town or The Adventures of the Browns At The Seaside; Comic Art-Manufactures; and The Ancient Story of the Old Dame and Her Pig* starting in 1847, but none of these seem to have ever been republished in America. They follow a definite Töpffer influence. This growing body of comic book production was made easier by the spreading understanding of transfer paper lithography, otherwise the panels would have had to have been drawn and lettered mirror reverse. Gombrich referred to Töpffer's comic books as "the innocent ancestors of today's manufactured dreams... everywhere in these countless episodes of almost surrealist inconsequence we find a mastery of physiognomic characterization which sets the standard for such influential humorous draftsmen in the 19th century as Wilhelm Busch in Germany."

A Register of The New York City Book Trades 1821-1842 by Sidney F. & Elizabeth Stege12, Huttner (The Bibliographical Society of America, NYC, 1993) mentions Benjamin H. Day bought into *Brother Jonathan*'s publisher, Wilson and Company, in this year, becoming at some point an equal partner with owner J. Gregg Wilson. The Register lists them both as publishers of *Brother Jonathan* at the same address of 162 Nassau Street. Other historical artifacts state Day eventually became sole-owner and publisher. Exactly when has not yet been determined, though we have figured out with certainly before 1850 .

This is the same Benjamin H. Day who started the first successful penny newspaper in 1833, *The (New York) Sun*, transforming it in four short years into the largest circulation daily in the world at that time. He sold out his ownership of the Sun to his brother-in-law during the financial "panic" of 1837, a mistake he regretted the rest of his life. He re-emerged heavily involved in *Brother Jonathan* definitely by 1840 and as a partner by 1841. *Brother Jonathan's* offices were right next door to Tamany Hall. (See the first 20 minutes of the 2002 movie *Gangs of New York* to visualize the period atmosphere and their customer base.) According to *The Brothers Harper* by Eugene Exmen (Harper & Row, 1965), on page 125, "*Brother Jonathan...* offered in its weekly edition and also in special supplements very cheap reprints of English novels. In effect, it began a price-cutting war against the older established 'pirates' among the book publishers..." Day, it appears, had found the perfect project on which to build a new empire.

Desirous of repeating the success they had with *Obadiah Oldbuck*, Wilson and Company published the first American edition of *Bachelor Butterfly* in 1846. Three years later, they reformatted *Obadiah Oldbuck* back into its original British shape using lithography, dropping a handful of comic panels and altering the text to hide these deletions. Soon thereafter, they published other comic books for a steadily growing market that they had helped to stimulate. In recognition of their significant role in the dissemination of sequential comics, Wilson and Company deserve to be remembered as the first comic book publisher in America.

Back in Europe, perhaps inspired by his involvement with Töpffer's *Obadiah Oldbuck*, George Cruikshank soon created several sequential comic books of his own. These too found their way to America. *The Bachelor's Own Book*, published first in Britain in 1844, became the second known U.S. published sequential comic book when it was reprinted by Burgess, Stringer and Company the following year. Next was Cruikshank's masterpiece *The Bottle*, the Hogarthian-style tale of a man whose addiction to alcohol brings himself and his family to ruin. After debuting in London in 1847, it was reprinted the same year in a British-American co-publication between David Bogue and Americans Wiley and Putnam. Both printings were in huge folio form, available in either black and white or professionally hand-tinted versions. In 1848, the story saw American print again, this time in smaller form, placed at the front of the otherwise prose volume *Temperance Tales; Or, Six Nights with the Washing-tonians*. It continued to be reprinted by a variety of publishers into the early 20th Century. *The Bottle* was even reproduced onto painted glass slides and then projected by magic lantern onto a screen for the moral edification of temperance audiences. *The Drunkard's Children, Cruikshank's sequel to The Bottle*, was issued July 1, 1848 as a British-American-Australian co-publishing venture, but was less successful, and had not nearly as many reprints.

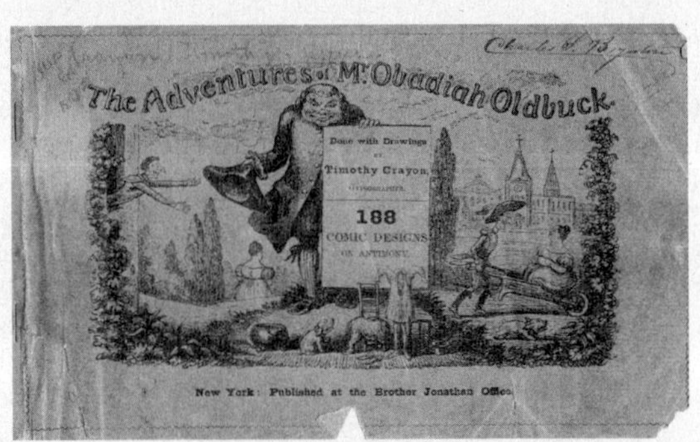

The Adventures of Obadiah Oldbuck, rare newly discovered 4th edition from mid 1850s. Says now "Published at Brother Jonathan Offices." Art & Story now accredited to the pseudonym "Timothy Crayon" - see Peter Piper ad previous page.

***The Strange and Wonderful Adventures of Bachelor Butterfly** by Rodolphe Töpffer (New York, 1846) was America's 3rd comic book; Wilson & Company's second comic book, this time out staying with the original European format.*

The most clearly sequential, as well as fun, of George Cruikshank's comic books was *The Tooth-Ache*, first issued in London in 1849. It was reprinted in America later that same year by Philadelphia map maker J.L. Smith. An additional concurrent version was also issued from Boston.

When closed, this booklet appears an unassuming 5-1/4 inches tall by 3-1/4 inches wide. Its striking feature is that the book folds open accordion style, stretching the entire 43-panel story along one single strip of paper, which when fully extended is seven feet, three inches long! *The Tooth-Ache* was issued in both black and white and professionally hand-colored editions. Abridged editions of the story, printed in black and white and with a "normal" page-turning rather than foldout presentation, appeared inside promotional giveaway comics issued by American companies in the 1880s.

Thanks to Töpffer, Cruikshank, and a handful of enterprising American publishers, the 1840s should be remembered as the decade when America first fell in love with the comics. It had seen the U.S. publication of six sequential comic books, as well as the importation of other comics with foreign imprints. America's growing interest in graphic humor was further stimulated by the growth of two other fields: the cartoon broadside and the humor magazine.

As mentioned before, the cartoon broadside had been a part of the American scene since pre-Revolution days, but it did not flourish until stone lithography (introduced in 1818 and in wide use by the 1830s) made the reproduction of images relatively fast and cheap. From the early 1830s into the mid 1840s, the leading producer of cartoon broadsides in America was New York printer H. R. Robinson, who either drew his own cartoons or employed others, especially E. W. Clay, to do it. Clay is notable for having produced the first sequential comic broadside in America. Published in 1834 and entitled, "This Is the House that Jack Built" (50 x 32 cm), the nine-panel parody of the classic nursery rhyme was an attack on the Jackson Administration. The dominant theme of American cartoon broadsides was political, as befitted a nation where politics was the leading spectator sport. As the American electorate grew increasingly educated and prosperous, the demand for cartoon broadside also increased. During the 1840s, lithographers in New York, Boston, and Philadelphia, entered the field to satisfy that demand. The best known of these, Nathaniel Currier, later Currier and Ives, joined the fray in 1848. The firm employed many artists, but its chief political cartoonist was Louis Maurer and its chief comic artist was Thomas Worth.

Except for the three previously cited sequential cartoon broadsides, nearly all of the cartoon broadsides published in America from 1832 to 1876, its dominant era, were single panels. From the 1860s onward, broadside series on a single comic theme became common, the most famous being Thomas Worth's *Darktown* series. These can be loosely categorized as sequential comics since they employed the same characters and formed a story of sorts when hung together on a wall, as was the publisher's expectation. Sequential art or not, the cartoon broadsides nearly always employed the speech balloons that later became one of the defining characteristic of the American comic strip.

During the same decade that sequential comics and cartoon broadsides were growing in popularity, the illustrated American humor magazine made its debut. The British comic weekly *Punch*, founded in 1841, was an immediate success, both in England and the United States. It was a handsomely printed quarto, initially twelve pages and later sixteen, with a repeating cover design, backed by a page of small advertisements, humorous text interspersed with comic spot art, and a single panel full-page cartoon. A significant subset of *Punch*'s subscriber base was located in the U.S., to which thousands of copies were exported on an ongoing trans-Atlantic basis. Inevitably, enterprising American publishers attempted to repulse this invader with a home-grown comic weekly. The first, *Yankee Doodle*, came to town (New York, that is) on October 10, 1846, for one year. *Judy* (November 28, 1846 to February 20, 1847), *The John-Donkey* (January 1 to October 21, 1848), and *The Elephant* (January 22 to February 19, 1848) soon followed. None of them was successful, but all of them continued to feed the growing American interest in comic art.

By the late 1840s, comic art was flourishing in America. The conditions were right for the production of the earliest known American-created sequential comic book. Brothers James and Donald Read, who had worked for a time as cartoonists on *Yankee Doodle*, were the creators of *Journey to the Gold Diggins by Jeremiah Saddlebags*. This spirited send-up of the California gold rush craze was published in June 1849 by Stringer and Townsend, the late publishers of *Judy*, and, soon after, by U. P. James of Cincinnati. This Töpffer-influenced comic book chronicles the adventures of its hero *Jeremiah Saddlebags* in his get-rich-quick quest for gold in California. It is highly sought by collectors of Western Americana. Interestingly, the back cover of the Stringer and Townsend edition carries an advertisement for *Rose and Gertrude* - a Genevese Story, one of Rodolphe Töpffer's non-comics prose novels.

Stringer and Townsend was making something of a name for itself as a publisher of comic art. It will be remembered that it was one of the 1845 participants in the American publication of *The Bachelor's Own Book*. And, then, in 1846-47, it published *Judy*. Its decision to issue *Jeremiah Saddlebags* was all in due course.

The Gold Rush proved to be a gold mine for American comic artists. Aside from being a featured topic in the 1849 edition of David Claypool Johnston's *Scraps*, in comic almanacs, and in Currier cartoon prints, it was the subject of several other significant sequential series. The first, *The Adventures of Mr. Tom Plump* (a fat man who nearly starves to death in his failed attempt at California Gold riches), saw print in 1850. The second, *The Adventures of Jeremiah Old-Pot* (a twelve-part burlesque narrative of a New York businessman who attempts to get rich selling tin in price-inflated California), ran throughout 1852 in *Yankee Notions*. Though the narrative was distinctly American in its humor, the artwork was probably German in origin. *Yankee Notions*' Publisher, T. W. Strong, built his business on recycling old woodcuts with new captions attached. It should be noted that the *Old-Pot* series, borrowed or otherwise, was the first sequential art to appear in an American humor magazine. *Yankee Notions*, published from 1852 to 1875, also has the distinction of being the first comic monthly published in America.

"Moses Keyser the Bowery Bully's Trip to the California Gold Mines," was a 13-page comic story that appeared in *Elton's Californian Comic All-My-Nack* for 1850. It was reprinted at least twice in the circa 1850-51 booklet *The Clown, Or The Banquet of Wit* and later again in *Sam Slick's Comic Almanac* in 1857. *The Clown* is also notable as the earliest known anthology of sequential comics, with the bonus that each multi-panel story is by a different artist. Many of the artists are as yet unidentified, and how much of it is original American material versus that reprinted from Europe is presently unknown. But verified are cartoons by George Cruikshank, Elton (American), the Read brothers, Grandville (French), and Richard Doyle (British). The Doyle contribution reprints the comics story "Brown, Jones and Robinson and How They Went to a Ball," which originally saw print in the August 24, 1850 issue of *Punch*. This is the first known American appearance of these Doyle characters, and was almost certainly pirated.

Richard Doyle's *The Foreign Tour of Messrs. Brown, Jones, and Robinson* is basically a travelogue in illustrated form, told via humorous episodes, part sequential cartoon sequences, and part snapshots of moments jumping forward in time. This halfway sequential format was ideal for most 19th Century cartoonists, who, with rare exception, had not quite grasped how to maintain a single sequential story for much longer than two dozen successive panels. Doyle had simplified Töpffer's formula in a manner most artists could attempt to emulate. Episodes of "*Brown, Jones, and Robinson*" originally appeared in *Punch* in 1850, until a dispute between the Roman Catholic Doyle and Punch's editors over an anti-Papal joke ended with Doyle's resignation. Doyle redrew and expanded the story into a single album, first seeing print in 1854 from British publisher Bradbury and Evans.

New York Publisher D. Appleton brought the album to America, reprinting it in 1860, 1871, and 1877. Next, Dick and Fitzgerald of New York pirated Doyle's story sometime in the early 1870s. Doyle's format from *Foreign Tour* was emulated again and again. Examples include: the 1857 *Mr. Hardy Lee, His Yacht*, by Charles Stedman; the 1860s- 1870s G. W. Carleton-published *Our Artist In...* series, set in various Latin American countries; the Augustus Hoppin 1870s sketch novels *On the Nile, Crossing the Atlantic*, and *Ups and Downs on Land and Water*; and *Life* founder John Ames Mitchell's 1881 (pre-Life) *The Summer School of Philosophy at Mt. Desert*. D. Appleton, the official, authorized American publisher of *Foreign Tour*, even commissioned an American artist - Toby - to create a sequel comic album involving Doyle's characters visiting the U.S. and Canada, published in 1872 as *The American Tour of Messrs Brown, Jones and Robinson*. In terms of influencing the development of mid-19th Century American comics, Doyle's *Foreign Tour* ranks with the works of Töpffer, Cruikshank, and Busch.

Doyle was also the author of an equally popular earlier cartoon series for Punch, titled, *In Manners and Customs of Ye Englyshe, Mr. Pips Hys Diary*, which was reprinted in 1849. In this work, Doyle told his story using a deliberately primitive almost stick-figure art style, combined with the Hogarthian structure of large single panel cartoons leaping forward in time with each picture.

Manners and Customs of Ye Harvard Studente, which ran in the first year of the *Harvard Lampoon* (1876-current), shows the clearest influence. The series by then student Francis Gilbert Attwood was collected in 1877 by Houghton Mifflin. Attwood followed it up with *Manners and Customs of Ye Bostonians*, again in the pages of the *Harvard Lampoon*, but it is unknown whether that series was ever reprinted in book form. Attwood later became one of the regular artists in *Life*.

The Extraordinary and Mirth-provoking Adventures by Sea and Land of Oscar Shanghai, inspired by Bachelor Butterfly, was issued May 1855 by Garrett and Company, Publishers, No. 18 Ann Street, New York. Oscar Shanghai has many misadventures including being swallowed by a whale, making a trip in a flying machine to Africa, where he is shot out of a huge bow by a "Black Prince" for refusing to marry a local princess of color. After more adventures, he makes it back home.

Oscar Shanghai's first publisher was confirmed in 2002 with the discovery of a very rare 36-page catalog from 1856 of books, pamphlets and prints handled by B.H. Day (successor to Wilson and Company) who was by this time publishing *Brother Jonathan* as a twice-a-year holiday pictorial only. The catalog has a few crossover advertisement pages from an associate publisher, Garrett and Company. This rediscovered treasure, which sold for $750 in 2002, contains within a sequential strip of one panel per page over 32 of those pages titled *"Peter Piper in Bengal,"* by John Tenniel, reprinted from four 1853 issues of *Punch*. In the narrative, Peter Piper tries his hand hunting all different kinds of wild game with many misadventures.

Amongst the many varied types of "Cheap Books" for sale in this rare catalog are the comic books *The Adventures of Obadiah Oldbuck, Bachelor Butterfly's Queer Love Adventures and Misfortunes*, and *The Fortunes of Ferdinand Flipper*, plus the aforementioned *Oscar Shanghai*. All were priced at "25¢ per copy, postage free, refunds paid out in stamps." There is also an advertisement for a comic book entitled *A Day's Sport - Or, Hunting Adventures of S. Winks Wattles, a Shopkeeper, Thomas Titt, a "legal gent," and Major Nicholas Noggin, a Jolly Good Fellow Generally* by Henry L. Stephens (1824-1882) of Philadelphia.

Stephens, later the political cartoonist for *Vanity Fair* (New York, 1859-1863) and a leading children's book illustrator, produced his first work, *Illustrations of the Poets: From Passages in the Life of Little Billy Vidkins*, a small wrappered album of 32 comic woodcuts, in 1849. It was first published by S. Robinson, of Philadelphia, and reprinted with variant titles several times in the 1850s including *Yankee Notions*. It is likely that Little *Billy Vidkins* was printed before *Jeremiah Saddlebags*, though more research is needed before making this claim.

Garrett and Company was also responsible for the 1856 publication of *The Sad Tale of the Courtship of Chevalier Slyfox-Wikof, Showing His Heart-Rending Astounding and Most Wonderful Love Adventures with Fanny Elssler and Miss Gambol*. This book parodied the very public relationship between the then-famous wealthy American aristocrat Henry Wikoff, and the even more famous European actress/ dancer Fanny Elssler. It is dated thusly because Wikoff's memoir is pictured in the comic book.

Apparently in late 1854 Garrett and Company formed a brief two-year partnership with Dick and Fitzgerald, officially becoming Garrett, Dick and Fitzgerald in November 1856, while continuing to operate out of the same 18 Ann Street address in New York. One month later they issued Richard Doyle's British published graphic novel *The Foreign Tour of Messrs. Brown, Jones, and Robinson,* reformatting it into the same oblong shape as Garrett's two prior comic books (which in turn were formatted in imitation of Töpffer's albums). This information came to light just this year. The interested scholar is encouraged to check out the new listings for Garrett's The Home Circle in the index.

In 1858, Garrett appears to have dropped out, leaving Dick and Fitzgerald alone with the former's book stock, his place of business, and most importantly, the printing plates for his comic books. For reasons unknown, Dick and Fitzgerald steered away from reprinting Garrett's comic books for more than a decade. But in the 1870s they resumed publication - not only of the three albums published by Garrett, but also of *Obadiah Oldbuck and Bachelor Butterfly* from Wilson and Company, and *Ferdinand Flipper* from *Brother Jonathan* - all of them also making use of the original printing plates. The inclusion of books from *Brother Jonathan*, Wilson and Company, and Garrett and Company all within the same promotional Peter Piper catalog from B.H. Day suggests that these early publishers of comic books had many over-lapping fields of interest,, and that Dick and Fitzgerald became the inheritor/acquirer of all of it. Dick and Fitzgerald also reprinted in the 1870s the earlier William T. Peter published *Ichabod Academicus* (how that title might have connected, if at all, with B.H. Day's business remains unclear). We can now say, though, that an evolving group of a handful of publishers was responsible, over a span of 46 years, beginning with the very first graphic novel published in America in 1842, for keeping in print in America a cluster of slightly over half a dozen graphic novels.

Tebbel's *History of Book Publishing* in the US (vol. 1, pages 351-2) states that Burgess and Stringer was dissolved in late 1840s and became two firms, Stringer and Townsend, and Burgess and Garrett. Burgess retired in 1850 and his nephew William Brisbane Dick stepped into the partnership, whereupon the new company was renamed Garrett, Dick and Fitzgerald. Garrett retired in 1851 and the firm became Dick and Fitzgerald. The firm persisted under that name until 1917.

Collections reprinting cartoons from Punch saw print in the U.S., such as *Merry Pictures by the Comic Hands*, imported for the 1859 Christmas Season, plus various John Leech, George Du Maurier, and Phil May books which appeared from the 1850s through 1910s. Finally, many American weekly newspapers and weekly and monthly magazines, humorous and non-humorous, reprinted cartoons from Punch. Such inclusions often became a prelude to switching to original material by American artists, if that publication find's cartoon section find American cartoonists of sufficient talent.

Harper's Monthly, the leading American monthly, was a prime example. Soon after it commenced publication in November 1850, it began to carry a few pages of single panel cartoons reprinted from *Punch* at the rear of each issue. This evolved into reprinting sequential comic pages from the British periodical *Town Talk*, and then, starting December 1853, original sequential comics by the great Frank Bellew.

Bellew (1828-1888) should be regarded as the "Father of American Sequential Comics." Born in India, educated in France and England, he emigrated to America in 1850. His earliest work shows an influence from Doyle, but he rapidly developed his own unique art style. Bellew's comics, both sequential and single panel, graced nearly every American comic periodical published from the 1850s into the 1870s.

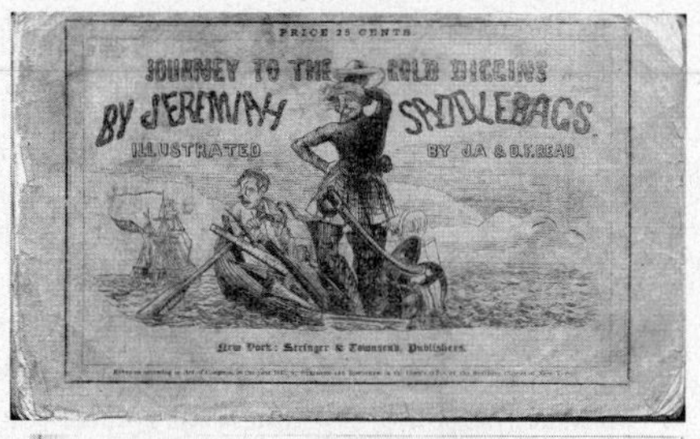

*Journey to the Gold Diggins By Jeremiah Saddlebags, June 1849, so far the earliest known sequential comic book by American creators, J.A. and D.F. Read. Above: a couple sample pages. Note similarity to Töpffer's comics especially **Bachelor Butterfly***

A month after the publication of the anonymous first installment of *Jeremiah Old-Pot* in *Yankee Notions*, Bellew began contributing his six-part, 18-panel comic series, *"Mr. Blobb in Search of a Physician"* to *The Lantern*, a New York comic weekly published from January 10, 1852 to July 2, 1853. The series ran in six of the nine issues published from January 31 through March 27, 1852. This was followed in April and May by the 16-panel, three-issue comic sequence "*Mr. Bulbear's Dream*", which concluded with the main character awakened from his dream by falling out of bed, exactly like *Little Nemo* would do five decades later.

These two series were just the beginning for Bellew, who contributed a voluminous amount of work to the *New York Picayune* (1850-1860) (which he also edited for a time in 1857-58), *The Comic Monthly* (1859-1881), *Momus*, an 1860 comic daily, *The Phunniest of Awl* (1864-1867) (which he also edited), *Punchinello* (1870), and *Wild Oats* (1870-1881), to name the most prominent.

The Comic Monthly deserves special mention. Started in March 1859 and published by J. C. Haney and Company, of 119 Nassau Street, New York, *The Comic Monthly* was a profusely illustrated 16-page folio, the same size as *Harper's Weekly*. It focused its graphic satire on politics, the theater, and the comedy of everyday life. A preponderance of the purely comic satire took the form of sequential art. Here are random samplings of highlights from issues from 1860:

• February: "A Day of Humiliation, Fasting, Supplica-tion, and Prayer (four panels, unsigned), "New Year Calls under the Influence of Hard Times" (twelve panels, unsigned), "Young Trouble-some; or, Master Jacky's Holidays" (nineteen panels covering three and half pages, unsigned);

• April: "Four Years After Marriage" (sixteen panels, unsigned), "Our Masked Ball" (twelve panel centerspread, Bellew), "Trials of a Witness" (eight panels, Bellew);

• May: "Precocities of Young Springles" (seven panels, unsigned), "The Fight for the Championship" (twenty-four panel centerspread, Bellew), "Steam Applied to Music" (three panels, unsigned), "The Course of True Love" (four panels, Bellew);

• June: "Further Particulars of the Fight" (nine panel cover, Bellew), "The Man Who Went to See the Fight" (twelve panels, unsigned);

• July: "Explaining American Politics to an Intelligent Foreigner" (twelve panels, unsigned), "The Meerschaum Mania" (two panels, Bellew), "The Art of Stump Speaking" (ten panels, unsigned), "Our Little Friend, Tom Noddy" (three panels, unsigned); "The Japanese in New York" (twelve panel centerspread, Bellew), "The Observant Child" (three panels, unsigned), "Mr. Dibbs Goes to Pike's Peak and Comes Back Again" (fourteen panel back cover, unsigned);

• September: "The Zouave Fever" (four panel cover, unsigned), "Mr. Lupell" (two panels, Bellew), "The Prince of Wales in America" (twenty-four panel centerspread, J. H. Howard), "D'ye Think It's True?" (three panels, Bellew);

• October: "The Duties of the Wide Awake" (four panels, Bellew), "Our Charley (two panels, unsigned), "The Three Young Friends" (eighteen panel back cover, unsigned);

• November: "The Hanlon's (sic) At Home" (nine panel back cover, unsigned);

• December: "The Target Excursion" (seventeen panel centerspread, signed with an unidentifiable monogram); "The Sporting Critic" two panels, Bellew).

The Comic Monthly also published many multi-panel cartoons grouped under a single heading, which were not strictly sequential in nature. Bellew was the monthly's chief artist, assisted by Thomas Nast, A. R Waud, and others. Some of the unsigned art was certainly by Bellew, some by journeymen artists, and some of it pirated from European journals.

The Comic Monthly was not the first folio-sized humor magazine. Those laurels go to *The New York Picayune,* which began as a newspaper, switched to a folio in 1856, adopted *Punch's* format for thirty-five issues in 1857-58, and returned to a folio for the remainder of its run.

Frank Leslie's *Budget of Fun*, the greatest of the folio monthlies, began in January 1859 and was published until June 1878. Its star cartoonist during the sixties was William Newman (c. 1817-1870), one of the founding artists of Punch. As we have noted, *The Comic Monthly* began two months later.

Frank Leslie was born Henry Cart in Ipswich, England in 1821. He became a very skilled engraver before coming over to

Yankee Notions #1, January, 1852. This title began the first sequential comic strips in an American humor magazine, The Adventures of Jerimiah Old-Pot.

America in 1948. He first worked as manager for P.T. Barnum's *New York Illustrated News* for several years. in 1850 he legally had his name changed to Frank Leslie. He died in 1880 and his wife continued the numerous publications he was publishing. Many of Frank Leslie's periodicals had a lot of sequental comic art.

Quarto-sized monthlies to compete with the successful *Yankee Notions* were also proliferating. *Nick-Nax* was the first (May 1856 to December 1875), followed by *Phunny Phellow* (October 1859- 1876) and *Merryman's Comic Monthly* (January 1863 to December 1875), to name the most prominent.

Enterprising publishers continued to attempt an American comic weekly in the style of *Punch*. The most notable efforts, *Vanity Fair* (1859-1863), *Mrs. Grundy* (1865), and *Punchinello* (1870), were distinguished but unsuccessful.

Nearly all of them, weeklies and monthlies, to varying degrees, featured sequential comic art. By the time of the American Civil War, sequential comic art was a part of the American graphic landscape.

While Bellew stood out for his sequential comics, Thomas Nast (1840-1902) brought a new style to American political cartoons, of which he is regarded the father. Even though he created several sequential strips early in his career (especially for Nick-Nax in 1859), Nast made his name in the pages of the national news periodical, *Harper's Weekly*, for which he worked from 1862 until 1886. Nast was influenced more by the dark wood engravings of Franco-German illustrator Gustave Dore than by the cartoonists of *Punch*. His somber cartoons were a novelty in American cartooning. Nast in the pages of *Harper's Weekly* (and Newman in the pages of the *Budget of Fun*) popularized the extravagant double-page folio-sized cartoon, which had no precedent in European or American cartooning, save for the separately published cartoon broadsides. This format would come to full maturity after 1876 in the pages of *Puck* (1876-1918) and then *Judge* (1881-1947).

As Nast grew in prominence and success, American cartoonists increasingly emulated him. U.S. humor publications evolved towards an amalgamation of Nast and Punch, rather than sheer imitation of the latter. After the War, with Nast's style of cartoons more entrenched in American readers' minds, efforts to launch *Punch*-like American periodicals floundered quickly. *Mrs. Grundy*, ironically most famous for its cover design by Nast, died after a mere twelve issues (running July 8 to September 23, 1865). *Punchinello* (April 2 to December 24, 1870) struggled nine months before its backers gave up. *Punchinello* had been financed by Tammany Hall politicians Tweed and Sweeney, as counter-propaganda against Nast's ongoing assault upon their corruption. They attempted to buy and threaten Nast into silence, to no avail.

American comics continued their pull away from Anglo-Franco imitation with the infusion of a third major European influence – the German humor magazine. The German-American community swelled significantly after the failed revolution of 1848. These émigrés brought with them a culture of humor, expressed most flamboyantly in their native humor magazines, the most famous being *Kladderadatsch, Fliegende Blätter*, and *Münchener Bilderbogen*. As high in quality, as were the graphic artists who contributed to them, one German comic artist in particular excelled beyond the rest, his stories breaking out and crossing over into English language translations, the demand for which resulted in numerous printings. This artist, of course, was Heinrich Christian Wilhelm Busch (1832-1908).

Busch's work appeared in English in the 1860s in both British and American periodicals, often uncredited. For example, four of Busch's strips appeared in English in the pages of *Merryman's Monthly* in 1864, while in 1879 his graphic story "Fipps der Affe" was serialized across a 10-issue run of Puck as "Troddledums the Simian." The earliest known English language appearance of Busch in book form was *The Flying Dutchman, or The Wrath of Herr von Stoppelnoze*, in 1862, from New York publisher G. W. Carleton. Carleton not only pirated Busch's strip, but went so far as to credit the entire story to American poet John G. Saxe, with Busch's cartoons mere illustrations accompanying Saxe's prose!

The next known English language Busch book was A *Bushel of Merry Thoughts*, an 1868 London-published anthology collecting various Busch strips. Some of these same stories later appeared in the U.S.-published *The Mischief Book* (1880), newly translated and with a few more Busch tales added. One of these additions was "Hans Huckebein," a tale of a mischievous pet raven who in the end gets drunk and accidentally hangs himself. It became, at least in the States, Busch's second most popular sequential comic story. The unrepentant bird was promoted to title character in two later collections: the rare *Hookeybeak the Raven and Other Tales* in 1878 and *Jack Huckaback, the Scapegrace Raven*, circa 1888. There were also at least three trade card series in the 1870s and 1880s that reprinted the ending sequence, as *Fritz Spindle-Shanks, The Raven Black*.

The most popular Busch tale, though, was easily Max und Moritz, which in the U.S. saw print as *Max and Maurice - A Juvenile History in Seven Tricks*. Published in Boston in 1871, this English language version saw at minimum of 60 reprintings by the century's end, plus countless more printings thereafter. A separate British translation debuted in 1874, under the title *Max and Moritz*. It is well known that the later Rudolph Dirks comic strip series, Katzenjammer Kids, beginning in late

1897, was based on *Max und Moritz*.

According to documents found by comics historian Alfredo Castelli, *Katzenjammer Kids* may not have been pirated as has been assumed but was licensed by William Randolph Hearst instead. Hearst's *New York Journal* was published in different language editions for New York City's immigrant communities. In the German edition, the strip was published under its original name, *Max und Moritz*. Numerous other translations of Busch were published in America - too many to name in this article. Several can be found in the Victorian Age Price Index.

The most significant humor magazine of the 1870s, prior to the founding of the German-language *Puck* in 1876, was *Wild Oats* (1870-1881), which for part of its run also published a German-language edition, *Schnedereddeng*. In terms of the quality of its cartoons and comics, this New York City publication was in 1872 at an artistic level *Puck* would not achieve until 1880. Published by Winchell and Small (later Collin and Small) and distributed through the New York News Company, *Wild Oats* carried a cross-section of old and new generation comic artists, from the more established W. M. Avery, Frank Beard, Frank Bellew, E.S. Bisbee, Michael Angelo Woolf, and Thomas Worth, to up-and-comers such as Livingston Hopkins, Frederick Burr Opper, Palmer Cox, and James A. Wales.

Wild Oats began carrying sequential comic strips as early as #26, dated March 14, 1872, with the Livingston Hopkins strip pictured on the next page (we do not know anything yet about the first 25 issues). The very next issue has a Worth double-page spread titled "The Political Humpty Dumpty... Horace Greeley" told in eleven panels plus the sequential fictional "Graphic Account of the Assassination of Queen Victoria" and "Love As the Angels Love." "The Doings of the Japanese Embassy At Washington" related in twelve panels by W. M. Avery follows up in #28 April 11, 1872. An unknown hand drew "The Physiology of Moving" in six panels in #30. Hopkins returns with a beautiful intense 28-panel double-page spread in #31 May 23. Hopkins and Worth alternated for many issues with sequential comic strips on baseball, horse racing and other pertinent subjects of the day. In #45 December 5, 1872, E.S. Bisbee contributed his first sequential in seventeen panels and Worth showed up in "Humor and Pathos of a New England Thanksgiving" in eleven panels. Issue 47 expands the concept with a twelve-panel job by Bisbee, twenty-panel effort on one page by Hopkins and a three-panel effort by Worth. And on it goes through 1873 as well - comic strip after comic strip. Issue 58 June 5, 1873, includes a particularly humorous nineteen-panel double-pager drawn by someone still unknown titled "The Terrible Adventures of Messrs. Buster and Stumps, with the Indians" which begins with two white men heading out west in an effort to exterminate Indians - and their misadventures of not quite getting the job done. It reads across both pages in a unique evolution similar to Popeye #2052 (found in the Platinum listings). Issue 65 contains two nine-panel Thomas Worth strips "Only a Mad Dog Scare - Another Lesson For Nervous People" and "Only a Cholera Scare - Something For Nervous People to Read and Ponder Over." Issue 66 Sept 18, 1873, has the very funny Hopkins twelve-panel strip as well as two more ten-panel Worth strips on the delights of Hunting and Fishing plus one by Hopkins titled "The Adventures of Mr Old Party with Jersey Mosquitoes" in twelve-panels. All told, four comic strips in this issue. They obviously liked what they were doing, judging from the exuberance of the work.

The next issue has Worth's nine-panel report on "The Adventures of Young Muttonhead among the Free Lovers" which was all about the "free sex" convention recently held in Chicago. Issue 68 has a nine-panel "An Adventure with a New Jersey Mosquito" which smacks of Winsor McCay in subject and even art style. Maybe McCay was inspired by this for his later animated cartoon as well as earlier Rarebit Fiend. We'll never know for sure. On through 1875, *Wild Oats* presented sequential comic strips issue after issue. With #148, October 27, 1875, Frederick Opper contributes his very first Wild Oats cover, a political cartoon on inflation then rampant in the US. He does covers through at least #161 before a short break and then comes back with many more. In #158, January 5, 1876, Palmer Cox - some five years before inventing The Brownies - begins a wonderful series of 24-panel double page spread comic strips, with a couple sample titles being "The Adventures of Mr. and Mrs. Sprowl And Their Christmas Turkey-A Crashing Chasing Tearful Tragedy But Happily Ending Well" and "Bachelor Broke and Widow Snuggi: A Pictorial Account of Their Sleigh Ride and What Became of It."

Even though he had been contributing many covers and interior single panel jobs to *Wild Oats* for years, Frank Bellew does not show up with his first comic strip until #190, August 16, 1876, with a nine-panel effort he titled, "Rodger's Patent Mosquito Armour." By this time America's "Father of the sequential comic strip" had inspired many other cartoonists to try their hand telling stories with words and pictures.

Another highly desirable American graphic novel, sought especially by collectors of Western lore, is *Quiddities of an Alaskan Trip* by William H. Bell which debuted in 1873. Bell was Timothy O'Sullivan's assistant photographer on the 1871-74 expeditions of Lt. George Wheeler, surveying and mapping the western territories for the U.S. government. The story panels are laid out within ornate frames like those of stereograph cards, such as Bell was involved in creating on the expedition. It involves a parody of a trip from Washington, D.C., to survey the newly purchased territory of Alaska, which at the time was derisively referred to as "Seward's Folly." Bell published *Quiddities* in Portland, Oregon, in 1873, meaning that he drew it while he was on just such an expedition.

The seemingly disparate influences of Thomas Nast and German comics came together in the work of Austrian immigrant Joseph Keppler (1838-1894). Like many cartoonists in America, Keppler desired to rival Nast. Unlike most, he possessed the talent and drive to accomplish it. Keppler, trained as an artist but working as an actor, began contributing comic art to *Kikeriki* (1861-1923) in his native Vienna. He emigrated to St. Louis in 1868, where he took his first stab at starting a comic weekly, the German language *Die Vehme* (Aug 28, 1869 - Aug. 20, 1870). Seven months later, still in St. Louis, he tried again, launching another German language humor periodical, titled *Puck*. This German *Puck* began on March 18, 1871, joined by an English language version one year later, but both ended on Aug. 24, 1872.

Keppler moved to New York City and began working for Frank Leslie. His cartoons appeared in *Frank Leslie's Illustrated Newspaper*, Frank Leslie's *Budget of Fun*, and the Leslie-owned *Jolly Joker* and *Day's Doings*. (To capitalize on the 1876 Centennial Exposition in Philadelphia, Leslie published in that year a paperback collection of Centennial-related humor, *Centennial Fun*, most of which was Keppler's work.) Four years after the first *Puck* died, Keppler was ready to try again. He re-launched the German language edition of *Puck* in New York City on September 27, 1876.

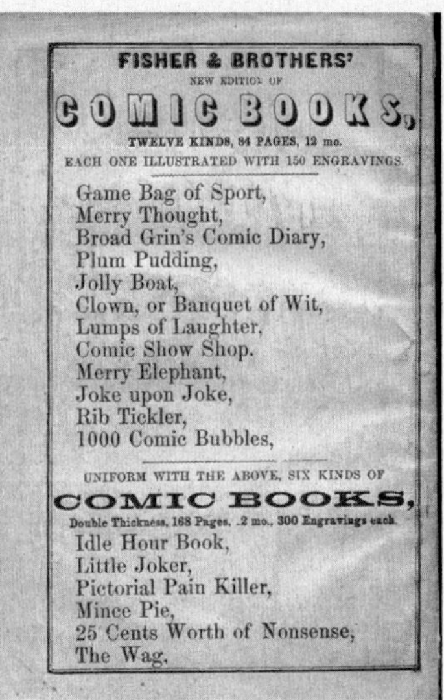

FISHER & BROTHERS'
NEW EDITION OF
COMIC BOOKS,
TWELVE KINDS, 84 PAGES, 12 mo.
EACH ONE ILLUSTRATED WITH 150 ENGRAVINGS.

Game Bag of Sport,
Merry Thought,
Broad Grin's Comic Diary,
Plum Pudding,
Jolly Boat,
Clown, or Banquet of Wit,
Lumps of Laughter,
Comic Show Shop.
Merry Elephant,
Joke upon Joke,
Rib Tickler,
1000 Comic Bubbles,

UNIFORM WITH THE ABOVE, SIX KINDS OF
COMIC BOOKS,
Double Thickness, 168 Pages, 12 mo., 300 Engravings each.
Idle Hour Book,
Little Joker,
Pictorial Pain Killer,
Mince Pie,
25 Cents Worth of Nonsense,
The Wag.

Earliest-known use of the description COMIC BOOKS dates from the early 1850s.

This *Puck* was both familiar and exotic. Its format of an extravagant center-spread cartoon sandwiched between front and back cover cartoons had by this time become something of a comic periodical standard, certainly for the monthlies. But *Puck* was different from what had come before. The cartoons were lithographed, not engraved, which lent to them a softer, more pleasing quality, and they were in color, something virtually without precedent in American comic periodical literature.

Initially, the magazine's cartoons were tinted in just one color, but *Puck* appeared, ambitiously, every week, and the coloring set it apart from anything else on American stands. The parallel English language edition of *Puck* was launched six months after the German version, on March 14, 1877. This English edition of *Puck* was a money-loser for several years, kept afloat by the German edition's profits and the determination of the English edition's literary editor, H.C. Bunner, not to give up. By 1880, *Puck* was a huge success. It became the new model for American humor publications. In time, Keppler hired other artists, most notably Frederick Burr Opper, Eugene Zimmerman ("Zim") and F. M. Howarth, and added black and white sequential comics to the magazine's interior and then, with increasing frequency in the early 1890s to the magazine's back cover. *Funny Folks* by F. M. Howarth, 1899, collected many early sequential comics from *Puck;* one of the titles many consider bridges the Victorian and Platinum Ages of comics. *Puck* was the model that inspired William Randolph Hearst to add a color comics section to his Sunday Journal in 1895.

With the first issue dated October 29, 1881, *Puck's* chief rival, *Judge*, was born. Founded by *Puck* artist James A. Wales, it also featured the work of Thomas Worth and Livingston Hopkins. *Judge* made several forays into *Puck*'s talent pool over the years. Its best capture was Eugene Zimmerman ("Zim"), who became for Judge the star artist that Frederick Burr Opper was for Puck.

Judge struggled financially for several years, and likely would have ceased publication had it not been for Puck's powerful performance during the 1884 election. *Puck*'s success galvanized Republican powerbrokers into recognizing the importance of the political cartoon weekly. They financed newspaperman W. J. Arkell's purchase of *Judge* in 1886 to turn it into a reliable Republican house organ.

Also worthy of mention is the New York City newspaper *The Daily Graphic* (March 4, 1873 to Sept 23, 1889), which claims the distinction of being the first regularly illustrated daily newspaper in the world, published every day except Sundays and holidays. The majority of its illustrations were portraits or depictions of news events, but nearly every issue contained some comic drawing, many of them gracing the front cover.

With so many pages to fill on a daily basis, *The Daily Graphic* became a rotating door for many young American cartoonists in the early stages of their careers (making one suspect that it was not the best paying gig in town). Within its pages, like needles to be found in the haystack of its more than 4800 issues, is early work by Livingston Hopkins (who mysteriously appears, vanishes, reappears, etc., for months to whole years at a time, right up to his 1884 departure to Australia), pre-*Life* work by Kemble, pre-*Harper*'s appearances by A.B. Frost and W.A. Rogers, pre-Puck and Judge Opper, C.J. Taylor, Hamilton, and Gillam. Old hats, too, appear at times, such as Michael Woolf and Frank Bellew, Sr.

Further, *The Daily Graphic* regularly plundered British periodicals for its back and sometimes center pages, not only perpetrating the usual swipes of single-panel *Punch* cartoons, but also stealing sequential strips from Punch's two main rival publications, *Judy* and *Fun*. This included occasionally reprinting (albeit at random) episodes of continuing British strips "The British Workman" by James Sullivan, and "McNab of that Ilk" by James Brown, though, strangely enough, not Marie Duval's *Ally Sloper*, despite the fact that *The Daily Graphic* did reprint some of Duval's non-"Sloper" strips. ("Ally Sloper" was a continuing sequential strip character who debuted in 1867, lasting into the 1920s, and had very successful solo British book collections of his strip appearances published as early as 1873, more than two decades prior to *Yellow Kid in McFadden*'s Flats).

Livingston Hopkins, whose art style changed like a chameleon from one year to the next, exhibited a definite Duval influence in his work within a year following the publication of the first *Ally Sloper* collection. Given that Hopkins worked for *The Daily Graphic* during the same period in which this newspaper was stealing cartoons from *Sloper*'s home publication, *Judy*, this can hardly be considered coincidental. Hopkins contributed a daily comic strip to *The Daily Graphic* in 1874-75, complete with word balloons. By the time Hopkins was preparing to emigrate to Australia to become lead cartoonist for the Sydney Bulletin, his art style was an imitation of Kemble's, who was also working at *The Daily Graphic*.

Life debuted on January 4, 1883, founded by J.A. Mitchell, and modeled after the Harvard Lampoon. It quickly rose to become the third main pillar of late 1800s American humor periodicals. Smaller in size, black and white, and priced the same as *Puck* and *Judge*, it nevertheless succeeded by appealing to a more genteel audience. Its earliest artists included Kemble and Palmer Cox, but its foremost artist was Charles Dana Gibson, becoming world renowned as the hand behind the graceful, aristocratic "Gibson Girls."

Unlike *Judge*, which had to become a low-brow imitation of *Life* to survive in the next century, and *Puck*, which attempted but failed to become an American version of the highbrow European humor magazines, Life transitioned into the 20th century virtually unaltered, and thrived. By the mid-1880s, with *Puck, Judge*, and *Life* all solidly in place, American comics and cartoon humor had come very much into their own, no longer looking first at Europe to take their cues.

Almanacs began to appear in America starting in 1639. Humor was introduced as early as 1647 by Samuel Danforth. A very important one was *Leed Almanac* beginning in 1687. John Tulley produced the first humorous almanac in 1688. James Franklin, brother of Ben, began the *Rhode Island Almanac* in 1728 using the name "Poor Robin" and his younger brother began *Poor Richard's Almanac* in 1732. Farmer's Almanac began in 1792 and used some humor.

The first comic almanac totally devoted to humor was published by Charles Ellm in Boston in 1831 and featured the artwork of D.C. Johnston. Perhaps the most famous comic almanacs (certainly the most valuable) are the *Davy Crockett* series (1835-1856) which began in Nashville, Tennessee. The comic periodicals all ended up issuing comic almanacs beginning with *Yankee Notions* in 1856 and continuing into the 1890s with a one-shot comic almanac published by *Judge* for the year 1894.

Beginning in the 1850s, a new breed of almanacs appeared. Usually created by medicine and farm product companies, they were distributed for free to promote the company's product. Competition amongst companies, whose goal was to get customers to read the almanacs and the advertisements contained therein again and again, meant that attention-getting humorous cartoons soon found their way back into these giveaway pamphlets. Initially their cartoons were done cheap, either poorly drawn or pirated from elsewhere, such as those found in the Hostetter's and Wright's almanac series. More elaborate promotional almanacs eventually did evolve, though, and amongst the best of these was *Barker's Illustrated Almanac*, first produced for the year 1878, and annually into the 1930s. Each *Barker's Almanac* contained ten to twelve full page cartoons, wonderful and bizarre in design, frequently racist, but also comically manic and crammed with details in a manner similar to Outcault's much later *Yellow Kid* pages. The cartoons in *Barker's Almanac* were so popular that in 1892, The Barker, Moore, and Mein Medicine Company published their first edition of *Barker's Komic Picture Souvenir*, reprinting nearly 150 pages of cartoons from their almanacs.

This first *Barker's Souvenir* features a wraparound color cover depicting people headed towards the Columbian World's Fair Exposition, which was to be held in Chicago the next year. It is the earliest confirmed "premium" comic book, sent to customers who mailed in a box label and outside wrapper from two different Barker's products. The *Souvenir* album was *Barker's* most in-demand premium. It was reprinted as a thick unnumbered booklet three more times in the 1890s, with the contents reorganized each time. Later, between 1901 and 1903, *Barker's* broke the album into three separate "Parts," each of which required still more box labels and wrappers to obtain. The 3-part series of reprint albums expanded to four parts circa 1906 or 1907. Both the 3 and 4-part album series had multiple printings.

Also very American in character were the country's promotional comics, which flourished throughout the latter half of the 19th century. They trace their beginnings to Comic Almanacs, which flourished in England and the United States since they first appeared in the 1830s. The first promotional comics which did not double as almanacs began to appear in the 1870s. They included the aforementioned reprints of Cruikshank and Busch strips, reprints of strips lifted from American sources (A.B. Frost's strip "The Bull Calf" was a particular favorite), and original material placing the product being promoted as the focus of the story. These original short cartoon dramas were in many ways similar in storyline to those found in modern television advertisements, except that the clothing is Victorian, and the claims, pre-F.D.A. and F.C.C., were unabashedly wild, over-the-top, and blunt. Chewing tobacco and snuff saved romances, calmed crying babies, and made the sick well. Stove polish that propelled you to wealth and power. Corsets that brought you a husband. The objective, of course, in an era before TV or radio, was to make each comic handout so entertaining that customers would want to keep and read the advertisement again and again.

The more wonderful graphics and outrageous claims tended to come from tobacco companies, who were using comic books and strips to sell their products more than a century before cries against "Joe Camel." The most elaborate of these were printed full color, and unfolded into a single long strip, just like Cruikshank's *The Tooth-Ache* from the 1840s, though usually limited to just the cover plus seven panels.

The earliest known anthology devoted to collecting the comic strips of a single American artist was A.B. Frost's *Stuff and Nonsense* in 1884. The next known American collection came in 1888, the very rare Frederick Burr Opper anthology, *Puck's Opper Book*. Both proved popular, so more Frost and Opper collections followed, to be joined within a few years by reprints collecting the cartoons and strips of Keppler, Kemble, Zim, Gibson, Mayer, Taylor, Frank Bellew's son "Chip," Howarth, Woolf, etc.

Puck, Judge, and *Texas Siftings* all began monthly Library series - 8-1/2" x 11" magazines, mostly black and white, which organized previously published material around one theme or one artist. For example, the first *Puck's Library* (July 1887) was titled "The National Game," and gathered beneath one cover *Puck* material poking fun at the game of baseball. The third (March 1888) and ninth (November 1889) issues of *Judge's Serial (later named Judge's Library)* were devoted entirely to the work of Zim.

Life tended more towards hardcover collections, such as its annual ten-issue series *The Good Things of Life* (1884-1893), which included cartoons and strips by Palmer Cox, T.S. Sullivant, Hy Mayer, and others. *The Good Things of Life* was published initially by the firm of White, Stokes, and Allen, but which by the fourth book, had become simply Frederick A. Stokes. Stokes published a number of other cartoon books in the 1880s and 1890s, the majority of them reprint collections. The experience he gained at this time with these reprint albums placed Stokes in the perfect position to pick up the wealth of material about to be created for the comics supplements of William R. Hearst's newspapers, making Stokes the first major publisher of the coming Platinum Age.

In 1892, Charles Scribner's Sons published A. B. Frost's *Bull Calf and Other Tales*. It contains sequential comic strip art on quite a few pages as well as single panel cartoons. By 1898, Charles Scribner's Sons also issued Kemble's *The Billy Goat and Other Comicalities* as a 112-page hardcover, which also has sequential comic strips.

In the early 1890s, the slum children cartoons of artist Michael Woolf (many of which were reprinted in the 1896 collection *99 Woolfs from Truth* and in the posthumous 1899 collection *Sketches of Lowly Life in a Great City*) were popular. *Truth* magazine, which followed Puck's format of color front cover, back cover and centerspread cartoons, but in style was more akin to the aristocratic Life, was initially unable to secure Woolf's services, creating an opportunity for the young cartoonist Richard F. Outcault, who desired to break into one of the weekly comic periodicals.

It was in his Woolf-inspired slum children cartoons for *Truth* that Outcault's prototype of the *Yellow Kid* first emerged. The bald, sack-clothed youngster made four appearances in *Truth*, starting with #372 on June 2, 1894, prior to his newspaper debut.

During the rise of Yellow Kid's popularity, he appeared in American comic magazines in parodies drawn by others, with politicians, even Hearst and Pulitzer, dressed up as the *Yellow Kid*. Such cartoons are known to have appeared in *Judge, Life, The Bee*, and *Vim* plus various newspapers across the country. More about the *Yellow Kid's* importance can be found in the Platinum Age section of this book.

While comics definitely have their roots in Europe, and the earliest American comic books either reprinted or emulated those of Europe, the direction of influence was by no means one way. By at least the 1870s, American cartoons were being published and seen in the Old World, as evidenced by the arrest in Spain of the on-the-lamb corrupt Tammany Hall politician Boss Tweed by Spanish police who recognized Tweed from a Nast cartoon.

European piracy of American cartoons was just as lucrative as the American piracy of Europeans. In the 1880s and '90s, the comics of Zim, Chip Bellew, and Charles Dana Gibson all saw reprint in Europe. In April 1899, *Pictorial Comedy*, a monthly magazine destined for a ten-year run, commenced publication in London. It was made up entirely of cartoons reprinted with permission from *Puck* and *Life*. F.M. Howarth's domestic comedies from *Puck* were favorites in France. American Hy Mayer was commissioned to create original comics work for *Black and White* (Britain), *Le Rire* (France), and *Fliegende Blätter*. Michael Woolf's slum children cartoons saw print in the British periodical *Pick-Me-Up*, during the same years that top British artist Phil May's first published work debuted in that publication. May later became famous for his Woolf-inspired street children cartoons as well as his influence on the development of comics in Australia.

As the 19th Century ended, American comics were coming to the fore worldwide, soon to explode into a position of dominance with the Platinum Age revolution brought about by the emergence of the color comic supplement in America's newspapers and the arrival of Richard F. Outcault's *Yellow Kid*.

END NOTE: Victorian Era comics were issued in many relatively obscure formats compared to what most of us are used to today. The Victorian Era section can only grow as there are many more heretofore undiscovered comics from the 1800s which have fallen off the radar of history. Some may wonder why some of the earlier items listed contain as of yet no prices. The reason is simple. These books are part of a relatively "new" market which is still establishing itself.

High-grade copies are almost unheard of in almost all instances. Some books may truly have only a handful left in existence. We are sure there are some known to have been published which no (as of yet) known copies have survived the ravages of time and neglect.

Each year expect another quantum leap in our ever-expanding knowledge of the fascinating earliest origins of the comic strip as it relates to North America. Your input in helping this section of the Guide grow and mature is most welcome!

Robert Lee Beerbohm first sold comics through the legendary RBCC beginning in 1966, set up at his first comicon in 1967, helped found the northern California Comics & Comix chain of stores in August 1972, co-hosted Berkeleycon 1973, the first UG creator-owned comix con and operated comic book stores from 1972-1994. He now owns Robert Beerbohm Comic Art that specializes in buying and selling scarce comics and related material from the 1840s-1980s. He has been compiling a detailed history book of the business of the American comic book for some time now and hopes to complete it soon.

Contact Robert directly at www.BLBComics.com

Richard Olson is an Research Professor Emeritus at the University of New Orleans. He published the Richard Outcault Collector for years. Reach Richard directly at: rolsonredoak@bellsouth.net

Richard Samuel West is the author of Satire on Stone: The Political Cartoons of Joseph Keppler (University of Illinois, 1988) and The San Francisco Wasp: An Illustrate History (Periodyssey Press, 2004) and editor of several cartoon collections. He is the owner of Periodyssey, a business that specializes in buying and selling significant and unusual American magazines. Richard can be reached at: www.oldmagazines.com

All three are life-long collectors and students of all forms of the comics who welcome corrections and additions to this concise compilation of our earliest American comics heritage dating back almost two centuries. Happy Hunting!

The American Comic Almanac #11
1835 © Charles Ellms, NYC

The Strange and Wonderful Adventures
of Bachelor Butterfly by Rodolphe Töpffer
1870s © Dick & Fitzgerald, NYC

Barker's "Komic" Picture Souvenir, 3rd Edition
1894 © Barker, Moore & Klein Medicine Co.

FR1.0 GD2.0 FN6.0

COLLECTOR'S NOTE: Most of the books listed in this section were published well over a century before organized comics fandom began archiving and helping to preserve these fragile popular culture artifacts. With some of these comics now over 160 years old, they almost never surface in Fine+ or better shape. Be happy when you simply find a copy.

This year has seen price growth in quite a few comic books in this era. Since this section began growing almost a decade now, comic books from Wilson, Brother Jonathan, Huestis & Cozans, Garrett, Dick & Fitzgerald, Frank Leslie, Street & Smith and others continue to be recognized by the more savvy in this fine hobby as legitimate comic book collectors' items. We had been more concerned with simply establishing what is known to exist. For the most part, that work is now a *fait accompli* in this section compiled, revised, and expanded by Robert Beerbohm with special thanks this year to Terrance Keegan plus acknowledgment to Bill Blackbeard, Chris Brown, Alfredo Castelli, Darrell Coons, Leonardo De Sá, Scott Deschaine, Joe Evans, Ron Friggle, Tom Gordon III, Michel Kempeneers, Andy Konkykru, Don Kurtz, Richard Olson, Robert Quesinberry, Joseph Rainone, Steve Rowe, Randy Scott, John Snyder, Art Spiegelman, Steve Thompson, Richard Samuel West, Doug Wheeler and Richard Wright. Special kudos to long-time collector and scholar Gabriel Laderman.

The prices given for Fair, Good and Fine categories are for strictly graded editions. If you need help grading your item, we refer you to the grading section in this book or contact the authors of this essay. Items marked Scarce, Rare or Very Rare we are still trying to figure out how many copies might still be in existence. We welcome additions and corrections from any interested collectors and scholars at robert@BLBcomics.com

For ease ascertaining the contents of each item of this listing and the Platinum index list, we offer the following list of categories found immediately following most of the titles:

E - EUROPEAN ORIGINAL COMICS MATERIAL; Printed in Europe or reprinted in USA
G - GRAPHIC NOVEL (LONGER FORMAT COMIC TELLING A SINGLE STORY)
H - "HOW TO DRAW CARTOONS" BOOKS
I - ILLUSTRATED BOOKS NOTABLE FOR THE ARTIST, BUT NOT A COMIC.
M - MAGAZINE / PERIODICAL COMICS MATERIAL REPRINTS
N - NEWSPAPER COMICS MATERIAL REPRINTS
O - ORIGINAL COMIC MATERIAL NOT REPRINTED FROM ANOTHER SOURCE
P - PROMOTIONAL COMIC, EITHER GIVEN AWAY FOR FREE, OR A PREMIUM GIVEN IN CONJUNCTION WITH THE PURCHASE OF A PRODUCT.
S - SINGLE PANEL / NON-SEQUENTIAL CARTOONS

Measurements are in inches. The first dimension given is Height and the second is Width. Some original British editions are included in the section, so as to better explain and differentiate their American counterparts.

ACROBATIC ANIMALS
R.H. Russell: 1899 (9x11-7/8", 72 pgs, B&W, hard-c)
nn (Scarce) 175.00 325.00 675.00
NOTE: *Animal strips by Gustave Verbeck, presented 1 panel per page.*

ALMY'S SANTA CLAUS (P,E)
Edward C. Almy & Co., Providence, R.I.: nd (1880's) (5-3/4x4-5/8", 20 pgs, B&W, paper-c
nn - (Rare) 12.50 40.00 100.00
NOTE: *Department store Christmas giveaway containing an abbreviated 28-panel reprinting of George Cruikshank's* ***The Tooth-ache****. Santa Claus cover.*

AMERICAN COMIC ALMANAC, THE (OLD AMERICAN COMIC ALMANAC 1839-1846)
Charles Ellms: 1831-1846 (5x8, 52 pgs, B&W)
1-First American comic almanac ever prrinted 650.00 1300.00 2600.00
2-16 125.00 210.00 450.00
NOTE:#1 from 1831 is the First American Comic Almanac

AMERICAN PUNCH
American Punch Publishing Co: Jan 1879-March 1881, J.A. Cummings Engraving Co (last 3 issues) (Quarto Monthly)
Most issues 25.00 50.00 175.00

THE AMERICAN WIT
Richardson & Collins, NY: 1867-68 (18-1/2x13. 8 pgs, B&W)
2/3 Frank Bellew single panels 50.00 100.00 250.00

AMERICAN WIT AND HUMOR
Harper & Bros, NY: 1859 (
nn - numerous McLenan sequential comic strips 130.00 260.00 525.00

ATTWOOD'S PICTURES - AN ARTIST'S HISTORY OF THE LAST TEN YEARS OF THE NINETEENTH CENTURY (M,S)
Life Publishing Company, New York: 1900 (11-1/4x9-1/8", 156 pgs, B&W, gilted blue hard-c)
nn - By Attwood 50.00 100.00 185.00
NOTE: *Reprints monthly calendar cartoons which appeared in* ***LIFE****, for 1887 through 1899.*

BACHELOR BUTTERFLY, THE VERITABLE HISTORY OF MR. (E,G)
D. Bogue, London: 1845 (5-1/2x10-1/4", 74 pgs, B&W, gilted hardcover)
nn - By Rodolphe Töpffer (Scarce) 500.00 1250.00 3000.00
nn - Hand colored edition (Very Rare) (no known sales)
NOTE: *This is the British Edition, translated from the re-engraved by Cham serialization found in* ***L'Illustration*** *- a periodical from Paris publisher Dubochet. Predates the first French collected edition. Third Töpffer comic book published in English. The first story page is numbered Page 3. Page 17 shows Bachelor Butterfly being swallowed by a whale.*

BACHELOR BUTTERFLY, THE STRANGE ADVENTURES OF (E,G)
Wilson & Co., New York: 1846 (5-3/8x10-1/8", 68 pgs, B&W, soft-c)
nn - By Rodolphe Töpffer (Very Rare) 600.00 1500.00 3300.00
nn - At least one hand colored copy exists (Very Rare) (no known sales)
NOTE: *2nd Töpffer comic book printed in the U.S., 3rd earliest known sequential comic book in the USA. Reprinted from the British D. Bogue 1845 edition, itself from the earlier French language* ***Histoire de Mr. Cryptogame****. Released the same year as the French Dubochet edition. Two variations known, the earlier printing with Page number 17 placed on the inside (left) bottom corner in error, with slightly later printings corrected to place page number 17 on the outside (right) bottom corner of that page. Another first printing indicator is pages 17 and 20 are printed on the wrong side of the page. For both printings: the first story page is numbered 2. Page 17 shows Bachelor Butterfly already in the whale. In most panels with 3 lines of text, the third line is indented further than the second, which is in turn indented further than the first.*

FR1.0 GD2.0 FN6.0

BACHELOR BUTTERFLY, THE STRANGE ADVENTURES
Brother Jonathan Press, NY: 1854 (5-1/2x10-5/8", 68 pgs, paper-c, B&W) (Very Rare)
nn - By Rodolphe Töpffer 250.00 500.00 1300.00

BACHELOR BUTTERFLY,THE STRANGE & WONDERFUL ADVENTURES OF
Dick & Fitzgerald, New York: 1870s-1888 (various printings 30 Cent cover price, 68 pgs, B&W, paper cover) (all versions Rare) (E,G)
nn - Black print on blue cover (5-1/2x10-1/2"); string bound 125.00 250.00 550.00
nn - Black print on green cover (5-1/2x10-1/2"); string bound 100.00 200.00 440.00
NOTE: *Reprints the earlier Wilson & Co. edition. Page 2 is the first story page. Page 17 shows Bachelor Butterfly already in the whale. In most panels with 3 lines of text, the second and third lines are equally indented in from the first. Unknown which cover (blue or green) is earlier.*

BACHELOR'S OWN BOOK. BEING THE PROGRESS OF MR. LAMBKIN, (GENT.) IN THE PURSUIT OF PLEASURE AND AMUSEMENT (E,O,G)
(See also PROGRESS OF MR. LAMBKIN)
D. Bogue, London: August 1, 1844 (5x8-1/4", 28 pgs printed one side only, cardboard cover & interior) (all versions Rare)
nn - First printing hand colored 200.00 400.00 1000.00
nn - First printing black & white 200.00 400.00 1000.00
NOTE: *First printing has misspellings in the title. "PURSUIT" is spelled "PERSUIT", and "AMUSEMENT" is spelled "AMUSEMEMT".*
nn - Second printing hand colored 200.00 400.00 1000.00
nn - Second printing black & white 200.00 400.00 1000.00
NOTE: Second printing. The misspelling of "PURSUIT" has been corrected, but "AMUSEMEMT" error is still present.
nn - Third printing hand colored No misspellings 200.00 400.00 1000.00
nn - Third printing black & white 200.00 400.00 1000.00
NOTE: *By George Cruikshank. This is the British Edition. Issued both in black & white, and professionally hand-colored editions. Hand-colored editions have survived in higher quantities than uncolored. Originally made with thin paper sheets covering the plates.*

BACHELOR'S OWN BOOK; OR, THE PROGRESS OF MR. LAMBKIN, (GENT.), IN THE PURSUIT OF PLEASURE AND AMUSEMENT, AND ALSO IN SEARCH OF HEALTH AND HAPPINESS, THE (E,O,G)
David Bryce & Son: Glasgow: 1884 (one shilling; 7-5/8 x5-7/8", 62 pgs printed one side only, illustrated hardcover, page edges guilt
nn - Reprints the 1844 edition with altered title 25.00 50.00 125.00
nn - soft cover edition exists 20.00 35.00 70.00

BACHELOR'S OWN BOOK. BEIN-G TWENTY-FOUR PASSAGES IN THE LIFE OF MR. LAMBKIN, GENT. (E,G)
Burgess, Stringer & Co., New York on cover; Carey & Hart, Philadelphia on title page: 1845 (31-1/4 cents, 7-1/2x4-5/8", 52 pgs, B&W, paper cover)
nn - By George Cruikshank (Very Rare) (no known sales)
NOTE: *This is the second known sequential comic book story published in America. Reprints the earlier British edition. Pages printed on one side only. New cover art by an unknown artist.*

BAD BOY'S FIRST READER (O,S)
G.W. Carleton & Co.: 1881 (5-3/4 x 4-1/8", 44 pgs, B&W, paper cover)
nn - By Frank Bellew (Senior) 60.00 125.00 275.00
NOTE: *Parody of a children's ABC primer, one cartoon illustration plus text per page. Includes one panel of Boss Tweed. Frank Bellew is considered the "Father of the American Sequential Comics."*

BALL OF YARN OR, QUEER, QUAINT & QUIZZICAL STORIES, UNRAVELED WITH NEARLY 200 COMIC ENGRAVINGS OF FREAKS, FOLLIES & FOIBLES OF QUEER FOLKS BY THAT PRINCE OF COMICS, ELTON, THE (M)
Philip. J. Cozans, 116 Nassau St, NY: early 1850s (7-1/4x3-1/2", 76 pgs, yellow-wraps)
nn - sequential comic strips plus singles (no known sales)
NOTE: Mose Keyser-r, Jones, Smith & Robinson Goes To A Ball-r; The Adventures of Mr Goliah Starvemouse-r are all sequential comic strips printed in a number of sources

BARKER'S ILLUSTRATED ALMANAC (O,P,S)
Barker, Moore & Mein Medicine Co: 1878-1932+ (36 pgs, B&W, color paper-cr)
1878-1879 (Rare) 60.00 125.00 300.00
NOTE: *Not known yet what the cover art is.*
1880 Farmer Plowing Field-c 50.00 100.00 250.00
1881-1883 (Scarce,7-3/4x6-1/8") *4-mast ships & lighthouse-c* 50.00 100.00 250.00
1884-1889 (8x6-1/4") *Horse & Rider jumping picket fence-c* 50.00 100.00 250.00
1890-1897 (8-1/8x6-1/4") 50.00 100.00 250.00
1898-1899 (7-3/8x5-7/8") 50.00 100.00 250.00
1900+: see the Platinum Age Comics section (7x5-7/8")
NOTE: *Barker's Almanacs were actually issued in November of the year preceding the year which appears on the almanac. For example, the 1878 dated almanac was issued November 1877. They were given away to retailers of Barker's farm animal medicinal products, to in turn be given away to customers. Each Barker's Almanac contains 10 full page cartoons. These frequently included racist stereotypes of blacks. Each cartoon*

The Comical Adventures of Beau Ogleby
1843 © Tlit & Bogue, London

The Bottle by George Cruikshank
1871 © Geo. Gebbie

Buzz A Buzz Or The Bees By Wilhelm Busch
1873 © Henry Holt And Company, New York

contained advertisements for Barker's products. It is unknown whether the cartoons appeared only in the almanacs, or if they also ran as newspaper ads or flyers. Originally issued with a metal hook attached in the upper left hand corner, which could be used to hang the almanac.

BARKER'S "KOMIC" PICTURE SOUVENIR (P,S)
Barker, Moore & Mein Medicine Co: nd (1892-94) (color cardboard cover, B&W interior) (all unnumbered editions Very Rare)

nn - (1892) (1st edition, 6-7/8x10-1/2, 150 pgs) wraparound cover showing people headed towards Chicago for the 1893 World's Fair	250.00	600.00	1200.00
nn - (1893) (2nd edition, ??? pgs) same cover as 1st edition	250.00	600.00	1200.00
nn - (1894) (3rd edition, 180 pgs, 6-3/4x10-3/8")	250.00	600.00	1200.00

NOTE: *New cover art showing crowd of people laughing with a copy of Barker's Almanac.The crowd picture is flanked on both sides by picture of a tall thin person.*

nn - (1894) (4th edition, 124 pgs, 6-3/8x9-3/8") same-c as 3rd edition	250.00	400.00	1000.00

NOTE: *Essentially same-c as 3rd edition, except flanking picture on left edge is now gone. The 2nd through 4th editions state their printing on the first interior page, in the paragraph beneath the picture of the Barker's Building. These have been confirmed as premium comic books, predating the Buster Brown premiums. They reprint advertising cartoons from Barker's Illustrated Almanac. For the 50 page booklets by this same name, numbered as "Part"s, see the PLATINUM AGE SECTION. All "Editions in Parts", without exception, were published after 1900.*

BEAU OGLEBY, THE COMICAL ADVENTURES OF (E,G)
Tilt & Bogue: nd (c1843) (5-7/8x9-1/8", 72 pgs, printed one side only, green gilted hard-c, B&W)

nn - By Rodolphe Töpffer (Rare)	500.00	1000.00	2300.00
nn - Hand coloured edition (Very Rare)	(no known sales)		

NOTE: *British Edition; no known American Edition. 2nd Töpffer comic book published in English. Translated from Paris publisher Aubert's unauthorized redrawn 1839 bootleg edition of Töpffer's* ***Histoire de Mr. Jabot****. The back most interior page is an advertisement for* ***Obadiah Oldbuck****, showing its comic book cover*

BEE, THE
Bee Publishing Co: May 16 1898-Aug 2 1898 (Chromolithographic Weekly)

most issues	50.00	100.00	200.00
8 June Yellow Kid Hearst cover issue	175.00	350.00	750.00

BEFORE AND AFTER. A LOCOFOCO CHRISTMAS PRESENT. (O, C)
D.C. Johnston, Boston: 1837 (4-3/4x3", 1 page, hand colored cardboard)

nn - (Very Rare) by David Claypoole Johnston (sold at auction for $400 in GD)
NOTE: *Pull-tab cartoon envelope, parodying the 1836 New York City mayoral election, picturing the candidate of the Locofoco Party smiling "Before the N.York election", then, when the tab is pulled, picturing him with an angry sneer "After the N.York election".*

BILLY GOAT AND OTHER COMICALITIES, THE (M)
Charles Scribner's Sons: 1898 (6-3/4x8-1/2", 116 pgs., B&W, Hardcover)

nn - By E. W. Kemble	125.00	250.00	600.00

BLACKBERRIES, THE (N.S) (see Coontown's 400)
R. H. Russell: 1897 (9"x12", 76 pgs, hard-c, every other page in color, every other page in one color sepia tone)

nn - By E. W. Kemble	200.00	400.00	1900.00

NOTE: *Tastefully done comics about Black Americana during the USA's Jim Crow days.*

BOOK OF BUBBLES, YE (S)
Endicott & Co., New York: March 1864 (6-1/4 x 9-7/8",160 pgs, guilt-illus. hard-c, B&W

nn - By unknown	150.00	300.00	600.00

NOTE: *Subtitle: A contribution to the New York Fair in aid of the Sanitary Commission; 68 single-sided pages of B&W cartoons, each with an accompanying limerick. A few are sequential.*

BOOK OF DRAWINGS BY FRED RICHARDSON (N,S)
Lakeside Press, Chicago: 1899 (13-5/8x10-1/2", 116 pgs, B&W, hard-c)

nn -	80.00	160.00	350.00

NOTE: *Reprinted from the* ***Chicago Daily News****. Mostly single panel. Includes one* ***Yellow Kid*** *parody, some Spanish-American War cartoons.*

BOTTLE, THE (E,O) (see also THE DRUNKARD'S CHILDREN, and TEA GARDEN TO TEA POT, and TEMPERANCE TALES; OR, SIX NIGHTS WITH THE WASHINGTONIANS)
D. Bogue, London, with others in later editions: nd (1846) (16-1/2x11-1/2", 16 pgs, printed one side only, paper cover)

D. Bogue, London (nd; 1846): first edition:

nn - Black & white (Scarce)	250.00	450.00	1200.00
nn - Hand colored (Rare)	(no known sales)		

D. Bogue, London, and Wiley and Putnam, New York (nd; 1847) : second edition, misspells American publisher "Putnam" as "Putman":

nn - Black & white (Scarce)	150.00	300.00	725.00
nn - Hand colored (Rare)	(no known sales)		

D. Bogue, London, and Wiley and Putnam, New York (nd; 1847) : third edition has "Putnam" spelled correctly.

nn - Black & white (Scarce)	150.00	300.00	725.00
nn - Hand colored (Rare)	(no known sales)		

D. Bogue, London, Wiley and Putnam, New York, and J. Sands, Sydney, New South Wales: (nd; 1847) : fourth edition with no misspellings

nn - Black & white (Scarce)	150.00	300.00	725.00
nn - Hand colored (Rare)	(no known sales)		

NOTE: *By George Cruikshank. Temperance/anti-alcohol story. All editions are in precisely identical format. The only difference is to be found on the cover, where it lists who published it. Cover is text only - no cover art.*

BOTTLE, THE HISTORY OF THE
J.C. Becket, 22 Grea St James St, Montreal, Canada: 1851 (9-1/8x6", B&W)

nn - From Engravings by Cruikshank	175.00	325.00	725.00

NOTE: *As published in The Canada Temperance Advocate.*

BOTTLE, THE (E)
W. Tweedie, London: nd (1862) (11-1/2x17-1/3", 16 pgs, printed one side only, paper cover)

nn - Black & white; By George Cruikshank (Scarce)	100.00	200.00	420.00
nn - Hand colored (Scarce)	(no known sales)		

BOTTLE, THE (E)
Geo. Gebbie, Philadelphia: nd (c.1871) (11-3/8x17-1/8", 42 pgs, tinted interior, hard-c)

nn - By George Cruikshank	100.00	200.00	420.00

NOTE: *New cover art (cover not by Cruikshank).*

BOTTLE, THE (E)
National Temperance, London: nd (1881) (11-1/2x16-1/2", 16 pgs, printed one side only, paper-c, color)

nn - By George Cruikshank	100.00	200.00	420.00

NOTE: *See Platinum Age section for 1900s printings.*

BOTTLE, THE (E)
Marques, Pittsburgh, PA: 1884/85 (6x8", 8 plates, full color, illustrated envelope)

nn - art not by Cruickshank; New Art	75.00	125.00	250.00

NOTE: Says Presented by J.M. Gusky, Dealer in Boots and Shoes

BROAD GRINS OF THE LAUGHING PHILOSOPHER
Dick & Fitzgerald,NY: 1870s

nn - (4) panel sequential strip	25.00	50.00	150.00

BROTHER JONATHAN
Wilson & Co/Benj H Day, 48 Beekman, NYC: 1839-???

July 4 1846 - ads for Obadiah & Butterfly	50.00	100.00	225.00
July 4 1856 catalog list - front cover comic strip	100.00	200.00	400.00
Xmas/New Years 1856	75.00	150.00	300.00
average large size issues	25.00	50.00	100.00

NOTE: has full page advert for Fredinand Flipper comic book116

BULL CALF, THE (P,M)
Various: nd (c1890's) (3-7/8x4-1/8", 16 pgs, B&W, paper-c)

nn - By A.B. Frost Creme Oatmeal Toilet Soap	50.00	75.00	200.00
nn - By A.B. Frost Thompson & Taylor Spice Co, Chicago	50.00	75.00	200.00

NOTE: *Reprints the popular strip story by Frost, with the art modified to place a sign for Creme Oatmeal Soap within each panel. The back cover advertises the specific merchant who gave this booklet away - multiple variations exist.*

BULL CALF AND OTHER TALES, THE (M)
Charles Scribner's Sons: 1892 (120 pgs., 6-3/4x8-7/8", B&W, illus. hard cover)

nn - By Arthur Burdett Frost	50.00	150.00	500.00

NOTE: *Blue, grey, tan hard covers known to exist.*

BULL CALF, THE STORY OF THE MAN OF HUMANITY AND THE (P,M)
C.H. Fargo & Co.: 1890 (5-1/4x6-1/4", 24 pgs, B&W, color paper-c)

nn - By A.B. Frost	50.00	100.00	200.00

NOTE: *Fargo shoe company giveaway; pages alternate between shoe advertisements and the strip story.*

BUSHEL OF MERRY THOUGHTS, A (see Mischief Book, The) (E)
Sampson Low Son & Marsten: 1868 (68 pgs, handcolored hardcover, B&W)

nn - (6-1/4 x 9-7/8", 138 pgs) red binding, publisher's name on title page only	250.00	500.00	1000.00
nn - (6-1/2 x 10", 134 pgs) green binding, publisher's name on cover & title page	250.00	500.00	1000.00

NOTE: *Cover plus story title pages designed by Leighton Brothers, based on Busch art. Translated by Harry Rogers (who is credited instead of Busch). This is a British publication, notable as the earliest known English language anthology collection of Wilhelm Busch comic strips. Page 13 of second story missing from all editions (panel dropped). Unknown which of the two editions was published first. A modern reprint, by Dover in 1971.*

BUTTON BURSTER, THE (M) (says on cover "ten cents hard cash")
M.J. Ivers & Co., 86 Nassau St., New York: 1873 (11x8-1/8", soft paper, B&W)

By various cartoonists (Very Rare)	150.00	300.00	600.00

NOTE: *Reprints from various 1873 issues of Wild Oats; has (5) different sequential comic strips: (3) by Livingston Hopkins, (1) by Thomas Worth, other one creator presently unknown; Bellew, Sr. single panel cartoons.*

BUZZ A BUZZ OR THE BEES (E)
Griffith & Farran, London: September 1872 (8-1/2x5-1/2", 168 pgs, printed one side only, orange, black & white hardcover, B&W interior)

nn - By Wilhelm Busch (Scarce)	112.00	225.00	500.00

NOTE: *Reprint published by Phillipson & Golder, Chester; text written by English to accompany Busch art.*

BUZZ A BUZZ OR THE BEES (E)
Henry Holt & Company, New York: 1873 (9x6", 96 pgs, gilted hardcover, hand colored)

nn - By Wilhelm Busch (Scarce)	125.00	250.00	500.00

NOTE: *Completely different translation than the Griffith & Farran version. Also, contains 28 additional illustrations by Park Benjamin. The lower page count is because the Henry Holt edition prints on both sides of each page, and the Griffith & Farran edition is printed one side only.*

CALENDAR FOR THE MONTH; YE PICTORIAL LYSTE OF YE MATTERS OF

The Carpet Bag #14
1851 © Snow & Wilder

Centennial Fun (Keppler cover)
July 1876 © Frank Leslie

Comic Monthly v6 #8
March 1865 © J.C.Haney, NY

FR1.0 GD2.0 FN6.0

INTEREST FOR SUMMER READING (P,M)
S.E. Bridgman & Company, Northampton, Mass: nd (c. late 1880's-1890's) (5-5/8x7-1/4", 64 pgs, paper-c, B&W)

nn - (Very Rare) T.S. Sullivant-c/a 125.00 250.00 500.00
NOTE: *Book seller's catalog, with every other page reprinting cartoons and strips (from Life??). Art by: Chips Bellew, Gibson, Howarth, Kemble, Sullivant, Townsend, Woolf.*

CARICATURE AND OTHER COMIC ART
Harper & Brothers, NY: 1877 (9-5/16x7-1/8", 360 pgs, B&W, green hard-c)

nn - By James Parton (over 200 illustrations) 30.00 60.00 250.00
NOTE: *This is the earliest known serious history of comics & related genre from around the world produced by an American. Parton was a cousin of Thomas Nast's wife Sarah. A large portion of this book was first serialized in **Harper's Monthly** in 1875.*

CARPET BAG, THE
Snow & Wilder, later Wilder & Pickard, Boston: March 21 1851-March 26 1853

Each average issue 25.00 50.00 100.00
Samuel "Mark Twain" Clemmons issues (first app in print) 800.00 1500.00 3200.00
NOTE: *Many issues contain cartoons by DC Johnston, Frank Bellew, others; literature includes Artemus Ward's Miss Partington who had a mischevious little Katzenjammer Kids-like brat. Carpet Bag was not considered derogatory pre-Civil War.*

CARROT-POMADE (O,G)
James G. Gregory, Publisher, New York: 1864 (9x6-7/8", 36 pgs, B&W)

nn - By Augustus Hoppin 75.00 150.00 300.00
NOTE: *The story of a quack remedy for baldness, sequentially told in the format parodying ABC primers. Has protective tissue pages (not part of page count).*

CARTOONS BY HOMER C. DAVENPORT (M,N,S)
De Witt Publishing House: 1898 (16-1/8x12", 102 pgs, hard-c, B&W)

nn 100.00 200.00 400.00
NOTE: *Reprinted from Harper's Weekly and the New York Journal. Includes cartoons about the Spanish-American War. Title page reads "Davenport's Cartoons".*

CARTOONS BY WILL E. CHAPIN (P,N,S)
The Times-Mirror Printing and Binding House, Los Angeles: 1899 (15-1/4x12", 98 pgs, hard-c, B&W)

nn - scarce 100.00 200.00 400.00
NOTE: *Premium item for subscribing to the Los-Angeles Times-Mirror newspaper, from which these cartoons were reprinted. Includes cartoons about the Spanish-American War.*

CARTOONS OF OUR WAR WITH SPAIN (N,S)
Frederick A. Stokes Company: 1898 (11-1/2x10", 72 pgs, hardcover, B&W)

nn - By Charles Nelan (r-New York Herald) 40.00 100.00 200.00
nn - 2nd printing noted on copy right page 30.00 60.00 120.00

CARTOONS OF THE WAR OF 1898 (E,M,N,S)
Belford, Middlebrook & Co., Chicago: 1898 (7x10-3/8",190 pgs, B&W, hard-c)

nn 50.00 100.00 200.00
NOTE: *Reprints single panel editorial cartoons on the Spanish-American War, from American, Spanish, Latino, and European newspapers and magazines, at rate of 2 to 6 cartoons per page. Art by Bart, Berryman, Bowman, Bradley, Chapin, Gillam, Nelan, Tenniel, others.*

CENTENNIAL FUN (O,S) (Rare)
Frank Leslie, Philadelphia: (July) 1876 (25¢, 11x8", 32 pgs, paper cover, B&W)

nn - By Joseph Keppler-c/a;Thomas Worth-a 175.00 350.00 700.00
NOTE: *Issued for the 1876 Centennial Exposition in Philadelphia. Exists with both black & white, and orange, black & white covers. One copy of the latter had an embossed newstand label from Partland, Maine, implying that the orange cover version, at least, was distributed and sold outside of Philadelphia.*

CHAMPAIGNE
Frank Leslie: June-Dec 1871

1-7 scarce 150.00 225.00 400.00

CHIC
Chic Publishing Co: 1880-81 (Chromolithographic Weekly)

1-38 Livingston Hopkins, Charles Kendrick, CW Weldon 75.00 150.00 325.00

CHILDREN'S CHRISTMAS BOOK, THE
The New York Sunday World: 1897 (10-1/4x8-3/4", 16 pgs, full color)

Dec 12, 1897 - By George Luks, G.H. Grant, Will Crawford, others) (Rare)
75.00 125.00 300.00

CHIP'S DOGS (M)
R.H. Russell and Son Publishers: 1895 hardcover, B&W)

nn - By Frank P. W. "Chip" Bellew 25.00 50.00 100.00
Early printing 80 pgs, 8-7/8x11-7/8"; dark green border of hardcover surrounds all four sides of pasted on cover image; pages arranged in error -- see NOTE below. (more scarce)
nn - By Frank P. W. "Chip" Bellew 12.50 25.00 50.00
Later printing 72 pgs, 8-7/8x11-3/4";green border only on the binding side (one side) of the cover image.
NOTE: *Both are strip reprints from **LIFE** . The difference in page count is due to more blank pages in the first printing -- all printings have the same comics contents, but with the pages in the first printing arranged differently. This is noticeable particularly in the 2-page strip "Getting a Pointer", which appears on the 2nd & 3rd to last pages of the later printings, but in the early printing the first half of this strip is near the middle of the book, while the last half appears on the 2nd to last story page.*

CHIP'S OLD WOOD CUTS (M,S)
R.H. Russell & Son: 1895 (8-7/8x11-3/4", 72 pgs, hardcover, B&W)

nn - By Frank P. W. ("Chip") Bellew 25.00 50.00 100.00
nn - 1897 reprint 15.00 30.00 60.00

CHIP'S UN-NATURAL HISTORY (O,S)
Frederick A. Stokes & Brother: 1888 (7x5-1/4", 64 pgs, hardcover, B&W)

nn - By Frank P. W. ("Chip") Bellew 12.50 25.00 50.00
NOTE: *Title page lists publisher as "Successors to White, Stokes & Allen."*

CLOWN, OR THE BANQUET OF WIT, THE (E,M,O)
Fisher & Brother, Philadelphia, Baltimore, New York, Boston: nd (c.1851) (7-3/8x4-1/2", 88 pgs, paper cover, B&W)

nn - (Very Rare; 3 known copies) 600.00 1200.00 2500.00
NOTE: *Earliest known multi-artist anthology of sequential comics; contains multiple sequential comics, plus numerous single panel cartoons. A mixture of reprinted and original material, involving both European and American artists. "Jones, Smith, and Robinson Goes to a Ball" by Richard Doyle (1st app. of Doyle's "Foreign Tour" in America, reprinted from PUNCH, August 24, 1850); "Moses Keyser The Bowery Bully's Trip to the Californian Gold Mines", by John H. Manning; "The Adventures of Mr. Gulp" (by the Read brothers?); more comics by artists unknown; cartoons by George Cruikshank, Grandville, Elton.*

COLD CUTS AND PICKLED EELS' FEET; DONE BROWN BY JOHN BROWN
P.J. Cozans, New York: nd (c1855-60) (B&W)

nn - (Very Rare) 100.00 200.00 300.00
NOTE: *Mostly a children's book. But, pages 87 to 110, and 111 to 122, contain narrative sequential stories.*

COLLEGE SCENES (O,G)
N. Hayward, Boston: 1850 (5x6-3/4", 72 pgs, printed one side only, B&W lithography)

nn - (Rare) by Nathan Hayward 200.00 400.00 700.00
NOTE: *This is the 2nd such production for an American University; the first issued at Yale circa 1845, decent funny art of story about life of a Harvard student from his entrance thru graduation entirely in caricature. Has art on back cover as well.*

COLLEGE CUTS Chosen From The Columbia Spectator 1880-81-82 (S)
White & Stokes, NY: 1882 (8x9-5/8", 92 pgs, B&W)

By F. Benedict Herzog, H. McVickar, W. Bard McVickar, others 20.00 40.00 100.00
nn - 2nd edition reprint (1888) (8-1/4x10-3/8) 10.00 20.00 50.00

COMICAL COONS (M)
R.H. Russell: 1898 (8-7/8 x 11-7/8", 68 pgs, hardcover, B&W)

nn - By E. W. Kemble 350.00 700.00 1500.00
NOTE: *Black Americana collection of 2-panel stories.*

COMICAL ALMANAC
Anton Bicker, Cinncinati, OH: 1885 (9x6, 260 pgs, B&W, illustrated-c)

nn - two (12) page sequential Busch comic strips 50.00 100.00 250.00

COMIC ALMANAC, THE
John Berger. Baltimore: 1854-? (7-1/2x6-1/4, 36 pgs, B&W)

nn - 65.00 125.00 275.00

COMIC ANNUAL, AMERICAN (O,I)
Richardson, Lord, & Holbrook, Boston: 1831 (6-7/8x4-3/8", 268 pgs, B&W, hard-c)

nn - (Scarce) 150.00 300.00 620.00
NOTE: *Mostly text; front & back cover illustrations, 13 full page, and scattered smaller illustrations by David Claypoole Johnston; edited by Henry J. Finn.*

COMIC HISTORY OF THE UNITED STATES, (I)
Carleton & Co., NY: 1876 (6-7/8x5-1/8", 336 pgs, hardcover, B&W)

nn - By Livingston Hopkins. 20.00 40.00 80.00
2nd printing: Cassell, Petter, Galpin & Co.: 1880 (6-7/8x5-1/8", 336 pgs, hardcover, B&W)
nn - By Livingston Hopkins. 20.00 40.00 80.00
NOTE: *Text with many B&W illustrations; some are multi-panel comics. Not to beconfused with **Bill Nye's Comic History Of The U.S.** which contains Frederick Opper illustrations.*

COMIC MONTHLY, THE
J.C. Haney, N.Y.: March 1859-1880 (16 x 11-1/2", 30 pgs average, B&W)

Certain average issues with sequential comics 50.00 100.00 200.00
11 (Jan 1860) Bellew-c 25.00 50.00 100.00
v2#2 (Apr 1860) Bellew-c 25.00 50.00 100.00
v2#3 (May 1860) Bellew-c 25.00 50.00 100.00
v2#4 (June 1860) Comic Strip Cover 50.00 100.00 200.00
v2#5 (July 1860) Bellew-c; (12) panel Explaining American Politics To An Intelligent Foreigner; (10) panel The Art of Stump Speaking; (15) panel Mr. Dibbs Goes to Pike's Peak and Comes Back Again 125.00 250.00 525.00
v2#7 (Sept 1860) Comic Strip Cover; (24) panel double page spread The Prince of Wales In America 50.00 100.00 200.00
v2#8 (18) panel The Three Young Friends Sillouette Strip 25.00 50.00 100.00
v2#9 (Nov 1860) (9) panel sequential 25.00 50.00 100.00
v2#10 11 not indexed 25.00 50.00 100.00
v2#12 (Jan 1861) (12) panel double page spread 25.00 50.00 100.00

COMIC TOKEN FOR 1836, A COMPANION TO THE COMIC ALMANAC, THE
Charles Ellms, Boston: 1836 (8x5', 48 pgs, B&W)

nn - 50.00 100.00 200.00

COMIC WEEKLY, THE
???, NYC: 1881-???

issues with comic strips (Chips, etc) 60.00 125.00 250.00

Comics From Scribner's Magazine
1891 © Scribner's

The Daily Graphic #158
Sept. 4, 1873 © The Graphic Company, NY

Elton's Californian Comic All-My-Nack #17
1850 © Elton's, NY

COMIC WORLD
???: 1876-1879 (Quarto Monthly)

	FR1.0	GD2.0	FN6.0
issues with comic strips	37.50	75.00	150.00

COMICS FROM SCRIBNER'S MAGAZINE (M)
Scribner's: nd (1891) (10 cents, 9-1/2x6-5/8", 24 pgs, paper cover, side stapled, B&W)

nn - (Rare) F.M.Howarth C&A	175.00	350.00	700.00

NOTE: *Advertised in SCRIBNER'S MAGAZINE in the June 1891 issue, page 793, as available by mail order for 10 cents. Collects together comics material which ran in the back pages of Scribner's Magazine. Art by Attwood, "Chip" Bellew, Dõe̅s, Frost, Gibson, Zim.*

COMUS OFFERING CONTAINING HUMOROUS SCRAPS OF DIVERTING COMICALITIES, THE (O, S)
B. Franklin Edmands, 25 Court St, Boston: c1830-31 (8-7/8x10-3/4", 16 pgs, thin brown paper-c, blank on backs,

nn - (William F Straton, Engraver, 15 Water St, Boston) (no known sales)
NOTE: All hand-colored single panel cartoons format definitely inspired by D.C. Johnston's Scraps with every panel character using well-defined word balloons. Might become a seminal step in the evolution of the American comic book. More research is needed.

CONTRASTS AND CONCEITS FOR CONTEMPLATION BY LUKE LIMNER (O)
Ackerman & Co, 96 Strand, London: c1848 (9-3/4x6-1/4, 48 pgs, B&W)

nn - By John Leighton	50.00	100.00	200.00

COONTOWN'S 400 (M) (see **Blackberries**) (M)
The Life (Magazine) Co.: 1899 (10-15/16x8-7/8, 68 pgs, cloth light-brown hard-c, B&W

nn - By E.W. Kemble (scarce)	325.00	600.00	1900.00

NOTE: *Tastefully drawn depictions of Black Americana over one hundred years ago during Jim Crow days.*

CROSSING THE ATLANTIC (O,G)
James R. Osgood & Co., Boston: 1872 (10-7/8x16", 68 pgs, hardcover, B&W);
Houghton, Osgood & Co., Boston: 1880

1st printing - by Augustus Hoppin	50.00	100.00	200.00
2nd printing (1880; 66 pgs; 8-1/8x11-1/8")	32.50	65.00	150.00

C.R. PITT'S COMIC ALMANAC
C.R. Pitt: 1880 (7-1/2x4-5/8", 28 pgs)

nn - contains (8) panel sequential	50.00	100.00	200.00

CRUIKSHANK'S OMNIBUS: A VEHICLE FOR FUN AND FROLIC (E,S)
E. Ferrett & Co., Philadelphia: 1845 (25 cents, 7-1/2" x 4-5/8", 96 pgs, B&W, paper-c)

nn - By George Cruikshank c/a (Very Rare)	150.00	300.00	750.00

NOTE: *Mostly prose, with 10 plates of cartoons printed on one-side (about half the plates with multiple cartoons), plus illustrated cover, all by George Cruikshank. First (perhaps only) American printing of Cruikshank's Omnibus, which was published first in Britain. It is only a partial reprinting.*

CYCLISTS' DICTIONARY (S)
Morgan & Wright, Chicago: 1894 (5 x3-3/4, 80 pgs, soft-c, B&W

nn - By Unknown	37.50	75.00	150.00

THE DAILY GRAPHIC
The Graphic Company, 39 Park Place, NY: 1873-Sept 23, 1889 (14x20-1/2, 8 pgs, B&W)

Average issues with comic strips	15.00	20.00	40.00
Average issues without comic strips	10.00	15.00	30.00

NOTE:

DAVY CROCKETT'S COMIC ALMANACK
???, Nashville, TN, then elsewhere: 1835-end (32 pages plus wraps)

1	550.00	1100.00	2200.00
2-13 15 end	275.00	550.00	1100.00
14 contains (17) panel Crocket comic strip bio 1848	1050.00	1600.00	3200.00

DAY'S DOINGS (was The Last Sensation) (Becomes New York Illustrated Times)
James Watts, NYC: #1 June 6 1868-early 1876 (11x16, 16 pgs, B&W)

average issue with comic strips	10.00	15.00	25.00
Paul Pry & Alley Sloper character issues	25.00	50.00	100.00
Aug 19 1871 - First Alley Sloper in America??	50.00	100.00	200.00

NOTE: *James Watts was a shadow company for Frank Leslie; outright sold to Frank Leslie in 1873. There are a lot of issues with comic strips from 1868 up.*

DAY'S SPORT - OR, HUNTING ADVENTURES OF S. WINKS WATTLES, A SHOPKEEPER, THOMAS TITT, A "LEGAL GENT," AND MAJOR NICHOLAS NOGGIN, A JOLLY GOOD FELLOW GENERALLY, A (O)
Brother Jonathan, NY: c1850s (5-7/8x8-1/4, 44 pgs)

nn - By Henry L. Stephens, Philadelphia (Very Rare) (no known sales)

DEVIL'S COMICAL OLDMANICK WITH COMIC ENGRAVINGS OF THE PRINCIPAL EVENTS OF TEXAS, THE
Turner & Fisher, NY & Philadelphia: 1837 (7-7/8x5", 24 pgs)

nn - many single panel cartoons	125.00	250.00	550.00

DIE VEHME, ILLUSTRIRTES WOCHENBLATT FUR SCHERZ UND ERNEST (M,O)
Heinrich Binder, St. Louis: No.1 Aug 28, 1869 - No.?? Aug 20, 1870 (10 cents, 8 pgs, B&W, paper-c) (see also PUCK)

1-?? (Very Rare) by Joseph Keppler	100.00	200.00	400.00

NOTE: *Joseph Keppler's first attempt at a weekly American humor periodical. Entirely in German. The title translates into: **"The Star Chamber: An Illustrated Weekly Paper in Fun and Ernest"**.*

DOMESTIC MANNERS OF THE AMERICANS
The Imprint Society, Barre, Mass: 1969 (9-3/4 x 7-1/4", 390 pgs, hard-c in slipcase, B&W)

nn -	15.00	25.00	60.00

NOTE: *Reprints the 1832 edition of this book by Mrs. Trollope with an added insert. The 28-page insert is what is of primary interest to us -- it reproduces SCRAPS No. 4 (1833) by D.C. Johnston.*

DRUNKARD'S CHILDREN, THE (see also THE BOTTLE) (E,O)
David Bogue, London; John Wiley and G.P. Putnam, New York; J. Sands, Sydney, New South Wales: July 1, 1848 (16x11", 16 pgs, printed on one side only, paper-c)

nn - Black & white edition (Scarce)	400.00	800.00	1200.00
nn - Hand colored edition (Rare)		(no known sales)	

NOTE: *Sequel story to THE BOTTLE, by George Cruikshank. Temperance/anti-alcohol story. British-American-Australian co-publication. Cover is text only - no cover art.*

DRUNKARD'S PROGRESS, OR THE DIRECT ROAD TO POVERTY, WRETCHEDNESS & RUIN, THE
J. W. Barber, New Haven, Conn.: Sept 1826 (single sheet)

nn - By John Warner Barber (Very Rare) (no known sales)
NOTE: *Broadside designed and printed by barber contains four large wood engravings showing "The Morning Dram" which is "The Beginning of Sorrow"; "The Grog Shop" with its "Bad Company"; "The Confirmed Drunkard" in a state of "Beastly Intoxication"; and the "Concluding Scene" with the family being drive off to the alms house. It is an interesting set of cuts, faintly reminiscent of Hogarth. Many modern reprints exist.*

DUEL FOR LOVE, A (O,P)
E.C. DeWitt & Co., Chicago: nd (c1880's) (3-3/8" x 2-5/8", 12 pgs, B&W, paper-c)

nn - Art by F.M. Howarth (Rare)	25.00	50.00	125.00

NOTE: *Advertising giveaway for DeWitt's Little Early Risers, featuring an 8-panel strip story, spread out 1 panel per page.*

DURHAM WHIFFS (O, P)
Blackwells Durham Tobacco Co: Jan 8 1878 (9x6.5", 8 pgs, color-c, B&W)

v1 #1 w/Trade Card Insert	37.50	75.00	200.00

NOTE: Sold in 2008 CGC 9.4 $1250

DYNALENE LAFLETS (P)
The Dynalene Company: nd (3 x 3-1/2", 16 pgs, B&W, paper cover)

nn - Dynalene Dyes promo (9) panel comic strip	25.00	50.00	75.00

ELEPHANT, THE
William H Graham, Tribune Building, NYC: Jan 22 1848-Feb 19 1848 (11x8.5", B&W)

1-5 Rare - single panel cartoons	175.00	325.00	650.00

ELTON'S COMIC ALL-MY-NACK (E,O.S)
Elton, Publisher, 18 Division & 98 Nassau St, NY: 1833-1852 (7-1/2x4-1/2", 36pgs, B&W

1-5 99% single panel cartoons	100.00	200.00	400.00
6 (1839)	100.00	200.00	400.00

NOTE: Two different covers & different interiors exist for this title and number

7-15 - 99% single panel cartoons	100.00	200.00	400.00
16 - contains 6 panel "A Tales of A Tayl-or" 1848-49	200.00	400.00	650.00
17 - contains "Moses Keyser, The Bowery Bully's Trip To the California Gold Mines" 1850 By John H. Manning, early comics creator, told in 15 panels	200.00	400.00	650.00
18-19 presently unknown contents	100.00	200.00	400.00

NOTE: *Contains both original American, and pirated European, cartoons. All single panel material, except where noted. Almanacs are published near the end of the year prior to that for which they are printed -- like calendars today. Thus, the 1833 No. 1 issue was really published in the last months of 1832. #17 has Elton's Californian Comic-All-My-Nack on the cover.*

ELTON'S COMIC ALMANAC (Publsiher change)
GW Cottrell & Co, Publishers & C Cornhill, Boston, Mass: 1853 (7-7/8x4-5/8,36pgs,B&W

20 - (2) sequential comic strips (9) panel "Jones, Smith and Robinson Goes To A Ball; (21) panel "The Adventures of Mr. Gulp" Rare	350.00	750.00	1500.00

NOTE: *Both strips appear in* The Clown, Or The Banquet of Wit

ELTON'S FUNNY ALMANACK (title change to Almanac)
Elton Publisher and Engraver, New York: 1846 (8x6-1/2", 36 pgs)

1 1846	50.00	100.00	225.00

ELTON'S FUNNY ALMANAC (#1 titled Almanack)
Elton & Co, New York: 1847-1853 (8x6-1/4, 36 pgs, B&W)

2 (1847) #3 (1848)	50.00	100.00	225.00

nn 1853 (8-1/8x4-7/8"; (5) panel comic strip "The Adventures of Mr. Goliah Starvemouse"

ELTON'S RIPSNORTER COMIC ALMANAC
Elton, 90 Nassau St, NY: 1850 (8x5, 24 pgs, B&W, paper-c)

nn - scarce	50.00	100.00	225.00

ENGLISH SOCIETY (S)
Harper & Brothers, Publishers, New York: 1897 (9-5/8x12-1/4", 206 pgs, B&W)

nn - by George Du Maurier	50.00	75.00	110.00

ENGLISH SOCIETY AT HOME (S)
James R. Osgood and Company: 1881 (10-7/8x8-5/8, 182 pgss, protective sheets on some pages - not included in pages count, hard-c, B&W 50.00 75.00 110.00

nn - by George Du Maurier

ENTER: THE COMICS (E,G)
University of Nebraska Press: 1965 (6-7/8x9-1/4", 120 pgs, hard-c)

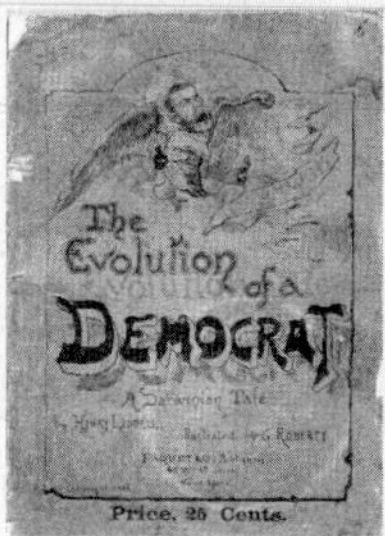

The Evolution Of A Democrat
1888 © Paquet & Co, NY

Flying Leaves
1880s © E.R. Herrick & Company, New York

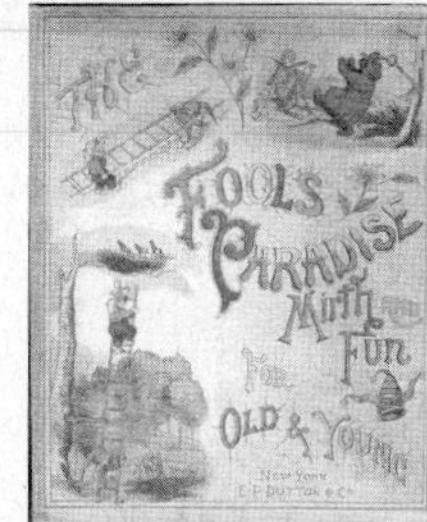

The Fools Paradise Mirth and Fun
For Old and Young
1883 © E.P. Dutton & Co, NYC

FR1.0 GD2.0 FN6.0

nn - By Ellen Weisse 25.00 50.00 100.00
NOTE: *Contains overview of Töpffer's life and career plus only published English translation of Töpffer's Monsieur Crepin (1837); appears to have been re-drawn by Weisse in the days before xerox machines.*

ESQUIRE BROWN AND HIS MULE, STORY OF
A.C. Meyer, Baltimore, Maryland: 1880s (5x3/7/8", 28 pgs, B&W)
Booklet (9 panel story plus cough remedies catalog) 35.00 70.00 150.00
Fold-Out of Booklet (9 panel version) 35.00 70.00 150.00

"EVENTS OF THE WEEK" REPRINTED FROM THE CHICAGO TRIBUNE
Henry O. Shepard Co, Chicago: 1894 (5-3/8x15-7/8", 110 pg, B&W, hard-c)
First Series, Second Series - By HR Heaton 37.50 75.00 150.00

EVERYBODY'S COMICK ALMANACK
Turner & Fisher, NY & Philadelphia: 1837 (7-7/8x5", 36 pgs, B&W)
nn 50.00 100.00 200.00

EVOLUTION OF A DEMOCRAT - A DARWINIAN TALE, THE (O,G)
Paquet & Co., New York: 1888 (25 cents, 7-7/8x5-1/2", 100 pgs, printed one side only, orange paper cover, B&W) (Very Rare)
nn - Written by Henry Liddell, art by G. Roberty 375.00 700.00 1500.00
NOTE: *Political parody about the rise of an Irishman through Tammany Hall. Grover Cleveland appears as linked with Tammany. Ireland becomes the next state in the USA.*

FABLES FOR THE TIMES (S, I)
R.H. Russell & Son, New York: 1896 (9-1/8x12-1/8", 52 pgs, yellow hard-c)
nn - By H.W. Phillips and T.S. Sullivant Scarce 75.00 150.00 300.00

FERDINAND FLIPPER, ESQ., THE FORTUNES OF (O,G)
Brother Jonathan, Publisher, NY: nd (1851) (5-3/4 x 9-3/8", 84 pgs, B&W, printed both sides)
nn - By Various (Very Rare) 700.00 1200.00 3300.00
NOTE: *Extended title: "...Commencing With A Period of Four Months And Anterior To His Birth Going Thru The Various Stages of His Infancy, Childhood, Verdant Years, Manhood, Middle Life, and Green and Ripe Old Age, And Ending A Short Time Subsequent to His Sudden Decease With His Final Exit, Funeral And Burial." Extremely unique comic book, put together by gathering 145 independent single illustrations and cartoons, by various artists, and stringing them together into a sequential story. The majority of panels are by Grandville. Also included are at least 19 signed Charles Martin, reprinted from 1847 issues of Yankee Doodle, 5 panels from D.C. Johnston, plus other panels by F.O.C. Darley, T.H. Matheson, and others. The story also contains several panels of Gold Rush content. Printed by E.A. Alverds. The 1851 date is derived from an advertisement found in the Oct-Dec 1851 issue of the Brother Jonathan newspaper. It ispossible, however, that it actually came out even earlier.*

FERDINAND FLIPPER, ESQ., THE FORTUNES OF (G)
Dick & Fitzgerald, New York: nd (1870's to 1888) (30 Cents, 84 pgs, B&W, paper cover)
nn - (Very Rare reprint - several editions possible) 375.00 750.00 1700.00

FINN'S COMIC ALMANAC
Marsh, Capen, & Lyon; Boston: 1835-??? (4.5x7.5, 36 pgs, B&W)
nn 100.00 200.00 400.00

FINN'S COMIC SKETCHBOOK (S)
Peabody & Co., 223 Broadway, NY: 1831 (10-1/2x16", 12 pgs, B&W)
nn - By Henry J. Finn (Very Rare) (no known sales)
NOTE: *Designs on copper plates; etched by J. Harris, NY; should have tissue paper in front of each plate.*

50 GREAT CARTOONS (M,P,S)
Ram's Horn Press: 1899 (14x10-3/4, 112 pgs, hard-c)
nn - By Frank Beard 30.00 60.00 125.00
NOTE: *Premium in return for a subscription to* ***The Ram's Horn*** *magazine.*

FISHER'S COMIC ALMANAC
Ames Fisher and Brother, No 12 North Sixth St, Philadelphia , Charles Small in NYC, Also in Boston: 1841-1868 (4-1/2 x 7-1/4, 36 pgs, B&W)
1-7 (1841-1847) 100.00 200.00 440.00
12 reprints mermaid-c with word balloon (1868) 100.00 200.00 440.00

F**** A*** K*****, OUTLINES ILLUSTRATIVE OF THE JOURNAL OF** (O,S)
D.C. Johnston, Boston: 1835 (9-5/16 x 6", 12 pgs, printed one side only, blue paper cover, B&W interior) (see also **SCRAPS**)
nn - by David Claypoole Johnston (Scarce) 650.00 1100.00 1750.00
NOTE: *This is a series of 8 plates parodying passages from the Journal of Fanny (Frances) A. Kemble, a British woman who wrote a highly negative book about American Culture after returning from the U.S. Though remembered now for her campaign against slavery, she was prejudiced against most everything American culture, thus inspiring Johnston's satire. Contains 4 protective sheets (not part of page count.)*

FLYING DUTCHMAN; OR, THE WRATH OF HERR VONSTOPPELNOZE, THE (E)
Carleton Publishing, New York: 1862 (7-5/8x5-1/4", 84 pgs, printed on one side only, gilted hardcover, B&W)
nn - By Wilhelm Busch (Scarce) 35.00 70.00 160.00
nn - 1975 Scarce 100 copy-r 74 pgs Visual Studies Workshop 5.00 10.00 20.00
NOTE: *This is the earliest known English language book publication of a Wilhelm Busch work. The story is plagiarized by American poet John G. Saxe, who is credited with the text, while the uncredited Busch cartoons are described merely as accompanying illustrations.*

FLYING LEAVES (E)
E.R. Herrick & Company, New York: nd (c1889/1890's) (8-1/4" x 11-1/2", 76 pgs, B&W interior, orange, b&w hard-c)
nn- (Scarce) 85.00 175.00 260.00

FR1.0 GD2.0 FN6.0

NOTE: *Reprints strips and single panel cartoons from 1888 Fliegende Blatter issues, translated into English. Various artists, including Bechstein, Adolf Hengeler, Lothar Meggendorfer, Emil Reinicke.*

FOOLS PARADISE WITH THE MANY ADVENTURES THERE AS SEEN IN THE STRANGE SURPRISING PEEP SHOW OF PROFESSOR WOLLEY COBBLE, THE (E)
(see also THE COMICAL PEEP SHOW)
John Camden Hotten, London: Nov 1871 (1 crown, 9-7/8x7-3/8", 172 pgs, printed one side only, gilted green hardcover, hand colored interior)
nn - By Wilhelm Busch (Rare) 500.00 1000.00 2000.00
NOTE: *Title on cover is:* ***WALK IN! WALK IN!! JUST ABOUT TO BEGIN!!! the FOOLS PARADISE****; below the above title page. Anthology of Wilhelm Busch comics, translated into English.*

FOOLS PARADISE WITH THE MANY WONDERFUL SIGHTS AS SEEN IN THE STRANGE SURPRISING PEEP SHOW OF PROFESSOR WOLLEY COBBLE, FURTHER ADVENTURES IN (E)
Chatto & Windus, London: 1873 (10x7-3/8", 128 pgs, printed one side only, brown hardcover, hand colored interior)
nn - By Wilhelm Busch (Rare) 400.00 800.00 1600.00
NOTE: *Sequel to the 1871* ***FOOLS PARADISE****, containing a completely different set of Busch stories, translated into English.*

FOOLS PARADISE MIRTH AND FUN FOR THE OLD & YOUNG (E)
Griffith & Farran, London: May 1883 (9-3/4x7-5/8", 78 pgs, color cover, color interior)
nn - By Wilhelm Busch (Rare) 100.00 200.00 425.00
NOTE: *Collection of selected stories reprinted from both the 1871 & 1873* ***FOOLS PARADISE****.*

FOOLS PARADISE - MIRTH AND FUN FOR THE OLD & YOUNG (E)
E.P. Dutton and Co., NY: May 1883 (9-3/4x7-5/8", 78 pgs, color cover, color interior)
nn - By Wilhelm Busch (Rare) 100.00 200.00 425.00
NOTE: *Collection of selected stories reprinted from both the 1871 & 1873* ***FOOLS PARADISE.***

FOREIGN TOUR OF MESSRS. BROWN, JONES, AND ROBINSON, THE (see Messrs....)

FRANK LESLIE'S BOYS AND GIRLS
Frank Leslie, NYC: Oct 13 1866-#905 Feb 9 1884
average issue with comic strip 20.00 30.00 50.00

FRANK LESLIE'S BUDGET OF FUN
Frank Leslie, Ross & Tousey, 121 Nassau St, NYC: Jan 1859-1878 (newspaper size)
1-5 no comic strips 50.00 100.00 250.00
6 June 1859 (9) panel "The Wonderful Hunting Tour of Mr Borridge After the Deer" 75.00 150.00 440.00
7-9 no comic strips 25.00 50.00 130.00
10 Sept 1859 sequential comic strip 50.00 100.00 250.00
11 (8) panel sequential "Apropos of the Great Eastern" 50.00 100.00 250.00
12-14 25.00 50.00 130.00
15 Feb 1860 (12) panel "The Ballet Girl" strip 50.00 100.00 240.00
16-18 25.00 50.00 130.00
19 June 1860 comic strip front cover 100.00 200.00 400.00
NOTE: Cover is (1) panel "The Very Latest Fashionable Amusement..."; Back cover comic strip "Mr Jogg's Reasons For Preferring to Board to Keeping House" (7) panels using word balloons. Plus centerfold double page (18) panel spread "The New York May, Moving in General, and Mrs. Grundy's In Particular."
20 24 25 no comic strips 25.00 50.00 130.00
21 (7/15/60) (8) panel Mr Septimus Verdilater Visits the Baltimore Convention" 50.00 100.00 260.00
22 (8/1/60) (3) panel 25.00 50.00 130.00
23 (8/15/60) (12) panel "Superb Scheme For Perfecting of Dramatic Entertainment" 50.00 100.00 260.00
25 (9/15/60 (9) panel sequential 25.00 50.00 130.00
27 AbrahamLincoln Word Balloon cover 50.00 100.00 260.00
28 Wilhelm Busch sequential strip-r begin 50.00 100.00 260.00
29, 31-51 25.00 50.00 130.00
30 (12/15/60) (3) panel sequential strip 25.00 50.00 130.00
31 (Jan 1861) (12) panel The Boarding School Miss 25.00 50.00 130.00
32 (Feb 1861) (10) panel Telegraphic Horrors; Or, Mr Buchanan Undergoing A Series of Electric Shocks 50.00 100.00 260.00
35 (4/1/61) Abraham Lincoln Word Balloon cover 50.00 100.00 260.00
43 44 no sequential comic strips 25.00 50.00 130.00
45 (Nov 1861) (6) panel sequential; (11) panel The Budget Army and Infantry Tactics; First Bellew here? - Many Bellew full pagers begin 50.00 100.00 260.00
48 (Feb 1862) Bellew-c; (2) panel Bellew strip plus singles 50.00 100.00 260.00
49 (Mar 1862) Bellew-c; (16) panel Wilhelm Busch "The Fly Or The Disturbed Dutchman A Story without Words" 50.00 100.00 260.00
50 (April 1862) Bellew-c "Succession Bath" plus singles 25.00 50.00 130.00
51 (May 1862) Bellew-c; (25) panel Busch The Toothache (6) panel Definitions of the Day 50.00 100.00 260.00
52 (June 1862) Bellew-c; (9) panel A Cock & A Bull Expedition; (6) panel Bellew The First Campaign of the Home Guard 50.00 100.00 260.00
NOTE: Johnny Bull & Louis Napolean with Brother Jonathan
53-67 To Be Indexed in the Future 25.00 50.00 130.00
68 (11/18///63) (6) panel Bellew strip "Cuts On Cowards" 25.00 50.00 130.00
NOTE: contains (1) panel William Newman 1817-1870, mentor to Thomas Nast
71 (Feb 1864) Word Balloon Jefferson Davis-c 25.00 50.00 130.00
72 (Mar 1864) Word Balloon-c 25.00 50.00 130.00
73 (April 1864) Word Balloon-c in (6) panels 25.00 50.00 130.00

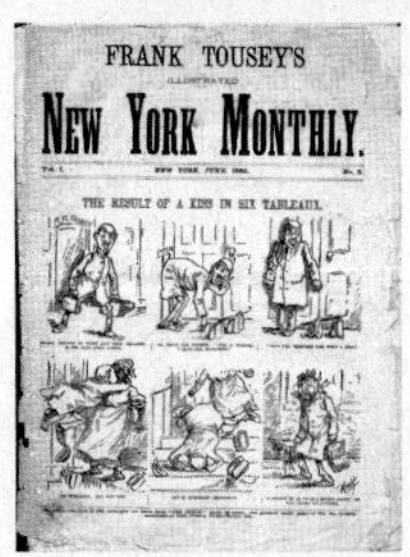

Frank Tousey's Illustrated New York Monthly #9
June 1882 © Frank Tousey

The Funnyest Of Awl And The Funniest Sort Of Phun v4#4
1865 © A.T. Bellew Word Balloon Cover

Funny Folk by F.M. Howarth
1899© E.P. Dutton

FR1.0 GD2.0 FN6.0

74 (May 1864) Newman Word Balloon-c 25.00 50.00 130.00
75 77 78 no sequentials 25.00 50.00 130.00
76 (July 1864) Newman Word Balloon-c 25.00 50.00 130.00
79 (Oct 1864) Word Balloon-c 25.00 50.00 130.00
80 (Nov 1864) Robt E Lee & Jeff Davis-c; no sequentials 25.00 50.00 130.00
81 (Dec 1864) Word Balloon "Abyss of War"-c 25.00 50.00 130.00
83 (2/18/65) Back-c (6) panel "Petroleum" 25.00 50.00 130.00
84 (Mar 1865) (6) panel sequential 25.00 50.00 130.00
85 (Apr 1865) Word Balloon-c 25.00 50.00 130.00
86 89 90 92 no sequentials 25.00 50.00 130.00
88 (7/6/65) (6) panel "Marriage" 25.00 50.00 130.00
91 (Oct 1865) (6) panel "Brief Confab At The Corner 25.00 50.00 130.00
93-98 yet to be indexed 25.00 50.00 130.00
99 (June 1866) (18) panel Mr Paul Peters Adventures
While Trout-Fishing In The Adirondacks 50.00 100.00 260.00
100 (July 1866) (4) panel sequential comic strip 25.00 50.00 130.00
102 (Sept 1866) (6) panel sequential comic strip 25.00 50.00 130.00
103 (Oct 1866) (9) panel strip; (12) pane;l back cover
Adventures of McTiffin At Long Branch 50.00 100.00 260.00
104 (Nov 1866) (4) panel; (23) panel "The Budget Rebuses; (2) panel
Glut On Treason Market;back-c; (6) sequential strip 25.00 50.00 130.00
105 (12/18/66) Word Balloon-c; (20) panel sequential back-c 37.50 65.00 156.00
NOTE: Artists include William Newman (1863-1868), William Henry Shelton, Joseph Keppler (1873-1876), James A. Wales (1876-1878), Frederick Burr Opper (1878)

FRANK LESLIE'S LADY'S MAGAZINE
Frank Leslie, NYC: Feb 1863-Dec 1882 (8.5x12", typically 152 pgs)
issues with comic strips 20.00 40.00 60.00

FRANK LESLIE'S PICTORIAL WEEKLY
Frank Leslie, Ross & Tousey, 121 Nassau St, NYC:
average issue (Very Rare) 50.00 100.00 210.00

FRANK TOUSEY'S NEW YORK COMIC MONTHLY
Frank Tousey, NYC: (no known sales)

FREAKS
???, Philadelphia: Jan 8, 1881-April? 1881 (Chromolithographic Weekly)
(Very Rare) 125.00 250.00 500.00

FREELANCE, THE
A.M. Soteldo Jr, Edito, 292 Broadway, NYC: 1874-75 (Folio Weekly)
(Rare) 25.00 50.00 100.00

FREE MASONRY EXPOSED
Winchell & Small, 113 Fulton, NY: 1871 (7-5/8x10-1/2", 36pgs, blue paper-c, B&W)
nn- Thomas Worth Scarce 100.00 200.00 450.00
NOTE: Scathing satircal look at Free Masons thru many cartoons, their power waning by the 1870s

FREETHINKERS' PICTORIAL TEXT-BOOK, THE (S,O)
The Truth Seeker Company, New York: 1890, 1896, 1898 (9x12, hard-c, B&W)
1 (1890 edition) - Scarce 382 pgs By Watson Heston 225.00 450.00 1000.00
1 (1896 edition) - Scarce 378 pgs By Watson Heston (1890-r)100.00 200.00 500.00
2 (1898 edition) - Scarce 408 pgs By Watson Heston 125.00 250.00 500.00
NOTE: *Sought after by collectors of Freethought/Atheism material. There is also 200 copy Modern Reprint.*

FRITZ SPINDLE-SHANKS, THE RAVEN BLACK
Cosack & C o, Buffalo, NY: 1870/80s (4-3/8x2-3/4", color)
(10) card comic strip set by Wilhelm Busch 25.00 50.00 100.00

FUN BY RALL
Unknown: circa 1865 (11x7-7/8", 68 pgs, soft-c, B&W)
nn - By presently unknown (Very Rare) 125.00 250.00 475.00
NOTE: *Wraparound soft cover like modern comic book; yellow paper cover with red & black ink.*

FUN FOR THE FAMILY IN PICTURES
D. Lothrop and Company: 1886 (4 x 7", 48 pgs, Silver & Red stiff-c; interior pages have various single color inks)
nn - By unknown hand 75.00 125.00 250.00
NOTE: *Single panel cartoons and sequential stories.*

FUN FROM LIFE
Frederick A Stokes & Brother, New York: 1889 (9 1/8 by 7 1/8, 72 pages, hard-c)
nn - Mostly by Frank "Chips" Bellew Jr 62.50 125.00 250.00
NOTE: *Contains both single panel and many sequential comics reprints from Life.*

FUNNYEST OF AWL AND THE FUNNIEST SORT OF PHUN, THE
AT Bellew Or W. Jennings Demorest, 121 Nassau St, NY : 1865-67 (30 issues, 16x11 tabloid 16 pgs B&W Monthly, 1-8 © American News; 9-on © A.T. Bellews)
1 (April 1864) Bellew-c 50.00 100.00 225.00
4 (1865) Bellew-c 50.00 100.00 225.00
5 (1865) Busch (20) panel comic srtip The Toothache 75.00 150.00 350.00
7 (1865) Bellew-c 50.00 100.00 225.00
8 (1865) Special Petroleum oil issue - much cartoon art 100.00 200.00 450.00
9 (July 1865) Bellew Bullfrog-c; centerfold double page spread hanging
many Confederates; (6) panel strip hanging Jeff Davis 100.00 200.00 450.00
10 (Aug 1865) Bellew-c (13) panel Busch strip with two ducks, a frog
and a butcher who gets the ducks in the end 100.00 200.00 450.00
11 (Sept 1865) Bellew Bull Frog Anti-French-c 50.00 100.00 225.00
13 14 15 (12/65-1/66) Bellew-c no sequential comic strips 50.00 100.00 225.00
16 (March 1866) address change to 39 Park Ave 50.00 100.00 225.00
22 (Sept 1866) 133 Nassau St 50.00 100.00 225.00
34 (Oct 1867) 133 Nassau St (7) panel Baseball comic strip;
Last Known Issue - were there more? 100.00 200.00 450.00
NOTE: *Radical Republican politics distributed by Great American News Company; owned by Frank Bellew's wife as a front for her husband. When the Civil War ended, the brutal anti-Confederate comic strips and jokes switched to frogs and began attacking France. Funny thing, history says without France's help in the 1700s, there just might not have been a United States.*

FUNNY ALMANAC
Elton & Co., NY: 1853 (8-1/8x4-7/8, 36 pgs)
nn - sequential comic strip 50.00 100.00 200.00
NOTE: (5) panel strip "The Adventures of Mr. Goliah Starvemouse"

FUNNY FELLOWS OWN BOOK, A COMPANION FOR THE LOVERS OF FROLIC AND GLEE, THE (M,N)
Philip. J. Cozans, 116 Nassau ST, NY: 1852 (4-1/2x7-1/2", 196 pgs, burnt orange paper-c)
nn - contains many sequential comic strips (Very Rare) (no known sales)
NOTE: Collected from many different Comic Alamac(k)s including Mose Keyser (Calif Gold Rush); Jones, Smith and Robinson Goes To A Ball; Adventures of Mr. Gulp, Or the Effects of A Dinner Party; The Bowery Bully's Trip To The California Gold Mines plus lots more. This one is a sleeper so far.

FUNNY FOLK (M)
E. P. Dutton: 1899 (12x16-1/2", 90 pgs,14 strips in color-rest in b&w, hard-c)
nn - By Franklin Morris Howarth 200.00 425.00 1800.00
nn - London: J.M. Dent, 1899 embossed-c; same interior 250.00 500.00 1100.00
NOTE: *Reprints many sequential strips & single panel cartoons from* ***Puck****. This is considered by many to be yet another "missing link" between Victorian & Platinum Age comic books. Most comic books 1900-1917 re-printing Sunday newspaper comic strips follow this size format, except using cardboard-c rather than hard-c.*

FUNNY SKETCHES...Also Embracing Comic Illustrations
Frank Harrison, New York: 1881 (6-5/8x5", 68 pgs, B&W, Color-c)
nn - contains (3) sequential comic strips; one strip is (6) pages long;
plus one (3) pages; one more (2) pager 75.00 150.00 350.00

GIBSON BOOK, THE (M,S)
Charles Scribner's Sons & R.H. Russell, New York: 1906 (11-3/8x17-5/8", gilted red hard-c, B&W)
Book I 50.00 100.00 200.00
NOTE: *Reprints in whole the books: Drawings, Pictures of People, London,Sketches and Cartoons, Education of Mr. Pipp, Americans. 414 pgs. 1907 2nd editions exist same value.*
Book II 50.00 100.00 200.00
NOTE: *Reprints in whole the books: A Widow and Her Friends, The Weaker Sex, Everyday People, Our Neighbors. 314 pgs 1907 second edition for both also exists. Same value.*

GIBSON'S PUBLISHED DRAWINGS, MR. (M,S) (see Plat index for later issues post 1900)
R.H. Russell, New York: No.1 1894 - No. 9 1904 (11x17-3/4", hard-c, B&W)
nn (No.1; 1894) Drawings 96 pgs 30.00 60.00 125.00
nn (No.2; 1896) Pictures of People 92 pgs 30.00 60.00 125.00
nn (No.3; 1898) Sketches and Cartoons 94 pgs 30.00 60.00 125.00
nn (No.4; 1899) The Education of Mr. Pipp 88 pgs 30.00 60.00 125.00
nn (No.5; 1900) Americans 30.00 60.00 125.00
NOTE: *By Charles Dana Gibson cartoons, reprinted from magazines, primarily* ***LIFE****. The Education of Mr. Pipp tells a story. Series continues how long after 1904? Each of these books originally came in a boxx and are worth more with the box.*

GIRL WHO WOULDN'T MIND GETTING MARRIED, THE (O)
Frederick Warne & Co., London & New York: nd (c1870's) (9-1/2x11-1/2", 28 pgs, printed 1 side, paper-c, B&W)
nn - By Harry Parkes 75.00 150.00 300.00
NOTE: *Published simultaneously with its companion volume,* ***The Man Who Would Like to Marry****.*

GOBLIN SNOB, THE (O)
DeWitt & Davenport, New York: nd (c1853-56) (24 x 17 cm, 96 pgs, B&W, color hard-c)
nn - (Rare) by H.L. Stephens 350.00 600.00 1250.00

GOLDEN ARGOSY
Frank A. Munsey, 81 Warren St, NYC: 1880s (10-1/2x12, 16 pgs, B&W)
issues with full page comic strips by Chips and Bisbee 20.00 40.00 60.00

GOLDEN DAYS, THE
James Elverson, Publisher, NYC: March 6 1880-May 11 1907 weekly, 16 pgs
issues with comic strips 4.00 7.50 15.00
Horatio Alger issues 10.00 20.00 40.00
v10 #49-v11#1 1889 first Stratemeyer story 25.00 50.00 100.00

GOLDEN WEEKLY, THE
Frank Tousey, NYC: #1 Sept 25 1889-#145 Aug 18 1892 (10-3/4x14-1/2, 16 pgs, B&W)
average issue with comic striips 15.00 25.00 50.00

GREAT LOCOFOCO JUGGERNAUT, THE (S)
publisher unknown: Fall/Winter 1837 (7-5/8x3-1/4, handbill single page)
nn - By David Claypoole Johnston (a VG copy sold for $2000 in 2005)

The Story of Han's The Swapper Cover & First Two Panels
1865 © L. Pranc & Co, Boston

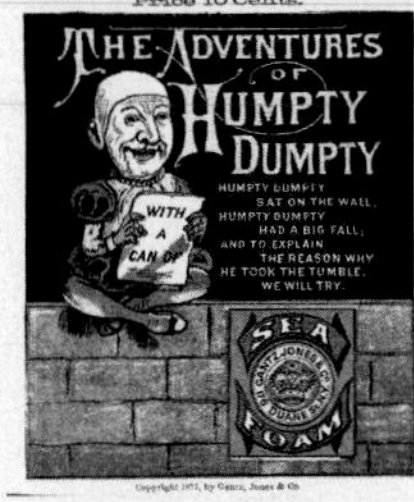

Humpty Dumpty, The Adventures of...
© Gantz, Jones and Co.

Imagerie d'Epinal
1888 © Mumoristic Publishing Co.

FR1.0 GD2.0 FN6.0

nn- **Imprint Society:** 1971 (reprint) 6.00 12.00 25.00

HALF A CENTURY OF ENGLISH HISTORY (S. M)
G.P. Putnam's Sons - The Knickerbocker Press, New York and London: 1884 (7-3/4 x 5-3/4", 316 pgs., illustrated hard-c)

nn - By Various 50.00 75.00 200.00
NOTE: *Subtitle: Pictorially Presented in a Series of Cartoons from the Collection of Mr. Punch. Comprising 150 plates by Doyle, Leech, Tenniel, and others, in which are portrayed the political careers of Peel, Palmerston, Russell, Cobden, Bright, Beaconsfield, Derby, Salisbury, Gladstone and other English statesmen.*

HAIL COLUMBIA! HISTORICAL, COMICAL, AND CENTENNIAL (O,S)
The Graphic Co., New York & Walter F. Brown, Providence, RI: 1876 (10x11-3/8", 60 pgs, red gilted hard-c, B&W)

nn - by Walter F. Brown (Scarce) 125.00 250.00 500.00

HANS HUCKEBEIN'S BATCH OF ODD STORIES ODDLY ILLUSTRATEDED
McLoughlin Bros., New York: 1880s (9-3/4x7-3/8, 36?? pg?

nn - By Wilhelm Busch (Rare) 75.00 150.00 300.00

HANS THE SWAPPER, THE STORY OF (O)
L. Pranc & Co., 159 Washington St, Boston: 1865 (33 inch long fold out in colors)

nn - unique fold out comic book on one long piece of paper 75.00 150.00 300.00

HARPER'S NEW MONTHLY MAGAZINE
Harper & Brothers, Franklin Square, NY: 1850-1870s (6-3/4x10, 140 pgs, paper-c, B&W)
1850s issues with comic strips in back advert section 20.00 30.00 75.00

HEALTH GUYED (I)
Frederick A. Stokes Company: 1890 (5-3/8 x 8-3/8, 56 pgs, hardcover, B&W)

nn - By Frank P.W. ("Chip") Bellew (Junior) 50.00 75.00 200.00
NOTE: *Text & cartoon illustration parody of a health guide.*

HEATHEN CHINEE, THE (O)
Western News Co.: 1870 (5-1/32x7-1/4, B&W, paper)
nn - 10 sheets printed on one side came in envelope 75.00 150.00 320.00

HITS AT POLITICS (M,S)
R.H. Russell, New York: 1899 (15" x 12", 156 pgs, B&W, hard-c)

nn - W.A. Rogers c/a 100.00 200.00 300.00
NOTE: *Collection of W.A. Rogers cartoons, all reprinted from Harper's Weekly. Includes Spanish-American War cartoons.*

THE HOME CIRCLE
Garrett & Co, NY: 1854-56 (26x19", 4 pgs, B&W)

1 (1/54) beautiful ad of Garrett Building 100.00 200.00 425.00
2/4 (4/66) Cover ad for Yale College Scraps 100.00 200.00 425.00
2/5 (5/55) First ad for Oscas Shanghai 75.00 150.00 310.00
2/6 (6/55) another ad forOscas Snanghai 75.00 150.00 310.00
2/8 (#20) (8/55) Oscar Shanghai comic book cover repro 200.00 400.00 1000.00
3/1 (#25) (1/56) 200.00 400.00 1000.00
NOTE: Garrett's 2nd comic book Courtship of Chavalier Slyfox-Wikoff
3/8 (#32) (8/56) 50.00 100.00 210.00
NOTE: First print ad for Foreign Tour of Messrs. Brown, Jones, and Robinson
35 (11/56) first official Garrett, Dick & Fitzgerald issue 50.00 100.00 210.00
37 (1/57) 100.00 200.00 425.00
NOTE: Front page comic strip repro ad for Messrs. Brown, Jones, and Robinson's Foreign Tour; Back cover full of short sequentials, singles panel

HOME MADE HAPPY. A ROMANCE FOR MARRIED MEN IN SEVEN CHAPTERS (O,P)
Genuine Durham Smoking Tobacco & The Graphic Co.: nd (c1870's) (5-1/4 tall x 3-3/8" wide folded, 27" wide unfolded, color cardboard)

nn - With all 8 panels attached (Scarce) 30.00 60.00 200.00
nn - Individual panels/cards 5.00 10.00 25.00
NOTE: *Consists of 8 attached cards, printed on one side, which unfold into a strip story of title card & 7 panels. Scrapbook hobbyists in the 19th Century tended to pull the panels apart to paste into their scrapbooks, making copies with all panels still attached scarce.*

HOME PICTURE BOOK FOR LITTLE CHILDREN (E,P)
Home Insurance Company, New York: July 1887 (8 x 6-1/8", 36 pgs, b&w, color paper-c)

nn (Scarce) 50.00 100.00 180.00
NOTE: *Contains an abbreviated 32-panel reprinting of "The Toothache" by George Cruikshank. Remainder of booklet does not contain comics. Some copies known to exist do not contain The Toothache - buyer beware!*

HOOD'S COMICALITIES. COMICAL PICTURES FROM HIS WORKS (E,S)
Porter & Coates: 1880 (8-1/2x10-3/8", 104 pgs, printed one side, hard-c, B&W)

nn 30.00 50.00 100.00
NOTE: *Reprints 4 cartoon illustrations per page from the British Hood's Comic Annuals, which were poetry books by Thomas Hood.*

HOOKEYBEAK THE RAVEN, AND OTHER TALES (see also JACK HUCKABACK, THE SCAPEGRACE RAVEN) (E)
George Routledge and Sons, London & New York: nd (1878) (7-1/4x5-5/8", 104 pgs, hardcover, B&W)

nn - By Wilhelm Busch (Rare) 100.00 200.00 450.00

HOW ADOLPHUS SLIM-JIM USED JACKSON'S BEST, AND WAS HAPPY. A LENGTHY TALE IN 7 ACTS. (O,P)
Jackson's Best Chewing Tobacco & Donaldson Brothers: nd(c1870's) (5-1/8 tall x 3-3/8" wide folded, 27" wide unfolded, color cardboard)

nn - With all 8 panels attached (Scarce) 30.00 60.00 250.00
nn - Individual panels/cards 10.00 15.00 30.00
NOTE: *Consists of 8 attached cards, printed on one side, which unfold into a strip story of title card & 7 panels. Scrapbook hobbyists in the 19th Century tended to pull the panels apart topaste into their scrapbooks, making copies with all panels still attached scarce.*

HOW DAYS' DURHAM STANDARD OF THE WORLD SMOKING TOBACCO MADE TWO PAIRS OF TWINS HAPPY (O,P)
J.R. Day & Bro. Standard Durham Smoking Tobacco, Durham, NC: nd (c late 1870's/early 1880's) (3-5/8" x 5-1/2", folded, 21-3/4" tall unfolded, color cardboard)

nn- With all 6 panels attached (Scarce) 150.00 300.00 600.00
nn- Individual panels/cards 20.00 40.00 60.00
NOTE: *Highly sought by both Black Americana and Tobacciana collectors. Recurring mid-19th Century story about two African-American twin brothers who romance and marry a pair of African-American twin sisters. Although the text is racist at points, the art is not. Consists of 6 attached cards, printed on one side, which unfold downwards into a strip story of title card & 5 panels. Scrapbook hobbyists in the 19th Century tended to pull the panels apart and paste into their scrapbooks, making copies with all panels attached scarce. Note, there are numerous cartoon tellings of this same story, including several card series versions (with different art, and story variations, each time). But, the above is the only version which unfolds as a strip of attached cards. The cards from all the unattached versions are smaller sized, and thus distinguishable.*

HUGGINIANA; OR, HUGGINS' FANTASY, BEING A COLLECTION OF THE MOST ESTEEMED MODERN LITERARY PRODUCTIONS (I,S,P)
H.C. Southwick, New York: 1808 (296 pgs, printed one side, B&W, hard-c)

nn - (Very Rare)) (no known sales)
NOTE: *The earliest known surviving collected promotional cartoons in America. This is a booklet collecting 7 folded plus 1 full page flyer advertisements for barber John Richard Desborus Huggins, who hired American artists Elkanah Tisdale and William S. Leney to modify previously published illustrations into cartoons referring to his barber shop.*

HUMOROUS MASTERPIECES - PICTURES BY JOHN LEECH (E,M)
Frederick A. Stokes: nd (late 1900's - early 1910's) No.1-2 (5-5/8x3-7/8", 68 pgs, cardboard covers, B&W)

1- John Leech (single panel cartoon-r from **Punch**) 25.00 50.00 110.00
2- John Leech (single panel cartoon-r from **Punch**) 25.00 50.00 110.00

HUMOURIST, THE (E,I,S)
C.V. Nickerson and Lucas and Deaver, Baltimore: No.1 Jan 1829 - No.12 Dec 1829 (5-3/4x3-1/2", B&W text w/hand colored cartoon pg.)

Bound volume No.1-12 (Very Rare; copies in libraries 270 pgs) (no known sales)
NOTE: *Earliest known American published periodical to contain a cartoon every issue. Surviving individual issues currently unknown -- all information comes from 1 surviving bound volume. Each issue is mostly text, with one full page hand-colored cartoon. Bound volume contains an additional hand-colored cartoons at front of each six month set (total of 14 cartoons in volume). Cartoons appear to be of British origin, possibly by George Cruikshank.*

HUMPTY DUMPTY, ADVENTURES OF...(I,P)
1877 (Promotional 4x3-1/2", 12 page chapbook from Gantz, Jones & Co, 10¢-c.)

nn-Promotes Gantz Sea Foam Baking Powder; early app. of a costumed character, dressed as Humpty Dumpty 125.00 150.00 600.00

HUSBAND AND WIFE, OR THE STORY OF A HAIR. (O,P)
Garland Stoves and Ranges, Michigan Stove Co.: 1883 (4-3/16 tall x 2-11/16" wide folded, 16" wide unfolded, color cardboard)

nn - With all 6 panels attached (Scarce) 50.00 75.00 150.00
nn - Individual panels/cards 5.00 10.00 25.00
NOTE: *Consists of 6 attached cards, printed on one side, which unfold into a strip story of title card & 5 panels. Scrapbook hobbyists in the 19th Century tended to pull the panels apart topaste into their scrapbooks, making copies with all panels still attached scarce.*

ICHABOD ACADEMICUS, THE COLLEGE EXPERIENCES OF (O,G)
William T. Peters, New Haven, CT: 1850 (5-1/2x9-3/4",108 pgs, B&W)

nn - By William T. Peters (Rare) 1000.00 2000.00 4300.00
NOTE: *Pages are not uniform in size. Also, a copy showed up on eBay with misspelled Acedemicus. Has "n" instead of "m" - not known yet which printing is earliest version.*

ICHABOD ACADEMICUS, THE COLLEGE EXPERIENCES OF (O,G)
Dick & Fitzgerald, New York: nd (1870s-1888) (paper-c, B&W)

nn - By William T. Peters (Very Rare) 275.00 550.00 1100.00
NOTE: *Pages are uniform in size.*

ILLUSTRATED SCRAP-BOOK OF HUMOR AND INTELLIGENCE (M)
John J. Dyer & Co.: nd (c1859-1860)

nn - Very Rare 225.00 450.00 1000.00
NOTE: *A "printed scrapbook" of images culled from some unidentified periodical. About half of it is illustrations that would have accompanied prose pieces. There are pages of single panel cartoons (multiple per page). And there are roughly 8 to 12 pages of sequential comics (all different stories, but appears to all be by the same presently unidentified artist).*

ILLUSTRATED WEEKLY, THE
Chars C Lucas & Co, 11 Dey St, NY: 1876 (15x18", 8pgs, 8¢ per issue)

2/8 (2/19/76) back-c all sequential comic strips 100.00 200.00 400.00
2/12 (3/18/76) full page of British-r sequentials 100.00 200.00 400.00
2/14 (4/1/76) April Fool Issue - (6) panel center; plus more 100.00 200.00 400.00
2/15 (4/8/76) (6) panel sequential 100.00 200.00 400.00
issues without comic strips 12.50 25.00 50.00

Jingo No. 3, Sept 24
1884 © Art Newspaper Co, Boston & NYC

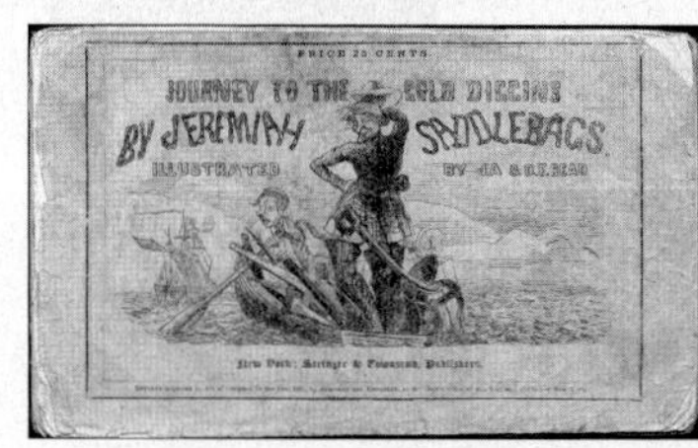

Journey To The Gold Diggings By Jeremiah Saddlebags
1849 © Various - First Original USA Comic Book

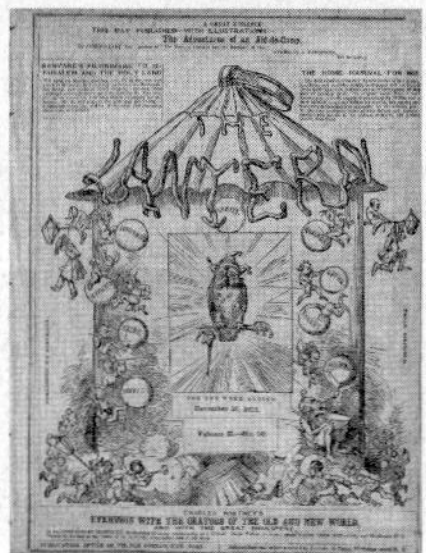

The Lantern Dec 18
1852 © Stringer & Townsend

ILLUSTRATIONS OF THE POETS: FROM PASSAGES IN THE LIFE OF LITTLE BILLY VIDKINS (See A Day's Sport...)
S. Robinson, Philadelphia: May 1849 (14.7 cm x 11.3 cm, 32 pgs, B&W)

nn - by Henry Stephens (very rare) (no known sales)
NOTE: *Predates Journey to the Gold Diggins By Jeremiah Saddlebags by a few months and is an original American proto-comic strip book. More research needs to be done. A later edition brought $800 in G/VG 2007*

IMAGERIE d'EPINAL (untrimmed individual sheets) (E)
Pellerin for Humoristic Publishing Co, Kansas City, Mo.: nd (1888) No.1-60 (15-7/8x11-3/4",single sheets, hand colored) (All are Rare)

1-14, 21, 22, 25-46, 49-60 - in the Album d'Images 17.50 35.00 70.00
15-20, 23,24, 47, 48 - not in the Album d'Images 30.00 60.00 125.00
NOTE: *Printed and hand colored in France expressly for the Humoristic Publishing Company. Printed on one side only. These are single sheets, sold separately. Reprints and translates the sheets from their original French.*

IMAGERIE d'EPINAL ALBUM d'IMAGES (E)
Pellerin for Humoristic Publishing Co., Kansas City. Mo: nd (1888) (15-1/2x11-1/2",108 pgs plus full color hard-c, hand colored interior)

nn - Various French artists (Rare) 500.00 1000.00 2300.00
NOTE: *Printed and hand colored in France expressly for the Humoristic Publishing Company. Printed on one side only. This is supposedly a collection of sixty broadsheets, originally sold separately. All copies known only have fifty of the sixty known of these broadsheets (slightly bigger, before binding, trimming the margins in the process, down to 15-1/4x11-3/8".). Three slightly different covers known to exist, with or without the indication in French "Textes en Anglais" ("Texts in Englishi), with or without the general title "Contes de FEes" ("Fairy Tales"). All known copies were collected with sheets 15-20, 23,24, 47, and 48 missing.*

IN LAUGHLAND (M)
R.H. Russell, New York: 1899 (14-9/16x12", 72 pgs, hard-c)

nn - By Henry "Hy" Mayer (scarce) 150.00 300.00 600.00
NOTE: *Mostly strips plus single panel cartoon-r from various magazines. The majority are reprinted from Life, with the rest from: Truth, Dramatic Mirror, Black and White, Figaro Illustre, Le Rire, and Fliegende Blatter.*

IN THE "400" AND OUT (M,S) (see also **THE TAILOR-MADE GIRL**)
Keppler & Schwarzmann, New York: 1888 (8-1/4x12", 64 pgs, hardc, B&W)

nn - By C.J. Taylor 42.50 85.00 200.00
NOTE: *Cartoons reprinted from **Puck**. The "400" is a reference to New York City's aristocratic elite.*

IN VANITY FAIR (M,S)
R.H.Russell & Son, New York: 1896 (11-7/8x17-7/8", 80 pgs, hard-c, B&W)

nn - By A.B.Wenzell, r-LIFE and HARPER'S 50.00 100.00 200.00

JACK HUCKABACK, THE SCAPEGRACE RAVEN (see also HOOKEYBEAK THE RAVEN) (E)
Stroefer & Kirchner, New York: nd (c1877) (9-3/8x6-3/8", 56 pgs, printed one side only, hand colored hardcover, B&W interior)

nn - By Wilhelm Busch (Rare) 100.00 200.00 400.00
NOTE: *The 1877 date is derived from a gift signature on one known copy. The publication date might in truth be earlier. There are also professionally hand colored copies known to exist which would be worth more.*

JEFF PETTICOATS
American News Company, NY: July 1865 (23 inches folded out; 6-1/4x8 folded,, B&W)
nn - Very Rare Frank Bellew (6) panel sequential foldout (10¢) (no known sales)
NOTE: printed also in **FUNNYEST OF AWL AND THE FUNNIEST SORT OF PHUN** #9 (July 1865) (6) panel strip hanging Jeff Davis; This sold hundreds of thousand of copies in its day

JINGO (M,O)
Art Newspaper Co., Boston & New York: No.1 Sept 10, 1884 - No.11 Nov 19, 1884 (10 cents, 13-7/8" x 10-1/4",16 pgs, color front/back-c and center, remainder B&W, paper-c)

1-11(Rare) 50.00 100.00 225.00
NOTE: *Satirical Republican propaganda magazine, modeled after **Puck** and **Judge**, which was published during the last couple months of the 1884 Presidential Election campaign. The Republicans lost, **Jingo** ceased publication, and Republican backers soon after purchased **Judge** magazine.*

JOHN-DONKEY, THE (O, S)
George Dexter, Burgess, Stringer & Co., NYC: 1848 (10x7.5",16 pgs,B&W, 6¢

1 Jan 1 1848 75.00 150.00 300.00
2-end (last issue Aug 12 1848) 50.00 100.00 200.00

JOLLY JOKER
Frank Leslie, NY: 1862-1878 (B&W, 10¢)

20/6 (July 1877) (Bellew Opper cover & single panels 150.00 300.00 600.00

JOLLY JOKER, OR LAUGH ALL-ROUND
Dick & Fitzgerald, NY: 1870s? (8-1/4x4-7/8", 148, B&W, illustrated green cover)

nn - cartoons on every page 100.00 200.00 400.00

JONATHAN'S WHITTLINGS OF THE WAR (O, S)
T.W. Strong, 98 Nassau St, NYC: April 1854-July 8 1854 (11.5x8.5", 16 pgs, B&W)

1 April 1854 100.00 200.00 400.00
NOTE: *Begins Frank Bellew's sequential comic strip "Mr. Hookemcumsnivey, A Russian Gentleman, Hears That His Country Is In A State of War"*
2-12 (July 8 1854) Many Bellew & Hopkins 100.00 200.00 400.00

JOURNAL CARRIER'S GREETING
???, Minn, Minn: 1897-98? (giveaway promo, 10-1/8x8-1/4, 36, B&W, paper-c)
nn - rare 50.00 100.00 200.00

JOURNEY TO THE GOLD DIGGINS BY JEREMIAH SADDLEBAGS (O,G)
Various publishers: 1849 (25 cents, 5-5/8 x 8-3/4", 68 pgs, green & black paper cover, B&W interior)

nn -- New York edition, Stringer & Townsend, Publishers (Very Rare) By J.A. and D.F. Read. 5500.00 8800.00 13,000.00
nn -- Cincinnati, Ohio edition, published by U.P. James (Very Rare) By J.A. and D.F. Read. 5500.00 8800.00 13,000.00
nn -- 1950 reprint, with introduction, published by William P. Wreden, Burlingame, California: 1950 (5-7/8 x 9", 92 pgs, hardcover, color interior) (390 copies printed) By J.A. and D.F. Read. 67.50 125.00 275.00
NOTE: *Earliest known original sequential comic book by an American creator; directly inspired by Töpffer's **Obadiah Oldbuck** and **Bachelor Butterfly** The New York and Cincinnati editions were both published in 1849, one soon after the other. Antiquarian Book sources have traditionally cited that the Cincinnati edition preceded the New York, but without referencing their evidence. Conflicting with this, the Cincinnati edition lists the New York publishers' 1849 copyright, while the New York edition makes no reference to the Cincinnati publishers. Such would indicate that the New York edition was first. Both are very rare, and until resolved both will be regarded as published simultaneously. A New York copy with missing back cover, detached front cover, and G/VG interior sold for $2000 in 2000. Two copies sold at auction in 2006 for $11,500 and 12,000. (Prices vary widely.)*

JUDGE (M,O)
Judge Publishing, New York: No.1 Oct 29, 1881 - No. 950, Dec ??, 1899 (10 cents, color front/back c and centerspread, remainder B&W, paper-c)

1 (Scarce) (no known sales)
2-26 (Volume 1; Scarce) 30.00 55.00 110.00
27-790,792-950 12.50 25.00 50.00
791 (12/12/1896; Vol.31) - classic satirical-c depicting Tammany Hall politicians as the Yellow Kid & Cox's Brownies 100.00 250.00 500.00
Bound Volumes (six month, 26 issue run each):
Vol. 1 (Scarce) (no known sales)
Vol. 2-30,32-37 140.00 280.00 600.00
Vol. 31 - includes issue 791 **YK/Brownies** parody 200.00 300.00 850.00
NOTE: *Rival publication to Puck. Purchased by Republican Party backers, following their loss in the 1884 Presidential Election, to become a Republican propaganda satire magazine.*

JUDGE, GOOD THINGS FROM
Judge Publishing Co., NY: 1887 (13-3/4x10.5", 68 pgs, color paper-c)

1 first printing 50.00 100.00 200.00
NOTE: Zimmerman, Hamilton, Victor, Woolf, Beard, Ehrhart, De Meza, Howarth, Smith, Alfred Mitchell

JUDGE'S LIBRARY (M)
Judge Publishing, New York: No.1, April 1890 - No. 141, Dec 1899 (10 cents, 11x8-1/8", 36 pgs, color paper-c, B&W)

1 15.00 30.00 60.00
2-141 15.00 30.00 60.00
151-??? (post-1900 issues; see Platinum Age section)
NOTE: ***Judge's Library** was a monthly magazine reprinting cartoons & prose from **Judge**, with each issue's material organized around the same subject. The cover art was often original. All issues were kept in print for the duration of the series, so later issues are more scarce than earlier ones.*

JUDGE'S QUARTERLY (M)
Judge Publishing Company/Arkell Publishing Company, New York: No.1 April 1892 - 31 Oct 1899 (25¢, 13-3/4x10-1/4", 64 pgs, color paper-c, B&W)

1-11 13-31 contents presently unknown to us 15.00 30.00 60.00
12 ZIM Sketches From Judge Jan 1895 100.00 200.00 425.00
NOTE: *Similar to **Judge's Library**, except larger in size, and issued quarterly. All reprint material, except for the cover art.*

JUDGE'S SERIALS (M,S)
Judge Publishing, New York: March 1888 (10x7.5", 36 pgs)

#3 - Eugene Zimmerman 100.00 200.00 400.00
NOTE: *A bit of sequential comic strips; mostly single panel cartoons. This series runs to at least #8.*

JUDY
Burgess, Stringer & Co., 17 Ann St, NYC: Nov 28 1846-Feb 20 47 (11x8.5",12 pgs,B&W)

1 Nov 28 1846 67.50 125.00 250.00
2-13 50.00 100.00 200.00

JUVENILE GEM, THE (see also THE ADVENTURES OF MR. TOM PLUMP, and OLD MOTHER MITTEN) (O,I)
Huestis & Cozans: nd (1850-1852) (6x3-7/8", 64 pgs, hand colored paper-c, B&W) (all versions Very Rare)

nn - First printing(s) publisher's address is 104 Nassau Street (1850-1851) (1 copy sold for $800.00 in Fair)
nn - 2nd printing(s) publisher's address is 116 Nassau Street (1851-1852) (no known sales)
nn - 3rd printing(s) publisher's address is 107 Nassau Street (1852+) (no known sales)
NOTE: *The JUVENILE GEM is a gathering of multiple booklets under a single, hand colored cover (none of the interior booklets have the covers which they were given when sold separately). The publisher appears to have gathered whichever printings of each booklet were available when copies of THE JUVENILE GEM was assembled, so that the booklets within, and the conglomerate cover, may be from a mixture of printings. Contains two sequential comic booklets: THE ADVENTURES OF MR. TOM PLUMP, and OLD MOTHER MITTEN AND HER FUNNY KITTEN, plus five heavily illustrated children's booklets - **The Pretty Primer**, **The Funny Book**, **The Picture Book**, **The Two Sisters**, and **Story Of The Little Drummer**. Six of these -- including the two comic books -- were reprinted in the 1960's by Americana Review as a set of individual booklets, and included in a folder collectively titled "Six Children's Books of the 1850's".*

LANTERN, THE
Stringer & Townsend:1852-1853 (11x8-3/8", 12 pgs, soft paper, 6 ¢)

Leslie's Young America #1
1881 © Leslie & Company, NYC

Life Jan 3
1884 © J.A. Mitchell

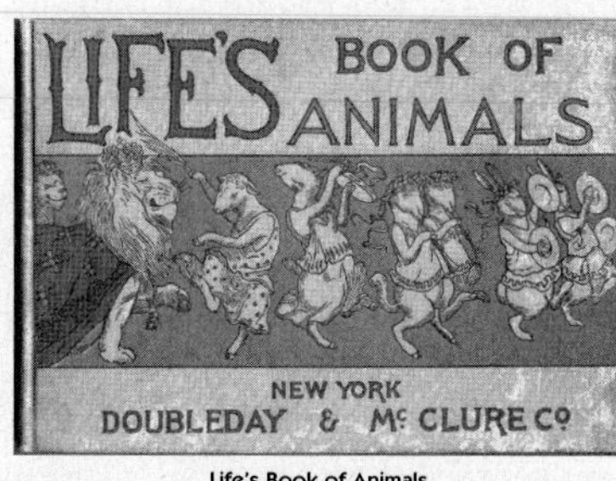

Life's Book of Animals
1888 © Doubleday & McClure Co.

FR1.0 GD2.0 FN6.0

1 Jan 10, 1852 37.50 75.00 175.00
2 25.00 50.00 110.00
3 First Frank Bellew cartoons onwards each issue 37.50 75.00 175.00
4 Bellew 's Mr Blobb begins 1/31/52 50.00 100.00 250.00
NOTE: *Bellew serial sequential comic strip "Mr Blobb In Search Of A Physician" becomes 2nd earliest known recurring character in American comic strips plus full page single panel Bellew cartoon "The Modern Frankenstein" take-off on Shelly's story.*
5 Hunsdale 2-panel "The Horrors of Slavery"; Mr Blobb 50.00 100.00 230.00
6 DF Read 15 panel "A Volley of Valentines"; Mr Blobb 50.00 100.00 230.00
7-8 10 Bellew's Mr Blobb continues 25.00 50.00 110.00
9 (4) panel "The Perils of Leap Year" MrBlobb 50.00 100.00 230.00
11 no Mr Blobb 20.00 40.00 100.00
12 Bellew's Mr Blobb continues 3/27/52 50.00 100.00 230.00
13 Bellew (10) panel sequential "Stump Speaking Studied" 50.00 100.00 230.00
14 no comic strips 20.00 40.00 100.00
15 Bellew's Mr Blobb ends (5) panel 4/17/52 50.00 100.00 230.00
16 Bellew begins new comic strip serial, "Mr. Bulbear, A Stockbroker, After having Supped at Delmonicos, Has A Dream", Part One, (6) panels 50.00 100.00 230.00
17 Bellew's Mr Bulbear continues 25.00 50.00 110.00
18 Bellew (8) panel "Trials of a Witness" 50.00 100.00 230.00
19 Bellew's Mr Bulbear's Dream continues 25.00 50.00 110.00
20-23 no comic strips 20.00 40.00 100.00
24 Bellew "Trials of a Publisher" (6) panel 50.00 100.00 230.00
25 comic strip "Travels of Jonathan Verdant"recurring character 25.00 50.00 110.00
26-49 contents to be indexed soon
50 (12/18/52) (2) panel Impertinent Smile 25.00 50.00 110.00
58 (2/12/53) (6) panel Trip to California 25.00 50.00 110.00
66 (4/9/53) (3) panel sequential strip 25.00 50.00 110.00

LAST SENSATION, THE (Becomes Day's Doings)
James Watts, NYC: Dec 27 1867-May 30 1868 (11x16 folio-size, 16 pgs, B&W)

issues with comic strips 50.00 100.00 200.00

LAUGH AND GROW FAT COMIC ALMANAC
Fisher & Brother, Philadelphia, New York & Boston: 1860-? (36 pgs)

nn 60.00 120.00 250.00

LEGEND OF SAM'L OF POSEN (O)
M.B. Curtis Company: 1884-85 (8x3-3/8", 44 pgs, Color-c, B&W interior)

nn - By M.B. Curtis 50.00 100.00 200.00
NOTE: Cover blurb says: From Early Days in Fatherland to affluence And Success in the Land of His Adoption, America

LESLIE'S YOUNG AMERICA (O. S)
Leslie & Co, 98 Chamber St, NY: 1881-82 (11-1/2x8", 5¢, B&W)

1 (7/9/81) back cover (6) panel strip 150.00 300.00 630.00
2 (7/16/81) back cover (9) panel strip 50.00 100.00 250.00
3 (7/23/81) back cover (16) panel Busch strip 67.50 125.00 275.00
9 (9/3/81) sequentials; Hopkins singles 50.00 100.00 250.00
15 (10/15/81) Zim or Frost? (6) panel strip 50.00 100.00 250.00
19 (11/12/81) (9) panel back-c strip 50.00 100.00 250.00
24 (4) panel strip 25 (2) panel back-c strip 50.00 100.00 250.00
26 27 (6) panel back-c strip 50.00 100.00 250.00
29 31 (12) panel strip 50.00 100.00 250.00
32 (2/11/82) (8) panel strip 50.00 100.00 250.00
issues without comic strips or Jules Verne 25.00 50.00 125.00
NOTE: Jules Verne stories begin with #1 and run thru at least #42

LIFE (M,O) (continues with Vol.35 No. 894+ in the Platinum Age section)
J.A.Mitchell: Vol.1 No.1 Jan. 4, 1883 - Vol.1 No.26 June 29, 1883 (10-1/4x8", 16 pgs, B&W, paper cover); J.A. Mitchell: Vol. 2 No. 27, July 5, 1883 - Vol. 6 No.148, Oct 29, 1885 (10-1/4x8-1/4", 16 pgs., B&W, paper cover); Mitchell & Miller: Vol.6 No.149, Nov. 5, 1885 - Vol. 31, No. 796, March 17, 1898 (10-3/8x8-3/8", 16 pgs., B&W, paper cover); Life Publishing Company: Vol. 31 No. 797, March 24, 1898 - Vol. 34 No. 893, Dec 28, 1899 (10-3/8 x 8-1/2", 20 pgs., B&W, paper cover)

1-26 (Scarce) (no known sales)
27-799 5.00 10.00 20.00
800 (4/7/1898) parody Yellow Kid / Spanish-American War cover (not by Outcault) 67.50 125.00 275.00
801-893 5.00 10.00 20.00
NOTE: *All covers for issues 1 - 26 are identical, apart from issue number & date.*
Hard bound collected volumes:
V. 1 (No.1-26) (Scarce) 67.50 125.00 250.00
V. 2-34 45.00 90.00 180.00
V. 31 YK #800 parody-c not by RFO 70.00 140.00 300.00
NOTE: *Because the covers of all issues in Volume 1 are identical, it was common practice to remove the covers before binding the issues together. This is not true of later volumes, though, in all volumes it was common to drop the advertising pages which appeared at the rear of each issue. Information on many more individual issues will expand next Guide.*

LIFE AND ADVENTURES OF JEFF DAVIS (I)
J.C. Haney & Co., NY: 1865 (10 cents, 7-1/2" x 4", 36 pgs, B&W, paper-c)

nn - By McArone (Scarce) 175.00 350.00 750.00
nn - 1974 Reprint (350) copies 6-3/4x4-3/8 50.00 10.00 20.00
nn - 1997 Reprint (7th Fla. Sutler, Clearwater, 6-3/4x4-1/4") – – 2.00
NOTE: *Humorous telling of the capture of Confederate President Jeff Davis in women's clothing, from the publisher of Merryman's Monthly. It contains an ad page for that publication; the material is perhaps reprinted from it. J.C. Haney licensed it to local printers, and so various publishers are found -- all printings currently regarded as simultaneous. (The Geo. H. Hees printing, Oswego, NY, contains an ad for the upcoming October 1865 issue of Merryman's Monthly, thus placing that printing in September 1865). Modern facsimile editions have been produced.*

LIFE IN PHILADELPHIA
W. Simpson, 66 Chestnut, Philadelphia; Siltart, No. 65 South Third St, Philadelphia: 1830 (7-3/4x6-7/8", 15 loose plates, hand colored copies exist, maybe B&W also)

nn - By Edward Williams Clay (1799-1857) (Very Rare) (no known sales)
NOTE: *First 13 plates etched, with many word balloons; scenes of exaggerated Black Americana in Philadelphia viewed one by one as broadsides. Had several publishers over the years. Was also eventually collected into a book of same name but only with the first 13 plates used; the last two not used in book. Collected book not yet viewed to share info.*

LIFE'S BOOK OF ANIMALS (M.S)
Doubleday & McClure Co.: 1898 (7-1/4x10-1/8", 88 pgs, color hardcover, B&W)

nn 30.00 55.00 110.00
NOTE: *Reprints funny animal single panel and strip cartoons reprinted from LIFE. Art by Blaisdell, Chip Bellew, Kemble, Hy Mayer, Sullivant, Woolf.*

LIFE'S COMEDY (M,S)
Charles Scribner's Sons: Series 1 1897 - Series 3 1898 (12x9-3/8", hardcover, B&W)

1 (142 pgs). 2, 3 (138 pgs) 60.00 120.00 250.00
NOTE: *Gibson a-1-3; c-3. Hy Mayer a-1-3. Rose O'Neill a-2-3. Stanlaws a-2-3. Sullivant a-1-2. Verbeek a-2. Wenzell a-1-3; c(painted)-2.*

LIFE, THE GOOD THINGS OF (M,S)
White, Stokes, & Allen, NY: 1884 - No.3 1886 ; Frederick A. Stokes, NY: No.4 1887; Frederick Stokes & Brother, NY: No.5 1888 - No.6 1889; Frederick A. Stokes Company, NY: No. 7 1890 - No.10 1893 (8-3/8x10-1/2", 74 pgs, gilted hardcover, B&W)

nn - 1884 (most common issue) 35.00 75.00 160.00
2 - 1885 35.00 75.00 160.00
3 - 1886 (76 pgs) 35.00 75.00 160.00
4 - 1887 (76 pgs) 35.00 75.00 160.00
5 - 1888 35.00 75.00 160.00
6 - 1889 35.00 75.00 160.00
7 - 1890 35.00 75.00 160.00
8 - 1891 (scarce) 75.00 150.00 300.00
9 - 1892 35.00 75.00 160.00
10 - 1893 35.00 75.00 160.00
NOTE: *Contains mostly single panel, and some sequential, comics reprinted from LIFE. Attwood a-1-4,10. Roswell Bacon a-5. Chip Bellew a-4-6. Frank Bellew a-4,6. Palmer Cox a-1. H. E. Dey a-5. C. D. Gibson a-4-10. F.M. Howarth a-5-6. Kemble a-1-3. Klapp a-5. Walt McDougall a-1-2. H. McVickar a-5; J. A. Mitchell a-5. Peter Newell a-2-3. Gray Parker a-4-5,7. J. Smith a-5. Albert E. Steiner a-5; T. S. Sullivant a-7-9. Wenzell a-8-10. Wilder a-3. Woolf a-3-6.)*

LIFE, THE SPICE OF (E,M,)
White and Allen: NY & London: 1888 (8-3/8x10-1/2",76 pgs, hard-c, B&W)

nn 50.00 100.00 225.00
NOTE: *Resembles **THE GOOD THINGS OF LIFE** in layout and format, and appears to be an attempt to compete with their former partner Frederick A. Stokes. However, the material is not from **LIFE**, but rather is reprinted and translated German sequential and single panel comics.*

LIFE'S PICTURE GALLERY (becomes LIFE'S PRINTS) (M,S,P)
Life Publishing Company, New York: nd (1898-1899) (paper cover, B&W) (all are scarce)

nn - (nd; 1898, 100 pgs, 5-1/4x8-1/2") Gibson-c of a woman with closed umbrella; 1st interior page announcing that after January 1, 1899 Gibson will draw exclusively for LIFE; the word "SPECIMEN" is printed in red, diagonally, across every print; a-Gibson, Rose O'Neill, Sullivant 37.50 75.00 150.00
nn - (nd; 1899, 128 pgs, 4-7/8x7-3/8") Gibson-c of a woman golfer; 1st interior page announcing that Gibson & Hanna, Jr. draw exclusively for LIFE; the word "SPECIMEN" is printed in red, horizontally, across every print. Includes prints from Gibson's **THE EDUCATION OF MR. PIPP**; a-Gibson, Sullivant 37.50 75.00 150.00
NOTE: *Catalog of prints reprinted from **LIFE** covers & centerspreads. The first catalog was given away free to anyone requesting it, but after many people got the catalog without ordering anything, subsequent catalogs were sold at 10 cents.*

LIGHT AND SHADE
William Drey Doppel Soap: 1892 (3-3/4x5-3/8", 20 pgs, B&W, color cover)

nn - By J.C. 50.00 100.00 200.00
NOTE: Contains (8) panel comic strip of black boy whose skin turns white using this soap.

LITTLE SICK BEAR, THE
Edwin W. Joy Co, San Francisco, CA: 1897 (6-1/4x5", 20 pgs, B&W, Scarce)

nn - By James Swinnerton one long sequential comic strip 200.00 400.00 850.00

LONDON OUT OF TOWN, OR THE ADVENTURES OF THE BROWNS AT THE SEA SIDE BY LUKE LIMNER, ESQ. (O)
David Bogue, 86 Fleet St, London: c1847 (5-1/2x4-1/4, 32 pgs, yellow paper hard-c, B&W

nn - By John Leighton 150.00 350.00 725.00
NOTE: one long sequential comic strip multiple-panel per page story; each page crammed with panels inspired by the Töpffer comic books Bogue began several years earlier.

LORGNETTE, THE (S)

Merryman's Monthly v3#5 with Bellew strip
May 1865 © J. C. Haney & Co., New York

Minneapolis Journal Cartoons Second Series
1895 © Minneapolis Journal

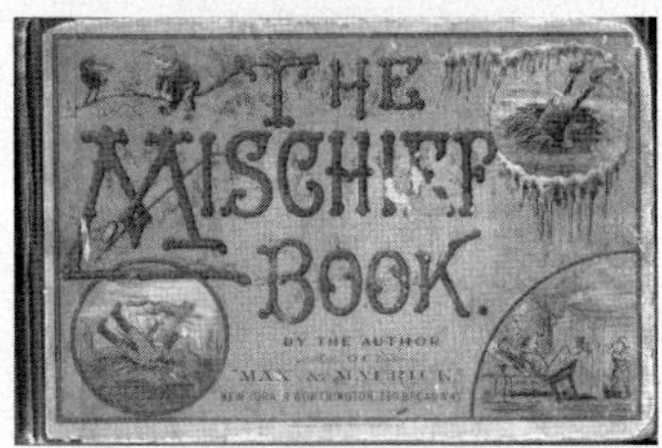

The Mischief Book by Wilhelm Busch
color cover art variation
1880 © R. Worthington, New York

George J Coombes, New York: 1886 (6-1/2x8-3/4, 38 pgs, hard-c, B&W)

nn - By J.K. Bangs 50.00 100.00 200.00

LOVING BALLAD OF LORD BATEMAN, THE (E,I)
G.W. Carleton & Co., Publishers, Madison Square, NY: 1871 (9x5-7/8",16 pgs, soft-c, 6¢)

nn - By George Cruikshank 50.00 100.00 200.00

MADISON'S EXPOSITION OF THE AWFUL & TERRIFYING CEREMONIES OF THE ODD FELLOWS
T.E. Peterson & Brothers, 306 Chestnut St, Phila: 1870s? (5-3/4x9-1/4, 68 pgs, B&W)
nn - single panel cartoons 50.00 100.00 200.00

MANNERS AND CUSTOMS OF YE HARVARD STUDENTE (M,S)
Houghton Mifflin & Co., Boston & Moses King, Cambridge: 1877 (7-7/8x11", 72 pgs, printed one side, hardc, B&W)

nn - by F.G. Attwood 100.00 225.00 450.00
NOTE: *Collection of cartoons originally serialized in the* ***Harvard Lampoon****. Attwood later became a major cartoonist for* ***Life****.*

MAN WHO WOULD LIKE TO MARRY, THE (O)
Frederick Warne & Co., London & New York: nd (c 1880's) (9-1/2x11-1/2", 28 pgs, printed 1 side, paper-c, B&W)

nn - By Harry Parkes 62.50 125.00 275.00
NOTE: *Published simultaneously with its companion volume,* ***The Girl Who Wouldn't Mind Getting Married****.*

MAX AND MAURICE: A JUVENILE HISTORY IN SEVEN TRICKS (E)
(see also Teasing Tom and Naughty Ned)
Roberts Brothers, Boston: 1871 first edition (8-1/8 x 5-1/2", 76 pgs, hard & soft-c B&W)

nn - By Wilhelm Busch (green or brown cloth hardbound) 300.00 600.00 1200.00
nn - exactly the same, but soft paper cover 175.00 350.00 700.00
NOTE: *Page count includes 56 pgs of art, two blank endpapers at the front (one colored), 8 pgs of ads at the back, two blank endpapers at the end (one colored), and the covers. Green or brown illustrated hardcover. The name of the author is given on the title page as "William Busch." We assume this to be the 1st edition. Back side of title page states: Entered according to Act of Congress, in the year 1870, by Roberts Brothers, In the office of the Librarian of Congress at Washington.*

nn - By Wilhelm Busch (1872 edition) 250.00 500.00 1200.00
nn - 1875 reprint 100.00 200.00 450.00
nn - 1882 reprint (76 pgs, hand colored- c/a, 75¢) 100.00 200.00 400.00
nn- 1889 reprint with new art on cover printed in full color 100.00 200.00 400.00
NOTE: *Each of the above contains 56 pages of art and text in a transitional format between a regular children's book and a comic book (the page count difference is ad pages in back). Seminal inspiration for William Randolph Hearst to acquire as a "new comic" (following the wild success of Outcault's Yellow Kid) to license M&M from Busch and hire Rudolph Dirks in late 1897 to create a New York American newspaper incarnation. In Hearst's English language newspapers it was called The Katzenjammer Kids and in his German language NYC newspaper it was titled Max & Moritz, Busch's original title. At least 50 other reprints versions are reputed to exist printed thru 1900. Translated from the 1865 German original. We are still sorting out the edition confusion.*

MAX AND MAURICE: A JUVENILE HISTORY IN SEVEN TRICKS (E)
(see also Teasing Tom and Naughty Ned)
Little, Brown, and Company, Boston: 1898-1902 (8-1/8 x 5-3/4", 72 pgs, hardcover, black ink on orange paper) (various early reprints)

nn - 1898 , 1899 By Wilhelm Busch 75.00 150.00 300.00
nn - 1902 (64 pages, B&W) 20.00 35.00 100.00

MERRY MAPLE LEAVES Or A Summer In The Country (S)
E.P. Dutton And Company, New York: 1872 (9-3/8x7-3/8", 90 and 86 pgs pgs, hard-c)

nn - By Abner Perk 25.00 50.00 150.00
NOTE: *Each drawing contained in a maple leaf motif by Livingston Hopkins and others.*

MERRYMAN'S MONTHLY A COMIC MAGAZINE FOR THE FAMILY (M,O,E)
J.C. Haney & Co, NY: 1863-1875 (10-7/8x7-13/16", 30 pgs average, B&W)

Certain issues with sequential comics 100.00 200.00 425.00
NOTE: *Sequential strips by Frank Bellew Sr, Wilhelm Busch found so far; others?*

MERRYTHOUGHT, OR LAUGHTER FROM YEAR TO YEAR, THE
Fisher & Brother, Phila, Baltimore: early 1850s (4-1/2x7", B&W)
nn - many singles, some sequential (Very Rare) (no known sales)
NOTE: See Vict article for back cover pic which is earliest known use of the term Comic Book

MESSRS. BROWN, JONES, AND ROBINSON, THE FOREIGN TOUR OF
(see also **THE CLOWN, OR THE BANQUET OF WIT**) (E,M,O,G)
Bradbury & Evans, London: 1854 (11-5/8x9-1/2", 196 pgs, gilted hard-c, B&W)

nn - By Richard Doyle 35.00 70.00 225.00
nn - Bradbury & Evans 1900 reprint 25.00 50.00 100.00
NOTE: *Protective sheets between each page (not part of page count). Expanded and redrawn sequential comics story from the serialized episodes originally published in PUNCH. Also comes in a 174 pg 8-3/4x11" version.*

MESSRS. BROWN, JONES, AND ROBINSON, THE LAUGHABLE ADVENTURES OF (E,M,G)
Garrett, Dick & Fitzgerald, NY: nd (1856 or 1857) (5-3/4x9-1/4", 100 pgs, printed one side only, paper-c, B&W)

nn - (Very Rare) by Richard Doyle c/a 325.00 550.00 1300.00
NOTE: *1st American reprinting of the "Foreign Tour"; reformatted into a small oblong format. Links the earlier Garrett & Co. to the later Dick & Fitzgerald. Back cover reprints full size the Garrett & Co. version cover for Oscar Shanghai. Interior front cover reprints full size the Garrett & Co. version cover for Slyfox-Wikof. Issued without a title page.*

MESSRS. BROWN, JONES, AND ROBINSON, THE FOREIGN TOUR OF (E,M,G)
D. Appleton & Co., New York: 1860 & 1877 (11-5/8x9-1/2", 196 pgs, gilted hard-c, B&W)

nn - (1860 printing) by Richard Doyle 30.00 60.00 220.00
nn - (1871 printing) by Richard Doyle 30.00 60.00 150.00
nn - (1877 printing) by Richard Doyle 30.00 60.00 150.00
NOTE: *Protective sheets between each page (not part of page count). Reprints the Bradbury & Evans edition.*

MESSRS BROWN JONES AND ROBINSON, THE AMERICAN TOUR OF (O,G)
D. Appleton & Co., New York: 1872 (11-5/8x9-1/2", 158 pgs, printed one side only, B&W, green gilted hard-c)

nn - By Toby 100.00 200.00 550.00
NOTE: *Original American graphic novel sequel to Richard Doyle's Foreign Tour of Brown, Jones, and Robinson, with the same characters visiting New York, Canada, and Cuba. Protective sheets between each page (not part of page count).*

MESSRS. BROWN, JONES, AND ROBINSON, THE LAUGHABLE ADVEN. OF (E,M,G)
Dick & Fitzgerald, NY: nd (late 1870's - 1888) (5-3/4x9-1/4", 100 pgs, printed one side only, green paper-c, B&W)

nn - (Scarce) by Richard Doyle 110.00 210.00 475.00
NOTE: *Reprints the Garrett, Dick & Fitzgerald printing, with the following changes: Takes what had been page 12 in the Garrett, D&F printing (art by M.H. Henry), and makes it a title page, which is numbered page 1. The first story page, "Go to the Races", is numbered 2 (whereas it is numbered 1 in the Garrett, Dick & Fitzgerald version). Numbering stays ahead of the G,D&F edition by 1 page up through page 12, after which the page numbering becomes identical.*

MINNEAPOLIS JOURNAL CARTOONS (N,S)
Minneapolis Journal: nn 1894 - No.2 1895 (7-3/4" x 10-7/8", 76 pgs, B&W, paper-c)

nn (1894) (Rare) 50.00 100.00 210.00
Second Series (1895) (Rare) 50.00 100.00 210.00
nn- "War Cartoons" Jan 1899 (9x8", 160 pgs, paperback, punched & string bound) (Scarce) 25.00 100.00 180.00
NOTE: *Reprints single panel cartoons from the prior year, by Charles "Bart" L. Bartholomew.*

MISCHIEF BOOK, THE (E)
R. Worthington, New York: 1880 (7-1/8 x 10-3/4", 176 pgs, hard-c, B&W)

nn - Green cloth binding; green on brown cover; cover art by R. Lewis based on Busch art by Wilhelm Busch 200.00 400.00 800.00
nn - Blue cloth binding; hand colored cover; completely different cover art based on Busch by Wilhelm Busch 200.00 400.00 800.00
NOTE: *Translated by Abby Langdon Alger. American published anthology collection of Wilhelm Busch comic strips. Includes two of the strips found in the British "Bushel of Merry-Thoughts" collection, translated better, and with the dropped panel restored. Unknown which cover version was first.*

MISSES BROWN, JONES AND ROBINSON, THE FOREIGN TOUR OF THE (E,O,G)
Bickers & Sons, London: nd (c1850's) (12-1/4" x 9-7/8", 108 pgs, printed on one side, B&W, hard-c)

nn- "by Miss Brown" (Rare) 100.00 200.00 410.00
NOTE: *A female take on Doyle's Foreign Tour, by an unknown woman artist, using the pseudonym "Miss Brown."*

MISS MILLY MILLEFLEUR'S CAREER (S)
Sheldon & Co., NY: 1869 (10-3/4x9-7/8", 74 pgs, purple hard-c)

nn - Artist unknown (Rare) 75.00 150.00 300.00

MR PODGER AT COUP'S GREATEST SHOW ON EARTH HIS HAPS AND MISHAPS, THE ADVENTURES OF (O,S)
W.C. Coup, New York: 1884 (5-5/8x4-1/4", 20 pgs, color-c, B&W)

nn - Circus Themes; Similar to Barker's Comic Almanacs 30.00 60.00 110.00

MR. TOODLES' GREAT ELEPHANT HUNT (See Peter Piper in Bengal)
Brother Jonathan, NYC: 1850s (4-1/4x7-7/8", page count presently unknown)

nn - catalog contains comic strip (Very Rare) (no known sales)

MR. TOODLES' TERRIFIC ELEPHANT HUNT
Dick & Fitzgerald, NYC: 1860s (5-3/4x9-1/4", 32 pgs, paper-c, B&W) (Very Rare)

nn - catalog reprint contains 28 panel comic strip 150.00 300.00 650.00

MRS GRUNDY
Mrs Grundy Publishing Co, NYC: July 8 1865-Sept 30 1865 (weekly)

1-13 Thomas Nast, Hoppin, Stephens, 50.00 100.00 200.00

MUSEUM OF WONDERS, A (O,I)
Routledge & Sons: 1894 (13x10", 64 pgs, color-c, color thru out)

nn - By Frederick Opper 125.00 250.00 520.00

MY FRIEND WRIGGLES, A (Laughter) Moving Panorama, of His Fortunes And Misfortunes, Illustrated With Over 200 Engravings, of Most Comic Catastrophes And Side-Splitting Merriment) (O,G)
Stearn & Co, 202 Williams St, NY: 1850s (5-7/8x9-3/4", 100 pgs, B&W)

nn - By S. P. Avery (also the engraver) (Very Rare) 250.00 500.00 1000.00

MY SKETCHBOOK (E,S)
Dana Estes & Charles E. Lauriat, Boston; J. Sabins & Sons, New York: circa 1880s (9-3/8x12", brown hard-c)

nn - By George Cruikshank 25.00 50.00 150.00
NOTE: *Reprints British editions 1834-36; extensive usage of word balloons.*

Nasby's Life Of Andy Jonson
1866 © Jesse Haney Company

99 "Woolf's" from Truth
1896 © Truth Company

The Adventures of Obadiah Oldbuck 4th printing
mid-1850s © Brother Jonathan Offices, NY

FR1.0 GD2.0 FN6.0

NASBY'S LIFE OF ANDY JONSON (O, M)
Jesse Haney Co., Publishers No. 119 Nassau St, NY: 1866 (4-1/2x7-1/2, 48 pgs, B&W)
nn - President Andrew Johnson satire 125.00 250.00 500.00
NOTE: Blurb further reads: With a True Pictorial History of His STumping Tour Out West By Petroleum V. Nasby, A Dimmicrat of Thirty Years Standing, And Who Allus Tuk His Licker Straight. Front of book has long sequential comic strip satire on President Andrew Johnson, misspelling his name on the cover on purpose.

NAST'S ILLUSTRATED ALMANAC
Harper & Brothers, Franklin Square, NYC: 1872-1874 (8x5.5", 80 pgs, B&W, 35¢)
nn 65.00 125.00 250.00

NAST'S WEEKLY (O,S)
???: 1892-93 (Quarto Weekly)
all issues scarce 50.00 100.00 200.00

NATIONAL COMIC ALMANAC
An Association of Gentlemen, Boston: 1838-?? (8.25x4.75", 34 pgs, B&W)
nn 60.00 120.00 250.00

NEW AMERICAN COMIC ALL-IMAKE (ELTON'S BASKET OF COMICAL SCRAPS), THE
Elton, Publisher, New York: 1839 (7-1/2x4-5/8, 24 pgs)
1 100.00 200.00 400.00

NEW BOOK OF NONSENSE, THE: A Contribution To The Great Central Fair In Aid of the Sanitary Commission (O,S)
Ashmead & Evans, No. 724 Chestnut St, Philadelphia: June 1864 (red hard-c)
nn - Artists unknown (Scarce) 50.00 150.00 300.00

NEW YORK ILLUSTRATED NEWS
Frank Leslie, NYC: 10/14/76-June 1884
average issues with comic strips 25.00 50.00 100.00

NEW YORK PICAYUNE (see PHUN FOTOCRAFT)
Woodward & Hutchings: 1850-1855 newspaper-size weekly; 1856-1857 Folio Monthly 16x10.5; 1857-1858 Quarto Weekly; 1858-1860 Quarto Weekly
Average Issue With Comic Strips 50.00 100.00 200.00
Issues with Full Front Page Comic Strip 100.00 200.00 400.00
NOTE: *Many issues contain Frank Bellew sequential comic strips & single panel cartoons. Later issues published by Woodward, Levison & Robert Gun (1853-1857) ; Levison & Thompson (1857-1860)*

NICK-NAX
Levison & Haney, NY: 1857-1858? (11x7-3/4", 32 pgs, B&W, paper-c)
v2 #10 Feb 1858 has many single panel cartoons 50.00 100.00 200.00

99 "WOOLFS" FROM TRUTH (see Sketches of Lowly Life in a Great City, Truth)
Truth Company, NY: 1896 (9x5-1/2", 72 pgs, varnished paper-like cloth hard-c, 25 cents)
nn - By Michael Angelo Woolf (Rare) 150.00 300.00 600.00
NOTE: *Woolf's cartoons are regarded as a primary influence on R.F. Outcault in the later development of The Yellow Kid newspaper strip. Copy sold in 2002 on eBay for $800.00.*

NONSENSE OR, THE TREASURE BOX OF UNCONSIDERED TRIFLES
Fisher & Brother, 12 North Sixth St, Phila, PA, 64 Baltimore St, Baltimore, MD: early 1850s (4-1/2x7", 128 pgs, B&W)
nn - much Davy Crocket sequential story-telling comic strips 300.00 600.00 1200.00

OBADIAH OLDBUCK, THE ADVENTURES OF MR. (E,G)
Tilt & Bogue, London: nd (1840-41) (5-15/16x9-3/16", 176 pgs,B&W, gilted hard-c)
nn - By Rodolphe Töpffer 800.00 1300.00 3100.00
nn - Hand coloured edition (Very Rare) (no known sales)
NOTE: *This is the British edition, translating the unauthorized redrawn 1839 edition from Parisian publisher Aubert, adapted from Töpffer's "Les Amours de Mr. Vieux Bois" (aka "Histoire de Mr. Vieux Bois"), originally published in French in Switzerland, in 1837 (2nd ed. 1839). Early 19th century books are often found rebound, with original cover and/or title page gone. To distinguish editions having no cover or title page: the British oblong editions (published by Tilt & Bogue) use Roman Numerals to number pages. American oblong shaped editions use Arabic Numerals. British are printed on one side only. This is the earliest known English language sequential comic book. Has a new title page with art by Robert Cruikshank.*

OBADIAH OLDBUCK, THE ADVENTURES OF MR. (E,G)
Wilson and Company, New York: September 14, 1842 (11-3/4x9", 44 pgs, B&W, yellow paper-c on bookstand editions, hemp paper interior)
Brother Jonathan Extra No. IX - Rare bookstand edition 2200.00 5000.00 10,000.00
Brother Jonathan Extra No. IX Very Rare subscriber/mailorder 2200.00 5000.00 10,000.00
NOTE: *By Rodolphe Töpffer. Earliest known sequential American comic book, reprinting the 1841 British edition. Pages are numbered via Roman numerals. States "BROTHER JONATHAN EXTRA - ADVENTURES OF MR. OBADIAH OLDBUCK." at the top of each page. Prints 2 to 3 tiers of panels on both sides of each page. Copies could be had for ten cents according to adverts in* ***Brother Jonathan***. *By Rodolphe Töpffer with cover masthead design by David Claypool Johnston, and cover art beneath the masthead reprinting Robert Cruikshank's title page art from the Tilt & Bogue edition. A special, additional cover was added for copies sold on stands (it was not issued with mail order or subscriber copies). Only 1 known copy possesses (partially) this very thin outer yellow cover. A decent (subscriber) copy sold on eBay in later October 2002 for over $3500.00. In 2005, a G/VG for $20,000; and a VG for $20,000. An apparent GD copy sold in auction in 2007 for $9560. A FA/GD copy sold in 2008 for $4182.50. A bound edition sold in 2010 for $2270.50. (Prices vary widely.)*

OBADIAH OLDBUCK, THE ADVENTURES OF MR. (E,G)
Wilson & Co, New York: nd (1849) (5-11/16x8-3/8", 84 pgs, B&W,paper-c)
nn - by Rodolphe Töpffer; title page by Robert Cruikshank (Very Rare) 500.00 1200.00 4100.00
NOTE: *2nd Wilson & Co printing, reformatted into a small oblong format, with nine panels edited out, and text modified to smooth out this removal. Results in four less printed tiers/strips. Pages are numbered via Arabic numerals. Every panel on Pages 11, 14, 19, 21, 24, 34, 35 has one line of text. Reformatted to conform with British first edition.*

OBADIAH OLDBUCK, THE ADVENTURES OF MR. (E,G)
Wilson & Co, 162 Nassau, NY: nd (early-1850s) (5-11/16x8-3/8", 84 pgs, B&W, yellow-c
nn - 3rd USA Printing by Rodolphe Töpffer; title page by Robert Cruikshank (Very Rare) Says By Timothy Crayon, an obvious pseudonym 800.00 1600.00 4100.00
NOTE: *Front cover banner the giant is holding says "Done With Drawings By Timothy Crayon, Gypsographer, 188 Comic Etchings On Antimony" Title page changes address to No. 15 Spruce-Street. (Late 162 Nassau Street.)*

OBADIAH OLDBUCK, THE ADVENTURES OF MR..
Brother Jonathan Offices: ND (mid-1850s) (5-11/16x8-3/8", 84 pages, B&W, oblong)
nn - 4th printing; Originally by Rodolphe Töpffer (Very Rare) 500.00 1200.00 4100.00
NOTE: *Cover States: "New York: Published at the Brother Jonathan Office". Front cover banner the giant is holding says "Done With Drawings By Timothy Crayon, Gypsographer, 188 Comic Designs On Antimony."*

OBADIAH OLDBUCK, THE ADVENTURES OF MR. (E,G)
Dick & Fitzgerald, New York: nd (various printings; est. 1870s to 1888) (Thirty Cents, 84 pgs, B&W, paper-c) (all versions scarce)
nn - Black print on green cover(5-11/16x8-15/16"); string bound 200.00 400.00 1000.00
nn - Black print on blue cover; same format as green-c 200.00 400.00 1000.00
nn - Black print on white cover(5-13/16x9-3/16"); staple bound beneath cover); this is a later printing than the blue or green-c 200.00 400.00 1000.00
NOTE: *Reprints the abbreviated 1849 Wilson & Co. 2nd printing. Pages are numbered via Arabic numerals. Many of the panels on Pages 11, 14, 19, 21, 24, 34, 35 take two lines to print the same words found in the Wilson & Co version, which used only one text line for the same panels. Unknown whether the blue or green cover is earlier. White cover version has "thirty cents" line blackened out on the two copies known to exist. Robert Cruikshank's title page has been made the cover in the D&F editions.*

OLD FOGY'S COMIC ALMANAC
Philip J. Cozans, NY: 1858 (4-7/8x7-1/4, 48 pgs)
nn - sequential comic strip told one panel per page 50.00 100.00 220.00
NOTE: Contains (12) panel "Fourth of July in New York" sequential

OLD MOTHER MITTEN AND HER FUNNY KITTEN (see also **The Juvenile Gem**) (O)
Huestis & Cozans: nd(1850-1852) (6x3-7/8"12pgs, hand colored paper-c, B&W)
nn - first printing(s) publisher's address is 104 Nassau Street (1850-1851) (Very Rare) (no known sales)
NOTE: *A hand colored outer cover is highly rare, with only 1 recorded copy possessing it. Front cover image and text is repeated precisely on page 3 (albeit b&w), and only interior pages are numbered, together leading owners of coverless copies to believe they have the cover. The true back cover has ads for the publisher. Cover was issued only with copies which were sold separately - books which were bound together as part of THE JUVENILE GEM never had such covers.*

OLD MOTHER MITTEN AND HER FUNNY KITTEN (see JUVENILE GEM) (O)
Philip J. Cozans: nd (1850-1852) (6x3-7/8",12 pgs, hand colored paper-c, B&W)
nn - Second printing(s) publisher's address is 116 Nassau Street (1851-1852) (Very Rare) (no known sales)
nn - Third printing(s) publisher's address is 107 Nassau Street (1852+) (Very Rare) (no known sales)

OLD MOTHER MITTEN AND HER FUNNY KITTEN
Americana Review, Scotia, NY: nd (1960's) (6-1/4x4-1/8", 8 pgs, side-stapled, cardboard, B&W)
nn - Modern reprint 5.00 10.00 15.00
NOTE: *Issued within a folder titled SIX CHILDREN'S BOOKS OF THE 1850'S. States "Reprinted by American Review" at bottom of front cover. Reprints the 104 Nassau Street address.*

ON THE NILE (O,G)
James R. Osgood & Co., Boston: 1874 ; **Houghton, Osgood & Co., Boston:** 1880 (112 pgs, gilted green hardcover, B&W)
1st printing (1874; 10-3/4x16") - by Augustus Hoppin 50.00 100.00 200.00
2nd printing (1880; smaller sized) 32.50 65.00 130.00

OSCAR SHANGHAI, THE EXTRAORDINARY AND MIRTH-PROVKING ADVENTURES BY SEA & LAND OF (O, G)
Garrett & Co., Publishers, No. 18 Ann Street, New York: May 1855 (5-3/4x9-1/4", 100 pgs, printed one side only, paper-c, 25¢, B&W)
nn - Samuel Avery-c; interior by ALC Very Rare) 1000.00 2000.00 4000.00
NOTE: *Not much is known of this first edition as the data comes from a recently rediscovered* ***Brother Jonathan*** *catalog issued circa 1853-55. No original known yet to exist.*

OSCAR SHANGHAI, THE WONDERFUL AND AMUSING DOINGS BY SEA AND LAND OF (G)
Dick & Fitzgerald, 10 Ann St, NY: nd (1870s-1888) (25 ¢, 5-3/4x9-1/4", 100 pgs, printed one side only, green paper c, B&W)
nn - Cover by Samuel Avery; interior by ALC (Rare) 300.00 500.00 1100.00
NOTE: *Exact reprint of Garrett & Co original.*

OUR ARTIST IN CUBA (O)
Carleton, New York: 1865 (6-5/8x4-3/8", 120 pgs, printed one side only, gilted hard-c, B&W)
nn - By Geo. W. Carleton 50.00 100.00 200.00

OUR ARTIST IN CUBA, PERU, SPAIN, AND ALGIERS (O)
Carleton: 1877 (6-1/2x5-1/8", 156 pgs, hard-c, B&W)
nn - By Geo. W. Carleton 50.00 100.00 200.00
nn - By Geo. W. Carleton (wraps paper cover) (Rare) 45.00 90.00 180.00

The Wonderful and Amusing Doings by Sea & Land of Oscar Shanghai
1870s © Dick & Fitzgerald, New York

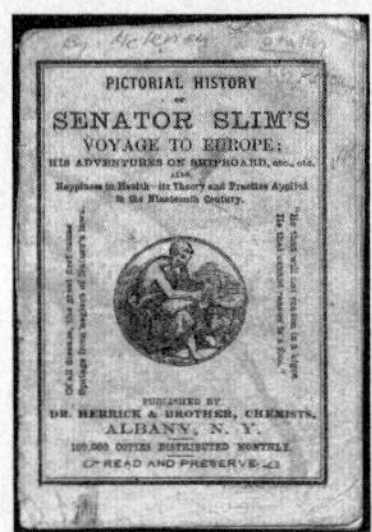

Pictorial History of Senator Slim's Voyage To Europe
1860 © Dr. Herrick & Brother, Albany, NY

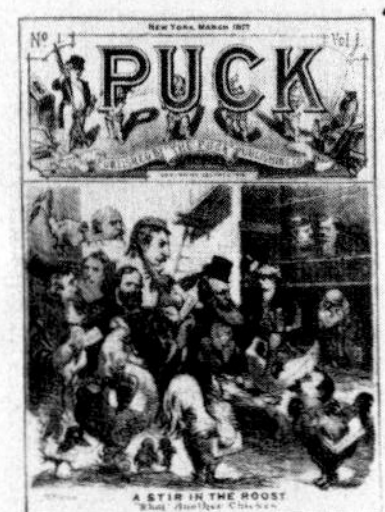

Puck #1
1877 © Keppler & Schwarzman, NY

FR1.0 GD2.0 FN6.0

NOTE: *Reprints OUR ARTIST IN CUBA and OUR ARTIST IN PERU, then adds new section on Spain and Algiers.*

OUR ARTIST IN PERU (O)
Carleton, New York: 1866 (7-3/4x5-7/8", 68 pgs, gilted hardcover, B&W)
nn- By Geo. W. Carleton 37.50 75.00 150.00
NOTE: *Contains advertisement for the upcoming books* ***OUR ARTIST IN ITALY*** *and* ***OUR ARTIST IN FRANCE***, *but no such publications have been found to date.*

PARSON SOURBALL'S EUROPEAN TOUR (O)
Duff and Ashmead: 1867 (6x7-1/2", 76 pgs, blue embossed title hard-c)
nn - By Horace Cope 100.00 200.00 400.00
NOTE: see **REV. MR. SOURBALL'S EUROPEAN TOUR, THE** for the soft paper cover version

PEN AND INK SKETCHES OF YALE NOTABLES (O,S)
Soule, Thomas and Winsor, St. Louis: 1872 (12-1/4x9-3/4", B&W)
By Squills 25.00 50.00 110.00
NOTE: *Printed by Steamlith Press, The R.P. Studley Company, St Louis.*

PETER PIPER IN BENGAL
Bengamin H Day.Publisher, Brother Jonathan Cheap Book Establishment, 48 Beekman, NY: 1953-55 (6-5/8x4-1/4, 36 pgs, yellow paper-c, B&W, 3 cents - two dollars per hundred) (Very Rare)
nn - By John Tenniel - 32 panel comic strip Punch-r 500.00 1000.00 2300.00
NOTE: *Actually also a catalog of inexpensive books, prints, maps and half a dozen comic books for sale on separate pages from publishers Day and Garrett - see full story of this brand new find in the Victorian Era essay. A complete copy with split spine sold in November 2002 for $750.00. Published date most likely 1855.*

THE PHILADELPHIA COMIC ALMANAC (S)
G. Strong, 44 Strawberry St, NYC: 1835 (8-1/2x5", 36 pgs)
nn - 100.00 200.00 600.00
NOTE: *77 engravings full of recurring cartoon characters but not sequential; early use of recurring characters.*

PHIL MAY'S SKETCH BOOK (E,S,M)
R.H. Russell, New York: 1899 (14-5/8x10", 64 pgs, brown hard-c, B&W)
nn - By Phil May 35.00 70.00 140.00
NOTE: *American reprint of the British edition.*

PHUNNY PHELLOW, THE
Oakie, Dayton & Jones: Oct 1859-1876; **Street & Smith** 1876: (Folio Monthly)
average issue with Thomas Nast 50.00 100.00 200.00

PHUN FOTOCRAFT, KEWREUS KONSEETS KOMICALLY ILLUSTRATED BY A KWEER FELLER (N) (see **NEW YORK PICAYUNE)**
The New York Picayune, NY: 1850s (104 pgs)
nn - Mostly Frank Bellew, some John Leach 250.00 550.00 1100.00
NOTE: Many sequential comic strips as well as single cartoons all collected from The New York Picayune. Ross & Tousey, Agents, 121 Nassau St, NY. The Picayune ran many sequential comic strips in its decade.

PICTORIAL HISTORY OF SENATOR SLIM'S VOYAGE TO EUROPE
Dr. Herrick & Brother, Chemists, Albany, NY: 1860 (3-1/4x4-3/4", 32 pgs, B&W)
nn - By John McLenan Very Rare 150.00 300.00 600.00

PICTURES OF ENGLISH SOCIETY (Parchment-Paper Series, No.4) (M,S,E)
D. Appleton & Co., New York: 1884 (5-5/8x4-3/8", 108 pgs, paper-c, B&W)
4 - By George du Maurier; Punch-r 30.00 60.00 125.00
NOTE: *Every other page is a full page cartoon, with the opposite page containing the cartoon's caption.*

PICTURES OF LIFE AND CHARACTER (M,S,E)
Bradbury and Evans, London: No.1 1855 - No.5 c1864 (12-1/2x18", 100 pgs, illustrated hard-c, B&W)
nn (No.1) (1855) 35.00 70.00 150.00
2 (1858), 3 (1860) 35.00 70.00 150.00
4 (nd; c1862) 5 (nd; c1864) 35.00 70.00 150.00
nn (nd (late 1860's) 32.50 65.00 140.00
NOTE: 2-1/2x18-1/4", 494 pgs, green gilted-c) reprints 1-5 in one book
1-3 John Leech's... (nd; 12-3/8x10", ? pgs, red gilted-c). 25.00 50.00 100.00
NOTE: *Reprints John Leech cartoons from* ***Punch***. *note that the Volume Number is mentioned only on the last page of these versions.*

PICTURES OF LIFE AND CHARACTER (E,M,S)
G.P. Putnam's Sons: 1880's (8-5/8x6-1/4", 218 pgs, hardcover, color-cr, B&W)
nn - John Leech (single panel **Punch** cartoon-r) 20.00 40.00 160.00
NOTE: *Leech reprints which extend back to the 1850s.*

PICTURES OF LIFE AND CHARACTER (Parchment-Paper Series) (E,M,S)
(see also Humerous Masterpieces)
D. Appleton & Co., NY: 1884 (30¢, 5-3/4 x 4-1/2", 104 pgs, paper-c, B&W)
nn - John Leech (single panel **Punch** cartoon-r) 20.00 40.00 160.00
NOTE: *An advertisment in the back refers to a cloth-bound edition for 50 cents.*

PIPPIN AMONG THE WIDE-AWAKES (O,S)
Werill & Chapin, 113 Nassau St, NYC, NY): 1860 (6x4-1/2", 36 pgs, 6 cents)
nn - Artist unknown (Very Rare) 100.00 200.00 400.00

PLISH AND PLUM (E.G)
Roberts Brothers, Boston: 1883 (8-1/8x5-3/4", 80 pgs, hardcover, B&W)
nn - By Wilhelm Busch 50.00 100.00 225.00

FR1.0 GD2.0 FN6.0

nn - Reprint (Roberts Brothers, 1895) 40.00 80.00 200.00
nn - Reprint (Little, Brown & Co., 1899) 40.00 80.00 200.00
NOTE: *The adventures of two dogs.*

POUNDS OF FUN
Frank Tousey, 34 North Moore St, NY: 1881 (6-1/2x9-1/2", 68pgs, B&W)
nn - Bellew, Worth, Woolf, Chips 40.00 80.00 200.00

PRESIDENTS MESSAGE, THE
G.P. Putnam's Sons, NY: 1887 (5-3/4x7-5/8, 44 pgs)
nn - (19) Thomas Nast single panel full page cartoons 40.00 80.00 200.00

PROTECT THE U.S. FROM JOHN BULL - PROTECTION PICTURES FROM JUDGE
Judge Publishing, New York: 1888 ((10 cents, 6-7/8x10-3/8", 36 pgs, paper-c, B&W)
nn - (Scarce) 30.00 60.00 130.00
NOTE: *Reprints both cartoons and commentary from* ***Puck***, *concerning the issue of tariffs which were then being debated in Congress. Art by Gillam, Hamilton, Victor.*

PUCK (German language edition, St. Louis) (M,O) (see also Die Vehme)
Publisher unknown, St. Louis: No.1, March 18, 1871 - No. ??, Aug. 24, 1872 (B&W, paper-c)
1-?? (Very Rare) by Joseph Keppler (no known sales)
NOTE: *Joseph Keppler's second attempt at a weekly humor periodical, following* ***Die Vehme*** *one year earlier. This was his first attempt to launch using the title* ***Puck***. *This German language version ran for a full year before being joined by an English language version.*

PUCK (English language edition, St. Louis) (M,O)
Publisher unknown, St. Louis: No.1, March ?? 1872 - No. ??, Aug. 24, 1872 (B&W, paper c)
1-?? (Very Rare) by Joseph Keppler (no known sales)
NOTE: *Same material as in the German language edition, but in English.*

PUCK, ILLUSTRIRTES HUMORISTISCHES WOCHENBLATT (German language edition, NYC) (M,O)
Keppler & Schwarzmann, New York: No.1 Sept (27) 1876 - 1164 Dec ?? 1899 (10 cents, color front/back-c and centerspread, remainder B&W, paper-c)
1-26 (Volume 1; Rare) by Joseph Keppler - these issues precede the English language version, and contain cartoons not found in them. Includes cartoons on the controversial Tilden-Hayes 1876 Presidential Election debacle. (no known sales)
27-52 (Volume 2; Rare) by Joseph Keppler - contains some cartoon material not found in the English language editions. Particularly in the earlier issues. (no known sales)
53-1164 15.00 30.00 60.00
Bound Volumes (six month, 26 issue run each):
Vol. 1 (Rare) (no known sales)
Vol. 2-4 (Rare) (no known sales)
Vol. 5-47 75.00 150.00 300.00
NOTE: *Joseph Keppler's second, and successful, attempt to launch* ***Puck***. *In German. The first six months precede the launch of the English language edition. Soon after (but not immediately after) the launch of the English edition, both editions began sharing the same cartoons, but, their prose material always remained different. The German language edition ceased publication at the end of 1899, while the English language edition continued into the early 20th Century. First American periodical to feature printed color every issue.*

PUCK (English language edition, NYC) (M,O)
Keppler & Schwarzmann, New York: No.1 March (14) 1877 - 1190 Dec ?? 1899 (10 cents, color front/back-c and centerspread, remainder B&W, paper-c)
1 (Rare) by Joseph Keppler (no known sales)
2-26 (Rare) by Joseph Keppler (no known sales)
27-1190 12.50 25.00 50.00
(see Platinum Age section for year 1900+ issues)
Bound volumes (six month, 26 issue run each):
Vol. 1 (Rare) (one set sold on eBay for $2300.00)
Vol. 2 (Scarce) (one set sold on eBay for $1500.00)
Vol. 3-6 (pre-1880 issues) 175.00 375.00 750.00
Vol. 7-46 140.00 300.00 600.00
NOTE: *The English language editions began six months after the German editions, and so the English edition numbering is always one volume number, and 26 issue numbers, behind its parallel German language edition. Pre-1880 & post-1900 issues are more scarce than 1880's & 1890's.*

PUCK (miniature) (M,P,I)
Keppler & Schwarzmann, New York: nd (c1895) (7x5-1/8", 12 pgs, color front & back paper-c, B&W interior)
nn - Scarce 25.00 50.00 110.00
NOTE: *C.J.Taylor-c; F.M.Howarth-a; F.Opper-a; giveaway item promoting* ***Puck's*** *various publications. Mostly text, with art reprinted from* ***Puck***.

PUCK, CARTOONS FROM (M,S)
Keppler & Schwarzmann, New York: 1893 (14-1/4x11-1/2", 244 pgs, hard-c, mostly B&W)
nn - by Joseph Keppler (Signed and Numbered) 105.00 225.00 450.00
NOTE: *Reprints Keppler cartoons from 1877 to 1893, mostly in B&W, though a few in color, with a text opposite each cartoon explaining the situation then being satirized. Issued only in an edition of 300 numbered issues, signed by Keppler. Only 1/4 of the pages are cartoons.*

PUCK'S LIBRARY (M)
Keppler & Schwarzmann, New York: No.1, July, 1887 - No. 174, Dec, 1899 (10 cents, 11-1/2x8-1/4", 36 pgs, color paper-c, B&W)
1- "The National Game" (Baseball) 65.00 125.00 250.00
2-149 10.00 20.00 50.00
NOTE: ***Puck's Library*** *was a monthly magazine reprinting cartoons & prose from* ***Puck***, *with each issue's*

Rays of Light
1886 © Morse Bros., Canton, Mass.

Scraps, New Series #1 by D.C. Johnston
1849 © D.C. Johnston, Boston

Shakespeare Would Ride The Bicycle If Alive Today
1896 © Cleveland Bicycles, Toledo, OH.

material organized around the same subject. The cover art was often original. All issues were kept in print for the duration of the series, so later issues are more scarce than earlier ones.

PUCK, PICKINGS FROM (M)
Keppler & Schwarzmann, New York: No.1, Sept, 1891 - No. 34, Dec, 1899 (25 cents, 13-1/4x10-1/4", 68 pgs, color paper-c, B&W)

1-34 Scarce 25.00 50.00 110.00
NOTE: *Similar to **Puck's Library**, except larger in size, and issued quarterly. All reprint material, except for the cover art. There also exist variations with "RAILROAD EDITION 30 CENTS" printed on the cover in place of the standard 25 cent price.*

PUCK'S OPPER BOOK (M)
Keppler & Schwarzmann, New York: 1888 (11-3/4x13-7/8", color paper-c, 68 pgs,interior B&W, 30¢)

nn - (Very Rare) by F. Opper 225.00 450.00 800.00
NOTE: *Puck's first book collecting work by a single artist.; mostly sequential comic strips.*

PUCK'S PRINTING BOOK FOR CHILDREN (S,O.I)
Keppler & Schwarzman, Pubs, NY: 1891 (10-3/8x7-7/8", 52 pgs, color-c, B&W and color)

nn - Frederick B Opper (Very Rare) (no known sales)

NOTE: *Left side printed in color; Right side B&W to be colored in.*

PUCK PROOFS (M,P,S)
Keppler & Schwarzmann, New York: nd (1906-1909) (74 pgs, paper cover; B&W) (all are Scarce)

nn - (c.1906, no price, 4-1/8x5-1/4") B&W painted -c of couple kissing over a chess board; 1905 & 1906-r 25.00 50.00 100.00
nn- (c.1909, 10 cents, 4-3/8x5-3/8") plain green paper-c; 76 pgs 1905-1909-r 25.00 50.00 100.00
NOTE: *Catalog of prints available from **Puck**, reprinting mostly cover & centerspread art from **Puck**. There likely exist more as yet unreported **Puck Proofs** catalogs. Art by Rose O'Neill.*

PUCK, THE TARIFF ?, CARTOONS AND COMMENTS FROM (M,S)
Keppler & Schwarzmann, New York: 1888 (10 cents, 6-7/8x10-3/8", 36 pgs, paper-c, B&W)

nn - (Scarce) 37.50 75.00 200.00
NOTE: *Reprints both cartoons and commentary from **Puck**, concerning the issue of tariffs which were then being debated in Congress. Art by Gillam, Keppler, Opper, Taylor.*

PUCK, WORLD'S FAIR
Keppler & Schwarzmann, PUCK BUILDING, World's Fair Grounds, Chicago: No.1 May 1, 1893 - No.26 Oct 30, 1893 (10 cents, 11-1/4x8-3/4, 14 pgs, paper-c, color front/back/center pages, rest B&W)(All issues Scarce to Rare)

1-26 35.00 70.00 140.00
1-26 bound volume: 500.00 1100.00 2300.00
NOTE: *Art by Joseph Keppler, F. Opper, F.M. Howarth, C.J. Taylor, W.A. Rogers. This was a separate, parallel run of **Puck**, published during the 1893 Chicago World's Fair from within the fairgrounds, and containing all new and different material than the regular weekly **Puck**. Smaller sized and priced the same, this originally sold poorly, and had not as wide distribution as **Puck**, and so consequently issues are much more rare than regular **Puck** issues from the same period. Not to be confused with the larger sized regular **Puck** issues from 1893 which sometimes also contained World's Fair related material, and sometimes had the words "World's Fair" appear on the cover. Can also be distinguished by the fact that **Puck's** issue numbering was in the 800's in 1893, while these issue number 1 through 26.*

PUNCHINELLO
Punchinello Publishing Co, NYC: April 2-Dec 24 1870 (weekly)

1-39 Henry L. Stephens, Frank Bellew, Bowlend 25.00 50.00 100.00
NOTE: *Funded by the Tweed Ring, mild politics attacking Grant Admin & other NYC newspapers. Bound copies exist.*

QUIDDITIES OF AN ALASKAN TRIP (O,G)
G.A. Steel & Co., Portland, OR: 1873 (6-3/4x10-1/2", 80 pgs, gilted hard-c, Red-c and Blue-c exist, B&W)

nn - By William H. Bell (Scarce) 350.00 750.00 1700.00
NOTE: *Highly sought Western Americana collectors. Parody of a trip from Washington DC to Alaska, by a member of the team which went to survey Alaska, purchase commonly known then as "Seward's Folly".*

"RAG TAGS" AND THEIR ADVENTURES, THE (N,S)
A. M. Robertson, San Francisco: 1899 (10-1/4x13-7/8, 84 pgs, color hard-c, B&W inside)

nn - By Arthur M. Lewis (SF Chronicle newspaper-r) (Scarce) 65.00 125.00 300.00

RAYS OF LIGHT (O,P)
Morse Bros., Canton, Mass.: No.1 1886 (7-1/8x5-1/8", 8 pgs, color paper-c, B&W)

1- (Rare) 50.00 100.00 200.00
NOTE: *Giveaway pamphlet in guise of an educational publication, consisting entirely of a sequential story in which a teacher instructs her classroom of young girls in the use of Rising Sun Stove Polish. Color front & back covers.*

RELIC OF THE ITALIAN REVOLUTION OF 1849, A
Gabici's Music Stores, New Orleans: 1849 (10-1/8x12-3/4", 144 pgs, hardcover)

nn - By G. Daelli (Scarce) 100.00 210.00 420.00
NOTE: *From the title page: "Album of fifty line engravings, executed on copper, by the most eminent artists at Rome in 1849; secreted from the papal police after the 'Restoration of Order,' And just imported into America."*

REMARKS ON THE JACOBINIAD (I,S)
E.W. Weld & W. Greenough, Boston: 1795-98 (8-1/4x5-1/8", 72 pgs, a number of B&W plates with text)

nn - Written by Rev. James Sylvester Gardner,artist unknown (Rare) (no known sales)
NOTE: *Early comics-type characters. Not sequential comics, but uses word balloons. Satire directed against "The Jacobin Club," supporters of the French Revolution and Radical Republicans. Gardner came to America from England in 1783, was minister of Trinity Church, Boston. There appears to be some reprints of this done as late as 1798.*

REV. MR. SOURBALL'S EUROPEAN TOUR, THE RECREATION OF A CITY, THE
Duffield Ashmead, Philadelphia: 1867 (7-5/8x6-1/4", 72 pgs, turquoise blue soft wrappers)

By Horace Cope (Rare) 50.00 100.00 225.00
NOTE: see **PARSON SOURBALL'S EUROPEAN TOUR** for the hard cover version.

RHYMES OF NONSENSE TRUTH & FICTION (S)
G.W. Carleton & Co, Publishers, NY: 1874 (10x7-3/4", 44 pgs, hard-c, B&W) (Very Rare)

nn - By Chaucer Jones and Michael Angelo Raphael Smith 100.00 200.00 450.00
NOTE: *Creator names obviously pseudonyms; looks like weak A.B. Frost.*

ROMANCE OF A HAMMOCK, THE - AS RECITED BY MR. GUS WILLIAMS IN "ONE OF THE FINEST" (O,P)
Unknown: 1880s (5-1/2x3-5/8" folded, 7 attached cardboard cards which fold out into a strip, color)

nn - By presently unknown Scarce 75.00 150.00 375.00
NOTE: *12-panel story, which one begins reading on one side of the folded-out strip, then flip to the other side to continue -- unlike the vast majority of folded strips, which are printed on only one side. This was a promotional handout, for a play titled "One of the Finest". The story pictured comes from a poem read in the play by then famous New York stage actor Gus Williams, who is pictured on the "cover"/title card."*

SAD TALE OF THE COURTSHIP OF CHEVALIER SLYFOX-WIKOF, SHOWING HIS HEART-RENDING ASTOUNDING & MOST WONDERFUL LOVE ADVENTURES WITH FANNY ELSSLER AND MISS GAMBOL, THE (O,G)
Garrett & Co., NY: Jan 1856 (25 ¢, 5-3/4x9-1/4", 100 pages, paper-c, B&W)

nn - By T.C. Bond ?? (Very Rare) 550.00 1100.00 2200.00
NOTE: *No surviving copies yet reported -- known via ads in Home Circle published by Garrett. Cover art by John McLenan and Samuel Avery. Graphic novel parodying the real-life romance between European actress/dancer Fanny Elssler and American aristocrat Henry Wikoff. The entire graphic novel is reprinted in the 1976 book "Fanny Elssler in America."*

SAD TALE OF THE COURTSHIP OF CHEVALIER SLYFOX-WIKOF, SHOWING HIS HEART-RENDING ASTOUNDING & MOST WONDERFUL LOVE ADVENTURES WITH FANNY ELSSLER AND MISS GUMBEL, THE (G) (25 cents printed on cover)
Dick And Fitzgerald, NY: 1870s-1888 (5-3/4x9-1/4", ??? pages, soft paper-c, B&W)

nn - By T.C. Bond ?? (Very Rare) 250.00 500.00 1100.00
NOTE: *Reprint of Garrett original printing before G,D&F partnership begins.*

SALT RIVER GUIDE FOR DISAPPOINTED POLITICIANS
Winchell, Small & Co., 113 Fulton St, NY: 1870s (16 pgs, 10¢)

nn - single panel cartoons from WIld Oats (Rare) 75.00 150.00 300.00

SAM SLICK'S COMIC ALMANAC
Philip J. Cozans, NYC: 1857 (7.5x4.5, 48 pgs, B&W) 100.00 200.00 400.00
NOTE: *Contains reprint of* "Moses Keyser the Bowery Bully's Trip to the California Gold Mines" *from* Elton's Comic Almanac #17 1850.

SCRAPS (O,S) (see also **F****** A*** K*****)
D.C. Johnston, Boston: 1828 - No.8 1840; New Series No.1 1849 (12 pgs, printed one side only, paper-c, B&W)

1 - 1828 (9-1/4 x 11-3/4") (Very Rare) (no known sales)
2 - 1830 (9-3/4 x 12-3/4") (Very Rare) (no known sales)
3 - 1832 (10-7/8 x 13-1/8") (Very Rare) (no known sales)
4 - 1833 (11 x 13-5/8") (Very Rare) (no known sales)
5- 1834 (10-3/8 x 13-3/8") (Very Rare) (no known sales)
6 - 1835 (10-3/8 x 13-1/4") red lettering in title SCRAPS (Very Rare) 300.00 600.00 1200.00
6 - 1835 (10-3/8 x 13-1/4") no red lettering in title (Rare) 220.00 440.00 1000.00
7 - 1837 (10-3/4 x 13-7/8") 1st Edition (Very Rare) 200.00 400.00 880.00
7 - 1837 (10-3/4 x 13-3/4") 2nd Edition (so stated) 100.00 175.00 375.00
NOTE: *20 pgs. of text (double-sided), 4 pgs. of art (single-sided), plus the covers. There are no protective sheets between the art pages.*
8 - 1840 (10-1/2 x 13-7/8") (Rare) 200.00 400.00 880.00
New Series 1- 1849 (10-7/8 x 13-3/4") 125.00 250.00 475.00
NOTE: *By David Claypoole Johnston. All issues consist of four one-sided sheets with 9 to 12 single panel cartoons per sheet. The other pages are blank or text. With #1-5 the size of the pages can vary up to an inch. Contains 4 protective sheets (not part of page count) Only 1 3 4 and the 1849 New Series Number 1 has cover art along with 4 art pgs. (single sided) with 4 protective sheets and no text pages.New Series Number 1, as well as #6 with bo red lettering and the second printing of issue 7, have survived in higher numbers due to a 1940s warehouse discovery.*

THE SETTLEMENT OF RHODE ISLAND (O)
The Graphic Co. Photo-Lith 39 & 41, Park Place, New York: 1874 (11-3/8x10, 40 pgs, gilted blue hard-c

nn - Charles T. Miller & Walter F. Brown 75.00 150.00 300.00
NOTE: *This is also the Same Walter F. Brown that did "Hail Columbia".*

SHAKESPEARE WOULD RIDE THE BICYCLE IF ALIVE TODAY. "THE REASON WHY" (O,P,S)
Cleveland Bicycles H.A. Lozier & Co., Toledo, OH: 1896 (5-1/2x4",16 pgs, paper-c, color)

nn - By F. Opper (Rare) 75.00 150.00 350.00
NOTE: *Original cartoons of Shakespearian characters riding bicycles; also popular amongst collectors of bicycle ephemera.*

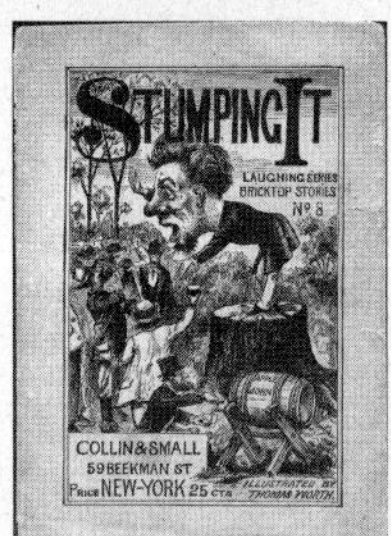

Stumping It
1876 © Collin & Lee, NY

Texas Siftings v6 #2 May 15
1886 ©Texas Siftings Publishing Co.

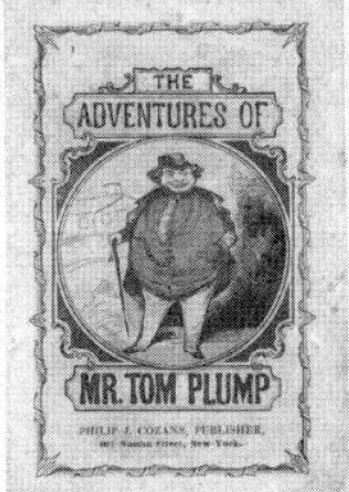

The Adventures Of Mr. Tom Plump
1851 © Huestis & Cozans, NY

FR1.0 GD2.0 FN6.0

SHAKINGS - ETCHINGS FROM THE NAVAL ACADEMY BY A MEMBER OF THE CLASS OF '67 (O,S)
Lee & Shepard, Boston: 1867 (7-7/8x10", 132 pages, blue hard-c)

By: Park Benjamin	38.00	75.00	150.00

NOTE: *Park Benjamin later became editor of Harper's Bazaar magazine.*

SHOO FLY PICTORIAL (S)
John Stetson, Chestnut sT Theatre, Phila, PA: June 1870 (15-1/2x11-1/2", 8 pgs, B&W)

1	75.00	150.00	275.00

SHYS AT SHAKSPEARE
J.P. and T.C.P., Philadelphia: 1869 (9-1/4x6", 52 pgs)

nn - Artist unknown	75.00	150.00	310.00

SKETCHES OF LOWLY LIFE IN A GREAT CITY (M,S) (See 99 "Woolfs" From Truth)
G. P. Puntam's Sons: 1899 (8-5/8x11-1/4", 200 pgs, hard-c, B&W)
(reprints from Life and Judge of Woolf's cartoons of NYC slum children)

nn - By Michael Angelo Woolf	75.00	150.00	350.00

NOTE: *Woolf's cartoons are regarded as a primary influence on R.F. Outcault in the later development of The Yellow Kid newspaper strip.*

SNAP (O,S)
Valentine & Townsend, Tribune Bldg, NYC: March 13,1885 (17x11, 8 pgs, B&W)

1-Contains a sequential comic strip	50.00	100.00	200.00

SOCIETY PICTURES (M,S,E)
Charles H. Sergel Company, Chicago: 1895 (5-1/4x7-3/4", 168 pgs, printed 1 side, paper-c, B&W)

nn - By George du Maurier; reprints from **Punch**.	25.00	50.00	120.00

SOLDIERS AND SAILORS HALF DIME TALES OF THE LATE REBELLION
Soldiers & Sailors Publishing Co: 1868 (5-1/4x7-7/8", 32 pgs)

v1#1-#16 v2#1-#10	15.00	30.00	60.00
v2 #11 contains (5) page comic strip	25.00	50.00	100.00

NOTE: *Changes to Soldiers & Sailors Half Dime Magazine with v2 #1.*

SOUVENIR CONTAINING CARTOONS ISSUED BY THE PRESS BUREAU OF THE OHIO STATE REPUBLICAN EXECUTIVE COMMITTEE, A (S)
Ohio State Republican Executive Committee, Columbus, OH: 1899 (10-3/8x13-1/2, 248 pgs, Hard-c, B&W

nn - By William L. Bloomer (Scarce)	105.00	225.00	450.00

SOUVENIR OF SOHMER CARTOONS FROM PUCK, JUDGE, AND FRANK LESLIE'S (M,S,P)
Sohmer Piano Co.: nd(c.1893) (6x4-3/4", 16 pgs, paper-c, B&W)

nn	25.00	50.00	100.00

NOTE: *Reprints painted "cartoon" Sohmer Piano advertisements which appeared in the above publications. Artists include Keppler, Gillam, others.*

SPORTING NEW YORKER, THE
Ornum & Co, Beekman ST, NYC: 1870s

issues with sequential comic strips (Rare)	50.00	100.00	200.00

STORY OF THE MAN OF HUMANITY AND THE BULL CALF, THE
(see Bull Calf, The Story of The Man Of Humanity And The)
NOTE: *Reprints of two of A. B. Frost's mostfamous sequential comic strips.*

STREET & SMITH'S LITERARY ALBUM
Street & Smith, NY: #1 Dec 23 1865-#225 Apr 9 1870 (11-3/4x16-3/4", 16 pgs, B&W)

1 (23 Dec 1865)	15.00	50.00	100.00
2-129 131-225 (issues with short sequential strips)	15.00	50.00	100.00
130 (Steam Man satire parody)	100.00	200.00	300.00

STUFF AND NONSENSE (Harper's Monthly strip-r) (M)
Charles Scribner's Sons: 1884 (10-1/4x7-3/4", 100 pgs, hardcover, B&W)

nn - By Arthur Burdett Frost	125.00	200.00	400.00
nn - By A.B. Frost (1888 reprint, 104 pgs)	50.00	100.00	200.00

NOTE: *Earliest known anthology devoted to collecting the comic strips of a single American artist. 1888 2nd printing has a different cover and is layed out somewhat differently inside with a new title page, 3 added pages of cartoons, and a couple more illustrations. For more Frost, the 2nd is worth checki ng out also.*

STUMPING IT (LAUGHING SERIES BRICKTOP STORIES #8) (O,S)
Collin & Small, NY: 1876 (6-5/8x9-1/4, 68 pgs, perfect bound, B&W)

nn - Thomas Worth art abounds (some sequentials)	100.00	175.00	375.00

NOTE: Mainly single panel cartoons w/text; however, some sequential comic strips inside worth picking up

SUMMER SCHOOL OF PHILOSOPHY AT MT. DESERT, THE
Henry Holt & Co.: 1881 (10-3/8x8-5/8", 60 pgs, illus. gilt hard-c, B&W)

nn - By J. A. Mitchell	60.00	120.00	250.00

NOTE: *J.A.Mitchell went on to found **LIFE** two years later in 1883. Also, the long-running mascot for **LIFE** was Cupid - which you see multitudes of Cupids flying around in this story.*

SURE WATER CURE, THE
Carey Grey & Hart, Phila, PA: c1841-43 (8-/2x5, 32 pgs, B&W

nn - proto-comic-strip Very Rare	175.00	350.00	700.00

TAILOR-MADE GIRL, HER FRIENDS, HER FASHIONS, AND HER FOLLIES, THE
(see also IN THE "400" AND OUT) (M)

Charles Scribner's Sons, New York: 1888 (8-3/8x10-1/2", 68 pgs, hard-c, B&W)

nn - Art by C.J. Taylor	25.00	50.00	110.00

NOTE: *Format is a full page cartoon on every other page, with a script style vignette, written by Philip H. Welch, on every page opposite the art.*

TALL STUDENT, THE
Roberts Brothers, Boston: 1873 (7x5", 48 pgs, printed one side only, gilted hard-c, B&W)

nn - By Wilhelm Busch (Scarce)	37.50	75.00	150.00

TARIFF ?, CARTOONS AND COMMENTS FROM PUCK, THE (see Puck, The Tariff...)

TEASING TOM AND NAUGHTY NED WITH A SPOOL OF CLARK'S COTTON, THE ADVENTURES OF (O,P)
Clark's O.N.T. Spool Cotton: 1879 (4-1/4x3", 12 pgs, B&W, paper-c)

nn	17.50	35.00	80.00

NOTE: *Knock-off of the "First Trick" in Wilhelm Busch's **Max and Maurice**, modified to involve Clark's Spool Cotton in the story, with similar but new art by an artist identified as "HB". The back cover advertises the specific merchant who gave this booklet away -- multiple variations of back cover suspected.*

TEMPERANCE TALES; OR, SIX NIGHTS WITH THE WASHINGTONIANS, VOL I & II
W.A. Leary & Co., Philadelphia: 1848 (50¢, 6-1/8x4", 328 pgs, B&W, hard-c)

nn	125.00	250.00	550.00

NOTE: *Mostly text. This edition gathers Volume I & II together. The first 8 pages reprints George Cruikshank's **THE BOTTLE**, re-drawn & re-engraved by Phil A. Pilliner. Later editions of this book do not include **THE BOTTLE** reprint and are therefore of little interest to comics collectors.*

TEXAS SIFTINGS
Texas Siftings Publishing Co, Austin, Texas (1881-1887), **NYC** (1887-1897): 1881-1885 newspaper-size weekly; 1886-1897 folio weekly (15x10-3/4", 16 pgs, B&W 10¢

1881-1885 issues	25.00	50.00	110.00
v6#1 (5/8/86) (8) panel strip Afterwhich He Emigrated; (16) panel The Tenor's Triumph Veni Vidi Vici	12.50	25.00	80.00
v6#2 (5/16/86 (5) panel sewuential	12.50	25.00	80.00
v6#3 no sequentials	12.50	25.00	80.00
v6#4 (5/29/86) Worth-c (4) panel Worth strip; (2) panel	12.50	25.00	80.00
v6#5 no sequentials	12.50	25.00	80.00
v6#6 (6/12/86) Comic Strip Cover (11) panels The Rise of a Great Artist (5) panel sequential	50.00	100.00	205.00
v6#7 (6/19/86) Worth-c (2) panel Wiorth; (10) panel Ha! Ha! The Honest Youth & the Lordly Villain	25.00	50.00	110.00
v6#8 (6/26/86) Worth-c; (15) panel The Kangaroo Hunter	25.00	50.00	110.00
v6#9 (7/3/86) Worth-c; Bellew (2) panel How Wives Get What They Want	12.50	25.00	80.00
v6#10 ((7/10/86) Baseball-c; (3) panel; (5) panel A Story Without Words from Fliegende Blätter	12.50	25.00	80.00
v6 #11 12 13 Worth-c no sequentials	12.50	25.00	80.00
v6#14 (8/7/86) Wiorth-c; (7) panel Mrs Cleveland Presents The President With A New Rocking Chair	12.50	25.00	80.00
v6#15 (8/14/86) Worth-c; (6) panel Worth strip	12.50	25.00	80.00
v6#16 (8/21/86) Worth-c Asleep At Post USA/Mexico Border (6) panel sequential	12.50	25.00	80.00
v6#17 no sequrntials	12.50	25.00	80.00
v6#18 (9/4/86) Worth-c; (3) panel from Fliegende	12.50	25.00	80.00
v6#19 (9/11/86) Worth Anarchist & Uncle Sam-c; (5) panel Duel of the Dudes	12.50	25.00	80.00
v6#20 (9/18/86) Worth-c (6) panel sequential	12.50	25.00	80.00
v6#21 (9/25/86) Worth-c; Verbeck single panel; (9) panel	12.50	25.00	80.00
v6#22 (10/2/86) Verbeck-c plus interiors	12.50	25.00	80.00
v6#23 (10/9/86) Worth-c Geronimo & Devil cover; Verbeck and Chips singles	25.00	50.00	110.00
v6#24 (10/16/86) Worth-c Verbeck strip "Evolution"	12.50	25.00	80.00
v6#25 no sequential strips	12.50	25.00	80.00
v6#26 (10/30/86) Worth-c; (6) panel Verbeck "A Warning To Smokers"	12.50	25.00	80.00

NOTE: *Many Thomas Worth sequential comic strips. Frank Bellew and Dan McCarthy appear. Wilhelm Busch-r from German Fligende Blaetter. Later issues in 1890s comics become sporadic*

THAT COMIC PRIMER (S)
G.W. Carleton & Co., Publishers: 1877 (6-5/8x5", 52 pgs, paper soft-c, B&W)

nn - By Frank Bellew	75.00	150.00	300.00

NOTE: *Premium for the United States Life Insurance Company, New York.*

TIGER, THE LEFTENANT AND THE BOSUN, THE
Prudential Insurance Home Office, 878 & 880 Broad St, Newark, NJ: 1889 (4.5x3.25", 12 pgs) (Scarce)

nn - 8 panel sequential story in color	50.00	100.00	225.00

TOM PLUMP, THE ADVENTURES OF MR. (see also The Juvenile Gem) (O)
Huestis & Cozans, New York: nd (c1850-1851) (6x3-7/8", 12 pgs, hand colored paper-c, B&W)

nn- First printing(s) publisher's address is 104 Nassau Street (1850-1851) (Very Rare)	750.00	1500.00	3200.00

NOTE: *California Gold Rush story. The hand colored outer cover is highly rare, with only 1 recorded copy possessing it. The front cover image and text is repeated precisely on page 3 (albeit b&w), and only interior pages are numbered, together leading owners of coverless copies to believe they have the cover. The true back*

Truth #372 (first app. The Yellow Kid)
June 2 1894 © Truth Company, NY

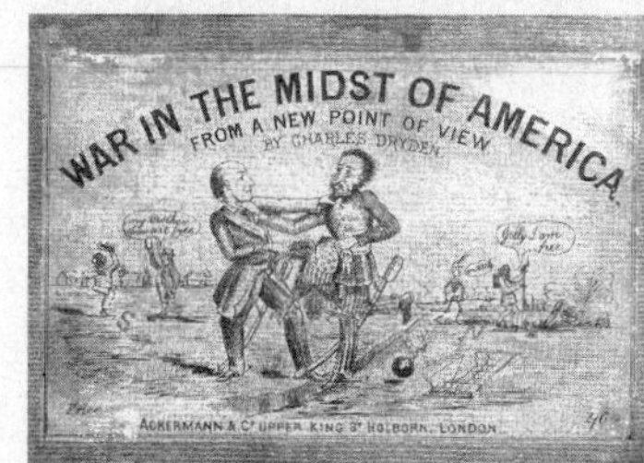

War in the Midst of America
1864 © Ackermann & Co.

Wild Oats #115 March 10
1875 © Winchell & Small, NYC

FR1.0 GD2.0 FN6.0

*cover contains ads for the publisher. The cover was issued only with copies which were sold separately - booklets which were bound together as part of **THE JUVENILE GEM** never had such covers.*

TOM PLUMP, THE ADVENTURES OF MR. (see also The Juvenile Gem) (O)
Philip J. Cozans: nd (1851-1852) (6x3-7/8", 12 pgs,hand colored paper-c, B&W)

nn- Second printing(s) publisher's address is 116 Nassau Street (1851-1852)
(Very Rare) 400.00 800.00 1600.00
nn- Third printing(s) publisher's address is 107 Nassau Street (1852+)
(Very Rare) 400.00 800.00 1600.00

TOM PLUMP, THE ADVENTURES OF MR.
Americana Review, Scotia, NY: nd(1960's) (6-1/4x4-1/8", 8 pgs, side-stapled, cardboard-c, B&W)

nn - Modern reprint - 25.00 50.00
NOTE: *Issued within a folder titled SIX CHILDREN'S BOOKS OF THE 1850'S. States "Reprinted by American Review" at bottom of front cover. Reprints the 104 Nassau Street address.)*
nn - Modern rep. (Scarce 1980s) (5-1/2x4-1/4", 8 pgs,side-stapled) - 10.00 20.00
NOTE: *Photocopy reprint by a comix zine publisher, from an Americana Review cop; vailable by mail order*

TOOTH-ACHE, THE (E,O)
D. Bogue, London: 1849 (5-1/4x3-3/4)

nn - By Cruikshank, B&W (Very Rare) 300.00 600.00 1300.00
nn - By Cruikshank, hand colored (Rare) (no known sales)
NOTE: *Scripted by Horace Mayhew, art by George Cruikshank. This is the British edition. Price 1/6 b&w, 3 hand colored. In British editions, the panels are not numbered. Publisher's name appears on cover. Booklet's "pages" unfold into a single, long, strip.*

J.L. Smith, Philadelphia, PA: nd (1849) (5-1/8"x 3-3/4" folded, 86-7/8" wide unfolded, 26 pgs, cardboard-c, color, 15¢)

nn - By Cruikshank, hand colored (Very Rare) 400.00 800.00 1700.00
NOTE: *Reprints the D. Bogue edition. In American editions, the panels are numbered (43 panels, not counting front & back cover). Publisher's name stamped on inside front cover, plus printed along left-hand side of first interior page. Page 1 is pasted to inside back cover, and unfolds from there. Front cover not attached to back cover by design. Booklet's "pages" unfold into a single, long, strip (made from four individual strips pasted together on the blank back side). There is a fairly common1974 British Arts Council reprint.*

TRAMP, THE: His Tricks, Tallies, and Tell-Tales, with His Signs, Countersigns, Grips, Passwords and Villainies Exposed (O,S)
Dick & Fitzgerald, New York: 1878 (11-3/8x8, 36 pgs, paper-c, B&W, 25¢) (Rare)

1 Frank Bellew 160.00 350.00 700.00
NOTE: *Edited by Frank Bellew, A Bee And A Chip (Bellew's daughter and son Frank).*

TRUTH (See Platinum Age section for 1900-1906 issues)
Truth Company, NY: 1886-1906? (13-11/16x10-5/16", 16 pgs, process color-c & centerfolds, rest B&W)

	FR1.0	GD2.0	FN6.0
1886-1887 issues	20.00	40.00	100.00
1888-1895 issues non Outcault issues	15.00	30.00	80.00
Mar 10 1894 - precursor Yellow Kid RFO	60.00	180.00	425.00
#372 June 2 1894 - first app Yellow Kid RFO	200.00	600.00	1200.00
June 23 1894 - precursor Yellow Kid R. F. Outcault	60.00	180.00	425.00
July 14 1894 -2nd app Yellow Kid RFO	110.00	330.00	675.00
Sept 15 1894 - (2) 3rd app YK RFO plus YK precursor	110.00	330.00	675.00
Feb 9 1895 - 4th app Yellow Kid RFO	110.00	330.00	675.00
1896-1899 issues	10.00	20.00	55.00

NOTE: *This magazine contains the earliest known appearances of **The Yellow Kid** by Richard Felton Outcault. Feb 9 1895 issue's YK cartoon was reprinted one week later in the **New York World** Feb 17 1895 edition. We are still sorting out further Outcault appearances. Truth also contained full color sequential strips by Hy Mayer on the back plus Woolf, Verbeek, etc.*

TRUTH, SELECTIONS FROM
Truth Company, NY: 1894-Spr 1897 (13-11/16x10-1/4, color-c, quarterly)

	FR1.0	GD2.0	FN6.0
1-4	25.00	50.00	100.00
5-Outcault's early Yellow Kid	100.00	225.00	475.00
6-13	20.00	40.00	80.00

NOTE: *#5 reprints all early Outcault Yellow Kid appearances*

TURNER'S COMIC ALMANAC
Charles Strong, 298 Pearl St, NYC: ???-1843 (7.25x4.5", 36 pgs, B&W)

nn 65.00 125.00 250.00

TURNER'S COMICK ALMA-NACK
Turner & Fisher, NYC: 1844-?? (7.25x4.5", 36 pgs, B&W)

nn 65.00 125.00 250.00

TWO HUNDRED SKETCHES, HUMOROUS AND GROTESQUE, BY GUSTAVE DORE (E)
Frederick Warne & Co, London: 1867 (13-3/4x11-3/8, 94 pgs, hard-c, B&W)

	FR1.0	GD2.0	FN6.0
nn - (1867) by Gustave Dore	100.00	200.00	500.00
nn - (Second Edition; 1871)- by Gustave Dore	60.00	125.00	250.00
nn - (Third Edition; 1870's)- by Gustave Dore	60.00	125.00	250.00
nn - (Fourth Edition; 1870's- by Gustave Dore	60.00	125.00	250.00

NOTE: *Contains sequential comics stories, single panel cartoons, and sketches. Reprints and translates material which originally appeared in the French publications "Le Journal pour Rire", circa 1848-49. Although dated 1867, it was likely published & available for the 1866 Christmas Season, as has been confirmed for the American edition. Printed by Dalziel. The American & first British editions were printed simultaneously, the American edition is not a reprint of the British.*

TWO HUNDRED SKETCHES, HUMOROUS AND GROTESQUE, BY GUSTAVE DORE (E)
Roberts Brothers, Boston: 1867 (13-3/4x11-3/8", 96 pgs, hard-c, B&W)

FR1.0 GD2.0 FN6.0

nn - By Gustave Dore 100.00 200.00 600.00
NOTE: *Although dated 1867, it was published & available for the 1866 Christmas Season. Printed by Dalziel, in England, and imported to the USA expressly for a USA publisher.*

UNCLE JOSH'S TRUNK-FUL OF FUN
Dick & Fitzgerald, 18 Ann St, NY: 1870s (5-3/4x9", 68 pgs, B&W & Red-c, B&W inside)

nn - Rare 75.00 125.00 200.00
NOTE: *Many single panel cartoons; (2) pages of early boxing sequential strip*

UNCLE SAM'S COMIC ALMANAC
M.J. Meyers, NY: 1879 (11x8", 32 pgs)

nn - 50.00 100.00 200.00

UNDER THE GASLIGHT
Gaslight Publishing Co (Frank Tousey): Oct 13 1878-Apr 12 1879 (Folio, 16pgs)

1-27 75.00 125.00 200.00

UNITED STATES COMIC ALMANAC
King & Baird, Philadelphia: 1851-?? (7.5x4.5", 36 pgs, B&W)

nn 60.00 120.00 250.00

UPS AND DOWNS ON LAND AND WATER (O.G)
James R. Osgood & Co., Boston: 1871 ; **Houghton, Osgood & Co., Boston:** 1880 (108 pgs, gilted hard-c, B&W)

1st printing (1871; 10-3/4x16") - By Augustus Hoppin 50.00 100.00 200.00
2nd printing (1880; smaller sized) 32.50 65.00 130.00
NOTE: *Exists as blue or orange hard covers.*

VANITY FAIR
William A. Stephens (for Thompson & Camac): Dec 29 1859-July 4 1863 Quarto Weekly

average issues with comic strips 20.00 30.00 100.00

VERDICT, THE
Verdict Publishing Co: Dec 19 1898-Nov 12 1900 (Chromolithographic Weekly)

Average Issues 50.00 100.00 225.00
NOTE: *Artists included George B. Luks, Horace Taylor, MIRS. Striking anti-Republican weekly full o fsome of the most savage political cartoons of the era. The last brilliant burst of energy for the political cartoon weekly*

VERY VERY FUNNY (M,S)
Dick & Fitzgerald, New York: nd(c1880's) (10¢, 7-1/2x5", 68 pgs, paper-c, B&W)

nn - (Rare) 75.00 150.00 325.00
NOTE: *Unauthorized reprints of prose and cartoons extracted from Puck, Texas Siftings, and other publications. Includes art by Chips Bellew, Bisbee, Graetz, Opper, Wales, Zim.*

VIM
H. Wimmel, NYC: June 22-Aug 24 1898 (Chromolithographic Weekly)

	FR1.0	GD2.0	FN6.0
average issue	50.00	100.00	200.00
Yellow Kid by Leon Barritt issues	75.00	150.00	350.00

WAR IN THE MIDST OF AMERICA. FROM A NEW POINT OF VIEW. (E,O,G)
Ackermann & Co., London: 1864 (4-3/8" x 5-7/8", folded, 36 feet wide unfolded, 80 pgs, hard-c, B&W)

nn- by Charles Dryden (rare) 450.00 950.00 2000.00
NOTE: *British graphic novel about the American Civil War, with a pro-Confederate bent. Adventures of a British artist who decides to visually summarize the American Civil War for his countrymen, from newspaper accounts. Reaching current events, he finds he can not finish the story until the War ends, and so he travels to America, to end it. Book unfolds into a single long strip (binding was issued split, to enable the unfolding).*

WASP, THE ILLUSTRATED SAN FRANCISCO
F. Korbel & Bros and Numerous Others: August 5 1876-April 25 1941 (Chromolithographic Weekly)

average 1800s issues with comic strips 50.00 100.00 200.00

WHAT I KNOW OF FARMING: Founded On The Experience of Horace Greeley (S)
The American News Company, New York: 1871 (7-1/4x4-1/2", paper-c, B&W)

nn - By Joseph Hull (Scarce) 35.00 70.00 175.00
NOTE: *Pay & Cox, Printers & Engravers, NY; political tract regarding Presidential elections.*

WILD FIRE
Wild Fire Co, NYC: Nov 30 1877-at least#16 Mar 1878 (Folio, 16 pgs)

1-16 30.00 60.00 125.00

WILD OATS, An Illustrated Weekly Journal of Fun, Satire, Burlesque, and Nits at Persons and Events of the Day (O)
Winchell & Small, 113 Fulton St /48 Ann St, NYC: Feb 1870-1881 (16-1/4x11", generally 16 pages, B&W, began as monthly, then bi-weekly, then weekly) All loose issues Very Rare (See *The Overstreet Price Guide* #35 2005 for a detailed index of single issue contents)

	FR1.0	GD2.0	FN6.0
1-25 Very Rare - contents to be indexed next year	50.00	100.00	250.00
26-28 30 32 35 36 39 40 41 43-46 1872 (sequential strips)	50.00	100.00	225.00
29 33 37 42 no sequential strips	40.00	80.00	160.00
31 34 38 47 Hopkins sequential comic strips	50.00	100.00	225.00
48 (1/16/73) Worth 13 panel sequential; first Woolf-c	50.00	100.00	225.00
49 51 53 54 60 62 61 64 65 66 67 69 1873 sequential strips	50.00	100.00	225.00
50 52 56 59 63 71 no sequential strips	40.00	80.00	160.00
51 (Worth 18 panel double page spread, Woolf 9 panel	50.00	100.00	225.00
55 Hopkins 22 panel double page spread; Bellew-c	50.00	150.00	320.00

57 intense unknown 6 panel "Two Relics of Barbarism, or A Few Contrasted Pictures,

Wild Oats #139 August 25 1875 © Winchell & Small, NY

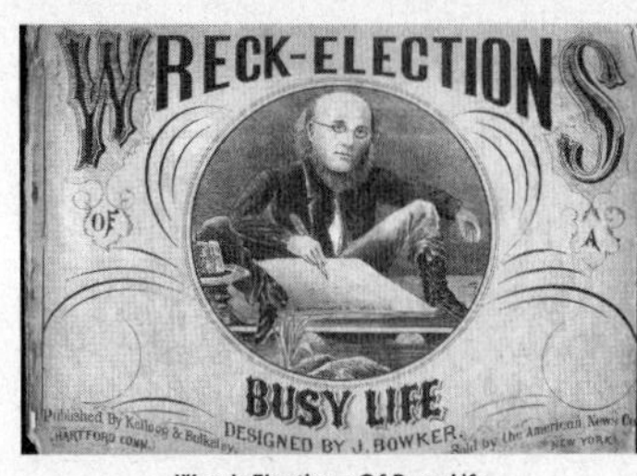

Wreck-Elections Of Busy Life Kellogg & Buckeley © 1864?

Yankee Notions #7 (v2#1) July 1852 © T.W. Strong, NY

FR1.0 GD2.0 FN6.0

Showing the origin of the North American Indian 50.00 100.00 225.00
58 (6/5/73) unknown 19 panel double pager "The Terrible Adventures of Messrs Buster & Stumps, About Exterminating the Indians" reads across both pages like Popeye #2095 (1933); Woolf-c 100.00 200.00 460.00
68 (10/16/73) unknown 9 panel "Adv of New jersey Mosquito" looks like Winsor McCay type style: early inspiration for McCay's animated cartoon? 50.00 100.00 250.00
70 unknown 6 panel; Hopkins 6 panel "Hopkins novel: A Tale of True Love, with all the variations"; Bellew-c 50.00 100.00 225.00
72 (12/11/73) Worth 11 panel; Wales President Grant war-c 50.00 100.00 225.00
73 74 75 Hopkins sequential comic strip 75.00 150.00 310.00
76 77 sequential strips 50.00 100.00 225.00
78 Bellew 5 panel double pager 50.00 100.00 225.00
79-105 (March 1874-Dec 1874) contents presently unknown 50.00 100.00 225.00
106 107 111 no sequentials;Bellew-c #106 110;Wales-c #107 50.00 100.00 225.00
108 (1/20/75) Wales 12 panel double pg spread; Bellew-c 50.00 100.00 225.00
109 (1/27/75) unknown 6 panel; Wales-c 50.00 100.00 225.00
111 Busch 13 panel "The Conundrum of the Day - Is Lager Beer Intoxicating?"; Bellew-c 50.00 100.00 225.00
112 116 sequential comic strips 50.00 100.00 225.00
113 114 115 no sequentials Worth-c #114 40.00 80.00 160.00
117 intense Wales 6 panel "One of the Oppresions of the Civil Rights Laws"' Bellew-c 75.00 150.00 330.00
118-137 (3/31/75-8/4/75) no sequential comic strips 40.00 80.00 160.00
138 (8/18/75) Bellew Sr & Bellew "Chips" Jr singles appear 50.00 100.00 225.00
139-143 145-147 154-157 159 no sequentials 40.00 80.00 160.00
144 (9/29/75) Hopkins 8 panel sequential; Wales-c 50.00 100.00 225.00
148 (10/27/75) Opper's first cover; many Opper singles 75.00 150.00 320.00
149 150 151 152 153 all Opper-c and much interior work 50.00 100.00 225.00
158 (1/5/76) Palmer Cox 1rst comic strip 24 panel double page spread "The Adv of Mr & Mrs Sprowl And Their Christmas Turkey - A Crashing Chasing Tearful Tragedy But Happily Ending Well"; Opper-c 100.00 200.00 450.00
159 160 162 165 167 169-173 no sequentials 40.00 80.00 160.00
161 163 164 166 168 179 182 Palmer Cox sequential strips 100.00 200.00 450.00
174 (4/26/76) Cox 24 panel double pager "The Tramp's Progress; A Story of the West And the Union Pacific Railroad" 100.00 200.00 450.00
175-178 183-189 no sequentials 40.00 80.00 160.00
180 (6/7/76) Beard & Opper jam; Woolf, Bellew singles 50.00 100.00 225.00
181 more Mann two panel jobs; Opper-c 50.00 100.00 225.00
190 Bellew 9 panel "Rodger's Patent Mosquito Armour" 75.00 150.00 320.00
191-end contents to be indexed in the near future 40.00 80.00 160.00
NOTE: *There are very few lknown oose issues. All loose issues are Very Rare. Prices vary widely on this magazine. Issues with sequential comic strips would be in higher demand than issues with no comic strips. We present this index from the Library of Congress and New York Historical Society bound sets. We would love to hear from any one who turns up loose copies. This scarce humor bi-weekly contains easily a couple hundred original first-time published sequential comic strips found in most issues plus innumerable single panel cartoons in every issue*

WOMAN IN SEARCH OF HER RIGHTS, THE ADVENTURES OF (G)
Lee & Shepard, Boston And New York: early 1870s (8-3/8x13", 40 pgs, hard-c)

By Florence Claxton (Very Rare) 450.00 900.00 1900.00
NOTE: *Earliest known original comic book sequential story by a woman; contains "nearly 100 original drawings by the author, which have been reproduced in fac-simile by the graphotype process of engraving." Tinted two color lithography; orange tint printed first, then printed 2nd time with black ink; early women's sufferage.*

WORLD OVER, THE (I)
G. W. Dillingham Company, New York: 1897 (192 pgs, hard-c)

nn - By Joe Kerr; 80 illustrations by R.F. Outcault (Rare) 330.00 660.00 1250.00
NOTE: soft cover editions also exist

WRECK-ELECTIONS OF BUSY LIFE (S)
Kellogg & Bulkeley: 1867 (9-1/4x11-3/4", ??? pages, soft-c)

nn - By J. Bowker (Rare) 110.00 225.00 450.00
NOTE: *Says "Sold by American News Company, New York" on cover.*

WYMAN'S COMIC ALMANAC FOR THE TIMES
T.W. Strong, NY: 1854 (8x5", 24 pgs)

nn - 50.00 100.00 200.00

YANKEE DOODLE
W.H. Graham, Tribune Building, NYC: Oct 10 1846-Oct 2 1847 (Quarto weekly)

average issue 110.00 125.00 250.00

YANKEE NOTIONS, OR WHITTLINGS OF JONATHAN'S JACK-KNIFE
T.W. Strong, 98 Nassau St, NYC: Jan. 1852-1875 (11x8, 32 pgs, paper-c, 12.5¢, monthly)

1 Brother Jonathan character single panel cartoons 60.00 125.00 250.00
NOTE: *Begins continuing character sequential comic strip,* "The Adventures of Jeremiah Oldpot" in "A Bird in the Hand Is Worth Two in The Bush"
2-4 25.00 50.00 115.00
5 British X-Over 25.00 50.00 115.00
NOTE: *Single panel of John Bull & Brother Jonathan exchanging civilities (issues of* Punch & Yankee Notions)
6 end of Jeremiah Oldpot continued strip 25.00 50.00 115.00
v2#1 begin "Hoosier Bragg" sequential strip - six issue serial 25.00 50.00 115.00
v2#2 Feb 1853 two pg 12 panel sequential "Mr Vanity's Exploits, Arising Out Of A Valentine" 37.50 75.00 195.00
v2#3-v2#5 continues Hoosier Bragg 25.00 50.00 115.00
v2#6 Juen 1853 Lion Eats Hoosier Bragg, end of story 25.00 50.00 115.00

FR1.0 GD2.0 FN6.0

v3#1 begins referring to its cartoons as "Comic Art" 37.50 75.00 195.00
v4#1-V4#6 v5#1-v5#2 no sequential comic strips 20.00 40.00 100.00
v5#3 two sequential comic strips 37.50 75.00 195.00
NOTE: *Mr Take-A-Drop And The Maine Law (5) panels and The First Segar (7) panels (about smoking tobacco)*
v5#4 April 1856 begin Billy Vidkins 37.50 75.00 195.00
NOTE: *Begins reprinting "From Passages in the Life of Little Billy Vidkins, first issued as a stand alone proto-comic book in 1849 Illustrations of the Poets*
v5#5 The McBargem Guards (9) panel sequential; Vidkins 25.00 50.00 115.00
v5#6 v5 #9 no comics 20.00 40.00 100.00
v5#7 Billy Vidkins continues 25.00 50.00 115.00
v5#8 end of Vidkins By HL Stephens, Esq. 25.00 50.00 115.00
v5#10 (6) panel "How We Learn To Ride"; Timber is hero 25.00 50.00 115.00
v5#11 (7) panel "How Mr. Green Sparrowgrass Voted-A Warning For the Benefit of Quiet Citizens About To Excercize the Elective Franchise" plus Pt Two "How We Learn to Ride" 37.50 75.00 195.00
v5#12 (6) panel "How Mr Pipp Got Struck"; "The Eclipse" featuring Mr Phips; Pt 3 "How We Learn to Ride" 25.00 50.00 115.00
v6#1 (Jan 1857) (12) panel "A Tale of An Umbrella; (4) panel begins a serial "The Man Who Bought The Elephant; (8) panel How Our Young New Yorkers Celebrate New Years Day 25.00 50.00 115.00
v6#2 (Feb 1857) Pt 2 (4) panels The Man Who Bought the Elephant; (7) panel A Game of All Fours 25.00 50.00 115.00
v6#3 (Mar 1857) Pt 3 (4) panels The Man Who Bought the Elephant ending; (4) panel Ye Great Crinoline Monopoly 25.00 50.00 115.00
v6#4 no comic strips 25.00 50.00 115.00
v6#5 (May 1850) (3) panel A Short Trip to Mr Bumps, And How It Ended; (2) panel How mr Trembles Was Garrotted 25.00 50.00 115.00
v6#6 no comic strips 25.00 50.00 115.00
v6#7 (July 1857) (5) panel Alma Mater; (3) panel Three Tableaux In the Life of A Broadway Swell 25.00 50.00 115.00
v6 #8 9 no comic strips 25.00 50.00 115.00
v6#10 (Oct 1857) (3) panel Adv of Mr Near-Sight 25.00 50.00 115.00
v6#11 (Nov 1857) (11) panel Mrs Champignon's Dinner Party And the Way She Arranged Her Guests; (4) panel A Stroll in August 25.00 50.00 115.00
v6#12 (Dec 1857) (8) panel strip; (12) panel Young Fitz At A Blow Out in the Fifth Ave 25.00 50.00 115.00
v10#1 (Jan 1860) comic strip Bibbs at Central Park Skating Pond using word balloons 25.00 50.00 115.00

YE TRUE ACCOUNTE OF YE VISIT TO SPRINGFIELDE BY YE CONSTABEL HIS SPECIAL REPORTER
Frank Leslie: 1861 (5-1/8 x 5-1/4 or 93 inches when folded out, paper-c, B&W)
nn - Very Rare fold-out of 18 comic strip panels plus covers - -
NOTE: *8 panels contain word balloons (Very Rare - only one copy known to exist.) First printed in Frank Leslie's Budget of Fun Jan 1 1861 issue. Abraham Lincoln Biography.*

YE VERACIOUS CHRONICLE OF GRUFF & POMPEY IN 7 TABLEAUX. (O,P)
Jackson's Best Chewing Tobacco & Donaldson Brothers: nd (c1870's) (5-1/8 tall x 3-3/8" wide folded, 27" wide unfolded, color cardboard)

nn - With all 8 panels attached (Scarce) 45.00 90.00 200.00
nn - Individual panels/cards 6.00 12.00 24.00
NOTE: *Black Americana interest. Consists of 8 attached cards, printed on one side, which unfold into a strip story of title card & 7 panels. Scrapbook hobbyists in the 19th Century tended to pull the panels apart and paste into their scrapbooks, making copies with all panels attached scarce.*

YOUNG AMERICA (continues as Yankee Doodle)
T.W. Strong, NYC: 1856

1-30 John McLennon 60.00 110.00 250.00

YOUNG AMERICA'S COMIC ALMANAC
T.W. Strong, NY: 1857 (7-1/2x5", 24 pgs)

nn 60.00 110.00 250.00

THE YOUNG MEN OF AMERICA (becomes Golden Weekly) (S)
Frank Tousey, NYC: 1887-88 (14x10-1/4", 16 pgs, B&W)

527 (10/13/87) Bellew strip "Story of A Black Eye" 25.00 50.00 110.00
530 (11/3/87) Thomas Worth (6) panel strip 32.00 64.00 125.00
531 (11/10/87) Thomas Worth(3) panel strip
537 (12/22/87) H.E. Patterson (3) panel strip
544 (2/9/88) Caran s'Ache (6) panel strip-r 37.50 75.00 110.00
555 (4/26/88) Thomas Worth (3) panel strip
556 (5/3/88) Thomas Worth (6) panel strip; Kit Carson-c 75.00 150.00 350.00
569 (8/21/88) Frank Bellew (2) panel strip
570 (8/9/88) Kemble (2) panel strip
571 (8/16/88) Kemble (2) panel strip; first Davy Crockett 75.00 150.00 350.00
Issues with just single panel cartoons 10.00 20.00 50.00

ZIM'S QUARTERLY (M)
(13-13/16x10-1/4", 60 pgs, color-c; most;y B&W, some interior color)

1 - Eugene Zimmerman 112.50 225.00 500.00
NOTE: *Approx. half sequential comic strips, other half single panel cartoons.*

Any addititions or corrections to this section are always welcome, very much encouraged and can be sent to **feedback@gemstonepub.com** to be processed for next year's Guide.

The American Comic Book: 1883-1938

A Concise History & Price Index Of The Field As Of 2018

NEWSPAPERS HARNESS COMICS POWER MYRIAD FORMATS COMPETE

by Robert Lee Beerbohm and Richard D. Olson, PhD ©2018

(This article was originally created by Robert L. Beerbohm and Richard D. Olson beginning in CBPG #27 1997 and is revised annually as new information comes to light.)

The story of the success of the modern comic strip as we know it today is tied closely to the companies who sponsored and bought licenses from the copyright holder for the purpose of advertising products. Platinum Age comic books have come back into their own after languishing mostly forgotten for a few decades. With this series of comics history research updates now marking its first decade, these historically important books are seem by many now as very collectible. Online sources such as eBay and bookfinder.com have demonstrate that many of these Platinum books are actually not scarce at all as previously thought, though they are in any type of higher-grade condition. Even so, most Platinum Age books are much rarer than so-called Golden Age comic books, yet despite this scarcity, *Mutt & Jeff, Bringing Up Father, The Katzenjammer Kids*, and many more were more popular than say Superman and Batman when they were introduced. Recent research has come up with some more amazing rediscoveries. There is much that can be learned and applied to today's comics market by a simple historical examination of the medium's evolution over more than 160 years.

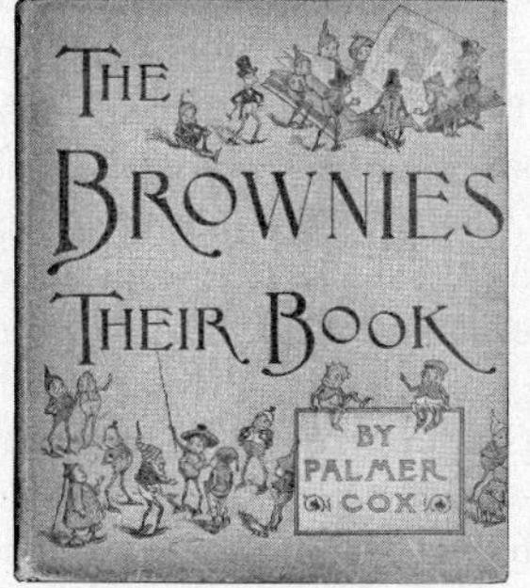

The Brownies' first book, 1887 by Palmer Cox, set a precedent for the Platinum Age, collecting and reprinting previously published material.

It should be noted that "ages" are applied to historical periods in the history of comics for convenience. In fact, ages typically overlap and there is no discrete beginning or ending for any given "age." This is the case with the Platinum Age, which clearly began with Palmer Cox's creation of *The Brownies* in 1883 even though it overlaps with the Victorian Age which ran through the end of the 19th Century. Cox introduced a qualitative change to the field, not an incremental quantitative change. Specifically, he produced art and verse for children in children's magazines and then merchandised those characters. He published work for children not only in books but in magazines and newspapers, and he merchandised his creations to an extent that had never been done previously.

Palmer Cox was born in 1840 near Granby, Quebec. He journeyed to Oakland, California in 1863, and began publishing cartoon, prose and poems in the local press and media outlets such as *The San Francisco Examiner* wherein by 1867 it has been reported he also began creating sequential comic strips, though none have yet surfaced.

His first book, *Squibs of California*, was published in 1874. He subsequently moved to New York in 1875 and almost immediately began working for the magazine *Wild Oats*, of which more is written about in the preceding Victorian Age history introduction as well as a sample of his sequential work. He drew dozens of sequential comic strips for *Wild Oats*, a humor magazine so scarce only one issue has been offered on eBay in the past six years.

Soon thereafter he became a major contributor to the Scribner publications, including *The St. Nicholas*, an illustrated magazine for young folk. His first cartoon for them was "The Wasp And The Bee," published in the March 1879 cover-

The Brownies in the Philippines by Palmer Cox, Oct 1904 - scarce original art from the book. President Roosevelt is pictured within these multitudes of Brownie madness, a Cox "signature trademark." Cox's stories are comic strip-oriented in nature of time sequence as he boldly took his Brownies around the world.

date issue. While it is now clear that Cox used elves and brownie-like characters in his art for several different magazines as early as 1877 in *Harper's Young People* magazine as well as using Brownies-type characters beginning in the Feb 1881 issue of *Wide Awake*, the first true appearance of the Brownies in their own story using that title, a combination of art and verse was February, 1883, in *St. Nicholas*. Palmer Cox's *The Brownies* were the first North American comics-type characters to be internationally merchandised. Even though Cox was continuously doing sequential comic strips in magazines like *Wild Oats*, he left the popular medium of comics when he hit paydirt with *The Brownies*. For over a quarter of a century, Cox deftly combined the popular advertising motifs of animals and fairies into a wonderful, whimsical world of society at its best and worst.

The Brownies' first book was issued in 1887, titled *The Brownies: Their Book*; many more followed. Cox also added a run of his hugely popular characters in *Ladies Home Journal* from October 1891 through February 1895, as well as a special for December 1910. With the 1892-93 World's Fair, the merchandising exploded with a host of products, including pianos, paper dolls and other figurines, chairs, stoves, puzzles, cough drops, coffee, soap, boots, candy, and many more. *Brownies* material was being produced in Europe as well as the United States of America.

Cox tried out *The Brownies* as a newspaper strip in the *San Francisco Examiner* during 1898, where he had begun his newspaper career over 30 years before, and then in the *New York World* in 1900. It was then syndicated from 1903 through 1907. He seems to have retired from regularly drawing *The Brownies* with the January 1914 issue of *St. Nicholas* when he was 74. A wealthy man, he lived to the ripe old age of 84, spending his last decade in his home he affectionately called Brownie Castle, back in Granby, Quebec.

By the mid-1890s, while keeping careful track of steadily rising circulations of magazines with graphic humor such as *Harper's, Puck, St. Nicholas, Judge, Life* and *Truth*, New York based newspaper publishers began to recognize that illustrated humor would sell extra papers. This is what *The Yellow Kid* taught these publishers. Thus was born the Sunday "comic supplement." Most of the super star favorites were under contract with these magazines. However, there was an artist working for *Truth* who wasn't. Roy L McCardell, then a staffer at *Puck*, informed Morrill Goddard, Sunday Editor of *The New York World*, that he knew someone who could fit what was needed at the then-largest newspaper in America.

Richard F. Outcault (1863-1928) first introduced his street children strip in *Truth* #372, June 2, 1894, somewhat inspired by Michael Angelo Woolf's slum kids single panel cartoons in **Life** which had begun in the mid 1880s. The interested collector should seek out a copy of Woolf's *Sketches of Lowly Life In A Great City* (1899) listed in the *Guide* for comparison study. Edward Harrigan's play "O'Reilly and the Four Hundred," which had a song beginning with the words "Down in Hogan's Alley..." also likely provided direct inspiration.

It's also probable that Outcault's *Hogan's Alley* cast, including the *Yellow Kid*, was inspired by Charles W. Saalburg's *The Ting Lings*, which began in the *Chicago Inter Ocean Jr* supplement post-dated May 1, 1894 in the April 29, 1894 edition of Chicago Inter Ocean. That first episode is titled: "The Brownies Welcome The Ting-Lings."

There is also a definite similarity in Mickey Dugan's appearance and clothing style to Saalburg's creation which we will now examine in more detail thanks to welcome, on-going research by long time comics historian Allan Holtz supplemented by living comics history legend Bill Blackbeard .

Charles Saalzburg was an artist who was also the genius behind color printing in newspapers. He seems to have pioneered the concept from whom all others learned their craft.

On June 23, 1892 the *Chicago Inter Ocean* introduced a section with mostly editorial cartoons titled the *Illustrated Supplement*, commemorating the Democratic National Convention held in that city. Early regulars included Thomas Nast and Art Young. Starting June 26, the *Inter Ocean* began steadily issuing this weekly four page supplement, typically featuring full page editorial cartoons on its front and back covers. In May 1893 the supplement began coming out twice a week, and even greater frequency to daily during the *World Columbian Exposition* held in Chicago later that same year as it was used as a wrapper to attract sales from fair goers. Art Young did some of the color cover art and comic strips for the early Fair supplements, printing them right at the Fair to goggle-eyed fair tourists. Thomas Nast did some art as well during a visit he made to the Fair.

By September 10, 1893 the *Inter Ocean* introduced color, a multi-panel editorial comic strip by Charles Saalburg. The supplement used yellow ink, a further nail in the coffin of various Yellow Kid myths which had clouded serious comics scholarship in earlier decades before being proven wrong.

On October 1, Tom E. Powers introduced their first sequential non-political comic strip in color, a humorous pantomime.

As the Exposition ended in November, the contents were soon aimed more at children, enhanced with color added to the center as well by December 24, 1893, then changing its title to *Inter Ocean Jr* in January 1894. This was accomplished easily by folding the single four page sheet into eight pages.

In the January 1894 Saalburg began using Brownies-inspired characters in his color comic strips. The present theory is the *Ting-Ling* characters took over solo five months later in response to a presumed cease and desist letter which inevitably must have been issued from Palmer Cox to the *Inter Ocean*.

However, on July 8 1894, the *Inter Ocean Jr* stopped color and full page comics-type work in this supplement, devolving back to simple small spot art works. By mid-1894, color comics printing genius Saalburg had been lured to Pulitzer's New York World, becoming Art Director in charge of coloring for the new color printing press at the *New York World*. The color supplement was soon to be unleashed in the largest city in America.

By the November 18, 1894 issue of the *World*, Outcault was working for Goddard and Saalburg. Outcault produced a successful Sunday newspaper sequential comic strip in color with "The Origin of a New Species" on the back page in the World's first colored Sunday supplement. Long time pro Walt McDougall, a famous cartoonist reputed to have turned the 1884 Presidential race with a single cartoon that ran in the *World*, handled the cartoon art on the front page. Earlier, *The World* began running full page color single panels on May 21, 1893. McDougall did various other page panels during 1893, but it was Jan. 28, 1894 when the first sequence of comic pictures in a New York World newspaper appeared in panels in the same format as our comic strips today. It was a full page cut up into nine panels. This historic sequence was drawn entirely in pantomime, with no words, by Mark Fenderson.

The second page to appear in panels was an eight panel strip from February 4, 1894, also lacking words except for the title. This page was a collaboration between Walt McDougall and Mark Fenderson titled "The Unfortunate Fate of a Well-Intentioned Dog." From then on, many full page color strips by McDougall and Fenderson appeared; they were the first cartoonists to draw for the Sunday newspaper comic section. It was Outcault, however, who soon became the most famous cartoonist featured. After first appearing in black and white in Pulitzer's *The New York World* on February 17, 1895 and again on March 10, 1895, *The Yellow Kid* was introduced to the public in color on May 5, 1895.

Some have erroneously reported in scholarly journals that perhaps it was Frank Ladendorf's "Uncle Reuben," first introduced May 26, 1895, which became the first regularly recurring comics character in newspapers. This is wrong, as even Outcault's "Yellow Kid" began in Pulitzer's paper a good three months before *Uncle Reuben*. Until firm evidence to the contrary comes to light, that honor will forever be enshrined with Jimmy Swinnerton's *Little Bears* cartoon characters, found all over inside Hearst's *San Francisco Examiner* beginning October 14, 1893 with the first one called "Baby Monarch. Though never actually a comic strip, they nonetheless were the earliest presently-known recurring comics-type characters in American newspapers. In June 1895, a semi-regular "Little Bears" feature began. On January 26, 1896, children were introduced, the title eventually changed to "Little Bears and Tykes," forever confusing some scholars decades later. There never was a strip titled *Little Bears and Tigers,* as the *Tigers* were strictly for New York consumption when Hearst ordered Swinnerton to move to the Big Apple to compete better in the brewing comic strip wars.

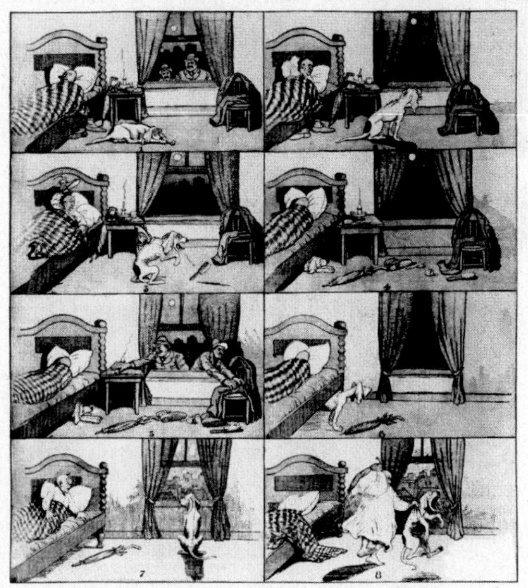

Walt McDougall & Mark Fenderson, the 2nd sequential comic strip in New York World, February 4, 1894, predates Yellow Kid in The World by over a year. Mark Fenderson drew the first NY World newspaper comic strip.

The Yellow Kid's importance is widely recognized today as the first newspaper comic strip to demonstrate without a doubt that the general public was ready for full color comics. *The Yellow Kid* was the first in the USA to show that comics could increase newspaper sales, and that comic characters could be merchandised. *The Yellow Kid* was the headlining spark of what was soon dubbed by Hearst as "eight pages of polychromatic effulgence that makes the rainbow look like a lead pipe."

Ongoing research suggests that Palmer Cox's fabulous success with *The Brownies* was a direct inspiration for Richard Outcault's future merchandising work. The ultimate proof lies in the fourth Yellow Kid cartoon, which appeared in the February 9, 1895 issue of *Truth*. It was reprinted in the *New York World* eight days later on February 17, 1895, becoming the first Yellow Kid cartoon in the newspapers. The caption read "FOURTH WARD BROWNIES. MICKEY, THE ARTIST (adding a finishing touch) Dere, Chimmy! If Palmer Cox wuz t' see yer, he'd git yer copyrighted in a minute." The Yellow Kid was widely licensed in the greater New York area for all kinds of products, including gum and cigarette cards, toys, pinbacks, cookies, postcards, tobacco products, and appliances. There was also a short-lived humor magazine from Street & Smith named *The Yellow Kid*, featuring exquisite Outcault covers, plus a 196-page comic book from Dillingham & Co. known as *The Yellow Kid in McFadden's Flats,* dated to early 1897. Check out the covers in "The Platinum Age" three-page comic strip elsewhere in this Guide. In addition, there were several Yellow Kid plays produced, spawning other collectibles like show posters, programs and illustrated sheet music. (For those interested in more information regarding the Yellow Kid, it is available on the Internet at www.neponset.com/yellowkid.)

Mickey Dugan burned brightly for a few years as Outcault secured a copyright on the character with the United States Government by September 1896. By the time he completed the necessary paperwork, however, hundreds of business people nationwide had pirated the image of The Yellow Kid and plastered it all over every product imaginable; mothers were even dressing their newborns to look like Dugan. Outcault, however, kept regularly utilizing images of *The Yellow Kid* in his comics style advertising work confirmed as late as 1915. Outcault soon found himself in a maelstrom not of his choosing, which probably pushed him to eventually drop the character. Outcault's creation went back and forth between newspaper giants Pulitzer and Hearst until Bennett's New York Herald mercifully snatched the cartoonist away in 1900 to do what amounted to a few relatively short-run strips. Later, he did one particular strip for a year–a satire of rural Black America titled *Pore Li'l Mose His Letters to his Mammy*, and then his newer creation, *Buster Brown*, debuted May 4, 1902. *Mose* had a very rare comic book collection published in 1902 by Cupples & Leon, now highly sought after by today's savvy collectors. Outcault continued drawing him in the background of occasional *Buster Brown* strips for many years to come.

William Randolph Hearst loved the comic strip medium ever since he was a little boy growing up on *Max & Moritz* by Wilhelm Busch in American collected book editions translated from the original German (these collections were first published in book form in 1871, serving as the influence for *The Katzenjammer Kids*). One of the ways Hearst responded to losing Outcault in 1900 was by purchasing the highly successful 23-year-old humor magazine *Puck* from the heirs of founder Joseph Keppler. With *Puck* and its exclusive cartoonist contracts, he commanded, among others, the very popular F. M. Howarth and Frederick Burr Opper's undivided attention. Opper first burst upon the comics scene in America back in 1880. Within a year Hearst had expanded this *National Lampoon* of its day into the colored Sunday comics section, *Puck-The Comic Weekly*. At first featuring Rudolph Dirk's *The Katzenjammer Kids* (1897), *Happy Hooligan* and other fine strips by the wildly popular Opper and a few others including Rudolph's brother Gus Dirks, the Hearst comic section steadily added more strips. For decades to come, there wasn't anything else that could compete with *Puck*. Hearst hired the best of the best and transformed *Puck* into the most popular comics section anywhere.

Outcault, meanwhile, followed in Palmer Cox's footprints a decade later by using the nexus of a World's Fair as a jumping off venue. *Buster Brown* was an instant sensation when he debuted as the new merchandising mascot of the Brown Shoe Company at the 1904 St. Louis World's Fair in a special Buster Brown Shoes pavilion. The character has the honor of being the first nationally licensed comic strip character in America with this time Outcault in almost full control. Many hundreds of different *Buster Brown* premiums have been issued. Comic books by Frederick A. Stokes Company featuring *Buster Brown & His Dog Tige* began as early as 1903 with *Buster Brown and His Resolutions*, simultaneously published in several different languages throughout the world.

After a few years, Buster and Outcault returned to Hearst in late 1905, joining what soon became the flagship of the comics world. Buster's popularity quickly spread all over the United States and then the world as he single-handedly spawned the first great comic strip licensing dynasty. For years, there were little people traveling from town to town performing as *Buster Brown* and selling shoes while accompanied by small dogs named Tige. Many other highly competitive licensed strips would soon follow. We suggest getting *Hake's Price Guide to Character Toys* for info on several hundred *Buster Brown* competitors, as well as several pages of the more fascinating *Buster Brown* material.

Soon there were many comic strip syndicates not only offering hundreds of various comic strips but also offering to license the characters for any company interested in paying the fee. The history of the comic strip with wide popularity since *The Yellow Kid* has been intertwined with giveaway premiums and character-based, store-bought merchandise of all kinds. Since its infancy as a profitable art form unto itself with *The Yellow Kid*, the comic strip world has profited from selling all sorts of "stuff" to the public featuring their favorite character or strip as its motif. American business gladly responded to the desire for comic character memorabilia with

Left: The Yellow Kid #1, March 20, 1897, Street & Smith as Howard Ainslee, NY.
Right: A rare full color "The Yellow Kid in McFadden's Flats" advertising sign promoting the first comic book featuring the Yellow Kid. The sign is from 1896 and measures 12x18".

The Adventures of Foxy Grandpa, late 1900, cover for the rare earliest known first edition of Carl "Bunny" Schultze's famous creation. He was one of the newspaper comics' first superstars.

Pore Li'l Mose by Richard Outcault, 1901. Bridges in between Yellow Kid and Buster Brown. Becoming scarce because many copies have been cut up.

thousands of fun items to enjoy and collect. Most of the early comics were not aimed specifically at kids, though children understandably enjoyed them as well.

Comic books have generally been associated with almost all of the licensed merchandise in this century. In the Platinum Age section beginning right after this essay, you will find a great many comic books in varied formats and sizes published before the advent of the first successful monthly newsstand comic magazine, *Famous Funnies*. What drove each of these evolutionary format changes was the need by their producers to make money so more books could be issued.

A very significant format was F. M. Howarth's *Funny Folks*, published in 1899 by E. P. Dutton and drawn from color as well as black and white pages of *Puck*. This rather large hardcover volume measured 16 1/2" wide by 12" tall. It contains numerous sequential comic strip pages as well as single gag illustrations. Howarth's art was a joy to behold and deserves wider recognition.

By Oct. 1900, Hearst had already caused Opper's *Folks In Funnyville* to be collected by publisher R. H. Russell, NY in a 12x9 hard cover format from his *New York Journal American Humorist* section. At the end of 1900, Carl Shultze had a first edition of *Vaudevilles and Other Things* published by Isaac H. Blanchard Co., NY. It measures 10 1/2" wide by 13" tall with 22 pages including covers. Each interior page is a 2 to 7 panel comic strip with lots of color.

There were also recently unearthed format variation second and third printings of *Vaudevilles* with the inscription "From the Originator of the 'Foxy Grandpa' Series" at the bottom of its front cover of the third printing. This note is lacking on the earlier first two editions, and it also switches format size to 11" tall by 13" wide. Discovered last year was a heretofore undocumented *The Adventures of Foxy Grandpa* - also issued in 1900 - new to the Platinum listings. The second number dated 1901 drops the words "The Adventures of..." from the title.

E. W. Kemble's *The Blackberries* had a color collection by 1901, also published by R. H. Russell, NY, as well as a few other comic-related volumes by Kemble still to be unearthed and properly identified. An earlier one was titled *Coontown's 400* (1899) newly listed this year. While the title is definitely not "PC" by today's standards, Kemble's drawings are excellent slices of African-American life in the USA with some humor injected. Kemble did a good job documenting aspects of life.

Confirmed is the exact format of Hearst's 1902 *The Katzenjammer Kids and Happy Hooligan And His Brother Gloomy Gus*. They both measure 15 5/16" wide by 10" tall and contain 88 pages including covers. Confirmed also is the fact that there are two separate editions with different covers for the pictured 1902 first edition and a 1903 Frederick Stokes edition of *Katzenjammer Kids* and *Happy Hooligan* with differing contents. They both are two different books entirely, and what confuses many collectors is that they have identical indicia title pages, but so does an entirely different *KK* from 1905.

Settling on a popular size of 17" wide by 11" tall, comic books were soon available that featured Charles "Bunny" Schultze's *Foxy Grandpa*, Rudolph Dirk's *The Katzenjammer Kids*, Winsor McCay's *Little Sammy Sneeze, Rarebit Fiend* and *Little Nemo*, and Fred Opper's *Happy Hooligan* and *Maud*, in addition to dozens of *Buster Brown* comic books. For well over a decade, these large-size, full-color volumes were the norm, retailing for 60¢. These collections offered full-size Sunday comics with the back side blank per page.

Though not the first daily newspaper strip, the very rare *Brainy Bowers and Drowsy Dugan* by R. W. Taylor is now crowned the first collection of strip reprints from a daily newspaper published in America. There are now four different collections of Brainy Bower known to exist.

The Outbursts of Everett True by A. D. Condo and J. W. Raper was first published by Saalfield in 1907 in an 88-page hardcover collection. It qualifies as the second daily comic strip collection as it predates the first *Mutt & Jeff* collection from Ball by three years. Condo & Raper's creation began its regular run several times a week in 1905 daily newspapers and lasted until 1927, when Condo became too sick to continue. This same *Everett True* collection was later truncated a bit by Saalfield in 1921 to 56 strips in just 32 pages measuring the standard 10"x10" Cupples & Leon size.

By 1908 Stokes had a large backlist of full color comic books for sale at 60¢ each. Some of these titles date back to 1903 and were reprinted over and over as demand warranted. Note the number of titles in the advertisement pulled from the back of *The Three Fun Makers* shown below.

With the ever-increasing popularity of Bud Fisher's new daily strip sensation, *Mutt & Jeff,* a new format was created for reprinting daily strips in black and white, a hardcover book about 15" wide by 5" tall, published by Ball starting in 1910 for five volumes. In 1912, Ball also branched out with at least the now-obscure *Doings of the Van Loons* by Fred I. Leipziger, a rare comic book in the same format as the *Mutt & Jeffs.*

Cartoons Magazine also began in 1912 and ran through 1921 before undergoing a radical format change. It is notable as a wonderful source for information on early comics and their creators. See also the Platinum index.

The next significant evolutionary change occurred in 1919, when Cupples & Leon began issuing their black and white daily strip reprint books in a new aforementioned format, about 10" wide by 10" tall, with four panels reprinted per page in a two by two matrix. These books were 52 pages for 25¢. The first ones featured *Bringing Up Father* and *Mutt & Jeff;* there were about 100 others.

By 1921, the last of the oblong (11"x15") color comic books were issued, with Cupples & Leon's *Jimmie Dugan* and *The Reg'lar Fellers* by Gene Byrne, and EmBee's *The Trouble Of Bringing Up Father* by self publisher George McManus. Of special historical interest, Embee issued the first 10¢ monthly comic book, *Comic Monthly,* with the first issue dated January 1922. A dozen 8-1/2"x9" issues were published, each featuring solo adventures of popular King Features strips. The monthly 10¢ comic book concept had finally arrived, though it would be more than a decade before it became truly successful.

Skippy by Percy Crosby debuted in the long-running humor magazine *Life* in the March 22, 1923 issue. By 1924 the first hard cover collection, *Life Presents Skippy*, was published. The newspaper comic strip debuted June 23, 1925 with the McClure syndicate. Hearst soon picked up a Sunday page a year later in mid-1926, then added a daily strip in 1929. By the 1930s it was red hot - think *Calvin & Hobbes or Peanuts* in popularity. In its day, it was one of the most popular comic strips ever created. Read the Modern era essay for more on *Skippy's* immense popularity.

In 1926, Cupples & Leon added a new 7" wide by 9" tall format with *Little Orphan Annie, Smitty,* and others. These were issued in both softcover and hardcover editions with dust jackets, and became extremely popular at 60¢ per copy.

Dell began publishing all original material in *The Funnies* in late 1929 in a larger tabloid format. At least three dozen issues were published before Delacorte threw in the towel. Even the extremely popular *Big Little Book*, introduced in 1932, can be viewed as a smaller version of the existing formats. The competition amongst publishers now included Dell, McKay, Sonnet, Saalfield and Whitman. The 1930s saw a definite shift in merchandising comic strip material from adults to children. This was the decade when Kellogg's placed *Buck Rogers* on the map, when Ovaltine issued tons of *Little Orphan Annie* material. Merchandising from such pioneers as Sam Gold and Kay Kamen spearheaded this next transformation of the comics biz beginning in the early 1930s.

Upwards of a thousand of these *Funnies On Parade* precursors, in all formats, were published through 1935 and were very popular. Towards the end of this era of once-popular comic book formats, beautiful collections of *Popeye, Mickey Mouse, Dick Tracy*, and many others were published which today command ever higher prices on the open market as they are rediscovered by the advanced collector who appreciates and enjoys truly great classic comics.

END NOTE: Each year we strive to add to the many 1930s variant formats. This Platinum Age section has grown as a result of advanced collectors who continue to report in with new finds. We encourage interested collectors and scholars to help with this section of the book, as each new data entry is very important for recovering our history. For corrections and additions to next year's next edition of *The Overstreet Guide* of some treasures you may have uncovered, please feel free to contact Gemstone Publishing at feedback@gemstonepub.com.

For further information on this era of American comic books, check out the previous evolving comics history essays in Guides #27,29-#40. Happy Hunting!

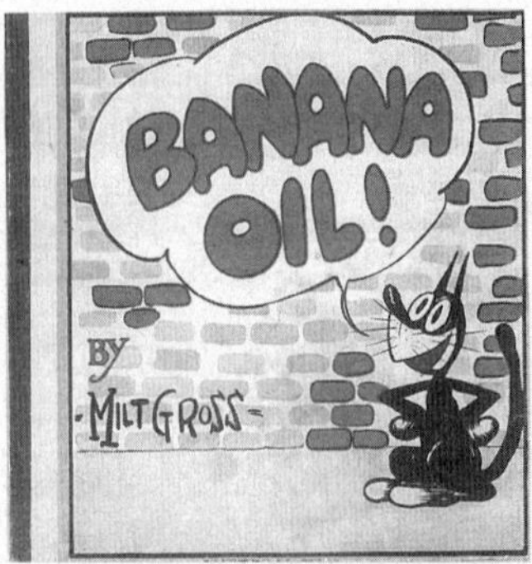

Banana Oil, a 1924 example of Cupples & Leon's then-revolutionary format from M.S. Publishers

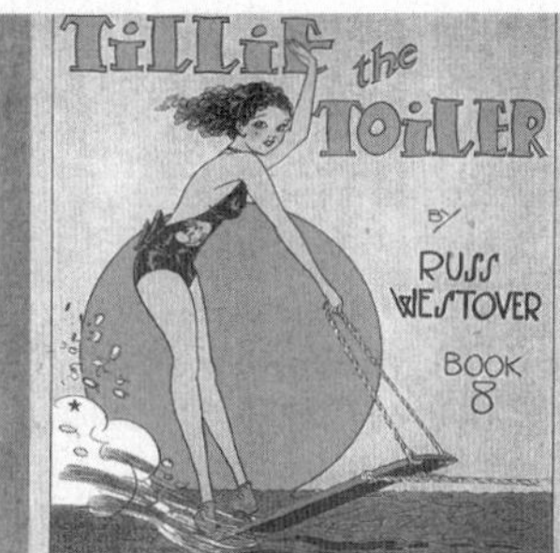

Tillie the Toiler #8 1933 from Cupples & Leon, another scarce number at the end of this once popular format.

David McKay published the last of the 10x10 comic books in 1935 as Famous Funnies grew in popularity.

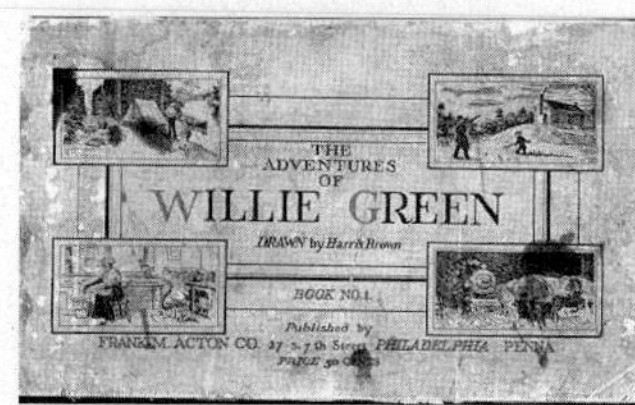

The Adventures of Willie Green
© Frank M. Acton

Alphonse and Gaston by Opper
1902 © Hearst's NY American & Journal

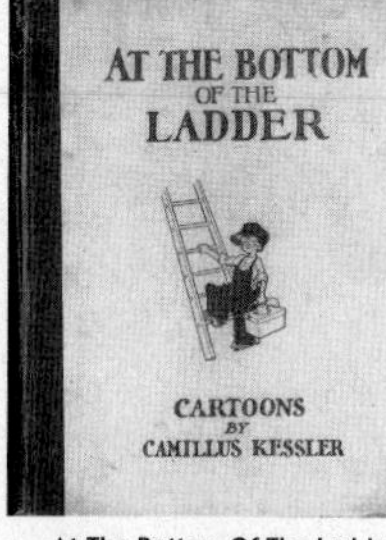

At The Bottom Of The Ladder
1926 © J.P. Lippincott Company

COLLECTOR'S NOTE: The books listed in this section were published many decades before organized comics fandom began archiving and helping to preserve these fragile popular culture artifacts. Consequently, copies of most all of these comics do not often surface in Fine+ or better shape. eBay has proven after more than a decade that many items once considered rare actually are not, though they almost always are in higher grades. For items marked scarce, we are trying to ascertain how many copies might still be in existence. Your input is always welcome.

Most Platinum Age comic books are in the Fair to VG range. If you want to collect these only in high grade, your collection will be extremely small. The prices given for Good, Fine and Very Fine categories are for strictly graded editions. If you need help grading your item, we refer you to the grading section in the front of this price guide or contact the authors of the Platinum essay. Most measurements are in inches. A few measurements are in centimeters. The first dimension given is Height and the second is Width.

For ease of ascertaining the contents of each item of this listing, there is a code letter or two following most titles we have been adding in over the years to aid you. A helpful list of categories pertaining to these codes can be found at the beginning of the Victorian Age pricing sections. This section created, revised, and expanded by Robert Beerbohm and Richard Olson with able assistance from Ray Agricola, Jon Berk, Bill Blackbeard, Roy Bonario, Ray Bottorff Jr., Chris Brown, Alfredo Castelli, Darrell Coons, Sol Davidson, Leonardo De Sá, Scott Deschaine, Mitchell Duval, Joe Evans, Tom Gordon III, Bruce Hamilton, Andy Konkykru, Don Kurtz, Gabriel Laderman, Bruce Mason, Donald Puff, Robert Quesinberry, Steve Rowe, Randy Scott, John Snyder, Art Spiegelman, Steve Thompson, Joan Crosby Tibbets, Richard Samuel West, Doug Wheeler, Richard Wright and Craig Yoe.

ADVENTURES OF EVA, PORA AND TED (M)
Evaporated Milk Association: 1932 (5x15", 16 pgs, B&W)

nn - By Steve 20.00 40.00 100.00
NOTE: *Appears to have had green, blue or white paper cover versions.*

ADVENTURES OF HAWKSHAW (N) (See Hawkshaw The Detective)
The Saalfield Publishing Co.: 1917 (9-3/4x13-1/2", 48 pgs., color & two-tone)

nn - By Gus Mager (only 24 pgs. of strips, reverse of each pg. is blank) 50.00 175.00 400.00
nn - 1927 Reprints 1917 issue 30.00 150.00 260.00
NOTE: *Started Feb 23, 1913-Sept 4, 1922, then begins again Dec 13, 1931-Feb 11, 1952.*

ADVENTURES OF SLIM AND SPUD, THE (M)
Prairie Farmer Publ. Co.: 1924 (3-3/4x 9-3/4", 104 pgs., B&W strip reprints)

nn 25.00 90.00 180.00
NOTE: *Illustrated mailing envelope exists postmarked out of Chicago, add 50%.*

ADVENTURES OF WILLIE WINTERS, THE (O,P)
Kelloggs Toasted Corn Flake Co.: 1912 (6-7/8x9-1/2", 20 pgs, full color)

nn - By Byron Williams & Dearborn Melvill 54.00 189.00 350.00

ADVENTURES OF WILLIE GREEN, THE (N) (see The Willie Green Comics)
Frank M. Acton Co.: 1915 (50¢, 52 pgs, 8-1/2X16", B&W, soft-c)

Book 1 - By Harris Brown; strip-r 54.00 189.00 350.00

A. E. F. IN CARTOONS BY WALLY, THE (N)
Don Sowers & Co.: 1933 (12x10-1/8", 88 pgs, hardcover B&W)

nn - By Wally Wallgren (WW One Stars & Stripes-r) 60.00 125.00 250.00

AFTER THE TOWN GOES DRY (I)
The Howell Publishing Co, Chicago: 1919 (48 pgs, 6-1/2x4", hardbound two color-c)

nn - By Henry C. Taylor; illus by Frank King 25.00 75.00 150.00

AIN'T IT A GRAND & GLORIOUS FEELING? (N) (Also see Mr. & Mrs.)
Whitman Publishing Co.: 1922 (9x9-3/4", 52 pgs., stiff cardboard-c)

nn - 1921 daily strip-r; B&W, color-c; Briggs-a 36.00 143.00 250.00
nn -(9x9-1/2", 28pgs., stiff cardboard-c)-Sunday strip-r in color (inside front-c says "More of the Married Life of Mr. & Mrs".) 36.00 143.00 250.00
NOTE: *Strip started in 1917; This is the 2nd Whitman comic book, after Brigg's MR. & MRS.*

ALL THE FUNNY FOLKS (I)
World Press Today, Inc.: 1926 (11-1/2x8-1/2", 112 pgs., color, hard-c)

nn-Barney Google, Spark Plug, Jiggs & Maggie, Tillie The Toiler, Happy Hooligan, Hans & Fritz, Toots & Casper, etc. 100.00 400.00 700.00
With Dust Jacket By Louis Biedermann 225.00 850.00 1600.00
NOTE: *Booklength race horse story masterfully enveloping all major King Features characters.*

ALPHONSE AND GASTON AND THEIR FRIEND LEON (N)
Hearst's New York American & Journal: 1902,1903 (10x15-1/4", Sunday strip reprints in color)

nn - (1902) - By Frederick Opper (scarce) 600.00 2100.00 –
nn - (1903) - By Frederick Opper (scarce) (72 pages) 600.00 2100.00 –
NOTE: *Strip ran Sept 22, 1901 to at least July 17, 1904.*

ALWAYS BELITTLIN' (see Skippy; That Rookie From the 13th Squad; Between Shots)
Henry Holt & Co.: 1927 (6x8", hard-c with DJ,

nn -By Percy Crosby (text with cartoons) 43.00 172.00 320.00

ALWAYS BELITTLIN' (I) (see Skippy; That Rookie From the 13th Squad, Between Shots)
Percy Crosby, Publisher: 1933 (14 1/4 x 11", 72 pgs, hard-c, B&W)

nn - By Percy Crosby 43.00 172.00 320.00
NOTE: *Self-published; primarily political cartoons with text pages denouncing prohibition's gang warfare effects and cuts in the national defense budget as Crosby saw war looming in Europe and with Japan.*

AMERICAN-JOURNAL-EXAMINER JOKE BOOK SPECIAL SUPPLEMENT (O)
New York American: 1911-12 (12 x 9 3/4", 16 pgs) (known issues) (Very Rare)

1 Tom Powers Joke Book(12/10/11) 80.00 320.00 –
2 Mutt & Jeff Joke Book (Bud Fisher 12/17/11) 100.00 365.00 –
3 TAD's Joke Book (Thomas Dorgan 12/24/11) 80.00 320.00 –
4 F. Opper's Joke Book (Frederick Burr Opper 12/31/11) (contains Happy Hooligan) 100.00 365.00 –
5 not known to exist
6 Swinnerton's Joke Book (Jimmy Swinnerton 01/14/12) (contains Mr. Jack) 100.00 400.00 –
7 The Monkey's Joke Book (Gus Mager 01/21/12) (contains Sherlocko the Monk) 100.00 365.00 –
8 Joys And Glooms Joke Book (T. E. Powers 01/28/12) 80.00 320.00 –
9 The Dingbat Family's Joke Book (George Herriman 02/04/12) (contains early Krazy Kat & Ignatz) 200.00 800.00 –
10 Valentine Joke Book, A (Opper, Howarth, Mager, T. E. Powers 02/11/12) 80.00 320.00 –
11 Little Hatchet Joke Book (T. E. Powers 02/18/12) 80.00 320.00 –
12 Jungle Joke Book (Dirks, McCay 02/25/12) 100.00 410.00 –
13 The Hayseeds Joke Book (03/03/12) 80.00 320.00 –
14 Married Life Joke Book (T.E. Powers 03/10/12) 80.00 320.00 –
NOTE: *These were insert newspaper supplements similar to Eisner's later Spirit sections. A Valentine Joke Book recently surfaced from Hearst's Boston Sunday American proving that other cities besides New York City had these special supplements. Each issue also contains work by other cartoonists besides the cover featured creator and those already listed above such as Sidney Smith, Winsor McCay, Hy Mayer, Grace Weiderseim (later Drayton), others.*

AMERICA'S BLACK & WHITE BOOK 100 Pictured Reasons Why We Are At War (N,S)
Cupples & Leon: 1917 (10 3/4 x 8", 216 pgs)

nn - W. A. Rogers (New York Herald-r) 35.00 118.00 225.00

AMONG THE FOLKS IN HISTORY
Rand McNally Print Guild: 1935 (192 pgs, 8-1/2x9-1/2", hard-c, B&W)

nn - By Gaar Williams 21.00 84.00 160.00

AMONG THE FOLKS IN HISTORY
The Book and Print Guild: 1935 (200 pgs, 8-1/2x9-1/2:,

nn - By Gaar Williams 21.00 84.00 160.00
NOTE: *Both the above are evidently different editions and contain largely full-page, single panel cartoons similar to Briggs' work of that sort. 8 or 10 pages are broken into panels, usually with a "this is how it was in the old days, this is how it is today theme."*

ANGELIC ANGELINA (N)
Cupples & Leon Company: 1909 (11-1/2x17", 56 pgs., 2 colors)

nn - By Munson Paddock 67.00 233.00 410.00
NOTE: *Strip ran March 22, 1908-Feb 7, 1909.*

ANDY GUMP, HIS LIFE STORY (I)
The Reilly & Lee Co, Chicago: 1924 (192 pgs, hardbound)

nn - By Sidney Smith (over 100 illustrations) 30.00 100.00 225.00

ANIMAL CIRCUS, THE (from Puggery Wee)
Rand McNally + Company: 1908 (48 pgs, 11x8-1/2", color-c, 3-color insides)

nn - By unknown 25.00 80.00 150.00
NOTE: *Illustrated verse, many pages with multiple illustrations.*

ANIMAL SERIALS
T. Y. Crowell: 1906 (9x6-7/8", 214 pgs, hard-c, B&W)

nn - By E Warde Blaisdell 20.00 80.00 160.00
NOTE: *Multi-page comic strip stories. Reprints of Sunday strip "Bunny Bright He's All-Right".*

A NOBODY'S SCRAP BOOK
Frederik A. Stokes Co., New York: 1900 (11" x 8-5/8", hard-c, color)

nn- (Scarce) 67.00 233.00 450.00
NOTE: *Designed in England, printed in Holland, on English paper -- which likely explains the mispelling of Frederick Stokes' name. Highly fragile paper. Strips and cartoons, all by the same unidentified artist, "A Nobody", almost certainly reprinted from somewhere, as they are very professional.*

AT THE BOTTOM OF THE LADDER (M)
J.P. Lippincott Company: 1926 (11x8-1/4", 296 pgs, hardcover, B&W)

nn - By Camillus Kessler 45.00 157.50 300.00
NOTE: *Hilarious single panel cartoons showing first jobs of then important "captains of industry."*

AUTO FUN, PICTURES AND COMMENTS FROM "LIFE"
Thomas Y. Crowell & Co.: 1905 (152 pgs, 9x7", hard-c, B&W)

nn -By various 45.00 157.00 375.00
NOTE: *The cover just has "Auto Fun" but the title page also has the subheading listed here. This is similar to other reprint books of Life cartoons printed in the guide. Largely single panel cartoons but also several sequential. One or more cartoons by Kemble, Levering, Dirks, Flagg, Sullivant. Sequential cartoons by Kemble, Levering, Sullivant, and the highpoint, a 2 pg 6 panel piece by Winsor McCay.*

BANANA OIL (N) (see also HE DONE HER WRONG)

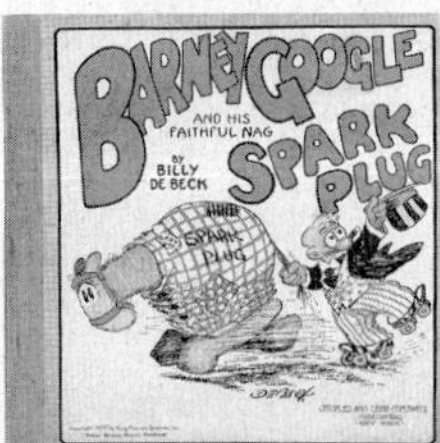

Barney Google and Spark Plug #1
© C&L

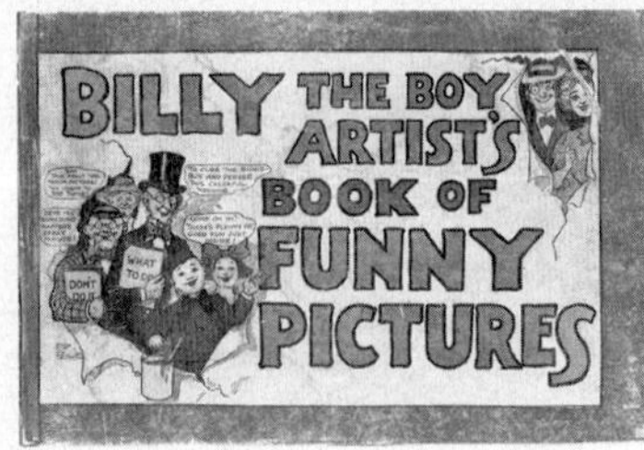

Bill the Boy Artist's Book by Ed Payne
1910 © C.M. Clark Publishing Co

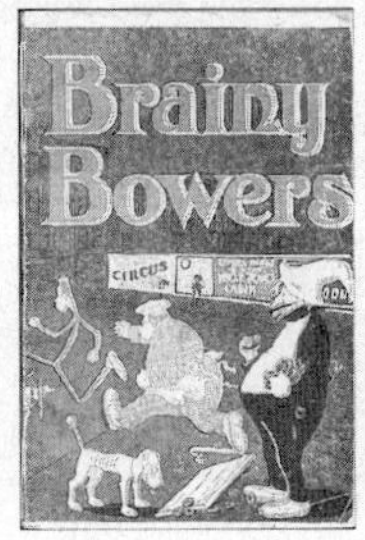

Brainy Bowers and Drowsy Duggan by R.W. Taylor
1905 © Star Publishing Co. - the first daily reprints

GD2.0 FN6.0 VF8.0

MS Publ. Co.: 1924 (9-7/8x10", 52 pgs., B&W)

nn - Milt Gross comic strips; not reprints 150.00 450.00 900.00

BARKER'S ILLUSTRATED ALMANAC (O,P,S) (See Barkers in Victorian Era section)
Barker, Moore & Mein Medicine Co: 1900-1932+ (36 pgs, B&W, color paper-c)

1900-1932+ (7x5-7/8") 50.00 100.00 225.00

BARKER'S "KOMIC" PICTURE SOUVENIR (P,S) (see Barker's in Victorian)
Barker, Moore & Mein Medicine Co: nd (Parts 1-3, 1901-1903; Parts 1-4, 1906+) (color cardboard-c, B&W interior, 50 pages)

Parts 1-3 (Rare, earliest printing, nd (1901)) 200.00 400.00 800.00
NOTE: *Same cover as 4th edition in Victorian Age Section, except has "Part 1", "Part 2", or "Part 3" printed in the blank space beneath the crate on which central figure is sitting. States "Edition in 3 Parts" on the first interior page, beneath the picture of the Barker's Building.*
Parts 1-3 (nd, c1901-1903) 100.00 250.00 650.00
NOTE: *New cover art on all Parts. States "Edition in 3 Parts" on the first interior page.*
Parts 1-4 (nd, c1906+) 100.00 200.00 450.00
NOTE: *States "Edition in 4 Parts" on the first interior page. Various printings known. These have been confirmed as premium comic books, predating the Buster Brown premiums. They reprint advertising cartoons from Barker's Illustrated Almanac. For the 50 page booklets by this same name, numbered as "Part"s, without exception, were published after 1900. Some editions are found to have 54 pages.*

BARNEY GOOGLE AND SPARK PLUG (N) (See **Comic Monthly**)
Cupples & Leon Co.: 1923 - No.6, 1928 (9-7/8x9-3/4"; 52 pgs., B&W, daily-r)

1 (nn)-By Billy DeBeck 60.00 240.00 550.00
2-4 (#5 & #6 do not exist) 46.00 186.00 350.00
NOTE: *Started June 17, 1919 as newspaper strip; Spark Plug introduced July 17, 1922; strip still running making it one of the oldest still in existence.*

BART'S CARTOONS FOR 1902 FROM THE MINNEAPOLIS JOURNAL (N,S)
Minneapolis Journal: 1903 (11x9", 102 pgs, paperback, B&W)

nn - By Charles L. Bartholomew 30.00 100.00 175.00

BELIEVE IT OR NOT! by Ripley (N,S)
Simon & Schuster: 1929 (8x 5-1/4", 68 pgs, red, B&W cover, B&W interior)

nn - By Robert Ripley (strip-r text & art) 60.00 125.00 275.00
NOTE: *1929 was the first printing of many reprintings . Strip began Dec 19, 1918 and is still running.*

BEN WEBSTER (N)
Standard Printing Company: 1928-1931 (13-3/4x4-7/16", 768 pgs, soft-c)

1 - "Bound to Win" 50.00 125.00 300.00
2 - "...in old Mexico 50.00 125.00 300.00
3 - "...At Wilderness Lake 50.00 125.00 300.00
4 - "...in the Oil Fields 50.00 125.00 300.00
NOTE: *Self Published by Edwin Alger, also contains fan's letter pages.*

BIG SMOKER
W.T. Blackwell & Co.: 1908 (16 pgs, 5-1/2x3-1/2", color-c & interior)

nn - By unknown 20.00 55.00 100.00
NOTE: *Stated reprint of 1878 version. no known copies yet of original printing.*

BILLY BOUNCE (I)
Donohue & Co.: 1906 (288 pgs, hardbound)

nn - By W.W. Denslow & Dudley Bragdon 150.00 525.00 1100.00
NOTE: *Billy Bounce was created in 1901 as a comic strip by W. W. Denslow (strip ran from 1901 NOV 11 to 1905 DEC 3), but the series is best remembered in the C. W. Kahles version (from 1902 SEP 28). Denslow resumed his character in the above illustrated book.*

BILLY HON'S FAMOUS CARTOON BOOK (H)
Wasley Publishing Co.: 1927 (7-1/2x10", 68 pgs, softbound wraparound)

nn - By Billy Hon 15.00 50.00 100.00

BILLY THE BOY ARTIST'S BOOK OF FUNNY PICTURES (N)
C.M.Clark Publishing Co.: 1910 (9x12", hardcover-c, Boston Globe strip-r)

nn - By Ed Payne 125.00 400.00 750.00
NOTE: *This long lived strip ran in **The Boston Globe** from Nov 5 1899-Jan 7 1955; one of the longer run strips.*

BILLY THE BOY ARTIST'S PAINTING BOOK OF FUNNY PICTURES
(known to exist; more data required) – – –

BIRD CENTER CARTOONS: A Chronicle of Social Happenings (N,S)
A. C. McClurg & Co.: 1904 (12-3/8x9-1/2", 216 pgs, hardcover, B&W, single panels)

nn - By John McCutcheon 40.00 140.00 260.00
NOTE: *Strip began in **The Chicago Tribune** in 1903. Satirical cartoons and text concerning a mythical town.*

BLASTS FROM THE RAM'S HORN
The Rams Horn Company: 1902 (330 pgs, 7x9", B&W)

nn - By various 25.00 80.00 125.00
NOTE: *Cartoons reprinted from what was, apparently, a religious newspaper. Many cartoons by Frank Beard. Mostly single panel but occasionally sequential. Allegorical cartoons similar to the Christian Cartoons book. This book mixes cartoons and text sort of like the Caricature books. One or more cartoons on every page.*

BOBBY THATCHER & TREASURE CAVE (N)
Altemus Co.: 1932 (9x7", 86 pgs., B&W, hard-c)

nn - Reprints; Storm-a 54.00 189.00 400.00

BOBBY THATCHER'S ROMANCE (N)
The Bell Syndicate/Henry Altemus Co.: 1931 (8-3/4x7", color cover, B&W)

GD2.0 FN6.0 VF8.0

nn - By Storm 54.00 189.00 400.00

BOOK OF CARTOONS, A (M,S)
Edward T. Miller: 1903 (12-1/4x9-1/4", 120 pgs, hardcover, B&W)

nn - By Harry J. Westerman (Ohio State Journal-r) 20.00 70.00 125.00

BOOK OF DRAWINGS BY A.B. FROST, A (M,S)
P.F. Collier & Son: 1904 (15-3/8 x 11", 96 pgs, B&W)

nn - A.B. Frost 55.00 105.00 310.00
NOTE: *Pages alternate verses by Wallace Irwin and full-page plated by A.B.Frost. 39 plates.*

BOTTLE, THE (E) (see Victorian Age section for earlier printings)
Gowans & Gray, London & Glasgow: June 1905 (3-3/4x6", 72 pgs, printed one side only, paper cover, B&W)

nn - 1st printing (June 1905) 20.00 50.00 125.00
nn - 2nd printing (March 1906) 20.00 50.00 100.00
nn - 3rd printing (January 1911) 20.00 50.00 100.00
NOTE: *By George Cruikshank. Reprints both THE BOTTLE and THE DRUNKARD'S CHILDREN. Cover is text only - no cover art.*

BOTTLE, THE (E)
Frederick A. Stokes: nd (c1906) (3-3/4x6", 72 pgs, printed one side only, paper-c, B&W)

nn- by George Cruikshank 20.00 40.00 100.00
NOTE: *Reprint of the Gowans & Gray edition. Reprints both THE BOTTLE and THE DRUNKARD'S CHILDREN. Cover is text only - no cover art.*

BOYS AND FOLKS (N).
George H. Dornan Company: 1917 (10-1/4 x 8-1/4", 232 pgs. (single-sided), B&W strip-r.

nn - By Webster 21.00 64.00 150.00
NOTE: *Four sections: Life's Darkest Moments, Mostly About Folks, The Thrill That Comes Once in a Lifetime, and Our Boyhood Ambitions. Most are single-panel cartoons, but there are some sequential comic strips.*

BOY'S & GIRLS' BIG PAINTING BOOK OF INTERESTING COMIC PICTURES (N)
M. A. Donohue & Co.: 1914-16 (9x15, 70 pgs)

nn - By Carl "Bunny" Schultze (Foxy Grandpa-r) 81.00 284.00 –
#2 (1914) 81.00 284.00 –
#337 (1914) (sez "Big Painting & Drawing Book") 81.00 284.00 –
nn - (1916) (sez "Big Painting Book")(9-1/4x15") 81.00 284.00 –
NOTE: *These are all **Foxy Grandpa** items.*

BRAIN LEAKS: Dialogues of Mutt & Flea (N)
O. K. Printing Co. (Rochester Evening Times): 1911 (76 pgs, 6-5/8x4-5/8, hard-c, B&W)

nn - By Leo Edward O'Melia; newspaper strip-r 29.00 100.00 200.00

BRAINY BOWERS AND DROWSY DUGGAN (N)
Star Publishing: 1905 (7-1/4 x 4-9/16", 98 pgs., blue, brown & white color cover, B&W interior, 25¢) (daily strip-r 1902-04 Chicago Daily News)

#74 - By R. W. Taylor (Scarce) 600.00 1900.00 –
NOTE: *Part of a series of Atlantic Library Heart Series. Strip begins in 1901 and runs thru 1915. Taylor also created Yen the Janitor for the **New York World.***

BRAIN BOWERS AND DROWSY DUGAN (N)
Max Stein Pub. House, Chicago: 1905 (6-3/16x4-3/8", 64 pgs, B&W)

nn - By R.W. Taylor (Scarce) 600.00 1900.00 –
NOTE: *A coverless copy of this surfaced on eBay in 2002 selling for $700.00.;*

BRAINY BOWERS AND DROWSY DUGGAN GETTING ON IN THE WORLD WITH NO VISIBLE MEANS OF SUPPORT (STORIES TOLD IN PICTURES TO MAKE THEIR TELLING SHORT) (N)
Max Stein/Star Publishing: 1905 (7-3/8x5 1/8", 164 pgs, slick black, red & tan color cover, interior newsprint) (daily strip-r 1902-04 Chicago Daily News)

nn - By R. W. Taylor (Scarce) 500.00 1800.00 –
nn - Possible hard cover edition also? – – –
NOTE: *These Brainy Bowers editions are the earliest known daily newspaper strip reprint books.*

BRINGING UP FATHER (N)
Star Co. (King Features): 1917 (5-1/2x16-1/2", 100 pgs., B&W, cardboard-c)

nn - (Scarcer)-Daily strip- by George McManus 158.00 553.00 1050.00

BRINGING UP FATHER (N)
Cupples & Leon Co.: 1919 - No. 26, 1934 (10x10", 52 pgs., B&W, stiff cardboard-c) (No. 22 is 9-1/4x9-1/2")

1-Daily strip-r by George McManus in all 30.00 110.00 400.00
2-10 28.00 105.00 285.00
11-20 40.00 200.00 400.00
21-26 (Scarcer) 65.00 310.00 600.00
The Big Book 1 (1926)-Thick book (hardcover, 142 pgs.) 127.00 508.00 1000.00
w/dust jacket (rare) 183.00 732.00 1400.00
The Big Book 2 (1929) 96.00 384.00 750.00
w/dust jacket (rare) 183.00 732.00 1375.00
NOTE: *The Big Books contain 3 regular issues rebound. Strip began Jan 2 1913-May 28 2000.*

BRINGING UP FATHER, THE TROUBLE OF (N)
Embee Publ. Co.: 1921 (9-3/4x15-3/4", 46 pgs, Sunday-r in color)

nn - (Rare) 100.00 350.00 700.00
NOTE: *Ties with Mutt & Jeff (EmBee) and Jimmie Dugan And The Reg'lar Fellers (C&L) as the last of the*

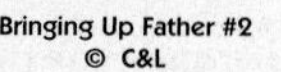

Bringing Up Father #2
© C&L

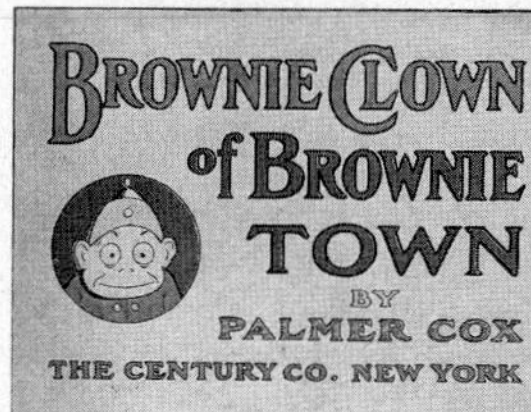

Brownie Clown of Brownie Town
© The Century Co.

Buster Brown Nuggets - Goes Swimming
1907 © Cupples & Leon

GD2.0 FN6.0 VF8.0

oblong size era. This was self published by George McManus.

BRINGING UP FATHER (N) (see SAGARA'S ENGLISH CARTOONS
Publisher unknown (actually, unreadable), Tokyo: October 1924 (9-7/8" x 7-1/2", 90 pgs, color hard-c, B&W)

nn- (Scarce) by George McManus C&A (no known sales)
NOTE: *Published in Tokyo, Japan, with all strips in both English and Japanese, to facilitate learning English. Introduction by George McManus. Scarce in USA.*

BRONX BALLADS (I)
Simon & Schuster, NY: 1927 (9-1/2x7-1/4", hard-c, B&W)

nn - By Robert Simon and Harry Hershfield 75.00 150.00 300.00

BROWNIES, THE (not sequential comic strips)
The Century Co.: 1887 - 1914 (all came with dust jackets; add $100-150 to value if original dust jacket is included and intact)

Book 1 - The Brownies: Their Book (1887) 200.00 800.00 1200.00
Book 2 - Another Brownies Book (1890) 150.00 635.00 1000.00
Book 3 - The Brownies at Home (1893) 125.00 530.00 825.00
Book 4 - The Brownies Around the World (1894) 100.00 425.00 675.00
Book 5 - The Brownies Through the Union (1895) 100.00 425.00 675.00
Book 6 - The Brownies Abroad (1899) 100.00 425.00 675.00
Book 7 - The Brownies in the Philippines (1904) 100.00 425.00 675.00
Book 8 - The Brownies' Latest Adventures (1910) 100.00 425.00 675.00
Book 9 - The Brownies Many More Nights (1914) 100.00 425.00 675.00
...Raid on Kleinmaier Bros. (c. 1910, 16 pages) Kleinmaier Bros. Clothing, Marion, Ohio (no known sales)

BROWNIE CLOWN OF BROWNIE TOWN (N)
The Century Co.: 1908 (6-7/8 x 9-3/8", 112 pgs, color hardcover & interior)

nn - By Palmer Cox (rare; 1907 newspaper comic strip-r) 250.00 800.00 1000.00
NOTE: *The Brownies created 1883 in* **St Nicholas Magazine.**

BUDDY TUCKER & HIS FRIENDS (N) (Also see **Buster Brown Nuggets**)
Cupples & Leon Co.: 1906 (11-5/8 x17", 58 pgs, color) (Scarce)

nn - 1905 Sunday strip-r by R. F. Outcault 525.00 1550.00 2650.00
NOTE: *Strip began Apr 30, 1905 thru at least Oct 1905.*

BUFFALO BILL'S PICTURE STORIES
Street & Smith Publications: 1909 (Soft cardboard cover)

nn - Very rare 100.00 275.00 450.00

BUGHOUSE FABLES (N) (see also **Comic Monthly**)
Embee Distributing Co. (King Features): 1921 (10¢, 4x4-1/2", 48 pgs.)

1-By Barney Google (Billy DeBeck) 46.00 186.00 350.00

BUG MOVIES (O) (Also see Clancy The Cop & Deadwood Gulch)
Dell Publishing Co.: 1931 (9-13/16x9-7/8", 52 pgs., B&W)

nn - Original material; Stookie Allen-a 150.00 300.00 600.00

BULL
Bull Publishing Company, New York: No.1, March, 1916 - No.12, Feb, 1917 (10 cents, 10-3/4x8-3/4", 24 pgs, color paper-c, B&W)

1-12 (Very Rare) – – –
NOTE: *Pro-German, Anti-British cartoon/humor monthly, whose goal was to keep the U.S. neutral and out of World War I. We know of no copies which have sold in the past few years.*

BUNNY'S BLUE BOOK (see also Foxy Grandpa) (N)
Frederick A. Stokes Co.: 1911 (10x15, 60¢)

nn - By Carl "Bunny" Schultze strip-r 125.00 360.00 –

BUNNY'S RED BOOK (see also Foxy Grandpa) (N)
Frederick A. Stokes Co.: 1912 (10-1/4x15-3/4", 64 pgs.)

nn - By Carl "Bunny" Schultze strip-r 125.00 360.00 –

BUNNY'S GREEN BOOK (see also Foxy Grandpa) (N)
Frederick A. Stokes Co.: 1913 (10x15")

nn - By Carl "Bunny" Schultze 125.00 360.00 –

BUSTER BROWN (C) (Also see Brown's Blue Ribbon Book of Jokes and Jingles & Buddy Tucker & His Friends)
Frederick A. Stokes Co.: 1903 - 1916 (Daily strip-r in color)

1903...& His Resolutions (11-1/4x16", 66 pgs.) by R. F. Outcault (Rare)-1st nationally distributed comic. Distr. through Sears & Roebuck 1600.00 3300.00 –
1904...His Dog Tige & Their Troubles (11-1/4x16-1/4", 66 pgs.)(Rare) 600.00 1800.00 –
1905...Pranks (11-1/4x16-3/8", 66 pgs.) 400.00 1450.00 –
1906...Antics (11x16-3/8", 66 pgs.) 400.00 1450.00 –
1906...And Company (11x16-1/2", 66 pgs.) 300.00 1050.00 –
1906...Mary Jane & Tige (11-1/4x16, 66 pgs.) 300.00 1050.00 –
NOTE: ***Yellow Kid** pictured on two pages.*
1908 Collection of Buster Brown Comics 250.00 835.00 –
1909 Outcault's Real Buster and The Only Mary Jane (11x16, 66 pgs, Stokes) 250.00 835.00 –
1910...Up to Date (10-1/8x15-3/4", 66 pgs.) 208.00 729.00 1000.00

GD2.0 FN6.0 VF8.0

1911...Fun And Nonsense (10-1/8x15-3/4", 66 pgs.) 183.00 642.00 1100.00
1912...The Fun Maker (10-1/8x15-3/4", 66 pgs.) -Yellow Kid (4 pgs.) 183.00 642.00 1100.00
1913...At Home (10-1/8x15-3/4", 56 pgs.) 167.00 583.00 1000.00
1914...And Tige Here Again (10x16, 62 pgs, Stokes) 153.00 535.00 900.00
1915...And His Chum Tige (10x16, Stokes) 153.00 535.00 900.00
1916...The Little Rogue (10-1/8x15-3/4", 62 pgs.) 162.00 567.00 1025.00
1917...And the Cat (5-1/2x 6-1/2, 26 pgs, Stokes) 115.00 402.00 700.00
1917...Disturbs the Family (5-1/2x 6 1/2, 26 pgs, Stokes
NOTE: *Story featuring statue of "the Chinese Yellow Kid"* 115.00 402.00 700.00
1917...The Real Buster Brown (5-1/2x 6 -/2, 26 pgs, Stokes 115.00 402.00 700.00

Frederick A. Stokes Co. Hard Cover Series (I)

...Abroad (1904, 10-1/4x8", 86 pgs., B&W, hard-c)-R. F. Outcault-a (Rare) 200.00 700.00 1000.00
...Abroad (1904, B&W, 67 pgs.)-R. F. Outcault-a 200.00 700.00 1000.00
NOTE: *Buster Brown Abroad is not an actual comic book, but prose with illustrations.*
..."Tige" His Story 1905 (10x8", 63 pgs., B&W) (63 illos.)
nn-By RF Outcault 143.00 500.00 –
...My Resolutions 1906 (10x8", B&W, 68 pgs.)-R.F. Outcault-a (Rare) 233.00 817.00 1350.00
...Autobiography 1907 (10x8", B&W, 71 pgs.) (16 color plates & 36 B&W illos) 67.00 233.00 400.00
...And Mary Jane's Painting Book 1907 (10x13-1/4", 60 pgs, both card & hardcover versions exist
nn-RFO (first printing blank on top of cover) 67.00 233.00 440.00
First Series- this is a reprint if it says First Series 67.00 233.00 440.00
Volume Two - By RFO 67.00 233.00 440.00
... My Resolutions by Buster Brown (1907, 68 pgs, small size, cardboard covers) scarce 43.00 150.00 285.00
NOTE: *Not actual comic book per se, but a compilation of the Resolutions panels found at the end of Outcault's Buster Brown newspaper strips.*

BUSTER BROWN (N)
Cupples & Leon Co./N. Y. Herald Co.: 1906 - 1917 (11x17", color, strip-r)
NOTE: *Early issues by R. F. Outcault; most C&L editions are not by Outcault.*

1906...His Dog Tige And Their Jolly Times (11-3/8x16-5/8", 68 pgs.) 300.00 1100.00 1800.00
1906...His Dog Tige & Their Jolly Times (11x16, 46 pgs.) 163.00 600.00 1000.00
1907...Latest Frolics (11-3/8x16-5/8", 66 pgs., r/'05-06 strips) 163.00 600.00 1000.00
1908...Amusing Capers (58 pgs.) 129.00 475.00 800.00
1909...The Busy Body (11-3/8x16-5/8", 62 pgs.) 129.00 475.00 800.00
1910...On His Travels (11x16", 58 pgs.) 115.00 402.00 800.00
1911...Happy Days (11-3/8x16-5/8", 58 pgs.) 115.00 402.00 800.00
1912...In Foreign Lands (10x16", 58 pgs) 115.00 402.00 800.00
1913...And His Pets (11x16", 58 pgs.) STOKES???? 115.00 402.00 800.00
1913...And His Pets (26 pg partial reprint) – – –
1914...Funny Tricks (11-3/8x16-5/8", 58 pgs.) 115.00 402.00 800.00
1916...At Play (10x16, 58 pgs) 115.00 402.00 800.00

BUSTER BROWN NUGGETS (N)
Cupples & Leon Co./N.Y.Herald Co.: 1907 (1905, 7-1/2x6-1/2", 36 pgs., color, strip-r, hard-c)(By R. F. Outcault) (NOTE: books are all unnumbered)

Buster Brown Goes Fishing, Goes Swimming, Plays Indian, Goes Shooting, Plays Cowboy, On Uncle Jack's Farm, Tige And the Bull, And Uncle Buster 40.00 150.00 350.00
Buddy Tucker Meets Alice in Wonderland 56.00 200.00 400.00
Buddy Tucker Visits The House That Jack Built 40.00 150.00 350.00

BUSTER BROWN MUSLIN SERIES (N)
Saalfield: 1907 (also contain copyright Cupples & Leon)

...Goes Fishing, Plays Indian, And the Donkey
(1907, 6-7/8x6-1/8", 24 pgs., color)-r/1905 Sunday comics page by Outcault (Rare) 50.00 175.00 325.00
...Plays Cowboy (1907, 6-3/4x6", 10 pgs., color)-r/1905 Sunday comics page by Outcault (Rare) 50.00 175.00 325.00
NOTE: *These are muslin versions of the C&L BB Nugget series. Muslin books are all cloth books, made to be washable so as not easily stained/destroyed by very young children. The Muslin books contain one strip each (the title strip), to the more common NUGGET's three strips.*

BUSTER BROWN PREMIUMS (Advertising premium booklets)
Various Publishers: 1904 - 1912 (3x5" to 5x7"; sizes vary)

American Fruit Product Company, Rochester, NY

Buster Brown Duffy's 1842 Cider (1904, 7x5". 12 pgs, C.E. Sherin Co, NYC)
nn - By R. F. Outcault (scarce) 100.00 350.00 600.00

The Brown Shoe Company, St. Louis, USA
Set of five books (5x7", 16 pgs., color)

Brown's Blue Ribbon Book of Jokes and Jingles Book 1 (nn, 1904)-By R. F. Outcault; Buster Brown & Tige, Little Tommy Tucker, Jack & Jill, Little Boy Blue, Dainty Jane; The Yellow Kid app. on back-c (1st BB comic book premium) 300.00 1050.00 2100.00
Buster Brown's Blue Ribbon Book of Jokes and Jingles Book 2 (1905)-

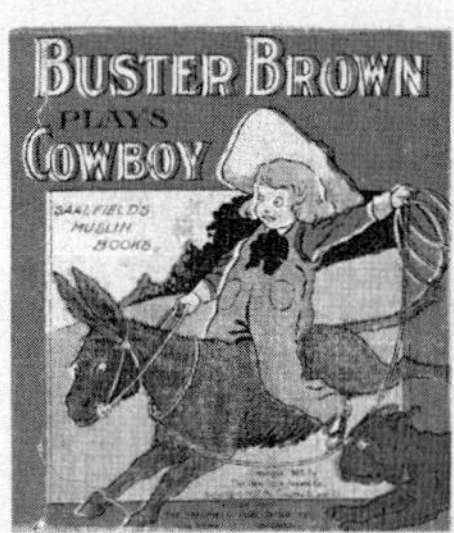

Buster Brown Nuggets -Buster Brown Plays Cowboy © C&L

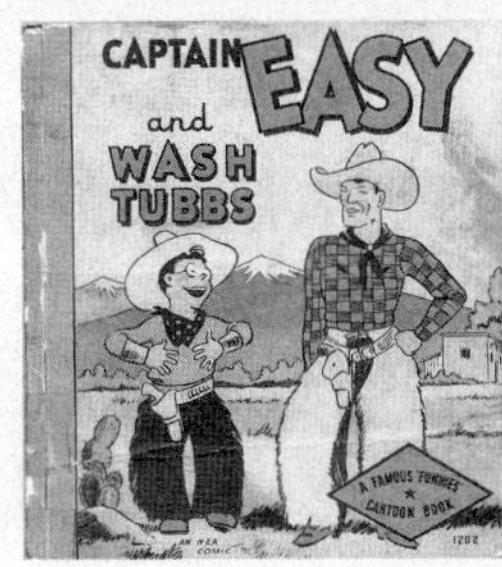

Captain Easy and Wash Tubbs by Roy Crane 1934 © Whitman Famous Comics Cartoon Book

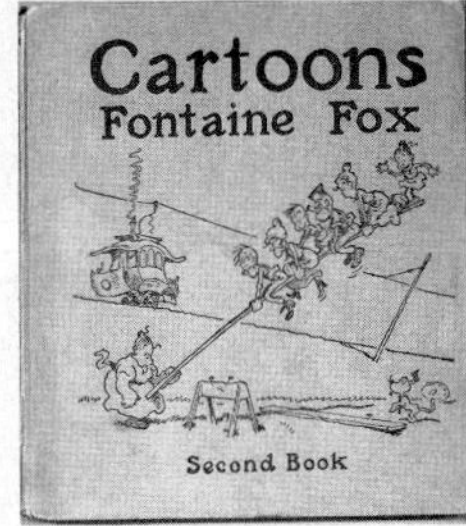

Cartoons Fontaine Fox Second Book early 1920s © Harper & Bros, NY

GD2.0 FN6.0 VF8.0

Original color art by Outcault 200.00 600.00 1200.00
Buster's Book of Jokes & Jingles Book 3 (1909)
not by R.F. Outcault 150.00 400.00 800.00
NOTE: *Reprinted from the Blue Ribbon post cards with advert jingles added.*
Buster's Book of Instructive Jokes and Jingles Book 4 (1910)-Original color art
not by R.F. Outcault 150.00 585.00 1000.00
...Book of Travels nn (1912, 3x5")-Original color art not signed by Outcault
117.00 408.00 735.00
NOTE: *Estimated 5 or 6 known copies exist of books #1-4.*

The Buster Brown Bread Company

"Buster Brown" Bread Book of Rhymes, The (1904, 4x6", 12 pgs., half color, half B&W)- Original color art not signed by RFO 158.00 553.00 1000.00

Buster Brown's Hosiery Mills

"How Buster Brown Got The Pie" nn (nd, 7x5-1/4". 16 pgs, color paper cover and color interior By R.F. Outcault 85.00 300.00 600.00
"The Autobiography of Buster Brown" nn (nd,9x6-1/8", 36 pgs, text story & art by R.F. Outcault 85.00 300.00 600.00
NOTE: *Similar to, but a distinctly different item than "Buster Brown's Autobiography."*

The Buster Brown Stocking Company

Buster Brown Drawing Book, The nn (nd, 5x6", 20 pgs.)-B&W reproductions of 1903 R.F. Outcault art to trace 50.00 150.00 350.00
NOTE: *Reprints a comic strip from Burr McIntosh Magazine, which includes Buster, Yellow Kid, and Pore Li'l Mose (only known story involving all three.)*
Buster Brown Stocking Magazine nn (Jan. 1906, 7-3/4x5-3/8", 36 pgs.) R.F. Outcault
50.00 100.00 225.00
NOTE: *This was actually a store bought item selling for 5 cents per copy.*

Collins Baking Company

Buster Brown Drawing Book nn (1904, 5x3", 12 pgs.)-Original B&W art to trace, not signed by R.F. Outcault 50.00 200.00 400.00

C. H. Morton, St. Albans, VT

Merry Antics of Buster Brown, Buddy Tucker & Tige nn (nd, 3-1/2x5-1/2", 16 pgs.) -Original B&W art by R.F. Outcault 83.00 292.00 525.00

Ivan Frank & Company

Buster Brown nn (1904, 3x5", 12 pgs.)-B&W repros of R. F. Outcault Sunday pages (First premium to actually reproduce Sunday comic pages – may be first premium comic strip-r book?) 125.00 438.00 800.00
Buster Brown's Pranks (1904, 3-1/2x5-1/8", 12 pgs.)-reprints intro of Buddy Tucker into the BB newspaper strip before he was spun off into his own short lived newspaper strip
125.00 438.00 800.00

Kaufmann & Strauss

Buster Brown Drawing Book (1906, 28 pages, 5x3-1/2") Color Cover, B+W original story signed by Outcault, tracing paper inserted as alternate pages. Back cover imprinted for Nox' Em All Shoes 50.00 150.00 325.00

Pond's Extract

Buster Brown's Experiences With Pond's Extract nn (1904, 6-3/4x4-1/2", 28 pgs.) Original color art by R.F. Outcault (may be the first BB premium comic book with original art) 100.00 250.00 575.00

C. A. Cross & Co.

Red Cross Drawing Book nn (1906, 4-7/8x3-1/2", color paper -c, B&W interior, 12 pgs.)
50.00 150.00 325.00
NOTE: *This is for Red Cross coffee; not the health organization.*

Ringen Stove Company

Quick Meal Steel Ranges nn (nd, 5x3", 16 pgs.)-Original B&W art not signed by R.F. Outcault 50.00 150.00 325.00

Steinwender Stoffregen Coffee Co.

"Buster Brown Coffee" (1905, 4-7/8x3", color paper cover, B&W interior, 12 printed pages, plus 1 tracing paper page above each interior image (total of 8 sheets) (Very Rare)
83.00 292.00 525.00
NOTE: *Part of a BB drawing contest. If instructions had been followed, most copies would have ended up destroyed.*

U. S. Playing Card Company

Buster Brown - My Own Playing Cards (1906, 2-1/2x1-3/4", full color)
nn - By R. F. Outcault 42.00 147.00 250.00
NOTE: *Series of full color panels tell stories, average about 5 cards per story.*

Publisher Unknown

The Drawing Book nn (1906, 3-9/16x5", 8 pgs.)-Original B&W art to trace not by R.F. Outcault 50.00 150.00 325.00

BUTLER BOOK A Series of Clever Cartoons of Yale Undergraduate Life
Yale Record: June 16, 1913 (10-3/4 x 17", 34 pgs, paper cover B&W)
nn - By Alban Bernard Butler 25.00 75.00 150.00
NOTE: *Cartoons and strips reprinted from The Yale Record student newspaper.*

BUTTONS & FATTY IN THE FUNNIES
Whitman Publishing Co.: nd 1927 (10-1/4x15-1/2", 28pg., color)
W936 - Signed "M.E.B.", probably M.E. Brady; strips in color copyright The Brooklyn Daily Eagle; (very rare) 61.00 244.00 450.00

BY BRIGGS (M,N,P) (see also OLD GOLD THE SMOOTHER AND BETTER CIGARETTE)
Old Gold Cigarettes: nd (c1920's) (11" x 9-11/16", 44 pgs, cardboard-c, B&W)
nn- (Scarce) 20.00 70.00 150.00

GD2.0 FN6.0 VF8.0

NOTE: *Collection reprinting strip cartoons by Clare Briggs, advertising Old Gold Cigarettes. These strips originally appeared in various magazines, play program booklets, newspapers, etc. Some of the strips involve regular Briggs strip series. Contains all of the strips in the smaller, color "OLD GOLD" giveaways, plus more.*

CAMION CARTOONS
Marshall Jones Company: 1919 (7-1/2x5", 136 pgs, B&W)
nn - By Kirkland H. Day (W.W.One occupation) 20.00 70.00 125.00

CANYON COUNTRY KIDDIES (M)
Doubleday, Page & Co: 1923 (8x10-1/4", 88 pgs, hard-c, B&W)
nn - By James Swinnerton 39.00 137.00 260.00

CARLO (H)
Doubleday, Page & Co.: 1913 (8 x 9-5/8, 120 pgs, hardcover, B&W)
nn - By A.B. Frost 40.00 140.00 300.00
NOTE: *Original sequential strips about a dog. Became short lived newspaper comic strip in 1914. Originally published with a dust jacket which increases value 50%.*

CARTOON BOOK, THE
Bureau of Publicity, War Loan Organization, Treasury Department, Washington, D.C.: 1918 (6-1/2x4-7/8", 48 pgs, paper cover, B&W)
nn - By various artists 31.00 108.00 200.00
NOTE: *U.S. government issued booklet of WW I propaganda cartoons by 46 artists promoting the third sale of Liberty Loan bonds. The artists include: Berryman, Clare Briggs, Cesare, J. N. "Ding" Darling, Rube Goldberg, Kemble, McCutcheon, George McManus, F. Opper, T. E. Powers, Ripley, Satterfield, H. T. Webster, Gaar Williams.*

CARTOON CATALOGUE (S)
The Lockwood Art School, Kalamazoo, Mich.: 1919 (11-5/8x9, 52 pgs, B&W)
nn - Edited by Mr. Lockwood 20.00 60.00 150.00
NOTE: *Jammed with 100s of single panel cartoons and some sequential comics; Mr Lockwood began the very first cartoonist school back in 1892. Clare Briggs was one of his students.*

CARTOON COMICS
Lasco Publications, Detroit, Mich: #1, April 1930 - #2, May 1930 (8-3/6x5-1/5")
1, 2 - By Lu Harris 20.00 60.00 120.00
NOTE: *Contains recurring characters Hollywood Horace, Campus Charlie, Pair-A-Dice Alley and Jocko Monkey. Not much is presently known about the creator(s) or publisher.*

CARTOON HISTORY OF ROOSEVELT'S CAREER, A
The Review of Reviews Company: 1910 (276 pgs, 8-1/4x11",
nn - By various 100.00 200.00 400.00
NOTE: *Reprints editorial cartoons about Teddy Roosevelt from U.S. and international newspapers and cartoons from the humor magaines (Puck, Judge, etc.). A few cartoonists whose work is included are Dalrymple, Opper, McDougall, McCutcheon, Remington, Rogers, Kemble. Mostly single panel but 10 or so are sequential strips.*

CARTOON HUMOR
Collegian Press: 1938 (102 pgs, squarebound, B&W)
nn 20.00 70.00 125.00
NOTE: *Contains cartoons & strips by Otto Soglow, Syd Hoff, Peter Arno, Abner Dean, others.*

CARTOONIST'S PHILOSOPHY, A
Percy Crosby: 1931, HC, 252 pgs, 5-1/2x7-1/2", hard-c, celluloid dust wrapper
nn - By Percy Crosby (10 plates, 6 are of Skippy) 30.00 70.00 140.00
NOTE: *Crosby's partial autobiography regarding his return to France in 1929, and portrayals of Normandy, the "cliff dwellers" on Normandy cliffs (destroyed in WWII), his visit to London, comments on art, philosophy, several poems, and political dialogue. His description of his Cockney driver, " Harold" is amusing. Also describes his experience visiting Chicago to speak out against Capone, his concerns over the evils of Prohibition, and the economy prior to the 1929 crash. This book reveals he was aware of the dangers of his outspoken views, and is prophetic, re: his later years as political prisoner. Also reveals his religious beliefs.*

CARTOONS BY BRADLEY: CARTOONIST OF THE CHICAGO DAILY NEWS
Rand McNally & Company: 1917 (11-1/4x8-3/4", 112 pgs, hardcover, B&W)
nn - By Luther D. Bradley (editorial) 20.00 70.00 120.00

CARTOONS BY FONTAINE FOX (Toonerville Trolley) (S)
Harper & Brothers Publishers: nd early '20s (9x7-7/8",102 pgs., hard-c, B&W)
Second Book- By Fontaine Fox (Toonerville-r) 150.00 300.00 550.00

CARTOONS BY HALLADAY (N,S)
Providence Journal Co., Rhode Island: Dec 1914 (116 pgs, 10-1/2x 7-3/4", hard-c, B&W)
nn- (Scarce) 50.00 125.00 250.00
NOTE: *Cartoons on Rhode Island politics, plus some Teddy Roosevelt & WW I cartoons.*

CARTOONS BY McCUTCHEON (S)
A. C. McClurg & Co.: 1903 (12-3/8x9-3/4", 212 pgs., hardcover, B&W)
nn - By John McCutcheon 20.00 70.00 125.00

CARTOONS BY W. A. IRELAND (S)
The Columbus-Evening Dispatch: 1907 (13-3/4 x 10-1/2", 66 pgs, hardcover)
nn - By W. A. Ireland (strip-r) 20.00 70.00 125.00

CARTOONS MAGAZINE (I,N,S)
H. H. Windsor, Publisher: Jan 1912-June 1921; July 1921-1923; 1923-1924; 1924-1927 (1912-July 1913 issues 12x9-1/4", 68-76 pgs; 1913-1921 issues 10x7", average 112 to 188 pgs, color covers)
1912-Jan-Dec 30.00 75.00 130.00
1913-1917 30.00 75.00 130.00

Cartoons Magazine Sept, 1917
by various creators © H. H. Windsor, Chicago

Charlie Chaplin in the Army by Segar
1917 © Essaney

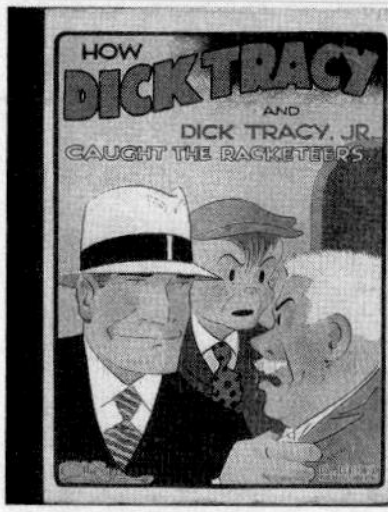

How Dick Tracy and Dick Tracy, Jr.
Caught the Racketeers by Chester Gould
1933 © Cupples & Leon

	GD2.0	FN6.0	VF8.0
1917-(Apr) "How Comickers Regard Their Characters"	30.00	105.00	160.00
1917-(June) "A Genius of the Comic Page" - long article on George Herriman, Krazy Kat, etc with lots of Herriman art; "Cartoonists and Their Cars"	150.00	300.00	700.00
1918-1919	30.00	75.00	130.00
1920-June 1921	30.00	75.00	130.00
July 1921-1923 titled Wayside Tales & Cartoons Magazine	30.00	75.00	130.00
1923-1924 becomes Cartoons Magazine again	30.00	75.00	130.00
1924-1927 becomes Cartoons & Movie Magazine	30.00	75.00	130.00

NOTE: *Many issues contain a wealth of historical background on then current cartoonists of the day with an international slant; each issue profusely illustrated with many cartoons. We are unsure if this magazine continued after 1927.*

CARTOONS BY J. N. DARLING (S,N - some sequantial strips)
The Register & Tribune Co., Des Moines, Iowa: 1909?-1920 (12x8-7/8",B&W)

	GD2.0	FN6.0	VF8.0
Book 1	20.00	55.00	130.00
Book 2 Education of Alonzo Applegate (1910)	18.00	52.00	110.00
2nd printing	18.00	52.00	110.00
Book 3 Cartoons From The Files (1911)	18.00	52.00	110.00
Book 4	18.00	52.00	110.00
Book 5 In Peace And War (1916)	18.00	52.00	110.00
Book 6 Aces & Kings War Cartoons (Dec 1, 1918)	18.00	52.00	110.00
Book 7 The Jazz Era (Dec 1920)	18.00	52.00	110.00
Book 8 Our Own Outlines of History (1922)	18.00	52.00	110.00

NOTE: *Some of the most inspired hard hitting cartoons ever printed. Are there more?*

CARTOONS THAT MADE PRINCE HENRY FAMOUS, THE (N,S)
The Chicago Record-Herald: Feb/March 1902 (12-1/8" x 9", 32 pgs, paper-c, B&W)

	GD2.0	FN6.0	VF8.0
nn- (Scarce) by McCutcheon	15.00	51.00	100.00

NOTE: *Cartoons about the visit of the British Prince Henry to the U.S.*

CAVALRY CARTOONS (O)
R. Montalboddi: nd (c1918) (14-1/4" x 11", 30 pgs, printed on one side, olive & black construction paper-c, B&W interior)

	GD2.0	FN6.0	VF8.0
nn - By R.Montalboddi	20.00	55.00	100.00

NOTE: *Comics about life in the U.S.Cavalry during World War I, by a soldier who was in the 1st Cavalry.*

CHARLIE CHAPLIN (N)
Essanay/M. A. Donohue & Co.: 1917 (9x16", B&W, large size soft-c)

	GD2.0	FN6.0	VF8.0
Series 1, #315-Comic Capers (9-3/4x15-3/4")-20 pgs. by Segar; Series 1, #316-In the Movies	165.00	525.00	1150.00
#317-Up in the Air (20 pgs), #318-In the Army	165.00	525.00	1375.00
Funny Stunts-(12-1/2x16-3/8",16 color pgs)	165.00	525.00	1375.00

NOTE: *All contain pre-Thimble Theatre Segar art. The thin paper used makes high grade copies very scarce.*

CHASING THE BLUES
Doubleday Page: 1912 (7-1/2x10", 108 pgs., B&W, hard-c)

	GD2.0	FN6.0	VF8.0
nn - By Rube Goldberg	150.00	525.00	1100.00

NOTE: *Contains a dozen Foolish Questions, baseball, a few Goldberg poems and lots of sequential strips.*

CHRISTIAN CARTOONS (N,S)
The Sunday School Times Company: 1922 (7-1/4 x 6-1/8,104 pgs, brown hard-c, B&W)

	GD2.0	FN6.0	VF8.0
nn - E.J. Pace	15.00	51.00	100.00

NOTE: *Religious cartoons reprinted from The Sunday School Times.*

CLANCY THE COP (O))
Dell Publishing Co.: 1930 - No. 2, 1931 (10x10", 52 pgs., B&W, cardboard-c)
(Also see Bug Movies & Deadwood Gulch)

	GD2.0	FN6.0	VF8.0
1, 2-By VEP Victor Pazimino (original material; not reprints)	10000	250.00	500.00

CLIFFORD MCBRIDE'S IMMORTAL NAPOLEON & UNCLE ELBY (N)
The Castle Press: 1932 (12x17"; soft-c cartoon book)

	GD2.0	FN6.0	VF8.0
nn - Intro. by Don Herod	36.00	144.00	250.00

COLLECTED DRAWINGS OF BRUCE BAIRNSFATHER, THE
W. Colston Leigh: 1931 (11-1/4x8-1/4 ", 168 pages, hardcover, B&W)

	GD2.0	FN6.0	VF8.0
nn - By Bruce Bairnsfather	24.00	96.00	175.00

COMICAL PEEP SHOW
McLoughlin Bros: 1902 (36 pgs, B&W)

	GD2.0	FN6.0	VF8.0
nn	24.00	96.00	165.00

NOTE: *Comic stories of Wilhelm Busch redrawn; two versions with green or gold front cover logos; back covers different.*

COMIC ANIMALS (I)
Charles E. Graham & Co.: 1903 (9-3/4x7-1/4", 90 pgs, color cover)

	GD2.0	FN6.0	VF8.0
nn - By Walt McDougall (not comic strips)	80.00	160.00	275.00

COMIC CUTS (O)
H. L. Baker Co., Inc.: 5/19/34-7/28/34 (Tabloid size 10-1/2x15-1/2", 24 pgs., 5¢)
(full color, not reprints; published weekly; created for news stand sales)

	GD2.0	FN6.0	VF8.0
V1#1 - V1#7(6/30/34), V1#8(7/14/34), V1#9(7/28/34)-Idle Jack strips	250.00	500.00	1000.00

NOTE: *According to a 1958 Lloyd Jacquet interview, this short-lived comics mag was the direct inspiration for Major Malcolm Wheeler-Nicholson's* ***New Fun Comics****, not* ***Famous Funnies****.*

COMIC MONTHLY (N)
Embee Dist. Co.: Jan, 1922 - No. 12, Dec, 1922 (10¢, 8-1/2"x9", 28 pgs., 2-color covers)
(1st monthly newsstand comic publication) (Reprints 1921 B&W dailies)

	GD2.0	FN6.0	VF8.0
1-Polly & Her Pals by Cliff Sterrett	400.00	1200.00	2600.00
2-Mike & Ike by Rube Goldberg	150.00	500.00	1150.00
3-S'Matter, Pop?	150.00	500.00	1150.00
4-Barney Google by Billy DeBeck	150.00	500.00	1150.00
5-Tillie the Toiler by Russ Westover	150.00	500.00	1150.00
6-Indoor Sports by Tad Dorgan	150.00	500.00	1150.00

NOTE: *#6 contains more Judge Rummy than Indoor Sports.*

	GD2.0	FN6.0	VF8.0
7-Little Jimmy by James Swinnerton	150.00	500.00	1150.00
8-Toots and Casper b y Jimmy Murphy	150.00	500.00	1150.00
9-New Bughouse Fables by Barney Google	150.00	500.00	1150.00
10-Foolish Questions by Rube Goldberg	150.00	500.00	1150.00
11-Barney Google & Spark Plug by Billy DeBeck	150.00	500.00	1150.00
12-Polly & Her Pals by Cliff Sterrett	150.00	500.00	1150.00

NOTE: *This series was published by George McManus (Bringing Up Father) as Em & Rudolph Block, Jr., son of Hearst's cartoon editor for many years, as "Bee." One would have thought this series would have done very well considering the tremendous amount of talent assembled. All issues are extremely hard to find these days and rarely show up in any type of higher grade.*

COMIC PAINTING AND CRAYONING BOOK (H)
Saalfield Publ. Co.: 1917 (13-1/2x10", 32 pgs.) (No price on-c)

	GD2.0	FN6.0	VF8.0
nn - Tidy Teddy by F. M. Follett, Clarence the Cop, Mr. & Mrs. Butt-In; regular comic stories to read or color	50.00	175.00	325.00

COMPLETE TRIBUNE PRIMER, THE (I)
Mutual Book Company: 1901 (7 1/4 x 5", 152 pgs, red hard-c)

	GD2.0	FN6.0	VF8.0
nn - By Frederick Opper; has 75 Opper cartoons	25.00	75.00	150.00

COURTSHIP OF TAGS, THE (N)
McCormick Press: pre-1910 (9x4", 88 pgs, red & B&W-c, B&W interior)

	GD2.0	FN6.0	VF8.0
nn - By O. E. Wertz (strip-r Wichita Daily Beacon)	25.00	75.00	150.00

DAFFYDILS (N)
Cupples & Leon Co.: 1911 (5-3/4x7-7/8", 52 pgs., B&W, hard-c)

	GD2.0	FN6.0	VF8.0
nn - By "Tad" Dorgan	58.00	204.00	375.00

NOTE: *Also exists in self-published TAD edition: The T.A. Dorgan Company; unknown which is first printing.*

DAN DUNN SECRET OPERATIVE 48 (Also See Detective Dan) (N)
Whitman Publishing: 1937 ((5 1/2 x 7 1/4", 68pgs., color cardboard-c, B&W)

	GD2.0	FN6.0	VF8.0
1010 And The Gangsters' Frame-Up	50.00	150.00	350.00

NOTE: *There are two versions of the book the later printing has a 5 cent cover price. Dick Tracy look-alike character by Norman Marsh.*

DANGERS OF DOLLY DIMPLE, THE (N)
Penn Tobacco Co.: nd (1930's) (9-3/8x7-7/8", 28 pgs, red cardboard-c, B&W)

	GD2.0	FN6.0	VF8.0
nn - (Rare) by Walter Enright	25.00	88.00	150.00

NOTE: *Reprints newspaper comic strip advertisements, in which in every episode, Dolly Dimple's life is saved by Penn's Smoking Tobacco. - how very un-P.C. by today's standards.*

DEADWOOD GULCH (O) (See The Funnies 1929)(also see Bug Movies & Clancy The Cop)
Dell Publishing Co.: 1931 (10x10", 52 pgs., B&W, color covers, B&W interior)

	GD2.0	FN6.0	VF8.0
nn - By Charles "Boody" Rogers (original material)	150.00	300.00	600.00

DESTINY A Novel In Pictures (O)
Farrar & Rinehart: 1930 (8x7", 424 pgs, B&W, hard-c, dust jacket?)

	GD2.0	FN6.0	VF8.0
nn - By Otto Nuckel (original graphic novel)	25.00	100.00	200.00

DICK TRACY & DICK TRACY JR. CAUGHT THE RACKETEERS, HOW
Cupples & Leon Co.: 1933 (8-1/2x7", 88 pgs., hard-c) (See Treasure Box of Famous Comics) (N)

	GD2.0	FN6.0	VF8.0
2-(Numbered on pg. 84)-Continuation of Stooge Viller book (daily strip reprints from 8/3/33 thru 11/8/33)(Rarer than #1)	100.00	400.00	800.00
With dust jacket...	175.00	500.00	1200.00

DICK TRACY & DICK TRACY JR. AND HOW THEY CAPTURED "STOOGE" VILLER (N)
Cupples & Leon Co.: 1933 (8-1/2x7", 100 pgs., hard-c, one-shot)
Reprints 1932 & 1933 Dick Tracy daily strips

	GD2.0	FN6.0	VF8.0
nn(No.1)-1st app. of "Stooge" Viller	94.00	376.00	750.00
With dust jacket...	175.00	500.00	1100.00

DIMPLES By Grace Drayton (N) (See Dolly Dimples)
Hearst's International Library Co.: 1915 (6 1/4 x 5 1/4, 12 pgs) (5 known)

	GD2.0	FN6.0	VF8.0
nn-Puppy and Pussy; nn-She Goes For a Walk; nn-She Had A Sneeze; nn-She Has a Naughty Play Husband; nn-Wait Till Fido Comes Home	21.00	74.00	175.00

DOINGS OF THE DOO DADS, THE (N)
Detroit News (Universal Feat. & Specialty Co.): 1922 (50¢, 7-3/4x7-3/4", 34 pgs, B&W, red & white-c, square binding)

	GD2.0	FN6.0	VF8.0
nn-Reprints 1921 newspaper strip "Text & Pictures" given away as prize in the Detroit News Doo Dads contest; by Arch Dale	43.00	173.00	360.00

DOING THE GRAND CANYON
Fred Harvey: 1922 (7 x 4-3/4", 24 pgs, B&W, paper cover)

	GD2.0	FN6.0	VF8.0
nn - John McCutcheon	25.00	55.00	110.00

'Erbie And 'Is Playmates By F. Opper
1932 © Democratic National Committee

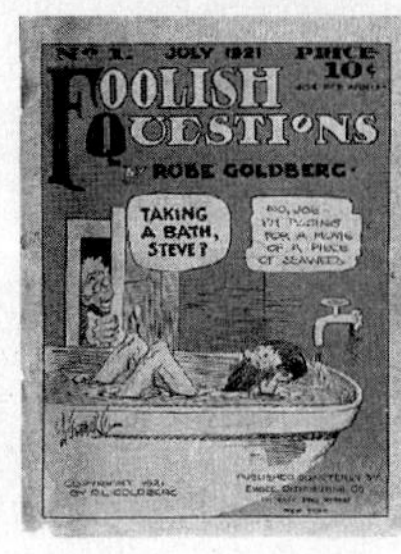

Foolish Questions by Rube Goldberg
1921 © EmBee Distributing Co., NY.

The Latest Adventures of Foxy Grandpa 1905
© Bunny Publ.

NOTE: *Text & 8 cartoons about visiting the Grand Canyon.*

DOINGS OF THE VAN-LOONS (N) (from same company as Mutt & Jeff #1-#5)
Ball Publications: 1912 (5-3/4X15-1/2", 68pg., B&W, hard-c)
nn - By Fred I. Leipziger (scarce) 72.00 252.00 600.00

DOLLY DIMPLES & BOBBY BOUNCE (See Dimples)
Cupples & Leon Co.: 1933 (8-3/4x7", color hardcover, B&W)
nn - Grace Drayton-a 24.00 96.00 165.00

DOO DADS, THE (Sleepy Sam and Tiny the Elephant)
Universal Feature * Specialty Co: 1922 (5-1/4x14", 36 pgs.,B&W, R&W-c,square binding)
nn - By Arch Dale 35.00 125.00 250.00

DRAWINGS BY HOWARD CHANDLER CHRISTIE (S, M)
Moffat, Yard & Company, NY: 1905 (11-7/8x16-1/2", 68 pgs, hard-c, B&W)
nn - Howard C. Christie 30.00 60.00 125.00
NOTE: *Reprints1898-1905 from Haprer & Bros, Ch. Scribners Sons, Leslie's, MacMillians, McLurg, Russell.*

DREAMS OF THE RAREBIT FIEND (N)
Frederick A. Stokes Co.:1905 (10-1/4x7-1/2", 68 pgs, thin paper cover all B&W) newspaper reprints from the New York Evening Telegram printed on yellow paper
nn-By Winsor "Silas" McCay (Very Rare) (Five copies known to exist)
Estimated value.... 1000.00 2600.00 -
NOTE: *A G/VG copy sold for $2,045 in May 2004. This item usually turns up with fragile paper.*

DRISCOLL'S BOOK OF PIRATES (O)
David McKay Publ.: 1934 (9x7", 124 pgs, B&W, hardcover)
nn - By Montford Amory ("Pieces of Eight strip-r) 21.00 64.00 150.00

DUCKY DADDLES
Frederick A. Stokes Co: July 1911 (15x10")
nn - By Grace Weiderseim (later Drayton) strip-r 50.00 175.00 300.00

DUMBUNNIES AND THEIR FRIENDS IN RABBITBORO, THE (O)
Albertine Randall Wheelan: 1931 (8-3/4x7-1/8", 82 pgs, color hardcover, B&W)
nn - By Albertine Randall Wheelan (self-pub) 75.00 125.00 250.00

EDISON - INSPIRATION TO YOUTH (N)(Also see Life of Thomas---)
Thomas A. Edison, Incorporated: 1939 (9-1/2 x 6-1/2, paper cover, B&W)
nn - Photo-c 50.00 150.00 275.00
NOTE: *Reprints strip material found in the 1928 Life of Thomas A. Edison in Word and Picture.*

'ERBIE AND 'IS PLAYMATES
Democratic National Committee: 1932 (8x9-1/2, 16 pgs, B&W)
nn - By Frederick Opper (Rare) 100.00 200.00 425.00
NOTE: *Anti-Hoover/Pro-Roosevelt political comics.*

EXPANSION BEING BART'S BEST CARTOONS FOR 1899
Minneapolis Journal: 1900 (10-1/4x8-1/4", 124 pgs, paperback, B&W)
v2#1 - By Charles L. Bartholomew 24.00 84.00 150.00

FAMOUS COMICS (N)
King Features Synd. (Whitman Pub. Co.): 1934 (100 pgs., daily newspaper-r) (3-1/2x8-1/2"; paper cover)(came in an illustrated box)
684 (#1) - Little Jimmy, Katz Kids & Barney Google 40.00 103.00 275.00
684 (#2) - Polly, Little Jimmy, Katzenjammer Kids 40.00 103.00 275.00
684 (#3) - Little Annie Rooney, Polly and Her Pals, Katzenjammer Kids
40.00 103.00 275.00
Box price... 75.00 150.00 450.00

FAMOUS COMICS CARTOON BOOKS (N)
Whitman Publishing Co.: 1934 (8x7-1/4", 72 pgs, B&W hard-c, daily strip-r)
1200-The Captain & the Kids; Dirks reprints credited to Bernard Dibble 29.00 86.00 210.00
1202-Captain Easy & Wash Tubbs by Roy Crane; 2 slightly different versions of cover exist 34.00 103.00 250.00
1203-Ella Cinders By Conselman & Plumb 28.00 84.00 210.00
1204-Freckles & His Friends 25.00 75.00 200.00
NOTE: *Called Famous Funnies Cartoon Books inside back area sales advertisement.*

FANTASIES IN HA-HA (M)
Meyer Bros & Co.: 1900 (14 x 11-7/8", 64 pgs, color cover hardcover, B&W)
nn - By Hy Mayer 50.00 150.00 300.00

FELIX (N)
Henry Altemus Company: 1931 (6-1/2"x8-1/4", 52 pgs., color, hard-c w/dust jacket)
1-3-Sunday strip reprints of Felix the Cat by Otto Messmer. Book No. 2 r/1931 Sunday panels mostly two to a page in a continuity format oddly arranged so each tier of panels reads across two pages, then drops to the next tier. (Books 1 & 3 have not been documented.)(Rare)
Each 250.00 500.00 1000.00
With dust jacket 250.00 750.00 1500.00

FELIX THE CAT BOOK (N)
McLoughlin Bros.: 1927 (8"x15-3/4", 52 pgs, half in color-half in B&W)
nn - Reprints 23 Sunday strips by Otto Messmer from 1926 & 1927, every other one in color, two pages per strip. (Rare) 200.00 900.00 1800.00
260-Reissued (1931), reformatted to 9-1/2"x10-1/4" (same color plates, but one strip per every three pages), retitled ("Book" dropped from title) and abridged (only eight strips repeated from first issue, 28 pgs.).(Rare) 90.00 350.00 650.00

F. FOX'S FUNNY FOLK (see Toonerville Trolley; Cartoons by Fontaine Fox) (C)
George H. Doran Company: 1917 (10-1/4x8-1/4", 228 pgs, red, B&W cover, B&W interior, hardcover; dust jacket?)
nn - By Fontaine Fox (Toonerville Trolley strip-r) 150.00 450.00 775.00

52 CAREY CARTOONS (O,S)
Carey Cartoon Service, NY: 1915 (25 cents, 6-3/4" x 10-1/2", 118 pgs, printed on one side, color cardboard-c, B&W)
nn - (1915) War - - -
NOTE: *The Carey Cartoon Service supplied a weekly, hand-colored single panel cartoon broadsheet, on current news events, starting in 1906 or 1907, for window display in Carey Fountain Pen chain stores. These broadsheets were 22-1/2" x 33" in size. Starting circa 1915, Carey Fountain Pens began offering subscriptions for the broadsheets to other merchants, for window display in their stores as well. This collects, in B&W, the cartoons for 1915. An "Edition Deluxe" was also advertised, with all cartoons hand colored. It is currently unknown whether a reprint collection was only issued in 1915, or if other editions exist.*

52 LETTERS TO SALESMEN
Steven-Davis Company: 1927 (???)
nn - (Rare) 25.00 100.00 150.00
NOTE: *52 motivational letters to salesmen, with page of comics for each week, bound into embossed leather binder.*

FOLKS IN FUNNYVILLE (S)
R.H. Russell: 1900 (12"x9-1/4", 48 pgs.)(cardboard-c)
nn - By Frederick Opper 300.00 1000.00 -
NOTE: *Reprinted from Hearst's NY Journal American Humorist supplements.*

FOOLISH QUESTIONS (S)
Small, Maynard & Co.: 1909 (6-7/8 x 5-1/2", 174 pgs, hardcover, B&W)
nn - By Rube Goldberg (first Goldberg item) 100.00 300.00 500.00
NOTE: *Comic strip began Oct 23, 1908 running thru 1941. Also drawn by George Frink in 1909.*

FOOLISH QUESTIONS THAT ARE ASKED BY ALL
Levi Strauss & Co./Small, Maynard & Co.: 1909 (5-1/2x5-3/4", 24 pgs, paper-c, B&W)
nn- (Rare) by Rube Goldberg 65.00 175.00 350.00

FOOLISH QUESTIONS (Boxed card set) (S)
Wallie Dorr Co., N.Y.: 1919 (5-1/4x3-3/4")(box & card backs are red)
nn - Boxed set w/52 B&W comics on cards; each a single panel gag complete set w/box
75.00 263.00 475.00
NOTE: *There are two diff sets put out simultaneously with the first set, by the same company. One set continues/picks up the numbering of the cards from the other set.*

FOOLISH QUESTIONS (S)
EmBee Distributing Co.: 1921 (10¢, 4x5 1/2; 52 pgs, 3 color covers; B&W)
1-By Rube Goldberg 46.00 160.00 300.00

FOXY GRANDPA
Foxy Grandpa Company, 33 Wall St, NY : 1900 (9x15", 84 pgs, full color, cardboard-c)
nn - By Carl Schultze (By Permission of New York Herald) 271.00 1200.00 -
NOTE: *This seminal comic strip began Jan 7, 1900 and was collected later that same year.*

FOXY GRANDPA (Also see The Funnies, 1st series) (N)
N. Y. Herald/Frederick A. Stokes Co./M. A. Donahue & Co./Bunny Publ. (L. R. Hammersly Co.): 1901 - 1916 (Strip-r in color, hard-c)
1901- 9x15" in color-N. Y. Herald 313.00 1000.00 -
1902- "Latest Larks of...", 32 pgs., 9-1/2x15-1/2" 164.00 575.00 -
1902- "The Many Advs. of...", 9x12", 148 pgs., Hammersly Co.
179.00 625.00 -
1903- "Latest Advs.", 9x15", 24 pgs., Hammersly Co. 164.00 575.00 -
1903- "...'s New Advs.", 11x15", 66 pgs., Stokes 164.00 575.00 -
1904- "Up to Date", 10x15", 66 pgs., Stokes 146.00 510.00 920.00
1904- "The Many Adventures of...", 9x15, 144pgs, Donohue 146.00 510.00 920.00
1905- "& Flip-Flaps", 9-1/2x15-1/2", 52 pgs. 146.00 510.00 920.00
1905- "The Latest Advs. of...", 9x15", 28, 52, & 68 pgs, M.A. Donohue Co.; re-issue of 1902 issue 104.00 365.00 700.00
1905- "Latest Larks of...", 9-1/2x15-1/2", 52 pgs., Donahue; re-issue of 1902 issue with more pages added 104.00 365.00 700.00
1905- "Latest Larks of...", 9-1/2x15-1/2", 24 pgs. edition, Donahue; re-issue of 1902 issue 104.00 365.00 700.00
1905- "Merry Pranks of...", 9-1/2x15-1/2", 28, 52 & 62 pgs., Donahue
104.00 365.00 700.00
1905-"...Surprises",10x15", color, 64 pg,Stokes, 60¢ 104.00 365.00 700.00
1906- "Frolics", 10x15", 30 pgs., Stokes 104.00 365.00 700.00
1907?-"...& His Boys",10x15", 64 color pgs, Stokes 104.00 365.00 700.00
1907- "Triumphs", 10x15", 62 pgs, Stokes 104.00 365.00 700.00
1908-"...Mother Goose", Stokes 104.00 365.00 700.00
1909- "...& Little Brother", 10x15, 58 pgs, Stokes 104.00 365.00 700.00

GD2.0 FN6.0 VF8.0

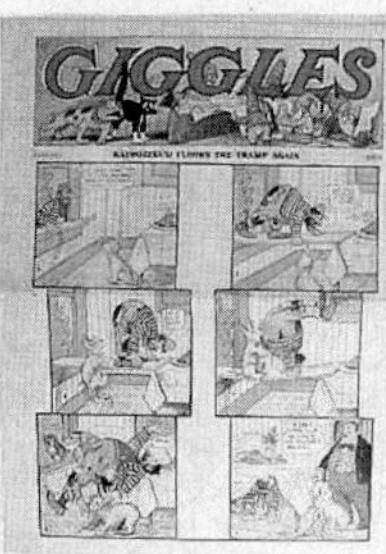

Giggles
© Pratt Food Co.

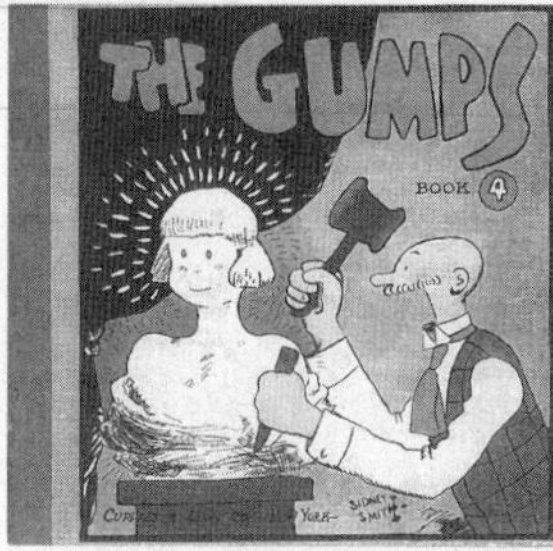

The Gumps by Sidney Smith
1927? © Cupples & Leon

Happy Hooligan Book 1 1902
© Frederick A. Stokes

GD2.0 FN6.0 VF8.0

1911- "Latest Tricks", r-1910,1911 Sundays-Stokes Co. 104.00 365.00 700.00
1914-(9-1/2x15-1/2", 24 pgs.)-6 color cartoons/page, Bunny Publ. Co.
88.00 306.00 610.00
1915 - ...Always Jolly (10x16, Stokes) 88.00 306.00 610.00
1916- "Merry Book", (10x15", 64 pgs, Stokes) 88.00 306.00 610.00
1917-"...Adventures (5 1/2 x 6 1/2, 26 pgs, Stokes) 57.00 200.00 450.00
1917-"...Frolics (5 1/2 x 6 1/2, 26 pgs, Stokes) 57.00 200.00 450.00
1917-"...Triumphs (5 1/2 x 6 1/2, 26 pgs, Stokes) 57.00 200.00 450.00

FOXY GRANDPA, FUNNY TRICKS OF (The Stump Books)
M.A. Donahue Co, Chicago: approx 1903 (1-7/8x6-3/8", 44 pgs, blue hardcover)
nn - By Carl Schultze 54.00 189.00 330.00
NOTE: *One of a series of ten "stump" books; the only comics one.*

FOXY GRANDPA'S MOTHER GOOSE (I)
Stokes: October 1903 (10-11/16x8-1/2", 86 pgs, hard-c)
nn - By Carl Schultze (not comics - illustrated book) 54.00 189.00 330.00

FOXY GRANDPA SPARKLETS SERIES (N)
M. A. Donahue & Co.: 1908 (7-3/4x6-1/2"; 24 pgs., color)
"... Rides the Goat", "...& His Boys", "...Playing Ball", "...Fun on the Farm", "...Fancy Shooting", "...Show His Boys Up-To-Date Sports", "...Plays Santa Claus"
each.... 88.00 306.00 525.00
900- "Playing Ball"; Bunny illos; 8 pgs., linen like pgs., no date
73.00 254.00 435.00

FOXY GRANDPA VISITS RICHMOND (O,P)
Dietz Printing Co., Richmond, VA / Hotel Rueger: nd (c1920's) (5-7/8" x 4-1/2", 16 pgs, paper-c, B&W)
nn - (Scarce) By Bunny 50.00 100.00 250.00
NOTE: *Promotional comic given away to its guests by the Hotel Rueger, about Foxy Grandpa visiting and enjoying the Hotel. Originally came in an envelope, with the words "Foxy Grandpa Visits Richmond -- and Rueger's" printed on it.*

FOXY GRANDPA VISITS WASHINGTON, D.C. (P)
Dietz Printing Co., Richmond, VA / Hamilton Hotel: nd (c1920's) (5-7/8" x 4-1/2", 16 pgs, paper-c, B&W)
nn - (Scarce) By Bunny 50.00 100.00 185.00
NOTE: *Mostly reprints "... Visits Richmond", changing all references to Hotel Rueger, to Hamilton Hotel instead. Also, changes depictions of a waiter and a cook from black to white, plus incompletely erases the cover art on a book Foxy Grandpa falls asleep with (the latter is how we know that the Richmond version was first).*

FRAGMENTS FROM FRANCE (S)
G. P. Putnam & Sons: 1917 (9x6-1/4", 168 pgs, hardcover, $1.75)
nn - By Bruce Bairnsfather 25.00 88.00 150.00
NOTE: *WW1 trench warfare cartoons; color dust jacket.*

FUNNIES, THE (H) (See Clancy the Cop, Deadwood Gulch, Bug Movies)
Dell Publishing Co.: 1929 - No. 36, 10/18/30 (10¢; 5¢ No. 22 on) (16 pgs.)
Full tabloid size in color; not reprints; published every Saturday
1-My Big Brudder, Jonathan, Jazzbo & Jim, Foxy Grandpa, Sniffy, Jimmy Jams & other strips begin; first four-color comic newsstand publication; also contains magic, puzzles & stories 200.00 700.00 1500.00
2-21 (1930, 10¢) 150.00 300.00 600.00
22(nn-7/12/30-5¢) 150.00 300.00 600.00
23(nn-7/19/30-5¢), 24(nn-7/26/30-5¢), 25(nn-8/2/30), 26(nn-8/9/30), 27(nn-8/16/30), 28(nn-8/23/30), 29(nn-8/30/30), 30(nn-9/6/30), 31(nn-9/13/30), 32(nn-9/20/30), 33(nn-9/27/30), 34(nn-10/4/30), 35(nn-10/11/30), 36(nn, no date-10/18/30)
each.... 150.00 300.00 600.00

GASOLINE ALLEY (Also see Popular Comics & Super Comics) (N)
Reilly & Lee Publishers: 1929 (8-3/4x7", B&W daily strip-r, hard-c)
nn - By King (96 pgs.) 125.00 300.00 600.00
with scarce Dust Wrapper 250.00 500.00 1000.00
NOTE: *Of all the Frank King reprint books, this is the only one to reprint actual complete newspaper strips - all others are illustrated prose text stories.*

GIBSON'S PUBLISHED DRAWINGS, MR. (M,S) (see Victorian index for earlier issues)
R.H. Russell, New York: No.1 1894 - No. 9 1904 (11x17-3/4", hard-c, B&W)
nn (No.6; 1901) A Widow and her Friends (90 pgs.) 30.00 60.00 120.00
nn (No.7; 1902) The Social Ladder (88 pgs.) 30.00 60.00 120.00
8 - 1903 The Weaker Sex (88 pgs.) 30.00 60.00 120.00
9 - 1904 Everyday People (88 pgs.) 30.00 60.00 120.00
NOTE: *By Charles Dana Gibson cartoons, reprinted from magazines, primarily LIFE. The Education of Mr. Pipp tells a story. Series continues how long after 1904?*

GIGGLES
Pratt Food Co., Philadelphia, PA: 1908-09? (12x9", 8 pgs, color, 5 cents-c)
1-8: By Walt McDougall (#8 dated March 1909) 40.00 175.00 -
NOTE: *Appears to be monthly; almost tabloid size; yearly subscriptions was 25 cents.*

GOD'S MAN (H)
Jonathan Cape and Harrison Smith Inc.: 1929 (8-1/4x6", 298 pgs, B&W hardcover w/dust jacket) (original graphic novel in wood cuts)
nn - By Lynd Ward 43.00 171.00 300.00

GOLD DUST TWINS
N. K. Fairbank Co.: 1904 (4-5/8x6-3/4", 18 pgs, color and B&W)
nn - By E. W. Kemble (Rare) 50.00 100.00 200.00
NOTE: *Promo comic for Gold DustWashing Powder; includes page of watercolor paints.*

GOLF
Volland Co.: 1916 (9x12-3/4", 132 pgs, hard-c, B&W)
nn - By Clair Briggs 100.00 200.00 400.00

GUMPS, THE (N)
Landfield-Kupfer: No. 1, 1918 - No. 6, 1921; (B&W Daily strip-r)
Book No. 1(1918)(scarce)-cardboard-c, 5-1/4x13-1/3", 64 pgs., daily strip-r by Sidney Smith 75.00 250.00 500.00
Book No.2(1918)-(scarce); 5-1/4x13-1/3"; paper cover; 36 pgs. daily strip reprints by Sidney Smith 75.00 250.00 500.00
Book No. 3 100.00 350.00 700.00
Book No. 4 (1918) 5-3/8x13-7/8", 20 pgs. Color card-c 100.00 350.00 700.00
Book No. 5 10-1/4x13-1/2", 20 pgs. Color paper-c 100.00 350.00 700.00
Book No. 6 (Rare, 20 pgs, 8x13-3/8, strip-r 1920-21) 121.00 423.00 750.00

GUMPS, ANDY AND MIN, THE (N)
Landfield-Kupfer Printing Co., Chicago/Morrison Hotel: nd (1920s) (Giveaway, 5-1/2"x14", 20 pgs., B&W, soft-c)
nn - Strip-r by Sidney Smith; art & logo embossed on cover w/hotel restaurant menu on back-c or a hotel promo ad; 4 different contents of issues known
50.00 175.00 300.00

GUMPS, THE (N)
Cupples & Leon: 1924-1930 (10x10, 52 pgs, B&W)
1 - By Sidney Smith 75.00 250.00 400.00
2-7 39.00 154.00 275.00

THE GUMPS (P)
Cupples & Leon Company: 1924 (9 x 7-1/2", 28 pgs, paper cover)
nn (1924) 50.00 175.00 275.00
NOTE: *Promotional comic for Sunshine Andy Gump Biscuits. Daily strip-r from 1922-24.*

GUMP'S CARTOON BOOK, THE (N)
The National Arts Company: 1931 (13-7/8x10", 36 pgs, color covers, B&W)
nn - By Sidney Smith 57.00 228.00 400.00

GUMPS PAINTING BOOK, THE (N)
The National Arts Company: 1931 (11 x 15 1/4", 20 pgs, half in full color)
nn - By Sidney Smith 57.00 228.00 400.00

HALT FRIENDS! (see also **HELLO BUDDY**)
???: 1918? (4-3/8x5-3/4", 36 pgs, color-c, B&W, no cover price listed)
nn - Unknown 20.00 40.00 100.00
NOTE: *Says on front cover: "Comics of War Facts of Service Sold on its merits by Unemployed or Disabled Ex-Service Men. Credentials Shown On Request. Price - Pay What You Please." These are very common; contents vary widely.*

HAMBONE'S MEDITATIONS
Jahl & Co.: no date 1920 (6-1/8 x 7-1/2, 108 pgs, paper cover, B&W)
nn - By J. P. Alley 50.00 150.00 300.00
NOTE: *Reprint of racist single panel newspaper series, 2 cartoons per page.*

HAN OLA OG PER (N)
Anundsen Publishing Co, Decorah, Iowa: 1927 (10-3/8 x 15-3/4", 54 pgs, paper-c, B&W)
nn - American origin Norwegian language strips-r 33.00 131.00 230.00
NOTE: *1940s and modern reprints exist.*

HANS UND FRITZ (N)
The Saalfield Publishing Co.: 1917, 1927-29 (10x13-1/2", 28 pgs., B&W)
nn - By R. Dirks (1917, r-1916 strips) 96.00 335.00 575.00
nn - By R. Dirks (1923 edition- reprint of 1917 edition) 58.00 204.00 300.00
nn - By R. Dirks (1926 edition- reprint of 1917 edition) 58.00 204.00 300.00
The Funny Larks Of... By R. Dirks (©1917 outside cover; ©1916 inside indicia)
96.00 335.00 575.00
The Funny Larks Of... (1927) reprints 1917 edition of 1916 strips
Halloween-c 58.00 204.00 300.00
The Funny Larks Of... 2 (1929) 58.00 204.00 300.00
193 - By R. Dirks; contains 1916 Sunday strip reprints of Katzenjammer Kids & Hawkshaw the Detective - reprint of 1917 nn edition (1929) this edition is not rare
58.00 204.00 300.00

HAPPY DAYS (S)
Coward-McCann Inc.: 1929 (12-1/2x9-5/8", 110 pgs, hardcover B&W)
nn - By Alban Butler (WW 1 cartoons) 20.00 60.00 125.00

HAPPY HOOLIGAN (See Alphonse...) (N)
Hearst's New York American & Journal: 1902,1903
Book 1-(1902)-"And His Brother Gloomy Gus", By Fred Opper; has 1901-02-r; (yellow & black)(86 pgs.)(10x15-1/4") 600.00 1800.00 3400.00
New Edition, 1903 -10x15" 82 pgs. in color 350.00 1400.00 -

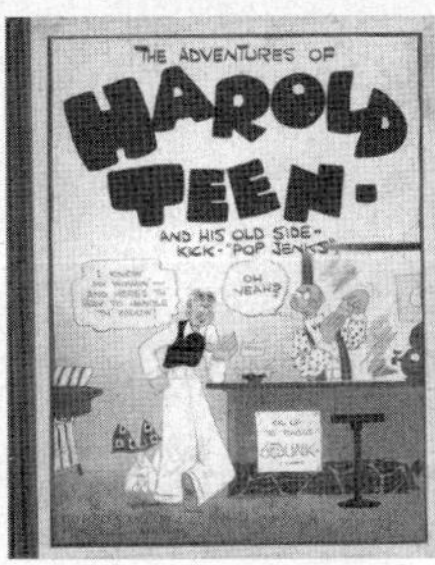

Harold Teen #2 by Carl Ed
1931 © Cupples & Leon

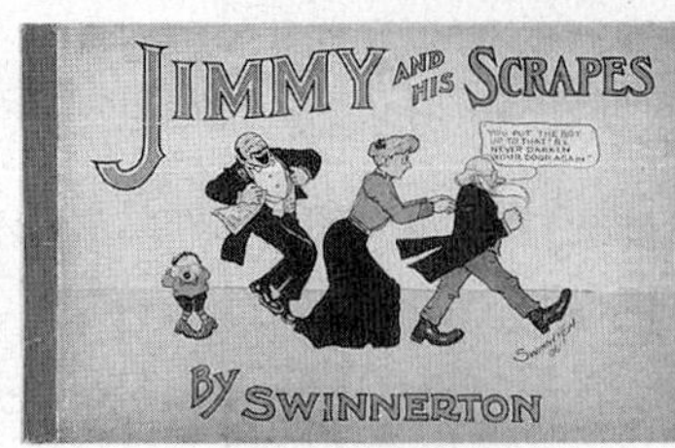

Jimmy and His Scrapes
© Frederick A. Stokes

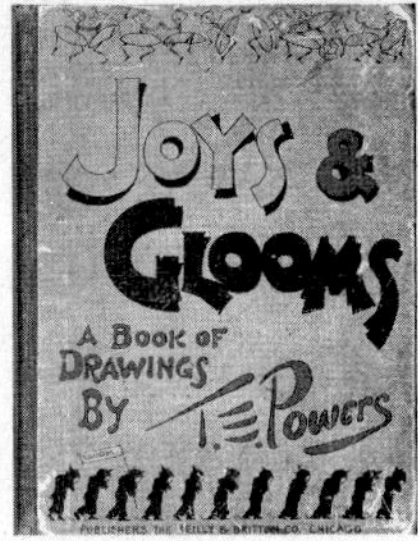

Joys & Glooms By T.E. Powers
1912 © Reilly & Britton Co.

GD2.0 FN6.0 VF8.0

NOTE: *Strip ran March 26, 1900-Aug 14, 1932 and is widely recognized as setting the format standard for all newspaper comic strips which came after it. Opper (1857-1937) was going blind towards the end.*

HAPPY HOOLIGAN (N) (By Fredrick Opper)
Frederick A. Stokes Co.: 1906-08 (10-1/4x15-3/4", cardboard color-c)

1906 - :Travels of...), 68 pgs,10-1/4x15-3/4", 1905-r 450.00 1000.00 –
1907 - "--Home Again", 68 pgs., 10x15-3/4", 60¢; full color-c 450.00 1000.00 –
1908 - "Handy--", 68 pgs, color 450.00 1000.00 –

HAPPY HOOLIGAN, THE STORY OF (G)
McLoughlin Bros.: No. 281, 1932 (12x9-1/2", 20 pgs., soft-c)

281-Three-color text, pictures on heavy paper 57.00 228.00 400.00
NOTE: *An homage to Opper's creation on its 30th Anniversary in 1932.*

HAROLD HARDHIKE'S REJUVENATION
O'Sullivan Rubber: 1917 (6-1/4x3-1/2, 16 pgs, B&W)

nn 25.00 100.00 200.00
NOTE: *Comic book to promote rubber shoe heels.*

HAROLD TEEN (N)
Cupples & Leon Co.: 1929 (9-7/8x9-7/8", 52 pgs, cardboard covers)

1 - By Carl Ed 50.00 200.00 500.00
nn - (1931, 8-11/16x6-7/8", 96 pgs, hardcover w/dj) 41.00 164.00 290.00
NOTE: *Title 2nd book:* ***HAROLD TEEN AND HIS OLD SIDE-KICK– POP JENKINS,*** *(Adv. of...). Precursor for Archie Andrews & crew; strip began May 4, 1919 running into 1959.*

HAROLD TEEN PAINT AND COLOR BOOK (N)
McLoughlin Bros Inc.: 1932 (13x9-3/4, 28 pgs, B&W and color)

#2054 25.00 100.00 200.00

HAWKSHAW THE DETECTIVE (See Advs. of..., Hans Und Fritz & Okay) (N)
The Saalfield Publishing Co.: 1917 (10-1/2x13-1/2", 24 pgs., B&W)

nn - By Gus Mager (Sunday strip-r) 54.00 190.00 325.00
nn - By Gus Mayer (1923 reprint of 1917 edition) 25.00 100.00 175.00
nn - By Gus Mager (1926 reprint of 1917 edition) 25.00 100.00 175.00
NOTE: *Runs Feb 23, 1913-Sept 4, 1922, starts again from Dec 13, 1931-Feb 11, 1952; Sherlock Holmes spoof.*

HEALTH IN PICTURES
American Public Health Association, NYC: 1930 (6-1/2" x 5-3/16", 76 pgs, green & black paper-c, B&W interior)

nn - By various 20.00 55.00 125.00
NOTE: *Collection of strips and cartoons put out by the Public Health Association, on topics ranging from boating and food safety, to small pox and typhoid prevention.*

HE DONE HER WRONG (O) (see also BANANA OIL)
Doubleday, Doran & Company: 1930 (8-1/4x 7-1/4", 276pgs, hard-c with dust jacket, B&W interiors)

nn - By Milt Gross 75.00 225.00 400.00
NOTE: *A seminal original-material wordless graphic novel, not reprints. Several modern reprints.*

HELLO BUDDY (see also **HALT FRIENDS**)
???: 1919? (4-3/8x5-3/4", 36 pgs, color-c, B&W, 15¢)

nn - Unknown 10.00 30.00 100.00
NOTE: *Says on front cover: "Comics of War Facts of Service Sold on its merits by Unemployed or Disabled Ex-Service Men." These are very common; contents vary widely.*

HENRY (N)
David McKay Co.: 1935 (25¢, soft-c)

Book 1 - By Carl Anderson 57.00 200.00 400.00
NOTE: *Strip began March 19 1932; this book ties with Popeye (David McKay) and Little Annie Rooney (David McKay) as the last of the 10x10" Platinum Age comic books.*

HENRY (M)
Greenberg Publishers Inc.: 1935 (11-1/4x 8-5/8", 72 pgs, red & blue color hard-c, dust jacket, B&W interiors) (strip-r from Saturday Evening Post)

nn - By Carl Anderson 57.00 200.00 400.00

HIGH KICKING KELLYS, THE (M)
Vaudeville News Corporation, NY: 1926 (5x11", B&W, two color soft-c)

nn - By Jack A. Ward (scarce) 40.00 160.00 280.00

HIGHLIGHTS OF HISTORY (N)
World Syndicate Publishing Co.: 1933-34 (4-1/2x4", 288 pgs)

nn - 5 different unnumbered issues; daily strip-r 25.00 50.00 100.00
NOTE: *Titles include Buffalo Bill, Daniel Boone, Kit Carson, Pioneers of the Old West, Winning of the Old Northwest. There are line drawing color covers and embossed hardcover versions. It is unknown which came out first.*

HOMER HOLCOMB AND MAY (N)
no publisher listed: 1920s (4 x 9-1/2", 40 pgs, paper cover, B&W)

nn - By Doc Bird Finch (strip-r) 10.00 40.00 70.00

HOME, SWEET HOME (N)
M.S. Publishing Co.: 1925 (10-1/4x10")

nn - By Tuthill 33.00 134.00 235.00

HOW THEY DRAW PROHIBITION (S)
Association Against Prohibition: 1930 (10x9", 100 pgs.)

nn - Single panel and multi-panel comics (rare) 71.00 285.00 550.00
NOTE: *Contains art by J.N. "Ding" Darling, James Flagg, Rollin Kirby, Winsor McCay, T.E. Powers, H.T. Webster, others. Also comes with a loose sheet listing all the newspapers where the cartoons originally appeared.*

HOW TO BE A CARTOONIST (H)
Saalfield Pub. Co: 1936 (10-3/8x12-1/2", 16 pgs, color-c, B&W)

nn - By Chas. H. Kuhn 15.00 50.00 100.00

HOW TO DRAW: A PRACTICAL BOOK OF INSTRUCTION (H)
Harper & Brothers: 1904 (9-1/4x12-3/8", 128 pgs, hardcover, B&W)

nn - Edited By Leon Barritt 57.00 228.00 400.00
NOTE: *Strips reprinted include: "Buster Brown" by Outcault, "Foxy Grandpa" by Bunny, "Happy Hooligan" by Opper, "Katzenjammer Kids" by Dirks, "Lady Bountiful" by Gene Carr, "Mr. Jack" by Swinnerton, "Panhandle Pete" by George McManus, "Mr E.Z. Mark" by F.M. Howarth others; non-character strips by Hy Mayer, Winsor McCay, T.E. Powers, others; single panel cartoons by Davenport, Frost, McDougall, Nast, W.A. Rogers, Sullivant, others.*

HOW TO DRAW CARTOONS (H)
Garden City Publishing Co.: 1926, 1937 (10 1/4 x 7 1/2, 150 pgs)

1926 first edition By Clare Briggs 25.00 75.00 150.00
1937 2nd edition By Clare Briggs 20.00 60.00 120.00
NOTE: *Seminal "how to" break into the comics syndicates with art by Briggs, Fisher, Goldberg, King, Webster, Opper, Tad, Hershfield, McCay, Ding, others. Came with Dust Jacket -add 50%.*

HOW TO DRAW FUNNY PICTURES: A Complete Course in Cartooning (H)
Frederick J. Drake & Co., Chicago: 1936 (10-3/8x6-7/8", 168 pgs, hardcover, B&W)

nn - By E.C. Matthews (200 illus by Eugene Zimmerman) 20.00 60.00 120.00

HY MAYER (M)
Puck Publishing: 1915 (13-1/2 x 20-3/4", 52 pgs, hardcover cover, color & B&W interiors)

nn - By Hy Mayer(strip reprints from Puck) 40.00 140.00 300.00

HYSTERICAL HISTORY OF THE CIVILIAN CONSERVATION CORPS
Peerless Engraving: 1934 (10-3/4x7-1/2", 104 pgs, soft-c, B&W)

nn - By various 20.00 60.00 125.00
NOTE: *Comics about CCC life, includes two color insert postcards in back.*

INDOOR SPORTS (N,S)
National Specials Co., New York: nd circa 1912 (25 cents, 6 x 9", 68 pgs, B&W)

nn - Tad 35.00 125.00 250.00
NOTE: *Cartoons reprinted from Hearst papers.*

IT HAPPENS IN THE BEST FAMILIES (N)
Powers Photo Engraving Co.: 1920 (52 pgs.)(9-1/2x10-3/4")

nn - By Briggs; B&W Sunday strips-r 29.00 114.00 220.00
Special Railroad Edition (30¢)-r/strips from 1914-1920 26.00 103.00 200.00

JIMMIE DUGAN AND THE REG'LAR FELLERS (N)
Cupples & Leon: 1921, 46 pgs. (11"x16")

nn - By Gene Byrne 71.00 284.00 500.00
NOTE: *Ties with EmBee's Mutt & Jeff and Trouble of Bringing Up Father as the last of this size.*

JIMMY (N) (see Little Jimmy Picture & Story Book)
N. Y. American & Journal: 1905 (10x15", 84 pgs., color)

nn - By Jimmy Swinnerton (scarce) 300.00 800.00 1800.00
NOTE: *James Swinnerton was one of the original first pioneers of the American newspaper comic strip.*

JIMMY AND HIS SCRAPES (N)
Frederick A. Stokes: 1906, (10-1/4x15-1/4", 66 pgs, cardboard-c, color)

nn - By Jimmy Swinnerton (scarce) 300.00 800.00 1700.00

JOE PALOOKA (N)
Cupples & Leon Co.: 1933 (9-13/16x10", 52 pgs., B&W daily strip-r)

nn - By Ham Fisher (scarce) 150.00 500.00 1000.00

JOHN, JONATHAN AND MR. OPPER BY F. OPPER (S,I,N)
Grant, Richards, 48 Leicester Square, W.C.: 1903 (9-5/8x8-3/8", 108 pgs, hard-c B&W)

nn - Opper (Scarce) 50.00 200.00 400.00
NOTE: *British precursor-type companion to* WIllie And His Poppa *reprints from Hearst's* NY American & Journal *Opper cartoons interfacing* Uncle Sam *precursor* Brother Jonathan, John Bull. *Uses name* Happy Hooligan *in one cartoon, has* John Bull *smoking opium in another.*

JOLLY POLLY'S BOOK OF ENGLISH AND ETIQUETTE (S)
Jos. J. Frisch: 1931 (60 cents, 8 x 5-1/8, 88 pgs, paper-c, B&W)

nn - By Jos. J. Frisch 20.00 60.00 125.00
NOTE: *Reprint of single panel newspaper series, 4 per page, of English and etiquette lessons taught by a flapper.*

JOYS AND GLOOMS (N)
Reilly & Britton Co.: 1912 (11x8", 72 pgs, hard-c, B&W interior)

nn - By T. E. Powers (newspaper strip-r) 39.00 156.00 325.00

JUDGE - yet to be indexed

JUDGE'S LIBRARY - yet to be indexed

The Cruise of the Katzenjammer Kids
© NY American & Journal

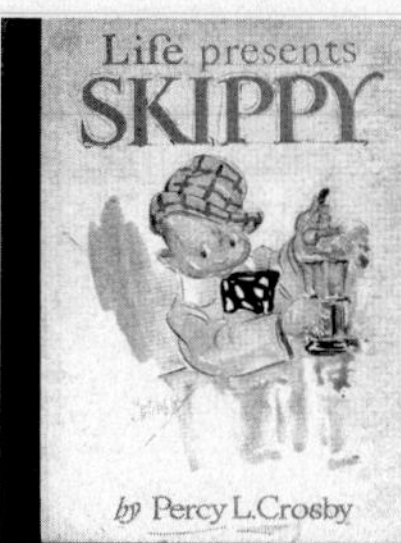

Life Presents Skippy by Percy L. Crosby
1924 © Life Publishing Company

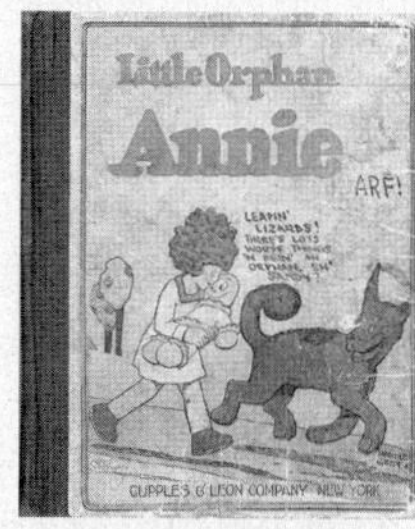

Little Orphan Annie 1926
© C&L

GD2.0 FN6.0 VF8.0

JUST KIDS COMICS FOR CRAYON COLORING
King Features. NYC: 1928 (11x8-1/2, 16 pgs, soft-c)

nn - By Ad Carter 33.00 100.00 210.00
NOTE: *Porous better grade paper; top pics printed in color; lower in b&w to color.*

JUST KIDS, THE STORY OF (I)
McLoughlin Bros.: 1932 (12x9-1/2", 20 pgs., paper-c)

283-Three-color text, pictures on heavy paper 30.00 125.00 260.00

KAPTIN KIDDO AND PUPPO (N)
Frederick A. Stokes Co.: 1910-1913 (11x16-1/2", 62 pgs)

1910-By Grace Wiederseim (later Drayton) 50.00 150.00 260.00
1910-Turr-ble Tales of... By Grace Wiederseim (Edward Stern & Co., 11x16-1/2", 64 pgs.) 50.00 150.00 260.00
1913- ...'Speriences By Grace Drayton 50.00 150.00 260.00
NOTE: *Strip ran approx. 1909-1912.*

KATZENJAMMER KIDS, THE (Also see Hans Und Fritz) (N)
New York American & Journal: 1902,1903 (10x15-1/4", 86 pgs., color)
(By Rudolph Dirks; strip first appeared in 1897) © W.R. Hearst
NOTE: *All KK books 1902-1905 all have the same exact title page with a 1902 copyright by W.R. Hearst; almost always look instead on the front cover.*

1902 (Rare) (red & black); has 1901-02 strips 1000.00 2700.00 –
1903- **A New Edition** (Rare), 86 pgs 800.00 2200.00 –
1904- 10x15", 84 pgs 250.00 900.00 –
1905?-The Cruise of the, 10x15", 60¢, in color 250.00 900.00 –
1905-A Series of Comic Pictures, 10x15", 84 pgs. in color, possible reprint of 1904 edition 250.00 800.00 –
1905-Tricks of... (10x15", 66 pgs, Stokes) 250.00 800.00 –
1906-Stokes (10x16", 32 pgs. in color) 186.00 800.00 –
1907- The Cruise of the, 10x15", 62 pgs 1905-r? 186.00 800.00 –
1910-The Komical...(10x15) 150.00 450.00 800.00
1921-Embee Dist. Co., 10x16", 20 pgs. in color 150.00 450.00 800.00

KATZENJAMMER KIDS MAGIC DRAWING AND COLORING BOOK (N)
Sam L Gabriel Sons And Company: 1931 (8 1/2 x 12", 36 pages, stiff-c

838-By Knerr 50.00 200.00 350.00

KEEPING UP WITH THE JONESES (N)
Cupples & Leon Co.: 1920 - No. 2, 1921 (9-1/4x9-1/4",52 pgs.,B&W daily strip-r)

1,2-By Pop Momand 39.00 154.00 290.00

KID KARTOONS (N,S)
The Century Co.: 1922 (232 pgs, printed 1 side, 9-3/4 x 7-3/4", hard-c, B&W)

nn - By Gene Carr (Metropolitan Movies strip-r) 60.00 240.00 –

KING OF THE ROYAL MOUNTED (Also See Dan Dunn) (N)
Whitman Publishing: 1937 (5 1/2 x 7 1/4", 68 pgs., color cardboard-c, B&W)

1010 36.00 144.00 250.00

LADY BOUNTIFUL (N)
Saalfield Publ. Co./Press Publ. Co.: 1917 (13-3/8x10", 36 pgs, color cardboard-c, B&W interiors)

nn - By Gene Carr; 2 panels per page 50.00 150.00 280.00
193S - 2nd printing (13-1/8x10",28 pgs color-c, B&W) 33.00 117.00 200.00

LAUGHS YOU MIGHT HAVE HAD From The Comic Pages of Six Week Day Issues of the Post-Dispatch (N)
St. Louis Post-Dispatch: 1921 (9 x 10 1/2", 28 pgs, B&W, red ink cover)

nn - Various comic strips 39.00 154.00 270.00

LIFE, DOGS FROM (M)
Doubleday, Page & Company: nn 1920 - No.2 1926 (130 pgs, 11-1/4 x 9", color painted-c, hard-c, B&W)

nn (No.1) 120.00 360.00 –
Second Litter 80.00 320.00 –
NOTE: *Reprints strips & cartoons featuring dogs, from Life Magazine. Editted by Thomas L. Masson. Highly sought by collectors of dog ephemera. Art in both books is mostly by Robert L. Dickey. Other art: Carl Anderson-1,2; Barbes-1; Chip Bellew-1; Lang Campbell-1,2; Percy Crosby-1,2; Edwina-2; Frueh-2; R.B. Fuller-1; Gibson-1,2; Don Herold-2; Gus Mager-2; Orr-1; J.R. Shaver-1,2; T.S. Sullivant-2; Russ Westover-1,2; Crawford Young-1.*

LIFE OF DAVY CROCKETT IN PICTURE AND STORY, THE
Cupples & Leon: 1935 (8-3/4x7", 64 pgs, B&W hard-c, dust jacket)

nn - By C. Richard Schaare 29.00 116.00 235.00

LIFE OF THOMAS A. EDISON IN WORD AND PICTURE, THE (N)(Also see Edison...)
Thomas A. Edison Industries: 1928 (10x8", 56 pgs, paper cover, B&W)

nn - Photo-c 100.00 250.00 400.00
NOTE: *Reprints newspaper strip which ran August to November 1927.*

LIFE'S LITTLE JOKES (S)
M.S. Publ. Co.: No date (1924)(10-1/16x10", 52 pgs., B&W)

nn - By Rube Goldberg 64.00 257.00 550.00

LIFE, MINIATURE (see also LIFE (miniature reprint of of issue No. 1)) (M,P,S)
Life Publishing Co.: No. 1 - No. 4 1913, 1916, 1919 (5-3/4x4-5/8", 20 pgs, color paper-c

1- 3 (1913) 4 (1916) 5 (1919) (no known sales)
NOTE: *Giveaway item from Life, to promote subscriptions. All reprint material. No.2: James Montgomery Flagg-c; a-Chip Bellew, Gus Dirks, Gibson, F.M.Howarth, Art Young.*

LIFE'S PRINTS (was **LIFE'S PICTURE GALLERY** - See Victorian Age section) (M,S,P)
Life Publishing Company, New York: nd (c1907) (7x4-1/2", 132 pgs, paper cover, B&W)

nn - (nd; c1907) unillustrated black construction paper cover; reprints art from 1895-1907; art by J.M.Flagg, A.B.Frost, Gibson (Scarce) – – –
nn - (nd; c1908) b&w cardboard painted cover by Gibson, showing angel raising a champagne glass; reprints art from 1901-1908; art by J.M.Flagg, A.B.Frost, Gibson, Walt Kuhn, Art Young (Scarce) – – –
NOTE: *Catalog of prints reprinted from LIFE covers & centerspreads. There are likely more as yet unreported catalogs.*

LIFE, THE COMEDY OF LIFE
Life Publishing Company: 1907 (130 pgs, 11-3/4x9-1/4",embossed printed cloth covered board-c, B+W

nn - By various 30.00 100.00 150.00
NOTE: *Single cartoons and some sequential cartoons). Artists include Charles Dana Gibson, Harrison Cady, E.W. Kemble, James Montgomery Flagg.*

LILY OF THE ALLEY IN THE FUNNIES
Whitman Publishing Co.: No date (1927) (10-1/4x15-1/2"; 28 pgs., color)

W936 - By T. Burke (Rare) 57.00 228.00 400.00

LITTLE ANNIE ROONEY (N)
David McKay Co.: 1935 (25¢, soft-c)

Book 1 43.00 172.00 350.00
NOTE: *Ties with Henry & Popeye (David McKay) as the last of the 10x10" size Plat comic books.*

LITTLE ANNIE ROONEY WISHING BOOK (G) (See Happy Hooligan, Story of #281)
McLoughlin Bros.: 1932 (12x9-1/2", 16 pgs., soft-c, 3-color text, heavier paper)

282 - By Darrell McClure 41.00 144.00 280.00

LITTLE BIRD TOLD ME, A (E)
Life Publishing Co.: 1905? (96 pgs, hardbound)

nn - By Walt Kuhn (Life-r) 41.00 144.00 280.00

LITTLE FOLKS PAINTING BOOK (N)
The National Arts Company: 1931 (10-7/8 x 15-1/4", 20 pgs, half in full color)

nn - By "Tack" Knight (strip-r) 41.00 144.00 280.00

LITTLE JIMMY PICTURE AND STORY BOOK (I) (see Jimmy)
McLaughlin Bros., Inc.: 1932 (13-1/4 x 9-3/4", 20 pgs, cardstock color cover)

284 Text by Marion Kincaird; illus by Swinnerton 57.00 228.00 400.00

LITTLE JOHNNY & THE TEDDY BEARS (Judge-r) (M) (see Teddy Bear Books)
Reilly & Britton Co.: 1907 (10x14".; 68 pgs, green, red, black interior color)

nn - By J. R. Bray-a/Robert D. Towne-s 67.00 233.00 400.00

LITTLE JOURNEY TO THE HOME OF BRIGGS THE SKY-ROCKET, THE
Lockhart Art School: 1917 (10-3/4x7-7/8", 20 pgs, B&W) (I)

nn - About Clare Briggs (bio & lots of early art) 41.00 144.00 280.00

LITTLE KING, THE (see New Yorker Cartoon Albums for 1st appearance) (M)
Farrar & Reinhart, Inc: 1933 (10-1/4 x 8-3/4, 80 pgs, hardcover w/dust jacket

nn - By Otto Soglow (strip-r The New Yorker) 125.00 250.00 500.00
NOTE: *Copies with dust jacket are worth 50% more. Also exists in a 12x8-3/4 edition.*

LITTLE LULU BY MARGE (M)
Rand McNally & Company, Chicago: 1936 (6-9/16x6", 68 pgs, yellow hard-c, B&W)

nn - By Marjorie Henderson Buell 50.00 130.00 300.00
NOTE: *Begins reprinting single panel Little Lulu cartoons which began with Saturday Evening Post Feb. 23, 1935. This book was reprinted several times as late as 1940.*

LITTLE NAPOLEON
No publisher listed: 1924 , 50 pages, 10" by 10"; Color cardstock-c, B&W

nn - By Bud Counihan (Cupples &Leon format) 25.00 100.00 250.00

LITTLE NEMO (...in Slumberland) (N) (see also Little Sammy Sneeze, Dreams...Rarebit F)
Doffield & Co.(1906)/Cupples & Leon Co.(1909): 1906, 1909 (Sunday strip-r in color, cardboard covers)

1906-11x16-1/2" by Winsor McCay; 30 pgs. (scarce) 1500.00 5500.00 –
1909-10x14" by Winsor McCay (scarce) 1300.00 4000.00 –

LITTLE ORPHAN ANNIE (See Treasure Box of Famous Comics) (N)
Cupples & Leon Co.: 1926 - 1934 (8-3/4x7", 100 pgs., B&W daily strip-r, hard-c)

1 (1926)-Little Orphan Annie (softback see Treasure Box) 50.00 200.00 400.00
2 (1927)-In the Circus (softback see Wonder Box...) 36.00 144.00 250.00
3 (1928)-The Haunted House (softback see Wonder Box...) 36.00 144.00 250.00
4 (1929)-Bucking the World 36.00 144.00 250.00
5 (1930)-Never Say Die 30.00 120.00 225.00
6 (1931)-Shipwrecked 30.00 120.00 225.00
7 (1932)-A Willing Helper 25.00 100.00 175.00

The Trials of Lulu and Leander by Howarth
1906 © NY American & Journal

Maud the Mirthful Mule by Opper
1908 © Frederick A. Stokes

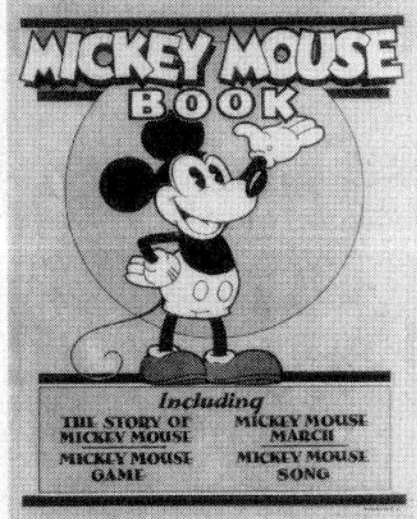

Mickey Mouse Book
1930 © Bibo & Lang

8 (1933)-In Cosmic City 25.00 100.00 175.00
9 (1934)-Uncle Dan (not rare) 25.00 100.00 175.00
NOTE: *Each book reprints dailies from the previous year. Each hardcover came with a dust jacket. Books with out dust jackets are worth 50% less. Many of copies of #9 Uncle Dan have been turning up on eBay recently.*

LITTLE ORPHAN ANNIE RUMMY CARDS (N)
Whitman Publishing Co., Racine: 1935 (box: 5 x 6 1/2" Cards: 3 1/2 x 2 1/4")
nn-Harold Gray 20.00 60.00 125.00
NOTE: *36 cards, including 1 instruction card, 5 character cards and 30 cards forming 5 sequential stories (6 cards each).*

LITTLE SAMMY SNEEZE (N) (see also Little Nemo, Dreams of A Rarebit Fiend)
New York Herald Co.: Dec 1905 (11x16-1/2", 72 pgs., color)
nn - By Winsor McCay (Very Rare) 3500.00 8000.00 –
NOTE: *Rarely found in fine to mint condition.*

LIVE AND LET LIVE
Travelers Insurance Co.: 1936 (5-3/4x7/3/4", 16 pgs. color and B&W)
nn - Bill Holman, Carl Anderson, etc 20.00 60.00 120.00

LULU AND LEANDER (N) (see also Funny Folk, 1899, in Victorian section)
New York American & Journal: 1904 (76 pgs); **William A Stokes & Co:** 1906
nn - By F.M. Howarth 300.00 750.00 1500.00
nn - The Trials of...(1906, 10x16", 68 pgs. in color) 300.00 750.00 1500.00
NOTE: *F. M. Howarth helped pioneer the American comic strip in the pages of PUCK magazine in the early 1890s before the Yellow Kid.*

MADMAN'S DRUM (O)
Jonathan Cape and Harrison Smith Inc.: 1930 (8-1/4x6", 274 pgs, B&W hardcover w/dust jacket) (original graphic novel in wood cuts)
nn - By Lynd Ward 50.00 175.00 310.00

MAMA'S ANGEL CHILD IN TOYLAND (I)
Rand McNally, Chicago: 1915 (128 pgs, hardbound)
nn - By M.T. "Penny" Ross & Marie C, Sadler 40.00 140.00 240.00
NOTE: *Mamma's Angel Child published as a comic strip by the "Chicago Tribune" 1908 Mar 1 to 1920 Oct 17. This novel dedicated to Esther Starring Richartz, "the original Mamma's Angel Kid."*

MAUD (N) (see also **Happy Hooligan**)
Frederick A. Stokes Co.: 1906 - 1908? (10x15-1/2", cardboard-c)
1906-By Fred Opper (Scarce), 66 pgs. color 400.00 1300.00 –
1907-The Matchless, 10x15" 70 pgs in color 300.00 1100.00 –
1908-The Mirthful Mule, 10x15", 64 pgs in color 300.00 1100.00 –
NOTE: *First run of strip began July 24, 1904 to at least Oct 6, 1907, spun out of **Happy Hooligan**.*

MEMORIAL EDITION The Drawings of Clare Briggs (S)
Wm H. Wise & Company: 1930 (7-1/2x8-3/4", 284 pgs, pebbled false black leather, B&W) (posthumous boxed set of 7 books by Clare Briggs)
nn - The Days of Real Sport; nn-Golf; nn-Real Folks at Home; nn-Ain't it a Grand and Glorious Feeling?; nn-That Guiltiest Feeling; nn-Somebody's Always Taking the Joy Out of Life; nn-When a Feller Needs a Friend
Each book... 30.00 110.00 160.00
NOTE: *Also exists in a whitish cream colored paper back edition; first edition unknown presently.*

MENACE CARTOONS (M, S)
Menace Publishing Company, Aurora, Missouri: 1914 (10-3/8x8", 80 pgs, cardboard-c, B&W)
nn - (Rare) 50.00 150.00 450.00
NOTE: *Reprints anti-Catholic cartoons from K.K.K. related publication **The Menace**.*

MEN OF DARING (N)
Cupples & Leon Co.: 1933 (8-3/4x7", 100 pgs)
nn - By Stookie Allen, intro by Lowell Thomas 30.00 90.00 200.00

MICKEY MOUSE BOOK
Bibo & Lang: 1930-1931 (12x9", stapled-c, 20 pgs., 4 printings)
nn - First Disney licensed publication (a magazine, not a book–see first book, Adventures of Mickey Mouse). Contains story of how Mickey met Walt and got his name; games, cartoons & song "Mickey Mouse (You Cute Little Feller)," written by Irving Bibo; Minnie, Clarabelle Cow, Horace Horsecollar & caricature of Walt shaking hands with Mickey. The changes made with the 2nd printing have been verified by billing affidavits in the Walt Disney Archives and include:Two Win Smith Mickey strips from 4/15/30 and 4/17/30 added to page 8 & back-c; "Printed in U.S.A." added to front cover; Bobette Bibo's age of 11 years added to title page; faulty type on the word "tail" corrected top of page 3; the word "start" added to bottom of page 7, removing the words "start 1 2 3 4" from the top of page 7; music and lyrics were rewritten on pages 12-14. A green ink border was added beginning with 2nd printing and some covers have inking variations. Art by Albert Barbelle, drawn in an Ub Iwerks style. Total circulation : 97,938 copies varying from 21,000 to 26,000 per printing.
1st printing. Contains the song lyrics **censored** in later printings, "When little Minnie's pursued by a big bad villain we feel so bad then we're glad when you up and kill him." Attached to the Nov. 15, 1930 issue of the Official Bulletin of the Mickey Mouse Club notes: "Attached to this Bulletin is a new Mickey Mouse Book that has just been published." This is thought to be the reason why a slightly disproportionate larger number of copies of the first printing still exist 600.00 1300.00 5300.00
1st printing (variant) All white-c and has advertising on inside front & back-cvrs. All other examples have blank inside cvrs. Has word "kill" in the song. One of the ads is for a Mickey Mouse Club. A Fine copy sold on 12/24/17 for $2375.
2nd printing with a theater/advertising. Christmas greeting added to inside front cover (1 copy known with Dec. 27, 1930 date) – 8000.00 –
2nd-4th printings 500.00 1100.00 3300.00
NOTE: *Theater/advertising copies do not qualify as separate printings. Most copies are missing pages 9 & 10 which had a puzzle to be cut out. Puzzle (pages 9 and 10) cut out or missing, subtract 60% to 75%.*

MICKEY MOUSE COLORING BOOK (S)
Saalfield Publishing Company: 1931 (15-1/4x10-3/4", 32 pgs, color soft cover, half printed in full color interior, rest B&W
871 - By Ub Iwerks & Floyd Gottfredson (rare) 450.00 1300.00 2500.00
NOTE: *Contains reprints of first MM daily strip ever, including the "missing" speck the chicken is after found only on the original daily strip art by Iwerks plus other very early MM art. There were several other Saalfield Mickey Mouse coloring books manufactured around the same time.*

MICKEY MOUSE, THE ADVENTURES OF (I)
David McKay Co., Inc.: Book I, 1931 - Book II, 1932 (5-1/2"x8-1/2", 32 pgs.)
Book I-First Disney book, by strict definition (1st printing-50,000 copies)(see Mickey Mouse Book by Bibo & Lang). Illustrated text refers to Clarabelle Cow as "Carolyn" and Horace Horsecollar as "Henry". The name "Donald Duck" appears with a non-costumed generic duck on back cover & inside, not in the context of the character that later debuted in the Wise Little Hen.
Hardback w/characters on back-c 75.00 300.00 800.00
Softcover w/characters on back-c 40.00 165.00 420.00
Version without characters on back-c 50.00 200.00 460.00
Book II-Less common than Book I. Character development brought into conformity with the Mickey Mouse cartoon shorts and syndicated strips. Captain Church Mouse, Tanglefoot, Peg-Leg Pete and Pluto appear with Mickey & Minnie 50.00 200.00 460.00

MICKEY MOUSE COMIC (N)
David McKay Co.: 1931 - No. 4, 1934 (10"x9-3/4", 52 pgs., card board-c)
(Later reprints exist)
1 (1931)-Reprints Floyd Gottfredson daily strips in black & white from 1930 & 1931, including the famous two week sequence in which Mickey tries to commit suicide 300.00 1000.00 2200.00
2 (1932)-1st app. of Pluto reprinted from 7/8/31 daily. All pgs. from 1931 164.00 656.00 1250.00
3 (1933)-Reprints 1932 & 1933 Sunday pages in color, one strip per page, including the "Lair of Wolf Barker" continuity pencilled by Gottfredson and inked by Al Taliaferro & Ted Thwaites. First app. Mickey's nephews, Morty & Ferdie, one identified by name of Mortimer Fieldmouse, not to be confused with Uncle Mortimer Mouse who is introduced in the Wolf Barker story 214.00 856.00 1700.00
4 (1934)-1931 dailies, include the only known reprint of the infamous strip of 2/4/31 where the villainous Kat Nipp snips off the end of Mickey's tail with a pair of scissors 140.00 560.00 1100.00

MICKEY MOUSE (N)
Whitman Publishing Co.: 1933-34 (10x8-3/4", 34 pgs, cardboard-c)
948-1932 & 1933 Sunday strips in color, printed from the same plates as Mickey Mouse Book #3 by David McKay, but only pages 5-17 & 32-48 (including all of the "Wolf Barker" continuity) 157.00 629.00 1300.00
NOTE: *Some copies bound with back cover upside down. Variance doesn't affect value. Same art appears on front and back covers of all copies. Height of Whitman reissue trimmed 1/2 inch.*

MILITARY WILLIE
J. I. Austen Co.: 1907 (7x9-1/2", 12 pgs., every other page in color, stapled)
nn - By F. R. Morgan 70.00 245.00 400.00

MINNEAPOLIS TRIBUNE CARTOON BOOK (S)
Minneapolis Tribune: 1899-1903 (11-3/8x9-3/8", B&W, paper cover)
nn (#1) (1899) 45.00 100.00 200.00
nn (#2) (1900) 45.00 100.00 200.00
nn (#3) (1901) (published Jan 01, 1901) 45.00 100.00 200.00
nn (#4) (1902) (114 pgs) 45.00 100.00 200.00
nn (#5) (1903) (9x10-3/4",110 pgs, B&W; color-c) 45.00 100.00 200.00
NOTE: *All by Roland C. Bowman (editorial-r).*

MINUTE BIOGRAPHIES: INTIMATE GLIMPSES INTO THE LIVES OF 150 FAMOUS MEN AND WOMEN
Grossett & Dunlap: 1931, 1933 (10-1/4x7-3/4", 168 pgs, hardcover, B&W)
nn - By Nisenson (art) & Parker(text) 25.00 75.00 160.00
More.... (1933) 25.00 75.00 160.00

MISCHIEVOUS MONKS OF CROCODILE ISLE, THE (N)
J. I. Austen Co., Chicago: 1908 (8-1/2x11-1/2", 12 pgs., 4 pgs. in color)
nn - By F. R. Morgan; reads longwise 125.00 375.00 600.00

MR. & MRS. (Also see Ain't It A Grand and Glorious Feeling?) (N)
Whitman Publishing Co.: 1922 (9x9-1/2", 52 & 28 pgs., cardboard-c)
nn - By Briggs (B&W, 52 pgs.) 37.00 149.00 260.00
nn - 28 pgs.-(9x9-1/2")-Sunday strips-r in color 41.00 163.00 285.00
NOTE: *The earliest presently-known Whitman comic books*

Moon Mullins #5 by Frank Willard
1931 @ Cupples & Leon

The Nebbs
© C&L

The Newlyweds by George McManus
1907 © Saalfield Publishing Co.

GD2.0 FN6.0 VF8.0

MR. BLOCK (N)
Industrial Workers of the World (IWW): 1913, 1919
nn - By Ernest Riebe (C) 55.00 160.00 –
...And The Profiteers (original material) (H) 55.00 160.00 –
NOTE: *Mr Block was a daily strip published from 1912 NOV 7 to 1913 SEP ? by the socialist newspaper "Industrial Worker"; Mr Block was a "square" guy (his head was in fact a block) who enthusiastically supported the same system that exploited him. The noted Joe Hill wrote a song about him (Mr Block,1913, on the air of "It loooks me like a big time tonight") for the "Industrial Worker Songbook".*

MR. TWEE-DEEDLE (N)
Cupples & Leon: 1913, 1917 (11-3/8 x 16-3/4" color strips-r from NY Herald)
nn - By John B. Gruelle (later of Raggedy Ann fame) 350.00 900.00 2000.00
nn - "Further Adventures of..." By Gruelle 350.00 900.00 2000.00
NOTE: *Strip ran Feb 5, 1911-March 10, 1918.*

MONKEY SHINES OF MARSELEEN AND SOME OF HIS ADVENTURES (C)
McLaughlin Bros. New York: 1906 (10 x 12-3/8", 36 pgs, full color hardcover)
nn - By Norman E. Jennett strip-r NY Evening Telegram 100.00 250.00 475.00
NOTE: *Strip began in 1906 until at least March 13, 1910.*

MONKEY SHINES OF MARSELEEN (N)
Cupples & Leon Co.: 1909 (11-1/2 x 17", 58 pgs. in two colors)
nn - By Norman E. Jennett (strip-r New York Herald) 100.00 250.00 475.00

MOON MULLINS (N)
Cupples & Leon Co.: 1927 - 1933 (52 pgs., B&W daily strip-r)
Series 1 ('27)-By Willard 63.00 250.00 550.00
Series 2 ('28), Series 3 ('29), Series 4 ('30) 39.00 156.00 300.00
Series 5 ('31), 6 ('32), 7 ('33) 39.00 156.00 300.00
Big Book 1 ('30)-B&W (scarce) 100.00 400.00 750.00
w/dust jacket (rare) 183.00 732.00 1150.00

MOVING PICTURE FUNNIES
Saml Gabriel Sons & Company: 1918 (5-1/4 x 10-1/4", 52 pgs, B&W, illustrated hard-c)
nn 25.00 50.00 100.00
NOTE: *823 Comical illustrations that show a different scene when folded.*

MUTT & JEFF (...Cartoon, The) (N)
Ball Publications: 1911 - No. 5, 1916 (5-3/4 x 15-1/2", 72 pgs, B&W, hard-c)
1 (1910)(50¢) very common 71.00 286.00 550.00
2,3: 2 (1911)-Opium den panels; Jeff smokes opium (pipe dreams).
3 (1912) both very common 71.00 286.00 500.00
2-(1913) Reprint of 1911 edition with black ink cover 50.00 175.00 300.00
4 (1915) (50¢) (Scarce) 150.00 350.00 650.00
5 (1916) (Rare) -Photos of Fisher, 1st pg. (68 pages) 200.00 480.00 1000.00
5-Scarce 84 page reprint edition 150.00 450.00 850.00
NOTE: *Mutt & Jeff first appeared in newspapers in 1907. Cover variations exist showing Mutt & Jeff reading various newspapers; i.e., The Oregon Journal, The American, and The Detroit News. Reprinting of each issue began soon after publication. No. 4 and 5 may not have been reprinted. Values listed include the reprints. Mutt & Jeff was the first successful American daily newspaper comic strip and as such remains one of the seminal strips of all time.*

MUTT & JEFF (N)
Cupples & Leon Co.: No. 6, 1919 - No. 22, 1934? (9-1/2x9-1/2", 52 pgs., B&W dailies, stiff-c)
6, 7 - By Bud Fisher (very common) 32.00 128.00 225.00
8-10 46.00 186.00 325.00
11-18 (Somewhat Scarcer) (#19-#22 do not exist) 60.00 â240.00 420.00
nn (1920) (Advs. of...) 11x16"; 44 pgs.; full color reprints of 1919 Sunday strips 93.00 372.00 675.00
Big Book nn (1926, 144 pgs., hardcovers) 114.00 456.00 800.00
w/dust jacket 193.00 772.00 1350.00
Big Book 1 (1928) - Thick book (hardcovers) 114.00 456.00 800.00
w/dust jacket (rare) 182.00 729.00 1275.00
Big Book 2 (1929) - Thick book (hardcovers) 114.00 456.00 800.00
w/dust jacket (rare) 182.00 729.00 1275.00
NOTE: *The Big Books contain three previous issues rebound.*

MUTT & JEFF (N)
Embee Publ. Co.: 1921 (9x15", color cardboard-c & interior)
nn - Sunday strips in color (Rare)- BY Bud Fisher 150.00 600.00 1200.00
NOTE: *Ties with The Trouble of Bringing Up Father (EmBee) and Jimmie Dugan & The Reg'lar Fellers (C&L) as the last of this size.*

MYSTERIOUS STRANGER AND OTHER CARTOONS, THE
McClure, Phillips & Co.: 1905 (12-3/8x9-3/4", 338 pgs, hardcover, B&W)
nn - By John McCutcheon 32.00 128.00 250.00

MY WAR - Szeged (Szuts)
Wm. Morrow Co.: 1932 (7x10-1/2", 210 pgs, hard-c, B&W)
nn - (All story panels, no words - powerful) 32.00 128.00 250.00

NAUGHTY ADVENTURES OF VIVACIOUS MR. JACK, THE
New York American & Journal: 1904 (15x10", color strips)
nn - By James Swinnerton; (Very Rare - 3 known copies) 1000.00 1700.00 2600.00

NEBBS, THE (N)
Cupples & Leon Co.: 1928 (52 pgs., B&W daily strip-r)
nn - By Sol Hess; Carlson-a 40.00 160.00 300.00

NERVY NAT'S ADVENTURES (E)
Leslie-Judge Co.: 1911 (90 pgs, 85¢, 1903 strip reprints from **Judge**)
nn - By James Montgomery Flagg 75.00 263.00 450.00

THE NEWLYWEDS AND THEIR BABY (N)
Saalfield Publ. Co.: 1907 (13x10", 52 pgs., hardcover)
...& Their Baby' by McManus; daily strips 50% color 350.00 1100.00 –
NOTE: *Strip ran Apr 10, 1904 thru Jan 14, 1906 and then May 19, 1907-Dec 5, 1916; was a huge success with Baby Snookums long before McManus invented Bringing Up Father; Snookums brought back as a topper strip over BUF Nov 19, 1944-Dec 30, 1956.*

THE NEWLYWEDS AND THEIR BABY'S COMIC PICTURES FOR PAINTING AND CRAYONING (N)
Saalfield Publishign Company: 1916 (10-1/4x14-3/4", 52 pgs. Cardboard-c)
nn - 44 B&W pages, covers, and one color wrap glued to B&W title page.
Color wrap: color title pg. & 3 pgs of color strips 83.00 290.00 550.00
nn - (1917, 10x14", 20 pgs, oblong, cardboard-c) partial reprint of 1916 edition 31.00 124.00 300.00

THE NEWLYWEDS AND THEIR BABY (N)
Saalfield Publishing Company: 1917 (10-1/8x13-9/16 ", 52 pgs, full color cardstock-c, some pages full color, others two color (orange, blue))
nn 83.00 290.00 475.00

NEW YORKER CARTOON ALBUM, THE (M)
Doubleday, Doran & Company Inc.: (1928-1931); **Harper & Brothers.:** (1931-1933); **Random House** (1935-1937), 12x9", various pg counts, hardcovers w/dust jackets)
1928: nn-114 pgs Arno, Held, Soglow, Williams, etc 20.00 60.00 130.00
1928: SECOND-114 pgs Arno, Bairnsfather, Gross, Held, Soglow, Williams 10.00 30.00 75.00
1930: THIRD-172 pgs Arno, Bairnsfather, Held, Soglow, Art Young 10.00 30.00 75.00
1931: FOURTH-154 pgs Arno, Held, Soglow, Steig, Thurber, Williams, Art Young, "Little King" by Soglow begins 10.00 30.00 75.00
1932: FIFTH-156 pgs Arno, Bairnsfather, Held, Hoff, Soglow, Steig, Thurber, Williams 10.00 30.00 75.00
1933: SIXTH-156 pgs same as above 10.00 30.00 75.00
1935: SEVENTH-164 pgs 10.00 30.00 75.00
1937: 168 pgs; Charles Addams plus same as above but no Little King, two page "Gone With The Wind" parody strip 10.00 30.00 75.00
NOTE: *Some sequential strips but mostly single panel cartoons.*

NIPPY'S POP (N)
The Saalfield Publishing Co.: 1917 (10-1/2x13-1/2", 36 pgs., B&W, Sunday strip-r)
nn - Charles M Payne (better known as S'Matter Pop) 50.00 160.00 270.00

OH, MAN (A Bully Collection of Those Inimitable Humor Cartoons) (S)
P.F. Volland & Co.: 1919 (8-1/2x13"; 136 pgs.)
nn - By Briggs 50.00 160.00 270.00
NOTE: *Originally came in illustrated box with Briggs art (box is Rare - worth 50% more with box).*

OH SKIN-NAY! (S)
P.F. Volland & Co.: 1913 (8-1/2x13", 136 pgs.)
nn - The Days Of Real Sport by Briggs 43.00 152.00 250.00
NOTE: *Originally came in illustrated box with Briggs art (box is Rare - worth 50% more with box).*

OLD GOLD THE SMOOTHER AND BETTER CIGARETTE...NOT A COUGH IN A CARLOAD (M,N,P) (see also BY BRIGGS)
Old Gold Cigarettes: nd (c1920's) (16 pgs, paper-c, color) (both Scarce)
nn- (4-1/4" x 3-7/8") cover strip is "Oh, Man!"; also contains: "Real Folks at Home", "Ain't It a Grand and Glorious Feelin?", "It Happens in the Best Regulated Families", and "Mr. and Mrs." (no known sales)
1440- (5-9/16" x 5-1/4") cover strip is "Frank and Ernest"; also contains: "That Guiltiest Feeling", "Real Folks at Home", "Oh, Man!", "When a Feller Needs a Friend". (no known sales)
NOTE: *Collection reprinting strip cartoons by Clare Briggs, advertising Old Gold Cigarettes. These strips originally appeared in various magazines, play program booklets, newspapers, etc. Some of the strips involve regular Briggs strip series. The two booklets contain a completely different set of comics.*

ON AND OFF MOUNT ARARAT (also see **Tigers**) (N)
Hearst's New York American & Journal: 1902, 86pgs. 10x15-1/4"
nn - Rare Noah's Ark satire by Jimmy Swinnerton (rare) 450.00 1600.00 –

ON THE LINKS (N)
Associated Feature Service: Dec, 1926 (9x10", 48 pgs.)
nn - Daily strip-r 50.00 125.00 200.00

ONE HUNDRED WAR CARTOONS (S)
Idaho Daily Statesman: 1918 (7-3/4x10", 102 pgs, paperback, B&W)
nn - By Villeneuve (WW I cartoons) 20.00 60.00 130.00

OUR ANTEDILUVIAN ANCESTORS (N,S)
New York Evening Journal, NY: 1903 (11-3/8x8-7/8", hardcover)

The Adventures of Peck's Bad Boy With the Teddy Bear Show by McDougall
1907 © Charles C. Thompson, Co.

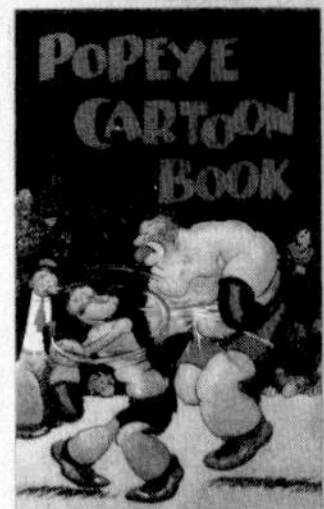

Popeye Cartoon Book
1934 © The Saalfield Co.

Roger Bean, R.G. #4
1917 © Indiana News Co., Distributors

GD2.0 FN6.0 VF8.0

nn - By F Opper 75.00 200.00 425.00
NOTE: *There is a simultaneously published British edition, identical size and contents, from C. Arthur Pearson Ltd, London. A collection of single panel cartoons about cavemen. Similar to an earlier British cartoon book "Prehistoric Peeps from Punch", by E.T. Reed.*

OUTBURSTS OF EVERETT TRUE, THE (N)
Saalfield Publ. Co.(Werner Co.): 1907 (92 pgs, 9-7/16x5-1/4")

1907 (2-4 panel strips-r)-By Condo & Raper 125.00 350.00 700.00
1921-Full color-c; reprints 56 of 88 cartoons from 1907 ed. (10x10", 32 pgs B&W) 125.00 225.00 350.00

OVER THERE COMEDY FROM FRANCE
Observer House Printing: nd (WW 1 era) (6x14", 60 pgs, paper cover)

nn - Artist(s) unknown 15.00 53.00 100.00

OWN YOUR OWN HOME (I)
Bobbs-Merrill Company, Indianapolis: 1919 (7-7/16x5-1/4")

nn - By Fontaine Fox – – –

PECKS BAD BOY (N)
Charles C. Thompson Co, Chicago (by Walt McDougal): 1906-1908 (strip-r)

The Adventures of... (1906) 11-1/2x16-1/4", 68 pgs 100.00 400.00 820.00
...& His Country Cousin Cynthia (1907) 12x16-1/2," 34 pgs In color 100.00 400.00 820.00
Advs. of...And His Country Cousins (1907) 5-1/2x10 1/2", 18 pgs In color 50.00 175.00 375.00
Advs. of...And His Country Cousins (1907) 11-1/2x16-1/4", 36 pgs 50.00 175.00 375.00
...& Their Advs With The Teddy Bear (1907) 5-1/2x10-1/2", 18 pgs in color 50.00 175.00 375.00
...& Their Balloon Trip To the Country (1907) 5-1/2x 10-1/2, 18 pgs in color 50.00 175.00 375.00
...With the Teddy Bear Show (1907) 5-1/2x 10-1/2 50.00 175.00 375.00
...With The Billy Whiskers Goats (1907) 5-1/2 x 10-1/2, 18 pgs in color 50.00 175.00 375.00
...& His Chums (1908) - 11x16-3/8", 36 pgs. Stanton & Van Vliet Co 100.00 400.00 820.00
...& His Chums (1908)-Hardcover; full color;16 pgs. 100.00 350.00 660.00
Advs. of...in Pictures (1908) (11x17, 36 pgs)-In color; Stanton & Van V. Liet Co. 100.00 400.00 820.00

PERCY & FERDIE (N)
Cupples & Leon Co.: 1921 (10x10", 52 pgs., B&W dailies, cardboard-c)

nn - By H. A. MacGill (Rare) 61.00 244.00 500.00

PETER RABBIT (N)
John H. Eggers Co. The House of Little Books Publishers: 1922 - 1923

B1-B4-(Rare)-(Set of 4 books which came in a cardboard box)-Each book reprints half of a Sunday page per page and contains 8 B&W and 2 color pages; by Harrison Cady (9-1/4x6-1/4", paper-c) each.... 43.00 172.00 300.00
Box only 57.00 228.00 400.00

PHILATELIC CARTOONS (M)
Essex Publishing Company, Lynn, Mass.: 1916 (8-11/16" x 5-7/8", 40 pgs, light blue construction paper-c, B&W interior)

nn - By Leroy S. Bartlett 50.00 100.00 200.00
NOTE: *Comics reprinted from The New England Philatelist.*

PICTORIAL HISTORY OF THE DEPARTMENT OF COMMERCE UNDER HERBERT HOOVER (see Picture Life of a Great American) (O)
Hoover-Curtis Campaign Committee of New York State: no date, 1928 (3-1/4 x 5-1/4, 32 pgs, paper cover, B&W)

nn - By Satterfield (scarce) 50.00 150.00 300.00
NOTE: *1928 Presidential Campaign giveaway. Original material, contents completely different from Picture Life of a Great American.*

PICTURE LIFE OF A GREAT AMERICAN (see Pictorial History of the Department of Commerce under Herbert Hoover) (O)
Hoover-Curtis Campaign Committee of New York State: no date, 1928 (paper cover, B&W)

nn - (8-3/4 x 7, 20 pgs) Text cover, 2 page text introduction, 18 pgs of comics (scarcer first print) 43.00 129.00 260.00
nn - (9 x 6-3/4,24 pgs) Illustrated cover,5 page text introduction, 18 pgs of comics (scarce) 43.00 129.00 260.00
NOTE: *1928 Presidential Campaign giveaway. Unknown which above version was published first. Both contain the same original comics material by Satterfield.*

PINK LAFFIN (I)
Whitman Publishing Co.: 1922 (9x12")(Strip-r; some of these actually text joke books)

...the Lighter Side of Life, ...He Tells 'Em, ...and His Family, ...Knockouts; Ray Gleason-a (All rare) each... 26.00 104.00 200.00

POLLY (AND HER PALS) - (N)
Newspaper Feature Service: 1916 (3x2-1/2", color)

Altogether: Three Rahs and a Tiger! by Cliff Sterrett 35.00 75.00 150.00

GD2.0 FN6.0 VF8.0

There Is A Limit To Pa's Patience by Cliff Sterrett 35.00 75.00 150.00
Pa's Lil Book Has Some Uncut Pages by Sterrett 35.00 75.00 150.00
NOTE: *Single newsprint sheet printed in full color on both sides, unfolds to show 12 panel story.*

POPEYE PAINT BOOK (N)
McLaughlin Bros, Inc., Springfield, Mass.: 1932 (9-7/8x13", 28 pgs, color-c)

2052 - By E. C. Segar 90.00 300.00 650.00
NOTE: *Contains a full color panel above and the exact same art in below panel n B&W which one was to color in; strip-r panels.*

POPEYE CARTOON BOOK (N)
The Saalfield Co.: 1934 (8-1/2x13", 40 pgs, cardboard-c)

2095-(scarce)-1933 strip reprints in color by Segar. Each page contains a vertical half of a Sunday strip, so the continuity reads row by row completely across each double page spread. If each page is read by itself, the continuity makes no sense. Each double page spread reprints one complete Sunday page from 1933 350.00 1000.00 2900.00
12 Page Version 125.00 350.00 1100.00

POPEYE (See **Thimble Theatre** for earlier Popeye-r from Sonnett) (N)
David McKay Publications: 1935 (25¢; 52 pgs, B&W) (By Segar)

1-Daily strip reprints- "The Gold Mine Thieves" 200.00 400.00 900.00
2-Daily strip-r (scarce) 200.00 400.00 1000.00
NOTE: *Ties with Henry & Little Annie Rooney (David McKay) as the last of the 10x10" size books.*

PORE LI'L MOSE (N)
New York Herald Publ. by Grand Union Tea
Cupples & Leon Co.: 1902 (10-1/2x15", 78 pgs., color)

nn - By R. F. Outcault; Earliest known C&L comic book (scarce in high grade - very high demand) 1200.00 4000.00 –
NOTE: *Black Americana one page newspaper strips; falls in between Yellow Kid & Buster Brown. Complete copies have become scarce. Some have cut this book apart thinking that reselling individual pages will bring them more money.*

PRETTY PICTURES (M)
Farrar & Rinehart: 1931 (12 x 8-7/8", 104 pgs, color hardcover w/dust jacket, B&W; reprints from New Yorker, Judge, Life, Collier's Weekly)

nn - By Otto Soglow (contains "The Little King") 33.00 134.00 245.00

QUAINT OLD NEW ENGLAND (S)
Triton Syndicate: 1936 (5-1/4x6-1/4", 100 pgs, soft-c squarebound, B&W)

nn - By Jack Withycomb 36.00 144.00 250.00
NOTE: *Comics about weird doings in Old New England.*

RED CARTOONS (S)
Daily Worker Publishing Company: 1926 (12 x 9", 68 pgs,cardboard cover, B&W)

nn - By Various (scarce) 40.00 160.00 280.00
NOTE: *Reprint of American Communist Party editorial cartoons, from The Daily Worker, The Workers Monthly, and the Liberator. Art by Fred Ellis, William Gropper, Clive Weed, Art Young.*

REG'LAR FELLERS (See All-American Comics, Jimmie Dugan & The..., Popular Comics & Treasure Box of Famous Comics) (N)
Cupples & Leon Co./MS Publishing Co.: 1921-1929

1 (1921)-52 pgs. B&W dailies (Cupples & Leon, 10x10") 43.00 171.00 325.00
1925, 48 pgs. B&W dailies (MS Publ.) 39.00 157.00 300.00
Hardcover (1929, 8-3/4x7-1/2"; 96 pgs.)-B&W-r 54.00 214.00 400.00

REG'LAR FELLERS STORY PAINT BOOK
Whitman, Racine, Wisc.: 1932 (8-3/4x12-1/8", 132 pgs, red soft-c)

By Gene Byrnes 25.00 75.00 150.00

ROGER BEAN, R. G. (Regular Guy) (N)
The Indiana News Co, Distributers.: 1915 - No. 2, 1915 (5-3/8x17", 68 pgs., B&W, hardcovers); #3-#5 published by **Chas. B. Jackson:** 1916-1919
(No. 1 2 4 & 5 bound on side, No. 3 bound at top)

1-By Chas B. Jackson (68pgs.)(Scarce) 60.00 210.00 375.00
2- 5-5/8x17-1/8", 66 pgs (says 1913 inside - an obvious printing error) (red or green binding) 60.00 210.00 375.00
3-Along the Firing Line... (1916; 68 pgs, 6x17") 60.00 210.00 375.00
3-Along the Firing Line side-bound version 60.00 210.00 375.00
4-Into the Trenches and Out Again with... (1917, 68 pgs) 60.00 210.00 375.00
5 ...And The Reconstruction Period (1919, 5-3/8x15-1/2", 84 pgs) (Scarce) (has $1 printed on cover) 60.00 210.00 375.00
Baby Grand Editions 1-5 (10x10", cardboard-c) 60.00 210.00 375.00
NOTE: *No. 1 & 2 of the Twin Baby Grands (nd) 8-1/4x10-7/8", 52 pgs. #3 & #4 9x10-7/8" Cardboard cover. B&W strip reprints. Cover also says "Politics Pickles People Police."*
nn - 9x11, 68 pgs 60.00 210.00 375.00
NOTE: Has picture of Chic Jackson and a posthumous dedication from his three children. strip-r 1931-32

ROGER BEAN PHILOSOPHER
Schnull & Co: 1917 (5-1/2x17", 36 pgs., B&W, brown & black paper-c, square binding)

nn - By Chic Jackson (no known sales)

ROOKIE FROM THE 13TH SQUAD, THAT (N) (also Between Shots; Always Belittlin';Skippy)
Harper & Brothers Publishers: Feb. 1918 (8x9-1/4", 72 pgs, hardcover, B&W)

nn - By Lieut. P(ercy) L. Crosby 75.00 225.00 400.00
NOTE: *Strip began in 1917 at an Army base during basic training.*

Seaman Si
© Pierce Publ. Co.

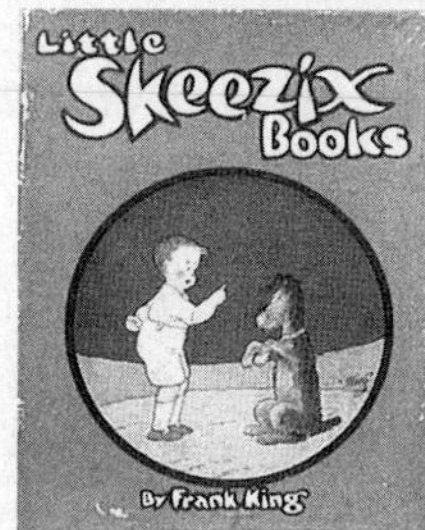

Little Skeezix Books by Frank King
1929 © Reilly & Lee

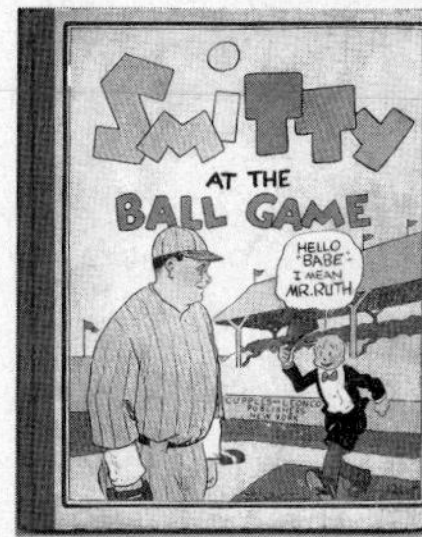

Smitty #2 By Walter Berndt
1929 © Cupples & Leon

GD2.0 FN6.0 VF8.0

ROUND THE WORLD WITH THE DOO-DADS (see Doings of the Doo-Dads, Doo Dads)
Universal Feature And Specialty Co, Chicago: 1922 (12x10-1/2", 52 pgs, B&W, red & light blue-c, square binding)

nn - By Arch Dale newspaper strip-r 43.00 173.00 300.00
NOTE: *Intermixed single panel and sequential comic strips with scenes from Scotland, Ireland, England, Holland, Italy, Spain, Egypt, Africa, and Lions & Elephants along the Nile River, China, Australia & back home.*

RUBAIYKT OF THE EGG
The John C Winston Co, Philadelphia: 1905 (7x5/12", 64 pgs, purple-c, B&W)

nn - By Clare Victor Dwiggins 35.00 75.00 160.00
NOTE: *Book is printed & cut into the shape of an egg.*

RULING CLAWSS, THE (N,S)
The Daily Worker: 1935 (192 pgs, 10-1/4 x 7-3/8", hard-c, B&W)

nn - By Redfield 60.00 240.00 –
NOTE: *Reprints cartoons from the American Communist Party newspaper The Daily Worker.*

SAGARA'S ENGLISH CARTOONS AND CARTOON STORIES (N)
Bunkosha, Tokyo: nd (c1925) (6-5/8" x 4-1/4", 272 pgs, hard-c, B&W)

nn- (Scarce) – – –
NOTE: *Published in Tokyo, Japan, with all strips in both English and Japanese, to facilitate learning English. Majority of book is Bringing Up Father by George McManus. Also contains Japanese strip Father Takes it Easy, by T. Sagara, reprinted from the Kokusai News Agency.*

SAM AND HIS LAUGH (N)
Frederick A. Stokes: 1906 (10x15", cardboard-c, Sunday strip-r in color)

nn - By Jimmy Swinnerton (Extremely Rare) 800.00 1400.00 3200.00
NOTE: *Strip ran July 24, 1904-Dec 26 1906; its ethnic humor might be considered racist by today's standards.*

SCHOOL DAYS (N)
Harper & Bros.: 1919 (9x8", 104 pgs.)

nn - By Clare Victor Dwiggins 75.00 150.00 300.00

SEAMAN SI - A Book of Cartoons About the Funniest "Gob" in the Navy (N)
Pierce Publishing Co.: 1916 (4x8-1/2, 200 pgs, hardcover, B&W); 1918 (4-1/8x8-1/4, 104 pgs, hardcover, B&W)

nn - By Perce Pearce (1916) 50.00 150.00 300.00
nn - 1918 - (Reilly & Britton Co.) 30.00 125.00 200.00
NOTE: *There exists two different covers for the 1918 reprints. The earlier edition was self published by the artist. The newspaper strip is sometimes also known as "The American Sailor."*

SECRET AGENT X-9 (N)
David McKay Pbll.: 1934 (Book 1: 84 pgs; Book 2: 124 pgs.) (8x7-1/2")

Book 1-Contains reprints of the first 13 weeks of the strip by Dashiell Hammett & Alex Raymond, complete except for 2 dailies 100.00 300.00 650.00
Book 2-Contains reprints immediately following contents of Book 1, for 20 weeks by Dashiell Hammett & Alex Raymond; complete except for two dailies. Last 5 strips misdated from 6/34, continuity correct 100.00 300.00 650.00

SILK HAT HARRY'S DIVORCE SUIT (N)
M. A. Donoghue & Co.: 1912 (5-3/4x15-1/2", oblong, B&W)

nn - Newspaper-r by Tad (Thomas A. Dorgan) 33.00 117.00 450.00

SINBAD A DOG'S LIFE (M)
Coward - McCann, Inc.: 1930 (11x 8-3/4", 104 pgs., single-sided, illustrated hard-c, B&W

nn - By Edwina 11.00 33.00 110.00
Sinbad...Again (1932, 10-15/16x 8-9/16", 104 pgs.) 11.00 33.00 110.00
NOTE: *Wordless comic strips from LIFE.*

SIS HOPKINS OWN BOOK AND MAGAZINE OF FUN
Leslie-Judge Co.: 1899-July 1911 (36 pgs, color-c, B&W) (merged into Judge's Library, later titled Film Fun)

any issue - By various 11.00 33.00 100.00
NOTE: *Zim, Flagg, Young, Newell, Adams, etc.*

SKEEZIX (Also see Gasoline Alley & Little Skeezix Books listed below) (I)
Reilly & Lee Co.: 1925 - 1928 (Strip-r, soft covers) (pictures & text)

...and Uncle Walt (1924)-Origin 26.00 104.00 225.00
...and Pal (1925), ...at the Circus (1926) 21.00 84.00 180.00
...& Uncle Walt (1927) (does this actually exist? reprint? never seen one yet)
...Out West (1928) 30.00 100.00 225.00
Hardback Editions... 34.00 136.00 245.00

SKEEZIX BOOKS, LITTLE (Also see Skeezix, Gasoline Alley) (G)
Reilly & Lee Co.: No date (1928, 1929) (Boxed set of three Skeezix books)

nn - Box with 3 issues of Skeezix. Skeezix & Pal, Skeezix at the Circus, Skeezix & Uncle Walt known. 1928 Set... 60.00 180.00 360.00
nn - Box with 4 issues of (3) above Skeezix plus "Out West" 80.00 330.00 550.00

SKEEZIX COLOR BOOK (N)
McLaughlin Bros. Inc, Springfield, Mass: 1929 (9-1/2x10-1/4", 28 pgs, one third in full color, rest in B&W)

2023 - By Frank King; strip-r to color 20.00 75.00 150.00

SKIPPY (see also Life Presents Skippy, Always Belittlin', That Rookie From 13th Squad)
No publisher listed: Circa 1920s (10x8", 16 pgs., color/B&W cartoons)

nn - By Percy Crosby 20.00 84.00 160.00

SKIPPY, LIFE PRESENTS (M)
Life Publishing Company & Henry Holt, NY: nd 1924 (134 pgs, 10-13/16x8-3/4", color hard-c, B&W

nn - By Percy L Crosby 100.00 300.00 550.00
NOTE: *Many sequential & single panel reprints from Skippy's earliest appearances in Life Magazine.*

SKIPPY
Greenberg, Publisher, Inc, NY: 1925. (11-14x8-5/8, 72 pgs, hard-c, B&W and color

nn - By Percy L. Crosby 50.00 150.00 300.00

NOTE: *Some but not all of these comics were also in Life Presents Skippy; issued with dust wrapper.*

SKIPPY AND OTHER HUMOR
Greenberg: Publisher, NY: 1929 (11-1/4x8-1/2",72 pgs,tan hard-c, B&W and color)

nn - By Percy L. Crosby 25.00 75.00 160.00
NOTE: *Came with a dust jacket.*

SKIPPY (I)
Grossett & Dunlap: 1929 (7-3/8x6, 370 pgs, hardcover text with some art)

nn - By Percy Crosby (issued with a dust jacket) 23.00 92.00 190.00
NOTE: *This is worth very little without the dust wrapper; very common without athe dust jacket.*

SKIPPY
Greenberg Press: 1930 (soft cover, ca. 16 pp.,

nn - By Percy Crosby (scarce) 50.00 175.00 300.00
NOTE: *Reprints from LIFE cartoons, color, b/w. Crosby told Greenberg to withdraw from the market as it cheapened the hard cover prior editions. Greenberg then stopped publishing per agreement, and sent Crosby all the copper & zinc bookplates, which were in Crosby estate until 1996.*

SKIPPY CRAYON AND COLORING BOOK (N)
McLoughlin Bros, Inc., Springfield, MA: 1931 (13x9-3/4", 28 pgs, color-c, color & B&W)

2050 - By Percy Crosby 30.00 90.00 200.00
NOTE: *This item says on the front cover: "Licensed by Percy Crosby" because he owned his creation. About half the pages have one panel pre-printed in full color with same one b&w below for person to copy the colors.*

SKIPPY RAMBLES (I)
G.P. Putnam's Sons: 1932 (7 1/8 x 5 1/8, 202 pgs)

nn - By Percy Crosby 25.00 84.00 160.00
NOTE: *Issued with a dustjacket. Has Skippy plates by Crosby every 4 or 5 pages.*

SKUDDABUD STARRY STORY SERIES - FOLK FROM THE FUTURE (O,G)
no publisher listed: 1936 (9" x 11-7/8", 48 pgs, cardboard-c, B&W)

Book One (Rare) "Parachuting" 21.00 84.00 160.00
NOTE: *By Columba Krebs. Top half of each page is a continuing strip story, while bottom half are different stories, in prose, about the same characters -- a race of aliens who have migrated to Earth, from their dying world.*

S'MATTER POP? (N)
Saalfield Publ. Co.: 1917 (10x14", 44 pgs., B&W, cardboard-c,)

nn - By Charlie Payne; in full color; pages printed on one side 48.00 169.00 300.00

S'MATTER POP? (N) (25 ¢ cover price)
E.I. Company, New York: 1927 (8-15/16x7-1/8", 52 pgs, yellow soft-c perfect bound

nn - By C.M. Payne (scarce) 24.00 84.00 150.00
NOTE: *First comic book published by Hugo Gernsback, noted for inventing Amazing Stories among other memorable science fiction pulps. The World Science Fiction Convention Award, The Hugo, is named for him.*

SMITTY (See Treasure Box of Famous Comics) (N)
Cupples & Leon Co.: 1928 - 1933 (9x7", 96 pgs., B&W strip-r, hardcover)

1928-(96 pgs. 7x8-3/4") By Walter Berndt 50.00 185.00 350.00
1929-At the Ball Game (Babe Ruth on cover) 60.00 235.00 500.00
1930-The Flying Office Boy, 1931-The Jockey, 1932-In the North Woods each... 45.00 150.00 300.00
1933-At Military School 45.00 150.00 300.00
NOTE: *Each hardbound was published with a dust jacket; worth 50% more with dust jacket. The 1929 edition is very popular with baseball collectors. Strip debuted Nov 27, 1922.*

SMOKEY STOVER (See Dan Dunn & King of the Royal Mounted) (N)
Whitman Publishing: 1937 (5 1/2 x 7 1/4", 68pgs., color cardboard-c, B&W)

1010 36.00 150.00 300.00

SOCIAL COMEDY (M)
Life Publishing Company: 1902 (11-3/4 x 9-1/2", 128 pgs, B&W, illustrated hardcover)

nn - Artists include C.D. Gibson & Kemble. 25.00 75.00 150.00
NOTE: *Reprints cartoons and a few sequential comics from LIFE. Came in unmarked slipcase.*

SOCIAL HELL, THE (O)
Rich Hill: 1902

nn - By Ryan Walker 25.00 75.00 150.00
NOTE: *"The conditions of workers and the corruption of a political system beholden to corporate interests have been a major focus of human rights concerns since the 19th century. This early graphic novel depicts the social evils of unreformed capitalism. Ryan Walker was a syndicate cartoonist for many mainstream newspapers as well as for the communist Daily Worker." This description comes from http://www.lib.uconn.edu/DoddCenter/ascexh3.html, where you can find also a reproduction of the cover. I add that Ryan Walker was the editor of "The Saint Louis Republic" comic section since its inception in 1897; the supplement published "Alma and Oliver", George McManus's first series.*

SPORT AND THE KID (see The Umbrella Man) (N)

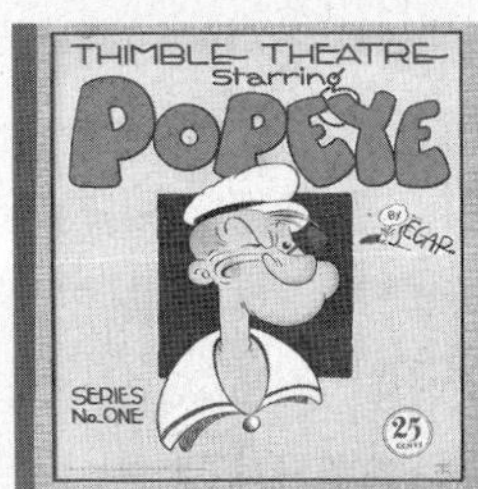

Thimble Theater #1 by E.C. Segar
1931 © Sonnet Publishing Co.

Tillie the Toiler #7 by Russ Westover
1932 © Cupples & Leon

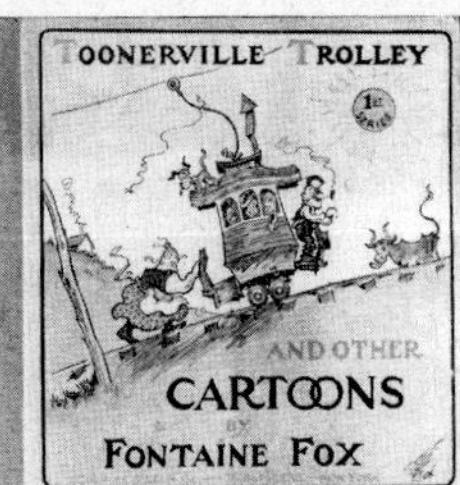

Toonerville Trolley And Other Cartoons
1921 © Cupples & Leon

GD2.0 FN6.0 VF8.0

Lowman & Hanford Co.: 1913 (6-1/4x6-5/8",114 pgs, hardcover, B&W&orange)
nn - By J.R. "Dok" Hager 20.00 70.00 150.00

STORY OF CONNECTICUT (N)
The Hartford Times: Vol.1 1935 - Vol.3 1936 (10-1/2" x 7-3/8",304 pgs,color hard-c, B&W)
Vol.1 - 3 20.00 70.00 150.00
NOTE: *Collects a newspaper strip on Connecticut State history, which ran in the Hartford Times. Strip is in a similar format to "Texas History Movies". Also published in a plain, blue hardcover.*

STORY OF JAPAN IN CHINA, THE (N,S)
Trans-Pacific News Service, NYC: Vol. 3, No.1 March 10, 1938 (9" x 6", 36 pgs, construction paper-c, B&W)
Vol.3 No.1 21.00 64.00 150.00
NOTE: *Part of the "China Reference Series" of booklets, detailing the Japanese occupation and brutalization of China. Consists entirely of cartoons. The other booklets in the series have no cartoons. Art by: Ding, Fitzpatrick, Herblock, Herman, Rollin Kirby, Knox, Low, Manning, Orr, Shoemaker, Talburt.*

STRANGE AS IT SEEMS (S)
Blue-Star Publishing Co.: 1932 (64 pgs., B&W, square binding)
1-Newspaper-r (*Published with & without No. 1 and price on cover.*) 32.00 128.00 200.00
Ex-Lax giveaway (1936, B&W, 24 pgs., 5x7") - McNaught Synd.
20.00 55.00 110.00

SULLIVANT'S ABC ZOO (I)
The Old Wine Press: 1946 (11-3/4x9-3/8", hardcover)
nn - By T.S. Sullivant (Rare) – – –
NOTE: *Reprints Mitchell & Miller material 1895-1898 and Life Publishing 1898-1926.*

TAILSPIN TOMMY STORY & PICTURE BOOK (N)
McLoughlin Bros.: No. 266, 1931? (nd) (10x10-1/2", color strip-r)
266 - By Forrest 43.00 172.00 300.00

TAILSPIN TOMMY (Also see Famous Feature Stories & The Funnies)(N)
Cupples & Leon Co.: 1932 (100 pgs., hard-c) (B&W 1930 strip reprints)
nn - (Scarce)- by Hal Forrest & Glenn Chaffin 50.00 150.00 400.00

TALES OF DEMON DICK AND BUNKER BILL (O)
Whitman Publishing Co.: 1934 (5-1/4x10-1/2", 80 pgs, color hardcover, B&W)
793 - By Spencer 33.00 100.00 300.00

TARZAN BOOK (The Illustrated...) (N)
Grosset & Dunlap: 1929 (9x7", 80 pgs.)
1(Rare)-Contains 1st B&W Tarzan newspaper comics from 1929. By Hal Foster Cloth reinforced spine & dust jacket (50¢); Foster-c
With dust jacket... 100.00 350.00 630.00
Without dust jacket... 55.00 200.00 325.00
2nd Printing(1934, 25¢, 76 pgs.)-4 Foster pgs. dropped; paper spine, circle in lower right cover with 25¢ price. The 25¢ is barely visible on some copies
40.00 145.00 250.00
1967-House of Greystoke reprint-7x10", using the complete 300 illustrations/text from the 1929 edition minus the original indicia, foreword, etc. Initial version bound in gold paper & sold for $5.00. Officially titled **Burroughs Bibliophile #2**. A very few additional copies were bound in heavier blue paper. Gold binding... 2.25 6.75 20.00
Blue binding... 2.50 7.50 27.00

TARZAN OF THE APES TO COLOR (N)
Saalfield Publishing Co.: No. 988, 1933 (15-1/4x10-3/4", 24 pgs) (Coloring book)
988-(Very Rare)-Contains 1929 daily reprints with some new art by Hal Foster. Two panels blown up large on each page with one at the top of opposing pages on every other double-page spread. Believed to be the only time these panels appeared in color. Most color panels are reproduced a second time in B&W to be colored
275.00 1100.00 2200.00

TARZAN OF THE APES The Big Little Cartoon Book (N)
Whitman Publishing Company: 1933 (4-1/2x3 5/8", 320 pgs, color-c, B&W)
744 - By Hal Foster (comic strips on every page) 60.00 175.00 350.00

TECK HASKINS AT OHIO STATE (S)
Lea-Mar Press: 1908 (7-1/4x5-3/8", 84 pgs, B&W hardcover)
nn - By W.A. Ireland; football cartoons-r from Columbus Ohio Evening Dispatch
30.00 100.00 180.00
NOTE: *Small blue & white patch of cover art pasted atop a color cloth quilt patter; pasted patch can easily peel off some copies.*

TECK 1909 (S)
Lea-Mar Press: 1909 (8-5/8 x 8-1/8", 124 pgs., B&W hardcover, 25¢)
nn - By W.A. Ireland; Ohio State University baseball cartoons-r from Columbus Evening Dispatch 30.00 100.00 180.00

TEDDY BEAR BOOKS, THE (M) (see also LITTLE JOHNNY AND THE TEDDY BEARS)
Reilly & Britton Co., Chicago: 1907 (7-1/16" x 5-3/8", 24 pgs, hard-c, color
The Teddy Bears Come to Life, The Teddy Bears at the Circus, The Teddy Bears in a Smashup, The Teddy Bears on a Lark, The Teddy Bears on a Toboggan, The Teddy Bears at School, The Teddy Bears Go Fishing, The Teddy Bears in Hot Water
25.00 75.00 150.00
NOTE: *Books are all unnumbered. C & A by J.R. Bray; s-Robert D. Towne. Reprints "Little Johnny & the Teddy Bears" strips, from Judge Magazine. Similar in format to the Buster Brown Nuggets series. All eight books debuted simultaneously.*

TEDDY BEARS IN FUN AND FROLIC (M) (see LITTLE JOHNNY & THE TEDDY BEARS)
Reilly & Britton Co., Chicago: 1908 (8-3/4" x 8-3/4", 50 pgs, cardboard-c, color)
nn - (Rare) by J.R. Bray-a; Robert D. Towne-s 100.00 400.00 725.00
NOTE: *Reprints "Little Johnny & the Teddy Bears" strips, from Judge Magazine. Unknown if there were any other "Teddy Bear" titles published in this format.*

THE TEENIE WEENIES
Reilly & Britton, Chicago: 1916 (16-3/8x10-1/2", 52 pgs, cardboard-c, full color)
nn - By Wm. Donahey (Chicago Tribune-r) 200.00 550.00 1000.00

TERROR OF THE TINY TADS (see also UPSIDE DOWNS OF LITTLE LADY LOVEKINS AND OLD MAN MUFFAROO)
Cupples & Leon: 1909 (11x17, 26 Sunday strips in Black & Red, Stiff cardboard-c)
nn - By Gustave Verbeek (Very Rare) (no known sales)

TEXAS HISTORY MOVIES (N)
Various editions, 1928 to 1986 (B&W)
Book I -1928 Southwest Press (7-1/4 x 5-3/8, 56 pgs, cardboard cover) for the Magnolia Petroleum Company 50.00 125.00 275.00
nn - 1928 Southwest Press (12-3/8 x 9-1/4, 232 pgs, HC) 75.00 200.00 400.00
nn - 1935 Magnolia Petroleum Company (6 x 9, 132 pgs, paper cover)
21.00 63.00 140.00
NOTE: *Exists with either Wagon Train or Texas Flag & Lafitte/pirate covers.*
nn - 1943 Magnolia Petroleum Company (132 pgs, paper cover)
25.00 55.00 120.00
nn - 1963 Graphic Ideas Inc (11 x 8-1/2, softcover) 12.00 37.00 75.00
NOTE: *Reprints daily newspaper strips from the Dallas News, on Texas history. 1935 editions onward distributed within the Texas Public School System. Prior to that they appear to be giveaway comic books for the Magnolia Petroleum Company. There are many more editions than the ones pointed out above.*

THAT SON-IN-LAW OF PA'S! (N)
Newspaper Feature Service: 1914 (2-1/2 by 3", color)
nn - *Imprinted on back for THE LESTER SHOE STORE.* 15.00 30.00 60.00
NOTE: *Single sheet printed in full color on both sides, unfolds to show 12 panel story.*

THIMBLE THEATRE STARRING POPEYE (See also Popeye) (N)
Sonnet Publishing Co.: 1931 - No. 2, 1932 (25¢, B&W, 52 pgs.)(Rare)
1-Daily strip serial-r in both by Segar 165.00 700.00 1500.00
2 140.00 600.00 1200.00
NOTE: *The very first Popeye reprint book. The first Thimble Theatre Sunday page appeared Dec 19, 1919. Popeye first entered Thimble Theatre on Jan 17, 1929.*

THREE FUN MAKERS, THE (N)
Stokes and Company: 1908 (10x15", 64 pgs., color) (1904-06 Sunday strip-r)
nn - Maud, Katzenjammer Kids, Happy Hooligan 800.00 2100.00 –
NOTE: *This is the first comic book to compile more than one newspaper strip together.*

TIGERS (Also see On and Off Mount Ararat) (N)
Hearst's New York American & Journal: 1902, 86 pgs. 10x15-1/4"
nn - Funny animal strip-r by Jimmy Swinnerton 600.00 1700.00 –
NOTE: *The strip began as The Journal Tigers in The New York Journal Dec 12, 1897-Sept 28 1903*

TILLIE THE TOILER (N)
Cupples & Leon Co.: 1925 - No. 8, 1933 (52 pgs., B&W, daily strip-r)
nn (#1) By Russ Westover 54.00 216.00 425.00
2-8 50.00 175.00 360.00
NOTE: *First newspaper strip appearance was in January, 1921.*

TILLIE THE TOILER MAGIC DRAWING AND COLORING BOOK
Sam L Gabriel Sons And Company: 1931 (8-1/2 x 12", 36 pages, stiff-c)
838-By Russ Westover 39.00 156.00 275.00

TIMID SOUL, THE (N)
Simon & Schuster: 1931 (12-1/4x9", 136 pgs, B&W hardcover, dust jacket?)
nn - By H. T. Webster (newspaper strip-r) 40.00 120.00 260.00

TIM McCOY, POLICE CAR 17 (O)
Whitman Publishing Co.: 1934 (14-3/4x11", 32 pgs, stiff color covers)
674-1933 original material 75.00 300.00 475.00
NOTE: *Historically important as first movie adaptation in comic books.*

TOAST BOOK
John C. Winston Co: 1905 (7-1/4 x 6,104 pgs, skull-shaped book, feltcover, B&W)
nn - By Clare Dwiggins 50.00 175.00 300.00
NOTE: *Cartoon illustrations accompanying toasts/poems, most involving alcohol.*

TOM SAWYER & HUCK FINN (N)
Stoll & Edwards Co.:1925 (10x10-3/4", 52 pgs, stiff covers)
nn - By "Dwig" Dwiggins; 1923, 1924-r color Sunday strips 50.00 200.00 350.00
NOTE: *By Permission of the Estate of Samuel L. Clemons and the Mark Twain Company.*

TOONERVILLE TROLLEY AND OTHER CARTOONS (N) (See Cartoons by Fontaine Fox)
Cupples & Leon Co.: 1921 (10 x10", 52 pgs., B&W, daily strip-r)
1 - By Fontaine Fox 75.00 300.00 600.00

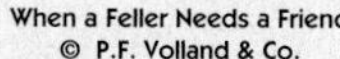
When a Feller Needs a Friend
© P.F. Volland & Co.

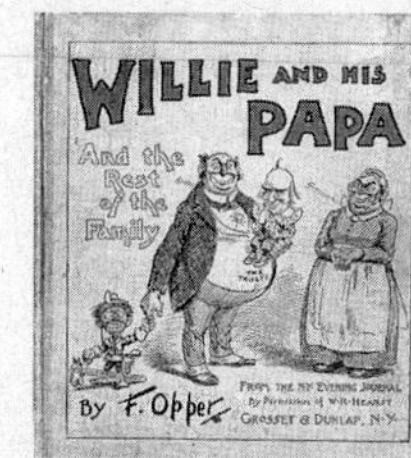

Willie and His Papa & the Rest of the Family by Opper
1901 © Grossett & Dunlap

The Yellow Kid #4 cover by Outcault
1897 © Howard, Ainslee & Co.

GD2.0 FN6.0 VF8.0

TRAINING FOR THE TRENCHES (M)
Palmer Publishing Company: 1917 (5-3/8 x 7", 20 pgs., paper-c, 10¢)

nn - By Lieut. Alban B. Butler, Jr. 21.00 84.00 150.00
NOTE: *Subtitle: "A book of humorous cartoons on a serious subject." Single-panels about military training.*

TREASURE BOX OF FAMOUS COMICS (N) (see Wonder Chest of Famous Comics)
Cupples & Leon Co.: 1934 8-1/2x(6-7/8", 36 pgs, soft covers) (Boxed set of 5 books)

Little Orphan Annie (1926) 21.00 84.00 180.00
Reg'lar Fellers (1928) 19.00 76.00 160.00
Smitty (1928) 19.00 76.00 160.00
Harold Teen (1931) 19.00 76.00 160.00
How Dick Tracy & Dick Tracy Jr. Caught The Racketeers (1933) 26.00 104.00 225.00
Softcover set of five books in box 160.00 640.00 1500.00
Box only 57.00 228.00 500.00
NOTE: *Dates shown are copyright dates; all books actually came out in 1934 or later. The softcovers are abbreviated versions of the hardcover editions listed under each character.*

T.R. IN CARTOONS (N)
A.C. McClurg & Co., Chicago: June 13, 1910 (10-5/8" x 8", 104? pgs, paper-c, B&W)

nn - By McCutcheon about Teddy Roosevelt - - -

TRUTH (See Victorian section for earlier issues including the first Yellow Kid appearances)
Truth Company, NY: 1886-1906? (13-11/16x10-5/16", 16 pgs, process color-c & center-folds, rest B&W)

1900-1906 issues 25.00 50.00 100.00

TRUTH SAVE IT FROM ABUSE & OVERWORK BEING THE EPISODE OF THE HIRED HAND & MRS. STIX PLASTER, CONCERTIST (N)
Radio Truth Society of WBAP: no date, 1924 (6-3/8 x 4-7/8, 40 pgs, paper cover, B&W)

nn - By V.T. Hamlin (Very Rare) 100.00 400.00 725.00
NOTE: *Radio station WBAP giveaway reprints strips from the Ft. Worth Texas Star-Telegram set at local radio station. 1st collected work by V.T. Hamlin, pre-Alley Oop.*

TWENTY FIVE YEARS AGO (see At The Bottom Of The Ladder) (M,S)
Coward-McCann: 1931 (5-3/4x8-1/4, 328 pgs, hardcover, B&W)

nn - By Camillus Kessler 32.00 128.00 250.00
NOTE: *Multi-image panel cartoons showing historical events for dates during the year.*

UMBRELLA MAN, THE (N) (See Sport And The Kid)
Lowman & Hanford Co.: 1911 (8-7/8x5-7/8",112 pgs, hard-c, B&W & orange)

nn - By J.R. "Dok" Hager (Seattle Times-r) 20.00 70.00 125.00

UNCLE REMUS AND BRER RABBIT (N)
Frederick A. Stokes Co.: 1907 (64 pgs, hardbound, color)

nn - By Joel C Harris & J.M. Conde 75.00 200.00 325.00

UPSIDE DOWNS OF LITTLE LADY LOVEKINS AND OLD MAN MUFFAROO
(see also TERROR OF THE TINY TADS)
New York Herald: 1905 (?) (N)

nn - By Gustav Verbeck 150.00 450.00 800.00

VAUDEVILLES AND OTHER THINGS (N)
Isaac H. Blandiard Co.: 1900 (13x10-1/2", 22 pgs., color) plus two reprints

nn - By Bunny (Scarce) 400.00 1000.00 -
nn - 2nd print "By the Creator of Foxy Grandpa" on-c but only has copyright info of 1900 (10-1/2x15 1/2, 28 pgs, color) 450.00 850.00 -
nn - 3rd print. "By the creator of Foxy Grandpa" on-c; has both 1900 and 1901 copyright info (11x13") 350.00 650.00 -

WALLY - HIS CARTOONS OF THE A.E.F. (N)
Stars & Stripes: 1917 (96 and 108 pgs, B&W)

nn - By Abian A "Wally" Wallgren (7x18; 96 pgs) 25.00 75.00 150.00
nn - another edition (108 pgs, 7x17-1/2) 25.00 75.00 150.00
NOTE: *World War One cartoons reprints from Stars & Stripes; sold to U.S. servicemen with profits to go to French War Orphans Fund. various editions from 1917-1920; there might be more than what we list here.*

WAR CARTOONS (S)
Dallas News: 1918 (11x9", 112 pgs, hardcover, B&W)

nn - By John Knott (WWOne cartoons) 20.00 70.00 130.00

WAR CARTOONS FROM THE CHICAGO DAILY NEWS (N,S)
Chicago Daily News: 1914 (10 cents, 7-3/4x10-3/4", 68 pgs, paper-c, B&W)

nn - By L.D. Bradley 20.00 70.00 130.00

WEBER & FIELD'S FUNNYISMS (S,M,O)
Arkell Comoany, NY: 1904 (10-7/8x8", 112 pgs, color-c, B&W)

1 - By various (only issue?) 20.00 70.00 150.00
NOTE: *Contains some sequential & many single panel strips by Outcault, George Luks, CA David, Houston, L Smith, Hy Mayer, Verbeck, Woolf, Sydney Adams, Frank "Chip" Bellew, Eugene "ZIM" Zimmerman, Phil May, FT Richards, Billy Marriner, Grosvenor and many others.*

WE'RE NOT HEROES (O,S)
E.C. Wells and J.W. Moss: 1933 (8-11/16" x 5-7/8", 52 pgs, B&W interior)

nn - By Eddie Wells; red & black paper-c 15.00 35.00 75.00
NOTE: *Amateurish cartoons about World War I vets in the Walter Reed Veteran's Hospital.*

WHEN A FELLER NEEDS A FRIEND (S)
P. F. Volland & Co.: 1914 (11-11/16x8-7/8)

nn - By Clare Briggs 37.00 131.00 220.00
NOTE: *Originally came in box with Briggs art (box is Rare); also numerous more modern reprints)*

WILD PILGRIMAGE (O)
Harrison Smith & Robert Haas: 1932 (9-7/8x7", 210 pgs, B&W hardcover w/dust jacket) (original wordless graphic novel in woodcuts)

nn - By Lynd Ward 50.00 175.00 300.00

WILLIE AND HIS PAPA AND THE REST OF THE FAMILY (I)
Grossett & Dunlap: 1901 (9-1/2x8", 200 pgs, hardcover from N.Y. Evening Journal by Permission of W. R. Hearst) (pictures & text)

nn - By Frederick Opper 100.00 260.00 400.00
NOTE: *Political satire series of single panel cartoons, involving whiny child Willie (President William McKinley), his rambunctious and uncontrollable cousin Teddy (Vice President Roosevelt), and Willie's Papa (trusts/monopolies) and their Maid (Senator) Hanna.*

WILLIE GREEN COMICS, THE (N) (see Adventures of Willie Green)
Frank M. Acton Co./Harris Brown: 1915 (8x15, 36 pgs); 1921 (6x10-1/8", 52 pgs, color paper cover, B&W interior, 25¢)

Book No. 1 By Harris Brown 45.00 158.00 300.00
Book 2 (#2 sold via mail order directly from the artist)(very rare) 45.00 172.00 325.00
NOTE: *Book No. 1 possible reprint of Adv. of Willie Green; definitely two different editions.*

WILLIE WESTINGHOUSE EDISON SMITH THE BOY INVENTOR (N)
William A. Stokes Co.: 1906 (10x16", 36 pgs. in color)

nn - By Frank Crane (Scarce) 375.00 900.00 1400.00
NOTE: *Comic strip began May 27, 1900 and ran thru 1914. Parody of inventors Westinghouse and Edison.*

WINNIE WINKLE (N)*Strip began as a daily Sept 20, 1920.*
Cupples & Leon Co.: 1930 - No. 4, 1933 (52 pgs., B&W daily strip-r)

1 40.00 160.00 360.00
2-4 25.00 110.00 300.00

WISDOM OF CHING CHOW, THE (see also The Gumps)
R. J. Jefferson Printing Co.: 1928 (4x3", 100 pgs, red & B&W cardboard cover) (newspaper strip-r The Chicago Tribune)

nn - By Sidney Smith (scarce) 30.00 90.00 150.00

WONDER CHEST OF FAMOUS COMICS (N) see Treasure Chest of Famous Comics)
Cupples & Leon Co.: 1935? 8-1/2x(6-7/8", 36 pgs, soft covers) (Boxed set of 5 books)

Little Orphan Annie #2 (1927) (Haunted House) 21.00 84.00 140.00
Little Orphan Annie #3 (1928) (in the Circus) 19.00 76.00 140.00
Smitty #2 (1929) (Babe Ruth app.) 19.00 76.00 140.00
Dolly Dimples and Bobby Bounce (1933) by Grace Drayton 19.00 76.00 140.00
How Dick Tracy & Dick Tracy Jr. Caught The Racketeers (1933) 26.00 104.00 200.00
Softcover set of five books in box 160.00 640.00 1250.00
Box only 57.00 228.00 425.00
NOTE: *Dates shown are original copyright dates of the first printings; all actually came out in 1934 or later. Extremely abbreviated versions of the hardcover editions listed under each character. It is suspected this came out the Christmas season following Treasure Chest of Famous Comics. which contains earlier editions.*

WORLD OF TROUBLE, A (S)
Minneapolis Journal: 1901 (10x8-3/4", 100 pgs, 40 pgs full color)

v3#1 - By Charles L. Bartholomew (editorial-r) 28.00 99.00 170.00

WRIGLEY'S "MOTHER GOOSE"
Wm. Wrigley Jr. Company, Chicago: 1915 (6" x 4", 28 pgs, full color)

nn - *Promotional comics for Wrigley's gum. Intro Wrigley's "Spearmen* 20.00 70.00 150.00
Book No. 2 20.00 70.00 150.00

YELLOW KID, THE (Magazine)(I) (becomes **The Yellow Book** #10 on)
Howard, Ainslee & Co., N.Y.: Mar. 20, 1897 - #9, July 17, 1897
(5¢, B&W w/color covers, 52p., stapled) (not a comic book)

1-R.F. Outcault Yellow kid on-c only #1-6. The same Yellow Kid color ad app. on back-c #1-6 (advertising the New York Sunday Journal) 900.00 3900.00 -
2-6 (#2 4/3/97, #5 5/22/97, #6, 6/5/97) 775.00 2950.00 -
7-9 (Yellow Kid not on-c) 145.00 500.00 -
NOTE: *Richard Outcault's Yellow Kid from the Hearst New York American represents the very first successful newspaper comic strip in America. Listed here due to historical importance.*

YELLOW KID IN MCFADDEN'S FLATS, THE (N)
G. W. Dillingham Co., New York: 1897 (50¢, 7-1/2x5-1/2", 196 pgs., B&W, squarebound)

nn - The first "comic" book featuring The Yellow Kid; E. W. Townsend narrative w/R. F. Outcault Sunday comic page art-r & some original drawings (Prices vary widely. Rare.) 7000.00 15,000.00 -
NOTE: *A Fair condition copy sold for $2,901 in August 2004.; restored app VF sold for $10,500 in 2005. A copy in Fine+ (spine intact) and loose back cover sold for $17,000 in 2006.*

YESTERDAYS (S)
The Reilly & Lee Co.: 1930 (8-3/4 x 7-1/2", 128 pgs, illustrated hard-c with dust jacket

nn - Text and cartoons about Victorian times by Frank Wing 25.00 50.00 100.00

Any addititions or corrections to this section are always welcome, very much encouraged and can be sent to **feedback@gemstonepub.com** to be processed for next year's Guide.

1968

The Marvel Age of Expansion

By Charles S. Novinskie

Limited by stifling policies by its distributor, Independent News, Marvel Comics used a variety of tactics to expand their ever-growing lineup of superheroes. The split book format, the likes of *Tales of Suspense* and *Tales to Astonish*, with bombastic stories featuring Captain America/Iron Man and Hulk/Sub-Mariner, respectively. *Strange Tales* featured the split adventures of Doctor Strange and Nick Fury, Agent of S.H.I.E.L.D. The ability to feature two characters under one title gave greater exposure to Marvel's superheroes while being limited to the number of books it published. The 1968 distribution deal that increased the number of titles Marvel could distribute monthly would have a dramatic effect on these titles – and much more so on the characters. Comic readers of that era were in for rapid increase in the number of titles, superhero and otherwise, that Marvel brought to the newsstand!

In 1968, Marvel was selling 50 million comic books a year, and company founder, Martin Goodman, was able to renegotiate his deal with Independent News, effectively allowing the company free reign as to the number of titles they published. Part of the push to expand was the desire to increase profitability in hopes of selling both Marvel Comics and Magazine Management. By late 1968, Goodman sold the companies to Perfect Film and Chemical Corporation, but remained on as publisher. In 1969, Goodman signed a new distribution deal, this time with Curtis Circulation Company.

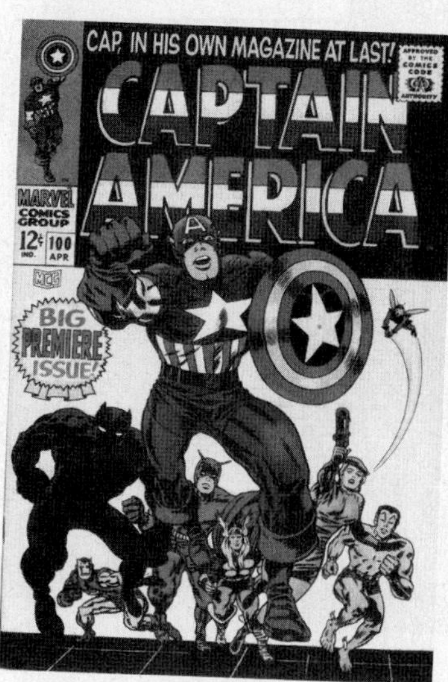

ATLAS CONNECTION

The origins of all three split books, *Tales of Suspense, Tales to Astonish*, and *Strange Tales* has its roots stretching back to the 1950s. Atlas titles featured classic tales by many of the greats; Krigstein, Crandall, Colan, Williamson, Ditko, Kirby, Everett, Heath, Davis and many more all developed stories that embodied the storytelling of that era. From science fiction to horror and everything in between, these titles slowly evolved into the split format books of the sixties.

Along the way, many prototype characters graced these stories, only to later be revived and refined to fit into the modern-day mythos. *Strange Tales* produced the prototypical characters for Quicksilver (#67), Magneto (#84), Fin Fang Foom (#89), and the Ancient One and Ant-Man (#92). Issue #97 even featured the first appearance of Aunt May and Uncle Ben, by Steve Ditko no less, before their appearance in *Amazing Fantasy* #15.

Tales of Suspense offered prototype appearances for the Lava Men (#7), Iron Man (#9)—before his origin in issue #39, The Stone Men, Doctor Doom, Watcher, and even Doctor Strange all had early prototype appearances ahead of their debut stories. *Tales To Astonish* featured early appearances of the Toad Men (#7), Groot (#13), and even a Hulk prototype (#21), before introducing Ant-Man to the world in issue #27.

DIVIDE AND CONQUER

During the course of 1968, no less than 13 #1 titles were added to the now rapidly expanding Marvel Universe. Many of those titles evolved from the aforementioned split books, taking the numbering with them. In April 1968, Captain America received a promotion with his first modern-age title all his own.

Captain America #100 featured a retelling of Cap's revival in the pages of *Avengers* #4 with artwork by Jack Kirby. The numbering rolled over from *Tales of Suspense* #99, thus ending the run on that title. Also in April, The Incredible Hulk made his debut with issue #102, back in his own series after a short-lived run of only six issues in 1962-1963. The numbering was a carry-over from the now-discontinued *Tales to Astonish*, which ended with issue #101. Also of note and published the same month is the hard to find *Iron Man and Sub-Mariner* #1. This one-shot title predates *Iron Man* #1 and *Sub-Mariner* #1 and continues tales begun in *Tales of Suspense* #99 and *Tales to Astonish* #101.

May started with a trio of new titles from the House of Ideas, with the *Invincible Iron Man* # 1 and *Sub-Mariner* #1 making their debut. Both characters were promoted to their own titles after a long run of split format stories. With artwork by the talented Gene Colan, Iron Man's inaugural solo tale continued the storyline from *Iron Man and Sub-Mariner* #1. The first issue of Namor's book also carried over from the same storyline.

A number of out-of-this-world titles made their debut as Marvel looked to expand into several genres. The first such launch was *Captain Marvel* #1, a title that has spawned numerous incarnations of the Kree superhero. The Kree captain's adventures were spun off his origin appearance in *Marvel Super-Heroes* #12, a 25 cent, 68-page book published in December 1967.

Captain Savage and His Leatherneck Raiders #1 started the lineup of new titles, premiering in January 1968. Lasting only 19 issues, the book hoped to emulate the success of *Sgt. Fury and His Howling Commandos*. The book was big on talent with great artists such as Dick Ayers, Syd Shores, John Severin, and Don Heck, but never gained an enthusiastic audience.

I SPY

One book to rise to prominence after a long run in *Strange Tales* was *Nick Fury, Agent of S.H.I.E.L.D.* Launched in June 1968, the spy-centric book, complete with espionage and great gadgets (such as a flying car), made this book the stand-out hit creatively. No other creator in modern time has spent such a short time in the medium while having such a lasting impact. Steranko's work on this title had all the over-the-top gadgets and artistry of an epic Kirby tale, but added a psychedelic, Salvador Dali style to his storytelling. Panel layouts were completely shattered, giving way to a style that used the blank page as a canvas for stories

that seemed to flow off the page. By today's standards, Steranko's artwork is rarely duplicated and has never been surpassed for its total, immersive experience. If Marvel's body of work in the sixties was the epitome of pop culture of that time, Steranko's Nick Fury was the benchmark that others aspired to.

THE NUMBERS GAME

While it was true that Marvel was now free to expand the number of titles in their growing stable of heroes, the sales figures weren't always favorable. Former editor in chief and writer for Marvel, Roy Thomas, recalls those chaotic days.

"I remember that the expansion was rapid with three anthology titles suddenly becoming six solo titles, plus a number of other titles to debut throughout that year," Thomas said. "I know that Stan [Lee] was enthusiastic about the expansion – he really liked the idea – although I'm sure the impetus for the expansion came from Martin Goodman. It was a great idea, but could have worked better. At the time comics began to lose sales over the coming years. Even titles like *Dr. Strange* and *S.H.I.E.L.D.* never sold very well, even with Steranko on the *S.H.I.E.L.D.* comic. Even *X-Men* failed at that time."

Thomas felt it was a shame because he felt that some of Marvel's best work came out of that era, with "Steranko on *S.H.I.E.L.D.*, Colan and myself on *Dr. Strange*, and of course my work with Neal Adams on *X-Men* – those titles didn't sell as well as what I felt were less inspired books in a number of cases." Eventually, numbers on *X-Men* did increase enough, leading to a run of reprints of early *X-Men* tales in that title.

THE B&W EXPERIMENT

Now that Marvel was well on their way to expanding their market share and giving readers what they wanted – more Marvel titles – they pulled out all the stops in July and gambled with a large format, black and white magazine. The hopes were that Marvel could capture a portion of the black-and-white magazine market that was popular with other publishers, such as Warren Publications. They even called in a familiar men's adventure magazine cover artist and painter, Harry Rosenbaum, to paint over layouts by John Romita, Sr.

THE SPECTACULAR SPIDER-MAN™
35c
40c IN CAN.
JULY
IND.

Thus was born the *Spectacular Spider-Man Magazine* #1, the first spinoff of the *Amazing Spider-Man* comic book. The 52-page, 35 cent experiment never had spectacular sales – maybe because of confusion as to where to rack the magazine-size title or it being too different for the times, and keeping in mind that regular sized comics were still selling for 12 cents at the time. Marvel did surge ahead with a second issue. This time, it featured a 58-page story in full color with the now-familiar Green Goblin as the adversary, and once again art by Romita and Mooney.

The appearance of these two issues of *Spectacular Spider-Man Magazine* in 1968 are of great significance as they served as the precursor to Marvel's black-and-white magazine explosion of the 1970s that launched titles like *Savage Sword of Conan*, *Deadly Hands of Kung Fu*, *Dracula Lives!*, *Tales of the Zombie*, *Marvel Preview*, *Savage Tales*, *Planet of the Apes*, and others that were later added to the lineup. The nature of the magazines allowed for more mature art and storytelling, outside the guidelines of the Comics Code Authority.

SOARING HIGH

August saw Norrin Radd take on the guise of the Herald of Galactus in *Silver Surfer* #1, in order to save his planet as well as the life of his beloved Shalla-Bal. Written by Stan Lee with art by John Buscema, the oversize, 25-cent first issue set the pace for the series that to this day is considered the gold standard of Silver Surfer tales. The book was also indicative of the direction Marvel was wanting to venture in now that their distribution limitations were resolved.

October saw the last of the 1968 expansion with two decidedly different titles: *Tales of Asgard* #1 and *Mighty Marvel Western* #1. *Tales of Asgard* only ran one issue, a 25 cent, 68-page special featuring reprints of stories of the same name from *Journey Into Mystery* #97-106. *Mighty Marvel Western* also ran various page counts, ranging from 52 to 68 pages. Stories included characters from Marvel's stable of western gunslingers from Kid Colt, to Rawhide Kid and Two Gun Kid. The western title ran 46 issues.

Looking back 50 years, it is hard to ignore that fact that the events of 1968 shaped the path of Marvel's future, paving the way for the company to grow into the powerhouse that it is today. Given that many of the characters that came out of that era have not only thrived, but have gone on to star in television and big-budget movie productions is true testimony to the fact that Marvel's expansion led directly to the growth of not only their company, but the entire comics industry as a whole.

Charles S. Novinskie has now been collecting comics for 50 years—and is thankful that his lifelong passion for comics began reading those Marvel classics back in 1968!

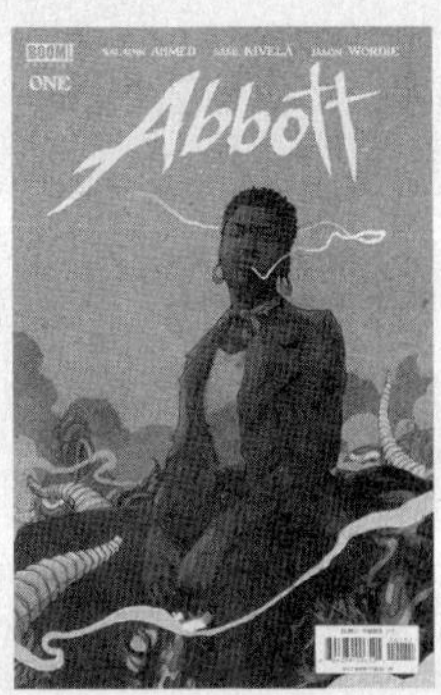

Abbott #1 © Saladin Ahmed

Abbott and Costello #3 © STJ

Ace Comics #26 © DMP

GD VG FN VF VF/NM NM-
2.0 4.0 6.0 8.0 9.0 9.2

The correct title listing for each comic book can be determined by consulting the indicia (publication data) on the beginning interior pages of the comic. The official title is determined by those words of the title in capital letters only, and not by what is on the cover. Titles are listed in this book as if they were one word, ignoring spaces, hyphens, and apostrophes, to make finding titles easier. Exceptions are made in rare cases. Comic books listed should be assumed to be in color unless noted "B&W".

Comic publishers are invited to send us sample copies for possible inclusion in future guides.

PRICING IN THIS GUIDE: Prices for **GD 2.0** (Good), **VG 4.0** (Very Good), **FN 6.0** (Fine), **VF 8.0** (Very Fine), **VF/NM 9.0** (Very Fine/Near Mint),and **NM– 9.2** (Near Mint–) are listed in whole U.S. dollars except for prices below $7 which show dollars and cents. **The minimum price listed is $3.00**, the cover price for current new comics. Many books listed at this price can be found in $1.00 boxes at conventions and dealers stores.

A-1 (See A-One)

A&A: THE ADVENTURES OF ARCHER & ARMSTRONG
Valiant Entertainment: Mar, 2016 - No. 12, Feb, 2017 ($3.99)

1-12: 1-Rafer Roberts-s/David Lafuente-a. 5-Faith app. 5-12-Norton-a 4.00
10-Cat cosplay photo variant-c 4.00

AARDVARK COMICS (Reprints from Cerebus in Hell)(Also see Batvark)
Aardvark-Vanaheim: Sept, 2017 ($4.00, B&W)

1-Cerebus figures placed over original Gustave Doré artwork of Hell; Action #1-c swipe 4.00

ABADAZAD
CrossGen (Code 6): Mar, 2004 - No. 3, May, 2004 ($2.95)

1-3-Ploog-a/c; DeMatteis-s 3.00
1-2nd printing with new cover 3.00

ABATTOIR
Radical Comics: Oct, 2010 - No. 6, Aug, 2011 ($3.99/$3.50, limited series)

1-($3.99) Cansino-a/Levin & Peteri-s 4.00
2-6-($3.50) 3.50

ABBIE AN' SLATS (...With Becky No. 1-4) (See Comics On Parade, Fight for Love, Giant Comics Edition 2, Giant Comics Editions #1, Sparkler Comics, Tip Topper, Treasury of Comics, & United Comics)
United Features Syndicate: 1940; March, 1948 - No. 4, Aug, 1948 (Reprints)

	GD	VG	FN	VF	VF/NM	NM-
Single Series 25 ('40)	40	80	120	246	411	575
Single Series 28	34	68	102	199	325	450
1 (1948)	17	34	51	98	154	210
2-4: 3-r/Sparkler #68-72	10	20	30	58	79	100

ABBOTT
BOOM! Studios: Jan, 2018 - No. 5 ($3.99, limited series)

1-Saladin Ahmed-s/Sami Kivelä 4.00

ABBOTT AND COSTELLO (...Comics)(See Giant Comics Editions #1 & Treasury of Comics)
St. John Publishing Co.: Feb, 1948 - No. 40, Sept, 1956 (Mort Drucker-a in most issues)

	GD	VG	FN	VF	VF/NM	NM-
1	87	174	261	553	952	1350
2	41	82	123	256	428	600
3-9 (#8, 8/49; #9, 2/50)	32	64	96	188	307	425
10-Son of Sinbad story by Kubert (new)	36	72	108	211	343	475
11,13-20 (#11, 10/50; #13, 8/51; #15, 12/52)	21	42	63	126	206	285
12-Movie issue	22	44	66	132	216	300
21-30: 28-r/#8. 29,30-Painted-c	16	32	48	94	147	200
31-40: 33,36,38-Reprints	14	28	42	78	112	145
3-D #1 (11/53, 25¢)-Infinity-c	32	64	96	188	307	425

ABBOTT AND COSTELLO (TV)
Charlton Comics: Feb, 1968 - No. 22, Aug, 1971 (Hanna-Barbera)

	GD	VG	FN	VF	VF/NM	NM-
1	7	14	21	46	86	125
2	4	8	12	27	44	60
3-10	3	6	9	21	33	45
11-22	3	6	9	17	26	35

ABC (See America's Best TV Comics)

ABC: A-Z (one-shots)
America's Best Comics: Nov, 2005 - July, 2006 ($3.99, one-shots)

... Greyshirt and Cobweb (1/06) character bios; Veitch-s/a; Gebbie-a; Dodson-c 4.00
... Terra Obscura and Splash Brannigan (3/06) character bios; Barta-a; Dodson-c 4.00
... Tom Strong and Jack B. Quick (11/05) character bios; Sprouse-a; Nowlan-a; Dodson-c 4.00
... Top Ten and Teams (7/06) character bios; Ha & Cannon-a; Veitch-a; Dodson-c 4.00

ABE SAPIEN... (Hellboy character)
Dark Horse Comics: Apr, 2013 - Present ($3.50/$3.99)

1-33: 1,2-Subtitled "Dark and Terrible"; Mignola & Allie-s/Fiumara-a/c. 8-Oeming-a. 23-Hellboy app.; Nowlan-a 3.50
34-36-($3.99) 4.00
...: Drums of the Dead (3/98, $2.95) 1-Thompson-a. Hellboy back-up; Mignola-s/a/c 4.00
...: The Abyssal Plain (6/10 - No. 2, 7/10, $3.50) 1,2-Mignola & Arcudi-s/Snejbjerg-a 3.50
...: The Devil Does Not Jest (9/11 - No. 2, 10/11, $3.50) Mignola & Arcudi-s. 1-Two covers by Johnson & Francavilla 3.50
...: The Drowning (2/08 - No. 5, 6/08, $2.99) 1-5-Mignola-s/c; Alexander-a 3.50
...: The Haunted Boy (10/09, $3.50) 1-Mignola & Arcudi-s/Reynolds-a/Johnson-c 3.50

ABIGAIL AND THE SNOWMAN
Boom Entertainment (KaBOOM!): Dec, 2014 - No. 4, Mar, 2015 ($3.99, limited series)

1-4-Roger Langridge-s/a. 1-Covers by Langridge & Liew 4.00

A. BIZARRO
DC Comics: Jul, 1999 - No. 4, Oct, 1999 ($2.50, limited series)

1-4-Gerber-s/Bright-a 3.00

ABOMINATIONS (See Hulk)
Marvel Comics: Dec, 1996 - No. 3, Feb, 1997 ($1.50, limited series)

1-3-Future Hulk storyline 3.00

ABRAHAM LINCOLN LIFE STORY (See Dell Giants)

ABRAHAM STONE
Marvel Comics (Epic): July, 1995 - No. 2, Aug, 1995 ($6.95, limited series)

1,2-Joe Kubert-s/a 7.00

ABSENT-MINDED PROFESSOR, THE (see Shaggy Dog & The... under Movie Comics)

ABSOLUTE VERTIGO
DC Comics (Vertigo): Winter, 1995 (99¢, mature)

	GD	VG	FN	VF	VF/NM	NM-
nn-1st app. Preacher. Previews upcoming titles including Jonah Hex: Riders of the Worm, The Invisibles (King Mob), The Eaters, Ghostdancing & Preacher	2	4	6	11	16	20

ABYSS, THE (Movie)
Dark Horse Comics: June, 1989 - No. 2, July, 1989 ($2.25, limited series)

1,2-Adaptation of film; Kaluta & Moebius-a 3.00

ACCELERATE
DC Comics (Vertigo): Aug, 2000 - No. 4, Nov, 2000 ($2.95, limited series)

1-4-Pander Bros.-a/Kadrey-s 3.00

ACCLAIM ADVENTURE ZONE
Acclaim Books: 1997 ($4.50, digest size)

1-Short stories of Turok, Troublemakers, Ninjak and others 4.50

ACCUSED, THE (Civil War II tie-in)
Marvel Comics: Oct, 2016 ($4.99, one-shot)

1-The trial of Hawkeye; Matt Murdock app.; Guggenheim-s/Bachs & Brown-a/Mack-c 5.00

ACE COMICS
David McKay Publications: Apr, 1937 - No. 151, Oct-Nov, 1949 (All contain some newspaper strip reprints)

	GD	VG	FN	VF	VF/NM	NM-
1-Jungle Jim by Alex Raymond, Blondie, Ripley's Believe It Or Not, Krazy Kat begin (1st app. of each)	349	698	1047	2443	4272	6100
2	103	206	309	659	1130	1600
3-5	69	138	207	442	759	1075
6-10	53	106	159	334	567	800
11-The Phantom begins (1st app., 2/38) (in brown costume)	400	800	1200	2800	4900	7000
12-20	42	84	126	265	445	625
21-25,27-30	39	78	117	231	378	525
26-Origin & 1st app. Prince Valiant (5/39); begins series?	142	284	426	909	1555	2200
31-40: 37-Krazy Kat ends	22	44	66	132	216	300
41-60	15	30	45	88	137	185
61-64,66-76-(7/43; last 68 pgs.)	14	28	42	80	115	150
65-(8/42)-Flag-c	15	30	45	88	137	185
77-84 (3/44; all 60 pgs.)	12	24	36	67	94	120
85-99 (52 pgs.)	11	22	33	60	83	105
100 (7/45; last 52 pgs.)	12	24	36	67	94	120
101-134: 128-(11/47)-Brick Bradford begins. 134-Last Prince Valiant (all 36 pgs.)	10	20	30	56	76	95
135-151: 135-(6/48)-Lone Ranger begins	9	18	27	52	69	85

ACE KELLY (See Tops Comics & Tops In Humor)

Aces High #4 © WMG

Action Comics #1 © DC

Action Comics #99 © DC

GD 2.0 | VG 4.0 | FN 6.0 | VF 8.0 | VF/NM 9.0 | NM- 9.2

ACE KING (See Adventures of Detective...)

ACES
Acme Press (Eclipse): Apr, 1988 - No. 5, Dec, 1988 ($2.95, B&W, magazine)

1-5 3.00

ACES HIGH
E.C. Comics: Mar-Apr, 1955 - No. 5, Nov-Dec, 1955

1-Not approved by code 26 52 78 208 329 450
2 14 28 42 112 181 250
3-5 13 26 39 104 165 225

NOTE: *All have stories by* **Davis**, **Evans**, **Krigstein**, *and* **Wood**. **Evans** *c-1-5.*

ACES HIGH
Gemstone Publishing: Apr, 1999 - No. 5, Aug, 1999 ($2.50)

1-5-Reprints E.C. issues 4.00
Annual 1 ($13.50) r/#1-5 14.00

ACME NOVELTY LIBRARY, THE
Fantagraphics Books: Winter 1993-94 - Present (quarterly, various sizes)

1-Introduces Jimmy Corrigan; Chris Ware-s/a in all 3 6 9 17 26 35
1-2nd and later printings 1 3 4 6 8 10
2,3: 2-Quimby 2 4 6 10 14 18
4-Sparky's Best Comics & Stories 3 6 9 14 20 25
5-12: Jimmy Corrigan in all 2 4 6 9 12 15
13,15-($10.95-c) 2 4 6 11 16 20
14-($12.95-c) Concludes Jimmy Corrigan saga 22.00
16,19-($15.95, hardcover) Rusty Brown 22.00
17-($16.95, hardcover) Rusty Brown 22.00
18-($17.95, hardcover) 22.00
Jimmy Corrigan, The Smartest Kid on Earth (2000, Pantheon Books, Hardcover, $27.50, 380 pgs.) Collects Jimmy Corrigan stories; folded dust jacket 35.00
Jimmy Corrigan, The Smartest Kid on Earth (2003, Softcover, $17.95) 20.00

NOTE: *Multiple printings exist for most issues.*

ACROSS THE UNIVERSE: THE DC UNIVERSE STORIES OF ALAN MOORE (Also see DC Universe: The Stories of Alan Moore)
DC Comics: 2003 ($19.95, TPB)

nn-Reprints selected Moore stories from '85-'87; Superman, Batman, Swamp Thing app. 20.00

ACTION ADVENTURE (War) (Formerly Real Adventure)
Gillmor Magazines: V1#2, June, 1955 - No. 4, Oct, 1955

V1#2-4 7 14 21 37 46 55

ACTION COMICS (...Weekly #601-642) (Also see The Comics Magazine #1, More Fun #14-17 & Special Edition) (Also see Promotional Comics section)
National Periodical Publ./Detective Comics/DC Comics: 6/38 - No. 583, 9/86; No. 584, 1/87 - No. 904, Oct, 2011

1-Origin & 1st app. Superman by Siegel & Shuster, Marco Polo, Tex Thompson, Pep Morgan, Chuck Dawson & Scoop Scanlon; 1st app. Zatara & Lois Lane; Superman story missing 4 pgs. which were included when reprinted in Superman #1; Clark Kent works for Daily Star; story continued in #2 200,000 400,000 700,000 1,400,000 2,600,000 3,800,000
1-Reprint, Oversize 13-1/2x10". **WARNING:** This comic is an exact reprint of the original except for its size. DC published it in 1974 with a second cover titling it as a Famous First Edition. There have been many reported cases of the outer cover being removed and the interior sold as the original edition. The reprint with the new outer cover removed is practically worthless. See Famous First Edition for value.
2-O'Mealia non-Superman covers thru #6 10,800 21,600 32,400 81,000 140,500 200,000
3 (Scarce)-Superman apps. in costume in only one panel 7730 15,460 23,190 58,000 100,500 143,000
4-6: 6-1st Jimmy Olsen (called office boy) 3570 7140 10,710 26,800 46,400 66,000
7-1st time the name Superman is printed on a comic cover; 2nd Superman cover 40,000 80,000 120,000 240,000 360,000 480,000
8,9 2700 5400 8100 20,250 35,125 50,000
10-3rd Superman cover by Shuster; splash panel used as cover art for Superman #1 23,600 47,200 70,800 141,600 220,800 300,000
11,14: 1st X-Ray Vision? 14-Clip Carson begins, ends #41; Zatara-c 1190 2380 3570 8900 15,450 22,000
12-Has 1 panel Batman ad for Det. #27 (5/39); Zatara sci-fi cover 2600 5200 7800 19,500 33,750 48,000
13-Shuster Superman-c; last Scoop Scanlon; centerspread has a 2-page ad for Superman #1 15,800 31,600 47,400 90,000 135,000 180,000
15-Guardineer Superman-c; has ad mentioning Detective Comics and Batman; full page ad for New York World's Fair 1939 with 25¢-c 2700 5400 8100 20,250 35,125 50,000
16-Has full page ad and 1 panel ad for New York World's Fair 1939 25¢ cover edition 700 1400 2100 5250 9125 13,000
17-Superman cover; last Marco Polo; full page ad for New York World's Fair 1939 with 15¢-c 1730 3460 5190 13,000 22,500 32,000
18-Origin 3 Aces; has a 1 panel ad for New York World's Fair 1939 at the end of the Superman story (ad also in #16,17,19) 700 1400 2100 5250 9125 13,000
19-Superman covers begin 1620 3240 4860 12,150 21,075 30,000
20-The 'S' left off Superman's chest; Clark Kent works at 'Daily Star' 1570 3140 4710 11,800 20,400 29,000
21-Has 2 ads for More Fun #52 (1st Spectre) 650 1300 1950 4875 8438 12,000
22 625 1250 1875 4688 8094 11,500
23-1st app. Luthor (w/red hair) & Black Pirate; Black Pirate by Moldoff; 1st mention of The Daily Planet (4/40)-Has 1 panel ad for Spectre in More Fun 4000 8000 12,000 28,400 46,700 65,000
24,25: 24-Kent at Daily Planet. 25-Last app. Gargantua T. Potts, Tex Thompson's sidekick 505 1010 1515 3788 6594 9400
26-28,30 454 908 1362 3314 5857 8400
29-1st Lois Lane-c (10/40) 497 994 1491 3628 6414 9200
31,32: 32-Intro/1st app. Krypto Ray Gun in Superman story by Burnley 314 628 942 2198 3849 5500
33-Origin Mr. America; Superman by Burnley; has half page ad for All Star Comics #3 331 662 993 2317 4059 5800
34,35,38,39 309 618 927 2163 3782 5400
36,40: 36-Classic robot-c. 40-(9/41)-Intro/1st app. Star Spangled Kid & Stripesy; Jerry Siegel photo 354 708 1062 2478 4339 6200
37-Origin Congo Bill 314 628 942 2198 3849 5500
41 300 600 900 1920 3310 4700
42-1st app./origin Vigilante; Bob Daley becomes Fat Man; origin Mr. America's magic flying carpet; The Queen Bee & Luthor app; Black Pirate ends; not in #41 300 600 900 2010 3505 5000
43-46,48-50: 44-Fat Man's i.d. revealed to Mr. America. 45-1st app. Stuff (Vigilante's oriental sidekick) 297 594 891 1900 3250 4600
47-1st Luthor cover in comics (4/42) 423 846 1269 3046 5323 7600
51-1st app. The Prankster 271 542 813 1734 2967 4200
52-Fat Man & Mr. America become the Ameri-commandos; origin Vigilante retold; classic Superman and back-ups-c 331 662 993 2317 4059 5800
53-56,59,60: 56-Last Fat Man. 60-First app. Lois Lane as Super-woman 252 504 756 1613 2757 3900
57-2nd Lois Lane-c in Action (3rd anywhere, 2/43) 258 516 774 1651 2826 4000
58-"Slap a Jap"-c 432 864 1296 3154 5577 8000
61-Historic Atomic Radiation-c (6/43) 290 580 870 1856 3178 4500
62-Japan war-c 239 478 717 1530 2615 3700
63-Japan war-c; last 3 Aces 277 554 831 1759 3030 4300
64-Intro Toyman 200 400 600 1280 2190 3100
65-70: 66-69-Kubert-i on Vigilante 168 336 504 1075 1838 2600
71-79: 74-Last Mr. America 132 264 396 838 1444 2050
80-2nd app. & 1st Mr. Mxyztplk-c (1/45) 161 322 483 1030 1765 2500
81-88,90: 83-Intro Hocus & Pocus 123 246 369 787 1344 1900
89-Classic rainbow cover 139 278 417 883 1517 2150
91-99: 93-X-Mas-c. 99-1st small logo (8/46) 103 206 309 659 1130 1600
100 139 278 417 883 1517 2150
101-Nuclear explosion-c (10/46) 245 490 735 1568 2684 3800
102-Mxyztplk-c 103 206 309 659 1130 1600
103-107,109-120: 105,117-X-Mas-c 94 188 282 597 1024 1450
108-Classic molten metal-c 113 226 339 718 1234 1750
121,122,124-126,128-140: 135,136,138-Zatara by Kubert 90 180 270 576 988 1400
123-(8/48) 1st time Superman flies, not leaps 110 220 330 704 1202 1700
127-Vigilante by Kubert; Tommy Tomorrow begins (12/48, see Real Fact #6) 90 180 270 576 988 1400
141-150,152-157,159-161: 156-Lois as Super Woman. 161- Last 52 pgs. 89 178 267 565 970 1375
151-Luthor/Mr. Mxyztplk/Prankster team-up 129 258 387 826 1413 2000
158-Origin Superman retold 145 290 435 921 1586 2250
162-180: 168,176-Used in **POP**, pg. 90. 173-Robot-c 84 168 252 538 919 1300
181-201: 191-Intro. Janu in Congo Bill. 198-Last Vigilante. 201-Last pre-code issue 79 158 237 502 864 1225
202-220,232: 212-(1/56)-Includes 1956 Superman calendar that is part of story. 232-1st Curt Swan-c in Action 61 122 183 390 670 950
221-231,233-240: 221-1st S.A. issue. 224-1st Golden Gorilla story. 228-(5/57)-Kongorilla in Congo Bill story (Congorilla try-out) 52 104 156 328 552 775
241,243-251: 241-Batman x-over. 248-Origin/1st app. Congorilla; Congo Bill renamed Congorilla. 251-Last Tommy Tomorrow 43 86 129 271 461 650
242-Origin & 1st app. Brainiac (7/58); 1st mention of Shrunken City of Kandor 625 1250 1875 7500 16,250 25,000
252-Origin & 1st app. Supergirl (5/59); 1st app. Metallo 625 1250 1875 7500 16,250 25,000
253-2nd app. Supergirl 84 168 252 538 919 1300

Action Comics #300 © DC

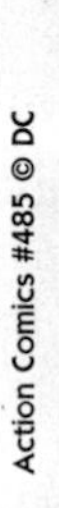

Action Comics #485 © DC

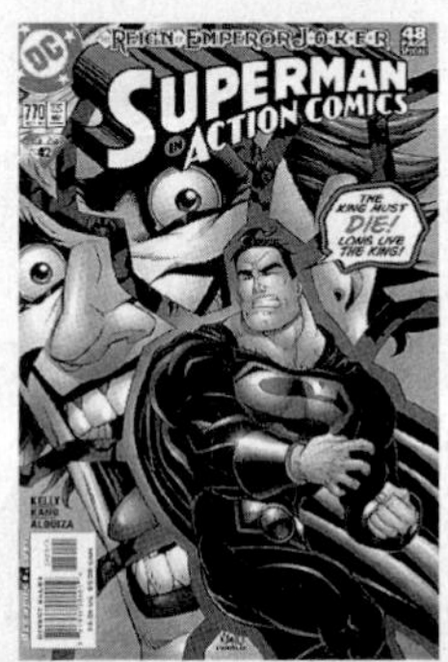

Action Comics #770 © DC

GD VG FN VF VF/NM NM-
2.0 4.0 6.0 8.0 9.0 9.2

254-1st meeting of Bizarro & Superman-c/story; 3rd app. Supergirl 55 110 165 352 601 850
255-1st Bizarro Lois Lane-c/story & both Bizarros leave Earth to make Bizarro World; 4th app. Supergirl 48 96 144 302 514 725
256-260: 259-Red Kryptonite used 36 72 108 211 343 475
261-1st X-Kryptonite which gave Streaky his powers; last Congorilla in Action; origin & 1st app. Streaky The Super Cat 39 78 117 240 395 550
262,264-266,268-270 31 62 93 184 300 415
263-Origin Bizarro World (continues in #264) 39 78 117 231 378 525
267(8/60)-3rd Legion app; 1st app. Chameleon Boy, Colossal Boy, & Invisible Kid, 1st app. of Supergirl as Superwoman. 71 142 213 454 777 1100
271-275,277-282: 274-Lois Lane as Superwoman. 280-Brief origin of Superman & Supergirl retold; Brainiac-c. 282-Last 10¢ issue 24 48 72 142 234 325
276(5/61)-6th Legion app; 1st app. Brainiac 5, Phantom Girl, Triplicate Girl, Bouncing Boy, Sun Boy, & Shrinking Violet; Supergirl joins Legion 58 116 174 371 636 900
283(12/61)-Legion of Super-Villains app. 1st 12¢ 13 26 39 89 195 300
284(1/62)-Mon-El app. 13 26 39 89 195 300
285(2/62)-12th Legion app; Brainiac 5 cameo; Supergirl's existence revealed to world; JFK & Jackie cameos 26 52 78 182 404 625
286-287,289-292,294-299: 286(3/62)-Legion of Super Villains app. 287(4/62)-15th Legion app. (cameo). 289(6/62)-16th Legion app. (Adult); Lightning Man & Saturn Woman's marriage 1st revealed. 290(7/62)-Legion app. (cameo); Phantom Girl app. 1st Supergirl emergency squad. 291-1st meeting Supergirl & Mr. Mxyzptlk. 292-2nd app. Superhorse (see Adv.#293). 297-General Zod, Phantom Zone villains & Mon-El app. 298-General Zod app.; Legion cameo 11 22 33 76 163 250
288-Mon-El app.; r-origin Supergirl 12 24 36 79 170 260
293-Origin Comet (Superhorse) 13 26 39 89 195 300
300-(5/63) 13 26 39 86 188 290
301-303,305,307,308,310-312,315-320: 307-Saturn Girl app. 317-Death of Nor-Kan of Kandor. 319-Shrinking Violet app. 9 18 27 58 114 170
304,306,313: 304-Origin/1st app. Black Flame (9/63). 306-Brainiac 5, Mon-El app. 313-Batman app. 9 18 27 59 117 175
309-(2/64)-Legion app.; Batman & Robin-c & cameo; JFK app. (he died 11/22/63; on stands last week of Dec, 1963) 9 18 27 61 123 185
314-Retells origin Supergirl; J.L.A. x-over 9 18 27 59 117 175
321-333,335-339: 336-Origin Akvar (Flamebird) 7 14 21 48 89 130
334-Giant G-20; origin Supergirl, Streaky, Superhorse & Legion (all-r) 10 20 30 66 138 210
340-Origin, 1st app. of the Parasite; 2 pg. pin-up 15 30 45 103 227 350
341,344,350,358: 341-Batman app. in Supergirl back-up story. 344-Batman x-over. 350-Batman, Green Arrow & Green Lantern app. in Supergirl back-up story. 358-Superboy meets Supergirl 6 12 18 41 76 110
342,343,345,346,348,349,351-357,359: 342-UFO story. 345-Allen Funt/Candid Camera story. 6 12 18 40 73 105
347,360-Giant Supergirl G-33,G-45; 347-Origin Comet-r plus Bizarro story. 360-Legion app.-r; r/origin Supergirl 8 16 24 55 105 155
361-2nd app. Parasite 7 14 21 46 86 125
362-364,367-372,374-378: 362-366-Leper/Death story. 370-New facts about Superman's origin. 376-Last Supergirl in Action; last 12¢-c. 377-Legion begins (thru #392) 5 10 15 33 57 80
365,366: 365-JLA & Legion app. 366-JLA app. 5 10 15 34 60 85
373-Giant Supergirl G-57; Legion-r 8 16 24 51 96 140
379-399,401: 388-Sgt. Rock app. 392-Batman-c/app.; last Legion in Action; Saturn Girl gets new costume. 393-401-All Superman issues. 395-Bonus "Secrets of Superman's Fortress" 2-page spread 3 6 9 19 30 40
400 4 8 12 23 37 50
402-Last 15¢ issue; Superman vs. Supergirl duel 3 6 9 20 31 42
403-413: All 52 pg. issues. 411-Origin Eclipso-(r). 413-Metamorpho begins, ends #418 3 6 9 19 30 40
414-424: 419-Intro. Human Target. 421-Intro Capt. Strong; Green Arrow begins. 422,423-Origin Human Target 2 4 6 9 13 16
425-Neal Adams-a(p); The Atom begins 3 6 9 15 22 28
426-431,433-436,438,439 2 4 6 8 10 12
432-1st Bronze Age Toyman app. (2/74) 2 4 6 13 18 22
437,443-(100 pg. Giants) 4 8 12 27 44 60
440-1st Grell-a on Green Arrow 2 4 6 10 14 18
441,442,444-448: 441-Grell-a on Green Arrow continues 2 4 6 8 10 12
449-(68 pgs.) 2 4 6 10 14 18
450-465,467-470,474-483,486,489-499: 454-Last Atom. 456-Grell Jaws-c. 458-Last Green Arrow 1 2 3 4 5 7
466,487,488: 466-Batman, Flash app. 487,488-(44 pgs.). 487-Origin & 1st app. Microwave Man; origin Atom retold 1 2 3 5 7 9
471-(5/77) 1st app. Faora Hu-Ul 2 4 6 12 16 20
472,473-Faora app. 473-Faora, General Zod app. 2 4 6 9 13 16
481-483,486-492,495-499,501-505,507,508-Whitman variants (low print run; none show issue # on cover) 2 4 6 8 10 12
484-Earth II Superman & Lois Lane wed; 40th anniversary issue(6/78) 2 4 6 8 10 12
484-Variant includes 3-D Superman punchout doll in cello. pack; 4 different inserts; (Canadian promo?) 6 12 18 41 76 110
485-Classic Neal Adams Superman-c 2 4 6 9 12 15
485-Whitman variant 2 4 6 11 16 20
500-($1.00, 68 pgs.)-Infinity-c; Superman life story retold; shows Legion statues in museum 2 4 6 8 10 12
501-520,522-543,545,547-551: 511-514-Airwave II solo stories. 513-The Atom begins. 517-Aquaman begins; ends #541. 532,536-New Teen Titans cameo. 535,536-Omega Men app. 551-Starfire becomes Red-Star 5.00
521-1st app. The Vixen 4 8 12 23 37 50
544-(6/83, Mando paper, 68 pgs.)-45th Anniversary issue; origins new Luthor & Brainiac; Omega Men cameo; Shuster-a (pin-up); article by Siegel 1 2 3 4 5 7
546-J.L.A., New Teen Titans app. 1 2 3 5 6 8
552,553-Animal Man, Cave Carson, Congorilla, Sea Devils-c/app.; Dolphin, Immortal Man, Rip Hunter, Suicide Squad app (2/84 & 3/84) 6.00
554-582: 577-Intro. Caitiff, the First Vampire 3.00
583-(9/86) Alan Moore scripts; last Earth 1 Superman story (cont'd from Superman #423) 2 4 6 11 16 20
584-(1/87) Byrne-a begins; New Teen Titans app. 6.00
585-599: 586-Legends x-over. 595-1st app. Silver Banshee. 596-Millennium x-over; Spectre app. 598-1st Checkmate 3.00
600-($2.50, 84 pgs., 5/88) 6.00
601-610,619-642: (#601-642 are weekly issues) ($1.50, 52 pgs.) 601-Re-intro The Secret Six; death of Katma Tui 4.00
611-618: 611-614-Catwoman stories (new costume in #611). 613-618-Nightwing stories 4.00
643-Superman & monthly issues begin again; Perez-c/a/scripts begin; swipes cover to Superman #1 6.00
644-649,651-661,663-666,668-673,675-683: 645-1st app. Maxima. 654-Part 3 of Batman storyline. 655-Free extra 8 pgs. 660-Death of Lex Luthor. 661-Begin $1.00-c. 675-Deathstroke cameo. 679-Last $1.00 issue. 683-Doomsday cameo 3.00
650,667: 650-($1.50, 52 pgs.)-Lobo cameo (last panel). 667-($1.75, 52 pgs.) 4.00
662-Clark Kent reveals i.d. to Lois Lane; story cont'd in Superman #53 4.00
674-Supergirl logo & c/story (reintro) 6.00
683-685-2nd & 3rd printings 3.00
684-Doomsday battle issue 4.00
685,686-Funeral for a Friend issues; Supergirl app. 4.00
687-($1.95)-Collector's Ed.w/die-cut-c 4.00
687-($1.50)-Newsstand Edition with mini-poster 3.00
688-699,701-703-($1.50): 688-Guy Gardner-c/story. 697-Bizarro-c/story. 703-(9/94)-Zero Hour 3.00
695-($2.50)-Collector's Edition w/embossed foil-c 4.00
700-($2.95, 68 pgs.)-Fall of Metropolis Pt 1, Guice-a; Pete Ross marries Lana Lang and Smallville flashbacks with Curt Swan art & Murphy Anderson inks 4.00
700-Platinum 18.00
700-Gold 20.00
0(10/94), 704(11/94)-719,721-731: 710-Begin $1.95-c. 714-Joker app. 719-Batman-c/app. 721-Mr. Mxyzptlk app. 723-Dave Johnson-c. 727-Final Night x-over. 3.00
720-Lois breaks off engagement w/Clark 4.00
720-2nd print. 3.00
732-749,751-764,767,767: 732-New powers. 733-New costume, Ray app. 738-Immonen-s/a(p) begins. 741-Legion app. 744-Millennium Giants x-over. 745-747-70's-style Superman vs. Prankster. 753-JLA-c/app. 757-Hawkman-c. 760-1st Encantadora. 761-Wonder Woman app. 766-Batman-c/app. 3.00
750-($2.95) 4.00
765-Joker & Harley-c/app. 1 2 3 5 6 8
768,769,771-774: 768-Begin $2.25-c; Marvel Family-c/app. 771-Nightwing-c/app. 772,773-Ra's al Ghul app. 774-Martian Manhunter-c/app. 3.00
770-($3.50) Conclusion of Emperor Joker x-over 4.00
775-($3.75) Bradstreet-c; intro. The Elite 2 4 6 9 12 15
775-(2nd printing) 1 3 4 6 8 10
776-799: 776-Farewell to Krypton; Rivoche-c. 780-782-Our Worlds at War x-over. 781-Hippolyta and Major Lane killed. 782-War ends. 784-Joker: Last Laugh; Batman & Green Lantern app. 793-Return to Krypton. 795-The Elite app. 798-Van Fleet-c 3.00
800-(4/03, $3.95) Struzan painted-c; guest artists include Ross, Jim Lee, Jurgens, Sale 4.00
801-811: 801-Raney-a. 809-The Creeper app. 811-Mr. Majestic app. 3.00
812-Godfall part 1; Turner-c; Caldwell-a(p) 4.00
812-2nd printing; B&W sketch-c by Turner 3.00

Action Comics #894 © DC

Action Comics (2011 series) #28 © DC

Action Comics #989 © DC

GD 2.0 | VG 4.0 | FN 6.0 | VF 8.0 | VF/NM 9.0 | NM- 9.2

813-Godfall pt. 4; Turner-c; Caldwell-a(p) 4.00
814-824,826-828,830-834,836: 814-Reis-a/Art Adams-c; Darkseid app.; begin $2.50-c.
815,816-Teen Titans-c/app. 820-Doomsday app. 826-Capt. Marvel app. 827-Byrne-c/a begin.
831-Villains United tie-in. 836-Infinite Crisis; revised origin 3.00
825-($2.99, 40 pgs.) Doomsday app. 4.00
829-Omac Project x-over Sacrifice pt. 2 5.00
829-(2nd printing) red tone cover 4.00
835-1st Livewire app. in regular DCU 2 4 6 8 10 12
837-843-One Year Later; powers return after Infinite Crisis; Johns & Busiek-s 3.00
844-Donner & Johns-s/Adam Kubert-a/c begin; brown-toned cover 4.00
844-Andy Kubert variant-c 5.00
844-2nd printing with red-toned Adam Kubert cover 3.00
845-849,851-857: 845-Bizarro-c/app.; re-intro. General Zod, Ursa & Non. 846-Jax-Ur app.
847-849-No Kubert-a. 851-Kubert-a/c. 855-857-Bizarro app.; Powell-a/c 3.00
850-($3.99) Supergirl and LSH app., origin re-told; Guedes-a/c 4.00
858-($3.50) Legion of Super-Heroes app.; 1st meeting re-told; Johns-s/Frank-a/c 4.00
858-Variant-c (Superman & giant Brainiac robot) by Frank 5.00
858-Second printing with regular cover with red background instead of yellow 3.00
858-Special Edition (7/10, $1.00) r/#858 with "What's Next?" cover logo 3.00
859-878: 859-863-Legion of Super-Heroes app.; var-c on each (859-Andy Kubert. 860-Lightle.
861-Grell. 862-Giffen. 863-Frank) 864-Batman and Lightning Lad app. 866-Brainiac returns
869-"Soda Pop" cover edition, 870-Pa Kent dies. 871-New Krypton; Ross-c 3.00
869-Initial printing recalled because of beer bottles on cover
5 10 15 33 57 80
879-896: 879-($3.99) Back-up Capt. Atom feature begins. 890-Luthor stories begin.
893-Comics debut of Chloe Sullivan (Smallville TV show) in regular DCU.
894-Death (Sandman) app. 896-Secret Six app. 4.00
897-899, 901-903-($2.99) 897-Joker app. 898-Larfleeze app. 899-Brainiac app. 3.00
900 (6/11, $5.99, 96 pgs.) Conclusion of Luthor Black Ring saga; Doomsday app.; bonus
short stories by various; Superman renounces U.S. citizenship 6.00
904-(10/11) Last issue of first volume; Doomsday app.; Rocafort-c 3.00
904-Variant-c by Ordway 5.00
#1,000,000 (11/98) Gene Ha-c; 853rd Century x-over 3.00
Annual 1 ('87, $2.95) Art Adams-c/a(p); Batman app. 5.00
Annual 2-6 ('89-'94, $2.95)-2-Pérez-c/a(i). 3-Armageddon 2001. 4-Eclipso vs. Shazam.
5-Bloodlines; 1st app. Loose Cannon. 6-Elseworlds story 4.00
Annual 7,9 ('95, '97, $3.95) 7-Year One story. 9-Pulp Heroes story 4.00
Annual 8 (1996, $2.95) Legends of the Dead Earth story 4.00
Annual 10 ('07, $3.99) Short stories by Johns & Donner and various incl. A. Adams, J. Kubert,
Wight, Morales; origin of Phantom Zone, Mon-El; Metallo app.; Adam & Joe Kubert-c 4.00
Annual 11 (7/08, $4.99) Conclusion to General Zod story continued from #851; Kubert-a 5.00
Annual 12 (8/09, $4.99) Origin of Nightwing and Flamebird 5.00
Annual 13 (2/11, $4.99) 1st meeting of Luthor and Darkseid; Ra's al Ghul app. 5.00

NOTE:***Supergirl's*** *origin in 262, 280, 285, 291, 305, 309.* ***N. Adams*** *c-356, 358, 359, 361-364, 366, 367, 370-374, 377-379i, 398-400, 402, 404,405, 419p, 466, 468, 469, 473i, 485.* ***Aparo*** *a-642.* ***Austin*** *c/a-682i.* ***Baily*** *a-24, 25.* ***Boring*** *a-164, 194, 211, 223, 233, 241, 250, 261, 266-268, 346, 348, 352, 356, 357.* ***Burnley*** *a-28-33; c-48?, 53-55, 58, 59?, 60-63, 65, 66p, 67p, 70p, 71p, 79p, 82p, 84-86p, 90-92p, 93p?, 94p, 107p, 108p.* ***Byrne*** *a-584-598p, 599i, 600p; c-584-591, 596-600.* ***Ditko*** *a-642.* ***Giffen*** *a-560, 563, 565, 577, 579; c-539, 560, 563, 565, 577, 579.* ***Grell*** *a-440-442, 444-446, 450-452, 456-458; c-456.* ***Guardineer*** *a-24, 25; c-8, 11, 12, 14-16, 18. 25.* ***Guice*** *a(p)-676-681, 683-698, 700; c-683, 685, 686, 687(direct), 688-693i, 694-696, 697i, 698-700.* ***Infantino*** *a-642.* ***Kaluta*** *c-613.* ***Bob Kane's*** *Clip Carson-14-41.* ***Gil Kane*** *a-443r, 493r, 539-541, 544-546, 551-554, 601-605, 642; c-535p, 540, 541, 544p, 545-549, 551-554, 580, 627.* ***Kirby*** *c-638.* ***Meskin*** *a-42-121(most).* ***Mignola*** *a-600, Annual 2; c-c-614.* ***Moldoff*** *a-23-25, 443r.* ***Mooney*** *a-667p.* ***Mortimer*** *c-153, 154, 159-172, 174, 178-181, 184, 186-189, 191-193, 196, 200, 206.* ***Orlando*** *a-617p; c-621.* ***Perez*** *a-600i, 643-652p, Annual 2p; c-529p, 602, 643-651, Annual 2p.* ***Quesada*** *c-Annual 4p.* ***Fred Ray*** *c-34, 36-46, 50-52.* ***Siegel & Shuster*** *a-1-27.* ***Paul Smith*** *c-608.* ***Starlin*** *a-509; c-631.* ***Leonard Starr*** *a-597i(part),* ***Staton*** *a-525p, 526p, 531p, 535p, 536p.* ***Swan/Moldoff*** *c-281, 286, 287, 293, 298, 334.* ***Thibert*** *c-676, 677p, 678-681, 684.* ***Toth*** *a-406, 407, 413, 431; c-616.* ***Tuska*** *a-486p, 550.* ***Williamson*** *a-568i.* ***Zeck*** *c-Annual 5*

ACTION COMICS (2nd series)(DC New 52)(Numbering reverts to original V1 #957 after #52)
DC Comics: Nov, 2011 - No. 52, Jul, 2016; No. 957, Aug, 2016 - Present ($3.99)

1-Grant Morrison-s/Rags Morales-a/c; re-introduces Superman
2 4 6 8 10 12
1-Variant-c by Jim Lee of Superman in new armor costume
2 4 6 10 14 18
1-(2nd - 5th printings) 4.00
2-12: 2-Morales & Brent Anderson-a; behind the scenes sketch art and commentary.
3-Gene Ha & Morales-a. 4-Re-intro. Steel. 5-Flashback to Krypton; Andy Kubert-a.
6-Legion of Super-Heroes app.; Andy Kubert-a. 7-Gets the new costume; intro. Steel 4.00
2-12-Variant covers. 2-Van Sciver. 3-Ha. 4-Choi. 5,6-Morales. 8-Frank 5.00
13-17,19-23: 13-Re-intro of Krypto. 14-Neil deGrasse Tyson app. 15-Legion app. 4.00
18-($4.99) Last Morrison-s; Mxyzptlk, The Legion and the Wanderers app. 5.00
23.1, 23.2, 23.3, 23.4 (11/13, $2.99, regular covers) 3.00
23.1 (11/13, $3.99, 3-D cover) "Cyborg Superman #1" on cover; Zor-El & Brainiac app. 5.00
23.2 (11/13, $3.99, 3-D cover) "Zod #1" on cover; origin of Zod on Krypton; Faora app. 5.00
23.3 (11/13, $3.99, 3-D cover) "Lex Luthor #1" on cover; Kuder-c 5.00
23.4 (11/13, $3.99, 3-D cover) "Metallo #1" on cover; Fisch-s/Pugh-a 5.00
24-49,51,52: 25-Zero Year. 30-Doomsday app. 31-35-Doomed x-over. 40-Bizarro app.
51-Supergirl app. 52-Wonder Woman, Batman and pre-Flashpoint Superman app. 4.00
50-($4.99) Vandal Savage and the Justice League app. 5.00
#0 (11/12, $3.99) Flashback to Lois' 1st Superman sighting; Oliver-a; 4.00
Annual 1 (12/12, $4.99) Superman vs. K-Man; Fisch-s/Hamner-a; Atomic Skull app. 5.00
Annual 2 (12/13, $4.99) Rocafort & Jurgens-a; H'El & Faora app.; back-up Mad sampler 5.00
Annual 3 (9/14, $4.99) Superman Doomed x-over; Brainiac app. 5.00
...: Futures End 1 (11/14, $2.99, regular-c) Five years later; Alixe-a 3.00
...: Futures End 1 (11/14, $3.99, 3-D cover) 4.00

ACTION COMICS (Numbering reverts to original V1 #957 after #52 from 2011-2016 series)
DC Comics: No. 957, Aug, 2016 - Present ($2.99)

957-974: 957-Jurgens-s/Zircher-a; the pre-52 Superman vs. Lex Luthor & Doomsday.
960-962-Wonder Woman app. 973-Superwoman & Steel app. 3.00
975-($3.99) Superman Reborn pt. 2; back-up with Mxyzptlk; Dini-s/Churchill-a 4.00
976-986,992-998: 976-Superman Reborn pt. 4. 977,978-Origin revised. 979-Cyborg Superman
returns. 984-Intro Ursa and Lor-Zod. 992-998-Booster Gold app. 3.00
987-991-($2.99) The Oz Effect regular covers; Jor-El returns 3.00
987-991-($3.99) The Oz Effect lenticular covers 4.00

ACTION COMICS
DC Comics: (no date)

1-Ashcan comic, not distributed to newsstands, only for in-house use. Cover art is the
rejected art to Detective Comics #2 and interior from Detective Comics #1.
A CGC certified 9.0 copy sold for $17,825 in 2002, $29,000 in 2008, and $50,000 in 2010.

ACTION FORCE (Also see G.I. Joe European Missions)
Marvel Comics Ltd. (British): Mar, 1987 - No. 50, 1988 ($1.00, weekly, magazine)

1,3: British G.I. Joe series. 3-w/poster insert 2 4 6 8 11 14
2,4 1 2 3 5 6 8
5-10 5.00
11-50 3.00
...Special 1 (7/87) Summer holiday special; Snake Eyes-c/app.
1 3 4 6 8 10
...Special 2 (10/87) Winter special 5.00

ACTION FUNNIES
DC Comics: 1937/1938

nn - Ashcan comic, not distributed to newsstands, only for in house use. Cover art is Action
Comics #3 and interior from Detective Comics #10. The Mallette/Brown copy in
VG+ condition sold for $15,000 in 2005. A VF+ copy sold for $10,157.50 in 2012.

ACTION GIRL
Slave Labor Graphics: Oct, 1994 - No. 19 ($2.50/$2.75/$2.95, B&W)

1-19: 4-Begin $2.75-c. 19-Begin $2.95-c 3.00
1-6 ($2.75, 2nd printings): All read 2nd Print in indicia. 1-(2/96). 2-(10/95). 3-(2/96). 4-(7/96).
5-(2/97). 6-(9/97) 3.00
1-4 ($2.75, 3rd printings): All read 3rd Print in indicia. 3.00

ACTION MAN (Based on the Hasbro G.I. Joe-type action figure)
IDW Publishing: Jun, 2016 - Present ($3.99)

1-4-John Barber-s/Paolo Villanelli-a 4.00
...: Revolution (110/16, $3.99) Tie-in to Hasbro toy titles x-over; Barber-s/Villanelli-a 4.00

ACTION PHILOSOPHERS!
Dark Horse Comics: Oct, 2014 ($1.00, one-shot)

1-Van Lente-s/Dunlavey-a 3.00

ACTION PLANET COMICS
Action Planet: 1996 - No. 3, Sept, 1997 ($3.95, B&W, 44 pgs.)

1-3: 1-Intro Monster Man by Mike Manley & other stories 4.00
Giant Size Action Planet Halloween Special (1998, $5.95, oversized) 6.00

ACTUAL CONFESSIONS (Formerly Love Adventures)
Atlas Comics (MPI): No. 13, Oct, 1952 - No. 14, Dec, 1952

13,14 12 24 36 69 97 125

ACTUAL ROMANCES (Becomes True Secrets #3 on?)
Marvel Comics (IPS): Oct, 1949 - No. 2, Jan, 1950 (52 pgs.)

1-Photo-c 19 38 57 111 176 240
2-Photo-c 14 28 42 76 108 140

A.D.: AFTER DEATH
Image Comics: Book 1, Nov, 2016 - Book 3, May, 2017 ($5.99, limited series, square-bound 8"x11")

1-3-Scott Snyder-s/Jeff Lemire-a 6.00

ADAM AND EVE
Spire Christian Comics (Fleming H. Revell Co.): 1975,1978 (35¢/39¢/49¢)

Adam Strange/Future Quest Special #1 © DC & H-B

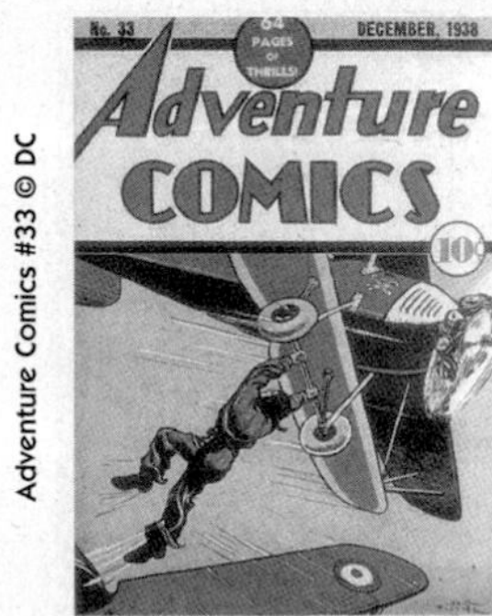

Adventure Comics #33 © DC

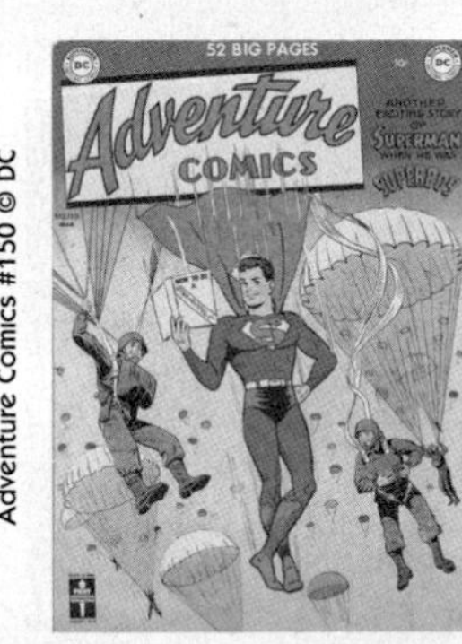

Adventure Comics #150 © DC

	GD	VG	FN	VF	VF/NM	NM-
	2.0	4.0	6.0	8.0	9.0	9.2

nn-By Al Hartley (1975 edition) 3 6 9 14 20 25
nn (1978 edition) 2 4 6 10 14 18

ADAM: LEGEND OF THE BLUE MARVEL
Marvel Comics: Jan, 2009 - No. 5, May, 2009 ($3.99, limited series)

1-5-Grevioux-s/Broome-a; Avengers app. 4.00

ADAM STRANGE (Also see Green Lantern #132, Mystery In Space #53 & Showcase #17)
DC Comics: 1990 - No. 3, 1990 ($3.95, 52 pgs, limited series, squarebound)

Book One - Three: Andy & Adam Kubert-c/a 4.00
...: The Man of Two Worlds (2003, $19.95, TPB) r/#1-3; sketch pages by Andy Kubert 20.00

ADAM STRANGE (Leads into the Rann/Thanagar War mini-series)
DC Comics: Nov, 2004 - No. 8, June, 2005 ($2.95, limited series)

1-8-Andy Diggle-s/Pascal Ferry-a/c. 1-Superman app. 3.00
...: Planet Heist TPB (2005, $19.99) r/series; sketch pages 20.00
... Special (11/08, $3.50) Takes place during Rann/Thanagar Holy War series; Starlin-s 4.00

ADAM STRANGE / FUTURE QUEST SPECIAL
DC Comics: May, 2017 ($4.99, one-shot)

1-Adam Strange meets Jonny Quest and team; back-up Top Cat story; Batman app. 5.00

ADAM-12 (TV)
Gold Key: Dec, 1973 - No. 10, Feb, 1976 (Photo-c)

1 6 12 18 37 66 95
2-10 3 6 9 21 33 45

ADDAMS FAMILY (TV cartoon)
Gold Key: Oct, 1974 - No. 3, Apr, 1975 (Hanna-Barbera)

1 7 14 21 48 89 130
2,3 5 10 15 33 57 80

ADLAI STEVENSON
Dell Publishing Co.: Dec, 1966

12-007-612-Life story; photo-c 3 6 9 21 33 45

ADOLESCENT RADIOACTIVE BLACK BELT HAMSTERS (See Clint)
Comic Castle/Eclipse Comics: 1986 - No. 9, Jan, 1988 ($1.50, B&W)

1-9: 1st & 2nd printings exist 3.00
1-Limited Edition 6.00
1-In 3-D (7/86), 2-4 ($2.50) 3.00
Massacre The Japanese Invasion #1 (8/89, $2.00) 3.00

ADOLESCENT RADIOACTIVE BLACK BELT HAMSTERS
Dynamite Entertainment: 2008 - No. 4, 2008 ($3.50, limited series)

1-4-Tom Nguyen-a/Keith Champagne-s; 2 covers by Nguyen and Oeming 3.50

ADRENALYNN (See The Tenth)
Image Comics: Aug, 1999 - No. 4, Feb, 2000 ($2.50)

1-4-Tony Daniel-s/Marty Egeland-a; origin of Adrenalynn 3.00

ADULT TALES OF TERROR ILLUSTRATED (See Terror Illustrated)

ADVANCED DUNGEONS & DRAGONS (Also see TSR Worlds)
DC Comics: Dec, 1988 - No. 36, Dec, 1991 (Newsstand #1 is Holiday, 1988-89) ($1.25-$1.75)

1-Based on TSR role playing game 4.00
2-36: 25-$1.75-c begins 3.00
Annual 1 (1990, $3.95, 68 pgs.) 4.00

ADVENTURE BOUND
Dell Publishing Co.: Aug, 1949

Four Color #239 6 12 18 37 66 95

ADVENTURE COMICS (Formerly New Adventure)(...Presents Dial H For Hero #479-490)
National Periodical Publications/DC Comics: No. 32, 11/38 - No. 490, 2/82; No. 491, 9/82 - No. 503, 9/83

32-Anchors Aweigh (ends #52), Barry O'Neil (ends #60, not in #33), Captain Desmo (ends #47), Dale Daring (ends #47), Federal Men (ends #70), The Golden Dragon (ends #36), Rusty & His Pals (ends #52) by Bob Kane, Todd Hunter (ends #38) and Tom Brent (ends #39) begin 520 1040 1560 2800 4200 5600
33-35,38 340 680 1020 1830 2765 3700
36 (scarce) 600 1200 1800 3240 4870 6500
37-Cover used on Double Action #2 385 770 1155 2080 3140 4200
39(6/39)- Jack Wood begins, ends #42; early mention of Marijuana in comics 340 680 1020 1830 2765 3700
40-(Rare, 7/39, on stands 6/10/39)-The Sandman begins by Bert Christman (who died in WWII); believed to be 1st conceived story (see N.Y. World's Fair for 1st published app.); Socko Strong begins, ends #54 7000 14,000 21,000 52,000 111,000 170,000
41-O'Mealia shark-c 660 1320 1980 4818 8509 12,200
42,44-Sandman-c by Flessel. 44-Opium story 876 1752 2628 6395 11,298 16,200
43,45: 45-Full page ad for Flash Comics #1 465 930 1395 3395 5998 8600
46,47-Sandman covers by Flessel. 47-Steve Conrad Adventurer begins, ends #76 660 1320 1980 4818 8509 12,200
48-1st app. The Hourman by Bernard Baily; Baily-c (Hourman c-48,50,52-59) 2750 5500 8250 20,500 41,750 63,000
49 300 600 900 2010 3505 5000
50-2nd Hourman-c; -Cotton Carver by Jack Lehti begins, ends #64 314 628 942 2198 3849 5500
51,60-Sandman-c: 51-Sandman-c by Flessel. 389 778 1167 2723 4762 6800
52-59: 53-1st app. Jimmy "Minuteman" Martin & the Minutemen of America in Hourman; ends #78. 58-Paul Kirk Manhunter begins (1st app.), ends #72 271 542 813 1734 2967 4200
61-1st app. Starman by Jack Burnley (4/41); Starman c-61-72; Starman by Burnley in #61-80 1200 2400 3600 9000 17,000 26,000
62-65,67,68,70: 67-Origin & 1st app. The Mist; classic Burnley-c. 70-Last Federal Men 258 516 774 1651 2826 4000
66-Origin/1st app. Shining Knight (9/41) 300 600 900 1950 3375 4800
69-1st app. Sandy the Golden Boy (Sandman's sidekick) by Paul Norris (in a Bob Kane style); Sandman dons new costume 298 596 894 1907 3279 4650
71-Jimmy Martin becomes costumed aide to the Hourman; 1st app. Hourman's Miracle Ray machine 258 516 774 1651 2826 4000
72-1st Simon & Kirby Sandman (3/42, 1st DC work) 975 1950 2919 7100 13,050 19,000
73-Origin Manhunter by Simon & Kirby; begin new series; Manhunter-c (scarce) 1275 2550 3825 9550 18,275 27,000
74-78,80: 74-Thorndyke replaces Jimmy, Hourman's assistant; new Sandman-c begin by S&K. 75-Thor app. by Kirby; 1st Kirby Thor (see Tales of the Unexpected #16). 77-Origin Genius Jones; Mist story. 80-Last S&K Manhunter & Burnley Starman 194 388 582 1242 2121 3000
79-Classic Manhunter-c 300 600 900 2010 3505 5000
81-90: 83-Last Hourman. 84-Mike Gibbs begins, ends #102 123 246 369 787 1344 1900
91-Last Simon & Kirby Sandman 119 238 357 762 1306 1850
92-99,101,102: 92-Last Manhunter. 101-Shining Knight origin retold. 102-Last Starman, Sandman, & Genius Jones; most-S&K-c (Genius Jones cont'd in More Fun #108) 97 194 291 621 1061 1500
100-S&K-c 135 270 405 864 1482 2100
103-Aquaman, Green Arrow, Johnny Quick & Superboy all move over from More Fun Comics #107; 8th app. Superboy; Superboy-c begin; 1st small logo (4/46) 309 618 927 2163 3782 5400
104 123 246 369 787 1344 1900
105-110 84 168 252 538 919 1300
111-120: 113-X-Mas-c 74 148 222 470 810 1150
121,122-126,128-130: 128-1st meeting Superboy & Lois Lane 69 138 207 442 759 1075
127-Brief origin Shining Knight retold 71 142 213 454 777 1100
131-141,143-149: 132-Shining Knight 1st return to King Arthur time; origin aide Sir Butch 61 122 183 390 670 950
142-Origin Shining Knight & Johnny Quick retold 65 130 195 416 708 1000
150,151,153,155,157,159,161,163-All have 6 pg. Shining Knight stories by Frank Frazetta. 159-Origin Johnny Quick. 161-1st Lana Lang app. in this title 74 148 222 470 810 1150
152,154,156,158,160,162,164-169: 166-Last Shining Knight. 168-Last 52 pg. issue 54 108 162 343 574 825
170-180 52 104 156 328 552 775
181-199: 189-B&W and color illo in **POP** 50 100 150 315 533 750
200 (5/54) 58 116 174 371 636 900
201-208: 207-Last Johnny Quick (not in 205) 47 94 141 296 498 700
209-Last pre-code issue; origin Speedy 48 96 144 302 514 725
210-1st app. Krypto (Superdog)-c/story (3/55) 600 1200 2400 5400 9450 13,500
211-213,215-219 43 86 129 271 461 650
214-2nd app. Krypto 87 174 261 553 952 1350
220-Krypto-c/sty 52 104 156 328 552 775
221-246: 229-1st S.A. issue; Green Arrow & Aquaman app. 237-1st Intergalactic Vigilante Squadron (6/57). 239-Krypto-c 37 74 111 222 361 500
247(4/58)-1st Legion of Super Heroes app.; 1st app. Cosmic Boy, Saturn Girl & Lightning Boy (later Lightning Lad in #267) (origin) 850 1700 3400 8500 17,750 27,000
248-252,254,255-Green Arrow in all: 255-Intro. Red Kryptonite in Superboy (used in #252 but with no effect) 34 68 102 199 325 450
253-1st meeting of Superboy & Robin; Green Arrow by Kirby in #250-255 (also see World's Finest #96-99) 39 78 117 231 378 525
256-Origin Green Arrow by Kirby 69 138 207 442 971 1500
257-259: 258-Green Arrow x-over in Superboy 27 54 81 158 259 360
260-1st Silver Age origin Aquaman (5/59) 90 180 270 720 1460 2200

Adventure Comics #288 © DC

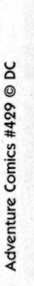

Adventure Comics #429 © DC

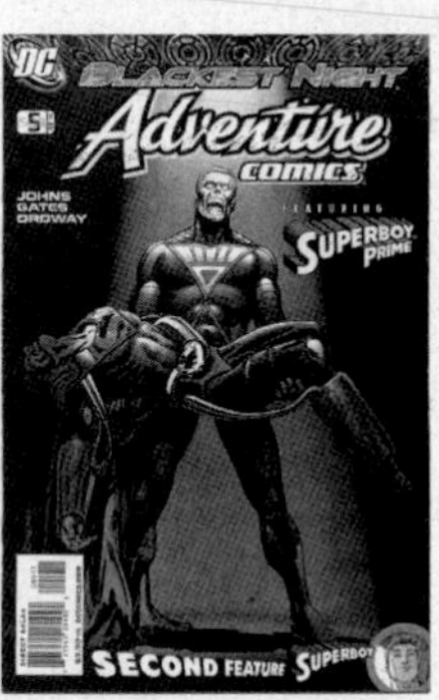

Adventure Comics (2009 series) #5 © DC

GD 2.0 | VG 4.0 | FN 6.0 | VF 8.0 | VF/NM 9.0 | NM- 9.2

261-265,268,270: 262-Origin Speedy in Green Arrow. 270-Congorilla begins, ends #281,283 22 44 66 128 209 290
266-(11/59)-Origin & 1st app. Aquagirl (tryout, not same as later character) 25 50 75 150 245 340
267(12/59)-2nd Legion of Super Heroes; Lightning Boy now called Lightning Lad; new costumes for Legion 97 194 291 611 1606 2600
269-Intro. Aqualad (2/60); last Green Arrow (not in #206) 53 106 159 334 567 800
271-Origin Luthor retold 43 86 129 271 461 650
272-274,277-280: 279-Intro White Kryptonite in Superboy. 280-1st meeting Superboy & Lori Lemaris 20 40 60 118 192 265
275-Origin Superman-Batman team retold (see World's Finest #94) 34 68 102 199 325 450
276-(9/60) Robinson Crusoe-like story 21 42 63 122 199 275
281,284,287-289: 281-Last Congorilla. 284-Last Aquaman in Adv.; Mooney-a. 287,288-Intro Dev-Em, the Knave from Krypton. 287-1st Bizarro Perry White & Jimmy Olsen. 288-Bizarro-c. 289-Legion cameo (statues) 19 38 57 111 176 240
282(3/61)-5th Legion app; intro/origin Star Boy 40 80 120 244 402 560
283-Intro. The Phantom Zone; 1st app. of General Zod (cameo in 2 panels) 77 154 231 493 847 1200
285-1st Tales of the Bizarro World-c/story (ends #299) in Adv. (see Action #255) 24 48 72 140 234 325
286-1st Bizarro Mxyzptlk; Bizarro-c 23 46 69 136 223 310
290(11/61)-9th Legion app; origin Sunboy in Legion (last 10¢ issue) 37 74 111 222 361 500
291,292,295-298: 291-1st 12¢ ish, (12/61). 292-1st Bizarro Lana Lang & Lucy Lane. 295-Bizarro-c; 1st Bizarro Titano 10 20 30 64 132 200
293(2/62)-13th Legion app; Mon-El app.; Legion of Super Pets 1st app./origin; 1st Superhorse; 2nd app. General Zod; 1st Bizarro Luthor & Kandor 37 74 111 222 361 500
294-1st Bizarro Marilyn Monroe, Pres. Kennedy. 12 24 36 83 182 280
299-1st Gold Kryptonite (8/62) 10 20 30 66 138 210
300-Tales of the Legion of Super-Heroes series begins (9/62); Mon-El leaves Phantom Zone (temporarily), joins Legion 54 108 162 432 1066 1700
301-Origin Bouncing Boy 15 30 45 105 233 360
302-305: 303-1st app. Matter-Eater Lad. 304-Death of Lightning Lad in Legion 13 26 39 86 188 290
306-310: 306-Intro. Legion of Substitute Heroes. 307-1st app. Element Lad in Legion. 308-1st app. Lightning Lass in Legion. 309-1st app. Legion of Super-Monsters 12 24 36 79 170 260
311-320: 312-Lightning Lad back in Legion. 315-Last new Superboy story; Colossal Boy app. 316-Origins & powers of Legion given. 317-Intro. Dream Girl in Legion; Lightning Lass becomes Light Lass; Hall of Fame series begins. 320-Dev-Em 2nd app. 10 20 30 64 132 200
321-Intro. Time Trapper 9 18 27 58 114 170
322-330: 327-Intro/1st app. Lone Wolf in Legion. 329-Intro The Bizarro Legionnaires; intro. Legion flight rings 8 16 24 55 105 155
331-340: 337-Chlorophyll Kid & Night Girl app. 340-Intro Computo in Legion 8 16 24 51 96 140
341-Triplicate Girl becomes Duo Damsel 7 14 21 44 82 120
342-345,347-351: 345-Last Hall of Fame; returns in 356,371. 348-Origin Sunboy; intro Dr. Regulus in Legion. 349-Intro Universo & Rond Vidar. 351-1st app. White Witch 6 12 18 42 79 115
346-1st app. Karate Kid, Princess Projectra, Ferro Lad, & Nemesis Kid. 17 34 51 117 259 400
352,354-360: 354,355-Superman meets the Adult Legion. 355-Insect Queen joins Legion (4/67) 6 12 18 38 69 100
353-Death of Ferro Lad in Legion 9 18 27 59 117 175
361-364,366,368-370: 369-Intro Mordru in Legion 5 10 15 35 63 90
365,367: 365-Intro Shadow Lass (memorial to Shadow Woman app. in #354's Adult Legion-s); lists origins & powers of L.S.H. 367-New Legion headquarters 6 12 18 38 69 100
371,372: 371-Intro. Chemical King (mentioned in #354's Adult Legion-s). 372-Timber Wolf & Chemical King join 6 12 18 38 69 100
373,374,376-380: 373-Intro. Tornado Twins (Barry Allen Flash descendants). 374-Article on comics fandom. 380-Last Legion in Adventure; last 12¢-c 5 10 15 34 60 85
375-Intro Quantum Queen & The Wanderers 5 10 15 35 63 90
381-Supergirl begins; 1st full length Supergirl story & her 1st solo book (6/69) 14 28 42 96 211 325
382-389 5 10 15 31 53 75
390-Giant Supergirl G-69 6 12 18 41 76 110
391-396,398 4 8 12 23 37 50
397-1st app. new Supergirl 5 10 15 31 53 75
399-Unpubbed G.A. Black Canary story 4 8 12 25 40 55
400-New costume for Supergirl (12/70) 5 10 15 31 53 75
401,402,404-408-(15¢-c) 3 6 9 17 26 35
403-68 pg. Giant G-81; Legion-r/#304,305,308,312 6 12 18 38 69 100
409-411,413-415,417-420-(52 pgs.): 413-Hawkman by Kubert r/B&B #44; G.A. Robotman-r/Det. #178; Zatanna by Morrow. 414-r-2nd Animal Man/Str. Advs. #184. 415-Animal Man-r/Str. Adv.#190 (origin recap). 417-Morrow Vigilante; Frazetta Shining Knight-r/Adv. #161; origin The Enchantress; no Zatanna. 418-Prev. unpub. Dr. Mid-Nite story from 1948; no Zatanna. 420-Animal Man-r/Str. Adv. #195 3 6 9 18 28 38
412-(52 pgs.) Reprints origin & 1st app. of Animal Man from Strange Adventures #180 3 6 9 18 28 38
416-Also listed as DC 100 Pg. Super Spectacular #10; Golden Age-r; r/1st app. Black Canary from Flash #86; no Zatanna 10 20 30 68 144 220
421-424: 424-Last Supergirl in Adventure 3 6 9 14 20 25
425-New look, content change to adventure; Kaluta-c; Toth-a, origin Capt. Fear 3 6 9 16 23 30
426,427: 426-1st Adventurers Club. 427-Last Vigilante 2 4 6 9 12 15
428-Origin/1st app. Black Orchid (c/story, 6-7/73) 6 12 18 41 76 110
429,430-Black Orchid-c/stories 3 6 9 20 31 42
431-Spectre by Aparo begins, ends #440. 5 10 15 35 63 90
432-439-Spectre app. 433-437-Cover title is Weird Adventure Comics. 436-Last 20¢ issue 3 6 9 21 33 45
440-New Spectre origin 4 8 12 23 37 50
441-458: 441-452-Aquaman app. 443-Fisherman app. 445-447-The Creeper app. 446-Flag-c. 449-451-Martian Manhunter app. 450-Weather Wizard app. in Aquaman story. 453-458-Superboy app. 453-Intro. Mighty Girl. 457,458-Eclipso app. 1 3 4 6 8 10
459,460 (68 pgs.): 459-New Gods/Darkseid storyline concludes from New Gods #19 (#459 is dated 9-10/78) without missing a month. 459-Flash (ends #466), Deadman (ends #466), Wonder Woman (ends #464), Green Lantern (ends #460). 460-Aquaman (ends #478) 3 6 9 14 20 26
461-($1.00, 68 pgs.) Justice Society begins; ends 466 4 8 12 25 40 55
462-($1.00, 68 pgs.) Death Earth II Batman 5 10 15 33 57 80
463-466 ($1.00 size, 68 pgs.) 2 4 6 10 14 18
467-Starman by Ditko & Plastic Man begins; 1st app. Prince Gavyn (Starman). 2 4 6 8 11 14
468-490: 470-Origin Starman. 479-Dial 'H' For Hero begins, ends #490. 478-Last Starman & Plastic Man. 480-490: Dial 'H' For Hero 5.00
491-503: 491-100pg. Digest size begins; r/Legion of Super Heroes/Adv. #247, 267; Spectre, Aquaman, Superboy, S&K Sandman, Black Canary-r & new Shazam by Newton begin. 492,495,496,499-S&K Sandman-r/Adventure in all. 493-Challengers of the Unknown begins by Tuska w/brief origin. 493-495,497-499-G.A. Captain Marvel-r. 494-499-Spectre-r/Spectre 1-3, 5-7. 496-Capt. Marvel Jr. new-s, Cockrum-a. 498-Mary Marvel new-s; Plastic Man-r begin; origin Bouncing Boy-r/ #301. 500-Legion-r (Digest size, 148 pgs.).
501-503: G.A.-r 2 4 6 9 13 16
... 80 Page Giant (10/98, $4.95) Wonder Woman, Shazam, Superboy, Supergirl, Green Arrow, Legion, Bizarro World stories 5.00

NOTE: *Bizarro covers-285, 286, 288, 294, 295, 329. Vigilante app.-420, 426, 427.* **N. Adams** *a(r)-495i-498i; c-365-369, 371-373, 375-379, 381-383.* **Aparo** *a-431-433, 434i, 435, 436, 437i, 438i, 439-452, 503r; c-431-452.* **Austin** *a-449i 451i.* **Bernard Baily** *c-48, 50, 52-59.* **Bolland** *c-475.* **Burnley** *c-61-72, 116-120p.* **Chaykin** *a-438.* **Ditko** *a-467-478p; c-467p.* **Creig Flessel** *c-32, 33, 40, 42, 44, 46, 47, 51, 60.* **Giffen** *c-491p-494p, 500p.* **Grell** *a-435-437, 440.* **Guardineer** *c-34, 35, 45.* **Infantino** *a-416r.* **Kaluta** *c-425.* **Bob Kane** *a-38.* **G. Kane** *a-414r, 425; c-496-499, 537.* **Kirby** *a-250-256.* **Kubert** *a-413.* **Meskin** *a-81,125,127.* **Moldoff** *a-494i; c-49.* **Morrow** *a-413-415, 417, 422, 502r, 503r.* **Netzer/Nasser** *a-449-451.* **Newton** *a-459-461, 464-466, 491p, 492p.* **Paul Norris** *a-69.* **Orlando** *a-457p, 458p.* **Perez** *c-484-486, 490p.* **Simon/Kirby** *a-503r; c-73-97, 100-102.* **Starlin** *c-471.* **Staton** *a-445-447i, 456-458p, 459, 460, 461p-465p, 466,467p-478p, 502p(r); c-458, 461(back).* **Toth** *a-418, 419, 425, 431, 495p-497p.* **Tuska** *a-494p.*

ADVENTURE COMICS (Also see All Star Comics 1999 crossover titles)
DC Comics: May, 1999 ($1.99, one-shot)

1-Golden Age Starman and the Atom; Snejbjerg-a 3.00

ADVENTURE COMICS (See Final Crisis: Legion of Three Worlds)
DC Comics: No. 0, Apr, 2009 - No. 12, Aug, 2010; No. 516, Sept, 2010 - No. 529, Oct, 2011 ($1.00/$3.99)

0-($1.00) R/Adventure Comics #247; new Luthor & Brainiac back-up-s; Lopresti-c 3.00
1-7-($3.99) Superboy stories; Johns-s/Manapul-a; Legion back-up-s. 5-7-Blackest Night 4.00
1-12-Variant 7-panel covers by various numbered with original #504-#515 5.00
8-12: 8-11-New Krypton x-over. 11-Mon-El leaves 21st century. 12-Legion; Levitz-s 4.00
516-521: 516-(9/10, resumes original numbering) flashback to Legion formation; Atom back-ups. 521-Adult Legion resumes; Mon-El joins Green Lanterns 4.00
522-529-($2.99) Legion Academy. 523-527-Jimenez-a/c 3.00

ADVENTURE COMICS SPECIAL (See New Krypton issues in 2009 Superman titles)
DC Comics: Jan, 2009 ($2.99, one-shot)

... Featuring the Guardian - James Robinson-s/Pere Pérez-a; origin re-told; intro. Gwen 3.00

ADVENTURE INTO MYSTERY

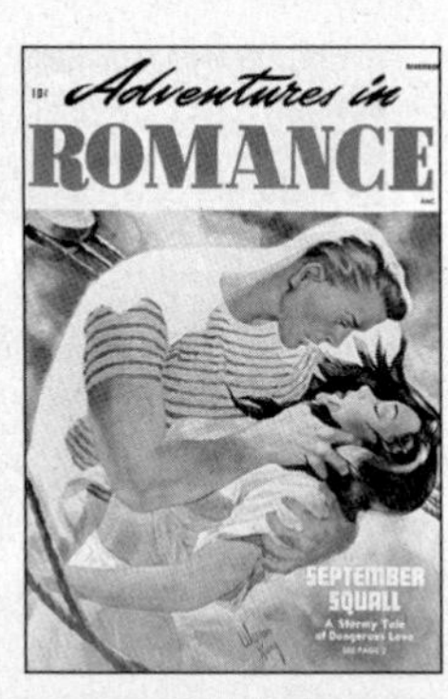

Adventures #1 © STJ

Adventures into Darkness #9 © STD

Adventures into the Unknown #14 © AC

Atlas Comics (BFP No. 1/OPI No. 2-8): May, 1956 - No. 8, July, 1957

	GD 2.0	VG 4.0	FN 6.0	VF 8.0	VF/NM 9.0	NM- 9.2
1-Powell s/f-a; Forte-a; Everett-c	65	130	195	416	708	1000
2-Flying Saucer story	36	72	108	211	343	475
3,6-Everett-c	32	64	96	188	307	425
4,5,7: 4-Williamson-a, 4 pgs; Powell-a. 5-Everett-c/a, Orlando-a. 7-Torres-a; Everett-c	34	68	102	199	325	450
8-Moreira, Sale, Torres, Woodbridge-a, Severin-c	32	64	96	188	307	425

ADVENTURE IS MY CAREER
U.S. Coast Guard Academy/Street & Smith: 1945 (44 pgs.)

	GD 2.0	VG 4.0	FN 6.0	VF 8.0	VF/NM 9.0	NM- 9.2
nn-Simon, Milt Gross-a	22	44	66	128	209	290

ADVENTURERS, THE
Aircel Comics/Adventure Publ.: Aug, 1986 - No. 10, 1987? ($1.50, B&W)
V2#1, 1987 - V2#9, 1988; V3#1, Oct, 1989 - V3#6, 1990

	GD 2.0	VG 4.0	FN 6.0	VF 8.0	VF/NM 9.0	NM- 9.2
1-Peter Hsu-a	1	2	3	5	6	8
1-Cover variant, limited ed.	2	4	6	9	12	15
1-2nd print (1986); 1st app. Elf Warrior						3.00
2,3, 0 (#4, 12/86)-Origin, 5-10, Book II, reg. & Limited Ed. #1						3.50
Book II, #2,3,0,4-9						3.00
Book III, #1 (10/89, $2.25)-Reg. & limited-c, Book III, #2-6						3.00

ADVENTURES (No. 2 Spectacular… on cover)
St. John Publishing Co.: Nov, 1949 - No. 2, Feb, 1950 (No. 1 …in Romance on cover)
(Slightly larger size)

	GD 2.0	VG 4.0	FN 6.0	VF 8.0	VF/NM 9.0	NM- 9.2
1(Scarce); Bolle, Starr-a(2)	37	74	111	222	361	500
2(Scarce)-Slave Girl; China Bombshell app.; Bolle, L. Starr-a	47	94	141	296	498	700

ADVENTURES FOR BOYS
Bailey Enterprises: Dec, 1954

	GD 2.0	VG 4.0	FN 6.0	VF 8.0	VF/NM 9.0	NM- 9.2
nn-Comics, text, & photos	8	16	24	40	50	60

ADVENTURES IN PARADISE (TV)
Dell Publishing Co.: Feb-Apr, 1962

	GD 2.0	VG 4.0	FN 6.0	VF 8.0	VF/NM 9.0	NM- 9.2
Four Color #1301	6	12	18	37	66	95

ADVENTURES IN ROMANCE (See Adventures)

ADVENTURES IN SCIENCE (See Classics Illustrated Special Issue)

ADVENTURES IN THE DC UNIVERSE
DC Comics: Apr, 1997 - No. 19, Oct, 1998 ($1.75/$1.95/$1.99)

	GD 2.0	VG 4.0	FN 6.0	VF 8.0	VF/NM 9.0	NM- 9.2
1-Animated style in all: JLA-c/app						5.00
2-11,13-17,19: 2-Flash app. 3-Wonder Woman. 4-Green Lantern. 6-Aquaman. 7-Shazam Family. 8-Blue Beetle & Booster Gold. 9-Flash. 10-Legion. 11-Green Lantern & Wonder Woman. 13-Impulse & Martian Manhunter. 14-Superboy/Flash race						3.50
12,18-JLA-c/app						3.50
Annual 1(1997, $3.95)-Dr. Fate, Impulse, Rose & Thorn, Superboy, Mister Miracle app.						4.50

ADVENTURES IN THE RIFLE BRIGADE
DC Comics (Vertigo): Oct, 2000 - No. 3, Dec, 2000 ($2.50, limited series)

	GD 2.0	VG 4.0	FN 6.0	VF 8.0	VF/NM 9.0	NM- 9.2
1-3-Ennis-s/Ezquerra-a/Bolland-c						3.00
TPB (2004, $14.95) r/series and Operation Bollock series						15.00

ADVENTURES IN THE RIFLE BRIGADE: OPERATION BOLLOCK
DC Comics (Vertigo): Oct, 2001 - No. 3, Jan, 2002 ($2.50, limited series)

	GD 2.0	VG 4.0	FN 6.0	VF 8.0	VF/NM 9.0	NM- 9.2
1-3-Ennis-s/Ezquerra-a/Fabry-c						3.00

ADVENTURES IN 3-D (With glasses)
Harvey Publications: Nov, 1953 - No. 2, Jan, 1954 (25¢)

	GD 2.0	VG 4.0	FN 6.0	VF 8.0	VF/NM 9.0	NM- 9.2
1-Nostrand, Powell-a, 2-Powell-a	14	28	42	80	115	150

ADVENTURES INTO DARKNESS (See Seduction of the Innocent 3-D)
Better-Standard Publications/Visual Editions: No. 5, Aug, 1952- No. 14, 1954

	GD 2.0	VG 4.0	FN 6.0	VF 8.0	VF/NM 9.0	NM- 9.2
5-Katz-c/a; Toth-a(p)	53	106	159	334	567	800
6-Tuska, Katz-a	42	84	126	265	445	625
7-9: 7-Katz-c/a. 8,9-Toth-a(p)	40	80	120	246	411	575
10-12: 10,11-Jack Katz-a. 12-Toth-a; lingerie panel	39	78	117	231	378	525
13-Toth-a(p); Cannibalism story cited by T. E. Murphy articles	48	96	144	302	514	725
14	34	68	102	199	325	450

NOTE: ***Fawcette** a-13. **Moreira** a-5. **Sekowsky** a-10, 11, 13(2).*

ADVENTURES INTO TERROR (Formerly Joker Comics)
Marvel/Atlas Comics (CDS): No. 43, Nov, 1950 - No. 31, May, 1954

	GD 2.0	VG 4.0	FN 6.0	VF 8.0	VF/NM 9.0	NM- 9.2
43(#1)	90	180	270	576	988	1400
44(#2, 2/51)-Sol Brodsky-c	50	100	150	315	533	750
3(4/51), 4	41	82	123	256	428	600
5-Wolverton-c panel/Mystic #6; Rico-c panel also; Atom Bomb story	43	86	129	271	461	650
6,8: 8-Wolverton text illo r-/Marvel Tales #104; prototype of Spider-Man villain The Lizard	41	82	123	256	428	600
7-Wolverton-a "Where Monsters Dwell", 6 pgs.; Tuska-c; Maneely-c panels	69	138	207	442	759	1075
9,10,12-Krigstein-a. 9-Decapitation panels	39	78	117	240	395	550
11,13-20	37	74	111	222	361	500
21-24,26-31	36	72	108	211	343	475
25-Matt Fox-a	39	78	117	240	395	550

NOTE: ***Ayers** a-21. **Colan** a-3, 5, 14, 21, 24, 25, 28, 29; c-27. **Colletta** a-30. **Everett** c-13, 21, 25. **Fass** a-28, 29. **Forte** a-28. **Heath** a-43, 44, 4-6, 22, 24, 26; c-43, 9, 11. **Lazarus** a-7. **Maneely** a-7(3 pg.), 10, 11, 21., 22 c-15, 29. **Don Rico** a-4, 5(3 pg.). **Sekowsky** a-43, 3, 4. **Sinnott** a-8, 9, 11, 24, 28. **Tuska** a-14; c-7.*

ADVENTURES INTO THE UNKNOWN
American Comics Group: Fall, 1948 - No. 174, Aug, 1967 (No. 1-33: 52 pgs.)
(1st continuous series Supernatural comic; see Eerie #1)

	GD 2.0	VG 4.0	FN 6.0	VF 8.0	VF/NM 9.0	NM- 9.2
1-Guardineer-a; adapt. of 'Castle of Otranto' by Horace Walpole	268	536	804	1702	2926	4150
2,3: 3-Feldstein-a (9 pgs)	90	180	270	576	988	1400
4,5: 5- 'Spirit Of Frankenstein' series begins, ends #12 (except #11)	45	90	135	284	480	675
6-10	37	74	111	222	361	500
11-16,18-20: 13-Starr-a. 15-Hitler app.	32	64	96	188	307	425
17-Story similar to movie 'The Thing'	36	72	108	211	343	475
21-26,28-30	26	52	78	154	252	350
27-Williamson/Krenkel-a (8 pgs.)	32	64	96	188	307	425
31-50: 38-Atom bomb panels; Devil-c	20	40	60	118	192	265
51-(1/54)-(3-D effect-c/story)-Only white cover	52	104	156	328	552	775
52-58: (3-D effect-c/stories with black covers). 52-E.C. swipe/Haunt Of Fear #14	48	96	144	302	514	725
59-3-D effect story only; new logo	34	68	102	199	325	450
60-Wood*esque*-a by Landau	15	30	45	88	137	185
61-Last pre-code issue (1-2/55)	15	30	45	88	137	185
62-70	7	14	21	46	86	125
71-90: 80-Hydrogen bomb panel	6	12	18	37	66	95
91,96(#95 on inside),107,116-All have Williamson-a	6	12	18	40	73	105
92-95,97-99,101-106,108-115,117-128: 109-113,118-Whitney painted-c. 128-Williamson/Krenkel/Torres-a(r)/Forbidden Worlds #63; last 10¢ issue	5	10	15	31	53	75
100	5	10	15	34	60	85
129-153,157: 153,157-Magic Agent app.	4	8	12	23	37	50
154-Nemesis series begins (origin), ends #170	4	8	12	28	47	65
155,156,158-167,170-174: 174-Flying saucer-c	4	8	12	22	35	48
168-Ditko-a(p)	4	8	12	27	44	60
169-Nemesis battles Hitler	4	8	12	27	44	60
Nemesis Archives: Vol. One (Dark Horse Books, 9/08, $59.95) r/#154-170; creator bios						60.00

NOTE: *"Spirit of Frankenstein" series in 5, 6, 8-10, 12, 16. **Buscema** a-100, 106, 108-110, 158r, 165r. **Cameron** a-34. **Craig** a-152, 160. **Goode** a-45, 47, 60. **Landau** a-51, 59-63. **Lazarus** a-34, 48, 51, 52, 56, 58, 79, 87; c-31-56, 58. **Reinman** a-102, 111, 112, 115-118, 124, 130, 137, 141, 145, 164. **Whitney** c-12-30, 57, 59-on (most.) **Torres/Williamson** a-116.*

ADVENTURES INTO WEIRD WORLDS
Marvel/Atlas Comics (ACI): Jan, 1952 - No. 30, June, 1954

	GD 2.0	VG 4.0	FN 6.0	VF 8.0	VF/NM 9.0	NM- 9.2
1-Atom bomb panels	132	264	396	838	1444	2050
2-Sci/fic stories (2); one by Maneely	50	100	150	315	533	750
3-10: 7-Tongue ripped out. 10-Krigstein, Everett-a	42	84	126	265	445	625
11-20	39	78	117	231	378	525
21-Hitler in Hell story	43	86	129	271	461	650
22-26: 24-Man holds hypo & splits in two-c	37	74	111	222	361	500
27-Matt Fox end of world story-a; severed head-c	55	110	165	352	601	850
28-Atom bomb story; decapitation panels	39	78	117	240	395	550
29,30	34	68	102	199	325	450

NOTE: ***Ayers** a-8, 26. **Everett** a-4, 5; c-6, 8, 10-13, 18, 19, 22, 24, 25; a-4, 25. **Fass** a-7. **Forte** a-21, 24. **Al Hartley** a-2. **Heath** a-1, 4, 17, 22; c-7, 9, 20. **Maneely** a-2, 3, 11, 20, 22, 23, 25; c-1, 3, 22, 25-27, 29. **Reinman** a-24, 28. **Rico** a-13. **Robinson** a-13. **Sinnott** a-25, 30. **Tuska** a-1, 2, 12, 15. **Whitney** a-7. **Wildey** a-28. Bondage c-22.*

ADVENTURES IN WONDERLAND (Also see Uncle Charlies Fables)
Lev Gleason Publications: April, 1955 - No. 5, Feb, 1956 (Jr. Readers Guild)

	GD 2.0	VG 4.0	FN 6.0	VF 8.0	VF/NM 9.0	NM- 9.2
1-Maurer-a	12	24	36	67	94	120
2-4	8	16	24	40	50	60
5-Christmas issue	8	16	24	42	54	65

ADVENTURES OF ALAN LADD, THE
National Periodical Publ.: Oct-Nov, 1949 - No. 9, Feb-Mar, 1951 (All 52 pgs.)

	GD 2.0	VG 4.0	FN 6.0	VF 8.0	VF/NM 9.0	NM- 9.2
1-Photo-c	81	162	243	518	884	1250
2-Photo-c	40	80	120	246	411	575

Adventures of Baron Munchausen #1 © Now Comics

Adventures of Dean Martin and Jerry Lewis #17 © DC

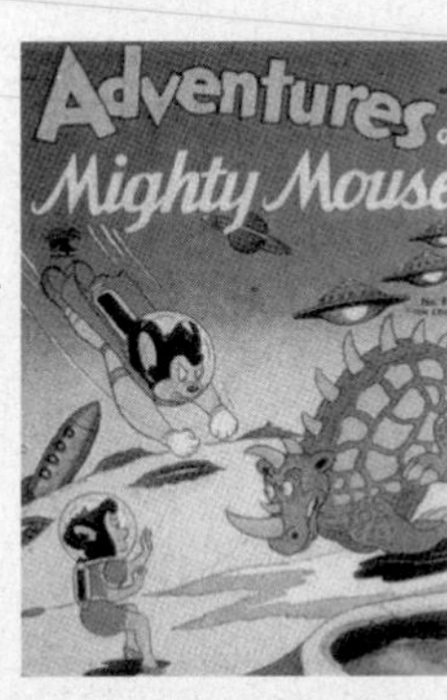

Adventures of Mighty Mouse #8 © Paul Terry

	GD 2.0	VG 4.0	FN 6.0	VF 8.0	VF/NM 9.0	NM- 9.2
3-6: Last photo-c	36	72	108	211	343	475
7-9	30	60	90	177	289	400

NOTE: *Dan Barry a-1. Moreira a-3-7.*

ADVENTURES OF ALICE (Also see Alice in Wonderland) (Becomes Alice at Monkey Island #3)
Civil Service Publ./Pentagon Publishing Co.: 1945

	GD 2.0	VG 4.0	FN 6.0	VF 8.0	VF/NM 9.0	NM- 9.2
1	15	30	45	85	130	175
2-Through the Magic Looking Glass	11	22	33	64	90	115

ADVENTURES OF BARON MUNCHAUSEN, THE
Now Comics: July, 1989 - No. 4, Oct, 1989 ($1.75, limited series)

1-4: Movie adaptation 3.00

ADVENTURES OF BARRY WEEN, BOY GENIUS, THE
Image Comics: Mar, 1999 - No. 3, May, 1999 ($2.95, B&W, limited series)

1-3-Judd Winick-s/a 3.00
...: Secret Crisis Origin Files (Oni, 7/04, Free Comic Book Day giveaway) - Winick-s/a 3.00
TPB (Oni Press, 11/99, $8.95) r/#1-3 9.00

ADVENTURES OF BARRY WEEN, BOY GENIUS 2.0, THE
Oni Press: Feb, 2000 - No. 3, Apr, 2000 ($2.95, B&W, limited series)

1-3-Judd Winick-s/a 3.00
TPB (2000, $8.95) 9.00

ADVENTURES OF BARRY WEEN, BOY GENIUS 3, THE : MONKEY TALES
Oni Press: Feb, 2001 - No. 6, Feb, 2002 ($2.95, B&W, limited series)

1-6-Judd Winick-s/a 3.00
TPB (2001, $8.95) r/#1-3; intro. by Peter David 9.00
...4 TPB (5/02, $8.95) r/#4-6 9.00

ADVENTURES OF BAYOU BILLY, THE (Based on video game)
Archie Comics: Sept, 1989 - No. 5, June, 1990 ($1.00)

1-5: Esposito-c/a(i). 5-Kelley Jones-c 3.00

ADVENTURES OF BOB HOPE, THE (Also see True Comics #59)
National Per. Publ.: Feb-Mar, 1950 - No. 109, Feb-Mar, 1968 (#1-10: 52pgs.)

	GD 2.0	VG 4.0	FN 6.0	VF 8.0	VF/NM 9.0	NM- 9.2
1-Photo-c	258	516	774	1651	2826	4000
2-Photo-c	92	184	276	584	1005	1425
3,4-Photo-c	57	114	171	362	619	875
5-10: 9-Horror-c	41	82	123	256	428	600
11-20	29	58	87	170	278	385
21-31 (2-3/55; last precode)	20	40	60	117	189	260
32-40	9	18	27	61	123	185
41-50	8	16	24	54	102	150
51-70	7	14	21	46	86	125
71-93	5	10	15	35	63	90
94-Aquaman cameo	6	12	18	38	69	100
95-1st app. Super-Hip & 1st monster issue (11/65)	8	16	24	51	96	140
96-105: Super-Hip and monster stories in all. 103-Batman, Robin, Ringo Starr cameos	5	10	15	34	60	85
106-109-All monster-c/stories by N. Adams-c/a	7	14	21	49	92	135

NOTE: *Buzzy in #34. Kitty Karr of Hollywood in #15, 17-20, 23, 28. Liz in #26, 109. Miss Beverly Hills of Hollywood in #7, 8, 10, 13, 14. Miss Melody Lane of Broadway in #15. Rusty in #23, 25. Tommy in #24. No 2nd feature in #2-4, 6, 8, 11, 12, 28-108.*

ADVENTURES OF CAPTAIN AMERICA
Marvel Comics: Sept, 1991 - No. 4, Jan, 1992 ($4.95, 52 pgs., squarebound, limited series)

1-4: 1-Origin in WW2; embossed-c; Nicieza scripts; Maguire-c/a(p) begins, ends #3. 2-4-Austin-c/a(i). 3,4-Red Skull app. 5.00

ADVENTURES OF CYCLOPS AND PHOENIX (Also See Askani'son & The Further Adventures of Cyclops And Phoenix)
Marvel Comics: May, 1994 - No. 4, Aug, 1994 ($2.95, limited series)

1-4-Characters from X-Men; origin of Cable 4.00
Trade paperback ($14.95)-reprints #1-4 15.00

ADVENTURES OF DEAN MARTIN AND JERRY LEWIS, THE
(The Adventures of Jerry Lewis #41 on) (See Movie Love #12)
National Periodical Publications: July-Aug, 1952 - No. 40, Oct, 1957

	GD 2.0	VG 4.0	FN 6.0	VF 8.0	VF/NM 9.0	NM- 9.2
1	145	290	435	921	1586	2250
2-3 pg origin on how they became a team	60	120	180	381	653	925
3-10: 3- I Love Lucy text featurette	36	72	108	211	343	475
11-19: Last precode (2/55)	22	44	66	132	216	300
20-30	17	34	51	98	154	210
31-40	15	30	45	83	124	165

ADVENTURES OF DETECTIVE ACE KING, THE (Also see Bob Scully-- & Detective Dan)
Humor Publ. Corp.: No date (1933) (36 pgs., 9-1/2x12") (10¢, B&W, one-shot) (paper-c)

	GD 2.0	VG 4.0	FN 6.0	VF 8.0	VF/NM 9.0	NM- 9.2
Book 1-Along with Bob Scully & Detective Dan, the first comic w/original art & the first of a single theme.; Not reprints; Ace King by Martin Nadle (The American Sherlock Holmes). A Dick Tracy look-alike	625	1250	1875	5000	-	-

ADVENTURES OF EVIL AND MALICE, THE
Image Comics: June, 1999 - No. 3, Nov, 1999 ($3.50/$3.95, limited series)

1-3-Jimmie Robinson-s/a. 3-($3.95-c) 4.00

ADVENTURES OF FELIX THE CAT, THE
Harvey Comics: May, 1992 ($1.25)

1-Messmer-r 5.00

ADVENTURES OF FORD FAIRLANE, THE
DC Comics: May, 1990 - No. 4, Aug, 1990 ($1.50, limited series, mature)

1-4: Andrew Dice Clay movie tie-in; Don Heck inks 4.00

ADVENTURES OF HOMER COBB, THE
Say/Bart Prod. : Sept, 1947 (Oversized) (Published in the U.S., but printed in Canada)

	GD 2.0	VG 4.0	FN 6.0	VF 8.0	VF/NM 9.0	NM- 9.2
1-(Scarce)-Feldstein-c/a	47	94	141	296	498	700

ADVENTURES OF HOMER GHOST (See Homer The Happy Ghost)
Atlas Comics: June, 1957 - No. 2, Aug, 1957

	GD 2.0	VG 4.0	FN 6.0	VF 8.0	VF/NM 9.0	NM- 9.2
V1#1,2: 2-Robot-c	16	32	48	94	147	200

ADVENTURES OF JERRY LEWIS, THE (Adventures of Dean Martin & Jerry Lewis No. 1-40) (See Super DC Giant)
National Periodical Publ.: No. 41, Nov, 1957 - No. 124, May-June, 1971

	GD 2.0	VG 4.0	FN 6.0	VF 8.0	VF/NM 9.0	NM- 9.2
41	9	18	27	62	126	190
42-60	7	14	21	49	92	135
61-67,69-73,75-80	6	12	18	41	76	110
68,74-Photo-c (movie)	9	18	27	60	120	180
81,82,85-87,90,91,94,96,98,99	5	10	15	34	60	85
83,84,88: 83-1st Monsters-c/s. 84-Jerry as a Super-hero-c/s. 88-1st Witch, Miss Kraft	6	12	18	38	69	100
89-Bob Hope app.; Wizard of Oz & Alfred E. Neuman in MAD parody	6	12	18	41	76	110
92-Superman cameo	6	12	18	41	76	110
93-Beatles parody as babies	6	12	18	38	69	100
95-1st Uncle Hal Wack-A-Boy Camp-c/s	6	12	18	38	69	100
97-Batman/Robin/Joker-c/story; Riddler & Penguin app; Dick Sprang-c.	8	16	24	56	108	160
100	6	12	18	40	73	105
101,103,104-Neal Adams-c/a	7	14	21	46	86	125
102-Beatles app.; Neal Adams c/a	9	18	27	57	111	165
105-Superman x-over	6	12	18	41	76	110
106-111,113-116	4	8	12	28	47	65
112,117: 112-Flash x-over. 117-W. Woman x-over	6	12	18	40	73	105
118-124	4	8	12	27	44	60

NOTE: *Monster-c/s-90,93,96,98,101. Wack-A-Buy Camp-c/s-96,99,102,107,108.*

ADVENTURES OF JO-JOY, THE (See Jo-Joy)

ADVENTURES OF LASSIE, THE (See Lassie)

ADVENTURES OF LUTHER ARKWRIGHT, THE
Valkyrie Press/Dark Horse Comics: Oct, 1987 - No. 9, Jan, 1989 ($2.00, B&W) V2, #1, Mar, 1990 - V2#9, 1990 ($1.95, B&W)

1-9: 1-Alan Moore intro., V2#1-9 (Dark Horse): r-1st series; new-c 4.00
TPB (1997, $14.95) r/#1-9 w/Michael Moorcock intro. 15.00

ADVENTURES OF MIGHTY MOUSE (Mighty Mouse Adventures No. 1)
St. John Publishing Co.: No. 2, Jan, 1952 - No. 18, May, 1955

	GD 2.0	VG 4.0	FN 6.0	VF 8.0	VF/NM 9.0	NM- 9.2
2	29	58	87	172	281	390
3-5	15	30	45	90	140	190
6-18	13	26	39	72	101	130

ADVENTURES OF MIGHTY MOUSE (2nd Series) (Becomes Mighty Mouse #161 on) (Two No. 144's; formerly Paul Terry's Comics; No. 129-137 have nn's)
St. John/Pines/Dell/Gold Key: No. 126, Aug, 1955 - No. 160, Oct, 1963

	GD 2.0	VG 4.0	FN 6.0	VF 8.0	VF/NM 9.0	NM- 9.2
126(8/55), 127(10/55), 128(11/55)-St. John	10	20	30	56	76	95
nn(129, 4/56)-144(8/59)-Pines	5	10	15	30	50	70
144(10-12/59)-155(7-9/62) Dell	4	8	12	27	44	60
156(10/62)-160(10/63) Gold Key	4	8	12	27	44	60

NOTE: *Early issues titled "Paul Terry's Adventures of ...."*

ADVENTURES OF MIGHTY MOUSE (Formerly Mighty Mouse)
Gold Key: No. 166, Mar, 1979 - No. 172, Jan, 1980

	GD 2.0	VG 4.0	FN 6.0	VF 8.0	VF/NM 9.0	NM- 9.2
166-172	1	2	3	5	6	8

ADVS. OF MR. FROG & MISS MOUSE (See Dell Junior Treasury No. 4)

ADVENTURES OF OZZIE & HARRIET, THE (See Ozzie & Harriet)

Adventures of Pinky Lee #2 © MAR

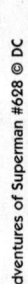

Adventures of Superman #628 © DC

Adventures of the Mask #4 © DH

ADVENTURES OF PATORUZU
Green Publishing Co.: Aug, 1946 - Winter, 1946
nn's-Contains Animal Crackers reprints 6 12 18 28 34 40

ADVENTURES OF PINKY LEE, THE (TV)
Atlas Comics: July, 1955 - No. 5, Dec, 1955
1 28 56 84 165 270 375
2-5 17 34 51 98 154 210

ADVENTURES OF PIPSQUEAK, THE (Formerly Pat the Brat)
Archie Publications (Radio Comics): No. 34, Sept, 1959 - No. 39, July, 1960
34 3 6 9 21 33 45
35-39 3 6 9 17 26 35

ADVENTURES OF QUAKE & QUISP, THE (See Quaker Oats "Plenty of Glutton")

ADVENTURES OF REX THE WONDER DOG, THE (Rex...No. 1)
National Periodical Publ.: Jan-Feb, 1952 - No. 45, May-June, 1959; No. 46, Nov-Dec, 1959
1-(Scarce)-Toth-c/a 213 426 639 1363 2332 3300
2-(Scarce)-Toth-c/a 84 168 252 538 919 1300
3-(Scarce)-Toth-a 61 122 183 390 670 950
4,5 48 96 144 302 514 725
6-10 40 80 120 246 411 575
11-Atom bomb-c/story; dinosaur-c/sty 45 90 135 284 480 675
12-19: 19-Last precode (1-2/55) 30 60 90 177 289 400
20-46 21 42 63 122 199 275
NOTE: *Infantino, Gil Kane* art in 5-19 (most)

ADVENTURES OF ROBIN HOOD, THE (Formerly Robin Hood)
Magazine Enterprises (Sussex Publ. Co.): No. 6, Jun, 1957 - No. 8, Nov, 1957 (Based on Richard Greene TV Show)
6-8-Richard Greene photo-c. 6,7-Powell-a 15 30 45 83 124 165

ADVENTURES OF ROBIN HOOD, THE
Gold Key: Mar, 1974 - No. 7, Jan, 1975 (Disney cartoon) (36 pgs.)
1(90291-403)-Part-r of $1.50 editions 2 4 6 13 18 22
2-7: 1-7 are part-r 2 4 6 8 11 14

ADVENTURES OF SNAKE PLISSKEN
Marvel Comics: Jan, 1997 ($2.50, one-shot)
1-Based on Escape From L.A. movie; Brereton-c 4.00

ADVENTURES OF SPAWN, THE
Image Comics (Todd McFarlane Prods.): Jan, 2007; Nov, 2008 ($5.99)
1,2-Printed adaptation of the Spawn.com web comic; Khary Randolph-a 6.00

ADVENTURES OF SPIDER-MAN, THE (Based on animated TV series)
Marvel Comics: Apr, 1996 - No. 12, Mar, 1997 (99¢)
1-12: 1-Punisher app. 2-Venom cameo. 3-X-Men. 6-Fantastic Four 3.00

ADVENTURES OF SUPERBOY, THE (See Superboy, 2nd Series)

ADVENTURES OF SUPERGIRL (Based on the TV series)
DC Comics: Early Jul, 2016 - No. 6, Sept, 2016 ($2.99)(Printing of stories first appearing online)
1-6: 1-Rampage app.; Bengal-a/Staggs-c 3.00

ADVENTURES OF SUPERMAN (Formerly Superman)
DC Comics: No. 424, Jan, 1987 - No. 499, Feb, 1993; No. 500, Early June, 1993 - No. 649, Apr, 2006 (This title's numbering continues with Superman #650, May, 2006)
424-Ordway-c/a; Wolfman-s begin following Byrne's Superman revamp; 1st Cat Grant 4.00
425-435,437-462: 426-Legends x-over. 432-1st app. Jose Delgado who becomes Gangbuster in #434. 437-Millennium x-over. 438-New Brainiac app. 440-Batman app. 449-Invasion 3.00
436-Byrne scripts begin; Millennium x-over 3.50
463-Superman/Flash race; cover swipe/Superman #199 5.00
464-Lobo-c & app. (pre-dates Lobo #1) 5.00
465-1st app. Hank Henshaw (later becomes Cyborg Superman) 1 2 3 5 6 8
466-479,481-495: 467-Part 2 of Batman story. 473-Hal Jordan, Guy Gardner x-over. 477-Legion app. 491-Last $1.00-c. 495-Forever People-c/story; Darkseid app. 3.00
480,496,497: 480-($1.75, 52 pgs.). 496-Doomsday cameo. 497-Doomsday battle issue 4.00
496,497-2nd printings 3.00
498,499-Funeral for a Friend; Supergirl app. 4.00
498-2nd & 3rd printings 3.00
500-($2.95, 68 pgs.)-Collector's edition w/card 5.00
500-($2.50, 68 pgs.)-Regular edition w/different-c 4.00
500-Platinum edition 45.00
501-($1.95)-Collector's edition with die-cut-c 3.50
501-($1.50)-Regular edition w/mini-poster & diff.-c 3.00
502-516: 502-Supergirl-c/story. 508-Challengers of the Unknown app. 510-Bizarro-c/story. 516-(9/94)-Zero Hour 3.00
505-($2.50)-Holo-grafx foil-c edition 3.50
0,517-523: 0-(10/94). 517-(11/94) 3.00
524-549,551-580: 524-Begin $1.95-c. 527-Return of Alpha Centurion (Zero Hour). 533-Impulse-c/app. 535-Luthor-c/app. 536-Brainiac app. 537-Parasite app. 540-Final Night x-over. 541-Superboy-c/app.; Lois & Clark honeymoon. 545-New powers. 546-New costume. 555-Red & Blue Supermen battle. 557-Millennium Giants x-over. 558-560: Superman Silver Age-style story; Krypto app. 561-Begin $1.99-c. 565-JLA app. 3.00
550-($3.50)-Double sized 4.00
581-588: 581-Begin $2.25-c. 583-Emperor Joker. 588-Casey-s 3.00
589-595: 589-Return to Krypton; Rivoche-c. 591-Wolfman-s. 593-595-Our Worlds at War x-over. 593-New Suicide Squad formed. 594-Doomsday-c/app. 3.00
596-Aftermath of "War" x-over has panel showing damaged World Trade Center buildings; issue went on sale the day after the Sept. 11 attack 6.00
597-599,601-624: 597-Joker: Last Laugh. 604,605-Ultraman, Owlman, Superwoman app. 606-Return to Krypton. 612-616,619-623-Nowlan-c. 624-Mr. Majestic app. 3.00
600-($3.95) Wieringo-a; painted-c by Adel; pin-ups by various 4.00
625,626-Godfall parts 2,5; Turner-c; Caldwell-a(p) 4.00
627-641,643-648: 627-Begin $2.50-c, Rucka-s/Clark-a/Ha-c begin. 628-Wagner-c. 631-Bagged with Sky Captain CD; Lois shot. 634-Mxyzptlk visits DC offices. 639-Capt. Marvel & Eclipso app. 641-OMAC app. 643-Sacrifice aftermath; Batman & Wonder Woman app. 3.00
642-OMAC Project x-over Sacrifice pt. 3; JLA app. 5.00
642-(2nd printing) red tone cover 3.00
649-Last issue; Infinite Crisis x-over, Superman vs. Earth-2 Superman 4.00
#1,000,000 (11/98) Gene Ha-c; 853rd Century x-over 3.00
Annual 1 (1987, $1.25, 52 pgs.)-Starlin-c & scripts 4.00
Annual 2,3 (1990, 1991, $2.00, 68 pgs.): 2-Byrne-c/a(i); Legion '90 (Lobo) app. 3-Armageddon 2001 x-over 4.00
Annual 4-6 ('92-'94, $2.50, 68 pgs.): 4-Guy Gardner/Lobo-c/story; Eclipso storyline; Quesada-c(p). 5-Bloodlines storyline. 6-Elseworlds sty. 4.00
Annual 7,9('95, '97, $3.95)-7-Year One story. 9-Pulp Heroes sty 4.00
Annual 8 (1996, $2.95)-Legends of the Dead Earth story 4.00
NOTE: *Erik Larsen a-431.*

ADVENTURES OF SUPERMAN
DC Comics: Jul, 2013 - No. 17, Nov, 2014 ($3.99)
1-17-Short story anthology by various. 1-Lemire-s/a. 4-Timm-c. 6-Mongul app. 14-Joker app.; Sugar & Spike app.; Hester-a 4.00

ADVENTURES OF THE DOVER BOYS
Archie Comics (Close-up): September, 1950 - No. 2, 1950 (No month given)
1,2 10 20 30 56 76 95

ADVENTURES OF THE FLY (The Fly #1-6; Fly Man No. 32-39; See The Double Life of Private Strong, The Fly, Laugh Comics & Mighty Crusaders)
Archie Publications/Radio Comics: Aug, 1959 - No. 30, Oct, 1964; No. 31, May, 1965
1-Shield app.; origin The Fly; S&K-c/a 52 104 156 411 931 1450
2-Williamson, S&K-a 27 54 81 194 435 675
3-Origin retold; Davis, Powell-a 23 46 69 161 356 550
4-Neal Adams-a(p)(1 panel); S&K-c; Powell-a; 2 pg. Shield story 15 30 45 103 227 350
5,6,9,10: 9-Shield app. 9-1st app. Cat Girl. 10-Black Hood app. 10 20 30 68 144 220
7,8: 7-1st S.A. app. Black Hood (7/60). 8-1st S.A. app. Shield (9/60) 11 22 33 76 163 250
11-13,15-20: 13-1st app. Fly Girl w/o costume. 16-Last 10¢ issue. 20-Origin Fly Girl retold 7 14 21 49 92 135
14-Origin & 1st app. Fly Girl in costume 8 16 24 55 105 155
21-30: 23-Jaguar cameo. 27-29-Black Hood 1 pg. strips. 30-Comet x-over (1st S.A. app.) in Fly Girl 6 12 18 38 69 100
31-Black Hood, Shield, Comet app. 6 12 18 40 73 105
Vol. 1 TPB ('04, $12.95) r/#1-4 & Double Life of Private Strong #1,2; foreward by Joe Simon 13.00
NOTE: *Simon c-2-4. Tuska a-1. Cover title to #31 is Flyman; Advs. of the Fly inside.*

ADVENTURES OF THE JAGUAR, THE (See Blue Ribbon Comics, Laugh Comics & Mighty Crusaders)
Archie Publications (Radio Comics): Sept, 1961 - No. 15, Nov, 1963
1-Origin Jaguar (1st app?) by J. Rosenberger 21 42 63 147 324 500
2,3: 3-Last 10¢ issue 10 20 30 69 147 225
4-6-Catgirl app. (#4's-c is same as splash pg.) 8 16 24 56 108 160
7-10: 10-Dinosaur-c 7 14 21 46 86 125
11-15:13,14-Catgirl, Black Hood app. in both 6 12 18 40 73 105

ADVENTURES OF THE MASK (TV cartoon)
Dark Horse Comics: Jan, 1996 - No. 12, Dec, 1996 ($2.50)

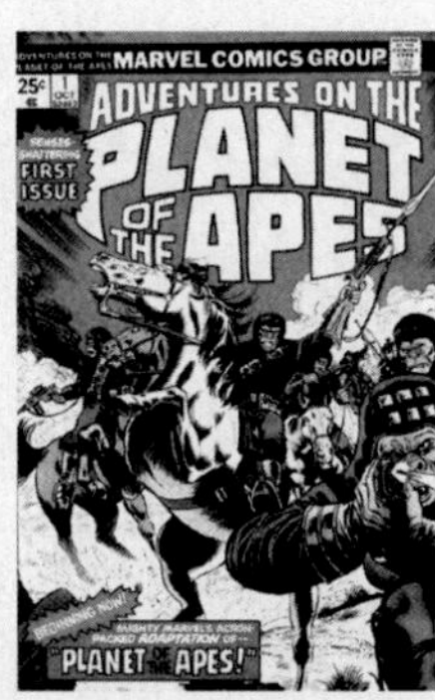

Adventures on the Planet of the Apes #1 © 20th Century Fox

Adventure Time #33 © CN

Afterlife with Archie #10 © ACP

	GD 2.0	VG 4.0	FN 6.0	VF 8.0	VF/NM 9.0	NM- 9.2

1-12: Based on animated series 3.00

ADVENTURES OF THE NEW MEN (Formerly Newmen #1-21)
Maximum Press: No. 22, Nov, 1996; No. 23, March, 1997 ($2.50)

22,23-Sprouse-c/a 3.00

ADVENTURES OF THE OUTSIDERS, THE (Formerly Batman & The Outsiders; also see The Outsiders)
DC Comics: No. 33, May, 1986 - No. 46, June, 1987

33-46: 39-45-r/Outsiders #1-7 by Aparo 3.00

ADVENTURES OF THE SUPER MARIO BROTHERS (See Super Mario Bros.)
Valiant: 1990 - No. 9, Oct, 1991 ($1.50)

V2#1	2	4	6	11	16	20
2-9	1	2	3	5	6	8

ADVENTURES OF THE THING, THE (Also see The Thing)
Marvel Comics: Apr, 1992 - No. 4, July, 1992, ($1.25, limited series)

1-4: 1-r/Marvel Two-In-One #50 by Byrne; Kieth-c. 2-4-r/Marvel Two-In-One #80,51 & 77; 2-Ghost Rider-c/story; Quesada-c. 3-Miller-r/Quesada-c; new Perez-a (4 pgs.) 3.00

ADVENTURES OF THE X-MEN, THE (Based on animated TV series)
Marvel Comics: Apr, 1996 - No. 12, Mar, 1997 (99¢)

1-12: 1-Wolverine/Hulk battle. 3-Spider-Man-c. 5,6-Magneto-c/app. 3.00

ADVENTURES OF TINKER BELL (See Tinker Bell, 4-Color No. 896 & 982)

ADVENTURES OF TOM SAWYER (See Dell Junior Treasury No. 10)

ADVENTURES OF YOUNG DR. MASTERS, THE
Archie Comics (Radio Comics): Aug, 1964 - No. 2, Nov, 1964

1	3	6	9	21	33	45
2	3	6	9	15	22	28

ADVENTURES ON OTHER WORLDS (See Showcase #17 & 18)

ADVENTURES ON THE PLANET OF THE APES (Also see Planet of the Apes)
Marvel Comics Group: Oct, 1975 - No. 11, Dec, 1976

1-Planet of the Apes magazine-r in color; Starlin-c; adapts movie thru #6	4	8	12	25	40	55
2-5: 5-(25¢-c edition)	3	6	9	14	20	25
5-7-(30¢-c variants, limited distribution)	5	10	15	31	53	75
6-10: 6,7-(25¢-c edition). 7-Adapts 2nd movie (thru #11)	3	6	9	14	20	25
11-Last issue; concludes 2nd movie adaptation	3	6	9	16	23	30

NOTE: *Alcala a-6-11r. Buckler c-2p. Nasser c-7. Ploog a-1-9. Starlin c-6. Tuska a-1-5r.*

ADVENTURES WITH THE DC SUPER HEROES (Interior also inserted into some DC issues)
DC Comics/Geppi's Entertainment Museum: 2007 Free Comic Book Day giveaway

"The Batman and Cal Ripken, Jr. Hall of Fame Edition "A Rare Catch" " in indicia 3.00

ADVENTURE TIME (With Finn & Jake) (Based on the Cartoon Network animated series)
Boom Entertainment (KaBOOM!): Feb, 2012 - Present ($3.99)

1-Cover A 25.00
1-Covers B & C; interlocking image 25.00
1-Cover D variant by Jeffrey Brown 30.00
1-Cover E wraparound 35.00
1-Second & third printings 5.00
2-Four covers 10.00
3-24,26-49,51-74-Multiple covers on all 4.00
25-($4.99) Art by Dustin Nguyen, Jess Fink, Jeffrey Brown & others; multiple covers 5.00
50-($4.99) Hastings-s/McGinty-a; multiple covers 5.00
2013 Annual #1 (5/13, $4.99) Three covers; s/a by Langridge, Nguyen & others 5.00
2013 Spoooktacular (10/13, $4.99) Halloween-themed; s/a by Fraser Irving & others 5.00
2013 Summer Special (7/13, $4.99) Multiple covers 5.00
2014 Annual #1 (4/14, $4.99) Three covers; stories printed sideways 5.00
2014 Winter Special (1/14, $4.99) Multiple covers 5.00
2015 Spoooktacular (10/15, $4.99) a Marceline story; s/a by Hanna K 5.00
2016 Spoooktacular (9/16, $4.99) Short stories by various; 2 covers by Bartel & McClaren 5.00
2017 Spoooktacular (10/17, $4.99) Short stories by various; 2 covers 5.00
... Cover Showcase (12/12, $3.99) Gallery of variant covers for #1-9; Paul Pope-c 4.00
... Free Comic Book Day Edition (5/12) Giveaway flip book with Peanuts 3.00

ADVENTURE TIME: BANANA GUARD ACADEMY (Cartoon Network)
Boom Entertainment (KaBOOM!): Jul, 2014 - No. 6, Dec, 2014 ($3.99, limited series)

1-6-Multiple covers on all; Mad Rupert-a 4.00

ADVENTURE TIME: CANDY CAPERS (Cartoon Network)
Boom Entertainment (KaBOOM!): Jul, 2013 - No. 6, Dec, 2013 ($3.99, limited series)

1-6-Multiple covers on all; McGinty-a 4.00

ADVENTURE TIME COMICS (Cartoon Network)
Boom Entertainment (KaBOOM!): Jul, 2016 - Present ($3.99)

1-20-Short stories by various. 1-Baltazar, Cook, Millionaire, Leyh-s/a 4.00

ADVENTURE TIME: ICE KING (Cartoon Network)
Boom Entertainment (KaBOOM!): Jan, 2016 - No. 6, Jun, 2016 ($3.99, limited series)

1-6-Multiple covers on all; Naujokaitis-s/Andrewson-a 4.00

ADVENTURE TIME: MARCELINE AND THE SCREAM QUEENS (Cartoon Network)
Boom Entertainment (KaBOOM!): Jul, 2012 - No. 6, Dec, 2012 ($3.99, limited series)

1-6-Multiple covers on all 4.00

ADVENTURE TIME: MARCELINE GONE ADRIFT (Cartoon Network)
Boom Entertainment (KaBOOM!): Jan, 2015 - No. 6, Jun, 2015 ($3.99, limited series)

1-6-Multiple covers on all; Meredith Gran-s/Carey Pietsch-a 4.00

ADVENTURE TIME/ REGULAR SHOW (Cartoon Network)
Boom Entertainment (KaBOOM!): Aug, 2017 - No. 6, Jan, 2018 ($3.99, limited series)

1-6-McCreery-s/Di Meo-a; multiple covers on each 4.00

ADVENTURE TIME: THE FLIP SIDE (Cartoon Network)
Boom Entertainment (KaBOOM!): Jan, 2014 - No. 6, Jun, 2014 ($3.99, limited series)

1-6-Multiple covers on all; Tobin & Coover-s; Wook Jin Clark-a 4.00

ADVENTURE TIME WITH FIONNA & CAKE (Cartoon Network)
Boom Entertainment (KaBOOM!): Jan, 2013 - No. 6, Jun, 2013 ($3.99, limited series)

1-6-Multiple covers on all 4.00

ADVENTURE TIME WITH FIONNA & CAKE CARD WARS (Cartoon Network)
Boom Entertainment (KaBOOM!): Jul, 2015 - No. 6, Dec, 2015 ($3.99, limited series)

1-6-Multiple covers on all; Jen Wang-s/Britt Wilson-a. 1-Polybagged with a game card 4.00

AEON FLUX (Based on the 2005 movie which was based on the MTV animated series)
Dark Horse Comics: Oct, 2005 - No. 4, Jan, 2006 ($2.99, limited series)

1-4-Timothy Green II-a/Mike Kennedy-s 3.00
TPB (5/06, $12.95) r/series; cover gallery 13.00

A-FORCE (Secret Wars tie-in)
Marvel Comics: Jul, 2015 - No. 5, Dec, 2015 ($3.99, limited series)

1-5-All-Female Avengers team; Bennett & Willow Wilson-s/Molina-a. 1-Intro. Singularity 4.00

A-FORCE (Follows Secret Wars)
Marvel Comics: Mar, 2016 - No. 10, Dec, 2016 ($3.99)

1-10: 1-Medusa, She-Hulk, Dazzler, Nico, Capt. Marvel, Singularity team; Wilson-s/Molina-a. 5-7-Thompson-s/Caldwell-a. 8-10-Civil War II tie-in 4.00

AFRICA
Magazine Enterprises: 1955

1(A-1#137)-Cave Girl, Thun'da; Powell-c/a(4)	30	60	90	177	289	400

AFRICAN LION (Disney movie)
Dell Publishing Co.: Nov, 1955

Four Color #665	5	10	15	34	60	85

AFTER DARK
Sterling Comics: No. 6, May, 1955 - No. 8, Sept, 1955

6-8-Sekowsky-a in all	9	18	27	52	69	85

AFTER DARK (Co-created by Wesley Snipes)
Radical Comics: No. 0, Jun, 2010 - No. 3 ($1.00/$4.99, limited series)

0-($1.00) Milligan-s/Nentrup & Mattina-a 3.00
1-3-($4.99) Milligan-s/Manco-a 5.00

AFTERLIFE WITH ARCHIE
Archie Comic Publications: Sept, 2013 - Present ($2.99/$3.99)

1-Aguirre-Sacasa-s/Francavilla-a; zombies in Riverdale; Sabrina app.; 4 covers 22.00
1-Second printing; new cover by Francavilla 6.00
2-Covers by Francavilla & Seeley; back-up short story r/Chilling Advs. in Sorcery 10.00
3-6: 3,4-Covers by Francavilla & Seeley on each; back-up r/Chilling Advs. in Sorcery. 5,6-Pepoy variant-c. 6-Back-up preview of Chilling Advs. of Sabrina #1 5.00
7-10-($3.99) 7-Covers by Francavilla & Pepoy; back-up r/Chilling Advs. in Sorcery 4.00
... Halloween ComicFest Edition 1 (2014, giveaway) Grey-toned reprint of #1 3.00
... Halloween ComicFest Edition 1 (2016, giveaway) Grey-toned reprint of #7 3.00

AFTERSHOCK GENESIS
AfterShock Comics: May, 2016 ($1.00, one-shot)

1-Short stories by various and previews of upcoming AfterShock titles 3.00

AFTER THE CAPE
Image Comics (Shadowline): Mar, 2007 - No. 3, May, 2007 ($2.99, B&W, limited series)

Agents of Atlas (2009 series) #1 © MAR

Agents of S.H.I.E.L.D. #1 © MAR

Aggie Mack #4 © SUPR

1-3-Jim Valentino-s/Marco Rudy-a 3.00
... Volume One TPB (9/07, $12.99) r/series; scripts, sketch pages, character profiles 13.00
...II (11/07 - No. 3, 1/08, $2.99) 1-3-Jim Valentino-s/Sergio Carrera-a 3.00

AGAINST BLACKSHARD 3-D (Also see SoulQuest)
Sirius Comics: August, 1986 ($2.25)

1 3.00

AGENCY, THE
Image Comics (Top Cow): August, 2001 - No. 6, Mar, 2002 ($2.50/$2.95/$4.95)

1-5: 1-Jenkins-s/Hotz-a; three covers by Hotz, Turner, Silvestri. 3-5-($2.95) 3.00
6-($4.95) Flip-c preview of Jeremiah TV series 5.00
Preview (2001, 16 pgs.) B&W pages, cover previews, sketch pages 3.00

AGENT CARTER: S.H.I.E.L.D. 50TH ANNIVERSARY
Marvel Comics: Nov, 2015 ($3.99, one-shot)

1-Kathryn Immonen-s/Rich Ellis-a; set in 1966; Sif, Dum Dum and Nick Fury app. 4.00

AGENT 47: BIRTH OF THE HITMAN (Based on the Io-Anteractive video game)
Dynamite Entertainment: 2017 - Present ($3.99)

1-4-Sebela-s/Lau-a; multiple covers on each 4.00

AGENT LIBERTY SPECIAL (See Superman, 2nd Series)
DC Comics: 1992 ($2.00, 52 pgs, one-shot)

1-1st solo adventure; Guice-c/a(i) 4.00

AGENTS, THE
Image Comics: Apr, 2003 - No. 6, Sept, 2003 ($2.95, B&W)

1-5-Ben Dunn-c/a in all 3.00
6-Five pg. preview of The Walking Dead #1 3 6 9 15 22 28

AGENTS OF ATLAS
Marvel Comics: Oct, 2006 - No. 6, Mar, 2007 ($2.99, limited series)

1-6: 1-Golden Age heroes Marvel Boy & Venus app.; Kirk-a 3.00
... MGC 1 (7/10, $1.00) r/#1 with "Marvel's Greatest Comics" logo on cover 3.00
HC (2007, $24.99, dustjacket) r/#1-6, What If? #9, agents' debuts in '40s-'50s Atlas comics, creator interviews, character design art 25.00

AGENTS OF ATLAS (Dark Reign)
Marvel Comics: Apr, 2009 - No. 11, Nov, 2009 ($3.99)

1-11: 1-Pagulayan-a; 2 covers by Art Adams and McGuinness; back-up with Wolverine app. 5-New Avengers app. 8-Hulk app. 4.00

AGENTS OF LAW (Also see Comic's Greatest World)
Dark Horse Comics: Mar, 1995 - No. 6, Sept, 1995 ($2.50)

1-6: 5-Predator app. 6-Predator app.; death of Law 3.00

AGENTS OF P.A.C.T. (Also see Captain Canuck)
Chapterhouse Publishing: Jan, 2017 - Present ($3.99)

1-3-Andrasofszky & Northcott-s/Manfredi-a; Agent Fleur De Lys app. 4.00

AGENTS OF S.H.I.E.L.D. (Characters from the TV series)
Marvel Comics: Mar, 2016 - No. 10, Dec, 2016 ($3.99)

1-10: 1-Guggenheim-s/Peralta-a; Tony Stark app. 3,4-Standoff tie-in. 5-Spider-Man app. 7-10-Civil War II tie-in. 9,10-Elektra app. 4.00

AGENT X (Continued from Deadpool)
Marvel Comics: Sept. 2002 - No. 15, Dec, 2003 ($2.99/$2.25)

1-($2.99) Simone-s/Udon Studios-a; Taskmaster app. 4.00
2-9-($2.25) 2-Punisher app. 3.00
10-15-($2.99) 10,11-Evan Dorkin-s. 12-Hotz-a 3.00

AGE OF APOCALYPSE (See Uncanny X-Force)
Marvel Comics: May, 2012 - No. 14, Jun, 2013 ($2.99)

1-14: 1-Lapham-s/De La Torre-a/Ramos-c. 13-Leads into X-Termination x-over 3.00

AGE OF APOCALYPSE (Secret Wars tie-in)
Marvel Comics: Sept, 2015 - No. 5, Dec, 2015 ($4.99/$3.99, limited series)

1-($4.99) Nicieza-s/Sandoval-a; alternate X-Men vs. Apocalypse 5.00
2-5-($3.99) Covers #1-5 form one image; Blink, Sabretooth & Magneto app. 4.00

AGE OF APOCALYPSE: THE CHOSEN
Marvel Comics: Apr, 1995 ($2.50, one-shot)

1-Wraparound-c 5.00

AGE OF BRONZE
Image Comics: Nov, 1998 - Present ($2.95/$3.50, B&W)

1-6-Eric Shanower-c/s/a 3.50
7-33-($3.50) 3.50
...Behind the Scenes (5/02, $3.50) background info and creative process 3.50
Image Firsts: Age of Bronze #1 (4/10, $1.00) r/#1 with "Image Firsts" cover logo 3.00
...Special (6/99, $2.95) Story of Agamemnon and Menelaus 3.50
A Thousand Ships (7/01, $19.95, TPB) r/#1-9 20.00
Sacrifice (9/04, $19.95, TPB) r/#10-19 20.00

AGE OF HEROES, THE
Halloween Comics/Image Comics #3 on: 1996 - No. 5, 1999 ($2.95, B&W)

1-5: James Hudnall scripts; John Ridgway-c/a 3.00
...Special ($4.95) r/#1,2 5.00
...Special 2 ($6.95) r/#3,4 7.00
...Wex 1 ('98, $2.95) Hudnall-s/Angel Fernandez-a 3.00

AGE OF HEROES (The Heroic Age)
Marvel Comics: Jul, 2010 - No. 4, Oct, 2010 ($3.99, limited series)

1-4-Short stories of Avengers members by various. 4-Jae Lee-c 4.00

AGE OF INNOCENCE: THE REBIRTH OF IRON MAN
Marvel Comics: Feb, 1996 ($2.50, one-shot)

1-New origin of Tony Stark 3.00

AGE OF REPTILES
Dark Horse Comics: Nov, 1993 - No. 4, Feb, 1994 ($2.50, limited series)

1-4: Delgado-c/a/scripts in all 3.00
... Ancient Egyptians 1-4 (6/15 - No. 4, 9/15, $3.99) Delgado-c/a/scripts; wraparound-c 4.00
... The Hunt 1-5 (5/96 - No. 5, 9/96, $2.95) Delgado-c/a/scripts in all; wraparound-c 3.00
... The Journey 1-4 (11/09 - No. 4, 7/10, $3.50) Delgado-c/a/scripts in all; wraparound-c 3.50

AGE OF THE SENTRY, THE
Marvel Comics: Nov, 2008 - No. 6, Mar, 2010 ($2.99, limited series)

1-6-Silver Age style stories. 1-Origin retold; Bullock-c. 3-Coover-a 3.00

AGE OF ULTRON
Marvel Comics: May, 2013 - No. 10, Aug, 2013 ($3.99, limited series)

1-Wraparound cardstock foil-c; Hitch-a/c 6.00
2-9: 2-5-Hitch-a/c. 6-Peterson & Pacheco-a, Hank Pym killed 4.00
10-Polybagged; Angela joins the Marvel Universe 6.00
10AU (8/13, $3.99) Waid-s/Aralijo-a/Pichelli-c; Hank Pym's origin re-told 1 3 4 6 8 10

AGE OF ULTRON VS. MARVEL ZOMBIES (Secret Wars tie-in)
Marvel Comics: Aug, 2015 - No. 4, Nov, 2015 ($3.99, limited series)

1-4-James Robinson-s/Steve Pugh-a; Vision, Wonder Man & Jim Hammond app. 4.00

AGE OF X (X-Men titles crossover)
Marvel Comics: ($3.99, limited series)

... Alpha 1 (3/11, $3.99) Short stories by various; covers by Bachalo & Coipel 4.00
...: Universe 1,2 (5/11 - No. 2, 6/11, $3.99) Pham-a; Bianchi-c; Avengers & Spider-Man app. 4.00

AGGIE MACK
Four Star Comics Corp./Superior Comics Ltd.: Jan, 1948 - No. 8, Aug, 1949

1-Feldstein-a, "Johnny Prep" 45 90 135 284 480 675
2,3-Kamen-c 26 52 78 154 252 350
4-Feldstein "Johnny Prep"; Kamen-c 34 68 102 199 325 450
5-8-Kamen-c/a. 7-Burt Lancaster app. on-c 28 56 84 165 270 375

AGGIE MACK
Dell Publishing Co.: Apr - Jun, 1962

Four Color #1335 5 10 15 31 53 75

AIR
DC Comics (Vertigo): Oct, 2008 - No. 24, Oct, 2010 ($2.99)

1-6,8-24-G. Willow Wilson-s/M.K. Perker-a 3.00
7-($1.00) Includes story re-cap 3.00
... A History of the Future TPB (2011, $14.99) r/#18-24 15.00
... Flying Machine TPB (2009, $12.99) r/#6-10; Wilson intro. 13.00
... Letters From Lost Countries TPB (2009, $9.99) r/#1-5; character sketch pages 10.00
... Pure Land TPB (2010, $14.99) r/#11-17 15.00

AIR ACE (Formerly Bill Barnes No. 1-12)
Street & Smith Publications: V2#1, Jan, 1944 - V3#8(No. 20), Feb-Mar, 1947

V2#1-Nazi concentration camp-c 53 106 159 334 567 800
V2#2-Classic Japanese WWII-c 213 426 639 1363 2332 3300
V2#3-12: 7-Powell-a 18 36 54 103 162 220
V3#1-6: 2-Atomic explosion on-c 14 28 42 82 121 160
V3#7-Powell bondage-c/a; all atomic issue 27 54 81 158 259 360
V3#8 (V5#8 on-c)-Powell-c/a 15 30 45 90 140 190

AIRBOY (Also see Airmaidens, Skywolf, Target: Airboy & Valkyrie)
Eclipse Comics: July, 1986 - No. 50, Oct, 1989 (#1-8, 50¢, 20 pgs., bi-weekly; #9-on, 36 pgs.;

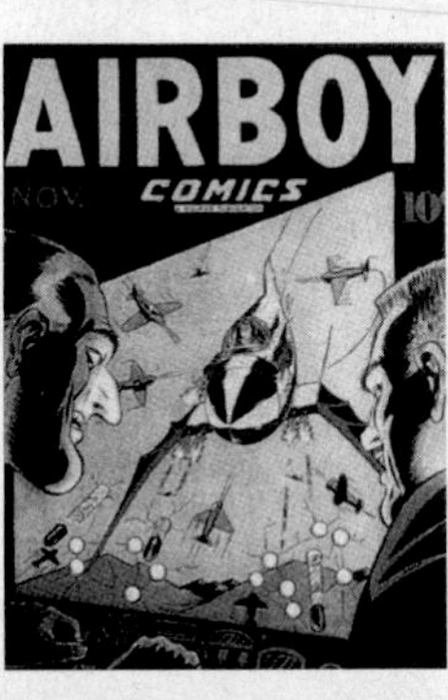

Airboy Comics V3 #10 © HILL

Air Fighters Comics V2 #2 © HILL

Akiko #29 © Mark Crilley

	GD 2.0	VG 4.0	FN 6.0	VF 8.0	VF/NM 9.0	NM- 9.2

	GD 2.0	VG 4.0	FN 6.0	VF 8.0	VF/NM 9.0	NM- 9.2

#34-on monthly)

Issue	GD	VG	FN	VF	VF/NM	NM-
1-4: 2-1st Marisa; Skywolf gets new costume. 3-The Heap begins						4.00
5-Valkyrie returns; Dave Stevens-c	1	3	4	6	8	10
6-49: 9-Begin $1.25-c; Skywolf begins. 11-Origin of G.A. Airboy & his plane Birdie. 28-Mr. Monster vs. The Heap. 33-Begin $1.75-c. 38-40-The Heap by Infantino. 41-r/1st app. Valkyrie from Air Fighters. 42-Begin $1.95-c. 46,47-part-r/Air Fighters. 48-Black Angel-r/A.F						3.00
50 ($4.95, 52 pgs.)-Kubert-c						5.00

NOTE: ***Evans*** *c-21.* ***Gulacy*** *c-7, 20.* ***Spiegle*** *a-34, 35, 37.* ***Ken Steacy*** *painted c-17, 33.*

AIRBOY
Image Comics: Jun, 2015 - No. 4, Nov, 2015 ($2.99, limited series, mature)

Issue	GD	VG	FN	VF	VF/NM	NM-
1-4: 1-Airboy meets writer James Robinson and artist Greg Hinkle. 3,4-Valkyrie app.						3.00

AIRBOY COMICS (Air Fighters Comics No. 1-22)
Hillman Periodicals: V2#11, Dec, 1945 - V10#4, May, 1953 (No V3#3)

Issue	GD	VG	FN	VF	VF/NM	NM-
V2#11	61	122	183	390	670	950
12-Valkyrie-c/app.	53	106	159	334	567	800
V3#1,2(no #3)	40	80	120	246	411	575
4-The Heap app. in Skywolf	37	74	111	222	361	500
5,7,8,10,11	33	66	99	194	317	440
6-Valkyrie-c/app.	36	72	108	216	351	485
9-Origin The Heap	37	74	111	222	361	500
12-Skywolf & Airboy x-over; Valkyrie-c/app.	39	78	117	240	395	550
V4#1-Iron Lady app.	33	66	99	194	317	440
2,3,12: 2-Rackman begins	26	52	78	154	252	350
4-Simon & Kirby-c	31	62	93	186	303	420
5-9,11-All S&K-a	30	60	90	177	289	400
10-Valkyrie-c/app.	32	64	96	192	314	435
V5#1-4,6-11: 4-Infantino Heap. 10-Origin The Heap	20	40	60	120	195	270
5-Skull-c.	24	48	72	140	230	320
12-Krigstein-a(p)	21	42	63	124	202	280
V6#1-3,5-12: 6,8-Origin The Heap	20	40	60	114	182	250
4-Origin retold	22	44	66	132	216	300
V7#1-12: 7,8,10-Origin The Heap. 12-(1/51)	19	38	57	112	179	245
V8#1-3,5-12: 5-UFO-c (6/51)	18	36	54	105	165	225
4-Krigstein-a	19	38	57	109	172	235
V9#1,3,4,6-12: 7-One pg. Frazetta ad	15	30	45	90	140	190
2-Valkyrie app.	16	32	48	94	147	200
5(#100)	16	32	48	94	147	200
V10#1-4	15	30	45	85	130	175

NOTE: ***Barry*** *a-V2#3, 7.* ***Bolle*** *a-V4#12.* ***McWilliams*** *a-V3#7, 9.* ***Powell*** *a-V7#2, 3, V8#1, 6.* ***Starr*** *a-V5#1, 12.* ***Dick Wood*** *a-V4#12. Bondage-c V5#8.*

AIRBOY MEETS THE PROWLER
Eclipse Comics: Aug, 1987 ($1.95, one-shot)

Issue	GD	VG	FN	VF	VF/NM	NM-
1-John Snyder, III-c/a						3.00

AIRBOY-MR. MONSTER SPECIAL
Eclipse Comics: Aug, 1987 ($1.75, one-shot)

Issue	GD	VG	FN	VF	VF/NM	NM-
1						3.00

AIRBOY VERSUS THE AIR MAIDENS
Eclipse Comics: July, 1988 ($1.95)

Issue	GD	VG	FN	VF	VF/NM	NM-
1						3.00

AIR FIGHTERS CLASSICS
Eclipse Comics: Nov, 1987 - No. 6, May, 1989 ($3.95, 68 pgs., B&W)

Issue	GD	VG	FN	VF	VF/NM	NM-
1-6: Reprints G.A. Air Fighters #2-7. 1-Origin Airboy						4.00

AIR FIGHTERS COMICS (Airboy Comics #23 (V2#11) on)
Hillman Periodicals: Nov, 1941; No. 2, Nov, 1942 - V2#10, Fall, 1945

Issue	GD	VG	FN	VF	VF/NM	NM-
V1#1-(Produced by Funnies, Inc.); No Airboy; Black Commander only app.	226	452	678	1446	2473	3500
2(11/42)-(Produced by Quality artists & Biro for Hillman); Origin & 1st app. Airboy & Iron Ace; Black Angel (1st app.), Flying Dutchman & Skywolf (1st app.) begin; Fuje-a; Biro-c/a	503	1006	1509	3672	6486	9300
3-Origin/1st app. The Heap; origin Skywolf; 2nd Airboy app./c	206	412	618	1318	2259	3200
4-Japan war-c	181	362	543	1158	1979	2800
5-Japanese octopus War-c	194	388	582	1242	2121	3000
6-Japanese soldiers as rats-c	226	452	678	1446	2473	3500
7-Classic Nazi swastika-c	206	412	618	1318	2259	3200
8-12: 8,10,11-War covers	90	180	270	576	988	1400
V2#1-Classic Nazi War-c	97	194	291	621	1061	1500
2-Skywolf by Giunta; Flying Dutchman by Fuje; 1st meeting Valkyrie & Airboy (she worked for the Nazis in beginning); 1st app. Valkyrie (11/43); Valkyrie-c	187	374	561	1197	2049	2900
3,4,6,8,9	61	122	183	390	670	950
5-Flag-c; Fuje-a	68	136	204	435	743	1050
7-Valkyrie app.	77	154	231	493	847	1200
10-Origin The Heap & Skywolf	70	140	210	445	765	1085

NOTE: ***Fuje*** *a-V1#2, 5, 7, V2#2, 3, 5, 7-9.* ***Giunta*** *a-V2#2, 3, 7, 9.*

AIRFIGHTERS MEET SGT. STRIKE SPECIAL, THE
Eclipse Comics: Jan, 1988 ($1.95, one-shot, stiff-c)

Issue	GD	VG	FN	VF	VF/NM	NM-
1-Airboy, Valkyrie, Skywolf app.						3.00

AIR FORCES (See American Air Forces)

AIRMAIDENS SPECIAL
Eclipse Comics: August, 1987 ($1.75, one-shot, Baxter paper)

Issue	GD	VG	FN	VF	VF/NM	NM-
1-Marisa becomes La Lupina (origin)						3.00

AIR RAIDERS
Marvel Comics (Star Comics)/Marvel #3 on: Nov, 1987- No. 5, Mar, 1988 ($1.00)

Issue	GD	VG	FN	VF	VF/NM	NM-
1,5: Kelley Jones-a in all						4.00
2-4: 2-Thunderhammer app.						3.00

AIRTIGHT GARAGE, THE (Also see Elsewhere Prince)
Marvel Comics (Epic Comics): July, 1993 - No. 4, Oct, 1993 ($2.50, lim. series, Baxter paper)

Issue	GD	VG	FN	VF	VF/NM	NM-
1-4: Moebius-c/a/scripts						5.00

AIR WAR STORIES
Dell Publishing Co.: Sept-Nov, 1964 - No. 8, Aug, 1966

Issue	GD	VG	FN	VF	VF/NM	NM-
1-Painted-c; Glanzman-c/a begins	4	8	12	27	44	60
2-8: 2,3-Painted-c	3	6	9	17	26	35

A.K.A. GOLDFISH
Caliber Comics: 1994 - 1995 (B&W, $3.50/$3.95)

Issue	GD	VG	FN	VF	VF/NM	NM-
...:Ace; ...:Jack; ...:Queen; ...:Joker; ...:King -Brian Michael Bendis-s/a						4.00
TPB (1996, $17.95)						20.00
Goldfish: The Definitive Collection (Image, 2001, $19.95) r/series plus promo art and new prose story; intro. by Matt Wagner						20.00
10th Anniversary HC (Image, 2002, $49.95)						50.00

AKIKO
Sirius: Mar, 1996 - No. 52, Feb, 2004 ($2.50/$2.95, B&W)

Issue	GD	VG	FN	VF	VF/NM	NM-
1-Crilley-c/a/scripts in all						5.00
2						4.00
3-39: 25-($2.95, 32 pgs.)-w/Asala back-up pages						3.00
40-49,51,52: 40-Begin $2.95-c						3.00
50-($3.50)						3.50
Flights of Fancy TPB (5/02, $12.95) r/various features, pin-ups and gags						13.00
TPB Volume 1,4 ('97, 2/00, $14.95) 1-r/#1-7. 4-r/#19-25						15.00
TPB Volume 2,3 ('98, '99, $11.95) 2-r/#8-13. 3- r/#14-18						12.00
TPB Volume 5 (12/01, $12.95) r/#26-31						13.00
TPB Volume 6,7 (6/03, 4/04, $14.95) 6-r/#32-38. 7-r/#40-47						15.00

AKIKO ON THE PLANET SMOO
Sirius: Dec, 1995 ($3.95, B&W)

Issue	GD	VG	FN	VF	VF/NM	NM-
V1#1-($3.95)-Crilley-c/a/scripts; gatefold-c						5.00
Ashcan ('95, mail offer)						3.00
Hardcover V1#1 (12/95, $19.95, B&W, 40 pgs.)						20.00
The Color Edition(2/00,$4.95)						5.00

AKIRA
Marvel Comics (Epic): Sept, 1988 - No. 38, Dec, 1995 ($3.50/$3.95/$6.95, deluxe, 68 pgs.)

Issue	GD	VG	FN	VF	VF/NM	NM-
1-Manga by Katsuhiro Otomo	3	6	9	16	23	30
1,2-2nd printings (1989, $3.95)						5.00
2	2	4	6	9	12	15
3-5	2	4	6	8	10	12
6-16	1	2	3	5	7	9
17-33: 17-$3.95-c begins						6.00
34-36: 34-(1994)-$6.95-c begins. 35-(1995)	2	4	6	10	14	18
37-Texeira back-up, Gibbons, Williams pin-ups	3	6	9	16	23	30
38-Moebius, Allred, Pratt, Toth, Romita, Van Fleet, O'Neill, Madureira pin-ups	4	8	12	28	47	65

ALABASTER: THE GOOD, THE BAD AND THE BIRD
Dark Horse Comics: Dec, 2015 - No. 5, Apr, 2016 ($3.99, limited series)

Issue	GD	VG	FN	VF	VF/NM	NM-
1-5-Caitlin Kiernan-s/Daniel Johnson-a						4.00

ALADDIN & HIS WONDERFUL LAMP (See Dell Jr Treasury #2)

ALAN LADD (See The Adventures of...)

Alarming Tales #2 © HARV

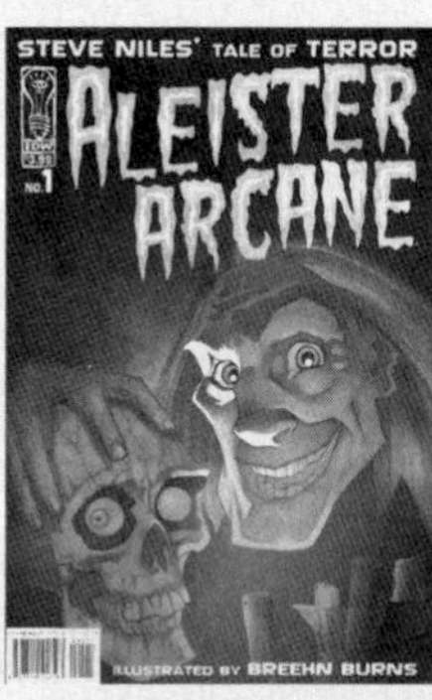

Aleister Arcane #1 © IDW

Alias #12 © MAR

	GD 2.0	VG 4.0	FN 6.0	VF 8.0	VF/NM 9.0	NM- 9.2
ALAN MOORE'S AWESOME UNIVERSE HANDBOOK (Also see Across the Universe:...) **Awesome Entertainment:** Apr, 1999 ($2.95, B&W)						
1-Alan Moore-text/ Alex Ross-sketch pages and 2 covers						5.00
ALAN MOORE... **DC Comics (WildStorm):** TPB						
...'s Complete WildC.A.T.S. (2007, $29.99) r/#21-34,50; ...Homecoming & ...Gang War						30.00
...: Wild Worlds (2007, $24.99) r/various WildStorm one-shots and limited series						25.00
ALARMING ADVENTURES **Harvey Publications:** Oct, 1962 - No. 3, Feb, 1963						
1-Crandall/Williamson-a	8	16	24	51	96	140
2-Williamson/Crandall-a	5	10	15	31	53	75
3-Torres-a	4	8	12	28	47	65
NOTE: ***Bailey** a-1, 3. **Crandall** a-1p, 2i. **Powell** a-2(2). **Severin** c-1-3. **Torres** a-2? **Tuska** a-1. **Williamson** a-1i, 2p.*						
ALARMING TALES **Harvey Publications (Western Tales):** Sept, 1957 - No. 6, Nov, 1958						
1-Kirby-c/a(4); Kamandi prototype story by Kirby	33	66	99	194	317	420
2-Kirby-a(4)	21	42	63	124	202	280
3,4-Kirby-a. 4-Powell, Wildey-a	17	34	51	98	154	210
5-Kirby/Williamson-a; Wildey-a; Severin-c	18	36	54	105	165	225
6-Williamson-a?; Severin-c	14	28	42	82	121	160
ALBEDO **Thoughts And Images:** Summer, 1983 - No. 14, Spring, 1989 (B&W) **Antarctic Press:** (Vol. 2) Jun, 1991 - No. 10 ($2.50)						
0-Yellow cover; 50 copies	15	30	45	103	227	350
0-White cover, 450 copies	8	16	24	56	108	160
0-Blue, 1st printing, 500 copies	7	14	21	49	92	135
0-Blue, 2nd printing, 1000 copies	4	8	12	27	44	60
0-3rd & 4th printing	3	6	9	14	19	24
1-Dark red, 1st printing - low print run	10	20	30	64	132	200
1-Bright red, later printings - low print run	6	12	18	38	69	100
2-(11/84) 1st app. Usagi Yojimbo by Stan Sakai; 2000 copies - no 2nd printing	100	200	300	700	1100	1500
3	3	6	9	21	33	45
4-Usagi Yojimbo-c	4	8	12	28	47	65
5-14						6.00
(Vol. 2) 1-10, Color Special						6.00
ALBEDO ANTHROPOMORPHICS **Antarctic Press:** (Vol. 3) Spring, 1994 - No. 4, Jan, 1996 ($2.95, color); (Vol. 4) Dec, 1999 - No. 2, Jan, 1999 ($2.95/$2.99, B&W)						
V3#1-4-Steve Gallacci-c/a. V4#1,2						3.00
ALBERTO (See The Crusaders)						
ALBERT THE ALLIGATOR & POGO POSSUM (See Pogo Possum)						
ALBION (Inspired by 1960s IPC British comics characters) **DC Comics (WildStorm):** Aug, 2005 - No. 6, Nov, 2006 ($2.99, limited series)						
1-6-Alan Moore, Leah Moore & John Reppion-s/Shane Oakley-a; Dave Gibbons-c						3.00
TPB (2007, $19.99) r/series; intro by Neil Gaiman; reprints from 1960s British comics						20.00
ALBUM OF CRIME (See Fox Giants)						
ALBUM OF LOVE (See Fox Giants)						
AL CAPP'S DOGPATCH (Also see Mammy Yokum) **Toby Press:** No. 71, June, 1949 - No. 4, Dec, 1949						
71(#1)-Reprints from Tip Top #112-114	16	32	48	92	144	195
2-4: 4-Reprints from Li'l Abner #73	13	26	39	72	101	130
AL CAPP'S SHMOO (Also see Oxydol-Dreft & Washable Jones & Shmoo) **Toby Press:** July, 1949 - No. 5, Apr, 1950 (None by Al Capp)						
1-1st app. Super-Shmoo	31	62	93	182	296	410
2-5: 3-Sci-fi trip to moon. 4-X-Mas-c	20	40	60	120	195	270
AL CAPP'S WOLF GAL **Toby Press:** 1951 - No. 2, 1952						
1-Edited-r from Li'l Abner #63	24	48	72	142	234	325
2-Edited-r from Li'l Abner #64	18	36	54	105	165	225
ALEISTER ARCANE **IDW Publishing:** Apr, 2004 - No. 3, June, 2004 ($3.99, limited series)						
1-3-Steve Niles-s/Breehn Burns-a						4.00
TPB (10/04, $17.99) r/series; sketch pages						18.00
ALEXANDER THE GREAT (Movie) **Dell Publishing Co.:** No. 688, May, 1956						
Four Color 688-Buscema-a; photo-c	6	12	18	42	79	115
ALEX + ADA **Image Comics:** Nov, 2013 - No. 15, Jun, 2015 ($2.99/$3.99)						
1-14-Jonathan Luna-a/c; Sarah Vaughn & Luna-s						3.00
15-($3.99) Conclusion						4.00
ALF (TV) (See Star Comics Digest) **Marvel Comics:** Mar, 1988 - No. 50, Feb, 1992 ($1.00)						
1-Photo-c	1	3	4	6	8	10
1-2nd printing						3.00
2-19: 6-Photo-c						3.00
20-22: 20-Conan parody. 21-Marx Brothers. 22-X-Men parody						3.50
23-30: 24-Rhonda-c/app. 29-3-D cover						3.00
31-43,46,47,49						3.00
44,45: 44-X-Men parody. 45-Wolverine, Punisher, Capt. America-c						4.00
48-(12/91) Risqué Alf with seal cover	3	6	9	19	30	40
50-($1.75, 52 pgs.)-Final issue; photo-c						4.00
Annual 1-3: 1-Rocky & Bullwinkle app. 2-Sienkiewicz-c. 3-TMNT parody						4.00
...Comics Digest 1,2: 1-(1988)-Reprints Alf #1,2	1	3	4	6	8	10
Holiday Special 1,2 ('88, Wint. '89, 68 pgs.): 2-X-Men parody-c						4.00
Spring Special 1 (Spr/89, $1.75, 68 pgs.) Invisible Man parody						4.00
TPB (68 pgs.) r/#1-3; photo-c						5.00
ALFRED HARVEY'S BLACK CAT **Lorne-Harvey Productions:** 1995 ($3.50, B&W/color)						
1-Origin by Mark Evanier & Murphy Anderson; contains history of Alfred Harvey & Harvey Publications; 5 pg. B&W Sad Sack story; Hildebrandts-c						6.00
ALGIE (LITTLE...) **Timor Publ. Co.:** Dec, 1953 - No. 3, 1954						
1-Teenage	8	16	24	44	57	70
1-Algie #1 cover w/Secret Mysteries #19 inside	10	20	30	54	72	90
2,3	6	12	18	28	34	40
Accepted Reprint #2(nd)	3	6	8	12	14	16
Super Reprint #15	2	4	6	8	11	14
ALIAS: **Now Comics:** July, 1990 - No. 5, Nov, 1990 ($1.75)						
1-5: 1-Sienkiewicz-c						3.00
ALIAS (Also see Jessica Jones apps. in New Avengers and The Pulse) **Marvel Comics (MAX Comics):** Nov, 2001 - No. 28, Jan, 2004 ($2.99)						
1-Bendis-s/Gaydos-a/Mack-c; intro Jessica Jones; Luke Cage app.	4	8	12	27	44	60
2-4	1	2	3	4	5	7
5-23: 7,8-Sienkiewicz-a (2 pgs.) 16-21-Spider-Woman app. 22,23-Jessica's origin						3.00
24-28-Purple Man app.; Avengers app.; flashback-a by Bagley						5.00
... MGC 1 (6/10, $1.00) r/#1 with "Marvel's Greatest Comics" logo on cover						3.00
HC (2002, $29.99) r/#1-9; intro. by Jeph Loeb						30.00
Omnibus (2006, $69.99, hardcover with dustjacket) r/#1-28 and What If Jessica Jones Had Joined the Avengers?; original pitch, script and sketch pages						70.00
Vol. 1: TPB (2003, $19.99) r/#1-9						20.00
Vol. 2: Come Home TPB (2003, $13.99) r/#11-15						14.00
Vol. 3: The Underneath TPB (2003, $16.99) r/#10,16-21						17.00
ALICE (New Adventures in Wonderland) **Ziff-Davis Publ. Co.:** No. 10, 7-8/51 - No. 11(#2), 11-12/51						
10-Painted-c; Berg-a	29	58	87	170	278	385
11-(#2 on inside) Dave Berg-a	19	38	57	109	172	235
ALICE AT MONKEY ISLAND (Formerly The Adventures of Alice) **Pentagon Publ. Co. (Civil Service):** No. 3, 1946						
3	11	22	33	60	83	105
ALICE COOPER (Also see Last Temptation) **Dynamite Entertainment:** 2014 - No. 6, 2015 ($3.99)						
1-6: 1-5-Joe Harris-s/Eman Casallos-a/David Mack-c. 6-Jerwa-s/Tenorio-a						4.00
ALICE COOPER VS. CHAOS! **Dynamite Entertainment:** 2015 - No. 6, 2016 ($3.99, limited series)						
1-6-Chastity, Purgatori, Evil Ernie, Lady Demon & The Queen of Sorrows app.						4.00
ALICE IN WONDERLAND (Disney; see Advs. of Alice, Dell Jr. Treasury #1, The Dreamery, Movie Comics,Walt Disney Showcase #22, and World's Greatest Stories) **Dell Publishing Co.:** No. 24, 1940; No. 331, 1951; No. 341, July, 1951						
Single Series 24 (#1)(1940)	55	110	165	352	601	850
Four Color 331, 341-"Unbirthday Party w/..."	15	30	45	103	227	350

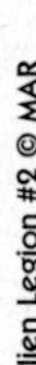
Alien Legion #2 © MAR

Aliens: Dead Orbit #1 © 20th Century Fox

Aliens Stronghold #2 © 20th Century Fox

GD VG FN VF VF/NM NM-
2.0 4.0 6.0 8.0 9.0 9.2

1-(Whitman, 3/84, pre-pack only)-r/4-Color #331 3 6 9 14 20 25

ALIEN ENCOUNTERS (Replaces Alien Worlds)
Eclipse Comics: June, 1985 - No. 14, Aug, 1987 ($1.75, Baxter paper, mature)
1-10: Nudity, strong language in all. 9-Snyder-a 4.00
11-14-Low print run 5.00

ALIEN LEGION (See Epic & Marvel Graphic Novel #25)
Marvel Comics (Epic Comics): Apr, 1984 - No. 20, Sept, 1987
nn-With bound-in trading card; Austin-i 4.00
2-20: 2-$1.50-c. 7,8-Portacio-i 3.00

ALIEN LEGION (2nd Series)
Marvel Comics (Epic): Aug, 1987(indicia)(10/87 on-c) - No. 18, Aug, 1990
V2#1-18-Stroman-a in all. 7-18-Farmer-i 3.00
...: Force Nomad TPB (Checker Book Pub. Group, 2001, $24.95) r/#1-11 25.00
...: Piecemaker TPB (Checker Book Pub. Group, 2002, $19.95) r/#12-18 20.00

ALIEN LEGION: (Series of titles; all Marvel/Epic Comics)
--BINARY DEEP, 1993 ($3.50, one-shot, 52 pgs.), nn-With bound-in trading card 4.00
--JUGGER GRIMROD, 8/92 ($5.95, one-shot, 52 pgs.) Book 1 6.00
--ONE PLANET AT A TIME, 5/93 - Book 3, 7/93 ($4.95, squarebound, 52 pgs.)
Book 1-3: Hoang Nguyen-a 5.00
--ON THE EDGE (The... #2 & 3), 11/90 - No. 3, 1/91 ($4.50, 52 pgs.)
1-3-Stroman & Farmer-a 4.50
--TENANTS OF HELL, '91 - No. 2, '91 ($4.50, squarebound, 52 pgs.)
Book 1,2-Stroman-c/a(p) 4.50

ALIEN LEGION: UNCIVIL WAR
Titan Comics: Jul, 2014 - No. 4, Oct, 2014 ($3.99)
1-4-Dixon-s/Stroman-a 4.00

ALIEN NATION (Movie)
DC Comics: Dec, 1988 ($2.50; 68 pgs.)
1-Adaptation of film; painted-c 4.00

ALIEN PIG FARM 3000
Image Comics (RAW Studios): Apr, 2007 - No. 4, July, 2007 ($2.99, limited series)
1-4-Steve Niles, Thomas Jane & Todd Farmer-s/Don Marquez-a 3.00

ALIEN RESURRECTION (Movie)
Dark Horse Comics: Oct, 1997 - No. 2, Nov, 1997 ($2.50; limited series)
1,2-Adaptation of film; Dave McKean-c 3.00

ALIENS, THE (Captain Johner and...)(Also see Magnus Robot Fighter...)
Gold Key: Sept-Dec, 1967; No. 2, May, 1982
1-Reprints from Magnus #1,3,4,6-10; Russ Manning-a in all
3 6 9 19 30 40
2-(Whitman) Same contents as #1 1 2 3 5 6 8

ALIENS (Movie) (See Alien: The Illustrated..., Dark Horse Comics & Dark Horse Presents #24)
Dark Horse Comics: May, 1988 - No. 6, July, 1989 ($1.95, B&W, limited series)
1-Based on movie sequel; 1st app. Aliens in comics 3 6 9 16 23 30
1-2nd - 6th printings; 4th w/new inside front-c 3.00
2 2 4 6 8 10 12
2-2nd & 3rd printing, 3-6-2nd printings 3.00
3 1 2 3 5 7 9
4-6 5.00
Mini Comic #1 (2/89, 4x6")-Was included with Aliens Portfolio 4.00
Collection 1 ($10.95,)-r/#1-6 plus Dark Horse Presents #24 plus new-a 12.00
Collection 1-2nd printing (1991, $11.95)-On higher quality paper than 1st print; Dorman painted-c 12.00
Hardcover ('90, $24.95, B&W)-r/1-6, DHP #24 30.00
... Omnibus Vol. 1 (7/07, $24.95, 9x6") r/1st & 2nd series and Aliens: Earth War 25.00
... Omnibus Vol. 2 (12/07, $24.95, 9x6") r/Genocide, Harvest and Colonial Marines series 25.00
... Omnibus Vol. 3 (3/08, $24.95, 9x6") r/Rogue, Salvation and Sacrifice, Labyrinth series 25.00
... Omnibus Vol. 4 (8/08, $24.95, 9x6") r/Music of the Spears, Stronghold, Berserker, Mondo Pest and Mondo Heat series and one-shots 25.00
... Omnibus Vol. 5 (11/08, $24.95, 9x6") r/Alchemy, Survival, Havoc series and various 25.00
... Omnibus Vol. 6 (2/09, $24.95, 9x6") r/Apocalypse GN, Xenogenesis & one-shots 25.00
... Outbreak (3rd printing, 8/96, $17.95)-Bolton-c 18.00
Platinum Edition - (See Dark Horse Presents: Aliens Platinum Edition) -

ALIENS
Dark Horse Comics: V2#1, Aug, 1989 - No. 4, 1990 ($2.25, limited series)
V2#1-Painted art by Denis Beauvais 5.00
1-2nd printing (1990), 2-4 3.00

GD VG FN VF VF/NM NM-
2.0 4.0 6.0 8.0 9.0 9.2

...: Nightmare Asylum TPB (12/96, $16.95) r/series; Bolton-c 17.00

ALIENS
Dark Horse Comics: May, 2009 - No. 4, Nov, 2009 ($3.50, limited series)
1-4-John Arcudi-s/Zach Howard-a. 1,2-Howard-c. 3,4-Swanland-c 3.50

ALIENS: (Series of titles, all Dark Horse)
--ALCHEMY, 10/97 - No. 3, 11/97 ($2.95),1-3-Corben-c/a, Arcudi-s 3.00
--APOCALYPSE - THE DESTROYING ANGELS, 1/99 - No. 4, 4/99 ($2.95)
1-4-Doug Wheatly-a/Schultz-s 3.00
--BERSERKERS, 1/95 - No. 4, 4/95 ($2.50) 1-4 3.00
--COLONIAL MARINES, 1/93 - No. 10, 7/94 ($2.50) 1-10 3.00
--DEAD ORBIT, 4/17 - No. 4, 12/17 ($3.99) 1-4-James Stokoe-s/a 4.00
--DEFIANCE, 4/16 - No. 12, 6/17 ($3.99) 1-12: 1,2-Brian Wood-s/Tristan Jones-a 4.00
--EARTH ANGEL, 8/94 ($2.95) 1-Byrne-a/story; wraparound-c 3.00
--EARTH WAR, 6/90 - No. 4, 10/90 ($2.50) 1-All have Sam Kieth-a & Bolton painted-c 5.00
1-2nd printing, 3,4 3.00
2 4.00
--GENOCIDE, 11/91 - No. 4, 2/92 ($2.50) 1-4-Suydam painted-c. 4-Wraparound-c, poster 3.00
--GLASS CORRIDOR, 6/98 ($2.95) 1-David Lloyd-s/a 3.00
--HARVEST (See Aliens: Hive)
--HAVOC, 6/97 - No. 2, 7/97 ($2.95) 1,2: Schultz-s, Kent Williams-c, 40 artists including Art Adams, Kelley Jones, Duncan Fegredo, Kevin Nowlan 3.00
--HIVE, 2/92 - No. 4,5/92 ($2.50) 1-4: Kelley Jones-c/a in all 3.00
...Harvest TPB ('98, $16.95) r/series; Bolton-c 17.00
--KIDNAPPED, 12/97 - No. 3, 2/98 ($2.50) 1-3 3.00
--LABYRINTH, 9/93 - No. 4, 1/94 ($2.50) 1-4: 1-Painted-c 3.00
--LIFE AND DEATH, 9/16 - No. 4, 12/16 ($3.99) 1-4-Abnett-s/Moritat-a 4.00
--LOVESICK, 12/96 ($2.95) 1 3.00
--MONDO HEAT, 2/96 ($2.50) nn-Sequel to Mondo Pest 3.00
--MONDO PEST, 4/95 ($2.95, 44 pgs.) nn-r/Dark Horse Comics #22-24 4.00
--MUSIC OF THE SPEARS, 1/94 - No. 4, 4/94 ($2.50) 1-4 3.00
--NEWT'S TALE, 6/92 - No. 2, 7/92 ($4.95) 1,2-Bolton-c 5.00
--PIG, 3/97 ($2.95)1 3.00
--PREDATOR: THE DEADLIEST OF THE SPECIES, 7/93 - No. 12,8/95 ($2.50)
1-Bolton painted-c; Guice-a(p) 5.00
1-Embossed foil platinum edition 10.00
2-12: Bolton painted-c. 2,3-Guice-a(p) 3.00
--PURGE, 8/97 ($2.95) nn-Hester-a 3.00
--ROGUE, 4/93 - No. 4, 7/93 ($2.50)1-4: Painted-c 3.00
--SACRIFICE, 5/93 ($4.95, 52 pgs.) nn-P. Milligan scripts; painted-c/a 5.00
--SALVATION, 11/93 ($4.95, 52 pgs.) nn-Mignola-c/a(p); Gibbons script 5.00
--SPECIAL, 6/97 ($2.50) 1 3.00
--STALKER, 6/98 ($2.50)1-David Wenzel-s/a 3.00
--STRONGHOLD, 5/94 - No. 4, 9/94 ($2.50) 1-4 3.00
--SURVIVAL, 2/98 - No. 3, 4/98 ($2.95) 1-3-Tony Harris-c 3.00
--TRIBES, 1992 ($24.95, hardcover graphic novel) Bissette text-s with Dorman painted-a 25.00
...softcover ($9.95) 10.00

ALIENS: FIRE AND STONE (Crossover with AvP, Predator, and Prometheus)
Dark Horse Comics: Sept, 2014 - No. 4, Dec, 2014 ($3.50, limited series)
1-4-Roberson-s/Reynolds-a 3.50

ALIENS/ VAMPIRELLA (See Vampirella/Aliens)

ALIENS VS. PARKER (Not based on the Alien movie series)
BOOM! Studios: Mar, 2013 - No. 4, May, 2013 ($3.99, limited series)
1-4: 1-Paul Scheer & Nick Giovannetti-s; Bracchi-a/Noto-c 4.00

ALIENS VS. PREDATOR (See Dark Horse Presents #36)
Dark Horse Comics: June, 1990 - No. 4, Dec, 1990 ($2.50, limited series)
1-Painted-c 2 4 6 8 10 12
1-2nd printing 3.00
0-(7/90, $1.95, B&W)-r/Dark Horse Pres. #34-36 2 4 6 8 10 12
2,3 5.00
4-Dave Dorman painted-c 4.00
Annual (7/99, $4.95) Jae Lee-c 5.00

Aliens vs. Predator: Three World War #6 © 20th Century Fox

All-American Comics #21 © DC

All-American Men of War #5 © DC

GD 2.0 | VG 4.0 | FN 6.0 | VF 8.0 | VF/NM 9.0 | NM- 9.2

... : Booty (1/96, $2.50) painted-c 3.00
... Omnibus Vol. 1 (5/07, $24.95, 9x6") r/#1-4 & Annual; ...: War; ...: Eternal 25.00
... Omnibus Vol. 2 (10/07, $24.95, 9x6") r/...: Xenogenesis #1-4; ...: Deadliest of the Species; ...: Booty and stories from ... Annual 25.00
...: One For One (8/10, $1.00) r/#1 with red cover frame 3.00
... : Thrill of the Hunt (9/04, $6.95, digest-size TPB) Based on 2004 movie 7.00
... Wraith 1 (7/98, $2.95) Jay Stephens-s 3.00

--VS. PREDATOR: DUEL, 3/95 - No. 2, 4/95 ($2.50) 1,2 3.00

--VS. PREDATOR: ETERNAL, 6/98 - No. 4, 9/98 ($2.50)1-4: Edginton-s/Maleev-a; Fabry-c3.00

--VS. PREDATOR: THREE WORLD WAR, 1/10 - No. 6, 9/10 ($3.50) 1-6-Leonardi-a 3.50

--VS. PREDATOR VS. THE TERMINATOR, 4/00 - No. 4, 7/00 ($2.95) 1-4: Ripley app. 3.00

--VS. PREDATOR: WAR, No. 0, 5/95 - No. 4, 8/95 ($2.50) 0-4: Corben painted-c 3.00

--VS. PREDATOR: XENOGENESIS, 12/99 - No. 4, 3/00 ($2.95) 1-4: Watson-s/Mel Rubi-a3.00

--XENOGENESIS, 8/99 - No. 4, 11/99 ($2.95) 1-4: T&M Bierbaum-s 3.00

ALIENS VS. ZOMBIES (Not based on the Alien movie series)
Zenescope Entertainment: Jul, 2015 - No. 5, Dec, 2015 ($3.99, limited series)

1-5: 1-Brusha-s/Riccardi-a; multiple covers on each 4.00

ALIEN TERROR (See 3-D Alien Terror)

ALIEN: THE ILLUSTRATED STORY (Also see Aliens)
Heavy Metal Books: 1980 ($3.95, soft-c, 8x11")

nn-Movie adaptation; Simonson-a 3 6 9 16 23 30

ALIEN[3] (Movie)
Dark Horse Comics: June, 1992 - No. 3, July, 1992 ($2.50, limited series)

1-3: Adapts 3rd movie; Suydam painted-c 3.00

ALIEN VS. PREDATOR: FIRE AND STONE (Crossover with Aliens, Predator, and Prometheus)
Dark Horse Comics: Oct, 2014 - No. 4, Jan, 2015 ($3.50, limited series)

1-4-Sebela-s/Olivetti-a 3.50

ALIEN VS. PREDATOR: LIFE AND DEATH (Crossover with Aliens, Predator, and Prometheus)
Dark Horse Comics: Dec, 2016 - No. 4, Mar, 2017 ($3.99, limited series)

1-4-Abnett-s/Theis-a 4.00

ALIEN WORLDS (Also see Eclipse Graphic Album #22)
Pacific Comics/Eclipse: Dec, 1982 - No. 9, Jan, 1985

1,2,4: 2,4-Dave Stevens-c/a 6.00
3,5-7 4.00
8,9 1 2 3 4 5 7
3-D No. 1-Art Adams 1st published art 1 2 3 4 5 7

ALISON DARE, LITTLE MISS ADVENTURES (Also see Return of ...)
Oni Press: Sept, 2000 ($4.50, B&W, one-shot)

1-J. Torres-s/J.Bone-c/a 4.50

ALISON DARE & THE HEART OF THE MAIDEN
Oni Press: Jan, 2002 - No. 2, Feb, 2002 ($2.95, B&W, limited series)

1,2-J. Torres-s/J.Bone-c/a 3.00

ALISTER THE SLAYER
Midnight Press: Oct, 1995 ($2.50)

1-Boris-c 3.00

ALL-AMERICAN COMICS (...Western #103-126, ...Men of War #127 on; also see The Big All-American Comic Book)
All-American/National Periodical Publ.: April, 1939 - No. 102, Oct, 1948

1-Hop Harrigan (1st app.), Scribbly by Mayer (1st DC app.), Toonerville Folks, Ben Webster, Spot Savage, Mutt & Jeff, Red White & Blue (1st app.), Adventures in the Unknown, Tippie, Reg'lar Fellers, Skippy, Bobby Thatcher, Mystery Men of Mars, Daiseybelle, Wiley of West Point begin 675 1350 2025 4725 8113 11,500
2-Ripley's Believe It or Not begins, ends #24 232 464 696 1485 2543 3600
3-5: 5-The American Way begins, ends #10 200 400 600 1280 2190 3100
6,7: 6-Last Spot Savage; Popsicle Pete begins, ends #26, 28. 7-Last Bobby Thatcher 135 270 405 864 1482 2100
8-The Ultra Man begins & 1st-c app. 443 886 1329 3234 5717 8200
9,10: 10-X-Mas-c 132 264 396 838 1444 2050
11,15: 11-Ultra Man-c. 15-Last Tippie & Reg'lar Fellars; Ultra Man-c 190 380 570 1207 2079 2950
12-14: 12-Last Toonerville Folks 129 258 387 826 1413 2000
16-(Rare)-Origin/1st app. Green Lantern by Sheldon Moldoff (c/a)(7/40) & begin series; appears in costume on-c & only one panel inside; created by Martin Nodell. Inspired in 1940 by a switchman's green lantern that would give trains the go ahead to proceed. G.L. cover pose swiped from last panel of a Jan, 1939 Flash Gordon Sunday page. 24,500 49,000 73,500 181,000 490,000 800,000
17-2nd Green Lantern 1300 2600 3900 9750 20,375 31,000
18-N.Y. World's Fair-c/story (scarce); The Atom app. in one panel announcing debut in next issue 1250 2500 3750 9400 19,700 30,000
19-Origin/1st app. The Atom (10/40); last Ultra Man 2575 5150 7725 19,300 39,650 60,000
20-Atom dons costume; Ma Hunkle becomes Red Tornado (1st app.)(1st DC costumed heroine, before Wonder Woman, 11/40); Rescue on Mars begins, ends #25; 1 pg. origin Green Lantern 649 1298 1947 4738 8369 12,000
21-Last Wiley of West Point & Skippy; classic Moldoff-c 530 1060 1590 3869 6835 9800
22,23: 23-Last Daiseybelle; 3 Idiots begin, end #82 366 732 1098 2562 4481 6400
24-Sisty & Dinky become the Cyclone Kids; Ben Webster ends; origin Dr. Mid-Nite & Sargon, The Sorcerer in text with app. 383 766 1149 2681 4691 6700
25-Origin & 1st story app. Dr. Mid-Nite by Stan Asch; Hop Harrigan becomes Guardian Angel; last Adventure in the Unknown (scarce) 1225 2450 3675 9200 19,100 29,000
26-Origin/1st story app. Sargon, the Sorcerer 389 778 1167 2723 4762 6800
27: #27-32 are misnumbered in indicia with correct No. appearing on-c. Intro. Doiby Dickles, Green Lantern's sidekick 400 800 1200 2800 4900 7000
28-Hop Harrigan gives up costumed i.d. 213 426 639 1363 2332 3300
29,30 213 426 639 1363 2332 3300
31-40: 35-Doiby learns Green Lantern's i.d. 177 354 531 1124 1937 2750
41-50: 50-Sargon ends 142 284 426 909 1555 2200
51-60: 59-Scribbly & the Red Tornado ends 119 238 357 762 1306 1850
61-Origin/1st app. Solomon Grundy (11/44) 1600 3200 4800 12,000 23,000 34,000
62-70: 70-Kubert Sargon; intro Sargon's helper, Maximillian O'Leary 103 206 309 659 1130 1600
71-88: 71-Last Red White & Blue. 72-Black Pirate begins (not in #74-82); last Atom. 73-Winky, Blinky & Noddy begins, ends #82. 79,83-Mutt & Jeff-c. 85-1st Crusher Crock (becomes Sportsmaster); Hasen "Derby" cover 82 164 246 528 902 1275
89-Origin & 1st app. Harlequin 258 516 774 1651 2826 4000
90,92,96-99: 90-Origin/1st app. Icicle. 98-Sportsmaster-c. 99-Last Hop Harrigan 158 316 474 1003 1727 2450
91,93,94,95-Harlequin-c 181 362 543 1158 1979 2800
100-1st app. Johnny Thunder by Alex Toth (8/48); western theme begins (Scarce) 206 412 618 1318 2259 3200
101-Last Mutt & Jeff (Scarce) 142 284 426 909 1555 2200
102-Last Green Lantern, Black Pirate & Dr. Mid-Nite (Scarce) 271 542 813 1734 2967 4200

NOTE: *No Atom in 47, 62-69.* ***Kinstler*** *Black Pirate-89.* ***Stan Aschmeier*** *a (Dr. Mid-Nite) 25-84; c-7.* ***Mayer*** *c-1, 2(part), 6, 10.* ***Moldoff*** *c-16-23.* ***Nodell*** *c-31.* ***Paul Reinman*** *a (Green Lantern)-53-55p, 56-84, 87; (Black Pirate)-83-88, 90; c-52, 55-76, 78, 80, 81, 87.* ***Toth*** *a-88, 92, 96, 98-102; c(p)-92, 96-102. Scribbly by* ***Mayer*** *in #1-59. Ultra Man by* ***Mayer*** *in #8-19.*

ALL AMERICAN COMICS
DC Comics: April 1939

nn - Ashcan comic, not distributed to newsstands, only for in house use. Cover art is Adventure Comics #33 and interior from Detective Comics #23. A CGC 7.5 copy sold for $7466 in December 2014.

ALL-AMERICAN COMICS (Also see All Star Comics 1999 crossover titles)
DC Comics: May, 1999 ($1.99, one-shot)

1-Golden Age Green Lantern and Johnny Thunder; Barreto-a 3.00

ALL-AMERICAN MEN OF WAR (Previously All-American Western)
National Periodical Publ.: No. 127, Aug-Sept, 1952 - No. 117, Sept-Oct, 1966

127 (#1, 1952) 134 268 402 1072 2411 3750
128 (1952) 57 114 171 456 1016 1575
2(12-1/'52-53)-5 50 100 150 400 900 1400
6-Devil Dog story; Ghost Squadron story 38 76 114 285 641 1000
7-10: 8-Sgt. Storm Cloud-s 38 76 114 285 641 1000
11-16,18: 18-Last precode; 1st Kubert-c (2/55) 35 70 105 252 564 875
17-1st Frogman-s in this title 36 72 108 259 580 900
19,20,22-27 27 54 81 194 435 675
21-Easy Co. prototype 34 68 102 245 548 850
28 (12/55)-1st Sgt. Rock prototype; Kubert-a 56 112 168 448 999 1550
29,30,32-Wood-a 27 54 81 194 435 675
31,33,34,36-38,40: 34-Gunner prototype-s. 36-Little Sure Shot prototype-s. 38-1st S.A. issue 25 50 75 175 388 600
35-Greytone-c 29 58 87 207 464 720
39 (11/56)-2nd Sgt. Rock prototype; 1st Easy Co.? 38 76 114 285 641 1000
41,43-47,49,50: 46-Tankbusters-c/s 21 42 63 150 330 510
42-Pre-Sgt. Rock Easy Co.-c/s 27 54 81 187 414 640
48-Easy Co.-c/s; Nick app.; Kubert-a 27 54 81 187 414 640
51-56,58-62,65,66: 61-Gunner-c/s 17 34 51 117 259 400

Allegra #3 © WSP

Alley Oop #13 © NEA Services

All-Flash #10 © DC

	GD 2.0	VG 4.0	FN 6.0	VF 8.0	VF/NM 9.0	NM- 9.2
57(5/58),63,64-Pre-Sgt. Rock Easy Co.-c/s	23	46	69	161	356	550
67-1st Gunner & Sarge by Andru & Esposito	50	100	150	400	900	1400
68,69: 68-2nd app. Gunner & Sarge. 69-1st Tank Killer-c/s	22	42	63	147	324	500
70	14	28	42	96	211	325
71-80: 71,72,76-Tank Killer-c/s. 74-Minute Commandos-c/s	12	24	36	82	179	275
81-Greytone-c	12	24	36	81	176	270
82-Johnny Cloud begins(1st app.), ends #117	28	56	84	202	451	700
83-2nd Johnny Cloud	14	28	42	94	207	320
84-88: 88-Last 10¢ issue	10	20	30	69	147	225
89-100: 89-Battle Aces of 3 Wars begins, ends #98. 89,90-Panels from these issues used by artist Roy Lichtenstein for famous paintings	8	16	24	56	108	160
101-111,113-116: 110,11-Greytone-c. 111,114,115-Johnny Cloud	6	12	18	40	73	105
112-Balloon Buster series begins, ends #114,116	6	12	18	41	76	110
117-Johnny Cloud-c & 3-part story	6	12	18	41	76	110

NOTE: *Frogman stories in 17, 38, 44, 45, 50, 51, 53, 55-58, 63, 65, 66, 72, 76, 77.* ***Colan*** *a-112.* ***Drucker*** *a-47, 58, 61, 63, 65, 69, 71, 74, 77.* ***Grandenetti*** *c(p)-127, 128, 2-17(most).* ***Heath*** *a-14, 27, 32, 38, 41, 45, 47, 50, 51, 55-58, 62, 64, 71, 75, 76, 78, 95, 111-117; c-85, 91, 94-96, 100, 101, 110-112, others?* ***Infantino*** *a-8.* ***Kirby*** *a-29.* ***Krigstein*** *a-128('52), 2, 3, 5.* ***Kubert*** *a-22, 24, 28, 29, 33, 34, 36, 38, 39, 41-43, 47-50, 52, 53, 55, 56, 59, 60, 63-65, 69, 71-73, 76, 102, 103, 105, 106, 108, 114; c-41, 44, 52, 54, 55, 58, 64, 69, 76, 77, 79, 102-106, 108, 113-117, others? Tank Killer in 69, 71, 76 by* ***Kubert. P. Reinman*** *c-55, 57, 61, 62, 71, 72, 74-76, 80.* ***J. Severin*** *a-58.*

ALL AMERICAN MEN OF WAR
DC Comics: Aug/Sept. 1952

nn - Ashcan comic, not distributed to newsstands, only for in-house use. Cover art is All Star Western #58 and interior from Mr. District Attorney #21. A GD+ copy sold for $1195 in 2012.

ALL-AMERICAN SPORTS
Charlton Comics: Oct, 1967

	GD	VG	FN	VF	VF/NM	NM-
1	3	6	9	19	30	45

ALL-AMERICAN WESTERN (Formerly All-American Comics; Becomes All-American Men of War)
National Periodical Publ.: No. 103, Nov, 1948 - No. 126, June-July, 1952 (103-121: 52 pgs.)

	GD	VG	FN	VF	VF/NM	NM-
103-Johnny Thunder & his horse Black Lightning continues by Toth, ends #126; Foley of The Fighting 5th, Minstrel Maverick, & Overland Coach begin; Captain Tootsie by Beck; mentioned in Love and Death	54	108	162	343	574	825
104-Kubert-a	39	78	117	234	385	535
105,107-Kubert-a	34	68	102	199	325	450
106,108-110,112: 112-Kurtzman's "Pot-Shot Pete" (1 pg.)	28	56	84	165	270	375
111,114-116-Kubert-a	29	58	87	172	281	390
113-Intro. Swift Deer, J. Thunder's new sidekick (4-5/50); classic Toth-c; Kubert-a	32	64	96	188	307	425
117-126: 121-Kubert-a; bondage-c	21	42	63	122	199	275

NOTE: ***G. Kane*** *c(p)-112, 119, 120, 123.* ***Kubert*** *a-103-105, 107, 111, 112(1 pg.), 113-116, 121.* ***Toth*** *a-103-125; c(p)-103-111,113-116, 121, 122, 124-126. Some copies of #125 have #12 on-c.*

ALL COMICS
Chicago Nite Life News: 1945

	GD	VG	FN	VF	VF/NM	NM-
1	15	30	45	85	130	175

ALLEGRA
Image Comics (WildStorm): Aug, 1996 - No. 4, Dec, 1996 ($2.50)

	NM-
1-4	3.00

ALLEY CAT (Alley Baggett)
Image Comics: July, 1999 - No. 6, Mar, 2000 ($2.50/$2.95)

	NM-
Preview Edition	6.00
Prelude	5.00
Prelude w/variant-c	6.00
1-Photo-c	3.00
1-Painted-c by Dorian	4.00
1-Another Universe Edition, 1-Wizard World Edition	7.00
2-4: 4-Twin towers on-c	3.00
5,6-($2.95)	3.00
Lingerie Edition (10/99, $4.95) Photos, pin-ups, cover gallery	5.00
...Vs. Lady Pendragon ('99, $3.00) Stinsman-c	3.00

ALLEY OOP (See The Comics, The Funnies, Red Ryder and Super Book #9)
Dell Publishing Co.: No. 3, 1942

	GD	VG	FN	VF	VF/NM	NM-
Four Color 3 (#1)	47	94	141	367	821	1275

ALLEY OOP
Argo Publ.: Nov, 1955 - No. 3, Mar, 1956 (Newspaper reprints)

	GD	VG	FN	VF	VF/NM	NM-
1	17	34	51	98	154	210
2,3	12	24	36	69	97	125

ALLEY OOP
Dell Publishing Co.: 12-2/62-63 - No. 2, 9-11/63

	GD	VG	FN	VF	VF/NM	NM-
1	5	10	15	35	63	90
2	5	10	15	31	53	75

ALLEY OOP
Standard Comics: No. 10, Sept, 1947 - No. 18, Oct, 1949

	GD	VG	FN	VF	VF/NM	NM-
10	32	64	96	188	307	425
11-18: 17,18-Schomburg-c	24	48	72	142	234	325

ALLEY OOP ADVENTURES
Antarctic Press: Aug, 1998 - No. 3, Dec, 1998 ($2.95)

	NM-
1-3-Jack Bender-s/a	3.00

ALLEY OOP ADVENTURES (Alley Oop Quarterly in indicia)
Antarctic Press: Sept, 1999 - No. 3, Mar, 2000 ($2.50/$2.99, B&W)

	NM-
1-3-Jack Bender-s/a	3.00

ALL-FAMOUS CRIME (2nd series - Formerly Law Against Crime #1-3; becomes All-Famous Police Cases #6 on)
Star Publications: No. 8, 5/51 - No. 10, 11/51; No. 4, 2/52 - No. 5, 5/52;

	GD	VG	FN	VF	VF/NM	NM-
8 (#1-1st series)	30	60	90	177	289	400
9 (#2)-Used in **SOTI**, illo- "The wish to hurt or kill couples in lovers' lanes is a not uncommon perversion;" L.B. Cole-c/a(r)/Law-Crime #3	42	84	126	265	445	625
10 (#3)	24	48	72	140	230	320
4 (#4-2nd series)-Formerly Law-Crime	22	44	66	132	216	300
5 (#5) Becomes All-Famous Police Cases #6	22	44	66	132	216	300

NOTE: *All have L.B. Cole covers.*

ALL FAMOUS CRIME STORIES (See Fox Giants)

ALL-FAMOUS POLICE CASES (Formerly All Famous Crime #5)
Star Publications: No. 6, Feb, 1952 - No. 16, Sept, 1954

	GD	VG	FN	VF	VF/NM	NM-
6	28	56	84	165	270	375
7,8: 7-Baker story. 8-Marijuana story	22	44	66	130	213	295
9-16	21	42	63	122	199	275

NOTE: ***L. B. Cole*** *c-all; a-15, 1pg.* ***Hollingsworth*** *a-15.*

ALL-FLASH (...Quarterly No. 1-5)
National Per. Publ./All-American: Summer, 1941 - No. 32, Dec-Jan, 1947-48

	GD	VG	FN	VF	VF/NM	NM-
1-Origin The Flash retold by E. E. Hibbard; Hibbard c-1-10,12-14,16,31p.	1250	2500	3750	8750	14,875	21,000
2-Origin recap	271	542	813	1734	2967	4200
3,4	161	322	483	1030	1765	2500
5-Winky, Blinky & Noddy begins (1st app.), ends #32	116	232	348	742	1271	1800
6-10: 6-Has full page ad for Wonder Woman #1	106	212	318	673	1162	1650
11,13: 13-The King app.	94	188	282	597	1024	1450
12-Origin/1st The Thinker	103	206	309	659	1130	1600
14-Green Lantern cameo	110	220	330	704	1202	1700
15-20: 18-Mutt & Jeff begins, ends #22	86	172	258	546	936	1325
21-31	71	142	213	454	777	1100
32-Origin/1st app. The Fiddler; 1st Star Sapphire	145	290	435	921	1586	2250

All-Flash Quarterly ashcan (a recently discovered CGC 7.0 copy sold for $8150 in 2012)

NOTE: *Book length stories in 2-13, 16. Bondage c-31, 32.* ***Martin Nodell*** *c-15, 17-28.*

ALL FLASH (Leads into Flash [2nd series] #231)
DC Comics: Sept, 2007 ($2.99, one-shot)

	NM-
1-Wally West hunts down Bart's killers; Waid-s; two covers by Middleton & Sienkiewicz	3.00

ALL FOR LOVE (Young Love V3#5-on)
Prize Publications: Apr-May, 1957 - V3#4, Dec-Jan, 1959-60

	GD	VG	FN	VF	VF/NM	NM-
V1#1	9	18	27	58	114	170
2-6: 5-Orlando-c	5	10	15	33	57	80
V2#1-5(1/59), 5(3/59)	5	10	15	30	50	70
V3#1(5/59), 1(7/59)-4: 2-Powell-a	4	8	12	27	44	60

ALL FUNNY COMICS
Tilsam Publ./National Periodical Publications (Detective): Winter, 1943-44 - No. 23, May-June, 1948

	GD	VG	FN	VF	VF/NM	NM-
1-Genius Jones (see Adventure #77 for debut), Buzzy (1st app., ends #4), Dover & Clover (see More Fun #93) begin; Bailey-a	48	96	144	302	514	725
2	22	44	66	132	216	300
3-10	15	30	45	85	130	175
11-13,15,18,19-Genius Jones app.	14	28	42	80	115	150
14,17,20-23	10	20	30	56	76	95
16-DC Super Heroes app.	31	62	93	182	296	410

ALL GOOD

All Humor Comics #10 © QUA

All New Atom #21 © DC

All-New Collectors' Edition C-56 © DC

GD 2.0 | VG 4.0 | FN 6.0 | VF 8.0 | VF/NM 9.0 | NM- 9.2

St. John Publishing Co.: Oct, 1949 (50¢, 260 pgs.)
nn-(8 St. John comics bound together) 113 226 339 718 1234 1750
NOTE: *Also see Li'l Audrey Yearbook & Treasury of Comics.*

ALL GOOD COMICS (See Fox Giants)
Fox Feature Syndicate: No.1, Spring, 1946 (36 pgs.)
1-Joy Family, Dick Transom, Rick Evans, One Round Hogan
27 54 81 158 259 360

ALL GREAT
William H. Wise & Co.: nd (1945?) (132 pgs.)
nn-Capt. Jack Terry, Joan Mason, Girl Reporter, Baron Doomsday; Torture scenes
48 96 144 302 514 725

ALL GREAT COMICS (See Fox Giants)
Fox Feature Syndicate: 1946 (36 pgs.)
1-Crazy House, Bertie Benson Boy Detective, Gussie the Gob
27 54 81 158 259 360

ALL GREAT COMICS (Formerly Phantom Lady #13? Dagar, Desert Hawk No. 14 on)
Fox Feature Syndicate: No. 14, Oct, 1947 - No. 13, Dec, 1947 (Newspaper strip reprints)
14(#12)-Brenda Starr & Texas Slim-r (Scarce) 57 114 171 362 621 880
13-Origin Dagar, Desert Hawk; Brenda Starr (all-r); Kamen-c; Dagar covers begin 65 130 195 416 708 1000

ALL-GREAT CONFESSION MAGAZINE (See Fox Giants)

ALL-GREAT CONFESSIONS (See Fox Giants)

ALL GREAT CRIME STORIES (See Fox Giants)

ALL GREAT JUNGLE ADVENTURES (See Fox Giants)

ALL HALLOW'S EVE
Innovation Publishing: 1991 ($4.95, 52 pgs.)
1-Painted-c/a 1 2 3 4 5 7

ALL HERO COMICS
Fawcett Publications: Mar, 1943 (100 pgs., cardboard-c)
1-Capt. Marvel Jr., Capt. Midnight, Golden Arrow, Ibis the Invincible, Spy Smasher, Lance O'Casey; 1st Banshee O'Brien; Raboy-c 194 388 582 1242 2121 3000

ALL HUMOR COMICS
Quality Comics Group: Spring, 1946 - No. 17, December, 1949
1 21 42 63 126 206 285
2-Atomic Tot story; Gustavson-a 14 28 42 76 108 140
3-9: 3-Intro Kelly Poole who is cover feature #3 on. 5-1st app. Hickory? 8-Gustavson-a 9 18 27 52 69 85
10-17 9 18 27 47 61 75

ALLIANCE, THE
Image Comics (Shadowline Ink): Aug, 1995 - No. 3, Nov, 1995 ($2.50)
1-3: 2-(9/95) 3.00

ALL LOVE (...Romances No. 26)(Formerly Ernie Comics)
Ace Periodicals (Current Books): No. 26, May, 1949 - No. 32, May, 1950
26 (No. 1)-Ernie, Lily Belle app. 14 28 42 76 108 140
27-L. B. Cole-a 15 30 45 84 127 170
28-32 10 20 30 58 79 100

ALL-NEGRO COMICS
All-Negro Comics: June, 1947 (15¢)
1 (Rare) 2300 4600 6900 12,500 17,250 22,000
NOTE: *Seldom found in fine or mint condition; many copies have brown pages.*

ALL-NEW ALL-DIFFERENT AVENGERS (Follows Secret Wars event)
Marvel Comics: Jan, 2016 - No. 15, Dec, 2015 ($4.99/$3.99)
1-($4.99) Spider-Man (Miles), Ms. Marvel, Nova join; Waid-s/Adam Kubert & Asrar-a 5.00
2-15-($3.99) Main cover by Alex Ross. 2,3-Warbringer app.; Kubert-a. 4-6,9,10-Asrar-a. 7,8-Standoff tie-ins; Adam Kubert-a. 9-Intro. new Wasp (Nadia). 13-15-Civil War II tie-in 4.00
Annual 1(10/16, $4.99) Fan-fic short stories by various incl. Waid/Zdarsky & Allegri 5.00

ALL-NEW ALL-DIFFERENT MARVEL UNIVERSE
Marvel Comics: May, 2016 ($4.99, one-shot)
1-Handbook-style entries; profiles of major characters; Marquez-c 5.00

ALL-NEW ALL-DIFFERENT POINT ONE (Follows Secret Wars event)
Marvel Comics: Dec, 2015 ($5.99, one-shot)
1-Preludes to new titles: Carnage, Daredevil, All-New Inhumans, Agents of S.H.I.E.L.D., Rocket Raccoon & Groot, and Contest of Champions; Del Mundo-c 6.00

ALL-NEW ATOM, THE (See The Atom and DCU Brave New World)
DC Comics: Sept, 2006 - No. 25, Sept, 2008 ($2.99)
1-25: 1-18-Simone-s. 1-Intro Ryan Choi; Byrne-a thru #3. 4-11-Barrows-a. 12,13-Chronos app. 14,15-Countdown x-over. 17,18-Wonder Woman app. 3.00
...: Future/Past TPB (2007, $14.99) r/#7-11 15.00
...: My Life in Miniature TPB (2007, $14.99) r/#1-6 and app. in DCU Brave New World #1 15.00
...: Small Wonder TPB (2008, $17.99) r/#17,18,21-25 18.00
...: The Hunt For Ray Palmer TPB (2008, $14.99) r/#12-16 15.00

ALL-NEW BATMAN: BRAVE & THE BOLD (See Batman: The Brave and the Bold)

ALL-NEW CAPTAIN AMERICA (See Captain America #25 - 2014 series)
Marvel Comics: Jan, 2015 - No. 6, Jun, 2015 ($3.99)
1-6: 1-Sam Wilson as Captain America, Ian as Nomad; Immonen-a 4.00
... Special 1 (7/15, $4.99) Loveness-s/Morgan-a; Inhumans & Spider-Man app. 5.00

ALL-NEW CAPTAIN AMERICA: FEAR HIM (Sam Wilson as Cap)
Marvel Comics: Jan, 2015 - No. 4, Apr, 2015 ($3.99, limited series)
1-4-Hopeless & Remender-s/Kudranski-a/Bianchi-c; The Scarecrow app. 4.00

ALL-NEW CLASSIC CAPTAIN CANUCK
Chapterhouse Comics: No. 0, Feb, 2016 - No. 4, Apr, 2017 ($4.99/$3.99)
0-($4.99) Short stories; Ed Brisson-s; art by various 5.00
1-4-($3.99) Brisson-s/Freeman-a; 2 covers on each 4.00

ALL-NEW COLLECTORS' EDITION (Formerly Limited Collectors' Edition: see for C-57, C-59)
DC Comics, Inc.: Jan, 1978 - Vol. 8, No. C-62, 1979 (No. 54-58: 76 pgs.)
C-53-Rudolph the Red-Nosed Reindeer 4 8 12 28 47 65
C-54-Superman Vs. Wonder Woman 4 8 12 27 44 60
C-55-Superboy & the Legion of Super-Heroes; Wedding of Lightning Lad & Saturn Girl; Grell-c/a 4 8 12 25 40 55
C-56-Superman Vs. Muhammad Ali: Wraparound Neal Adams-c/a; Adams & O'Neil-s (see "Superman Vs. Muhammad Ali" for reprint) 10 20 30 64 132 200
C-56-Superman Vs. Muhammad Ali (Whitman variant)-low print
11 22 33 76 163 250
C-57,C-59-(See Limited Collectors' Edition)
C-58-Superman Vs. Shazam; Buckler-c/a; Black Adam's 2nd Bronze Age app.
4 8 12 27 44 60
C-60-Rudolph's Summer Fun(8/78) 4 8 12 25 40 55
C-61-(See Famous First Edition-Superman #1)
C-62-Superman the Movie (68 pgs.; 1979)-Photo-c from movie plus photos inside (also see DC Special Series #25 for Superman II) 3 6 9 15 22 28

ALL-NEW COMICS (...Short Story Comics No. 1-3)
Family Comics (Harvey Publications): Jan, 1943 - No. 14, Nov, 1946; No. 15, Mar-Apr, 1947 (10 x 13-1/2")
1-Steve Case, Crime Rover, Johnny Rebel, Kayo Kane, The Echo, Night Hawk, Ray O'Light, Detective Shane begin (all 1st app.?); Red Blazer on cover only; Sultan-a; Nazi WWII-c
300 600 900 1980 3440 4900
2-Origin Scarlet Phantom by Kubert; Nazi WWII-c 135 270 405 864 1482 2100
3-Nazi WWII-c 119 238 357 762 1305 1850
4-Nazi WWII-c 107 214 321 680 1165 1650
5-Classic Schomburg Japanese WWII-c showing Japanese using Human Suicide bombs falling on the Capitol building 161 322 483 1030 1765 2500
6-11: Schomburg-c on all. 9-11-Japanese WWII-c. 6-8 Nazi WWII-c. 6-The Boy Heroes & Red Blazer (text story) begin, end #12; Black Cat app.; intro. Sparky in Red Blazer. 7-Kubert, Powell-a; Black Cat & Zebra app. 8,9: 8-Shock Gibson app.; Kubert, Powell-a; Schomburg-c. 9-Black Cat app.; Kubert-a. 10-The Zebra app. (from Green Hornet Comics); Kubert-a(3). 11-Girl Commandos, Man In Black app.
148 296 444 947 1624 2300
12-Kubert-a; Japanese WWII-c 61 122 183 390 670 950
13-Stuntman by Simon & Kirby; Green Hornet, Joe Palooka, Flying Fool app.; Green Hornet-c 50 100 150 315 533 750
14-The Green Hornet & The Man in Black Called Fate by Powell, Joe Flying Fool app.; Flying Fool app.; J. Palooka-c by Ham Fisher 41 82 123 256 428 600
15-(Rare)-Small size (5-1/2x8-1/2"; B&W; 32 pgs.). Distributed to mail subscribers only. Black Cat and Joe Palooka app. 174 348 522 1114 1907 2700
NOTE: *Also see Boy Explorers No. 2, Flash Gordon No. 5, and Stuntman No. 3.* **Powell** *a-11.* **Schomburg** *c-5-11. Captain Red Blazer & Spark on c-5-11 (w/Boy Heroes #12).*

ALL-NEW DOOP (X-Men)
Marvel Comics: Jun, 2014 - No. 5, Nov, 2014 ($3.99, limited series)
1-5-Milligan-s/Lafuente-a; Kitty Pryde and X-Men app. 3-5-The Anarchist app. 4.00

ALL-NEW EXECUTIVE ASSISTANT: IRIS (Volume 4) (Also see Executive Assistant: Iris)
Aspen MLT: Sept, 2013 - No. 5, Jun, 2014 ($1.00/$3.99)
1-($1.00) Buccellato-s/Qualano-a; multiple covers 3.00
2-5-($3.99) Multiple covers 4.00

ALL-NEW EXECUTIVE ASSISTANT: IRIS: ENEMIES AMONG US

All-New Ghost Rider #2 © MAR

All-Select Comics #5 © MAR

All Star Batman #3 © DC

GD VG FN VF VF/NM NM-
2.0 4.0 6.0 8.0 9.0 9.2

Aspen MLT: Dec, 2016 - Present ($4.99)
1-Wohl-s/Cafaro-a; Hernandez-s/Green-a; multiple covers 5.00

ALL NEW FATHOM (See Fathom)

ALL-NEW GHOST RIDER (Also see the 2017 Ghost Rider series)
Marvel Comics: May, 2014 - No. 12, May, 2015 ($3.99)
1-12: 1-Felipe Smith-s/Tradd Moore-a; origin of Robbie Reyes. 6-10-Damion Scott-a 4.00

ALL-NEW GUARDIANS OF THE GALAXY (Continues in Guardians of the Galaxy #146)
Marvel Comics: Jul, 2017 - No. 12, Dec, 2017 ($3.99)
1-12: 1-Grandmaster app.; Duggan-s/Kuder-a. 2,4-The Collector app. 3-Irving-a 4.00
Annual 1 (8/17, $4.99) Tie-in to Secret Empire; Beyruth-a; Yondu & Mantis app. 5.00

ALL-NEW HAWKEYE
Marvel Comics: May, 2015 - No. 5, Nov, 2015 ($3.99)
1-5-Jeff Lemire-s/Ramón Pérez-a/c; Kate Bishop app.; flashback to circus childhood 4.00

ALL-NEW HAWKEYE
Marvel Comics: Jan, 2016 - No. 6, Jun, 2016 ($3.99)
1-6-Lemire-s/Pérez-a/c; Kate Bishop app. 1-3-Flashforward 30 years; Mandarin app. 4.00

ALL-NEW INHUMANS
Marvel Comics: Feb, 2016 - No. 11, Nov, 2016 ($3.99)
1-($4.99)-Asmus & Soule-s/Caselli-a; Crystal & Gorgon app. 5.00
2-11-($3.99) 2-4-The Commissar app. 5,6-Spider-Man app. 4.00

ALL-NEW INVADERS
Marvel Comics: Mar, 2014 - No. 15, Apr, 2015 ($3.99)
1-15: 1-Capt. America, Bucky, Namor & Jim Hammond team; Robinson-s/Pugh-a. 6,7-Original Sin tie-in 4.00

ALL-NEW MARVEL NOW! POINT ONE
Marvel Comics: Mar, 2014 ($5.99, one-shot preview of upcoming series)
1-Previews of Loki, Silver Surfer, Black Widow, Ms. Marvel, Avengers, All-New Invaders 6.00

ALL NEW MICHAEL TURNER'S FATHOM (See Fathom)

ALL NEW MICHAEL TURNER'S SOULFIRE (See Soulfire)

ALL-NEW OFFICIAL HANDBOOK OF THE MARVEL UNIVERSE A TO Z
Marvel Comics: 2006 - No. 12, 2006 ($3.99, limited series)
1-12-Profile pages of Marvel characters not covered in 2004-2005 Official Handbooks 4.00
...: Update 1-4 (2007, $3.99) Profile pages 4.00

ALL-NEW ULTIMATES
Marvel Comics: Jun, 2014 - No. 12, Mar, 2015 ($3.99)
1-12: 1-Miles Morales Spider-Man, Spider-Woman, Cloak and Dagger, Kitty Pryde and Bombshell team. 5,6-Crossbones app. 4.00

ALL-NEW WOLVERINE (Laura Kinney X-23 as Wolverine)
Marvel Comics: Jan, 2016 - Present ($4.99/$3.99)
1-($4.99) Tom Taylor-s/David Lopez-a; Angel app. 5.00
2-31-($3.99) 2-Intro. Gabby. 2,3-Taskmaster app. 4-Doctor Strange app. 5-Janet Van Dyne app. 7-Squirrel Girl app. 8,9-Fin Fang Foom app. 10-12-Civil War II tie-in. 16-18-Gambit app.19-21-Ironheart app. 22-24-Guardians of the Galaxy app.; Yu-c. 25-30-Daken app. 31-Deadpool app. 4.00
Annual 1 (10/16, $4.99) Gwen Stacy app.; Tom Taylor-s/Marcio Takara-a 5.00

ALL-NEW X-FACTOR
Marvel Comics: Mar, 2014 - No. 20, Mar, 2015 ($3.99)
1-20: 1-12-David-s/DiGiandomenico-a; Gambit, Polaris, Quicksilver, Danger app. 13,14-Mhan-a. 14-Scarlet Witch app. 15-17-Axis tie-in 4.00

ALL-NEW X-MEN
Marvel Comics: Jan, 2013 - No. 41, Aug, 2015 ($3.99)
1-Bendis-s; Immonen-a and wraparound-c; original X-Men time travel to present 4.00
2-24: 6-8-Marquez-a; Mystique app. 8-Avengers app. 16,17-Battle of the Atom tie-ins. 18-New uniforms. 22-24-Trial of Jean Grey; Guardians of the Galaxy app. 4.00
25-($4.99) Art by Marquez with pages by Timm, Mack, Young, Campbell & many others 5.00
26-41: 30-Pichelli-a. 31-36-X-Men in Ultimate universe; Miles Morales app. 38,39-Black Vortex x-over; Ronan & Guardians of the Galaxy app.; Sorrentino-a. 40-Iceman revealed as gay 4.00
Annual 1 (2/15, $4.99) Sorrentino-a; Eva Bell and Morgana Le Fey in the past 5.00
Special #1 (12/13, $4.99) Superior Spider-Man and the Hulk app. 5.00

ALL-NEW X-MEN
Marvel Comics: Feb, 2016 - No. 19, May, 2017 ($3.99)
1-8-Hopeless-s/Bagley-a; original X-Men, Wolverine (X-23), Kid Apocalypse app. 4.00
9-($4.99) Apocalypse Wars x-over; Beast & Kid Apocalypse in ancient Egypt 5.00
10-19: 10,11-Apocalypse Wars; young Apocalypse app. 17,18-Inhumans app. 4.00
Annual 1 (1/17, $4.99) Spotlight on Idie; Sina Grace-s/Cory Smith-a 5.00
#1.MU (4/17, $4.99) Monsters Unleashed tie-in; Barberi & Lim-a; Gambit app. 5.00

ALL NIGHTER
Image Comics: Jun, 2011 - No. 5, Oct, 2011 ($2.99, B&W, limited series)
1-5-David Haun-s/a/c 3.00

ALL-OUT WAR
DC Comics: Sept-Oct, 1979 - No. 6, Aug, 1980 ($1.00, 68 pgs.)
1-The Viking Commando (origin), Force Three(origin), & Black Eagle Squadron begin 2 4 6 13 18 22
2-6 2 4 6 8 10 12
NOTE: *Ayers a(p)-1-6. Elias r-2. Evans a-1-6. Kubert c-16.*

ALL PICTURE ADVENTURE MAGAZINE
St. John Publishing Co.: Oct, 1952 - No. 2, Nov, 1952 (100 pg. Giants, 25¢, squarebound)
1-War comics 50 100 150 315 533 750
2-Horror-crime comics 60 120 180 381 653 925
NOTE: *Above books contain three St. John comics rebound; variations possible. Baker art known in both.*

ALL PICTURE ALL TRUE LOVE STORY
St. John Publishing Co.: Oct., 1952 - No. 2, Nov., 1952 (100 pgs., 25¢)
1-Canteen Kate by Matt Baker 71 142 213 454 777 1100
2-Baker-c/a 66 132 198 419 722 1025

ALL-PICTURE COMEDY CARNIVAL
St. John Publishing Co.: October, 1952 (100 pgs., 25¢)(Contains 4 rebound comics)
1-Contents can vary; Baker-a 47 94 141 296 498 700

ALL REAL CONFESSION MAGAZINE (See Fox Giants)

ALL ROMANCES (Mr. Risk No. 7 on)
A. A. Wyn (Ace Periodicals): Aug, 1949 - No. 6, June, 1950
1 18 36 54 103 162 220
2 11 22 33 62 86 110
3-6 10 20 30 56 76 95

ALL-SELECT COMICS (Blonde Phantom No. 12 on)
Timely Comics (Daring Comics): Fall, 1943 - No. 11, Fall, 1946
1-Capt. America (by Rico #1), Human Torch, Sub-Mariner begin; Black Widow story (4 pgs.); Classic Schomburg-c 1850 3700 5550 12,300 25,650 39,000
2-Red Skull app. 703 1406 2109 5132 9066 13,000
3-The Whizzer begins 443 886 1329 3234 5717 8200
4,5-Last Sub-Mariner 366 732 1098 2562 4481 6400
6-9: 6-The Destroyer app. 8-No Whizzer 300 600 900 1920 3310 4700
10-The Destroyer & Sub-Mariner app.; last Capt. America & Human Torch issue 300 600 900 1920 3310 4700
11-1st app. Blonde Phantom; Miss America app.; all Blonde Phantom-c by Shores 300 600 900 1980 3440 4900
NOTE: *Schomburg c-1-10. Sekowsky a-7. #7 & 8 show 1944 in indicia, but should be 1945.*

ALL SELECT COMICS 70th ANNIVERARY SPECIAL
Marvel Comics: Sept, 2009 ($3.99, one-shot)
1-New stories of Blonde Phantom and Marvex the Super Robot; r/Marvex G.A. app. 5.00

ALL SPORTS COMICS (Formerly Real Sports Comics; becomes All Time Sports Comics No. 4 on)
Hillman Periodicals: No. 2, Dec-Jan, 1948-49; No. 3, Feb-Mar, 1949
2-Krigstein-a(p), Powell, Starr-a 36 72 108 211 343 475
3-Mort Lawrence-a 22 44 66 132 216 300

ALL STAR BATMAN
DC Comics: Oct, 2016 - No. 14, Dec, 2017 ($4.99)
1-5-Snyder-s/Romita Jr.-a; Two-Face app.; back-up with Shalvey-a 5.00
1-Director's Cut ($5.99) r/#1 with B&W art and original script; variant cover gallery 6.00
6-9-Back-up w/Francavilla-a. 6-Jock-a; Mr. Freeze app. 7-Lotay-a; Poison Ivy app 5.00
10-14-Albuquerque-a; back-up with Fiumara-a 5.00

ALL STAR BATMAN & ROBIN, THE BOY WONDER
DC Comics: Sept, 2005 - No. 10, Aug, 2008 ($2.99)
1-Two covers; retelling of Robin's origin; Frank Miller-s/Jim Lee-a/c 4.00
1-Diamond Retailer Summit Edition (9/05) sketch-c 60.00
2-10: 2-7-Two covers by Lee and Miller. 3-Black Canary app. 4-Six pg. Batcave gatefold. 10-Edition without profanity 3.00
8-10: 8,9-Variant cover by Neal Adams. 10-Variant-c by Quitely 5.00
10-Recalled edition with insufficiently covered profanity inside; Jim Lee-c 20.00
10-Recalled edition with variant Quitely-c 40.00
... Special Edition (2/06, $3.99) r/#1 with Lee pencil pages and Miller script; new Miller-c 4.00

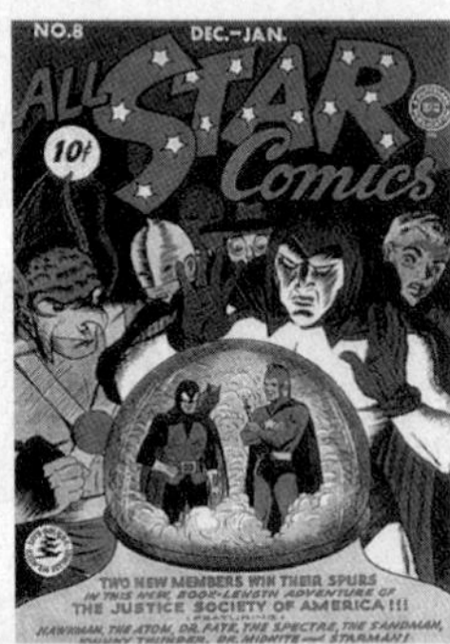

All Star Comics #8 © DC

All-Star Squadron #41 © DC

All Star Western #87 © DC

GD VG FN VF VF/NM NM-
2.0 4.0 6.0 8.0 9.0 9.2

GD VG FN VF VF/NM NM-
2.0 4.0 6.0 8.0 9.0 9.2

Vol. 1 HC (2008, $24.99, dustjacket) r/#1-9; cover gallery, sketch pages; Schreck intro. 25.00
Vol. 1 SC (2009, $19.99) r/#1-9; cover gallery, sketch pages; Schreck intro. 20.00

ALL STAR COMICS
DC Comics: Spring 1940

1-Ashcan comic, not distributed to newsstands, only for in-house use. Cover art is Flash Comics #1 and interior from Detective Comics #37. A CGC certified 7.0 copy sold for $15,600 in 2002 and for $21,000 in May 2014.

ALL STAR COMICS (All Star Western No. 58 on)
National Periodical Publ./All-American/DC Comics: Sum, 1940 - No. 57, Feb-Mar, 1951; No. 58, Jan-Feb, 1976 - No. 74, Sept-Oct, 1978

1-The Flash (#1 by E.E. Hibbard), Hawkman (by Shelly), Hourman (by Bernard Baily), The Sandman (by Creig Flessel), The Spectre (by Baily), Biff Bronson, Red White & Blue (ends #2) begin; Ultra Man's only app. (#1-3 are quarterly; #4 begins bi-monthly issues) 1200 2400 3600 9000 17,000 25,000
2-Green Lantern (by Martin Nodell), Johnny Thunder begin; Green Lantern figure swipe from the cover of All-American Comics #16; Flash figure swipe from cover of Flash Comics #8; Moldoff/Bailey-c (cut & paste-c.) 530 1060 1590 3869 6835 9800
3-Origin & 1st app. The Justice Society of America (Win/40); Dr. Fate & The Atom begin, Red Tornado cameo 5800 11,600 17,400 46,400 93,200 140,000
3-Reprint, Oversize 13-1/2x10". **WARNING:** This comic is an exact reprint of the original except for its size. DC published it in 1974 with a second cover titling it as a Famous First Edition. There have been many reported cases of the outer cover being removed and the interior sold as the original edition. The reprint with the new outer cover removed is practically worthless. See Famous First Edition for value.
4-1st adventure for J.S.A. 595 1190 1785 4350 7675 11,000
5-1st app. Shiera Sanders as Hawkgirl (1st costumed super-heroine, 6-7/41) 497 994 1491 3628 6414 9200
6-Johnny Thunder joins JSA 300 600 900 1980 3440 4900
7-First time ever Superman and Batman appear in a story together; Superman, Batman and Flash become honorary members; last Hourman; Doiby Dickles app. 423 846 1269 3046 5323 7600
8-Origin & 1st app. Wonder Woman (12-1/41-42)(added as 9 pgs. making book 76 pgs.; origin cont'd in Sensation #1; see W.W. #1 for more detailed origin); Dr. Fate dons new helmet; Hop Harrigan text stories & Starman begin; Shiera app.; Hop Harrigan JSA guest; Starman & Dr. Mid-Nite become members 17,300 34,600 51,900 138,400 219,200 300,000
9-11: 9-JSA's girlfriends cameo; Shiera app.; J. Edgar Hoover of FBI made associate member of JSA. 10-Flash, Green Lantern cameo; Sandman new costume. 11-Wonder Woman begins; Spectre cameo; Shiera app.; Moldoff Hawkman-c 300 600 900 2040 3570 5100
12-Wonder Woman becomes JSA Secretary 300 600 900 1980 3440 4900
13,15: Sandman w/Sandy in #14 & 15. 13-Hitler app. in book-length sci-fi story. 15-Origin & 1st app. Brain Wave; Shiera app. 252 504 756 1613 2757 3900
14-(12/42) Junior JSA Club begins; w/membership offer & premiums 258 516 774 1651 2826 4000
16-20: 19-Sandman w/Sandy. 20-Dr. Fate & Sandman cameo 239 478 717 1530 2615 3700
21-23: 21-Spectre & Atom cameo; Dr. Fate by Kubert; Dr. Fate, Sandman end. 22-Last Hop Harrigan; Flag-c. 23-Origin/1st app. Psycho Pirate; last Spectre & Starman 181 362 543 1158 1979 2800
24-Flash & Green Lantern cameo; Mr. Terrific only app.; Wildcat, JSA guest; Kubert Hawkman begins; Hitler-c 187 374 561 1197 2049 2900
25-27: 25-Flash & Green Lantern start again. 26-Robot-c. 27-Wildcat, JSA guest (#24-26: only All-American imprint) 161 322 483 1030 1765 2500
28-32 148 296 444 947 1624 2300
33-Solomon Grundy & Doiby Dickles app; classic Solomon Grundy cover & last G.A. app. 406 812 1218 2842 4971 7100
34,35-Johnny Thunder cameo in both 135 270 405 864 1482 2100
36-Batman & Superman JSA guests 300 600 900 2010 3505 5000
37-Johnny Thunder cameo; origin & 1st app. Injustice Society; last Kubert Hawkman 187 374 561 1197 2049 2900
38-Black Canary begins; JSA Death issue 252 504 756 1613 2757 3900
39,40: 39-Last Johnny Thunder 129 258 387 826 1413 2000
41-Black Canary joins JSA; Injustice Society app. (2nd app.?) 129 258 387 826 1413 2000
42-Atom & the Hawkman don new costumes 129 258 387 826 1413 2000
43-49,51-56: 43-New logo; Robot-c. 55-Sci/Fi story. 56-Robot-c 129 258 387 826 1413 2000
50-Frazetta art, 3 pgs. 134 268 402 851 1463 2075
57-Kubert-a, 6 pgs. (Scarce); last app. G.A. Green Lantern, Flash & Dr. Mid-Nite 194 388 582 1242 2121 3000
V12 #58-(1976) JSA (Flash, Hawkman, Dr. Mid-Nite, Wildcat, Dr. Fate, Green Lantern, Robin & Star Spangled Kid) app.; intro. Power Girl 9 18 27 59 117 175
V12 #59,60: 59-Estrada & Wood-a 3 6 9 20 31 42
V12 #61-68: 62-65-Superman app. 64,65-Wood-c/a; Vandal Savage app. 66-Injustice Society app. 68-Psycho Pirate app. 3 6 9 20 31 42
V12 #69-1st Earth-2 Huntress (Helena Wayne) 6 12 18 40 73 105
V12 #70-73: 70-Full intro. of Huntress. 72-Thorn on-c 3 6 9 20 31 42
V12 #74-(44 pgs.) Last issue, story continues in Adventure Comics #461 & 462 (death of Earth-2 Batman; Staton-c/a 4 8 12 28 47 65
(See Justice Society Vol. 1 TPB for reprints of V12 revival)
NOTE: *No Atom-27, 36; no Dr. Fate-13; no Flash-8, 9, 11-23; no Green Lantern-8, 9,11-23; Hawkman in 1-57 (only one to app. in all 57 issues); no Johnny Thunder-5, 36; no Wonder Woman-9, 10, 23. Book length stories in 4-9, 11-14, 18-22, 25, 26, 29, 30, 32-36, 40, 42, 43. Johnny Peril in #42-46, 48, 49, 51, 52,54-57.* ***Baily*** *a-1-10, 12, 13, 14i, 15-20.* ***Burnley*** *Starman-8-13; c-12, 13.* ***Grell*** *c-58.* ***E.E. Hibbard*** *c-3, 4, 6-10.* ***Infantino*** *c-40.* ***Kubert*** *Hawkman-24-30, 33-37.* ***Lampert/Baily/Flessel*** *c-1, 2.* ***Moldoff*** *Hawkman-3-23; c-11.* ***Mart Nodell*** *c-25i, 26i, 27-32.* ***Purcell*** *c-5.* ***Simon & Kirby*** *Sandman 14-17, 19.* ***Staton*** *a-66-74p. c-74p.* ***Toth*** *a-37(2), 38(2), 40, 41; c-38, 41.* ***Wood*** *a-58i-63i, 64, 65; c-63i, 64, 65. Issues 1-7, 9-16 are 68 pgs.; #8 is 76 pgs.; #17-19 are 60 pgs.; #20-57 are 52 pgs.*

ALL STAR COMICS (Also see crossover 1999 editions of Adventure, All-American, National, Sensation, Smash, Star Spangled and Thrilling Comics)
DC Comics: May, 1999 - No. 2, May, 1999 ($2.95, bookends for JSA x-over)

1,2-Justice Society in World War 2; Robinson-s/Johnson-c 3.00
1-RRP Edition 45.00
...80-Page Giant (9/99, $4.95) Phantom Lady app. 5.00

ALL STAR INDEX, THE
Independent Comics Group (Eclipse): Feb, 1987 ($2.00, Baxter paper)

1 1 2 3 5 6 8

ALL-STAR SECTION EIGHT (Also see Sixpack and Dogwelder: Hard Travelin' Heroz)
DC Comics: Aug, 2015 - No. 6, Feb, 2016 ($2.99, limited series)

1-6-Ennis-s/McCrea-a/Conner-c. 1-Batman app. 4-Wonder Woman app. 6-Superman 3.00

ALL-STAR SQUADRON (See Justice League of America #193)
DC Comics: Sept, 1981 - No. 67, Mar, 1987

1-Original Atom, Hawkman, Dr. Mid-Nite, Robotman (origin), Plastic Man, Johnny Quick, Liberty Belle, Shining Knight begin 1 3 4 6 8 10
2-10: 3-Solomon Grundy app. 4,7-Spectre app. 8-Re-intro Steel, the Indestructable Man 5.00
11-24,26-46,48,49: 12-Origin G.A. Hawkman retold. 15-JLA, JSA & Crime Syndicate app. 23-Origin/1st app. The Amazing Man. 24-Batman app. 26-Origin Infinity, Inc.(2nd app.); Robin app. 27-Dr. Fate vs. The Spectre. 30-35-Spectre app. 33-Origin Freedom Fighters of Earth-X. 36,37-Superman vs. Capt. Marvel; Ordway-c. 41-Origin Starman 4.00
25-1st app. Nuklon (Atom Smasher) & Infinity, Inc. (9/83) 1 3 4 6 8 10
47-Origin Dr. Fate; McFarlane-a (1st full story)/part-c (7/85) 2 4 6 10 14 18
50-Double size; Crisis x-over 1 2 3 5 6 8
51-66: 51-56-Crisis x-over. 61-Origin Liberty Belle. 62-Origin The Shining Knight. 63-Origin Robotman. 65-Origin Johnny Quick. 66-Origin Tarantula 6.00
67-Last issue; retells first case of the Justice Society 1 2 3 5 6 8
Annual 1-3: 1(11/82)-Retells origin of G.A. Atom, Guardian & Wildcat; Jerry Ordway's 1st pencils for DC. (1st work was inking Carmine Infantino in Mystery in Space #117). 2(11/83)-Infinity, Inc. app. 3(9/84) 6.00
NOTE: ***Buckler*** *a-1-5; c-1, 3-5, 51.* ***Kubert*** *c-2, 7-18. JLA app. in 14, 15. JSA app. in 4, 14, 15, 19, 27, 28.*

ALL-STAR STORY OF THE DODGERS, THE
Stadium Communications: Apr, 1979 ($1.00)

1 2 4 6 9 13 16

ALL-STAR SUPERMAN (Also see FCBD edition in the Promotional Comics section)
DC Comics: Jan, 2006 - No. 12, Oct, 2008 ($2.99)

1-Grant Morrison-s/Frank Quitely-a/c 5.00
1-Variant-c by Neal Adams 20.00
1-Special Edition (2009, $1.00) r/#1 with "After Watchmen" cover logo frame 3.00
2-12: 3-Lois gets super powers. 7,8-Bizarro app. 3.00
Free Comic Book Day giveaway (6/08) reprints #1 3.00
Vol. 1 HC (2007, $19.99, dustjacket) r/#1-6; Bob Schreck intro. 20.00
Vol. 1 SC (2008, $12.99) r/#1-6; Schreck intro. 13.00
Vol. 2 HC (2009, $19.99, dustjacket) r/#7-12; Mark Waid intro. 20.00
Vol. 2 SC (2009, $12.99) r/#7-12; Mark Waid intro. 13.00

ALL STAR WESTERN (Formerly All Star Comics No. 1-57)
National Periodical Publ.: No. 58, Apr-May, 1951 - No. 119, June-July, 1961

58-Trigger Twins (ends #116), Strong Bow, The Roving Ranger & Don Caballero begin 52 104 156 328 552 775
59,60: Last 52 pgs. 31 62 93 186 303 420
61-66: 61-64-Toth-a 25 50 75 150 245 340
67-Johnny Thunder begins; Gil Kane-a 36 72 108 211 343 475
68-81: Last precode (2-3/55) 17 34 51 98 154 210
82-98: 97-1st S.A. issue 15 30 45 84 127 170
99-Frazetta-r/Jimmy Wakely #4 15 30 45 85 130 175
100 15 30 45 85 130 175

All Star Western (2011 series) #27 © DC

All Top Comics #16 © FOX

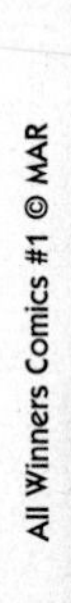
All Winners Comics #1 © MAR

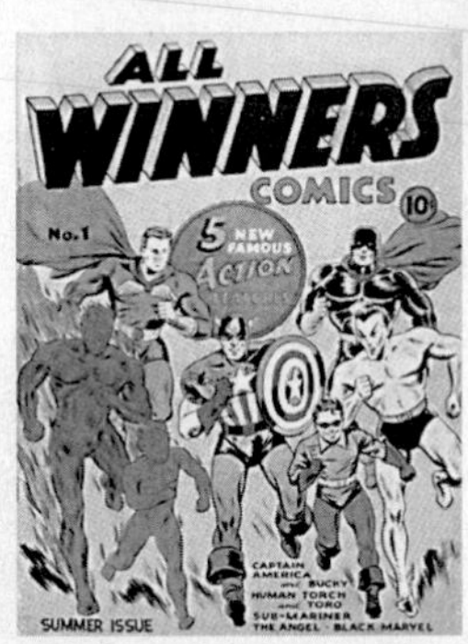

	GD 2.0	VG 4.0	FN 6.0	VF 8.0	VF/NM 9.0	NM- 9.2
101-107,109-116,118,119: 103-Grey tone-c	14	28	42	80	115	150
108-Origin J. Thunder; J. Thunder logo begins	26	52	78	154	252	350
117-Origin Super Chief	16	32	48	94	147	200

NOTE: *Gil Kane c(p)-58, 59, 61, 63, 64, 68, 69, 70-95(most), 97-199(most).* ***Infantino*** *art in most issues. Madame .44 app.- #117-119.*

ALL-STAR WESTERN (Weird Western Tales No. 12 on)
National Periodical Publications: Aug-Sept, 1970 - No. 11, Apr-May, 1972

1-Pow-Wow Smith-r; Infantino-a 5 10 15 35 63 90
2-Outlaw begins; El Diablo by Morrow begins; has cameos by Williamson, Torres, Kane, Giordano & Phil Seuling 5 10 15 34 60 85
3-Origin El Diablo 5 10 15 31 53 75
4-6: 5-Last Outlaw issue. 6-Billy the Kid begins, ends #8 4 8 12 23 37 50
7-9-(52 pgs.) 9-Frazetta-a, 3pgs.(r) 4 8 12 25 40 55
10-(52 pgs.) Jonah Hex begins (1st app., 2-3/72) 34 68 102 245 548 850
11-(52 pgs.) 2nd app. Jonah Hex; 1st cover 13 26 39 89 195 300

NOTE: ***Neal Adams*** *c-2-5;* ***Aparo*** *a-5.* ***G. Kane*** *a-3, 4, 6, 8.* ***Kubert*** *a-4r, 7-9r.* ***Morrow*** *a-2-4, 10, 11. No. 7-11 have 52 pgs.*

ALL STAR WESTERN (DC New 52)
DC Comics: Nov, 2011 - No. 34, Oct, 2014 ($3.99)

1-34: 1-Jonah Hex in 1880s Gotham City; Gray & Palmiotti-s/Moritat-a. 2,3-El Diablo back-up. 9-11-Court of Owls. 10-Bat Lash back-up; Garcia-López-a. 13-16-Tomahawk back-up. 19-21-Booster Gold app. 21-28-Hex in present day. 22-Batman app. 27-Superman app. 30,31-Madame .44 back-up; Garcia-López-a. 34-Darwyn Cooke-c/a 4.00
#0 (11/12, $3.99) Jonah Hex's full origin; Gray & Palmiotti-s/Moritat-a 4.00

ALL SURPRISE (Becomes Jeanie #13 on) (Funny animal)
Timely/Marvel (CPC): Fall, 1943 - No. 12, Winter, 1946-47

1-Super Rabbit, Gandy & Sourpuss begin 57 114 171 362 619 875
2 24 48 72 142 234 325
3-10,12 20 40 60 114 182 250
11-Kurtzman "Pigtales" art 20 40 60 117 189 260

ALL TEEN (Formerly All Winners; All Winners & Teen Comics No. 21 on)
Marvel Comics (WFP): No. 20, January, 1947

20-Georgie, Mitzi, Patsy Walker, Willie app.; Syd Shores-c 37 74 111 222 361 500

ALL-TIME SPORTS COMICS (Formerly All Sports Comics)
Hillman Per.: V2, No. 4, Apr-May, 1949 - V2, No. 7, Oct-Nov, 1949 (All 52 pgs.)

V2#4 23 46 69 136 223 310
5-7: 5-(V1#5 inside)-Powell-a; Ty Cobb sty. 7-Krigstein-p; Walter Johnson & Knute Rockne sty 18 36 54 105 165 225

ALL TOP
William H. Wise Co.: 1944 (132 pgs.)

nn-Capt. V, Merciless the Sorceress, Red Robbins, One Round Hogan, Mike the M.P., Snooky, Pussy Katnip app. 41 82 123 256 428 600

ALL TOP COMICS (My Experience No. 19 on)
Fox Feature Synd./Green Publ./Norlen Mag.: 1945; No. 2, Sum, 1946 - No. 18, Jul, 1949; 1957 - 1959

1-Cosmo Cat & Flash Rabbit begin (1st app.) 34 68 102 199 325 450
2 (#1-7 are funny animal) 16 32 48 94 147 200
3-7: 7-Two diff. issues (7/47 & 9/47) 14 28 42 80 115 150
8-Blue Beetle, Phantom Lady, & Rulah, Jungle Goddess begin (11/47); Kamen-c 300 600 900 2010 3505 5000
9-Kamen-c 161 322 483 1030 1765 2500
10-Classic Kamen bondage/torture/dwarf-c 194 388 582 1242 2121 3000
11-13,15,17: 11,12-Rulah-c. 15-No Blue Beetle 132 264 396 838 1444 2050
14-No Blue Beetle; used in **SOTI**, illo- "Corpses of colored people strung up by their wrists" 200 400 600 1280 2190 3100
16-Classic Good Girl octopus-c 174 348 522 1114 1907 2700
18-Dagar, Jo-Jo app; no Phantom Lady or Blue Beetle 87 174 261 553 952 1350
6(1957-Green Publ.)-Patoruzu the Indian; Cosmo Cat on cover only. 6(1958-Literary Ent.)-Muggy Doo; Cosmo Cat on cover only. 6(1959-Norlen)-Atomic Mouse; Cosmo Cat on-c only. 6(1959)-Little Eva. 6(Cornell)-Supermouse on-c 5 10 15 24 30 35

NOTE: *Jo-Jo by* ***Kamen****-12,18.*

ALL TRUE ALL PICTURE POLICE CASES
St. John Publishing Co.: Oct, 1952 - No. 2, Nov, 1952 (100 pgs.)

1-Three rebound St. John crime comics 54 108 162 343 574 825
2-Three comics rebound 42 84 126 265 445 625

NOTE: *Contents may vary.*

ALL-TRUE CRIME (...Cases No. 26-35; formerly Official True Crime Cases)
Marvel/Atlas Comics: No. 26, Feb, 1948 - No. 52, Sept, 1952
(OFI #26,27/CFI #28,29/LCC #30-46/LMC #47-52)

26(#1)-Syd Shores-c 39 78 117 240 395 550
27(4/48)-Electric chair-c 34 68 102 199 325 450
28-41,43-48,50-52: 35-37-Photo-c 15 30 45 86 133 180
42,49-Krigstein-a. 49-Used in **POP**, Pg 79 15 30 45 90 140 190

NOTE: ***Colan*** *a-46.* ***Keller*** *a-46.* ***Robinson*** *a-47, 50.* ***Sale*** *a-46.* ***Shores*** *c-26.* ***Tuska*** *a-48(3).*

ALL-TRUE DETECTIVE CASES (Kit Carson No. 5 on)
Avon Periodicals: #2, Apr-May, 1954 - No. 4, Aug-Sept, 1954

2(#1)-Wood-a 28 56 84 165 270 375
3-Kinstler-c 15 30 45 90 140 190
4-r/Gangsters And Gun Molls #2; Kamen-a 21 42 63 122 199 275
nn(100 pgs.)-7 pg. Kubert-a, Kinstler back-c 50 100 150 315 533 750

ALL TRUE ROMANCE (...Illustrated No. 3)
Artful Publ. #1-3/Harwell(Comic Media) #4-20?/Ajax-Farrell(Excellent Publ.) No. 22 on/Four Star Comic Corp.: 3/51 - No. 20, 12/54; No. 22, 3/55 - No. 30?, 7/57; No. 3(#31), 9/57;No. 4(#32), 11/57; No. 33, 2/58 - No. 34, 6/58

1 (3/51) 24 48 72 142 234 325
2 (10/51; 11/51 on-c) 15 30 45 83 124 165
3(12/51) - #5(5/52) 14 28 42 76 108 140
6-Wood-a, 9 pgs. (exceptional) 22 44 66 132 216 300
7-10 [two #7s: #7(11/52, 9/52 inside), #7(11/52, 11/52 inside)]. 10-Hollingsworth-c 13 26 39 72 101 130
11-13,16-19(9/54),20(12/54) (no #21): 11,13-Heck-a 11 22 33 62 86 110
14-Marijuana story 11 22 33 64 90 115
22: Last precode issue (1st Ajax, 3/55) 11 22 33 62 86 110
23-27,29,30(7/57): 29-Disbrow-a 10 20 30 54 72 95
28 (9/56)-L. B. Cole, Disbrow-a 14 28 42 78 112 145
3(#31, 9/57),4(#32, 11/57),33,34 (Farrell, '57- '58) 9 18 27 50 65 80

ALL WESTERN WINNERS (Formerly All Winners; becomes Western Winners with No. 5; see Two-Gun Kid No. 5)
Marvel Comics(CDS): No. 2, Winter, 1948-49 - No. 4, April, 1949

2-Black Rider (origin/1st app.) & his horse Satan, Kid Colt & his horse Steel, & Two-Gun Kid & his horse Cyclone begin; Shores c-2-4 77 154 231 493 847 1200
3-Anti-Wertham editorial 39 78 117 236 388 540
4-Black Rider i.d. revealed; Heath, Shores-a 39 78 117 236 388 540

ALL WINNERS COMICS (All Teen #20) (Also see Timely Presents: ...)
USA No. 1-7/WFP No. 10-19/YAI No. 21: Summer, 1941 - No. 19, Fall, 1946; No. 21, Winter, 1946-47; (No #20) (No. 21 continued from Young Allies No. 20)

1-The Angel & Black Marvel only app.; Capt. America by Simon & Kirby, Human Torch & Sub-Mariner begin (#1 was advertised as All Aces); 1st app. All-Winners Squad in text story by Stan Lee 1900 3800 5700 13,500 25,250 37,000
2-The Destroyer & The Whizzer begin; Simon & Kirby Captain America 595 1190 1785 4350 7675 11,000
3 465 930 1395 3395 5990 8600
4-Classic War-c by Al Avison 524 1048 1572 3825 6763 9700
5 383 766 1149 2681 4691 6700
6-The Black Avenger only app.; no Whizzer story; Hitler, Hirohito & Mussolini-c 622 1244 1866 4541 8021 11,500
7-10 383 766 1149 2681 4691 6700
11,13-15: 11-1st Atlas globe on-c (Winter, 1943-44; also see Human Torch #14). 14,15-No Human Torch 300 600 900 1920 3310 4700
12-Red Skull story; last Destroyer; no Whizzer story 360 720 1080 2520 4410 6300
16-18: 16-No Human Torch 239 478 717 1530 2615 3700
19-(Scarce)-1st story app. & origin All Winners Squad (Capt. America & Bucky, Human Torch & Toro, Sub-Mariner, Whizzer, & Miss America; r-in Fantasy Masterpieces #10 892 1784 2676 6512 13,256 20,000
21-(Scarce)-All Winners Squad; bondage-c 687 1374 2061 5015 10,508 16,000

NOTE: ***Everett*** *Sub-Mariner-1, 3, 4;* ***Burgos*** *Torch-1, 3, 4.* ***Schomburg*** *c-1, 7-18.* ***Shores*** *c-19p, 21.*

(2nd Series - August, 1948, Marvel Comics (CDS))
(Becomes All Western Winners with No. 2)

1-The Blonde Phantom, Capt. America, Human Torch, & Sub-Mariner app. 309 618 927 2163 3782 5400

ALL WINNERS COMICS 70th ANNIVERARY SPECIAL
Marvel Comics: Oct, 2009 ($3.99, one-shot)

1-New story of All Winners Squad; r/G.A. Capt Anerica app. from All Winners #12 5.00

ALL-WINNERS SQUAD: BAND OF HEROES
Marvel Comics: Aug, 2011 - No. 5, Dec, 2011 ($2.99, unfinished limited series of 8 issues)

1-5-WWII story of the Young Avenger and Captain Flame; Jenkins-s/DiGiandomenico-a 3.00

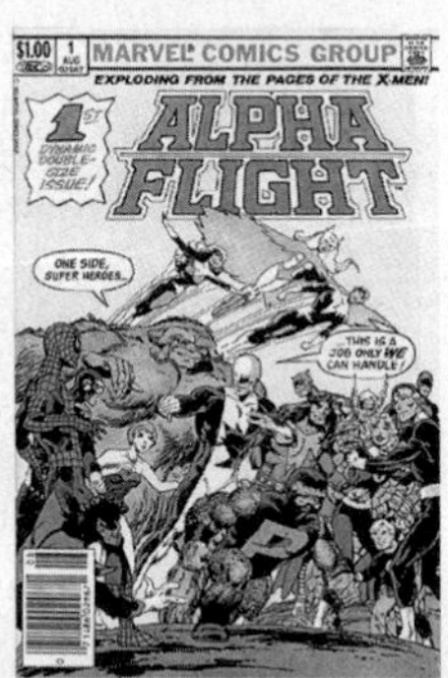

Alpha Flight #1 © MAR

Alpha Flight (2011 series) #1 © MAR

Amazing Adult Fantasy #7 © MAR

	GD 2.0	VG 4.0	FN 6.0	VF 8.0	VF/NM 9.0	NM- 9.2

ALL YOUR COMICS (See Fox Giants)
Fox Feature Syndicate (R. W. Voight): Spring, 1946 (36 pgs.)

1-Red Robbins, Merciless the Sorceress app. 22 44 66 132 216 300

ALMANAC OF CRIME (See Fox Giants)

AL OF FBI (See Little Al of the FBI)

ALOHA, HAWAIIAN DICK (Also see Hawaiian Dick)
Image Comics: Apr, 2016 - No. 5, Aug, 2016 ($3.99, limited series)

1-5-B. Clay Moore-s. 1-4-Jacob Wyatt-a. 5-Paul Reinwand-a 4.00

ALONE IN THE DARK (Based on video game)
Image Comics: Feb, 2003 ($4.95)

1-Matt Haley-c/a; Jean-Marc & Randy Lofficier-s 5.00

ALPHA AND OMEGA
Spire Christian Comics (Fleming H. Revell): 1978 (49¢)

nn 2 4 6 9 13 16

ALPHA: BIG TIME (See Amazing Spider-Man #692-694)
Marvel Comics: Apr, 2013 - No. 5, Aug, 2015 ($2.99)

1-5-Fialkov-s/Plati-a/Ramos-c. 1,3,5-Superior Peter Parker app. 4-Thor app. 3.00

ALPHA CENTURION (See Superman, 2nd Series & Zero Hour)
DC Comics: 1996 ($2.95, one-shot)

1 3.00

ALPHA FLIGHT (See X-Men #120,121 & X-Men/Alpha Flight)
Marvel Comics: Aug, 1983 - No. 130, Mar, 1994 (#52-on are direct sales only)

1-(52 pgs.) Byrne-a begins (thru #28) -Wolverine & Nightcrawler cameo
2 4 6 8 10 12
2-11,13-28: 2-Vindicator becomes Guardian; origin Marrina & Alpha Flight. 3-Concludes origin Alpha Flight. 6-Origin Shaman. 7-Origin Snowbird. 10,11-Origin Sasquatch. 13-Wolverine app. 16,17-Wolverine cameo. 17-X-Men x-over (mostly r-/X-Men #109). 19-Origin/1st app. Talisman. 20-New headquarters. 25-Return of Guardian. 28-Last Byrne issue 3.50
12-(52 pgs.)-Death of Guardian 4.00
29-32,35-49: 39-47,49-Portacio-a(i) 3.00
33-1st app. Lady Deathstrike; Wolverine app. 2 4 6 9 12 15
34-2nd app. Lady Deathstrike; origin Wolverine 6.00
50-Double size; Portacio-a(i) 4.00
51-Jim Lee's 1st work at Marvel (10/87); Wolverine cameo; 1st Lee Wolverine; Portacio-a(i)
1 2 3 5 6 8
52,53-Wolverine app.; Lee-a on Wolverine; Portacio-a(i); 53-Lee/Portacio-a 4.00
54-73,76-86,91-99,101-105: 54,63,64-No Jim Lee-a. 54-Portacio-a(i). 55-62-Jim Lee-a(p). 71-Intro The Sorcerer (villain). 91-Dr. Doom app. 94-F.F. x-over. 99-Galactus, Avengers app. 102-Intro Weapon Omega 3.00
74,75,87-90,100: 74-Wolverine, Spider-Man & The Avengers app. 75-Double size ($1.95, 52 pgs.). 87-90-Wolverine. 4 part story w/Jim Lee-c. 89-Original Guardian returns. 100-($2.00, 52 pgs.)-Avengers & Galactus app. 4.00
106-Northstar revealed to be gay 3.50
106-2nd printing (direct sale only) 3.00
107-109,112-119,121-129: 107-X-Factor x-over. 112-Infinity War x-overs. 115-1st Wyre 3.00
110,111: Infinity War x-overs, Wolverine app. (brief). 111-Thanos cameo 3.00
120-($2.25)-Polybagged w/Paranormal Registration Act poster 4.00
130-($2.25, 52 pgs.) 4.00
Annual 1,2 (9/86, 12/87) 4.00
...Classics Vol. 1 TPB (2007, $24.99) r/#1-8; character profile pages; Byrne interview 25.00
Special V2#1(6/92, $2.50, 52 pgs.)-Wolverine-c/story 4.00
NOTE: ***Austin*** *c-1i, 2i, 53i.* ***Byrne*** *c-81, 82.* ***Guice*** *c-85, 91-99.* ***Jim Lee*** *a(p)-51, 53, 55-62, 64; c-53, 87-90.* ***Mignola*** *a-29-31p.* ***Whilce Portacio*** *a(i)-39-47, 49-54.*

ALPHA FLIGHT (2nd Series)
Marvel Comics: Aug, 1997 - No. 20, Mar, 1999 ($2.99/$1.99)

1-($2.99)-Wraparound cover 6.00
2,3: 2-Variant-c 4.00
4-11: 8,9-Wolverine-c/app. 3.00
12-($2.99) Death of Sasquatch; wraparound-c 4.00
13-15,18-20 3.00
16-1st app. cameo Honey Lemon (Big Hero 6) 1 2 3 5 6 8
17-1st app. Big Hero 6 2 4 6 10 14 18
.../Inhumans '98 Annual ($3.50) Raney-a 4.00

ALPHA FLIGHT (3rd Series)
Marvel Comics: May, 2004 - No. 12, April, 2005 ($2.99)

1-12: 1-6-Lobdell-s/Henry-c/a 3.00
... Vol. 1: You Gotta Be Kiddin' Me (2004, $14.99) r/#1-6 15.00

ALPHA FLIGHT (4th Series)
Marvel Comics: No. 0.1, Jul, 2011 - No. 8, Mar, 2012 ($2.99)

0.1-Pak & Van Lente-s/Oliver & Green-a; Kara Killgrave app. 3.00
1-(8/11, $3.99) Fear Itself tie-in; Eaglesham-a/Jimenez-c; bonus design sketch pages 4.00
2-8-($2.99) Fear Itself tie-ins. 2-Puck returns. 5-Taskmaster app. 7,8-Wolverine app. 3.00

ALPHA FLIGHT: IN THE BEGINNING
Marvel Comics: July, 1997 ($1.95, one-shot)

(-1)-Flashback w/Wolverine 3.00

ALPHA FLIGHT SPECIAL
Marvel Comics: July, 1991 - No. 4, Oct, 1991 ($1.50, limited series)

1-4: 1-3-r-A. Flight #97-99 w/covers. 4-r-A.Flight #100 3.00

ALPHA KING (3 FLOYDS:...)
Image Comics: May, 2016 - No. 5, Nov, 2017 ($3.99)

1-5-Azzarello & Floyd-s/Bisley-a/c 4.00

ALTERED IMAGE
Image Comics: Apr, 1998 - No. 3, Sept, 1998 ($2.50, limited series)

1-3-Spawn, Witchblade, Savage Dragon; Valentino-s/a 3.00

ALTERED STATES
Dynamite Entertainment: 2015 ($3.99, series of one-shots)

...: Doc Savage - Alternate reality Doc Savage in caveman past; Philip Tan-c 4.00
...: Red Sonja - Alternate reality Sonja in modern day New York City; Philip Tan-c 4.00
...: The Shadow - Alternate reality Shadow in sci-fi future; Philip Tan-c 4.00
...: Vampirella - Alternate reality Vampirella as a mortal on Drakulon; Collins-s 4.00

ALTER EGO
First Comics: May, 1986 - No. 4, Nov, 1986 (Mini-series)

1-4 3.00

ALTER NATION
Image Comics: Feb, 2004 - No. 4, Jun, 2004 ($2.95, limited series)

1-4: 1-Two covers by Art Adams and Barberi; Barberi-a 3.00

ALTERS
AfterShock Comics: Sept, 2016 - No. 10, Feb, 2018 ($3.99)

1-10: 1-Paul Jenkins-s/Leila Leiz-a 4.00

ALVIN (TV) (See Four Color Comics No. 1042 or Three Chipmunks #1)
Dell Publishing Co.: Oct-Dec, 1962 - No. 28, Oct, 1973

12-021-212 (#1) 8 16 24 51 96 140
2 5 10 15 31 53 75
3-10 4 8 12 28 47 65
11-"Chipmunks sing the Beatles' Hits" 5 10 15 31 53 75
12-28 4 8 12 23 37 50
Alvin For President (10/64) 4 8 12 28 47 65
...& His Pals in Merry Christmas with Clyde Crashcup & Leonardo 1 (25¢ Giant)
(02-120-402)-(12-2/64) 6 12 18 42 79 115
Reprinted in 1966 (12-023-604) 4 8 12 23 37 50

ALVIN & THE CHIPMUNKS
Harvey Comics: July, 1992 - No. 5, May, 1994

1-5: 1-Richie Rich app. 5.00

AMALGAM AGE OF COMICS, THE: THE DC COMICS COLLECTION
DC Comics: 1996 ($12.95, trade paperback)

nn-r/Amazon, Assassins, Doctor Strangefate, JLX, Legends of the Dark Claw, & Super Soldier 13.00

AMANDA AND GUNN
Image Comics: Apr, 1997 - No. 4, Oct, 1997 ($2.95, B&W, limited series)

1-4 3.00

AMAZING ADULT FANTASY (Formerly Amazing Adventures #1-6; becomes Amazing Fantasy #15) (See Amazing Fantasy for Omnibus HC reprint of #1-15)
Marvel Comics Group (AMI): No. 7, Dec, 1961 - No. 14, July, 1962

7-Ditko-c/a begins, ends #14 52 104 156 406 916 1425
8-Last 10¢ issue 46 92 138 340 770 1200
9-13: 12-1st app. Mailbag. 13-Anti-communist story
45 90 135 333 754 1175
13-2nd printing (1994) 2 4 6 8 10 12
14-Prototype issue (Professor X) 49 98 147 382 854 1325

AMAZING ADVENTURE FUNNIES (Fantoman No. 2 on)
Centaur Publications: June, 1940 - No. 2, Sept. 1940

1-The Fantom of the Fair by Gustavson (r/Amaz. Mystery Funnies V2#7,V2#8),

Amazing Adventures (1979 series) #2 © MAR

Amazing Detective Cases #9 © MAR

Amazing Fantasy #15 © MAR

GD 2.0 | VG 4.0 | FN 6.0 | VF 8.0 | VF/NM 9.0 | NM- 9.2

The Arrow, Skyrocket Steele From the Year X by Everett (r/AMF #2);
Burgos-a 206 412 618 1318 2259 3200
2-Reprints; Published after Fantoman #2 135 270 405 864 1482 2100
NOTE: ***Burgos** a-1(2). **Everett** a-1(3). **Gustavson** a-1(5), 2(3). **Pinajian** a-2.*

AMAZING ADVENTURES (Also see Boy Cowboy & Science Comics)
Ziff-Davis Publ. Co.: 1950; No. 1, Nov, 1950 - No. 6, Fall, 1952 (Painted covers)

1950 (no month given) (8-1/2x11) (8 pgs.) Has the front & back cover plus Schomburg story used in Amazing Advs. #1 (Sent to subscribers of Z-D s/f magazines & ordered through mail for 10¢. Used to test market) 81 162 243 518 884 1250
1-Wood, Schomburg, Anderson, Whitney-a 100 200 300 635 1093 1550
2,3,5: 2-Schomburg-a. 2,5-Anderson-a. 3,5-Starr-a 48 96 144 302 514 725
4-Classic-c; Anderson-a 65 130 195 416 708 1000
6-Krigstein-a 50 100 150 315 533 750

AMAZING ADVENTURES (Becomes Amazing Adult Fantasy #7 on) (See Amazing Fantasy for Omnibus HC reprint of #1-15)
Atlas Comics (AMI)/Marvel Comics No. 3 on: June, 1961 - No. 6, Nov, 1961

1-Origin Dr. Droom (1st Marvel-Age Superhero) by Kirby; Kirby/Ditko-a (5 pgs.) Ditko & Kirby-a in all; Kirby monster c-1-6 132 264 396 1056 2378 3700
2 50 100 150 400 900 1400
3-6: 6-Last Dr. Droom 46 92 138 359 805 1250

AMAZING ADVENTURES
Marvel Comics Group: Aug, 1970 - No. 39, Nov, 1976

1-Inhumans by Kirby(p) & Black Widow (1st app. in Tales of Suspense #52) double feature begins 7 14 21 49 92 135
2-4: 2-F.F. brief app. 4-Last Inhumans by Kirby 3 6 9 21 33 45
5-8: Adams-a(p); 8-Last Black Widow; last 15¢-c 5 10 15 30 50 70
9,10: Magneto app. 10-Last Inhumans (origin-r by Kirby) 4 8 12 25 40 55
11-New Beast begins(1st app. in mutated form; origin in flashback); X-Men cameo in flashback (#11-17 are X-Men tie-ins) 18 36 54 124 275 425
12-17: 12-Beast battles Iron Man. 13-Brotherhood of Evil Mutants x-over from X-Men. 15-X-Men app. 16-Rutland Vermont - Bald Mountain Halloween x-over; Juggernaut app. 17-Last Beast (origin); X-Men app. 7 14 21 48 89 130
18-War of the Worlds begins (5/73); 1st app. Killraven; Neal Adams-a(p) 4 8 12 27 44 60
19-35,38,39: 19-Chaykin-a. 25-Buckler-a. 35-Giffen's first published story (art), along with Deadly Hands of Kung-Fu #22 (3/76) 1 3 4 6 8 10
36,37-(Regular 25¢ edition)(7-8/76) 1 3 4 6 8 10
36,37-(30¢-c variants, limited distribution) 4 8 12 27 44 60
NOTE: ***N. Adams** c-6-8. **Buscema** a-1p, 2p. **Colan** a-3-5p, 26p. **Ditko** a-24r. **Everett** a(i)3-5, 7-9. **Giffen** a-35i, 38p. **G. Kane** c-11, 25p, 29p. **Ploog** a-12i. **Russell** a-27-32, 34-37, 39; c-28, 30-32, 33i, 34, 35, 37, 39i. **Starlling** a-17. **Starlin** c-15p, 16, 17, 27. **Sutton** a-11-15p.*

AMAZING ADVENTURES
Marvel Comics Group: Dec, 1979 - No. 14, Jan, 1981

V2#1-Reprints story/X-Men #1 & 38 (origins) 3 6 9 14 20 25
2-14: 2-6-Early X-Men-r. 7,8-Origin Iceman 2 4 6 8 10 12
NOTE: ***Byrne** c-6p, 9p. **Kirby** a-1-14r; c-7, 9. **Steranko** a-12r. **Tuska** a-7-9.*

AMAZING ADVENTURES
Marvel Comics: July, 1988 ($4.95, squarebound, one-shot, 80 pgs.)

1-Anthology; Austin, Golden-a 5.00

AMAZING ADVENTURES OF CAPTAIN CARVEL AND HIS CARVEL CRUSADERS, THE
(See Carvel Comics in the Promotional Comics section)

AMAZING CEREBUS (Reprints from Cerebus in Hell)(Also see Aardvark Comics)
Aardvark-Vanaheim: Feb, 2018 ($4.00, B&W)

1-Cerebus figures placed over original Doré artwork; Amazing Spider-Man #300-c swipe 4.00

AMAZING CHAN & THE CHAN CLAN, THE (TV)
Gold Key: May, 1973 - No. 4, Feb, 1974 (Hanna-Barbera)

1-Warren Tufts-a in all 3 6 9 21 33 45
2-4 3 6 9 16 23 30

AMAZING COMICS (Complete Comics No. 2)
Timely Comics (EPC): Fall, 1944

1-The Destroyer, The Whizzer, The Young Allies (by Sekowsky), Sergeant Dix; Schomburg-c 290 580 870 1856 3178 4500

AMAZING DETECTIVE CASES (Formerly Suspense No. 2?)
Marvel/Atlas Comics (CCC): No. 3, Nov, 1950 - No. 14, Sept, 1952

3 34 68 102 199 325 450
4-6: 6-Jerry Robinson-a 20 40 60 114 182 250
7-10 18 36 54 105 165 225
11,12: 11-(3/52)-Horror format begins. 12-Krigstein-a 53 106 159 334 567 800
13-(Scarce)-Everett-a; electrocution-c/story 58 116 174 371 636 900
14 50 100 150 315 533 750
NOTE: ***Colan** a-9. **Maneely** c-13. **Sekowsky** a-12. **Sinnott** a-13. **Tuska** a-10.*

AMAZING FANTASY (Formerly Amazing Adult Fantasy #7-14)
Atlas Magazines/Marvel: #15, Aug, 1962 (Sept, 1962 shown in indicia); #16, Dec, 1995 - #18, Feb, 1996

15-Origin/1st app. of Spider-Man by Steve Ditko (11 pgs.); 1st app. Aunt May & Uncle Ben; Kirby/Ditko-c 8000 16,000 32,000 92,000 233,500 375,000
16-18 ('95-'96, $3.95): Kurt Busiek scripts; painted-c/a by Paul Lee 4.00
Amazing Fantasy #15: Spider-Man! (8/12, $3.99) recolored rep. of #15 and ASM #1 4.00
Amazing Fantasy Omnibus HC ("Amazing Adult Fantasy" on-c) (2007, $75.00, dustjacket) r/Amazing Adventures #1-6, Amazing Adult Fantasy #7-14 and Amazing Fantasy #15 with letter pages; foreword by Bissette; cover gallery from '70s reprint titles 75.00

AMAZING FANTASY (Continues from #6 in Araña: The Heart of the Spider)
Marvel Comics: Aug, 2004 - No. 20, June, 2006 ($2.99)

1-Intro. Anya Corazon; Fiona Avery-s/Mark Brooks-c/a 4.00
2-14,16-20: 3,4-Roger Cruz-a. 7-Intro. new Scorpion; Kirk-a. 10-Intro. Vampire By Night 13,14-Back-up Captain Universe stories. 16-20-Death's Head 3.00
15-($3.99, 1/06) Spider-Man app.; intro 6 new characters incl. Amadeus Cho/Mastermind Excello seen in World War Hulk series; s/a by various 5 10 15 24 30 35
Death's Head 3.0: Unnatural Selection TPB (2006, $13.99) r/#16-20 14.00
Scorpion: Poison Tomorrow (2005, $7.99, digest) r/#7-13 8.00

AMAZING GHOST STORIES (Formerly Nightmare)
St. John Publishing Co.: No. 14, Oct, 1954 - No. 16, Feb, 1955

14-Pit & the Pendulum story by Kinstler; Baker-c 50 100 150 315 533 750
15-r/Weird Thrillers #5; Baker-c, Powell-a 39 78 117 231 378 525
16-Kubert reprints of Weird Thrillers #4; Baker-c; Roussos, Tuska-a; Kinstler-a (1 pg.) 36 72 108 211 343 475

AMAZING HIGH ADVENTURE
Marvel Comics: 8/84; No. 2, 10/85; No. 3, 10/86 - No. 5, 1986 ($2.00)

1-5: Painted-c on all. 3,4-Baxter paper. 4-Bolton-c/a. 5-Bolton-a 4.00
NOTE: ***Bissette** a-4. **Severin** a-1, 3. **Sienkiewicz** a-1,2. **Paul Smith** a-2. **Williamson** a-2i.*

AMAZING JOY BUZZARDS
Image Comics: 2005 - No. 4, 2005 ($2.95, B&W with pink spot color in #1)

1-4-Mark Andrew Smith-s/Dan Hipp-a. 1-Mahfood back-c. 2-Morse back-c 3.00
Vol. 1 TPB (2005, $11.95) r/#1-4; bonus art and character design sketches 12.00
TPB (2008, $19.99) r/#1-4 and Vol. 2 #1-5 20.00

AMAZING JOY BUZZARDS (Volume 2)
Image Comics: Oct, 2005 - No. 5, Aug, 2006 ($2.99, B&W)

1-5: 1-Mark Andrew Smith-s/Dan Hipp-a. 4-Mahfood-a; Crosland-a. 5-Holgate-a 3.00
Vol. 2 TPB (2006, $12.99) r/#1-4; bonus art, pin-ups and character sketches 13.00

AMAZING-MAN COMICS (Formerly Motion Picture Funnies Weekly?)
(Also see Stars And Stripes Comics)
Centaur Publications: No. 5, Sept, 1939 - No. 26, Jan, 1942

5(#1)(Rare)-Origin/1st app. A-Man the Amazing Man by Bill Everett; The Cat-Man by Tarpe Mills (also #8), Mighty Man by Filchock, Minimidget & sidekick Ritty, & The Iron Skull by Burgos begins 2100 4200 6300 17,000 29,500 42,000
6-Origin The Amazing Man retold; The Shark begins; Ivy Menace by Tarpe Mills app. 432 864 1296 3154 5577 8000
7-Magician From Mars begins; ends #11 300 600 900 2070 3635 5200
8-Cat-Man dresses as woman 252 504 756 1613 2757 3900
9-Magician From Mars battles the 'Elemental Monster,' swiped into The Spectre in More Fun #54 & 55. Ties w/Marvel Mystery #4 for 1st Nazi War-c on a comic (2/40) 265 530 795 1694 2897 4100
10,11: 11-Zardi, the Eternal Man begins; ends #16; Amazing Man dons costume; last Everett issue 194 388 582 1242 2121 3000
12,13 181 362 543 1158 1979 2800
14-Reef Kinkaid, Rocke Wayburn (ends #20), & Dr. Hypno (ends #21) begin; no Zardi or Chuck Hardy 155 310 465 992 1696 2400
15,17-20: 15-Zardi returns; no Rocke Wayburn. 17-Dr. Hypno returns; no Zardi 132 264 396 838 1444 2050
16-Mighty Man's powers of super strength & ability to shrink & grow explained; Rocke Wayburn returns; no Dr. Hypno; Al Avison (a character) begins, ends #18 (a tribute to the famed artist) 139 278 417 883 1517 2150
21-Origin Dash Dartwell (drug-use story); origin & only app. T.N.T. 148 296 444 947 1624 2300
22-Dash Dartwell, the Human Meteor & The Voice app; last Iron Skull & The Shark; Silver Streak app. (classic-c) 459 918 1377 3350 5925 8500
23-Two Amazing Man stories; intro/origin Tommy the Amazing Kid; The Marksman only app.

Amazing Man Comics #25 © CEN

Amazing Spider-Girl #25 © MAR

Amazing Spider-Man #47 © MAR

GD VG FN VF VF/NM NM-
2.0 4.0 6.0 8.0 9.0 9.2

129 258 387 826 1413 2000
24-King of Darkness, Nightshade, & Blue Lady begin; end #26; 1st app. Super-Ann
129 258 387 826 1413 2000
25 (Scarce) Meteor Martin by Wolverton 423 846 1269 3067 5384 7700
26 (Scarce) Meteor Martin by Wolverton; Electric Ray app.
470 940 1410 3431 6066 8700

NOTE: ***Everett*** *a-5-11; c-5-11.* ***Gilman*** *a-14-20.* ***Giunta/Mirando*** *a-7-10.* ***Sam Glanzman*** *a-14-16, 18-21, 23.* ***Louis Glanzman*** *a-6, 9-11, 14-21; c-13-19, 21.* ***Robert Golden*** *a-9.* ***Gustavson*** *a-6; c-22, 23.* ***Lubbers*** *a-14-21.* ***Simon*** *a-10.* ***Frank Thomas*** *a-6, 9-11, 14, 15, 17-21.*

AMAZING MYSTERIES (Formerly Sub-Mariner Comics No. 31)
Marvel Comics (CCC): No. 32, May, 1949 - No. 35, Jan, 1950 (1st Marvel Horror Comic)

32-The Witness app. 123 246 369 787 1344 1900
33-Horror format 58 116 174 371 636 900
34,35: Changes to Crime. 34,35-Photo-c 23 46 69 136 223 310

AMAZING MYSTERY FUNNIES
Centaur Publications: Aug, 1938 - No. 24, Sept, 1940 (All 52 pgs.)

V1#1-Everett-c(1st); Dick Kent Adv. story; Skyrocket Steele in the Year X on cover only
541 1082 1623 3950 6975 10,000
2-Everett 1st-a (Skyrocket Steele) 343 686 1029 2400 4200 6000
3 226 452 678 1446 2473 3500
3(#4, 12/38)-nn on cover, #3 on inside; bondage-c
258 516 774 1651 2826 4000
V2#1,3,4,6: 3-Air-Sub DX begins by Burgos. 4-Dan Hastings, Sand Hog begins (ends #5).
6-Last Skyrocket Steele 194 388 582 1242 2121 3000
2-Classic-c; drug use story 258 516 774 1651 2826 4000
5-Classic Everett-c 432 864 1296 3154 5577 8000
7 (Scarce)-Intro. The Fantom of the Fair & begins; Everett, Gustavson, Burgos-a
459 918 1377 3350 5925 8500
8-Origin & 1st app. Speed Centaur 194 388 582 1242 2121 3000
9-11: 11-Self portrait and biog. of Everett; Jon Linton begins; early Robot cover (11/39)
155 310 465 992 1696 2400
12 (Scarce)-1st Space Patrol; Wolverton-a (12/39); new costume Phantom of the Fair
245 490 735 1568 2684 3800
V3#1(#17, 1/40)-Intro. Bullet; Tippy Taylor serial begins, ends #24
(continued in The Arrow #2) 129 258 387 826 1413 2000
18,20: 18-Fantom of the Fair by Gustavson 126 252 378 806 1378 1950
19,21-24: Space Patrol by Wolverton in all 142 284 426 909 1555 2200

NOTE: ***Burgos*** *a-V2#3-9.* ***Eisner*** *a-V1#2, 3(2).* ***Everett*** *a-V1#2-4, V2#1, 3-6; c-V1#1-4,V2#3, 5, 18.* ***Filchock*** *a-V2#9.* ***Flessel*** *a-V2#6.* ***Guardineer*** *a-V1#4, V2#4-6;* ***Gustavson*** *a-V2#4, 5, 9-12, V3#1, 18, 19; c-V2#7, 9, 12, V3#1, 21, 22;* ***McWilliams*** *a-V2#9, 10.* ***TarpeMills*** *a-V2#2, 4-6, 9-12, V3#1.* ***Leo Morey****(Pulp artist) c-V2#10; text illo-V2#11.* ***FrankThomas*** *a-6-V2#11.* ***Webster*** *a-V2#4.*

AMAZING SAINTS
Logos International: 1974 (39¢)

nn-True story of Phil Saint 2 4 6 9 13 16

AMAZING SCARLET SPIDER
Marvel Comics: Nov, 1995 - No. 2, Dec, 1995 ($1.95, limited series)

1,2: Replaces "Amazing Spider-Man" for two issues. 1-Venom/Carnage cameos.
2-Green Goblin & Joystick-c/app. 3.00

AMAZING SCREW-ON HEAD, THE
Dark Horse Comics (Maverick): May, 2002 ($2.99, one-shot)

1-Mike Mignola-s/a/c 3.00

AMAZING SPIDER-GIRL (Also see Spider-Girl and What If...? (2nd series) #105)
Marvel Comics: No. 0, 2006; No. 1, Dec, 2006 - No. 30, May, 2009 ($2.99)

0-($1.99) Recap of the Spider-Girl series and character profiles; A.F. #15 cover swipe 3.00
1-14,16-24,26-($2.99) Frenz & Buscema-a. 9-Carnage returns. 19-Has #17 on cover 3.00
15,25,30-($3.99) 15-10th Anniversary issue. 25-Three covers 4.00
... Vol. 1: What Ever Happened to the Daughter of Spider-Man? TPB (2007, $14.99) r/#0-6 15.00
... Vol. 2: Comes the Carnage! TPB (2007, $13.99) r/#7-12 14.00
... Vol. 3: Mind Games TPB (2008, $13.99) r/#13-18 14.00

AMAZING SPIDER-MAN, THE (See All Detergent Comics, Amazing Fantasy, America's Best TV Comics, Aurora, Deadly Foes of..., Fireside Book Series, Friendly Neighborhood..., Giant-Size..., Giant Size Super-Heroes Featuring..., Marvel Age..., Marvel Collectors Item Classics, Marvel Fanfare, Marvel Graphic Novel, Marvel Knights..., Marvel Spec. Ed., Marvel Tales, Marvel Team-Up, Marvel Treasury Ed., New Avengers, Nothing Can Stop the Juggernaut, Official Marvel Index To..., Peter Parker..., Power Record Comics, Spectacular..., Spider-Man, Spider-Man Digest, Spider-Man Saga, Spider-Man 2099, Spider-Man Vs. Wolverine, Spidey Super Stories, Strange Tales Annual #2, Superior Spider-Man, Superman Vs. ..., Try-Out Winner Book, Ultimate Marvel Team-Up, Ultimate Spider-Man, Web of Spider- Man & Within Our Reach)

AMAZING SPIDER-MAN, THE
Marvel Comics Group: March, 1963 - No. 441, Nov, 1998

1-Retells origin by Steve Ditko; 1st Fantastic Four x-over (ties with F.F. #12 as first Marvel x-over); intro. John Jameson & The Chameleon; Spider-Man's 2nd app.; Kirby/Ditko-c; Ditko-c/a #1-38 2400 4800 7200 18,000 45,000 72,000

GD VG FN VF VF/NM NM-
2.0 4.0 6.0 8.0 9.0 9.2

1-Reprint from the Golden Record Comic set 28 56 84 202 451 700
With record (1966) 40 80 120 296 673 1050
2-1st app. the Vulture & the Terrible Tinkerer 450 900 1350 3825 8663 13,500
3-1st app. Doc Octopus; 1st full-length story; Human Torch cameo;
Spider-Man pin-up by Ditko 367 734 1101 3120 7060 11,000
4-Origin & 1st app. The Sandman (see Strange Tales #115 for 2nd app.); 1st monthly issue;
intro. Betty Brant & Liz Allen 290 580 870 2393 5397 8400
5-Dr. Doom app. 224 448 672 1848 4174 6500
6-1st app. Lizard 190 380 570 1568 3534 5500
7-Vs. The Vulture 136 272 408 1088 2444 3800
8-Fantastic Four app. in back-up story by Kirby & Ditko
96 192 288 768 1734 2700
9-Origin & 1st app. Electro (2/64) 132 264 396 1056 2378 3700
10-1st app. Big Man & The Enforcers 98 196 294 784 1767 2750
11-1st app. Bennett Brant 118 236 354 944 2122 3300
12-Doc Octopus unmasks Spider-Man-c/story 89 178 267 712 1606 2500
13-1st app. Mysterio 145 290 435 1196 2698 4200
14-(7/64)-1st app. The Green Goblin (c/story)(Norman Osborn); Hulk x-over
214 428 642 1766 3983 6200
15-1st app. Kraven the Hunter; 1st mention of Mary Jane Watson (not shown)
96 192 288 768 1734 2700
16-Spider-Man battles Daredevil (1st x-over 9/64); still in old yellow costume
75 150 225 600 1350 2100
17-2nd app. Green Goblin (c/story); Human Torch x-over (also in #18 & #21)
79 158 237 632 1416 2200
18-1st app. Ned Leeds who later becomes Hobgoblin; Fantastic Four cameo;
3rd app. Sandman 49 98 147 376 851 1325
19-Sandman app. 38 76 114 281 628 975
20-Origin & 1st app. The Scorpion 71 142 213 568 1284 2000
21-2nd app. The Beetle (see Strange Tales #123) 40 80 120 296 673 1050
22-1st app. Princess Python 39 78 117 289 657 1025
23-3rd app. The Green Goblin-c/story; Norman Osborn app.; Marvel Masterwork pin-up by
Ditko; fan letter by Jim Shooter 46 92 138 368 834 1300
24 36 72 108 266 596 925
25-(6/65)-1st brief app. Mary Jane Watson (face not shown); 1st app. Spencer Smythe;
Norman Osborn app. 40 80 120 296 673 1050
26-4th app. The Green Goblin-c/story; 1st app. Crime Master; dies in #27
41 82 123 303 689 1075
27-5th app. The Green Goblin-c/story; Norman Osborn app.
40 80 120 296 673 1050
28-Origin & 1st app. Molten Man (9/65, scarcer in high grade)
96 192 288 768 1734 2700
29,30 28 56 84 202 451 700
31-(12/65)-1st app. Gwen Stacy, Harry Osborn who later becomes 2nd Green Goblin &
Prof. Warren. 46 92 138 368 834 1300
32-38: 34-4th app. Kraven the Hunter. 36-1st app. Looter. 37-Intro. Norman Osborn.
38-(7/66)-2nd brief app. Mary Jane Watson (face not shown); last Ditko issue
23 46 69 161 356 550
39-The Green Goblin-c/story; Green Goblin's identity revealed as Norman Osborn; Osborn learns Spider-Man's secret identity; Romita-a begins (8/66; see Daredevil #16 for
1st Romita-a on Spider-Man) 46 92 138 340 770 1200
40-1st told origin The Green Goblin-c/story 38 76 114 285 641 1000
41-1st app. Rhino 44 88 132 326 738 1150
42-(11/66)-3rd app. Mary Jane Watson (cameo in last 2 panels); 1st time
face is shown 23 46 69 161 356 550
43-45,47-49: 43-Origin of the Rhino. 44,45-2nd & 3rd app. The Lizard. 47-M.J. Watson & Peter Parker 1st date. 47-Green Goblin cameo; Harry & Norman Osborn app.
47,49-5th & 6th app. Kraven the Hunter. 48-1st new Vulture (Blackie Drago)
18 36 54 124 275 425
46-Intro/origin The Shocker 27 54 81 189 420 650
50-1st app. Kingpin (7/67) 93 186 279 744 1672 2600
51-2nd app. Kingpin; Joe Robertson 1-panel cameo 22 44 66 154 340 525
52-58,60: 52-1st app. Joe Robertson & 3rd app. Kingpin. 56-1st app. Capt. George Stacy.
57,58-Ka-Zar app. 12 24 36 84 185 285
59-1st app. Brainwasher (alias Kingpin); 1st-c app. M. J. Watson
13 26 39 89 195 300
61-74: 61-1st Gwen Stacy cover app. 67-1st app. Randy Robertson. 69-Kingpin-c.
69,70-Kingpin app. 70-1st app. Vanessa Fisk (Kingpin's wife)(only seen in shadow).
73-1st app. Silvermane. 74-Last 12¢ issue 10 20 30 66 138 210
75-77,79-83,87-89,91,92,95,99: 79-The Prowler app. 83-1st app. Schemer; Vanessa Fisk app.
(only previously seen in shadow in #70) 9 18 27 58 114 170
78-1st app. The Prowler 10 20 30 69 147 225
84,85,93: 84,85-Kingpin-c/story. 93-1st app. Arthur Stacy
9 18 27 59 117 175

Amazing Spider-Man #185 © MAR

Amazing Spider-Man #252 © MAR

Amazing Spider-Man #276 © MAR

	GD 2.0	VG 4.0	FN 6.0	VF 8.0	VF/NM 9.0	NM- 9.2
86-Re-intro & origin Black Widow in new costume	11	22	33	73	157	240
90-Death of Capt. Stacy	11	22	33	73	157	240
94-Origin retold	10	20	30	64	132	200
96-98-Green Goblin app. (97,98-Green Goblin-c); drug books not approved by CCA	10	20	30	69	147	225
100-Anniversary issue (9/71); Green Goblin cameo (2 pgs.)	14	28	42	96	211	325
101-1st app. Morbius the Living Vampire; Lizard cameo; Stan Lee co-plots with Roy Thomas; last 15¢ issue (10/71)	28	56	84	202	451	700
101-Silver ink 2nd printing (9/92, $1.75)	2	4	6	10	14	18
102-Origin & 2nd app. Morbius (25¢, 52 pgs.)	12	24	36	79	170	260
103-118: 103,104-Roy Thomas-s. 104,111-Kraven the Hunter-c/stories. 105-109-Stan Lee-s. 108-1st app. Sha-Shan. 109-Dr. Strange-c/story. 110-1st app. Gibbon; Conway-s begin. 113-1st app. Hammerhead. 116-118-Reprints story from Spectacular Spider-Man Mag. in color with some changes	6	12	18	41	76	110
119,120-Spider-Man vs. Hulk (4 & 5/73)	9	18	27	58	114	170
121-Death of Gwen Stacy (6/73) (killed by Green Goblin)(reprinted in Marvel Tales #98 & 192); Harry Osborn LSD overdose	29	58	87	209	467	725
122-Death of The Green Goblin-c/story (7/73) (reprinted in Marvel Tales #99 & 192)	24	48	72	168	372	575
123-Cage app.	7	14	21	44	82	120
124-1st app. Man-Wolf (9/73)	7	14	21	49	92	135
125-Man-Wolf origin	6	12	18	40	73	105
126-128: 126-1st mention of Harry Osborn becoming Green Goblin	6	12	18	38	69	100
129-1st app. The Punisher (2/74); 1st app. Jackal	170	340	510	850	1275	1700
130-133: 131-Last 20¢ issue	5	10	15	34	60	85
134-(7/74); 1st app. Tarantula; Harry Osborn discovers Spider-Man's ID; Punisher cameo	6	12	18	41	76	110
135-2nd full Punisher app. (8/74)	10	20	30	64	132	200
136-1st app. Harry Osborn in Green Goblin costume	8	16	24	51	96	140
137-Green Goblin-c/story (2nd Harry Osborn Goblin)	6	12	18	37	66	95
138-141: 139-1st Grizzly. 140-1st app. Glory Grant	4	8	12	25	40	55
142,143-Gwen Stacy clone cameos: 143-1st app. Cyclone	4	8	12	25	40	55
144-147: 144-Full app. of Gwen Stacy clone. 145,146-Gwen Stacy clone storyline continues. 147-Spider-Man learns Gwen Stacy is clone	4	8	12	25	40	55
148-Jackal revealed	4	8	12	28	47	65
149-Spider-Man clone story begins, clone dies (?); origin of Jackal	8	16	24	51	96	140
150-Spider-Man decides he is not the clone	4	8	12	28	47	65
151-Spider-Man disposes of clone body; Len Wein-s begins; thru #180	5	10	15	31	53	75
152-160-(Regular 25¢ editions). 152-vs. the Shocker. 154-vs. Sandman. 156-1st Mirage. 157-159-Doc Octopus & Hammerhead app. 159-Last 25¢ issue(8/76). 160-Spider-Mobile destroyed	3	6	9	19	30	40
155-159-(30¢-c variants, limited distribution)	8	16	24	51	96	140
161-Nightcrawler app. from X-Men; Punisher cameo; Wolverine & Colossus app.	4	8	12	25	40	55
162-Punisher, Nightcrawler app.; 1st Jigsaw	4	8	12	25	40	55
163-168: 163-164-vs. the Kingpin. 165-vs. Stegron. 166-Stegron & the Lizard app. 167-1st app. Will O' The Wisp. 168-Will O' The Wisp app.	3	6	9	16	23	30
169-170,172-173: 169-Clone story recapped; Stan Lee Cameo. 170-Dr. Faustus app. 172-1st Rocket Racer. 173-vs Molten Man	3	6	9	16	23	30
171-Nova app. x-over w/Nova #12	3	6	9	17	26	35
169-173-(35¢-c variants, limited dist.)(6-10/77)	18	36	54	124	275	425
174,175-Punisher app.	3	6	9	19	30	40
176-180-Green Goblin (Barton Hamilton) app.; Harry Osborn Green Goblin in #180 only. 177-180-Silvermane app.	3	6	9	18	28	38
181-186: 181-Origin retold; gives life history of Spidey; Punisher cameo in flashback (1 panel). 182-(7/78)-Peter's first proposal to Mary Jane, but she declines (in #183). 183-Rocket Racer & the Big Wheel app. 184-vs. the second White Dragon. 185-Peter graduates college	3	6	9	14	20	25
187,188: 187-Captain America app. 188-vs. Jigsaw	3	6	9	16	23	30
189,190-Byrne-a; Man-Wolf app.	3	6	9	16	23	30
191-193,196-199: 191-vs. the Spider-Slayer. 192-Death of Spencer Smythe. 193-Peter & Mary Jane break up; the Fly app. 196-Faked death of Aunt May. 197-vs. the Kingpin. 198,199-Mysterio app.	2	4	6	11	16	20

NOTE: *Whitman 3-packs containing #192-194,196 exist.*

	GD 2.0	VG 4.0	FN 6.0	VF 8.0	VF/NM 9.0	NM- 9.2
194-1st app. Black Cat	9	18	27	62	126	190
195-2nd app. Black Cat & origin Black Cat	3	6	9	19	30	40
200-Giant origin issue (1/80); death of the burglar (from Amazing Fantasy #15)	3	6	9	21	33	45
201,202-Punisher app. 201-Classic bullseye-c	3	6	9	14	19	24
203-208,210,211,213-219: 203-3rd Dazzler (4/80). 204,205-Black Cat app. 204-Last Wolfman-s. 206-Byrne-a. 207-vs Mesmero. 210-1st app. Madame Web. 211-Sub-Mariner app. 214,215-New Frightful Four app: Wizard, Trapster, Sandman & Llyra (Namor foe). 216-Madame Web app. 217-Sandman vs Hydro-Man. 219-Grey Gargoyle app.; Frank Miller-c	2	4	6	9	12	15
209-Kraven the Hunter app; 1st app. origin Calypso	2	4	6	11	16	20
212-1st app. & origin Hydro-Man	2	4	6	11	16	20
220-225,228: 220-Moon Knight app. 222-1st app. of the Whizzer as Speed Demon. 223-vs. The Red Ghost & the Super-Apes; Roger Stern-s begins. 224-Vulture app. 225-Foolkiller II-c/story.	1	3	4	6	8	10
226,227-Black Cat returns	2	4	6	9	12	15
229,230: Classic 'Nothing can stop the Juggernaut' story	2	4	6	13	18	22
231-237: 231,232-Cobra & Mr Hyde app. 233-Tarantula app. 234-Free 16 pg. insert "Marvel Guide to Collecting Comics", Tarantula & Will O' The Wisp app. 235-Origin Will 'O The Wisp. 236-Tarantula dies. 237-Stilt-Man app.	1	3	4	6	8	10
238-(3/83)-1st app. Hobgoblin (Ned Leeds); came with skin "Tattooz" decal.						

NOTE: The same decal appears in the more common Fantastic Four #252 which is being removed & placed in this issue as incentive to increase value. (No "Tattooz" were included in the Canadian edition)

	GD 2.0	VG 4.0	FN 6.0	VF 8.0	VF/NM 9.0	NM- 9.2
(Value with tattooz)	8	16	24	56	108	160
(Value without tattooz)	5	10	15	23	57	80
239-2nd app. Hobgoblin & 1st battle w/Spidey	4	8	12	28	47	65
240-243,246-248: 240,241-Vulture app. (origin in #241). 242-Mary Jane Watson cameo (last panel). 243-Reintro Mary Jane after 4 year absence. 248-'The Kid Who Collects Spider-Man' story	1	3	4	6	8	10
244-3rd app. Hobgoblin (cameo)	2	4	6	9	12	15
245-(10/83)-4th app. Hobgoblin (cameo); Lefty Donovan gains powers of Hobgoblin & battles Spider-Man	2	4	6	11	16	20
249-251: 3 part Hobgoblin/Spider-Man battle. 249-Retells origin & death of 1st Green Goblin. 251-Last old costume	2	4	6	9	13	16
252-Spider-Man dons new black costume (5/84); ties with Marvel Team-Up #141 & Spectacular Spider-Man #90 for 1st new costume in regular title (See Marvel Super-Heroes Secret Wars #8 (12/84) for acquisition of costume); last Roger Stern-s	6	12	18	37	66	95
253-1st app. The Rose; Tom DeFalco-s begin	2	4	6	9	12	15
254,255,257,258: 254-Jack O' Lantern app. 255-1st app Black Fox. 257-Hobgoblin cameo; 2nd app. Puma; M.J. Watson reveals she knows Spidey's i.d. 258-Hobgoblin app.	1	3	4	6	8	10
256-1st app. Puma	2	4	6	10	14	18
259-Full Hobgoblin app.; Spidey back to old costume; origin Mary Jane Watson	2	4	6	10	14	18
260-Hobgoblin app.	2	4	6	10	14	18
261-Hobgoblin-c/story; painted-c by Vess	2	4	6	9	11	14
262-Spider-Man unmasked; photo-c	1	3	4	6	8	10
263,264,266-268: 266-Toad & Frogman app.; Peter David-s. 268-Secret Wars II x-over	1	2	3	5	6	8
265-1st app. Silver Sable (6/85)	3	6	9	19	30	40
265-Silver ink 2nd printing ($1.25)	1	3	4	6	8	10
269-270: 269-Spider-Man vs Firelord. 270 Avengers app.	1	3	4	6	8	10
271-274,277-280,282-283: 272-1st app. Slyde. 273-Secret Wars II x-over; Beyonder app. 274-Secret Wars II x-over; Zarathos app. (The Spirit of Vengeance). 277-Vess-c & back-up art. 278-Scourge app; death of the Wraith. 279-Jack O' Lantern-c/s. 280-1st Sinister Syndicate: Beetle, Boomerang, Hydro-Man, Rhino, Speed Demon. 282-X-Factor app.	1	2	3	5	6	8
275-($1.25, 52 pgs.)-Hobgoblin-c/story; origin-r by Ditko	3	6	9	15	22	28
276-Hobgoblin app.	2	4	6	8	10	12
281-Hobgoblin battles Jack O'Lantern	1	3	4	6	8	10
284,285: 284-Punisher cameo; Gang War Pt. 1; Hobgoblin-c/story. 285-Punisher app.; minor Hobgoblin app.; last Tom DeFalco-s; Gang War Pt. 2	1	3	4	6	8	10
286-288: Gang War Parts 3-5. 286-Hobgoblin-c & app. (minor). 287-Hobgoblin app. (minor). 288-Full Hobgoblin app.; Gang War ends	1	3	4	6	8	10
289-(6/87, $1.25, 52 pgs.)-Hobgoblin's i.d. revealed as Ned Leeds; death of Ned Leeds; Macendale (Jack O'Lantern) becomes new Hobgoblin (1st app.)	3	6	9	14	20	25
290-292,295-297: 290-Peter proposes to Mary Jane; 1st David Michelinie-s. 291,292-Spider-Slayer app. 292-She accepts; leads into wedding in Amazing Spider-Man Annual #21. 295-'Mad Dog Ward' Pt. 2; x-over w/Web of Spider-Man #33 & Spectacular Spider-Man #133. 296-297-Doc Octopus app.	1	2	3	5	6	8
293,294-Part 2 & 5 of Kraven story from Web of Spider-Man. 293-Continued from Web of Spider-Man #31; continues into Spectacular Spider-Man #131. 294-Death of Kraven; continued from Web of Spider-Man #32; continues in Spectacular Spider-Man #132	2	4	6	9	12	15

Amazing Spider-Man #327 © MAR

Amazing Spider-Man #383 © MAR

Amazing Spider-Man #436 © MAR

	GD 2.0	VG 4.0	FN 6.0	VF 8.0	VF/NM 9.0	NM- 9.2

298-Todd McFarlane-c/a begins (3/88); 1st brief app. Eddie Brock who becomes Venom; (last pg.) 5 10 15 33 57 80
299-1st brief app. Venom with costume 5 10 15 30 50 70
300 ($1.50, 52 pgs.; 25th Anniversary)-1st full Venom app.; last black costume (5/88) 42 84 126 210 280 350
301-$1.00 issues begin. Classic McFarlane-c 3 6 9 17 26 35
302-305: 302-303-Silver Sable app. 304,305-Black Fox app. 304-1st bi-weekly issue 2 4 6 10 14 18
306-311,313,314: 306-Swipes-c from Action #1. 307-Chameleon app. 308-Taskmaster app. 309-1st app. Styx & Stone. 310-Killer Shrike app. 311-Inferno x-over; Mysterio app. 314-Christmas-c 2 4 6 9 13 16
312-Hobgoblin battles Green Goblin; Inferno x-over 2 4 6 13 18 22
315,317-Venom app. 3 6 9 16 23 30
316-Classic Venom-c 4 8 12 25 40 55
318-323,325: 318-Scorpion app. 319-Bi-weekly begins again; Scorpion, Rhino, Backlash app. 320-'Assassination Nation Plot' Pt.1 (ends in issue #325); Paladin & Silver Sable app. 321-Paladin & Silver Sable app. 322-Silver Sable app. 323-Captain America app. 325-Captain America & Red Skull app. 1 3 4 6 8 10
324-Sabretooth app.; McFarlane cover only 2 4 6 9 12 15
326,327,329: 326-Acts of Vengeance x-over; vs Graviton. 327-Acts of Vengeance x-over; vs. Magneto; Cosmic storyline continues from Spectacular Spider-Man; Erik Larsen-a. 329-Acts of Vengeance x-over; vs. the Tri-Sentinel; Sebastian Shaw app.; Erik Larsen-a (continuous through issue #344) 6.00
328-Acts of Vengeance x-over; vs. the Hulk; last McFarlane issue 2 4 6 10 14 18
330,331-Punisher app. 331-Minor Venom app. 6.00
332,333-Venom-c/story 2 4 6 8 11 14
334-336,338-343: 334-339-Return of the Sinister Six. 341-Tarantula app; Spider-Man loses his cosmic powers. 342,343-Black Cat app. 4.00
337-Hobgoblin app. 5.00
344-(2/91) 1st app. Cletus Kasady (Carnage) 3 6 9 15 22 28
345-1st full app. Cletus Kasady; Venom cameo on last pg.; 1st Mark Bagley-a on Spider-Man 2 4 6 11 16 20
346,347-Venom app. 2 4 6 9 12 15
348,349,351-359: 348-Avengers x-over. 351-Bagley-a begins. 351,352-Nova of New Warriors app. 353-Darkhawk app.; brief Punisher app. 354-Punisher cameo & Nova, Night Thrasher (New Warriors), Darkhawk & Moon Knight app. 357,358-Punisher, Darkhawk, Moon Knight, Night Thrasher, Nova x-over. 358-3 part gatefold-c; last $1.00-c 4.00
350-($1.50, 52pgs.)-Origin retold; Spidey vs. Dr. Doom; last Erik Larsen-a pin-ups; Uncle Ben app. 5.00
360-Carnage cameo 2 4 6 8 10 12
361-(4/92) Intro. Carnage (the Spawn of Venom); begin 3 part story; recap of how Spidey's alien costume became Venom 5 10 15 30 50 70
361-($1.25)-2nd printing; silver-c 3 6 9 17 26 35
362,363-Carnage & Venom-c/story 2 4 6 9 12 15
362-2nd printing 2 4 6 9 12 15
364,366-373,376,377,381-387: 364-The Shocker app. (old villain). 366-Peter's parents-c/story; Red Skull, Viper & Taskmaster app. 367-Red Skull, Viper & Taskmaster app. 368-Invasion of the Spider-Slayers Pt.1 (through Pt.6 in #373). 369-Harry Osborn back-up (Gr. Goblin II). Electro app. 370-Black Cat & Scorpion app. 373-Venom back-up. 376,377-Cardiac app. 381,382-Hulk app. 383-The Jury app. 383-385-vs The Jury. 384-Venom/Carnage app. 386-Vulture app. 387-Vulture is de-aged & gets new costume 3.00
365-($3.95, 84 pgs.)-30th anniversary issue w/silver hologram on-c; Spidey/Venom/Carnage pull-out poster; contains 5 pg. preview of Spider-Man 2099 (1st app.); Spidey's origin retold; Lizard app.; reintro Peter's parents in Stan Lee 3 pg. text w/illo (story continues thru #370) 2 4 6 10 14 18
374-Venom-c/story 6.00
375-($3.95, 68 pgs.)-Holo-grafx foil-c; vs. Venom story; ties into Venom: Lethal Protector #1; Pat Olliffe-a. 1 3 4 6 8 10
378-380: Parts 3,7 and 11 of Maximum Carnage. 378-Continued from Web of Spider-Man #101; Venom vs Carnage; continues in Spider-Man #35. 379-Continued from Web of Spider-Man #102; Deathlok, Firestar, Black Cat & Morbius app.; continued in Spider-Man #36. 380-Continued from Web of Spider-Man #103; Captain America & Cloak and Dagger app.; continued in Spider-Man #37 5.00
388-($2.25, 68 pgs.)-Newsstand edition; Venom back-up & Cardiac & chance back-up; last David Michelinie-s (6-year run) 4.00
388-($2.95, 68 pgs.)-Collector's edition w/foil-c 5.00
389-1st JM DeMatteis-s; Trading Card insert (3 cards) attached to the staples; harder to find in true high grade due to indents caused by the cards; Green Goblin app. 4.00
390-393,395,396: 390-393-vs. Shriek. 395-Puma app. 396-Daredevil & the Owl app. 3.00
390-($2.95)-Collector's edition polybagged w/16 pg. insert of new animated Spidey TV show plus animation cel 5.00
394-($2.95, 48 pgs.)-Deluxe edition; flip book w/Birth of a Spider-Man Pt. 2; silver foil both-c; Power & Responsibility Pt. 2; Judas Traveller, the Jackal and the Gwen Stacy Clone app. 1st app. Scrier 5.00
394-Newstand edition ($1.50-c) 7.00
397-($2.25)-Flip book w/Ultimate Spider-Man 4.00
398,399: 398-Web of Death Pt.3; continued from Spectacular Spider-Man #220; Doc Octopus & Kaine app.; continued in Spectacular Spider-Man #221. 399-Smoke and Mirrors Pt.2; continued from Web of Spider-Man #122; Jackal, Scarlet Spider, Gwen Stacy Clone app; continued in Spider-Man #56 5.00
400-($2.95)-Death of Aunt May; newsstand edition 3 6 9 16 24 32
400-($3.95)-Death of Aunt May; embossed grey overlay cover 2 4 6 11 16 20
400-Collector's Edition; white embossed-c; (10,000 print run) 5 10 15 30 50 70
401,402,405,406-409: 401-The Mark of Kaine Pt.2; continued from Web of Spider-Man #124; Scarlet Spider app; continues in Spider-Man #58. 402-Judas Traveller & Scrier app. 405-Exiled Pt.2; continued from Web of Spider-Man #128; Scarlet Spider app.; continues in Spider-Man #62. 406-1st full app. of the female Doc Octopus (Carolyn Trainer); continues in Spider-Man #63; Marvel Overpower card insert; harder to find in higher grades due to card indenting; last JM DeMatteis-s. 407-Human Torch, Sandman & Silver Sable app. Tom DeFalco-s (returns to Spider-Man; last-s in 1987). 408-Regular ed; Media Blizzard pt.2; Mysterio app; continued from Sensational Spider-Man #1; continues in Spider-Man #65. 409-The Return of Kaine Pt.3; continued from Spectacular Spider-Man #231; Kaine & Rhino app.; continues in Spider-Man #66 4.00
403-The Trial of Peter Parker Pt. 2; continued from Web of Spider-Man #126; Carnage app; continues in Spider-Man #60. 1 2 3 5 6 8
404-Maximum Clonage Pt.3; continued from Web of Spider-Man #127; Scarlet Spider, Jackal, Scrier & Kaine app; continued in Spider-Man #61 5.00
408-($2.95)-Polybagged version with TV theme song cassette; scarce in high grade due to damage caused by the cassette indenting the actual comic 9 18 27 58 114 170
408-Direct edition (without cassette & out of polybag) 5 10 15 34 60 85
408-Newstand edition; variant cover 5 10 15 35 63 90
410-Web of Carnage Pt.2; continued from Sensational Spider-Man #3; Carnage app; continues in Spider-Man #67 3 6 9 15 22 28
411,412,414,417-419,421-424: 411-Blood Brothers Pt.2; continued from Sensational Spider-Man #4; Gaunt app; continued in Spider-Man #68. 412-Blood Brothers Pt.6; continued from Sensational Spider-Man #5; vs Gaunt. 414-The Rose app. 417-Death of Scrier. 418-Revelations Pt.3; continued from Spectacular Spider-Man #240; Norman Osborn returns; 'death' of Peter and Mary Jane's baby (May Parker); continued in Spider-Man #75. 419-1st minor app. of The Black Tarantula. 422,423-Electro app. 424-Elektra app. 4.00
413-Contains a free packet of Island Twists Kool-Aid and Spider-Man For Kids magazine subscriber card; harder to find in true high grade 6.00
415-Onslaught Impact 2; Green Goblin (Phil Urich) app. vs. Mark IV Sentinels; last Mark Bagley-a (5 year run) 6.00
416-Epilogue to Onslaught; harder to find in high grade due to Marvel Overpower card insert 1 3 4 6 8 10
420-X-Man app. 1 2 3 4 5 7
425-($2.99)-48 pgs., wraparound-c; X-Man app 1 2 3 4 5 7
426,428,429,432,435-437,440: 426-Female Dr. Octopus app. 428-Dr. Octopus app. 429-Absorbing Man app. 432-Spider-Hunt Pt.2; continued from Sensational Spider-Man #25; Black Tarantula & Norman Osborn app. 433-Mr. Hyde app. 435-Identity Crisis; Black Tarantula & Kaine app. 436-Black Tarantula app. 437-Plantman app. 440-Gathering of Five Pt.2; continued from Sensational Spider-Man #32; John Byrne-s; Molten Man & Norman Osborn app; continued in Spider-Man #96 6.00
427-Return of Dr. Octopus; double-gatefold-c. 1 2 3 4 5 7
430-Carnage & Silver Surfer app. 3 6 9 14 20 25
431-Cosmic-Carnage vs Silver Surfer; Galactus cameo 3 6 9 21 33 45
432-Variant yellow-c 'Wanted Dead or Alive' 2 4 6 9 12 15
434-Identity Crisis; Black Tarantula app. 1 3 4 6 8 10
434-Variant 'Amazing Ricochet #1'-c 2 4 6 9 12 15
438-Daredevil app. 7.00
439-Alternate future story; Avengers app; last Tom DeFalco-s 1 2 3 5 6 8
441-The Final Chapter Pt.1; John Byrne-s; Norman Osborn app; last issue (Dec. 1998); story continues in Spider-Man #97 1 2 3 5 7 9
#500-up (See Amazing Spider-Man Vol. 2; series resumed original numbering after Vol. 2 #58)
#(-1) Flashback issue (7/97, $1.95-c) 3.00
Annual 1 (1964, 72 pgs.) Origin Spider-Man; 1st app. Sinister Six (Dr. Octopus, Electro, Kraven the Hunter, Mysterio, Sandman, Vulture) (new 41 pg. story); plus gallery of Spidey foes; early X-Men app. 141 282 423 1142 2571 4000
Annual 2 (1965, 25¢, 72 pgs.) Reprints from #1,2,5 plus new Doctor Strange story 35 70 105 252 564 875
Special 3 (11/66, 25¢, 72 pgs.) New Avengers story & Hulk x-over; Doctor Octopus-r

Amazing Spider-Man Annual #25 © MAR

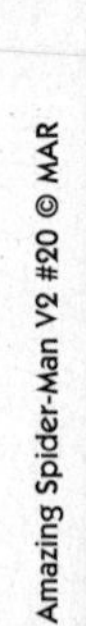

Amazing Spider-Man V2 #20 © MAR

Amazing Spider-Man #626 © MAR

	GD 2.0	VG 4.0	FN 6.0	VF 8.0	VF/NM 9.0	NM- 9.2

from #11,12; Romita-a 18 36 54 124 275 425
Special 4 (11/67, 25¢, 68 pgs.) Spidey battles Human Torch (new 41 pg. story)
13 26 39 89 195 300
Special 5 (11/68, 25¢, 68 pgs.) New 40 pg. Red Skull story; 1st app. Peter Parker's parents; last annual with new-a 11 22 33 73 157 240
Special 5-2nd printing (1994) 2 4 6 8 10 12
Special 6 (11/69, 25¢, 68 pgs.) Reprints 41 pg. Sinister Six story from annual #1 plus 2 Kirby/Ditko stories (r) 6 12 18 42 79 115
Special 7 (12/70, 25¢, 68 pgs.) All-r(#1,2) new Vulture-c
5 10 15 35 63 90
Special 8 (12/71) All-r 5 10 15 35 63 90
King Size 9 ('73) Reprints Spectacular Spider-Man (mag.) #2; 40 pg. Green Goblin-c/story (re-edited from 58 pgs.) 5 10 15 35 63 90
Annual 10 (1976) Origin Human Fly (vs. Spidey); new-a begins
3 6 9 16 23 30
Annual 11-13 ('77-'79): 12-Spidey vs. Hulk-r/#119,120. 13-New Byrne/Austin-a; Dr. Octopus x-over w/Spectacular S-M Ann. #1 2 4 6 11 16 20
Annual 14 (1980) Miller-c/a(p); Dr. Strange app. 3 6 9 14 20 25
Annual 15 (1981) Miller-c/a(p); Punisher app. 3 6 9 17 26 35
Annual 16 (1982)-Origin/1st app. new Capt. Marvel (female heroine Monica Rambeau)
2 4 6 9 12 15
Annual 17-20: 17 ('83)-Kingpin app. 18 ('84)-Scorpion app.; JJJ weds. 19 ('85). 20 ('86)-Origin Iron Man of 2020 1 2 3 4 5 7
Annual 21 (1987) Special wedding issue; newsstand & direct sale versions exist & are worth same 3 6 9 14 20 25
Annual 22 (1988, $1.75, 68 pgs.) 1st app. Speedball; Evolutionary War x-over; Daredevil app. 2 4 6 8 11 14
Annual 23 (1989, $2.00, 68 pgs.) Atlantis Attacks; origin Spider-Man retold; She-Hulk app.; Byrne-c; Liefeld-a(p), 23 pgs. 5.00
Annual 24 (1990, $2.00, 68 pgs.) -Ant-Man app. 4.00
Annual 25 (1991, $2.00, 68 pgs.) 3 pg. origin recap; Iron Man app.; 1st Venom solo story; Ditko-a (6 pgs.) 5.00
Annual 26 (1992, $2.25, 68 pgs.) New Warriors-c/story; Venom solo story cont'd in Spectacular Spider-Man Annual #12 5.00
Annual 27 ('93, $2.95, 68 pgs.) Bagged w/card; 1st app. Annex 4.00
Annual 28 ('94, $2.95, 68 pgs.) Carnage-c/story 1 3 4 6 8 10
'96 Special-($2.95, 64 pgs.)-"Blast From The Past" 4.00
'97 Special-($2.99)-Wraparound-c,Sundown app. 4.00
... : Carnage (6/93, $6.95)-r/ASM #344,345,359-363 1 3 4 6 8 10
Marvel Graphic Novel - Parallel Lives (3/89, $8.95) 2 4 6 8 10 12
...: Parallel Lives 1 (2012, $4.99) r/1989 GN 5.00
Marvel Graphic Novel - Spirits of the Earth (1990, $18.95, HC)
3 6 9 15 22 28
Super Special 1 (4/95, $3.95)-Flip Book 4.00
...: Skating on Thin Ice 1(1990, $1.25, Canadian)-McFarlane-c; anti-drug issue; Electro app.
1 2 3 5 7 9
...: Skating on Thin Ice 1 (2/93, $1.50, American) 4.00
...: Double Trouble 2 (1990, $1.25, Canadian) 6.00
...: Double Trouble 2 (2/93, $1.50, American) 3.00
...: Hit and Run 3 (1990, $1.25, Canadian)-Ghost Rider-c/story
1 2 3 5 7 9
...: Hit and Run 3 (2/93. $1.50, American) 3.00
...: Chaos in Calgary 4 (Canadian; part of 5 part series)-Turbine,Night Rider, Frightful app. 2 4 6 8 11 14
...: Chaos in Calgary 4 (2/93, $1.50, American) 3.00
...: Deadball 5 (1993, $1.60, Canadian)-Green Goblin-c/story; features Montreal Expos 2 4 6 10 14 18
Note: Prices listed above are for English Canadian editions. French editions are worth double.
...: Soul of the Hunter nn (8/92, $5.95, 52 pgs.)-Zeck-c/a(p) 6.00
Wizard #1 Ace Edition ($13.99) r/#1 w/ new Ramos acetate-c 14.00
Wizard #129 Ace Edition ($13.99) r/#129 w/ new Ramos acetate-c 14.00

NOTE: ***Austin*** *a(i)-248, 335, 337, Annual 13; c(i)-188, 241, 242, 248, 331, 334, 343, Annual 25.* ***J. Buscema*** *a(p)-72, 73, 76-81, 84, 85.* ***Byrne*** *a-189p, 190p, 206p, Annual 3r, 6r, 7r, 13p; c-189p, 268, 296, Annual 12.* ***Ditko*** *a-1-38, Annual 1, Special 3(r), 2, 24(2); c-1i, 2-38, Annual 1.* ***Guice*** *c/a-Annual 18i.* ***Gil Kane*** *a(p)-89-105, 120-124, 150, Annual 10, 12i, 24p; c-90p, 96, 98, 99, 101-105p, 129p, 131p, 132p, 137-140p, 143p, 148p, 149p, 151p, 153p, 160p, 161p, Annual 10p, 24.* ***Kirby*** *a-8.* ***Erik Larsen*** *a-324, 327, 329-350; c-327, 329-350, 354i, Annual 25.* ***McFarlane*** *a-298p, 299p, 300-303, 304-323p, 325p, 328; c-298-325, 328.* ***Miller*** *c-218, 219.* ***Mooney*** *a-65i, 67-82i, 84-88i, 173i, 178i, 189i, 190i, 192i, 193i, 196-202i, 207i, 211-219i, 221i, 222i, 226i, 227i, 229-233i, Annual 11i, 17i.* ***Nasser*** *c-228p.* ***Nebres*** *a-Annual 24i.* ***Russell*** *c-357i.* ***Simonson*** *c-222, 337i.* ***Starlin*** *a-113i, 114i, 187p.* ***Williamson*** *a-365i.*

AMAZING SPIDER-MAN (Volume 2) (Some issues reprinted in "Spider-Man, Best Of" hardcovers)
Marvel Comics: Jan, 1999 - No. 700, Feb, 2013 ($2.99/$1.99/$2.25)

1-($2.99)-Byrne-a; Avengers, Fantastic Four & Green Goblin app.
1 3 4 6 8 10
1-Sunburst variant-c 2 4 6 9 12 15
1-($6.95) Dynamic Forces variant-c by the Romitas 2 4 6 10 14 18
1-Marvel Matrix sketch variant-c 1 3 4 6 8 10
2-($1.99) Two covers -by John Byrne and Andy Kubert 4.00
3-11: 4-Fantastic Four app. 5-Spider-Woman-c 3.00
12-($2.99) Sinister Six return (cont. in Peter Parker #12) 4.00
13-17: 13-Mary Jane's plane explodes 3.00
18,19,21-24,26-28: 18-Begin $2.25-c. 19-Venom-c. 24-Maximum Security 3.00
20-($2.99, 100 pgs.) Spider-Slayer issue; new story and reprints 4.00
25-($2.99) Regular cover; Peter Parker becomes the Green Goblin 4.00
25-($3.99) Holo-foil enhanced cover 5.00
29-Peter is reunited with Mary Jane 4.00
30-Straczynski-s/Campbell-c begin; intro. Ezekiel 6.00
31-35: Battles Morlun 4.00
36-Black cover; aftermath of the Sept. 11 tragedy in New York
3 6 9 19 30 40
37-49: 39-'Nuff Said issue 42-Dr. Strange app. 43-45-Doctor Octopus app. 46-48-Cho-c 3.00
50-Peter and MJ reunite; Captain America & Dr. Doom app.; Campbell-c 4.00
51-58: 51,52-Campbell-c. 55,56-Avery scripts. 57,58-Avengers, FF, Cyclops app. 3.00
(After #58 [Nov, 2003] numbering reverts back to original Vol. 1 with #500, Dec, 2003)
500-($3.50) J. Scott Campbell-c; Romita Jr. & Sr.-a; Uncle Ben app.
2 4 6 8 10 12
501-524: 501-Harris-c. 503-504-Loki app. 506-508-Ezekiel app. 509-514-Sins Past; intro. Gabriel and Sarah Osborn; Deodato-a. 519-Moves into Avengers HQ. 521-Begin $2.50-c 524-Harris-c 3.00
525,526-Evolve or Die x-over. 525-David-s. 526-Hudlin-s; Spider-Man loses eye 4.00
525-528-2nd printings with variant-c. 525-Ben Reilly costume. 526-Six-Armed Spidey. 527-Spider-Man 2099. 528-Spider-Ham 5.00
527,528: Evolve or Die pt. 9,12 3.00
529-Debut of red and gold costume (Iron Spider); Garney-a 20.00
529-2nd printing 5.00
529-3rd printing with Wieringo-c 3.00
530,531-Titanium Man app.; Kirkham-a. 531-Begin $2.99-c 6.00
532-538-Civil War tie-in. 538-Aunt May shot 5.00
539-543-Back in Black. 539-Peter wears the black costume 3.00
544-($3.99) "One More Day" pt. 1; Quesada-a/Straczynski-s 4.00
545-(12/08, $3.99) "One More Day" pt. 4; Quesada-a/Straczynski-s, Peter & MJ's marriage un-done; r/wedding from ASM Annual #21; 2 covers by Quesada and Djurdjevic 4.00
546-($3.99) Brand New Day begins; McNiven-a; Deodato, Winslade, Land, Romita Jr.-a; 1st app. Mr. Negative 5.00
546-Variant-c by Bryan Hitch 8.00
546-Second printing with new McNiven-c of Peter Parker 4.00
546-MGC (7/10, $1.00) r/#546 with "Marvel's Greatest Comics" logo on cover 3.00
547-567: 547,548-McNiven-a. 549-551-Larroca-a. 550-Intro. Menace. 555-557-Bachalo-a. 559-Intro. Screwball. 560,561-MJ app. 565-New Kraven intro. 566,567-Spidey in Daredevil costume 3.00
568-($3.99) Romita Jr.-a begins; two covers by Romita Jr. and Alex Ross 6.00
568-Variant-c by John Romita Sr. 22.00
568-2nd printing with Romita Jr. Anti-Venom costume cover 4.00
569-Debut of Anti-Venom; Norman Osborn and Thunderbolts app.;Romita Jr.-c 4.00
569-Variant Venom-c by Granov 6.00
570-572-Two covers on each 3.00
573-($3.99) New Ways to Die conclusion; Spidey meets Stephen Colbert back-up; Ollife-a; two covers by Romita Jr. and Maguire 5.00
573-Variant cover with Stephen Colbert; cover swipe of AF #15 by Quesada 12.00
574-582: 577-Punisher app. 3.00
583-($3.99) Spidey meets Obama back-up story; regular Romita Sr. "Cougars" cover 10.00
583-($3.99) Obama variant-c with Spidey on left; Spidey meets Obama back-up story 42.00
583-($3.99) Second printing Obama variant-c with Spidey on right and yellow bkgrd 8.00
583-($3.99) 3rd-5th printings Obama variant-c: 3rd-Blue bkgrd w/flag. 4th-White bkgrd w/flag. 5th-Lincoln Memorial bkgrd 5.00
584-587, 589-599: 585-Menace ID revealed. 590,591-Fantastic Four app. 594-Aunt May engaged. 595-599-American Son; Osborn Avengers app. app. 3.00
588-($3.99) Conclusion to "Character Assassination"; Romita Jr.-a 4.00
600-(9/09, $4.99) Aunt May's wedding; Romita Jr.-a; Doc Octopus, FF app.; Mary Jane cameo; back-up story by Stan Lee; back-up with Doran-a; 2 covers by Romita Jr. & Ross 8.00
600-Variant covers by Romita Sr. and Quesada 12.00
601-604,606-611,613-616,618-621,623-627: 601-Back-up w/Quesada-a. 606,607-Black Cat app.; Campbell-c. 611-Deadpool-c/app. 612-The Gauntlet begins; Waid-s. 615,616-Sandman app. 621-Black Cat app. 624-Peter Parker fired. 626-Gaydos-a 3.00
605,612,617,622,628-($3.99): 605-Mayhew-c. 613-Rhino back-up story. 617-New Rhino. 622-Bianchi-c; Morbius app. 628-Captain Universe app. 4.00
629-633-($2.99)-Bachalo-a; Lizard app. 3.00
634-641-($3.99) 634-637-Grim Hunt; Kaine app. 635-Kraven returns. 638-641-"One Moment in Time" wedding flashback/ret-con; Quesada-s 4.00
638-641-Variant covers by Quesada 15.00

Amazing Spider-Man #671 © MAR

Amazing Spider-Man (2015 series) #25 © MAR

Amazing World of DC Comics #15 © DC

GD 2.0 | VG 4.0 | FN 6.0 | VF 8.0 | VF/NM 9.0 | NM- 9.2

642-646-($2.99) Waid-s/Azaceta-a; interlocking covers by Djurdjevic 3.00
647-($4.99) Short stories by various; Djurdjevic-c; cover gallery of Brand New Day issues 5.00
648-691-($3.99) 648-Big Time begins; Ramos-a; Hobgoblin app. 654-Flash Thompson becomes Venom; Marla Jameson killed. 655-Martin-a. 657-660-Fantastic Four app. 666-673-Spider Island. 667-672-Ramos-a; Avengers app. 677-X-over w/Daredevil #8. 682-687-Avengers app. 4.00
654.1-(4/11, $2.99) Flash Thompson as Venom; Ramos-a 3.00
679.1-(4/12, $2.99) Morbius the Living Vampire app. 3.00
692-($5.99) Debut of Alpha; Ramos-a; back-up short stories 6.00
693-697: 694-Cover swipe of Superman vs. Spider-Man 4.00
698, 699, 699.1: 698-Doctor Octopus brain switch revealed. 699.1-Morbius origin 4.00
700-($7.99) Collage cover; Leads into Superior Spider-Man #1; back-up short stories 25.00
700-Variant skyline-c by Marcos 45.00
700-Second printing cover with Doctor Octopus on an ASM #300 swipe 8.00
700.1 - 700.5 (2/14, weekly limited series, $3.99) 700.1-Janson-a/Ferry-c 4.00
1999, 2000 Annual (6/99, '00, $3.50) 1999-Buscema-a 4.00
2001 Annual ($2.99) Follows Peter Parker: S-M #29; last Mackie-s 4.00
Annual 1 (2008, $3.99) McKone-a; secret of Jackpot revealed; death of Jackpot 4.00
Annual 36 (9/09, $3.99) Debut of Raptor; Olliffe-a 4.00
Annual 37 (7/10, $3.99) Untold 1st meeting with Captain America; back-up w/Olliffe-a 4.00
Annual 38 (6/11, $3.99) Deadpool & Hulk app.; Garbett-a/McNiven-c 4.00
Annual 39 (7/12, $3.99) Avengers app.; Garbett-a/c 4.00
...: Big Time 1 (8/11, $5.99) r/#648-650 6.00
Collected Edition #30-32 ($3.95) reprints #30-32 w/cover #30 4.00
... 500 Covers HC (2004, $49.99) reprints covers for #1-500 & Annuals; yearly re-caps 50.00
...: Ends of the Earth (7/12, $3.99) Silas-a/Fiumara-c; Big Hero Six app. 4.00
...: Family Business HC (2014, $24.99) Kingpin app.; Waid & Robinson-s/Dell'Otto-a 25.00
Free Comic Book Day 2011 (Spider-Man) 1-Ramos-c/a; Spider-Woman & Shang-Chi app. 3.00
.../Ghost Rider: Motorstorm 1 ('11, $2.99) r/#558-560 3.00
...: Hooky 1 (2012, $4.99) r/Marvel Graphic Novel #22 (1986) with Wrightson-a 5.00
...: Infested 1 (11/11, $3.99) Spider Island tie-in; short stories by various; Ramos-c 4.00
... Omnibus HC (2007, $99.99, dustjacket) r/Amazing Fantasy #15, Amazing Spider-Man #1-38, Annual #1,2, Strange Tales Annual #2 & Fantastic Four Annual #1; letter pages, bonus art, intro. by Stan Lee; bios, essays, Marvel Tales cover gallery 100.00
Spider-Man: Brand New Day - Extra!! #1 (9/08, $3.99) short stories; Bachalo,Olliffe-a 4.00
Spider-Man: Brand New Day Yearbook #1 (2008, $4.99) plot synopses; profile pages 5.00
... Spidey Sunday Spectacuar (7/11, $3.99) collects back-ups from ASM #634-645 4.00
...: Swing Shift (2007 FCBD Edition) Jimenez-c/a; Slott-s 4.00
...: Swing Shift Director's Cut (2008, $3.99) story from 2007 FCBD; Brand New Day info 4.00
The Many Loves of the Amazing Spider-Man (7/10, $3.99) short stories of Black Cat, Gwen & Carlie, and Mary Jane; s/a by various 4.00
...: The Short Halloween (7/09, $3.99) Bill Hader & Seth Meyers-s/Maguire-a 4.00
...: You're Hired 1 (5/11, $3.99) r/story from New York Daily News insert 4.00
...Vol. 1: Coming Home (2001, $15.95) r/#30-35; J. Scott Campbell-c 16.00
...Vol. 2: Revelations (2002, $8.99) r/#36-39; Kaare Andrews-c 9.00
...Vol. 3: Until the Stars Turn Cold (2002, $12.99) r/#40-45; Romita Jr.-c 13.00
...Vol. 4: The Life and Death of Spiders (2003, $11.99) r/#46-50; Campbell-c 12.00
...Vol. 5: Unintended Consequences (2003, $12.99) r/#51-56; Dodson-c 13.00
...Vol. 6: Happy Birthday (2003, $12.99) r/#57,58,500-502 13.00
...Vol. 7: The Book of Ezekiel (2004, $12.99) r/#503-508; Romita Jr.-c 13.00
...Vol. 8: Sins Past (2005, $12.99) r/#509-514; cover sketch gallery 13.00
...Vol. 9: Skin Deep (2005, $9.99) r/#515-518 10.00
...Vol. 10: New Avengers (2005, $14.99) r/#519-524 15.00
Brand New Day #1-3 (11/08-1/09, $3.99) reprints #546-551 4.00
Civil War: Amazing Spider-Man TPB (2007, $17.99) r/#532-538; variant covers 18.00

AMAZING SPIDER-MAN (Follows Superior Spider-Man)(Also see Spider-Verse Team-Up)
Marvel Comics: Jun, 2014 - No. 20.1 , Oct, 2015 ($3.99)(there was no #19 or 20)

1-($5.99) 1st app. Cindy Moon (cameo, becomes Silk in #3); Slott-s/Ramos-a; bonus shorts with Electro, Black Cat, Spider-Man 2099, Kaine; bonus r/Inhuman #1; Ramos-c 6.00
1-Variant-c by J. Scott Campbell 8.00
2,3-Cindy Moon app.; Electro app. 2-Avengers app. 3-Black Cat app. 4.00
4-1st app. Silk (Cindy Moon); Original Sin tie-in 20.00
5-8: 5,6-Silk, Black Cat app. 7,8-Ms. Marvel app.; back-up Spider-Verse; Morlun app. 4.00
9-($4.99) Spider-Verse part 1; Variant Spider-Men & Spider-Gwen app.; Coipel-a 6.00
10-15-Spider-Verse; Superior Spider-Man returns. 13,14-Uncle Ben app.; Camuncoli-a 4.00
16-18-Ghost app.; Ramos-a; back-up with Black Cat 4.00
16.1, 17.1, 18.1, 19.1, 20.1-($3.99) Spiral parts 1-5; Conway-s/Barberi-a 4.00
Annual 1 (2/15, $4.99) Sean Ryan-s/Peterson-a/c; Nitz-s/Salas-a 5.00
Special 1(5/15, $4.99) Crossover with Inhumans and All-New Captain America specials 5.00
#1.1-1.5 (Learning to Crawl) (7/14-11/14, $3.99) Re-tells early career; Alex Ross-c 4.00

AMAZING SPIDER-MAN (Follows Secret Wars)
Marvel Comics: Dec, 2015 - No. 32, Nov, 2017; No. 789, Dec, 2017 - Present ($5.99/$3.99)

1-($5.99) Slott-s/Camuncoli-a; main-c by Alex Ross; back-up previews of Spider-titles 6.00
2-18-($3.99) 3,5-Human Torch app. 6-8-Cloak & Dagger app. 13-15-Iron Man app. 15-Mary Jane in the Iron Spider suit. 17-New female Electro 4.00
19-($4.99) Clone Conspiracy tie-in; Kingpin & Rhino app. 5.00
20-24: Clone Conspiracy tie-ins. 20-Doctor Octopus gets his body back. 21-Kaine returns 4.00
25-($9.99) Osborn Identity begins; Silver Sable returns; debut of The Superior Octopus 10.00
26-32: 26-28,32-Norman Osborn app.; Immonen-a. 29-31-Secret Empire tie-ins 4.00

[Title switches to legacy numbering after #32 (11/17)]

789-797: 789-791-"Fall of Parker"; Immonen-a. 792,793-Venom Inc. x-over. 795-Osborn merges with Carnage; Loki app. 4.00
#1.1-1.6 (Amazing Grace) (2/16-9/16, $3.99) The Santerians app.; Bianchi-a 4.00
Annual 1 (1/17, $4.99) Short stories by various incl. Wayne Brady, Ramos, Gage, Asmus 5.00
Annual 42 (4/18, $4.99) Dan Slott-s/Cory Smith-a 5.00

AMAZING SPIDER-MAN & SILK: THE SPIDER(FLY) EFFECT
Marvel Comics: May, 2016 - No. 4, Aug, 2016 ($4.99, limited series)

1-4: 1-Robbie Thompson-s/Todd Nauck-a; time-travelling Peter & Silk meet Ben Parker 5.00

AMAZING SPIDER-MAN EXTRA! (Continued from Spider-Man: Brand New Day - Extra!! #1)
Marvel Comics: No. 2, Mar, 2009 - No. 3, May, 2009 ($3.99)

2,3: 2-Anti-Venom app.; Bachalo-a. 3-Ana Kraven app.; Jimenez-a 4.00

AMAZING SPIDER-MAN FAMILY (Also see Spider-Man Family)
Marvel Comics: Oct, 2008 - No. 8, Sept, 2009 ($4.99, anthology)

1-8-New tales and reprints. 1-Includes r/ASM #300; Granov-c. 2-Deodato-c. 5-Spider-Girl new story. 6-Origin of Jackpot 5.00

AMAZING SPIDER-MAN PRESENTS: AMERICAN SON
Marvel Comics: Jul, 2010 - No. 4, Oct, 2010 ($3.99, limited series)

1-4-Reed-s/Briones-a/Djurdjevic-c; Gabriel Stacy app. 4.00

AMAZING SPIDER-MAN PRESENTS: ANTI-VENOM - NEW WAYS TO LIVE
Marvel Comics: Nov, 2009 - No. 3, Feb, 2010 ($3.99, limited series)

1-3-Wells-s/Siqueira-a; Punisher app. 4.00

AMAZING SPIDER-MAN PRESENTS: JACKPOT
Marvel Comics: Mar, 2010 - No. 3, Jun, 2010 ($3.99, limited series)

1-3-Guggenheim-s/Melo-a; Boomerang and White Rabbit app. 4.00

AMAZING SPIDER-MAN: RENEW YOUR VOWS (Secret Wars tie-in)
Marvel Comics: Aug, 2015 - No. 5, Nov, 2015 ($3.99, limited series)

1-5-Adam Kubert-a; wife Mary Jane and daughter Annie app. 1-Venom app. 4.00

AMAZING SPIDER-MAN: RENEW YOUR VOWS (Series)
Marvel Comics: Jan, 2017 - Present ($4.99/$3.99)

1-($4.99) Conway-s/Stegman-a; Mole Man app.; back-up Holden-s/a; Leth-s/Sauvage-a 5.00
2-16-($3.99) 6,7-X-Men & Magneto app. 8,9-Venom app. 13-Jumps to 8 years later 4.00

AMAZING SPIDER-MAN: THE MOVIE
Marvel Comics: Aug, 2012 - No. 2, Aug, 2012 ($3.99, limited series)

1,2-Partial adaptation of the 2012 movie; Neil Edwards-a; photo covers 4.00

AMAZING SPIDER-MAN: THE MOVIE ADAPTATION
Marvel Comics: Mar, 2014 - No. 2, Apr, 2014 ($2.99, limited series)

1,2-Adaptation of the 2012 movie; Wellington Alves-a; photo covers 3.00

AMAZING SPIDER-MAN: VENOM INC. (Crossover with ASM #792,793 & Venom #159,160)
Marvel Comics: 2018 ($4.99, bookends of crossover series)

... Alpha 1 (2/18, $4.99) Part 1 of x-over; Stegman-a; Eddie Brock & Anti-Venom app. 5.00
... Omega 1 (3/18, $4.99) Concluding Part 6 of x-over; Stegman-a 5.00

AMAZING WILLIE MAYS, THE
Famous Funnies Publ.: No date (Sept, 1954)

nn 87 174 261 553 952 1350

AMAZING WORLD OF DC COMICS
DC Comics: Jul, 1974 - No. 17, 1978 ($1.50, B&W, mail-order DC Pro-zine)

1-Kubert interview; unpublished Kirby-a; Infantino-c 6 12 18 42 79 115
2-4: 3-Julie Schwartz profile. 4-Batman; Robinson-c 5 10 15 31 53 75
5-Sheldon Mayer 4 8 12 28 47 65
6,8,13: 6-Joe Orlando; EC-r; Wrightson pin-up. 8-Infantino; Batman-r from Pop Tart giveaway. 13-Humor; Aragonés-c; Wood/Ditko-a; photos from serials of Superman, Batman, Captain Marvel 4 8 12 22 35 48
7,10-12: 7-Superman; r/1955 Pep comic giveaway. 10-Behind the scenes at DC; Showcase article. 11-Super-Villains; unpubl. Secret Society of S.V. story. 12-Legion; Grell-c/interview; 4 8 12 23 37 50
9-Legion of Super-Heroes; lengthy bios and history; Cockrum-c 6 12 18 42 79 115
14-Justice League 4 8 12 25 40 55
15-Wonder Woman; Nasser-c 5 10 15 30 50 70

Amazing World of Gumball #5 © TBS

America #3 © MAR

American Flagg Definitive Collection Vol. 1 © First Comics & Howard Chaykin

	GD 2.0	VG 4.0	FN 6.0	VF 8.0	VF/NM 9.0	NM- 9.2
16-Golden Age heroes	4	8	12	28	47	65
17-Shazam; G.A., 70s, TV and Fawcett heroes	4	8	12	25	40	55
Special 1 (Digest size)	3	6	9	20	31	42

AMAZING WORLD OF GUMBALL, THE (Based on the Cartoon Network series)
Boom Entertainment (kaBOOM!): Jun, 2014 - No. 8, Mar, 2015 ($3.99)

1-8-Multiple covers on each 4.00
... 2015 Grab Bag Special (9/15, $4.99) Short stories and pin-ups by various; 3 covers 5.00
... 2015 Special (1/15, $4.99) Short stories by various; 3 covers 5.00
... 2016 Grab Bag Special (8/16, $4.99) Short stories and pin-ups by various 5.00
... 2017 Grab Bag Special (8/17, $7.99) Short stories and pin-ups by various 8.00

AMAZING WORLD OF SUPERMAN (See Superman)

AMAZING X-MEN
Marvel Comics: Mar, 1995 - No. 4, July, 1995 ($1.95, limited series)

1-Age of Apocalypse; Andy Kubert-c/a 4.00
2-4 3.00

AMAZING X-MEN
Marvel Comics: Jan, 2014 - No. 19, Jun, 2015 ($3.99)

1-19: 1-Nightcrawler returns; Aaron-s/McGuinness-a; wraparound-c. 7-Firestar, Iceman and Spider-Man app. 8-12-World War Wendigo. 19-Colossus vs. The Juggernaut 4.00
Annual 1 (8/14, $4.99) Larroca-a/c; back-up w/Juan Doe-a 5.00

AMAZON
Comico: Mar, 1989 - No. 3, May, 1989 ($1.95, limited series)

1-3: Ecological theme; Steven Seagle-s/Tim Sale-a 3.00
1-3-(Dark Horse, 3/09 - No. 3, 5/09, $3.50) recolored reprint with creator interviews 3.50

AMAZON (Also see Marvel Versus DC #3 & DC Versus Marvel #4)
DC Comics (Amalgam): Apr, 1996 ($1.95, one-shot)

1-John Byrne-c/a/scripts 3.00

AMAZON ATTACK 3-D
The 3-D Zone: Sept, 1990 ($3.95, 28 pgs.)

1-Chaykin-a 6.00

AMAZONS ATTACK (See Wonder Woman #8 - 2006 series)
DC Comics: Jun, 2007 - No. 6, Late Oct, 2007 ($2.99, limited series)

1-6-Queen Hippolyta and Amazons attacks Wash., DC; Pfeifer-s/Woods-a 3.00

AMAZON WOMAN (1st Series)
FantaCo: Summer, 1994 - No. 2, Fall, 1994 ($2.95, B&W, limited series, mature)

1,2: Tom Simonton-c/a/scripts 3.00

AMAZON WOMAN (2nd Series)
FantaCo: Feb, 1996 - No. 4, May, 1996 ($2.95, B&W, limited series, mature)

1-4: Tom Simonton-a/scripts 3.00
...: Invaders of Terror ('96, $5.95) Simonton-a/s 6.00

AMBUSH BUG (Also see Son of...)
DC Comics: June, 1985 - No. 4, Sept, 1985 (75¢, limited series)

1-4: Giffen-c/a in all 4.00
Nothing Special 1 (9/92, $2.50, 68 pg.)-Giffen-c/a 4.00
Stocking Stuffer (2/86, $1.25)-Giffen-c/a 4.00

AMBUSH BUG: YEAR NONE
DC Comics: Sept, 2008 - No. 5, Jan, 2009; No. 7, Dec, 2009 ($2.99, limited series, no #6)

1-5,7-Giffen-s/a; Jonni DC app. 4-Conner-c. 7-Baltazar & Franco-a; Giffen-a 3.00

AME-COMI GIRLS (Based on the Anime-styled statue series)
DC Comics: Dec, 2012 - No. 5, Apr, 2013 ($3.99, printed version of digital-first series)

1-5: 1-Wonder Woman; Conner-c/a. 2-Batgirl. 3-Duela Dent; Naifeh-a 4.00

AME-COMI GIRLS (Based on the Anime-styled statue series)
DC Comics: May, 2013 - No. 8, Dec, 2013 ($3.99)

1-8: 1-Palmiotti & Gray-s/Francisco-a; story continues from earlier series 4.00

AMERICA (From Young Avengers and The Ultimates)
Marvel Comics: May, 2017 - No. 12, Apr, 2018 ($3.99)

1-12: 1-Gabby Rivera-s/Joe Quinones-a; Captain Marvel & Spectrum app. 2-Moon Girl app. 3-Storm & the X-Men app. 4.00

AMERICA AT WAR - THE BEST OF DC WAR COMICS (See Fireside Book Series)

AMERICA IN ACTION
Dell (Imp. Publ. Co.)/ Mayflower House Publ.: 1942; Winter, 1945 (36 pgs.)

	GD	VG	FN	VF	VF/NM	NM-
1942-Dell-(68 pgs.)	20	40	60	114	182	250
1-(1945)-Has 3 adaptations from American history; Kiefer, Schrotter & Webb-a	15	30	45	83	124	165

AMERICAN, THE
Dark Horse Comics: July, 1987 - No. 8, 1989 ($1.50/$1.75, B&W)

1-8: ($1.50) 3.00
Collection ($5.95, B&W)-Reprints 6.00
Special 1 (1990, $2.25, B&W) 3.00

AMERICAN AIR FORCES, THE (See A-1 Comics)
William H. Wise(Flying Cadet Publ. Co./Hasan(No.1)/Life's Romances/ Magazine Ent. No. 5 on): Sept-Oct, 1944-No. 4, 1945; No. 5, 1951-No. 12, 1954

	GD	VG	FN	VF	VF/NM	NM-
1-Article by Zack Mosley, creator of Smilin' Jack; German war-c	43	86	129	271	461	650
2-Classic-Japan war-c	87	174	261	553	952	1350
3,4-Japan war-c	20	40	60	114	182	250

NOTE: *All part comic, part magazine. Art by* **Whitney, Chas. Quinlan, H. C. Kiefer,** *and* **Tony Dipreta.**

	GD	VG	FN	VF	VF/NM	NM-
5(A-1 45)(Formerly Jet Powers), 6(A-1 54), 7(A-1 58), 8(A-1 65), 9(A-1 67), 10(A-1 74), 11(A-1 79), 12(A-1 91)	10	20	30	54	72	90

NOTE: **Powell** *c/a-5-12.*

AMERICAN CENTURY
DC Comics (Vertigo): May, 2001 - No. 27, Oct, 2003 ($2.50/$2.75)

1-Chaykin-s/painted-c; Tischman-a 4.00
2-27: 5-New story arc begins. 10-16,22-27-Orbik-c. 17-21-Silke-c. 18-$2.75-c begins 3.00
Hollywood Babylon (2002, $12.95, TPB) r/#5-9; w/sketch-to-art pages 13.00
Scars & Stripes (2001, $8.95, TPB) r/#1-4; Tischman intro. 9.00

AMERICAN DREAM (From the M2 Avengers)
Marvel Comics: Jul, 2008 - No. 5, Sept, 2008 ($2.99, limited series)

1-5-DeFalco-s/Nauck-a 3.00

AMERICAN FLAGG! (See First Comics Graphic Novel 3,9,12,21 & Howard Chaykin's..)
First Comics: Oct, 1983 - No. 50, Mar, 1988

1,21-27: 1-Chaykin-c/a begins. 21-27-Alan Moore scripts 4.00
2-20,28-49: 31-Origin Bob Violence 3.00
50-Last issue 4.00
Special 1 (11/86)-Introduces Chaykin's Time² 4.00
...: Hard Times TPB (6/85, $11.95) r/#1-7; intro. by Michael Moorcock; bonus materials 12.00
...: Definitive Collection Volume 1 HC (2008, $49.99) r/#1-14 and material from the...: Hard Times TPB; intro by Michael Chabon; afterword by Jim Lee 50.00

AMERICAN FREAK: A TALE OF THE UN-MEN
DC Comics (Vertigo): Feb, 1994 - No. 5, Jun, 1994 ($1.95, mini-series, mature)

1-5 3.00

AMERICAN GODS (Based on the Neil Gaiman novel)
Dark Horse Comics: Mar, 2017 - Present ($3.99)

1-9: 1-Gaiman & Russell-s/Scott Hampton-a. 3-Simonson-a (4 pgs). 4-Doran-a (9 pgs.) 4.00

AMERICAN GRAPHICS
Henry Stewart: No. 1, 1954; No. 2, 1957 (25¢)

	GD	VG	FN	VF	VF/NM	NM-
1-The Maid of the Mist, The Last of the Eries (Indian Legends of Niagara) (sold at Niagara Falls)	12	24	36	67	94	120
2-Victory at Niagara & Laura Secord (Heroine of the War of 1812)	8	16	24	42	54	65

AMERICAN INDIAN, THE (See Picture Progress)

AMERICAN LIBRARY
David McKay Publ.: 1943 - No. 6, 1944 (15¢, 68 pgs., B&W, text & pictures)

	GD	VG	FN	VF	VF/NM	NM-
nn (#1)-Thirty Seconds Over Tokyo (movie)	48	96	144	302	514	725
nn (#2)-Guadalcanal Diary; painted-c (only 10¢)	36	72	108	211	343	475
3-6: 3-Look to the Mountain. 4-Case of the Crooked Candle (Perry Mason). 5-Duel in the Sun. 6-Wingate's Raiders	18	36	54	105	165	225

AMERICAN: LOST IN AMERICA, THE
Dark Horse Comics: July, 1992 - No. 4, Oct, 1992 ($2.50, limited series)

1-4: 1-Dorman painted-c. 2-Phillips painted-c. 3-Mignola-c. 4-Jim Lee-c 3.00

AMERICAN MONSTER
AfterShock Comics: Jan, 2016 - No. 6, May, 2017 ($3.99)

1-6-Brian Azzarello-s/Juan Doe-a 4.00

AMERICAN MYTHOLOGY DARK: WEREWOLVES VS DINOSAURS
American Mythology Prods.: 2016 - No. 2, 2017 ($3.99)

1,2-Chris Scalf & Eric Dobson-s/a; 3 covers 4.00

AMERICAN SPLENDOR: (Series of titles)
Dark Horse Comics: Aug, 1996 - Apr, 2001 (B&W, all one-shots)

--**COMIC-CON COMICS** (8/96) 1-H. Pekar script. --**MUSIC COMICS** (11/97) nn-H. Pekar-s/ Sacco-a; r/Village Voice jazz strips. --**ODDS AND ENDS** (12/97) 1-Pekar-s. --**ON THE JOB**

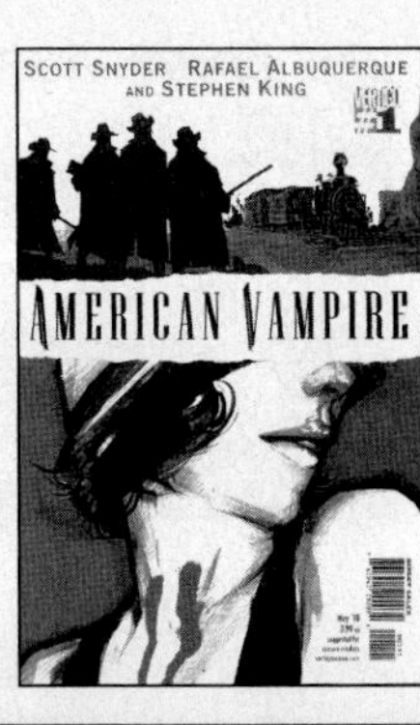

American Vampire #1 © Snyder & King

America's Best Comics #28 © STD

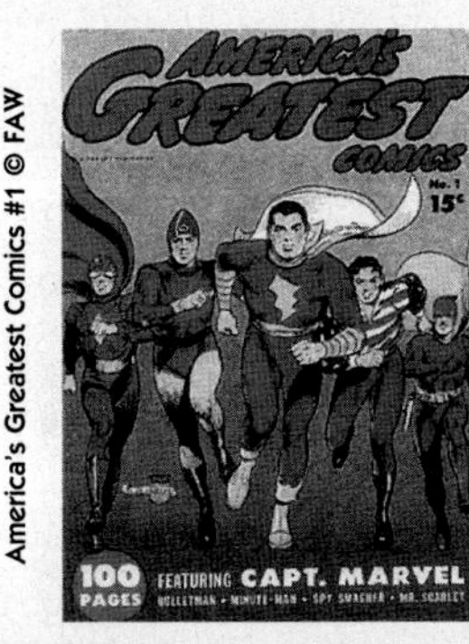

America's Greatest Comics #1 © FAW

GD 2.0 | VG 4.0 | FN 6.0 | VF 8.0 | VF/NM 9.0 | NM- 9.2

(5/97) 1-Pekar-s. --**A STEP OUT OF THE NEST** (8/94) 1-Pekar-s. --**TERMINAL** (9/99) 1-Pekar-s. --**TRANSATLANTIC** (7/98) 1-"American Splendour" on cover; Pekar-s 3.00
--**A PORTRAIT OF THE AUTHOR IN HIS DECLINING YEARS** (4/01, $3.99) 1-Photo-c. --**BEDTIME STORIES** (6/00, $3.95) 4.00

AMERICAN SPLENDOR
DC Comics: Nov, 2006 - No. 4, Feb, 2007 ($2.99, B&W)

1-4-Pekar-s/art by Haspiel and various. 1-Fabry-c 3.00
...: Another Day TPB (2007, $14.99) r/#1-4 15.00

AMERICAN SPLENDOR (Volume 2)
DC Comics (Vertigo): Jun, 2008 - No. 4, Sept, 2008 ($2.99, B&W)

1-4-Pekar-s/art by Haspiel and various. 1-Bond-c. 3-Cooke-c 3.00
...: Another Dollar TPB (2009, $14.99) r/#1-4 15.00

AMERICAN SPLENDOR: UNSUNG HERO
Dark Horse Comics: Aug, 2002 - No. 3, Oct, 2002 ($3.99, B&W, limited series)

1-3-Pekar script/Collier-a; biography of Robert McNeill 4.00
TPB (8/03, $11.95) r/#1-3 12.00

AMERICAN SPLENDOR: WINDFALL
Dark Horse Comics: Sept, 1995 - No. 2, Oct,1995 ($3.95, B&W, limited series)

1,2-Pekar script 4.00

AMERICAN TAIL: FIEVEL GOES WEST, AN
Marvel Comics: Early Jan, 1992 - No. 3, Early Feb, 1992 ($1.00, limited series)

1-3-Adapts Universal animated movie; Wildman-a 3.00
1-($2.95-c, 69 pgs.) Deluxe squarebound edition 5.00

AMERICAN VAMPIRE
DC Comics (Vertigo): May, 2010 - No. 34, Feb, 2013 ($3.99/$2.99)

1-10: 1-9-Snyder-s/Albuquerque-a. 1-5-Back-up story by Stephen King 4.00
1-5-Variant-c: 1-Jim Lee. 2-Berni Wrightson. 3-Andy Kubert. 5-Paul Pope 6.00
11-34-($2.99) 11-Santolouco-a. 12-Zezelj-a. 19-21-Bernet-a 3.00
... Anthology 1 (10/13, $7.99) Short stories by various; Albuquerque-c 8.00
...: The Long Road to Hell 1 (8/13, $6.99) Snyder-s/Albuquerque-a 7.00
HC (2010, $24.99, d.j.) r/#1-5; intro. by Stephen King; script pages and sketch art 25.00
...Volume Two HC (2011, $24.99, d.j.) r/#6-11; cover design art 25.00

AMERICAN VAMPIRE: LORD OF NIGHTMARES
DC Comics (Vertigo): Aug, 2012 - No. 5, Dec, 2012 ($2.99, limited series)

1-5-Set in 1954 England; Snyder-s/Nguyen-a/c. 2-Origin of Dracula 3.00

AMERICAN VAMPIRE: SECOND CYCLE
DC Comics (Vertigo): May, 2014 - No. 11, Jan, 2016 ($3.99/$2.99, limited series)

1,8-10-($3.99) Snyder-s/Albuquerque-a/c 4.00
2-7-($2.99) 5-Bergara-a 3.00
11-($4.99) Snyder-s/Albuquerque-a/c 5.00

AMERICAN VAMPIRE: SURVIVAL OF THE FITTEST
DC Comics (Vertigo): Aug, 2011 - No. 5, Dec, 2011 ($2.99, limited series)

1-5-Set during WWII; Snyder-s/Murphy-a/c 3.00

AMERICAN VIRGIN
DC Comics (Vertigo): May, 2006 - No. 23, Mar, 2008 ($2.99)

1-23-Steven Seagle-s/Becky Cloonan-a in most. 1-3-Quitely-c. 4-14-Middleton-c 3.00
...: Head (2006, $9.99, TPB) r/#1-4; interviews with the creators and page development 10.00
...: Going Down (2007, $14.99, TPB) r/#5-9 15.00
...: Wet (2007, $12.99, TPB) r/#10-14 13.00
...: Around the World (Vol. 4) (2008, $17.99, TPB) r/#15-23 18.00

AMERICAN WAY, THE
DC Comics (WildStorm): Apr, 2006 - No. 8, Nov, 2006 ($2.99, limited series)

1-8-John Ridley-s/Georges Jeanty-a/c 3.00

AMERICAN WAY, THE: THOSE ABOVE AND THOSE BELOW
DC Comics (Vertigo): Sept, 2017 - No. 6, Apr, 2018 ($3.99, limited series)

1-6-John Ridley-s/Georges Jeanty-a/c; sequel set in 1972 4.00

AMERICA'S BEST COMICS
Nedor/Better/Standard Publications: Feb, 1942; No. 2, Sept, 1942 - No. 31, July, 1949 (New logo with #9)

1-The Woman in Red, Black Terror, Captain Future, Doc Strange, The Liberator, & Don Davis, Secret Ace begin 377 754 1131 2639 4620 6600
2-Origin The American Eagle; The Woman in Red ends
168 336 504 1075 1838 2600
3-Pyroman begins (11/42, 1st app.; also see Startling Comics #18, 12/42)
161 322 483 1030 1765 2500
4-6: 5-Last Capt. Future (not in #4); Lone Eagle app. 6-American Crusader app.
123 246 369 787 1344 1900
7-Hitler, Mussolini & Hirohito-c 326 652 978 2282 3991 5700
8-Last Liberator 115 230 345 730 1253 1775
9-The Fighting Yank begins; The Ghost app. 116 232 348 742 1271 1800
10-Flag-c 111 222 333 705 1215 1725
11-Hirohito & Tojo-c. (10/44) 135 270 405 864 1482 2100
12 87 174 261 553 952 1350
13-Japanese WWII-c 107 214 321 680 1165 1650
14-17: 14-American Eagle ends; Doc Strange vs. Hitler story
73 146 219 467 796 1125
18-Classic-c 103 206 309 659 1130 1600
19-21: 21-Infinity-c 65 130 195 416 708 1000
22-Capt. Future app. 57 114 171 362 619 875
23-Miss Masque begins; last Doc Strange 79 158 237 502 864 1225
24-Miss Masque bondage-c 76 152 228 486 831 1175
25-Last Fighting Yank; Sea Eagle app. 60 120 180 381 653 925
26-Miss Masque motorcycle-c; The Phantom Detective & The Silver Knight app.; Frazetta text illo & some panels in Miss Masque 66 132 198 419 722 1025
27-31: 27,28-Commando Cubs. 27-Doc Strange. 28-Tuska Black Terror. 29-Last Pyroman
54 108 162 343 574 825

NOTE: *American Eagle not in 3, 8, 9, 13. Fighting Yank not in 10, 12. Liberator not in 2, 6, 7. Pyroman not in 9, 11, 14-16, 23, 25-27.* ***Schomburg (Xela)*** *c-5, 7-31. Bondage c-18, 24.*

AMERICA'S BEST COMICS
America's Best Comics: 1999 - 2008

... Preview (1999, Wizard magazine supplement) - Previews Tom Strong, Top Ten, Promethea, Tomorrow Stories 3.00
... Primer (2008, $4.99, TPB) r/Tom Strong #1, Tom Strong's Terrific Tales, Top Ten #1, Promethea #1, Tomorrow Stories #1,6 5.00
... Sketchbook (2002, $5.95, square-bound)-Design sketches by Sprouse, Ross, Adams, Nowlan, Ha and others 6.00
Special 1 (2/01, $6.95)-Short stories of Alan Moore's characters; art by various; Ross-c 7.00
TPB (2004, $17.95) Reprints short stories and sketch pages from ABC titles 18.00

AMERICA'S BEST TV COMICS (TV)
American Broadcasting Co. (Prod. by Marvel Comics): 1967 (25¢, 68 pgs.)

1-Spider-Man, Fantastic Four (by Kirby/Ayers), Casper, King Kong, George of the Jungle, Journey to the Center of the Earth stories (promotes new TV cartoon show)
10 20 30 69 147 225

AMERICA'S BIGGEST COMICS BOOK
William H. Wise: 1944 (196 pgs., one-shot)

1-The Grim Reaper, The Silver Knight, Zudo, the Jungle Boy, Commando Cubs, Thunderhoof app. 50 100 150 315 533 750

AMERICA'S FUNNIEST COMICS
William H. Wise: 1944 - No. 2, 1944 (15¢, 80 pgs.)

nn(#1), 2-Funny Animal 24 48 72 142 234 325

AMERICA'S GOT POWERS
Image Comics: Apr, 2012 - No. 7, Oct, 2013 ($2.99, limited series)

1-7-Jonathan Ross-s/Bryan Hitch-a/c. 1-Wraparound-c 3.00

AMERICA'S GREATEST COMICS
Fawcett Publications: May?, 1941 - No. 8, Summer, 1943 (15¢, 100 pgs., soft cardboard-c)

1-Bulletman, Spy Smasher, Capt. Marvel, Minute Man & Mr. Scarlet begin; Classic Mac Raboy-c. 1st time that Fawcett's major super-heroes appear together as a group on a cover. Fawcett's 1st squarebound comic 349 698 1047 2443 4272 6100
2 145 290 435 921 1586 2250
3 113 226 339 718 1234 1750
4,5: 4-Commando Yank begins; Golden Arrow, Ibis the Invincible & Spy Smasher cameo in Captain Marvel 77 154 231 489 837 1185
6,7: 7-Balbo the Boy Magician app.; Captain Marvel, Bulletman cameo in Mr. Scarlet
68 136 204 435 743 1050
8-Capt. Marvel Jr. & Golden Arrow app.; Spy Smasher x-over in Capt. Midnight; no Minute Man or Commando Yank 68 136 204 435 743 1050

AMERICA'S SWEETHEART SUNNY (See Sunny, ...)

AMERICA VS. THE JUSTICE SOCIETY
DC Comics: Jan, 1985 - No. 4, Apr, 1985 ($1.00, limited series)

1-Double size; Alcala-a(i) in all 2 4 6 8 10 12
2-4: 3,4-Spectre cameo 1 2 3 5 7 9

AMERICOMICS
Americomics: April, 1983 - No. 6, Mar, 1984 ($2.00, Baxter paper/slick paper)

1-Intro/origin The Shade; Intro. The Slayer, Captain Freedom and The Liberty Corps; Perez-c 5.00

Anarky #8 © DC

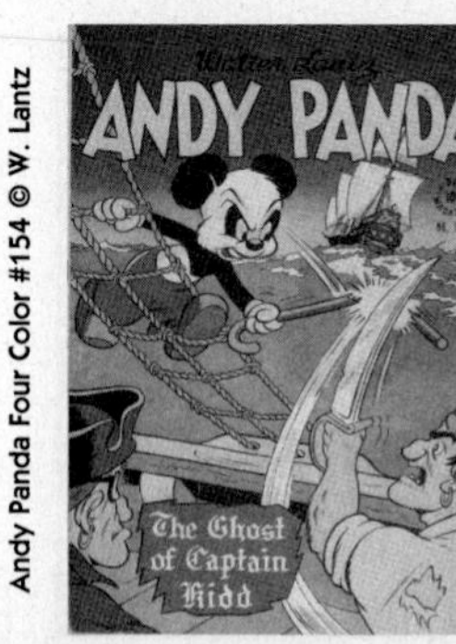

Andy Panda Four Color #154 © W. Lantz

Angel (2009 series) #26 © 20th Century Fox

	GD 2.0	VG 4.0	FN 6.0	VF 8.0	VF/NM 9.0	NM- 9.2

1,2-2nd printings ($2.00) 3.00
2-6: 2-Messenger app. & 1st app. Tara on Jungle Island. 3-New & old Blue Beetle battle. 4-Origin Dragonfly & Shade. 5-Origin Commando D. 6-Origin the Scarlet Scorpion 3.00
Special 1 (8/83, $2.00)-Sentinels of Justice (Blue Beetle, Captain Atom, Nightshade & The Question) 5.00

AMETHYST
DC Comics: Jan, 1985 - No. 16, Aug, 1986 (75¢)

1-16: 8-Fire Jade's i.d. revealed 3.00
Special 1 (10/86, $1.25) 4.00
1-4 (11/87 - 2/88)(Limited series) 3.00

AMETHYST, PRINCESS OF GEMWORLD (See Legion of Super-Heroes #298)
DC Comics: May, 1983 - No. 12, Apr, 1984 (Maxi-series)

1-(60¢) 5.00
1,2-(35¢): tested in Austin & Kansas City 5 10 15 33 57 80
2-12, Annual 1(9/84): 5-11-Pérez-c(p) 4.00
NOTE: *Issues #1 & 2 also have Canadian variants with a 75¢ cover price.*

AMORY WARS (Based on the Coheed and Cambria album The Second Stage Turbine Blade)
Image Comics: Jun, 2007 - No. 5, Jan, 2008 ($2.99, limited series)

1-5: 1-Claudio Sanchez-s/Gus Vasquez-a 3.00

AMORY WARS II
Image Comics: Jun, 2008 - No. 5, Oct, 2008 ($2.99, limited series)

1-5-Claudio Sanchez-s/Gabriel Guzman-a 3.00

AMORY WARS: GOOD APOLLO, I'M BURNING STAR IV
BOOM! Studios: Apr, 2017 - Present ($3.99)

1-10: 1-Claudio Sanchez & Chondra Echert-s/Rags Morales-a. 1-Four covers 4.00

AMORY WARS IN KEEPING SECRETS OF SILENT EARTH: 3
BOOM! Studios: May, 2010 - No. 12, Jun, 2011 ($3.99)

1-12: 1-Claudio Sanchez & Peter David-s/Chris Burnham-a. 1-Four covers 4.00

AMY RACECAR COLOR SPECIAL (See Stray Bullets)
El Capitán Books: July, 1997; Oct, 1999 ($2.95/$3.50)

1,2-David Lapham-a/scripts. 2-($3.50) 3.50

ANARCHO DICTATOR OF DEATH (See Comics Novel)

ANARKY (See Batman titles)
DC Comics: May, 1997 - No. 4, Aug, 1997 ($2.50, limited series)

1 3.50
2-4 3.00

ANARKY (See Batman titles)
DC Comics: May, 1999 - No. 8, Dec, 1999 ($2.50)

1-8: 1-JLA app.; Grant-s/Breyfogle-a. 3-Green Lantern app. 7-Day of Judgment; Haunted Tank app. 8-Joker-c/app. 3.00

ANCHORS ANDREWS (The Saltwater Daffy)
St. John Publishing Co.: Jan, 1953 - No. 4, July, 1953 (Anchors the Saltwater... No. 4)

1-Canteen Kate by Matt Baker (9 pgs.) 25 50 75 150 245 340
2-4 10 20 30 56 76 95

ANDY & WOODY (See March of Comics No. 40, 55, 76)

ANDY BURNETT (TV, Disney)
Dell Publishing Co.: Dec, 1957

Four Color 865-Photo-c 8 16 24 54 102 150

ANDY COMICS (Formerly Scream Comics; becomes Ernie Comics)
Current Publications (Ace Magazines): No. 20, June, 1948-No. 21, Aug, 1948

20,21: Archie-type comic 10 20 30 58 79 100

ANDY DEVINE WESTERN
Fawcett Publications: Dec, 1950 - No. 2, 1951

1-Photo-c 47 94 141 296 498 700
2-Photo-c 32 64 96 192 314 435

ANDY GRIFFITH SHOW, THE (TV)(1st show aired 10/3/60)
Dell Publishing Co.: #1252, Jan-Mar, 1962; #1341, Apr-Jun, 1962

Four Color 1252(#1) 36 72 108 266 596 925
Four Color 1341-Photo-c 34 68 102 245 548 850

ANDY HARDY COMICS (See Movie Comics #3 by Fiction House)
Dell Publishing Co.: April, 1952 - No. 6, Sept-Nov, 1954

Four Color 389(#1) 6 12 18 37 66 95
Four Color 447,480,515, #5,#6 4 8 12 27 44 60

ANDY PANDA (Also see Crackajack Funnies #39, The Funnies, New Funnies & Walter Lantz...)
Dell Publishing Co.: 1943 - No. 56, Nov-Jan, 1961-62 (Walter Lantz)

Four Color 25(#1, 1943) 50 100 150 390 870 1350
Four Color 54(1944) 25 50 75 175 388 600
Four Color 85(1945) 15 30 45 103 227 350
Four Color 130(1946),154,198 10 20 30 70 150 230
Four Color 216,240,258,280,297 8 16 24 55 105 155
Four Color 326,345,358 6 12 18 41 76 110
Four Color 383,409 5 10 15 35 63 90
16(11-1/52-53) - 30 4 8 12 28 47 65
31-56 4 8 12 23 37 50
(See March of Comics #5, 22, 79, & Super Book #4, 15, 27.)

A-NEXT (See Avengers)
Marvel Comics: Oct, 1998 - No. 12, Sept, 1999 ($1.99)

1-6,8-12: 1-Next generation of Avengers; Frenz-a. 2-Two covers. 3-Defenders app. 3.00
7-1st app. of Hope Pym 2 4 6 9 12 15
Spider-Girl Presents Avengers Next Vol. 1: Second Coming (2006, $7.99, digest) r/#1-6 8.00

ANGEL
Dell Publishing Co.: Aug, 1954 - No. 16, Nov-Jan, 1958-59

Four Color 576(#1, 8/54) 5 10 15 30 50 70
2(5-7/55) - 16 3 6 9 17 26 35

ANGEL (TV) (Also see Buffy the Vampire Slayer)
Dark Horse Comics: Nov, 1999 - No. 17, Apr, 2001 ($2.95/$2.99)

1-17: 1-3,5-7,10-14-Zanier-a. 1-4,7,10-Matsuda & photo-c. 16-Buffy-c/app. 3.00
...: Earthly Possessions TPB (4/01, $9.95) r/#5-7, photo-c 10.00
...: Surrogates TPB (12/00, $9.95) r/#1-3; photo-c 10.00

ANGEL (Buffy the Vampire Slayer)
Dark Horse Comics: Sept, 2001 - No. 4, May, 2002 ($2.99, limited series)

1-4-Joss Whedon & Matthews-s/Rubi-a; photo-c and Rubi-c on each 3.00

ANGEL (Buffy the Vampire Slayer) (Previously titled Angel: After the Fall)
IDW Publishing: No. 18, Feb, 2009 - No. 44, Apr, 2011 ($3.99)

18-44: Multiple covers on all. 25-Juliet Landau-s 4.00

ANGEL (one-shots) (Buffy the Vampire Slayer)
IDW Publishing: ($3.99/$7.49)

...: Connor (8/06, $3.99) Jay Faerber-s/Bob Gill-a; 4 covers + 1 retailer cover 4.00
...: Doyle (7/06, $3.99) Jeff Mariotte-s/David Messina-a; 4 covers + 1 retailer cover 4.00
...: Gunn (5/06, $3.99) Dan Jolley-s/Mark Pennington-a; 4 covers + 2 retailer covers 4.00
...: Illyria (4/06, $3.99) Peter David-s/Nicola Scott-a; 4 covers + 2 retailer covers 4.00
...: Masks (10/06, $7.49) short stories of Angel, Illyria, Cordilia & Lindsay; puppet Angel app. 8.00
... 100-Page Spectacular (4/11, $7.99) reprints of 4 issues; Runge-c 8.00
... Special • Lorne (3/10, $7.99) John Byrne-s/a; The Groosalugg app. 8.00
Team Angel 100-Page Spectacular (4/11, $7.99) reprints; Runge-c 8.00
...: Vs. Frankenstein (10/09, $3.99) John Byrne-s/a/c 4.00
...: Vs. Frankenstein II (10/10, $3.99) John Byrne-s/a/c 4.00
...: Wesley (6/06, $3.99) Scott Tipton-s/Mike Norton-a; 4 covers + 1 retailer cover 4.00
Spotlight TPB (12/06, $19.99) r/Connor, Doyle, Gunn, Illyria & Wesley one-shots 20.00
... Yearbook (5/11, $7.99) short stories by various; 3 covers 8.00

ANGELA
Image Comics (Todd McFarlane Prod.): Dec, 1994 - No. 3, Feb, 1995 ($2.95, lim. series)

1-Gaiman scripts & Capullo-c/a in all; Spawn app. 1 2 3 5 6 8
2 6.00
3 5.00
Special Edition (1995)-Pirate Spawn-c 3 6 9 14 20 25
Special Edition (1995)-Angela-c 3 6 9 14 20 25
TPB ($9.95, 1995) reprints #1-3 & Special Ed. w/additional pin-ups 10.00

ANGELA: ASGARD'S ASSASSIN (The Image Comics character in the Marvel Universe)
Marvel Comics: Feb, 2015 - No. 6, Jul, 2015 ($3.99)

1-6: 1-Gillen-s/Jimenez-a; multiple covers. 4-6-Guardians of the Galaxy app. 4.00

ANGEL: AFTER THE FALL (Buffy the Vampire Slayer) (Follows the last TV episode)
IDW Publishing: Nov, 2007 - No. 17, Feb, 2009 ($3.99)(Continues as Angel with #18)

1-Whedon & Lynch-s; multiple covers 5.00
2-17: Multiple covers on all 4.00

ANGELA/GLORY: RAGE OF ANGELS (See Glory/Angela: Rage of Angels)
Image Comics (Todd McFarlane Productions): Mar, 1996 ($2.50, one-shot)

1-Liefeld-c/Cruz-a(p); Darkchylde preview flip book 4.00
1-Variant-c 4.00

ANGEL: A HOLE IN THE WORLD (Adaptation of the 2-part TV episode)
IDW Publishing: Dec, 2009 - No. 5, Apr, 2010 ($3.99, limited series)

Angel and the Ape (2001 series) #1 © DC

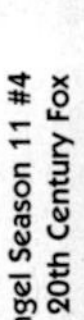
Angel Season 11 #4 © 20th Century Fox

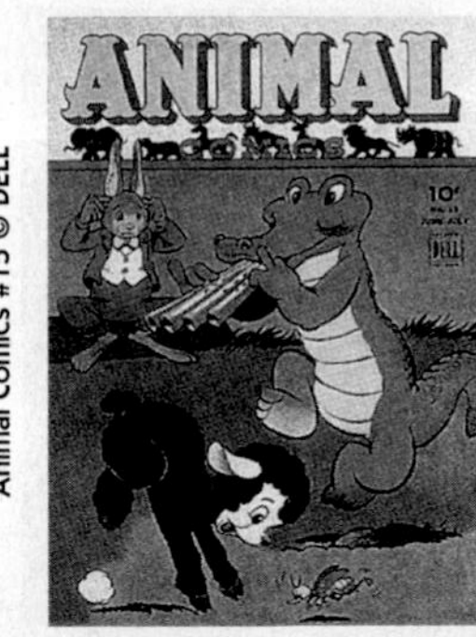

Animal Comics #15 © DELL

	GD 2.0	VG 4.0	FN 6.0	VF 8.0	VF/NM 9.0	NM- 9.2

1-5-Fred becomes Illyria; Casagrande-a/c 4.00

ANGEL & FAITH (Follows Buffy the Vampire Slayer Season Eight)
Dark Horse Comics: Aug, 2011 - No. 25, Aug, 2013 ($2.99)

1-Gage-s/Isaacs-a; two covers by Morris & Chen 3.00
2-25-Two covers by Morris & Isaacs. 5-Harmony & Clem app.; Noto-a. 7-Drusilla app. 11-14-Willow & Connor app. 20-Spike app.; Archie style-c 3.00

ANGEL & FAITH SEASON 10 (Buffy the Vampire Slayer)
Dark Horse Comics: Apr, 2014 - No. 25, Apr, 2016 ($3.50/$3.99)

1-15-Two covers on each. 1-Gischler-s/Conrad-a. 5-Santacruz-a. 6-10-Amy app. 10-Fred returns 3.50
16-25-($3.99) 17-Drusilla returns 4.00

ANGEL AND THE APE (Meet Angel No. 7) (See Limited Collector's Edition C-34 & Showcase No. 77)
National Periodical Publications: Nov-Dec, 1968 - No. 6, Sept-Oct, 1969

	GD	VG	FN	VF	VF/NM	NM-
1-(11-12/68)-Not Wood-a	5	10	15	30	50	70
2-5-Wood inks in all. 4-Last 12¢ issue	3	6	9	20	31	42
6-Wood inks	4	8	12	22	35	48

ANGEL AND THE APE (2nd Series)
DC Comics: Mar, 1991 - No. 4, June, 1991 ($1.00, limited series)

1-4 3.00

ANGEL AND THE APE (3rd Series)
DC Comics (Vertigo): Oct, 2001 - No. 4, Jan 2002 ($2.95, limited series)

1-4-Chaykin & Tischman-s/Bond-a/Art Adams-c 3.00

ANGELA: QUEEN OF HEL (The Image Comics character in the Marvel Universe)
Marvel Comics: Dec, 2015 - No. 7, Jun, 2016 ($3.99)

1-5: 1-Bennett-s/Jacinto & Hans-a. 4,5-Hela app. 6,7-Thor (Jane) app. 4.00

ANGEL: AULD LANG SYNE (Buffy the Vampire Slayer)
IDW Publishing: Nov, 2006 - No. 5, Mar, 2007 ($3.99, limited series)

1-5: 1-Three covers plus photo-c; Tipton-s/Messina-a 4.00

ANGEL: BARBARY COAST (Buffy the Vampire Slayer)
IDW Publishing: Apr, 2010 - No. 3, Jun, 2010 ($3.99, limited series)

1-3-Angel in 1906 San Francisco; Tischman-s/Urru-a; 2 covers on each 4.00

ANGEL: BLOOD & TRENCHES (Buffy the Vampire Slayer)
IDW Publishing: Mar, 2009 - No. 4, June, 2009 ($3.99, B&W&Red, limited series)

1-4-Angel in World War II Europe; John Byrne-s/a/c 4.00

ANGEL: ILLYRIA: HAUNTED (Buffy the Vampire Slayer)
IDW Publishing: Nov, 2010 - No. 4, Feb, 2011 ($3.99, limited series)

1-4-Tipton & Huehner-s/Casagrande-a; 2 covers 4.00

ANGEL LOVE
DC Comics: Aug, 1986 - No. 8, Mar, 1987 (75¢, limited series)

1-8, Special 1 (1987, $1.25, 52 pgs.) 4.00

ANGEL: NOT FADE AWAY (Buffy the Vampire Slayer)
IDW Publishing: May, 2009 - No. 3, July, 2009 ($3.99, limited series)

1-3-Adaptation of TV show's final episodes; Mooney-a 4.00

ANGEL OF LIGHT, THE (See The Crusaders)

ANGEL: OLD FRIENDS (Buffy the Vampire Slayer)
IDW Publishing: Nov, 2005 - No. 5, Mar, 2006 ($3.99, limited series)

1-5: Four covers plus photo-c on each; Mariotte-s/Messina-a; Gunn, Spike and Illyria app. 4.00
... Cover Gallery (6/06, $3.99) gallery of variant covers for the series 4.00
... Cover Gallery (12/06, $3.99) gallery of variant covers; preview of Angel: Auld Lang Syne 4.00
TPB (2006, $19.99) r/series; gallery of Messina covers 20.00

ANGEL: ONLY HUMAN (Buffy the Vampire Slayer)
IDW Publishing: Aug, 2009 - No. 5, Dec, 2009 ($3.99, limited series)

1-5-Lobdell-s/Messina-a; covers by Messina and Dave Dorman 4.00

ANGEL: REVELATIONS (X-Men character)
Marvel Comics: July, 2008 - No. 5, Nov, 2008 ($3.99, limited series)

1-5-Origin from childhood re-told; Adam Pollina-a/Aquirre-Sacasa-s 4.00

ANGEL SEASON 11 (Buffy the Vampire Slayer)
Dark Horse Comics: Jan, 2017 - No. 12, Dec, 2017 ($3.99)

1-12: 1-4-Bechko-s/Borges-a; Fred & Illyria app. 4.00

ANGEL: SMILE TIME (Buffy the Vampire Slayer)
IDW Publishing: Dec, 2008 - No. 3, Apr, 2009 ($3.99, limited series)

1-3-Adaptation of TV episode; Messina-a; Messina and photo covers for each 4.00

ANGEL: THE CURSE (Buffy the Vampire Slayer)
IDW Publishing: June, 2005 - No. 5, Oct, 2005 ($3.99, limited series)

1-5-Four covers on each; Mariotte-s/Messina-a 4.00
TPB (1/06, $19.99) r/#1-5; cover gallery of Messina covers 20.00

ANGELTOWN
DC Comics (Vertigo): Jan, 2005 - No. 5, May, 2005 ($2.95, limited series)

1-5-Gary Phillips-s/Shawn Martinbrough-a 3.00

ANGELUS
Image Comics (Top Cow): Dec, 2007; Dec, 2009 - Nov, 2010 ($2.99)

... Pilot Season 1-(12/07) Sejic-a/c; Edington-s; origin re-told 3.00
1-6-Marz-s/Sejic-a; multiple covers on each 3.00

ANGRY BIRDS COMICS (Based on the Rovio videogame)(Also see Super Angry Birds)
IDW Publishing: Jun, 2014 - No. 12, Jun, 2015 ($3.99)

1-12-Short stories by Jeff Parker, Paul Tobin and various; wraparound-c on most 4.00
Volume 2 (1/16 - 12/16, $3.99) 1-12-Wraparound-c on all 4.00
...: Holiday Special (12/14, $5.99) Terence in charge of the North Pole 6.00
... Quarterly: Furious Fowl (8/17, $5.99) Short stories by various 6.00
... Quarterly: Monsters and Mistletoe (12/17, $5.99) Short stories by various 6.00

ANGRY BIRDS: FLIGHT SCHOOL (Based on the Rovio videogame)
IDW Publishing: Feb, 2017 - No. 3, Jun, 2017 ($3.99)

1-3-Short stories by various 4.00

ANGRY BIRDS GAME PLAY (Based on the Rovio videogame)
IDW Publishing: Jan, 2017 - No. 3, May, 2017 ($3.99)

1-3-Short stories by various; wraparound-c 4.00

ANGRY BIRDS TRANSFORMERS (Based on the Rovio videogame)
IDW Publishing: Nov, 2014 - No. 4, Feb, 2015 ($3.99, limited series)

1-4-Barber-s; the Eggspark lands on Piggy Island 4.00

ANGRY CHRIST COMIX (See Cry For Dawn)

ANIMA
DC Comics: Mar, 1994 - No. 15, July, 1995 ($1.75/$1.95/$2.25)

1-7,0,8-15: 7-(9/94)-Begin $1.95-c; Zero Hour x-over 3.00

ANIMAL ADVENTURES
Timor Publications/Accepted Publ. (reprints): Dec, 1953 - No. 3, May?, 1954

	GD	VG	FN	VF	VF/NM	NM-
1-Funny animal	8	16	24	44	57	70
2,3: 2-Featuring Soopermutt (2/54)	7	14	21	35	43	50
1-3 (reprints, nd)	3	6	8	11	13	15

ANIMAL ANTICS
DC Comics: Feb, 1946

nn - Ashcan comic, not distributed to newsstands, only for in-house use. Cover art is Star Spangled Comics #49 and interior is Boy Commandos #12; a NM cover sold for $1000 in 2012, and FN/VF copy sold for $1553.50 in 2012.

ANIMAL ANTICS (Movietown... No. 24 on)
National Periodical Publ: Mar-Apr, 1946 - No. 23, Nov-Dec, 1949 (All 52 pgs.?)

	GD	VG	FN	VF	VF/NM	NM-
1-Raccoon Kids begins by Otto Feuer; many-c by Grossman; Seaman Sy Wheeler by Kelly in some issues; Grossman-a in most issues	45	90	135	284	480	675
2	25	50	75	147	241	335
3-10: 10-Post-c/a	16	32	48	94	147	200
11-23: 14,15,18,19-Post-a	12	24	36	69	97	125

ANIMAL COMICS
Dell Publishing Co.: Dec-Jan, 1941-42 - No. 30, Dec-Jan, 1947-48

	GD	VG	FN	VF	VF/NM	NM-
1-1st Pogo app. by Walt Kelly (Dan Noonan art in most issues)	126	252	378	806	1378	1950
2-Uncle Wiggily begins	57	114	171	362	619	875
3,5	27	54	81	189	420	650
4,6,7-No Pogo	16	32	48	110	243	375
8-10	19	38	57	131	291	450
11-15	12	24	36	79	170	260
16-20	9	18	27	58	114	170
21-30: 24-30- "Jigger" by John Stanley	8	16	24	51	96	140

NOTE: ***Dan Noonan*** *a-18-30.* ***Gollub*** *art in most later issues; c-29, 30.* ***Kelly*** *c-7-26, part #27-30.*

ANIMAL CRACKERS (Also see Adventures of Patoruzu)
Green Publ. Co./Norlen/Fox Feat.(Hero Books): 1946; No. 31, July, 1950; No. 9, 1959

	GD	VG	FN	VF	VF/NM	NM-
1-Super Cat begins (1st app.)	20	40	60	120	195	270
2	11	22	33	64	90	115
31(Fox)-Formerly My Love Secret	9	18	27	50	65	80

Animal Man #75 © DC

Animaniacs #23 © WB

Animosity #2 © Marguerite Bennett

	GD 2.0	VG 4.0	FN 6.0	VF 8.0	VF/NM 9.0	NM- 9.2

9(1959-Norlen)-Infinity-c 5 10 15 22 26 30
nn, nd ('50s), no publ.; infinity-c 5 10 15 22 26 30

ANIMAL FABLES
E. C. Comics (Fables Publ. Co.): July-Aug, 1946 - No. 7, Nov-Dec, 1947

1-Freddy Firefly (clone of Human Torch), Korky Kangaroo, Petey Pig, Danny Demon begin 68 136 204 435 743 1050
2-Aesop Fables begin 39 78 117 240 395 550
3-6 36 72 108 211 343 475
7-Origin Moon Girl 84 168 252 538 919 1300

ANIMAL FAIR (Fawcett's...)
Fawcett Publications: Mar, 1946 - No. 11, Feb, 1947

1-Hoppy the Marvel Bunny-c 29 58 87 174 285 395
2 14 28 42 82 121 160
3-6 12 24 36 67 94 120
7-11 10 20 30 54 72 90

ANIMAL FUN
Premier Magazines: 1953 (25¢, came w/glasses)

1-(3-D)-Ziggy Pig, Silly Seal, Billy & Buggy Bear 39 78 117 240 395 550

ANIMAL MAN (See Action Comics #552, 553, DC Comics Presents #77, 78, Last Days of Animal Man, Secret Origins #39, Strange Adventures #180 & Wonder Woman #267, 268)
DC Comics (Vertigo imprint #57 on): Sept, 1988 - No. 89, Nov, 1995 ($1.25/$1.50/$1.75/$1.95/$2.25, mature)

1-Grant Morrison scripts begin, ends #26 2 4 6 8 10 12
2-10: 2-Superman cameo. 6-Invasion tie-in. 9-Manhunter-c/story. 10-Psycho Pirate app. 1 2 3 4 5 7
11-49,51-55,57-89: 23,24-Psycho Pirate app. 24-Arkham Asylum story; Bizarro Superman app. 25-Inferior Five app. 26-Morrison apps. in story; part photo-c (of Morrison?) 3.00
50-($2.95, 52 pgs.)-Last issue w/Veitch scripts 5.00
56-($3.50, 68 pgs.) 5.00
Annual 1 (1993, $3.95, 68 pgs.)-Bolland-c; Children's Crusade Pt. 3 6.00
...: Deus Ex Machina TPB (2003, $19.95) r/#18-26; Morrison-s; new Bolland-c 20.00
...: Origin of the Species TPB (2002, $19.95) r/#10-17 & Secret Origins #39 20.00
NOTE: *Bolland c-1-63. 71-Sutton-a(i)*

ANIMAL MAN (DC New 52)
DC Comics: Nov, 2011 - No. 29, May, 2014 ($2.99)

1-Jeff Lemire-s/Travel Foreman-a/c; 1st printing with yellow cover background 8.00
1-Second printing (red cover background), Third printing (grey cover background) 3.00
2-29: 2-4 Foreman-a. 5-Huat-a. 10 Justice League Dark app. 13-17-Rotworld 3.00
#0 (11/12, $2.99) Lemire-s/Pugh-a/c; Buddy Baker's origin re-told 3.00
Annual 1 (7/12, $4.99) Swamp Thing app.; Lemire-s/Green-a 5.00
Annual 2 (9/13, $4.99) Lemire-s/Foreman-a 5.00

ANIMAL MYSTIC (See Dark One...)
Cry For Dawn/Sirius: 1993 - No. 4, 1995 ($2.95?/$3.50, B&W)

1 6.00
1-Alternate 2 4 6 9 12 15
1-2nd printing 4.00
2 4.00
2,3-2nd prints (Sirius) 3.50
3,4: 4-Color poster insert, Linsner-s 4.00
TPB ($14.95) r/series 15.00

ANIMAL MYSTIC WATER WARS
Sirius: 1996 - No. 6 ($2.95, limited series)

1-6-Dark One-c/a/scripts 5.00

ANIMAL WORLD, THE (Movie)
Dell Publishing Co.: No. 713, Aug, 1956

Four Color 713 5 10 15 31 53 75

ANIMANIACS (TV)
DC Comics: May, 1995 - No. 59, Apr, 2000 ($1.50/$1.75/$1.95/$1.99)

1 1 2 3 4 5 7
2-20: 13-Manga issue. 19-X-Files parody; Miran Kim-c; Adlard-a (4 pgs.) 4.00
21-59: 26-E.C. parody-c. 34-Xena parody. 43-Pinky & the Brain take over 3.00
A Christmas Special (12/94, $1.50, "1" on-c) 5.00

ANIMATED COMICS
E. C. Comics: No date given (Summer, 1947?)

1 (Rare) Funny Animal 100 200 300 635 1093 1550

ANIMATED FUNNY COMIC TUNES (See Funny Tunes)

ANIMATED MOVIE-TUNES (Movie Tunes No. 3)
Margood Publishing Corp. (Timely): Fall, 1945 - No. 2, Sum, 1946

1,2-Super Rabbit, Ziggy Pig & Silly Seal 40 80 120 246 411 575

ANIMAX
Marvel Comics (Star Comics): Dec, 1986 - No. 4, June, 1987

1-4: Based on toys; Simonson-a 3.00

ANIMOSITY (Also see World of Animosity one-shot)
AfterShock Comics: Aug, 2016 - Present ($3.99)

1-Marguerite Bennett-s/Rafael de Latorre-a; 2 covers 15.00
2 8.00
3-12 4.00

ANIMOSITY: EVOLUTION
AfterShock Comics: Oct, 2017 - Present ($3.99, limited series)

1-4-Bennett-s/Gapstur-a; San Francisco one month after the awakening 4.00

ANIMOSITY: THE RISE
AfterShock Comics: Jan, 2017 - No. 3, Sept, 2017 ($3.99, limited series)

1-3-Bennett-s/Juan Doe-a; the early days after the animals awoke 4.00

ANITA BLAKE (Circus of the Damned - The Charmer on cover)
Marvel Comics: July, 2010 - No. 5, Dec, 2010 ($3.99, limited series)

1-5-Laurell K. Hamilton & Jess Ruffner-s/Ron Lim-a/ Brett Booth-c 4.00
... - The Ingenue 1-5 (3/11 - No. 5, 10/11, $3.99) Hamilton & Ruffner-s/Lim-a/Booth-c 4.00
... - The Scoundrel 1-4 (11/11 - No. 5, 5/12, $3.99) Hamilton & Ruffner-s/Lim-a/Booth-c 4.00

ANITA BLAKE: VAMPIRE HUNTER GUILTY PLEASURES
Marvel Comics (Dabel Brothers): Dec, 2006 - No. 12, Aug, 2008 ($2.99)

1-Laurell K. Hamilton-s/Brett Booth-a; blue cover 6.00
1-Variant-c by Greg Horn 20.00
1-Sketch cover 25.00
1-2nd printing with red cover 3.00
2-Two covers 5.00
3-12 3.00
...: Handbook (2007, $3.99) profile pages of characters; glossary 4.00
... Volume One HC (6/07, $19.99, dust jacket) r/#1-6; cover gallery 20.00

ANITA BLAKE: VAMPIRE HUNTER THE FIRST DEATH, (LAURELL K. HAMILTON'S...)
Marvel Comics (Dabel Brothers): July, 2007 - No. 2, Dec, 2007 ($3.99)

1,2-Laurell K. Hamilton & Jonathon Green-s/Wellington Alves-a. 2-Marvel Zombie var-c 4.00
... HC (2008, $19.99, dust jacket) r/#1,2 & Guilty Pleasures Handbook 20.00

ANITA BLAKE, VAMPIRE HUNTER: THE LAUGHING CORPSE
Marvel Comics: Dec, 2008 - No. 5, Apr, 2009 ($3.99)

... - Book One (12/08 - No. 5, 4/09) 1-5-Laurell K. Hamilton-s/Ron Lim-a/c 4.00
... - Necromancer 1-5 (6/09 - No. 5, 11/09, $3.99) Lim-a/c 4.00
Anita Blake (Executioner on-c) #11-15 (12/09 - No. 15, 5/10) numbering continued; Lim-a 4.00

ANNE RICE'S INTERVIEW WITH THE VAMPIRE
Innovation Books: 1991 - No. 12, Jan, 1994 ($2.50, limited series)

1-12: Adapts novel; Moeller-a 3.00

ANNE RICE'S THE MASTER OF RAMPLING GATE
Innovation Books: 1991 ($6.95, one-shot)

1-Bolton painted-c; Colleen Doran painted-a 7.00

ANNE RICE'S THE MUMMY OR RAMSES THE DAMNED
Millennium Publications: Oct, 1990 - No. 12, Feb, 1992 ($2.50, limited series)

1-12: Adapts novel; Mooney-p in all 3.00

ANNE RICE'S THE WITCHING HOUR
Millennium Publ./Comico: 1992 - No. 13, Jan, 1993 ($2.50, limited series)

1-13 3.00

ANNETTE (Disney, TV)
Dell Publishing Co.: No. 905, May, 1958; No. 1100, May, 1960 (Mickey Mouse Club)

Four Color 905-Annette Funicello photo-c 21 42 63 147 324 500
Four Color 1100-...'s Life Story (Movie); A. Funicello photo-c 17 34 51 117 259 400

ANNEX (See Amazing Spider-Man Annual #27 for 1st app.)
Marvel Comics: Aug, 1994 - No. 4, Nov, 1994 ($1.75)

1-4: 1,4-Spider-Man app. 3.00

ANNIE
Marvel Comics Group: Oct, 1982 - No. 2, Nov, 1982 (60¢)

1,2-Movie adaptation 4.00

Annie Oakley and Tagg #13 © DELL

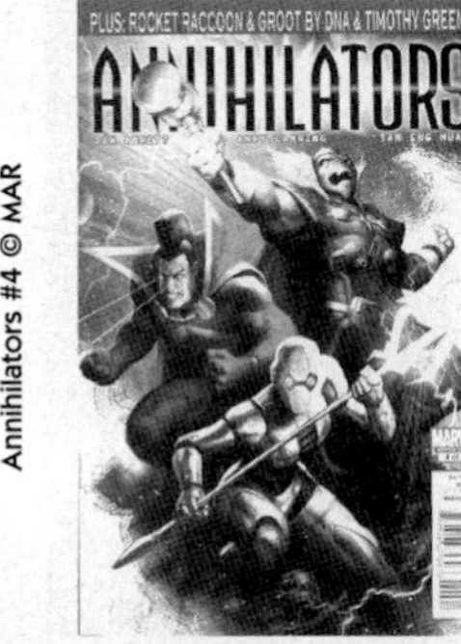

Annihilators #4 © MAR

A-1 Comics #27 © ME

	GD 2.0	VG 4.0	FN 6.0	VF 8.0	VF/NM 9.0	NM- 9.2

Treasury Edition ($2.00, tabloid size) 3 6 9 17 26 35

ANNIE OAKLEY (See Tessie The Typist #19, Two-Gun Kid & Wild Western)
Marvel/Atlas Comics(MPI No. 1-4/CDS No. 5 on): Spring, 1948 - No. 4, 11/48; No. 5, 6/55 - No. 11, 6/56

1 (1st Series, 1948)-Hedy Devine app. 58 116 174 371 636 900
2 (7/48, 52 pgs.)-Kurtzman-a, "Hey Look", 1 pg; Intro. Lana; Hedy Devine app; Captain Tootsie by Beck 36 72 108 211 343 475
3,4 28 56 84 165 270 375
5 (2nd Series, 1955)-Reinman-a; Maneely-c 21 42 63 122 199 275
6-9: 6,8-Woodbridge-a. 9-Williamson-a (4 pgs.) 15 30 45 85 130 175
10,11: 11-Severin-c 14 28 42 82 121 160

ANNIE OAKLEY AND TAGG (TV)
Dell Publishing Co./Gold Key: 1953 - No. 18, Jan-Mar, 1959; July, 1965 (Gail Davis photo-c #3 on)

Four Color 438 (#1) 13 26 39 89 195 300
Four Color 481,575 (#2,3) 9 18 27 59 117 175
4(7-9/55)-10 7 14 21 46 86 125
11-18(1-3/59) 6 12 18 38 69 100
1(7/65-Gold Key)-Photo-c (c-r/#6) 4 8 12 27 44 60
NOTE: ***Manning** a-13. Photo back c-4, 9, 11.*

ANNIHILATION
Marvel Comics: May, 2006 - No. 6, Mar, 2007 ($3.99/$2.99, limited x-over series)

Prologue (5/06, $3.99, one-shot) Nova, Thanos and Silver Surfer app. 4.00
1-6: 1-(10/06) Giffen-s/DiVito-a; Annihilus app. 3.00
...: Heralds of Galactus 1,2 (4/07-5/07, $3.99) 2-Silver Surfer app. 4.00
...: Nova 1-4 (6/06-9/06, $2.99) Abnett & Lanning-s/Walker-a/Dell'Otto-c. 2,3-Quasar app. 3.00
...: Ronan 1-4 (6/06-9/06, $2.99) Furman-s/Lucas-a/Dell'Otto-c 3.00
... Saga (2007, $1.99) re-cap of the series; DiVito-c 3.00
...: Silver Surfer 1-4 (6/06-9/06, $2.99) Giffen-s/Arlem-a/Dell'Otto-c 3.00
...: Super-Skrull 1-4 (6/06-9/06, $2.99) Grillo-Marxuach-s/Titus-a/Dell'Otto-c 3.00
...: The Nova Corps Files (2006, $3.99) profile pages of characters and alien races 4.00
Annihilation Book 1 HC (2007, $29.99, dustjacket) r/Drax the Destroyer #1-4, Annihilation Prologue and Annihilation: Nova #1-4; sketch and layout pages 30.00
Annihilation Book 1 SC (2007, $24.99) same content as HC 25.00
Annihilation Book 2 HC (2007, $29.99, dustjacket) r/Annihilation: Silver Surfer #1-4, ...: Super Skrull #1-4 and ...: Ronan #1-4; sketch and layout pages 30.00
Annihilation Book 2 SC (2007, $24.99) same content as HC 25.00
Annihilation Book 3 HC (2007, $29.99, dustjacket) r/Annihilation #1-6, Annihilation: Heralds of Galactus #1,2 and Annihilation: Nova Corps Files; sketch pages 30.00
Annihilation Book 3 SC (2007, $24.99) same content as HC 25.00

ANNIHILATION: CONQUEST (Also see Nova 2007 series)
Marvel Comics: Jan, 2008 - No. 6, Jun, 2008 ($3.99/$2.99, limited x-over series)

Prologue (8/07, $3.99, one-shot) the new Quasar, Moondragon app.; Perkins-a 5.00
1-5-Raney-a; Ultron app. 3-Moondragon dies 5.00
6-($3.99) Guardians of the Galaxy team forms 3 6 9 16 23 30
... - Quasar 1-4 (9/07-No. 4, 12/07, $2.99) Gage-s/Lilly-a. 1-Super-Adaptoid app. 3.00
... - Starlord 1-4 (9/07-No. 4, 12/07, $2.99) Giffen-s/Green-a 6.00
... - Wraith 1-4 (9/07-No. 4, 12/07, $2.99) Hotz-a/Grillo-Marxuach-s 3.00
Annihilation: Conquest Book 1 HC (2008, $29.99, dustjacket) r/Prologue; ...Quasar #1-4, ...Star-Lord #1-4; Annihilation Saga; design pages 30.00

ANNIHILATOR
Legendary Comics: Sept, 2014 - No. 6, Jun, 2015 ($3.99)

1-6-Grant Morrison-s/Frazer Irving-a/c 4.00

ANNIHILATORS
Marvel Comics: May, 2011 - No. 4, Aug, 2011 ($4.99, limited series)

1-4: Quasar, Silver Surfer, Beta-Ray Bill, Ronan, Gladiator app.; Huat-a 5.00

ANNIHILATORS: EARTHFALL
Marvel Comics: Nov, 2011 - No. 4, Feb, 2012 ($3.99, limited series)

1-4-Avengers app.; Abnett & Lanning-s/Huat-a/Christopher-c 4.00

ANNO DRACULA: 1895 SEVEN DAYS IN MAYHEM (Based on the Kim Newman novels)
Titan Comics: Apr, 2017 - No. 5, Sept, 2017 ($3.99, limited series)

1-5-Kim Newman-s/Paul McCaffrey-a; multiple covers on each 4.00

ANOTHER WORLD (See Strange Stories From...)

ANSWER!, THE
Dark Horse Comics: Jan, 2013 - No. 4 ($3.99, limited series)

1-3-Dennis Hopeless-s/Mike Norton-a 4.00

ANT
Image Comics: Aug, 2005 - No. 11 ($2.99)

	GD 2.0	VG 4.0	FN 6.0	VF 8.0	VF/NM 9.0	NM- 9.2

1-11: 1-Mario Gulley-s/a. 2-Savage Dragon & Spawn app. 3-Spawn-c/app. 3.00
Vol. 1: Reality Bites TPB (2006, $12.99) r/#1-4; sketch and concept art 13.00

ANTHRO (See Showcase #74)
National Periodical Publications: July-Aug, 1968 - No. 6, July-Aug, 1969

1-(7-8/68)-Howie Post-a in all 5 10 15 33 57 80
2-5: 5-Last 12¢ issue 3 6 9 21 33 45
6-Wood-c/a (inks) 4 8 12 23 37 50

ANTI-HITLER COMICS
New England Comics Press: Summer, 1992 ($2.75, B&W, one-shot)

1-Reprints Hitler as Devil stories from wartime comics 6.00

ANT-MAN (See Irredeemable Ant-Man, The)

ANT-MAN (Also see Astonishing Ant-Man)
Marvel Comics: Mar, 2015 - No. 5, Jul, 2015 ($3.99)

1-($4.99) Scott Lang as Ant-Man; Spencer-s/Rosanas-a; main-c by Brooks 5.00
2-5-($3.99) 2,3-Taskmaster app. 4-Darren Cross returns 4.00
Annual 1 (9/15, $4.99) Giant-Man & Egghead app.; intro. Raz Malhotra 5.00
...: Larger Than Life 1 (8/15, $3.99) movie Hank Pym story; r/Tales to Astonish #27 & #35 4.00
...: Last Days 1 (10/15, $3.99) Secret Wars tie-in; Spencer-s; Miss Patroit app. 4.00

ANT-MAN & WASP
Marvel Comics: Jan, 2011 - No. 3, Mar, 2011 ($3.99, limited series)

1-3-Tim Seeley-s/a; Espin-c; Tigra app. 5.00

ANT-MAN'S BIG CHRISTMAS
Marvel Comics: Feb, 2000 ($5.95, square-bound, one-shot)

1-Bob Gale-s/Phil Winslade-a; Avengers app. 6.00

ANT-MAN: SEASON ONE
Marvel Comics: 2012 ($24.99, hardcover graphic novel)

HC - Origin story; DeFalco-s/Domingues-a/Tedesco painted-c 25.00

ANTONY AND CLEOPATRA (See Ideal, a Classical Comic)

ANYTHING GOES
Fantagraphics Books: Oct, 1986 - No. 6, 1987 ($2.00, #1-5 color & B&W/#6 B&W, lim. series)

1-6: 1-Flaming Carrot app. (1st in color?); G. Kane-c. 2-6: 2-Miller-c(p); Alan Moore scripts; Kirby-a; early Sam Kieth-a (2 pgs.). 3-Capt. Jack, Cerebus app.; Cerebus-c by N. Adams. 4-Perez-c. 5-3rd color Teenage Mutant Ninja Turtles app. 3.50

A-1
Marvel Comics (Epic Comics): 1992 - No. 4, 1993 ($5.95, limited series, mature)

1-4: 1-Fabry-c/a, Russell-a, S. Hampton-a. 3-Bisley-c; Kent Williams-a. 4-McKean-a; Dorman-s/a 1 2 3 4 5 7

A-1 COMICS (A-1 appears on covers No. 1-17 only)(See individual title listings for #11-139) (1st two issues not numbered.)
Life's Romances Publ.-No. 1/Compix/Magazine Ent.: 1944 - No. 139, Sept-Oct, 1955 (No #2)

nn-(1944) (See Kerry Drake Detective Cases)
1-Dotty Dripple (1 pg.), Mr. Ex, Bush Berry, Rocky, Lew Loyal (20 pgs.) 20 40 60 115 185 255
3-8,10: Texas Slim & Dirty Dalton, The Corsair, Teddy Rich, Dotty Dripple, Inca Dinca, Tommy Tinker, Little Mexico & Tugboat Tim, The Masquerader & others. 7-Corsair-c/s. 8-Intro Rodeo Ryan 12 24 36 69 97 125
9-All Texas Slim 13 26 39 72 101 130

(See Individual Alphabetical listings for prices)

11-Teena; Ogden Whitney-c
13-Guns of Fact & Fiction (1948). Used in **SOTI**, pg. 19; Ingels & Johnny Craig-a
17-Tim Holt #2; photo-c; last issue to carry A-1 on cover (9-10/48)
19-Tim Holt #3; photo-c
22-Dick Powell (1949)-Photo-c
23-Cowboys and Indians #6; Doc Holiday-c/story
25-Fibber McGee & Molly (1949) (Radio)
26-Trail Colt #2-Ingels-c
28-Christmas-(Koko & Kola #6) ("50)
30-Jet Powers #1-Powell-a
32-Jet Powers #2
33-Muggsy Mouse #1('51)
35-Jet Powers #3-Williamson/Evans-a
37-Ghost Rider #5-Frazetta-c (1951)
39-Muggsy Mouse #3
12,15-Teena
14-Tim Holt Western Adventures #1
16-Vacation Comics; The Pixies, Tom Tom, Flying Fredd, & Koko & Kola
18,20-Jimmy Durante; photo covers on both
21-Joan of Arc (1949)-Movie adaptation; Ingrid Bergman photo-covers & interior photos; Whitney-a
24-Trail Colt #1-Frazetta-r in-Manhunt #13; Ingels-c; L. B. Cole-a
27-Ghost Rider #1(1950)-Origin
29-Ghost Rider #2-Frazetta-c (1950)
31-Ghost Rider #3-Frazetta-c & origin ('51)
34-Ghost Rider #4-Frazetta-c (1951)
36-Muggsy Mouse #2; Racist-c
38-Jet Powers #4-Williamson/Wood-a
40-Dogface Dooley #1('51)

A-1 Comics #64 © ME

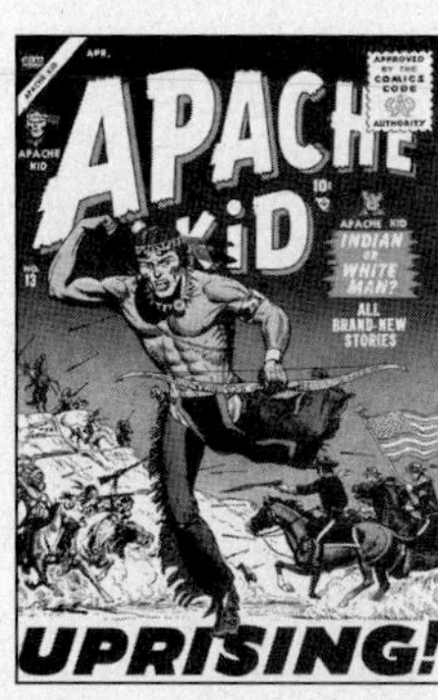

Apache Kid #13 © MAR

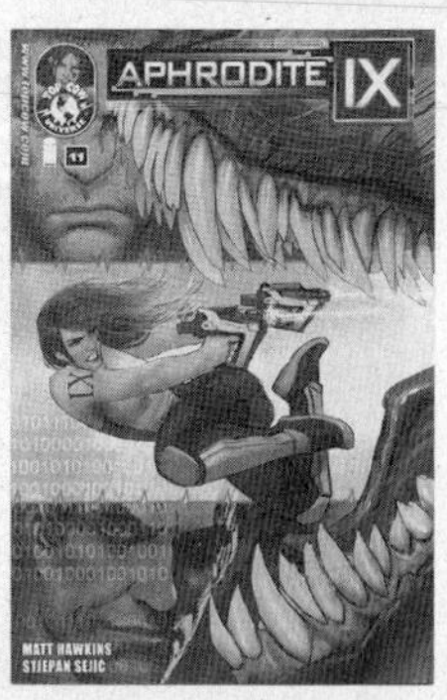

Aphrodite IX V2 #11 © TCOW

	GD 2.0	VG 4.0	FN 6.0	VF 8.0	VF/NM 9.0	NM- 9.2

41-Cowboys 'N' Indians #7 (1951)
42-Best of the West #1-Powell-a
43-Dogface Dooley #2
44-Ghost Rider #6
45-American Air Forces #5-Powell-c/a
46-Best of the West #2
47-Thun'da, King of the Congo #1-Frazetta-c/a('52)
48-Cowboys 'N' Indians #8
49-Dogface Dooley #3
50-Danger Is Their Business #11 ('52)-Powell-a
51-Ghost Rider #7 ('52)
52-Best of the West #3
53-Dogface Dooley #4
54-American Air Forces #6(8/52)-Powell-a
55-U.S. Marines #5-Powell-a
56-Thun'da #2-Powell-c/a
57-Ghost Rider #8
58-American Air Forces #7-Powell-a
59-Best of the West #4
60-The U.S. Marines #6-Powell-a
61-Space Ace #5('53)-Guardineer-a
62-Starr Flagg, Undercover Girl #5 (#1) reprinted from A-1 #24
63-Manhunt #13-Frazetta
64-Dogface Dooley #5
65-American Air Forces #8-Powell-a
66-Best of the West #5
67-American Air Forces #9-Powell-a
68-U.S. Marines #7-Powell-a
69-Ghost Rider #9(10/52)
70-Best of the West #6
71-Ghost Rider #10(12/52)-Vs. Frankenstein
72-U.S. Marines #8-Powell-a(3)
73-Thun'da #3-Powell-c/a
74-American Air Forces #10-Powell-a
75-Ghost Rider #11(3/52)
76-Best of the West #7
77-Manhunt #14
78-Thun'da #4-Powell-c/a
79-American Air Forces #11-Powell-a
80-Ghost Rider #12(6/52)-One-eyed Devil-c
81-Best of the West #8
82-Cave Girl #11(1953)-Powell-c/a; origin (#1)
83-Thun'da #5-Powell-c/a
84-Ghost Rider #13(7-8/53)
85-Best of the West #9
86-Thun'da #6-Powell-c/a
87-Best of the West #10(9-10/53)
88-Bobby Benson's B-Bar-B Riders #20
89-Home Run #3-Powell-a; Stan Musial photo-c
90-Red Hawk #11(1953)-Powell-c/a
91-American Air Forces #12-Powell-a
92-Dream Book of Romance #5-Photo-c; Guardineer-a
93-Great Western #8('54)-Origin The Ghost Rider; Powell-a
94-White Indian #11-Frazetta-a(r); Powell-c
95-Muggsy Mouse #4
96-Cave Girl #12, with Thun'da; Powell-c/a
97-Best of the West #11
98-Undercover Girl #6-Powell-c
99-Muggsy Mouse #5
100-Badmen of the West #1-Meskin-a(?)
101-White Indian #12-Frazetta-a(r)
101-Dream Book of Romance #6 (4-6/54); Marlon Brando photo-c; Powell, Bolle, Guardineer-a
103-Best of the West #12-Powell-a
104-White Indian #13-Frazetta-a(r) ('54)
105-Great Western #9-Ghost Rider app.; Powell-a, 6 pgs.; Bolle-c
106-Dream Book of Love #1 (6-7/54) -Powell, Bolle-a; Montgomery Clift, Donna Reed photo-c
107-Hot Dog #1
108-Red Fox #15 (1954)-L.B. Cole-c/a; Powell-a
109-Dream Book of Romance #7 (7-8/54). Powell-a; movie photo-c
110-Dream Book of Romance #8 (10/54)-Movie photo-c
111-I'm a Cop #1 ('54); drug mention story; Powell-a
112-Ghost Rider #14 ('54)
113-Great Western #10; Powell-a
114-Dream Book of Love #2- Guardineer, Bolle-a; Piper Laurie, Victor Mature photo-c
115-Hot Dog #3
116-Cave Girl #13-Powell-c/a
117-White Indian #14
118-Undercover Girl #7-Powell-c
119-Straight Arrow's Fury #1 (origin); Fred Meagher-c/a
120-Badmen of the West #2
121-Mysteries of Scotland Yard #1; reprinted from Manhunt (5 stories)
122-Black Phantom #1 (11/54)
123-Dream Book of Love #3 (10-11/54)-Movie photo-c
124-Dream Book of Romance #8 (10-11/54)
125-Cave Girl #14-Powell-c/a
126-I'm a Cop #2-Powell-a
127-Great Western #11('54)-Powell-a
128-I'm a Cop #3-Powell-a
129-The Avenger #1('55)-Powell-c
130-Strongman #1-Powell-a (2-3/55)
131-The Avenger #2('55)-Powell-c/a
132-Strongman #2
133-The Avenger #3-Powell-c/a
134-Strongman #3
135-White Indian #15
136-Hot Dog #4
137-Africa #1-Powell-c/a(4)
138-The Avenger #4-Powell-c/a
139-Strongman #4-Powell-a

NOTE: *Bolle a-110. Photo-c-17-22, 89, 92, 101, 106, 109, 110, 114, 123, 124.*

APACHE
Fiction House Magazines: 1951

	GD 2.0	VG 4.0	FN 6.0	VF 8.0	VF/NM 9.0	NM- 9.2
1	23	46	69	136	223	310
I.W. Reprint No. 1-r/#1 above	3	6	9	17	26	35

APACHE KID (Formerly Reno Browne; Western Gunfighters #20 on)
(Also see Two-Gun Western & Wild Western)
Marvel/Atlas Comics(MPC No. 53-10/CPS No. 11 on): No. 53, 12/50 - No. 10, 1/52; No. 11, 12/54 - No. 19, 4/56

	GD 2.0	VG 4.0	FN 6.0	VF 8.0	VF/NM 9.0	NM- 9.2
53(#1)-Apache Kid & his horse Nightwind (origin), Red Hawkins by Syd Shores begins	39	78	117	240	395	550
2(2/51)	19	38	57	111	176	240
3-5	14	28	42	82	121	160
6-10 (1951-52): 7-Russ Heath-a	13	26	39	72	101	130
11-19 (1954-56)	11	22	33	60	83	105

NOTE: *Heath a-7. c-11, 13.* ***Maneely*** *a-53; c-53(#1), 12, 14-16.* ***Powell*** *a-14.* ***Severin*** *c-17.*

APACHE MASSACRE (See Chief Victorio's...)

APACHE SKIES
Marvel Comics: Sept, 2002 - No. 4, Dec, 2002 ($2.99, limited series)

	GD 2.0	VG 4.0	FN 6.0	VF 8.0	VF/NM 9.0	NM- 9.2
1-4-Apache Kid app.; Ostrander-s/Manco-c/a						3.00
TPB (2003, $12.99) r/#1-4						13.00

APACHE TRAIL
Steinway/America's Best: Sept, 1957 - No. 4, June, 1958

	GD 2.0	VG 4.0	FN 6.0	VF 8.0	VF/NM 9.0	NM- 9.2
1	11	22	33	64	90	115
2-4: 2-Tuska-a	8	16	24	40	50	60

APE (Magazine)
Dell Publishing Co.: 1961 (52 pgs., B&W)

	GD 2.0	VG 4.0	FN 6.0	VF 8.0	VF/NM 9.0	NM- 9.2
1-Comics and humor	5	10	15	30	50	70

APHRODITE IX
Image Comics (Top Cow): Sept, 2000 - No. 4, Mar, 2002 ($2.50)

	GD 2.0	VG 4.0	FN 6.0	VF 8.0	VF/NM 9.0	NM- 9.2
1-3: 1-Four covers by Finch, Turner, Silvestri, Benitez						4.00
1-Tower Record Ed.; Finch-c						3.00
1-DF Chrome ($14.99)						15.00
4-($4.95) Double-sized issue; Finch-c						5.00
Convention Preview						10.00
...: Time Out of Mind TPB (6/04, $14.99) r/#1-4, & #0; cover gallery						15.00
Wizard #0 (4/00, bagged w/Tomb Raider magazine) Preview & sketchbook						5.00
#0-(6/01, $2.95) r/Wizard #0 with cover gallery						3.00

APHRODITE IX (Volume 2)
Image Comics (Top Cow): May, 2013 - No. 11, Jun, 2014 ($2.99/$3.99)

	GD 2.0	VG 4.0	FN 6.0	VF 8.0	VF/NM 9.0	NM- 9.2
1-Free Comic Book Day giveaway; Hawkins-s/Sejic-a						3.00
2-10-($2.99) Hawkins-s/Sejic-a						3.00
11-($3.99) Leads into Aphrodite IX Cyber Force #1						4.00
... Cyber Force #1 (7/14, $5.99) Hawkins-s/Sejic-a; leads into IXth Generation #1						6.00
... Hidden Files 1 (1/14, $2.99) Character profiles; Sejic-a						3.00

A+X (Avengers Plus X-Men)
Marvel Comics: Dec, 2012 - No. 18, May, 2014 ($3.99)

	GD 2.0	VG 4.0	FN 6.0	VF 8.0	VF/NM 9.0	NM- 9.2
1-18: 1-Hulk & Wolverine team-up; Keown-c. 2-Black Widow/Rogue; Bachalo-c/a. 14-Superior Spider-Man app.						4.00
1-Variant baby-c by Skottie Young						5.00

APOCALYPSE AL
Image Comics: Feb, 2014 - No. 4 ($2.99, B&W)

	GD 2.0	VG 4.0	FN 6.0	VF 8.0	VF/NM 9.0	NM- 9.2
1-3-Straczynski-s/Kotian-a; 2 covers on each						3.00

APOCALYPSE NERD
Dark Horse Comics: January, 2005 - No. 6, Oct, 2007 ($2.99, B&W)

	GD 2.0	VG 4.0	FN 6.0	VF 8.0	VF/NM 9.0	NM- 9.2
1-6-Peter Bagge-s/a						3.00

APOLLO IX (See Aphrodite IX)
Image Comics (Top Cow): Aug, 2015 ($3.99, one-shot)

	GD 2.0	VG 4.0	FN 6.0	VF 8.0	VF/NM 9.0	NM- 9.2
1-Ashley Robinson-s/Fernando Argosino-a; 2 covers						4.00

APPARITION
Caliber Comics: 1995 ($3.95, 52 pgs., B&W)

	GD 2.0	VG 4.0	FN 6.0	VF 8.0	VF/NM 9.0	NM- 9.2
1 ($3.95)						4.00
V2#1-6 ($2.95)						3.00
Visitations						4.00

APPLESEED
Eclipse Comics: Sept, 1988 - Book 4, Vol. 4, Aug, 1991 ($2.50/$2.75/$3.50, 52/68 pgs, B&W)

	GD 2.0	VG 4.0	FN 6.0	VF 8.0	VF/NM 9.0	NM- 9.2
Book One, Vol. 1-5: 5-(1/89), Book Two, Vol. 1(2/89) -5(7/89): Art Adams-c, Book Three, Vol. 1(8/89) -4 ($2.75), Book Three, Vol. 5 ($3.50), Book Four, Vol. 1 (1/91) - 4 (8/91) ($3.50, 68 pgs.)						6.00

APPLESEED DATABOOK
Dark Horse Comics: Apr, 1994 - No. 2, May, 1994 ($3.50, B&W, limited series)

	GD 2.0	VG 4.0	FN 6.0	VF 8.0	VF/NM 9.0	NM- 9.2
1,2: 1-Flip book format						4.00

APPROVED COMICS (Also see Blue Ribbon Comics)
St. John Publishing Co. (Most have no c-price): March, 1954 - No. 12, Aug, 1954 (Painted-c on #1-5,7,8,10)

Approved Comics #11 © STJ

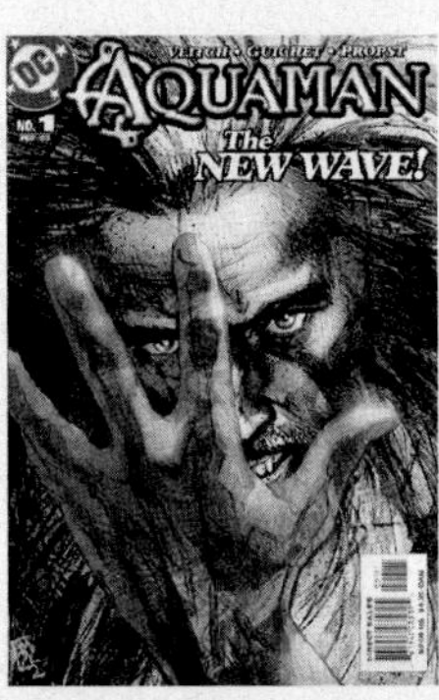

Aquaman (2003 series) #1 © DC

Aquaman (2016 series) #25 © DC

	GD 2.0	VG 4.0	FN 6.0	VF 8.0	VF/NM 9.0	NM- 9.2
1-The Hawk #5-r	10	20	30	56	76	95
2-Invisible Boy (3/54)-Origin; Saunders-c	16	32	48	92	144	195
3-Wild Boy of the Congo #11-r (4/54)	10	20	30	56	76	95
4,5: 4-Kid Cowboy-r. 5-Fly Boy-r	10	20	30	56	76	95
6-Daring Adv.-r (5/54); Krigstein-a(2); Baker-c	15	30	45	85	130	175
7-The Hawk #6-r	10	20	30	56	76	95
8-Crime on the Run (6/54); Powell-a; Saunders-c	10	20	30	56	76	95
9-Western Bandit Trails #3-r, with new-c; Baker-c/a	18	36	54	105	165	225
10-Dinky Duck (Terrytoons)	7	14	21	35	43	50
11-Fightin' Marines #3-r (8/54); Canteen Kate app; Baker-c/a	20	40	60	117	189	260
12-Northwest Mounties #4-r(8/54); new Baker-c	18	36	54	105	165	225

AQUAMAN (See Adventure Comics #260, Brave & the Bold, DC Comics Presents #5, DC Special #28, DC Special Series #1, DC Super Stars #7, Detective Comics, JLA, Justice League of America, More Fun #73, Showcase #30-33, Super DC Giant, Super Friends, and World's Finest Comics)

AQUAMAN (1st Series)
National Periodical Publications/DC Comics: Jan-Feb, 1962 - No. 56, Mar-Apr, 1971; No. 57, Aug-Sept, 1977 - No. 63, Aug-Sept, 1978

	GD 2.0	VG 4.0	FN 6.0	VF 8.0	VF/NM 9.0	NM- 9.2
1-(1-2/62)-Intro. Quisp	166	332	498	1370	3085	4800
2	34	68	102	245	548	850
3-5	21	42	63	147	324	500
6-10	14	28	42	96	211	325
11-1st app. Mera	54	108	162	432	966	1500
12-17,19,20	11	22	33	76	163	250
18-Aquaman weds Mera; JLA cameo	14	28	42	96	211	325
21-28,30-32: 23-Birth of Aquababy. 26-Huntress app.(3-4/66). 30-Batman & Superman-c & cameo	8	16	24	52	99	145
29-1st app. Ocean Master, Aquaman's step-brother	37	74	111	274	612	950
33-1st app. Aqua-Girl (see Adventure #266)	13	26	39	89	195	300
34,36-40: 40-Jim Aparo's 1st DC work (8/68)	6	12	18	42	79	115
35-1st app. Black Manta	54	108	162	432	966	1500
41,43-46,47,49: 45-Last 12¢-c	6	12	18	37	66	95
42-Black Manta-c	12	24	36	79	170	260
48-Origin reprinted	6	12	18	38	69	100
50-52-Deadman by Neal Adams	8	16	24	51	96	140
53-56('71): 56-1st app. Crusader; last 15¢-c	3	6	9	21	33	45
57-('77) Black Manta-c	3	6	9	14	20	25
58-63: 58-Origin retold	2	4	6	9	12	15
...: Death of a Prince TPB (2011, $29.99) r/#58-63 and Adventure #435-437,441-455						30.00

NOTE: ***Aparo** a-40-45, 46p, 47-59; c-58-63.* ***Nick Cardy** c-1-40.* ***Newton** a-60-63.*

AQUAMAN (1st limited series)
DC Comics: Feb, 1986 - No. 4, May, 1986 (75¢, limited series)

	GD 2.0	VG 4.0	FN 6.0	VF 8.0	VF/NM 9.0	NM- 9.2
1-New costume; 1st app. Nuada of Thierna Na Oge	1	3	4	6	8	10
2-4: 3-Retelling of Aquaman & Ocean Master's origins.						5.00
Special 1 (1988, $1.50, 52 pgs.)						4.00

NOTE: ***Craig Hamilton** c/a-1-4p.* ***Russell** c-2-4i.*

AQUAMAN (2nd limited series)
DC Comics: June, 1989 - No. 5, Oct, 1989 ($1.00, limited series)

	NM- 9.2
1-5: Giffen plots/breakdowns; Swan-a(p).	4.00
Special 1 (Legend of..., $2.00, 1989, 52 pgs.)-Giffen plots/breakdowns; Swan-a(p)	4.00

AQUAMAN (2nd Series)
DC Comics: Dec, 1991 - No. 13, Dec, 1992 ($1.00/$1.25)

	NM- 9.2
1-5	3.00
6-13: 6-Begin $1.25-c. 9-Sea Devils app.	3.00

AQUAMAN (3rd Series)(Also see Atlantis Chronicles)
DC Comics: Aug, 1994 - No. 75, Jan, 2001 ($1.50/$1.75/$1.95/$1.99/$2.50)

	NM- 9.2
1-(8/94)-Peter David scripts begin; reintro Dolphin	6.00
2-(9/94)-Aquaman loses hand	6.50
0-(10/94)-Aquaman replaces lost hand with hook.	6.50
3-8: 3-(11/94)-Superboy-c/app. 4-Lobo app. 6-Deep Six app.	3.50
9-69: 9-Begin $1.75-c. 10-Green Lantern app. 11-Reintro Mera. 15-Re-intro Kordax. 16-vs. JLA. 18-Reintro Ocean Master & Atlan (Aquaman's father). 19-Reintro Garth (Aqualad). 23-1st app. Deep Blue (Neptune Perkins & Tsunami's daughter). 23,24-Neptune Perkins, Nuada, Tsunami, Arion, Power Girl, & The Sea Devils app. 26-Final Night. 28-Martian Manhunter-c/app. 29-Black Manta-c/app. 32-Swamp Thing-c/app. 37-Genesis x-over. 41-Maxima-c/app. 43-Millennium Giants x-over; Superman-c/app. 44-G.A. Flash & Sentinel app. 50-Larsen-s begins. 53-Superman app. 60-Tempest marries Dolphin; Teen Titans app. 63-Kaluta covers begin. 66-JLA app.	3.00
70-75: 70-Begin $2.50-c. 71-73-Warlord-c/app. 75-Final issue	3.00
#1,000,000 (11/98) 853rd Century x-over	3.00
Annual 1 (1995, $3.50)-Year One story	4.00
Annual 2 (1996, $2.95)-Legends of the Dead Earth story	4.00
Annual 3 (1997, $3.95)-Pulp Heroes story	4.00
Annual 4,5 ('98, '99, $2.95)-4-Ghosts; Wrightson-c. 5-JLApe	4.00
...Secret Files 1 (12/98, $4.95) Origin-s and pin-ups	5.00

NOTE: ***Art Adams**-c, Annual 5.* ***Mignola** c-6.* ***Simonson** c-15.*

AQUAMAN (4th Series)(Titled Aquaman: Sword of Atlantis #40-on) (Also see JLA #69-75)
DC Comics: Feb, 2003 - No. 57, Dec, 2007 ($2.50/$2.99)

	NM- 9.2
1-Veitch-s/Guichet-a/Maleev-c	4.00
2-14: 2-Martian Manhunter app. 8-11-Black Manta app.	3.00
15-39: 15-San Diego flooded; Pfeifer-s/Davis-c begin. 23,24-Sea Devils app. 33-Mera returns. 39-Black Manta app.	3.00
40-Sword of Atlantis; One Year Later begins ($2.99-c) Guice-a ; two covers	4.00
41-49,51-57: 41-Two covers. 42-Sea Devils app. 44-Ocean Master app.	3.00
50-($3.99) Tempest app.; McManus-a	4.00
...Secret Files 2003 (5/03, $4.95) background on Aquaman's new powers; pin-ups	5.00
...: Once and Future TPB (2006, $12.99) r/#40-45	13.00
...: The Waterbearer TPB (2003, $12.95) r/#1-4, stories from Aquaman Secret Files and JLA/JSA Secret Files #1; JG Jones-c	13.00

AQUAMAN (DC New 52)
DC Comics: Nov, 2011 - No. 52, Jul, 2016 ($2.99/$3.99)

	GD 2.0	VG 4.0	FN 6.0	VF 8.0	VF/NM 9.0	NM- 9.2
1-Geoff Johns-s/Ivan Reis-a/c	1	2	3	4	5	7
2-23,24,26-40: 7-13-Black Manta app. 14-17-Throne of Atlantis. 15,16-Justice League app. 24-Story of Atlan. 26-Pelletier-a. 31-Swamp Thing app. 37-Grodd app.						3.00
23.1, 23.2 (11/13, $2.99, regular covers)						3.00
23.1 (11/13, $3.99, 3-D cover) "Black Manta #1" on cover; Crime Syndicate app.						5.00
23.2 (11/13, $3.99, 3-D cover) "Ocean Master #1" on cover; Crime Syndicate app.						5.00
25-($3.99) "Death of a King" finale; last Johns-s						4.00
41-49,51,52: 41-($3.99-c begin)						4.00
50-($4.99) Booth-a						5.00
#0 (11/12, $2.99) Aquaman & Vulko's return to Atlantis; Johns-s/Reis-a/c						3.00
Annual 1 (12/13, $4.99) The Others app.; Pelletier-c/Ostrander-s						5.00
Annual 2 (9/14, $4.99) Wonder Woman app.; Parker-s/Guichet-a						5.00
...: Futures End 1 (11/14, $2.99, regular-c) Five years later; Jurgens-s						3.00
...: Futures End 1 (11/14, $3.99, 3-D cover)						4.00

AQUAMAN (DC Rebirth) (Also see Mera: Queen of Atlantis)
DC Comics: Aug, 2016 - Present ($2.99/$3.99)

	NM- 9.2
1-24: 1-Abnett-s/Walker-a; Black Manta app. 5,6-Superman app. 14,15-Black Manta app.	3.00
25-33-($3.99) 25-Sejic-a; leads into Justice League #24	4.00
...: Rebirth (8/16, $2.99) Abnett-s/Eaton & Jiménez-a; Black Manta app.	3.00
Annual 1 (1/18, $4.99) Fiumara-a; future Aquaman & Mera with son Tom	5.00

AQUAMAN AND THE OTHERS (DC New 52)
DC Comics: Jun, 2014 - No. 11, May, 2015 ($2.99)

	NM- 9.2
1-11: 1-Jurgens-s/Medina-a	3.00
...: Futures End 1 (11/14, $2.99, regular-c) Five years later; Cont'd from Aquaman: FE #1	3.00
...: Futures End 1 (11/14, $3.99, 3-D cover)	4.00

AQUAMAN: TIME & TIDE (3rd limited series) (Also see Atlantis Chronicles)
DC Comics: Dec, 1993 - No. 4, Mar, 1994 ($1.50, limited series)

	NM- 9.2
1-4: Peter David scripts; origin retold.	3.00
Trade paperback ($9.95)	10.00

AQUANAUTS (TV)
Dell Publishing Co.: May - July, 1961

	GD 2.0	VG 4.0	FN 6.0	VF 8.0	VF/NM 9.0	NM- 9.2
Four Color 1197-Photo-c	6	12	18	41	76	110

ARABIAN NIGHTS (See Cinema Comics Herald)

ARACHNOPHOBIA (Movie)
Hollywood Comics (Disney Comics): 1990 ($5.95, 68 pg. graphic novel)

	NM- 9.2
nn-Adaptation of film; Spiegle-a	6.00
Comic edition ($2.95, 68 pgs.)	4.00

ARAK/SON OF THUNDER (See Warlord #48)
DC Comics: Sept, 1981 - No. 50, Nov, 1985

	NM- 9.2
1,24,50: 1-1st app. Angelica, Princess of White Cathay. 24,50-(52 pgs.)	4.00
2-23,25-49: 3-Intro Valda. 12-Origin Valda. 20-Origin Angelica	3.00
Annual 1(10/84)	4.00

ARAÑA THE HEART OF THE SPIDER (See Amazing Fantasy (2004) #1-6)
Marvel Comics: March, 2005 - No. 12, Feb, 2006 ($2.99)

	NM- 9.2
1-12: 1-Avery-s/Cruz-a. 4-Spider-Man-c/app.	3.00
Vol. 1: Heart of the Spider (2005, $7.99, digest) r/Amazing Fantasy (2004) #1-6	8.00
Vol. 2: In the Beginning (2005, $7.99, digest) r/#1-6	8.00
Vol. 3: Night of the Hunter (2006, $7.99, digest) r/#7-12	8.00

Archard's Agents #1 © CRO

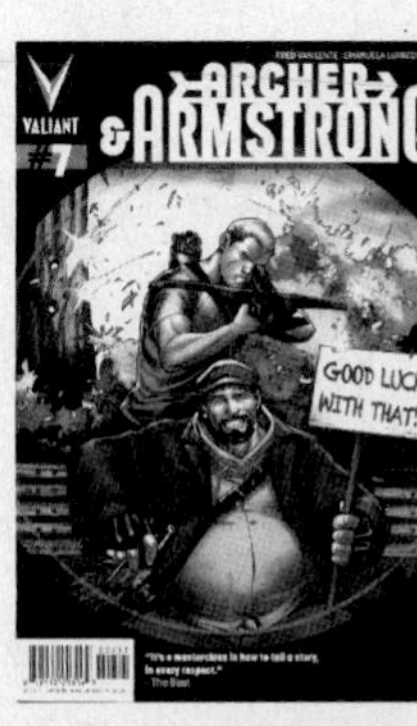

Archer & Armstrong (2012 series) #7 © VAL

Archie #14 © ACP

	GD 2.0	VG 4.0	FN 6.0	VF 8.0	VF/NM 9.0	NM- 9.2

ARCADIA
BOOM! Studios: May, 2015 - No. 8, Feb, 2016 ($3.99)
1-8-Paknadel-s/Pfeiffer-a 4.00

ARCANA (Also see Books of Magic limited & ongoing series and Mister E)
DC Comics (Vertigo): 1994 ($3.95, 68 pgs., annual)
1-Bolton painted-c; Children's Crusade/Tim Hunter story 4.00

ARCANUM
Image Comics (Top Cow Productions): Apr, 1997 - No. 8, Feb, 1998 ($2.50)
1/2 Gold Edition 12.00
1-Brandon Peterson-s/a(p), 1-Variant-c, 4-American Ent. Ed. 3.50
2-8 3.00
3-Variant-c 4.00
...: Millennium's End TPB (2005, $16.99) r/#1-8 & #1/2; cover gallery and sketch pages 17.00

ARCHANGEL (See Uncanny X-Men, X-Factor & X-Men)
Marvel Comics: Feb, 1996 ($2.50, B&W, one-shot)
1-Milligan story 3.00

ARCHARD'S AGENTS (See Ruse)
CrossGeneration Comics: Jan, 2003; Nov, 2003; Apr, 2004 ($2.95)
1-Dixon-s/Perkins-a 3.00
...: The Case of the Puzzled Pugilist (11/03) Dixon-s/Perkins-a 3.00
Vol. 3 - Deadly Dare (4/04) Dixon-s/McNiven-a; preview of Lady Death: The Wild Hunt 3.00

ARCHENEMIES
Dark Horse Comics: Apr, 2006 - No. 4, July, 2006 ($2.99, limited series)
1-4-Melbourne-s/Guichet-a 3.00

ARCHER & ARMSTRONG
Valiant: July (June inside), 1992 - No. 26, Oct, 1994 ($2.50)
0-(7/92)-B. Smith-c/a; Reese-i assists 6.00
0-(with Gold Valiant Logo) 5 10 15 34 60 85
1,2: 1-(8/92)-Origin & 1st app. Archer; Miller-c; B. Smith/Layton-a. 2-2nd app. Turok (c/story); Smith/Layton-a; Simonson-c 5.00
3-7: 3,4-Smith-c&a(p) & scripts 4.00
8-($4.50, 52 pgs.)-Combined with Eternal Warrior #8; B. Smith-c/a & scripts; 1st app. Ivar the Time Walker 5.00
9-26: 10-2nd app. Ivar. 10,11-B. Smith-c. 21,22-Shadowman app. 22-w/bound-in trading card. 25-Eternal Warrior app. 26-Flip book w/Eternal Warrior #26 3.00
...: First Impressions HC (2008, $24.95) recolored reprints #0-6; new "Formation of the Sect" story by Jim Shooter and Sal Velutto; Shooter commentary; new cover by Golden 25.00

ARCHER & ARMSTRONG
Valiant Entertainment: Aug, 2012 - No. 25, Oct, 2014 ($3.99)
1-24: 1-Van Lente-s/Henry-a; two covers; origin. 5-8-Eternal Warrior app. 4.00
1,4-8-Pullbox variants: 1-Clayton Henry. 4-Juan Doe. 7,8-Emanuela Lupacchino 4.00
1-Variant-c by David Aja 10.00
1-Variant-c by Neal Adams 25.00
25-($4.99) Van Lente-s/Henry-a; back-up short stories by various; cover gallery 5.00
#0-(5/13, $3.99) Van Lente-s/Henry-a 4.00
...Archer #0-(2/14, $3.99) Van Lente-s/Pere Pérez-a; childhood origin 4.00
...: The One Percent #1 (11/14, $3.99) Fawkes-s/Eisma-a/Juan Doe-c 4.00

ARCHIE (See Archie Comics) (Also see Afterlife With..., Christmas & Archie, Everything's..., Explorers of the Unknown, Jackpot, Life With..., Little..., Oxydol-Dreft, Pep, Riverdale High, Teenage Mutant Ninja Turtles Adventures & To Riverdale and Back Again)

ARCHIE
Archie Comic Publications: Sept, 2015 - Present ($3.99)
1-29-Mark Waid-s; multiple covers on all; back-up classic reprints. 1-3-Fiona Staples-a. 4-Annie Wu-a. 5-10-Veronica Fish-a. 13-Re-intro. Cheryl Blossom; back-up r/1st app. from B&V #320. 13-17-Eisma-a. 18-22-Pete Woods-a. 23-29-Audrey Mok-a 4.00
... Collector's Edition (2/16, $9.99) r/#1-3 with creator intros and variant cover gallery 10.00
FCBD Edition (2016, giveaway) r/#1; Staples-c; back-up Jughead story 3.00

ARCHIE ALL CANADIAN DIGEST
Archie Publications: Aug, 1996 ($1.75, 96 pgs.)
1 1 2 3 5 6 8

ARCHIE AMERICANA SERIES, BEST OF THE FORTIES
Archie Publications: 1991, 2002 ($10.95, trade paperback)
Vol. 1,2-r/early strips from 1940s 1-Intro. by Steven King. 2-Intro. by Paul Castiglia 12.00

ARCHIE AMERICANA SERIES, BEST OF THE FIFTIES
Archie Publications: 1991 ($8.95, trade paperback)
Vol. 2-r/strips from 1950's 12.00
2nd printing (1998, $9.95) 12.00

	GD 2.0	VG 4.0	FN 6.0	VF 8.0	VF/NM 9.0	NM- 9.2

Book 2 (2003, $10.95) 12.00

ARCHIE AMERICANA SERIES, BEST OF THE SIXTIES
Archie Publications: 1995 ($9.95, trade paperback)
Vol. 3-r/strips from 1960s; intro. by Frankie Avalon 12.00

ARCHIE AMERICANA SERIES, BEST OF THE SEVENTIES
Archie Publications: 1997, 2008 ($9.95/$10.95, trade paperback)
Vol. 4 (1997, $9.95)-r/strips from 1970s 12.00
Vol. 8 Book 2 (2008, $10.95)-r/other strips from 1970s 12.00

ARCHIE AMERICANA SERIES, BEST OF THE EIGHTIES
Archie Publications: 2001 ($10.95, trade paperback)
Vol. 5-r/strips from 1980s; foreward by Steve Geppi 12.00

ARCHIE AMERICANA SERIES, BEST OF THE '90S
Archie Publications: 2008 ($11.95, trade paperback)
Vol. 9-r/strips from 1990s; new Lindsey cover 12.00

ARCHIE AND BIG ETHEL
Spire Christian Comics (Fleming H. Revell Co.): 1982 (69¢)
nn-(Low print run) 2 4 6 13 18 22

ARCHIE & FRIENDS
Archie Comics: Dec, 1992 - No. 159, Feb, 2012 ($1.25-$2.99)
1 5.00
2,4,10-14,17,18,20-Sabrina app. 20-Archie's Band-c 4.00
3,5-9,16 3.00
15-Babewatch-s with Sabrina app. 6.00
19-Josie and the Pussycats app.; E.T. parody-c/s 5.00
21-46 3.00
47-All Josie and the Pussycats issue; movie and actress profiles/photos 4.00
48-142: 48-56,58,60,96-Josie and the Pussycats-c/s. 79-Cheryl Blossom returns. 100-The Veronicas-c/app. 101-Katy Keene begins. 129-Begin $2.50. 130,131-Josie and the Pussycats. 137-Cosmo, Super Duck, Pat the Brat and other old characters app. 3.00
143-159: 143-Begin $2.99-c. 145-Jersey Shore spoof. 146,147-Twilite. 154-Little Archie 3.00

ARCHIE & FRIENDS DOUBLE DIGEST MAGAZINE
Archie Comics: Feb, 2011 - No. 33, Jan, 2014 ($3.99, digest-size)
1-32: 1-Staton-a. 7-13-SuperTeens app. 4.00
33-($5.99, 320 pages) Double Double Digest 6.00

ARCHIE AND ME (See Archie Giant Series Mag. #578, 591, 603, 616, 626)
Archie Publications: Oct, 1964; No. 2, Aug, 1965 - No. 161, Feb, 1987
1 17 34 51 117 259 400
2-(8/65) 9 18 27 60 120 180
3-5: 3-(12/65) 6 12 18 40 73 105
6-10: 6-(8/66) 5 10 15 30 50 70
11-20: 11-(4/68) 3 6 9 21 33 45
21(6/68)-26,28-30: 21-UFO story. 26-X-Mas-c 3 6 9 16 24 32
27-Groovyman & Knowman superhero-s; UFO-sty 3 6 9 19 30 40
31-42: 37-Japan Expo '70-c/s 3 6 9 14 19 24
43-48,50-63-(All Giants): 43-(8/71) Mummy-s. 44-Mermaid-s. 62-Elvis cameo-c. 63-(2/74) 3 6 9 15 22 28
49-(Giant) Josie & the Pussycats-c/app. 3 6 9 20 31 42
64-66,68-99-(Regular size): 85-Bicentennial-s. 98-Collectors Comics 2 4 6 8 10 12
67-Sabrina app.(8/74) 2 4 6 10 14 18
100-(4/78) 2 4 6 8 11 14
101-120: 107-UFO-s 1 2 3 5 6 8
121(8/80)-159: 134-Riverdale 2001 6.00
160,161: 160-Origin Mr. Weatherbee; Caveman Archie gang story. 161-Last issue 1 2 3 5 6 8

ARCHIE & ME COMICS DIGEST
Archie Comics: Dec, 2017 - Present ($6.99, digest-size)
1-6-Reprints incl. Archie Babies 7.00

ARCHIE AND MR. WEATHERBEE
Spire Christian Comics (Fleming H. Revell Co.): 1980 (59¢)
nn - (Low print run) 2 4 6 13 18 22

ARCHIE...ARCHIE ANDREWS, WHERE ARE YOU? (...Comics Digest #9, 10; ...Comics Digest Mag. No. 11 on)
Archie Publications: Feb, 1977 - No. 114, May, 1998 (Digest size, 160-128 pgs., quarterly)
1 3 6 9 17 26 35
2,3,5,7-9-N. Adams-a; 8-r-/origin The Fly by S&K. 9-Steel Sterling-r 2 4 6 10 14 18

Archie Comics #26 © ACP

Archie Comics #378 © ACP

Archie Comics #641 © ACP

	GD 2.0	VG 4.0	FN 6.0	VF 8.0	VF/NM 9.0	NM- 9.2
4,6,10 ($1.00/$1.50)	2	4	6	8	11	14
11-20: 17-Katy Keene story	2	3	4	6	8	10
21-50,100	1	2	3	5	6	8
51-70						4.00
71-99,101-114: 113-Begin $1.95-c						3.00

ARCHIE AS PUREHEART THE POWERFUL (Also see Archie Giant Series #142, Jughead as Captain Hero, Life With Archie & Little Archie)
Archie Publications (Radio Comics): Sept, 1966 - No. 6, Nov, 1967

	GD	VG	FN	VF	VF/NM	NM-
1-Super hero parody	11	22	33	76	163	250
2	6	12	18	41	76	110
3-6	6	12	18	37	66	95

NOTE: *Evilheart cameos in all. Title: Archie As Pureheart the Powerful #1-3; ...As Capt. Pureheart-#4-6.*

ARCHIE AT RIVERDALE HIGH (See Archie Giant Series Magazine #573, 586, 604 & Riverdale High)
Archie Publications: Aug, 1972 - No. 113, Feb, 1987

	GD	VG	FN	VF	VF/NM	NM-
1	7	14	21	46	86	125
2	4	8	12	25	40	55
3-5	3	6	9	16	23	30
6-10	2	4	6	11	16	20
11-30	2	4	6	8	10	12
31(12/75)-46,48-50(12/77)	1	3	4	6	8	10
47-Archie in drag-s; Betty mud wrestling-s	2	4	6	10	14	18
51-80,100 (12/84)	1	2	3	5	6	8
81(8/81)-88, 91,93-95,98						6.00
89,90-Early Cheryl Blossom app. 90-Archies Band app.	3	6	9	14	20	26
92,96,97,99-Cheryl Blossom app. 96-Anti-smoking issue	2	4	6	11	16	20
101,102,104-109,111,112: 102-Ghost-c						6.00
103-Archie dates Cheryl Blossom-s	2	4	6	11	16	20
110,113: 110-Godzilla-s. 113-Last issue	1	2	3	5	6	8

ARCHIE CHRISTMAS SPECTACULAR
Archie Comics: Feb, 2018 ($2.99)

	GD	VG	FN	VF	VF/NM	NM-
1-Christmas-themed reprints						3.00

ARCHIE COMICS (See Pep Comics #22 [12/41] for Archie's debut) (1st Teen-age comic; Radio show first aired 6/2/45 by NBC)
MLJ Magazines No. 1-19/Archie Publ. No. 20 on: Winter, 1942-43 - No. 19, 3-4/46; No. 20, 5-6/46 - No. 666, Jul, 2015

	GD	VG	FN	VF	VF/NM	NM-
1 (Scarce)-Jughead, Veronica app.; 1st app. Mrs. Andrews	12,300	24,600	43,000	86,000	138,000	190,000
2 (Scarce)	1750	3500	5250	13,000	21,500	30,000
3 (60 pgs.)(scarce)	865	1730	2595	6315	11,158	16,000
4-Article about Archie radio series	519	1038	1557	3789	6695	9600
5-Halloween-c	465	930	1395	3395	5998	8600
6,8-10: 6-X-Mas-c. 9-1st Miss Grundy cover	300	600	900	2040	3570	5100
7-1st definitive love triangle story	377	754	1131	2639	4620	6600
11-15: 15-Dotty & Ditto by Woggon	161	322	483	1030	1765	2500
16-20: 15,17,18-Dotty & Ditto by Woggon. 16,19-Woggon-a. 18-Halloween pumpkin-c.	145	290	435	921	1586	2250
21-30: 23-Betty & Veronica by Woggon. 25-Woggon-a. 30-Coach Piffle app., a Coach Kleats prototype. 34-Pre-Dilton try-out (named Dilbert)	87	174	261	553	952	1350
31-40	53	106	159	334	567	800
41-49	41	82	123	256	428	600
50-Classic Montana Betty-c (5-6/51)	161	322	483	1030	1765	2500
51-60	18	36	54	124	275	425
61-70 (1954): 65-70, Katy Keene app.	13	26	39	89	195	300
71-80: 72-74-Katy Keene app.	11	22	33	73	157	240
81-93,95-99	9	18	27	60	120	180
94-1st Coach Kleats in this title (see Pep #24)	10	20	30	64	132	200
100	10	20	30	66	138	210
101-122,126,128-130 (1962)	6	12	18	40	73	105
123-125,127-Horror/SF covers. 123-UFO-c/s	9	18	27	59	117	175
131,132,134-157,159,160: 137-1st Caveman Archie gang story	4	8	12	27	44	60
133 (12/62)-1st app. Cricket O'Dell	5	10	15	30	50	70
158-Archie in drag story	5	10	15	30	50	70
161(2/66)-184,186-188,190-195,197-199: 168-Superhero gag-c. 176,178-Twiggy-c 183-Caveman Archie gang story	3	6	9	17	26	35
185-1st "The Archies" Band story	4	8	12	25	40	55
189 (3/69)-Archie's band meets Don Kirshner who developed the Monkees	3	6	9	19	30	40
196 (12/69)-Early Cricket O'Dell app.	3	6	9	19	30	40
200 (6/70)	3	6	9	18	28	38
201-230(11/73): 213-Sabrina/Josie-c cameos. 229-Lost Child issue	2	4	6	11	16	20
231-260(3/77): 253-Tarzan parody	2	4	6	8	11	14
261-282, 284-299	1	3	4	6	8	10
283(8/79)-Cover/story plugs "International Children's Appeal" which was a fraudulent charity, according to TV's 20/20 news program broadcast July 20, 1979	2	4	6	8	10	12
300(1/81)-Anniversary issue	2	4	6	8	11	14
301-321,323-325,327-335,337-350: 323-Cheryl Blossom pin-up. 325-Cheryl Blossom app.						6.00
322-E.T. story	1	2	3	5	6	8
326-Early Cheryl Blossom story	2	4	6	11	16	20
336-Michael Jackson/Boy George parody	2	4	6	8	10	12
351-399: 356-Calgary Olympics Special. 393-Infinity-c; 1st comic book printed on recycled paper						5.00
400 (6/92)-Shows 1st meeting of Little Archie and Veronica						6.00
401-428						4.00
429-Love Showdown part 1						5.00
430-599: 467- "A Storm Over Uniforms" x-over parts 3,4. 538-Comic-Con issue						3.00
600-602: 600-(10/09) Archie proposes to Veronica. 601-Marries Veronica. 602-Twins born						4.00
603-605: 603-(1/10) Archie proposes to Betty. 604-Marries Betty. 605-Twins born						4.00
606-615,618-626: 609-Begin $2.99-c. 610-613-Man From RIVERDALE. 625-70th Anniversary. 626-Michael Strahan app.						3.00
616,617-Obama & Palin app.; two covers on each						4.00
627-630-Archie Meets KISS; 2 covers on each by Parent & Francavilla						4.00
631-658: 632-634-Archie marries Valerie from the Pussycats. 635-Jill Thompson var-c. 636-Gender swap. 641-644-Crossover with Glee; 2 covers. 648-Simonson var-c. 655-Cosmo the Merry Martian app. 656-Intro. Harper Lodge						3.00
650-Variant "Battle of the Bands" cover by Fiona Staples						5.00
659-665-($3.99) Two covers on each. 664-Game of Thrones parody. 665-Harper app.						4.00
666-Last issue; 6 interlocking covers with vintage title logos (Archie Comics, Blue Ribbon Comics, Top-Notch Comics, Pep Comics, Zip Comics, and Jackpot Comics)						4.00
Annual 1 ('50)-116 pgs. (Scarce)	300	600	900	1950	3975	6100
Annual 2 ('51)	116	232	348	742	1471	2200
Annual 3 ('52)	66	132	198	419	797	1175
Annual 4,5 (1953-54)	46	92	138	290	520	750
Annual 6-10 (1955-59): 8,9-(100 pgs.). 10-(84 pgs.) Elvis record on-c	16	32	48	110	243	375
Annual 11-15 (1960-65): 12,13-(84 pgs.) 14,15-(68 pgs.)	9	18	27	62	126	190
Annual 16-20 (1966-70)(all 68 pgs.): 20-Archie's band-c	6	12	18	38	69	100
Annual 21,22,24-26 (1971-75): 21,22-(68 pgs.). 22-Archie's band-s. 24-26-(52 pgs.). 25-Cavemen-s	4	8	12	23	37	50
Annual 23-Archie's band-c/s; Josie/Sabrina-c	5	10	15	30	50	70
Annual Digest 27 ('75)	4	8	12	23	37	50
...28-30	3	6	9	14	20	25
...31-34	2	4	6	9	13	16
...35-40 (...Magazine #35 on)	1	3	4	6	8	10
...41-65 ('94)						5.00
...66-69						3.00
...All-Star Specials (Winter '75, $1.25)-6 remaindered Archie comics rebound in each; titles: "The World of Giant Comics", "Giant Grab Bag of Comics", "Triple Giant Comics" & "Giant Spec. Comics	5	10	15	30	50	70

NOTE: *Archies Band-s-185, 188-192, 197, 198, 201, 204, 205, 208, 209, 215, 329, 330; Band-c-191, 330. Cavemen Archie Gang-s-183, 192, 197, 208, 210, 220, 223, 282, 333, 335, 338, 340.* ***Al Fagly*** *c-17-35.* ***Bob Montana*** *c-38, 41-50, 58, Annual 1-4.* ***Bill Woggon*** *c-53, 54.*

ARCHIE COMICS DIGEST (...Magazine No. 37-95)
Archie Publications: Aug, 1973 - No. 267, Nov, 2010 (Digest-size, 160-128 pgs.)

	GD	VG	FN	VF	VF/NM	NM-
1-1st Archie digest	9	18	27	60	120	180
2	5	10	15	30	50	70
3-5	4	8	12	23	37	50
6-10	3	6	9	16	23	30
11-33: 32,33-The Fly-r by S&K	2	4	6	10	14	18
34-60	1	3	4	6	8	10
61-80,100	1	2	3	5	6	8
81-99						5.00
101-140: 36-Katy Keene story						4.00
141-165						3.00
166-235,237-267: 194-Begin $2.39-c. 225-Begin $2.49-c						3.00
236-65th Anniversary issue, r/1st app. in Pep #22 and entire Archie Comics #1 (1942)						5.00

NOTE: ***Neal Adams*** *a-1, 2, 4, 5, 19-21, 24, 25, 27, 29, 31, 33. X-mas c-88, 94, 100, 106.*

ARCHIE COMICS DIGEST (Continues from Archie's Double Digest #252)
Archie Publications: No. 253, Sept, 2014 - Present ($4.99-$6.99, digest-size)

Archie Comics Digest #278 © ACP

Archie Giant Series #18 © ACP

Archie Giant Series #187 © ACP

GD 2.0 | VG 4.0 | FN 6.0 | VF 8.0 | VF/NM 9.0 | NM- 9.2

253,254,257-259,261,262,264,267,269,270,272,273,275,277,279,281-($4.99) 5.00
255,260,266,274,276,282,283,285-287-($6.99) Titled Archie Jumbo Comics Digest 7.00
256,263,265,268,271,278,280,284-($5.99): 256,263,268,278-Titled Archie Comics Annual 6.00

ARCHIE COMICS (Free Comic Book Day editions) (Also see Pep Comics)
Archie Publications: 2003 - Present

... Free Comic Book Day Edition 1,2: 1-(7/03). 2-(9/04) 3.00
Little Archie "The Legend of the Lost Lagoon" FCBD Edition (5/07) Bolling-s/a 3.00
... Presents the Mighty Archie Art Players ('09) Free Comic Book Day giveaway 3.00
...'s 65th Anniversary Bash ('06) Free Comic Book Day giveaway 3.00
...'s Summer Splash FCBD Edition (5/10) Parent-a; Cheryl Blossom app. 3.00

ARCHIE COMICS PRESENTS: THE LOVE SHOWDOWN COLLECTION
Archie Publications: 1994 ($4.95, squarebound)

nn-r/Archie #429, Betty #19, Betty & Veronica #82, & Veronica #39 1 2 3 5 6 8

ARCHIE COMICS SUPER SPECIAL
Archie Publications: Dec, 2012 - No. 7, Jan, 2017 ($9.99, squarebound magazine-sized, quarterly)

1-7: 1-Christmas themed. 2-Valentine's themed 10.00

ARCHIE DIGEST (Free Comic Book Day edition)
Archie Comic Publications: June/July 2014 (digest-size giveaway)

1-Reprints; Parent-c 3.00

ARCHIE DOUBLE DIGEST (See Archie's Double Digest Quarterly Magazine)

ARCHIE GETS A JOB
Spire Christian Comics (Fleming H. Revell Co.): 1977

nn 2 4 6 13 18 22

ARCHIE GIANT SERIES MAGAZINE
Archie Publications: 1954 - No. 632, July, 1992 (No #36-135, no #252-451)
(#1 not code approved) (#1-233 are Giants; #12-184 are 68 pgs.,#185-194,197-233 are 52 pgs.; #195,196 are 84 pgs.; #234-up are 36 pgs.)

1-Archie's Christmas Stocking 165 330 495 1048 1799 2550
2-Archie's Christmas Stocking('55) 81 162 243 518 884 1250
3-6-Archie's Christmas Stocking('56- '59) 53 106 159 334 567 800
7-10: 7-Katy Keene Holiday Fun(9/60); Bill Woggon-c. 8-Betty & Veronica Summer Fun (10/60); baseball story w/Babe Ruth & Lou Gehrig. 9-The World of Jughead (12/60); Neal Adams-a. 10-Archie's Christmas Stocking(1/61) 39 78 117 240 395 550
11,13,16,18: 11-Betty & Veronica Spectacular (6/61). 13-Betty & Veronica Summer Fun (10/61). 16-Betty & Veronica Spectacular (6/62). 18-Betty & Veronica Summer Fun (10/62) 25 50 75 150 245 340
12,14,15,17,19,20: 12-Katy Keene Holiday Fun (9/61). 14-The World of Jughead (12/61); Vampire-s. 15-Archie's Christmas Stocking (1/62). 17-Archie's Jokes (9/62); Katy Keene app. 19-The World of Jughead (12/62). 20-Archie's Christmas Stocking (1/63) 19 38 57 112 179 245
21,23,28: 21-Betty & Veronica Spectacular (6/63). 23-Betty & Veronica Summer Fun (10/63). 28-Betty & Veronica Summer Fun (9/64) 9 18 27 59 117 175
22,24,25,27,29,30: 22-Archie's Jokes (9/63). 24-The World of Jughead (12/63). 25-Archie's Christmas Stocking (1/64). 27-Archie's Jokes (8/64). 29-Around the World with Archie (10/64); Doris Day-s. 30-The World of Jughead (12/64) 8 16 24 54 102 150
26-Betty & Veronica Spectacular (6/64); all pin-ups; DeCarlo-c/a 9 18 27 60 120 180
31,33-35: 31-Archie's Christmas Stocking (1/65). 33-Archie's Jokes (8/65). 34-Betty & Veronica Summer Fun (9/65). 35-Around the World with Archie (10/65). 6 12 18 38 69 100
32-Betty & Veronica Spectacular (6/65); all pin-ups; DeCarlo-c/a 7 14 21 48 89 130
36-135-**Do not exist**
136-141: 136-The World of Jughead (12/65). 137-Archie's Christmas Stocking (1/66). 138-Betty & Veronica Spect. (6/66). 139-Archie's Jokes (6/66). 140-Betty & Veronica Summer Fun (8/66). 141-Around the World with Archie (9/66) 6 12 18 38 69 100
142-Archie's Super-Hero Special (10/66)-Origin Capt. Pureheart, Capt. Hero, and Evilheart 7 14 21 49 92 135
143-The World of Jughead (12/66); Capt. Hero-c/s; Man From R.I.V.E.R.D.A.L.E., Pureheart, Superteen app. 6 12 18 38 69 100
144-160: 144-Archie's Christmas Stocking (1/67). 145-Betty & Veronica Spectacular (6/67). 146-Archie's Jokes (6/67). 147-Betty & Veronica Summer Fun (8/67) 148-World of Archie (9/67). 149-World of Jughead (10/67). 150-Archie's Christmas Stocking (1/68). 151-World of Archie (2/68). 152-World of Jughead (2/68). 153-Betty & Veronica Spectacular (6/68). 154-Archie Jokes (6/68). 155-Betty & Veronica Summer Fun (8/68). 156-World of Archie (10/68). 157-World of Jughead (12/68). 158-Archie's Christmas Stocking (1/69). 159-Betty & Veronica Christmas Spectacular (1/69). 160-World of Archie (2/69); Frankenstein-s each... 4 8 12 23 37 50
161-World of Jughead (2/69); Super-Jughead-s; 11 pg. early Cricket O'Dell-s 4 8 12 25 40 55
162-183: 162-Betty & Veronica Spectacular (6/69). 163-Archie's Jokes(8/69). 164-Betty & Veronica Summer Fun (9/69). 165-World of Archie (9/69). 166-World of Jughead (9/69). 167-Archie's Christmas Stocking (1/70). 168-Betty & Veronica Christmas Spect. (1/70). 169-Archie's Christmas Love-In (1/70). 170-Jughead's Eat-Out Comic Book Mag. (12/69). 171-World of Archie (2/70). 172-World of Jughead (2/70). 173-Betty & Veronica Spectacular (6/70). 174-Archie's Jokes (8/70). 175-Betty & Veronica Summer Fun (9/70). 176-Li'l Jinx Giant Laugh-Out (8/70). 177-World of Archie (9/70). 178-World of Jughead (9/70). 179-Archie's Christmas Stocking(1/71). 180-Betty & Veronica Christmas Spect. (1/71). 181-Archie's Christmas Love-In (1/71). 182-World of Archie (2/71). 183-World of Jughead (2/71)-Last squarebound each... 3 6 9 17 26 35
184-189,193,194,197-199 (52 pgs.): 184-Betty & Veronica Spectacular (6/71). 185-Li'l Jinx Giant Laugh-Out (6/71). 186-Archie's Jokes (8/71). 187-Betty & Veronica Summer Fun (9/71). 188-World of Archie (9/71). 189-World of Jughead (9/71). 193-World of Archie (3/72).194-World of Jughead (4/72). 197-Betty & Veronica Spectacular (6/72). 198-Archie's Jokes (8/72). 199-Betty & Veronica Summer Fun (9/72) each... 3 6 9 15 22 28
190-Archie's Christmas Stocking (12/71); Sabrina-c 4 8 12 27 44 60
191-Betty & Veronica Christmas Spect.(2/72); Sabrina app. 4 8 12 23 37 50
192-Archie's Christmas Love-In (1/72); Archie Band-c/s 3 6 9 20 31 42
195-(84 pgs.)-Li'l Jinx Christmas Bag (1/72). 3 6 9 21 33 45
196-(84 pgs.)-Sabrina's Christmas Magic (1/72) 5 10 15 33 57 80
200-(52 pgs.)-World of Archie (10/72) 3 6 9 20 31 42
201-206,208-219,221-230,232,233 (All 52 pgs.): 201-Betty & Veronica Spectacular (10/72). 202-World of Jughead (11/72). 203-Archie's Christmas Stocking (12/72). 204-Betty & Veronica Christmas Spectacular (2/73). 205-Archie's Christmas Love-In (1/73). 206-Li'l Jinx Christmas Bag (12/72). 208-World of Archie (3/73). 209-World of Jughead (4/73). 210-Betty & Veronica Spectacular (6/73). 211-Archie's Jokes (8/73). 212-Betty & Veronica Summer Fun (9/73). 213-World of Archie (10/73). 214-Betty & Veronica Spectacular (10/73). 215-World of Jughead (11/73). 216-Archie's Christmas Stocking (12/73). 217-Betty & Veronica Christmas Spectacular (2/74). 218-Archie's Christmas Love-In (1/74). 219-Li'l Jinx Christmas Bag (12/73). 221-Betty & Veronica Spectacular (Advertised as World of Archie) (6/74). 222-Archie's Jokes (advertised as World of Jughead) (8/74). 223-Li'l Jinx (8/74). 224-Betty & Veronica Summer Fun (9/74). 225-World of Archie (9/74). 226-Betty & Veronica Spectacular (10/74). 227-World of Jughead (10/74). 228-Archie's Christmas Stocking (12/74). 229-Betty & Veronica Christmas Spectacular (12/74). 230-Archie's Christmas Love-In (1/75). 232-World of Archie (3/75). 233-World of Jughead (4/75) each... 2 4 6 11 16 20
207,220,231,243: Sabrina's Christmas Magic. 207-(12/72). 220-(12/73). 231-(1/75). 243-(1/76) each... 3 6 9 16 24 32
234-242,244-251 (36 pgs.): 234-Betty & Veronica Spectacular (6/75). 235-Archie's Jokes (8/75). 236-Betty & Veronica Summer Fun (9/75). 237-World of Archie (9/75) 238-Betty & Veronica Spectacular (10/75). 239-World of Jughead (10/75). 240-Archie's Christmas Stocking (12/75). 241-Betty & Veronica Christmas Spectacular (12/75). 242-Archie's Christmas Love-In (1/76). 244-World of Archie (3/76). 245-World of Jughead (4/76). 246-Betty & Veronica Spectacular (6/76). 247-Archie's Jokes (8/76). 248-Betty & Veronica Summer Fun (9/76). 249-World of Archie (9/76). 250-Betty & Veronica Spectacular (10/76). 251-World of Jughead each.... 2 4 6 9 12 15
252-451-**Do not exist**
452-454,456-466,468-478, 480-490,492-499: 452-Archie's Christmas Stocking (12/76). 453-Betty & Veronica Christmas Spectacular (12/76). 454-Archie's Christmas Love-In (1/77). 456-World of Archie (3/77). 457-World of Jughead (4/77). 458-Betty & Veronica Spectacular (6/77). 459-Archie's Jokes (8/77)-Shows 8/76 in error. 460-Betty & Veronica Summer Fun (9/77). 461-World of Archie (9/77). 462-Betty & Veronica Spectacular (10/77). 463-World of Jughead (10/77). 464-Archie's Christmas Stocking (12/77). 465-Betty & Veronica Christmas Spectacular (12/77). 466-Archie's Christmas Love-In (1/78). 468-World of Archie (2/78). 469-World of Jughead (2/78). 470-Betty & Veronica Spectacular(6/78). 471-Archie's Jokes (8/78). 472-Betty & Veronica Summer Fun (9/78). 473-World of Archie (9/78). 474-Betty & Veronica Spectacular (10/78). 475-World of Jughead (10/78). 476-Archie's Christmas Stocking (12/78). 477-Betty & Veronica Christmas Spectacular (12/78). 478-Archie's Christmas Love-In (1/79). 480-The World of Archie (3/79). 481-World of Jughead (4/79). 482-Betty & Veronica Spectacular (6/79). 483-Archie's Jokes (8/79). 484-Betty & Veronica Summer Fun(9/79). 485-The World of Archie (9/79). 486-Betty & Veronica Spectacular (10/79). 487-The World of Jughead (10/79). 488-Archie's Christmas Stocking (12/79). 489-Betty & Veronica Christmas Spectacular (1/80). 490-Archie's Christmas Love-in (1/80). 492-The World of Archie (2/80). 493-The World of Jughead (4/80). 494-Betty & Veronica Spectacular (6/80). 495-Archie's Jokes (8/80). 496-Betty & Veronica Summer Fun (9/80). 497-The World of Archie (9/80). 498-Betty & Veronica Spectacular (10/80). 499-The World of Jughead (10/80) each... 2 4 6 8 10 12
455,467,479,491,503-Sabrina's Christmas Magic: 455-(1/77). 467-(1/78). 479-(1/79) Dracula/Werewolf-s. 491-(1/80), 503(1/81) 2 4 6 11 16 20

Archie Giant Series #612 © ACP

The Archies #1 © ACP

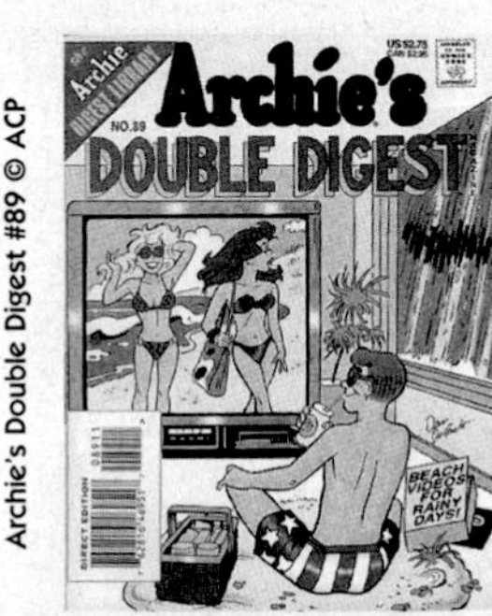

Archie's Double Digest #89 © ACP

GD 2.0 | VG 4.0 | FN 6.0 | VF 8.0 | VF/NM 9.0 | NM- 9.2

500-Archie's Christmas Stocking (12/80) 2 4 6 8 11 14
501-514,516-527,529-532,534-539,541-543,545-550: 501-Betty & Veronica Christmas Spectacular (12/80). 502-Archie's Christmas Love-in (1/81). 504-The World of Archie (3/81). 505-The World of Jughead (4/81). 506-Betty & Veronica Spectacular (6/81). 507-Archie's Jokes (8/81). 508-Betty & Veronica Summer Fun (9/81). 509-The World of Archie (9/81). 510-Betty & Veronica Spectacular (9/81). 511-The World of Jughead (10/81). 512-Archie's Christmas Stocking (12/81). 513-Betty & Veronica Christmas Spectacular (12/81). 514-Archie's Christmas Love-in (1/82). 516-The World of Archie(3/82). 517-The World of Jughead (4/82). 518-Betty & Veronica Spectacular (6/82). 519-Archie's Jokes (8/82). 520-Betty & Veronica Summer Fun (9/82). 521-The World of Archie (9/82). 522-Betty & Veronica Spectacular (10/82). 523-The World of Jughead (10/82).524-Archie's Christmas Stocking (1/83). 525-Betty and Veronica Christmas Spectacular (1/83). 526-Betty and Veronica Spectacular (5/83). 527-Little Archie (8/83). 529-Betty and Veronica Summer Fun (8/83). 530-Betty and Veronica Spectacular (9/83). 531-The World of Jughead (9/83). 532-The World of Archie (10/83). 534-Little Archie (1/84). 535-Archie's Christmas Stocking (1/84). 536-Betty and Veronica Christmas Spectacular (1/84). 537-Betty and Veronica Spectacular (6/84). 538-Little Archie (8/84). 539-Betty and Veronica Summer Fun (8/84). 541-Betty and Veronica Spectacular (9/84). 542-The World of Jughead (9/84). 543-The World of Archie (10/84). 545-Little Archie (12/84). 546-Archie's Christmas Stocking (12/84). 547-Betty and Veronica Christmas Spectacular (12/84). 548-Betty and Veronica Spectacular (6/85). 549-Little Archie. 550-Betty and Veronica Summer Fun
each... 1 2 3 5 7 9
515,528,533,540,544: 515-Sabrina's Christmas Magic (1/82). 528-Josie and the Pussycats (8/83). 533-Sabrina; Space Pirates by Frank Bolling (10/83). 540-Josie and the Pussycats (8/84). 544-Sabrina the Teen-Age Witch (10/84).
each... 2 4 6 10 14 18
551,562,571,584,597-Josie and the Pussycats 2 4 6 8 10 12
552-561,563-570,572-583,585-596,598-600: 552-Betty & Veronica Spectacular. 553-The World of Jughead. 554-The World of Archie. 555-Betty's Diary. 556-Little Archie (1/86). 557-Archie's Christmas Stocking (1/86). 558-Betty & Veronica Christmas Spectacular (1/86). 559-Betty & Veronica Spectacular. 560-Little Archie. 561-Betty & Veronica Summer Fun. 563-Betty & Veronica Spectacular. 564-World of Jughead. 565-World of Archie. 566-Little Archie. 567-Archie's Christmas Stocking. 568-Betty & Veronica Christmas Spectacular. 569-Betty & Veronica Spring Spectacular. 570-Little Archie. 571-Dracula-c/s. 572-Betty & Veronica Summer Fun. 573-Archie At Riverdale High. 574-World of Archie. 575-Betty & Veronica Spectacular. 576-Pep. 577-World of Jughead. 578-Archie And Me. 579-Archie's Christmas Stocking. 580-Betty and Veronica Christmas Spectacular. 581-Little Archie Christmas Special. 582-Betty & Veronica Spring Spectacular. 583-Little Archie. 585-Betty & Veronica Summer Fun. 586-Archie At Riverdale High. 587-The World of Archie (10/88); 1st app. Explorers of the Unknown. 588-Betty & Veronica Spectacular. 589-Pep (10/88). 590-The World of Jughead. 591-Archie & Me. 592-Archie's Christmas Stocking. 593-Betty & Veronica Christmas Spectacular. 594-Little Archie. 595-Betty & Veronica Spring Spectacular. 596-Little Archie. 598-Betty & Veronica Summer Fun. 599-The World of Archie (10/89); 2nd app. Explorers of the Unknown. 600-Betty and Veronica Spectacular
each.... 6.00
601,602,604-609,611-629: 601-Pep. 602-The World of Jughead. 604-Archie at Riverdale High. 605-Archie's Christmas Stocking. 606-Betty and Veronica Christmas Spectacular. 607-Little Archie. 608-Betty and Veronica Spectacular. 609-Little Archie. 611-Betty and Veronica Summer Fun. 612-The World of Archie. 613-Betty and Veronica Spectacular. 614-Pep (10/90). 615-Veronica's Summer Special. 616-Archie and Me. 617-Archie's Christmas Stocking. 618-Betty & Veronica Christmas Spectacular. 619-Little Archie. 620-Betty and Veronica Spectacular. 621-Betty and Veronica Summer Fun. 622-Josie & the Pussycats; not published. 623-Betty and Veronica Spectacular. 624-Pep Comics. 625-Veronica's Summer Special. 626-Archie and Me. 627-World of Archie. 628-Archie's Pals 'n' Gals Holiday Special. 629-Betty & Veronica Christmas Spectacular.
each.... 4.00
603-Archie and Me; Titanic app. 5.00
610-Josie and the Pussycats 1 2 3 4 5 7
630-631: 630-Archie's Christmas Stocking. 631-Archie's Pals 'n' Gals 4.00
632-Last issue; Betty & Veronica Spectacular 1 2 3 4 5 7
NOTE: *Archies Band-c-173,180,192; s-189,192. Archie Cavemen-165,225,232,244,249. Little Sabrina-527,534, 538,545,556,566. UFO-s-178,487,594.*

ARCHIE HALLOWEEN SPECTACULAR
Archie Comic Publications: Dec, 2017 ($2.99)
1-Halloween-themed reprints; Shultz-c 3.00

ARCHIE JUMBO COMICS DIGEST (See Archie Comic Digest)

ARCHIE MEETS RAMONES
Archie Comic Publications: 2016 ($4.99, one-shot)
1-Segura & Rosenberg-s/Lagacé-a; multiple covers; The Archies go to 1976; Sabrina app. 5.00

ARCHIE MEETS THE PUNISHER (Same contents as The Punisher Meets Archie)
Marvel Comics & Archie Comics Publ.: Aug, 1994 ($2.95, 52 pgs., one-shot)
1-Batton Lash story, John Buscema-a on Punisher, Stan Goldberg-a on Archie
1 2 3 5 6 8

ARCHIES, THE
Archie Comic Publications: Jul, 2017; Nov, 2017 - Present ($4.99/$3.99)
1-5-($3.99) Segura & Rosenberg-s/Eisma-a. 3-Chvrches app. 4-The Monkees app. 4.00
..., One-Shot (7/17, $4.99) Segura & Rosenberg-s/Eisma-a; Archie forms the band 5.00

ARCHIE'S ACTIVITY COMICS DIGEST MAGAZINE
Archie Enterprises: 1985 - No. 4 (Annual, 128 pgs., digest size)
1 (Most copies are marked) 2 4 6 9 13 16
2-4 1 2 3 5 7 9

ARCHIE'S CAR
Spire Christian Comics (Fleming H. Revell co.): 1979 (49¢)
nn 2 4 6 13 18 22

ARCHIE'S CHRISTMAS LOVE-IN (See Archie Giant Series Mag. No. 169, 181,192, 205, 218, 230, 242, 454, 466, 478, 490, 502, 514)

ARCHIE'S CHRISTMAS STOCKING (See Archie Giant Series Mag. No. 1-6,10, 15, 20, 25, 31, 137, 144, 150, 158, 167, 179, 190, 203, 216, 228, 240, 452, 464, 476, 488, 500, 512, 524, 535, 546, 557, 567, 579, 592, 605, 617, 630)

ARCHIE'S CHRISTMAS STOCKING
Archie Comics: 1993 - No. 7, 1999 ($2.00-$2.29, 52 pgs.)(Bound-in calendar poster in all)
1-Dan DeCarlo-c/a 5.00
2-5 4.00
6,7: 6-(1998, $2.25). 7-(1999, $2.29) 4.00

ARCHIE'S CIRCUS
Barbour Christian Comics: 1990 (69¢)
nn 2 4 6 10 14 18

ARCHIE'S CLASSIC CHRISTMAS STORIES
Archie Comics: 2002 ($10.95, TPB)
Volume 1 - Reprints stories from 1955-1964 Archie's Christmas Stocking issues 12.00

ARCHIE'S CLEAN SLATE
Spire Christian Comics (Fleming H. Revell Co.): 1973 (35/49¢)
1-(35¢-c edition)(Some issues have nn) 3 6 9 14 19 24
1-(49¢-c edition) 2 4 6 10 14 18

ARCHIE'S DATE BOOK
Spire Christian comics (Fleming H. Revell Co.): 1981
nn-(Low print) 2 4 6 13 18 22

ARCHIE'S DOUBLE DIGEST QUARTERLY MAGAZINE
Archie Comics: 1981 - No. 252, Aug, 2014 ($1.95-$3.99, 256 pgs.) (Archie's Double Digest Magazine No. 10 on)(Title becomes Archie's Comics Digest #253 on)
1 3 6 9 16 23 30
2-10; 6-Katy Keene story. 2 4 6 10 14 18
11-30: 29-Pureheart story 2 4 6 8 10 12
31-50 1 2 3 4 5 7
51-70,100 5.00
71-99 4.00
101-237,239-251: 123-Begin $3.29-c. 170-Begin $3.69. 197-Begin $3.99-c. 4.00
238-Titled Archie Double Double Digest (4/13, $5.99, 320 pages) 6.00
252-($4.99) Title changes to Archie's Comics Digest with #253 5.00

ARCHIE'S FAMILY ALBUM
Spire Christian Comics (Fleming H. Revell Co.): 1978 (39¢/49¢, 36 pgs.)
nn 2 4 6 13 18 22
nn (49¢-c edition) 2 4 6 9 13 16

ARCHIE'S FESTIVAL
Spire Christian Comics (Fleming H. Revell Co.): 1980 (49¢)
nn 2 4 6 13 18 22

ARCHIE'S FUNHOUSE DOUBLE DIGEST
Archie Comics: Feb, 2014 - Present ($3.99-$7.99, digest-size)
1-5 4.00
6,19,21: 6,19-Titled Archie's Funhouse Double Double Digest ($5.99, 320 pgs.) 6.00
7-10,12-14,16,18,25,28-($4.99) Title becomes Archie's Funhouse Comics Digest 5.00
11-($7.99) Titled Archie's Funhouse Jumbo Comics Digest 8.00
15,17,20,22-($6.99) Archie's Funhouse Jumbo Comics Digest 7.00
23,24,26,27-($5.99) 23-Titled Archie's Funhouse Christmas Annual Double Digest 6.00

ARCHIE'S GIRLS, BETTY AND VERONICA (Becomes Betty & Veronica)(Also see Veronica)
Archie Publications (Close-Up): 1950 - No. 347, Apr, 1987
1 331 662 993 2317 4059 5800
2 142 284 426 909 1555 2200

Archie's Girls, Betty and Veronica #17 © ACP

Archie's Girls, Betty and Veronica Annual #3 © ACP

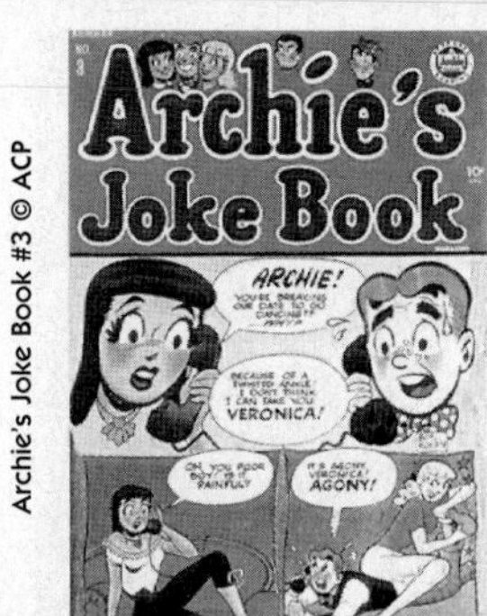

Archie's Joke Book #3 © ACP

	GD 2.0	VG 4.0	FN 6.0	VF 8.0	VF/NM 9.0	NM- 9.2
3-5: 3-Betty's 1st ponytail. 4-Dan DeCarlo's 1st Archie work	84	168	252	538	919	1300
6-10: 10-Katy Keene app. (2 pgs.)	60	120	180	381	653	925
11-20: 11,13,14,17-19-Katy Keene app. 17-Last pre-code issue (3/55). 20-Debbie's Diary (2 pgs.)	43	86	129	271	461	650
21-30: 27,30-Katy Keene app. 29-Tarzan	36	72	108	211	343	475
31-43,45-50: 41-Marilyn Monroe and Brigitte Bardot mentioned. 45-Fabian 1 pg. photo & bio. 46-Bobby Darin 1 pg. photo & bio	21	42	63	126	206	285
44-Elvis Presley 1 pg. photo & bio	24	48	72	144	237	330
51-55,57-74: 67-Jackie Kennedy homage. 73-Sci-fi-c	9	18	27	57	111	165
56-Elvis and Bobby Darin records parody	10	20	30	66	138	210
75-Betty & Veronica sell souls to Devil	22	44	66	154	340	525
76-99: 82-Bobby Rydell 1 pg. illustrated bio; Elvis mentioned on-c. 83-Rick Nelson illo/text page. 84-Connie Francis 1 pg. illustrated bio	6	12	18	38	69	100
100	6	12	18	42	79	115
101-104, 106-117,120 (12/65): 113-Monsters-s	4	8	12	28	47	65
105-Beatles wig parody (5 pg. story)(9/64)	5	10	15	31	53	75
118-(10/65) 1st app./origin Superteen (also see Betty & Me #3)	6	12	18	41	76	110
119-2nd app./last Superteen story	5	10	15	31	53	75
121,122,124-126,128-140 (8/67): 135,140-Mod-c. 136-Slave Girl-s	3	6	9	19	30	40
123-"Jingo"-Ringo parody-c	4	8	12	23	37	50
127-Beatles Fan Club-s	5	10	15	31	53	75
141-156,158-163,165-180 (12/70)	3	6	9	15	22	28
157,164-Archies Band	3	6	9	18	28	38
181-193,195-199	2	4	6	11	16	20
194-Sabrina-c/s	3	6	9	20	31	42
200-(8/72)	3	6	9	14	19	24
201-205,207,209,211-215,217-240	2	4	6	8	10	12
206,208,210, 216: 206,208,216-Sabrina c/app. 206-Josie-c. 210-Sabrina app.	3	6	9	15	22	28
241 (1/76)-270 (6/78)	1	3	4	6	8	10
271-299: 281-UFO-s	1	2	3	5	7	9
300 (12/80)-Anniversary issue	2	4	6	8	10	12
301-309	1	2	3	4	5	7
310-John Travolta parody story	1	3	4	6	8	10
311-319						6.00
320 (10/82)-Intro. of Cheryl Blossom on cover and inside story (she also appears, but not on the cover, in Jughead #325 with same 10/82 publication date)	18	36	54	121	268	415
321-Cheryl Blossom app.	6	12	18	38	69	100
322-Cheryl Blossom app.; Cheryl meets Archie for the 1st time	7	14	21	46	86	125
323,326,329,330,331,333-338: 333-Monsters-s						6.00
324,325-Crickett O'Dell app.	2	4	6	9	12	15
327,328-Cheryl Blossom app.	3	6	9	20	31	42
332,339: 332-Superhero costume party. 339-(12/85) Betty dressed as Madonna.	2	4	6	10	14	18
340-346 Low print	1	3	4	6	8	10
347 (4/87) Last issue; low print	2	4	6	8	10	12
Annual 1 (1953)	135	270	405	864	1482	2100
Annual 2 (1954)	52	104	156	328	552	775
Annual 3-5 (1955-1957)	40	80	120	246	411	575
Annual 6-8 (1958-1960)	28	56	84	165	270	375

ARCHIE'S HOLIDAY FUN DIGEST
Archie Comics: 1997 - Present ($1.75/$1.95/$1.99/$2.19/$2.39/$2.49, annual)

	GD 2.0	VG 4.0	FN 6.0	VF 8.0	VF/NM 9.0	NM- 9.2
1-12-Christmas stories						3.00

ARCHIE'S JOKEBOOK COMICS DIGEST ANNUAL (See Jokebook...)

ARCHIE'S JOKE BOOK MAGAZINE (See Joke Book ...)
Archie Publ: 1953 - No. 3, Sum, 1954; No. 15, Fall, 1954 - No. 288, 11/82 (subtitled...Laugh-In #127-140; ...Laugh-Out #141-194)

	GD 2.0	VG 4.0	FN 6.0	VF 8.0	VF/NM 9.0	NM- 9.2
1953-One Shot (#1)	148	296	444	947	1624	2300
2	54	108	162	343	574	825
3 (no #4-14)	41	82	123	256	428	600
15-20: 15-Formerly Archie's Rival Reggie #14; last pre-code issue (Fall/54). 15-17-Katy Keene app.	27	54	81	158	259	360
21-30	16	32	48	94	147	200
31-43: 42-Bio of Ed "Kookie" Byrnes. 43-story about guitarist Duane Eddy	14	28	42	76	108	140
44-1st professional comic work by Neal Adams, 4 pgs.	32	64	96	192	314	435
45-47-N. Adams-a in all, 2-6 pgs.	19	38	57	111	176	240
48-Four pgs. N. Adams-a	19	38	57	111	176	240
49,50	6	12	18	41	66	90
51-56,60 (1962)	4	8	12	27	44	60
57-Elvis mentioned; Marilyn Monroe cameo	6	12	18	37	66	95
58,59-Horror/Sci-Fi-c	7	14	21	48	89	130
61-80 (8/64): 66-(12¢ cover). 76-Robot-c	3	6	9	17	26	35
66-(15¢ cover variant)	4	8	12	23	37	50
81-89,91,92,94-99	3	6	9	14	20	25
90,93: 90-Beatles gag. 93-Beatles cameo	3	6	9	16	24	32
100 (5/66)	3	6	9	16	23	30
101,103-117,119-123,127,129,131-140 (9/69): 105-Superhero gag-c. 108-110-Archies Archers Band-s. 116-Beatles/Monkees/Bob Dylan cameos (posters)	2	4	6	11	16	20
102 (7/66) Archie Band prototype-c; Elvis parody panel, Rolling Stones mention	3	6	9	17	26	35
118,124,125,126,128,130: 118-Archie Band-c; Veronica & Groovers band-s. 124-Archies Band-c/app. 125-Beatles cameo (poster). 126,130-Monkees cameo. 128-Veronica/Archies Band app.	3	6	9	16	23	30
141-173,175-181,183-199	2	4	6	8	11	14
174-Sabrina-c. 182-Sabrina cameo	2	4	6	9	13	16
200 (9/74)	2	4	6	9	13	16
201-230 (3/77)	1	2	3	5	6	8
231-239,241-287						6.00
240-Elvis record-c	2	3	4	6	8	10
288-Last issue	1	2	3	4	5	7

NOTE: *Archies Band-c-118,124,147,172; 1 pg.-s-127,128,138,140,143,147,167; 2 pg.-s-124,131, 155. Sabrina app.-247,248,252-259,261,262,264,266-270,274,277,284-286.*

ARCHIE'S JOKES (See Archie Giant Series Mag. No. 17, 22, 27, 33, 139, 146, 154, 163, 174, 186, 198, 211, 222, 235, 247, 459, 471, 483, 495, 519)

ARCHIE'S LOVE SCENE
Spire Christian Comics (Fleming H. Revell Co.): 1973 (35¢/39¢/49¢/no price)

	GD 2.0	VG 4.0	FN 6.0	VF 8.0	VF/NM 9.0	NM- 9.2
1-(35¢ Edition)	3	6	9	14	19	24
1-(39¢/49¢ Edition/no price) (Some copies have nn)	2	4	6	10	14	18

ARCHIE'S LOVE SHOWDOWN SPECIAL
Archie Publications: 1994 ($2.00, one-shot)

	GD 2.0	VG 4.0	FN 6.0	VF 8.0	VF/NM 9.0	NM- 9.2
1-Concludes x-over from Archie #429, Betty #19, B&V #82, Veronica #39						4.00

ARCHIE'S MADHOUSE (Madhouse Ma-ad No. 67 on)
Archie Publications: Sept, 1959 - No. 66, Feb, 1969

	GD 2.0	VG 4.0	FN 6.0	VF 8.0	VF/NM 9.0	NM- 9.2
1-Archie begins	25	50	75	175	388	600
2	12	24	36	82	179	275
3-5	9	18	27	58	114	170
6-10	6	12	18	41	76	110
11-17 (Last w/regular characters)	5	10	15	35	63	90
18-21,23,29: 18-New format begins. 23-No Sabrina. 29-Flying saucer-c	5	10	15	31	53	75
22-1st app. Sabrina, the Teen-age Witch (10/62)	114	228	342	912	2056	3200
24-2nd app.Sabrina a	15	30	45	103	227	350
25,26,28-Sabrina app. 25-1st app. Captain Sprocket (4/63); 3rd app. Sabrina; sci-fi/horror-c	11	22	33	76	163	250
27-Sabrina-c; no story	8	16	24	54	102	150
30,34,38-40: No Sabrina. 34-Bordered-c begin.	4	8	12	25	40	55
31-33,37-Sabrina app.	8	16	24	51	96	140
35-Beatles cameo. No Sabrina	4	8	12	28	47	65
36-1st Salem the Cat w/Sabrina story	12	24	36	79	170	260
41-48,51,52,54,56,57,60-62,64-66; No Sabrina 43-Mighty Crusaders cameo. 44-Swipes Mad #4 (Super-Duperman) in "Bird Monsters From Outer Space"	3	6	9	20	31	42
49,50,53,55,58,59,63-Sabrina stories	6	12	18	37	66	95
Annual 1 (1962-63) no Sabrina	9	18	27	59	117	175
Annual 2 (1964) no Sabrina	5	10	15	33	57	80
Annual 3 (1965)-r/1st app. Sabrina from #22	12	24	36	79	170	260
Annual 4,5('66-68)(Becomes Madhouse Ma-ad Annual #7 on); no Sabrina	4	8	12	27	44	60
Annual 6 (1969)-Sabrina the Teen-Age Witch-sty	6	12	18	38	69	100

NOTE: *Cover title to #61-65 is "Madhouse" and to #66 is "Madhouse Ma-ad Jokes". Sci-Fi/Horror covers 6, 8, 11, 13, 15-26, 29, 35, 36, 38, 42, 43, 48, 51, 58, 60.*

ARCHIE'S MECHANICS
Archie Publications: Sept, 1954 - No. 3, 1955

	GD 2.0	VG 4.0	FN 6.0	VF 8.0	VF/NM 9.0	NM- 9.2
1-(15¢; 52 pgs.)	108	216	324	686	1181	1675
2-(10¢)-Last pre-code issue	57	114	171	362	619	875
3-(10¢)	48	96	144	302	514	725

ARCHIE'S MYSTERIES (Continued from Archie's Weird Mysteries)

Archie's Pal, Jughead #20 © ACP

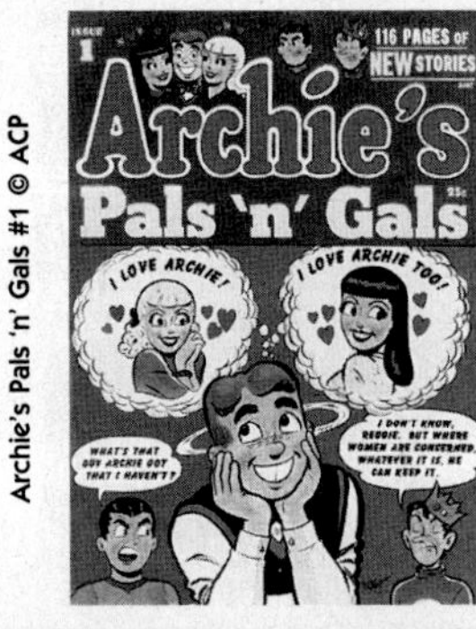

Archie's Pals 'n' Gals #1 © ACP

Archie's Rival Reggie #6 © ACP

	GD 2.0	VG 4.0	FN 6.0	VF 8.0	VF/NM 9.0	NM- 9.2

Archie Comics: No. 25, Feb, 2003 - No. 34, June, 2004 ($2.19)

25-34- Archie and gang as "Teen Scene Investigators" 3.00

ARCHIE'S ONE WAY
Spire Christian Comics (Fleming H. Revell Co.): 1972 (35¢/39¢/49¢, 36 pgs.)

nn-(35¢ Edition) 3 6 9 14 19 24
nn-(39¢, 49¢, no price editions) 2 4 6 10 14 18

ARCHIE'S PAL, JUGHEAD (Jughead No. 127 on)
Archie Publications: 1949 - No. 126, Nov, 1965

1 (1949)-1st app. Moose (see Pep #33) 300 600 900 1950 3375 4800
2 (1950) 103 206 309 659 1130 1600
3-5 58 116 174 371 636 900
6-10: 7-Suzie app. 39 78 117 240 395 550
11-20: 20-Jughead as Sherlock Holmes parody 26 52 78 154 252 350
21-30: 23-25,28-30-Katy Keene app. 23-Early Dilton-s. 28-Debbie's Diary app.
18 36 54 103 162 220
31-50: 49-Archies Rock 'N' Rollers band-c 7 14 21 48 89 130
51-57,59-70: 59- Bio of Will Hutchins of TV's Sugarfoot. 68-Early Archie Gang Cavemen-s
5 10 15 34 60 85
58-Neal Adams-a 6 12 18 40 73 105
71-76,83,89-99: 72-Jughead dates Betty & Veronica. 83 (4/62) 1st mention of Secret Society of Jughead Hating Girls. 95-2nd app. Cricket O'Dell
4 8 12 27 44 60
77,78,80-82,85,86,88-Horror/Sci-Fi-c. 86(7/62) 1st app. The Brain
8 16 24 51 96 140
79-Creature From the Black Lagoon-c 9 18 27 59 117 175
84-1st app. Big Ethyl (5/62) 5 10 15 33 57 80
87-2nd app. of Big Ethyl; UGAJ (United Girls Against Jughead)-s
5 10 15 30 50 70
100 4 8 12 28 47 65
101-Return of Big Ethyl 4 8 12 27 44 60
102-126 3 6 9 19 30 40
Annual 1 (1953, 25¢) 97 194 291 621 1061 1500
Annual 2 (1954, 25¢)-Last pre-code issue 47 94 141 296 498 700
Annual 3-5 (1955-57, 25¢) 34 68 102 199 325 450
Annual 6-8 (1958-60, 25¢) 21 42 63 126 206 285

ARCHIE'S PAL JUGHEAD COMICS (Formerly Jughead #1-45)
Archie Comic Publ.: No. 46, June, 1993 - No. 214, Sept, 2012 ($1.25-$2.99)

46-214: 100-"A Storm Over Uniforms" x-over part 1,2. 166-Three Geeks cameo. 200-Tom Root-s; Sabrina cameo. 201-Begin $2.99-c 3.00

ARCHIE'S PALS 'N' GALS (Also see Archie Giant Series Magazine #628)
Archie Publ: 1952-53 - No. 6, 1957-58; No. 7, 1958 - No. 224, Sept, 1991
(...All News Stories on-c #49-59)

1-(116 pgs., 25¢) 123 246 369 787 1344 1900
2(Annual)('54, 25¢) 52 104 156 328 552 775
3-5(Annual, '55-57, 25¢): 3-Last pre-code issue 39 78 117 231 378 525
6-10('58-'60) 24 48 72 142 234 325
11,13,14,16,17,20-(84 pgs.): 17-B&V paper dolls 14 28 42 80 115 150
12,15-(84 pgs.) Neal Adams-a. 12-Harry Belafonte 2 pg. photos & bio.
15 30 45 90 140 190
18-(84 pgs.) Horror/Sci-Fi-c 18 36 54 105 165 225
19-Marilyn Monroe app. 20 40 60 114 182 250
21,22,24-28,30 (68 pgs.) 6 12 18 41 76 110
23-(Wint./62) 6 pg. Josie-s with Pepper and Melody (1st app.) by DeCarlo; Betty in towel pin-up 46 92 138 368 834 1300
29-Beatles satire (68 pgs.) 9 18 27 60 120 180
31(Wint. 64/65)-39 -(68 pgs.) 5 10 15 33 57 80
40-Early Superteen-s; with Pureheart 6 12 18 41 76 110
41(8/67)-43,45-50(2/69) (68 pgs.) 4 8 12 25 40 55
44-Archies Band-s; WEB cameo 4 8 12 28 47 65
51(4/69),52,55-64(6/71): 62-Last squarebound 3 6 9 18 28 38
53-Archies Band-c/s 3 6 9 21 33 45
54-Satan meets Veronica-s 5 10 15 34 60 85
65(8/70),67-70,73,74,76-81,83(6/74) (52 pgs.) 3 6 9 21 33 45
66,82-Sabrina-c 4 8 12 22 34 45
71,72-Two part drug story (8/72,9/72) 3 6 9 21 33 45
75-Archies Band-s 3 6 9 16 24 32
84-99 2 4 6 8 10 12
100 (12/75) 2 4 6 9 13 16
101-130(3/79): 125,126-Riverdale 2001-s 1 2 3 5 6 8
131-160,162-170 (7/84) 6.00
161 (11/82) 3rd app./1st solo Cheryl Blossom-s and pin-up; 2nd Jason Blossom
5 10 15 34 60 85
171-173,175,177-197,199: 197-G. Colan-a 5.00
174,176,198: 174-New Archies Band-s. 176-Cyndi Lauper-c. 198-Archie gang on strike at Archie Ent. offices 6.00
200(9/88)-Illiteracy-s 6.00
201,203-223: Later issues $1.00 cover 4.00
202-Explains end of Archie's jalopy; Dezerland-c/s; James Dean cameo 6.00
224-Last issue 6.00
NOTE: *Archies Band-c-45,47,49,53,56; s-44,53,75,174. UFO-s-50,63,209,220.*

ARCHIE'S PALS 'N' GALS DOUBLE DIGEST MAGAZINE
Archie Comic Publications: Nov, 1992 - No. 146, Dec, 2010 ($2.50-$3.99)

1-Capt. Hero story; Pureheart app. 2 4 6 8 10 12
2-10: 2-Superduck story; Little Jinx in all. 4-Begin $2.75-c
1 2 3 4 5 7
11-29 4.00
30-146: 40-Begin $2.99-c. 48-Begin $3.19-c. 56-Begin $3.29-c. 72-Begin $3.59-c. 100-Story uses screen captures from classic animated series. 102-Begin $3.69-c 125-128-"New Look" art; Moose and Midge break up. 130-Begin $3.99-c. 133-Reggie spotlight, also reprints early apps. 4.00

ARCHIE'S PARABLES
Spire Christian Comics (Fleming H. Revell Co.): 1973,1975 (39/49¢, 36 pgs.)

nn-By Al Hartley; 39¢ Edition 3 6 9 14 19 24
49¢, no price editions 2 4 6 9 13 16

ARCHIE'S R/C RACERS (Radio controlled cars)
Archie Comics: Sept, 1989 - No. 10, Mar, 1991 (95¢/$1)

1 6.00
2,5-7,10: 5-Elvis parody. 7-Supervillain-c/s. 10-UFO-c/s 4.00
3,4,8,9 3.00

ARCHIE'S RIVAL REGGIE (Reggie & Archie's Joke Book #15 on)
Archie Publications: 1949 - No. 14, Aug, 1954

1-Reggie 1st app. in Jackpot Comics #5 107 214 321 680 1165 1650
2 48 96 144 302 514 725
3-5 36 72 108 211 343 475
6-10 24 48 72 142 234 325
11-14: Katy Keene in No. 10-14, 1-2 pgs. 19 38 57 111 176 240

ARCHIE'S RIVERDALE HIGH (See Riverdale High)

ARCHIE'S ROLLER COASTER
Spire Christian Comics (Fleming H. Revell Co.): 1981 (69¢)

nn-(Low print) 2 4 6 13 18 22

ARCHIE'S SOMETHING ELSE
Spire Christian Comics (Fleming H. Revell Co.): 1975 (39/49¢, 36 pgs.)

nn-(39¢-c) Hell's Angels Biker on motorcycle-c 3 6 9 14 19 24
nn-(49¢-c) 2 4 6 10 14 18
Barbour Christian Comics Edition ('86, no price listed) 2 3 4 6 8 10

ARCHIE'S SONSHINE
Spire Christian Comics (Fleming H. Revell Co.): 1973, 1974 (39/49¢, 36 pgs.)

39¢ Edition 3 6 9 14 19 24
49¢, no price editions 2 4 6 9 13 16

ARCHIE'S SPORTS SCENE
Spire Christian Comics (Fleming H. Revell Co.): 1983 (no cover price)

nn-(Low print) 2 4 6 13 18 22

ARCHIE'S SPRING BREAK
Archie Comics: 1996 - No. 5, 2000 ($2.00/$2.49, 48 pgs., annual)

1-5: 1,2-Dan DeCarlo-c 4.00

ARCHIE'S STORY & GAME COMICS DIGEST MAGAZINE
Archie Enterprises: Nov, 1986 - No. 39, Jan, 1998 ($1.25-$1.95, 128 pgs., digest-size)

1: Marked-up copies are common 2 4 6 11 16 20
2-10 2 4 6 8 10 12
11-20 1 2 3 4 5 7
21-39: 39-($1.95) 4.00

ARCHIE'S SUPER HERO SPECIAL (See Archie Giant Series Mag. No. 142)

ARCHIE'S SUPER HERO SPECIAL (...Comics Digest Mag. 2)
Archie Publications (Red Circle): Jan, 1979 - No. 2, Aug, 1979 (95¢, 148 pgs.)

1-Simon & Kirby r-/Double Life of Pvt. Strong #1,2; Black Hood, The Fly, Jaguar, The Web app. 3 6 9 14 20 25
2-Contains contents to the never published Black Hood #1; origin Black Hood; N. Adams, Wood, Channing, McWilliams, Morrow, S&K-a(r); N. Adams-c. The Shield, The Fly, Jaguar,

Archie vs. Sharknado #1 © ACP

Archie 3000 #5 © ACP

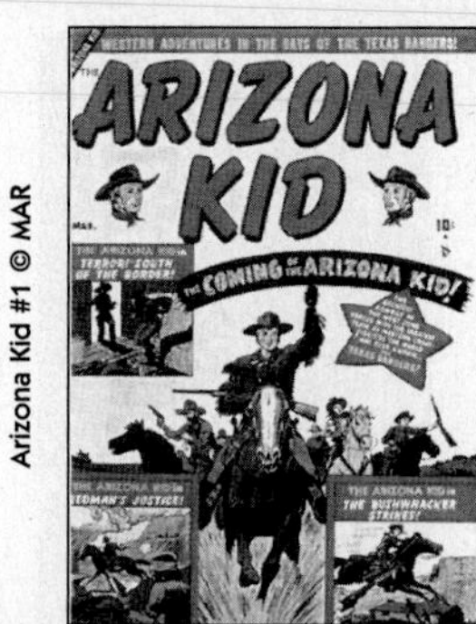

Arizona Kid #1 © MAR

	GD 2.0	VG 4.0	FN 6.0	VF 8.0	VF/NM 9.0	NM- 9.2
Hangman, Steel Sterling, The Web, The Fox-r	3	6	9	14	20	25

ARCHIE'S SUPER TEENS
Archie Comic Publications, Inc.: 1994 - No. 4, 1996 ($2.00, 52 pgs.)

1-Staton/Esposito-c/a; pull-out poster						5.00
2-4: 2-Fred Hembeck script; Bret Blevins/Terry Austin-a						4.00

ARCHIE'S TV LAUGH-OUT ("...Starring Sabrina" on-c #1-50)
Archie Publications: Dec, 1969 - No. 105, Feb, 1986 (#1-7: 68 pgs.)

1-Sabrina begins, thru #105	10	20	30	69	147	225
2 (68 pgs.)	5	10	15	35	63	90
3-6 (68 pgs.)	5	10	15	30	50	70
7-Josie begins, thru #105; Archie's & Josie's Bands cover logos begin	7	14	21	46	86	125
8-23 (52 pgs.): 10-1st Josie on-c. 12-1st Josie and Pussycats on-c. 14-Beatles cameo on poster	4	8	12	25	40	55
24-40: 37,39,40-Bicenntennial-c	3	6	9	14	20	25
41,47,56: 41-Alexandra rejoins J&P band. 47-Fonz cameo; voodoo-s. 56-Fonz parody; B&V with Farrah hair-c	3	6	9	15	22	28
42-46,48-55,57-60	2	4	6	9	12	15
61-68,70-80: 63-UFO-s. 79-Mummy-s	1	3	4	6	8	10
69-Sherlock Holmes parody	1	3	4	6	8	10
81-90,94,95,97-99: 84 Voodoo-s	1	2	3	5	6	8
91-Early Cheryl Blossom-s; Sabrina/Archies Band-c	3	6	9	19	30	40
92-A-Team parody	1	3	4	6	8	10
93-(2/84) Archie in drag-s; Hill Street Blues-s; Groucho Marx parody; cameo parody app. of Batman, Spider-Man, Wonder Woman and others	2	4	6	9	12	15
96-MASH parody-s; Jughead in drag; Archies Band-c	1	3	4	6	8	10
100-(4/85) Michael Jackson parody-c/s; J&P band and Archie band on-c	2	4	6	10	14	18
101-104-Lower print run. 104-Miami Vice parody-c	1	2	3	5	7	9
105-Wrestling/Hulk Hogan parody-c; J&P band-s	2	4	6	9	12	15

NOTE: ***Dan DeCarlo-a** 78-up(most), c-89-up(most). **Archies Band-s** 2,7,9-11,15,20,25,37,64,65,67,68,70,73, 76,78,79,83,84,86,90,96,100,101; **Archies Band-c** 2,17,20,91,94,96,99-103. **Josie-s** 12,21,26,35,52,78,80,90. **Josie-c** 10,91,94. **Josie and the Pussycats (as a band in costume)-s** 7,9,10,37,38,41,42,66,84,99-101,105. **Josie w/Pussycats member Valerie &/or Melody-s** 17,20,22,25,27-29,31,33,36,39,40,43-51,53-65,67-77,79,81-83,85-89,92-94,102-104. **Josie w/Pussycats band-c** 12,14,17,18,22,24. **Sabrina-s** 1-9,11-86,88-106. **Sabrina-c** 1-18,21,23,27,49,91,94.*

ARCHIE'S VACATION SPECIAL
Archie Publications: Winter, 1994 - Present ($2.00/$2.25/$2.29/$2.49, annual)

1						5.00
2-8: 8-(2000, $2.49)						4.00

ARCHIE'S WEIRD MYSTERIES (Continues as Archie's Mysteries)
Archie Comics: Feb, 2000 - No. 24, Dec, 2002 ($1.79/$1.99)

1						3.50
2-24: 3-Mighty Crusaders app. 14-Super Teens-c/app.; Mighty Crusaders app.						3.00

ARCHIE'S WORLD
Spire Christian Comics (Fleming H. Revell Co.): 1973, 1976 (39/49¢)

39¢ Edition	3	6	9	14	19	24
49¢ Edition, no price editions	2	4	6	9	13	16

ARCHIE 3000
Archie Comics: May, 1989 - No. 16, July, 1991 (75¢/95¢/$1.00)

1,16: 16-Aliens-c/s						4.00
2-15: 6-Begin $1.00-c; X-Mas-c						3.00

ARCHIE VS. PREDATOR
Dark Horse Comics: Apr, 2015 - No. 4, Jul, 2015 ($3.99, limited series)

1-4-The Archie gang hunted by the Predator; de Campi-s/Ruiz-a; 3 covers on each 4.00

ARCHIE VS. SHARKNADO
Archie Comics: 2015 ($4.99, one-shot)

1-Based on the Sharknado movie series; Ferrante-s/Parent-a; 3 covers 5.00

ARCOMICS PREMIERE
Arcomics: July, 1993 ($2.95)

1-1st lenticular-c on a comic (flicker-c) 4.00

AREA 52
Image Comics: Jan, 2001 - No. 4, June, 2001 ($2.95)

1-4-Haberlin-s/Henry-a 3.00

ARES
Marvel Comics: Mar, 2006 - No. 5, July, 2006 ($2.99, limited series)

1-5-Oeming-s/Foreman-a						3.00
...: God of War TPB (2006, $13.99) r/series						14.00

ARGUS (See Flash, 2nd Series) (Also see Showcase '95 #1,2)
DC Comics: Apr, 1995 - No. 6, Oct, 1995 ($1.50, limited series)

1-6: 4-Begin $1.75-c 3.00

ARIA
Image Comics (Avalon Studios): Jan, 1999 - No. 4, Nov, 1999 ($2.50)

	GD 2.0	VG 4.0	FN 6.0	VF 8.0	VF/NM 9.0	NM- 9.2
Preview (11/98, $2.95)						5.00
1-Anacleto-c/a	1	2	3	5	6	8
1-Variant-c by Michael Turner	1	2	3	5	6	8
1-($10.00) Alternate-c by Turner	1	3	4	6	8	10
1,2-(Blanc & Noir) Black and white printing of pencil art						3.00
1-(Blanc & Noir) DF Edition						5.00
2-4: 2,4-Anacleto-c/a. 3-Martinez-a						3.00
4-($6.95) Glow in the Dark-c	1	3	4	6	8	10
Aria Angela 1 (2/00, $2.95) Anacleto-a; 4 covers by Anacleto, JG Jones, Portacio and Quesada						3.00
Aria Angela Blanc & Noir 1 (4/00, $2.95) Anacleto-c						3.00
Aria Angela European Ashcan						10.00
Aria Angela 2 (10/00, $2.95) Anacleto-a/c						3.00
...: A Midwinter's Dream 1 (1/02, $4.95, 7"x7") text-s w/Anacleto panels						5.00
...: The Enchanted Collection (5/04, $16.95) r/Summer's Spell & The Uses of Enchantment						17.00

ARIA: SUMMER'S SPELL
Image Comics (Avalon Studios): Mar, 2002 - No. 2, Jun, 2002 ($2.95)

1,2-Anacleto-c/Holguin-s/Pajarillo & Medina-a 3.00

ARIA: THE SOUL MARKET
Image Comics (Avalon Studios): Mar, 2001 - No. 6, Dec, 2001 ($2.95)

1-6-Anacleto-c/Holguin-s						3.00
HC (2002, $26.95, 8.25" x 12.25") oversized r/#1-6						27.00
SC (2004, $16.95, 8.25" x 12.25") oversized r/#1-6						17.00

ARIA: THE USES OF ENCHANTMENT
Image Comics (Avalon Studios): Feb, 2003 - No. 4, Sept, 2003 ($2.95)

1-4-Anacleto-c/Holguin-s/Medina-a 3.00

ARIANE AND BLUEBEARD (See Night Music #8)

ARIEL & SEBASTIAN (See Cartoon Tales & The Little Mermaid)

ARION, LORD OF ATLANTIS (Also see Crisis on Infinite Earths & Warlord #55)
DC Comics: Nov, 1982 - No. 35, Sept, 1985

1-Story cont'd from Warlord #62						4.00
2-35						3.00
... Special #1 (11/85)						4.00

ARION THE IMMORTAL (Also see Arion, Lord of Atlantis & Showcase '95 #7)
DC Comics: July, 1992 - No. 6, Dec, 1992 ($1.50, limited series)

1-6: 4-Gustovich-a(i) 3.00

ARISTOCATS (See Movie Comics & Walt Disney Showcase No. 16)

ARISTOKITTENS, THE (...Meet Jiminy Cricket No. 1)(Disney)
Gold Key: Oct, 1971 - No. 9, Oct, 1975

1	3	6	9	19	30	40
2-5,7-9	3	6	9	14	19	24
6-(52 pgs.)	3	6	9	15	22	28

ARIZONA KID, THE (Also see The Comics & Wild Western)
Marvel/Atlas Comics(CSI): Mar, 1951 - No. 6, Jan, 1952

1	25	50	75	150	245	340
2-4: 2-Heath-a(3)	14	28	42	76	108	140
5,6	11	22	33	62	86	110

NOTE: ***Heath** a-1-3; c-1-3. **Maneely** c-4-6. **Morisi** a-4-6. **Sinnott** a-6.*

ARK, THE (See The Crusaders)

ARKAGA
Image Comics: Sept, 1997 ($2.95, one-shot)

1-Jorgensen-s/a 3.00

ARKANIUM
Dreamwave Productions: Sept, 2002 - No. 5 ($2.95)

1-5: 1-Gatefold wraparound-c 3.00

ARKHAM ASYLUM: LIVING HELL
DC Comics: July, 2003 - No. 6, Dec, 2003 ($2.50, limited series)

1-6-Ryan Sook-a; Batman app. 3-Batgirl-c/app. 3.00

ARKHAM ASYLUM: MADNESS
DC Comics: 2010 ($19.99, HC graphic novel, dustjacket)

Armegeddon #1 © Chaos!

Armor Hunters: Harbinger #3 © VAL

Army of Darkness V3 #1 © Orion

GD VG FN VF VF/NM NM-
2.0 4.0 6.0 8.0 9.0 9.2

GD VG FN VF VF/NM NM-
2.0 4.0 6.0 8.0 9.0 9.2

HC-Sam Kieth-s/a/c; Joker, Two-Face, Harley and Ivy app. 20.00
SC-(2011, $14.99) Sam Kieth-s/a/c; Joker, Two-Face, Harley and Ivy app. 15.00

ARKHAM MANOR (Follows events in Batman Eternal #30)
DC Comics: Dec, 2014 - No. 6, May, 2015 ($2.99)
1-6-Arkham Asylum re-opens in Wayne Manor; Duggan-s/Crystal-a 3.00
...: Endgame 1 (6/15, $2.99) Tieri-s/Albuquerque-c; tie-in with other Batman titles 3.00

ARKHAM REBORN
DC Comics: Dec, 2009 - No. 3, Feb, 2010 ($2.99, limited series)
1-3-David Hine-s/Jeremy Haun-a 3.00
Batman: Arkham Reborn TPB (2010, $12.99) r/#1-3, Detective Comics #864,865 and Batman: Battle For the Cowl: Arkham Asylum #1 13.00

ARMAGEDDON
Chaos! Comics: Oct, 1999 - No. 4, Jan, 2000 ($2.95, limited series)
Preview 5.00
1-4-Lady Death, Evil Ernie, Purgatori app. 3.00

ARMAGEDDON: ALIEN AGENDA
DC Comics: Nov, 1991 - No. 4, Feb, 1992 ($1.00, limited series)
1-4 3.00

ARMAGEDDON FACTOR, THE
AC Comics: 1987 - No. 2, 1987; No. 3, 1990 ($1.95)
1,2: Sentinels of Justice, Dragonfly, Femforce 3.00
3-($3.95, color)-Almost all AC characters app. 4.00

ARMAGEDDON: INFERNO
DC Comics: Apr, 1992 - No. 4, July, 1992 ($1.00, limited series)
1-4: Many DC heroes app. 3-A. Adams/Austin-a 3.00

ARMAGEDDON 2001
DC Comics: May, 1991 - No. 2, Oct, 1991 ($2.00, squarebound, 68 pgs.)
1-Features many DC heroes; intro Waverider 5.00
1-2nd & 3rd printings; 3rd has silver ink-c 4.00
2 4.00

ARMED & DANGEROUS
Acclaim Comics (Armada): Apr, 1996 - No.4, July, 1996 ($2.95, B&W)
1-4-Bob Hall-c/a & scripts 3.00
Special 1 (8/96, $2.95, B&W)-Hall-c/a & scripts. 3.00

ARMED & DANGEROUS HELL'S SLAUGHTERHOUSE
Acclaim Comics (Armada): Oct, 1996 - No. 4, Jan, 1997 ($2.95, B&W)
1-4: Hall-c/a/scripts. 3.00

ARMOR (AND THE SILVER STREAK) (Revengers Featuring... in indicia for #1-3)
Continuity Comics: Sept, 1985 - No.13, Apr, 1992 ($2.00)
1-13: 1-Intro/origin Armor & the Silver Streak; Neal Adams-c/a. 7-Origin Armor; Nebres-i 3.50

ARMOR (DEATHWATCH 2000)
Continuity Comics: Apr, 1993 - No. 6, Nov, 1993 ($2.50)
1-6: 1-3-Deathwatch 2000 x-over 3.00

ARMOR HUNTERS
Valiant Entertainment: Jun, 2014 - No. 4, Sept, 2014 ($3.99)
1-4-Venditti-s/Braithwaite-a; X-O vs. the Hunters. 2-4-Bloodshot app. 4-Ninjak app. 4.00
...: Aftermath 1 (10/14, $3.99) Venditti-s/Cafu-a; leads into Unity #0 4.00

ARMOR HUNTERS: BLOODSHOT
Valiant Entertainment: Jul, 2014 - No. 3, Sept, 2014 ($3.99, limited series)
1-3-Joe Harris-s/Hairsine-a; Malgam app. 4.00

ARMOR HUNTERS: HARBINGER
Valiant Entertainment: Jul, 2014 - No. 3, Sept, 2014 ($3.99, limited series)
1-3-Dysart-s/Gill-a 4.00

ARMORINES (See X-O Manowar #25 for 16 pg. bound-in Armorines #0)
Valiant: June, 1994 - No. 12, June, 1995 ($2.25)
0-Stand-alone edition with cardstock-c 30.00
0-Gold 25.00
1 4.00
2-12: 7-Wraparound-c. 12-Byrne-c/swipe (X-Men, 1st Series #138) 3.00

ARMORINES (Volume 2)
Acclaim Comics: Oct, 1999 - No. 4 ($3.95/$2.50, limited series)
1-($3.95) Calafiore & P. Palmiotti-a 4.00
2,3-($2.50) 3.00

ARMOR WARS (Secret Wars tie-in)
Marvel Comics: Aug, 2015 - No. 5, Nov, 2015 ($3.99, limited series)
1-5-Tony Stark and other armor-clad citizens of Technopolis; Robinson-s/Takara-a 4.00

ARMOR X
Image Comics: March, 2005 - No. 4, June, 2005 ($2.95, limited series)
1-Keith Champagne-s/Andy Smith-a; flip covers on #2-4 3.00

ARMSTRONG AND THE VAULT OF SPIRITS (Archer and Armstrong)
Valiant Entertainment: Feb, 2018 ($3.99, one-shot)
1-Van Lente-s/Cafu & Robertson-a; Archer, Faith, Quantum & Woody, Ivar app. 4.00

ARMY AND NAVY COMICS (Supersnipe No. 6 on)
Street & Smith Publications: May, 1941 - No. 5, July, 1942

	GD 2.0	VG 4.0	FN 6.0	VF 8.0	VF/NM 9.0	NM- 9.2
1-Cap Fury & Nick Carter	55	110	165	352	601	850
2-Cap Fury & Nick Carter	34	68	102	199	325	450
3,4: 4-Jack Farr-c/a	26	52	78	154	252	350
5-Supersnipe app.; see Shadow V2#3 for 1st app.; Story of Douglas MacArthur; George Marcoux-c/a	54	108	162	343	574	825

ARMY @ LOVE
DC Comics (Vertigo): May, 2007 - No. 12, Apr, 2008;
V2 #1, Oct, 2008 - No. 6, Mar, 2009 ($2.99)
1-12-Rick Veitch-s/a(p); Gary Erskine-a(i) 3.00
(Vol. 2) 1-6-Veitch-s/a(p); Erskine-a(i) 3.00
...: Generation Pwned TPB (2008, $12.99) r/#6-12 13.00
...: The Hot Zone Club TPB (2007, $9.99) r/#1-5; intro. by Peter Kuper 10.00

ARMY ATTACK
Charlton Comics: July, 1964 - No. 4, Feb, 1965; V2#38, July, 1965 - No. 47, Feb, 1967

	GD 2.0	VG 4.0	FN 6.0	VF 8.0	VF/NM 9.0	NM- 9.2
V1#1	5	10	15	30	50	70
2-4(2/65)	3	6	9	19	30	40
V2#38(7/65)-47 (formerly U.S. Air Force #1-37)	3	6	9	16	23	30

NOTE: *Glanzman a-1-3. Montes/Bache a-44.*

ARMY AT WAR (Also see Our Army at War & Cancelled Comic Cavalcade)
DC Comics: Oct-Nov, 1978

	GD 2.0	VG 4.0	FN 6.0	VF 8.0	VF/NM 9.0	NM- 9.2
1-Kubert-c; all new story and art	2	4	6	11	16	20

ARMY OF DARKNESS (Movie)
Dark Horse Comics: Nov, 1992 - No. 2, Dec, 1992; No. 3, Oct, 1993 ($2.50, limited series)

	GD 2.0	VG 4.0	FN 6.0	VF 8.0	VF/NM 9.0	NM- 9.2
1-3-Bolton painted-c/a	2	4	6	9	12	15

... Movie Adaptation TPB (2006, $14.99) r/#1-3; intro. by Busiek; Bruce Campbell interview 15.00

ARMY OF DARKNESS (Also see Marvel Zombies vs. Army of Darkness)
Dynamite Entertainment: 2005 - No. 13, 2007 ($2.99)
1-4 (Vs. Re-Animator):1,2-Four covers; Greene-a/Kuhoric-s. 3,4-Three covers 4.00
5-13: 5-7-Kuhoric-s/Sharpe-a; four covers. 8-11-Ash Vs. Dracula. 12,13-Death of Ash 4.00

ARMY OF DARKNESS: ...
Dynamite Entertainment: 2007 - No. 27, 2010 ($3.50/$3.99)
... From the Ashes 1-4-Kuhoric-s/Blanco-a; covers by Blanco & Suydam 4.00
5-8-(The Long Road Home); two covers on each 4.00
9-25: 9-12-(Home Sweet Hell), 13-King For a Day. 14-17-Hellbillies and Deadnecks 4.00
26,27-($3.99) Raicht-s/Cohn-a/c 4.00
#1992.1 (2014, $7.99, squarebound) Short stories by Kuhoric, Niles and others 8.00
...: Ash's Christmas Horror Special (2008, $4.99) Kuhoric-s/Simons-a; 2 covers 5.00
...: Convention Invasion (2014, $7.99, squarebound) Moreci-s/Peeples-a 8.00
... Election Special 1 (2016, $5.99) Serrano-s/Galindo-a 6.00
.../ Reanimator One Shot (2013, $4.99) Rahner-s/Valiente-a 5.00

ARMY OF DARKNESS VOLUME 3
Dynamite Entertainment: 2012 - No. 13, 2013 ($3.99)
1-13: 1-Female Ash; Michaels-a 4.00

ARMY OF DARKNESS VOLUME 4
Dynamite Entertainment: 2014 - No. 5, 2015 ($3.99)
1-5-Ash in space; Bunn-s/Watts-a; multiple covers 4.00

ARMY OF DARKNESS: ASHES 2 ASHES (Movie)
Devil's Due Publ.: July, 2004 - No. 4, 2004 ($2.99, limited series)
1-4-Four covers for each; Nick Bradshaw-a 4.00
1-Director's Cut (12/04, $4.99) r/#1, cover gallery, script and sketch pages 5.00
TPB (2005, $14.99) r/series; cover gallery; Bradshaw interview and sketch pages 15.00

ARMY OF DARKNESS: ASH GETS HITCHED
Dynamite Entertainment: 2014 - No. 4, 2014 ($3.99, limited series)
1-4-Ash in medieval times; Niles-s/Tenorio-a; multiple covers 4.00

The Arrow #3 © CEN

Artifacts #31 © TCOW

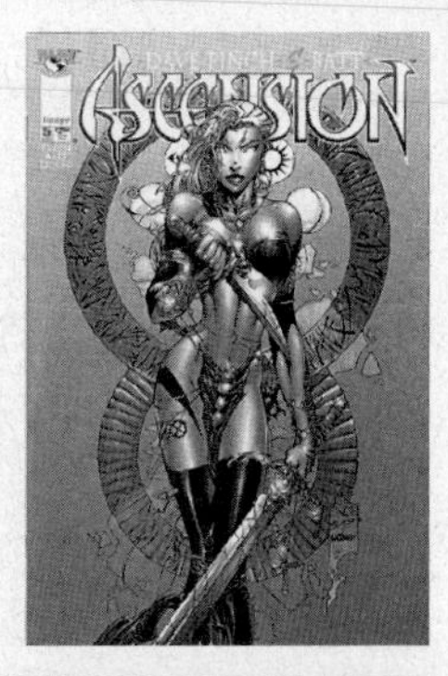

Ascension #5 © Banning & Finch

	GD 2.0	VG 4.0	FN 6.0	VF 8.0	VF/NM 9.0	NM- 9.2

ARMY OF DARKNESS: ASH SAVES OBAMA
Dynamite Entertainment: 2009 - No. 4, 2009 ($3.50, limited series)
1-4-Serrano-s/Padilla-a; covers by Parrillo and Nauck. 4-Obama app. 4.00

ARMY OF DARKNESS FURIOUS ROAD
Dynamite Entertainment: 2016 - No. 6, 2016 ($3.99, limited series)
1-6-Nancy Collins-s/Kewber Baal-a. 1-Multiple covers 4.00

ARMY OF DARKNESS: SHOP TILL YOU DROP DEAD (Movie)
Devil's Due Publ.: Jan, 2005 - No. 4, July, 2005 ($2.99, limited series)
1-4:1-Five covers; Bradshaw-a/Kuhoric-s. 2-4: Two covers. 3-Greene-a 4.00

ARMY OF DARKNESS VS. HACK/SLASH
Dynamite Entertainment: 2013 - No. 6, 2014 ($3.99, limited series)
1-6-Tim Seeley-s/Daniel Leister-a; multiple covers on each 4.00

ARMY OF DARKNESS / XENA
Dynamite Entertainment: 2008 - No. 4, 2008 ($3.50, limited series)
1-4-Layman-s/Montenegro-a; two covers on each 4.00

ARMY OF DARKNESS XENA: WARRIOR PRINCESS FOREVER... AND A DAY
Dynamite Entertainment: 2016 - No. 6, 2017 ($3.99, limited series)
1-6-Lobdell-s. 1-Multiple covers. 1,2-Fernandez-a. 3-6-Galindo-a 4.00

ARMY SURPLUS KOMIKZ FEATURING CUTEY BUNNY
Army Surplus Komikz/Eclipse Comics: 1982 - No. 5, 1985 ($1.50, B&W)
1-Cutey Bunny begins 2 4 6 8 10 12
2-5: 5-(Eclipse)-JLA/X-Men/Batman parody 4.50

ARMY WAR HEROES (Also see Iron Corporal)
Charlton Comics: Dec, 1963 - No. 38, June, 1970
1 5 10 15 35 63 90
2-10 3 6 9 21 33 45
11-21,23-30: 24-Intro. Archer & Corp. Jack series 3 6 9 16 23 30
22-Origin/1st app. Iron Corporal series by Glanzman 5 10 15 30 50 70
31-38 2 4 6 10 14 18
Modern Comics Reprint 36 ('78) 5.00
NOTE: *Montes/Bache a-1, 16, 17, 21, 23-25, 27-30.*

AROUND THE BLOCK WITH DUNC & LOO (See Dunc and Loo)

AROUND THE WORLD IN 80 DAYS (Movie) (See A Golden Picture Classic)
Dell Publishing Co.: Feb, 1957
Four Color 784-Photo-c 7 14 21 46 86 125

AROUND THE WORLD UNDER THE SEA (See Movie Classics)

AROUND THE WORLD WITH ARCHIE (See Archie Giant Series Mag. #29, 35, 141)

AROUND THE WORLD WITH HUCKLEBERRY & HIS FRIENDS (See Dell Giant No. 44)

ARRGH! (Satire)
Marvel Comics Group: Dec, 1974 - No. 5, Sept, 1975 (25¢)
1-Dracula story; Sekowsky-a(p) 3 6 9 19 30 40
2-5: 2-Frankenstein. 3-Mummy. 4-Nightstalker(TV); Dracula-c/app., Hunchback. 5-Invisible Man, Dracula 3 6 9 14 20 25
NOTE *Alcala a-2; c-3. Everett a-1r, 2r. Grandenetti a-4. Maneely a-4r. Sutton a-1-3.*

ARROW (See Protectors)
Malibu Comics: Oct, 1992 ($1.95, one-shot)
1-Moder-a(p) 3.00

ARROW (Based on the 2012 television series)
DC Comics: Jan, 2013 - No. 12, Dec, 2013 ($3.99, printings of digital-first stories)
1-Photo-c; origin retold; Grell-a 1 2 3 5 6 8
1-Special Edition (2012, giveaway) Grell-c; back-up preview of Green Arrow #0 3.00
2-12: 8-12-Photo-c 4.00

ARROW SEASON 2.5 (Follows the second season of the 2012 television series)
DC Comics: Dec, 2014 - No. 12, Nov, 2015 ($2.99, printings of digital-first stories)
1-12-Photo-c on most. 1-5-Brother Blood app. 5,6-Suicide Squad app. 3.00

ARROW, THE (See Funny Pages)
Centaur Publications: Oct, 1940 - No. 2, Nov, 1940; No. 3, Oct, 1941
1-The Arrow begins(r/Funny Pages) 389 778 1167 2723 4762 6800
2,3: 2-Tippy Taylor serial continues from Amazing Mystery Funnies #24. 3-Origin Dash Dartwell, the Human Meteor; origin The Rainbow-r; bondage-c 206 412 618 1318 2259 3200
NOTE: *Gustavson a-1, 2; c-3.*

ARROWHEAD (See Black Rider and Wild Western)
Atlas Comics (CPS): April, 1954 - No. 4, Nov, 1954
1-Arrowhead & his horse Eagle begin 20 40 60 114 182 250
2-4: 4-Forte-a 12 24 36 67 94 120
NOTE: *Heath c-3. Jack Katz a-3. Maneely c-2. Pakula a-2. Sinnott a-1-4; c-1.*

ARROWSMITH (Also see Astro City/Arrowsmith flip book)
DC Comics (Cliffhanger): Sept, 2003 - No. 6, May, 2004 ($2.95)
1-6-Pacheco-a/Busiek-s 3.00
...: So Smart in Their Fine Uniforms TPB (2004, $14.95) r/#1-6 15.00

ARSENAL (Teen Titans' Speedy)
DC Comics: Oct, 1998 - No. 4, Jan, 1999 ($2.50, limited series)
1-4: Grayson-s. 1-Black Canary app. 2-Green Arrow app. 3.00

ARSENAL SPECIAL (See New Titans, Showcase '94 #7 & Showcase '95 #8)
DC Comics: 1996 ($2.95, one-shot)
1 3.00

ARTBABE
Fantagraphics Books: May, 1996 - Apr, 1999 ($2.50/$2.95/$3.50, B&W)
V1 #5, V2 #1-3 3.00
#4-($3.50) 3.50

ARTEMIS IX (See Aphrodite IX)
Image Comics (Top Cow): Aug, 2015 ($3.99, one-shot)
1-Dan Wickline-s/Johnny Desjardins-a; 2 covers 4.00

ARTEMIS: REQUIEM (Also see Wonder Woman, 2nd Series #90)
DC Comics: June, 1996 - No. 6, Nov, 1996 ($1.75, limited series)
1-6: Messner-Loebs scripts & Benes-c/a in all. 1,2-Wonder Woman app. 3.00

ARTIFACTS
Image Comics (Top Cow): Jul, 2010 - No. 40, Nov, 2014 ($3.99, intended as a limited series)
0-(5/10, free) Free Comic Book Day edition; Sejic-a 3.00
1-39: 1-6-Marz-s/Broussard-a. 1-Multiple covers; back-up origin of Witchblade. 7,8-Portacio-a. 9-12-Haun-a. 10-Wraparound-c by Sejic. 13-Keown-a. 14-25-Sejic-a 4.00
40-($5.99) Steve Foxe-s/Adalor Alvarez-a/Sejic-c; back-up stories 6.00
... Lost Tales 1 (5/15, $3.99) Short stories by Talent Hunt runners-up 4.00
...Origins (1/12, $3.99) Two-page spread origins of the 13 artifacts; wraparound-c 4.00

ART OF HOMAGE STUDIOS, THE
Image Comics: Dec, 1993 ($4.95, one-shot)
1-Short stories and pin-ups by Jim Lee, Silvestri, Williams, Portacio & Chiodo 5.00

ART OF ZEN INTERGALACTIC NINJA, THE
Entity Comics: 1994 - No. 2, 1994 ($2.95)
1,2 3.00

ART OPS
DC Comics (Vertigo): Dec, 2015 - No. 12, Dec, 2016 ($3.99)
1-12: Shaun Simon-s/Mike Allred-c. 1-5,8,9,12-Mike Allred-a. 6,7-Eduardo Risso-a 4.00

ARZACH (See Moebius...)
Dark Horse Comics: 1996 ($6.95, one-shot)
nn-Moebius-c/a/scripts 2 4 6 9 12 15

ASCENSION
Image Comics (Top Cow Productions): Oct, 1997 - No. 22, Mar, 2000 ($2.50)
Preview 5.00
Preview Gold Edition 8.00
Preview San Diego Edition 2 4 6 8 10 12
0 4.00
1/2 6.00
1-David Finch-s/a(p)/Batt-s/a(i) 4.00
1-Variant-c w/Image logo at lower right 6.00
2-22 3.00
... Collected Edition 1,2 (1998 - No. 2, $4.95, squarebound) 1-r/#1,2. 2-r/#3,4 5.00
Fan Club Edition 5.00

ASH
Event Comics: Nov, 1994 - No. 6, Dec, 1995; No. 0, May, 1996 ($2.50/$3.00)
0-Present & Future (Both 5/96, $3.00, foil logo-c)-w/pin-ups 3.00
0-Blue Foil logo-c (Present and Future) (1000 each) 4.00
0-Silver Prism logo-c (Present and Future) (500 each) 10.00
0-Red Prism logo-c (Present and Future) (250 each) 20.00
0-Gold Hologram logo-c (Present and Future) (1000 each) 8.00
1-Quesada-p/story; Palmiotti-i/story: Barry Windsor-Smith pin-up 2 4 6 8 10 12
2-Mignola Hellboy pin-up 1 2 3 4 5 7
3,4: 3-Big Guy pin-up by Geoff Darrow. 4-Jim Lee pin-up 4.00

Ash: Cinder & Smoke #5 © Q&P

Aspen #1 © Aspen MLT

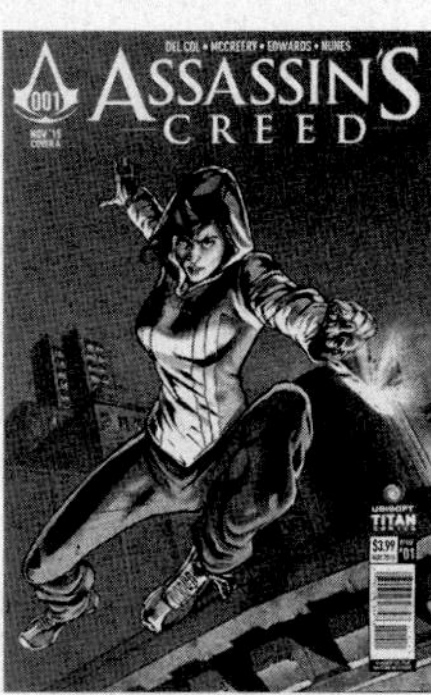

Assassin's Creed #1 © Ubisoft

4-Fahrenheit Gold 7.00
4-6-Fahrenheit Red (5,6-1000) 8.00
4-6-Fahrenheit White 12.00
5, 6-Double-c w/Hildebrandt Bros.-a, Quesada & Palmiotti. 6-Texeira-c 3.00
5,6-Fahrenheit Gold (2000) 4.00
6-Fahrenheit White (500)-Texeira-c 12.00
Volume 1 (1996, $14.95, TPB)-r/#1-5, intro by James Robinson 15.00
Wizard Mini-Comic (1996, magazine supplement) 3.00
Wizard #1/2 (1997, mail order) 4.00

ASH AND THE ARMY OF DARKNESS (Leads into Army of Darkness: Ash Gets Hitched)
Dynamite Entertainment: 2013 - No. 8, 2014 ($3.99)

1-8: 1-5-Niles-s/Calero-a. 1-Three covers. 2-8-Two covers. 6-8-Tenorio-a 4.00

ASH: CINDER & SMOKE
Event Comics: May, 1997 - No. 6, Oct, 1997 ($2.95, limited series)

1-6: Ramos-a/Waid, Augustyn-s in all. 2-6-variant covers by Ramos and Quesada 3.00

ASH: FILES
Event Comics: Mar, 1997 ($2.95, one-shot)

1-Comics w/text 3.00

ASH: FIRE AND CROSSFIRE
Event Comics: Jan, 1999 - No. 5 ($2.95, limited series)

1,2-Robinson-s/Quesada & Palmiotti-c/a 3.00

ASH: FIRE WITHIN, THE
Event Comics: Sept, 1996 - No. 2, Jan, 1997 ($2.95, unfinished limited series)

1,2: Quesada & Palmiotti-c/s/a 3.00

ASH/ 22 BRIDES
Event Comics: Dec, 1996 - No. 2, Apr, 1997 ($2.95, limited series)

1,2: Nicieza-s/Ramos-c/a 3.00

ASH VS. THE ARMY OF DARKNESS
Dynamite Entertainment: No. 0, 2017 - No. 5, 2017 ($3.99)

0-5: 0-Sims & Bowers-s/Vargas-a; multiple covers on each 4.00

ASKANI'SON (See Adventures of Cyclops & Phoenix limited series)
Marvel Comics: Jan, 1996 - No. 4, May, 1996 ($2.95, limited series)

1-4: Story cont'd from Advs. of Cyclops & Phoenix; Lobdell/Loeb story; Gene Ha-c/a(p) 3.00
TPB (1997, $12.99) r/#1-4; Gene Ha painted-c 13.00

ASPEN (MICHAEL TURNER PRESENTS:...) (Also see Fathom)
Aspen MLT, Inc.: July, 2003 - No. 3, Aug, 2003 ($2.99)

1-Fathom story; Turner-a/Johns-s; interviews w/Turner & Johns; two covers by Turner 3.00
2,3:2-Fathom story; Turner-a/Johns-s; two covers by Turner; pin-ups and interviews 3.00
... Presents: The Adventures of the Aspen Universe (10/16, free) coloring book; Oum-a 3.00
... Seasons: Fall 2005 (12/05, $2.99) short stories by various; Turner-c 3.00
... Seasons: Spring 2005 (4/05, $2.99) short stories by various; Turner-c 3.00
... Seasons: Summer 2006 (10/06, $2.99) short stories by various; Turner-c 3.00
... Seasons: Winter 2009 (3/09, $2.99) short stories by various; Benitez-c 3.00
... Showcase: Aspen Matthews 1 (7/08, $2.99) Caldwell-a 3.00
... Showcase: Kiani 1 (10/09, $2.99) Scott Clark-a; covers by Clark and Caldwell 3.00
... Sketchbook 1 (2003, $2.99) sketch pages by Michael Turner and Talent Caldwell 3.00
... Splash: 2006 Swimsuit Spectacular 1 (3/06, $2.99) pin-up pages by various; Turner-c 3.00
... Splash: 2007 Swimsuit Spectacular 1 (8/07, $2.99) pin-up pages by various; Turner-c 3.00
... Splash: 2008 Swimsuit Spectacular 1 (7/08, $2.99) pin-up pages by various; Turner-c 3.00
... Splash: 2010 Swimsuit Spectacular 1 (8/10, $2.99) pin-up pages by various; 2 covers 3.00
... Universe Sourcebook 1 (7/16, $5.99) Character profiles for Fathom, Soulfire, Iris 6.00

ASPEN SHOWCASE
Aspen MLT: Oct, 2008 ($2.99)

...: Benoist 1 (10/08) - Krul-s/Gunnell-a; two covers by Gunnell & Manapul 3.00
...: Ember 1 (2/09) - Randy Green-a; two covers by Gunnell & Green 3.00

ASPEN UNIVERSE: DECIMATION
Aspen MLT: No. 0, May, 2017; No. 1, Oct, 2017 - No. 4, Jan, 2018 (free/$3.99)

0-(5/17, free) Prelude to Aspen crossover series; Hernandez-s/Renna & Bazaldua-a 3.00
1-4-($3.99) Hernandez-s/Renna-a 4.00

ASPEN UNIVERSE: REVELATIONS
Aspen MLT: Jul, 2016 - No. 5, Dec, 2016 ($3.99)

1-5-Fathom & Soulfire crossover; Fialkov & Krul-s/Gunderson-a; multiple covers 4.00

ASSASSINISTAS
IDW Publishing (Black Crown): Dec, 2017 - Present ($3.99)

1-3-Tini Howard-s/Gilbert Hernandez-a 4.00

GD 2.0 | VG 4.0 | FN 6.0 | VF 8.0 | VF/NM 9.0 | NM- 9.2

ASSASSINS
DC Comics (Amalgam): Apr, 1996 ($1.95)

1 3.00

ASSASSIN'S CREED (Based on the Ubisoft Entertainment videogame)
Titan Comics: Nov, 2015 - No. 14, Feb, 2017 ($3.99/$4.99)

1-12: 1-Del Col & McCreery-s/Edwards-a; multiple-c. 1-5-Trial By Fire. 6-11-Setting Sun 4.00
13,14-($4.99) Homecoming 5.00
... Free Comic Book Day (5/16, giveaway) Alves-a; Great Wall back-up w/Calero-a 3.00

ASSASSIN'S CREED: AWAKENING (Based on the Ubisoft Entertainment videogame)
Titan Comics: Dec, 2016 - No. 6, May, 2017 ($4.99, B&W manga style, reads right to left)

1-6-Takashi Yano-s/Kenji Oiwa-a 5.00

ASSASSIN'S CREED: LOCUS (Based on the Ubisoft Entertainment videogame)
Titan Comics: Oct, 2016 - No. 4, Jan, 2017 ($3.99, limited series)

1-4-Edginton-s/Wijngaard-a 4.00

ASSASSIN'S CREED: ORIGINS (Based on the Ubisoft Entertainment videogame)
Titan Comics: Mar, 2018 - No. 4 ($3.99, limited series)

1-Del Col-s/Kaiowa-a; 4 covers 4.00

ASSASSIN'S CREED: REFLECTIONS (Based on the Ubisoft Entertainment videogame)
Titan Comics: Apr, 2017 - No. 4, Aug, 2017 ($3.99, limited series)

1-4-Edginton-s/Favoccia-a 4.00

ASSASSIN'S CREED: THE FALL (Based on the Ubisoft Entertainment videogame)
DC Comics: Jan, 2011 - No. 3, Mar, 2011 ($3.99, limited series)

1-3-Cam Stewart & Karl Kerschl-s/a 4.00

ASSASSIN'S CREED: UPRISING (Based on the Ubisoft Entertainment videogame)
Titan Comics: Feb, 2017 - No. 8, Nov, 2017 ($3.99)

1-8-Paknadel & Watters-s/Holder-a; multiple covers 4.00

ASSIGNMENT, THE (Adapts screenplay of 2017 movie The Assignment)
Titan Comics (Hard Case Crime): Feb, 2017 - Present ($5.99)

1-3-Walter Hill & Denis Hamill-s/Jef-a; English version of French comic 6.00

ASSAULT ON NEW OLYMPUS PROLOGUE
Marvel Comics: Jan, 2010 ($3.99, one-shot)

1-Spider-Man, Hercules, Amadeus Cho app.; Granov-c; leads into Inc. Hercules #138 4.00

ASTONISHING (Formerly Marvel Boy No. 1, 2)
Marvel/Atlas Comics(20CC): No. 3, Apr, 1951 - No. 63, Aug, 1957

	GD 2.0	VG 4.0	FN 6.0	VF 8.0	VF/NM 9.0	NM- 9.2
3-Marvel Boy continues; 3-5-Marvel Boy-c	155	310	465	992	1696	2400
4-6-Last Marvel Boy; 4-Stan Lee app.	103	206	309	659	1130	1600
7-10: 7-Maneely s/f story. 10-Sinnott s/f story	53	106	159	334	567	800
11,12,15,17,20	47	94	141	296	498	700
13,14,16,18,19-Krigstein-a. 18-Jack The Ripper sty	48	96	144	302	514	725
21,22,24	39	78	117	231	378	525
23-E.C. swipe "The Hole In The Wall" from Vault Of Horror #16	39	78	117	240	395	550
25,29: 25-Crandall-a. 29-Decapitation-c	37	74	111	222	361	500
26-28	37	74	111	218	354	490
30-Tentacled eyeball-c/story; classic-c	71	142	213	454	777	1100
31-Classic story: man develops atomic powers after exposure to A-bomb; four A-bomb panels	34	68	102	199	325	450
32-37-Last pre-code issues	32	64	96	188	307	425
38-43,46,48-52,56,58,59,61	24	48	72	142	234	325
44,45,47,53-55,57,60: 44-Crandall swipe/Weird Fantasy #22. 45,47-Krigstein-a. 53-Ditko-a. 54-Torres-a, 55-Crandall, Torres-a. 57-Williamson/Krenkel-a (4 pgs.). 60-Williamson/Mayo-a (4 pgs.)	27	54	81	158	259	360
62,63: 62-Torres, Powell-a. 63-Woodbridge-a	25	50	75	150	245	340

NOTE: ***Ayers** a-16, 49. **Berg** a-36, 53, 56. **Cameron** a-50. **Gene Colan** a-12, 20, 29, 56. **Ditko** a-53. **Drucker** a-41, 62. **Everett** a-3-6(3), 6, 10, 12, 37, 47, 48, 58; c-3-5, 13,15, 16, 18, 29, 47, 49, 51, 53-55, 57, 59-63. **Fass** a-11, 34. **Forte** a-26, 48, 53, 58, 60. **Fuje** a-11. **Heath** a-8, 29; c-8, 9, 19, 22, 25, 26. **Kirby** a-56. **Lawrence** a-28, 37, 38, 42. **Maneely** a-7(2), 19; c-7, 31, 33, 34, 56. **Moldoff** a-33. **Morisi** a-10, 60. **Morrow** a-52, 61. **Orlando** a-47, 58, 61. **Pakula** a-10. **Powell** a-43, 44, 48. **Ravielli** a-26, 28. **Reinman** a-32, 34, 38. **Robinson** a-20. **J. Romita** a-7, 18, 24, 43, 57,61. **Roussos** a-55. **Sale** a-28, 38, 59; c-32. **Sekowsky** a-13. **Severin** c-46. **Shores** a-16, 60. **Sinnott** a-11, 30, 31. **Whitney** a-13. **Ed Win** a-20. Canadian reprints exist.*

ASTONISHING ANT-MAN (Scott Lang)
Marvel Comics: Dec, 2015 - No. 13, Dec, 2016($3.99)

1-12: 1-Spencer-s/Rosanas-a; Cassie Lang app. 2,3-Capt. America (Sam Wilson) app. 4.00
13-($4.99) Spencer-s/Schoonover & Rosanas-a; Yellowjacket app. 5.00

ASTONISHING SPIDER-MAN AND WOLVERINE
Marvel Comics: Jul, 2010 - No. 6, Jul. 2011 ($3.99, limited series)

1-6-Adam Kubert-a/Jason Aaron-s. 1-Bonus pin-up gallery; wraparound-c 4.00

Astonishing Tales (2009 series) #1 © MAR

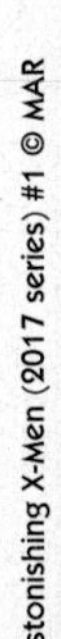

Astonishing X-Men (2017 series) #1 © MAR

Astro City (2013 series) #41 © Juke Box Prods.

GD 2.0 | VG 4.0 | FN 6.0 | VF 8.0 | VF/NM 9.0 | NM- 9.2

1-Director's Cut (10/10, $4.99) r/#1 with full script & B&W art 5.00
...: Another Fine Mess (6/11, $4.99) r/#1-3; wraparound-c 5.00

ASTONISHING TALES (See Ka-Zar)
Marvel Comics Group: Aug, 1970 - No. 36, July, 1976 (#1-7: 15¢; #8: 25¢)

	GD 2.0	VG 4.0	FN 6.0	VF 8.0	VF/NM 9.0	NM- 9.2
1-Ka-Zar (by Kirby(p) #1,2; by B. Smith #3-6) & Dr. Doom (by Wood #1-4; by Tuska #5,6; by Colan #7,8; 1st Marvel villain solo series) double feature begins; Kraven the Hunter-c/story; Nixon cameo	6	12	18	38	69	100
2-Kraven the Hunter-c/story; Kirby, Wood-a	3	6	9	21	33	45
3-5: B. Smith-p; Wood-a-#3,4. 5-Red Skull app.	4	8	12	23	37	50
6-1st app. Bobbi Morse (later becomes Mockingbird); Doctor Doom vs. Black Panther-c/sty;	5	10	15	34	60	85
7-Last 15¢ issue; Black Panther app.	3	6	9	17	26	35
8-(25¢, 52 pgs.)-Last Dr. Doom of series	4	8	12	23	37	50
9-All Ka-Zar issues begin; Lorna-r/Lorna #14	2	4	6	11	16	20
10-B. Smith/Sal Buscema-a.	3	6	9	14	20	25
11-Origin Ka-Zar & Zabu; death of Ka-Zar's father	2	4	6	13	18	22
12-2nd app.Man-Thing; by Neal Adams (see Savage Tales #1 for 1st app.)	5	10	15	35	63	90
13-3rd app.Man-Thing	4	8	12	25	40	55
14-20: 14-Jann of the Jungle-r (1950s); reprints censored Ka-Zar-s from Savage Tales #1. 17-S.H.I.E.L.D. begins. 19-Starlin-a(p). 20-Last Ka-Zar (continues into 1974 Ka-Zar series)	1	3	4	6	8	10
21-(12/73)-It! the Living Colossus begins, ends #24 (see Supernatural Thrillers #1)	4	8	12	23	37	50
22	3	6	9	17	26	35
23,24-It! the Living Colossus vs. Fin Fang Foom	4	8	12	23	37	50
25-1st app. Deathlok the Demolisher; full length stories begin, end #36; Perez's 1st work, 2 pgs. (8/74)	8	16	24	51	96	140
26-28,30	3	6	9	14	20	25
29-Reprints origin/1st app. Guardians of the Galaxy from Marvel Super-Heroes #18 plus-c w/4 pgs. omitted; no Deathlok story	3	6	9	19	30	40
31-34: 31-Watcher-r/Silver Surfer #3	2	4	6	10	14	18
35,36-(Regular 25¢ edition)(5,7/76)	2	4	6	10	14	18
35,36-(30¢-c, low distribution)	6	12	18	37	66	95

NOTE: ***Buckler** a-13i, 16p, 25, 26p, 27p, 28, 29p-36p; c-13, 25p, 26-30, 32-35p, 36. **John Buscema** a-9, 12p-14p, 16p; c-4-6p, 12p. **Colan** a-7p, 8p. **Ditko** a-21r. **Everett** a-6i. **G. Kane** a-11p, 15p; c-9, 10p, 11p, 14, 15p, 21p. **McWilliams** a-30i. **Starlin** a-19p; c-16p. **Sutton & Trimpe** a-8. **Tuska** a-5p, 6p, 8p. **Wood** a-1-4. **Wrightson** c-31i.*

ASTONISHING TALES (Anthology)
Marvel Comics: Apr, 2009 - No. 6, Sept, 2009 ($3.99, limited series)

1-6-Wolverine, Punisher, Iron Man and Iron Man 2020 app. 1-Wraparound-c 4.00

ASTONISHING THOR
Marvel Comics: Jan, 2011 - No. 5, Sept, 2011 ($3.99, limited series)

1-5: 1-Robert Rodi-s/Mike Choi-a/Esad Ribic-c 4.00

ASTONISHING X-MEN
Marvel Comics: Mar, 1995 - No. 4, July, 1995 ($1.95, limited series)

1-Age of Apocalypse; Magneto-c 4.00
2-4 3.00

ASTONISHING X-MEN
Marvel Comics: Sept, 1999 - No. 3, Nov, 1999 ($2.50, limited series)

1-3-New team, Cable & X-Man app.; Peterson-a 3.00
TPB (11/00, $15.95) r/#1-3, X-Men #92 & #95, Uncanny X-Men #375 16.00

ASTONISHING X-MEN (See Giant-Size Astonishing X-Men for story folllowing #24)
Marvel Comics: July, 2004 - No. 68, Dec, 2013 ($2.99/$3.99)

1-Whedon-s/Cassaday-c/a; team of Cyclops, Beast, Wolverine, Emma Frost & Kitty Pryde 4.00
1-Director's Cut (2004, $3.99) different Cassaday partial sketch-c; cover gallery, sketch pages and script excerpt 5.00
1-Variant-c by Cassaday 10.00
1-Variant-c by Dell'Otto 5.00
2,3,5,6-X-Men battle Ord 3.00
4-Colossus returns 4.00
4-Variant Colossus cover by Cassaday 5.00
7-24: 7-Fantastic Four app. 9,10-X-Men vs. the Danger Room 3.00
7,9,10-12,19-24-Second printing variant covers 3.00
25-35: 25-Ellis-s/Bianchi-a begins; Bianchi wraparound-c. 31-Jimenez-a begins 3.00
36-68-($3.99): 36-Pearson wraparound-c; Way-s/Pearson-a. 44-47-McKone-a. 51-Northstar wedding; wraparound-c. 60-X-Termination tie-in 4.00
Annual 1 (1/13, $4.99) Gage-s/Baldeon-a; bonus r/Alpha Flight #106 5.00
.../Amazing Spider-Man: The Gauntlet Sketchbook ('09, giveaway) flip book preview 3.00
...: Ghost Boxes 1,2 (12/08-1/09, $3.99) Ellis-s/Davis & Granov-a; full Ellis script 4.00
... Saga (2006, $3.99) reprints highlights from #1-12; sketch pages and cover gallery 4.00
... Sketchbook Special ('08, $2.99) Costume sketches & blueprints by Bianchi & Larroca 3.00
...Vol. 1 HC (2006, $29.99, dust jacket) r/#1-12; interviews, sketch pages and covers 30.00
...Vol. 1: Gifted (2004, $14.99) r/#1-6; variant cover gallery 15.00
...Vol. 2: Dangerous (2005, $14.99) r/#7-12; variant cover gallery 15.00
...Vol. 3: Torn (2007, $14.99) r/#13-18; variant & sketch cover gallery 15.00

ASTONISHING X-MEN
Marvel Comics: Sept, 2017 - Present ($4.99/$3.99)

1-($4.99) Soule-s/Cheung-a; Old Man Logan, Rogue, Bishop, Gambit, Psylocke app. 5.00
2-8-($3.99) 2-Deodato-a; Mystique app. 3-McGuinness-a. 4-Pacheco-a. 7-Xavier returns; Noto-a 4.00

ASTONISHING X-MEN: XENOGENESIS
Marvel Comics: July, 2010 - No. 5, Apr, 2011 ($3.99, limited series)

1-5-Warren Ellis-s/Kaare Andrews-a/c. 1-Wraparound-c; script 4.00
1-Director's Cut (10/10, $4.99) r/#1 with full script & B&W art; cover sketches 5.00

ASTOUNDING SPACE THRILLS: THE COMIC BOOK
Image Comics: Apr, 2000 - No. 4, Dec, 2000 ($2.95, limited series)

1-4-Steve Conley-s/a. 2,3-Flip book w/Crater Kid 3.00
Galaxy-Sized Astounding Space Thrills 1 (10/01, $4.95) 5.00

ASTOUNDING WOLF-MAN
Image Comics: Jun, 2007 - No. 25, Nov, 2010 ($2.99)

1-Free Comic Boy Day issue; Kirkman-s/Howard-a; origin story 3.00
2-24: 11-Invincible x-over from Invincble #57 3.00
25-($4.99) Wraparound-c; Wolfcorps app. 5.00
Vol. 1 TPB (2008, $14.99) r/#1-7; sketch pages; Kirkman intro. 15.00

ASTRA
CPM Manga: 2001 - No. 8 ($2.95, B&W, limited series)

1-8: Created by Jerry Robinson; Tanaka-a. 1-Balent variant-c 3.00
TPB (2002, $15.95) r/#1-8; JH Williams III-c from #3 16.00

ASTRO BOY (TV) (See March of Comics #285 & The Original...)
Gold Key: August, 1965 (12¢)

	GD 2.0	VG 4.0	FN 6.0	VF 8.0	VF/NM 9.0	NM- 9.2
1(10151-508) 1st app. Astro Boy in comics	27	54	81	189	420	650

ASTRO BOY THE MOVIE (Based on the 2009 CGI movie)
IDW Publishing: 2009 ($3.99, limited series)

...Official Movie Adaptation 1-4 (8/09 - No. 4, 9/09, $3.99) EJ Su-a 4.00
...Official Movie Prequel 1-4 (5/09 - No. 4, 8/09) Jourdan-a/c; Ashley Wood var-c on each 4.00

ASTRO CITY (Also see Kurt Busiek's Astro City)
DC Comics (WildStorm Productions): Dec, 2004 - Dec, 2009 (one-shots)

...#1 Special Edition (8/10, $1.00) reprints first issue with "What's Next? cover logo 3.00
...: Astra Special 1,2 (11/09, 12/09, $3.99) Busiek-s/Anderson-a/Ross-c 4.00
... A Visitor's Guide (12/04, $5.95) short story, city guide and pin-ups by various; Ross-c 6.00
...: Beautie (4/08, $3.99) Busiek-s/Anderson-a/Ross-c; origin 4.00
...: Samaritan (9/06, $3.99) Busiek-s/Anderson-a/Ross-c; origin of Infidel 4.00
...: Shining Stars HC (2011, $24.99, d.j) r/...: Astra Special 1,2, ...: Beautie, ...: Samaritan, and ...: Silver Agent 1,2; bonus design art and Ross cover sketch art 25.00
...: Silver Agent 1,2 (8,9/10, $3.99) Busiek-s/Anderson-a/Ross-c 4.00

ASTRO CITY (Also see Kurt Busiek's Astro City)
DC Comics (Vertigo): Aug, 2013 - Present ($3.99)

1-50-Busiek-s/Ross-c; Anderson-a in most. 12-Nolan-a. 17-Grummett-a. 22,25-Merino-a. 35,36-Ron Randall-a; Jack-In-The Box app. 39,40-Carnero-a. 47-Origin G-Dog 4.00

ASTRO CITY / ARROWSMITH (Flip book)
DC Comics (WildStorm Productions): Jun, 2004 ($2.95, one-shot flip book)

1-Intro. Black Badge; Ross-c; Arrowsmith a/c by Pacheco 3.00

ASTRO CITY: DARK AGE
DC Comics (WildStorm Productions): Aug, 2005 - No. 4, Dec, 2005 ($2.95, limited series)

Book One 1-4-Busiek-s/Anderson-a/Ross-c; Silver Agent and The Blue Knight app. 3.00
Book Two #1-4 (1/07-11/07, $2.99) Busiek-s/Anderson-a/Ross-c 3.00
Book Three #1-4 (7/09-10/09, $3.99) Busiek-s/Anderson-a/Ross-c 4.00
Book Four #1-4 (3/10-6/10, $3.99) Busiek-s/Anderson-a/Ross-c 4.00
... 1: Brothers and Other Strangers HC (2008, $29.99, d.j.) r/Book One #1-4, Book Two #1-4, and story from Astro City/Arrowsmith #1; Marc Guggenheim intro.; new Ross-c 30.00
... 1: Brothers and Other Strangers SC (2009, $19.99) same contents as HC 20.00
... 2: Brothers in Arms HC ('10, $29.99, d.j.) r/Book Three #1-4, Book Four #1-4, Ross-c 30.00

ASTRO CITY: LOCAL HEROES
DC Comics (WildStorm Productions): Apr, 2003 - No. 5, Feb, 2004 ($2.95, limited series)

1-5-Busiek-s/Anderson-a/Ross-c 3.00
HC (2005, $24.95) r/series; Kurt Busiek's Astro City V2 #21,22; stories from Astro City/ Arrowsmith #1; and 9-11, The World's Finest... Vol. 2; Alex Ross sketch pages 25.00

Atari Force #4 © Atari

The Atom #4 © DC

Atom-Age Combat #3 © STJ

	GD 2.0	VG 4.0	FN 6.0	VF 8.0	VF/NM 9.0	NM- 9.2

SC (2005, $17.99) same contents as HC 18.00

ASTRONAUTS IN TROUBLE
Image Comics: Jun, 2015 - No. 11 ($2.99, B&W, reprints of earlier Astronauts in Trouble)

1-11-Larry Young-s. 1-3-Reprints the Space: 1959 series; Charlie Adlard-a. 4-9-Reprints the Live From the Moon series. 4-6-Matt Smith-a. 7-11-Adlard-a 3.00

ASYLUM
Millennium Publications: 1993 ($2.50)

1-3: 1-Bolton-c/a; Russell 2-pg. illos 3.00

ASYLUM
Maximum Press: Dec, 1995 - No. 11, Jan, 1997 ($2.95/$2.99, anthology) (#1-6 are flip books)

1-11: 1-Warchild by Art Adams, Beanworld, Avengelyne, Battlestar Galactica. 2-Intro Mike Deodato's Deathkiss. 4-1st app.Christian; painted Battlestar Galactica story begins. 6-Intro Bionix (Six Million Dollar Man & the Bionic Woman). 7-Begin $2.99-c. 8-B&W-a. 9- Foot Soldiers & Kid Supreme. 10-Lady Supreme by Terry Moore-c/app. 4.00

ATARI FORCE (Also see Promotional comics section)
DC Comics: Jan, 1984 - No. 20, Aug, 1985 (Mando paper)

1-(1/84)-Intro Tempest, Packrat, Babe, Morphea, & Dart; García-López-a 4.00
2-20 3.00
Special 1 (4/86) 4.00

NOTE: ***Byrne*** *c-Special 1i.* ***Giffen*** *a-12p, 13i.* ***Rogers*** *a-18p, Special 1p.*

A-TEAM, THE (TV) (Also see Marvel Graphic Novel)
Marvel Comics Group: Mar, 1984 - No. 3, May, 1984 (limited series)

	GD	VG	FN	VF	VF/NM	NM-
1-3						6.00
1,2-(Whitman bagged set) w/75¢-c	2	4	6	8	10	12
3-(Whitman, no bag) w/75¢-c	1	2	3	5	6	8

A-TEAM: SHOTGUN WEDDING (Based on the 2010 movie)
IDW Publishing: Mar, 2010 - No. 4, Apr, 2010 ($3.99, limited series)

1-4-Co-plotted by Joe Carnahan; Stephen Mooney-a; Snyder III-c 4.00

A-TEAM: WAR STORIES (Based on the 2010 movie)
IDW Publishing: Mar, 2010 - Apr, 2010 ($3.99, series of one-shots)

...: B.A. (3/10) Dixon & Burnham-s/Maloney-a/Gaydos & photo-c 4.00
...: Face (4/10) Dixon & Burnham-s/Muriel-a/Gaydos & photo-c 4.00
...: Hannibal (3/10) Dixon & Burnham-s/Petrus-a/Gaydos & photo-c 4.00
...: Murdock (4/10) Dixon & Burnham-s/Vilanova-a/Gaydos & photo-c 4.00

ATHENA INC. THE MANHUNTER PROJECT
Image Comics: Dec, 2001; Apr, 2002 - No. 6 ($2.95/$4.95/$5.95)

...The Beginning (12/01, $5.95) Anacleto-c/a; Haberlin-s 6.00
1-5: 1-(4/02, $2.95) two covers by Anacleto 3.00
6-($4.95) 5.00
...: Agents Roster #1 (11/02, $5.95, 8 1/2 x 11") bios and sketch pages by Anacleto 6.00
Vol. 1 TPB (4/03, $19.95) r/#1-6 & Agents Roster; cover gallery 20.00

ATHENA
Dynamite Entertainment: 2009 - No. 4, 2010 ($3.50)

1-4-Murray-s/Neves-a; multiple covers on each. 1-Obama flip cover 3.50

ATHENA IX (See Aphrodite IX)
Image Comics (Top Cow): Jul, 2015 ($3.99, one-shot)

1-Ryan Cady-s/Phillip Sevy; 3 covers 4.00

ATLANTIS CHRONICLES, THE (Also see Aquaman, 3rd Series & Aquaman: Time & Tide)
DC Comics: Mar, 1990 - No. 7, Sept, 1990 ($2.95, limited series, 52 pgs.)

1-7: 1-Peter David scripts. 7-True origin of Aquaman; nudity panels 4.00

ATLANTIS, THE LOST CONTINENT
Dell Publishing Co.: May, 1961

	GD	VG	FN	VF	VF/NM	NM-
Four Color #1188-Movie, photo-c	9	18	27	60	120	180

ATLAS (See 1st Issue Special)

ATLAS
Dark Horse Comics: Feb, 1994 - No. 4, 1994 ($2.50, limited series)

1-4 3.00

ATLAS (Agents of Atlas)(The Heroic Age)
Marvel Comics: Jul, 2010 - No. 5, Nov, 2010 ($3.99/$2.99)

1-($3.99) Parker-s/Hardman-a/Dodson-c; 3-D Man app.; profile page 4.00
2-5-($2.99) 2,3,5-Pagulayan-c. 4-Jae Lee-c 3.00

ATLAS UNIFIED
Atlas Comics: No. 0, Oct, 2011 - No. 2, Feb, 2012 ($2.99, unfinished limited series)

0 Prelude: Midnight (10/11) Phoenix, Kromag, Sgt. Hawk app.; bonus sketch pages 3.00
1,2: 1-Three covers; Peyer-s/Salgado-a; x-over of Grim Ghost, Wulf, Phoenix & others 3.00

ATMOSPHERICS
Avatar Press: June, 2002 ($5.95, B&W, one-shot graphic novel)

1-Warren Ellis-s/Ken Meyer Jr.-painted-a/c 6.00

ATOM, THE (See Action #425, All-American #19, Brave & the Bold, D.C. Special Series #1, Detective Comics, Flash Comics #80, Hawkman, Identity Crisis, JLA, Power Of The Atom, Showcase #34 -36, Super Friends, Sword of The Atom, Teen Titans & World's Finest)

ATOM, THE (...& the Hawkman No. 39 on)
National Periodical Publ.: June-July, 1962 - No. 38, Aug-Sept, 1968

	GD	VG	FN	VF	VF/NM	NM-
1-(6-7/62)-Intro Plant-Master; 1st app. Maya	102	204	306	816	1858	2850
2	31	62	93	223	499	775
3-1st Time Pool story; 1st app. Chronos (origin)	21	42	63	147	324	500
4,5: 4-Snapper Carr x-over	15	30	45	103	227	350
6,9,10	11	22	33	76	163	250
7-Hawkman x-over (6-7/63; 1st Atom & Hawkman team-up); 1st app. Hawkman since Brave & the Bold tryouts	23	46	69	161	356	550
8-Justice League, Dr. Light app.	12	24	36	82	179	275
11-15: 13-Chronos-c/story	9	18	27	60	120	180
16-18,20	7	14	21	46	86	125
19-Zatanna x-over; 2nd app.	9	18	27	59	117	175
21-28,30: 26-Two-page pin-up. 28-Chronos-c/story	6	12	18	41	76	110
29-1st solo Golden Age Atom x-over in S.A.	13	26	39	89	195	300
31-35,37,38: 31-Hawkman x-over. 37-Intro. Major Mynah; Hawkman cameo	5	10	15	35	63	90
36-G.A. Atom x-over	6	12	18	41	76	110

NOTE: ***Anderson*** *a-1-11i, 13i; c-inks-1-25, 31-35, 37.* ***Sid Greene*** *a-8i-37i.* ***Gil Kane*** *a-1p-37p; c-1p-28p, 29, 33p, 34; c-26i.* ***George Roussos*** *a-38i.* ***Mike Sekowsky*** *a-38p. Time Pool stories also in 6, 9,12, 17, 21, 27, 35.*

ATOM, THE (See All New Atom and Tangent Comics/ The Atom)

ATOM AGE (See Classics Illustrated Special Issue)

ATOM-AGE COMBAT
St. John Publishing Co.: June, 1952 - No. 5, Apr, 1953; Feb, 1958

	GD	VG	FN	VF	VF/NM	NM-
1-Buck Vinson in all	55	110	165	352	601	850
2-Flying saucer story	34	68	102	199	325	450
3,5: 3-Mayo-a (6 pgs.). 5-Flying saucer-c/story	30	60	90	177	289	400
4 (Scarce)	34	68	102	199	325	450
1(2/58-St. John)	26	52	78	154	252	350

ATOM-AGE COMBAT
Fago Magazines: No. 2, Jan, 1959 - No. 3, Mar, 1959

	GD	VG	FN	VF	VF/NM	NM-
2-A-Bomb explosion-c;	32	64	96	188	307	425
3	23	46	69	138	227	315

ATOMAN
Spark Publications: Feb, 1946 - No. 2, April, 1946

	GD	VG	FN	VF	VF/NM	NM-
1-Origin & 1st app. Atoman; Robinson/Meskin-a; Kidcrusaders, Wild Bill Hickok, Marvin the Great app.	74	148	222	470	810	1150
2-Robinson/Meskin-a; Robinson c-1,2	45	90	135	284	480	675

ATOM & HAWKMAN, THE (Formerly The Atom)
National Periodical Publ: No. 39, Oct-Nov, 1968 - No. 45, Oct-Nov, 1969; No. 46, Mar, 2010

	GD	VG	FN	VF	VF/NM	NM-
39-43: 40-41-Kubert/Anderson-a. 43-(7/69)-Last 12¢ issue; 1st S.A. app. Gentleman Ghost	5	10	15	34	60	85
44,45: 44-(9/69)-1st 15¢-c; origin Gentleman Ghost	5	10	15	34	60	85
46-(3/10, $2.99) Blackest Night crossover one-shot; Geoff Johns-s/Ryan Sook-a/c						3.00

NOTE: ***M. Anderson*** *a-39, 40i, 41i, 43, 44.* ***Sid Greene*** *a-40i-45i.* ***Kubert*** *a-40p, 41p; c-39-45.*

ATOM ANT (TV) (See Golden Comics Digest #2) (Hanna-Barbera)
Gold Key: January, 1966 (12¢)

	GD	VG	FN	VF	VF/NM	NM-
1(10170-601)-1st app. Atom Ant, Precious Pup, and Hillbilly Bears	15	30	45	103	227	350

ATOM ANT & SECRET SQUIRREL (See Hanna-Barbera Presents)

ATOMIC AGE
Marvel Comics (Epic Comics): Nov, 1990 - No. 4, Feb, 1991 ($4.50, limited series, square-bound, 52 pgs.)

1-4: Williamson-a(i); sci-fi story set in 1957 4.50

ATOMIC ATTACK (True War Stories; formerly Attack, first series)
Youthful Magazines: No. 5, Jan, 1953 - No. 8, Oct, 1953 (1st story is sci/fi in all issues)

	GD	VG	FN	VF	VF/NM	NM-
5-Atomic bomb-c; science fiction stories in all	47	94	141	296	498	700
6-8	32	64	96	188	307	425

ATOMIC BOMB
Jay Burtis Publications: 1945 (36 pgs.)

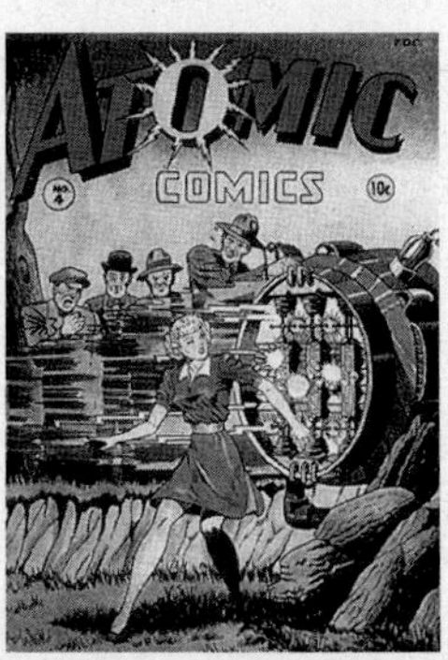

Atomic Comics #4 © Green Pub. Co.

Attack #54 © CC

Attack on Planet Mars #1 © AVON

	GD 2.0	VG 4.0	FN 6.0	VF 8.0	VF/NM 9.0	NM- 9.2
1-Superheroes Airmale & Stampy (scarce)	71	142	213	454	777	1100

ATOMIC BUNNY (Formerly Atomic Rabbit)
Charlton Comics: No. 12, Aug, 1958 - No. 19, Dec, 1959

	GD 2.0	VG 4.0	FN 6.0	VF 8.0	VF/NM 9.0	NM- 9.2
12	12	24	36	69	97	125
13-19	8	16	24	42	54	65

ATOMIC COMICS
Daniels Publications (Canadian): Jan, 1946 (Reprints, one-shot)

	GD 2.0	VG 4.0	FN 6.0	VF 8.0	VF/NM 9.0	NM- 9.2
1-Rocketman, Yankee Boy, Master Key app.	43	86	129	271	461	650

ATOMIC COMICS
Green Publishing Co.: Jan, 1946 - No. 4, July-Aug, 1946 (#1-4 were printed w/o cover gloss)

	GD 2.0	VG 4.0	FN 6.0	VF 8.0	VF/NM 9.0	NM- 9.2
1-Radio Squad by Siegel & Shuster; Barry O'Neal app.; Fang Gow cover-r/ Detective Comics (Classic-c)	82	164	246	528	902	1275
2-Inspector Dayton; Kid Kane by Matt Baker; Lucky Wings, Congo King, Prop Powers (only app.) begin; atomic monster-c	57	114	171	362	619	875
3,4: 3-Zero Ghost Detective app.; Baker-a(2) each; 4-Baker-c	40	80	120	246	411	575

ATOMIC KNIGHTS (See Strange Adventures #117)
DC Comics: 2010 ($39.99, HC with dustjacket)

	GD 2.0	VG 4.0	FN 6.0	VF 8.0	VF/NM 9.0	NM- 9.2
HC-Reprints the original 1960-64 run from debut in Strange Adventures #117 to S.A. #160; new intro. by Murphy Anderson						40.00

ATOMIC MOUSE (TV, Movies) (See Blue Bird, Funny Animals, Giant Comics Edition & Wotalife Comics)
Capitol Stories/Charlton Comics: 3/53 - No. 52, 2/63; No. 1, 12/84; V2#10, 9/85 - No. 12, 1/86

	GD 2.0	VG 4.0	FN 6.0	VF 8.0	VF/NM 9.0	NM- 9.2
1-Origin & 1st app.; Al Fago-c/a in most	39	78	117	231	378	525
2	15	30	45	86	133	180
3-10: 5-Timmy The Timid Ghost app.; see Zoo Funnies	10	20	30	58	79	100
11-13,16-25	8	16	24	40	50	60
14,15-Hoppy The Marvel Bunny app.	9	18	27	50	65	80
26-(68 pgs.)	12	24	36	67	94	120
27-40: 36,37-Atom The Cat app.	6	12	18	29	36	42
41-52	5	10	15	22	26	30
1 (1984)-Low print run; rep/#7-c w/diff. stories	2	4	6	8	10	12
V2#10 (9/85) -12(1/86)-Low print run	1	3	4	6	8	10

ATOMIC RABBIT (Atomic Bunny #12 on; see Giant Comics #3 & Wotalife)
Charlton Comics: Aug, 1955 - No. 11, Mar, 1958

	GD 2.0	VG 4.0	FN 6.0	VF 8.0	VF/NM 9.0	NM- 9.2
1-Origin & 1st app.; Al Fago-c/a in all?	34	68	102	199	325	450
2	14	28	42	80	115	150
3-10	10	20	30	56	76	95
11-(68 pgs.)	14	28	42	80	115	150

ATOMICS, THE
AAA Pop Comics: Jan, 2000 - No. 15, Nov, 2001 ($2.95)

	GD 2.0	VG 4.0	FN 6.0	VF 8.0	VF/NM 9.0	NM- 9.2
1-11-Mike Allred-s/a; 1-Madman-c/app.						3.00
12-15-($3.50): 13-15-Savage Dragon-c/app. 15-Afterword by Alex Ross; colored reprint of 1st Frank Einstein story						3.50
...King-Size Giant Spectacular: Jigsaw (2000, $10.00) r/#1-4						10.00
...King-Size Giant Spectacular: Lessons in Light, Lava, & Lasers (2000, $8.95) r/#5-8						9.00
...King-Size Giant Spectacular: Running With the Dragon ('02, $8.95) r/#13-15 and r/1st Frank Einstein app. in color						9.00
...King-Size Giant Spectacular: Worlds Within Worlds ('01, $8.95) r/#9-12						9.00
Madman and the Atomics, Vol. 1 TPB (2007, $24.99) r/#1-15, cover gallery, pin-ups, afterword by Alex Ross						25.00
...: Spaced Out & Grounded in Snap City TPB (10/03, $12.95) r/one-shots - It Girl, Mr. Gum, Spaceman and Crash Metro & the Star Squad; sketch pages						13.00

ATOMIC SPY CASES
Avon Periodicals: Mar-Apr, 1950 (Painted-c)

	GD 2.0	VG 4.0	FN 6.0	VF 8.0	VF/NM 9.0	NM- 9.2
1-No Wood-a; A-bomb blast panels; Fass-a	42	84	126	265	445	625

ATOMIC THUNDERBOLT, THE
Regor Company: Feb, 1946 (one-shot) (scarce)

	GD 2.0	VG 4.0	FN 6.0	VF 8.0	VF/NM 9.0	NM- 9.2
1-Intro. Atomic Thunderbolt & Mr. Murdo	81	162	243	518	884	1250

ATOMIC TOYBOX
Image Comics: Dec, 1999 ($2.95)

	GD 2.0	VG 4.0	FN 6.0	VF 8.0	VF/NM 9.0	NM- 9.2
1- Aaron Lopresti-c/s/a						3.00

ATOMIC WAR!
Ace Periodicals (Junior Books): Nov, 1952 - No. 4, Apr, 1953

	GD 2.0	VG 4.0	FN 6.0	VF 8.0	VF/NM 9.0	NM- 9.2
1-Atomic bomb-c	181	362	543	1158	1979	2800
2,3: 3-Atomic bomb-c	70	140	210	445	765	1085
4-Used in **POP**, pg. 96 & illo.	70	140	210	445	765	1085

ATOMIKA
Speakeasy Comics/Mercury Comics: Mar, 2005 - No. 6 ($2.99)

	GD 2.0	VG 4.0	FN 6.0	VF 8.0	VF/NM 9.0	NM- 9.2
1-6: 1-Alex Ross-c/Sal Abbinanti-a/Dabb-s. 3-Fabry-c. 4-Four covers; Romita back-c						3.00
... God is Red TPB (5/06, $19.99) r/#1-6; cover gallery; Dabb foreword						20.00

ATOMIK ANGELS
Crusade Comics: May, 1996 - No. 4, Nov. 1996 ($2.50)

	GD 2.0	VG 4.0	FN 6.0	VF 8.0	VF/NM 9.0	NM- 9.2
1-4: 1-Freefall from Gen 13 app.						3.00
1-Variant-c						4.00
Intrep-Edition (2/96, B&W, giveaway at launch party)-Previews Atomik Angels #1; includes Billy Tucci interview.						4.00

ATOM SPECIAL (See Atom & Justice League of America)
DC Comics: 1993/1995 ($2.50/$2.95)(68pgs.)

	GD 2.0	VG 4.0	FN 6.0	VF 8.0	VF/NM 9.0	NM- 9.2
1,2: 1-Dillon-c/a. 2-McDonnell-a/Bolland-c/Peyer-s						4.00

ATOM THE CAT (Formerly Tom Cat; see Giant Comics #3)
Charlton Comics: No. 9, Oct, 1957 - No. 17, Aug, 1959

	GD 2.0	VG 4.0	FN 6.0	VF 8.0	VF/NM 9.0	NM- 9.2
9	10	20	30	54	72	90
10,13-17	7	14	21	35	43	50
11,12: 11(64 pgs)-Atomic Mouse app. 12(100 pgs.)	11	22	33	62	86	110

ATTACK
Youthful Mag./Trojan No. 5 on: May, 1952 - No. 4, Nov, 1952; No. 5, Jan, 1953 - No. 5, Sept, 1953

	GD 2.0	VG 4.0	FN 6.0	VF 8.0	VF/NM 9.0	NM- 9.2
1-(1st series)-Extreme violence	48	96	144	302	514	725
2,3-Both Harrison-c/a; bondage, whipping	28	56	84	165	270	375
4-Krenkel-a (7 pgs.); Harrison-a (becomes Atomic Attack #5 on)	28	56	84	165	270	375
5-(#1, Trojan, 2nd series)	18	36	54	105	165	225
6-8 (#2-4), 5	14	28	42	80	115	150

ATTACK
Charlton Comics: No. 54, 1958 - No. 60, Nov, 1959

	GD 2.0	VG 4.0	FN 6.0	VF 8.0	VF/NM 9.0	NM- 9.2
54 (25¢, 100 pgs.)	12	24	36	69	97	125
55-60	7	14	21	35	43	50

ATTACK!
Charlton Comics: 1962 - No. 15, 3/75; No. 16, 8/79 - No. 48, 10/84

	GD 2.0	VG 4.0	FN 6.0	VF 8.0	VF/NM 9.0	NM- 9.2
nn(#1)-('62) Special Edition	6	12	18	41	76	110
2('63), 3(Fall, '64)	4	8	12	23	37	50
V4#3(10/66), 4(10/67)-(Formerly Special War Series #2; becomes Attack At Sea V4#5): 3-Tokyo Rose story	3	6	9	19	30	40
1(9/71)-D-Day story	3	6	9	16	23	30
2-5: 2-Hitler app. 4-American Eagle app.	2	4	6	9	12	15
6-15(3/75): 8-Nixon app.	1	3	4	6	8	10
16(8/79) - 40						5.00
41-47 Low print run						7.00
48(10/84)-Wood-r; S&K-c (low print)	1	3	4	6	8	10
Modern Comics 13('78)-r						5.00

NOTE: ***Sutton** a-9,10,13.*

ATTACK!
Spire Christian Comics (Fleming H. Revell Co.): 1975 (39¢/49¢, 36 pgs.)

	GD 2.0	VG 4.0	FN 6.0	VF 8.0	VF/NM 9.0	NM- 9.2
nn	2	4	6	10	14	18

ATTACK AT SEA (Formerly Attack!, 1967)
Charlton Comics: V4#5, Oct, 1968 (one-shot)

	GD 2.0	VG 4.0	FN 6.0	VF 8.0	VF/NM 9.0	NM- 9.2
V4#5	3	6	9	19	30	40

ATTACK ON PLANET MARS (See Strange Worlds #18)
Avon Periodicals: 1951

	GD 2.0	VG 4.0	FN 6.0	VF 8.0	VF/NM 9.0	NM- 9.2
nn-Infantino, Fawcette, Kubert & Wood-a; adaptation of Tarrano the Conqueror by Ray Cummings	103	206	309	659	1130	1600

ATTITUDE LAD
Slave Labor Graphics: Apr, 1994 - No. 3, Nov, 1994 ($2.95, B&W)

	GD 2.0	VG 4.0	FN 6.0	VF 8.0	VF/NM 9.0	NM- 9.2
1-3						3.00

AUDREY & MELVIN (Formerly Little...)(See Little Audrey & Melvin)
Harvey Publications: No. 62, Sept, 1974

	GD 2.0	VG 4.0	FN 6.0	VF 8.0	VF/NM 9.0	NM- 9.2
62	2	4	6	9	13	16

AUGIE DOGGIE (TV) (See Hanna-Barbera Band Wagon, Quick-Draw McGraw, Spotlight #2, Top Cat & Whitman Comic Books)
Gold Key: October, 1963 (12¢)

	GD 2.0	VG 4.0	FN 6.0	VF 8.0	VF/NM 9.0	NM- 9.2
1-Hanna-Barbera character	15	30	45	100	220	340

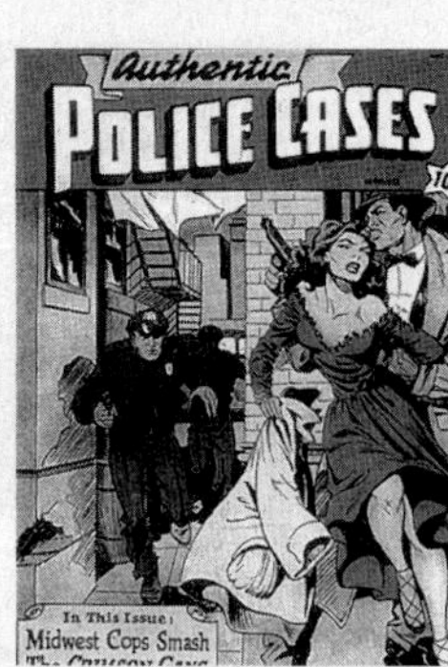

Authentic Police Cases #10 © STJ

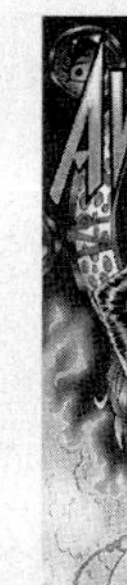
The Authority #1 © WSP

Avengelyne V2 #7 © Rob Liefeld

GD 2.0 | VG 4.0 | FN 6.0 | VF 8.0 | VF/NM 9.0 | NM- 9.2

AUTHENTIC POLICE CASES
St. John Publishing Co.: 2/48 - No. 6, 11/48; No. 7, 5/50 - No. 38, 3/55

	GD	VG	FN	VF	VF/NM	NM-
1-Hale the Magician by Tuska begins	60	120	180	381	653	925
2-Lady Satan, Johnny Rebel app.	40	80	120	246	411	575
3-Veiled Avenger app.; blood drainage story plus 2 Lucky Coyne stories; used in **SOTI**, illo. from Red Seal #16	63	126	189	403	689	975
4,5: 4-Masked Black Jack app. 5-Late 1930s Jack Cole-a(r); transvestism story	40	80	120	246	411	575
6-Matt Baker-c; used in **SOTI**, illo- "An invitation to learning", r-in Fugitives From Justice #3; Jack Cole-a; also used by the N.Y. Legis. Comm.	123	246	369	787	1344	1900
7,8,10-14: 7-Jack Cole-a; Matt Baker-a begins #8, ends #?; Vic Flint in #10-14. 10-12-Baker-a(2 each)	52	104	156	328	552	775
9-No Vic Flint	50	100	150	315	533	750
15-Drug-c/story; Vic Flint app.; Baker-c	52	104	156	328	552	775
16,17,19,22-Baker-c	42	84	126	265	445	625
18,20,21,23: Baker-a(i)	36	72	108	211	343	475
24-28 (All 100 pgs.): 26-Transvestism	54	108	162	343	574	825
29,31,32-Baker-c	39	78	117	231	378	525
30	28	56	84	165	270	375
33-38: 33-Baker-c. 34-Baker-c; drug story; r/#9. 35-Baker-c/a(2); r/#10. 36-r/#11; Vic Flint strip-r; Baker-c/a(2) unsigned. 37-Baker-c; r/#17. 38- Baker-c/a; r/#18	39	78	117	231	378	525

NOTE: ***Matt Baker** c-6-16, 17, 19, 22, 27, 29, 31-38; a-13, 16. Bondage c-1, 3.*

AUTHORITY, THE (See Stormwatch and Jenny Sparks: The Secret History of...)
DC Comics (WildStorm): May, 1999 - No. 29, Jul, 2002 ($2.50)

	GD	VG	FN	VF	VF/NM	NM-
1-Wraparound-c; Warren Ellis-s/Bryan Hitch and Paul Neary-a	1	2	3	4	5	7
1-Special Edition (7/10, $1.00) r/#1 with "What's Next?" logo on cover						3.00
2-4						5.00
5-12: 12-Death of Jenny Sparks; last Ellis-s						4.00
13-Mark Millar-s/Frank Quitely-c/a begins						6.00
14-16-Authority vs. Marvel-esque villains						4.00
17-29: 17,18-Weston-a. 19,20,22-Quitely-a. 21-McCrea-a. 23-26-Peyer-s/Nguyen-a; new Authority. 25,26-Jenny Sparks app. 27,28-Millar-s/Art Adams-a/c						3.00
Annual 2000 ($3.50) Devil's Night x-over; Hamner-a/Bermejo-c						4.00
Absolute Authority Slipcased Hardcover (2002, $49.95) oversized r/#1-12 plus script pages by Ellis and sketch pages by Hitch						50.00
...: Earth Inferno and Other Stories TPB (2002, $14.95) r/#17-20, Annual 2000, and Wildstorm Summer Special; new Quitely-c						15.00
...: Human on the Inside HC (2004, $24.95, dust jacket) Ridley-s/Oliver-a/c						25.00
...: Human on the Inside SC (2004, $17.99) Ridley-s/Oliver-a/c						18.00
...: Kev (10/02, $4.95) Ennis-s/Fabry-c/a						5.00
...: Relentless TPB (2000, $17.95) r/#1-8						18.00
...: Scorched Earth (2/03, $4.95) Robbie Morrison-s/Frazer Irving-a/Ashley Wood-c						5.00
...: Transfer of Power TPB (2002, $17.95) r/#22-29						18.00
...: Under New Management TPB (2000, $17.95) r/#9-16; new Quitely-c						18.00

AUTHORITY, THE (See previews in Sleeper, Stormwatch: Team Achilles and Wildcats Version 3.0)
DC Comics (WildStorm): Jul, 2003 - No. 14, Oct, 2004 ($2.95)

	NM-
1-14: 1-Robbie Morrison-s/Dwayne Turner-a. 5-Huat-a. 14-Portacio-a	3.00
#0 (10/03, $2.95) r/preview back-up-s listed above; Turner sketch pages	3.00
...: Fractured Worlds TPB (2005, $17.95) r/#6-14; cover gallery	18.00
...: Harsh Realities TPB (2004, $14.95) r/#0-5; cover gallery	15.00
.../Lobo: Jingle Hell (2/04, $4.95) Bisley-c/a; Giffen & Grant-s	5.00
.../Lobo: Spring Break Massacre (8/05, $4.99) Bisley-c/a; Giffen & Grant-s	5.00

AUTHORITY, THE (Volume 4) (The Lost Year)
DC Comics (WildStorm): Dec, 2006 - No. 2, May 2007; No. 3, Jan, 2010 - No. 12, Oct, 2010 ($2.99)

	NM-
1,2-Grant Morrison-s/Gene Ha-a/c	3.00
1-Variant cover by Art Adams	5.00
3-12: 3-(1/10) Morrison & Giffen-s/Robertson-a. 3-12-Ha-c. 12-Ordway-a	3.00
...Reader: The Lost Year (1/10, $2.99) r/#1,2	3.00
... Book One (2010, $17.99) r/#1-7; cover sketch art	18.00

AUTHORITY, THE (Volume 5) (World's End)
DC Comics (WildStorm): Oct, 2008 - No. 29, Jan, 2011 ($2.99)

	NM-
1-29: 1-5-Simon Coleby-a/c; Lynch back-up story w/Hairsine-a/Gage-s. 21-Simonson-c	3.00
...: Rule Britannia TPB (2010, $19.99) r/#8-17	20.00
...: World's End TPB (2009, $17.99) r/#1-7	18.00

AUTHORITY, THE: MORE KEV
DC Comics (WildStorm): Jul, 2004 - No. 4, Dec, 2004 ($2.95, limited series)

	NM-
1-4-Garth Ennis-s/Glenn Fabry-c/a	3.00
...: Kev TPB (2005, $14.99) r/Authority: Kev one-shot and Authority: More Kev series	15.00

AUTHORITY, THE: PRIME
DC Comics (WildStorm): Dec, 2007 - No. 6, May, 2008 ($2.99, limited series)

	NM-
1-6-Gage-s/Robertson-c/a; Bendix app.	3.00
TPB (2008, $17.99) r/#1-6	18.00

AUTHORITY, THE: REVOLUTION
DC Comics (WildStorm): Dec, 2004 - No. 12, Dec, 2005 ($2.95/$2.99)

	NM-
1-12-Brubaker-s/Nguyen-a. 5-Henry Bendix returns. 7-Jenny Sparks app.	3.00
...: Book One TPB (2005, $14.99) r/#1-6; cover gallery and Nguyen sketch pages	15.00
...: Book Two TPB (2006, $14.99) r/#7-12; cover gallery and Nguyen sketch pages	15.00

AUTHORITY, THE: THE MAGNIFICENT KEV
DC Comics (WildStorm): Nov, 2005 - No. 5, Feb, 2006 ($2.99, limited series)

	NM-
1-5-Garth Ennis-s/Carlos Ezquerra-a/Glenn Fabry-c	3.00
TPB (2006, $14.99) r/#1-5	15.00

AUTOMATIC KAFKA
DC Comics (WildStorm): Sept, 2002 - No. 9, Jul, 2003 ($2.95)

	NM-
1-9-Ashley Wood-c/a; Joe Casey-s	3.00

AUTUMN ADVENTURES (Walt Disney's...)
Disney Comics: Autumn, 1990; No. 2, Autumn, 1991 ($2.95, 68 pgs.)

	NM-
1-Donald Duck-r(2) by Barks, Pluto-r, & new-a	4.00
2-D. Duck-r by Barks; new Super Goof story	4.00

AUTUMNLANDS: TOOTH & CLAW (Titled Tooth & Claw for issue #1)
Image Comics: Nov, 2014 - Present ($2.99)

	NM-
1-14: 1-Busiek-s/Dewey-a. 2-Variant-c by Alex Ross	3.00

AVATAARS: COVENANT OF THE SHIELD
Marvel Comics: Sept, 2000 - No. 3, Nov, 2000 ($2.99, limited series)

	NM-
1-3-Kaminski-s/Oscar Jimenez-a	3.00

AVATAR
DC Comics: Feb, 1991 - No. 3, Apr, 1991 ($5.95, limited series, 100 pgs.)

	NM-
1-3: Based on TSR's Forgotten Realms	6.00

AVENGELYNE
Maximum Press: May, 1995 - No. 3, July, 1995 ($2.50/$3.50, limited series)

	GD	VG	FN	VF	VF/NM	NM-
1/2	2	4	6	8	10	12
1/2 Platinum						15.00
1-Newstand ($2.50)-Photo-c; poster insert						6.00
1-Direct Market ($3.50)-Chromium-c; poster	1	2	3	4	5	7
1-Glossy edition	2	4	6	12	16	20
1-Gold						12.00
2-3: 2-Polybagged w/card						3.00
3-Variant-c; Deodato pin-up						5.00
...Bible (10/96, $3.50)						4.00
.../Glory (9/95, $3.95) 2 covers						4.00
.../Glory Swimsuit Special (6/96, $2.95) photo and illos. covers						3.00
.../Glory: The Godyssey (9/96, $2.99) 2 covers (1 photo)						3.00
...Revelation One (Avatar, 1/01, $3.50) 3 covers by Haley, Rio, Shaw; Shaw-a						3.50
.../Shi (Avatar, 11/01, $3.50) Eight covers; Waller-a						3.50
...Swimsuit (8/95, $2.95)-Pin-ups/photos. 3-Variant-c exist (2 photo, 1 Liefeld-a)						4.00
...Swimsuit (1/96, $3.50, 2nd printing)-photo-c						4.00
Trade paperback (12/95, $9.95)						10.00
.../Warrior Nun Areala 1 (11/96, $2.99) also see Warrior Nun/Avengelyne						3.00

AVENGELYNE
Maximum Press: V2#1, Apr, 1996 - No. 14, Apr, 1997 ($2.95/$2.50)

	NM-
V2#1-Four covers exist (2 photo-c).	4.00
V2#2-Three covers exist (1 photo-c); flip book w/Darkchylde	5.00
V2#0, 3-14: 0-(10/96).3-Flip book w/Priest preview. 5-Flip book w/Blindside	3.00

AVENGELYNE (Volume 3)
Awesome Comics: Mar, 1999 ($2.50)

	NM-
1-Fraga & Liefeld-a	3.00

AVENGELYNE (4th series)
Image Comics: Jul, 2011 - No. 8, May, 2012 ($2.99)

	NM-
1-8-Liefeld & Poulson-s/Gieni-a. 1-Three covers by Liefeld, Gieni, and Benitez	3.00

AVENGELYNE: ARMAGEDDON
Maximum Press: Dec, 1996 - No. 3, Feb, 1997 ($2.99, limited series)

	NM-
1-3-Scott Clark-a(p)	3.00

AVENGELYNE: DEADLY SINS
Maximum Press: Feb, 1996 - No. 2, Mar, 1996 ($2.95, limited series)

Avengers #9 © MAR

Avengers #23 © MAR

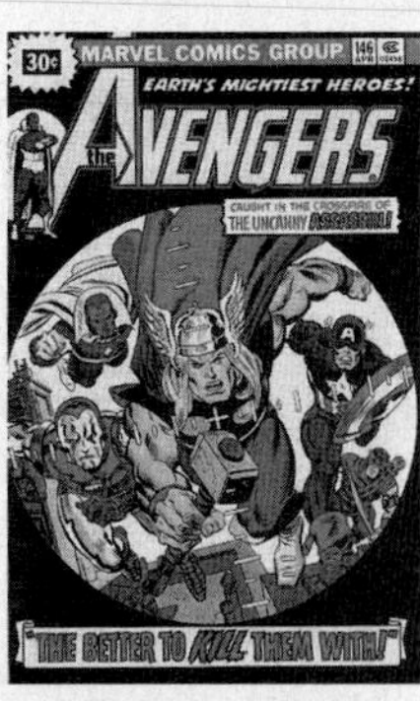

Avengers #146 © MAR

	GD 2.0	VG 4.0	FN 6.0	VF 8.0	VF/NM 9.0	NM- 9.2
1,2: 1-Two-c exist (1 photo, 1 Liefeld-a). 2-Liefeld-c; Pop Mhan-a(p)						3.00

AVENGELYNE/POWER
Maximum Press: Nov, 1995 - No.3, Jan, 1996 ($2.95, limited series)

	GD 2.0	VG 4.0	FN 6.0	VF 8.0	VF/NM 9.0	NM- 9.2
1-3: 1,2-Liefeld-c. 3-Three variant-c. exist (1 photo-c)						3.00

AVENGELYNE • PROPHET
Maximum Press: May, 1996; No. 2, Feb. 1997 ($2.95, unfinished lim. series)

	GD 2.0	VG 4.0	FN 6.0	VF 8.0	VF/NM 9.0	NM- 9.2
1,2-Liefeld-c/a(p)						3.00

AVENGER, THE (See A-1 Comics)
Magazine Enterprises: Feb-Mar, 1955 - No. 4, Aug-Sept, 1955

	GD 2.0	VG 4.0	FN 6.0	VF 8.0	VF/NM 9.0	NM- 9.2
1(A-1 #129)-Origin	40	80	120	246	411	575
2(A-1 #131), 3(A-1 #133) Robot-c, 4(A-1 #138)	27	54	81	160	263	365
IW Reprint #9('64)-Reprints #1 (new cover)	3	6	9	19	30	40

NOTE: *Powell a-2-4; c-1-4.*

AVENGER, THE (Pulp Hero from Justice Inc.)
Dynamite Entertainment: 2014 ($7.99)

	GD 2.0	VG 4.0	FN 6.0	VF 8.0	VF/NM 9.0	NM- 9.2
... Special 2014: The Television Killers - Rahner-s/Menna-a/Hack-c						8.00

AVENGERS, THE (TV)(Also see Steed and Mrs. Peel)
Gold Key: Nov, 1968 ("John Steed & Emma Peel" cover title) (15¢)

	GD 2.0	VG 4.0	FN 6.0	VF 8.0	VF/NM 9.0	NM- 9.2
1-Photo-c	13	26	39	89	195	300
1-(Variant with photo back-c)	17	34	51	117	259	400

AVENGERS, THE (See Essential..., Giant-Size..., JLA/..., Kree/Skrull War Starring..., Marvel Graphic Novel #27, Marvel Super Action, Marvel Super Heroes('66), Marvel Treasury Ed., Marvel Triple Action, New Avengers, Solo Avengers, Tales Of Suspense #49, West Coast Avengers & X-Men Vs....)

AVENGERS, THE (The Mighty Avengers on cover only #63-69)
Marvel Comics Group: Sept, 1963 - No. 402, Sept, 1996

	GD 2.0	VG 4.0	FN 6.0	VF 8.0	VF/NM 9.0	NM- 9.2
1-Origin & 1st app. The Avengers (Thor, Iron Man, Hulk, Ant-Man, Wasp); Loki app.	840	1680	3360	9400	23,000	42,000
2-Hulk leaves Avengers	114	228	342	912	2056	3200
3-2nd Sub-Mariner x-over outside the F.F. (see Strange Tales #107 for 1st); Sub-Mariner & Hulk team-up & battle Avengers; Spider-Man cameo (1/64)	89	178	267	712	1606	2500
4-Revival of Captain America who joins the Avengers; 1st Silver Age app. of Captain America & Bucky (3/64)	276	552	828	2277	5139	8000
4-Reprint from the Golden Record Comic set	15	30	45	103	227	350
With Record (1966)	22	44	66	154	340	525
5-Hulk app.	50	100	150	400	900	1400
6-1st app. original Zemo & his Masters of Evil	44	88	132	326	738	1150
7-Rick Jones app. in Bucky costume	40	80	120	296	673	1050
8-Intro Kang	38	76	114	285	641	1000
9-Intro Wonder Man who dies in same story	56	112	168	448	999	1550
10-Intro/1st app. Immortus; early Hercules app. (11/64)	30	60	90	216	483	750
11-Spider-Man-c & x-over (12/64)	37	74	111	274	612	950
12-15: 15-Death of original Zemo	19	38	57	131	291	450
16-New Avengers line-up (Hawkeye, Quicksilver, Scarlet Witch join; Thor, Iron Man, Giant-Man, Wasp leave)	36	72	108	259	580	900
17,18: 17-Minor Hulk app.	13	26	39	89	195	300
19-1st app. Swordsman; origin Hawkeye (8/65)	15	30	45	103	227	350
20-22: Wood inks. 20-Intro. Power Man (Erik Josten)	10	20	30	69	147	225
23,24,26,27,29,30: 23-Romita Sr. inks (1st Silver Age Marvel work). 23,24-Avengers vs. Kang.	9	18	27	61	123	185
25-Dr. Doom-c/story	19	38	57	131	291	450
28-(5/66) First app. of The Collector; Giant-Man becomes Goliath	27	54	81	194	435	675
31-40: 32-1st Sons of the Serpent. 34-Last full Stan Lee plot/script. 35-1st Roy Thomas script w/Stan Lee plot. 38-40-Hercules app. 40-Sub-Mariner app.	8	16	24	51	96	140
41-46,50: 43-1st app. Red Guardian (dies in #44). 45-Hercules joins. 46-Ant-Man returns (re-intro, 11/67)	7	14	21	46	86	125
47,49-Magneto-c/story	7	14	21	48	89	130
48-Origin/1st app. new Black Knight (1/68)	7	14	21	48	89	130
51-The Collector app.	8	16	24	51	96	140
52-Black Panther joins; 1st app. The Grim Reaper	8	16	24	56	108	160
53-X-Men app.	9	18	27	61	123	185
54-1st Ultron app. (1 panel); new Masters of Evil	11	22	33	76	163	250
55-1st full app. Ultron (8/68) (1 panel reveal in #54)	19	38	57	131	291	450
56-Zemo app; story explains how Capt. America became imprisoned in ice during WWII, only to be rescued in Avengers #4	8	16	24	56	108	160
57-1st app. S.A. Vision (10/68); death of Ultron-5	46	92	138	359	805	1250
58-Origin The Vision	10	20	30	69	147	225
59-Intro. Yellowjacket	11	22	33	76	163	250
60-65: 60-Wasp & Yellowjacket wed. 61-Dr. Strange app. 62-1st Man-Ape. 63-Goliath becomes Yellowjacket; Hawkeye becomes the new Goliath. 65-Last 12¢ issue	6	12	18	41	76	110
66-B. Smith-a; vs. Ultron-6; 1st mention of adamantium metal	8	16	24	51	96	140
67-Ultron-6 cvr/sty; B. Smith-a	9	18	27	61	123	185
68-Buscema-a	6	12	18	38	69	100
69-1st brief app. Squadron Sinister (Dr. Spectrum, Hyperion, Nighthawk)	10	20	30	64	132	200
70-1st full app. Nighthawk	7	14	21	46	86	125
71-1st app. The Invaders (12/69); Black Knight joins	9	18	27	63	129	195
72-79,81,82,84,86,90-91: 72-1st Zodiak; Captain Marvel & Nick Fury app. 73,74-Sons of the Serpent. 75-1st app. Arkon. 78-1st app. Lethal Legion (Man-Ape, Living Laser, Power Man, Grimm Reaper, Swordsman). 82-Daredevil app. 86-2nd Squadron Supreme app.	5	10	15	35	63	90
80-1st app. Red Wolf	7	14	21	46	86	125
83-Intro. The Liberators (Wasp, Valkyrie, Scarlet Witch, Medusa & the Black Widow)	12	24	36	79	170	260
85-1st app. Squadron Supreme (American Eagle, Dr. Spectrum, Hawkeye (Wyatt McDonald), Hyperion, Lady Lark, Nighthawk (Kyle Richmond), Tom Thumb, Whizzer)	6	12	18	41	76	110
87-Origin The Black Panther	10	20	30	64	132	200
88-Written by Harlan Ellison; Hulk app.	6	12	18	37	66	95
88-2nd printing (1994)	2	4	6	8	10	12
89-Classic Captain Marvel execution-c; beginning of Kree/Skrull War (runs through issue #97)	7	14	21	44	82	120
92-Last 15¢ issue; Neal Adams-c	6	12	18	41	76	110
93-(52 pgs.)-Neal Adams-c/a	15	30	45	100	220	340
94-96-Neal Adams-c/a	8	16	24	54	102	150
97-G.A. Capt. America, Sub-Mariner, Human Torch, Patriot, Vision, Blazing Skull, Fin, Angel, & new Capt. Marvel x-over	7	14	21	46	86	125
98,99: 98-Goliath becomes Hawkeye; Smith c/a(i). 99-Smith-c, Smith/Sutton-a	5	10	15	31	53	75
100-(6/72)-Smith-c/a; featuring everyone who was an Avenger	9	18	27	61	123	185
101-Harlan Ellison scripts	4	8	12	27	44	60
102-106,108,109	4	8	12	23	37	50
107-Starlin-a(p)	4	8	12	25	40	55
110,111-X-Men and Magneto app.	5	10	15	35	63	90
112-1st app. Mantis	13	26	39	89	195	300
113-115,119-124,126,128-130: 114-Swordsman returns; joins Avengers, first Mantis-c. 115-Prologue to Avengers/Defenders War. 119-Rutland, Vermont Halloween issue. 120-123-vs. Zodiac. 123,124-Mantis origin. 124-1st Star-Stalker. 126-Klaw & Solarr app. 129-Kang app; story continues in Giant-Size Avengers #2	3	6	9	19	30	40
116-118-Avengers/Defenders War; x-over w/Defenders #8-11. 116-Silver Surfer vs Vision. 117-Captain America vs. Sub-Mariner. 118-Avengers & Defenders vs. Loki & Dormammu	5	10	15	33	57	80
125-Thanos-c & brief app.; story continues in Captain Marvel #33	5	10	15	35	63	90
127-Ultron-7 app; story continues in Fantastic Four #150	4	8	12	23	37	50
131-133,136-140: 131,132-Vs. Kang. 131-1st Legion of the Unliving. 132-Continues in Giant-Size Avengers #3. 133-Origin of the Kree. 136-Ploog-r/Amazing Advs. #12. 137-Moondragon joins; Beast app; becomes provisional member; officially joins in #151; Wasp & Yellowjacket return	3	6	9	16	23	30
134,135-Origin of the Vision revised (also see Avengers Forever mini-series). 135-Continues in Giant-Size Avengers #4	4	8	12	23	37	50
141-143: 141-Squadron Supreme app; Pérez-a(p) begins. 142,143-Marvel Western heroes app. (Kid Colt, Rawhide Kid, Two-Gun Kid, Ringo Kid, Night Rider). 143-Vs. Kang (last 1970s app.)	2	4	6	12	15	20
144-Origin & 1st app. Hellcat (Patsy Walker)	6	12	18	37	66	95
145,146: Published out of sequence; Tony Isabella-s; originally intended to be in Giant-Size Avengers #5	2	4	6	9	12	15
146-149-(30¢-c variants, limited distribution)	5	10	15	33	57	80
147-149-(Reg. 25¢ editions)(5-7/76) Squadron Supreme app.	2	4	6	11	16	20
150-Kirby-a(r) pgs. 7-18 (from issue #16); pgs. 1-6 feature new-a by Pérez; new line-up: Capt. America, Iron Man, Scarlet Witch, Wasp, Yellowjacket, Vision & The Beast	2	4	6	13	18	22
150-(30¢-c variant, limited distribution)	5	10	15	33	57	80
151-Wonder Man returns w/new costume; Champions app.; The Collector app.	3	6	9	14	19	24

152-154,157,159,160,163: 152-1st app Black Talon. 154-vs. Attuma; continues in Super-Villain

Avengers #190 © MAR

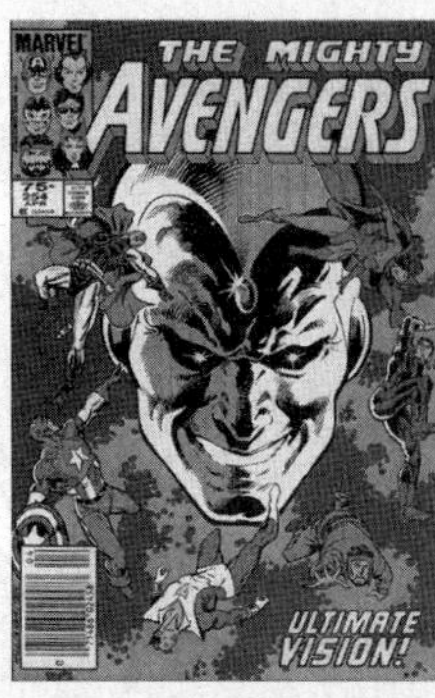

Avengers #254 © MAR

Avengers #376 © MAR

	GD 2.0	VG 4.0	FN 6.0	VF 8.0	VF/NM 9.0	NM- 9.2
Team-up #9. 160-Grimm Reaper app. 163-Vs. The Champions	2	4	6	9	12	15
155,156-Dr. Doom app.	2	4	6	10	14	18
158-1st app. Graviton; Wonder Man vs. Vision; Jim Shooter plots begin	2	4	6	11	16	20
160-164-(35¢-c variants, limited dist.)(6-10/77)	8	16	24	54	102	150
161,162-Ultron-8 app; Henry Pym appears as Ant-Man. 162-1st app. Jocasta	3	6	9	14	20	25
164,165-Byrne-a; vs. Lethal Legion	2	4	6	10	14	18
166-Byrne-a; vs. Count Nefaria	2	4	6	13	18	22
167,168-Guardians of the Galaxy app.	2	4	6	11	16	20
169,172,178-180: 172-Hawkeye rejoins	1	3	4	6	8	10
170,171-Ultron & Jocasta app. 170-Minor Guardians of the Galaxy app.	2	4	6	11	16	20
173-177-Korvac Saga issues; 173-175-The Collector app. 173,177-Guardians of the Galaxy app. 174-Thanos cameo. 176-Starhawk app.	2	4	6	8	10	12
181-(3/79) Byrne-a/Pérez-c; new line-up: Capt. America, Scarlet Witch, Iron Man, Wasp, Vision, Beast & The Falcon; debut of Scott Lang who becomes Ant-Man in Marvel Premiere #47 (4/79)	6	12	18	40	73	105
182-191-Byrne-a: 183-Ms. Marvel joins. 184-vs. Absorbing Man. 185-Origin Quicksilver & Scarlet Witch. 186-187-vs. Morded the Mystic. 188-Intro. The Elements of Doom. 189-Deathbird app. 190,191-vs. Grey Gargoyle	2	4	6	8	10	12
192-194,197-199: 197-199-vs Red Ronin	1	2	3	5	6	8
195-1st Taskmaster cameo	2	4	6	9	12	15
196-1st full Taskmaster app.	6	12	18	37	66	95
200-(10/80, 52 pgs.)-Ms. Marvel leaves; 1st actual app. of Marcus Immortus	2	4	6	10	14	18
201,203-210,212: 204,205-vs. Yellow Claw						5.00
202-Ultron app.	2	4	6	10	14	18
211-New line-up: Capt. America, Iron Man, Tigra, Thor, Wasp & Yellowjacket; Angel, Beast, Dazzler app.	1	2	3	4	5	7
213,215,216,239,240,250: 213-Controversial Yellowjacket slapping Wasp issue; Yellowjacket leaves. 215,216-Silver Surfer app. 216-Tigra leaves. 239-(1/84) Avengers app. on David Letterman show. 240-Spider-Woman revived. 250-($1.00, 52 pgs; West Coast Avengers app. vs. Maelstrom						6.00
214-Ghost Rider app.	1	2	3	4	5	7
217-218,222,224-226,228-235,238: 217-Yellowjacket & Wasp return. 222-1st app. Egghead's Masters of Evil. 225,226-Black Knight app. 229-Death of Egghead. 230-Yellowjacket quits. 231-Iron Man leaves. 232-Starfox (Eros) joins. 233-Byrne-a. 234-Origin Quicksilver & Scarlet Witch. 238-Origin Blackout						5.00
219,220-Drax the Destroyer app. 220-Moondragon vs. Drax	1	2	3	5	6	8
221-Hawkeye & She-Hulk join; Spider-Man, Spider-Woman, Dazzler app.						6.00
223-Taskmaster app.	2	4	6	13	18	22
227-Captain Marvel (Monica Rambeau) joins; Roger Stern plots begin	1	3	4	6	8	10
236,237-Spider-Man tries to join the Avengers						6.00
241-249,251-256,258-262: 242-Dr. Strange app. 243-Vision becomes chairman. 244,245-vs. Dire Wraiths. 246-248-Eternals app. 249-x-over with Thor #350. 252-vs. the Blood Brothers. 253-Vision vs. Quasimodo. 254-West Coast Avengers app. 255-John Buscema & Tom Palmer return as artists; 1st app Nebula's pirate crew. 256-Terminus app. 258-x-over with Amazing Spider-Man #269-270; Spider-Man & Firelord app. 258-260-Nebula app. 260-261-Secret Wars II X-over; Beyonder app. 262-Hercules vs. Sub-Mariner						4.00
257-1st app. Nebula (from the Guardians of the Galaxy movie)	3	6	9	17	26	35
263-(1/86) Return of Jean Grey, leading into X-Factor #1(story continues in FF #286)						6.00
264-265,267-269: 264-1st new Yellowjacket (Rita Demara) 266-Secret Wars II x-over; vs. The Beyonder. 267-269-Kang app.						3.00
266-Secret Wars II epilogue; Silver Surfer & Molecule Man app.						4.00
270-273-Baron Zemo and the new Masters of Evil app. 272-Alpha Flight app.						4.00
274-277-Baron Zemo and the new Masters of Evil app. in 'Siege of Avengers mansion'. 274-Hercules injured. 275-Jarvis severely beaten. 276-Thor returns. 277-Capt. America vs. Baron Zemo						5.00
278-283: 279-Capt. Marvel (Monica Rambeau) becomes Avengers leader; Dr. Druid joins. 280-Jarvis flashback issue. 281-283-Olympian Gods app. 282-Sub-Mariner rejoins						3.00
284,285-vs. the Olympian Gods. 285 Avengers vs. Zeus; Hercules recovers						4.00
286-299: 286-Fixer app. Awesome Android & Super Adaptoid app. 287-Mentallo app. 288-1st app. 'Heavy Metal' (TESS-One, Intergalactic Sentry #459, Machine Man, Super-Adaptoid). 290-West Coast Avengers app. 291-$1.00 issues begin. 292-1st app. the Leviathan (Marrina). 293-Death of Marrina. 294-Capt. Marvel (Monica Rambeau) leaves. 295-vs. the Cross-Time Kangs. 297-Dr. Druid leaves; Thor, Black Knight & She-Hulk resign. 298-Inferno x-over. 299-Inferno x-over; New Mutants app.						3.00
300-(2/89, $1.75, 68 pgs., squarebound) New line-up; the Captain (Steve Rogers), Thor, Invisible Woman, Mr. Fantastic & Gilgamesh (formerly the Forgotten one) Inferno x-over; Simonson-a						4.00

	GD 2.0	VG 4.0	FN 6.0	VF 8.0	VF/NM 9.0	NM- 9.2
301-304,306-313,319-325,327,330-343: 301-Firelord app; 1st app. Super-Nova. 302-Re-intro Quasar; Firelord app. 303-vs. Super-Nova. Quasar, Firelord & West Coast Avengers app.; Mr. Fantastic & Invisible Woman leave. 308-310-Eternals app. 311-313-Acts of Vengeance x-over. 312-Freedom Force app. 320-324-Alpha Flight app. 327-2nd app. Rage. 332,333-Dr. Doom app. 334-Intro. Thane Ector & the Brethren; Inhumans & Quicksilver app. 335-339-vs. the Brethren. 335-1st Steve Epting art. 341,342-New Warriors & Sons of the Serpent app. 343-Intro. the Gatherers; Bob Harras scripts begin (end #395); last $1.00-c						3.00
305,314-318: 305-Byrne scripts begin; most current & non-active Avengers app. 314-318-Spider-Man x-over.						4.00
326-1st app. Rage (11/90)						5.00
328,329: 328-Origin Rage. 329-New line-up (Capt. America, Quasar, Sersi, She-Hulk, Thor, Vision, Black Widow) Spider-Man becomes a reserve member; Rage & Sandman become probationary members						4.00
344,348-349,351-359: 344-1st app. Proctor, leader of the Gatherers. 349-Thor vs. Hercules. 351-Starjammers app. 352-354-Grimm Reaper app.						3.00
345,346-Operation Galactic Storm x-overs. 345-Pt.5-Deathbird app. 346-Pt.12-Intro. Starforce (super-powered Kree warriors)						4.00
347-Double-sized issue ($1.75, 39, pgs.) Operation Galactic Storm conclusion (Pt.19) end of the Kree/Shi'ar War; 'death' of the Supreme Intelligence						5.00
350-($2.50, 68 pgs.) Double gatefold-c showing-c to #1; r/#53 w/cover in flip book format; vs. The Starjammers						5.00
360-($2.95, 52 pgs.) Embossed all-foil-c; 30th ann.						5.00
361,362,364,365,367: 361-362-vs. the Gatherers. 364-365-vs. Galen-Kor of the Kree						4.00
363-($2.95, 52 pgs.)-All silver foil-c; vs. Proctor & the Gatherers; 1st cameo app. Deathcry (unnamed)						5.00
366-($3.95, 68 pgs.)-Embossed all gold foil-c; Deadpool app. in back-up story						5.00
368,376-378: 368-Bloodties pt.1; Avengers/X-Men x-over						3.00
369-($2.95)-Foil embossed-c; Bloodties pt.5; X-Men/Avengers vs. Exodus						5.00
370-373: 370-371-Ghaur the Deviant app. 372-373-vs. Proctor & the Gatherers						4.00
374-Bound-in trading card sheet; origin of Proctor as an alternate-Earth Black Knight revealed (scarcer in NM due to the card insert)						5.00
375-($2.00, 52 pgs.)-Regular ed.; Thunderstrike returns; leads into Malibu Comic's Black September; end of the Gatherers saga (since #343); death of Proctor; Black Knight & Sersi leave; last Epting-a						4.00
375-($2.50, 52 pgs.)-Collectors ed.						5.00
379-382-Regular editions: 379-Galen Kor & Kree Lunatic Legion app. 380-382-High Evolutionary app. 380-1st Mike Deodato-a. 381-Exodus app.						3.00
379-382-Marvel Double Feature editions ($2.50, 45 pgs.)-All have Giant-Man stories in a flip-book format						4.00
383-385: 383-Fantastic Force app. 384-Hercules stripped of immortality & banished from Olympus. 385-Red Skull app.						4.00
386-389, 398-399: 386-Red Skull app.; 'Taking of AIM' prelude; continues in Capt. America #440. 387-Taking of AIM Pt.2; Red Skull app.; re-intro Modok; continues in Capt. America #441. 388-Taking of AIM Pt.4; Red Skull & Modok app.						6.00
390-393: 390-'The Crossing' prelude; leads into Avengers: the Crossing #1. 391,392-The Crossing. 391-Overpower game card insert; scarcer in NM. 392-393-The Crossing						5.00
394,397: 394-The Crossing; 1st new Wasp; story cont. in Avengers Timeslide #1; 397-x-over w/Hulk #440-441	1	2	3	4	5	7
395-The Crossing/Timeslide; 'death' of Tony Stark; Bob Harras co-plot only, last work on Avengers	1	2	3	5	6	8
396-First Sign Pt.4; vs. the Zodiac						8.00
400-(Double-size, 32 pgs.)-Mark Waid scripts; Loki app.						7.00
401,402: 401-Onslaught Impact #1; Magneto app. 402-Onslaught Impact #2; vs. Onslaught & Holocaust; last issue; continues in X-Men #56						6.00
#500-503 (See Avengers Vol. 3; series resumed original numbering after Vol. 3 #84)						
Special 1 (9/67, 25¢, 68 pgs.)-New-a; original & new Avengers team-up	13	26	39	86	188	290
Special 2 (9/68, 25¢, 68 pgs.)-New-a; original vs. new Avengers	9	18	27	59	117	175
Special 3 (9/69, 25¢, 68 pgs.)-r/Avengers #4 plus 3 Capt. America stories by Kirby (art); origin Red Skull	5	10	15	34	60	85
Special 4 (1/71, 25¢, 68 pgs.)-Kirby-r/Avengers #5,6	4	8	12	23	37	50
Special 5 (1/72, 52 pgs.)-All-reprint issue; Kirby-r Avengers #8/Heck-r w/Spider-Man from issue #11	3	6	9	21	33	45
Annual 6 (11/76) Pérez-a; Kirby-c; vs. Nuklo	2	4	6	11	16	20
Annual 7 (11/77)-Starlin-c/a; Warlock dies; Thanos app.; x-over w/Marvel Two-in-one Ann #2	5	10	15	35	63	90
Annual 8 (1978)-Dr. Strange, Ms. Marvel app. vs. Hyperion, Dr. Spectrum & Whizzer	2	4	6	8	11	14
Annual 9 (1979)-Newton-a(p); Intro. Arsenal	2	3	4	6	8	10
Annual 10 (1981)-Golden-a; X-Men cameo; 1st app. Rogue & Madelyne Pryor						

Avengers V3 #2 © MAR

Avengers V3 #39 © MAR

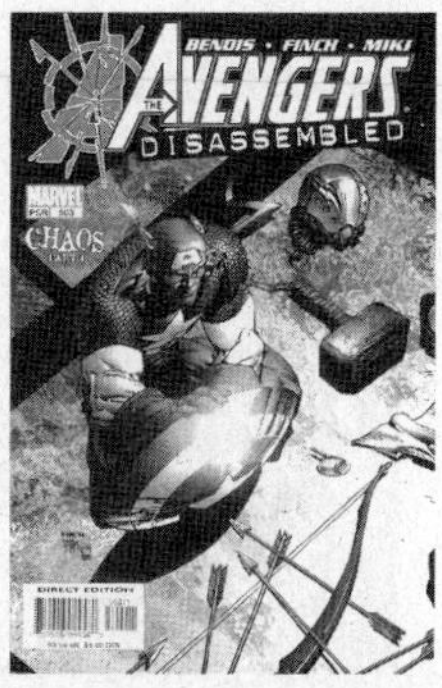

Avengers #503 © MAR

	GD 2.0	VG 4.0	FN 6.0	VF 8.0	VF/NM 9.0	NM- 9.2
	5	10	15	33	57	80

Annual 11-13: 11 (1982)-Vs. The Defenders. 12 ('83)-Inhumans app. 13 ('84)-Ditko/Byrne-a 5.00

Annual 14-15,17-18: 14 ('85)-x-over w/Fantastic Four Ann. #19; vs. the Skrulls. 15 ('86)-vs. Freedom Force; x-over w/Avengers West Coast Ann. #1. 17('88)-Evolutionary War x-over. 18('89)-Atlantis Attacks 4.00

Annual 16 (1987)-x-over w/Avengers West Coast Ann. #2; Silver Surfer app. vs. the Grandmaster and Legion of the Unliving (including Drax, Captain Marvel & Green Goblin) 5.00

Annual 19-22: 19 ('90)-Terminus Factor Pt.5 (conclusion) continued from Avengers West Coast Ann. #5. 20 ('91)-Subterranean Saga Pt.1; cont. in Hulk Ann. #17. 21 ('92)-Citizen Kang pt.4; vs. Terminatrix. 22 ('93)-Bagged w/card; 1st app. Bloodwraith 4.00

Annual 23 (1994)-Buscema-a; Roy Thomas-s; vs. Loki & Pluto; x-over w/Thor Ann. #19 5.00

Avengers 1: The Coming of the Avengers! (2012, $3.99) recolored reprint/#1 5.00

...: Galactic Storm Vol. 1 ('06, $29.99, TPB) r/Kree-Shi'ar war from Avengers #345-346, Capt. America #398-399, Avengers West Coast #80-81, Quasar #32-33, Wonder Man #7-8, Iron Man #278 and Thor #445; new Epting-c 30.00

...: Galactic Storm Vol. 2 ('06, $29.99, TPB) r/Kree-Shi'ar war from Avengers #347, Capt. America #400-401, Avengers West Coast #82, Quasar #34-36, Wonder Man #9, Iron Man #279, Thor #446 and What If #55-56 30.00

...: Kang - Time and Time Again ('05, $19.99, TPB) r/Avengers #69-71 & 267-269, Thor #140 and Incredible Hulk #135 20.00

...Kree-Skrull War ('00, $24.95, TPB) new Neal Adams-c 25.00

...: Legends Vol. 3: George Perez ('03, $16.99)-r/#161,162,194-196,201, Ann. #6 & 8 17.00

Marvel Double Feature...Avengers/Giant-Man #379 ($2.50, 52 pgs.)-Same as Avengers #379 w/Giant-Man flip book 4.00

Marvel Graphic Novel - Deathtrap: The Vault (1991, $9.95) Venom-c/app. 2 4 6 8 11 14

The Korvac Saga TPB (2003, $19.95)-r/#167,168,170-177; Perez-c 20.00

The Serpent Crown TPB (2005, $15.99)-r/#141-144,147-149; Hellcat app. 16.00

The Yesterday Quest ($6.95)-r/#181,182,185-187 1 2 3 4 5 7

Under Siege ('98, $16.95, TPB) r/#270,271,273-277 17.00

...: Vision and the Scarlet Witch TPB (2005, $15.99) r/wedding from Giant-Size Avengers #4 and "Vision and the Scarlet Witch" mini-series #1-4 16.00

...: Visionaries ('99, $16.95)-r/early George Perez art 17.00

NOTE: ***Austin** c(i)-157, 167, 168, 170-177, 181, 183-188, 198-201, Annual 8. **John Buscema** a-41-44p, 46p, 47p, 49, 50, 51-62p, 74-77, 79-85, 87-91, 97, 105p, 121p, 124p,125p, 152, 153p, 255-279p, 281-302p; c-41-66, 68-71, 73-91, 97-99, 178, 256-259p, 261-279p, 281-302p. **Byrne** a-164-166p, 181-191p, 233p, Annual 13i, 14p; c-186-190p, 233p, 260, 305p; scripts-305-312. **Colan** a(p)-63-65, 111, 206-208, 210, 211; c(p)-65, 206-208, 210, 211. **Ditko** a-Annual 13. **Guice** a-Annual 12p. **Don Heck** a-9-15, 17-40, 157. **Kane** c-37p, 159p. **Kane/Everett** c-97. **Kirby** a-1-8p, Special 3r, 4r(p); c-1-30, 148, 151-158; layouts-14-16. **Ron Lim** c(p)-335-341. **Miller** c-193p. **Mooney** a-86i, 179p, 180p. **Nebres** a-178i; c-179i. **Newton** a-204p, Annual 9p. **Perez** a(p)-141, 143, 144, 148, 150, 154, 155, 160, 161, 162, 167,168, 170, 171, 194-196, 198-202, Annual 6, 8; c(p)-160-162, 164-166, 170-174, 181,183-185, 191, 192, 194-201, 379-382, Annual 8. **Starlin** c-121, 135. **Staton** a-127-134i. **Tuska** a-47i,48i, 51i, 53i, 54i, 106p, 107p, 135p, 137-140p, 163p. Guardians of the Galaxy app. in #167, 168, 170, 173, 175, 181.*

AVENGERS, THE (Volume Two)
Marvel Comics: V2#1, Nov, 1996 - No. 13, Nov, 1997 ($2.95/$1.95/$1.99) (Produced by Extreme Studios)

1-($2.95)-Heroes Reborn begins; intro new team (Captain America, Swordsman, Scarlet Witch, Vision, Thor, Hellcat & Hawkeye); 1st app. Avengers Island; Loki & Enchantress app.; Rob Liefeld-p & plot; Chap Yaep-p; Jim Valentino scripts; variant-c exists 5.00

1-($1.95)-Variant-c 6.00

2-13: 2,3-Jeph Loeb scripts begin, Kang app. 4-Hulk-c/app. 5-Thor/Hulk battle; 2 covers. 10,11,13-"World War 3"-pt. 2, x-over w/Image characters. 12-($2.99) "Heroes Reunited"-pt. 2 4.00

Heroes Reborn: Avengers (2006, $29.99, TPB) r/#1-12; pin-up and cover gallery 30.00

AVENGERS, THE (Volume Three)(See New Avengers for next series)
Marvel Comics: Feb, 1998 - No. 84, Aug, 2004; No. 500, Sept, 2004 - No. 503, Dec, 2004 ($2.99/$1.99/$2.25)

1-($2.99, 48 pgs.) Busiek-s/Pérez-a/wraparound-c; Avengers reassemble after Heroes Return; many Avengers app. vs. Morgan Le Fey 5.00

1-Variant Heroes Return sunburst cover 1 2 3 4 5 7

1-Dynamic Forces Ltd Edition (1500 copies); sunburst-c signed by Perez 4 8 12 23 37 50

1-Rough Cut-Features original script and pencil pages 4.00

2-($1.99) Pérez-c; vs. Morgan Le Fey, alternate painted-c by Lago 4.00

3,4: 3-Wonder Man-c/app. & "dies". 4-Final roster chosen; Captain America, Thor, Hawkeye, Iron Man, Scarlet Witch, Vision, Warbird (formally Ms. Marvel: Carol Danvers) 3.00

5-6,8-11; 5-6: Squadron Supreme-c/app.: Hyperion, Dr. Spectrum, Power Princess, Whizzer, Haywire, Lady Lark, Shape & Moonglow. 8-1st app; Triathlon & Silverclaw; vs. Moses Magnum. 9-1st mention of the Triune Understanding. 10-Grimm Reaper & Ultron app; return of the Legion of the Unliving: Captain Mar-Vell, Dr. Druid, Mockingbird, Swordsman, Wonder Man & Thunderstrike. 11-Legion of the Unliving app; Hellcat, Spider-Man, Daredevil & Fantastic Four guest app; Wonder Man returns to life 3.00

7-Live Kree or Die pt. 4; continued from Quicksilver #10; Warbird leaves; vs. Kree Lunatic Legion 4.00

GD VG FN VF VF/NM NM- 2.0 4.0 6.0 8.0 9.0 9.2

12-($2.99, 38 pgs.) Thunderbolts app; Firebird and Justice (of the New Warriors) join the Avengers. 4.00

12-Alternate-c of Avengers w/white background; no logo 3 6 9 16 23 30

12-Dynamic Forces alternate-c; ltd. to 5000 copies 1 3 4 6 8 10

12-Dynamic Forces alternate-c; ltd. to 1500 copies; signed by Pérez, Vey and Smith 3 6 9 14 20 25

13-18,23,26: 13-New Warriors app.; 1st app. Lord Templar; 1st (shadowed) app. Jonathan Tremont – leader of the Triune Understanding. 14-Beast app. vs. Lord Templar; 1st app. Pagan. 15-1st full app. of Jonathan Tremont; Pagan and Lord Templar, the Wrecking Crew and Ultron app. 16-18-Ordway-s/a; vs. the Doomsday Man in #17; vs. the Wrecking Crew in #18. 23-Vision & Scarlet Witch history retold. 26-Immonen-a; Lord Templar & Taskmaster app. 3.00

16-Variant-c w/purple background 5.00

19,20: Ultron Unlimited pt. 1-2; Black Panther app.; Giant-Man (Henry Pym app. in #20-22) 1 3 4 6 8 10

21,22-Ultron Unlimited pt. 3-4; vs. Ultron; Black Panther app. 6.00

24-Continued from Juggernaut: the Eighth Day #1; vs. the Exemplars 4.00

25-Vs. the Exemplars; Spider-Man, New Warriors, Juggernaut and Quicksilver app. 5.00

27-($2.99, 100 pgs. 'Monster') New line up - Justice, Firestar & Thor leave, Triathlon & She-Hulk join, Wonder Man becomes a reserve member; Ant-Man app.; reprints issues (all Vol.1) #101,150,151, Annual #19; Note: Due to the 100 pages, this issue often suffers from tears around the staples. 6.00

28-32: 28-30-vs. Kulan Gath. 31-Vision rejoins; vs. Grimm Reaper. 32-Life story & secret origin of Madame Masque revealed 3.00

33-Thunderbolts x-over w/Thunderbolts #44; Madame Masque & Count Nefaria app. 1 3 4 6 9 12

34-($2.99, 38 pgs.) Last Perez-a; continued from Thunderbolts #44; vs. Count Nefaria; Black Widow app 6.00

35-37: 35-Maximum Security x-over; Romita Jr.-a; 36-37; vs. Bloodwraith; Epting-a 4.00

38-Davis-a begins ($1.99-c); new line-up: Captain America, Goliath (Henry Pym), Thor, Quicksilver, Wasp, Iron Man, Vision, Scarlet Witch, Triathlon, Wonder Man & Warbird (Carol Danvers) 4.00

39,40: Hulk app. 5.00

41-47,49: 41-Vs. Scarlet Centurion; Kang app. 42-44-Kang, Scarlet Centurion & the Presence app. 43-Jack of Hearts joins; last Davis-a. 45-Origin of the Scarlet Centurion; Kang & the Master of the World (from Alpha Flight issues) app. 46-Vs. Kang and his army; Scarlet Centurion & the Master of the World app. 47-Origin of Scarlet Centurion continued with flashback to issue #200 w/Ms. Marvel (Carol Danvers); 1st full app of the Triple Evil (ancient cosmic menace). 49-'Nuff Said story; Kang attacks Washington DC 3.00

48-($3.50, 100 pgs); vs. Kang and his legions; Scarlet Centurion app; death of Master of the World; Triple Evil app.; r/#98-100 4.00

50-($3.50); vs. the Triple Evil (destroyed); Lord Pagan & Templar app. (both die); Jonathan Tremont & the Triune Understanding revealed as villains; 3-D Man app. 5.00

51,52: 51-Kang app. as ruler of the Earth; Wonder Man and Scarlet Witch app.; features 2 pg. tribute to the late John Buscema who passed away on January 10th 2002. 52-Avengers vs. Kang; Scarlet Centurion & the Presence app. 4.00

53-Avengers vs. Kang; death of Jonathan Tremont. 6.00

54-56: 54-Conclusion of the Kang war w/Kang defeated; death of Scarlet Centurion. 55-Kang war aftermath; Thor leaves. 56-Beast app; last Busiek issue 4.00

57-62,65-84: 57-Geoff Johns-s begins; 'World Trust' pt. 1; ends with pt. 4 in issue #60. 64-Solo Falcon story; vs Scarecrow. 65-70-Red Zone pt. 1-6; vs. the Red Skull. Wasp and Yellowjacket (Henry Pym) story; vs. Plantman and Whirlwind. 71-74; Search for She-Hulk pt. 1-4; Hulk app. in #73-74. 77-Last Johns issue. 78-81; Chuck Austen-s begin; Lionheart of Avalon pt. 1-5; special 50-¢t issue. 79-81; Captain Britain (Brian Braddock) app. 82-84-Once an Invader pt. 1-4; intro. New invaders team: Blazing Skull, Spitfire, US Agent & Union Jack; Namor app. in #83-84 4.00

63-Standoff pt. 3; continued from Thor (Vol. 2) #58; Thor vs. Iron Man; Dr. Doom app. 2 4 6 9 12 15

(After #84 [Aug, 2004], numbering reverted back to original Vol. 1 with #500, Sept, 2004)

500-($3.50) "Avengers Disassembled" begins; Bendis-s/Finch-a; Ant-Man (Scott Lang) and Jack of Hearts killed, Vision destroyed by the Scarlet Witch 5.00

500-Director's Cut ($4.99) Cassaday foil variant-c plus interviews and galleries 1 3 4 6 8 10

501, 502-($2.25): 501-Numerous Avengers and ex-team members app. 502-Hawkeye killed 5.00

503-($3.50) "Avengers Disassembled" ends; reprint pages from Avengers V1#16; Dr. Strange and Magneto app; story continues in Avengers Finale #1 4.00

#11/2 (12/99, $2.50) Timm-c/a; Stern-s; 1963-style issue 3.00

.../ Squadron Supreme '98 Annual ($2.99) 4.00

1999, 2000 Annual (7/99, '00, $3.50) 1999-Manco-a. 2000-Breyfogle-a 4.00

2001 Annual ($2.99) Reis-a; back-up-s art by Churchill 4.00

...: Above and Beyond TPB ('05, $24.99) r/#36-40,56, Annual 2001, & Avengers: The Ultron

Avengers (2011 series) #12.1 © MAR

Avengers #674 © MAR

Avengers Academy #31 © MAR

GD VG FN VF VF/NM NM-
2.0 4.0 6.0 8.0 9.0 9.2

GD VG FN VF VF/NM NM-
2.0 4.0 6.0 8.0 9.0 9.2

Imperative; Alan Davis-c 25.00
... Assemble HC ('04, $29.95, oversized) r/#1-11 & '98 Annual; Busiek intro.; Pérez pencil art and Busiek script from Avengers #1 30.00
... Assemble Vol. 2 HC ('05, $29.95, oversized) r/#12-22, #0 & Ann. 1999; Ordway intro. 30.00
... Assemble Vol. 3 HC ('06, $34.99, oversized) r/#23-34, #1 1/2 & Thunderbolts #42-44 35.00
... Assemble Vol. 4 HC ('07, $34.99, oversized) r/#35-40, Avengers 2000, Avengers 2001, Avengers: The Ultron Imperative, Maximum Security #1-3 & ...Dangerous Planet 35.00
... Assemble Vol. 5 HC ('07, $39.99, oversized) r/#41-56 and Avengers 2001 40.00
...: Clear and Present Dangers TPB ('01, $19.95) r/#8-15 20.00
...: Defenders War HC ('07, $19.99) r/#115-118 & Defenders #8-11; Englehart intro. 20.00
...: Disassembled HC ('06, $24.99) r/#500-503 & Avengers Finale; Director's Cut extras 25.00
...: Disassembled TPB ('05, $15.99) r/#500-503 & Avengers Finale; Director's Cut extras 16.00
...Finale 1 (1/05, $3.50) Epilogue to Avengers Disassembled; Neal Adams-c; art by various incl. Peréz, Maleev, Oeming, Powell, Mayhew, Mack, McNiven, Cheung, Frank 4.00
Free Comic Book Day (5/09, giveaway) New Avengers 1st battle vs. Dark Avengers 3.00
...: Living Legends TPB ('04, $19.99) r/#23-30; last Busiek/Pérez arc 20.00
...Supreme Justice TPB (4/01, $17.95) r/Squadron Supreme appearances in Avengers #5-7, '98 Annual, Iron Man #7, Capt. America #8, Quicksilver #10; Pérez-c 18.00
The Kang Dynasty TPB ('02, $29.99) r/#41-55 & 2001 Annual 30.00
The Morgan Conquest TPB ('00, $14.95) r/#1-4 15.00
.../Thunderbolts Vol. 1: The Nefaria Protocols (2004, $19.99) r/#31-34, 42-44 20.00
Ultron Unleashed TPB (8/99, $3.50) reprints early app. 4.00
Ultron Unlimited TPB (4/01, $14.95) r/#19-22 & #0 prelude 15.00
Wizard #0-Ultron Unlimited prelude 3.00
Vol. 1: World Trust TPB ('03, $14.99) r/#57-62 & Marvel Double-Shot #2 15.00
Vol. 2: Red Zone TPB ('04, $14.99) r/#64-70 15.00
Vol. 3: The Search For She-Hulk TPB ('04, $12.99) r/#71-76 13.00
Vol. 4: The Lionheart of Avalon TPB ('04, $11.99) r/#77-81 12.00
Vol. 5: Once an Invader TPB ('04, $14.99) r/#82-84, V1 #71; Invaders #0 & Ann #1 ('77) 15.00

AVENGERS (The Heroic Age)
Marvel Comics: July, 2010 - No. 34, Jan, 2013 ($3.99)

1-New team assembled; Bendis-s/Romita Jr.-a; Kang app.; back-up text Avengers history 6.00
1-Variant-c by Land 8.00
1-Variant covers by Djurdjevic and John Romita Sr. 12.00
1-3-Second printings 4.00
2,3: 2-Wonder Man app. 5.00
4-12: 4-6-Ultron app. 7-Red Hulk app. 12-Red Hulk joins 4.00
12.1 -(6/11, $2.99) Hitch & Neary-c/a; The Wizard & The Intelligencia app.; Ultron returns 3.00
13-24: 13-17-Fear Itself tie-ins. 13,15-Bachalo-a. 17-New Avengers app. 18-20-Acuña-a. 19-Vision returns, Storm joins 4.00
24.1 -(5/12, $2.99) Peterson-a; Magneto, She-Hulk app. 3.00
25-33: 25-30-Avengers vs. X-Men tie-in; Simonson-a. 31-34-Janet Van Dyne app. 4.00
34-($4.99) Art by Peterson, Mayhew & Dodson; Deodato, Simonson, Yu, Cheung, Coipel art pages; Bendis afterword 5.00
... Annual 1 (3/12, $4.99) Bendis-s/Dell'Otto-c/a; Wonder Man app. 5.00
... Assemble 1 (7/10, $3.99) Handbook-style profiles of Avengers, enemies, allies 4.00
...: Infinity Quest 1 (8/11, $4.99) r/#7-9 with variant covers 5.00
... Roll Call 1 (2012, $4.99) Updated handbook-style profiles of Avengers & enemies 5.00
... Spotlight (7/10, $3.99) Creator interviews, previews, history of the team; trivia 4.00

AVENGERS (Marvel NOW!)
Marvel Comics: Feb, 2013 - No. 44, Jun, 2015 ($3.99)

1-13: 1-Hickman-s/Opeña-a/Weaver-c. 4-6-Adam Kubert-a 4.00
14-23: 14-17-Prelude to Infinity. 18-23-Infinity tie-ins 4.00
24-($4.99) Rogue Planet; Ribic-a; Iron Man 3030 app. 5.00
25-28-Hickman-s/Larroca-a. 27-Includes reprint of All-New Invaders #1 4.00
29-($4.99) Original Sin tie-in; Yu-a/Cho-c 5.00
30-34-Original Sin tie-in; Hickman-s/Yu-a 4.00
34.1 (11/14), 34.2 (3/15), 35-($4.99) 34.1-Spotlight on Hyperion; Keown-a. 34.2-Spotlight on Starbrand; Bengal-a. 35-Cheung, Medina-a 5.00
36-39,41-43: 37,39,41-Deodato-a. 39-Leads into New Avengers #28 4.00
40-($4.99) Thanos-c/app.; Caselli-a 5.00
44-($4.99) Follows New Avengers #33; Thanos app.; leads into Secret Wars #1 5.00
Annual (2/14, $4.99) Christmas-themed; Lafuente-a 5.00
...: Endless Wartime HC (2013, $24.99, OGN) Ellis-s/McKone-a; intro by Clark Gregg 25.00
...: No More Bullying (3/15, $1.99) Short stories; Avengers, Spider-Man, GOTG app. 3.00
... Now! Handbook 1 (2/15, $4.99) Updated version with new characters from 2014 5.00
...: The Enemy Within (7/13, $2.99) DeConnick-s/Hepburn-a; Captain Marvel tie-in 3.00
...: Vs 1 (7/15, $5.99) Printing of 4 digital-first stories; Raney-c 6.00
100th Anniversary Special: Avengers 1 (9/14, $3.99) James Stokoe-s/a 4.00

AVENGERS (After Secret Wars)
Marvel Comics: No. 0, Dec, 2015 ($5.99)

0-Short story preludes for the various Avengers 2016 titles; Deadpool app. 6.00

AVENGERS (Follows events of Civil War II)
Marvel Comics: Jan, 2017 - No. 11, Nov, 2017; No. 672, Dec, 2017 - Present ($4.99/$3.99)

1-($4.99) Spider-Man, Capt. America (Sam), Thor (Jane), Wasp, Vision, Hercules team 5.00
2-11-($3.99) 2-6-Kang app.; Waid-s/del Mundo-a. 7,8-Infamous Iron Man app.; Noto-a. 9,10-Secret Empire tie-ins 4.00
[Title switches to legacy numbering after #11 (11/17)]
672-674,676-683: 672-674-The Champions app. 676-683-No Surrender. 681-Origin of Voyager. 682-Hulk returns 4.00
675-($4.99) No Surrender Part 1; "return" of Voyager; lenticular wraparound-c by Brooks 5.00
#1.MU (3/17, $4.99) Monsters Unleashed tie-in; Zub-s/Izaakse-a 5.00

AVENGERS (Flashback to new team roster from Avengers #16 [1965])
Marvel Comics: No. 1.1, Jan, 2017 - No. 5.1, May, 2017 ($3.99)

1.1, 2.1, 3.1, 4.1, 5.1- Hawkeye, Quicksilver and Scarlet Witch join team; Waid-s/Kitson-a 4.00

AVENGERS ACADEMY (The Heroic Age)(Also see Avengers Arena)
Marvel Comics: Aug, 2010 - No. 39, Jan, 2013 ($3.99/$2.99)

1-($3.99) Gage-s/McKone-a/c; Intro. team of Veil, Hazmat, Striker, Mettle, Finesse, Reptil 4.00
1-Variant-c by Djurdjevic 8.00
2-14,14.1 -($2.99) 3,4-Juggernaut app. 5-Molina-a. 7-Absorbing Man app.; Raney-a. 3.00
15-39: 15-20-Fear Itself tie-in. 22-Magneto app. 27,28-Runaways app. 29-33-Tie in to Avengers vs. X-Men event 3.00
... Giant Size 1 (7/11, $7.99) Young Allies and Arcade app.; Tobin-s/Baldeon-a 8.00

AVENGERS: AGE OF ULTRON POINT ONE (Free Comic Book Day)
Marvel Comics: 2012 (Free giveaway)

#0.1 - Reprints Avengers 12.1 (6/11); Bendis-s/Hitch & Neary-c/a 4.00

AVENGERS: A.I. (Follows Age of Ultron series)
Marvel Comics: Sept, 2013 - No. 12, Jun, 2014 ($2.99)

1-12: 1-Humphries-s/Araújo-a; Hank Pym, Vision app. 7-Daredevil app. 3.00

AVENGERS AND POWER PACK ASSEMBLE!
Marvel Comics: June, 2006 - No. 4, Sept, 2006 ($2.99, limited series)

1-4-GuriHiru-a/Sumerak-s. 1-Capt. America app. 2-Iron Man. 3-Spider-Man, Kang app. 3.00
TPB (2006, $6.99, digest-size) r/#1-4 7.00

AVENGERS AND THE INFINITY GAUNTLET
Marvel Comics: Oct, 2010 - No. 4, Jan, 2011 ($2.99, limited series)

1-4: 1-Clevinger-s/Churilla-a; Dr. Doom and Thanos app. 1-Ramos-c. 2-Lim-c 3.00

AVENGERS & X-MEN: AXIS
Marvel Comics: Dec, 2014 - No. 9, Feb, 2015 ($4.99/$3.99, limited series)

1-($4.99) Remender-s/Adam Kubert-a; Red Skull as Red Onslaught 5.00
2-8-($3.99): 2,7-Kubert-a. 3,4,8-Yu-a. 3-Adult Apocalypse app. 5,6-Dodson-a 4.00
9-($4.99) Cheung, Dodson, Yu & Kubert-a 5.00

AVENGERS ARENA
Marvel Comics: Feb, 2013 - No. 18, Jan, 2014 ($2.99)

1-18: 1-Avengers Academy members & Runaways in Arcade's Murder World; Walker-a 3.00

AVENGERS ASSEMBLE (Also see Marvel Universe Avengers Assemble)
Marvel Comics: May, 2012 - No. 25, May, 2014 ($3.99)

1-25: 1-Bendis-s/Bagley-a/c; movie roster in regular Marvel universe. 3-Thanos returns. 4-8-Guardians of the Galaxy app. 9-DeConnick-s begin. 13,14-Age of Ultron tie-in. 18-20-Infinity tie-in. 21-23-Inhumanity 4.00
Annual 1 (3/13, $4.99) Gage-s/Coker-a; spotlight on The Vision 5.00

AVENGERS: CELESTIAL QUEST
Marvel Comics: Nov, 2001 - No. 8, June, 2002 ($2.50/$3.50, limited series)

1-7-Englehart-s/Santamaría-a; Thanos app. 3.00
8-($3.50) 4.00

AVENGERS: CLASSIC
Marvel Comics: Aug, 2007 - No. 12, Juy, 2008 ($3.99/$2.99)

1,12-($3.99) 1-Reprints Avengers #1 ('63) with new stories about that era; Art Adams-c 4.00
2-11-($2.99) R/#2-11 with back-up w/art by Oeming and others 3.00

AVENGERS COLLECTOR'S EDITION, THE
Marvel Comics: 1993 (Ordered through mail w/candy wrapper, 20 pgs.)

1-Contains 4 bound-in trading cards 5.00

AVENGERS: EARTH'S MIGHTIEST HEROES
Marvel Comics: Jan, 2005 - No. 8, Apr, 2005 ($3.50, limited series)

1-8-Retells origin; Casey-s/Kolins-a 4.00
HC (2005, $24.99, 7 1/2" x 11" with dustjacket) r/#1-8 25.00

AVENGERS: EARTH'S MIGHTIEST HEROES (Based on the Disney animated series)
Marvel Comics: Jan, 2011 - No. 4, Apr, 2011 ($3.99)

Avengers Forever #1 © MAR

Avengers Origins: Thor #1 © MAR

Avengers: The Initiative #2 © MAR

GD 2.0 | VG 4.0 | FN 6.0 | VF 8.0 | VF/NM 9.0 | NM- 9.2

1-4-Yost-s/Wegener-a. 1-Hero profile pages. 2-Villain profile pages 4.00

AVENGERS EARTH'S MIGHTIEST HEROES (Titled Marvel Universe... for #1)
Marvel Comics: Jun, 2012 - No. 17, Oct, 2013 ($2.99)
1-17-All ages title. 13-FF & Dr. Doom app. 17-Ant-Man, Luke Cage & Iron Fist app. 4.00

AVENGERS: EARTH'S MIGHTIEST HEROES II
Marvel Comics: Jan, 2007 - No. 8, May, 2007 ($3.99, limited series)
1-8-Retells time when the Vision joined; Casey-s/Rosado-a. 6-Hank & Janet's wedding 4.00
HC (2007, $24.99, 7 1/2" x 11" with dustjacket) r/#1-8; cover sketches 25.00

AVENGERS FAIRY TALES
Marvel Comics: May, 2008 - No. 4, Dec, 2008 ($2.99, limited series)
1-4: 1-Peter Pan-style tale; Cebulski-a/Lemos-a. 2-The Vision. 3-Miyazawa-a 3.00

AVENGERS FOREVER
Marvel Comics: Dec, 1998 - No. 12, Feb, 2000 ($2.99)
1-Busiek-s/Pacheco-a in all 4.00
2-12: 4-Four covers. 6-Two covers. 8-Vision origin revised. 12-Rick Jones becomes Capt. Marvel 3.00
TPB (1/01, $24.95) r/#1-12; Busiek intro.; new Pacheco-c 25.00

AVENGERS INFINITY
Marvel Comics: Sept, 2000 - No. 4, Dec, 2000 ($2.99, limited series)
1-4-Stern-s/Chen-a 3.00

AVENGERS/ INVADERS
Marvel Comics: Jul, 2008 - No. 12, Aug, 2009 ($2.99, limited series)
1-Invaders journey to the present; Alex Ross-c/Sadowski-a; Thunderbolts app. 3.00
2-12: 2-New Avengers app.; Perkins variant-c. 3-12-Variant-c on each 3.00
... Sketchbook (2008, giveaway) Ross and Sadowski sketch art; Krueger commentary 3.00

AVENGERS/ JLA (See JLA/Avengers for #1 & #3)
DC Comics: No, 2, 2003; No. 4, 2003 ($5.95, limited series)
2-Busiek-s/Pérez-a; wraparound-c; Krona, Galactus app. 6.00
4-Busiek-s/Pérez-a; wraparound-c 6.00

AVENGERS LOG, THE
Marvel Comics: Feb, 1994 ($1.95)
1-Gives history of all members; Pérez-c 3.00

AVENGERS: MILLENNIUM
Marvel Comics: Jun, 2015 - No. 4, Jun, 2015 ($3.99, weekly limited series)
1-4-Di Giandomenico-a; Scarlet Witch & Quicksilver app. 1-Yu-c. 2-4-Deodato-c. 4.00

AVENGERS NEXT (See A-Next and Spider-Girl)
Marvel Comics: Jan, 2007 - No. 5, Mar, 2007 ($2.99, limited series)
1-5-Lim-a/Wieringo-c; Spider-Girl app. 1-Avengers vs. zombies. 2-Thena app. 3.00
...: Rebirth TPB (2007, $13.99) r/#1-5 14.00

AVENGERS 1959
Marvel Comics: Dec, 2011 - No. 5, Mar, 2012 ($2.99, limited series)
1-5-Chaykin-s/a/c; Nick Fury, Kraven, Namora, Sabretooth, Dominic Fortune app. 3.00

AVENGERS: OPERATION HYDRA
Marvel Comics: Jun, 2015 ($3.99, one-shot)
1-Movie team; Pilgrim-s/Di Vito-a; bonus reprint of Avengers #16 (1965) 4.00

AVENGERS ORIGINS (Series of one-shots)
Marvel Comics: Jan, 2012 ($3.99)
...: Ant-Man & The Wasp 1 (1/12) Aguirre-Sacasa-s/Hans-a/Djurdjevic-c; origin of both 4.00
...: Luke Cage 1 (1/12) Glass & Benson-s/Talajic-a/Djurdjevic-c; 4.00
...: Scarlet Witch & Quicksilver 1 (1/12) McKeever-s/Pierfederici-a/Djurdjevic-c 4.00
...: Thor 1 (1/12) K. Immonen-s/Barrionuevo-a/Djurdjevic-c 4.00
...: Vision 1 (1/12) Higgins & Siegel-s/Perger-a/Djurdjevic-c; Ultron-5 app. 4.00

AVENGERS PRIME (The Heroic Age)
Marvel Comics: Aug, 2010 - No. 5, Mar, 2011 ($3.99, limited series)
1-5-Thor, Iron Man & Steve Rogers; Bendis-s/Davis-a; Enchantress app. 4.00
1-Variant-c by Djurdjevic 8.00

AVENGERS: RAGE OF ULTRON
Marvel Comics: 2015 ($24.99, hardcover graphic novel)
HC - Remender-s/Opeña-a; intro by Busiek 25.00

AVENGERS: SEASON ONE
Marvel Comics: 2013 ($24.99, hardcover graphic novel)
HC - Origin story; Peter David-a/Tedesco painted-c; bonus script outline 25.00

AVENGERS: SOLO
Marvel Comics: Dec, 2011 - No. 5, Apr, 2012 ($3.99, limited series)
1-5-Hawkeye; back-up Avengers Academy 4.00

AVENGERS SPOTLIGHT (Formerly Solo Avengers #1-20)
Marvel Comics: No. 21, Aug, 1989 - No. 40, Jan, 1991 (75¢/$1.00)
21-Byrne-c/a 3.50
22-40: 26-Acts of Vengeance story. 31-34-U.S. Agent series. 36-Heck-i. 37-Mortimer-i. 40-The Black Knight app. 3.00

AVENGERS STANDOFF (Crossover with Avengers titles and other Marvel titles)
Marvel Comics: Apr, 2016 - Jun, 2016 ($4.99)
...: Assault on Pleasant Hill Alpha 1 (5/16) Part 2 of crossover; Spencer-s/Saiz-a 5.00
...: Assault on Pleasant Hill Omega 1 (6/16) Part 3 of crossover; Spencer-s/Acuña-a; new Quasar debut; Red Skull app. 5.00
...: Welcome to Pleasant Hill 1 (4/16) Part 1 of crossover; Spencer-s/Bagley-a/Acuña-c 5.00

AVENGERS STRIKEFILE
Marvel Comics: Jan, 1994 ($1.75, one-shot)
1 3.00

AVENGERS: THE CHILDREN'S CRUSADE
Marvel Comics: Sept, 2010 - No. 9, May, 2012 ($3.99, limited series)
1-9-Young Avengers search for Scarlet Witch; Heinberg-s/Cheung-a. 6-9-X-Men app. 4.00
1-4-Variant-c. 1-Jelena Djurdjevic. 2-Travis Charest. 3,4-Art Adams 6.00
... - Young Avengers (5/11, $3.99) Takes place between #4&5; Alan Davis-a/c 4.00

AVENGERS: THE CROSSING
Marvel Comics: July, 1995 ($4.95, one-shot)
1-Deodato-c/a; 1st app. Thor's new costume 5.00

AVENGERS: THE INITIATIVE (See Civil War and related titles)
Marvel Comics: Jun, 2007 - No. 35, Jun, 2010 ($2.99)
1-Caselli-a/Slott-s/Cheung-c; War Machine app. 4.00
2-35: 4,5-World War Hulk. 6-Uy-a. 14-19-Secret Invasion; 3-D Man app. 16-Skrull Kill Krew returns. 20-Tigra pregnancy revealed, 21-25-Ramos-a. 32-35-Siege 3.00
Annual 1 (1/08, $3.99) Secret Invasion tie-in; Cheung-c 4.00
... Featuring Reptil (5/09, $3.99) Gage-s/Uy-a 4.00
... Special 1 (1/09, $3.99) Slott & Gage-s/Uy-a 4.00
...: Vol. 1 - Basic Training HC (2007, $19.99, d.j.) r/#1-6 20.00
...: Vol. 1 - Basic Training SC (2008, $14.99) r/#1-6 15.00

AVENGERS: THE ORIGIN
Marvel Comics: Jun, 2010 - No. 5, Oct, 2010 ($3.99, limited series)
1-5-Casey-s/Noto-a/c; team origin (pre-Capt. America) re-told; Loki app. 4.00

AVENGERS: THE TERMINATRIX OBJECTIVE
Marvel Comics: Sept, 1993 - No. 4, Dec, 1993 ($1.25, limited series)
1 ($2.50)-Holo-grafx foil-c 4.00
2-4-Old vs. current Avengers 3.00

AVENGERS: THE ULTRON IMPERATIVE
Marvel Comics: Nov, 2001 ($5.99, one-shot)
1-Follow-up to the Ultron Unlimited ending in Avengers #42; BWS-c 6.00

AVENGERS, THOR & CAPTAIN AMERICA: OFFICIAL INDEX TO THE MARVEL UNIVERSE
Marvel Comics: Jun, 2010 - No. 15, 2001 ($3.99)
1-15-Each issue has chronological synopsies, creator credits, character lists for 30-40 issues of Avengers, Captain America and Journey Into Mystery starting with debuts 4.00

AVENGERS/THUNDERBOLTS
Marvel Comics: May, 2004 - No. 6, Sept, 2004 ($2.99, limited series)
1-6: Busiek & Nicieza-s/Kitson-c. 1,2-Kitson-a. 3-6-Grummett-a 3.00
Vol. 2: Best Intentions (2004, $14.99) r/#1-6 15.00

AVENGERS: TIMESLIDE
Marvel Comics: Feb, 1996 ($4.95, one-shot)
1-Foil-c 5.00

AVENGERS TWO: WONDER MAN & BEAST
Marvel Comics: May, 2000 - No. 3, July, 2000 ($2.99, limited series)
1-3: Stern-s/Bagley-c/a 3.00

AVENGERS/ULTRAFORCE (See Ultraforce/Avengers)
Marvel Comics: Oct, 1995 ($3.95, one-shot)
1-Wraparound foil-c by Pérez 4.00

AVENGERS: ULTRON FOREVER
Marvel Comics: Jun, 2015 ($4.99)(Continues in New Avengers: Ultron Forever)
1-Part 1 of 3-part crossover with New Avengers and Uncanny Avengers; Ewing-s/

Avengers Unplugged #3 © MAR

Avenging Spider-Man #1 © MAR

Axcend #4 © Shane Davis

GD 2.0 | VG 4.0 | FN 6.0 | VF 8.0 | VF/NM 9.0 | NM- 9.2

Alan Davis-a; team-up of past, present and future Avengers vs. Ultron 5.00

AVENGERS UNDERCOVER (Follows Avengers Arena series)
Marvel Comics: May, 2014 - No. 10, Nov, 2014 ($2.99)
1-10: Hopeless-s in all; Masters of Evil app. 1,2,4,5,7,Kev Walker-a. 3,6,9-Green-a 3.00

AVENGERS UNITED THEY STAND
Marvel Comics: Nov, 1999 - No. 7, June, 2000 ($2.99/$1.99)
1-Based on the animated series 4.00
2-6-($1.99) 2-Avengers battle Hydra. 6-The Collector app. 3.00
7-($2.99) Devil Dinosaur-c/app.; The Collector app.; r/Avengers Action Figure Comic 4.00

AVENGERS UNIVERSE
Marvel Comics: Jun, 2000 - No. 3, Oct, 2000 ($3.99)
1-3-Reprints recent stories 4.00

AVENGERS UNPLUGGED
Marvel Comics: Oct, 1995 - No. 6, Aug, 1996 (99¢, bi-monthly)
1-6 3.00

AVENGERS VS. ATLAS (Leads into Atlas #1)
Marvel Comics: Mar, 2010 - No. 4, Jun, 2010 ($3.99, limited series)
1-4-Hardman-a; Ramos-c. 1-Back-up w/Miyazawa-a. 2-4-Original Avengers app. 4.00

AVENGERS VS INFINITY
Marvel Comics: Jan, 2016 ($5.99, one-shot)
1-Short stories with The Wrecker, Doctor Doom, Bossman & Dracula; Alves & Lim-a 6.00

AVENGERS VS. PET AVENGERS
Marvel Comics: Dec, 2010 - No. 4, Mar, 2011 ($2.99, limited series)
1-4-Eliopoulos-s/Guara-a; Fin Fang Foom app. 3.00

AVENGERS VS. X-MEN (Also see AVX: VS and AVX: Consequences)
Marvel Comics: No. 0, May, 2012 - No. 12, Dec, 2012 ($3.99/$4.99, bi-weekly limited series)
0-Bendis & Aaron-s; Frank Cho-a/c; Scarlet Witch and Hope featured 4.00
1-11: 1-5-Romita Jr. -a. 6,7,11-Coipel-a. 8-10-Adam Kubert-a. 11-Hulk app. 4.00
12-($4.99) Adam Kubert-a; Cyclops as Dark Phoenix 5.00

AVENGERS WEST COAST (Formerly West Coast Avengers)
Marvel Comics: No. 48, Sept, 1989 - No. 102, Jan, 1994 ($1.00/$1.25)
48,49: 48-Byrne-c/a & scripts continue thru #57 3.50
50-Re-intro original Human Torch 4.00
51-69,71-74,76-83,85,86,89-99: 54-Cover swipe/F.F. #1. 78-Last $1.00-c. 79-Dr. Strange x-over. 93-95-Darkhawk app. 3.00
70,75,84,87,88: 70-Spider-Woman app. 75 (52 pgs.)-Fantastic Four x-over. 84-Origin Spider-Woman retold; Spider-Man app. (also in #85,86). 87,88-Wolverine-c/story 4.00
100-($3.95, 68 pgs.)-Embossed all red foil-c 4.00
101,102: 101-X-Men x-over 5.00
Annual 5-8 ('90- '93, 68 pgs.)-5,6-West Coast Avengers in indicia. 7-Darkhawk app. 8-Polybagged w/card 4.00
...: Darker Than Scarlet TPB (2008, $24.99) r/#51-57,60-62; Byrne-s/a 25.00
...: Vision Quest TPB (2005, $24.99) r/#42-50; Byrne-s/a 25.00

AVENGERS WORLD
Marvel Comics: Mar, 2014 - No. 21, Jul, 2015 ($3.99)
1-21: 1-Hickman & Spencer-s/Caselli-a. 6-Neal Adams-c. 15,16-Doctor Doom app. 16-Cassie Lang brought back to life. 21-Leads into Secret Wars #1 4.00

AVENGERS: X-SANCTION
Marvel Comics: Feb, 2012 - No. 4, May, 2012 ($3.99, limited series)
1-4-Loeb-s/McGuinness-a/c; Cable battles the Avengers. 3,4-Wolverine & Spidey app. 4.00

AVENGING SPIDER-MAN (Spider-Man and Avengers member team-ups)
Marvel Comics: Jan, 2012 - No. 22, Aug, 2013 ($3.99)
1-8,10-15: 1-3-Madureira-a/Wells-s; Madureira-c. 1-3-Red Hulk & Avengers app. 4-Hawkeye. 5-Captain America app.; Yu-a. 11-Dillon-a. 12,13-Deadpool app. 14,15-Devil Dinosaur 4.00
1-Variant-c by Ramos 1 2 3 5 6 8
1-Variant-c by J. Scott Campbell 1 2 3 5 6 8
9-(9/12) Carol Danvers (Ms. Marvel) takes the name Captain Marvel 4 8 12 23 37 50
15.1 (2/13, $2.99) Follows Amazing Spider-Man #700; 1st Superior Spider-Man 5.00
16-22-Superior Spider-Man. 16-Wolverine & X-Men app. 18-Thor app. 22-Punisher app. 4.00
Annual 1 (12/12, $4.99) Spider-Man (Peter Parker) and The Thing; Zircher-c 5.00

AVIATION ADVENTURES AND MODEL BUILDING (True Aviation Advs. ...No. 15)
Parents' Magazine Institute: No. 16, Dec, 1946 - No. 17, Feb, 1947
16,17-Half comics and half pictures 8 16 24 42 54 65

AVIATION CADETS
Street & Smith Publications: 1943
nn 19 37 57 111 176 240

A-V IN 3-D
Aardvark-Vanaheim: Dec, 1984 ($2.00, 28 pgs. w/glasses)
1-Cerebus, Flaming Carrot, Normalman & Ms. Tree 4.00

AVX: CONSEQUENCES (Aftermath of Avengers Vs. X-Men series)
Marvel Comics: Dec, 2012 - No. 5, Jan, 2013 ($3.99, weekly limited series)
1-5-Cyclops in prison; Gillen-s/art by various 4.00

AVX: VS (Tie-in to Avengers Vs. X-Men series)
Marvel Comics: Jun, 2012 - No. 6, Nov, 2012 ($3.99, limited series)
1-6-Spotlight on the individual fights from Avengers Vs. X-Men #2; art by various 4.00

AWESOME ADVENTURES
Awesome Entertainment: Aug, 1999 ($2.50)
1-Alan Moore-s/ Steve Skroce-a; Youngblood story 3.00

AWESOME HOLIDAY SPECIAL
Awesome Entertainment: Dec, 1997 ($2.50, one-shot)
1-Flip book w/covers of Fighting American & Coven. Holiday stories also featuring Kaboom and Shaft by regular creators. 3.00
1-Gold Edition 5.00

AWFUL OSCAR (Formerly & becomes Oscar Comics with No. 13)
Marvel Comics: No. 11, June, 1949 - No. 12, Aug, 1949
11,12 16 32 48 94 147 200

AW YEAH COMICS: ACTION CAT & ADVENTURE BUG
Dark Horse Graphics: Mar, 2016 - No. 4, Jun, 2016 ($2.99, limited series)
1-4-Art Baltazar & Franco-s/a 3.00

AXA
Eclipse Comics: Apr, 1987 - No. 2, Aug, 1987 ($1.75)
1,2 3.00

AXCEND
Image Comics: Oct, 2015 - Present ($3.50/$3.99)
1-3-Shane Davis-s/a 3.50
4,5-($3.99) 4.00

AXE COP: BAD GUY EARTH
Dark Horse Comics: Mar, 2011 - No. 3, May, 2011 ($3.50, limited series)
1-3-Malachai Nicolle-s/Ethan Nicolle-a 3.50

AXE COP: PRESIDENT OF THE WORLD
Dark Horse Comics: Jul, 2012 - No. 3, Sept, 2012 ($3.50, limited series)
1-3-Malachai Nicolle-s/Ethan Nicolle-a 3.50

AXE COP: THE AMERICAN CHOPPERS
Dark Horse Comics: May, 2014 - No. 3, Jul, 2014 ($3.99, limited series)
1-3-Malachai Nicolle-s/Ethan Nicolle-a. 3-Origin of Axe Cop 4.00

AXEL PRESSBUTTON (Pressbutton No. 5; see Laser Eraser &...)
Eclipse Comics: Nov, 1984 - No. 6, July, 1985 ($1.50/$1.75, Baxter paper)
1-6: Reprints Warrior (British mag.). 1-Bolland-c; origin Laser Eraser & Pressbutton 3.00

AXIS ALPHA
Axis Comics: Feb, 1994 ($2.50, one-shot)
V1-Previews Axis titles including, Tribe, Dethgrip, B.E.A.S.T.I.E.S. & more; Pitt app. in Tribe story. 3.00

AXIS: CARNAGE (Tie-in to Avengers & X-Men Axis series)
Marvel Comics: Dec, 2014 - No. 3, Feb, 2015 ($3.99, limited series)
1-3-Spears-s/Peralta-a; Carnage as a hero; Sin-Eater app. 4.00

AXIS: HOBGOBLIN (Tie-in to Avengers & X-Men Axis series)
Marvel Comics: Dec, 2014 - No. 3, Feb, 2015 ($3.99, limited series)
1-3-Shinick-s/Rodriguez-a; Hobgoblin as a hero; Goblin King app. 4.00

AXIS: RESOLUTIONS (Tie-in to Avengers & X-Men Axis series)
Marvel Comics: Dec, 2014 - No. 4, Feb, 2015 ($3.99, limited series)
1-4-Two stories per issue; s/a by various. 1-Lashley-a. 4-Chaykin-s/a 4.00

AZRAEL (...Agent of the Bat #47 on)(Also see Batman: Sword of Azrael)
DC Comics: Feb, 1995 - No. 100, May, 2003 ($1.95/$2.25/$2.50/$2.95)
1-Dennis O'Neil scripts begin 5.00
2,3 3.50
4-46,48-62: 5,6-Ras Al Ghul app. 13-Nightwing-c/app. 15-Contagion Pt. 5 (Pt. 4 on-c).

GD 2.0 | VG 4.0 | FN 6.0 | VF 8.0 | VF/NM 9.0 | NM- 9.2

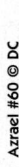

Azrael #60 © DC

Babe #7 © PRIZE

Babyteeth #1 © Cates & Brown

	GD 2.0	VG 4.0	FN 6.0	VF 8.0	VF/NM 9.0	NM- 9.2

16-Contagion Pt. 10. 22-Batman-c/app. 23,27-Batman app. 27,28-Joker app. 35-Hitman app. 36-39-Batman, Bane app. 50-New costume. 53-Joker-c/app. 56,57,60-New Batgirl app. 3.00
47-($3.95) Flip book with Batman: Shadow of the Bat #80 4.00
63-74,76-92: 63-Huntress-c/app.; Azrael returns to old costume. 67-Begin $2.50-c. 70-79-Harris-c. 83-Joker x-over. 91-Bruce Wayne: Fugitive pt. 15 3.00
75-($3.95) New costume; Harris-c 4.00
93-100: 93-Begin $2.95-c. 95,96-Two-Face app. 100-Last issue; Zeck-c 3.00
#1,000,000 (11/98) Giarrano-a 3.00
Annual 1 (1995, $3.95)-Year One story 4.00
Annual 2 (1996, $2.95)-Legends of the Dead Earth story 4.00
Annual 3 (1997, $3.95)-Pulp Heroes story; Orbik-c 4.00
.../Ash (1997, $4.95) O'Neil-s/Quesada, Palmiotti-a 5.00
Plus (12/96, $2.95)-Question-c/app. 4.00

AZRAEL
DC Comics: Dec, 2009 - No. 18, May, 2011 ($2.99)

1-18: 1-9-Nicieza-s/Bachs-a. 1-Covers by Jock & Irving. 2,3-Jock-c. 5-Ragman app. 3.00
...: Angel in the Dark TPB (2010, $17.99) r/#1-6; cover gallery 18.00

AZRAEL: DEATH'S DARK KNIGHT
DC Comics: May, 2009 - No. 3, Jul, 2009 ($2.99, limited series)

1-Battle For the Cowl tie-in; Nicieza-s/Irving-a/March-c 3.00
TPB (2010, $14.99) r/#1-3, Batman Annual #27 and Detective Annual #11 15.00

AZTEC ACE
Eclipse Comics: Mar, 1984 - No. 15, Sept, 1985 ($2.25/$1.50/$1.75, Baxter paper)

1-$2.25-c (52 pgs.) 4.00
2-15: 2-Begin 36 pgs. 3.00
NOTE: *N. Redondo a-1i-8i, 10i. c-6-8i.*

AZTEK: THE ULTIMATE MAN
DC Comics: Aug, 1996 - No. 10, May 1997 ($1.75)

1-1st app. Aztek & Synth; Grant Morrison & Mark Millar scripts in all 6.00
2-9: 2-Green Lantern app. 3-1st app. Death-Doll. 4-Intro The Lizard King. 5-Origin. 6-Joker app.; Batman cameo. 7-Batman app. 8-Luthor app. 9-vs. Parasite-c/app. 4.00
10-Joins the JLA; JLA-c/app. 1 2 4 6 8 10
JLA Presents: Aztek the Ultimate Man TPB (2008, $19.99) r/#1-10 20.00
NOTE: *Breyfogle c-5p. N. Steven Harris a-1-5p. Porter c-1p. Wieringo c-2p.*

BABE (...Darling of the Hills, later issues)(See Big Shot and Sparky Watts)
Prize/Headline/Feature: June-July, 1948 - No. 11, Apr-May, 1950

1-Boody Rogers-a 50 100 150 315 533 750
2-Boody Rogers-a 30 60 90 177 289 400
3-11-All by Boody Rogers 24 48 72 142 234 325

BABE
Dark Horse Comics (Legend): July, 1994 - No. 4, Jan, 1994 ($2.50, lim. series)

1-4: John Byrne-c/a/scripts; ProtoTykes back-up story 3.00

BABE RUTH SPORTS COMICS (Becomes Rags Rabbit #11 on?)
Harvey Publications: April, 1949 - No. 11, Feb, 1951

1-Powell-a 40 80 120 246 411 575
2-Powell-a 27 54 81 158 259 360
3-11: Powell-a in most 22 44 66 130 213 295
NOTE: *Baseball c-2-4, 9. Basketball c-1, 6. Football c-5. Yogi Berra c/story-8. Joe DiMaggio c/story-3. Bob Feller c/story-4. Stan Musial c-9.*

BABES IN TOYLAND (Disney, Movie) (See Golden Pix Story Book ST-3)
Dell Publishing Co.: No. 1282, Feb-Apr, 1962

Four Color 1282-Annette Funicello photo-c 12 24 36 83 182 280

BABES OF BROADWAY
Broadway Comics: May, 1996 ($2.95, one-shot)

1-Pin-ups of Broadway Comics' female characters; Alan Davis, Michael Kaluta, J.G. Jones, Alan Weiss, Guy Davis & others-a; Giordano-c. 3.00

BABE 2
Dark Horse Comics (Legend): Mar, 1995 - No. 2, May, 1995 ($2.50, lim. series)

1,2: John Byrne-c/a/scripts 3.00

BABY HUEY
Harvey Comics: No. 1, Oct, 1991 - No. 9, June, 1994 ($1.00/$1.25/$1.50, quarterly)

1 ($1.00): 1-Cover says "Big Baby Huey" 5.00
2-9 ($1.25-$1.50) 3.00

BABY HUEY AND PAPA (See Paramount Animated...)
Harvey Publications: May, 1962 - No. 33, Jan, 1968 (Also see Casper The Friendly Ghost)

1 13 26 39 86 188 290
2 7 14 21 49 92 135
3-5 5 10 15 33 57 80
6-10 3 6 9 20 31 42
11-20 3 6 9 15 22 28
21-33 2 4 6 13 18 22

BABY HUEY DIGEST
Harvey Publications: June, 1992 (Digest-size, one-shot)

1-Reprints 1 3 4 6 8 10

BABY HUEY DUCKLAND
Harvey Publications: Nov, 1962 - No. 15, Nov, 1966 (25¢ Giants, 68 pgs.)

1 10 20 30 66 138 210
2-5 5 10 15 34 60 85
6-15 3 6 9 21 33 45

BABY HUEY, THE BABY GIANT (Also see Big Baby Huey, Casper, Harvey Hits #22, Harvey Comics Hits #60, & Paramount Animated Comics)
Harvey Publ: 9/56 - #97, 10/71; #98, 10/72; #99, 10/80; #100, 10/90; #101, 11/90

1-Infinity-c 50 100 150 400 900 1400
2 21 42 63 147 324 500
3-Baby Huey takes anti-pep pills 13 26 39 89 195 300
4,5 9 18 27 61 123 185
6-10 6 12 18 40 73 105
11-20 5 10 15 31 53 75
21-40 4 8 12 23 37 50
41-60 3 6 9 16 23 30
61-79 (12/67) 2 4 6 13 18 22
80(12/68) - 95-All 68 pg. Giants 3 6 9 16 24 32
96,97-Both 52 pg. Giants 3 6 9 14 19 24
98-Regular size 2 4 6 9 12 15
99-Regular size 1 2 3 5 6 8
100,101 ($1.00) 4.00

BABYLON 5 (TV)
DC Comics: Jan, 1995 - No. 11, Dec, 1995 ($1.95/$2.50)

1 2 4 6 8 11 14
2-5 1 2 3 5 7 9
6-11: 7-Begin $2.50-c 1 2 3 4 5 7
... The Price of Peace (1998, $9.95, TPB) r/#1-4,11 10.00

BABYLON 5: IN VALEN'S NAME
DC Comics: Mar, 1998 - No. 3, May, 1998 ($2.50, limited series)

1-3 4.00

BABY SNOOTS (Also see March of Comics #359,371,396,401,419,431,443,450,462,474,485)
Gold Key: Aug, 1970 - No. 22, Nov, 1975

1 3 6 9 19 30 40
2-11 2 4 6 11 16 20
12-22: 22-Titled Snoots, the Forgetful Elefink 2 4 6 8 10 12

BABYTEETH
AfterShock Comics: Jun, 2017 - Present ($3.99)

1-8-Donny Cates-s/Garry Brown-a 4.00
... #1: Halloween Edition (10/17, giveaway) r/#1 in B&W; Elizabeth Torque-c 3.00

BACCHUS (Also see Eddie Campbell's ...)
Harrier Comics (New Wave): 1988 - No. 2, Aug, 1988 ($1.95, B&W)

1,2: Eddie Campbell-c/a/scripts. 3.00

BACHELOR FATHER (TV)
Dell Publishing Co.: No. 1332, 4-6/62 - No. 2, Sept.-Nov., 1962

Four Color 1332 (#1), 2-Written by Stanley 7 14 21 44 82 120

BACHELOR'S DIARY
Avon Periodicals: 1949 (15¢)

1(Scarce)-King Features panel cartoons & text-r; pin-up, girl wrestling photos; similar to Sideshow 132 264 396 838 1444 2050

BACKLASH (Also see The Kindred)
Image Comics (WildStorm Prod.): Nov,1994 - No. 32, May, 1997 ($1.95/$2.50)

1-Double-c; variant-double-c 4.00
2-24,26-32: 5-Intro Mindscape; 2 pinups. 8-Wildstorm Rising Pt 8 (newsstand & Direct Market versions. 19-Fire From Heaven Pt 2. 20-Fire From Heaven Pt 10. 31-WildC.A.T.S app. 3.00
25-($3.95)-Double-size 4.00
...& Taboo's African Holiday (9/99, $5.95) Booth-s/a(p) 6.00

BACKLASH/SPIDER-MAN
Image Comics (WildStorm Productions): Aug, 1996 - No. 2, Sept, 1996 ($2.50, lim. series)

Bad Ass #4 © Guy Delcourt Prods.

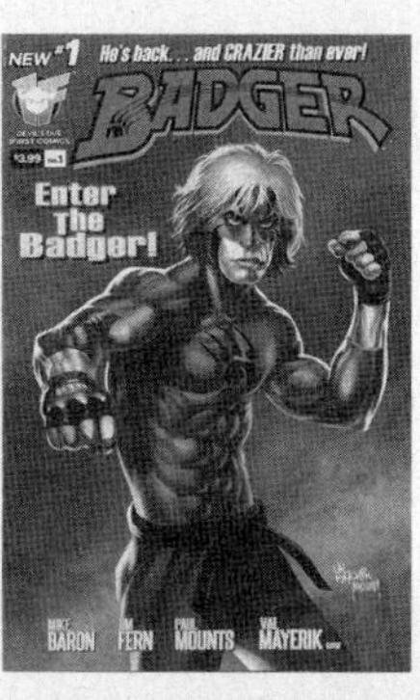

Badger (2016 series) #1 © 1First Comics

Baffling Mysteries #6 © ACE

	GD 2.0	VG 4.0	FN 6.0	VF 8.0	VF/NM 9.0	NM- 9.2

1,2: Pike (villain from WildC.A.T.S) & Venom app. 3.00

BACKPACK MARVELS (B&W backpack-sized reprint collections)
Marvel Comics: Nov, 2000 ($6.95, B&W, digest-size)

Avengers 1 -r/Avengers #181-189; profile pages 7.00
Spider-Man 1-r/ASM #234-240 7.00
X-Men 1-r/Uncanny X-Men #167-173 7.00
X-Men 2-r/Uncanny X-Men #174-179; new painted-c by Greg Horn 7.00

BACKSTAGERS, THE
Boom Entertainment (BOOM! Box): Aug, 2016 - No. 8, Mar, 2017 ($3.99)

1-8: 1-James Tynion IV-s/Rian Sygh-a/Veronica Fish-c 4.00
...: Valentine's Intermission 1 (2/18, $7.99) Short stories by Tynion, Sygh and others 8.00

BACK TO THE FUTURE (Movie, TV cartoon)
Harvey Comics: Nov, 1991 - No. 4, June, 1992 ($1.25)

1-4: 1,2-Gil Kane-c; based on animated cartoon 3.00

BACK TO THE FUTURE (Movie, TV cartoon)
IDW Publishing: Oct, 2015 - No. 25, Oct, 2017 ($3.99)

1-Story by Bob Gale; multiple covers; Doc & Marty's first meeting 6.00
2-24-Multiple covers. 3-Archie variant-c 4.00
25-($4.99)

BACK TO THE FUTURE: BIFF TO THE FUTURE
IDW Publishing: Jan, 2017 - No. 6, JUn, 2017 ($3.99, limited series)

1-5-Biff's rise to power with the sports almanac; Gale & Fridolfs-s/Alan Robinson-a 4.00

BACK TO THE FUTURE: CITIZEN BROWN (Based on the Telltale Games video game)
IDW Publishing: May, 2016 - No. 5, Sept, 2016 ($4.99, limited series)

1-5-Erik Burnham-s/Alan Robinson-a; multiple covers on all 5.00

BACK TO THE FUTURE: FORWARD TO THE FUTURE
Harvey Comics: Oct, 1992 - No. 3, Feb, 1993 ($1.50, limited series)

1-3 3.00

BACK TO THE FUTURE: TALES FROM THE TIME TRAIN
IDW Publishing: Dec, 2017 - Present ($3.99, limited series)

1,2-Doc Brown, Clara and their kids; Gale & Barber-s/Levens-a. 2-1939 World's Fair 4.00

BACKWAYS
AfterShock Comics: Dec, 2107 - Present ($3.99)

1-3-Justin Jordan-s/Eleonora Carlini-a 4.00

BAD ASS
Dynamite Entertainment: 2014 - No. 4. 2014 ($3.99)

1-4-Hanna-s/Bessadi-a 4.00

BAD BLOOD
Dark Horse Comics: Jan, 2014 - No. 5, May, 2014 ($3.99, limited series)

1-5-Vampire story; Jonathan Maberry-s/Tyler Crook-a 4.00

BAD BOY
Oni Press: Dec, 1997 ($4.95, one-shot)

1-Frank Miller-s/Simon Bisley-a/painted-c 5.00

BAD COMPANY
Quality Comics/Fleetway Quality #15 on: Aug, 1988 - No. 19?, 1990 ($1.50/$1.75, high quality paper)

1-19: 5,6-Guice-c 3.00

BADGE OF JUSTICE (Formerly Crime And Justice #21)
Charlton Comics: No. 22, Jan, 1955; No. 2, Apr, 1955 - No. 4, Oct, 1955

	GD	VG	FN	VF	VF/NM	NM-
22(#1)-Giordano-c	10	20	30	58	79	100
2-4	7	14	21	35	43	50

BADGER, THE
Capital Comics(#1-4)/First Comics: Dec, 1983 - No. 70, Apr, 1991; V2#1, Spring, 1991

1 5.00
2-49,51-70: 52-54-Tim Vigil-c/a 3.00
50-($3.95, 52 pgs.) 4.00
V2#1 (Spring, 1991, $4.95) 5.00

BADGER, THE
Image Comics: V3#78, May, 1997 - V3#88 ($2.95, B&W)

78-Cover lists #1, Baron-s 3.00
79/#2, 80/#3, 81(indicia lists #80)/#4,82-88/#5-11 3.00

BADGER, THE
Devil's Due/1First Comics: 2016 - Present ($3.99)

	GD 2.0	VG 4.0	FN 6.0	VF 8.0	VF/NM 9.0	NM- 9.2

1-5: 1-Mike Baron-s/Jim Fern-a/Val Mayerik-c; origin story. 2-5-Putin app. 4.00

BADGER GOES BERSERK
First Comics: Sept, 1989 - No. 4, Dec, 1989 ($1.95, lim. series, Baxter paper)

1-4: 2-Paul Chadwick-c/a(2pgs.) 3.00

BADGER: SHATTERED MIRROR
Dark Horse Comics: July, 1994 - No. Oct, 1994 ($2.50, limited series)

1-4 3.00

BADGER: ZEN POP FUNNY-ANIMAL VERSION
Dark Horse Comics: July, 1994 - No. 2, Aug, 1994 ($2.50, limited series)

1,2 3.00

BAD GIRLS
DC Comics: Oct, 2003 - No. 5, Feb, 2004 ($2.50, limited series)

1-5-Steve Vance-s/Jennifer Graves-a/Darwyn Cooke-c 3.00
TPB (2009, $14.99) r/#1-5; Graves sketch pages 15.00

BAD IDEAS
Image Comics: Apr, 2004 - No. 2, July, 2004 ($5.95, B&W, limited series)

1,2-Chinsang-s/Mahfood & Crosland-a 6.00
..., Vol. 1: Collected! (2005, $12.99) r/#1,2 13.00

BAD KITTY ONE SHOT (CHAOS!...)
Dynamite Entertainment: 2014 ($5.99)

1-Spence-s/Rafael-a/c; origin 6.00

BADLANDS
Vortex Comics: May, 1990 ($3.00, glossy stock, mature)

1-Chaykin-c 3.00

BADLANDS
Dark Horse Comics: July, 1991 - No. 6, Dec, 1991 ($2.25, B&W, limited series)

1-6: 1-John F. Kennedy-c; reprints Vortex Comics issue 3.00

BADMEN OF THE WEST
Avon Periodicals: 1951 (Giant) (132 pgs., painted-c)

	GD	VG	FN	VF	VF/NM	NM-
1-Contains rebound copies of Jesse James, King of the Bad Men of Deadwood, Badmen of Tombstone; other combinations possible. Issues with Kubert-a...	47	94	141	296	498	700

BADMEN OF THE WEST! (See A-1 Comics)
Magazine Enterprises: 1953 - No. 3, 1954

	GD	VG	FN	VF	VF/NM	NM-
1 (A-1 100)-Meskin-a?	23	46	69	136	223	310
2 (A-1 120), 3: 2-Larsen-a	15	30	45	88	137	185

BADMEN OF TOMBSTONE
Avon Periodicals: 1950

	GD	VG	FN	VF	VF/NM	NM-
nn	19	38	57	111	176	240

BAD PLANET
Image Comics (Raw Studios): Dec, 2005 - No. 6, Nov, 2008 ($2.99)

1-6: 1-Thomas Jane & Steve Niles-s/Larosa & Bradstreet-a/c. 2-Wrightson-c. 3-3-D pages 3.00

BADROCK (Also see Youngblood)
Image Comics (Extreme Studios): Mar, 1995 - No. 2, Jan, 1996 ($1.75/$2.50)

1-Variant-c (3) 4.00
2-Liefeld-c/a & story; Savage Dragon app, flipbook w/Grifter/Badrock #2; variant-c exist 3.00
Annual 1(1995,$2.95)-Arthur Adams-c 4.00
Annual 1 Commemorative ($9.95)-3,000 printed 10.00
.../Wolverine (6/96, $4.95, squarebound)-Sauron app; pin-ups; variant-c exists 5.00
.../Wolverine (6/96)-Special Comicon Edition 5.00

BADROCK AND COMPANY (Also see Youngblood)
Image Comics (Extreme Studios): Sept, 1994 - No.6, Feb, 1995 ($2.50)

1-6 : 6-Indicia reads "October 1994"; story cont'd in Shadowhawk #17 3.00

BAFFLING MYSTERIES (Formerly Indian Braves No. 1-4; Heroes of the Wild Frontier No. 26-on)
Periodical House (Ace Magazines): No. 5, Nov, 1951 - No. 26, Oct, 1955

	GD	VG	FN	VF	VF/NM	NM-
5	48	96	144	302	514	725
6-19,21-24: 8-Woodish-a by Cameron. 10-E.C. Crypt Keeper swipe on-c. 24-Last pre-code issue	36	72	108	211	343	475
20-Classic bondage-c	42	84	126	265	445	625
25-Reprints; surrealistic-c	26	52	78	154	252	350
26-Reprints	23	46	69	138	227	315

NOTE: ***Cameron** a-8, 10, 16-18, 20-22. **Colan** a-5, 11, 25r/5. **Sekowsky** a-5, 6, 22. Bondage c-20, 23. Reprints in 18(1), 19(1), 24(3).*

BAKER STREET PECULIARS, THE

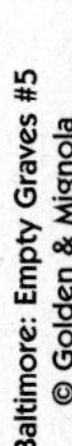

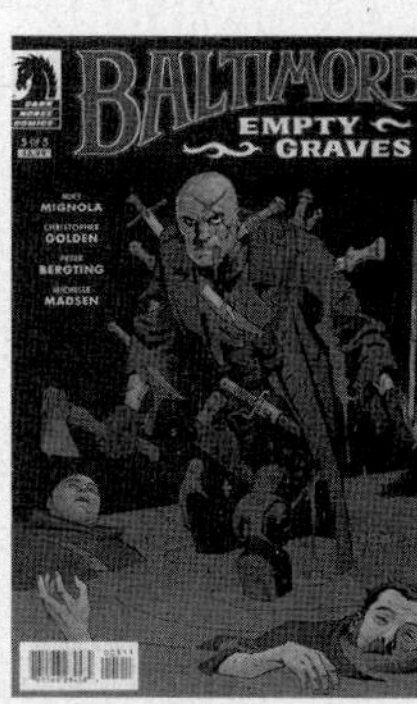

Baltimore: Empty Graves #5 © Golden & Mignola

Bane: Conquest #2 © DC

Barbie #16 © Mattel

	GD 2.0	VG 4.0	FN 6.0	VF 8.0	VF/NM 9.0	NM- 9.2

Boom Entertainment (kaboom!): Mar, 2016 - No. 4, Jun, 2016 ($3.99, limited series)
1-4-Roger Langridge-s/Andy Hirsch-a 4.00

BALBO (See Master Comics #33 & Mighty Midget Comics)

BALDER THE BRAVE
Marvel Comics Group: Nov, 1985 - No. 4, 1986 (Limited series)
1-4: Simonson-c/a; character from Thor 4.00

BALLAD OF HALO JONES, THE
Quality Comics: Sept, 1987 - No. 12, Aug, 1988 ($1.25/$1.50)
1-12: Alan Moore scripts in all 3.00

BALL AND CHAIN
DC Comics (Homage): Nov, 1999 - No. 4, Feb, 2000 ($2.50, limited series)
1-4-Lobdell-s/Garza-a 3.00

BALLISTIC (Also See Cyberforce)
Image Comics (Top Cow Productions): Sept, 1995 - No. 3, Dec, 1995 ($2.50, limited series)
1-3: Wetworks app, Turner-c/a 3.00
... Action (5/96, $2.95) Pin-ups of Top Cow characters participating in outdoor sports 3.00
... Imagery (1/96, $2.50, anthology) Cyberforce app. 3.00
.../ Wolverine (2/97, $2.95) Devil's Reign pt. 4; Witchblade cameo (1 page) 4.00

BALOO & LITTLE BRITCHES (Disney)
Gold Key: Apr, 1968
1-From the Jungle Book 4 8 12 23 37 50

BALTIMORE: ... (One-shots)
Dark Horse Comics: ($3.50)
... The Inquisitor (6/13) Mignola & Golden-s; Stenbeck-a/c 3.50
... The Play (11/12) Mignola & Golden-s; Stenbeck-a/c 3.50
... The Widow and the Tank (2/13) Mignola & Golden-s; Stenbeck-a/c 3.50

BALTIMORE: CHAPEL OF BONES
Dark Horse Comics: Jan, 2014 - No. 2, Feb, 2014 ($3.50, limited series)
1,2-Mignola & Golden-s; Stenbeck-a/c 3.50

BALTIMORE: EMPTY GRAVES
Dark Horse Comics: Apr, 2016 - No. 5, Aug, 2016 ($3.99, limited series)
1-5-Mignola & Golden-s; Bergting-a; Stenbeck-c 4.00

BALTIMORE: DR. LESKOVAR'S REMEDY
Dark Horse Comics: Jun, 2012 - No. 2, Jul, 2012 ($3.50, limited series)
1,2-Mignola & Golden-s; Stenbeck-a/c 3.50

BALTIMORE: THE CULT OF THE RED KING
Dark Horse Comics: May, 2015 - No. 5, Sept, 2015 ($3.99, limited series)
1-5-Mignola & Golden-s; Bergting-a; Stenbeck-c 4.00

BALTIMORE: THE CURSE BELLS
Dark Horse Comics: Aug, 2011 - No. 5, Dec, 2011 ($3.50, limited series)
1-5-Mignola-s/c; Stenbeck-a. 1-Variant-c by Francavilla 3.50

BALTIMORE: THE INFERNAL TRAIN
Dark Horse Comics: Sept, 2013 - No. 3, Nov, 2013 ($3.50, limited series)
1-3-Mignola & Golden-s; Stenbeck-a/c 3.50

BALTIMORE: THE PLAGUE SHIPS
Dark Horse Comics: Aug, 2010 - No. 5, Dec, 2010 ($3.50, limited series)
1-5-Mignola-s/c; Stenbeck-a; Lord Baltimore hunting vampires in 1916 Europe 3.50

BALTIMORE: THE RED KINGDOM
Dark Horse Comics: Feb, 2017 - No. 5, Jun, 2017 ($3.99, limited series)
1-5-Mignola & Golden-s; Bergting-a; Stenbeck-c 4.00

BALTIMORE: THE WITCH OF HARJU
Dark Horse Comics: Jul, 2014 - No. 3, Sept, 2014 ($3.50, limited series)
1-3-Mignola & Golden-s; Bergting-a; Stenbeck-c 3.50

BALTIMORE: THE WOLF AND THE APOSTLE
Dark Horse Comics: Oct, 2014 - No. 2, Nov, 2014 ($3.50, limited series)
1,2-Mignola & Golden-s; Stenbeck-a/c 3.50

BAMBI (Disney) (See Movie Classics, Movie Comics, and Walt Disney Showcase No. 31)
Dell Publishing Co.: No. 12, 1942; No. 30, 1943; No. 186, Apr, 1948; 1984
Four Color 12-Walt Disney's... 46 92 138 340 770 1200
Four Color 30-Bambi's Children (1943) 40 80 120 296 673 1050
Four Color 186-Walt Disney's...; reprinted as Movie Classic Bambi #3 (1956)
14 28 42 96 211 325
1-(Whitman, 1984; 60¢)-r/Four Color #186 (3-pack) 2 4 6 10 14 18

BAMBI (Disney)
Grosset & Dunlap: 1942 (50¢, 7"x8-1/2", 32pg, hard-c w/dust jacket)
nn-Given away w/a copy of Thumper for a $2.00, 2-yr. subscription to WDC&S
in 1942 (Xmas offer). Book only 22 44 66 132 216 300
w/dust jacket 39 78 117 240 395 550

BAMM BAMM & PEBBLES FLINTSTONE (TV)
Gold Key: Oct, 1964 (Hanna-Barbera)
1 8 16 24 51 96 140

BANANA SPLITS, THE (TV) (See Golden Comics Digest & March of Comics No. 364)
Gold Key: June, 1969 - No. 8, Oct, 1971 (Hanna-Barbera)
1-Photo-c on all 8 16 24 56 108 160
2-8 5 10 15 34 60 85

BANANA SUNDAY
Oni Press: July, 2005 - No. 4, Oct, 2005 ($2.99, B&W, limited series)
1-4-Root Nibot-s/Colleen Coover-a 3.00
TPB (3/06, $11.95) r/#1-4; sketch gallery 12.00

BAND WAGON (See Hanna-Barbera Band Wagon)

BANE: CONQUEST
DC Comics: Jul, 2017 - No. 12 ($3.99, limited series)
1-10: 1-Chuck Dixon-s/Graham Nolan-a; covers by Nolan and Kelley Jones. 4,5-Catwoman app. 6-10-Kobra app. 4.00

BANG! TANGO
DC Comics (Vertigo): Apr, 2009 - No. 6, Sept, 2009 ($2.99, limited series)
1-6-Kelly-s/Sibar-a/Chaykin-c 3.00

BANG-UP COMICS
Progressive Publishers: Dec, 1941 - No. 3, June, 1942
1-Nazi WWII-c; Cosmo Mann & Lady Fairplay begin; Buzz Balmer by Rick Yager in all
(origin #1) 119 238 357 762 1306 1850
2-Nazi zeppelin WWII-c 71 142 213 454 777 1100
3-Japanese WWII-c 63 126 189 403 689 975

BANISHED KNIGHTS (See Warlands)
Image Comics: Dec, 2001 - No. 4, June, 2002 ($2.95)
1-4-Two covers (Alvin Lee, Pat Lee) 3.00

BANKSHOT
Dark Horse Comics: Jun, 2017 - No. 5 ($3.99, limited series)
1-4-Alex de Campi-s/Chriscross-a 4.00

BANNER COMICS (Becomes Captain Courageous No. 6)
Ace Magazines: No. 3, Sept, 1941 - No. 5, Jan, 1942
3-Captain Courageous (1st app.) & Lone Warrior & Sidekick Dicky begin;
Nazi WWII-c by Jim Mooney 219 438 657 1402 2401 3400
4,5: 4-Flag-c 155 310 465 992 1696 2400

BARACK OBAMA (See Presidential Material: Barack Obama, Amazing Spider-Man #583, Savage Dragon #137)

BARACK THE BARBARIAN
Devil's Due Publishing: Jun, 2009 - No. 4, Oct, 2009 ($3.50/$3.99, limited series)
...Quest For The Treasure of Stimuli 1-3-($3.50) Conan spoof with Barack Obama; Hama-s 3.50
...Quest For The Treasure of Stimuli 4-($3.99) 4.00
...: The Red of Red Sarah 1 ($5.99, B&W) Sarah Palin satire; Hama-s 6.00

BARBARELLA (Volume 1)
Dynamite Entertainment: 2017 - Present ($3.99)
1-3-Mike Carey-s/Kenan Yarar-a; multiple covers on each 4.00

BARBARIANS, THE
Atlas Comics/Seaboard Periodicals: June, 1975
1-Origin, only app. Andrax; Iron Jaw app.; Marcos-a 2 4 6 13 18 22

BARBIE
Marvel Comics: Jan, 1991 - No. 63, Mar, 1996 ($1.00/$1.25/$1.50)
1-Polybagged w/doorknob hanger; Romita-c 2 4 6 9 12 15
2-49,51-62 1 2 3 5 7 9
50,63: 50-(Giant). 63-Last issue 2 4 6 8 10 12
... And Baby Sister Kelly (1995, 99¢-c, part of a Marvel 4-pack) scarce
3 6 9 14 20 25

BARBIE & KEN
Dell Publishing Co.: May-July, 1962 - No. 5, Nov-Jan, 1963-64
01-053-207(#1)-Based on Mattel toy dolls 36 72 108 259 580 900

Barb Wire #4 © DH

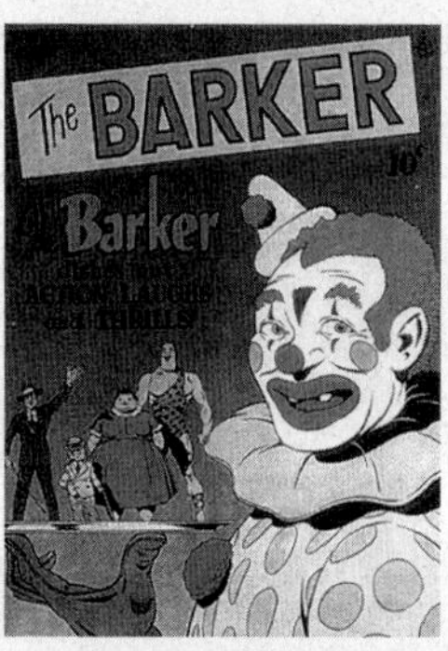

The Barker #2 © QUA

Baseball Comics #1 © Will Eisner

	GD 2.0	VG 4.0	FN 6.0	VF 8.0	VF/NM 9.0	NM- 9.2
2-4	26	52	78	182	404	625
5 (Last issue)	27	54	81	189	420	650

BARBIE FASHION
Marvel Comics: Jan, 1991 - No. 53, May, 1995 ($1.00/$1.25/$1.50)

	GD 2.0	VG 4.0	FN 6.0	VF 8.0	VF/NM 9.0	NM- 9.2
1-Polybagged w/Barbie Pink Card	2	4	6	9	12	15
2-49,51,52: 4-Contains preview to Sweet XVI	1	2	3	5	7	9
50,53: 50-(Giant). 53-Last issue	2	4	6	8	10	12

BARB WIRE (See Comics' Greatest World)
Dark Horse Comics: Apr, 1994 - No. 9, Feb, 1995 ($2.00/$2.50)

	GD 2.0	VG 4.0	FN 6.0	VF 8.0	VF/NM 9.0	NM- 9.2
1-9: 1-Foil logo						3.00
Trade paperback (1996, $8.95)-r/#2,3,5,6 w/Pamela Anderson bio						9.00

BARB WIRE (Volume 2)
Dark Horse Comics: Jul, 2015 - No. 8, Feb, 2016 ($3.99)

	GD 2.0	VG 4.0	FN 6.0	VF 8.0	VF/NM 9.0	NM- 9.2
1-8-Adam Hughes-c on all. 1-Warner-s/Olliffe-a; two covers by Hughes						4.00

BARB WIRE: ACE OF SPADES
Dark Horse Comics: May, 1996 - No. 4, Sept, 1996 ($2.95, limited series)

	GD 2.0	VG 4.0	FN 6.0	VF 8.0	VF/NM 9.0	NM- 9.2
1-4: Chris Warner-c/a(p)/scripts; Tim Bradstreet-c/a(i) in all						3.00

BARB WIRE COMICS MAGAZINE SPECIAL
Dark Horse Comics: May, 1996 ($3.50, B&W, magazine, one-shot)

	GD 2.0	VG 4.0	FN 6.0	VF 8.0	VF/NM 9.0	NM- 9.2
nn-Adaptation of film; photo-c; poster insert.						3.50

BARB WIRE MOVIE SPECIAL
Dark Horse Comics: May, 1996 ($3.95, one-shot)

	GD 2.0	VG 4.0	FN 6.0	VF 8.0	VF/NM 9.0	NM- 9.2
nn-Adaptation of film; photo-c; 1st app. new look						4.00

BARKER, THE (Also see National Comics #42)
Quality Comics Group/Comic Magazine: Autumn, 1946 - No. 15, Dec, 1949

	GD 2.0	VG 4.0	FN 6.0	VF 8.0	VF/NM 9.0	NM- 9.2
1	27	54	81	158	259	360
2	15	30	45	86	133	180
3-10	13	26	39	72	101	130
11-14	10	20	30	54	72	90
15-Jack Cole-a(p)	10	20	30	56	76	95

NOTE: ***Jack Cole*** art in some issues.

BARNABY
Civil Service Publications Inc.: 1945 (25¢,102 pgs., digest size)

	GD 2.0	VG 4.0	FN 6.0	VF 8.0	VF/NM 9.0	NM- 9.2
V1#1-r/Crocket Johnson strips from 1942	5	10	14	20	24	28

BARNEY AND BETTY RUBBLE (TV) (Flintstones' Neighbors)
Charlton Comics: Jan, 1973 - No. 23, Dec, 1976 (Hanna-Barbera)

	GD 2.0	VG 4.0	FN 6.0	VF 8.0	VF/NM 9.0	NM- 9.2
1	4	8	12	23	37	50
2-11: 11(2/75)-1st Mike Zeck-a (illos)	3	6	9	14	20	25
12-23: 17-Columbo parody	2	4	6	10	14	18
Digest Annual (1972, B&W, 100 pgs.) (scarce)	4	8	12	25	40	55

BARNEY BAXTER (Also see Magic Comics)
David McKay/Dell Publishing Co./Argo: 1938 - No. 2, 1956

	GD 2.0	VG 4.0	FN 6.0	VF 8.0	VF/NM 9.0	NM- 9.2
Feature Books 15(McKay-1938)	42	84	126	268	452	635
Four Color 20(1942)	24	48	72	170	378	585
1,2 (1956-Argo)	9	18	27	50	65	80

BARNEY BEAR ...
Spire Christian Comics (Fleming H. Revell Co.): 1977-1982

	GD 2.0	VG 4.0	FN 6.0	VF 8.0	VF/NM 9.0	NM- 9.2
...Home Plate nn-(1979, 49¢), ...In Toyland nn-(1982, 49¢),...Lost and Found nn-(1979, 49¢), Out of The Woods nn-(1980, 49¢), Sunday School Picnic nn-(1981, 69¢), The Swamp Gang!-(1977, 39¢)	2	4	6	9	13	16

BARNEY GOOGLE & SNUFFY SMITH
Dell Publishing Co./Gold Key: 1942 - 1943; April, 1964

	GD 2.0	VG 4.0	FN 6.0	VF 8.0	VF/NM 9.0	NM- 9.2
Four Color 19(1942)	52	104	156	323	549	775
Four Color 40(1944)	20	40	60	135	300	465
Large Feature Comic 11(1943)	39	78	117	240	395	550
1(10113-404)-Gold Key (4/64)	4	8	12	25	40	55

BARNEY GOOGLE & SNUFFY SMITH
Toby Press: June, 1951 - No. 4, Feb, 1952 (Reprints)

	GD 2.0	VG 4.0	FN 6.0	VF 8.0	VF/NM 9.0	NM- 9.2
1	14	28	42	80	115	150
2,3	9	18	27	47	61	75
4-Kurtzman-a "Pot Shot Pete", 5 pgs.; reprints John Wayne #5	12	24	36	69	97	125

BARNEY GOOGLE AND SNUFFY SMITH
Charlton Comics: Mar, 1970 - No. 6, Jan, 1971

	GD 2.0	VG 4.0	FN 6.0	VF 8.0	VF/NM 9.0	NM- 9.2
1	3	6	9	16	24	32
2-6	2	4	6	11	16	20

BARNUM!
DC Comics (Vertigo): 2003; 2005 ($29.95, $19.95)

	GD 2.0	VG 4.0	FN 6.0	VF 8.0	VF/NM 9.0	NM- 9.2
Hardcover (2003, $29.95, with dust jacket)-Chaykin & Tischman-s/Henrichon-a						30.00
Softcover (2005, $19.95)-Chaykin & Tischman-s/Henrichon-a						20.00

BARNYARD COMICS (Dizzy Duck No. 32 on)
Nedor/Polo Mag./Standard(Animated Cartoons): June, 1944 - No. 31, Sept, 1950; No. 10, 1957

	GD 2.0	VG 4.0	FN 6.0	VF 8.0	VF/NM 9.0	NM- 9.2
1 (nn, 52 pgs.)-Funny animal	25	50	75	150	245	340
2 (52 pgs.)	15	30	45	84	127	170
3-5	11	22	33	64	90	115
6-12,16	10	20	30	58	79	100
13-15,17,21,23,26,27,29-All contain Frazetta text illos	11	22	33	64	90	115
18-20,22,24,25-All contain Frazetta-a & text illos	14	28	42	80	115	150
28,30,31	9	18	27	52	69	85
10 (1957)(Exist?)	4	7	10	14	17	20

BARRY M. GOLDWATER
Dell Publishing Co.: Mar, 1965 (Complete life story)

	GD 2.0	VG 4.0	FN 6.0	VF 8.0	VF/NM 9.0	NM- 9.2
12-055-503-Photo-c	4	8	12	23	37	50

BARRY WINDSOR-SMITH: STORYTELLER
Dark Horse Comics: Oct, 1996 - No. 9, July, 1997 ($4.95, oversize)

	GD 2.0	VG 4.0	FN 6.0	VF 8.0	VF/NM 9.0	NM- 9.2
1-9: 1-Intro Young Gods, Paradox Man & the Freebooters; Barry Smith-c/a/scripts						5.00
Preview						4.00

BAR SINISTER (Also see Shaman's Tears)
Acclaim Comics (Windjammer): Jun, 1995 - No. 4, Sept, 1995 ($2.50, lim. series)

	GD 2.0	VG 4.0	FN 6.0	VF 8.0	VF/NM 9.0	NM- 9.2
1-4: Mike Grell-c/a/scripts						3.00

BARTMAN (Also see Simpsons Comics & Radioactive Man)
Bongo Comics: 1993 - No. 6, 1994 ($1.95/$2.25)

	GD 2.0	VG 4.0	FN 6.0	VF 8.0	VF/NM 9.0	NM- 9.2
1-($2.95)-Foil-c; bound-in jumbo Bartman poster						6.00
2-6: 3-w/trading card						4.00

BART SIMPSON (See Simpsons Comics Presents Bart Simpson)

BASEBALL COMICS
Will Eisner Productions: Spring, 1949 (Reprinted later as a Spirit section)

	GD 2.0	VG 4.0	FN 6.0	VF 8.0	VF/NM 9.0	NM- 9.2
1-Will Eisner-c/a	70	140	210	445	765	1085

BASEBALL COMICS
Kitchen Sink Press: 1991 ($3.95, coated stock)

	GD 2.0	VG 4.0	FN 6.0	VF 8.0	VF/NM 9.0	NM- 9.2
1-r/1949 ish. by Eisner; contains trading cards						6.00

BASEBALL HEROES
Fawcett Publications: 1952 (one-shot)

	GD 2.0	VG 4.0	FN 6.0	VF 8.0	VF/NM 9.0	NM- 9.2
nn (Scarce)-Babe Ruth photo-c; baseball's Hall of Fame biographies	86	172	258	546	936	1325

BASEBALL'S GREATEST HEROES
Magnum Comics: Dec, 1991 - No. 2, May, 1992 ($1.75)

	GD 2.0	VG 4.0	FN 6.0	VF 8.0	VF/NM 9.0	NM- 9.2
1-Mickey Mantle #1; photo-c; Sinnott-a(p)						5.00
2-Brooks Robinson #1; photo-c; Sinnott-a(i)						4.00

BASEBALL THRILLS
Ziff-Davis Publ. Co.: No. 10, Sum, 1951 - No. 3, Sum, 1952 (Saunders painted-c No.1,2)

	GD 2.0	VG 4.0	FN 6.0	VF 8.0	VF/NM 9.0	NM- 9.2
10(#1)-Bob Feller, Musial, Newcombe & Boudreau stories	44	88	132	277	469	660
2-Powell-a(2)(Late Sum, '51); Feller, Berra & Mathewson stories	32	64	96	188	307	425
3-Kinstler-c/a; Joe DiMaggio story	32	64	96	188	307	425

BASEBALL THRILLS 3-D
The 3-D Zone: May, 1990 ($2.95, w/glasses)

	GD 2.0	VG 4.0	FN 6.0	VF 8.0	VF/NM 9.0	NM- 9.2
1-New L.B. Cole-c; life stories of Ty Cobb & Ted Williams						6.00

BASICALLY STRANGE (Magazine)
John C. Comics (Archie Comics Group): Dec, 1982 ($1.95, B&W)

	GD 2.0	VG 4.0	FN 6.0	VF 8.0	VF/NM 9.0	NM- 9.2
1-(21,000 printed; all but 1,000 destroyed; pgs. out of sequence)	3	6	9	16	23	30
1-Wood, Toth-a; Corben-c; reprints & new art	2	4	6	13	18	22

BASIC HISTORY OF AMERICA ILLUSTRATED
Pendulum Press: 1976 (B&W) (Soft-c $1.50; Hard-c $4.50)

07-1999-America Becomes a World Power 1890-1920. 07-2251-The Industrial Era 1865-1915. 07-226x-Before the Civil War 1830-1860. 07-2278-Americans Move Westward 1800-1850. 07-2286-The Civil War 1850-1876;

Batgirl #1 © DC

Batgirl (2011 series) #42 © DC

Batman #4 © DC

GD VG FN VF VF/NM NM-
2.0 4.0 6.0 8.0 9.0 9.2

GD VG FN VF VF/NM NM-
2.0 4.0 6.0 8.0 9.0 9.2

Redondo-a. 07-2294-The Fight for Freedom 1750-1783. 07-2308-The New World 1500-1750. 07-2316-Problems of the New Nation 1800-1830. 07-2324-Roaring Twenties and the Great Depression 1920-1940. 07-2332-The United States Emerges 1783-1800. 07-2340-America Today 1945-1976. 07-2359-World War II 1940-1945

Softcover editions each 1 2 3 4 5 7
Hardcover editions each 14.00

BASIL (...the Royal Cat)
St. John Publishing Co.: Jan, 1953 - No. 4, Sept, 1953

1-Funny animal 9 18 27 47 61 75
2-4 6 12 18 28 34 40
I.W. Reprint 1 2 4 6 9 12 15

BASIL WOLVERTON'S FANTASTIC FABLES
Dark Horse Comics: Oct, 1993 - No. 2, Dec, 1993 ($2.50, B&W, limited series)

1,2-Wolverton-c/a(r) 6.00

BASIL WOLVERTON'S GATEWAY TO HORROR
Dark Horse Comics: June, 1988 ($1.75, B&W, one-shot)

1-Wolverton-r 6.00

BASIL WOLVERTON'S PLANET OF TERROR
Dark Horse Comics: Oct, 1987 ($1.75, B&W, one-shot)

1-Wolverton-r; Alan Moore-c 6.00

BASTARD SAMURAI
Image Comics: Apr, 2002 - No. 3, Aug, 2002 ($2.95)

1-3-Oeming & Gunter-s; Shannon-a/Oeming-i 3.00
TPB (2003, $12.95) r/#1-3; plus sketch pages and pin-ups 13.00

BATGIRL (See Batman: No Man's Land stories)
DC Comics: Apr, 2000 - No. 73, Apr, 2006 ($2.50)

1-Scott & Campanella-a 1 3 4 6 8 10
1-(2nd printing) 3.00
2-10: 8-Lady Shiva app. 4.50
11-24: 12-"Officer Down" x-over. 15-Joker-c/app. 24-Bruce Wayne: Murderer pt. 2. 4.00
25-($3.25) Batgirl vs Lady Shiva 4.50
26-29: 27- Bruce Wayne: Fugitive pt. 5; Noto-a. 29-B.W.:F. pt. 13 3.50
30-49,51-73: 30-32-Connor Hawke app. 39-Intro. Black Wind. 41-Superboy-c/app. 53-Robin (Spoiler) app. 54-Bagged with Sky Captain CD. 55-57-War Games. 63,64-Deathstroke app. 67-Birds of Prey app. 70-1st app. Lazara (Nora Fries). 73-Lady Shiva origin; Sale-c 3.00
50-($3.25) Batgirl vs Batman 4.00
Annual 1 ('00, $3.50) Planet DC; intro. Aruna 5.00
...: A Knight Alone (2001, $12.95, TPB) r/#7-11,13,14 13.00
...: Death Wish (2003, $14.95, TPB) r/#17-20,22,23,25 & Secret Files and Origins #1 15.00
...: Destruction's Daughter (2006, $19.99, TPB) r/#65-73 20.00
...: Fists of Fury (2004, $14.95, TPB) r/#15,16,21,26-28 15.00
...: Kicking Assassins (2005, $14.99, TPB) r/#60-64 15.00
... Secret Files and Origins (8/02, $4.95) origin-s Noto-a; profile pages and pin-ups 5.00
...: Silent Running (2001, $12.95, TPB) r/#1-6 13.00

BATGIRL (Cassandra Cain)
DC Comics: Sept, 2008 - No. 6, Feb, 2009 ($2.99)

1-6-Beechen-s/Calafiore-a 3.00

BATGIRL (Spoiler/Stephanie Brown)(Batman: Reborn)
DC Comics: Oct, 2009 - No. 24, Oct, 2011 ($2.99)

1-24: 1-7-Garbett-a/Noto-c. 3-New costume. 8-Caldwell-a. 9-14-Lau-c. 14-Supergirl app. 3.00
1-Variant-c by Hamner 5.00
...: Batgirl Rising TPB (2010, $17.99) r/#1-7 20.00
...: The Flood TPB (2011, $14.99) r/#9-14 15.00

BATGIRL (Barbara Gordon)(DC New 52)(See Secret Origins #10)
DC Comics: Nov, 2011 - No. 52, Jul, 2016 ($2.99)

1-Barbara Gordon back in costume; Simone-s/Syaf-a/Hughes-c 12.00
1-Second & Third printings 3.00
2-12: 2-6-Hughes-c. 3-Nightwing app. 7-12-Syaf-c. 9-Night of the Owls. 12-Batwoman app. 3.00
13-Die-cut cover; Death of the Family tie-in; Batwoman app. 10.00
13-24: 14-16-Death of the Family tie-in; Joker app. 20,21-Intro. The Ventriloquist 3.00
25-($3.99) Zero Year tie-in; Bennett-s/Pasarin-a 4.00
26-34: 27-Gothtopia tie-in. 28,29-Strix app. 31-34-Simone-s. 31-Ragdoll app. 3.00
35-49,51,52: 35-New costume; Tarr-a/Stewart-c. 37-Dagger Type app. 41,42-Batman (Gordon) & Livewire app. 45-Dick Grayson app. 48,49-Black Canary app. 3.00
50-($4.99) Black Canary, Spoiler & Bluebird app.; Tarr-a 5.00
#0 (11/12, $2.99) Batgirl origin updated; Simone-s/Benes-a 3.00
Annual 1 (12/12, $4.99) Catwoman and the Talons app.; Simone-s/Wijaya-a/Benes-c 5.00
Annual 2 (6/14, $4.99) Poison Ivy app.; Simone-s/Gill-a/Benes-c 5.00
Annual 3 (9/15, $4.99) Dick Grayson, Spoiler & Batwoman app. 5.00
...: Endgame 1 (5/15, $2.99) Tie-in with other Endgame stories in Batman titles 3.00
...: Futures End 1 (11/14, $2.99, regular-c) Five years later; Bane app.; Simone-s 3.00
...: Futures End 1 (11/14, $3.99, 3-D cover) 4.00

BATGIRL (DC Rebirth)
DC Comics: Sept, 2016 - Present ($2.99/$3.99)

1-9: 1-Hope Larson-s/Rafael Albuquerque-a. 6-Poison Ivy app. 9-Penguin app. 3.00
10-20-($3.99): 10,11-Penguin app. 13-Catwoman app. 18-Harley Quinn app. 4.00
Annual 1 (5/17, $4.99) Supergirl app. (story cont'd in Supergirl #9); Larson-s; Bengal-c 5.00

BATGIRL ADVENTURES (See Batman Adventures, The)
DC Comics: Feb, 1998 ($2.95, one-shot) (Based on animated series)

1-Harley Quinn and Poison Ivy app.; Timm-c 4 8 12 23 37 50

BATGIRL AND THE BIRDS OF PREY (DC Rebirth)
DC Comics: Aug, 2016 - Present ($2.99/$3.99)

1-8: 1-Julie & Shawna Benson-s/Claire Roe-a. 3-6,8-Antonio-a. 8-Nightwing app. 3.00
9-19-($3.99) 10-Nightwing & Green Arrow app. 12-17-Catwoman & Poison Ivy app. 4.00
...: Rebirth 1 (9/16, $2.99) Batgirl, Black Canary & Huntress team up; Claire Roe-a 3.00

BATGIRL SPECIAL
DC Comics: 1988 ($1.50, one-shot, 52 pgs)

1-Kitson-a/Mignola-c 2 4 6 8 10 12

BATGIRL: YEAR ONE
DC Comics: Feb, 2003 - No. 9, Oct, 2003 ($2.95, limited series)

1-Barbara Gordon becomes Batgirl; Killer Moth app.; Beatty & Dixon-s 1 3 4 6 8 10
2-9 3.00
TPB (2003, $17.95) r/#1-9 18.00

BAT LASH (See DC Special Series #16, Showcase #76, Weird Western Tales)
National Periodical Publications: Oct-Nov, 1968 - No. 7, Oct-Nov, 1969 (12¢/15¢)

1-(10-11/68, 12¢-c)-2nd app. Bat Lash; classic Nick Cardy-c/a in all 7 14 21 44 82 120
2-7: 6,7-(15¢-c) 4 8 12 27 44 60

BAT LASH
DC Comics: Feb, 2008 - No. 6, Jul, 2008 ($2.99, limited series)

1-6-Aragonés & Brandvold-s/John Severin-a. 1-Two covers by Severin and Simonson 3.00
...: Guns and Roses TPB (2008, $17.99) r/#1-6 18.00

BATMAN (See All Star Batman & Robin, Anarky, Aurora [in Promo. Comics section], Azrael, The Best of DC #2, Blind Justice, The Brave & the Bold, Cosmic Odyssey, DC 100-Page Super Spec. #14,20, DC Special, DC Special Series, Detective, Dynamic Classics, 80-Page Giants, Gotham By Gaslight, Gotham Nights, Greatest Batman Stories Ever Told, Greatest Joker Stories Ever Told, Heroes Against Hunger, JLA,The Joker, Justice League of America, Justice League Int., Legends of the Dark Knight, Limited Coll. Ed., Man-Bat, Nightwing, Power Record Comics, Real Fact #5, Robin, Saga of Ra's al Ghul, Shadow of the..., Star Spangled, Super Friends, 3-D Batman, Untold Legend of..., Wanted... & World's Finest Comics)

BATMAN
National Per. Publ./Detective Comics/DC Comics: Spring, 1940 - No. 713, Oct, 2011 (#1-5 were quarterly)

1-Origin The Batman reprinted (2 pgs.) from Det. #33 w/splash from #34 by Bob Kane; see Detective #33 for 1st origin; 1st app. Joker (2 stories intended for 2 separate issues of Det. Comics which would have been 1st & 2nd app.); splash pg. to 2nd Joker story is similar to cover of Det. #40 (story intended for #40); 1st app. The Cat (Catwoman) (1st villainess in comics); has Batman story (w/Hugo Strange) without Robin originally planned for Det. #38; mentions location (Manhattan) where Batman lives (see Det. #31). This book was created entirely from the inventory of Det. Comics; 1st Batman/Robin pin-up on back-c; has text piece & photo of Bob Kane 50,000 100,000 150,000 340,000 545,000 750,000
1-Reprint, oversize 13-1/2x10". **WARNING:** This comic is an exact duplicate reprint of the original except for its size. DC published it in 1974 with a second cover titling it as a Famous First Edition. There have been many reported cases of the outer cover being removed and the interior sold as the original edition. The reprint with the new outer cover removed is practically worthless. See Famous First Edition for value.
2-2nd app. The Joker; 2nd app. Catwoman (out of costume) in Joker story; 1st time called Catwoman (NOTE: A 15¢-c for Canadian distr. exists.) 2800 5600 8400 20,000 37,500 55,000
3-3rd app Catwoman (1st in costume & 1st costumed villainess); 1st Puppet Master app.; classic Kane & Robinson-c 1245 2490 3735 9300 18,150 27,000
4-4th app. The Joker (see Det. #45 for 3rd); 1st mention of Gotham City in a Batman comic (on newspaper)(Win/40) 1000 2000 3000 7600 13,800 20,000
5-1st app. the Batmobile with its bat-head front 811 1622 2433 5920 10,460 15,000
6,7: 7-Bullseye-c; Joker app. 649 1298 1947 4738 8369 12,000
8-Infinity-c by Fred Ray; Joker app. 530 1060 1590 3869 6835 9800
9-10:9-1st Batman x-mas story; Burnley-c. 10-Catwoman story (gets new costume) 514 1028 1542 3750 6625 9500

Batman #19 © DC

Batman #60 © DC

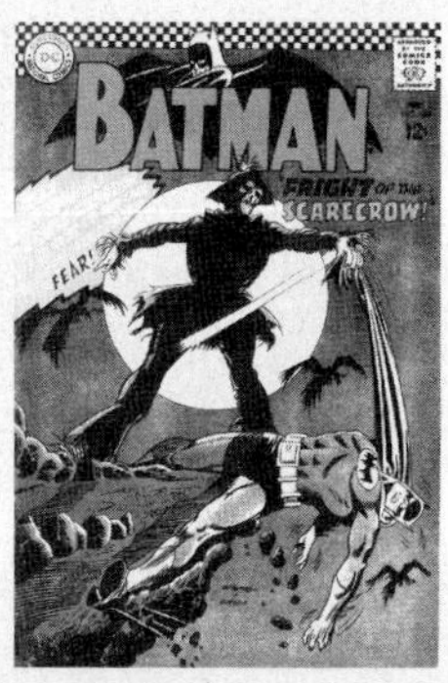

Batman #189 © DC

	GD 2.0	VG 4.0	FN 6.0	VF 8.0	VF/NM 9.0	NM- 9.2
11-Classic Joker-c by Ray/Robinson (3rd Joker-c, 6-7/42); Joker & Penguin app.	1250	2500	3750	9500	17,250	25,000
12,15: 12-Joker app. 15-New costume Catwoman	383	766	1149	2681	4691	6700
13-Jerry Siegel (Superman's co-creator) appears in a Batman story; Batman parachuting on black-c	421	842	1263	2947	5174	7400
14-2nd Penguin-c; Penguin app. (12-1/42-43)	394	788	1182	2758	4829	6900
16-Intro/origin Alfred (4-5/43); cover is a reverse of #9 cover by Burnley; 1st small logo	757	1514	2271	5526	9763	14,000
17,20: 17-Classic war-c; Penguin app. 20-1st Batmobile-c (12-1/43-44); Joker app.	337	674	1011	2359	4130	5900
18-Hitler, Hirohito, Mussolini-c.	486	972	1458	3550	6275	9000
19-Joker app.	252	504	756	1613	2757	3900
21,22,24,26,28-30: 21-1st skinny Alfred in Batman (2-3/44). 21,30-Penguin app. 22-1st Alfred solo-c/story (Alfred solo stories in 22-32,36); Catwoman & The Cavalier app. 28-Joker story	200	400	600	1280	2190	3100
23-Joker-c/story; classic black-c	432	864	1296	3154	5577	8000
25-Only Joker/Penguin team-up; 1st team-up between two major villains	300	600	900	2040	3570	5100
27-Classic Burnley Christmas-c; Penguin app.	252	504	756	1613	2757	3900
31,32,34-36,39: 32-Origin Robin retold; Joker app. 35-Catwoman story (in new costume w/o cat head mask). 36-Penguin app.	148	296	444	947	1624	2300
33-Christmas-c	174	348	522	1114	1907	2700
37-Joker spotlight on black-c	300	600	900	1950	3375	4800
38-Penguin-c/story	181	362	543	1158	1979	2800
40-Joker-c/story	252	504	756	1613	2757	3900
41-1st Sci-fi cover/story in Batman; Penguin app.(6-7/47)	135	270	405	864	1482	2100
42-2nd Catwoman-c (1st in Batman)(8-9/47); Catwoman story also.	277	554	831	1759	3030	4300
43-Penguin-c/story	155	310	465	992	1696	2400
44-Classic Joker-c	309	618	927	2163	3782	5400
45,46: 45-Christmas-c/story; Catwoman story. 46-Joker app.	119	238	357	762	1306	1850
47-1st detailed origin The Batman (6-7/48); 1st Bat-signal-c this title (see Detective #108); Batman tracks down his parent's killer and reveals i.d. to him	595	1190	1785	4350	7675	11,000
48-1000 Secrets of the Batcave; r-in #203; Penguin story	155	310	465	992	1696	2400
49-Joker-c/story; 1st app. Mad Hatter; 1st app. Vicki Vale	314	628	942	2198	3849	5500
50-Two-Face impostor app.	174	348	522	1114	1907	2700
51,54,56,57,60: 57-Centerfold is a 1950 calendar; Joker app.	116	232	348	742	1271	1800
52-Joker-c/story	258	516	774	1651	2826	4000
53-Joker story	129	258	387	826	1413	2000
55-Joker-c/stories	245	490	735	1568	2684	3800
58,61: 58-Penguin-c. 61-Origin Batplane II	161	322	483	1030	1765	2500
59-1st app. Deadshot; Batman in the future-c/sty	343	686	1029	2400	4200	6000
62-Origin Catwoman; Catwoman-c	248	496	744	1575	2713	3850
63-1st app. Killer Moth; Joker story; flying saucer story(2-3/51)	135	270	405	864	1482	2100
64,70-72,74-77,79: 70-Robot-c. 72-Last 52 pg. issue. 74-Used in **POP**, Pg. 90. 75-Gorilla-c. 76-Penguin story. 79-Vicki Vale in "The Bride of Batman"	100	200	300	635	1093	1550
65,69-Catwoman-c/stories	181	362	543	1158	1979	2800
66,73-Joker-c/stories. 66-Pre-2nd Batman & Robin team try-out. 73-Vicki Vale story	194	388	582	1242	2121	3000
67-Joker story	113	226	339	718	1234	1750
68,81-Two-Face-c/stories	126	252	378	806	1378	1950
78-(8-9/53)-Roh Kar, The Man Hunter from Mars story-the 1st lawman of Mars to come to Earth (green skinned)	119	238	357	762	1306	1850
80-Joker stories	113	226	339	718	1234	1750
82,83,87-89: 89-Last pre-code issue	94	188	282	597	1024	1450
84-Catwoman-c/story; Two-Face app.	161	322	483	1030	1765	2500
85,86-Joker story. 86-Intro Batmarine (Batman's submarine)	97	194	291	621	1061	1500
90,91,93-96,98,99: 99-(4/56)-Last G.A. Penguin app.	81	162	243	518	884	1250
92-1st app. Bat-Hound-c/story	194	388	582	1242	2121	3000
97-2nd app. Bat-Hound-c/story; Joker story	94	188	282	597	1024	1450
100-(6/56)	309	618	927	2163	3782	5400
101-(8/56)-Clark Kent x-over who protects Batman's i.d. (3rd story)	77	154	231	493	847	1200
102-104,106-109: 103-1st S.A. issue; 3rd Bat-Hound-c/story	74	148	222	470	810	1150
105-1st Batwoman in Batman (2nd anywhere)	152	304	456	965	1658	2350
110-Joker story	77	154	231	493	847	1200
111-120: 112-1st app. Signalman (super villain). 113-1st app. Fatman; Batman meets his counterpart on Planet X w/a chest plate similar to S.A. Batman's design (yellow oval w/black design inside).	63	126	189	403	689	975
121- Origin/1st app. of Mr. Zero (Mr. Freeze).	432	864	1296	3154	5577	8000
122,124-126,128,130: 122,126-Batwoman-c/story. 124-2nd app. Signal Man. 128-Batwoman cameo. 130-Lex Luthor app.	54	108	162	343	574	825
123,127: 123-Joker story; Bat-Hound-c/app. 127-(10/59)-Batman vs. Thor the Thunder God c/story; Joker story; Superman cameo	55	110	165	352	601	850
129-Origin Robin retold; bondage-c; Batwoman-c/story (reprinted in Batman Family #8)	65	130	195	416	708	1000
131-135,137,138,141-143: 131-Intro 2nd Batman & Robin series (see #66; also in #135,145, 154,159,163). 133-1st Bat-Mite in Batman (3rd app. anywhere). 134-Origin The Dummy (not Vigilante's villain). 141-2nd app. original Bat-Girl. 143-(10/61)-Last 10¢ issue	43	86	129	271	461	650
136-Joker-c/story	52	104	156	328	552	775
139-Intro 1st original Bat-Girl; only app. Signalman as the Blue Bowman	103	206	309	659	1130	1600
140-Joker story, Batwoman-c/s; Superman cameo	47	94	141	296	498	700
144-(12/61)-1st 12¢ issue; Joker story	27	54	81	194	435	675
145,148-Joker-c/stories	30	60	90	216	483	750
146,147,149,150	21	42	63	147	324	500
151-154,156-158,160-162,164-168,170: 152-Joker story. 156-Ant-Man/Robin team-up(6/63). 164-New Batmobile(6/64) new look & Mystery Analysts series begins	17	34	51	117	259	400
155-1st S.A. app. The Penguin (5/63)	46	92	138	340	770	1200
159,163-Joker-c/stories. 159-Bat-Girl app. 163-Last Bat-Girl app. until Teen Titans #50	24	48	72	168	372	575
169-2nd SA Penguin app.	21	42	63	147	324	500
171-1st Riddler app.(5/65) since Dec. 1948	66	132	198	528	1189	1850
172-175,177,178,180,184	10	20	30	70	150	230
176-(80-Pg. Giant G-17); Joker-c/story; Penguin app. in strip-r; Catwoman reprint	13	26	39	86	188	290
179-2nd app. Silver Age Riddler	18	36	54	124	275	425
181-Intro. Poison Ivy; Batman & Robin poster insert	64	128	192	512	1156	1800
182,187-(80 Pg. Giants G-24, G-30); Joker-c/stories	11	22	33	76	163	250
183-2nd app. Poison Ivy	15	30	45	103	227	350
185-(80 Pg. Giant G-27)	11	22	33	73	157	240
186-Joker-c/story	11	22	33	75	160	245
188,191,192,194-196,199	9	18	27	58	114	170
189-1st S.A. app. Scarecrow; retells origin of G.A. Scarecrow from World's Finest #3(1st app.)	28	56	84	202	451	700
190-Penguin-c/app.	11	22	33	76	163	250
193-(80-Pg. Giant G-37)	10	20	30	68	144	220
197-4th S.A. Catwoman app. cont'd from Det. #369; 1st new Batgirl app. in Batman (5th anywhere)	15	30	45	103	227	350
198-(80-Pg. Giant G-43); Joker-c/story-r/World's Finest #61; Catwoman-r/Det. #211; Penguin-r; origin-r/#47	10	20	30	70	150	230
200-(3/68)-Joker cameo; retells origin of Batman & Robin; 1st Neal Adams work this title (cover only)	12	24	36	84	185	285
201-Joker story	7	14	21	46	86	125
202,204-207,209-212: 210-Catwoman-c/app. 212-Last 12¢ issue	6	12	18	42	79	115
203-(80 Pg. Giant G-49); r/#48, 61, & Det. 185; Batcave Blueprints	8	16	24	56	108	160
208-(80 Pg. Giant G-55); New origin Batman by Gil Kane plus 3 G.A. Batman reprints w/Catwoman, Vicki Vale & Batwoman	8	16	24	56	108	160
213-(80-Pg. Giant G-61); 30th anniversary issue (7-8/69); origin Alfred (r/Batman #16), Joker(r/Det. #168), Clayface; new origin Robin with new facts	9	18	27	61	123	185
214-217: 214-Alfred given a new last name- "Pennyworth" (see Detective #96)	6	12	18	37	66	95
218-(68 pg. Giant G-67)	9	18	27	63	129	195
219-Neal Adams-a	9	18	27	60	120	180
220,221,224-226,229-231	5	10	15	34	60	85
222-Beatles take-off; art lesson by Joe Kubert	17	34	51	117	259	400
223,228,233: 223,228-(68 pg. Giants G-73,G-79). 233-G-85-(68 pgs., "64 pgs." on-c)	7	14	21	46	86	125
227-Neal Adams cover swipe of Detective #31	37	74	111	274	612	950
232-(6/71) Adams-a. Intro/1st app. Ra's al Ghul; origin Batman & Robin retold; last 15¢ issue (see Detective #411 (5/71) for Talia's debut)	34	68	102	245	548	850
234-(9/71)-1st modern app. of Harvey Dent/Two-Face with origin re-told in brief; (see World's						

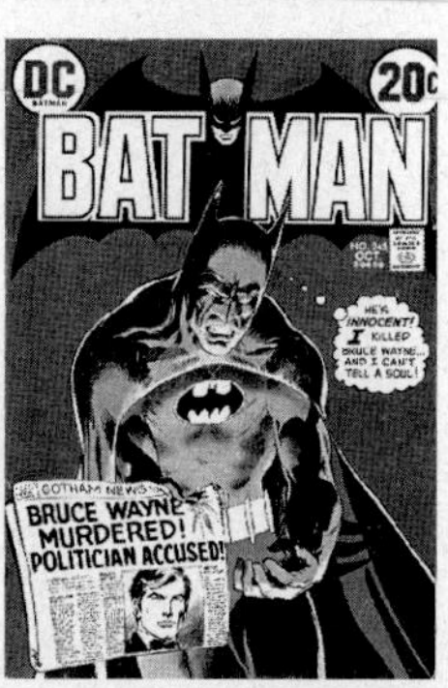

Batman #245 © DC

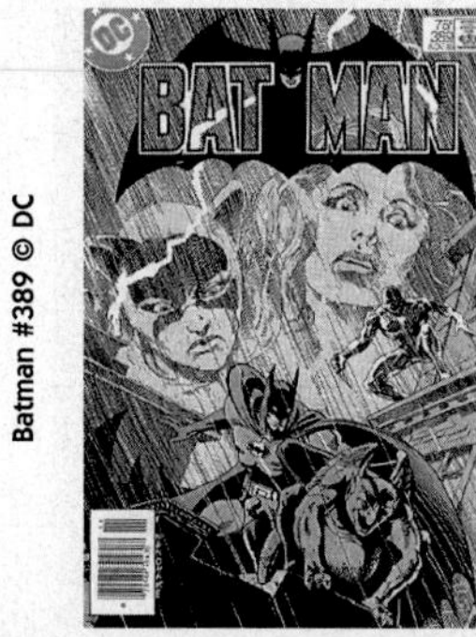

Batman #389 © DC

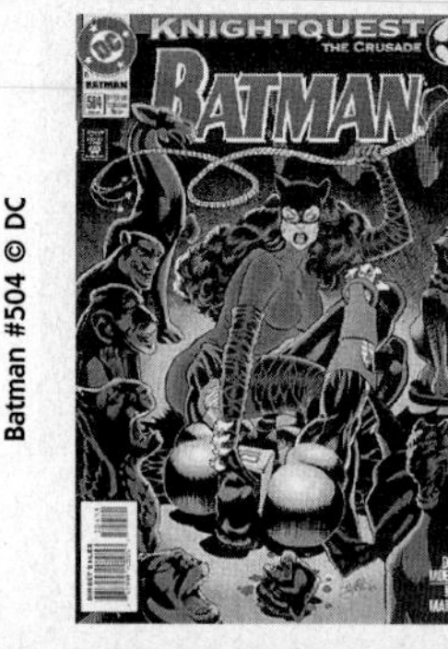

Batman #504 © DC

GD VG FN VF VF/NM NM-
2.0 4.0 6.0 8.0 9.0 9.2

Finest #173 for Batman as Two-Face; only S.A. mention of character); N. Adams-a; 52 pg. issues begin, end #242 21 42 63 147 324 500
235,236,239-242: 239-XMas-c. 241-Reprint/#5 6 12 18 41 76 110
237-N. Adams-c/a. 1st Rutland Vermont - Bald Mountain Halloween x-over. 1st app. The Reaper; Holocaust reference; Wrightson/Ellison plots; G.A. Batman-r/Detective #37 15 30 45 100 220 340
238-Also listed as DC 100 Page Super Spectacular #8; Batman, Legion, Aquaman-r; G.A. Atom, Sargon (r/Sensation #57), Plastic Man (r/Police #14) stories; Doom Patrol origin-r; N. Adams wraparound-c 12 24 36 84 185 285
243-245-Neal Adams-a 9 18 27 61 123 185
246-250,252,253: 246-Scarecrow app. 253-Shadow-c & app. 5 10 15 34 60 85
251-(9/73)-N. Adams-c/a; Joker-c/story 36 72 108 266 596 925
254,256,257,259,261-All 100 pg. editions; part-r: 254-(2/74)-Man-Bat-c/app. 256-Catwoman app. 257-Joker & Penguin app. 259-Shadow-c/app. 7 14 21 44 82 120
255-(100 pgs.)-N. Adams-c/a; tells of Bruce Wayne's father who wore bat costume & fought crime (r/Det. #235); r/story Batman #22 8 16 24 51 96 140
258-First mention of Arkham (Hospital, renamed Arkham Asylum in #260) 8 16 24 54 102 150
260-(100 pgs.) Joker-c/story; 2nd Arkham Asylum (see #258 for 1st mention) 8 16 24 51 96 140
262 (68 pgs.) 5 10 15 33 57 80
263,264,266-285,287-290,292,293,295-299: 266-Catwoman back to old costume 3 6 9 14 20 25
265-Wrightson-a(i) 3 6 9 15 22 28
286,291,294: 294-Joker-c/stories 3 6 9 17 26 35
300-Double-size 4 8 12 23 37 50
301-(7/78)-306,308-310,312-315,317-320,325-331,333-352: 304-(44 pgs.). 306-3rd app. Black Spider. 308-Mr. Freeze app. 310-1st modern app. The Gentleman Ghost in Batman; Kubert-c. 312,314-Two-Face-c/stories. 313-2nd app. Calendar Man. 318-Intro Firebug. 319-2nd modern age app. The Gentleman Ghost; Kubert-c. 331-1st app./death original Electrocutioner. 344-Poison Ivy app. 345-1st app. new Dr. Death. 345,346,351-Catwoman back-ups. 346-Two-Face-c/app. 2 4 6 9 12 15
306-308,311-320,323,324,326-(Whitman variants; low print run; none show issue # on cover) 2 4 6 13 18 22
307-1st app. Lucius Fox (1/79) 2 4 6 11 16 20
311,316,322-324: 311-Batgirl-c/story; Batgirl reteams w/Batman. 316-Robin returns. 322-324-Catwoman (Selina Kyle) app. 322,323-Cat-Man cameos (1st in Batman, 1 panel each). 323-1st meeting Catwoman & Cat-Man. 324-1st full app. Cat-Man this title 2 4 6 10 14 18
321,353,359-Joker-c/stories 3 6 9 14 20 25
332-Catwoman's 1st solo 2 4 6 11 16 20
354-356,358,360,362-365,369,370: 362-Riddler-c/story with origin retold in brief 1 3 4 6 8 10
357-1st app. Jason Todd (3/83); see Det. #524; brief app. Croc (see Detective #523 (2/83) for earlier cameo 8 16 24 51 96 140
361-Debut of Harvey Bullock (7/83)(see Detective #441,('74) for a similar Lt. Bullock, no first name given, appeared in 3 panels) 3 6 9 14 20 25
366-Jason Todd 1st in Robin costume; Joker-c/story 3 6 9 21 33 45
367-Jason in red & green costume (not as Robin) 2 4 6 8 11 14
368-1st new Robin in costume (Jason Todd) 3 6 9 19 30 40
371-385,388-399,401-403: 371-Cat-Man-c/story; brief origin Cat-Man (cont'd in Det. #538). 390-391-Catwoman app. 398-Catwoman & Two-Face app. 401-2nd app. Magpie (see Man of Steel #3 for 1st). 403-Joker cameo 1 2 3 5 6 8

NOTE: *Issues 397-399, 401-403, 408-416, 421-425, 430-432 all have 2nd printings in 1989; some with up to 8 printings. Some are not identified as reprints but have newer ads copyrighted after cover dates. All reprints have different back-c ads. All reprints are scarcer than 1st prints and have same value to variant collectors.*

386-Intro Black Mask (villain) 5 10 15 33 57 80
387-Intro Black Mask continues 2 4 6 11 16 20
400 ($1.50, 68pgs.)-Dark Knight special; intro by Stephen King; Art Adams/Austin-a 3 6 9 19 30 40
404-Miller scripts begin (end 407); Year 1; 1st modern app. Catwoman (2/87) 3 6 9 19 30 40
405-407: 407-Year 1 ends (See Detective Comics #575-578 for Year 2) 3 6 9 14 20 25
408-410: New Origin Jason Todd (Robin) 2 4 6 13 18 22
411-416,421,422,424,425: 411-Two-face app. 412-Origin/1st app. Mime. 414-Starlin scripts begin, end #429. 416-Nightwing-c/story 6.00
417-420: "Ten Nights of the Beast" storyline 2 4 6 8 10 12
423-McFarlane-c 3 6 9 16 23 30
426-($1.50, 52 pgs.)- "A Death In The Family" storyline begins, ends #429 3 6 9 16 23 30
427- "A Death In The Family" part 2. (Direct Sales version has inside back-c page for phone poll; newsstand version has an ad on inside back-c and UPC code on front-c) 2 4 6 11 16 20
428-Death of Robin (Jason Todd) 3 6 9 21 33 45
429-Joker-c/story; Superman app. 2 4 6 11 16 20
430-432 5.00
433-435-Many Deaths of the Batman story by John Byrne-c/scripts 5.00
436-Year 3 begins (ends #439); origin original Robin retold by Nightwing (Dick Grayson); 1st app. Timothy Drake (8/89) 2 4 6 9 12 15
436-441: 436-2nd printing. 437-Origin Robin cont. 440,441: "A Lonely Place of Dying" Parts 1 & 3 5.00
442-1st app. Timothy Drake in Robin costume 1 2 3 5 6 8
443-456,458,459,462-464: 445-447-Batman goes to Russia. 448,449-The Penguin Affair Pts 1 & 3. 450-Origin Joker. 450,451-Joker-c/stories. 452-454-Dark Knight Dark City storyline; Riddler app. 455-Alan Grant scripts begin, ends #466, 470. 464-Last solo Batman story; free 16 pg. preview of Impact Comics line 4.00
457-Timothy Drake officially becomes Robin & dons new costume 2 4 6 8 10 12
457-Direct sale edition (has #000 in indicia) 2 4 6 8 10 12
460,461,465-487: 460,461-Two part Catwoman story. 465-Robin returns to action with Batman. 470-War of the Gods x-over. 475-1st app. Renee Montoya. 475,476-Return of Scarface. 476-Last $1.00-c. 477,478-Photo-c 4.00
488-Cont'd from Batman: Sword of Azrael #4; Azrael-c & app. 1 2 3 5 6 8
489-Bane-c/story; 1st app. Azrael in Bat-costume 2 4 6 8 10 12
490-Riddler-c/story; Azrael & Bane app. 6.00
491,492: 491-Knightfall lead-in; Joker-c/story; Azrael & Bane app.; Kelley Jones-c begin. 492-Knightfall part 1; Bane app. 6.00
492-Platinum edition (promo copy) 2 4 6 10 14 18
493-496: 493-Knightfall Pt. 3. 494-Knightfall Pt. 5; Joker-c & app. 495-Knightfall Pt. 7; brief Bane & Joker apps. 496-Knightfall Pt. 9, Joker-c/story; Bane cameo 6.00
497-(Late 7/93)-Knightfall Pt. 11; Bane breaks Batman's back; B&W outer-c; Aparo-a(p); Giordano-a(i) 2 4 6 8 10 12
497-499: 497-2nd printing. 497-Newsstand edition w/o outer cover. 498-Knightfall part 15; Bane & Catwoman-c & app. (see Showcase 93 #7 & 8) 499-Knightfall Pt. 17; Bane app. 5.00
500-($2.50, 68 pgs.)-Knightfall Pt. 19; Azrael in new Bat-costume; Bane-c/story 5.00
500-($3.95, 68 pgs.)-Collector's Edition w/die-cut double-c w/foil by Joe Quesada & 2 bound-in post cards 1 2 3 5 6 8
501-508,510,511: 501-Begin $1.50-c. 501-508-Knightquest. 503,504-Catwoman app. 507-Ballistic app.; Jim Balent-a(p). 510-KnightsEnd Pt. 7. 511-(9/94)-Zero Hour; Batgirl-c/story 3.00
509-($2.50, 52 pgs.)-KnightsEnd Pt. 1 4.00
512-514,516-518: 512-(11/94)-Dick Grayson assumes Batman role 3.00
515-Special Ed.($2.50)-Kelley Jones-a begins; all black embossed-c; Troika Pt. 1 5.00
515-Regular Edition 3.00
519-534,536-549: 519-Begin $1.95-c. 521-Return of Alfred, 522-Swamp Thing app. 525-Mr. Freeze app. 527,528-Two Face app. 529-Contagion Pt. 6. 530-532-Deadman app. 533-Legacy prelude. 534-Legacy Pt. 5. 536-Final Night x-over; Man-Bat-c/app. 540,541-Spectre-c-app. 544-546-Joker & The Demon. 548,549-Penguin-c/app. 3.00
530-532 ($2.50)-Enhanced edition; glow-in-the-dark-c. 4.00
535-(10/96, $2.95)-1st app. The Ogre 4.00
535-(10/96, $3.95)-1st app. The Ogre; variant, cardboard, foldout-c 5.00
550-($3.50)-Collector's Ed., includes 4 collector cards; intro. Chase, return of Clayface; Kelley Jones-c 5.00
550-($2.95)-Standard Ed.; Williams & Gray-c 4.00
551,552,554-562: 551,552-Ragman c/app. 554-Cataclysm pt. 12. 3.00
553-Cataclysm pt.3 4.00
563-No Man's Land; Joker-c by Campbell; Gale-s 1 2 3 5 6 8
564-566,568,569,571-574: 569-New Batgirl-c/app. 3.00
567-1st Cassandra Cain 2 4 6 11 16 20
570-Joker and Harley Quinn story 3 6 9 16 23 30
575-579: 575-New look Batman begins; McDaniel-a 3.00
580-598: 580-Begin $2.25-c. 587-Gordon shot. 591,592-Deadshot-c/app. 3.00
599-Bruce Wayne: Murderer pt. 7 3.50
600-($3.95) Bruce Wayne: Fugitive pt. 1; back-up homage stories in '50s, 60's, & 70s styles; by Aragonés, Gaudiano, Shanower and others 5.00
600-(2nd printing) 4.00
601-604, 606,607: 601,603-Bruce Wayne: Fugitive pt.3,13. 606,607-Deadshot-c/app. 3.00
605-($2.95) Conclusion to Bruce Wayne: Fugitive x-over; Noto-c 4.00
608-(12/02) Hush begins; Jim Lee-a/c & Jeph Loeb-s begin; Poison Ivy & Catwoman app. 15.00
608-2nd printing; has different cover with Batman standing on gargoyle 80.00
608-Special Edition; has different cover; 200 printed; used for promotional purposes (a CGC certified 9.2 copy sold for $700, and a CGC certified 9.8 copy sold for $2,100)
608-Special Edition (9/09, $1.00) printing has new "After Watchmen" logo cover frame 5.00
609-Huntress app. 9.00
610,611: 610-Killer Croc-c/app.; Batman & Catwoman kiss 8.00

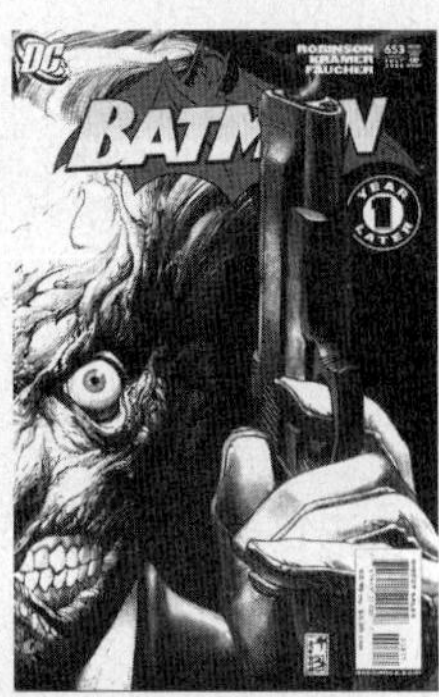

Batman #653 © DC

Batman (2011 series) #41 © DC

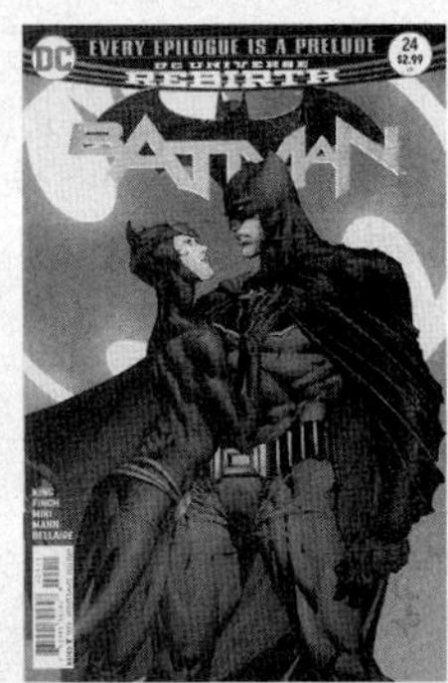

Batman (2016 series) #24 © DC

612-Batman vs. Superman; 1st printing with full color cover 22.00
612-2nd printing with B&W sketch cover 32.00
613-Harley Quinn & Joker-c/app. 2 4 6 8 10 12
614-Joker-c/app. 8.00
615-617: 615-Reveals ID to Catwoman. 616-Ra's al Ghul app. 617-Scarecrow app. 5.00
618-Batman vs. "Jason Todd" 4.00
619-Newsstand cover; Hush story concludes; Riddler app. 5.00
619-Two variant tri-fold covers; one Heroes group, one Villains group 5.00
619-2nd printing with Riddler chess cover 5.00
620-Broken City pt. 1; Azzarello-s/Risso-a/c begin; Killer Croc app. 4.00
621-633: 621-625-Azzarello-s/Risso-a/c. 626-630-Winick-s/Nguyen-a/Wagner-c; Penguin & Scarecrow app. 631-633-War Games. 633-Conclusion to War Games x-over 3.00
634,636,637-Winick-s/Nguyen-a/Wagner-c; Red Hood app. 637-Amazo app. 4.00
635-1st app. Red Hood (later revealed as Jason Todd in #638) 50.00
638-Red Hood unmasked as Jason Todd; Nguyen-a 1 3 4 6 8 10
639-650: 640-Superman app. 641-Begin $2.50-c. 643,644-War Crimes; Joker app. 650-Infinite Crisis; Joker and Jason Todd app. 3.00
651-654-One Year Later; Bianchi-c 3.50
655-Begin Grant Morrison-s/Andy Kubert-a; Kubert-c w/red background 30.00
655-Variant cover by Adam Kubert, brown-toned image 90.00
656-Intro. Damian, son of Talia and Batman (see Batman: Son of the Demon) 15.00
657-Damian in Robin costume 8.00
658-665: 659-662-Mandrake-a. 663-Van Fleet-a. 664-Bane app. 3.00
666-Future story of adult Damian; Andy Kubert-a 2 4 6 11 16 20
667-675: 667-669-Williams III-a. 670,671-Resurrection of Ra's al Ghul; Daniel-a. 671-2nd printing 3.00
676-Batman R.I.P. begins; Morrison-s/Daniel-a/Alex Ross-c 4.00
676-Variant-c by Tony Daniel 12.00
676-Second (red-tinted Daniel-c) & third (B&W Daniel-c) printings 3.00
677-680,682-685: Batman R.I.P.; Alex Ross-c. 678-Bat-Mite app. 682-685-Last Rites 3.00
677-Variant-c with Red Hood by Tony Daniel 10.00
677-Second printing with B&W&red-tinted Daniel-c 3.00
681-($3.99) Batman R.I.P. conclusion 4.00
686-($3.99) Gaiman-s/Andy Kubert-a; continues in Detective #853; Kubert sketch pgs.; covers by Kubert and Ross; 2nd & 3rd printings exist 4.00
687-($3.99) Batman: Reborn begins; Dick Grayson becomes Batman; Winick-s/Benes-a 4.00
688-699: 688-691-Bagley-a. 692-697,699-Tony Daniel-s/a. 692-Catwoman app. 3.00
700-(8/10, $4.99) Morrison-s; art by Daniel, Quitely, Finch & Andy Kubert; Finch-c 12.00
700-Variant-c by Mignola 50.00
701-712: 701,702-Morrison-s; R.I.P story. 704-Batman Inc. begins; Daniel-s/a 3.00
713-(10/11) Last issue of first volume; Nicieza-s; Robin flashbacks 8.00
#0 (10/94)-Zero Hour issue released between #511 & #512; Origin retold 3.00
#1,000,000 (11/98) 853rd Century x-over 3.00
Annual 1 (8-10/61)-Swan-c 54 108 162 432 966 1500
Annual 2 24 48 72 168 372 575
Annual 3 (Summer, '62)-Joker-c/story 25 50 75 175 388 600
Annual 4,5 13 26 39 89 195 300
Annual 6,7 (7/64, 25¢, 80 pgs.) 11 22 33 73 157 240
Annual V5#8 (1982)-Painted-c 1 3 4 6 8 10
Annual 9,10,12: 9(7/85). 10(1986). 12(1988, $1.50) 1 2 3 4 5 7
Annual 11 (1987, $1.25)-Penguin-c/story; Moore-s 1 2 3 5 7 9
Annual 13 (1989, $1.75, 68 pgs.)-Gives history of Bruce Wayne, Dick Grayson, Jason Todd, Alfred, Comm. Gordon, Barbara Gordon (Batgirl) & Vicki Vale; Morrow-i 6.00
Annual 14-17 ('90-'93, 68 pgs.)-14-Origin Two-Face. 15-Armageddon 2001 x-over; Joker app. 15 (2nd printing). 16-Joker-c/s; Kieth-c. 17 (1993, $2.50, 68 pgs.)-Azrael in Bat-costume; intro Ballistic 4.00
Annual 18 (1994, $2.95) 4.00
Annual 19 (1995, $3.95)-Year One story; retells Scarecrow's origin 4.00
Annual 20 (1996, $2.95)-Legends of the Dead Earth story; Giarrano-a 4.00
Annual 21 (1997, $3.95)-Pulp Heroes story 4.00
Annual 22,23 ('98, '99, $2.95)-22-Ghosts; Wrightson-c. 23-JLApe; Art Adams-c 4.00
Annual 24 ('00, $3.50) Planet DC; intro. The Boggart; Aparo-a 4.00
Annual 25 ('06, $4.99) Infinite Crisis-revised story of Jason Todd; unused Aparo page 10.00
Annual 26 ('07, $3.99) Origin of Ra's al Ghul; Damian app. 4.00
Annual 27 ('09, $4.99) Azrael app.; Calafiore-a; back-up story w/Kelley Jones-a 5.00
Annual 28 (2/11, $4.99) The Question, Nightrunner and Veil app.; Lau-c 5.00

NOTE: ***Art Adams*** *a-400p.* ***Neal Adams*** *c-200, 203, 210, 217, 219-222, 224-227, 229, 230, 232, 234, 236-241, 243-246, 251, 255, Annual 14.* ***Aparo*** *a-414-420, 426-435, 440-448, 450, 451, 480-483, 486-491, 494-500; c-414-416, 481, 482, 463i, 486, 487i.* ***Bolland*** *a-400; c-445-447.* ***Burnley*** *a-10, 12-18, 20, 22, 25, 27; c-9, 15, 16, 27, 28p, 40p, 42p.* ***Byrne*** *c-401, 433-435, 533-535, Annual 11.* ***Travis Charest*** *c-488-490p.* ***Colan*** *a-340p, 343-345p, 348-351p, 373p, 383p; c-343p, 345p, 350p.* ***J. Cole*** *a-238r.* ***Cowan*** *a-Annual 10p.* ***Golden*** *a-295p, 303p, 484, 485.* ***Alan Grant*** *scripts-455-466, 470, 474-476, 479, 480, Annual 16(part).* ***Grell*** *a-287, 288p, 289p, 290; c-287-290.* ***Infantino/Anderson*** *c-167, 173, 175, 181, 186, 191, 192, 194, 195, 198, 199.* ***Infantino/Giella*** *c-190.* ***Kelley Jones*** *a-513-519, 521-525, 527; c-491-499, 500(newsstand), 501-510, 513.* ***Kaluta*** *c-242, 248, 253, Annual 12.* ***G. Kane/Anderson*** *c-178-180.* ***Bob Kane*** *a-1, 2, 5; c-1-5, 7, 17.* ***G. Kane*** *a-(r)-254, 255, 259, 261, 353i.* ***Kubert*** *a-238r, 400; c-310, 319p, 327, 328, 344.* ***McFarlane*** *c-423.* ***Mignola*** *c-426-429, 452-454, Annual 18.* ***Moldoff*** *c-101-140.* ***Moldoff/Giella*** *a-164-175, 177-181, 183, 184, 186.* ***Moldoff/Greene*** *a-169, 172-174, 177-179, 181, 184.* ***Mooney*** *a-255r.* ***Morrow*** *a-Annual 13i.* ***Newton*** *a-305, 306, 328p, 331p, 332p, 337p, 338p, 346p, 352-357p, 360-372p, 374-378p; c-374p, 378p.* ***Nino*** *a-Annual 9.* ***Irv Novick*** *c-201, 202.* ***Perez*** *a-400; c-436-442.* ***Fred Ray*** *c-8, 10; w/Robinson-11.* ***Robinson/Roussos*** *a-12-17, 20, 22, 24, 25, 27, 28, 31, 33, 37.* ***Robinson*** *a-12, 14, 18, 22-32,34, 36, 37, 255r, 260r, 261r; c-6, 10, 12-14, 18, 21, 24, 26, 30, 37, 39.* ***Simonson*** *a-300p, 312p, 321p; c-300p, 312p, 366, 413i.* ***P. Smith*** *a-Annual 9.* ***Dick Sprang*** *c-19, 20, 22, 23, 25, 29, 31-36, 38, 51, 55, 66, 73, 76.* ***Starlin*** *c/a-402.* ***Staton*** *a-334.* ***Sutton*** *a-400.* ***Wrightson*** *a-265i, 400; c-320r. Bat-Hound app. in 92, 97, 103, 123, 125, 133, 156, 158. Bat-Mite app. in 133, 136, 144, 146, 158, 161. Batwoman app. in 105, 116, 122, 125, 128, 129, 131, 133, 139, 140, 141, 144, 145, 150, 151, 153, 154, 157, 159, 162, 163.* ***Zeck*** *c-417-420. Catwoman back-ups in 332, 345, 346, 348-351. Joker app. in 1, 2, 4, 5, 7-9, 11-13, 19, 20, 23, 25, 28, 32 & many more. Robin solo back-up stories in 337-339, 341-343.*

GD VG FN VF VF/NM NM-
2.0 4.0 6.0 8.0 9.0 9.2

BATMAN (DC New 52)
DC Comics: Nov, 2011 - No. 52, Jul, 2016 ($2.99/$3.99)

1-Snyder-s/Capullo-a/c 5 10 15 31 53 75
1-Variant-c by Van Sciver 4 8 12 28 47 65
1-2nd-5th printings 3 6 9 17 26 35
2-4 2 4 6 9 12 15
2-5-Variant covers. 2-Jim Lee. 3-Ivan Reis. 4-Mike Choi, 5-Burnham. 6-Gary Frank 2 4 6 9 12 15
5-7-Court of Owls. 7-Debut Harper Row 1 3 4 6 8 10
5-7 Combo Pack ($3.99) polybagged with digital download code 1 3 4 6 8 10
8-11: 8-Begin $3.99-c. 8,9-Night of the Owls. 11-Court of the Owls finale 6.00
12-Story of Harper Row; Cloonan-a 5.00
13-Death of the Family; Joker and Harley Quinn app.; die-cut-c 2 4 6 8 10 12
14-20: 14-17-Death of the Family. 17-Death of the Family conclusion. 18-Andy Kubert-a 5.00
21-23: 21-Zero Year begins; 1st app. Duke Thomas (unnamed) 5.00
23.1, 23.2, 23.3, 23.4 (11/13, $2.99, regular covers) 4.00
23.1 (11/13, $3.99, 3-D cover) "Joker #1" on cover; Andy Kubert-s/Andy Clarke-a 10.00
23.2 (11/13, $3.99, 3-D cover) "Riddler #1" on cover; Jeremy Haun-a 6.00
23.3 (11/13, $3.99, 3-D cover) "Penguin #1" on cover; Tieri-s/Duce-a/Fabok-c 6.00
23.4 (11/13, $3.99, 3-D cover) "Bane #1" on cover; Nolan-a/March-c 6.00
24-(12/13, $6.99) Batman vs. Red Hood at Ace Chemicals re-told; Dark City begins 10.00
24-New York Comic Con variant with Detective #27 cover swipe 3 6 9 14 20 25
25,29,33-($4.99) 25-All black cover; Doctor Death app. 33-Zero Year finale 6.00
26-28,30-32,34: 28-Nguyen-a; Harper Row as Bluebird; Stephanie Brown returns 4.00
35-($4.99) Endgame pt. 1; Justice League app.; back-up with Kelley Jones-a 5.00
36-39-Endgame; Joker app.; (back-up stories in each; 37-McCrea-a, 38-Kieth-a, 39-Nguyen) 39-Alfred attacked 4.00
40-($4.99) Endgame conclusion 5.00
41-43,45-49,51,52: 41-Gordon dons the robot suit. 49-Paquette-a. 52-Tynion-s 4.00
44-($4.99) Snyder & Azzarello-s/Jock-a 5.00
50-($5.99) Bruce Wayne back as Batman; new costume 6.00
#0 (11/12, $3.99) Flashbacks; Red Hood gang app. 5.00
Annual 1 (7/12, $4.99) Origin of Mr. Freeze; Snyder-s/Fabok-a 2 4 6 11 16 20
Annual 2 (9/13, $4.99) Origin of the Anchoress; Jock-c 6.00
Annual 3 (2/15, $4.99) Joker app.; Tynion-s/Antonio-a/Albuquerque-c 5.00
Annual 4 (11/15, $4.99) Joker app.; Tynion-s/Antonio-a/Murphy-c 5.00
... Endgame 40 Director's Cut 1 (1/16, $5.99) Pencil art and original script for #40 6.00
...: Futures End 1 (11/14, $2.99, regular-c) Five years later; Fawkes-s; Bizarro app. 3.00
...: Futures End 1 (11/14, $3.99, 3-D cover) 4.00
... Zero Year Director's Cut (9/13, $5.99) Reprints Batman #21 original pencil art pages with word balloons; Scott Snyder's script 6.00

BATMAN (DC Rebirth)
DC Comics: Aug, 2016 - Present ($2.99)

1-King-s/Finch-a/c; intro. Gotham and Gotham Girl 5.00
1-Director's Cut (1/17, $5.99) r/#1 in pencil-a; original script; variant cover gallery 6.00
2-20: 2-Hugo Strange app. 3-Psycho Pirate returns. 5-Justice League app. 7,8-Night of the Monster Men x-overs; Batwoman & Nightwing app. 9-13-I Am Suicide; Bane app. 3.00
21,22-The Button x-over with Flash #21,22; Eobard Thawne & Flashpoint Batman app. 3.00
23,24: 23-Swamp Thing app. 24-Batman proposes to Catwoman 3.00
25-($3.99) War of Jokes and Riddles part 1; Joker & Riddler app. 4.00
26-35,38-41: 26-32-War of Jokes and Riddles. 27-Kite Man app. 33-35,39,40-Joëlle Jones-a. 42-Justice League app. 3.00
36,37-Superman & Lois app.; Clay Mann-a 3.00
Annual 1 (1/17, $4.99) Short stories by various incl. Adams, Dini, Snyder Finch; Finch-c 5.00
Annual 2 (1/18, $4.99) King-s/Weeks & Lark-a; Batman & Catwoman's early encounters 5.00
...: Rebirth 1 (8/16, $2.99) King & Snyder-s/Janín-a; Duke Thomas & Calendar Man app. 3.00

BATMAN (Hardcover books and trade paperbacks)
...: ABSOLUTION (2002, $24.95)-Hard-c.; DeMatteis-s/Ashmore painted-a 25.00
...: ABSOLUTION (2003, $17.95)-Soft-c.; DeMatteis-s/Ashmore painted-a 18.00
...: A LONELY PLACE OF DYING (1990, $3.95, 132 pgs.)-r/Batman #440-442 & New Titans

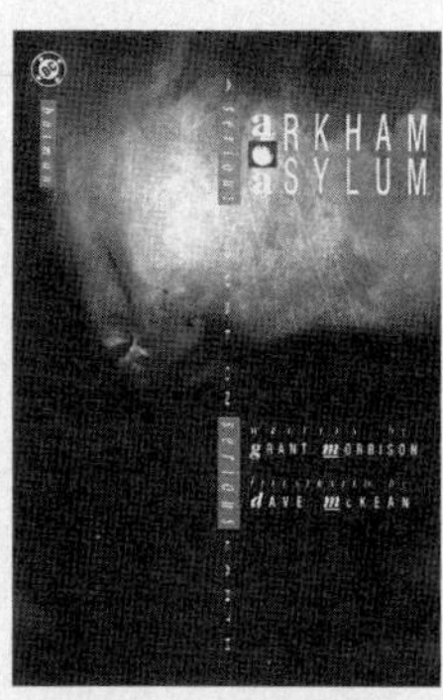

Batman: Arkham Asylum HC © DC

Batman: Blind Justice SC © DC

Batman: Going Sane SC © DC

GD VG FN VF VF/NM NM-
2.0 4.0 6.0 8.0 9.0 9.2

#60,61; Perez-c 8.00
...: ANARKY TPB (1999, $12.95) r/early appearances 13.00
...AND DRACULA: RED RAIN nn (1991, $24.95)-Hard-c.; Elseworlds storyline 32.00
...AND DRACULA: RED RAIN nn (1992, $9.95)-SC 12.00
...AND SON HC (2007, $24.99, dustjacket) r/Batman #655-658,663-666 25.00
...AND SON SC (2008, $14.99) r/Batman #655-658,663-666 15.00
...ANNUALS (See DC Comics Classics Library for reprints of early Annuals)
ARKHAM ASYLUM Hard-c; Morrison-s/McKean-a (1989, $24.95) 35.00
ARKHAM ASYLUM Soft-c ($14.95) 20.00
ARKHAM ASYLUM 15TH ANNIVERSARY EDITION Hard-c (2004, $29.95) reprint with Morrison's script and annotations, original page layouts; Karen Berger afterword 30.00
ARKHAM ASYLUM 15TH ANNIVERSARY EDITION Soft-c (2005, $17.99) 18.00
...: AS THE CROW FLIES-(2004, $12.95) r/#626-630; Nguyen sketch pages 13.00
BIRTH OF THE DEMON Hard-c (1992, $24.95)-Origin of Ra's al Ghul 35.00
BIRTH OF THE DEMON Soft-c (1993, $12.95) 15.00
BLIND JUSTICE nn (1992, $7.50)-r/Det. #598-600 8.00
BLOODSTORM (1994, $24.95,HC) Kelley Jones-c/a 28.00
BRIDE OF THE DEMON Hard-c (1990, $19.95) 25.00
BRIDE OF THE DEMON Soft-c ($12.95) 15.00
...: BROKEN CITY HC-(2004, $24.95) r/#620-625; new Johnson-c; intro by Schreck 25.00
...: BROKEN CITY SC-(2004, $14.99) r/#620-625; new Johnson-c; intro by Schreck 15.00
...: BRUCE WAYNE: FUGITIVE Vol. 1 ('02, $12.95)-r/ story arc 13.00
...: BRUCE WAYNE: FUGITIVE Vol. 2 ('03, $12.95)-r/ story arc 13.00
...: BRUCE WAYNE: FUGITIVE Vol. 3 ('03, $12.95)-r/ story arc 13.00
...: BRUCE WAYNE-MURDERER? ('02, $19.95)-r/ story arc 20.00
...: BRUCE WAYNE - THE ROAD HOME HC ('11, $24.99) r/Bruce Wayne: The Road Home one-shots 25.00
...: CATACLYSM ('99, $17.95)-r/ story arc 18.00
...: CHILD OF DREAMS (2003, $24.95, B&W, HC) Reprint of Japanese manga with Kia Asamiya-s/a/c; English adaptation by Max Allan Collins; Asamiya interview 25.00
...: CHILD OF DREAMS (2003, $19.95, B&W, SC) 20.00
...CHRONICLES VOL. 1 (2005, $14.99)-r/apps. in Detective Comics #27-38; Batman #1 15.00
...CHRONICLES VOL. 2 (2006, $14.99)-r/apps. in Detective Comics #39-45 and NY World's Fair 1940; Batman #2,3 15.00
...CHRONICLES VOL. 3 (2007, $14.99)-r/apps. in Detective Comics #46-50 and World's Best Comics #1; Batman #4,5 15.00
...CHRONICLES VOL. 4 (2007, $14.99)-r/apps. in Detective Comics #51-56 and World's Finest Comics #2,3; Batman #6,7 15.00
...CHRONICLES VOL. 5 (2008, $14.99)-r/apps. in Detective Comics #57-61 and World's Finest Comics #4; Batman #8,9 15.00
...CHRONICLES VOL. 6 (2008, $14.99)-r/apps. in Detective Comics #62-65 and World's Finest Comics #5,6; Batman #10,11 15.00
...CHRONICLES VOL. 7 (2009, $14.99)-r/apps. in Detective Comics #66-70 and World's Finest Comics #7; Batman #12,13 15.00
...CHRONICLES VOL. 8 (2009, $14.99)-r/apps. in Detective Comics #71-74 and World's Finest Comics #8,9; Batman #14,15 15.00
...CHRONICLES VOL. 9 (2010, $14.99)-r/apps. in Detective Comics #75-77 and World's Finest Comics #10; Batman #16,17 15.00
...CHRONICLES VOL. 10 (2010, $14.99)-r/apps. in Detective Comics #78-81 and World's Finest Comics #11; Batman #18,19 15.00
...: CITY OF CRIME (2006, $19.99) r/Detective Comics #800-808,811-814; Lapham-s 20.00
...: COLLECTED LEGENDS OF THE DARK KNIGHT nn (1994, $12.95)-r/Legends of the Dark Knight #32-34,38,42,43 13.00
...: CRIMSON MIST (1999, $24.95,HC)-Vampire Batman Elseworlds story Doug Moench-s/Kelley Jones-c/a 25.00
...: CRIMSON MIST (2001, $14.95,SC) 15.00
...: DARK JOKER-THE WILD (1993, $24.95,HC)-Elseworlds story; Moench-s/Jones-c/a 30.00
...: DARK JOKER-THE WILD (1993, $9.95,SC) 12.00
...DARK KNIGHT DYNASTY nn (1997, $24.95)-Hard-c.; 3 Elseworlds stories; Barr-s/ S. Hampton painted-a, Gary Frank, McDaniel-a(p) 28.00
...DARK KNIGHT DYNASTY Softcover (2000, $14.95) Hampton-c 15.00
...DEADMAN: DEATH AND GLORY nn (1996, $24.95)-Hard-c.; Robinson-s/ Estes-c/a 28.00
...DEADMAN: DEATH AND GLORY ($12.95)-SC 15.00
DEATH AND THE CITY (2007, $14.99, TPB)-r/Detective #827-834 15.00
DEATH BY DESIGN (2012, $24.99, HC)-Chip Kidd-s/Dave Taylor-s 25.00
DEATH IN THE FAMILY (1988, $3.95, trade paperback)-r/Batman #426-429 by Aparo 12.00
DEATH IN THE FAMILY: (2nd - 5th printings) 8.00
...: DETECTIVE (2007, $14.99, SC)-r/Detective Comics #821-826 15.00
...: DETECTIVE #27 HC (2003, $19.95)-Elseworlds; Uslan-s/Snejbjerg-a 20.00
...: DETECTIVE #27 SC (2004, $12.95)-Elseworlds; Uslan-s/Snejbjerg-a 13.00
DIGITAL JUSTICE nn (1990, $24.95, Hard-c.)-Computer generated art 30.00
... EARTH ONE HC (2012, $22.99)-Updated re-imagining of Batman's origin & debut; Geoff Johns-s/Gary Frank-a 23.00
... : EGO AND OTHER TALES HC (2007, $24.99)-r/Batman: Ego, Catwoman: Selina's Big Score, and stories from Batman Black and White and Solo; Darwyn Cooke-s/a 25.00
... : EGO AND OTHER TALES SC (2008, $17.99) same contents as HC 18.00
... :EVOLUTION (2001, $12.95, SC)-r/Detective Comics #743-750 13.00
... FACES (1995, $9.95, TPB) r/Legends of the Dark Knight #28-30 15.00
... FACES (2008, $12.99, TPB) Second printing 13.00
...: FACE THE FACE (2006, $14.99, TPB)-r/Batman #651-654, Detective #817-820 15.00
...: FALSE FACES HC (2008, $19.99)-r/Batman #588-590, Wonder Woman #160,161; Batman: Gotham City Secret Files #1 and Detective #787; Brian K. Vaughn intro. 20.00
...: FALSE FACES SC (2008, $14.99)-r/Batman #588-590, Wonder Woman #160,161; Batman: Gotham City Secret Files #1 and Detective #787; Brian K. Vaughn intro. 15.00
...: FORTUNATE SON HC (1999, $24.95) Gene Ha-a 25.00
...: FORTUNATE SON SC (2000, $14.95) Gene Ha-a 15.00
FOUR OF A KIND TPB (1998, $14.95)-r/1995 Year One Annuals featuring Poison Ivy, Riddler, Scarecrow, & Man-Bat 15.00
... GOING SANE (2008, $14.95, TPB) r/Legends of the Dark Knight #65-68,200 15.00
...: GOTHAM BY GASLIGHT (2006, $12.99, TPB) r/Gotham By Gaslight & Master of the Future one-shots; Elseworlds Batman vs. Jack the Ripper 13.00
...GOTHIC (1992, $12.95, TPB)-r/Legends of the Dark Knight #6-10 15.00
...GOTHIC (2007, $14.99, TPB)-r/Legends of the Dark Knight #6-10 15.00
...: HARVEST BREED-(2000, $24.95) George Pratt-s/painted-a 25.00
...: HARVEST BREED-(2003, $17.95) George Pratt-s/painted-a 18.00
...: HAUNTED KNIGHT-(1997, $12.95) r/ Halloween specials 15.00
...: HEART OF HUSH HC-(2009, $19.99) r/#Detective #846-850; pin-ups 20.00
...: HEART OF HUSH SC-(2010, $14.99) r/#Detective #846-850; pin-ups 15.00
...: HONG KONG HC (2003, $24.95, with dustjacket) Doug Moench-s/Tony Wong-a 25.00
...: HONG KONG SC (2004, $17.95) Doug Moench-s/Tony Wong-a 18.00
...: HUSH DOUBLE FEATURE-(2003, $3.95) r/#608,609(1st 2 Jim Lee-a issues) 6.00
...: HUSH SC-(2009, $24.99) r/#608-619; Wizard 0; variant cover gallery; Loeb intro 25.00
...: HUSH UNWRAPPED-(2011, $39.99, HC) r/#608-619's original Jim Lee pencil art 40.00
...: HUSH VOLUME 1 HC-(2003, $19.95) r/#608-612; & new 2 pg. origin w/Lee-a 20.00
...: HUSH VOLUME 1 SC-(2004, $12.95) r/#608-612; includes CD of DC GN art 13.00
...: HUSH VOLUME 2 HC-(2003, $19.95) r/#613-619; Lee intro & sketchpages 20.00
...: HUSH VOLUME 2 SC-(2004, $12.95) r/#613-619; Lee intro & sketchpages 13.00
...: ILLUSTRATED BY NEAL ADAMS VOLUME 1 HC-(2003, $49.95) r/Batman, Brave and the Bold, and Detective Comics stories and covers 50.00
...: ILLUSTRATED BY NEAL ADAMS VOLUME 2 HC-(2004, $49.95) r/Adams' Batman art from 1969-71; intro. by Dick Giordano 50.00
...: ILLUSTRATED BY NEAL ADAMS VOLUME 3 HC-(2006, $49.99) r/Adams' Batman art from 1971-74; covers, pin-ups and design art; intro. by Denny O'Neil 50.00
... IMPOSTERS TPB (2011, $14.99) r/Detective Comics #867-870 15.00
... INTERNATIONAL TPB (2010, $17.99) R/Batman: Scottish Connection, Batman in Barcelona: Dragon's Knight and Batman: Legends of the DK #52,53; Jim Lee-c 18.00
... IN THE FORTIES TPB ($19.95) Intro. by Bill Schelly 20.00
... IN THE FIFTIES TPB ($19.95) Intro. by Michael Uslan 20.00
... IN THE SIXTIES TPB ($19.95) Intro. by Adam West 20.00
... IN THE SEVENTIES TPB ($19.95) Intro. by Dennis O'Neil 20.00
... IN THE EIGHTIES TPB ($19.95) Intro. by John Wells 20.00
.../ JUDGE DREDD FILES (2004, $14.95) reprints cross-overs 15.00
... :KING TUT'S TOMB TPB (2010, $14.99) r/Batman Confidential #26-28, Batman #353 and Brave and the Bold #164,171 15.00
... LEGACY-(1996, $17.95) reprints Legacy 18.00
...: LIFE AFTER DEATH HC-(2010, $19.99, dustjacket) r/#Batman #692-699 20.00
...: LONG SHADOWS HC-(2010, $19.99, dustjacket) r/#Batman #687-691 20.00
...: LONG SHADOWS SC-(2011, $14.99) r/#Batman #687-691 15.00
...: LOVERS & MADMEN-(See Batman Confidential)
...: MAD LOVE AND OTHER STORIES HC (2009, $19.99) r/Batman Adventures: Mad Love, Batman Advs. Holiday Special and other Dini/Timm collaborations; commentary 20.00
...: THE MANY DEATHS OF THE BATMAN (1992, $3.95, 84 pgs.)-r/Batman #433-435 w/new Byrne-c 8.00
...: MONSTERS (2009, $19.99, TPB)-r/Legends of the Dark Knight #71-73,83,84,89,90 20.00
...: THE MOVIES (1997, $19.95)-r/movie adaptations of Batman, Batman Returns, Batman Forever, Batman and Robin 20.00
...: NINE LIVES HC (2002, $24.95, sideways format) Motter-s/Lark-a 25.00
...: NINE LIVES SC (2003, $17.95, sideways format) Motter-s/Lark-a 18.00
...: OFFICER DOWN (2001, $12.95)-r/Commissioner shot x-over; Talon-c 13.00
.../ PLANETARY DELUXE HC (2011, $22.99)-r/Planetary/Batman: Night on Earth; script 23.00
...: PREY (1992, $12.95)-Gulacy/Austin-a 15.00
...: PRIVATE CASEBOOK HC (2008, $19.99)-r/Detective Comics #840-845 and story from DC Infinite Halloween Special #1 20.00
...: PRODIGAL (1997, $14.95)-Gulacy/Austin-a 15.00
...: R.I.P.: THE DELUXE EDITION HC (2009, $24.99)-r/Batman #676-683 and story from DC Universe #0 25.00
...: R.I.P.: SC (2010, $14.99)-r/Batman #676-683 and story from DC Universe #0 15.00
... SCARECROW TALES (2005, $19.99, TPB) r/Scarecrow stories & pin-ups from World's

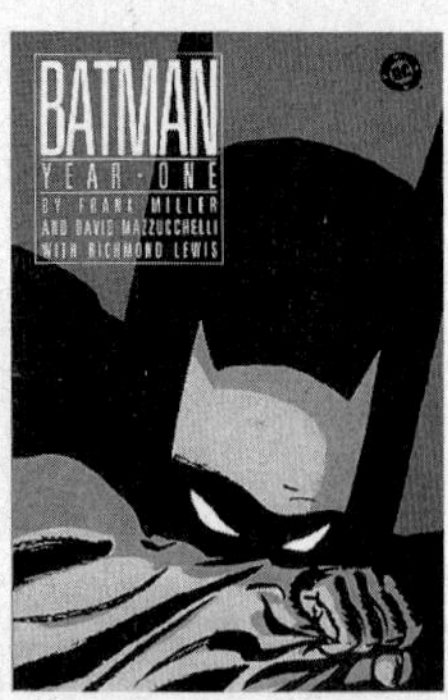

Batman: Year One SC © DC

Batman: Batgirl #1 © DC

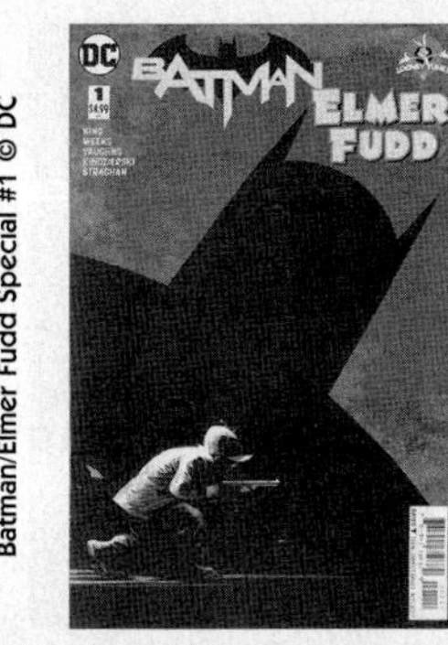

Batman/Elmer Fudd Special #1 © DC

	GD	VG	FN	VF	VF/NM	NM-
	2.0	4.0	6.0	8.0	9.0	9.2

Finest #3 to present 20.00
...: SECRETS OF THE BATCAVE (2007, $17.99, TPB) r/Batcave stories 18.00
SHAMAN (1993, $12.95)-r/Legends/D.K. #1-5 15.00
...: SNOW (2007, $14.99, TPB)-r/Legends of the Dark Knight #192-196; Fisher-a 15.00
...: SON OF THE DEMON Hard-c (9/87, $14.95) (see Batman #655-658) 35.00
...: SON OF THE DEMON limited signed & numbered Hard-c (1,700) 60.00
...: SON OF THE DEMON Soft-c w/new-c ($8.95) 15.00
...: SON OF THE DEMON Soft-c (1989, $9.95, 2nd printing - 5th printing) 10.00
... : STRANGE APPARITIONS ($12.95) r/'77-'78 Englehart/Rogers stories from Detective #469-479; also Simonson-a 13.00
...: TALES OF THE DEMON (1991, $17.95, 212 pgs.)-Intro by Sam Hamm; reprints by Neal Adams(3) & Golden; contains Saga of Ra's al Ghul #1 20.00
TALES OF THE MULTIVERSE: BATMAN - VAMPIRE (2007, $19.99) r/Batman & Dracula: Red Rain, Batman: Bloodstorm and Batman: Crimson Mist; Van Lustbader foreword 20.00
...: TEN NIGHTS OF THE BEAST (1994, $5.95)-r/Batman #417-420 10.00
...: TERROR (2003, $12.95, TPB)-r/Legends of the Dark Knight #137-141; Gulacy-c 13.00
...: THE BLACK GLOVE (2009, $17.99, TPB) r/Batman #667-669,672-675 18.00
...: THE CHALICE (HC, '99, $24.95) Van Fleet painted-a 25.00
...: THE CHALICE (SC, '00, $14.95) Van Fleet painted-a 15.00
...: THE GREATEST STORIES EVER TOLD (2005, $19.99, TPB) Les Daniels intro. 20.00
...: THE GREATEST STORIES EVER TOLD VOLUME TWO (2007, $19.99, TPB) 20.00
...: THE JOKER'S LAST LAUGH ('08, $17.99) r/Joker's Last Laugh series #1-6 18.00
...: THE LAST ANGEL (1994, $12.95, TPB) Lustbader-s 15.00
...: THE RESURRECTION OF RA'S AL GHUL (2008, $29.99, HC w/DJ) r/x-over 30.00
...: THE RESURRECTION OF RA'S AL GHUL (2009, $19.99, SC) r/x-over 20.00
...: THE RING, THE ARROW AND THE BAT (2003, $19.95, TPB) r/Legends of the DCU #7-9 & Batman: Legends of the Dark Knight #127-131; Green Lantern & Green Arrow app. 20.00
...: THE STRANGE DEATHS OF BATMAN ('09, $19.99) r/Batman #291-294, Det. #347, World's Finest #184,269, Brave & the Bold #115, Nightwing #52; Aparo-c 20.00
...: THE WRATH ('09, $17.99) r/Batman Special #1 and Batman Confidential #13-16 18.00
...: THRILLKILLER (1998, $12.95, TPB)-r/series & Thrillkiller '62 15.00
...: TIME AND THE BATMAN HC ('11, $19.99) r/Batman #700-703; cover gallery 20.00
...: TWO-FACE AND SCARECROW YEAR ONE (2009, $19.99, TPB)-r/Year One: Batman Scarecrow #1,2 and Two Face: Year One #1,2 20.00
...: UNDER THE COWL (2010, $17.99, TPB)-r/app. Dick Grayson, Tim Drake, Damian Wayne, Jean Paul Valley and Terry McGinnis as Batman 18.00
...: UNDER THE HOOD (2005, $9.99, TPB)-r/Batman #635-641 10.00
...: UNDER THE HOOD Vol. 2 (2006, $9.99, TPB)-r/Batman #645-650 & Annual #25 10.00
...: UNDER THE RED HOOD (2011, $29.99, TPB)-r/Batman #635-641,645-650, Ann. #25 30.00
...: VENOM (1993, $9.95, TPB)-r/Legends of the Dark Knight #16-20; embossed-c 15.00
... VS. TWO-FACE (2008, $19.99, TPB) r/initial (Det. #80) & classic battles; Bianchi-c 20.00
...: WAR CRIMES (2006, $12.99, TPB) r/x-over; James Jean-c 13.00
... WAR DRUMS (2004, $17.95) r/Detective #790-796 & Robin #126-128 18.00
...: WAR GAMES ACT 1,2,3 (2005, $14.95/$14.99, TPB) r/x-over; James Jean-c; each.. 15.00
...: WHATEVER HAPPENED TO THE CAPED CRUSADER? HC-(2009, $24.99, d.j.) r/Batman #686, Detective #853 and other Gaiman Batman stories; Gaiman intro.; Andy Kubert sketch pages; new Kubert cover 25.00
...: WHATEVER HAPPENED TO THE CAPED CRUSADER? SC-(2010, $14.99) 15.00
YEAR ONE Hard-c (1988, $12.95) r/Batman #404-407 25.00
YEAR ONE (1988, $9.95, TPB)-r/Batman #404-407 by Miller; intro by Miller 15.00
YEAR ONE (TPB, 2nd & 3rd printings) 10.00
YEAR ONE Deluxe HC (2005, $19.99, die-cut d.j.) new intro. by Miller and developmental material from Mazzucchelli; script pages and sketches 20.00
YEAR ONE (Deluxe) SC (2007, $14.99) r/story plus bonus material from 2005 HC 15.00
YEAR TWO (1990, $9.95, TPB)-r/Det. 575-578 by McFarlane; wraparound-c 15.00

BATMAN (one-shots)
... ABDUCTION, THE (1998, $5.95) 6.00
... ALLIES SECRET FILES AND ORIGINS 2005 (8/05, $4.99) stories/pin-ups by various 5.00
... & ROBIN (1997, $5.95)-Movie adaptation 6.00
...: ARKHAM ASYLUM - TALES OF MADNESS (5/98, $2.95) Cataclysm x-over pt. 16 4.00
... : BANE (1997, $4.95)-Dixon-s/Burchett-a; Stelfreeze-c; cover art interlocks w/Batman:(Batgirl, Mr. Freeze, Poison Ivy) 6.00
... : BATGIRL (1997, $4.95)-Puckett-s/Haley,Kesel-a; Stelfreeze-c; cover art interlocks w/Batman:(Bane, Mr. Freeze, Poison Ivy) 6.00
... : BATGIRL (6/98, $1.95)-Girlfrenzy; Balent-a 4.00
... : BLACKGATE (1/97, $3.95) Dixon-s 5.00
... : BLACKGATE - ISLE OF MEN (4/98, $2.95) Cataclysm x-over pt. 8; Moench-s/Aparo-a 4.00
... BOOK OF SHADOWS, THE (1999, $5.95) 6.00
BROTHERHOOD OF THE BAT (1995, $5.95)-Elseworlds-s 6.00
... BULLOCK'S LAW (8/99, $4.95) Dixon-s 5.00
.../CAPTAIN AMERICA (1996, $5.95, DC/Marvel) Elseworlds story; Byrne-c/s/a 8.00
...: CASTLE OF THE BAT ($5.95)-Elseworlds story 6.00
... : CATWOMAN DEFIANT nn (1992, $4.95, prestige format)-Milligan scripts; cover art interlocks w/Batman: Penguin Triumphant; special foil logo 6.00

	GD	VG	FN	VF	VF/NM	NM-
	2.0	4.0	6.0	8.0	9.0	9.2

.../CATWOMAN: FOLLOW THE MONEY (1/11, $4.99) Chaykin-c/s/a 5.00
... /DANGER GIRL (2/05, $4.95)-Leinil Yu-a/c; Joker, Harley Quinn & Catwoman app. 8.00
... /DAREDEVIL (2000, $5.95)-Barreto-a 6.00
...: DARK ALLEGIANCES (1996, $5.95)-Elseworlds story, Chaykin-c/a 7.00
...: DARK KNIGHT GALLERY (1/96, $3.50)-Pin-ups by Pratt, Balent, & others 4.00
...:DAY OF JUDGMENT (11/99, $3.95) 5.00
... DAY SPECIAL EDITION 1 (10/17, giveaway) r/Batman #16 (2017) with Harley Quinn framing pages by Palmiotti & Conner-s/Blevins-a 3.00
...:DEATH OF INNOCENTS (12/96, $3.95)-O'Neil-s/ Staton-a(p) 5.00
.../DEMON (1996, $4.95)-Alan Grant scripts 6.00
.../DEMON: A TRAGEDY (2000, $5.95)-Grant-s/Murray painted-a 6.00
...:D.O.A. (1999, $6.95)-Bob Hall-s/a 7.00
...:/DOC SAVAGE SPECIAL (2010, $4.99)-Azzarello-s/Noto-a/covers by JG Jones & Morales; preview of First Wave line (Batman, Doc Savage, The Spirit, Blackhawks) 5.00
...:DREAMLAND (2000, $5.95)-Grant-s/Breyfogle-a 6.00
... : EGO (2000, $6.95)-Darwyn Cooke-s/a 7.00
... 80-PAGE GIANT (8/98, $4.95) Stelfreeze-c 6.00
... 80-PAGE GIANT 1 (2/10, $5.99) Andy Kubert-c; Catwoman, Poison Ivy app. 6.00
... 80-PAGE GIANT 2 (10/99, $4.95) Luck of the Draw 6.00
... 80-PAGE GIANT 3 (7/00, $5.95) Calendar Man 6.00
... 80-PAGE GIANT 2011 (2/11, $5.95) Nguyen-c; short stories of villains by various 6.00
... 80-PAGE GIANT 2011 (10/11, $5.99) Nguyen-c; art by Naifeh & others 6.00
... /ELMER FUDD SPECIAL 1 (8/17, $4.99) Tom King-s/Lee Weeks-a; cartoony back-up with Bugs Bunny; King-s/Vaughns-a 10.00
... /ELMER FUDD SPECIAL 1 (10/17, $4.99) 2nd printing; brighter red bkgd on cover 6.00
... FOREVER (1995, $5.95, direct market) 6.00
... FOREVER (1995, $3.95, newsstand) 4.00
FULL CIRCLE nn (1991, $5.95, 68 pgs.)-Sequel to Batman: Year Two 8.00
...GALLERY, The 1 (1992, $2.95)-Pin-ups by Miller, N. Adams & others 4.00
...GOLDEN STREETS OF GOTHAM (2003, $6.95) Elseworlds in early 1900s 7.00
...GOTHAM BY GASLIGHT (1989, $3.95) Elseworlds; Mignola-a/Augustyn-s 8.00
...GOTHAM CITY SECRET FILES 1 (4/00, $4.95) Batgirl app. 6.00
...: GOTHAM NOIR (2001, $6.95)-Elseworlds; Brubaker-s/Phillips-c/a 7.00
.../GREEN ARROW: THE POISON TOMORROW nn (1992, $5.95, square-bound, 68 pgs.) Netzer-c/a 8.00
... HALLOWEEN COMIC FEST SPECIAL EDITION 1 (11/17, giveaway) r/Batman #7 ('16) 3.00
...: HIDDEN TREASURES 1 (12/10, $4.99) unpubl. story Wrightson-a; r/Swamp Thing #7 5.00
HOLY TERROR nn (1991, $4.95, 52 pgs.)-Elseworlds story 6.00
.../HOUDINI: THE DEVIL'S WORKSHOP (1993, $5.95) 7.00
... :HUNTRESS/SPOILER - BLUNT TRAUMA (5/98, $2.95) Cataclysm pt. 13; Dixon-s/Barreto & Sienkiewicz-a 4.00
...: I, JOKER nn (1998, $4.95)-Elseworlds story; Bob Hall-s/a 6.00
...: IN BARCELONA: DRAGON'S KNIGHT 1 (7/09, $3.99) Waid-s/Olmos-a/Jim Lee-c 4.00
...: IN DARKEST KNIGHT nn (1994, $4.95, 52 pgs.)-Elseworlds story; Batman w/Green Lantern's ring. 6.00
...:JOKER'S APPRENTICE (5/99, $3.95) Von Eeden-a 5.00
...:JOKER'S DAUGHTER (4/14, $4.99) Bennett-s/Hetrick-a/Jeanty-c 5.00
.../ JOKER: SWITCH (2003, $6.95)-Bolton-a/Grayson-s 7.00
...:JUDGE DREDD: JUDGEMENT ON GOTHAM nn (1991, $5.95, 68 pgs.) Simon Bisley-c/a; Grant/Wagner scripts 8.00
...:JUDGE DREDD: JUDGEMENT ON GOTHAM nn (2nd printing) 6.00
...:JUDGE DREDD: THE ULTIMATE RIDDLE (1995, $4.95) 6.00
...:JUDGE DREDD: VENDETTA IN GOTHAM (1993, $5.95) 7.00
...: KNIGHTGALLERY (1995, $3.50)-Elseworlds sketchbook. 4.00
.../ LOBO (2000, $5.95)-Elseworlds; Joker app.; Bisley-a 6.00
...: MASK OF THE PHANTASM (1994, $2.95)-Movie adapt. 4.00
...: MASK OF THE PHANTASM (1994, $4.95)-Movie adapt. 6.00
...: MASQUE (1997, $6.95)-Elseworlds; Grell-c/s/a 7.00
...: MASTER OF THE FUTURE nn (1991, $5.95, 68 pgs.)-Elseworlds; sequel to Gotham By Gaslight; Barreto-a; embossed-c 6.00
...: MITEFALL (1995, $4.95)-Alan Grant script, Kevin O'Neill-a 6.00
... : MR. FREEZE (1997, $4.95)-Dini-s/Buckingham-a; Stelfreeze-c; cover art interlocks w/Batman:(Bane, Batgirl, Poison Ivy) 6.00
... /NIGHTWING: BLOODBORNE (2002, $5.95) Cypress-a; McKeever-c 6.00
...: NOEL (2011, $22.99, HC graphic novel with dustjacket) Lee Bermejo-s/a; Jim Lee intro.; Catwoman, Superman & The Joker app.; bonus sketch & layout art pages 23.00
...: NOSFERATU (1999, $5.95) McKeever-a 6.00
...: OF ARKHAM (2000, $5.95)-Elseworlds; Grant-s/Alcatena-a 6.00
...: OUR WORLDS AT WAR (8/01, $2.95)-Jae Lee-c 3.00
...: PENGUIN TRIUMPHANT nn (1992, $4.95)-Staton-a(p); foil logo 6.00
...•PHANTOM STRANGER nn (1997, $4.95) nn-Grant-s/Ransom-a 6.00
... : PLUS (2/97, $2.95) Arsenal-c/app. 4.00
... : POISON IVY (1997, $4.95)-J.F. Moore-s/Apthorp-a; Stelfreeze-c; cover art interlocks w/Batman:(Bane, Batgirl, Mr. Freeze) 6.00

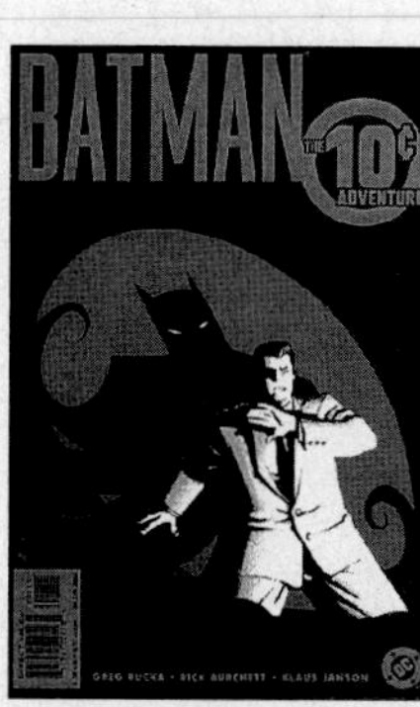

Batman: The 10-Cent Adventure #1 © DC

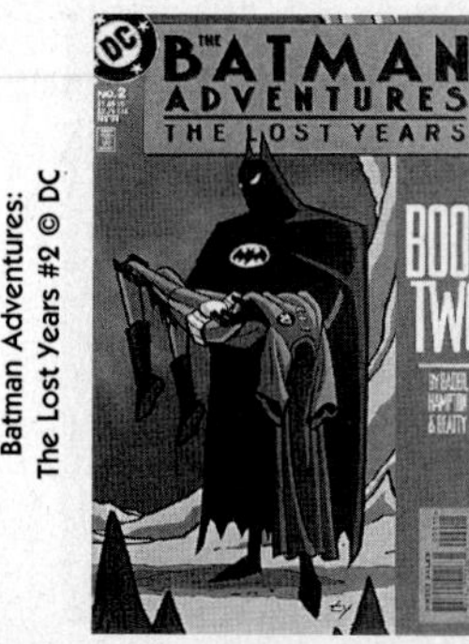

Batman Adventures: The Lost Years #2 © DC

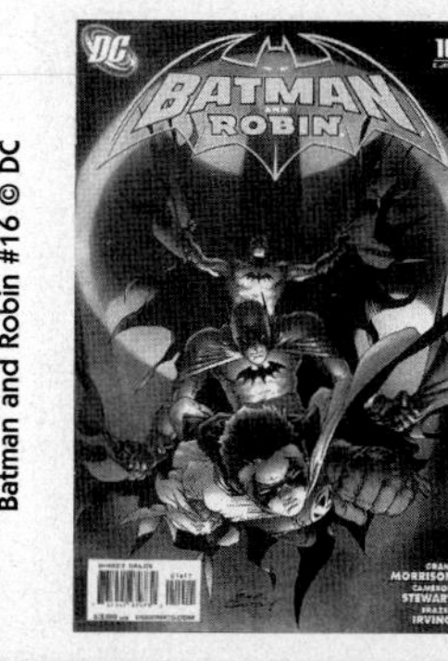

Batman and Robin #16 © DC

GD 2.0 | VG 4.0 | FN 6.0 | VF 8.0 | VF/NM 9.0 | NM- 9.2

.../POISON IVY: CAST SHADOWS (2004, $6.95) Van Fleet-c/a; Nocenti-s 7.00
.../PUNISHER: LAKE OF FIRE (1994, $4.95, DC/Marvel) 6.00
... :REIGN OF TERROR ('99, $4.95) Elseworlds 6.00
...RETURNS MOVIE SPECIAL (1992, $3.95) 4.00
...RETURNS MOVIE PRESTIGE (1992, $5.95, squarebound)-Dorman painted-c 6.00
...:RIDDLER-THE RIDDLE FACTORY (1995, $4.95)-Wagner script 6.00
...: ROOM FULL OF STRANGERS (2004, $5.95) Scott Morse-s/c/a 6.00
...: SCARECROW 3-D (12/98, $3.95) w/glasses 5.00
.../ SCARFACE: A PSYCHODRAMA (2001, $5.95)-Adlard-a/Sienkiewicz-c 6.00
...: SCAR OF THE BAT nn (1996, $4.95)-Elseworlds; Max Allan Collins script; Barreto-a 6.00
... :SCOTTISH CONNECTION (1998, $5.95) Quitely-a 6.00
... :SEDUCTION OF THE GUN nn (1992, $2.50, 68 pgs.) 5.00
.../SPAWN: WAR DEVIL nn (1994, $4.95, 52 pgs.) 6.00
... SPECIAL 1 (4/84)-Mike W. Barr story; Golden-c/a 1 2 3 5 6 8
.../SPIDER-MAN (1997, $4.95) Dematteis-s/Nolan & Kesel-a 6.00
... : THE ABDUCTION ('98, $5.95) 6.00
...: THE BLUE, THE GREY, & THE BAT (1992, $5.95)-Weiss/Lopez-a 7.00
... :THE HILL (5/00, $2.95)-Priest-s/Martinbrough-a 3.00
... :THE KILLING JOKE (1988, deluxe 52 pgs., mature readers)-Bolland-c/a; Alan Moore scripts; Joker cripples Barbara Gordon 5 10 15 30 50 70
...: THE KILLING JOKE (2nd thru 14th printings) 3 6 9 14 20 25
...: THE KILLING JOKE : THE DELUXE EDITION (2008, $17.99, HC) re-colored version along with Bolland-s/a from Batman Black and White #4; sketch pages; Tim Sale intro. 18.00
...: THE MAN WHO LAUGHS (2005, $6.95)-Retells 1st meeting with the Joker; Mahnke-a 7.00
...: THE OFFICIAL COMIC ADAPTATION OF THE WARNER BROS. MOTION PICTURE (1989, $2.50, regular format, 68 pgs.)-Ordway-c 4.00
...: THE OFFICIAL COMIC ADAPTATION OF THE WARNER BROS. MOTION PICTURE (1989, $4.95, prestige format, 68 pgs.)-same interiors but different-c 6.00
...: THE ORDER OF BEASTS (2004, $5.95)-Elseworlds; Eddie Campbell-a 6.00
...: THE SPIRIT (1/07, $4.99)-Loeb-s/Cooke-a; P'Gell & Commissioner Dolan app. 5.00
...: THE 10-CENT ADVENTURE (3/02, 10¢) intro. to the "Bruce Wayne: Murderer" x-over; Rucka-s/Burchett & Janson-a/Dave Johnson-c 3.00

NOTE: (Also see Promotional Comics section for alternate copies with special outer half-covers promoting local comic shops)

...: THE 12-CENT ADVENTURE (10/04, 12¢) intro. to the "War Games" x-over; Grayson-s/Bachs-a; Catwoman & Spoiler app. 3.00
...: TWO-FACE-CRIME AND PUNISHMENT-(1995, $4.95)-McDaniel-a 6.00
... : TWO FACES (11/98, $4.95) Elseworlds 6.00
...Vs. THE INCREDIBLE HULK (1995, $3.95)-r/DC Special Series #27 6.00
...: VILLAINS SECRET FILES (10/98, $4.95) Origin-s 6.00
... VILLAINS SECRET FILES AND ORIGINS 2005 (7/05, $4.99) Clayface origin w/ Mignola-a; Black Mask story, pin-up of villains by various; Barrionuevo-c 6.00

BATMAN ADVENTURES, THE (Based on animated series)
DC Comics: Oct, 1992 - No. 36, Oct, 1995 ($1.25/$1.50)

1-Penguin-c/story 2 4 6 9 12 15
1 ($1.95, Silver Edition)-2nd printing 3.00
2,4-6,8-11,13-15,17-19: 2-Catwoman-c/story. 5-Scarecrow-c/story. 10-Riddler-c/story. 11-Man-Bat-c/story. 18-Batgirl-c/story. 19-Scarecrow-c/story 4.00
3-Joker-c/story 2 4 6 9 12 15
7-Special edition polybagged with Man-Bat trading card 6.00
12-(9/93) 1st Harley Quinn app. in comics; 1st animated-version Batgirl app. in title 50 100 150 225 350 475
16-Joker-c/story; begin $1.50-c 3 6 9 16 23 30
20-24,26,27,29-32: 26-Batgirl app. 3.00
25-($2.50, 52 pgs.)-Superman app. 4.00
28-Joker & Harley Quinn-c; 2nd app. Harley Quinn 3 6 9 17 26 35
33-36: 33-Begin $1.75-c 3.00
Annual 1 ('94) 3rd app. Harley Quinn 3 6 9 19 30 40
Annual 2 ('95) Demon-c/story; Ra's al Ghul app. 4.00
...: Dangerous Dames & Demons (2003, $14.95, TPB) r/Annual 1,2, Mad Love & Adventures in the DC Universe #3; Bruce Timm painted-c 30.00
Holiday Special 1 (1995, $2.95) Harley Quinn app. 3 6 9 14 19 24
The Collected Adventures Vol. 1,2 ('93, '95, $5.95) 10.00
TPB ('98, $7.95) r/#1-6; painted wraparound-c 10.00

BATMAN ADVENTURES (Based on animated series)
DC Comics: Jun, 2003 - No. 17, Oct, 2004 ($2.25)

1-Timm-c 1 2 3 5 6 8
1-Free Comic Book Day edition (6/03) Timm-c 4.00
1-Halloween Fest Special Edition (12/15) Timm-c 3.00
2,4-9,11-15,17: 4-Ra's al Ghul app. 6-8-Phantasm app. 14-Grey Ghost app. 3.00
3-Joker & Harley Quinn-c/app. 3 6 9 16 24 32
10-Catwoman-c/app. 2 4 6 11 16 20
16-Joker & Harley Quinn-c/app. 4 8 12 25 40 55

Batman/Scooby-Doo Halloween Fest 1 (12/12, giveaway flipbook with Scooby-Doo) r/#1 5.00
Vol. 1: Rogues Gallery (2004, $6.95, digest size) r/#1-4 & Batman: Gotham Advs. #50 7.00
Vol. 2: Shadows & Masks (2004, $6.95, digest size) r/#5-9 7.00

BATMAN ADVENTURES, THE: MAD LOVE
DC Comics: Feb, 1994 ($3.95/$4.95)

1-Origin of Harley Quinn; Dini-s/Timm-c/a 7 14 21 46 86 125
1-($4.95, Prestige format) new Timm painted-c 5 10 15 33 57 80

BATMAN ADVENTURES, THE: THE LOST YEARS (TV)
DC Comics: Jan, 1998 - No. 5, May, 1998 ($1.95) (Based on animated series)

1-5-Leads into Fall '97's new animated episodes. 4-Tim Drake becomes Robin. 5-Dick becomes Nightwing 3.00
TPB-(1999, $9.95) r/series 12.00

BATMAN/ALIENS
DC Comics/Dark Horse: Mar, 1997 - No. 2, Apr, 1997 ($4.95, limited series)

1,2: Wrightson-c/a. 6.00
TPB-(1997, $14.95) w/prequel from DHP #101,102 15.00

BATMAN/ALIENS II
DC Comics/Dark Horse: 2003 - No. 3, 2003 ($5.95, limited series)

1-3-Edginton-s/Staz Johnson-a 6.00
TPB-(2003, $14.95) r/#1-3 15.00

BATMAN AND... (See Batman and Robin [2011 series] #19-on)

BATMAN AND ROBIN (See Batman R.I.P. and Batman: Battle For The Cowl series)
DC Comics: Aug, 2009 - No. 26, Oct, 2011 ($2.99)

1-Grant Morrison-s/Frank Quitely-a/c; Dick Grayson & Damian Wayne team 8.00
1-Variant cover by J.G. Jones 20.00
1-Second thru Fourth printings - recolored Quitely covers 3.00
2-16-Quitely-c. 2-Three printings. 4-6-Tan-a. 7-9-Stewart-a; Batwoman & Squire app. 13-15-Joker app.; Irving-a. 16-Bruce Wayne returns; Batman Inc. announced 3.00
2-Variant-c by Adam Kubert 10.00
17-26: 17-McDaniel-a/March-c. 21,22-Gleason-a. 23-25-Red Hood app. 3.00
... #1 Special Edition (6/10, $1.00) r/#1 with "What's Next?" cover logo 3.00
...: Batman and Robin Must Die - The Deluxe Edition HC (2011, $24.99) r/#13-16; cover and costume design sketch art 25.00
...: Batman Reborn - The Deluxe Edition HC (2010, $24.99) r/#1-6; design sketch art 25.00
...: Batman Reborn SC (2011, $14.99) r/#1-6; cover and character design sketch art 15.00
...: Batman vs. Robin - The Deluxe Edition HC (2010, $24.99) r/#7-12; cover sketch art 25.00

BATMAN AND ROBIN (DC New 52)(Cover title changes each issue from #19-32)
DC Comics: Nov, 2011 - No. 40, May, 2015 ($2.99)

1-Bruce and Damian Wayne in costume; Tomasi-s/Gleason-a 4.00
2-14: 5,6-Ducard flashback. 9-Night of the Owls 3.00
15-Death of the Family tie-in; die-cut Joker cover 5.00
16-18: 16-Death of the Family tie-in. 18-Requiem 3.00
19-23: 19-Red Robin. 20-Red Hood. 21-Batgirl. 22-Catwoman. 23-Nightwing 3.00
23.1, 23.2, 23.3, 23.4 (11/13, $2.99, regular covers) 3.00
23.1 (11/13, $3.99, 3-D cover) "Two Face #1" on cover; March-a; Scarecrow app. 6.00
23.2 (11/13, $3.99, 3-D cover) "Court of Owls #1" on cover; history of the Owls 5.00
23.3 (11/13, $3.99, 3-D cover) "Ra's al Ghul #1" on cover; history of Ra's retold 5.00
23.4 (11/13, $3.99, 3-D cover) "Killer Croc #1" on cover; Croc's origin 5.00
24-40: 24-28-Two-Face. 25-Matches Malone app. 29-Aquaman. 30-Wonder Woman. 31-Frankenstein. 32-Ra's al Ghul. 33-38-Title back to Batman and Robin. 37-Darkseid app.; Damien returns; cont'd in Robin Rises: Alpha. 39,40-Justice League app. 3.00
#0 (11/12, $2.99) Damian's childhood training with Talia; Tomasi-s/Gleason-a 3.00
Annual 1 (3/13, $4.99) Damian in the Batman #666 costume; Andy Kubert-c 5.00
Annual 2 (3/14, $4.99) Mahnke-a; flashback to Dick Grayson's first week as Robin 5.00
Annual 3 (6/15, $4.99) Ryp-a/Syaf-c 5.00
...: Futures End 1 (11/14, $2.99, regular-c) Five years later; Nguyen-a; 1st app. Duke Thomas as future Robin 3.00
...: Futures End 1 (11/14, $3.99, 3-D cover) 4.00

BATMAN AND ROBIN ADVENTURES (TV)
DC Comics: Nov, 1995 - No. 25, Dec, 1997 ($1.75) (Based on animated series)

1-Dini-s 1 2 3 5 6 8
2-4,6,7,9-15,17,19,20,22,23: 2-4-Dini script. 4-Penguin-c/app. 9-Batgirl & Talia-c/app. 10-Ra's al Ghul-c/app. 11-Man-Bat app. 12-Bane-c/app. 13-Scarecrow-c/app. 15 Deadman-c/app. 3.00
5-Joker-c/story 6.00
8-Poison Ivy & Harley Quinn-c/app. 2 4 6 13 18 22
16,18,24: 16-Catwoman-c/app. 18-Joker-c/app. 24-Poison Ivy app. 2 4 6 8 10 12
21-Batgirl-c 3 6 9 17 26 35

Batman & Robin Eternal #3 © DC

Batman Beyond (2015 series) #1 © DC

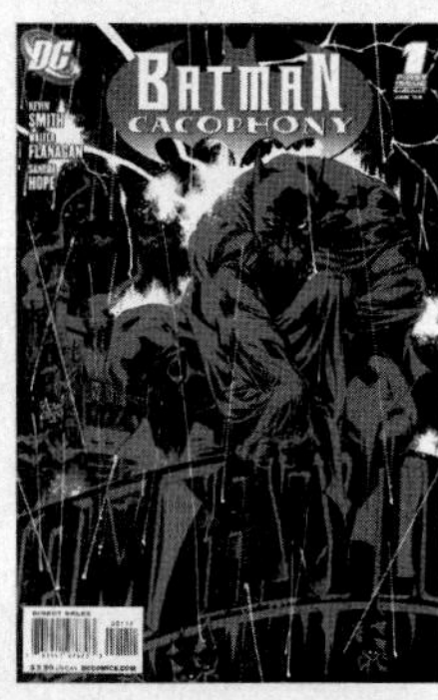
Batman Cacophony #1 © DC

	GD 2.0	VG 4.0	FN 6.0	VF 8.0	VF/NM 9.0	NM- 9.2

25-($2.95, 48 pgs.) 4.00
Annual 1,2 (11/96, 11/97): 1-Phantasm-c/app. 2-Zatara & Zatanna-c/app. 4.00
...: Sub-Zero(1998, $3.95) Adaptation of animated video 4.00

BATMAN & ROBIN ETERNAL (Sequel to Batman Eternal)
DC Comics: Dec, 2015 - No. 26, May, 2016 ($3.99/$2.99, weekly series)

1-($3.99) Tynion IV & Snyder-s/Daniel-a; Cassandra Cain app. 4.00
2-25-($2.99) Dick Grayson, Red Hood, Red Robin, Bluebird, Spoiler app. 6-1st app. Mother. 9,10,15,16,24,25-Azrael app. 23-25-Midnighter app. 3.00
26-($3.99) Conclusion; Tony Daniel-c 4.00

BATMAN AND SUPERMAN ADVENTURES: WORLD'S FINEST
DC Comics: 1997 ($6.95, square-bound, one-shot) (Based on animated series)

1-Adaptation of animated crossover episode; Dini-s/Timm-c; Harley Quinn on cover 2 4 6 8 11 14

BATMAN AND SUPERMAN: WORLD'S FINEST
DC Comics: Apr, 1999 - No. 10, Jan, 2000 ($4.95/$1.99, limited series)

1,10-($4.95, squarebound) Taylor-a 5.00
2-9-($1.99) 5-Batgirl app. 8-Catwoman-c/app. 3.00
TPB (2003, $19.95) r/#1-10 20.00

BATMAN AND THE OUTSIDERS (The Adventures of the Outsiders #33 on)
(Also see Brave & The Bold #200 & The Outsiders) (Replaces The Brave and the Bold)
DC Comics: Aug, 1983 - No. 32, Apr, 1986 (Mando paper #5 on)

1-Batman, Halo, Geo-Force, Katana, Metamorpho & Black Lightning begin 5.00
2-32: 5-New Teen Titans x-over. 9-Halo begins. 11,12-Origin Katana. 18-More info on Metamorpho's origin. 28-31-Lookers origin. 32-Team disbands 3.00
Annual 1,2 (9/84, 9/85): 2-Metamorpho & Sapphire Stagg wed 4.00
NOTE: ***Aparo** a-1-9, 11-13p, 16-20; c-1-4, 5i, 6-21, Annual 1, 2. **B. Kane** a-3r. **Layton** a-19i, 20i. **Lopez** a-3p. **Miller** c-Annual 1. **Perez** c-5p. **B. Willingham** a-14p.*

BATMAN AND THE OUTSIDERS (Continues as The Outsiders for #15-39)
DC Comics: Dec, 2007 - No. 14, Feb, 2009; No. 40, Jul, 2011 ($2.99)

1-14: 1-Batman, Catwoman, Martian Manhunter, Katana, Metamorpho, Thunder & Grace begin. 4-Batgirl joins. 11-13-Batman R.I.P. 3.00
40 (7/11) Final issue; Didio-s/Tan-a; history of the team 3.00
... Special (3/09, $3.99) Alfred assembles a new team; Andy Kubert-a; two covers 4.00
...: The Chrysalis TPB (2008, $14.99) r/#1-5 15.00
...: The Snare TPB (2008, $14.99) r/#6-10 15.00

BATMAN & THE SIGNAL
DC Comics: Mar, 2018 - No. 3 ($3.99)

1,2-Batman and Duke Thomas; Hamner-a 4.00

BATMAN: ARKHAM CITY (Prequel to the video game)
DC Comics: Early Jul, 2011 - No. 5, Oct, 2011 ($2.99, limited series)

1-5-Dini-s/D'Anda-a; Joker app. 3.00
...: End Game (1/13, $6.99) Story bridges Arkham City and Arkham Unhinged series 7.00

BATMAN: ARKHAM KNIGHT (Prequel to the Arkham video game trilogy finale)
DC Comics: May, 2015 - No. 12, Feb, 2016 ($3.99)

1-Tomasi-s/Bogdanovic-a/Panosian-c; 1st comic app. of Arkham Knight 6.00
2-12: 2-Harley Quinn cover 4.00
Annual 1 (11/15, $4.99) Tomasi-s/Segovia-a; Firefly app. 5.00
...: Robin 1 (1/16, $2.99) Tomasi-s/Rocha-a 3.00

BATMAN: ARKHAM KNIGHT: GENESIS
DC Comics: Oct, 2015 - No. 6 ($2.99, limited series)

1-4: 1-Tomasi-s/Borges-a/Sejic-c; Jason Todd's origin. 4-Harley Quinn cover 3.00

BATMAN: ARKHAM UNHINGED (Based on the Batman: Arkham City video game)
DC Comics: Jun, 2012 - No. 20, Jan, 2014 ($2.99)

1-20: 1-Wilkins-c; Catwoman, Two-Face & Hugo Strange app. 3.00

BATMAN: BANE OF THE DEMON
DC Comics: Mar, 1998 - No. 4, June, 1998 ($1.95, limited series)

1-4-Dixon-s/Nolan-a; prelude to Legacy x-over 3.00

BATMAN: BATTLE FOR THE COWL (Follows Batman R.I.P. storyline)
DC Comics: May, 2009 - No. 3, Jul, 2009 ($3.99, limited series)

1-3-Tony Daniel-s/a/c; 2 covers on each 4.00
...: Arkham Asylum (6/09, $2.99) Hine-s/Haun-a/Ladronn-c 3.00
...: Commissioner Gordon (5/09, $2.99) Mandrake-a/Ladronn-c; Mr. Freeze app. 3.00
...: Man-Bat (6/09, $2.99) Harris-s/Calafiore-a/Ladronn-c; Dr. Phosphorus app. 3.00
...: The Network (7/09, $2.99) Nicieza-s/Calafiore & Kramer-a/Ladronn-c 3.00
...: The Underground (6/09, $2.99) Yost-s/Raimondi-a/Ladronn-c; Harley Quinn app. 3.00
Companion SC (2009, $14.99) r/ five one-shots 15.00
HC (2009, $19.99) r/#1-3 & Gotham Gazette: Batman Dead & Gotham Gazette: Batman Alive; gallery of variant covers and sketch art 20.00
SC (2010, $14.99) same contents as HC 15.00

BATMAN BEYOND (Based on animated series)
DC Comics: Mar, 1999 - No. 6, Aug, 1999 ($1.99, limited series)

1-Adaptation of pilot episode, Timm-c 4 8 12 23 37 50
2-6: 2-Adaptation of pilot episode cont., Timm-c. 4-Darwyn Cooke-c; The Demon app. 1 2 3 5 6 8
TPB (1999, $9.95) r/#1-6 15.00

BATMAN BEYOND (Based on animated series)(Continuing series)
DC Comics: Nov, 1999 - No. 24, Oct, 2001 ($1.99)

1-Rousseau-a; Batman vs. Batman 1 3 4 6 8 10
2-24: 14-Demon-c/app. 21,22-Justice League Unlimited-c/app. 4.00
...: Return of the Joker (2/01, $2.95) adaptation of video release 3 6 9 19 30 40

BATMAN BEYOND (Animated series)(See Superman/Batman Annual #4)
DC Comics: Aug, 2010 - No. 6, Jan, 2011 ($2.99, limited series)

1-6: 1-Benjamin-a; Nguyen-c; return of Hush 3.00
1-Variant-c by J.H. Williams III 6.00
...: Hush Beyond TPB (2011, $14.99) r/#1-6 15.00

BATMAN BEYOND
DC Comics: Mar, 2011 - No. 8, Oct, 2011 ($2.99)

1-8: 1-3-Justice League app.; Beechen-s/Benjamin-a/Nguyen-c. 8-Inque app. 3.00
1-Variant-c by Darwyn Cooke 4.00

BATMAN BEYOND (Tim Drake as Batman)
DC Comics: Aug, 2015 - No. 16, Nov. 2016 ($2.99)

1-16: 1-Jurgens-s/Chang-a. 2-Inque app. 5-New suit. 7,16-Stephen Thompson-a. 10-Tuftan app. 11-Superman's son app. 12-Tan-a. 16-Terry McGinnis back as Batman 3.00

BATMAN BEYOND (DC Rebirth)
DC Comics: Dec, 2016 - Present ($2.99/$3.99)

1-6: 1-3,6-Dan Jurgens-s/Bernard Chang-a. 4,5-Pete Woods-a 3.00
7-17-($3.99) 8-11-Damian app. 4.00
...: Rebirth 1 (11/16, $2.99) Terry McGinnis in the suit; Jurgens-s/Sook-a 3.00

BATMAN BEYOND UNIVERSE
DC Comics: Oct, 2013 - No. 16, Jan, 2015 ($3.99)

1-12: 1-Superman & the JLB app.; Sean Murphy-c. 8-12-Wonder Woman app. 9-12-Justice Lords app. 13,14-Phantasm returns. 15-Royal Flush Gang app. 4.00

BATMAN BEYOND UNLIMITED
DC Comics: Apr, 2012 - No. 18, Sept, 2013 ($3.99)

1-18: 1-Beechen-s/Breyfogle-a; Superman & Justice League back-ups; Nguyen-c. 17-Metal Men return; Marvel Family app. 18-New Batgirl 4.00

BATMAN: BLACK & WHITE
DC Comics: June, 1996 - No. 4, Sept, 1996 ($2.95, B&W, limited series)

1-Stories by McKeever, Timm, Kubert, Chaykin, Goodwin; Jim Lee-c; Allred inside front-c; Moebius inside back-c 4.00
2-4: 2-Stories by Simonson, Corben, Bisley & Gaiman; Miller-c. 3-Stories by M. Wagner, Janson, Sienkiewicz, O'Neil & Kristiansen; B. Smith-c; Russell inside front-c; Silvestri inside back-c. 4-Stories by Bolland, Goodwin & Gianni, Strnad & Nowlan, O'Neil & Stelfreeze; Toth-c; pin-ups by Neal Adams & Alex Ross 3.00
Hardcover ('97, $39.95) r/series w/new art & cover plate 40.00
Softcover ('00, $19.95) r/series 20.00
Volume 2 HC ('02, $39.95, 7 3/4"x12") r/B&W back-up-s from Batman: Gotham Knights #1-16; stories and art by various incl. Ross, Buscema, Byrne, Ellison, Sale; Mignola-c 40.00
Volume 2 SC ('03, $19.95, 7 3/4"x12") same contents as HC 20.00
Volume 2 SC ('08, $19.99, reg. size) same contents as HC 20.00
Volume 3 HC ('07, $24.99, reg. size) r/B&W back-up-s from Batman: Gotham Knights #17-49; stories and art by various incl. Davis, DeCarlo, Morse, Schwartz, Thompson; Miller-c 25.00

BATMAN: BLACK & WHITE
DC Comics: Nov, 2013 - No. 6, Apr, 2014 ($4.99, B&W, limited series)

1-6-Short story anthology by various. 1-Silvestri-c; Neal Adams-a. 2-Steranko-c; Nino-a. 3-Bermejo-s/a. 4-Conner-c; Allred-s/a. 6-Mahnke-c; Hughes, Cloonan, Chiang-a 5.00

BATMAN: BOOK OF THE DEAD
DC Comics: Jun, 1999 - No. 2, July, 1999 ($4.95, limited series, prestige format)

1,2-Elseworlds; Kitson-a 6.00

BATMAN CACOPHONY
DC Comics: Jan, 2009 - No. 3, Mar, 2009 ($3.99, limited series)

1-3-Kevin Smith-s/Walt Flanagan-a; Joker and Onomatoapoeia app.; Adam Kubert-c 4.00

Batman Eternal #50 © DC

Batman Family #1 © DC

Batman: Gotham Adventures #3 © DC

GD 2.0 VG 4.0 FN 6.0 VF 8.0 VF/NM 9.0 NM- 9.2

GD 2.0 VG 4.0 FN 6.0 VF 8.0 VF/NM 9.0 NM- 9.2

1-3-Variant-c by Sienkiewicz 15.00
HC (2009, $19.99, d.j.) r/#1-3; Kevin Smith intro.; script for #3, cover gallery 20.00
SC (2010, $14.99) r/#1-3; Kevin Smith intro.; script for #3, cover gallery 15.00

BATMAN: CATWOMAN DEFIANT (See Batman one-shots)

BATMAN/ CATWOMAN: TRAIL OF THE GUN
DC Comics: 2004 - No. 2, 2004 ($5.95, limited series, prestige format)
1,2-Elseworlds; Van Sciver-a/Nocenti-s 6.00

BATMAN CHRONICLES, THE (See the Batman TPB listings for the Golden Age reprint series that shares this title)
DC Comics: Summer, 1995 - No. 23, Winter, 2001 ($2.95, quarterly)
1-3,5-19: 1-Dixon/Grant/Moench script. 3-Bolland-c. 5-Oracle Year One story, Richard Dragon app., Chaykin-c. 6-Kaluta-c; Ra's al Ghul story. 7-Superman-c/app.11-Paul Pope-s/a. 12-Cataclysm pt. 10. 18-No Man's Land 5.00
4-Hitman story by Ennis, Contagion tie-in; Balent-c 2 4 6 9 12 15
20,22,23: 20-Catwoman and Relative Heroes-c/app. 4.00
21-Brian Michael Bendis-s (1st for DC)/Gaydos-a; Giordano-a; Pander Bros.-a/c 6.00
...Gallery (3/97, $3.50) Pin-ups 4.00
...Gauntlet, The (1997, $4.95, one-shot) 6.00

BATMAN: CITY OF LIGHT
DC Comics: Dec, 2003 - No. 8, July, 2004 ($2.95, limited series)
1-8-Pander Brothers-a/s; Paniccia-s 3.00

BATMAN CONFIDENTIAL
DC Comics: Feb, 2007 - No. 54, May, 2011 ($2.99)
1-49,51-54: 1-6-Diggle-s/Portacio-a/c. 7-12-Cowan-a; Joker's origin. 13-16-Morales-a. 17-21-Batgirl vs. Catwoman; Maguire-a. 22-25-McDaniel-a; Joker app. 26-28-King Tut app.; Garcia-Lopez-a. 40-43-Kieth-s/a. 44-48-Mandrake-a/c 3.00
50-($4.99) Bingham-a; back-up Silver Age-style JLA story 5.00
...: Dead to Rights SC (2010, $14.99) r/#22-25,29,30 15.00
...: Lovers and Madmen HC (2008, $24.99, dustjacket) r/#7-12; Brad Meltzer intro. 25.00
...: Lovers and Madmen SC (2009, $14.99) r/#7-12; Brad Meltzer intro. 15.00
...: Rules of Engagement HC (2007, $24.99, dustjacket) r/#1-6 25.00
...: The Bat and the Beast SC (2010, $12.99) r/#31-35 13.00
...: The Cat and the Bat SC (2009, $12.99) r/#17-21 13.00
...: Vs. The Undead SC (2010, $14.99) r/#44-48 15.00

BATMAN: CREATURE OF THE NIGHT
DC Comics: Jan, 2018 - No. 4 ($5.99, squarebound, limited series)
1,2-Kurt Busiek-s/John Paul Leon-a; story of Bruce Wainwright 6.00

BATMAN: DARK DETECTIVE
DC Comics: Early July, 2005 - No. 6, Late September, 2005 ($2.99, limited series)
1-6-Englehart-s/Rogers & Austin-a; Silver St. Cloud and The Joker app. 3.00

BATMAN: DARK KNIGHT OF THE ROUND TABLE
DC Comics: 1999 - No. 2, 1999 ($4.95, limited series, prestige format)
1,2-Elseworlds; Giordano-a 7.00

BATMAN: DARK VICTORY
DC Comics: 1999 - No. 13, 2000 ($4.95/$2.95, limited series)
Wizard #0 Preview 3.00
1-($4.95) Loeb-s/Sale-c/a 5.00
2-12-($2.95) 3.00
13-($4.95) 5.00
Hardcover (2001, $29.95) with dust jacket; r/#0,1-13 30.00
Softcover (2002, $19.95) r/#0,1-13 20.00

BATMAN: DEATH AND THE MAIDENS
DC Comics: Oct, 2003 - No. 9, Aug, 2004 ($2.95, limited series)
1-Ra's al Ghul app.; Rucka-s/Janson-a 4.00
2-9: 9-Ra's al Ghul dies 3.00
TPB (2004, $19.95) r/#1-9 & Detective #783 20.00

BATMAN/ DEATHBLOW: AFTER THE FIRE
DC Comics/WildStorm: 2002 - No. 3, 2002 ($5.95, limited series)
1-3-Azzarello-s/Bermejo & Bradstreet-a 6.00
TPB (2003, $12.95) r/#1-3; plus concept art 13.00

BATMAN: DEATH MASK
DC Comics/CMX: Jun, 2008 - No. 4, Sept, 2008 ($2.99, B&W, limited series, right-to-left manga style)
1-4-Yoshinori Natsume-s/a 3.00
TPB (2008, $9.99, digest size) r/#1-4; interview with Yoshinori Natsume 10.00

BATMAN ETERNAL (Also see Arkham Manor series)
DC Comics: Jun, 2014 - No. 52, Jun, 2015 ($2.99, weekly series)
1-Snyder-s/Fabok-a; Professor Pyg & Jason Bard app. 5.00
2-51: 2-Carmine Falcone returns. 3-Stephanie Brown app. 6,14-17,26,29,30,37-Joker's Daughter app. 20-Spoiler dons costume. 30-Arkham Asylum destroyed. 41-Bluebird in costume 3.00
52-($3.99) Jae Lee-c; art by various 4.00

BATMAN: EUROPA
DC Comics: Jan, 2016 - No. 4, Apr, 2016 ($4.99, limited series)
1-4: 1-Joker app.; Casali & Azzarello-a/Camuncoli & Jim Lee-a. 2-Camuncoli-a 5.00
... Director's Cut 1 (8/16, $5.99) r/#1 with Jim Lee's pencil art; bonus original script 6.00

BATMAN FAMILY, THE
National Periodical Pub./DC Comics: Sept-Oct, 1975 - No. 20, Oct-Nov, 1978 (#1-4, 17-on: 68 pgs.) (Combined with Detective Comics with No. 481)
1-Origin/2nd app. Batgirl-Robin team-up (The Dynamite Duo); reprints plus one new story begins; N. Adams-a(r); r/1st app. Man-Bat from Det. #400 5 10 15 30 50 70
2-5: 2-r/Det. #369. 3-Batgirl & Robin learn each's i.d.; r/Batwoman app. from Batman #105. 4-r/1st Fatman app. from Batman #113. 5-r/1st Bat-Hound app. from Batman #92 3 6 9 16 23 30
6-(7-8/76) Joker's daughter on cover (1st app.) 7 14 21 46 86 125
7,8,14-16: 8-r/Batwoman app.14-Batwoman app. 15-3rd app. Killer Moth. 16-Bat-Girl cameo (last app. in costume until New Teen Titans #47) 2 4 6 13 18 22
9-Joker's daughter-c/app. 5 10 15 30 50 70
10-1st revival Batwoman; Cavalier app.; Killer Moth app. 3 6 9 18 28 38
11-13,17-20: 11-13-Rogers-a(p): 11-New stories begin; Man-Bat begins. 13-Batwoman cameo. 17-($1.00 size)-Batman, Huntress begin; Batwoman & Catwoman 1st meet. 18-20: Huntress by Staton in all. 20-Origin Ragman retold 3 6 9 17 26 35

NOTE: *Aparo a-17; c-11-16.* ***Austin*** *a-12i.* ***Chaykin*** *a-14p.* ***Michael Golden*** *a-15-17,18-20p.* ***Grell*** *a-1; c-1.* ***Gil Kane*** *a-2r.* ***Kaluta*** *c-17, 19.* ***Newton*** *a-13.* ***Robinson*** *a-1r, 3i(r), 9r.* ***Russell*** *a-18i, 19i.* ***Starlin*** *a-17; c-18, 20.*

BATMAN: FAMILY
DC Comics: Dec, 2002 - No. 8, Feb, 2003 ($2.95/$2.25, weekly limited series)
1,8-($2.95): 1-John Francis Moore-s/Hoberg & Gaudiano-a 4.00
2-7-($2.25): 3-Orpheus & Black Canary app. 3.00

BATMAN: GATES OF GOTHAM
DC Comics: Jul, 2011 - No. 5, Late Oct, 2011 ($2.99, limited series)
1-5-Flashbacks to 1880s Gotham City; Snyder-s/Higgins-a 3.00

BATMAN: GCPD
DC Comics: Aug, 1996 - No. 4, Nov, 1996 ($2.25, limited series)
1-4: Features Jim Gordon; Aparo/Sienkiewicz-a 3.00

BATMAN: GORDON OF GOTHAM
DC Comics: June, 1998 - No. 4, Sept, 1998 ($1.95, limited series)
1-4: Gordon's early days in Chicago 3.00

BATMAN: GORDON'S LAW
DC Comics: Dec, 1996 - No. 4, Mar, 1997 ($1.95, limited series)
1-4: Dixon-s/Janson-c/a 3.00

BATMAN: GOTHAM ADVENTURES (Based on Kids WB Batman animated series)
DC Comics: June, 1998 - No. 60, May, 2003 ($2.95/$1.95/$1.99/$2.25)
1-($2.95) 2 4 6 11 16 20
2-3-($1.95): 2-Two-Face-c/app. 3.00
4-9,11-13,15-28: 4-Begin $1.99-c. 5-Deadman-c. 13-MAD #1 cover swipe 3.00
10,14-Harley Quinn c/app. 2 4 6 11 16 20
29,43-Harley Quinn c/app. 2 4 6 11 16 20
30,32-42,44,46-52,54-59: 50-Catwoman-c/app. 58-Creeper-c/app. 3.00
31-Joker-c/app. 6.00
45-Harley Quinn c/app. 3 6 9 16 24 32
53-Poison Ivy-c/app.; Harley Quinn cameo 1 3 4 6 8 10
60-Joker-c/app. 1 3 4 6 8 10
TPB (2000, $9.95) r/#1-6 15.00

BATMAN: GOTHAM AFTER MIDNIGHT
DC Comics: July, 2008 - No. 12, Jun, 2009 ($2.99, limited series)
1-12-Steve Niles-s/Kelley Jones-a/c. 1-Scarecrow app. 2-Man-Bat app. 5,6-Joker app. 3.00
TPB (2009, $19.99) r/#1-12; John Carpenter intro.; Jones sketch pages 20.00

BATMAN: GOTHAM COUNTY LINE
DC Comics: 2005 - No. 3, 2005 ($5.99, square-bound, limited series)
1-3-Steve Niles-s/Scott Hampton-a. 2,3-Deadman app. 6.00
TPB (2006, $17.99) r/#1-3 18.00

Batman/Grendel #1 © DC & Matt Wagner

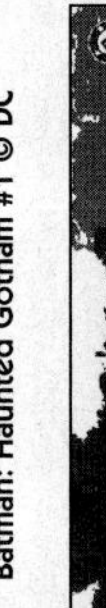

Batman: Haunted Gotham #1 © DC

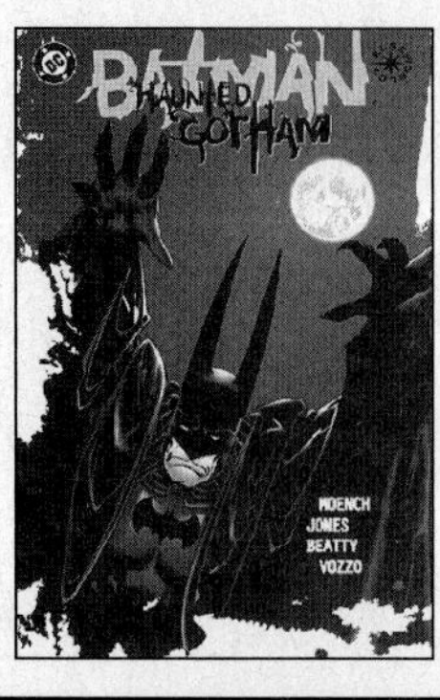

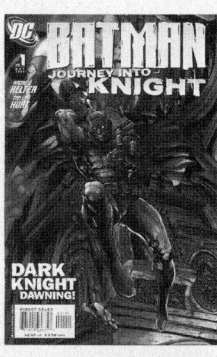

Batman: Journey Into Knight #1 © DC

GD	VG	FN	VF	VF/NM	NM-
2.0	4.0	6.0	8.0	9.0	9.2

BATMAN: GOTHAM KNIGHTS
DC Comics: Mar, 2000 - No. 74, Apr, 2006 ($2.50/$2.75)

1-Grayson-s; B&W back-up by Warren Ellis & Jim Lee 4.00
2-10-Grayson-s; B&W back-ups by various. 6-Killing Joke flashback 3.00
11-($3.25) Bolland-c; Kyle Baker back-up story 4.00
12-24: 13-Officer Down x-over; Ellison back-up-s. 15-Colan back-up. 20-Superman-c/app. 3.00
25,26-Bruce Wayne: Murderer pt. 4,10 3.50
27-31: 28,30,31-Bruce Wayne: Fugitive pt. 7,14,17 3.00
32-49: 32-Begin $2.75-c; Kaluta-a back-up. 33,34-Bane-c/app. 35-Mahfood-a back-up. 38-Bolton-a back-up. 43-Jason Todd & Batgirl app. 44-Jason Todd flashback 3.00
50-54-Hush returns-Barrionuevo-a/Bermejo-c. 53,54-Green Arrow app. 4.00
55-($3.75) Batman vs. Hush; Joker & Riddler app. 5.00
56-74: 56-58-War Games; Jae Lee-c. 60-65-Hush app. 66-Villains United tie-in; Talia app. 3.00
Batman: Hush Returns TPB (2006, $12.99) r/#50-55,66; cover gallery 13.00

BATMAN: GOTHAM NIGHTS II (First series listed under Gotham Nights)
DC Comics: Mar, 1995 - No. 4, June, 1995 ($1.95, limited series)

1-4 3.00

BATMAN/GRENDEL (1st limited series)
DC Comics: 1993 - No. 2, 1993 ($4.95, limited series, squarebound; 52 pgs.)

1,2: Batman vs. Hunter Rose. 1-Devil's Riddle; Matt Wagner-c/a/scripts. 2-Devil's Masque; Matt Wagner-c/a/scripts 7.00

BATMAN/GRENDEL (2nd limited series)
DC Comics: June, 1996 - No. 2, July, 1996 ($4.95, limited series, squarebound)

1,2: Batman vs. Grendel Prime. 1-Devil's Bones. 2-Devil's Dance; Wagner-c/a/s 6.00

BATMAN: HARLEY & IVY
DC Comics: Jun, 2004 - No. 3, Aug, 2004 ($2.50, limited series)

1-Paul Dini-s/Bruce Timm-c/a in all 3 6 9 19 30 40
2,3 3 6 9 14 20 25
TPB (2007, $14.99) r/series; newly colored story from Batman: Gotham Knights #14 and Harley and Ivy: Love on the Lam series 15.00

BATMAN: HARLEY QUINN
DC Comics: 1999 ($5.95, prestige format)

1-Intro. of Harley Quinn into regular DC continuity; Dini-s/Alex Ross-c 7 14 21 49 92 135
1-(2nd printing) 4 8 12 23 37 50

BATMAN: HAUNTED GOTHAM
DC Comics: 2000 - No. 4, 2000 ($4.95, limited series, squarebound)

1-4-Doug Moench-s/Kelley Jones-c/a 6.00
TPB (2009, $19.99) r/#1-4 20.00

BATMAN/ HELLBOY/STARMAN
DC Comics/Dark Horse: Jan, 1999 - No. 2, Feb, 1999 ($2.50, limited series)

1,2: Robinson-s/Mignola-a. 2-Harris-c 5.00

BATMAN: HOLLYWOOD KNIGHT
DC Comics: Apr, 2001 - No. 3, Jun, 2001 ($2.50, limited series)

1-3-Elseworlds Batman as a 1940's movie star; Giordano-a/Layton-s 3.00

BATMAN/ HUNTRESS: CRY FOR BLOOD
DC Comics: Jun, 2000 - No. 6, Nov, 2000 ($2.50, limited series)

1-6: Rucka-s/Burchett-a; The Question app. 3.00
TPB (2002, $12.95) r/#1-6 13.00

BATMAN, INC.
DC Comics: Jan, 2011 - No. 8, Aug, 2011 ($3.99/$2.99)

1-3-Morrison-s/Paquette-a; covers by Paquette & Williams 4.00
4-8-($2.99) 4-Burnham-a, original Batwoman (Kathy Kane) app. 3.00
...: Leviathan Strikes (2/12, $6.99) Morrison-s/Burnham & Stewart-a; cover gallery 7.00

BATMAN INCORPORATED
DC Comics: Jul, 2012 - No. 13, Sept, 2013 ($2.99)

1-7-Morrison-s/Burnham-a/c. 2-Origin of Talia. 3-Matches Malone returns 3.00
1-Variant-c by Quitely 5.00
8-Death of Damian 5.00
9-13: 9,10,12,13-Morrison-s/Burnham-a/c 3.00
#0 (11/12, $2.99) Frazer Irving-a; the start of Batman Incorporated 3.00
... Special 1 (10/13, $4.99) Short stories about international Batmen; s/a by various 5.00

BATMAN: JEKYLL & HYDE
DC Comics: June, 2005 - No. 6, Nov, 2005 ($2.99, limited series)

1-6-Paul Jenkins-s; Two-Face app. 1-3-Jae Lee-a. 4-6-Sean Phillips-a 3.00
TPB (2008, $14.99) r/#1-6 15.00

BATMAN: JOKER TIME (...: It's Joker Time! on cover)
DC Comics: 2000 - No. 3 ($4.95, limited series, squarebound)

1-3-Bob Hall-s/a 6.00

BATMAN: JOURNEY INTO KNGHT
DC Comics: Oct, 2005 - No. 12, Nov, 2006 ($2.50/$2.99, limited series)

1-9-Andrew Helfer-s/Tan Eng Huat-a/Pat Lee-c 3.00
10-12-($2.99) Joker app. 3.00

BATMAN/ JUDGE DREDD "DIE LAUGHING"
DC Comics: 1998 - No. 2, 1999 ($4.95, limited series, squarebound)

1,2: 1-Fabry-c/a. 2-Jim Murray-c/a 6.00

BATMAN: KNIGHTGALLERY (See Batman one-shots)

BATMAN: LEAGUE OF BATMEN
DC Comics: 2001 - No. 2, 2001 ($5.95, limited series, squarebound)

1,2-Elseworlds; Moench-s/Bright & Tanghal-a/Van Fleet-c 6.00

BATMAN: LEGENDS OF THE DARK KNIGHT (Legends of the Dark...#1-36)
DC Comics: Nov, 1989 - No. 214, Mar, 2007 ($1.50/$1.75/$1.95/$1.99/$2.25/$2.50/$2.99)

1- "Shaman" begins, ends #5; outer cover has four different color variations, all worth same 5.00
2-10: 6-10- "Gothic" by Grant Morrison (scripts) 4.00
11-15: 11-15-Gulacy/Austin-a. 13-Catwoman app. 4.00
16-Intro drug Bane uses; begin Venom story 6.00
17-20 5.00
21-49,51-63: 38-Bat-Mite-c/story. 46-49-Catwoman app. w/Heath-c/a. 51-Ragman app.; Joe Kubert-c. 59,60,61-Knightquest x-over. 62,63-KnightsEnd Pt. 4 & 10 3.00
50-($3.95, 68 pgs.)-Bolland embossed gold foil-c; Joker-c/story; pin-ups by Chaykin, Simonson, Williamson, Kaluta, Russell, others 5.00
64-99: 64-(9/94)-Begin $1.95-c. 71-73-James Robinson-s,Watkiss-c/a. 74,75-McKeever-c/a/s. 76-78-Scott Hampton-c/a/s. 81-Card insert. 83,84-Ellis-s. 85-Robinson-s. 91-93-Ennis-s. 94-Michael T. Gilbert-s/a. 3.00
100-($3.95) Alex Ross painted-c; gallery by various 5.00
101-115: 101-Ezquerra-a. 102-104-Robinson-s 3.00
116-No Man's Land stories begin; Huntress-c 4.00
117-119,121-126: 122-Harris-c 3.00
120-ID of new Batgirl revealed 4.00
127-131: Return to Legends stories; Green Arrow app. 3.00
132-199, 201-204: 132-136 ($2.25-c) Archie Goodwin-s/Rogers-a. 137-141-Gulacy-a. 142-145-Joker and Ra's al Ghul app. 146-148-Kitson-a. 158-Begin $2.50-c 169-171-Tony Harris-c/a. 182-184-War Games. 182-Bagged with Sky Captain CD 3.00
200-($4.99) Joker-c/app. 5.00
205-214: 205-Begin $2.99-c. 207,208-Olivetti-a. 214-Deadshot app. 3.00
#0-(10/94)-Zero Hour; Quesada/Palmiotti-c; released between #64&65 3.00
Annual 1-7 ('91-'97, $3.50-$3.95, 68 pgs.): 1-Joker app. 2-Netzer-c/a. 3-New Batman (Azrael) app. 4-Elseworlds story. 5-Year One; Man-Bat app. 6-Legend of the Dead Earth story. 7-Pulp Heroes story 4.00
... Halloween Special 1 (12/93, $6.95, 84 pgs.)-Embossed & foil stamped-c 1 2 3 5 6 8
... Halloween Special Edition 1 (12/14, giveaway) Sale-a/c 3.00
Batman Madness-...Halloween Special (1994, $4.95) 6.00
Batman Ghosts-...Halloween Special (1995, $4.95) 6.00
NOTE: *Aparo a-Annual 1. **Chaykin** scripts-24-26. **Giffen** a-Annual 1. **Golden** a-Annual 1. **Alan Grant** scripts-38, 52, 53. **Gil Kane** c/a-24-26. **Mignola** a-54; c-54, 62. **Morrow** a-Annual 3i. **Quesada** a-Annual 1. **James Robinson** scripts- 71-73. **Russell** c/a-42, 43. **Sears** a-21, 23; c-21, 23. **Zeck** a-69, 70; c-69, 70.*

BATMAN-LEGENDS OF THE DARK KNIGHT: JAZZ
DC Comics: Apr, 1995 - No. 3, June, 1995 ($2.50, limited series)

1-3 3.00

BATMAN: LI'L GOTHAM
DC Comics: Jun, 2013 - No. 12, May, 2014 ($2.99, printings of stories that 1st appeared online)

1-12-Dustin Nguyen-a/c; Nguyen & Fridolfs-s; holiday themed short stories 3.00
Halloween Comic Fest 2013 (12/13, no cover price) Halloween giveaway; r/#1 3.00

BATMAN/LOBO
DC Comics: Oct, 2007 - No. 2, Nov, 2007 ($5.99, squarebound, limited series)

1,2-Sam Kieth-s/a 6.00

BATMAN: LOST (Tie-in to Dark Nights: Metal series)
DC Comics: Jan, 2018 ($4.99, one-shot)

1-Snyder, Tynion IV & Williamson-s/Mahnke, Paquette & Jimenez-a; Coipel foil-c 5.00

BATMAN: MANBAT
DC Comics: Oct, 1995 - No. 3, Dec, 1995 ($4.95, limited series)

1-3-Elseworlds-Delano-script; Bolton-a 6.00

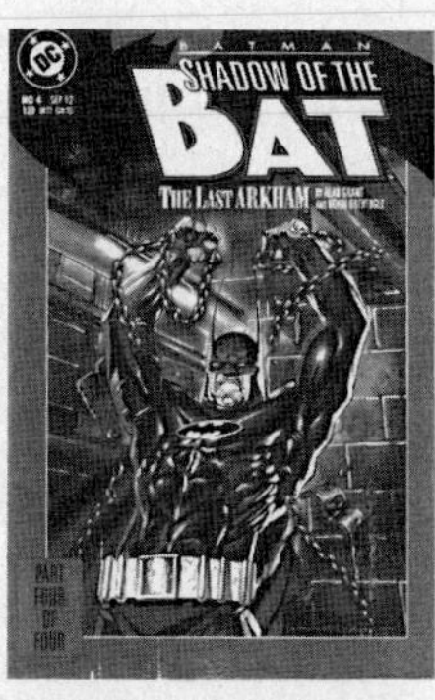

Batman: Shadow of the Bat #4 © DC

Batman '66 #30 © DC

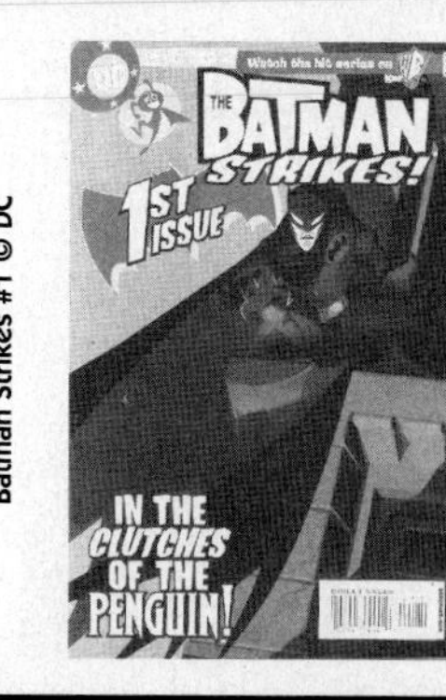

Batman Strikes #1 © DC

GD	VG	FN	VF	VF/NM	NM-
2.0	4.0	6.0	8.0	9.0	9.2

TPB-(1997, $14.95) r/#1-3 15.00

BATMAN: MITEFALL (See Batman one-shots)

BATMAN MINIATURE (See Batman Kellogg's)

BATMAN: NEVERMORE
DC Comics: June, 2003 - No. 5, Oct, 2003 ($2.50, limited series)
1-5-Elseworlds Batman & Edgar Allan Poe; Wrightson-c/Guy Davis-a/Len Wein-s 3.00

BATMAN: NO MAN'S LAND (Also see 1999 Batman titles)
DC Comics: (one shots)
nn (3/99, $2.95) Alex Ross-c; Bob Gale-s; begins year-long story arc 4.00
Collector's Ed. (3/99, $3.95) Ross lenticular-c 6.00
#0 (: Ground Zero on cover) (12/99, $4.95) Orbik-c 6.00
...: Gallery (7/99, $3.95) Jim Lee-c 4.00
...: Secret Files (12/99, $4.95) Maleev-c 6.00
TPB ('99, $12.95) r/early No Man's Land stories; new Batgirl early app. 13.00
No Law and a New Order TPB(1999, $5.95) Ross-c 8.00
Volume 2 ('00, $12.95) r/later No Man's Land stories; Batgirl(Huntress) app.; Deodato-c 13.00
Volume 3-5 ('00,'01 $12.95) 3-Intro. new Batgirl. 4-('00). 5-('01) Land-c 13.00

BATMAN: ODYSSEY
DC Comics: Sept, 2010 - No. 6, Feb, 2011 ($3.99, limited series)
1-6-Neal Adams-s/a/c. 1-Man-Bat app.; bonus sketch pages. 5,6-Joker app. 4.00
1-6-Variant B&W-version cover 5.00
Vol. 2 (12/11 - No. 7, 6/12) 1-7-Neal Adams-s/a/c 4.00

BATMAN: ORPHANS
DC Comics: Early Feb, 2011 - No. 2, Late Feb, 2011 ($3.99, limited series)
1,2-Berganza-s/Barberi-a/c 4.00

BATMAN: ORPHEUS RISING
DC Comics: Oct, 2001 - No. 5, Feb, 2002 ($2.50, limited series)
1-5-Intro. Orpheus; Simmons-s/Turner & Miki-a 3.00

BATMAN: OUTLAWS
DC Comics: 2000 - No. 3, 2000 ($4.95, limited series)
1-3-Moench-s/Gulacy-a 6.00

BATMAN: PENGUIN TRIUMPHANT (See Batman one-shots)

BATMAN/PREDATOR III: BLOOD TIES
DC Comics/Dark Horse Comics: Nov, 1997 - No. 4, Feb, 1998 ($1.95, lim. series)
1-4: Dixon-s/Damaggio-c/a 4.00
TPB-(1998, $7.95) r/#1-4 10.00

BATMAN/RA'S AL GHUL (See Year One:...)

BATMAN RETURNS MOVIE SPECIAL (See Batman one-shots)

BATMAN: RIDDLER-THE RIDDLE FACTORY (See Batman one-shots)

BATMAN: RUN, RIDDLER, RUN
DC Comics: 1992 - Book 3, 1992 ($4.95, limited series)
Book 1-3: Mark Badger-a & plot 6.00

BATMAN SCARECROW (See Year One:...)

BATMAN: SECRET FILES
DC Comics: Oct, 1997 ($4.95)
1-New origin-s and profiles 6.00

BATMAN: SECRETS
DC Comics: May, 2006 - No. 5, Sept, 2006 ($2.99, limited series)
1-5-Sam Kieth-s/a/c; Joker app. 3.00
TPB (2007, $12.99) r/series 13.00

BATMAN / SHADOW (Pulp hero)
DC Comics: June, 2017 - No. 6, Nov, 2017 ($3.99, limited series)
1-6: Snyder & Orlando-s/Rossmo-a; Lamont Cranston in current Gotham City 4.00

BATMAN: SHADOW OF THE BAT
DC Comics: June, 1992 - No. 94, Feb, 2000 ($1.50/$1.75/$1.95/$1.99)
1-The Last Arkham-c/story begins; Alan Grant scripts in all 6.00
1-($2.50)-Deluxe edition polybagged w/poster, pop-up & book mark 8.00
2-7: 4-The Last Arkham ends. 7-Last $1.50-c 3.00
8-28: 14,15-Staton-a(p). 16-18-Knightfall tie-ins. 19-28-Knightquest tie-ins w/Azrael as Batman. 25-Silver ink-c; anniversary issue 3.00
29-($2.95, 52 pgs.)-KnightsEnd Pt. 2 4.00
30-72: 30-KnightsEnd Pt. 8. 31-(9/94)-Begin $1.95-c; Zero Hour. 32-(11/94). 33-Robin-c. 35-Troika-Pt.2. 43,44-Cat-Man & Catwoman-c. 48-Contagion Pt. 1; card insert. 49-Contagion Pt.7. 56,57,58-Poison Ivy-c/app. 62-Two-Face app. 69,70-Fate app. 3.00
35-($2.95)-Variant embossed-c 4.00
73,74,76-78: Cataclysm x-over pts. 1,9. 76-78-Orbik-c 3.00
75-($2.95) Mr. Freeze & Clayface app.; Orbik-c 4.00
79,81,82: 79-Begin $1.99-c; Orbik-c 3.00
80-($3.95) Flip book with Azrael #47 4.00
83-No Man's Land; intro. new Batgirl (Huntress) 8.00
84,85-No Man's Land 4.00
86-92,94: 87-Deodato-a. 90-Harris-c. 92-Superman app. 94-No Man's Land ends 3.00
93-Joker and Harley app. 5.00
#0 (10/94) Zero Hour; released between #31&32 3.00
#1,000,000 (11/98) 853rd Century x-over; Orbik-c 3.00
Annual 1-5 ('93-'97 $2.95-$3.95, 68 pgs.): 3-Year One story; Poison Ivy app. 4-Legends of the Dead Earth story; Starman cameo. 5-Pulp Heroes story; Poison Ivy app. 4.00

BATMAN: SINS OF THE FATHER (Based on the Batman: The Telltale Series video game)
DC Comics: Apr, 2018 - Present ($2.99, printing of digital first stories)
1-Gage-s/Ienco-a; Deadshot app. 4.00

BATMAN '66 (Characters and likenesses based on the 1966 television series)
DC Comics: Sept, 2013 - No. 30, Feb, 2016 ($3.99/$2.99, printings of stories that first appeared online)
1-Jeff Parker-s/Jonathan Case-a/Mike Allred-c; Riddler & Catwoman app. 6.00
1-Variant-c by Jonathan Case 1 3 4 6 8 10
1-San Diego Comic-Con variant action figure photo-c 3 6 9 17 26 35
2-12: 2-Penguin & Mr. Freeze app.; Templeton-a. 3,11,20-Joker app. 5,10,11-Batgirl app. 8-King Tut app. 4.00
13-24,26-30: 14-Selfie variant-c. 16,20-Egghead app. 18,21,27,29-Batgirl app. 21-Lord Death Man app. 22-Oeming-a. 26-Poison Ivy app. 27-Bane app. 30-Allred-a 3.00
25-1st app. The Harlequin; back-up Mad Men spoof with Batgirl 6.00
... The Lost Episode 1 (1/15, $9.99) Harlan Ellison 1960s script adapted by Len Wein; García-López-a; Two-Face app.; covers by García-López & Ross; original pencil art 10.00

BATMAN '66 MEETS STEED AND MRS. PEEL (TV's The Avengers)
DC Comics: Sept, 2016 - No. 6, Feb, 2017 ($2.99, printings of stories that first appeared online)
1-6-Edginton-s/Dow Smith-a/Allred-c. 1,2-Catwoman app. 3-6-Mr. Freeze app. 3.00

BATMAN '66 MEETS THE GREEN HORNET
DC Comics: Aug, 2014 - No. 6, Jan, 2015 ($2.99, printings of stories that first appeared online)
1-6-Kevin Smith & Ralph Garman-s/Ty Templeton-a/Alex Ross-c 3.00

BATMAN '66 MEETS THE MAN FROM U.N.C.L.E.
DC Comics: Feb, 2016 - No. 6, Jul, 2016 ($2.99, limited series)
1-6-Jeff Parker-s/David Haun-a/Allred-c. 1-Olga and Penguin app. 3.00

BATMAN '66 MEETS WONDER WOMAN '77
DC Comics: Mar, 2017 - No. 6, Aug, 2017 ($3.99, limited series)
1-6-Parker & Andreyko-s/Haun-a; Ra's al Ghul & Talia app. 5,6-Robin as Nightwing 5.00

BATMAN: SON OF THE DEMON (Also see Batman #655-658 and Batman Hardcovers)
DC Comics: 2006 ($5.99, reprints the 1987 HC in comic book format)
nn-Talia has Batman's son; Mike W. Barr-s/Jerry Bingham-a; new Andy Kubert-c 6.00

BATMAN-SPAWN: WAR DEVIL (See Batman one-shots)

BATMAN SPECTACULAR (See DC Special Series No. 15)

BATMAN: STREETS OF GOTHAM (Follows Batman: Battle For The Cowl series)
DC Comics: Aug, 2009 - No. 21, May, 2011 ($3.99$2.99)
1-18: 1-Dini-s/Nguyen-a; back-up Manhunter feature; Jeanty-a. 10,11-Zsasz app. 4.00
19-21-($2.99) 19-Joker app. 3.00
...- Hush Money HC (2010, $19.99) r/#1-4, Detective #852 and Batman #685 20.00
...- Hush Money SC (2011, $14.99) r/#1-4, Detective #852 and Batman #685 15.00
...- Leviathan HC (2010, $19.99) r/#5-11 20.00
...- The House of Hush HC (2011, $22.99) r/#12-14,16-21 23.00

BATMAN STRIKES!, THE (Based on the 2004 animated series)
DC Comics: Nov, 2004 - No. 50, Dec, 2008 ($2.25)
1,2,4-27,29-31,33,34,36-38,40,42,44,46,48-50: 1,11-Penguin app. 2-Man-Bat app. 4-Bane app. 9-Joker app. 18-Batgirl debut. 29-Robin debuts. 33-Cal Ripken 8-pg. insert. 44-Superman app. 3.00
1-Free Comic Book Day edition (6/05) Penguin app. 3.00
3-($2.95) Joker-c/app.; Catwoman & Wonder Woman-r from Advs. in the DCU 4.00
28,32-Joker-c/app. 32-Cal Ripken 8-pg. insert. 5.00
35-Joker & Harley Quinn-c/app. 2 4 6 9 12 15
39,47-Black Mask-c/app. 6.00
41-Harley Quinn & Poison Ivy-c/app. 2 4 6 9 12 15
43-Harley Quinn-c/app. 2 4 6 9 12 15
45-Harley Quinn, Poison Ivy, Catwoman-c/app. 2 4 6 10 14 18
Jam Packed Action (2005, $7.99, digest) adaptations of two TV episodes 8.00

Batman/Superman #1 © DC

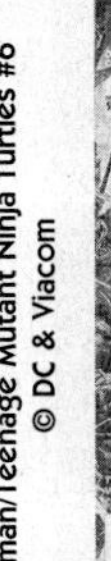
Batman/Teenage Mutant Ninja Turtles #6 © DC & Viacom

Batman: The Dark Knight #1 © DC

	GD 2.0	VG 4.0	FN 6.0	VF 8.0	VF/NM 9.0	NM- 9.2

... Vol. 1: Crime Time (2005, $6.99, digest) r/#1-5 7.00
... Vol. 2: In Darkest Knight (2005, $6.99, digest) r/#6-10 7.00

BATMAN/ SUPERMAN
DC Comics: Aug, 2013 - No. 32, Jul, 2016 ($3.99)

1-4-Greg Pak-s/Jae Lee-a/c; Catwoman & Wonder Woman app. 4.00
3.1 (11/13, $2.99, regular cover) 3.00
3.1 (11/13, $3.99, 3-D cover) "Doomsday #1" on cover; Booth-a; Zod app. 6.00
5-7-Booth-a; reads sideways; Mongul app. 4.00
8,9-First Contact x-over with Worlds' Finest #20,21; Power Girl & Huntress app.; Lee-a 4.00
10-31: 11-Doomed tie-in. 13-Jae Lee-a. 13-15-Catwoman app. 17-Lobo app. 21-Batman (Gordon in robot suit). 23,24-Aquaman app. 25-27-Vandal Savage app. 4.00
32-The Great Ten app.; 1st app. Chinese Super-Man (Kong Kenan) 5.00
Annual 1 (5/14, $5.99) Supergirl, Krypto, Cyborg, Batgirl, Red Hood app.; Jae Lee-c 6.00
Annual 2 (5/15, $4.99) Killer Croc, Cheshire & Bane app.; Syaf-c 5.00
...: Futures End 1 (11/14, $2.99, regular-c) Five years later; Pak-s 3.00
...: Futures End 1 (11/14, $3.99, 3-D cover) 4.00

BATMAN/ SUPERMAN/WONDER WOMAN: TRINITY
DC Comics: 2003 - No. 3, 2003 ($6.95, limited series, squarebound)

1-3-Matt Wagner-s/a/c. 1-Ra's al Ghul & Bizarro app. 7.00
HC (2004, $24.95, with dust-jacket) r/series; intro. by Brad Meltzer 30.00
SC (2004, $17.99) r/series; intro. by Brad Meltzer 18.00

BATMAN: SWORD OF AZRAEL (Also see Azrael & Batman #488,489)
DC Comics: Oct, 1992 - No. 4, Jan, 1993 ($1.75, limited series)

	GD	VG	FN	VF	VF/NM	NM-
1-Wraparound gatefold-c; Quesada-c/a(p) in all; 1st app. Azrael	2	4	6	11	16	20
2-4: 4-Cont'd in Batman #488	1	2	3	5	6	8

Silver Edition 1-4 (1993, $1.95)-Reprints #1-4 3.00
Trade Paperback (1993, $9.95)-Reprints #1-4 12.00
Trade Paperback Gold Edition 18.00

BATMAN/ TARZAN: CLAWS OF THE CAT-WOMAN
Dark Horse Comics/DC Comics: Sept, 1999 - No. 4, Dec, 1999 ($2.95, limited series)

1-4: Marz-s/Kordey-a 3.00

BATMAN/ TEENAGE MUTANT NINJA TURTLES
DC Comics: Feb, 2016 - No. 6, Jul, 2016 ($3.99, limited series)

1-6-Tynion IV-s/Williams II-a; Penguin, Croc & Shredder app. 4.00
... Director's Cut 1 (11/16, $5.99) r/#1 in B&W and pencil-a; original script 6.00

BATMAN/ TEENAGE MUTANT NINJA TURTLES II
DC Comics: Feb, 2018 - No. 6, ($3.99, limited series)

1-4-Tynion IV-s/Williams II-a; Bane app. 4.00

BATMAN/ TEENAGE MUTANT NINJA TURTLES ADVENTURES
IDW Publishing: Nov, 2016 - No. 6, Apr, 2017 ($3.99, limited series)

1-6-Manning-s/Sommariva-a; Clayface, Joker and Harley Quinn app.; multiple covers 4.00
... Director's Cut 1 (2/17, $4.99) r/#1 in B&W and pencil-a; original script 5.00

BATMAN: TENSES
DC Comics: 2003 - No. 2, 2003 ($6.95, limited series)

1,2-Joe Casey-s/Cully Hamner-a; Bruce Wayne's first year back in Gotham 7.00

BATMAN: THE ANKH
DC Comics: 2002 - No. 2, 2002 ($5.95, limited series)

1,2-Dixon-s/Van Fleet-a 6.00

BATMAN: THE BRAVE AND THE BOLD (Based on the 2008 animated series)
DC Comics: Mar, 2009 - No. 22, Dec, 2010 ($2.50/$2.99)

1-18: 1-Power Girl app. 4-Sugar & Spike cameo. 7-Doom Patrol app. 9-Catman app. 3.00
19-22-($2.99) Cyborg Superman and the Green Lantern Corps app. 22-Aquaman app. 3.00
TPB (2009, $12.99) r/#1-6 13.00
...: Emerald Knight TPB (2011, $12.99) r/#13,14,16,18,19,21 13.00
...: The Fearsome Fangs Strike Again TPB (2010, $12.99) r/#7-12 13.00

BATMAN: THE BRAVE AND THE BOLD (Titled "All New Batman: Brave & the Bold" for #1-13)
DC Comics: Jan, 2011 - No. 16, Apr, 2012 ($2.99)

1-16: 1-Superman. 4-Wonder Woman app. 8-Aquaman app. 9-Hawkman app. 3.00

BATMAN: THE CULT
DC Comics: 1988 - No. 4, Nov, 1988 ($3.50, deluxe limited series)

	GD	VG	FN	VF	VF/NM	NM-
1-Wrightson-a/painted-c in all	1	2	3	5	6	8

2-4 6.00
Trade Paperback (1991, $14.95)-New Wrightson-c; Starlin intro. 25.00
Trade Paperback (2009, $19.99) 20.00

BATMAN: THE DARK KNIGHT
DC Comics: Jan, 2011 - No. 5, Oct, 2011 ($3.99/$2.99)

1-David Finch-s/a; Penguin & Killer Croc app.; covers by Finch and Clarke 4.00
2-5-($2.99) Demon app. 3.00

BATMAN: THE DARK KNIGHT (DC New 52)
DC Comics: Nov, 2011 - No. 29, May, 2014 ($2.99)

1-29: 1-Jenkins & Finch-s/Finch-a/c; White Rabbit debut. 3-Flash app. 5,6-Superman app. 6,7-Bane app. 9-Night of the Owls. 22-25-Maleev-a. 28-Van Sciver-a/c 3.00
23.1, 23.2, 23.3, 23.4 (11/13, $2.99, regular covers) 3.00
23.1 (11/13, $3.99, 3-D cover) "Ventriloquist #1" on cover; Simone-s/Santacruz-a 6.00
23.2 (11/13, $3.99, 3-D cover) "Mr. Freeze #1" on cover; Gray & Palmiotti-s 5.00
23.3 (11/13, $3.99, 3-D cover) "Clayface#1" on cover; Richards-a 5.00
23.4 (11/13, $3.99, 3-D cover) "Joker's Daughter #1" on cover; origin story; Jeanty-a 12.00
#0 (11/12, $2.99) Hurwitz-s/Suayan & Ryp-a; flashback to aftermath of parents' murder 3.00
Annual 1 (7/13, $4.99) Hurwitz-s/Kudranski-a/Maleev-c; Scarecrow, Penguin Mad Hatter 5.00

BATMAN: THE DARK KNIGHT RETURNS (Also see Dark Knight Strikes Again)
DC Comics: Mar, 1986 - No. 4, 1986 ($2.95, squarebound, limited series)

	GD	VG	FN	VF	VF/NM	NM-
1-Miller story & c/a(p); set in the future	7	14	21	44	82	120
1,2-2nd & 3rd printings, 3-2nd printing	3	6	9	14	20	25
2-Carrie Kelley becomes 1st female Robin	4	8	12	23	37	50
3-Death of Joker; Superman app.	3	6	9	17	26	35
4-Death of Alfred; Superman app.	3	6	9	17	26	35

Hardcover, signed & numbered edition ($40.00)(4000 copies) 275.00
Hardcover, trade edition 60.00

	GD	VG	FN	VF	VF/NM	NM-
Softcover, trade edition (1st printing only)	2	4	6	11	16	20
Softcover, trade edition (2nd thru 8th printings)	2	4	6	8	10	12

10th Anniv. Slipcase set ('96, $100.00): Signed & numbered hard-c edition (10,000 copies), sketchbook, copy of script for #1, 2 color prints 135.00
10th Anniv. Hardcover ('96, $45.00) 50.00
10th Anniv. Softcover ('97, $14.95) 18.00
Hardcover 2nd printing ('02, $24.95) with 3 1/4" tall partial dustjacket 25.00
NOTE: *The #2 second printings can be identified by matching the grey background colors on the inside front cover and facing page. The inside front cover of the second printing has a dark grey background which does not match the lighter grey of the facing page. On the true 1st printings, the backgrounds are both light grey. All other issues are clearly marked.*

BATMAN: THE DARK PRINCE CHARMING
DC Comics: Jan, 2018 - No. 2 ($12.99, HC, limited series)

1-Enrico Marini-s/a; Joker & Harley Quinn app. 13.00

BATMAN: THE DAWNBREAKER (Tie-in to Dark Nights: Metal series)
DC Comics: Dec, 2017 ($3.99, one-shot)

1-Humphries-s/Van Sciver-a; Fabok foil-c; Wayne as Dark Multiverse Green Lantern 4.00

BATMAN: THE DOOM THAT CAME TO GOTHAM
DC Comics: 2000 - No. 3, 2001 ($4.95, limited series)

1-3-Elseworlds; Mignola-c/s; Nixey-a; Etrigan app. 6.00

BATMAN: THE DEVASTATOR (Tie-in to Dark Nights: Metal series)
DC Comics: Jan, 2018 ($3.99, one-shot)

1-Tieri-s/Daniel-a; Fabok foil-c; Bruce Wayne as Dark Multiverse Doomsday 4.00

BATMAN: THE DROWNED (Tie-in to Dark Nights: Metal series)
DC Comics: Dec, 2017 ($3.99, one-shot)

1-Abnett-s/Tan-a; Fabok foil-c; female Bryce Wayne as Dark Multiverse Aquawoman 4.00

BATMAN: THE KILLING JOKE (See Batman one-shots)

BATMAN: THE LONG HALLOWEEN
DC Comics: Oct, 1996 - No. 13, Oct, 1997 ($2.95/$4.95, limited series)

	GD	VG	FN	VF	VF/NM	NM-
1-($4.95)-Loeb-s/Sale-c/a in all	2	4	6	8	10	12

2-5($2.95): 2-Solomon Grundy-c/app. 3-Joker-c/app., Catwoman, Poison Ivy app. 6.00
6-10: 6-Poison Ivy-c. 7-Riddler-c/app. 5.00
11,12 4.00
13-($4.95, 48 pgs.)-Killer revelations 6.00
Special Edition (Halloween Comic Fest 2013) (12/13, free giveaway) r/#1 3.00
Absolute Batman: The Long Halloween (2007, $75.00, oversized HC) r/series; interviews with the creators; Sale sketch pages; action figure line; unpubbed 4-page sequence 75.00
HC-($29.95) r/series 50.00
SC-($19.95) 20.00

BATMAN: THE MAD MONK ("Batman & the Mad Monk" on cover)
DC Comics: Oct, 2006 - No. 6, Mar, 2007 ($3.50, limited series)

1-6-Matt Wagner-s/a/c. 1-Catwoman app. 3.50
TPB (2007, $14.99) r/#1-6 15.00

BATMAN: THE MERCILESS (Tie-in to Dark Nights: Metal series)

Batman: White Knight #1 © DC

Bat-Mite #6 © DC

Battle #2 © MAR

	GD 2.0	VG 4.0	FN 6.0	VF 8.0	VF/NM 9.0	NM- 9.2

DC Comics: Dec, 2017 ($3.99, one-shot)
1-Tomasi-s/Manapul-a; Fabok foil-c; Bruce Wayne as Dark Multiverse God of War 4.00

BATMAN: THE MONSTER MEN ("Batman & the Monster Men" on cover)
DC Comics: Jan, 2006 - No. 6, June, 2006 ($2.99, limited series)
1-6-Matt Wagner-s/a/c 3.00
TPB (2006, $14.99) r/#1-6 15.00

BATMAN: THE MURDER MACHINE (Tie-in to Dark Nights: Metal series)
DC Comics: Nov, 2017 ($3.99, one-shot)
1-Tieri-s/Federici-a; Fabok foil-c; Bruce Wayne as Dark Multiverse Cyborg 4.00

BATMAN: THE OFFICIAL COMIC ADAPTATION OF THE WARNER BROS. MOTION PICTURE (See Batman one-shots)

BATMAN: THE RED DEATH (Tie-in to Dark Nights: Metal series)
DC Comics: Nov, 2017 ($3.99, one-shot)
1-Williamson-s/Di Giandomenico-a; Fabok foil-c; Bruce Wayne as Dark Multiverse Flash 4.00

BATMAN: THE RETURN
DC Comics: Jan, 2011 ($4.99, one-shot)
1-Morrison-s/Finch-a; covers by Finch & Ha; costume design sketch art; script pages 5.00

BATMAN: THE RETURN OF BRUCE WAYNE (Follows Batman's "death" in Final Crisis #6)
DC Comics: Early Jul, 2010 - No. 6, Dec, 2010 ($3.99, limited series)
1-6-Bruce Wayne's time travels; Morrison-s/Andy Kubert-c. 1-Sprouse-a. 4-Jeanty-a 4.00
1-Second & third printings; 4.00
1-6-Variant covers: 1-Sprouse. 2-Irving. 3-Paquette. 4-Jeanty. 5-Sook. 6-Garbett 8.00
... - The Deluxe Edition HC (2011, $29.99) r/#1-6; sketch pages 30.00

BATMAN: THE ULTIMATE EVIL
DC Comics: 1995 ($5.95, limited series, prestige format)
1,2-Barrett, Jr. adaptation of Vachss novel. 6.00

BATMAN: THE WIDENING GYRE
DC Comics: Oct, 2009 - No. 6, Sept, 2010 ($3.99/$2.99/$4.99, limited series)
1-($3.99) Kevin Smith-s/Walt Flanagan-a; debut Baphomet; Demon app.; Sienkiewicz-c 4.00
1-5-Variant covers by Gene Ha 8.00
2-5-($2.99) 2-Silver St. Cloud returns. 5-Catwoman app. 3.00
6-($4.99) Joker, Deadshot & Catwoman app. 5.00
6-Variant cover by Gene Ha 10.00
HC (2010, $19.99, dj) r/#1-6; variant covers; afterword by Kevin Smith 20.00

BATMAN 3-D (Also see 3-D Batman)
DC Comics: 1990 ($9.95, w/glasses, 8-1/8x10-3/4")
nn-Byrne-a/scripts; Riddler, Joker, Penguin & Two-Face app. plus r/1953 3-D Batman; pin-ups by many artists 2 4 6 8 10 12

BATMAN: TOYMAN
DC Comics: Nov, 1998 - No. 4, Feb, 1999 ($2.25, limited series)
1-4-Hama-s 3.00

BATMAN: TURNING POINTS
DC Comics: Jan, 2001 - No. 5, Jan, 2001 ($2.50, weekly limited series)
1-5: 2-Giella-a. 3-Kubert-c/Giordano-a. 4-Chaykin-c/Brent Anderson-a. 5-Pope-c/a 3.00
TPB (2007, $14.99) r/#1-5 15.00

BATMAN: TWO-FACE-CRIME AND PUNISHMENT (See Batman one-shots)

BATMAN: TWO-FACE STRIKES TWICE
DC Comics: 1993 - No. 2, 1993 ($4.95, 52 pgs.)
1,2-Flip book format w/Staton-a (G.A. side) 6.00

BATMAN UNSEEN
DC Comics: Early Dec, 2009 - No. 5, Feb, 2010 ($2.99, limited series)
1-5-Doug Moench-s/Kelley Jones-a/c. Black Mask app. 3.00
SC (2010, $14.99) r/#1-5 15.00

BATMAN: VENGEANCE OF BANE (Also see Batman #491)
DC Comics: Jan, 1993; 1995 ($2.50, 68 pgs.)
... Special 1 - Origin & 1st app. Bane; Dixon-s/Nolan & Barreto-a/Fabry-c 5 10 15 30 50 70
... Special 1 (2nd printing) 2 4 6 9 12 15
.... II nn (1995, $3.95)-sequel; Dixon-s/Nolan & Barreto-a/Fabry-c 2 4 6 9 12 15

BATMAN VERSUS PREDATOR
DC Comics/Dark Horse Comics: 1991 - No. 3, 1992 ($4.95/$1.95, limited series)
(1st DC/Dark Horse x-over)
1 (Prestige format, $4.95)-1 & 3 contain 8 Batman/Predator trading cards; Andy & Adam Kubert-a; Suydam painted-c 1 2 3 5 6 8
1-3 (Regular format, $1.95)-No trading cards 4.00
2,3-(Prestige)-2-Extra pin-ups inside; Suydam-c 6.00
TPB (1993, $5.95, 132 pgs.)-r/#1-3 w/new introductions & forward plus new wraparound-c by Dave Gibbons 1 3 4 6 8 10

BATMAN VERSUS PREDATOR II: BLOODMATCH
DC Comics: Late 1994 - No. 4, 1995 ($2.50, limited series)
1-4-Huntress app.; Moench scripts; Gulacy-a 4.00
TPB (1995, $6.95)-r/#1-4 1 3 4 6 8 10

BATMAN VS. THE INCREDIBLE HULK (See DC Special Series No. 27)

BATMAN: WAR ON CRIME
DC Comics: Nov, 1999 ($9.95, treasury size, one-shot)
nn-Painted art by Alex Ross; story by Alex Ross and Paul Dini 15.00

BATMAN: WHITE KNIGHT
DC Comics: Dec, 2017 - No. 8 ($3.99, limited series)
1-6-Sean Murphy-s/a; Joker is cured. 2-6-Harley Quinn app. 4.00

BATMAN/ WILDCAT
DC Comics: Apr, 1997 - No. 3, June, 1997 ($2.25, mini-series)
1-3: Dixon/Smith-s: 1-Killer Croc app. 3.00

BATMAN: YEAR 100
DC Comics: 2006 - No. 4, 2006 ($5.99, squarebound, limited series)
1-4-Paul Pope-s/a/c 6.00
TPB (2007, $19.99) r/series 20.00

BAT MASTERSON (TV) (Also see Tim Holt #28)
Dell Publishing Co.: Aug-Oct, 1959; Feb-Apr, 1960 - No. 9, Nov-Jan, 1961-62
Four Color 1013 (#1) (8-10/59) 10 20 30 67 141 215
2-9: Gene Barry photo-c on all. 2,3,6-Two different back-c exist; variants have a comic strip on the back-c 6 12 18 38 69 100

BAT-MITE
DC Comics: Aug, 2015 - No. 6, Jan, 2016 ($2.99, limited series)
1-6: 1-Jurgens-s/Howell-a; Batman app. 4-Booster Gold app. 5-Inferior Five app. 3.00

BATS (See Tales Calculated to Drive You Bats)

BATS, CATS & CADILLACS
Now Comics: Oct, 1990 - No. 2, Nov, 1990 ($1.75)
1,2: 1-Gustovich-a(i); Snyder-c 3.00

BAT-THING
DC Comics (Amalgam): June, 1997 ($1.95, one-shot)
1-Hama-s/Damaggio & Sienkiewicz-a 3.00

BATTLE
Marvel/Atlas Comics(FPI #1-62/ Male #63 on): Mar, 1951 - No. 70, Jun, 1960

	GD	VG	FN	VF	VF/NM	NM-
1	61	122	183	390	670	950
2	34	68	102	199	325	450
3-10: 4-1st Buck Pvt. O'Toole. 10-Pakula-a	28	56	84	165	270	375
11-20: 11-Check-a. 17-Classic Hitler story	22	44	66	132	216	300
21,23-Krigstein-a	22	44	66	128	209	290
22,24-36: 32-Tuska-a. 36-Everett-a	20	40	60	117	189	260
37-Kubert-a (Last precode, 2/55)	21	42	63	122	199	275
38-40,42-48	19	38	57	111	176	240
41,49: 41-Kubert/Moskowitz-a. 49-Davis-a	20	40	60	114	182	250
50-54,56-58: 56-Colan-a; Ayers-a	18	36	54	105	165	225
55-Williamson-a (5 pgs.)	19	38	57	111	176	240
59-Torres-a	18	36	54	107	169	230
60-62: 60,62-Combat Kelly app. 61-Combat Casey app.	18	36	54	105	165	225
63-Ditko-a	25	50	75	150	245	340
64-66-Kirby-a. 66-Davis-a; has story of Fidel Castro in pre-Communism days (an admiring profile)	28	56	84	165	270	375
67,68: 67-Williamson/Crandall-a (4 pgs.); Kirby, Davis-a. 68-Kirby/Williamson-a (4 pgs.); Kirby/Ditko-a	30	60	90	177	289	400
69,70: 69-Kirby-a. 70-Kirby/Ditko-a	28	56	84	165	270	375

NOTE: ***Andru** a-37. **Berg** a-8, 38, 14, 60-62. **Colan** a-19, 33, 43, 55. **Everett** a-36, 50, 70; c-56, 57. **Heath** a-6, 9, 13, 31, 69; c-6, 9, 12, 26, 35, 37. **Kirby** c-64-69. **Maneely** a-4-7, 31, 61; c-4, 22, 27, 33, 43, 48, 59, 61. **Orlando** a-47. **Powell** a-53, 55. **Reinman** a-4, 8-10, 14, 26, 32, 48. **Robinson** a-9, 39. **Romita** a-14, 26. **Severin** a-28, 32-34, 66-69; c-36, 50, 55. **Sinnott** a-33, 37, 63, 66. **Whitney** s-10. **Woodbridge** a-52, 55.*

BATTLE ACTION
Atlas Comics (NPI): Feb, 1952 - No. 12, 5/53; No. 13, 10/54 - No. 30, 8/57
1-Pakula-a 43 86 129 271 461 650

Battleaxes #4 © Terry LaBan

Battle Beasts #1 © DST

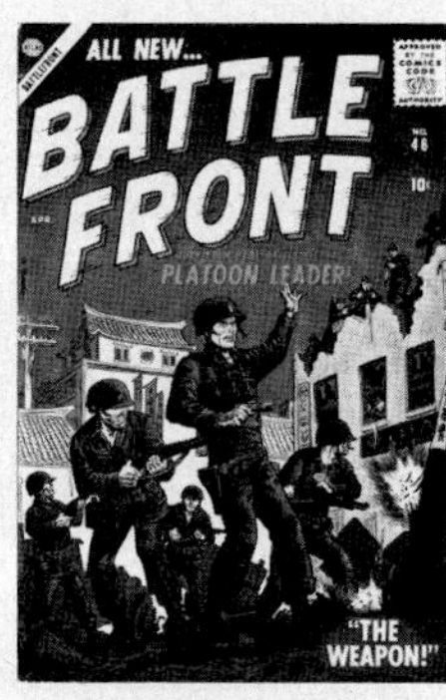

Battlefront #46 © MAR

GD 2.0 | VG 4.0 | FN 6.0 | VF 8.0 | VF/NM 9.0 | NM- 9.2

2 24 48 72 140 230 320
3,4,6,7,9,10: 6-Robinson-c/a. 7-Partial nudity 18 36 54 103 162 220
5-Used in **POP**, pg. 93,94 18 36 54 105 165 225
8-Krigstein-a 18 36 54 107 169 230
11-15 (Last precode, 2/55) 17 34 51 98 154 210
16-30: 20-Romita-a. 22-Pakula-a. 27,30-Torres-a 15 30 45 88 137 185
NOTE: *Battle Brady app. 5-7, 10-12.* ***Berg*** *a-3.* ***Check*** *a-11.* ***Everett*** *a-7; c-13, 25.* ***Heath*** *a-3, 8, 18; c-3,15, 18, 21.* ***Maneely*** *a-1; c-5.* ***Reinman*** *a-1, 2, 20.* ***Robinson*** *a-6, 7; c-6.* ***Shores*** *a-7(2), 12, 20; c-11.* ***Sinnott*** *a-3, 27.* ***Woodbridge*** *a-28, 30.*

BATTLE ATTACK
Stanmor Publications: Oct, 1952 - No. 8, Dec, 1955
1 16 32 48 92 144 195
2 10 20 30 54 72 90
3-8: 3-Hollingsworth-a 9 18 27 50 65 80

BATTLEAXES
DC Comics (Vertigo): May, 2000 - No. 4, Aug, 2000 ($2.50, limited series)
1-4: Terry LaBan-s/Alex Horley-a 3.00

BATTLE BEASTS
Blackthorne Publishing: Feb, 1988 - No. 4, 1988 ($1.50/$1.75, B&W/color)
1-4: 1-3- (B&W)-Based on Hasbro toys. 4-Color 3.00

BATTLE BEASTS
IDW Publishing: Jul, 2012 - No. 4, Oct, 2012 ($3.99, limited series)
1-4-Curnow-s/Schiti-a; 2 covers on each 4.00

BATTLE BRADY (Formerly Men in Action No. 1-9; see 3-D Action)
Atlas Comics (IPC): No. 10, Jan, 1953 - No. 14, June, 1953
10: 10-12-Syd Shores-c 26 52 78 154 252 350
11-Used in **POP**, pg. 95 plus B&W & color illos 18 36 54 103 162 220
12-14 15 30 45 90 140 190

BATTLE CHASERS
Image Comics (Cliffhanger): Apr, 1998 - No. 4, Dec, 1998;
DC Comics (Cliffhanger): No. 5, May, 1999 - No. 8, May, 2001 ($2.50)
Image Comics: No. 9, Sept, 2001 ($3.50)
Prelude (2/98) 1 3 4 6 8 10
Prelude Gold Ed. 1 3 4 6 8 10
1-Madureira & Sharrieff-s/Madureira-a(p)/Charest-c 1 2 3 5 7 9
1-American Ent. Ed. w/"racy" cover 1 3 4 6 8 10
1-Gold Edition 9.00
1-Chromium cover 20.00
1-2nd printing 3.00
2 5.00
2-Dynamic Forces BattleChrome cover 2 4 6 8 10 12
3-Red Monika cover by Madureira 4.00
4-8: 4-Four covers. 6-Back-up by Adam Warren-s/a. 7-Three covers (Madureira, Ramos, Campbell) 3.00
9-($3.50, Image) Flip cover/story by Adam Warren 4.00
...: A Gathering of Heroes HC ('99, $24.95) r/#1-5, Prelude, Frank Frazetta Fantasy Ill.; cover gallery 25.00
...: A Gathering of Heroes SC ('99, $14.95) 15.00
...Collected Edition 1,2 (11/98, 5/99, $5.95) 1-r/#1,2. 2-r/#3,4 6.00

BATTLE CLASSICS (See Cancelled Comic Cavalcade)
DC Comics: Sept-Oct, 1978 (44 pgs.)
1-Kubert-r; new Kubert-c 2 4 6 8 10 12

BATTLE CRY
Stanmor Publications: 1952 (May) - No. 20, Sept, 1955
1 21 42 63 122 199 275
2-(7/52) 12 24 36 69 97 125
3,5-10: 8-Pvt. Ike begins, ends #13,17 10 20 30 58 76 95
4-Classic E.C. swipe 11 22 33 62 86 110
11-20 9 18 27 52 69 85
NOTE: ***Hollingsworth*** *a-9; c-20.*

BATTLEFIELD (War Adventures on the...)
Atlas Comics (ACI): April, 1952 - No. 11, May, 1953
1-Pakula, Reinman-a 40 80 120 246 411 575
2-5: 2-Heath, Maneely, Pakula, Reinman-a 20 40 60 117 189 260
6-11 17 34 51 98 154 210
NOTE: ***Colan*** *a-11.* ***Everett*** *a-8.* ***Heath*** *a-1, 2, 5p,7; c-2, 8, 9, 11.* ***Ravielli*** *a-11.*

BATTLEFIELD ACTION (Formerly Foreign Intrigues)
Charlton Comics: No. 16, Nov, 1957 - No. 62, 2-3/66; No. 63, 7/80 - No. 89, 11/84
V2#16 9 18 27 50 65 80
17,20-30: 29-D-Day story 6 12 18 28 34 40
18,19-Check-a (2 stories in #18) 3 6 9 21 33 45
31-34,36-62(1966): 40-Panel from this issue used by artist Roy Lichtenstein for famous painting. 55,61-Hitler app. 3 6 9 16 23 30
35-Hitler-c 4 8 12 25 40 55
63-80(1983-84) 5.00
81-83,85-89 (Low print run) 1 2 3 4 5 7
84-Kirby reprints; 3 stories 1 3 4 6 8 10
NOTE: ***Montes/Bache*** *a-43, 55, 62.* ***Glanzman*** *a-87r.*

BATTLEFIELDS
Dynamite Entertainment: 2008 - No. 9, 2010 ($3.50, limited series then numbered issues)
...: Dear Billy 1-3 ('09 - No. 3, '09, $3.50) Ennis-s/Snejbjerg-a/Cassaday-c.1-Leach var-c 3.50
...: Happy Valley 1-3 ('09 - No. 3, '09, $3.50) Ennis-s/Holden-a/Leach-c 3.50
...: The Night Witches 1-3 ('08 - No. 3, '09, $3.50) Ennis-s/Braun-a/Cassaday-c; Russian female pilots in WW2. 1-Leach var-c 3.50
...: The Tankies 1-3 ('09 - No. 3, '09, $3.50) Ennis-s/Ezquerra-a/Cassaday-c.1-Leach var-c 3.50
4-9: 4-6-Ezquerra-a/Leach-c. 7-9-Sequel to "The Night Witches"; Braun-a 3.50

BATTLEFIELDS (Volume 2)
Dynamite Entertainment: 2012 - No. 6, 2013 ($3.99, limited series)
1-6: 1-3-Ennis-s/Ezquerra-a/Leach-c. 4-6-Braun-a 4.00

BATTLE FIRE
Aragon Magazine/Stanmor Publications: Apr, 1955 - No. 7, 1955
1 15 30 45 86 133 180
2-(6/55) 10 20 30 54 72 90
3-7 9 18 27 50 65 80

BATTLE FOR A THREE DIMENSIONAL WORLD
3D Cosmic Publications: May, 1983 (20 pgs., slick paper w/stiff-c, $3.00)
nn-Kirby c/a in 3-D; shows history of 3-D 2 4 6 8 11 14

BATTLEFORCE
Blackthorne Publishing: Nov, 1987 - No. 2, 1988 ($1.75, color/B&W)
1,2: Based on game. 1-In color. 2-B&W 3.00

BATTLE FOR INDEPENDENTS, THE (Also See Cyblade/Shi & Shi/Cyblade: The Battle For Independents)
Image Comics (Top Cow Productions)/Crusade Comics: 1995 ($29.95)
nn-Boxed set of all editions of Shi/Cyblade & Cyblade/Shi plus new variant 3 6 9 19 30 40

BATTLE FOR THE PLANET OF THE APES (See Power Record Comics)

BATTLEFRONT
Atlas Comics (PPI): June, 1952 - No. 48, Aug, 1957
1-Heath-c 50 100 150 315 533 750
2-Robinson-a(4) 26 52 78 154 252 350
3-5-Robinson-a 21 42 63 126 206 285
6-10: Combat Kelly in No. 6-10. 6-Romita-a 19 38 57 112 179 245
11-22,24-28: 14,16-Battle Brady app. 22-Teddy Roosevelt & His Rough Riders story. 28-Last pre-code (2/55) 18 36 54 103 162 220
23,43-Check-a 18 36 54 105 165 225
29-39,41,44-47 16 32 48 94 147 200
40,42-Williamson-a 18 36 54 103 162 220
48-Crandall-a 17 34 51 98 154 210
NOTE: ***Ayers*** *a-18, 19, 25, 32, 35.* ***Berg*** *a-44.* ***Colan*** *a-21, 22, 24, 25, 32, 33-35, 38, 40, 42, 43, 45.* ***Drucker*** *a-28, 29.* ***Everett*** *a-44.* ***Heath*** *c-23, 26, 27, 29, 32.* ***Maneely*** *a-21-23, 26; c-2, 7, 13, 22, 24, 25, 34, 35, 41.* ***Morisi*** *a-42.* ***Morrow*** *a-41.****Orlando*** *a-47.* ***Powell*** *a-19, 21, 25, 29, 32, 40, 47.* ***Robinson*** *a-1-3, 4&5(4); c-4, 5.* ***Robert Sale*** *a-19, 24.* ***Severin*** *a-32; c-40, 42, 45.* ***Sinnott*** *a-26, 45, 48.* ***Woodbridge*** *a-45, 46.*

BATTLEFRONT
Standard Comics: No. 5, June, 1952
5-Toth-a 16 32 48 92 144 195

BATTLE GODS: WARRIORS OF THE CHAAK
Dark Horse Comics: Apr, 2000 - No. 4, July, 2000 ($2.95)
1-4-Francisco Ruiz Velasco-s/a 3.00

BATTLE GROUND
Atlas Comics (OMC): Sept, 1954 - No. 20, Sept, 1957
1 39 78 117 231 378 525
2-Jack Katz-a (11/54) 20 40 60 117 189 260
3,4: 3-Jack Katz-a. 4-Last precode (3/55) 18 36 54 103 162 220
5-8,10 (3/56) 16 32 48 94 147 200
9,11,13,18: 9-Krigstein-a. 11,13,18-Williamson-a in each 18 36 54 103 162 220
12,15-17,19,20 15 30 45 90 140 190

Battle Hymn #1 © B. Clay Moore

Battle Report #1 © AJAX

Battlestar Galactica #4 © MAR

	GD 2.0	VG 4.0	FN 6.0	VF 8.0	VF/NM 9.0	NM- 9.2

14-Kirby-a 20 40 60 115 185 255

NOTE: ***Ayers** a-4, 6, 13, 16. **Colan** a-3, 11, 13. **Drucker** a-7, 12, 13, 20. **Heath** c-2, 3, 5, 7, 13. **Maneely** a-3, 14, 19; c-1, 6, 18, 19. **Orlando** a-17. **Pakula** a-6, 11. **Reinman** a-2. **Severin** a-4, 5, 12, 19. c-20. **Sinnott** a-7, 16. **Tuska** a-11.*

BATTLE HEROES
Stanley Publications: Sept, 1966 - No. 2, Nov, 1966 (25¢, squarebound giants)

1 4 8 12 23 37 50
2 3 6 9 17 26 35

BATTLE HYMN
Image Comics: Jan, 2005 - No. 5, Oct, 2005 ($2.95/$2.99, limited series)

1-5-WW2 super team; B. Clay Moore-s/Jeremy Haun-a; flip cover on #1-4 3.00

BATTLE OF THE BULGE (See Movie Classics)

BATTLE OF THE PLANETS (Based on syndicated cartoon by Sandy Frank)
Gold Key/Whitman No. 6 on: 6/79 - No. 10, 12/80

1: Mortimer a-1-4,7-10 5 10 15 35 63 90
2-6,10 3 6 9 21 33 45
7-Low print run 6 12 18 38 69 100
8,9-Low print run: 8(11/80). 9-(3-pack only?) 5 10 15 34 60 85

BATTLE OF THE PLANETS (Also see Thundercats/...)
Image Comics (Top Cow): Aug, 2002 - No. 12, Sept, 2003 ($2.95/$2.99)

1-($2.95) Alex Ross-c & art director; Tortosa-a(p); re-intro. G-Force 3.00
1-($5.95) Holofoil-c by Ross 6.00
2-11-($2.99) Ross-c on all 3.00
12-($4.99) 5.00
#1/2 (7/03, $2.99) Benitez-c; Alex Ross sketch pages 3.00
... Battle Book 1 (5/03, $4.99) background info on characters, equipment, stories 5.00
... : Jason 1 (7/03, $4.99) Ross-c; Erwin David-a; preview of Tomb Raider: Epiphany 5.00
... : Mark 1 (5/03, $4.99) Ross-c; Erwin David-a; preview of BotP: Jason 5.00
.../Thundercats 1 (Image/WildStorm, 5/03, $4.99) 2 covers by Ross & Campbell 5.00
.../Witchblade 1 (2/03, $5.95) Ross-c; Christina and Jo Chen-a 6.00
Vol. 1: Trial By Fire (2003, $7.99) r/#1-3 8.00
Vol. 2: Blood Red Sky (9/03, $16.95) r/#4-9 17.00
Vol. 3: Destroy All Monsters (11/03, $19.95) r/#10-12, ...: Jason, ...: Mark, .../Witchblade 20.00
Vol. 1: Digest (1/04, $9.99, 7-3/8x5", B&W) r/#1-9 & ...: Mark 10.00
Vol. 2: Digest (8/04, $9.99, B&W) r/#10-12, ...: Jason, ...: Manga #1-3, .../Witchblade 10.00

BATTLE OF THE PLANETS: MANGA
Image Comics (Top Cow): Nov, 2003 - No. 3, Jan, 2004 ($2.99, B&W)

1-3-Edwin David-a/David Wohl-s; previews for Wanted & Tomb Raider #35 3.00

BATTLE OF THE PLANETS: PRINCESS
Image Comics (Top Cow): Nov, 2004 - No. 6, May, 2005 ($2.99, B&W, limited series)

1-6-Tortosa-a/Wohl-s. 1-Ross-c. 2-Tortosa-c 3.00

BATTLE POPE
Image Comics: June, 2005 - No. 14, Apr, 2007 ($2.99/$3.50, reprints 2000 B&W series in color)

1-5-Kirkman-s/Moore-a 3.50
6-10,12-14-($3.50) 14-Wedding 3.50
11-($4.99) Christmas issue 5.00
... Vol. 1: Genesis TPB (2006, $12.95) r/#1-4; sketch pages 13.00
... Vol. 2: Mayhem TPB (2006, $12.99) r/#5-8; sketch pages 13.00
... Vol. 3: Pillow Talk TPB (2007, $12.99) r/#9-11; sketch pages 13.00

BATTLER BRITTON (British comics character who debuted in 1956)
DC Comics (WildStorm): Sept, 2006 - No. 5, Jan, 2007 ($2.99, limited series)

1-5-WWII fighter pilots; Garth Ennis-s/Colin Wilson-a 3.00
TPB (2007, $19.99) r/#1-5; background of the character's British origins in the 1950s 20.00

BATTLE REPORT
Ajax/Farrell Publications: Aug, 1952 - No. 6, June, 1953

1 15 30 45 85 130 175
2-6 10 20 30 54 72 90

BATTLE SCARS
Marvel Comics: Jan, 2012 - No. 6, Jun, 2012 ($2.99, limited series)

1-Intro. Marcus Johnson and Cheese (later ID'd as Phil Coulson in #6); Eaton-a/Pagulayan-c
2 4 6 8 10 12
2-5: 4-Deadpool app. 5-Nick Fury app. 4.00
6-Marcus Johnson becomes Nick Fury Jr.; resembles movie version; Cheese joins SHIELD and is ID'd as Agent Coulson 2 4 6 8 10 12

BATTLE SQUADRON
Stanmor Publications: April, 1955 - No. 5, Dec, 1955

1 14 28 42 81 118 155
2-5: 3-Iwo Jima & flag-c 9 18 27 50 65 80

BATTLESTAR GALACTICA (TV) (Also see Marvel Comics Super Special #8)
Marvel Comics Group: Mar, 1979 - No. 23, Jan, 1981

1: 1-5 adapt TV episodes 2 4 6 13 18 22
2-23: 1-3-Partial-r 1 3 4 6 8 10

NOTE: ***Austin** c-9i, 10i. **Golden** c-18. **Simonson** a(p)-4, 5, 11-13, 15-20, 22, 23; c(p)-4, 5,11-17, 19, 20, 22, 23.*

BATTLESTAR GALACTICA (TV) (Also see Asylum)
Maximum Press: July, 1995 - No. 4, Nov, 1995 ($2.50, limited series)

1-4: Continuation of 1978 TV series 4.00
Trade paperback (12/95, $12.95)-reprints series 13.00

BATTLESTAR GALACTICA (1978 TV series)
Realm Press: Dec, 1997 - No. 5, July, 1998 ($2.99)

1-5-Chris Scalf-s/painted-a/c 3.00
...Search For Sanctuary (9/98, $2.99) Scalf & Kuhoric-s 3.00
...Search For Sanctuary Special (4/00, $3.99) Kuhoric-s/Scalf & Scott-a 4.00

BATTLESTAR GALACTICA (2003-2009 TV series)
Dynamite Entertainment: No. 0, 2006 - No. 12, 2007 (25¢/$2.99)

0-(25¢-c) Two covers; Pak-s/Raynor-a 3.00
1-($2.99) Covers by Turner, Tan, Raynor & photo-c; Pak-s/Raynor-a 3.00
2-12-Four covers on each 3.00
... Pegasus (2007, $4.99) story of Battlestar Pegasus & Admiral Cain; 2 covers 5.00
... Volume 1 HC (2007, $19.99) r/#0-4; cover gallery; Raynor sketch pages; commentary 20.00
... Volume 1 TPB (2007, $14.99) r/#0-4; cover gallery; Raynor sketch pages; commentary 15.00
... Volume 2 HC (2007, $19.99) r/#5-8; cover gallery; Raynor sketch pages 20.00
... Volume 2 TPB (2007, $14.99) r/#5-8; cover gallery; Raynor sketch pages 15.00

BATTLESTAR GALACTICA, (Classic...) (1978 TV series characters)
Dynamite Entertainment: 2006 - No. 5,2006 ($2.99)

1-5: 1-Two covers by Dorman & Caldwell; Rafael-a. 2-Two covers 3.00

BATTLESTAR GALACTICA, (Classic...) (Volume 2) (1978 TV series characters)
Dynamite Entertainment: 2013 - No. 12, 2014 ($3.99)

1-12: 1-5-Two covers by Alex Ross & Chris Eliopoulos on each; Abnett & Lanning-s 4.00

BATTLESTAR GALACTICA, (Classic...) (Volume 3) (1978 TV series characters)
Dynamite Entertainment: 2016 - Present ($3.99)

1-5: 1-Cullen Bunn-s/Alex Sanchez-a; multiple covers 4.00

BATTLESTAR GALACTICA: APOLLO'S JOURNEY (1978 TV series)
Maximum Press: Apr, 1996 - No. 3, June, 1996 ($2.95, limited series)

1-3: Richard Hatch scripts 4.00

BATTLESTAR GALACTICA: BSG VS. BSG (1978 characters meet 2003 characters)
Dynamite Entertainment: 2018 - Present ($3.99, limited series)

1,2-Peter David-s/Johnny DesJardins-a; multiple covers 3.00

BATTLESTAR GALACTICA: CYLON APOCALYPSE (1978 TV series characters)
Dynamite Entertainment: 2007 - No. 4, 2007 ($2.99, limited series)

1-4-Carlos Rafael-a; 4 covers on each 3.00
TPB (2007, $14.99) r/series with cover gallery 15.00

BATTLESTAR GALACTICA: CYLON WAR (2003-2009 TV series)
Dynamite Entertainment: 2009 - No. 4, 2010 ($3.99, limited series)

1-3-First cylon war 40 years before the Caprica attack; Raynor-a; 2 covers 4.00

BATTLESTAR GALACTICA 1880, STEAMPUNK... (1978 TV series characters)
(Title changes from "(Classic) Battlestar Galactica Vol. 2" after #1)
Dynamite Entertainment: 2014 - No. 4, 2014 ($3.99, limited series)

1-4-Tony Lee-s/Aneke-a; multiple covers 4.00

BATTLESTAR GALACTICA: GHOSTS (2003-2009 TV series)
Dynamite Entertainment: 2008 - No. 4, 2009 ($4.99, 40 pgs., limited series)

1-4-Intro. of the Ghost Squadron; Jerwa-s/Lau-a/Calero-c 5.00

BATTLESTAR GALACTICA: GODS AND MONSTERS (2003-2009 TV series)
Dynamite Entertainment: 2016 - No. 5, 2017 ($3.99, limited series)

1-5-Karl Kesel-s/Alec Morgan & Dan Schkade-a 4.00

BATTLESTAR GALACTICA: JOURNEY'S END (1978 TV series)
Maximum Press: Aug, 1996 - No. 4, Nov, 1996 ($2.99, limited series)

1-4-Continuation of the T.V. series 4.00

BATTLESTAR GALACTICA: ORIGINS (2003-2009 TV series)
Dynamite Entertainment: 2007 - No. 11, 2008 ($3.50)

1-11: 1-4-Baltar's origin; multiple covers. 5-8-Adama's origin. 9-11-Starbuck & Helo 3.50

BATTLESTAR GALACTICA: SEASON III

Battlestar Galactica: Season Zero #8 © Universal

Batwoman #40 © DC

Beanbags #2 © Z-D

	GD 2.0	VG 4.0	FN 6.0	VF 8.0	VF/NM 9.0	NM- 9.2

Realm Press: June/July, 1999 - No. 3, Sept, 1999 ($2.99)

1-3: 1-Kuhoric-s/Scalf & Scott-a; two covers by Scalf & Jae Lee. 2,3-Two covers 3.00
Gallery (4/00, $3.99) short story and pin-ups 4.00
1999 Tour Book (5/99, $2.99) 3.00
1999 Tour Book Convention Edition (6.99) 7.00
...Special: Centurion Prime (12/99, $3.99) Kuhoric-s 4.00

BATTLESTAR GALACTICA: SEASON ZERO (2003-2009 TV series)
Dynamite Entertainment: 2007 - No. 12, 2008 ($2.99)

1-12-Set 2 years before the Cylon attack; multiple covers 3.00
.../The Lone Ranger 2007 Free Comic Book Day Edition; flip book with Cassaday Lone Ranger-c 3.00

BATTLESTAR GALACTICA: SIX (2003-2009 TV series)
Dynamite Entertainment: No. 1, 2014 - No. 5, 2015 ($3.99, limited series)

1-5: 1-J.T. Krul-s/Igor Lima-a; multiple covers. 3-5-Rodolfo-a. 5-Baltar app. 4.00

BATTLESTAR GALACTICA: SPECIAL EDITION (TV)
Maximum Press: Jan, 1997 ($2.99, one-shot)

1-Fully painted; Scalf-c/s/a; r/Asylum 3.00

BATTLESTAR GALACTICA: STARBUCK (TV)
Maximum Press: Dec, 1995 - No. 3, Mar, 1996 ($2.50, limited series)

1-3 4.00

BATTLESTAR GALACTICA: STARBUCK, (Classic...) (1978 TV series characters)
Dynamite Entertainment: 2013 - No. 4, 2014 ($3.99, limited series)

1-4-Tony Lee-s/Eman Casallos-a. 1-Childhood flashback 4.00

BATTLESTAR GALACTICA: THE COMPENDIUM (TV)
Maximum Press: Feb, 1997 ($2.99, one-shot)

1 3.00

BATTLESTAR GALACTICA: THE DEATH OF APOLLO, (Classic...) (1978 TV series)
Dynamite Entertainment: 2014 - No. 6, 2015 ($3.99, limited series)

1-6-Dan Abnett-s/Dietrich Smith-a; multiple covers on each 4.00

BATTLESTAR GALACTICA: THE ENEMY WITHIN (TV)
Maximum Press: Nov, 1995 - No. 3, Feb, 1996 ($2.50, limited series)

1-3: 3-Indicia reads Feb, 1995 in error. 4.00

BATTLESTAR GALACTICA: THE FINAL FIVE (2003 series)
Dynamite Entertainment: 2009 - No. 4, 2009 ($3.99, limited series)

1-4-Raynor-a; 2 covers on each 4.00

BATTLESTAR GALACTICA ZAREK (2003 series)
Dynamite Entertainment: 2007 - No. 4, 2007 ($3.50, limited series)

1-4-Origin story of political activist Tom Zarek; 2 covers on each 3.50

BATTLE STORIES (See XMas Comics)
Fawcett Publications: Jan, 1952 - No. 11, Sept, 1953

	GD	VG	FN	VF	VF/NM	NM-
1-Evans-a (Korean War)	18	36	54	103	162	220
2	11	22	33	62	86	110
3-11	9	18	27	52	69	85

BATTLE STORIES
Super Comics: 1963 - 1964

Reprints #10-13,15-18: 10-r/U.S Tank Commandos #? 11-r/? 11, 12,17-r/Monty Hall #?; 13-Kintsler-a (1pg).15-r/American Air Forces #7 by Powell; Bolle-r. 18-U.S. Fighting Air Force #? 2 4 6 9 13 16

BATTLETECH (See Blackthorne 3-D Series #41 for 3-D issue)
Blackthorne Publishing: Oct, 1987 - No. 6, 1988 ($1.75/$2.00)

1-6: Based on game. 1-Color. 2-Begin B&W 3.00
Annual 1 ($4.50, B&W) 5.00

BATTLETECH
Malibu Comics: Feb, 1995 ($2.95)

0 3.00

BATTLETECH FALLOUT
Malibu Comics: Dec, 1994 - No. 4, Mar, 1995 ($2.95)

1-4-Two edi. exist #1; normal logo 3.00
1-Gold version w/foil logo stamped "Gold Limited Edition 8.00
1-Full-c holographic limited edition 6.00

BATTLETIDE (Death's Head II & Killpower...)
Marvel Comics UK, Ltd.: Dec, 1992 - No. 4, Mar, 1993 ($1.75, mini-series)

1-4: Wolverine, Psylocke, Dark Angel app. 3.00

BATTLETIDE II (Death's Head II & Killpower...)
Marvel Comics UK, Ltd.: Aug, 1993 - No. 4, Nov, 1993 ($1.75, mini-series)

1-($2.95)-Foil embossed logo 4.00
2-4: 2-Hulk-c/story 3.00

BATVARK (Reprints from Cerebus in Hell)
Aardvark-Vanaheim: Aug, 2017 ($4.00, B&W)

1-Cerebus figures placed over original Gustave Doré artwork of Hell; Batman #1-c swipe 4.00

BATWING (DC New 52)
DC Comics: Nov, 2011 - No. 34, Oct, 2014 ($2.99)

1-24: 1-3,5-Judd Winick-s/Ben Oliver-a. 4-Origin; Chriscross-a. 9-Night of the Owls 3.00
25-($3.99) Zero Year tie-in; Luke Fox's first meeting with Batman; Conner-c 4.00
26-34: 26,27-Darwyn Cooke-c 3.00
#0 (11/12, $2.99) origin of David Zavimbe; Winick-s/To-a 3.00
...: Futures End 1 (11/14, $2.99, regular-c) Five years later; Panosian-c 3.00
...: Futures End 1 (11/14, $3.99, 3-D cover) 4.00

BATWOMAN (See 52 #9 & 11 for debut and Detective Comics #854-860)
DC Comics: No. 0, Jan, 2011; No. 1, Nov, 2011 - No. 40, May, 2015 ($2.99)

0-(1/11) Williams III-s; art by Williams III and Reeder; Williams III-c 3.00
0-(1/11)-Variant-c by Reeder 5.00
1-New DC 52; Williams III-a; Williams III & Blackman-s; Bette Kane app. 5.00
2-24: 2-Cameron Chase returns. 6-8-Reeder-a/c. 9-11,15,18-20,22,23-McCarthy-a. 12-17-Wonder Woman app. 21-Francavilla-a; Killer Croc app. 3.00
25-($3.99) Zero Year tie-in; Maggie Sawyer & Bruce Wayne app. 4.00
26-40: 26-31-Wolf Spider. 35-Etrigan, Clayface, Ragman & Alice app. 3.00
#0 (11/12, $2.99) Flashback to Kate's training; Williams III-a 3.00
Annual 1 (6/14, $4.99) Continued from #24; Batman app.; McCarthy & Moritat-a 5.00
Annual 2 (6/15, $4.99) Continued from #40; Jeanty-c/a 5.00
... Elegy The Deluxe Edition HC (2010, $24.99, d.j.) r/Detective #854-860; gallery of variant covers, sketch art and script pages; intro. by Rachel Maddow 25.00
... Elegy SC (2011, $17.99) same contents as Deluxe HC 18.00
...: Futures End 1 (11/14, $2.99, regular-c) Five years later; Red Alice app. 3.00
...: Futures End 1 (11/14, $3.99, 3-D cover) 4.00

BATWOMAN (DC Rebirth)
DC Comics: May, 2017 - Present ($2.99/$3.99)

1-12: 1-($3.99) M. Bennett & Tynion IV-s/Epting-a; covers by Epting & JG Jones. 6-Arlem-a 8-10-Scarecrow app. 4.00
...: Rebirth 1 (4/17, $2.99) Bennett & Tynion-s/Epting-a; origin re-capped 3.00

BAY CITY JIVE
DC Comics (WildStorm): Jul, 2001 - No. 3, Sept, 2001 ($2.95, limited series)

1-3: Intro Sugah Rollins in 1970s San Francisco; Layman-s/Johnson-a 3.00

BAYWATCH COMIC STORIES (TV) (Magazine)
Acclaim Comics (Armada): May, 1996 - No. 4, 1997 ($4.95) (Photo-c on all)

1-4: Photo comics based on TV show 5.00

BEACH BLANKET BINGO (See Movie Classics)

BEAGLE BOYS, THE (Walt Disney)(See The Phantom Blot)
Gold Key: 11/64; No. 2, 11/65; No. 3, 8/66 - No. 47, 2/79 (See WDC&S #134)

	GD	VG	FN	VF	VF/NM	NM-
1	5	10	15	31	53	75
2-5	3	6	9	17	26	35
6-10	3	6	9	15	22	28
11-20: 11,14,19-r	2	4	6	11	16	20
21-30: 27-r	2	4	6	8	11	14
31-47	1	3	4	6	8	10

BEAGLE BOYS VERSUS UNCLE SCROOGE
Gold Key: Mar, 1979 - No. 12, Feb, 1980

	GD	VG	FN	VF	VF/NM	NM-
1	2	4	6	9	13	16
2-12: 9-r	1	2	3	5	6	8

BEANBAGS
Ziff-Davis Publ. Co. (Approved Comics): Winter, 1951 - No. 2, Spring, 1952

	GD	VG	FN	VF	VF/NM	NM-
1,2	15	30	45	83	124	165

BEANIE THE MEANIE
Fago Publications: No. 3, May, 1959

	GD	VG	FN	VF	VF/NM	NM-
3	5	10	15	24	30	35

BEANY AND CECIL (TV) (Bob Clampett's...)
Dell Publishing Co.: Jan, 1952 - 1955; July-Sept, 1962 - No. 5, July-Sept, 1963

	GD	VG	FN	VF	VF/NM	NM-
Four Color 368	22	44	66	154	340	525
Four Color 414,448,477,530,570,635(1/55)	12	24	36	84	185	285

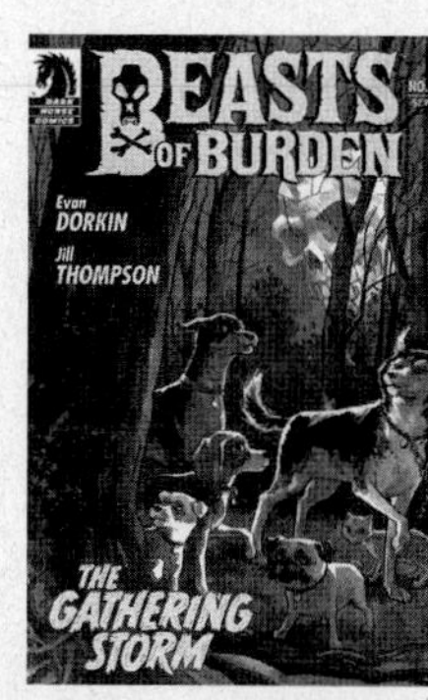

Beasts of Burden #1
© Dorkin & Thompson

The Beauty #4 © Haun & Hurley

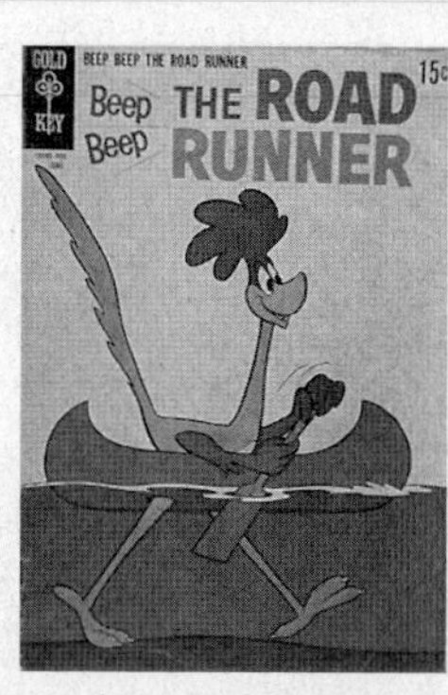

Beep Beep, the Road Runner #12 © WB

	GD 2.0	VG 4.0	FN 6.0	VF 8.0	VF/NM 9.0	NM- 9.2

01-057-209 (#1) 11 22 33 77 166 255
2-5 9 18 27 58 114 170

BEAR COUNTRY (Disney)
Dell Publishing Co.: No. 758, Dec, 1956
Four Color 758-Movie 5 10 15 34 60 85

BEAST (See X-Men)
Marvel Comics: May, 1997 - No. 3, 1997 ($2.50, mini-series)
1-3-Giffen-s/Nocon-a 3.00

BEAST BOY (See Titans)
DC Comics: Jan, 2000 - No. 4, Apr, 2000 ($2.95, mini-series)
1-4-Justiano-c/a; Raab & Johns-s 3.00

B.E.A.S.T.I.E.S. (Also see Axis Alpha)
Axis Comics: Apr, 1994 ($1.95)
1-Javier Saltares-c/a/scripts 3.00

BEASTS OF BURDEN (See Dark Horse Book of Hauntings, ...Monsters, ...The Dead, ...Witchcraft)
Dark Horse Comics: Sept, 2009 - No. 4, Dec, 2009 ($2.99, limited series)
1-4-Evan Dorkin-s/Jill Thompson-a/c 3.00
...: Hunters & Gatherers (3/14, $3.50) Evan Dorkin-s/Jill Thompson-a/c 3.50
...: Neighborhood Watch (8/12, $3.50) Evan Dorkin-s/Jill Thompson-a/c 3.50
...: What the Cat Dragged In (5/16, $3.99) Evan Dorkin & Sarah Dyer-s/Jill Thompson-a/c 4.00
Volume 1: Animal Rites HC (6/10, $19.99) r/#1-4 & short stories from Dark Horse Books 20.00

BEATLES, THE (See Girls' Romances #109, Go-Go, Heart Throbs #101, Herbie #5, Howard the Duck Mag. #4, Laugh #166, Marvel Comics Super Special #4, My Little Margie #54, Not Brand Echh, Strange Tales #130, Summer Love, Superman's Pal Jimmy Olsen #79, Teen Confessions #37, Tippy's Friends & Tippy Teen)

BEATLES, THE (Life Story)
Dell Publishing Co.: Sept-Nov, 1964 (35¢)
1-(Scarce)-Stories with color photo pin-ups; Paul S. Newman-s (photo-c)
46 92 138 368 834 1300

BEATLES EXPERIENCE, THE
Revolutionary Comics: Mar, 1991 - No. 8, 1991 ($2.50, B&W, limited series)
1-8: 1-Gold logo 5.00

BEATLES YELLOW SUBMARINE (See Movie Comics under Yellow...)

BEAUTIFUL KILLER
Black Bull Comics: Sept., 2002 - No. 3, Jan, 2003 ($2.99, limited series)
...Limited Preview Edition (5/02, $5.00) preview pgs. & creator interviews 5.00
1-Noto-a/Palmiotti-s; Hughes-c; intro Brigit Cole 3.00
2,3: 2-Jusko-c. 3-Noto-c 3.00
TPB (5/03, $9.99) r/#1-3; cover gallery and Adam Hughes sketch pages 10.00

BEAUTIFUL PEOPLE
Slave Labor Graphics: Apr, 1994 ($4.95, 8-1/2x11", one-shot)
nn 5.00

BEAUTIFUL STORIES FOR UGLY CHILDREN
DC Comics (Piranha Press): 1989 - No. 30, 1991 ($2.00/$2.50, B&W, mature)
Vol. 1-20: 12-$2.50-c begins 4.00
21-25 5.00
26-30-(Lower print run) 1 2 3 4 5 7
A Cotton Candy Autopsy ($12.95, B&W)-Reprints 1st two volumes 13.00

BEAUTY, THE (Also see Pilot Season: The Beauty)
Image Comics: Aug, 2015 - Present ($3.50/$3.99)
1-6-Jeremy Haun & Jason Hurley-s/Haun-a. 1-Three covers; reprints Pilot Season issue 4.00
7-19-($3.99) 7-Huddleston-a. 8-10-Weldele-a. 12-Haun-a. 13-16-Nachlik-a 4.00

BEAUTY AND THE BEAST, THE
Marvel Comics Group: Jan, 1985 - No. 4, Apr, 1985 (limited series)
1-4: Dazzler & the Beast from X-Men; Sienkiewicz-c on all 4.00

BEAUTY AND THE BEAST (Graphic novel)(Also see Cartoon Tales & Disney's New Adventures of...)
Disney Comics: 1992
nn-($4.95, prestige edition)-Adapts animated film 7.00
nn-($2.50, newsstand edition) 4.00

BEAUTY AND THE BEAST
Disney Comics: Sept., 1992 - No. 2, 1992 ($1.50, limited series)
1,2 3.00

BEAUTY AND THE BEAST: PORTRAIT OF LOVE (TV)
First Comics: May, 1989 - No. 2, Mar, 1990 ($5.95, 60 pgs., squarebound)
1,2: 1-Based on TV show, Wendy Pini-a/scripts. 2-...: Night of Beauty; by Wendy Pini 6.00

BEAVER VALLEY (Movie)(Disney)
Dell Publishing Co.: No. 625, Apr, 1955
Four Color 625 6 12 18 37 66 95

BEAVIS AND BUTTHEAD (MTV's...)(TV cartoon)
Marvel Comics: Mar, 1994 - No. 28, June, 1996 ($1.95)
1-Silver ink-c. 1, 2-Punisher & Devil Dinosaur app. 1 3 4 6 8 10
1-2nd printing 4.00
2,3: 2-Wolverine app. 3-Man-Thing, Spider-Man, Venom, Carnage, Mary Jane & Stan Lee cameos; John Romita, Sr. art (2 pgs.) 5.00
4-28: 5-War Machine, Thor, Loki, Hulk, Captain America & Rhino cameos. 6-Psylocke, Polaris, Daredevil & Bullseye app. 7-Ghost Rider & Sub-Mariner app. 8-Quasar & Eon app. 9-Prowler & Nightwatch app. 11-Black Widow app. 12-Thunderstrike & Bloodaxe app. 13-Night Thrasher app. 14-Spider-Man 2099 app. 15-Warlock app. 16-X-Factor app. 25-Juggernaut app. 4.00

BECK & CAUL INVESTIGATIONS
Gauntlet Comics (Caliber): Jan, 1994 - No. 5, 1995? ($2.95, B&W)
1-5 3.00
Special 1 ($4.95) 5.00

BEDKNOBS AND BROOMSTICKS (See Walt Disney Showcase No. 6 & 50)

BEDLAM!
Eclipse Comics: Sept, 1985 - No. 2, Sept, 1985 (B&W-r in color)
1,2: Bissette-a 4.00

BEDTIME STORIES FOR IMPRESSIONABLE CHILDREN
Moonstone Books/American Mythology: Nov, 2010; Feb, 2017 ($3.99, B&W)
1-(11/10) Short story anthology; Vaughn, Kuhoric & Tinnell-s; 3 covers 4.00
1-(2/17) Short story anthology; Vaughn, Shooter & Nelms-s; 4 covers 4.00

BEDTIME STORY (See Cinema Comics Herald)

BEE AND PUPPYCAT
Boom Entertainment (KaBOOM!): May, 2014 - No. 11, Apr, 2016 ($3.99)
1-11: Multiple covers on each. 1,2-Natasha Allegri-s/a 4.00

BEELZELVIS
Slave Labor Graphics: Feb, 1994 ($2.95, B&W, one-shot)
1 3.00

BEEP BEEP, THE ROAD RUNNER (TV) (See Dell Giant Comics Bugs Bunny Vacation Funnies #8 for 1st app.) (Also see Daffy & Kite Fun Book)
Dell Publishing Co./Gold Key No. 1-88/Whitman No. 89 on: July, 1958 - No. 14, Aug-Oct, 1962; Oct, 1966 - No. 105, 1984

	GD 2.0	VG 4.0	FN 6.0	VF 8.0	VF/NM 9.0	NM- 9.2
Four Color 918 (#1, 7/58)	12	24	36	82	179	275
Four Color 1008,1046 (11-1/59-60)	8	16	24	51	96	140
4(2-4/60)-14(Dell)	6	12	18	37	66	95
1(10/66, Gold Key)	6	12	18	42	79	115
2-5	4	8	12	27	44	60
6-14	3	6	9	19	30	40
15-18,20-40	3	6	9	16	23	30
19-With pull-out poster	4	8	12	25	40	55
41-50	3	6	9	14	19	24
51-70	2	4	6	9	13	16
71-88	2	3	4	6	8	10
89,90,94-101: 100(3/82), 101(4/82)	2	4	6	8	10	12
91(8/80), 92(9/80), 93 (3-pack?) (low printing)	8	16	24	51	96	140
102-105 (All #90189 on-c; nd or date code; pre-pack) 102(6/83), 103(7/83), 104(5/84), 105(6/84)	3	6	9	19	30	40
#63-2970 (Now Age Books/Pendulum Pub. Comic Digest, 1971, 75¢, 100 pages, B&W) collection of one-page gags	4	8	12	27	44	60

NOTE: *See March of Comics #351, 353, 375, 387, 397, 416, 430, 442, 455. #5, 8-10, 35, 53, 59-62, 68-r; 96-102, 104 are 1/3-r.*

BEETLE BAILEY (See Giant Comic Album, Sarge Snorkel; also Comics Reading Libraries in the Promotional Comics section)
Dell Publishing Co./Gold Key #39-53/King #54-66/Charlton #67-119/Gold Key #120-131/ Whitman #132: #459, 5/53 - #38, 5-7/62; #39, 11/62 - #53, 5/66; #54, 8/66 - #65, 12/67;#67, 2/69 - #119, 11/76; #120, 4/78 - #132, 4/80

	GD 2.0	VG 4.0	FN 6.0	VF 8.0	VF/NM 9.0	NM- 9.2
Four Color 469 (#1)-By Mort Walker	13	26	39	86	188	290
Four Color 521,552,622	7	14	21	49	92	135
5(2-4/56)-10(5-7/57)	5	10	15	35	63	90
11-20(4-5/59)	4	8	12	28	47	65
21-38(5-7/62)	3	6	9	20	31	42
39-53(5/66)	3	6	9	17	26	35

Before Watchmen: Silk Spectre #1 © DC

Ben Reilly: Scarlet Spider #1 © MAR

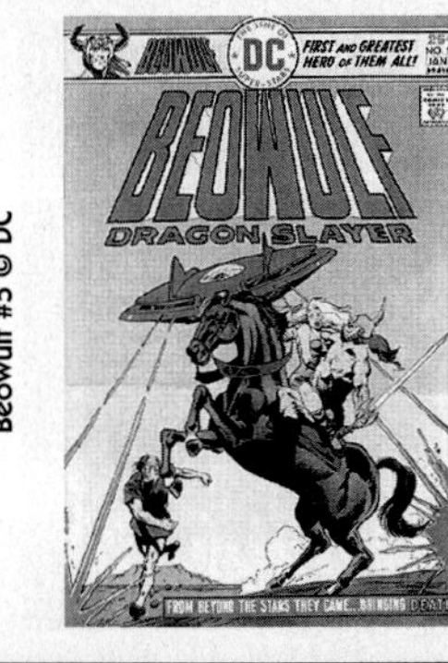

Beowulf #5 © DC

	GD 2.0	VG 4.0	FN 6.0	VF 8.0	VF/NM 9.0	NM- 9.2
54-65 (No. 66 publ. overseas only?)	3	6	9	16	23	30
67-69: 69-Last 12¢ issue	3	6	9	14	20	25
70-99	2	4	6	9	13	16
100	2	4	6	11	16	20
101-111,114-119	1	3	4	6	8	10
112,113-Byrne illos. (4 each)	2	4	6	9	12	18
120-132	1	2	3	4	5	7

BEETLE BAILEY
Harvey Comics: V2#1, Sept, 1992 - V2#9, Aug, 1994 ($1.25/$1.50)

	GD 2.0	VG 4.0	FN 6.0	VF 8.0	VF/NM 9.0	NM- 9.2
V2#1						5.00
2-9-($1.50)						3.50
Big Book 1(11/92),2(5/93)(Both $1.95, 52 pgs.)						4.00
Giant Size V2#1(10/92),2(3/93)(Both $2.25,68 pgs.)						4.00

BEETLEJUICE (TV)
Harvey Comics: Oct, 1991 ($1.25)

	GD 2.0	VG 4.0	FN 6.0	VF 8.0	VF/NM 9.0	NM- 9.2
1						5.00

BEETLEJUICE CRIMEBUSTERS ON THE HAUNT
Harvey Comics: Sept, 1992 - No. 3, Jan, 1993 ($1.50, limited series)

	GD 2.0	VG 4.0	FN 6.0	VF 8.0	VF/NM 9.0	NM- 9.2
1-3						4.00

BEE 29, THE BOMBARDIER
Neal Publications: Feb, 1945

	GD 2.0	VG 4.0	FN 6.0	VF 8.0	VF/NM 9.0	NM- 9.2
1-(Funny animal)	37	74	111	222	361	500

BEFORE THE FANTASTIC FOUR: BEN GRIMM AND LOGAN
Marvel Comics: July, 2000 - No. 3, Sept, 2000 ($2.99, limited series)

	GD 2.0	VG 4.0	FN 6.0	VF 8.0	VF/NM 9.0	NM- 9.2
1-3-The Thing and Wolverine app.; Hama-s						3.00

BEFORE THE FANTASTIC FOUR: REED RICHARDS
Marvel Comics: Sept, 2000 - No. 3, Dec, 2000 ($2.99, limited series)

	GD 2.0	VG 4.0	FN 6.0	VF 8.0	VF/NM 9.0	NM- 9.2
1-3-Peter David-s/Duncan Fegredo-c/a						3.00

BEFORE THE FANTASTIC FOUR: THE STORMS
Marvel Comics: Dec, 2000 - No. 3, Feb, 2001 ($2.99, limited series)

	GD 2.0	VG 4.0	FN 6.0	VF 8.0	VF/NM 9.0	NM- 9.2
1-3-Adlard-a						3.00

BEFORE WATCHMEN: COMEDIAN (Prequel to 1986 Watchmen series)
DC Comics: Aug, 2012 - No. 6, Jun, 2013 ($3.99, limited series)

	GD 2.0	VG 4.0	FN 6.0	VF 8.0	VF/NM 9.0	NM- 9.2
1-6-Brian Azzarello-s/J.G. Jones-a/c; The Comedian during the Vietnam War; back-up Crimson Corsair serial in #1-4; Higgins-a						4.00
1-Variant-c by Jim Lee						60.00
1-6-Variant covers. 1-Risso. 2-Bradstreet. 3-Leon. 4-Stelfreeze. 5-Frank. 6-Albuquerque						8.00

BEFORE WATCHMEN: DOLLAR BILL (Prequel to 1986 Watchmen series)
DC Comics: Mar, 2013 ($3.99, one-shot)

	GD 2.0	VG 4.0	FN 6.0	VF 8.0	VF/NM 9.0	NM- 9.2
1-Len Wein-s/Steve Rude-a/c; origin and demise of Dollar Bill						4.00
1-Variant-c by Jim Lee						60.00
1-Variant-c by Darwyn Cooke						8.00

BEFORE WATCHMEN: DR. MANHATTAN (Prequel to 1986 Watchmen series)
DC Comics: Oct, 2012 - No. 4, Apr, 2013 ($3.99, limited series)

	GD 2.0	VG 4.0	FN 6.0	VF 8.0	VF/NM 9.0	NM- 9.2
1-4-Straczynski-s/Hughes-a/c; back-up Crimson Corsair serial in #1-3; Higgins-a						4.00
1-Variant-c by Jim Lee						60.00
1-4-Variant covers. 1-Pope. 2-Russell. 3-Neal Adams. 4-Sienkiewicz						8.00

BEFORE WATCHMEN: MINUTEMEN (Prequel to 1986 Watchmen series)
DC Comics: Aug, 2012 - No. 6, Mar, 2013 ($3.99, limited series)

	GD 2.0	VG 4.0	FN 6.0	VF 8.0	VF/NM 9.0	NM- 9.2
1-6-Darwyn Cooke-a/c; The team flashback to 1939; back-up Crimson Corsair serial in #1-5; Higgins-a						4.00
1-Variant-c by Jim Lee						40.00
1-6-Variant covers. 1-Golden. 2-Garcia-Lopez-c. 3-Chiang. 4-Rude. 6-Cloonan						8.00

BEFORE WATCHMEN: MOLOCH (Prequel to 1986 Watchmen series)
DC Comics: Jan, 2013 - No. 2, Feb, 2013 ($3.99, limited series)

	GD 2.0	VG 4.0	FN 6.0	VF 8.0	VF/NM 9.0	NM- 9.2
1,2-Straczynski-s/Risso-a/c; origin; back-up Crimson Corsair serial in both; Higgins-a						4.00
1-Variant-c by Jim Lee						40.00
1,2-Variant covers. 1-Matt Wagner. 2-Olly Moss						8.00

BEFORE WATCHMEN: NITE OWL (Prequel to 1986 Watchmen series)
DC Comics: Aug, 2012 - No. 4, Feb, 2013 ($3.99, limited series)

	GD 2.0	VG 4.0	FN 6.0	VF 8.0	VF/NM 9.0	NM- 9.2
1-4-Straczynski-s/Andy Kubert-a/c; Joe Kubert-a(i) in #1-3; back-up Crimson Corsair serial in #1-3; Higgins-a						4.00
1-Variant-c by Jim Lee						50.00
1-4-Variant covers. 1-Nowlan. 2-Finch. 3-Samnee. 4-Van Sciver						8.00

BEFORE WATCHMEN: OZYMANDIAS (Prequel to 1986 Watchmen series)
DC Comics: Sept, 2012 - No. 6, Apr, 2013 ($3.99, limited series)

	GD 2.0	VG 4.0	FN 6.0	VF 8.0	VF/NM 9.0	NM- 9.2
1-6-Len Wein-s/Jae Lee-a/c; origin of master plan; back-up Crimson Corsair serial in #1-4; Higgins-a						4.00
1-Variant-c by Jim Lee						50.00
1-6-Variant covers. 1-Jimenez. 2-Noto. 3-Carnevale. 4-Kaluta. 5-Thompson. 6-Sook						8.00

BEFORE WATCHMEN: RORSCHACH (Prequel to 1986 Watchmen series)
DC Comics: Oct, 2012 - No. 4, Apr, 2013 ($3.99, limited series)

	GD 2.0	VG 4.0	FN 6.0	VF 8.0	VF/NM 9.0	NM- 9.2
1-4-Azzarello-s/Bermejo-a/c; back-up Crimson Corsair serial in #1-3; Higgins-a						5.00
1-Variant-c by Jim Lee						75.00
1-4-Variant covers. 1-Steranko. 2-Jock. 3-Kidd. 4-Reis						10.00

BEFORE WATCHMEN: SILK SPECTRE (Prequel to 1986 Watchmen series)
DC Comics: Aug, 2012 - No. 4, Dec, 2013 ($3.99, limited series)

	GD 2.0	VG 4.0	FN 6.0	VF 8.0	VF/NM 9.0	NM- 9.2
1-4-Cooke & Conner-s/Conner-a/c; back-up Crimson Corsair serial in all; Higgins-a						4.00
1-Variant-c by Jim Lee						60.00
1-4-Variant covers. 1-Dave Johnson. 2-Middleton. 3-Allred. 4-Timm						8.00

BEHIND PRISON BARS
Realistic Comics (Avon): 1952

	GD 2.0	VG 4.0	FN 6.0	VF 8.0	VF/NM 9.0	NM- 9.2
1-Kinstler-c	39	78	117	231	378	525

BEHOLD THE HANDMAID
George Pflaum: 1954 (Religious) (25¢ with a 20¢ sticker price)

	GD 2.0	VG 4.0	FN 6.0	VF 8.0	VF/NM 9.0	NM- 9.2
nn	6	12	18	31	38	45

BELIEVE IT OR NOT (See Ripley's...)

BEN AND ME (Disney)
Dell Publishing Co.: No. 539, Mar, 1954

	GD 2.0	VG 4.0	FN 6.0	VF 8.0	VF/NM 9.0	NM- 9.2
Four Color 539	5	10	15	30	50	70

BEN BOWIE AND HIS MOUNTAIN MEN
Dell Publishing Co.: 1952 - No. 17, Nov-Jan, 1958-59

	GD 2.0	VG 4.0	FN 6.0	VF 8.0	VF/NM 9.0	NM- 9.2
Four Color 443 (#1)	9	18	27	61	123	185
Four Color 513,557,599,626,657	5	10	15	34	60	85
7(5-7/56)-11: 11-Intro/origin Yellow Hair	4	8	12	25	40	55
12-17	4	8	12	23	37	50

BEN CASEY (TV)
Dell Publishing Co.: June-July, 1962 - No. 10, June-Aug, 1965 (Photo-c)

	GD 2.0	VG 4.0	FN 6.0	VF 8.0	VF/NM 9.0	NM- 9.2
12-063-207 (#1)	5	10	15	35	63	90
2(10/62),3,5-10	4	8	12	23	37	50
4-Marijuana & heroin use story	4	8	12	27	44	60

BEN CASEY FILM STORIES (TV)
Gold Key: Nov, 1962 (25¢) (Photo-c)

	GD 2.0	VG 4.0	FN 6.0	VF 8.0	VF/NM 9.0	NM- 9.2
30009-211-All photos	6	12	18	38	69	100

BENEATH THE PLANET OF THE APES (See Movie Comics & Power Record Comics)

BEN FRANKLIN (See Kite Fun Book)

BEN HUR
Dell Publishing Co.: No. 1052, Nov, 1959

	GD 2.0	VG 4.0	FN 6.0	VF 8.0	VF/NM 9.0	NM- 9.2
Four Color 1052-Movie, Manning-a	9	18	27	61	123	185

BEN ISRAEL
Logos International: 1974 (39¢)

	GD 2.0	VG 4.0	FN 6.0	VF 8.0	VF/NM 9.0	NM- 9.2
nn-Christian religious	2	4	6	10	14	18

BEN REILLY: SCARLET SPIDER
Marvel Comics: Jun, 2017 - Present ($3.99)

	GD 2.0	VG 4.0	FN 6.0	VF 8.0	VF/NM 9.0	NM- 9.2
1-14: 1-Peter David-s/Mark Bagley-a. 6,7-Sliney-a. 7-Death app. 8-10-The Hornet app.						4.00

BEN 10 (Cartoon Network)
IDW Publishing: Nov, 2013 - No. 4, Feb, 2014 ($3.99, limited series)

	GD 2.0	VG 4.0	FN 6.0	VF 8.0	VF/NM 9.0	NM- 9.2
1-4: Henderson-s/Purcell-a; multiple covers on each						4.00

BEOWULF (Also see First Comics Graphic Novel #1)
National Periodical Publications: Apr-May, 1975 - No. 6, Feb-Mar, 1976

	GD 2.0	VG 4.0	FN 6.0	VF 8.0	VF/NM 9.0	NM- 9.2
1	2	4	6	9	12	15
2,3,5,6: 5-Flying saucer-c/story	1	2	3	5	6	8
4-Dracula-c/s	1	3	4	6	8	10

BERNI WRIGHTSON, MASTER OF THE MACABRE
Pacific Comics/Eclipse Comics No. 5: July, 1983 - No. 5, Nov, 1984 ($1.50, Baxter paper)

	GD 2.0	VG 4.0	FN 6.0	VF 8.0	VF/NM 9.0	NM- 9.2
1-5: Wrightson-c/a(r). 4-Jeff Jones-r (11 pgs.)						6.00

BERRYS, THE (Also see Funny World)
Argo Publ.: May, 1956

Best Comics #2 © BP

Best of DC #1 © DC

Best of the Brave and the Bold #1 © DC

	GD 2.0	VG 4.0	FN 6.0	VF 8.0	VF/NM 9.0	NM- 9.2

1-Reprints daily & Sunday strips & daily Animal Antics by Ed Nofziger 6 12 18 29 36 42

BERZERKER (Milo Ventimiglia Presents...)
Image Comics (Top Cow): No. 0, Feb, 2009 - No. 6, Jun, 2010 ($2.99/$3.99)

0-3-Jeremy Haun-a/Rick Loverd-s/Dale Keown-c. 0-Creator interviews 3.00
4-6-($3.99) Covers by Haun & Keown 4.00

BERZERKERS (See Youngblood V1#2)
Image Comics (Extreme Studios): Aug, 1995 - No. 3, Oct, 1995 ($2.50, limited series)

1-3: Beau Smith scripts, Fraga-a 3.00

BEST COMICS
Better Publications: Nov, 1939 - No. 4, Feb, 1940(10-11/16" wide x 8" tall, reads sideways)

1-(Scarce)-Red Mask begins (1st app., 1st African American superhero in comics) & c/s-all 300 600 900 2010 3505 5000
2-4: 3-Racist-c. 4-Cannibalism story 155 310 465 992 1696 2400

BEST FROM BOY'S LIFE, THE
Gilberton Company: Oct, 1957 - No. 5, Oct, 1958 (35¢)

1-Space Conquerors & Kam of the Ancient Ones begin, end #5; Bob Cousy photo/story 13 26 39 72 101 130
2,3,5 8 16 24 42 54 65
4-L.B. Cole-a 8 16 24 44 57 70

BEST LOVE (Formerly Sub-Mariner Comics No. 32)
Marvel Comics (MPI): No. 33, Aug, 1949 - No. 36, April, 1950 (Photo-c 33-36)

33-Kubert-a 17 34 51 98 154 210
34 (10/49) 12 24 36 69 97 125
35,36-Everett-a 14 28 42 76 108 140

BEST OF ARCHIE, THE
Perigee Books: 1980 ($7.95, softcover TPB)

nn-Intro by Michael Uslan & Jeffrey Mendel 5 10 15 34 60 85

BEST OF BUGS BUNNY, THE
Gold Key: Oct, 1966 - No. 2, Oct, 1968

1,2-Giants 4 8 12 27 44 60

BEST OF DC, THE (Blue Ribbon Digest) (See Limited Coll. Ed. C-52)
DC Comics: Sept-Oct, 1979 - No. 71, Apr, 1986 (100-148 pgs; mostly reprints)

1-Superman, w/"Death of Superman"-r 2 4 6 11 16 20
2,5-9: 2-Batman 40th Ann. Special. 5-Best of 1979. 6,8-Superman. 7-Superboy. 9-Batman, Creeper app. 2 4 6 8 10 12
3-Superfriends 2 4 6 9 12 15
4-Rudolph the Red Nosed Reindeer 2 4 6 9 13 16
10-Secret Origins of Super Villains; 1st ever Penguin origin-s 3 6 9 15 22 28
11-16,18-20: 11-The Year's Best Stories. 12-Superman Time and Space Stories.13-Best of DC Comics Presents. 14-New origin stories of Batman villains. 15-Superboy. 16-Superman Anniv. 18-Teen Titans new-s., Adams, Kane-a; Perez-c. 19-Superman. 20-World's Finest 1 2 3 5 7 9
17-Supergirl 2 4 6 8 10 12
21,22: 21-Justice Society. 22-Christmas; unpublished Sandman story w/Kirby-a 2 4 6 10 14 18
23-27: 23-(148 pgs.)-Best of 1981. 24 Legion, new story and 16 pgs. new costumes. 25-Superman. 26-Brave & Bold. 27-Superman vs. Luthor 2 4 6 9 12 15
28,29: 28-Binky, Sugar & Spike app. 29-Sugar & Spike, 3 new stories; new Stanley & his Monster story 2 4 6 9 13 16
30,32-36,38,40: 30-Detective Comics. 32-Superman. 33-Secret origins of Legion Heroes and Villains. 34-Metal Men; has #497 on-c from Adv. Comics. 35-The Year's Best Comics Stories (148 pgs.). 36-Superman vs. Kryptonite. 38-Superman. 40-World of Krypton 2 4 6 9 12 15
31-JLA 2 4 6 10 14 18
34-Corrected version with "#34" on cover 2 4 6 10 14 18
37,39: 37-"Funny Stuff", Mayer-a. 39-Binky 2 4 6 10 14 18
41,43,45,47,49,53,55,58,60,63,65,68,70: 41-Sugar & Spike new stories with Mayer-a. 43,49,55-Funny Stuff. 45,53,70-Binky. 47,65,68-Sugar & Spike. 58-Super Jrs. Holiday Special; Sugar & Spike. 60-Plop!; Wood-c(r) & Aragonés-r (5/85). 63-Plop!; Wrightson-a(r) 3 6 9 14 19 24
42,44,46,48,50-52,54,56,57,59,61,62,64,66,67,69,71: 42,56-Superman vs. Aliens. 44,57,67-Superboy & LSH. 46-Jimmy Olsen. 48-Superman Team-ups. 50-Year's best Superman. 51-Batman Family. 52 Best of 1984. 54,56,59-Superman. 61-(148 pgs.)Year's best. 62-Best of Batman 1985. 69-Year's best Team stories. 71-Year's best 2 4 6 10 14 18

NOTE: ***N. Adams** a-2r, 14r, 18r, 26, 51. **Aparo** a-9, 14, 26, 30; c-9, 14, 26. **Austin** a-51i. **Buckler** a-40p; c-16, 22. **Giffen** a-50, 52; c-33p. **Grell** a-33p. **Grossman** a-37. **Heath** a-26. **Infantino** a-10r, 18. **Kaluta** a-40. **G. Kane** a-10r, 18r; c-40, 44. **Kubert** a-10r, 21, 26. **Layton** a-21. **S. Mayer** c-29, 37, 41, 43, 47; a-28, 29, 37, 41, 43, 47, 58, 65, 68. **Moldoff** c-64p. **Morrow** a-40; c-40. **W. Mortimer** a-39p. **Newton** a-5, 51. **Perez** a-24, 50p; c-18, 21, 23. **Rogers** a-14, 51p. **Simonson** a-11r. **Spiegle** a-52. **Starlin** a-51. **Staton** a-5, 21. **Tuska** a-24. **Wolverton** a-60. **Wood** a-60, 63; c-60, 63. **Wrightson** a-60. New art in #14, 18, 24.*

BEST OF DENNIS THE MENACE, THE
Hallden/Fawcett Publications: Summer, 1959 - No. 5, Spring, 1961 (100 pgs.)

1-All reprints; Wiseman-a 7 14 21 44 72 100
2-5: 2-Christmas-c 4 8 12 28 44 60

BEST OF DONALD DUCK, THE
Gold Key: Nov, 1965 (12¢, 36 pgs.)(Lists 2nd printing in indicia)

1-Reprints Four Color #223 by Barks 7 14 21 46 86 125

BEST OF DONALD DUCK & UNCLE SCROOGE, THE
Gold Key: Nov, 1964 - No. 2, Sept, 1967 (25¢ Giants)

1(30022-411)('64)-Reprints 4-Color #189 & 408 by Carl Barks; cover of F.C. #189 redrawn by Barks 8 16 24 54 102 150
2(30022-709)('67)-Reprints 4-Color #256 & "Seven Cities of Cibola" & U.S. #8 by Barks 7 14 21 44 82 120

BEST OF HORROR AND SCIENCE FICTION COMICS
Bruce Webster: 1987 ($2.00)

1-Wolverton, Frazetta, Powell, Ditko-r 1 3 4 6 8 10

BEST OF JOSIE AND THE PUSSYCATS
Archie Comics: 2001 ($10.95, TPB)

1-Reprints 1st app. and noteworthy stories 12.00

BEST OF MARMADUKE, THE
Charlton Comics: 1960

1-Brad Anderson's strip reprints 3 6 9 21 33 45

BEST OF MS. TREE, THE
Pyramid Comics: 1987 - No. 4, 1988 ($2.00, B&W, limited series)

1-4 3.00

BEST OF THE BRAVE AND THE BOLD, THE (See Super DC Giant)
DC Comics: Oct, 1988 - No. 6, Jan, 1989 ($2.50, limited series)

1-6: Neal Adams-r, Kubert-r & Heath-r in all 4.00

BEST OF THE SPIRIT, THE
DC Comics: 2005 ($14.99, TPB)

nn-Reprints 1st app. and noteworthy stories; intro by Neil Gaiman; Eisner bio. 15.00

BEST OF THE WEST (See A-1 Comics)
Magazine Enterprises: 1951 - No. 12, April-June, 1954

1(A-1 42)-Ghost Rider, Durango Kid, Straight Arrow, Bobby Benson begin 41 82 123 256 428 600
2(A-1 46) 22 44 66 128 209 290
3(A-1 52), 4(A-1 59), 5(A-1 66) 18 36 54 105 165 225
6(A-1 70), 7(A-1 76), 8(A-1 81), 9(A-1 85), 10(A-1 87), 11(A-1 97), 12(A-1 103) 15 30 45 84 127 170

NOTE: ***Bolle** a-9. **Borth** a-12. **Guardineer** a-5, 12. **Powell** a-1, 12.*

BEST OF UNCLE SCROOGE & DONALD DUCK, THE
Gold Key: Nov, 1966 (25¢)

1(30030-611)-Reprints part 4-Color #159 & 456 & Uncle Scrooge #6,7 by Carl Barks 7 14 21 44 82 120

BEST OF WALT DISNEY COMICS, THE
Western Publishing Co.: 1974 ($1.50, 52 pgs.) (Walt Disney)
(8-1/2x11" cardboard covers; 32,000 printed of each)

96170-Reprints 1st two stories less 1 pg. each from 4-Color #62 6 12 18 37 66 95
96171-Reprints Mickey Mouse and the Bat Bandit of Inferno Gulch from 1934 (strips) by Gottfredson 6 12 18 37 66 95
96172-r/Uncle Scrooge #386 & two other stories 6 12 18 37 66 95
96173-Reprints "Ghost of the Grotto" (from 4-Color #159) & "Christmas on Bear Mountain" (from 4-Color #178) 6 12 18 37 66 95

BEST ROMANCE
Standard Comics (Visual Editions): No. 5, Feb-Mar, 1952 - No. 7, Aug, 1952

5-Toth-a; photo-c 17 34 51 98 154 210
6,7-Photo-c 11 22 33 64 90 115

BEST SELLER COMICS (See Tailspin Tommy)

BEST WESTERN (Formerly Terry Toons? or Miss America Magazine
Marvel Comics (IPC): V7#24(#57)?; Western Outlaws & Sheriffs No. 60 on)
No. 58, June, 1949 - No. 59, Aug, 1949

Betrayal of the Planet of the Apes #1 © 20th Century Fox

Bettie Page (2017 series) #3 © Bettie Page LLC

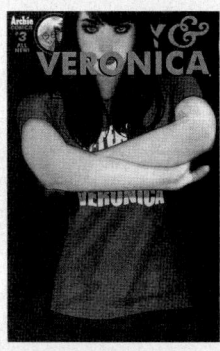

Betty and Veronica V3 #3 © ACP

GD VG FN VF VF/NM NM-
2.0 4.0 6.0 8.0 9.0 9.2

GD VG FN VF VF/NM NM-
2.0 4.0 6.0 8.0 9.0 9.2

58,59-Black Rider, Kid Colt, Two-Gun Kid app.; both have Syd Shores-c 21 42 63 122 199 275

BETA RAY BILL: GODHUNTER
Marvel Comics: Aug, 2009 - No. 3, Oct, 2009 ($3.99, limited series)

1-3-Kano-a; Thor and Galactus app.; reprints form Thor #337-339. 2,3-Silver Surfer app. 4.00

BETRAYAL OF THE PLANET OF THE APES (Set 20 years before the first movie)
BOOM! Studios: Nov, 2011 - No. 4, Feb, 2012 ($3.99, limited series)

1-4-Dr. Zaius app.; Bechko-s/Hardman-a. 1-Three covers. 2-Two covers 4.00

BETTIE PAGE
Dynamite Entertainment: 2017 - No. 8, 2018 ($3.99, limited series)

1-8: 1-Bettie Page in 1951 Hollywood; Avallone-s/Worley-a; multiple covers on each 4.00

BETTIE PAGE COMICS
Dark Horse Comics: Mar, 1996 ($3.95)

1-Dave Stevens-c; Blevins & Heath-a; Jaime Hernandez pin-up 2 4 6 11 16 20

BETTIE PAGE COMICS: QUEEN OF THE NILE
Dark Horse Comics: Dec, 1999 - No. 3, Apr, 2000 ($2.95, limited series)

1-3-Silke-s/a; Stevens-c 2 4 6 8 10 12

BETTIE PAGE COMICS: SPICY ADVENTURE
Dark Horse Comics: Jan, 1997 ($2.95, one-shot, mature)

nn-Silke-c/s/a 2 4 6 8 10 12

BETTY (See Pep Comics #22 for 1st app.)
Archie Comics: Sept, 1992 - No. 195, Jan, 2012 ($1.25-$2.99)

1 6.00
2-18,20-24: 20-1st Super Sleuther-s 4.00
19-Love Showdown part 2 5.00
25-Pin-up page of Betty as Marilyn Monroe, Madonna, Lady Di 5.00
26-50 3.00
51-195: 57- "A Storm Over Uniforms" x-over part 5,6. 186-Begin $2.99-c 3.00

BETTY AND HER STEADY (Going Steady with Betty No. 1)
Avon Periodicals: No. 2, Mar-Apr, 1950

2 13 26 39 74 105 135

BETTY AND ME
Archie Publications: Aug, 1965 - No. 200, Aug, 1992

1 12 24 36 82 179 275
2,3: 3-Origin Superteen 6 12 18 38 69 100
4-8: Superteen in new costume #4-7; dons new helmet in #5, ends #8. 5 10 15 31 53 75
9,10: Girl from R.I.V.E.R.D.A.L.E. 9-UFO-s 4 8 12 27 44 60
11-15,17-20(4/69) 3 6 9 21 33 45
16-Classic cover; w/risqué cover dialogue 17 34 51 117 259 400
21,24-35: 33-Paper doll page 3 6 9 16 23 30
22-Archies Band-s 3 6 9 16 24 32
23-I Dream of Jeannie parody 3 6 9 19 30 40
36(8/71),37,41-55 (52 pgs.): 42-Betty as vamp-s 3 6 9 16 23 30
38-Sabrina app. 4 8 12 23 37 50
39-Josie and Sabrina cover cameos 3 6 9 19 30 40
40-Archie & Betty share a cabin 3 6 9 17 26 35
56(4/71)-80(12/76): 79 Betty Cooper mysteries thru #86. 79-81-Drago the Vampire-s 2 4 6 9 13 16
81-99: 83-Harem-c. 84-Jekyll & Hyde-c/s 2 4 6 8 10 12
100(3/79) 2 4 6 9 12 15
101,118: 101-Elvis mentioned. 118-Tarzan mentioned 1 2 3 5 7 9
102-117,119-130(9/82): 103,104-Space-s. 124-DeCarlo-c begins 7.00
131-138,140,142-147,149-154,156-158: 135,136-Jason Blossom app. 136-Cheryl Blossom cameo. 137-Space-s. 138-Tarzan parody 5.00
139,141,148: 139-Katy Keene collecting-s; Archie in drag-s. 141-Tarzan parody-s. 148-Cyndi Lauper parody-s 6.00
155,159,160(8/87): 155-Archie in drag-s. 159-Superhero gag-c. 160-Wheel of Fortune parody 6.00
161-169,171-199 4.00
170,200: 170-New Archie Superhero-s 6.00

BETTY AND VERONICA (Also see Archie's Girls...)
Archie Enterprises: June, 1987 - No. 278, Dec, 2015 (75¢-$3.99)

1 2 3 4 6 8 10
2-10 6.00
11-30 4.00
31-81 3.00
82-Love Showdown part 3 5.00
83-271: 242-Begin $2.50-c. 247-Begin $2.99-c. 264-271-Two covers 3.00
267-Mermaid variant-c by Fiona Staples 10.00
272-274,276-278-($3.99): 272-274,276,277-Two covers. 278-Last issue; 6 covers 4.00
275-($4.99) Five covers by Adam Hughes, Ramona Fradon & others 5.00
... Free Comic Book Day Edition #1 (6/05) Katy Keene-c/app.; Cheryl Blossom app. 3.00

BETTY AND VERONICA (Volume 3)
Archie Comic Publications: Sept, 2016 - No. 3, Aug, 2017 ($3.99, limited series)

1-3-Adam Hughes-s/a; multiple covers on each; back-up classic pin-ups 4.00
... No. 1: FCBD Edition (5/17, giveaway) r/#1; bonus Riverdale TV show character guide 3.00

BETTY & VERONICA ANNUAL DIGEST (...Digest Magazine #1-4, 44 on; ...Comics Digest Mag. #5-43)(Continues as Betty & Veronica Friends Double Digest #209-on)
Archie Publications: Nov, 1980 - No. 208, Nov, 2010 ($1.00/-$2.69, digest size)

1 3 6 9 15 22 28
2-10: 2(11/81-Katy Keene story), 3(8/82) 2 4 6 9 13 16
11-30 1 3 4 6 8 10
31-50 1 2 3 4 5 7
51-70 4.00
71-191: 110-Begin $2.19-c. 135-Begin $2.39-c. 165-Begin $2.49. 185-Includes reprint of Archie's Girls B&V #1 (1950) and new story where 1950 & 2008 B&V meet 3.00
192-208: 192-Begin $2.69-c 3.00

BETTY & VERONICA ANNUAL DIGEST MAGAZINE
Archie Comics: Sept, 1989 - No. 16, Aug, 1997 ($1.50/$1.75/$1.79, 128 pgs.)

1 1 2 3 5 7 9
2-10: 9-Neon ink logo 5.00
11-16: 16-Begin $1.79-c 3.00

BETTY & VERONICA CHRISTMAS SPECTACULAR (See Archie Giant Series Magazine #159, 168, 180, 191, 204, 217, 229, 241, 453, 465, 477, 489, 501, 513, 525, 536, 547, 558, 568, 580, 593, 606, 618)

BETTY & VERONICA DOUBLE DIGEST MAGAZINE
Archie Enterprises: 1987 - Present ($2.25-$6.99, digest size, 256 pgs.)(...Digest #12 on)

1 2 4 6 8 10 12
2-10 1 2 3 4 5 7
11-25: 5,17-Xmas-c. 16-Capt. Hero story 5.00
26-50 4.00
51-150: 87-Begin $3.19-c. 95-Begin $3.29-c. 114-Begin $3.59-c. 142-Begin $3.69-c 4.00
151-211,213-222: 151-(7/07)-Realistic style Betty & Veronica debuts (thru #154). 160-Cheryl Blossom spotlight. 170-173-Realistic style 4.00
212,223,237,240-($5.99) Titled Betty & Veronica Double Double Digest (320 pages) 6.00
224-($5.99) Titled Betty & Veronica Comics Annual (192 pgs.) 6.00
225,228,238,242,247,250,255,257,260-262-($6.99) Titled Betty & Veronica Jumbo Comics Digest (320 pgs.) 7.00
226,227,229-232,234-236,239,241,243,245,246,249,251,254,256-($4.99) Titled Betty & Veronica Comics Digest or Comics Double Digest 5.00
244,248,252,253,258-($5.99) 244,253-Titled Betty & Veronica Summer Ann. 6.00
Betty & Veronica: in Bad Boy Trouble Vol.1 TPB (2007, $7.49) r/new style from #151-154 8.00

BETTY & VERONICA FRIENDS DOUBLE DIGEST (Continues from B&V Digest Mag. #208)
Archie Publications: No. 209, Jan, 2011 - Present ($3.99-$6.99, digest size)

209-236,238: 209-Cheryl Blossom app. 4.00
237,246-Titled Betty & Veronica Friends Double Double Digest ($5.99, 320 pages) 6.00
239-($4.99) Double Digest 5.00
240,245,250,252,254,256,257-260-($6.99) 257-Winter Annual 7.00
241-244,248-($4.99) Titled Betty & Veronica Friends Comics Digest. 244-Pussycats app. 5.00
247,249,251,253,255-($5.99) 247-Easter Annual. 251-Halloween Annual 6.00

BETTY & VERONICA SPECTACULAR (See Archie Giant Series Mag. #11, 16, 21, 26, 32, 138, 145, 153, 162, 173, 184, 197, 201, 210, 214, 221, 226, 234, 238, 246, 250, 458, 462, 470, 482, 486, 494, 498, 506, 510, 518, 522, 526, 530, 537, 552, 559, 563, 569, 575, 582, 588, 600, 608, 613, 620, 623, and Betty & Veronica)

BETTY AND VERONICA SPECTACULAR
Archie Comics: Oct, 1992 - No. 90, Sept, 2009 ($1.25/$1.50/$1.75/$1.99/$2.19/$2.25/$2.50)

1-Dan DeCarlo-c/a 5.00
2-90: 48-Cheryl Blossom leaves Riverdale. 64-Cheryl Blossom returns 3.00

BETTY & VERONICA SPRING SPECTACULAR (See Archie Giant Series Magazine #569, 582, 595)

BETTY & VERONICA SUMMER FUN (See Archie Giant Series Mag. #8, 13, 18, 23, 28, 34, 140, 147, 155, 164, 175, 187, 199, 212, 224, 236, 248, 460, 484, 496, 508, 520, 529, 539, 550, 561, 572, 585, 598, 611, 621)
Archie Comics: 1994 - Present ($2.00/$2.25/$2.29)

1-($2.00, 52 pgs. plus poster) 4.00
2-6: 5-($2.25-c). 6-($2.29-c) 3.00
Vol. 1 (2003, $10.95) reprints stories from Archie Giant Series editions 12.00

BETTY & VERONICA: VIXENS
Archie Comics Publications: Jan, 2018 - Present ($3.99)

Betty Boop #1 © KFS

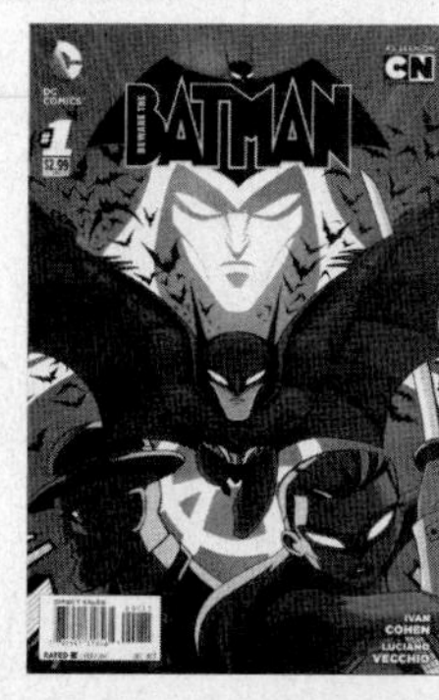

Beware the Batman #1 © DC

The Beyond #11 © ACE

GD 2.0 | VG 4.0 | FN 6.0 | VF 8.0 | VF/NM 9.0 | NM- 9.2

1-4-Betty & Veronica form a biker gang; Rotante-s/Cabrera-a; South Side Serpents app. 4.00

BETTY BOOP (Volume 1)
Dynamite Entertainment: 2016 - No. 4, 2017 ($3.99)
1-4-Langridge-s/Lagacé-a; Koko app.; multiple covers on each 4.00

BETTY BOOP'S BIG BREAK
First Publishing: 1990 ($5.95, 52 pgs.)
nn-By Joshua Quagmire; 60th anniversary ish. 6.00

BETTY PAGE 3-D COMICS
The 3-D Zone: 1991 ($3.95, "7-1/2x10-1/4," 28 pgs., no glasses)
1-Photo inside covers; back-c nudity 2 4 6 8 11 14

BETTY'S DIARY (See Archie Giant Series Magazine No. 555)
Archie Enterprises: April, 1986 - No. 40, Apr, 1991 (#1:65¢; 75¢/95¢)
1 1 2 3 4 5 7
2-10 4.00
11-40 3.00

BETTY'S DIGEST
Archie Enterprises: Nov, 1996 - No. 2 ($1.75/$1.79)
1,2 3.00

BEVERLY HILLBILLIES (TV)
Dell Publishing Co.: 4-6/63 - No. 18, 8/67; No. 19, 10/69; No. 20, 10/70; No. 21, Oct, 1971
1-Photo-c 13 26 39 86 188 290
2-Photo-c 8 16 24 51 96 140
3-9: All have photo covers 6 12 18 40 73 105
10: No photo cover 5 10 15 30 50 70
11-21: All have photo covers. 18-Last 12¢ issue. 19-21-Reprint #1-3 (covers and insides)
5 10 15 33 57 80
NOTE: *#1-9, 11-21 are photo covers.*

BEWARE (Formerly Fantastic; Chilling Tales No. 13 on)
Youthful Magazines: No. 10, June, 1952 - No. 12, Oct, 1952
10-E.A. Poe's Pit & the Pendulum adaptation by Wildey; Harrison/Bache-a; atom bomb and shrunken head-c 69 138 207 442 759 1075
11-Harrison-a; Ambrose Bierce adapt. 48 96 144 302 514 725
12-Used in **SOTI**, pg. 388; Harrison-a 48 96 144 302 514 725

BEWARE
Trojan Magazines/Merit Publ. No. ?: No. 13, 1/53 - No. 16, 7/53; No. 5, 9/53 - No. 15, 5/55
13(#1)-Harrison-a 69 138 207 442 759 1075
14(#2, 3/53)-Krenkel/Harrison-c; dismemberment, severed head panels
48 96 144 302 514 725
15,16(#3, 5/53; #4, 7/53)-Harrison-a 43 86 129 271 461 650
5,9,12,13(1/55) 42 84 126 265 445 625
6-Ill. in **SOTI**- "Children are first shocked and then desensitized by all this brutality." Corpse on cover swipe/V.O.H. #26; girl on cover swipe/Advs. Into Darkness #10
90 180 270 576 988 1400
7,8-Check-a 48 96 144 302 514 725
10-Frazetta/Check-c; Disbrow, Check-a 194 388 582 1242 2121 3000
11-Disbrow-a; heart torn out, blood drainage 48 96 144 302 514 725
14,15: 14-Myron Fass-c. 15-Harrison-a 40 80 120 246 411 575
NOTE: ***Fass** a-5, 6, 8; c-6, 11, 14. **Forte** a-8. **Hollingsworth** a-15(#3), 16(#4), 9; c-16(#4), 8, 9. **Kiefer** a-16(#4), 5, 6, 10.*

BEWARE (Becomes Tomb of Darkness No. 9 on)
Marvel Comics Group: Mar, 1973 - No. 8, May, 1974 (All reprints)
1-Everett-c; Kirby & Sinnott-r ('54) 4 8 12 25 40 55
2-8: 2-Forte, Colan-r. 6-Tuska-a. 7-Torres-r/Mystical Tales #7
3 6 9 16 24 32
NOTE: ***Infantino** a-4r. **Gil Kane** c-4. **Wildey** a-7r.*

BEWARE TERROR TALES
Fawcett Publications: May, 1952 - No. 8, July, 1953
1-E.C. art swipe/Haunt of Fear #5 & Vault of Horror #26
58 116 174 371 636 900
2 39 78 117 240 395 550
3-5,7 36 72 108 211 343 475
6-Classic skeleton-c 41 82 123 256 428 600
8-Tothish-a; people being cooked-c 47 94 141 296 498 700
NOTE: ***Andru** a-2. **Bernard Bailey** a-1; c-1-5. **Powell** a-1, 2, 8. **Sekowsky** a-2.*

BEWARE THE BATMAN (Based on the Cartoon Network series)
DC Comics: Dec, 2013 - No. 6, May, 2014 ($2.99)
1-6: 1-Anarky app. 4-Man-Bat app. 6-Killer Croc app. 3.00

BEWARE THE CREEPER (See Adventure, Best of the Brave & the Bold, Brave & the Bold, 1st Issue Special, Flash #318-323, Showcase #73, World's Finest Comics #249)
National Periodical Publications: May-June, 1968 - No. 6, Mar-Apr, 1969 (All 12¢ issues)
1-(5-6/68)-Classic Ditko-c; Ditko-a in all 8 16 24 54 102 150
2-6: 2-5-Ditko-c. 2-Intro. Proteus. 6-Gil Kane-c 5 10 15 31 53 75

BEWARE THE CREEPER
DC Comics (Vertigo): June, 2003 - No. 5, Oct, 2003 ($2.95, limited series)
1-5-Female vigilante in 1920s Paris; Jason Hall-s/Cliff Chiang-a 3.00

BEWITCHED (TV)
Dell Publishing Co.: 4-6/65 - No. 11, 10/67; No. 12, 10/68 - No. 13, 1/69; No. 14, 10/69
1-Photo-c 13 26 39 87 191 295
2-No photo-c 7 14 21 46 86 125
3-13-All have photo-c. 12-Rep. #1. 13-Last 12¢-c 6 12 18 40 73 105
14-No photo-c; reprints #2 5 10 15 31 53 75

BEYOND!
Marvel Comics: Sept, 2006 - No. 6, Feb, 2007 ($2.99, limited series)
1-6-McDuffie-s/Kolins-a; Spider-Man, Venom, Gravity, Wasp app. 6-Gravity dies 3.00

BEYOND, THE
Ace Magazines: Nov, 1950 - No. 30, Jan, 1955
1-Bakerish-a(p) 55 110 165 352 601 850
2-Bakerish-a(p) 39 78 117 231 378 525
3-10: 10-Woodish-a by Cameron 32 64 96 188 307 425
11-20: 18-Used in **POP**, pgs. 81,82 26 52 78 154 252 350
21-26,28-30 24 48 72 142 234 325
27-Used in **SOTI**, pg. 111 26 52 78 154 252 350
NOTE: ***Cameron** a-10, 11p, 12p, 15, 16, 21-27, 30; c-20. **Colan** a-6, 13, 17. **Sekowsky** a-2, 3, 5, 7, 11, 14, 27r. No. 1 was to appear as Challenge of the Unknown No. 7.*

BEYOND THE FRINGE (Based on the TV series Fringe)
DC Comics: May, 2012 ($3.99, one-shot)
1-Joshua Jackson-s/Jorge Jimenez-a/Drew Johnson-c 4.00

BEYOND THE GRAVE
Charlton Comics: July, 1975 - No. 6, June, 1976; No. 7, Jan, 1983 - No. 17, Oct, 1984
1-Ditko-a (6 pgs.); Sutton painted-c 4 8 12 25 40 55
2-6: 2-5-Ditko-a; Ditko c-2,3,6 3 6 9 16 23 30
7-17: ('83-'84) Reprints. 8,11,16-Ditko-a. 11-Staton-a. 13-Aparo-c(r). 15-Sutton-c (low print run). 16-Palais-a 1 2 3 5 6 8
Modern Comics Reprint 2('78) 6.00
NOTE: ***Howard** a-4. **Kim** a-1. **Larson** a-4, 6.*

BIBLE, THE: EDEN
IDW Publishing: 2003 ($21.99, hardcover graphic novel)
HC-Scott Hampton painted-a; adaptation of Genesis by Dave Elliot and Keith Giffen 22.00

BIBLE TALES FOR YOUNG FOLK (...Young People No. 3-5)
Atlas Comics (OMC): Aug, 1953 - No. 5, Mar, 1954
1 29 58 87 170 278 385
2-Everett, Krigstein, Maneely-a; Robinson-c 18 36 54 105 165 225
3-5: 4,5-Robinson-c 15 30 45 88 137 185

BIG (Movie)
Hit Comics (Dark Horse Comics): Mar, 1989 ($2.00)
1-Adaptation of film; Paul Chadwick-c 3.00

BIG ALL-AMERICAN COMIC BOOK, THE (See All-American Comics)
All-American/National Per. Publ.: 1944 (132 pgs., one-shot) (Early DC Annual)
1-Wonder Woman, Green Lantern, Flash, The Atom, Wildcat, Scribbly, The Whip, Ghost Patrol, Hawkman by Kubert (1st on Hawkman), Hop Harrigan, Johnny Thunder, Little Boy Blue, Mr. Terrific, Mutt & Jeff app.; Sargon on cover only; cover by Kubert/Hibbard/Mayer and others 60 1300 1950 4750 8875 13,000

BIG BABY HUEY (See Baby Huey)

BIG BANG COMICS (Becomes Big Bang #4)
Caliber Press: Spring, 1994 - No. 4, Feb, 1995; No. 0, May, 1995 ($1.95, lim. series)
1-4-($1.95-c) 3.00
0-(5/95, $2.95) Alex Ross-c; color and B&W pages 3.00
Your Big Book of Big Bang Comics TPB ('98, $11.00) r/#0-2 11.00

BIG BANG COMICS (Volume 2)
Image Comics (Highbrow Ent.): V2#1, May, 1996 - No. 35, Jan, 2001 ($1.95-$3.95)
1-23,26: 1-Mighty Man app. 2-4-S.A. Shadowhawk app. 5-Begin $2.95-c. 6-Curt Swan/Murphy Anderson-c. 7-Begin B&W. 12-Savage Dragon-c/app. 16,17,21-Shadow Lady 3.00
24,25,27-35-($3.95): 35-Big Bang vs. Alan Moore's "1963" characters 4.00
...Presents the Ultiman Family (2/05, $3.50) 3.50

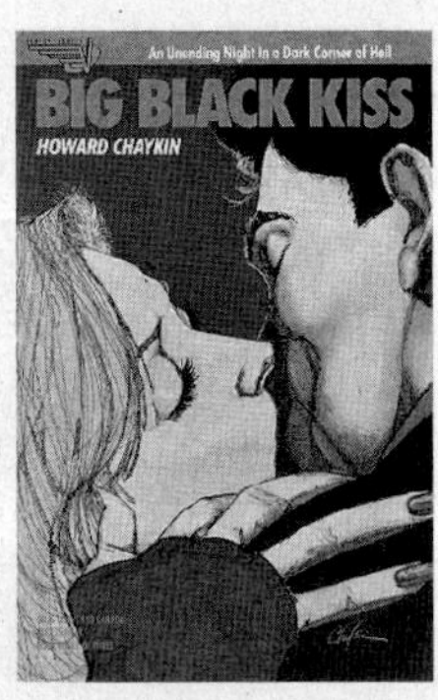

Big Black Kiss #3 © Howard Chaykin

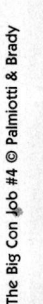

The Big Con Job #4 © Palmiotti & Brady

Big Shot Comics #5 © CCG

	GD 2.0	VG 4.0	FN 6.0	VF 8.0	VF/NM 9.0	NM- 9.2

...Round Table of America (2/04, $3.95) Don Thomas-a 4.00
...Summer Special (8/03, $4.95) World's Nastiest Nazis app. 5.00

BIG BANG PRESENTS (Volume 3)
Big Bang Comics: July, 2006 - No. 5 ($2.95/$3.95, B&W)

1,2: 1-Protoplasman (Plastic Man homage) 3.00
3-5-($3.95) 3-Origin of Protoplasman. 4-Flip book 4.00

BIG BANG UNIVERSE
AC Comics: 2015 ($9.95, B&W)

1-Four new stories; Ultiman, Knight Watchman, Galahad & Whiz Kids app. 10.00

BIG BLACK KISS
Vortex Comics: Sep, 1989 - No. 3, Nov, 1989 ($3.75, B&W, lim. series, mature)

1-3-Chaykin-s/a 4.00

BIG BLOWN BABY (Also see Dark Horse Presents)
Dark Horse Comics: Aug, 1996 - No. 4, Nov, 1996 ($2.95, lim. series, mature)

1-4: Bill Wray-c/a/scripts 3.00

BIG BOOK OF ..., THE
DC Comics (Paradox Press): 1994 - 1999 (B&W)($12.95 - $14.95)

nn-...**BAD,**1998 ($14.95),...**CONSPIRACIES,** 1995 ($12.95), ...**DEATH,**1994 ($12.95), ...**FREAKS,** 1996 ($14.95), ...**GRIMM,** 1999 ($14.95), ...**HOAXES,** 1996 ($14.95), ...**LITTLE CRIMINALS,** 1996 ($14.95), ...**LOSERS,**1997 ($14.95), **MARTYRS,** 1997 ($14.95), ...**SCANDAL,**1997 ($14.95), ...**THE WEIRD WILD WEST,**1998 ($14.95), ...**THUGS,** 1997 ($14.95), ...**UNEXPLAINED,** 1997 ($14.95), ...**URBAN LEGENDS,** 1994 ($12.95), ...**VICE,** 1999 ($14.95), ...**WEIRDOS,** 1995 ($12.95) cover price

BIG BOOK OF FUN COMICS (See New Book of Comics)
National Periodical Publications: Spring, 1936 (Large size, 52 pgs.)
(1st comic book annual & DC annual)

1 (Very rare)-r/New Fun #1-5 2300 4600 6900 15,000 - -

BIG BOOK ROMANCES
Fawcett Publications: Feb, 1950 (no date given) (148 pgs.)

1-Contains remaindered Fawcett romance comics - several combinations possible
84 168 252 538 919 1300

BIG CHIEF WAHOO
Eastern Color Printing/George Dougherty (distr. by Fawcett): July, 1942 - No. 7, Wint., 1943/44?(no year given)(Quarterly)

1-Newspaper-r (on sale 6/15/42) 43 86 129 271 461 650
2-Steve Roper app. 23 46 69 136 223 310
3-5: 4-Chief is holding a Katy Keene comic in one panel
18 36 54 105 165 225
6-7 14 28 42 82 121 160

NOTE: *Kerry Drake in some issues.*

BIG CIRCUS, THE (Movie)
Dell Publishing Co.: No. 1036, Sept-Nov, 1959

Four Color 1036-Photo-c 6 12 18 40 73 105

BIG CON JOB, THE (PALMIOTTI & BRADY'S...)
BOOM! Studios: Mar, 2015 - No. 4, Jun, 2015 ($3.99, limited series)

1-4-Palmiotti & Brady-s/Stanton-a/Conner-c 4.00

BIG COUNTRY, THE (Movie)
Dell Publishing Co.: No. 946, Oct, 1958

Four Color 946-Photo-c 6 12 18 42 79 115

BIG DADDY DANGER
DC Comics: Oct, 2002 - No. 9, June, 2003 ($2.95, limited series)

1-9-Adam Pollina-s/a/c 3.00

BIG DADDY ROTH (Magazine)
Millar Publications: Oct-Nov, 1964 - No. 4, Apr-May, 1965 (35¢)

1-Toth-a; Batman & Robin parody 18 36 54 124 275 425
2-4-Toth-a 12 24 36 82 179 275

BIGFOOT
IDW Publishing: Feb, 2005 - No. 4, May, 2005 ($3.99, limited series)

1-4-Steve Niles & Rob Zombie-s/Richard Corben-a/c 4.00

BIGG TIME
DC Comics (Vertigo): 2002 ($14.95, B&W, graphic novel)

nn-Ty Templeton-s/c/a 15.00

BIG GUY AND RUSTY THE BOY ROBOT, THE (Also See Madman Comics #6,7 & Martha Washington Stranded In Space)
Dark Horse (Legend): July, 1995 - No. 2, Aug, 1995 ($4.95, oversize, limited series)

1,2-Frank Miller scripts & Geoff Darrow-c/a 1 2 3 4 5 7

BIG HAIR PRODUCTIONS
Image Comics: Feb, 2000 - No. 2, Mar, 2000 ($3.50, B&W)

1,2 3.50

BIG HERO ADVENTURES (See Jigsaw)

BIG HERO 6 (Also see Sunfire & Big Hero Six)
Marvel Comics: Nov, 2008 - No. 5, Mar, 2009 ($3.99, limited series)

1-Claremont-s/Nakayama-a; 1-Character design pages & Handbook entries
3 6 9 16 23 30
2-5 1 2 3 5 6 8
...: Brave New Heroes 1 (11/12, $8.99) r/#1-5 9.00

BIG JON & SPARKIE (Radio)(Formerly Sparkie, Radio Pixie)
Ziff-Davis Publ. Co.: No. 4, Sept-Oct, 1952 (Painted-c)

4-Based on children's radio program 19 38 57 111 176 240

BIG LAND, THE (Movie)
Dell Publishing Co.: No. 812, July, 1957

Four Color 812-Alan Ladd photo-c 8 16 24 52 99 145

BIG LIE, THE
Image Comics: Sept, 2011 ($3.99, one-shot)

1-Revisits the 9-11 attacks; Rick Veitch-s/a(p); Thomas Yeates-c 4.00

BIG MAN PLANS
Image Comics: Mar, 2015 - No. 4 ($3.50, limited series)

1-4-Eric Powell & Tim Wiesch-s/Powell-a/c 3.50

BIG MOOSE (Character from Archie Comics)
Archie Comics Publications: Jun, 2017 ($4.99, limited series)

..., One Shot - short stories by various; art by Cory Smith, Pitilli & Jampole 4.00

BIG RED (See Movie Comics)

BIG SHOT COMICS
Columbia Comics Group: May, 1940 - No. 104, Aug, 1949

1-Intro. Skyman; The Face (1st app.; Tony Trent), The Cloak (Spy Master), Marvelo, Monarch of Magicians, Joe Palooka, Charlie Chan, Tom Kerry, Dixie Dugan, Rocky Ryan begin; Charlie Chan moves over from Feature Comics #31 (4/40)
300 600 900 1920 3310 4700
2 100 200 300 635 1093 1550
3-The Cloak called Spy Chief; Skyman-c 90 180 270 576 988 1400
4,5 61 122 183 390 670 950
6-10: 8-Christmas-c 50 100 150 315 533 750
11-13 47 94 141 296 498 700
14-Origin & 1st app. Sparky Watts (6/41) 50 100 150 315 533 750
15-Origin The Cloak 58 116 174 371 636 900
16-20 39 78 117 240 395 550
21-23,27,30: 30-X-Mas-c, WWII-c 34 68 102 204 332 460
24-Classic Tojo-c. 123 246 369 787 1344 1900
25-Hitler-c 84 168 252 538 919 1300
26,29-Japanese WWII-c. 29-Intro. Capt. Yank; Bo (a dog) newspaper strip-r by Frank Beck begin, ends #104. 41 82 123 250 418 585
28-Hitler, Tojo & Mussolini-c 126 252 378 806 1378 1950
31,33-40 24 48 72 142 234 325
32-Vic Jordan newspaper strip reprints begin, ends #52; Hitler, Tojo & Mussolini-c
113 226 339 718 1234 1750
41,42,44,45,47-50: 42-No Skyman. 50-Origin The Face retold
21 42 63 122 199 275
43-Hitler-c 103 206 309 659 1130 1600
46-Hitler, Tojo-c (6/44) 97 194 291 621 1061 1500
51-Tojo Japanese war-c 39 78 117 240 395 550
52-56,58-60: 18 36 54 105 165 225
57-Hitler, Tojo Halloween mask-c 41 82 123 256 428 600
61-70: 63 on-Tony Trent, the Face 14 28 42 82 121 160
71-80: 73-The Face cameo. 74-(2/47)-Mickey Finn begins. 74,80-The Face app. in Tony Trent. 78-Last Charlie Chan strip-r 14 28 42 76 108 140
81-90: 85-Tony Trent marries Babs Walsh. 86-Valentines-c
11 22 33 62 86 110
91-99,101-104: 69-94-Skyman in Outer Space. 96-Xmas-c
10 20 30 56 76 95
100 11 22 33 64 90 115

NOTE: ***Mart Bailey** art on "The Face" No. 1-104. **Guardineer** a-5. Sparky Watts by **Boody Rogers**-No. 14-42, 77-104, (by others No. 43-76). Others than Tony Trent wear "The Face" mask in No. 46-63, 93. Skyman by **Ogden Whitney**-No. 1, 2, 4, 12-37, 49, 70-101. Skyman covers-No. 1, 3, 7-12, 14, 16, 20, 27, 89, 95, 100.*

Big Town #3 © DC

Big Trouble in Little China #10 © 20th Century Fox

Billy Batson and the Magic of Shazam! #6 © DC

BIG SMASH BARGAIN COMICS
No publisher listed: Early 1950s (25¢, 160pgs., Canadian reprints)

	GD 2.0	VG 4.0	FN 6.0	VF 8.0	VF/NM 9.0	NM- 9.2
1-4: Contains 4 comics from various companies bundled with new cover (scarce)	41	82	123	256	428	600

BIG TEX
Toby Press: June, 1953

	GD 2.0	VG 4.0	FN 6.0	VF 8.0	VF/NM 9.0	NM- 9.2
1-Contains (3) John Wayne stories-r with name changed to Big Tex	14	28	42	76	108	140

BIG-3
Fox Feature Syndicate: Fall, 1940 - No. 7, Jan, 1942

	GD 2.0	VG 4.0	FN 6.0	VF 8.0	VF/NM 9.0	NM- 9.2
1-Blue Beetle, The Flame, & Samson begin	252	504	756	1613	2757	3900
2	103	206	309	659	1130	1600
3-5	77	154	231	493	847	1200
6,7: 6-Last Samson. 7-WWII Nazi-c; V-Man app.	58	116	174	371	636	900

BIG THUNDER MOUNTAIN RAILROAD (Disney Kingdoms)
Marvel Comics: May, 2015 - No. 5, Oct, 2015 ($3.99, limited series)

	GD 2.0	VG 4.0	FN 6.0	VF 8.0	VF/NM 9.0	NM- 9.2
1-5: 1-Dennis Hopeless-s/Tigh Walker-a/Pasqual Ferry-c. 3-Ruiz-a						4.00

BIG TOP COMICS, THE (TV's Great Circus Show)
Toby Press: 1951 - No. 2, 1951 (No month)

	GD 2.0	VG 4.0	FN 6.0	VF 8.0	VF/NM 9.0	NM- 9.2
1	12	24	36	69	97	125
2	9	18	27	52	69	85

BIG TOWN (Radio/TV) (Also see Movie Comics, 1946)
National Periodical Publ: Jan, 1951 - No. 50, Mar-Apr, 1958 (No. 1-9: 52pgs.)

	GD 2.0	VG 4.0	FN 6.0	VF 8.0	VF/NM 9.0	NM- 9.2
1-Dan Barry-a begins	69	138	207	442	759	1075
2	37	74	111	222	361	500
3-10	22	44	66	132	216	300
11-20	18	36	54	105	165	225
21-31: Last pre-code (1-2/55)	14	28	42	76	108	140
32-50: 46-Grey tone cover	10	20	30	56	76	95

BIG TROUBLE IN LITTLE CHINA (Based on the 1986 Kurt Russell movie)
BOOM! Studios: Jun, 2014 - No. 25, Jun, 2016 ($3.99)

	GD 2.0	VG 4.0	FN 6.0	VF 8.0	VF/NM 9.0	NM- 9.2
1-12-Continuing advs. of Jack Burton; John Carpenter & Eric Powell-s; Brian Churilla-a; multiple covers by Powell and others on each						4.00
13-24: 13-16-Van Lente-s/Eisma-a. 17-20-McDaid-a. 21-24-Santos-a						4.00
25-($4.99) Van Lente-s/Santos-a						5.00

BIG TROUBLE IN LITTLE CHINA / ESCAPE FROM NEW YORK (Based on the movies)
BOOM! Studios: Oct, 2016 - No. 6, Mar, 2017 ($3.99)

	GD 2.0	VG 4.0	FN 6.0	VF 8.0	VF/NM 9.0	NM- 9.2
1-6-Jack Burton meets Snake Plisskin; Greg Pak-s/Daniel Bayliss-a						4.00

BIG TROUBLE IN LITTLE CHINA: OLD MAN JACK (Based on the movie)
BOOM! Studios: Sept, 2017 - Present ($3.99)

	GD 2.0	VG 4.0	FN 6.0	VF 8.0	VF/NM 9.0	NM- 9.2
1-6-Old Jack Burton battles Lo Pan; Carpenter & Burch-s/Corona-a; multiple covers						4.00

BIG VALLEY, THE (TV)
Dell Publishing Co.: June, 1966 - No. 5, Oct, 1967; No. 6, Oct, 1969

	GD 2.0	VG 4.0	FN 6.0	VF 8.0	VF/NM 9.0	NM- 9.2
1: Photo-c #1-5	5	10	15	31	53	75
2-6: 6-Reprints #1	3	6	9	21	33	45

BIKER MICE FROM MARS (TV)
Marvel Comics: Nov, 1993 - No. 3, Jan, 1994 ($1.50, limited series)

	GD 2.0	VG 4.0	FN 6.0	VF 8.0	VF/NM 9.0	NM- 9.2
1-3: 1-Intro Vinnie, Modo & Throttle. 2-Origin						4.00

BILL & TED GO TO HELL (Movie)
BOOM! Studios: Feb, 2016 - No. 4, May, 2016 ($3.99, limited series)

	GD 2.0	VG 4.0	FN 6.0	VF 8.0	VF/NM 9.0	NM- 9.2
1-4-Joines-s/Bachan-a						4.00

BILL & TED SAVE THE UNIVERSE (Movie)
BOOM! Studios: Jun, 2017 - No. 5, Oct, 2017 ($3.99, limited series)

	GD 2.0	VG 4.0	FN 6.0	VF 8.0	VF/NM 9.0	NM- 9.2
1-5-Joines-s/Bachan-a						4.00

BILL & TED'S BOGUS JOURNEY
Marvel Comics: Sept, 1991 ($2.95, squarebound, 84 pgs.)

	GD 2.0	VG 4.0	FN 6.0	VF 8.0	VF/NM 9.0	NM- 9.2
1-Adapts movie sequel						4.00

BILL & TED'S EXCELLENT COMIC BOOK (Movie)
Marvel Comics: Dec, 1991 - No. 12, 1992 ($1.00/$1.25)

	GD 2.0	VG 4.0	FN 6.0	VF 8.0	VF/NM 9.0	NM- 9.2
1-12: 3-Begin $1.25-c						3.00

BILL & TED'S MOST TRIUMPHANT RETURN (Movie)
BOOM! Studios: Mar, 2015 - No. 6, Aug, 2015 ($3.99, limited series)

	GD 2.0	VG 4.0	FN 6.0	VF 8.0	VF/NM 9.0	NM- 9.2
1-6: 1-Follows the end of the second movie; Lynch-s/Gaylord-a/Guillory-c						4.00

BILL BARNES COMICS (...America's Air Ace Comics No. 2 on) (Becomes Air Ace V2#1 on; also see Shadow Comics)
Street & Smith Publications: Oct, 1940(No. month given) - No. 12, Oct, 1943

	GD 2.0	VG 4.0	FN 6.0	VF 8.0	VF/NM 9.0	NM- 9.2
1-23 pgs.-comics; Rocket Rooney begins	107	214	321	680	1165	1650
2-Barnes as The Phantom Flyer app.; Tuska-a	53	106	159	334	567	825
3-5	42	84	126	269	452	635
6,8,10,12	39	78	117	233	384	535
7-(1942) Story about dropping atomic bomb on Japan	71	142	213	454	777	1100
9-Classic WWII cover	58	116	174	371	636	900
11-Japanese WWII Gremlin cover	40	80	120	246	411	575

BILL BATTLE, THE ONE MAN ARMY (Also see Master Comics No. 133)
Fawcett Publications: Oct, 1952 - No. 4, Apr, 1953 (All photo-c)

	GD 2.0	VG 4.0	FN 6.0	VF 8.0	VF/NM 9.0	NM- 9.2
1	14	28	42	82	121	160
2	9	18	27	47	61	75
3,4	8	16	24	42	54	65

BILL BLACK'S FUN COMICS
Paragon #1-3/Americomics #4: Dec, 1982 - No. 4, Mar, 1983 ($1.75/$2.00, Baxter paper) (1st AC comic)

	GD 2.0	VG 4.0	FN 6.0	VF 8.0	VF/NM 9.0	NM- 9.2
1-(B&W fanzine; 7x8-1/2"; low print) Intro. Capt. Paragon, Phantom Lady & Commando D	2	4	6	13	18	22
2-4: 2,3-(B&W fanzines; 8-1/2x11"). 3-Kirby-c. 4-($2.00, color)-Origin Nightfall (formerly Phantom Lady); Nightveil app.; Kirby-a	1	3	4	6	8	10

BILL BOYD WESTERN (Movie star; see Hopalong Cassidy & Western Hero)
Fawcett Publ: Feb, 1950 - No. 23, June, 1952 (1-3,7,11,14-on: 36 pgs.)

	GD 2.0	VG 4.0	FN 6.0	VF 8.0	VF/NM 9.0	NM- 9.2
1-Bill Boyd & his horse Midnite begin; photo front/back-c	30	60	90	177	289	400
2-Painted-c	16	32	48	94	147	200
3-Photo-c begin, end #23; last photo back-c	14	28	42	80	115	150
4-6(52 pgs.)	12	24	36	69	97	125
7,11(36 pgs.)	10	20	30	56	76	95
8-10,12,13(52 pgs.)	10	20	30	58	79	100
14-22	9	18	27	52	69	85
23-Last issue	10	20	30	56	76	95

BILL BUMLIN (See Treasury of Comics No. 3)

BILL ELLIOTT (See Wild Bill Elliott)

BILLI 99
Dark Horse Comics: Sept, 1991 - No. 4, 1991 ($3.50, B&W, lim. series, 52 pgs.)

	GD 2.0	VG 4.0	FN 6.0	VF 8.0	VF/NM 9.0	NM- 9.2
1-4: Tim Sale-c/a						4.00

BILL STERN'S SPORTS BOOK
Ziff-Davis Publ. Co.(Approved Comics): Spring-Sum, 1951 - V2#2, Win, 1952

	GD 2.0	VG 4.0	FN 6.0	VF 8.0	VF/NM 9.0	NM- 9.2
V1#10-(1951) Whitney painted-c	21	42	63	122	199	275
2-(Sum/52; reg. size)	16	32	48	94	147	200
V2#2-(1952, 96 pgs.)-Krigstein, Kinstler-a	21	42	63	126	206	285

BILL THE BULL: ONE SHOT, ONE BOURBON, ONE BEER
Boneyard Press: Dec, 1994 ($2.95, B&W, mature)

	GD 2.0	VG 4.0	FN 6.0	VF 8.0	VF/NM 9.0	NM- 9.2
1						3.00

BILLY AND BUGGY BEAR (See Animal Fun)
I.W. Enterprises/Super: 1958; 1964

	GD 2.0	VG 4.0	FN 6.0	VF 8.0	VF/NM 9.0	NM- 9.2
I.W. Reprint #1, #7('58)-All Surprise Comics #?(Same issue-r for both)	2	4	6	10	14	18
Super Reprint #10(1964)	2	4	6	8	11	14

BILLY BATSON AND THE MAGIC OF SHAZAM! (Follows Shazam: The Monster Society of Evil mini-series)
DC Comics: Sept, 2008 - No. 21, Dec, 2010 ($2.25/$2.50, all ages title)

	GD 2.0	VG 4.0	FN 6.0	VF 8.0	VF/NM 9.0	NM- 9.2
1-17: 1-4-Mike Kunkel-s/a/c; Theo (Black) Adam app. 5-DeStefano-a. 13-16-Black Adam						4.00
1-Variant B&W sketch cover						4.00
18-21 ($2.99) 21-Justice League cameo						4.00
TPB (2010, $12.99) r/#1-6; cover and haracter sketches						13.00
...: Mr. Mind Over Matter TPB (2011, $12.99) r/#7-12						13.00

BILLY BUCKSKIN WESTERN (2-Gun Western No. 4)
Atlas Comics (IMC No. 1/MgPC No. 2,3): Nov, 1955 - No. 3, Mar, 1956

	GD 2.0	VG 4.0	FN 6.0	VF 8.0	VF/NM 9.0	NM- 9.2
1-Mort Drucker-a; Maneely-c/a	18	36	54	107	169	230
2-Mort Drucker-a	11	22	33	64	90	115
3-Williamson, Drucker-a	14	28	42	76	108	140

BILLY BUNNY (Black Cobra No. 6 on)
Excellent Publications: Feb-Mar, 1954 - No. 5, Oct-Nov, 1954

	GD 2.0	VG 4.0	FN 6.0	VF 8.0	VF/NM 9.0	NM- 9.2
1	10	20	30	56	76	95

Billy the Kid #8 © TOBY

Billy West #6 © STD

Birds of Prey #23 © DC

	GD 2.0	VG 4.0	FN 6.0	VF 8.0	VF/NM 9.0	NM- 9.2
2	7	14	21	35	43	50
3-5	6	12	18	28	34	40

BILLY BUNNY'S CHRISTMAS FROLICS
Farrell Publications: 1952 (25¢ Giant, 100 pgs.)

	GD 2.0	VG 4.0	FN 6.0	VF 8.0	VF/NM 9.0	NM- 9.2
1	22	44	66	132	216	300

BILLY MAKE BELIEVE
United Features Syndicate: No. 14, 1939

	GD 2.0	VG 4.0	FN 6.0	VF 8.0	VF/NM 9.0	NM- 9.2
Single Series 14	32	64	96	192	314	435

BILLY NGUYEN, PRIVATE EYE
Caliber Press: V2#1, 1990 ($2.50)

	GD 2.0	VG 4.0	FN 6.0	VF 8.0	VF/NM 9.0	NM- 9.2
V2#1						3.00

BILLY THE KID (Formerly The Masked Raider; also see Doc Savage Comics & Return of the Outlaw)
Charlton Publ. Co.: No. 9, Nov, 1957 - No. 121, Dec, 1976; No. 122, Sept, 1977 - No. 123, Oct, 1977; No. 124, Feb, 1978 - No. 153, Mar, 1983

	GD 2.0	VG 4.0	FN 6.0	VF 8.0	VF/NM 9.0	NM- 9.2
9	10	20	30	58	79	100
10,12,14,17-19: 12-2 pg Check-sty	8	16	24	40	50	60
11-(68 pgs.)-Origin & 1st app. The Ghost Train	9	18	27	50	65	80
13-Williamson/Torres-a	8	16	24	44	57	70
15-Origin; 2 pgs. Williamson-a	8	16	24	44	57	70
16-Williamson-a, 2 pgs.	8	16	24	42	54	65
20-26-Severin-a(3-4 each)	8	16	24	44	57	70
27-30: 30-Masked Rider app.	3	6	9	18	28	38
31-40	3	6	9	15	22	28
41-60	2	4	6	13	18	22
61-65	2	4	6	10	14	18
66-Bounty Hunter series begins.	3	6	9	14	20	25
67-80: Bounty Hunter series; not in #79,82,84-86	2	4	6	10	14	18
81-84,86-90: 87-Last Bounty Hunter. 88-1st app. Mr. Young of the Boothill Gazette	2	4	6	8	10	12
85-Early Kaluta-a (4 pgs.)	2	4	6	9	13	16
91-123: 110-Mr. Young of Boothill app. 111-Origin The Ghost Train. 117-Gunsmith & Co., The Cheyenne Kid app.	1	2	3	5	6	8
124(2/78)-153						6.00
Modern Comics 109 (1977 reprint)						5.00

NOTE: ***Boyette** a-88-110. **Kim** a-73. **Morsi** a-12,14. **Sattler** a-118-123. **Severin** a(r)-121-129, 134; c-23, 25. **Sutton** a-111.*

BILLY THE KID ADVENTURE MAGAZINE
Toby Press: Oct, 1950 - No. 29, 1955

	GD 2.0	VG 4.0	FN 6.0	VF 8.0	VF/NM 9.0	NM- 9.2
1-Williamson/Frazetta-a (2 pgs) r/from John Wayne Adventure Comics #2; photo-c	31	62	93	182	296	410
2-Photo-c	12	24	36	69	97	125
3-Williamson/Frazetta "The Claws of Death", 4 pgs. plus Williamson art	34	68	102	199	325	450
4,5,7,8,10: 4,7-Photo-c	9	18	27	52	69	85
6-Frazetta assist on "Nightmare"; photo-c	15	30	45	83	124	165
9-Kurtzman Pot-Shot Pete; photo-c	11	22	33	64	90	115
11,12,15-20: 11-Photo-c	8	16	24	42	54	65
13-Kurtzman-r/John Wayne #12 (Genius)	9	18	27	47	61	75
14-Williamson/Frazetta; r-of #1 (2 pgs.)	10	20	30	56	76	95
21,23-29	7	14	21	37	46	55
22-Williamson/Frazetta-r(1pg.)/#1; photo-c	8	16	24	42	54	65

BILLY THE KID AND OSCAR (Also see Fawcett's Funny Animals)
Fawcett Publications: Winter, 1945 - No. 3, Fall, 1946 (Funny animal)

	GD 2.0	VG 4.0	FN 6.0	VF 8.0	VF/NM 9.0	NM- 9.2
1	15	30	45	86	133	180
2,3	10	20	30	58	79	100

BILLY THE KID'S OLD TIMEY ODDITIES
Dark Horse Comics: Apr, 2005 - No. 4, July, 2005 ($2.99, limited series)

	GD 2.0	VG 4.0	FN 6.0	VF 8.0	VF/NM 9.0	NM- 9.2
1-4-Eric Powell-s/c; Kyle Hotz-a						4.00
TPB (2005, $13.95) r/series						14.00
... and the Ghostly Fiend of London (9/10 - No. 4, 12/10, $3.99) 1-4-Powell-s/c; Kyle Hotz-a; Goon back-up; Powell-s/a						4.00
... and the Orm of Loch Ness (10/12 - No. 4, 1/13, $3.50) 1-4-Powell-s/Hotz-a/c						4.00

BILLY WEST (Bill West No. 9,10)
Standard Comics (Visual Editions): 1949-No. 9, Feb, 1951; No. 10, Feb, 1952

	GD 2.0	VG 4.0	FN 6.0	VF 8.0	VF/NM 9.0	NM- 9.2
1	18	36	54	103	162	220
2	11	22	33	62	86	110
3-6,9,10	10	20	30	54	72	90
7,8-Schomburg-c	11	22	33	62	86	110

NOTE: ***Celardo** a-1-6, 9; c-1-3. **Moreira** a-3. **Roussos** a-2.*

BING CROSBY (See Feature Films)

BINGO (...Comics) (H. C. Blackerby)
Howard Publ.: 1945 (Reprints National material)

	GD 2.0	VG 4.0	FN 6.0	VF 8.0	VF/NM 9.0	NM- 9.2
1-L. B. Cole opium-c; blank back-c	39	78	117	240	395	550

BINGO, THE MONKEY DOODLE BOY
St. John Publishing Co.: Aug, 1951; Oct, 1953

	GD 2.0	VG 4.0	FN 6.0	VF 8.0	VF/NM 9.0	NM- 9.2
1(8/51)-By Eric Peters	10	20	30	54	72	90
1(10/53)	8	16	24	40	50	60

BINKY (Formerly Leave It to...)
National Periodical Publ./DC Comics: No. 72, 4-5/70 - No. 81, 10-11/71; No. 82, Summer/77

	GD 2.0	VG 4.0	FN 6.0	VF 8.0	VF/NM 9.0	NM- 9.2
72-76	4	8	12	27	44	60
77-79: (68 pgs.). 77-Bobby Sherman 1pg. story w/photo. 78-1 pg. sty on Barry Williams of Brady Bunch. 79-Osmonds 1pg. story	5	10	15	35	63	90
80,81 (52 pgs.)-Sweat Pain story	5	10	15	31	53	75
82 (1977, one-shot)	4	8	12	27	44	60

BINKY'S BUDDIES
National Periodical Publications: Jan-Feb, 1969 - No. 12, Nov-Dec, 1970

	GD 2.0	VG 4.0	FN 6.0	VF 8.0	VF/NM 9.0	NM- 9.2
1	8	16	24	51	96	140
2-12: 3-Last 12¢ issue	4	8	12	27	44	60

BIONIC MAN (TV)
Dynamite Entertainment: 2011 - No. 26, 2013 ($3.99)

	GD 2.0	VG 4.0	FN 6.0	VF 8.0	VF/NM 9.0	NM- 9.2
1-26: 1-Kevin Smith & Phil Hester-s; Lau-a; multiple covers. 12-15-Bigfoot app.						4.00
Annual 1 (2013, $4.99) The Venus Probe; Beatty-s/Mayhew-c						5.00

BIONIC MAN VS. THE BIONIC WOMAN (TV)
Dynamite Entertainment: 2013 - No. 5, 2013 ($3.99, limited series)

	GD 2.0	VG 4.0	FN 6.0	VF 8.0	VF/NM 9.0	NM- 9.2
1-5-Champagne-s/Luis-a; 3 covers on each						4.00

BIONIC WOMAN, THE (TV)
Charlton Publications: Oct, 1977 - No. 5, June, 1978

	GD 2.0	VG 4.0	FN 6.0	VF 8.0	VF/NM 9.0	NM- 9.2
1	5	10	15	30	50	70
2-5	3	6	9	19	30	40

BIONIC WOMAN, THE (TV)
Dynamite Entertainment: 2013 - No. 10, 2013 ($3.99)

	GD 2.0	VG 4.0	FN 6.0	VF 8.0	VF/NM 9.0	NM- 9.2
1-10: 1-Tobin-s/Renaud-c/Carvalho-a; origin re-told						4.00

BIONIC WOMAN, THE: SEASON FOUR (TV)
Dynamite Entertainment: 2014 - No. 4, 2014 ($3.99, limited series)

	GD 2.0	VG 4.0	FN 6.0	VF 8.0	VF/NM 9.0	NM- 9.2
1-4-Jerwa-s/Cabrera-a. 1-Reg & photo-c						4.00

BIRDS OF PREY (Also see Black Canary/Oracle: Birds of Prey)
DC Comics: Jan, 1999 - No. 127, Apr, 2009 ($1.99/$2.50/$2.99)

	GD 2.0	VG 4.0	FN 6.0	VF 8.0	VF/NM 9.0	NM- 9.2
1-Dixon-s/Land-c/a	2	4	6	8	10	12
2-4						6.00
5-7,9-15: 15-Guice-a begins.						4.00
8-Nightwing-c/app.; Barbara & Dick's circus date	4	8	12	23	37	50
16-38: 23-Grodd-c/app. 26-Bane app. 32-Noto-c begin						3.00
39,40-Bruce Wayne: Murderer pt. 5,12						3.50
41-Bruce Wayne: Fugitive pt. 2						4.00
42-46: 42-Fabry-a. 45-Deathstroke-c/app.						3.00
47-74,77-91: 47-49-Terry Moore-s/Conner & Palmiotti-a; Noto-c. 50-Gilbert Hernandez-s begin. 52,54-Metamorpho app. 56-Simone-s/Benes-a begin. 65,67,68,70-Land-c. 86-Timm-a (7 pgs.)						3.00
75-($2.95) Pearson-c; back-up story of Lady Blackhawk						4.00
76-Debut of Black Alice (from Day of Vengeance)	1	2	3	5	6	8
92-99,101-127: 92-One Year Later. 94-Begin $2.99-c; Prometheus app. 96,97-Black Alice app. 98,99-New Batgirl app. 99-Black Canary leaves the team. 104-107-Secret Six app.						3.00
100-($3.99) new team recruited; Black Canary origin re-told						4.00
TPB (1999, $17.95) r/ previous series and one-shots						18.00
...: Batgirl 1 (2/98, $2.95) Dixon-s/Frank-c						5.00
...: Batgirl/Catwoman 1 ('03, $5.95) Robertson-a; cont'd in BOP: Catwoman/Oracle 1						6.00
...: Between Dark & Dawn TPB (2006, $14.99) r/#69-75						15.00
...: Blood and Circuits TPB (2007, $17.99) r/#96-103						18.00
...: Catwoman/Oracle 1 ('03, $5.95) Cont'd from BOP: Batgirl/Catwoman 1; David Ross-a						6.00
...: Club Kids TPB (2008, $17.99) r/#109-112,118						18.00
...: Dead of Winter TPB (2008, $17.99) r/#104-108						18.00
...: Metropolis or Dust TPB (2008, $17.99) r/#113-117						18.00
...: Of Like Minds TPB (2004, $14.95) r/#55-61						15.00
...: Old Friends, New Enemies TPB (2003, $17.95) r/#1-6, ...: Batgirl, ...: Wolves						18.00
...: Perfect Pitch TPB (2007, $17.99) r/#86-90,92-95						18.00
...: Platinum Flats TPB (2009, $17.99) r/#119-124						18.00

Birds of Prey (2010 series) #3 © DC

Birthright #18 © Skybound

Black Bolt (2017 series) #5 © MAR

GD VG FN VF VF/NM NM-
2.0 4.0 6.0 8.0 9.0 9.2

GD VG FN VF VF/NM NM-
2.0 4.0 6.0 8.0 9.0 9.2

...: Revolution 1 (1997, $2.95) Frank-c/Dixon-s 5.00
... Secret Files 2003 (8/03, $4.95) Short stories, pin-ups and profile pages; Noto-c 5.00
...: Sensei and Student TPB (2005, $17.95) r/#62-68 18.00
...: The Battle Within TPB (2006, $17.99) r/#76-85 18.00
...: The Ravens 1 (6/98, $1.95)-Dixon-s; Girlfrenzy issue 4.00
...: Wolves 1 (10/97, $2.95) Dixon-s/Giordano & Faucher-a 5.00

BIRDS OF PREY (Brightest Day)
DC Comics: Jul, 2010 - No. 15, Oct, 2011 ($2.99)
1-Simone-s/Benes-a/c; Hawk and Dove join team, Penguin app. 3.00
1-Variant cover by Chiang 5.00
2-15: 2-4-Penguin app. 7-10-"Death of Oracle". 11-Catman app. 14,15-Tucci-a 3.00
... End Run HC (2011, $22.99, d.j.) r/#1-6 23.00

BIRDS OF PREY (DC New 52)
DC Comics: Nov, 2011 - No. 34, Oct, 2014 ($2.99)
1-24: 1-Swierczynski-s/Saiz-a; intro. Starling. 2-Katana & Poison Ivy join. 4-Batgirl joins. 9-Night of the Owls. 16-Strix joins. 18-20-Mr. Freeze app. 3.00
25-($3.99) Zero Year tie-in; flashback to Dinah's childhood; John Lynch app. 4.00
26-34: 26-Birds vs. Basilisk. 28-Gothtopia tie-in; Ra's al Ghul app. 32-34-Suicide Squad 3.00
#0 (11/12, $2.99) Black Canary and Batgirl first meeting; Molenaar-a/Lau-c 3.00
...: Futures End 1 (11/14, $2.99, regular-c) Five years later; The Red League 3.00
...: Futures End 1 (11/14, $3.99, 3-D cover) 4.00

BIRDS OF PREY: MANHUNT
DC Comics: Sept, 1996 - No. 4, Dec, 1996 ($1.95, limited series)
1-Features Black Canary, Oracle, Huntress, & Catwoman; Chuck Dixon scripts; Gary Frank-c on all. 1-Catwoman cameo only 1 2 3 5 6 8
2-4 6.00
NOTE: *Gary Frank c-1-4. Matt Haley a-1-4p. Wade Von Grawbadger a-1i.*

BIRTH CAUL, THE
Eddie Campbell Comics: 1999 ($5.95, B&W, one-shot)
1-Alan Moore-s/Eddie Campbell-a 6.00

BIRTH OF THE DEFIANT UNIVERSE, THE
Defiant: May, 1993
nn-Contains promotional artwork & text; limited print run of 1000 copies. 2 4 6 10 14 18

BIRTHRIGHT
Image Comics (Skybound): Oct, 2014 - Present ($2.99/$3.99)
1-25-Joshua Williamson-s/Andrei Bressan-a 3.00
26-30-($3.99) 27-Regular and Walking Dead tribute covers 4.00

BISHOP (See Uncanny X-Men & X-Men)
Marvel Comics: Dec, 1994 - No.4, Mar, 1995 ($2.95, limited series)
1-4: Foil-c; Shard & Mountjoy in all. 1-Storm app. 4.00

BISHOP THE LAST X-MAN
Marvel Comics: Oct, 1999 - No. 16, Jan, 2001 ($2.99/$1.99/$2.25)
1-($2.99)-Jeanty-a 4.00
2-8-($1.99): 2-Two covers 3.00
9-11,13-16: 9-Begin $2.25-c. 15-Maximum Security x-over; Xavier app. 3.00
12-($2.99) 4.00

BISHOP: XAVIER SECURITY ENFORCER
Marvel Comics: Jan, 1998 - No.3, Mar, 1998 ($2.50, limited series)
1-3: Ostrander-s 3.00

BITCH PLANET
Image Comics: Dec, 2014 - Present ($3.50/$3.99)
1-DeConnick-s/De Landro-a/c 5.00
2-9: 3-Origin of Penny Rolle. 5-Begin $3.99-c. 6-Meiko flashback 4.00

BITCH PLANET: TRIPLE FEATURE
Image Comics: Jun, 2017 - Present ($3.99)
1-5-Short story anthology by various; De Landro-c. 5-Charretier-a 4.00

BITE CLUB
DC Comics (Vertigo): Jun, 2004 - No. 6, Nov, 2004 ($2.95, limited series)
1-6-Chaykin-s/Tischman-a/Quitely-c 3.00
TPB Digest (2005, $9.99) r/#1-6; cover gallery 10.00
The Complete Bite Club TPB (2007, $19.99) r/#1-6 and ...: Vampire Crime Unit #1-5 20.00

BITE CLUB: VAMPIRE CRIME UNIT
DC Comics (Vertigo): Jun, 2006 - No. 5 ($2.99, limited series)
1-5:1-Chaykin & Tischman-s/Hahn-a/Quitely-c. 4-Chaykin-c 3.00

BIZARRE ADVENTURES (Formerly Marvel Preview)
Marvel Comics Group: No. 25, 3/81 - No. 34, 2/83 (#25-33: Magazine-$1.50)
25,26: 25-Lethal Ladies. 26-King Kull; Bolton-c/a 2 4 6 8 11 14
27,28: 27-Phoenix, Iceman & Nightcrawler app. 28-The Unlikely Heroes; Elektra by Miller; Neal Adams-a 2 4 6 11 16 20
29,30,32,33: 29-Stephen King's Lawnmower Man. 30-Tomorrow; 1st app. Silhouette. 32-Gods; Thor-c/s. 33-Horror; Dracula app.; photo-c 2 3 4 6 8 10
31-After The Violence Stops; new Hangman story; Miller-a 2 4 6 8 11 14
34 ($2.00, Baxter paper, comic size)-Son of Santa; Christmas special; Howard the Duck by Paul Smith 1 2 3 5 7 9
NOTE: *Alcala a-27i. Austin a-25i, 28i. Bolton a-26, 32. J. Buscema a-27p, 29, 30p; c-26. Byrne a-31 (2 pg.). Golden a-25p, 28p. Perez a-27p. Rogers a-25p. Simonson a-29; c-29. Paul Smith a-34.*

BIZARRO
DC Comics: Aug, 2015 - No. 6, Jan, 2016 ($2.99, limited series)
1-6-Corson-s/Duarte-a; Jimmy Olsen app. 4-Zatanna app. 6-Superman app. 3.00

BIZARRO COMICS!
DC Comics: 2001 ($29.95, hardcover, one-shot)
HC-Short stories of DC heroes by various alternative cartoonists including Dorkin, Pope, Haspiel, Kidd, Kochalka, Millionaire, Stephens, Wray; includes "Superman's Babysitter" by Kyle Baker from Elseworlds 80-Page Giant recalled by DC; Groening-c 30.00
Softcover (2003, $19.95) 20.00

BIZARRO WORLD
DC Comics: 2005 ($29.95, hardcover, one-shot)
HC-Short stories by various alternative cartoonists including Bagge, Baker, Dorkin, Dunn, Kupperman, Morse, Oswalt, Pekar, Simpson, Stewart; Jaime Hernandez-c 30.00
Softcover (2006, $19.99) 20.00

BLACK ADAM (See 52 and Countdown)
DC Comics: Oct, 2007 - No. 6, Mar, 2008 ($2.99, limited series)
1-6: 1-Mahnke-a/c; Isis returns; Felix Faust app. 5.00
...: The Dark Age TPB (2008, $17.99) r/#1-6; Alex Ross-c 18.00

BLACK AND WHITE (See Large Feature Comic, Series I)

BLACK & WHITE (Also see Codename: Black & White)
Image Comics (Extreme): Oct, 1994 - No. 3, Jan, 1995 ($1.95, limited series)
1-3: Thibert-c/story 3.00

BLACK & WHITE MAGIC
Innovation Publishing: 1991 ($2.95, 98 pgs., B&W w/30 pgs. color, squarebound)
1-Contains rebound comics w/covers removed; contents may vary 4.00

BLACK AXE
Marvel Comics (UK): Apr, 1993 - No. 7, Oct, 1993 ($1.75)
1-4: 1-Romita Jr.-c. 2-Sunfire-c/s 3.00
5-7: 5-Janson-c; Black Panther app. 6,7-Black Panther-c/s 3.00

BLACK BAG
Legendary Comics: Nov, 2015 - Present ($3.99)
1-3-Roberson-s/Bastos-a 4.00

BLACKBALL COMICS
Blackball Comics: Mar, 1994 ($3.00)
1-Trencher-c/story by Giffen; John Pain by O'Neill 3.00

BLACK BAT, THE
Dynamite Entertainment: 2013 - No. 12, 2014 ($3.99)
1-12-Buccellato-s/Cliquet-a; multiple covers on each 4.00

BLACKBEARD'S GHOST (See Movie Comics)

BLACK BEAUTY (See Son of Black Beauty)
Dell Publishing Co.: No. 440, Dec, 1952
Four Color 440 5 10 15 34 60 85

BLACK BEETLE, THE
Dark Horse Comics: Jan, 2013 - No. 4, Jun, 2013 ($3.99, limited series)
1-4-Francavilla-s/a/c 4.00

BLACK BOLT (The Inhumans)
Marvel Comics: Jul, 2017 - Present ($3.99)
1-11: 1-6-Saladin Ahmed-s/Christian Ward-a; Absorbing Man app. 7-Irving-a 4.00

BLACK BOLT: SOMETHING INHUMAN THIS WAY COMES
Marvel Comics: Sept, 2013 ($7.99, one-shot)
1-Reprints Black Bolt app. in Amazing Adventures #5-10 & Avengers #95 8.00

BLACKBURNE COVENANT, THE

Black Canary (2015 series) #6 © DC

Black Cat Comics #1 © HARV

Black Diamond Western #16 © LEV

	GD	VG	FN	VF	VF/NM	NM-
	2.0	4.0	6.0	8.0	9.0	9.2

Dark Horse Comics: Apr, 2003 - No. 4, July, 2003 ($2.99, limited series)

1-4-Nicieza-s/Raffaele-a 3.00
TPB (2003, $12.95) r/#1-4 13.00

BLACK CANARY (See All Star Comics #38, Flash Comics #86, Justice League of America #75 & World's Finest #244)
DC Comics: Nov, 1991 - No. 4, Feb, 1992 ($1.75, limited series)

1-4 3.00

BLACK CANARY
DC Comics: Jan, 1993 - No. 12, Dec, 1993 ($1.75)

1-7 3.00
8-12: 8-The Ray-c/story. 9,10-Huntress-c/story 3.00

BLACK CANARY (Follows Oliver Queen's marriage proposal in Green Arrow #75)
DC Comics: Early Sept, 2007 - No. 4, Late Oct, 2007 ($2.99, bi-weekly limited series)

1-4-Bedard-s/Siqueira-a 3.00
... Wedding Planner 1 (11/07, $2.99) Roux-c/Ferguson & Norrie-a 3.00

BLACK CANARY
DC Comics: Aug, 2015 - No. 12, Aug, 2016 ($2.99)

1-12: 1-Fletcher-s/Annie Wu-a/c. 4,5-Guerra-a. 8-Vixen app. 9-Moritat-a. 10-Batgirl app. 3.00

BLACK CANARY AND ZATANNA; BLOODSPELL
DC Comics: 2014 ($22.99, hardcover graphic novel, dustjacket)

HC-Paul Dini-s/Joe Quinones-a; includes script and sketch art 23.00

BLACK CANARY/ORACLE: BIRDS OF PREY (Also see Showcase '96 #3)
DC Comics: 1996 ($3.95, one-shot)

1-Chuck Dixon scripts & Gary Frank-c/a. 3 6 9 14 20 25

BLACK CAT (AMAZING SPIDER-MAN PRESENTS...)
Marvel Comics: Aug, 2010 - No. 4, Dec, 2010 ($3.99, limited series)

1-4-Van Meter-s/Pulido-a/Conner-c; Spider-Man & Ana Kraven app. 5.00

BLACK CAT COMICS (...Western #16-19; ...Mystery #30 on)
(See All-New #7,9, The Original Black Cat, Pocket & Speed Comics)
Harvey Publications (Home Comics): June-July, 1946 - No. 29, June, 1951

1-Kubert-a; Joe Simon c-1,2 84 168 252 538 919 1300
2-Kubert-a 41 82 123 256 428 600
3,4: 4-The Red Demons begin (The Demon #4 & 5)
34 68 102 206 336 465
5,6,7: 5,6-The Scarlet Arrow app. in ea. by Powell; S&K-a in both. 6-Origin Red Demon. 7-Vagabond Prince by S&K plus 1 more story 39 78 117 240 395 550
8-S&K-a; Kerry Drake begins, ends #13 37 74 111 222 361 500
9-Origin Stuntman (r/Stuntman #1) 39 78 117 231 378 525
10-20: 14,15,17-Mary Worth app. plus Invisible Scarlet O'Neil-#15,20,24
27 54 81 160 263 365
21-26 22 44 66 128 209 290
27,28: 27-Used in **SOTI**, pg. 193; X-Mas-c; 2 pg. John Wayne story. 28-Intro. Kit, Black Cat's new sidekick 24 48 72 140 230 320
29-Black Cat bondage-c; Black Cat stories 22 44 66 132 216 300

BLACK CAT MYSTERY (Formerly Black Cat; ...Western Mystery #54; ...Western #55,56; ...Mystery #57; ...Mystic #58-62; Black Cat #63-65)
Harvey Publications: No. 30, Aug, 1951 - No. 65, Apr, 1963

30-Black Cat on cover and first page only 39 78 117 231 378 525
31,32,34,37,38,40 31 62 93 182 296 410
33-Used in **POP**, pg. 89; electrocution-c 47 94 141 296 498 700
35-Atomic disaster cover/story 40 80 120 244 402 560
36,39-Used in **SOTI**: #36-Pgs. 270,271; #39-Pgs. 386-388
39 78 117 231 378 525
41-43 30 60 90 177 289 400
44-Eyes, ears, tongue cut out; Nostrand-a 36 72 108 211 343 475
45-Classic "Colorama" by Powell; Nostrand-a 81 162 243 518 884 1250
46-49,51-Nostrand-a in all. 51-Story has blank panel covering censored art (post-Code)
34 68 102 199 325 450
50-Check-a; classic Warren Kremer-c showing a man's face & hands burning away
377 754 1131 2639 4620 6600
52,53 (r/#34 & 35) 20 40 60 114 182 250
54-Two Black Cat stories (2/55, last pre-code) 21 42 63 122 199 275
55,56-Black Cat app. 20 40 60 114 182 250
57(7/56)-Kirby-c 21 42 63 124 202 280
58-60-Kirby-a(4). 58,59-Kirby-c. 60,61-Simon-c 24 48 72 144 237 330
61-Nostrand-a; "Colorama" r/#45 22 44 66 132 216 300
62 (3/58)-E.C. story swipe 20 40 60 114 182 250
63-65: Giants(10/62,1/63, 4/63); Reprints; Black Cat app. 63-origin Black Kitten.
65-1 pg. Powell-a 21 42 63 126 206 285

NOTE: ***Kremer** a-37, 39, 43; c-36, 37, 47. **Meskin** a-51. **Palais** a-30, 31(2), 32(2), 33-35, 37-40. **Powell** a-32-35, 36(2), 40, 41, 43-53, 57. **Simon** c-63-65. **Sparling** a-44. Bondage c-32, 34, 43.*

BLACK CLOUD
Image Comics: Apr, 2017 - Present ($3.99)

1-7: 1-Latour & Brandon-s/Hinkle-a 4.00

BLACK COBRA (Bride's Diary No. 4 on) (See Captain Flight #8)
Ajax/Farrell Publications(Excellent Publ.): No. 1, 10-11/54; No. 6(No. 2), 12-1/54-55; No. 3, 2-3/55

1-Re-intro Black Cobra & The Cobra Kid (costumed heroes)
39 78 117 240 395 550
6(#2)-Formerly Billy Bunny 21 42 63 126 206 285
3-(Pre-code)-Torpedoman app. 21 42 63 122 199 275

BLACK CONDOR (Also see Crack Comics, Freedom Fighters & Showcase '94 #10,11)
DC Comics: June, 1992 - No. 12, May, 1993 ($1.25)

1-8-Heath-c 3.00
9-12: 9,10,12-Heath-c. 9,10-The Ray app. 12-Batman-c/app. 3.00

BLACK CROSS SPECIAL (See Dark Horse Presents)
Dark Horse Comics: Jan, 1988 ($1.75, B&W, one-shot)(Reprints & new-a)

1-1st printing 4.00
1-(2nd printing) has 2 pgs. new-a 3.00
...: Dirty Work 1 (4/97, $2.95) Chris Warner-c/s/a 3.00

BLACK CROWN QUARTERLY
IDW Publishing: Oct, 2017 - Present ($6.99, quarterly)

1,2-Short story anthology with creator interviews and series previews 7.00

BLACK DIAMOND
Americomics: May, 1983 - No. 5, 1984 (no month)($2.00-$1.75, Baxter paper)

1-3-Movie adapt.; 1-Colt back-up begins 4.00
4,5 3.00

NOTE: ***Bill Black** a-1i; c-1. **Gulacy** c-2-5. Sybil Danning photo back-c-1.*

BLACK DIAMOND WESTERN (Formerly Desperado No. 1-8)
Lev Gleason Publ: No. 9, Mar, 1949 - No. 60, Feb, 1956 (No. 9-28: 52 pgs.)

9-Black Diamond & his horse Reliapon begin; origin & 1st app. Black Diamond
21 42 63 122 199 275
10 12 24 36 69 97 125
11-15 10 20 30 54 72 90
16-28(11/49-11/51)-Wolverton's Bingbang Buster 14 28 42 76 108 140
29-40: 31-One pg. Frazetta anti-drug ad 9 18 27 47 61 75
41-50,53-59 8 16 24 40 50 60
51-3-D effect-c/story 15 30 45 85 130 175
52-3-D effect story 14 28 42 81 118 155
60-Last issue 8 16 24 44 57 70

NOTE: ***Biro** c-9-35?. **Cooper** a-12. **Myron Foss** a-54-58, c-54-56, 58. **Guardineer** a-9, 12, 15, 18. **Jack Keller** a-12. **Kida** a-9. **Maurer** a-10. **Ed Moore** a-16. **Morisi** a-55. **William Overgard** a-9-23. **Tuska** a-10, 48. **Bill Walton** a-57.*

BLACK DRAGON, THE
Marvel Comics (Epic Comics): May, 1985 - No. 6, Oct, 1985 (Baxter paper, mature)

1-6: 1-Chris Claremont story & John Bolton painted-c/a in all 4.00
TPB (Dark Horse, 4/96, $17.95, B&W, trade paperback) r/#1-6; intro by Anne McCaffrey 18.00

BLACK DYNAMITE (Based on the Michael Jai White film)
IDW Publishing: Dec, 2013 - No. 4, Aug, 2014 ($3.99)

1-4: 1-Ash-s/Wimberly-a; multiple covers. 2,3-Ferreira-a 4.00

BLACKEST NIGHT (2009 Green Lantern & DC crossover) (Leads into Brightest Day series)
DC Comics: No. 0, Jun, 2009 - No. 8, May, 2010 ($3.99, limited series)

0-Free Comic Book Day edition; Johns-s/Reis-a; profile pages of different corps 3.00
1-8: 1-($3.99) Black Lantern Corps arises; Johns-s/Reis-c/a; Hawkman & Hawkgirl killed. 4-Nekron rises. 8-Dead heroes return 5.00
1-Variant cover by Van Sciver 10.00
1-3,5: 2nd-4th printings 4.00
2-8: 2-Cascioli variant-c. 3-Van Sciver variant-c. 4-7-Migliari variant-c. 8-Mahnke var-c 8.00
... Director's Cut (6/10, $5.99) Commentary with story panels; cover gallery, script pgs. 6.00
HC (2010, $29.99, d.j.) r/#0-8 & Blackest Night Director's Cut; variant cover gallery 30.00
SC (2011, $19.99) r/#0-8 & Blackest Night Director's Cut; variant cover gallery 20.00
...: Black Lantern Corps Vol. 1 HC (2010, $24.99, d.j.) r/BN: Batman, BN: Superman, and BN: Titans series; cover gallery and character sketch designs 25.00
...: Black Lantern Corps Vol. 1 SC (2011, $19.99) same contents as HC edition 20.00
...: Black Lantern Corps Vol. 2 HC (2010, $24.99, d.j.) r/BN: The Flash, BN: JSA, and BN: Wonder Woman series; cover gallery and character sketch designs 25.00
...: Rise of the Black Lanterns HC (2010, $24.99) r/one-shots Atom and Hawkman #46,

Black-Eyed Kids #14 © Joe Pruett

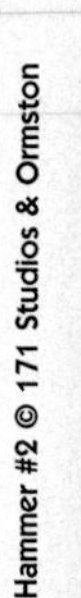

Black Hammer #2 © 171 Studios & Ormston

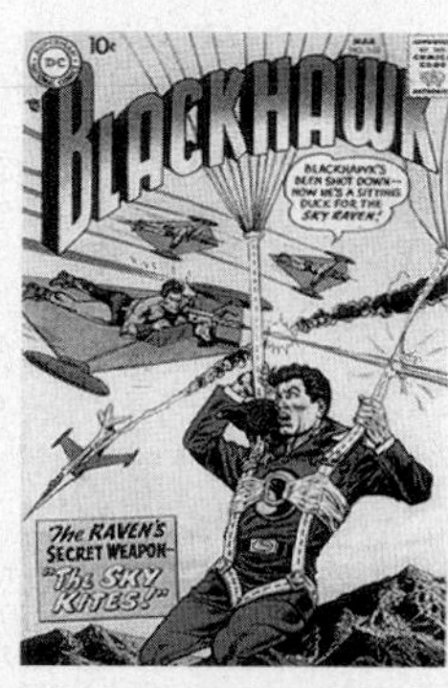

Blackhawk #122 © DC

	GD 2.0	VG 4.0	FN 6.0	VF 8.0	VF/NM 9.0	NM- 9.2

Catwoman #83, Phantom Stranger #42, Power of Shazam #48, The Question #37, Starman #81, Weird Western Tales #71, Green Arrow #30 & Adventure Comics #7; sketch art 25.00
...: Rise of the Black Lanterns SC (2011, $19.99) same contents as HC edition 20.00

BLACKEST NIGHT: BATMAN (2009 Green Lantern & DC crossover)
DC Comics: Oct, 2009 - No. 3, Dec, 2009 ($2.99, limited series)

1-3: 1-Bat-parents rise as Black Lanterns; Deadman app.; Syaf-a/Andy Kubert-c; 2 printings. 3-Flying Graysons return 3.00
1-3-Variant-c by Sienkiewicz 5.00

BLACKEST NIGHT: JSA (2009 Green Lantern & DC crossover)
DC Comics: Feb, 2010 - No. 3, Apr, 2010 ($2.99, limited series)

1-3-Original Sandman, Dr. Midnite and Mr. Terrific rise; Barrows-a/c 3.00
1-3-Variant-c by Gene Ha 5.00

BLACKEST NIGHT: SUPERMAN (2009 Green Lantern & DC crossover)
DC Comics: Oct, 2009 - No. 3, Dec, 2009 ($2.99, limited series)

1-3-Earth-2 Superman and Lois become Black Lanterns; Barrows-a/c; 2 printings 3.00
1-3-Variant-c by Shane Davis 5.00

BLACKEST NIGHT: TALES OF THE CORPS (2009 Green Lantern & DC crossover)
DC Comics: Sept, 2009 - No. 3, Sept, 2009 ($3.99, weekly limited series)

1-3-Short stories by various; interlocking cover images. 3-Commentary on B.N. #0 4.00
HC (2010, $24.99) r/#1-3 & Adventure Comics #4,5 & Green Lantern #49; sketch art 25.00
SC (2011, $19.99) r/#1-3 & Adventure Comics #4,5 & Green Lantern #49; sketch art 20.00

BLACKEST NIGHT: THE FLASH (2009 Green Lantern & DC crossover)
DC Comics: Feb, 2010 - No. 3, Apr, 2010 ($2.99, limited series)

1-3-Rogues vs. Dead Rogues; Johns-s/Kolins-a 3.00
1-3-Variant-c by Manapul 5.00

BLACKEST NIGHT: TITANS (2009 Green Lantern & DC crossover)
DC Comics: Oct, 2009 - No. 3, Dec, 2009 ($2.99, limited series)

1-3-Terra and the original Hawk return; Benes-a/c 3.00
1-3-Variant-c by Brian Haberlin 5.00

BLACKEST NIGHT: WONDER WOMAN (2009 Green Lantern & DC crossover)
DC Comics: Feb, 2010 - No. 3, Apr, 2010 ($2.99, limited series)

1-3-Maxwell Lord returns; Rucka-s/Scott-a/Horn-c. 2,3-Mera app.; Star Sapphire 3.00
1-3-Variant-c by Ryan Sook 5.00

BLACK-EYED KIDS
AfterShock Comics: Apr, 2016 - No. 15, Dec, 2017 ($3.99)

1-15: 1-($1.99) Joe Pruett-s/Szymon Kudranski-a/Francesco Francavilla-c. 2-15-($3.99) 4.00

BLACK FLAG (See Asylum #5)
Maximum Press: Jan, 1995 - No.4, 1995; No. 0, July, 1995 ($2.50, B&W) (No. 0 in color)

Preview Edition (6/94, $1.95, B&W)-Fraga/McFarlane-c. 3.00
0-4: 0-(7/95)-Liefeld/Fraga-c. 1-(1/95). 3.00
1-Variant cover 5.00
2,4-Variant covers 3.00

NOTE: ***Fraga*** *a-0-4, Preview Edition; c-1-4.* ***Liefeld/Fraga*** *c-0.* ***McFarlane/Fraga*** *c-Preview Edition.*

BLACK FURY (Becomes Wild West No. 58) (See Blue Bird)
Charlton Comics Group: May, 1955 - No. 57, Mar-Apr, 1966 (Horse stories)

	GD	VG	FN	VF	VF/NM	NM-
1	12	24	36	67	94	120
2	7	14	21	37	46	55
3-10	6	12	18	28	34	40
11-15,19,20	4	8	10	18	22	25
16-18-Ditko-a	12	24	36	67	94	120
21-30	4	7	10	14	17	20
31-57	3	6	8	12	14	16

BLACK GOLIATH (See Avengers #32-35,41,54 and Civil War #4)
Marvel Comics Group: Feb, 1976 - No. 5, Nov, 1976

	GD	VG	FN	VF	VF/NM	NM-
1-Tuska-a(p) thru #3	3	6	9	19	30	40
2-5: 2-4-(Regular 25¢ editions). 4-Kirby-c/Buckler-a	2	4	6	9	13	16
2-4-(30¢-c variants, limited distribution)(4,6,8/76)	4	8	12	25	40	55

BLACK HAMMER
Dark Horse Comics: Jul, 2016 - Present ($3.99)

1-13: 1-8,10,11,13-Lemire-s/Ormston-a; covers by Ormston & Lemire. 9,12-Rubín-a 4.00
...: Giant-Sized Annual (1/17, $5.99) Short stories by various incl. Nguyen, Allred, Kindt 6.00

BLACKHAWK (Formerly Uncle Sam #1-8; see Military Comics & Modern Comics)
Comic Magazines(Quality)No. 9-107(12/56); National Periodical Publications No. 108 (1/57) -250; DC Comics No. 251 on: No. 9, Winter, 1944 - No. 243, 10-11/68; No. 244, 1-2/76 - No. 250, 1-2/77; No. 251, 10/82 - No. 273, 11/84

	GD	VG	FN	VF	VF/NM	NM-
9 (1944)	265	530	795	1694	2897	4100
10 (1946)	116	232	348	742	1271	1800
11-15: 14-Ward-a; 13,14-Fear app.	84	168	252	538	919	1300
16-19	68	136	204	435	743	1050
20-Classic Crandall bondage-c; Ward Blackhawk	107	214	321	680	1165	1650
21-30 (1950)	52	104	156	328	552	775
31-40: 31-Chop Chop by Jack Cole	41	82	123	250	418	585
41-49,51-60: 42-Robot-c	36	72	108	216	351	485
50-1st Killer Shark; origin in text	39	78	117	236	388	540
61,62: 61-Used in **POP**, pg. 91. 62-Used in **POP**, pg. 92 & color illo	32	64	96	192	314	435
63-70,72-80: 65-H-Bomb explosion panel. 66-B&W & color illos **POP**. 67-Hitler-s. 70-Return of Killer Shark; atomic explosion panel. 75-Intro. Blackie the Hawk	31	62	93	182	296	410
71-Origin retold; flying saucer-c; A-Bomb panels	35	70	105	208	339	470
81-86: Last precode (3/55)	27	54	81	162	266	370
87-92,94-99,101-107: 91-Robot-c. 105-1st S.A.	22	44	66	132	216	300
93-Origin in text	23	46	69	136	223	310
100	27	54	81	162	266	370
108-1st DC issue (1/57); re-intro. Blackie, the Hawk, their mascot; not in #115	38	76	114	281	628	975
109-117: 117-(10/57)-Mr. Freeze app.	15	30	45	100	220	340
118-(11/57)-Frazetta-r/Jimmy Wakely #4 (3 pgs.)	15	30	45	103	227	350
119-130 (11/58): 120-Robot-c	12	24	36	79	170	260
131,132,134-140 (9/59)	10	20	30	66	138	210
133-Intro. Lady Blackhawk	65	130	195	416	708	1000
141-150,152-163,165,166: 141-Cat-Man returns-c/s. 143-Kurtzman-r/Jimmy Wakely #4. 150-(7/60)-King Condor returns. 166-Last 10¢ issue	8	16	24	54	102	150
151-Lady Blackhawk receives & loses super powers	8	16	24	56	108	160
164-Origin retold	8	16	24	56	108	160
167-180	6	12	18	37	66	95
181-190	5	10	15	31	53	75
191-196,199: 196-Combat Diary series begins	4	8	12	27	44	60
197,198,200: 197-New look for Blackhawks. 198-Origin retold	4	8	12	28	47	65
201,202,204-210	3	6	9	21	33	45
203-Origin Chop Chop (12/64)	4	8	12	25	40	55
211-227,229-243(1968): 230-Blackhawks become superheroes; JLA cameo 242-Return to old costumes	3	6	9	17	26	35
228-Batman, Green Lantern, Superman, The Flash cameos.	4	8	12	23	37	50
244 ('76) -250: 250-Chuck dies	1	2	3	5	6	8

251-273: 251-Origin retold; Black Knights return. 252-Intro Domino. 253-Part origin Hendrickson. 258-Blackhawk's Island destroyed. 259-Part origin Chop-Chop. 265-273 (75¢ cover price) 4.00

NOTE: ***Chaykin*** *a-260; c-257-260, 262.* ***Crandall*** *a-10, 11, 13, 16?, 18-20, 22-26, 30-33, 35p, 36(2), 37, 38?, 39-44, 46-50, 52-58, 60, 63, 64, 66, 67; c-14-20, 22-63(most except #28-33, 36, 37, 39).* ***Evans*** *a-244, 245,246i, 248-250i.* ***G. Kane*** *c-263, 264.* ***Kubert c****-244, 245.* ***Newton*** *a-266p.* ***Severin*** *a-257.****Spiegle*** *a-261-267, 269-273; c-265-272.* ***Toth*** *a-260p.* ***Ward*** *a-16-27(Chop Chop, 8pgs. ea.); pencilled stories-No. 17-63(approx.).* ***Wildey*** *a-268. Chop Chop solo stories in #10-95?*

BLACKHAWK
DC Comics: Mar, 1988 - No. 3, May, 1988 ($2.95, limited series, mature)

1-3: Chaykin painted-c/a/scripts 4.00

BLACKHAWK (Also see Action Comics #601)
DC Comics: Mar, 1989 - No. 16, Aug, 1990 ($1.50, mature)

1 4.00
2-6,8-16: 16-Crandall-c swipe 3.00
7-($2.50, 52 pgs.)-Story-r/Military #1 4.00
Annual 1 (1989, $2.95, 68 pgs.)-Recaps origin of Blackhawk, Lady Blackhawk, and others 4.00
Special 1 (1992, $3.50, 68 pgs.)-Mature readers 4.00

BLACKHAWK INDIAN TOMAHAWK WAR, THE
Avon Periodicals: 1951 (Also see Fighting Indians of the Wild West)

	GD	VG	FN	VF	VF/NM	NM-
nn-Kinstler-c; Kit West story	21	42	63	126	206	285

BLACKHAWKS (DC New 52)
DC Comics: Nov, 2011 - No. 8, Jun, 2012 ($2.99)

1-8: 1-Costa-s/Nolan & Lashley-a 3.00

BLACK HOLE (See Walt Disney Showcase #54) (Disney, movie)
Whitman Publishing Co.: Mar, 1980 - No. 4, Sept, 1980

	GD	VG	FN	VF	VF/NM	NM-
11295(#1) (1979, Golden, $1.50-c, 52 pgs., graphic novel; 8 1/2x11") Photo-c; Spiegle-a.	3	6	9	14	20	25
1-3: 1,2-Movie adaptation. 2,3-Spiegle-a. 3-McWilliams-a; photo-c. 3-New stories	2	4	6	10	14	18

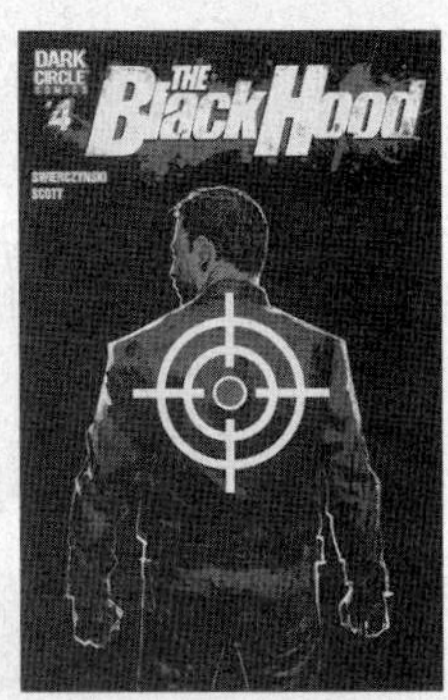

The Black Hood V2 #4 © ACP

Black Lightning #2 © DC

Black Magic V2 #1 © Headline

GD 2.0 | VG 4.0 | FN 6.0 | VF 8.0 | VF/NM 9.0 | NM- 9.2

4-Sold only in pre-packs; new story; Spiegle-a 24 48 72 168 372 575

BLACK HOOD, THE (See Blue Ribbon, Flyman & Mighty Comics)
Red Circle Comics (Archie): June, 1983 - No. 3, Oct, 1983 (Mandell paper)

1-Morrow, McWilliams, Wildey-a; Toth-c 6.00
2,3: The Fox by Toth-c/a; Boyette-a. 3-Morrow-a; Toth wraparound-c 4.00
NOTE: *Also see Archie's Super-Hero Special Digest #2*

BLACK HOOD
DC Comics (Impact Comics): Dec, 1991 - No. 12, Dec, 1992 ($1.00)

1 4.00
2-12: 11-Intro The Fox. 12-Origin Black Hood 3.00
Annual 1 (1992, $2.50, 68 pgs.)-w/Trading card 4.00

BLACK HOOD, THE
Archie Comic Publications (Dark Circle Comics): Apr, 2015 - No. 11, Aug, 2016 ($3.99)

1-11: 1-Origin retold; Swierczynski-s/Gaydos-a; five covers. 6-Chaykin-a. 8-Hack-a 4.00

BLACK HOOD, THE (Volume 2)
Archie Comic Publications (Dark Circle Comics): Dec, 2016 - No. 5, Aug, 2017 ($3.99)

1-5-Swierczynski-s/Greg Scott-a 4.00

BLACK HOOD COMICS (Formerly Hangman #2-8; Laugh Comics #20 on; also see Black Swan, Jackpot, Roly Poly & Top-Notch #9)
MLJ Magazines: No. 9, Wint., 1943-44 - No. 19, Sum., 1946 (on radio in 1943)

9-The Hangman & The Boy Buddies cont'd 135 270 405 864 1482 2100
10-Hangman & Dusty, the Boy Detective app. 81 162 243 518 884 1250
11-Dusty app.; no Hangman 68 136 204 435 743 1050
12,13,15-18: 17-Hal Foster swipe from Prince Valiant; 1st issue with "An Archie Magazine" on-c 61 122 183 390 670 950
14-Kinstler blood-c 110 220 330 704 1202 1700
19-I.D. exposed; last issue 77 154 231 493 847 1200
NOTE: *Hangman by* ***Fuje*** *in 9, 10.* ***Kinstler*** *a-15, c-14-16.*

BLACK JACK (Rocky Lane's...; formerly Jim Bowie)
Charlton Comics: No. 20, Nov, 1957 - No. 30, Nov, 1959

20 9 18 27 52 69 85
21,27,29,30 6 12 18 31 38 45
22,23: 22-(68 pgs.). 23-Williamson/Torres-a 8 16 24 42 54 65
24-26,28-Ditko-a 10 20 30 56 76 95

BLACK JACK KETCHUM
Image Comics: Dec, 2015 - No. 4, Mar, 2016 ($3.99)

1-4: 1-Brian Schirmer-s/Claudia Balboni-a 4.00

BLACK KNIGHT, THE
Toby Press: May, 1953; 1963

1-Bondage-c 37 74 111 222 361 500
Super Reprint No. 11 (1963)-Reprints 1953 issue 3 6 9 19 25 32

BLACK KNIGHT, THE
Atlas Comics (MgPC): May, 1955 - No. 5, April, 1956

1-Origin Crusader; Maneely-c/a 142 284 426 909 1555 2200
2-Maneely-c/a(4) 84 168 252 538 919 1300
3-5: 4-Maneely-c/a. 5-Maneely-c, Shores-a 68 136 204 435 743 1050

BLACK KNIGHT (See The Avengers #48, Marvel Super Heroes & Tales To Astonish #52)
Marvel Comics: June, 1990 - No. 4, Sept, 1990 ($1.50, limited series)

1-4: 1-Original Black Knight returns. 3,4-Dr. Strange app. 3.00
... (MDCU) 1 (01/10, $3.99) Origin re-told; Frenz-a; originally from Marvel Digital Comics 4.00
NOTE: ***Buckler*** *c-1-4p*

BLACK KNIGHT (See Weirdworld and Secret Wars 2015 series)
Marvel Comics: Jan, 2016 - No. 5, May, 2016 ($3.99)

1-5: 1-Tieri-s/Pizzari-a. 2-5-Uncanny Avengers app. 4.00

BLACK KNIGHT: EXODUS
Marvel Comics: Dec, 1996 ($2.50, one-shot)

1-Raab-s; Apocalypse-c/app. 3.00

BLACK LAMB, THE
DC Comics (Helix): Nov, 1996 - No, 6, Apr, 1997 ($2.50, limited series)

1-6: Tim Truman-c/a/scripts 3.00

BLACKLIGHT (From ShadowHawk)
Image Comics: June, 2005 - No. 2, Jul, 2005 ($2.99)

1,2-Toledo & Deering-a/Wherle-s 3.00

BLACK LIGHTNING (See The Brave & The Bold, Cancelled Comic Cavalcade, DC Comics Presents #16, Detective #490 and World's Finest #257)
National Periodical Publ./DC Comics: Apr, 1977 - No. 11, Sept-Oct, 1978

1-Origin Black Lightning 5 10 15 30 50 70
2,3,6-10: 2-Talia and Merlyn app. 2 4 6 8 11 14
4,5-Superman-c/s. 4-Intro Cyclotronic Man 2 4 6 9 13 16
11-The Ray new solo story 2 4 6 10 14 18
NOTE: ***Buckler*** *c-1-3p, 6-11p. #11 is 44 pgs.*

BLACK LIGHTNING (2nd Series)
DC Comics: Feb, 1995 - No. 13, Feb, 1996 ($1.95/$2.25)

1-Tony Isabella scripts begin, ends #8 1 2 3 5 6 8
2-13: 6-Begin $2.25-c. 13-Batman-c/app. 3.00

BLACK LIGHTNING: COLD DEAD HANDS
DC Comics: Jan, 2018 - No. 6, ($3.99, limited series)

1-5-Tony Isabella-s/Clayton Henry-a; Tobias Whale app. 4.00

BLACK LIGHTNING: YEAR ONE
DC Comics: Mar, 2009 - No. 6, May, 2009 ($2.99, bi-weekly limited series)

1-6-Van Meter-s/Hamner-a. 1-Two printings (white and yellow cover title logos) 3.00
TPB (2009, $17.99) r/#1-6 18.00

BLACK LIST, THE (Based on the TV show)
Titan Comics: Aug, 2015 - No. 10, Jul, 2016 ($3.99)

1-10-Art & photo-c for each: 1-Nicole Phillips-s/Beni Lobel-a. 4.00

BLACK MAGIC (...Magazine) (Becomes Cool Cat V8#6 on)
Crestwood Publ. V1#1-4,V6#1-V7#5/Headline V1#5-V5#3,V7#6-V8#5: 10-11/50 - V4#1, 6-7/53: V4#2, 9-10/53 - V5#3, 11-12/54; V6#1, 9-10/57 - V7#2, 11-12/58: V7#3, 7-8/60 - V8#5, 11-12/61 (V1#1-5, 52pgs.; V1#6-V3#3, 44pgs.)

V1#1-S&K-a, 10 pgs.; Meskin-a(2) 174 348 522 1114 1907 2700
2-S&K-a, 17 pgs.; Meskin-a 74 148 222 470 810 1150
3-6(8-9/51)-S&K, Roussos, Meskin-a 61 122 183 390 670 950
V2#1(10-11/51),4,5,7(#13),9(#15),12(#18)-S&K-a 41 82 123 250 418 585
2,3,6,8,10,11(#17) 34 68 102 204 332 460
V3#1(#19, 12/52) - 6(#24, 5/53)-S&K-a 35 70 105 208 339 470
V4#1(#25, 6-7/53), 2(#26, 9-10/53)-S&K-a(3-4) 37 74 111 218 354 490
3(#27, 11-12/53)-S&K-a; Ditko-a (2nd published-a); also see Captain 3-D, Daring Love #1, Strange Fantasy #9, & Fantastic Fears #5 (Fant. Fears was 1st drawn, but not 1st publ.) 68 136 204 435 743 1050
4(#28)-Eyes ripped out/story-S&K, Ditko-a 50 100 150 315 533 750
5(#29, 3-4/54)-S&K, Ditko-a 39 78 117 229 375 520
6(#30, 5-6/54)-S&K, Powell?-a 31 62 93 186 303 420
V5#1(#31, 7-8/54 - 3(#33, 11-12/54)-S&K-a 21 42 63 122 199 275
V6#1(#34, 9-10/57), 2(#35, 11-12/57) 12 24 36 69 97 125
3(1-2/58) - 6(7-8/58) 12 24 36 69 97 125
V7#1(9-10/58) - 3(7-8/60), 4(9-10/60) 10 20 30 56 76 95
5(11-12/60)-Hitler-c; Torres-a 20 40 60 114 182 250
6(1-2/61)-Powell-a(2) 10 20 30 56 76 95
V8#1(3-4/61)-Powell-c/a 10 20 30 56 76 95
2(5-6/61)-E.C. story swipe/W.F. #22; Ditko, Powell-a 11 22 33 60 83 105
3(7-8/61)-E.C. story swipe/W.F. #22; Powell-a(2) 11 22 33 60 83 105
4(9-10/61)-Powell-a(5) 10 20 30 56 76 95
5-E.C. story swipe/W.S.F. #28; Powell-a(3) 11 22 33 60 83 105
NOTE: ***Bernard Baily*** *a-V4#6?, V5#3(2).* ***Grandenetti*** *a-V2#3, 11.* ***Kirby*** *c-V1#1-6, V2#1-12, V3#1-6, V4#1, 2, 4-6, V5#1-3.* ***McWilliams*** *a-V3#2i.* ***Meskin*** *a-V1#1(2), 2, 3, 4(2), 5(2), 6, V2/1, 2, 3(2), 4(3), 5, 6(2), 7-9, 11, 12i, V3#1(2), 5, 6, V5#1(2), 2.* ***Orlando*** *a-V6#1, 4, V7#2; c-V6/1-6.* ***Powell*** *a-V5#1?.* ***Roussos*** *a-V1#3-5, 6(2), V2#3(2), 4, 5(2), 6, 8, 9, 10(2), 11, 12p, V3#1(2), 2i, 5, V5#2.* ***Simon*** *a-V2#12, V3#2, V7#5? c-V4#3?, V7#3?, 4, 5?, 6?, V8#1-5.* ***Simon & Kirby*** *a-V1#1, 2(2), 3-6, V2#1, 4, 5, 7, 9, 12, V3#1-6, V4#1(3), 2(4), 3(2), 4(2), 5, 6, V5#1-3; c-V2#1.* ***Leonard Starr*** *a-V1#1.* ***Tuska*** *a-V6#3, 4.* ***Woodbridge*** *a-V7#4.*

BLACK MAGIC
National Periodical Publications: Oct-Nov, 1973 - No. 9, Apr-May, 1975

1-S&K reprints 3 6 9 16 24 32
2-8-S&K reprints 2 4 6 10 14 18
9-S&K reprints 2 4 6 11 16 20

BLACK MAGICK
Image Comics: Oct, 2015 - Present ($3.99)

1-10-Greg Rucka-s/Nicola Scott-a 4.00

BLACKMAIL TERROR (See Harvey Comics Library)

BLACK MARKET
BOOM! Studios: Jul, 2014 - No. 4, Oct, 2014 ($3.99, limited series)

1-4-Barbiere-s/Santos-a 4.00

BLACK MASK
DC Comics: 1993 - No. 3, 1994 ($4.95, limited series, 52 pgs.)

Black Orchid #10 © DC

Black Panther V2 #1 © MAR

Black Panther #166 © MAR

GD 2.0 | VG 4.0 | FN 6.0 | VF 8.0 | VF/NM 9.0 | NM- 9.2

1-3 5.00

BLACK MONDAY MURDERS, THE
Image Comics: Aug, 2016 - Present ($4.99/$3.99, limited series)

1-4-Jonathan Hickman-s/Tomm Coker-a 5.00
5-8-($3.99) 4.00

BLACK OPS
Image Comics (WildStorm): Jan, 1996 - No. 5, May, 1996 ($2.50, lim. series)

1-5 3.00

BLACK ORCHID (See Adventure Comics #428 & Phantom Stranger)
DC Comics: Holiday, 1988-89 - No. 3, 1989 ($3.50, lim. series, prestige format)

Book 1,3: Gaiman scripts & McKean painted-a in all 6.00
Book 2-Arkham Asylum story; Batman app. 1 2 3 5 6 8
TPB (1991, $19.95) r/#1-3; new McKean-c 20.00

BLACK ORCHID
DC Comics: Sept, 1993 - No. 22, June, 1995 ($1.95/$2.25)

1-22: Dave McKean-c all issues 3.00
1-Platinum Edition 12.00
Annual 1 (1993, $3.95, 68 pgs.)-Children's Crusade 4.00

BLACKOUT
Dark Horse Comics: Mar, 2014 - No. 4, Jul, 2014 ($2.99, limited series)

1-4-Barbiere-s/Lorimer-a; King Tiger back-up by Stradley-s/Doug Wheatley-a 3.00

BLACKOUTS (See Broadway Hollywood...)

BLACK PANTHER, THE (Also see Avengers #52, Fantastic Four #52, Jungle Action, Marvel Premiere #51-53 and Rise of the Black Panther)
Marvel Comics Group: Jan, 1977 - No. 15, May, 1979

1-Jack Kirby-s/a thru #12 8 16 24 54 102 150
2-13: 4,5-(Regular 30¢ editions). 8-Origin 3 6 9 17 26 35
4,5-(35¢-c variants, limited dist.)(7,9/77) 8 16 24 55 105 155
14,15-Avengers x-over. 14-Origin 3 6 9 17 26 35
...By Jack Kirby Vol. 1 TPB (2005, $19.99) r/#1-7; unused covers and sketch pages 20.00
...By Jack Kirby Vol. 2 TPB (2006, $19.99) r/#8-12 by Kirby and #13 non-Kirby 20.00
NOTE: *J. Buscema c-15p. Layton c-13i.*

BLACK PANTHER
Marvel Comics Group: July, 1988 - No. 4, Oct, 1988 ($1.25)

1-4-Gillis-s/Cowan & Delarosa-a 1 2 3 5 6 8

BLACK PANTHER (Marvel Knights)
Marvel Comics: Nov, 1998 - No. 62, Sept, 2003 ($2.50)

1-Texeira-a/c; Priest-s 2 4 6 9 12 15
1-($6.95) DF edition w/Quesada & Palmiotti-c 3 4 6 9 12 15
2,3: 2-Two covers by Texeira and Timm. 3-Fantastic Four app. 5.00
4-1st White Wolf 2 4 6 11 16 20
5-22,24-35,37-40: 5-Evans-a. 6-8-Jusko-a. 8-Avengers-c/app. 15-Hulk app. 22-Moon Knight app. 25-Maximum Security x-over. 26-Storm-c/app. 28-Magneto & Sub-Mariner-c/app. 29-WWII flashback meeting w/Captain America. 35-Defenders-c/app. 37-Luke Cage and Falcon-c/app. 3.00
23-Deadpool & the Avengers app. 2 4 6 11 16 20
36-($3.50, 100 pgs.) 35th Anniversary issue incl. r/1st app. in FF #52 4.00
41-56: 41-44-Wolverine app. 47-Thor app. 48,49-Magneto app. 3.00
57-62: 57-Begin $2.99-c. 59-Falcon app. 3.00
...: The Client (6/01, $14.95, TPB) r/#1-5 15.00
... 2099 #1 (11/04, $2.99) Kirkman-s/Hotz-a/Pat Lee-c 3.00

BLACK PANTHER (Marvel Knights)
Marvel Comics: Apr, 2005 - No. 41, Nov, 2008 ($2.99)

1-Reginald Hudlin-s/John Romita Jr. & Klaus Janson-a; covers by Romita & Ribic 1 2 3 5 6 8
2-1st app. Shuri 3 6 9 14 20 25
3-7,9-15,17-20: 7-House of M; Hairsine-a. 10-14-Luke Cage app. 12,13-Blade app. 17-Linsner-c. 19-Doctor Doom app. 3.00
8-Cho-c; X-Men app. 4.00
8-2nd printing variant-c 3.00
16-($3.99) Wedding of T'Challa and Storm; wraparound Cho-c; Hudlin-s/Eaton-a 4.00
21-Civil War x-over; Namor app. 8.00
21-2nd printing with new cover and Civil War logo 3.00
22-25-Civil War: 23-25-Turner-c 4.00
26-41: 26-30-T'Challa and Storm join the Fantastic Four. 27-30-Marvel Zombies app. 28-30-Suydam-c. 39-41-Secret Invasion 3.00
Annual 1 (4/08, $3.99) Hudlin-s/Stroman & Lashley-a; alternate future; Uatu app. 4.00
...: Bad Mutha TPB (2006, $10.99) r/#10-13 11.00
...: Civil War TPB (2007, $17.99) r/#19-25 18.00
...: Four the Hard Way TPB (2007, $13.99) r/#26-30; page layouts and character designs 14.00
...: Little Green Men TPB (2008, $10.99) r/#31-34 11.00
...: The Bride TPB (2006, $14.99) r/#14-18; interview with the dress designer 15.00
...: Who Is The Black Panther HC (2005, $21.99) r/#1-6; Hudlin afterword; cover gallery 22.00
...: Who Is The Black Panther SC (2006, $14.99) r/#1-6; Hudlin afterword; cover gallery 15.00

BLACK PANTHER
Marvel Comics: Apr, 2009 - No. 12, Mar, 2010 ($3.99/$2.99)

1-($3.99) Hudlin-s/Lashley-a; covers by Campbell & Lashley; Dr. Doom & Shuri app. 2 4 6 11 16 20
2-12-($2.99) 2-6-Campbell-c. 6-Shuri becomes female Black Panther 4.00

BLACK PANTHER
Marvel Comics: Jun, 2016 - No. 18, Nov, 2017; No. 166, Dec, 2017 - Present ($4.99/$3.99)

1-($4.99) Ta-Nehisi Coates-s/Brian Stelfreeze-a; bonus Stelfreeze interview & art 1 2 3 5 6 8
2-18-($3.99) 2-4,9,12-Stelfreeze-a. 5-8,10-12,16-18-Sprouse-a. 13-17-Ororo app. 4.00
[Title switches to legacy numbering after #18 (11/17)]
166-170: 166-Klaw app.; Coates-s/Kirk-a 4.00
Annual 1 (4/18, $4.99) Stories by Priest, Perkins, McGregor, Acuña, Hudlin & Lashley 5.00

BLACK PANTHER AND THE CREW
Marvel Comics: Jun, 2017 - No. 6, Oct, 2017 ($3.99)

1-6-Storm, Luke Cage, Misty Knight & Manifold app.; Ta-Nehisi Coates-s/Butch Guice-a 4.00

BLACK PANTHER/CAPTAIN AMERICA: FLAGS OF OUR FATHERS
Marvel Comics: Jun, 2010 - No. 4, Sept, 2010 ($3.99, limited series)

1-4-Hudlin-s/Cowan-a; WW2 story; Howling Commandos & Red Skull app. 4.00

BLACK PANTHER: PANTHER'S PREY
Marvel Comics: May, 1991 - No. 4, Oct, 1991 ($4.95, squarebound, lim. series, 52 pgs.)

1-4: McGregor-s/Turner-a 6.00

BLACK PANTHER: THE MAN WITHOUT FEAR (Continues from Daredevil #512)
Marvel Comics: No. 513, Feb, 2011 - No. 523, Nov, 2011 ($2.99)

513-523: 513-Shadowland aftermath; Liss-s/Francavilla-a/Bianchi-c. 521-523-Fear Itself 3.00
513-Variant-c by Francavilla 5.00

BLACK PANTHER: THE MOST DANGEROUS MAN ALIVE
Marvel Comics: No. 523.1, Nov, 2011 - No. 529, Apr, 2012 ($2.99)

523.1, 524-529: 523.1-Palo-a/Zircher-c. 524-Spider Island tie-in; Lady Bullseye app. 3.00

BLACK PANTHER: THE SOUND AND THE FURY
Marvel Comics: Apr, 2018 ($3.99, one-shot)

1-Klaw app.; Macchio-s/Di Vito-a; reprint of Fantastic Four #53 (origin/1st app. Klaw) 4.00

BLACK PANTHER: WORLD OF WAKANDA
Marvel Comics: Jan, 2017 - No. 6, Jun, 2017 ($4.99/$3.99, limited series)

1-($4.99) Roxanne Gay-s/Alitha E. Martinez-a; spotlight on The Dora Milaje 5.00
2-6-($3.99) 6-Rembert Browne-s/Joe Bennett-a; White Tiger app. 4.00

BLACK PEARL, THE
Dark Horse Comics: Sept, 1996 - No. 5, Jan, 1997 ($2.95, limited series)

1-5: Mark Hamill scripts 3.00

BLACK PHANTOM (See Tim Holt #25, 38)
Magazine Enterprises: Nov, 1954 (one-shot) (Female outlaw)

1 (A-1 #122)-The Ghost Rider story plus 3 Black Phantom stories; Headlight-c/a 39 78 117 240 395 550

BLACK PHANTOM
AC Comics: 1989 - No. 3, 1990 ($2.50, B&W; #2 color)(Reprints & new-a)

1-3: 1-Ayers-r, Bolle-r/B.P. #1-3-Redmask-r 3.00

BLACK PHANTOM, RETURN OF THE (See Wisco)

BLACK RACER AND SHILO NORMAN SPECIAL, THE (Jack Kirby 100th Birthday tribute)
DC Comics: Oct, 2017 ($4.99, one-shot)

1-Black Racer origin; Hudlin-s/Cowan-a; reprint pages from New Gods #5,7,8 5.00

BLACK RIDER (Western Winners #1-7; Western Tales of Black Rider #28-31; Gunsmoke Western #32 on)(See All Western Winners, Best Western, Kid Colt, Outlaw Kid, Rex Hart, Two-Gun Kid, Two-Gun Western, Western Gunfighters, Western Winners, & Wild Western)
Marvel/Atlas Comics(CDS No. 8-17/CPS No. 19 on): No. 8, 3/50 - No. 18, 1/52; No. 19, 11/53 - No. 27, 3/55

8 (#1)-Black Rider & his horse Satan begin; 36 pgs; Stan Lee photo-c as Black Rider) 53 106 159 334 567 800
9-52 pgs. begin, end #14 27 54 81 158 259 360
10-Origin Black Rider 32 64 96 192 314 435

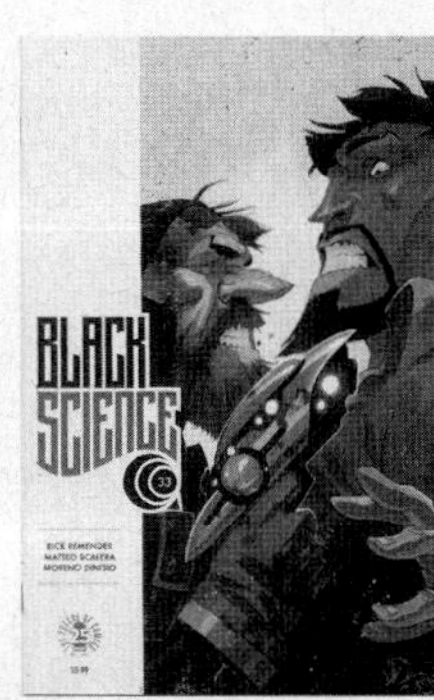

Black Science #33 © Remender & Scalera

Black Terror #1 © Superpowers

Black Widow (2014 series) #13 © MAR

	GD 2.0	VG 4.0	FN 6.0	VF 8.0	VF/NM 9.0	NM- 9.2
11-14: 14-Last 52pgs.	19	38	57	111	176	240
15-19: 19-Two-Gun Kid app.	16	32	48	94	147	200
20-Classic-c; Two-Gun Kid app.	18	36	54	107	169	230
21-27: 21-23-Two-Gun Kid app. 24,25-Arrowhead app. 26-Kid Colt app. 27-Last issue; last precode. Kid Colt app. The Spider (a villain) burns to death	15	30	45	86	133	180

NOTE: *Ayers c-22. **Jack Keller** a-15, 26, 27. **Maneely** a-14; c-9, 16, 17, 24, 25, 27. **Syd Shores** a-19, 21, 22, 23(3), 24(3), 25-27; c-19, 21, 23. **Sinnott** a-24, 25. **Tuska** a-12, 19-21.*

BLACK RIDER RIDES AGAIN!, THE
Atlas Comics (CPS): Sept, 1957

1-Kirby-a(3); Powell-a; Severin-c 37 74 111 222 361 500

BLACK ROAD
Image Comics: Apr, 2016 - No. 10, May, 2017 ($3.99)

1-10-Brian Wood-s/Garry Brown-a 4.00

BLACK SCIENCE
Image Comics: Nov, 2013 - Present ($3.50/$3.99)

1-Remender-s/Scalera-a; multiple covers 10.00
2 6.00
3-33: 11,16,21-33-$3.99-c 4.00
34-($4.99) 5.00

BLACK SEPTEMBER (Also see Avengers/Ultraforce, Ultraforce (1st series) #10 & Ultraforce/Avengers)
Malibu Comics (Ultraverse): 1995 ($1.50, one-shot)

Infinity-Intro to the new Ultraverse; variant-c exists. 3.00

BLACKSTONE (See Super Magician Comics & Wisco Giveaways)

BLACKSTONE, MASTER MAGICIAN COMICS
Vital Publ./Street & Smith Publ.: Mar-Apr, 1946 - No. 3, July-Aug, 1946

1	39	78	117	231	378	525
2,3	21	42	63	126	206	285

BLACKSTONE, THE MAGICIAN (...Detective on cover only #3 & 4)
Marvel Comics (CnPC): No. 2, May, 1948 - No. 4, Sept, 1948 (No #1) (Cont'd from E.C. #1?)

2-The Blonde Phantom begins, ends #4	94	188	282	597	1024	1450
3,4: 3-Blonde Phantom by Sekowsky	54	108	162	343	574	825

BLACKSTONE, THE MAGICIAN DETECTIVE FIGHTS CRIME
E. C. Comics: Fall, 1947

1-1st app. Happy Houlihans 58 116 174 371 636 900

BLACK SUN (X-Men Black Sun on cover)
Marvel Comics: Nov, 2000 - No. 5, Nov, 2000 ($2.99, weekly limited series)

1-(...: X-Men), 2-(...: Storm), 3-(...: Banshee and Sunfire), 4-(...: Colossus and Nightcrawler), 5-(...: Wolverine and Thunderbird); Claremont-s in all; Evans interlocking painted covers; Magik returns 3.00

BLACK SUN
DC Comics (WildStorm): Nov, 2002 - No. 6, Jun, 2003 ($2.95, limited series)

1-6-Andreyko-s/Scott-a 3.00

BLACK SWAN COMICS
MLJ Magazines (Pershing Square Publ. Co.): 1945

1-The Black Hood reprints from Black Hood No. 14; Bill Woggon-a; Suzie app. Caribbean Pirates-c 24 48 72 140 230 320

BLACK TARANTULA (See Feature Presentations No. 5)

BLACK TERROR (See America's Best Comics & Exciting Comics)
Better Publications/Standard: Winter, 1942-43 - No. 27, June, 1949

1-Black Terror, Crime Crusader begin; Japanese WWII-c	400	800	1200	2800	4900	7000
2	181	362	543	1158	1979	2800
3-Nazi WWII-c	168	336	504	1075	1838	2600
4,5-Nazi & Japanese WWII-c	142	284	426	909	1555	2200
6-8: 6,8-Classic Nazi WWII-c. 7-Classic Japanese WWII-c; The Ghost app.	168	336	504	1075	1838	2600
9,10-Nazi & Japanese WWII-c	123	246	369	787	1344	1900
11,13-19	61	122	183	390	670	950
12-Japanese WWII-c	81	162	243	518	884	1250
20-Classic-c; The Scarab app.	97	194	291	621	1061	1500
21-Miss Masque app.	77	154	231	493	847	1200
22-Part Frazetta-a on one Black Terror story	65	130	195	416	708	1000
23,25-27	54	108	162	343	574	825
24-Frazetta-a (1/4 pg.)	84	168	252	538	919	1300

NOTE: *Schomburg (Xela) c-2-27; bondage c-2, 17, 24. **Meskin** a-27. **Moreira** a-27. **Robinson/Meskin** a-23, 24(3), 25, 26. **Roussos/Mayo** a-24. **Tuska** a-26, 27.*

BLACK TERROR, THE (Also see Total Eclipse)
Eclipse Comics: Oct, 1989 - No. 3, June, 1990 ($4.95, 52 pgs., squarebound, limited series)

1-3: Beau Smith & Chuck Dixon scripts; Dan Brereton painted-c/a 5.00

BLACK TERROR (Also see Project Superpowers)
Dynamite Entertainment: 2008 - No. 14, 2011 ($3.50/$3.99)

1-14-Golden Age hero. 1-Alex Ross-c/Mike Lilly-a; various variant-c exist 4.00

BLACKTHORNE 3-D SERIES
Blackthorne Publishing Co.: May, 1985 - No. 80, 1989 ($2.25/$2.50)

1-Sheena in 3-D #1. D. Stevens-c/retouched-a	1	2	3	5	6	8
2-10: 2-MerlinRealm in 3-D #1. 3-3-D Heroes #1. Goldyn in 3-D #1. 5-Bizarre 3-D Zone #1. 6-Salimba in 3-D #1. 7-Twisted Tales in 3-D #1. 8-Dick Tracy in 3-D #1. 9-Salimba in 3-D #2. 10-Gumby in 3-D #1						6.00
11-19: 11-Betty Boop in 3-D #1. 12-Hamster Vice in 3-D #1. 13-Little Nemo in 3-D #1. 14-Gumby in 3-D #2. 15-Hamster Vice #6 in 3-D. 16-Laffin' Gas #6 in 3-D. 17-Gumby in 3-D #3. 18-Bullwinkle and Rocky in 3-D #1. 19-The Flintstones in 3-D #1						6.00
20(#1),26(#2),35(#3),39(#4),52(#5),62,71(#6)-G.I. Joe in 3-D. 62-G.I. Joe Annual	2	4	6	8	11	14
21-24,27-28: 21-Gumby in 3-D #4. 22-The Flintstones in 3-D #2. 23-Laurel & Hardy in 3-D #1. 24-Bozo the Clown in 3-D #1. 27-Bravestarr in 3-D #1. 28- Gumby in 3-D #5						6.00
25,29,37-The Transformers in 3-D	2	4	6	10	14	18
30-Star Wars in 3-D #1	3	6	9	16	23	30
31-34,36,38,40: 31-The California Raisins in 3-D #1. 32-Richie Rich & Casper in 3-D #1. 33-Gumby in 3-D #6. 34-Laurel & Hardy in 3-D #2. 36-The Flintstones in 3-D #3. 38-Gumby in 3-D #7. 40-Bravestarr in 3-D #2						6.00
41-46,49,50: 41-Battletech in 3-D #1. 42-The Flintstones in 3-D #4. 43-Underdog in 3-D #1 44-The California Raisins in 3-D #2. 45-Red Heat in 3-D #1 (movie adapt.). 46-The California Raisins in 3-D #3. 49-Rambo in 3-D #1. 49-Sad Sack in 3-D #1. 50-Bullwinkle For President in 3-D #1						6.00
47,48-Star Wars in 3-D #2,3	2	4	6	11	16	20
51,53-60: 51-Kull in 3-D #1. 53-Red Sonja in 3-D #1. 54-Bozo in 3-D #2. 55-Waxwork in 3-D #1 (movie adapt.). 57-Casper in 3-D #1. 58-Baby Huey in 3-D #1. 59-Little Dot in 3-D #1. 60-Solomon Kane in 3-D #1						6.00
61,63-70,72-74,76-80: 61-Werewolf in 3-D #1. 63-The California Raisins in 3-D #4. 64-To Die For in 3-D #1. 65-Capt. Holo in 3-D #1. 66-Playful Little Audrey in 3-D #1. 67-Kull in 3-D #2. 69-The California Raisins in 3-D #5. 70-Wendy in 3-D #1. 72-Sports Hall of Shame #1. 74-The Noid in 3-D #1. 80-The Noid in 3-D #2	1	2	3	4	5	7
75-Moonwalker in 3-D #1 (Michael Jackson movie adapt.)	4	8	12	27	44	60

BLACK VORTEX (See Guardians of the Galaxy & X-Men: The Black Vortex)

BLACK WIDOW (Marvel Knights) (Also see Marvel Graphic Novel)
Marvel Comics: May, 1999 - No. 3, Aug, 1999 ($2.99, limited series)

1-(June on-c) Devin Grayson-s/J.G. Jones-c/a; Daredevil app. 5.00
1-Variant-c by J.G. Jones 6.00
2,3 4.00
...Web of Intrigue (6/99, $3.50) r/origin & early appearances 4.00
TPB (7/01, $15.95) r/Vol. 1 & 2; Jones-c 16.00

BLACK WIDOW (Marvel Knights) (Volume 2)
Marvel Comics: Jan, 2001 - No. 3, May, 2001 ($2.99, limited series)

1-3-Grayson & Rucka-s/Scott Hampton-c/a; Daredevil app. 3.00

BLACK WIDOW (Marvel Knights)
Marvel Comics: Nov, 2004 - No. 6, Apr, 2005 ($2.99, limited series)

1-6-Sienkiewicz-a/Land-c 3.00

BLACK WIDOW (Continues in Widowmaker #1)
Marvel Comics: Jun, 2010 - No. 8, Jan, 2011 ($3.99/$2.99)

1-($3.99) Liu-s/Acuña-a; Wolverine app.; back-up history text						4.00
1-Variant photo-c of Scarlett Johansson from Iron Man 2 movie	3	6	9	14	20	25
2-8-($2.99) 2-5-Acuña-a. 2,3-Elektra app.						3.00

BLACK WIDOW (All-New Marvel Now!)
Marvel Comics: Mar, 2014 - No. 20, Sept, 2015 ($3.99)

1-20: 1-Edmonson-s/Noto-a/c. 7-Daredevil app. 8-Winter Soldier app. 11-X-23 app. 4.00

BLACK WIDOW
Marvel Comics: May, 2016 - No. 12, May, 2017 ($3.99)

1-12: 1-Waid-s/Samnee-s&a. 6-Iron Man app. 9,10-Winter Soldier app. 4.00

BLACK WIDOW & THE MARVEL GIRLS
Marvel Comics: Feb, 2010 - No. 4, Apr, 2010 ($2.99, limited series)

1-4-Tobin-s. 1-Enchantress app. 2-Avengers app. 4-Storm app.; Miyazawa-a 3.00

Blade #3 © MAR

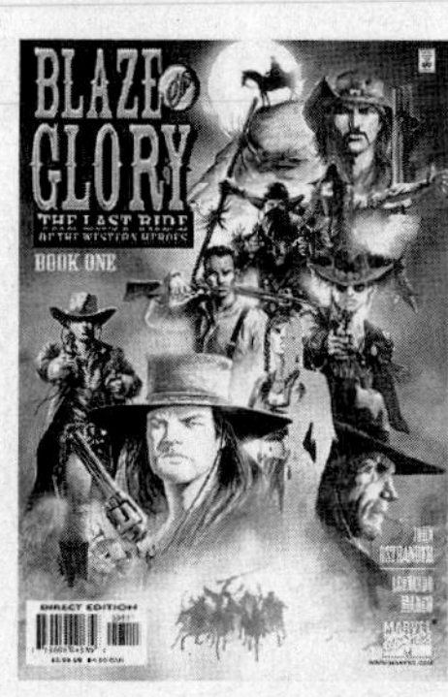

Blaze of Glory #1 © MAR

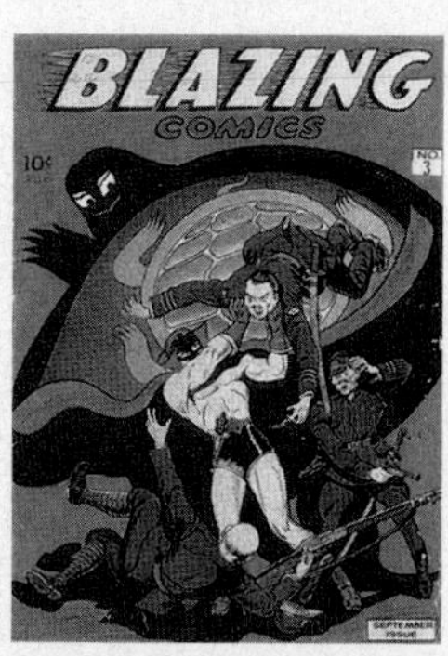

Blazing Comics #3 © ENWIL

GD VG FN VF VF/NM NM-
2.0 4.0 6.0 8.0 9.0 9.2

BLACK WIDOW: DEADLY ORIGIN
Marvel Comics: Jan, 2010 - No. 4, Apr, 2010 ($3.99, limited series)

1-4-Granov-c; origin retold. 1-Wolverine and Bucky app. 3-Daredevil app. 4.00

BLACK WIDOW: PALE LITTLE SPIDER (Marvel Knights) (Volume 3)
Marvel Comics: Jun, 2002 - No. 3, Aug, 2002 ($2.99, limited series)

1-3-Rucka-s/Kordey-a/Horn-c 3.00

BLACK WIDOW 2 (THE THINGS THEY SAY ABOUT HER) (Marvel Knights)
Marvel Comics: Nov, 2005 - No. 6, Apr, 2006 ($2.99, limited series)

1-6-Phillips & Sienkiewicz-a/Morgan-s; Daredevil app. 3.00
TPB (2006, $15.99) r/#1-6 16.00

BLACKWULF
Marvel Comics: June, 1994 - No. 10, Mar, 1995 ($1.50)

1-($2.50)-Embossed-c; Angel Medina-a 4.00
2-10 3.00

BLADE (The Vampire Hunter)
Marvel Comics

1-(3/98, $3.50) Colan-a(p)/Christopher Golden-s 4.00
... Black & White TPB (2004, $15.99, B&W) reprints from magazines Vampire Tales #8,9; Marvel Preview #3,6; Crescent City Blues #1 and Marvel Shadow and Light #1 16.00
San Diego Con Promo (6/97) Wesley Snipes photo-c 3.00
...Sins of the Father (10/98, $5.99) Sears-a; movie adaption 6.00
Blade 2: Movie Adaptation (5/02, $5.95) Ponticelli-a/Bradstreet-c 6.00

BLADE (The Vampire Hunter)
Marvel Comics: Nov, 1998 - No. 3, Jan, 1999 ($3.50/$2.99)

1-($3.50) Contains Movie insider pages; McKean-a 4.00
2,3-($2.99): 2-Two covers 3.00

BLADE (Volume 2)
Marvel Comics (MAX): May, 2002 -No. 6, Oct, 2002 ($2.99)

1-6-Bradstreet-c/Hinz-s. 1-5-Pugh-a. 6-Homs-a 3.00

BLADE
Marvel Comics: Nov, 2006 - No. 12, Oct, 2007 ($2.99)

1-12: 1-Chaykin-a/Guggenheim-s; origin retold; Spider-Man app. 2-Dr. Doom-c/app. 5-Civil War tie-in; Wolverine app. 6-Blade loses a hand. 10-Spider-Man app. 3.00
...: Sins of the Father TPB (2007, $14.99) r/#7-12; afterword by Guggenheim 15.00
...: Undead Again TPB (2007, $14.99) r/#1-6; letters pages from #1&2 15.00

BLADE OF THE IMMORTAL (Manga)
Dark Horse Comics: June, 1996 - No. 131, Nov, 2007 ($2.95/$2.99/$3.95, B&W)

1-Hiroaki Samura-s/a in all 1 3 4 6 8 10
2-5: 2-#1 on cover in error 6.00
6-10 5.00
11,19,20,34-($3.95, 48 pgs.): 34-Food one-shot 4.00
12-18,21-33,35-41,43-105,107-131: 12-20-Dreamsong. 21-28-On Silent Wings. 29-33-Dark Shadow. 35-42-Heart of Darkness. 43-57-The Gathering 3.00
42-($3.50) Ends Heart of Darkness 3.50
106-($3.99) 4.00

BLADE RUNNER (Movie)
Marvel Comics Group: Oct, 1982 - No. 2, Nov, 1982

1,2-r/Marvel Super Special #22; 1-Williamson-c/a. 2-Williamson-a
2 4 6 8 10 12

BLADE: THE VAMPIRE-HUNTER
Marvel Comics: July, 1994 - No. 10, Apr, 1995 ($1.95)

1-($2.95)-Foil-c; Dracula returns; Wheatley-c/a 4.00
2-10: 2,3,10-Dracula-c/app. 8-Morbius app. 3.00

BLADE: VAMPIRE-HUNTER
Marvel Comics: Dec, 1999 - No. 6, May, 2000 ($3.50/$2.50)

1-($3.50)-Bart Sears-s; Sears and Smith-a 4.00
2-6-($2.50): 2-Regular & Wesley Snipes photo-c 3.00

BLAIR WITCH CHRONICLES, THE
Oni Press: Mar, 2000 - No. 4, July, 2000 ($2.95, B&W, limited series)

1-4-Van Meter-s.1-Guy Davis-a. 2-Mireault-a 3.00
1-DF Alternate-c by John Estes 4.00
TPB (9/00, $15.95) r/#1-4 & Blair Witch Project one-shot 16.00

BLAIR WITCH: DARK TESTAMENTS
Image Comics: Oct, 2000 ($2.95, one-shot)

1-Edington-s/Adlard-a; story of murderer Rustin Parr 3.00

GD VG FN VF VF/NM NM-
2.0 4.0 6.0 8.0 9.0 9.2

BLAIR WITCH PROJECT, THE (Movie companion, not adaptation)
Oni Press: July, 1999 ($2.95, B&W, one-shot)

1-(1st printing) History of the Blair Witch, art by Edwards, Mireault, and Davis; Van Meter-s; only the stick figure is red on the cover 5.00
1-(2nd printing) Stick figure and title lettering are red on cover 4.00
1-(3rd printing) Stick figure, title, and creator credits are red on cover 3.00
DF Glow in the Dark variant-c ($10.00) 10.00

BLAST (Satire Magazine)
G & D Publications: Feb, 1971 - No. 2, May, 1971

1-Wrightson & Kaluta-a/Everette-c 7 14 21 48 89 130
2-Kaluta-c/a 5 10 15 35 63 90

BLAST CORPS
Dark Horse Comics: Oct, 1998 ($2.50, one-shot, based on Nintendo game)

1-Reprints from Nintendo Power magazine; Mahn-a 3.00

BLASTERS SPECIAL
DC Comics: 1989 ($2.00, one-shot)

1-Peter David scripts; Invasion spin-off 4.00

BLAST-OFF (Three Rocketeers)
Harvey Publications (Fun Day Funnies): Oct, 1965 (12¢)

1-Kirby/Williamson-a(2); Williamson/Crandall-a; Williamson/Torres/Krenkel-a; Kirby/Simon-c
6 12 18 41 76 110

BLAZE
Marvel Comics: Aug, 1994 - No. 12, July, 1995 ($1.95)

1-($2.95)-Foil embossed-c 4.00
2-12: 2-Man-Thing-c/story. 11,12-Punisher app. 3.00

BLAZE CARSON (Rex Hart #6 on)(See Kid Colt, Tex Taylor, Wild Western, Wisco)
Marvel Comics (USA): Sept, 1948 - No. 5, June, 1949

1-Tex Taylor app.; Shores-c 32 64 96 188 307 425
2,4,5: 2-Tex Morgan app.; Shores-c. 4-Two-Gun Kid app. 5-Tex Taylor app.
20 40 60 117 189 260
3-Used by N.Y. State Legis. Comm. (injury to eye splash); Tex Morgan app.
21 42 63 122 199 275

BLAZE: LEGACY OF BLOOD (See Ghost Rider & Ghost Rider/Blaze)
Marvel Comics (Midnight Sons imprint): Dec, 1993 - No. 4, Mar, 1994 ($1.75, limited series)

1-4 3.00

BLAZE OF GLORY
Marvel Comics: Feb, 2000 - No. 4, Mar, 2000 ($2.99, limited series)

1-4-Ostrander-s/Manco-a; Two-Gun Kid, Rawhide Kid, Red Wolf and Ghost Rider app. 3.00
TPB (7/02, $9.99) r/#1-4 10.00

BLAZE THE WONDER COLLIE (Formerly Molly Manton's Romances #1?)
Marvel Comics(SePI): No. 2, Oct, 1949 - No. 3, Feb, 1950 (Both have photo-c)

2(#1), 3-(Scarce) 28 56 84 168 274 380

BLAZING BATTLE TALES
Seaboard Periodicals (Atlas): July, 1975

1-Intro. Sgt. Hawk & the Sky Demon; Severin, McWilliams, Sparling-a; Nazi-c by Thorne
3 6 9 14 19 24

BLAZING COMBAT (Magazine)
Warren Publishing Co.: Oct, 1965 - No. 4, July, 1966 (35¢, B&W)

1-Frazetta painted-c on all 30 60 90 216 483 750
2 8 16 24 56 108 160
3,4: 4-Frazetta half pg. ad 8 16 24 51 96 140
nn-Anthology (reprints from No. 1-4) (low print) 8 16 24 51 96 140

NOTE: ***Adkins*** *a-4.* ***Colan*** *a-3,4,nn.* ***Crandall*** *a-all.* ***Evans*** *a-1,4.* ***Heath*** *a-4,nn.* ***Morrow*** *a-1-3,nn.* ***Orlando*** *a-1-3,nn.* ***J. Severin*** *a-all.* ***Torres*** *a-1-4.* ***Toth*** *a-all.* ***Williamson*** *a-2. and* ***Wood*** *a-3,4,nn.*

BLAZING COMBAT: WORLD WAR I AND WORLD WAR II
Apple Press: Mar, 1994 ($3.75, B&W)

1,2: 1-r/Colan, Toth, Goodwin, Severin, Wood-a. 2-r/Crandall, Evans, Severin, Torres, Williamson-a 4.00

BLAZING COMICS (Also see Blue Circle Comics and Red Circle Comics)
Enwil Associates/Rural Home: 6/44 - #3, 9/44; #4, 2/45; #5, 3/45; #5(V2#2), 3/55 - #6(V2#3), 1955?

1-The Green Turtle, Red Hawk, Black Buccaneer begin; origin Jun-Gal; classic Japanese WWII splash 58 116 174 371 636 900
2-5: 2-Japanese WWII-c. 3-Briefer-a. 5-(V2#2 inside)
40 80 120 246 411 575
5(3/55, V2#2-inside)-Black Buccaneer-c, 6(V2#3-inside, 1955)-Indian/

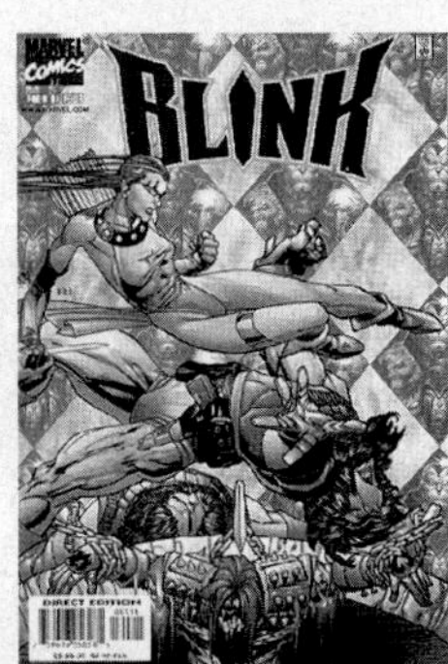

Blink #4 © MAR

Blonde Phantom #16 © MAR

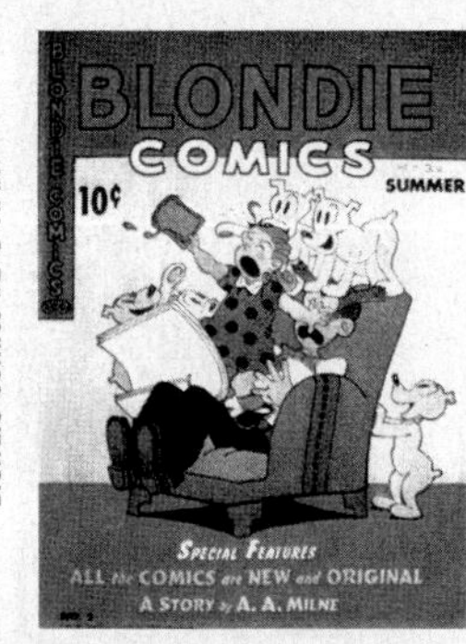

Blondie Comics #2 © HARV

GD VG FN VF VF/NM NM-
2.0 4.0 6.0 8.0 9.0 9.2

Japanese-c; cover is from Apr. 1945 22 44 66 132 216 300
NOTE: *No. 5 & 6 contain remaindered comics rebound and the contents can vary. Cloak & Dagger, Will Rogers, Superman 64, Star Spangled 130, Kaanga known. Value would be half of contents.*

BLAZING SIXGUNS
Avon Periodicals: Dec, 1952

1-Kinstler-c/a; Larsen/Alascia-a(2), Tuska?-a; Jesse James, Kit Carson, Wild Bill Hickok app. 26 52 78 154 252 350

BLAZING SIXGUNS
I.W./Super Comics: 1964

I.W. Reprint #1,8,9: 1-r/Wild Bill Hickok #26, Western True Crime #? & Blazing Sixguns #1 by Avon; Kinstler-c. 8-r/Blazing Western #?; Kinstler-c. 9-r/Blazing Western #1; Ditko-r; Kintsler-c reprinted from Dalton Boys #1 2 4 6 10 14 18
Super Reprint #10,11,15-17: 10,11-r/The Rider #2,1. 15-r/Silver Kid Western #?. 16-r/Buffalo Bill #?; Wildey-r; Severin-c. 17(1964)-r/Western True Crime #? 2 4 6 10 14 18
12-Reprints Bullseye #3; S&K-a 3 6 9 18 28 38
18-r/Straight Arrow #? by Powell; Severin-c 2 4 6 10 14 18

BLAZING SIX-GUNS (Also see Sundance Kid)
Skywald Comics: Feb, 1971 - No. 2, Apr, 1971 (52 pgs.)

1-The Red Mask (3-D effect, not true 3-D), Sundance Kid begin (new-s), Avon's Geronimo reprint by Kinstler; Wyatt Earp app. 3 6 9 14 20 25
2-Wild Bill Hickok, Jesse James, Kit Carson-r plus M.E. Red Mask-r (3-D effect) 2 4 6 10 14 18

BLAZING WEST (The Hooded Horseman #21 on)(52 pgs.)
American Comics Group (B&I Publ./Michel Publ.): Fall, 1948 - No. 20, Nov-Dec, 1951

1-Origin & 1st app. Injun Jones, Tenderfoot & Buffalo Belle; Texas Tim & Ranger begins, ends #13 21 42 63 124 202 280
2,3 (1-2/49) 13 26 39 72 101 130
4-Origin & 1st app. Little Lobo; Starr-a (3-4/49) 11 22 33 64 90 115
5-10: 5-Starr-a 10 20 30 54 72 90
11-13 9 18 27 47 61 75
14(11-12/50)-Origin/1st app. The Hooded Horseman 14 28 42 82 121 160
15-20: 15,16,18,19-Starr-a 10 20 30 54 72 90

BLAZING WESTERN
Timor Publications: Jan, 1954 - No. 5, Sept, 1954

1-Ditko-a (1st Western-a?); text story by Bruce Hamilton 20 40 60 120 195 270
2-4 10 20 30 54 72 90
5-Disbrow-a; L.B. Cole-c 10 20 30 56 76 95

BLINDSIDE
Image Comics (Extreme Studios): Aug, 1996 ($2.50)

1-Variant-c exists 3.00

BLINK (See X-Men Age of Apocalypse storyline)
Marvel Comics: March, 2001 - No. 4, June, 2001 ($2.99, limited series)

1-4-Adam Kubert-c/Lobdell-s/Winick-script; leads into Exiles #1 3.00

BLIP
Marvel Comics Group: 2/1983 - 1983 (Video game mag. in comic format)

1-1st app. Donkey Kong & Mario Bros. in comics, 6pgs. comics; photo-c 2 4 6 11 16 20
2-Spider-Man photo-c; 6pgs. Spider-Man comics w/Green Goblin 2 4 6 8 10 12
3,4,6 6.00
5-E.T., Indiana Jones; Rocky-c 1 2 3 4 5 7
7-6pgs. Hulk comics; Pac-Man & Donkey Kong Jr. Hints 1 2 3 5 6 8

BLISS ALLEY
Image Comics: July, 1997 - No. 2, Sept, 1997 ($2.95, B&W)

1,2-Messner-Loebs-s/a 3.00

BLITZKRIEG
National Periodical Publications: Jan-Feb, 1976 - No. 5, Sept-Oct, 1976

1-Kubert-c on all 4 8 12 25 40 55
2-5 3 6 9 16 24 32

BLOCKBUSTERS OF THE MARVEL UNIVERSE
Marvel Comics: March, 2011 ($4.99, one-shot)

1-Handbook-style summaries of Marvel crossover events like Civil War & Heroes Reborn 5.00

BLONDE PHANTOM (Formerly All-Select #1-11; Lovers #23 on)(Also see Blackstone, Marvel Mystery, Millie The Model #2, Sub-Mariner Comics #25 & Sun Girl)
Marvel Comics (MPC): No. 12, Winter, 1946-47 - No. 22, Mar, 1949

GD VG FN VF VF/NM NM-
2.0 4.0 6.0 8.0 9.0 9.2

12-Miss America begins, ends #14 213 426 639 1363 2332 3300
13-Sub-Mariner begins (not in #16) 126 252 378 806 1378 1950
14,15: 15-Kurtzman's "Hey Look" 119 238 357 762 1306 1850
16-Captain America with Bucky story by Rico(p), 6 pgs.; Kurtzman's "Hey Look" (1 pg.) 148 296 444 947 1624 2300
17-22: 22-Anti Wertham editorial 107 214 321 680 1165 1650
NOTE: ***Shores** c-12-18.*

BLONDIE (See Ace Comics, Comics Reading Libraries (Promotional Comics section), Dagwood, Daisy & Her Pups, Eat Right to Work..., King & Magic Comics)
David McKay Publications: 1942 - 1946

Feature Books 12 (Rare) 90 180 270 576 988 1400
Feature Books 27-29,31,34(1940) 22 44 66 128 209 290
Feature Books 36,38,40,42,43,45,47 20 40 60 114 182 250
...1944 (Hard-c, 1938, B&W, 128 pgs.)-1944 daily strip-r 16 32 48 94 147 200

BLONDIE & DAGWOOD FAMILY
Harvey Publ. (King Features Synd.): Oct, 1963 - No. 4, Dec, 1965 (68 pgs.)

1 5 10 15 30 50 70
2-4 3 6 9 19 30 40

BLONDIE COMICS (...Monthly No. 16-141)
David McKay #1-15/Harvey #16-163/King #164-175/Charlton #177 on: Spring, 1947 - No. 163, Nov, 1965; No. 164, Aug, 1966 - No. 175, Dec, 1967; No. 177, Feb, 1969 - No. 222, Nov, 1976

1 41 82 123 256 428 600
2 21 42 63 122 199 275
3-5 15 30 45 90 140 190
6-10 14 28 42 80 115 150
11-15 10 20 30 56 76 95
16-(3/50; 1st Harvey issue) 11 22 33 62 86 110
17-20: 20-(3/51)-Becomes Daisy & Her Pups #21 & Chamber of Chills #21 5 10 15 34 60 85
21-30 5 10 15 31 53 75
31-50 4 8 12 27 44 60
51-80 4 8 12 23 37 50
81-99 3 6 9 21 33 45
100 4 8 12 25 40 55
101-124,126-130 3 6 9 17 26 35
125 (80 pgs.) 4 8 12 27 44 60
131-136,138,139 3 6 9 16 24 32
137,140-(80 pgs.) 4 8 12 25 40 55
141-147,149-154,156,160,164-167 3 6 9 16 23 30
148,155,157-159,161-163 are 68 pgs. 3 6 9 21 33 45
168-175 2 4 6 11 16 20
177-199 (no #176)-Moon landing-c/s 2 4 6 9 13 16
200-Anniversary issue; highlights of the Bumsteads 2 4 6 10 14 18
201-210,213-222 2 4 6 8 10 12
211,212-1st & 2nd app. Super Dagwood 2 4 6 9 13 16
Blondie, Dagwood & Daisy by Chic Young #1(Harvey, 1953, 100 pg. squarebound giant) new stories; Popeye (1 pg.) and Felix (1pg.) app. 36 72 108 211 343 475

BLOOD
Marvel Comics (Epic Comics): Feb, 1988 - No. 4, Apr, 1988 ($3.25, mature)

1-4: DeMatteis scripts & Kent Williams-c/a 5.00

BLOOD AND GLORY (Punisher & Captain America)
Marvel Comics: Oct, 1992 - No. 3, Dec, 1992 ($5.95, limited series)

1-3: 1-Embossed wraparound-c by Janson; Chichester & Clarke-s 6.00

BLOOD & ROSES: FUTURE PAST TENSE (Bob Hickey's...)
Sky Comics: Dec, 1993 ($2.25)

1-Silver ink logo 3.00

BLOOD & ROSES: SEARCH FOR THE TIME-STONE (Bob Hickey's...)
Sky Comics: Apr, 1994 ($2.50)

1 3.00

BLOOD AND SHADOWS
DC Comics (Vertigo): 1996 - Book 4, 1996 ($5.95, squarebound, mature)

Books 1-4: Joe R. Lansdale scripts; Mark A. Nelson-c/a. 6.00

BLOOD AND WATER
DC Comics (Vertigo): May, 2003 - No. 5, Sept, 2003 ($2.95, limited series)

1-5-Judd Winick-s/Tomm Coker-a/Brian Bolland-c 3.00
TPB (2009, $14.99) r/#1-5 15.00

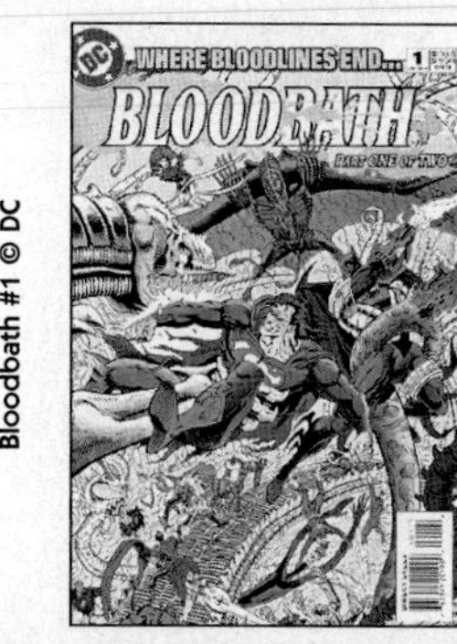

Bloodbath #1 © DC

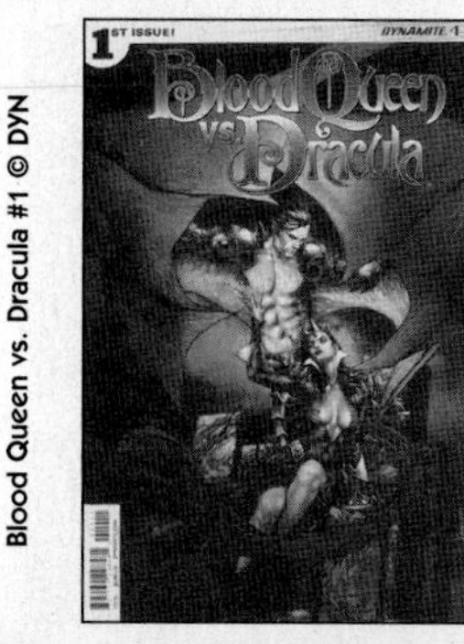

Blood Queen vs. Dracula #1 © DYN

Bloodshot Reborn #16 © VAL

BLOOD: A TALE
DC Comics (Vertigo): Nov, 1996 - No. 4, Feb, 1997 ($2.95, limited series)
1-4: Reprints Epic series w/new-c; DeMatteis scripts; Kent Williams-c/a 3.00
TPB (2004, $19.95) r/#1-4 20.00

BLOODBATH
DC Comics: Early Dec, 1993 - No. 2, Late Dec, 1993 ($3.50, 68 pgs.)
1-Neon ink-c; Superman app.; new Batman-c /app. 4.00
2-Hitman 2nd app. 1 2 3 4 5 7

BLOOD BLISTER
AfterShock Comics: Jan, 2017 - Present ($3.99)
1,2-Phil Hester-s/Tony Harris-a 4.00

BLOODBORNE: THE DEATH OF SLEEP (Based on the Sony computer game)
Titan Comics: Mar, 2018 - Present ($3.99)
1-Ales Kot-s/Piotr Kowalski-a 4.00

BLOODHOUND
DC Comics: Sept, 2004 - No. 10, June, 2005 ($2.95)
1-10: 1-Jolley-s/Kirk-a/Johnson-c. 5-Firestorm app. (cont. from Firestorm #7) 3.00

BLOODHOUND: CROWBAR MEDICINE
Dark Horse Comics: Oct, 2013 - No. 5, Mar, 2014 ($3.99)
1-5-Jolley-s/Kirk-a/c 4.00

BLOOD LEGACY
Image Comics (Top Cow): May, 2000 - No. 4, Nov, 2000; Apr, 2003 ($2.50/$4.99)
...: The Story of Ryan 1-4-Kerri Hawkins-s. 1-Andy Park-a(p); 3 covers 3.00
...: The Young Ones 1 (4/03, $4.99, one-shot) Basaldua-c/a 5.00
Preview Special ('00, $4.95) B&W flip-book w/The Magdalena Preview 5.00

BLOODLINES
DC Comics: Jun, 2016 - No. 6, Nov, 2016 ($2.99, limited series)
1-6: 1-Krul-s/Marion-a 3.00

BLOODLINES: A TALE FROM THE HEART OF AFRICA (See Tales From the Heart of Africa)
Marvel Comics (Epic Comics): 1992 ($5.95, 52 pgs.)
1-Story cont'd from Tales From... 6.00

BLOOD OF DRACULA
Apple Comics: Nov, 1987 - No. 20?, 1990 ($1.75/$1.95, B&W)($2.25 #14,16 on)
1-3,5-14,20: 1-10-Chadwick-c 4.00
4,16-19-Lost Frankenstein pgs. by Wrightson 1 2 3 4 5 7
15-Contains stereo flexidisc ($3.75) 5.00

BLOOD OF THE DEMON (Etrigan the Demon)
DC Comics: May, 2005 - No. 17, Sept, 2006 ($2.50/$2.99)
1-14-Byrne-a(p) & plot/Pfeifer-script. 3,4-Batman app. 13-One Year Later 3.00
15-17-($2.99) 3.00

BLOOD OF THE INNOCENT (See Warp Graphics Annual)
WaRP Graphics: 1/7/86 - No. 4, 1/28/86 (Weekly mini-series, mature)
1-4 3.00

BLOODPACK
DC Comics: Mar, 1995 - No. 4, June,1995 ($1.50, limited series)
1-4 3.00

BLOODPOOL
Image Comics (Extreme): Aug, 1995 - No. 4, Nov, 1995 ($2.50, limited series)
1-4: Jo Duffy scripts in all 3.00
Special (3/96, $2.50)-Jo Duffy scripts 3.00
Trade Paperback (1996, $12.95)-r/#1-4 13.00

BLOOD QUEEN, THE
Dynamite Entertainment: 2014 - No. 6, 2014 ($3.99, limited series)
1-6-Brownfield-s/Casas-a/Anacleto-c; variant covers on each 4.00
Annual 2014 ($7.99) Prequel stories to the series 8.00

BLOOD QUEEN VS. DRACULA
Dynamite Entertainment: 2015 - No. 4, 2015 ($3.99, limited series)
1-4-Brownfield-s/Baal-a/Anacleto-c; variant covers on each 4.00

BLOOD RED DRAGON (Stan Lee and Yoshiki's...)
Image Comics: No. 0, Aug, 2011 - No. 3, Nov, 2011 ($3.99)
0-3-Goff-s/Soriano-a 4.00

BLOODSCENT
Comico: Oct, 1988 ($2.00, one-shot, Baxter paper)
1-Colan-p 3.00

BLOODSEED
Marvel Comics (Frontier Comics): Oct, 1993 - No. 2, Nov, 1993 ($1.95)
1,2: Sharp/Cam Smith-a 3.00

BLOODSHOT (See Eternal Warrior #4 & Rai #0)
Valiant/Acclaim Comics (Valiant): Feb, 1993 - No. 51, Aug, 1996 ($2.25/$2.50)
0-(3/94, $3.50)-Wraparound chromium-c by Quesada(p); origin 5.00
0-Gold variant; no cover price 30.00
Note: There is a "Platinum variant" ; press run error of Gold ed. (25 copies exist)
(A CGC certified 9.8 copy sold for $2,067 in 2004)
1-($3.50)-Chromium embossed-c by B. Smith w/poster
1 2 3 5 6 8
2-5,8-14: 3-$2.25-c begins; cont'd in Hard Corps #5. 4-Eternal Warrior-c/story. 5-Rai & Eternal Warrior app. 14-(3/94)-Reese-c(i) 4.00
6,7: 6-1st app. Ninjak (out of costume). 7-Ninjak in costume
1 3 4 6 8 10
15(4/94)-50: 16-w/bound-in trading card 3.00
51-Bloodshot dies? 3 6 9 19 30 40
Yearbook 1 (1994, $3.95) 4.00
Special 1 (3/94, $5.95)-Zeck-c/a(p); Last Stand 6.00
...: Blood of the Machine HC (2012, $24.99) r/#1-8; new 8 pg. story; intro. by VanHook 25.00

BLOODSHOT (Volume Two)
Acclaim Comics (Valiant): July, 1997 - No. 16, Oct, 1998 ($2.50)
1-16: 1-Two covers. 5-Copycat-c. X-O Manowar-c/app 3.00

BLOODSHOT (Re-titled Bloodshot and H.A.R.D.Corps for #14-23)
Valiant Entertainment: July, 2012 - No. 25, Nov, 2014 ($3.99)
1-13: 1-Sweirczynski-s/Garcia & Lozzi-a. 10-13-Harbinger Wars tie-ins 4.00
1-9-Pullbox variants 4.00
1-Variant-c by David Aja 15.00
1-Variant-c by Esad Ribic 20.00
14-24: 14-23-Bloodshot and H.A.R.D.Corps 4.00
25-($4.99) Milligan-s/Larosa-a; back-up Chaykin-s/a; short features by various 5.00
#0 (8/13) Kindt-s/ChrisCross-a; covers by Lupacchino & Bullock 4.00
Bloodshot and H.A.R.D.Corps #0 (2/14, $3.99) History of Project Rising Spirit 4.00
Bloodshot's Day Off 1 (7/17, $3.99) Rahal-s/Evans-a; Viet Man app. 4.00

BLOODSHOT REBORN
Valiant Entertainment: Apr, 2015 - No. 18, Oct, 2016 ($3.99)
1-18: 1-4-Lemire-s/Suayan-a. 1-1st app. Bloodsquirt. 6-9-Guice-a. 10-13-Set 30 years later. 14-1st app. Deathmate 4.00
#0 (3/17, $3.99) Lemire-s/Guedes-a 4.00
Annual 2016 #1 (3/16, $5.99) Short stories by various incl. Kano, Lemire, Bennett 6.00
...: Bloodshot Island - Director's Cut 1 (6/16, $4.99) r/#1 in B&W; original script 5.00

BLOODSHOT SALVATION
Valiant Entertainment: Sept, 2017 - Present ($3.99)
1-7: 1-Lemire-s/LaRosa-a; bonus Ninjak #1 preview 4.00

BLOODSHOT U.S.A.
Valiant Entertainment: Oct, 2016 - No. 4, Jan, 2017 ($3.99, limited series)
1-4-Lemire-s/Braithwaite-a; Ninjak and Deathmate app. 4.00

BLOODSTONE
Marvel Comics: Dec, 2001 - No. 4, Mar, 2002 ($2.99)
1-4-Intro. Elsa Bloodstone; Abnett & Lanning-s/Lopez-a 3.00

BLOODSTREAM
Image Comics: Jan, 2004 - No. 4, Dec, 2004 ($2.95)
1-4-Adam Shaw painted-a 3.00

BLOODSTRIKE (See Supreme V2#3)
Image Comics (Extreme Studios): 1993 - No. 22, May, 1995; No. 25, May, 1994 ($1.95/$2.50)
1-22, 25: Liefeld layouts in early issues. 1-Blood Brothers prelude. 2-1st app. Lethal. 5-1st app. Noble. 9-Black and White part 6 by Art Thibert; Liefeld pin-up. 9,10-Have coupon #3 & 7 for Extreme Prejudice #0. 10-(4/94). 11-(7/94). 16:Platt-c; Prophet app. 17-19-polybagged w/card . 25-(5/94)-Liefeld/Fraga-c 3.00
... #1 Remastered Edition (7/17, $3.99) Two covers by Fraga & Liefeld 4.00
NOTE: ***Giffen** story/layouts-4-6. **Jae Lee** c-7, 8. **Rob Liefeld** layouts-1-3. **Art Thibert** c-6i.*

BLOODSTRIKE
Image Comics: No. 26, Mar, 2012 - No. 33, Dec, 2012 ($2.99/$3.99)
26-29: 26-Two covers by Seeley & Liefeld; Seeley-s/Gaston-a 3.00
30-33-($3.99) 32,33-Suprema app. 4.00

BLOODSTRIKE (Volume 2)

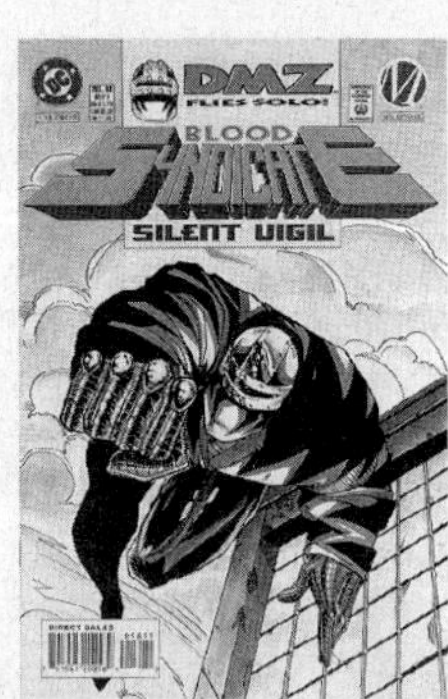

Blood Syndicate #18 © Milestone

The Blue Beetle #5 © FOX

Blue Beetle (2016 series) #9 © DC

GD 2.0 | VG 4.0 | FN 6.0 | VF 8.0 | VF/NM 9.0 | NM- 9.2

Image Comics: Jul, 2015 - Present ($2.99/$3.99)

1-($3.99) Liefeld-s/a 4.00
2-(9/15, $2.99) Liefeld-s/a 3.00

BLOODSTRIKE ASSASSIN
Image Comics (Extreme Studios): June, 1995 - No. 3, Aug, 1995; No. 0, Oct, 1995 ($2.50, limited series)

0-3: 3-(8/95)-Quesada-c. 0-(10/95)-Battlestone app. 3.00

BLOOD SWORD, THE
Jademan Comics: Aug, 1988 - No. 53, Dec, 1992 ($1.50/$1.95, 68 pgs.)

1-53-Kung Fu stories in all 4.00

BLOOD SWORD DYNASTY
Jademan Comics: 1989 -No. 41, Jan, 1993 ($1.25, 36 pgs.)

1-Ties into Blood Sword 4.00
2-41: Ties into Blood Sword 3.00

BLOOD SYNDICATE
DC Comics (Milestone): Apr, 1993 - No. 35, Feb, 1996 ($1.50/-$3.50)

1-($2.95)-Collector's Edition; polybagged with poster, trading card, & acid-free backing board (direct sale only) 4.00
1-9,11-24,26,27,29,33-34: 8-Intro Kwai. 15-Byrne-c. 16-Worlds Collide Pt. 6; Superman-c/app. 17-Worlds Collide Pt. 13. 29-(99¢); Long Hot Summer x-over 3.00
10,28,30-32: 10-Simonson-c. 30-Long Hot Summer x-over 3.00
25-($2.95, 52 pgs.) 4.00
35-Kwai disappears; last issue 4.00

BLOODWULF
Image Comics (Extreme): Feb, 1995 - No. 4, May, 1995 ($2.50, limited series)

1-4: 1-Liefeld-c w/4 diferent captions & alternate-c. 3.00
Summer Special (8/95, $2.50)-Jeff Johnson-c/a; Supreme app; story takes place between Legend of Supreme #3 & Supreme #23. 3.00

BLOODY MARY
DC Comics (Helix): Oct, 1996 - No. 4, Jan, 1997 ($2.25, limited series)

1-4: Garth Ennis scripts; Ezquerra-c/a in all 3.50
TPB (2005, $19.99) r/#1-4 and Bloody Mary: Lady Liberty #1-4 20.00

BLOODY MARY: LADY LIBERTY
DC Comics (Helix): Sept, 1997 - No. 4, Dec, 1997 ($2.50, limited series)

1-4: Garth Ennis scripts; Ezquerra-c/a in all 3.00

BLUE
Image Comics (Action Toys): Aug, 1999 - No. 2, Apr, 2000 ($2.50)

1,2-Aronowitz-s/Struzan-c 3.00

BLUEBEARD
Slave Labor Graphics: Nov, 1993 - No. 3, Mar, 1994 ($2.95, B&W, lim. series)

1-3: James Robinson scripts. 2-(12/93) 3.00
Trade paperback (6/94, $9.95) 13.00
Trade paperback (2nd printing, 7/96, $12.95)-New-c 13.00

BLUE BEETLE, THE (Also see All Top, Big-3, Mystery Men & Weekly Comic Magazine)
Fox Publ. No. 1-11, 31-60; Holyoke No. 12-30: Winter, 1939-40 - No. 57, 7/48; No. 58, 4/50 - No. 60, 8/50

1-Reprints from Mystery Men #1-5; Blue Beetle origin; Yarko the Great-r/from Wonder Comics /Wonderworld #2-5 all by Eisner; Master Magician app.; (Blue Beetle in 4 different costumes) 568 1136 1704 4146 7323 10,500
2-K-51-r by Powell/Wonderworld #8,9 245 490 735 1568 2684 3800
3-Simon-c 168 336 504 1075 1838 2600
4-Marijuana drug mention story 123 246 369 787 1344 1900
5-Zanzibar The Magician by Tuska 100 200 300 635 1093 1550
6-Dynamite Thor begins (1st); origin Blue Beetle 97 194 291 621 1061 1500
7,8-Dynamo app. in both. 8-Last Thor 94 188 282 597 1024 1450
9-12: 9,10-The Blackbird & The Gorilla app. 10-Bondage/hypo-c. 11(2/42)-Bondage-c; The Gladiator app. 12(6/42)-The Black Fury app. 84 168 252 538 919 1300
13-V-Man begins (1st app.), ends #19; Kubert-a; centerfold spread 87 174 261 553 952 1350
14,15-Kubert-a in both. 14-Intro. side-kick (c/text only), Sparky (called Spunky #17-19); BB vs. The Red Robe (Red Skull swipe) 77 154 231 493 847 1200
16-18: 17-Brodsky-c 58 116 174 371 636 900
19-Kubert-a 60 120 180 388 657 925
20-Origin/1st app. Tiger Squadron; Arabian Nights begin 61 122 183 390 670 950
21-26: 24-Intro. & only app. The Halo. 26-General Patton story & photo 52 104 156 328 552 775
27-Tamaa, Jungle Prince app. 45 90 135 284 480 675
28-30(2/44): 29-WWII Nazi bondage-c(1/44) 42 84 126 265 445 625
31(6/44), 33,34,36-40: 34-38-"The Threat from Saturn" serial. 40-Shows #20 in indicia 37 74 111 222 361 500
32-Hitler-c 119 238 357 762 1306 1850
35-Extreme violence 41 82 123 256 428 600
41-45 (#43 exist?) 36 72 108 211 343 475
46-The Puppeteer app. 39 78 117 240 395 550
47-Kamen & Baker-a begin 181 362 543 1158 1979 2800
48-50 129 258 387 826 1413 2000
51,53 113 226 339 718 1234 1750
52-Kamen bondage-c; true crime stories begin 187 374 561 1197 2049 2900
54-Used in **SOTI**. Illo, "Children call these 'headlights' comics"; classic-c 432 864 1296 3154 5577 8000
55-57: 56-Used in **SOTI**, pg. 145. 57(7/48)-Last Kamen issue; becomes Western Killers? 110 220 330 704 1202 1700
58(4/50)-60-No Kamen-a 24 48 72 140 230 320

NOTE: ***Kamen** a-47-51, 53, 55-57; c-47, 49-52. **Powell** a-4(2). Bondage-c 9-12, 46, 52. Headlight-c 46, 48, 57.*

BLUE BEETLE (Formerly The Thing; becomes Mr. Muscles No. 22 on)
(See Charlton Bullseye & Space Adventures)
Charlton Comics: No. 18, Feb, 1955 - No. 21, Aug, 1955

18,19-(Pre-1944-r). 18-Last pre-code issue. 19-Bouncer, Rocket Kelly-r 24 48 72 140 230 320
20-Joan Mason by Kamen 29 58 87 174 285 395
21-New material 23 46 69 136 223 310

BLUE BEETLE (Unusual Tales #1-49; Ghostly Tales #55 on)(See Captain Atom #83 & Charlton Bullseye)
Charlton Comics: V2#1, June, 1964 - V2#5, Mar-Apr, 1965; V3#50, July, 1965 - V3#54, Feb-Mar, 1966; #1, June, 1967 - #5, Nov, 1968

V2#1-Origin/1st S.A. app. Dan Garrett-Blue Beetle 23 46 69 161 356 550
2-5: 5-Weiss illo; 1st published-a? 6 12 18 37 66 95
V3#50-54-Formerly Unusual Tales 5 10 15 34 60 85
1(1967)-Question series begins by Ditko 21 42 63 147 324 500
2-Origin Ted Kord-Blue Beetle (see Capt. Atom #83 for 1st Ted Kord Blue Beetle); Dan Garrett x-over 7 14 21 48 89 130
3-5 (All Ditko-c/a in #1-5) 6 12 18 37 66 95
1,3(Modern Comics-1977)-Reprints 2 4 6 9 12 15

NOTE: *#6 only appeared in the fanzine 'The Charlton Portfolio.'*

BLUE BEETLE (Also see Americomics, Crisis On Infinite Earths, Justice League & Showcase '94 #2-4)
DC Comics: June, 1986 - No. 24, May, 1988

1-Origin retold; intro. Firefist 1 2 3 5 6 8
2-10,15-19,21-24: 2-Origin Firefist. 5-7-The Question app. 21-Millennium tie-in 4.00
11-14,20: 11-14-New Teen Titans x-over. 20-Justice League app.; Millennium tie-in 4.00

BLUE BEETLE (See Infinite Crisis, Teen Titans, and Booster Gold #21)
DC Comics: May, 2006 - No. 36, Apr, 2009 ($2.99)

1-Hamner-a/Giffen & Rogers-s; Guy Gardner app. 4.00
1-2nd & 3rd printings 3.00
2-36: 2-2nd printing exists. 2-4-Oracle app. 5-Phantom Stranger app. 16-Eclipso app. 18,33-Teen Titans app. 20-Sinestro Corps. 21-Spectre app. 26-Spanish issue 3.00
...: Black and Blue TPB (2010, $17.99) r/#27,28,35,36 & Booster Gold #21-25,28,29 18.00
...: Boundaries TPB (2009, $14.99) r/#29-34 15.00
...: End Game TPB (2008, $14.99) r/#20-26; English script for #26 15.00
...: Reach For the Stars TPB (2008, $14.99) r/#13-19 15.00
...: Road Trip TPB (2007, $12.99) r/#7-12 13.00
...: Shellshocked TPB (2006, $12.99) r/#1-6 13.00

BLUE BEETLE (DC New 52) (Also see Threshold)
DC Comics: Nov, 2011 - No. 16, Mar, 2013 ($2.99)

1-16: 1-Bedard-s/Ig Guara-a; new origin. 9-Green Lantern (Kyle) app. 11-Booster Gold 3.00
#0 (11/12, $2.99) Origin of the scarab 3.00

BLUE BEETLE (DC Rebirth)
DC Comics: Nov, 2016 - No. 18, Apr, 2018 ($2.99/$3.99)

1-7-Giffen-s/Kolins-a. 4-7-Doctor Fate app. 3.00
8-18-($3.99) 8-11-Doctor Fate, Arion and OMAC app. 12-Batman app. 4.00
...: Rebirth 1 (10/16, $2.99) Giffen-s/Kolins-a; Ted Kord & Doctor Fate app. 3.00

BLUEBERRY (See Lt. Blueberry & Marshal Blueberry)
Marvel Comics (Epic Comics): 1989 - No. 5, 1990 ($12.95/$14.95, graphic novel)

1,3,4,5-($12.95)-Moebius-a in all 3 6 9 15 22 28
2-($14.95) 3 6 9 15 22 28

Blue Bolt #2 © NOVP

Blue Devil #15 © DC

Blue Ribbon Comics #3 © MLJ

BLUE BOLT
Funnies, Inc. No. 1/Novelty Press/Premium Group of Comics: June, 1940 - No. 101 (V10#2), Sept-Oct, 1949

	GD 2.0	VG 4.0	FN 6.0	VF 8.0	VF/NM 9.0	NM- 9.2
V1#1-Origin Blue Bolt by Joe Simon, Sub-Zero Man, White Rider & Super Horse, Dick Cole, Wonder Boy & Sgt. Spook (1st app. of each)	394	788	1182	2758	4829	6900
2-Simon & Kirby's 1st art & 1st super-hero (Blue Bolt)	271	542	813	1734	2967	4200
3-1 pg. Space Hawk by Wolverton; 2nd S&K-a on Blue Bolt (same cover date as Red Raven #1); Simon-c	245	490	735	1568	2684	3800
4-S&K-a; classic Everett shark-c	219	438	657	1402	2401	3400
5-S&K-a; Everett-a begins on Sub-Zero; 1st time S&K names app. in a comic	187	374	561	1197	2049	2900
6,8-10-S&K-a	161	322	483	1030	1765	2500
7-Classic S&K-c/a (scarce)	232	464	696	1485	2543	3600
11-Classic Everett Giant Robot-c (scarce)	206	412	618	1318	2259	3200
12-Nazi submarine-c	161	322	483	1030	1765	2500
V2#1-Origin Dick Cole & The Twister; Twister x-over in Dick Cole, Sub-Zero, & Blue Bolt; origin Simba Karno who battles Dick Cole thru V2#5 & becomes main supporting character V2#6 on; battle-c	50	100	150	315	533	750
2-Origin The Twister retold in text	40	80	120	246	411	575
3-5: 5-Intro. Freezum	34	68	102	204	332	460
6-Origin Sgt. Spook retold	31	62	93	182	296	410
7-12: 7-Lois Blake becomes Blue Bolt's costume aide; last Twister. 12-Text-sty by Mickey Spillaine	25	50	75	150	245	340
V3#1-3	20	40	60	120	195	270
4-12: 4-Blue Bolt abandons costume	18	36	54	103	162	220
V4#1-Hitler, Tojo, Mussolini-c	103	206	309	659	1130	1600
V4#2-Liberty Bell-c	17	34	51	98	154	210
V4#3-12: 3-Shows V4#3 on-c, V4#4 inside (9-10/43). 5-Infinity-c. 8-Last Sub-Zero	15	30	45	84	127	170
V5#1-8, V6#1-3,5-7,9,10, V7#1-12	14	28	42	76	108	140
V6#4-Racist cover	37	74	111	222	361	500
V6#8-Girl fight-c	15	30	45	86	133	180
V8#1-6,8-12, V9#1-4,7,8, V10#1(#100),V10#2(#101)-Last Dick Cole, Blue Bolt	11	22	33	60	83	105
V8#7,V9#6,9-L. B. Cole-c	22	44	66	128	209	290
V9#5-Classic fish in the face-c	30	60	90	177	289	400

NOTE: ***Everett*** *c-V1#4, 11, V2#1, 2.* ***Gustavson*** *a-V1#1-12, V2#1-7.* ***Kiefer*** *c-V3#1.* ***Rico*** *a-V6#10, V7#4. Blue Bolt not in V9#8.*

BLUE BOLT (Becomes Ghostly Weird Stories #120 on; continuation of Novelty Blue Bolt) (...Weird Tales of Terror #111,112,...Weird Tales #113-119)
Star Publications: No. 102, Nov-Dec, 1949 - No. 119, May-June, 1953

	GD 2.0	VG 4.0	FN 6.0	VF 8.0	VF/NM 9.0	NM- 9.2
102-The Chameleon, & Target app.	41	82	123	256	428	600
103,104-The Chameleon app. 104-Last Target	39	78	117	240	395	550
105-Origin Blue Bolt (from #1) retold by Simon; Chameleon & Target app.; opium den story	116	232	348	742	1271	1800
106-Blue Bolt by S&K begins; Spacehawk reprints from Target by Wolverton begin, ends #110; Sub-Zero begins; ends #109	84	168	252	538	919	1300
107-110: 108-Last S&K Blue Bolt reprint. 109-Wolverton-c(r)/inside Spacehawk splash. 110-Target app.	74	148	222	470	810	1150
111,112: 111-Red Rocket & The Mask-r; last Blue Bolt; 1pg. L. B. Cole-a. 112-Last Torpedo Man app.	77	154	231	493	847	1200
113-Wolverton's Spacehawk-r/Target V3#7	74	148	222	470	810	1150
114,116: 116-Jungle Jo-r	73	146	219	467	796	1125
115-Sgt. Spook app.	84	168	252	538	919	1300
117-Jo-Jo & Blue Bolt-r; Hollingsworth-a	76	152	228	486	831	1175
118-"White Spirit" by Wood	74	148	222	470	810	1150
119-Disbrow/Cole-c; Jungle Jo-r	73	146	219	467	796	1125
Accepted Reprint #103(1957?, nd)	14	28	42	80	115	150

NOTE: ***L. B. Cole*** *c-102-108, 110 on.* ***Disbrow*** *a-112(2), 113(3), 114(2), 115(2), 116-118.* ***Hollingsworth*** *a-117.* ***Palais*** *a-112r. Sci/Fi c-105-110. Horror c-111.*

BLUE BULLETEER, THE (Also see Femforce Special)
AC Comics: 1989 ($2.25, B&W, one-shot)

	NM- 9.2
1-Origin by Bill Black; Bill Ward-a	4.00

BLUE BULLETEER (Also see Femforce Special)
AC Comics: 1996 ($5.95, B&W, one-shot)

	NM- 9.2
1-Photo-c	6.00

BLUE CIRCLE COMICS (Also see Red Circle Comics, Blazing Comics & Roly Poly Comic Book)
Enwil Associates/Rural Home: June, 1944 - No. 6, Apr, 1945

	GD 2.0	VG 4.0	FN 6.0	VF 8.0	VF/NM 9.0	NM- 9.2
1-The Blue Circle begins (1st app.); origin & 1st app. Steel Fist	39	78	117	240	395	550
2	22	44	66	128	209	290
3-Hitler parody-c	50	100	150	315	533	750
4-6: 5-Last Steel Fist.	20	40	60	117	189	260
6-(Dated 4/45, Vol. 2#3 inside)-Leftover covers to #6 were later restapled over early 1950's coverless comics; variations of the coverless comics exist. Colossal Features known.	20	40	60	117	189	260

BLUE DEVIL (See Fury of Firestorm #24, Underworld Unleashed, Starman (2nd) #38, Infinite Crisis and Shadowpact)
DC Comics: June, 1984 - No. 31, Dec, 1986 (75¢/$1.25)

	NM- 9.2
1	4.00
2-16,19-31: 4-Origin Nebiros. 7-Gil Kane-a. 8-Giffen-a	3.00
17,18-Crisis x-over	3.50
Annual 1 (11/85)-Team-ups w/Black Orchid, Creeper, Demon, Madame Xanadu, Man-Bat & Phantom Stranger	4.00

BLUE MONDAY: ... (one-shots)
Oni Press: Feb, 2002 - Dec, 2008 (B&W, Chynna Clugston-Major-s/a/c in all)

	NM- 9.2
Dead Man's Party (10/02, $2.95) Dan Brereton painted back-c	3.00
Inbetween Days (9/03, $9.95, 8" x 5-1/2") r/Dead Man's Party, Lovecats, & Nobody's Fool	10.00
Lovecats (2/02, $2.95) Valentine's Day themed	3.00
Nobody's Fool (2/03, $2.95) April Fool's Day themed	3.00
Thieves Like Us (12/08, $3.50) Part 1 of an unfinished 5-part series	3.50

BLUE MONDAY: ABSOLUTE BEGINNERS
Oni Press: Feb, 2001 - No. 4, Sept, 2001 ($2.95, B&W, limited series)

	NM- 9.2
1-4-Chynna Clugston-Major-s/a/c	3.00
TPB (12/01, $11.95, 8" x 6") r/series	12.00

BLUE MONDAY: PAINTED MOON
Oni Press: Feb, 2004 - No. 4, Mar, 2005 ($2.99, B&W, limited series)

	NM- 9.2
1-4-Chynna Clugston-Major-s/a/c	3.00
TPB (4/05, $11.95, digest-sized) r/series; sketch pages	12.00

BLUE MONDAY: THE KIDS ARE ALRIGHT
Oni Press: Feb, 2000 - No. 3, May, 2000 ($2.95, B&W, limited series)

	NM- 9.2
1-3-Chynna Clugston-Major-s/a/c. 1-Variant-c by Warren. 2-Dorkin-c	3.00
3-Variant cover by J. Scott Campbell	4.00
TPB (12/00, $10.95, digest-sized) r/#1-3 & earlier short stories	11.00

BLUE PHANTOM, THE
Dell Publishing Co.: June-Aug, 1962

	GD 2.0	VG 4.0	FN 6.0	VF 8.0	VF/NM 9.0	NM- 9.2
1(01-066-208)-by Fred Fredericks	3	6	9	20	31	42

BLUE RIBBON COMICS (...Mystery Comics No. 9-18)
MLJ Magazines: Nov, 1939 - No. 22, Mar, 1942 (1st MLJ series)

	GD 2.0	VG 4.0	FN 6.0	VF 8.0	VF/NM 9.0	NM- 9.2
1-Dan Hastings, Richy the Amazing Boy, Rang-A-Tang the Wonder Dog begin (1st app. of each); Little Nemo app. (not by W. McCay); Jack Cole-a(3) (1st MLJ comic)	258	516	774	1651	2826	4000
2-Bob Phantom, Silver Fox (both in #3), Rang-A-Tang Club & Cpl. Collins begin (1st app. of each); Jack Cole-a	129	258	387	826	1413	2000
3-J. Cole-a	87	174	261	553	952	1350
4-Doc Strong, The Green Falcon, & Hercules begin (1st app. each); origin & 1st app. The Fox & Ty-Gor, Son of the Tiger	97	194	291	621	1061	1500
5-8: 8-Last Hercules; 6,7-Biro, Meskin-a. 7-Fox app. on-c	77	154	231	493	847	1200
9-(Scarce)-Origin & 1st app. Mr. Justice (2/41)	331	662	993	2317	4059	5800
10-13: 12-Last Doc Strong. 13-Inferno, the Flame Breather begins, ends #19; Devil-c	142	284	426	909	1555	2200
14,15,17,18: 15-Last Green Falcon	123	246	369	767	1344	1900
16-Origin & 1st app. Captain Flag (9/41)	174	348	522	1114	1907	2700
19-22: 20-Last Ty-Gor. 22-Origin Mr. Justice retold	107	214	321	680	1165	1650

NOTE: ***Biro*** *c-3-5; a-2 (Cpl. Collins & Scoop Cody).* ***S. Cooper*** *c-9-17. 20-22 contain "Tales From the Witch's Cauldron" (same strip as "Stories of the Black Witch" in Zip Comics). Mr. Justice c-9-18. Captain Flag c-16-18 (w/Mr. Justice), 19-22.*

BLUE RIBBON COMICS (Becomes Teen-Age Diary Secrets #4)
(Also see Approved Comics, Blue Ribbon Comics and Heckle & Jeckle)
Blue Ribbon (St. John): Feb, 1949 - No. 6, Aug, 1949

	GD 2.0	VG 4.0	FN 6.0	VF 8.0	VF/NM 9.0	NM- 9.2
1-Heckle & Jeckle (Terrytoons)	16	32	48	92	144	195
2(4/49)-Diary Secrets; Baker-c	58	116	174	371	636	900
3-Heckle & Jeckle (Terrytoons)	11	22	33	62	86	110
4(6/49)-Diary Secrets; Baker c/a(2)	61	122	183	390	670	950
5(8/49)-Teen-Age Diary Secrets; Oversize; photo-c; Baker-a(2)- Continues as Teen-Age Diary Secrets	77	154	231	493	847	1200
6-Dinky Duck(8/49)(Terrytoons)	8	16	24	44	57	70

BLUE RIBBON COMICS
Red Circle Prod./Archie Ent. No. 5 on: Nov, 1983 - No. 14, Dec, 1984

Bobby Benson's B-Bar-B Riders #15 © ME

Bob's Burgers #11 © 20th Century Fox

Bodycount #3 © Mirage

GD 2.0 VG 4.0 FN 6.0 VF 8.0 VF/NM 9.0 NM- 9.2

1-S&K-r/Advs. of the Fly #1,2; Williamson/Torres-r/Fly #2; Ditko-c 1 2 3 5 6 8
2-7,9,10: 3-Origin Steel Sterling. 5-S&K Shield-r; new Kirby-c. 6,7-The Fox app. 8-Toth centerspread; Black Hood app.; Neal Adams-a(r) 6.00
1 2 3 4 5 7
11,13,14: 11-Black Hood. 13-Thunder Bunny. 14-Web & Jaguar 6.00
12-Thunder Agents; Noman new Ditko-a 1 2 3 5 6 8
NOTE: ***N. Adams** a(r)-8. **Buckler** a-4i. **Nino** a-2i. **McWilliams** a-8. **Morrow** a-8.*

BLUE STREAK (See Holyoke One-Shot No. 8)

BLUNTMAN AND CHRONIC TPB(Also see Jay and Silent Bob, Clerks, and Oni Double Feature)
Image Comics: Dec, 2001 ($14.95, TPB)
nn-Tie-in for "Jay & Silent Bob Strike Back" movie; new Kevin Smith-s/Michael Oeming-a; r/app. from Oni Double Feature #12 in color; Ben Affleck & Jason Lee afterwords 15.00

BLYTHE (Marge's)
Dell Publishing Co.: No. 1072, Jan-Mar, 1960
Four Color 1072 5 10 15 34 60 85

B-MAN (See Double-Dare Adventures)

BO (Tom Cat #4 on) (Also see Big Shot #29 & Dixie Dugan)
Charlton Comics Group: June, 1955 - No. 3, Oct, 1955 (A dog)
1-3: Newspaper reprints by Frank Beck; Noodnik the Eskimo app. 8 16 24 40 50 60

BOATNIKS, THE (See Walt Disney Showcase No. 1)

BOB BURDEN'S ORIGINAL MYSTERYMEN PRESENTS
Dark Horse Comics: 1999 - No. 4 ($2.95/$3.50)
1-3-Bob Burden-s/Sadowski-a(p) 3.50
4-($3.50) All Villain issue 3.50

BOBBY BENSON'S B-BAR-B RIDERS (Radio) (See Best of The West, The Lemonade Kid & Model Fun)
Magazine Enterprises/AC Comics: May-June, 1950 - No. 20, May-June, 1953
1-The Lemonade Kid begins; Powell-a (Scarce) 42 84 126 267 451 635
2 18 36 54 103 162 220
3-5: 4,5-Lemonade Kid-c (#4-Spider-c) 14 28 42 78 112 145
6-8,10 13 26 39 74 105 135
9,11,13-Frazetta-c; Ghost Rider in #13-15 by Ayers-a. 13-Ghost Rider-c 39 78 117 240 395 550
12,17-20: 20-(A-1 #88) 12 24 36 67 94 120
14-Decapitation/Bondage-c & story; classic horror-c 30 60 90 177 289 400
15-Ghost Rider-c 23 46 69 136 223 310
16-Photo-c 14 28 42 81 118 155
1 (1990, $2.75, B&W)-Reprints; photo-c & inside covers 3.00
NOTE: ***Ayers** a-13-15, 20. **Powell** a-1-12(4 ea.), 13(3), 14-16(Red Hawk only); c-1-8,1 0, 12. Lemonade Kid in most 1-13.*

BOBBY COMICS
Universal Phoenix Features: May, 1946
1-By S. M. Iger 14 28 42 76 108 140

BOBBY SHERMAN (TV)
Charlton Comics: Feb, 1972 - No. 7, Oct, 1972
1-Based on TV show "Getting Together" 5 10 15 33 57 80
2-7: Photo-c on all. 7-Bobby Sherman for President 4 8 12 23 37 50

BOB COLT (See XMas Comics)
Fawcett Publications: Nov, 1950 - No. 10, May, 1952
1-Bob Colt, his horse Buckskin & sidekick Pablo begin; photo front/back-c begin 24 48 72 142 234 325
2 14 28 42 80 115 150
3-5 12 24 36 67 94 120
6-Flying Saucer story 10 20 30 58 79 100
7-10: 9-Last photo back-c 9 18 27 52 69 85

BOB HOPE (See Adventures of... & Calling All Boys #12)

BOB MARLEY, TALE OF THE TUFF GONG (Music star)
Marvel Comics: Aug, 1994 - No, 3, Nov, 1994 ($5.95, limited series)
1-3 6.00

BOB POWELL'S TIMELESS TALES
Eclipse Comics: March, 1989 ($2.00, B&W)
1-Powell-r/Black Cat #5 (Scarlet Arrow), 9 & Race for the Moon #1 3.00

BOB'S BURGERS (TV)
Dynamite Entertainment: 2014 - No. 5, 2014 ($3.99)
1-5-Short stories by various. 1-Multiple covers 4.00

BOB'S BURGERS (Volume 2)(TV)
Dynamite Entertainment: 2015 - No. 16, 2016 ($3.99)
1-16-Short stories by various; multiple covers on all 4.00
... Free Comic Book Day 2015 (giveaway) Reprints various short stories from Vol. 1 3.00
... Free Comic Book Day 2016 (giveaway) Reprints various short stories 3.00

BOB SCULLY, THE TWO-FISTED HICK DETECTIVE (Also see Advs. of Detective Ace King and Detective Dan)
Humor Publ. Co.: No date (1933) (36 pgs., 9-1/2x11", B&W, paper-c; 10¢-c)
nn-By Howard Dell; not reprints; along with Advs. of Det. Ace King and Detective Dan, the first comic w/original art & the first of a single theme; has a blue 2-tone cover 600 1200 1800 4800 - -

BOB SON OF BATTLE
Dell Publishing Co.: No. 729, Nov, 1956
Four Color 729 4 8 12 28 47 65

BOB STEELE WESTERN (Movie star)
Fawcett Publications/AC Comics: Dec, 1950 - No. 10, June, 1952; 1990
1-Bob Steele & his horse Bullet begin; photo front/back-c begin 37 74 111 222 361 500
2 19 38 57 109 172 235
3-5: 4-Last photo back-c 14 28 42 82 121 160
6-10: 10-Last photo-c 13 26 39 72 101 130
1 (1990, $2.75, B&W)-Bob Steele & Rocky Lane reprints; photo-c & inside covers 3.00

BOB SWIFT (Boy Sportsman)
Fawcett Publications: May, 1951 - No. 5, Jan, 1952
1 10 20 30 58 79 100
2-5: Saunders painted-c #1-5 7 14 21 35 43 50

BOB, THE GALACTIC BUM
DC Comics: Feb, 1995 - No. 4, June, 1995 ($1.95, limited series)
1-4: 1-Lobo app. 3.00

BODIES
DC Comics (Vertigo): Sept, 2014 - No. 8, Apr, 2015 ($3.99, limited series)
1-8-Spencer-s; art by Hetrick, Ormston, Lotay & Winslade 4.00

BODY BAGS
Dark Horse Comics (Blanc Noir): Sept, 1996 - No. 4, Jan, 1997 ($2.95, mini-series, mature) (1st Blanc Noir series)
1,2-Jason Pearson-c/a/scripts in all. 1-Intro Clownface & Panda 5.00
3,4 4.00
Body Bags 1 (Image Comics, 7/05, $5.99) r/#1&2 6.00
Body Bags 2 (Image Comics, 8/05, $5.99) r/#3&4 6.00
...: 3 The Hard Way (Image, 2/06, $5.99) new story & r/Dark Horse Presents Annual 1997 and Dark Horse Maverick 2000; Pearson-c 6.00
...: One Shot (Image, 11/08, $5.99) wraparound-c; Pearson-c/a/s 6.00

BODYCOUNT (Also see Casey Jones & Raphael)
Image Comics (Highbrow Entertainment): Mar, 1996 - No. 4, July, 1996 ($2.50, lim. series)
1-4: Kevin Eastman-a(p)/scripts; Simon Bisley-c/a(i); Turtles app. 3.00

BODY DOUBLES (See Resurrection Man)
DC Comics: Oct, 1999 - No. 4, Jan, 2000 ($2.50, limited series)
1-4-Lanning & Abnett-s. 2-Black Canary app. 4-Wonder Woman app. 3.00
... (Villains) (2/98, $1.95, one-shot) 1-Pearson-c; Deadshot app. 3.00

BOFFO LAFFS
Paragraphics: 1986 - No. 5 ($2.50/$1.95)
1-($2.50) First comic cover with hologram 4.00
2-5 3.00

BOLD ADVENTURE
Pacific Comics: Nov, 1983 - No. 3, June, 1984 ($1.50)
1-Time Force, Anaconda, & The Weirdling begin 3.00
2,3: 2-Soldiers of Fortune begins. 3-Spitfire 3.00
NOTE: ***Kaluta** c-3. **Nebres** a-1-3. **Nino** a-2, 3. **Severin** a-3.*

BOLD STORIES (Also see Candid Tales & It Rhymes With Lust)
Kirby Publishing Co.: Mar, 1950 - July, 1950 (Digest size, 144 pgs.)
March issue (Very Rare) - Contains "The Ogre of Paris" by Wood 265 530 795 1694 2897 4100
May issue (Very Rare) - Contains "The Cobra's Kiss" by Graham Ingels (21 pgs.) 219 438 657 1402 2401 3400
July issue (Very Rare) - Contains "The Ogre of Paris" by Wood

Bombshells United #1 © DC

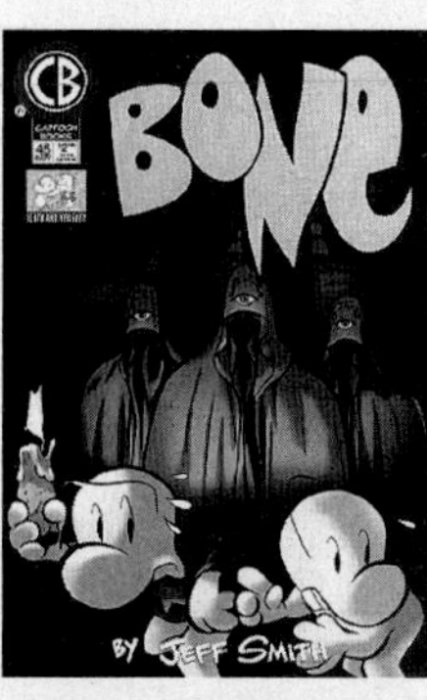

Bone #45 © Jeff Smith

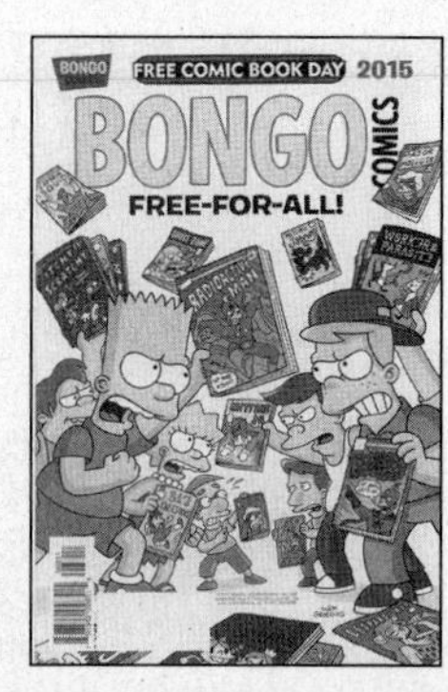

Bongo Comics Free-For-All 2015 © Bongo

	GD 2.0	VG 4.0	FN 6.0	VF 8.0	VF/NM 9.0	NM- 9.2
	219	438	657	1402	2401	3400

BOLT AND STAR FORCE SIX
Americomics: 1984 ($1.75)

	GD 2.0	VG 4.0	FN 6.0	VF 8.0	VF/NM 9.0	NM- 9.2
1-Origin Bolt & Star Force Six						3.00
Special 1 (1984, $2.00, 52pgs., B&W)						4.00

BOMBARDIER (See Bee 29, the Bombardier & Cinema Comics Herald)

BOMBAST
Topps Comics: 1993 ($2.95, one-shot) (Created by Jack Kirby)

	GD 2.0	VG 4.0	FN 6.0	VF 8.0	VF/NM 9.0	NM- 9.2
1-Polybagged w/Kirbychrome trading card; Savage Dragon app.; Kirby-c; has coupon for Amberchrome Secret City Saga #0						4.00

BOMBA THE JUNGLE BOY (TV)
National Periodical Publ.: Sept-Oct, 1967 - No. 7, Sept-Oct, 1968 (12¢)

	GD 2.0	VG 4.0	FN 6.0	VF 8.0	VF/NM 9.0	NM- 9.2
1-Intro. Bomba; Infantino/Anderson-c	4	8	12	27	44	60
2-7	3	6	9	17	26	35

BOMBER COMICS
Elliot Publ. Co./Melverne Herald/Farrell/Sunrise Times: Mar, 1944 - No. 4, Winter, 1944-45

	GD 2.0	VG 4.0	FN 6.0	VF 8.0	VF/NM 9.0	NM- 9.2
1-Wonder Boy, & Kismet, Man of Fate begin	97	194	291	621	1061	1500
2-Hitler-c and 8 pg. story	135	270	405	864	1482	2100
3: 2-4-Have Classics Comics ad to HRN 20	53	106	159	334	567	800
4-Hitler, Tojo & Mussolini-c; Sensation Comics #13-c/swipe; has Classics Comics ad to HRN 20.	129	258	387	826	1413	2000

BOMB QUEEN
Image Comics (Shadowline): Feb, 2006 - No. 4, May, 2006 ($3.50, mature)

	GD 2.0	VG 4.0	FN 6.0	VF 8.0	VF/NM 9.0	NM- 9.2
1-4-Jimmie Robinson-s/a						3.50
... Vs. Blacklight One Shot #1 (8/06, $3.50) Robinson-a; Shadowhawk app.						3.50
..., Vol. 1: WMD: Woman of Mass Destruction TPB (7/06, $12.99) r/#1-4; bonus art						13.00

BOMB QUEEN II
Image Comics (Shadowline): Oct, 2006 - No. 3, Dec, 2006 ($3.50, mature)

	GD 2.0	VG 4.0	FN 6.0	VF 8.0	VF/NM 9.0	NM- 9.2
1-3-Jimmie Robinson-s/a; intro. The Four Queens						3.50
..., Vol. 2: Dirty Bomb - Queen of Hearts TPB (7/07, $14.99) r/#1-3 & Blacklight One Shot; bonus art; Robinson interview						15.00

BOMB QUEEN III THE GOOD, THE BAD & THE LOVELY
Image Comics (Shadowline): Mar, 2007 - No. 4, Jun, 2007 ($3.50, mature)

	GD 2.0	VG 4.0	FN 6.0	VF 8.0	VF/NM 9.0	NM- 9.2
1-4-Jimmie Robinson-a/Jim Valentino-s; Blacklight & Rebound app. 1-Linsner-c						3.50

BOMB QUEEN IV SUICIDE BOMBER
Image Comics (Shadowline): Aug, 2007 - No. 4, Dec, 2007 ($3.50, mature)

	GD 2.0	VG 4.0	FN 6.0	VF 8.0	VF/NM 9.0	NM- 9.2
1-4-Jim Robinson-s/a. 3-She-Spawn app.						3.50

BOMB QUEEN (Volume 5)
Image Comics (Shadowline): May, 2008 - No. 6, Mar, 2009 ($3.50, mature)

	GD 2.0	VG 4.0	FN 6.0	VF 8.0	VF/NM 9.0	NM- 9.2
Vol. 5 #1-6-Jim Robinson-s/a						3.50
Vol. 6 #1-4: 1-(9/09 - No. 4, 1/11, $3.50) Obama satire						3.50
Vol. 7 #1-4 (12/11 - No. 4, 5/12) Bomb Queen returns in 2112						3.50
... Presents: All Girl Comics (5/09, $3.50) Dee Rail, Blacklight, Rebound, Tempest app.						3.50
... Presents: All Girl Special (7/11, $3.50) President Palin app.						3.50
... vs. Hack/Slash (2/11, $3.50) Cassie and Vlad app.; Robinson-s/a						3.50

BOMBSHELLS: UNITED (Continued from DC Comics: Bombshell series)
DC Comics: Nov, 2017 - Present ($2.99)

	GD 2.0	VG 4.0	FN 6.0	VF 8.0	VF/NM 9.0	NM- 9.2
1-13: 1-Bennett-s/Sauvage-a/Dodson-c; intro. Dawnstar & Clayface. 9-Siya Oum-a						3.00

BONANZA (TV)
Dell/Gold Key: June-Aug, 1960 - No. 37, Aug, 1970 (All Photo-c)

	GD 2.0	VG 4.0	FN 6.0	VF 8.0	VF/NM 9.0	NM- 9.2
Four Color 1110 (6-8/60)	30	60	90	216	483	750
Four Color 1221,1283, & #01070-207, 01070-210	15	30	45	100	220	340
1(12/62-Gold Key)	16	32	48	110	243	375
2	9	18	27	58	114	170
3-10	7	14	21	44	82	120
11-20	5	10	15	34	60	85
21-37: 29-Reprints	5	10	15	30	50	70

BONE
Cartoon Books #1-20, 28 on/Image Comics #21-27: Jul, 1991 - No. 55, Jun, 2004 ($2.95, B&W)

	GD 2.0	VG 4.0	FN 6.0	VF 8.0	VF/NM 9.0	NM- 9.2
1-Jeff Smith-c/a in all	34	68	102	245	548	850
1-2nd printing	2	4	6	10	14	18
1-3rd thru 5th printings						4.00
2-1st printing	9	18	27	59	117	175
2-2nd & 3rd printings						4.00
3-1st printing	6	12	18	38	69	100
3-2nd thru 4th printings						4.00
4,5	5	10	15	30	50	70
6-10	2	4	6	13	18	22
11-20						6.00
13 1/2 (1/95, Wizard)	2	4	6	8	10	12
13 1/2 (Gold)	2	4	6	9	12	15
21-37: 21-1st Image issue						5.00
38-($4.95) Three covers by Miller, Ross, Smith	1	2	3	4	5	7
39-55-($2.95)						4.00
1-27-($2.95): 1-Image reprints begin w/new-c. 2-Allred pin-up.						3.00
nn (2008, 8-1/2" x 5-3/8" Halloween mini-comic giveaway)						3.00
... Holiday Special (1993, giveaway)	2	3	4	6	8	10
... Reader -($9.95) Behind the scenes info						10.00
... Sourcebook-San Diego Edition						3.00
...10th Anniversary Edition (8/01, $5.95) r/#1 in color; came with figure						6.00
Complete Bone Adventures Vol 1,2 ('93, '94, $12.95, r/#1-6 & #7-12)						15.00
...: One Volume Edition (2004, $39.95, 1300 pgs.) r/#1-54; extra material						40.00
Volume 1-($19.95, hard-c)-"Out From Boneville"						20.00
Volume 1-($12.95, soft-c)						13.00
Volume 2,5-($22.95, hard-c)-"The Great Cow Race" & "Rock Jaw"						23.00
Volume 2,5-($14.95, soft-c)						15.00
Volume 3,4-($24.95, hard-c)-"Eyes of the Storm" & "The Dragonslayer"						25.00
Volume 3,4,7-($16.95, soft-c)						17.00
Volume 6-($15.95, soft-c)-"Old Man's Cave"						16.00
Volume 7-($24.95, hard-c)-"Ghost Circles"						25.00
Volume 8-($23.95, hard-c)-"Treasure Hunters"						24.00

NOTE: *Printings not listed sell for cover price.*

BONGO (See Story Hour Series)

BONGO & LUMPJAW (Disney, see Walt Disney Showcase #3)
Dell Publishing Co.: No. 706, June, 1956; No. 886, Mar, 1958

	GD 2.0	VG 4.0	FN 6.0	VF 8.0	VF/NM 9.0	NM- 9.2
Four Color 706 (#1)	6	12	18	38	69	100
Four Color 886	4	8	12	28	47	65

BONGO COMICS ...
Bongo Comics: 2005 - Present (Free Comic Book Day giveaways)

	GD 2.0	VG 4.0	FN 6.0	VF 8.0	VF/NM 9.0	NM- 9.2
Gimme Gimme Giveaway! (2005) - Short stories from Simpsons Comics, Futurama Comics and Radioactive Man						3.00
Free-For-All! (2006, 2007, 2008, 2009, 2010, 2011, 2013-2017) - Short stories						3.00
Free-For-All! 2012 - Flip book with SpongeBob Comics						3.00

BONGO COMICS PRESENTS RADIOACTIVE MAN (See Radioactive Man)

BON VOYAGE (See Movie Classics)

BOOF
Image Comics (Todd McFarlane Prod.): July, 1994 - No. 6, Dec, 1994 ($1.95)

	GD 2.0	VG 4.0	FN 6.0	VF 8.0	VF/NM 9.0	NM- 9.2
1-6						3.00

BOOF AND THE BRUISE CREW
Image Comics (Todd McFarlane Prod.): July, 1994 - No. 6, Dec, 1994 ($1.95)

	GD 2.0	VG 4.0	FN 6.0	VF 8.0	VF/NM 9.0	NM- 9.2
1-6						3.00

BOOK AND RECORD SET (See Power Record Comics)

BOOK OF ALL COMICS
William H. Wise: 1945 (196 pgs.)(Inside f/c has Green Publ. blacked out)

	GD 2.0	VG 4.0	FN 6.0	VF 8.0	VF/NM 9.0	NM- 9.2
nn-Green Mask, Puppeteer & The Bouncer	65	130	195	416	708	1000

BOOK OF ANTS, THE
Artisan Entertainment: 1998 ($2.95, B&W)

	GD 2.0	VG 4.0	FN 6.0	VF 8.0	VF/NM 9.0	NM- 9.2
1-Based on the movie Pi; Aronofsky-s						3.00

BOOK OF BALLADS AND SAGAS, THE
Green Man Press: Oct, 1995 - No. 4 ($2.95/$3.50/$3.25, B&W)

	GD 2.0	VG 4.0	FN 6.0	VF 8.0	VF/NM 9.0	NM- 9.2
1-4: 1-Vess-c/a; Gaiman story.						3.50

BOOK OF COMICS, THE
William H. Wise: No date (1944) (25¢, 132 pgs.)

	GD 2.0	VG 4.0	FN 6.0	VF 8.0	VF/NM 9.0	NM- 9.2
nn-Captain V app.; WWII-c	50	100	150	315	533	750

BOOK OF DEATH
Valiant Entertainment: Jul, 2015 - No. 4, Oct, 2015 ($3.99, limited series)

	GD 2.0	VG 4.0	FN 6.0	VF 8.0	VF/NM 9.0	NM- 9.2
1-4-Venditti-s/Gill & Braithwaite-a; multiple covers on each. 4-Flip book with preview for Wrath of the Eternal Warrior series						4.00
...: Fall of Bloodshot (7/15, $3.99) Lemire-s/Braithwaite-a; Armstrong app.						4.00
...: Fall of Harbinger (9/15, $3.99) Dysart-s/Kano-a; future deaths of the team						4.00
...: Fall of Ninjak (8/15, $3.99) Kindt-s/Hairsine-a						4.00
...: Fall of X-O Manowar (10/15, $3.99) Venditti-s/Henry-a; future death of Aric						4.00

BOOK OF FATE, THE (See Fate)

Books of Doom #1 © MAR

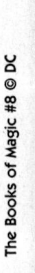

The Books of Magic #8 © DC

Booster Gold: Futures End #1 © DC

	GD 2.0	VG 4.0	FN 6.0	VF 8.0	VF/NM 9.0	NM- 9.2

DC Comics: Feb, 1997 - No. 12, Jan, 1998 ($2.25/$2.50)
1-12: 4-Two-Face-c/app. 6-Convergence. 11-Sentinel app. 3.00

BOOK OF LOST SOULS, THE
Marvel Comics (Icon): Dec, 2005 - No. 6, June, 2006 ($2.99)
1-6-Colleen Doran-a/c; J. Michael Straczynski-s 3.00
... Vol. 1: Introductions All Around (2006, $16.99, TPB) r/series 17.00

BOOK OF LOVE (See Fox Giants)

BOOK OF NIGHT, THE
Dark Horse Comics: July, 1987 - No. 3, 1987 ($1.75, B&W)
1-3: Reprints from Epic Illustrated; Vess-a 3.00
TPB-r/#1-3 15.00
Hardcover-Black-c with red crest 100.00
Hardcover w/slipcase (1991) signed and numbered 50.00

BOOK OF THE DEAD
Marvel Comics: Dec, 1993 - No. 4, Mar, 1994 ($1.75, limited series, 52 pgs.)
1-4: 1-Ploog Frankenstein & Morrow Man-Thing-r begin; Wrightson-r/Chamber of Darkness #7. 2-Morrow new painted-c; Chaykin/Morrow Man-Thing; Krigstein-r/Uncanny Tales #54; r/Fear #10. 3-r/Astonishing Tales #10 & Starlin Man-Thing. 3,4-Painted-c 1 2 3 5 6 8

BOOKS OF DOOM (Dr. Doom from Fantastic Four)
Marvel Comics: Jan, 2006 - No. 6, June, 2006 ($2.99, limited series)
1-6-Life story/origin of Dr. Doom; Brubaker-s/Raimondi-a/Rivera-c 3.00
Fantastic Four: Books of Doom HC (2006, $19.99) r/#1-6 20.00
Fantastic Four: Books of Doom SC (2007, $14.99) r/#1-6 15.00

BOOKS OF FAERIE, THE
DC Comics (Vertigo): Mar, 1997 - No. 3, May, 1997 ($2.50, limited series)
1-3-Gross-a 3.00
TPB (1998, $14.95) r/#1-3 & Arcana Annual #1 15.00

BOOKS OF FAERIE, THE : AUBERON'S TALE
DC Comics (Vertigo): Aug, 1998 - No. 3, Oct, 1998 ($2.50, limited series)
1-3-Gross-a 3.00

BOOKS OF FAERIE, THE : MOLLY'S STORY
DC Comics (Vertigo): Sept, 1999 - No. 4, Dec, 1999 ($2.50, limited series)
1-4-Ney Rieber-s/Mejia-a 3.00

BOOKS OF MAGIC
DC Comics: 1990 - No. 4, 1991 ($3.95, 52 pgs., limited series, mature)
1-Bolton painted-c/a; Phantom Stranger app.; Gaiman scripts in all 1 3 4 6 8 10
2,3: 2-John Constantine, Dr. Fate, Spectre, Deadman app. 3-Dr. Occult app.; minor Sandman app. 1 2 3 4 5 7
4-Early Death-c/app. (early 1991) 1 2 3 5 6 8
Trade paperback-($19.95)-Reprints limited series 20.00

BOOKS OF MAGIC (Also see Hunter: The Age of Magic and Names of Magic)
DC Comics (Vertigo): May, 1994 - No. 75, Aug, 2000 ($1.95/$2.50, mature)
1-Charles Vess-c 2 4 6 8 10 12
1-Platinum 2 4 6 13 18 22
2-4: 4-Death app. 1 2 3 4 5 7
5-14: Charles Vess-c 4.00
15-75: 15-$2.50-c begins. 22-Kaluta-c. 25-Death-c/app; Bachalo-c. 51-Peter Gross-s/a begins. 55-Medley-a 3.00
Annual 1-3 (2/97, 2/98, '99, $3.95) 4.00
Bindings (1995, $12.95, TPB)-r/#1-4 13.00
Death After Death (2001, $19.95, TPB)-r/#42-50 20.00
Girl in the Box (1999, $14.95, TPB)-r/#26-32 15.00
Reckonings (1997, $12.95, TPB)-r/#14-20 13.00
Summonings (1996, $17.50, TPB)-r/#5-13, Vertigo Rave #1 17.50
The Burning Girl (2000, $17.95, TPB)-r/#33-41 18.00
Transformations (1998, $12.95, TPB)-r/#21-25 13.00

BOOKS OF MAGICK, THE : LIFE DURING WARTIME (See Books of Magic)
DC Comics (Vertigo): Sept, 2004 - No. 15, Dec, 2005 ($2.50/$2.75)
1-15: 1-Spencer-s/Ormston-a/Quitely-c; Constantine app. 2-Bagged with Sky Captain CD 6-Fegredo-a. 7-Constantine & Zatanna-c 3.00
... Book One TPB (2005, $9.95) r/#1-5 10.00

BOOM! STUDIOS...
BOOM! Studios
... Ten Year Celebration 2015 Free Comic Book Day Special (5/15, giveaway) short stories of Adventure Time, Peanuts, Garfield, Lumberjanes, Regular Show & others 3.00
... Summer Blast (5/16, FCBD giveaway) Mouse Guard, Labyrinth, Adventure Time 3.00
... 2017 Summer Blast (5/17) FCBD giveaway; Mouse Guard, Brave Chef Brianna 3.00

BOONDOCK SAINTS (Based on the movie)
12-Gauge Comics: May, 2010 - No. 2, Jun, 2010 ($3.99, limited series)
...: In Nomine Patris 1,2-Troy Duffy-s/Guus Floor-a 4.00
...: In Nomine Patris Vol. 2 (10/10 - No. 2, 11/10): 1,2-Duffy-s/Floor-a 4.00
...: In Nomine Patris Vol. 3 (3/11 - No. 2, 4/11): 1,2-Duffy-s/Floor-a 4.00

BOOSTER GOLD (See Justice League #4)
DC Comics: Feb, 1986 - No. 25, Feb, 1988 (75¢)
1-Dan Jurgens-s/a(p); 1st app. of Booster Gold 3 6 9 17 26 35
2-25: 4-Rose & Thorn app. 6-Origin. 6,7,23-Superman app. 8,9-LSH app. 22-JLI app. 24,25-Millennium tie-ins 5.00
NOTE: *Austin c-22i. Byrne c-23i.*

BOOSTER GOLD (See DC's weekly series 52)
DC Comics: Oct, 2007 - No. 47, Oct, 2011 ($3.50/$2.99/$3.99)
1-Geoff Johns-s/Dan Jurgens-a(p); covers by Jurgens and Art Adams; Rip Hunter app. 5.00
2-4,6-20: 3-Jonah Hex app. 4-Barry Allen app. 8-Superman app. 3.00
5-Joker and Batgirl app.; Killing Joke-style-c 6.00
21-29-($3.99) 21-Blue Beetle back-ups begin. 22-New Teen Titans app. 23-Photo-c. 26,27-Blackest Night; Ted Kord rises. 29-Cyborg Superman app. 4.00
30-47-($2.99): 32-34-Giffen & DeMatteis-s. 32-Emerald Empress app. 40-Origin retold. 43-Legion of S.H. app. 44-47-Flashpoint tie-in; Doomsday app. 3.00
#0-(4/08) Blue Beetle (Ted Cord) returns; takes place between #6&7 3.00
#1,000,000-(9/08) Michelle Carter returns; takes place between #10&11 3.00
...: Futures End 1 (11/14, $2.99, regular-c) Jurgens-s; Kamandi, LSH, Captain Atom app. 3.00
...: Futures End 1 (11/14, $3.99, 3-D cover) 4.00
.../ The Flintstones Special 1 (5/17, $4.99) Russell-s/Leonardi-a; Jetsons back-up 5.00

BOOTS AND HER BUDDIES
Standard Comics/Visual Editions/Argo (NEA Service):
No. 5, 9/48 - No. 9, 9/49; 12/55 - No. 3, 1956

	GD	VG	FN	VF	VF/NM	NM-
5-Strip-r	20	40	60	114	182	250
6,8	14	28	42	76	108	140
7-(Scarce)	15	30	45	88	137	185
9-(Scarce)-Frazetta-a (2 pgs.)	29	58	87	172	281	390
1-3(Argo-1955-56)-Reprints	6	12	18	31	38	45

BOOTS & SADDLES (TV)
Dell Publ. Co.: No. 919, July, 1958; No. 1029, Sept, 1959; No. 1116, Aug, 1960

	GD	VG	FN	VF	VF/NM	NM-
Four Color 919 (#1)-Photo-c	7	14	21	48	89	130
Four Color 1029, 1116-Photo-c	5	10	15	34	60	85

BORDERLANDS: ... (Based on the video game)
IDW Publishing: Jul, 2014 - No. 8, Feb, 2015 ($3.99)
1-8: 1-4-The Fall of Fyerstone. 5-8-Tannis and the Vault 4.00

BORDERLANDS: ORIGINS (Based on the video game)
IDW Publishing: Nov, 2012 - No. 4, Feb, 2013 ($3.99, limited series)
1-4: 1-Spotlight on Roland. 2-Lilith. 3-Mordecai. 4-Brick 4.00

BORDER PATROL
P. L. Publishing Co.: May-June, 1951 - No. 3, Sept-Oct, 1951

	GD	VG	FN	VF	VF/NM	NM-
1	15	30	45	86	133	180
2,3	10	20	30	56	76	95

BORDER WORLDS (Also see Megaton Man)
Kitchen Sink Press: 7/86 - No. 7, 1987; V2#1, 1990 - No. 4, 1990 ($1.95-$2.00, B&W, mature)
1-7, V2#1-4: Donald Simpson-c/a/scripts 3.00

BORIS KARLOFF TALES OF MYSTERY (TV) (...Thriller No. 1,2)
Gold Key: No. 3, April, 1963 - No. 97, Feb, 1980

	GD	VG	FN	VF	VF/NM	NM-
3-5-(Two #5's, 10/63,11/63): 5-(10/63)-11 pgs. Toth-a.	5	10	15	31	53	75
6-8,10: 10-Orlando-a	4	8	12	25	40	55
9-Wood-a	4	8	12	27	44	60
11-Williamson-a, 8 pgs.; Orlando-a, 5 pgs.	4	8	12	27	44	60
12-Torres, McWilliams-a; Orlando-a(2)	4	8	12	21	33	45
13,14,16-20	3	6	9	18	28	38
15-Crandall	3	6	9	19	30	40
21-Jeff Jones-a(3 pgs.) "The Screaming Skull"	3	6	9	19	30	40
22-Last 12¢ issue	3	6	9	16	23	30
23-30: 23-Reprint; photo-c	3	6	9	15	22	28
31-50: 36-Weiss-a	3	6	9	14	19	24

Born #1 © MAR

Bounty #1 © Wiebe & Lee

Boy Commandos #15 © DC

GD VG FN VF VF/NM NM-
2.0 4.0 6.0 8.0 9.0 9.2

51-74: 74-Origin & 1st app. Taurus 2 4 6 10 14 18
75-79,87-97: 90-r/Torres, McWilliams-a/#12; Morrow-c 2 4 6 9 12 15
80-86-(52 pgs.) 2 4 6 10 14 18
Story Digest 1(7/70-Gold Key)-All text/illos.; 148 pp. 5 10 15 31 53 75
(See Mystery Comics Digest No. 2, 5, 8, 11, 14, 17, 20, 23, 26)
NOTE: ***Bolle*** *a-51-54, 56, 58, 59.* ***McWilliams*** *a-12, 14, 18, 19, 72, 80, 81, 93.* ***Orlando*** *a-11-15, 21. Reprints: 78, 81-86, 88, 90, 92, 95, 97.*

BORIS KARLOFF THRILLER (TV) (Becomes Boris Karloff Tales...)
Gold Key: Oct, 1962 - No. 2, Jan, 1963 (84 pgs.)
1-Photo-c 10 20 30 66 138 210
2 6 12 18 40 73 105

BORIS THE BEAR
Dark Horse Comics/Nicotat Comics #13 on: Aug, 1986 - No. 34, 1990 ($1.50/$1.75/$1.95, B&W)
1, 8, Annual 1 (1988, $2.50): 8-(44 pgs.) 4.00
1 (2nd printing),2,3,4A,4B,5-12, 14-34 3.00
13-1st Nicotat Comics issue 3.00

BORIS THE BEAR INSTANT COLOR CLASSICS
Dark Horse Comics: July, 1987 - No. 3, 1987 ($1.75/$1.95)
1-3 3.00

BORN
Marvel Comics: 2003 - No. 4, 2003 ($3.50, limited series)
1-4-Frank Castle (the Punisher) in 1971 Vietnam; Ennis-s/Robertson-a 3.50
HC (2004, $17.99) oversized reprint of series; proposal, layout pages 18.00
Punisher: Born SC (2004, $13.99) r/series; proposal, layout pages 14.00

BORN AGAIN
Spire Christian Comics (Fleming H. Revell Co.): 1978 (39¢)
nn-Watergate, Nixon, etc. 3 6 9 19 30 40

BOUNCE, THE
Image Comics: May, 2013 - No. 12, May, 2014 ($2.99)
1-12-Casey-s/Messina-a 3.00

BOUNCER, THE (Formerly Green Mask #9)
Fox Feature Syndicate: 1944 - No. 14, Jan, 1945
nn(1944, #10?) 34 68 102 199 325 450
11 (9/44)-Origin; Rocket Kelly, One Round Hogan app.
24 48 72 142 234 325
12-14: 14-Reprints no # issue 20 40 60 114 182 250

BOUNTY
Dark Horse Comics: Jul, 2016 - No. 5, Dec, 2016 ($3.99, limited series)
1-5-Kurtis Wiebe-s/Mindy Lee-a 4.00

BOUNTY GUNS (See Luke Short's..., Four Color 739)

BOX OFFICE POISON
Antarctic Press: 1996 - No. 21, Sept, 2000 ($2.95, B&W)
1-Alex Robinson-s/a in all 1 2 3 4 5 7
2-5 4.00
6-21, ...Kolor Karnival 1 (5/99, $2.99) 3.00
...Super Special 0 (5/97, $4.95) 5.00
Sherman's March: Collected BOP Vol. 1 (9/98, $14.95) r/#0-4 15.00
TPB (2002, $29.95, 608 pgs.) r/entire series 30.00

BOX OFFICE POISON COLOR COMICS
IDW Publishing: Jan, 2017 - Present ($3.99)
1-4-Colored reprints of 1996 series; Alex Robinson-s/a in all; bonus commentary 4.00

BOY AND THE PIRATES, THE (Movie)
Dell Publishing Co.: No. 1117, Aug, 1960
Four Color 1117-Photo-c 6 12 18 37 66 95

BOY COMICS (Captain Battle No. 1 & 2; Boy Illustories No. 43-108) (Stories by Charles Biro) (Also see Squeeks)
Lev Gleason Publ. (Comic House): No. 3, Apr, 1942 - No. 119, Mar, 1956
3 (No.1)-1st app. & origin Crimebuster (ends #110), Bombshell (ends #8) Young Robin Hood (ends # 32), Yankee Longago (ends #28), Hero of the Month (ends #31), Case 1001-1005, 1006-1009 (ends #10); Swoop Storm begins (ends #32); Pepper Casey only app.; 1st app. Iron Jaw; Crimebuster's pet monkey Squeeks begins
331 662 993 2317 4059 5800
4-Hitler, Tojo Mussolini-c; Iron Jaw app. Little Wise Guys (prototype of later version) begins, ends #5 200 400 600 1280 2190 3100
5-Japanese war-c 135 270 405 864 1482 2100
6-Origin Iron Jaw; origin & death of Iron Jaw's son killed by his father; Hitler app.; Little Dynamite begins, ends #39; 1st Iron Jaw-c 331 662 993 2317 4059 5800
7-Flag & Hitler, Tojo, Mussolini-c; Dickey Dean app. 200 400 600 1280 2190 3100
8-Death of Iron Jaw; Iron Jaw-c & spash pg. 103 206 309 659 1130 1600
9-Iron Jaw classic-c (does not appear in story) 168 336 504 1075 1838 2600
10-Return of Iron Jaw; classic Biro Iron Jaw/Nazi-c 200 400 600 1280 2190 3100
11-Iron Jaw sty/classic-c 129 258 387 826 1413 2000
12-Classic Japanese WWII bondage torture interrogation-c
119 238 357 762 1306 1850
13-Nazi firing squad-c 87 174 261 553 952 1350
14-Iron Jaw-c 84 168 252 538 919 1300
15-Death of Iron Jaw, killed by The Rodent 97 194 291 621 1061 1500
16,18,20 (2/45) 47 94 141 296 498 700
17-(8/44)-Flag-c; The Moth app. 50 100 150 315 533 750
19-One of the greatest all-time stories 53 106 159 334 567 800
21-24: 24-Concentration camp story 34 68 102 199 325 450
25-Devil-c; hanging story (52 pgs.) 40 80 120 246 411 575
26-Bondage, torture-c/story (68 pgs.) 47 94 141 296 498 700
27-29,31,32-(All 68 pgs.). 28-Yankee Longago ends. 32-Swoop Storm & Young Robin Hood end 36 72 108 211 343 475
30-(10/46, 68 pgs.)-Origin Crimebuster retold from #3 w/Iron Jaw; Nazi work camp story
40 80 120 246 411 575
33-40: 34-Crimebuster story (2); suicide-c/story 22 44 66 132 216 300
41-50-41-Daredevil illus. text story 19 38 57 111 176 240
51-59: 57(9/50)-Dilly Duncan begins, ends #71 16 32 48 94 147 200
60-(12/50)-Iron Jaw returns c/sty 18 36 54 105 165 225
61-Origin Crimebuster & Iron Jaw retold c/sty 20 40 60 114 182 250
62-(2/51)-Death of Iron Jaw explained w/Iron Jaw-c 19 38 57 111 176 240
63-67,69-72: 63-McWilliams-a 14 28 42 76 108 140
68,73-Iron Jaw c/sty; 73-Frazetta 1 pg. ad 14 28 42 80 115 150
74,78,81-Iron Jaw c/sty (2-3) 12 24 36 67 94 120
75-77,84 11 22 33 62 86 110
79,80-Iron Jaw sty: 80(8/52)-1st app. Rocky X of the Rocketeers; becomes "Rocky X" #101; Iron Jaw, Sniffer & the Deadly Dozen in #80-118 11 22 33 64 90 115
82-Iron Jaw-c (apps. in one panel) 11 22 33 62 86 110
83,85-88-Iron Jaw c/sty. 87-The Deadly Dozen begins; becomes Iron Jaw #88 (4/53)
11 22 33 64 90 115
89(5/53)-92-The Claw serial app. in Rocky X (also see Silver Streak & Daredevil); on-c. 89-"Iron Jaw" becomes "Sniffrer & Iron Jaw" (ends #118); Iron Jaw c/story in all
12 24 36 67 94 120
93-Claw cameo & last app.; Woodesque-a on Rocky X by Sid Check; Iron Jaw-c/sty
11 22 33 64 90 115
94-97-Iron Jaw-c/sty in all 11 22 33 60 83 105
98,100:(4/54): 98-Rocky X by Sid Check 11 22 33 62 86 110
99,101-107,109,111,119: 101-Rocky X becomes spy strip. 106-Robin Hood app. 111-Crimebuster becomes Chuck Chandler, ends #119
10 20 30 54 72 90
108-(2/55)-Kubert & Ditko-a (Crimebuster, 8 pgs.) 11 22 33 62 86 110
110,112-118-Kubert-a 10 20 30 58 79 100
(See Giant Boy Book of Comics)
NOTE: *Boy Movies in 3-5,40,41. Iron Jaw app. 3,4,6,8,10,11,13-15; returns-60,62, 68, 69, 72-79, 81-118; c-60-62, 73, 74, 78, 81-83, 85-97.* ***Biro*** *c-all.* ***Jack Alderman*** *a-26.* ***Dan Barry*** *a-31,32, 35-38.* ***Al Borth*** *a- 51.* ***Dick Briefer*** *a-3-28, 124.* ***Sid Check*** a-93, 98. ***Ditko*** a-108. ***Bob Fujitani*** (***Fuje***) *a-55, 18pgs.* ***Jerry Gandenetti*** *a-52.* ***R. W. Hall*** *a-19-22.* ***Hubbell*** *a-30, 106, 108, 110, 111.* ***Joe Kubert*** *a-108, 110, 112-118.* ***Kenneth Landau*** *a-92.* ***George Mandel*** *a-3-30.* ***Norman Maurer*** *a-4-9, 11-13, 31, 32, 35, 41, 43, 46, 51, 57, 61, 73, 74, 78-83.* ***Bob Montana*** *a-4, 16, 19.* ***Pete Morisi*** *a-111.* ***William Overgard*** *a-68, 71, 74, 86, 88.* ***Palais*** *a-14, 16, 17, 19, 20, 25, 26. among others.* ***Tuska*** *a-30.* ***Bob Wood*** *a-8-13.*

GD VG FN VF VF/NM NM-
2.0 4.0 6.0 8.0 9.0 9.2

BOY COMMANDOS (See Detective #64 & World's Finest Comics #8)
National Periodical Publications: Winter, 1942-43 - No. 36, Nov-Dec, 1949
1-Origin Liberty Belle; The Sandman & The Newsboy Legion x-over in Boy Commandos; S&K-a, 48 pgs.; S&K cameo? (classic WWII-c) 400 800 1200 2800 4900 7000
2-Last Liberty Belle; Hitler-c; S&K-a, 46 pgs.; WWII-c
245 490 735 1568 2684 3800
3-S&K-a, 45 pgs.; WWII-c 135 270 405 864 1482 2100
4-6: All WWII-c. 6-S&K-a 84 168 252 538 919 1300
7-10: All WWII-c 53 106 159 334 567 800
11-13: All WWII-c. 11-Infinity-c 39 78 117 240 395 550
14,16,18-19-All have S&K-a. 18-2nd Crazy Quilt-c 34 68 102 199 325 450
15-1st app. Crazy Quilt, their arch nemesis 41 82 123 256 428 600
17,20-Sci/fi-c/stories 40 80 120 246 411 575
21,22,25: 22-3rd Crazy Quilt-c; Judy Canova x-over 27 54 81 158 259 360
23-S&K-c/a(all) 36 72 108 214 347 480
24-1st costumed superhero satire-c (11-12/47). 34 68 102 199 325 450
26-Flying Saucer story (3-4/48)-4th of this theme; see The Spirit 9/28/47(1st), Shadow Comics V7#10 (2nd, 1/48) & Captain Midnight #60 (3rd, 2/48)
32 64 96 190 310 430

Boy Explorers Comics #1 © HARV

The Boys #41 © Spitfire & Robertson

B.P.R.D.: War on Frogs #3 © Mignola

GD 2.0 | VG 4.0 | FN 6.0 | VF 8.0 | VF/NM 9.0 | NM- 9.2

27,28,30: 30-Cleveland Indians story 26 52 78 154 252 350
29-S&K story (1) 27 54 81 162 266 370
31-35: 32-Dale Evans app. on-c & in story. 33-Last Crazy Quilt-c. 34-Intro. Wolf, their mascot 23 46 69 136 223 310
36-Intro The Atomobile c/sci-fi story (Scarce) 41 82 123 256 428 600
The Boy Commandos by Joe Simon & Jack Kirby Volume One HC (2010, $49.99) reprints apps. in Detective #64-72, World's Finest #8,9 & Boy Commandos #1,2; Buhle intro. 50.00
NOTE: *Most issues signed by **Simon & Kirby** are not by them. **S&K** c-1-9, 13, 14, 17, 21, 23, 24, 30-32. **Feller** c-30.*

BOY COMMANDOS
National Per. Publ.: Sept-Oct, 1973 - No. 2, Nov-Dec, 1973 (G.A. S&K reprints)

1,2: 1-Reprints story from Boy Commandos #1 plus-c & Detective #66 by S&K. 2-Infantino/Orlando-c 2 4 6 10 14 18

BOY COMMANDOS COMICS
DC Comics: Sept/Oct. 1942

1-Ashcan comic, not distributed to newsstands, only for in-house use. Cover art is the splash page from the Boy Commandos story in Detective Comics #68 interior is from an unidentified issue of Detective Comics (A FN- copy sold for $1912 in 2012)
nn - (9-10/42) Ashcan comic, not distributed to newsstands, only for in-house use. Cover art is the splash page from the Boy Commandos story in Detective Comics #68 interior is from Detective Comics #68 (no known sales)

BOY COWBOY (Also see Amazing Adventures & Science Comics)
Ziff-Davis Publ. Co.: 1950 (8 pgs. in color)

nn-Sent to subscribers of Ziff-Davis mags. & ordered through mail for 10¢; used to test market for Kid Cowboy 36 72 108 211 343 475

BOY DETECTIVE
Avon Periodicals: May-June, 1951 - No. 4, May, 1952

1 22 44 66 132 216 300
2-4: 3,4-Kinstler-c 15 30 45 85 130 175

BOY EXPLORERS COMICS (Terry and The Pirates No. 3 on)
Family Comics (Harvey Publ.): May-June, 1946 - No. 2, Sept-Oct, 1946

1-Intro The Explorers, Duke of Broadway, Calamity Jane & Danny Dixon...Cadet; S&K-c/a, 24 pgs. 77 154 231 493 847 1200
2-(Rare)-Small size (5-1/2x8-1/2"; B&W; 32 pgs.) Distributed to mail subscribers only; S&K-a 155 310 465 992 1696 2400
(Also see All New No. 15, Flash Gordon No. 5, and Stuntman No. 3)

BOY ILLUSTORIES (See Boy Comics)

BOY LOVES GIRL (Boy Meets Girl No. 1-24)
Lev Gleason Publications: No. 25, July, 1952 - No. 57, June, 1956

25(#1) 15 30 45 83 124 165
26,27,29-33: 30-33-Serial, 'Loves of My Life 10 20 30 56 76 95
34-42: 39-Lingerie panels 10 20 30 54 72 90
28-Drug propaganda story 10 20 30 56 76 95
43-Toth-a 10 20 30 58 79 100
44-50: 47-Toth-a? 49-Roller Derby-c. 50-Last pre-code (2/55) 9 18 27 52 69 85
51-57: 57-Ann Brewster-a 9 18 27 47 61 75

BOY MEETS GIRL (Boy Loves Girl No. 25 on)
Lev Gleason Publications: Feb, 1950 - No. 24, June, 1952 (No. 1-17: 52 pgs.)

1-Guardineer-a 21 42 63 124 202 280
2 13 26 39 74 105 135
3-10 12 24 36 67 94 120
11-24 11 22 33 60 83 105
NOTE: ***Briefer** a-24. **Fuje** c-3,7. Painted-c 1-17. Photo-c 19-21, 23.*

BOYS, THE
DC Comics (WildStorm)/Dynamite Ent. #7 on: Oct, 2006 - No. 72, 2012 ($2.99/$3.99)

1-Garth Ennis-s/Darick Robertson-a 1 3 4 6 8 10
2-6 5.00
7-42-(Dynamite Ent.,). 19-Origin of the Homelander. 23-Variant-c by Cassaday 3.00
43-64,66-71-($3.99) Russ Braun-a in most. 54,55-McCrea-a 4.00
65,72-($4.99): 65-End of the Homelander. 72-Last issue; bonus pin-ups; cover gallery 5.00
#1: Dynamite Edition (2009, $1.00) r/#1; flip book with Battlefields Night Witches 3.00
...: Herogasm 1-6 (2009 - No. 6, 2009, $2.99) Ennis-s/McCrea-a 3.00
... Volume 1: The Name of the Game TPB (2007, $14.99) r/#1-6; intro. by Simon Pegg 15.00
... Volume 2: Get Some TPB (2008, $19.99) r/#7-14 20.00
... Volume 3: Good For The Soul TPB (2008, $19.99) r/#15-22 20.00
... Volume 4: We Gotta Go Now TPB (2009, $19.99) r/#23-30; cover gallery 20.00
... Volume 5: Herogasm TPB (2009, $19.99) r/#Herogasm #1-6 20.00

BOYS, THE: BUTCHER, BAKER, CANDLESTICKMAKER
Dynamite Entertainment: 2011 - No. 6, 2011 ($3.99, mature)

1-6-Garth Ennis-s/Darick Robertson-a; Billy Butcher's early years 4.00

BOYS, THE: HIGHLAND LADDIE
Dynamite Entertainment: 2010 - No. 6, 2011 ($3.99, mature)

1-6-Garth Ennis-s/John McCrea-a 4.00

BOYS' AND GIRLS' MARCH OF COMICS (See March of Comics)

BOYS' RANCH (Also see Western Tales & Witches' Western Tales)
Harvey Publ.: Oct, 1950 - No. 6, Aug, 1951 (No.1-3, 52 pgs.; No. 4-6, 36 pgs.)

1-S&K-c/a(3) 58 116 174 371 636 900
2-S&K-c/a(3) 40 80 120 246 411 575
3-S&K-c/a(2); Meskin-a 39 78 117 231 378 525
4-S&K-c/a, 5 pgs. 34 68 102 199 325 450
5,6-S&K-c, splashes & centerspread only; Meskin-a 20 40 60 114 182 250

BOZO (Larry Harmon's Bozo, the World's Most Famous Clown)
Innovation Publishing: 1992 ($6.95, 68 pgs.)

1-Reprints Four Color #285(#1) 1 2 3 4 5 7

BOZO THE CLOWN (TV) (Bozo No. 7 on)
Dell Publishing Co.: July, 1950 - No. 4, Oct-Dec, 1963

Four Color 285(#1) 17 34 51 117 259 400
2(7-9/51)-7(10-12/52) 9 18 27 63 129 195
Four Color 464,508,551,594(10/54) 9 18 27 58 114 170
1(nn, 5-7/62) 7 14 21 44 82 120
2 - 4(1963) 5 10 15 35 63 90

BOZZ CHRONICLES, THE
Marvel Comics (Epic Comics): Dec, 1985 - No. 6, 1986 (Lim. series, mature)

1-6-Logan/Wolverine look alike in 19th century. 1,3,5-Blevins-a 3.00

B.P.R.D. (Bureau of Paranormal Research and Defense) (Also see Hellboy titles)
Dark Horse Comics: (one-shots)

... Dark Waters (7/03, $2.99) Guy Davis-c/a; Augustyn-s 3.00
... Night Train (9/03, $2.99) Johns & Kolins-s; Kolins & Stewart-a 3.00
... The Ectoplasmic Man (6/08, $2.99) Stenbeck-a/Mignola-c; origin of Johann Kraus 3.00
... There's Something Under My Bed (11/03, $2.99) Pollina-a/c 3.00
... The Soul of Venice (5/03, $2.99) Oeming-a/c; Gunter & Oeming-s 3.00
... The Soul of Venice and Other Stories TPB (8/04, $17.95) r/one-shots & new story by Mignola and Cam Stewart; sketch pages by various 18.00
... War on Frogs (6/08,12/08, 6/09, 12/09, $2.99) 1-Trimpe-a/Mignola-c; Abe Sapien app. 2-Severin-a. 3-Moline-a. 4-Snejbjerg 3.00

B.P.R.D.: GARDEN OF SOULS
Dark Horse Comics: Mar, 2007 - No. 5, July, 2007 ($2.99, limited series)

1-5-Mignola & Arcudi-s/Guy Davis-a/Mignola-c 3.00

B.P.R.D.: HELL ON EARTH
Dark Horse Comics: ($3.50, limited series)

... Exorcism (6/12 - No. 2, 7/12) 1,2-Mignola-s/Stewart-a/Kalvachev-c 3.50
... Gods (1/11 - No. 3, 3/11) 1-Mignola & Arcudi-s/Guy Davis-a; Ryan Sook-c 3.50
... Monsters (7/11 - No. 2, 8/11) 1,2-Mignola & Arcudi-s. 1-Sook & Francavilla covers 3.50
... New World (8/10 - No. 5, 12/10) 1-5-Mignola & Arcudi-s/Guy Davis-a/c 3.50
... Russia (9/11 - No. 5, 1/12) 1-5-Mignola & Arcudi-s/Crook-a 3.50
... The Devil's Engine (5/12 - No. 3, 7/12) 1-3-Mignola & Arcudi-s/Crook-a/Fegredo-c 3.50
... The Long Death (2/12 - No. 3, 4/12) 1-3-Mignola & Arcudi-s/Harren-a/Fegredo-c 3.50
... The Pickens County Horror (3/12 - No. 2, 4/12) 1,2-Mignola & Allie-s/Latour-a 3.50
... The Transformation of J.H. O'Donnell (5/12) 1-Mignola & Allie-s/Fiumara-a 3.50
... The Return of the Master (8/12 - No. 5, 12/12) 1-5-Mignola & Arcudi-s/Crook-a; 3-5-Also numbered as #100-102 on cover and indicia 3.50
103-141: 103-(1/13). 103,104-The Abyss of Time. 105,106-A Cold Day in Hell 3.50
142-147-($3.99) 4.00

B.P.R.D.: HOLLOW EARTH (Mike Mignola's...)
Dark Horse Comics: Jan, 2002 - No. 3, June, 2002 ($2.99, limited series)

1-3-Mignola, Golden & Sniegoski-s/Sook-a/Mignola-c; Hellboy and Abe Sapien app. 3.00
... and Other Stories TPB (1/03; 7/04, $17.95) r/#1-3, Hellboy: Box Full of Evil, Abe Sapien: Drums of the Dead, and Dark Horse Extra; plus sketch pages 18.00

B.P.R.D.: KILLING GROUND
Dark Horse Comics: Aug, 2007 - No. 5, Dec, 2007 ($2.99, limited series)

1-5-Mignola & Arcudi-s/Guy Davis-a/c 3.00

B.P.R.D.: KING OF FEAR
Dark Horse Comics: Jan, 2010 - No. 5, May, 2010 ($2.99, limited series)

1,2-Mignola & Arcudi-s/Guy Davis-a; Mignola-c 3.00

The Bradleys #5 © Peter Bagge

Brass (2000 series) #1 © WSP

Brave and the Bold #30 © DC

GD 2.0 | VG 4.0 | FN 6.0 | VF 8.0 | VF/NM 9.0 | NM- 9.2

B.P.R.D.: 1946
Dark Horse Comics: Jan, 2008 - No. 5, May, 2008 ($2.99, limited series)
1-5-Mignola & Dysart-s/Azaceta-a; Mignola-c 3.00

B.P.R.D.: 1947
Dark Horse Comics: Jul, 2009 - No. 5, Nov, 2009 ($2.99, limited series)
1-5-Mignola & Dysart-s/Bá & Moon-a; Mignola-c 3.00

B.P.R.D.: 1948
Dark Horse Comics: Oct, 2012 - No. 5, Feb, 2013 ($3.50, limited series)
1-5-Mignola & Arcudi-s/Fiumara-a; Johnson-c 3.50

B.P.R.D.: PLAGUE OF FROGS
Dark Horse Comics: Mar, 2004 - No. 5, July, 2004 ($2.99, limited series)
1-5-Mignola-s/Guy Davis-c/a 3.00
TPB (1/05, $17.95) r/series; sketchbook pages & afterword by Davis & Mignola 18.00

B.P.R.D.: THE BLACK FLAME
Dark Horse Comics: Sept, 2005 - No. 6, Jan, 2006 ($2.99, limited series)
1-6-Mignola & Arcudi-s/Guy Davis-a/ Mignola-c 3.00
TPB (7/06, $17.95) r/series; sketchbook pages & afterword by Davis & Mignola 18.00

B.P.R.D.: THE BLACK GODDESS
Dark Horse Comics: Jan, 2009 - No. 5, May, 2009 ($2.99, limited series)
1-5-Mignola & Arcudi-s/Guy Davis-a/Nowlan-c 3.00

B.P.R.D.: THE DEAD
Dark Horse Comics: Nov, 2004 - No. 5, Mar, 2005 ($2.99, limited series)
1-5-Mignola-s/Guy Davis-c/a 3.00

B.P.R.D.: THE DEAD REMEMBERED
Dark Horse Comics: Apr, 2011 - No. 3, Jun, 2011 ($3.50, limited series)
1-3-Mignola-s; Moline-a; Jo Chen-c. 1-Variant-c by Moline 3.50

B.P.R.D.: THE DEVIL YOU KNOW
Dark Horse Comics: Jul, 2017 - Present ($3.99, limited series)
1-5-Mignola & Allie-s/Laurence Campbell-a/Fegredo-c. 1-Mignola var-c 4.00

B.P.R.D.: THE UNIVERSAL MACHINE
Dark Horse Comics: Apr, 2006 - No. 5, Aug, 2006 ($2.99, limited series)
1-5-Mignola & Arcudi-s/Guy Davis-a/Mignola-c. 5-Mignola-a (5 pgs.) 3.00
TPB (1/07, $17.95) r/series; sketchbook pages by Davis; Mignola afterword 18.00

B.P.R.D.: THE WARNING
Dark Horse Comics: July, 2008 - No. 5, Nov, 2008 ($2.99, limited series)
1-5-Mignola & Arcudi-s/Guy Davis-c/a 3.00

B.P.R.D.: VAMPIRE
Dark Horse Comics: Mar, 2013 - No. 5, Jul, 2013 ($3.50, limited series)
1-5-Mignola-s/Bá & Moon-a; Moon-c 3.50

BRADLEYS, THE (Also see Hate)
Fantagraphics Books: Apr, 1999 - No. 6, Jan, 2000 ($2.95, B&W, limited series)
1-6-Reprints Peter Bagge's-s/a 3.00

BRADY BUNCH, THE (TV)(See Kite Fun Book and Binky #78)
Dell Publishing Co.: Feb, 1970 - No. 2, May, 1970 (photo-c)
1 10 20 30 70 150 230
2 8 16 24 55 105 155

BRAIN, THE
Sussex Publ. Co./Magazine Enterprises: Sept, 1956 - No. 7, 1958
1-Dan DeCarlo-a in all including reprints 13 26 39 74 105 135
2,3 9 18 27 47 61 75
4-7 4 8 12 27 44 60
I.W. Reprints #1-4,8-10('63),14: 2-Reprints Sussex #2 with new cover added 2 4 6 9 13 16
Super Reprint #17,18(nd) 2 4 6 9 13 16

BRAINBANX
DC Comics (Helix): Mar, 1997 - No. 6, Aug, 1997 ($2.50, limited series)
1-6: Elaine Lee-s/Temujin-a 3.00

BRAIN BOY
Dell Publishing Co.: Apr-June, 1962 - No. 6, Sept-Nov, 1963 (Painted c-#1-6)
Four Color 1330(#1)-Gil Kane-a; origin 10 20 30 64 132 200
2(7-9/62),3-6: 4-Origin retold 6 12 18 41 76 110

BRAIN BOY
Dark Horse Comics: Sept, 2013 - No. 3, Nov, 2013 ($2.99, limited series)
1-3-Van Lente-s/Silva-a/Olivetti-c 3.00
#0-(12/13, $2.99) Reprints stories from Dark Horse Presents #23-25; Olivetti-c 3.00

BRAIN BOY: THE MEN FROM G.E.S.T.A.L.T.
Dark Horse Comics: May, 2014 - No. 4, Aug, 2014 ($2.99, limited series)
1-4-Van Lente-s/Freddie Williams II-a/c 3.00

BRAM STOKER'S DRACULA (Movie)(Also see Dracula: Vlad the Impaler)
Topps Comics: Oct, 1992 - No. 4, Jan, 1993 ($2.95, limited series, polybagged)
1-(1st & 2nd printing)-Adaptation of film begins; Mignola-c/a in all; 4 trading cards & poster; photo scenes of movie 5.00
1-Crimson foil edition (limited to 500) 20.00
2-4: 2-Bound-in poster & cards. 4 trading cards in both. 3-Contains coupon to win 1 of 500 crimson foil-c edition of #1. 4-Contains coupon to win 1 of 500 uncut sheets of all 16 trading cards 4.00

BRAND ECHH (See Not Brand Echh)

BRAND OF EMPIRE (See Luke Short's...Four Color 771)

BRASS
Image Comics (WildStorm Productions): Aug, 1996 - No. 3, May, 1997 ($2.50, lim. series)
1-($4.50) Folio Ed.; oversized 4.50
1-3: Wiesenfeld-s/Bennett-a. 3-Grunge & Roxy(Gen 13) cameo 3.00

BRASS
DC Comics (WildStorm): Aug, 2000 - No. 6, Jan, 2001 ($2.50, limited series)
1-6-Arcudi-s 3.00

BRATH
CrossGeneration Comics: Feb, 2003 - No. 14, June, 2004 ($2.95)
Prequel-Dixon-s/Di Vito-a 3.00
1-14: 1-(3/03)-Dixon-s/Di Vito-a 3.00
Vol. 1: Hammer of Vengeance (2003, $9.95) Digest-sized reprint of Prequel & #1-6 10.00

BRATS BIZARRE
Marvel Comics (Epic/Heavy Hitters): 1994 - No. 4, 1994 ($2.50, limited series)
1-4: All w/bound-in trading cards 3.00

BRAVADOS, THE (See Wild Western Action)
Skywald Publ. Corp.: Aug, 1971 (52 pgs., one-shot)
1-Red Mask, The Durango Kid, Billy Nevada-r; Bolle-a; 3-D effect story 3 6 9 15 22 28

BRAVE AND THE BOLD, THE (See Best Of... & Super DC Giant) (Replaced by Batman & The Outsiders)
National Periodical Publ./DC Comics: Aug-Sept, 1955 - No. 200, July, 1983
1-Viking Prince by Kubert, Silent Knight, Golden Gladiator begin; part Kubert-c 327 654 981 2747 6274 9800
2 132 264 396 1056 2378 3700
3,4 70 140 210 560 1255 1950
5-Robin Hood begins (4-5/56, 1st DC app.), ends #15; see Robin Hood Tales #7 73 146 219 584 1317 2050
6-10: 6-Robin Hood by Kubert; last Golden Gladiator app.; Silent Knight; no Viking Prince. 8-1st S.A. issue 46 92 138 368 834 1300
11-22,24: 12,14-Robin Hood-c. 18,21-23-Grey tone-c. 22-Last Silent Knight. 24-Last Viking Prince by Kubert (2nd solo book) 38 76 114 281 628 975
23-Viking Prince origin by Kubert; 1st B&B single theme issue & 1st Viking Prince solo book 46 92 138 359 805 1250
25-1st app. Suicide Squad (8-9/59) 286 572 858 2402 5451 8500
26,27-Suicide Squad 40 80 120 296 673 1050
28-(2-3/60)-Justice League intro./1st app.; origin/1st app. Snapper Carr 1400 2800 5600 18,000 53,000 88,000
29-Justice League (4-5/60)-2nd app. battle the Weapons Master; robot-c 276 552 828 2277 5139 6800
30-Justice League (6-7/60)-3rd app.; vs. Amazo 190 380 570 1568 3534 5500
31-1st app. Cave Carson (8-9/60); scarce in high grade; 1st try-out series 46 92 138 340 770 1200
32,33-Cave Carson 23 46 69 164 362 560
34-Origin/1st app. Silver-Age Hawkman, Hawkgirl & Byth (2-3/61); Gardner Fox story, Kubert-c/a ; 1st S.A. Hawkman tryout series; 2nd in #42-44; both series predate Hawkman #1 (4-5/64) 159 318 477 1312 2956 4600
35-Hawkman by Kubert (4-5/61)-2nd app. 37 74 111 274 612 950
36-Hawkman by Kubert; origin & 1st app. Shadow Thief (6-7/61)-3rd app. 34 68 102 245 548 850
37-Suicide Squad (2nd tryout series) 24 48 72 168 372 575
38,39-Suicide Squad. 38-Last 10¢ issue 19 38 57 131 291 450
40,41-Cave Carson Inside Earth (2nd try-out series). 40-Kubert-a. 41-Meskin-a

Brave and the Bold #62 © DC

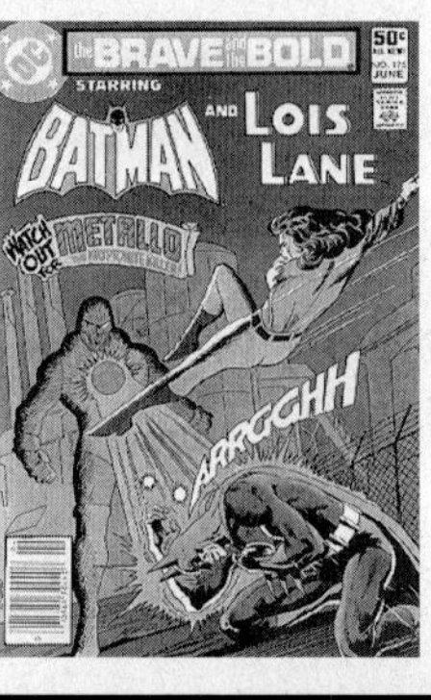

Brave and the Bold #175 © DC

Brave and the Bold #184 © DC

	GD 2.0	VG 4.0	FN 6.0	VF 8.0	VF/NM 9.0	NM- 9.2
	12	24	36	84	185	285
42-Hawkman by Kubert (2nd tryout series); Hawkman earns helmet wings; Byth app.	19	38	57	133	297	460
43-Hawkman by Kubert; more detailed origin	23	46	69	161	356	550
44-Hawkman by Kubert; grey-tone-c	19	38	57	133	297	460
45-49-Strange Sports Stories by Infantino	8	16	24	56	108	160
50-The Green Arrow & Manhunter From Mars (10-11/63); 1st Manhunter x-over outside of Detective Comics (pre-dates House of Mystery #143); team-ups begin	17	34	51	117	259	400
51-Aquaman & Hawkman (12-1/63-64); pre-dates Hawkman #1	18	36	54	124	275	425
52-(2-3/64)-3 Battle Stars; Sgt. Rock, Haunted Tank, Johnny Cloud, & Mlle. Marie team-up for 1st time by Kubert (c/a)	22	44	66	154	340	525
53-Atom & The Flash by Toth	9	18	27	59	117	175
54-Kid Flash, Robin & Aqualad; 1st app./origin Teen Titans (6-7/64)	68	136	204	544	1222	1900
55-Metal Men & The Atom	8	16	24	54	102	150
56-The Flash & Manhunter From Mars	8	16	24	54	102	150
57-Origin & 1st app. Metamorpho (12-1/64-65)	21	42	63	147	324	500
58-2nd app. Metamorpho by Fradon	9	18	27	61	123	185
59-Batman & Green Lantern; 1st Batman team-up in Brave and the Bold	11	22	33	76	163	250
60-Teen Titans (2nd app.)-1st app. new Wonder Girl (Donna Troy), who joins Titans (6-7/65)	44	88	132	326	738	1150
61-Origin Starman & Black Canary by Anderson	12	24	36	82	179	275
62-Origin Starman & Black Canary cont'd. 62-1st S.A. app. Wildcat (10-11/65); 1st S.A. app. of G.A. Huntress (W.W. villain)	10	20	30	69	147	225
63-Supergirl & Wonder Woman	8	16	24	56	108	160
64-Batman Versus Eclipso (see H.O.S. #61)	8	16	24	51	96	140
65-Flash & Doom Patrol (4-5/66)	6	12	18	37	66	95
66-Metamorpho & Metal Men (6-7/66)	6	12	18	37	66	95
67-Batman & The Flash by Infantino; Batman team-ups begin, end #200 (8-9/66)	7	14	21	44	82	120
68-Batman/Metamorpho/Joker/Riddler/Penguin-c/story; Batman as Bat-Hulk (Hulk parody)	8	16	24	51	96	140
69-Batman & Green Lantern	6	12	18	38	69	100
70-Batman & Hawkman; Craig-a(p)	6	12	18	38	69	100
71-Batman & Green Arrow	6	12	18	38	69	100
72-Spectre & Flash (6-7/67); 4th app. The Spectre; predates Spectre #1	6	12	18	40	73	105
73-Aquaman & The Atom	6	12	18	37	66	95
74-Batman & Metal Men	6	12	18	37	66	95
75-Batman & The Spectre (12-1/67-68); 6th app. Spectre; came out between Spectre #1 & #2	6	12	18	41	76	110
76-Batman & Plastic Man (2-3/68); came out between Plastic Man #8 & #9	6	12	18	37	66	95
77-Batman & The Atom	6	12	18	37	66	95
78-Batman, Wonder Woman & Batgirl	6	12	18	41	76	110
79-Batman & Deadman by Neal Adams (8-9/68); early Deadman app.	9	18	27	61	123	185
80-Batman & Creeper (10-11/68); N. Adams-a; early app. The Creeper; came out between Creeper #3 & #4	8	16	24	52	99	145
81-Batman & Flash; N. Adams-a	8	16	24	52	99	145
82-Batman & Aquaman; N. Adams-a; origin Ocean Master retold (2-3/69)	8	16	24	55	105	155
83-Batman & Teen Titans; N. Adams-a (4-5/69)	8	16	24	52	99	145
84-Batman (G.A., 1st S.A. app.) & Sgt. Rock; N. Adams-a; last 12¢ issue (6-7/69)	8	16	24	52	99	145
85-Batman & Green Arrow; 1st new costume for Green Arrow by Neal Adams (8-9/69)	12	24	36	84	185	285
86-Batman & Deadman (10-11/69); N. Adams-a; story concludes from Strange Adventures #216 (1-2/69)	8	16	24	52	99	145
87-Batman & Wonder Woman	4	8	12	27	44	60
88-Batman & Wildcat	4	8	12	27	44	60
89-Batman & Phantom Stranger (4-5/70); early Phantom Stranger app. (came out between Phantom Stranger #6 & 7	4	8	12	25	40	55
90-Batman & Adam Strange	4	8	12	25	40	55
91-Batman & Black Canary (8-9/70)	4	8	12	25	40	55
92-Batman; intro the Bat Squad	4	8	12	25	40	55
93-Batman-House of Mystery; N. Adams-a	8	16	24	51	96	140
94-Batman-Teen Titans	4	8	12	27	44	60
95-Batman & Plastic Man	3	6	9	20	31	42
96-Batman & Sgt. Rock; last 15¢ issue	3	6	9	21	33	45
97-Batman & Wildcat; 52 pg. issues begin, end #102; reprints origin & 1st app. Deadman from Strange Advs. #205	3	6	9	21	33	45
98-Batman & Phantom Stranger; 1st Jim Aparo Batman-a?	3	6	9	21	33	45
99-Batman & Flash	3	6	9	21	33	45
100-(2-3/72, 25¢, 52 pgs.)-Batman-Green Lantern-Green Arrow-Black Canary-Robin; Deadman-r by Adams/Str. Advs. #210	5	10	15	35	63	90
101-Batman & Metamorpho; Kubert Viking Prince	3	6	9	20	31	42
102-Batman-Teen Titans; N. Adams-a(p)	5	10	15	30	50	70
103-107,109,110: Batman team-ups: 103-Metal Men. 104-Deadman. 105-Wonder Woman. 106-Green Arrow. 107-Black Canary. 109-Demon. 110-Wildcat	3	6	9	14	20	26
108-Sgt. Rock	3	6	9	15	22	28
111-Batman/Joker-c/story	3	6	9	21	33	42
112-117: All 100 pgs.; Batman team-ups: 112-Mr. Miracle. 113-Metal Men; reprints origin/1st Hawkman from Brave and the Bold #34; r/origin Multi-Man/Challengers #14. 114-Aquaman. 115-Atom; r/origin Viking Prince from #23; r/Dr. Fate/Hourman/Solomon Grundy/Green Lantern from Showcase #55. 116-Spectre. 117-Sgt. Rock; last 100 pg. issue	5	10	15	30	50	70
118-Batman/Wildcat/Joker-c/story	3	6	9	16	24	32
119,121-123,125-128,132-140: Batman team-ups: 119-Man-Bat. 121-Metal Men. 122-Swamp Thing. 123-Plastic Man/Metamorpho. 125-Flash. 126-Aquaman. 127-Wildcat. 128-Mr. Miracle. 132-Kung-Fu Fighter. 133-Deadman. 134-Green Lantern. 135-Metal Men. 136-Metal Men/Green Arrow. 137-Demon. 138-Mr. Miracle. 139-Hawkman. 140-Wonder Woman	2	4	6	8	10	12
120-Kamandi (68 pgs.)	3	6	9	14	19	24
124-Sgt. Rock; Jim Aparo app. on cover & in story`	2	4	6	9	12	15
129,130-Batman/Green Arrow/Atom parts 1 & 2; Joker & Two Face-c/stories	3	6	9	15	22	28
131-Batman & Wonder Woman vs. Catwoman-c/sty	2	4	6	10	14	18
141-Batman/Black Canary vs. Joker-c/story	2	4	6	13	18	22
142-160: Batman team-ups: 142-Aquaman. 143-Creeper; origin Human Target (44 pgs.). 144-Green Arrow; origin Human Target part 2 (44 pgs.). 145-Phantom Stranger. 146-G.A. Batman/Unknown Soldier. 147-Supergirl. 148-Plastic Man; X-Mas-c. 149-Teen Titans. 150-Anniversary issue; Superman. 151-Flash. 152-Atom. 153-Red Tornado. 154-Metamorpho. 155-Green Lantern. 156-Dr. Fate. 157-Batman vs. Kamandi (ties into Kamandi #59). 158-Wonder Woman. 159-Ra's Al Ghul. 160-Supergirl.	1	3	4	6	8	10
145(11/79)-147,150-159,165(8/80)-(Whitman variants; low print run; none show issue # on cover)	2	4	6	10	14	18
161-181,183-190,192-195,198,199: Batman team-ups: 161-Adam Strange. 162-G.A. Batman/Sgt. Rock. 163-Black Lightning. 164-Hawkman. 165-Man-Bat. 166-Black Canary; Nemesis (intro) back-up story begins, ends #192; Penguin-c/story. 167-G.A. Batman/Blackhawk; origin Nemesis. 168-Green Arrow. 169-Zatanna. 170-Nemesis. 171-Scalphunter. 172-Firestorm. 173-Guardians of the Universe. 174-Green Lantern. 175-Lois Lane. 176-Swamp Thing. 177-Elongated Man. 178-Creeper. 179-Legion. 180-Spectre. 181-Hawk & Dove. 183-Riddler. 184-Huntress & Earth II Batman. 185-Green Arrow. 186-Hawkman. 187-Metal Men. 188,189-Rose & the Thorn. 190-Adam Strange. 192-Superboy vs. Mr. I.Q. 194-Flash. 195-I...Vampire. 198-Karate Kid. 199-Batman vs. The Spectre						6.00
182-G.A. Robin; G.A. Starman app.; 1st modern app. G.A. Batwoman	2	4	6	8	11	14
191-Batman/Joker-c/story; Nemesis app.	2	4	6	9	13	16
196-Ragman; origin Ragman retold.	1	2	3	5	6	8
197-Catwoman; Earth II Batman & Catwoman marry; 2nd modern app. of G.A. Batwoman; Scarecrow story in Golden Age style	2	4	6	13	18	22
200-Double-sized (64 pgs.); printed on Mando paper; Earth One & Earth Two Batman app. in separate stories; intro/1st app. Batman & The Outsiders; 1st app. Katana	3	6	9	16	23	30

NOTE: ***Neal Adams*** *a-79-86, 93, 100r, 102; c-75, 76, 79-86, 88-90, 93, 95, 99, 100r.* ***M. Anderson*** *a-115r; c-72i, 96i.* ***Andru/Esposito*** *c-25-27.* ***Aparo*** *a-98, 100-102, 104-125, 126i, 127-136, 138-145, 147, 148i, 149-152, 154, 155, 157-162, 168-170, 173-178, 180-182, 184, 186i-189i, 191i-193i, 195, 196, 200; c-105-109, 111-136, 137i, , 138-175, 177, 180-184, 186-200.* ***Austin*** *a-166i.* ***Bernard Baily*** *c-32, 33, 58.* ***Buckler*** *a-185, 186p; c-137, 178p, 185p, 186p.* ***Giordano*** *a-143, 144.* ***Infantino*** *a-67p, 72p, 97r, 98r, 115r, 172p, 183p, 190p, 194p; c-45-49, 67p, 69p, 70p, 72p, 96p, 98r.* ***Kaluta*** *c-176.* ***Kane*** *a-115r; c-59, 64.* ***Kubert &/or Heath*** *a-1-24; reprints-101, 113, 115, 117.* ***Kubert*** *a-99r; c-22-24, 34-36, 40, 42-44, 52.* ***Mooney*** *a-114r.* ***Mortimer*** *a-64, 69.* ***Newton*** *a-153p, 156p, 165p.* ***Irv Novick*** *c-1(part), 2-21.* ***Fred Ray*** *a-78r.* ***Roussos*** *a-50, 76i, 114r.* ***Staton*** *148p. 52 pgs.-97, 100; 68 pgs.-120; 100 pgs.-112-117.*

BRAVE AND THE BOLD, THE
DC Comics: Dec, 1991 - No. 6, June, 1992 ($1.75, limited series)

1-6: Green Arrow, The Butcher, The Question in all; Grell scripts in all — 4.00

NOTE: ***Grell*** *c-3, 4-6.*

BRAVE AND THE BOLD, THE
DC Comics: Apr, 2007 - No. 35, Aug, 2010 ($2.99)

1-Batman & Green Lantern team-up; Roulette app.; Waid-s/Peréz-c/a; 2 covers — 5.00

2-32,34,35: 2-GL & Supergirl. 3-Batman & Blue Beetle vs. Fatal Five; Lobo app. 4-6-LSH app. 12-Megistus conclusion; Ordway-a. 14-Kolins-a. 16-Superman & Catwoman.

Brave and the Bold #33 © DC

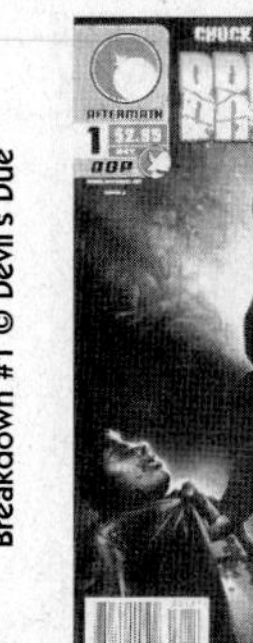

Breakdown #1 © Devil's Due

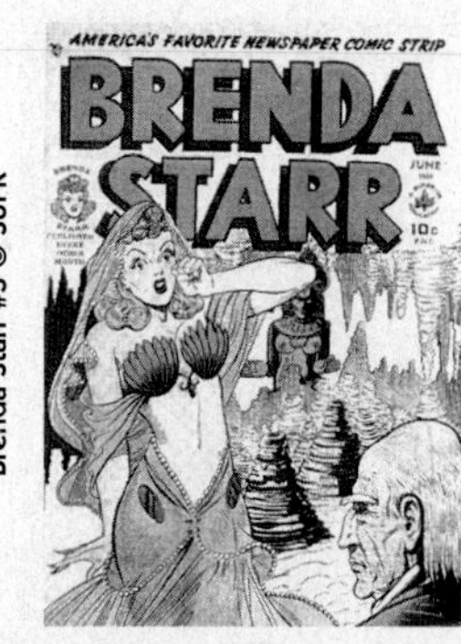

Brenda Starr #3 © SUPR

	GD 2.0	VG 4.0	FN 6.0	VF 8.0	VF/NM 9.0	NM- 9.2

28-Blackhawks app. 29-Batman/Brother Power the Geek. 31-Atom/Joker 3.00
33-Batgirl, Zatanna & W.W.; prelude to Killing Joke 3 6 9 15 22 28
...: Demons and Dragons HC (2009, $24.99, dustjacket) r/#13-16; Brave & the Bold V1 #181, Flash V3 #107 and Impulse #17; Mark Waid commentary 25.00
...: Demons and Dragons SC (2010, $17.99) same contents as HC 18.00
...: Milestone SC (2010, $17.99) r/#24-26 and Static #12, Hardware #16, Xombi #6 18.00
Team-ups of the Brave and the Bold HC (2010, $24.99) r/#27-33 25.00
...: The Book of Destiny HC (2008, $24.99, dustjacket) r/#7-12; Ordway sketch pages 25.00
...: The Book of Destiny SC (2009, $17.99) r/#7-12; Ordway sketch pages 18.00
...: The Lords of Luck HC (2007, $24.99, dustjacket) r/#1-6 with Waid intro & annotations 25.00
...: The Lords of Luck SC (2008, $17.99) r/#1-6 with Waid intro & annotations 18.00
...: Without Sin SC (2009, $17.99) r/#17-22 18.00

BRAVE AND THE BOLD ANNUAL NO. 1 1969 ISSUE, THE
DC Comics: 2001 ($5.95, one-shot)
1-Reprints Silver Age team-ups in 1960s-style 80 pg. Giant format 6.00

BRAVE AND THE BOLD: BATMAN AND WONDER WOMAN, THE
DC Comics: Apr, 2018 - No. 6 (3.99, limited series)
1-Liam Sharp-s/a 4.00

BRAVE AND THE BOLD SPECIAL, THE (See DC Special Series No. 8)

BRAVE EAGLE (TV)
Dell Publishing Co.: No. 705, June, 1956 - No. 929, July, 1958
Four Color 705 (#1)-Photo-c 6 12 18 42 79 115
Four Color 770, 816, 879 (2/58), 929-All photo-c 5 10 15 31 53 75

BRAVE NEW WORLD (See DCU Brave New World)

BRAVE OLD WORLD (V2K)
DC Comics (Vertigo): Feb, 2000 - No. 4, May, 2000 ($2.50, mini-series)
1-4-Messner-Loeb-s/Guy Davis & Phil Hester-a 3.00

BRAVE ONE, THE (Movie)
Dell Publishing Co.: No. 773, Mar, 1957
Four Color 773-Photo-c 5 10 15 34 60 85

BRAVEST WARRIORS (Based on the animated web series)
BOOM! Entertainment (KaBOOM): Oct, 2012 - No. 36, Sept, 2015 ($3.99)
1-36-Multiple covers on each 4.00
2014 Annual (1/14, $4.99) Short stories featuring Catbug; multiple covers 5.00
2014 Impossibear Special 1 (6/14, $4.99) Short stories; multiple covers 5.00
... Paralyzed Horse Giant 1 (11/14, $4.99) Short stories; multiple covers 5.00
...: Tales From the Holo John 1 (5/15, $4.99) Short stories; multiple covers 5.00

BRAVURA
Malibu Comics (Bravura): 1995 (mail-in offer)
0-wraparound holographic-c; short stories and promo pin-ups of Chaykin's Power & Glory, Gil Kane's & Steven Grant's Edge, Starlin's Breed, & Simonson's Star Slammers 5.00
1 1/2 7.00

BREACH
DC Comics: Mar, 2005 - No. 11, Jan, 2006 ($2.95/$2.50)
1-11: 1-Marcos Martin-a/Bob Harras-s; origin. 4-JLA-c/app. 3.00

BREAKDOWN
Devil's Due Publ.: Oct, 2004 - No. 6, Apr, 2005 ($2.95)
1-6: 1-Two covers by Dave Ross and Leinil Yu; Dixon-s/Ross-a 3.00

BREAKFAST AFTER NOON
Oni Press: May, 2000 - No. 6, Jan, 2001 ($2.95, B&W, limited series)
1-6-Andi Watson-s/a 3.00
TPB (2001, $19.95) r/series 20.00

BREAKING INTO COMICS THE MARVEL WAY
Marvel Comics: May, 2010 - No. 2, May, 2010 ($3.99, limited series)
1,2-Short stories by various newcomer artists; artist profiles 4.00

BREAKNECK BLVD.
MotioN Comics/Slave Labor Graphics Vol. 2: No. 0, Feb, 1994 - No. 2, Nov, 1994; Vol. 2#1, Jul, 1995 - #6, Dec., 1996 ($2.50/$2.95, B&W)
0-2, V2#1-6: 0-Pérez/Giordano-c 3.00

BREAK-THRU (Also see Exiles V1#4)
Malibu Comics (Ultraverse): Dec, 1993 - No. 2, Jan, 1994 ($2.50, 44 pgs.)
1,2-Pérez-c/a(p); has x-overs in Ultraverse titles 4.00

BREATH OF BONES: A TALE OF THE GOLEM
Dark Horse Comics: Jun, 2013 - No. 3, Aug, 2013 ($3.99, B&W, limited series)
1-3-Niles-s/Wachter-a 4.00

BREATHTAKER
DC Comics: 1990 - No. 4, 1990 ($4.95, 52 pgs., prestige format, mature)
Book 1-4: Mark Wheatley-painted-c/a & scripts; Marc Hempel-a 5.00
TPB (1994, $14.95) r/#1-4; intro by Neil Gaiman 15.00

'BREED
Malibu Comics (Bravura): Jan, 1994 - No. 6, 1994 ($2.50, limited series)
1-(48 pgs.)-Origin/1st app. of 'Breed by Starlin; contains Bravura stamps; spot varnish-c 4.00
2-6: 2-5-contains Bravura stamps. 6-Death of Rachel 3.00
...:Book of Genesis (1994, $12.95)-reprints #1-6 13.00

'BREED II
Malibu Comics (Bravura): Nov, 1994 - No. 6, Apr, 1995 ($2.95, limited series)
1-6: Starlin-c/a/scripts in all. 1-Gold edition 3.00

'BREED III
Image Comics: May, 2011 - No. 7, Dec, 2011 ($2.99)
1-7: Starlin-c/a/scripts in all 3.00

BREEZE LAWSON, SKY SHERIFF (See Sky Sheriff)

BRENDA LEE'S LIFE STORY
Dell Publishing Co.: July-Sept., 1962
01-078-209 8 16 24 51 86 120

BRENDA STARR (Also see All Great)
Four Star Comics Corp./Superior Comics Ltd.: No. 13, 9/47; No. 14, 3/48; V2#3, 6/48 - V2#12, 12/49
V1#13-By Dale Messick 100 200 300 635 1093 1550
14-Classic Kamen bondage-c 432 864 1296 3154 5577 8000
V2#3-Baker-a? 81 162 243 518 884 1250
4-Used in **SOTI**, pg. 21; Kamen-c 97 194 291 621 1061 1500
5-10 71 142 213 454 777 1100
11,12 (Scarce) 74 148 222 470 810 1150
NOTE: *Newspaper reprints plus original material through #6. All original #7 on.*

BRENDA STARR (...Reporter)(Young Lovers No. 16 on?)
Charlton Comics: No. 13, June, 1955 - No. 15, Oct, 1955
13-15-Newspaper-r 32 64 96 188 307 425

BRENDA STARR REPORTER
Dell Publishing Co.: Oct, 1963
1 10 20 30 68 144 220

BRER RABBIT (See Kite Fun Book, Walt Disney Showcase #28 and Wheaties)
Dell Publishing Co.: No. 129, 1946; No. 208, Jan, 1949; No. 693, 1956 (Disney)
Four Color 129 (#1)-Adapted from Disney movie "Song of the South"
23 46 69 164 362 560
Four Color 208 (1/49) 10 20 30 66 138 210
Four Color 693-Part-r #129 7 14 21 49 92 135

BRIAN PULIDO'S LADY DEATH... (See Lady Death)

BRICK BRADFORD (Also see Ace Comics & King Comics)
King Features Syndicate/Standard: No. 5, July, 1948 - No. 8, July, 1949 (Ritt & Grey reprints)
5 20 40 60 117 189 260
6-Robot-c (by Schomburg?). 65 130 195 416 708 1000
7-Schomburg-c. 8-Says #7 inside, #8 on-c 18 36 54 103 162 220

BRICKLEBERRY (Based on the animated series)
Dynamite Entertainment: 2016 - No. 4, 2016 ($3.99, limited series)
1-4-Waco O'Guin & Roger Black-s 4.00

BRIDE'S DIARY (Formerly Black Cobra No. 3)
Ajax/Farrell Publ.: No. 4, May, 1955 - No. 10, Aug, 1956
4 (#1) 12 24 36 67 94 120
5-8 9 18 27 50 65 80
9,10-Disbrow-a 10 20 30 58 79 100

BRIDES IN LOVE (Hollywood Romances & Summer Love No. 46 on)
Charlton Comics: Aug, 1956 - No. 45, Feb, 1965
1 14 28 42 76 108 140
2 8 16 24 40 50 60
3-6,8-10 3 6 9 21 33 45
7-(68 pgs.) 4 8 12 27 44 60
11-20 3 6 9 16 23 30
21-45 2 4 6 11 16 20

BRIDES OF HELHEIM

Brides Romances #6 © QUA

Briggs Land #6 © Brian Wood

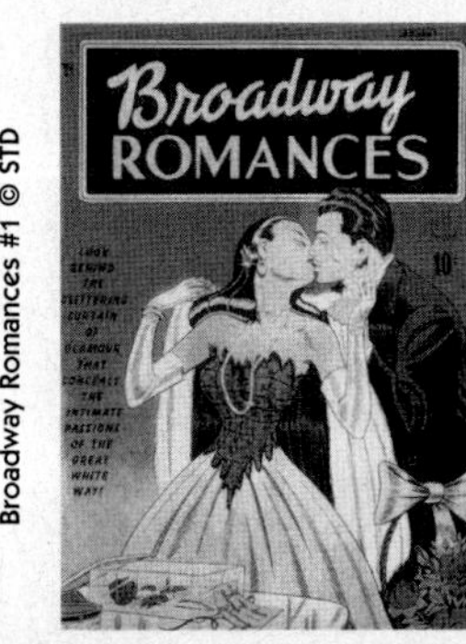

Broadway Romances #1 © STD

	GD 2.0	VG 4.0	FN 6.0	VF 8.0	VF/NM 9.0	NM- 9.2

Oni Press: Oct, 2014 - No. 6, May, 2015 ($3.99)

1-6-Cullen Bunn-s/Joëlle Jones-a 4.00

BRIDES ROMANCES
Quality Comics Group: Nov, 1953 - No. 23, Dec, 1956

	GD 2.0	VG 4.0	FN 6.0	VF 8.0	VF/NM 9.0	NM- 9.2
1	20	40	60	117	189	260
2	12	24	36	69	97	125
3-10: Last precode (3/55)	11	22	33	64	90	115
11-17,19-22: 15-Baker-a(p)?; Colan-a	10	20	30	58	79	100
18-Baker-a	14	28	42	76	108	140
23-Baker-c/a	20	40	60	117	189	260

BRIDE'S SECRETS
Ajax/Farrell(Excellent Publ.)/Four-Star: Apr-May, 1954 - No. 19, May, 1958

	GD 2.0	VG 4.0	FN 6.0	VF 8.0	VF/NM 9.0	NM- 9.2
1	17	34	51	98	154	210
2	11	22	33	60	83	105
3-6: Last precode (3/55)	10	20	30	54	72	90
7-11,13-19: 18-Hollingsworth-a	9	18	27	50	65	80
12-Disbrow-a	10	20	30	56	76	95

BRIDE-TO-BE ROMANCES (See True...)

BRIGADE
Image Comics (Extreme Studios): Aug, 1992 - No. 4, 1993 ($1.95, lim. series)

1-Liefeld part plots/scripts in all, Liefeld-c(p); contains 2 Brigade trading cards 4.00
1-Gold foil stamped logo edition 8.00
2-Contains coupon for Image Comics #0 & 2 trading cards 3.00
2-With coupon missing 2.00
3,4: 3-Contains 2 trading cards; 1st Birds of Prey. 4-Flip book featuring Youngblood #5 3.00

BRIGADE
Image Comics (Extreme): V2#1, May, 1993 - V2#22, July, 1995, V2#25, May, 1996 ($1.95/$2.50)

V2#1-22,25: 1-Gatefold-c; Liefeld co-plots; Blood Brothers part 1; Bloodstrike app. 2-(6/93, V2#1 on inside)-Foil merricote-c (newsstand ed. w/out foil-c exists). 3-Perez-c(i); Liefeld scripts. 8,9-Coupons #2 & 6 for Extreme Prejudice #0 bound-in. 11-(8/94, $2.50) WildC.A.T.S app. 16-Polybagged w/ trading card. 22-"Supreme Apocalypse" Pt. 4; w/ trading card 3.00
0-(9/93)-Liefeld scripts; 1st app. Warcry; Youngblood & Wildcats app.; 3.00
20-Variant-c. by Quesada & Palmiotti 3.00
Sourcebook 1 (8/94, $2.95) 3.00
1-(Awesome Ent., 7/00, $2.99) Flip book w/Century preview 4.00
1-(6/10, $3.99) Liefeld-s/Mychaels-a; covers by Liefeld & Mychaels 4.00

BRIGAND, THE (See Fawcett Movie Comics No. 18)

BRIGGS LAND
Dark Horse Comics: Aug, 2016 - No. 6, Jan, 2017 ($3.99)

1-6-Brian Wood-s/Mack Chater-a/Tula Lotay-c 4.00

BRIGGS LAND: LONE WOLVES
Dark Horse Comics: Jun, 2017 - No. 6, Nov, 2017 ($3.99)

1-6: 1-Brian Wood-s/Mack Chater-a/Matthew Woodson-c. 4-Del Ray-a 4.00

BRIGHTEST DAY (Also see Blackest Night and Green Lantern)
DC Comics: No. 0, Jun, 2010 - No. 24, Late Jun, 2011 ($3.99/$2.99)

0-($3.99) Johns & Tomasi-s/Pasarin-a/Finch-c 4.00
0-Variant-c by Reis 8.00
1-23-($2.99) 1-Black Manta returns. 4-Intro. Jackson (new Aqualad) 16-Aqualad origin. 18-Hawkman & Hawkgirl killed. 20-Aquaman killed 3.00
1-23: Variant covers. 1-6,9-18,20-23-by Reis, 7,8 White Lantern by Sook. 19-by Frank 6.00
24-($4.99) Swamp Thing and John Constantine return to DC universe 5.00
24-($4.99) Variant cover by Reis 8.00
...: The Atom Special (9/10, $2.99) Lemire-s/Asrar-a/Frank-c 3.00
... Volume 1 HC (2010, $29.99) r/#0-7; cover gallery 30.00
... Volume 2 HC (2011, $29.99) r/#8-16; cover gallery 30.00

BRIGHTEST DAY AFTERMATH: THE SEARCH FOR SWAMP THING
DC Comics: Aug, 2011 - No. 3, Oct, 2011 ($2.99, limited series)

1-3-Vankin-s/Castiello-a; covers by Syaf & Jones; John Constantine & Zatanna app. 3.00

BRILLIANT
Marvel Comics (Icon): Jul, 2011 - No. 5, Mar, 2014 ($3.95, limited series)

1-5-Bendis-s/Bagley-a/c 4.00

BRILLIANT TRASH
AfterShock Comics: Nov, 2017 - Present ($3.99)

1-4-Tim Seeley-s/Priscilla Petraites-a 4.00

BRING BACK THE BAD GUYS (Also see Fireside Book Series)
Marvel Comics: 1998 ($24.95, TPB)

1-Reprints stories of Marvel villains' secrets 25.00

BRINGING UP FATHER
Dell Publishing Co.: No. 9, 1942 - No. 37, 1944

	GD 2.0	VG 4.0	FN 6.0	VF 8.0	VF/NM 9.0	NM- 9.2
Large Feature Comic 9	34	68	102	204	332	460
Four Color 37	18	36	54	124	275	425

BRING ON THE BAD GUYS (See Fireside Book Series)

BRING THE THUNDER
Dynamite Entertainment: 2010 - No. 4, 2011 ($3.99)

1-4-Alex Ross-c/Ross & Nitz-s/Tortosa-a 4.00

BRITANNIA
Valiant Entertainment: Sept, 2016 - No. 4, Dec, 2016 ($3.99, limited series)

1-MIlligan-a/Ryp-a; set in 60-66 A.D.; Emperor Nero app. 4.00

BRITANNIA: WE WHO ARE ABOUT TO DIE
Valiant Entertainment: Apr, 2017 - No. 4, Jul, 2017 ($3.99, limited series)

1-4-MIlligan-a/Ryp-a; further story of Antonius Axia; multiple covers on each 4.00

BROADWAY HOLLYWOOD BLACKOUTS
Stanhall: Mar-Apr, 1954 - No. 3, July-Aug, 1954

	GD 2.0	VG 4.0	FN 6.0	VF 8.0	VF/NM 9.0	NM- 9.2
1	23	46	69	136	223	310
2,3	15	30	45	86	133	180

BROADWAY ROMANCES
Quality Comics Group: January, 1950 - No. 5, Sept, 1950

	GD 2.0	VG 4.0	FN 6.0	VF 8.0	VF/NM 9.0	NM- 9.2
1-Ward-c/a (9 pgs.); Gustavson-a	42	84	126	265	445	625
2-Ward-a (9 pgs.); photo-c	29	58	87	170	278	385
3-5: All-Photo-c	16	32	48	94	147	200

BROKEN ARROW (TV)
Dell Publishing Co.: No. 855, Oct, 1957 - No. 947, Nov, 1958

	GD 2.0	VG 4.0	FN 6.0	VF 8.0	VF/NM 9.0	NM- 9.2
Four Color 855 (#1)-Photo-c	6	12	18	37	66	95
Four Color 947-Photo-c	5	10	15	31	53	75

BROKEN CROSS, THE (See The Crusaders)

BROKEN MOON
American Gothic Press: Sept, 2015 - No. 4, Jan, 2016 ($3.99, limited series)

1-4-Steve Niles-s/Nat Jones-a; covers by Jones & Sanjulian 4.00

BROKEN PIECES
Aspen MLT: No. 0, Sept, 2011; Oct, 2011 - No. 5, Dec, 2012 ($2.50/$3.50, limited series)

0-($2.50)-Roslan-s/Kaneshiro-a; three covers 3.00
1-5: 1-($3.50)-Roslan-s/Kaneshiro-a; three covers 3.50

BROKEN TRINITY
Image Comics (Top Cow): July, 2008 - No. 3, Nov, 2008 ($2.99, limited series)

1-3-Witchblade, Darkness & Angelus app.; Marz-s/Sejic & Hester-a; two covers 3.00
...: Aftermath 1 (4/09, $2.99) Marz & Hill-s/Lucas & Kirkham-a 3.00
...: Angelus 1 (12/08, $2.99) Marz-s/Stelfreeze-a; two covers 3.00
...: Pandora's Box 1-6 (2/10 - No. 6, 4/11 $3.99) Tommy Lee Edwards-c 4.00
...: The Darkness 1 (8/08, $2.99) Hester-s/Lucas-a; two covers 3.00
...: Witchblade 1 (12/08, $2.99) Marz-s/Blake-a; two covers 3.00

BRONCHO BILL (See Comics On Parade, Sparkler & Tip Top Comics)
United Features Syndicate/Standard(Visual Editions) No. 5-on: 1939 - 1940; No. 5, 1?/48 - No. 16, 8?/50

	GD 2.0	VG 4.0	FN 6.0	VF 8.0	VF/NM 9.0	NM- 9.2
Single Series 2 ('39)	55	110	165	352	601	850
Single Series 19 ('40)(#2 on cvr)	42	84	126	267	451	635
5	15	30	45	85	130	175
6(4/48)-10(4/49)	10	20	30	56	76	95
11(6/49)-16	9	18	27	50	65	80

NOTE: *Schomburg c-6, 7, 9-13, 15, 16.*

BROOKLYN ANIMAL CONTROL
IDW Publishing: Dec, 2015 ($7.99, square-bound, one-shot)

1-J.T. Petty-s/Stephen Thompson-a; werewolves in Brooklyn 8.00

BROOKS ROBINSON (See Baseball's Greatest Heroes #2)

BROTHER BILLY THE PAIN FROM PLAINS
Marvel Comics Group: 1979 (68pgs.)

	GD 2.0	VG 4.0	FN 6.0	VF 8.0	VF/NM 9.0	NM- 9.2
1-B&W comics, satire, Jimmy Carter-c & x-over w/Brother Billy peanut jokes. Joey Adams-a (scarce)	5	10	15	31	53	75

BROTHERHOOD, THE (Also see X-Men titles)
Marvel Comics: July, 2001 - No. 9, Mar, 2002 ($2.25)

Brother Power, The Geek #1 © DC

The Brute #2 © Nemesis

BubbleGun V2 #1 © Aspen MLT

GD 2.0 | VG 4.0 | FN 6.0 | VF 8.0 | VF/NM 9.0 | NM- 9.2

1-Intro. Orwell & the Brotherhood; Ribic-a/X-s/Sienkiewicz-c 3.00
2-9: 2-Two covers (JG Jones & Sienkiewicz). 4-6-Fabry-c. 7-9-Phillips-c/a 3.00

BROTHER POWER, THE GEEK (See Saga of Swamp Thing Annual & Vertigo Visions)
National Periodical Publications: Sept-Oct, 1968 - No. 2, Nov-Dec, 1968

1-Origin; Simon-c(i?) 5 10 15 31 53 75
2 3 6 9 19 30 40

BROTHERS, HANG IN THERE, THE
Spire Christian Comics (Fleming H. Revell Co.): 1979 (49¢)

nn 2 4 6 13 18 22

BROTHERS IN ARMS (Based on the World War II military video game)
Dynamite Entertainment: 2008 - No. 4, 2008 ($3.99/$3.50)

1-($3.99) Fabbri-a; two covers by Fabbri & Sejic 4.00
2-4-($3.50) Two covers by Fabbri & Sejic on each 3.50

BROTHERS OF THE SPEAR (Also see Tarzan)
Gold Key/Whitman No. 18: June, 1972 - No. 17, Feb, 1976; No. 18, May, 1982

1 5 10 15 31 53 75
2-Painted-c begin, end #17 3 6 9 18 28 38
3-10 3 6 9 15 22 28
11-18: 12-Line drawn-c. 13-17-Spiegle-a. 18(5/82)-r/#2; Leopard Girl-r
2 4 6 11 16 20

BROTHERS, THE CULT ESCAPE, THE
Spire Christian Comics (Fleming H. Revell Co.): 1980 (49¢)

nn 3 6 9 14 19 24

BROWNIES (See New Funnies)
Dell Publishing Co.: No. 192, July, 1948 - No. 605, Dec, 1954

Four Color 192(#1)-Kelly-a 13 26 39 89 195 300
Four Color 244(9/49), 293 (9/50)-Last Kelly c/a 10 20 30 64 132 200
Four Color 337(7-8/51), 365(12-1/51-52), 398(5/52) 6 12 18 38 69 100
Four Color 436(11/52), 482(7/53), 522(12/53), 605 5 10 15 35 63 90

BRUCE GENTRY
Better/Standard/Four Star Publ./Superior No. 3: Jan, 1948 - No. 8, Jul, 1949

1-Ray Bailey strip reprints begin, end #3; E.C. emblem appears as a monogram on stationery in story; negligee panels 65 130 195 416 708 1000
2,3 39 78 117 240 395 550
4-8 28 56 84 165 270 375

NOTE: *Kamenish a-2-7; c-1-8.*

BRUCE JONES' OUTER EDGE
Innovation: 1993 ($2.50, B&W, one-shot)

1-Bruce Jones-c/a/script 3.00

BRUCE LEE (Also see Deadly Hands of Kung Fu)
Malibu Comics: July, 1994 - No. 6, Dec, 1994 ($2.95, 36 pgs.)

1-6: 1-(44 pgs.)-Mortal Kombat prev., 1st app. in comics. 2,6-(36 pgs.) 5.00

BRUCE WAYNE: AGENT OF S.H.I.E.L.D. (Also see Marvel Vs. DC #3 & DC Vs. Marvel #4)
Marvel Comics (Amalgam): Apr, 1996 ($1.95, one-shot)

1-Chuck Dixon scripts & Cary Nord-c/a. 3.00

BRUCE WAYNE: THE ROAD HOME (See Batman: The Return of Bruce Wayne)
(See Batman: Bruce Wayne - The Road Home HC for reprints)
DC Comics: Dec, 2010 ($2.99, series of one-shots with interlocking covers)

...: Batgirl 1 - Bryan Miller-s/Pere Pérez-a 3.00
...: Batman and Robin 1 - Nicieza-s/Richards-a; Vicki Vale app. 3.00
...: Catwoman 1 - Fridolfs-s/Nguyen-a; Harley & Ivy app. 3.00
...: Commissioner Gordon 1 - Beechen-s/Kudranski-a; Penguin app. 3.00
...: Oracle 1 - Andreyko-s/Padilla-a; Man-Bat & Manhunter app. 3.00
...: Outsiders 1 - Barr-s/Saltares-a 3.00
...: Ra's al Ghul 1 - Nicieza-s/McDaniel-a 3.00
...: Red Robin 1 - Nicieza-s/Bachs-a; Ra's al Ghul app. 3.00

BRUISER
Anthem Publications: Feb, 1994 ($2.45)

1 3.00

BRUTAL NATURE
IDW Publishing: May, 2016 - No. 4, Aug, 2016 ($3.99, limited series)

1-4-Ariel Olivetti-a/Luciano Saracino-s 4.00

BRUTAL NATURE: CONCRETE FURY
IDW Publishing: Mar, 2017 - No. 5, Jul, 2017 ($3.99, limited series)

1-5-Ariel Olivetti-a/Luciano Saracino-s 4.00

BRUTE, THE
Seaboard Publ. (Atlas): Feb, 1975 - No. 3, July, 1975

1-Origin & 1st app; Sekowsky-a(p) 3 6 9 16 23 30
2-Sekowsky-a(p); Fleisher-s 2 4 6 10 14 18
3-Brunner/Starlin/Weiss-a(p) 2 4 6 13 18 22

BRUTE & BABE
Ominous Press: July, 1994 - No. 2, Aug, 1994

1-($3.95, 8 tablets plus-c)-"...It Begins..."; tablet format 4.00
2-($2.50, 36 pgs.)-"Mael's Rage", 2-(40 pgs.)-Stiff additional variant-c 3.00

BRUTE FORCE
Marvel Comics: Aug, 1990 - No. 4, Nov, 1990 ($1.00, limited series)

1-4: Animal super-heroes; Delbo & DeCarlo-a 3.00

B-SIDES (The Craptacular...)
Marvel Comics: Nov, 2002 - No. 3, Jan, 2003 ($2.99, limited series)

1-3-Kieth-c/Weldele-a. 2-Dorkin-a (1 pg.) 2-FF cameo. 3-FF app. 3.00

BUBBLEGUM CRISIS: GRAND MAL
Dark Horse Comics: Mar, 1994 - No. 4, June, 1994 ($2.50, limited series)

1-4-Japanese manga 3.00

BUBBLEGUN
Aspen MLT: Jun, 2013 - No. 5, Mar, 2014 ($1.00/$3.99)

1-($1.00) Roslan-s/Bowden-a; multiple covers 3.00
2-5-($3.99) Multiple covers on each 4.00

BUBBLEGUN (Volume 2)
Aspen MLT: May, 2017 - No. 5, Sept, 2017 ($3.99)

1-5-Roslan-s/Tovar-a; multiple covers 4.00

BUCCANEER
I. W. Enterprises: No date (1963)

I.W. Reprint #1(r-/Quality #20), #8(r-/#23): Crandall-a in each
3 6 9 16 23 30

BUCCANEERS (Formerly Kid Eternity)
Quality Comics: No. 19, Jan, 1950 - No. 27, May, 1951 (No. 24-27: 52 pgs.)

19-Captain Daring, Black Roger, Eric Falcon & Spanish Main begin; Crandall-a 48 96 144 302 514 725
20,23-Crandall-a 36 72 108 215 350 485
21-Crandall-c/a 39 78 117 236 388 540
22-Bondage-c 28 56 84 165 270 375
24-26: 24-Adam Peril, U.S.N. begins. 25-Origin & 1st app. Corsair Queen. 26-Last Spanish Main 24 48 72 142 234 325
27-Crandall-c/a 34 68 102 205 335 465
Super Reprint #12 (1964)-Crandall-r/#21 3 6 9 16 23 30

BUCCANEERS, THE (TV)
Dell Publishing Co.: No. 800, 1957

Four Color 800-Photo-c 6 12 18 42 79 115

BUCKAROO BANZAI (Movie)
Marvel Comics Group: Dec, 1984 - No. 2, Feb, 1985

1,2-Movie adaptation; r/Marvel Super Special #33; Texiera-c/a 4.00

BUCKAROO BANZAI: RETURN OF THE SCREW
Moonstone: 2006 - No. 3, 2006 ($3.50, limited series)

1-3: 1-Three covers by Haley, Stribling, Beck; Thompson-a 3.50
Preview (2006, 50¢) B&W preview; history of movie and spin-off projects 3.00

BUCK DUCK
Atlas Comics (ANC): June, 1953 - No. 4, Dec, 1953

1-Funny animal stories in all 20 40 60 117 189 260
2-4: 2-Ed Win-a(5) 13 26 39 72 101 130

BUCK JONES (Also see Crackajack Funnies, Famous Feature Stories, Master Comics #7 & Wow Comics #1, 1936)
Dell Publishing Co.: No. 299, Oct, 1950 - No. 850, Oct, 1957 (All Painted-c)

Four Color 299(#1)-Buck Jones & his horse Silver-B begin; painted back-c begins, ends #5
12 24 36 83 182 280
2(4-6/51) 7 14 21 44 82 120
3-8(10-12/52) 6 12 18 37 66 95
Four Color 460,500,546,589 6 12 18 41 76 110
Four Color 652,733,850 5 10 15 35 63 90

BUCK ROGERS (Also see Famous Funnies, Pure Oil Comics, Salerno Carnival of Comics, 24 Pages of Comics, & Vicks Comics)

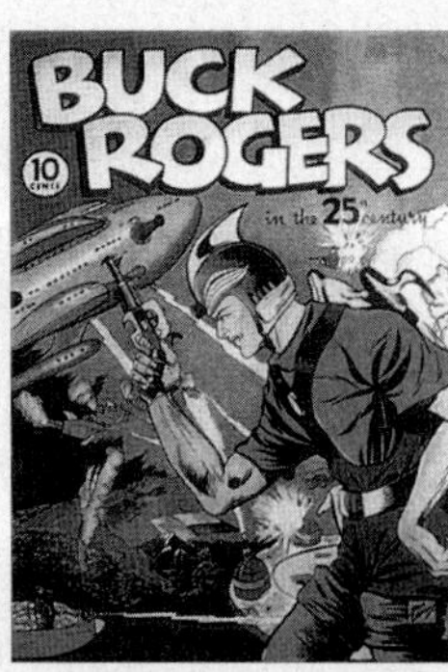

Buck Rogers #1 © KFS

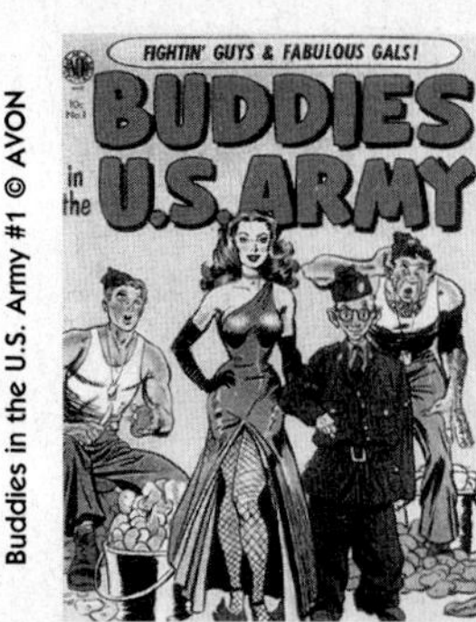

Buddies in the U.S. Army #1 © AVON

Buffy the Vampire Slayer #61 © 20th Century Fox

GD VG FN VF VF/NM NM-
2.0 4.0 6.0 8.0 9.0 9.2

Famous Funnies: Winter, 1940-41 - No. 6, Sept, 1943
NOTE: Buck Rogers first appeared in the pulp magazine Amazing Stories Vol. 3 #5 in Aug, 1928.
1-Sunday strip reprints by Rick Yager; begins with strip #190; Calkins-c 349 698 1047 2443 4272 6100
2 (7/41)-Calkins-c 142 284 426 909 1555 2200
3 (12/41), 4 (7/42) 119 238 357 762 1306 1850
5,6: 5-Story continues with Famous Funnies No. 80; Buck Rogers, Sky Roads. 6-Reprints of 1939 dailies; contains B.R. story "Crater of Doom" (2 pgs.) by Calkins not-r from Famous Funnies 100 200 300 635 1093 1550

BUCK ROGERS
Toby Press: No. 100, Jan, 1951 - No. 9, May-June, 1951
100(#7)-All strip-r begin; Anderson, Chatton-a 34 68 102 199 325 450
101(#8), 9-All Anderson-a(1947-49-r/dailies) 26 52 78 154 252 350

BUCK ROGERS (...in the 25th Century No. 5 on) (TV)
Gold Key/Whitman No. 7 on: Oct, 1964; No. 2, July, 1979 - No. 16, May, 1982 (No #10; story was written but never released. #17 exists only as a press proof without covers and was never published)
1(10128-410, 12¢)-1st S.A. app. Buck Rogers & 1st new B. R. in comics since 1933 giveaway; painted-c; back-c pin-up 11 22 33 73 157 240
2(7/79)-6: 3,4,6-Movie adaptation; painted-c 2 4 6 9 12 15
7,11 (Whitman) 2 4 6 11 16 20
8,9 (prepack)(scarce) 4 8 12 27 44 60
12-16: 14(2/82), 15(3/82), 16(5/82) 2 4 6 8 10 12
Giant Movie Edition 11296(64pp, Whitman, $1.50), reprints GK #2-4 minus cover; tabloid size; photo-c (See Marvel Treasury) 3 6 9 17 26 35
Giant Movie Edition 02489(Western/Marvel, $1.50), reprints GK #2-4 minus cover 3 6 9 16 24 32
NOTE: ***Bolle*** *a-2p,3p, Movie Ed.(p).* ***McWilliams*** *a-2i,3i, 5-11, Movie Ed.(i). Painted c-1-9,11-13.*

BUCK ROGERS (Comics Module)
TSR, Inc.: 1990 - No. 10, 1991 ($2.95, 44 pgs.)
1-10 (1990): 1-Begin origin in 3 parts. 2-Indicia says #1. 2,3-Black Barney back-up story. 4-All Black Barney issue; B. B.-c. 5-Indicia says #6; Black Barney-c & lead story; Buck Rogers back-up story. 10-Flip book (72pgs.) 4.00

BUCK ROGERS
Dynamite Entertainment: No. 0, 2009 - No. 12, 2010 (25¢/$3.50)
0-(25¢) Beatty-s/Rafael-a/Cassaday-c 3.00
1-12: 1-($3.50) Three covers by Cassaday, Ross and Wagner; origin re-told 3.50
Annual 1 (2011, $4.99) Rafael-a; covers by Rafael & Sadowski 5.00

BUCK ROGERS
Hermes Press: 2013 - No. 4, 2013 ($3.99)
1-4-Howard Chaykin-s/a/c 4.00

BUCKSKIN (TV)
Dell Publishing Co.: No. 1011, July, 1959 - No. 1107, June-Aug, 1960
Four Color 1011 (#1)-Photo-c 7 14 21 44 82 120
Four Color 1107-Photo-c 6 12 18 40 73 105

BUCKY BARNES: THE WINTER SOLDIER (See Captain America titles)
Marvel Comics: Dec, 2014 - No. 11, Nov, 2015 ($3.99)
1-11: 1-Ales Kot-s/Marco Rudy-a; Daisy Johnson app. 2,8,9,10-Loki app. 4-7,9-Crossbones app. 7-Foss-a 4.00

BUCKY O'HARE (Funny Animal)
Continuity Comics: 1988 ($5.95, graphic novel)
1-Golden-c/a(r); r/serial-Echo of Futurepast #1-6 1 3 4 6 8 10
Deluxe Hardcover ($40.00, 52 pg., 8 x 11") 40.00

BUCKY O'HARE
Continuity Comics: Jan, 1991 - No. 5, 1991 ($2.00)
1-6: 1-Michael Golden-c/a 3.00

BUDDIES IN THE U.S. ARMY
Avon Periodicals: Nov, 1952 - No. 2, 1953
1-Lawrence-c 15 30 45 85 130 175
2-Mort Lawrence-c/a 11 22 33 60 83 105

BUFFALO BEE (TV)
Dell Publishing Co.: No. 957, Nov, 1958 - No. 1061, Dec-Feb, 1959-60
Four Color 957 (#1) 8 16 24 52 99 145
Four Color 1002 (8-10/59), 1061 6 12 18 40 73 105

BUFFALO BILL (See Frontier Fighters, Super Western Comics & Western Action Thrillers)
Youthful Magazines: No. 2, Oct, 1950 - No. 9, Dec, 1951

GD VG FN VF VF/NM NM-
2.0 4.0 6.0 8.0 9.0 9.2

2-Annie Oakley story 15 30 45 84 127 170
3-9: 2-4-Walter Johnson-c/a. 9-Wildey-a 11 22 33 60 83 105

BUFFALO BILL CODY (See Cody of the Pony Express)

BUFFALO BILL, JR. (TV) (See Western Roundup)
Dell/Gold Key: Jan, 1956 - No. 13, Aug-Oct, 1959; 1965 (All photo-c)
Four Color 673 (#1) 8 16 24 56 108 160
Four Color 742,766,798,828,856(11/57) 5 10 15 35 63 90
7(2-4/58)-13 5 10 15 31 53 75
1(6/65, Gold Key)-Photo-c(r/F.C. #798); photo-b/c 4 8 12 23 37 50

BUFFALO BILL PICTURE STORIES
Street & Smith Publications: June-July, 1949 - No. 2, Aug-Sept, 1949
1,2-Wildey, Powell-a in each 14 28 42 80 115 150

BUFFY: THE HIGH SCHOOL YEARS (Based on the TV series)
Dark Horse Comics
... – Glutton For Punishment (10/16, $10.99, 6" x 9") McDonald-s/Li-a 11.00
... – Parental Parasite (6/17, $10.99, 6" x 9") McDonald-s/Li-a 11.00

BUFFY THE VAMPIRE SLAYER (Based on the TV series)(Also see Angel and Faith, Spike, Tales of the Vampires and Willow)
Dark Horse Comics: 1998 - No. 63, Nov, 2003 ($2.95/$2.99)
1-Bennett-a/Watson-s; Art Adams-c 1 2 3 6 8 10
1-Variant photo-c 1 2 3 6 8 10
1-Gold foil logo Art Adams-c 15.00
1-Gold foil logo photo-c 20.00
2-4-Photo-c 1 3 4 6 8 10
5-15-Regular and photo-c. 4-7-Gomez-a. 5,8-Green-c 5.00
16-49: 29,30-Angel x-over. 43-45-Death of Buffy. 47-Lobdell-s begin. 48-Pike returns 3.00
50-($3.50) Scooby gang battles Adam; back-up story by Watson 4.00
51-63: 51-54-Viva Las Buffy; pre-Sunnydale Buffy & Pike in Vegas 3.00
Annual '99 ($4.95)-Two stories and pin-ups 1 2 3 4 5 7
...: A Stake to the Heart TPB (3/04, $12.95) r/#60-63 13.00
...: Chaos Bleeds (6/03, $2.99) Based on the video game; photo & Campbell-c 3.00
...: Creatures of Habit (3/02, $17.95) text with Horton & Paul Lee-a 18.00
...: Jonathan 1 (1/01, $2.99) two covers; Richards-a 3.00
...: Lost and Found 1 (3/02, $2.99) aftermath of Buffy's death; Richards-a 3.00
... Lovers Walk (2/01, $2.99) short stories by various; Richards & photo-c 3.00
...: Note From the Underground (3/03, $12.95) r/#47-50 13.00
...: Omnibus Vol. 1 (7/07, $24.95, 9x6") r/Spike & Dru #3, Origin #1-3 and Buffy #51-59 25.00
...: Omnibus Vol. 2 (9/07, $24.95, 9x6") r/Buffy #60-63 and various one-shots & specials 25.00
...: Omnibus Vol. 3 (1/08, $24.95, 9x6") r/Buffy #1-8,12,16, Annual '99 25.00
...: Omnibus Vol. 4 (5/08, $24.95, 9x6") r/Buffy #9-11,13-15,17-20,50 and various 25.00
...: Omnibus Vol. 5 (9/08, $24.95, 9x6") r/Buffy #21-28 and various one-shots & specials 25.00
...: Omnibus Vol. 6 (2/09, $24.95, 9x6") r/Buffy #29-38 and various one-shots & specials 25.00
...: One For One (9/10, $1.00) r/#1 with red cover frame 3.00
...: Reunion (6/02, $3.50) Buffy & Angel's; Espenson-s; art by various 3.50
...: Slayer Interrupted TPB (2003, $14.95) r/#56-59 15.00
...: Tales of the Slayers (10/02, $3.50) art by Matsuda and Colan; art & photo-c 3.50
...: The Death of Buffy TPB (8/02, $15.95) r/#43-46 16.00
...: Viva Las Buffy TPB (7/03, $12.95) r/#51-54 13.00
Wizard #1/2 1 2 3 6 8 9

BUFFY THE VAMPIRE SLAYER ("Season Eight" of the TV series)
Dark Horse Comics: Mar, 2007 - No. 40, Jan, 2011 ($2.99)
1-Joss Whedon-s/Georges Jeanty-a/Jo Chen-c 6.00
1-Variant cover by Jeanty 6.00
1-RRP with B&W Jeanty cover (edition of 1000) 85.00
1-4: 1-2nd thru 5th printings. 2-2nd-4th printings. 3,4-2nd & 3rd printings 3.00
2-5-Jeanty-a; covers by Chen & Jeanty 4.00
6-13,16-19-Two covers by Chen & Jeanty. 6-9-Faith app.; Vaughan-s. 10,11-Whedon-s. 12-15-Goddard-s; Dracula app. 16-19-Fray app.; Whedon-s/Moline-a 3.00
20-40: 20-28,31-40-Two covers by Chen and Jeanty. 20-Animation style flashback. 21,26-30-Espenson-s. 30-Hughes-c. 31-Whedon-s. 32-35-Meltzer-s. 36-40-Whedon-s 3.00
...: Riley (8/10, $3.50) Espensen-s/Moline-a; Riley Finn and Sam; Angel app. 3.50
... Tales of the Vampires (6/09, $2.99) Cloonan-s/Lolos-a; covers by Chen & Bá/Moon 3.00
...: Willow (12/09, $3.50) Whedon-s/Moline-a; Willow meets the Snake Guide 3.50

BUFFY THE VAMPIRE SLAYER ("Season Nine" of the TV series)
Dark Horse Comics: Sept, 2011 - No. 25, Sept, 2013 ($2.99)
1-25: 1-Whedon-s/Jeanty-a; covers by Morris & Chen. 2-5-Chambliss-s; two covers by Morris & Jeanty. 5-Moline-a; Nikki flashback. 6,7-Two covers by Jeanty & Noto. 8-10-Richards-a. 14-Espenson-s; intro. Billy. 16-19-Illyria app. 3.00
....: Buffyverse Sampler (1/13, $4.99) r/#1, Angel & Faith #1, Spike #1, Willow #1 5.00
FCBD (5/12, giveaway) Buffy vs. Alien; Jeanty-a; flip book with The Guild 3.00

Buffy the Vampire Slayer Season Eleven #1 © 20th Century Fox

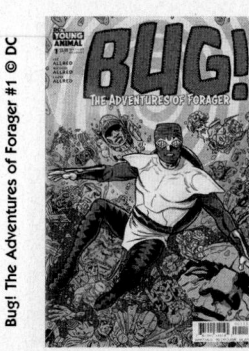

Bug! The Adventures of Forager #1 © DC

Bulletman #5 © FAW

GD 2.0 | VG 4.0 | FN 6.0 | VF 8.0 | VF/NM 9.0 | NM- 9.2

BUFFY THE VAMPIRE SLAYER (SEASON TEN)
Dark Horse Comics: Mar, 2014 - No. 30, Aug, 2016 ($3.50/$3.99)

1-16: 1-Gage-s/Isaacs-a; covers by Morris & Isaacs. 2-5-Dracula app. 3-5,7,12,13-Nicholas Brendon & Gage-s. 8-Corben-a (3 pgs) 3.50
17-30-($3.99) 19-Nicholas Brendon & Gage-s. 25-Levens-a 4.00

BUFFY THE VAMPIRE SLAYER SEASON ELEVEN
Dark Horse Comics: Nov, 2016 - No. 12, Oct, 2017 ($3.99)

1-12: 1-Gage-s/Isaacs-a; covers by Morris & Isaacs. 5,9-Jeanty-a 4.00

BUFFY THE VAMPIRE SLAYER: ANGEL
Dark Horse Comics: May, 1999 - No. 3, July, 1999 ($2.95, limited series)

1-3-Gomez-a; Matsuda-c & photo-c for each 3.00

BUFFY THE VAMPIRE SLAYER: GILES
Dark Horse Comics: Oct, 2000 ($2.95, one-shot)

1-Eric Powell-a; Powell & photo-c 3.00

BUFFY THE VAMPIRE SLAYER: HAUNTED
Dark Horse Comics: Dec, 2001 - No. 4, Mar, 2002 ($2.99, limited series)

1-4-Faith and the Mayor app.; Espenson-s/Richards-a 3.00
TPB (9/02, $12.95) r/series; photo-c 13.00

BUFFY THE VAMPIRE SLAYER: OZ
Dark Horse Comics: July, 2001 - No. 3, Sept, 2001 ($2.99, limited series)

1-3-Totleben & photo-c; Golden-s 3.00

BUFFY THE VAMPIRE SLAYER: SPIKE AND DRU
Dark Horse Comics: Apr, 1999; No. 2, Oct, 1999; No. 3, Dec, 2000 ($2.95)

1-3: 1,2-Photo-c. 3-Two covers (photo & Sook) 3.00

BUFFY THE VAMPIRE SLAYER: THE ORIGIN (Adapts movie screenplay)
Dark Horse Comics: Jan, 1999 - No. 3, Mar, 1999 ($2.95, limited series)

1-3-Brereton-s/Bennett-a; reg & photo-c for each 3.00

BUFFY THE VAMPIRE SLAYER: WILLOW & TARA
Dark Horse Comics: Apr, 2001 ($2.99, one-shot)

1-Terry Moore-a/Chris Golden & Amber Benson-s; Moore-c & photo-c 3.00
TPB (4/03, $9.95) r/#1 & W&T - Wilderness; photo-c 10.00

BUFFY THE VAMPIRE SLAYER: WILLOW & TARA - WILDERNESS
Dark Horse Comics: Jul, 2002 - No. 2, Sept, 2002 ($2.99, limited series)

1,2-Chris Golden & Amber Benson-s; Jothikaumar-c & photo-c 3.00

BUG
Marvel Comics: Mar, 1997 ($2.99, one-shot)

1-Micronauts character 3.00

BUGALOOS (Sid & Marty Krofft TV show)
Charlton Comics: Sept, 1971 - No. 4, Feb, 1972

1 5 10 15 30 50 70
2-4 3 6 9 19 30 40
NOTE: *No. 3(1/72) went on sale late in 1972 (after No. 4) with the 1/73 issues.*

BUGHOUSE (Satire)
Ajax/Farrell (Excellent Publ.): Mar-Apr, 1954 - No. 4, Sept-Oct, 1954

V1#1 26 52 78 154 252 350
2-4 15 30 45 86 133 180

BUGS BUNNY (See The Best of..., Camp Comics, Comic Album #2, 6, 10, 14, Dell Giant #28, 32, 46, Dynabrite, Golden Comics Digest #1, 3, 5, 6, 8, 10, 14, 15, 17, 21, 26, 30, 34, 39, 42, 47, Kite Fun Book, Large Feature Comic #8, Looney Tunes and Merry Melodies, March of Comics #44, 59, 75, 83, 97, 115, 132, 149, 160, 179, 188, 201, 220, 231, 245, 259, 273, 287, 301, 315, 329, 343, 363, 367, 380, 392, 403, 415, 428, 440, 452, 464, 476, 487, Porky Pig, Puffed Wheat, Story Hour Series #802, Super Book #14, 26 and Whitman Comic Books)

BUGS BUNNY (See Dell Giants for annuals)
Dell Publishing Co./Gold Key No. 86-218/Whitman No. 219 on: 1942 - No. 245, April, 1984

Large Feature Comic 8(1942)-(Rarely found in fine-mint condition)
300 600 900 1920 3310 4700
Four Color 33 ('43) 111 222 333 888 1994 3100
Four Color 51 36 72 108 259 580 900
Four Color 88 23 46 69 156 348 540
Four Color 123('46),142,164 15 30 45 105 233 360
Four Color 187,200,217,233 11 22 33 76 163 250
Four Color 250-Used in **SOTI**, pg. 309 12 24 36 79 170 260
Four Color 266,274,281,289,298('50) 9 18 27 61 123 185
Four Color 307,317(#1),327(#2),338,347,355,366,376,393
8 16 24 55 105 155
Four Color 407,420,432(10/52) 7 14 21 48 89 130

GD 2.0 | VG 4.0 | FN 6.0 | VF 8.0 | VF/NM 9.0 | NM- 9.2

Four Color 498(9/53),585(9/54), 647(9/55) 6 12 18 38 69 100
Four Color 724(9/56),838(9/57),1064(12/59) 5 10 15 34 60 85
28(12-1/52-53)-30 5 10 15 34 60 85
31-50 4 8 12 28 47 65
51-85(7-9/62) 4 8 12 23 37 50
86(10/62)-88-Bugs Bunny's Showtime-(25¢, 80pgs.) 5 10 15 35 63 90
89-99 3 6 9 16 24 32
100 3 6 9 17 26 35
101-118: 108-1st Honey Bunny. 118-Last 12¢ issue 3 6 9 14 19 24
119-140 2 4 6 11 16 20
141-170 2 4 6 9 12 15
171-218: 218-Publ. by Whitman only? 2 4 6 8 10 12
219,220,225-237(5/82): 229-Swipe of Barks story/WDC&S #223. 233(2/82)
2 4 6 8 10 12
221(9/80),222(11/80)-Pre-pack? (Scarce) 4 8 12 28 47 65
223 (1/81, 50¢-c), 224 (3/81)-Low distr. 3 6 9 14 20 25
223 (1/81, 40¢-c) Cover price error variant 3 6 9 17 26 35
238-245 (#90070 on-c, nd, nd code; pre-pack): 238(5/83), 239(6/83), 240(7/83), 241(7/83), 242(8/83), 243(8/83), 244(3/84), 245(4/84) 3 6 9 15 22 28
NOTE: *Reprints-100,102-104,110,115,123,143,144,147,167,173,175-177,179-185,187,190.*
nn (Xerox Pub. Comic Digest, 1971, 100 pages, B&W) collection of one-page gags 4 8 12 23 37 50
...Comic-Go-Round 11196-(224 pgs.)($1.95)(Golden Press, 1979)
4 8 12 25 40 55
...Winter Fun 1(12/67-Gold Key)-Giant 5 10 15 30 50 70

BUGS BUNNY
DC Comics: June, 1990 - No. 3, Aug, 1990 ($1.00, limited series)

1-3: Daffy Duck, Elmer Fudd, others app. 4.00

BUGS BUNNY (...Monthly on-c)
DC Comics: 1993 - No. 3, 1994? ($1.95)

1-3-Bugs, Porky Pig, Daffy, Road Runner 3.50

BUGS BUNNY (Digest-size reprint from Looney Tunes)
DC Comics: 2005 ($6.99, digest)

Vol. 1: What's Up Doc? - Reprints from Looney Tunes #37,41,43-45,48,52,55,57-59,63 7.00

BUGS BUNNY & PORKY PIG
Gold Key: Sept, 1965 (Paper-c, giant, 100 pgs.)

1(30025-509) 6 12 18 38 69 100

BUGS BUNNY'S ALBUM (See Bugs Bunny, Four Color No. 498,585,647,724)

BUGS BUNNY LIFE STORY ALBUM (See Bugs Bunny, Four Color No. 838)

BUGS BUNNY MERRY CHRISTMAS (See Bugs Bunny, Four Color No. 1064)

BUG! THE ADVENTURES OF FORAGER (From New Gods)
DC Comics (Young Animal): Jul, 2017 - No. 6, Feb, 2018 ($3.99)

1-6-Lee Allred-s/Mike Allred-a/c. 1-Sandman, Brute & Glob app. 2-G.A. Sandman, Sandy, Blue Beetle and The Losers app. 3-Atlas app. 5-Omac app. 4.00

BUILDING, THE
Kitchen Sink Press: 1987; 2000 (8 1/2" x 11" sepia toned graphic novel)

nn-Will Eisner-s/c/a 15.00
nn-(DC Comics, 9/00, $9.95) reprints 1987 edition 10.00

BULLET CROW, FOWL OF FORTUNE
Eclipse Comics: Mar, 1987 - No. 2, Apr, 1987 ($2.00, B&W, limited series)

1,2-The Comic Reader-r & new-a 3.00

BULLETMAN (See Fawcett Miniatures, Master Comics, Mighty Midget Comics, Nickel Comics & XMas Comics)
Fawcett Publications: Sum, 1941 - #12, 2/12/43; #14, Spr, 1946 - #16, Fall, 1946 (No #13)

1-Silver metallic-c 400 800 1200 2800 4900 7000
2-Raboy-c 177 354 531 1124 1937 2750
3,5-Raboy-c each 142 284 426 909 1555 2200
4 98 196 294 622 1074 1525
6,8-10: 10-Intro. Bulletdog 84 168 252 538 919 1300
7-Ghost Stories told by night watchman of cemetery begins; Eisnerish-a; hidden message "Chic Stone is a jerk". 94 188 282 597 1024 1450
11,12,14-16 (nn 13): 12-Robot-c 61 122 183 390 670 950
NOTE: ***Mac Raboy*** *c-1-3, 5, 6, 10. "Bulletman the Flying Detective" on cover #8 on.*

BULLET POINTS
Marvel Comics: Jan, 2007 - No. 5, May, 2007 ($2.99, limited series)

1-5: 1-Steve Rogers becomes Iron Man; Straczynski-s/Edwards-a. 4,5-Galactus app. 3.00
TPB (2007, $13.99) r/#1-5; layout pages by Edwards 14.00

Bullseye (2017 series) #4 © MAR

Burke's Law #1 © DELL

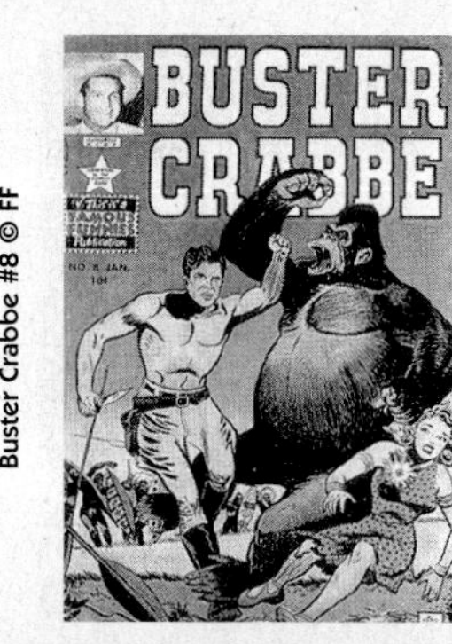

Buster Crabbe #8 © FF

GD VG FN VF VF/NM NM-
2.0 4.0 6.0 8.0 9.0 9.2

BULLETPROOF MONK (Inspired the 2003 film)
Image Comics (Flypaper Press): 1998 - No. 3, 1999 ($2.95, limited series)
1-3-Oeming-a 3.00
...: Tales of the BPM (3/03, $2.95) Flip book; 2 covers by Sale; art by Sale, Oeming, Dave Johnson; Seann William Scott afterword 3.00
TPB (2002, $9.95) r/#1-3; foreword by John Woo 10.00

BULLETS AND BRACELETS (Also see Marvel Versus DC #3 & DC Versus Marvel #4)
Marvel Comics (Amalgam): Apr, 1996 ($1.95)
1-John Ostrander script & Gary Frank-c/a 3.00

BULLSEYE (Daredevil villain)
Marvel Comics: Apr, 2017 - No. 5, Aug, 2017 ($4.99/$3.99, limited series)
1-($4.99) Brisson-s/Sanna-a; back-up with Wolfman-s/Morgan-a 5.00
2-5-($3.99) Brisson-s/Sanna-a 4.00

BULLS-EYE (Cody of The Pony Express No. 8 on)
Mainline No. 1-5/Charlton No. 6,7: 7-8/54-No. 5, 3-4/55; No. 6, 6/55; No. 7, 8/55
1-S&K-c, 2 pgs.-a 74 148 222 470 810 1150
2-S&K-c/a 54 108 162 343 574 825
3-5-S&K-c/a(2 each). 4-Last pre-code issue (1-2/55). 5-Censored issue with tomahawks removed in battle scene 45 90 135 284 480 675
6-S&K-c/a 40 80 120 246 411 575
7-S&K-c/a(3) 45 90 135 284 480 675

BULLS-EYE COMICS (Formerly Komik Pages #10; becomes Kayo #12)
Harry 'A' Chesler: No. 11, 1944
11-Origin K-9, Green Knight's sidekick, Lance; The Green Knight, Lady Satan, Yankee Doodle Jones app. 129 258 387 826 1413 2000

BULLSEYE: GREATEST HITS (Daredevil villain)
Marvel Comics: Nov, 2004 - No. 5, Mar, 2005 ($2.99, limted series)
1-5-Origin of Bullseye; Steve Dillon-a/Deodato-c. 3-Punisher app. 3.00
TPB (2005, $13.99) r/#1-5 14.00

BULLSEYE: PERFECT GAME (Daredevil villain)
Marvel Comics: Jan, 2011 - No. 2, Feb, 2011 ($3.99, limited series)
1,2-Huston-s/Martinbrough-a; Bullseye as baseball pitcher 4.00

BULLWHIP GRIFFIN (See Movie Comics)

BULLWINKLE (...and Rocky No. 22 on; See March of Comics #233 and Rocky & Bullwinkle) (TV) (Jay Ward)
Dell/Gold Key: 3-5/62 - #11, 4/74; #12, 6/76 - #19, 3/78; #20, 4/79 - #25, 2/80
Four Color 1270 (3-5/62) 16 32 48 110 243 375
01-090-209 (Dell, 7-9/62) 13 26 39 86 188 290
1(11/62, Gold Key) 12 24 36 80 173 265
2(2/63) 8 16 24 54 102 150
3(4/72)-11(4/74-Gold Key) 5 10 15 31 53 75
12-14: 12(6/76)-Reprints. 13(9/76), 14-New stories 3 6 9 17 26 35
15-25 2 4 6 11 16 20
Mother Moose Nursery Pomes 01-530-207 (5-7/62, Dell) 15 30 45 103 227 350
NOTE: *Reprints: 6, 7, 20-24.*

BULLWINKLE AND ROCKY (TV)
Charlton Comics: July, 1970 - No. 7, July, 1971
1-Has 1 pg. pin-up 6 12 18 40 73 105
2-7: 3-Snidely Whiplash app. 5 10 15 30 50 70

BULLWINKLE AND ROCKY
Star Comics/Marvel Comics No. 3 on: Nov, 1987 - No. 9, Mar, 1989
1-9: Boris & Natasha in all. 3,5,8-Dudley Do-Right app. 4-Reagan-c 5.00
Marvel Moosterworks (1/92, $4.95) 2 4 6 8 10 12

BUMMER
Fantagraphics Books: June, 1995 ($3.50, B&W, mature)
1 3.50

BUNNY (Also see Harvey Pop Comics and Fruitman Special)
Harvey Publications: Dec, 1966 - No. 20, Dec, 1971; No. 21, Nov, 1976
1-68 pg. Giants begin 7 14 21 49 92 135
2-10: 3-1st app. Fruitman. 6,8-10-Fruitman 4 8 12 28 47 65
11-18: 18-Last 68 pg. Giant 4 8 12 27 44 60
19-21-52 pg. Giants: 21-Fruitman app. 4 8 12 25 40 55

BURKE'S LAW (TV)
Dell Publ.: 1-3/64; No. 2, 5-7/64; No. 3, 3-5/65 (All have Gene Barry photo-c)
1-Photo-c 5 10 15 31 53 75
2,3-Photo-c 4 8 12 23 37 50

BURNING FIELDS
BOOM! Studios: Jan, 2015 - No. 8, Sept, 2015 ($3.99, limited series)
1-6-Moreci & Daniel-s/Lorimer-a 4.00

BURNING ROMANCES (See Fox Giants)

BUSTER BEAR
Quality Comics Group (Arnold Publ.): Dec, 1953 - No. 10, June, 1955
1-Funny animal 13 26 39 74 105 135
2 7 14 21 37 46 55
3-10 6 12 18 31 38 45
I.W. Reprint #9,10 (Super on inside) 2 4 6 9 13 16

BUSTER BROWN COMICS (See Promotional Comics section)

BUSTER BUNNY
Standard Comics(Animated Cartoons)/Pines: Nov, 1949 - No. 16, Oct, 1953
1-Frazetta 1 pg. text illo. 14 28 42 76 108 140
2 7 14 21 37 46 55
3-14,16 6 12 18 31 38 45
15-Racist-c 12 24 36 69 97 125

BUSTER CRABBE (TV)
Famous Funnies Publ.: Nov, 1951 - No. 12, 1953
1-1st app.(?) Frazetta anti-drug ad; text story about Buster Crabbe & Billy the Kid 40 80 120 246 411 575
2-Williamson/Evans-c; text story about Wild Bill Hickok & Pecos Bill 38 76 114 225 368 510
3-Williamson/Evans-c/a 39 78 117 240 395 550
4-Frazetta-c/a, 1pg.; bondage-c 61 122 183 390 670 950
5-Frazetta-c; Williamson/Krenkel/Orlando-a, 11pgs. (per Mr. Williamson) 161 322 483 1030 1765 2500
6,8 22 44 66 132 216 300
7-Frazetta one pg. ad 21 42 63 122 199 275
9-One pg. Frazetta Boy Scouts ad (1st?) 17 34 51 98 154 210
10-12 13 26 39 72 101 130
NOTE: Eastern Color sold 3 dozen each NM file copies of #s 9-12 a few years ago.

BUSTER CRABBE (The Amazing Adventures of...)(Movie star)
Lev Gleason Publications: Dec, 1953 - No. 4, June, 1954
1,4: 1-Photo-c. 4-Flash Gordon-c 22 44 66 130 213 295
2,3-Toth-a 20 40 60 114 182 250

BUTCH CASSIDY
Skywald Comics: June, 1971 - No. 3, Oct, 1971 (52 pgs.)
1-Pre-code reprints and new material; Red Mask reprint, retitled Maverick; Bolle-a; Sutton-a 3 6 9 15 22 28
2,3: 2-Whip Wilson-r. 3-Dead Canyon Days reprint/Crack Western No. 63; Sundance Kid app.; Crandall-a 2 4 6 10 14 18

BUTCH CASSIDY (...& the Wild Bunch)
Avon Periodicals: 1951
1-Kinstler-c/a 22 44 66 128 209 290
NOTE: ***Reinman** story; Issue number on inside spine.*

BUTCH CASSIDY (See Fun-In No. 11 & Western Adventure Comics)

BUTCHER, THE (Also see Brave and the Bold, 2nd Series)
DC Comics: May, 1990 - No. 5, Sept, 1990 ($1.50, mature)
1-5: 1-No indicia inside 3.00

BUTCHER KNIGHT
Image Comics (Top Cow): Jan, 2001 - No. 4, June, 2001 ($2.95, limited series)
Preview (B&W, 16 pgs.) Dwayne Turner-c/a 3.00
1-4-Dwayne Turner-c/a 3.00

BUTTERFLY
Archaia: Sept, 2014 - No. 4, Dec, 2014 ($3.99, limited series)
1-4: Phil Noto-c on all. 1-Marguerite Bennett-s/Antonio Fuso-a. 3,4-Simeone-a 4.00

BUZ SAWYER (Sweeney No. 4 on)
Standard Comics: June, 1948 - No. 3, 1949
1-Roy Crane-a 30 60 90 177 289 400
2-Intro his pal Sweeney 17 34 51 98 154 210
3 13 26 39 72 101 130

BUZ SAWYER'S PAL, ROSCOE SWEENEY (See Sweeney)

BUZZ, THE (Also see Spider-Girl)
Marvel Comics: July, 2000 - No. 3, Sept, 2000 ($2.99, limited series)

Buzzy #49 © DC

Cable #82 © MAR

Cage #9 © MAR

	GD 2.0	VG 4.0	FN 6.0	VF 8.0	VF/NM 9.0	NM- 9.2

1-3-Buscema-a/DeFalco & Frenz-s 3.00

BUZZARD (See The Goon)
Dark Horse Comics: Jun, 2010 - No. 3, Aug, 2010 ($3.50, limited series)

1-3-Eric Powell-c; Buzzard story w/Powell-s/a; Billy The Kid back-up; Powell-s/Hotz-a 3.50

BUZZ BUZZ COMICS MAGAZINE
Horse Press: May, 1996 ($4.95, B&W, over-sized magazine)

1-Paul Pope-c/a/scripts; Moebius-a 5.00

BUZZY (See All Funny Comics)
National Periodical Publications/Detective Comics: Winter, 1944-45 - No. 75, 1-2/57; No. 76, 10/57; No. 77, 10/58

	GD 2.0	VG 4.0	FN 6.0	VF 8.0	VF/NM 9.0	NM- 9.2
1 (52 pgs. begin); "America's favorite teenster"	39	78	117	240	395	550
2 (Spr, 1945)	21	42	63	122	199	275
3-5	16	32	48	94	147	200
6-10	14	28	42	82	121	160
11-20	14	28	42	76	108	140
21-30	12	24	36	69	97	125
31,35-38	11	22	33	62	86	110
32-34,39-Last 52 pgs. Scribbly story by Mayer in each (these four stories were done for Scribbly #14 which was delayed for a year)	12	24	36	67	94	120
40-77: 62-Last precode (2/55)	11	22	33	60	83	105

BUZZY THE CROW (See Harvey Comics Hits #60 & 62, Harvey Hits #18 & Paramount Animated Comics #1)

BY BIZARRE HANDS
Dark Horse Comics: Apr, 1994 - No. 3, June, 1994 ($2.50, B&W, mature)

1-3: Lansdale stories 3.00

CABBOT: BLOODHUNTER (Also see Bloodstrike & Bloodstrike: Assassin)
Maximum Press: Jan, 1997 ($2.50, one-shot)

1-Rick Veitch-a/script; Platt-c; Thor, Chapel & Prophet cameos 3.00

CABLE (See Ghost Rider &..., & New Mutants #87) (Title becomes Soldier X)
Marvel Comics: May, 1993 - No. 107, Sept, 2002 ($3.50/$1.95/$1.50-$2.25)

1-($3.50, 52 pgs.)-Gold foil & embossed-c; Thibert a-1-4p; c-1-3 5.00
2,4-15: 4-Liefeld-a assist; last Thibert-a(p). 6-8-Reveals that Baby Nathan is Cable; gives background on Stryfe. 9-Omega Red-c/story. 11-Bound-in trading card sheet 4.00

	GD 2.0	VG 4.0	FN 6.0	VF 8.0	VF/NM 9.0	NM- 9.2
3-1st Weasel; extra 16 pg. X-Men/Avengers ann. preview	1	2	3	5	6	8

16-Newsstand edition 3.00
16-Enhanced edition 5.00
17-20-($1.95)-Deluxe edition, 20-w/bound in '95 Fleer Ultra cards 4.00
17-20-($1.50)-Standard edition 3.00
21-24, 26-44, -1(7/97): 21-Begin $1.95-c; return from Age of Apocalyse. 24-Grizzly dies. 28-vs. Sugarman; Mr. Sinister app. 30-X-Man-c/app.; Exodus app. 31-vs. X-Man. 32-Post app. 33-Post-c/app; Mandarin app (flashback); includes "Onslaught Update". 34-Onslaught x-over; Hulk-c/app; Apocalypse app. (cont'd in Hulk #444). 35-Onslaught x-over; Apocalypse vs. Cable. 36-w/card insert. 38-Weapon X-c/app; Psycho Man & Micronauts app. 40-Scott Clark-a(p). 41-Bishop-c/app. 3.00
25 ($3.95)-Foil gatefold-c 5.00
45-49,51-74: 45-Operation Zero Tolerance. 51-1st Casey-s. 54-Black Panther. 55-Domino-c/app. 62-Nick Fury-c/app.63-Stryfe-c/app. 67,68-Avengers-c/app. 71,73-Liefeld-a 3.00
50-($2.99) Double sized w/wraparound-c 4.00
75 -($2.99) Liefeld-c/a; Apocalypse: The Twelve x-over 4.00
76-79: 76-Apocalypse: The Twelve x-over 3.00
80-96: 80-Begin $2.25-c. 87-Mystique-c/app. 3.00
97-99,101-107: 97-Tischman-s/Kordey-a/c begin 3.00
100-($3.99) Dialogue-free 'Nuff Said back-up story 4.00
... Classic Vol. 1 TPB (2008, $29.99) r/#1-4, New Mutants #87, Cable: Blood & Metal #1,2 30.00
.../Machine Man '98 Annual ($2.99) Wraparound-c 4.00
.../X-Force '96 Annual ($2.95) Wraparound-c 4.00
...'99 Annual ($3.50) vs. Sinister; computer photo-c 4.00
...Second Genesis 1 (9/99, $3.99) r/New Mutants #99, 100 and X-Force #1; Liefeld-c 4.00
...: The End (2002, $14.99, TPB) r/#101-107 15.00

CABLE
Marvel Comics: May, 2008 - No. 25, Jun, 2010 ($2.99/$3.99)

1-23: 1-10-Olivetti-c/a. 1-Liefeld var-c. 2-Finch var-c. 3-Romita Jr. var-c. 4-Bishop app.; Djurdjevic var-c. 5-Silvestri var-c. 6-Liefeld var-c. 13-15-Messiah War x-over; Deadpool app. 16,17-Gulacy-a 3.00
24-($3.99) Bishop app. 4.00

	GD 2.0	VG 4.0	FN 6.0	VF 8.0	VF/NM 9.0	NM- 9.2
25-($3.99) Deadpool app.; Medina-a	1	2	3	5	6	8

CABLE
Marvel Comics: Jul, 2017 - No. 5, Nov, 2017; No. 150, Dec, 2017 - Present ($3.99)

1-5: 1-Robinson-s/Pacheco-a. 4,5-Cinar-a. 4-Rasputin app. 4.00

[Title switches to legacy numbering after #5 (11/17)]

150-154-The Externals app. 4.00

CABLE AND X-FORCE (Marvel NOW!)
Marvel Comics: Feb, 2013 - Present ($3.99)

1-19: 1-Hopeless-s/Larroca-a; Cable, Colossus, Domino, Forge & Dr. Nemesis team 4.00

CABLE - BLOOD AND METAL (Also see New Mutants #87 & X-Force #8)
Marvel Comics: Oct, 1992 - No. 2, Nov, 1992 ($2.50, limited series, 52 pgs.)

1-Fabian Nicieza scripts; John Romita, Jr.-c/a in both; Cable vs. Stryfe; 2nd app. of The Wild Pack (becomes The Six Pack); wraparound-c 5.00
2-Prelude to X-Cutioner's Song 5.00

CABLE/DEADPOOL ("Cable & Deadpool" on cover)
Marvel Comics: May, 2004 - No. 50, Apr, 2008 ($2.99)

	GD 2.0	VG 4.0	FN 6.0	VF 8.0	VF/NM 9.0	NM- 9.2
1-Nicieza-s/Liefeld-c	4	8	12	27	44	60
2,3	1	3	4	6	8	10

4-23,25-37: 7-9-X-Men app. 17-House of M. 21-Heroes For Hire app. 30,31-Civil War. 30-Great Lakes Avengers app. 33-Liefeld-c 5.00

	GD 2.0	VG 4.0	FN 6.0	VF 8.0	VF/NM 9.0	NM- 9.2
24-Spider-Man app.	1	3	4	6	8	10
38-1st Bob, Agent of HYDRA	2	4	6	13	18	22

39-49: 43,44-Wolverine app. 4.00

	GD 2.0	VG 4.0	FN 6.0	VF 8.0	VF/NM 9.0	NM- 9.2
50-($3.99) Final issue; Spider-Man and the Avengers app.	2	4	6	10	14	18

Cable & Deadpool MCG 1 (7/11, $1.00) r/#1 with "Marvel's Greatest Comics" cover logo 3.00
... Vol. 1: If Looks Could Kill TPB (2004, $14.99) r/#1-6 15.00
... Vol. 2: The Burnt Offering TPB (2005, $14.99) r/#7-12 15.00
... Vol. 3: The Human Race TPB (2005, $14.99) r/#13-18 15.00
... Vol. 4: Bosom Buddies TPB (2006, $14.99) r/#19-24 15.00
... Vol. 5: Living Legends TPB (2006, $13.99) r/#25-29 14.00
... Vol. 6: Paved With Good Intentions TPB (2007, $14.99) r/#30-35 15.00
... Vol. 7: Separation Anxiety TPB (2007, $17.99) r/#36-42; sketch pages 18.00
Deadpool Vs. The Marvel Universe TPB (2008, $24.99) r/#43-50 25.00

CADET GRAY OF WEST POINT (See Dell Giants)

CADILLACS & DINOSAURS (TV)
Marvel Comics (Epic Comics): Nov, 1990 - No. 6, Apr, 1991 ($2.50, limited series)

1-6: r/Xenozoic Tales in color w/new-c 3.00
...In 3-D #1 (7/92, $3.95, Kitchen Sink)-With glasses 6.00

CADILLACS AND DINOSAURS (TV)
Topps Comics: V2#1, Feb, 1994 - V2#9, 1995 ($2.50, limited series)

V2#1-($2.95)-Collector's edition w/Stout-c & bound-in poster; Buckler-a; foil stamped logo; Giordano-a in all 6.00
V2#1-9: 1-Newsstand edition w/Giordano-c. 2,3-Collector's editions w/Stout-c & posters. 2,3-Newsstand ed. w/Giordano-c; w/o posters. 4-6-Collectors & Newsstand editions; Kieth-c. 7-9-Linsner-c 3.00

CAGE (Also see Hero for Hire, Power Man & Punisher)
Marvel Comics: Apr, 1992 - No. 20, Nov, 1993 ($1.25)

1,3,10,12: 3-Punisher-c & minor app. 10-Rhino & Hulk-c/app. 12-(52 pgs.)-Iron Fist app. 4.00
2,4-9,11,13-20: 9-Rhino-c/story; Hulk cameo 3.00

CAGE (Volume 3)
Marvel Comics (MAX): Mar, 2002 - No. 5, Sept, 2002 ($2.99, mature)

1-5-Corben-c/a; Azzarello-s 3.00
HC (2002, $19.99, with dustjacket) r/#1-5; intro. by Darius James; sketch pages 20.00
SC (2003, $13.99) r/#1-5; intro. by Darius James 14.00

CAGE! (Luke Cage)
Marvel Comics: Dec, 2016 - No. 4, Mar, 2017 ($3.99, limited series)

1-4-Genndy Tartakovsky-s/a; set in 1977 4.00

CAGED HEAT 3000 (Movie)
Roger Corman's Cosmic Comics: Nov, 1995 - No. 3, Jan, 1996 ($2.50)

1-3: Adaptation of film 3.00

CAGE HERO
Dynamite Entertainment: 2015 - No. 4, 2016 ($3.99, limited series)

1-4-Kevin Eastman & Ian Parker-s/Renalto Rei-a 4.00

CAGES
Tundra Publ.: 1991 - No. 10, May, 1996 ($3.50/$3.95/$4.95, limited series)

	GD 2.0	VG 4.0	FN 6.0	VF 8.0	VF/NM 9.0	NM- 9.2
1-Dave McKean-c/a in all	2	4	6	8	10	12
2-Misprint exists	1	2	3	5	6	8

3-9: 5-$3.95-c begins 4.00
10-($4.95) 5.00

Calling All Boys #8 © PMI

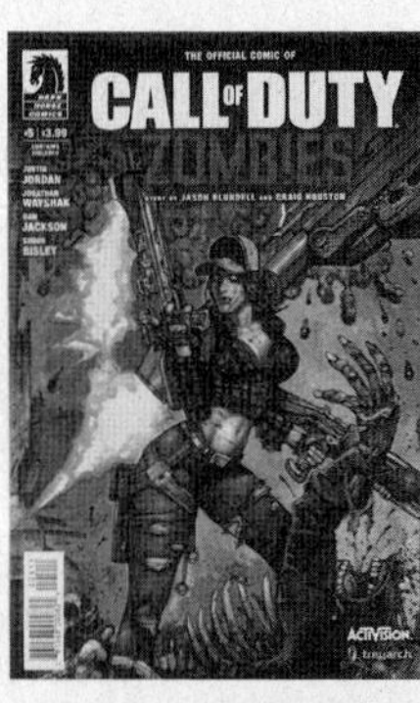

Call of Duty: Zombies #5 © Activision

Campus Romances #2 © AVON

CAIN'S HUNDRED (TV)
Dell Publishing Co.: May-July, 1962 - No. 2, Sept-Nov, 1962

	GD 2.0	VG 4.0	FN 6.0	VF 8.0	VF/NM 9.0	NM- 9.2
nn(01-094-207)	3	6	9	19	30	40
2	3	6	9	15	22	28

CAIN/VAMPIRELLA FLIP BOOK
Harris Comics: Oct, 1994 ($6.95, one-shot, squarebound)

	GD 2.0	VG 4.0	FN 6.0	VF 8.0	VF/NM 9.0	NM- 9.2
nn-contains Cain #3 & #4; flip book is r/Vampirella story from 1993 Creepy Fearbook	1	2	3	5	7	9

CALIBER PRESENTS
Caliber Press: Jan, 1989 - No. 24, 1991 ($1.95/$2.50, B&W, 52 pgs.)

	GD 2.0	VG 4.0	FN 6.0	VF 8.0	VF/NM 9.0	NM- 9.2
1-Anthology; 1st app. The Crow; Tim Vigil-c/a	9	18	27	59	117	175
2-Deadworld story; Tim Vigil-a	2	4	6	10	14	18
3-24: 15-24 ($3.50, 68 pgs.)						4.00

CALIBER PRESENTS: CINDERELLA ON FIRE
Caliber Press: 1994 ($2.95, B&W, mature)

	GD 2.0	VG 4.0	FN 6.0	VF 8.0	VF/NM 9.0	NM- 9.2
1						3.00

CALIBER SPOTLIGHT
Caliber Press: May, 1995 ($2.95, B&W)

	GD 2.0	VG 4.0	FN 6.0	VF 8.0	VF/NM 9.0	NM- 9.2
1-Kabuki app						3.50

CALIFORNIA GIRLS
Eclipse Comics: June, 1987 - No. 8, May, 1988 ($2.00, 40 pgs, B&W)

	GD 2.0	VG 4.0	FN 6.0	VF 8.0	VF/NM 9.0	NM- 9.2
1-8: All contain color paper dolls						4.00

CALL, THE
Marvel Comics: June, 2003 - No. 4, Sept, 2003 ($2.25)

	GD 2.0	VG 4.0	FN 6.0	VF 8.0	VF/NM 9.0	NM- 9.2
1-4-Austen-s/Olliffe-a						3.00

CALLING ALL BOYS (Tex Granger No. 18 on)
Parents' Magazine Institute: Jan, 1946 - No. 17, May, 1948 (Photo c-1-5,7,8)

	GD 2.0	VG 4.0	FN 6.0	VF 8.0	VF/NM 9.0	NM- 9.2
1	18	36	54	107	169	230
2-Contains Roy Rogers article	11	22	33	62	86	110
3-7,9,11,14-17: 6-Painted-c. 11-Rin Tin Tin photo on-c; Tex Granger begins. 14-J. Edgar Hoover photo on-c. 15-Tex Granger-c begin	9	18	27	52	69	85
8-Milton Caniff story	11	22	33	62	86	110
10-Gary Cooper photo on-c	11	22	33	62	86	110
12-Bob Hope photo on-c	15	30	45	86	133	180
13-Bing Crosby photo on-c	14	28	42	81	118	155

CALLING ALL GIRLS
Parents' Magazine Institute: Sept, 1941 - No. 89, Sept, 1949 (Part magazine, part comic)

	GD 2.0	VG 4.0	FN 6.0	VF 8.0	VF/NM 9.0	NM- 9.2
1-Photo-c	26	52	78	154	252	350
2-Photo-c	14	28	42	82	121	160
3-Shirley Temple photo-c	19	38	57	112	179	245
4-10: 4,5,7,9-Photo-c. 9-Flag-c	13	26	39	72	101	130
11-Tina Thayer photo-c; Mickey Rooney photo-b/c; B&W photo inside of Gary Cooper as Lou Gehrig in "Pride of Yankees"	14	28	42	81	118	155
12-20	10	20	30	58	79	100
21-39,41-43(10-11/45)-Last issue with comics	10	20	30	54	72	90
40-Liz Taylor photo-c	28	56	84	165	270	375
44-51(7/46)-Last comic book size issue	9	18	27	47	61	75
52-89	8	16	24	42	54	65

NOTE: ***Jack Sparling*** *art in many issues; becomes a girls' magazine "Senior Prom" with #90.*

CALLING ALL KIDS (Also see True Comics)
Parents' Magazine Institute: Dec-Jan, 1945-46 - No. 26, Aug, 1949

	GD 2.0	VG 4.0	FN 6.0	VF 8.0	VF/NM 9.0	NM- 9.2
1-Funny animal	18	36	54	105	165	225
2	11	22	33	62	86	110
3-10	9	18	27	52	69	85
11-26	9	18	27	47	61	75

CALL OF DUTY: BLACK OPS III (Based on the Activision video game)
Dark Horse Comics: Nov, 2015 - No. 6, Oct, 2016 ($3.99, limited series)

	GD 2.0	VG 4.0	FN 6.0	VF 8.0	VF/NM 9.0	NM- 9.2
1-6-Prequel to the game; Hama-s/Ferreira-a						4.00

CALL OF DUTY: ZOMBIES (Based on the Activision video game)
Dark Horse Comics: Oct, 2016 - No. 6, Aug, 2017 ($3.99, limited series)

	GD 2.0	VG 4.0	FN 6.0	VF 8.0	VF/NM 9.0	NM- 9.2
1-6-Justin Jordan-s/Jonathan Wayshak-a/Simon Bisley-c						4.00

CALL OF DUTY, THE : THE BROTHERHOOD
Marvel Comics: Aug, 2002 - No. 6, Jan, 2003 ($2.25)

	GD 2.0	VG 4.0	FN 6.0	VF 8.0	VF/NM 9.0	NM- 9.2
1-Exploits of NYC Fire Dept.; Finch-c/a; Austen & Bruce Jones-s						4.00
2-6-Austen-s						3.00
...Vol 1: The Brotherhood & The Wagon TPB (2002, $14.99) r/#1-6 & ...The Wagon #1-4						15.00

CALL OF DUTY, THE : THE PRECINCT
Marvel Comics: Sept, 2002 - No. 5, Jan, 2003 ($2.25, limited series)

	GD 2.0	VG 4.0	FN 6.0	VF 8.0	VF/NM 9.0	NM- 9.2
1-Exploits of NYC Police Dept.; Finch-c; Bruce Jones-s/Mandrake-a						3.00
2-4						3.00
...Vol 2: The Precinct TPB (2003, $9.99) r/#1-4						10.00

CALL OF DUTY, THE : THE WAGON
Marvel Comics: Oct, 2002 - No. 4, Jan, 2003 ($2.25, limited series)

	GD 2.0	VG 4.0	FN 6.0	VF 8.0	VF/NM 9.0	NM- 9.2
1-4-Exploits of NYC EMS Dept.; Finch-c; Austen-s/Zelzej-a						3.00

CALVIN (See Li'l Kids)

CALVIN & THE COLONEL (TV)
Dell Publishing Co.: No. 1354, Apr-June, 1962 - No. 2, July-Sept, 1962

	GD 2.0	VG 4.0	FN 6.0	VF 8.0	VF/NM 9.0	NM- 9.2
Four Color 1354(#1) (The last Four Color issue)	8	16	24	54	102	150
2	5	10	15	35	63	90

CAMELOT 3000
DC Comics: Dec, 1982 - No. 11, July, 1984; No. 12, Apr, 1985 (Direct sales, maxi series, Mando paper)

	GD 2.0	VG 4.0	FN 6.0	VF 8.0	VF/NM 9.0	NM- 9.2
1-12: 1-Mike Barr scripts & Brian Bolland-c/a begin. 5-Intro Knights of New Camelot						5.00
TPB (1988, $12.95) r/#1-12						15.00
...: The Deluxe Edition (2008, $34.99, HC) r/#1-12; oversized & recolored; Barr intro.; design and promotional art; original proposal page						40.00

NOTE: ***Austin*** *a-7i-12i.* ***Bolland*** *a-1-12p; c-1-12.*

CAMERA COMICS
U.S. Camera Publishing Corp./ME: July, 1944 - No. 9, Summer, 1946

	GD 2.0	VG 4.0	FN 6.0	VF 8.0	VF/NM 9.0	NM- 9.2
nn (7/44)	39	78	117	231	378	525
nn (9/44)	27	54	81	158	259	360
1(10/44)-The Grey Comet (slightly smaller page size than subsequent issues); WWII-c	31	62	93	186	303	420
2-16 pgs. of photos with 32 pgs. of comics	20	40	60	117	189	260
3-Nazi WW II-c; photos	26	52	78	154	252	350
4-9: All 1/3 photos	17	34	51	98	154	210

CAMP CANDY (TV)
Marvel Comics: May, 1990 - No. 6, Oct, 1990 ($1.00, limited series)

	GD 2.0	VG 4.0	FN 6.0	VF 8.0	VF/NM 9.0	NM- 9.2
1-6: Post-c/a(p); featuring John Candy						5.00

CAMP COMICS
Dell Publishing Co.: Feb, 1942 - No. 3, April, 1942 (All have photo-c)(All issues are scarce)

	GD 2.0	VG 4.0	FN 6.0	VF 8.0	VF/NM 9.0	NM- 9.2
1- "Seaman Sy Wheeler" by Kelly, 7 pgs.; Bugs Bunny app.; Mark Twain adaptation	90	180	270	576	988	1400
2-Kelly-a, 12 pgs.; Bugs Bunny app.; classic-c	90	180	270	576	988	1400
3-(Scarce)-Dave Berg & Walt Kelly-a	63	126	189	403	689	975

CAMP RUNAMUCK (TV)
Dell Publishing Co.: Apr, 1966

	GD 2.0	VG 4.0	FN 6.0	VF 8.0	VF/NM 9.0	NM- 9.2
1-Photo-c	3	6	9	21	33	45

CAMPUS LOVES
Quality Comics Group (Comic Magazines): Dec, 1949 - No. 5, Aug, 1950

	GD 2.0	VG 4.0	FN 6.0	VF 8.0	VF/NM 9.0	NM- 9.2
1-Ward-c/a (9 pgs.)	40	80	120	246	411	575
2-Ward-c/a	32	64	96	188	307	425
3-5	17	34	51	100	158	215

NOTE: ***Gustavson*** *a-1-5. Photo c-3-5.*

CAMPUS ROMANCE (...Romances on cover)
Avon Periodicals/Realistic: Sept-Oct, 1949 - No. 3, Feb-Mar, 1950

	GD 2.0	VG 4.0	FN 6.0	VF 8.0	VF/NM 9.0	NM- 9.2
1-Walter Johnson-a; c-/Avon paperback #348	43	86	129	271	461	650
2-Grandenetti-a; c-/Avon paperback #151	30	60	90	177	289	400
3-c-/Avon paperback #201	30	60	90	177	289	400
Realistic reprint	16	32	48	94	147	200

CANADA DRY PREMIUMS (See Swamp Fox, The & Terry & The Pirates in the Promotional Comics section)

CANCELLED COMIC CAVALCADE (See the Promotional Comics section)

CANDID TALES (Also see Bold Stories & It Rhymes With Lust)
Kirby Publ. Co.: April, 1950; June, 1950 (Digest size) (144 pgs.) (Full color)

	GD 2.0	VG 4.0	FN 6.0	VF 8.0	VF/NM 9.0	NM- 9.2
nn-(Scarce) Contains Wood female pirate story, 15 pgs., and 14 pgs. in June issue; Powell-a	181	362	543	1158	1979	2800

NOTE: *Another version exists with Dr. Kilmore by Wood; no female pirate story.*

CANDY (Teen-age)(Also see Police Comics #37)
Quality Comics Group (Comic Magazines): Autumn, 1947 - No. 64, Jul, 1956

	GD 2.0	VG 4.0	FN 6.0	VF 8.0	VF/NM 9.0	NM- 9.2
1-Gustavson-a	32	64	96	188	307	425
2-Gustavson-a	15	30	45	90	140	190
3-10	11	22	33	64	90	115

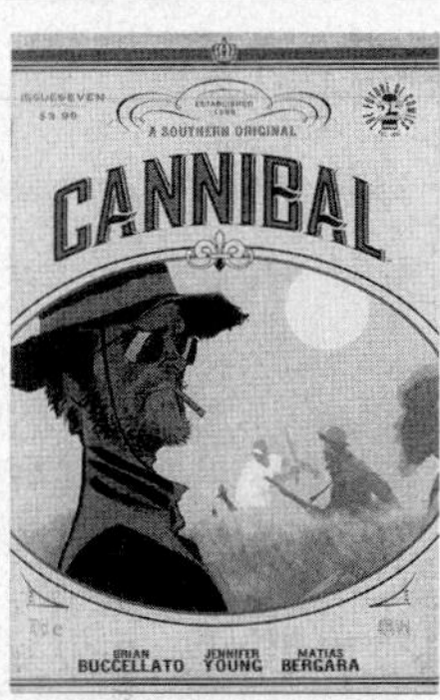

Cannibal #7 © Young & Buccellato

The Cape: 1969 #3 © Joe Hill

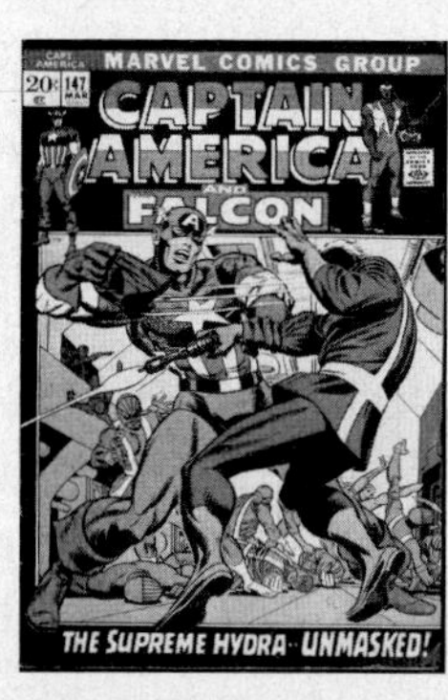

Captain America #147 © MAR

	GD	VG	FN	VF	VF/NM	NM-
	2.0	4.0	6.0	8.0	9.0	9.2

11-30 9 18 27 52 69 85
31-64: 64-Ward-c(p)? 8 16 24 42 54 65
Super Reprint No. 2,10,12,16,17,18('63- '64):17-Candy #12
2 4 6 10 14 18
NOTE: *Jack Cole 1-2 pg. art in many issues.*

CANDY COMICS
William H. Wise & Co.: Fall, 1944 - No. 3, Spring, 1945
1-Two Scoop Scuttle stories by Wolverton 40 80 120 246 411 575
2,3-Scoop Scuttle by Wolverton, 2-4 pgs. 26 52 78 154 252 350

CANNON (See Heroes, Inc. Presents Cannon)

CANNIBAL
Image Comics: Oct, 2016 - No. 8, Oct, 2017 ($3.99)
1-8-Young & Buccellato-s/Bergara-a 4.00

CANNON: DAWN OF WAR (Michael Turner's...)
Aspen MLT, Inc.: Nov, 2004 ($2.99)
1-Turnbull-a; two covers by Turnbull and Turner 3.00

CANNONBALL COMICS
Rural Home Publishing Co.: Feb, 1945 - No. 2, Mar, 1945
1-The Crash Kid, Thunderbrand, The Captive Prince & Crime Crusader begin; skull-c
148 296 444 947 1624 2300
2-Devil-c 116 232 348 742 1271 1800

CANTEEN KATE (See All Picture All True Love Story & Fightin' Marines)
St. John Publishing Co.: June, 1952 - No. 3, Nov, 1952
1-Matt Baker-c/a 87 174 261 553 952 1350
2-Matt Baker-c/a 53 106 159 334 567 800
3-(Rare)-Used in **POP**, pg. 75; Baker-c/a 61 122 183 390 670 950

CAPE, THE
IDW Publishing: Dec, 2010; Jul, 2011 - No. 4, Jan, 2012 ($3.99)
1-(12/10) Zach Howard-c/a; Jason Ciaramella-s 4.00
1-4: 1-(7/11) Story continues from 12/10 issue 4.00
...: Legacy Edition (6/11, $5.99) r/#1 (12/10) with Joe Hill's original short story 6.00
...: 1969 (7/12 - No. 4, 10/12, $3.99) 1-4-Ciaramella-s; origin in Vietnam 4.00

CAPER
DC Comics: Dec, 2003 - No. 12, Nov, 2004 ($2.95, limited series)
1-12: 1-4-Judd Winick-s/Farel Dalrymple-a. 5-8-John Severin-a. 9-12-Fowler-a 3.00

CAPES
Image Comics: Sept, 2003 - No. 3, Nov, 2003 ($3.50)
1-Robert Kirkman-s; 5 pg. preview of The Walking Dead #1
3 6 9 21 33 45
2,3-Robert Kirkman-s/Mark Englert-a/c 3.50

CAP'N QUICK & A FOOZLE (Also see Eclipse Mag. & Monthly)
Eclipse Comics: July, 1984 - No. 3, Nov, 1985 ($1.50, color, Baxter paper)
1-3-Rogers-c/a 3.00

CAPTAIN ACTION (Toy)
National Periodical Publications: Oct-Nov, 1968 - No. 5, June-July, 1969 (Based on Ideal toy)
1-Origin; Wally Wood-a; Superman-c app. 6 12 18 41 76 110
2,3,5-Gil Kane/Wally Wood-a 5 10 15 31 53 75
4- Gil Kane-c 4 8 12 27 44 60

CAPTAIN ACTION CAT: THE TIMESTREAM CATASTROPHE
Dynamite Entertainment: 2014 - No. 4, 2014 ($3.99, limited series)
1-4-Art Baltazar-s/a; Franco & Smits-s; all ages cat version of Capt. Action characters; Ghost, X, Captain Midnight, Skyman & The Occultist app. 4.00

CAPTAIN ACTION COMICS (Toy)
Moonstone: No. 0, 2008 - Present (Based on the Ideal toy)
0-($1.99) Origin re-told; Sparacio-a; three covers; character history by Michael Eury 3.00
1-5: 1-($3.99) Sparacio-a; intro. by Jim Shooter 4.00
... Comics Special 1 (2010, $5.99) 3 covers by Barreto, Ordway & Spiegle 6.00
... Exclusive Special 1 (2011, no price) Gulacy-c; Barreto-a 4.00
...: First Mission, Last Day (2008, $3.99) origin story re-told; Nicieza-s/Procopio-a 4.00
... King Size Special 1 (2011, $6.99) 1-Covers by Byrne, Wheatley & M. Benes 7.00
... Season 2 (2010, $3.99) 1-3: 1-Covers by Allred & Texiera; Obama app. 4.00
... Winter Special (2011, $4.99) Green Hornet & Kato on-c & text story 5.00

CAPTAIN AERO COMICS (Samson No. 1-6; also see Veri Best Sure Fire & Veri Best Sure Shot Comics)
Holyoke Publishing Co.: V1#7(#1), Dec, 1941 - V2#4(#10), Jan, 1943; V3#9(#11), Sept, 1943 -V4#3(#17), Oct, 1944; #21, Dec, 1944 - #26, Aug, 1946 (No #18-20)
V1#7(#1)-Flag-Man & Solar, Master of Magic, Captain Aero, Cap Stone, Adventurer begin; Nazi WWII-c 206 412 618 1318 2259 3200
8,10: 8(#2)-Pals of Freedom app. 10(#4)-Origin The Gargoyle; Kubert-a
100 200 300 635 1093 1550
9(#3)-Hitler-sty; Catman back-c; Alias X begins; Pals of Freedom app.; Nazi WWII-c
113 226 339 718 1234 1750
11,12(#5,6)-Kubert-a; Miss Victory in #6 81 162 243 518 884 1250
V2#1,2(#7,8): 8-Origin The Red Cross; Miss Victory app.; Brodsky-c(i)
63 126 189 403 689 975
3(#9)-Miss Victory app. 110 220 330 704 1202 1700
4(#10)-Miss Victory app.; Japanese WWII-c 97 194 291 621 1061 1500
V3#9 - V3#12(#11-14): All Quinlan Japanese WWII-c. 9-Miss Victory app.
81 162 243 518 884 1250
V3#13(#15),V4#2(#16): Schomburg Japanese WWII-c. 13-Miss Victory app.
97 194 291 621 1061 1500
V4#3(#17)-Miss Victory app.; L.B. Cole Japanese WWII-c
71 142 213 454 777 1100
21-24-L.B. Cole Japanese WWII covers. 22-Intro/origin Mighty Mite
60 120 180 381 653 925
25-L.B. Cole Sci-fi-c 74 148 222 470 810 1150
26-L.B. Cole Sci-fi-c; Palais-a(2) (scarce) 239 478 717 1530 2615 3700
NOTE: ***L.B. Cole** c-17, 21-26. **Hollingsworth** a-23. **Infantino** a-23, 26. **Schomburg** c-15, 16.*

CAPTAIN AMERICA (See Adventures of..., All-Select, All Winners, Aurora, Avengers #4, Blood and Glory, Captain Britain 16-20, Giant-Size..., The Invaders, Marvel Double Feature, Marvel Fanfare, Marvel Mystery, Marvel Super-Action, Marvel Super Heroes V2#3, Marvel Team-Up, Marvel Treasury Special, Power Record Comics, Ultimates, USA Comics, Young Allies & Young Men)

CAPTAIN AMERICA (Formerly Tales of Suspense #1-99) (Captain America and the Falcon #134-223 & Steve Rogers: Captain America #444-454 appears on cover only)
Marvel Comics Group: No. 100, Apr, 1968 - No. 454, Aug, 1996
100-Flashback on Cap's revival with Avengers & Sub-Mariner; story continued from Tales of Suspense #99; Kirby-c/a begins 50 100 150 350 638 925
101-The Sleeper-c/story; Red Skull app. 9 18 27 60 120 180
102-104: 102-Sleeper-c/s. 103,104-Red Skull-c/sty 7 14 21 48 89 130
105-108: 107-Red Skull & Hitler-c 6 12 18 37 66 95
109-Origin Capt. America retold in detail 9 18 27 60 120 180
109-2nd printing (1994) 2 4 6 8 10 12
110-Rick Jones dons Bucky's costume & becomes Cap's partner; Hulk x-over; Steranko-a Classic Steranko-c 10 20 30 68 144 220
111,113-Classic Steranko-c/a: 111-Death of Steve Rogers. 113-Cap's funeral; Avengers app.
9 18 27 60 120 180
112-S.A. recovery retold; last Kirby-c/a 6 12 18 41 76 110
114-116,119,120: 114-Red Skull Cosmic Cube story. 115,116-Red Skull app; last 12¢ issue. 119-Cap vs. Red Skull; Cosmic Cube "destroyed"; Falcon app.
4 8 12 28 47 65
117-1st app. The Falcon (9/69) 27 54 81 194 435 675
118-2nd app. The Falcon 8 16 24 55 105 155
121-136,139,140: 121-Retells origin; Avengers app. 122-Cap vs. Scorpion. 124-Modok app. 125-Mandarin app. 129-Red Skull app. 133-The Falcon becomes Cap's partner; origin Modok. 139,140-Grey Gargoyle app; origin in #140
3 6 9 21 33 45
137,138-Spider-Man x-over 4 8 12 27 44 60
141,142-Grey Gargoyle app. 141-Last Stan Lee issue. 142-Last 15¢ issue
3 6 9 17 26 35
143-(52 pgs) Cap vs. Red Skull 4 8 12 23 37 50
144-New costume Falcon 3 6 9 19 30 40
145-152: 145-147-Cap vs. the Supreme Hydra. 148-Red Skull app. 151,152- Cap vs. Mr. Hyde 3 6 9 14 20 25
153-155: 153-1st brief app. Jack Monroe; return of 1950s Captain America. 154-1st full app. Jack Monroe (Nomad); 1950s Captain America and Avengers app. 155-Origin retold; origin Jack Monroe and the 1950s Captain America
3 6 9 19 30 40
156-Cap vs. the 1950s Captain America; Jack Monroe app; classic Cap vs Cap cover
3 6 9 16 23 30
157-170,177-179: 160-1st app. Solarr. 161,162-Peggy Carter app. 163-1st Serpent Squad: Viper, Eel and Cobra. 164-1st Nightshade. 165-167-Cap vs. Yellow Claw. 168-1st Helmut Zemo (as the Phoenix). 169,170-Vs. original Moonstone
2 4 6 9 12 15
171-Black Panther app. 3 6 9 19 30 40
172,173: X-Men x-over 3 6 9 16 23 30
174,175: X-Men x-over 2 4 6 18 22 25
176-End of Cap. Avengers app. 2 4 6 13 18 22
180-Intro/origin of Nomad (Steve Rogers) 3 6 9 17 26 35
181-Intro/origin new Cap. 2 4 6 11 16 20
182,184,185,187-192: 182,184,185-Red Skull app. 189,190-Cap vs. Nightshade.

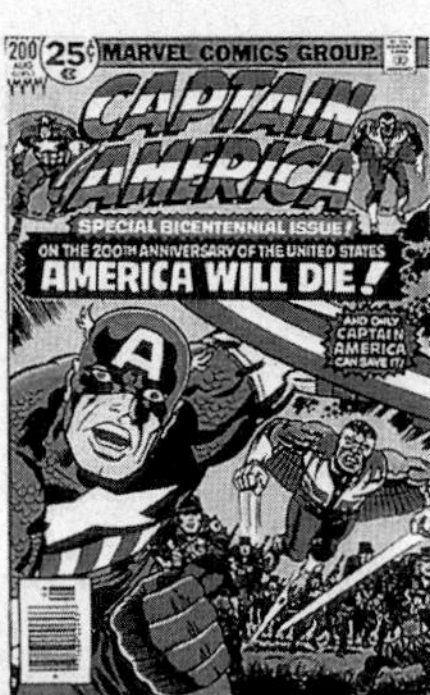

Captain America #200 © MAR

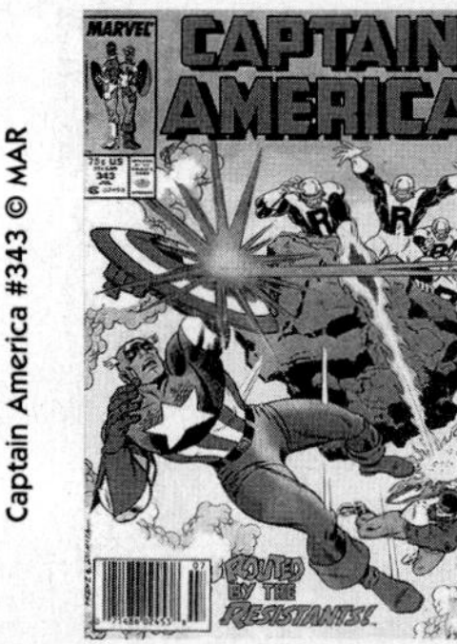

Captain America #343 © MAR

Captain America V2 #13 © MAR

GD 2.0 | VG 4.0 | FN 6.0 | VF 8.0 | VF/NM 9.0 | NM- 9.2

191-Iron Man app. 192-Intro Dr. Karla Sofen (later becomes Moonstone) 2 4 6 8 10 12
183-Death of new Cap; Steve Rogers drops Nomad I.D; returns to being Capt. America 2 4 6 9 12 15
186-True origin The Falcon; Red Skull app. 2 4 6 11 16 20
193-Kirby-c/a begins 3 6 9 16 23 30
194-199-(Regular 25¢ edition)(4-7/76) 2 4 6 10 14 18
196-199-(30¢-c variants, limited distribution) 5 10 15 33 57 80
200-(Regular 25¢ edition)(8/76) 2 4 6 11 16 20
200-(30¢-c variant, limited distribution) 5 10 15 35 63 90
201-214-Kirby-c/a. 208-1st Arnim Zola. 209,210- Arnim Zola app. 210-212 –vs Red Skull 2 4 6 8 11 14
210-214-(35¢-c variants, limited dist.)(6-10/77) 9 18 27 61 123 185
215,216,218-229: 215-Origin retold. 216-r/Strange Tales #114. 226,227-Red Skull app. 228-Cap vs. Constrictor. 229-Marvel Man app. 1 2 4 5 6 9
217-Intro. Marvel Boy (Wendell Vaughan); becomes Marvel Man in #218; later becomes Quasar (2/78) 5 10 15 31 53 75
230,235: 230-Battles Hulk-c/story cont'd in Inc. Hulk #232. 235-(7/79) Daredevil x-over; Miller-a(p) 1 2 4 5 7 10
231-233,236-240,242-246: 233-"Death" of Sharon Carter. 244,245-Miller-c 1 2 3 4 5 7
234-Daredevil app. 1 2 3 4 6 8
241-Punisher app.; Miller-c 4 8 12 27 44 60
241-2nd print 1 2 3 5 6 8
247-252-Byrne-a 1 3 4 6 8 10
253,255: 253-Byrne-a; Baron Blood app. 255-Origin retold; Miller-c 2 4 6 9 12 15
254-Byrne-a; death of Baron Blood; intro new Union Jack 2 4 6 13 18 22
256-262: 257-Hulk app. 258-Zeck-a begins. 259-Cap vs. Dr. Octopus. 261,262-Red Skull app. 5.00
263-266: 263-Red Skull-c/story. 264-Original X-Men app. 265,266-Spider-Man app. 6.00
267-280: 267-1st app. Everyman. 268-Defenders app. 269-1st Team America. 272-1st Vermin. 273,274-Baron Strucker. 275-1st Baron Zemo (formally the Phoenix). 276-278-Cap vs. Baron Zemo. 279-(3/83)-Contains Tattooz skin decals. 280-Scarecrow app. 5.00
281-1950's Bucky returns. Spider-Woman and Viper app. 1 2 3 4 6 8
282-Bucky becomes new Nomad (Jack Monroe) 2 4 6 8 10 12
282-Silver ink 2nd print ($1.75) w/original date (6/83) 3.00
283-Cap vs. Viper 5.00
284,285,289,291-300: 284-Patriot (Jack Mace) app. 285-Death of Patriot. 293,294-Nomad app. 293-299-Red Skull and Baron Zemo app. 298-Origin Red Skull. 300- "Death" of Red Skull. 4.00
286-288-Deathlok app. 5.00
290-1st Mother Superior (Red Skull's daughter, later becomes Sin) 1 3 4 6 8 10
301-304,307-318,322,324-326,328-331: 301-Avengers app. 307-1st Madcap; 1st Mark Gruenwald-s (begins 8-year run). 308-Secret Wars II x-over. 310-1st Serpent Society. 312-1st Flag Smasher. 313-Death of Modok. 314-Squadron Supreme x-over. 317-Hawkeye & Mockingbird app. 318-Scourge app; death of Blue Streak and Adder. 322-Cap vs. Flag Smasher. 325-Nomad app. 328,330-Demolition Man (D-Man) app. 3.00
305,306-Captain Britain app. 4.00
319-321,327: 319-Scourge kills numerous villians 320-"Death"'of Scourge. 321-Cap vs. Flag Smasher; classic Zeck cover Cap with machine gun. 327-Cap vs Super-Patriot 4.00
323-1st app. new Super-Patriot (see Nick Fury) 5.00
332-Old Captain America resigns 2 4 6 8 10 12
333-340; 333- Super Patriot becomes new Cap. 334-Intro new Bucky; Freedom Force app. 337-Serpent Society app; Avengers #4 homage-c; Steve Rogers becomes 'the Captain'; becomes Captain America again in issue #350. 339-Fall of the Mutants tie-in 4.00
341-343,345-349: 341-Cap vs Iron Man; x-over with Iron Man #228. 342-Cap vs. Viper and the Serpent Squad 3.00
344-($1.50, 52 pgs.)-Ronald Reagan cameo as a snake man 4.00
350-($1.75, 68 pgs.)-Return of Steve Rogers (original Cap) to original costume 6.00
351-358,360-382,384-396: 351-Nick Fury app. 357-Bloodstone hunt Pt. 1 (of 6). 358-Baron Zemo app. 365,366-Acts of Vengeance x-overs. 367-Magneto vs Red Skull. 372-378-Streets of Poison. 374-Bullseye app. 375-Daredevil app. 376-Black Widow app. 377-Bullseye vs. Crossbones; Red Skull app. 379-Quasar app. 380-382-Serpent Society app. 386-U.S. Agent app. 387-392-Superia Stratagem. 387-389-Red Skull back-up stories. 394-Red Skull app. 395-Thor app. (Eric Masterson; also in 396-397); Red Skull app. 396-Red Skull and new (1st) Jack O Lantern app; last $1.00-c 3.00
359-Crossbones debut (cameo); Baron Zemo app. 1 3 4 6 8 10
360-1st app. Crossbones; Baron Zemo app. 3 6 9 16 23 30
383-($2.00, 68 pgs., squarebound)-50th anniversary issue; Red Skull story; Jim Lee-c(i) 5.00
397-399,401-424: 397-New Jack O Lantern app. 398,399-Operation Galactic Storm x-overs. 401-Operation Galactic storm epilogue. 402-Begin 6 part Man-Wolf story w/Wolverine in #403-407. 405-410-New Jack O Lantern app. in back-up story. 406-Cable & Shatterstar cameo. 407-Capwolf vs. Cable-c/story. 408-Infinity War x-over; Falcon back-up story. 409-Red Skull & Crossbones app. 410-Crossbones app. 414-Black Panther app. 419-Red Skull app; x-over with Silver Sable #15. 423- Cap vs. Namor-c/story 3.00
400-($2.25, 84 pgs.) Flip book format w/double gatefold-c; Operation Galactic Storm x-over; r/Avengers #4 plus-c contains cover pin-ups 1 2 3 5 6 8
425-($2.95, 52 pgs.)-Embossed Foil-c edition; Fighting Chance Pt. 1 4.00
425-($1.75, 52 pgs.)-non-embossed-c edition; Fighting Chance Pt. 1 5.00
426-439,442,443: 426-437-Fighting Chance Pt. 2-12. 427-Begins $1.50-c; bound-in trading card sheet. 428-1st Americop. 431-1st Free Spirit. 434-1st Jack Flag. 438-Fighting Chance epilogue. 443-Last Gruenwald issue 4.00
440,441-Avengers x-overs; 'Taking A.I.M" story 5.00
444-Mark Waid-s (1st on Cap) & Ron Garney-c/a(p) begins, ends #454; Avengers app. 5.00
445-Operation rebirth Pt.1; vs Red Skull; Sharon Carter returns 5.00
446,447 – Operation Rebirth; Red Skull app. 446-Hitler app. 6.00
448-($2.95, double-sized issue) Waid script & Garney-c/a; Red Skull "dies" 5.00
449-Thor app; story x-overs with Thor, Iron Man and Avengers titles 5.00
450- "Man Without a Country" begins; Steve Rogers-c 4.00
450-Captain America-c with white background 6.00
451-453: 451-1st app. Cap's new costume. 453-Cap gets old costume back; Bill Clinton app. 4.00
454-Last issue of the regular series (8/96) 5.00
#600-up (See Captain America 2005 series, resumed original numbering after #50)
Special 1(1/71)-All reprint issue from Tales Of Suspense #63,69,70,71,75 5 10 15 35 63 90
Special 2(1/72, 52 pgs.)-All reprint issue from Tales Of Suspense #72-74 and Not Brand Echh #5 4 8 12 23 37 50
Annual 3('76, 52 pgs.)-Kirby-c/a(new) 3 6 9 16 23 30
Annual 4('77, 34 pgs.)-Magneto-c/story 3 6 9 16 23 30
Annual 5-7: (52 pgs.)('81-'83) 5.00
Annual 8(9/86)-Wolverine-c/story 3 6 9 19 30 40
Annual 9-13('90-'94, 68 pgs.)-9-Nomad back-up. 10-Origin retold (2 pgs.). 11-Falcon solo story. 12-Bagged w/card. 13-Red Skull-c/story 4.00
...Ashcan Edition ('95, 75¢) 3.00
... and the Falcon: Madbomb TPB (2004, $16.99) r/#193-200; Kirby-s/a 17.00
... and the Falcon: Nomad TPB (2006, $24.99) r/#177-186; Cap becomes Nomad 25.00
... and the Falcon: Secret Empire TPB (2005, $19.99) r/#169-176 20.00
... and the Falcon: The Swine TPB (2006, $29.99) r/#206-214 & Annual #3,4 30.00
... By Jack Kirby: Bicentennial Battles TPB (2005, $19.99) r/#201-205 & Marvel Treasury Special Featuring Captain America's Bicentennial Battles; Kirby-s/a 20.00
...: Deathlok Lives! nn(10/93, $4.95)-r/#286-288 6.00
...Drug War 1-(1994, $2.00, 52 pgs.)-New Warriors app. 4.00
...Man Without a Country(1998, $12.99, TPB)-r/#450-453 13.00
...Medusa Effect 1 (1994, $2.95, 68 pgs.)-Origin Baron Zemo 4.00
...Operation Rebirth (1996, $9.95)-r/#445-448 10.00
... 65th Anniversary Special (5/06, $3.99) WWII flashback with Bucky; Brubaker-s 5.00
...Streets of Poison ($15.95)-r/#372-378 16.00
...: The Movie Special nn (5/92, $3.50, 52 pgs.)-Adapts movie; printed on coated stock; The Red Skull app. 4.00

NOTE: ***Austin*** *c-225i, 239i, 246i.* ***Buscema*** *a-115p, 217p; c-136p, 217, 297.* ***Byrne*** *c-223(part), 238, 239, 247p-254p, 290, 291, 313p; a-247-254p, 255, 313p, 350.* ***Colan*** *a(p)-116-137, 256, Annual 5; c(p)-116-123, 126, 129.* ***Everett*** *a-136i, 137i; c-126i.* ***Garney*** *a(p)-444-454.* ***Gil Kane*** *a-145p; c-147p, 149p, 150p, 170p, 172-174, 180, 181p, 183-190p, 215, 216, 220, 221.* ***Kirby*** *a(p)-100-109, 112, 193-214, 216, Special 1, 2(layouts), Annual 3, 4; c-100-109, 112, 126p, 193-214.* ***Ron Lim*** *a(p)-366, 368-378, 380-386; c-366p, 368-378p, 379, 380-393p.* ***Miller*** *c-241p, 244p, 245p, 255p, Annual 5.* ***Mooney*** *a-149i.* ***Morrow*** *a-144.* ***Perez*** *c-243p, 246p.* ***Robbins*** *c(p)-183-187, 189-192, 225.* ***Roussos*** *a-140i, 168i.* ***Shores*** *a-102i, 107i, 109i.* ***Starlin/Sinnott*** *c-162.* ***Sutton*** *a-244i.* ***Tuska*** *a-112i, 215p, Special 2.* ***Waid*** *scripts-444-454.* ***Williamson*** *a-313i.* ***Wood*** *a-127i.* ***Zeck*** *a-263-289; c-300.*

CAPTAIN AMERICA (Volume Two)
Marvel Comics: V2#1, Nov, 1996 - No. 13, Nov, 1997($2.95/$1.95/$1.99)
(Produced by Extreme Studios)

1-($2.95)-Heroes Reborn begins; Liefeld-c/a; Loeb scripts; reintro Nick Fury 1 2 3 5 6 8
1-($2.95)-(Variant-c)-Liefeld-c/a 1 2 3 5 6 8
1-(7/96, $2.95)-(Exclusive Comicon Ed.)-Liefeld-c/a 2 4 6 8 10 12
2-11,13: 5-Two-c. 6-Cable-c/app. 13-"World War 3"-pt. 4, x-over w/Image 3.00
12-($2.99) "Heroes Reunited"-pt. 4 4.00
Heroes Reborn: Captain America (2006, $29.99, TPB) r/#1-12 & Heroes Reborn #1/2 30.00

CAPTAIN AMERICA (Vol. Three) (Also see Capt. America: Sentinel of Liberty)
Marvel Comics: Jan, 1998 - No. 50, Feb, 2002 ($2.99/$1.99/$2.25)

1-($2.99) Mark Waid-s/Ron Garney-a 4.00
1-Variant cover 6.00
2-($1.99): 2-Two covers 3.00
3-11: 3-Returns to old shield. 4-Hawkeye app. 5-Thor-c/app. 7-Andy Kubert-c/a begin.

Captain America V3 #32 © MAR

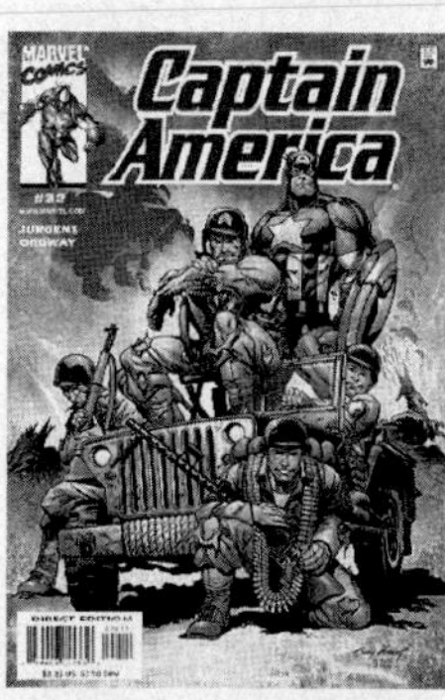

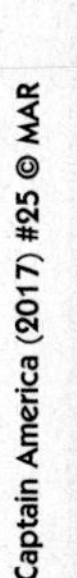

Captain America Comics #3 © MAR

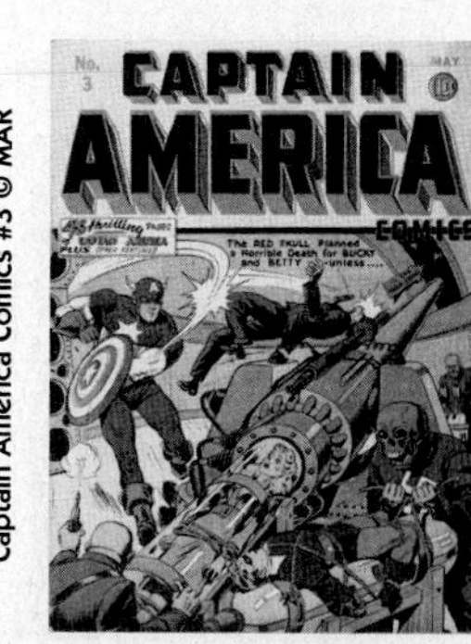

	GD 2.0	VG 4.0	FN 6.0	VF 8.0	VF/NM 9.0	NM- 9.2

9-New shield 3.00
12-($2.99) Battles Nightmare; Red Skull back-up story 4.00
13-17,19-Red Skull returns 3.00
18-($2.99) Cap vs. Korvac in the Future 4.00
20-24,26-29: 20,21-Sgt. Fury back-up story painted by Evans 3.00
25-($2.99) Cap & Falcon vs. Hatemonger 4.00
30-49: 30-Begin $2.25-c. 32-Ordway-a. 33-Jurgens-s/a begins; U.S. Agent app. 36-Maximum Security x-over. 41,46-Red Skull app. 3.00
50-($5.95) Stories by various incl. Jurgens, Quitely, Immonen; Ha-c 6.00
.../Citizen V '98 Annual ($3.50) Busiek & Kesel-s 4.00
1999 Annual ($3.50) Flag Smasher app. 4.00
2000 Annual ($3.50) Continued from #35 vs. Protocide; Jurgens-s 4.00
2001 Annual ($2.99) Golden Age flashback; Invaders app. 4.00
...: To Serve and Protect TPB (2/02, $17.95) r/Vol. 3 #1-7 18.00

CAPTAIN AMERICA (Volume 4)
Marvel Comics: Jun, 2002 - No. 32, Dec, 2004 ($3.99/$2.99)

1-Ney Rieber-s/Cassaday-c/a 4.00
2-9-($2.99) 3-Cap reveals Steve Rogers ID. 7-9-Hairsine-a 3.00
10-32: 10-16-Jae Lee-a. 17-20-Gibbons-s/Weeks-a. 21-26-Bachalo-a. 26-Bucky flashback. 27,28-Eddie Campbell-a. 29-32-Red Skull app. 3.00
...Vol. 1: The New Deal HC (2003, $22.99) r/#1-6; foreward by Max Allan Collins 23.00
...Vol. 2: The Extremists TPB (2003, $13.99) r/#7-11; Cassaday-c 14.00
...Vol. 3: Ice TPB (2003, $12.99) r/#12-16; Jae Lee-a; Cassaday-c 13.00
...Vol. 4: Cap Lives TPB (2004, $12.99) r/#17-22 & Tales of Suspense #66 13.00
Avengers Disassembled: Captain America TPB (2004, $17.99) r/#29-32 and Captain America and the Falcon #5-7 18.00

CAPTAIN AMERICA
Marvel Comics: Jan, 2005 - No. 619, Aug, 2011 ($2.99/$3.99)

1-Brubaker-s/Epting-c/a; Red Skull app. 2 4 6 9 12 15
2-5 5.00
6-1st full app. of the Winter Soldier; Swastika-c 3 6 9 17 26 35
6-Retailer variant cover 3 6 9 21 33 45
7-24: 10-House of M. 11-Origin of the Winter Soldier. 13-Iron Man app. 24-Civil War 4.00
8-Variant Red Skull cover 2 4 6 8 10 12
25-($3.99) Captain America shot dead; handcuffed red glove cover by Epting 12.00
25-($3.99) Variant edition with running Cap cover by McGuinness 8.00
25-($3.99) 2nd printing with "The Death of The Dream" cover by Epting 5.00
25-Director's Cut-($4.99) w/script with Brubaker commentary; pencil pages, variant and un-used covers gallery; article on media hype 6.00
26-33-Falcon & Winter Soldier app. 3.00
34-(3/08) Bucky becomes the new Captain America; Alex Ross-c 10.00
34-Variant-c by Steve Epting 8.00
34-($3.99) Director's Cut; includes script; pencil art, costume designs, cover gallery 5.00
34-DF Edition with Alex Ross portrait cover; signed by Ross 30.00
35-49-Bucky as Captain America. 43-45-Batroc app. 46,47-Sub-Mariner app. 3.00
50-(7/09, $3.99) Bucky's birthday flashbacks; Captain America's life synopsis; Martin-a 4.00

(After #50, numbering reverts to original with #600, Aug, 2009)

600-(8/09, $4.99) Covers by Ross and Epting; leads into Captain America: Reborn series; art by Guice, Chaykin, Ross, Eaglesham; commentary by Joe Simon; cover gallery 5.00
601-615,617-619-($3.99) 601-Gene Colan-a; 3 covers. 602-Nomad back-up feature begins. 606-Baron Zemo returns. 611-615-Trial of Captain America 4.00
615.1 (5/11, $2.99) Brubaker-s/Breitweiser-a/Acuña-c 3.00
616-(5/11, $4.99) 70th Anniversary Issue; short stories by Brubaker, Chaykin, Deodato, McGuinness, Grist and others, Charest-c 5.00
616-Variant-c by Epting 8.00
...: America's Avenger (8/11, $4.99) Handbook format profiles of friends and foes 5.00
... and Batroc (5/11, $3.99) Gillen-s/Arlem-a; Bucky vs. Batroc in Paris 4.00
... and Crossbones (5/11, $3.99) Harms-s/Shalvey-a/Tocchini-c 4.00
... and Falcon (5/11, $3.99) Williams-s/Isaacs-a/Tocchini-c 4.00
... and the First Thirteen (5/11, $3.99) Peggy Carter in WWII France 1943 4.00
... and the Secret Avengers (5/11, $3.99) DeConnick-s/Tocchini-a/c; Black Widow app. 4.00
... and Thor: Avengers 1 (9/11, $4.99) Movie version Cap; prequel to Thor movie; Lim-c 5.00
... By Ed Brubaker Omnibus Vol. 1 HC (2007, $74.99, dustjacket) r/#1-25; Capt. America 65th Anniv. Spec. and Winter Soldier: Winter Kills; Brubaker intro.; bonus material 75.00
Civil War: Captain America TPB (2007, $11.99) r/#22-24 & Winter Soldier: Winter Kills 12.00
...: Fighting Avenger (6/11, $4.99) 1st WWII mission; Gurihiru-a/c; Kitson var-c 5.00
...MGC #1 (5/10, $1.00) r/#1 with "Marvel's Greatest Comics" cover logo 3.00
...: Rebirth 1 (8/11, $4.99) r/origin & Red Skull apps. from Tales of Suspense #63,65-68 5.00
...: Red Menace Vol. 1 SC (2006, $11.99) r/#15-17 and 65th Anniversary Special 12.00
...: Red Menace Vol. 2 SC (2006, $10.99) r/#18-21; Brubaker interview 11.00
... Spotlight (7/11, $3.99) creator interviews; features on the movie and The Invaders 4.00
... Theater of War: America First! (2/09, $4.99) 1950s era tale; Chaykin-s/a; reprints 5.00
... Theater of War: America the Beautiful (3/09, $4.99) WW2 tale; Jenkins-s/Erskine-a 5.00
... Theater of War: Operation Zero-Point (12/08, $3.99) WW2 tale; Breitweiser-a 4.00
...: The Death of Captan America Vol. 1 HC (2007, $19.99) r/#25-30; variant covers 20.00
...: The Death of Captan America Vol. 2 HC (2008, $19.99) r/#31-36; variant covers 20.00
...Vol. 1: Winter Soldier HC (2005, $21.99) r/#1-7; concept sketches 22.00
...Vol. 1: Winter Soldier SC (2006, $16.99) r/#1-7; concept sketches 17.00
...: Who Won't Wield the Shield (6/10, $3.99) Deadpool & Forbush Man app. 4.00
...: Winter Soldier Vol. 2 HC (2006, $19.99) r/#8,9,11-14 20.00
...: Winter Soldier Vol. 2 SC (2006, $14.99) r/#8,9,11-14 15.00

CAPTAIN AMERICA
Marvel Comics: Sept, 2011 - No. 19, Dec, 2012 ($3.99)

1-19: 1-5-Brubaker-s/McNiven-c/a. 1-Nick Fury & Baron Zemo app. 6-10-Davis-a/c 4.00
1-Variant-c by John Romita Sr. 8.00
1-Movie photo variant-c of Chris Evans in costume 5.00

CAPTAIN AMERICA (Marvel NOW!)
Marvel Comics: Jan, 2013 - No. 25, Dec, 2014 ($3.99)

1-10-Remender-s/Romita Jr.-a/c; Cap in Dimension Z; Arnim Zola app.; 1st app. Jet Black. 10-Sharon Carter supposedly killed 4.00
11-24: 11,12,14,15-Pacheco-a; Nuke returns. 16-Red Skull app.; Alixe-a. 21-Steve Rogers rapidly aged. 22-24-Pacheco-a; Avengers app. 23-Sharon Carter returns 4.00
25-($4.99) Sam Wilson becomes the new Captain America; Pacheco-a 5.00
...: Homecoming 1 (5/14, $3.99) Van Lente-s/Grummett-a; bonus rep of Capt. Am. #117 4.00
...: Peggy Carter, Agent of S.H.I.E.L.D. (2014, $7.99) r/notable appearances 8.00

CAPTAIN AMERICA (Secret Empire tie-in)(Follows Captain America: Sam Wilson #24)
Marvel Comics: No. 25, Oct, 2017 ($4.99)

25-Leads into Secret Empire #8; Black Panther, Namor app.; Spencer-s/Saiz-a 5.00

CAPTAIN AMERICA (Marvel Legacy)
Marvel Comics: No. 695, Jan, 2018 - Present ($3.99)

695-699: 695-Follows Secret Empire; Waid-s/Samnee-a. 697-Kraven app. 4.00

CAPTAIN AMERICA AND ... (Numbering continues from Captain America #619)
Marvel Comics: No. 620, Sept, 2011 - No. 640, Feb, 2013 ($2.99)

... Bucky 620-628: 620-624-Brubaker & Andreyko-s/Samnee-a/McGuinness-c. 620-Bucky's early WWII days. 625-628-Francavilla-c/a 3.00
... Hawkeye 629-632: 629-(6/12) Bunn-s/Vitti-aDell'Otto-c 3.00
... Iron Man 633-635: 635-(8/12) Bunn-s/Kitson-a/Andrasofszky-c; Batroc app. 3.00
... Namor 635.1 (10/12) World War II flashback; Will Conrad-a/Immonen-c 3.00
... Black Widow 636-640: 636-(11/12) Bunn-s/Francavilla-a/c 3.00

CAPTAIN AMERICA AND THE FALCON
Marvel Comics: May, 2004 - No. 14, June, 2005 ($2.99, limited series)

1-4-Priest-s/Sears-a 3.00
5-14: 5-8-Avengers Disassembled x-over. 6,7-Scarlet Witch app. 8-12-Modok app. 3.00
... Vol. 1: Two Americas (2005, $9.99) r/#1-4 10.00
... Vol. 2: Brothers and Keepers (2005, $17.99) r/#8-14 18.00

CAPTAIN AMERICA & THE KORVAC SAGA
Marvel Comics: Feb, 2011 - No. 4, May, 2011 ($2.99, limited series)

1-4-McCool-s/Rousseau-a/c. 4-Galactus app. 3.00

CAPTAIN AMERICA & THE MIGHTY AVENGERS (Sam Wilson as Captain America)
Marvel Comics: Jan, 2015 - No. 9, Aug, 2015 ($3.99)

1-9: 1-3-AXIS tie-ins; Luke Ross-a. 8,9-Secret Wars tie-in 4.00

CAPTAIN AMERICA/BLACK PANTHER (See Black Panther/Captain America: Flags of Our Fathers)

CAPTAIN AMERICA COMICS
Timely/Marvel Comics (TCI 1-20/CmPS 21-68/MjMC 69-75/Atlas Comics (PrPI 76-78):
Mar, 1941 - No. 75, Feb, 1950; No. 76, 5/54 - No. 78, 9/54
(No. 74 & 75 titled Capt. America's Weird Tales)

1-Origin & 1st app. Captain America & Bucky by Simon & Kirby; Hurricane, Tuk the Caveboy begin by S&K; 1st app. Red Skull; Hitler-c (by Simon?); intro of the "Capt. America Sentinels of Liberty Club" (advertised on inside front-c.); indicia reads Vol. 2, Number 1
24,000 48,000 72,000 160,000 260,000 460,000
2-S&K Hurricane; Tuk by Avison (Kirby splash); classic Hitler-c; 1st app. Cap's round shield
2500 5000 7500 18,750 40,375 62,000
3-Classic Red Skull-c & app; Stan Lee's 1st text (1st work for Marvel)
2500 5000 7500 18,750 36,875 55,000
4-Early use of full pg. panel in comic; back-c pin-up of Captain America and Bucky
1175 2350 3525 8800 16,650 24,500
5-Classic Kirby Nazi/torture Wheel of Death/Red Skull-c
1075 2150 3225 8000 14,750 21,500
6-Origin Father Time; Tuk the Caveboy ends 1000 2000 3000 7400 13,200 19,000
7-Red Skull app.; classic-c 1075 2150 3225 8000 14,750 21,500
8-10-Last S&K issue, (S&K centerfold #6-10) 838 1676 2514 6117 10,809 15,500

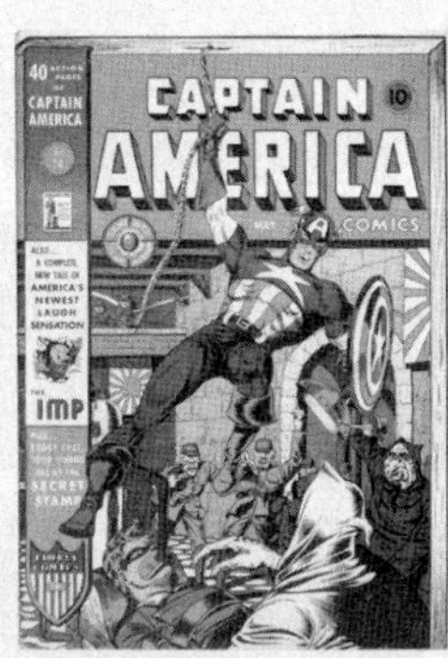

Captain America Comics #14 © MAR

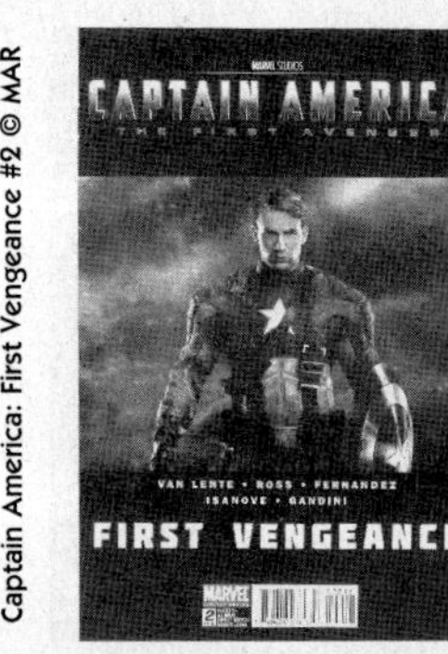

Captain America: First Vengeance #2 © MAR

Captain America: Sam Wilson #10 © MAR

	GD 2.0	VG 4.0	FN 6.0	VF 8.0	VF/NM 9.0	NM- 9.2
11-Last Hurricane, Headline Hunter; Al Avison Captain America begins, ends #20; Avison-c(p)	595	1190	1785	4350	7675	11,000
12-The Imp begins, ends #16; last Father Time	595	1190	1785	4350	7675	11,000
13-Origin The Secret Stamp; classic "Remember Pearl Harbor"-c	975	1950	2919	7100	12,550	18,000
14,15: 14-"Remember Pearl Harbor" Japanese bondage/torture-c	595	1190	1785	4350	7675	11,000
16-Red Skull unmasks Cap; Red Skull-c	838	1676	2514	6117	10,809	15,500
17-The Fighting Fool only app.	492	984	1476	3592	6346	9100
18-Classic-c	519	1038	1557	3789	6695	9600
19-Human Torch begins #19	465	930	1395	3395	5998	8600
20-Sub-Mariner app.; no Human Torch	459	918	1377	3350	5925	8500
21-25: 25-Cap drinks liquid opium	454	908	1362	3314	5857	8400
26-30: 27-Last Secret Stamp; last 68 pg. issue. 28-60 pg. issues begin.	449	898	1347	3278	5789	8300
31-35,38-40: 34-Centerfold poster of Cap	421	842	1263	2947	5174	7400
36-Classic Hitler-c	703	1406	2109	5132	9066	13,000
37-Red Skull app.	676	1352	2028	4935	8718	12,500
41-Last Japan War-c	354	708	1062	2478	4339	6200
42-45	297	594	891	1900	3250	4600
46-German Holocaust-c; classic	1500	3000	4500	10,000	17,500	25,000
47-Last German War-c	320	640	960	2240	3920	5600
48-58,60	226	452	678	1446	2473	3500
59-Origin retold	366	732	1098	2562	4481	6400
61-Red Skull-c/story	415	830	1245	2905	5103	7300
62,64,65: 65-Kurtzman's "Hey Look"	265	530	795	1694	2897	4100
63-Intro/origin Asbestos Lady	277	554	831	1759	3030	4300
66-Bucky is shot; Golden Girl teams up with Captain America & learns his i.d; origin Golden Girl	354	708	1062	2478	4339	6200
67-69: 67-Captain America/Golden Girl team-up; Mxyztplk swipe; last Toro in Human Torch. 68-Sub-Mariner/Namora, and Captain America/Golden Girl team-up. 69-Human Torch/ Sun Girl team-up.	331	662	993	2317	4059	5800
70-73: 70-Sub-Mariner/Namora, and Captain America/Golden Girl team-up. 70-SciFi-c/story. 71-Anti Wertham editorial; The Witness, Bucky app.	377	754	1131	2639	4620	6600
74-(Scarce)(10/49)-Titled "Captain America's Weird Tales"; Red Skull-c & app.; classic-c	1750	3500	5250	13,000	24,500	36,000
75(2/50)-Titled "C.A.'s Weird Tales"; no C.A. app.; horror cover/stories	366	732	1098	2562	4481	6400
76-78(1954): Human Torch/Toro stories; all have communist-c/stories	258	516	774	1651	2826	4000
132-Pg. Issue (B&W-1942)(Canadian)-Very rare. Has blank inside-c and back-c; contains Marvel Mystery #33 & Captain America #18 w/cover from Captain America #22; same contents as one version of the Marvel Mystery annuals	5050	10,100	15,150	38,000	-	-

*NOTE: **Crandall** a-2i, 3i, 9i, 10i. **Kirby** c-1, 2, 5-8p. **Rico** c-69-71. **Romita** c-77, 78. **Schomburg** c-3, 4, 26-29, 31, 33, 37-39, 41, 42, 45-54, 58. **Sekowsky** c-55, 56. **Shores** c-1i, 2i, 5-7i, 11i, 20-25, 30, 32, 34, 35, 40, 57, 59-67. **S&K** c-9, 10. Bondage c-3, 7, 15, 16, 34, 38.*

CAPTAIN AMERICA COMICS #1 70TH ANNIVERSARY EDITION
Marvel Comics: May, 2011 ($4.99, one-shot)

1-Recolored reprint of entire 1941 issue including Hurricane & Tuk stories; Ching-c 6.00

CAPTAIN AMERICA COMICS 70TH ANNIVERSARY SPECIAL
Marvel Comics: June, 2009 ($3.99, one-shot)

1-WWII flashback; Marcos Martin-a; Marcos-2 covers; r/Capt. America Comics #7 5.00

CAPTAIN AMERICA CORPS
Marvel Comics: Aug, 2011 - No. 5, Dec, 2011 ($2.99, limited series)

1-5-Stern-s/Briones-a/Jimenez-a; various versions of Captain America team-up 3.00

CAPTAIN AMERICA: DEAD MEN RUNNING
Marvel Comics: Mar, 2002 - No. 3, May, 2002 ($2.99, limited series)

1-3-Macan-s/Zezelj-a 3.00

CAPTAIN AMERICA: FIRST VENGEANCE (Based on the 2011 movie version)
Marvel Comics: Jul, 2011 - No. 4, Aug, 2011 ($2.99, limited series)

1-4-Van Lente-s; art by Luke Ross & others. 2-Movie photo-c 3.00

CAPTAIN AMERICA: FOREVER ALLIES
Marvel Comics: Oct, 2010 - No. 4, Jan, 2011 ($3.99, limited series)

1-4-Stern-s/Dragotta-a; Bucky in present & WW2 flashbacks; Young Allies app. 4.00

CAPTAIN AMERICA: HAIL HYDRA
Marvel Comics: Mar, 2011 - No. 5, Jul, 2011 ($2.99, limited series)

1-5-Cap vs. Hydra; Granov-c. 1-WWII flashback. 2-Kirby-style art by Scioli. 4-Hotz-a 3.00

CAPTAIN AMERICA: LIVING LEGEND
Marvel Comics: Dec, 2013 - No. 4, Feb, 2014 ($3.99, limited series)

1-4: 1-Diggle-s/Granov-a/c. 2-4-Alessio-a 4.00

CAPTAIN AMERICA: MAN OUT OF TIME
Marvel Comics: Jan, 2011 - No. 5, May, 2011 ($3.99, limited series)

1-5-Waid-s/Molina-a/Hitch-c; Cap's unfreezing in modern times re-told 4.00

CAPTAIN AMERICA/NICK FURY: BLOOD TRUCE
Marvel Comics: Feb, 1995 ($5.95, one-shot, squarebound)

nn-Chaykin story 6.00

CAPTAIN AMERICA/NICK FURY: THE OTHERWORLD WAR
Marvel Comics: Oct, 2001 ($6.95, one-shot, squarebound)

nn-Manco-a; Bucky and Red Skull app. 7.00

CAPTAIN AMERICA: PATRIOT
Marvel Comics: Nov, 2010 - No. 4, Feb, 2011 ($3.99, limited series)

1-4-Kesel-s/Breitweiser-a; 1-WW2 story; Patriot & the Liberty Legion app. 4.00

CAPTAIN AMERICA: REBORN (Titled Reborn in #1-3)
Marvel Comics: Sept, 2009 - No. 6, Mar, 2010 ($3.99, limited series)

1-6-Steve Rogers returns from the dead; Brubaker-s/Hitch & Guice-a. 1-Covers by Hitch, Ross & Quesada. 2-Origin re-told. 4-Joe Kubert var-c. 5-Cassaday var-c 4.00
1-4-Variant-c by Cassaday. 2-Variant-c by Sale. 5-Finch var-c 10.00
... MGC #1 (5/11, $1.00) r/#1 with "Marvel's Greatest Comics" logo on cover 3.00
...: Who Will Wield the Shield? (2/10, $3.99) Aftermath of series; Guice & Luke Ross-a 4.00

CAPTAIN AMERICA: RED, WHITE & BLUE
Marvel Comics: Sept, 2002 ($29.99, one-shot, hardcover with dustjacket)

nn-Reprints from Lee & Kirby, Steranko, Miller and others; and new short stories and pin-ups by various incl. Ross, Dini, Timm, Waid, Dorkin, Sienkiewicz, Miller, Bruce Jones, Collins, Piers-Rayner, Pope, Deodato, Quitely, Nino; Stelfreeze-c 30.00
TPB (2007, $19.99) 20.00

CAPTAIN AMERICA: ROAD TO WAR
Marvel Comics: Jun, 2016 ($4.99, one-shot)

1-Prelude to Captain America: Civil War movie; bonus r/Tales of Suspense #58 5.00

CAPTAIN AMERICA: SAM WILSON (Leads into Captain America #25 (Oct. 2017))
Marvel Comics: Dec, 2015 - No. 24, Sept, 2017 ($3.99)

1-6: 1-Spencer-s/Acuña-a; Misty Knight & D-Man app. 3-6-Sam as CapWolf 4.00
7-($5.99) 75th Anniversary issue; Steve Rogers regains his youth; Standoff tie-in; bonus short stories by Whedon & Cassaday, Tim Sale, and Rucka & Perkins 6.00
8-24: 8-Standoff tie-in; Baron Zemo app. 10-13-Civil War II tie-in. 11-13-U.S. Agent app. 22-24-Secret Empire tie-ins 4.00

CAPTAIN AMERICA, SENTINEL OF LIBERTY (See Fireside Book Series)

CAPTAIN AMERICA: SENTINEL OF LIBERTY
Marvel Comics: Sept, 1998 - No. 12, Aug, 1999 ($1.99)

1-Waid-s/Garney-a 3.00
1-Rough Cut ($2.99) Features original script and pencil pages 3.00
2-5: 2-Two-c; Invaders WW2 story 3.00
6-($2.99) Iron Man-c/app. 4.00
7-11: 8-Falcon-c/app. 9-Falcon poses as Cap 3.00
12-($2.99) Final issue; Bucky-c/app. 4.00

CAPTAIN AMERICA SPECIAL EDITION
Marvel Comics Group: Feb, 1984 - No. 2, Mar, 1984 ($2.00, Baxter paper)

	GD 2.0	VG 4.0	FN 6.0	VF 8.0	VF/NM 9.0	NM- 9.2
1-Steranko-c/a(r) in both; r/Capt. America #110,111	1	2	3	5	6	8
2-Reprints the scarce Our Love Story #5, and C.A. #113	1	2	3	5	6	8

CAPTAIN AMERICA: STEVE ROGERS (Also see Captain America: Sam Wilson)
Marvel Comics: Jul, 2016 - No. 19, Sept, 2017 ($4.99/$3.99)

1-Spencer-s/Saiz-a; childhood flashbacks to Hydra recruitment; Red Skull app. 5.00
2-19-($3.99) 2-Kobik app. 4-6-Civil War II tie-in. 14,15-Red Skull app. 16-19-Secret Empire tie-ins. 18-Namor app. 19-Leads into Captain America #25 (10/17) 4.00

CAPTAIN AMERICA THEATER OF WAR
Marvel Comics: 2009 - 2010 ($3.99, series of one-shots)

...: A Brother in Arms (6/09) Jenkins-s/McCrea-a; WWII story 4.00
...: Ghosts of My Country (12/09) Jenkins-s/Bonetti-a/Guice-c 4.00
...: Prisoners of Duty (2/10) Higgins & Siegel-s/Padilla-a; WWII story 4.00
...: To Soldier On (10/09) Jenkins-s/Blanco-a/Noto-c; Captain America in Iraq 4.00

CAPTAIN AMERICA: THE CHOSEN
Marvel Comics: Nov, 2007 - No. 6, Mar, 2008 ($3.99, limited series)

1-6-Breitweiser-a/Morrell-s 4.00

Captain America: White #0 © MAR

Captain Atom (2011 series) #1 © DC

Captain Britain #2 © MAR

GD 2.0 VG 4.0 FN 6.0 VF 8.0 VF/NM 9.0 NM- 9.2

CAPTAIN AMERICA: THE CLASSIC YEARS
Marvel Comics: Jun, 1998 - No. 2 (trade paperbacks)

1-($19.95) Reprints Captain America Comics #1-5 25.00
2-($24.95) Reprints Captain America Comics #6-10 25.00

CAPTAIN AMERICA: THE FIRST AVENGER ADAPTATION (MARVEL'S...)
Marvel Comics: Jan, 2014 - No. 2, Feb, 2014 ($2.99, limited series)

1,2-Adaptation of the 2011 movie; Peter David-s/Wellinton Alves-a/photo-c 3.00

CAPTAIN AMERICA: THE LEGEND
Marvel Comics: Sept, 1996 ($3.95, one-shot)

1-Tribute issue; wraparound-c 5.00

CAPTAIN AMERICA: THE 1940S NEWSPAPER STRIP
Marvel Comics: Aug, 2010 - No. 3, Oct, 2010 ($3.99, limited series)

1-3-Karl Kesel-s/a; new stories set in WW2, formatted like 1940s newspaper comics 4.00

CAPTAIN AMERICA: WHAT PRICE GLORY
Marvel Comics: May, 2003 - No. 4, May, 2003 ($2.99, weekly limited series)

1-4-Bruce Jones-s/Steve Rude & Mike Royer-a 3.00

CAPTAIN AMERICA: WHITE
Marvel Comics: No. 0, Sept, 2008; No. 1, Nov, 2015 - No. 5, Feb, 2016 (limited series)

0-Bucky's origin retold; Loeb-s/Sale-a in all; interviews with creators; Sale sketch art 3.00
1-($4.99) Flashback to 1941; Sgt. Fury and the Howling Commandos app. 5.00
2-5-($3.99) 3-5-Red Skull app. 4.00

CAPTAIN AMERICA: WINTER SOLDIER DIRECTOR'S CUT
Marvel Comics: Jun, 2014 ($4.99, one-shot)

1-Reprints Captain America (2005) #1; bonus Brubaker script & series proposal 5.00

CAPTAIN AND THE KIDS, THE (See Famous Comics Cartoon Books)

CAPTAIN AND THE KIDS, THE (See Comics on Parade, Katzenjammer Kids, Okay Comics & Sparkler Comics)
United Features Syndicate/Dell Publ. Co.: 1938 -12/39; Sum, 1947 - No. 32, 1955; Four Color No. 881, Feb, 1958

	GD	VG	FN	VF	VF/NM	NM-
Single Series 1(1938)	116	232	348	742	1271	1800
Single Series 1(Reprint)(12/39- "Reprint" on-c)	48	96	144	302	514	725
1(Summer, 1947-UFS)-Katzenjammer Kids	19	38	57	111	176	240
2	11	22	33	62	86	110
3-10	10	20	30	54	72	90
11-20	8	16	24	44	57	70
21-32 (1955)	8	16	24	40	50	60
50th Anniversary issue-(1948)-Contains a 2 pg. history of the strip, including an account of the famous Supreme Court decision allowing both Pulitzer & Hearst to run the same strip under different names	19	38	57	111	176	240
Special Summer issue, Fall issue (1948)	12	24	36	69	97	125
Four Color 881 (Dell)	5	10	15	30	50	70

CAPTAIN ATOM
Nationwide Publishers: 1950 - No. 7, 1951 (5¢, 5x7-1/4", 52 pgs.)

	GD	VG	FN	VF	VF/NM	NM-
1-Science fiction	42	84	126	265	445	625
2-7	26	52	78	154	252	350

CAPTAIN ATOM (Formerly Strange Suspense Stories #77)(Also see Space Adventures and Thunderbolt)
Charlton Comics: V2#78, Dec, 1965 - V2#89, Dec, 1967

	GD	VG	FN	VF	VF/NM	NM-
V2#78-Origin retold; Bache-a (3 pgs.)	8	16	24	51	96	145
79-81: 79-1st app. Dr. Spectro; 3 pg. Ditko cut & paste /Space Adventures #24.	5	10	15	35	63	90
82-Intro. Nightshade (9/66)	10	20	30	70	150	230
83-(11/66)-1st app. Ted Kord/Blue Beetle	36	72	108	259	580	900
84-86: Ted Kord Blue Beetle in all. 84-1st app. new Captain Atom. 85-1st app. Punch and Jewelee	5	10	15	33	57	80
87-89: Nightshade by Aparo in all	5	10	15	33	57	80
83-(Modern Comics-1977)-reprints	3	6	9	19	30	40
84,85-(Modern Comics-1977)-reprints	1	2	3	5	6	8

NOTE: *Aparo a-87-89. Ditko c/a(p) 78-89. #90 only published in fanzine 'The Charlton Bullseye' #1, 2.*

CAPTAIN ATOM (Also see Americomics & Crisis On Infinite Earths)
DC Comics: Mar, 1987 - No. 57, Sept, 1991 (Direct sales only #35 on)

1-(44 pgs.)-Origin/1st app. with new costume 5.00
2-49: 5-Firestorm x-over. 6-Intro. new Dr. Spectro. 11-Millennium tie-in. 14-Nightshade app. 16-Justice League app. 17-$1.00-c begins; Swamp Thing app. 20-Blue Beetle x-over. 24,25-Invasion tie-in 3.00
50-($2.00, 52 pgs.) 4.00
51-57: 57-War of the Gods x-over 3.00
Annual 1,2 ('88, '89)-1-Intro Major Force 4.00

CAPTAIN ATOM (DC New 52)
DC Comics: Nov, 2011 - No. 12, Oct, 2012; No. 0, Nov, 2012 ($2.99)

1-12-J.T. Krul-s/Freddie Williams II-a. 3-Flash app. 3.00
#0 (11/12, $2.99) origin of Captain Atom re-told 3.00

CAPTAIN ATOM: ARMAGEDDON (Restarts the WildStorm Universe)
DC Comics (WildStorm): Dec, 2005 - No. 9, Aug, 2006 ($2.99, limited series)

1-9-Captain Atom appears in WildStorm Universe; Pfeifer-s/Camuncoli-a. 1-Lee-c 3.00
TPB (2007, $19.99) r/series 20.00

CAPTAIN BATTLE (Boy Comics #3 on) (See Silver Streak Comics)
New Friday Publ./Comic House: Summer, 1941 - No. 2, Fall, 1941

	GD	VG	FN	VF	VF/NM	NM-
1-Origin Blackout by Rico; Captain Battle begins (1st appeared in Silver Streak #10, 5/41) classic hooded villain bondage/torture-c	200	600	900	1280	2190	3100
2-Origin Doctor Horror & only app.; classic story "House of Giants"	94	188	282	597	1024	1450

CAPTAIN BATTLE (2nd Series)
Magazine Press/Picture Scoop No. 5: No. 3, Wint, 1942-43; No. 5, Sum, 1943 (No #4)

	GD	VG	FN	VF	VF/NM	NM-
3-Origin Silver Streak-r/SS#3; origin Lance Hale-r/SS #2; Cloud Curtis, Presto Martin 1st app.-r/SS #7; Simon-a(r) (52 pgs., nd)	90	180	270	576	988	1400
5-Origin Blackout-r/#1 (68 pgs.); Japanese WWII-c	90	180	270	576	988	1400

CAPTAIN BATTLE, JR.
Comic House (Lev Gleason): Fall, 1943 - No. 2, Winter, 1943-44

	GD	VG	FN	VF	VF/NM	NM-
1-Nazi WWII-c by Rico. Hitler/Claw sty; The Claw vs. The Ghost	148	296	444	947	1624	2300
2-Wolverton's Scoop Scuttle; Don Rico-c/a; The Green Claw story is reprinted from Silver Streak #6; Japanese WWII bondage/torture-c by Rico	87	174	261	553	952	1350

CAPTAIN BEN DIX (See Promotional Comics section)

CAPTAIN BRITAIN (Also see Marvel Team-Up No. 65, 66)
Marvel Comics International: Oct. 13, 1976 - No. 39, July 6, 1977 (Weekly)

	GD	VG	FN	VF	VF/NM	NM-
1-1st app & origin of Captain Britain (Brian Broddock); with Capt. Britain's face mask inside Claremont-s/Trimpe-a	9	18	27	59	117	175
2-Origin, part II; Capt. Britain's Boomerang inside	3	6	9	17	26	35
3-7: 3-Vs. Bank Robbers. 4-7-Vs. Hurricane	2	4	6	8	10	12
8-(12/76) 1st app. Betsy Braddock, the sister of Capt. Britain (Brian Braddock) who later becomes Psylocke (X-Men); 1st app. Dr. Synne	12	24	36	80	173	265
9-11-Battles Dr. Synne. 9,10-Betsy Braddock app.	2	4	6	8	10	12
12-23,25-27: (low print run)-12,13-Vs. Dr. Synne. 14,15-Vs. Mastermind. 16-23,25,26-With Captain America. 17-Misprinted & color section reprinted in #18. 27-Origin retold	3	6	9	14	20	25
24-With Capt. Britain's Jet Plane inside	3	6	9	19	30	40
28-32,36-39: 28-32-Vs. Lord Hawk. 30-32-Inhumans app. 35-Dr. Doom app. 37-39-Vs. Highwayman & Munipulator	1	2	3	5	6	8
33-35-More on origin	1	2	3	5	7	9
Annual (1978, Hardback, 64 pgs.)-Reprints #1-7 with pin-ups of Marvel characters	3	6	9	15	22	28
Summer Special (1980, 52 pgs.)-Reprints	1	2	3	5	6	8

NOTE: *No. 1, 2, & 24 are rarer in mint due to inserts. Distributed in Great Britain only. Nick Fury-r by **Steranko** in 1-20, 24-31, 35-37. Fantastic Four-r by **J. Buscema** in all. New **Buscema**-a in 24-30. Story from No. 39 continues in Super Spider-Man (British weekly) No. 231-247. Following cancellation of his series, new Captain Britain stories appeared in "Super Spider-Man" (British weekly) No. 231-247. Captain Britain stories which appear in Super-Spider-Man No 248-253 are reprints of Marvel Team-Up No. 65&66. Capt. Britain strips also appeared in Hulk Comic (weekly) 1, 3-30, 42-55, 57-60, in Marvel Superheroes (monthly) 377-388, in Daredevils (monthly) 1-11, Mighty World of Marvel (monthly) 7-16 & Captain Britain (monthly) 1-14. Issues 1-23 have B&W & color, paper-c, & are 32 pgs. Issues 24 on are all B&W w/glossy-c & are 36 pgs.*

CAPTAIN BRITAIN AND MI: 13 (Also see Secret Invasion x-over titles)
Marvel Comics: Jul, 2008 - No. 15, Sept, 2009 ($2.99)

1-Skrull invasion; Black Knight app.; Kirk-a 4.00
1-2nd printing with Kirk variant-c; 3rd printing with B&W cover 3.00
2-15: 5-Blade app. 9,10-Dracula app. 3.00
... Annual 1 (8/09, $3.99) Land-c; Meggan in Hell; Dr. Doom cameo; Collins-a 4.00

CAPTAIN BRITAIN AND THE MIGHTY DEFENDERS (Secret Wars tie-in)
Marvel Comics: Sept, 2015 - No. 2, Oct, 2015 ($3.99, limited series)

1,2-Ho Yinsen, Faiza Hussain, White Tiger, She-Hulk app.; Al Ewing-s/Alan Davis-a 4.00

CAPTAIN CANUCK
Comely Comix (Canada)(All distr. in U. S.): Jul,1975 - No. 4, Jul, 1977; No. 4, Jul-Aug, 1979 - No. 14, Mar-Apr, 1981

	GD	VG	FN	VF	VF/NM	NM-
1-1st app. Captain Canuck, C.I.S.O. & Bluefox; Richard Comely-c/a	2	4	6	10	14	18

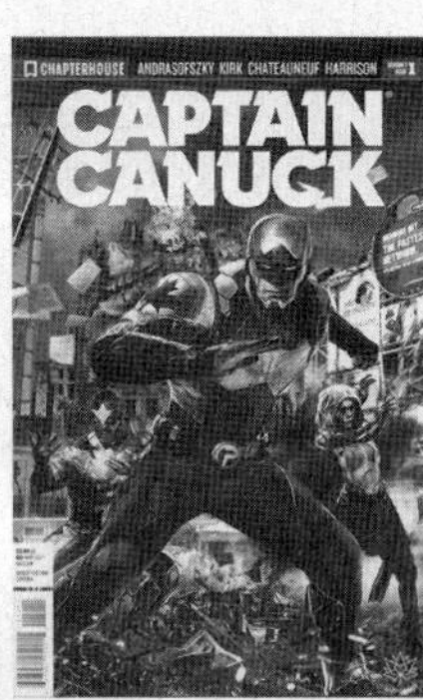

Captain Canuck (2015 series) #12 © Comely

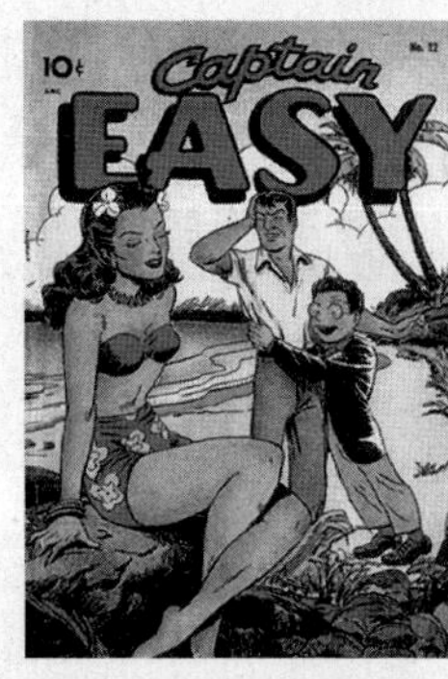

Captain Easy #12 © NEA

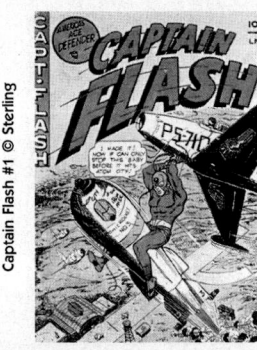

Captain Flash #1 © Sterling

	GD 2.0	VG 4.0	FN 6.0	VF 8.0	VF/NM 9.0	NM- 9.2

2,3(5-7/76): 2-1st app. Dr. Walker, Redcoat & Kebec. 3-1st app. Heather 6.00
4 (1st printing-2/77)-10x14-1/2"; (5.00); B&W; 300 copies serially numbered and signed with one certificate of authenticity 9 18 27 61 123 185
4 (2nd printing-7/77)-11x17", B&W; only 15 copies printed; signed by creator Richard Comely, serially #'d and two certificates of authenticity inserted; orange cardboard covers (Very Rare) 12 24 36 84 185 285
4-14: 4(7-8/79)-1st app. Tom Evans & Mr. Gold; origin The Catman. 5-Origin Capt. Canuck's powers; 1st app. Earth Patrol & Chaos Corps. 5-7-Three-part neo-Nazi story set in 1994. 8-Jonn 'The Final Chapter'; 1st app. Mike & Saskia. 9-1st World Beyond. 11-1st 'Chariots of Fire' story. 12-A-bomb explosion panel 6.00
15-(8/04, $15.00) Limited edition of unpublished issue from 1981; serially #'d edition of 150; signed by creator Richard Comely 7 14 21 44 82 120
... Legacy 1 (9-10/06) Comely-s/a 4.00
... Legacy Special Edition ($7.95, 52 pgs., limited ed. of 1000) Comely-s/a 1 3 4 6 8 10
Special Collectors Pack (#1 & #2 polybagged) 2 4 6 8 10 12
Summer Special 1(7-9/80, 95¢, 64 pgs.) George Freeman-c/a; pin-ups by Gene Day, Tom Grummett, Dave Sim and others 6.00
Summer Special / Canada Day Edition #1 (2014, no cover price) 2 new stories, background on animated web series; regular-c shows a parade; variants exist 5.00
NOTE: *30,000 copies of No. 2 were destroyed in Winnipeg.*

CAPTAIN CANUCK
Chapterhouse Comics: May, 2015 - Present ($3.99)
1-13: 1-Kalman Andrasofszky-s/a; 3 covers. 3-12-Leonard Kirk-a 4.00
#0/FCBD Edition (5/15, giveaway) previews #1; origin re-told; character profiles 3.00

CAPTAIN CANUCK: UNHOLY WAR
Comely Comix: Oct, 2004 - No. 3, Jan, 2005; No. 4, Sept, 2007 ($2.50, limited series)
1-3-Riel Langlois-s/Drue Langlois-a: 1-1st app. David Semple (West Coast Capt. Canuck); Clair Sinclair as Bluefox 3.00
4-(Low print run) Black Mack the Lumberjack, Torchie, Splatter app. 6.00

CAPTAIN CANUCK YEAR ONE
Chapterhouse Comics: May, 2017; Nov, 2017 - Present ($1.99)
1-($1.99) Baruchel & Andrasofszky-s; Marcus To-a; back-up Die Kitty Die story 3.00
#1/FCBD Edition (5/17, giveaway) back-up Die Kitty Die story 3.00

CAPTAIN CARROT AND HIS AMAZING ZOO CREW (Also see New Teen Titans & Oz-Wonderland War)
DC Comics: Mar, 1982 - No. 20, Nov, 1983
1-Superman app. 6.00
2-20: 3-Re-intro Dodo & The Frog. 9-Re-intro Three Mouseketeers, the Terrific Whatzit. 10,11-Pig Iron reverts back to Peter Porkchops. 20-Changeling app. 4.00

CAPTAIN CARROT AND THE FINAL ARK (DC Countdown tie-in)
DC Comics: Dec, 2007 - No. 3, Feb, 2008 ($2.99, limited series)
1-3-Bill Morrison-s/Scott Shaw!-a. 3-Batman, Red Arrow, Hawkgirl & Zatanna app. 3.00
TPB (2008, $19.99) r/#1-3; Captain Carrot and His Amazing Zoo Crew #1,14,15; New Teen Titans #16 and stories from Teen Titans (2003 series) #30,31; cover gallery 20.00

CAPTAIN CARVEL AND HIS CARVEL CRUSADERS (See Carvel Comics)

CAPTAIN CONFEDERACY
Marvel Comics (Epic Comics): Nov, 1991 - No. 4, Feb, 1992 ($1.95)
1-4: All new stories 3.00

CAPTAIN COURAGEOUS COMICS (Banner #3-5; see Four Favorites #5)
Periodical House (Ace Magazines): No. 6, March, 1942
6-Origin & 1st app. The Sword; Lone Warrior, Capt. Courageous app.; Capt. moves to Four Favorites #5 in May 116 232 348 742 1271 1800

CAPT'N CRUNCH COMICS (See Cap'n...)

CAPTAIN DAVY JONES
Dell Publishing Co.: No. 598, Nov, 1954
Four Color 598 6 12 18 37 66 95

CAPTAIN EASY (See The Funnies & Red Ryder #3-32)
Hawley/Dell Publ./Standard(Visual Editions)/Argo: 1939 - No. 17, Sept, 1949; April, 1956
nn-Hawley(1939)-Contains reprints from The Funnies & 1938 Sunday strips by Roy Crane 97 194 291 621 1061 1500
Four Color 24 (1943) 54 108 162 346 591 835
Four Color 111(6/46) 12 24 36 82 179 275
10(Standard-10/47) 14 28 42 78 112 145
11,12,14,15,17: 11-17 all contain 1930s & '40s strip-r 10 20 30 56 76 95
13,16: Schomburg-c 13 26 39 72 101 130
Argo 1(4/56)-Reprints 7 14 21 37 46 55

CAPTAIN EASY & WASH TUBBS (See Famous Comics Cartoon Books)

CAPTAIN ELECTRON
Brick Computer Science Institute: Aug, 1986 ($2.25)
1-Disbrow-a 3.00

CAPTAIN EO 3-D (Michael Jackson Disney theme parks movie)
Eclipse Comics: July, 1987 (Eclipse 3-D Special #18, $3.50, Baxter)
1-Adapts 3-D movie; Michael Jackson-c/app. 3 6 9 16 23 30
1-2-D limited edition 5 10 15 33 57 80
1-Large size (11x17", 8/87)-Sold only at Disney Theme parks ($6.95) 4 8 12 25 40 55

CAPTAIN FEARLESS COMICS (Also see Holyoke One-Shot #6, Old Glory Comics & Silver Streak #1)
Helnit Publishing Co. (Holyoke Publ. Co.): Aug, 1941 - No. 2, Sept, 1941
1-Origin Mr. Miracle, Alias X, Captain Fearless, Citizen Smith Son of the Unknown Soldier; Miss Victory (1st app.) begins (1st patriotic heroine? before Wonder Woman) 107 214 321 680 1165 1650
2-Grit Grady, Captain Stone app. 55 110 165 352 601 850

CAPTAIN FLAG (See Blue Ribbon Comics #16)

CAPTAIN FLASH
Sterling Comics: Nov, 1954 - No. 4, July, 1955
1-Origin; Sekowsky-a; Tomboy (female super hero) begins; only pre-code issue; atomic rocket-c 47 94 141 296 498 700
2-4: 4-Flying saucer invasion-c 28 56 84 165 270 375

CAPTAIN FLEET (Action Packed Tales of the Sea)
Ziff-Davis Publishing Co.: Fall, 1952
1-Painted-c 19 38 57 111 176 240

CAPTAIN FLIGHT COMICS
Four Star Publications: May, 1944 - No. 10, Dec, 1945; No. 11, Feb-Mar, 1947
nn-Captain Flight begins 71 142 213 454 777 1100
2-4: 4-Rock Raymond begins, ends #7 48 96 144 302 514 725
5-Bondage, classic torture-c; Red Rocket begins; the Grenade app. (scarce) 219 438 657 1402 2401 3400
6-L. B. Cole-a, 8 pgs. 42 84 126 265 445 625
7-10: 7-L. B. Cole covers begin, end #11. 7-9-Japanese WWII-c. 8-Yankee Girl begins; intro. Black Cobra & Cobra Kid & begins. 9-Torpedoman app.; last Yankee Girl; Kinstler-a. 10-Deep Sea Dawson, Zoom of the Jungle, Rock Raymond, Red Rocket, & Black Cobra app; bondage-c 61 122 183 390 670 950
11-Torpedoman, Blue Flame (Human Torch clone) app.; last Black Cobra, Red Rocket; classic L. B. Cole sci-fi robot-c (scarce) 258 516 774 1651 2826 4000

CAPTAIN GALLANT (...of the Foreign Legion) (TV) (Texas Rangers in Action No. 5 on?)
Charlton Comics: 1955; No. 2, Jan, 1956 - No. 4, Sept, 1956
Non-Heinz version (#1)-Buster Crabbe photo on-c; full page Buster Crabbe photo inside front-c 8 16 24 44 57 70
(Heinz version is listed in the Promotional Comics section)
2-4: Buster Crabbe in all. 2-Crabbe photo back-c 6 12 18 31 38 45

CAPTAIN GLORY
Topps Comics: Apr, 1993 ($2.95) (Created by Jack Kirby)
1-Polybagged w/Kirbychrome trading card; Ditko-a & Kirby-c; has coupon for Amberchrome Secret City Saga #0 4.00

CAPTAIN HERO (See Jughead as...)

CAPTAIN HERO COMICS DIGEST MAGAZINE
Archie Publications: Sept, 1981
1-Reprints of Jughead as Super-Guy 2 4 6 10 14 18

CAPTAIN HOBBY COMICS
Export Publication Ent. Ltd. (Dist. in U.S. by Kable News Co.): Feb, 1948 (Canadian)
1 12 24 36 69 97 125

CAPT. HOLO IN 3-D (See Blackthorne 3-D Series #65)

CAPTAIN HOOK & PETER PAN (Movie)(Disney)
Dell Publishing Co.: No. 446, Jan, 1953
Four Color 446 9 18 27 59 117 175

CAPTAIN JET (Fantastic Fears No. 7 on)
Four Star Publ./Farrell/Comic Media: May, 1952 - No. 5, Jan, 1953
1-Bakerish-a 26 52 78 154 252 350
2 15 30 45 86 133 180
3-5,6(?) 12 24 36 69 97 125

CAPTAIN JOHNER & THE ALIENS
Valiant: May, 1995 - No. 2, May, 1995 ($2.95, shipped in same month)

Captain Kronos - Vampire Hunter #1 © Hammer

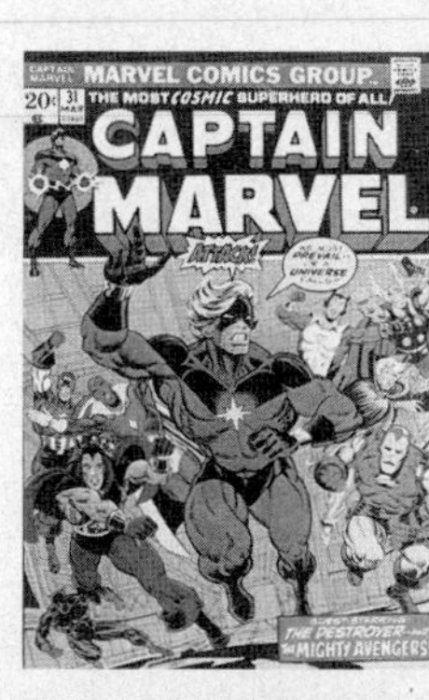

Captain Marvel #31 © MAR

Captain Marvel (2013 series) #14 © MAR

GD VG FN VF VF/NM NM-
2.0 4.0 6.0 8.0 9.0 9.2

1,2: Reprints Magnus Robot Fighter 4000 A.D. back-up stories; new Paul Smith-c 3.00

CAPTAIN JUSTICE (TV)
Marvel Comics: Mar, 1988 - No. 2, Apr, 1988 (limited series)

1,2-Based on the 1987 "Once a Hero" television series 3.00

CAPTAIN KANGAROO (TV)
Dell Publishing Co.: No. 721, Aug, 1956 - No. 872, Jan, 1958

Four Color 721 (#1)-Photo-c 13 26 39 89 195 300
Four Color 780, 872-Photo-c 11 22 33 76 163 250

CAPTAIN KID
AfterShock Comics: Jul, 2016 - No. 5, Mar, 2017 ($3.99)

1-5-Mark Waid & Tom Peyer-s/Wilfredo Torres-a 4.00

CAPTAIN KIDD (Formerly Dagar; My Secret Story #26 on)(Also see Comic Comics & Fantastic Comics)
Fox Feature Syndicate: No. 24, June, 1949 - No. 25, Aug, 1949

24,25: 24-Features Blackbeard the Pirate 15 30 45 85 130 175

CAPTAIN KRONOS - VAMPIRE HUNTER (Based on the 1974 Hammer film)
Titan Comics (Hammer Comics): Oct, 2017 - No. 4, Jan, 2018 ($3.99)

1-4-Abnett-s/Mandrake-a; multiple covers on each (art & photo) 4.00

CAPTAIN MARVEL (See All Hero, All-New Collectors' Ed., America's Greatest, Fawcett Miniature, Gift, JSA, Kingdom Come, Legends, Limited Collectors' Ed., Marvel Family, Master No. 21, Mighty Midget Comics, Power of Shazam!, Shazam, Special Edition Comics, Whiz, Wisco (in Promotional Comics section), World's Finest #253 and XMas Comics)

CAPTAIN MARVEL (Becomes ...Presents the Terrible 5 No. 5)
M. F. Enterprises: April, 1966 - No. 4, Nov, 1966 (25¢ Giants)

nn-(#1 on pg. 5)-Origin; created by Carl Burgos 5 10 15 34 60 85
2-4: 3-(#3 on pg. 4)-Fights the Bat 4 8 12 23 37 50

CAPTAIN MARVEL (Marvel's Space-Born Super-Hero! Captain Marvel #1-6; see Giant-Size..., Life Of..., Marvel Graphic Novel #1, Marvel Spotlight V2#1 & Marvel Super-Heroes #12)
Marvel Comics Group: May, 1968 - No. 19, Dec, 1969; No. 20, June, 1970 - No. 21, Aug, 1970; No. 22, Sept, 1972 - No. 62, May, 1979

1 16 32 48 111 246 380
2-Super Skrull-c/story 8 16 24 51 96 140
3-5: 4-Captain Marvel battles Sub-Mariner 6 12 18 38 69 100
6-11: 11-Capt. Marvel given great power by Zo the Ruler; Smith/Trimpe-c;
Death of Una 4 8 12 25 40 55
12,13,15,19,20 3 6 9 17 26 35
14-Capt. Marvel vs. Iron Man; last 12¢ issue. 4 8 12 28 47 65
16-1st new Captain Marvel (cameo) 4 8 12 28 47 65
17-1st new Captain Marvel app. 8 16 24 54 102 150
18-Carol Danvers gets powers 7 14 21 46 86 125
21-Capt. Marvel battles Hulk; last 15¢ issue 4 8 12 28 47 65
22-24 3 6 9 17 26 35
25-Starlin-c/a begins; Starlin's 1st Thanos saga begins (3/73), ends #34; Thanos cameo
(5 panels) 7 14 21 49 92 135
26-2nd app. Thanos (see Iron Man #55); 1st Thanos-c
8 16 24 56 108 160
27-3rd app. Thanos 7 14 21 44 82 120
28-Thanos-c/s (4th app.); Avengers app. 8 16 24 56 108 160
29,30-Thanos cameos. 29-C.M. gains more powers 4 8 12 28 47 65
31-Thanos app.; last 20¢ issue; Avengers app. 5 10 15 30 50 70
32-Thanos-c & app.; Avengers app. 5 10 15 31 53 75
33-Thanos-c & app.; Capt. Marvel battles Thanos; Thanos origin re-told
8 16 24 54 102 150
34-1st app. Nitro; C.M. contracts cancer which eventually kills him; last Starlin-c/a
4 8 12 25 40 55
35,37-40,42,46-48,50,53-56,59-62: 39-Origin Watcher. 42,59-62-Drax app.
2 4 6 8 10 12
36,41,43,49: 36-R-origin/1st app. Capt. Marvel from Marvel Super-Heroes #12.
41,43-Drax app.; Wrightson part inks; #43-c(i). 49-Starlin & Weiss-p assists
2 4 6 8 11 14
44,45-(Regular 25¢ editions)(5,7/76) 2 4 6 8 10 12
44,45-(30¢-c variants, limited distribution) 4 8 12 27 44 60
51,52-(Regular 30¢ editions)(7,9/77) 2 4 6 8 10 12
51,52-(35¢-c variants, limited distribution) 7 14 21 46 86 125
57-Thanos appears in flashback 2 4 6 13 18 22
58-Thanos cameo; Drax app. 2 4 6 10 14 18

NOTE: ***Alcala** a-35. **Austin** a-46i, 49-53i; c-52i. **Buscema** a-18p-21p. **Colan** a(p)-1-4; c(p)-1-4, 8, 9. **Heck** a-5-10p, 16p. **Gil Kane** a-17-21p; c-17-24p, 37p, 53. **Starlin** a-36. **McWilliams** a-40i. #25-34 were reprinted in The Life of Captain Marvel.*

CAPTAIN MARVEL
Marvel Comics: Nov, 1989 ($1.50, one-shot, 52 pgs.)

1-Super-hero from Avengers; new powers 4.00

CAPTAIN MARVEL
Marvel Comics: Feb, 1994 ($1.75, 52 pgs.)

1-(Indicia reads Vol 2 #2)-Minor Captain America app. 4.00

CAPTAIN MARVEL
Marvel Comics: Dec, 1995 - No. 6, May, 1996 ($2.95/$1.95)

1 ($2.95)-Advs. of Mar-Vell's son begins; Fabian Nicieza scripts; foil-c 4.00
2-6: 2-Begin $1.95-c 3.00

CAPTAIN MARVEL (Vol. 3) (See Avengers Forever)
Marvel Comics: Jan, 2000 - No. 35, Oct, 2002 ($2.50)

1-Peter David-s in all; two covers 4.00
2-10: 2-Two covers; Hulk app. 9-Silver Surfer app. 3.00
11-35: 12-Maximum Security x-over. 17,18-Starlin-a. 27-30-Spider-Man 2099 app. 3.00
Wizard #0-Preview and history of Rick Jones 4.00
...: First Contact (8/01, $16.95, TPB) r/#0,1-6 17.00

CAPTAIN MARVEL (Vol. 4) (See Avengers Forever)
Marvel Comics: Nov, 2002 - No. 25, Sept, 2004 ($2.25/$2.99)

1-Peter David-s/Chriscross-a ; 3 covers by Ross, Jusko & Chriscross 4.00
2-7: 2,3-Punisher app. 3-Alex Ross-c; new costume debuts. 4-Noto-c. 7-Thor app. 3.00
3-Sketchbook Edition-($3.50) includes Ross' concept design pages for new costume 4.00
8-25: 8-Begin $2.99-c; Thor app.; Manco-c. 10-Spider-Man-c/app. 15-Neal Adams-c 3.00
Vol. 1: Nothing To Lose (2003, $14.99, TPB) r/#1-6 15.00
Vol. 2: Coven (2003, $14.99, TPB) r/#7-12 15.00
Vol. 3: Crazy Like a Fox (2004, $14.99, TPB) r/#13-18 15.00
Vol. 4: Odyssey (2004, $16.99, TPB) r/#19-25 17.00

CAPTAIN MARVEL (Vol. 5) (See Secret Invasion x-over titles)
Marvel Comics: Jan, 2008 - No. 5, Jun, 2008 ($2.99)

1-5-Mar-Vell "from the past in the present"; McGuinness-c/Weeks-a 3.00
3,4-Skrull variant-c 4.00

CAPTAIN MARVEL
Marvel Comics: Sept, 2012 - No. 17, Jan, 2014 ($2.99)

1-Carol Danvers as Captain Marvel; DeConnick-s/Soy-a
2 4 6 10 14 18
2-5 6.00
6-13,15,16: 13-The Enemy Within. 15,16-Infinity tie-in 5.00
14-1st cameo of Kamala Khan (new Ms. Marvel); Andrade-a; The Enemy Within cont'd
4 8 12 27 44 60
17-($3.99) Cameo of Kamala Khan (new Ms. Marvel); Andrade-a
2 4 6 10 14 18
17-($3.99, 2nd printing) Kamala Khan (new Ms. Marvel) in costume on cover
10 20 30 64 132 200

CAPTAIN MARVEL
Marvel Comics: May, 2014 - No. 15, Jul, 2015 ($3.99)

1-Carol Danvers; DeConnick-s/Lopez-a 2 4 6 10 14 18
2,3-Guardians of the Galaxy app. 6.00
4-9,11-15: 7,8-Rocket Raccoon app. 14-Black Vortex x-over 4.00
10-($4.99) 100th issue; War Machine & Spider-Woman app.; Lopez & Takara-a 5.00

CAPTAIN MARVEL (Follows Secret Wars event)(Also see Mighty Captain Marvel)
Marvel Comics: Mar, 2016 - No. 10, Jan, 2017 ($3.99)

1-5-Carol Danvers; Fazekas & Butters-s/Anka-a; Aurora, Sasquatch & Puck app. 4.00
6-9-Civil War II tie-ins 4.00
10-($4.99) Civil War II tie-in; Gage & Gage-s/Silas-a; Alpha Flight app. 5.00

CAPTAIN MARVEL (Follows Mighty Captain Marvel)
Marvel Comics: No. 125, Dec, 2017 - Present ($3.99)

125-129-Carol Danvers; Stohl-s/Bandini-a; Alpha Flight app. 4.00

CAPTAIN MARVEL ADVENTURES (See Special Edition Comics for pre #1)
Fawcett Publications: 1941 (March) - No. 150, Nov, 1953 (#1 on stands 1/16/41)

nn(#1)-Captain Marvel & Sivana by Jack Kirby. The cover was printed on unstable paper stock and is rarely found in Fine or Mint condition; blank back inside-c
5000 10,000 20,000 40,000 65,000 90,000
2-(Advertised as #3, which was counting Special Edition Comics as the
real #1); Tuska-a 465 930 1395 3395 5998 8600
3-Metallic silver-c 334 668 1002 2338 4094 5850
4-Three Lt. Marvels app. 226 452 678 1446 2473 3500
5 174 348 522 1114 1907 2700
6-10: 9-1st Otto Binder scripts on Capt. Marvel 129 258 387 826 1413 2000

Captain Marvel Adventures #17 © FAW

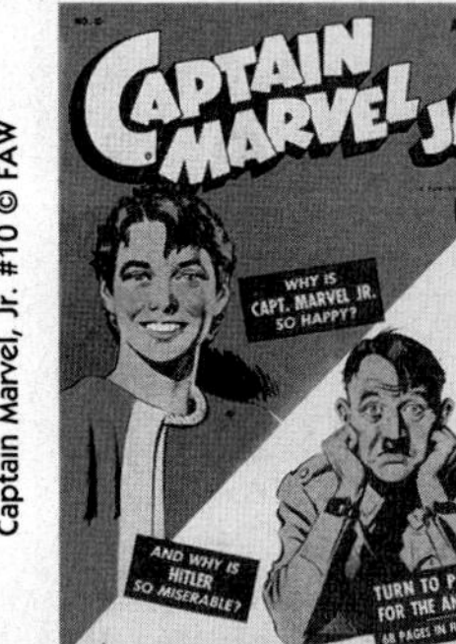

Captain Marvel, Jr. #10 © FAW

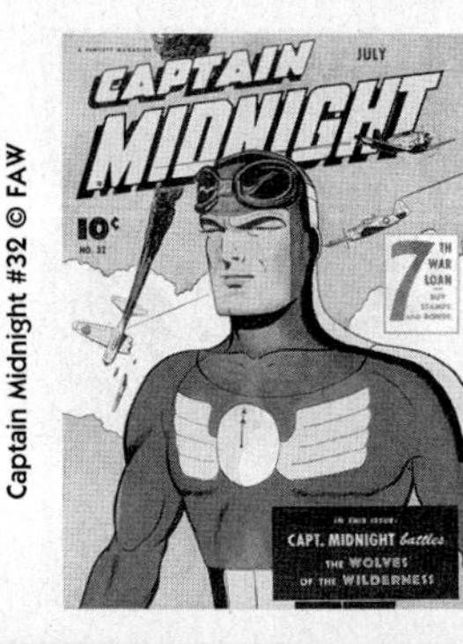

Captain Midnight #32 © FAW

GD VG FN VF VF/NM NM-
2.0 4.0 6.0 8.0 9.0 9.2

11-15: 12-Capt. Marvel joins the Army. 13-Two pg. Capt. Marvel pin-up.
15-Comix Cards on back-c begin, end #26 103 206 309 659 1130 1600
16,17: 17-Painted-c 94 188 282 597 1024 1450
18-Origin & 1st app. Mary Marvel & Marvel Family (12/11/42); classic painted-c;
Mary Marvel by Marcus Swayze 514 1028 1542 3750 6625 9500
19-Mary Marvel x-over; classic Christmas-c 87 174 261 553 952 1350
20,21,23-Attached to the cover, each has a miniature comic just like the Mighty Midget Comics #11, except that each has a full color promo ad on the back cover. Most copies were circulated without the miniature comic. These issues with miniatures attached are very rare, and should not be mistaken for copies with the similar Mighty Midget glued in its place. The Mighty Midgets had blank back covers except for a small victory stamp seal. Only the Capt. Marvel, Captain Marvel Jr. and Golden Arrow No. 11 miniatures have been positively documented as having been affixed to these covers. Each miniature was only partially glued by its back cover to the Captain Marvel comic making it easy to see if it's the genuine miniature rather than a Mighty Midget.
with comic attached.... 459 918 1377 3350 5925 8500
20,23-Without miniature 71 142 213 454 777 1100
21-Without miniature; Hitler-c 135 270 405 864 1482 2100
22-Mr. Mind serial begins; Mr. Mind first heard 97 194 291 621 1061 1500
24,25 68 136 204 432 746 1060
26-28,30: 26-Flag-c; subtle Mr. Mind 2-panel cameo. 27-1st full Mr. Mind app. (his voice was only heard over the radio before now) (9/43) 57 114 171 362 619 875
29-1st Mr. Mind-c (11/43) 63 126 189 403 689 975
31-35: 35-Origin Radar (5/44, see Master #50) 51 102 153 318 539 760
36-40: 37-Mary Marvel x-over 47 94 141 296 498 700
41-46: 42-Christmas-c. 43-Capt. Marvel 1st meets Uncle Marvel; Mary Batson cameo.
46-Mr. Mind serial ends 39 78 117 240 395 550
47-50 37 74 111 222 361 500
51-53,55-60: 51-63-Bi-weekly issues. 52-Origin & 1st app. Sivana Jr.; Capt. Marvel Jr. x-over
34 68 102 199 325 450
54-Special oversize 68 pg. issue 34 68 102 204 332 460
61-The Cult of the Curse serial begins 36 72 108 216 351 485
62-65-Serial cont.; Mary Marvel x-over in #65 34 68 102 199 325 450
66-Serial ends; Atomic War-c 39 78 117 233 384 535
67-77,79: 69-Billy Batson's Christmas; Uncle Marvel, Mary Marvel, Capt. Marvel Jr. x-over. 71-Three Lt. Marvels app. 72-Empire State Building photo-c. 79-Origin Mr. Tawny
31 62 93 182 296 410
78-Origin Mr. Atom 34 68 102 204 322 460
80-Origin Capt. Marvel retold; origin scene-c 97 194 291 621 1061 1500
81-84,86-90: 81,90-Mr. Atom app. 82-Infinity-c. 82,86,88,90-Mr. Tawny app.
31 62 93 182 296 410
85-Freedom Train issue 34 68 102 199 325 450
91-99: 92-Mr. Tawny app. 96-Gets 1st name "Tawky" 30 60 90 177 289 400
100-Origin retold; silver metallic-c 50 100 150 315 533 750
101-115,117-120 30 60 90 177 289 400
116-Flying Saucer issue (1/51) 34 68 102 199 325 450
121-Origin retold 37 74 111 222 361 500
122-137,139,140 30 60 90 177 289 400
138-Flying Saucer issue (11/52) 34 68 102 204 332 460
141-Pre-code horror story "The Hideous Head-Hunter"
34 68 102 199 325 450
142-149: 142-used in **POP**, pgs. 92,96 33 66 99 194 317 440
150-(Low distribution) 58 116 174 371 636 900
NOTE: ***Swayze*** *a-12, 14, 15, 18, 19, 40; c-12, 15, 19.*

CAPTAIN MARVEL AND THE CAROL CORPS (Secret Wars tie-in)
Marvel Comics: Aug, 2015 - No. 4, Nov, 2015 ($3.99, limited series)
1-4: 1-Carol Danvers' squad; DeConnick & Thompson-s/Lopez-a. 4-Braga-a 4.00

CAPTAIN MARVEL AND THE GOOD HUMOR MAN (Movie)
Fawcett Publications: 1950
nn-Partial photo-c w/Jack Carson & the Captain Marvel Club Boys
50 100 150 315 533 750

CAPTAIN MARVEL COMIC STORY PAINT BOOK (See Comic Story...)

CAPTAIN MARVEL, JR. (See Fawcett Miniatures, Marvel Family, Master Comics, Mighty Midget Comics, Shazam & Whiz Comics)

CAPTAIN MARVEL, JR.
Fawcett Publications: Nov, 1942 - No. 119, June, 1953 (No #34)
1-Origin Capt. Marvel Jr. retold (Whiz #25); Capt. Nazi app. Classic Raboy-c
595 1190 1785 4350 7675 11,000
2-Vs. Capt. Nazi; origin Capt. Nippon 213 426 639 1363 2332 3300
3 116 232 348 742 1271 1800
4-Classic Raboy-c 123 246 369 787 1344 1900
5-Vs. Capt. Nazi 97 194 291 621 1061 1500
6-8: 8-Vs. Capt. Nazi 81 162 243 518 884 1250
9-Classic flag-c 97 194 291 621 1061 1500
10-Hitler-c 181 362 543 1158 1979 2800
11,12,15-Capt. Nazi app. 68 136 204 435 743 1050
13-Classic Hitler, Tojo and Mussolini football-c 181 362 543 1158 1979 2800
14,16-20: 14-Christmas-c. 16-Capt. Marvel & Sivana x-over. 17-Futuristic city-c; Raboy-c/a(3).
19-Capt. Nazi & Capt. Nippon app. 57 114 171 362 619 875
21-30: 25-Flag-c 45 90 135 284 480 675
31-33,36-40: 37-Infinity-c 33 66 99 194 317 440
35-#34 on inside; cover shows origin of Sivana Jr. which is not on inside. Evidently the cover to #35 was printed out of sequence and bound with contents to #34
33 66 99 194 317 440
41-70: 42-Robot-c. 53-Atomic Bomb-c/story 27 54 81 160 263 365
71-99,101-104: 87,93-Robot-c. 104-Used in **POP**, pg. 89
24 48 72 142 234 325
100 29 58 87 170 278 385
105-114,116-118: 116-Vampira, Queen of Terror app.
28 56 84 165 270 375
115-Classic injury to eye-c; Eyeball story w/injury-to-eye panels
148 296 444 947 1624 2300
119-Electric chair-c (scarce) 81 162 243 518 884 1250
NOTE: ***Mac Raboy*** *c-1-28, 30-32, 57, 59 among others.*

CAPTAIN MARVEL PRESENTS THE TERRIBLE FIVE
M. F. Enterprises: Aug, 1966; V2#5, Sept, 1967 (No #2-4) (25¢)
1 5 10 15 31 53 75
V2#5-(Formerly Captain Marvel) 4 8 12 23 37 50

CAPTAIN MARVEL'S FUN BOOK
Samuel Lowe Co.: 1944 (1/2" thick) (cardboard covers)(25¢)
nn-Puzzles, games, magic, etc.; infinity-c 45 90 135 284 480 675

CAPTAIN MARVEL SPECIAL EDITION (See Special Edition)

CAPTAIN MARVEL STORY BOOK
Fawcett Publications: Summer, 1946 - No. 4, Summer?, 1948
1-Half text 60 120 180 381 653 925
2-4 42 84 126 265 445 625

CAPTAIN MARVEL THRILL BOOK (Large-Size)
Fawcett Publications: 1941 (B&W w/color-c)
1-Reprints from Whiz #8,10, & Special Edition #1 (Rare)
400 800 1200 4000 - -
NOTE: *Rarely found in Fine or Mint condition.*

CAPTAIN MIDNIGHT (TV, radio, films) (See The Funnies, Popular Comics & Super Book of Comics)(Becomes Sweethearts No. 68 on)
Fawcett Publications: Sept, 1942 - No. 67, Fall, 1948 (#1-14: 68 pgs.)
1-Origin Captain Midnight, star of radio and movies; Captain Marvel cameo on cover
320 640 960 2240 3920 5600
2-Smashes the Jap Juggarnaut 158 316 474 1003 1727 2450
3-Classic Nazi war-c 145 290 435 921 1586 2250
4,5: 4-Grapples the Gremlins 116 232 348 742 1271 1800
6-8 69 138 207 442 759 1075
9-Raboy-c 73 146 219 467 796 1125
10-Raboy Flag-c/WWII-c 74 148 222 470 810 1150
11-20: 11,17,18-Raboy-c. 16 (1/44) 50 100 150 315 533 750
21-Classic WWII-c 58 116 174 371 636 900
22,25-30: 22-War savings stamp-c 40 80 120 246 411 575
23-WWII Concentration Camp-c 55 110 165 352 601 850
24-Japan flag sunburst-c 61 122 183 390 670 950
31-40 32 64 96 188 307 425
41-59,61-67: 50-Sci/fi theme begins? 25 50 75 150 245 340
60-Flying Saucer issue (2/48)-3rd of this theme; see The Spirit 9/28/47 (1st), Shadow Comics V7#10 (2nd, 1/48) & Boy Commandos #26 (4th, 3-4/48)
39 78 117 233 384 535

CAPTAIN MIDNIGHT
Dark Horse Comics: No. 0, Jun, 2013 - No. 24, Jun, 2015 ($2.99)
0-24: 0-Williamson-s/Ibáñez-a; WWII hero appears in modern times. 4,5-Skyman app. 3.00
One For One: Captain Midnight #1 (1/14, $1.00) r/#1 3.00

CAPTAIN NICE (TV)
Gold Key: Nov, 1967 (one-shot)
1(10211-711)-Photo-c 6 12 18 37 66 95

CAPTAIN N: THE GAME MASTER (TV)
Valiant Comics: 1990 - No. 5, 1990 ($1.95, thick stock, coated-c)
1-5: 3-Quesada-a (1st pro work). 4,5-Layton-c 5.00

CAPTAIN PARAGON (See Bill Black's Fun Comics)
Americomics: Dec, 1983 - No. 4, 1985

Captain Science #2 © YM

Capt. Storm #15 © DC

Captain Video #6 © FAW

GD VG FN VF VF/NM NM-
2.0 4.0 6.0 8.0 9.0 9.2

1-Intro/1st app. Ms. Victory 4.00
2-4 3.00

CAPTAIN PARAGON AND THE SENTINELS OF JUSTICE
AC Comics: April, 1985 - No. 6, 1986 ($1.75)
1-6: 1-Capt. Paragon, Commando D., Nightveil, Scarlet Scorpion, Stardust & Atoman 3.00

CAPTAIN PLANET AND THE PLANETEERS (TV cartoon)
Marvel Comics: Oct, 1991 - No. 12, Oct, 1992 ($1.00/$1.25)
1-N. Adams painted-c 4.00
2-12: 3-Romita-c 3.00

CAPTAIN POWER AND THE SOLDIERS OF THE FUTURE (TV)
Continuity Comics: Aug, 1988 - No. 2, 1988 ($2.00)
1,2: 1-Neal Adams-c/layouts/inks; variant-c exists. 3.00

CAPTAIN PUREHEART (See Archie as...)

CAPTAIN ROCKET
P. L. Publ. (Canada): Nov, 1951
1 54 108 162 343 574 825

CAPT. SAVAGE AND HIS LEATHERNECK RAIDERS (...And His Battlefield Raiders #9 on)
Marvel Comics Group (Animated Timely Features): Jan, 1968 - No. 19, Mar, 1970
(See Sgt. Fury No. 10)
1-Sgt. Fury & Howlers cameo 6 12 18 41 76 110
2,7,11: 2-Origin Hydra. 7-Pre-"Thing" Ben Grimm story. 11-Sgt. Fury app.
3 6 9 17 26 35
3-6,8-10,12-14: 4-Origin Hydra. 14-Last 12¢ issue 3 6 9 16 23 30
15-19 3 6 9 14 19 24
*NOTE: **Ayres/Shores** a-1-8,11. **Ayres/Severin** a-9,10,17-19. **Heck/Shores** a-12-15.*

CAPTAIN SCIENCE (Fantastic No. 8 on)
Youthful Magazines: Nov, 1950; No. 2, Feb, 1951 - No. 7, Dec, 1951
1-Wood-a; origin; 2 pg. text w/ photos of George Pal's "Destination Moon."
100 200 300 635 1093 1550
2-Flying saucer-c swiped Weird Science #13(#2)-c 55 110 165 352 601 850
3,6,7; 3,6-Bondage c-swipes/Wings #94,91 52 104 156 328 552 775
4,5-Wood/Orlando-c/a(2) each 89 178 267 565 970 1375
NOTE: *Fass a-4. Bondage c-3, 6, 7.*

CAPTAIN SILVER'S LOG OF SEA HOUND (See Sea Hound)

CAPTAIN SINBAD (Movie Adaptation) (See Fantastic Voyages of... & Movie Comics)

CAPTAIN STERNN: RUNNING OUT OF TIME
Kitchen Sink Press: Sept, 1993 - No. 5, 1994 ($4.95, limited series, coated stock, 52 pgs.)
1-5: Berni Wrightson-c/a/scripts 6.00
1-Gold ink variant 10.00

CAPTAIN STEVE SAVAGE (...& His Jet Fighters, No. 2-13)
Avon Periodicals: 1950 - No. 8, 1/53; No. 5, 9-10/54 - No. 13, 5-6/56
nn(1st series)-Harrison/Wood art, 22 pgs. (titled "...Over Korea")
47 94 141 296 498 700
1(4/51)-Reprints nn issue (Canadian) 22 44 66 128 209 290
2-Kamen-a 18 36 54 105 165 225
3-11 (#6, 11-12/54, last precode) 15 30 45 83 124 165
12-Wood-a (6 pgs.) 18 36 54 103 162 220
13-Check, Lawrence-a 15 30 45 84 127 170
NOTE: ***Kinstler** c-2-5, 7-9, 11. **Lawrence** a-8. **Ravielli** a-5, 9.*
5(9-10/54-2nd series)(Formerly Sensational Police Cases)
12 24 36 67 94 120
6-Reprints nn issue; Harrison/Wood-a 12 24 36 69 97 125
7-13: 9,10-Kinstler-c. 10-r/cover #2 (1st series). 13-r/cover #8 (1st series)
10 20 30 56 76 95

CAPTAIN STONE (See Holyoke One-Shot No. 10)

CAPT. STORM (Also see G. I. Combat #138)
National Periodical Publications: May-June, 1964 - No. 18, Mar-Apr, 1967
1-Origin 10 20 30 69 147 225
2-7,9-18: 3,6,13-Kubert-a. 4-Colan-a. 12-Kubert-c 7 14 21 44 82 120
8-Grey-tone-c 8 16 24 54 102 150

CAPTAIN 3-D (Super hero)
Harvey Publications: December, 1953 (25¢, came with 2 pairs of glasses)
1-Kirby/Ditko-a (Ditko's 3rd published work tied with Strange Fantasy #9, see also Daring Love #1 & Black Magic V4 #3); shows cover in 3-D on inside;
Kirby/Meskin-c 12 24 36 69 97 125
NOTE: *Half price without glasses*

CAPTAIN THUNDER AND BLUE BOLT
Hero Comics: Sept, 1987 - No. 10, 1988 ($1.95)
1-10: 1-Origin Blue Bolt. 3-Origin Capt. Thunder. 6-1st app. Wicket. 8-Champions x-over 3.00

CAPTAIN TOOTSIE & THE SECRET LEGION (Advs. of...)(Also see Monte Hale #30,39 & Real Western Hero)
Toby Press: Oct, 1950 - No. 2, Dec, 1950
1-Not Beck-a; both have sci/fi covers 34 68 102 199 325 450
2-The Rocketeer Patrol app.; not Beck-a 20 40 60 117 189 260

CAPTAIN TRIUMPH (See Crack Comics #27)

CAPTAIN UNIVERSE... (5-part x-over)
Marvel Comics: 2005; Jan, 2006
.../ Daredevil 1 (1/06, $2.99) Part 2; Faerber-s/Santacruz-a 3.00
.../ Hulk 1 (1/06, $2.99) Part 1; Faerber-s/Magno-a 3.00
.../ Invisible Woman 1 (1/06, $2.99) Part 4; Faerber-s/Raiz-a; Gladiator app. 3.00
.../ Silver Surfer 1 (1/06, $2.99) Part 5; Faerber-s/Magno-a 3.00
.../ X-23 1 (1/06, $2.99) Part 3; Faerber-s/Portella-a; Scorpion app. 3.00
...: Power Unimaginable TPB (2005, $19.99)-Reprints from Marvel Spotlight #9-11, Incredible Hulk Ann. #10, Marvel Fanfare #25, Web of Spider-Man Ann. #5&6, Marvel Comics Presents #148, Cosmic Power Unlimited #5 20.00
...: The Hero Who Could Be You 1 (7/13, $7.99) r/Marvel Spotlight #9-11 & early apps. 8.00
...: Universal Heroes TPB (2005, $13.99) reprints .../Hulk, .../Daredevil, ...X-23 and back-up stories from Amazing Fantasy (2005) #13,14 14.00

CAPTAIN VENTURE & THE LAND BENEATH THE SEA (See Space Family Robinson)
Gold Key: Oct, 1968 - No. 2, Oct, 1969
1-r/Space Family Robinson serial; Spiegle-a 4 8 12 27 44 60
2-Spiegle-a 4 8 12 23 37 50

CAPTAIN VICTORY AND THE GALACTIC RANGERS (Also see Kirby: Genesis)
Pacific Comics: Nov, 1981 - No. 13, Jan, 1984 ($1.00, direct sales, 36-48 pgs.)
(Created by Jack Kirby)
1-1st app. Mr. Mind 4.00
2-13: 3-N. Adams-a 3.00
Special 1-(10/83)-Kirby c/a(p) 4.00
*NOTE: **Conrad** a-10, 11. **Ditko** a-6. **Kirby** a-1-3p; c-1-13.*

CAPTAIN VICTORY AND THE GALACTIC RANGERS
Jack Kirby Comics: July, 2000 - No. 2, Sept, 2000 ($2.95, B&W)
1,2-New Jeremy Kirby-s with reprinted Jack Kirby-a; Liefeld pin-up art 3.00

CAPTAIN VICTORY AND THE GALACTIC RANGERS
Dynamite Entertainment: 2014 - No. 6, 2015 ($3.99)
1-6-Joe Casey-s; art by various. 3-Dalrymple & Mahfood-a 4.00

CAPTAIN VIDEO (TV) (See XMas Comics)
Fawcett Publications: Feb, 1951 - No. 6, Dec, 1951 (No. 1,5,6-36 pgs.; 2-4, 52 pgs.)
1-George Evans-a(2); 1st TV hero comic 103 206 309 659 1130 1600
2-Used in **SOTI**, pg. 382 66 132 198 419 722 1025
3-6-All Evans-a except #5 mostly Evans 55 110 165 352 601 850
NOTE: *Minor **Williamson** assists on most issues. Photo c-1, 5, 6; painted c-2-4.*

CAPTAIN WILLIE SCHULTZ (Also see Fightin' Army)
Charlton Comics: No. 76, Oct, 1985 - No. 77, Jan, 1986
76,77-Low print run 1 2 3 5 6 8

CAPTAIN WIZARD COMICS (See Meteor, Red Band & Three Ring Comics)
Rural Home: 1946
1-Capt. Wizard dons new costume; Impossible Man, Race Wilkins app.
40 80 120 246 411 575

CAPTAIN WONDER
Image Comics: Feb, 2011 ($4.99, 3-D comic with glasses)
1-Haberlin-s/Tan-a; sketch pages, crossword puzzle, paper dolls 5.00

CAPTURE CREATURES
BOOM! Entertainment (kaboom!): Nov, 2014 - No. 4, May, 2015 ($3.99)
1-4-Frank Gibson-s/Becky Dreistadt-a; multiple covers on each 4.00

CARBON GREY
Image Comics: Mar, 2011 - No. 3, May, 2011 ($2.99, limited series)
1-3-Khari Evans, Kinsun Loh & Hoang Nguyen-a; Nguyen-c 3.00
... Origins 1,2 (11/11 - No. 2, 3/12, $3.99) 1-Pop Mhan-a 4.00
Vol. 2 (7/12 - No. 3, 2/13, $3.99) 1-3-Gardner-s/Evans & Nguyen-a 4.00
Vol. 3 (12/13 - Present) 1,2-Gardner-s/Evans & Nguyen-a 4.00

CARE BEARS (TV, Movie)(See Star Comics Magazine)
Star Comics/Marvel Comics No. 15 on: Nov, 1985 - No. 20, Jan, 1989

Carnage (2016 series) #15 © MAR

Cars #2 © DIS/Pixar

Cartoon Network Action Pack #61 © CN

GD 2.0 | VG 4.0 | FN 6.0 | VF 8.0 | VF/NM 9.0 | NM- 9.2

1-Post-a begins 2 4 6 10 14 18
2-20: 11-$1.00-c begins. 13-Madballs app. 1 3 4 6 8 10

CAREER GIRL ROMANCES (Formerly Three Nurses)
Charlton Comics: June, 1964 - No. 78, Dec, 1973

V4#24-31 3 6 9 14 20 25
32-Elvis Presley, Herman's Hermits, Johnny Rivers line drawn-c 10 20 30 64 132 200
33-37,39-50: 39-Tiffany Sinn app. 2 4 6 13 18 22
38-(2/67) 1st app. Tiffany Sinn, C.I.A. Sweetheart, Undercover Agent (also see Secret Agent #10; Dominguel-a 3 6 9 16 24 32
51-78: 54-Jonnie Love anti-drup PSA. 67-Susan Dey pin-up. 70-David Cassidy pin-up 2 4 6 10 14 18

CAR 54, WHERE ARE YOU? (TV)
Dell Publishing Co.: Mar-May, 1962 - No. 7, Sept-Nov, 1963; 1964 - 1965 (All photo-c)

Four Color 1257(#1, 3-5/62) 8 16 24 54 102 150
2(6-8/62)-7 5 10 15 30 50 70
2,3(10-12/64), 4(1-3/65)-Reprints #2,3,&4 of 1st series 3 6 9 19 30 40

CARL BARKS LIBRARY OF WALT DISNEY'S GYRO GEARLOOSE COMICS AND FILLERS IN COLOR, THE
Gladstone: 1993 ($7.95, 8-1/2x11", limited series, 52 pgs.)

1-6: Carl Barks reprints 1 3 4 6 8 10

CARL BARKS LIBRARY OF WALT DISNEY'S COMICS AND STORIES IN COLOR, THE
Gladstone: Jan, 1992 - No. 51, Mar, 1996 ($8.95, 8-1/2x11", 60 pgs.)

1,2,6,8-51: 1-Barks Donald Duck-r/WDC&S #31-35; 2-r/#36,38-41; 6-r/#57-61; 8-r/#67-71; 9-r/#72-76; 10-r/#77-81; 11-r/#82-86; 12-r/#87-91; 13-r/#92-96; 14-r/#97-101; 15-r/#102-106; 16-r/#107-111; 17-r/#112,114,117,124,125; 18-r/#126-130; 19-r/#131,132(2),133,134; 20-r/#135-139; 21-r/#140-144; 22-r/#145-149; 23-r/#150-154; 24-r/#155-159; 25-r/#160-164; 26-r/#165-169; 27-r/#170-174;28-r/#175-179; 29-r/#180-184; 30-r/#185-189; 31-r/#190-194; 32-r/#195-199;33-r/#200-204; 34-r/#205-209; 35-r/#210-214; 36-r/#215-219; 37-r/#220-224; 38-r/#225-229; 39-r/#230-234; 40-r/#235-239; 41-r/#240-244; 42r/#245-249; 43-r/#250-254; 44-50; All contain one Heroes & Villains trading card each 2 4 6 9 12 15
3,4,7: 3-r/#42-46. 4-r/#47-51. 7-r/#62-66. 2 4 6 11 16 20
5-r/#52-56 3 6 9 16 23 30

CARL BARKS LIBRARY OF WALT DISNEY'S DONALD DUCK ADVENTURES IN COLOR, THE
Gladstone: Jan, 1994 - No. 25, Jan, 1996 ($7.95-$9.95, 44-68 pgs., 8-1/2"x11")
(all contain one Donald Duck trading card each)

1-5,7-25-Carl Barks-r: 1-r/FC #9; 2-r/FC #29; 3-r/FC #62; 4-r/FC #108; 5-r/FC #147 & #79(Mickey Mouse); 7-r/FC #159. 8-r/FC #178 & 189. 9-r/FC #199 & 203; 10-r/FC 223 & 238; 11-r/Christmas Parade #1 & 2; 12-r/FC #296; 13-r/FC #263; 14-r/MOC #20 & 41; 15-r/FC 275 & 282; 16-r/FC #291&300; 17-r/FC #308 & 318; 18-r/Vac. Parade #1 & Summer Fun #2; 19-r/FC #328 & 367 2 4 6 9 12 15
6-r/MOC #4, Cheerios "Atom Bomb," D.D. Tells About Kites 3 6 9 14 20 25

CARL BARKS LIBRARY OF WALT DISNEY'S DONALD DUCK CHRISTMAS STORIES IN COLOR, THE
Gladstone: 1992 ($7.95, 44pgs., one-shot)

nn-Reprints Firestone giveaways 1945-1949 2 4 6 10 14 18

CARL BARKS LIBRARY OF WALT DISNEY'S UNCLE SCROOGE COMICS ONE PAGERS IN COLOR, THE
Gladstone: 1992 - No. 2, 1993 ($8.95, limited series, 60 pgs., 8-1/2x11")

1-Carl Barks one pg. reprints 3 6 9 16 23 30
2-Carl Barks one pg. reprints 2 4 6 10 14 18

CARNAGE
Marvel Comics: Dec, 2010 - No. 5, Aug, 2011 ($3.99, limited series)

1-5-Spider-Man & Iron Man app.; Clayton Crain-a/c; Wells-s 4.00
...: It's a Wonderful Life (10/96, $1.95) David Quinn scripts 3.00
...: Mind Bomb (2/96, $2.95) Warren Ellis script; Kyle Hotz-a 4.00

CARNAGE
Marvel Comics: Jan, 2016 - No. 16, Mar, 2017 ($3.99)

1-16: 1-Conway-s/Perkins-a; Eddie Brock app. 3-Man-Wolf app. 4,5-Toxin app. 4.00

CARNAGE, U.S.A.
Marvel Comics: Feb, 2012 - No. 5, Jun, 2012 ($3.99, limited series)

1-4-Clayton Crain-a/c; Wells-s; Spider-Man & Avengers app. 3,4-Venom app. 4.00

CARNATION MALTED MILK GIVEAWAYS (See Wisco)

CARNEYS, THE
Archie Comics: Summer, 1994 ($2.00, 52 pgs)

1-Bound-in pull-out poster 4.00

CARNIVAL COMICS (Formerly Kayo #12; becomes Red Seal Comics #14)
Harry 'A' Chesler/Pershing Square Publ. Co.: 1945

nn (#13)-Guardineer-a 20 40 60 115 185 255

CAROLINE KENNEDY
Charlton Comics: 1961 (one-shot)

nn-Interior photo covers of Kennedy family 10 20 30 64 132 200

CAROUSEL COMICS
F. E. Howard, Toronto: V1#8, April, 1948

V1#8 12 24 36 69 97 125

CARS (Based on the 2006 Pixar movie)
Boom Entertainment: No. 0, Nov, 2009 - No. 7, Jun, 2010 ($2.99)

0-7: 0,1-Three covers on each. 2-7-Two covers on each 3.00
...: Adventures of Tow Mater 1-4 (7/10 - No. 4, 10/10, $2.99) 1-Two covers 3.00
...: Radiator Springs 1-4 (7/09 - No. 4, 10/09, $2.99) Two covers on each 3.00
...: The Rookie 1-4 (3/09 - No. 4, 6/09, $2.99) Origin of Lightning McQueen 3.00

CARS 2 (Based on the 2011 Pixar movie)
Marvel Worldwide (Disney Comics): Aug, 2011 - No. 2, Aug, 2011 ($3.99)

1,2-Movie adaptation; car profile pages 4.00

CARS, WORLD OF (Free Comic Book Day giveaway)
BOOM Kids!: May, 2009

1-Based on the Disney/Pixar movie 3.00

CARTOON CARTOONS (Anthology)
DC Comics: Mar, 2001 - No. 33, Oct, 2004 ($1.99/$2.25)

1-33-Short stories of Cartoon Network characters. 3,6,10,13,15-Space Ghost. 13-Begin $2.25-c. 17-Dexter's Laboratory begins 3.00

CARTOON KIDS
Atlas Comics (CPS): 1957 (no month)

1-Maneely-c/a; Dexter The Demon, Willie The Wise-Guy, Little Zelda app. 16 32 48 94 147 200

CARTOON NETWORK ACTION PACK (Anthology)
DC Comics: July, 2006 - No. 67, May, 2012 ($2.25/$2.50/$2.99)

1-31-Short stories of Cartoon Network characters. 1,4,6-Rowdyruff Boys app. 3.00
32-67: 32-Begin $2.50-c. 50-Ben 10/Generator Rex team-up 3.00

CARTOON NETWORK BLOCK PARTY (Anthology)
DC Comics: Nov, 2004 - No. 59, Sept, 2009 ($2.25/$2.50)

1,2,4-51-Short stories of Cartoon Network characters 3.00
3-($2.95) Bonus pages 4.00
52-59: 52-Begin $2.50-c. 59-Last issue; Powerpuff Girls app. 3.00
Cartoon Network 2-in-1: Ben 10 Alien Force/The Secret Saturdays TPB (2010, $12.99) reprints stories from #26-42 13.00
Cartoon Network 2-in-1: Foster's Home For Imaginary Friends/Powerpuff Girls TPB (2010, $12.99) reprints stories from #19-21,23,25,26,28,30-32,34-38,41 13.00
... Vol. 1: Get Down! (2005, $6.99, digest) reprints from Dexter's Lab and Cartoon Cartoons 7.00
... Vol. 2: Read All About It! (2005, $6.99, digest) reprints 7.00
... Vol. 3: Can You Dig It?; ... Vol. 4: Blast Off! (2006, $6.99, digest) reprints 7.00

CARTOON NETWORK PRESENTS
DC Comics: Aug, 1997 - No. 24, Aug, 1999 ($1.75-$1.99, anthology)

1-Dexter's Lab 5.00
1-Platinum Edition 1 2 3 5 7 9
2-10: 2-Space Ghost 3.50
11-24: 12-Bizarro World 3.00

CARTOON NETWORK PRESENTS SPACE GHOST
Archie Comics: Mar, 1997 ($1.50)

1-Scott Rosema-p 6.00

CARTOON NETWORK STARRING... (Anthology)
DC Comics: Sept, 1999 - No. 18, Feb, 2001 ($1.99)

1-Powerpuff Girls 5.00
2-18: 2,8,11,14,17-Johnny Bravo. 12,15,18-Space Ghost 3.00

CARTOON TALES (Disney's...)
W.D. Publications (Disney): nd, nn (1992) ($2.95, 6-5/8x9-1/2", 52 pgs.)

nn-Ariel & Sebastian-Serpent Teen; Beauty and the Beast; A Tale of Enchantment; Darkwing Duck - Just Us Justice Ducks; 101 Dalmatians - Canine Classics; Tale Spin - Surprise in the Skies; Uncle Scrooge - Blast to the Past 4.00

Casanova: Acedia #1 © Milkfed

Casey - Crime Photographer #2 © MAR

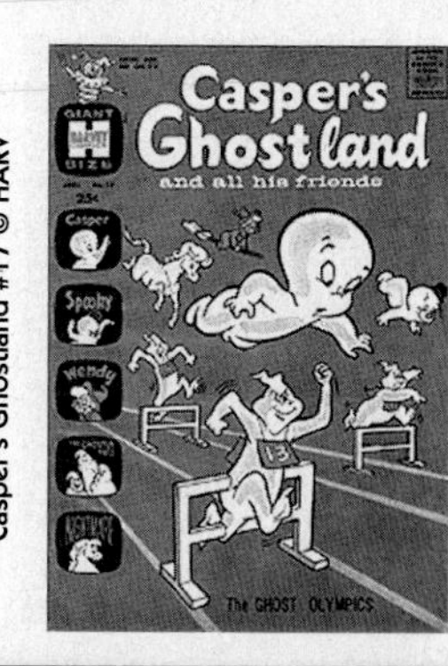

Casper's Ghostland #17 © HARV

CARVERS
Image Comics (Flypaper Press): 1998 - No. 3, 1999 ($2.95)

	GD 2.0	VG 4.0	FN 6.0	VF 8.0	VF/NM 9.0	NM- 9.2
1-3-Pander Bros.-a/Fleming-s						3.00

CAR WARRIORS
Marvel Comics (Epic): June, 1991 - No. 4, Sept, 1991 ($2.25, lim. series)

	GD 2.0	VG 4.0	FN 6.0	VF 8.0	VF/NM 9.0	NM- 9.2
1-4: 1-Says April in indicia						3.00

CASANOVA
Image Comics: June, 2006 - No. 14, May, 2008 ($1.99, B&W & olive green or blue)

	GD 2.0	VG 4.0	FN 6.0	VF 8.0	VF/NM 9.0	NM- 9.2
1-14: 1-7-Matt Fraction-s/Gabriel Bá-a/c. 8-14-Fabio Moon-a						3.00
...: Luxuria TPB (2008, $12.99) r/#1-7; sketch pages and cover gallery						13.00
1-4 (Marvel Comics, 10/10 - No. 4, 12/10, $3.99) Recolored reprints Image series #1-7						4.00
...: Acedia 1-8 (Image, 1/15 - No. 8, 3/17) Fraction-s/Moon-a; back-up by Chabon-s/Bá-a						4.00
...: Avaritia (III) 1-4 (Marvel, 11/11 - No. 4, 8/12, $4.99) new story; Fraction-s/Bá-a						5.00
...: Gula (Marvel, 1/11 - No. 4, 4/11) r/Image series #8-14. 4-New story pages						4.00

CASE FILES: SAM & TWITCH (Also see the Spawn titles)
Image Comics: May, 2003 - No. 25, July, 2006 ($2.50/$2.95, color #1-6/B&W #7-on)

	GD 2.0	VG 4.0	FN 6.0	VF 8.0	VF/NM 9.0	NM- 9.2
1-25: 1-5-Scott Morse-a/Marc Andreyko-s. 7-13-Paul Lee-a. 13-Niles-s						3.00

CASE OF THE SHOPLIFTER'S SHOE (See Perry Mason, Feature Book No.50)

CASE OF THE WINKING BUDDHA, THE
St. John Publ. Co.: 1950 (132 pgs.; 25¢; B&W; 5-1/2x7-5-1/2x8")

	GD 2.0	VG 4.0	FN 6.0	VF 8.0	VF/NM 9.0	NM- 9.2
nn-Charles Raab-a; reprinted in Authentic Police Cases No. 25	47	94	141	296	498	700

CASEY BLUE
DC Comics (WildStorm): Jul, 2008 - No. 6, Dec, 2008 ($2.99, limited series)

	GD 2.0	VG 4.0	FN 6.0	VF 8.0	VF/NM 9.0	NM- 9.2
1-6-B. Clay Moore-s/Carlos Barberi-a						3.00
...: Beyond Tomorrow TPB (2009, $19.99) r/#1-6; Barberi sketch pages						20.00

CASEY-CRIME PHOTOGRAPHER (Two-Gun Western No. 5 on)(Radio)
Marvel Comics (BFP): Aug, 1949 - No. 4, Feb, 1950

	GD 2.0	VG 4.0	FN 6.0	VF 8.0	VF/NM 9.0	NM- 9.2
1-Photo-c; 52 pgs.	32	64	96	188	307	425
2-4: Photo-c	20	40	60	120	195	270

CASEY JONES (TV)
Dell Publishing Co.: No. 915, July, 1958

	GD 2.0	VG 4.0	FN 6.0	VF 8.0	VF/NM 9.0	NM- 9.2
Four Color 915-Alan Hale photo-c	5	10	15	34	60	85

CASEY JONES & RAPHAEL (See Bodycount)
Mirage Studios: Oct, 1994 ($2.75, unfinished limited series)

	GD 2.0	VG 4.0	FN 6.0	VF 8.0	VF/NM 9.0	NM- 9.2
1-Bisley-c; Eastman story & pencils						3.00

CASEY JONES: NORTH BY DOWNEAST
Mirage Studios: May, 1994 - No. 2, July, 1994 ($2.75, limited series)

	GD 2.0	VG 4.0	FN 6.0	VF 8.0	VF/NM 9.0	NM- 9.2
1,2-Rick Veitch script & pencils; Kevin Eastman story & inks						3.00

CASPER ADVENTURE DIGEST
Harvey Comics: V2#1, Oct, 1992 - V2#8, Apr, 1994 ($1.75/$1.95, digest-size)

	GD 2.0	VG 4.0	FN 6.0	VF 8.0	VF/NM 9.0	NM- 9.2
V2#1: Casper, Richie Rich, Spooky, Wendy						5.00
2-8						3.50

CASPER AND...
Harvey Comics: Nov, 1987 - No. 12, June, 1990 (.75/$1.00, all reprints)

	GD 2.0	VG 4.0	FN 6.0	VF 8.0	VF/NM 9.0	NM- 9.2
1-Ghostly Trio						5.00
2-12: 2-Spooky; begin $1.00-c. 3-Wendy. 4-Nightmare. 5-Ghostly Trio. 6-Spooky. 7-Wendy. 8-Hot Stuff. 9-Baby Huey. 10-Wendy.11-Ghostly Trio. 12-Spooky						3.00

CASPER AND FRIENDS
Harvey Comics: Oct, 1991 - No. 5, July, 1992 ($1.00/$1.25)

	GD 2.0	VG 4.0	FN 6.0	VF 8.0	VF/NM 9.0	NM- 9.2
1-Nightmare, Ghostly Trio, Wendy, Spooky						4.00
2-5						3.00

CASPER AND FRIENDS MAGAZINE: Mar, 1997 - No. 3, July, 1997 ($3.99)

	GD 2.0	VG 4.0	FN 6.0	VF 8.0	VF/NM 9.0	NM- 9.2
1-3						4.00

CASPER AND NIGHTMARE (See Harvey Hits# 37, 45, 52, 56, 59, 62, 65, 68,71, 75)

CASPER AND NIGHTMARE (Nightmare & Casper No. 1-5)
Harvey Publications: No. 6, 11/64 - No. 44, 10/73; No. 45, 6/74 - No. 46, 8/74 (25¢)

	GD 2.0	VG 4.0	FN 6.0	VF 8.0	VF/NM 9.0	NM- 9.2
6: 68 pg. Giants begin, ends #32	5	10	15	31	53	75
7-10	3	6	9	21	33	45
11-20	3	6	9	17	26	35
21-37: 33-37-(52 pg. Giants)	3	6	9	14	20	26
38-46	2	4	6	10	14	18

NOTE: *Many issues contain reprints.*

CASPER AND SPOOKY (See Harvey Hits No. 20)
Harvey Publications: Oct, 1972 - No. 7, Oct, 1973

	GD 2.0	VG 4.0	FN 6.0	VF 8.0	VF/NM 9.0	NM- 9.2
1	3	6	9	17	26	35
2-7	2	4	6	10	14	18

CASPER AND THE GHOSTLY TRIO
Harvey Pub.: Nov, 1972 - No. 7, Nov, 1973; No. 8, Aug, 1990 - No. 10, Dec, 1990

	GD 2.0	VG 4.0	FN 6.0	VF 8.0	VF/NM 9.0	NM- 9.2
1	3	6	9	17	26	35
2-7	2	4	6	10	14	18
8-10						6.00

CASPER AND WENDY
Harvey Publications: Sept, 1972 - No. 8, Nov, 1973

	GD 2.0	VG 4.0	FN 6.0	VF 8.0	VF/NM 9.0	NM- 9.2
1: 52 pg. Giant	3	6	9	17	26	35
2-8	2	4	6	10	14	18

CASPER BIG BOOK
Harvey Comics: V2#1, Aug, 1992 - No. 3, May, 1993 ($1.95, 52 pgs.)

	GD 2.0	VG 4.0	FN 6.0	VF 8.0	VF/NM 9.0	NM- 9.2
V2#1-Spooky app.						4.00
2,3						4.00

CASPER CAT (See Dopey Duck)
I. W. Enterprises/Super: 1958; 1963

	GD 2.0	VG 4.0	FN 6.0	VF 8.0	VF/NM 9.0	NM- 9.2
1,7: 1-Wacky Duck #?.7-Reprint, Super No. 14('63)	2	4	6	9	13	16

CASPER DIGEST (...Magazine #?; ...Halloween Digest #8, 10)
Harvey Publications: Oct, 1986 - No. 18, Jan, 1991 ($1.25/$1.75, digest-size)

	GD 2.0	VG 4.0	FN 6.0	VF 8.0	VF/NM 9.0	NM- 9.2
1	1	3	4	6	8	10
2-18: 11-Valentine-c. 18-Halloween-c						6.00

CASPER DIGEST (...Magazine #? on)
Harvey Comics: V2#1, Sept, 1991 - V2#14, Nov, 1994 ($1.75/$1.95, digest-size)

	GD 2.0	VG 4.0	FN 6.0	VF 8.0	VF/NM 9.0	NM- 9.2
V2#1						5.00
2-14						3.50

CASPER DIGEST STORIES
Harvey Publications: Feb, 1980 - No. 4, Nov, 1980 (95¢, 132 pgs., digest size)

	GD 2.0	VG 4.0	FN 6.0	VF 8.0	VF/NM 9.0	NM- 9.2
1	2	4	6	9	13	16
2-4	1	2	3	5	7	9

CASPER DIGEST WINNERS
Harvey Publications: Apr, 1980 - No. 3, Sept, 1980 (95¢, 132 pgs., digest size)

	GD 2.0	VG 4.0	FN 6.0	VF 8.0	VF/NM 9.0	NM- 9.2
1	2	4	6	9	13	16
2,3	1	2	3	5	7	9

CASPER ENCHANTED TALES DIGEST
Harvey Comics: May, 1992 - No. 10, Oct, 1994 ($1.75, digest-size, 98 pgs.)

	GD 2.0	VG 4.0	FN 6.0	VF 8.0	VF/NM 9.0	NM- 9.2
1-Casper, Spooky, Wendy stories						5.00
2-10						4.00

CASPER GHOSTLAND
Harvey Comics: May, 1992 ($1.25)

	GD 2.0	VG 4.0	FN 6.0	VF 8.0	VF/NM 9.0	NM- 9.2
1						3.00

CASPER GIANT SIZE
Harvey Comics: Oct, 1992 - No. 4, Nov, 1993 ($2.25, 68 pgs.)

	GD 2.0	VG 4.0	FN 6.0	VF 8.0	VF/NM 9.0	NM- 9.2
V2#1-Casper, Wendy, Spooky stories						5.00
2-4						4.00

CASPER HALLOWEEN TRICK OR TREAT
Harvey Publications: Jan, 1976 (52 pgs.)

	GD 2.0	VG 4.0	FN 6.0	VF 8.0	VF/NM 9.0	NM- 9.2
1	3	6	9	17	26	35

CASPER IN SPACE (Formerly Casper Spaceship)
Harvey Publications: No. 6, June, 1973 - No. 8, Oct, 1973

	GD 2.0	VG 4.0	FN 6.0	VF 8.0	VF/NM 9.0	NM- 9.2
6-8	2	4	6	10	14	18

CASPER'S GHOSTLAND
Harvey Publications: Winter, 1958-59 - No. 97, 12/77; No. 98, 12/79 (25¢)

	GD 2.0	VG 4.0	FN 6.0	VF 8.0	VF/NM 9.0	NM- 9.2
1-84 pgs. begin, ends #10	18	36	54	124	275	425
2	9	18	27	59	117	175
3-10	7	14	21	44	82	120
11-20: 11-68 pgs. begin, ends #61. 13-X-Mas-c	5	10	15	35	63	90
21-40	4	8	12	28	47	65
41-61	3	6	9	16	24	32
62-77: 62-52 pgs. begin	2	4	6	9	13	16
78-98: 94-X-Mas-c	2	4	6	8	10	12

NOTE: *Most issues contain reprints w/new stories.*

CASPER SPACESHIP (Casper in Space No. 6 on)
Harvey Publications: Aug, 1972 - No. 5, April, 1973

Casper the Frtiendly Ghost #17 © DC

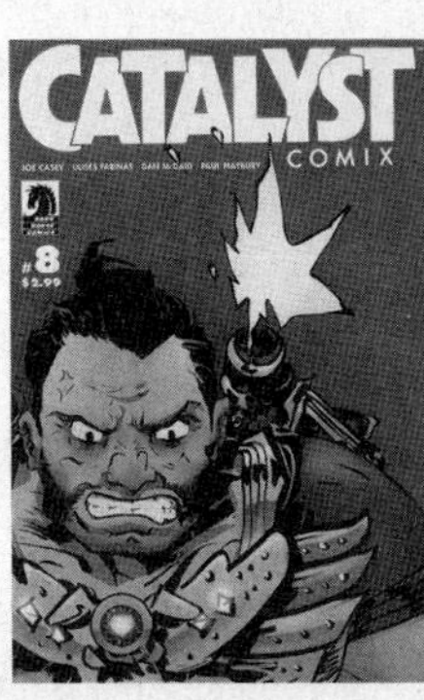

Catalyst Comix #8 © DH

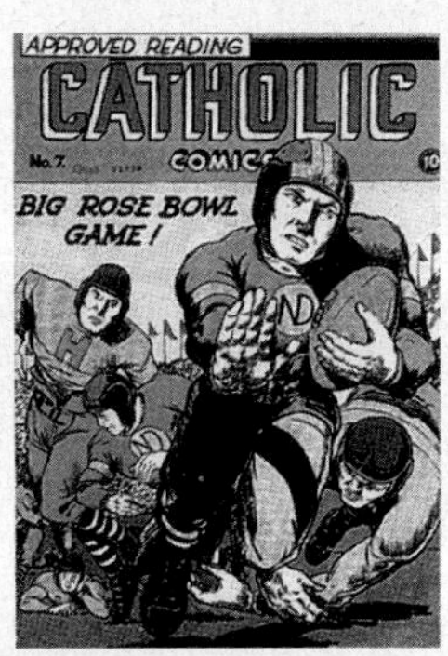

Catholic Comics #7 © Cath. Pub.

	GD 2.0	VG 4.0	FN 6.0	VF 8.0	VF/NM 9.0	NM- 9.2
1: 52 pg. Giant	3	6	9	18	28	38
2-5	2	4	6	11	16	20

CASPER'S SCARE SCHOOL
Ape Entertainment: 2011 - No. 4 ($3.99, limited series)

1,2-New short stories and classic reprints 4.00

CASPER STRANGE GHOST STORIES
Harvey Publications: October, 1974 - No. 14, Jan, 1977 (All 52 pgs.)

1	3	6	9	18	28	38
2-14	2	4	6	11	16	20

CASPER, THE FRIENDLY GHOST (See America's Best TV Comics, Famous TV Funday Funnies, The Friendly Ghost..., Nightmare &..., Richie Rich and..., Tastee-Freez, Treasury of Comics, Wendy the Good Little Witch & Wendy Witch World)

CASPER, THE FRIENDLY GHOST (Becomes Harvey Comics Hits No. 61 (No. 6), and then continued with Harvey issue No. 7)(1st Series)
St. John Publishing Co.: Sept, 1949 - No. 5, Aug, 1951

1(1949)-Origin & 1st app. Baby Huey & Herman the Mouse (1st comic app. of Casper and the 1st time the name Casper app. in any media, even films)	541	1082	1623	3950	6975	10,000
2,3 (2/50 & 8/50)	142	284	426	909	1555	2200
4,5 (3/51 & 8/51)	94	188	282	597	1024	1450

CASPER, THE FRIENDLY GHOST (Paramount Picture Star...)(2nd Series)
Harvey Publications (Family Comics): No. 7, Dec, 1952 - No. 70, July, 1958
Note: No. 6 is Harvey Comics Hits No. 61 (10/52)

7-Baby Huey begins, ends #9	38	76	114	285	641	1000
8,9	21	42	63	147	324	500
10-Spooky begins (1st app., 6/53), ends #70?	37	74	111	274	612	950
11,12: 2nd & 3rd app. Spooky	15	30	45	100	220	340
13-18: Alfred Harvey app. in story	12	24	36	79	170	260
19-1st app. Nightmare (4/54)	25	50	75	175	388	600
20-Wendy the Witch begins (1st app., 5/54)	46	92	138	359	805	1250
21-30: 24-Infinity-c	9	18	27	59	117	175
31-40: 38-Early Wendy app. 39-1st app. Samson Honeybun. 40-1st app. Dr. Brainstorm	7	14	21	46	86	125
41-1st Wendy app. on-c	13	26	39	89	195	300
42-50: 43-2nd Wendy-c. 46-1st app. Spooky's girl Pearl.	6	12	18	37	66	95
51-70 (Continues as Friendly Ghost... 8/58) 58-Early app. Bat Balfrey. 63-2nd app. Something the Baby Ghost. 66-1st app. Wildcat Witch	5	10	15	31	53	75

Harvey Comics Classics Vol. 1 TPB (Dark Horse Books, 6/07, $19.95) Reprints Casper's earliest appearances in this title, Little Audrey, and The Friendly Ghost Casper, mostly B&W with some color stories; history, early concept drawings and animation art 20.00

NOTE: *Baby Huey app. 7-9, 11, 121, 14, 16, 20. Buzzy app. 14, 16, 20. Nightmare app. 19, 27, 36, 37, 42, 46, 51, 53, 56, 70. Spooky app. 10-70. Wendy app. 20, 29-31, 35, 37, 38, 41-49, 51, 52, 54-58, 61, 64, 68.*

CASPER THE FRIENDLY GHOST (Formerly The Friendly Ghost...)(3rd Series)
Harvey Comics: No. 254, July, 1990 - No. 260, Jan, 1991 ($1.00)

254-260 3.00

CASPER THE FRIENDLY GHOST (4th Series)
Harvey Comics: Mar, 1991 - No. 28, Nov, 1994 ($1.00/$1.25/$1.50)

1-Casper becomes Mighty Ghost; Spooky & Wendy app. 5.00
2-28: 7,8-Post-a. 11-28-($1.50) 3.00

CASPER THE FRIENDLY GHOST (5th Series)
American Mythology Prods.: 2017 - Present ($3.99)

1,2-New stories and reprints; Hot Stuff, Spooky & Wendy app. 4.00

CASPER T.V. SHOWTIME
Harvey Comics: Jan, 1980 - No. 5, Oct, 1980

1	2	4	6	9	13	16
2-5	1	2	3	5	7	9

CASSETTE BOOKS (Classics Illustrated)
Cassette Book Co./I.P.S. Publ.: 1984 (48 pgs, b&w comic with cassette tape)
NOTE: *This series was illegal. The artwork was illegally obtained, and the Classics Illustrated copyright owner, Twin Circle Publ. sued to get an injunction to prevent the continued sale of this series. Many C.I. collectors obtained copies before the 1987 injunction, but now they are already scarce. Here again the market is just developing, but sealed mint copies of com ic and tape should be worth at least $25.*

1001 (CI#1-A2)New-PC 1002(CI#3-A2)CI-PC 1003(CI#13-A2)CI-PC
1004(CI#25)CI-LDC 1005(CI#10-A2)New-PC 1006(CI#64)CI-LDC

CASTILIAN (See Movie Classics)

CASTLE: A CALM BEFORE STORM (Based on the ABC TV series Castle)
Marvel Comics: Feb, 2013 - No. 5, Jul, 2013 ($3.99, limited series)

1-5-Peter David-s/Robert Atkins-a/Mico Suayan-c 4.00

CASTLE: RICHARD CASTLE'S ... (Based on the ABC TV series Castle)
Marvel Comics: 2011, 2012 ($19.99, hardcover graphic novels with dustjacket)

Deadly Storm HC (2011) - An "adaptation" of the show's fictional Derrick Storm novel; Bendis & DeConnick-s 20.00
Storm Season HC (2012) - Bendis & DeConnick-s/Lupacchino-a 20.00

CASTLEVANIA: THE BELMONT LEGACY
IDW Publishing: March 2005 - No. 5, July, 2005 ($3.99, limited series)

1-5-Marc Andreyko-s/E.J. Su-a 4.00

CASTLE WAITING
Olio: 1997 - No. 7, 1999 ($2.95, B&W)
Cartoon Books: Vol. 2, Aug, 2000 - No. 16 ($2.95/$3.95, B&W)
Fantagraphics Books: Vol. 3, 2006 - Present ($5.95/$3.95, B&W)

1-Linda Medley-s/a in all	1	2	3	5	6	8

2 4.00
3-7 3.00
The Lucky Road TPB r/#1-7 17.00
Hiatus Issue (1999) Crilley-c; short stories and previews 3.00
Vol. 2 #1-6,14-16 (#5&6 also have #12&13 on cover, for series numbering) 3.00
Vol. 3 #1 ($5.95) r/#15,16 and new story 6.00
Vol. 3 #2-15 ($3.95) 4.00

CASUAL HEROES
Image Comics (Motown Machineworks): Apr, 1996 ($2.25, unfinished lim. series)

1-Steve Rude-c 3.00

CAT, T.H.E. (TV) (See T.H.E. Cat)

CAT, THE (See Movie Classics)

CAT, THE (Female hero)
Marvel Comics Group: Nov, 1972 - No. 4, June, 1973

1-Origin & 1st app. The Cat (who later becomes Tigra); Mooney-a(i); Wood-c(i)/a(i)	8	16	24	56	108	160
2,3: 2-Marie Severin/Mooney-a. 3-Everett inks	3	6	9	17	26	35
4-Starlin/Weiss-a(p)	3	6	9	18	28	38

CATACLYSM
Marvel Comics: No. 0.1, Dec, 2013 ($3.99)

0.1-Fialkov-s; Galactus threatens the Ultimate Universe 4.00

CATACLYSM: THE ULTIMATES LAST STAND (Leads into Survive #1)
Marvel Comics: Jan, 2014 - No. 5, Apr, 2014 ($3.99, limited series)

1-5-Galactus in the Ultimate Universe; Ultimates & Spider-Man app.; Bendis-s/Bagley-a 4.00

CATACLYSM: ULTIMATES
Marvel Comics: Jan, 2014 - No. 3, Mar, 2014 ($3.99, limited series)

1-3-Ultimates vs. Galactus; Fialkov-s/Giandomenico-a 4.00

CATACLYSM: ULTIMATE SPIDER-MAN
Marvel Comics: Jan, 2014 - No. 3, Mar, 2014 ($3.99, limited series)

1-3-Spider-Man vs. Galactus; Bendis-s/Marquez-a 4.00

CATACLYSM: ULTIMATE X-MEN
Marvel Comics: Jan, 2014 - No. 3, Mar, 2014 ($3.99, limited series)

1-3-Fialkov-s/Martinez-a; Captain Marvel app. 4.00

CATALYST: AGENTS OF CHANGE (Also see Comics' Greatest World)
Dark Horse Comics: Feb, 1994 - No. 7, Nov, 1994 ($2.00, limited series)

1-7: 1-Foil stamped logo 3.00

CATALYST COMIX (From Comics' Greatest World)
Dark Horse Comics: Jul, 2013 - No. 9, Mar, 2014 ($2.99)

1-9: Amazing Grace, Frank Wells, and Agents of Change app.; Casey-s/Grampá-c 3.00

CATECHISM IN PICTURES
Catechetical Guild: Jan, 1958

311-Addison Burbank-a	8	16	24	42	54	65

CAT FROM OUTER SPACE (See Walt Disney Showcase #46)

CATHOLIC COMICS (See Heroes All Catholic...)
Catholic Publications: June, 1946 - V3#10, July, 1949

1	30	60	90	177	289	400
2	16	32	48	94	147	200
3-13(7/47): 11-Hollingsworth-a	14	28	42	82	121	160
V2#1-10	11	22	33	62	86	110
V3#1-10: Reprints 10-part Treasure Island serial from Target V2#2-11 (see Key Comics #5)	11	22	33	64	90	115

NOTE: ***Orlando** c-V2#10, V3#5, 6, 8.*

Cat-Man Comics #7 © HOKE

Catwoman #13 © DC

Catwoman (2nd series) #70 © DC

GD VG FN VF VF/NM NM-
2.0 4.0 6.0 8.0 9.0 9.2

CATHOLIC PICTORIAL
Catholic Guild: 1947

1-Toth-a(2) (Rare) 39 78 117 240 395 550

CAT-MAN COMICS (Formerly Crash Comics No. 1-5)
Holyoke Publishing Co./Continental Magazines V2#12, 7/44 on:
5/41 - No. 17, 1/43; No. 18, 7/43 - No. 22, 12/43; No. 23, 3/44 - No. 26, 11/44; No. 27, 4/45 - No. 30, 12/45; No. 31, 6/46 - No. 32, 8/46

1(V1#6)-The Cat-Man new costume (see Crash Comics for 1st app.) by Charles Quinlan; Origin The Deacon & Sidekick Mickey, Dr. Diamond & Rag-Man; The Black Widow app. Blaze Baylor begins 595 1190 1785 4350 7675 11,000
2(V1#7) 258 516 774 1651 2826 4000
3(V1#8)-The Pied Piper begins; classic Hitler, Stalin & Mussolini-c 400 800 1200 2800 4900 7000
4(V1#9) 226 452 678 1446 2473 3500
5(V2#10, 12/41)-Origin/1st app. The Kitten, Cat-Man's sidekick; The Hood begins. (cover re-dated w/cat image printed over Nov. date). Most of The Kitten's cover image blocked with sidebar 271 542 813 1734 2967 4200
6(V2#11), 7(V2#12) 226 452 678 1446 2473 3500
8(V2#13,3/42)-Origin Little Leaders; Volton by Kubert begins (his 1st comic book work) 300 600 900 1950 3375 4800
9 (V2#14, 4/42)-Classic-c showing a laughing Kitten slaughtering Japanese soldiers with a machine gun 314 628 942 2198 3849 5500
10 (V2#15, 5/42)-Origin Blackout; Phantom Falcon begins 206 412 618 1318 2259 3200
11 (V3#1, 6/42)-Kubert-a 206 412 618 1318 2259 3200
12 (V3#2),15,17(1/43): 12-Volton by Brodsky, not Kubert 194 388 582 1242 2121 3000
13-(9/42)(scarce) Weed of Doom (marijuana) 649 1298 1947 4738 8369 12,000
14-(10/42) World War II-c; Brodsky-a 213 426 639 1363 2332 3300
16 (V3#5, 12/42)-Hitler, Tojo, Mussolini, Goehring-c 692 1384 2076 3633 6317 9000
18 (V3#8, 7/43)-(scarce) 269 538 807 1412 2456 3500
19 (V2#6, 9/43)-Hitler, Tojo, Mussolini-c 654 1308 1962 3434 5967 8500
20 (V2#7, 10/43)-Classic Hitler-c 1077 2154 3231 5654 9827 14,000
21,22 (V2#8, V2#9) 168 336 504 1075 1838 2600
23 (V2#10, 3/44) World War II-c 194 388 582 1242 2121 3000
nn(V3#13, 5/44) Rico-a; Schomburg Japanese WWII bondage-c (Rare) 343 686 1029 2400 4200 6000
nn(V2#12, 7/44) L.B. Cole-a (4 pgs) 142 284 426 909 1555 2200
nn(V3#1, 9/44)-Origin The Golden Archer; Leatherface app. 142 284 426 909 1555 2200
nn(V3#2, 11/44)-L. B. Cole-c 161 322 483 1030 1765 2500
27-Origins Catman & Kitten retold; L. B. Cole Flag-c; Infantino-a 206 412 618 1318 2259 3200
28-Dr. Macabre app.; L. B. Cole-c/a 300 600 900 1950 3375 4800
29-32-L. B. Cole-c; bondage-#30 206 412 618 1318 2259 3200
NOTE: *Fuje a-11, 27, 28(2), 29(3), 30. Palais a-11, 16, 27, 28, 29(2), 30(2), 32; c-25(7/44). Rico a-11(2), 23, 27, 28.*

CAT TALES (3-D)
Eternity Comics: Apr, 1989 ($2.95)

1-Felix the Cat-r in 3-D 5.00

CATWOMAN (Also see Action Comics Weekly #611, Batman #404-407, Detective Comics, & Superman's Girlfriend Lois Lane #70, 71)
DC Comics: Feb, 1989 - No. 4, May, 1989 ($1.50, limited series, mature)

1 1 3 4 6 8 10
2-4: 3-Batman cameo. 4-Batman app. 1 2 3 5 7 9
Her Sister's Keeper (1991, $9.95, trade paperback)-r/#1-4 12.00

CATWOMAN (Also see Showcase '93, Showcase '95 #4, & Batman #404-407)
DC Comics: Aug, 1993 - No. 94, Jul, 2001 ($1.50-$2.25)

0-(10/94)-Zero Hour; origin retold. Released between #14&15 4.00
1-($1.95)-Embossed-c; Bane app.; Balent c-1-10; a-1-10p 6.00
2-20: 3-Bane flashback cameo. 4-Brief Bane app. 6,7-Knightquest tie-ins; Batman (Azrael) app. 8-1st app. Zephyr. 12-KnightsEnd pt. 6. 13-new Knights End Aftermath. 14-(9/94)-Zero Hour 4.00
21-24, 26-30, 33-49: 21-$1.95-c begins. 28,29-Penguin cameo app. 36-Legacy pt. 2. 38-40-Year Two; Batman, Joker, Penguin & Two-Face app. 46-Two-Face app. 3.00
25,31,32: 25-($2.95)-Robin app. 31,32-Contagion pt. 4 (Reads pt. 5 on-c) & pt. 9. 4.00
50-($2.95, 48 pgs.)-New armored costume 4.00
50-($2.95, 48 pgs.)-Collector's Ed.w/metallic ink-c 5.00
51-77: 51-Huntress-c/app. 54-Grayson-s begins. 56-Cataclysm pt.6. 57-Poison Ivy-c/app. 63-65-Joker-c/app. 72-No Man's Land; Ostrander-s begins 3.00
78-82: 80-Catwoman goes to jail 3.00
83,84,89-Harley Quinn-c/app. 83-Begin $2.25-c 1 3 4 6 8 10

GD VG FN VF VF/NM NM-
2.0 4.0 6.0 8.0 9.0 9.2

85-88,90-94 3.00
#1,000,000 (11/98) 853rd Century x-over 3.00
Annual 1 (1994, $2.95, 68 pgs.)-Elseworlds story; Batman app.; no Balent-a 4.00
Annual 2,4 ('95, '97, $3.95) 2-Year One story. 4-Pulp Heroes 4.00
Annual 3 (1996, $2.95)-Legends of the Dead Earth story 4.00
...Plus 1 (11/97, $2.95) Screamqueen (Scare Tactics) app. 4.00
TPB ($9.95) r/#15-19, Balent-c 12.00

CATWOMAN (Also see Detective Comics #759-762)
DC Comics: Jan, 2002 - No. 82, Oct, 2008; No. 83, Mar, 2010 ($2.50/$2.99)

1-Darwyn Cooke & Mike Allred-a; Ed Brubaker-s 6.00
2-4 4.00
5-43: 5-9-Rader-a/Paul Pope-c. 10-Morse-c. 16-JG Jones-c. 22-Batman-c/app. 34-36-War Games. 43-Killer Croc app. 3.00
44-Adam Hughes-c begin 5.00
45,46 2 4 6 13 18 22
47,49,52-57,59-68,71,73,75-79: 52-Catwoman kills Black Mask. 53-One Year Later; Helena born. 55-Begin $2.99-c. 56-58-Wildcat app. 75-78-Salvation Run 5.00
48,69 1 2 3 5 6 8
50,58,72-Zatanna-c/app. 1 3 4 6 8 10
51-Classic Selina Kyle mugshot-c 5 10 15 33 57 80
70-Classic-c; "Amazons Attack" tie-in 3 6 9 16 23 30
74-Zatanna app. 3 6 9 19 30 40
80-82 1 3 4 6 8 10
83-(3/10, $2.99) Blackest Night one-shot; Harley Quinn & Black Mask app.; Adam Hughes-c 1 2 3 5 6 8
...: Catwoman Dies TPB (2008, $14.99) r/#66-72; Hughes cover gallery 15.00
...: Crime Pays TPB (2008, $14.99) r/#73-77 15.00
...: Crooked Little Town TPB (2003, $14.95) r/#5-10 & Secret Files; Oeming-c 15.00
...: It's Only a Movie TPB (2007, $19.99) r/#59-65 20.00
...: Relentless TPB (2005, $19.95) r/#12-19 & Secret Files 20.00
... Secret Files and Origins (10/02, $4.95) origin-s Oeming-a; profiles and pin-ups 5.00
...Selina's Big Score HC (2002, $24.95) Cooke-s/a; pin-ups by various 25.00
...Selina's Big Score SC (2003, $17.95) Cooke-s/a; pin-ups by various 18.00
...: The Dark End of the Street TPB (2002, $12.95) r/#1-4 & Slam Bradley back-up stories from Detective Comics #759-762 13.00
...: The Long Road Home TPB (2009, $17.99) r/#78-82 18.00
...: The Replacements TPB (2007, $14.99) r/#53-58 15.00
...: Wild Ride TPB (2005, $14.99) r/#20-24 & Secret Files #1 15.00

CATWOMAN (DC New 52)
DC Comics: Nov, 2011 - No. 52, Jul, 2016 ($2.99)

1-Winick-s/March-a; Batman app. 5.00
2-12: 2-6-March-a. 7,8-Melo-a. 9-Night of the Owls 3.00
13-(12/12) Death of the Family tie-in; die-cut Joker mask-c 12.00
13-Second printing with chessboard-c 5.00
14-22: 14-Death of the Family tie-in; Joker app 3.00
23,24: 23-(10/13) Debut of Joker's Daughter in final panel. 24-Joker's Daughter app. 5.00
25,26,28-49: 25-Zero Year. 26-Joker's Daughter app. 28-Gothtopia. 35-40-Jae Lee-c 3.00
27-($3.99) Gothtopia x-over with Detective Comics #27; Olliffe & Richards-a 4.00
50-($4.99) Harley Quinn, Poison Ivy app.; back-up origin of Black Mask's mask 5.00
51,52: Black Mask & the False Face Society app.; Middleton-c 3.00
#0 (11/12, $2.99) Origin re-told; Nocenti-s/Melo-a/March-c 3.00
Annual 1 (7/13, $4.99) Nocenti-s/Duce-a; Penguin app. 5.00
Annual 2 (2/15, $4.99) Olliffe & McCrea-a 5.00
...: Election Night 1 (1/17, $4.99) Meredith Finch-s/Shane Davis-a; Prez app. 5.00
...: Futures End 1 (11/14, $2.99, regular-c) Five years later; Olliffe-a/Dodson-c 3.00
...: Futures End 1 (11/14, $3.99, 3-D cover) 4.00

CATWOMAN/ GUARDIAN OF GOTHAM
DC Comics: 1999 - No. 2, 1999 ($5.95, limited series)

1,2-Elseworlds; Moench-s/Balent-a 6.00

CATWOMAN: NINE LIVES OF A FELINE FATALE
DC Comics: 2004 ($14.95, TPB)

nn-Reprints notable stories from Batman #1 to the present; pin-ups by various; Bolland-c 15.00

CATWOMAN: THE MOVIE (2004 Halle Berry movie)
DC Comics: 2004 ($4.95/$9.95)

1-($4.95) Movie adaptation; Jim Lee-c and sketch pages; Derenick-a 5.00
... & Other Cat Tales TPB (2004, $9.95)-r/Movie adaptation; Jim Lee sketch pages, r/Catwoman #0, Catwoman (2nd series) #11 & 25; photo-c 10.00

CATWOMAN/VAMPIRELLA: THE FURIES
DC Comics/Harris Publ.: Feb, 1997 ($4.95, squarebound, 46 pgs.) (1st DC/Harris x-over)

nn-Reintro Pantha; Chuck Dixon scripts; Jim Balent-c/a 6.00

Cave Carson Has a Cybernetic Eye #7 © DC

Centipede (2017 series) #1 © Atari

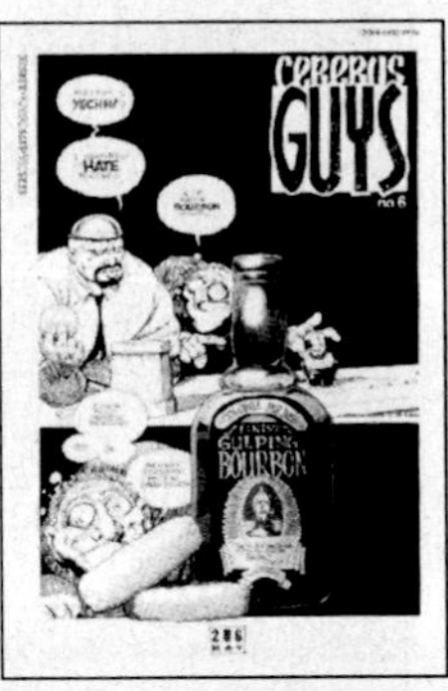

Cerebus #206 © Dave Sim

GD VG FN VF VF/NM NM-
2.0 4.0 6.0 8.0 9.0 9.2

GD VG FN VF VF/NM NM-
2.0 4.0 6.0 8.0 9.0 9.2

CATWOMAN: WHEN IN ROME
DC Comics: Nov, 2004 - No. 6, Aug, 2005 ($3.50, limited series)
1-6-Jeph Loeb-s/Tim Sale-a/c; Riddler app. 3.50
HC (2005, $19.99, dustjacket) r/series; intro by Mark Chiarello; sketch pages 20.00
SC (2007, $12.99) r/series; intro by Mark Chiarello; sketch pages 13.00

CATWOMAN/WILDCAT
DC Comics: Aug, 1998 - No. 4, Nov, 1998 ($2.50, limited series)
1-4-Chuck Dixon & Beau Smith-s; Stelfreeze-c 3.00

CAUGHT
Atlas Comics (VPI): Aug, 1956 - No. 5, Apr, 1957
1 26 52 78 154 252 350
2-4: 3-Maneely, Pakula, Torres-a. 4-Maneely-a 15 30 45 84 127 170
5-Crandall, Krigstein-a 15 30 45 86 133 180
NOTE: ***Drucker** a-2. **Heck** a-4. **Severin** c-1, 2, 4, 5. **Shores** a-4.*

CAVALIER COMICS
A. W. Nugent Publ. Co.: 1945; 1952 (Early DC reprints)
2(1945)-Speed Saunders, Fang Gow 20 40 60 120 195 270
2(1952) 12 24 36 67 94 120

CAVALRY, THE : S.H.I.E.L.D. 50TH ANNIVERSARY
Marvel Comics: Nov, 2015 ($3.99, one-shot)
1-Agent Melinda May on a training mission; Luke Ross-a; Keown-c 4.00

CAVE CARSON HAS A CYBERNETIC EYE
DC Comics (Young Animal): Dec, 2016 - No. 12, Nov, 2017 ($3.99)
1-12-Jonathan Rivera & Gerald Way-s/Michael Avon Oeming-a; back-up Tom Scioli-s/a in #1-6. 7-Superman-c/app. 4.00
.../ Swamp Thing Special 1 (4/18, $4.99) Part 4 of Milk Wars crossover; Rivera-a/Foss-a 5.00

CAVE GIRL (Also see Africa)
Magazine Enterprises: No. 11, 1953 - No. 14, 1954
11(A-1 82)-Origin; all Cave Girl stories 53 106 159 334 567 800
12(A-1 96), 13(A-1 116), 14(A-1 125)-Thunda by Powell in each
39 78 117 236 388 540
NOTE: ***Powell** c/a in all.*

CAVE GIRL
AC Comics: 1988 ($2.95, 44 pgs.) (16 pgs. of color, rest B&W)
1-Powell-r/Cave Girl #11; Nyoka photo back-c from movie; Powell/Bill Black-c; Special Limited Edition on-c 4.00

CAVE KIDS (TV) (See Comic Album #16)
Gold Key: Feb, 1963 - No. 16, Mar, 1967 (Hanna-Barbera)
1 6 12 18 38 69 100
2-5 4 8 12 23 37 50
6-16: 7,12-Pebbles & Bamm Bamm app. 16-1st Space Kidettes
3 6 9 19 30 40

CAVEWOMAN
Basement Comics: Jan, 1994 - No. 6, 1995 ($2.95)
1 6 12 18 37 66 95
2 3 6 9 19 30 40
3-6 2 4 6 9 13 16
...: Meets Explorers ('97, $2.95) 5.00
...: One-Shot Special (7/00, $2.95) Massey-s/a 5.00

CBLDF (Comic Book Legal Defense Fund) (See Liberty Comics)

CELESTINE (See Violator Vs. Badrock #1)
Image Comics (Extreme): May, 1996 - No. 2, June, 1996 ($2.50, limited series)
1,2: Warren Ellis scripts 3.00

CENTIPEDE (Based on Atari videogame)
Dynamite Entertainment: 2017 - No. 5, 2017 ($3.99)
1-5: 1-Bemis-s/Marron-a; covers by Marron, Francavilla & Schkade 4.00

CENTURION OF ANCIENT ROME, THE
Zondervan Publishing House: 1958 (no month listed) (B&W, 36 pgs.)
(Rare) All by Jay Disbrow 110 220 330 704 1202 1700

CENTURIONS (TV)
DC Comics: June, 1987 - No. 4, Sept, 1987 (75¢, limited series)
1-4 4.00

CENTURY: DISTANT SONS
Marvel Comics: Feb, 1996 ($2.95, one-shot)
1-Wraparound-c 4.00

CENTURY OF COMICS (See Promotional Comics section)

CENTURY WEST
Image Comics: Sept, 2013 ($7.99, squarebound, graphic novel)
nn-Howard Chaykin-s/a/c 8.00

CEREBUS BI-WEEKLY
Aardvark-Vanaheim: Dec. 2, 1988 - No. 27, Nov. 24, 1989 ($1.25, B&W)
Reprints Cerebus The Aardvark #1-27
1-16, 18, 19, 21-27: 3.00
17-Hepcats app. 2 4 6 8 10 12
20-Milk & Cheese app. 2 4 6 10 12 15

CEREBUS: CHURCH & STATE
Aardvark-Vanaheim: Feb, 1991 - No. 30, Apr, 1992 ($2.00, B&W, bi-weekly)
1-30: r/Cerebus #51-80 3.00

CEREBUS: HIGH SOCIETY
Aardvark-Vanaheim: Feb, 1990 - No. 25, 1991 ($1.70, B&W)
1-25: r/Cerebus #26-50 3.00

CEREBUS IN HELL?
Aardvark-Vanaheim: No. 0, 2016; No. 1, Jan, 2017 - No. 4, Apr, 2017 ($4.00, B&W)
0-4-Sim & Atwal-s; Cerebus figures placed over original Gustave Doré artwork of Hell 4.00
Cerebus The Vark Knight Returns 1 (12/17, $4.00) new pages and reprints 4.00
The Death of Cerebus in Hell 1 (11/17, $4.00) new pages and reprints 4.00

CEREBUS JAM
Aardvark-Vanaheim: Apr, 1985
1-Eisner, Austin, Dave Sim-a (Cerebus vs. Spirit) 6.00

CEREBUS THE AARDVARK (See A-V in 3-D, Nucleus, Power Comics)
Aardvark-Vanaheim: Dec, 1977 - No. 300, March, 2004 ($1.70/$2.00/$2.25, B&W)
0 3.00
0-Gold 20.00
1-1st app. Cerebus; 2000 print run; most copies poorly printed
104 208 312 832 1866 2900
Note: *There is a counterfeit version known to exist. It can be distinguished from the original in the following ways: inside cover is glossy instead of flat, black background on the front cover is blotted or spotty. Reports show that a counterfeit #2 also exists.*
2-Dave Sim art in all 14 28 42 94 207 320
3-Origin Red Sophia 11 22 33 73 157 240
4-Origin Elrod the Albino 9 18 27 60 120 180
5,6 7 14 21 49 92 135
7-10 6 12 18 37 66 95
11,12: 11-Origin The Cockroach 5 10 15 31 53 75
13-15: 14-Origin Lord Julius 4 8 12 28 47 65
16-20 3 6 9 21 33 45
21-B. Smith letter in letter column 5 10 15 35 63 90
22-Low distribution; no cover price 4 8 12 25 40 55
23-30: 23-Preview of Wandering Star by Teri S. Wood. 26-High Society begins, ends #50
3 6 9 16 23 30
31-Origin Moonroach 3 6 9 16 24 32
32-40, 53-Intro. Wolveroach (brief app.) 2 4 6 8 10 12
41-50,52: 52-Church & State begins, ends #111; Cutey Bunny app.
1 2 3 5 7 9
51,54: 51-Cutey Bunny app. 54-1st full Wolveroach story
2 4 6 8 11 14
55,56-Wolveroach app.; Normalman back-ups by Valentino
1 3 4 6 8 10
57-100: 61,62: Flaming Carrot app. 65-Gerhard begins 4.00
101-160: 104-Flaming Carrot app. 112/113-Double issue. 114-Jaka's Story begins, ends #136. 139-Melmoth begins, ends #150. 151-Mothers & Daughters begins, ends #200 3.00
161-Bone app. 1 3 4 6 8 10
162-231: 175-($2.25, 44 pgs). 186-Strangers in Paradise cameo. 201-Guys storyline begins; Eddie Campbell's Bacchus app. 220-231-Rick's Story 3.00
232-265-Going Home 3.00
266-288,291-299-Latter Days: 267-Five-Bar Gate. 276-Spore (Spawn spoof) 3.00
289&290 ($4.50) Two issues combined 5.00
300-Final issue 3.00
Free Cerebus (Giveaway, 1991-92?, 36 pgs.)-All-r 4.00

CHAIN GANG WAR
DC Comics: July, 1993 - No. 12, June, 1994 ($1.75)
1-($2.50)-Embossed silver foil-c, Dave Johnson-c/a 4.00
2-4,6-12: 3-Deathstroke app. 4-Brief Deathstroke app. 6-New Batman (Azrael) cameo. 11-New Batman-c/story. 12-New Batman app. 3.00
5-($2.50)-Foil-c; Deathstroke app; new Batman cameo (1 panel) 4.00

The Challenger #2 © IP

Challengers of the Unknown #4 © DC

Champion Comics #4 © HARV

GD VG FN VF VF/NM NM-
2.0 4.0 6.0 8.0 9.0 9.2

CHAINS OF CHAOS
Harris Comics: Nov, 1994 - No. 3, Jan, 1995 ($2.95, limited series)

1-3-Re-Intro of The Rook w/ Vampirella 5.00

CHALLENGE OF THE UNKNOWN (Formerly Love Experiences)
Ace Magazines: No. 6, Sept, 1950 (See Web Of Mystery No. 19)

6- "Villa of the Vampire" used in N.Y. Joint Legislative Comm. Publ; Sekowsky-a
48 96 144 302 514 725

CHALLENGER, THE
Interfaith Publications/T.C. Comics: 1945 - No. 4, Oct-Dec, 1946

nn; nd; 32 pgs.; Origin the Challenger Club; Anti-Fascist with funny animal filler
97 194 291 621 1061 1500

2-Classic Pandora's Box demons-c; Kubert-a 84 168 252 538 919 1300

3,4: Kubert-a; 4-Fuje-a 50 100 150 315 533 750

CHALLENGERS OF THE FANTASTIC
Marvel Comics (Amalgam): June 1997 ($1.95, one-shot)

1-Karl Kesel-s/Tom Grummett-a 3.00

CHALLENGERS OF THE UNKNOWN (See Showcase #6, 7, 11, 12, Super DC Giant, and Super Team Family) (See Showcase Presents for B&W reprints)
National Per. Publ./DC Comics: 4-5/58 - No. 77, 12-1/70-71; No. 78, 2/73 - No. 80, 6-7/73; No. 81, 6-7/77 - No. 87, 6-7/78

1-(4-5/58)-Kirby/Stein-a(2); Kirby-c 234 468 702 1930 4365 6800

2-Kirby/Stein-a(2) 66 132 198 528 1189 1850

3-Kirby/Stein-a(2); Rocky returns from space with powers similar to the Fantastic Four (9/58)
59 118 177 472 1061 1650

4-8-Kirby/Wood-a plus cover to #8 42 84 126 311 706 1100

9,10 25 50 75 175 388 600

11-Grey tone-c 31 62 93 223 499 775

12-15: 14-Origin/1st app. Multi-Man (villain) 17 34 51 119 265 410

16-22: 18-Intro. Cosmo, the Challengers Spacepet. 22-Last 10¢ issue
12 24 36 81 176 270

23-30 8 16 24 56 108 160

31-Retells origin of the Challengers 9 18 27 57 111 165

32-40 6 12 18 41 76 110

41-47,49,50,52-60: 43-New look begins. 47-1st Sponge-Man. 49-Intro. Challenger Corps. 55-Death of Red Ryan. 60-Red Ryan returns 5 10 15 31 53 75

48,51: 48-Doom Patrol app. 51-Sea Devils app. 5 10 15 33 57 80

61-68: 64,65-Kirby origin-r, parts 1 & 2. 66-New logo. 68-Last 12¢ issue.
4 8 12 23 37 50

69-73,75-80: 69-1st app. Corinna. 77-Last 15¢ issue 3 6 9 16 23 30

74-Deadman by Tuska/Adams; 1 pg. Wrightson-a 6 12 18 41 76 110

81,83-87: 81-(6-7/77). 83-87-Swamp Thing app. 84-87-Deadman app.
2 4 6 8 10 12

82-Swamp Thing begins (thru #87, c/s 2 4 6 9 12 15

NOTE: ***N. Adams*** *c-67, 68, 70, 72, 74i, 81i.* ***Buckler*** *c-83-86p.* ***Giffen*** *a-83-87p.* ***Kirby*** *a-75-80r; c-75, 77, 78.* ***Kubert*** *c-64, 66, 69, 76, 79.* ***Nasser*** *c/a-81p, 82p.* ***Tuska*** *a-73.* ***Wood*** *r-76.*

CHALLENGERS OF THE UNKNOWN
DC Comics: Mar, 1991 - No. 8, Oct, 1991 ($1.75, limited series)

1-Jeph Loeb scripts & Tim Sale-a in all (1st work together); Bolland-c 4.00

2-8: 2-Superman app. 3-Dr. Fate app. 6-G. Kane-c(p). 7-Steranko-c/swipe by Art Adams 3.00

... Must Die! (2004, $19.95, TPB) r/series; intro by Bendis; Sale sketch pages 20.00

NOTE: ***Art Adams*** *c-7.* ***Hempel*** *c-5.* ***Gil Kane*** *c-6p.* ***Sale*** *a-1-8; c-3, 8.* ***Wagner*** *c-4.*

CHALLENGERS OF THE UNKNOWN
DC Comics: Feb, 1997 - No. 18, July, 1998 ($2.25)

1-18: 1-Intro new team; Leon-c/a(p) begins. 4-Origin of new team. 11,12-Batman app. 15-Millennium Giants x-over; Superman-c/app. 3.00

CHALLENGERS OF THE UNKNOWN
DC Comics: Aug, 2004 - No. 6, Jan, 2005 ($2.95, limited series)

1-6-Intro. new team; Howard Chaykin-s/a 3.00

CHALLENGE TO THE WORLD
Catechetical Guild: 1951 (10¢, 36 pgs.)

nn 6 12 18 31 38 45

CHAMBER (See Generation X and Uncanny X-Men)
Marvel Comics: Oct, 2002 - No. 4, Jan, 2003 ($2.99, limited series)

1-4-Bachalo-c/Vaughan-s/Ferguson-a. 1-Cyclops app. 3.00

CHAMBER OF CHILLS (Formerly Blondie Comics #20; ...of Clues No. 27 on)
Harvey Publications/Witches Tales: No. 21, June, 1951 - No. 26, Dec, 1954

21 (#1) 61 122 183 390 670 950

22,24 (#2,4) 41 82 123 256 428 600

23 (#3)-Excessive violence; eyes torn out 42 84 126 265 445 625

5(2/52)-Decapitation, acid in face scene 42 84 126 265 445 625

6-Woman melted alive 41 82 123 256 428 600

7-Used in **SOTI**, pg. 389; decapitation/severed head panels
41 82 123 256 428 600

8-10: 8-Decapitation panels 39 78 117 231 378 525

11,12,14: 14-Spider-Man precursor (11/52) 32 64 96 190 310 430

13,15-18,20-22,24-Nostrand-a in all. 13,21-Decapitation panels. 18-Atom bomb panels. 20-Nostrand-c 37 74 111 222 361 500

19-Classic-c; Nostrand-a 206 412 618 1318 2259 3200

23-Classic-c of corpse kissing woman; Nostrand-a 206 412 618 1318 2259 3200

25,26 25 50 75 150 245 340

NOTE: *About half the issues contain bondage, torture, sadism, perversion, gore, cannabalism, eyes ripped out, acid in face, etc.* ***Elias*** *c-4-11, 14-19, 21-26.* ***Kremer*** *a-12, 17.* ***Palais*** *a-21(1), 23.* ***Nostrand/Powell*** *a-13, 15, 16.* ***Powell*** *a-21, 23, 24('51), 5-8, 11, 13, 18-21, 23-25. Bondage-c-21, 24('51), 7. 25-r/#5; 26-r/#9.*

CHAMBER OF CHILLS
Marvel Comics Group: Nov, 1972 - No. 25, Nov, 1976

1-Harlan Ellison adaptation 5 10 15 31 53 75

2-5: 2-1st app. John Jakes' Brak the Barbarian 3 6 9 17 26 35

6-25: 22,23-(Regular 25¢ editions) 3 6 9 16 23 30

22,23-(30¢-c variants, limited distribution)(5,7/76) 5 10 15 33 57 80

NOTE: ***Adkins*** *a-1i, 2i.* ***Brunner*** *a-2-4; c-4.* ***Chaykin*** *a-4.* ***Ditko*** *r-14, 16, 19, 23, 24.* ***Everett*** *a-3i, 11r,21r.* ***Heath*** *a-1r.* ***Gil Kane*** *c-2p.* ***Kirby*** *r-11, 18, 19, 22.* ***Powell*** *a-13r.* ***Russell*** *a-1p, 2p.* ***Shores*** *a-5 .* ***Williamson/Mayo*** *a-13r.* ***Robert E. Howard*** *horror story adaptation-2, 3.*

CHAMBER OF CLUES (Formerly Chamber of Chills)
Harvey Publications: No. 27, Feb, 1955 - No. 28, April, 1955

27-Kerry Drake-r/#19; Powell-a; last pre-code 7 14 21 37 46 55

28-Kerry Drake 6 12 18 29 36 42

CHAMBER OF DARKNESS (Monsters on the Prowl #9 on)
Marvel Comics Group: Oct, 1969 - No. 8, Dec, 1970

1-Buscema-a(p) 7 14 21 48 89 130

2,3: 2-Neal Adams scripts. 3-Smith, Buscema-a 4 8 12 28 47 65

4-A Conan-esque tryout by Smith (4/70); reprinted in Conan #16; Marie Severin/Everett-c 8 16 24 56 108 160

5,8: 5-H.P. Lovecraft adaptation. 8-Wrightson-c 4 8 12 25 40 55

6 3 6 9 21 33 45

7-Wrightson-c/a, 7pgs. (his 1st work at Marvel); Wrightson draws himself in 1st & last panels; Kirby/Ditko-r; last 15¢-c 5 10 15 35 63 90

1-(1/72; 25¢ Special, 52 pgs.) 4 8 12 25 40 55

NOTE: ***Adkins/Everett*** *a-8.* ***Buscema*** *a-Special 1r.* ***Craig*** *a-5.* ***Ditko*** *a-6-8r.* ***Heck*** *a-1, 2, 8, Special 1r.* ***Kirby*** *a(p)-4, 5, 7r.* ***Kirby/Everett*** *c-5.* ***Severin/Everett*** *c-6.* ***Shores*** *a-2, 3i, Special 1r.* ***Sutton*** *a-1, 2i, 4, 7, Special 1r.* ***Wrightson*** *c-7, 8.*

CHAMP COMICS (Formerly Champion No. 1-10)
Worth Publ. Co./Champ Publ./Family Comics(Harvey Publ.): No. 11, Oct, 1940 - No. 24, Dec, 1942; No. 25, April, 1943

11-Human Meteor cont'd. from Champion 142 284 426 909 1555 2200

12-17,20: 14,15-Crandall-c. 20-The Green Ghost app.; Japanese WWII-c
116 232 348 742 1271 1800

18,19-Simon-c. 19-The Wasp app. 142 284 426 909 1555 2200

21-23,25: 22-The White Mask app. 23-Flag-c 90 180 270 576 988 1400

24-Hitler, Tojo & Mussolini-c 168 336 504 1075 1838 2600

CHAMPION (See Gene Autry's...)

CHAMPION COMICS
Worth Publ. Co.: Oct, 1939 (ashcan)

nn-Ashcan comic, not distributed to newsstands, only for in house use. A FN/VF copy sold for $2,261.76 in 2010.

CHAMPION COMICS (Formerly Speed Comics #1?; Champ Comics No. 11 on)
Worth Publ. Co.(Harvey Publications): No. 2, Dec, 1939 - No. 10, Aug, 1940 (no No.1)

2-The Champ, The Blazing Scarab, Neptina, Liberty Lads, Jungleman, Bill Handy, Swingtime Sweetie begin 129 258 387 826 1413 2000

3-7: 7-The Human Meteor begins? 87 174 261 553 952 1350

8,10: 8-Simon-c. 10-Bondage-c by Kirby 284 568 852 1818 3109 4400

9-1st S&K-c (1st collaboration together) 300 600 900 2010 3505 5000

CHAMPIONS, THE
Marvel Comics Group: Oct, 1975 - No. 17, Jan, 1978

1-Origin & 1st app. The Champions (The Angel. Black Widow, Ghost Rider, Hercules, Iceman) Venus x-over 4 8 12 24 38 52

2-10: 2-3 vs. Pluto, Venus x-over. 5-7-(Regular 25¢ edition)(4-8/76). 5-1st Rampage. 6-Kirby-c. 7-1st Darkstar, Griffin & Titanium Man app. 8-Champions vs. Darkstar, Griffin & Titanium Man; 1st Yuri Petrovitch as new Crimson Dynamo. 10-Champions vs. Crimson Dynamo & Titanium Man 2 4 6 11 16 20

Champions (2016 series) #5 © MAR

Chaos War #1 © MAR

Charlie Chan #4 © Prize

	GD 2.0	VG 4.0	FN 6.0	VF 8.0	VF/NM 9.0	NM- 9.2

5-7-(30¢-c variants, limited distribution) 4 8 12 28 47 65
11-15: 11-Byrne-a begins; Black Goliath app; Darkstar joins. 12-Stilt-Man, Black Goliath & The Stranger app. 13-Black Goliath & The Stranger app. 14,15-(Regular 30¢ edition). 14-1st Swarm; Iceman dons new costume. 15-Origin Swarm 2 4 6 13 18 22
14,15-(35¢-c variant, limited distribution) 6 12 18 38 69 100
16-Continued from Super-Villain Team-Up #14; Magneto & Dr. Doom app; Hulk & Beast guest app. 2 4 6 13 18 25
17-Last issue; vs. The Brotherhood of Evil Mutants; Sentinels app.; Champions app. next in Spectacular Spider-Man #17 2 4 6 13 18 22
... Classic Vol. 1 TPB (2006, $19.99) r/#1-11; unused cover to #7 20.00
... Classic Vol. 2 TPB (2007, $19.99) r/#12-17, Iron Man Ann. #4, Avengers #163, Super-Villain Team-Up #14 and Peter Parker, The Spectacular Spider-Man #17-18 20.00
...: No Time For Losers (2016, $7.99) r/#1-3,14,15; art by Heck, Tuska & Byrne 8.00
NOTE: ***Buckler/Adkins** c-3. **Byrne** a-11-15, 17. **Kane/Adkins** c-1. **Kane/Layton** c-11. **Tuska** a-3p, 4p, 6p, 7p. Ghost Rider c-1-4, 7, 8, 10, 14, 16, 17 (4, 10, 14 are more prominent).*

CHAMPIONS (Game)
Eclipse Comics: June, 1986 - No. 6, Feb, 1987 (limited series)
1-6: 1-Intro Flare; based on game. 5-Origin Flare 3.00

CHAMPIONS (Also see The League of Champions)
Hero Comics: Sept, 1987 - No. 12, 1989 ($1.95)
1-12: 1-Intro The Marksman & The Rose. 4-Origin Malice 3.00
Annual 1(1988, $2.75, 52 pgs.)-Origin of Giant 4.00

CHAMPIONS
Marvel Comics: Dec, 2016 - Present ($4.99/$3.99)
1-($4.99) Ms. Marvel, Spider-Man (Miles), Hulk (Amadeus), Nova, Viv Vision team 5.00
2-17-($3.99) 3-Young Cyclops joins. 5-Gwenpool app. 9-Intro. Red Locust. 10,11-Secret Empire tie-ins. 13-15-Avengers app. 4.00
#1.MU (4/17, $4.99) Monsters Unleashed tie-in; Whitely-s/Stein & Brandt-a 5.00

CHAMPION SPORTS
National Periodical Publications: Oct-Nov, 1973 - No. 3, Feb-Mar, 1974
1 3 6 9 16 23 30
2,3 2 4 6 9 12 15

CHANNEL ZERO
Image Comics: Feb, 1998 - No. 5 ($2.95, B&W, limited series)
1-5, ...Dupe (1/99) -Brian Wood-s/a 3.00

CHAOS (See The Crusaders)

CHAOS!
Dynamite Entertainment: 2014 - No. 6, 2014 ($3.99, limited series)
1-6-Seeley-s/Andolfo-a; multiple covers on each. Purgatori, Evil Ernie, Chastity app. 4.00
... Holiday Special 2014 ($5.99) Short stories by various; Lupacchino-c 6.00
...: Smiley The Psychotic Button 1 (2015, $4.99) origin re-told; Andolfo-c 5.00

CHAOS! BIBLE
Chaos! Comics: Nov, 1995 ($3.30, one-shot)
1-Profiles of characters & creators 3.50

CHAOS! CHRONICLES
Chaos! Comics: Feb, 2000 ($3.50, one-shot)
1-Profiles of characters, checklist of Chaos! comics and products 3.50

CHAOS EFFECT, THE
Valiant: 1994
Alpha (Giveaway w/trading card checklist) 3.00
Alpha-Gold variant, Alpha-Red variant, Omega-Gold variant 5.00
Omega (11/94, $2.25); Epilogue Pt. 1, 2 (12/94, 1/95; $2.95) 3.00

CHAOS! GALLERY
Chaos! Comics: Aug, 1997 ($2.95, one-shot)
1-Pin-ups of characters 3.00

CHAOS! QUARTERLY
Chaos! Comics: Oct, 1995 -No. 3, May, 1996 ($4.95, quarterly)
1-3: 1-Anthology; Lady Death-c by Julie Bell. 2-Boris "Lady Demon"-c 5.00
1-Premium Edition (7,500) 25.00

CHAOS WAR
Marvel Comics: Dec, 2010 - No. 4, Mr, 2011 ($3.99, limited series)
1-5-Hercules, Thor and others vs. Chaos King; Pham-a. 3-5-Galactus app. 4.00
...: Alpha Flight 1 (1/11, $3.99) McCann-s/Brown-a 4.00
...: Ares 1 (2/11, $3.99) Oeming-s/Segovia-a 4.00
...: Chaos King 1 (1/11, $3.99) Kaluta-a/c; Monclair-s 4.00
...: Dead Avengers 1-3 (1/11 - No. 3, 3/11, $3.99) Grummett-a; Capt. Marvel app. 4.00
...: God Squad 1 (2/11, $3.99) Sumerak-s/Panosian-a 4.00
...: Thor 1,2 (1/11 - No. 2, 2/11, $3.99) DeMatteis-s/Ching-a 4.00
...: X-Men 1,2 (2/11 - No. 2, 3/11, $3.99) Braithwaite-a; Thunderbird, Banshee app. 4.00

CHAPEL (Also see Youngblood & Youngblood Strikefile #1-3)
Image Comics (Extreme Studios): No. 1 Feb, 1995 - No. 2, Mar, 1995 ($2.50, limited series)
1,2 3.00

CHAPEL (Also see Youngblood & Youngblood Strikefile #1-3)
Image Comics (Extreme Studios): V2 #1, Aug, 1995 - No. 7, Apr, 1996 ($2.50)
V2#1-7: 4-Babewatch x-over. 5-vs. Spawn. 7-Shadowhawk-c/app; Shadowhunt x-over 3.00
#1-Quesada & Palmiotti variant-c 3.00

CHAPEL (Also see Youngblood & Youngblood Strikefile #1-3)
Awesome Entertainment: Sept, 1997 ($2.99, one-shot)
1 (Reg. & alternate covers) 3.00

CHARISMAGIC
Aspen MLT: No. 0, Mar, 2011 - No. 6, Jul, 2012 ($1.99/$2.99/$3.50)
0-($1.99) Khary Randolph-a/ Vince Hernandez-s; 3 covers 3.00
1-4-($2.99) 1-4-Four covers on each 3.00
5,6-($3.50) Multiple covers on each 3.50
... Primer 1 (2/18, 25¢) Character profiles and story histories 3.00
...: The Death Princess 1-3 (11/12 - No. 3, 7/13, $3.99) Hernandez-s/Emilio Lopez-a 4.00

CHARISMAGIC (Volume 2)
Aspen MLT: May, 2013 - No. 6, Nov, 2013 ($1.00/$3.99)
1-($1.00) Vincenzo Cucca-a/ Vince Hernandez-s; multiple covers 3.00
2-6-($3.99) Multiple covers on each 4.00

CHARISMAGIC (Volume 3)
Aspen MLT: Feb, 2018 - No. 6 ($3.99)
1-Joey Vazquez-a/ Vince Hernandez-s; multiple covers 4.00

CHARLEMAGNE (Also see War Dancer)
Defiant: Mar, 1994 - No. 5, July, 1994 ($2.50)
1-(3/94, $3.50, 52 pgs.)-Adam Pollina-c/a. 4.00
2,3,5: Adam Pollina-c/a. 2-War Dancer app. 5-Pre-Schism issue. 3.00
4-($3.25, 52 pgs.) 4.00
#0 (Hero Illustrated giveaway)-Adam Pollina-c/a; 1st app. of Ngu 3.00

CHARLIE CHAN (See Big Shot Comics, Columbia Comics, Feature Comics & The New Advs. of...)

CHARLIE CHAN (The Adventures of...) (Zaza The Mystic No. 10 on) (TV)
Crestwood(Prize) No. 1-5; Charlton No. 6(6/55) on: 6-7/48 - No. 5, 2-3/49; No. 6, 6/55 - No. 9, 3/56
1-S&K-c, 2 pgs.; Infantino-a 87 174 261 553 952 1350
2-5-S&K-c: 3-S&K-c/a 50 100 150 315 533 750
6 (6/55-Charlton)-S&K-c 37 74 111 222 361 500
7-9 20 40 60 118 192 265

CHARLIE CHAN
Dell Publishing Co.: Oct-Dec, 1965 - No. 2, Mar, 1966
1-Springer-a/c 5 10 15 31 53 75
2-Springer-a/c 3 6 9 21 33 45

CHARLIE McCARTHY (See Edgar Bergen Presents...)
Dell Publishing Co.: No. 171, Nov, 1947 - No. 571, July, 1954 (See True Comics #14)
Four Color 171 25 50 75 175 388 600
Four Color 196-Part photo-c; photo back-c 16 32 48 108 239 370
1(3-5/49)-Part photo-c; photo back-c 12 24 36 82 179 275
2-9(7/52; #5,6-52 pgs.) 7 14 21 48 89 130
Four Color 445,478,527,571 6 12 18 41 76 110

CHARLTON ACTION: FEATURING "STATIC" (Also see Eclipse Monthly)
Charlton Comics: No, 11, Oct, 1985 - No. 12, Dec, 1985
11,12-Ditko-c/a; low print run 1 2 3 5 6 8

CHARLTON ARROW
Charlton Neo: 2017 - Present ($7.99)
1-New E-Man and Nova by Cuti & Staton; Monster Hunter, Mr. Mixit 8.00

CHARLTON BULLSEYE
CPL/Gang Publications: 1975 - No. 5, 1976 ($1.50, B&W, bi-monthly, magazine format)
1: 1 & 2 are last Capt. Atom by Ditko/Byrne intended for the never published Capt. Atom #90; Nightshade app.; Jeff Jones-a 5 10 15 30 50 70
2-Part 2 Capt. Atom story by Ditko/Byrne 3 6 9 21 33 45
3-Wrong Country by Sanho Kim 2 4 6 13 18 22

Chase #9 © DC

Chastity: Rocked #1 © Chaos

Cheval Noir #22 © DH

GD 2.0 VG 4.0 FN 6.0 VF 8.0 VF/NM 9.0 NM- 9.2

4-Doomsday + 1 by John Byrne 3 6 9 16 24 32
5-Doomsday + 1 by Byrne, The Question by Toth; Neal Adams back-c; Toth-c
5 10 15 31 53 75

CHARLTON BULLSEYE
Charlton Publications: June, 1981 - No. 10, Dec, 1982; Nov, 1986
1-1st Blue Beetle app. since '74, 1st app. The Question since '75; 1st app. Rocket Rabbit; Neil The Horse shown on preview page 3 6 9 17 26 35
2-5: 2-Charlton debut of Neil The Horse; Rocket Rabbit app. 4-Vanguards 6.00
6-10: Low print run. 6-Origin & 1st app. Thunderbunny. 7-1st apps. of Captain Atom & Nightshade since '75. 9-1st app. Bludd. 2 4 6 8 10 12
NOTE: *Material intended for issue #11-up was published in* ***Scary Tales*** *#37-up.*

CHARLTON CLASSICS
Charlton Comics: Apr, 1980 - No. 9, Aug, 1981
1-Hercules-r by Glanzman in all 6.00
2-9 5.00

CHARLTON CLASSICS LIBRARY (1776)
Charlton Comics: V10 No.1, Mar, 1973 (one-shot)
1776 (title) - Adaptation of the film musical "1776"; given away at movie theatres; also a newsstand version 3 6 9 14 19 24

CHARLTON PREMIERE (Formerly Marine War Heroes)
Charlton Comics: V1#19, July, 1967; V2#1, Sept, 1967 - No. 4, May, 1968
V1#19, V2#1,2,4: V1#19-Marine War Heroes. V2#1-Trio; intro. Shape, Tyro Team & Spookman. 2-Children of Doom; Boyette classic-a. 4-Unlikely Tales; Aparo, Ditko-a
3 6 9 15 22 28
V2#3-Sinistro Boy Fiend; Blue Beetle & Peacemaker x-over
3 6 9 17 26 35

CHARLTON SPORT LIBRARY - PROFESSIONAL FOOTBALL
Charlton Comics: Winter, 1969-70 (Jan. on cover) (68 pgs.)
1 3 6 9 19 30 40

CHARMED (TV)
Zenescope Entertainment: No. 0, Jun, 2010 - No. 24, Oct, 2012 ($3.50)
0-24-Multiple covers on most 3.50

CHARMED SEASON 10 (TV)
Zenescope Entertainment: Oct, 2014 - No. 17, Mar, 2016 ($3.99)
1-17: 1-Shand-s/Feliz-a/Seidman-c 4.00

CHARMED (Volume 1) (TV)
Dynamite Entertainment: 2017 - No. 5, 2017 ($3.99)
1-5-Schultz-s/Sanapo-a; multiple covers on all 4.00

CHASE (See Batman #550 for 1st app.)(Also see Batwoman)
DC Comics: Feb, 1998 - No. 9, Oct, 1998; #1,000,000 Nov, 1998 ($2.50)
1-9: Williams III & Gray-a. 1-Includes 4 Chase cards. 4-Teen Titans app. 7,8-Batman app. 9-GL Hal Jordan-c/app. 3.00
#1,000,000 (11/98) Final issue; 853rd Century x-over 3.00

CHASING DOGMA (See Jay and Silent Bob)

CHASSIS
Millenium Publications: 1996 - No. 3 ($2.95)
1-3: 1-Adam Hughes-c. 2-Conner var-c. 3.00

CHASSIS
Hurricane Entertainment: 1998 - No. 3 ($2.95)
0,1-3: 1-Adam Hughes-c. 0-Green var-c. 3.00

CHASSIS (Vol. 3)
Image Comics: Nov, 1999 - No. 4 ($2.95, limited series)
1-4: 1-Two covers by O'Neil and Green. 2-Busch var-c. 3.00
1-($6.95) DF Edition alternate-c by Wieringo 7.00

CHASTITY
Chaos! Comics: (one-shots)
#1/2 (1/01, $2.95) Batista-a 3.00
Heartbreaker (3/02, $2.99) Adrian-a/Molenaar-c 3.00
Love Bites (3/01, $2.99) Vale-a/Romano-c 3.00
Reign of Terror 1 (10/00, $2.95) Grant-s/Ross-a/Rio-c 3.00
Re-Imagined 1 (7/02, $2.99) Conner-c; Toledo-a 3.00

CHASTITY
Dynamite Entertainment: 2014 - No. 6, 2014 ($3.99, limited series)
1-6: 1-Andreyko-s/Acosta-a; origin retold. Multiple covers on each 4.00

CHASTITY: CRAZYTOWN
Chaos! Comics: Apr, 2002 - No. 3, June, 2002 ($2.99, limited series)
1-3-Nicieza-s/Batista-c/a 3.00

CHASTITY: LUST FOR LIFE
Chaos! Comics: May, 1999 - No. 3, July, 1999 ($2.95, limited series)
1-3-Nutman-s/Benes-c/a 3.00

CHASTITY: ROCKED
Chaos! Comics: Nov, 1998 - No. 4, Feb, 1999 ($2.95, limited series)
1-4-Nutman-s/Justiniano-c/a 3.00

CHASTITY: SHATTERED
Chaos! Comics: Jun, 2001 - No. 3, Sept, 2001 ($2.99, limited series)
1-3-Kaminski & Pulido-s/Batista-c/a 3.00

CHASTITY: THEATER OF PAIN
Chaos! Comics: Feb, 1997 - No. 3, June, 1997 ($2.95, limited series)
1-3-Pulido-s/Justiniano-c/a 3.00
TPB (1997, $9.95) r/#1-3 10.00

CHECKMATE (TV)
Gold Key: Oct, 1962 - No. 2, Dec, 1962
1-Photo-c on both 5 10 15 33 57 80
2 5 10 15 30 50 70

CHECKMATE! (See Action Comics #598 and The OMAC Project)
DC Comics: Apr, 1988 - No. 33, Jan, 1991 ($1.25)
1-33: 13: New format begins 3.00
NOTE: ***Gil Kane*** *c-2, 4, 7, 8, 10, 11, 15-19.*

CHECKMATE (See Infinite Crisis and The OMAC Project)
DC Comics: Jun, 2006 - No. 31, Dec, 2008 ($2.99)
1-Rucka-s/Saiz-a/Bermejo-c; Alan Scott, Mr. Terrific, Sasha Bordeaux app. 4.00
1-2nd printing with B&W cover 3.00
2-31: 2,3-Kobra, King Faraday, Amanda Waller, Fire app. 4-The Great Ten app. 13-15-Outsiders app. 26-Chimera origin 3.00
...: A King's GameTPB (2007, $14.99) r/#1-7 15.00
...: Chimera TPB (2009, $17.99) r/#26-31 18.00
...: Fall of the Wall TPB (2008, $14.99) r/#16-22 15.00
...: Pawn Breaks TPB (2007, $14.99) r/#8-12 15.00

CHERYL BLOSSOM (See Archie's Girls, Betty and Veronica #320 for 1st app.)
Archie Publications: Sept, 1995 - No. 3, Nov, 1995 ($1.50, limited series)
1 2 4 6 10 14 18
2,3 1 2 3 5 7 9
Special 1-4 ('95, '96, $2.00) 1 2 3 5 7 9

CHERYL BLOSSOM (Cheryl's Summer Job)
Archie Publications: July, 1996 - No. 3, Sept, 1996 ($1.50, limited series)
1-3 1 2 3 4 5 7

CHERYL BLOSSOM (...Goes Hollywood)
Archie Publications: Dec, 1996 - No. 3, Feb, 1997 ($1.50, limited series)
1-3 1 2 3 4 5 7

CHERYL BLOSSOM
Archie Publications: Apr, 1997 - No. 37, Mar, 2001 ($1.50/$1.75/$1.79/$1.99)
1-Dan DeCarlo-c/a 2 4 6 8 10 12
2-10: 2-7-Dan DeCarlo-c/a 6.00
11-37: 32-Begin $1.99-c. 34-Sabrina app. 4.00

CHESTY SANCHEZ
Antarctic Press: Nov, 1995 - No. 2, Mar, 1996 ($2.95, B&W)
1,2 3.00
...Super Special (2/99, $5.99) 6.00

CHEVAL NOIR
Dark Horse Comics: 1989 - No. 48, Nov, 1993 ($3.50, B&W, 68 pgs.)
1 ($3.50) Dave Stevens-c 2 4 6 10 14 18
2-6,8,10 ($3.50): 6-Moebius poster insert 5.00
7-Dave Stevens-c 2 4 6 8 10 12
9,11,13,15,17,20,22 ($4.50, 84 pgs.) 6.00
12,18,19,21,23 ($3.95): 12-Geary-a; Mignola-c 5.00
14 ($4.95, 76 pgs.)(7 pgs. color) 6.00
16,24 ($3.75): 16-19-Contain trading cards 5.00
25,26 ($3.95): 26-Moebius-a begins 5.00
27-48 ($2.95): 33-Snyder III-c 4.00
NOTE: ***Bolland*** *a-2, 6, 7, 13, 14.* ***Bolton*** *a-2, 4, 45; c-4, 20.* ***Chadwick*** *c-13.* ***Dorman*** *painted c-16.* ***Geary*** *a-13, 14.* ***Kelley Jones*** *c-27.* ***Kaluta*** *a-6; c-6, 18.* ***Moebius*** *c-5, 9, 26.* ***Dave Stevens*** *c-1, 7.* ***Sutton*** *painted c-36.*

Chew #8 © John Layman

Cheyenne #24 © DELL

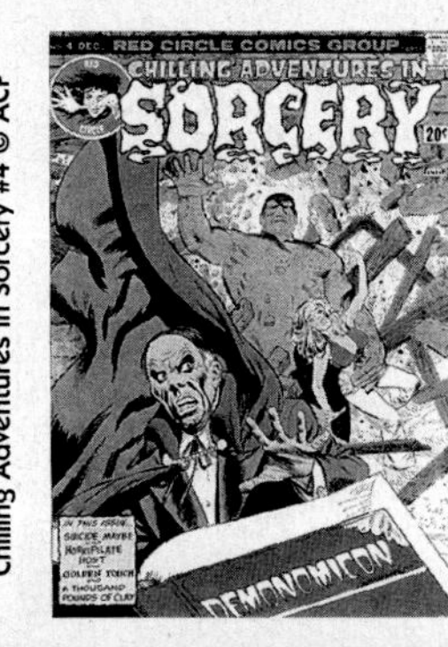

Chilling Adventures in Sorcery #4 © ACP

CHEW (See Walking Dead #61 for preview)
Image Comics: Jun, 2009 - No. 60, Nov, 2016 ($2.99/$3.50/$3.99)

	GD 2.0	VG 4.0	FN 6.0	VF 8.0	VF/NM 9.0	NM- 9.2
1-Layman-s/Guillory-a	10	20	30	69	147	225
1-(2nd-4th printings)	2	4	6	9	12	15
2-1st printing	3	6	9	19	30	40
2-5-(2nd & 3rd printings)						6.00
3-1st printing	2	4	6	11	16	20
4,5-1st printings	2	4	6	9	12	15
6-10	1	3	4	6	8	10
11-15: 15-Gatefold wraparound-c	1	2	3	5	6	8
16-24: 19-Neon green cover ink						5.00
25-44,46-49: 27-(6/12) Second Helping Edition						3.00
27-(5/11) Future issue released between #18 & #19						5.00
45,50-55-($3.50) 49-Poyo cover. 53-Flintstones cover						3.50
56-59-($3.99)						4.00
60-($5.99) Final issue; double cover with gatefold; set in the future						6.00
...: Demon Chicken Poyo One-Shot (4/16, $3.99) Layman-s/Guillory-a; pin-up gallery						4.00
.../ Revival One Shot (5/14, $4.99) Flip book: Layman-s/Guillory-a & Selley-s/Norton-a						5.00
...: Warrior Chicken Poyo (7/14, $3.50) Layman-s/Guillory-a; bonus pin-up gallery						3.50
Image Firsts: Chew #1 (4/10, $1.00) r/#1 with "Image Firsts" cover logo						5.00

CHEWBACCA (Star Wars)
Marvel Comics: Dec, 2015 - No. 5, Feb, 2016 ($3.99, limited series)

	GD 2.0	VG 4.0	FN 6.0	VF 8.0	VF/NM 9.0	NM- 9.2
1-5-Duggan-s/Noto-a; takes place after Episode 4 Battle of Yavin						4.00

CHEYENNE (TV)
Dell Publishing Co.: No. 734, Oct, 1956 - No. 25, Dec-Jan, 1961-62

	GD 2.0	VG 4.0	FN 6.0	VF 8.0	VF/NM 9.0	NM- 9.2
Four Color 734(#1)-Clint Walker photo-c	13	26	39	86	188	290
Four Color 772,803: Clint Walker photo-c	8	16	24	51	96	140
4(8-10/57) - 20: 4-9,13-20-Clint Walker photo-c. 10-12-Ty Hardin photo-c	6	12	18	37	66	95
21-25-Clint Walker photo-c on all	6	12	18	38	69	100

CHEYENNE AUTUMN (See Movie Classics)

CHEYENNE KID (Formerly Wild Frontier No. 1-7)
Charlton Comics: No. 8, July, 1957 - No. 99, Nov, 1973

	GD 2.0	VG 4.0	FN 6.0	VF 8.0	VF/NM 9.0	NM- 9.2
8 (#1)	8	16	24	42	54	65
9,15-19	6	12	18	29	36	42
10-Williamson/Torres-a(3); Ditko-c	11	22	33	60	83	105
11-(68 pgs.)-Cheyenne Kid meets Geronimo	10	20	30	58	79	100
12-Williamson/Torres-a(2)	10	20	30	58	79	100
13-Williamson/Torres-a (5 pgs.)	8	16	24	44	57	70
14-Williamson-a (5 pgs.?)	8	16	24	42	54	65
20-22,24,25-Severin c/a(3) each	4	8	12	21	33	45
23,27-29	3	6	9	15	22	28
26,30-Severin-a	3	6	9	17	26	35
31-59	2	4	6	10	14	18
60-65	2	4	6	8	11	14
66-Wander by Aparo begins, ends #87	2	4	6	10	14	18
67-80	2	4	6	8	11	14
81-99: Apache Red begins #88, origin in #89	2	4	6	8	11	14
Modern Comics Reprint 87,89(1978)						5.00

CHIAROSCURO (THE PRIVATE LIVES OF LEONARDO DA VINCI)
DC Comics (Vertigo): July, 1995 - No. 10, Apr, 1996 ($2.50/$2.95, limited series, mature)

	GD 2.0	VG 4.0	FN 6.0	VF 8.0	VF/NM 9.0	NM- 9.2
1-9: McGreal and Rawson-s/Truog & Kayanan-a						3.00
10-($2.95)						3.00
TPB (2005, $24.99) r/series; intro. by Alisa Kwitney, afterword by Pat McGreal						25.00

CHICAGO MAIL ORDER (See C-M-O Comics in the Promotional Comics section)

CHIEF, THE (Indian Chief No. 3 on)
Dell Publishing Co.: No. 290, Aug, 1950 - No. 2, Apr-June, 1951

	GD 2.0	VG 4.0	FN 6.0	VF 8.0	VF/NM 9.0	NM- 9.2
Four Color 290(#1)	8	16	24	51	96	140
2	5	10	15	35	63	90

CHIEF CRAZY HORSE (See Wild Bill Hickok #21)
Avon Periodicals: 1950 (Also see Fighting Indians of the Wild West!)

	GD 2.0	VG 4.0	FN 6.0	VF 8.0	VF/NM 9.0	NM- 9.2
nn-Fawcette-c	24	48	72	142	234	325

CHIEF VICTORIO'S APACHE MASSACRE (See Fight Indians of/Wild West!)
Avon Periodicals: 1951

	GD 2.0	VG 4.0	FN 6.0	VF 8.0	VF/NM 9.0	NM- 9.2
nn-Williamson/Frazetta-a (7 pgs.); Larsen-a; Kinstler-c	60	120	180	381	653	925

CHILD IS BORN, A
Apostle Arts: Nov, 2011 ($5.99, one-shot)

	GD 2.0	VG 4.0	FN 6.0	VF 8.0	VF/NM 9.0	NM- 9.2
nn-Story of the birth of Jesus; Billy Tucci-s/a; cover by Tucci & Sparacio						6.00
HC (7/12, $15.99) Includes bonus interview with Billy Tucci and sketch art						16.00

CHILDREN OF FIRE
Fantagor Press: Nov, 1987 - No. 3, 1988 ($2.00, limited series)

	GD 2.0	VG 4.0	FN 6.0	VF 8.0	VF/NM 9.0	NM- 9.2
1-3: by Richard Corben						4.00

CHILDREN OF THE VOYAGER (See Marvel Frontier Comics Unlimited)
Marvel Frontier Comics: Sept, 1993 - No. 4, Dec, 1993 ($1.95, limited series)

	GD 2.0	VG 4.0	FN 6.0	VF 8.0	VF/NM 9.0	NM- 9.2
1-($2.95)-Embossed glow-in-the-dark-c; Paul Johnson-c/a						4.00
2-4						3.00

CHILDREN'S BIG BOOK
Dorene Publ. Co.: 1945 (25¢, stiff-c, 68 pgs.)

	GD 2.0	VG 4.0	FN 6.0	VF 8.0	VF/NM 9.0	NM- 9.2
nn-Comics & fairy tales; David Icove-a	15	30	45	90	140	190

CHILDREN'S CRUSADE, THE
DC Comics (Vertigo): Dec, 1993 - No. 2, Jan, 1994 ($3.95, limited series)

	GD 2.0	VG 4.0	FN 6.0	VF 8.0	VF/NM 9.0	NM- 9.2
1,2-Gaiman scripts & Bachalo-a; framing issues for Children's Crusade x-over						4.00

CHILD'S PLAY: THE SERIES (Movie)
Innovation Publishing: May, 1991 - #3, 1991 ($2.50, 28pgs.)

	GD 2.0	VG 4.0	FN 6.0	VF 8.0	VF/NM 9.0	NM- 9.2
1-3						3.00

CHILD'S PLAY 2 THE OFFICIAL MOVIE ADAPTATION (Movie)
Innovation Publishing: 1990 - No. 3, 1990 ($2.50, bi-weekly limited series)

	GD 2.0	VG 4.0	FN 6.0	VF 8.0	VF/NM 9.0	NM- 9.2
1-3: Adapts movie sequel						3.00

CHILI (Millie's Rival)
Marvel Comics Group: 5/69 - No. 17, 9/70; No. 18, 8/72 - No. 26, 12/73

	GD 2.0	VG 4.0	FN 6.0	VF 8.0	VF/NM 9.0	NM- 9.2
1	9	18	27	58	114	170
2,4,5	5	10	15	34	60	85
3-Millie & Chili visit Marvel and meet Stan Lee & Stan Goldberg (6 pgs.)	6	12	18	37	66	95
6-17	5	10	15	30	50	70
18-26	4	8	12	27	44	60
Special 1(12/71, 52 pgs.)	5	10	15	35	63	90

CHILLER
Marvel Comics (Epic): Nov, 1993 - No. 2, Dec, 1993 ($7.95, lim. series)

	GD 2.0	VG 4.0	FN 6.0	VF 8.0	VF/NM 9.0	NM- 9.2
1,2-(68 pgs.)	1	2	3	5	6	8

CHILLING ADVENTURES IN SORCERY (...as Told by Sabrina #1, 2)
(Red Circle Sorcery No. 6 on)
Archie Publications (Red Circle Prods.): 9/72 - No. 2, 10/72; No. 3, 10/73 - No. 5, 2/74

	GD 2.0	VG 4.0	FN 6.0	VF 8.0	VF/NM 9.0	NM- 9.2
1-Sabrina cameo as narrator	5	10	15	31	53	75
2-Sabrina cameo as narrator	3	6	9	19	30	40
3-5: Morrow-c/a, all. 4,5-Alcazar-a	2	4	6	11	16	20

CHILLING ADVENTURES OF SABRINA
Archie Comic Publications: Dec, 2014 - Present ($3.99, mature content)

	GD 2.0	VG 4.0	FN 6.0	VF 8.0	VF/NM 9.0	NM- 9.2
1-8: 1-Aguirre-Sacasa-s/Hack-a; two covers; origin re-told, set in the 1960s						4.00
... - Halloween ComicFest Edition 1 (2015, free) r/#1 in B&W						3.00
... - Halloween ComicFest Edition #1 2017 (free) r/#7 in B&W						3.00

CHILLING TALES (Formerly Beware)
Youthful Magazines: No. 13, Dec, 1952 - No. 17, Oct, 1953

	GD 2.0	VG 4.0	FN 6.0	VF 8.0	VF/NM 9.0	NM- 9.2
13(No.1)-Harrison-a; Matt Fox-c/a	110	220	330	704	1202	1700
14-Harrison-a	71	142	213	454	777	1100
15-Matt Fox-c; Harrison-a	84	168	252	538	919	1300
16-Poe adapt.-'Metzengerstein'; Rudyard Kipling adapt.- 'Mark of the Beast,' by Kiefer; bondage-c	90	180	270	576	988	1400
17-Matt Fox-c; Sir Walter Scott & Poe adapt.	77	154	231	493	847	1200

CHILLING TALES OF HORROR (Magazine)
Stanley Publications: V1#1, 6/69 - V1#7, 12/70; V2#2, 2/71 - V2#6, 10/71(50¢, B&W, 52 pgs.)

	GD 2.0	VG 4.0	FN 6.0	VF 8.0	VF/NM 9.0	NM- 9.2
V1#1	9	18	27	57	111	165
2-4,(no #5),6,7: 7-Cameron-a	6	12	18	38	69	100
V2#2-6: 2-Two different #2 issues exist (2/71 & 4/71). 2-(2/71) Spirit of Frankenstein -r/Adventures into the Unknown #16. 4-(8/71) different from other V2#4(6/71)	5	10	15	35	63	90
V2#4-(6/71) r/9 pg. Feldstein-a from Adventures into the Unknown #3	6	12	18	37	66	95

NOTE: *Two issues of V2#2 exist, Feb, 1971 and April, 1971. Two issues of V2#4 exist, Jun, 1971 and Aug, 1971.*

CHILLY WILLY (Also see New Funnies #211)
Dell Publ. Co.: No. 740, Oct, 1956 - No. 1281, Apr-June, 1962 (Walter Lantz)

	GD 2.0	VG 4.0	FN 6.0	VF 8.0	VF/NM 9.0	NM- 9.2
Four Color 740 (#1)	8	16	24	51	96	140
Four Color 852 (2/58),967 (2/59),1017 (9/59),1074 (2-4/60),1122 (8/60),						

Chip 'N' Dale Rescue Rangers #1 © DIS

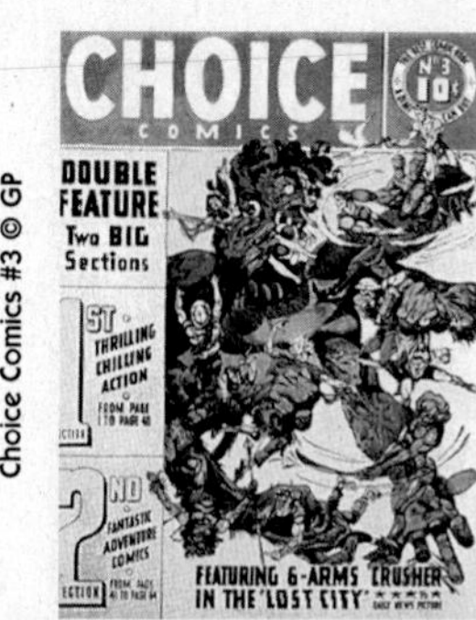

Choice Comics #3 © GP

Christmas Parade #2 © DIS

	GD 2.0	VG 4.0	FN 6.0	VF 8.0	VF/NM 9.0	NM- 9.2
1177 (4-6/61),1212 (7-9/61),1281	5	10	15	34	60	85

CHIMERA
CrossGeneration Comics: Mar, 2003 - No. 4, July, 2003 ($2.95, limited series)

1-4-Marz-s/Peterson-c/a						3.00
Vol. 1 TPB (2003, $15.95) r/#1-4 plus sketch pages, 3-D models, how-to guides						16.00

CHIMICHANGA
Albatross Exploding Funny Books: 2010 ($3.00, B&W)

1-3-Eric Powell-s/a/c						3.00

CHIMICHANGA: THE SORROW OF THE WORLD'S WORST FACE
Dark Horse Comics: Oct, 2016 - No. 4, Dec, 2017 ($3.99, limited series)

1-4-Eric Powell-s/Stephanie Buscema-a						4.00

CHINA BOY (See Wisco in the Promotional Comics section)

CHIN MUSIC
Image Comics: May, 2013 - No. 2, Aug, 2013 ($2.99)

1,2-Steve Niles-s/Tony Harris-a/c						3.00

CHIP 'N' DALE (Walt Disney)(See Walt Disney's C&S #204)
Dell Publishing Co./Gold Key/Whitman No. 65 on: Nov, 1953 - No. 30, June-Aug, 1962; Sept, 1967 - No. 83, July, 1984

Four Color 517(#1)	11	22	33	73	157	240
Four Color 581,636	6	12	18	42	79	115
4(12/55-2/56)-10	5	10	15	33	57	80
11-30	4	8	12	28	47	65
1(Gold Key, 1967)-Reprints	3	6	9	19	30	40
2-10	2	4	6	13	18	22
11-20	2	4	6	9	12	15
21-40	2	4	6	8	10	12
41-64,70-77: 75(2/82), 76(2-3/82), 77(3/82)	1	2	3	5	7	9
65,66 (Whitman)	2	4	6	8	11	14
67-69 (3-pack? 1980): 67(8/80), 68(10/80) (scarce)	4	8	12	28	47	65
78-83 (All #90214; 3-pack, nd, nd code): 78(4/83), 79(5/83), 80(7/83), 81(8/83), 82(5/84), 83(7/84)	3	6	9	15	22	28

NOTE: *All Gold Key/Whitman issues have reprints except No. 32-35, 38-41, 45-47. No. 23-28, 30-42, 45-47, 49 have new covers.*

CHIP 'N DALE RESCUE RANGERS
Disney Comics: June, 1990 - No. 19, Dec, 1991 ($1.50)

1-New stories; origin begins						4.00
2-19: 2-Origin continued						3.00

CHIP 'N DALE RESCUE RANGERS
BOOM! Studios: Dec, 2010 - No. 8, Jul, 2011 ($3.99)

1-8: 1-Brill-s/Castellani-a; 3 covers						4.00
... Free Comic Book Day Edition (5/11) Flip book with Darkwing Duck						3.00

CHITTY CHITTY BANG BANG (See Movie Comics)

C.H.I.X.
Image Comics (Studiosaurus): Jan, 1998 ($2.50)

1-Dodson, Haley, Lopresti, Randall, and Warren-s/c/a						3.00
1-($5.00) "X-Ray Variant" cover						5.00
C.H.I.X. That Time Forgot 1 (8/98, $2.95)						3.00

CHOICE COMICS
Great Publications: Dec, 1941 - No. 3, Feb, 1942

1-Origin Secret Circle; Atlas the Mighty app.; Zomba, Jungle Fight, Kangaroo Man, & Fire Eater begin	155	310	465	992	1696	2400
2	77	154	231	493	847	1200
3-Double feature; Features movie "The Lost City" (classic cover); continued from Great Comics #3	194	388	582	1242	2121	3000

CHOLLY AND FLYTRAP (Arthur Suydam's...)(Also see New Adventures of...)
Image Comics: Nov, 2004 - No. 4, June, 2005 ($4.95/$5.95, limited series)

1-($4.95) Arthur Suydam-s/a/c						6.00
2-4-($5.95)						6.00

CHOO CHOO CHARLIE
Gold Key: Dec, 1969

1-John Stanley-a	5	10	15	35	63	90

CHOSEN
Dark Horse Comics: Jan, 2004 - No. 3, Aug, 2004 ($2.99, limited series)

1-Story of the second coming; Mark Millar-s/Peter Gross-a						4.00
2,3						3.00

CHRISTIAN (See Asylum)

Maximum Press: Jan, 1996 ($2.99, one-shot)

1-Pop Mhan-a						3.00

CHRISTIAN HEROES OF TODAY
David C. Cook: 1964 (36 pgs.)

nn	3	6	9	17	26	35

CHRISTMAS (Also see A-1 Comics)
Magazine Enterprises: No. 28, 1950

A-1 28	10	20	30	56	76	95

CHRISTMAS ADVENTURE, A (See Classics Comics Giveaways, 12/69)

CHRISTMAS ALBUM (See March of Comics No. 312)

CHRISTMAS ANNUAL
Golden Special: 1975 ($1.95, 100 pgs., stiff-c)

nn-Reprints Mother Goose stories with Walt Kelly-a	3	6	9	21	33	45

CHRISTMAS & ARCHIE
Archie Comics: Jan, 1975 ($1.00, 68 pgs., 10-1/4x13-1/4" treasury-sized)

1-(scarce)	5	10	15	34	60	85

CHRISTMAS BELLS (See March of Comics No. 297)

CHRISTMAS CARNIVAL
Ziff-Davis Publ. Co./St. John Publ. Co. No. 2: 1952 (25¢, one-shot, 100 pgs.)

nn	39	78	117	231	378	525
2-Reprints Ziff-Davis issue plus-c	18	36	54	105	165	225

CHRISTMAS CAROL, A (See March of Comics No. 33)

CHRISTMAS EVE, A (See March of Comics No. 212)

CHRISTMAS IN DISNEYLAND (See Dell Giants)

CHRISTMAS PARADE (See Dell Giant No. 26, Dell Giants, March of Comics No. 284, Walt Disney Christmas Parade & Walt Disney's...)

CHRISTMAS PARADE (Walt Disney's)
Gold Key: 1962 (no month listed) - No. 9, Jan, 1972 (#1,5: 80 pgs.; #2-4,7-9: 36 pgs.)

1 (30018-301)-Giant	8	16	24	51	96	140
2-6: 2-r/F.C. #367 by Barks. 3-r/F.C. #178 by Barks. 4-r/F.C. #203 by Barks. 5-r/Christmas Parade #1 (Dell) by Barks; giant. 6-r/Christmas Parade #2 (Dell) by Barks (64 pgs.); giant	5	10	15	35	63	90
7-Pull-out poster (half price w/o poster)	5	10	15	30	50	70
8-r/F.C. #367 by Barks; pull-out poster	5	10	15	35	63	90
9	4	8	12	25	40	55

CHRISTMAS PARTY (See March of Comics No. 256)

CHRISTMAS STORIES (See Little People No. 959, 1062)

CHRISTMAS STORY (See March of Comics No. 326 in the Promotional Comics section)

CHRISTMAS STORY, THE
Catechetical Guild: 1955 (15¢)

393-Addison Burbank-a	8	16	24	40	50	60

CHRISTMAS STORY BOOK (See Woolworth's Christmas Story Book)

CHRISTMAS TREASURY, A (See Dell Giants & March of Comics No. 227)

CHRISTMAS WITH ARCHIE
Spire Christian Comics (Fleming H. Revell Co.): 1973, 1974 (49¢, 52 pgs.)

nn-Low print run	3	6	9	15	22	28

CHRISTMAS WITH MOTHER GOOSE
Dell Publishing Co.: No. 90, Nov, 1945 - No. 253, Nov, 1949

Four Color 90 (#1)-Kelly-a	15	30	45	103	227	350
Four Color 126 ('46), 172 (11/47)-By Walt Kelly	11	22	33	76	163	250
Four Color 201 (10/48), 253-By Walt Kelly	10	20	30	64	132	200

CHRISTMAS WITH SANTA (See March of Comics No. 92)

CHRISTMAS WITH THE SUPER-HEROES (See Limited Collectors' Edition)
DC Comics: 1988; No. 2, 1989 ($2.95)

1,2: 1-(100 pgs.)-All reprints; N. Adams-r, Byrne-c; Batman, Superman, JLA, LSH Christmas stories; r-Miller's 1st Batman/DC Special Series #21. 2-(68 pgs.)-Superman by Chadwick; Batman, Wonder Woman, Deadman, Green Lantern, Flash app.; Morrow-a; Enemy Ace by Byrne; all new-a						6.00

CHROMA-TICK, THE (...Special Edition, #1,2) (Also see The Tick)
New England Comics Press: Feb, 1992 - No. 8, Nov, 1993 ($3.95/$3.50, 44 pgs.)

1,2-Includes serially numbered trading card set						5.00
3-8 ($3.50, 36 pgs.): 6-Bound-in card						4.00

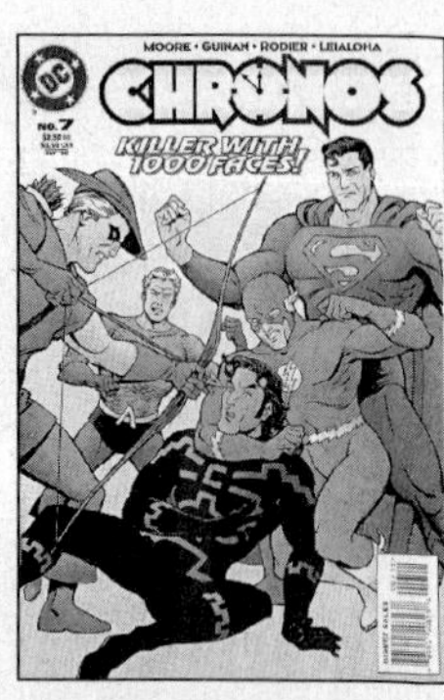

Chronos #7 © DC

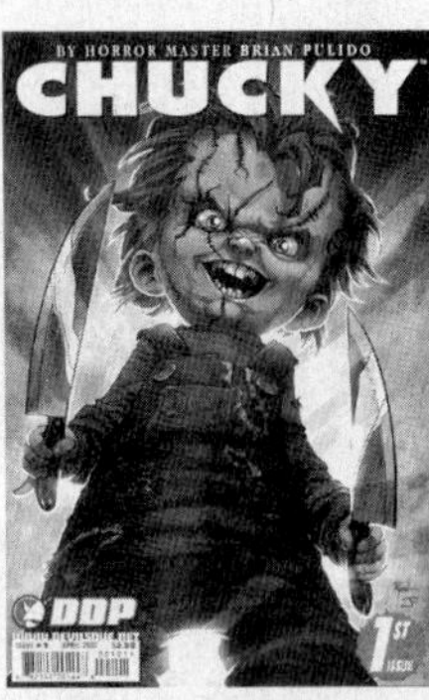

Chucky #1 © Universal Studios

Cinderella Love #25 © STJ

	GD 2.0	VG 4.0	FN 6.0	VF 8.0	VF/NM 9.0	NM- 9.2

CHROME
Hot Comics: 1986 - No. 3, 1986 ($1.50, limited series)

1-3 3.00

CHROMIUM MAN, THE
Triumphant Comics: Aug, 1993 - No.10, May, 1994 ($2.50)

1-1st app. Mr. Death; all serially numbered 3.00
2-10: 2-1st app. Prince Vandal. 3-1st app. Candi, Breaker & Coil. 4,5-Triumphant Unleashed x-over. 8,9-(3/94). 10-(5/94) 3.00
0-(4/94)-Four color-c, 0-All pink-c & all blue-c; no cover price 3.00

CHROMIUM MAN: VIOLENT PAST, THE
Triumphant Comics: Jan, 1994 - No. 2, Jan, 1994 ($2.50, limited series)

1,2-Serially numbered to 22,000 each 3.00

CHRONICLES OF CONAN, THE (See Conan the Barbarian)

CHRONICLES OF CORUM, THE (Also see Corum...)
First Comics: Jan, 1987 - No. 12, Nov, 1988 ($1.75/$1.95, deluxe series)

1-12: Adapts Michael Moorcock's novel; Thomas-s; Mignola-a/c 3.00

CHRONONAUTS
Image Comics: Mar, 2015 - No. 4, Jun, 2015 ($3.50/$5.99)

1-3-Mark Millar-s/Sean Murphy-a 3.50
4-($5.99) 6.00

CHRONOS
DC Comics: Mar, 1998 - No. 11, Feb. 1999 ($2.50)

1-11-J.F. Moore-s/Guinan-a 3.00
#1,000,000 (11/98) 853rd Century x-over 3.00

CHUCK (Based on the NBC TV series)
DC Comics (WildStorm): Aug, 2008 - No. 6, Jan, 2009 ($2.99, limited series)

1-6-Jeremy Haun-a/Kristian Donaldson-c; Noto back-up-a 3.00
TPB (2009, $19.99) r/#1-6; photo-c 20.00

CHUCKLE, THE GIGGLY BOOK OF COMIC ANIMALS
R. B. Leffingwell Co.: 1945 (132 pgs., one-shot)

1-Funny animal 25 50 75 150 245 340

CHUCK NORRIS (TV)
Marvel Comics (Star Comics): Jan, 1987 - No. 4, July, 1987

1-Ditko-a 2 4 6 11 16 20
2,3: Ditko-a 6.00
4-No Ditko-a (low print run) 1 2 3 4 5 8

CHUCK WAGON (See Sheriff Bob Dixon's...)

CHUCKY (Based on the 1988 killer doll movie Child's Play)
Devil's Due Publishing: Apr, 2007 - No. 4, Nov, 2007 ($3.50/$5.50)

1-3-Pulido-s/Medors-a; art & photo covers 5.00
4-($5.50) 1 2 3 4 5 7
TPB (2007, $18.99) r/series; gallery of variant covers; 4 pages of script and sketch art 19.00

CHYNA (WWF Wrestling)
Chaos! Comics: Sept, 2000; July, 2001 ($2.95/$2.99, one-shots)

1-Grant-s/Barrows-a; photo-c 3.00
1-($9.95) Premium Edition; Cleavenger-c 10.00
II -(7/01, $2.99) Deodato-a; photo-c 3.00

CICERO'S CAT
Dell Publishing Co.: July-Aug, 1959 - No. 2, Sept-Oct, 1959

1-Cat from Mutt & Jeff 4 8 12 28 47 65
2 4 8 12 25 40 55

CIMARRON STRIP (TV)
Dell Publishing Co.: Jan, 1968

1-Stuart Whitman photo-c 4 8 12 23 37 50

CINDER AND ASHE
DC Comics: May, 1988 - No. 4, Aug, 1988 ($1.75, limited series)

1-4: Mature readers 3.00

CINDERELLA (Disney) (See Movie Comics)
Dell Publishing Co.: No. 272, Apr, 1950 - No. 786, Apr, 1957

Four Color 272 12 24 36 82 179 275
Four Color 786-Partial-r #272 6 12 18 41 76 110

CINDERELLA
Whitman Publishing Co.: Apr, 1982

nn-Reprints 4-Color #272 1 2 3 4 5 7

CINDERELLA: FABLES ARE FOREVER (See Fables)
DC Comics (Vertigo): Apr, 2011 - No. 6, Sept, 2011 ($2.99, limited series)

1-6-Roberson-s/McManus-a/Zullo-c; Dorothy Gale app. 3.00

CINDERELLA: FROM FABLETOWN WITH LOVE (See Fables)
DC Comics (Vertigo): Jan, 2010 - No. 6, Jun, 2010 ($2.99, limited series)

1-6: Roberson-s/McManus-a/Zullo-c 3.00
TPB (2010, $14.99) r/#1-6 15.00

CINDERELLA LOVE
Ziff-Davis/St. John Publ. Co. No. 12 on: No. 10, 1950; No. 11, 4-5/51; No. 12, 9/51; No. 4, 10-11/51 - No. 11, Fall, 1952; No. 12, 10/53 - No. 15, 8/54; No. 25, 12/54 - No. 29, 10/55 (No #16-24)

10(#1)(1st Series, 1950)-Painted-c 26 52 78 154 252 350
11(#2, 4-5/51)-Crandall-a; Saunders painted-c 18 36 54 105 165 225
12(#3, 9/51)-Photo-c 15 30 45 90 140 190
4-8: 4,6,7-Photo-c 15 30 45 86 133 180
9-Kinstler-a; photo-c 16 32 48 92 144 195
10,11(Fall/'52): 10,11-Photo-c 15 30 45 86 133 180
12(St. John-10/53)-#13:13-Painted-c. 15 30 45 85 130 175
14-Matt Baker-a 30 60 90 177 289 400
15(8/54)-Matt Baker-c 84 168 252 538 919 1300
25(2nd Series)(Formerly Romantic Marriage) Classic Matt Baker-c 135 270 405 864 1482 2100
26-Matt Baker-c; last precode (2/55) 103 206 309 659 1130 1600
27-29: Matt Baker-c 84 168 252 538 919 1300

CINDY COMICS (...Smith No. 39, 40; Crime Can't Win No. 41 on)(Formerly Krazy Komics) (See Junior Miss & Teen Comics)
Timely Comics: No. 27, Fall, 1947 - No. 40, July, 1950

27-Kurtzman-a, 3 pgs: Margie, Oscar begin 41 82 123 256 428 600
28-31-Kurtzman-a 26 52 78 154 252 350
32-36,38-40: 33-Georgie story; anti-Wertham editorial 22 44 66 132 216 300
37-Classic greytone-c 300 600 900 1500 2250 3000

NOTE: *Kurtzman's "Hey Look"-#27(3), 29(2), 30(2), 31; "Giggles 'n' Grins"-28.*

CINNAMON: EL CICLO
DC Comics: Oct, 2003 - No. 5, Feb, 2004 ($2.50, limited series)

1-5-Van Meter-s/Chaykin-c/Paronzini-a 3.00

CIRCUS (...the Comic Riot)
Globe Syndicate: June, 1938 - No. 3, Aug, 1938

1-(Scarce)-Spacehawks (2 pgs.), & Disk Eyes by Wolverton (2 pgs.), Pewee Throttle by Cole (2nd comic book work; see Star Comics V1#11), Beau Gus, Ken Craig & The Lords of Crillon, Jack Hinton by Eisner, Van Bragger by Kane 508 1016 1524 3708 6554 9400
2,3-(Scarce)-Eisner, Cole, Wolverton, Bob Kane-a in each 290 580 870 1856 3178 4500

CIRCUS BOY (TV) (See Movie Classics)
Dell Publishing Co.: No. 759, Dec, 1956 - No. 813, July, 1957

Four Color 759 (#1)-The Monkees' Mickey Dolenz photo-c 12 24 36 81 176 270
Four Color 785 (4/57), 813-Mickey Dolenz photo-c 9 18 27 62 126 190

CIRCUS COMICS
Farm Women's Pub. Co./D. S. Publ.: Apr, 1945 - No. 2, Jun, 1945; Wint., 1948-49

1-Funny animal 15 30 45 85 130 175
2 10 20 30 56 76 95
1(1948)-D.S. Publ.; 2 pgs. Frazetta 26 52 78 152 249 345

CIRCUS OF FUN COMICS
A. W. Nugent Publ. Co.: 1945 - No. 3, Dec, 1947 (A book of games & puzzles)

1 15 30 45 90 140 190
2,3 10 20 30 54 72 90

CISCO KID, THE (TV)
Dell Publishing Co.: July, 1950 - No. 41, Oct-Dec, 1958

Four Color 292(#1)-Cisco Kid, his horse Diablo, & sidekick Pancho & his horse Loco begin; line drawn cover 21 42 63 147 324 500
2(1/51) Painted-c begin 10 20 30 64 132 200
3-5 9 18 27 59 117 175
6-10 8 16 24 51 96 140
11-20 7 14 21 44 82 120
21-36-Last painted-c 6 12 18 37 66 95
37-41: All photo-c 7 14 21 46 86 125

NOTE: ***Buscema** a-40. **Ernest Nordli** painted c-5-16, 20, 35.*

City of the Living Dead nn © AVON

Civil War #3 © MAR

Civil War II: Choosing Sides #1 © MAR

GD 2.0 | VG 4.0 | FN 6.0 | VF 8.0 | VF/NM 9.0 | NM- 9.2

CISCO KID COMICS
Bernard Bailey/Swappers Quarterly: Winter, 1944 (one-shot)

1-Illustrated Stories of the Operas: Faust; Funnyman by Giunta; Cisco Kid (1st app.) & Superbaby begin; Giunta-c 47 94 141 296 498 700

CITIZEN JACK
Image Comics: Nov, 2015 - No. 6, May, 2016 ($3.99, limited series)

1-6-Sam Humphries-s/Tommy Patterson-a 4.00

CITIZEN SMITH (See Holyoke One-Shot No. 9)

CITIZEN V AND THE V-BATTALION (See Thunderbolts)
Marvel Comics: June, 2001 - No. 3, Aug, 2001 ($2.99, limited series)

1-3-Nicieza-a; Michael Ryan-c/a 3.00
...: The Everlasting 1-4 (3/02 - No. 4, 7/02) Nicieza-s/LaRosa-a(p) 3.00

CITY OF HEROES (Online game)
Dark Horse Comics/Blue King Studios: Sept, 2002; May, 2004 - No. 7 ($2.95)

1-(no cover price) Dakan-s/Zombo-a 3.00
1-7-($2.95) 3.00

CITY OF HEROES (Online game)
Image Comics: June, 2005 - No. 20, Aug, 2007 ($2.99)

1-20: 1-Waid-s; Pérez-c. 6-Flip-c with City of Villains. 7-9-Jurgens-s 3.00

CITY OF OTHERS
Dark Horse Comics: Apr, 2007 - No. 4, Aug, 2007 ($2.99, limited series)

1-4-Bernie Wrightson-a/c; Steve Niles & Wrightson-s 3.00
TPB (2/08, $14.95) r/#1-4; Wrightson sketch pages 15.00

CITY OF SILENCE
Image Comics: May, 2000 - No. 3, July, 2000 ($2.50)

1-3-Ellis-s/Erskine-a 3.00
TPB (6/04, $9.95) r/#1-3; pin-up gallery 10.00

CITY OF THE LIVING DEAD (See Fantastic Tales No. 1)
Avon Periodicals: 1952

nn-Hollingsworth-c/a 77 154 231 493 847 1200

CITY OF TOMORROW
DC Comics (WildStorm): June, 2005 - No. 6, Nov, 2005 ($2.99, limited series)

1-6-Howard Chaykin-s/a 3.00
TPB (2006, $19.99) r/#1-6 20.00

CITY PEOPLE NOTEBOOK
Kitchen Sink Press: 1989 ($9.95, B&W, magazine sized)

nn-Will Eisner-s/a 15.00
nn-(DC Comics, 2000) Reprint 10.00

CITY SURGEON (Blake Harper...)
Gold Key: August, 1963

1(10075-308)-Painted-c 4 8 12 23 37 50

CITY: THE MIND IN THE MACHINE
IDW (Darby Pop Publishing): Feb, 2014 - No. 4, May, 2014 ($3.99)

1-4-Eric Garcia-s; 2 covers on each. 1-Fernandez-a. 3-Drew Moss-a. 4-Montenat-a 4.00

CIVIL WAR (Also see Amazing Spider-Man for TPB)
Marvel Comics: July, 2006 - No. 7, Jan, 2007 ($3.99/$2.99, limited series)

1-($3.99) Millar-s/McNiven-a & wraparound-c 2 4 6 11 16 20
1-Variant cover by Michael Turner 3 6 9 17 26 35
1-Aspen Comics Variant cover by Turner 3 6 9 19 30 40
1-Sketch Variant cover 4 8 12 23 37 50
1-Director's Cut (2006, $4.99) r/#1 plus promo art, variant covers, sketches and script 1 2 3 5 6 8
2-($2.99) Spider-Man unmasks 2 4 6 8 10 12
2-Turner variant cover 2 4 6 11 16 20
2-B&W sketch variant cover 3 6 9 17 26 35
2-2nd printing 5.00
3-7: 3-Thor returns. 4-Goliath killed 1 2 3 5 6 8
3-7-Turner variant covers 1 2 3 6 8 10
3-7-B&W sketch variant covers 3 6 9 14 20 25
TPB (2007, $24.99) r/#1-7; gallery of variant covers 25.00
...: Battle Damage Report (2007, $3.99) Post-Civil War character profiles; McGuinness-c 4.00
...: Choosing Sides (2/07, $3.99) Colan-c; Howard the Duck app.; 2 covers by Yu & Colan 5.00
... Companion TPB (2007, $13.99) r/Civil War Files, ...:Battle Damage Report, Marvel Spotlight: Millar/McNiven, Marvel Spotlight: Civil War Aftermath and Daily Bugle CW 14.00
Daily Bugle Civil War Newspaper Special #1 (9/06, 50¢, newsprint) Daily Bugle "newspaper" overview of the crossover; Mayhew-a 3.00
...Files (2006, $3.99) profile pages of major Civil War characters; McNiven-c 4.00
...: Marvel Universe TPB (2007, $11.99) r/Civil War: Choosing Sides, CW: The Return, She-Hulk #8, CW: The Initiative; She-Hulk sketch page; variant cover gallery 12.00
...: MGC #1 (6/10, $1.00) r/#1 with "Marvel's Greatest Comics" cover logo 3.00
...: The Confession (5/07, $2.99) Maleev-c/a; Bendis-s 3.00
...: The Initiative (4/07, $4.99) Silvestri-c/a; previews of post-Civil War series 5.00
...: The Return (3/07, $2.99) Captain Marvel returns; The Sentry app.; Raney-a 3.00
...: The Road to Civil War TPB (2007, $14.99) r/New Avengers: Illuminati, Fantastic Four #536 & 537, Amazing Spider-Man #529-531; Spider-Man costume sketches by Bachalo 15.00
... War Crimes (2/07, $3.99) Kingpin in prison; Tieri-s/Staz Johnson-a 4.00
... War Crimes TPB (2007, $17.99) r/Civil War: War Crimes one-shot and Underworld #1-5 18.00
... X-Men Universe TPB (2007, $13.99) r/Cable & Deadpool #30-32; X-Factor #8,9 14.00

CIVIL WAR (Secret Wars tie-in)
Marvel Comics: Sept, 2015 - No. 5, Dec, 2015 ($4.99/$3.99, limited series)

1-($4.99) Soule-s/Yu-a; Stark vs. Rogers on Battleworld 5.00
2-5-($3.99) 4.00

CIVIL WAR CHRONICLES (Reprints of Civil War and related Marvel issues)
Marvel Comics: Oct, 2007 - No. 12, Sept, 2008 ($4.99, limited series)

1-12: Reprints Civil War, Civil War: Frontline and x-over issues 5.00

CIVIL WAR: FRONTLINE (Tie-in to Civil War and related Marvel issues)
Marvel Comics: Aug, 2006 - No. 11, Apr, 2007 ($2.99, limited series)

1-Jenkins-s/Bachs-a/Watson-c; back-up stories by various 4.00
2-11: 3-Green Goblin app. 11-Aftermath of Civil War #7 3.00
... Book 1 TPB (2007, $14.99) r/#1-6 15.00
... Book 2 TPB (2007, $14.99) r/#7-11 15.00

CIVIL WAR: HOUSE OF M
Marvel Comics: Nov, 2008 - No. 5, Mar, 2009 ($2.99, limited series)

1-5-Gage-s/DiVito-a 3.00

CIVIL WAR MUSKET, THE (Kadets of America Handbook)
Custom Comics, Inc.: 1960 (25¢, half-size, 36 pgs.)

nn 3 6 9 15 22 28

CIVIL WAR II
Marvel Comics: No. 0, Jul, 2016 - No. 8, Feb, 2017 ($4.99/$5.99, limited series)

0-($4.99) Bendis-s/Coipel-a; intro. Ulysses 5.00
1-($5.99) Bendis-s/Marquez-a; Thanos kills War Machine 6.00
2-8-($4.99) 3-Banner killed. 4,5-Guardians of the Galaxy app. 7-Sorrentino-a (2 pgs.) 5.00
...: The Oath 1 (3/17, $4.99) Spencer-s; Capt. America named Director of SHIELD 5.00

CIVIL WAR II: AMAZING SPIDER-MAN
Marvel Comics: Aug, 2016 - No. 4, Nov, 2016 ($3.99, limited series)

1-4-Gage-s/Foreman-a; Ulysses app.; Clash returns 4.00

CIVIL WAR II: CHOOSING SIDES
Marvel Comics: Aug, 2016 - No. 6, Nov, 2016 ($4.99/$3.99, limited series)

1-($4.99) Short stories; Nick Fury, Night Thrasher & Damage Control app. 5.00
2-6-($3.99) Nick Fury story in all. 2-War Machine. 4-Punisher. 6-Jessica Jones 4.00

CIVIL WAR II: GODS OF WAR
Marvel Comics: Aug, 2016 - No. 4, Nov, 2016 ($3.99, limited series)

1-4-Abnett-s/Laiso-a/Anacleto-c. 1-Amadeus Cho app. 3-Avengers app. 4.00

CIVIL WAR II: KINGPIN
Marvel Comics: Sept, 2016 - No. 4, Dec, 2016 ($4.99/$3.99, limited series)

1-($4.99) Two stories; Rosenberg-s/Ortiz-a; Talajic-a; intro./origin Janus Jardeesh 5.00
2-4-($3.99) Rosenberg-s/Ortiz-a. 3-Punisher app. 4.00

CIVIL WAR II: ULYSSES
Marvel Comics: Oct, 2016 - No. 3, Dec, 2016 ($4.99, limited series)

1-3-Ewing-s/Kesel & Palo-a/Francavilla-c; Karnak and the Inhumans app. 4.00

CIVIL WAR II: X-MEN
Marvel Comics: Aug, 2016 - No. 4, Nov, 2016 ($3.99, limited series)

1-4-Bunn-s/Broccardo-a; Magneto app. 2-The Brood & Fantomex app. 4-Ulysses app. 4.00

CIVIL WAR: X-MEN (Tie-in to Civil War)
Marvel Comics: Sept, 2006 - No. 4, Dec, 2006 ($2.99, limited series)

1-4-Paquette-a/Hine-s; Bishop app. 3.00
1-Variant cover by Michael Turner 10.00
TPB (2007, $11.99) r/#1-4, profile pages of minor characters 12.00

CIVIL WAR: YOUNG AVENGERS & RUNAWAYS (Tie-in to Civil War)
Marvel Comics: Sept, 2006 - No. 4, Dec, 2006 ($2.99, limited series)

1-4-Caselli-a/Wells-s/Cheung-c 3.00

Claire Voyant #4 © STD

Clandestine #3 © MAR

Clash #3 © Veitch & Adam Kubert

	GD 2.0	VG 4.0	FN 6.0	VF 8.0	VF/NM 9.0	NM- 9.2

TPB (2007, $11.99) r/#1-4, profile pages of characters 12.00

CLAIRE VOYANT (Also see Keen Teens)
Leader Publ./Standard/Pentagon Publ.: 1946 - No. 4, 1947 (Sparling strip reprints)

	GD 2.0	VG 4.0	FN 6.0	VF 8.0	VF/NM 9.0	NM- 9.2
nn	87	174	261	553	952	1350
2-Kamen-c	65	130	195	416	708	1000
3-Kamen bridal-c; contents mentioned in Love and Death, a book by Gershom Legman(1949) referenced by Dr. Wertham in **SOTI**	97	194	291	621	1061	1500
4-Kamen bondage-c	84	168	252	538	919	1300

CLANDESTINE (Also see Marvel Comics Presents & X-Men: ClanDestine)
Marvel Comics: Oct, 1994 - No.12, Sept, 1995 ($2.95/$2.50)

1-($2.95)-Alan Davis-c/a(p)/scripts & Mark Farmer-c/a(i) begin, ends #8; Modok app.; Silver Surfer cameo; gold foil-c 4.00
2-12: 2-Wraparound-c. 2,3-Silver Surfer app. 5-Origin of ClanDestine. 6-Capt. America, Hulk, Spider-Man, Thing & Thor-c; Spider-Man cameo. 7-Spider-Man-c/app; Punisher cameo. 8-Invaders & Dr. Strange app. 10-Captain Britain-c/app. 11-Sub-Mariner app. 3.00
Preview (10/94, $1.50) 3.00
... Classic HC (2008, $29.99, DJ) r/#1-8, Marvel Comics Presents #158, X-Men and Clandestine #1&2, sketch pages and cover gallery; Alan Davis afterword 30.00

CLANDESTINE
Marvel Comics: Apr, 2008 - No. 5, Aug, 2008 ($2.99, limited series)

1-5: 1-Alan Davis-c/a(p)/scripts & Mark Farmer-c/a(i). 2-5-Excalibur app. 3.00

CLARENCE (Based on the Cartoon Network series)
BOOM! Studios (kaboom): Jun, 2015 - No. 4, Sept, 2015 ($3.99)

1-4-Short stories by various; multiple covers on each 4.00
...: Quest 1 (6/16, $4.99) Cron-DeVico-s; art by Smigiel & Omac 5.00
...: Rest Stops 1 (12/15, $4.99) Short stories by various; two covers 5.00

CLASH
DC Comics: 1991 - No. 3, 1991 ($4.95, limited series, 52 pgs.)

Book One - Three: Adam Kubert-c/a 5.00

CLASSIC BATTLESTAR GALACTICA (See Battlestar Galactica, Classic...)

CLASSIC COMICS/ILLUSTRATED - INTRODUCTION
by Dan Malan

Since the first publication of this special introduction to the **Classics** section, a number of revisions have been made to further clarify the listings. **Classics** reprint editions prior to 1963 had either incorrect dates or no dates listed. Those reprint editions should be identified only by the highest number on the reorder list (HRN). Past *Guides* listed what were calculated to be approximately correct dates, but many people found it confusing for the *Guide* to list a date not listed in the comic itself.

We have also attempted to clear up confusion about edition variations, such as color, printer, etc. Such variations are identified by letters. Editions are determined by three categories. Original edition variations are designated as Edition 1A, 1B, etc. All reprint editions prior to 1963 are identified by HRN only. All reprint editions from 9/63 on are identified by the correct date listed in the comic.

Information is also included on four reprintings of **Classics**. From 1968-1976, Twin Circle, the Catholic newspaper, serialized over 100 **Classics** titles. That list can be found under non-series items at the end of this section. In 1972, twelve **Classics** were reissued as **Now Age Books Illustrated**. They are listed under **Pendulum Illustrated Classics**. In 1982, 20 **Classics** were reissued, adapted for teaching English as a second language. They are listed under **Regents Illustrated Classics**. Then in 1984, six **Classics** were reissued with cassette tapes. See the listing under **Cassette Books**.

UNDERSTANDING CLASSICS ILLUSTRATED
by Dan Malan

Since **Classics Illustrated** is the most complicated comic book series, with all its reprint editions and variations, changes in covers and artwork, a variety of means of identifying editions, and the most extensive worldwide distribution of any comic-book series, this introductory section is provided to assist you in gaining expertise about this series.

THE HISTORY OF CLASSICS

The **Classics** series was the brain child of Albert L. Kanter, who saw in the new comic-book medium a means of introducing children to the great classics of literature. In October of 1941 his Gilberton Co. began the **Classic Comics** series with **The Three Musketeers**, with 64 pages of storyline. In those early years, the struggling series saw irregular schedules and numerous printers, not to mention variable art quality and liberal story adaptations. With No.13 the page total was reduced to 56 (except for No. 33, originally scheduled to be No. 9), and with No. 15 the coming-next ad on the outside back cover moved inside. In 1945 the Jerry Iger Shop began producing all new CC titles, beginning with No. 23. In 1947 the search for a classier logo resulted in **Classics Illustrated**, beginning with No. 35, **Last Days of Pompeii**. With No. 45 the page total dropped again to 48, which was to become the standard.

Two new developments in 1951 had a profound effect upon the success of the series. One was the introduction of painted covers, instead of the old line drawn covers, beginning with No. 81, **The Odyssey**. The second was the switch to the major national distributor Curtis. They raised the cover price from 10 to 15 cents, making it the highest priced comic-book, but it did not slow the growth of the series, because they were marketed as books, not comics. Because of this higher quality image, **Classics** flourished during the fifties while other comic series were reeling from outside attacks. They diversified with their new **Juniors**, **Specials**, and **World Around Us** series.

Classics artwork can be divided into three distinct periods. The pre-Iger era (1941-44) was mentioned above for its variable art quality. The Iger era (1945-53) was a major improvement in art quality and adaptations. It came to be dominated by artists Henry Kiefer and Alex Blum, together accounting for some 50 titles. Their styles gave the first real personality to the series. The EC era (1954-62) resulted from the demise of the EC horror series, when many of their artists made the major switch to classical art.

But several factors brought the production of new CI titles to a complete halt in 1962. Gilberton lost its 2nd class mailing permit. External factors like television, cheap paperback books, and Cliff Notes were all eating away at their market. Production halted with No.167, **Faust**, even though many more titles were already in the works. Many of those found their way into foreign series, and are very desirable to collectors. In 1967, **Classics Illustrated** was sold to Patrick Frawley and his Catholic publication, Twin Circle. They issued two new titles in 1969 as part of an attempted revival, but succumbed to major distribution problems in 1971. In 1988, First Publishing acquired the rights to use the old CI series art, logo, and name from the Frawley Group, and released a short-lived series featuring contributions of modern creators. Acclaim Books and Twin Circles issued a series of **Classics** reprints from 1997-1998.

One of the unique aspects of the **Classics Illustrated** (CI) series was the proliferation of reprint variations. Some titles had as many as 25 editions. Reprinting began in 1943. Some **Classic Comics** (CC) reprints (r) had the logo format revised to a banner logo, and added a motto under the banner. In 1947 CC titles changed to the CI logo, but kept their line drawn covers (LDC). In 1948, Nos. 13, 18, 29 and 41 received second covers (LDC2), replacing covers considered too violent, and reprints of Nos. 13-44 had pages reduced to 48, except for No. 26, which had 48 pages to begin with.

Starting in the mid-1950s, 70 of the 80 LDC titles were reissued with new painted covers (PC). Thirty of them also received new interior artwork (A2). The new artwork was generally higher quality with larger art panels and more faithful but abbreviated storylines. Later on, there were 29 second painted covers (PC2), mostly by Twin Circle. Altogether there were 199 interior art variations (169 (O)s and 30 A2 editions) and 272 different covers (169 (O)s, four LDC2s, 70 new PCs of LDC (O)s, and 29 PC2s). It is mildly astounding to realize that there are nearly 1400 different editions in the U.S. CI series.

FOREIGN CLASSICS ILLUSTRATED

If U.S. Classics variations are mildly astounding, the veritable plethora of foreign CI variations will boggle your imagination. While we still anticipate additional discoveries, we presently know about series in 25 languages and 27 countries. There were 250 new CI titles in foreign series, and nearly 400 new foreign covers of U.S. titles. The 1400 U.S. CI editions pale in comparison to the 4000 plus foreign editions. The very nature of CI lent itself to flourishing as an international series. Worldwide, they published over one billion copies! The first foreign CI series consisted of six Canadian Classic Comic reprints in 1946.

The following chart shows when CI series first began in each country:
1946: Canada. 1947: Australia. 1948: Brazil/The Netherlands. 1950: Italy. 1951: Greece/Japan/Hong Kong(?)/England/Argentina/Mexico. 1952: West Germany. 1954: Norway. 1955: New Zealand/South Africa. 1956: Denmark/Sweden/Iceland. 1957: Finland/France. 1962: Singapore(?). 1964: India (8 languages). 1971: Ireland (Gaelic). 1973: Belgium(?)/Philippines(?) & Malaysia(?).

Significant among the early series were Brazil and Greece. In 1950, Brazil was the first country to begin doing its own new titles. They issued nearly 80 new CI titles by Brazilian authors. In Greece in 1951 they actually had debates in parliament about the effects of Classics Illustrated on Greek culture, leading to the inclusion of 88 new Greek History & Mythology titles in the CI series.

But by far the most important foreign CI development was the joint European series which began in 1956 in 10 countries simultaneously. By 1960, CI had the largest European distribution of any American publication, not just comics! So when all the problems came up with U.S. distribution, they literally moved the CI operation to Europe in 1962, and continued producing new titles in all four CI series. Many of them were adapted and drawn in the U.S., the most famous of which was the British CI #158A. Dr. No, drawn by Norman Nodel. Unfortunately, the British CI series ended in late 1963, which limited the European CI titles available in English to 15. Altogether there were 82 new CI art titles in the joint European series, which ran until 1976.

IDENTIFYING CLASSICS EDITIONS

HRN: This is the highest number on the reorder list. It should be listed in ( ) after the title number. It is crucial to understanding various CI editions.

ORIGINALS (O): This is the all-important First Edition. To determine (O)s,there is one primary rule and two secondary rules (with exceptions):

Rule No. 1: All (O)s and only (O)s have coming-next ads for the next number. **Exceptions**:

Classic Comics #1 © GIL

Classic Comics #2 © GIL

Classic Comics #3 © GIL

No. 14(15) (reprint) has an ad on the last inside text page only. No. 14(0) also has a full-page outside back cover ad (also rule 2). Nos.55(75) and 57(75) have coming-next ads. (Rules 2 and 3 apply here). Nos. 168(0) and 169(0) do not have coming-next ads. No.168 was never reprinted; No. 169(0) has HRN (166). No. 169(169) is the only reprint.

Rule No. 2: On nos.1-80, all (O)s and only (O)s list 10c on the front cover. **Exceptions**: Reprint variations of Nos. 37(62), 39(71), and 46(62) list 10c on the front cover. (Rules 1 and 3 apply here.)

Rule No. 3: All (O)s have HRN close to that title No. **Exceptions**: Some reprints also have HRNs close to that title number: a few CC(r)s, 58(62), 60(62), 149(149), 152(149) 153(149), and title nos. in the 160's. (Rules 1 and 2 apply here.)

DATES: Many reprint editions list either an incorrect date or no date. Since Gilberton apparently kept track of CI editions by HRN, they often left the (O) date on reprints. Often, someone with a CI collection for sale will swear that all their copies are originals. That is why we are so detailed in pointing out how to identify original editions. Except for original editions, which should have a coming-next ad, etc., all CI dates prior to 1963 are incorrect! So you want to go by HRN only if it is (165) or below, and go by listed date if it is 1963 or later. There are a few (167) editions with incorrect dates. They could be listed either as (167) or (62/3), which is meant to indicate that they were issued sometime between late 1962 and early 1963.

COVERS: A change from CC to LDC indicates a logo change, not a cover change; while a change from LDC to LDC2, LDC to PC, or from PC to PC2 does indicate a new cover. New PCs can be identified by HRN, and PC2s can be identified by HRN and date. Several covers had color changes, particularly from purple to blue.

Notes: If you see 15 cents in Canada on a front cover, it does not necessarily indicate a Canadian edition. Editions with an HRN between 44 and 75, with 15 cents on the cover are Canadian. Check the publisher's address. An HRN listing two numbers with a / between them indicates that there are two different reorder lists in the front and back covers. Official Twin Circle editions have a full-page back cover ad for their TC magazine, with no CI reorder list. Any CI with just a Twin Circle sticker on the front is not an official TC edition.

TIPS ON LISTING CLASSICS FOR SALE

It may be easy to just list Edition 17, but Classics collectors keep track of CI editions in terms of HRN and/or date, (O) or (r), CC or LDC, PC or PC2, A1 or A2, soft or stiff cover, etc. Try to help them out. For originals, just list (0), unless there are variations such as color (Nos. 10 and 61), printer (Nos. 18-22), HRN (Nos. 95, 108, 160), etc. For reprints, just list HRN if it's (165) or below. Above that, list HRN and date. Also, please list type of logo/cover/art for the convenience of buyers. They will appreciate it.

CLASSIC COMICS (Also see Best from Boys Life, Cassette Books, Famous Stories, Fast Fiction, Golden Picture Classics, King Classics, Marvel Classics Comics, Pendulum Illustrated Classics, Picture Parade, Picture Progress, Regents Ill. Classics, Spitfire, Stories by Famous Authors, Superior Stories, and World Around Us.)

CLASSIC COMICS (Classics Illustrated No. 35 on)
Elliot Publishing #1-3 (1941-1942)/Gilberton Publications #4-167 (1942-1967) /Twin Circle Pub. (Frawley) #168-169 (1968-1971):
10/41 - No. 34, 2/47; No. 35, 3/47 - No. 169, Spring 1969
(Reprint Editions of almost all titles 5/43 - Spring 1971)
(Painted Covers (0)s No. 81 on, and (r)s of most Nos. 1-80)

Abbreviations:
A–Art; C or c–Cover; CC–Classic Comics; CI–Classics Ill.; Ed–Edition; LDC–Line Drawn Cover; PC–Painted Cover; r–Reprint

1. The Three Musketeers

Ed	HRN	Date	Details	A	C	GD 2.0	VG 4.0	FN 6.0	VF 8.0	VF/NM 9.0	NM- 9.2
1	–	10/41	Date listed-1941; Elliot Pub; 68 pgs.	1	1	514	1014	1542	3750	6625	9500
2	10	–	10¢ price removed on all (r)s; Elliot Pub; CC-r	1	1	36	72	108	211	343	475
3	15	–	Long Isl. Ind. Ed.; CC-r	1	1	26	52	78	154	252	350
4	18/20	–	Sunrise Times Ed.; CC-r	1	1	19	38	57	109	172	235
5	21	–	Richmond Courier Ed.; CC-r	1	1	17	34	51	98	154	210
6	28	1946	CC-r	1	1	14	28	42	80	115	150
7	36	–	LDC-r	1	1	8	16	24	42	54	65
8	60	–	LDC-r	1	1	6	12	18	27	33	38
9	64	–	LDC-r	1	1	5	10	15	22	26	30
10	78	–	C-price 15¢;LDC-r	1	1	4	9	13	18	22	26
11	93	–	LDC-r	1	1	4	9	13	18	22	26
12	114	–	Last LDC-r	1	1	4	8	11	16	19	22
13	134	–	New-c; old-a; 64 pg. PC-r	1	2	3	6	9	18	28	38
14	143	–	Old-a; PC-r; 64 pg.	1	2	2	4	6	11	16	20
15	150	–	New-a; PC-r; Evans/Crandall-a	2	2	3	6	9	16	24	32
16	149	–	PC-r	2	2	2	4	6	8	11	14
17	167	–	PC-r	2	2	2	4	6	8	11	14
18	167	4/64	PC-r	2	2	2	4	6	8	11	14
19	167	1/65	PC-r	2	2	2	4	6	8	11	14
20	167	3/66	PC-r	2	2	2	4	6	8	11	14
21	166	11/67	PC-r	2	2	2	4	6	8	11	14
22	166	Spr/69	C-price 25¢ ; stiff-c; PC-r	2	2	2	4	6	8	11	14
23	169	Spr/71	PC-r; stiff-c	2	2	2	4	6	8	11	14

2. Ivanhoe

Ed	HRN	Date	Details	A	C	GD 2.0	VG 4.0	FN 6.0	VF 8.0	VF/NM 9.0	NM- 9.2
1	(O)	12/41?	Date listed-1941; Elliot Pub; 68 pgs.	1	1	245	490	735	1568	2684	3800
2	10	–	Price & 'Presents' removed; Elliot Pub; CC-r	1	1	32	64	96	188	307	425
3	15	–	Long Isl. Ind. ed.; CC-r	1	1	21	42	63	124	202	280
4	18/20	–	Sunrise Times ed.; CC-r	1	1	18	36	54	103	162	225
5	21	–	Richmond Courier ed.; CC-r	1	1	16	32	48	94	147	200
6	28	1946	Last 'Comics'-r	1	1	14	28	42	80	115	150
7	36	–	1st LDC-r	1	1	9	18	27	47	61	75
8	60	–	LDC-r	1	1	6	12	18	27	33	38
9	64	–	LDC-r	1	1	5	10	15	22	26	30
10	78	–	C-price 15¢; LDC-r	1	1	4	9	13	18	22	26
11	89	–	LDC-r	1	1	4	8	12	17	21	24
12	106	–	LDC-r	1	1	4	7	10	14	17	20
13	121	–	Last LDC-r	1	1	4	7	10	14	17	20
14	136	–	New-c&a; PC-r	2	2	5	10	15	25	31	36
15	142	–	PC-r	2	2	2	4	6	9	13	16
16	153	–	PC-r	2	2	2	4	6	9	13	16
17	149	–	PC-r	2	2	2	4	6	9	13	16
18	167	–	PC-r	2	2	2	4	6	8	11	14
19	167	5/64	PC-r	2	2	2	4	6	8	11	14
20	167	1/65	PC-r	2	2	2	4	6	8	11	14
21	167	3/66	PC-r	2	2	2	4	6	8	11	14
22A	166	9/67	PC-r	2	2	2	4	6	8	11	14
22B	166	–	Center ad for Children's Digest & Young Miss; rare; PC-r	2	2	6	12	18	40	73	105
23	166	R/68	C-Price 25¢; PC-r	2	2	2	4	6	8	11	14
24	169	Win/69	Stiff-c	2	2	2	4	6	8	11	14
25	169	Win/71	PC-r; stiff-c	2	2	2	4	6	8	11	14

3. The Count of Monte Cristo

Ed	HRN	Date	Details	A	C	GD 2.0	VG 4.0	FN 6.0	VF 8.0	VF/NM 9.0	NM- 9.2
1	(O)	3/42	Elliot Pub; 68 pgs.	1	1	155	310	465	992	1696	2400
2	10	–	Conray Prods; CC-r	1	1	27	54	81	158	259	360
3	15	–	Long Isl. Ind. ed.; CC-r	1	1	20	40	60	120	195	270
4	18/20	–	Sunrise Times ed.; CC-r	1	1	18	36	54	107	169	230
5	20	–	Sunrise Times ed.; CC-r	1	1	17	34	51	98	154	210
6	21	–	Richmond Courier ed.; CC-r	1	1	16	32	48	94	147	200
7	28	1946	CC-r; new Banner logo	1	1	14	28	42	80	115	150
8	36	–	1st LDC-r	1	1	9	18	27	47	61	75
9	60	–	LDC-r	1	1	6	12	18	27	33	38
10	62	–	LDC-r	1	1	6	12	18	29	36	42
11	71	–	LDC-r	1	1	5	10	14	20	24	28
12	87	–	C-price 15¢; LDC-r	1	1	4	9	13	18	22	26
13	113	–	LDC-r	1	1	4	7	10	14	17	20
14	135	–	New-c&a; PC-r; Cameron-a	2	2	3	6	9	17	26	35
15	143	–	PC-r	2	2	2	4	6	8	13	16
16	153	–	PC-r	2	2	2	4	6	8	13	16
17	161	–	PC-r	2	2	2	4	6	8	13	16
18	167	–	PC-r	2	2	2	4	6	8	11	14
19	167	7/64	PC-r	2	2	2	4	6	8	11	14

Classic Comics #5 © GIL

Classic Comics #7 © GIL

Classic Comics #8 © GIL

Ed	HRN	Date	Details	A	C	GD 2.0	VG 4.0	FN 6.0	VF 8.0	VF/NM 9.0	NM- 9.2
20	167	7/65	PC-r	2	2	2	4	6	8	11	14
21	167	7/66	PC-r	2	2	2	4	6	8	11	14
22	166	R/68	C-price 25¢; PC-r	2	2	2	4	6	8	11	14
23	169	–	Win/69 Stiff-c; PC-r	2	2	2	4	6	8	11	14

4. The Last of the Mohicans

Ed	HRN	Date	Details	A	C	GD 2.0	VG 4.0	FN 6.0	VF 8.0	VF/NM 9.0	NM- 9.2
1	(O)	8/42	Date listed-1942; Gilberton #4(0) on; 68 pgs.	1	1	135	270	405	864	1482	2100
2	12	–	Elliot Pub; CC-r	1	1	27	54	81	158	259	360
3	15	–	Long Isl. Ind. ed.; CC-r	1	1	20	40	60	120	195	270
4	20	–	Long Isl. Ind. ed.; CC-r; banner logo	1	1	18	36	54	105	165	225
5	21	–	Queens Home News ed.; CC-r	1	1	16	32	48	94	147	200
6	28	1946	Last CC-r; new	1	1	14	28	42	80	115	150
7	36	–	1st LDC-r	1	1	9	18	27	47	61	75
8	60	–	LDC-r	1	1	6	12	18	27	33	38
9	64	–	LDC-r	1	1	5	10	14	20	24	28
10	78	–	C-price 15¢; LDC-r	1	1	4	9	13	18	22	26
11	89	–	LDC-r	1	1	4	8	12	17	21	24
12	117	–	Last LDC-r	1	1	4	7	10	14	17	20
13	135	–	New-c; PC-r	1	2	5	10	15	24	30	35
14	141	–	PC-r	1	2	4	7	9	14	16	18
15	150	–	New-a; PC-r; Severin, L.B. Cole-a	2	2	6	12	18	27	33	38
16	161	–	PC-r	2	2	2	4	6	8	11	14
17	167	–	PC-r	2	2	2	4	6	8	11	14
18	167	6/64	PC-r	2	2	2	4	6	8	11	14
19	167	8/65	PC-r	2	2	2	4	6	8	11	14
20	167	8/66	PC-r	2	2	2	4	6	8	11	14
21	166	R/67	C-price 25¢; PC-r	2	2	2	4	6	8	11	14
22	169	Spr/69	Stiff-c; PC-r	2	2	2	4	6	8	11	14

5. Moby Dick

Ed	HRN	Date	Details	A	C	GD 2.0	VG 4.0	FN 6.0	VF 8.0	VF/NM 9.0	NM- 9.2
1A	(O)	9/42	Date listed-1942; Gilberton; 68 pgs.	1	1	168	336	504	1075	1838	2600
1B			inside-c, rare free promo			252	504	756	1613	2757	3900
2	10	–	Conray Prods; Pg. 64 changed from 105 title list to letter from Editor; CC-r	1	1	28	56	84	165	270	375
3	15	–	Long Isl. Ind. ed.; Pg. 64 changed from Letter to the Editor to Ill. poem-Concord Hymn; CC-r	1	1	23	46	69	136	223	310
4	18/20	–	Sunrise Times ed.; CC-r	1	1	19	38	57	109	172	235
5	20	–	Sunrise Times ed.; CC-r	1	1	18	36	54	105	165	225
6	21	–	Sunrise Times ed.; CC-r	1	1	16	32	48	94	147	200
7	28	1946	CC-r; new banner logo	1	1	14	28	42	81	118	155
8	36	–	1st LDC-r	1	1	9	18	27	47	61	75
9	60	–	LDC-r	1	1	6	12	18	27	33	38
10	62	–	LDC-r	1	1	6	12	18	29	36	42
11	71	–	LDC-r	1	1	5	10	15	22	26	30
12	87	–	C-price 15¢; LDC-r	1	1	5	10	14	20	24	28
13	118	–	LDC-r	1	1	4	8	12	17	21	24
14	131	–	New c&a; PC-r	2	2	5	10	15	25	31	36
15	138	–	PC-r	2	2	2	4	6	9	12	16
16	148	–	PC-r	2	2	2	4	6	9	12	16
17	158	–	PC-r	2	2	2	4	6	9	12	16
18	167	–	PC-r	2	2	2	4	6	8	11	14
19	167	6/64	PC-r	2	2	2	4	6	8	11	14
20	167	7/65	PC-r	2	2	2	4	6	8	11	14
21	167	3/66	PC-r	2	2	2	4	6	8	11	14
22	166	9/67	PC-r	2	2	2	4	6	8	11	14
23	166	Win/69	New-c & c-price 25¢; Stiff-c; PC-r	2	3	3	6	9	16	23	30
24	169	Win/71	PC-r	2	3	3	6	9	14	19	24

6. A Tale of Two Cities

Ed	HRN	Date	Details	A	C	GD 2.0	VG 4.0	FN 6.0	VF 8.0	VF/NM 9.0	NM- 9.2
1	(O)	10/42	Date listed-1942; 68 pgs. Zeckerberg c/a	1	1	129	258	387	826	1413	2000
2	14	–	Elliot Pub; CC-r	1	1	24	48	72	142	234	325
3	18	–	Long Isl. Ind. ed.; CC-r	1	1	20	40	60	114	182	250
4	20	–	Sunrise Times ed.; CC-r	1	1	18	36	54	105	165	225
5	28	1946	Last CC-r; new banner logo	1	1	14	28	42	80	115	150
6	51	–	1st LDC-r	1	1	8	16	24	42	54	65
7	64	–	LDC-r	1	1	5	10	15	23	28	32
8	78	–	C-price 15¢; LDC-r	1	1	5	10	14	20	24	28
9	89	–	LDC-r	1	1	4	7	10	14	17	20
10	117	–	LDC-r	1	1	4	7	10	14	17	20
11	132	–	New-c&a; PC-r; Joe Orlando-a	2	2	5	10	15	25	31	36
12	140	–	PC-r	2	2	2	4	6	8	11	14
13	147	–	PC-r	2	2	2	4	6	8	11	14
14	152	–	PC-r; very rare	2	2	17	34	51	98	154	210
15	153	–	PC-r	2	2	2	4	6	9	13	16
16	149	–	PC-r	2	2	2	4	6	9	13	16
17	167	–	PC-r	2	2	2	4	6	8	11	14
18	167	6/64	PC-r	2	2	2	4	6	8	11	14
19	167	8/65	PC-r	2	2	2	4	6	8	11	14
20	166	5/67	PC-r	2	2	2	4	6	8	11	14
21	166	Fall/68	New-c & 25¢; PC-r	2	3	3	6	9	16	24	32
22	169	Sum/70	Stiff-c; PC-r	2	3	2	4	6	13	18	22

7. Robin Hood

Ed	HRN	Date	Details	A	C	GD 2.0	VG 4.0	FN 6.0	VF 8.0	VF/NM 9.0	NM- 9.2
1	(O)	12/42	Date listed-1942; first Gift Box ad-bc; 68 pgs.	1	1	100	200	300	635	1093	1550
2	12	–	Elliot Pub; CC-r	1	1	24	48	72	140	230	320
3	18	–	Long Isl. Ind. ed.; CC-r	1	1	19	38	57	111	176	240
4	20	–	Nassau Bulletin ed.; CC-r	1	1	18	36	54	103	162	220
5	22	–	Queens Cty. Times ed.; CC-r	1	1	16	32	48	94	147	200
6	28	–	CC-r	1	1	14	28	42	81	118	155
7	51	–	LDC-r	1	1	8	16	24	42	54	65
8	64	–	LDC-r	1	1	5	10	15	24	30	35
9	78	–	LDC-r	1	1	4	9	13	18	22	26
10	97	–	LDC-r	1	1	4	8	12	17	21	24
11	106	–	LDC-r	1	1	4	7	10	14	17	20
12	121	–	LDC-r	1	1	4	7	10	14	17	20
13	129	–	New-c; PC-r	1	2	5	10	15	25	31	36
14	136	–	New-a; PC-r	2	2	5	10	15	24	29	34
15	143	–	PC-r	2	2	2	4	6	9	13	16
16	153	–	PC-r	2	2	2	4	6	9	13	16
17	164	–	PC-r	2	2	2	4	6	8	11	14
18	167	–	PC-r	2	2	2	4	6	8	11	14
19	167	6/64	PC-r	2	2	2	4	6	8	11	14
20	167	5/65	PC-r	2	2	2	4	6	8	11	14
21	167	7/66	PC-r	2	2	2	4	6	8	11	14
22	166	12/67	PC-r	2	2	2	4	6	8	11	14
23	169	Sum/69	Stiff-c; c-price 25¢; PC-r	2	2	2	4	6	8	11	14

8. Arabian Nights

Ed	HRN	Date	Details	A	C	GD 2.0	VG 4.0	FN 6.0	VF 8.0	VF/NM 9.0	NM- 9.2
1	(O)	2/43	Original; 68 pgs. Lilian Chestney-c/a	1	1	152	304	456	965	1658	2350
2	17	–	Long Isl. ed.; pg. 64 changed from Gift Box ad to Letter from British Medical Worker; CC-r	1	1	52	104	156	323	549	775
3	20	–	Nassau Bulletin;	1	1	42	84	126	265	445	625

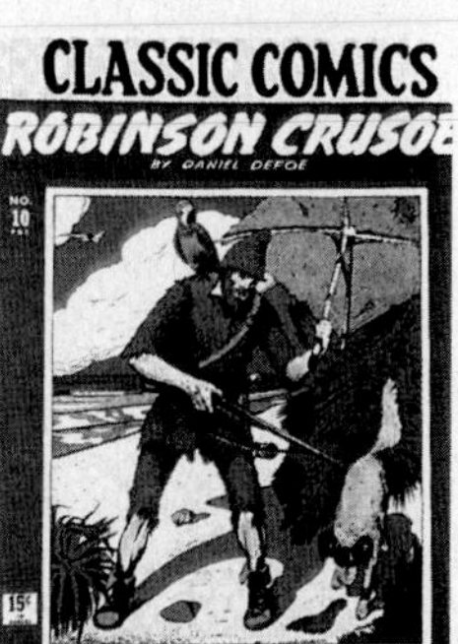

Classic Comics #10 © GIL

Classic Comics #12 © GIL

Classic Comics #14 © GIL

Ed	HRN	Date	Details	A	C	GD 2.0	VG 4.0	FN 6.0	VF 8.0	VF/NM 9.0	NM- 9.2
			Pg. 64 changed from letter to article-Three Men Named Smith; CC-r								
4A	28	1946	CC-r; new banner logo, slick-c	1	1	31	62	93	182	296	410
4B	28	1946	Same, but w/stiff-c	1	1	31	62	93	182	296	410
5	51	–	LDC-r	1	1	22	44	66	128	209	290
6	64	–	LDC-r	1	1	19	38	57	111	176	240
7	78	–	LDC-r	1	1	18	36	54	105	165	225
8	164	–	New-c&a; PC-r	2	2	15	30	45	90	140	190

9. Les Miserables

Ed	HRN	Date	Details	A	C	GD 2.0	VG 4.0	FN 6.0	VF 8.0	VF/NM 9.0	NM- 9.2
1A	(O)	3/43	Original; slick paper cover; 68 pgs.	1	1	103	206	309	659	1130	1600
1B	(O)	3/43	Original; rough, pulp type-c; 68 pgs.	1	1	116	232	348	742	1271	1800
2	14	–	Elliot Pub; CC-r	1	1	26	52	78	154	252	350
3	18	3/44	Nassau Bul. Pg. 64 changed from Gift Box ad to Bill of Rights article; CC-r	1	1	22	44	66	128	209	290
4	20	–	Richmond Courier ed.; CC-r	1	1	19	38	57	111	176	240
5	28	1946	Gilberton; pgs. 60-64 rearranged/ illos added; CC-r	1	1	14	28	42	81	118	155
6	51	–	LDC-r	1	1	9	18	27	47	61	75
7	71	–	LDC-r	1	1	6	12	18	29	36	42
8	87	–	C-price 15¢; LDC-r	1	1	6	12	18	27	33	38
9	161	–	New-c&a; PC-r	2	2	7	14	21	37	46	55
10	167	9/63	PC-r	2	2	2	4	6	11	16	20
11	167	12/65	PC-r	2	2	2	4	6	11	16	20
12	166	R/1968	New-c & price 25¢; PC-r	2	3	3	6	9	17	26	35

10. Robinson Crusoe (Used in **SOTI**, pg. 142)

Ed	HRN	Date	Details	A	C	GD 2.0	VG 4.0	FN 6.0	VF 8.0	VF/NM 9.0	NM- 9.2
1A	(O)	4/43	Original; Violet-c; 68 pgs; Zuckerberg c/a	1	1	86	172	258	546	936	1325
1B	(O)	4/43	Original; blue-grey-c, 68 pgs.	1	1	94	188	282	597	1024	1450
2A	14	–	Elliot Pub; violet-c; 68 pgs; CC-r	1	1	29	58	87	170	278	385
2B	14	–	Elliot Pub; blue-grey-c; CC-r	1	1	25	50	75	147	241	335
3	18	–	Nassau Bul. Pg. 64 changed from Gift Box ad to Bill of Rights article; CC-r	1	1	19	38	57	111	176	240
4	20	–	Queens Home News ed.; CC-r	1	1	16	32	48	94	147	200
5	28	1946	Gilberton; pg. 64 changes from Bill of Rights to WWII article-One Leg Shot Away; last CC-r	1	1	14	28	42	80	115	150
6	51	–	LDC-r	1	1	8	16	24	42	54	65
7	64	–	LDC-r	1	1	6	12	18	27	33	38
8	78	–	C-price 15¢; LDC-r	1	1	5	10	14	20	24	28
9	97	–	LDC-r	1	1	4	9	13	18	22	26
10	114	–	LDC-r	1	1	4	7	10	14	17	20
11	130	–	New-c; PC-r	1	2	5	10	15	25	31	36
12	140	–	New-a; PC-r	2	2	5	10	15	24	29	34
13	153	–	PC-r	2	2	2	4	6	8	11	14
14	164	–	PC-r	2	2	2	4	6	8	11	14
15	167	–	PC-r	2	2	2	4	6	8	11	14
16	167	7/64	PC-r	2	2	2	4	6	10	14	18
17	167	5/65	PC-r	2	2	2	4	6	10	14	18
18	167	6/66	PC-r	2	2	2	4	6	8	11	14
19	166	Fall/68	C-price 25¢; PC-r	2	2	2	4	6	8	11	14
20	166	R/68	(No Twin Circle ad)	2	2	2	4	6	9	13	16
21	169	Sm/70	Stiff-c; PC-r	2	2	2	4	6	9	13	16

11. Don Quixote

Ed	HRN	Date	Details	A	C	GD 2.0	VG 4.0	FN 6.0	VF 8.0	VF/NM 9.0	NM- 9.2
1	10	5/43	First (O) with HRN list; 68 pgs.	1	1	89	178	267	565	970	1375
2	18	–	Nassau Bulletin ed.; CC-r	1	1	23	46	69	136	223	310
3	21	–	Queens Home News ed.; CC-r	1	1	19	38	57	111	176	240
4	28	–	CC-r	1	1	14	28	42	81	118	155
5	110	–	New-PC; PC-r	1	2	7	14	21	35	43	50
6	156	–	Pgs. reduced 68 to 52; PC-r	1	2	4	7	10	14	17	20
7	165	–	PC-r	1	2	2	4	6	9	13	16
8	167	1/64	PC-r	1	2	2	4	6	9	13	16
9	167	11/65	PC-r	1	2	2	4	6	9	13	16
10	166	R/1968	New-c & price 25¢; PC-r	1	3	3	6	9	18	27	36

12. Rip Van Winkle and the Headless Horseman

Ed	HRN	Date	Details	A	C	GD 2.0	VG 4.0	FN 6.0	VF 8.0	VF/NM 9.0	NM- 9.2
1	11	6/43	Original; 68 pgs.	1	1	92	184	276	584	1005	1425
2	15	–	Long Isl. Ind. ed.; CC-r	1	1	24	48	72	142	234	325
3	20	–	Long Isl. Ind. ed.;	1	1	20	40	60	114	182	250
4	22	–	Queens Cty. Times ed.; CC-r	1	1	16	32	48	94	147	200
5	28	–	CC-r	1	1	14	28	42	80	115	150
6	60	–	1st LDC-r	1	1	8	16	24	40	50	60
7	62	–	LDC-r	1	1	5	10	15	23	28	32
8	71	–	LDC-r	1	1	4	9	13	18	22	26
9	89	–	C-price 15¢; LDC-r	1	1	4	8	12	17	21	24
10	118	–	LDC-r	1	1	4	7	10	14	17	20
11	132	–	New-c; PC-r	1	2	5	10	15	25	31	36
12	150	–	New-a; PC-r	2	2	5	10	15	24	29	34
13	158	–	PC-r	2	2	2	4	6	9	13	16
14	167	–	PC-r	2	2	2	4	6	9	13	16
15	167	12/63	PC-r	2	2	2	4	6	8	11	14
16	167	4/65	PC-r	2	2	2	4	6	8	11	14
17	167	4/66	PC-r	2	2	2	4	6	8	11	14
18	166	R/1968	New-c&price 25¢; PC-r; stiff-c	2	3	3	6	9	14	20	26
19	169	Sm/70	PC-r; stiff-c	2	3	2	4	6	10	14	18

13. Dr. Jekyll and Mr. Hyde (Used in **SOTI**, pg. 143)(1st horror comic?)

Ed	HRN	Date	Details	A	C	GD 2.0	VG 4.0	FN 6.0	VF 8.0	VF/NM 9.0	NM- 9.2
1	12	8/43	Original 60 pgs.	1	1	139	278	417	883	1517	2150
2	15	–	Long Isl. Ind. ed.; CC-r	1	1	36	72	108	211	343	475
3	20	–	Long Isl. Ind. ed.; CC-r	1	1	24	48	72	142	234	325
4	28	–	No c-price; CC-r	1	1	18	36	54	105	165	225
5	60	–	New-c; Pgs. reduced from 60 to 52; H.C. Kiefer-c; LDC-r	1	2	9	18	27	47	61	75
6	62	–	LDC-r	1	2	6	12	18	28	34	40
7	71	–	LDC-r	1	2	5	10	15	23	28	32
8	87	–	Date returns (erroneous); LDC-r	1	2	5	10	15	22	26	30
9	112	–	New-c&a; PC-r; Cameron-a	2	3	7	14	21	35	43	50
10	153	–	PC-r	2	3	2	4	6	9	13	16
11	161	–	PC-r	2	3	2	4	6	9	13	16
12	167	–	PC-r	2	3	2	4	6	8	11	14
13	167	8/64	PC-r	2	3	2	4	6	8	11	14
14	167	11/65	PC-r	2	3	2	4	6	8	11	14
15	166	R/68	C-price 25¢; PC-r	2	3	2	4	6	8	11	14
16	169	Wn/69	PC-r; stiff-c	2	3	2	4	6	8	11	14

14. Westward Ho!

Ed	HRN	Date	Details	A	C	GD 2.0	VG 4.0	FN 6.0	VF 8.0	VF/NM 9.0	NM- 9.2
1	13	9/43	Original; last out-side bc coming-next ad; 60 pgs.	1	1	194	388	582	1242	2121	3000
2	15	–	Long Isl. Ind. ed.; CC-r	1	1	58	116	174	371	636	900
3	21	–	Queens Home	1	1	46	92	138	290	488	685

Classic Comics #15 © GIL

Classic Comics #17 © GIL

Classic Comics #19 © GIL

Ed	HRN	Date	Details	A	C	GD 2.0	VG 4.0	FN 6.0	VF 8.0	VF/NM 9.0	NM- 9.2
			News; Pg. 56 changed from coming-next ad to Three Men Named Smith; CC-r								
4	28	1946	Gilberton; Pg. 56 changed again to WWII article-Speaking for America; last CC-r	1	1	39	78	117	242	401	560
5	53	–	Pgs. reduced from 60 to 52; LDC-r	1	1	36	72	108	216	351	485

15. Uncle Tom's Cabin (Used in **SOTI**, pgs. 102, 103)

Ed	HRN	Date	Details	A	C	GD 2.0	VG 4.0	FN 6.0	VF 8.0	VF/NM 9.0	NM- 9.2
1	14	11/43	Original; Outside-bc ad: 2 Gift Boxes; 60 pgs.; color var. on-c; green trunk,root on left & brown trunk, root on left	1	1	82	164	246	528	902	1275
2	15	–	Long Isl. Ind. listed- bottom inside-fc; also Gilberton listed bottom-pg. 1; CC-r; portion of root to the left of the price circle can be green or brown	1	1	26	52	78	154	252	350
3	21	–	Nassau Bulletin ed.; CC-r	1	1	20	40	60	117	189	260
4	28	–	No c-price; CC-r	1	1	14	28	42	82	121	160
5	53	–	Pgs. reduced 60 to 52; LDC-r	1	1	8	16	24	42	54	65
6	71	–	LDC-r	1	1	6	12	18	27	33	38
7	89	–	C-price 15¢; LDC-r	1	1	5	10	15	24	30	35
8	117	–	New-c/lettering changes; PC-r	1	2	5	10	15	25	31	36
9	128	–	'Picture Progress' promo; PC-r	1	2	2	4	6	10	14	18
10	137	–	PC-r	1	2	2	4	6	9	13	16
11	146	–	PC-r	1	2	2	4	6	9	13	16
12	154	–	PC-r	1	2	2	4	6	9	13	16
13	161	–	PC-r	1	2	2	4	6	8	11	14
14	167	–	PC-r	1	2	2	4	6	8	11	14
15	167	6/64	PC-r	1	2	2	4	6	8	11	14
16	167	5/65	PC-r	1	2	2	4	6	8	11	14
17	166	5/67	PC-r	1	2	2	4	6	8	11	14
18	166	Wn/69	New-stiff-c; PC-r	1	3	3	6	9	15	22	28
19	169	Sm/70	PC-r; stiff-c	1	3	2	4	6	10	14	18

16. Gulliver's Travels

Ed	HRN	Date	Details	A	C	GD 2.0	VG 4.0	FN 6.0	VF 8.0	VF/NM 9.0	NM- 9.2
1	15	12/43	Original-Lilian Chestney c/a; 60 pgs.	1	1	81	162	243	518	884	1250
2	18/20	–	Price deleted; Queens Home News ed; CC-r	1	1	22	44	66	128	209	290
3	22	–	Queens Cty. Times ed.; CC-r	1	1	18	36	54	105	165	225
4	28	–	CC-r	1	1	14	28	42	80	115	150
5	60	–	Pgs. reduced to 48; LDC-r	1	1	6	12	18	31	38	45
6	62	–	LDC-r	1	1	5	10	15	23	28	32
7	78	–	C-price 15¢; LDC-r	1	1	5	10	14	20	24	28
8	89	–	LDC-r	1	1	4	8	12	17	21	24
9	155	–	New-c; PC-r	1	2	5	10	15	25	31	36
10	165	–	PC-r	1	2	2	4	6	8	11	14
11	167	5/64	PC-r	1	2	2	4	6	8	11	14
12	167	11/65	PC-r	1	2	2	4	6	8	11	14
13	166	R/1968	C-price 25¢; PC-r	1	2	2	4	6	8	11	14
14	169	Wn/69	PC-r; stiff-c	1	2	2	4	6	8	11	14

17. The Deerslayer

Ed	HRN	Date	Details	A	C	GD 2.0	VG 4.0	FN 6.0	VF 8.0	VF/NM 9.0	NM- 9.2
1	16	1/44	Original; Outside-bc ad: 3 Gift Boxes; 60 pgs.	1	1	66	132	198	419	872	1025
2A	18	–	Queens Cty Times (inside-fc); CC-r	1	1	23	46	69	136	223	310
2B	18	–	Gilberton (bottom-pg. 1); CC-r; Scarce	1	1	33	66	99	194	317	440
3	22	–	Queens Cty. Times ed.; CC-r	1	1	19	38	57	109	172	235
4	28	–	CC-r	1	1	14	28	42	81	118	155
5	60	–	Pgs.reduced to 52; LDC-r	1	1	7	14	21	37	46	55
6	64	–	LDC-r	1	1	5	10	15	22	26	30
7	85	–	C-price 15¢; LDC-r	1	1	4	8	12	17	21	24
8	118	–	LDC-r	1	1	4	7	10	14	17	20
9	132	–	LDC-r	1	1	4	7	10	14	17	20
10	167	11/66	Last LDC-r	1	1	2	4	6	11	16	20
11	166	R/1968	New-c & price 25¢; PC-r	1	2	3	6	9	17	26	35
12	169	Spr/71	Stiff-c; letters from parents & educators; PC-r	1	2	2	4	6	10	14	18

18. The Hunchback of Notre Dame

Ed	HRN	Date	Details	A	C	GD 2.0	VG 4.0	FN 6.0	VF 8.0	VF/NM 9.0	NM- 9.2
1A	17	3/44	Orig.; Gilberton ed; 60 pgs.	1	1	100	200	300	635	1093	1550
1B	17	3/44	Orig.; Island Pub. Ed.; 60 pgs.	1	1	87	174	261	553	952	1350
2	18/20	–	Queens Home News ed.; CC-r	1	1	28	56	84	165	270	375
3	22	–	Queens Cty. Times ed.; CC-r	1	1	22	44	66	132	216	300
4	28	–	CC-r	1	1	21	42	63	122	199	275
5	60	–	New-c; 8pgs. deleted; Kiefer-c; LDC-r	1	2	9	18	27	50	65	80
6	62	–	LDC-r	1	2	5	10	15	22	26	30
7	78	–	C-price 15¢; LDC-r	1	2	5	10	14	20	24	28
8A	89	–	H.C.Kiefer on bottom right-fc; LDC-r	1	2	4	9	13	18	22	26
8B	89	–	Name omitted; LDC-r	1	2	5	10	15	24	30	35
9	118	–	LDC-r	1	2	4	8	12	17	21	24
10	140	–	New-c; PC-r	1	3	7	14	21	35	43	50
11	146	–	PC-r	1	3	4	9	13	18	22	26
12	158	–	New-c&a; PC-r; Evans/Crandall-a	2	4	5	10	15	25	31	36
13	165	–	PC-r	2	4	2	4	6	9	13	16
14	167	9/63	PC-r	2	4	2	4	6	9	13	16
15	167	10/64	PC-r	2	4	2	4	6	9	13	16
16	167	4/66	PC-r	2	4	2	4	6	8	11	14
17	166	R/1968	New price 25¢; PC-r	2	4	2	4	6	8	11	14
18	169	Sp/70	Stiff-c; PC-r	2	4	2	4	6	8	11	14

19. Huckleberry Finn

Ed	HRN	Date	Details	A	C	GD 2.0	VG 4.0	FN 6.0	VF 8.0	VF/NM 9.0	NM- 9.2
1A	18	4/44	Orig.; Gilberton ed.; 60 pgs.	1	1	54	108	162	343	574	825
1B	18	4/44	Orig.; Island Pub.; 60 pgs.	1	1	57	114	171	362	619	875
2	18	–	Nassau Bulletin ed.; fc-price 15¢-Canada; no coming-next ad; CC-r	1	1	23	46	69	136	223	310
3	22	–	Queens City Times ed.; CC-r	1	1	19	38	57	111	176	240
4	28	–	CC-r	1	1	14	28	42	80	115	150
5	60	–	Pgs. reduced to 48; LDC-r	1	1	6	12	18	31	38	45
6	62	–	LDC-r	1	1	5	10	15	23	28	32
7	78	–	LDC-r	1	1	4	9	13	18	22	26
8	89	–	LDC-r	1	1	4	8	12	17	21	24
9	117	–	LDC-r	1	1	4	7	10	14	17	20
10	131	–	New-c&a; PC-r	2	2	5	10	15	24	30	35
11	140	–	PC-r	2	2	2	4	6	9	13	16
12	150	–	PC-r	2	2	2	4	6	9	13	16
13	158	–	PC-r	2	2	2	4	6	9	13	16
14	165	–	PC-r (scarce)	2	2	3	6	9	14	19	24
15	167	–	PC-r	2	2	2	4	6	8	11	14

Classic Comics #21 © GIL

Classic Comics #24 © GIL

Classic Comics #26 © GIL

Ed	HRN	Date	Details	A	C	GD 2.0	VG 4.0	FN 6.0	VF 8.0	VF/NM 9.0	NM- 9.2
16	167	6/64	PC-r	2	2	2	4	6	8	11	14
17	167	6/65	PC-r	2	2	2	4	6	8	11	14
18	167	10/65	PC-r	2	2	2	4	6	8	11	14
19	166	9/67	PC-r	2	2	2	4	6	8	11	14
20	166	Win/69	C-price 25¢; PC-r; stiff-c	2	2	2	4	6	8	11	14
21	169	Sm/70	PC-r; stiff-c	2	2	2	4	6	8	11	14

20. The Corsican Brothers

Ed	HRN	Date	Details	A	C	GD 2.0	VG 4.0	FN 6.0	VF 8.0	VF/NM 9.0	NM- 9.2
1A	20	6/44	Orig.; Gilberton ed.; bc-ad: 4 Gift Boxes; 60 pgs.	1	1	48	96	114	302	514	725
1B	20	6/44	Orig.; Courier ed.; 60 pgs.	1	1	41	82	123	256	428	600
1C	20	6/44	Orig.; Long Island Ind. ed.; 60 pgs.	1	1	41	82	123	256	428	600
2	22	–	Queens Cty. Times ed.; white logo banner; CC-r	1	1	20	40	60	114	182	250
3	28	–	CC-r	1	1	19	38	57	109	172	235
4	60	–	CI logo; no price; 48 pgs.; LDC-r	1	1	15	30	45	90	140	190
5A	62	–	LDC-r; Classics Ill. logo at top of pgs.	1	1	15	30	45	83	124	165
5B	62	–	w/o logo at top of pg. (scarcer)	1	1	15	30	45	86	133	180
6	78	–	C-price 15¢; LDC-r	1	1	14	28	42	81	118	155
7	97	–	LDC-r	1	1	14	28	42	78	112	145

21. 3 Famous Mysteries ("The Sign of the 4", "The Murders in the Rue Morgue", "The Flayed Hand")

Ed	HRN	Date	Details	A	C	GD 2.0	VG 4.0	FN 6.0	VF 8.0	VF/NM 9.0	NM- 9.2
1A	21	7/44	Orig.; Gilberton ed.; 60 pgs.	1	1	98	196	294	630	1078	1525
1B	21	7/44	Orig. Island Pub. Co.; 60 pgs.	1	1	102	204	306	650	1113	1575
1C	21	7/44	Original; Courier Ed.; 60 pgs.	1	1	89	178	267	565	970	1375
2	22	–	Nassau Bulletin ed.; CC-r	1	1	40	80	120	244	402	560
3	30	–	CC-r	1	1	28	56	84	165	270	375
4	62	–	LDC-r; 8 pgs. deleted; LDC-r	1	1	22	44	66	128	209	290
5	70	–	LDC-r	1	1	20	40	60	117	189	260
6	85	–	C-price 15¢; LDC-r	1	1	18	36	54	107	169	230
7	114	–	New-c; PC-r	1	2	18	36	54	107	169	230

22. The Pathfinder

Ed	HRN	Date	Details	A	C	GD 2.0	VG 4.0	FN 6.0	VF 8.0	VF/NM 9.0	NM- 9.2
1A	22	10/44	Orig.; No printer listed; ownership statement inside fc lists Gilberton & date; 60 pgs.	1	1	47	94	141	296	498	700
1B	22	10/44	Orig.; Island Pub. ed.; 60 pgs.	1	1	41	82	123	256	428	600
1C	22	10/44	Orig.; Queens Cty Times ed. 60 pgs.	1	1	41	82	123	256	428	600
2	30	–	C-price removed; CC-r	1	1	15	30	45	85	130	175
3	60	–	Pgs. reduced to 52; LDC-r	1	1	6	12	18	27	33	38
4	70	–	LDC-r	1	1	5	10	15	22	26	30
5	85	–	C-price 15¢; LDC-r	1	1	4	9	13	18	22	26
6	118	–	LDC-r	1	1	4	8	12	17	21	24
7	132	–	LDC-r	1	1	4	7	10	14	17	20
8	146	–	LDC-r	1	1	4	7	10	14	17	20
9	167	11/63	New-c; PC-r	1	2	4	8	12	23	37	50
10	167	12/65	PC-r	1	2	2	4	6	11	16	20
11	166	8/67	PC-r	1	2	2	4	6	11	16	20

23. Oliver Twist (1st Classic produced by the Iger Shop)

Ed	HRN	Date	Details	A	C	GD 2.0	VG 4.0	FN 6.0	VF 8.0	VF/NM 9.0	NM- 9.2
1	23	7/45	Original; 60 pgs.	1	1	47	94	141	296	498	700
2A	30	–	Printers Union logo on bottom left-fc same as 23(Orig.) (very rare); CC-r	1	1	30	60	90	177	289	400
2B	30	–	Union logo omitted; CC-r	1	1	15	30	45	84	127	170
3	60	–	Pgs. reduced to 48; LDC-r	1	1	6	12	18	29	36	42
4	62	–	LDC-r	1	1	5	10	15	23	28	32
5	71	–	LDC-r	1	1	5	10	14	20	24	28
6	85	–	C-price 15¢; LDC-r	1	1	4	9	13	18	22	26
7	94	–	LDC-r	1	1	4	7	10	14	17	20
8	118	–	LDC-r	1	1	4	7	10	14	17	20
9	136	–	New-PC, old-a; PC-r	1	2	5	10	15	24	30	35
10	150	–	Old-a; PC-r	1	2	4	7	10	14	17	20
11	164	–	Old-a; PC-r	1	2	4	8	11	16	19	22
12	164	–	New-a; PC-r; Evans/Crandall-a	2	2	4	8	12	23	37	50
13	167	–	PC-r	2	2	2	4	6	11	16	20
14	167	8/64	PC-r	2	2	2	4	6	8	11	14
15	167	12/65	PC-r	2	2	2	4	6	8	11	14
16	166	R/1968	New 25¢; PC-r	2	2	2	4	6	8	11	14
17	169	Win/69	Stiff-c; PC-r	2	2	2	4	6	8	11	14

24. A Connecticut Yankee in King Arthur's Court

Ed	HRN	Date	Details	A	C	GD 2.0	VG 4.0	FN 6.0	VF 8.0	VF/NM 9.0	NM- 9.2
1	–	9/45	Original	1	1	41	82	123	256	428	600
2	30	–	No price circle; CC-r	1	1	15	30	45	84	127	170
3	60	–	8 pgs. deleted; LDC-r	1	1	6	12	18	27	33	38
4	62	–	LDC-r	1	1	5	10	15	23	28	32
5	71	–	LDC-r	1	1	5	10	15	22	26	30
6	87	–	C-price 15¢; LDC-r	1	1	4	9	13	18	22	26
7	121	–	LDC-r	1	1	4	8	12	17	21	24
8	140	–	New-c&a; PC-r	2	2	5	10	15	25	31	36
9	153	–	PC-r	2	2	2	4	6	9	13	16
10	164	–	PC-r	2	2	2	4	6	8	11	14
11	167	–	PC-r	2	2	2	4	6	8	11	14
12	167	7/64	PC-r	2	2	2	4	6	8	11	14
13	167	6/66	PC-r	2	2	2	4	6	8	11	14
14	166	R/1968	C-price 25¢; PC-r	2	2	2	4	6	8	11	14
15	169	Spr/71	PC-r; stiff-c	2	2	2	4	6	8	11	14

25. Two Years Before the Mast

Ed	HRN	Date	Details	A	C	GD 2.0	VG 4.0	FN 6.0	VF 8.0	VF/NM 9.0	NM- 9.2
1	–	10/45	Original; Webb/Heames-a&c	1	1	41	82	123	256	428	600
2	30	–	Price circle blank; CC-r	1	1	15	30	45	84	127	170
3	60	–	8 pgs. deleted; LDC-r	1	1	6	12	18	27	33	38
4	62	–	LDC-r	1	1	5	10	15	23	28	32
5	71	–	LDC-r	1	1	4	9	13	18	22	26
6	85	–	C-price 15¢; LDC-r	1	1	4	8	12	17	21	24
7	114	–	LDC-r	1	1	4	7	10	14	17	20
8	156	–	3 pgs. replaced by fillers; new-c; PC-r	1	2	5	10	15	25	31	36
9	167	12/63	PC-r	1	2	2	4	6	8	11	14
10	167	12/65	PC-r	1	2	2	4	6	8	11	14
11	166	9/67	PC-r	1	2	2	4	6	8	11	14
12	169	Win/69	C-price 25¢; stiff-c PC-r	1	2	2	4	6	8	11	14

26. Frankenstein (2nd horror comic?)

Ed	HRN	Date	Details	A	C	GD 2.0	VG 4.0	FN 6.0	VF 8.0	VF/NM 9.0	NM- 9.2
1	26	12/45	Orig.; Webb/Brewster a&c; 52 pgs.	1	1	115	230	345	730	1253	1775
2A	30	–	Price circle blank; no indicia; CC-r	1	1	32	64	96	192	314	435
2B	30	–	With indicia; scarce; CC-r	1	1	37	74	111	222	361	500
3	60	–	LDC-r	1	1	17	34	51	98	154	210
4	62	–	LDC-r	1	1	15	30	45	88	137	185
5	71	–	LDC-r	1	1	8	16	24	42	54	65
6A	82	–	C-price 15¢; soft-c LDC-r	1	1	7	14	21	37	46	55

Classic Comics #28 © GIL

Classic Comics #30 © GIL

Classics Illustrated #35 © GIL

Ed	HRN	Date	Details	A	C	GD 2.0	VG 4.0	FN 6.0	VF 8.0	VF/NM 9.0	NM- 9.2
6B	82	–	Stiff-c; LDC-r	1	1	8	16	24	42	54	65
7	117	–	LDC-r	1	1	5	10	15	22	26	30
8	146	–	New Saunders-c; PC-r	1	2	6	12	18	31	38	45
9	152	–	Scarce; PC-r	1	2	8	16	24	42	54	65
10	153	–	PC-r	1	2	2	4	6	10	14	18
11	160	–	PC-r	1	2	2	4	6	10	14	18
12	165	–	PC-r	1	2	2	4	6	9	13	16
13	167	–	PC-r	1	2	2	4	6	9	13	16
14	167	6/64	PC-r	1	2	2	4	6	9	13	16
15	167	6/65	PC-r	1	2	2	4	6	9	13	16
16	167	10/65	PC-r	1	2	2	4	6	9	13	16
17	166	9/67	PC-r	1	2	2	4	6	9	13	16
18	169	Fall/69	C-price 25¢; stiff-c PC-r	1	2	2	4	6	9	13	16
19	169	Spr/71	PC-r; stiff-c	1	2	2	4	6	9	13	16

27. The Adventures of Marco Polo

Ed	HRN	Date	Details	A	C	GD 2.0	VG 4.0	FN 6.0	VF 8.0	VF/NM 9.0	NM- 9.2
1	–	4/46	Original	1	1	41	82	123	256	428	600
2	30	–	Last 'Comics' reprint; CC-r	1	1	15	30	45	84	127	170
3	70	–	8 pgs. deleted; no c-price; LDC-r	1	1	5	10	15	24	30	35
4	87	–	C-price 15¢; LDC-r	1	1	4	9	13	18	22	26
5	117	–	LDC-r	1	1	4	7	10	14	17	20
6	154	–	New-c; PC-r	1	2	5	10	15	24	30	35
7	165	–	PC-r	1	2	2	4	6	8	11	14
8	167	4/64	PC-r	1	2	2	4	6	8	11	14
9	167	6/66	PC-r	1	2	2	4	6	8	11	14
10	169	Spr/69	New price 25¢; stiff-c; PC-r	1	2	2	4	6	8	11	14

28. Michael Strogoff

Ed	HRN	Date	Details	A	C	GD 2.0	VG 4.0	FN 6.0	VF 8.0	VF/NM 9.0	NM- 9.2
1	–	6/46	Original	1	1	41	82	123	256	428	600
2	51	–	8 pgs. cut; LDC-r	1	1	15	30	45	84	127	170
3	115	–	New-c; PC-r	1	2	6	12	18	31	38	45
4	155	–	PC-r	1	2	4	7	10	14	17	20
5	167	11/63	PC-r	1	2	2	4	6	9	13	16
6	167	7/66	PC-r	1	2	2	4	6	9	13	16
7	169	Sm/69	C-price 25¢; stiff-c PC-r	1	3	3	6	9	15	21	26

29. The Prince and the Pauper

Ed	HRN	Date	Details	A	C	GD 2.0	VG 4.0	FN 6.0	VF 8.0	VF/NM 9.0	NM- 9.2
1	–	7/46	Orig.; "Horror"-c	1	1	60	120	180	381	653	925
2	60	–	8 pgs. cut; new-c by Kiefer; LDC-r	1	2	9	18	27	52	69	85
3	62	–	LDC-r	1	2	5	10	15	24	30	35
4	71	–	LDC-r	1	2	4	9	13	18	22	26
5	93	–	LDC-r	1	2	4	8	12	17	21	24
6	114	–	LDC-r	1	2	4	7	10	14	17	20
7	128	–	New-c; PC-r	1	3	5	10	15	24	30	35
8	138	–	PC-r	1	3	2	4	6	9	13	16
9	150	–	PC-r	1	3	2	4	6	9	13	16
10	164	–	PC-r	1	3	2	4	6	8	11	14
11	167	–	PC-r	1	3	2	4	6	8	11	14
12	167	7/64	PC-r	1	3	2	4	6	8	11	14
13	167	11/65	PC-r	1	3	2	4	6	8	11	14
14	166	R/68	C-price 25¢; PC-r	1	3	2	4	6	8	11	14
15	169	Sm/70	PC-r; stiff-c	1	3	2	4	6	8	11	14

30. The Moonstone

Ed	HRN	Date	Details	A	C	GD 2.0	VG 4.0	FN 6.0	VF 8.0	VF/NM 9.0	NM- 9.2
1	–	9/46	Original; Rico-c/a	1	1	41	82	123	256	428	600
2	60	–	LDC-r; 8pgs. cut	1	1	9	18	27	50	65	80
3	70	–	LDC-r	1	1	8	16	24	42	54	65
4	155	–	New L.B. Cole-c; PC-r	1	2	4	8	12	28	44	60
5	165	–	PC-r; L.B. Cole-c	1	2	3	6	9	16	23	30
6	167	1/64	PC-r; L.B. Cole-c	1	2	2	4	6	11	16	20
7	167	9/65	PC-r; L.B. Cole-c	1	2	2	4	6	10	14	18
8	166	R/1968	C-price 25¢; PC-r	1	2	2	4	6	9	13	16

31. The Black Arrow

Ed	HRN	Date	Details	A	C	GD 2.0	VG 4.0	FN 6.0	VF 8.0	VF/NM 9.0	NM- 9.2
1	30	10/46	Original	1	1	39	78	117	235	385	535
2	51	–	CI logo; LDC-r 8pgs. deleted	1	1	6	12	18	33	41	48
3	64	–	LDC-r	1	1	4	9	13	18	22	26
4	87	–	C-price 15¢; LDC-r	1	1	4	8	12	17	21	24
5	108	–	LDC-r	1	1	4	7	10	14	17	20
6	125	–	LDC-r	1	1	4	7	10	14	17	20
7	131	–	New-c; PC-r	1	2	5	10	15	24	30	35
8	140	–	PC-r	1	2	2	4	6	9	13	16
9	148	–	PC-r	1	2	2	4	6	9	13	16
10	161	–	PC-r	1	2	2	4	6	8	11	14
11	167	–	PC-r	1	2	2	4	6	8	11	14
12	167	7/64	PC-r	1	2	2	4	6	8	11	14
13	167	11/65	PC-r	1	2	2	4	6	8	11	14
14	166	R/1968	C-price 25¢; PC-r	1	2	2	4	6	8	11	14

32. Lorna Doone

Ed	HRN	Date	Details	A	C	GD 2.0	VG 4.0	FN 6.0	VF 8.0	VF/NM 9.0	NM- 9.2
1	–	12/46	Original; Matt Baker c&a	1	1	41	82	123	250	418	585
2	53/64	–	8 pgs. deleted; LDC-r	1	1	9	18	27	47	61	75
3	85	1951	C-price 15¢; LDC-r; Baker c&a	1	1	7	14	21	37	46	55
4	118	–	LDC-r	1	1	4	9	13	18	22	26
5	138	–	New-c; old-c becomes new title pg.; PC-r	1	2	6	12	18	28	34	40
6	150	–	PC-r	1	2	2	4	6	8	11	14
7	165	–	PC-r	1	2	2	4	6	8	11	14
8	167	1/64	PC-r	1	2	2	4	6	9	13	16
9	167	11/65	PC-r	1	2	2	4	6	9	13	16
10	166	R/1968	New-c; PC-r	1	3	3	6	9	16	24	32

33. The Adventures of Sherlock Holmes

Ed	HRN	Date	Details	A	C	GD 2.0	VG 4.0	FN 6.0	VF 8.0	VF/NM 9.0	NM- 9.2
1	33	1/47	Original; Kiefer-c; contains Study in Scarlet & Hound of the Baskervilles; 68 pgs.	1	1	132	264	396	838	1444	2050
2	53	–	"A Study in Scarlet" (17 pgs.) deleted; LDC-r	1	1	48	96	144	302	514	725
3	71	–	LDC-r	1	1	39	78	117	231	378	525
4A	89	–	C-price 15¢; LDC-r	1	1	30	60	90	117	289	400
4B	89	–	Kiefer's name omitted from-c	1	1	31	62	93	186	303	420

34. Mysterious Island (Last "Classic Comics" issue)

Ed	HRN	Date	Details	A	C	GD 2.0	VG 4.0	FN 6.0	VF 8.0	VF/NM 9.0	NM- 9.2
1	35	2/47	Original; Webb/Heames-c/a	1	1	41	82	123	250	418	585
2	60	–	8 pgs. deleted; LDC-r	1	1	7	14	21	37	46	55
3	62	–	LDC-r	1	1	5	10	15	23	28	32
4	71	–	LDC-r	1	1	6	12	18	31	38	45
5	78	–	C-price 15¢ in circle; LDC-r	1	1	5	10	14	20	24	28
6	92	–	LDC-r	1	1	4	9	13	18	22	26
7	117	–	LDC-r	1	1	4	7	10	14	17	20
8	140	–	New-c; PC-r	1	2	5	10	15	24	30	35
9	156	–	PC-r	1	2	2	4	6	9	13	16
10	167	10/63	PC-r	1	2	2	4	6	8	11	14
11	167	5/64	PC-r	1	2	2	4	6	8	11	14
12	167	6/66	PC-r	1	2	2	4	6	8	11	14
13	166	R/1968	C-price 25¢; PC-r	1	2	2	4	6	8	11	14

35. Last Days of Pompeii (First "Classics Illustrated")

Ed	HRN	Date	Details	A	C	GD 2.0	VG 4.0	FN 6.0	VF 8.0	VF/NM 9.0	NM- 9.2
1	35	3/47	Original; LDC; Kiefer-c/a	1	1	41	82	123	250	418	585
2	161	–	New c&a; 15¢; PC-r; Kirby/Ayers-a	2	2	5	10	15	32	51	70
3	167	1/64	PC-r	2	2	3	6	9	16	22	28
4	167	7/66	PC-r	2	2	3	6	9	16	22	28
5	169	Spr/70	New price 25¢; stiff-c; PC-r	2	2	3	6	9	16	22	28

Classics Illustrated #36 © GIL

Classics Illustrated #40 © GIL

Classics Illustrated #46 © GIL

36. Typee

Ed	HRN	Date	Details	A	C	GD 2.0	VG 4.0	FN 6.0	VF 8.0	VF/NM 9.0	NM- 9.2
1	36	4/47	Original	1	1	29	58	87	170	278	385
2	64	–	No c-price; 8 pg. ed.; LDC-r	1	1	7	14	21	37	46	55
3	155	–	New-c; PC-r	1	2	5	10	15	24	30	35
4	167	9/63	PC-r	1	2	2	4	6	9	13	16
5	167	7/65	PC-r	1	2	2	4	6	9	13	16
6	169	Sm/69	C-price 25¢; stiff-c PC-r	1	2	2	4	6	9	13	16

37. The Pioneers

Ed	HRN	Date	Details	A	C	GD 2.0	VG 4.0	FN 6.0	VF 8.0	VF/NM 9.0	NM- 9.2
1	37	5/47	Original; Palais-c/a	1	1	27	54	81	158	259	360
2A	62	–	8 pgs. cut; LDC-r; price circle blank	1	1	6	12	18	28	34	40
2B	62	–	10¢; LDC-r;	1	1	29	58	87	170	278	385
3	70	–	LDC-r	1	1	4	8	12	17	21	24
4	92	–	15¢; LDC-r	1	1	4	8	11	16	19	22
5	118	–	LDC-r	1	1	4	7	10	14	17	20
6	131	–	LDC-r	1	1	4	7	10	14	17	20
7	132	–	LDC-r	1	1	4	7	10	14	17	20
8	153	–	LDC-r	1	1	4	7	10	14	17	20
9	167	5/64	LDC-r	1	1	2	4	6	9	13	16
10	167	6/66	LDC-r	1	1	2	4	6	9	13	16
11	166	R/1968	New-c; 25¢; PC-r	1	2	3	6	9	18	27	36

38. Adventures of Cellini

Ed	HRN	Date	Details	A	C	GD 2.0	VG 4.0	FN 6.0	VF 8.0	VF/NM 9.0	NM- 9.2
1	–	6/47	Original; Froehlich c/a	1	1	32	64	96	192	314	435
2	164	–	New-c&a; PC-r	2	2	3	6	9	18	27	36
3	167	12/63	PC-r	2	2	2	4	6	10	14	18
4	167	7/66	PC-r	2	2	2	4	6	10	14	18
5	169	Spr/70	Stiff-c; new price 25¢; PC-r	2	2	2	4	6	11	16	20

39. Jane Eyre

Ed	HRN	Date	Details	A	C	GD 2.0	VG 4.0	FN 6.0	VF 8.0	VF/NM 9.0	NM- 9.2
1	–	7/47	Original	1	1	31	62	93	186	303	420
2	60	–	No c-price; 8 pgs. cut; LDC-r	1	1	6	12	18	31	38	45
3	62	–	LDC-r	1	1	5	10	15	24	30	35
4	71	–	LDC-r; c-price 10¢	1	1	5	10	15	22	26	30
5	92	–	C-price 15¢; LDC-r	1	1	4	9	13	18	22	26
6	118	–	LDC-r	1	1	4	8	12	17	21	24
7	142	–	New-c; old-a; PC-r	1	2	6	12	18	28	34	40
8	154	–	Old-a; PC-r	1	2	4	8	12	17	21	24
9	165	–	New-a; PC-r	2	2	3	6	9	17	26	35
10	167	12/63	PC-r	2	2	3	6	9	14	19	24
11	167	4/65	PC-r	2	2	2	4	6	13	18	22
12	167	8/66	PC-r	2	2	2	4	6	13	18	22
13	166	R/1968	New-c; PC-r	2	3	5	10	15	31	53	75

40. Mysteries ("The Pit and the Pendulum", "The Advs. of Hans Pfall" & "The Fall of the House of Usher")

Ed	HRN	Date	Details	A	C	GD 2.0	VG 4.0	FN 6.0	VF 8.0	VF/NM 9.0	NM- 9.2
1	40	8/47	Original; Kiefer-c/a, Froehlich, Griffiths-a	1	1	58	116	174	371	636	900
2	62	–	LDC-r; 8pgs. cut	1	1	24	48	72	142	234	325
3	75	–	LDC-r	1	1	19	38	57	111	176	240
4	92	–	C-price 15¢; LDC-r	1	1	15	30	45	94	147	200

41. Twenty Years After

Ed	HRN	Date	Details	A	C	GD 2.0	VG 4.0	FN 6.0	VF 8.0	VF/NM 9.0	NM- 9.2
1	–	9/47	Original; 'horror'-c	1	1	39	78	117	235	385	535
2	62	–	New-c; no c-price 8 pgs. cut; LDC-r; Kiefer-c	1	2	7	14	21	37	46	55
3	78	–	C-price 15¢; LDC-r	1	2	5	10	15	23	28	32
4	156	–	New-c; PC-r	1	3	5	10	15	24	30	35
5	167	12/63	PC-r	1	3	2	4	6	8	11	14
6	167	11/66	PC-r	1	3	2	4	6	8	11	14
7	169	Spr/70	New price 25¢; stiff-c; PC-r	1	3	2	4	6	8	11	14

42. Swiss Family Robinson

Ed	HRN	Date	Details	A	C	GD 2.0	VG 4.0	FN 6.0	VF 8.0	VF/NM 9.0	NM- 9.2
1	42	10/47	Orig.; Kiefer-c&a;	1	1	24	48	72	140	230	320
2A	62	–	8 pgs. cut; outside bc: Gift Box ad; LDC-r	1	1	6	12	18	31	38	45
2B	62	–	8 pgs. cut; outside-bc: Reorder list; scarce; LDC-r	1	1	10	20	30	58	79	100
3	75	–	LDC-r	1	1	5	10	14	20	24	28
4	93	–	LDC-r	1	1	5	10	14	20	24	28
5	117	–	LDC-r	1	1	3	6	9	14	19	24
6	131	–	New-c; old-a; PC-r	1	2	3	6	9	15	21	26
7	137	–	Old-a; PC-r	1	2	2	4	6	10	14	18
8	141	–	Old-a; PC-r	1	2	2	4	6	10	14	18
9	152	–	New-a; PC-r	2	2	3	6	9	16	23	30
10	158	–	PC-r	2	2	2	4	6	8	11	14
11	165	–	PC-r	2	2	3	6	9	16	24	32
12	167	12/63	PC-r	2	2	2	4	6	8	11	14
13	167	4/65	PC-r	2	2	2	4	6	8	11	14
14	167	5/66	PC-r	2	2	2	4	6	8	11	14
15	166	11/67	PC-r	2	2	2	4	6	8	11	14
16	169	Spr/69	PC-r; stiff-c	2	2	2	4	6	8	11	14

43. Great Expectations (Used in **SOTI**, pg. 311)

Ed	HRN	Date	Details	A	C	GD 2.0	VG 4.0	FN 6.0	VF 8.0	VF/NM 9.0	NM- 9.2
1	43	11/47	Original; Kiefer-a/c	1	1	90	180	270	576	988	1400
2	62	–	No c-price; 8 pgs. cut; LDC-r	1	1	57	114	171	362	624	885

44. Mysteries of Paris (Used in **SOTI**, pg. 323)

Ed	HRN	Date	Details	A	C	GD 2.0	VG 4.0	FN 6.0	VF 8.0	VF/NM 9.0	NM- 9.2
1A	44	12/47	Original; 56 pgs.; Kiefer-c/a	1	1	65	130	195	416	708	1000
1B	44	12/47	Orig.; printed on white/heavier paper; (rare)	1	1	76	152	228	486	831	1175
2A	62	–	8 pgs. cut; outside-bc: Gift Box ad; LDC-r	1	1	30	60	90	177	289	400
2B	62	–	8 pgs. cut; outside-bc: reorder list; LDC-r	1	1	30	60	90	177	289	400
3	78	–	C-price 15¢; LDC-r	1	1	25	50	75	147	241	335

45. Tom Brown's School Days

Ed	HRN	Date	Details	A	C	GD 2.0	VG 4.0	FN 6.0	VF 8.0	VF/NM 9.0	NM- 9.2
1	44	1/48	Original; 1st 48pg. issue	1	1	20	40	60	114	182	250
2	64	–	No c-price; LDC-r	1	1	7	14	21	35	43	50
3	161	–	New-c&a; PC-r	2	2	3	6	9	16	24	32
4	167	2/64	PC-r	2	2	2	4	6	9	13	16
5	167	8/66	PC-r	2	2	2	4	6	9	13	16
6	166	R/1968	C-price 25¢; PC-r	2	2	2	4	6	9	13	16

46. Kidnapped

Ed	HRN	Date	Details	A	C	GD 2.0	VG 4.0	FN 6.0	VF 8.0	VF/NM 9.0	NM- 9.2
1	47	4/48	Original; Webb-c/a	1	1	20	40	60	114	182	250
2A	62	–	Price circle blank; LDC-r	1	1	7	14	21	35	43	50
2B	62	–	C-price 10¢; rare; LDC-r	1	1	31	62	93	182	296	410
3	78	–	C-price 15¢; LDC-r	1	1	5	10	14	20	24	28
4	87	–	LDC-r	1	1	4	9	13	18	22	26
5	118	–	LDC-r	1	1	4	7	10	14	17	20
6	131	–	New-c; PC-r	1	2	5	10	15	23	28	32
7	140	–	PC-r	1	2	2	4	6	9	13	16
8	150	–	PC-r	1	2	2	4	6	9	13	16
9	164	–	Reduced pg.width; PC-r	1	2	2	4	6	8	11	14
10	167	–	PC-r	1	2	2	4	6	8	11	14
11	167	3/64	PC-r	1	2	2	4	6	8	11	14
12	167	6/65	PC-r	1	2	2	4	6	8	11	14
13	167	12/65	PC-r	1	2	2	4	6	8	11	14
14	166	9/67	PC-r	1	2	2	4	6	8	11	14
15	166	Win/69	New price 25¢; PC-r; stiff-c	1	2	2	4	6	8	11	14
16	169	Sm/70	PC-r; stiff-c	1	2	2	4	6	8	11	14

Classics Illustrated #47 © GIL

Classics Illustrated #49 © GIL

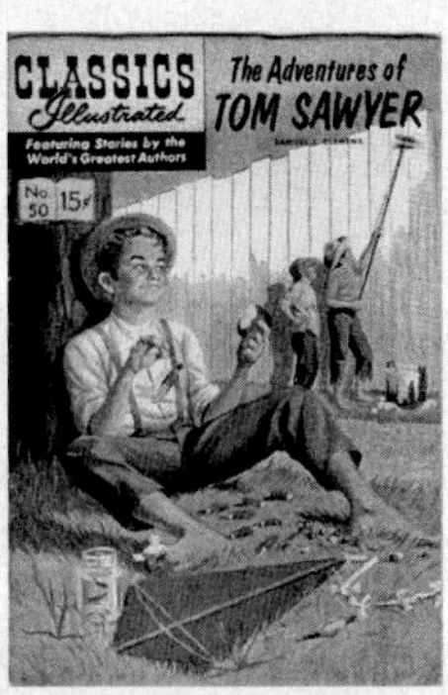

Classics Illustrated #50 © GIL

47. Twenty Thousand Leagues Under the Sea

Ed	HRN	Date	Details	A	C	GD 2.0	VG 4.0	FN 6.0	VF 8.0	VF/NM 9.0	NM- 9.2
1	47	5/48	Orig.; Kiefer-a&c;	1	1	20	40	60	120	195	270
2	64	–	No c-price; LDC-r	1	1	6	12	18	28	34	40
3	78	–	C-price 15¢; LDC-r	1	1	4	9	13	18	22	26
4	94	–	LDC-r	1	1	4	8	12	17	21	24
5	118	–	LDC-r	1	1	4	7	10	14	17	20
6	128	–	New-c; PC-r	1	2	5	10	15	24	30	35
7	133	–	PC-r	1	2	2	4	6	10	14	18
8	140	–	PC-r	1	2	2	4	6	9	13	16
9	148	–	PC-r	1	2	2	4	6	9	13	16
10	156	–	PC-r	1	2	2	4	6	9	13	16
11	165	–	PC-r	1	2	2	4	6	9	13	16
12	167	–	PC-r	1	2	2	4	6	9	13	16
13	167	3/64	PC-r	1	2	2	4	6	9	13	16
14	167	8/65	PC-r	1	2	2	4	6	9	13	16
15	167	10/66	PC-r	1	2	2	4	6	9	13	16
16	166	R/1968	C-price 25¢; new-c PC-r	1	3	3	6	9	15	22	28
17	169	Spr/70	Stiff-c; PC-r	1	3	2	4	6	13	18	22

48. David Copperfield

Ed	HRN	Date	Details	A	C	GD 2.0	VG 4.0	FN 6.0	VF 8.0	VF/NM 9.0	NM- 9.2
1	47	6/48	Original; Kiefer-c/a	1	1	20	40	60	114	182	250
2	64	–	Price circle replaced by motif of boy reading; LDC-r	1	1	6	12	18	28	34	40
3	87	–	C-price 15¢; LDC-r	1	1	4	8	12	17	21	24
4	121	–	New-c; PC-r	1	2	5	10	15	22	26	30
5	130	–	PC-r	1	2	2	4	6	9	13	16
6	140	–	PC-r	1	2	2	4	6	9	13	16
7	148	–	PC-r	1	2	2	4	6	9	13	16
8	156	–	PC-r	1	2	2	4	6	9	13	16
9	167	–	PC-r	1	2	2	4	6	8	11	14
10	167	4/64	PC-r	1	2	2	4	6	8	11	14
11	167	6/65	PC-r	1	2	2	4	6	8	11	14
12	166	5/67	PC-r	1	2	2	4	6	8	11	14
13	166	R/67	PC-r; C-price 25¢	1	2	2	4	6	10	14	18
14	166	Spr/69	C-price 25¢; stiff-c PC-r	1	2	2	4	6	8	11	14
15	169	Win/69	Stiff-c; PC-r	1	2	2	4	6	8	11	14

49. Alice in Wonderland

Ed	HRN	Date	Details	A	C	GD 2.0	VG 4.0	FN 6.0	VF 8.0	VF/NM 9.0	NM- 9.2
1	47	7/48	Original; 1st Blum a & c	1	1	30	60	90	177	289	400
2	64	–	No c-price; LDC-r	1	1	8	16	24	44	57	70
3A	85	–	C-price 15¢; soft-c LDC-r	1	1	8	16	24	40	50	60
3B	85	–	Stiff-c; LDC-r	1	1	8	16	24	42	54	65
4	155	–	New PC, similar to orig.; PC-r	1	2	4	8	12	27	44	60
5	165	–	PC-r	1	2	3	6	9	18	28	38
6	167	3/64	PC-r	1	2	3	6	9	16	24	32
7	167	6/66	PC-r	1	2	4	8	12	28	47	65
8A	166	Fall/68	New-c; soft-c; 25¢ c-price; PC-r	1	3	4	8	12	27	44	60
8B	166	Fall/68	New-c; stiff-c; 25¢ c-price; PC-r	1	3	6	12	18	40	73	105

50. Adventures of Tom Sawyer (Used in **SOTI**, pg. 37)

Ed	HRN	Date	Details	A	C	GD 2.0	VG 4.0	FN 6.0	VF 8.0	VF/NM 9.0	NM- 9.2
1A	51	8/48	Orig.; Aldo Rubano a&c	1	1	20	40	60	114	182	250
1B	51	9/48	Orig.; Rubano c&a	1	1	20	40	60	114	182	250
1C	51	9/48	Orig.; outside-bc: blue & yellow only; rare	1	1	25	50	75	147	241	335
2	64	–	No c-price; LDC-r	1	1	5	10	15	23	28	32
3	78	–	C-price 15¢; LDC-r	1	1	4	8	12	17	21	24
4	94	–	LDC-r	1	1	4	7	10	14	17	20
5	117	–	LDC-r	1	1	2	4	6	10	14	18
6	132	–	LDC-r	1	1	2	4	6	10	14	18
7	140	–	New-c; PC-r	1	2	3	6	9	17	26	35
8	150	–	PC-r	1	2	2	4	6	9	13	16
9	164	–	New-a; PC-r	2	2	3	6	9	17	26	35
10	167	–	PC-r	2	2	2	4	6	9	13	16
11	167	1/65	PC-r	2	2	2	4	6	8	11	14
12	167	5/66	PC-r	2	2	2	4	6	8	11	14
13	166	12/67	PC-r	2	2	2	4	6	8	11	14
14	169	Fall/69	C-price 25¢; stiff-c; PC-r	2	2	2	4	6	8	11	14
15	169	Win/71	PC-r	2	2	2	4	6	8	11	14

51. The Spy

Ed	HRN	Date	Details	A	C	GD 2.0	VG 4.0	FN 6.0	VF 8.0	VF/NM 9.0	NM- 9.2
1A	51	9/48	Original; inside-bc illo: Christmas Carol	1	1	19	38	57	109	172	235
1B	51	9/48	Original; inside-bc illo: Man in Iron Mask	1	1	19	38	57	109	172	235
1C	51	8/48	Original; outside-bc: full color	1	1	19	38	57	109	172	235
1D	51	8/48	Original; outside-bc: blue & yellow only; scarce	1	1	20	40	60	115	185	255
2	89	–	C-price 15¢; LDC-r	1	1	5	10	14	20	24	28
3	121	–	LDC-r	1	1	4	8	12	17	21	24
4	139	–	New-c; PC-r	1	2	3	6	9	18	27	35
5	156	–	PC-r	1	2	2	4	6	9	13	16
6	167	11/63	PC-r	1	2	2	4	6	8	11	14
7	167	7/66	PC-r	1	2	2	4	6	8	11	14
8A	166	Win/69	C-price 25¢; soft-c; scarce; PC-r	1	2	3	6	9	15	21	26
8B	166	Win/69	C-price 25¢; stiff-c; PC-r	1	2	2	4	6	8	11	14

52. The House of the Seven Gables

Ed	HRN	Date	Details	A	C	GD 2.0	VG 4.0	FN 6.0	VF 8.0	VF/NM 9.0	NM- 9.2
1	53	10/48	Orig.; Griffiths a&c	1	1	19	38	57	109	172	235
2	89	–	C-price 15¢; LDC-r	1	1	5	10	14	20	24	28
3	121	–	LDC-r	1	1	4	8	12	17	21	24
4	142	–	New-c&a; PC-r; Woodbridge-a	2	2	5	10	15	25	31	36
5	156	–	PC-r	2	2	2	4	6	9	13	16
6	165	–	PC-r	2	2	2	4	6	8	11	14
7	167	5/64	PC-r	2	2	2	4	6	9	13	16
8	167	3/66	PC-r	2	2	2	4	6	8	11	14
9	166	R/1968	C-price 25¢; PC-r	2	2	2	4	6	8	11	14
10	169	Spr/70	Stiff-c; PC-r	2	2	2	4	6	8	11	14

53. A Christmas Carol

Ed	HRN	Date	Details	A	C	GD 2.0	VG 4.0	FN 6.0	VF 8.0	VF/NM 9.0	NM- 9.2
1	53	11/48	Original & only ed; Kiefer-c/a	1	1	26	52	78	154	252	350

54. Man in the Iron Mask

Ed	HRN	Date	Details	A	C	GD 2.0	VG 4.0	FN 6.0	VF 8.0	VF/NM 9.0	NM- 9.2
1	55	12/48	Original; Froehlich-a, Kiefer-c	1	1	19	38	57	109	172	235
2	93	–	C-price 15¢; LDC-r	1	1	5	10	15	23	28	32
3A	111	–	(O) logo lettering; scarce; LDC-r	1	1	6	12	18	31	38	45
3B	111	–	New logo as PC; LDC-r	1	1	5	10	15	23	28	32
4	142	–	New-c&a; PC-r	2	2	5	10	15	24	30	35
5	154	–	PC-r	2	2	2	4	6	9	13	16
6	165	–	PC-r	2	2	2	4	6	8	11	14
7	167	5/64	PC-r	2	2	2	4	6	8	11	14
8	167	4/66	PC-r	2	2	2	4	6	8	11	14
9A	166	Win/69	C-price 25¢; soft-c PC-r	2	2	3	6	9	15	21	26
9B	166	Win/69	Stiff-c	2	2	2	4	6	8	11	14

55. Silas Marner (Used in **SOTI**, pgs. 311, 312)

Ed	HRN	Date	Details	A	C	GD 2.0	VG 4.0	FN 6.0	VF 8.0	VF/NM 9.0	NM- 9.2
1	55	1/49	Original-Kiefer-c	1	1	19	38	57	109	172	235
2	75	–	Price circle blank; 'Coming Next' ad; LDC-r	1	1	5	10	15	24	30	35
3	97	–	LDC-r	1	1	3	6	9	14	19	24
4	121	–	New-c; PC-r	1	2	3	6	9	18	27	35
5	130	–	PC-r	1	2	2	4	6	9	13	16
6	140	–	PC-r	1	2	2	4	6	9	13	16

Classics Illustrated #54 © GIL

Classics Illustrated #61 © GIL

Classics Illustrated #64 © GIL

Ed	HRN	Date	Details	A	C	GD 2.0	VG 4.0	FN 6.0	VF 8.0	VF/NM 9.0	NM- 9.2
7	154	–	PC-r	1	2	2	4	6	9	13	16
8	165	–	PC-r	1	2	2	4	6	8	11	14
9	167	2/64	PC-r	1	2	2	4	6	8	11	14
10	167	6/65	PC-r	1	2	2	4	6	8	11	14
11	166	5/67	PC-r	1	2	2	4	6	8	11	14
12A	166	Win/69	C-price 25¢; soft-c PC-r	1	2	3	6	9	15	21	26
12B	166	Win/69	C-price 25¢; stiff-c PC-r	1	2	2	4	6	8	11	14

56. The Toilers of the Sea

Ed	HRN	Date	Details	A	C	GD 2.0	VG 4.0	FN 6.0	VF 8.0	VF/NM 9.0	NM- 9.2
1	55	2/49	Original; A.M. Froehlich-c/a	1	1	24	48	72	142	234	325
2	165	–	New-c&a; PC-r; Angelo Torres-a	2	2	8	16	24	40	50	60
3	167	3/64	PC-r	2	2	3	6	9	16	23	30
4	167	10/66	PC-r	2	2	3	6	9	16	23	30

57. The Song of Hiawatha

Ed	HRN	Date	Details	A	C	GD 2.0	VG 4.0	FN 6.0	VF 8.0	VF/NM 9.0	NM- 9.2
1	55	3/49	Original; Alex Blum-c/a	1	1	18	36	54	103	162	220
2	75	–	No c-price w/15¢ sticker; 'Coming Next' ad; LDC-r	1	1	5	10	15	24	30	35
3	94	–	C-price 15¢; LDC-r	1	1	5	10	14	20	24	28
4	118	–	LDC-r	1	1	3	6	9	14	19	24
5	134	–	New-c; PC-r	1	2	3	6	9	17	26	35
6	139	–	PC-r	1	2	2	4	6	9	13	16
7	154	–	PC-r	1	2	2	4	6	9	13	16
8	167	–	Has orig.date; PC-r	1	2	2	4	6	8	11	14
9	167	9/64	PC-r	1	2	2	4	6	8	11	14
10	167	10/65	PC-r	1	2	2	4	6	8	11	14
11	166	F/1968	C-price 25¢; PC-r	1	2	2	4	6	8	11	14

58. The Prairie

Ed	HRN	Date	Details	A	C	GD 2.0	VG 4.0	FN 6.0	VF 8.0	VF/NM 9.0	NM- 9.2
1	60	4/49	Original; Palais c/a	1	1	18	36	54	103	162	220
2A	62	–	No c-price; no coming-next ad; LDC-r	1	1	9	18	27	47	61	75
2B	62		10¢ (rare)	1	1	19	38	57	112	179	245
3	78	–	C-price 15¢ in dbl. circle; LDC-r	1	1	5	10	15	22	26	30
4	114	–	LDC-r	1	1	4	8	12	17	21	24
5	131	–	LDC-r	1	1	4	7	10	14	17	20
6	132	–	LDC-r	1	1	4	7	10	14	17	20
7	146	–	New-c; PC-r	1	2	5	10	15	23	28	32
8	155	–	PC-r	1	2	2	4	6	9	13	16
9	167	5/64	PC-r	1	2	2	4	6	8	11	14
10	167	4/66	PC-r	1	2	2	4	6	8	11	14
11	169	Sm/69	New price 25¢; stiff-c; PC-r	1	2	2	4	6	8	11	14

59. Wuthering Heights

Ed	HRN	Date	Details	A	C	GD 2.0	VG 4.0	FN 6.0	VF 8.0	VF/NM 9.0	NM- 9.2
1	60	5/49	Original; Kiefer-c/a	1	1	19	38	57	109	172	235
2	85	–	C-price 15¢; LDC-r	1	1	6	12	18	28	34	40
3	156	–	New-c; PC-r	1	2	5	10	15	25	31	36
4	167	1/64	PC-r	1	2	2	4	6	9	13	16
5	167	10/66	PC-r	1	2	2	4	6	9	13	16
6	169	Sm/69	C-price 25¢; stiff-c; PC-r	1	2	2	4	6	9	13	16

60. Black Beauty

Ed	HRN	Date	Details	A	C	GD 2.0	VG 4.0	FN 6.0	VF 8.0	VF/NM 9.0	NM- 9.2
1	62	6/49	Original; Froehlich-c/a	1	1	18	36	54	103	162	220
2	62	–	No c-price; no coming-next ad; LDC-r (rare)	1	1	20	40	60	114	182	250
3	85	–	C-price 15¢; LDC-r	1	1	5	10	15	23	28	32
4	158	–	New L.B. Cole-c/a; PC-r	2	2	7	14	21	35	43	50
5	167	2/64	PC-r	2	2	2	4	6	11	16	20
6	167	3/66	PC-r	2	2	2	4	6	11	16	20
7	166	R/1968	New-c&price, 25¢; PC-r	2	3	5	10	15	30	50	70

61. The Woman in White

Ed	HRN	Date	Details	A	C	GD 2.0	VG 4.0	FN 6.0	VF 8.0	VF/NM 9.0	NM- 9.2
1A	62	7/49	Original; Blum-c/a fc-purple; bc: top illos light blue	1	1	20	40	60	114	182	250
1B	62	7/49	Original; Blum-c/a fc-pink; bc: top illos light violet	1	1	20	40	60	114	182	250
2	156	–	New-c; PC-r	1	2	6	12	18	28	34	40
3	167	1/64	PC-r	1	2	2	4	6	11	16	20
4	166	R/1968	C-price 25¢; PC-r	1	2	2	4	6	11	16	20

62. Western Stories ("The Luck of Roaring Camp" and "The Outcasts of Poker Flat")

Ed	HRN	Date	Details	A	C	GD 2.0	VG 4.0	FN 6.0	VF 8.0	VF/NM 9.0	NM- 9.2
1	62	8/49	Original; Kiefer-c/a	1	1	17	34	51	98	154	210
2	89	–	C-price 15¢; LDC-r	1	1	5	10	15	23	28	32
3	121	–	LDC-r	1	1	3	6	9	15	21	26
4	137	–	New-c; PC-r	1	2	3	6	9	17	26	35
5	152	–	PC-r	1	2	2	4	6	8	11	14
6	167	10/63	PC-r	1	2	2	4	6	8	11	14
7	167	6/64	PC-r	1	2	2	4	6	8	11	14
8	167	11/66	PC-r	1	2	2	4	6	8	11	14
9	166	R/1968	New-c&price 25¢; PC-r	1	3	3	6	9	16	24	32

63. The Man Without a Country

Ed	HRN	Date	Details	A	C	GD 2.0	VG 4.0	FN 6.0	VF 8.0	VF/NM 9.0	NM- 9.2
1	62	9/49	Original; Kiefer-c/a	1	1	20	40	60	114	182	250
2	78	–	C-price 15¢ in double circle; LDC-r	1	1	5	10	15	23	28	32
3	156	–	New-c, old-a; PC-r	1	2	6	12	18	28	34	40
4	165	–	New-a & text pgs.; PC-r; A. Torres-a	2	2	5	10	15	23	28	32
5	167	3/64	PC-r	2	2	2	4	6	8	11	14
6	167	8/66	PC-r	2	2	2	4	6	8	11	14
7	169	Sm/69	New price 25¢; stiff-c; PC-r	2	2	2	4	6	8	11	14

64. Treasure Island

Ed	HRN	Date	Details	A	C	GD 2.0	VG 4.0	FN 6.0	VF 8.0	VF/NM 9.0	NM- 9.2
1	62	10/49	Original; Blum-c/a	1	1	19	38	57	109	172	235
2A	82	–	C-price 15¢; soft-c LDC-r	1	1	5	10	15	22	26	30
2B	82	–	Stiff-c; LDC-r	1	1	5	10	15	23	28	32
3	117	–	LDC-r	1	1	3	6	9	15	21	26
4	131	–	New-c; PC-r	1	2	3	6	9	17	26	35
5	138	–	PC-r	1	2	2	4	6	9	13	16
6	146	–	PC-r	1	2	2	4	6	9	13	16
7	158	–	PC-r	1	2	2	4	6	9	13	16
8	165	–	PC-r	1	2	2	4	6	8	11	14
9	167	–	PC-r	1	2	2	4	6	8	11	14
10	167	6/64	PC-r	1	2	2	4	6	8	11	14
11	167	12/65	PC-r	1	2	2	4	6	8	11	14
12A	166	10/67	PC-r	1	2	2	4	6	8	11	14
12B	166	10/67	w/Grit ad stapled in book	1	2	10	20	30	66	138	210
13	169	Spr/69	New price 25¢; stiff-c; PC-r	1	2	2	4	6	9	13	16
14	–	1989	Long John Silver's Seafood Shoppes; $1.95, First/Berkley Publ.; Blum-r	1	2						5.00

65. Benjamin Franklin

Ed	HRN	Date	Details	A	C	GD 2.0	VG 4.0	FN 6.0	VF 8.0	VF/NM 9.0	NM- 9.2
1	64	11/49	Original; Kiefer-c; Iger Shop-a	1	1	10	20	30	68	144	220
2	131	–	New-c; PC-r	1	2	5	10	15	24	30	35
3	154	–	PC-r	1	2	2	4	6	9	13	16
4	167	2/64	PC-r	1	2	2	4	6	9	13	16
5	167	4/66	PC-r	1	2	2	4	6	9	13	16
6	169	Fall/69	New price 25¢; stiff-c; PC-r	1	2	2	4	6	9	13	16

66. The Cloister and the Hearth

Classics Illustrated #67 © GIL

Classics Illustrated #72 © GIL

Classics Illustrated #76 © GIL

Ed	HRN	Date	Details	A	C	GD 2.0	VG 4.0	FN 6.0	VF 8.0	VF/NM 9.0	NM- 9.2
1	67	12/49	Original & only ed; Kiefer-a & c	1	1	34	68	102	199	325	450

67. The Scottish Chiefs

Ed	HRN	Date	Details	A	C	GD 2.0	VG 4.0	FN 6.0	VF 8.0	VF/NM 9.0	NM- 9.2
1	67	1/50	Original; Blum-a&c	1	1	15	30	45	90	140	190
2	85	–	C-price 15¢; LDC-r	1	1	5	10	15	23	28	32
3	118	–	LDC-r	1	1	3	6	9	15	21	26
4	136	–	New-c; PC-r	1	2	3	6	9	18	27	36
5	154	–	PC-r	1	2	2	4	6	9	13	16
6	167	11/63	PC-r	1	2	2	4	6	10	14	18
7	167	8/65	PC-r	1	2	2	4	6	9	13	16

68. Julius Caesar (Used in **SOTI**, pgs. 36, 37)

Ed	HRN	Date	Details	A	C	GD 2.0	VG 4.0	FN 6.0	VF 8.0	VF/NM 9.0	NM- 9.2
1	70	2/50	Original; Kiefer-c/a	1	1	15	30	45	90	140	190
2	85	–	C-price 15¢; LDC-r	1	1	5	10	15	22	26	30
3	108	–	LDC-r	1	1	4	9	13	18	22	26
4	156	–	New L.B. Cole-c; PC-r	1	2	6	12	18	28	34	40
5	165	–	New-a by Evans, Crandall; PC-r	2	2	5	10	15	24	30	35
6	167	2/64	PC-r	2	2	2	4	6	8	11	14
7	167	10/65	Tarzan books inside cover; PC-r	2	2	2	4	6	8	11	14
8	166	R/1967	PC-r	2	2	2	4	6	8	11	14
9	169	Win/69	PC-r; stiff-c	2	2	2	4	6	8	11	14

69. Around the World in 80 Days

Ed	HRN	Date	Details	A	C	GD 2.0	VG 4.0	FN 6.0	VF 8.0	VF/NM 9.0	NM- 9.2
1	70	3/50	Original; Kiefer-c/a	1	1	15	30	45	90	140	190
2	87	–	C-price 15¢; LDC-r	1	1	5	10	15	22	26	30
3	125	–	LDC-r	1	1	4	9	13	18	22	26
4	136	–	New-c; PC-r	1	2	5	10	15	25	31	36
5	146	–	PC-r	1	2	2	4	6	9	13	16
6	152	–	PC-r	1	2	2	4	6	9	13	16
7	164	–	PC-r	1	2	2	4	6	8	11	14
8	167	–	PC-r	1	2	2	4	6	8	11	14
9	167	7/64	PC-r	1	2	2	4	6	8	11	14
10	167	11/65	PC-r	1	2	2	4	6	8	11	14
11	166	7/67	PC-r	1	2	2	4	6	8	11	14
12	169	Spr/69	C-price 25¢; stiff-c; PC-r	1	2	2	4	6	8	11	14

70. The Pilot

Ed	HRN	Date	Details	A	C	GD 2.0	VG 4.0	FN 6.0	VF 8.0	VF/NM 9.0	NM- 9.2
1	71	4/50	Original; Blum-c/a	1	1	14	28	42	81	118	155
2	92	–	C-price 15¢; LDC-r	1	1	5	10	15	23	28	32
3	125	–	LDC-r	1	1	4	9	13	18	22	26
4	156	–	New-c; PC-r	1	2	6	12	18	28	34	40
5	167	2/64	PC-r	1	2	2	4	6	11	16	20
6	167	5/66	PC-r	1	2	2	4	6	9	13	16

71. The Man Who Laughs

Ed	HRN	Date	Details	A	C	GD 2.0	VG 4.0	FN 6.0	VF 8.0	VF/NM 9.0	NM- 9.2
1	71	5/50	Original; Blum-c/a	1	1	20	40	60	114	182	250
2	165	–	New-c&a; PC-r	2	2	14	28	42	80	115	155
3	167	4/64	PC-r	2	2	11	22	33	62	86	115

72. The Oregon Trail

Ed	HRN	Date	Details	A	C	GD 2.0	VG 4.0	FN 6.0	VF 8.0	VF/NM 9.0	NM- 9.2
1	73	6/50	Original; Kiefer-c/a	1	1	14	28	42	81	118	155
2	89	–	C-price 15¢; LDC-r	1	1	5	10	15	23	28	32
3	121	–	LDC-r	1	1	4	9	13	18	22	26
4	131	–	New-c; PC-r	1	2	5	10	15	25	31	36
5	140	–	PC-r	1	2	2	4	6	9	13	16
6	150	–	PC-r	1	2	2	4	6	9	13	16
7	164	–	PC-r	1	2	2	4	6	8	11	14
8	167	–	PC-r	1	2	2	4	6	8	11	14
9	167	8/64	PC-r	1	2	2	4	6	8	11	14
10	167	10/65	PC-r	1	2	2	4	6	8	11	14
11	166	R/1968	C-price 25¢; PC-r	1	2	2	4	6	8	11	14

73. The Black Tulip

Ed	HRN	Date	Details	A	C	GD 2.0	VG 4.0	FN 6.0	VF 8.0	VF/NM 9.0	NM- 9.2
1	75	7/50	1st & only ed.; Alex Blum-c/a	1	1	39	78	117	231	378	525

74. Mr. Midshipman Easy

Ed	HRN	Date	Details	A	C	GD 2.0	VG 4.0	FN 6.0	VF 8.0	VF/NM 9.0	NM- 9.2
1	75	8/50	1st & only edition	1	1	38	76	114	228	369	510

75. The Lady of the Lake

Ed	HRN	Date	Details	A	C	GD 2.0	VG 4.0	FN 6.0	VF 8.0	VF/NM 9.0	NM- 9.2
1	75	9/50	Original; Kiefer-c/a	1	1	14	28	42	81	118	155
2	85	–	C-price 15¢; LDC-r	1	1	5	10	15	24	30	35
3	118	–	LDC-r	1	1	5	10	14	20	24	28
4	139	–	New-c; PC-r	1	2	5	10	15	25	31	36
5	154	–	PC-r	1	2	2	4	6	9	13	16
6	165	–	PC-r	1	2	2	4	6	8	11	14
7	167	4/64	PC-r	1	2	2	4	6	8	11	14
8	167	5/66	PC-r	1	2	2	4	6	8	11	14
9	169	Spr/69	New price 25¢; stiff-c; PC-r	1	2	2	4	6	8	11	14

76. The Prisoner of Zenda

Ed	HRN	Date	Details	A	C	GD 2.0	VG 4.0	FN 6.0	VF 8.0	VF/NM 9.0	NM- 9.2
1	75	10/50	Original; Kiefer-c/a	1	1	14	28	42	81	118	155
2	85	–	C-price 15¢; LDC-r	1	1	5	10	15	23	28	32
3	111	–	LDC-r	1	1	3	6	9	16	21	26
4	128	–	New-c; PC-r	1	2	3	6	9	17	26	35
5	152	–	PC-r	1	2	2	4	6	9	13	16
6	165	–	PC-r	1	2	2	4	6	8	11	14
7	167	4/64	PC-r	1	2	2	4	6	8	11	14
8	167	9/66	PC-r	1	2	2	4	6	8	11	14
9	169	Fall/69	New price 25¢; stiff-c; PC-r	1	2	2	4	6	8	11	14

77. The Iliad

Ed	HRN	Date	Details	A	C	GD 2.0	VG 4.0	FN 6.0	VF 8.0	VF/NM 9.0	NM- 9.2
1	78	11/50	Original; Blum-c/a	1	1	14	28	42	81	118	155
2	87	–	C-price 15¢; LDC-r	1	1	5	10	15	24	30	35
3	121	–	LDC-r	1	1	3	6	9	15	21	26
4	139	–	New-c; PC-r	1	2	3	6	9	16	24	32
5	150	–	PC-r	1	2	2	4	6	9	13	16
6	165	–	PC-r	1	2	2	4	6	8	11	14
7	167	10/63	PC-r	1	2	2	4	6	8	11	14
8	167	7/64	PC-r	1	2	2	4	6	8	11	14
9	167	5/66	PC-r	1	2	2	4	6	8	11	14
10	166	R/1968	C-price 25¢; PC-r	1	2	2	4	6	8	11	14

78. Joan of Arc

Ed	HRN	Date	Details	A	C	GD 2.0	VG 4.0	FN 6.0	VF 8.0	VF/NM 9.0	NM- 9.2
1	78	12/50	Original; Kiefer-c/a	1	1	14	28	42	81	118	155
2	87	–	C-price 15¢; LDC-r	1	1	5	10	15	23	28	32
3	113	–	LDC-r	1	1	3	6	9	15	21	26
4	128	–	New-c; PC-r	1	2	3	6	9	17	26	35
5	140	–	PC-r	1	2	2	4	6	9	13	16
6	150	–	PC-r	1	2	2	4	6	9	13	16
7	159	–	PC-r	1	2	2	4	6	9	13	16
8	167	–	PC-r	1	2	2	4	6	8	11	14
9	167	12/63	PC-r	1	2	2	4	6	8	11	14
10	167	6/65	PC-r	1	2	2	4	6	8	11	14
11	166	6/67	PC-r	1	2	2	4	6	8	11	14
12	166	Win/69	New-c&price, 25¢; PC-r; stiff-c	1	3	3	6	9	16	24	32

79. Cyrano de Bergerac

Ed	HRN	Date	Details	A	C	GD 2.0	VG 4.0	FN 6.0	VF 8.0	VF/NM 9.0	NM- 9.2
1	78	1/51	Orig.; movie promo inside front-c; Blum-c/a	1	1	14	28	42	81	118	155
2	85	–	C-price 15¢; LDC-r	1	1	5	10	15	23	28	32
3	118	–	LDC-r	1	1	3	6	9	17	23	28
4	133	–	New-c; PC-r	1	2	3	6	9	16	24	32
5	156	–	PC-r	1	2	2	4	6	11	16	20
6	167	8/64	PC-r	1	2	2	4	6	11	16	20

80. White Fang (Last line drawn cover)

Ed	HRN	Date	Details	A	C	GD 2.0	VG 4.0	FN 6.0	VF 8.0	VF/NM 9.0	NM- 9.2
1	79	2/51	Orig.; Blum-c/a	1	1	14	28	42	81	118	155
2	87	–	C-price 15¢; LDC-r	1	1	5	10	15	24	30	35
3	125	–	LDC-r	1	1	3	6	9	15	21	26
4	132	–	New-c; PC-r	1	2	3	6	9	16	24	32
5	140	–	PC-r	1	2	2	4	6	9	13	16
6	153	–	PC-r	1	2	2	4	6	9	13	16
7	167	–	PC-r	1	2	2	4	6	8	11	14

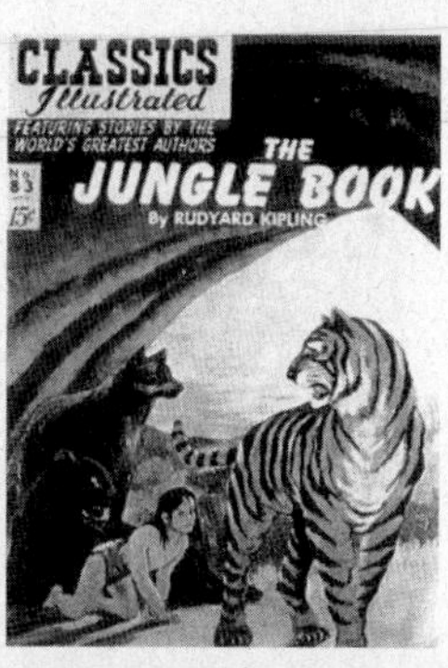

Classics Illustrated #83 © GIL

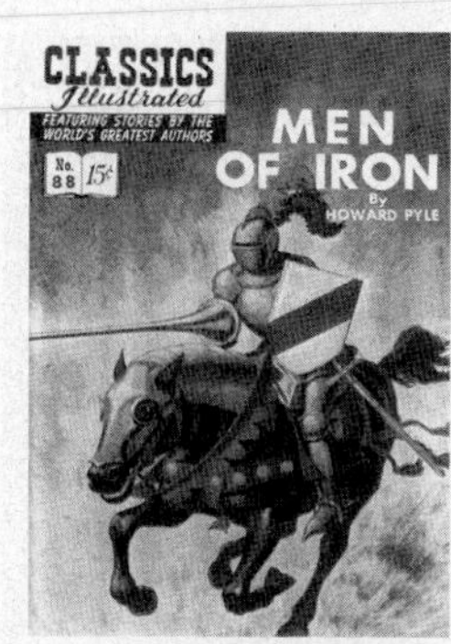

Classics Illustrated #88 © GIL

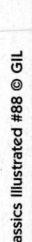

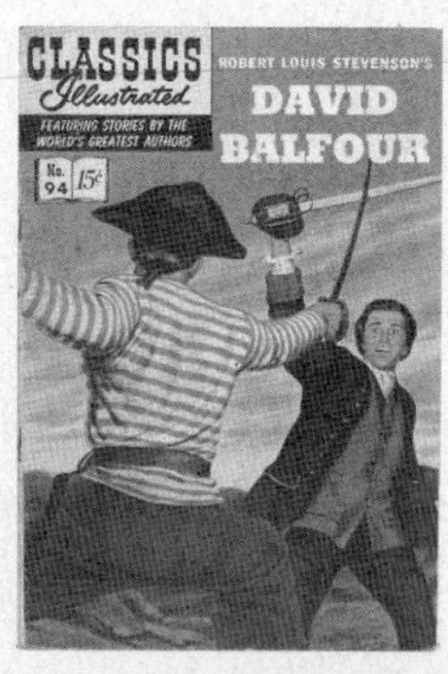

Classics Illustrated #94 © GIL

Ed	HRN	Date	Details	A	C	GD 2.0	VG 4.0	FN 6.0	VF 8.0	VF/NM 9.0	NM- 9.2
8	167	9/64	PC-r	1	2	2	4	6	8	11	14
9	167	7/65	PC-r	1	2	2	4	6	8	11	14
10	166	6/67	PC-r	1	2	2	4	6	8	11	14
11	169	Fall/69	New price 25¢; PC-r; stiff-c	1	2	2	4	6	8	11	14

81. The Odyssey (1st painted cover)

Ed	HRN	Date	Details	A	C	GD 2.0	VG 4.0	FN 6.0	VF 8.0	VF/NM 9.0	NM- 9.2
1	82	3/51	First 15¢ Original; Blum-c	1	1	14	28	42	81	118	155
2	167	8/64	PC-r	1	1	2	4	6	11	16	20
3	167	10/66	PC-r	1	1	2	4	6	11	16	20
4	169	Spr/69	New, stiff-c; PC-r	1	2	3	6	9	18	27	36

82. The Master of Ballantrae

Ed	HRN	Date	Details	A	C	GD 2.0	VG 4.0	FN 6.0	VF 8.0	VF/NM 9.0	NM- 9.2
1	82	4/51	Original; Blum-c	1	1	13	26	39	72	101	130
2	167	8/64	PC-r	1	1	3	6	9	14	19	24
3	166	Fall/68	New, stiff-c; PC-r	1	2	3	6	9	18	27	36

83. The Jungle Book

Ed	HRN	Date	Details	A	C	GD 2.0	VG 4.0	FN 6.0	VF 8.0	VF/NM 9.0	NM- 9.2
1	85	5/51	Original; Blum-c Bossert/Blum-a	1	1	13	26	39	72	101	130
2	110	–	PC-r	1	1	2	4	6	10	14	18
3	125	–	PC-r	1	1	2	4	6	9	13	16
4	134	–	PC-r	1	1	2	4	6	9	13	16
5	142	–	PC-r	1	1	2	4	6	9	13	16
6	150	–	PC-r	1	1	2	4	6	9	13	16
7	159	–	PC-r	1	1	2	4	6	9	13	16
8	167	–	PC-r	1	1	2	4	6	8	11	14
9	167	3/65	PC-r	1	1	2	4	6	8	11	14
10	167	11/65	PC-r	1	1	2	4	6	8	11	14
11	167	5/66	PC-r	1	1	2	4	6	8	11	14
12	166	R/1968	New c&a; stiff-c; PC-r	2	2	3	6	9	18	28	38

84. The Gold Bug and Other Stories ("The Gold Bug", "The Tell-Tale Heart", "The Cask of Amontillado")

Ed	HRN	Date	Details	A	C	GD 2.0	VG 4.0	FN 6.0	VF 8.0	VF/NM 9.0	NM- 9.2
1	85	6/51	Original; Blum-c/a; Palais, Laverly-a	1	1	15	30	45	84	127	170
2	167	7/64	PC-r	1	1	11	22	33	62	86	110

85. The Sea Wolf

Ed	HRN	Date	Details	A	C	GD 2.0	VG 4.0	FN 6.0	VF 8.0	VF/NM 9.0	NM- 9.2
1	85	7/51	Original; Blum-c/a	1	1	11	22	33	64	90	115
2	121	–	PC-r	1	1	2	4	6	9	13	16
3	132	–	PC-r	1	1	2	4	6	9	13	16
4	141	–	PC-r	1	1	2	4	6	9	13	16
5	161	–	PC-r	1	1	2	4	6	8	11	14
6	167	2/64	PC-r	1	1	2	4	6	8	11	14
7	167	11/65	PC-r	1	1	2	4	6	8	11	14
8	169	Fall/69	New price 25¢; stiff-c; PC-r	1	1	2	4	6	8	11	14

86. Under Two Flags

Ed	HRN	Date	Details	A	C	GD 2.0	VG 4.0	FN 6.0	VF 8.0	VF/NM 9.0	NM- 9.2
1	87	8/51	Original; first delBourgo-a	1	1	11	22	33	64	90	115
2	117	–	PC-r	1	1	2	4	6	10	14	18
3	139	–	PC-r	1	1	2	4	6	9	13	16
4	158	–	PC-r	1	1	2	4	6	9	13	16
5	167	2/64	PC-r	1	1	2	4	6	8	11	14
6	167	8/66	PC-r	1	1	2	4	6	8	11	14
7	169	Sm/69	New price 25¢; stiff-c; PC-r	1	1	2	4	6	8	11	14

87. A Midsummer Nights Dream

Ed	HRN	Date	Details	A	C	GD 2.0	VG 4.0	FN 6.0	VF 8.0	VF/NM 9.0	NM- 9.2
1	87	9/51	Original; Blum c/a	1	1	11	22	33	64	90	115
2	161	–	PC-r	1	1	2	4	6	9	13	16
3	167	4/64	PC-r	1	1	2	4	6	8	11	14
4	167	5/66	PC-r	1	1	2	4	6	8	11	14
5	169	Sm/69	New price 25¢; stiff-c; PC-r	1	1	2	4	6	8	11	14

88. Men of Iron

Ed	HRN	Date	Details	A	C	GD 2.0	VG 4.0	FN 6.0	VF 8.0	VF/NM 9.0	NM- 9.2
1	89	10/51	Original	1	1	11	22	33	64	90	115
2	154	–	PC-r	1	1	2	4	6	9	13	16
3	167	1/64	PC-r	1	1	2	4	6	8	11	14
4	166	R/1968	C-price 25¢; PC-r	1	1	2	4	6	8	11	14

89. Crime and Punishment (Cover illo. in **POP**)

Ed	HRN	Date	Details	A	C	GD 2.0	VG 4.0	FN 6.0	VF 8.0	VF/NM 9.0	NM- 9.2
1	89	11/51	Original; Palais-a	1	1	13	26	39	72	101	130
2	152	–	PC-r	1	1	2	4	6	9	13	16
3	167	4/64	PC-r	1	1	2	4	6	8	11	14
4	167	5/66	PC-r	1	1	2	4	6	8	11	14
5	169	Fall/69	New price 25¢ stiff-c; PC-r	1	1	2	4	6	8	11	14

90. Green Mansions

Ed	HRN	Date	Details	A	C	GD 2.0	VG 4.0	FN 6.0	VF 8.0	VF/NM 9.0	NM- 9.2
1	89	12/51	Original; Blum-c/a	1	1	11	22	33	64	90	115
2	148	–	New L.B. Cole-c; PC-r	1	2	5	10	15	22	26	30
3	165	–	PC-r	1	2	2	4	6	8	11	14
4	167	4/64	PC-r	1	2	2	4	6	8	11	14
5	167	9/66	PC-r	1	2	2	4	6	8	11	14
6	169	Sm/69	New price 25¢; stiff-c; PC-r	1	2	2	4	6	8	11	14

91. The Call of the Wild

Ed	HRN	Date	Details	A	C	GD 2.0	VG 4.0	FN 6.0	VF 8.0	VF/NM 9.0	NM- 9.2
1	92	1/52	Orig.; delBourgo-a	1	1	11	22	33	64	90	115
2	112	–	PC-r	1	1	2	4	6	9	13	16
3	125	–	'Picture Progress' on back-c; PC-r	1	1	2	4	6	9	13	16
4	134	–	PC-r	1	1	2	4	6	9	13	16
5	143	–	PC-r	1	1	2	4	6	9	13	16
6	165	–	PC-r	1	1	2	4	6	9	13	16
7	167	–	PC-r	1	1	2	4	6	8	11	14
8	167	4/65	PC-r	1	1	2	4	6	8	11	14
9	167	3/66	PC-r	1	1	2	4	6	8	11	14
10	166	11/67	PC-r	1	1	2	4	6	8	11	14
11	169	Spr/70	New price 25¢; stiff-c; PC-r	1	1	2	4	6	8	11	14

92. The Courtship of Miles Standish

Ed	HRN	Date	Details	A	C	GD 2.0	VG 4.0	FN 6.0	VF 8.0	VF/NM 9.0	NM- 9.2
1	92	2/52	Original; Blum-c/a	1	1	11	22	33	64	90	115
2	165	–	PC-r	1	1	2	4	6	9	13	16
3	167	3/64	PC-r	1	1	2	4	6	9	13	16
4	166	5/67	PC-r	1	1	2	4	6	9	13	16
5	169	Win/69	New price 25¢ stiff-c; PC-r	1	1	2	4	6	9	13	16

93. Pudd'nhead Wilson

Ed	HRN	Date	Details	A	C	GD 2.0	VG 4.0	FN 6.0	VF 8.0	VF/NM 9.0	NM- 9.2
1	94	3/52	Orig.; Kiefer-c/a;	1	1	11	22	33	64	90	115
2	165	–	New-c; PC-r	1	2	2	4	6	11	16	25
3	167	3/64	PC-r	1	2	2	4	6	9	13	16
4	166	R/1968	New price 25¢; soft-c; PC-r	1	2	2	4	6	9	13	16

94. David Balfour

Ed	HRN	Date	Details	A	C	GD 2.0	VG 4.0	FN 6.0	VF 8.0	VF/NM 9.0	NM- 9.2
1	94	4/52	Original; Palais-a	1	1	11	22	33	64	90	115
2	167	5/64	PC-r	1	1	2	4	6	11	16	20
3	166	R/1968	C-price 25¢; PC-r	1	1	2	4	6	13	18	22

95. All Quiet on the Western Front

Ed	HRN	Date	Details	A	C	GD 2.0	VG 4.0	FN 6.0	VF 8.0	VF/NM 9.0	NM- 9.2
1A	96	5/52	Orig.; del Bourgo-a	1	1	14	28	42	81	118	155
1B	99	5/52	Orig.; del Bourgo-a	1	1	13	26	39	72	101	130
2	167	10/64	PC-r	1	1	3	6	9	15	22	28
3	167	11/66	PC-r	1	1	3	6	9	15	22	28

96. Daniel Boone

Ed	HRN	Date	Details	A	C	GD 2.0	VG 4.0	FN 6.0	VF 8.0	VF/NM 9.0	NM- 9.2
1	97	6/52	Original; Blum-a	1	1	11	22	33	62	86	110
2	117	–	PC-r	1	1	2	4	6	9	13	16
3	128	–	PC-r	1	1	2	4	6	9	13	16
4	132	–	PC-r	1	1	2	4	6	9	13	16
5	134	–	"Story of Jesus" on back-c; PC-r	1	1	2	4	6	9	13	16
6	158	–	PC-r	1	1	2	4	6	9	13	16
7	167	1/64	PC-r	1	1	2	4	6	8	11	14

Classics Illustrated #98 © GIL

Classics Illustrated #104 © GIL

Classics Illustrated #108 © GIL

Ed	HRN	Date	Details	A	C	GD 2.0	VG 4.0	FN 6.0	VF 8.0	VF/NM 9.0	NM- 9.2
8	167	5/65	PC-r	1	1	2	4	6	8	11	14
9	167	11/66	PC-r	1	1	2	4	6	8	11	14
10	166	Win/69	New-c; price 25¢; PC-r; stiff-c	1	2	3	6	9	15	22	28

97. King Solomon's Mines

Ed	HRN	Date	Details	A	C	GD 2.0	VG 4.0	FN 6.0	VF 8.0	VF/NM 9.0	NM- 9.2
1	96	7/52	Orig.; Kiefer-a	1	1	11	22	33	62	86	110
2	118	–	PC-r	1	1	2	4	6	9	13	16
3	131	–	PC-r	1	1	2	4	6	9	13	16
4	141	–	PC-r	1	1	2	4	6	9	13	16
5	158	–	PC-r	1	1	2	4	6	9	13	16
6	167	2/64	PC-r	1	1	2	4	6	8	11	14
7	167	9/65	PC-r	1	1	2	4	6	8	11	14
8	169	Sm/69	New price 25¢; stiff-c; PC-r	1	1	2	4	6	8	11	14

98. The Red Badge of Courage

Ed	HRN	Date	Details	A	C	GD 2.0	VG 4.0	FN 6.0	VF 8.0	VF/NM 9.0	NM- 9.2
1	98	8/52	Original	1	1	11	22	33	62	86	110
2	118	–	PC-r	1	1	2	4	6	9	13	16
3	132	–	PC-r	1	1	2	4	6	9	13	16
4	142	–	PC-r	1	1	2	4	6	9	13	16
5	152	–	PC-r	1	1	2	4	6	9	13	16
6	161	–	PC-r	1	1	2	4	6	9	13	16
7	167	–	Has orig.date; PC-r	1	1	2	4	6	9	13	16
8	167	9/64	PC-r	1	1	2	4	6	9	13	16
9	167	10/65	PC-r	1	1	2	4	6	9	13	16
10	166	R/1968	New-c&price 25¢; PC-r; stiff-c	1	2	3	6	9	16	23	30

99. Hamlet (Used in **POP**, pg. 102)

Ed	HRN	Date	Details	A	C	GD 2.0	VG 4.0	FN 6.0	VF 8.0	VF/NM 9.0	NM- 9.2
1	98	9/52	Original; Blum-a	1	1	11	22	33	64	90	115
2	121	–	PC-r	1	1	2	4	6	9	13	16
3	141	–	PC-r	1	1	2	4	6	9	13	16
4	158	–	PC-r	1	1	2	4	6	9	13	16
5	167	–	Has orig.date; PC-r	1	1	2	4	6	8	11	14
6	167	7/65	PC-r	1	1	2	4	6	8	11	14
7	166	4/67	PC-r	1	1	2	4	6	8	11	14
8	169	Spr/69	New-c&price 25¢; PC-r; stiff-c	1	2	3	6	9	16	23	30

100. Mutiny on the Bounty

Ed	HRN	Date	Details	A	C	GD 2.0	VG 4.0	FN 6.0	VF 8.0	VF/NM 9.0	NM- 9.2
1	100	10/52	Original	1	1	11	22	33	62	86	110
2	117	–	PC-r	1	1	2	4	6	9	13	16
3	132	–	PC-r	1	1	2	4	6	9	13	16
4	142	–	PC-r	1	1	2	4	6	9	13	16
5	155	–	PC-r	1	1	2	4	6	9	13	16
6	167	–	Has orig. date;PC-r	1	1	2	4	6	8	11	14
7	167	5/64	PC-r	1	1	2	4	6	8	11	14
8	167	3/66	PC-r	1	1	2	4	6	8	11	14
9	169	Spr/70	PC-r; stiff-c	1	1	2	4	6	8	11	14

101. William Tell

Ed	HRN	Date	Details	A	C	GD 2.0	VG 4.0	FN 6.0	VF 8.0	VF/NM 9.0	NM- 9.2
1	101	11/52	Original; Kiefer-c delBourgo-a	1	1	11	22	33	62	86	110
2	118	–	PC-r	1	1	2	4	6	9	13	16
3	141	–	PC-r	1	1	2	4	6	9	13	16
4	158	–	PC-r	1	1	2	4	6	9	13	16
5	167	–	Has orig.date; PC-r	1	1	2	4	6	8	11	14
6	167	11/64	PC-r	1	1	2	4	6	8	11	14
7	166	4/67	PC-r	1	1	2	4	6	8	11	14
8	169	Win/69	New price 25¢; stiff-c; PC-r	1	1	2	4	6	8	11	14

102. The White Company

Ed	HRN	Date	Details	A	C	GD 2.0	VG 4.0	FN 6.0	VF 8.0	VF/NM 9.0	NM- 9.2
1	101	12/52	Original; Blum-a	1	1	14	28	42	76	108	140
2	165	–	PC-r	1	1	3	6	9	16	23	30
3	167	4/64	PC-r	1	1	3	6	9	16	23	30

103. Men Against the Sea

Ed	HRN	Date	Details	A	C	GD 2.0	VG 4.0	FN 6.0	VF 8.0	VF/NM 9.0	NM- 9.2
1	104	1/53	Original; Kiefer-c; Palais-a	1	1	11	22	33	64	90	115
2	114	–	PC-r	1	1	4	8	11	16	19	22
3	131	–	New-c; PC-r	1	2	5	10	15	24	30	35
4	158	–	PC-r	1	2	4	7	10	14	17	20
5	149	–	White reorder list; came after HRN-158; PC-r	1	2	5	10	15	22	26	30
6	167	3/64	PC-r	1	2	2	4	6	9	13	16

104. Bring 'Em Back Alive

Ed	HRN	Date	Details	A	C	GD 2.0	VG 4.0	FN 6.0	VF 8.0	VF/NM 9.0	NM- 9.2
1	105	2/53	Original; Kiefer-c/a	1	1	11	22	33	62	86	110
2	118	–	PC-r	1	1	2	4	6	9	13	16
3	133	–	PC-r	1	1	2	4	6	9	13	16
4	150	–	PC-r	1	1	2	4	6	9	13	16
5	158	–	PC-r	1	1	2	4	6	9	13	16
6	167	10/63	PC-r	1	1	2	4	6	8	11	14
7	167	9/65	PC-r	1	1	2	4	6	8	11	14
8	169	Win/69	New price 25¢; stiff-c; PC-r	1	1	2	4	6	8	11	14

105. From the Earth to the Moon

Ed	HRN	Date	Details	A	C	GD 2.0	VG 4.0	FN 6.0	VF 8.0	VF/NM 9.0	NM- 9.2
1	106	3/53	Original; Blum-a	1	1	11	22	33	62	86	110
2	118	–	PC-r	1	1	2	4	6	9	13	16
3	132	–	PC-r	1	1	2	4	6	9	13	16
4	141	–	PC-r	1	1	2	4	6	9	13	16
5	146	–	PC-r	1	1	2	4	6	9	13	16
6	156	–	PC-r	1	1	2	4	6	9	13	16
7	167	–	Has orig. date; PC-r	1	1	2	4	6	8	11	14
8	167	5/64	PC-r	1	1	2	4	6	8	11	14
9	167	5/65	PC-r	1	1	2	4	6	8	11	14
10A	166	10/67	PC-r	1	1	2	4	6	8	11	14
10B	166	10/67	w/Grit ad stapled in book	1	1	9	18	27	59	117	175
11	169	Sm/69	New price 25¢; stiff-c; PC-r	1	1	2	4	6	8	11	14
12	169	Spr/71	PC-r	1	1	2	4	6	8	11	14

106. Buffalo Bill

Ed	HRN	Date	Details	A	C	GD 2.0	VG 4.0	FN 6.0	VF 8.0	VF/NM 9.0	NM- 9.2
1	107	4/53	Orig.; delBourgo-a	1	1	11	22	33	60	83	105
2	118	–	PC-r	1	1	2	4	6	9	13	16
3	132	–	PC-r	1	1	2	4	6	9	13	16
4	142	–	PC-r	1	1	2	4	6	9	13	16
5	161	–	PC-r	1	1	2	4	6	8	11	14
6	167	3/64	PC-r	1	1	2	4	6	8	11	14
7	166	7/67	PC-r	1	1	2	4	6	8	11	14
8	169	Fall/69	PC-r; stiff-c	1	1	2	4	6	8	11	14

107. King of the Khyber Rifles

Ed	HRN	Date	Details	A	C	GD 2.0	VG 4.0	FN 6.0	VF 8.0	VF/NM 9.0	NM- 9.2
1	108	5/53	Original	1	1	11	22	33	60	83	105
2	118	–	PC-r	1	1	2	4	6	9	13	16
3	146	–	PC-r	1	1	2	4	6	9	13	16
4	158	–	PC-r	1	1	2	4	6	9	13	16
5	167	–	Has orig.date; PC-r	1	1	2	4	6	8	11	14
6	167	10/66	PC-r	1	1	2	4	6	8	11	14

108. Knights of the Round Table

Ed	HRN	Date	Details	A	C	GD 2.0	VG 4.0	FN 6.0	VF 8.0	VF/NM 9.0	NM- 9.2
1A	108	6/53	Original; Blum-a	1	1	11	22	33	64	90	115
1B	109	6/53	Original; scarce	1	1	12	24	36	67	94	120
2	117	–	PC-r	1	1	2	4	6	9	13	16
3	165	–	PC-r	1	1	2	4	6	8	11	14
4	167	4/64	PC-r	1	1	2	4	6	8	11	14
5	166	4/67	PC-r	1	1	2	4	6	8	11	14
6	169	Sm/69	New price 25¢; stiff-c; PC-r	1	1	2	4	6	8	11	14

109. Pitcairn's Island

Ed	HRN	Date	Details	A	C	GD 2.0	VG 4.0	FN 6.0	VF 8.0	VF/NM 9.0	NM- 9.2
1	110	7/53	Original; Palais-a	1	1	11	22	33	64	90	115
2	165	–	PC-r	1	1	2	4	6	9	13	16
3	167	3/64	PC-r	1	1	2	4	6	9	13	16
4	166	6/67	PC-r	1	1	2	4	6	9	13	16

110. A Study in Scarlet

Ed	HRN	Date	Details	A	C

Classics Illustrated #114 © GIL

Classics Illustrated #115 © GIL

Classics Illustrated #127 © GIL

Ed	HRN	Date	Details	A	C	GD 2.0	VG 4.0	FN 6.0	VF 8.0	VF/NM 9.0	NM- 9.2
1	111	8/53	Original	1	1	15	30	45	84	127	170
2	165	–	PC-r	1	1	11	22	33	62	86	110

111. The Talisman

Ed	HRN	Date	Details	A	C	GD 2.0	VG 4.0	FN 6.0	VF 8.0	VF/NM 9.0	NM- 9.2
1	112	9/53	Original; last H.C. Kiefer-a	1	1	11	22	33	64	90	115
2	165	–	PC-r	1	1	2	4	6	9	13	16
3	167	5/64	PC-r	1	1	2	4	6	9	13	16
4	166	Fall/68	C-price 25¢; PC-r	1	1	2	4	6	9	13	16

112. Adventures of Kit Carson

Ed	HRN	Date	Details	A	C	GD 2.0	VG 4.0	FN 6.0	VF 8.0	VF/NM 9.0	NM- 9.2
1	113	10/53	Original; Palais-a	1	1	11	22	33	62	86	110
2	129	–	PC-r	1	1	2	4	6	9	13	16
3	141	–	PC-r	1	1	2	4	6	9	13	16
4	152	–	PC-r	1	1	2	4	6	9	13	16
5	161	–	PC-r	1	1	2	4	6	8	11	14
6	167	–	PC-r	1	1	2	4	6	8	11	14
7	167	2/65	PC-r	1	1	2	4	6	8	11	14
8	167	5/66	PC-r	1	1	2	4	6	8	11	14
9	166	Win/69	New-c&price 25¢; PC-r; stiff-c	1	2	3	6	9	14	20	25

113. The Forty-Five Guardsmen

Ed	HRN	Date	Details	A	C	GD 2.0	VG 4.0	FN 6.0	VF 8.0	VF/NM 9.0	NM- 9.2
1	114	11/53	Orig.; delBourgo-a	1	1	14	28	42	76	108	140
2	166	7/67	PC-r	1	1	4	8	12	23	37	50

114. The Red Rover

Ed	HRN	Date	Details	A	C	GD 2.0	VG 4.0	FN 6.0	VF 8.0	VF/NM 9.0	NM- 9.2
1	115	12/53	Original	1	1	14	28	42	76	108	140
2	166	7/67	PC-r	1	1	4	8	12	23	37	50

115. How I Found Livingstone

Ed	HRN	Date	Details	A	C	GD 2.0	VG 4.0	FN 6.0	VF 8.0	VF/NM 9.0	NM- 9.2
1	116	1/54	Original	1	1	14	28	42	80	115	150
2	167	1/67	PC-r	1	1	4	8	12	27	44	60

116. The Bottle Imp

Ed	HRN	Date	Details	A	C	GD 2.0	VG 4.0	FN 6.0	VF 8.0	VF/NM 9.0	NM- 9.2
1	117	2/54	Orig.; Cameron-a	1	1	14	28	42	80	115	150
2	167	1/67	PC-r	1	1	4	8	12	27	44	60

117. Captains Courageous

Ed	HRN	Date	Details	A	C	GD 2.0	VG 4.0	FN 6.0	VF 8.0	VF/NM 9.0	NM- 9.2
1	118	3/54	Orig.; Costanza-a	1	1	13	26	39	74	105	135
2	167	2/67	PC-r	1	1	3	6	9	14	20	26
3	169	Fall/69	New price 25¢; stiff-c; PC-r	1	1	3	6	9	14	20	26

118. Rob Roy

Ed	HRN	Date	Details	A	C	GD 2.0	VG 4.0	FN 6.0	VF 8.0	VF/NM 9.0	NM- 9.2
1	119	4/54	Original; Rudy & Walter Palais-a	1	1	14	28	42	80	115	150
2	167	2/67	PC-r	1	1	4	8	12	27	44	60

119. Soldiers of Fortune

Ed	HRN	Date	Details	A	C	GD 2.0	VG 4.0	FN 6.0	VF 8.0	VF/NM 9.0	NM- 9.2
1	120	5/54	Schaffenberger-a	1	1	13	26	39	72	101	130
2	166	3/67	PC-r	1	1	3	6	9	14	20	26
3	169	Spr/70	New price 25¢; stiff-c; PC-r	1	1	3	6	9	14	20	26

120. The Hurricane

Ed	HRN	Date	Details	A	C	GD 2.0	VG 4.0	FN 6.0	VF 8.0	VF/NM 9.0	NM- 9.2
1	121	6/54	Orig.; Cameron-a	1	1	13	26	39	72	101	130
2	166	3/67	PC-r	1	1	4	8	12	22	34	50

121. Wild Bill Hickok

Ed	HRN	Date	Details	A	C	GD 2.0	VG 4.0	FN 6.0	VF 8.0	VF/NM 9.0	NM- 9.2
1	122	7/54	Original	1	1	11	22	33	60	83	105
2	132	–	PC-r	1	1	2	4	6	9	13	16
3	141	–	PC-r	1	1	2	4	6	9	13	16
4	154	–	PC-r	1	1	2	4	6	9	13	16
5	167	–	PC-r	1	1	2	4	6	8	11	14
6	167	8/64	PC-r	1	1	2	4	6	8	11	14
7	166	4/67	PC-r	1	1	2	4	6	8	11	14
8	169	Win/69	PC-r; stiff-c	1	1	2	4	6	8	11	14

122. The Mutineers

Ed	HRN	Date	Details	A	C	GD 2.0	VG 4.0	FN 6.0	VF 8.0	VF/NM 9.0	NM- 9.2
1	123	9/54	Original	1	1	11	22	33	64	90	115
2	136	–	PC-r	1	1	2	4	6	9	13	16
3	146	–	PC-r	1	1	2	4	6	9	13	16
4	158	–	PC-r	1	1	2	4	6	9	13	16
5	167	11/63	PC-r	1	1	2	4	6	8	11	14
6	167	3/65	PC-r	1	1	2	4	6	8	11	14
7	166	8/67	PC-r	1	1	2	4	6	8	11	14

123. Fang and Claw

Ed	HRN	Date	Details	A	C	GD 2.0	VG 4.0	FN 6.0	VF 8.0	VF/NM 9.0	NM- 9.2
1	124	11/54	Original	1	1	11	22	33	64	90	115
2	133	–	PC-r	1	1	2	4	6	9	13	16
3	143	–	PC-r	1	1	2	4	6	9	13	16
4	154	–	PC-r	1	1	2	4	6	9	13	16
5	167	–	Has orig.date; PC-r	1	1	2	4	6	8	11	14
6	167	9/65	PC-r	1	1	2	4	6	8	11	14

124. The War of the Worlds

Ed	HRN	Date	Details	A	C	GD 2.0	VG 4.0	FN 6.0	VF 8.0	VF/NM 9.0	NM- 9.2
1	125	1/55	Original; Cameron-c/a	1	1	14	28	42	80	115	150
2	131	–	PC-r	1	1	2	4	6	10	14	18
3	141	–	PC-r	1	1	2	4	6	10	14	18
4	148	–	PC-r	1	1	2	4	6	10	14	18
5	156	–	PC-r	1	1	2	4	6	10	14	18
6	165	–	PC-r	1	1	2	4	6	13	18	22
7	167	–	PC-r	1	1	2	4	6	9	13	16
8	167	11/64	PC-r	1	1	2	4	6	10	14	18
9	167	11/65	PC-r	1	1	2	4	6	9	13	16
10	166	R/1968	C-price 25¢; PC-r	1	1	2	4	6	9	13	16
11	169	Sm/70	PC-r; stiff-c	1	1	2	4	6	9	13	16

125. The Ox Bow Incident

Ed	HRN	Date	Details	A	C	GD 2.0	VG 4.0	FN 6.0	VF 8.0	VF/NM 9.0	NM- 9.2
1	–	3/55	Original; Picture Progress replaces reorder list	1	1	11	22	33	60	83	105
2	143	–	PC-r	1	1	2	4	6	9	13	16
3	152	–	PC-r	1	1	2	4	6	9	13	16
4	149	–	PC-r	1	1	2	4	6	9	13	16
5	167	–	PC-r	1	1	2	4	6	8	11	14
6	167	11/64	PC-r	1	1	2	4	6	8	11	14
7	166	4/67	PC-r	1	1	2	4	6	8	11	14
8	169	Win/69	New price 25¢; stiff-c; PC-r	1	1	2	4	6	8	11	14

126. The Downfall

Ed	HRN	Date	Details	A	C	GD 2.0	VG 4.0	FN 6.0	VF 8.0	VF/NM 9.0	NM- 9.2
1	–	5/55	Orig.; 'Picture Progress' replaces reorder list; Cameron-c/a	1	1	11	22	33	64	90	115
2	167	8/64	PC-r	1	1	2	4	6	13	18	22
3	166	R/1968	C-price 25¢; PC-r	1	1	2	4	6	13	18	22

127. The King of the Mountains

Ed	HRN	Date	Details	A	C	GD 2.0	VG 4.0	FN 6.0	VF 8.0	VF/NM 9.0	NM- 9.2
1	128	7/55	Original	1	1	11	22	33	64	90	115
2	167	6/64	PC-r	1	1	2	4	6	11	16	20
3	166	F/1968	C-price 25¢; PC-r	1	1	2	4	6	11	16	20

128. Macbeth (Used in **POP**, pg. 102)

Ed	HRN	Date	Details	A	C	GD 2.0	VG 4.0	FN 6.0	VF 8.0	VF/NM 9.0	NM- 9.2
1	128	9/55	Orig.; last Blum-a	1	1	11	22	33	64	90	115
2	143	–	PC-r	1	1	2	4	6	9	13	16
3	158	–	PC-r	1	1	2	4	6	9	13	16
4	167	–	PC-r	1	1	2	4	6	8	11	14
5	167	6/64	PC-r	1	1	2	4	6	8	11	14
6	166	4/67	PC-r	1	1	2	4	6	8	11	14
7	166	R/1968	C-Price 25¢; PC-r	1	1	2	4	6	8	11	14
8	169	Spr/70	Stiff-c; PC-r	1	1	2	4	6	8	11	14

129. Davy Crockett

Ed	HRN	Date	Details	A	C	GD 2.0	VG 4.0	FN 6.0	VF 8.0	VF/NM 9.0	NM- 9.2
1	129	11/55	Orig.; Cameron-a	1	1	14	28	42	82	121	160
2	167	9/66	PC-r	1	1	11	22	33	62	86	110

130. Caesar's Conquests

Ed	HRN	Date	Details	A	C	GD 2.0	VG 4.0	FN 6.0	VF 8.0	VF/NM 9.0	NM- 9.2
1	130	1/56	Original; Orlando-a	1	1	11	22	33	64	90	115

Classics Illustrated #132 © GIL

Classics Illustrated #133 © GIL

Classics Illustrated #145 © GIL

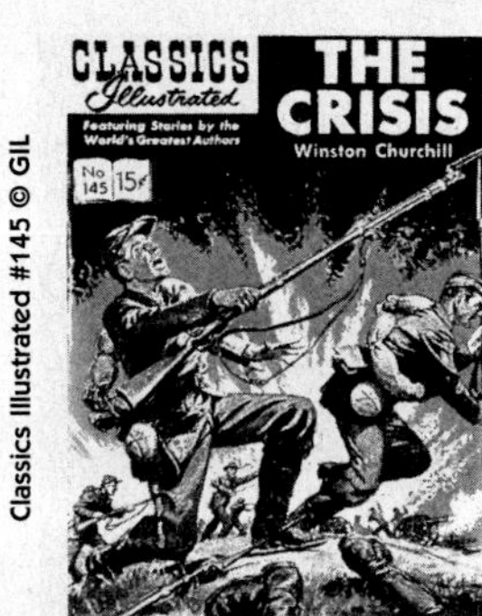

Ed	HRN	Date	Details	A	C	GD 2.0	VG 4.0	FN 6.0	VF 8.0	VF/NM 9.0	NM- 9.2
2	142	–	PC-r	1	1	2	4	6	9	13	16
3	152	–	PC-r	1	1	2	4	6	9	13	16
4	149	–	PC-r	1	1	2	4	6	9	13	16
5	167	–	PC-r	1	1	2	4	6	8	11	14
6	167	10/64	PC-r	1	1	2	4	6	8	11	14
7	167	4/66	PC-r	1	1	2	4	6	8	11	14

131. The Covered Wagon

Ed	HRN	Date	Details	A	C	GD 2.0	VG 4.0	FN 6.0	VF 8.0	VF/NM 9.0	NM- 9.2
1	131	3/56	Original	1	1	6	12	18	40	73	105
2	143	–	PC-r	1	1	2	4	6	9	13	16
3	152	–	PC-r	1	1	2	4	6	9	13	16
4	158	–	PC-r	1	1	2	4	6	9	13	16
5	167	–	PC-r	1	1	2	4	6	8	11	14
6	167	11/64	PC-r	1	1	2	4	6	8	11	14
7	167	4/66	PC-r	1	1	2	4	6	8	11	14
8	169	Win/69	New price 25¢; stiff-c; PC-r	1	1	2	4	6	8	11	14

132. The Dark Frigate

Ed	HRN	Date	Details	A	C	GD 2.0	VG 4.0	FN 6.0	VF 8.0	VF/NM 9.0	NM- 9.2
1	132	5/56	Original	1	1	11	22	33	64	90	115
2	150	–	PC-r	1	1	2	4	6	9	13	16
3	167	1/64	PC-r	1	1	2	4	6	9	13	16
4	166	5/67	PC-r	1	1	2	4	6	9	13	16

133. The Time Machine

Ed	HRN	Date	Details	A	C	GD 2.0	VG 4.0	FN 6.0	VF 8.0	VF/NM 9.0	NM- 9.2
1	132	7/56	Orig.; Cameron-a	1	1	7	14	21	46	86	125
2	142	–	PC-r	1	1	2	4	6	10	14	18
3	152	–	PC-r	1	1	2	4	6	10	14	18
4	158	–	PC-r	1	1	2	4	6	9	13	16
5	167	–	PC-r	1	1	2	4	6	9	13	16
6	167	6/64	PC-r	1	1	2	4	6	10	14	18
7	167	3/66	PC-r	1	1	2	4	6	9	13	16
8	166	12/67	PC-r	1	1	2	4	6	9	13	16
9	169	Win/71	New price 25¢; stiff-c; PC-r	1	1	2	4	6	9	13	16

134. Romeo and Juliet

Ed	HRN	Date	Details	A	C	GD 2.0	VG 4.0	FN 6.0	VF 8.0	VF/NM 9.0	NM- 9.2
1	134	9/56	Original; Evans-a	1	1	6	12	18	42	79	115
2	161	–	PC-r	1	1	2	4	6	9	13	16
3	167	9/63	PC-r	1	1	2	4	6	8	11	14
4	167	5/65	PC-r	1	1	2	4	6	8	11	14
5	166	6/67	PC-r	1	1	2	4	6	8	11	14
6	166	Win/69	New c&price 25¢; stiff-c; PC-r	1	2	3	6	9	17	25	32

135. Waterloo

Ed	HRN	Date	Details	A	C	GD 2.0	VG 4.0	FN 6.0	VF 8.0	VF/NM 9.0	NM- 9.2
1	135	11/56	Orig.; G. Ingels-a	1	1	6	12	18	42	79	115
2	153	–	PC-r	1	1	2	4	6	9	13	16
3	167	–	PC-r	1	1	2	4	6	8	11	14
4	167	9/64	PC-r	1	1	2	4	6	8	11	14
5	166	R/1968	C-price 25¢; PC-r	1	1	2	4	6	8	11	14

136. Lord Jim

Ed	HRN	Date	Details	A	C	GD 2.0	VG 4.0	FN 6.0	VF 8.0	VF/NM 9.0	NM- 9.2
1	136	1/57	Original; Evans-a	1	1	6	12	18	42	79	115
2	165	–	PC-r	1	1	2	4	6	8	11	14
3	167	3/64	PC-r	1	1	2	4	6	8	11	14
4	167	9/66	PC-r	1	1	2	4	6	8	11	14
5	169	Sm/69	New price 25 ¢; stiff-c; PC-r	1	1	2	4	6	8	11	14

137. The Little Savage

Ed	HRN	Date	Details	A	C	GD 2.0	VG 4.0	FN 6.0	VF 8.0	VF/NM 9.0	NM- 9.2
1	136	3/57	Original; Evans-a	1	1	6	12	18	42	79	115
2	148	–	PC-r	1	1	2	4	6	9	13	16
3	156	–	PC-r	1	1	2	4	6	9	13	16
4	167	–	PC-r	1	1	2	4	6	8	11	14
5	167	10/64	PC-r	1	1	2	4	6	8	11	14
6	166	8/67	PC-r	1	1	2	4	6	8	11	14
7	169	Spr/70	New price 25¢; stiff-c; PC-r	1	1	2	4	6	8	11	14

138. A Journey to the Center of the Earth

Ed	HRN	Date	Details	A	C	GD 2.0	VG 4.0	FN 6.0	VF 8.0	VF/NM 9.0	NM- 9.2
1	136	5/57	Original	1	1	8	16	24	51	96	140
2	146	–	PC-r	1	1	2	4	6	11	16	20
3	156	–	PC-r	1	1	2	4	6	11	16	20
4	158	–	PC-r	1	1	2	4	6	9	13	16
5	167	–	PC-r	1	1	2	4	6	8	11	14
6	167	6/64	PC-r	1	1	2	4	6	13	18	22
7	167	4/66	PC-r	1	1	2	4	6	13	18	22
8	166	R/68	C-price 25¢; PC-r	1	1	2	4	6	10	14	18

139. In the Reign of Terror

Ed	HRN	Date	Details	A	C	GD 2.0	VG 4.0	FN 6.0	VF 8.0	VF/NM 9.0	NM- 9.2
1	139	7/57	Original; Evans-a	1	1	6	12	18	40	73	105
2	154	–	PC-r	1	1	2	4	6	9	13	16
3	167	–	Has orig.date; PC-r	1	1	2	4	6	8	11	14
4	167	7/64	PC-r	1	1	2	4	6	8	11	14
5	166	R/1968	C-price 25¢; PC-r	1	1	2	4	6	8	11	14

140. On Jungle Trails

Ed	HRN	Date	Details	A	C	GD 2.0	VG 4.0	FN 6.0	VF 8.0	VF/NM 9.0	NM- 9.2
1	140	9/57	Original	1	1	6	12	18	40	73	105
2	150	–	PC-r	1	1	2	4	6	9	13	16
3	160	–	PC-r	1	1	2	4	6	9	13	16
4	167	9/63	PC-r	1	1	2	4	6	8	11	14
5	167	9/65	PC-r	1	1	2	4	6	8	11	14

141. Castle Dangerous

Ed	HRN	Date	Details	A	C	GD 2.0	VG 4.0	FN 6.0	VF 8.0	VF/NM 9.0	NM- 9.2
1	141	11/57	Original	1	1	7	14	21	44	82	120
2	152	–	PC-r	1	1	2	4	6	9	13	16
3	167	–	PC-r	1	1	2	4	6	9	13	16
4	166	7/67	PC-r	1	1	2	4	6	9	13	16

142. Abraham Lincoln

Ed	HRN	Date	Details	A	C	GD 2.0	VG 4.0	FN 6.0	VF 8.0	VF/NM 9.0	NM- 9.2
1	142	1/58	Original	1	1	6	12	18	42	79	115
2	154	–	PC-r	1	1	2	4	6	9	13	16
3	158	–	PC-r	1	1	2	4	6	9	13	16
4	167	10/63	PC-r	1	1	2	4	6	8	11	14
5	167	7/65	PC-r	1	1	2	4	6	8	11	14
6	166	11/67	PC-r	1	1	2	4	6	8	11	14
7	169	Fall/69	New price 25¢; stiff-c; PC-r	1	1	2	4	6	8	11	14

143. Kim

Ed	HRN	Date	Details	A	C	GD 2.0	VG 4.0	FN 6.0	VF 8.0	VF/NM 9.0	NM- 9.2
1	143	3/58	Original; Orlando-a	1	1	6	12	18	40	73	105
2	165	–	PC-r	1	1	2	4	6	8	11	14
3	167	11/63	PC-r	1	1	2	4	6	8	11	14
4	167	8/65	PC-r	1	1	2	4	6	8	11	14
5	169	Win/69	New price 25¢; stiff-c; PC-r	1	1	2	4	6	8	11	14

144. The First Men in the Moon

Ed	HRN	Date	Details	A	C	GD 2.0	VG 4.0	FN 6.0	VF 8.0	VF/NM 9.0	NM- 9.2
1	143	5/58	Original; Woodbridge/Williamson/Torres-a	1	1	7	14	21	46	86	125
2	152	–	(Rare)-PC-r	1	1	8	16	24	51	96	140
3	153	–	PC-r	1	1	2	4	6	9	13	16
4	161	–	PC-r	1	1	2	4	6	8	11	14
5	167	–	PC-r	1	1	2	4	6	8	11	14
6	167	12/65	PC-r	1	1	2	4	6	8	11	14
7	166	Fall/68	New-c&price 25¢; PC-r; stiff-c	1	2	3	6	9	16	23	30
8	169	Win/69	Stiff-c; PC-r	1	2	2	4	6	10	16	20

145. The Crisis

Ed	HRN	Date	Details	A	C	GD 2.0	VG 4.0	FN 6.0	VF 8.0	VF/NM 9.0	NM- 9.2
1	143	7/58	Original; Evans-a	1	1	6	12	18	42	79	115
2	156	–	PC-r	1	1	2	4	6	9	13	16
3	167	10/63	PC-r	1	1	2	4	6	8	11	14
4	167	3/65	PC-r	1	1	2	4	6	8	11	14
5	166	R/68	C-price 25¢; PC-r	1	1	2	4	6	8	11	14

146. With Fire and Sword

Ed	HRN	Date	Details	A	C	GD 2.0	VG 4.0	FN 6.0	VF 8.0	VF/NM 9.0	NM- 9.2
1	143	9/58	Original; Woodbridge-a	1	1	6	12	18	42	79	115
2	156	–	PC-r	1	1	2	4	6	10	14	18
3	167	11/63	PC-r	1	1	2	4	6	9	13	16
4	167	3/65	PC-r	1	1	2	4	6	9	13	16

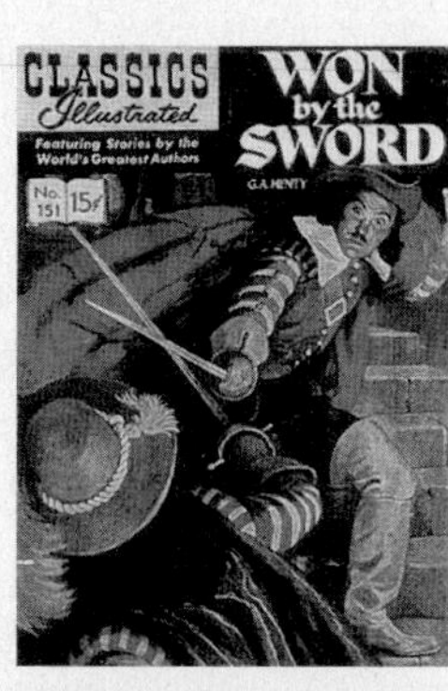

Classics Illustrated #151 © GIL

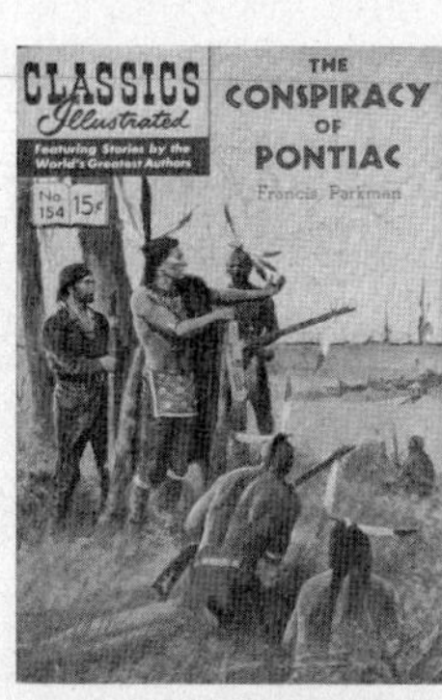

Classics Illustrated #154 © GIL

Classics Illustrated #160 © GIL

147. Ben-Hur

Ed	HRN	Date	Details	A	C	GD 2.0	VG 4.0	FN 6.0	VF 8.0	VF/NM 9.0	NM- 9.2
1	147	11/58	Original; Orlando-a	1	1	6	12	18	41	76	110
2	152	–	Scarce; PC-r	1	1	6	12	18	42	79	115
3	153	–	PC-r	1	1	2	4	6	9	13	16
4	158	–	PC-r	1	1	2	4	6	9	13	16
5	167	–	Orig.date; but PC-r	1	1	2	4	6	8	11	14
6	167	2/65	PC-r	1	1	2	4	6	8	11	14
7	167	9/66	PC-r	1	1	2	4	6	8	11	14
8A	166	Fall/68	New-c&price 25¢; PC-r; soft-c	1	2	3	6	9	16	24	32
8B	166	Fall/68	New-c&price 25¢; PC-r; stiff-c; scarce	1	2	3	6	9	21	33	45

148. The Buccaneer

Ed	HRN	Date	Details	A	C	GD 2.0	VG 4.0	FN 6.0	VF 8.0	VF/NM 9.0	NM- 9.2
1	148	1/59	Orig.; Evans/Jenny-a; Saunders-c	1	1	6	12	18	40	73	105
2	568	–	Juniors list only PC-r	1	1	2	4	6	9	13	16
3	167	–	PC-r	1	1	2	4	6	8	11	14
4	167	9/65	PC-r	1	1	2	4	6	8	11	14
5	169	Sm/69	New price 25¢; PC-r; stiff-c	1	1	2	4	6	8	11	14

149. Off on a Comet

Ed	HRN	Date	Details	A	C	GD 2.0	VG 4.0	FN 6.0	VF 8.0	VF/NM 9.0	NM- 9.2
1	149	3/59	Orig.;G.McCann-a; blue reorder list	1	1	6	12	18	42	79	115
2	155	–	PC-r	1	1	2	4	6	9	13	16
3	149	–	PC-r; white reorder list; no coming-next ad	1	1	2	4	6	9	13	16
4	167	12/63	PC-r	1	1	2	4	6	8	11	14
5	167	2/65	PC-r	1	1	2	4	6	8	11	14
6	167	10/66	PC-r	1	1	2	4	6	8	11	14
7	166	Fall/68	New-c & price 25¢; PC-r	1	2	3	6	9	16	23	30

150. The Virginian

Ed	HRN	Date	Details	A	C	GD 2.0	VG 4.0	FN 6.0	VF 8.0	VF/NM 9.0	NM- 9.2
1	150	5/59	Original	1	1	7	14	21	44	82	120
2	164	–	PC-r	1	1	2	4	6	11	16	20
3	167	10/63	PC-r	1	1	3	6	9	15	21	26
4	167	12/65	PC-r	1	1	2	4	6	11	16	20

151. Won By the Sword

Ed	HRN	Date	Details	A	C	GD 2.0	VG 4.0	FN 6.0	VF 8.0	VF/NM 9.0	NM- 9.2
1	150	7/59	Original	1	1	6	12	18	42	79	115
2	164	–	PC-r	1	1	2	4	6	10	14	18
3	167	10/63	PC-r	1	1	2	4	6	10	14	18
4	166	7/67	PC-r	1	1	2	4	6	10	14	18

152. Wild Animals I Have Known

Ed	HRN	Date	Details	A	C	GD 2.0	VG 4.0	FN 6.0	VF 8.0	VF/NM 9.0	NM- 9.2
1	152	9/59	Orig.; L.B. Cole c/a	1	1	7	14	21	46	86	125
2A	149	–	PC-r; white reorder list; no coming-next ad; IBC: Jr. list #572	1	1	2	4	6	9	13	16
2B	149	–	PC-r; inside-bc: Jr. list to #555	1	1	2	4	6	9	13	16
2C	149	–	PC-r; inside-bc: has World Around Us ad; scarce	1	1	3	6	9	15	21	26
3	167	9/63	PC-r	1	1	2	4	6	8	11	14
4	167	8/65	PC-r	1	1	2	4	6	8	11	14
5	169	Fall/69	New price 25¢; stiff-c; PC-r	1	1	2	4	6	8	11	14

153. The Invisible Man

Ed	HRN	Date	Details	A	C	GD 2.0	VG 4.0	FN 6.0	VF 8.0	VF/NM 9.0	NM- 9.2
1	153	11/59	Original	1	1	7	14	21	49	92	135
2A	149	–	PC-r; white reorder list; no coming-next ad; inside-bc: Jr. list to #572	1	1	2	4	6	11	16	20
2B	149	–	PC-r; inside-bc: Jr. list to #555	1	1	2	4	6	13	18	22
3	167	–	PC-r	1	1	2	4	6	9	13	16
4	167	2/65	PC-r	1	1	2	4	6	9	13	16
5	167	9/66	PC-r	1	1	2	4	6	9	13	16
6	166	Win/69	New price 25¢; PC-r; stiff-c	1	1	2	4	6	9	13	16
7	169	Spr/71	Stiff-c; letters spelling 'Invisible Man' are 'solid' not 'invisible;' PC-r	1	1	2	4	6	9	13	16

154. The Conspiracy of Pontiac

Ed	HRN	Date	Details	A	C	GD 2.0	VG 4.0	FN 6.0	VF 8.0	VF/NM 9.0	NM- 9.2
1	154	1/60	Original	1	1	7	14	21	41	82	120
2	167	11/63	PC-r	1	1	2	4	6	13	18	22
3	167	7/64	PC-r	1	1	2	4	6	13	18	22
4	166	12/67	PC-r	1	1	2	4	6	13	18	22

155. The Lion of the North

Ed	HRN	Date	Details	A	C	GD 2.0	VG 4.0	FN 6.0	VF 8.0	VF/NM 9.0	NM- 9.2
1	154	3/60	Original	1	1	6	12	18	42	79	115
2	167	1/64	PC-r	1	1	2	4	6	11	16	20
3	166	R/1967	C-price 25¢; PC-r	1	1	2	4	6	10	14	18

156. The Conquest of Mexico

Ed	HRN	Date	Details	A	C	GD 2.0	VG 4.0	FN 6.0	VF 8.0	VF/NM 9.0	NM- 9.2
1	156	5/60	Orig.; Bruno Premiani-c/a	1	1	6	12	18	42	79	115
2	167	1/64	PC-r	1	1	2	4	6	10	14	18
3	166	8/67	PC-r	1	1	2	4	6	10	14	18
4	169	Spr/70	New price 25¢; stiff-c; PC-r	1	1	2	4	6	9	13	16

157. Lives of the Hunted

Ed	HRN	Date	Details	A	C	GD 2.0	VG 4.0	FN 6.0	VF 8.0	VF/NM 9.0	NM- 9.2
1	156	7/60	Orig.; L.B. Cole-c	1	1	7	14	21	44	82	120
2	167	2/64	PC-r	1	1	2	4	6	13	18	22
3	166	10/67	PC-r	1	1	2	4	6	13	18	22

158. The Conspirators

Ed	HRN	Date	Details	A	C	GD 2.0	VG 4.0	FN 6.0	VF 8.0	VF/NM 9.0	NM- 9.2
1	156	9/60	Original	1	1	7	14	21	44	82	120
2	167	7/64	PC-r	1	1	2	4	6	13	18	22
3	166	10/67	PC-r	1	1	2	4	6	13	18	22

159. The Octopus

Ed	HRN	Date	Details	A	C	GD 2.0	VG 4.0	FN 6.0	VF 8.0	VF/NM 9.0	NM- 9.2
1	159	11/60	Orig.; Gray Morrow-a; L.B. Cole-c	1	1	7	14	21	44	82	120
2	167	2/64	PC-r	1	1	2	4	6	13	18	22
3	166	R/1967	C-price 25¢; PC-r	1	1	2	4	6	13	18	22

160. The Food of the Gods

Ed	HRN	Date	Details	A	C	GD 2.0	VG 4.0	FN 6.0	VF 8.0	VF/NM 9.0	NM- 9.2
1A	159	1/61	Original	1	1	7	14	21	46	86	125
1B	160	1/61	Original; same, except for HRN	1	1	7	14	21	44	82	120
2	167	1/64	PC-r	1	1	2	4	6	13	18	22
3	166	6/67	PC-r	1	1	2	4	6	13	18	22

161. Cleopatra

Ed	HRN	Date	Details	A	C	GD 2.0	VG 4.0	FN 6.0	VF 8.0	VF/NM 9.0	NM- 9.2
1	161	3/61	Original	1	1	7	14	21	44	82	120
2	167	1/64	PC-r	1	1	3	6	9	14	19	24
3	166	8/67	PC-r	1	1	3	6	9	14	19	24

162. Robur the Conqueror

Ed	HRN	Date	Details	A	C	GD 2.0	VG 4.0	FN 6.0	VF 8.0	VF/NM 9.0	NM- 9.2
1	162	5/61	Original	1	1	7	14	21	44	82	120
2	167	7/64	PC-r	1	1	3	6	9	14	19	24
3	166	8/67	PC-r	1	1	3	6	9	14	19	24

163. Master of the World

Ed	HRN	Date	Details	A	C	GD 2.0	VG 4.0	FN 6.0	VF 8.0	VF/NM 9.0	NM- 9.2
1	163	7/61	Original; Gray Morrow-a	1	1	7	14	21	44	82	120
2	167	1/65	PC-r	1	1	2	4	6	13	18	22
3	166	R/1968	C-price 25¢; PC-r	1	1	2	4	6	13	18	22

164. The Cossack Chief

Ed	HRN	Date	Details	A	C	GD 2.0	VG 4.0	FN 6.0	VF 8.0	VF/NM 9.0	NM- 9.2
1	164	(1961)	Orig.; nd(10/61?)	1	1	6	12	18	41	76	110

Classics Illustrated #166 © GIL

Classics Illustrated #169 © GIL

Classics Illustrated Junior #503 © GIL

						GD 2.0	VG 4.0	FN 6.0	VF 8.0	VF/NM 9.0	NM- 9.2
2	167	4/65	PC-r	1	1	2	4	6	13	18	22
3	166	Fall/68	C-price 25¢; PC-r	1	1	2	4	6	13	18	22

165. The Queen's Necklace

Ed	HRN	Date	Details	A	C	GD	VG	FN	VF	VF/NM	NM-
1	164	1/62	Original; Morrow-a	1	1	7	14	21	44	82	120
2	167	4/65	PC-r	1	1	2	4	6	13	18	22
3	166	Fall/68	C-price 25¢; PC-r	1	1	2	4	6	13	18	22

166. Tigers and Traitors

Ed	HRN	Date	Details	A	C	GD	VG	FN	VF	VF/NM	NM-
1	165	5/62	Original	1	1	8	16	24	55	105	155
2	167	2/64	PC-r	1	1	3	6	9	21	33	45
3	167	11/66	PC-r	1	1	3	6	9	21	33	45

167. Faust

Ed	HRN	Date	Details	A	C	GD	VG	FN	VF	VF/NM	NM-
1	165	8/62	Original	1	1	11	22	33	75	160	245
2	167	2/64	PC-r	1	1	5	10	15	34	60	85
3	166	6/67	PC-r	1	1	5	10	15	34	60	85

168. In Freedom's Cause

Ed	HRN	Date	Details	A	C	GD	VG	FN	VF	VF/NM	NM-
1	169	Win/69	Original; Evans/ Crandall-a; stiff-c; 25¢; no coming-next ad;	1	1	13	26	39	86	188	290

169. Negro Americans The Early Years

Ed	HRN	Date	Details	A	C	GD	VG	FN	VF	VF/NM	NM-
1	166	Spr/69	Orig. & last issue; 25¢; Stiff-c; no coming-next ad; other sources indicate publication date of 5/69	1	1	12	24	36	80	173	265
2	169	Spr/69	Stiff-c	1	1	7	14	21	44	82	120

NOTE: *Many other titles were prepared or planned but were only issued in British/European series.*

CLASSIC POPEYE (See Popeye, Classic)

CLASSIC PUNISHER (Also see Punisher)
Marvel Comics: Dec, 1989 ($4.95, B&W, deluxe format, 68 pgs.)

1-Reprints Marvel Super Action #1 & Marvel Preview #2 plus new story 5.00

CLASSIC RED SONJA
Dynamite Entertainment: 2010 - No. 4, 2010 ($3.99)

1-4-Newly colored reprints of stories from Savage Sword of Conan magazine 4.00

CLASSICS ILLUSTRATED
First Publishing/Berkley Publishing: Feb, 1990 - No. 27, July, 1991 ($3.75/$3.95, 52 pgs.)

1-27: 1-Gahan Wilson-c/a. 4-Sienkiewicz painted-c/a. 6-Russell scripts/layouts. 7-Spiegle-a. 9-Ploog-c/a. 16-Staton-a. 18-Gahan Wilson-c/a; 20-Geary-a. 26-Aesop's Fables (6/91). 26,27-Direct sale only 5.00

CLASSICS ILLUSTRATED
Acclaim Books/Twin Circle PublishingCo.: Feb, 1997 - Jan, 1998 ($4.99, digest-size) (Each book contains study notes)

A Christmas Carol-(12/97), A Connecticut Yankee in King Arthur's Court-(5/97), All Quiet on the Western Front-(1/98), A Midsummer's Night Dream-(4/97) Around the World in 80 Days-(1/98), A Tale of Two Cities-(2/97)Joe Orlando-r, Captains Courageous-(11/97), Crime and Punishment-(3/97), Dr. Jekyll and Mr. Hyde-(10/97), Don Quixote-(12/97), Frankenstein-(10/97), Great Expectations-(4/97), Hamlet-(3/97), Huckleberry Finn-(3/97), Jane Eyre-(2/97), Kidnapped-(1/98), Les Miserables-(5/97), Lord Jim-(9/97), Macbeth-(5/97), Moby Dick-(4/97), Oliver Twist-(5/97), Robinson Crusoe-(9/97), Romeo & Juliet-(2/97), Silas Marner-(11/97), The Call of the Wild-(9/97), The Count of Monte Cristo-(1/98), The House of the Seven Gables-(9/97), The Iliad-(12/97), The Invisible Man-(10/97), The Last of the Mohicans-(12/97), The Master of Ballantrae-(11/97), The Odyssey-(3/97), The Prince and the Pauper-(4/97), The Red Badge Of Courage-(9/97), Tom Sawyer-(2/97) Wuthering Heights-(11/97) 5.00

NOTE: *Stories reprinted from the original Gilberton Classic Comics and Classics Illustrated.*

CLASSICS ILLUSTRATED GIANTS
Gilberton Publications: Oct, 1949 (One-Shots - "OS")

These Giant Editions, all with new front and back covers, were advertised from 10/49 to 2/52. They were 50¢ on the newsstand and 60¢ by mail. They are actually four Classics in one volume. All the stories are reprints of the Classics Illustrated Series.

NOTE: There were also British hardback Adventure & Indian Giants in 1952, with the same covers but different contents: Adventure - 2, 7, 10; Indian - 17, 22, 37, 58. They are also rare.

	GD	VG	FN	VF	VF/NM	NM-
"An Illustrated Library of Great Adventure Stories" - reprints of No. 6,7,8,10 (Rare); Kiefer-c	161	322	483	1030	1765	2500
"An Illustrated Library of Exciting Mystery Stories" - reprints of No. 30,21,40, 13 (Rare); Blum-c	171	342	513	1086	1868	2650
"An Illustrated Library of Great Indian Stories" - reprints of No. 4,17,22,37 (Rare); Blum-c	161	322	483	1030	1765	2500

INTRODUCTION TO CLASSICS ILLUSTRATED JUNIOR

Collectors of Juniors can be put into one of two categories: those who want any copy of each title, and those who want all the originals. Those seeking every original and reprint edition are a limited group, primarily because Juniors have no changes in art or covers to spark interest, and because reprints are so low in value it is difficult to get dealers to look for specific reprint editions.

In recent years it has become apparent that most serious Classics collectors seek Junior originals. Those seeking reprints seek them for low cost. This has made the previous note about the comparative market value of reprints inadequate. Three particular reprint editions are worth even more. For the 535-Twin Circle edition, see Giveaways. There are also reprint editions of 501 and 503 which have a full-page bc ad for the very rare Junior record. Those may sell as high as $10-$15 in mint. Original editions of 557 and 558 also have that ad.

There are no reprint editions of 577. The only edition, from 1969, is a 25 cent stiff-cover edition with no ad for the next issue. All other original editions have coming-next ad. But 577, like C.I. #168, was prepared in 1962 but not issued. Copies of 577 can be found in 1963 British/European series, which then continued with dozens of additional new Junior titles.

PRICES LISTED BELOW ARE FOR ORIGINAL EDITIONS, WHICH HAVE AN AD FOR THE NEXT ISSUE.

NOTE: *Non HRN 576 copies- many are written on or colored . Reprints with 576 HRN are worth about 1/3 original prices. All other HRN #'s are 1/2 original price*

CLASSICS ILLUSTRATED JUNIOR
Famous Authors Ltd. (Gilberton Publications): Oct, 1953 - Spring, 1971

	GD	VG	FN	VF	VF/NM	NM-
501-Snow White & the Seven Dwarfs; Alex Blum-a	12	24	36	69	97	125
502-The Ugly Duckling	9	18	27	47	61	75
503-Cinderella	8	16	24	40	50	60
504-512: 504-The Pied Piper. 505-The Sleeping Beauty. 506-The Three Little Pigs. 507-Jack & the Beanstalk. 508-Goldilocks & the Three Bears. 509-Beauty and the Beast. 510-Little Red Riding Hood. 511-Puss-N Boots. 512-Rumpelstiltskin	6	12	18	27	33	38
513-Pinocchio	7	14	21	37	46	55
514-The Steadfast Tin Soldier	8	16	24	44	57	70
515-Johnny Appleseed	6	12	18	27	33	38
516-Aladdin and His Lamp	6	12	18	29	36	42
517-519: 517-The Emperor's New Clothes. 518-The Golden Goose. 519-Paul Bunyan	6	12	18	27	33	38
520-Thumbelina	6	12	18	29	36	42
521-King of the Golden River	6	12	18	27	33	38
522,523,530: 522-The Nightingale. 523-The Gallant Tailor. 530-The Golden Bird	5	10	15	24	30	35
524-The Wild Swans	6	12	18	29	36	42
525,526: 525-The Little Mermaid. 526-The Frog Prince	6	12	18	29	36	42
527-The Golden-Haired Giant	6	12	18	27	33	38
528-The Penny Prince	6	12	18	27	33	38
529-The Magic Servants	6	12	18	27	33	38
531-Rapunzel	6	12	18	27	33	38
532-534: 532-The Dancing Princesses. 533-The Magic Fountain. 534-The Golden Touch	5	10	15	23	28	32
535-The Wizard of Oz	8	16	24	44	57	70
536-The Chimney Sweep	6	12	18	27	33	38
537-The Three Fairies	6	12	18	28	34	40
538-Silly Hans	5	10	15	23	28	32
539-The Enchanted Fish	6	12	18	31	38	45
540-The Tinder-Box	6	12	18	31	38	45
541-Snow White & Rose Red	5	10	15	24	30	35
542-The Donkey's Tale	5	10	15	24	30	35
543-The House in the Woods	6	12	18	27	33	38
544-The Golden Fleece	6	12	18	31	38	45
545-The Glass Mountain	5	10	15	24	30	35
546-The Elves & the Shoemaker	5	10	15	24	30	35
547-The Wishing Table	6	12	18	27	33	38
548-551: 548-The Magic Pitcher. 549-Simple Kate. 550-The Singing Donkey. 551-The Queen Bee	5	10	15	23	28	32
552-The Three Little Dwarfs	6	12	18	27	33	38
553,556: 553-King Thrushbeard. 556-The Elf Mound	5	10	15	23	28	32
554-The Enchanted Deer	6	12	18	29	36	42
555-The Three Golden Apples	5	10	15	24	30	35
557-Silly Willy	6	12	18	28	34	40
558-The Magic Dish; L.B. Cole-c; soft and stiff-c exist on original	7	14	21	35	43	50

Classics Illustrated Special Issue #159A © GIL

Classic Star Wars #17 © Lucasfilm

Clean Room #17 © Gail Simone

GD VG FN VF VF/NM NM-
2.0 4.0 6.0 8.0 9.0 9.2

559-The Japanese Lantern; 1 pg. Ingels-a; L.B. Cole-c
7 14 21 35 43 50
560-The Doll Princess; L.B. Cole-c 7 14 21 35 43 50
561-Hans Humdrum; L.B. Cole-c 6 12 18 29 36 42
562-The Enchanted Pony; L.B. Cole-c 7 14 21 35 43 50
563,565-568,570: 563-The Wishing Well; L.B. Cole-c. 565-The Silly Princess; L.B. Cole-c. 566-Clumsy Hans; L.B. Cole-c. 567-The Bearskin Soldier; L.B. Cole-c. 570-The Pearl Princess 6 12 18 27 33 38
564-The Salt Mountain; L.B.Cole-c. 568-The Happy Hedgehog; L.B. Cole-c.
6 12 18 28 34 40
569,573: 569-The Three Giants.573-The Crystal Ball 5 10 15 23 28 32
571,572: 571-How Fire Came to the Indians. 572-The Drummer Boy
6 12 18 29 36 42
574-Brightboots 5 10 15 24 30 35
575-The Fearless Prince 6 12 18 28 34 40
576-The Princess Who Saw Everything 7 14 21 35 43 50
577-The Runaway Dumpling 8 16 24 44 57 70
NOTE: *Prices are for original editions. Last reprint - Spring, 1971.* ***Costanza*** *&* ***Schaffenberger*** *art in many issues.*

CLASSICS ILLUSTRATED SPECIAL ISSUE
Gilberton Co.: (Came out semi-annually) Dec, 1955 - Jul, 1962 (35¢, 100 pgs.)

129-The Story of Jesus (titled ...Special Edition) "Jesus on Mountain" cover
18 36 54 105 165 225
"Three Camels" cover (12/58) 19 38 57 109 172 235
"Mountain" cover (no date)-Has checklist on inside b/c to HRN #161 & different testimonial on back-c 14 28 42 76 108 140
"Mountain" cover (1968 re-issue; has white 50¢ circle) 10 20 30 56 76 95
132A-The Story of America (6/56); Cameron-a 12 24 36 67 94 120
135A-The Ten Commandments(12/56) 11 22 33 64 90 115
138A-Adventures in Science(6/57); HRN to 137 11 22 33 60 83 105
138A-(6/57)-2nd version w/HRN to 149 7 14 21 35 43 50
138A-(12/61)-3rd version w/HRN to 149 7 14 21 35 43 50
141A-The Rough Rider (Teddy Roosevelt)(12/57); Evans-a
11 22 33 62 86 110
144A-Blazing the Trails West(6/58)- 73 pgs. of Crandall/Evans plus Severin-a 11 22 33 64 90 115
147A-Crossing the Rockies(12/58)-Crandall/Evans-a 11 22 33 62 86 110
150A-Royal Canadian Police(6/59)-Ingels, Sid Check-a
11 22 33 62 86 110
153A-Men, Guns & Cattle(12/59)-Evans-a (26 pgs.); Kinstler-a
11 22 33 62 86 110
156A-The Atomic Age(6/60)-Crandall/Evans, Torres-a
11 22 33 62 86 110
159A-Rockets, Jets and Missiles(12/60)-Evans, Morrow-a
11 22 33 62 86 110
162A-War Between the States(6/61)-Kirby & Crandall/Evans-a; Ingels-a
17 34 51 100 158 215
165A-To the Stars(12/61)-Torres, Crandall/Evans, Kirby-a
14 28 42 76 108 140
166A-World War II('62)-Torres, Crandall/Evans, Kirby-a
15 30 45 83 124 165
167A-Prehistoric World(7/62)-Torres & Crandall/Evans-a; two versions exist (HRN to 165 & HRN to 167) 14 28 42 81 118 155
nn Special Issue-The United Nations (1964; 50¢; scarce); this is actually part of the European Special Series, which cont'd on after the U.S. series stopped issuing new titles in 1962. This English edition was prepared specifically for sale at the U.N. It was printed in Norway
50 100 150 315 533 750
NOTE: *There was another U.S. Special Issue prepared in 1962 with artwork by* ***Torres*** *entitled World War I. Unfortunately, it was never issued in any English-language edition. It was issued in 1964 in West Germany, The Netherlands, and some Scandanavian countries, with another edition in 1974 with a new cover.*

CLASSICS LIBRARY (See King Classics)

CLASSIC STAR WARS (Also see Star Wars)
Dark Horse Comics: Aug, 1992 - No. 20, June, 1994 ($2.50)

1-Begin Star Wars strip-r by Williamson; Williamson redrew portions of the panels to fit comic book format 6.00
2-10: 8-Polybagged w/Star Wars Galaxy trading card. 8-M. Schultz-c 4.00
11-19: 13-Yeates-c. 17-M. Schultz-c. 19-Evans-c 3.00
20-($3.50, 52 pgs.)-Polybagged w/trading card 4.00
Escape To Hoth TPB ($16.95) r/#15-20 17.00
The Rebel Storm TPB - r/#8-14 17.00
Trade paperback ($29.95, slip-cased)-Reprints all movie adaptations 30.00
NOTE: *Williamson c-1-5,7,9,10,14,15,20.*

CLASSIC STAR WARS: (Title series). **Dark Horse Comics**

--A NEW HOPE, 6/94 - No. 2, 7/94 ($3.95)

GD VG FN VF VF/NM NM-
2.0 4.0 6.0 8.0 9.0 9.2

1,2: 1-r/Star Wars #1-3, 7-9 publ; 2-r/Star Wars #4-6, 10-12 publ. by Marvel Comics 4.00
--DEVILWORLDS, 8/96 - No.2, 9/96 ($2.50s)1,2: r/Alan Moore-s 3.00
--HAN SOLO AT STARS' END, 3/97 - No. 3, 5/97 ($2.95)
1-3: r/strips by Alfredo Alcala 3.00
--RETURN OF THE JEDI, 10/94 - No.2, 11/94 ($3.50)
1,2: 1-r/1983-84 Marvel series; polybagged with w/trading card 3.50
--THE EARLY ADVENTURES, 8/94 - No. 9, 4/95 ($2.50)1-9 3.00
--THE EMPIRE STRIKES BACK, 8/94 - No. 2, 9/94 ($3.95)
1-r/Star Wars #39-44 published by Marvel Comics 4.00

CLASSIC X-MEN (Becomes X-Men Classic #46 on)
Marvel Comics Group: Sept, 1986 - No. 45, Mar, 1990

1-Begins-r of New X-Men 2 4 6 8 10 12
2-10: 10-Sabretooth app. 4.00
11-42,44,45: 11-1st origin of Magneto in back-up story. 17-Wolverine-c. 27-r/X-Men #121. 26-r/X-Men #120; Wolverine-c/app. 35-r/X-Men #129. 39-New Jim Lee back-up story (2nd-a on X-Men) 3.00
43-Byrne-c/a(r); ($1.75, double-size) 4.00
NOTE: ***Art Adams*** *c(p)-1-10, 12-16, 18-23.* ***Austin*** *c-10,15-21,24-28i.* ***Bolton*** *back up stories in 1-28,30-35.* ***Williamson*** *c-12-14i.*

CLAW (See Capt. Battle, Jr., Daredevil Comics & Silver Streak Comics)

CLAWS (See Wolverine & Black Cat: Claws 2 for sequel)
Marvel Comics: Oct, 2006 - No. 3, Dec, 2006 ($3.99, limited series)

1-3-Wolverine and Black Cat team-up; Linsner-a/c 4.00
Wolverine & Black Cat: Claws HC (2007, $17.99, dustjacket) r/#1-3 & bonus Linsner art 18.00

CLAW THE UNCONQUERED (See Cancelled Comic Cavalcade)
National Periodical Publications/DC Comics: 5-6/75 - No. 9, 9-10/76; No. 10, 4-5/78 - No. 12, 8-9/78

1-1st app. Claw 2 4 6 8 10 12
2-12: 3-Nudity panel. 9-Origin 1 2 3 4 5 7
NOTE: ***Giffen*** *a-8-12p.* ***Kubert*** *c-10-12.* ***Layton*** *a-9i, 12i.*

CLAW THE UNCONQUERED (See Red Sonja/Claw: The Devil's Hands)
DC Comics: Aug, 2006 - No. 6, Jan, 2007 ($2.99)

1-6: 1,2-Chuck Dixon-s/Andy Smith; two covers by Smith & Van Sciver 3.00
TPB (2007, $17.99) r/#1-6; cover gallery 18.00

CLAY CODY, GUNSLINGER
Pines Comics: Fall, 1957

1-Painted-c 6 12 18 31 38 45

CLEAN FUN, STARRING "SHOOGAFOOTS JONES"
Specialty Book Co.: 1944 (10¢, B&W, oversized covers, 24 pgs.)

nn-Humorous situations involving Negroes in the Deep South
White cover issue... 26 52 78 154 252 350
Dark grey cover issue... 27 54 81 158 259 360

CLEAN ROOM
DC Comics (Vertigo): Dec, 2015 - No. 18, Jun, 2017 ($3.99)

1-18: 1-Gail Simone-s/Jon Davis-Hunt-a/Jenny Frison-c 4.00

CLEMENTINA THE FLYING PIG (See Dell Jr. Treasury)

CLEOPATRA (See Ideal, a Classical Comic No. 1)

CLERKS: THE COMIC BOOK (Also see Tales From the Clerks and Oni Double Feature #1)
Oni Press: Feb, 1998 ($2.95, B&W, one-shot)

1-Kevin Smith-s 2 4 6 11 16 20
1-Second printing 4.00
...Holiday Special (12/98, $2.95) Smith-s 5.00
...The Lost Scene (12/99, $2.95) Smith-s/Hester-a 5.00

CLIFFHANGER (See Battle Chasers, Crimson, and Danger Girl)
WildStorm Prod./Wizard Press: 1997 (Wizard supplement)

0-Sketchbook preview of Cliffhanger titles 6.00

CLIMAX! (Mystery)
Gillmor Magazines: July, 1955 - No. 2, Sept, 1955

1 17 34 51 98 154 210
2 14 28 42 76 108 140

CLINT (Also see Adolescent Radioactive Black Belt Hamsters)
Eclipse Comics: Sept, 1986 - No. 2, Jan, 1987 ($1.50, B&W)

1,2 3.00

CLINT & MAC (TV, Disney)
Dell Publishing Co.: No. 889, Mar, 1958

Clive Barker's Hellraiser (2011 series) #1 © BOOM & Clive Barker

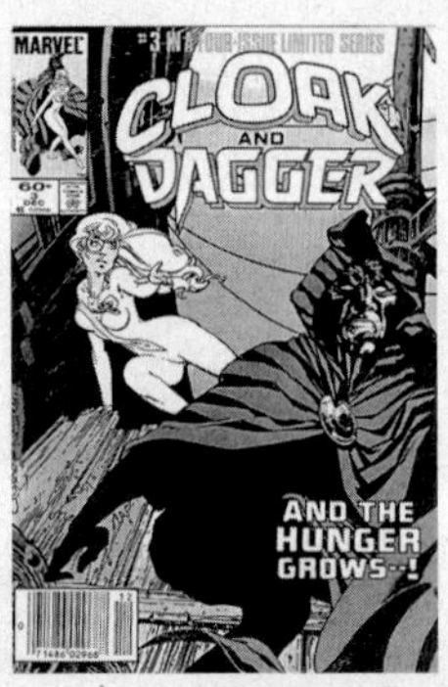

Cloak and Dagger #3 © MAR

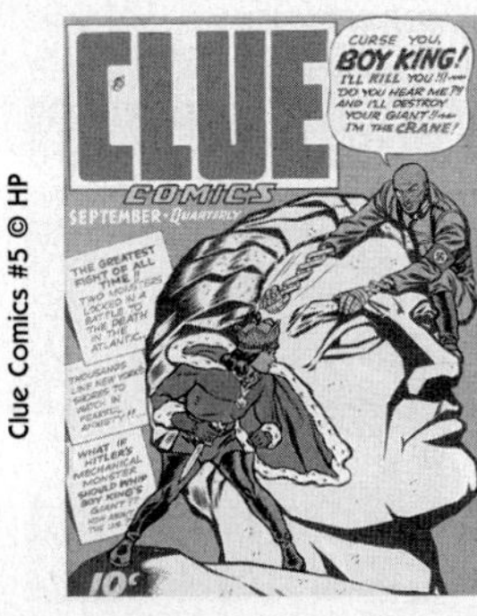

Clue Comics #5 © HP

GD 2.0 | VG 4.0 | FN 6.0 | VF 8.0 | VF/NM 9.0 | NM- 9.2

GD 2.0 | VG 4.0 | FN 6.0 | VF 8.0 | VF/NM 9.0 | NM- 9.2

Four Color 889-Alex Toth-a, photo-c 10 20 30 64 132 200

CLIVE BARKER'S BOOK OF THE DAMNED: A HELLRAISER COMPANION
Marvel Comics (Epic): Oct, 1991 - No. 3, Nov, 1992 ($4.95, semi-annual)
Volume 1-3-(52 pgs.): 1-Simon Bisley-c. 2-(4/92). 3-(11/92)-McKean-a (1 pg.) 5.00

CLIVE BARKER'S HELLRAISER (Also see Epic, Hellraiser Nightbreed –Jihad, Revelations, Son of Celluloid, Tapping the Vein & Weaveworld)
Marvel Comics (Epic Comics): 1989 - No. 20, 1993 ($4.50-6.95, mature, quarterly, 68 pgs.)
Book 1-4,10-16,18,19: Based on Hellraiser & Hellbound movies; Bolton-c/a; Spiegle & Wrightson-a (graphic album). 10-Foil-c. 12-Sam Kieth-a 6.00
Book 5-9 ($5.95): 7-Bolton-a. 8-Morrow-a 6.00
Book 17-Alex Ross-a, 34 pgs. 2 4 6 8 10 12
Book 20-By Gaiman/McKean 1 2 3 5 6 8
...Collected Best (Checker Books, '02, $21.95)-r/by various incl. Ross, Gaiman, Mignola 22.00
...Collected Best II ('03, $19.95)-r/by various incl. Bolton, L. Wachowski, Dorman 20.00
...Collected Best III ('04, $26.95)-r/by various incl. Bolton, L. Wachowski, Wrightson 27.00
...Dark Holiday Special ('92, $4.95)-Conrad-a 6.00
...Spring Slaughter 1 ('94, $6.95, 52 pgs.)-Painted-c 7.00
...Summer Special 1 ('92, $5.95, 68 pgs.) 6.00

CLIVE BARKER'S HELLRAISER
BOOM! Studios: Mar, 2011 - No. 20, Nov, 2012 ($3.99)
1-20: 1-Barker & Monfette-s/Manco-a; preview of Hellraiser Masterpieces; 3 covers 4.00
Annual 1 (3/12, $4.99) Hervás-a; three covers 5.00
2013 Annual (10/13, $4.99) Seifert-s/Hervás-a; Barker & Meares-s/Ordon-a 5.00
...: Bestiary 1-6 (8/14 - No. 6, 1/15, $3.99) short stories by various; multiple covers 4.00
... Masterpieces 1-12 (11/11 - No. 12, 4/12, $3.99) reps from Marvel series. 1-Wrightson-a 4.00
...: The Dark Watch 1-12 (2/13 - No. 12, 1/14, $3.99) Tom Garcia-a; multiple covers 4.00
...: The Road Below 1-4 (10/12 - No. 4, 1/13, $3.99) Haemi Jang-a; multiple covers 4.00

CLIVE BARKER'S NEXT TESTAMENT
BOOM! Studios: May, 2013 - No. 12, Aug, 2014 ($3.99)
1-12: 1-Clive Barker & Mark Miller-s/Haemi Jang-a. 1-Four covers 4.00

CLIVE BARKER'S NIGHTBREED (Also see Epic)
Marvel Comics (Epic Comics): Apr, 1990 - No. 25, Mar, 1993 ($1.95/$2.25/$2.50, mature)
1-25: 1-4-Adapt horror movie. 5-New stories; Guice-a(p) 3.00

CLIVE BARKER'S NIGHTBREED
BOOM! Studios: May, 2014 - No. 12, Apr, 2015 ($3.99)
1-12: 1-8-Andreyko-s/Kowalski-a. 9-11-Javier & Pramanik-a 4.00

CLIVE BARKER'S THE HARROWERS
Marvel Comics (Epic Comics): Dec, 1993 - No. 6, May, 1994 ($2.50)
1-($2.95)-Glow-in-the-dark-c; Colan-c/a in all 4.00
2-6 3.00
NOTE: ***Colan*** *a(p)-1-6; c-1-3, 4p, 5p.* ***Williamson*** *a(i)-2, 4, 5(part).*

CLOAK AND DAGGER
Ziff-Davis Publishing Co.: Fall, 1952
1-Saunders painted-c 37 74 111 222 361 500

CLOAK AND DAGGER (Also see Marvel Fanfare and Spectacular Spider-Man #64)
Marvel Comics Group: Oct, 1983 - No. 4, Jan, 1984 (Mini-series)
1-4-Austin-c/a(i) in all. 4-Origin 4.00

CLOAK AND DAGGER (2nd Series)(Also see Marvel Graphic Novel #34 & Strange Tales)
Marvel Comics Group: July, 1985 - No. 11, Jan, 1987
1-11: 7,8-Mignola-c. 9-Art Adams-p 3.00
...And Power Pack (1990, $7.95, 68 pgs.) 8.00

CLOAK AND DAGGER (3rd Series listed as Mutant Misadventures Of...)

CLOAK AND DAGGER
Marvel Comics: May, 2010 ($3.99, one-shot)
1-Stuart Moore-s/Mark Brooks-a; X-Men app. 4.00

CLOAKS
BOOM! Studios: Sept, 2014 - No. 4, Dec, 2014 ($3.99, limited series)
1-4-Monroe-s/Navarro-a 4.00

CLOBBERIN' TIME
Marvel Comics: Sept, 1995 ($1.95) (Based on card game)
nn-Overpower game guide; Ben Grimm story 3.00

CLOCK MAKER, THE
Image Comics: Jan, 2003 - No. 4, May, 2003 ($2.50, comic unfolds to 10"x13" pages)
1-4-Krueger-s 3.00
... Act Two (4/04, $4.95, standard format) Krueger-s/Matt Smith-c 5.00

CLOCKWORK ANGELS (Based on Neil Peart's story and lyrics from Rush's album)
BOOM! Studios: Mar, 2014 - No. 6, Nov, 2014 ($3.99, limited series)
1-6-Kevin J. Anderson-s/Nick Robles-a; two covers on each 4.00

CLONE CONSPIRACY, THE (Also see Amazing Spider-Man [2017] #18)
Marvel Comics: Dec, 2016 - Present ($4.99/$3.99)
1-($4.99) Slott-s/Cheung-a; Miles Warren, Gwen Stacy, Doc Ock & Rhino app. 5.00
2-5-($3.99) Kaine app. 3-Ben Reilly returns 4.00
...: Omega 1 (5/17, $4.99) Three short stories by various; aftermath of series 5.00

CLONEZONE SPECIAL
Dark Horse Comics/First Comics: 1989 ($2.00, B&W)
1-Back-up series from Badger & Nexus 3.00

CLOSE ENCOUNTERS (See Marvel Comics Super Special & Marvel Special Edition)

CLOSE SHAVES OF PAULINE PERIL, THE (TV cartoon)
Gold Key: June, 1970 - No. 4, March, 1971
1 4 8 12 23 37 50
2-4 3 6 9 16 23 30

CLOUDBURST
Image Comics: June, 2004 ($7.95, squarebound)
1-Gray & Palmiotti-s/Shy & Gouveia-a 8.00

CLOUDFALL
Image Comics: Nov, 2003 ($4.95, B&W, squarebound)
1-Kirkman-s/Su-a/c 5.00

CLOWN COMICS (No. 1 titled Clown Comic Book)
Clown Comics/Home Comics/Harvey Publ.: 1945 - No. 3, Win, 1946
nn (#1) 15 30 45 83 124 165
2,3 9 18 27 52 69 85

CLOWNS, THE (I Pagliacci)
Dark Horse Comics: 1998 ($2.95, B&W, one-shot)
1-Adaption of the opera; P. Craig Russell-script 3.00

CLUBHOUSE RASCALS (#1 titled ...Presents?) (Also see Three Rascals)
Sussex Publ. Co. (Magazine Enterprises): June, 1956 - No. 2, Oct, 1956
1-The Brain app. in both; DeCarlo-a 8 16 24 44 57 70
2 7 14 21 35 43 50

CLUB "16"
Famous Funnies: June, 1948 - No. 4, Dec, 1948
1-Teen-age humor 14 28 42 80 115 150
2-4 9 18 27 47 61 75

CLUE (Based on the boardgame)
IDW Publishing: Jun, 2017 - No. 6, Nov, 2017 ($3.99)
1-6-Paul Allor-s/Nelson Daniel-a; multiple covers on each 4.00

CLUE COMICS (Real Clue Crime V2#4 on)
Hillman Periodicals: Jan, 1943 - No. 15(V2#3), May, 1947
1-Origin The Boy King, Nightmare, Micro-Face, Twilight, & Zippo
184 368 552 1168 2009 2850
2 (scarce) 87 174 261 553 952 1350
3-5 (9/43) 47 94 141 296 498 700
6,8,9: 8-Palais-c/a(2) 36 72 108 211 343 475
7-Classic concentration camp torture-c (3/44) 84 168 252 538 919 1300
10-Origin/1st app. The Gun Master & begin series; content changes to crime
(10/46) 37 74 111 222 361 500
11 (12/46) 26 52 78 154 252 350
12-Origin Rackman; McWilliams-a, Guardineer-a(2) 36 72 108 211 343 475
V2#1-Nightmare new origin; Iron Lady app.; Simon & Kirby-a (3/47)
55 110 165 352 601 850
V2#2-S&K-a(2)-Bondage/torture-c; man attacks & kills people with electric iron. Infantino-a 81 162 243 518 884 1250
V2#3-S&K-a(3) 57 114 171 362 619 875

CLUELESS: SENIOR YEAR (Movie)
Boom Entertainment (BOOM Box): Aug, 2017 ($14.99, SC, graphic novel)
nn-Sarah Kuhn & Amber Benson-s/Siobhan Keenan-a; sequel to the movie; bonus art 15.00

CLUELESS SPRING SPECIAL (TV)
Marvel Comics: May, 1997 ($3.99, magazine sized, one-shot)
1-Photo-c from TV show 4.00

CLUSTER
BOOM! Studios: Feb, 2015 - No. 8, Oct, 2015 ($3.99, limited series)

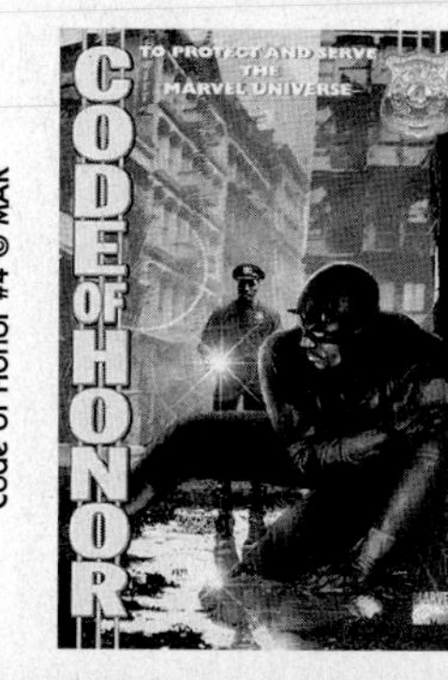

Code of Honor #4 © MAR

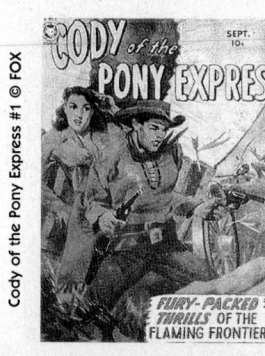

Cody of the Pony Express #1 © FOX

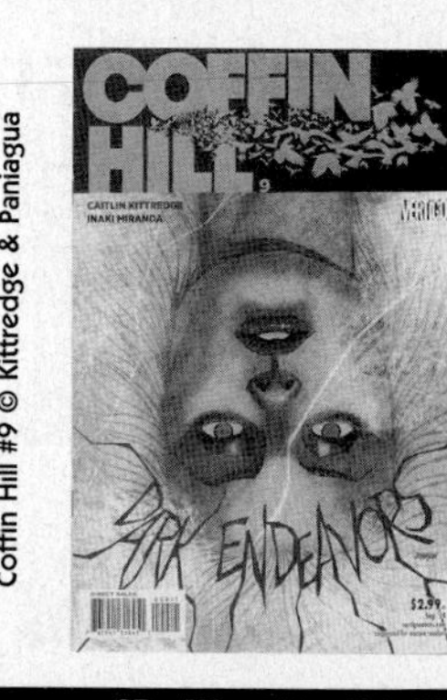

Coffin Hill #9 © Kittredge & Paniagua

	GD 2.0	VG 4.0	FN 6.0	VF 8.0	VF/NM 9.0	NM- 9.2
1-8-Ed Brisson-s/Damian Couceiro-a						4.00
CLUTCHING HAND, THE						
American Comics Group: July-Aug, 1954						
1-Gustavson, Moldoff-a	50	100	150	315	533	750
CLYDE BEATTY COMICS (Also see Crackajack Funnies)						
Commodore Productions & Artists, Inc.: October, 1953 (84 pgs.)						
1-Photo front/back-c; movie scenes and comics	22	44	66	132	216	300
CLYDE CRASHCUP (TV)						
Dell Publishing Co.: Aug-Oct, 1963 - No. 5, Sept-Nov, 1964						
1-All written by John Stanley	6	12	18	41	76	110
2-5	4	8	12	27	44	60
COBB						
IDW Publishing: May, 2006 - No. 3, July, 2007 ($3.99, B&W)						
1-3-Beau Smith-s/Eduardo Barreto-a/c; regular and retailer incentive covers						4.00
COBRA (G.I. Joe)						
IDW Publishing: No. 10, Feb, 2012 - No. 21, Jan, 2013 ($3.99)						
10-21						4.00
... Annual 2012: The Origin of Cobra Commander (1/12, $7.99) Dixon-s						8.00
CODENAME: ACTION						
Dynamite Entertainment: 2013 - No. 5, 2014 ($3.99, limited series)						
1-5-Captain Action; Chris Roberson-s/Jonathan Lau-a; multiple covers on each						4.00
CODE NAME: ASSASSIN (See 1st Issue Special)						
CODENAME: BABOUSHKA						
Image Comics: Oct, 2015 - Present ($3.99)						
1-5: 1-Antony Johnston-s/Shari Chankhamma-a						4.00
CODENAME: DANGER						
Lodestone Publishing: Aug, 1985 - No. 4, May, 1986 ($1.50)						
1-4						3.00
CODENAME: FIREARM (Also see Firearm)						
Malibu Comics (Ultraverse): June, 1995 - No. 5, Sept, 1995 ($2.95, bimonthly limited series)						
0-5: 0-2-Alec Swan back-up story by James Robinson. 0-Pérez-c						3.00
CODENAME: GENETIX						
Marvel Comics UK: Jan, 1993 - No. 4, May, 1993 ($1.75, limited series)						
1-4: Wolverine in all						3.00
CODENAME: KNOCKOUT						
DC Comics (Vertigo): No. 0, Jun, 2001 - No. 23, June, 2003 ($2.50/$2.75)						
0-15: Rodi-s in all. 0-5-Small Jr. -a. 1-Two covers by Chiodo & Cho. 7,8,10,11,12-Paquette-a. 6,9,13,14-Conner-a						3.00
16-23: 16-Begin $2.75-c. 23-Last issue; JG Jones-c						3.00
CODENAME SPITFIRE (Formerly Spitfire And The Troubleshooters)						
Marvel Comics Group: No. 10, July, 1987 - No. 13, Oct, 1987						
10-13: 10-Rogers-c/a (low printing)						3.50
CODENAME: STRYKE FORCE (Also See Cyberforce V1#4 & Cyberforce/Stryke Force: Opposing Forces						
Image Comics (Top Cow Productions): Jan, 1994 - No. 14, Sept, 1995 ($1.95-$2.25)						
0,1-14: 1-12-Silvestri stories, Peterson-a. 4-Stormwatch app. 14-Story continues in Cyberforce/Stryke Force: Opposing Forces; Turner-a						3.00
1-Gold, 1-Blue						4.00
CODE OF HONOR						
Marvel Comics: Feb, 1997 - No. 4, May, 1997 ($5.95, limited series)						
1-4-Fully painted by various; Dixon-s						6.00
CODY OF THE PONY EXPRESS (See Colossal Features Magazine)						
Fox Feature Syndicate: Sept, 1950 (See Women Outlaws)(One shot)						
1-Painted-c	15	30	45	86	133	180
CODY OF THE PONY EXPRESS (Buffalo Bill...) (Outlaws of the West #11 on; Formerly Bullseye)						
Charlton Comics: No. 8, Oct, 1955; No. 9, Jan, 1956; No. 10, June, 1956						
8-Bullseye on splash pg; not S&K-a	8	16	24	44	57	70
9,10: Buffalo Bill app. in all	6	12	18	29	36	42
CODY STARBUCK (1st app. in Star Reach #1)						
Star Reach Productions: July, 1978						
nn-Howard Chaykin-c/a	3	6	9	14	20	25
2nd printing	2	4	6	8	10	12

	GD 2.0	VG 4.0	FN 6.0	VF 8.0	VF/NM 9.0	NM- 9.2
NOTE: *Both printings say First Printing. True first printing is on lower-grade paper, somewhat off-register, and snow in snow sequence has green tint.*						
CO-ED ROMANCES						
P. L. Publishing Co.: November, 1951						
1	12	24	36	69	97	125
COFFEE WORLD						
World Comics: Oct, 1995 ($1.50, B&W, anthology)						
1-Shannon Wheeler's Too Much Coffee Man story						3.00
COFFIN, THE						
Oni Press: Sept, 2000 - No. 4, May, 2001 ($2.95, B&W, limited series)						
1-4-Hester-s/Huddleston-a						3.00
COFFIN HILL						
DC Comics (Vertigo): Dec, 2013 - No. 20, Sept, 2015 ($2.99/$3.99)						
1-18: 1-Caitlin Kittredge-s/Inaki Miranda-a; covers by Dave Johnson & Gene Ha						3.00
19,20-($3.99) Johnson-c						4.00
COLDER						
Dark Horse Comics: Nov, 2012 - No. 5, Mar, 2013 ($3.99, limited series)						
1-5-Tobin-s/Ferreyra-a/c						4.00
COLDER: THE BAD SEED						
Dark Horse Comics: Oct, 2014 - No. 5, Feb, 2015 ($3.99, limited series)						
1-5-Tobin-s/Ferreyra-a/c						4.00
COLDER: TOSS THE BONES						
Dark Horse Comics: Sept, 2015 - No. 5, Jan, 2016 ($3.99, limited series)						
1-5-Tobin-s/Ferreyra-a/c						4.00
COLD WAR						
IDW Publishing: Oct, 2011 - No. 4, Jan, 2012 ($3.99, limited series)						
1-4-John Byrne-s/a/c; two covers on each						4.00
COLD WAR						
AfterShock Comics: Feb, 2018 - Present ($3.99)						
1-Sebela-a/Sherman-a						4.00
COLLIDER (See FBP: Federal Bureau Of Physics; title changed after issue #1)						
COLLECTORS DRACULA, THE						
Millennium Publications: 1994 - No. 2, 1994 ($3.95, color/B&W, 52 pgs., limited series)						
1,2-Bolton-a (7 pgs.)						4.00
COLLECTORS ITEM CLASSICS (See Marvel Collectors Item Classics)						
COLONIZED, THE						
IDW Publishing: Apr, 2013 - No. 4, Jul, 2013 ($3.99, limited series)						
1-4-Aliens vs. Zombies; Dave Sim-c/Chris Ryall-s/Drew Moss-a						4.00
COLORS IN BLACK						
Dark Horse Comics: Mar, 1995 - No. 4, June, 1995 ($2.95, limited series)						
1-4						3.00
COLOSSAL FEATURES MAGAZINE (Formerly I Loved) (See Cody of the Pony Express)						
Fox Feature Syndicate: No. 33, 5/50 - No. 34, 7/50; No. 3, 9/50 (Based on Columbia serial)						
33,34: Cody of the Pony Express begins. 33-Painted-c. 34-Photo-c	15	30	45	84	127	170
3-Authentic criminal cases	15	30	45	84	127	170
COLOSSAL SHOW, THE (TV cartoon)						
Gold Key: Oct, 1969						
1	5	10	15	30	50	70
COLOSSUS (See X-Men)						
Marvel Comics: Oct, 1997 ($2.99, 48 pgs., one-shot)						
1-Raab-s/Hitch & Neary-a, wraparound-c						4.00
COLOSSUS COMICS (See Green Giant & Motion Picture Funnies Weekly)						
Sun Publications (Funnies, Inc.?): March, 1940						
1-(Scarce)-Tulpa of Tsang(hero); Colossus app.	1000	2000	3000	7600	13,800	20,000
NOTE: *Cover by artist that drew Colossus in Green Giant Comics.*						
COLOUR OF MAGIC, THE (Terry Pratchett's...)						
Innovation Publishing: 1991 - No. 4, 1991 ($2.50, limited series)						
1-4: Adapts 1st novel of the Discworld series						3.00
COLT .45 (TV)						
Dell Publishing Co.: No. 924, 8/58 - No. 1058, 11-1/59-60; No. 4, 2-4/60 - No. 9, 5-7/61						
Four Color 924(#1)-Wayde Preston photo-c on all	9	18	27	62	126	190

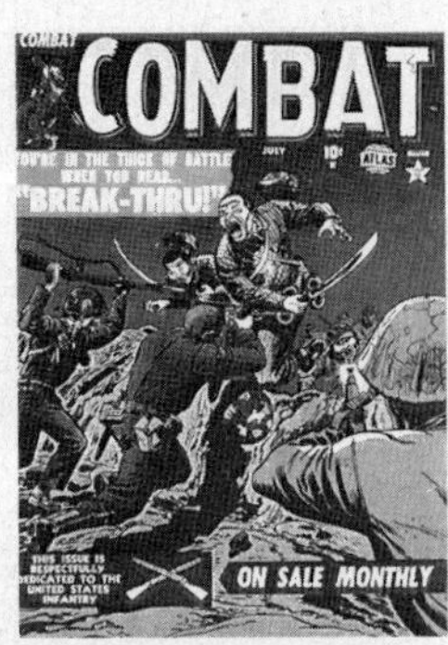

Combat #2 © MAR

Combat Kelly #2 © MAR

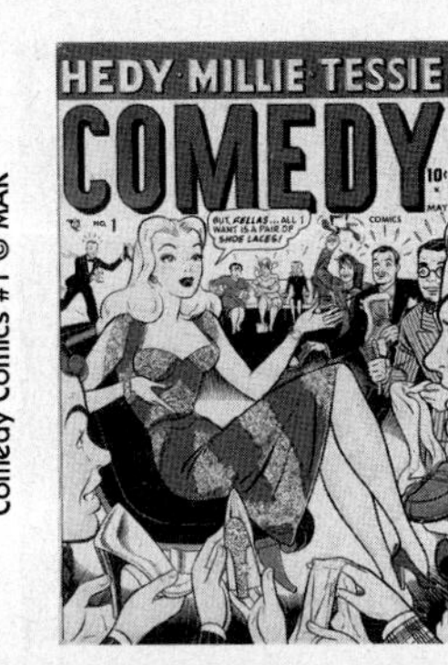

Comedy Comics #1 © MAR

	GD 2.0	VG 4.0	FN 6.0	VF 8.0	VF/NM 9.0	NM- 9.2
Four Color 1004,1058: 1004-Photo-b/c	7	14	21	48	89	130
4,5,7-9	7	14	21	48	89	130
6-Toth-a	8	16	24	51	96	140

COLUMBIA COMICS
William H. Wise Co.: 1943

	GD 2.0	VG 4.0	FN 6.0	VF 8.0	VF/NM 9.0	NM- 9.2
1-Joe Palooka, Charlie Chan, Capt. Yank, Sparky Watts, Dixie Dugan app.	32	64	96	188	307	425

COMANCHE
Dell Publishing Co.: No. 1350, Apr-Jun, 1962

	GD 2.0	VG 4.0	FN 6.0	VF 8.0	VF/NM 9.0	NM- 9.2
Four Color 1350-Disney movie; reprints FC #966 with title change from "Tonka" to "Comanche"; Sal Mineo photo-c	5	10	15	33	57	80

COMANCHEROS, THE
Dell Publishing Co.: No. 1300, Mar-May, 1962

	GD 2.0	VG 4.0	FN 6.0	VF 8.0	VF/NM 9.0	NM- 9.2
Four Color 1300-Movie, John Wayne photo-c	14	28	42	94	207	320

COMBAT
Atlas Comics (ANC): June, 1952 - No. 11, April, 1953

	GD 2.0	VG 4.0	FN 6.0	VF 8.0	VF/NM 9.0	NM- 9.2
1	43	86	129	271	461	650
2-Heath-c/a	24	48	72	142	234	325
3,5-9,11: 3-Romita-a. 6-Robinson-c; Romita-a	18	36	54	105	165	225
4-Krigstein-a	18	36	54	103	162	220
10-B&W and color illos. in **POP**; Sale-a, Forte-a	18	36	54	107	169	230

NOTE: *Combat Casey in 7-11.* ***Heath*** *a-2, 3; c-1, 2, 5, 9.* ***Maneely*** *a-1; c-3, 10.* ***Pakula*** *a-1.* ***Reinman*** *a-1.*

COMBAT
Dell Publishing Co.: Oct-Nov, 1961 - No. 40, Oct, 1973 (No #9)

	GD 2.0	VG 4.0	FN 6.0	VF 8.0	VF/NM 9.0	NM- 9.2
1-Painted-c (thru #17)	7	14	21	44	82	120
2,3,5	4	8	12	27	44	60
4-John F. Kennedy c/story (P.T. 109)	5	10	15	33	57	80
6,7,8(4-6/63), 8(7-9/63)	4	8	12	25	40	55
10-26: 26-Last 12¢ issue	3	6	9	21	33	45
27-40(reprints #1-14). 30-r/#4	3	6	9	14	19	24

COMBAT CASEY (Formerly War Combat)
Atlas Comics (SAI): No. 6, Jan, 1953 - No. 34, July, 1957

	GD 2.0	VG 4.0	FN 6.0	VF 8.0	VF/NM 9.0	NM- 9.2
6 (Indicia shows 1/52 in error)	31	62	93	186	303	420
7-R.Q. Sale-a	18	36	54	107	169	230
8-Used in **POP**, pg. 94	17	34	51	100	158	215
9,10,13-19-Violent art by R.Q. Sale; Battle Brady x-over #10	20	40	60	117	189	260
11,12,20-Last Precode (2/55)	15	30	45	86	133	180
21-34: 22,25-R.Q. Sale-a	15	30	45	84	127	170

NOTE: ***Everett*** *a-6.* ***Heath*** *c-10, 17, 19, 23, 30.* ***Maneely*** *c-6, 8, 15.* ***Powell*** *a-29(5), 30(5), 34.* ***Severin*** *c-26, 33, 34.*

COMBAT KELLY
Atlas Comics (SPI): Nov, 1951 - No. 44, Aug, 1957

	GD 2.0	VG 4.0	FN 6.0	VF 8.0	VF/NM 9.0	NM- 9.2
1-1st app. Combat Kelly; Heath-a	43	86	129	271	461	650
2	24	48	72	140	230	320
3-10	19	38	57	109	172	235
11-Used in **POP**, pgs. 94,95 plus color illo.	19	38	57	109	172	235
12-Color illo. in **POP**	17	34	51	100	158	215
13-16	15	30	45	90	140	190
17-Violent art by R. Q. Sale; Combat Casey app.	20	40	60	114	182	250
18-20,22-28: 18-Battle Brady app. 28-Last precode (1/55)	15	30	45	86	133	180
21-Transvestism-c	17	34	51	98	154	210
29-44: 38-Green Berets story (8/56)	15	30	45	83	124	165

NOTE: ***Berg*** *a-8, 12-14, 15-17, 19-23, 25, 26, 28, 31-37, 39, 41-44; c-2.* ***Colan*** *a-42.* ***Heath*** *a-4, 18; c-31.* ***Lawrence*** *a-23.* ***Maneely*** *a-3-5(2), 6, 7(3), 8, 9(2), 11; c-4, 5, 7, 8, 10, 11, 25, 29, 39.* ***R.Q. Sale*** *a-17, 25.* ***Severin*** *c-41, 42.* ***Whitney*** *a-5.*

COMBAT KELLY (...and the Deadly Dozen)
Marvel Comics Group: June, 1972 - No. 9, Oct, 1973

	GD 2.0	VG 4.0	FN 6.0	VF 8.0	VF/NM 9.0	NM- 9.2
1-Intro & origin new Combat Kelly; Ayers/Mooney-a; Severin-c (20¢)	3	6	9	21	33	45
2,5-8	2	4	6	13	18	22
3,4: 3-Origin. 4-Sgt. Fury-c/s	3	6	9	15	22	28
9-Death of the Deadly Dozen	3	6	9	17	26	35

COMBAT ZONE: TRUE TALES OF GIS IN IRAQ
Marvel Comics: 2005 ($19.99, squarebound)

	GD 2.0	VG 4.0	FN 6.0	VF 8.0	VF/NM 9.0	NM- 9.2
Vol. 1-Karl Zinsmeister scripts adapted from his non-fiction books; Dan Jurgens-a						20.00

COMBINED OPERATIONS (See The Story of the Commandos)

COMEBACK (See Zane Grey 4-Color 357)

COMEDY CARNIVAL
St. John Publishing Co.: no date (1950's) (100 pgs.)

	GD 2.0	VG 4.0	FN 6.0	VF 8.0	VF/NM 9.0	NM- 9.2
nn-Contains rebound St. John comics	39	78	117	231	378	525

COMEDY COMICS (1st Series) (Daring Mystery #1-8) (Becomes Margie Comics #35 on)
Timely Comics (TCI 9,10): No. 9, April, 1942 - No. 34, Fall, 1946

	GD 2.0	VG 4.0	FN 6.0	VF 8.0	VF/NM 9.0	NM- 9.2
9-(Scarce)-The Fin by Everett, Capt. Dash, Citizen V, & The Silver Scorpion app.; Wolverton-a; 1st app. Comedy Kid; satire on Hitler & Stalin; The Fin, Citizen V & Silver Scorpion cont. from Daring Mystery	300	600	900	2070	3635	5200
10-(Scarce)-Origin The Fourth Musketeer, Victory Boys; Monstro, the Mighty app.	232	464	696	1485	2543	3600
11-Vagabond, Stuporman app.	68	136	204	435	743	1050
12,13	32	64	96	188	307	425
14-Origin/1st app. Super Rabbit (3/43) plus-c	87	174	261	553	952	1350
15-19	28	56	84	165	270	375
20-Hitler parody-c	68	136	204	435	743	1050
21-Tojo-c	53	106	159	334	567	800
22-Hitler parody-c	94	188	282	597	1024	1450
23-32	20	40	60	117	189	260
33-Kurtzman-a (5 pgs.)	21	42	63	122	199	275
34-Intro Margie; Wolverton-a (5 pgs.)	39	78	117	231	378	525

COMEDY COMICS (2nd Series)
Marvel Comics (ACI): May, 1948 - No. 10, Jan, 1950

	GD 2.0	VG 4.0	FN 6.0	VF 8.0	VF/NM 9.0	NM- 9.2
1-Hedy, Tessie, Millie begin; Kurtzman's "Hey Look" (he draws himself)	65	130	195	416	708	1000
2	30	60	90	177	289	400
3,4-Kurtzman's "Hey Look": 3-(1 pg). 4-(3 pgs)	58	116	174	371	636	900
5-10	22	44	66	132	216	300

COMET, THE (See The Mighty Crusaders & Pep Comics #1)
Red Circle Comics (Archie): Oct, 1983 - No. 2, Dec, 1983

	GD 2.0	VG 4.0	FN 6.0	VF 8.0	VF/NM 9.0	NM- 9.2
1-Re-intro & origin The Comet; The American Shield begins. Nino & Infantino art in both. Hangman in both						6.00
2-Origin continues.						5.00

COMET, THE
DC Comics (Impact Comics): July, 1991 - No. 18, Dec, 1992 ($1.00/$1.25)

	GD 2.0	VG 4.0	FN 6.0	VF 8.0	VF/NM 9.0	NM- 9.2
1						4.00
2-18: 4-Black Hood app. 6-Re-intro Hangman. 8-Web x-over. 10-Contains Crusaders trading card. 4-Origin. Netzer (Nasser) c(p)-11,14-17						3.00
Annual 1 (1992, $2.50, 68 pgs.)-Contains Impact trading card; Shield back-up story						4.00

COMET MAN, THE (Movie)
Marvel Comics Group: Feb, 1987 - No. 6, July, 1987 (limited series)

	GD 2.0	VG 4.0	FN 6.0	VF 8.0	VF/NM 9.0	NM- 9.2
1-6: 3-Hulk app. 4-She-Hulk shower scene-c/s. Fantastic 4 app. 5-Fantastic 4 app.						3.00

NOTE: ***Kelley Jones*** *a-1-6p.*

COMIC ALBUM (Also see Disney Comic Album)
Dell Publishing Co.: Mar-May, 1958 - No. 18, June-Aug, 1962

	GD 2.0	VG 4.0	FN 6.0	VF 8.0	VF/NM 9.0	NM- 9.2
1-Donald Duck	8	16	24	54	102	150
2-Bugs Bunny	5	10	15	31	53	75
3-Donald Duck	6	12	18	41	76	110
4-6,8-10: 4-Tom & Jerry. 5-Woody Woodpecker. 6,10-Bugs Bunny. 8-Tom & Jerry. 9-Woody Woodpecker	4	8	12	27	44	60
7,11,15: Popeye. 11-(9-11/60)	4	8	12	28	47	65
12-14: 12-Tom & Jerry. 13-Woody Woodpecker. 14-Bugs Bunny	4	8	12	27	44	60
16-Flintstones (12-2/61-62)-3rd app. Early Cave Kids app.	7	14	21	46	86	125
17-Space Mouse (3rd app.)	5	10	15	30	50	70
18-Three Stooges; photo-c	7	14	21	46	86	125

COMIC BOOK
Marvel Comics-#1/Dark Horse Comics-#2: 1995 ($5.95, oversize)

	GD 2.0	VG 4.0	FN 6.0	VF 8.0	VF/NM 9.0	NM- 9.2
1-Spumco characters by John K.	1	2	3	4	5	7
2-(Dark Horse)						6.00

COMIC BOOK GUY: THE COMIC BOOK (BONGO COMICS PRESENTS...) (Simpsons)
Bongo Comics: 2010 - No. 5, 2010 ($3.99/$2.99, limited series)

	GD 2.0	VG 4.0	FN 6.0	VF 8.0	VF/NM 9.0	NM- 9.2
1-($3.99) Four-layer cover w/classic swipes incl. FF#1; intro Graphic Novel Kid	2	4	6	11	16	20
2-5-($2.99) 2-Stan Lee cameo. 3-Includes Little Lulu spoof. 4-Comic Book Guy origin						6.00

COMIC CAPERS
Red Circle Mag./Marvel Comics: Fall, 1944 - No. 6, Fall, 1946

	GD 2.0	VG 4.0	FN 6.0	VF 8.0	VF/NM 9.0	NM- 9.2
1-Super Rabbit, The Creeper, Silly Seal, Ziggy Pig, Sharpy Fox begin	41	82	123	256	428	600

Comic Cavalcade #8 © DC

The Comics #8 © DELL

Comics on Parade #21 © UFS

	GD 2.0	VG 4.0	FN 6.0	VF 8.0	VF/NM 9.0	NM- 9.2

2 22 44 66 130 213 295
3-6: 4-(Summer 1945) 21 42 63 122 199 275

COMIC CAVALCADE
All-American/National Periodical Publications: Winter, 1942-43 - No. 63, June-July, 1954 (Contents change with No. 30, Dec-Jan, 1948-49 on)

1-The Flash, Green Lantern, Wonder Woman, Wildcat, The Black Pirate by Moldoff (also #2), Ghost Patrol, and Red White & Blue begin; Scribbly app.; Minute Movie
975 1950 2925 7100 12,550 18,000
2-Mutt & Jeff begin; last Ghost Patrol & Black Pirate; Minute Movies
277 554 831 1760 3030 4300
3-Hop Harrigan & Sargon, the Sorcerer begin; The King app.
181 362 543 1158 1979 2800
4,5: 4-The Gay Ghost, The King, Scribbly, & Red Tornado app. 5-Christmas-c. 5-Prints ad for Jr. JSA membership kit that includes "The Minute Man Answers The Call"
174 348 522 1114 1907 2700
6-10: 7-Red Tornado & Black Pirate app.; last Scribbly. 9-Fat & Slat app.; X-Mas-c
148 296 444 947 1624 2300
11-Wonder Woman vs. The Cheetah 119 238 357 762 1306 1850
12,14: 12-Last Red White & Blue 110 220 330 704 1202 1700
13-Solomon Grundy app.; X-Mas-c 213 426 639 1363 2332 3300
15-Just a Story begins 111 222 333 705 1215 1725
16-20: 19-Christmas-c 103 206 309 659 1130 1600
21-23: 22-Johnny Peril begins. 23-Harry Lampert-c (Toth swipes)
94 188 282 597 1024 1450
24-Solomon Grundy x-over in Green Lantern 123 246 369 787 1344 1900
25-28: 25-Black Canary app.; X-Mas-c. 26-28-Johnny Peril app. 28-Last Mutt & Jeff
87 174 261 553 952 1350
29-(10-11/48)-Last Flash, Wonder Woman, Green Lantern & Johnny Peril; Wonder Woman invents "Thinking Machine"; 2nd computer in comics (after Flash Comics #52); Leave It to Binky story (early app.) 116 232 348 742 1271 1800
30-(12-1/48-49)-The Fox & the Crow, Dodo & the Frog & Nutsy Squirrel begin
42 84 126 265 445 625
31-35 23 46 69 136 223 310
36-49: 41-Last squarebound issue 17 34 51 100 158 215
50-62(Scarce) 21 42 63 122 199 275
63(Rare) 34 68 102 204 332 460

NOTE: ***Grossman** a-30-63. **E.E. Hibbard** c-(Flash only)-1-4, 7-14, 16-19, 21. **Sheldon Mayer** a(2-3)-40-63. **Moulson** c(G.L.)-7, 15. **Nodell** c(G.L.)-9. **H.G. Peter** c(W. Woman only)-1, 3-21, 24. **Post** a-31, 36. **Purcell** c(G.L.)-2-5, 10. **Reinman** a(Green Lantern)-4-6, 8, 9, 13, 15-21; c(Gr. Lantern)-6, 8, 19. **Toth** a(Green Lantern)-26-28; c-27. Atom app.-22, 23.*

COMIC COMICS
Fawcett Publications: Apr, 1946 - No. 10, Feb, 1947

1-Captain Kid; Nutty Comics #1 in indicia 15 30 45 86 133 180
2-10-Wolverton-a, 4 pgs. each. 5-Captain Kidd app. Mystic Moot by Wolverton in #2-10? 15 30 45 85 130 175

COMIC LAND
Fact and Fiction Publ.: March, 1946

1-Sandusky & the Senator, Sam Stupor, Sleuth, Marvin the Great, Sir Passer, Phineas Gruff app.; Irv Tirman & Perry Williams art 15 30 45 85 130 175

COMICO CHRISTMAS SPECIAL
Comico: Dec, 1988 ($2.50, 44 pgs.)

1-Rude/Williamson-a; Dave Stevens-c 5.00

COMICO COLLECTION (Also see Grendel)
Comico: 1987 ($9.95, slipcased collection)

nn-Contains exclusive Grendel: Devil's Vagary, 9 random Comico comics, a poster and newsletter in black slipcase w/silver ink 25.00

COMICO PRIMER (See Primer)

COMIC PAGES (Formerly Funny Picture Stories)
Centaur Publications: V3#4, July, 1939 - V3#6, Dec, 1939

V3#4-Bob Wood-a 103 206 309 659 1130 1600
5,6: 6-Schwab-c 90 180 270 576 988 1400

COMICS (See All Good)

COMICS, THE
Dell Publ. Co.: Mar, 1937 - No. 11, Nov, 1938 (Newspaper strip-r; bi-monthly)

1-1st app. Tom Mix in comics; Wash Tubbs, Tom Beatty, Myra North, Arizona Kid, Erik Noble & International Spy w/Doctor Doom begin
187 374 561 1197 2049 2900
2 87 174 261 553 952 1350
3-11: 3-Alley Oop begins 71 142 213 454 777 1100

	GD 2.0	VG 4.0	FN 6.0	VF 8.0	VF/NM 9.0	NM- 9.2

COMICS AND STORIES (See Walt Disney's Comics and Stories)

COMICS & STORIES (Also see Wolf & Red)
Dark Horse Comics: Apr, 1996 - No. 4, July, 1996 ($2.95, lim. series) (Created by Tex Avery)

1-4: Wolf & Red app; reads Comics and Stories on-c. 1-Terry Moore-a. 2-Reed Waller-a 3.00

COMICS CALENDAR, THE (The 1946...)
True Comics Press (ordered through the mail): 1946 (25¢, 116 pgs.) (Stapled at top)

nn-(Rare) Has a "strip" story for every day of the year in color
40 80 120 246 411 575

COMICS DIGEST (Pocket size)
Parents' Magazine Institute: Winter, 1942-43 (B&W, 100 pgs)

1-Reprints from True Comics (non-fiction World War II stories)
10 20 30 56 76 95

COMICS EXPRESS
Eclipse Comics: Nov, 1989 - No. 2, Jan, 1990 ($2.95, B&W, 68pgs.)

1,2: Collection of strip-r; 2(12/89-c, 1/90 inside) 4.00

COMICS FOR KIDS
London Publ. Co./Timely: 1945 (no month); No. 2, Sum, 1945 (Funny animal)

1-Puffy Pig, Sharpy Fox 36 72 108 211 343 475
2-Puffy Pig, Sharpy Fox 24 48 72 142 234 325

COMICS' GREATEST WORLD
Dark Horse Comics: Jun, 1993 - V4#4, Sept, 1993 ($1.00, weekly, lim. series)

Arcadia (Wk 1): V1#1,2,4: 1-X: Frank Miller-c. 2-Pit Bulls. 4-Monster. 3.00
1-B&W Press Proof Edition (1500 copies) 1 3 4 6 8 10
1-Silver-c; distr. retailer bonus w/print & cards 1 2 3 5 6 8
3-Ghost, Dorman-c; Hughes-a 4.00
Retailer's Prem. Emb. Silver Foil Logo-r/V1#1-4 1 3 4 6 8 10
Golden City (Wk 2: V2#1-4: 1-Rebel; Ordway-c. 2-Mecha; Dave Johnson-c.
3-Titan; Walt Simonson-c. 4-Catalyst; Perez-c. 3.00
1-Gold-c; distr. retailer bonus w/print & cards. 6.00
Retailer's Prem. Embos. Gold Foil Logo-r/V2#1-4 1 2 3 5 6 8
Steel Harbor (Week 3): V3#1-Barb Wire; Dorman-c; Gulacy-a(p) 4.00
2-4: 2-The Machine. 3-Wolfgang. 4-Motorhead 3.00
1-Silver-c; distr. retailer bonus w/print & cards 1 2 3 5 6 8
Retailer's Prem. Emb. Red Foil Logo-r/V3#1-4. 1 3 4 6 8 10
Vortex (Week 4): V4#1-4: 1-Division 13; Dorman-c. 2-Hero Zero; Art Adams-c.
3-King Tiger; Chadwick-a(p); Darrow-c. 4-Vortex; Miller-c. 3.00
1-Gold-c; distr. retailer bonus w/print & cards. 6.00
Retailer's Prem. Emb. Blue Foil Logo-r/V4#1-4. 1 2 3 5 6 8

COMICS' GREATEST WORLD: OUT OF THE VORTEX (See Out of The Vortex)

COMICS HITS (See Harvey Comics Hits)

COMICS MAGAZINE, THE (...Funny Pages #3)(Funny Pages #6 on)
Comics Magazine Co. (1st Comics Mag./Centaur Publ.): May, 1936 - No. 5, Sept, 1936 (Paper covers)

1-1st app. Dr. Mystic (a.k.a. Dr. Occult) by Siegel & Shuster (the 1st app. of a Superman prototype in comics). Dr. Mystic is not in costume but later appears in costume as a more pronounced prototype in More Fun #14-17. (1st episode of "The Koth and the Seven"; continues in More Fun #14; originally scheduled for publication at DC). 1 pg. Kelly-a; Sheldon Mayer-a 3800 7600 11,400 23,000 - -
2-Federal Agent (a.k.a. Federal Men) by Siegel & Shuster; 1 pg. Kelly-a
420 840 1260 2520 3360 4200
3-5 360 720 1080 2160 2880 3600

COMICS NOVEL (Anarcho, Dictator of Death)
Fawcett Publications: 1947

1-All Radar; 51 pg anti-fascism story 39 78 117 231 378 525

COMICS ON PARADE (No. 30 on are a continuation of Single Series)
United Features Syndicate: Apr, 1938 - No. 104, Feb, 1955

1-Tarzan by Foster; Captain & the Kids, Little Mary Mixup, Abbie & Slats, Ella Cinders, Broncho Bill, Li'l Abner begin 394 788 1182 2758 4829 6900
2 (Tarzan & others app. on-c of #1-3,17) 142 284 426 909 1555 2200
3 113 226 339 718 1234 1750
4,5 81 162 243 518 884 1250
6-10 55 110 165 352 601 850
11-16,18-20 42 84 126 267 451 635
17-Tarzan-c 55 110 165 352 601 850
21-29: 22-Son of Tarzan begins. 22,24,28-Tailspin Tommy-c. 29-Last Tarzan issue
36 72 108 216 351 485
30-Li'l Abner 20 40 60 114 182 250
31-The Captain & the Kids 15 30 45 85 130 175

Comics on Parade #57 © UFS

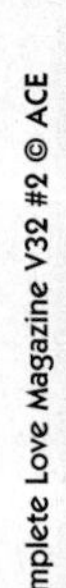
Complete Love Magazine V32 #2 © ACE

Conan #1 © CPI

	GD 2.0	VG 4.0	FN 6.0	VF 8.0	VF/NM 9.0	NM- 9.2
32-Nancy & Fritzi Ritz	14	28	42	78	112	145
33,36,39,42-Li'l Abner	16	32	48	94	147	200
34,37,40-The Captain & the Kids (10/41,6/42,3/43)	15	30	45	83	124	165
35,38-Nancy & Fritzi Ritz. 38-Infinity-c	14	28	42	76	108	140
41-Nancy & Fritzi Ritz	12	24	36	67	94	120
43-The Captain & the Kids	15	30	45	83	124	165
44 (3/44),47,50: Nancy & Fritzi Ritz	12	24	36	67	94	120
45-Li'l Abner	15	30	45	84	127	170
46,49-The Captain & the Kids	13	26	39	74	105	135
48-Li'l Abner (3/45)	15	30	45	84	127	170
51,54-Li'l Abner	14	28	42	76	108	140
52-The Captain & the Kids (3/46)	12	24	36	69	97	125
53,55,57-Nancy & Fritzi Ritz	11	22	33	62	86	110
56-The Captain & the Kids (r/Sparkler)	11	22	33	62	86	110
58-Li'l Abner; continues as Li'l Abner #61?	14	28	42	76	108	140
59-The Captain & the Kids	10	20	30	54	72	90
60-70-Nancy & Fritzi Ritz	9	18	27	47	61	75
71-99,101-104-Nancy & Sluggo: 71-76-Nancy only	8	16	24	42	54	65
100-Nancy & Sluggo	14	28	42	76	108	140
Special Issue, 7/46; Summer, 1948 - The Captain & the Kids app.	14	28	42	76	108	140

NOTE: Bound Volume (Very Rare) includes No. 1-12; bound by publisher in pictorial comic boards & distributed at the 1939 World's Fair and through mail order from ads in comic books (also see Tip Top)

	300	600	900	2010	3505	5000

NOTE: *Li'l Abner reprinted from Tip Top.*

COMICS READING LIBRARIES (See the Promotional Comics section)

COMICS REVUE
St. John Publ. Co. (United Features Synd.): June, 1947 - No. 5, Jan, 1948

1-Ella Cinders & Blackie	14	28	42	81	118	155
2,4: 2-Hap Hopper (7/47). 4-Ella Cinders (9/47)	9	18	27	50	65	80
3,5: 3-Iron Vic (8/47). 5-Gordo No. 1 (1/48)	9	18	27	47	61	75

COMIC STORY PAINT BOOK
Samuel Lowe Co.: 1943 (Large size, 68 pgs.)

1055-Captain Marvel & a Captain Marvel Jr. story to read & color; 3 panels in color per pg. (reprints)	82	164	246	528	902	1275

COMING OF RAGE
Liquid Comics: 2015 - No. 5, 2016 ($3.99, limited series)

1-5-Wes Craven & Steve Niles-s/Francesco Biagini-a. 1-Afterword by Wes Craven 4.00

COMIX BOOK
Marvel Comics Group/Krupp Comics Works No. 4,5: 1974 - No. 5, 1976 ($1.00, B&W, magazine) (#1-3 newsstand; #4,5 were direct distribution only)

1-Underground comic artists; 2 pgs. Wolverton-a	3	6	9	15	22	28
2,3: 2-Wolverton-a (1 pg.)	3	6	9	14	19	24
4(2/76), 4(5/76), 5 (Low distribution)	3	6	9	16	23	30

NOTE: *Print run No. 1-3: 200,000-250,000; No. 4&5: 10,000 each.*

COMIX INTERNATIONAL
Warren Magazines: Jul, 1974 - No. 5, Spring, 1977 (Full color, stiff-c, mail only)

1-Low distribution; all Corben story remainders from Warren; Corben-c on all	9	18	27	62	126	190
2,4: 2-Two Dracula stories; Wood, Wrightson-r; Crandall-a; Maroto-a. 4-Printing w/ 3 Corben sty	6	12	18	37	66	95
3-5: 3-Dax story. 4-(printing without Corben story). 4-Crandall-a. 4,5-Vampirella stories. 5-Spirit story; Eisner-a	5	10	15	33	57	80

NOTE: *No. 4 had two printings with extra **Corben** story in one. No. 3 may also have a variation. No. 3 has two Jeff Jones reprints from Vampirella.*

COMMANDER BATTLE AND THE ATOMIC SUB
Amer. Comics Group (Titan Publ. Co.): Jul-Aug, 1954 - No. 7, Aug-Sep, 1955

1 (3-D effect)-Moldoff flying saucer-c	61	122	183	390	670	950
2,4-7: 2-Moldoff-c. 4-(1-2/55)-Last pre-code; Landau-a. 5-3-D effect story (2 pgs.). 6,7-Landau-a. 7-Flying saucer-c	39	78	117	231	378	525
3-H-Bomb-c; Atomic Sub becomes Atomic Spaceship	39	78	117	236	388	540

COMMANDO ADVENTURES
Atlas Comics (MMC): June, 1957 - No. 2, Aug, 1957

1-Severin-c	17	34	51	98	154	210
2-Severin-c; Reinman & Romita-a; Drucker-a?	12	24	36	69	97	125

COMMANDOS
DC Comics: Oct. 1942

1-Ashcan comic, not distributed to newsstands, only for in-house use. Cover art is Boy Commandos #1 with interior being a Boy Commandos story from an unidentified issue of Detective Comics (a VF copy sold for $2629 in 2018)

COMMANDO YANK (See The Mighty Midget Comics & Wow Comics)

COMMON GROUNDS
Image Comics (Top Cow): Feb, 2004 - No. 6, July, 2004 ($2.99)

1-6: 1-Two covers; art by Jurgens and Oeming. 3-Bachalo, Jurgens-a. 4-Peréz-a 3.00
...: Baker's Dozen TPB (12/04, $14.99) r/#1-6; cover gallery; Holey Crullers pages 15.00

COMPLETE ALICE IN WONDERLAND (Adaptation of Carroll's original story)
Dynamite Entertainment: 2009 - No. 4 ($4.99, limited series)

1-4-Leah Moore & John Reppion-s/Erica Awano-a/John Cassaday-c 5.00

COMPLETE BOOK OF COMICS AND FUNNIES
William H. Wise & Co.: 1944 (25¢, one-shot, 196 pgs.)

1-Origin Brad Spencer, Wonderman; The Magnet, The Silver Knight by Kinstler, & Zudo the Jungle Boy app.	61	122	183	390	670	950

COMPLETE BOOK OF TRUE CRIME COMICS
William H. Wise & Co.: No date (Mid 1940's) (25¢, 132 pgs.)

nn-Contains Crime Does Not Pay rebound (includes #22)	174	348	522	1114	1907	2700

COMPLETE COMICS (Formerly Amazing Comics No. 1)
Timely Comics (EPC): No. 2, Winter, 1944-45

2-The Destroyer, The Whizzer, The Young Allies & Sergeant Dix; Schomburg-c	184	368	552	1168	2009	2850

COMPLETE DRACULA (Adaptation of Stoker's original story)
Dynamite Entertainment: 2009 - No. 5, 2009 ($4.99, limited series)

1-5-Leah Moore & John Reppion-s/Colton Worley-a/John Cassaday-c 5.00

COMPLETE FRANK MILLER BATMAN, THE
Longmeadow Press: 1989 ($29.95, hardcover, silver gilded pages)

HC-Reprints Batman: Year One, Wanted: Santa Claus--Dead or Alive, and The Dark Knight Returns 45.00

COMPLETE GUIDE TO THE DEADLY ARTS OF KUNG FU AND KARATE
Marvel Comics: 1974 (68 pgs., B&W magazine)

V1#1-Bruce Lee-c and 5 pg. story (scarce)	7	14	21	46	86	125

COMPLETE LOVE MAGAZINE (Formerly a pulp with same title)
Ace Periodicals (Periodical House): V26#2, May-June, 1951 - V32#4(#191), Sept, 1956

V26#2-Painted-c (52 pgs.)	15	30	45	85	130	175
V26#3-6(2/52), V27#1(4/52)-6(1/53)	11	22	33	64	90	115
V28#1(3/53), V28#2(5/53), V29#3(7/53)-6(12/53)	11	22	33	60	83	105
V30#1(2/54), V30#1(#176, 4/54),2,4-6(#181, 1/55)	11	22	33	60	83	105
V30#3(#178)-Rock Hudson photo-c	11	22	33	62	86	110
V31#1(#182, 3/55)-Last precode	10	20	30	58	79	100
V31#2(5/55)-6(#187, 1/56)	10	20	30	56	76	95
V32#1(#188, 3/56)-4(#191, 9/56)	10	20	30	56	76	95

NOTE: *(34 total issues). Photo-c V27#5-on. Painted-c V26#3.*

COMPLETE MYSTERY (True Complete Mystery No. 5 on)
Marvel Comics (PrPI): Aug, 1948 - No. 4, Feb, 1949 (Full length stories)

1-Seven Dead Men	55	110	165	352	601	850
2-4: 2-Jigsaw of Doom!; Shores-a. 3-Fear in the Night; Burgos-c/a (28 pgs.). 4-A Squealer Dies Fast	42	84	126	265	445	625

COMPLETE ROMANCE
Avon Periodicals: 1949

1-(Scarce)-Reprinted as Women to Love	57	114	171	362	619	875

CONAN (See Chamber of Darkness #4, Giant-Size..., Handbook of..., King Conan, Marvel Graphic Novel #19, 28, Marvel Treasury Ed., Power Record Comics, Robert E. Howard's.., Savage Sword of Conan, and Savage Tales)

CONAN
Dark Horse Comics: Feb, 2004 - No. 50, May, 2008 ($2.99)

0-(11/03, 25¢-c) Busiek-s/Nord-a 3.00
1-($2.99) Linsner-c/Busiek-s/Nord-a 5.00
1-(2nd printing) J. Scott Campell-c 3.00
1-(3rd printing) Nord-c 3.00
2-49: 18-Severin & Timm-a. 22-Kaluta-a (6 pgs.) 24-Harris-c. 29-31-Mignola-s 3.00
24-Variant-c with nude woman (also see Conan and the Demons of Khitai #3 for ad) 35.00
50-($4.99) Harris-c; new story and reprint from Conan the Barbarian #30 5.00
... and the Daughters of Midora (10/04, $4.99) Texiera-a/c 5.00
...: Born on the Battlefield TPB (6/08, $17.95) r/#0,8,15,23,32,45,46; Ruth sketch pages 18.00
...: FCBD 2006 Special (5/06) Paul Lee-a; flip book with Star Wars FCBD 2006 Special 3.00
...: One For One (8/10, $1.00) r/#1 with red cover frame 3.00

Conan Classic #4 © CPI

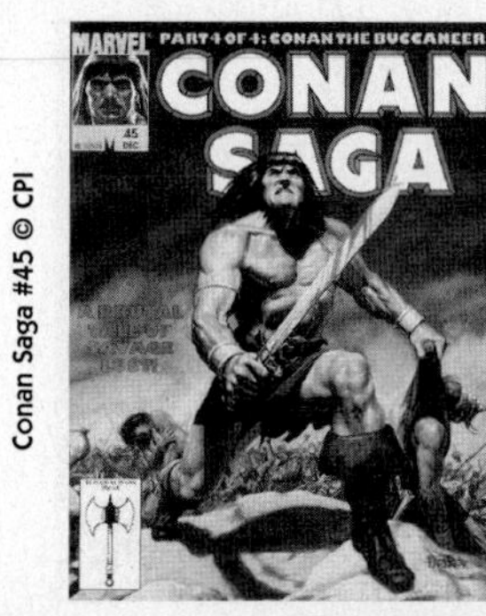

Conan Saga #45 © CPI

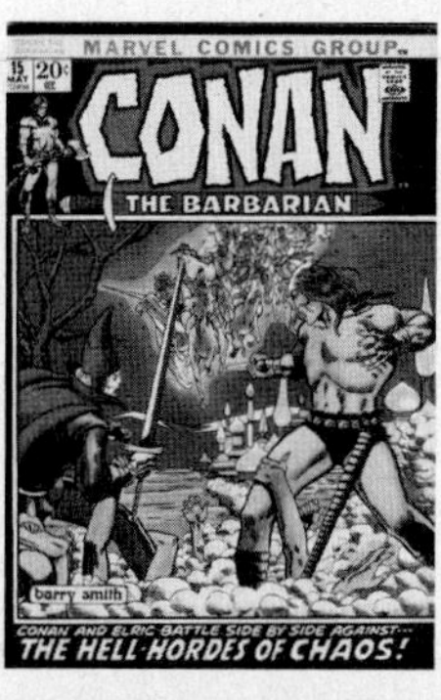

Conan the Barbarian #15 © CPI

GD 2.0 | VG 4.0 | FN 6.0 | VF 8.0 | VF/NM 9.0 | NM- 9.2

GD 2.0 | VG 4.0 | FN 6.0 | VF 8.0 | VF/NM 9.0 | NM- 9.2

...: The Blood-Stained Crown and Other Stories TPB (1/08, $14.95) r/#18,26-28,39 15.00
...: The Weight of the Crown (1/10, $3.50) Darick Robertson-s/a; 2 covers by Robertson 3.50
HC Vol. 1: The Frost Giant's Daughter and Other Stories (2005, $24.95) r/#1-6, partial #7; signed by Busiek; Nord sketch pages 25.00
Vol. 1: The Frost Giant's Daughter and Other Stories (2005, $15.95) r/#1-6, partial #7 16.00
Vol. 2: The God in the Bowl and Other Stories HC (2005, $24.95) r/#9-14 25.00
Vol. 2: The God in the Bowl and Other Stories SC (2006, $15.95) r/#9-14 16.00
Vol. 3: The Tower of the Elephant and Other Stories HC (5/06, $24.95) r/#0,16,17,19-22 25.00
Vol. 3: The Tower of the Elephant and Other Stories SC (6/06, $15.95) r/#0,16,17,19-22 16.00
Vol. 4: The Hall of the Dead and Other Stories HC (5/07, $24.95) r/#0,24,25,29-31,33,34 25.00
Vol. 4: The Hall of the Dead and Other Stories SC (6/07, $17.95) r/#0,24,25,29-31,33,34 18.00
Vol. 5: Rogues in the House and Other Stories SC (3/08, $17.95) r/#0,37,38,41-44 18.00
Vol. 6: The Hand of Nergal HC (10/08, $24.95) r/#0,47-50; sketch pages 25.00

CONAN AND THE DEMONS OF KHITAI
Dark Horse Comics: Oct, 2005 - No. 4, Jan, 2006 ($2.99, limited series)

1,2,4-Paul Lee-a/Akira Yoshida-s/Pat Lee-c 3.00
3-1st printing with red cover logo; letters page has image of Conan #24 nude variant-c 5.00
3-2nd printing with black cover logo; letters page has image of Conan #24 regular-c 3.00
TPB (7/06, $12.95) r/series 13.00

CONAN AND THE JEWELS OF GWAHLUR
Dark Horse Comics: Apr, 2005 - No. 3, June, 2005 ($2.99, limited series)

1-3-P. Craig Russell-s/a/c 3.00
HC (12/05, $13.95) r/series; P. Craig Russell interview and sketch pages 14.00

CONAN AND THE MIDNIGHT GOD
Dark Horse Comics: Dec, 2006 - No. 5, May, 2007 ($2.99, limited series)

1-5-Dysart-s/Conrad-a/Alexander-c 3.00
TPB (10/07, $14.95) r/#1-5 and Age of Conan: Hyborian Adventures one-shot 15.00

CONAN AND THE PEOPLE OF THE BLACK CIRCLE
Dark Horse Comics: Oct, 2013 - No. 4, Jan, 2014 ($3.50, limited series)

1-4-Van Lente-s/Olivetti-a/c 3.50

CONAN AND THE SONGS OF THE DEAD
Dark Horse Comics: July, 2006 - No. 5, Nov, 2006 ($2.99, limited series)

1-5-Timothy Truman-a/c; Joe Lansdale-s 3.00
TPB (4/07, $14.95) r/series; Truman sketch pages 15.00

CONAN: (Title Series): Marvel Comics

CONAN, 8/95 - No. 11, 6/96 ($2.95), 1-11: 4-Malibu Comic's Rune app. 3.00

...CLASSIC, 6/94 - No. 11, 4/95 ($1.50), 1-11: 1-r/Conan #1 by B. Smith, r/covers w/changes. 2-11-r/Conan #2-11 by Smith. 2-Bound w/cover to Conan The Adventurer #2 by mistake 3.00

...DEATH COVERED IN GOLD, 9/99 - No. 3, 11/99 ($2.99), 1-3-Roy Thomas-s/ John Buscema-a 3.00

...FLAME AND THE FIEND, 8/00 - No. 3, 10/00 ($2.99), 1-3-Thomas-s 3.00

...RETURN OF STYRM, 9/98 - No. 3, 11/98 ($2.99), 1-3-Parente & Soresina-a; painted-c 3.00

...RIVER OF BLOOD, 6/98 - No. 3, 8/98 ($2.50), 1-3 3.00

...SCARLET SWORD, 12/98 - No. 3, 2/99 ($2.99), 1-3-Thomas-s/Raffaele-a 3.00

CONAN: ISLAND OF NO RETURN
Dark Horse Comics: Jun, 2011 - No. 2, Jul, 2011 ($3.50, limited series)

1,2-Marz-s/Sears-a 3.50

CONAN RED SONJA
Dark Horse Comics: Jan, 2015 - No. 4, Apr, 2015 ($3.99, limited series)

1-4-Gail Simone & Jim Zub-s/Dan Panosian-a/c 4.00

CONAN: ROAD OF KINGS
Dark Horse Comics: Dec, 2010 - No. 12, Jan, 2012 ($3.50)

1-12: 1-Roy Thomas-s/Mike Hawthorne-a; covers by Wheatley & Keown 3.50

CONAN SAGA, THE
Marvel Comics: June, 1987 - No. 97, Apr, 1995 ($2.00/$2.25, B&W, magazine)

1-Barry Smith-r; new Smith-c 2 4 6 8 11 14
2-27: 2-9,11-new Barry Smith-c. 13,15-Boris-c. 17-Adams-r.18,25-Chaykin-r. 22-r/Giant-Size Conan 1,2 4.00
28-90: 28-Begin $2.25-c. 31-Red Sonja-r by N. Adams/SSOC #1; 1 pg. Jeff Jones-r. 32-Newspaper strip-r begin by Buscema. 33-Smith/Conrad-a. 39-r/Kull #1('71) by Andru & Wood. 44-Swipes-c/Savage Tales #1. 57-Brunner-r/SSOC #30. 66-r/Conan Annual #2 by Buscema. 79-r/Conan #43-45 w/Red Sonja. 85-Based on Conan #57-63 3.00
91-96 5.00
97-Last issue 1 2 3 5 6 8

NOTE: ***J. Buscema*** *r-32-on; c-86.* ***Chaykin*** *r-34.* ***Chiodo*** *painted c-63, 65, 66, 82.* ***G. Colan*** *a-47p.* ***Jusko*** *painted c-64, 83.* ***Kaluta*** *c-84.* ***Nino*** *a-37.* ***Ploog*** *a-50.* ***N. Redondo*** *painted c-48, 50, 51, 53, 57, 62.* ***Simonson*** *r-50-54, 56.* ***B. Smith*** *r-51.* ***Starlin*** *c-34.* ***Williamson*** *r-50i.*

CONAN THE ADVENTURER
Marvel Comics: June, 1994 - No. 14, July, 1995 ($1.50)

1-($2.50)-Embossed foil-c; Kayaran-a 4.00
2-14 3.00
2-Contents are Conan Classics #2 by mistake 3.00

CONAN THE AVENGER
Dark Horse Comics: Apr, 2014 - No. 25, Apr, 2016 ($3.99/$3.50)

1-25: 1-Van Lente-s/Ching-a. 4-Staples-c. 13-15-Powell-c. 25-Bisley-c 4.00

CONAN THE BARBARIAN
Marvel Comics: Oct, 1970 - No. 275, Dec, 1993

1-Origin/1st app. Conan (in comics) by Barry Smith; 1st brief app. Kull; #1-9 are 15¢ issues 25 50 75 175 388 600
2 9 18 27 59 117 175
3-(Low distribution in some areas) 12 24 36 84 185 285
4,5 7 14 21 49 92 135
6-9: 8-Hidden panel message, pg. 14. 9-Last 15¢-c 6 12 18 37 66 95
10,11 (25¢ 52 pg. giants): 10-Black Knight-r; Kull story by Severin 6 12 18 42 79 115
12,13: 12-Wrightson-c(i) 5 10 15 34 60 85
14,15-Elric app. 6 12 18 38 69 100
16,19,20: 16-Conan-r/Savage Tales #1 5 10 15 33 57 80
17,18-No Barry Smith-a 4 8 12 27 44 60
21,22: 22-Has reprint from #1 4 8 12 28 47 65
23-1st app. Red Sonja (2/73) 7 14 21 49 92 135
24-1st full Red Sonja story; last Smith-a 6 12 18 41 76 110
25-John Buscema-c/a begins 3 6 9 16 23 30
26-30: 28-Centerfold ad by Mark Jewelers 2 4 6 13 18 22
31-36,38-40 2 4 6 9 12 15
37-Neal Adams-c/a; last 20¢ issue; contains pull-out subscription form 3 6 9 17 26 34
41-43,46-50: 48-Origin retold 2 4 6 8 10 12
44,45-N. Adams-i(Crusty Bunkers). 45-Adams-c 2 4 6 9 12 15
51-57,59,60: 59-Origin Belit 1 2 3 5 6 8
58-2nd Belit app. (see Giant-Size Conan #1) 2 4 6 8 11 14
61-65-(Regular 25¢ editions)(4-8/76) 1 2 3 4 5 7
61-65-(30¢-c variants, limited distribution) 5 10 15 31 53 75
66-99: 68-Red Sonja story cont'd from Marvel Feature #7. 75-79-(Reg. 30¢-c). 84-Intro. Zula. 85-Origin Zula. 87-r/Savage Sword of Conan #3 in color 6.00
75-79-(35¢-c variants, limited distribution) 6 12 18 42 79 115
100-(52 pg. Giant)-Death of Belit 1 3 4 6 8 10
101-114 4.00
115-Double size 5.00
116-199,201-231,233-249: 116-r/Power Record Comic PR31. 244-Zula returns 4.00
200,232: 200-(52 pgs.). 232-Young Conan storyline begins; Conan is born 5.00
250-(60 pgs.) 6.00
251-270: 262-Adapted from R.E. Howard story 5.00
271-274 1 2 3 5 6 8
275-($2.50, 68 pgs.)-Final issue; painted-c (low print) 3 6 9 19 30 40
King Size 1(1973, 35¢)-Smith-r/#2,4; Smith-c 3 6 9 19 30 40
Annual 2(1976, 50¢)-New full length story 2 4 6 10 14 18
Annual 3,4: 3('78)-Chaykin/N. Adams-r/SSOC #2. 4('78)-New full length story 2 4 6 8 10 12
Annual 5,6: 5(1979)-New full length Buscema story & part-c, 6(1981)-Kane-c/a 6.00
Annual 7-12: 7('82)-Based on novel "Conan of the Isles" (new-a). 8(1984). 9(1984). 10(1986). 11(1986). 12(1987) 4.00
Special Edition 1 (Red Nails) 4.00
The Chronicles of Conan Vol. 1: Tower of the Elephant and Other Stories (Dark Horse, 2003, $15.95) r/#1-8; afterword by Roy Thomas 16.00
The Chronicles of Conan Vol. 2: Rogues in the House and Other Stories (Dark Horse, 2003, $15.95) r/#9-13,16; afterword by Roy Thomas 16.00
The Chronicles of Conan Vol. 3: The Monster of the Monoliths and Other Stories (Dark Horse, 2003, $15.95) r/#14,15,17-21; afterword by Roy Thomas 16.00
The Chronicles of Conan Vol. 4: The Song of Red Sonja and Other Stories (Dark Horse, 2004, $15.95) r/#23-26 & "Red Nails" from Savage Tales; afterword by Roy Thomas 16.00
The Chronicles of Conan Vol. 5: The Shadow in the Tomb and Other Stories (Dark Horse, 2004, $15.95) r/#27-34; afterword by Roy Thomas 16.00
The Chronicles of Conan Vol. 6: The Curse of the Skull and Other Stories (Dark Horse, 2004, $15.95) r/#35-42; afterword by Roy Thomas 16.00
The Chronicles of Conan Vol. 7: The Dweller in the Pool and Other Stories (Dark Horse, 2005, $15.95) r/#43-51; afterword by Roy Thomas 16.00
The Chronicles of Conan Vol. 8: Brothers of the Blade and Other Stories (Dark Horse,

Conan the Barbarian (2012 series) #11 © CPI

Conan the Slayer #12 © CPI

Condorman #1 © DIS

GD 2.0 VG 4.0 FN 6.0 VF 8.0 VF/NM 9.0 NM- 9.2

2005, $16.95) r/#52-59; afterword by Roy Thomas 17.00
The Chronicles of Conan Vol. 9: Riders of the River-Dragons and Other Stories (Dark Horse, 11/05, $16.95) r/#60-63,65,69-71; afterword by Roy Thomas 17.00
The Chronicles of Conan Vol. 10: When Giants Walk the Earth and Other Stories (Dark Horse, 3/06, $16.95) r/#72-77,79-82; afterword by Roy Thomas 17.00
The Chronicles of Conan Vol. 11: The Dance of the Skull and Other Stories (Dark Horse, 2/07, $16.95) r/#82-86,88-90; afterword by Roy Thomas 17.00
The Chronicles of Conan Vol. 12: The King Beast of Abombi and Other Stories (Dark Horse, 7/07, $16.95) r/#91,93-100; afterword by Roy Thomas 17.00
The Chronicles of Conan Vol. 13: Whispering Shadows and Other Stories (Dark Horse, 12/07, $16.95) r/#92,100-107; afterword by Roy Thomas 17.00
The Chronicles of Conan Vol. 14: Shadow of the Beast and Other Stories (Dark Horse, 3/08, $16.95) r/#92,108-115; afterword by Roy Thomas 17.00
The Chronicles of Conan Vol. 15: The Corridor of Mullah-Kajar and Other Stories (Dark Horse, 7/08, $16.95) r/#116-121 & Annual #2; afterword by Roy Thomas 17.00

NOTE: **Arthur Adams** *c-248, 249.* **Neal Adams** *a-116r(i); c-49i.* **Austin** *a-125, 126; c-125i, 126i.* **Brunner** *c-17i. c-40.* **Buscema** *a-25-36p, 38, 39, 41-56p, 58-63p, 65-67p, 68, 70-78p, 84-86p, 88-91p, 93-126p, 136p, 140, 141-144p, 146-158p, 159, 161, 162, 163p, 165-185p, 187-190p, Annual 2(3pgs.). 3-5p, 7p; c(p)-26, 36, 44, 46, 52, 56, 58, 59, 64, 65, 72, 78-80, 83-91, 93-103, 105-126, 136-151, 155-159, 161, 162, 168, 169, 171, 172, 174, 175, 178-185, 188, 189, Annual 4, 5, 7.* **Chaykin** *a-79-83.* **Golden** *c-152.* **Kaluta** *c-167.* **Gil Kane** *a-12p, 17p, 18p, 127-130, 131-134p; c-12p, 17p, 18p, 23, 25, 27-32, 34, 35, 38, 39, 41-43, 45-51, 53-55, 57, 60-63, 65-71, 73p, 76p, 127-134.* **Jim Lee** *c-242.* **McFarlane** *c-241p.* **Ploog** *a-57.* **Russell** *a-21; c-251i.* **Simonson** *c-135.* **B. Smith** *a-1-11p, 12, 13-15p, 16, 19-21, 23, 24; c-1-11, 13-16, 19-24p.* **Starlin** *a-64.* **Wood** *a-47r. Issue Nos. 3-5, 7-9, 11, 16-18, 21, 23, 25, 27-30, 35, 37, 38, 42, 45, 52, 57, 58, 65, 69-71, 73, 79-83, 99, 100, 104, 114, Annual 2 have original Robert E. Howard stories adapted. Issues #32-34 adapted from Norvell Page's novel* **Flame Winds**.

CONAN THE BARBARIAN (Volume 2)
Marvel Comics: July, 1997 - No. 3, Oct, 1997 ($2.50, limited series)

1-3-Castellini-a 3.00

CONAN THE BARBARIAN
Dark Horse Comics: Feb, 2012 - No. 25, Feb, 2014 ($3.50)

1-25: 1-3-Brian Wood-s/Becky Cloonan-a. 1-Two covers by Carnevale & Cloonan 3.50
One for One: Conan the Barbarian #1 (1/14, $1.00) r/#1 3.00

CONAN THE BARBARIAN MOVIE SPECIAL (Movie)
Marvel Comics Group: Oct, 1982 - No. 2, Nov, 1982

1,2-Movie adaptation; Buscema-a 4.00

CONAN THE BARBARIAN: THE MASK OF ACHERON (Based on the 2011 movie)
Dark Horse Comics: Jul, 2011 ($6.99, one-shot)

1-Stuart Moore-s/Gabriel Guzman-a/c 7.00

CONAN THE BARBARIAN: THE USURPER
Marvel Comics: Dec, 1997 - No. 3, Feb, 1998 ($2.50, limited series)

1-3-Dixon-s 3.00

CONAN: THE BOOK OF THOTH
Dark Horse Comics: Mar, 2006 - No. 4, June, 2006 ($4.99, limited series)

1-4-Origin of Thoth-amon; Len Wein & Kurt Busiek-s/Kelley Jones-a/c 5.00
TPB (12/06, $17.95) r/#1-4 18.00

CONAN THE CIMMERIAN
Dark Horse Comics: No. 0, Jun, 2008 - No. 25, Nov, 2010 (99¢/$2.99)

0-Follows Conan #50; Truman-s/Giorello-a/c 3.00
1-(7/08, $2.99) Two covers by Joe Kubert and Cho; Giorello & Corben-a 3.00
2-25: 2-7-Cho-c; Giorello & Corben-a. 8-18-Linsner-c. 14-Joe Kubert-a (7 pgs.) 3.00

CONAN THE DESTROYER (Movie)
Marvel Comics Group: Jan, 1985 - No. 2, Mar, 1985

1,2-r/Marvel Super Special 4.00

CONAN THE FRAZETTA COVER SERIES
Dark Horse Comics: Dec, 2007 - No. 8 ($3.50/$5.99/$6.99)

1-($3.50) Reprints from Dark Horse series with Frazetta covers 6.00
2,3-($5.99) 6.00
4-8-($6.99) 7.00

CONAN THE KING (Formerly King Conan)
Marvel Comics Group: No. 20, Jan, 1984 - No. 55, Nov, 1989

20-49 4.00
50-54 5.00
55-Last issue 1 3 4 6 8 10

NOTE: **Kaluta** *c-20-23, 24i, 26, 27, 30, 50, 52.* **Williamson** *a-37i; c-37i, 38i.*

CONAN: THE LEGEND (See Conan 2004 series)

CONAN: THE LORD OF THE SPIDERS
Marvel Comics: Mar, 1998 - No. 3, May, 1998 ($2.50, limited series)

1-3-Roy Thomas-s/Raffaele-a 3.00

CONAN THE SAVAGE
Marvel Comics: Aug, 1995 - No. 10, May, 1996 ($2.95, B&W, Magazine)

1-10: 1-Bisley-c. 4-vs. Malibu Comics' Rune. 5,10-Brereton-c 4.00

CONAN THE SLAYER
Dark Horse Comics: Jul, 2016 - No. 12, Aug, 2017 ($3.99)

1-12: 1-Bunn-s/Dávila-a/Bermejo-c. 11-Verma-a 4.00

CONAN VS. RUNE (Also See Conan #4)
Marvel Comics: Nov, 1995 ($2.95, one-shot)

1-Barry Smith-c/a/scripts 4.00

CONCRETE (Also see Dark Horse Presents & Within Our Reach)
Dark Horse Comics: March, 1987 - No. 10, Nov, 1988 ($1.50, B&W)

1-Paul Chadwick-c/a in all 2 4 6 8 10 12
1-2nd print 3.00
2 6.00
3-Origin 5.00
4-10 4.00
A New Life 1 (1989, $2.95, B&W)-r/#3,4 plus new-a (11 pgs.) 4.00
Celebrates Earth Day 1990 ($3.50, 52 pgs.) 6.00
Color Special 1 (2/89, $2.95, 44 pgs.)-r/1st two Concrete apps. from Dark Horse Presents #1,2 plus new-a 6.00
Depths TPB (7/05, $12.95)-r/#1-5, stories from DHP #1,8,10,150; other short stories 13.00
Land And Sea 1 (2/89, $2.95, B&W)-r/#1,2 6.00
Odd Jobs 1 (7/90, $3.50)-r/5,6 plus new-a 4.00
...Vol. 1: Depths ('05, $12.95, 9"x6") r/#1-5 & short stories 13.00
...Vol. 2: Heights ('05, $12.95, 9"x6") r/#6-10 & short stories 13.00
...Vol. 3: Fragile Creatures (1/06, $12.95, 9"x6") r/mini-series & short stories from DHP 13.00
...Vol. 4: Killer Smile (3/06, $12.95, 9"x6") r/mini-series & short stories from various 13.00
...Vol. 5: Think Like a Mountain (5/06, $12.95, 9"x6") r/mini-series & short stories 13.00
...Vol. 6: Strange Armor (7/06, $12.95, 9"x6") r/mini-series & short stories 13.00
...Vol. 7: The Human Dilemma (4/06, $12.95, 9"x6") r/mini-series 13.00

CONCRETE: (Title series), **Dark Horse Comics**

--ECLECTICA, 4/93 - No. 2, 5/93 ($2.95) 1,2 4.00

--FRAGILE CREATURE, 6/91 - No. 4, 2/92 ($2.50) 1-4 4.00

--KILLER SMILE, (Legend), 7/94 - No. 4, 10/94 ($2.95) 1-4 4.00

--STRANGE ARMOR, 12/97 - No. 5, 5/98 ($2.95, color) 1-5-Chadwick-s/c/a; retells origin 4.00

--THE HUMAN DILEMMA, 12/04 - No. 6, 5/05 ($3.50)
1-6: Chadwick-a/c & scripts; Concrete has a child 3.50

--THINK LIKE A MOUNTAIN, (Legend), 3/96 - No. 6, 8/96 ($2.95)
1-6: Chadwick-a/scripts & Darrow-c in all 4.00

CONDORMAN (Walt Disney)
Whitman Publishing: Oct, 1981 - No. 3, Jan, 1982

1-3: 1,2-Movie adaptation; photo-c 1 3 4 6 8 10

CONEHEADS
Marvel Comics: June, 1994 - No. 4, 1994 ($1.75, limited series)

1-4 3.00

CONFESSIONS ILLUSTRATED (Magazine)
E. C. Comics: Jan-Feb, 1956 - No. 2, Spring, 1956

1-Craig, Kamen, Wood, Orlando-a 30 60 90 177 289 400
2-Craig, Crandall, Kamen, Orlando-a 22 44 66 132 216 300

CONFESSIONS OF LOVE
Artful Publ.: Apr, 1950 - No. 2, July, 1950 (25¢, 7-1/4x5-1/4", 132 pgs.)

1-Bakerish-a 77 154 231 493 847 1200
2-Art & text; Bakerish-a 48 96 144 302 514 725

CONFESSIONS OF LOVE (Formerly Startling Terror Tales #10; becomes Confessions of Romance No. 7 on)
Star Publications: No. 11, 7/52 - No. 14, 1/53; No. 4, 3/53- No. 6, 8/53

11-13: 12,13-Disbrow-a 21 42 63 122 199 275
14,5,6 18 36 54 105 165 225
4-Disbrow-a 19 38 57 109 172 235

NOTE: *All have* **L. B. Cole** *covers.*

CONFESSIONS OF ROMANCE (Formerly Confessions of Love)
Star Publications: No. 7, Nov, 1953 - No. 11, Nov, 1954

7 22 44 66 128 209 290
8 18 36 54 105 165 225
9-Wood-a 19 38 57 112 179 245
10,11-Disbrow-a 19 38 57 109 172 235

Congo Bill #3 © DC

Constantine: The Hellblazer #4 © DC

Contact Comics #12 © Aviation

GD 2.0 VG 4.0 FN 6.0 VF 8.0 VF/NM 9.0 NM- 9.2

NOTE: *All have* **L. B. Cole** *covers.*

CONFESSIONS OF THE LOVELORN (Formerly Lovelorn)
American Comics Group (Regis Publ./Best Synd. Features): No. 52, Aug, 1954 - No. 114, June-July, 1960

52 (3-D effect) 39 78 117 240 395 550
53,55 15 30 45 85 130 175
54 (3-D effect) 37 74 111 222 361 500
56-Anti-communist propaganda story, 10 pgs; last pre-code (2/55)
18 36 54 105 165 225
57-90,100 10 20 30 58 79 100
91-Williamson-a 12 24 36 67 94 120
92-99,101-114 9 18 27 50 65 80
NOTE: **Whitney** *a-most issues; c-52, 53. Painted c-106, 107.*

CONFIDENTIAL DIARY (Formerly High School Confidential Diary; Three Nurses #18 on)
Charlton Comics: No. 12, May, 1962 - No. 17, Mar, 1963

12-17 3 6 9 15 22 28

CONGO BILL (See Action Comics & More Fun Comics #56)
National Periodical Publication: Aug-Sept, 1954 - No. 7, Aug-Sept, 1955

1 200 400 600 1600 - -
2,7 125 250 375 1000 - -
3-6: 4-Last pre-Code issue 100 200 300 800 - -
NOTE: *(Rarely found in fine to mint condition.)* **Nick Cardy** *c-1-7.*

CONGO BILL
DC Comics (Vertigo): Oct, 1999 - No. 4, Jan, 2000 ($2.95, limited series)

1-4-Corben-c 3.00

CONGORILLA (Also see Actions Comics #224)
DC Comics: Nov, 1992 - No. 4, Feb, 1993 ($1.75, limited series)

1-4: 1,2-Brian Bolland-c 3.00

CONJURORS
DC Comics: Apr, 1999 - No. 3, Jun, 1999 ($2.95, limited series)

1-3-Elseworlds; Phantom Stranger app.; Barreto-c/a 3.00

CONNECTICUT YANKEE, A (See King Classics)

CONNOR HAWKE: DRAGON'S BLOOD (Also see Green Arrow titles)
DC Comics: Jan, 2007 - No. 6, Jun, 2007 ($2.99, limited series)

1-6-Chuck Dixon-s/Derec Donovan-a/c 3.00
SC (2008, $19.99) r/#1-6 20.00

CONQUEROR, THE
Dell Publishing Co.: No., 690, Mar, 1956

Four Color 690-Movie, John Wayne photo-c 15 30 45 103 227 350

CONQUEROR COMICS
Albrecht Publishing Co.: Winter, 1945

nn 24 48 72 142 234 325

CONQUEROR OF THE BARREN EARTH (See The Warlord #63)
DC Comics: Feb, 1985 - No. 4, May, 1985 (Limited series)

1-4: Back-up series from Warlord 3.00

CONQUEST
Store Comics: 1953 (6¢)

1-Richard the Lion Hearted, Beowulf, Swamp Fox 8 16 24 40 50 60

CONQUEST
Famous Funnies: Spring, 1955

1-Crandall-a, 1 pg.; contains contents of 1953 ish. 5 10 15 22 26 30

CONSPIRACY
Marvel Comics: Feb, 1998 - No. 2, Mar, 1998 ($2.99, limited series)

1,2-Painted art by Korday/Abnett-s 3.00

CONSTANTINE (Also see Hellblazer)
DC Comics (Vertigo): 2005 (Based on the 2005 Keanu Reeves movie)

...: The Hellblazer Collection (2005, $14.95) Movie adaptation and r/#1, 27, 41; photo-c 15.00
...: The Official Movie Adaptation (2005, $6.95) Seagle-s/Randall-a/photo-c 7.00

CONSTANTINE (Also see Justice League Dark)
DC Comics: May, 2013 - No. 23, May, 2015 ($2.99)

1-Lemire & Fawkes-s/Guedes-a; two covers by Reis & Guedes
1 2 3 5 6 8
2-20: 2-The Spectre app. 5-Trinity War tie-in; Shazam app. 9-Forever Evil tie-in. 20-23-Constantine on Earth 2. 23-Darkseid app. 3.00
...: Futures End 1 (11/14, $2.99, regular-c) Five years later; Ferreyra-a/c 3.00
...: Futures End 1 (11/14, $3.99, 3-D cover) 4.00
.../Hellblazer Special Edition 1 (12/14, $1.00) Flipbook r/#1 and Hellblazer #1 3.00

CONSTANTINE: THE HELLBLAZER
DC Comics: Aug, 2015 - No. 13, Aug, 2016 ($2.99)

1-13: 1-Doyle & Tynion IV-s/Rossmo-a, covers by Rossmo & Doyle. 3,4-Doyle-a. 7-Swamp Thing app. 8-12-Neron app. 10,11-Foreman-a 3.00

CONSTRUCT
Caliber (New Worlds): 1996 - No. 6, 1997 ($2.95, B&W, limited series)

1-6: Paul Jenkins scripts 3.00

CONSUMED
Platinum Studios: July, 2007 - No. 4, Oct, 2007 ($2.99, limited series)

1-4-Linsner-c/Budd-a/Shumskas-Tait-s 3.00

CONTACT COMICS
Aviation Press: July, 1944 - No. 12, May, 1946

nn-Black Venus, Flamingo, Golden Eagle, Tommy Tomahawk begin
71 142 213 454 777 1100
2-Classic sci-fi-c 68 136 204 435 743 1050
3-5: 3-Last Flamingo. 3,4-Black Venus by L. B. Cole. 5-The Phantom Flyer app.
50 100 150 315 533 750
6,11-Kurtzman's Black Venus; 11-Last Golden Eagle, last Tommy Tomahawk; Feldstein-a 53 106 159 334 567 800
7-10 42 84 126 265 445 625
12-Sky Rangers, Air Kids, Ace Diamond app.; L.B. Cole sci-fi cover
187 374 561 1197 2049 2900
NOTE: **L. B. Cole** *a-3, 9; c-1-12.* **Giunta** *a-3.* **Hollingsworth** *a-5, 7, 10.* **Palais** *a-11, 12.*

CONTEMPORARY MOTIVATORS
Pendelum Press: 1977 - 1978 ($1.45, 5-3/8x8", 31 pgs., B&W)

14-3002 The Caine Mutiny; 14-3010 Banner in the Sky; 14-3029 God Is My Co-Pilot; 14-3037 Guadalcanal Diary; 14-3045 Hiroshima; 14-3053 Hot Rod; 14-3061 Just Dial a Number; 14-3088 The Diary of Anne Frank; 14-3096 Lost Horizon
2 4 6 8 10 12
NOTE: *Also see Pendulum Illustrated Classics. Above may have been distributed the same.*

CONTEST OF CHAMPIONS (See Marvel Super-Hero...)

CONTEST OF CHAMPIONS
Marvel Comics: Dec, 2015 - No. 10, Sept, 2016 ($4.99/$3.99, limited series)

1-($4.99) The Collector, Venom, Mr. Fixit, Iron Man, Gamora & Maestro app.; Medina-a 5.00
2-9-($3.99) 2-Ares and Punisher 2099 app. 3-5-The Sentry app. 7,8-Ultimates app. 9-Revisits Civil War 4.00
10-($4.99) Finale; Ewing-s/Marcellius-a 5.00

CONTEST OF CHAMPIONS II
Marvel Comics: Sept, 1999 - No. 5, Nov, 1999 ($2.50, limited series)

1-5-Claremont-s/Jimenez-a 3.00

CONTRACT WITH GOD, A
Baronet Publishing Co./Kitchen Sink Press: 1978 ($4.95/$7.95, B&W, graphic novel)

nn-Will Eisner-s/a 3 6 9 14 20 25
Reprint (DC Comics, 2000, $12.95) 13.00

CONVERGENCE
DC Comics: No. 0, Jun, 2015 - No. 8, July, 2015 ($4.99/$3.99, weekly limited series)

0-Superman & multiple Brainiacs app.; intro Telos; Van Sciver-a/Jurgens & King-s 5.00
1-($4.99) Earth-2 heroes vs. Telos; Pagulayan-a; wraparound-c by Reis 5.00
2-7-($3.99) 2-Intro. Deimos; Pagulayan-a. 4,5-Warlord app. 5-Andy Kubert-a 4.00
8-($4.99) Conclusion; art by Segovia, Pagulayan, Pansica & Van Sciver 5.00

CONVERGENCE
DC Comics: June, 2015 - July, 2015 ($3.99, 2-part tie-in miniseries, each issue has a variant cover designed by Chip Kidd)

... Action Comics 1,2 - Pre-Crisis Earth Two Superman & Power Girl; Red Son Superman, Wonder Woman & Lex Luthor app.; Conner-c. 2-Bonus preview of Sinestro #12 4.00
... Adventures of Superman 1,2 - Pre-Crisis Earth One Superman & Supergirl app.; Wolfman-s. 2-Kamandi app.; bonus preview of Martian Manhunter #1 4.00
... Aquaman 1,2 - Harpoon-hand Aquaman & Deathblow app.; Cloonan-c; Richards-a. 2-Bonus preview of Doctor Fate #1 4.00
... Atom 1,2 - Pre-Flashpoint Ray Palmer & Deathstroke app.; Dillon-c/Yeowell-a. 2-Ryan Choi app.; bonus preview of Green Lantern #41 4.00
... Batgirl 1,2 - Stephanie Brown, Cassadra Cain, Tim Drake & Catman app; Leonardi-a. 2-Grodd app.; bonus preview of Prez #1 4.00
... Batman and Robin 1,2 - Pre-Flashpoint Batman, Damian & Red Hood app.; Cowan & Janson-a. 2-Superman app.; bonus preview of Omega Men #1 4.00

Convergence Shazam! #1 © DC

"Cookie" #12 © ACG

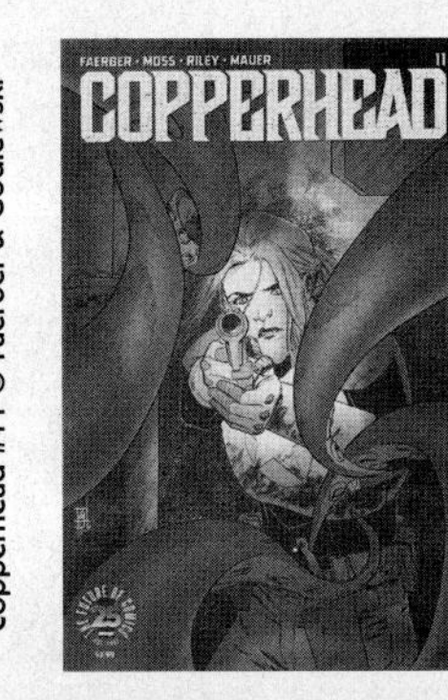

Copperhead #11 © Faerber & Godlewski

GD VG FN VF VF/NM NM-
2.0 4.0 6.0 8.0 9.0 9.2

... Batman and The Outsiders 1,2 - Pre-Crisis Outsiders and Omac app.; Andy Kubert-c. 2-Bonus preview of Batman Beyond #1 4.00
... Batman: Shadow of the Bat 1,2 - Pre-Zero Hour Batman & Azrael app. 1-Philip Tan-a/c. 2-Leonardi-a; bonus preview of Deathstroke #7 4.00
... Blue Beetle 1,2 - Charlton Blue Beetle, Captain Atom & The Question app.; Blevins-c. 2-Legion of Super-Heroes app.; bonus preview of Black Canary #1 4.00
... Booster Gold 1,2 - Rip Hunter & the Legion of Super-Heroes app.; Jurgens-c. 2-Blue Beetle app.; bonus preview of Earth-2: Society #1 4.00
... Catwoman 1,2 - Pre-Zero Hour purple suit Catwoman & Kingdom Come Batman app.; Ron Randall-a. Bonus preview of Gotham By Midnight #6 4.00
... Crime Syndicate 1,2 - Earth-Three villains & 853rd Century JLA app.; Winslade-a. 2-Bonus preview of Cyborg #1 4.00
... Detective Comics 1,2 - Earth-Two pre-Crisis Robin & Huntress vs. Red Son Superman; Cowan & Sienkiewicz-a. 2-Red Son Batman app.; bonus preview of Flash #41 4.00
... Flash 1,2 - Earth-One pre-Crisis Barry Allen vs. Tangent Superman; Abnett-s/Dallocchio-a; 2-Bonus preview of New Suicide Squad #9 4.00
... Green Arrow 1,2 - Pre-Zero Hour Oliver Queen & Connor Hawke vs. Kingdom Come Black Canary & Dinah Lance; Morales-a; 2-Bonus preview of G.L.C. Lost Army #1 4.00
... Green Lantern Corps 1,2 - Earth-One pre-Crisis Guy Gardner, John Stewart & Hal Jordan; Hercules from Durvale app. 2-Bonus preview of Gotham Academy #7 4.00
... Green Lantern/Parallax 1,2 - Pre-Zero Hour Hal Jordan & Kyle Rayner; Ron Wagner-a. Princess Fern of Electropolis app. 2-Bonus preview of Lobo #7 4.00
... Harley Quinn 1,2 - Pre-Flashpoint Harley, Poison Ivy & Catwoman; Winslade-a. 2-Harley battles Captain Carrot. 2-Bonus preview of Section Eight #1 4.00
... Hawkman 1,2 - Earth-One pre-Crisis Katar Hol & Shayera; Parker-s/Truman-a. 2-Bonus preview of Grayson #9 4.00
... Infinity Inc. 1,2 - Earth-Two pre-Crisis Infinity Inc. vs. Future Jonah Hex & The Dogs of War; Ordway-s, 1-Ben Caldwell-a. 2-Bonus preview of Batgirl #41 4.00
... Justice League 1,2 - Pre-Flashpoint female Justice League vs. Flashpoint Aquaman; Buckingham-c. 2-Bonus preview of Detective Comics #41 4.00
... Justice League International 1,2 - Pre-Zero Hour JLI vs. Kingdom Come; Manley-a. 2-Bonus preview of Justice League 3001 #1 4.00
... Justice League of America 1,2 - Earth-One pre-Crisis Detroit JLA vs. Tangent Secret Six; ChrisCross-a. 2-Bonus preview of Batman/Superman #21 4.00
... Justice Society of America 1,2 - Earth-Two pre-Crisis JSA vs. Weaponers of Qward; Derenick-a. 2-Bonus preview of Superman/Wonder Woman #18 4.00
... New Teen Titans 1,2 - Earth-One pre-Crisis Teen Titans vs. Tangent Doom Patrol; Nicola Scott-a. 2-Bonus preview of Robin: Son of Batman #1 4.00
... Nightwing and Oracle 1,2 - Pre-Flashpoint version vs. Flashpoint Hawkman; Duursema-a/Thompson-c. 2-Bonus preview of Midnighter #1 4.00
... Plastic Man and the Freedom Fighters 1,2 - Earth-X team vs. Futures End cyborgs; Silver Ghost app.; McCrea-a/Barta-c. 2-Bonus preview of Harley Quinn #17 4.00
... The Question 1,2 - Pre-Flashpoint Question (Renee Montoya); Huntress, Batwoman & Two-Face app.; Rucka-s/Hamner-a. 2-Bonus preview of Starfire #1 4.00
... Shazam! 1,2 - Earth-S Marvel Family vs. Gotham By Gaslight Batman; Shaner-a Sivana, Ibac, Mr. Atom app. 2-Bonus preview of Constantine The Hellblazer #1 4.00
... Speed Force 1,2 - Pre-Flashpoint Flash (Wally West) vs. Flashpoint Wonder Woman Grummett-a; Fastback (Zoo Crew) app. 2-Bonus preview of Green Arrow #41 4.00
... Suicide Squad 1,2 - Pre-Zero Hour vs. Kingdom Come Green Lantern Mandrake-a; Lex Luthor app. 2-Bonus preview of Aquaman #41 4.00
... Superboy 1,2 - Pre-Zero Hour Kon-El vs. Kingdom Come Superman, Flash & Red Robin; Moline-a/Tarr-c. 2-Bonus preview of Action Comics #41 4.00
... Superboy and the Legion of Super-Heroes 1,2 - Pre-Crisis Legion vs. The Atomic Knights; Storms-a/Guerra-c. 2-Bonus preview of Teen Titans #9 4.00
... Supergirl: Matrix 1,2 - Pre-Zero Hour Supergirl vs. Lady Quark (Electropolis); Ambush Bug app.; Giffen-s/Green II-a/Porter-c. 2-Bonus preview of Bat-Mite #1 4.00
... Superman 1,2 - Pre-Flashpoint Superman & Lois vs. Flashpoint heroes; Jurgens-s/Weeks-a; 2-Baby born (Jonathan Kent); bonus preview of Doomed #1 (See Superman: Lois & Clark series) 4.00
... Superman: Man of Steel 1,2 - Pre-Zero Hour Steel vs. Gen-13; Parasite app.; Louise Simonson-s/June Brigman-a/Walt Simonson-c. 2-Bonus preview of Bizarro #1 4.00
... Swamp Thing 1,2 - Earth-One pre-Crisis Swamp Thing vs. Red Rain vampire Batman; Len Wein-s/Kelley Jones-a. 2-Bonus preview of Catwoman #41 4.00
... Titans 1,2 - Pre-Flashpoint Titans vs. The Extremists; Nicieza-s/Wagner-a; 2-Bonus preview of Red Hood & Arsenal #1 4.00
... Wonder Woman 1,2 - Earth-One pre-Crisis Wonder Woman vs. Red Rain vampire Joker, Catwoman & Poison Ivy. 1-Middleton-a/c. 2-Lopresti-a; bonus preview of Secret Six 4.00
... World's Finest 1,2 - Earth-Two pre-Crisis Seven Soldiers of Victory vs. Weaponers of Qward; Scribbly Jibbet app.; Levitz-s. 2-Bonus preview of We Are Robin #1 4.00

CONVOCATIONS: A MAGIC THE GATHERING GALLERY
Acclaim Comics (Armada): Jan, 1996 ($2.50, one-shot)
1-pin-ups by various artists including Kaluta, Vess, and Dringenberg 3.00

COO COO COMICS (...the Bird Brain No. 57 on)
Nedor Publ. Co./Standard (Animated Cartoons): Oct, 1942 - No. 62, Apr, 1952

	GD 2.0	VG 4.0	FN 6.0	VF 8.0	VF/NM 9.0	NM- 9.2
1-Origin/1st app. Super Mouse & begin series (cloned from Superman); the first funny animal super hero series (see Looney Tunes #5 for 1st funny animal super hero)	47	94	141	296	498	700
2	20	40	60	117	189	260
3-10: 10-(3/44)	15	30	45	85	130	175
11-33: 33-1 pg. Ingels-a	12	24	36	69	97	125
34-40,43-46,48-50Text illos by Frazetta in all. 36-Super Mouse covers begin	15	30	45	86	133	180
41-Frazetta-a (6-pg. story & 3 text illos)	25	50	75	150	245	340
42,47-Frazetta-a & text illos.	19	18	57	111	176	240
51-62: 56-58,61-Super Mouse app.	11	22	33	62	86	110

"COOKIE" (Also see Topsy-Turvy)
Michel Publ./American Comics Group(Regis Publ.): Apr, 1946 - No. 55, Aug-Sept, 1955

	GD 2.0	VG 4.0	FN 6.0	VF 8.0	VF/NM 9.0	NM- 9.2
1-Teen-age humor	29	58	87	172	281	390
2-1st app. Tee-Pee Tim who takes over Ha Ha Comics later	15	30	45	90	140	190
3-10: 8-Bing Crosby app.	14	28	42	76	108	140
11-20: 12-Hedy Lamarr app. 13-Jackie Robinson mentioned. 15-Gregory Peck app. 16-Ub Iwerks (a creator of Mickey Mouse) name used. 18-Jane Russell-type Jane Bustle. 19-Cookie takes a dog to see Lassie movie	12	24	36	67	94	120
21-23,26,28-30: 26-Milt Gross & Starlett O'Hara stories. 28,30-Starlett O'Hara stories	10	20	30	56	76	95
24,25,27-Starlett O'Hara stories	10	20	30	58	79	100
31-34,37-48,52-55	9	18	27	50	65	80
35,36-Starlett O'Hara stories	10	20	30	54	72	90
49-51: 49-(6-7/54)-3-D effect-c/s. 50-3-D effect. 51-(10-11/54) 8pg. TrueVision 3-D effect story	15	30	45	83	124	165

COOL CAT (What's Cookin' With...) (Formerly Black Magic)
Prize Publications: V8#6, Mar-Apr, 1962 - V9#2, July-Aug, 1962

	GD 2.0	VG 4.0	FN 6.0	VF 8.0	VF/NM 9.0	NM- 9.2
V8#6, nn(V9#1, 5-6/62), V9#2	3	6	9	19	30	40

COOL WORLD (Movie by Ralph Bakshi)
DC Comics: Apr, 1992 - No. 4, Sept, 1992 ($1.75, limited series)
1-4: Prequel to animated/live action movie. 1-Bakshi-c. Bill Wray inks in all 3.00
Movie Adaptation nn ('92, $3.50, 68pg.)-Bakshi-c 4.00

COPPER CANYON (See Fawcett Movie Comics)

COPPERHEAD
Image Comics: Sept, 2014 - Present ($3.50/$3.99)
1-18: 1-Faerber-s/Godlewski-a; multiple covers. 11-$3.99-c begins. 11-18-Moss-a 4.00

COPS (TV)
DC Comics: Aug, 1988 - No. 15, Aug, 1989 ($1.00)
1 ($1.50, 52 pgs.)-Based on Hasbro Toys 4.00
2-15: 14-Orlando-c(p) 3.00

COPS: THE JOB
Marvel Comics: June, 1992 - No. 4, Sept, 1992 ($1.25, limited series)
1-4: All have Jusko scripts & Golden-c 3.00

CORBEN SPECIAL, A
Pacific Comics: May, 1984 (one-shot)
1-Corben-c/a; E.A. Poe adaptation 6.00

CORE, THE
Image Comics: July, 2008 ($3.99)
Pilot Season - Hickman-s/Rocafort-a 4.00

CORKY & WHITE SHADOW (Disney, TV)
Dell Publishing Co.: No. 707, May, 1956 (Mickey Mouse Club)

	GD 2.0	VG 4.0	FN 6.0	VF 8.0	VF/NM 9.0	NM- 9.2
Four Color 707-Photo-c	6	12	18	42	79	115

CORLISS ARCHER (See Meet Corliss Archer)

CORMAC MAC ART (Robert E. Howard's...)
Dark Horse Comics: 1990 - No. 4, 1990 ($1.95, B&W, mini-series)
1-4: All have Bolton painted-c; Howard adapts. 3.00

CORPORAL RUSTY DUGAN (See Holyoke One-Shot #2)

CORPSES OF DR. SACOTTI, THE (See Ideal a Classical Comic)

CORSAIR, THE (See A-1 Comics No. 5, 7, 10 under Texas Slim)

CORUM: THE BULL AND THE SPEAR (See Chronicles Of Corum)
First Comics: Jan, 1989 - No. 4, July, 1989 ($1.95)
1-4: Adapts Michael Moorcock's novel 3.00

Cosmic Slam #1 © USF

Countdown to Adventure #1 © DC

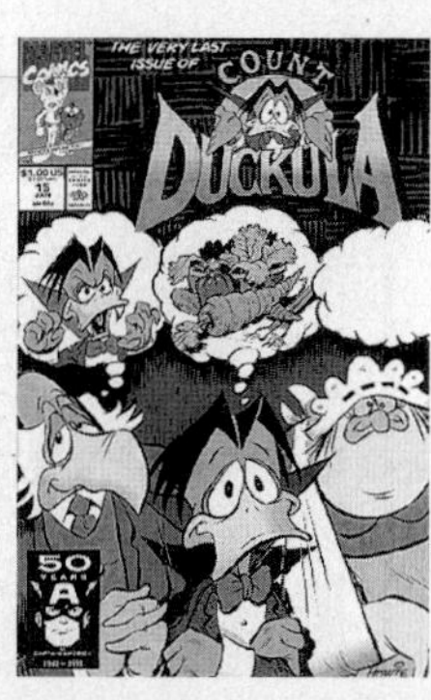

Count Duckula #15 © Cosgrove-Hall

	GD 2.0	VG 4.0	FN 6.0	VF 8.0	VF/NM 9.0	NM- 9.2

COSMIC BOOK, THE
Ace Comics: Dec, 1986 - No. 1, 1987 ($1.95)
1,2: 1-(44pgs.)-Wood, Toth-a. 2-(B&W) 4.00

COSMIC BOY (Also see The Legion of Super-Heroes)
DC Comics: Dec, 1986 - No. 4, Mar, 1987 (limited series)
1-4: Legends tie-ins all issues 4.00

COSMIC GUARD
Devil's Due Publ.: Aug, 2004 - No. 6, Dec, 2005 ($2.99)
1-6-Jim Starlin-s/a 3.00

COSMIC HEROES
Eternity/Malibu Graphics: Oct, 1988 - No. 11, Dec, 1989 ($1.95, B&W)
1-11: Reprints 1934-1936's Buck Rogers newspaper strips #1-728 3.00

COSMIC ODYSSEY
DC Comics: 1988 - No. 4, 1988 ($3.50, limited series, squarebound)
1-4: Reintro. New Gods into DC continuity; Superman, Batman, Green Lantern (John Stewart) app; Starlin scripts, Mignola-c/a in all. 2-Darkseid merges Demon & Jason Blood (separated in Demon limited series #4) 5.00
TPB (1992,2009, $19.99) r/#1-4; Robert Greenberger intro. 20.00

COSMIC POWERS
Marvel Comics: Mar, 1994 - No. 6, Aug, 1994 ($2.50, limited series)
1,2-Thanos app. 1-Ron Lim-c/a(p). 2-Terrax 5.00
3-6: 3-Ganymede & Jack of Hearts app. 4.00

COSMIC POWERS UNLIMITED
Marvel Comics: May, 1995 - No. 5, May, 1996 ($3.95, quarterly)
1-5 4.00

COSMIC SLAM
Ultimate Sports Entertainment: 1999 ($3.95, one-shot)
1-McGwire, Sosa, Bagwell, Justice battle aliens; Sienkiewicz-c 4.00

COSMO (The Merry Martian)
Archie Comic Publications: Feb, 2018 - Present ($2.99)
1,2-Cosmo, Astra, and Orbi app.; Ian Flynn-s/Tracy Yardley-a; multiple covers 3.00

COSMO CAT (Becomes Sunny #11 on; also see All Top & Wotalife Comics)
Fox Publications/Green Publ. Co./Norlen Mag.: July-Aug, 1946 - No. 10, Oct, 1947; 1957; 1959

	GD 2.0	VG 4.0	FN 6.0	VF 8.0	VF/NM 9.0	NM- 9.2
1	30	60	90	177	289	400
2	15	30	45	86	133	180
3-Origin (11-12/46)	19	38	57	111	176	240
4-Robot-c	15	30	45	85	130	175
5-10	11	22	33	60	83	105
2-4(1957-Green Publ. Co.)	6	12	18	27	33	38
2-4(1959-Norlen Mag.)	5	10	15	23	28	32
I.W. Reprint #1	2	4	6	11	16	20

COSMO THE MERRY MARTIAN
Archie Publications (Radio Comics): Sept, 1958 - No. 6, Oct, 1959

	GD 2.0	VG 4.0	FN 6.0	VF 8.0	VF/NM 9.0	NM- 9.2
1-Bob White-a in all	18	36	54	105	165	225
2-6	12	24	36	69	97	125

COTTON WOODS (All-American athlete)
Dell Publishing Co.: No. 837, Sept, 1957

	GD 2.0	VG 4.0	FN 6.0	VF 8.0	VF/NM 9.0	NM- 9.2
Four Color 837	5	10	15	30	50	70

COUGAR, THE (Cougar No. 2)
Seaboard Periodicals (Atlas): April, 1975 - No. 2, July, 1975

	GD 2.0	VG 4.0	FN 6.0	VF 8.0	VF/NM 9.0	NM- 9.2
1,2: 1-Vampire; Adkins-a(p). 2-Cougar origin; werewolf-s; Buckler-c(p)	2	4	6	11	16	20

COUNTDOWN (See Movie Classics)

COUNTDOWN
DC Comics (WildStorm): June, 2000 - No. 8, Jan, 2001 ($2.95)
1-8-Mariotte-s/Lopresti-a 3.00

COUNTDOWN (Continued from 52 weekly series)
DC Comics: No. 51, July, 2007 - No. 1, June, 2008 ($2.99, weekly, limited series) (issue #s go in reverse)
51-Gatefold wraparound-c by Andy Kubert; Duela Dent killed; the Monitors app. 3.00
50-1: 50-Joker-c. 48-Lightray dies. 47-Mary Marvel gains Black Adam's powers. 46-Intro. Forerunner. 43-Funeral for Bart Allen. 39-Karate Kid-c 3.00
Countdown to Final Crisis Vol. 1 TPB (2008, $19.99) r/#51-39 20.00
Countdown to Final Crisis Vol. 2 TPB (2008, $19.99) r/#38-26 20.00
Countdown to Final Crisis Vol. 3 TPB (2008, $19.99) r/#25-13 20.00
Countdown to Final Crisis Vol. 4 TPB (2008, $19.99) r/#12-1 20.00

COUNTDOWN: ARENA (Takes place during Countdown #21-18)
DC Comics: Feb, 2008 - No. 4, Feb, 2008 ($3.99, weekly, limited series)
1-4-Battles between alternate Earth heroes; McDaniel-a; Andy Kubert variant-c on each 4.00
TPB (2008, $17.99) r/#1-4; variant covers 18.00

COUNTDOWN PRESENTS: LORD HAVOK & THE EXTREMISTS
DC Comics: Dec, 2007 - No. 8 ($2.99, limited series)
1-6: 1-Tieri-s/Sharp-a/c; Challengers From Beyond app. 3.00
TPB (2008, $17.99) r/#1-6 18.00

COUNTDOWN PRESENTS THE SEARCH FOR RAY PALMER (Leads into Countdown #18)
DC Comics: Nov, 2007 - Feb, 2008 ($2.99, series of one-shots)
...: Wildstorm (11/07) Part 1; The Authority app.; Art Adams-c/Unzueta-a 3.00
...: Crime Society (12/07) Earth-3 Owlman & Jokester app.; Igle-a 3.00
...: Red Rain (1/08) Vampire Batman app.; Kelley Jones-c; Jones, Battle & Unzueta-a 3.00
...: Gotham By Gaslight (1/08) Victorian Batman app.; Tocchini-a/Nguyen-c 3.00
...: Red Son (2/08) Soviet Superman app.; Foreman-a 3.00
...: Superwoman/Batwoman (2/08) Conclusion; gender-reversed heroes; Sook-c 3.00
TPB (2008, $17.99) r/one-shots 18.00

COUNTDOWN SPECIAL
DC Comics: Dec, 2007 - Jun, 2008 ($4.99, collection of reprints related to Countdown)
...: Eclipso (5/08) r/Eclipso #10 & Spectre #17,18 (1994); Sook-c 5.00
...: Jimmy Olsen (1/08) r/Superman's Pal, Jimmy Olsen #136,147,148; Kirby-s/a; Sook-c 5.00
...: Kamandi (6/08) r/Kamandi: The Last Boy on Earth #1,10,29; Kirby-s/a; Sook-c 5.00
...: New Gods (3/08) r/Forever People #1, Mr. Miracle #1, New Gods #7; Kirby-s/a; Sook-c 5.00
...: Omac (4/08) r/Omac (1974) #1, Warlord #37-39, DC Comics Presents #61; Sook-c 5.00
...: The Atom 1,2 (2/08) r/stories from Super-Team Family #11-14; Sook-c on both 5.00
...: The Flash (12/07) r/Rogues Gallery in Flash (1st series) #106,113,155,174; Sook-c 5.00

COUNTDOWN TO ADVENTURE
DC Comics: Oct, 2007 - No. 8, May, 2008 ($3.99, limited series)
1-8: 1-Adam Strange, Animal Man and Starfire app.; origin of Forerunner 4.00
TPB (2008, $17.99) r/#1-8 18.00

COUNTDOWN TO INFINITE CRISIS (See DC Countdown)

COUNTDOWN TO MYSTERY (See Eclipso: The Music of the Spheres TPB for reprint)
DC Comics: Nov, 2007 - No. 8, Jun, 2008 ($3.99, limited series)
1-8: 1-Doctor Fate, Eclipso, The Spectre and Plastic Man app. 4.00
TPB (2008, $17.99) r/#1-8 18.00

COUNT DUCKULA (TV)
Marvel Comics: Nov, 1988 - No. 15, Jan, 1991 ($1.00)
1,8: 1-Dangermouse back-up. 8-Geraldo Rivera photo-c/& app.; Sienkiewicz-a(i) 5.00
2-7,9-15: Dangermouse back-ups in all 4.00

COUNT OF MONTE CRISTO, THE
Dell Publishing Co.: No. 794, May, 1957

	GD 2.0	VG 4.0	FN 6.0	VF 8.0	VF/NM 9.0	NM- 9.2
Four Color 794-Movie, Buscema-a	8	16	24	51	96	140

COUP D'ETAT (Oneshots)
DC Comics (WildStorm): April, 2004 ($2.95, weekly limited series)
...: Sleeper 1 (part 1 of 4) Jim Lee-a; 2 covers by Lee and Bermejo 3.00
...: Stormwatch 1 (part 2 of 4) D'Anda-a; 2 covers by D'Anda and Bermejo 3.00
...: Wildcats Version 3.0 1 (part 3 of 4) Garza-a; 2 covers by Garza and Bermejo 3.00
...: The Authority 1 (part 4 of 4) Portacio-a; 2 covers by Portacio and Bermejo 3.00
...: Afterword 1 (5/04) Profile pages and prelude stories for Sleeper & Wetworks 3.00
TPB (2004, $12.95) r/series and profile pages from Afterword 13.00

COURAGE COMICS
J. Edward Slavin: 1945

	GD 2.0	VG 4.0	FN 6.0	VF 8.0	VF/NM 9.0	NM- 9.2
1,2,77	16	32	48	94	147	200

COURTNEY CRUMRIN
Oni Press: Apr, 2012 - No. 10, Feb, 2013 ($3.99)
1-10-Ted Naifeh-s/a 4.00
#1 (5/14, Free Comic Book Day giveaway) r/#1 3.00

COURTNEY CRUMRIN...
Oni Press: July, 2005; July 2007; Dec, 2008 ($5.95, B&W, series of one-shots)
... And The Fire Thief's Tale (7/07) Naifeh-s/a 6.00
... And The Prince of Nowhere (12/08) Naifeh-s/a 6.00
... Tales (5/11) sequel to Tales Portrait of the Warlock...; Naifeh-s/a 6.00
... Tales Portrait of the Warlock as a Young Man (7/05) origin Uncle Aloysius; Naifeh-s/a 6.00

Coven Black & White #1 © Awesome

Cowboy Love #9 © FAW

Cowgirl Romances #8 © FH

COURTNEY CRUMRIN & THE COVEN OF MYSTICS
Oni Press: Dec, 2002 - No. 4, March, 2003 ($2.95, B&W, limited series)

	GD 2.0	VG 4.0	FN 6.0	VF 8.0	VF/NM 9.0	NM- 9.2
1-4-Ted Naifeh-s/a						3.00
TPB (9/03, $11.95, 8" x 5-1/2") r/#1-4						12.00

COURTNEY CRUMRIN & THE NIGHT THINGS
Oni Press: Mar, 2002 - No. 4, June, 2002 ($2.95, B&W, limited series)

	GD 2.0	VG 4.0	FN 6.0	VF 8.0	VF/NM 9.0	NM- 9.2
1-4-Ted Naifeh-s/a						3.00
Free Comic Book Day Edition (5/03) Naifeh-s/a						3.00
TPB (12/02, $11.95) r/#1-4						12.00

COURTNEY CRUMRIN IN THE TWILIGHT KINGDOM
Oni Press: Dec, 2003 - No. 4, May, 2004 ($2.99, B&W, limited series)

	GD 2.0	VG 4.0	FN 6.0	VF 8.0	VF/NM 9.0	NM- 9.2
1-4-Ted Naifeh-s/a						3.00
TPB (9/04, $11.95, digest-size) r/#1-4						12.00

COURTSHIP OF EDDIE'S FATHER (TV)
Dell Publishing Co.: Jan, 1970 - No. 2, May, 1970

	GD 2.0	VG 4.0	FN 6.0	VF 8.0	VF/NM 9.0	NM- 9.2
1-Bill Bixby photo-c on both	5	10	15	34	60	85
2	4	8	12	23	37	50

COVEN
Awesome Entertainment: Aug, 1997 - No. 5, Mar, 1998 ($2.50)

	GD 2.0	VG 4.0	FN 6.0	VF 8.0	VF/NM 9.0	NM- 9.2
Preview	1	2	3	5	6	8
1-Loeb-s/Churchill-a; three covers by Churchill, Liefeld, Pollina	1	2	3	5	6	8
1-Fan Appreciation Ed.(3/98); new Churchill-c						3.00
1+ :Includes B&W art from Kaboom	1	3	4	6	8	10
2-Regular-c w/leaping Fantom						6.00
2-Variant-c w/circle of candles	1	2	3	5	6	8
3-6-Contains flip book preview of ReGex						3.00
3-White variant-c	1	2	3	4	5	7
3,4: 3-Halloween wraparound-c. 4-Purple variant-c						3.00
...Black & White (9/98) Short stories						3.00
...Fantom Special (2/98) w/sketch pages						5.00

COVEN
Awesome Entertainment: Jan, 1999 - No. 3, June, 1999 ($2.50)

	GD 2.0	VG 4.0	FN 6.0	VF 8.0	VF/NM 9.0	NM- 9.2
1-3: 1-Loeb-s/Churchill-a; 6 covers by various. 2-Supreme-c/app. 3-Flip book w/Kaboom preview						3.00
... Dark Origins (7/99, 2.50) w/Lionheart gallery						3.00

COVENANT, THE
Image Comics (Top Cow): 2005 ($9.99, squarebound, one-shot)

	GD 2.0	VG 4.0	FN 6.0	VF 8.0	VF/NM 9.0	NM- 9.2
nn-Tone Rodriguez-a/Aron Coleite-s						10.00

COVENANT, THE
Image Comics: Jun, 2015 - No. 5, Dec, 2015 ($3.99)

	GD 2.0	VG 4.0	FN 6.0	VF 8.0	VF/NM 9.0	NM- 9.2
1-5-Rob Liefeld-s/c; Matt Horak-a; story of the Ark of the Covenant						4.00

COVERED WAGONS, HO (Disney, TV)
Dell Publishing Co.: No. 814, June, 1957 (Donald Duck)

	GD 2.0	VG 4.0	FN 6.0	VF 8.0	VF/NM 9.0	NM- 9.2
Four Color 814-Mickey Mouse app.	5	10	15	34	60	85

COWBOY ACTION (Formerly Western Thrillers No. 1-4; Becomes Quick-Trigger Western No. 12 on)
Atlas Comics (ACI): No. 5, March, 1955 - No. 11, March, 1956

	GD 2.0	VG 4.0	FN 6.0	VF 8.0	VF/NM 9.0	NM- 9.2
5	15	30	45	90	140	190
6-10: 6-8-Heath-c	12	24	36	67	94	120
11-Williamson-a (4 pgs.); Baker-a	14	28	42	76	108	140

NOTE: ***Ayers** a-8. **Drucker** a-6. **Maneely** c/a-5, 6. **Severin** c-10. **Shores** a-7.*

COWBOY COMICS (Star Ranger #12, Stories #14)(Star Ranger Funnies #15)
Centaur Publishing Co.: No. 13, July, 1938 - No. 14, Aug, 1938

	GD 2.0	VG 4.0	FN 6.0	VF 8.0	VF/NM 9.0	NM- 9.2
13-(Rare)-Ace and Deuce, Lyin Lou, Air Patrol, Aces High, Lee Trent, Trouble Hunters begin	226	452	678	1446	2473	3500
14-(Rare)-Filchock-c	161	322	483	1030	1765	2500

NOTE: ***Guardineer** a-13, 14. **Gustavson** a-13, 14.*

COWBOY IN AFRICA (TV)
Gold Key: Mar, 1968

	GD 2.0	VG 4.0	FN 6.0	VF 8.0	VF/NM 9.0	NM- 9.2
1(10219-803)-Chuck Connors photo-c	4	8	12	25	40	55

COWBOY LOVE (Becomes Range Busters?)
Fawcett Publications/Charlton Comics No. 28 on: 7/49 - V2#10, 6/50; No. 11, 1951; No. 28, 2/55 - No. 31, 8/55

	GD 2.0	VG 4.0	FN 6.0	VF 8.0	VF/NM 9.0	NM- 9.2
V1#1-Rocky Lane photo back-c	15	30	45	90	140	190
2	8	16	24	44	57	70
V1#3,4,6 (12/49)	8	16	24	40	50	60
5-Bill Boyd photo back-c (11/49)	9	18	27	47	61	75
V2#7-Williamson/Evans-a	10	20	30	54	72	90
V2#8-11	7	14	21	35	43	50
V1#28 (Charlton)-Last precode (2/55) (Formerly Romantic Story?)	6	12	18	31	38	45
V1#29-31 (Charlton; becomes Sweetheart Diary #32 on)	6	12	18	28	34	40

NOTE: ***Powell** a-10. **Marcus Swayze** a-2, 3. Photo c-1-11. No. 1-3, 5-7, 9, 10 are 52 pgs.*

COWBOY ROMANCES (Young Men No. 4 on)
Marvel Comics (IPC): Oct, 1949 - No. 3, Mar, 1950 (All photo-c & 52 pgs.)

	GD 2.0	VG 4.0	FN 6.0	VF 8.0	VF/NM 9.0	NM- 9.2
1-Photo-c	26	52	78	154	252	350
2-William Holden, Mona Freeman "Streets of Laredo" photo-c	18	36	54	107	169	230
3-Photo-c	15	30	45	90	140	190

COWBOYS 'N' INJUNS (...and Indians No. 6 on)
Compix No. 1-5/Magazine Enterprises No. 6 on: 1946 - No. 5, 1947; No. 6, 1949 - No. 8, 1952

	GD 2.0	VG 4.0	FN 6.0	VF 8.0	VF/NM 9.0	NM- 9.2
1-Funny animal western	16	32	48	92	144	195
2-5-All funny animal western	10	20	30	56	76	95
6(A-1 23)-Half violent, half funny; Ayers-a	15	30	45	85	130	175
7(A-1 41, 1950), 8(A-1 48)-All funny	9	18	27	52	69	85
I.W. Reprint No. 1,7,10 (Reprinted in Canada by Superior, No. 7), 10('63)	2	4	6	11	16	20

COWBOY WESTERN COMICS (TV)(Formerly Jack In The Box; Becomes Space Western No. 40-45 & Wild Bill Hickok & Jingles No. 68 on; title: Cowboy Western Heroes No. 47 & 48; Cowboy Western No. 49 on)
Charlton (Capitol Stories): No. 17, 7/48 - No. 39, 8/52; No. 46, 10/53; No. 47, 12/53; No. 48, Spr, '54; No. 49, 5-6/54 - No. 67, 3/58 (nn 40-45)

	GD 2.0	VG 4.0	FN 6.0	VF 8.0	VF/NM 9.0	NM- 9.2
17-Jesse James, Annie Oakley, Wild Bill Hickok begin; Texas Rangers app.	16	32	48	94	147	200
18,19-Orlando-c/a. 18-Paul Bunyan begins. 19-Wyatt Earp story	10	20	30	58	79	100
20-25: 21-Buffalo Bill story. 22-Texas Rangers-c/story. 24-Joel McCrea photo-c & adaptation from movie "Three Faces West". 25-James Craig photo-c & adaptation from movie "Northwest Stampede"	9	18	27	52	69	85
26-George Montgomery photo-c and adaptation from movie "Indian Scout"; 1 pg. bio on Will Rogers	10	20	30	58	79	100
27-Sunset Carson photo-c & adapts movie "Sunset Carson Rides Again" plus 1 other Sunset Carson story	39	78	117	240	395	550
28-Sunset Carson line drawn-c; adapts movies "Battling Marshal" & "Fighting Mustangs" starring Sunset Carson	20	40	60	114	182	250
29-Sunset Carson line drawn-c; adapts movies "Rio Grande" with Sunset Carson & "Winchester '73" w/James Stewart plus 5 pg. life history of Sunset Carson featuring Tom Mix	20	40	60	114	182	250
30-Sunset Carson photo-c; adapts movie "Deadline" starring Sunset Carson plus 1 other Sunset Carson story	39	78	117	240	395	550
31-34,38,39,47-50 (no #40-45): 50-Golden Arrow, Rocky Lane & Blackjack (r?) stories	9	18	27	47	61	75
35,36-Sunset Carson-c/stories (2 in each). 35-Inside front-c photo of Sunset Carson plus photo on-c	20	40	60	120	195	270
37-Sunset Carson stories (2)	15	30	45	94	147	200
46-(Formerly Space Western)-Space western story	15	30	45	94	147	200
51-57,59-66: 51-Golden Arrow(r?) & Monte Hale-r renamed Rusty Hall. 53,54-Tom Mix-r. 55-Monte Hale story(r?). 66-Young Eagle story. 67-Wild Bill Hickok and Jingles-c/story	7	14	21	35	43	50
58-(1/56)-Wild Bill Hickok, Annie Oakley & Jesse James stories; Forgione-a	8	16	24	44	57	70
67-(15¢, 68 pgs.)-Williamson/Torres-a, 5 pgs.	9	18	27	50	65	80

NOTE: *Many issues trimmed 1" shorter. **Maneely** a-67(5). Inside front/back photo c-29.*

COWGIRL ROMANCES
Marvel Comics (CCC): No. 28, Jan, 1950 (52 pgs.)

	GD 2.0	VG 4.0	FN 6.0	VF 8.0	VF/NM 9.0	NM- 9.2
28(#1)-Photo-c	23	46	69	136	223	310

COWGIRL ROMANCES
Fiction House Magazines: 1950 - No. 12, Winter, 1952-53 (No. 1-3: 52 pgs.)

	GD 2.0	VG 4.0	FN 6.0	VF 8.0	VF/NM 9.0	NM- 9.2
1-Kamen-a	50	100	150	315	533	750
2	28	56	84	165	270	375
3-5: 5-12-Whitman-c (most)	24	48	72	142	234	325
6-9,11,12	22	44	66	132	216	300
10-Frazetta?/Williamson?-a; Kamen?/Baker-a; r/Mitzi story from Movie Comics #4 w/all new dialogue	39	78	117	240	395	550

C.O.W.L. #6 © Higgins & Siegel

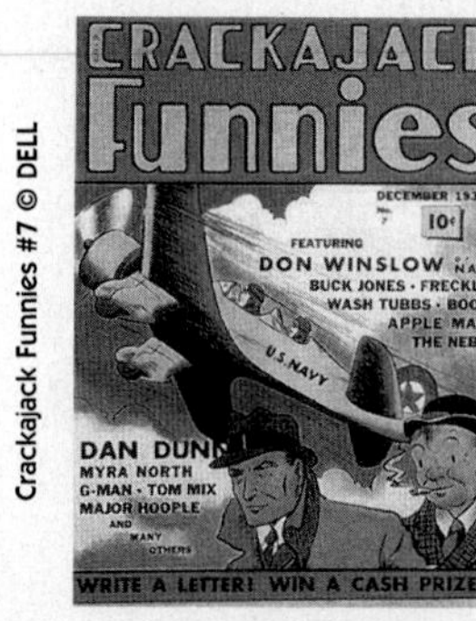

Crackajack Funnies #7 © DELL

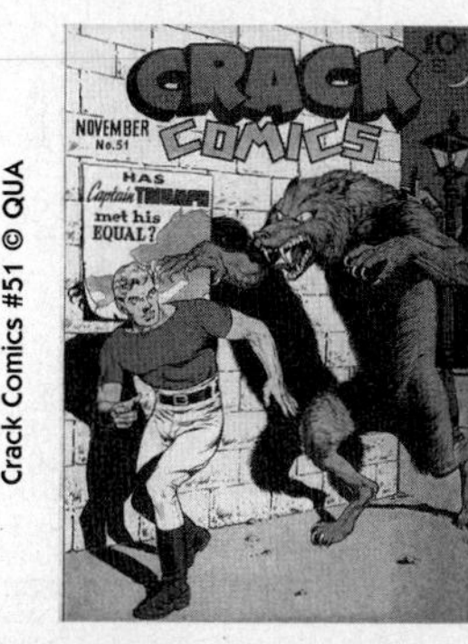

Crack Comics #51 © QUA

GD 2.0 | VG 4.0 | FN 6.0 | VF 8.0 | VF/NM 9.0 | NM- 9.2

C.O.W.L.
Image Comics: May, 2014 - No. 11, Jul, 2015 ($3.50)
1-11: 1-Higgins & Siegel-s/Reis-a. 6-Origin of Grey Raven; Charretier-a 3.50

COW PUNCHER (...Comics)
Avon Periodicals: Jan, 1947; No. 2, Sept, 1947 - No. 7, 1949
1-Clint Cortland, Texas Ranger, Kit West, Pioneer Queen begin; Kubert-a; Alabam stories begin 58 116 174 371 636 900
2-Kubert, Kamen/Feldstein-a; Kamen-c 48 96 144 302 514 725
3-5,7: 3-Kiefer story 37 74 111 222 361 500
6-Opium drug mention story; bondage, headlight-c; Reinman-a 45 90 135 284 480 675

COWPUNCHER
Realistic Publications: 1953 (nn) (Reprints Avon's No. 2)
nn-Kubert-a 15 30 45 85 130 175

COWSILLS, THE (See Harvey Pop Comics)

COW SPECIAL, THE
Image Comics (Top Cow): Spring-Summer 2000; 2001 ($2.95)
1-Previews upcoming Top Cow projects; Yancy Butler photo-c 3.00
Vol. 2 #1-Witchblade-c; previews and interviews 3.00

COYOTE
Marvel Comics (Epic Comics): June, 1983 - No. 16, Mar, 1986
1-10,15: 7-10-Ditko-a 4.00
11-1st McFarlane-a. 3 6 9 14 19 24
12-14,16: 12-14-McFarlane-a. 14-Badger x-over. 16-Reagan c/app. 6.00
Coyote Collection Vol. 1 (2005, $14.99) reprints from Coyote #1-7 & Scorpio Rose #1,2 plus Rogers layout pages for unpublished #3; Englehart intro. 15.00
Coyote Collection Vol. 2 (2005, $12.99) reprints from Coyote #1-4 13.00
Coyote Collection Vol. 3 (2006, $12.99) reprints from Coyote #5-8 13.00
Coyote Collection Vol. 4 (2007, $14.99) reprints from Coyote #9-12 15.00
Coyote Collection Vol. 5 (2007, $12.99) reprints from Coyote #13-16 13.00

COYOTES
Image Comics: Nov, 2017 - Present ($3.99)
1-3-Sean Lewis-s/Caitlin Yarsky-a 4.00

CRACKAJACK FUNNIES (Also see The Owl)
Dell Publishing Co.: June, 1938 - No. 43, Jan, 1942
1-Dan Dunn, Freckles, Myra North, Wash Tubbs, Apple Mary, The Nebbs, Don Winslow, Tom Mix, Buck Jones, Major Hoople, Clyde Beatty, Boots begin 194 388 582 1242 2121 3000
2 77 154 231 493 847 1200
3 58 116 174 371 636 900
4 48 96 144 302 514 725
5-Nude woman on cover (10/38) 54 108 162 343 574 825
6-8,10: 8-Speed Bolton begins (1st app.) 42 84 126 265 445 625
9-(3/39)-Red Ryder strip-r begin by Harman; 1st app. in comics & 1st cover app. 174 348 522 1114 1907 2700
11-14 36 72 108 216 351 485
15-Tarzan text feature begins by Burroughs (9/39); not in #26,35 39 78 117 234 385 535
16-24: 18-Stratosphere Jim begins (1st app., 12/39). 23-Ellery Queen begins plus-c (1st comic book app., 5/40) 32 64 96 188 307 425
25-The Owl begins (1st app., 7/40); in new costume #26 by Frank Thomas (also see Popular Comics #72) 87 174 261 553 952 1350
26,27,29,30 50 100 150 315 533 750
28-Part Owl-c 58 116 174 371 636 900
31-Owl covers begin, end #42 61 122 183 390 670 950
32-Origin Owl Girl 63 126 189 403 689 975
33-37: 36-Last Tarzan issue. 37-Cyclone & Midge begin (1st app.) 55 110 165 352 601 850
38-(scarce) Classic giant gorilla vs. Owl-c 81 162 243 518 884 1250
39-Andy Panda begins (intro/1st app., 9/41) 71 142 213 454 777 1100
40-42: 42-Last Owl-c. 53 106 159 334 567 800
43-Terry & the Pirates-r 26 52 78 154 252 350
NOTE: *McWilliams art in most issues.*

CRACK COMICS (Crack Western No. 63 on)
Quality Comics Group: May, 1940 - No. 62, Sept, 1949
1-Origin & 1st app. The Black Condor by Lou Fine, Madame Fatal, Red Torpedo, Rock Bradden & The Space Legion; The Clock, Alias the Spider (by Gustavson), Wizard Wells, & Ned Brant begin; Powell-a; Note: Madame Fatal is a man dressed as a woman 465 930 1395 3395 5998 8600
2 219 438 657 1402 2401 3400
3 155 310 465 992 1696 2400
4 126 252 378 806 1378 1950
5-10: 5-Molly The Model begins. 10-Tor, the Magic Master begins 103 206 309 659 1130 1600
11-20: 13-1 pg. J. Cole-a. 15-1st app. Spitfire 87 174 261 553 952 1350
21-24: 23-Pen Miller begins; continued from National Comics #22. 24-Last Fine Black Condor 68 136 204 435 743 1050
25 54 108 162 343 574 825
26-Flag-c 68 136 204 435 743 1050
27-(1/43)-Intro & origin Captain Triumph by Alfred Andriola (Kerry Drake artist) & begin series 116 232 348 742 1271 1800
28-30 42 84 126 265 445 625
31-39: 31-Last Black Condor 24 48 72 142 234 325
40-46 17 34 51 100 158 215
47-57,59,60-Capt. Triumph by Crandall 18 36 54 107 169 230
58,61,62-Last Captain Triumph 15 30 45 85 130 175
NOTE: *Black Condor by* ***Fine****: No. 1, 2, 5, 6, 8, 10-24; by* ***Sultan****: No. 3, 7; by* ***Fugitani****: No. 9.* ***Cole*** *a-34.* ***Crandall*** *a-61(unsigned); c-48, 49, 51-61.* ***Guardineer*** *a-17.* ***Gustavson*** *a-1, 2, 4, 7, 13, 17, 23.* ***McWilliams*** *a-15-27. Black Condor c-2, 4, 6, 8, 10, 12, 14, 16, 18, 20-26. Capt. Triumph c-27-62. The Clock c-1, 3, 5, 7, 9, 11, 13, 15, 17, 19.*

CRACK COMICS (Next Issue Project)
Image Comics: No. 63, Oct, 2011 ($4.99, one-shot)
63-Mimics style & format of a 1949 issue; Weiss-c; s/a by various; Capt Triumph app. 5.00

CRACK COMICS
Quality Comics: May 1940
1-Ashcan comic, not distributed to newsstands, only for in-house use. Cover art is the same as published version of Crack Comics #1with exception of text panel on bottom left of cover. A CGC certified 4.0 copy sold for $1,495 in 2005.

CRACKED (Magazine) (Satire) (Also see The 3-D Zone #19)
Major Magazines(#1-212)/Globe Communications(#213-346/American Media #347 on):
Feb-Mar, 1958 - No. 365, Nov, 2004
1-One pg. Williamson-a; Everett-c; Gunsmoke-s 34 68 102 245 548 850
2-1st Shut-Ups & Bonus Cut-Outs; Superman parody-c by Severin (his 1st cover on the title) Frankenstein-s 16 32 48 110 243 375
3-5 12 24 36 79 170 260
6-10: 7-Reprints 1st 6 covers on-c. 8-Frankenstein-c. 10-Wolverton-a 9 18 27 62 126 190
11-12, 13(nn,3/60), 7 14 21 48 89 130
14-Kirby-a 8 16 24 54 102 150
15-17, 18(nn,2/61), 19,20 6 12 18 40 73 105
21-27(11/62), 27(No.28, 2/63; mis-#d), 29(5/63) 5 10 15 35 63 90
30-40(11/64): 37-Beatles and Superman cameos 4 8 12 27 44 60
41-45,47-56,59,60: 47,49,52-Munsters. 51-Beatles inside-c. 59-Laurel and Hardy photos 4 8 12 23 37 50
46,57,58: 46,58-Man From U.N.C.L.E. 46-Beatles. 57-Rolling Stones 4 8 12 25 40 55
61-80: 62-Beatles cameo. 69-Batman, Superman app. 70-(8/68) Elvis cameo. 71-Garrison's Gorillas; W.C. Fields photos 3 6 9 16 23 30
81-99: 99-Alfred E. Neuman on-c 3 6 9 14 20 25
100 3 6 9 17 26 35
101-119: 104-Godfather-c/s. 108-Archie Bunker-s. 112,119-Kung Fu (TV). 113-Tarzan-s. 115-MASH. 117-Cannon. 118-The Sting-c/s 2 4 6 10 14 18
120(12/74) Six Million Dollar Man-c/s; Ward-a 2 4 6 13 18 22
121,122,124-126,128-133,136-140: 121-American Graffiti. 122-Korak-c/s. 124,131-Godfather-c/s. 128-Capone-c. 129,131-Jaws. 132-Baretta-c/s. 133-Space 1999. 136-Laverne and Shirley/Fonz-c. 137-Travolta/Kotter-c/s. 138-Travolta/Laverne and Shirley/ Fonz-c. 139-Barney Miller-c/s. 140-King Kong-c/s; Fonz-s 2 4 6 10 14 18
123-Planet of the Apes-c/s; Six Million Dollar Man 2 4 6 13 18 22
127,134,135: 127-Star Trek-c/s; Ward-a. 134-Fonz-c/s; Starsky and Hutch. 135-Bionic Woman-c/s; Ward-a 2 4 6 11 16 20
141,151-Charlie's Angels-c/s. 151-Frankenstein 2 4 6 11 16 20
142,143,150,152-155,157: 142-MASH-c/s. 143-Rocky-c/s; King Kong-s. 150-(5/78) Close Encounters-c/s. 152-Close Enc./Star Wars-c/s. 153-Close Enc./Fonz-c/s. 154-Jaws II-c/s; Star Wars-s. 155-Star Wars/Fonz-c 2 4 6 9 13 16
144,149,156,158-160: 144-Fonz/Happy Days-c. 149-Star Wars/Six Mil.$ Man-c/s. 156-Grease/Travolta-c. 158-Mork & Mindy. 159-Battlestar Galactica-c/s; MASH-s. 160-Superman-c/s 2 4 6 11 16 20
145,147-Both have insert postcards: 145-Fonz/Rocky/L&S-c/s. 147-Star Wars-s; Farrah photo page (missing postcards-1/2 price) 3 6 9 14 20 26
146,148: 46-Star Wars-c/s with stickers insert (missing stickers-1/2 price). 148-Star Wars-c/s with inside-c color poster 3 6 9 16 23 30
161,170-Ward-a: 161-Mork & Mindy-c/s. 170-Dukes of Hazzard-c/s

Cracked #226 © GCC

Cracked #260 © GCC

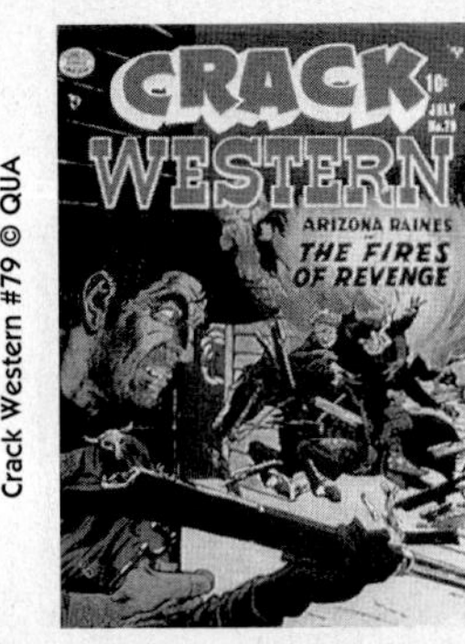

Crack Western #79 © QUA

GD 2.0 | VG 4.0 | FN 6.0 | VF 8.0 | VF/NM 9.0 | NM- 9.2

2 4 6 8 11 14

162,165-168,171,172,175-178,180-Ward-a: 162-Sherlock Holmes-s. 165-Dracula-c/s. 167-Mork-c/s. 168,175-MASH-c/s. 168-Mork-s. 172-Dukes of Hazzard/CHiPs-c/s. 176-Barney Miller-c/s 2 4 6 8 10 12

163,179:163-Postcard insert; Mork & Mindy-c/s. 179-Insult cards insert; Popeye, Dukes of Hazzard-c/s 3 6 9 14 19 24

164,169,173,174: 164-Alien movie-c/s; Mork & Mindy-s. 169-Star Trek. 173,174-Star Wars-Empire Strikes Back. 173-SW poster 2 4 6 9 13 16

181,182,185-191,193,194,196-198-most Ward-a: 182-MASH-c/s. 185-Dukes of Hazzard-c/s; Jefferson-s. 187-Love Boat. 188-Fall Guy-s. 189-Fonz/Happy Days-c. 190,194-MASH-c/s. 191-Magnum P.I./Rocky-c; Magnum-s. 193-Knight Rider-s. 196-Dukes of Hazzard/Knight Rider-c/s. 198-Jaws III-c/s; Fall Guy-s 1 2 3 5 7 9

183,184,192,195,199,200-Ward-a in all: 183-Superman-c/s. 184-Star Trek-c/s. 192-E.T.-c/s; Rocky-s. 195-E.T.-c/s. 199-Jabba-c; Star Wars-s. 200-(12/83) 1 3 4 6 8 10

201,203,210-A-Team-c/s 6.00

202,204-206,211-224,226,227,230-233: 202-Knight Rider-s. 204-Magnum P.I.; A-Team-s. 206-Michael Jackson/Mr. T-c/s. 212-Prince-s; Cosby-s. 213-Monsters issue-c/s. 215-Hulk Hogan/Mr. T-c/s. 216-Miami Vice-s; James Bond-s. 217-Rambo-s; Cosby-s; A-Team-s. 218-Rocky-c/s. 219-Arnold/Commando-c/s; Rocky-s; Godzilla. 220-Rocky-c/s. 221-Stephen King app. 223-Miami Vice-s. 224-Cosby-s. 226-29th Anniv.; Tarzan-s; Aliens-s; Family Ties-s. 227-Cosby, Family Ties, Miami Vice-s. 230-Monkees-c/s; Elvis on-c; 232-Alf, Cheers, StarTrek-s. 233-Superman/James Bond-c/s; Robocop, Predator-s 5.00

207-209,225,234: 207-Michael Jackson-c/s. 208-Indiana Jones-c/s. 209-MichaelJackson/Gremlins-c/s; Star Trek III-s. 225-Schwarzenegger/Stallone/G.I. Joe-c/s. 234-Don Martin-a begins; Batman/Robocop/Clint Eastwood-c/s 6.00

228,229: 228-Star Trek-c/s; Alf, Pee Wee Herman-s. 229-Monsters issue-c/s; centerfold with many superheroes 6.00

235,239,243,249: 235-1st Martin-c; Star Trek:TNG-s; Alf-s. 239-Beetlejuice-c/s; Mike Tyson-s. 243-X-Men and other heroes app. 249-Batman/Indiana Jones/Ghostbusters-c/s 6.00

236,244,245,248: 236-Madonna/Stallone-c/s; Twilight Zone-s. 244-Elvis-c/s; Martin-c. 245-Roger Rabbit-c/s. 248-Batman issue 6.00

237,238,240-242,246,247,250: 237-Robocop-s. 238-Rambo-c/s; Star Trek-s. 242-Dirty Harry-s, Ward-a. 246-Alf-s; Star Trek-s., Ward-a. 247-Star Trek-s. 250-Batman/Ghostbusters-s 4.00

251-253,255,256,259,261-265,275-278,281,284,286-297,299: 252-Star Trek-s. 253-Back to the Future-c/s. 255-TMNT-c/s. 256-TMNT-c/s; Batman, Bart Simpson on-c. 259-Die Hard II, Robocop-s. 261-TMNT, Twin Peaks-s. 262-Rocky-c/s; Rocky Horror-s. 265-TMNT-s. 276-Aliens III, Batman-s. 277-Clinton-c. 284-Bart Simpson-c; 90210-s. 297-Van Damme-s/photo-c. 299-Dumb & Dumber-c/s 4.00

254,257,266,267,272,280,282,285,298,300: 254-Back to the Future, Punisher-s; Wolverton-a, Batman-s, Ward-a. 257-Batman, Simpsons-s; Spider-Man and other heroes app. 266-Terminator-c/s. 267-Toons-c/s. 272-Star Trek VI-s. 280-Swimsuit issue. 282-Cheers-c/s. 285-Jurassic Park-c/s. 298-Swimsuit issue; Martin-c. 300-(8/95) Brady Bunch-c/s 5.00

258,260,274,279,283: 258-Simpsons-c/s; Back to the Future-s. 260-Spider-Man-c/s; Simpsons-s. 274-Batman-c/s. 279-Madonna-c/s. 283-Jurassic Park-c/s; Wolverine app. inside back-c 5.00

301-305,307-365: 365-Freas-c 3.00

306-Toy Story-c/s 4.00

Biggest... (Winter, 1977) 2 4 6 13 18 22

Biggest, Greatest... nn('65) 4 8 12 28 47 65

Biggest, Greatest... 2('66/67) - #5('69/70) 3 6 9 19 30 40

Biggest, Greatest... 6('70) - #12(Wint. '77) 3 6 9 14 19 24

Biggest, Greatest...13(Fall '78) - #21(Fall/Wint. '86) 2 4 6 8 11 14

...Blockbuster 1(Sum '87), 2('88), 3(Sum. '89) 1 3 4 6 8 10

...Blockbuster 4 - 6(Sum. '92) 6.00

...Collectors' Edition 4 ('73; formerly ...Special) 2 4 6 13 18 22

5-9,10(10/75) 2 4 6 11 16 20

11-19,20(11/17) 2 4 6 8 11 14

21,22,23(5/78): 23-Ward-a 2 4 6 8 11 14

(#24-62,64 not numbered)

1978 (nn; July, Sept, Nov, Dec) (#24-27) 2 4 6 8 11 14

1979 (nn; May, July, Sept, Nov, Dec) (#28-33) 2 4 6 8 11 14

1980 (nn; Feb, May, July, Sept, Nov, Dec) (#34-39) 1 3 4 6 8 10

1981 (nn; Feb, May, July, Sept, Nov, Dec) (#40-45) 1 3 4 6 8 10

1982 (nn; Feb, May, July, Sept, Nov, Dec) (#46-51) 1 3 4 6 8 10

1983 (nn; Feb, May, Sept, Nov, Dec) (#52-56) 1 3 4 6 8 10

1984 (nn; Feb, May, July, Nov) (#57-60) 1 2 3 4 5 7

1985 (nn; Feb) (#61) 1 2 3 4 5 7

62(9/85), nn(#63,11/85), 64(12/85), 65-69, 70(4/87) 1 2 3 4 5 7

71,72,73(100 pgs., 1/88), 74-79, 80(9/89) 5.00

81-96, 97(two diff. issues), 98-115: 83-Elvis, Batman parodies 5.00

116('98)-Last issue? 6.00

...Digest 1(Fall, '86, 148 pgs.), 2(1/87) 1 2 3 6 8 10

...Digest 3-5 1 2 3 4 5 7

...Party Pack 1,2('88) - 4('90) 4.00

...Shut-Ups 1(2/72) 3 6 9 17 26 35

...Shut-Ups 2('72) becomes Cracked Spec. #3 3 6 9 14 19 24

...Special 3('73; formerly Cracked Shut-Ups; ...Collectors' Edition#4 on) 2 4 6 13 18 22

... Summer Special 1(Sum. '91), 2(Sum. '92)-Don Martin-a 4.00

... Summer Special 3(Sum. '93) - 8(Sum. '98) 3.00

... Super (Vol. 2, formerly Super Cracked) 5(Wint. '91/92) - 14(Wint.'97/98) 3.00

Extra Special... 1(Spr. '76) 2 4 6 11 16 20

Extra Special... 2(Spr./Sum. '77) 2 4 6 10 14 18

Extra Special... 3(Wint. '79) - 9(Wint. '86) 1 2 3 4 5 7

Giant... nn('65) 5 10 15 33 57 80

Giant... 2('66) - 5('69) 3 6 9 21 33 45

Giant...6('70) - 12('76) 3 6 9 16 24 32

Giant...nn(9/77, #13), nn(1/78, #14), nn(3/78, #15), nn(5/78, #16), nn(7/78, #17), nn(11/78, #18), nn(3/79, #19), nn(7/79, #20), nn(10/79, #21), nn(12/79, #22), nn(3/80, #23), nn(7/80, #24) 2 4 6 11 16 20

Giant...nn(10/80, #25), nn(12/80, #26), nn(3/81, #27), nn(7/81, #28), nn(10/81, #29), nn(12/81, #30), nn(7/82, #31), nn(10/82, #32), nn(12/82, #33), nn(7/83, #34), 2 4 6 8 11 14

Giant...nn(10/83, #35), nn(12/83, #36), nn(3/84, #37), nn(7/84, #38), nn(10/84, #39), nn(3/85, #40), nn(7/85, #41), nn(10/85, #42) 1 2 3 5 7 9

Giant...43(3/86) - 46(1/87), 47(Wint. '88), 48(Wint. '89) 1 2 3 4 5 7

King Sized... 1('67) 4 8 12 25 40 55

King Sized... 2('68) - 5('71) 3 6 9 17 26 35

King Sized... 6('72) - 11('77) 3 6 9 14 20 26

King Sized... 12(Fall '78) - 17(Sum. '83) 2 4 6 8 11 14

King Sized... 18-20 (Sum/'86) (#21,22 exist?) 1 3 4 6 8 10

Spaced Out... 1-4 ('93 - '94) 5.00

Super... 1('68) 4 8 12 25 40 55

Super... 2('69) - 6('73) 3 6 9 19 30 40

Super... 7('74), 8(Spr. '75) - 10(Spr. '77) 3 6 9 15 22 28

Super... 11(Sum. '78) - 16(Fall '81) 2 4 6 11 16 20

Super... 17(Spr. '82) - 22(Fall '83) 2 4 6 8 11 14

Super... 23(Sum. '84, mis-numbered as #24) 2 4 6 8 11 14

Super... 24(Fall '84, correctly numbered) 2 4 6 8 11 14

Super... 25(Wint. '85) - 32(Fall '86) 2 4 6 8 10 12

Super... (Vol. 2) 1('87, 100 pgs.)-Severin & Elder-a 1 3 4 6 8 10

Super... (Vol. 2) 2(Sum. '88), 3(Wint. '89), 4(exist?)(Becomes Cracked Super) 6.00

NOTE: ***Burgos*** *a-1-10.* ***Colan*** *a-257.* ***Davis*** *a-5, 11-17, 24, 40, 80; c-12-14, 16.* ***Elder*** *a-5, 6, 10-13; c-10.* ***Everett*** *a-1-10, 23-25, 61; c-1.* ***Heath*** *a-1-3, 6, 13, 14, 17, 110; c-6.* ***Jaffee*** *a-5, 6.* ***Don Martin*** *c-235, 244, 247, 259, 261, 264.* ***Morrow*** *a-8-10.* ***Reinman*** *a-1-4.* ***Severin*** *c/a-in most all issues.* ***Shores*** *a-3-7.* ***Torres*** *a-7-10.* ***Ward*** *a-22-24, 27, 35, 40, 120-193, 195, 197-205, 242, 244, 246, 247, 250, 252-257.* ***Williamson*** *a-1 (1 pg.).* ***Wolverton*** *a-10 (2 pgs.), Giant nn('65).* ***Wood*** *a-27, 35, 40. Alfred E. Neuman c-177, 200, 202. Batman c-234, 248, 249, 256, 274. Captain America c-256. Christmas c-234, 243. Spider-Man c-260. Star Trek c-127, 169, 207, 228. Star Wars c-145, 146, 148, 149, 152, 155, 173, 174, 199. Superman c-183, 233. #144, 146 have free full-color pre-glued stickers. #145, 147, 155, 163 have free full-color postcards. #123, 137, 154, 157 have free iron-ons.*

CRACKED MONSTER PARTY
Globe Communications: July, 1988 - No. 27, Wint. 1999/2000

1 2 4 6 11 16 20

2-10 2 4 6 8 10 12

11-26 1 2 3 4 5 7

27-Interview with a Vampire-c/s 2 4 6 8 10 12

CRACKED'S FOR MONSTERS ONLY
Major Magazines: Sept, 1969 - No. 9, Sept, 1969; June, 1972

1 4 8 12 28 47 65

2-9, nn(6/72) 3 6 9 19 30 40

CRACK WESTERN (Formerly Crack Comics; Jonesy No. 85 on)
Quality Comics Group: No. 63, Nov, 1949 - No. 84, May, 1953 (36 pgs., 63-68,74-on)

63(#1)-Ward-c; Two-Gun Lil (origin & 1st app.)(ends #84), Arizona Ames, his horse Thunder (with sidekick Spurs & his horse Calico), Frontier Marshal (ends #70), & Dead Canyon Days (ends #69) begin; Crandall-a 18 36 54 107 169 230

64,65: 64-Ward-c. Crandall-a in both. 15 30 45 83 124 165

66,68-Photo-c. 66-Arizona Ames becomes A. Raines (ends #84) 13 26 39 72 101 130

67-Randolph Scott photo-c; Crandall-a 14 28 42 80 115 150

69(52pgs.)-Crandall-a 13 26 39 72 101 130

70(52pgs.)-The Whip (origin & 1st app.) & his horse Diablo begin (ends #84); Crandall-a 13 26 39 72 101 130

71(52pgs.)-Frontier Marshal becomes Bob Allen F. Marshal (ends #84); Crandall-c/a 14 28 42 80 115 150

72(52pgs.)-Tim Holt photo-c 12 24 36 67 94 120

73(52pgs.)-Photo-c 10 20 30 58 79 100

74-76,78,79,81,83-Crandall-c. 83-Crandall-a(p) 11 22 33 62 86 110

Crash Comics #1 © TPC

Crazy #3 © MAR

Crazy #52 © MAR

GD 2.0 | VG 4.0 | FN 6.0 | VF 8.0 | VF/NM 9.0 | NM- 9.2

77,80,82 8 16 24 44 57 70
84-Crandall-c/a 12 24 36 67 94 120
NOTE: ***Crandall** c-71p, 74-81, 83p(w/**Cuidera**-i).*

CRASH COMICS (Cat-Man Comics No. 6 on)
Tem Publishing Co.: May, 1940 - No. 5, Nov, 1940

1-The Blue Streak, Strongman (origin), The Perfect Human, Shangra begin (1st app. of each); Kirby-a 360 720 1080 2520 4410 6300
2-Simon & Kirby-a 200 400 600 1280 2190 3100
3-Simon & Kirby-a 181 362 543 1158 1979 2800
4-Origin & 1st app. The Cat-Man; S&K-a 459 918 1377 3350 5925 8500
5-1st Cat-Man-c & 2nd app.; Simon & Kirby-a 252 504 756 1613 2757 3900
NOTE: *Solar Legion by **Kirby** No. 1-5 (5 pgs. each). Strongman c-1-4. Catman c-5.*

CRASH DIVE (See Cinema Comics Herald)

CRASH METRO AND THE STAR SQUAD
Oni Press: May, 1999 ($2.95, B&W, one-shot)

1-Allred-s/Ontiveros-a 3.00

CRASH RYAN (Also see Dark Horse Presents #44)
Marvel Comics (Epic): Oct, 1984 - No. 4, Jan, 1985 (Baxter paper, lim. series)

1-4 3.00

CRAZY (Also see This Magazine is Crazy)
Atlas Comics (CSI): Dec, 1953 - No. 7, July, 1954

1-Everett-c/a 47 94 141 296 498 700
2 30 60 90 177 289 400
3-7: 4-I Love Lucy satire. 5-Satire on censorship 26 52 78 154 252 350
NOTE: ***Ayers** a-5. **Berg** a-1, 2. **Burgos** c-5, 6. **Drucker** a-6. **Everett** a-1-4. **Al Hartley** a-4. **Heath** a-3, 7; c-7. **Maneely** a-1-7, c-3, 4. **Post** a-3-6. Funny monster c-1-4.*

CRAZY (Satire)
Marvel Comics Group: Feb, 1973 - No. 3, June, 1973

1-Not Brand Echh-r; Beatles cameo (r) 3 6 9 17 26 35
2,3-Not Brand Echh-r; Kirby-a 2 4 6 10 16 20

CRAZY MAGAZINE (Satire)
Oct, 1973 - No. 94, Apr, 1983 (40-90¢, B&W magazine)
Marvel Comics: (#1, 44 pgs; #2-90, reg. issues, 52 pgs; #92-95, 68 pgs)'

1-Wolverton(1 pg.), Bode-a; 3 pg. photo story of Neal Adams & Dick Giordano; Harlan Ellison story; TV Kung Fu sty. 5 10 15 30 50 70
2-"Live & Let Die" c/s; 8pgs; Adams/Buscema-a; McCloud w5 pgs. Adams-a; Kurtzman's "Hey Look" 2 pg.-r 3 6 9 19 30 40
3-5: 3-"High Plains Drifter" w/Clint Eastwood c/s; Waltons app; Drucker, Reese-a. 4-Shaft-c/s; Ploog-a; Nixon 3 pg. app; Freas-a. 5-Michael Crichton's "Westworld" c/s; Nixon app. 3 6 9 16 24 32
6,7,18: 6-Exorcist c/s; Nixon app. 7-TV's Kung Fu c/s; Nixon app.; Ploog & Freas-a. 18-Six Million Dollar Man/Bionic Woman c/s; Welcome Back Kotter story 3 6 9 15 22 28
8-10: 8-Serpico c/s; Casper parody; TV's Police Story. 9-Joker cameo; Chinatown story; Eisner s/a begins; Has 1st 8 covers on-c. 10-Playboy Bunny-c; M. Severin-a; Lee Marrs-a begins; "Deathwish" story 3 6 9 14 20 26
11-17,19: 11-Towering Inferno. 12-Rhoda. 13-"Tommy" the Who Rock Opera. 14-Mandingo. 15-Jaws story. 16-Santa/Xmas-c; "Good Times" TV story; Jaws. 17-Bicentennial issue; Baretta; Woody Allen. 19-King Kong c/s; Reagan, J. Carter, Howard the Duck cameos, "Laverne & Shirley" 2 4 6 11 16 20
20,24,27: 20-Bicentennial-c; Space 1999 sty; Superheroes song sheet, 4pgs. 24-Charlie's Angels. 27-Charlie's Angels/Travolta/Fonz-c; Bionic Woman sty 3 6 9 14 19 24
21-23,25,26,28-30: 21-Starsky & Hutch. 22-Mount Rushmore/J. Carter-c; TV's Barney Miller; Superheroes spoof. 23-Santa/Xmas-c; "Happy Days" sty; "Omen" sty. 25-J. Carter-c/s; Grandenetti-a begins; TV's Alice; Logan's Run. 26-TV Stars-c; Mary Hartman, King Kong. 28-Donny & Marie Osmond-c/s; Marathon Man. 29-Travolta/Kotter-c; "One Day at a Time", Gong Show. 30-1977, 84 pgs. w/bonus; Jaws, Baretta, King Kong, Happy Days 2 4 6 9 12 15
31,33-35,38,40: 31-"Rocky"-c/s; TV game shows. 33-Peter Benchley's "Deep". 34-J. Carter-c; TV's "Fish". 35-Xmas-c with Fonz/Six Million Dollar Man/Wonder Woman/Darth Vader/ Travolta, TV's "Mash" & "Family Matters". 38-Close Encounters of the Third Kind-c/s. 40-"Three's Company-c/s 1 3 4 6 8 11
32-Star Wars/Darth Vader-c/s; "Black Sunday" 3 6 9 14 19 24
36,42,47,49: 36-Farrah Fawcett/Six Million Dollar Man-c; TV's Nancy Drew & Hardy Boys; 1st app. Howard The Duck in Crazy, 2 pgs. 42-84 pgs. w/bonus; TV Hulk/Spider-Man-c; Mash, Gong Show, One Day at a Time, Disco, Alice. 47-Battlestar Galactica xmas-c; movie "Foul Play". 49-1979, 84 pgs. w/bonus; Mork & Mindy-c; Jaws, Saturday Night Fever, Three's Company 2 4 6 9 12 15
37-1978, 84 pgs. w/bonus. Darth Vader-c; Barney Miller, Laverne & Shirley, Good Times, Rocky, Donny & Marie Osmond, Bionic Woman 2 4 6 13 18 22

GD 2.0 | VG 4.0 | FN 6.0 | VF 8.0 | VF/NM 9.0 | NM- 9.2

39,44: 39-Saturday Night Fever-c/s. 44-"Grease"-c w/Travolta/O. Newton-John 2 4 6 11 16 20
41-Kiss-c & 1pg. photos; Disaster movies, TV's "Family", Annie Hall 4 8 12 27 44 60
43,45,46,48,51: 43-Jaws-c; Saturday Night Fever. 43-E.C. swipe from Mad #131. 45-Travolta/O. Newton-John/J. Carter-c; Eight is Enough. 46-TV Hulk-c/s; Punk Rock. 48-"Wiz"-c, Battlestar Galactica-s. 51-Grease/Mork & Mindy/D&M Osmond-c, Mork & Mindy-sty. "Boys from Brazil" 1 3 4 6 8 11
50,58: 50-Superman movie-c/sty, Playboy Mag., TV Hulk, Fonz; Howard the Duck, 1 pg. 58-1980, 84 pgs. w/32 pg. color comic bonus insert-Full reprint of Crazy Comic #1, Battlestar Galactica, Charlie's Angels, Starsky & Hutch 2 4 6 11 16 20
52,59,60,64: 52-1979, 84 pgs. w/bonus. Marlon Brando-c; TV Hulk, Grease. Kiss, 1 pg. photos. 59-Santa Ptd-c by Larkin; "Alien", "Moonraker", Rocky-2, Howard the Duck, 1 pg. 60-Star Trek w/Muppets-c; Star Trek sty; 1st app/origin Teen Hulk; Severin-a. 64-84 pgs. w/bonus Monopoly game satire. "Empire Strikes Back", 8 pgs., One Day at a Time 2 4 6 11 16 20
53,54,65,67-70: 53-"Animal House"-c/sty; TV's "Vegas", Howard the Duck, 1 pg. 54-Love at First Bite-c/sty, Fantasy Island sty, Howard the Duck 1 pg. 65-(Has #66 on-c, Aug/'80). "Black Hole" w/Janson-a; Kirby,Wood/Severin-a(r), 5 pgs. Howard the Duck, 3 pgs.; Broderick-a; Buck Rogers, Mr. Rogers. 67-84 pgs. w/bonus; TV's Kung Fu, Exorcist; Ploog-a(r). 68-American Gigolo, Dukes of Hazzard, Teen Hulk; Howard the Duck, 3 pgs. Broderick-a; Monster sty/5 pg. Ditko-a(r). 69-Obnoxio the Clown-c/sty; Stephen King's "Shining", Teen Hulk, Richie Rich, Howard the Duck, 3pgs; Broderick-a. 70-84 pgs. Towering Inferno, Daytime TV; Trina Robbins-a 1 3 4 6 8 10
55-57,61,63: 55-84 pgs. w/bonus; Love Boat, Mork & Mindy, Fonz, TV Hulk. 56-Mork/Rocky/ J. Carter-c; China Syndrome. 57-TV Hulk with Miss Piggy-c, Dracula, Taxi, Muppets. 61-1980, 84 pgs. Adams-a(r), McCloud, Pro wrestling, Casper, TV's Police Story. 63-Apocalypse Now-Coppola's cult movie; 3rd app. Teen Hulk, Howard the Duck, 3 pgs. 2 4 6 8 11 14
62-Kiss-c & 2 pg. app; Quincy, 2nd app. Teen Hulk 4 8 12 23 37 50
66-Sept/'80, Empire Strikes Back-c/sty; Teen Hulk by Severin, Howard the Duck, 3pgs. by Broderick 2 4 6 10 14 18
71,72,75-77,79: 71-Blues Brothers parody, Teen Hulk, Superheroes parody, WKRP in Cincinnati, Howard the Duck, 3pgs. by Broderick. 72-Jackie Gleason/Smokey & the Bandit II-c/sty, Shogun, Teen Hulk. Howard the Duck, 3pgs. by Broderick. 75-Flash Gordon movie c/sty; Teen Hulk, Cat in the Hat, Howard the Duck 3pgs. by Broderick. 76-84 pgs. w/bonus; Monster-sty w/ Crandall-a(r), Monster-stys(2) w/Kirby-a(r), 5pgs. ea; Mash, TV Hulk, Chinatown. 77-Popeye movie/R. Williams-c/sty; Teen Hulk, Love Boat, Howard the Duck 3 pgs. 79-84 pgs. w/bonus color stickers; has new material; "9 to 5" w/Dolly Parton, Teen Hulk, Magnum P.I., Monster-sty w/5pgs, Ditko-a(r), "Rat" w/Sutton-a(r), Everett-a, 4 pgs.(r) 1 3 4 6 8 10
73,74,78,80: 73-84 pgs. w/bonus Hulk/Spiderman Finger Puppets-c & bonus; "Live & Let Die, Jaws, Fantasy Island. 74-Dallas/"Who Shot J.R."-c/sty; Elephant Man, Howard the Duck 3pgs. by Broderick. 78-Clint Eastwood-c/sty; Teen Hulk, Superheroes parody, Lou Grant. 80-Star Wars, 2 pg. app; "Howling", TV's "Greatest American Hero" 2 4 6 8 11 14
81,84,86,87,89: 81-.Superman Movie II-c/sty; Wolverine cameo, Mash, Teen Hulk. 84-American Werewolf in London, Johnny Carson app; Teen Hulk. 86-Time Bandits-c/sty; Private Benjamin. 87-Rubix Cube-c; Hill Street Blues, "Ragtime", Origin Obnoxio the Clown; Teen Hulk. 89-Burt Reynolds "Sharkey's Machine", Teen Hulk 1 3 4 6 8 10
82-X-Men-c w/new Byrne-a, 84 pgs. w/new material; Fantasy Island, Teen Hulk, "For Your Eyes Only", Spiderman/Human Torch-r by Kirby/Ditko; Sutton-a(r); Rogers-a; Hunchback of Notre Dame, 5 pgs. 2 4 6 11 16 20
83-Raiders of the Lost Ark-c/sty; Hart to Hart; Reese-a; Teen Hulk 2 4 6 9 13 20
85,88: 85-84 pgs; Escape from New York, Teen Hulk; Kirby-a(r), 5 pgs, Poseidon Adventure, Flintstones, Sesame Street. 88-84 pgs. w/bonus Dr. Strange Game; some new material; Jeffersons, X-Men/Wolverine, 10 pgs.; Byrne-a; Apocalypse Now, Teen Hulk 1 3 4 6 8 11
90-94: 90-Conan-c/sty; M. Severin-a; Teen Hulk. 91-84 pgs, some new material; Bladerunner-c/sty, "Deathwish-II, Teen Hulk, Black Knight, 10 pgs.-'50s-r w/Maneely-a. 92-Wrath of Khan Star Trek-c/sty; Joanie & Chachi, Teen Hulk. 93-"E.T."-c/sty, Teen Hulk, Archie Bunkers Place, Dr. Doom Game. 94-Poltergeist, Smurfs, Teen Hulk, Casper, Avengers parody-8pgs. Adams-a 2 4 6 10 14 18
Crazy Summer Special #1 (Sum, '75, 100 pgs.)-Nixon, TV Kung Fu, Babe Ruth, Joe Namath, Waltons, McCloud, Chariots of the Gods 3 6 9 14 19 24
NOTE: ***N. Adams** a-2, 61r, 94p. **Austin** a-82i. **Buscema** a-2, 82. **Byrne** c-82p. **Nick Cardy** c-7, 8, 10, 12-16, Super Special 1. **Crandall** a-76r. **Ditko** a-68r, 79r, 82r. **Drucker** a-3. **Eisner** a-9-16. **Kelly Freas** c-1-6, 9, 11; a-7. **Kirby/Wood** a-66r. **Ploog** a-1, 4, 7, 67r, 73r. **Rogers** a-82. **Sparling** a-92. **Wood** a-65r. Howard the Duck in 36, 50, 51, 53, 54, 59, 63, 65, 66, 68, 69, 71, 72, 74, 75, 77. Hulk in 46, c-42, 46, 57, 73. Star Wars in 32, 66; c-37.*

CRAZYMAN
Continuity Comics: Apr, 1992 - No. 3, 1992 ($2.50, high quality paper)

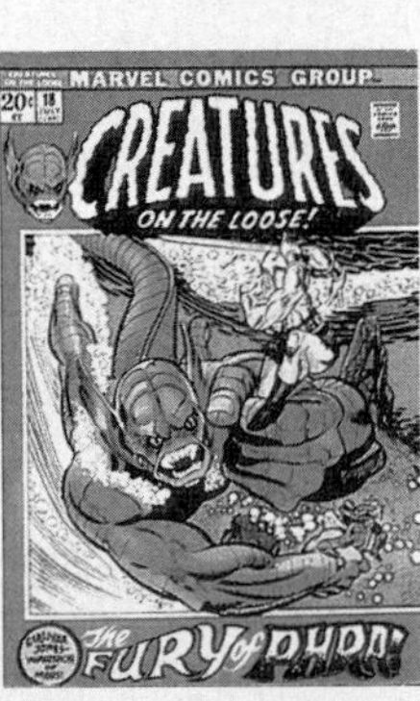

Creatures on the Loose #18 © MAR

The Creep #0 © John Arcudi

Creepy #4 © WP

GD 2.0 VG 4.0 FN 6.0 VF 8.0 VF/NM 9.0 NM- 9.2

1-($3.95, 52 pgs.)-Embossed-c; N. Adams part-i 4.00
2,3 ($2.50): 2-N. Adams/Bolland-c 3.00

CRAZYMAN
Continuity Comics: V2#1, 5/93 - No. 4, 1/94 ($2.50, high quality paper)
V2#1-4: 1-Entire book is die-cut. 2-(12/93)-Adams-c(p) & part scripts. 3-(12/93). 4-Indicia says #3, Jan. 1993 3.00

CRAZY, MAN, CRAZY (Magazine) (Becomes This Magazine is...?)
(Formerly From Here to Insanity)
Humor Magazines (Charlton): V2#1, Dec, 1955 - V2#2, June, 1956
V2#1,V2#2-Satire; Wolverton-a, 3 pgs. 19 38 57 109 172 235

CREATOR-OWNED HEROES
Image Comics: Jun, 2012 - No. 8, Jan, 2013 ($3.99)
1-8-Anthology of short stories by various and creator interviews 4.00

CREATURE, THE (See Movie Classics)

CREATURE COMMANDOS (See Weird War Tales #93 for 1st app.)
DC Comics: May, 2000 - No. 8, Dec, 2000 ($2.50, limited series)
1-8: Truman-s/Eaton-a 3.00

CREATURES OF THE ID
Caliber Press: 1990 ($2.95, B&W)
1-Frank Einstein (Madman) app.; Allred-a 5 10 15 31 53 75

CREATURES OF THE NIGHT
Dark Horse Books: Nov, 2004 ($12.95, hardcover graphic novel)
HC-Neil Gaiman-s/Michael Zulli-a/c 13.00

CREATURES ON THE LOOSE (Formerly Tower of Shadows No. 1-9)(See Kull)
Marvel Comics: No. 10, March, 1971 - No. 37, Sept, 1975 (New-a & reprints)
10-(15¢)-1st full app. King Kull; see Kull the Conqueror; Wrightson-a 8 16 24 51 96 140
11-Classic story about an underground comic artist going to Hell 4 8 12 27 44 60
12-15: 13-Last 15¢ issue 4 8 12 23 37 50
16-Origin Warrior of Mars (begins, ends #21) 3 6 9 15 22 28
17-20 2 4 6 9 13 16
21-Steranko-c 3 6 9 16 24 32
22-Steranko-c; Thongor stories begin 3 6 9 17 26 35
23-29-Thongor-c/stories 1 3 4 6 8 10
30-Manwolf begins 3 6 9 19 30 40
31-33 2 4 6 9 13 16
34-37 2 4 6 8 10 12

NOTE: ***Crandall** a-13. **Ditko** r-15, 17, 18, 20, 22, 24, 27, 28. **Everett** a-16i(new). **Matt Fox** r-21i. **Howard** a-26i. **Gil Kane** a-16p, 17p, 19i; c-16, 17, 19, 20, 25, 29, 33p, 35p, 36p. **Kirby** a-10-15r, 16(2)r, 17r, 19r. **Morrow** a-20, 21. **Perez** a-33-37; c-34p. **Shores** a-11. **innott** r-21. **Sutton** c-10. **Tuska** a-30-32p.*

CREECH, THE
Image Comics: Oct, 1997 - No. 3, Dec, 1997 ($1.95/$2.50, limited series)
1-3: 1-Capullo-s/c/a(p) 3.00
TPB (1999, $9.95) r/#1-3, McFarlane intro. 10.00
Out for Blood 1-3 (7/01 - No. 3, 11/01; $4.95) Capullo-s/c/a 5.00

CREED
Hall of Heroes Comics: Dec, 1994 - No. 2, Jan, 1995 ($2.50, B&W)
1-Trent Kaniuga-s/a 2 4 6 10 14 18
2 2 4 6 8 10 12

CREED
Lightning Comics: June, 1995 - No. 3 ($2.75/$3.00, B&W/color)
1-($2.75) 4.00
1-($3.00, color) 5.00
1-($9.95)-Commemorative Edition 10.00
1-TwinVariant Edition (1250? print run) 10.00
1-Special Edition; polybagged w/certificate 4.00
1 Gold Collectors Edition; polybagged w/certificate 3.00
2,3-($3.00, color)-Butt Naked Edition & regular-c 3.00
3-($9.95)-Commemorative Edition; polybagged w/certificate & card 10.00

CREED: CRANIAL DISORDER
Lightning Comics: Oct, 1996 ($3.00, limited series)
1-3-Two covers 3.00
1-($5.95)-Platinum Edition 6.00
2,3-($9.95)Ltd. Edition 10.00

CREED/TEENAGE MUTANT NINJA TURTLES
Lightning Comics: May, 1996 ($3.00, one-shot)

GD 2.0 VG 4.0 FN 6.0 VF 8.0 VF/NM 9.0 NM- 9.2

1-Kaniuga-a(p)/scripts; Laird-c; variant-c exists 3.00
1-($9.95)-Platinum Edition 10.00
1-Special Edition; polybagged w/certificate 5.00

CREEP, THE
Dark Horse Books: No. 0, Aug, 2012 - No. 4, Dec, 2012 ($2.99/$3.50)
0-Frank Miller-c; Arcudi-s/Case-a 3.50
1-4-($3.50): 1-Mignola-c. 2-Sook-c 3.50

CREEPER BY STEVE DITKO, THE
DC Comics: 2010 ($39.99, hardcover with dustjacket)
HC-Reprints Showcase #73, Beware the Creeper #1-6, First Issue Special #7 and apps. in World's Finest #249-255 and Cancelled Comic Cavalcade #2; intro. by Steve Niles 40.00

CREEPER, THE (See Beware... , Showcase #73 & 1st Issue Special #7)
DC Comics: Dec, 1997 - No. 11; #1,000,000 Nov, 1998 ($2.50)
1-11-Kaminski-s/Martinbrough-a(p). 7,8-Joker-c/app. 3.00
#1,000,000 (11/98) 853rd Century x-over 3.00

CREEPER, THE (See DCU Brave New World)
DC Comics: Oct, 2006 - No. 6, Mar, 2007 ($2.99, limited series)
1-6-Niles-s/Justiniano-a/c; Jack Ryder becomes the Creeper. 2-6-Batman app. 3.00
... - Welcome to Creepsville TPB ('07, $19.99) r/#1-6 & story from DCU Brave New World 20.00

CREEPS
Image Comics: Oct, 2001 - No. 4, May, 2002 ($2.95)
1-4-Mandrake-a/Mishkin-s 3.00

CREEPSHOW
Plume/New American Library Pub.: July, 1982 (softcover graphic novel)
1st edition-nn-(68 pgs.) Kamen-c/Wrightson-a; screenplay by Stephen King for the George Romero movie 5 10 15 31 53 75
2nd-7th printings 3 6 9 17 26 35

CREEPY (See Warren Presents)
Warren Publishing Co./Harris Publ. #146: 1964 - No. 145, Feb, 1983; No. 146, 1985 (B&W, magazine)
1-Frazetta-a (his last story in comics?); Jack Davis-c; 1st Warren all comics magazine; 1st app. Uncle Creepy 13 26 39 86 188 290
2-Frazetta-c & 1 pg. strip 10 20 30 64 132 200
3-8,11-13,15-17: 3-7,9-11,15-17-Frazetta-c. 7-Frazetta 1 pg. strip. 15,16-Adams-a. 16-Jeff Jones-a 6 12 18 37 66 95
9-Creepy fan club sketch by Wrightson (1st published-a); has 1/2 pg. anti-smoking strip by Frazetta; Frazetta-c; 1st Wood and Ditko art on this title; Toth-a (low print) 7 14 21 49 92 135
10-Brunner fan club sketch (1st published work) 6 12 18 38 69 100
14-Neal Adams 1st Warren work 6 12 18 38 69 100
18-28,30,31: 27-Frazetta-c 4 8 12 28 47 65
29,34: 29-Jones-a 5 10 15 30 50 70
32-(scarce) Frazetta-c; Harlan Ellison sty 8 16 24 51 96 140
33,35,37,39,40,42-47,49: 35-Hitler/Nazi-s. 39-1st Uncle Creepy solo-s, Cousin Eerie app.; early Brunner-a. 42-1st San Julian-c. 44-1st Ploog-a. 46-Corben-a 4 8 12 23 37 50
36-(11/70)1st Corben art at Warren 5 10 15 30 50 70
38,41-(scarce): 38-1st Kelly-c. 41-Corben-a 5 10 15 33 57 80
48,55,65-(1972, 1973, 1974 Annuals) #55 & 65 contain an 8 pg. slick comic insert. 48-(84 pgs.). 55-Color poster bonus (1/2 price if missing). 65-(100 pgs.) Summer Giant 5 10 15 30 50 70
50-Vampirella/Eerie/Creepy-c 5 10 15 33 57 80
51,54,56-61,64: All contain an 8 pg. slick comic insert in middle. 59-Xmas horror. 54,64-Chaykin-a 4 8 12 27 44 60
52,53,66,71,72,75,76,78-80: 71-All Bermejo-a; Space & Time issue. 72-Gual-a. 78-Fantasy issue. 79,80-Monsters issue 3 6 9 19 30 40
62,63-1st & 2nd full Wrightson story art; Corben-a; 8 pg. color comic insert 4 8 12 27 44 60
67,68,73 3 6 9 21 33 45
69,70-Edgar Allan Poe issues; Corben-a 4 8 12 23 37 50
74,77: 74-All Crandell-a. 77-Xmas Horror issue; Corben-a,Wrightson-a 4 8 12 23 37 50
81,84,85,88-90,92-94,96-99,102,104-112,114-118,120,122-130: 84,93-Sports issue. 85,97,102-Monster issue. 89-All war issue; Nino-a. 94-Weird Children issue. 96,109-Aliens issue. 99-Disasters. 103-Corben-a. 104-Robots issue. 106-Sword & Sorcery.107-Sci-fi. 116-End of Man. 125-Xmas Horror 2 4 6 10 14 18
82,100,101: 82-All Maroto issue. 100-(8/78) Anniversary. 101-Corben-a 3 6 9 14 20 26
83,95-Wrightson-a. 83-Corben-a. 95-Gorilla/Apes. 2 4 6 13 18 22
86,87,91,103-Wrightson-a. 86-Xmas Horror 2 4 6 13 18 22

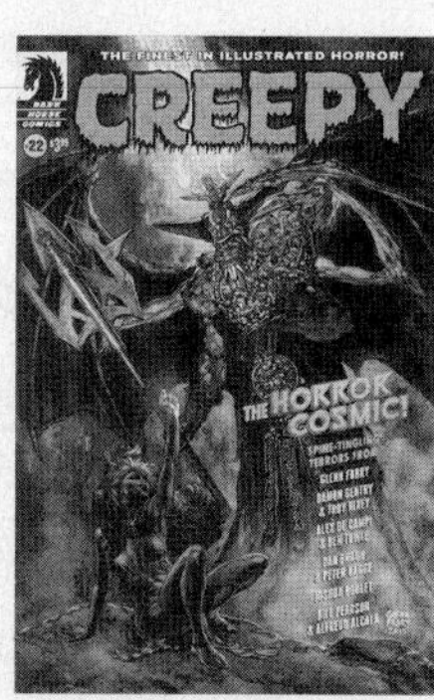
Creepy (2009 series) #22 © New Comic Co.

Crime and Punishment #31 © LEV

Crime Detective Comics #6 © HILL

GD 2.0 VG 4.0 FN 6.0 VF 8.0 VF/NM 9.0 NM- 9.2

113-All Wrightson-r issue 3 6 9 19 29 38
119,121: 119-All Nino issue.121-All Severin-r issue 2 4 6 13 18 22
131,133-136,138,140: 135-Xmas issue 2 4 6 13 18 22
132,137,139: 132-Corben. 137-All Williamson-r issue. 139-All Toth-r issue
3 6 9 14 20 26
141,143,144 (low dist.): 144-Giant, $2.25; Frazetta-c 3 6 9 17 26 35
142,145 (low dist.): 142-(10/82, 100 pgs.) All Torres issue. 145-(2/83) last Warren issue
3 6 9 19 30 40
146 ($2.95)-1st from Harris; resurrection issue 6 12 18 42 79 115
Year Book '68-'70: '70-Neal Adams, Ditko-a(r) 5 10 15 33 57 80
Annual 1971,1972 5 10 15 31 53 75
1993 Fearbook ($3.95)-Harris Publ.; Brereton-c; Vampirella by Busiek-s/Art Adams-a; David-s; Paquette-a 3 6 9 17 26 35
...:The Classic Years TPB (Harris/Dark Horse, '91, $12.95) Kaluta-c; art by Frazetta,Torres, Crandall, Ditko, Morrow, Williamson, Wrightson 25.00

NOTE: *All issues contain many good artists works:* ***Neal Adams, Brunner, Corben, Craig (Taycee), Crandall, Ditko, Evans, Frazetta, Heath, Jeff Jones, Krenkel, McWilliams, Morrow, Nino, Orlando, Ploog, Severin, Torres, Toth, Williamson, Wood, & Wrightson****; covers by* ***Crandall, Davis, Frazetta, Morrow, San Julian, Todd/Bode****; Otto Binder's "Adam Link" stories in No. 2, 4, 6, 8, 9, 12, 13, 15 with* ***Orlando*** *art.* ***Frazetta*** *c-2-7, 9-11, 15-17, 27, 32, 83r, 89r, 91r.* ***E.A. Poe*** *adaptations in 66, 69, 70.*

CREEPY (Mini-series)
Harris Comics/Dark Horse: 1992 - Book 4, 1992 (48 pgs, B&W, squarebound)

Book 1-4: Brereton painted-c on all. Stories and art by various incl. David (all), Busiek(2), Infantino(2), Guice(3), Colan(1) 2 4 6 8 10 12

CREEPY
Dark Horse Comics: July, 2009 - No. 24, Jun, 2016 ($4.99/$3.99, 48 pgs, B&W, quarterly)

1-13: 1-Powell-c; art by Wrightson, Toth, Alexander. 8,12-Corben-c. 5.00
14-24-($3.99) 18-Nguyen-c. 20,23,24-Corben-a 4.00

CREEPY THINGS
Charlton Comics: July, 1975 - No. 6, June, 1976

1-Sutton-c/a 3 6 9 14 19 24
2-6: Ditko-a in 3,5. Sutton c-3,4. 6-Zeck-c 2 4 6 8 10 12
Modern Comics Reprint 2-6(1977) 5.00

NOTE: ***Larson*** *a-2,6.* ***Sutton*** *a-1,2,4,6.* ***Zeck*** *a-2.*

CREW, THE
Marvel Comics: July, 2003 - No. 7, Jan, 2004 ($2.50)

1-7-Priest-s/Bennett-a; James Rhodes (War Machine) app. 3.00

CRIME AND JUSTICE (Badge Of Justice #22 on; Rookie Cop? No. 27 on)
Capitol Stories/Charlton Comics: March, 1951 - No. 21, Nov, 1954; No. 23, Mar, 1955 - No. 26, Sept, 1955 (No #22)

1 42 84 126 265 445 625
2 21 42 63 122 199 275
3-8,10-13: 6-Negligee panels 19 38 57 111 176 240
9-Classic story "Comics Vs. Crime" 37 74 111 222 361 500
14-Color illos in **POP**; story of murderer who beheads women
34 68 102 199 325 450
15-17,19-21,23,24: 15-Negligee panels. 23-Rookie Cop (1st app.)
14 28 42 80 115 150
18-Ditko-a 33 66 99 194 317 440
25,26: (scarce) 20 40 60 117 189 260

NOTE: ***Alascia*** *c-20.* ***Ayers*** *a-17.* ***Shuster*** *a-19-21; c-19. Bondage c-11, 12.*

CRIME AND PUNISHMENT (Title inspired by 1935 film)
Lev Gleason Publications: April, 1948 - No. 74, Aug, 1955

1-Mr. Crime app. on-c 42 84 126 265 445 625
2-Narrator, Officer Common Sense (a ghost) begins, ends #27? (see Crime Does Not Pay #41) 21 42 63 122 199 275
3-(6/48)-Used in **SOTI**, pg. 112; contains Biro & Gleason self censorship code of 12 listed restrictions 22 44 66 132 216 300
4,5 15 30 45 90 140 190
6-10 14 28 42 80 115 150
11-20 12 24 36 69 97 125
21-30 11 22 33 60 83 105
31-38,40-44,46: 46-One pg. Frazetta-a 10 20 30 54 72 90
39-Drug mention story "The Five Dopes" 16 32 48 94 147 200
45- "Hophead Killer" drug story 16 32 48 94 147 200
47-53,55,57,60-65,70-74: 9 18 27 52 69 85
54-Electric Chair-c 10 20 30 56 76 95
56-Classic dagger/torture-c 11 22 33 64 90 115
58-Used in **POP**, pg. 79 11 22 33 62 86 110
59-Used in **SOTI**, illo "What comic-book America stands for"
36 72 108 216 351 485
66-Toth-c/a(4); 3-D effect issue (3/54); 1st "Deep Dimension" process
41 82 123 250 418 585
67- "Monkey on His Back" heroin story; 3-D effect issue
39 78 117 231 378 525
68-3-D effect issue; Toth-c (7/54) 32 64 96 188 307 425
69- "The Hot Rod Gang" dope crazy kids 15 30 45 85 130 175

NOTE: ***Belfi*** *a- 2, 3, 5.* ***Biro*** *c-most.* ***Al Borth*** *a-9, 35.* ***Cooper*** *a-9.* ***Joe Certa*** *a-8.* ***Tony Dipreta*** *a-3, 5, 15, 34.* ***Everett*** *a-31.* ***Bob Fujitani (Fuje)*** *a-2-20, 26, 27.* ***Joseph Gaguardi*** *a-15, 18, 20.* ***Fred Guardineer*** *a-2-5, 10-12, 14, 15, 17, 18, 20, 26-28, 32, 34, 35, 38-44, 51, 54.* ***Jack Keller*** *a-18.* ***Kinstler*** *c-69.* ***Martinott*** *a-13.* ***Al McWilliams*** *a-36, 41, 48, 49.* ***William Overgard*** *a-36.* ***Dick Rockwell*** *a-35, 51.* ***Robert Q. Sale*** *a-43.* ***George Tuska*** *a-28, 30, 51, 64, 70. Painted-c-31.*

CRIME AND PUNISHMENT: MARSHALL LAW TAKES MANHATTAN
Marvel Comics (Epic Comics): 1989 ($4.95, 52 pgs., direct sales only, mature)

nn-Graphic album featuring Marshall Law 5.00

CRIME BIBLE: THE FIVE LESSONS (Aftermath of DC's 52 series)
DC Comics: Dec, 2007 - No. 5, Apr, 2008 ($2.99, limited series)

1-5-Rucka-s; The Question (Renee Montoya) app. 3-Batwoman app. 3.00
The Question: The Five Books of Blood HC (2008, $19.99) r/#1-5 20.00
The Question: The Five Books of Blood SC (2009, $14.99) r/#1-5 15.00

CRIME CAN'T WIN (Formerly Cindy Smith)
Marvel/Atlas Comics (TCI 41/CCC 42,43,4-12): No. 41, 9/50 - No. 43, 2/51; No. 4, 4/51 - No. 12, 9/53

41(#1)-"The Girl Who Planned Her Own Murder" 32 64 96 190 310 430
42(#2) 18 36 54 107 169 230
43(#3)-Horror story 22 44 66 128 209 290
4(4/51),5-12: 10-Possible use in **SOTI**, pg. 161 15 30 45 88 137 185

NOTE: ***Robinson*** *a-9-11.* ***Tuska*** *a-43.*

CRIME CASES COMICS (Formerly Willie Comics)
Marvel/Atlas Comics(CnPC No.24-8/MJMC No.9-12): No. 24, 8/50 - No. 27, 3/51; No. 5, 5/51 - No. 12, 7/52

24 (#1, 52 pgs.)-True police cases 24 48 72 140 230 320
25-27(#2-4): 27-Maneely & Morisi-a 18 36 54 103 162 220
5-12: 11-Robinson-a. 12-Tuska-a 15 30 45 88 137 185

CRIME CLINIC
Ziff-Davis Publishing Co.: No. 10, July-Aug, 1951 - No. 5, Summer, 1952

10(#1)-Painted-c; origin Dr. Tom Rogers 33 66 99 194 317 440
11(#2),4,5: 4,5-Painted-c 21 42 63 124 202 280
3-Used in **SOTI**, pg. 18 22 44 66 128 209 290

NOTE: *All have painted covers by* ***Saunders****.* ***Starr*** *a-10.*

CRIME CLINIC
Slave Labor Graphics: May, 1995 - No. 2, Oct, 1995 ($2.95, B&W, limited series)

1,2 3.00

CRIME DETECTIVE COMICS
Hillman Periodicals: Mar-Apr, 1948 - V3#8, May-June, 1953

V1#1-The Invisible 6, costumed villains app; Fuje-c/a, 15 pgs.
39 78 117 231 378 525
2,5: 5-Krigstein-a 19 38 57 111 176 240
3,4,6,7,10-12: 6-McWilliams-a 16 32 48 92 144 195
8-Kirbyish-a by McCann 16 32 48 92 144 195
9-Used in **SOTI**, pg. 16 & "Caricature of the author in a position comic book publishers wish he were in permanently" illo. 43 86 129 271 461 650
V2#1,4,7-Krigstein-a: 1-Tuska-a 15 30 45 83 124 165
2,3,5,6,8-12 (1-2/52) 14 28 42 78 112 145
V3#1-Drug use-c 14 28 42 81 118 155
2-8 12 24 36 67 94 120

NOTE: ***Briefer*** *a-11, V3#1.* ***Kinstlerish****-a by* ***McCann****-V2#7, V3#2.* ***Powell*** *a-10, 11.* ***Starr*** *a-10.*

CRIME DETECTOR
Timor Publications: Jan, 1954 - No. 5, Sept, 1954

1 27 54 81 158 259 360
2 15 30 45 88 137 185
3,4 14 28 42 82 121 160
5-Disbrow-a (classic) 27 54 81 158 259 360

CRIME DOES NOT PAY (Formerly Silver Streak Comics No. 1-21)
Comic House/Lev Gleason/Golfing: No. 22, June, 1942 - No. 147, July, 1955 (1st crime comic)(Title inspired by film)

22 (23 on cover, 22 on indicia)-Origin The War Eagle & only app.; Chip Gardner begins; #22 was rebound in Complete Book of True Crime (Scarce)
676 1352 2028 4935 8718 12,500
23-(9/42) (Scarce) 320 640 960 2240 3920 5600
24-(11/42) Intro. & 1st app. Mr. Crime; classic Biro-c showing woman's head on fire being pushed onto hot stovetop burner 950 1900 2850 4750 8375 12,000

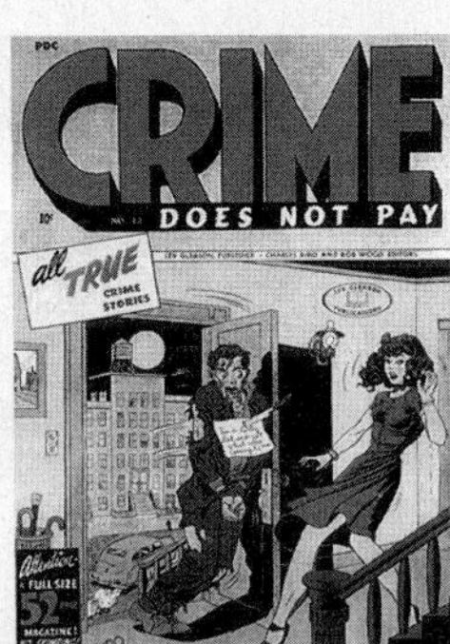

Crime Does Not Pay #43 © LEV

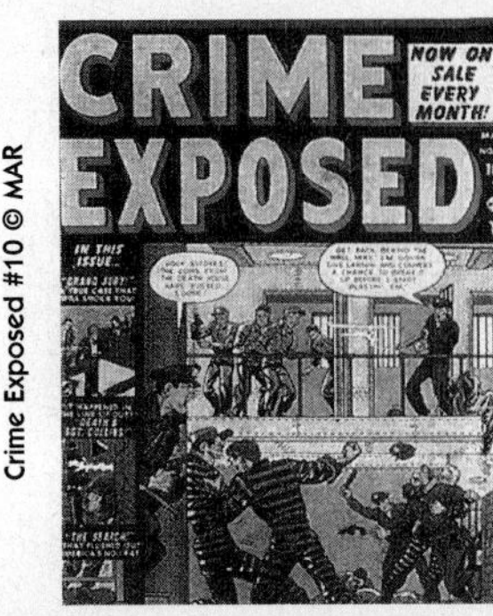

Crime Exposed #10 © MAR

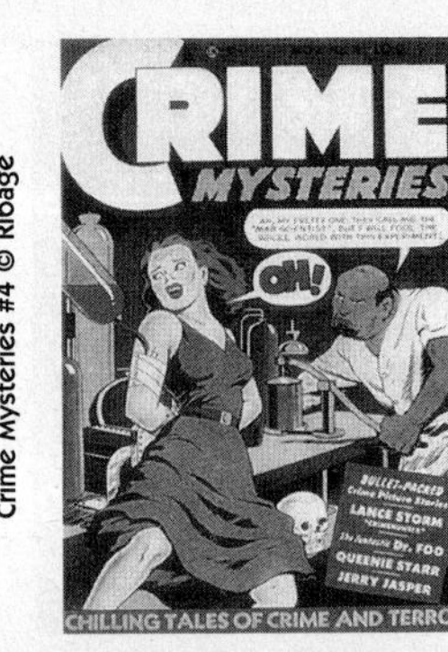

Crime Mysteries #4 © Ribage

GD VG FN VF VF/NM NM-
2.0 4.0 6.0 8.0 9.0 9.2

GD VG FN VF VF/NM NM-
2.0 4.0 6.0 8.0 9.0 9.2

25-(1/43) 2nd app. Mr. Crime; classic '40s crime-c 142 284 426 901 1555 2200
26-(3/43) 3rd app. Mr. Crime 116 232 348 742 1271 1800
27-Classic Biro-c pushing man into hot oven 142 284 426 909 1555 2200
28-30: 30-Wood and Biro app. 82 164 246 528 902 1275
31,32,34-40 45 90 135 284 480 675
33-(5/44) Classic Biro hanging & hatchet-c 219 438 657 1402 2401 3400
41-(9/45) Origin & 1st app. Officer Common Sense 41 82 123 256 428 600
42-(11/45) Classic electrocution-c 71 142 213 454 777 1100
43-46,48-50: 44-50 are 68 pg. issues. 44-"Legs" Diamond story. 50-(3/47)-1st issue to advertise 5 million readers on front-c. 58-(12/47)-shows 6 million readers (these ads believed to have influenced the crime comic wave of 1948)
29 58 87 170 278 385
47-(9/46)-Electric chair-c 45 90 135 284 480 675
51-70: 58(12/47)-Thomas Dun, killer of thousands (1565) story. 63,64-Possible use in **SOTI**, pg. 306. 63-Contains Biro & Gleason self censorship code of 12 listed restrictions (5/48) 21 42 63 122 199 275
71-99: 87-Chip Gardner begins, ends #100. 87-99-Painted-c
17 34 51 98 154 210
100-Painted-c 19 38 57 109 172 235
101-104,107-110: 101,102-Painted-c. 102-Chip Gardner app.
14 28 42 81 118 155
105-Used in **POP**, pg. 84 15 30 45 85 130 175
106,114-Frazetta-a, 1 pg. 14 28 42 82 121 160
111-Used in **POP**, pgs. 80 & 81; injury-to-eye sty illo 16 32 48 94 147 200
112,113,115-130 12 24 36 67 94 120
131-140 11 22 33 60 83 105
141,142-Last pre-code issue; Kubert-a(1) 12 24 36 69 97 125
143-Kubert-a in one story 12 24 36 69 97 125
144-146 11 22 33 60 83 105
147-Last issue (scarce); Kubert-a 17 34 51 98 154 210
1(Golfing-1945) 10 20 30 54 72 90
The Best of...(1944, 128 pgs.)-Series contains 4 rebound issues
116 232 348 742 1271 1800
...1945 issue 76 152 228 486 831 1175
...1946-48 issues 57 114 171 362 619 875
...1949-50 issues 47 94 147 296 498 700
...1951-53 issues (25¢) 40 80 120 246 411 575

NOTE: *Many issues contain violent covers and stories. Who Dunit by* ***Guardineer****-39-42, 44-105, 108-110; Chip Gardner by* ***Bob Jujitani (Fuge)****-88-103.* ***Alderman*** *a-29, 41-44, 49.* ***Dan Barry*** *a-67, 75.* ***Charles Biro*** *c-1-76, 122, 142.* ***Dick Briefer*** *a-29(2), 30, 31, 33, 37, 39.* ***G. Colan*** *a-105.* ***Tony Dipreta*** *a-79, 90, 92.* ***Fuje*** *c-88, 89, 91-94, 96, 98, 99, 102, 103.* ***Fred Guardineer*** *a-51, 57, 58(2), 66-68, 71, 74, 79, 81, 90, 92.* ***Joe Kubert*** *c-143.* ***Landau*** *a-118.* ***Al Mandell*** *a-37.* ***Norman Maurer*** *a-29, 39, 41, 42.* ***McWilliams*** *a-91, 93, 95, 100-103.* ***Rudy Palais*** *a-30, 33.* ***Bob Powell*** *a-146, 147.* ***George Tuska*** *a-48-50(2ea.), 51, 52 56, 57(2), 58, 60-64, 66-68, 71, 74, 81. Painted c-87-103. Bondage c-43, 62, 98.*

CRIME EXPOSED
Marvel Comics (PPI)/Marvel Atlas Comics (PrPI): June, 1948; Dec, 1950 - No. 14, June, 1952

1(6/48) 39 78 117 236 388 540
1(12/50) 26 52 78 154 252 350
2 17 34 51 98 154 210
3-9,11,14 15 30 45 85 130 175
10-Used in **POP**, pg. 81 15 30 45 88 137 185
12-Krigstein & Robinson-a 15 30 45 88 137 185
13-Used in **POP**, pg. 81; Krigstein-a 15 30 45 90 140 190

NOTE: ***Keller*** *a-8, 10.* ***Maneely*** *c-8.* ***Robinson*** *a-11, 12.* ***Sale*** *a-4.* ***Tuska*** *a-3, 4.*

CRIMEFIGHTERS
Marvel Comics (CmPS 1-3/CCC 4-10): Apr, 1948 - No. 10, Nov, 1949

1-Some copies are undated & could be reprints 32 64 96 188 307 425
2,3: 3-Morphine addict story 17 34 51 98 154 210
4-10: 4-Early John Buscema-a. 6-Anti-Wertham editorial. 9,10-Photo-c
15 30 45 85 130 175

CRIME FIGHTERS (...Always Win)
Atlas Comics (CnPC): No. 11, Sept, 1954 - No. 13, Jan, 1955

11-13: 11-Maneely-a,13-Pakula, Reinman, Severin-a
14 28 42 81 118 155

CRIME-FIGHTING DETECTIVE (Shock Detective Cases No. 20 on; formerly Criminals on the Run)
Star Publications: No. 11, Apr-May, 1950 - No. 19, June, 1952 (Based on true crime cases)

11-L. B. Cole-c/a (2 pgs.); L. B. Cole-c on all 22 44 66 132 216 300
12,13,15-19: 17-Young King Cole & Dr. Doom app. 17 34 51 100 158 215
14-L. B. Cole-c/a, r/Law-Crime #2 19 38 57 111 176 240

CRIME FILES
Standard Comics: No. 5, Sept, 1952 - No. 6, Nov, 1952

5-1pg. Alex Toth-a; used in **SOTI**, pg. 4 (text) 27 54 81 158 259 360
6-Sekowsky-a 15 30 45 85 130 175

CRIME ILLUSTRATED (Magazine)
E. C. Comics: Nov-Dec, 1955 - No. 2, Spring, 1956 (25¢, Adult Suspense Stories on-c)

1-Ingels & Crandall-a 21 42 63 122 199 275
2-Ingels & Crandall-a 15 30 45 90 140 190

NOTE: ***Craig*** *a-2.* ***Crandall*** *a-1, 2; c-2.* ***Evans*** *a-1.* ***Davis*** *a-2.* ***Ingels*** *a-1, 2.* ***Krigstein/Crandall*** *a-1.* ***Orlando*** *a-1, 2; c-1.*

CRIME INCORPORATED (Formerly Crimes Incorporated)
Fox Feature Syndicate: No. 2, Aug, 1950; No. 3, Aug, 1951

2 30 60 90 177 289 400
3(1951)-Hollingsworth-a 20 40 60 117 189 260

CRIME MACHINE (Magazine reprints pre-code crime and gangster comics)
Skywald Publications: Feb, 1971 - No. 2, May, 1971 (B&W, 68 pgs., roundbound)

1-Kubert-a(2)(r)(Avon); bikini girl in cake-c 5 10 15 35 63 90
2-Torres, Wildey-a; violent-c/a 4 8 12 27 44 60

CRIME MUST LOSE! (Formerly Sports Action?)
Sports Action (Atlas Comics): No. 4, Oct, 1950 - No. 12, April, 1952

4-Ann Brewster-a in all; c-used in N.Y. Legis. Comm. documents
23 46 69 138 227 315
5-10,12: 9-Robinson-a 16 32 48 94 147 200
11-Used in **POP**, pg. 89 17 34 51 98 154 210

CRIME MUST PAY THE PENALTY (Formerly Four Favorites; Penalty #47, 48)
Ace Magazines (Current Books): No. 33, Feb, 1948; No. 2, Jun, 1948 - No. 48, Jan, 1956

33(#1, 2/48)-Becomes Four Teeners #34? 43 86 129 271 461 650
2(6/48)-Extreme violence; Palais-a? 28 56 84 165 270 375
3,4,8: 3- "Frisco Mary" story used in Senate Investigation report, pg. 7. 4,8-Transvestism stories 21 42 63 126 206 285
5-7,9,10 17 34 51 98 154 210
11-19 15 30 45 90 140 190
20-Drug story "Dealers in White Death" 24 48 72 142 234 325
21-32,34-40,42-48: 44-Last pre-code 14 28 42 76 108 140
33(7/53)- "Dell Fabry-Junk King" drug story; mentioned in Love and Death
20 40 60 114 182 250
41-reprints "Dealers in White Death" 14 28 42 80 115 150

NOTE: ***Cameron*** *a-29-31, 34, 35, 39-41.* ***Colan*** *a-20, 31.* ***Kremer*** *a-3, 37r.* ***Larsen*** *a-32.* ***Palais*** *a-5?,37.*

CRIME MUST STOP
Hillman Periodicals: October, 1952 (52 pgs.)

V1#1(Scarce)-Similar to Monster Crime; Mort Lawrence, Krigstein-a
126 252 378 806 1378 1950

CRIME MYSTERIES (Secret Mysteries #16 on; combined with Crime Smashers #7 on)
Ribage Publ. Corp. (Trojan Magazines): May, 1952 - No. 15, Sept, 1954

1-Transvestism story; crime & terror stories begin 90 180 270 576 988 1400
2-Marijuana story (7/52) 58 116 174 371 636 900
3-One pg. Frazetta-a 50 100 150 315 533 750
4-Cover shows girl in bondage having her blood drained; 1 pg. Frazetta-a
129 258 387 826 1413 2000
5-10 42 84 126 265 445 625
11,12,14 39 78 117 240 395 550
13-(5/54)-Angelo Torres 1st comic work (inks over Check's pencils); Check-a
43 86 129 271 461 650
15-Acid in face-c 55 110 165 352 601 850

NOTE: ***Fass*** *a-13; c-4, 6, 10.* ***Hollingsworth*** *a-10-13, 15; c-2, 12, 13, 15.* ***Kiefer*** *a-4.* ***Woodbridge*** *a-13? Bondage-c-1, 8, 12.*

CRIME ON THE RUN (See Approved Comics #8)

CRIME ON THE WATERFRONT (Formerly Famous Gangsters)
Realistic Publications: No. 4, May, 1952 (Painted cover)

4 34 68 102 199 325 450

CRIME PATROL (Formerly International #1-5; International Crime Patrol #6; becomes Crypt of Terror #17 on)
E. C. Comics: No. 7, Summer, 1948 - No. 16, Feb-Mar, 1950

7-Intro. Captain Crime 90 180 270 576 988 1400
8-14: 12-Ingels-a 77 154 231 493 847 1200
15-Intro. of Crypt Keeper (inspired by Witches Tales radio show) & Crypt of Terror (see Tales From the Crypt #33 for origin); used by N.Y. Legis. Comm.; last pg. Feldstein-a
286 572 858 2288 3644 5000
16-2nd Crypt Keeper app.; Roussos-a 183 366 549 1464 2332 3200

NOTE: ***Craig*** *c/a in most issues.* ***Feldstein*** *a-9-16.* ***Kiefer*** *a-8, 10, 11.* ***Moldoff*** *a-7.*

CRIME PATROL

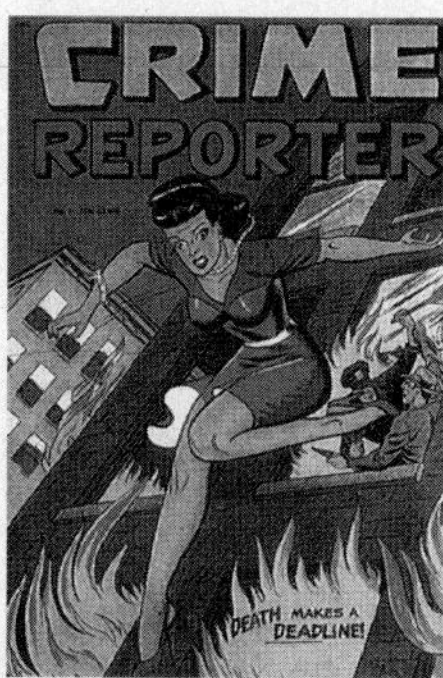

Crime Reporter #1 © STJ

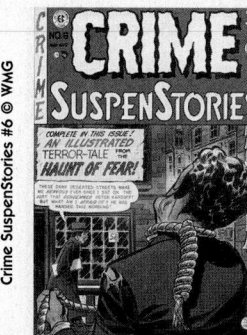

Crime SuspenStories #6 © WMG

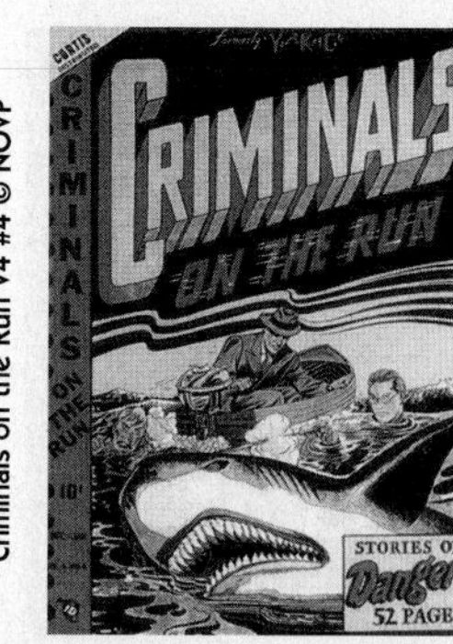

Criminals on the Run V4 #4 © NOVP

	GD 2.0	VG 4.0	FN 6.0	VF 8.0	VF/NM 9.0	NM- 9.2

Gemstone Publishing: Apr, 2000 - No. 10, Jan, 2001 ($2.50)

1-10: E.C. reprints 4.00
Volume 1,2 (2000, $13.50) 1-r/#1-5. 2-r/#6-10 14.00

CRIME PHOTOGRAPHER (See Casey...)

CRIME REPORTER
St. John Publ. Co.: Aug, 1948 - No. 3, Dec, 1948 (Indicia shows Oct.)

1-Drug club story 84 168 252 538 919 1300
2-Used in **SOTI**: illo- "Children told me what the man was going to do with the red-hot poker;" r/Dynamic #17 with editing; Baker-c; Tuska-a 129 258 387 826 1413 2000
3-Baker-c; Tuska-a 77 154 231 493 847 1200

CRIMES BY WOMEN
Fox Feature Syndicate: June, 1948 - No. 15, Aug, 1951; 1954 (True crime cases)

1-True story of Bonnie Parker 129 258 387 826 1413 2000
2 77 154 231 493 847 1200
3-Used in **SOTI**, pg. 234 110 220 330 704 1202 1700
4,5,7-9,11-15: 8-Used in **POP**. 14-Bondage-c 69 138 207 442 759 1075
6-Classic girl fight-c; acid-in-face panel 110 220 330 704 1202 1700
10-Used in **SOTI**, pg. 72; girl fight-c 81 162 243 518 884 1250
54(M.S. Publ.-'54)-Reprint; (formerly My Love Secret) 28 56 84 165 270 375

CRIMES INCORPORATED (Formerly My Past)
Fox Feature Syndicate: No. 12, June, 1950 (Crime Incorporated No. 2 on)

12 32 64 96 188 307 425

CRIMES INCORPORATED (See Fox Giants)

CRIME SMASHER (See Whiz #76)
Fawcett Publications: Summer, 1948 (one-shot)

1-Formerly Spy Smasher 41 82 123 256 428 600

CRIME SMASHERS (Becomes Secret Mysteries No. 16 on)
Ribage Publishing Corp.(Trojan Magazines): Oct, 1950 - No. 15, Mar, 1953

1-Used in **SOTI**, pg. 19,20, & illo "A girl raped and murdered;" Sally the Sleuth begins 90 180 270 576 988 1400
2-Kubert-c 48 96 144 302 514 725
3,4 39 78 117 240 395 550
5-Wood-a 47 94 141 296 498 700
6,8-11: 8-Lingerie panel 32 64 96 188 307 425
7-Female heroin junkie story 36 72 108 211 343 475
12-Injury to eye panel; 1 pg. Frazetta-a 34 68 102 204 332 460
13-Used in **POP**, pgs. 79,80; 1 pg. Frazetta-a 34 68 102 204 332 460
14,15 26 52 78 154 252 350

NOTE: ***Hollingsworth** a-14. **Kiefer** a-15. Bondage c-7, 9.*

CRIME SUSPENSTORIES (Formerly Vault of Horror No. 12-14)
E. C. Comics: No. 15, Oct-Nov, 1950 - No. 27, Feb-Mar, 1955

15-Identical to #1 in content; #1 printed on outside front cover. #15 (formerly "The Vault of Horror") printed and blackened out on inside front cover with Vol. 1, No. 1 printed over it. Evidently, several of No. 15 were printed before a decision was made not to drop the Vault of Horror and Haunt of Fear series. The print run was stopped on No. 15 and continued on No. 1. All of the No. 15 issues were changed as described above. 206 412 618 1648 2624 3600
1 160 320 480 1280 2040 2800
2 80 160 240 640 1020 1400
3-5: 3-Poe adaptation. 3-Old Witch stories begin 56 112 168 448 712 975
6-10: 9-Craig bio. 50 100 150 400 638 875
11,12,14,15: 15-The Old Witch guest stars 39 78 117 312 494 675
13,16-Williamson-a 40 80 120 320 510 700
17-Classic "bullet in the head" cover; Williamson/Frazetta-a (6 pgs.); Williamson bio. 77 154 231 616 983 1350
18,19: 19-Used in **SOTI**, pg. 235 34 68 102 272 436 600
20-Classic hanging cover used in **SOTI**, illo "Cover of a children's comic book"; issue was on display at the 1954 Senate hearing 86 172 258 688 1094 1500
21,24-26: 24- "Food For Thought" similar to "Cave In" in Amazing Detective Cases #13 (1952) 27 54 81 216 346 475
22-Classic ax decapitation-c; exhibited in the 1954 Senate Investigation on juvenile delinquency trial; decapitation story 571 1142 1713 4568 7284 10,000

NOTE: *Senator Kefauver questioning Bill Gaines: "Here is your May issue. This seems to be a man with a bloody ax holding a woman's head up which has been severed from her body. Do you think that's in good taste?" Gaines: "Yes I do - for the cover of a horror comic. A cover in bad taste, for example, might be defined as holding her head a little higher so that blood could be seen dripping from it and moving the body over a little further so that the neck of the body could be seen to be bloody." It was actually drawn this way first and Gaines had Craig change it to the published version.*

23-Used in Senate investigation on juvenile delinquency 40 80 120 320 510 700
27-Last issue (Low distribution) 37 74 111 259 455 650

NOTE: ***Craig** a-1-21; c-1-18, 20-22. **Crandall** a-18-26. **Davis** a-4, 5, 7, 9-12, 20. **Elder** a-17,18. **Evans** a-15, 19, 21, 23, 25, 27; c-23, 24. **Feldstein** c-19. **Ingels** a-1-12, 14, 15, 27. **Kamen** a-2, 4-18, 20-27; c-25-27. **Krigstein** a-22, 24, 25, 27. **Kurtzman** a-1, 3. **Orlando** a-16, 22, 24, 26. **Wood** a-1, 3. Issues No. 1-3 were printed in Canada as "Weird Suspenstories." Issues No. 11-15 have E. C. "quickie" stories. No. 25 contains the famous "Are You a Red Dupe?" editorial. Ray Bradbury adaptations-15, 17.*

CRIME SUSPENSTORIES
Russ Cochran/Gemstone Publ.: Nov, 1992 - No. 27, May, 1999 ($1.50/$2.00/$2.50)

1-27: Reprints Crime SuspenStories series 4.00

CRIMINAL (Also see Criminal: The Sinners)
Marvel Comics (Icon): Oct, 2006 - No. 10, Oct, 2007 ($2.99)
Volume 2: Feb, 2008 - No. 7, Nov, 2008 ($3.50)

1-10-Ed Brubaker-s/Sean Phillips-a/c 3.00
Volume 2: 1-7-Brubaker-s/Phillips-a 3.50
...: Tenth Anniversary Special Edition (Image Comics, 4/16, $5.99) Brubaker-s/Phillips-a; 1970s Kung Fu magazine pastishe within story; intro. Fang the Kung Fu Werewolf 6.00
...: The Special Edition (Image Comics, 2/15, $4.99) Brubaker-s/Phillips-a; 1970s Conan B&W magazine pastishe within story 5.00
... Vol. 1: Coward TPB (2007, $14.99) r/#1-5; intro. by Tom Fontana 15.00
... Vol. 2: Lawless TPB (2007, $14.99) r/#6-10; intro. by Frank Miller 15.00
... Vol. 3: The Dead and the Dying TPB (2008, $11.99) r/V2#1-4; intro. by John Singleton 12.00

CRIMINAL MACABRE: (limited series and one-shots)
Dark Horse Comics: ($2.99)

...: Cellblock 666 (9/08 - No. 4, 5/09)(#25-28 in series) 1-4-Niles-s/Stakal-a/Bradstreet-c 3.00
...: Die, Die, My Darling (4/12, $3.50) reprints serial from DHP #4-6; Staples-c 3.50
...: Feat of Clay (6/06, $2.99) Niles-s/Hotz-a/c 3.00
Free Comic Book Day: Criminal Macabre - Call Me Monster (5/11) flip book w/Baltimore 3.00
...: My Demon Baby (9/07 - No. 4, 4/08)(#21-24 in the series) 1-4-Niles-s/Stakal-a 3.00
...: No Peace For Dead Men (9/11, $3.99) Niles-s/Mitten-a/Staples-c 4.00
...: The Eyes of Frankenstein (9/13 - No. 4, 12/13 $3.99) 1-4-Niles-s/Mitten-a 4.00
...: The Goon (7/11, $3.99) Niles-s/Mitten-a; covers by Powell & Staples 4.00
...: They Fight By Night (11/12, $3.99) reprints serial from DHP #10-13; Staples-c 4.00
...: Two Red Eyes (12/06 - No. 4, 3/07) 1-4-Niles-s/Hotz-a/Bradstreet-c 3.00

CRIMINAL MACABRE: A CAL MCDONALD MYSTERY (Also see Last Train to Deadsville)
Dark Horse Comics: May, 2003 - No. 5, Sept, 2003 ($2.99)

1-5-Niles-s/Templesmith-a 3.00

CRIMINAL MACABRE: FINAL NIGHT - THE 30 DAYS OF NIGHT CROSSOVER
Dark Horse Comics: Dec, 2012 - No. 4, Mar, 2013 ($3.99, limited series)

1-4-Niles-s/Mitten-a/Erickson-c 4.00

CRIMINAL MACABRE:THE THIRD CHILD
Dark Horse Comics: Sept, 2014 - No. 4, Dec, 2014 ($3.99, limited series)

1-4-Niles-s/Mitten-a/Erickson-c 4.00

CRIMINALS ON THE RUN (Formerly Young King Cole) (Crime Fighting Detective No. 11 on)
Premium Group (Novelty Press): V4#1, Aug-Sep, 1948-#10, Dec-Jan, 1949-50

V4#1-Young King Cole continues 30 60 90 177 289 400
2-6: 6-Dr. Doom app. 25 50 75 150 245 340
7-Classic "Fish in the Face" c by L. B. Cole 63 126 189 403 689 975
V5#1,2 (#8,9),10: 9,10-L. B. Cole-c 22 44 66 132 216 300

NOTE: *Most issues have **L. B. Cole** covers. **McWilliams** a-V4#6, 7, V5#2, 10; c-V4#5.*

CRIMINAL: THE LAST OF THE INNOCENT
Marvel Comics (Icon): Jun, 2011 - No. 4, Sept, 2011 ($3.50)

1-4-Ed Brubaker-s/Sean Phillips-a/c 3.50

CRIMINAL: THE SINNERS
Marvel Comics (Icon): Sept, 2009 - No. 5, Mar, 2010 ($3.50)

1-5-Ed Brubaker-s/Sean Phillips-a/c 3.50

CRIMSON (Also see Cliffhanger #0)
Image Comics (Cliffhanger Productions): May, 1998 - No. 7, Dec, 1998;
DC Comics (Cliffhanger Prod.): No. 8, Mar, 1999 - No. 24, Apr, 2001 ($2.50)

1-Humberto Ramos-a/Augustyn-s 5.00
1-Variant-c by Warren 8.00
1-Chromium-c 15.00
2-Ramos-c with street crowd, 2-Variant-c by Art Adams 4.00
2-Dynamic Forces CrimsonChrome cover 15.00
3-7: 3-Ramos Moon background-c. 7-Three covers by Ramos, Madureira, & Campbell 3.50
8-23: 8-First DC issue 3.00
24-($3.50) Final issue; wraparound-c 4.00
DF Premiere Ed. 1998 ($6.95) covers by Ramos and Jae Lee 7.00
Crimson: Scarlet X Blood on the Moon (10/99, $3.95) 4.00
Crimson Sourcebook (11/99, $2.95) Pin-ups and info 3.00
Earth Angel TPB (2001, $14.95) r/#13-18 15.00

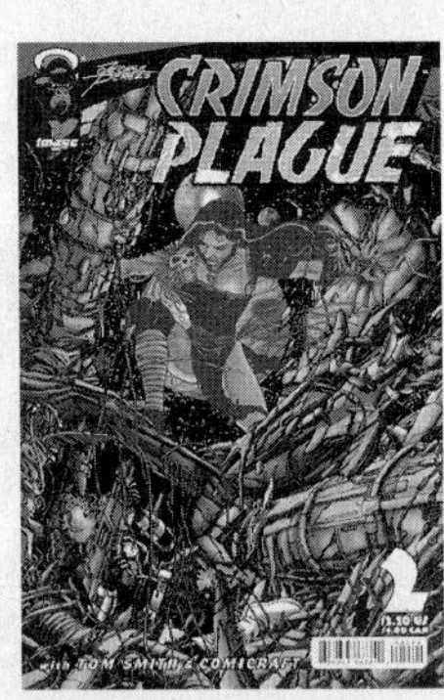

Crimson Plague #2 © George Pérez

Crisis on Infinite Earths #9 © DC

Crosswind #1 © Staggs & Simone

GD VG FN VF VF/NM NM-
2.0 4.0 6.0 8.0 9.0 9.2

Heaven and Earth TPB (1/00, $14.95) r/#7-12 15.00
Loyalty and Loss TPB ('99, $12.95) r/#1-6 15.00
Redemption TPB ('01, $14.95) r/#19-24 15.00

CRIMSON AVENGER, THE (See Detective Comics #20 for 1st app.)(Also see Leading Comics #1 & World's Best/Finest Comics)
DC Comics: June, 1988 - No. 4, Sept, 1988 ($1.00, limited series)
1-4 4.00

CRIMSON DYNAMO
Marvel Comics (Epic): Oct, 2003 - No. 6, Apr, 2004 ($2.50/$2.99)
1-4,6: 1-John Jackson Miller-s/Steve Ellis-a/c 3.00
5-($2.99) Iron Man-c/app. 4.00

CRIMSON PLAGUE
Event Comics: June, 1997 ($2.95, unfinished mini-series)
1-George Perez-a 3.00

CRIMSON PLAGUE (George Pérez's...)
Image Comics (Gorilla): June, 2000 - No. 2, Aug, 2000 ($2.95, mini-series)
1-George Pérez-a; reprints 6/97 issue with 16 new pages 3.00
2-($2.50) 3.00

CRISIS AFTERMATH: THE BATTLE FOR BLUDHAVEN (Also see Infinite Crisis)
DC Comics: Jun, 2006 - No. 6, Sept, 2006 ($2.99, limited series)
1-Atomic Knights return; Teen Titans app.; Jurgens-a/Acuna-c 4.00
1-2nd printing with pencil cover 3.00
2-6: 2-Intro S.H.A.D.E. (new Freedom Fighters) 3.00
TPB (2007, $12.99) r/#1-6 13.00

CRISIS AFTERMATH: THE SPECTRE (Also see Infinite Crisis, Gotham Central and Tales of the Unexpected)
DC Comics: Jul, 2006 - No. 3, Sept, 2006 ($2.99, limited series)
1-3-Crispus Allen becomes the Spectre; Pfeifer-s/Chiang-a/c 3.00
TPB (2007, $12.99) r/#1-3 and Tales of the Unexpected #1-3 13.00

CRISIS ON INFINITE EARTHS (Also see Official... Index and Legends of the DC Universe)
DC Comics: Apr, 1985 - No. 12, Mar, 1986 (maxi-series)
1-1st DC app. Blue Beetle & Detective Karp from Charlton; Pérez-c on all
2 4 6 11 16 20
2-6: 6-Intro Charlton's Capt. Atom, Nightshade, Question, Judomaster, Peacemaker & Thunderbolt into DC Universe 2 4 6 8 10 12
7-Double size; death of Supergirl 3 6 9 16 23 30
8-Death of the Flash (Barry Allen) 3 6 9 15 22 28
9-11: 9-Intro. Charlton's Ghost into DC Universe. 10-Intro. Charlton's Banshee, Dr. Spectro, Image, Punch & Jewelee into DC Universe; Starman (Prince Gavyn) dies
2 4 6 8 10 12
12-(52 pgs.)-Deaths of Dove, Kole, Lori Lemaris, Sunburst, G.A. Robin & Huntress; Kid Flash becomes new Flash; 3rd & final DC app. of the 3 Lt. Marvels; Green Fury gets new look (becomes Green Flame in Infinity, Inc. #32) 2 4 6 9 13 16
Slipcased Hardcover (1998, $99.95) Wraparound dust-jacket cover pencilled by Pérez and painted by Alex Ross; sketch pages by Pérez; Wolfman intro.; afterword by Giordano 125.00
TPB (2000, $29.95) Wraparound-c by Pérez and Ross 30.00
NOTE: *Crossover issues: All Star Squadron 50-56,60; Amethyst 13; Blue Devil 17,18; DC Comics Presents 78,86-88,95; Detective Comics 558; Fury of Firestorm 41,42; G.I. Combat 274; Green Lantern 194-196,198; Infinity, Inc. 18-25 & Annual 1, Justice League of America 244,245 & Annual 3; Legion of Super-Heroes 16,18; Losers Special 1; New Teen Titans 13,14; Omega Men 31,33; Superman 413-415; Swamp Thing 44,46; Wonder Woman 327-329.*

CRISIS ON MULTIPLE EARTHS
DC Comics: 2002 - 2010 ($14.95, trade paperbacks)
TPB-(2003) Reprints 1st 4 Silver Age JLA/JSA crossovers from J.L.ofA. #21,22; 29,30; 37,38; 46,47; new painted-c by Alex Ross; intro. by Mark Waid 15.00
Volume 2 (2003, $14.95) r/J.L.ofA. #55,56; 64,65; 73,74; 82,83; new Ordway-c 15.00
Volume 3 (2004, $14.95) r/J.L.ofA. #91,92; 100-102; 107,108; 113; Wein intro., Ross-c 15.00
Volume 4 (2006, $14.99) r/J.L.ofA. #123-124 (Earth-Prime),135-137 (Fawcett's Shazam characters), 147-148 (Legion of Super-Heroes); Ross-c 15.00
Volume 5 (2010, $19.99) r/J.L.ofA. #159-160 (Jonah Hex, Enemy Ace), #171-172 (Murder of Mr. Terrific), 1#83-185 (New Gods & Darkseid); Pérez-c 20.00
... The Team-Ups Volume 1 (2005, $14.99) r/Flash #123,129,137,151; Showcase #55,56; Green Lantern #40, Brave and the Bold #61 and Spectre #7; new Ordway-c 15.00

CRITICAL MASS (See A Shadowline Saga: Critical Mass)

CRITTER
Big Dog Press: Jul, 2011 - No. 4, 2011; Jun, 2012 - No. 20, Apr, 2014 ($3.50)
1-4-Multiple covers on all 3.50
Vol. 2 1-20-Multiple covers on all 3.50

CRITTER
Aspen MLT: Jul, 2015 - No. 4, Oct, 2015 ($3.99)
1-4-Reprints the 2011 series; multiple covers on all 4.00

CRITTERS (Also see Usagi Yojimbo Summer Special)
Fantagraphics Books: 1986 - No. 50, 1990 ($1.70/$2.00, B&W)
1-Cutey Bunny, Usagi Yojimbo app. 2 4 6 11 16 20
2,4,5,8,9 6.00
3,6,7,10-Usagi Yojimbo app. 1 2 3 5 6 8
11,14-Usagi Yojimbo app. 11-Christmas Special (68 pgs.) 5.00
12,13,15-22,24-37,39,40: 22-Watchmen parody; two diff. covers exist 3.00
23-With Alan Moore Flexi-disc ($3.95) 5.00
38-($2.75-c) Usagi Yojimbo app. 5.00
41-49 4.00
50 ($4.95, 84 pgs.)-Neil the Horse, Capt. Jack, Sam & Max & Usagi Yojimbo app.; Quagmire, Shaw-a 1 2 3 4 5 7
Special 1 (1/88, $2.00) 4.00

CROSS
Dark Horse Comics: No. 0, Oct, 1995 - No. 6, Apr, 1995 ($2.95, limited series, mature)
0-6: Darrow-c & Vachss scripts in all 3.00

CROSS AND THE SWITCHBLADE, THE
Spire Christian Comics (Fleming H. Revell Co.): 1972 (35-49¢)
1-Some issues have nn 3 6 9 17 26 35

CROSS BRONX, THE
Image Comics: Sept, 2006 - No. 4, Dec, 2006 ($2.99, limited series)
1-4: 1-Oeming-a/c; Oeming & Brandon-s; Ribic var-c. 2-Johnson var-c. 4-Mack var-c 3.00

CROSSFIRE
Spire Christian Comics (Fleming H. Revell Co.): 1973 (39/49¢)
nn 2 4 6 13 18 22

CROSSFIRE (Also see DNAgents)
Eclipse Comics: 5/84 - No. 17, 3/86; No. 18, 1/87 - No. 26, 2/88 ($1.50, Baxter paper) (#18-26 are B&W)
1-11,14-26: 1-DNAgents x-over; Spiegle-c/a begins 3.00
12-Death of Marilyn Monroe; Dave Stevens-c 2 4 6 11 16 20
13-Death of Marilyn Monroe 1 2 3 5 6 8

CROSSFIRE AND RAINBOW (Also see DNAgents)
Eclipse Comics: June, 1986 - No. 4, Sept, 1986 ($1.25, deluxe format)
1-3: Spiegle-a 3.00
4-Dave Stevens-c 6.00

CROSSGEN...
CrossGeneration Comics
CrossGenesis (1/00) Previews CrossGen universe; cover gallery 3.00
...Primer (1/00) Wizard supplement; intro. to the CrossGen universe 3.00
...Sampler (2/00) Retailer preview book 3.00

CROSSGEN CHRONICLES
CrossGeneration Comics: June, 2000 - No. 8 ($3.95)
1-Intro. to CrossGen characters & company 4.00
1-(no cover price) same contents, customer preview 4.00
2-8: 2-(3/01) George Pérez-c/a. 3-5-Pérez-a/Waid-s. 6,7-Nebres-c/a 4.00

CROSSING MIDNIGHT
DC Comics (Vertigo): Jan, 2007 - No. 19, Jul, 2008 ($2.99)
1-19: 1-Carey-s/Fern-a/Williams III-c. 10-12-Nguyen-a 3.00
...: Cut Here TPB (2007, $9.99) r/#1-5 10.00
...: A Map of Midnight TPB (2008, $14.99) r/#6-12; afterword by Carey 15.00
...: The Sword in the Soul TPB (2008, $14.99) r/#13-19 15.00

CROSSING THE ROCKIES (See Classics Illustrated Special Issue)

CROSSOVERS, THE
CrossGeneration Comics: Feb, 2003 - No. 12 ($2.95)
1-12-Robert Rodi-s. 1-6-Mauricet & Ernie Colon-a. 7-Staton-a begins 3.00
Vol. 1: Cross Currents (2003, $9.95) digest-sized reprints #1-6 10.00

CROSSWIND
Image Comics: Jun, 2017 - Present ($3.99)
1-6-Gail Simone-s/Cat Staggs-a 4.00

CROW, THE (Also see Caliber Presents)
Caliber Press: Feb, 1989 - No. 4, 1989 ($1.95, B&W, limited series)
1-James O'Barr-c/a/scripts 9 18 27 60 120 180
1-3-2nd printing 2 4 6 13 18 22

The Crow: Wild Justice #2 © James O'Barr

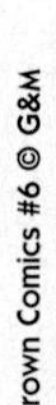

	GD 2.0	VG 4.0	FN 6.0	VF 8.0	VF/NM 9.0	NM- 9.2
2	5	10	15	31	53	75
2-3rd printing						5.00
3,4	4	8	12	28	47	65

CROW, THE
Tundra Publishing, Ltd.: Jan, 1992 - No. 3, 1992 ($4.95, B&W, 68 pgs.)

	GD	VG	FN	VF	VF/NM	NM-
1-r/#1,2 of Caliber series	2	4	6	11	16	20
2,3: 2-r/#3 of Caliber series w/new material. 3-All new material	2	4	6	8	10	12

CROW, THE
Kitchen Sink Press: 1/96 - No. 3, 3/96 ($2.95, B&W)

	NM-
1-3: James O'Barr-c/scripts	5.00
#0-A Cycle of Shattered Lives (12/98, $3.50) new story by O'Barr	4.00

CROW, THE
Image Comics (Todd McFarlane Prod.): Feb, 1999 - No. 10, Nov, 1999 ($2.50)

	NM-
1-10: 1-Two covers by McFarlane and Kent Williams; Muth-s in all. 2-6,10-Paul Lee-a	3.00
Book 1 - Vengeance (2000, $10.95, TPB) r/#1-3,5,6	11.00
Book 2 - Evil Beyond Reach (2000, $10.95, TPB) r/#4,7-10	11.00
Todd McFarlane Presents The Crow Magazine 1 (3/00, $4.95)	5.00

CROW, THE: CITY OF ANGELS (Movie)
Kitchen Sink Press: July, 1996 - No. 3, Sept, 1996 ($2.95, limited series)

	NM-
1-3: Adaptation of film; two-c (photo & illos.). 1-Vincent Perez interview	3.00

CROW, THE: CURARE
IDW Publishing: Jun, 2013 - No. 3, Aug, 2013 ($3.99, limited series)

	NM-
1-3-James O'Barr-s/Antoine Dodé-a; multiple covers on each	4.00

CROW, THE: DEATH AND REBIRTH
IDW Publishing: Jul, 2012 - No. 5, Nov, 2012 ($3.99, limited series)

	NM-
1-5-Shirley-s/Colden-a; multiple covers on each	4.00

CROW, THE: FLESH AND BLOOD
Kitchen Sink Press: May, 1996 - No. 3, July, 1996 ($2.95, limited series)

	NM-
1-3: O'Barr-c	3.00

CROW, THE: RAZOR - KILL THE PAIN
London Night Studios: Apr, 1998 - No. 3, July, 1998 ($2.95, B&W, lim. series)

	NM-
1-3-Hartsoe-s/O'Barr-painted-c	3.00
0(10/98) Dorien painted-c, Finale (2/99)	3.00
The Lost Chapter (2/99, $4.95), Tour Book-(12/97) pin-ups; 4 diff.-c	5.00

CROW, THE: PESTILENCE
IDW Publishing: Mar, 2014 - No. 4, Jun, 2014 ($3.99, limited series)

	NM-
1-4-Frank Bill-s/Drew Moss-a; two covers	4.00

CROW, THE: SKINNING THE WOLVES
IDW Publishing: Dec, 2012 - No. 3, Feb, 2013 ($3.99, limited series)

	NM-
1-3-James O'Barr-s/Jim Terry-s/a; multiple covers on each	4.00

CROW, THE: WAKING NIGHTMARES
Kitchen Sink Press: Jan, 1997 - No. 4, 1998 ($2.95, B&W, limited series)

	NM-
1-4-Miran Kim-c	5.00

CROW, THE: WILD JUSTICE
Kitchen Sink Press: Oct, 1996 - No. 3, Dec, 1996 ($2.95, B&W, limited series)

	NM-
1-3-Prosser-s/Adlard-a	3.00

CROWN COMICS (Also see Vooda)
Golfing/McCombs Publ.: Wint, 1944-45; No. 2, Sum, 1945 - No. 19, July, 1949

	GD	VG	FN	VF	VF/NM	NM-
1- "The Oblong Box" E.A. Poe adaptation	50	100	150	315	533	750
2-Baker-a	34	68	102	204	332	460
3-Baker-a; Voodah by Baker	41	82	123	256	428	600
4-6-Baker-c/a; Voodah app. #4,5	39	78	117	231	378	525
7-Feldstein, Baker, Kamen-a; Baker-c	39	78	117	240	395	550
8-Baker-a; Voodah app.	29	58	87	170	278	385
9-11,13-19: Voodah in #10-19. 13-New logo	20	40	60	114	182	250
12-Master Marvin by Feldstein, Starr-a; Voodah-c	20	40	60	117	189	260

NOTE: *Bolle a-11, 13-16, 18, 19; c-11p, 15.* ***Powell*** *a-19.* ***Starr*** *a-11-13; c-11i.*

CRUCIBLE
DC Comics (Impact): Feb, 1993 - No. 6, July, 1993 ($1.25, limited series)

	NM-
1-6: 1-(99¢)-Neon ink-c. 1,2-Quesada-c(p). 1-4-Quesada layouts	3.00

CRUEL AND UNUSUAL
DC Comics (Vertigo): June, 1999 - No. 4, Sept, 1999 ($2.95, limited series)

	NM-
1-4-Delano & Peyer-s/McCrea-c/a	3.00

CRUSADER FROM MARS (See Tops in Adventure)
Ziff-Davis Publ. Co.: Jan-Mar, 1952 - No. 2, Fall, 1952 (Painted-c)

	GD	VG	FN	VF	VF/NM	NM-
1-Cover is dated Spring	84	168	252	538	919	1300
2-Bondage-c	58	116	174	371	636	900

CRUSADER RABBIT (TV)
Dell Publishing Co.: No. 735, Oct, 1956 - No. 805, May, 1957

	GD	VG	FN	VF	VF/NM	NM-
Four Color 735 (#1)	21	42	63	147	324	500
Four Color 805	16	32	48	111	246	380

CRUSADERS, THE (Religious)
Chick Publications: 1974 - Vol. 17, 1988 (39/69¢, 36 pgs.)

	GD	VG	FN	VF	VF/NM	NM-
Vol.1-Operation Bucharest ('74). Vol.2-The Broken Cross ('74). Vol.3-Scarface ('74). Vol.4-Exorcists ('75). Vol.5-Chaos ('75)	3	6	9	16	23	30
Vol.6-Primal Man? ('76)-(Disputes evolution theory). Vol.7-The Ark-(claims proof of existence, destroyed by Bolsheviks). Vol.8-The Gift-(Life story of Christ). Vol.9-Angel of Light-(Story of the Devil). Vol.10-Spellbound?-(Tells how rock music is Satanic & produced by witches). 11-Sabotage?. 12-Alberto. 13-Double Cross. 14-The Godfathers. (No. 6-14 low in distribution; loaded with religious propaganda.). 15-The Force. 16-The Four Horsemen	3	6	9	16	23	30
Vol. 17-The Prophet (low print run)	3	6	9	17	26	35

CRUSADERS (Southern Knights No. 2 on)
Guild Publications: 1982 (B&W, magazine size)

	GD	VG	FN	VF	VF/NM	NM-
1-1st app. Southern Knights	2	4	6	10	14	18

CRUSADERS, THE (Also see Black Hood, The Jaguar, The Comet, The Fly, Legend of the Shield, The Mighty... & The Web)
DC Comics (Impact): May, 1992 - No. 8, Dec, 1992 ($1.00/$1.25)

	NM-
1-8-Contains 3 Impact trading cards	4.00

CRUSADES, THE
DC Comics (Vertigo): 2001 - No. 20, Dec, 2002 ($3.95/$2.50)

	NM-
...: Urban Decree ('01, $3.95) Intro. the Knight; Seagle-s/Kelley Jones-c/a	4.00
1-(5/01, $2.50) Sienkiewicz-c	3.00
2-20: 2-Moeller-c. 18-Begin $2.95-c	3.00

CRUSH
Dark Horse Comics: Oct, 2003 - No. 4, Jan, 2004 ($2.99, limited series)

	NM-
1-4-Jason Hall-s/Sean Murphy-a	3.00

CRUSH, THE
Image Comics (Motown Machineworks): Jan, 1996 - No. 5, July, 1996 ($2.25, limited series)

	NM-
1-5: Baron scripts	3.00

CRUX
CrossGeneration Comics: May, 2001 - No. 33, Feb, 2004 ($2.95)

	NM-
1-33: 1-Waid-s/Epting & Magyar-a/c. 6-Pelletier-a. 13-Dixon-s begin. 25-Cover has fake creases and other aging	3.00
Atlantis Rising Vol. 1 TPB (2002, $15.95) r/#1-6	16.00
Test of Time Vol. 2 TPB (12/02, $15.95) r/#7-12	16.00
Vol. 3: Strangers in Atlantis (2003, $15.95) r/#13-18	16.00
Vol. 4: Chaos Reborn (2003, $15.95) r/#19-24	16.00

CRY FOR DAWN
Cry For Dawn Pub.: 1989 - No. 9 ($2.25, B&W, mature)

	GD	VG	FN	VF	VF/NM	NM-
1	7	14	21	46	86	125
1-2nd printing	3	6	9	19	30	40
1-3rd printing	3	6	9	14	20	25
2	4	8	12	23	37	50
2-2nd printing	2	4	6	11	16	20
3	3	6	9	16	23	30
3a-HorrorCon Edition (1990, less than 400 printed, signed inside-c)						200.00
4-6	2	4	6	11	16	20
5-2nd printing	1	2	3	5	6	8
7-9	2	4	6	9	12	15
4-9-Signed & numbered editions	3	6	9	14	20	25
Angry Christ Comix HC (4/03, $29.99) reprints various stories; and 30 pgs. new material						30.00
...Calendar (1993)						35.00

CRY HAVOC
Image Comics: Jan, 2016 - No. 6, Jun, 2016 ($3.99)

	NM-
1-6-Simon Spurrier-s/Ryan Kelly-a; 2 covers on each	4.00

CRYIN' LION COMICS
William H. Wise Co.: Fall, 1944 - No. 3, Spring, 1945

	GD	VG	FN	VF	VF/NM	NM-
1-Funny animal	18	36	54	107	169	230
2-Hitler and Tojo app.	15	30	45	84	127	170

Crypt of Terror #19 © WMG

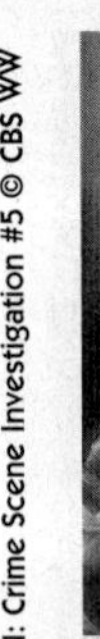
CSI: Crime Scene Investigation #5 © CBS WW

Curse of the Spawn #12 © TMP

GD 2.0 | VG 4.0 | FN 6.0 | VF 8.0 | VF/NM 9.0 | NM- 9.2

3 11 22 33 62 86 110

CRYPT
Image Comics (Extreme): Aug, 1995 - No. 2, Oct. 1995 ($2.50, limited series)
1,2-Prophet app. 3.00

CRYPTIC WRITINGS OF MEGADETH
Chaos! Comics: Sept, 1997 - No. 4, Jun, 1998 ($2.95, quarterly)
1-4-Stories based on song lyrics by Dave Mustaine 3.00

CRYPTOCRACY
Dark Horse Comics: Jun, 2016 - No. 6, Nov, 2016 ($3.99)
1-6: 1-Van Jensen-s/Pete Woods-a 4.00

CRYPT OF DAWN (see Dawn)
Sirius: 1996 ($2.95, B&W, limited series)
1-Linsner-c/s; anthology. 5.00
2, 3 (2/98) 4.00
4,5: 4- (6/98), 5-(11/98) 3.00
Ltd. Edition 20.00

CRYPT OF SHADOWS
Marvel Comics Group: Jan, 1973 - No. 21, Nov, 1975 (#1-9 are 20¢)
1-Wolverton-r/Advs. Into Terror #7 5 10 15 31 53 75
2-10: 2-Starlin/Everett-c 3 6 9 17 25 34
11-21: 18,20-Kirby-a 3 6 9 15 22 28
NOTE: ***Briefer*** *a-2r.* ***Ditko*** *a-13r, 18-20r.* ***Everett*** *a-6, 14r; c-2i.* ***Heath*** *a-1r.* ***Gil Kane*** *c-1, 6.* ***Mort Lawrence*** *a-1r, 8r.* ***Maneely*** *a-2r.* ***Moldoff*** *a-8.* ***Powell*** *a-12r, 14r.* ***Tuska*** *a-2r.*

CRYPT OF TERROR (Formerly Crime Patrol; Tales From the Crypt No. 20 on)
(Also see EC Archives • Tales From the Crypt)
E. C. Comics: No. 17, Apr-May, 1950 - No. 19, Aug-Sept, 1950
17-1st New Trend to hit stands 343 686 1029 2744 4372 6000
18,19 183 366 549 1464 2332 3200
NOTE: ***Craig*** *c/a-17-19.* ***Feldstein*** *a-17-19.* ***Ingels*** *a-19.* ***Kurtzman*** *a-18.* ***Wood*** *a-18. Canadian reprints known; see Table of Contents.*

CRYPTOZOIC MAN (Comic Book Men)
Dynamite Entertainment: 2013 - No. 4, 2014 ($3.99, limited series)
1-Bryan Johnson-s/Walt Flanagan-a/c 2 4 6 10 14 18
2-4 1 3 4 6 8 10

CRYSIS (Based on the EA videogame)
IDW Publishing: Jun, 2011 - No. 6, Oct, 2011 ($3.99, limited series)
1-6: 1-Richard K. Moran-s/Peter Bergting-a; two covers 4.00

CSI: CRIME SCENE INVESTIGATION (Based on TV series)
IDW Publishing: Jan, 2003 - No. 5, May, 2003 ($3.99, limited series)
1-Two covers (photo & Ashley Wood); Max Allan Collins-s 4.00
2-5 4.00
Free Comic Book Day edition (7/04) Previews CSI: Bad Rap; The Shield: Spotlight; 24: One Shot; and 30 Days of Night 3.00
...: Case Files Vol. 1 TPB (8/06, $19.99) B&W rep/Serial TPB, CSI - Bad Rap and CSI - Demon House limited series 20.00
...: Serial TPB (2003, $19.99) r/#1-5; bonus short story by Collins/Wood 20.00
...: Thicker Than Blood (7/03, $6.99) Mariotte-s/Rodriguez-a 7.00

CSI: CRIME SCENE INVESTIGATION - BAD RAP
IDW Publishing: Aug, 2003 - No. 5, Dec, 2003 ($3.99, limited series)
1-5-Two photo covers; Max Allan Collins-s/Rodriguez-a 4.00
TPB (3/04, $19.99) r/#1-5 20.00

CSI: CRIME SCENE INVESTIGATION - DEMON HOUSE
IDW Publishing: Feb, 2004 - No. 5, Jun, 2004 ($3.99, limited series)
1-5-Photo covers on all; Max Allan Collins-s/Rodriguez-a 4.00
TPB (10/04, $19.99) r/#1-5 20.00

CSI: CRIME SCENE INVESTIGATION - DOMINOS
IDW Publishing: Aug, 2004 - No. 5, Dec, 2004 ($3.99, limited series)
1-5-Photo covers on all; Oprisko-s/Rodriguez-a 4.00

CSI: CRIME SCENE INVESTIGATION - DYING IN THE GUTTERS
IDW Publishing: Aug, 2006 - No. 5, Dec, 2006 ($3.99, limited series)
1-5-"Rich Johnston" murdered; comic creators (Quesada, Rucka, David, Brubaker, Silvestri and others) appear as suspects; Stephen Mooney-a; photo-c 4.00

CSI: CRIME SCENE INVESTIGATION - SECRET IDENTITY
IDW Publishing: Feb, 2005 - No. 5, Jun, 2005 ($3.99, limited series)
1-5-Photo covers on all; Steven Grant-s/Gabriel Rodriguez-a 4.00

CSI: MIAMI
IDW Publishing: Oct, 2003; Apr, 2004 ($6.99, one-shots)
... - Blood Money (9/04)-Oprisko-s/Guedes & Perkins-a 7.00
... - Smoking Gun (10/03)-Mariotte-s/Avilés & Wood-a 7.00
... - Thou Shalt Not... (4/04)-Oprisko-s/Guedes & Wood-a 7.00
TPB (2/05, $19.99) reprints one-shots 20.00

CSI: NY - BLOODY MURDER
IDW Publishing: July, 2005 - No. 5, Nov, 2005 ($3.99, limited series)
1-5-Photo covers on all; Collins-s/Woodward-a 4.00

C•23 (Jim Lee's...) (Based on Wizards of the Coast card game)
Image Comics: Apr, 1998 - No. 8, Nov, 1998 ($2.50)
1-8: 1,2-Choi & Mariotte-s/ Charest-c. 2-Variant-c by Jim Lee. 4-Ryan Benjamin-c. 5,8-Corben var-c. 6-Flip book with Planetary preview; Corben-c 3.00

CUD
Fantagraphics Books: 8/92 - No. 8, 12/94 ($2.25-$2.75, B&W, mature)
1-8: Terry LaBan scripts & art in all. 6-1st Eno & Plum 3.00

CUD COMICS
Dark Horse Comics: Jan, 1995 - No. 8, Sept, 1997 ($2.95, B&W)
1-8: Terry LaBan-c/a/scripts. 5-Nudity; marijuana story 3.00
Eno and Plum TPB (1997, $12.95) r/#1-4, DHP #93-95 13.00

CUPID
Marvel Comics (U.S.A.): Dec, 1949 - No. 2, Mar, 1950
1-Photo-c 24 48 72 140 230 320
2-Bettie Page ('50s pin-up queen) photo-c; Powell-a (see My Love #4)
74 148 222 470 810 1150

CURB STOMP
BOOM! Studios: Feb, 2015 - No. 4, May, 2015 ($3.99, limited series)
1-4-Ryan Ferrier-s/Devaki Neogi-a 4.00

CURIO
Harry 'A' Chesler: 1930's(?) (Tabloid size, 16-20 pgs.)
nn 21 42 63 122 199 275

CURLY KAYOE COMICS (Boxing)
United Features Syndicate/Dell Publ. Co.: 1946 - No. 8, 1950; Jan, 1958
1 (1946)-Strip-r (Fritzi Ritz); biography of Sam Leff, Kayoe's artist
24 48 72 140 230 320
2 16 32 48 94 147 200
3-8 14 28 42 80 115 150
United Presents...(Fall, 1948) 14 28 42 80 115 150
Four Color 871 (Dell, 1/58) 5 10 15 30 50 70

CURSED
Image Comics (Top Cow): Oct, 2003 - No. 4, Feb, 2004 ($2.99)
1-4-Avery & Blevins-s/Molenaar-a 3.00

CURSE OF DRACULA, THE
Dark Horse Comics: July, 1998 - No. 3, Sept, 1998 ($2.95, limited series)
1-3-Marv Wolfman-s/Gene Colan-a 3.00
TPB (2005, $9.95) r/series; intro. by Marv Wolfman 10.00

CURSE OF RUNE (Becomes Rune, 2nd Series)
Malibu Comics (Ultraverse): May, 1995 - No. 4, Aug, 1995 ($2.50, lim. series)
1-4: 1-Two covers form one image 3.00

CURSE OF THE SPAWN
Image Comics (Todd McFarlane Prod.): Sept, 1996 - No. 29, Mar, 1999 ($1.95)
1-Dwayne Turner-a(p) 1 3 4 6 8 10
1-B&W Edition 2 4 6 10 14 18
2-3 5.00
4-29: 12-Movie photo-c of Melinda Clarke (Priest) 4.00
Blood and Sutures ('99, $9.95, TPB) r/#5-8 10.00
Lost Values ('00, $10.95, TPB) r/#12-14,22; Ashley Wood-c 11.00
Sacrifice of the Soul ('99, $9.95, TPB) r/#1-4 10.00
Shades of Gray ('00, $9.95, TPB) r/#9-11,29 10.00
The Best of the Curse of the Spawn (6/06, $16.99, TPB) B&W r/#1-8,12-16,20-29 17.00

CURSE OF THE WEIRD
Marvel Comics: Dec, 1993 - No. 4, Mar, 1994 ($1.25, limited series)
(Pre-code horror-r)
1-4: 1,3,4-Wolverton-r(1-Eye of Doom; 3-Where Monsters Dwell; 4-The End of the World). 2-Orlando-r. 4-Zombie-r by Everett; painted-c 1 2 3 5 6 8
NOTE: ***Briefer*** *r-2.* ***Davis*** *a-4r.* ***Ditko*** *a-1r, 2r, 4r; c-1r.* ***Everett*** *r-1.* ***Heath*** *r-1-3.* ***Kubert*** *r-3.* ***Wolverton*** *a-1r, 3r, 4r.*

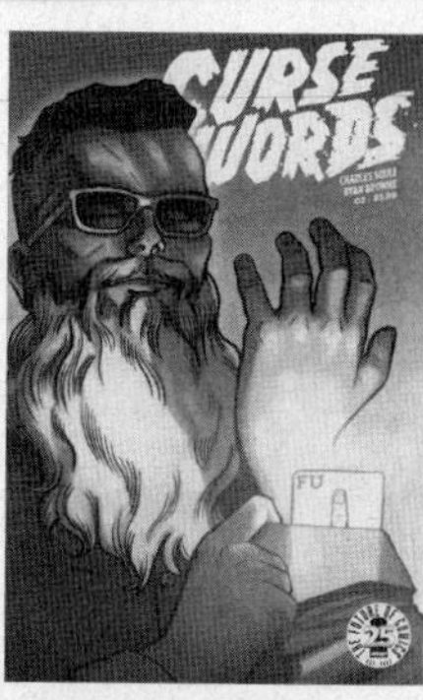
Curse Words #2 © Silent E Prods.

Cyber Force V4 #4 © TCOW

Cyberfrog #1 © HoH

	GD 2.0	VG 4.0	FN 6.0	VF 8.0	VF/NM 9.0	NM- 9.2

CURSE WORDS
Image Comics: Jan, 2017 - Present ($3.99)

1-11-Charles Soule-s/Ryan Browne-a 4.00
Holiday Special (12/17, $3.99) Mike Norton-a 4.00

CUSTER'S LAST FIGHT
Avon Periodicals: 1950

	GD 2.0	VG 4.0	FN 6.0	VF 8.0	VF/NM 9.0	NM- 9.2
nn-Partial reprint of Cowpuncher #1	18	36	54	105	165	225

CUTEY BUNNY (See Army Surplus Komikz Featuring...)

CUTIE PIE
Junior Reader's Guild (Lev Gleason): May, 1955 - No. 3, Dec, 1955; No. 4, Feb, 1956; No. 5, Aug, 1956

	GD 2.0	VG 4.0	FN 6.0	VF 8.0	VF/NM 9.0	NM- 9.2
1	9	18	27	52	69	85
2-5: 4-Misdated 2/55	6	12	18	31	38	45

CUTTING EDGE
Marvel Comics: Dec, 1995 ($2.95)

1-Hulk-c/story; Messner-Loebs scripts 3.00

CVO: COVERT VAMPIRIC OPERATIONS
IDW Publishing: June, 2003 ($5.99, one-shot)

1-Alex Garner-s/Mindy Lee-a(p) 6.00
... - Human Touch 1 (8/04, $3.99, one-shot) Hernandez & Garner-a 4.00
... - 100-Page Spectacular (4/11, $7.99) r/#1, African Blood #2 Rogue State #5 8.00
TPB (9/04, $19.99) r/#1 and ... - Artifact #1-3; intro. by Garner 20.00

CVO: COVERT VAMPIRIC OPERATIONS - AFRICAN BLOOD
IDW Publishing: Sept, 2006 - No. 4, May, 2007 ($3.99, limited series)

1-4-El Torres-s/Luis Czerniawski-a 4.00

CVO: COVERT VAMPIRIC OPERATIONS - ARTIFACT
IDW Publishing: Oct, 2003 - No. 3, Dec, 2003 ($3.99, limited series)

1-3-Jeff Mariotte-s/Gabriel Hernandez-a/Alex Garner-c 4.00

CVO: COVERT VAMPIRIC OPERATIONS - ROGUE STATE
IDW Publishing: Nov, 2004 - No. 5, Mar, 2005 ($3.99, limited series)

1-5-Jeff Mariotte-s/Vazquez-a 4.00
TPB (7/05, $19.99) r/#1-5; cover gallery 20.00

CYBERELLA
DC Comics (Helix): Sept, 1996 - No. 12, Aug, 1997 ($2.25/$2.50)(1st Helix series)

1-12: 1-5-Chaykin & Cameron-a. 1,2-Chaykin-c. 3-5-Cameron-c 3.00

CYBERFORCE
Image Comics (Top Cow Productions): Oct, 1992 - No. 4, 1993; No. 0, Sept, 1993 ($1.95, limited series)

1-Silvestri-c/a in all; coupon for Image Comics #0; 1st Top Cow Productions title 6.00
1-With coupon missing 2.00
2-4,0: 2-(3/93). 3-Pitt-c/story. 4-Codename: Stryke Force back-up (1st app.); foil-c. 0-(9/93)-Walt Simonson-c/a/scripts 3.00

CYBERFORCE
Image Comics (Top Cow Productions)/Top Cow Comics No. 28 on: V2#1, Nov, 1993 - No. 35, Sept. 1997 ($1.95)

V2#1-24: 1-7-Marc Silvestri/Keith Williams-c/a. 8-McFarlane-c/a. 10-Painted variant-c exists. 18-Variant-c exists. 23-Velocity-c. 3.00
1-3: 1-Gold Logo-c. 2-Silver embossed-c. 3-Gold embossed-c 10.00
1-(99¢, 3/96, 2nd printing) 3.00
25-($3.95)-Wraparound, foil-c 4.00
26-35: 28-(11/96)-1st Top Cow Comics iss. Quesada & Palmiotti's Gabriel app. 27-Quesada & Palmiotti's Ash app. 3.00
Annual 1,2 (3/95, 8/96, $2.50, $2.95) 4.00
NOTE: *Annuals read Volume One in the indica.*

CYBERFORCE (Volume 3)
Image Comics (Top Cow): Apr, 2006 - No. 6, Nov, 2006 ($2.99)

1-6: 1-Pat Lee-a/Ron Marz-s; three covers by Pat Lee, Marc Silvestri and Dave Finch 3.00
#0-(6/06, $2.99) reprints origin story from Image Comics Hardcover Vol. 1 3.00
.../X-Men 1 (1/07, $3.99) Pat Lee-a/Ron Marz-s; 2 covers by Lee and Silvestri 4.00
Vol. 1 TPB (12/06, $14.99) r/#1-6, #0 & story from The Cow Quarterly; cover gallery 15.00

CYBER FORCE (Volume 4)
Image Comics (Top Cow): Dec, 2012 - Present (no cover price/$2.99)

1-11: 1-Silvestri & Hawkins-s/Pham-a; multiple covers on each 3.00
...: Artifacts #0 (12/16, $3.99) Short stories by various; Khoi Pham-c 4.00

CYBERFORCE/HUNTER-KILLER
Image Comics (Top Cow Productions): July, 2009 - No. 5, Mar, 2010 ($2.99)

1-5-Waid-s/Rocafort-a; multiple covers on each 3.00

CYBERFORCE ORIGINS
Image Comics (Top Cow Productions): Jan, 1995 - No. 3, Nov, 1995 ($2.50)

1-Cyblade (1/95) 5.00
1-Cyblade (3/96, 99¢, 2nd printing) 3.00
1A-Exclusive Ed.; Tucci-c 4.00
2,3: 2-Stryker (2/95)-1st Mike Turner-a. 3-Impact 3.00
(#4) Misery (12/95, $2.95) 3.00

CYBERFORCE/STRYKEFORCE: OPPOSING FORCES (See Codename: Stryke Force #15)
Image Comics (Top Cow Productions): Sept, 1995 - No. 2, Oct, 1995 ($2.50, limited series)

1,2: 2-Stryker disbands Strykeforce. 3.00

CYBERFORCE UNIVERSE SOURCEBOOK
Image Comics (Top Cow Productions): Aug, 1994/Feb, 1995 ($2.50)

1,2-Silvestri-c 3.00

CYBERFROG
Hall of Heroes: June, 1994 - No. 2, Dec, 1994 ($2.50, B&W, limited series)

	GD 2.0	VG 4.0	FN 6.0	VF 8.0	VF/NM 9.0	NM- 9.2
1-Ethan Van Sciver-c/a/scripts	3	6	9	15	22	28
2	2	4	6	8	10	12

CYBERFROG
Harris Comics: Feb, 1996 - No. 3, Apr, 1996 ($2.95)

0-3: Van Sciver-c/a/scripts. 2-Variant-c exists 6.00

CYBERFROG: (Title series), **Harris Comics**

--RESERVOIR FROG, 9/96 - No. 2, 10/96 ($2.95) 1,2: Van Sciver-c/a/scripts; wraparound-c 4.00
--3RD ANNIVERSARY SPECIAL, 1/97 - #2, ($2.50, B&W) 1,2 4.00
--VS. CREED, 7/97 ($2.95, B&W)1 4.00

CYBERNARY (See Deathblow #1)
Image Comics (WildStorm Productions): Nov, 1995 - No.5, Mar, 1996 ($2.50)

1-5 3.00

CYBERNARY 2.0
DC Comics (WildStorm): Sept, 2001 - No. 6, Apr, 2002 ($2.95, limited series)

1-6: Joe Harris-s/Eric Canete-a. 6-The Authority app. 3.00

CYBERPUNK
Innovation Publishing: Sept, 1989 - No. 2, Oct, 1989 ($1.95, 28 pgs.) Book 2, #1, May, 1990 - No. 2, 1990 ($2.25, 28 pgs.)

1,2, Book 2 #1,2:1,2-Ken Steacy painted-covers (Adults) 3.00

CYBERPUNK: THE SERAPHIM FILES
Innovation Publishing: Nov, 1990 - No. 2, Dec, 1990 ($2.50, 28 pgs., mature)

1,2: 1-Painted-c; story cont'd from Seraphim 3.00

CYBERPUNX
Image Comics (Extreme Studios): Mar, 1996 ($2.50)

1 3.00

CYBERRAD
Continuity Comics: 1991 - No. 7, 1992 ($2.00)(Direct sale & newsstand-c variations) V2#1, 1993 ($2.50)

1-7: 5-Glow-in-the-dark-c by N. Adams (direct sale only). 6-Contains 4 pg. fold-out poster; N. Adams layouts 3.00
V2#1-($2.95, direct sale ed.)-Die-cut-c w/B&W hologram on-c; Neal Adams sketches 4.00
V2#1-($2.50, newsstand ed.)-Without sketches 3.00

CYBERRAD DEATHWATCH 2000 (Becomes CyberRad w/#2, 7/93)
Continuity Comics: Apr, 1993 - No. 2, 1993 ($2.50)

1,2: 1-Bagged w/2 cards; Adams-c & layouts & plots. 2-Bagged w/card; Adams scripts 3.00

CYBER 7
Eclipse Comics: Mar, 1989 - #7, Sept, 1989; V2#1, Oct, 1989 - #10, 1990 ($2.00, B&W)

1-7, Book 2 #1-10: Stories translated from Japanese 3.00

CYBLADE
Image Comics (Top Cow Productions): Oct, 2008 - No. 4, Mar, 2009 ($2.99)

1-4: 1,2-Mays-a/Fialkov-s. 1-Two covers. 3,4-Ferguson-a 3.00
.../ Ghost Rider 1 (Marvel/Top Cow, 1/97, $2.95) Devil's Reign pt. 2 4.00
...: Pilot Season 1 (9/07, $2.99) Rick Mays-a 3.00

CYBLADE/SHI (Also see Battle For The Independents & Shi/Cyblade: The Battle For The Independents)
Image Comics (Top Cow Productions): 1995 ($2.95, one-shot)

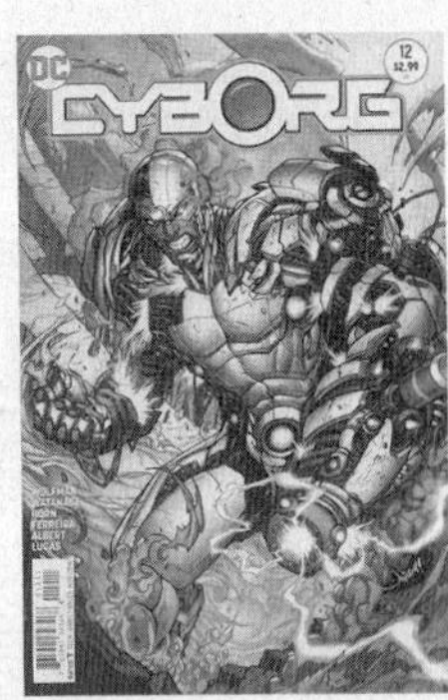

Cyborg #12 © DC

Cyclops #3 © MAR

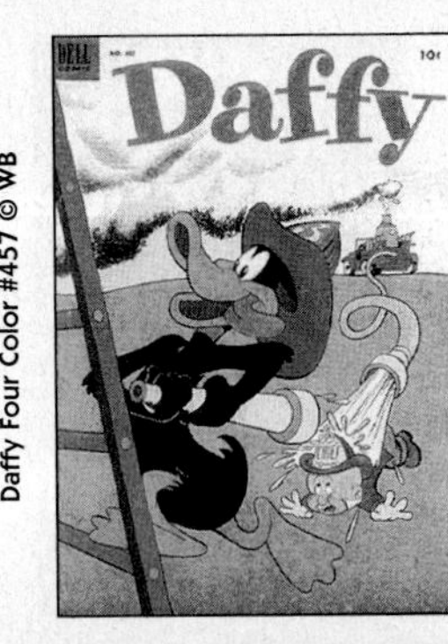

Daffy Four Color #457 © WB

	GD 2.0	VG 4.0	FN 6.0	VF 8.0	VF/NM 9.0	NM- 9.2
San Diego Preview	2	4	6	10	14	18
1-($2.95)-1st app. Witchblade	2	4	6	8	10	12
1-($2.95)-variant-c; Tucci-a						5.00

CYBORG (From Justice League)
DC Comics: Sept, 2015 - No. 12, Aug, 2016 ($2.99)

	GD 2.0	VG 4.0	FN 6.0	VF 8.0	VF/NM 9.0	NM- 9.2
1-12: 1-Walker-s/Reis-a. 3-6-Metal Men app. 9,10-Shazam app.						3.00

CYBORG (DC Rebirth)
DC Comics: Nov, 2016 - Present ($2.99/$3.99)

	GD 2.0	VG 4.0	FN 6.0	VF 8.0	VF/NM 9.0	NM- 9.2
1-10: 1-Semper Jr.-s/Pelletier-a; Kilg%re app. 6-Intro. Variant						3.00
11-20: 11-Begin $3.99-c. 15-Metal Men app. 15-17-Beast Boy app.						4.00
...: Rebirth 1 (11/16, $2.99) Semper Jr.-s/Pelletier-a; origin retold						3.00

CYBRID
Maximum Press: July, 1995; No. 0, Jan, 1997 ($2.95/$3.50)

	GD 2.0	VG 4.0	FN 6.0	VF 8.0	VF/NM 9.0	NM- 9.2
1-(7/95)						3.50
0-(1/97)-Liefeld-a/script; story cont'd in Avengelyne #4						3.50

CYCLONE COMICS (Also see Whirlwind Comics)
Bilbara Publishing Co.: June, 1940 - No. 5, Nov, 1940

	GD 2.0	VG 4.0	FN 6.0	VF 8.0	VF/NM 9.0	NM- 9.2
1-Origin Tornado Tom; Volton (the human generator), Tornado Tom, Kingdom of the Moon, Mister Q begin (1st app. of each)	81	162	243	518	884	1250
2	58	116	174	371	636	900
3-Classic-c (scarce)	123	246	369	787	1344	1900
4-(9/40)	65	130	195	416	708	1000
5-(Scarce)	90	180	270	576	988	1400

Ashcan - (5/40) Not distributed to newsstands, only for in house use. Cover produced on green stock paper. A CGC certified FN (6.0) copy sold for $2,000 in 2006.

CYCLOPS (X-Men)
Marvel Comics: Oct, 2001 - No. 4, Jan, 2002 ($2.50, limited series)

	GD 2.0	VG 4.0	FN 6.0	VF 8.0	VF/NM 9.0	NM- 9.2
1-4-Texeira-c/a. 1,2-Black Tom and Juggernaut app.						3.00
1-(5/11, $2.99, one-shot) Haspiel-a; Batroc and the Circus of Crime app.						3.00

CYCLOPS (All-New X-Men)
Marvel Comics: Jul, 2014 - No. 12, Jun, 2015 ($3.99)

	GD 2.0	VG 4.0	FN 6.0	VF 8.0	VF/NM 9.0	NM- 9.2
1-10: 1-Rucka-s/Dauterman-a; Corsair app. 6-12-Layman-s. 12-Black Vortex x-over						4.00

CYCLOPS: RETRIBUTION
Marvel Comics: 1994 ($5.95, trade paperback)

	GD 2.0	VG 4.0	FN 6.0	VF 8.0	VF/NM 9.0	NM- 9.2
nn-r/Marvel Comics Presents #17-24	1	2	3	5	6	8

CY-GOR (See Spawn #38 for 1st app.)
Image Comics (Todd McFarlane Prod.): July, 1999 - No. 6, Dec, 1999 ($2.50)

	GD 2.0	VG 4.0	FN 6.0	VF 8.0	VF/NM 9.0	NM- 9.2
1-6-Veitch-s						3.00

CYNTHIA DOYLE, NURSE IN LOVE (Formerly Sweetheart Diary)
Charlton Publications: No. 66, Oct, 1962 - No. 74, Feb, 1964

	GD 2.0	VG 4.0	FN 6.0	VF 8.0	VF/NM 9.0	NM- 9.2
66-74	3	6	9	14	19	24

DAFFODIL
Marvel Comics (Soleil): 2010 - No. 3, 2010 ($5.99, limited series)

	GD 2.0	VG 4.0	FN 6.0	VF 8.0	VF/NM 9.0	NM- 9.2
1-3-English version of French comic; Brrémaud-s/Rigano-a						6.00

DAFFY (Daffy Duck No. 18 on)(See Looney Tunes)
Dell Publishing Co./Gold Key No. 31-127/Whitman No. 128 on: #457, 3/53 - #30, 7-9/62; #31, 10-12/62 - #145, 6/84 (No #132,133)

	GD 2.0	VG 4.0	FN 6.0	VF 8.0	VF/NM 9.0	NM- 9.2
Four Color 457(#1)-Elmer Fudd x-overs begin	12	24	36	81	176	270
Four Color 536,615('55)	7	14	21	49	92	135
4(1-3/56)-11('57)	5	10	15	33	57	80
12-19(1958-59)	4	8	12	28	47	65
20-40(1960-64)	3	6	9	20	31	42
41-60(1964-68)	3	6	9	16	23	30
61-90(1969-74)-Road Runner in most. 76-82-"Daffy Duck and the Road Runner" on-c	2	4	6	11	16	20
90-Whitman variant	3	6	9	14	19	24
91-110	2	4	6	8	11	14
111-127	1	3	4	6	8	10
128,134-141: 139(2/82), 140(2-3/82), 141(4/82)	2	4	6	8	10	12
129(8/80),130,131 (pre-pack?) (scarce). 129-Sherlock Holmes parody-s	4	8	12	28	47	65
142-145(#90029 on-c; nd, nd code, pre-pack): 142(6/83), 143(8/83), 144(3/84), 145(6/84)	3	6	9	17	26	35
Mini-Comic 1 (1976; 3-1/4x6-1/2")	1	3	4	6	8	10

NOTE: *Reprint issues-No.41-46, 48, 50, 53-55, 58, 59, 65, 67, 69, 73, 81, 96, 103-108; 136-142, 144, 145(1/3-2/3-r). (See March of Comics No. 277, 288, 303, 313, 331, 347, 357,375, 387, 397, 402, 413, 425, 437, 460).*

DAFFY DUCK (Digest-size reprints from Looney Tunes)
DC Comics: 2005 ($6.99, digest)

Vol. 1: You're Despicable! - Reprints from Looney Tunes #38,43,45,47,51,53,54,58,61,62,66,70 7.00

DAFFY TUNES COMICS
Four-Star Publications: June, 1947; No. 12, Aug, 1947

	GD 2.0	VG 4.0	FN 6.0	VF 8.0	VF/NM 9.0	NM- 9.2
nn	11	22	33	62	86	110
12-Al Fago-c/a; funny animal	10	20	30	56	76	95

DAGAR, DESERT HAWK (Captain Kidd No. 24 on; formerly All Great)
Fox Feature Syndicate: No. 14, Feb, 1948 - No. 23, Apr, 1949 (No #17,18)

	GD 2.0	VG 4.0	FN 6.0	VF 8.0	VF/NM 9.0	NM- 9.2
14-Tangi & Safari Cary begin; Good bondage-c/a	110	220	330	704	1202	1700
15,16-E. Good-a; 15-Headlight-c	58	116	174	371	636	900
19,20,22: 19-Used in **SOTI**, pg. 180 (Tangi)	54	108	162	343	574	825
21,23: 21-Bondage-c; "Bombs & Bums Away" panel in "Flood of Death" story used in **SOTI.** 23-Bondage-c	57	114	171	362	619	875

NOTE: *Tangi by **Kamen**-14-16, 19, 20; c-20, 21.*

DAGAR THE INVINCIBLE (Tales of Sword & Sorcery...) (Also see Dan Curtis Giveaways & Gold Key Spotlight)
Gold Key: Oct, 1972 - No. 18, Dec, 1976; No. 19, Apr, 1982

	GD 2.0	VG 4.0	FN 6.0	VF 8.0	VF/NM 9.0	NM- 9.2
1-Origin; intro. Villains Olstellon & Scor	4	8	12	23	37	50
2-5: 3-Intro. Graylin, Dagar's woman; Jarn x-over	3	6	9	14	19	24
6-1st Dark Gods story	2	4	6	9	13	16
7-10: 9-Intro. Torgus. 10-1st Three Witches story	2	4	6	9	13	16
11-18: 13-Durak & Torgus x-over; story continues in Dr. Spektor #15. 14-Dagar's origin retold. 18-Origin retold	2	4	6	8	10	12
19(4/82)-Origin-r/#18						6.00

NOTE: *Durak app. in 7, 12, 13. Tragg app. in 5, 11.*

DAGWOOD (Chic Young's) (Also see Blondie Comics)
Harvey Publications: Sept, 1950 - No. 140, Nov, 1965

	GD 2.0	VG 4.0	FN 6.0	VF 8.0	VF/NM 9.0	NM- 9.2
1	17	34	51	117	259	400
2	8	16	24	56	108	160
3-10	7	14	21	44	82	120
11-20	5	10	15	35	63	90
21-30	5	10	15	31	53	75
31-50: 33-Sci-Fi-c	4	8	12	28	47	65
51-70	3	6	9	21	33	45
71-100	3	6	9	17	26	35
101-121,123-128,130,135	3	6	9	16	23	30
122,129,131-134,136-140-All are 68-pg. issues	3	6	9	21	33	45

NOTE: *Popeye and other one page strips appeared in early issues.*

DAI KAMIKAZE!
Now Comics: June, 1987 - No. 12, Aug, 1988 ($1.75)

	GD 2.0	VG 4.0	FN 6.0	VF 8.0	VF/NM 9.0	NM- 9.2
1-1st app. Speed Racer						5.00
1-Second printing						3.00
2-12						3.00

DAILY BUGLE (See Spider-Man)
Marvel Comics: Dec, 1996 - No. 3, Feb, 1997 ($2.50, B&W, limited series)

	GD 2.0	VG 4.0	FN 6.0	VF 8.0	VF/NM 9.0	NM- 9.2
1-3-Paul Grist-s						3.00

DAISY AND DONALD (See Walt Disney Showcase No. 8)
Gold Key/Whitman No. 42 on: May, 1973 - No. 59, July, 1984 (no No. 48)

	GD 2.0	VG 4.0	FN 6.0	VF 8.0	VF/NM 9.0	NM- 9.2
1-Barks-r/WDC&S #280,308	3	6	9	21	33	45
2-5: 4-Barks-r/WDC&S #224	2	4	6	11	16	20
6-10	2	4	6	9	12	15
11-20	1	3	4	6	8	10
21-41: 32-r/WDC&S #308	1	2	3	5	6	8
36,42-44 (Whitman)	2	4	6	8	11	14
45 (8/80),46-(pre-pack?)(scarce)	4	8	12	27	44	60
47-(12/80)-Only distr. in Whitman 3-pack (scarce)	5	10	15	35	63	90
48(3/81)-50(8/81): 50-r/#3	2	4	6	10	14	18
51-54: 51-Barks-r/4-Color #1150. 52-r/#2. 53(2/82), 54(4/82)	2	4	6	9	13	16
55-59-(all #90284 on-c, nd, nd code, pre-pack): 55(5/83), 56(7/83), 57(8/83), 58(8/83), 59(7/84)	3	6	9	19	30	40

DAISY & HER PUPS (Dagwood & Blondie's Dogs)(Formerly Blondie Comics #20)
Harvey Publications: No. 21, 7/51 - No. 27, 7/52; No. 8, 9/52 - No. 18, 5/54

	GD 2.0	VG 4.0	FN 6.0	VF 8.0	VF/NM 9.0	NM- 9.2
21 (#1)-Blondie's dog Daisy and her 5 pups led by Elmer begin. Rags Rabbit app.	5	10	15	35	63	90
22-27 (#2-7): 26 has No. 6 on cover but No. 26 on inside. 23,25-The Little King app. 24-Bringing Up Father by McManus app. 25-27-Rags Rabbit app.	4	8	12	27	44	60

8-18: 8,9-Rags Rabbit app. 8,17-The Little King app. 11-The Flop Family Swan begins.

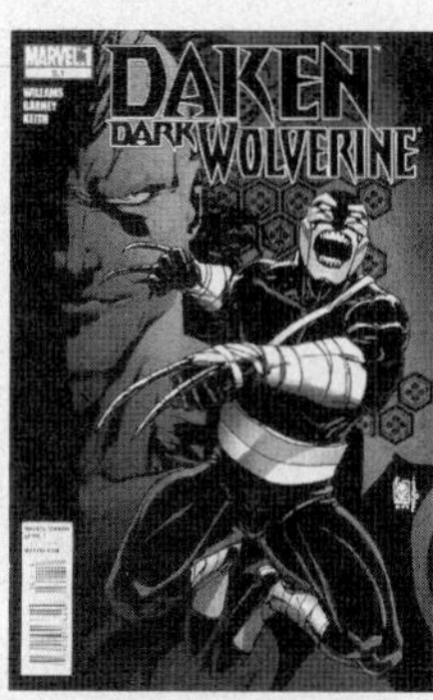

Daken: Dark Wolverine #9.1 © MAR

Dale Evans Comics #12 © DC

Dandy Comics #5 © WMG

GD 2.0 | VG 4.0 | FN 6.0 | VF 8.0 | VF/NM 9.0 | NM- 9.2

22-Cookie app. 11-Felix The Cat app. by 17,18-Popeye app.
4 8 12 25 40 55

DAISY DUCK & UNCLE SCROOGE PICNIC TIME (See Dell Giant #33)

DAISY DUCK & UNCLE SCROOGE SHOW BOAT (See Dell Giant #55)

DAISY DUCK'S DIARY (See Dynabrite Comics, & Walt Disney's C&S #298)
Dell Publishing Co.: No. 600, Nov, 1954 - No. 1247, Dec-Fef, 1961-62 (Disney)

Four Color 600 (#1) 8 16 24 51 96 140
Four Color 659, 743 (11/56) 6 12 18 40 73 105
Four Color 858 (11/57), 948 (11/58), 1247 (12-2/61-62)
5 10 15 35 63 90
Four Color 1055 (11-1/59-60), 1150 (12-1/60-61)-By Carl Barks)
8 16 24 56 108 160

DAISY HANDBOOK
Daisy Manufacturing Co.: 1946; No. 2, 1948 (10¢, pocket-size, 132 pgs.)

1-Buck Rogers, Red Ryder; Wolverton-a (2 pgs.) 22 44 66 132 216 300
2-Captain Marvel & Ibis the Invincible, Red Ryder, Boy Commandos & Robotman; Wolverton-a (2 pgs.); contains 8 pg. color catalog 22 44 66 132 216 300

DAISY MAE (See Oxydol-Dreft)

DAISY'S RED RYDER GUN BOOK
Daisy Manufacturing Co.: 1955 (25¢, pocket-size, 132 pgs.)

nn-Boy Commandos, Red Ryder; 1pg. Wolverton-a 15 30 45 85 130 175

DAKEN: DARK WOLVERINE
Marvel Comics: Nov, 2010 - No. 23, May, 2012 ($3.99/$2.99)

1-Camuncoli-a/c; Way & Liu-s; back-up history of the character 4.00
2-9, 9.1, 10-23-($2.99) 3,4-Fantastic Four app. 7-9-Crossover with X-23 #8,9; Gambit app. 9.1-Avengers app. 13-16-Moon Knight app. 17-19-Runaways app. 3.00

DAKKON BLACKBLADE ON THE WORLD OF MAGIC: THE GATHERING
Acclaim Comics (Armada): June, 1996 ($5.95, one-shot)

1-Jerry Prosser scripts; Rags Morales-c/a. 6.00

DAKOTA LIL (See Fawcett Movie Comics)

DAKTARI (Ivan Tors) (TV)
Dell Publishing Co.: July, 1967 - No. 3, Oct, 1968; No. 4, Oct, 1969

1-Marshall Thompson photo-c on all 4 8 12 23 37 50
2-4 3 6 9 17 26 35

DALE EVANS COMICS (Also see Queen of the West...)(See Boy Commandos #32)
National Periodical Publications: Sept-Oct, 1948 - No. 24, Jul-Aug, 1952 (No. 1-19: 52 pgs.)

1-Dale Evans & her horse Buttermilk begin; Sierra Smith begins by Alex Toth
58 116 174 371 636 900
2-Alex Toth-a 30 60 90 177 289 400
3-11-Alex Toth-a 20 40 60 114 182 250
12-20: 12-Target-c 14 28 42 80 115 150
21-24 14 28 42 82 121 160
NOTE: *Photo-c-1, 2, 4-14.*

DALGODA
Fantagraphics Books: Aug, 1984 - No. 8, Feb, 1986 (High quality paper)

1,8: 1- Fujitake-c/a in all. 8-Alan Moore story 4.00
2-7: 2,3-Debut Grimwood's Daughter. 3.00

DALTON BOYS, THE
Avon Periodicals: 1951

1-(Number on spine)-Kinstler-c 20 40 60 114 182 250

DAMAGE
DC Comics: Apr, 1994 - No. 20, Jan, 1996 ($1.75/$1.95/$2.25)

1-20: 6-(9/94)-Zero Hour. 0-(10/94). 7-(11/94). 14-Ray app. 3.00

DAMAGE
DC Comics: Mar, 2018 - Present ($2.99)

1,2: 1-Venditti-s/Daniel-a; intro. Ethan Avery. 2-Suicide Squad & Wonder Woman app. 3.00

DAMAGE CONTROL (See Marvel Comics Presents #19)
Marvel Comics: 5/89 - No. 4, 8/89; V2#1, 12/89 - No. 4, 2/90 ($1.00)
V3#1, 6/91 - No. 4, 9/91 ($1.25, all are limited series)

V1#1-4,V2#1-4,V3#1-4: V1#4-Wolverine app. V2#2,4-Punisher app. 1-Spider-Man app. 2-New Warriors app. 3,4-Silver Surfer app. 4-Infinity Gauntlet parody 3.00

DAMAGED
Radical Comics: Jul, 2011 - No. 6 ($3.99/$3.50, limited series)

1-($3.99) Lapham-s/Manco-a; covers by Maleev & Manco 4.00
2-4-($3.50) Maleev-c 3.50

GD 2.0 | VG 4.0 | FN 6.0 | VF 8.0 | VF/NM 9.0 | NM- 9.2

DAMIAN: SON OF BATMAN
DC Comics: Dec, 2013 - No. 4, Mar, 2014 ($3.99, limited series)

1-4-Andy Kubert-s/c/a; near-future Damian; Ra's al Ghul & Talia app. 4.00
1-Variant-c by Tony Daniel 8.00

DAMNED
Image Comics (Homage Comics): June, 1997 - No. 4, Sept, 1997 ($2.50, limited series)

1-4-Steven Grant-s/Mike Zeck-c/a in all 3.00

DAMN NATION
Dark Horse Comics: Feb, 2005 - No. 3, Apr, 2005 ($2.99, limited series)

1-3-J. Alexander-a/Andrew Cosby-s 3.00

DAMSELS
Dynamite Entertainment: 2012 - No. 13, 2014 ($3.99)

1-13: 1-Leah Moore & John Reppion-s/Aneke-a. 1-Campbell-c. 2-8-Linsner-c 4.00
... Giant Killer One Shot (2013, $4.99) Leah Moore & John Reppion-s/Dietrich Smith-a 5.00

DAMSELS IN EXCESS
Aspen MLT: Jul, 2014 - No. 5, May, 2015 ($3.99, limited series)

1-5-Vince Hernandez-s/Mirka Andolfo-a; multiple covers on each 4.00

DAMSELS: MERMAIDS
Dynamite Entertainment: No. 0, 2013 - No. 5, 2013 ($3.99)

0-Free Comic Book Day giveaway; Sturges-s/Deshong-a/Hans-c 3.00
1-5-($3.99) Sturges-s/Deshong-a. 1-Two covers by Anacleto & Renaud. 2-5-Renaud-c 4.00

DANCES WITH DEMONS (See Marvel Frontier Comics Unlimited)
Marvel Frontier Comics: Sept, 1993 - No. 4, Dec, 1993 ($1.95, limited series)

1-($2.95)-Foil embossed-c; Charlie Adlard & Rod Ramos-a 4.00
2-4 3.00

DAN DARE
Virgin Comics: Nov, 2007 - No. 7, July, 2008 ($2.99/$5.99)

1-6-Ennis-s/Erskine-a. 1-Two covers by Talbot and Horn. 2-6-Two covers on each 3.00
7-($5.99) Double sized finale with wraparound Erskine-c; Gibbons variant-c 6.00

DAN DARE
Titan Comics: Nov, 2017 - No. 4, Jan, 2018 ($3.99)

1-4-MIlligan-s/Foche-a; multiple covers on each 4.00

DANDEE: Four Star Publications: 1947 (Advertised, not published)

DAN DUNN (See Crackajack Funnies, Detective Dan, Famous Feature Stories & Red Ryder)

DANDY COMICS (Also see Happy Jack Howard)
E. C. Comics: Spring, 1947 - No. 7, Spring, 1948

1-Funny animal; Vince Fago-a in all; Dandy in all 47 94 141 296 498 700
2 33 66 99 194 317 440
3-7: 3-Intro Handy Andy who is c-feature #3 on 27 54 81 162 266 370

DANGER
Comic Media/Allen Hardy Assoc.: Jan, 1953 - No. 11, Aug, 1954

1-Heck-c/a 34 68 102 199 325 450
2,3,5,7,9-11: 18 36 54 107 169 230
4-Marijuana cover/story 21 42 63 124 202 280
6- "Narcotics" story; begin spy theme 20 40 60 114 182 250
8-Bondage/torture/headlights panels 22 44 66 128 209 290
NOTE: *Morisi a-2, 5, 6(3), 10; c-2. Contains some reprints from Danger & Dynamite.*

DANGER (Formerly Comic Media title)
Charlton Comics Group: No. 12, June, 1955 - No. 14, Oct, 1955

12(#1) 14 28 42 80 115 150
13,14: 14-r/#12 11 22 33 62 86 110

DANGER
Super Comics: 1964

Super Reprint #10-12 (Black Dwarf; #10-r/Great Comics #1 by Novack. #11-r/Johnny Danger #1. #12-r/Red Seal #14), #15-r/Spy Cases #26. #16-Unpublished Chesler material (Yankee Girl), #17-r/Scoop #8 (Capt. Courage & Enchanted Dagger), #18(nd)-r/Guns Against Gangsters #5 (Gun-Master, Annie Oakley, The Chameleon; L.B. Cole-r)
2 4 6 11 16 20

DANGER AND ADVENTURE (Formerly This Magazine Is Haunted; Robin Hood and His Merry Men No. 28 on)
Charlton Comics: No. 22, Feb, 1955 - No. 27, Feb, 1956

22-Ibis the Invincible-c/story (last G.A. app.); Nyoka app.; last pre-code issue
11 22 33 62 86 110
23-Lance O'Casey-c/sty; Nyoka app.; Ditko-a thru #27
13 26 39 72 101 130

Danger Girl: Renegade #3 © JS Campbell

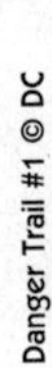
Danger Trail #1 © DC

Dante's Inferno #4 © EA

	GD 2.0	VG 4.0	FN 6.0	VF 8.0	VF/NM 9.0	NM- 9.2
24-27: 24-Mike Danger & Johnny Adventure begin	9	18	27	50	65	80

DANGER GIRL (Also see Cliffhanger #0)
Image Comics (Cliffhanger Productions): Mar, 1998 - No. 4, Dec, 1998;
DC Comics (Cliffhanger Prod.): No. 5, July, 1999 - No. 7, Feb, 2001

	GD	VG	FN	VF	VF/NM	NM-
Preview-Bagged in DV8 #14 Voyager Pack						4.00
Preview Gold Edition						10.00
1-($2.95) Hartnell & Campbell-s/Campbell/Garner-a	1	2	3	5	6	8
1-($4.95) Chromium cover						55.00
1-American Entertainment Ed.						8.00
1-American Entertainment Gold Ed., 1-Tourbook edition						12.00
1-"Danger-sized" ed.; over-sized format	3	6	9	16	24	32
2-($2.50)						4.00
2-Smoking Gun variant cover	4	8	12	27	44	60
2-Platinum Ed.	5	10	15	34	60	85
2-Dynamic Forces Omnichrome variant-c	2	4	6	10	14	18
2-Gold foil cover						9.00
2-Ruby red foil cover	12	24	36	81	176	270
3,4: 3-c by Campbell, Charest and Adam Hughes. 4-Big knife variant-c						3.00
3,5: 3-Gold foil cover. 5-DF Bikini variant-c						5.00
4-6						3.00
7-($5.95) Wraparound gatefold-c; Last issue						6.00
...: Danger-Sized Treasury Edition #1 (IDW, 1/12, $9.99, 13" x 8-1/2") r/#1,2 & Preview						10.00
...: Hawaiian Punch (5/03, $4.95) Campbell-c; Phil Noto-a						5.00
...: Odd Jobs TPB (2004, $14.95) r/one-shots Hawaiian Punch, Viva Las Danger & Special; Campbell-c						15.00
San Diego Preview (8/98, B&W) flip book w/Wildcats preview						5.00
Sketchbook (2001, $6.95) Campbell-a; sketches for comics, toys, games						7.00
...Special (2/00, $3.50) art by Campbell, Chiodo, and Art Adams						3.50
... 3-D #1 (4/03, $4.95, bagged with 3-D glasses) r/ Preview & #1 in 3-D						5.00
...: Viva Las Danger (1/04, $4.95) Noto-a/Campbell-c						5.00
... :The Dangerous Collection nn (8/98; r-#1)						6.00
... :The Dangerous Collection 2,3: 2-(11/98, $5.95) r/#2,3. 3-('99) r/#4,5						6.00
... :The Dangerous Collection nn, 2-($10.00) Gold foil logo						10.00
... :The Ultimate Collection HC ($29.95) r/#1-7; intro by Bruce Campbell						30.00
... :The Ultimate Collection SC ($19.95) r/#1-7; intro by Bruce Campbell						20.00

DANGER GIRL AND THE ARMY OF DARKNESS
Dynamite Entertainment/ IDW Publ.: 2011 - No. 6, 2012 ($3.99, limited series)

1-6-Hartnell-s/Bolson-a. 1,2 Covers by Campbell, Bradshaw & Renaud — 4.00

DANGER GIRL: BACK IN BLACK
DC Comics (Cliffhanger): Jan, 2006 - No. 4, Apr, 2006 ($2.99, limited series)

1-4-Hartnell-s/Bradshaw-a. 1-Campbell-c — 3.00
TPB (2007, $12.99) r/series & covers — 13.00

DANGER GIRL: BODY SHOTS
DC Comics (WildStorm): Jun, 2007 - No. 4, Sept, 2007 ($2.99, limited series)

1-4-Hartnell-s/Bradshaw-a — 3.00
TPB (2007, $12.99) r/series & covers — 13.00

DANGER GIRL/ G.I. JOE
IDW Publishing: Jul, 2012 - No. 5, Nov, 2012 ($3.99, limited series)

1-5-Hartnell-s/Royle-a; 2 covers by Campbell on each — 4.00

DANGER GIRL KAMIKAZE
DC Comics (Cliffhanger): Nov, 2001 - No. 2, Dec., 2001 ($2.95, lim. series)

1,2-Tommy Yune-s/a — 3.00

DANGER GIRL: MAYDAY
IDW Publishing: Apr, 2014 - No. 4, Aug, 2014 ($3.99, limited series)

1-4-Hartnell-s/Royle-a; 2 covers by Royle on each — 4.00

DANGER GIRL: RENEGADE
IDW Publishing: Sept, 2015 - No. 4, Jan, 2016 ($3.99, limited series)

1-4-Hartnell-s/Molnar-a/Campbell-c — 4.00

DANGER GIRL: REVOLVER
IDW Publishing: Jan, 2012 - No. 4, Apr, 2012 ($3.99, limited series)

1-4-Hartnell-s/Madden-a; covers by Campbell & Madden — 4.00

DANGER GIRL: THE CHASE
IDW Publishing: Sept, 2013 - No. 4, Dec, 2013 ($3.99, limited series)

1-4-Hartnell-s/Tolibao-a. 1-Three covers (Panosian, Wallace & photo) — 4.00

DANGER GIRL: TRINITY
IDW Publishing: Apr, 2013 - No. 4, Jul, 2013 ($3.99, limited series)

1-4-Hartnell-s/Campbell-c; art by Royle, Tolibao, & Molnar. 1-Variant-c by Garner — 4.00

DANGER IS OUR BUSINESS!
Toby Press: 1953(Dec.) - No. 10, June, 1955

	GD	VG	FN	VF	VF/NM	NM-
1-Captain Comet by Williamson/Frazetta-a, 6 pgs. (science fiction)	52	104	156	328	552	775
2	15	30	45	86	133	180
3-10	14	28	42	78	112	145
I.W. Reprint #9('64)-Williamson/Frazetta-r/#1; Kinstler-c	8	16	24	51	96	140

DANGER IS THEIR BUSINESS (Also see A-1 Comic)
Magazine Enterprises: No. 50, 1952

	GD	VG	FN	VF	VF/NM	NM-
A-1 50-Powell-a	15	30	45	84	127	170

DANGER MAN (TV)
Dell Publishing Co.: No. 1231, Sept-Nov, 1961

	GD	VG	FN	VF	VF/NM	NM-
Four Color 1231-Patrick McGoohan photo-c	10	20	30	66	138	210

DANGER TRAIL (Also see Showcase #50, 51)
National Periodical Publ.: July-Aug, 1950 - No. 5, Mar-Apr, 1951 (52 pgs.)

	GD	VG	FN	VF	VF/NM	NM-
1-King Faraday begins, ends #4; Toth-a in all	142	284	426	909	1555	2200
2	97	194	291	621	1061	1500
3-(Rare) one of the rarest early '50s DCs	155	310	465	992	1696	2400
4,5: 5-Johnny Peril-c/story (moves to Sensation Comics #107); new logo (also see Comic Cavalcade #15-29)	74	148	222	470	810	1150

DANGER TRAIL
DC Comics: Apr, 1993 - No. 4, July, 1993 ($1.50, limited series)

1-4: Gulacy-c on all — 3.00

DANGER UNLIMITED (See San Diego Comic Con Comics #2 & Torch of Liberty Special)
Dark Horse (Legend): Feb, 1994 - No. 4, May, 1994 ($2.00, limited series)

1-4: Byrne-c/a/scripts in all; origin stories of both original team (Doc Danger, Thermal, Miss Mirage, & Hunk) & future team (Thermal, Belebet, & Caucus). 1-Intro Torch of Liberty & Golgotha (cameo) in back-up story. 4-Hellboy & Torch of Liberty cameo in lead story — 3.00
TPB (1995, $14.95)-r/#1-4; includes last pg. originally cut from #4 — 15.00

DAN HASTINGS (See Syndicate Features)

DANIEL BOONE (See The Exploits of..., Fighting... Frontier Scout...,The Legends of... & March of Comics No. 306)
Dell Publishing Co.: No. 1163, Mar-May, 1961

	GD	VG	FN	VF	VF/NM	NM-
Four Color 1163-Marsh-a	5	10	15	35	63	90

DANIEL BOONE (TV) (See March of Comics No. 306)
Gold Key: Jan, 1965 - No. 15, Apr, 1969 (All have Fess Parker photo-c)

	GD	VG	FN	VF	VF/NM	NM-
1-Back-c and last eight pages fold in half to form "Official Handbook Fess Parker as Daniel Boone Trail Blazers Club"	7	14	21	48	89	130
2-Back-c pin-up	5	10	15	30	50	70
3-5-Back-c pin-ups	4	8	12	25	40	55
6-15: 7,8-Back-c pin-up	3	6	9	19	30	40

DAN'L BOONE
Sussex Publ. Co.: Sept, 1955 - No. 8, Sept, 1957

	GD	VG	FN	VF	VF/NM	NM-
1	14	28	42	80	115	150
2	10	20	30	54	72	90
3-8	8	16	24	40	50	60

DANNY BLAZE (...Firefighter) (Nature Boy No. 3 on)
Charlton Comics: Aug, 1955 - No. 2, Oct, 1955

	GD	VG	FN	VF	VF/NM	NM-
1-Authentic stories of fire fighting	13	26	39	74	105	135
2	9	18	27	50	65	80

DANNY DINGLE (See Sparkler Comics)
United Features Syndicate: No. 17, 1940

	GD	VG	FN	VF	VF/NM	NM-
Single Series 17	28	56	84	165	270	375

DANNY THOMAS SHOW, THE (TV)
Dell Publishing Co.: No. 1180, Apr-June, 1961 - No. 1249, Dec-Feb, 1961-62

	GD	VG	FN	VF	VF/NM	NM-
Four Color 1180-Toth-a, photo-c	13	26	39	89	195	300
Four Color 1249-Manning-a, photo-c	12	24	36	80	173	265

DANTE
Image Comics (Top Cow): Jan, 2017 - Present ($5.99)

1-Matt Hawkins-s/Darick Robertson-a/c — 6.00

DANTE'S INFERNO (Based on the video game)
DC Comics (WildStorm): Feb, 2010 - No. 6, Jul, 2010 ($3.99, limited series)

1-6-Christos Gage-s/Diego Latorre-a — 4.00

Daredevil #14 © LEV

Daredevil #31 © LEV

Daredevil #4 © MAR

GD 2.0 | VG 4.0 | FN 6.0 | VF 8.0 | VF/NM 9.0 | NM- 9.2

TPB (2010, $19.99) r/#1-6 20.00

DAOMU (Based on a novel series from China)
Image Comics: Feb, 2011 - No. 8, Dec, 2011 ($2.99)

1-8-Kennedy Xu-s/Ken Chou-a 3.00

DARBY O'GILL & THE LITTLE PEOPLE (Movie)(See Movie Comics)
Dell Publishing Co.: 1959 (Disney)

Four Color 1024-Toth-a; photo-c. 9 18 27 57 111 165

DAREDEVIL ("Daredevil Comics" on cover of #2) (See Silver Streak Comics)
Lev Gleason Publications (Funnies, Inc. No. 1): July, 1941 - No. 134, Sept, 1956
(52 pgs. #52-80; 64 pgs. #35-41)(Charles Biro stories)

1-No. 1 titled "Dardedevil Battles Hitler," Classic battle issue as Daredevil teams up in each strip - The Silver Streak, Lance Hale, Cloud Curtis, Dickey Dean & Pirate Prince to battle Hitler; The Claw unites with Hitler and Japanese and battles Daredevil; Origin of Hitler feature story "The Man of Hate." Classic Hitler photo app. on-c 1275 2550 3825 9500 16,750 24,000

2-London (by Jerry Robinson), Pat Patriot (by Reed Crandall), Nightro, Real American No. 1 (by Briefer #2-11), Dash Dillon, Whirlwind begin; Dickie Dean, Pirate Prince end; intro. & only app. Pioneer, Champion of America & Times Square. The Claw continues #2-4 389 778 1167 2723 4762 6800

3-Intro./origin of 13. Newspaper editor has name "Roussos." Daredevil battles the Claw ill. text story 265 530 795 1694 2897 4100

4-The Claw captured and taken to New York Central Park Zoo. Whirlwind, the Blond Bomber begins, ends #6 226 452 678 1446 2473 3500

5-Ghost vs. Claw begins by Bob Wood, ends #20; 13 & Jinx begin; origin 13 retold in text; intro./origin Jinx, 13's sidekick; intro. Sniffer in Daredevil 187 374 561 1197 2049 2900

6-(12/41)-Classic horror-c; Daredevil battles wolf with human brain; Dash Dillon ends 168 336 504 1075 1838 2600

7,9: 7-(2/42), shows #6 on cover; delayed one month due to Pearl Harbor attack. 9-Daredevil vs. Daredevil-c; Sniffer strip begins, ends #69 123 246 369 787 1344 1900

8-Nazi WWII war-c. Nightro ends. Sniffer/Daredevil fight Nazi insurgents; 135 270 405 864 1482 2100

10-(5-42), "Remember Pearl Harbor" Japanese WWII-c; classic splash page w/American flag. Daredevil joins Air Corps. to fight Japanese. Ghost Battles Claw & Japanese. Last Whirlwind 168 336 504 1075 1838 2600

11-Classic Quasimodo (hunchback of Notre Dame) bondage/torture-c/sty. London, Pat Patriot, Real America #1 end 574 1094 1641 3500 5500 7500

12-Origin of The Claw; Scoop Scuttle by Wolverton begins (2-4 pgs.), ends #22, not in #21. Charles Biro biography. Dickey Dean, Pirate Prince return (both end #32) 139 278 417 883 1517 2150

13-Intro of Little Wise Guys (10/42)(also see Boy #4); Daredevil fights Nazi hooded cult; Ghost battles Claw, Hitler & Nazis in Britain; Bob Wood biography 108 216 324 686 1181 1675

14-Classic Daredevil facial portrait-c; Hitler app.; "Slap the Jap" game included 87 174 261 553 952 1350

15-Death of Meatball 108 216 324 686 1181 1675

16-WWII-c w/freighter hit by German torpedo. Meatball is buried & Curly joins Little Wise Guys team 79 158 237 502 864 1225

17-Little Wise Guys hanging and beating Japanese soldiers on cover 194 388 582 1242 2121 3000

18-New origin of Daredevil (not same as Silver Streak #6). Hitler, Mussolini Tojo and Mickey Mouse app. on-c at carnival 129 258 387 826 1413 2000

19,20: Last Ghost vs. Claw 65 130 195 416 708 1000

21-Reprints cover of Silver Streak #6 (on inside) plus intro. of The Claw from Silver Streak #1. The Claw strip begins by Bob Q. Siege, ends #31 84 168 252 538 919 1300

22,23: 22-Daredevil fights the Tramp. 23-Dickie Dean by Bob Montana 46 92 138 290 488 685

24-Bloody puppet show-c; classic Claw splash pg. 53 106 159 334 567 800

25-1st Little Wise Guys-c without Daredevil 37 74 111 222 361 500

26,28-30 41 82 123 256 428 600

27-Bondage/torture-c 97 194 291 621 1061 1500

31-Death of The Claw 84 168 252 538 919 1300

32-34: 32,33-Egbert app. 33-Roger Wilco begins, ends #35 34 68 102 206 336 465

35-37,39-41: 35-Two Daredevil stories begin, end #68; Chauncey app. 37-39-Go Along Gallagher app. (#35-41 are 64 pgs.); 41-Dickie Dean ends 36 72 108 216 351 485

38-Origin Daredevil retold from #18 47 94 141 296 498 700

42-Intro. Kilroy in Daredevil who unveils Daredevil's I.D.-c/sty 31 62 93 182 296 410

43-45,47,48-All Daredevil-c. 43-Daredevil in costume on-c & 1 panel only inside; 44-DD back in costume; i.d. revealed on-c. 29 58 87 172 281 390

46,50: DD not on-c 24 48 72 142 234 325

49-Wise Guys fight secret hooded group c/sty. DD not on-c 29 58 87 172 281 390

51,52,56-60,63-66,68,69-Last Daredevil & Sniffer (12/50). 56-Wise Guys start their own circus. DD not on-c 20 40 60 115 185 255

53-Daredevil/Wise Guys find lost palace of Zanzarah, an underground Egyptian tomb w/mummy & treasure; classic c/story. DD-c 22 44 66 128 209 290

54,55-Daredevil-c 21 42 63 124 202 280

61-Daredevil & Wise Guys in haunted house classic c/story. Daredevil/Wise Guys fly rocket into stratosphere. DD not on-c 22 44 66 128 209 290

62-Wise Guys in medieval times, a dream by Peewee locked in a medieval museum; classic c/story. DD not on-c 22 44 66 128 209 290

67-Last Daredevil-c 21 42 63 124 202 280

70-Little Wise Guys take over book without Daredevil. Daredevil removed from-c & logo; Air Devils w/Hot Rock Flanagan begins, ends #80 14 28 42 80 115 150

71-78,81: 81-Dilly Duncan begins, ends #134 11 22 33 60 83 105

79,80: 79-(10/51)-Daredevil returns; Wise Guys go to Africa. 80-Daredevil & Wise Guys blast into space & land on Mars; last Daredevil app. in title 12 24 36 69 97 125

82,90: One pg. Frazetta ad in both 11 22 33 60 83 105

83-89,91-99,101-134 10 20 30 56 76 95

100-(7/53) 12 24 36 69 97 125

NOTE: ***Biro** a-1-22, 38; c-1-134; script-1-134. **Dan Barry** a(Daredevil) 40-48; **Roy Belft**-a (Daredevil) 49-55. **Bolle** a-125. **Al Borth**-a(Daredevil) #57-59. **Briefer** a-1-11 (Real American #1); Pirate Prince-#1, 2, 12-31. **Tony Dipreta**-a(Wise Guys) #108-110, 112-134. **R.W. Hall** a-22. **Carl Hubbell** a-9-21, 23-26, 27(Daredevil), 28-32. **Al Mandel** a-13. **Hy Mankin**-a(Wise Guys)-#80, 81. **Maurer**-a(Daredevil)-23, 31, 37, 38, 41, 43-51, 53-67, 69; (Little Wise Guys)-70-89. **McWilliams** a-70, 73-80. **Bob Montana** a-12, 23, 27, 28, 31-33. **Wm. Overgard**-a(Daredevil) #67, (Wise Guys) 74-79, 83-85, 87. **Jerry Robinson** a(London) #2-8. **Roussos** a(Nightro)-2-8. **Bob Q. Siege**-a(Claw) 27-31; (Daredevil)-#35. **Wolverton** a-12-22. **Bob Wood**-a(The Claw)-1-20; (The Ghost)-5-20. **Dick Wood** sty-2-10, 13-22, 27-32. **Daredevil** not on-c #46,49-52,56-66,68-134.*

DAREDEVIL (...& the Black Widow #92-107 on-c only; see Giant-Size...,Marvel Advs., Marvel Graphic Novel #24, Marvel Super Heroes, '66 & Spider-Man &...)
Marvel Comics Group: Apr, 1964 - No. 380, Oct, 1998

1-Origin/1st app. Daredevil; intro Foggy Nelson & Karen Page; death of Battling Murdock; Bill Everett-c/a; reprinted in Marvel Super Heroes #1 (1966) 567 1134 1700 3950 7475 11,000

2-Fantastic Four cameo; 2nd app. Electro (Spidey villain); Thing guest star 73 146 219 584 1317 2050

3-Origin & 1st app. The Owl (villain) 42 84 126 311 706 1100

4-Origin & 1st app. The Purple Man 37 74 111 274 612 950

5-Minor costume change; Wood-a begins 28 56 84 196 441 685

6-Mr. Fear app. 21 42 63 147 324 500

7-Daredevil battles Sub-Mariner & dons red costume for 1st time (4/65); Marvel Masterwork pin-up by Wood 93 186 279 744 1672 2600

8-10: 8-Origin/1st app. Stilt Man. 10-1st app. Cat Man, Bird Man, Ape Man & Frog Man 15 30 45 103 227 350

11-15: 11-Last Wally Wood. 12-1st app. Plunderer; Ka-Zar app. Kirby/Romita-a begins. 13-Facts about Ka-Zar's origin; vs. the Plunderer; Kirby/Romita-a. 14-Romita-a begins; Ka-Zar & the Plunderer app. 15-1st app. the Ox 10 20 30 66 138 210

16,17- Spider-Man x-over. 16-1st Romita-a on Spider-Man (5/66) 20 40 60 138 307 475

18-Origin & 1st app. Gladiator 11 22 33 73 157 240

19,20: 19-DD vs. the Gladiator. 20-DD vs. the Owl; 1st Gene Colan-a 8 16 24 56 108 160

21-26,28-30: 21-DD vs. the Owl. 22-DD vs. the Owl, Gladiator & and Masked Marauder; 1st app the Tri-Man. 23-Owl, Gladiator, Masked Marauder & Tri-Man app. 24-Ka-Zar app. 25-1st app. Leap-Frog; 1st app. 'Mike Murdock' Daredevil's fake twin brother. 26-Stilt-Man app. 30-Thor app vs. Cobra and Mr. Hyde 6 12 18 41 76 110

27-Spider-Man x-over; Stilt-Man & the Masked Marauder app. 7 14 21 48 89 150

31-36,39,40: 31,32-DD vs. Cobra & Mr. Hyde. 33,34-DD vs. the Beetle. 35-DD vs. the Trapster. 36-DD vs. the Trapster; Dr. Doom cameo. 39-1st app. Exterminator (later becomes Death-Stalker); Ape Man, Cat Man & Bird Man app. as the Unholy Three. 40-DD vs. the Unholy Three 6 12 18 37 66 95

37,38: 37-Daredevil vs. Dr. Doom. 38-Dr. Doom app; Fantastic Four x-over; continued in Fantastic Four #73 6 12 18 41 76 110

41,42-44-49: 41- 'Death' of Mike Murdock; Daredevil drops the fake twin persona; DD vs. the Exterminator and the Unholy Three. 42-1st app. Jester. 44-46-DD vs. the Jester. 48-DD vs. Stilt-Man. 49-1st app. Star Saxon & the Plastoid 5 10 15 34 60 85

43-Daredevil vs. Captain America; origin partially retold; Kirby-c 8 16 24 56 108 160

50-51,53: 50-Barry Smith-a; last Stan Lee-s; vs. Star Saxon & the Plastoid. 51-1st Roy Thomas-s; Barry Smith-a; vs. Star Saxon & the Plastoid. 53-Gene Colan-a returns;

Daredevil #72 © MAR

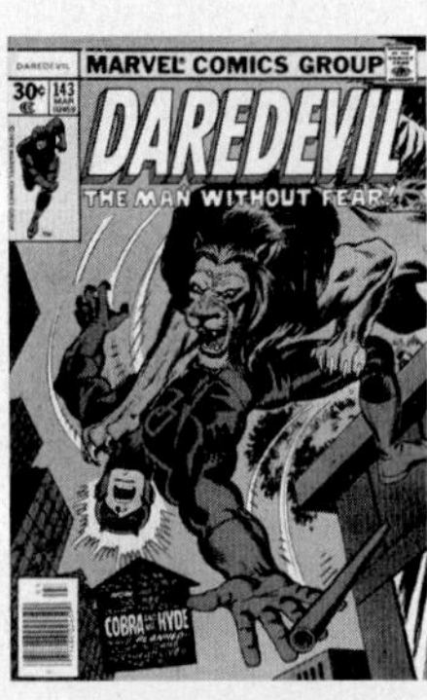

Daredevil #143 © MAR

Daredevil #248 © MAR

	GD 2.0	VG 4.0	FN 6.0	VF 8.0	VF/NM 9.0	NM- 9.2
origin retold	5	10	15	35	63	90
52-Barry Smith-a; Black Panther app.; learns Daredevil's secret identity	6	12	18	42	79	115
54-56,58-60: 54-Spider-Man cameo; vs. Mr. Fear. 55-DD vs. Mr. Fear. 56-1st app. Death's Head (Star Saxon) (9/69); story continued in #57. 58-1st app. Stunt-Master. 59-1st app. Torpedo (dies this issue)	4	8	12	27	44	60
57-Reveals i.d. to Karen Page; Death's Head app.	6	12	18	37	66	95
61,63-68,70-72,74-76,78-80: 61-DD vs. the Jester, Cobra & Mr. Hyde. 63-vs. Gladiator. 64-Stunt-Master app. 67-Stilt-Man app. 71-Last Roy Thomas-s. 72-1st app Tagak 'Lord of Leopards'; 1st Gerry Conway-s. 75-1st app. El Condor. 76-Death El Condor. 78-1st app. Man-Bull. 79-DD vs. Man-Bull. 80-vs the Owl	4	8	12	23	37	50
62,69,73: 62-Origin of Nighthawk (Kyle Richmond). 69-Black Panther app. 73-Continued from Iron Man #35; Nick Fury app. vs. the Zodiac; concluded in Iron Man #36.	4	8	12	27	44	60
77-Spider-Man & Sub-Mariner app.; story continues in Sub-Mariner #40	5	10	15	30	50	70
81-(52 pgs.)-Black Widow becomes regular guest star (11/71); receives co-billing w/issue #92 through issue #107; vs. Mr. Kline and the Owl	8	12	18	38	69	125
82,84-87,89-98: 82-DD vs. Mr. Kline. 84-Conclusion of the Mr. Kline story; see Iron Man #41-45 & Sub-Mariner #42. 85-DD vs. Gladiator. 86-Death of the Ox. 87-Daredevil & the Black Widow relocate to San Francisco; Electro app. 89-Purple Man & Electro app. 90-Mr. Fear app. 91-Death of Mr. Fear. 92-Black Widow gets co-billing as of this issue. 93,94-DD vs. the Indestructible Man. 95,96-DD vs. the Man-Bull. 97-99-DD vs. the Dark Messiah; Steve Gerber co-script; 98-Last Conway-s	3	6	9	19	30	40
83,99: 83-Barry Smith layouts/Weiss-p. 99-Hawkeye app; Steve Gerber-s begin; plot continues in Avengers #111	3	6	9	21	33	45
88-Purple Man app; early life of Black Widow revealed	4	8	12	23	37	50
100-1st app. Angar the Screamer; origin retold; Jann Wenner, editor of Rolling Stone app.	5	10	15	30	50	70
101,102,104,106,108-110: 101-vs Angar the Screamer. 102-vs. Stilt Man. 104-Kraven the Hunter app. 106-Moondragon app; vs. Terrex. 108-Title returns to 'Daredevil'. Moondragon app.; 1st app. Black Spectre; Beetle app; Daredevil and Black Widow break-up. 109-Shanna the She-Devil app.; vs. Nekra & Black Spectre; story continues in Marvel Two-in-One #3. 110-Continued from Marvel Two-in-One #3; vs. the Mandrill, Nekra & Black Spectre; brief Thing app.	3	6	9	16	23	30
103-1st app. & origin of Ramrod; Spider-Man app.	3	6	9	19	30	40
105-Origin of Moondragon by Starlin (12/73) Thanos cameo in flashback (early app.)	5	10	15	35	63	90
107-Starlin-c; Thanos cameo; Moondragon & Captain Marvel app; death of Terrex	3	6	9	19	30	40
111-1st app. Silver Samurai; Shanna the She-Devil, Mandrill, Nekra & Black Spectre app.	6	12	18	38	69	100
112-114,116-120: 112-Conclusion of the Black Spectre story; Mandrill & Nekra app. 113-1st brief app. Death-Stalker; Gladiator app. 114-1st full Death-Stalker app; Man-Thing & Gladiator app. 116,117-DD vs. the Owl; 117-Last Gerber-s. 118-1st app. Blackwing; vs. the Circus of Crime. 119-Tony Isabella-s begin. 120-1st app. El Jaguar Agent of HYDRA	3	6	9	16	23	30
115-Death-Stalker app.; advertisement for Wolverine in Incredible Hulk #181 (on pg. 19)	3	6	9	19	30	40
121-123,125-130,137: 121-vs. HYDRA; El Jaguar and the Dreadnaught app; Nick Fury app. 122-Return of Silvermane as the new Supreme HYDRA. 123-Silvermane, El Jaguar, Dreadnaught, Mentallo & HYDRA app; Nick Fury and SHIELD app; last Isabella-s. 125-Death of Copperhead; Wolfman-s begin. 126-1st app. the second and third Torpedos; 1st app. Heather Glenn. 127-vs. the third Torpedo (Brock Jones). 128-Death-Stalker app. 129-vs the Man-Bull	3	6	9	14	20	25
124-1st app. Copperhead; Black Widow leaves; Len Wein & Marv Wolfman co-plot	3	6	9	17	26	35
131-Origin/1st app. Bullseye (see Nick Fury #15)	15	30	45	100	220	340
132-2nd Bullseye app. new Bullseye (regular 25c edition)	5	10	15	35	63	90
132-(30¢-c variant, limited distribution)(4/76)	10	20	30	64	132	200
133-136: 133-Uri Geller & the Jester app. 134-Torpedo app. vs. the Chameleon. 135,136-vs. the Jester	3	6	9	14	20	25
133-136-(30¢-c variants, limited distribution)(5-8/76)	4	8	12	28	47	65
138-Ghost Rider-c/story; Death's Head is reincarnated; Byrne-a	3	6	9	19	30	40
139,140,142-145,147-154: 140-vs the Beetle & Gladiator. 142-vs. Cobra & Hyde; Nova cameo. 143-Cobra & Hyde app; last Wolfman-s. 144-vs the Man-Bull & Owl. 145-vs the Owl. 147-Purple Man app. 148-Death-Stalker app. 149-1st app. the third Smasher. 150-1st app. Paladin. 151-Reveals i.d. to Heather Glenn. 152-vs Death-Stalker; Roger McKenzie-s begin. 153-vs Cobra & Hyde. 154-vs Purple Man, Cobra & Hyde & Jester	2	4	6	13	18	22

	GD 2.0	VG 4.0	FN 6.0	VF 8.0	VF/NM 9.0	NM- 9.2
141,146-Bullseye app.	4	8	12	23	37	50
146-(35¢-c variant, limited distribution)	10	20	30	64	132	200
147,148-(35¢-c variants, limited distribution)	8	16	24	54	102	150
155-157-DD vs. Death-Stalker; Black Widow, Hercules, Captain America & the Beast app.	3	6	9	14	20	25
158-Frank Miller-a begins (5/79) origin/death of Death-Stalker (see Captain America #235 & Spectacular Spider-Man #27)	8	16	24	56	108	160
159-Brief Bullseye app.	5	10	15	30	50	70
160,161-Bullseye and Black Widow app.	4	8	12	25	40	55
162-Ditko-a; no Miller-a; origin retold	3	6	9	14	20	25
163,164: 163-vs. the Hulk. 164-Origin retold and expanded	3	6	9	18	28	38
165-167,170: 165-1st Miller co-plot w/McKenzie; Dr. Octopus app. 166-vs. Gladiator. 167-Last McKenzie co-plot; 1st app. Mauler. 170-Kingpin app.	3	6	9	16	24	32
168-(1/81) Origin/1st app. Elektra; 1st Miller scripts	11	22	33	73	157	240
169-2nd Elektra app; Bullseye app.	4	8	12	28	47	65
171-173: 171,172-vs. the Kingpin	3	6	9	17	16	35
174-1st app. the Hand (Ninjas who trained Elektra)	3	6	9	21	33	45
175-Elektra & Daredevil vs. the Hand	3	6	9	19	30	40
176-180-Elektra app: 176-1st app. Stick (Daredevil's mentor). 177-Kingpin & the Hand app. 178-Kingpin & Power Man & Iron Fist app. 179-Anti-smoking issue mentioned in the Congressional Record	3	6	9	16	24	32
181-(4/82, 52-pgs)-Death of Elektra; Punisher cameo out of costume	4	8	12	25	40	55
182-184: 182-Bullseye app. 183,184 -'Angel Dust' drug story; Punisher app.	3	6	9	16	23	30
185-191: 186-Stilt-Man app. 187-New Black Widow vs. the Hand. 188-Black Widow app. 189-Death of Stick; Black Widow app. 190-Elektra returns, part origin; 2 pin-ups. 191-Classic 'Russian Roulette' story with Bullseye; last Miller Daredevil	2	4	6	8	11	14
192-195,198,199: 192-Alan Brennert story; Klaus Janson (p)&(i) begin. 193-Larry Hama-s. 194-Denny O'Neil-s begin. 198-Bullseye receives Adamantium bones. 199-Bullseye app; death of Dark Wind						4.00
196-Wolverine-c/app; 1st app. Dark Wind. Bullseye app.	2	4	6	10	14	18
197-Bullseye-c/app; 1st app, Yuriko Oyama (becomes Lady Deathstrike in Alpha Flight #33)	2	4	6	8	10	12
200-Bulleye vs. Daredevil; Byrne-c	1	3	4	6	8	10
201-207,209-218: 201-Black Widow solo story. 202-1st app. Micah Synn. 203-1st app. the Trump; Byrne-c. 204-1st app. Crossbow (Green Arrow homage?) 205-1st app. Gael (Irish Republican Army hitman). 206-DD vs. Micah Synn; 1st Mazzucchelli-p on DD. Kingpin app. 207-HYDRA & Black Widow app. 209-Harlan Ellison plot. 210-Crossbow & Kingpin app. 211,212-DD & Kingpin team-up vs. Micah Synn. 215-Two-Gun Kid flashback. 216-Gael app. 217-Gael app; 1st app. the Cossack; Barry-Windsor-Smith-c. 218-DD appears as the Jester						4.00
208,219: 208-Harlan Ellison scripts borrowed from Avengers TV episode 'House that Jack Built'. 219-Miller-c/script						5.00
220-226,234-237: 220-Death of Heather Glenn. 222-Black Widow app. 223-Secret Wars II crossover; Beyonder gives DD his sight back; DD rejects the gift. 225-Vulture app. 226-Gladiator app.; last Denny O'Neil-s. 234-Madcap app. 235-DD vs. Mr. Hyde. 237-DD vs. Klaw; Black Widow app.						4.00
227-(2/86, 36 pgs.)-Miller scripts begin; classic 'Born Again' Pt.1 story begins; Kingpin learns DD's secret identity.						6.00
228-233: 'Born Again'; Kingpin ruins Matt Murdock's life. 232-1st app Nuke. 233-Last Miller script; Captain America app.; death of Nuke						5.00
238-Mutant massacre; Sabretooth app; 1st Ann Nocenti-s						6.00
239,240,242-247: 239-1st app. Rotgut. 243-1st app. Nameless One. 245-Black Panther app. 246-1st app. Chance. 247-Black Widow app.						3.00
241-Todd McFarlane-a(p)						5.00
248-Wolverine cameo; 1st app. Bushwacker. 249-DD vs. Wolverine; Bushwacker app.						6.00
250,251,253,258: 250-1st app. Bullet; Romita Jr-a begins. 251-vs. Bullet. 253-Kingpin app. 258-1st app. Bengal						3.00
252-(52 pgs)-Fall of the Mutants tie-in; 1st app. Ammo. 260-(52 pgs)-Bushwacker, Bullet, Ammo & Typhoid Mary vs. DD						5.00
254-Origin & 1st app. Typhoid Mary (5/88)	3	6	9	19	30	40
255,256: 2nd&3rd app. Typhoid Mary. 259-Typhoid Mary app.						5.00
257-Punisher app. (x-over w/Punisher #10)	2	4	6	8	11	14
261-269,271-281: 261-Typhoid Mary & Human Torch app. 262-Inferno tie-in. 263-Inferno tie-in; 1st new look 'monstrous' Mephisto. 264-vs the Owl. 265-Inferno tie-in; Mephisto app. 266-Mephisto app. 267-Bullet app. 269-Blob & Pyro (from Freedom Force) app. 272-1st app. Shotgun; Inhumans app. 273-DD vs. Shotgun; Inhumans app. 274-Black Bolt & the Inhumans app. 275,276-'Acts of Vengeance' x-over; Ultron app. 278-Mephisto & Blackheart app. 279-Mephisto app. 280-DD in Hell; Mephisto app. 281-Silver Surfer cameo;						

Daredevil Annual #10 © MAR

Daredevil V2 #46 © MAR

Daredevil #500 © MAR

GD 2.0 | VG 4.0 | FN 6.0 | VF 8.0 | VF/NM 9.0 | NM- 9.2

Mephisto & Blackheart app. 3.00
270-1st app. Blackheart (the son of Mephisto); Spider-Man app. 5.00
282-DD escapes Hell; Silver Surfer, Mephisto & Blackheart app. 4.00
283-287,289 294-299: 283-Captain America app. 284-287,289-Bullseye impersonates DD; 284-1st Lee Weeks-a. 291-vs. Bullet; last Nocenti-s. 292,293-Punisher app. 295-Ghost Rider app. 297-'Last Rights' Pt.1; Typhoid Mary app. 298-Pt.2; Nick Fury & SHIELD app. 299-Pt. 3; Baron Strucker & Hydra vs. the Kingpin 3.00
287-Bulleye-c/s; Kingpin app; Elektra dream sequence 5.00
290-Bullseye vs. Daredevil 1 3 4 6 8 10
300-(52 pgs.)-'Last Rights' Pt.4; Kingpin loses criminal empire; last Weeks-a 4.00
301-318: 301-303-vs. the Owl. 305-306-Spider-Man app. 307-'Dead Man's Hand' Pt. 1; Nomad & Tombstone app.; continued in Nomad #4. 308-'Dead Man's Hand' Pt. 5; continued from Punisher War Journal #45; Punisher app; continues in Punisher War Journal #46. 309-'Dead Man's Hand' Pt. 7; continued from Nomad #5; continued in Punisher War Journal #47. 310-Infinity War tie-in; Calypso vs. DD doppelganger. 311-Calypso & Brother Voodoo app. 314,315-Shock & Mr. Fear app. 317,318-Taskmaster, Stilt-Man & Tatterdemalion app. 3.00
319-Prologue to Fall From Grace Pt. 1; Elektra returns; Silver Sable app. 6.00
319-2nd printing w/black-c 3.00
320-(9/93) Fall From Grace Pt. 1; Silver Sable app. 5.00
321-Fall From Grace regular ed; Pt. 2 new armored costume; Venom app. 3.00
321-($2.00)-Wraparound Glow-in-the-dark-c 5.00
322-Fall From Grace Pt. 3; Eddie Brock app. 4.00
323,324: Fall From Grace Pt. 4 & 5; 323-vs. Venom-c/story; 324-Morbius-c/story 4.00
325-($2.50, 52 pgs.) Fall From Grace ends; contains bound-in poster; Elektra app. 4.00
326-338: 326-New logo; Captain America app. 327-Captain America-c/story. 328-Captain America & Baron Strucker app. 329-Iron Fist app. 330-Gambit app. 331,332-vs. Baron Strucker. 334-336-Bushwacker app. 338-Kingpin app. 3.00
339-343: 339-342-Kingpin app. 4.00
344-(9/95)-Title becomes part of the 'Marvel Edge' imprint; story continued from Double Edge: Alpha; Punisher & Nick Fury app.; continued in Ghost Rider #65 5.00
345-Original red costume returns; Marvel Overpower card insert 6.00
346-349: 348-1st Cary Nord-a in DD (1/96) 'Dec' on-c 4.00
350-($2.95)-Double-Sized 4.00
350-($3.50)-Double-Sized; gold ink-c 5.00
351-353,355-360: 351-Last 'Marvel Edge' imprint issue. 353-Karl Kessel scripts; Nord-c/a begins. 354-Bullseye (illusion)-c. 355-Pyro app. 357-Enforcers app. 358-Mysterio app. 360-Absorbing Man app. 4.00
354-Spider-Man app.; $1.50-c begins 1 2 3 5 6 8
361,365-367: 361-Black Widow & DD vs. Grey Gargoyle. 365-367: 365-Molten Man & Mr. Fear app. 366-Mr. Fear app.; Colan-c/a. 367-Colan-c/a; Mr. Fear & Gladiator app. 5.00
362-364: 363-Colan-c/a. 364-Mr. Fear app. 4.00
368-Omega Red & Black Widow app. 1 3 4 6 8 10
369-Black Widow app. 6.00
370-374: 370-Darkstar, Vanguard & Ursa Major app; last Colan-a. 371-Black Widow app. 372-Ghost Rider (Daniel Ketch) app. 373,374-Mr. Fear app. 5.00
375-($2.99)-Wraparound-c; Mr. Fear-c/app. 5.00
376-379: "Flying Blind", DD goes undercover for SHIELD 3.00
380-($2.99) Final issue; flashback story; Kingpin, Bullseye & Bushwacker app.
1 3 4 6 8 10
#(-1) Flashback issue (7/97, $1.95); Gene Colan-c/a 3.00
Special 1 (9/67, 25¢, 68-pgs)-New art/story by Lee/Colan; DD vs. the 'Emissaries of Evil' (Electro, Leapfrog, Stilt-Man, Matador & Gladiator) 7 14 21 48 89 130
Special 2,3: 2 (2/71, 25¢, 52 pgs.) Reprints issues #10-11 by Wood. 3-(1/72, 25¢, 52 pgs.) Reprints issues #16-17 3 6 9 21 33 45
Annual 4 (10/76, squarebound) Sub-Mariner & Black Panther app.
3 6 9 17 26 35
Annual 4 (#5, 1989) Atlantis Attacks; continued from Spectacular Spider-Man Annual #9; Spider-Man app.; continued in Avengers Annual #18 5.00
Annual 6-9: 6-('90) Lifeform Pt. 2; continued from Punisher Annual #3; continues in Silver Surfer Annual #3. 7-('91) The Von Strucker Gambit Pt. 1; continued in Punisher Annual #4. Guice-a (7 pgs.). 8-('92) System Bites Pt. 2; Deathlok & Bushwacker app; continued in Wonder Man Annual #1. 9-('93) Polybagged w/card; 1st app. Devourer 4.00
Annual 10-('94) Elektra, Nick Fury, Shang-Chi (Master of Kung-Fu) vs. Ghostmaker 5.00
...: Born Again TPB ($17.95)-r/#227-233; Miller-s/Mazzucchelli-a & new-c 20.00
... By Frank Miller and Klaus Janson Omnibus HC (2007, $99.99, dustjacket) r/#158-161, 163-191 and What If...? #28; intros by Miller and Janson; interviews, bonus art 100.00
... By Frank Miller and Klaus Janson Omnibus Companion HC (2007, $59.99, die-cut d.j.) r/#219,226-233, Daredevil: The Man Without Fear #1-5, Daredevil: Love and War, and Peter Parker, the Spect. Spider-Man #27-28; bonus materials 60.00
.../Deadpool (Annual '97, $2.99)-Wraparound-c 6.00
...: Fall From Grace TPB ($19.95)-r/#319-325 20.00
...: Gang War TPB ($15.95)-r/#169-172,180; Miller-s/a(p) 16.00
...Legends: (Vol. 4) Typhoid Mary TPB (2003, $19.95) r/#254-257,259-263 20.00

GD 2.0 | VG 4.0 | FN 6.0 | VF 8.0 | VF/NM 9.0 | NM- 9.2

... :Love's Labors Lost TPB ($19.99)-r/#215-217,219-222,225,226; Mazzucchelli-c 20.00
.../Punisher TPB (1988, $4.95)-r/D.D. #182-184 (all printings) 6.00
...Visionaries: Frank Miller Vol. 1 TPB ($17.95) r/#158-161,163-167 18.00
...Visionaries: Frank Miller Vol. 2 TPB ($24.95) r/#168-182; new Miller-c 25.00
...Visionaries: Frank Miller Vol. 3 TPB ($24.95) r/#183-191, What If? #28,35 & Bizarre Adventures #28; new Miller-c 25.00
... Vs. Bullseye Vol. 1 TPB (2004, $15.99) r/#131-132,146,169,181,191 16.00
Wizard Ace Edition: Daredevil (Vol. 1) #1 (4/03, $13.99) Acetate Campbell-c 14.00
NOTE: ***Art Adams*** *c-238p, 239.* ***Austin*** *a-191i; c-151i, 200i.* ***John Buscema*** *a-136, 137p, 234p, 235p; c-86p, 136i, 137p, 142, 219.* ***Byrne*** *c-200p, 201, 203, 223.* ***Capullo*** *a-286p.* ***Colan*** *a(p)-20-49, 53-82, 84-98, 100, 110, 112, 124, 153, 154, 156, 157, 363, 366-370, Spec. 1p; c(p)-20-42, 44-49, 53-60, 71, 92, 98, 138, 153, 154, 156, 157, Annual 1.* ***Craig*** *a-50i, 52i.* ***Ditko*** *a-162, 234p, 235p, 264p; c-162.* ***Everett*** *c/a-1; inks-21, 83.* ***Garney*** *c/a-304.* ***Gil Kane*** *a-141p, 146-148p, 151p; c(p)-85, 90, 91, 93, 94, 115, 116, 119, 120, 125-128, 133, 139, 147, 152.* ***Kirby*** *c-2-4, 5p, 12p, 13p, 43.* ***Layton*** *c-202.* ***Miller*** *scripts-168-182, 183(part), 184-191, 219, 227-233; a-158-161p, 163-184p, 191p; c-158-161p, 163-184p, 185-189, 190p, 191.* ***Orlando*** *a-2-4p.* ***Powell*** *a-9p, 11p, Special 1r, 2r.* ***Simonson*** *c-199, 236p.* ***B. Smith*** *a-236p; c-51p, 52p, 217.* ***Starlin*** *a-105p.* ***Steranko*** *c-44i.* ***Tuska*** *a-39i, 145p.* ***Williamson*** *a(i)-237, 239, 240, 243, 248-257, 259-282, 283(part), 284, 285, 287, 288(part), 289(part), 293-300; c(i)-237, 243, 244, 248-257, 259-263, 265-278, 280-289, Annual 8.* ***Wood*** *a-5-8, 9i, 10, 11i, Spec. 2i; c-5i, 6-11, 164i.*

DAREDEVIL (Volume 2)(Marvel Knights)(Becomes Black Panther: The Man Without Fear #513)
Marvel Comics: Nov, 1998 - No. 512, Feb, 2011 ($2.50/$2.99)

1-Kevin Smith-s/Quesada & Palmiotti-a 12.00
1-($6.95) DF Edition w/Quesada & Palmiotti var.-c 15.00
1-($6.00) DF Sketch Ed. w/B&W-c 10.00
2-Two covers by Campbell and Quesada/Palmiotti 9.00
3-8: 4,5-Bullseye app. 5-Variant-c exists. 8-Spider-Man-c/app.; last Smith-s 6.00
9-15: 9-11-David Mack-s; intro Echo. 12-Begin $2.99-c; Haynes-a. 13,14-Quesada-a 4.00
16-19-Direct editions; Bendis-s/Mack-c/painted-a 4.00
18,19,21,22-Newsstand editions with variant cover logo "Marvel Unlimited Featuring... 4.00
20-($3.50) Gale-s/Winslade-a; back-up by Stan Lee-s/Colan-a; Mack-c 5.00
21-40: 21-25-Gale-s. 26-38-Bendis-s/Maleev-a. 32-Daredevil's ID revealed. 35-Spider-Man-c/app. 38-Iron Fist & Luke Cage app. 40-Dodson-a 3.50
41-(25¢-c) Begins "Lowlife" arc; Maleev-a; intro Milla Donovan 3.00
41-(Newsstand edition with 2.99¢-c) 3.00
42-45-"Lowlife" arc; Maleev-a 3.00
46-50-($2.99). 46-Typhoid Mary returns. 49-Bullseye app. 50-Art panels by various incl. Romita, Colan, Mack, Janson, Oeming, Quesada 3.00
51-64,66-74,76-81: 51-55-Mack-s/a; Echo app. 54-Wolverine-c/app. 61-64-Black Widow app. 71-Decalogue begins. 76-81-The Murdock Papers. 81-Last Bendis-s/Maleev-a 3.00
65-($3.99) 40th Anniversary issue; Land-c; art by Maleev, Horn, Bachalo and others 4.00
75-($3.99) Decalogue ends; Jester app. 4.00
82-99,101-119: 82-Brubaker-s/Lark-a begin; Foggy "killed". 84-86-Punisher app. 87-Other Daredevil ID revealed. 94-Romita-c. 111-Lady Bullseye debut 3.00
82-Variant-c by McNiven 4.00
100-($3.99) Three covers (Djurdjevic, Bermejo and Turner); art by Romita Sr., Colan, Lark, Sienkiewicz, Maleev, Bermejo & Djurdjevic; sketch art gallery; r/Daredevil #90 (1972) 4.00

(After Vol. 2 #119, Aug, 2009, numbering reverts to original Vol. 1 with #500)

500-(10/09, $4.99) Kingpin, Lady Bullseye app.; back-up stories, pin-up & cover galleries; r/#191; five covers by Djurdjevic, Darrow, Dell'Otto, Ross and Zircher 5.00
501-512: 501-Daredevil takes over The Hand; Diggle-s begins; Ribic-c. 508-Shadowland begins. 512-Black Panther app. 3.00
Annual #1 (12/07, $3.99) Brubaker-s/Fernandez-a/Djurdjevic-c; Black Tarantula app. 4.00
... & Captain America: Dead on Arrival (2008, $4.99) English version of Italian story 5.00
... Black & White 1 (10/10, $3.99) B&W short stories by various; Aja-c 4.00
... Blood of the Tarantula (6/08, $3.99) Parks & Brubaker-s/Samnee-a/Djurdjevic-c 4.00
... By Brian Michael Bendis Omnibus Vol. 1 HC (2008, $99.99) oversized r/#16-19,26-50, and 56-60 100.00
... By Ed Brubaker Saga (2008, giveaway) synopsis of issues #82-110, preview of #111 3.00
... Cage Match 1 (7/10, $2.99) flashback early Luke Cage team-up; Chen-a 3.00
... MGC #26 (8/10, $1.00) r/#26 with "Marvel's Greatest Comics" logo on cover 3.00
...2099 #1 (11/04, $2.99) Kirkman-s/Moline-a 3.00
TPB ($9.95) r/#1-3 10.00
...Vol. 1 HC (2001, $29.99, with dustjacket) r/#1-11,13-15 30.00
...Vol. 1 HC (2003, $29.99, with dustjacket) r/#1-11,13-15; larger page size 30.00
...Vol. 2 HC (2002, $29.99, with dustjacket) r/#26-37; afterword by Bendis 30.00
...Vol. 3 HC (2004, $29.99, with dustjacket) r/#38-50; Maleev sketch pages 30.00
...Vol. 4 HC (2005, $29.99, with dustjacket) r/#56-65; Vol. 1 #81 (1971) Black Widow 30.00
...Vol. 5 HC (2006, $29.99, with dustjacket) r/#66-75 30.00
...Vol. 6 HC (2006, $34.99, with dustjacket) r/#76-81 & What If Karen Page Had Lived? 35.00
(Vol. 1) Visionaries TPB ($19.95) r/#1-8; Ben Affleck intro. 20.00
(Vol. 2) Parts of a Hole TPB (1/02, $17.95) r/#9-15; David Mack intro. 18.00
(Vol. 3) Wake Up TPB (7/02, $9.99) r/#16-19 10.00
...Vol. 4: Underboss TPB (8/02, $14.99) r/#26-31 15.00
...Vol. 5: Out TPB (2003, $19.99) r/#32-40 20.00
...Vol. 6: Lowlife TPB (2003, $13.99) r/#41-45 14.00
...Vol. 7: Hardcore TPB (2003, $13.99) r/#46-50 14.00

Daredevil (2016 series) #1 © MAR

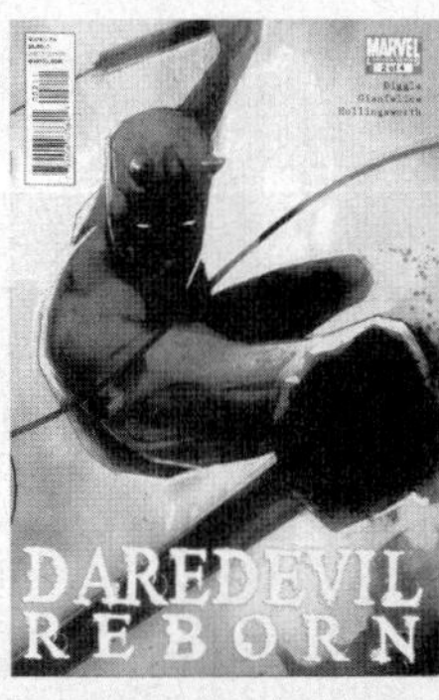

Daredevil: Reborn #2 © MAR

Daredevil: The Target #1 © MAR

GD 2.0 VG 4.0 FN 6.0 VF 8.0 VF/NM 9.0 NM- 9.2

...Vol. 8: Echo - Vision Quest TPB (2004, $13.99) r/#51-55; David Mack-s/a 14.00
...Vol. 9: King of Hell's Kitchen TPB (2004, $13.99) r/#56-60 14.00
...Vol. 10: The Widow TPB (2004, $16.99) r/#61-65 & Vol. 1 #81 17.00
...Vol. 11: Golden Age TPB (2005, $13.99) r/#66-70 14.00
...Vol. 12: Decalogue TPB (2005, $14.99) r/#71-75 15.00
...Vol. 13: The Murdock Papers TPB (2006, $14.99) r/#76-81 15.00
...: The Devil Inside and Out Vol. 1 (2006, $14.99) r/#82-87; Brubaker & Lark interview 15.00
...: The Devil Inside and Out Vol. 2 (2007, $14.99) r/#88-93; Bermejo cover sketches 15.00
...: Hell To Pay Vol. 1 TPB (2007, $14.99) r/#94-99; Djurdjevic cover sketches 15.00
...: Hell To Pay Vol. 2 TPB (2008, $15.99) r/#100-105 16.00

DAREDEVIL (Volume 3)
Marvel Comics: Sept, 2011 - No. 36, Apr, 2014 ($3.99/$2.99)

1-($3.99) Mark Waid-s/Paolo Rivera-a; back-up tale with Marcos Martin-a 4.00
1-Variant-c by Marcos Martin 8.00
1-Variant-c by Neal Adams 10.00
2-10,10.1,11-20,23,24,25,27-36-($2.99) 2-Capt. America app. 3-Klaw returns. 4-6-Marcos Martin-a. 8-X-over w/Amazing Spider-Man #677; Spider-Man and Black Cat app. 11-Spider-Man app. 17-Allred-a. 30-Silver Surfer app. 32,33-Satana & monsters app. 3.00
21,22: 21-1st Superior Spider-Man app. (cameo). 22-Superior Spider-Man app. 5.00
26-($3.99) Bullseye and Lady Bullseye app.; back-up "Fighting Cancer" story 4.00
Annual 1 (10/12, $4.99) Alan Davis-s/a/c; Dr. Strange & ClanDestine app. 5.00

DAREDEVIL (Volume 4)
Marvel Comics: May, 2014 - No. 18, Nov, 2015 ($3.99)

1-18-($3.99) Mark Waid-s/Chris Samnee-a; Murdock moves to San Francisco. 6,7-Original Sin tie-in. 8-10-Purple Man app. 14-Owl's daughter app. 15-18-Kingpin app. 4.00
#0.1-(9/14, $4.99) Waid-s/Krause-a/Samnee-c 5.00
#1.50-($4.99) 50th Anniversary issue; Murdock at 50; back-up Bendis-s/Maleev-a 5.00
#15.1-(7/15, $4.99) Waid-s/Samnee-a; Guggenheim-s/Krause-a 5.00

DAREDEVIL (Follows Secret Wars)
Marvel Comics: Feb, 2016 - No. 28, Dec, 2017; No. 595, Jan, 2018 - Present ($3.99)

1-28: 1-Soule-s/Garney-a; Blindspot app. 2,3-The Hand app. 4-Steve Rogers app. 6,7-Elektra app.; Sienkiewicz-c. 9-Spider-Man app. 16-Bullseye app. 18,19-Purple Man app. 23-She-Hulk app. 28-Kingpin becomes mayor of New York 4.00
[Title switches to legacy numbering after #28 (12/17)]
595-599: 595-(1/18) Soule-s/Landini-a 4.00
Annual 1 (10/16, $4.99) Echo returns; Vanesa Del Ray-a 5.00

DAREDEVIL/ BATMAN (Also see Batman/Daredevil)
Marvel Comics/ DC Comics: 1997 ($5.99, one-shot)

nn-McDaniel-c/a 6.00

DAREDEVIL BATTLES HITLER (See Daredevil #1 [1941 series])

DAREDEVIL: BATTLIN' JACK MURDOCK
Marvel Comics: Aug, 2007 - No. 4, Nov, 2007 ($3.99, limited series)

1-4-Wells-s/DiGiandomenico-a; flashback to the fixed fight 4.00
TPB (2007, $12.99) r/#1-4; page layouts and cover inks 13.00

DAREDEVIL COMICS (Golden Age title) (See Daredevil)

DAREDEVIL: DARK NIGHTS
Marvel Comics: Aug, 2013 - No. 8, Mar, 2014 ($3.99, limited series)

1-8: 1-3-Lee Weeks-s/a. 4,5-David Lapham-s/a; The Shocker app. 6-8-Conner-c 4.00

DAREDEVIL/ ELEKTRA: LOVE AND WAR
Marvel Comics: 2003 ($29.99, hardcover with dust jacket)

HC-Larger-size reprints of Daredevil: Love and War (Marvel Graphic Novel #24) & Elektra: Assassin; Frank Miller-s; Bill Sienkiewicz-a 30.00

DAREDEVIL: END OF DAYS
Marvel Comics: Dec, 2012 - No. 8, Aug, 2013 ($3.99, limited series)

1-8-Bendis & Mack-s/Janson & Sienkiewicz-a; death of Daredevil in the future 4.00

DAREDEVIL: FATHER
Marvel Comics: June, 2004 - No. 6, Feb, 2007 ($3.50/$2.99, limited series)

1-Quesada-s/a; Isanove-painted color 3.50
1-Director's Cut ($2.99) cover and page development art; partial sketch-c 3.00
2-6: 2-($2.99,10/05). 3-Santerians app. 3.00
HC (2006, $24.99) r/series; Lindelof intro.; sketch pages, cover pencils and bonus art 25.00

DAREDEVIL: NINJA
Marvel Comics: Dec, 2000 - No. 3, Feb, 2001 ($2.99, limited series)

1-3: Bendis-s/Haynes-a 3.00
1-Dynamic Forces foil-c 10.00
TPB (7/01, $12.95) r/#1-3 with cover and sketch gallery 13.00

DAREDEVIL NOIR
Marvel Comics: June, 2009 - No. 4, Sept, 2009 ($3.99, limited series)

1-4-Irvine-s/Coker-a; covers by Coker and Calero 4.00

DAREDEVIL / PUNISHER: SEVENTH CIRCLE
Marvel Comics: Jul, 2016 - Present ($4.99, limited series)

1-4-Soule-s/Kudranski-a; Blindspot app. 3,4-Crimson Dynamo app. 5.00

DAREDEVIL: REBORN (Follows Shadowland x-over)
Marvel Comics: Mar, 2011 - No. 4, Jul, 2011 ($3.99, limited series)

1-4-Diggle-s/Gianfelice-a 4.00

DAREDEVIL: REDEMPTION
Marvel Comics: Apr, 2005 - No. 6, Aug, 2005 ($2.99, limited series)

1-6-Hine-s/Gaydos-a/Sienkiewicz-c 3.00
TPB (2005, $14.99) r/#1-6 15.00

DAREDEVIL: SEASON ONE
Marvel Comics: 2012 ($24.99, hardcover graphic novel)

HC - Story of early career, yellow costume; Johnston-s/Alves-a/Tedesco painted-c 25.00

DAREDEVIL/ SHI (See Shi/ Daredevil)
Marvel Comics/ Crusade Comics: Feb,1997 ($2.95, one-shot)

1 3.00

DAREDEVIL/ SPIDER-MAN
Marvel Comics: Jan, 2001 - No. 4, Apr, 2001 ($2.99, limited series)

1-4-Jenkins-s/Winslade-a/Alex Ross-c; Stilt Man app. 3.00
TPB (8/01, $12.95) r/#1-4; Ross-c 13.00

DAREDEVIL THE MAN WITHOUT FEAR
Marvel Comics: Oct, 1993 - No. 5, Feb, 1994 ($2.95, limited series) (foil embossed covers)

1-Miller scripts; Romita, Jr./Williamson-c/a 6.00
2-5 5.00
Hardcover 100.00
Trade paperback 20.00

DAREDEVIL: THE MOVIE (2003 movie adaptation)
Marvel Comics: March, 2003 ($3.50/$12.95, one-shot)

1-Photo-c of Ben Affleck; Bruce Jones-s/Manuel Garcia-a 3.50
TPB ($12.95) r/movie adaptation; Daredevil #32; Ultimate Daredevil & Elektra #1 and Spider-Man's Tangled Web #4; photo-c of Ben Affleck 13.00

DAREDEVIL: THE TARGET (Daredevil Bullseye on cover)
Marvel Comics: Jan, 2003 ($3.50, unfinished limited series)

1-Kevin Smith-s/Glenn Fabry-c/a 3.50

DAREDEVIL VS. PUNISHER
Marvel Comics: Sept, 2005 - No. 6, Jan, 2006 ($2.99, limited series)

1-5-David Lapham-s/a 3.00
TPB (2005, $15.99) r/#1-6 16.00

DAREDEVIL: YELLOW
Marvel Comics: Aug, 2001 - No. 6, Jan, 2002 ($3.50, limited series)

1-6-Jeph Loeb-s/Tim Sale-a/c; origin & yellow costume days retold 3.50
HC (5/02, $29.95) r/#1-6 with dustjacket; intro by Stan Lee; sketch pages 30.00
Daredevil Legends Vol. 1: Daredevil Yellow (2002, $14.99, TPB) r/#1-6 15.00

DARING ADVENTURES (Also see Approved Comics)
St. John Publishing Co.: Nov, 1953 (25¢, 3-D, came w/glasses)

1 (3-D)-Reprints lead story from Son of Sinbad #1 by Kubert 26 52 78 154 252 350

DARING ADVENTURES
I.W. Enterprises/Super Comics: 1963 - 1964

I. W. Reprint #8-r/Fight Comics #53; Matt Baker-a 4 8 12 28 47 65
I.W. Reprint #9-r/Blue Bolt #115; Disbrow-a(3) 5 10 15 30 50 70
Super Reprint #10,11('63)-r/Dynamic #24,16; 11-Marijuana story; Yankee Boy app.; Mac Raboy-a 4 8 12 21 33 45
Super Reprint #12('64)-Phantom Lady from Fox (r/#14 only? w/splash pg. omitted); Matt Baker-a 9 18 27 57 111 165
Super Reprint #15('64)-r/Hooded Menace #1 6 12 18 37 66 95
Super Reprint #16('64)-r/Dynamic #12 3 6 9 19 30 40
Super Reprint #17('64)-r/Green Lama #3 by Raboy 4 8 12 25 40 55
Super Reprint #18-Origin Atlas from unpublished Atlas Comics #1 4 8 12 23 37 50

DARING COMICS (Formerly Daring Mystery) (Jeanie Comics No. 13 on)
Timely Comics (HPC): No. 9, Fall, 1944 - No. 12, Fall, 1945

9-Human Torch, Toro & Sub-Mariner begin 200 400 600 1280 2190 3100

Daring Mystery Comics #1 © MAR

Dark Ages #1 © Abnett & Culbard

Darkchylde #4 © Randy Queen

10-12: 10-The Angel only app. 11,12-The Destroyer app.
174 348 522 1114 1907 2700

NOTE: ***Schomburg** c-9-11. **Sekowsky** c-12? Human Torch, Toro & Sub-Mariner c-9-12.*

DARING CONFESSIONS (Formerly Youthful Hearts)
Youthful Magazines: No. 4, 11/52 - No. 7, 5/53; No. 8, 10/53

4-Doug Wildey-a; Tony Curtis story 21 42 63 122 199 275
5-8: 5-Ray Anthony photo on-c. 6,8-Wildey-a 15 30 45 88 137 185

DARING ESCAPES
Image Comics: Sept, 1998 - No. 4, Mar, 1999 ($2.95/$2.50, mini-series)

1-Houdini; following app. in Spawn #19,20 3.00
2-4-($2.50) 3.00

DARING LOVE (Radiant Love No. 2 on)
Gilmor Magazines: Sept-Oct, 1953

1–Steve Ditko's 1st published work (1st drawn was Fantastic Fears #5)(Also see Black Magic #27)(scarce) 265 530 795 1694 2897 4100

DARING LOVE (Formerly Youthful Romances)
Ribage/Pix: No. 15, 12/52; No. 16, 2/53-c, 4/53-Indicia; No. 17-4/53-c & indicia

15 15 30 45 90 140 190
16,17: 17-Photo-c 14 28 42 82 121 160

NOTE: ***Colletta** a-15. **Wildey** a-17.*

DARING LOVE STORIES (See Fox Giants)

DARING MYSTERY COMICS (Comedy Comics No. 9 on; title changed to Daring Comics with No. 9)
Timely Comics (TPI 1-6/TCI 7,8): 1/40 - No. 5, 6/40; No. 6, 9/40; No. 7, 4/41 - No. 8, 1/42

1-Origin The Fiery Mask (1st app.) by Joe Simon; Monako, Prince of Magic (1st app.), John Steele, Soldier of Fortune (1st app.), Doc Denton (1st app.) begin; Flash Foster & Barney Mullen, Sea Rover only app; bondage-c
2200 4400 6600 17,000 34,500 52,000
2-(Rare)-Origin The Phantom Bullet (1st & only app.); The Laughing Mask & Mr. E only app.; Trojak the Tiger Man begins, ends #6; Zephyr Jones & K-4 & His Sky Devils app., also #4
1150 2300 3450 8700 16,850 25,000
3-The Phantom Reporter, Dale of FBI, Captain Strong only app.; Breeze Barton, Marvex the Super-Robot, The Purple Mask begin 622 1244 1866 4541 8021 11,500
4,5: 4-Last Purple Mask; Whirlwind Carter begins; Dan Gorman, G-Man app. 5-The Falcon begins (1st app.); The Fiery Mask, Little Hercules app. by Sagendorf in the Segar style; bondage-c 459 918 1377 3350 5925 8500
6-Origin & only app. Marvel Boy by S&K; Flying Flame, Dynaman, & Stuporman only app.; The Fiery Mask by S&K; S&K-c 514 1028 1542 3750 6625 9500
7-Origin and 1st app. The Blue Diamond, Captain Daring by S&K, The Fin by Everett, The Challenger, The Silver Scorpion & The Thunderer by Burgos; Mr. Millions app
423 846 1269 3000 5250 7500
8-Origin Citizen V; Last Fin, Silver Scorpion, Capt. Daring by Borth, Blue Diamond & The Thunderer; Kirby & part solo Simon-c; Rudy the Robot only app.; Citizen V, Fin & Silver Scorpion continue in Comedy #9 371 742 1113 2600 4550 6500

NOTE: ***Schomburg** c-1-4, 7. **Simon** a-2, 3, 5. Cover features: 1-Fiery Mask; 2-Phantom Bullet; 3-Purple Mask; 4-G-Man; 5-The Falcon; 6-Marvel Boy; 7, 8-Multiple characters.*

DARING MYSTERY COMICS 70th ANNIVERARY SPECIAL
Marvel Comics: Nov, 2009 ($3.99, one-shot)

1-New story of The Phantom Reporter; r/app. in Daring Mystery #3 (1940); 2 covers 5.00

DARING NEW ADVENTURES OF SUPERGIRL, THE
DC Comics: Nov, 1982 - No. 13, Nov, 1983 (Supergirl No. 14 on)

1-Origin retold; Lois Lane back-ups in #2-12 2 4 6 11 16 20
2-13: 8,9-Doom Patrol app. 13-New costume; flag-c 5.00

NOTE: ***Buckler** c-1p, 2p. **Giffen** c-3p, 4p. **Gil Kane** c-6,8, 9, 11-13.*

DARK, THE
Continum Comics: Nov, 1990 - No. 4, Feb, 1993; V2#1, May, 1993 - V2#7, Apr?, 1994 ($1.95)

1-4: 1-Bright-p; Panosian, Hanna-i; Stroman-c. 2-(1/92)-Stroman-c/a(p). 4-Perez-c & part-i 3.00
V2#1,V2#2-6: V2#1-Red foil Bart Sears-c. V2#1-Red non-foil variant-c. V2#1-2nd printing w/blue foil Bart Sears-c. V2#2-Stroman/Bryant-a. 3-Perez-c(i). 3-6-Foil-c. 4-Perez-c & part-i; bound-in trading cards. 5,6-(2,3/94)-Perez-c(i). 7-(B&W)-Perez-c(i) 3.00
Convention Book 1 ,2(Fall/94, 10/94)-Perez-c 3.00

DARK AGES
Dark Horse Comics: Aug, 2014 - No. 4, Nov, 2014 ($3.99, limited series)

1-4-Abnett-s/Culbard-a/c 4.00

DARK AND BLOODY, THE
DC Comics (Vertigo): Apr, 2016 - No. 6, Sept, 2016 ($3.99, limited series)

1-6-Aldridge-s/Godlewski-a 4.00

DARK ANGEL (Formerly Hell's Angel)
Marvel Comics UK, Ltd.: No. 6, Dec, 1992 - No. 16, Dec, 1993 ($1.75)

6-8,13-16: 6-Excalibur-c/story. 8-Psylocke app. 3.00
9-12-Wolverine/X-Men app. 3.50

DARK ANGEL: PHOENIX RESURRECTION (Kia Asamiya's...)
Image Comics: May, 2000 - No. 4, Oct, 2001 ($2.95)

1-4-Kia Asamiya-s/a. 3-Van Fleet variant-c 3.00

DARK ARK
AfterShock Comics: Sept, 2017 - Present ($3.99)

1-5-Cullen Bunn-s/Juan Doe-a 4.00

DARK AVENGERS (See Secret Invasion and Dark Reign titles)
Marvel Comics: Mar, 2009 - No. 16, Jul, 2010 ($3.99)

1-Norman Osborn assembles his Avengers; Bendis-s/Deodato-a/c 4.00
1-Variant Iron Patriot armor cover by Djurdjevic 8.00
2-16: 2-6-Bendis-s/Deodato-a/c. 2-4 Dr. Doom app. 7,8-Utopia x-over; X-Men app. 9-Nick Fury app. 11,12-Deodato & Horn-a. 13-16-Siege. 13-Sentry origin 4.00
Annual 1 (2/10, $4.99) Bendis-s/Bachalo-a; Marvel Boy new costume; Siege preview 5.00
,,,/ Uncanny X-Men: Exodus (11/09, $3.99) Conclusion of x-over; Deodato & Dodson-a 4.00
,,,/ Uncanny X-Men: Utopia (8/09, $3.99) Part 1 of x-over w/Uncanny X-Men #513,514 4.00

DARK AVENGERS (Title continues from Thunderbolts #174)
Marvel Comics: No. 175, Aug, 2012 - No. 190, Jul, 2013 ($2.99)

175-190: 175-New team assembles; Parker-s/Shalvey-a/Deodato-c 3.00

DARK AVENGERS: ARES
Marvel Comics: Dec, 2009 - No. 3, Feb, 2010 ($3.99, limited series)

1-3-Garcia-a/Gillen-s. 1-Nord-c. 2-Tan-c. 3-McGuinness-c 4.00

DARKCHYLDE (Also see Dreams of the Darkchylde)
Maximum Press #1-3/ Image Comics #4 on: June, 1996 - No. 5, Sept, 1997 ($2.95/ $2.50)

1-Randy Queen-c/a/scripts; "Roses" cover 6.00
1-American Entertainment Edition-wraparound-c 6.00
1-"Fashion magazine-style" variant-c 1 2 3 4 5 7
1-Special Comicon Edition (contents of #1) Winged devil variant-c 5.00
1-($2.50)-Remastered Ed.-wraparound-c 4.00
2(Reg-c),2-Spiderweb and Moon variant-c 6.00
3(Reg-c),3-"Kalvin Clein" variant-c by Drew 4.00
4,5(Reg-c), 4-Variant-c 4.00
5-B&W Edition, 5-Dynamic Forces Gold Ed. 8.00
0-(3/98, $2.50) 3.00
0-Remastered (1/01, $2.95) includes Darkchylde: Redemption preview 3.00
1/2-WIzard offer 4.00
1/2 Variant-c 6.00
... The Descent TPB ('98, $19.95) r/#1-5; bagged with Darkchylde The Legacy Preview Special 1998; listed price is for TPB only 20.00

DARKCHYLDE LAST ISSUE SPECIAL
Darkchylde Entertainment: June, 2002 ($3.95)

1-Wraparound-c; cover gallery 4.00

DARKCHYLDE REDEMPTION
Darkchylde Entertainment: Feb, 2001 - No. 2, Dec, 2001 ($2.95)

1,2: 1-Wraparound-c 3.00
1-Dynamic Forces alternate-c 6.00
1-Dynamic Forces chrome-c 16.00

DARKCHYLDE SKETCH BOOK
Image Comics (Dynamic Forces): 1998

1-Regular-c 8.00
1-DarkChrome cover 16.00

DARKCHYLDE SUMMER SWIMSUIT SPECTACULAR
DC Comics (WildStorm): Aug, 1999 ($3.95, one-shot)

1-Pin-up art by various 4.00

DARKCHYLDE SWIMSUIT ILLUSTRATED
Image Comics: 1998 ($2.50, one-shot)

1-Pin-up art by various 3.00
1-(6.95) Variant cover 7.00
1-Chromium cover 15.00

DARKCHYLDE THE DIARY
Image Comics: June, 1997 ($2.50, one-shot)

1-Queen-c/s/ art by various 3.00
1-Variant-c 5.00

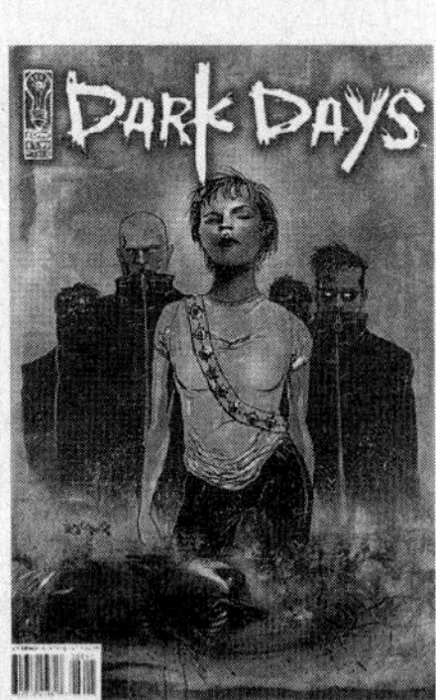

Dark Days #2 © Niles & Templesmith

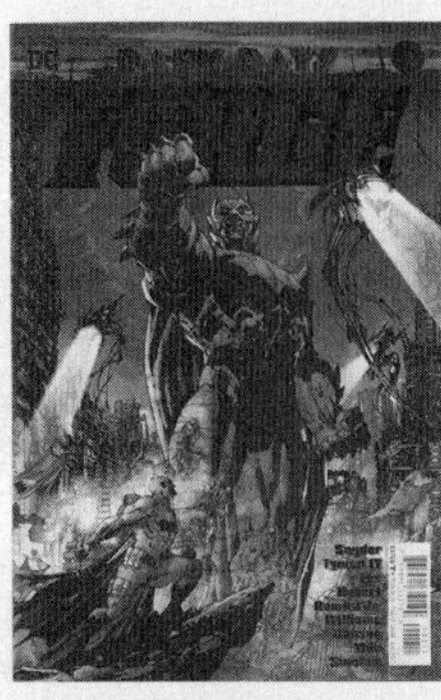

Dark Days: The Forge #1 © DC

Dark Fantasies #1 © Dark Fantasy

GD 2.0 | VG 4.0 | FN 6.0 | VF 8.0 | VF/NM 9.0 | NM- 9.2

1-Holochrome variant-c 8.00

DARKCHYLDE THE LEGACY
Image Comics/DC (WildStorm) #3 on: Aug, 1998 - No. 3, June, 1999 ($2.50)
1-3: 1-Queen-c. 2-Two covers by Queen and Art Adams 3.00

DARK CLAW ADVENTURES
DC Comics (Amalgam): June, 1997 ($1.95, one-shot)
1-Templeton-c/s/a & Burchett-a 3.00

DARK CROSSINGS: DARK CLOUDS RISING
Image Comics (Top Cow): June, 2000; Oct, 2000 ($5.95, limited series)
1-Witchblade, Darkness, Tomb Raider crossover; Dwayne Turner-a 6.00
1-(Dark Clouds Overhead) 6.00

DARK CRYSTAL, THE (Movie)
Marvel Comics Group: April, 1983 - No. 2, May, 1983
1,2-Adaptation of film 4.00

DARK DAYS (See 30 Days of Night)
IDW Publishing: June, 2003 - No. 6, Dec, 2003 ($3.99, limited series)
1-6-Sequel to 30 Days of Night; Niles-s/Templesmith-a 4.00
1-Retailer variant (Diamond/Alliance Fort Wayne 5/03 summit) 15.00
TPB (2004, $19.99) r/#1-6; cover gallery; intro. by Eric Red 20.00

DARK DAYS (Tie-ins to Dark Nights: Metal series)
DC Comics: Aug, 2017 - Sept, 2017 ($4.99, one-shots)
...: The Casting 1 (9/17, $4.99) Snyder & Tynion IV-s; Jim Lee, Andy Kubert & Romita Jr.-a; Joker, Green Lantern & Hawkman app. 5.00
...: The Forge (8/17, $4.99) Lee, Kubert & Romita Jr.-a; Mister Miracle, Mr. Terrific app. 5.00
...: The Forge/The Casting Director's Cut (1/18, $7.99) reprints 2 issues with B&W pencil-a; original script for The Forge 8.00

DARKDEVIL (See Spider-Girl)
Marvel Comics: Nov, 2000 - No. 3, Jan, 2001 ($2.99, limited series)
1-3: 1-Origin of Darkdevil; Kingpin-c/app. 3.00

DARK DOMINION
Defiant: Oct, 1993 - No. 10, July, 1994 ($2.50)
1-10-Len Wein scripts begin. 1-Intro Chasm. 4-Free extra 16 pgs. 7-9-J.G. Jones-c/a (his 1st pro work). 10-Pre-Schism issue; Shooter/Wein script; John Ridgway-a 3.00

DARK ENGINE
Image Comics: Jul, 2014 - No. 5, Mar, 2015 ($3.50)
1-5-Burton-s/Bivens-a 3.50

DARKER IMAGE (Also see Deathblow, The Maxx, & Bloodwulf)
Image Comics: Mar, 1993 ($1.95, one-shot)
1-The Maxx by Sam Kieth begins; Bloodwulf by Rob Liefeld & Deathblow by Jim Lee begin (both 1st app.); polybagged w/1 of 3 cards by Kieth, Lee or Liefeld 3.00
1-B&W interior pgs. w/silver foil logo 6.00

DARK FANG
Image Comics: Nov, 2017 - Present ($3.99)
1-4-Gunter-s/Shannon-a 4.00

DARK FANTASIES
Dark Fantasy: 1994 - No. 8, 1995 ($2.95)
1-Test print Run (3,000)-Linsner-c 1 2 3 5 6 8
1-Linsner-c 5.00
2-8: 2-4 (Deluxe), 2-4 (Regular), 5-8 (Deluxe; $3.95) 4.00
5-8 (Regular; $3.50) 3.50

DARK GUARD
Marvel Comics UK: Oct, 1993 - No. 4, Jan, 1994 ($1.75)
1-($2.95)-Foil stamped-c 4.00
2-4 3.00

DARKHAWK (Also see War of Kings)
Marvel Comics: Mar, 1991 - No. 50, Apr, 1995 ($1.00/$1.25/$1.50)
1-Origin/1st app. Darkhawk; Hobgoblin cameo 2 4 6 9 12 15
2,3,13,14: 2-Spider-Man & Hobgoblin app. 3-Spider-Man & Hobgoblin app. 13,14-Venom-c/story 4.00
4-12,15-24,26-49: 6-Capt. America & Daredevil x-over. 9-Punisher app. 11,12-Tombstone app. 19-Spider-Man & Brotherhood of Evil Mutants-c/story. 20-Spider-Man app. 22-Ghost Rider-c/story. 23-Origin begins, ends #25. 27-New Warriors-c/story. 35-Begin 3 part Venom story. 39-Bound-in trading card sheet 3.00
25,50: (52 pgs.)-Red holo-grafx foil-c w/double gatefold poster; origin of Darkhawk armor 4.00
Annual 1-3 ('92-'94,68 pgs.)-1-Vs. Iron Man. 2 -Polybagged w/card 4.00

DARKHAWK (Marvel Legacy)
Marvel Comics: No. 51, Jan, 2018 ($3.99, one-shot)
51-Bowers & Sims-s/Kev Walker-a/Nakayama-c 4.00

DARKHOLD: PAGES FROM THE BOOK OF SINS (See Midnight Sons Unlimited)
Marvel Comics (Midnight Sons imprint #15 on): Oct, 1992 - No. 16, Jan, 1994
1-($2.75, 52 pgs.)-Polybagged w/poster by Andy & Adam Kubert; part 4 of Rise of the Midnight Sons storyline 4.00
2-10,12-16: 3-Reintro Modred the Mystic (see Marvel Chillers #1). 4-Sabertooth-c/sty. 5-Punisher & Ghost Rider app. 15-Spot varnish-c. 15,16-Siege of Darkness pt. 4&12 3.00
11-($2.25)-Outer-c is a Darkhold envelope made of black parchment w/gold ink 4.00

DARK HORSE BOOK OF... , THE
Dark Horse Comics: Aug, 2003 - Nov, 2006 ($14.95/$15.95, HC, 9 1/4" x 6 1/4")
... Hauntings (8/03, $14.95)-Short stories by various incl. Mignola (Hellboy), Thompson, Dorkin, Russell; Gianni-c 15.00
... Monsters (11/06, $15.95)-Short-s by Mignola, Thompson, Dorkin, Giffen, Busiek; Gianni-c 16.00
... The Dead (6/05, $14.95)-Short-s by Mignola, Thompson, Dorkin, Powell; Gianni-c 15.00
... Witchcraft (6/04, $14.95)-Short-s by Mignola, Thompson, Dorkin, Millionaire; Gianni-c 15.00

DARK HORSE CLASSICS (Title series), **Dark Horse Comics**
1992 ($3.95, B&W, 52 pgs. nn's): The Last of the Mohicans. 20,000 Leagues Under the Sea 4.00

DARK HORSE CLASSICS, 5/96 ($2.95) 1-r/Predator: Jungle Tales 3.00
--ALIENS VERSUS PREDATOR, 2/97 - No. 6, 7/97 ($2.95,) 1-6: r/Aliens Versus Predator 3.00
--GODZILLA: KING OF THE MONSTERS, 4/98 ($2.95) 1-6: 1-r/Godzilla: Color Special; Art Adams-a 3.00
--STAR WARS: DARK EMPIRE, 3/97 - No. 6, 8/97 ($2.95) 1-6: r/Star Wars: Dark Empire 3.00
--TERROR OF GODZILLA, 8/98 - No. 6, 1/99 ($2.95) 1-6-r/manga Godzilla in color; Art Adams-c 3.00

DARK HORSE COMICS
Dark Horse Comics: Aug, 1992 - No. 25, Sept, 1994 ($2.50)
1-Dorman double gategold painted-c; Predator, Robocop, Timecop (3-part) & Renegade stories begin 4.00
2-6,11-25: 2-Mignola-c. 3-Begin 3-part Aliens story; Aliens-c. 4-Predator-c. 6-Begin 4 part Robocop story. 12-Begin 2-part Aliens & 3-part Predator stories. 13-Thing From Another World begins w/Nino-a(i). 15-Begin 2-part Aliens: Cargo story. 16-Begin 3-part Predator story. 17-Begin 3-part Star Wars: Droids story & 3-part Aliens: Alien story; Droids-c. 19-Begin 2-part X story; X cover 3.00
7-Begin Star Wars: Tales of the Jedi 3-part story 1 2 3 4 5 7
8-1st app. X and begins; begin 4-part James Bond 6.00
9,10: 9-Star Wars ends. 10-X ends; Begin 3-part Predator & Godzilla stories 4.00
NOTE: *Art Adams c-11.*

DARK HORSE DAY SAMPLER 2016
Dark Horse Comics: Jun, 2016 (no price, promotional one-shot)
nn-New Buffy the Vampire Slayer story; reprint stories of Sin City, AvP, Umbrella Academy 3.00

DARK HORSE DOWN UNDER
Dark Horse Comics: Jun, 1994 - No. 3, Oct, 1994 ($2.50, B&W, limited series)
1-3 3.00

DARK HORSE MAVERICK
Dark Horse Comics: July, 2000; July, 2001; Sept, 2002 (B&W, annual)
2000-($3.95) Short stories by Miller, Chadwick, Sakai, Pearson 4.00
2001-($4.99) Short stories by Sakai, Wagner and others; Miller-c 5.00
...: Happy Endings (9/02, $9.95) Short stories by Bendis, Oeming, Mahfood, Mignola, Miller, Kieth and others; Miller-c 10.00

DARK HORSE MONSTERS
Dark Horse Comics: Feb, 1997 ($2.95, one-shot)
1-Reprints 3.00

DARK HORSE PRESENTS
Dark Horse Comics: July, 1986 - No. 157, Sept, 2000 ($1.50-$2.95, B&W)
1-1st app. Concrete by Paul Chadwick 2 4 6 11 16 20
1-2nd printing (1988, $1.50) 3.00
1-Silver ink 3rd printing (1992, $2.25)-Says 2nd printing inside 3.00
2-9: 2-6,9-Concrete app. 6.00
10-1st app. The Mask; Concrete app. 2 4 6 10 14 18
11-19,21-23: 11-19,21-Mask stories. 12,14,16,18,22-Concrete app. 15(2/88). 17-All Roachmill issue 6.00
20-(68 pgs.)-Concrete, Flaming Carrot, Mask 1 3 4 6 8 10
24-Origin Aliens-c/story (11/88); Mr. Monster app. 3 6 9 14 20 25
25-27,29-31,37-39,41,44,45,47-49: 38-Concrete. 44-Crash Ryan. 48,49-Contain 2 trading

Dark Horse Presents #89 © DH

Dark Horse Presents V3 #21 © DH

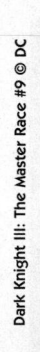

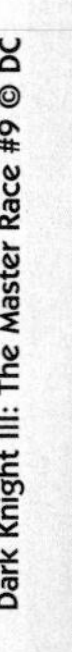
Dark Knight III: The Master Race #9 © DC

GD 2.0 | VG 4.0 | FN 6.0 | VF 8.0 | VF/NM 9.0 | NM- 9.2

cards 3.00
28,33,40: 28-(52 pgs.)-Concrete app.; Mr. Monster story (homage to Graham Ingels). 33-(44 pgs.). 40-(52 pgs.)-1st Argosy story 4.00
32,34,35: 32-(68 pgs.)-Annual; Concrete, American. 34-Aliens-c/story. 35-Predator-c/app. 4.00
36-1st Aliens Vs. Predator story; painted-c 2 4 6 10 14 18
36-Variant line drawn-c 3 6 9 16 23 30
42,43,46: 42,43-Aliens-c/stories. 46-Prequel to new Predator II mini-series 3.00
50-S/F story by Perez; contains 2 trading cards 4.00
51-53-Sin City by Frank Miller, parts 2-4; 51,53-Miller-c (see D.H.P. Fifth Anniversary Special for pt. 1) 1 2 3 4 6 8
54-61: 54-(9/91) The Next Men begins (1st app.) by Byrne; Miller-a/Morrow-c. Homocide by Morrow (also in #55). 55-2nd app. The Next Men; parts 5 & 6 of Sin City by Miller; Miller-c. 56-(68 pg. annual)-part 7 of Sin City by Miller; part prologue to Aliens: Genocide; Next Men by Byrne. 57-(52 pgs.)-Part 8 of Sin City by Miller; Next Men by Byrne; Byrne & Miller-c; Alien Fire story; swipes cover to Daredevil #1. 58,59-Alien Fire stories. 58-61- Part 9-12 Sin City by Miller 5.00
62-Last Sin City (entire book by Miller, c/a; 52 pgs.) 2 4 6 8 10 12
63-66,68-79,81-84-($2.25): 64-Dr. Giggles begins (1st app.), ends #66; Boris the Bear story. 66-New Concrete-c/story by Chadwick. 71-Begin 3 part Dominque story by Jim Balent; Balent-c. 72-(3/93)-Begin 3-part Eudaemon (1st app.) story by Nelson 3.00
67-($3.95, 68 pgs.)-Begin 3-part prelude to Predator: Race War mini-series; Oscar Wilde adapt. by Russell 4.00
80-Art Adams-c/a (Monkeyman & O'Brien) 4.00
85-87,92-99: 85-Begin $2.50-c. 92, 93, 95-Too Much Coffee Man 3.00
88-Hellboy by Mignola. 2 4 6 8 10 12
89-91-Hellboy by Mignola. 1 2 3 5 6 8
NOTE: *There are 5 different Dark Horse Presents #100 issues*
100-1-Intro Lance Blastoff by Miller; Milk & Cheese by Evan Dorkin 4.00
100-2-Hellboy-c by Wrightson; Hellboy story by Mignola; includes Roberta Gregory & Paul Pope stories 6.00
100-3-100-5: 100-3-Darrow-c, Concrete by Chadwick; Pekar story. 100-4-Gibbons-c: Miller story, Geary story/a. 100-5-Allred-c, Adams, Dorkin, Pope 3.00
101-125: 101-Aliens c/a by Wrightson, story by Pope. 103-Kirby gatefold-c. 106-Big Blown Baby by Bill Wray. 107-Mignola-c/a. 109-Begin $2.95-c; Paul Pope-c. 110-Ed Brubaker-a/s. 114-Flip books begin; Lance Blastoff by Miller; Star Slammers by Simonson. 115-Miller-c. 117-Aliens-c/app. 118-Evan Dorkin-c/a. 119-Monkeyman & O'Brien. 124-Predator. 125-Nocturnals 3.00
126-($3.95, 48 pgs.)-Flip book: Nocturnals, Starship Troopers 4.00
127-134,136-140: 127-Nocturnals. 129-The Hammer. 132-134-Warren-a 3.00
135-($3.50) The Mark 3.50
141-All Buffy the Vampire Slayer issue 4.00
142-149: 142-Mignola-c. 143-Tarzan. 146,147-Aliens vs. Predator. 148-Xena 3.00
150-($4.50) Buffy-c by Green; Buffy, Concrete, Fish Police app. 4.50
151-157: 151-Hellboy-c/app. 153-155-Angel flip-c. 156,157-Witch's Son 3.00
Annual 1997 ($4.95, 64 pgs.)-Flip book; Body Bags, Aliens. Pearson-c; stories by Allred & Stephens, Pope, Smith & Morrow 1 2 3 5 6 8
Annual 1998 ($4.95, 64 pgs.) 1st Buffy the Vampire Slayer comic app.; Hellboy story and cover by Mignola 1 2 3 5 6 8
Annual 1999 (7/99, $4.95) Stories of Xena, Hellboy, Ghost, Luke Skywalker, Groo, Concrete, the Mask and Usagi Yojimbo in their youth. 5.00
Annual 2000 ($4.95) Girl sidekicks; Chiodo-c and flip photo Buffy-c 5.00
...Aliens Platinum Edition (1992)-r/DHP #24,43,43,56 & Special 11.00
...Fifth Anniversary Special nn (4/91, $9.95)-Part 1 of Sin City by Frank Miller (c/a); Aliens, Aliens vs. Predator, Concrete, Roachmill, Give Me Liberty & The American stories 35.00
The One Trick Rip-off (1997, $12.95, TPB)-r/stories from #101-112 13.00
NOTE: ***Geary** a-59, 60. **Miller** a-Special, 51-53, 55-62; c-59-62, 100-1; c-51, 53, 55, 59-62, 100-1. **Moebius** a-63; c-63, 70. **Vess** a-78; c-75, 78.*

DARK HORSE PRESENTS
Dark Horse Comics: Apr, 2011 - No. 36, May, 2014 ($7.99, anthology)
1-36: 1-Frank Miller-c & Xerxes preview; Neal Adams-s/a. 1-3-Concrete by Chadwick. 1-8-Chaykin-s/a. 2,3,9-Corben-a. 3-Steranko interview. 7-Hellboy app. 10-Milk & Cheese. 12-17-Aliens; Kieth-a. 14-Flipbook. 18-Capt. Midnight. 23-26,29-34-Nexus. 25,26-Buffy. 28,29-Neal Adams-s/a. 31,32-Hellboy; McMahon-a 8.00

DARK HORSE PRESENTS (Volume 3)
Dark Horse Comics: Aug, 2014 - No. 33, Apr, 2017 ($4.99, anthology)
1-6: 1-Two covers. 1,2-Rusty & Big Guy by Darrow-s/a. 2-Aliens. 5-Alex Ross-c 5.00
7-(2/15) 200th Issue; Hellboy by Mignola & Bá, Groo, Mind Mgmt; Gibbons, Darrow-a 5.00
8-15,17-33: 8-10-Tarzan by Grell. 14,15-The Rook; Gulacy-a. 17,18-Levitz-s 5.00
16-($5.99) Flip book with Hellboy by Mignola; art by Calero, Ordway, McCarthy 6.00

DARK HORSE TWENTY YEARS
Dark Horse Comics: 2006 (25¢, one-shot)
nn-Pin-ups by Dark Horse artists of other artists' Dark Horse characters; Mignola-c 3.00

DARK IVORY
Image Comics: Mar, 2008 - No. 4, Jan, 2009 ($2.99, limited series)
1-4-Eva Hopkins & Joseph Michael Linsner-s/Linsner-a/c 3.00

DARK KNIGHT (See Batman: The Dark Knight Returns & Legends of the...)

DARK KNIGHT RETURNS, THE: THE LAST CRUSADE
DC Comics: Aug, 2016 ($6.99, squarebound, one-shot)
1-Miller & Azzarello-s/Romita Jr.-a; Jason Todd Robin vs. The Joker; Poison Ivy app. 7.00

DARK KNIGHTS RISING: THE WILD HUNT (See Dark Nights: Metal series and other tie-ins)
DC Comics: Apr, 2018 ($4.99, one-shot)
1-Snyder & Morrison-s/Porter & Mahnke-a; Detective Chimp app.; foil-c 5.00

DARK KNIGHT STRIKES AGAIN, THE (Also see Batman: The Dark Knight Returns)
DC Comics: 2001 - No. 3, 2002 ($7.95, prestige format, limited series)
1-Frank Miller-s/a/c; sequel set 3 years after Dark Knight Returns; 2 covers 10.00
2,3 10.00
HC (2002, $29.95) intro. by Miller; sketch pages and exclusive artwork; cover has 3 1/4" tall partial dustjacket 30.00
SC (2002, $19.95) intro. by Miller; sketch pages 20.00

DARK KNIGHT III: THE MASTER RACE (Also see Batman: The Dark Knight Returns)
DC Comics: Jan, 2016 - No. 9, Jul, 2017 ($5.99, cardstock cover, limited series)
1-9: 1-Miller & Azzarello-s/Andy Kubert-a; Dark Knight Universe Presents: The Atom mini-comic attached at centerfold, Miller-a. 2-Wonder Woman mini-comic. 3-Superman returns; Green Lantern mini-comic. 4-Batgirl mini-comic. 5-Lara mini-comic. 6-World's Finest mini-comic. 7-Strange Adventures mini-comic. 8-Detective mini. 9-Action mini 6.00
1-8-Deluxe Edition ($12.99, HC) reprints story plus mini-comic at full size; cover gallery 13.00
9-Deluxe Edition ($12.99, HC) Sold with slipcase fitting all 9 Deluxe Edition HCs 13.00
... Book One - Director's Cut (11/16, $7.99) r/ #1 in B&W art; script, variant cover gallery 8.00

DARKLON THE MYSTIC (Also see Eerie Magazine #79,80)
Pacific Comics: Oct, 1983 (one-shot)
1-Starlin-c/a(r) 4.00

DARKMAN (Movie)
Marvel Comics: Sept, 1990; Oct, 1990 - No. 3, Dec, 1990 ($1.50)
1 (9/90, $2.25, B&W mag., 68 pgs.)-Adaptation of film 4.00
1-3: Reprints B&W magazine 3.00

DARKMAN
Marvel Comics: V2#1, Apr, 1993 -No. 6, Sept, 1993 ($2.95, limited series)
V2#1 ($3.95, 52 pgs.) 4.00
2-6 3.00

DARK MANSION OF FORBIDDEN LOVE, THE (Becomes Forbidden Tales of Dark Mansion No. 5 on)
National Periodical Publ.: Sept-Oct, 1971 - No. 4, Mar-Apr, 1972 (52 pgs.)
1-Greytone-c on all 17 34 51 119 265 410
2-4: 2-Adams-c. 3-Jeff Jones-c 9 18 27 60 120 180

DARKMAN VS. THE ARMY OF DARKNESS (Movie crossover)
Dynamite Entertainment: 2006 - No. 4, 2007 ($3.50)
1-4: 1-Busiek & Stern-s/Fry-a; photo-c and Perez and Bradshaw covers 3.50

DARKMINDS
Image Comics (Dreamwave Prod.): July, 1998 - No. 8, Apr, 1999 ($2.50)
1-Manga; Pat Lee-s/a; 2 covers 1 3 4 6 8 10
1-2nd printing 3.00
2, 0-(1/99, $5.00) Story and sketch pages 5.00
3-8, 1/2-(5/99, $2.50) Story and sketch pages 3.00
... Collected 1,2 (1/99,3/99; $7.95) 1-r/#1-3. 2-r/#4-6 8.00
... Collected 3 (5/99; $5.95) r/#7,8 6.00

DARKMINDS (Volume 2)
Image Comics (Dreamwave Prod.): Feb, 2000 - No. 10, Apr, 2001 ($2.50)
1-10-Pat Lee-c 3.00
0-(7/00) Origin of Mai Murasaki; sketchbook 3.00

DARKMINDS: MACROPOLIS
Image Comics (Dreamwave Prod.): Jan, 2002 - No. 4, Dec, 2002 ($2.95)
Preview (8/01) Flip book w/Banished Knights preview 3.00
1-4-Jo Chen-a 3.00

DARK MATTER (Inspired 2015 TV series on SyFy channel)
Dark Horse Comics.: Jan, 2012 - No. 4, Apr, 2012 ($3.50, limited series)
1-4-Joseph Mallozzi & Paul Mullie-s/Garry Brown-a 4.00

DARKMINDS: MACROPOLIS (Volume 2)

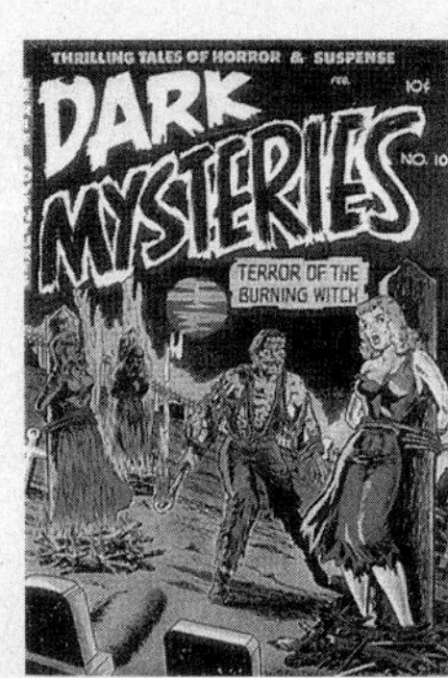

Dark Mysteries #10 © Merit

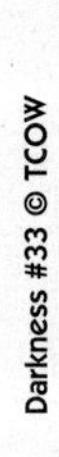
Darkness #33 © TCOW

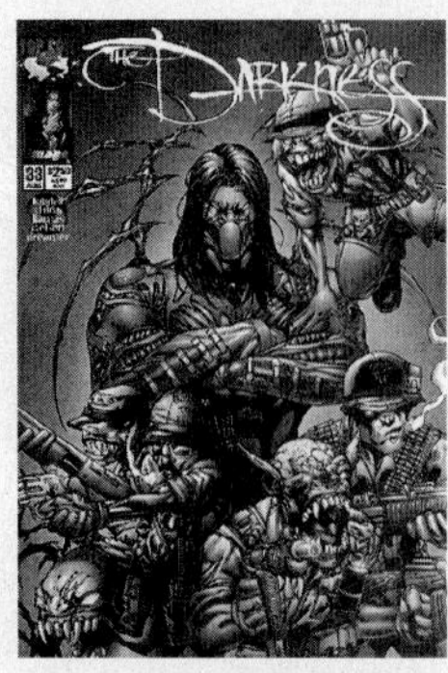

Dark Nights: Metal #1 © DC

GD 2.0 | VG 4.0 | FN 6.0 | VF 8.0 | VF/NM 9.0 | NM- 9.2

Dreamwave Prod.: Sept, 2003 - No. 4, Jul, 2004 ($2.95)
1-4-Chris Sarracini-s/Kwang Mook Lim-a 3.00

DARKMINDS / WITCHBLADE (Also see Witchblade/Dark Minds)
Image Comics (Top Cow/Dreamwave Prod.): Aug, 2000 ($5.95, one-shot)
1-Wohl-s/Pat Lee-a; two covers by Silvestri and Lee 6.00

DARK MYSTERIES (Thrilling Tales of Horror & Suspense)
"Master" - "Merit" Publications: June-July, 1951 - No. 24, July, 1955
1-Wood-c/a (8 pgs.) 148 296 444 947 1624 2300
2-Classic skull-c; Wood/Harrison-c/a (8 pgs.) 148 296 444 947 1624 2300
3-9: 7-Dismemberment, hypo blood drainage stys 60 120 180 381 653 925
10-Cannibalism story; witch burning-c 116 232 348 742 1271 1800
11-13,15-17: 11-Severed head panels. 13-Dismemberment-c/story. 17-The Old Gravedigger host 54 108 162 343 574 825
14-Several E.C. Craig swipes 55 110 165 352 601 850
18-Bondage, skeletons-c 84 168 252 538 919 1300
19-Injury-to-eye panel; E.C. swipe; torture-c 239 478 717 1530 2615 3700
20-Female bondage, blood drainage story 63 126 189 403 689 975
21,22: 21-Devil-c. 22-Last pre-code issue, misdated 3/54 instead of 3/55 43 86 129 271 461 650
23,24 36 72 108 211 343 475
NOTE: ***Cameron** a-1, 2. **Myron Fass** c/a-21. **Harrison** a-3, 7; c-3. **Hollingsworth** a-7-17, 20, 21, 23. **Wildey** a-5. Woodish art by **Fleishman**-9; c-10, 14-17. Bondage c-10, 18, 19.*

DARK NEMESIS (VILLAINS) (See Teen Titans)
DC Comics: Feb, 1998 ($1.95, one-shot)
1-Jurgens-s/Pearson-c 3.00

DARKNESS, THE (See Witchblade #10)
Image Comics (Top Cow Productions): Dec, 1996 - No. 40, Aug, 2001 ($2.50)
Special Preview Edition-(7/96, B&W)-Ennis script; Silvestri-a(p) 2 4 6 9 13 16
0 2 4 6 8 10 12
0-Gold Edition 16.00
1/2 1 3 4 6 8 10
1/2-Christmas-c 3 6 9 14 19 24
1/2-(3/01, $2.95) r/#1/2 w/new 6 pg. story & Silvestri-c 3.00
1-Ennis-s/Silvestri-a, 1-Black variant-c 2 4 6 9 12 15
1-Platinum variant-c 20.00
1-DF Green variant-c 12.00
1,2: 1-Fan Club Ed. 1 3 4 6 8 10
3-5 6.00
6-10: 9,10-Witchblade "Family Ties" x-over pt. 2,3 4.00
7-Variant-c w/concubine 1 2 3 5 7 9
8-American Entertainment 6.00
8-10-American Entertainment Gold Ed. 7.00
11-Regular Ed.; Ennis-s/Silverstri & D-Tron-c 3.00
11-Nine (non-chromium) variant-c (Benitez, Cabrera, the Hildebrandts, Finch, Keown, Peterson, Portacio, Tan, Turner 4.50
11-Chromium-c by Silvestri & Batt 20.00
12-19: 13-Begin Benitez-a(p) 3.00
20-24,26-40: 34-Ripclaw app. 3.00
25-($3.99) Two covers (Benitez, Silvestri) 4.00
25-Chromium-c variant by Silvestri 8.00
.../ Batman (8/99, $5.95) Silvestri, Finch, Lansing-a(p) 6.00
...Collected Editions #1-4 ($4.95,TPB) 1-r/#1,2. 2-r/#3,4. 3- r/#5,6. 4- r/#7,8 6.00
...Collected Editions #5,6 ($5.95, TPB)5- r/#11,12. 6-r/#13,14 6.00
Deluxe Collected Editions #1 (12/98, $14.95, TPB) r/#1-6 & Preview 15.00
...: Heart of Darkness (2001, $14.95, TPB) r/ #7,8, 11-14 15.00
Holiday Pin-up-American Entertainment 5.00
Holiday Pin-up Gold Ed.-American Entertainment 7.00
Image Firsts: Darkness #1 (9/10, $1.00) r/#1 with "Image Firsts" logo on cover 3.00
Infinity #1 (8/99, $3.50) Lobdell-s 3.50
Prelude-American Entertainment 4.00
Prelude Gold Ed.-American Entertainment 9.00
Volume 1 Compendium (2006, $59.99) r/#1-40, V2 #1, Tales of the Darkness #1-4; #1/2, Darkness/Witchblade #1/2, Darkness: Wanted Dead; cover and sketch gallery 60.00
...: Wanted Dead 1 (8/03, $2.99) Texiera-a/Tieri-s 3.00
Wizard ACE Ed.- Reprints #1 2 4 6 8 10 12

DARKNESS (Volume 2)
Image Comics (Top Cow Productions): Dec, 2002 - No. 24, Oct, 2004 ($2.99)
1-24: 1-6-Jenkins-s/Keown-a. 17-20-Lapham-s. 23,24-Magdalena app. 3.00
... Black Sails (3/05, $2.99) Marz-s/Cha-a; Hunter-Killer preview 3.00
... and Tomb Raider (4/05, $2.99) r/Darkness Prelude & Tomb Raider/Darkness Special 3.00

GD 2.0 | VG 4.0 | FN 6.0 | VF 8.0 | VF/NM 9.0 | NM- 9.2

...: Resurrection TPB (2/04, $16.99) r/#1-6 & Vol. 1 #40 17.00
.../ The Incredible Hulk (7/04, $2.99) Keown-a/Jenkins-s 3.00
.../ Vampirella (7/05, $2.99) Terry Moore-s; two covers by Basaldua and Moore 3.00
... Vol. 5 TPB (2006, $19.99) r/#7-16 & The Darkness: Wanted Dead #1; cover gallery 20.00
... vs. Mr Hyde Monster War 2005 (9/05, $2.99) x-over w/Witchblade, Tomb Raider and Magdalena; two covers 3.00
.../ Wolverine (2006, $2.99) Kirkham-a/Tieri-s 3.00

DARKNESS (Volume 3) (Numbering jumps from #10 to #75)
Image Comics (Top Cow Productions): Dec, 2007 - Present ($2.99)
1-10: 1-Hester-s/Broussard-a. 1-Three covers. 7-9-Lucas-a. 8-Aphrodite IV app. 3.00
75 (2/09, $4.99) Four covers; Hester-s/art by various 5.00
76-99,101-113,115-($2.99) 76-99,101-Multiple covers on each 3.00
100 (2/12, $4.99) Four covers; Hester-s/art by various; cover gallery; series timeline 5.00
114-($4.99) The Age of Reason Part 1; Hine-s/Haun-a; bonus Darkness timeline 5.00
116-($3.99) The Age of Reason Part 3; Hine-s/Haun-a 4.00
... : Butcher (4/08, $3.99) Story of Butcher Joyce; Levin-s/Broussard-a/c 4.00
... : Close Your Eyes (6/14, $3.99) Story of Adelmo Estacado in 1912; Kot-s/Oleksicki-a/c 4.00
...: Confession (5/11) Free Comic Boy Day giveaway; Broussard & Molnar-a 3.00
... / Darkchylde: Kingdom Pain 1 (5/10, $4.99) Randy Queen-s/a 5.00
... First Look (11/07, 99¢) Previews series; sketch pages 3.00
... : Hope (4/16, $3.99) Harmon-s/Dwyer-a/Linda Sejic-c 4.00
... : Lodbrok's Hand (12/08, $2.99) Hester-s/Oeming-a/c; variant-c by Carnevale 3.00
... : Shadows and Flame 1 (1/10, $2.99) Lucas-c/a 3.00
... : Vicious Traditions 1 (3/14, $3.99) Ales Kot-s/Dean Ormston-a/Dale Keown-c 4.00

DARKNESS: FOUR HORSEMEN
Image Comics (Top Cow): Aug, 2010 - No. 4, May, 2011 ($3.99, limited series)
1-4-Hine-s/Wamester-a 4.00

DARKNESS: LEVEL...
Image Comics (Top Cow): No. 0, Dec, 2006 - No. 5, Aug, 2007 ($2.99, limited series)
0-5: 0-Origin of The Darkness in WW1; Jenkins-s. 1-Jackie's origin retold; Sejic-a 3.00

DARKNESS/ PITT
Image Comics (Top Cow): Dec, 2006; Aug, 2009 - No. 3, Nov, 2009 ($2.99)
...: First Look (12/06) Jenkins script pages with Keown B&W and color art 3.00
1-3: 1-(8/09) Jenkins-s/Keown-a; covers by Keown and Sejic. 2,3-Two covers 3.00

DARKNESS/ SUPERMAN
Image Comics (Top Cow Productions): Jan, 2005 - No. 2, Feb, 2005 ($2.99, limited series)
1,2-Marz-s/Kirkham & Banning-a/Silvestri-c 3.00

DARKNESS VISIBLE
IDW Publishing: Feb, 2017 - Present ($3.99)
1-6: 1-Mike Carey & Arvind David-s/Brendan Cahill-a. 3,6-Ramondelli-a 4.00

DARKNESS VS. EVA: DAUGHTER OF DRACULA
Dynamite Entertainment: 2008 - No. 4, 2008 ($3.50, limited series)
1-4-Leah Moore & John Reppion-s/Salazar-a; three covers on each 3.50

DARK NIGHT: A TRUE BATMAN STORY
DC Comics: 2016 ($22.99, HC Graphic Novel)
HC - Paul Dini-s/Eduardo Risso-a 23.00

DARK NIGHTS: METAL (Also see Dark Days prelude one-shots)
DC Comics: Nov, 2017 - No. 6 ($4.99/$3.99)
1-($4.99) Snyder-s/Capullo-a; Justice League & Dream of the Endless app.; foil logo-c 5.00
1-Second printing; red title logo on cover 5.00
2-5-($3.99) 2-Barbatos app. 4.00
Director's Cut 1 (2/18, $6.99) r/#1 pencil art; gallery of variant covers 7.00

DARK NIGHTS: THE BATMAN WHO LAUGHS (Dark Nights: Metal) (Also see Teen Titans #12 [11/17])
DC Comics: Jan, 2018 ($3.99, one-shot)
1-Tynion IV-s/Rossmo-a; Fabok foil-c; Bruce Wayne as Dark Multiverse Joker 10.00

DARK REIGN (Follows Secret Invasion crossover)
Marvel Comics: 2009 ($3.99/$4.99, one-shots)
...: Files 1 (2009, $4.99) profile pages of villains tied in to Dark Reign x-over 5.00
...: Made Men 1 (11/09, $3.99) short stories by various incl. Pham, Leon, Oliver 4.00
...: New Nation 1 (2/09, $3.99) previews of various series tied in to Dark Reign x-over 4.00
...: The Cabal 1 (6/09, $3.99) Cabal members stories by various incl. Granov, Acuña 4.00
...: The Goblin Legacy 1 (2009, $3.99) r/ASM #39,40; Osborn history; Mayhew-a 4.00

DARK REIGN: ELEKTRA
Marvel Comics: May, 2009 - No. 5, Oct, 2009 ($3.99, limited series)
1-5-Mann-a/Bermejo-c; Elektra after the Skrull replacement. 2,3-Bullseye app. 4.00

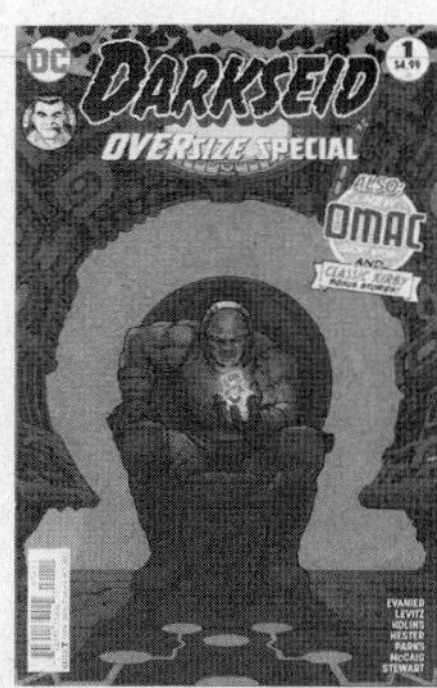

Darkseid Special #1 © DC

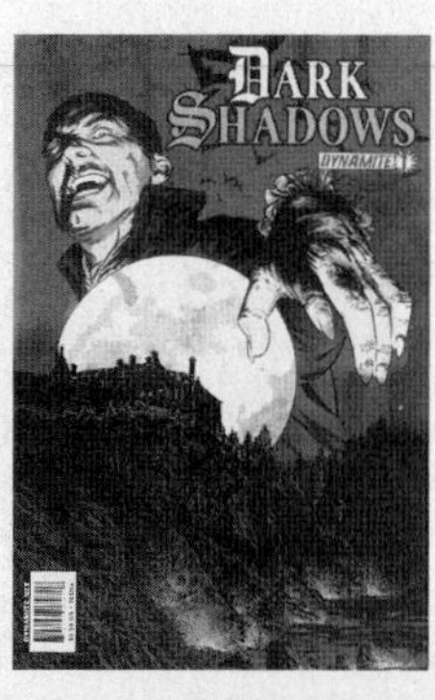

Dark Shadows (2011 series) #1 © Dan Curtis

Darkstars #12 © DC

	GD 2.0	VG 4.0	FN 6.0	VF 8.0	VF/NM 9.0	NM- 9.2

DARK REIGN: FANTASTIC FOUR
Marvel Comics: May, 2009 - No. 5, Sept, 2009 ($2.99, limited series)

1-5-Chen-a 3.00

DARK REIGN: HAWKEYE
Marvel Comics: June, 2009 - No. 5, Mar, 2010 ($3.99, limited series)

1-5-Bullseye in the Dark Avengers; Raney-a/Langley-c. 5-Guinaldo-a 4.00

DARK REIGN: LETHAL LEGION
Marvel Comics: Aug, 2009 - No. 3, Nov, 2009 ($3.99, limited series)

1-3-Santolouco-a/Edwards-c; Grim Reaper and Wonder Man app. 4.00

DARK REIGN: MR. NEGATIVE (Also see Amazing Spider-Man #546)
Marvel Comics: Aug, 2009 - No. 3, Oct, 2009 ($3.99, limited series)

1-3-Jae Lee-c/Gugliotta-a; Spider-Man app. 4.00

DARK REIGN: SINISTER SPIDER-MAN
Marvel Comics: Aug, 2009 - No. 4, Nov, 2009 ($3.99, limited series)

1-4-Bachalo-c/a; Venom/Scorpion as Dark Avenger Spider-Man 4.00

DARK REIGN: THE HOOD
Marvel Comics: Jul, 2009 - No. 5, Nov, 2009 ($3.99, limited series)

1-5-Hotz-a/Djurdjevic-c 4.00

DARK REIGN: THE LIST
Marvel Comics: 2009 - 2010 ($3.99, one-shots)

... - Amazing Spider-Man (1/10, $3.99) Adam Kubert-c/a; back-up r/Pulse #5 4.00
... - Avengers (11/09, $3.99) Bendis-s/Djurdjevic-c/a; Ronin (Hawkeye) app. 4.00
... - Daredevil (11/09, $3.99) Diggle-s/Tan-c/a; Bullseye app.; leads into Daredevil #501 4.00
... - Hulk (12/09, $3.99) Pak-s/Oliver-a; Skaar app.; back-up r/Amaz. Spider-Man #14 4.00
... - Punisher (12/09, $3.99) Romita Jr.-a/c; Castle killed by Daken; preview of Franken-Castle in Punisher #11 6.00
... - Secret Warriors (12/09, $3.99) McGuinness-a/c; Nick Fury; back-up r/Steranko-a 4.00
... - Wolverine (12/09, $3.99) Ribic-a/c; Marvel Boy and Fantomex app. 4.00
... - X-Men (11/09, $3.99) Alan Davis-a/c; Namor app.; back-up r/Kieth-a 4.00

DARK REIGN: YOUNG AVENGERS
Marvel Comics: Jul, 2009 - No. 5, Dec, 2009 ($3.99, limited series)

1-5-Brooks-a; Osborn's Young Avengers vs. original Young Avengers 4.00

DARK REIGN: ZODIAC
Marvel Comics: Aug, 2009 - No. 3, Nov, 2009 ($3.99, limited series)

1-3-Casey-s/Fox-a. 1-Human Torch app. 4.00

DARKSEID SPECIAL (Jack Kirby 100th Birthday tribute)
DC Comics: Oct, 2017 ($4.99, one-shot)

1-Evanier-s/Kolins-a; Omac story with Levitz-s/Hester-a; r/Forever People #6 (4 pgs) 5.00

DARKSEID (VILLAINS) (See Jack Kirby's New Gods and New Gods)
DC Comics: Feb, 1998 ($1.95, one-shot)

1-Byrne-s/Pearson-c 3.00

DARKSEID VS. GALACTUS: THE HUNGER
DC Comics: 1995 ($4.95, one-shot) (1st DC/Marvel x-over by John Byrne)

nn-John Byrne-c/a/script 6.00

DARK SHADOWS
Steinway Comic Publ. (Ajax)(America's Best): Oct, 1957 - No. 3, May, 1958

	GD	VG	FN	VF	VF/NM	NM-
1	32	64	96	188	307	425
2,3	21	42	63	122	199	275

DARK SHADOWS (TV) (See Dan Curtis Giveaways)
Gold Key: Mar, 1969 - No. 35, Feb, 1976 (Photo-c: 1-7)

	GD	VG	FN	VF	VF/NM	NM-
1(30039-903)-With pull-out poster (25¢)	21	42	63	147	324	500
1-With poster missing	7	14	21	48	89	130
2	8	16	24	54	102	150
3-With pull-out poster	9	18	27	60	120	180
3-With poster missing	5	10	15	35	63	90
4-7: 7-Last photo-c	6	12	18	38	69	100
8-10	5	10	15	30	50	70
11-20	4	8	12	27	44	60
21-35: 30-Last painted-c	4	8	12	23	37	50
Story Digest 1 (6/70, 148pp.)-Photo-c (low print)	7	14	21	46	86	125

DARK SHADOWS (TV) (See Nightmare on Elm Street)
Innovation Publishing: June, 1992 - No. 4, Spring, 1993 ($2.50, limited series, coated stock)

1-Based on 1991 NBC TV mini-series; painted-c 5.00
2-4 4.00

DARK SHADOWS: BOOK TWO
Innovation Publishing: 1993 - No. 4, July, 1993 ($2.50, limited series)

1-4-Painted-c. 4-Maggie Thompson scripts 4.00

DARK SHADOWS: BOOK THREE
Innovation Publishing: Nov, 1993 ($2.50)

1-(Whole #9) 4.00

DARK SHADOWS/VAMPIRELLA
Dynamite Entertainment: 2012 - No. 5, 2012 ($3.99, limited series)

1-5-Andreyko-s/Berkenkotter-a/Neves-c 4.00

DARK SHADOWS, VOLUME 1
Dynamite Entertainment: 2011 - No. 23, 2013 ($3.99)

1-23-Set in 1971. 1-Aaron Campbell-a; covers by Campbell & Francavilla 4.00

DARK SHADOWS: YEAR ONE
Dynamite Entertainment: 2013 - No. 6, 2013 ($3.99, limited series)

1-6-Origin of Barnabas Collins; Andreyko-s/Vilanova-a 4.00

DARK SOULS: LEGENDS OF THE FLAME (Based on the Bandai Namco video game)
Titan Comics: Sept, 2016 - No. 2, Nov, 2016 ($3.99, limited series)

1,2-Short stories by various; multiple covers on each 4.00

DARK SOULS: THE BREATH OF ANDOLUS (Based on the Bandai Namco video game)
Titan Comics: May, 2016 - No. 4, Sept, 2016 ($3.99, limited series)

1-4-George Mann-s/Alan Quah-a; multiple covers on each 4.00

DARK SOULS: WINTER'S SPITE (Based on the Bandai Namco video game)
Titan Comics: Dec, 2016 - No. 4, Apr, 2017 ($3.99, limited series)

1-4-George Mann-s/Alan Quah-a; multiple covers on each 4.00

DARKSTAR AND THE WINTER GUARD
Marvel Comics: Aug, 2010 - No. 3, Oct, 2010 ($3.99, limited series)

1-3-Gallaher-s/Ellis-a/Henry-c; back-up reprint from X-Men Unlimited #28 4.00

DARKSTARS, THE
DC Comics: Oct, 1992 - No. 38, Jan, 1996 ($1.75/$1.95)

1-1st app. The Darkstars 4.00
2-24,0,25-38: 5-Hawkman & Hawkwoman app. 18-20-Flash app. 24-(9/94)-Zero Hour. 0-(10/94). 25-(11/94). 30-Green Lantern app. 31-...vs. Darkseid. 32-Green Lantern app. 3.00

NOTE: ***Travis Charest** a(p)-4-7; c(p)-2-5; c-6-11. **Stroman** a-1-3; c-1.*

DARK TALES FROM THE VOKESVERSE
American Mythology: 2016 ($4.99, B&W)

1-Short horror stories by Neil Vokes and various; 2 covers 5.00

DARK TOWER: THE BATTLE OF JERICHO HILL (Based on Stephen King's Dark Tower)
Marvel Comics: Feb, 2010 - No. 5, Jun, 2010 ($3.99, limited series)

1-5-Peter David & Robin Furth-s/Jae Lee & Richard Isanove-a/c; variant-c for each 4.00

DARK TOWER: THE DRAWING OF THE THREE - BITTER MEDICINE (Stephen King)
Marvel Comics: Jun, 2016 - No. 5, Oct, 2016 ($3.99, limited series)

1-5-Peter David & Robin Furth-s/Jonathan Marks-a/Nimit Malavia-c 4.00

DARK TOWER: THE DRAWING OF THE THREE - HOUSE OF CARDS (Stephen King)
Marvel Comics: May, 2015 - No. 5, Sept, 2015 ($3.99, limited series)

1-5-Peter David & Robin Furth-s/Piotr Kowalski-a/J.T. Tedesco-c 4.00

DARK TOWER: THE DRAWING OF THE THREE - LADY OF SHADOWS (Stephen King)
Marvel Comics: Nov, 2015 - No. 5, Mar, 2016 ($3.99, limited series)

1-5-Peter David & Robin Furth-s/Jonathan Marks-a/Nimit Malavia-c 4.00

DARK TOWER: THE DRAWING OF THE THREE - THE PRISONER (Stephen King)
Marvel Comics: Nov, 2014 - No. 5, Feb, 2015 ($3.99, limited series)

1-5-Peter David & Robin Furth-s/Piotr Kowalski-a/J.T. Tedesco-c 4.00

DARK TOWER: THE DRAWING OF THE THREE - THE SAILOR (Stephen King)
Marvel Comics: Dec, 2016 - No. 5, Apr, 2017 ($3.99, limited series)

1-5-Peter David & Robin Furth-s/Ramirez-a/Anacleto-c 4.00

DARK TOWER: THE FALL OF GILEAD (Based on Stephen King's Dark Tower)
Marvel Comics: July, 2009 - No. 6, Jan, 2010 ($3.99, limited series)

1-6-Peter David & Robin Furth-s/Richard Isanove-a/Jae Lee-c; variant-c for each 4.00
Dark Tower: Guide to Gilead (2009, $3.99) profile pages of people and places 4.00

DARK TOWER: THE GUNSLINGER BORN (Based on Stephen King's Dark Tower series)
Marvel Comics: Apr, 2007 - No. 7, Oct, 2007 ($3.99, limited series)

1-Peter David & Robin Furth-s/Jae Lee & Richard Isanove-a; boyhood of Roland Deschain; afterword by Ralph Macchio; map of New Canaan 6.00

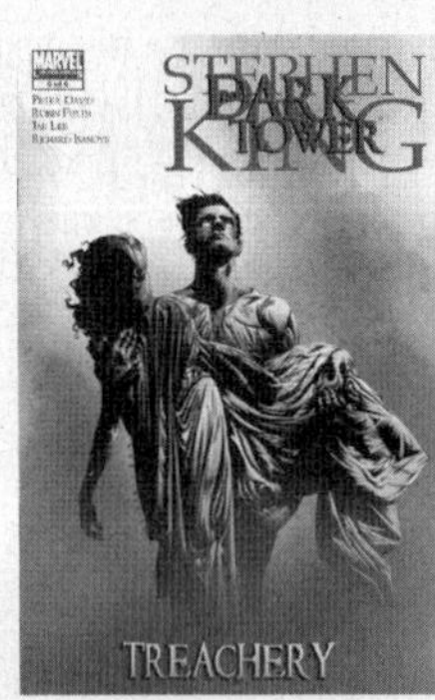

Dark Tower: Treachery #6 © Stephen King

Darth Vader (2017 series) #1 © Lucasfilm

Dastardly & Muttley #1 © H-B

	GD 2.0	VG 4.0	FN 6.0	VF 8.0	VF/NM 9.0	NM- 9.2

1-Variant cover by Quesada 8.00
1-Second printing with variant-c by Quesada 5.00
1-Sketch cover variant by Jae Lee 30.00
2-6-Jae Lee-c 4.00
2-Second printing with variant-c by Immonen 4.00
2-7-Variant covers. 2-Finch-c. 3-Yu-c. 4-McNiven-c. 5-Land-c. 6-Campbell. 7-Coipel 6.00
2-7-B&W sketch-c by Jae Lee 20.00
... MGC #1 (5/11, $1.00) r/#1 with "Marvel's Greatest Comics" logo on cover 3.00
... Sketchbook (2006, no cover price) pencil art and designs by Lee; coloring process 5.00
Dark Tower: Gunslinger's Guidebook (2007, $3.99) profile pages with Jae Lee-a 4.00
HC (2007, $24.99) r/#1-7; variant covers and sketch pages; Macchio intro. 25.00

DARK TOWER: THE GUNSLINGER - EVIL GROUND (Stephen King's Dark Tower)
Marvel Comics: Jun, 2013 - No. 2, Aug, 2013 ($3.99, limited series)
1,2-Robin Furth & Peter David-s/Richard Isanove-a/c 4.00

DARK TOWER: THE GUNSLINGER - SHEEMIE'S TALE (Stephen King's Dark Tower)
Marvel Comics: Mar, 2013 - No. 2, Apr, 2013 ($3.99, limited series)
1,2-Robin Furth-s/Richard Isanove-a/c 4.00

DARK TOWER: THE GUNSLINGER - SO FELL LORD PERTH (Stephen King's Dark Tower)
Marvel Comics: Sept, 2013 ($3.99, one-shot)
1-Robin Furth & Peter David-s/Richard Isanove-a/c 4.00

DARK TOWER: THE GUNSLINGER - THE BATTLE OF TULL (Stephen King's Dark Tower)
Marvel Comics: Aug, 2011 - No. 5, Dec, 2011 ($3.99, limited series)
1-5-Peter David & Robin Furth-s/Michael Lark-a/c 4.00

DARK TOWER: THE GUNSLINGER - THE JOURNEY BEGINS (Stephen King's Dark Tower)
Marvel Comics: Jul, 2010 - No. 5, Nov, 2010 ($3.99, limited series)
1-5-Peter David & Robin Furth-s/Sean Phillips-a/c 4.00
1-Variant cover by Jae Lee 5.00

DARK TOWER: THE GUNSLINGER - THE LITTLE SISTERS OF ELURIA (Stephen King)
Marvel Comics: Feb, 2011 - No. 5, Jun, 2011 ($3.99, limited series)
1-5: 1-Peter David & Robin Furth-s/Luke Ross-a/c 4.00

DARK TOWER: THE GUNSLINGER - THE MAN IN BLACK (Stephen King)
Marvel Comics: Aug, 2012 - No. 5, Dec, 2012 ($3.99, limited series)
1-5-Peter David & Robin Furth-s/Maleev-a/c 4.00

DARK TOWER: THE GUNSLINGER - THE WAY STATION (Stephen King)
Marvel Comics: Feb, 2012 - No. 5, Jun, 2012 ($3.99, limited series)
1-5-Peter David & Robin Furth-s/Laurence Campbell-a/c 4.00

DARK TOWER: THE LONG ROAD HOME (Based on Stephen King's Dark Tower series)
Marvel Comics: May, 2008 - No. 5, Sept, 2008 ($3.99, limited series)
1-Peter David & Robin Furth-s/Jae Lee & Richard Isanove-a 4.00
1-Variant cover by Deodato 6.00
1-Sketch cover variant by Jae Lee 30.00
2-5-Jae Lee-c 4.00
2-5: 2-Variant-c by Quesada. 3-Djurdjevic var-c. 4-Garney var-c. 5-Bermejo var-c 6.00
2-5-B&W sketch-c by Jae Lee 20.00
2-Second printing with variant-c by Lee 4.00
Dark Tower: End-World Almanac (2008, $3.99) guide to locations and inhabitants 4.00

DARK TOWER: THE SORCEROR (Based on Stephen King's Dark Tower)
Marvel Comics: June, 2009 ($3.99, one-shot)
1-Robin Furth-s/Richard Isanove-a/c; the story of Marten Broadcloak 4.00

DARK TOWER: TREACHERY (Based on Stephen King's Dark Tower series)
Marvel Comics: Nov, 2008 - No. 6, Apr, 2009 ($3.99, limited series)
1-6-Peter David & Robin Furth-s/Jae Lee & Richard Isanove-a 4.00
1-Variant cover by Dell'otto 10.00

DARKWING DUCK (TV cartoon) (Also see Cartoon Tales)
Disney Comics: Nov, 1991 - No. 4, Feb, 1992 ($1.50, limited series)
1-4: Adapts hour-long premiere TV episode 3.00

DARKWING DUCK (TV cartoon)
BOOM! Studios (KABOOM!): Jun, 2010 - No. 18, Nov, 2011 ($3.99)
1-Brill-s/Silvani-a; Launchpad McQuack app.; 3 covers 5.00
2-18-Multiple covers on all. 7-Batman #1 cover swipe. 8-Detective #31 cover swipe 4.00
Annual 1 (3/11, $4.99) Three covers; Quackerjack app. 5.00
... Free Comic Book Day Edition (5/11) Flip book with Chip 'N' Dale Rescue Rangers 3.00

DARK WOLVERINE (See Wolverine 2003 series)

DARK X-MEN (See Dark Avengers and the Dark Reign mini-series)
Marvel Comics: Jan, 2010 - No. 5, May, 2010 ($3.99, limited series)
1-5-Cornell-s/Kirk-a. 1-3-Bianchi-c. 1-Nate Grey returns 4.00
...: The Confession (11/09, $3.99) Cansino-a; Paquette-c 4.00

DARK X-MEN: THE BEGINNING (See Dark Avengers and the Dark Reign mini-series)
Marvel Comics: Sept, 2009 - No. 3, Oct, 2009 ($3.99, limited series)
1-3: 1-Cornell-s/Kirk-a; Jae Lee-c on all. 2-Daken app. 3-Mystique app.; Jock-a 4.00

DARLING LOVE
Close Up/Archie Publ. (A Darling Magazine): Oct-Nov, 1949 - No. 11, 1952 (no month) (52 pgs.)(Most photo-c)

	GD	VG	FN	VF	VF/NM	NM-
1-Photo-c	26	52	78	152	249	345
2-Photo-c	15	30	45	84	127	170
3-8,10,11: 3-6-photo-c	14	28	42	76	108	140
9-Krigstein-a	14	28	42	80	115	150

DARLING ROMANCE
Close Up (MLJ Publications): Sept-Oct, 1949 - No. 7, 1951 (All photo-c)

	GD	VG	FN	VF	VF/NM	NM-
1-(52 pgs.)-Photo-c	28	56	84	165	270	375
2	15	30	45	84	127	170
3-7	14	28	42	76	108	140

DARQUE PASSAGES (See Master Darque)
Acclaim (Valiant): April, 1998 ($2.50)
1-Christina Z.-s/Manco-c/a 3.00

DART (Also see Freak Force & Savage Dragon)
Image Comics (Highbrow Entertainment): Feb, 1996 - No. 3, May, 1996 ($2.50, lim. series)
1-3 3.00

DARTH MAUL (See Star Wars: Darth Maul)

DARTH VADER (Follows after the end of Star Wars Episode IV)
Marvel Comics: Apr, 2015 - No. 25, Dec, 2016 ($4.99/$3.99)
1-($4.99) Gillen-s/Larroca-a/Granov-c; Jabba the Hut & Boba Fett app. 5.00
2,4-12-($3.99) 6-Boba Fett app. 4.00
3-Intro. Doctor Aphra and Triple Zero 5.00
13-19,21-24: 13-15-Vader Down x-over pts. 2,4,6. 24-Flashbacks to Episode III 4.00
20-($4.99) The Emperor app.; back-up Triple-Zero & Beetee story w/Norton-a 5.00
25-($5.99) Gillen-s/Larroca-a; back-up story with Fiumara-a; bonus cover gallery 6.00
Annual 1 (2/16, $4.99) Gillen-s/Yu-a/c 5.00
...: Doctor Aphra No. 1 Halloween Comic Fest 2016 (12/16, giveaway) r/#3 3.00

DARTH VADER (Follows after the end of Star Wars Episode III)
Marvel Comics: Aug, 2017 - Present ($4.99/$3.99)
1-($4.99) Soule-s/Camuncoli-a/Cheung-c; back-up by Eliopoulos-s/a 5.00
2-12-($3.99) Soule-s/Camuncoli-a. 5-Vader acquires the red light saber 4.00

DASTARDLY & MUTTLEY (See Fun-In No. 1-4, 6 and Kite Fun Book)
DC Comics: Nov, 2017 - No. 6, Apr, 2018 ($3.99, limited series)
1-6: 1-New origin for the pair; Ennis-s/Mauricet-a 4.00

DATE WITH DANGER
Standard Comics: No. 5, Dec, 1952 - No. 6, Feb, 1953

	GD	VG	FN	VF	VF/NM	NM-
5,6-Secret agent stories: 6-Atom bomb story	11	22	33	62	86	110

DATE WITH DEBBI (Also see Debbi's Dates)
National Periodical Publ.: Jan-Feb, 1969 - No. 17, Sept-Oct, 1971; No. 18, Oct-Nov, 1972

	GD	VG	FN	VF	VF/NM	NM-
1-Teenage	8	16	24	51	96	140
2-5,17-(52 pgs) James Taylor sty.	4	8	12	25	40	55
6-12,18-Last issue	4	8	12	23	37	50
13-16-(68 pgs.): 14-1 pg. story on Jack Wild. 15-Marlo Thomas/"That Girl" story	4	8	12	27	44	60

DATE WITH JUDY, A (Radio/TV, and 1948 movie)
National Periodical Publications: Oct-Nov, 1947 - No. 79, Oct-Nov, 1960 (No. 1-25: 52 pgs.)

	GD	VG	FN	VF	VF/NM	NM-
1-Teenage	36	72	108	211	343	475
2	17	34	51	100	158	215
3-10	14	28	42	81	118	155
11-20	11	22	33	64	90	115
21-40	11	22	33	60	83	105
41-45: 45-Last pre-code (2-3/55)	10	20	30	56	76	95
46-79: 79-Drucker-c/a	9	18	27	52	69	85

DATE WITH MILLIE, A (Life With Millie No. 8 on)(Teenage)
Atlas/Marvel Comics (MPC): Oct, 1956 - No. 7, Aug, 1957; Oct, 1959 - No. 7, Oct, 1960

	GD	VG	FN	VF	VF/NM	NM-
1(10/56)-(1st Series)-Dan DeCarlo-a in #1-7	53	106	159	334	567	800
2	37	74	111	222	361	500
3-7	22	44	66	132	216	300
1(10/59)-(2nd Series)	30	60	90	177	289	400

David Cassidy #2 © CC

Day of Judgment #5 © DC

Dazzler One-shot #1 © MAR

GD VG FN VF VF/NM NM-
2.0 4.0 6.0 8.0 9.0 9.2

2-7 15 30 45 88 137 185

DATE WITH PATSY, A (Also see Patsy Walker)
Atlas Comics: Sept, 1957 (One-shot)
1-Starring Patsy Walker 22 44 66 132 216 300

DAUGHTERS OF THE DRAGON (See Heroes For Hire)
Marvel Comics: 2005; Mar, 2006 - No. 6, Aug, 2006 ($2.99, limited series)
1-6-Palmiotti & Gray-s/Evans-a. 1-Rhino app. 5,6-Iron Fist app. 3.00
... Deadly Hands Special (2005, $3.99) reprints app. from Deadly Hands of Kung Fu #32,33 & Bizarre Adventures #25; Claremont-s/Rogers-a; new Rogers-c & interview 4.00
...: Samurai Bullets TPB (2006, $15.99) r/#1-6 16.00

DAVID AND GOLIATH (Movie)
Dell Publishing Co.: No. 1205, July, 1961
Four Color 1205-Photo-c 6 12 18 42 79 115

DAVID BORING (See Eightball)
Pantheon Books: 2000 ($24.95, hardcover w/dust jacket)
Hardcover - reprints David Boring stories from Eightball; Clowes-s/a 25.00

DAVID CASSIDY (TV)(See Partridge Family, Swing With Scooter #33 & Time For Love #30)
Charlton Comics: Feb, 1972 - No. 14, Sept, 1973
1-Most have photo covers 6 12 18 38 69 100
2-5 4 8 12 25 40 55
6-14 4 8 12 23 37 50

DAVID LADD'S LIFE STORY (See Movie Classics)

DAVY CROCKETT (See Dell Giants, Fightin..., Frontier Fighters, It's Game Time, Power Record Comics, Western Tales & Wild Frontier)

DAVY CROCKETT (Frontier Fighter...)
Avon Periodicals: 1951
nn-Tuska?, Reinman-a; Fawcette-c 22 44 66 132 216 300

DAVY CROCKETT (...King of the Wild Frontier No. 1,2)(TV)
Dell Publishing Co./Gold Key: 5/55 - No. 671, 12/55; No. 1, 12/63; No. 2, 11/69 (Walt Disney)
Four Color 631(#1)-Fess Parker photo-c 14 28 42 96 211 325
Four Color 639-Photo-c 11 22 33 76 163 260
Four Color 664,671(Marsh-a)-Photo-c 11 22 33 75 160 245
1(12/63-Gold Key)-Fess Parker photo-c; reprints 7 14 21 46 86 125
2(11/69)-Fess Parker photo-c; reprints 4 8 12 28 44 60

DAVY CROCKETT (...Frontier Fighter #1,2; Kid Montana #9 on)
Charlton Comics: Aug, 1955 - No. 8, Jan, 1957
1 10 20 30 58 79 100
2 7 14 21 37 46 55
3-8 6 12 18 28 34 40

DAWN
Sirius Entertainment/Image Comics: June, 1995 - No. 6, 1996 ($2.95)
1/2-w/certificate 1 2 3 5 6 8
1/2-Variant-c 2 4 6 10 14 18
1-Linsner-c/a 1 2 3 5 6 8
1-Black Light Edition 2 4 6 9 13 16
1-White Trash Edition 3 6 9 16 23 30
1-Look Sharp Edition 3 6 9 18 28 38
2-4: Linsner-c/a 4.50
2-Variant-c, 3-Limited Edition 2 4 6 13 18 22
4-6-Vibrato-c 3.50
4, 5-Limited Edition 2 4 6 8 10 12
6-Limited Edition 2 4 6 8 10 12
...Convention Sketchbook (Image Comics, 2002, $2.95) pin-ups 3.00
...2003 Convention Sketchbook (Image Comics, 3/03, $2.95) pin-ups 3.00
...2004 Convention Sketchbook (Image Comics, 4/04, $2.95) pin-ups 3.00
...2005 Convention Sketchbook (Image Comics, 5/05, $2.95) pin-ups 3.00
Genesis Edition ('99, Wizard supplement) previews Return of the Goddess 3.00
Lucifer's Halo TPB (11/97, $19.95) r/Drama, Dawn #1-6 plus 12 pages of new artwork 20.00
...: Not to Touch The Earth (9/10, $5.99) Linsner-s/c/a; pin-ups by various incl. Turner 6.00
...: Tenth Anniversary Special (9/99, $2.95) Interviews 3.00
The Portable Dawn ($9.95, 5"x4", 64 pgs.) Pocket-sized cover gallery 10.00
...: The Swordmaster's Daughter & Other Stories (2013, $3.99) Linsner-s/c/a 4.00

DAWN OF THE DEAD (George A. Romaro's...)
IDW Publishing: Apr, 2004 - No. 3, Jun, 2004 ($3.99, limited series)
1-3-Adaptation of the 2004 movie; Niles-s 4.00
TPB (9/04, $17.99) r/#1-3; intro. by George A. Romero 18.00

DAWN OF THE PLANET OF THE APES
BOOM! Studios: Nov, 2014 - No. 6, Apr, 2015 ($3.99, limited series)
1-6: 1-Takes place between the 2011 and 2014 movies; Moreci-s/McDaid-a 4.00

DAWN: THE RETURN OF THE GODDESS
Sirius Entertainment: Apr, 1999 - No. 4, July, 2000 ($2.95, limited series)
1-4-Linsner-s/a 3.00
TPB (4/02, $12.95) r/#1-4; intro. by Linsner 13.00

DAWN: THREE TIERS
Image Comics: Jun, 2003 - No. 6, Aug, 2005 ($2.95, limited series)
1-6-Linsner-s/a. 2-Preview of Vampire's Christmas 3.00

DAWN / VAMPIRELLA
Dynamite Entertainment: 2014 - No. 5, 2015 ($3.99, limited series)
1-5-Linsner-s/a/c. 3-Vampirella origin re-told 4.00

DAYDREAMERS (See Generation X)
Marvel Comics: Aug, 1997 - No. 3, Oct, 1997 ($2.50, limited series)
1-3-Franklin Richards, Howard the Duck, Man-Thing app. 3.00

DAY MEN
BOOM! Studios: Jul, 2013 - No. 8, Oct, 2015 ($3.99)
1-Stelfreeze-a/c; Gagnon & Nelson-s 5.00
2-8: 2-Covers by Stelfreeze & Pérez 4.00
...: Pen & Ink No. 1 (12/13, $9.99, 11"x17") Pen and ink art for #1&2 with commentary 10.00

DAY OF JUDGMENT
DC Comics: Nov, 1999 - No. 5, Nov, 1999 ($2.95/$2.50, limited series)
1-($2.95) Spectre possessed; Matt Smith-a 3.00
2-5: Parallax returns. 5-Hal Jordan becomes the Spectre 3.00
...Secret Files 1 (11/99, $4.95) Harris-c 5.00

DAY OF VENGEANCE (Prelude to Infinite Crisis)(Also see Birds of Prey #76 for 1st app. of Black Alice)
DC Comics: June, 2005 - No. 6, Nov, 2005 ($2.50, limited series)
1-6: 1-Jean Loring becomes Eclipso; Spectre, Ragman, Enchantress, Detective Chimp, Shazam app.; Justiniano-a. 2,3-Capt. Marvel app. 4-6-Black Alice app. 3.00
...: Infinite Crisis Special 1 (3/06, $4.99) Justiniano-a/Simonson-c 5.00
TPB (2005, $12.99) r/series & Action #826, Advs. of Superman #639, Superman #216 13.00

DAYS OF HATE
Image Comics: Jan, 2018 - Present ($3.99)
1,2-Ales Kot-s/Danijel Zezelj-a 4.00

DAYS OF THE DEFENDERS (See Defenders, The)
Marvel Comics: Mar, 2001 ($3.50, one-shot)
1-Reprints early team-ups of members, incl. Marvel Feature #1; Larsen-c 3.50

DAYS OF THE MOB (See In the Days of the Mob)

DAYTRIPPER
DC Comics (Vertigo): Feb, 2010 - No. 10, Nov, 2010 ($2.99, limited series)
1-10-Gabriel Bá & Fábio Moon-s/a 3.00
TPB (2010, $19.99) r/#1-10; sketch art pages 20.00

DAZEY'S DIARY
Dell Publishing Co.: June-Aug, 1962
01-174-208: Bill Woggon-c/a 4 8 12 27 44 60

DAZZLER, THE (Also see Marvel Graphic Novel & X-Men #130)
Marvel Comics Group: Mar, 1981 - No. 42, Mar, 1986
1-X-Men app. 2 4 6 11 16 20
2-20,23,25,26,29-32,34-37,39-41: 2-X-Men app. 10,11-Galactus app. 23-Rogue/Mystique 1 pg. app. 26-Jusko-c. 40-Secret Wars II 4.00
21,22,24,27,28,38,42: 21-Double size; photo-c. 22 (12/82)-vs. Rogue Battle-c/sty. 24-Full app. Rogue w/Powerman (Iron Fist). 27-Rogue app. 28-Full app. Rogue; Mystique app. 38-Wolverine-c/app.; X-Men app. 42-Beast-c/app. 5.00
33-Michael Jackson "Thriller" swipe-c/sty 2 4 6 8 10 12
One-shot (7/10, $3.99) Andrasofszky-a/c; Arcade app. 4.00
NOTE: *No. 1 distributed only through comic shops.* **Alcala** *a-1i, 2i.* **Chadwick** *a-38-42p; c(p)-39, 41, 42.* **Guice** *a-38i, 42i; c-38, 40.*

DC CHALLENGE (Most DC superheroes appear)
DC Comics: Nov, 1985 - No. 12, Oct, 1986 ($1.25/$2.00, maxi-series)
1-11: 1-Colan-a. 2,8-Batman-c/app. 4-Gil Kane-c/a 3.00
12-($2.00-c) Giant; low print 4.00
NOTE: *Batman app. in 1-4, 6-12. Joker app. in 7.* **Infantino** *a-3.* **Ordway** *c-12.* **Swan/Austin** *c-10.*

DC COMICS: BOMBSHELLS (Continues in Bombshelss: United)
DC Comics: Oct, 2015 - No. 33, Oct, 2017 ($3.99, printings of digital-first stories)

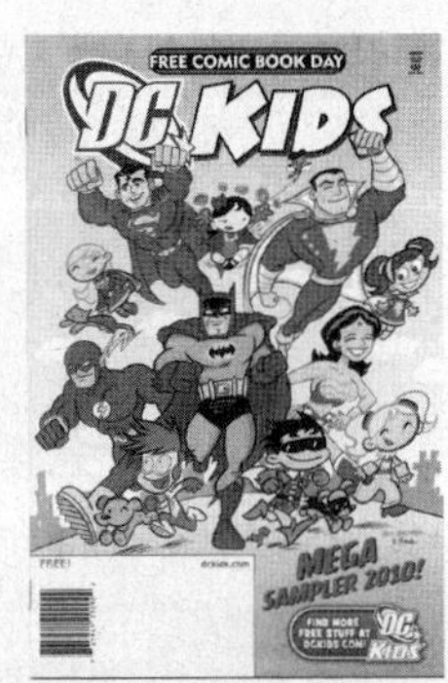

DC Comics Mega Sampler 2010 © DC

DC Comics Presents #32 © DC

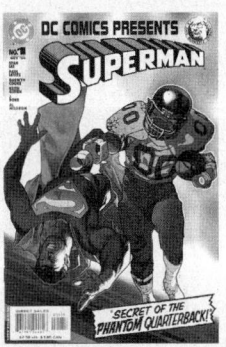

DC Comics Presents: Superman #1 © DC

	GD 2.0	VG 4.0	FN 6.0	VF 8.0	VF/NM 9.0	NM- 9.2

1-24: 1-Bennett-s/Sauvage-a/Lucia-a; set in 1940 WWII. 4,14-18-Harley Quinn-c/app. 4.00
25-($4.99) Suicide Squad app.; intro. Faora Hu-Ul; Aneke-a 5.00
26-33: 27,32,33-Harley Quinn/Poison Ivy-c. 29-Superman app. 4.00
Annual 1 (10/16, $4.99) Bennett-s/Charretier-a; origin of vampire Batgirl 5.00

DC COMICS CLASSICS LIBRARY (Hardcover collections of classic DC stories)
DC Comics: 2009 - Present ($39.99, hardcover with dustjacket)

Batman: A Death in the Family ('09)- r/Batman #426-429, 440-442, New Titans #60,61 40.00
Batman Annuals ('09)- r/Batman Annual #1-3; afterword by Richard Bruning 40.00
Batman Annuals Volume 2 ('10)- r/Batman Annual #4-7; intro. by Michael Uslan 40.00
Flash of Two Worlds ('09)- r/Flash #123,129,137,151,170&173 team-ups with G.A. Flash 40.00
Justice League of America by George Pérez ('09) r/J.L.of A. #184-186, 192-194 40.00
Justice League of America by George Pérez Vol. 2 ('10) r/J.L.of A. #195-197,200 40.00
Legion of Super-Heroes: The Life and Death of Ferro Lad ('09) - r/Adventure Comics # 346, 347,352-355,357; intro. by Paul Levitz; afterword by Jim Shooter 40.00
Roots of the Swamp Thing ('09)- r/House of Secrets #92 & Swamp Thing #1-13; Wein intro. 40.00
Superman: Kryptonite Nevermore ('09)- r/Superman #233-238,240-242; afterword by Denny O'Neil 40.00

DC COMICS ESSENTIALS
DC Comics: ($1.00, flipbooks with DC Graphic Novel catalog of recommended titles)

...: Action Comics #1 (2/14, $1.00) Reprints Action #1 (2011) with flipbook of DC GNs 3.00
...: Batman #1 (12/13, $1.00) Reprints Batman #1 (2011) with flipbook of DC GNs 3.00
...: Batman and Robin #1 (4/16, $1.00) Reprints Batman and Robin #1 (2011) with flipbook 3.00
...: Batman and Son Special Ed. ('14, $1.00) Reprints Batman #655 with flipbook 3.00
...: Batman: Death of the Family (6/16, $1.00) Reprints Batman #13 (2011) with flipbook 3.00
...: Batman: Hush Spec. Ed. ('14, $1.00) Reprints Batman #608 with flipbook of DC GNs 3.00
...: Batman: The Black Mirror Special Ed. ('14, $1.00) Reprints Detective #871 w/flipbook 3.00
...: Batman: The Dark Knight Returns #1 (5/16, $1.00) Reprints #1 with flipbook 3.00
...: Batman: The Dark Knight Returns Special Ed. ('14, $1.00) Reprints #1 with flipbook 3.00
...: Batman: Year One #1 ('14, $1.00) Reprints Batman #404 with flipbook of DC GNs 3.00
...: DC: The New Frontier #1 (3/16, $1.00) Reprints first issue with flipbook 3.00
...: Green Lantern #1 (1/14, $1.00) Reprints Green Lantern #1 (2011) with flipbook 3.00
...: JLA #1 (6/16, $1.00) Reprints JLA #1 with flipbook of DC GNs 3.00
...: Justice League #1 (1/14, $1.00) Reprints Justice League #1 (2011) with flipbook 3.00
...: Superman Unchained #1 (5/16, $1.00) Reprints Superman Unchained #1 with flipbook 3.00
...: Watchmen #1 (2/14, $1.00) Reprints Watchmen #1 (1986) with flipbook 3.00
...: Wonder Woman #1 (12/13, $1.00) Reprints Wonder Woman #1 (2011) with flipbook 3.00

DC COMICS MEGA SAMPLER
DC Comics: 2009; Jul, 2010 (6-1/4" x 9-1/2", FCBD giveaways)

1, 2010- Short stories of kid-friendly titles; Tiny Titans, Billy Batson, Super Friends app. 3.00

DC COMICS PRESENTS
DC Comics: July-Aug, 1978 - No. 97, Sept, 1986 (Superman team-ups in all)

	GD 2.0	VG 4.0	FN 6.0	VF 8.0	VF/NM 9.0	NM- 9.2
1-4th Superman/Flash race	4	8	12	28	47	65
1-(Whitman variant)	5	10	15	33	57	80
2-Part 2 of Superman/Flash race	3	6	9	15	22	28
2-(Whitman variant)	3	6	9	17	26	35
3,4,9-12,14-16,19,21,22-(Whitman variants, low print run, none have issue # on cover)	3	6	9	14	20	25
3-10: 3-Adam Strange. 4-Metal Men. 5-Aquaman. 6-Green Lantern. 7-Red Tornado. 8-Swamp Thing. 9-Wonder Woman. 10-Sgt. Rock	2	4	6	8	10	12
11-25,28-40: 12-Mister Miracle. 13-Legion of Super-Heroes. 19-Batgirl. 21-Elongated Man. 23-Dr. Fate. 24-Deadman. 30-Black Canary. 31-Robin. 34-Marvel Family. 35-Man-Bat. 36-Starman. 37-Hawkgirl. 38-The Flash						6.00
26-(10/80)-Green Lantern; intro Cyborg, Starfire, Raven (1st app. New Teen Titans in 16 pg. preview); Starlin-c/a; Sargon the Sorcerer back-up	9	18	27	58	114	170
27-1st app. Mongul	3	6	9	21	33	45
41-Superman/Joker-c/story; 1st app. New Wonder Woman in 16 pg. preview; Colan-a	1	3	4	6	8	10
42-46,48,50,52-71,73-76,79-83: 42-Sandman. 43,80-Legion of Super-Heroes. 52-Doom Patrol; 1st app. Ambush Bug. 58-Robin. 64-Kamandi. 82-Adam Strange. 83-Batman & Outsiders						4.00
47-(7/82) He-Man-c/s (1st app. in comics)	6	12	18	42	79	115
49-Black Adam & Captain Marvel app.	3	6	9	17	26	35
51-Preview insert (16 pgs.) of He-Man (2nd app.)	2	4	6	9	12	15
72,77,78,97: 72-Joker/Phantom Stranger-c/story. 77,78-Animal Man app. (77-c also). 97-Phantom Zone						6.00
84-Challengers of the Unknown; Kirby-c/s.						6.00
85-Swamp Thing; Alan Moore scripts						6.00
86,88-96: 86-88-Crisis x-over. 88-Creeper						4.00
87-Origin/1st app. Superboy of Earth Prime	3	6	9	16	23	30
Annual 1(9/82)-G.A. Superman; 1st app. Alexander Luthor	1	2	3	5	6	8
Annual 2,3: 2(7/83)-Intro/origin Superwoman. 3(9/84)-Shazam						4.00
Annual 4(10/85)-Superwoman						4.00

NOTE: ***Adkins** a-2, 54; c-2. **Buckler** a-33, 34; c-30, 33, 34. **Giffen** a-39; c-59. **Gil Kane** a-28, 35, Annual 3; c-48p, 56, 58, 60, 62, 64, 68, Annual 2, 3. **Kirby** c/a-84. **Kubert** c/a-66. **Morrow** c/a-65. **Newton** c/a-54p. **Orlando** c-53i. **Perez** a-26p, 61p; c-38, 61, 94. **Starlin** a-26-29p, 36p, 37p; c-26-29, 36, 37, 93. **Toth** a-84. **Williamson** i-79, 85, 87.*

DC COMICS PRESENTS: ...(Julie Schwartz tribute series of one-shots based on classic covers)
DC Comics: Sept, 2004 - Oct, 2004 ($2.50)

The Atom -(Based on cover of Atom #10) Gibbons-s/Oliffe-a; Waid-s/Jurgens-a; Bolland-c 3.00
Batman -(Batman #183) Johns-s/Infantino-a; Wein-s/Kuhn-a; Hughes-c 3.00
The Flash -(Flash #163) Loeb-s/McGuinness-a; O'Neil-s/Mahnke-a; Ross-c 3.00
Green Lantern -(Green Lantern #31) Azzarello-s/Breyfogle-a; Pasko-s/McDaniel-a; Bolland-c 3.00
Hawkman -(Hawkman #6) Bates-s/Byrne-a; Busiek-s/Simonson-a; Garcia-Lopez-c 3.00
Justice League of America -(J.L. of A. #53) Ellison & David-s/Giella-a; Wolfman-s/Nguyen-a; Garcia-Lopez-c 3.00
Mystery in Space -(M.I.S. #82) Maggin-s/Williams-a; Morrison-s/Ordway-a; Ross-c 3.00
Superman -(Superman #264) Stan Lee-s/Cooke-a; Levitz-s/Giffen-a; Hughes-c 3.00

DC COMICS PRESENTS: ...
DC Comics: Dec, 2010 - Present ($7.99/$9.99, squarebound, one-shot reprints)

The Atom 1 (3/11) r/Legends of the DC Universe #28,29,40,41; Gil Kane-a 8.00
Batman 1 (12/10) r/Batman #582-585,600 8.00
Batman 2 (1/11) r/Batman #591-594 8.00
Batman 3 (2/11) r/Batman #595-598 8.00
Batman Adventures 1 (9/14) reprints; Burchett, Parobeck, Templeton, Timm-a 8.00
Batman: Arkham 1 (6/11) r/Batman Chronicles #6, Batman; Arkham Asylum - Tales of Madness #1, Batman Villains Secret Files #1 & Justice Leagues: J.L. of Arkham #1 8.00
Batman - Bad 1 (1/12) r/Batman: Legends of the D.K. #146-148 8.00
Batman Beyond 1 (2/11) r/Batman Beyond #13,14,21,22 8.00
Batman: Blaze of Glory 1 (2/12) r/Batman: Legends of the D.K. #197-199,212 8.00
Batman - Blink 1 (12/11) r/Batman: Legends of the D.K. #156-158 8.00
Batman/Catwoman 1 (12/10) r/Batman and Catwoman: Trail of the Gun 8.00
Batman - Conspiracy 1 (4/11) r/Batman: Legends of the D.K. #86-88; Detective #821 8.00
Batman - Dark Knight, Dark City 1 (7/11) r/Batman #452-454; Detective #633 8.00
Batman - Don't Blink 1 (1/12) r/Batman: Legends of the D.K. #164-167 8.00
Batman: Gotham Noir 1 (9/11) r/Batman: Gotham Noir #1 & Batman #604 8.00
Batman - Irresistible 1 (5/11) r/Batman: Legends of the D.K. #169-171; Hourman #22 8.00
Batman - The Demon Laughs 1 (12/11) r/Batman: Legends of the D.K. #142-145; Aparo-a 8.00
Batman: The Secret City 1 (2/12) r/Batman: Legends of the D.K. #180,181,190,191 8.00
Batman: Urban Legends 1 (2/12) r/Batman: Legends of the D.K. #168,177-179 8.00
Brightest Day 1 (12/10) r/Strange Advs. #205, Hawkman #27,34,36, Solo #8, DC Hol. '09 8.00
Brightest Day 2 (1/11) r/Firestorm #11-13 & Martian Manhuner #11,24 8.00
Brightest Day 3 (2/11) r/Legends of the DC Univ. #25-27 & Teen Titans #27,28 8.00
Captain Atom 1 (2/12) r/back-up stories from Action Comics #879-889 8.00
Catwoman - Guardian of Gotham 1 (12/11) r/Catwoman: Guardian of Gotham #1,2 8.00
Chase 1 (1/11) r/Chase #1,6-8 8.00
Darkseid War 1 (2/16, $7.99) r/New Gods #1,7, Mister Miracle #1 & Forever People #1 8.00
Demon Driven Out, The 1 (7/14, $9.99) r/The Demon: Driven Out #1-6 10.00
Elseworlds 80-Page Giant 1 (1/12) r/Elseworlds 80-Page Giant (pulled from distribution) 8.00
Flash 1 (7/11) r/Showcase #4,14 and Flash #125,130,139 8.00
Flash/Green Lantern: Faster Friends (1/11) r/G.L./Flash: Faster Friends & Flash/G.L. : FF 8.00
Green Lantern 1 (12/10) r/Green Lantern #137-140 (2001) 8.00
Green Lantern - Fear Itself 1 (4/11) r/Green Lantern: Fear Itself GN 8.00
Green Lantern - Willworld 1 (7/11) r/Green Lantern: Willworld GN 8.00
Harley Quinn 1 (4/14) r/Batman: Harley Quinn #1, Joker's Asylum II: HQ #1 and others 8.00
Impulse 1 (8/11) r/Impulse #50-53 8.00
Jack Kirby Omnibus Sampler 1 (12/11) r/Kirby art stories from 1957,1958 8.00
JLA 1 (2/11) r/JLA #90-93 8.00
JLA - Age of Wonder 1 (12/11) r/JLA: Age of Wonder 8.00
JLA: Black Baptism 1 (8/11) r/JLA: Black Baptism #1-4 8.00
JLA Heaven's Ladder 1 (10/11) comic-sized reprint; and r/Green Lantern #1,000,000 8.00
Legion of Super-Heroes 1 (6/11) r/Legion of Super-Heroes #122,123 & Legionnaires 79,80 8.00
Legion of Super-Heroes 2 (2/12) r/Adv. #247 and recent Legion short stories 8.00
Lobo 1 (3/11) r/Lobo #63,64 & DC First: Superman/Lobo #1 8.00
Metal Men 1 (4/11) r/Doom Patrol ('09) #1-7 and Silver Age: The Brave and the Bold #1 8.00
Night Force 1 (4/11) r/Night Force #1-4; Gene Colan-a 8.00
Ninja Boy 1 (6/11) r/Ninja Boy #1-4 8.00
Robin War 100-Page Super Spectacular 1 (2/16) Ryan Sook-c 8.00
Shazam! 1,2 (9/11,10/11) 1-r/Power of Shazam #38-41. 2-r/ #42-46 8.00
Son of Superman 1 (7/11) r/Son of Superman GN 8.00
Superboy's Legion 1 (12/11) r/Superboy's Legion #1,2 (Elseworlds) 8.00
Superman 1 (12/10) r/Superman: The Man of Steel #121 & Superman #179,180,185 8.00
Superman 2 (1/11) r/Action #798, Superman: The Man of Steel #133, Superman #189 & Advs. of Superman #611 8.00
Superman 3 (2/11) r/Superman #177,178,181,182 8.00
Superman 4 (9/11) r/Action #768,771-773 8.00
Superman Adventures 1 (8/12) r/Superman Adventures #16,19,22,23 8.00

DC First: Flash / Superman #1 © DC

DC House of Horror #1 © DC

DC Retroactive: Wonder Woman - The '70s #1 © DC

GD 2.0 VG 4.0 FN 6.0 VF 8.0 VF/NM 9.0 NM- 9.2

Superman/Doomsday 1 (5/11) r/Doomsday Annual #1 & Superman #175 8.00
Superman - Infestation 1 (8/11) r/Action #778, Advs. of Superman #591, Superman #169 and Superman: The Man of Steel #113 8.00
Superman: Lois and Clark 100-Page S.S. 1 (1/16) r/Superman: The Wedding Album 8.00
Superman - Secret Identity 1 (12/11) r/Superman: Secret Identity #1,2 8.00
Superman - Secret Identity 2 (1/12) r/Superman: Secret Identity #3,4 8.00
Superman - Sole Survivor 1 (3/11) r/Legends of the DC Universe #1-3,39 8.00
Superman - The Kents 1,2 (1/12, 2/12) 1-r/The Kents #1-4. 2-The Kents #5-8 8.00
Teen Titans 1 (10/11) Teen Titans Lost Annual #1 and Solo #7; Allred-a 8.00
Titans Hunt 100-Page Super Spectacular 1 (1/16) r/Teen Titans early apps.; Sook-c 8.00
The Life Story of the Flash 1 (1/12) r/The Life Story of the Flash GN 8.00
T.H.U.N.D.E.R. Agents 1 (2/11) r/T.H.U.N.D.E.R. Agents #1,2,7 (1966) 8.00
Wonder Woman 1 (4/11) r/Wonder Woman #139-142 (1998) 8.00
Wonder Woman Adventures 1 (9/12) r/Advs. in the DC Universe #1,3,11,19 8.00
Young Justice 1 (12/10) r/JLA World Without Grownups #1,2 8.00
Young Justice 2 (1/11) r/Y.J: The Secret, Y.J. Secret Files #1, Y.J. In No Man's Land 8.00
Young Justice 3 (2/11) r/Young Justice #7 & Y.J Secret Origins 80-Page Giant #1 8.00

DC COMICS - THE NEW 52 FCBD SPECIAL EDITION
DC Comics: Jun, 2012 (giveaway one-shot)

1-Origin of The Trinity of Sin (Pandora, The Question, Phantom Stranger); Justice League app.; Jim Lee, Reis, Ha, Rocafort-a; previews Earth 2, G.I. Combat, Ravagers 3.00

DC COMICS THE NEW 52 PRESENTS: ...
DC Comics: Mar, 2012 - Present ($7.99, squarebound, one-shot reprints)

The Dark 1 (3/12) r/Animal Man #1, Swamp Thing #1, I, Vampire #1, and J.L. Dark #1 8.00

DC COUNTDOWN (To Infinite Crisis)
DC Comics: May, 2005 ($1.00, 80 pages, one-shot)

1-Death of Blue Beetle; prelude to OMAC Project, Day of Vengeance, Rann/Thanagar War and Villains United mini-series; s/a by various; Jim Lee/Alex Ross-c 4.00

DC FIRST: ...(series of one-shots)
DC Comics: July, 2002 ($3.50)

Batgirl/Joker 1-Sienkiewicz & Terry Moore-a; Nowlan-c 3.50
Green Lantern/Green Lantern 1-Alan Scott & Hal Jordan vs. Krona 3.50
Flash/Superman 1-Superman races Jay Garrick; Abra Kadabra app. 3.50
Superman/Lobo 1-Giffen-s; Nowlan-c 3.50

DC GOES APE
DC Comics: 2008 ($19.99, trade paperback)

Vol. 1 - Reprints app. of Grodd, Beppo, Titano and other monkey tales; Art Adams-c 20.00

DC GRAPHIC NOVEL (Also see DC Science Fiction...)
DC Comics: Nov, 1983 - No. 7, 1986 ($5.95, 68 pgs.)

1-3,5,7: 1-Star Raiders; García-López-c/a; prequel to Atari Force #1. 2-Warlords; not from regular Warlord series. 3-The Medusa Chain; Ernie Colon story/a. 5-Me and Joe Priest; Chaykin-c. 7-Space Clusters; Nino-c/a 2 4 6 9 12 15
4-The Hunger Dogs by Kirby; Darkseid kills Himon from Mister Miracle & destroys New Genesis 5 10 15 31 53 75
6-Metalzoic; Sienkiewicz-c ($6.95) 2 4 6 9 12 15

DC HOLIDAY SPECIAL
DC Comics: Feb, 2010 ($5.99/$9.99, one-shots)

... '09 (2/10, $5.99) 1-Christmas short stories by various incl. Tucci, Chaykin; Nguyen-c 6.00
... 2017 (2/18, $9.99) 1-Story/art by various incl. Rucka, King, Francavilla; Andy Kubert-c 10.00

DC HOUSE OF HORROR
DC Comics: Dec, 2017 ($9.99, square-bound one-shot)

1-Horror short stories by various incl. Giffen, Porter, Baker, Raney, Chaykin; Kaluta-c 6.00

DC INFINITE HALLOWEEN SPECIAL
DC Comics: Dec, 2007 ($5.99, one-shot)

1-Halloween short stories by various incl. Dini, Waid, Hairsine, Kelley Jones; Gene Ha-c 6.00

DC/MARVEL: ALL ACCESS (Also see DC Versus Marvel & Marvel Versus DC)
DC Comics: 1996 - No. 4, 1997 ($2.95, limited series)

1-4: 1-Superman & Spider-Man app. 2-Robin & Jubilee app. 3-Dr. Strange & Batman-c/app., X-Men, JLA app. 4-X-Men vs. JLA-c/app. rebirth of Amalgam 3.00

DC/MARVEL: CROSSOVER CLASSICS
DC Comics: 1998; 2003 ($14.95, TPB)

Vol. II-Reprints Batman/Punisher: Lake of Fire, Punisher/Batman: Deadly Knights, Silver Surfer/Superman, Batman & Capt. America 15.00
Vol. 4 (2003, $14.95) Reprints Green Lantern/Silver Surfer: Unholy Alliances, Darkseid/ Galactus: The Hunger, Batman & Spider-Man, and Superman/Fantastic Four 15.00

DC NATION FCBD SUPER SAMPLER
DC Comics: (Giveaway)

.../ Superman Adventures Flip Book (6/12) stories from Superman Family Adventures, Young Justice, Green Lantern: The Animated Series 3.00
... (7/13) Stories from Beware the Batman and Teen Titans Go! 3.00

DC 100 PAGE SUPER SPECTACULAR
(Title is 100 Page... No. 14 on)(Square bound) (Reprints, 50¢)
National Periodical Publications: No. 4, Summer, 1971 - No. 13, 6/72; No. 14, 2/73 - No. 22, 11/73 (No #1-3)

4-Weird Mystery Tales; Johnny Peril & Phantom Stranger; cover & splashes by Wrightson; origin Jungle Boy of Jupiter 24 48 72 168 372 575
5-Love Stories; Wood inks (7 pgs.)(scarcer) 46 92 138 368 834 1300
6- "World's Greatest Super-Heroes"; JLA, JSA, Spectre, Johnny Quick, Vigilante & Hawkman; contains unpublished Wildcat story; N. Adams wrap-around-c; r/JLA #21,22 18 36 54 124 275 425
6-Replica Edition (2004, $6.95) complete reprint w/wraparound-c 7.00
7-(Also listed as Superman #245) Air Wave, Kid Eternity, Hawkman-r; Atom-r/Atom #3 9 18 27 60 120 180
8-(Also listed as Batman #238) Batman, Legion, Aquaman-r; G.A. Atom, Sargon (r/Sensation #57), Plastic Man (r/Police #14) stories; Doom Patrol origin-r; Neal Adams wraparound-c 12 24 36 84 185 285
9-(Also listed as Our Army at War #242) Kubert-c 9 18 27 58 114 170
10-(Also listed as Adventure Comics #416) Golden Age-reprints; r/1st app. Black Canary from Flash #86; no Zatanna 10 20 30 68 144 220
11-(Also listed as Flash #214) origin Metal Men-r/Showcase #37; never before published G.A. Flash story. 8 16 24 54 102 150
12,14: 12-(Also listed as Superboy #185) Legion-c/story; Teen Titans, Kid Eternity (r/Hit #46), Star Spangled Kid-r(S.S. #55). 14-Batman-r/Detective #31,32,156; Atom-r/Showcase #34 7 14 21 46 86 125
13-(Also listed as Superman #252) Ray(r/Smash #17), Black Condor, (r/Crack #18), Hawkman(r/Flash #24); Starman-r/Adv. #67; Dr. Fate & Spectre-r/More Fun #57; Neal Adams-c 10 20 30 66 138 210
15,16,18,19,21,22: 15-r/2nd Boy Commandos/Det. #64. 16-Sgt. Rock; r/Capt. Storm #1, 1st Johnny Cloud/All-American Men of War #82. 18-Superman. 21-Superboy; r/Brave & the Bold #54. 22-r/All-Flash #13 6 12 18 37 66 95
17,20: 17-JSA-r/All Star #37 (10-11/47, 38 pgs.), Sandman-r/Adv. #65 (8/41), JLA #23 (11/63) & JLA #43 (3/66). 20-Batman-r/Det. #66,68, Spectre; origin Two-Face 6 12 18 38 69 100
... : Love Stories Replica Edition (2000, $6.95) reprints #5 7.00

NOTE: ***Anderson*** *r-11, 14, 18i, 22.* ***B. Baily*** *r-18, 20.* ***Burnley*** *r-18, 20.* ***Crandall*** *r-14p, 20.* ***Drucker*** *r-4.* ***Grandenetti*** *a-22(2)r.* ***Heath*** *a-22r.* ***Infantino*** *r-17, 20, 22.* ***G. Kane*** *r-18.* ***Kirby*** *r-15.* ***Kubert*** *r-6, 7, 16, 17; c-16, 19.* ***Manning*** *a-19r.* ***Meskin*** *r-4, 22.* ***Mooney*** *r-15, 21.* ***Toth*** *r-17, 20.*

DC ONE MILLION (Also see crossover #1,000,000 issues and JLA One Million TPB)
DC Comics: Nov, 1998 - No. 4, Nov, 1998 ($2.95/$1.99, weekly lim. series)

1-($2.95) JLA travels to the 853rd century; Morrison-s 4.00
2-4-($1.99) 3.00
... Eighty-Page Giant (8/99, $4.95) 5.00
TPB ('99, $14.95) r/#1-4 and several x-over stories 15.00

DC REBIRTH HOLIDAY SPECIAL
DC Comics: Feb, 2017 ($9.99, one-shot)

1-Short stories by various; framing pages of Harley Quinn by Dini-s/Charretier-a 10.00

DC RETROACTIVE (New stories done in old style plus reprint from decade)
DC Comics: Sept, 2011 - Oct, 2011 ($4.99, series of one-shots)

...: Batman - The '70s (9/11, $4.99) Len Wein-s/Tom Mandrake-a; r/Batman #307 5.00
...: Batman - The '80s (10/11, $4.99) Mike Barr-s/Jerry Bingham-a; The Reaper app. 5.00
...: Batman - The '90s (10/11, $4.99) Grant-s/Breyfogle-a; Scarface & Ventriloquist app. 5.00
...: Flash - The '70s (9/11, $4.99) Bates-s/Gallego-a; r/DC Comics Presents #2 5.00
...: Flash - The '80s (10/11, $4.99) Messner-Loebs-s/LaRocque-a; r/Flash v2 #18 5.00
...: Flash - The '90s (10/11, $4.99) Augustyn-s/Bowden-a; r/Flash v2 #142 5.00
...: Green Lantern - The '70s (9/11, $4.99) O'Neil-s/Grell-a; r/Green Lantern #76 5.00
...: Green Lantern - The '80s (10/11, $4.99) Wein-s/Staton-a; r/Green Lantern #172 5.00
...: Green Lantern - The '90s (10/11, $4.99) Marz-s/Banks-a; r/Green Lantern v3 #78 5.00
...: JLA - The '70s (9/11, $4.99) Bates-s; Adam Strange app.; r/J.L. of A. #123 5.00
...: JLA - The '80s (10/11, $4.99) Conway-s/Randall-a; Felix Faust app.; r/J.L.of A. #239 5.00
...: JLA - The '90s (10/11, $4.99) Giffen & DeMatteis-s/Maguire-a; r/J.L.A. #6 5.00
...: Superman - The '70s (9/11, $4.99) Pasko-s/Barreto-a; r/Action Comics #484 5.00
...: Superman - The '80s (10/11, $4.99) Wolfman-s/Cariello-a; r/Superman #352 5.00
...: Superman - The '90s (10/11, $4.99) L. Simonson-s/Bogdanove-a; Guardian app. 5.00
...: Wonder Woman - The '70s (9/11, $4.99) O'Neil-s/J. Bone-a; r/Wonder Woman #201 5.00
...: Wonder Woman - The '80s (10/11, $4.99) Thomas-s/Buckler-a; r/W.W. #288 5.00
...: Wonder Woman - The '90s (10/11, $4.99) Messner-Loebs-s/Moder-a; r/W.W. v2 #66 5.00

DC SCIENCE FICTION GRAPHIC NOVEL
DC Comics: 1985 - No. 7, 1987 ($5.95)

SF1-SF7: SF1-Hell on Earth by Robert Bloch; Giffen-p. SF2-Nightwings by Robert Silverberg;

DC Special #29 © DC

DC Special Series #1 © DC

DC Super-Stars #10 © DC

	GD 2.0	VG 4.0	FN 6.0	VF 8.0	VF/NM 9.0	NM- 9.2

G. Colan-p. SF3-Frost & Fire by Bradbury. SF4-Merchants of Venus. SF5-Demon With A Glass Hand by Ellison; M. Rogers-a. SF6-The Magic Goes Away by Niven. SF7-Sandkings by George R.R. Martin 2 4 6 8 11 14

DC SILVER AGE CLASSICS
DC Comics: 1992 ($1.00, all reprints)

...Action Comics #252-r/1st Supergirl. Adventure Comics #247-r/1st Legion of Super-Heroes. The Brave and the Bold #28-r/1st JLA. Detective Comics #225-r/1st Martian Manhunter. Detective Comics #327-r/1st new look Batman. Green Lantern #76-r/1st Green Lantern/Green Arrow. House of Secrets #92-r/1st Swamp Thing. Showcase #4-r/1st S.A. Flash. Showcase #22-r/1st S.A. Green Lantern 4.00
...Sugar and Spike #99; includes 2 unpublished stories 5.00

DC SPECIAL (Also see Super DC Giant)
National Per. Publ.: 10-12/68 - No. 15, 11-12/71; No. 16, Spr/75 - No. 29, 8-9/77

1-All Infantino issue; Flash, Batman, Adam Strange-r; begin 68 pg. issues, end #21 8 16 24 54 102 150
2-Teen humor; Binky, Buzzy, Harvey app. 9 18 27 62 126 190
3-All-Girl issue; unpubl. GA Wonder Woman story 9 18 27 57 111 165
4,11: 4-Horror (1st Abel, brief). 11-Monsters 5 10 15 33 57 80
5-10,12-15: 5-All Kubert issue; Viking Prince, Sgt. Rock-r. 6-Western. 7,9,13-Strangest Sports. 12-Viking Prince; Kubert-c/a (r/B&B almost entirely). 15-G.A. Plastic Man origin-r/Police #1; origin Woozy by Cole; 14,15-(52 pgs.) 4 8 12 27 44 60
16-27: 16-Super Heroes Battle Super Gorillas. 17-Early S.A. Green Lantern-r. 22-Origin Robin Hood. 26-Enemy Ace. 27-Captain Comet story 3 6 9 16 23 30
28-Earth Shattering Disaster Stories; Legion of Super-Heroes story 3 6 9 16 24 32
29-New "The Untold Origin of the Justice Society"; Staton-a/Neal Adams-c; Hitler app. in story and on cover 5 10 15 31 53 75

NOTE: ***N. Adams*** *c-3, 4, 6, 11, 29.* ***Grell*** *a-20; c-17, 20.* ***Heath*** *a-12r.* ***G. Kane*** *a-6p, 13r, 17r, 19-21r.* ***Kirby*** *a-4, 11.* ***Kubert*** *a-6r, 12r, 22.* ***Meskin*** *a-10.* ***Moreira*** *a-10.* ***Staton*** *a-29p.* ***Toth*** *a-13, 20r. #1-15: 25¢; 16-27: 50¢; 28, 29: 60¢. #1-13, 16-21: 68 pgs.; 14, 15: 52 pgs.; 25-27: oversized.*

DC SPECIAL BLUE RIBBON DIGEST
DC Comics: Mar-Apr, 1980 - No. 24, Aug, 1982

1,2,4,5: 1-Legion reprints. 2-Flash. 4-Green Lantern. 5-Secret Origins; new Zatara and Zatanna 2 4 6 8 11 14
3-Justice Society reprints; new Dr. Fate story 2 4 6 10 14 18
6,8-10: 6-Ghosts. 8-Legion. 9-Secret Origins. 10-Warlord-"The Deimos Saga"-Grell-s/c/a 2 4 6 8 11 14
7-Sgt. Rock's Prize Battle Tales 2 4 6 13 18 22
11,16: 11-Justice League. 16-Green Lantern/Green Arrow-r; all Adams-a 2 4 6 11 16 20
12-Haunted Tank; reprints 1st app. 2 4 6 13 18 22
13-15,17-19: 13-Strange Sports Stories. 14-UFO Invaders; Adam Strange app. 15-Secret Origins of Super Villains; JLA app. 17-Ghosts. 18-Sgt. Rock; Kubert front & back-c. 19-Doom Patrol; new Perez-c 2 4 6 9 13 16
20-Dark Mansion of Forbidden Love (scarce) 4 8 12 28 47 65
21-Our Army at War 3 6 9 15 22 28
22-24: 22-Secret Origins. 23-Green Arrow, w/new 7 pg. story (Spiegle-a). 24-House of Mystery; new Kubert wraparound-c 2 4 6 13 18 22

NOTE: ***N. Adams*** *a-16(6)r, 17r, 23r; c-16.* ***Aparo*** *a-6r, 24r; c-23.* ***Grell*** *a-8, 10; c-10.* ***Heath*** *a-14.* ***Infantino*** *a-15r.* ***Kaluta*** *a-17r.* ***Gil Kane*** *a-15r, 22r.* ***Kirby*** *a-5, 9, 23r.* ***Kubert*** *a-3, 18r, 21r; c-7, 12, 14, 17, 18, 21, 24.* ***Morrow*** *a-24r.* ***Orlando*** *a-17r, 22r; c-1, 20.* ***Toth*** *a-21r, 24r.* ***Wood*** *a-3, 17r, 24r.* ***Wrightson*** *a-16r, 17r, 24r.*

DC SPECIAL: CYBORG (From Teen Titans) (See Teen Titans 2003 series for TPB collection)
DC Comics: Jul, 2008 - No. 6, Dec, 2008 ($2.99, limited series)

1-6: 1-Sable-s/Lashley-a; origin re-told. 3-6-Magno-a 3.00

DC SPECIAL: RAVEN (From Teen Titans) (See Teen Titans 2003 series for TPB collection)
DC Comics: May, 2008 - No. 5, Sept, 2008 ($2.99, limited series)

1-5-Marv Wolfman-s/Damion Scott-a 3.00

DC SPECIAL SERIES
National Periodical Publications/DC Comics: 9/77 - No. 16, Fall, 1978; No. 17, 8/79 - No. 27, Fall, 1981 (No. 18, 19, 23, 24 - digest size, 100 pgs.; No. 25-27 - Treasury sized)

1-"5-Star Super-Hero Spectacular 1977"; Batman, Atom, Flash, Green Lantern, Aquaman, in solo stories, Kobra app.; 1st app. Patty Spivot in Flash story; N. Adams-c 5 10 15 33 57 80
2(#1)-"The Original Swamp Thing Saga 1977"-r/Swamp Thing #1&2 by Wrightson; new Wrightson wraparound-c. 2 4 6 11 16 20
3,4,6-8: 3-Sgt Rock. 4-Unexpected. 6-Secret Society of Super Villains, Jones-a. 7-Ghosts Special. 8-Brave and Bold w/ new Batman, Deadman & Sgt Rock team-up 2 4 6 13 18 22
5-"Superman Spectacular 1977"-(84 pg, $1.00)-Superman vs. Brainiac & Lex Luthor, new 63 pg. story 3 6 9 15 22 28
9-Wonder Woman; Ditko-a (11 pgs.) 3 6 9 15 22 28
10-"Secret Origins of Superheroes Special 1978"-(52 pgs.)-Dr. Fate, Lightray & Black Canary on-c/new origin stories; Staton, Newton-a 3 6 9 14 20 26
11-"Flash Spectacular 1978"-(84 pgs.) Flash, Kid Flash, GA Flash & Johnny Quick vs. Grodd; Wood-i on Kid Flash chapter 2 4 6 13 18 22
12-"Secrets of Haunted House Special Spring 1978" 2 4 6 13 18 22
13-"Sgt. Rock Special Spring 1978", 50 pg new story 3 6 9 14 19 24
14,17,20-"Original Swamp Thing Saga", Wrightson-a: 14-Sum '78, r/#3,4. 17-Sum '79 r/#5-7. 20-Jan/Feb '80, r/#8-10 2 4 6 9 13 16
15-"Batman Spectacular Summer 1978", Ra's Al Ghul-app.; Golden-a. Rogers-a/front & back-c 4 8 12 25 40 55
16-"Jonah Hex Spectacular Fall 1978"; death of Jonah Hex, Heath-a; Bat Lash and Scalphunter stories 6 12 18 37 66 95
18,19-Digest size: 18-"Sgt. Rock's Prize Battle Tales Fall 1979". 19-"Secret Origins of Super-Heroes Fall 1979"; origins Wonder Woman (new-a),r/Robin, Batman-Superman team, Aquaman, Hawkman and others 2 4 6 13 18 22
21-"Super-Star Holiday Special Spring 1980", Frank Miller-a in "Batman--Wanted Dead or Alive" (1st Batman story); Jonah Hex, Sgt. Rock, Superboy & LSH and House of Mystery/Witching Hour-c/stories 5 10 15 30 50 70
22-"G.I. Combat Sept. 1980", Kubert-c. Haunted Tank-s 3 6 9 14 19 24
23,24-Digest size: 23-World's Finest-r. 24-Flash 2 4 6 11 16 20
V5#25-($2.95)-"Superman II, the Adventure Continues Summer 1981"; photos from movie & photo-c (see All-New Coll. Ed. C-62 for first Superman movie) 3 6 9 14 19 24
26-($2.50)-"Superman and His Incredible Fortress of Solitude Summer 1981" 3 6 9 14 19 24
27-($2.50)-"Batman vs. The Incredible Hulk Fall 1981" 4 8 12 23 37 50

NOTE: ***Aparo*** *c-8.* ***Heath*** *a-12i, 16.* ***Infantino*** *a-19r.* ***Kirby*** *a-23, 19r.* ***Kubert*** *c-13, 19r.* ***Nasser/Netzer*** *a-1, 10i, 15.* ***Newton*** *a-10.* ***Nino*** *a-4, 7.* ***Starlin*** *c-12.* ***Staton*** *a-1.* ***Tuska*** *a-19r. #25 & 26. were advertised as All-New Collectors' Edition C-63, C-64. #26 was originally planned as All-New Collectors' Ed. C-30?; has C-630 & A.N.C.E. on cover.*

DC SPECIAL: THE RETURN OF DONNA TROY
DC Comics: Aug, 2005 - No. 4, Late Oct, 2005 ($2.99, limited series)

1-4-Jimenez-s/Garcia-Lopez-a(p)/Pérez-i 3.00

DC SUPERHERO GIRLS
DC Comics: May, 2016; May, 2017 (All-ages FCBD giveaway)

1 FCBD 2017 Special Edition (5/17); teenage girl heroes; Fontana-s/Labat-a 3.00
1 Special Edition (5/16); teenage girl heroes at Super Hero High; Fontana-s/Labat-a 3.00
... 2017 Halloween Comic Fest Special Edition (11/17) Labat & Garbowska-a 3.00
... Halloween Fest Special Edition (12/16); teenage girl heroes at Super Hero High 3.00

DC SUPER-STARS
National Periodical Publ./DC Comics: March, 1976 - No. 18, Winter, 1978 (No. 3-18: 52 pgs.)

1-(68 pgs.)-Re-intro Teen Titans (predates T. T. #44 (11/76); tryout iss.) plus r/Teen Titans; W.W. as girl was original Wonder Girl 3 6 9 19 30 40
2-6,9,12,16: 2,4,6,8-Adam Strange; 2-(68 pgs.)-r/1st Adam Strange/Hawkman team-up from Mystery in Space #90 plus Atomic Knights origin-r. 3-Legion issue. 4-r/Tales/Unexpected #45. 2 4 6 8 11 14
7-Aquaman spotlight; Aqualad, Aquagirl, Ocean Master & Black Manta app.; Aparo-c 3 6 9 21 33 45
8-r/1st Space Ranger from Showcase #15, Adam Strange-r/Mystery in Space #89 & Star Rovers-r/M.I.S. #80 2 4 6 9 13 16
10-Strange Sports Stories; Batman/Joker-c/story 2 4 6 10 14 18
11-Magic; Zatanna-c/reprint from Adv. #413-415 with Morrow-a; Morrow-c; Flash vs. Abra Kadabra (r/Flash #128) 4 8 12 23 34 50
13-Sergio Aragonés Special 3 6 9 15 22 28
14,15,18: 15-Sgt. Rock 2 4 6 9 13 16
17-Secret Origins of Super-Heroes (origin of The Huntress); origin Green Arrow by Grell; Legion app.; Earth II Batman & Catwoman marry (1st revealed; also see B&B #197 & Superman Family #211) 8 16 24 54 102 150

NOTE: ***M. Anderson*** *r-2, 4, 6.* ***Aparo*** *c-7, 14, 18.* ***Austin*** *a-11i.* ***Buckler*** *a-14p; c-10.* ***Grell*** *a-17.* ***G. Kane*** *a-1r, 10r.* ***Kubert*** *c-15.* ***Layton*** *c/a-16i, 17i.* ***Mooney*** *a-4r, 6r.* ***Morrow*** *c/a-11r.* ***Nasser*** *a-11.* ***Newton*** *c/a-16p.* ***Staton*** *a-17; c-17. No. 10, 12-18 contain all new material; the rest are reprints. #1 contains new and reprint material.*

DC: THE NEW FRONTIER (Also see Justice League: The New Frontier Special)
DC Comics: Mar, 2004 - No. 6, Nov, 2004 ($6.95, limited series)

1-6-DCU in the 1940s-60s; Darwyn Cooke-c/s/a in all. 1-Hal Jordan and The Losers app. 2-Origin Martian Manhunter; Barry Allen app. 3-Challengers of the Unknown 7.00
...Volume One (2004, $19.95, TPB) r/#1-3; cover gallery & intro. by Paul Levitz 20.00
...Volume Two (2005, $19.99, TPB) r/#4-6; cover gallery & afterword by Cooke 20.00

DC TOP COW CROSSOVERS
DC Comics/Top Cow Productions: 2007 ($14.99, TPB)

SC-r/The Darkness/Batman; JLA/Witchblade; The Darkness/Superman; JLA/Cyberforce 15.00

DC 2000
DC Comics: 2000 - No. 2, 2000 ($6.95, limited series)

DCU: Legacies #1 © DC

DC Universe: Rebirth #1 © DC

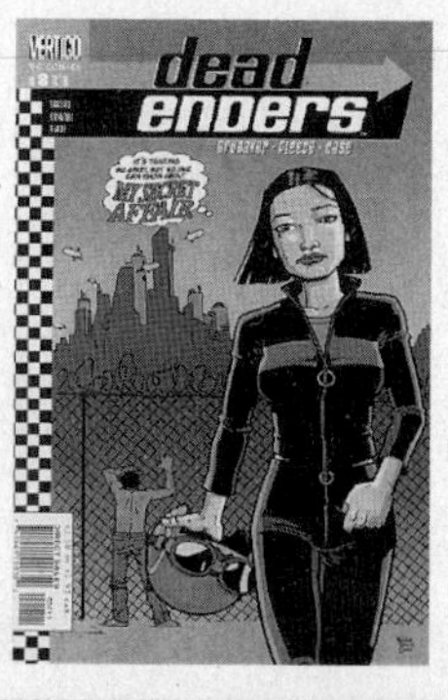
Dead Enders #8 © Brubaker & Pleece

GD 2.0 | VG 4.0 | FN 6.0 | VF 8.0 | VF/NM 9.0 | NM- 9.2

1,2-JLA visit 1941 JSA; Semeiks-a 7.00

DCU BRAVE NEW WORLD (See Infinite Crisis and tie-ins)
DC Comics: Aug, 2006 ($1.00, 80 pgs., one-shot)

1-Previews 2006 series Martian Manhunter, OMAC, The Creeper, The All-New Atom, The Trials of Shazam, and Uncle Sam and the Freedom Fighters; the Monitor app. 4.00

DCU (Halloween and Christmas one-shot anthologies)
DC Comics

... Halloween Special '09 (12/09, $5.99) Ha-c; art from Bagley, Tucci, K. Jones, Nguyen 6.00
... Halloween Special 2010 (12/10, $4.99) Ha-c; art from Tucci, Garbett; I...Vampire app. 5.00
... Holiday Special (2/09, $5.99) Christmas by various incl. Dini, Maguire, Reis; Quitely-c 6.00
... Holiday Special 2010 (2/11, $4.99) Jonah Hex, Spectre, Legion of S.H., Anthro app. 5.00
... Infinite Halloween Special (12/08, $5.99) Ralph & Sue Dibny app.; Gene Ha-c 6.00
... Infinite Holiday Special (2/07, $4.99) by various; Batwoman app.; Porter-c 5.00

DCU HEROES SECRET FILES
DC Comics: Feb, 1999 ($4.95, one-shot)

1-Origin-s and pin-ups; new Star Spangled Kid app. 5.00

DCU: LEGACIES
DC Comics: Jul, 2010 - No. 10, Apr, 2011 ($3.99, limited series)

1-10: 1,2-Andy Kubert-c; JSA app.; two covers on each. 3-JLA app.; Garcia-Lopez-a. 4-Sgt. Rock back-up; Joe Kubert-a. 5-Pérez-a. 8-Back-up Quitely-a 4.00

DC UNIVERSE CHRISTMAS, A
DC Comics: 2000 ($19.95)

TPB-Reprints DC Christmas stories by various 20.00

DC UNIVERSE: DECISIONS
DC Comics: Early Nov, 2008 - No. 4, Late Dec, 2008 ($2.99, limited series)

1-4-Assassination plot in the Presidential election; Winick & Willingham-s/Porter-a 3.00

DC UNIVERSE HOLIDAY BASH
DC Comics: 1997- 1999 ($3.95)

I,II-(X-mas '96,'97) Christmas stories by various 5.00
III (1999, for Christmas '98, $4.95) 5.00

DC UNIVERSE ILLUSTRATED BY NEAL ADAMS (Also see Batman Illustrated by Neal Adams HC Vol. 1-3)
DC Comics: 2008 ($39.99, hardcover with dustjacket)

Vol. 1 - Reprints Adams' non-Batman/non-Green Lantern work from 1967-1972; incl. Teen Titans, DC war, Enemy Ace, Superman and PSAs; promo art; Levitz foreword 40.00

DC UNIVERSE: LAST WILL AND TESTAMENT
DC Comics: Oct, 2008 ($3.99, one-shot)

1-Geo-Force vs. Deathstroke; DC heroes prepare for Final Crisis; Brad Meltzer-s; Adam Kubert & Joe Kubert-a; two covers 4.00

DC UNIVERSE ONLINE LEGENDS (Based on the online game)
DC Comics: Early Apr. 2011 - Late May, 2012 ($2.99)

1-26: 1-Wolfman & Bedard-s/Porter-a; DC heroes & Luthor vs. Brainiac. 1-Wraparound-c 3.00

DC UNIVERSE: ORIGINS
DC Comics: 2009 ($14.99, TPB)

nn-Reprints 2-page origins of DC characters from back-ups in 52, Countdown and Justice League: Cry For Justice #1-3; s/a by various; Alex Ross-c 15.00

DC UNIVERSE PRESENTS (DC New 52)
DC Comics: Nov, 2011 - No. 19, Jun, 2013 ($2.99)

1-5-Deadman. 1-Deadman origin re-told; Jenkins-s/Chang-a/Sook-c 3.00
6-8-Challengers of the Unknown; DiDio-s/Ordway-a/Sook-c 3.00
9-19: 9-11-Savage; Chang-a. 12-Kid Flash. 13-16-Black Lightning & Blue Devil 3.00
#0 (11/12, $5.99) O.M.A.C., Mr. Terrific, Hawk & Dove, Blackhawks, Deadman origins 6.00

DC UNIVERSE: REBIRTH
DC Comics: Jul, 2016 ($2.99, one-shot)

1-($2.99) Wally West returns; Johns-s; art by Frank, Van Sciver, Reis & Jimenez; wraparound-c by Gary Frank 3.00
1-2nd printing ($5.99, squarebound) same wraparound-c by Gary Frank 6.00
1-3rd printing ($5.99, squarebound) variant Kid Flash cover by Gary Frank 6.00

DC UNIVERSE SPECIAL
DC Comics: July, 2008 - Aug, 2008 ($4.99, collection of reprints related to Final Crisis)

...: Justice League of America (7/08) r/J.L. of A. #111,166-168 & Detective #274; Sook-c 5.00
...: Reign in Hell (8/08) r/Blaze/Satanus War x-over; Sook-c 5.00
...: Superman (7/08) r/Mongul app. in Superman #32, Showcase '95 #7,8, Flash #102 5.00

DC UNIVERSE: THE STORIES OF ALAN MOORE (Also see Across the Universe:...)
DC Comics: 2006 ($19.99)

GD 2.0 | VG 4.0 | FN 6.0 | VF 8.0 | VF/NM 9.0 | NM- 9.2

TPB-Reprints Batman: The Killing Joke, "Whatever Happened to the Man of Tomorrow", "For The Man Who Has Everything, and other classic Moore DC stories; Bolland-c 20.00

DC UNIVERSE: TRINITY
DC Comics: Aug, 1993 - No. 2, Sept, 1993 ($2.95, 52 pgs, limited series)

1,2-Foil-c; Green Lantern, Darkstars, Legion app. 4.00

DC UNIVERSE VS. MASTERS OF THE UNIVERSE
DC Comics: Oct, 2013 - No. 6, May, 2014 ($2.99, limited series)

1-6: 1-3-Giffen-s/Soy-a/Benes-c; Constantine app. 4-6-Mhan-a 3.00

DCU VILLAINS SECRET FILES
DC Comics: Apr, 1999 ($4.95, one-shot)

1-Origin-s and profile pages 5.00

DC VERSUS MARVEL (See Marvel Versus DC) (Also see Amazon, Assassins, Bruce Wayne: Agent of S.H.I. E. L.D., Bullets & Bracelets, Doctor Strangefate, JLX, Legend of the Dark Claw, Magneto & The Magnetic Men, Speed Demon, Spider-Boy, Super Soldier, X-Patrol)
DC Comics: No. 1, 1996, No. 4, 1996 ($3.95, limited series)

1,4: 1-Marz script, Jurgens-a(p); 1st app. of Access. 5.00
.../Marvel Versus DC ($12.95, trade paperback) r/1-4 13.00

DC/WILDSTORM DREAMWAR
DC Comics: Jun, 2008 - No. 6, Nov, 2008 ($2.99, limited series)

1-6-Giffen-s; Silver Age JLA, Teen Titans, JSA, Legion app. on WildStorm Earth 3.00
1-Variant-c of Superman & Midnighter by Garbett 6.00
TPB (2009, $19.99) r/series 20.00

DC: WORLD WAR III (See 52/WWIII)

D-DAY (Also see Special War Series)
Charlton Comics (no No. 3): Sum/63; No. 2, Fall/64; No. 4, 9/66; No. 5, 10/67; No. 6, 11/68

	GD 2.0	VG 4.0	FN 6.0	VF 8.0	VF/NM 9.0	NM- 9.2
1,2: 1(1963)-Montes/Bache-c. 2(Fall '64)-Wood-a(4)	3	6	9	21	33	45
4-6('66-'68)-Montes/Bache-a #5	3	6	9	14	20	25

DEAD AIR
Slave Labor Graphics: July, 1989 ($5.95, graphic novel)

	GD 2.0	VG 4.0	FN 6.0	VF 8.0	VF/NM 9.0	NM- 9.2
nn-Mike Allred's 1st published work	1	2	3	5	6	8

DEAD BOY DETECTIVES
DC Comics (Vertigo): Feb, 2014 - No. 12, Feb, 2015 ($2.99, limited series)

1-12-Litt-s/Buckingham-a. 1-Covers by Buckingham & Chiang 3.00

DEAD CORPSE
DC Comics (Helix): Sept, 1998 - No. 4, Dec, 1998 ($2.50, limited series)

1-4-Pugh-a/Hinz-s 3.00

DEAD DROP
Valiant Entertainment: May, 2015 - No. 4, Aug, 2015 ($3.99, limited series)

1-4-Ales Kot-s/Adam Gorham-a; X-O Manowar app. 2-Archer app. 4.00

DEAD END CRIME STORIES
Kirby Publishing Co.: April, 1949 (52 pgs.)

	GD 2.0	VG 4.0	FN 6.0	VF 8.0	VF/NM 9.0	NM- 9.2
nn-(Scarce)-Powell, Roussos-a; painted-c	61	122	183	390	670	950

DEAD ENDERS
DC Comics (Vertigo): Mar, 2000 - No. 16, June, 2001 ($2.50)

1-16-Brubaker-s/Pleece & Case-a 3.00
Stealing the Sun (2000, $9.95, TPB) r/#1-4, Vertigo Winter's Edge #3 10.00

DEAD-EYE WESTERN COMICS
Hillman Periodicals: Nov-Dec, 1948 - V3#1, Apr-May, 1953

	GD 2.0	VG 4.0	FN 6.0	VF 8.0	VF/NM 9.0	NM- 9.2
V1#1-(52 pgs.)-Krigstein, Roussos-a	22	44	66	132	216	300
V1#2,3-(52 pgs.)	14	28	42	80	115	150
V1#4-12-(52 pgs.)	10	20	30	58	79	100
V2#1,2,5-8,10-12: 1-7-(52 pgs.)	9	18	27	47	61	75
3,4-Krigstein-a	9	18	27	52	69	85
9-One pg. Frazetta ad	9	18	27	47	61	75
V3#1	9	18	27	47	61	75

NOTE: *Briefer a-V1#8. Kinstleresque stories by **McCann**-12, V2#1, 2, V3#1. **McWilliams** a-V1#5. **Ed Moore** a-V1#4.*

DEADFACE: DOING THE ISLANDS WITH BACCHUS
Dark Horse Comics: July, 1991 - No. 3, Sept, 1991 ($2.95, B&W, lim. series)

1-3: By Eddie Campbell 3.00

DEADFACE: EARTH, WATER, AIR, AND FIRE
Dark Horse Comics: July, 1992 - No. 4, Oct, 1992 ($2.50, B&W, limited series; British-r)

1-4: By Eddie Campbell 3.00

DEAD INSIDE

Dead Irons #4 © Classic Monsters

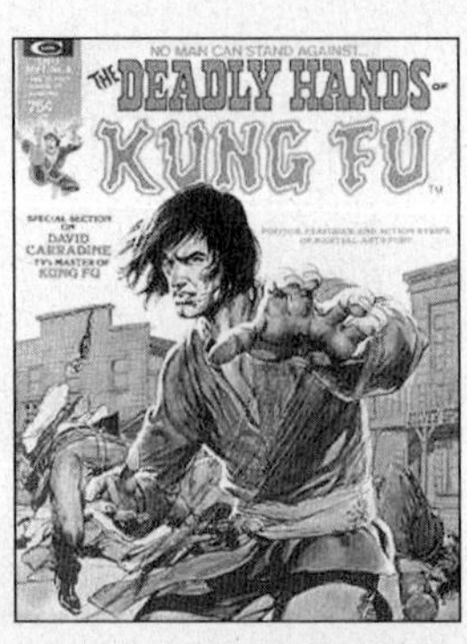

Deadly Hands of Kung Fu #4 © MAR

Deadman (2018 series) #1 © DC

GD 2.0 | VG 4.0 | FN 6.0 | VF 8.0 | VF/NM 9.0 | NM- 9.2

GD 2.0 | VG 4.0 | FN 6.0 | VF 8.0 | VF/NM 9.0 | NM- 9.2

Dark Horse Comics: Dec, 2016 - No. 5, May, 2017 ($3.99)

1-5-Arcudi-s/Fejzula-a/Dave Johnson-c 4.00

DEAD IN THE WEST
Dark Horse Comics: Oct, 1993 - No. 2, Mar, 1994 ($3.95, B&W, 52 pgs.)

1,2-Timothy Truman-c 4.00

DEAD IRONS
Dynamite Entertainment: 2009 - No. 4, 2009 ($3.99)

1-4-Kuhoric-s/Alexander-a/Jae Lee-c 4.00

DEADLANDER (Becomes Dead Rider for #2)
Dark Horse Comics: Oct, 2007 - No. 4, ($2.99, limited series)

1-2-Kevin Ferrara-s/a 3.00

DEADLANDS (Old West role playing game)
Image Comics: Jul, 2011; Aug, 2011; Jan, 2012 ($2.99, one-shots)

...: Black Water (1/12) Mariotte-s/Brook Turner-a 3.00
...: Death Was Silent (8/11) Marz-s/Sears-a/c 3.00
...: Massacre at Red Wing (7/11) Palmiotti & Gray-s/Moder-a/c 3.00

DEADLIEST HEROES OF KUNG FU (Magazine)
Marvel Comics Group: Summer, 1975 (B&W)(76 pgs.)

1-Bruce Lee vs. Carradine painted-c; TV Kung Fu, 4pgs. photos/article; Enter the Dragon, 24 pgs. photos/article w/ Bruce Lee; Bruce Lee photo pinup 5 10 15 33 57 80

DEADLINE
Marvel Comics: June, 2002 - No. 4, Sept, 2002 ($2.99, limited series)

1-4: 1-Intro. Kat Farrell; Bill Rosemann-s/Guy Davis-a; Horn painted-c 3.00
TPB (2002. $9.99) r/#1-4 10.00

DEADLY DUO, THE
Image Comics (Highbrow Entertainment): Nov, 1994 - No. 3, Jan, 1995 ($2.50, lim. series)

1-3: 1-1st app. of Kill Cat 3.00

DEADLY DUO, THE
Image Comics (Highbrow Entertainment): June, 1995 - No. 4, Oct, 1995 ($2.50, lim. series)

1-4: 1-Spawn app. 2-Savage Dragon app. 3-Gen 13 app. 3.00

DEADLY FOES OF SPIDER-MAN (See Lethal Foes of...)
Marvel Comics: May, 1991 - No. 4, Aug, 1991 ($1.00, limited series)

1-4: 1-Punisher, Kingpin, Rhino app. 3.00

DEADLY HANDS OF KUNG FU, THE (See Master of Kung Fu)
Marvel Comics Group: April, 1974 - No. 33, Feb, 1977 (75¢) (B&W, magazine)

1(V1#4 listed in error)-Origin Sons of the Tiger; Shang-Chi, Master of Kung Fu begins (ties w/Master of Kung Fu #17 as 3rd app. Shang-Chi); Bruce Lee painted-c by Neal Adams; 2pg. memorial photo pinup w/8 pgs. photos/articles; TV Kung Fu, 9 pgs. photos/articles; 15 pgs. Starlin-a 6 12 18 37 66 95
2-Adams painted-c; 1st time origin of Shang-Chi, 34 pgs. by Starlin. TV Kung Fu, 6 pgs. photos & article w/2 pg. pinup. Bruce Lee, 11 pgs. ph/a 4 8 12 28 47 65
3,4,7,10: 3-Adams painted-c; Gulacy-a. Enter the Dragon, photos/articles, 8 pgs. 4-TV Kung Fu painted-c by Neal Adams; TV Kung Fu 7 pg. article/art; Fu Manchu; Enter the Dragon, 10 pg. photos/article w/Bruce Lee. 7-Bruce Lee painted-c & 9 pgs. photos/articles-Return of Dragon plus 1 pg. photo pinup. 10-(3/75)-Iron Fist painted-c & 34 pg. sty-Early app. 3 6 9 21 33 45
5,6: 5-1st app. Manchurian, 6 pgs. Gulacy-a. TV Kung Fu, 4 pg. article; reprints books w/Barry Smith-a. Capt. America-sty, 10 pgs. Kirby-a(r). 6-Bruce Lee photos/article, 6 pgs.; 15 pgs. early Perez-a 3 6 9 20 31 42
8,9,11: 9-Iron Fist, 2 pg. Preview pinup; Nebres-a. 11-Billy Jack painted-c by Adams; 17 pgs. photos/article 3 6 9 18 28 38
12,13: 12-James Bond painted-c by Adams; 14 pg. photos/article. 13-16 pgs. early Perez-a; Piers Anthony, 7 pgs. photos/article 3 6 9 17 26 35
14-Classic Bruce Lee painted-c by Adams. Lee pinup by Chaykin. Lee 16 pg. photos/article w/2 pgs. Green Hornet TV 6 12 18 38 69 100
15,19: 15-Sum, '75 Giant Annual #1. 20pgs. Starlin-a. Bruce Lee photo pinup & 3 pg. photos/article re book; Man-Thing app. Iron Fist-c/sty; Gulacy-a 18pgs. 19-Iron Fist painted-c & series begins; 1st White Tiger 3 6 9 18 28 38
16,18,20: 16-1st app. Corpse Rider, a Samurai w/Sanho Kim-a. 20-Chuck Norris painted-c & 16 pgs. interview w/photos/article; Bruce Lee vs. C. Norris pinup by Ken Barr. Origin The White Tiger, Perez-a 3 6 9 16 24 32
17-Bruce Lee painted-c by Adams; interview w/R. Clouse, director Enter Dragon 7 pgs. w/B. Lee app. 1st Giffen-a (1pg. 11/75) 4 8 12 28 47 65
21-Bruce Lee 1pg. photos/article 3 6 9 16 24 32
22-1st brief app. Jack of Hearts. 1st Giffen sty-a (along w/Amazing Adv. #35, 3/76) 3 6 9 19 30 40
23-1st full app. Jack of Hearts 4 8 12 23 37 50
24-26,29: 24-Iron Fist-c & centerfold pinup. early Zeck-a; Shang Chi pinup; 6 pgs. Piers Anthony text sty w/Pérez/Austin-a; Jack of Hearts app. early Giffen-a. 25-1st app. Shimuru, "Samurai", 20 pgs. Mantlo-sty/Broderick-a; "Swordquest"-c & begins 17 pg. sty by Sanho Kim; 11 pg. photos/article; partly Bruce Lee. 26-Bruce Lee painted-c & pinup; 16 pgs. interviews w/Kwon & Clouse; talk about Bruce Lee re-filming of Lee legend. 29-Ironfist vs. Shang Chi battle-c/sty; Jack of Hearts app. 3 6 9 18 28 38
27 3 6 9 15 22 28
28-All Bruce Lee Special Issue; (1st time in comics). Bruce Lee painted-c by Ken Barr & pinup. 36 pgs. comics chronicaling Bruce Lee's life; 15 pgs. B. Lee photos/article (Rare in high grade) 7 14 21 46 86 125
30-32: 30-Swordquest-c/sty & conclusion; Jack of Hearts app. 31-Jack of Hearts app; Staton-a. 32-1st Daughters of the Dragon-c/sty, 21 pgs. M. Rogers-a/Claremont-sty; Iron Fist pinup 3 6 9 16 23 30
33-Shang Chi-c/sty; Classic Daughters of the Dragon, 21 pgs. M. Rogers-a/Claremont-story with nudity; Bob Wall interview, photos/article, 14 pgs. 3 6 9 20 31 42
...Special Album Edition 1(Summer, '74)-Iron Fist-c/story (early app., 3rd?); 10 pgs. Adams-i; Shang Chi/Fu Manchu, 10 pgs.; Sons of Tiger, 11 pgs.; TV Kung Fu, 6 pgs. photos/article 4 8 12 23 37 50

NOTE: ***Bruce Lee:*** *1-7, 14, 15, 17, 25, 26, 28.* ***Kung Fu (TV):*** *1, 2, 4.* ***Jack of Hearts****: 22, 23, 29-33.* ***Shang Chi Master of Kung Fu****: 1-9, 11-18, 29, 31, 33.* ***Sons of Tiger:*** *1, 3, 4, 6-14, 16-19.* ***Swordquest:*** *25-27, 29-33.* ***White Tiger****: 19-24, 26, 27, 29-33.* ***N. Adams*** *a-1i(part), 27i; c-1, 2-4, 11, 12, 14, 17.* ***Giffen*** *a-22p, 24p.* ***G. Kane*** *a-23p.* ***Kirby*** *a-5r.* ***Nasser*** *a-27p, 28.* ***Perez*** *a(p)-6-14, 16, 17, 19, 21.* ***Rogers*** *a-26, 32, 33.* ***Starlin*** *a-1, 2r, 15r.* ***Staton*** *a-28p, 31, 32.*

DEADLY HANDS OF KUNG FU
Marvel Comics: Jul, 2014 - No. 4, Oct, 2014 ($3.99, limited series)

1-4-Benson-s/Huat-a/Johnson-c. 2-4-Misty Knight & Colleen Wing app. 4.00

DEADMAN (See The Brave and the Bold & Phantom Stranger #39)
DC Comics: May, 1985 - No. 7, Nov, 1985 ($1.75, Baxter paper)

1-7: 1-Deadman-r by Infantino, N. Adams in all. 5-Batman-c/story-r/Strange Adventures. 7-Batman-r 4.00
... Book One TPB (2011, $19.99) r/apps. in Strange Adventures #205-213 20.00

DEADMAN
DC Comics: Mar, 1986 - No. 4, June, 1986 (75¢, limited series)

1-4: Lopez-c/a. 4-Byrne-c(p) 4.00

DEADMAN
DC Comics: Feb, 2002 - No. 9, Oct, 2002 ($2.50)

1-9: 1-4-Vance-s/Beroy-a. 3,4-Mignola-c. 5,6-Garcia-Lopez-a 3.00

DEADMAN
DC Comics (Vertigo): Oct, 2006 - No. 13, Oct, 2007 ($2.99)

1-13: 1-Bruce Jones-s/John Watkiss-a/c; intro Brandon Cayce 3.00
...: Deadman Walking TPB (2007, $9.99) r/#1-5 10.00

DEADMAN
DC Comics: Jan, 2018 - No. 6 ($3.99, limited series)

1-4-Neal Adams-s/a; Hook and Commissioner Gordon app. 4.00

DEADMAN: DARK MANSION OF FORBIDDEN LOVE
DC Comics: Dec, 2016 - No. 3, Apr, 2017 ($5.99, limited series, squarebound)

1-3-Sarah Vaughn-s/Lan Medina-a/Stephanie Hans-c 6.00

DEADMAN: DEAD AGAIN (Leads into 2002 series)
DC Comics: Oct, 2001 - No. 5, Oct, 2001 ($2.50, weekly limited series)

1-5: Deadman at the deaths of the Flash, Robin, Superman, Hal Jordan 3.00

DEADMAN: EXORCISM
DC Comics: 1992 - No. 2, 1992 ($4.95, limited series, 52 pgs.)

1,2: Kelley Jones-c/a in both 5.00

DEADMAN: LOVE AFTER DEATH
DC Comics: 1989 - No. 2, 1990 ($3.95, 52 pgs., limited series, mature)

Book One, Two: Kelley Jones-c/a in both. 1-Contains nudity 5.00

DEAD MAN'S RUN
Aspen MLT: No. 0, Dec, 2011 - No. 6, Jul, 2013 ($2.50/$3.50)

0-($2.50) Greg Pak-s/Tony Parker-a; 3 covers; bonus design sketch art 3.00
1-6: 1-(2/12, $3.50) Greg Pak-s/Tony Parker-a; 2 covers 3.50

DEAD OF NIGHT
Marvel Comics Group: Dec, 1973 - No. 11, Aug, 1975

1-Horror reprints 5 10 15 30 50 70
2-10: 10-Kirby-a. 6-Jack the Ripper-c/s 3 6 9 17 26 35

Deadpool #54 © MAR

Deadpool (2008 series) #37 © MAR

Deadpool (2016 series) #1 © MAR

GD 2.0 VG 4.0 FN 6.0 VF 8.0 VF/NM 9.0 NM- 9.2

11-Intro Scarecrow; Kane/Wrightson-c 4 8 12 28 47 65
NOTE: *Ditko* r-7, 10. *Everett* c-2. *Sinnott* r-1.

DEAD OF NIGHT FEATURING DEVIL-SLAYER
Marvel Comics (MAX): Nov, 2008 - No. 4, Feb, 2009 ($3.99, limited series)
1-4-Keene-s/Samnee-a/Andrews-c 4.00

DEAD OF NIGHT FEATURING MAN-THING
Marvel Comics (MAX): Apr, 2008 - No. 4, July, 2008 ($3.99, limited series)
1-4: 1-Man-Thing origin re-told; Kano-a. 2-4-Jennifer Kale app. 4.00

DEAD OF NIGHT FEATURING WEREWOLF BY NIGHT
Marvel Comics (MAX): Mar, 2009 - No. 4, Jun, 2009 ($3.99, limited series)
1-4: 1-Werewolf By Night origin re-told; Swierczynski-s/Suayan-a 4.00

DEAD OR ALIVE - A CYBERPUNK WESTERN
Image Comics (Shok Studio): Apr, 1998 - No. 4, July, 1998 ($2.50, limited series)
1-4 3.00

DEADPOOL (See New Mutants #98 for 1st app.)
Marvel Comics: Aug, 1994 - No. 4, Nov, 1994 ($2.50, limited series)
1-Mark Waid's 1st Marvel work; Ian Churchill-c/a 2 4 6 13 18 22
2-4 1 2 3 5 6 8

DEADPOOL (... : Agent of Weapon X on cover #57-60) (title becomes Agent X)
Marvel Comics: Jan, 1997 - No. 69, Sept, 2002 ($2.95/$1.95/$1.99)
1-($2.95)-Wraparound-c; Kelly-s/McGuinness-a 6 12 18 37 66 95
2-Begin-$1.95-c. 2 4 6 9 12 15
3,5-10,12,13,15-22,24: 12-Variant-c. 22-Cable app. 6.00
4-Hulk-c/app. 2 4 6 13 18 22
11-($3.99)-Deadpool replaces Spider-Man from Amazing Spider-Man #47; Kraven, Gwen Stacy app. 3 6 9 17 26 35
14-1st Ajax; begin McDaniel-a 3 6 9 14 20 25
23,25-($2.99); 23-Dead Reckoning pt. 1; wraparound-c 1 2 3 4 5 7
26-40: 27-Wolverine-c/app. 37-Thor app. 5.00
41,43-49,51-53,56-60: 41-Begin $2.25-c. 44-Black Panther-c/app. 46-49-Chadwick-a 51-Cover swipe of Detective #38. 57-60-BWS-c 4.00
42-G.I. Joe #21 cover swipe; silent issue 2 4 6 11 16 20
50-1st Kid Deadpool 2 4 6 11 16 20
54,55-Punisher-c/app. 54-Dillon-c. 55-Bradstreet-c 3 6 9 14 20 25
61-64,66-68: 61-64-Funeral For a Freak on cover. 66-69-Udon Studios-a. 67-Dazzler-c/app. 1 3 4 6 8 10
65-Girl in bunny suit-c; Udon Studios-a 3 6 9 19 30 40
69-Udon Studios-a 2 4 6 9 12 15
#(-1) Flashback (7/97) Lopresti-a; Wade Wilson's early days 2 4 6 9 12 15
.../Death '98 Annual ($2.99) Kelly-s 3 6 9 16 23 30
... Team-Up (12/98, $2.99) Widdle Wade-c/app. 2 4 6 8 10 12
Baby's First Deadpool Book (12/98, $2.99) 3 6 9 16 23 30
Encyclopædia Deadpoolica (12/98, $2.99) Synopses 3 6 9 14 20 25
.../GLI - Summer Fun Spectacular #1 (9/07, $3.99) short stories; Pelletier-c 1 3 4 6 8 10
... Classic Vol. 1 TPB (2008, $29.99) r/#1, New Mutants #98, Deadpool: The Circle Chase #1-4 and Deadpool (1994 series) #1-4 30.00
Mission Improbable TPB (9/98, $14.95) r/#1-5 20.00
Wizard #0 ('98, bagged with Wizard #87) 6.00

DEADPOOL
Marvel Comics: Nov, 2008 - No. 63, Dec, 2012 ($3.99/$2.99)
1-($3.99) Medina-a; Secret Invasion x-over; Crain-c 3 6 9 16 23 30
1-Variant cover by Liefeld 4 8 12 27 44 60
2 1 3 4 6 8 10
3-10: 4-10-Pearson-c. 8,9-Thunderbolts x-over. 10-Dark Reign 6.00
11-24,26-33, 33.1, 34-44,46-49-($2.99): 11-20-Pearson-c. 16-18-X-Men app. 19-21-Spider-Man & Hit-Monkey app. 26-Ghost Rider app. 27-29-Secret Avengers app. 30,31-Curse of the Mutants. 37-39-Hulk app. 4.00
25-($3.99) 3-D cover, fake 3-D glasses on back-c; back-up story w/Bond-a 5.00
45-1st full app. of Evil Deadpool 2 4 6 9 12 15
49.1, 51-63 ($2.99) 49-McCrea-a. 51-Garza-a. 61-Hit-Monkey app. 4.00
50-($3.99) Uncanny X-Force & Kingpin app.; Barberi-a 1 2 3 5 6 8
900-(12/09, $4.99) Stories by various incl. Liefeld, Baker; wraparound-c by Johnson 6.00
1000-(10/10, $4.99) Stories by various; gallery of variant covers; Johnson-c 6.00
Annual 1 (7/11, $3.99) "Identity Wars" crossover; Spider-Man & Hulk app. 5.00
... & Cable #26 (4/11, $3.99) Swierczynski-s/Fernandez-a 4.00
... Family 1 (6/11, $3.99) short stories by various; Pearson-c 4.00
...: Games of Death 1 (5/09, $3.99) Benson-s/Crystal-a/Land-c 4.00
... MCG (7/10, $1.00) r/#1 with "Marvel's Greatest Comics" logo on cover 3.00

DEADPOOL
Marvel Comics: Jan, 2013 - No. 45, Jun, 2015 ($2.99)
1-Posehn & Duggan-s/Tony Moore-a/Darrow-c; Deadpool vs. Zombie ex-Presidents 2 4 6 8 11 14
2-5 6.00
6-26: 7-Iron Man app.; spoof in 1980s style; Koblish-a/Maguire-c. 10-Spider-Man app. 13-Spoof in 1970s style; Heroes For Hire app. 15-19-Wolverine & Capt. America app. 4.00
27-($9.99) Wedding of Deadpool & Shiklah; wraparound-c with 236 characters 15.00
28-33,35-44-($3.99): 30-32-Dazzler app. 36-39-AXIS tie-in. 40-Gracking issue 4.00
34-($4.99) Original Sin tie-in; flashback in 1990s style; Sabretooth & Alpha Flight app. 1 2 3 5 6 8
45-(#250 on cover, 5/15, $9.99) Death of Deadpool; back-up short stories by various 10.00
Annual 1 (1/14, $4.99) Madcap and Avengers app.; Acker & Blacker-s/Shaner-a 5.00
Annual 2 (7/14, $4.99) Spider-Man and The Chameleon app.; Camagni-a/Nakayama-c 5.00
Bi-Annual 1 (11/14, $4.99) Scheer & Giovannetti-s/Espin-a; Brute Force app. 5.00
...: The Gauntlet (3/14, giveaway) printing of Marvel digital comics content; Cho-c 3.00

DEADPOOL (Continues in Despicable Deadpool #287)
Marvel Comics: Jan, 2016 - No. 36, Nov, 2017 ($4.99/$3.99)
1-($4.99) Duggan-s/Hawthorne-a; Deadpool starts a Heroes For Hire 5.00
2-6,8-12-($3.99) 3,4-Steve Rogers app. 6-Intro. Deadpool 2099; Koblish-a. 8-11-Sabretooth app. 12-Deadpool 2099 app. 4.00
7-($9.99) 25th Anniversary issue; back-up short stories about the Mercs For Money 10.00
13-($9.99) Crossover with Daredevil & Power Man and Iron Fist 10.00
14-20,22-24,26-29: 14-17-Civil War II tie-ins. 14-Ulysses app. 15-Black Panther app. 4.00
21-($9.99) Duggan-s/Lolli-a; Shakespeare-style story by Doescher-s/Oliveira-a 10.00
25-($5.99) Duggan-s/Koblish-a; Deadpool 2099 story 6.00
30-($9.99) Duggan-s/Hawthorne-a; Deadpool in space; Agent Adsit & Rocket app. 10.00
31-36: 31-35-Secret Empire tie-ins 4.00
#3.1-(2/16, $3.99) All-Spanish issue about the Mexican Deadpool Masacre; Koblish-a 4.00
Annual 1 (11/16, $4.99) Spoof of Spider-Man and His Amazing Friends cartoon; Koblish-a 5.00
...: Last Days of Magic 1 (7/16, $4.99) Koblish-a/Ramos-c; Doctor Strange app. 5.00
...: Masacre 1 (7/16, $3.99) Reprints #3.1 in English 4.00

DEADPOOL & CABLE: SPLIT SECOND
Marvel Comics: Feb, 2016 - No. 3, Apr, 2016 ($3.99, limited series)
1-3-Nicieza-s/Reilly Brown-a 4.00

DEADPOOL & THE MERCS FOR MONEY
Marvel Comics: Apr, 2016 - No. 5, Aug, 2016 ($3.99)
1-5: 1-Bunn-s/Espin-a; bonus reprint of Spidey #1 4.00

DEADPOOL & THE MERCS FOR MONEY
Marvel Comics: Sept, 2016 - No. 10, Jun, 2017 ($3.99)
1-10: 1-Bunn-s/Coello-a; Negasonic Teenage Warhead app.10-Dracula app. 4.00

DEADPOOL: BACK IN BLACK (Deadpool with the Venom symbiote right before ASM #300)
Marvel Comics: Dec, 2016 - No. 5, Feb, 2017 ($3.99, limited series)
1-5: 2-Power Pack app. 5-Spider-Man in black costume app.; Eddie Brock app. 4.00

DEADPOOL: BAD BLOOD
Marvel Comics: 2017 ($24.99, HC, original graphic novel)
1-Rob Liefeld-s/a/c; Cable, Domino and X-Force app. 25.00

DEADPOOL: DRACULA'S GAUNTLET (Printing of Marvel digital comic mini-series)
Marvel Comics: Sept, 2014 - No. 7, Oct, 2014 ($3.99, weekly limited series)
1-7-Duggan & Posehn-s; Deadpool meets Shiklah. 2,3,6-Blade app. 4-Frightful Four app. 4.00

DEADPOOL CORPS (Continues from Prelude to Deadpool Corps series)
Marvel Comics: Jun, 2010 - No. 12, May, 2011 ($3.99/$2.99)
1-($3.99) Liefeld-a/c; Gischler-s; 2 covers by Liefeld 1 2 3 5 6 8
2-12-($2.99) 2-5,7,9-Liefeld-a. 6-Mychaels-a 3.00
...: Rank and Foul 1 (5/10, $3.99) Handbook-style profile pages of allies and enemies 4.00

DEADPOOL KILLS DEADPOOL
Marvel Comics: Sept, 2013 - No. 4, Dec, 2013 ($2.99, limited series)
1-Bunn-s/Espin-a; Deadpool Corps app. 1 2 3 5 6 8
2-4 3.00

DEADPOOL KILLS THE MARVEL UNIVERSE
Marvel Comics: Oct, 2012 - No. 4, Oct, 2012 ($2.99, weekly limited series)
1-Bunn-s/Talajic-a/Andrews-c 3 6 9 17 26 35
2-4 2 4 6 8 10 12

DEADPOOL KILLS THE MARVEL UNIVERSE AGAIN

Deadpool Pulp #3 © MAR

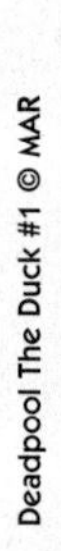
Deadpool The Duck #1 © MAR

Deadshot #2 © DC

	GD 2.0	VG 4.0	FN 6.0	VF 8.0	VF/NM 9.0	NM- 9.2

Marvel Comics: Sept, 2017 - No. 5, Nov, 2017 ($3.99, limited series)
1-5-Bunn-s/Talajic-a/Johnson-c. 3-Gwenpool app. 1,5-Red Skull app. 4.00

DEADPOOL KILLUSTRATED
Marvel Comics: Mar, 2013 - No. 4, Jun, 2013 ($2.99, limited series)
1-Bunn-s/Lolli-a/Del Mundo-c; stories/covers styled like Classics Illustrated
1 2 3 5 6 8
2-4 4.00

DEADPOOL MAX
Marvel Comics (MAX): Dec, 2010 - No. 12, Nov, 2011 ($3.99)
1-12: 1-8,10-12-David Lapham-s/Kyle Baker-a/c. 6,7-Domino app. 9-Crystal-a 4.00
... X-Mas Special 1 (2/12, $4.99) Lapham-s; art by Lapham, Baker & Crystal; Baker-c 5.00

DEADPOOL MAX 2
Marvel Comics (MAX): Dec, 2011 - No. 6, May, 2012 ($3.99)
1-6: 1,2-David Lapham-s/Kyle Baker-a/c. 3-Crystal-a 4.00

DEADPOOL: MERC WITH A MOUTH
Marvel Comics: Sept, 2009 - No. 13, Sept, 2010 ($3.99/$2.99)
1-($3.99) Suydam-c/Dazo-a; Zombie-head Deadpool & Ka-Zar app.; r/Deadpool #4 ('97)
1 3 4 6 8 10
2-6,8-12-($2.99) Suydam-c on all. 8-Deadpool goes to Zombie dimension 4.00
7-($3.99) Covers by Suydam & Liefeld; art by Liefeld, Baker, Pastoras, Dazo;
1st app. Lady Deadpool 3 6 9 21 33 45
13-($3.99) Silence of the Lambs-c 2 4 6 10 14 18

DEADPOOL PULP
Marvel Comics: Nov, 2010 - No. 4, Feb, 2011 ($3.99, limited series)
1-4-Alternate Deadpool in 1955; Glass & Benson-s/Laurence Campbell-a/Jae Lee-c 4.00

DEADPOOL'S ART OF WAR
Marvel Comics: Dec, 2014 - No. 4, Mar, 2015 ($3.99, limited series)
1-4-David-s/Koblish-a; Loki and Thor app. 4.00

DEADPOOL'S SECRET SECRET WARS (Secret Wars tie-in)
Marvel Comics: Jul, 2015 - No. 4, Oct, 2015 ($4.99/$3.99, limited series)
1-($4.99) Deadpool inserts himself into the 1984 Secret Wars series; Bunn-s/Harris-c 5.00
2-4-($3.99) Spider-Man, Avengers & X-Men app. 3-Black costume created 4.00
2-Gwenpool variant-c by Bachalo; 1st app. of Gwenpool 20.00

DEADPOOL: SUICIDE KINGS
Marvel Comics: Jun, 2009 - No. 5, Oct, 2009 ($3.99, limited series)
1-Barberi-a; Punisher, Daredevil, & Spider-Man app.1 3 4 6 8 10
2-5 5.00

DEADPOOL TEAM-UP
Marvel Comics: No. 899, Jan, 2010 - No. 883, May, 2011 ($2.99, numbering runs in reverse)
899-883: 899-Hercules app.; Ramos-c. 897-Ghost Rider app. 894-Franken-Castle app.
887-Thor app. 883-Galactus & Silver Surfer app. 3.00

DEADPOOL: THE CIRCLE CHASE (See New Mutants #98)
Marvel Comics: Aug, 1993 - No. 4, Nov, 1993 ($2.00, limited series)
1-($2.50)-Embossed-c 3 6 9 14 20 25
2-4 1 3 4 6 8 10

DEADPOOL: THE DUCK
Marvel Comics: Mar, 2017 - No. 5, May, 2017 ($3.99, limited series)
1-5-Deadpool & Howard the Duck merge; Rocket Raccoon app.; Camagni-a 4.00

DEADPOOL: TOO SOON
Marvel Comics: Dec, 2016 - No. 4, Mar, 2017 ($4.99, limited series)
1-4-Corin-s/Nauck-a; Squirrel Girl, Howard the Duck, Punisher, Forbush Man app. 5.00

DEADPOOL V GAMBIT
Marvel Comics: Aug, 2016 - No. 5, Nov, 2016 ($3.99, limited series)
1-5-Acker & Blacker-s/Beyruth-s. 1-Spider-Man & Daredevil app. 4.00

DEADPOOL VS. CARNAGE
Marvel Comics: Jun, 2014 - No. 4, Aug, 2014 ($3.99, limited series)
1-Bunn-s/Espin-a/Fabry-c 2 4 6 8 10 12
2-4 6.00

DEADPOOL VS. OLD MAN LOGAN
Marvel Comics: Dec, 2017 - No. 5, Apr, 2018 ($3.99, limited series)
1-5-Declan Shalvey-s/Mike Henderson-a 4.00

DEADPOOL VS. THANOS
Marvel Comics: Nov, 2015 - No. 4, Dec, 2015 ($3.99, limited series)
1-4-Seeley-s/Bondoc-a; Death app. 2-Guardians of the Galaxy app. 4.00

DEADPOOL VS. THE PUNISHER
Marvel Comics: Jun, 2017 - No. 5, Aug, 2017 ($3.99, limited series)
1-5-Van Lente-s/Pere Pérez-a/Shalvey-c 4.00

DEADPOOL VS. X-FORCE
Marvel Comics: Sept, 2014 - No. 4, Nov, 2014 ($3.99, limited series)
1-4-Swierczynski-s/Larraz-a/Shane Davis-c 4.00

DEADPOOL: WADE WILSON'S WAR
Marvel Comics: Aug, 2010 - No. 4, Nov, 2010 ($3.99, limited series)
1-4-Swierczynski-s/Pearson-a/c; Bullseye, Domino & Silver Sable app. 4.00

DEAD RIDER (See Deadlander)

DEAD ROMEO
DC Comics: June, 2009 - No. 6, Nov, 2009 ($2.99, limited series)
1-6-Ryan Benjamin-a/Jesse Snider-s 3.00
TPB (2010, $19.99) r/#1-6; cover gallery 20.00

DEAD, SHE SAID
IDW Publishing: May, 2008 - No. 3, Sept, 2008 ($3.99, limited series)
1-3-Bernie Wrightson-a/Steve Niles-s 4.00

DEADSHOT (See Batman #59, Detective Comics #474, & Showcase '93 #8)
DC Comics: Nov, 1988 - No. 4, Feb, 1989 ($1.00, limited series)
1-Ostrander & Yale-s/Luke McDonnell-a 1 2 3 5 6 8
2-4 5.00

DEADSHOT
DC Comics: Feb, 2005 - No. 5, June 2005 ($2.95, limited series)
1-5-Zeck-c/Gage-s/Cummings-a. 3-Green Arrow app. 4.00

DEAD SPACE (Based on the Electronics Arts videogame)
Image Comics: Mar, 2008 - No. 6, Sept, 2008 ($2.99, limited series)
1-6-Templesmith-a/Johnston-s 3.00
... Extraction (9/09, $3.50) Templesmith-a/Johnston-s 3.50

DEAD SQUAD
IDW Publishing (Darby Pop): Oct, 2014 - Present ($3.99)
1-4-Federman-s/Scaia-a. 1-Two covers 4.00

DEAD VENGEANCE
Dark Horse Comics: Oct, 2015 - No. 4, Jan, 2016 ($3.99, limited series)
1-4-Bill Morrison-s. 1-Morrison-a. 2-4-Tone Rodriguez-a 4.00

DEAD WHO WALK, THE (See Strange Mysteries-Super Reprint #15,16 {1963-64})
Realistic Comics: 1952 (one-shot)
nn 81 162 243 518 884 1250

DEADWORLD (Also see The Realm)
Arrow Comics/Caliber Comics: Dec, 1986 - No. 26 ($1.50/$1.95/#15-28: $2.50, B&W)
1-4 4.00
5-26-Graphic cover version 4.00
5-26-Tame cover version 3.00
...Archives 1-3 (1992, $2.50) 3.00

DEAN KOONTZ'S FRANKENSTEIN: STORM SURGE
Dynamite Entertainment: 2015 - No. 6, 2016 ($3.99)
1-6-Chuck Dixon-s/Andres Ponce-a 4.00

DEAN MARTIN & JERRY LEWIS (See Adventures of...)

DEAR BEATRICE FAIRFAX
Best/Standard Comics (King Features): No. 5, Nov, 1950 - No. 9, Sept, 1951
(Vern Greene art)
5-All have Schomburg air brush-c 17 34 51 98 154 210
6-9 14 28 42 76 108 140

DEAR HEART (Formerly Lonely Heart)
Ajax: No. 15, July, 1956 - No. 16, Sept, 1956
15,16 10 20 30 54 72 90

DEAR LONELY HEART (...Illustrated No. 1-6)
Artful Publications: Mar, 1951; No. 2, Oct, 1951 - No. 8, Oct, 1952
1 21 42 63 122 199 275
2 12 24 36 69 97 125
3-Matt Baker Jungle Girl story 22 44 66 130 213 295
4-8 11 22 33 62 86 110

DEAR LONELY HEARTS (Lonely Heart #9 on)

Death: At Death's Door #1 © DC

Death Head #5 © Zach & Nick Keller

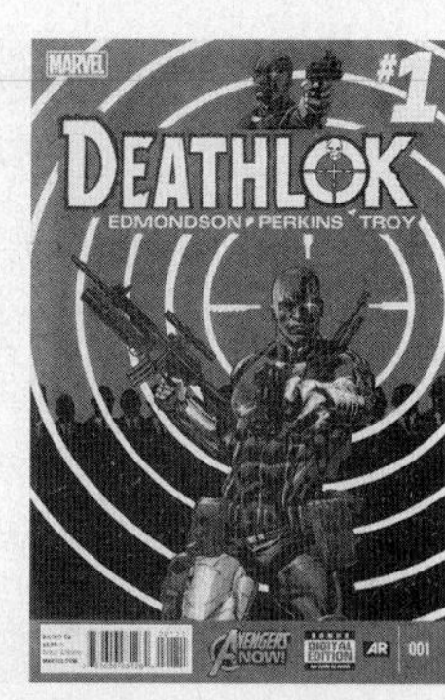

Deathlok (2014 series) #1 © MAR

	GD 2.0	VG 4.0	FN 6.0	VF 8.0	VF/NM 9.0	NM- 9.2

Harwell Publ./Mystery Publ. Co. (Comic Media): Aug, 1953 -No. 8, Oct, 1954

1	15	30	45	90	140	190
2-8	12	24	36	67	94	120

DEARLY BELOVED
Ziff-Davis Publishing Co.: Fall, 1952

1-Photo-c	20	40	60	114	182	250

DEAR NANCY PARKER
Gold Key: June, 1963 - No. 2, Sept, 1963

1-Painted-c on both	4	8	12	23	37	50
2	3	6	9	17	26	35

DEATH, THE ABSOLUTE... (From Neil Gaiman's Sandman titles)
DC Comics (Vertigo): 2009 ($99.99, oversized hardcover in slipcase)

nn-Reprints 1st app. in Sandman #8, Sandman #20, Death: The High Cost of Living #1-3, Death: the Time of Your Life #1-3, Death Talks About Life; short stories and pin-ups; merchandise pics; script and sketch art for Sandman #8; Gaiman afterword 100.00

DEATH: AT DEATH'S DOOR (See Sandman: The Season of Mists)
DC Comics (Vertigo): 2003 ($9.95, graphic novel one-shot, B&W, 7-1/2" x 5")

1-Jill Thompson-s/a/c; manga-style; Morpheus and the Endless app. 10.00

DEATHBED
DC Comics (Vertigo): Apr, 2018 - Present ($3.99)

1-Joshua Williamson-s/Riley Rossmo-a 4.00

DEATH BE DAMNED
BOOM! Studios: Feb, 2017 - No. 4, May, 2017 ($3.99, limited series)

1-4-Ben Acker, Ben Blacker & Andrew Miller-s/Hannah Christenson-a 4.00

DEATHBLOW (Also see Batman/Deathblow and Darker Image)
Image Comics (WildStorm Productions): May (Apr. inside), 1993 - No. 29, Aug, 1996 ($1.75/$1.95/$2.50)

0-(8/96, $2.95, 32 pgs.)-r/Darker Image w/new story & art; Jim Lee & Trevor Scott-a; new Jim Lee-c 3.00
1-($2.50)-Red foil stamped logo on black varnish-c; Jim Lee-c/a; flip-book side has Cybernary -c/story (#2 also) 4.00
1-($1.95)-Newsstand version w/o foil-c & varnish 3.00
2-29: 2-(8/93)-Lee-a; with bound-in poster. 2-($1.75)-Newsstand version w/o poster. 4-Jim Lee-c/Tim Sale-a begin. 13-W/pinup poster by Tim Sale & Jim Lee. 16-($1.95 Newsstand & $2.50 Direct Market editions)-Wildstorm Rising Pt. 6. 17-Variant "Chicago Comicon" edition exists. 20,21-Gen 13 app. 23-Backlash-c/app. 24,25-Grifter-c/app; Gen 13 & Dane from Wetworks app. 28-Deathblow dies. 29-Memorial issue 3.00
5-Alternate Portacio-c (Forms larger picture when combined with alternate-c for Gen 13 #5, Kindred #3, Stormwatch #10, Team 7 #1, Union #0, Wetworks #2 & WildC.A.T.S #11) 6.00
...:Sinners and Saints TPB ('99, $19.95) r/#1-12; Sale-c 20.00

DEATHBLOW (Volume 2)
DC Comics (WildStorm): Dec, 2006 - No. 9, Apr, 2008 ($2.99)

1-9: 1-Azzarello-s/D'Anda-a; two covers by D'Anda & Platt 3.00
...: And Then You Live! TPB (2008, $19.99) r/#1-9 20.00

DEATHBLOW BY BLOWS
DC Comics (WildStorm): Nov, 1999 - No. 3, Jan, 2000 ($2.95, limited series)

1-3-Alan Moore-s/Jim Baikie-a 3.00

DEATHBLOW/WOLVERINE
Image Comics (WildStorm Productions)/ Marvel Comics: Sept, 1996 - No. 2, Feb, 1997 ($2.50, limited series)

1,2: Wiesenfeld-s/Bennett-a 3.00
TPB (1997, $8.95) r/#1,2 9.00

DEATH DEALER (Also see Frank Frazetta's...)
Verotik: July, 1995 - No. 4, July, 1997 ($5.95)

1-Frazetta-c; Bisley-a	2	4	6	8	10	12
1-2nd print, 2-4-($6.95)-Frazetta-c; embossed logo	1	2	3	4	5	7

DEATH-DEFYING 'DEVIL, THE (Also see Project Superpowers)
Dynamite Entertainment: 2008 - No. 4, 2009 ($3.50, limited series)

1-4-Casey & Ross-s/Salazar-a; multiple covers; the Dragon app. 3.50

DEATH-DEFYING DOCTOR MIRAGE, THE
Valiant Entertainment: Sept, 2014 - No. 5, Jan, 2015 ($3.99, limited series)

1-5-Van Meter-s/de la Torre-a. 1-3-Foreman-c. 4,5-Wada-c 4.00

DEATH-DEFYING DOCTOR MIRAGE, THE: SECOND LIVES
Valiant Entertainment: Dec, 2015 - No. 4, Mar, 2016 ($3.99, limited series)

1-4-Van Meter-s/de La Torre-a 4.00

DEATH HEAD
Dark Horse Comics: Jul, 2015 - No. 6, Feb, 2016 ($3.99, limited series)

1-6-Zach & Nick Keller-s/Joanna Estep-a 4.00

DEATH, JR.
Image Comics: Apr, 2005 - No. 3, Aug, 2005 ($4.99, squarebound, limited series)

1-3-Gary Whitta-s/Ted Naifeh-a 5.00
Vol. 1 TPB (2005, $14.99) r/series; concept and promotional art 15.00

DEATH, JR. (Volume 2)
Image Comics: Jul, 2006 - No. 3, May, 2007 ($4.99, squarebound, limited series)

1-3-Gary Whitta-s/Ted Naifeh-a. 1-Dan Brereton-c 5.00
Vol. 2 TPB (2007, $14.99) r/series; Halloween story w/Guy Davis-a; promotional art 15.00

DEATHLOK (Also see Astonishing Tales #25)
Marvel Comics: July, 1990 - No. 4, Oct, 1990 ($3.95, limited series, 52 pgs.)

1-4: 1,2-Guice-a(p). 3,4-Denys Cowan-a, c-4 5.00

DEATHLOK
Marvel Comics: July, 1991 - No. 34, Apr, 1994 ($1.75)

1-Silver ink cover; Denys Cowan-c/a(p) begins 4.00
2-18,20-24,26-34: 2-Forge (X-Men) app. 3-Vs. Dr. Doom. 5-X-Men & F.F. x-over. 6,7-Punisher x-over. 9,10-Ghost Rider-c/story. 16-Infinity War x-over. 17-Jae Lee-c. 22-Black Panther app. 27-Siege app. 3.00
19-($2.25)-Foil-c 4.00
25-($2.95, 52 pgs.)-Holo-grafx foil-c 4.00
Annual 1 (1992, $2.25, 68 pgs.)-Guice-p; Quesada-c(p) 4.00
Annual 2 (1993, $2.95, 68 pgs.)-Bagged w/card; intro Tracer 4.00
NOTE: *Denys Cowan a(p)-9-13, 15, Annual 1; c-9-12, 13p, 14. Guice/Cowan c-8.*

DEATHLOK
Marvel Comics: Sept, 1999 - No. 11, June, 2000 ($1.99)

1-11: 1-Casey-s/Manco-a. 2-Two covers. 4-Canete-a 3.00

DEATHLOK (... The Demolisher on cover)
Marvel Comics: Jan, 2010 - No. 7, Jul, 2010 ($3.99, limited series)

1-7-Huston-s/Medina-a/Peterson-c 4.00

DEATHLOK
Marvel Comics: Dec, 2014 - No. 10, Sept, 2015 ($3.99)

1-10: 1-Edmonson-s/Perkins-a; intro. Henry Hayes. 2-5,8-10-Domino app. 4.00

DEATHLOK SPECIAL
Marvel Comics: May, 1991 - No. 4, June, 1991 ($2.00, bi-weekly lim. series)

1-4: r/1-4(1990) w/new Guice-c #1,2; Cowan c-3,4 3.00
1-2nd printing w/white-c 3.00

DEATHMASK
Future Comics: Mar, 2003 - No. 3, June, 2003 ($2.99)

1-3-Giordano-a(p)/Michelinie & Layton-s 3.00

DEATHMATCH
BOOM! Studios: Dec, 2012 - No. 12, Nov, 2013 ($2.99)

1-($1.00) Jenkins-s/Magno-a; multiple covers 3.00
2-12 ($3.99) Multiple covers on each 4.00

DEATHMATE
Valiant (Prologue/Yellow/Blue)/Image Comics (Black/Red/Epilogue): Sept, 1993 - Epilogue (#6), Feb, 1994 ($2.95/$4.95, limited series)

Preview-(7/93, 8 pgs.) 3.00
Prologue (#1)–Silver foil; Jim Lee/Layton-c; B. Smith/Lee-a; Liefeld-a(p) 3.00
Prologue–Special gold foil ed. of silver ed. 4.00
Black (#2)-(9/93, $4.95, 52 pgs.)-Silvestri/Jim Lee-c; pencils by Peterson/Silvestri/Capullo/ Jim Lee/Portacio; 1st story app. Gen 13 telling their rebellion against the Troika (see WildC.A.T.S. Trilogy) 6.00
Black-Special gold foil edition 7.00
Yellow (#3)-(10/93, $4.95, 52 pgs)-Yellow foil-c; Indicia says Prologue Sept 1993 by mistake; 3rd app. Ninjak; Thibert-c(i) 5.00
Yellow-Special gold foil edition 6.00
Blue (#4)-(10/93, $4.95, 52 pgs.)-Thibert blue foil-c(i); Reese-a(i) 5.00
Blue-Special gold foil edition 6.00
Red (#5), Epilogue (#6)-(2/94, $2.95)-Silver foil Quesada/Silvestri-c; Silvestri-a(p) 3.00

DEATH METAL
Marvel Comics UK: Jan, 1994 - No. 4, Apr, 1994 ($1.95, limited series)

1-4: 1-Silver ink-c. Alpha Flight app. 3.00

Death of X #1 © MAR

Deathstroke (2016 series) #11 © DC

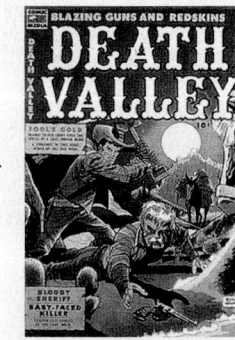

Death Valley #2 © CM

	GD	VG	FN	VF	VF/NM	NM-
	2.0	4.0	6.0	8.0	9.0	9.2

DEATH METAL VS. GENETIX
Marvel Comics UK: Dec, 1993 - No. 2, Jan, 1994 (Limited series)
1-($2.95)-Polybagged w/2 trading cards 3.00
2-($2.50)-Polybagged w/2 trading cards 3.00

DEATH OF CAPTAIN MARVEL (See Marvel Graphic Novel #1)

DEATH OF DRACULA
Marvel Comics: Aug, 2010 ($3.99, one shot)
1-Gischler-s/Camuncoli-a/c 4.00

DEATH OF HAWKMAN, THE
DC Comics: Dec, 2016 - No. 6, May, 2017 ($3.99, limited series)
1-6-Andreyko-s/Lopresti-a; Adam Strange app. 2-6-Despero app. 4.00

DEATH OF MR. MONSTER, THE (See Mr. Monster #8)

DEATH OF SUPERMAN (See Superman, 2nd Series)

DEATH OF THE NEW GODS (Tie-in to the Countdown series)
DC Comics: Early Dec, 2007 - No. 8, Jun, 2008 ($3.50, limited series)
1-8-Jim Starlin-s/a/c. 1-Barda killed. 6-Orion dies. 7-Scott Free and Metron die 3.50
TPB (2009, $19.99) r/#1-8; Starlin intro.; cover gallery 20.00

DEATH OF WOLVERINE
Marvel Comics: Nov, 2014 - No. 4, Dec, 2014 ($4.99, limited series)
1-4-Soule-s/McNiven-a; multiple covers on each; bonus art & commentary in each 5.00
...: Deadpool & Captain America (12/14, $4.99) Duggan-s/Kolins-a 5.00
...: Life After Logan (1/15, $4.99) Short stories by various; Cyclops, Nightcrawler app. 5.00

DEATH OF WOLVERINE: THE LOGAN LEGACY (Continues in Wolverines #1)
Marvel Comics: Dec, 2014 - No. 7, Feb, 2015 ($3.99, bi-weekly limited series)
1-7: 1-Soule-s; X-23, Daken, Deathstrike, Mystique & Sabretooth app. 4.00

DEATH OF WOLVERINE: THE WEAPON X PROGRAM
Marvel Comics: Jan, 2015 - No. 5, Mar, 2015 ($3.99, bi-weekly limited series)
1-5-Soule-s. 1-3-Larroca-a. 3-Sabretooth app. 4.00

DEATH OF X (Leads into X-Men vs. Inhumans)
Marvel Comics: Dec, 2016 - No. 4, Jan, 2017 ($4.99/$3.99, limited series)
1-($4.99) Soule & Lemire-s; Kuder-a; X-Men, Inhumans & Hydra app. 5.00
2-4-($3.99) 2-Kuder-a. 3,4-Kuder & Garrón-a. 4-Death of Cyclops 4.00

DEATH RACE 2020
Roger Corman's Cosmic Comics: Apr, 1995 - No. 8, Nov, 1995 ($2.50)
1-8: Sequel to the Movie 3.00

DEATH RATTLE (Formerly an Underground)
Kitchen Sink Press: V2#1, 10/85 - No. 18, 1988, 1994 ($1.95, Baxter paper, mature); V3#1, 11/95 - No. 5, 6/96 ($2.95, B&W)
V2#1-7,9-18: 1-Corben-c. 2-Unpubbed Spirit story by Eisner. 5-Robot Woman-r by Wolverton. 6-B&W issues begin. 10-Savage World-r by by Williamson/Torres/Krenkel/Frazetta from Witzend #1. 16-Wolverton Spacehawk-r 5.00
8-(12/86)-1st app. Mark Schultz's Xenozoic Tales/Cadillacs & Dinosaurs 2 4 6 11 16 20
8-(1994)-r plus interview w/Mark Schultz 3.50
V3#1-5 ($2.95-c): 1-Mark Schultz-c 3.50

DEATH SENTENCE
Titan Comics: Nov, 2003 - No. 6, Apr, 2014 ($3.99)
1-6-Montynero-s/c; Dowling-a 4.00

DEATH SENTENCE LONDON
Titan Comics: Jun, 2015 - No. 6, Jan, 2016 ($3.99)
1-6-Montynero-s/c; Simmonds-a 4.00

DEATH'S HEAD (See Daredevil #56, Dragon's Claws #5 & Incomplete...)(See Amazing Fantasy (2004) for Death's Head 3.0)
Marvel Comics: Dec, 1988 - No. 10, Sept, 1989 ($1.75)
1-Dragon's Claws spin-off 3.00
2-Fantastic Four app.; Dragon's Claws x-over 3.00
3-10: 8-Dr. Who app. 9-F. F. x-over; Simonson-c(p) 3.00

DEATH'S HEAD II (Also see Battletide)
Marvel Comics UK, Ltd.: Mar, 1992 - No. 4, June (May inside), 1992 ($1.75, color, lim. series)
1-4: 2-Fantastic Four app. 4-Punisher, Spider-Man, Daredevil, Dr. Strange, Capt. America & Wolverine in the year 2020 3.00
1,2-Silver ink 2nd printiings 3.00

DEATH'S HEAD II (Also see Battletide)
Marvel Comics UK, Ltd.: Dec, 1992 - No. 16, Mar, 1994 ($1.75/$1.95)
V2#1-13,15,16: 1-Gatefold-c. 1-4-X-Men app. 15-Capt. America & Wolverine app. 3.00
V2# 14-($2.95)-Foil flip-c w/Death's Head II Gold #0 4.00
...Gold 1 (1/94, $3.95, 68 pgs.)-Gold foil-c 4.00

DEATH'S HEAD II & THE ORIGIN OF DIE CUT
Marvel Comics UK, Ltd.: Aug, 1993 - No. 2, Sept, 1993 (limited series)
1-($2.95)-Embossed-c 4.00
2 ($1.75) 3.00

DEATHSTROKE (DC New 52)
DC Comics: Nov, 2011 - No. 20, Jul, 2013 ($2.99)
1-Higgins-s/Bennett-a/Bisley-c 6.00
2-20: 4-Blackhawks app. 9-12-Liefeld-s/a/c; Lobo app. 3.00
#0 (11/12, $2.99) Origin story, Team 7 app.; Liefeld-s/a/c 3.00

DEATHSTROKE (DC New 52)
DC Comics: Dec, 2014 - No. 20, Sept, 2016 ($2.99)
1-20: 1-Tony Daniel-s/a; I Ching app. 3-6-Harley Quinn app. 7-10-Wonder Woman app. 11-13-Harley Quinn & Suicide Squad app. 3.00
Annual 1 (9/15, $4.99) Takes place between #8 & 9; Wonder Woman app.; Kirkham-a 5.00
Annual 1 (8/16, $4.99) Hester-s/Colak & Viacava-a 5.00

DEATHSTROKE (DC Rebirth)
DC Comics: Oct, 2016 - Present ($2.99)
1-19: 1-Priest-s/Pagulayan-a; Clock King app. 4,5-Batman & Robin (Damian) app. 8-Superman app. 11-The Creeper app.; Cowan & Sienkiewicz-a. 19-Lazarus Contract tie-in with Teen Titans and Titans 3.00
20-29-($3.99) 21-The Defiance team forms; Terra app. 22-Dr. Light app. 4.00
Annual 1 (3/18, $4.99) Priest-s/Cowan & Sienkiewicz-a; Power Girl app. 5.00
... Rebirth 1 (10/16, $2.99) Priest-s/Pagulayan-a; Clock King app. 3.00

DEATHSTROKE: THE TERMINATOR (Deathstroke: The Hunted #0-47; Deathstroke #48-60) (Also see Marvel & DC Present, New Teen Titans #2, New Titans, Showcase '93 #7,9 & Tales of the Teen Titans #42-44)
DC Comics: Aug, 1991 - No. 60, June, 1996 ($1.75-$2.25)
1-New Titans spin-off; Mike Zeck c-1-28 2 4 6 10 14 18
1-Gold ink 2nd printing ($1.75) 1 2 3 5 6 8
2 5.00
3-40,0(10/94),41(11/94)-49,51-60: 6,8-Batman cameo. 7,9-Batman-c/story. 9-1st brief app. new Vigilante (female). 10-1st full app. new Vigilante; Perez-i. 13-Vs. Justice League; Team Titans cameo on last pg. 14-Total Chaos, part 1; Team Titans-c/story cont'd in New Titans #90. 15-1st app. Rose Wilson. 40-(9/94). 0-(10/94)-Begin Deathstroke, The Hunted, ends #47. 3.00
50 ($3.50) 4.00
Annual 1-4 ('92-'95, 68 pgs.): 1-Nightwing & Vigilante app.; minor Eclipso app. 2-Bloodlines Deathstorm; 1st app. Gunfire. 3-Elseworlds story. 4-Year One story 4.00
NOTE: ***Golden** a-12. **Perez** a-11i. **Zeck** c-Annual 1, 2.*

DEATH: THE HIGH COST OF LIVING (See Sandman #8) (Also see the Books of Magic limited & ongoing series)
DC Comics (Vertigo): Mar, 1993 - No. 3, May, 1993 ($1.95, limited series)
1-Bachalo/Buckingham-a; Dave McKean-c; Neil Gaiman scripts in all 6.00
1-Platinum edition 40.00
2 3.50
3-Pgs. 19 & 20 had wrong placement 3.00
3-Corrected version w/pgs. 19 & 20 facing each other 4.00
Death Talks About Life-giveaway about AIDS prevention 5.00
Hardcover (1994, $19.95)-r/#1-3 & Death Talks About Life; intro. by Tori Amos 20.00
Trade paperback (6/94, $12.95, Titan Books)-r/#1-3 & Death Talks About Life; prism-c 13.00

DEATH: THE TIME OF YOUR LIFE (See Sandman #8)
DC Comics (Vertigo): Apr, 1996 - No. 3, July, 1996 ($2.95, limited series)
1-3: Neil Gaiman story & Bachalo/Buckingham-a; Dave McKean-c. 2-(5/96) 3.00
Hardcover (1997, $19.95)-r/#1-3 w/3 new pages & gallery art by various 20.00
TPB (1997, $12.95)-r/#1-3 & Visions of Death gallery; Intro. by Claire Danes 13.00

DEATH 3
Marvel Comics UK: Sept, 1993 - No. 4, Dec, 1993 ($1.75, limited series)
1-($2.95)-Embossed-c 4.00
2-4 3.00

DEATH VALLEY (Cowboys and Indians)
Comic Media: Oct, 1953 - No. 6, Aug, 1954
1-Billy the Kid; Morisi-a; Andru/Esposito-c/a 24 48 72 142 234 325
2-Don Heck-c 15 30 45 86 133 180
3-6: 3,5-Morisi-a. 5-Discount-a 14 28 42 80 115 150

DEATH VALLEY (Becomes Frontier Scout, Daniel Boone No.10-13)

Deathwish #3 © Milestone Media

Deep State #1 © Justin Jordan

The Defenders #55 © MAR

GD VG FN VF VF/NM NM-
2.0 4.0 6.0 8.0 9.0 9.2

Charlton Comics: No. 7, 6/55 - No. 9, 10/55 (Cont'd from Comic Media series)
7-9: 8-Wolverton-a (half pg.) 11 22 33 62 86 110

DEATH VIGIL
Image Comics (Top Cow): Jul, 2014 - No. 8, Sept, 2015 ($3.99)
1-8-Stjepan Sejic-s/a/c 4.00

DEATHWISH
DC Comics (Milestone Media): Dec, 1994 - No. 4, Mar, 1995 ($2.50, lim. series)
1-4 3.00

DEATH WRECK
Marvel Comics UK: Jan, 1994 - No. 4, Apr, 1994 ($1.95, limited series)
1-4: 1-Metallic ink logo; Death's Head II app. 3.00

DEBBIE DEAN, CAREER GIRL
Civil Service Publ.: April, 1945 - No. 2, July, 1945
1,2-Newspaper reprints by Bert Whitman 15 30 45 83 124 165

DEBBI'S DATES (Also see Date With Debbi)
National Periodical Publications: Apr-May, 1969 - No. 11, Dec-Jan, 1970-71
1 7 14 21 46 86 125
2,3,5,7-11: 2-Last 12¢ issue 4 8 12 25 40 55
4-Neal Adams text illo 4 8 12 28 47 65
6-Superman cameo 6 12 18 37 66 95

DECADE OF DARK HORSE, A
Dark Horse Comics: Jul, 1996 - No. 4, Oct, 1996 ($2.95, B&W/color, lim. series)
1-4: 1-Sin City-c/story by Miller; Grendel by Wagner; Predator. 2-Star Wars wraparound-c. 3-Aliens-c/story; Nexus, Mask stories 3.00

DECAPITATOR (Randy Bowen's...)
Dark Horse Comics: Jun, 1998 - No. 4, ($2.95)
1-4-Bowen-s/art by various. 1-Mahnke-c. 3-Jones-c 4.00

DECEPTION, THE
Image Comics (Flypaper Press): 1999 - No. 3, 1999 ($2.95, B&W, mini-series)
1-3-Horley painted-c 3.00

DECIMATION: THE HOUSE OF M
Marvel Comics: Jan, 2006 ($3.99)
... - The Day After (one-shot) Claremont-s/Green-a 4.00

DECISION 2012 (Biographies of the main 2012 presidential candidates)
BOOM! Studios: Nov, 2011 ($3.99, series of one-shots)
...: Barack Obama 1 (11/11, $3.99) biography; Damian Couceiro-a; 2 covers 4.00
...: Michelle Bachman 1 (11/11) biography; Aaron McConnell-a; 2 covers 4.00
...: Ron Paul 1 (11/11) biography; Dean Kotz-a; 2 covers 4.00
...: Sarah Palin 1 (11/11) biography; Damian Couceiro-a; 2 covers 4.00

DEEP, THE (Movie)
Marvel Comics Group: Nov, 1977 (Giant)
1-Infantino-c/a 1 3 4 6 8 10

DEEP GRAVITY
Dark Horse Comics: Jul, 2014 - No. 4, Oct, 2014 ($3.99, limited series)
1-4-Hardman & Bechko-s/Baldó-a/Hardman-c 4.00

DEEP SLEEPER
Oni Press/Image Comics: Feb, 2004 - No. 4, Sept, 2004 ($3.50/$2.95, B&W, limited series)
1,2-(Oni Press, $3.50)-Hester-s/Huddleston-a 3.50
3,4-(Image Comics, $2.95) 3.00
... Omnibus (Image, 8/04, $5.95) r/#1,2 6.00
... Vol. 1 TPB (2005, $12.95) r/#1-4; cover gallery 13.00

DEEP STATE
BOOM! Studios: Nov, 2014 - No. 8, Jul, 2015 ($3.99)
1-8-Justin Jordan-s/Ariela Kristantina-a 4.00

DEFCON 4
Image Comics (WildStorm Productions): Feb, 1996 - No. 4, Sept, 1996 ($2.50, lim. series)
1/2 1 2 3 5 7 9
1/2 Gold-(1000 printed) 14.00
1-Main Cover by Mat Broome & Edwin Rosell 3.00
1-Hordes of Cymulants variant-c by Michael Golden 5.00
1-Backs to the Wall variant-c by Humberto Ramos & Alex Garner 5.00
1-Defcon 4-Way variant-c by Jim Lee 1 2 3 4 5 7
2-4 3.00

DEFEND COMICS (The CBLDF Presents...)
Comic Book Legal Defense Fund: May, 2015 (giveaway)
FCBD Edition - Short stories incl. Kevin Keller, Beanworld; art by Liew, Parent, Watson 3.00

DEFENDERS, THE (TV)
Dell Publishing Co.: Sept-Nov, 1962 - No. 2, Feb-Apr, 1963
12-176-211(#1) 4 8 12 25 40 55
12-176-304(#2) 3 6 9 20 31 42

DEFENDERS, THE (Also see Giant-Size..., Marvel Feature, Marvel Treasury Edition, Secret Defenders & Sub-Mariner #34, 35; The New...#140-on)
Marvel Comics Group: Aug, 1972 - No. 152, Feb, 1986
1-Englehart-s/Sal Buscema-a begins; The Hulk, Doctor Strange, Sub-Mariner app.; last app. as Defenders in Marvel Feature #3; 1st Necrodamus; plot continued from Incredible Hulk #126; minor Omegatron app. 13 26 39 87 191 295
2-Silver Surfer x-over; 1st Calizuma (a wizard in the service of the Nameless Ones) 7 14 21 46 86 125
3,5: 3-Silver Surfer x-over; vs. The Nameless Ones; Barbara Norris app. from Incredible Hulk #126. 5-vs. The Omegatron (destroyed) 5 10 15 31 53 75
4-Barbara Norris becomes the third incarnation of the Valkyrie (previously seen in Avengers #83 & Incredible Hulk #142; Enchantress, the Executioner & The Black Knight app (turned to stone); Valkyrie joins the Defenders 6 12 18 37 66 95
6,7: 6-Silver Surfer x-over. 7-Silver Surfer, Hawkeye app. vs. Red Ghost & Attuma 3 6 9 21 33 45
8,9: 8-Silver Surfer & Hawkeye app. vs. Red Ghost & Attuma; 4-pg story begins "Avengers/Defenders War"; Dormammu & Loki team-up; story continues in Avengers #116. 9-Continued from Avengers #116; Iron Man vs. Hawkeye, Dr. Strange vs. Mantis; continued in Avengers #117. 4 8 12 25 40 55
10-Hulk vs. Thor; continued in Avengers #118 8 16 24 54 102 150
11-"Avengers/Defenders War" concludes; Silver Surfer, Black Knight & King Richard app.; last Englehart-s 4 8 12 25 40 55
12-Last 20¢ issue; Wein-s begin; brief origin Valkyrie retold; vs. Xemnu the Titan; Defenders app. next in Giant-Size Defenders #1 3 6 9 14 20 25
13,14: 13-Nighthawk app. vs. The Squadron Sinister (Hyperion, Dr. Spectrum & the Whizzer; 1st app. Nebulon the Celestial Man. 14-vs. The Squadron Sinister & Nebulon; Sub-Mariner leaves; Nighthawk joins 3 6 9 14 20 25
15,16: 15-Magneto & Brotherhood of Evil Mutants app.; first Alpha the Ultimate Mutant; Professor X app. 16-Magneto & the Brotherhood of Evil mutants turned into children; Defenders app. next in Giant-Size Defenders #2 3 6 9 16 23 30
17-Power Man x-over (11/74); 1st app. of the Wrecking Crew (Thunderball, Bulldozer & Piledriver); Valkyrie leaves 3 6 9 14 20 25
18-20: 18-19-vs. the Wrecking Crew. 20-Continued from Marvel Two-in-one #7; Valkyrie returns (origin retold) 1st Gerber-s 2 4 6 9 12 15
21-25: 21-1st Headmen (Chondu the Mystic, Dr. Arthur Nagan, Jerold Morgan); Valkyrie origin continued from last issue; Hulk returns; story continued in Giant-Size Defenders #4. 22-25-vs. Sons of the Serpent. 23-Yellowjacket app. 24-25-Son of Satan, Daredevil, Yellowjacket & Power Man app; story continues in Giant-Size Defenders #5; 25-1st app. "Elf with a gun" 1 3 4 6 8 10
26-Continued from Giant-Size Defenders #5; Guardians of the Galaxy app. (pre-dates Marvel Presents #3); origin of Vance Astro; Killraven & Badoon x-over 2 4 6 9 12 15
27-1st brief app. Starhawk (unnamed); Guardians of the Galaxy & Defenders vs. the Badoon 3 6 9 17 26 35
28-1st full app. Starhawk; Guardians of the Galaxy & Badoon app. 6 12 18 38 69 100
29-Starhawk joins the Guardians of the Galaxy; 1st app. Aleta (Starhawks wife); Guardians story continues in Marvel Presents #3 2 4 6 9 12 15
30-Mantlo-s (fill-in issue) 6.00
31-40: 31-Headman app. 32-Origin of Nighthawk; Headmen & Son of Satan app; 1st app. Ruby Thursday; 2nd app. "Elf with a gun". 33-Origin Nighthawk continued; return of Nebulon. 34-38-(Regular 25¢ editions). 34-vs. Nebulon. 35-1st new Red Guardian (Dr. Tania Belinsky); Headmen & Nebulon app. 36-Red Guardian & Plant Man app. 37-Power Man guest app.; vs. Plant Man, Eel & Porcupine; Nebulon app. 38-Power Man app.; vs. Eel & Porcupine; "Elf with a gun" app. 39-Power Man app. 40-1st new Valkyrie (gold) costume; "Elf with a gun" app.; story continued in Defenders Annual # 6.00
34-38 (30¢-c variants, limited distribution 4-8/76) 4 8 12 25 40 55
41-46: 41-Last Gerber-s/Sal Buscema-a. 42,43-Egg Head, Rhino, Solarr & Cobalt Man app.; Giffen-a; 43-1st Red Rajah; Power Man app. 44-Power Man & Hellcat app. 45-Power Man & Hellcat app. 46-Dr. Strange & Red Guardian leave; "Elf with a gun" app; vs. Scorpio 6.00
47-50-Moon Knight guest app. 47,48-Wonder Man app. 47-49-vs. Scorpio (Jacob Fury). 48-50-(Regular 30¢ editions). 50-Death Scorpio; SHIELD app. 6.00
48-52-(35¢-c variants, limited distribution)(6-10/77) 7 14 21 44 82 120
51-60: 51,52-(Regular 30¢ editions). 51-Nighthawk vs. The Ringer. 52-Hulk vs. Sub-Mariner. 53-1st brief app. Lunatik (Lobo lookalike) created by Roger Slifer & Keith Giffen, six years before they create Lobo in Omega Men #3; 1st app. Sergie Krylov (The Presence). 54,55-vs. the Presence. 54-last Giffen-a. 55-Origin Red Guardian; Lunatik cameo. 56-Red

The Defenders (2017 series) #1 © MAR

Dejah Thoris (2016 series) #6 © DYN

Delete #1 © 1First Comics

Guardian leaves; Valkyrie vs. Lunatik. 57-Ms. Marvel (Carol Danvers) app. 58-60-Devil Slayer app. 5.00
61-vs. Lunatik; Spider-Man app. 4.00
62-"Defender for a day" issue; Jack of Hearts, Ms. Marvel (Carol Danvers), Hercules, Iron Man, White Tiger, Nova, Marvel Man (later Quasar), Son of Satan, Havok, Prowler, Paladin, Falcon, Torpedo, Black Goliath, Stingray, Polaris, Captain Ultra, Iron Fist, Captain Marvel (Mar-Vell), Tagak app. (all try to join Defenders) 5.00
63,64: 63-Various villains form their own Defenders team. 64-Villains defeated; the various new Defenders leave 4.00
65-75: 66-68-Defenders in Asgard. 66-Hulk returns. 68-Hela app. 69-Omegatron app. 70-vs. Lunatik. 71-Origin Lunatik; Dr. Strange returns. 72,73-Lunatik app. 73-Foolkiller app. 74-Nighthawk resigns as leader; Foolkiller app. 75-vs. Foolkiller 4.00
76-93,97-99: 76-Wasp, Omega the Unknown & Ruby Thursday app. 77-Origin Omega the Unknown; Moondragon & Wasp app. 78-Original Defenders return (Hulk, Dr. Strange & Namor; continue thru #101); Wasp, Yellowjacket & Moondragon app. 79,80-Mandrill app; Wasp & Yellowjacket app. 84-Atlantis vs. Wakanda; Namor vs. Black Panther. 85,86-Black Panther app. 87-Origin Hellcat retold. 90,91-vs. Mandrill; Daredevil app. 97,98-Devil Slayer & Man-Thing app. 98-Nighthawk leaves; Avengers app. 99-Mephisto app. 3.00
94-1st Gargoyle (Isaac Christians) 1 2 3 5 6 8
95,96: Ghost Rider app. 95-Dracula app. 3.00
100-(52-pgs.)-Hellcat (Patsy Walker) revealed as Satan's daughter; Silver Surfer app. 1 3 4 6 8 10
101-Silver Surfer app. 3.00
102-111,115-119-124: 104-Beast joins. 105-Son of Satan joins; Mr. Fantastic app. 106-Captain America app.; death of Nighthawk. 107-Daredevil & Captain America app. 109-Spider-Man app; Defenders app. next in Avengers Annual #11. 111-Overmind cameo. 120-122-Son of Satan-c/stories. 122-"Elf with a gun" returns; Silver Surfer & Iceman app. 123-"Elf with a Gun" app.; Moondragon cameo; 1st app. Cloud; Vision & Scarlet Witch app. 124-Origin of the "Elf with a gun" 3.00
112-114-Overmind & Squadron Supreme app. 3.00
125-(52 pgs)-Intro new Defenders (Angel, Beast, Iceman, Valkyrie, Gargoyle & Moondragon); Hulk, Dr. Strange, Namor & Silver Surfer resign; "Elf with a Gun" mystery resolved 5.00
126-149,151: 126-130-Secret Empire story. 129-New Mutants cameo (3/84, early x-over). 134-1st full app. Manslaughter. 139-Odin app. 140-New Moondragon costume. 145-Johnny Blaze (Ghost Rider) app. 147-1st app. Interloper; Sgt. Fury app. 151-Manslaughter app. 3.00
150-(52 pgs.)-Origin Cloud 5.00
152-(52 pgs.)-Continued from Secret Wars II #7; Beyonder app.; vs. The Dragon of the Moon; leads into X-Factor #1 6.00
Annual 1 (1976, 52 pgs-) Continued from Defenders #40; Power Man app.; vs. Nebulon, the Bozos and the Headmen 3 6 9 19 30 40

NOTE: ***Art Adams** c-142p. **Austin** a-53i; c-65i, 119i, 145i. **Frank Bolle** a-7i, 10i, 11i. **Buckler** c(p)-34, 38, 76, 77, 79-86, 90, 91. **J. Buscema** c-66. **Giffen** a-42-49p, 50, 51-54p. **Golden** a-53p, 54p; c-94, 96. **Guice** c-129. **G. Kane** c(p)-13, 16, 18, 19, 21-26, 31-33, 35-37, 40, 41, 52, 55. **Kirby** c-42-45. **Mooney** a-3i, 31-34i, 62i, 63i, 85i. **Nasser** c-88p. **Perez** c(p)-51, 53, 54. **Rogers** c-98. **Starlin** c-110. **Tuska** a-57p. Silver Surfer in No. 2, 3, 6, 8-11, 92, 98-101, 107, 112-115, 122-125.*

DEFENDERS, THE (Volume 2) (Continues in The Order)
Marvel Comics: Mar, 2001 - No. 12, Feb, 2002 ($2.99/$2.25)

1-Busiek & Larsen-s/Larsen & Janson-a/c 3.00
2-11: 2-Two covers by Larsen & Art Adams; Valkyrie app. 4-Frenz-a 3.00
12-($3.50) 'Nuff Said issue; back-up-s Reis-a 4.00
...: From the Vault (9/11, $2.99) Previously unpublished story; Bagley-a 3.00

DEFENDERS, THE
Marvel Comics: Sept, 2005 - No. 5, Jan, 2006 ($2.99, limited series)

1-5-Giffen & DeMatteis-s/Maguire-a. 2-Dormammu app. 3.00
...: Indefensible HC (2006, $19.99, dust jacket) r/#1-5; Giffen & Maguire sketch page 20.00
...: Indefensible SC (2007, $13.99) r/#1-5; Giffen & Maguire sketch page 14.00

DEFENDERS, THE
Marvel Comics: Feb, 2012 - No. 12, Jan, 2013 ($3.99)

1-12: 1-Dr. Strange, Namor, Silver Surfer, Red She-Hulk, Iron Fist team; Dodson-a 4.00
...: Strange Heroes 1 (2/12, $4.99) Handbook-style profiles of team members and foes 5.00
...: The Coming of the Defenders 1 (2/12, $5.99) r/Marvel Feature #1-3; recolored-c of #1 6.00
...: Tournament of Heroes 1 (3/12, $5.99) r/Defenders #62-65 (1978); recolored-c of #62 6.00

DEFENDERS
Marvel Comics: Aug, 2017 - No. 10, Apr, 2018 ($4.99/$3.99)

1-($4.99) Luke Cage, Jessica Jones, Daredevil, Iron Fist team; Bendis-s/Marquez-a 5.00
2-10-($3.99) 3-Punisher app. 6-8-Deadpool app. 4.00

DEFENDERS OF DYNATRON CITY
Marvel Comics: Feb, 1992 - No. 6, July, 1992 ($1.25, limited series)

1-6-Lucasarts characters. 2-Origin 3.00

DEFENDERS OF THE EARTH (TV)
Marvel Comics (Star Comics): Jan, 1987 - No. 4, July, 1987

1-4: The Phantom, Mandrake The Magician, Flash Gordon begin. 3-Origin Phantom. 4-Origin Mandrake 4.00

DEFEX
Devil's Due Publ.: Oct, 2004 - No. 6, Apr, 2005 ($2.95)

1-6: 1-Wolfman-s/Caselli-a. 6-Pérez-c 3.00

DEFIANCE
Image Comics: Feb, 2002 - No. 8, Jun, 2003 ($2.95)

Preview Edition (12/01) 3.00
1-8-Barré-s/Kang & Suh-a 3.00

DEFINITIVE DIRECTORY OF THE DC UNIVERSE, THE (See Who's Who...)

DEJAH OF MARS (Warlord of Mars)
Dynamite Entertainment: 2014 - No. 4, 2014 ($3.99)

1-4-Rahner-s/Morales-a; multiple covers on each 4.00

DEJAH THORIS (Warlord of Mars)
Dynamite Entertainment: 2016 - No. 6, 2016 ($3.99)

1-6-Barbarie-s/Manna-a; multiple covers 4.00

DEJAH THORIS AND THE GREEN MEN OF MARS (Warlord of Mars)
Dynamite Entertainment: 2013 - No. 12, 2014 ($3.99)

1-12: 1-8-Rahner-s/Antonio-a; multiple covers on each. 9-12-Morales-a 4.00

DEJAH THORIS AND THE WHITE APES OF MARS (Warlord of Mars)
Dynamite Entertainment: 2012 - No. 3, 2012 ($3.99)

1-3-Rahner-s/Antonio-a; 2 covers by Peterson & Garza 4.00

DEJAH THORIS, VOLUME 2
Dynamite Entertainment: No. 0, 2018 - Present ($3.99)

0-(25¢-c) Amy Chu-s/Pasquale Qualano-a; multiple covers 3.00
1,2-($3.99) Chu-s/Qualano-a; multiple covers 4.00

DELECTA OF THE PLANETS (See Don Fortune & Fawcett Miniatures)

DELETE
1First Comics: 2016 - No. 4, 2016 ($4.99, limited series)

1-4-Palmiotti & Gray-s/Timms-a/Conner-c 5.00

DELICATE CREATURES
Image Comics (Top Cow): 2001 ($16.95, hardcover with dust jacket)

nn-Fairy tale storybook; J. Michael Straczynski-s; Michael Zulli-a 17.00

DELINQUENTS
Valiant Entertainment: Aug, 2014 - No. 4, Nov, 2014 ($3.99, limited series)

1-4-Quantum & Woody meet Archer & Armstrong; Asmus & Van Lente-s/Kano-a 4.00

DELIRIUM'S PARTY: A LITTLE ENDLESS STORYBOOK (Characters from The Sandman titles and The Little Endless Storybook)
DC Comics: 2011 ($14.99, hardcover, one-shot)

HC-Jill Thompson-s/painted-a/c; Little Delirium throws a party; watercolor page process 15.00

DELLA VISION (...The Television Queen) (Patty Powers #4 on)
Atlas Comics: April, 1955 - No. 3, Aug, 1955

	GD 2.0	VG 4.0	FN 6.0	VF 8.0	VF/NM 9.0	NM- 9.2
1-Al Hartley-c	53	106	159	334	567	800
2,3	30	60	90	177	289	400

DELLEC
Aspen MLT.: Aug, 2009 - No. 6, Oct, 2011 ($2.50)

1-6-Gunnell-a/c 3.00

DELL GIANT COMICS

Dell Publishing began to release square bound comics in 1949 with a 132-page issue called Christmas Parade #1. The covers were of a heavier stock to accommodate the increased number of pages. The books proved profitable at 25 cents, but the average number of pages was quickly reduced to 100. Ten years later they were converted to a numbering system similar to the Four Color Comics, for greater ease in distribution and the page counts cut back to mostly 84 pages. The label "Dell Giant" began to appear on the covers in 1954. Because of the size of the books and the heavier, less pliant cover stock, they are rarely found in high grade condition, and with the exception of a small quantity of copies released from Western Publishing's warehouse–are almost never found in near mint.

	GD 2.0	VG 4.0	FN 6.0	VF 8.0	VF/NM 9.0	NM- 9.2
Abraham Lincoln Life Story 1(3/58)	8	16	24	64	107	150
Bugs Bunny Christmas Funnies 1(11/50, 116pp)	21	42	63	168	289	410
...Christmas Funnies 2(11/51, 116pp)	12	24	36	96	171	245
...Christmas Funnies 3-5(11/52-11/54,)-Becomes Christmas Party #6	10	20	30	80	140	200
...Christmas Funnies 7-9(12/56-12/58)	9	18	27	72	124	175
...Christmas Party 6(11/55)-Formerly Bugs Bunny Christmas Funnies						

Dell Giant - Christmas Parade #2 © DIS

Dell Giant - Marge's Little Lulu on Vacation #1 © M. Buell

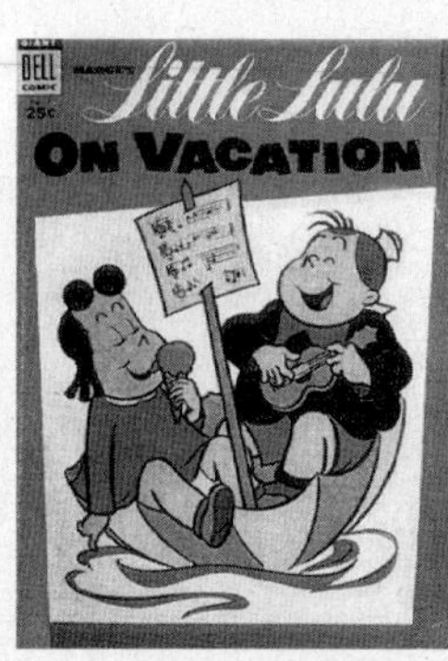

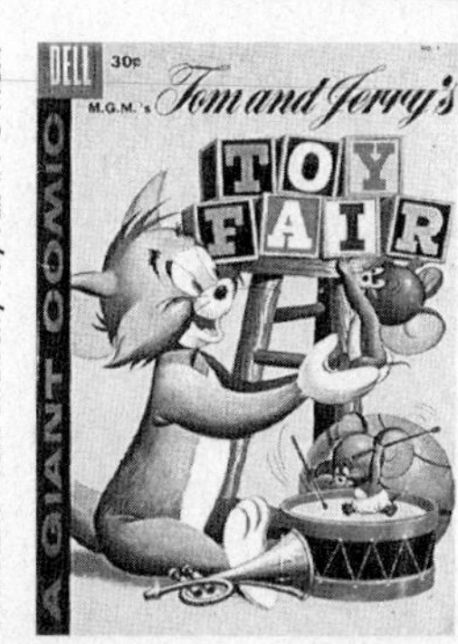

Dell Giant - Tom and Jerry Toy Fair #1 © MGM

GD VG FN VF VF/NM NM-
2.0 4.0 6.0 8.0 9.0 9.2

9 18 27 72 124 175
...County Fair 1(9/57) 11 22 33 88 149 210
...Halloween Parade 1(10/53) 12 24 36 96 166 235
...Halloween Parade 2(10/54)-Trick 'N' Treat Halloween Fun #3 on
10 20 30 80 135 190
...Trick 'N' Treat Halloween Fun 3,4(10/55-10/56)-Formerly Halloween Parade #2
9 18 27 72 129 185
...Vacation Funnies 1(7/51, 112pp) 20 40 60 160 280 400
...Vacation Funnies 2('52) 13 26 39 104 180 255
...Vacation Funnies 3-5('53-'55) 10 20 30 80 138 195
...Vacation Funnies 6,7,9('56-'59) 9 18 27 72 124 175
...Vacation Funnies 8('58) 1st app. Beep Beep the Road Runner, Wile E. Coyote (1st meeting), Mathilda (Mrs. Beep Beep) and their 3 children who hatch from eggs; one month before Four Color #918 11 22 33 88 157 225
Cadet Gray of West Point 1(4/58)-Williamson-a, 10pgs.; Buscema-a; photo-c
8 16 24 64 107 150
Christmas In Disneyland 1(12/57)-Barks-a, 18 pgs. 25 50 75 200 350 500
Christmas Parade 1(11/49)(132 pgs.)(1st Dell Giant)-Donald Duck (25 pgs. by Barks, r-in G.K. Christmas Parade #5); Mickey Mouse & other film oriented stories; Cinderella (prior to movie), 7 Dwarfs, Bambi & Thumper, So Dear To My Heart, Flying Mouse, Dumbo, Cookieland & others 63 126 189 504 877 1250
Christmas Parade 2('50)-Donald Duck (132 pgs.)(25 pgs. by Barks, r-in Gold Key's Christmas Parade #6). Mickey, Pluto, Chip & Dale, etc. Contents shift to a holiday expansion of W.D. C&S type format 42 84 126 336 588 840
Christmas Parade 3-7('51-'55, #3-116pgs; #4-7, 100 pgs.)
14 28 42 112 196 280
Christmas Parade 8(12/56)-Barks-a, 8 pgs. 22 44 66 176 306 435
Christmas Parade 9(12/58)-Barks-a, 20 pgs. 25 50 75 200 350 500
Christmas Treasury, A 1(11/54) 10 20 30 80 135 190
Davy Crockett, King Of The Wild Frontier 1(9/55)-Fess Parker photo-c; Marsh-a
19 38 57 152 269 385
Disneyland Birthday Party 1(10/58)-Barks-a, 16 pgs. r-by Gladstone
25 50 75 200 350 500
Donald and Mickey In Disneyland 1(5/58) 11 22 33 88 157 225
Donald Duck Beach Party 1(7/54)-Has an Uncle Scrooge story (not by Barks) that prefigures the later rivalry with Flintheart Glomgold and tells of Scrooge's wild rivalry with another millionaire 16 32 48 128 224 320
...Beach Party 2(1955)-Lady & Tramp 11 22 33 88 157 225
...Beach Party 3-5(1956-58) 11 22 33 88 152 215
...Beach Party 6(8/59, 84pp)-Stapled 8 16 24 64 115 165
Donald Duck Fun Book 1,2 (1953 & 10/54)-Games, puzzles, comics & cut-outs (very rare in unused condition)(most copies commonly have defaced interior pgs.)
63 126 189 504 877 1250
Donald Duck In Disneyland 1(9/55)-1st Disneyland Dell Giant
15 30 45 120 210 300
Golden West Rodeo Treasury 1(10/57) 10 20 30 80 135 190
Huey, Dewey and Louie Back To School 1(9/58) 9 18 27 72 126 180
Lady and The Tramp 1(6/55) 17 34 51 136 233 330
Life Stories of American Presidents 1(11/57)-Buscema-a
8 16 24 64 107 150
Lone Ranger Golden West 3(8/55)-Formerly Lone Ranger Western Treasury
18 36 54 144 255 365
Lone Ranger Movie Story nn(3/56)-Origin Lone Ranger in text; Clayton Moore photo-c
36 72 108 288 507 725
...Western Treasury 1(9/53)-Origin Lone Ranger, Silver, & Tonto; painted cover
23 46 69 184 325 465
...Western Treasury 2(8/54)-Becomes Lone Ranger Golden West #3
18 36 54 144 255 365
Marge's Little Lulu & Alvin Story Telling Time 1(3/59)-r/#2,5,3,11,30,10,21,17,8, 14,16; Stanley-a 14 28 42 112 196 280
...& Her Friends 4(3/56)-Tripp-a 14 28 42 112 191 270
...& Her Special Friends 3(3/55)-Tripp-a 15 30 45 120 210 300
...& Tubby At Summer Camp 5,2: 5(10/57)-Tripp-a. 2(10/58)-Tripp-a
13 26 39 104 182 260
...& Tubby Halloween Fun 6,2: 6(10/57)-Tripp-a. 2(10/58)-Tripp-a
13 26 39 104 182 260
...& Tubby In Alaska 1(7/59)-Tripp-a 13 26 39 104 177 250
...On Vacation 1(7/54)-r/4C-110,14,4C-146,5,4C-97,4,4C-158,3,1;Stanley-a
25 50 75 200 350 500
...& Tubby Annual 1(3/53)-r/4C-165,4C-74,4C-146,4C-97,4C-158, 4C-139, 4C-131; Stanley-a (1st Lulu Dell Giant) 30 60 90 240 420 600
...& Tubby Annual 2('54)-r/4C-139,6,4C-115,4C-74,5,4C-97,3,4C-146,18; Stanley-a
25 50 75 200 350 500
Marge's Tubby & His Clubhouse Pals 1(10/56)-1st app. Gran'pa Feeb;1st app. Janie; written by Stanley; Tripp-a 15 30 45 120 210 300
Mickey Mouse Almanac 1(12/57)-Barks-a, 8pgs. 27 54 81 216 378 540
...Birthday Party 1(9/53)-r/entire 48pgs. of Gottfredson's "Mickey Mouse in Love Trouble" from WDC&S 36-39. Quality equal to original. Also reprints one story each from Four Color 27, 79, & 181 plus 6 panels of highlights in the career of Mickey Mouse
31 62 93 248 434 620
...Club Parade 1(12/55)-r/4-Color 16 with some death trap scenes redrawn by Paul Murry & recolored with night turned into day; quality less than original
22 44 66 176 308 440
...In Fantasy Land 1(5/57) 13 26 39 104 180 255
...In Frontier Land 1(5/56)-Mickey Mouse Club iss. 13 26 39 104 180 255
...Summer Fun 1(8/58)-Mobile cut-outs on back-c; becomes Summer Fun with #2; Canadian version exists with 30¢-c price 13 26 39 104 180 255
Moses & The Ten Commandments 1(8/57)-Not based on movie; Dell's adaptation; Sekowsky-a; variant version has "Gods of Egypt" comic back-c 8 16 24 64 107 150
Nancy & Sluggo Travel Time 1(9/58) 8 16 24 64 115 165
Peter Pan Treasure Chest 1(1/53, 212pp)-Disney; contains 54-page movie adaptation & other Peter Pan stories; plus Donald & Mickey stories w/P. Pan; a 32-page retelling of "D. Duck Finds Pirate Gold" with yellow beak, called "Capt. Hook & the Buried Treasure"
140 280 420 1120 1960 2800
Picnic Party 6,7(7/55-6/56)(Formerly Vacation Parade)-Uncle Scrooge, Mickey & Donald
12 24 36 96 166 235
Picnic Party 8(7/57)-Barks-a, 6pgs 21 42 63 168 289 410
Pogo Parade 1(9/53)-Kelly-a(r-/Pogo from Animal Comics in this order: #11,13,21,14,27,16,23,9,18,15,17) 25 50 75 200 350 500
Raggedy Ann & Andy 1(2/55) 16 32 48 128 224 320
Santa Claus Funnies 1(11/52)-Dan Noonan -A Christmas Carol adaptation
9 18 27 72 126 180
Silly Symphonies 1(9/52)-Redrawing of Gotfredson's Mickey Mouse strip of "The Brave Little Tailor;" 2 Good Housekeeping pages (from 1943); Lady and the Two Siamese Cats, three years before "Lady & the Tramp;" a retelling of Donald Duck's first app. in "The Wise Little Hen" & other stories based on 1930's Silly Symphony cartoons
33 66 99 264 457 650
Silly Symphonies 2(9/53)-M. Mouse in "The Sorcerer's Apprentice", 2 Good Housekeeping pages (from 1944); The Pelican & the Snipe, Elmer Elephant, Peculiar Penguins, Little Hiawatha, & others 24 48 72 192 339 485
Silly Symphonies 3(2/54)-r/Mickey & The Beanstalk (4-Color #157, 39pgs.), Little Minnehaha, Pablo, The Flying Gauchito, Pluto, & Bongo, & 2 Good Housekeeping pages (1944)
20 40 60 160 275 390
Silly Symphonies 4(8/54)-r/Dumbo (4-Color 234), Morris The Midget Moose, The Country Cousin, Bongo, & Clara Cluck 20 40 60 160 275 390
Silly Symphonies 5-8: 5(2/55)-r/Cinderella (4-Color 272), Bucky Bug, Pluto, Little Hiawatha, The 7 Dwarfs & Dumbo, Pinocchio. 6(8/55)-r/Pinocchio (WDC&S 63), The 7 Dwarfs & Thumper (WDC&S 45), M. Mouse "Adventures With Robin Hood" (40 pgs.), Johnny Appleseed, Pluto & Peter Pan, & Bucky Bug; Cut-out on back-c. 7(2/57)-r/Reluctant Dragon, Ugly Duckling, M. Mouse & Peter Pan, Jiminy Cricket, Peter & The Wolf, Brer Rabbit, Bucky Bug; Cut-out on back-c. 8(2/58)-r/Thumper Meets The 7 Dwarfs (4-Color #19), Jiminy Cricket, Niok, Brer Rabbit; Cut-out on back-c
16 32 48 128 224 320
Silly Symphonies 9(2/59)-r/Paul Bunyan, Humphrey Bear, Jiminy Cricket, The Social Lion, Goliath II; cut-out on back-c 15 30 45 120 210 300
Sleeping Beauty 1(4/59) 25 50 75 200 350 500
Summer Fun 2(8/59, 84pp, stapled binding)(Formerly Mickey Mouse...)-Barks-a(2), 24 pgs.
24 48 72 192 336 480
Tarzan's Jungle Annual 1(8/52)-Lex Barker photo on-c of #1,2
15 30 45 120 210 300
...Annual 2(8/53) 11 22 33 88 152 215
...Annual 3-7('54-9/58)(two No. 5s)-Manning-a-No. 3,5-7; Marsh-a in No. 1-7 plus painted-c 1-7 9 18 27 72 124 175
Tom And Jerry Back To School 1(9/56) 2 different back-c, variant has "Apple for the Teacher" cut-out 12 24 36 96 168 240
...Picnic Time 1(7/58) 10 20 30 80 135 190
...Summer Fun 1(7/54)-Droopy written by Barks 15 30 45 120 205 290
...Summer Fun 2-4(7/55-7/57) 8 16 24 64 107 150
...Toy Fair 1(6/58) 9 18 27 72 126 180
...Winter Carnival 1(12/52)-Droopy written by Barks 20 40 60 160 280 400
...Winter Carnival 2(12/53)-Droopy written by Barks 16 32 48 128 224 320
...Winter Fun 3(12/54) 8 16 24 64 115 165
...Winter Fun 4-7(12/55-11/58) 7 14 21 56 101 145
Treasury of Dogs, A 1(10/56) 8 16 24 64 107 150
Treasury of Horses, A (9/55) 8 16 24 64 107 150
Uncle Scrooge Goes To Disneyland 1(8/57p)-Barks-a, 20 pgs. r-by Gladstone; 2 different back-c; variant shows 6 snapshots of Scrooge 26 52 78 208 359 510
Vacation In Disneyland 1(8/58) 11 22 33 88 157 225

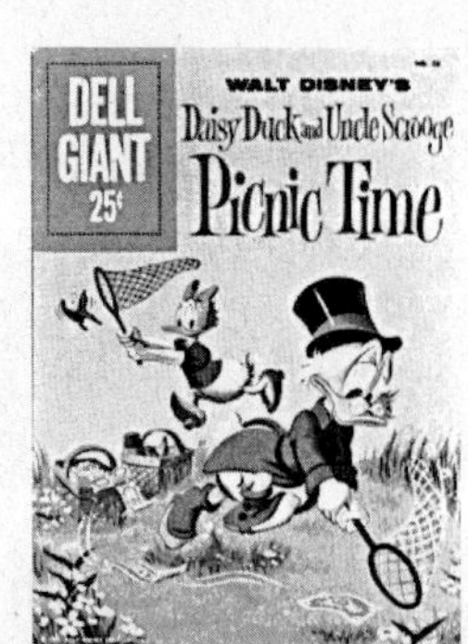

Dell Giant #33 © DIS

Dell Junior Treasury #8 © DELL

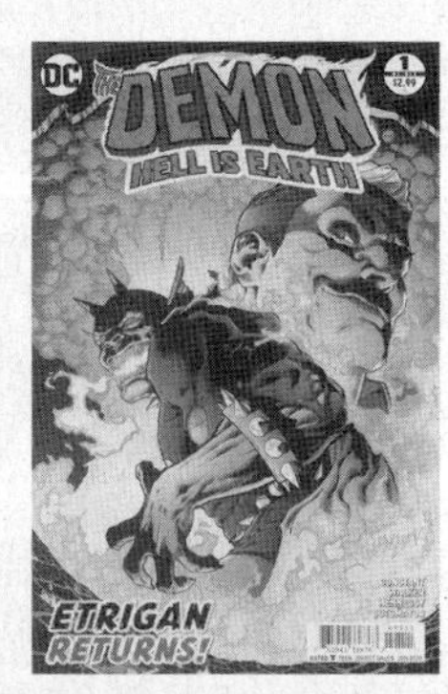

The Demon: Hell is Earth #1 © DC

GD 2.0 | VG 4.0 | FN 6.0 | VF 8.0 | VF/NM 9.0 | NM- 9.2

Vacation Parade 1(7/50, 132pp)-Donald Duck & Mickey Mouse; Barks-a, 55 pgs. 95 190 285 760 1330 1900
Vacation Parade 2(7/51,116pp) 25 50 75 200 350 500
Vacation Parade 3-5(7/52-7/54)-Becomes Picnic Party No. 6 on. #4-Robin Hood Advs. 14 28 42 112 194 275
Western Roundup 1(6/52)-Photo-c; Gene Autry, Roy Rogers, Johnny Mack Brown, Rex Allen, & Bill Elliott begin; photo back-c begin, end No. 14,16,18 25 50 75 200 350 500
Western Roundup 2(2/53)-Photo-c 14 28 42 112 196 280
Western Roundup 3-5(7-9/53 - 1-3/54)-Photo-c 11 22 33 88 157 225
Western Roundup 6-10(4-6/54 - 4-6/55)-Photo-c 11 22 33 88 149 210
Western Roundup 11-17,25: 11-17-Photo-c; 11-13,16,17-Manning-a. 11-Flying A's Range Rider, Dale Evans begin 9 18 27 72 129 185
Western Roundup 18-Toth-a; last photo-c; Gene Autry ends 11 22 33 88 149 210
Western Roundup 19-24-Manning-a. 19-Buffalo Bill Jr. begins (7-9/57; early app.). 19,20,22-Toth-a. 21-Rex Allen, Johnny Mack Brown end. 22-Jace Pearson's Texas Rangers, Rin Tin Tin, Tales of Wells Fargo (2nd app., 4-6/58) & Wagon Train (2nd app.) begin 9 18 27 72 129 185
Woody Woodpecker Back To School 1(10/52) 10 20 30 80 140 200
...Back To School 2-4,6('53-10/57)-County Fair No. 5 8 16 24 64 112 160
...County Fair 5(9/56)-Formerly Back To School 8 16 24 64 112 160
...County Fair 2(11/58) 7 14 21 56 101 145

DELL GIANTS (Consecutive numbering)
Dell Publishing Co.: No. 21, Sept, 1959 - No. 55, Sept, 1961 (Most 84 pgs., 25¢)

21-(#1)-M.G.M.'s Tom & Jerry Picnic Time (84pp, stapled binding)-Painted-c 11 22 33 88 157 225
22-Huey, Dewey & Louie Back to School (Disney; 10/59, 84pp, square binding begins) 9 18 27 72 129 185
23-Marge's Little Lulu & Tubby Halloween Fun (10/59)-Tripp-a 12 24 36 96 168 240
24-Woody Woodpecker's Family Fun (11/59)(Walter Lantz) 8 16 24 64 112 160
25-Tarzan's Jungle World(11/59)-Marsh-a; painted-c 11 22 33 88 152 215
26-Christmas Parade(Disney; 12/59)-Barks-a, 16pgs.; Barks draws himself on wanted poster on pg. 13 21 42 63 168 289 410
27-Walt Disney's Man in Space (10/59) r-/4-Color 716,866, & 954 (100 pgs., 35¢)(TV) 9 18 27 72 129 185
28-Bugs Bunny's Winter Fun (2/60) 9 18 27 72 126 180
29-Marge's Little Lulu & Tubby in Hawaii (4/60)-Tripp-a 12 24 36 96 166 235
30-Disneyland USA(Disney; 6/60) 9 18 27 72 124 175
31-Huckleberry Hound Summer Fun (7/60)(TV)(HannaBarbera)-Yogi Bear & Pixie & Dixie app. 12 24 36 96 173 250
32-Bugs Bunny Beach Party 7 14 21 56 101 145
33-Daisy Duck & Uncle Scrooge Picnic Time (Disney; 9/60) 9 18 27 72 124 175
34-Nancy & Sluggo Summer Camp (8/60) 7 14 21 56 101 145
35-Huey, Dewey & Louie Back to School (Disney; 10/60)-1st app. Daisy Duck's Nieces, April, May & June 12 24 36 96 163 230
36-Marge's Little Lulu & Witch Hazel Halloween Fun (10/60)-Tripp-a 11 22 33 88 157 225
37-Tarzan, King of the Jungle (11/60)-Marsh-a; painted-c 9 18 27 72 129 185
38-Uncle Donald & His Nephews Family Fun (Disney; 11/60)-Cover painting based on a pencil sketch by Barks 12 24 36 96 173 250
39-Walt Disney's Merry Christmas (Disney; 12/60)-Cover painting based on a pencil sketch by Barks 12 24 36 96 173 250
40-Woody Woodpecker Christmas Parade (12/60)(Walter Lantz) 6 12 18 48 87 125
41-Yogi Bear's Winter Sports (12/60)(TV)(Hanna-Barbera)-Huckleberry Hound, Pixie & Dixie, Augie Doggie app. 12 24 36 96 173 250
42-Marge's Little Lulu & Tubby in Australia (4/61) 11 22 33 88 157 225
43-Mighty Mouse in Outer Space (5/61) 18 36 54 144 252 360
44-Around the World with Huckleberry and His Friends (7/61)(TV)(Hanna-Barbera)-Yogi Bear, Pixie & Dixie, Quick Draw McGraw, Augie Doggie app.; 1st app. Yakky Doodle 13 26 39 104 182 260
45-Nancy & Sluggo Summer Camp (8/61) 7 14 21 56 96 135
46-Bugs Bunny Beach Party (8/61) 7 14 21 56 96 135
47-Mickey & Donald in Vacationland (Disney; 8/61) 8 16 24 64 115 165
48-The Flintstones (No. 1)(Bedrock Bedlam)(7/61)(TV)(Hanna-Barbera) 1st app. in comics 21 42 63 168 294 420
49-Huey, Dewey & Louie Back to School (Disney; 9/61) 9 18 27 72 124 175
50-Marge's Little Lulu & Witch Hazel Trick 'N' Treat (10/61) 11 22 33 88 157 225
51-Tarzan, King of the Jungle by Jesse Marsh (11/61)-Painted-c 8 16 24 64 110 155
52-Uncle Donald & His Nephews Dude Ranch (Disney; 11/61) 8 16 24 64 115 165
53-Donald Duck Merry Christmas (Disney; 12/61) 8 16 24 64 112 160
54-Woody Woodpecker's Christmas Party (12/61)-Issued after No. 55 7 14 21 56 98 140
55-Daisy Duck & Uncle Scrooge Showboat (Disney; 9/61) 8 16 24 64 117 170
NOTE: All issues printed with & without ad on back cover.

DELL JUNIOR TREASURY
Dell Publishing Co.: June, 1955 - No. 10, Oct, 1957 (15¢) (All painted-c)

1-Alice in Wonderland; r/4-Color #331 (52 pgs.) 8 16 24 54 102 150
2-Aladdin & the Wonderful Lamp 6 12 18 41 76 110
3-Gulliver's Travels (1/56) 6 12 18 37 66 95
4-Adventures of Mr. Frog & Miss Mouse 6 12 18 38 69 100
5-The Wizard of Oz (7/56) 6 12 18 41 76 110
6-10: 6-Heidi (10/56). 7-Santa and the Angel. 8-Raggedy Ann and the Camel with the Wrinkled Knees. 9-Clementina the Flying Pig. 10-Adventures of Tom Sawyer 6 12 18 37 66 95

DEMOLITION MAN
DC Comics: Nov, 1993 - No. 4, Feb, 1994 ($1.75, color, limited series)

1-4-Movie adaptation 3.00

DEMON, THE (See Detective Comics No. 482-485)
National Periodical Publications: Aug-Sept, 1972 - V3#16, Jan, 1974

1-Origin; Kirby-s/c/a in all; 1st Morgaine Le Fey 11 22 33 76 163 250
2-5 4 8 12 27 44 60
6-16: 7-1st app. Klarion the Witch Boy 3 6 9 19 30 40

DEMON, THE (1st limited series)(Also see Cosmic Odyssey #2)
DC Comics: Nov, 1986 - No. 4, Feb, 1987 (75¢, limited series)(#2 has #4 of 4 on-c)

1-4: Matt Wagner-a(p) & scripts in all. 4-Demon & Jason Blood become separate entities. 4.00

DEMON, THE (2nd Series)
DC Comics: July, 1990 - No. 58, May, 1995 ($1.50/$1.75/$1.95)

1-Grant scripts begin, ends #39: 1-4-Painted-c 5.00
2-18,20-27,29-39,41,42: 3,8-Batman app. (cameo #4). 12-Bisley painted-c. 12-15,21-Lobo app. (1 pg. cameo #11). 23-Robin app. 29-Superman app. 31,33-39-Lobo app. 3.00
19-($2.50, 44 pgs.)-Lobo poster stapled inside 5.00
28,40: 28-Superman-c/story; begin $1.75-c. 40-Garth Ennis scripts begin 4.00
43-45-Hitman app. 1 2 3 5 7 9
46-48 Return of The Haunted Tank-c/s. 48-Begin $1.95-c. 5.00
49,51,0-(10/94),55-58: 51-(9/94) 3.00
50 ($2.95, 52 pgs.) 4.00
52-54-Hitman-s 5.00
Annual 1 (1992, $3.00, 68 pgs.)-Eclipso-c/story 4.00
Annual 2 (1993, $3.50, 68 pgs.)-1st app. of Hitman 3 6 9 14 19 24
NOTE: *Alan Grant scripts in #1-16, 20, 21, 23-25, 30-39, Annual 1.* ***Wagner*** *a/scripts-22.*

DEMON DREAMS
Pacific Comics: Feb, 1984 - No. 2, May, 1984

1,2-Mostly r-/Heavy Metal 3.00

DEMON: DRIVEN OUT
DC Comics: Nov, 2003 - No. 6, Apr, 2004 ($2.50, limited series)

1-6-Dysart-s/Mhan-a 3.00

DEMON, THE: HELL IS EARTH (Etrigan)
DC Comics: Jan, 2018 - No. 6 ($2.99, limited series)

1-4-Andrew Constant-s/Brad Walker-a; Xanadu app. 3.00

DEMON-HUNTER
Seaboard Periodicals (Atlas): Sept, 1975

1-Origin/1st app. Demon-Hunter; Buckler-c/a 3 6 9 14 20 25

DEMON KNIGHT: A GRIMJACK GRAPHIC NOVEL
First Publishing: 1990 ($8.95, 52 pgs.)

nn-Flint Henry-a 9.00

DEMON KNIGHTS (New DC 52) (Set in the Dark Ages)
DC Comics: Nov, 2011 - No. 23, Oct, 2013 ($2.99)

1-23: 1-Cornell-s/Neves-a/Daniel-c; Etrigan, Madame Xanadu & The Shining Knight app. 3.00

Dennis the Menace #20 © KFS

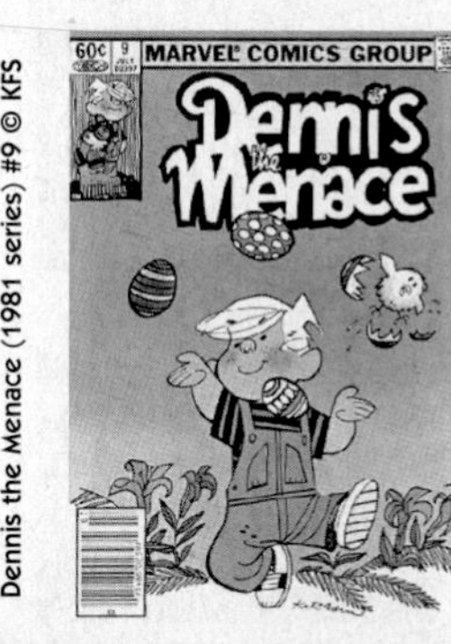

Dennis the Menace (1981 series) #9 © KFS

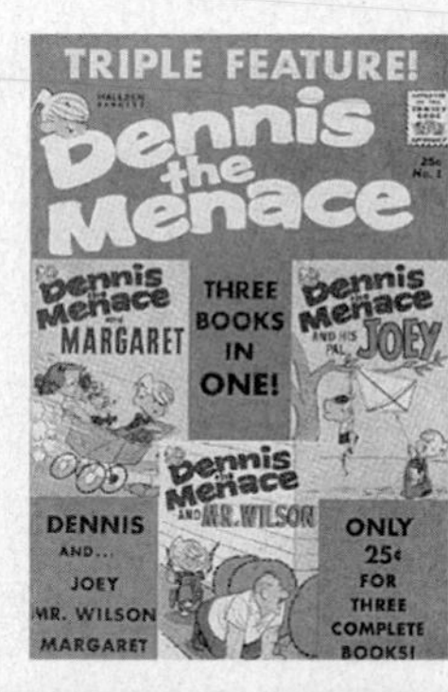

Dennis the Menace Tripe Feature #1 © KFS

	GD 2.0	VG 4.0	FN 6.0	VF 8.0	VF/NM 9.0	NM- 9.2
#0 (11/12, $2.99) Origin of Etrigan The Demon; Merlin app.; Cornell-s/Chang-a						3.00

DENNIS THE MENACE (TV with 1959 issues) (Becomes ...Fun Fest Series; See The Best of... & The Very Best of...)(...Fun Fest on-c only to #156-166)
Standard Comics/Pines No.15-31/Hallden (Fawcett) No.32 on: 8/53 - #14, 1/56; #15, 3/56 - #31, 11/58; #32, 1/59 - #166, 11/79

	GD 2.0	VG 4.0	FN 6.0	VF 8.0	VF/NM 9.0	NM- 9.2
1-1st app. Dennis, Mr. & Mrs. Wilson, Ruff & Dennis' mom & dad; Wiseman-a, written by Fred Toole-most issues	258	516	774	1651	2826	4000
2	60	120	180	381	653	925
3-5	39	78	117	231	378	525
6-10: 8-Last pre-code issue	32	64	96	188	307	425
11-20	21	42	63	122	199	275
21,23-30	14	28	42	76	108	140
22-1st app. Margaret w/blonde hair	16	32	48	94	147	200
31-1st app. Joey	16	32	48	94	147	200
32-38,40(1/60): 37-A-Bomb blast panel	9	18	27	52	69	85
39-1st app. Gina (11/59)	12	24	36	67	94	120
41-60(7/62)	4	8	12	22	34	45
61-80(9/65),100(1/69)	3	6	9	14	20	25
81-99	2	4	6	11	16	20
101-117: 102-Last 12¢ issue	2	4	6	9	12	15
118(1/72)-131 (All 52 pages)	2	4	6	10	14	18
132(1/74)-142,144-160	1	2	3	5	7	9
143(3/76) Olympic-c/s; low print	2	4	6	10	14	18
161-166	1	3	4	6	8	10

NOTE: ***Wiseman** c/a-1-46, 53, 68, 69.*

DENNIS THE MENACE (Giants) (No. 1 titled Giant Vacation Special; becomes Dennis the Menace Bonus Magazine No. 76 on)
(#1-8,18,23,25,30,38: 100 pgs.; rest to #41: 84 pgs.; #42-75: 68 pgs.)
Standard/Pines/Halldén(Fawcett): Summer, 1955 - No. 75, Dec, 1969

	GD 2.0	VG 4.0	FN 6.0	VF 8.0	VF/NM 9.0	NM- 9.2
nn-Giant Vacation Special(Summ/55-Standard)	18	36	54	105	165	225
nn-Christmas issue (Winter '55)	15	30	45	90	140	190
2-Giant Vacation Special (Summer '56-Pines)	14	28	42	80	115	150
3-Giant Christmas issue (Winter '56-Pines)	13	26	39	74	105	135
4-Giant Vacation Special (Summer '57-Pines)	12	24	36	69	97	125
5-Giant Christmas issue (Winter '57-Pines)	12	24	36	69	97	125
6-In Hawaii (Giant Vacation Special)(Summer '58-Pines)	11	22	33	64	90	115
6-In Hawaii (Summer '59-Hallden)-2nd printing; says 3rd large printing on-c; 6-In Hawaii (Summer '60)-3rd printing; says 4th large printing on-c; 6-In Hawaii (Summer '62)-4th printing; says 5th large printing on-c each....	8	16	24	44	57	70
6-Giant Christmas issue (Winter '58)	11	22	33	64	90	115
7-In Hollywood (Winter '59-Hallden)	5	10	15	31	53	75
7-In Hollywood (Summer '61)-2nd printing	3	6	9	20	31	42
8-In Mexico (Winter '60, 100 pgs.-Hallden/Fawcett)	5	10	15	31	53	75
8-In Mexico (Summer '62, 2nd printing)	3	6	9	20	31	42
9-Goes to Camp (Summer '61, 84 pgs.)-1st CCA approved issue	5	10	15	30	50	70
9-Goes to Camp (Summer '62)-2nd printing	3	6	9	20	31	42
10-12: 10-X-Mas issue (Winter '61), 11-Giant Christmas issue (Winter '62), 12-Triple Feature (Winter '62)	5	10	15	33	57	80
13-17: 13-Best of Dennis the Menace (Spring '63)-Reprints, 14-And His Dog Ruff (Summer '63), 15-In Washington, D.C. (Summer '63), 16-Goes to Camp (Summer '63)-Reprints No. 9, 17-& His Pal Joey (Winter '63)	4	8	12	23	37	50
18-In Hawaii (Reprints No. 6)	3	6	9	19	30	40
19-Giant Christmas issue (Winter '63)	4	8	12	23	37	50
20-Spring Special (Spring '64)	4	8	12	23	37	50
21-40 (Summer '66): 30-r/#6. #35-Xmas spec.Wint,'65	3	6	9	17	26	35
41-60 (Fall '68)	3	6	9	14	19	24
61-75 (12/69): 68-Partial-r/#6	2	4	6	11	16	20

NOTE: ***Wiseman** c/a-1-8, 12, 14, 15, 17, 20, 22, 27, 28, 31, 35, 36, 41, 49.*

DENNIS THE MENACE
Marvel Comics Group: Nov, 1981 - No. 13, Nov, 1982

	GD 2.0	VG 4.0	FN 6.0	VF 8.0	VF/NM 9.0	NM- 9.2
1-New-a	2	4	6	9	12	15
2-13: 2-New art. 3-Part-r. 4,5-r. 5-X-Mas-c & issue, 7-Spider Kid-c/sty	1	2	3	4	5	7

NOTE: ***Hank Ketcham** c-most; a-3, 12. **Wiseman** a-4, 5.*

DENNIS THE MENACE AND HIS DOG RUFF
Hallden/Fawcett: Summer, 1961

	GD 2.0	VG 4.0	FN 6.0	VF 8.0	VF/NM 9.0	NM- 9.2
1-Wiseman-c/a	5	10	15	34	60	85

DENNIS THE MENACE AND HIS FRIENDS
Fawcett Publ.: 1969; No. 5, Jan, 1970 - No. 46, April, 1980 (All reprints)

	GD 2.0	VG 4.0	FN 6.0	VF 8.0	VF/NM 9.0	NM- 9.2
Dennis the Menace & Joey No. 2 (7/69)	2	4	6	13	18	22
Dennis the Menace & Ruff No. 2 (9/69)	2	4	6	13	18	22
Dennis the Menace & Mr. Wilson No. 1 (10/69)	3	6	9	15	22	28
Dennis & Margaret No. 1 (Winter '69)	3	6	9	15	22	28
5-12: 5-Dennis the Menace & Margaret. 6-...& Joey. 7-...& Ruff. 8-...& Mr. Wilson	2	4	6	8	11	14
13-21-(52 pg Giants): 13-(1/72). 21-(1/74)	2	4	6	10	14	18
22-37	1	3	4	6	8	10
38-46 (Digest size, 148 pgs., 4/78, 95¢)	2	4	6	8	11	14

NOTE: *Titles rotate every four issues, beginning with No. 5. Joey issues: #2(7/69),6,10,14,18,22,26,30,34. Ruff issues: #2(9/69), 7,11,15,19,23,27,31,35. Mr. Wilson issues: #1(10/69),8,12,16,20,24,28,32,36. Margaret issues: #1(Wint./69),5,9,13,17,21,25,29,33,37.*

DENNIS THE MENACE AND HIS PAL JOEY
Fawcett Publ.: Summer, 1961 (10¢) (See Dennis the Menace Giants No. 45)

	GD 2.0	VG 4.0	FN 6.0	VF 8.0	VF/NM 9.0	NM- 9.2
1-Wiseman-c/a	5	10	15	34	60	85

DENNIS THE MENACE AND THE BIBLE KIDS
Word Books: 1977 (36 pgs.)

	GD 2.0	VG 4.0	FN 6.0	VF 8.0	VF/NM 9.0	NM- 9.2
1-6: 1-Jesus. 2-Joseph. 3-David. 4-The Bible Girls. 5-Moses. 6-More About Jesus	2	4	6	9	12	15
7-9-Low print run: 7-The Lord's Prayer. 8-Stories Jesus told. 9-Paul, God's Traveller	3	6	9	19	30	40
10-Low print run; In the Beginning	5	10	15	33	57	80

NOTE: ***Ketcham** c/a in all.*

DENNIS THE MENACE BIG BONUS SERIES
Fawcett Publications: No. 10, Feb, 1980 - No. 11, Apr, 1980

	GD 2.0	VG 4.0	FN 6.0	VF 8.0	VF/NM 9.0	NM- 9.2
10,11	1	2	3	5	6	8

DENNIS THE MENACE BONUS MAGAZINE (Formerly Dennis the Menace Giants Nos. 1-75) (...Big Bonus Series on-c for #174-194)
Fawcett Publications: No. 76, 1/70 - No. 95, 7/71; No. 95, 7/71; No. 97, '71; No. 194, 10/79; (No. 76-124: 68 pgs.; No. 125-163: 52 pgs.; No. 164 on: 36 pgs.)

	GD 2.0	VG 4.0	FN 6.0	VF 8.0	VF/NM 9.0	NM- 9.2
76-90(3/71)	2	4	6	10	14	18
91-95, 97-110(10/72): Two #95's with same date(7/71) A-Summer Games, and B-That's Our Boy. No #96	2	4	6	9	13	16
111-124	2	4	6	8	10	12
125-163-(52 pgs.)	2	4	6	8	10	12
164-194: 166-Indicia printed backwards	1	2	3	4	5	7

DENNIS THE MENACE COMICS DIGEST
Marvel Comics Group: April, 1982 - No. 3, Aug, 1982 ($1.25, digest-size)

	GD 2.0	VG 4.0	FN 6.0	VF 8.0	VF/NM 9.0	NM- 9.2
1-3-Reprints	1	3	4	6	8	10
1-Mistakenly printed with DC emblem on cover	2	4	6	10	12	15

NOTE: ***Ketcham** c-all. **Wiseman** a-all. A few thousand #1's were published with a DC emblem on cover.*

DENNIS THE MENACE FUN BOOK
Fawcett Publications/Standard Comics: 1960 (100 pgs.)

	GD 2.0	VG 4.0	FN 6.0	VF 8.0	VF/NM 9.0	NM- 9.2
1-Part Wiseman-a	5	10	15	35	63	90

DENNIS THE MENACE FUN FEST SERIES (Formerly Dennis the Menace #166)
Hallden (Fawcett): No. 16, Jan, 1980 - No. 17, Mar, 1980 (40¢)

	GD 2.0	VG 4.0	FN 6.0	VF 8.0	VF/NM 9.0	NM- 9.2
16,17-By Hank Ketcham	1	2	3	4	5	7

DENNIS THE MENACE POCKET FULL OF FUN!
Fawcett Publications (Hallden): Spring, 1969 - No. 50, March, 1980 (196 pgs.) (Digest size)

	GD 2.0	VG 4.0	FN 6.0	VF 8.0	VF/NM 9.0	NM- 9.2
1-Reprints in all issues	5	10	15	33	57	80
2-10	4	8	12	23	37	50
11-20	3	6	9	15	22	28
21-28	2	4	6	11	16	20
29-50: 35,40,46-Sunday strip-r	2	4	6	8	11	14

NOTE: *No. 1-28 are 196 pgs.; No. 29-36: 164 pgs.; No. 37: 148 pgs.; No. 38 on: 132 pgs. No. 8, 11, 15, 21, 25, 29 all contain strip reprints.*

DENNIS THE MENACE TELEVISION SPECIAL
Fawcett Publ. (Hallden Div.): Summer, 1961 - No. 2, Spring, 1962 (Giant)

	GD 2.0	VG 4.0	FN 6.0	VF 8.0	VF/NM 9.0	NM- 9.2
1	5	10	15	34	60	85
2	3	6	9	21	33	45

DENNIS THE MENACE TRIPLE FEATURE
Fawcett Publications: Winter, 1961 (Giant)

	GD 2.0	VG 4.0	FN 6.0	VF 8.0	VF/NM 9.0	NM- 9.2
1-Wiseman-c/a	5	10	15	34	60	85

DEPT. H
Dark Horse Comics: Apr, 2016 - No. 24 ($3.99)

	GD 2.0	VG 4.0	FN 6.0	VF 8.0	VF/NM 9.0	NM- 9.2
1-23-Matt Kindt-s/a. 1-Two covers						4.00

DEPUTY, THE (TV)

Descender #23 © 171 Studios & D. Nguyen

Desperado #4 © LEV

Detective Comics #22 © DC

	GD	VG	FN	VF	VF/NM	NM-
	2.0	4.0	6.0	8.0	9.0	9.2

Dell Publishing Co.: No. 1077, Feb-Apr, 1960 - No. 1225, Oct-Dec, 1961 (all-Henry Fonda photo-c)

Four Color 1077 (#1)-Buscema-a 10 20 30 64 132 200
Four Color 1130 (9-11/60)-Buscema-a,1225 8 16 24 54 102 150

DEPUTY DAWG (TV) (Also see New Terrytoons)
Dell Publishing Co./Gold Key: Oct-Dec, 1961 - No. 1299, 1962; No. 1, Aug, 1965

Four Color 1238,1299 9 18 27 63 129 195
1(10164-508)(8/65)-Gold Key 9 18 27 63 129 195

DEPUTY DAWG PRESENTS DINKY DUCK AND HASHIMOTO-SAN (TV)
Gold Key: August, 1965

1(10159-508) 9 18 27 57 111 165

DESCENDER
Image Comics: Mar, 2015 - Present ($2.99/$3.99)

1-Lemire-s/Nguyen-a/c in all; bonus concept-a 5.00
1-Variant-c by Lemire 6.00
2-18-Lemire-s/Nguyen-a/c 3.00
19-27-($3.99) 4.00

DESERT GOLD (See Zane Grey 4-Color 467)

DESIGN FOR SURVIVAL (Gen. Thomas S. Power's...)
American Security Council Press: 1968 (36 pgs. in color) (25¢)

nn-Propaganda against the Threat of Communism-Aircraft cover; H-Bomb panel
3 6 9 17 26 35
Twin Circle Edition-Cover shows panels from inside 2 4 6 13 18 22

DESOLATION JONES
DC Comics (WildStorm): July, 2005 - No. 8, Feb, 2007 ($2.95/$2.99)

1-8: 1-6-Warren Ellis-s/J.H. Williams-a. 7,8-Zezelj-a 3.00

DESPERADO (Becomes Black Diamond Western No. 9 on)
Lev Gleason Publications: June, 1948 - No. 8, Feb, 1949 (All 52 pgs.)

1-Biro-c on all; contains inside photo-c of Charles Biro, Lev Gleason & Bob Wood
17 34 51 98 154 210
2 10 20 30 58 79 100
3-Story with over 20 killings 11 22 33 60 83 105
4-8 8 16 24 44 57 70

NOTE: ***Barry** a-2. **Fuje** a-4, 8. **Guardineer** a-5-7. **Kida** a-3-7. **Ed Moore** a-4, 6.*

DESPERADO PRIMER
Image Comics (Desperado): Apr, 2005 ($1.99, one-shot)

1-Previews of Roundeye, World Traveler, A Mirror To The Soul; Bolland-c 3.00

DESPERADOES
Image Comics (Homage): Sept, 1997 - No. 5, June, 1998 ($2.50/$2.95)

1-5-Mariotte-s/Cassaday-c/a: 1-($2.50-c). 2-5-($2.95) 3.00
...: A Moment's Sunlight TPB ('98, $16.95) r/#1-5 17.00
...: Epidemic! (11/99, $5.95) Mariotte-s 6.00

DESPERADOES: BANNERS OF GOLD
IDW Publishing: Dec, 2004 - No. 5, Apr, 2005 ($3.99, limited series)

1-5: Mariotte-s/Haun-a. 1-Cassaday-c 4.00

DESPERADOES: BUFFALO DREAMS
IDW Publishing: Jan, 2007 - No. 4, Apr, 2007 ($3.99, limited series)

1-4: Mariotte-s/Dose-a/c 4.00

DESPERADOES: QUIET OF THE GRAVE
DC Comics (Homage): Jul, 2001 - No. 5, Nov, 2001 ($2.95)

1-5-Jeff Mariotte-s/John Severin-c/a 3.00
TPB (2002, $14.95) r/#1-5; intro. by Brian Keene 15.00

DESPERATE TIMES (See Savage Dragon)
Image Comics: Jun, 1998 - No. 4, Dec, 1998; Nov, 2000 - No. 4, July, 2001 ($2.95, B&W)

1-4-Chris Eliopoulos-s/a 3.00
(Vol. 2) 1-4 3.00
(Vol. 3) 0-(1/04, $3.50) Pages read sideways 3.50
(Vol. 3) 1-Pages read sideways 3.00

DESPICABLE DEADPOOL (Marvel Legacy)
Marvel Comics: No. 287, Dec, 2017 - Present ($3.99)

287-295-Duggan-s/Koblish-a; Cable app. 293-Rogue app. 4.00

DESTINATION MOON (See Fawcett Movie Comics, Space Adventures #20, 23, & Strange Adventures #1)

DESTINY: A CHRONICLE OF DEATHS FORETOLD (See Sandman)
DC Comics (Vertigo): 1997 - No. 3, 1998 ($5.95, limited series)

1-3-Alisa Kwitney-s in all: 1-Kent Williams & Michael Zulli-a, Williams painted-c. 2-Williams & Scott Hampton-painted-c/a. 3-Williams & Guay-a 6.00
TPB (2000, $14.95) r/series 15.00

DESTROY!!
Eclipse Comics: 1986 ($4.95, B&W, magazine-size, one-shot)

1 5.00
3-D Special 1-r-/#1 ($2.50) 5.00

DESTROYER
Marvel Comics: June, 2009 - No. 5, Oct, 2009 ($3.99, limited series)

1-5-Kirkman-s/Walker-a/Pearson-c 4.00

DESTROYER, THE
Marvel Comics (MAX): Nov, 1989 - No. 9, Jun, 1990 ($2.25, B&W, magazine, 52 pgs.)

1-Based on Remo Williams movie, paperbacks 6.00
2-9: 2-Williamson part inks. 4-Ditko-a 4.00

DESTROYER, THE
Marvel Comics: V2#1, March, 1991 ($1.95, 52 pgs.)
V3#1, Dec, 1991 - No. 4, Mar, 1992 ($1.95, mini-series)

V2#1,V3#1-4: Based on Remo Williams paperbacks. V3#1-4-Simonson-c. 3-Morrow-a 4.00

DESTROYER, THE (Also see Solar, Man of the Atom)
Valiant: Apr, 1995 ($2.95, color, one-shot)

0-Indicia indicates #1 3.00

DESTROYER (VICTOR LAVALLE'S...)
BOOM! Studios: May, 2017 - No. 6, Oct, 2017 ($3.99, limited series)

1-6-LaValle-s/Dietrich Smith-a; Frankenstein's monster app. 4.00

DESTROYER DUCK
Eclipse Comics: Feb, 1982 - No. 7, May, 1984 (#2-7: Baxter paper) ($1.50)

1-Origin Destroyer Duck; 1st app. Groo; Kirby-c/a(p) 2 4 6 10 14 18
2-5: 2-Starling back-up begins; Kirby-c/a(p) thru #5 5.00
6,7 4.00

NOTE: ***Neal Adams** c-1i. **Kirby** c/a-1-5p. **Miller** c-7.*

DESTRUCTOR, THE
Atlas/Seaboard: February, 1975 - No. 4, Aug, 1975

1-Origin/1st app.; Ditko/Wood-a; Wood-c(i) 2 4 6 13 18 22
2-4: 2-Ditko/Wood-a. 3,4-Ditko-a(p) 2 4 6 9 13 16

DETECTIVE COMICS (Also see other Batman titles)
National Periodical Publications/DC Comics: Mar, 1937 - No. 881, Oct, 2011

1-(Scarce)-Slam Bradley & Spy by Siegel & Shuster, Speed Saunders by Stoner and Flessel, Cosmo, the Phantom of Disguise, Buck Marshall, Bruce Nelson begin; Chin Lung in 'Claws of the Red Dragon' serial begins; Vincent Sullivan-c
13,500 27,000 40,500 100,000 - -
2 (Rare)-Creig Flessel-c begin; new logo 6150 12,300 18,450 40,000 - -
3 (Rare) 3700 7400 11,000 27,000 - -
4,5: 5-Larry Steele begins 1950 3900 5850 10,725 15,113 19,500
6,7,9,10 1400 2800 4200 7700 10,850 14,000
8-Mister Chang-c; classic-c 2000 4000 6000 11,000 15,500 20,000
11-14,17,19: 17-1st app. Fu Manchu in Detective 1200 2400 3600 6600 9300 12,000
15,16-Have interior ad for Action Comics #1 1400 2800 4200 7700 10,850 14,000
18-Classic Fu Manchu-c; last Flessel-c 1900 3800 5700 10,450 14,725 19,000
20-The Crimson Avenger begins (1st app.) 1400 2800 4200 7700 10,850 14,000
21,23-25 1000 2000 3000 5500 7750 10,000
22-1st Crimson Avenger-c by Chambers (12/38) 1200 2400 3600 6600 9300 12,000
26 1150 2300 3450 6325 8913 11,500
27-The Bat-Man & Commissioner Gordon begin (1st app.), created by Bill Finger & Bob Kane (5/39); Batman-c (1st)(by Kane). Bat-Man's secret identity revealed as Bruce Wayne in six pg. story. Signed Rob't Kane (also see Det. Picture Stories #5 & Funny Pages V3#1)
170,000 340,000 510,000 1,134,000 1,817,000 2,500,000
27-Reprint, Oversize 13-1/2x10". WARNING: This comic is an exact duplicate reprint of the original except for its size. DC published it in 1974 with a second cover titling it as Famous First Edition. There have been many reported cases of the outer cover being removed and the interior sold as the original edition. The reprint with the new outer cover removed is practically worthless; see Famous First Edition for value.
28-2nd app. The Batman (6 pg. story); non-Bat-Man-c; signed Rob't Kane
8400 16,800 25,200 46,200 75,600 105,000
29-1st app. Doctor Death-c/story, Batman's 1st name villain. 1st 2 part story (10 pgs.). 2nd Batman-c by Kane 18,000 36,000 54,000 100,000 175,000 250,000
30-Dr. Death app. Story concludes from issue #29. Classic Batman splash panel by Kane.
2200 4400 6600 15,500 25,250 35,000
31-Classic Batman over castle cover; 1st app. The Monk & 1st Julie Madison (Bruce Wayne's 1st love interest); 1st Batplane (Bat-Gyro) and Batarang; 2nd 2-part Batman adventure. Gardner Fox takes over script from Bill Finger. 1st mention of locale (New York City) where

Detective Comics #35 © DC

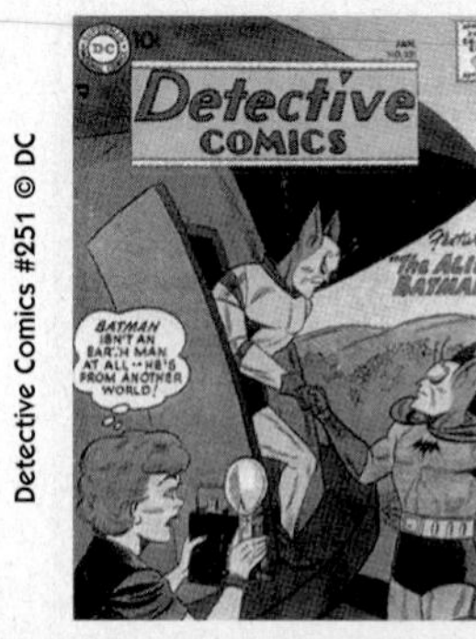

Detective Comics #251 © DC

Detective Comics #290 © DC

	GD 2.0	VG 4.0	FN 6.0	VF 8.0	VF/NM 9.0	NM- 9.2
Batman lives	27,500	55,000	82,500	154,000	227,000	300,000
32-Batman story concludes from issue #31. 1st app. Dala (Monk's assistant). Batman uses gun for 1st time to slay The Monk and Dala. This was the 1st time a costumed hero used a gun in comic books. 1st Batman head logo on cover	1700	3400	5100	11,700	20,850	30,000
33-Origin The Batman (2 pgs.)(1st told origin); Batman gun holster-c; Batman w/smoking gun panel at end of story. Batman story now 12 pgs. Classic Batman-c	13,000	26,000	39,000	81,000	145,500	210,000
34-2nd Crimson Avenger-c by Creig Flessel and last non Batman-c. Story from issue #32 x-over as Bruce Wayne sees Julie Madison off to America from Paris. Classic Batman splash panel used later in Batman #1 for origin story. Steve Malone begins	1400	2800	4200	10,000	17,000	24,000
35-Classic Batman hypodermic needle-c that reflects story in issue #34. Classic Batman with smoking .45 automatic splash panel. Batman-c begin	15,600	31,200	46,800	101,000	145,500	190,000
36-Batman-c that reflects adventure in issue #35. Origin/1st app. of Dr. Hugo Strange (1st major villain, 2/40). 1st finned-gloves worn by Batman	6200	12,400	18,600	45,000	67,500	90,000
37-Last solo Golden-Age Batman adventure in Detective Comics. Panel at end of story reflects solo Batman adventure in Batman #1 that was originally planned for Detective #38. Cliff Crosby begins	4600	9200	13,800	32,800	52,400	72,000
38-Origin/1st app. Robin the Boy Wonder (4/40); Batman and Robin-c begin; cover by Kane	10,700	21,400	32,100	75,000	110,000	145,000
39-Opium story; Clayface app. in 1 panel ad at the end of the Batman story	975	1950	2919	7100	12,550	18,000
40-Origin & 1st app. Clayface (Basil Karlo); 1st Joker cover app. (6/40); Joker story intended for this issue was used in Batman #1 instead; cover is similar to splash page in 2nd Joker story in Batman #1	2100	4200	6300	14,000	24,500	35,000
41-Robin's 1st solo	465	930	1395	3395	5998	8600
42-44: 44-Crimson Avenger-new costume	389	778	1167	2723	4762	6800
45-1st Joker story in Det. (3rd book app. & 4th story app. over all, 11/40)	514	1028	1542	3750	6625	9500
46-50: 46-Death of Hugo Strange. 48-1st time car called Batmobile (2/41); Gotham City 1st mention in Detective (1st mentioned in Wow #1; also see Batman #4). 49-Last Clayface	354	708	1062	2478	4339	6200
51-53,55-57	284	568	852	1818	3109	4400
54-Cover mimics Detective #33 cover	297	594	891	1901	3251	4600
58-1st Penguin app. (12/41); last Speed Saunders; Fred Ray-c	1333	2666	4000	10,000	15,000	20,000
59,60: 59-Last Steve Malone; 2nd Penguin; Wing becomes Crimson Avenger's aide. 60-Intro. Air Wave; Joker app. (2nd in Det.)	277	554	831	1759	3030	4300
61,63: 63-Last Cliff Crosby; 1st app. Mr. Baffle	252	504	756	1613	2757	3900
62-Joker-c/story (2nd Joker-c, 4/42)	811	1622	2433	5920	10,460	15,000
64-Origin & 1st app. Boy Commandos by Simon & Kirby (6/42); Joker app.	459	918	1377	3350	5925	8500
65-1st Boy Commandos-c (S&K-a on Boy Commandos & Ray/Robinson-a on Batman & Robin on-c; 4 artists on one-c)	320	640	960	2240	3920	5600
66-Origin & 1st app. Two-Face (originally named Harvey Kent)	1550	3100	4650	11,000	17,500	24,000
67-1st Penguin-c (9/42)	389	778	1167	2723	4762	6800
68-Two-Face-c/story; 1st Two-Face-c	423	846	1269	3088	5444	7800
69-Classic Joker with 2 guns in his hands-c	1333	2666	4000	10,000	15,000	20,000
70	252	504	756	1613	2757	3900
71-Classic Joker black background calendar-c	900	1800	2700	6000	10,500	15,000
72,74,75: 74-1st Tweedledum & Tweedledee plus-c; S&K-a	206	412	618	1318	2259	3200
73-Scarecrow-c/story (1st Scarecrow-c)	900	1800	2700	6000	10,500	15,000
76-Newsboy Legion & The Sandman x-over in Boy Commandos; S&K-a; Joker-c/story	423	846	1269	3000	5250	7500
77-79: All S&K-a	174	348	522	1114	1907	2700
80-Two-Face-c/sty; S&K-a	252	504	756	1613	2757	3900
81,82,84,86-90: 81-1st Cavalier-c & app. 87-Penguin app. 89-Last Crimson Avenger; 2nd Cavalier-c & app.	142	284	426	909	1555	2200
83-1st "skinny" Alfred (1/44)(see Batman #21; last S&K Boy Commandos (also #92,128); most issues #84 on signed S&K are not by them	155	310	465	992	1696	2400
85-Joker-c/story; last Spy; Kirby/Klech Boy Commandos	290	580	870	1856	3178	4500
91,102,109-Joker-c/stories	277	554	831	1759	3030	4300
92-98: 96-Alfred's last name 'Beagle' revealed, later changed to 'Pennyworth' in #214	116	232	348	742	1271	1800
99-Penguin-c/story	177	354	531	1124	1937	.2750
100 (6/45)	152	304	456	965	1658	2350
101,103-107,110-113,115-117,119	103	206	309	659	1130	1600
108-1st Bat-signal-c (2/46)	129	258	387	826	1413	2000
114,118-Joker-c/stories. 114-1st small logo (8/46)	245	490	735	1568	2684	3800
120-Penguin-c/story	187	374	561	1197	2049	2900
121,123,125,127,129,130	100	200	300	635	1093	1550
122-1st Catwoman-c (4/47)	432	864	1296	3154	5577	8000
124,128-Joker-c/stories	226	452	678	1446	2473	3500
126-Penguin-c	158	316	474	1003	1727	2450
131-134,136,139	94	188	282	597	1024	1450
135-Frankenstein-c/story	119	238	357	762	1306	1850
137-Joker-c/story; last Air Wave	206	412	618	1318	2259	3200
138-Origin Robotman (see Star Spangled #7 for 1st app.); series ends #202	142	284	426	909	1555	2200
140-The Riddler-c/story (1st app., 10/48)	2200	4400	6600	14,600	24,825	35,000
141,143-148,150: 150-Last Boy Commandos	94	188	282	597	1024	1450
142-2nd Riddler-c/story	343	686	1029	2400	4200	6000
149-Joker-c/story	187	374	561	1197	2049	2900
151-Origin & 1st app. Pow Wow Smith, Indian lawman (9/49) & begins series	103	206	309	659	1130	1600
152,154,155,157-160: 152-Last Slam Bradley	94	188	282	597	1024	1450
153-1st app. Roy Raymond TV Detective (11/49); origin The Human Fly	97	194	291	621	1061	1500
156(2/50)-The new classic Batmobile	161	322	483	1030	1765	2500
161-167,169,170,172-176: Last 52 pg. issue	90	180	270	576	988	1400
168-Origin the Joker	2800	5600	8400	17,500	27,750	38,000
171-Penguin-c	126	252	378	806	1378	1950
177-179,181-186,188,189,191,192,194-199,201,202,204,206-210,212,214-216: 184-1st app. Fire Fly. 185-Secret of Batman's utility belt. 202-Last Robotman & Pow Wow Smith. 215-1st app. of Batmen of all Nations. 216-Last precode (2/55)	87	174	261	553	952	1350
180,193-Joker-c/story	161	322	483	1030	1765	2500
187-Two-Face-c/story	239	478	717	1530	2615	3700
190-Origin Batman retold	110	220	330	704	1202	1700
200(10/53), 205: 205-Origin Batcave	103	206	309	659	1130	1600
203,211-Catwoman-c/stories	123	246	369	787	1344	1900
213-Origin & 1st app. Mirror Man	103	206	309	659	1130	1600
217-224: 218-Batman Jr. & Robin Sr. app.	74	148	222	470	810	1150
225-(11/55)-1st app. Martian Manhunter (J'onn J'onzz); origin begins; also see Batman #78	1200	2400	3600	8400	19,200	30,000
226-Origin Martian Manhunter cont'd (2nd app.)	194	388	582	1242	2121	3000
227-229: Martian Manhunter stories in all	87	174	261	553	952	1350
230-1st app. Mad Hatter (imposter, not the one from Batman #49, this one's appearance inspired the 1966 TV version); brief recap origin of Martian Manhunter	123	246	369	787	1344	1900
231-Brief origin recap Martian Manhunter	63	126	189	403	689	975
232,234,237,238,240	60	120	180	380	653	925
233-Origin & 1st app. Batwoman (7/56)	400	800	1200	2800	4900	7000
235-Origin Batman & his costume; tells how Bruce Wayne's father (Thomas Wayne) wore Bat costume & fought crime (reprinted in Batman #255)	103	206	309	659	1130	1600
236-1st S.A. issue; J'onn J'onzz talks to parents and Mars-1st since being stranded on Earth; 1st app. Bat-Tank?	65	130	195	416	708	1000
239-Early DC grey tone-c	90	180	270	576	988	1400
241-260: 246-Intro. Diane Meade, John Jones' girl. 249-Batwoman-c/app. 253-1st app. The Terrible Trio. 254-Bat-Hound-c/story. 257-Intro. & 1st app. Whirly Bats. 259-1st app. The Calendar Man	48	96	144	302	514	725
261-264,266,268-271: 261-J. Jones tie-in to sci/fi movie "Incredible Shrinking Man"; 1st app. Dr. Double X. 262-Origin Jackal. 268,271-Manhunter origin recap	39	78	117	231	378	525
265-Batman's origin retold with new facts	53	106	159	334	567	800
267-Origin & 1st app. Bat-Mite (5/59)	100	200	300	635	1093	1550
272,274,275,277-280	34	68	102	199	325	450
273-J'onn J'onzz i.d. revealed for 1st time	34	68	102	206	336	465
276-2nd app. Bat-Mite	47	94	141	296	498	700
281-292, 294-297: 286,292-Batwoman-c/app. 287-Origin J'onn J'onzz retold. 289-Bat-Mite-c/story. 292-Last Roy Raymond. 297-Last 10¢ issue (11/61)	26	52	78	154	252	350
293-(7/61)-Aquaman begins (pre #1); ends #300	30	60	90	177	289	400
298-(12/61)-1st modern Clayface (Matt Hagen)	50	100	150	390	870	1350
299, 300-(2/62)-Aquaman ends	14	28	42	94	207	320
301-(3/62)-J'onn J'onzz returns to Mars (1st time since stranded on Earth six years before)	13	26	39	89	195	300
302-Batwoman-c/app.	13	26	39	89	195	300
303-306,308-310,312-317,319-321,323,324,326,329,330: 321-2nd Terrible Trio. 326-Last J'onn J'onzz, story cont'd in House of Mystery #143; intro. Idol-Head of						

Detective Comics #438 © DC

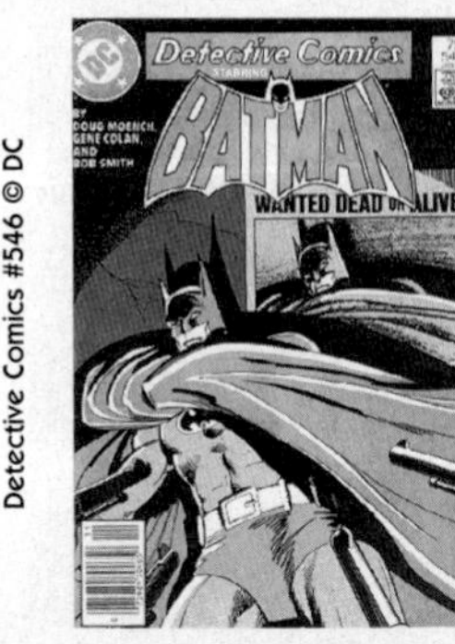

Detective Comics #546 © DC

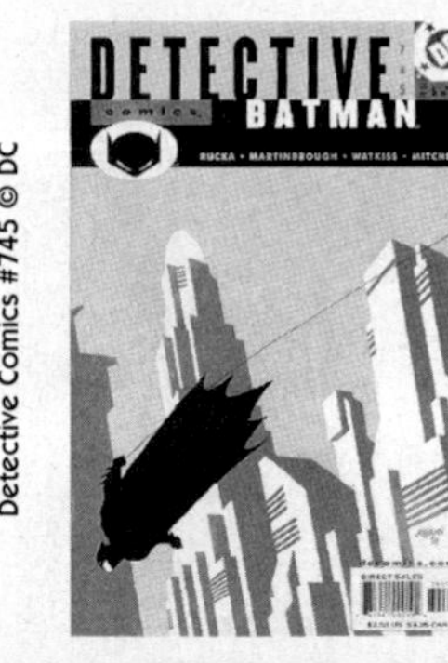

Detective Comics #745 © DC

	GD 2.0	VG 4.0	FN 6.0	VF 8.0	VF/NM 9.0	NM- 9.2
Diabolu	10	20	30	64	132	200
307-Batwoman-c/app.	10	20	30	67	141	215
311-1st app. Cat-Man; intro. Zook in John Jones	21	42	63	147	324	500
318,322,325: 318,325-Cat-Man-c/story (2nd & 3rd app.); also 1st & 2nd app. Batwoman as the Cat-Woman. 322-Bat-Girl's 1st/only app. in Det. (6th in all); Batman cameo in J'onn J'onzz (only hero to app. in series)	12	24	36	82	179	275
327-(5/64)-Elongated Man begins, ends #383; 1st new look Batman with new costume; Infantino/Giella new look-a begins; Batman with gun	16	32	48	111	246	375
328-Death of Alfred; Bob Kane biog, 2 pgs.	12	24	36	81	176	270
331,333-340: 334-1st app. The Outsider	8	16	24	54	102	150
332,341,365-Joker-c/stories	11	22	33	73	157	240
342-358,360,361,366-368: 345-Intro Block Buster. 347-"What If" theme story (1/66). 350-Elongated Man new costume. 355-Zatanna x-over in Elongated Man. 356-Alfred brought back in Batman, early SA app.	7	14	21	49	92	135
359-Intro/origin Batgirl (Barbara Gordon)-c/story (1/67); 1st Silver Age app. Killer Moth; classic Batgirl-c	150	300	600	1440	2720	4000
362,364-S.A. Riddler app. (early)	9	18	27	58	114	170
363-2nd app. new Batgirl	14	28	42	96	211	325
369(11/67)-N. Adams-a (Elongated Man); 3rd app. S.A. Catwoman (cameo; leads into Batman #197); 4th app. new Batgirl	15	30	45	100	220	340
370-1st Neal Adams-a on Batman (cover only, 12/67)	9	18	27	62	126	190
371-(1/68) 1st new Batmobile from TV show; classic Batgirl-c	12	24	36	82	179	275
372-376,378-386,389,390: 375-New Batmobile-c	6	12	18	38	69	100
377-S.A. Riddler-c/sty	7	14	21	46	86	125
387-r/1st Batman story from #27 (30th anniversary, 5/69); Joker-c; last 12¢ issue	9	18	27	61	123	185
388-Joker-c/story	9	18	27	63	129	195
391-394,396,398,399,401,403,406,409: 392-1st app. Jason Bard. 401-2nd Batgirl/Robin team-up	6	12	18	37	66	95
395,397,402,404,407,408,410-Neal Adams-a. 402-Man-Bat-c/app. (2nd app.). 404-Tribute to Enemy Ace	11	22	33	72	154	235
400-(6/70)-Origin & 1st app. Man-Bat; 1st Batgirl/Robin team-up (cont'd in #401); Neal Adams-a	28	56	84	202	451	700
405-Debut League of Assassins	17	34	51	117	259	400
411-(5/71) Intro. Talia, daughter of Ra's al Ghul (Ra's mentioned, but doesn't appear until Batman #232 (6/71); Bob Brown-a	33	66	99	238	532	825
412-413: 413-Last 15¢ issue	6	12	18	37	66	95
414-424: All-25¢, 52 pgs. 418-Creeper x-over. 424-Last Batgirl.	6	12	18	38	69	100
425-436: 426,430,436-Elongated Man app. 428,434-Hawkman begins, ends #467	5	10	15	30	50	70
437-New Manhunter begins (10-11/73, 1st app.) by Simonson, ends #443	5	10	15	34	60	85
438-440,442-445 (All 100 Page Super Spectaculars): 438-Kubert Hawkman-r. 439-Origin Manhunter. 440-G.A. Manhunter(Adv. #79) by S&K, Hawkman, Dollman, Green Lantern; Toth-a. 442-G.A. Newsboy Legion, Black Canary, Elongated Man, Dr. Fate-r. 443-Origin The Creeper-r; death of Manhunter; G.A. Green Lantern, Spectre-r; Batman-r/Batman #18. 444-G.A. Kid Eternity-r. 445-G.A. Dr. Midnite-r	6	12	18	38	69	100
441-(6,7/74)(100 Page S.S.) 1st app. Lt. (Harvey) Bullock, first name not given, appears in only 3 panels; G.A. Plastic Man, Batman, Ibis-r	7	14	21	46	86	125
446-460: 457-Origin retold & updated	3	6	9	17	26	35
461-465,470,480: 480-(44 pgs.). 463-1st app. Black Spider. 464-2nd app. Black Spider 470-Intro. Silver St. Cloud.	3	6	9	16	23	30
466-468,471-473,478,479-Rogers-a in all: 466-1st app. Signalman since Batman #139. 470,471-1st modern app. Hugo Strange. 478-1st app. 3rd Clayface (Preston Payne). 479-(44 pgs.)	4	8	12	25	40	55
469-Intro/origin Dr. Phosphorous; Simonson-a	4	8	12	23	37	50
474-1st app. new Deadshot	6	12	18	41	76	110
475,476-Joker-c/stories; Rogers-a	7	14	21	48	89	130
477-Neal Adams-a(r); Rogers-a (3 pgs.)	4	8	12	23	37	50
481-(Combined with Batman Family, 12-1/78-79, begin $1.00, 68 pg. issues, ends #495); 481-495-Batgirl, Robin solo stories	3	6	9	21	33	45
482-Starlin/Russell, Golden-a; The Demon begins (origin-r), ends #485 (by Ditko #483-485)	3	6	9	14	20	25
483-40th Anniversary issue; origin retold; Newton Batman begins	3	6	9	15	22	28
484-495 (68 pgs): 484-Origin Robin. 485-Death of Batwoman. 486-Killer Moth app. 487-The Odd Man by Ditko. 489-Robin/Batgirl team-up. 490-Black Lightning begins. 491-(#492 on inside). 493-Intro. The Swashbuckler	2	4	6	9	13	16
496-499: 496-Clayface app.	2	4	6	8	10	12
500-($1.50, 52 pgs.)-Batman/Deadman team-up with Infantino-a; new Hawkman story by Joe Kubert; incorrectly says 500th Anniv. of Det.	2	4	6	13	18	22

	GD 2.0	VG 4.0	FN 6.0	VF 8.0	VF/NM 9.0	NM- 9.2
501-503,505-522: 509-Catman-c. 510-Mad Hatter-c. 512-2nd app. new Dr. Death. 513-Two-Face app. 519-Last Batgirl. 521-Green Arrow series begins	1	2	3	5	6	8
504-Joker-c/story	2	4	6	11	16	20
523-1st Killer Croc (cameo); Solomon Grundy app.	3	6	9	20	31	42
524-2nd app. Jason Todd (cameo)(3/83)	2	4	6	9	12	15
525-3rd app. Jason Todd (See Batman #357)	2	4	6	9	12	15
526-Batman's 500th app. in Detective Comics ($1.50, 68 pgs.); Death of Jason Todd's parents, Joker-c/story (55 pgs.); Bob Kane pin-up	3	6	9	15	22	28
527-531,533,534,536-553,555-568,571,573: 538-Cat-Man-c/story cont'd from Batman #371. 542-Jason Todd quits as Robin (becomes Robin again #547). 549,550-Alan Moore scripts (Green Arrow). 566-Batman villains profiled. 567-Harlan Ellison scripts						6.00
532,569,570-Joker-c/stories	2	4	6	9	13	16
535-Intro new Robin (Jason Todd)-1st appeared in Batman	1	3	4	6	8	10
554-1st new Black Canary (9/85)	1	2	3	5	6	8
572-(3/87, $1.25, 60 pgs.)-50th Anniv. of Det. Comics	1	3	4	6	8	10
574-Origin Batman & Jason Todd retold	2	4	6	8	10	12
575-Year 2 begins, ends #578	3	6	9	15	22	28
576-578: McFarlane-c/a; The Reaper app.	3	6	9	15	22	28
579-597,599,601-607,609,610: 579-New bat wing logo. 583-1st app. villains Scarface & Ventriloquist. 589,595-(52 pgs.)-Each contain free 16 pg. Batman stories. 604-607-Mudpack storyline; 604,607-Contain Batman mini-posters. 610-Faked death of Penguin; artists names app. on tombstone on-c						4.00
598-($2.95, 84 pgs.)- "Blind Justice" storyline begins by Batman movie writer Sam Hamm, ends #600						6.00
600-(5/89, $2.95, 84 pgs.)-50th Anniv. of Batman in Det.; 1 pg. Neal Adams pin-up, among other artists						6.00
608-1st app. Anarky						6.00
611-626,628-646,649-658: 612-1st new look Cat-Man; Catwoman app. 615- "The Penguin Affair" part 2 (See Batman #448,449). 617-Joker-c/story. 624-1st new Catwoman (w/death) & 1st new Batwoman. 626-Batman's 600th app. in Detective. 642-Return of Scarface, part 2. 644-Last $1.00-c. 644-646-The (2nd) Electrocutioner (Lester Buchinsky) app. 652,653-Huntress-c/story w/new costume plus Charest-c on both						4.00
627-($2.95, 84 pgs.)-Batman's 601st app. in Det.; reprints 1st story/#27 plus 3 versions (2 new) of same story						6.00
647-1st app. Stephanie Brown	2	4	6	10	14	18
648-1st full app. Spoiler (Stephanie Brown)						5.00
659-664: 659-Knightfall part 2; Kelley Jones-c. 660-Knightfall part 4; Bane-c by Sam Kieth. 661-Knightfall part 6; brief Joker & Riddler app. 662-Knightfall part 8; Riddler app.; Sam Kieth-c. 663-Knightfall part 10; Kelley Jones-c. 664-Knightfall part 12; Bane-c/story; Joker app.; continued in Showcase 93 #7 & 8; Jones-c						6.00
665-675: 665,666-Knightfall parts 16 & 18; 666-Bane-c/story. 667-Knightquest: The Crusade & new Batman begins (1st app. in Batman #500). 669-Begin $1.50-c; Knightquest, cont'd in Robin #1. 671,673-Joker app.						4.00
675-($2.95)-Collectors edition w/foil-c						5.00
676-($2.50, 52 pgs.)-KnightsEnd pt. 3						5.00
677,678: 677-KnightsEnd pt. 9. 678-(9/94)-Zero Hour tie-in.						4.00
679-685: 679-(11/94). 682-Troika pt. 3						3.00
682-($2.50) Embossed-c Troika pt. 3						4.00
686-699,701-719: 686-Begin $1.95-c. 693,694-Poison Ivy-c/app. 695-Contagion pt. 2; Catwoman, Penguin app. 696-Contagion pt. 8. 698-Two-Face-c/app. 701-Legacy pt. 6; Batman vs. Bane-c/app. 702-Legacy Epilogue. 703-Final Night x-over. 705-707-Riddler-app. 714,715-Martian Manhunter-app.						3.00
700-($4.95, Collectors Edition)-Legacy pt. 1; Ra's Al Ghul-c/app; Talia & Bane app; book displayed at shops in envelope						6.00
700-($2.95, Regular Edition)-Different-c						4.00
720-736,738,739: 720,721-Cataclysm pts. 5,14. 723-Green Arrow app. 730-740-No Man's Land stories. 735-1st app. Mercy Graves in regular DCU						3.00
737-Harley Quinn-c/app. (1st app. in Detective); No Man's Land	2	4	6	10	14	18
740-Joker, Bane-c/app.; Harley Quinn app.; No Man's Land	1	3	4	6	8	10
741-($2.50) Endgame; Joker-c/app.; Harley Quinn app.						5.00
742-749,751-765: 742-New look Batman begins; 1st app. Crispus Allen (who later becomes the Spectre). 751,752-Poison Ivy app. 756-Superman-c/app. 759-762-Catwoman back-up						3.00
750-($4.95, 64 pgs.) Ra's al Ghul-c						6.00
766-772: 766,767-Bruce Wayne: Murderer pt. 1,8. 769-772-Bruce Wayne: Fugitive pts. 4,8,12,16						3.00
773,774,776-782,784-799: 773-Begin $2.75-c; Sienkiewicz-c. 777-784-Sale-c. 784-786-Alan Scott app. 787-Mad Hatter app. 797-799-War Games						3.00
775-($3.50) Sienkiewicz-c						4.00
783-1st Nyssa						5.00
800-($3.50) Jock-c; aftermath of War Games; back-up by Lapham						4.00

Detective Comics (2011 series) #37 © DC

Detective Comics #934 © DC

Dethklok #1 © Cartoon Network

GD 2.0 | VG 4.0 | FN 6.0 | VF 8.0 | VF/NM 9.0 | NM- 9.2

801-816: 801-814-Lapham-s. 804-Mr. Freeze app. 809-War Crimes 3.00
817-830,832-836,838-849,851,852: 817-820: One Year Later 8-part x-over with Batman #651-654; Robinson-s/Bianchi-c. 819-Begin $2.99-c. 820-Dini-s/Williams III-a. 821-Harley Quinn app. 825-Doctor Phosphorus app. 827-Debut of new Scarface. 833,834-Zatanna & Joker app. 838,839-Resurrection of Ra's al Ghul x-over. 846-847-Batman R.I.P. x-over 3.00
817,818,838,839-2nd printings. 817-Combo-c of #817̳ cover images. 818-Combo-c of #818 and Batman #653 cover images. 838-Andy Kubert variant-c. 839-Red bkgd-c 3.00
831,837-Harley Quinn-c/app. 831-Dini-s 1 3 4 6 8 10
850-($3.99) Batman vs. Hush; Dini-s/Nguyen-a 6.00
853-($3.99) Gaiman-s/Andy Kubert-a; continued from Batman #686; Kubert sketch pgs. 4.00
853-Variant-c with red background by Andy Kubert 12.00
854-872-($3.99) 854-Batwoman features begin; Rucka-a/J.H. Williams-a/c; The Question back-ups begin. 858-860-Batwoman origin. 871-1st Scott Snyder Batman-s 4.00
854,858,859,860-Variant-c: 854-JG Jones. 858-Hughes. 859-Jock. 860-Alex Ross 6.00
854-Special Edition (8/10, $1.00) reprints issue with "What's Next?" logo on cover 3.00
873-880-($2.99) 874,875,879-Francavilla-a. 880-Jock-a 3.00
881-(10/11) Last issue of first volume; Snyder-s/Jock & Francavilla-a 3.00
#0-(10/94) Zero Hour tie-in, released between #678 & 679 3.00
#1,000,000 (11/98) 853rd Century x-over 3.00
Annual 1 (1988, $1.50) 5.00
Annual 2-7,9 ('89-'94, '96, 68 pgs.)-4-Painted-c. 5-Joker-c/story (54 pgs.) continued in Robin Annual #1; Sam Kieth-c; Eclipso app. 6-Azrael as Batman in new costume; intro Geist the Twilight Man; Bloodlines storyline. 7-Elseworlds story. 9-Legends of the Dead Earth story 5.00
Annual 8 (1995, $3.95, 68 pgs.)-Year One story 5.00
Annual 10 (1997, $3.95)-Pulp Heroes story 5.00
Annual 11 (12/09, $4.99)-Azrael & The Question app.; continued from Batman Ann. #27 5.00
Annual 12 (2/11, $4.99)-Nightrunner & The Question app.; continued in Batman Ann. #28 5.00

NOTE: **Neal Adams** *c-370, 372, 385, 389, 391, 392, 394-422, 439.* **Aparo** *a-437, 438, 444-446, 500, 625-632p, 638-643p; c-430, 437, 440-446, 448, 468-470, 480, 484(back), 492-502,508, 509, 515, 518-522, 641, 716, 719, 722, 724.* **Austin** *a(i)-450, 451, 463-468, 471-476; c(i)-474-476, 478.* **Baily** *a-443r.* **Buckler** *a-434, 446p, 479p; c(p)-467, 482, 505-507, 511, 513-516, 518.* **Burnley** *a(Batman)-65, 75, 78, 83, 100, 103, 125; c-62i, 63i, 64, 73i, 78, 83p, 96p, 103p, 105p, 106, 108, 121p, 123p, 125p.* **Chaykin** *a-441.* **Colan** *a(p)-510, 512, 517, 523, 528-538, 540-546, 555-567; c(p)-510, 512, 528, 530-535, 537, 538, 540, 541, 543-545, 556-558, 560-564.* **J. Craig** *a-488.* **Ditko** *a-443r, 483-485, 487.* **Golden** *a-482p; c-625, 626, 628-631, 633, 644-646.* **Alan Grant** *scripts-584-597, 601-621, 641, 642, Annual 5.* **Grell** *a-445, 455, 463p, 464p; c-455.* **Guardineer** *c-23, 24, 26, 28, 30, 32.* **Gustavson** *a-441r.* **Infantino** *a-354, 442(2)r, 500, 572.* **Infantino/Anderson** *c-333, 337-340, 343, 344, 347, 351, 352, 359, 361-368, 371.* **Kelley Jones** *c-651, 657i, 658i, 659, 661, 663-675.* **Kaluta** *c-423, 424, 426-428, 431, 434, 438, 484, 486, 572.* **Bob Kane** *a-Most early issues #27 on, 297r, 356r, 438-440r, 442r, 443r.* **Kane/Robinson** *c-33.* **Gil Kane** *a(p)-368, 370-374, 384, 385, 388-407, 438r, 439r, 520.* **Kane/Anderson** *c-369.* **Sam Kieth** *c-654-656 (657, 658 w/***Kelley Jones***), 660, 662, Annual #5.* **Kubert** *a-438r, 439r, 500; c-348-350.* **McFarlane** *c/a(p)-576-578.* **Meskin** *a-420r.* **Mignola** *c-583.* **Moldoff** *c-233-354, 259, 266, 267, 275, 287, 289, 290, 297, 300.* **Moldoff/Giella** *a-328, 330, 332, 334, 336, 338, 340, 342, 344, 346, 348, 350, 352, 354, 356.* **Mooney** *a-444r.* **Moreira** *a-153-300, 419r, 444r, 445r.* **Nasser/Netzer** *a-654, 655, 657, 658.* **Newton** *a(p)-480, 481, 483-499, 501-509, 511, 513-516, 518-520, 524, 526, 539; c-526p.* **Irv Novick** *c-375-377, 383.* **Robbins** *a-426p, 429p.* **Robinson** *a-part: 66, 68, 71-73; all: 74-76, 79, 80; c-62, 64, 66, 68-74, 76, 79, 82, 86, 88, 442r, 443r.* **Rogers** *a-466-468, 471-479p, 481p; c-471p, 472p, 473, 474-479p.* **Roussos** *Airwave-76-105(most); c(i)-71, 72, 74-76, 79, 107.* **Russell** *a-481i, 482i.* **Simon/Kirby** *a-440r, 442r.* **Simonson** *a-437-443, 450, 469, 470, 500.* **Dick Sprang** *c-77, 82, 84, 85, 87, 89-93, 95-100, 102, 103i, 104i, 106, 108, 114, 117, 118, 122, 123, 128, 129, 131, 133, 135, 141, 148, 149, 168, 622-624.* **Starlin** *a-481p, 482p; c-503, 504, 567p.* **Starr** *a-444r.* **Toth** *a-442; r-414, 416, 418, 424, 440-441, 443, 444.* **Tuska** *a-486p, 490p.* **Matt Wagner** *c-647-649.* **Wrightson** *c-425.*

DETECTIVE COMICS (DC New 52)(Numbering reverts to original series #934 after #52)
DC Comics: Nov, 2011 - Present ($2.99/$3.99)

1-Joker app.; Tony Daniel-s/a/c 3 6 9 14 20 25
2-7: 2-Intro of The Dollmaker. 5-7-Penguin app. 5.00
8,10-14,16-18: 8-($3.99) Catwoman & Scarecrow app.; back-up Two-Face story begins 4.00
9-Night of the Owls 5.00
15-Die-cut Joker cover; Death of the Family tie-in 8.00
19-(6/13, $7.99) 900th issue of Detective; bonus back-up stories and pin-up art 8.00
20-24,26: 21-23-Man-Bat back-up story. 26-Man-Bat app. 4.00
23.1, 23.2, 23.3, 23.4 (11/13, $2.99, regular covers) 3.00
23.1 (11/13, $3.99, 3-D cover) "Poison Ivy #1" on cover; Fridolfs-s/Pina-a 1 3 4 6 8 10
23.2 (11/13, $3.99, 3-D cover) "Harley Quinn #1" on cover; Googe-a/Kindt-s; origin 2 4 6 13 18 22
23.3 (11/13, $3.99, 3-D cover) "Scarecrow #1" on cover; Kudranski-a 5.00
23.4 (11/13, $3.99, 3-D cover) "Man-Bat #1" on cover; Tieri-s/Eaton-a 5.00
25-($3.99) Zero Year focus on Lt. Gordon; Fabok-a/c; Man-Bat back-up 4.00
27-($7.99) Start of Gothtopia; short stories by Meltzer, Hitch, Neal Adams, Francavilla, Murphy 8.00
28-49,51,52: 28,29-Gothtopia. 30-34,37-40-Manupul-a. 37-40-Anarky app. 43,44-Joker's Daughter. 45,46-Justice League app. 47-"Robin War" tie-in 4.00
50-($4.99) Bonus pin-up swipes of classic Detective covers by various 5.00
#0 (11/12, $3.99) Flashback to training and return to Alfred 4.00
Annual 1 (10/12, $4.99) Black Mask app.; Daniel-s/c; Molenaar-a 5.00
Annual 2 (9/13, $4.99) The Wrath app.; Eaton-a/Clarke-c 5.00
Annual 3 (9/14, $4.99) March-c 5.00
...: Endgame 1 (5/15, $2.99) Tie-in to Endgame story in Batman #35-40; Anarky app. 3.00
...: Futures End 1 (11/14, $2.99, regular-c) Five years later; Riddler app. 3.00
...: Futures End 1 (11/14, $3.99, 3-D cover) 4.00

DETECTIVE COMICS (Numbering reverts to original V1 #934 after #52 from 2011-2016 series)
DC Comics: No. 934, Aug, 2016 - Present ($2.99)

934-Tynion IV-s/Barrows-a; Batwoman, Spoiler, Red Robin, Clayface app. 3.00
935-949,951-974: 936-938-Alvaro Martinez-a. 937-Intro. Ulysses Armstrong. 940-Apparent death of Tim Drake. 941,942-Night of the Monster Men x-over. 944-Batwing returns. 948,949-Batwoman begins. 951-956-"League of Shadows." 958-961-Zatanna app. 965-Tim Drake vs. Mr. Oz. 965-967-Future Batman (Tim Drake) app. 3.00
950-($3.99) Prologue to "League of Shadows"; Takara-a; Shiva & Azrael app. 4.00
975-($3.99) Trial of Batwoman; Tynion IV-s/Martinez-a 4.00
Annual 1 (3/18, $4.99)Tynion IV-s/Barrows-a; Clayface origin re-told 5.00

DETECTIVE DAN, SECRET OP. 48 (Also see Adventures of Detective Ace King and Bob Scully, The Two-Fisted Hick Detective)
Humor Publ. Co. (Norman Marsh): 1933 (10¢, 10x13", 36 pgs., B&W, one-shot) (3 color, cardboard-c)

nn-By Norman Marsh, 1st comic w/ original-a; 1st newsstand-c; Dick Tracy look-alike; forerunner of Dan Dunn. (Title and Wu Fang character inspired Detective Comics #1 four years later.) (1st comic of a single theme) 2000 4000 6000 12,000 - -

DETECTIVE EYE (See Keen Detective Funnies)
Centaur Publications: Nov, 1940 - No. 2, Dec, 1940

1-Air Man (see Keen Detective) & The Eye Sees begins; The Masked Marvel & Dean Denton app. 277 554 831 1759 3030 4300
2-Origin Don Rance and the Mysticape; Binder-a; Frank Thomas-c 187 374 561 1197 2049 2900

DETECTIVE PICTURE STORIES (Keen Detective Funnies No. 8 on?)
Comics Magazine Company: Dec, 1936 - No. 5, Apr, 1937

1 (All issues are very scarce) 600 1200 1800 3400 5600 7800
2-The Clock app. (1/37, early app.) 295 590 885 1685 2743 3800
3,4: 4-Eisner-a 230 460 690 1300 2150 3000
5-The Clock-c/story (4/37); "The Case of the Missing Heir" 1st detective/adventure art by Bob Kane; Bruce Wayne prototype app. (story reprinted in Funny Pages V3 #1) 425 850 1275 2425 3963 5500

DETECTIVES, THE (TV)
Dell Publishing Co.: No. 1168, Mar-May, 1961 - No. 1240, Oct-Dec, 1961

Four Color 1168 (#1)-Robert Taylor photo-c 9 18 27 61 123 185
Four Color 1219-Robert Taylor, Adam West photo-c 9 18 27 61 123 185
Four Color 1240-Tufts-a; Robert Taylor photo-c; 2 different back-c 8 16 24 51 96 140

DETECTIVES, INC. (See Eclipse Graphic Album Series)
Eclipse Comics: Apr, 1985 - No. 2, Apr, 1985 ($1.75, both w/April dates)

1,2: 2-Nudity 3.00

DETECTIVES, INC.: A TERROR OF DYING DREAMS
Eclipse Comics: Jun, 1987 - No. 3, Dec, 1987 ($1.75, B&W& sepia)

1-3: Colan-a 3.00
TPB ('99, $19.95) r/series 20.00

DETENTION COMICS
DC Comics: Oct, 1996 ($3.50, 56 pgs., one-shot)

1-Robin story by Dennis O'Neil & Norm Breyfogle; Superboy story by Ron Marz & Ron Lim; Warrior story by Ruben Diaz & Joe Phillips; Phillips-c 5.00

DETHKLOK (Based on the animated series Metalocalypse)
Dark Horse Comics: Oct, 2010 - No. 3, Feb, 2011 ($3.99, limited series)

1-3-Small & Schnepp-s; covers by Schnepp & Eric Powell 4.00
...: Versus the Goon 1-(7/09, $3.50) Powell-s/a/c; Dethklok visits the Goon universe 3.50
...: Versus the Goon 1-Variant cover by Jon Schnepp 5.00
HC (7/11, $19.99) r/#1-3 & Dethklok: Versus the Goon 20.00

DETONATOR (Mike Baron's...)
Image Comics: Nov, 2004 - No. 4 ($2.50/$2.95)

1-4-Mike Baron-s/Mel Rubi-a 3.00

DEUS EX (Based on the Square Enix videogame)
DC Comics: Apr, 2011 - No. 6, Sept, 2011 ($2.99, limited series)

1-6-Robbie Morrison-s/Trevor Hairsine-a 3.00

DEUS EX: CHILDREN'S CRUSADE (Based on the Square Enix videogame)
Titan Comics: Mar, 2016 - No. 5, Jul, 2016 ($3.99, limited series)

1-5-Alex Irvine-s/John Aggs-a; 3 covers on each 4.00

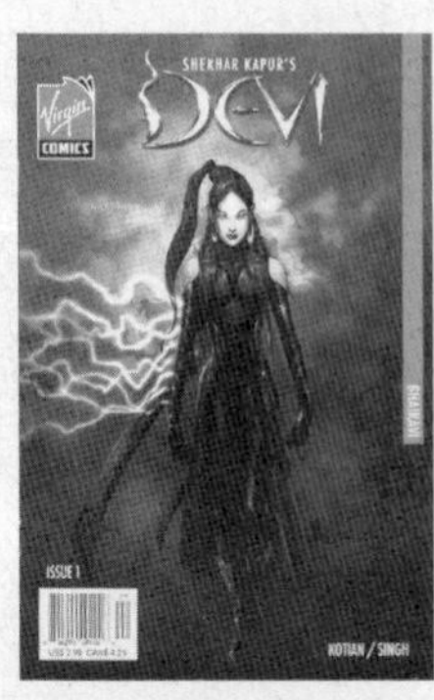

Devi #1 © Virgin Comics

Devolution #4 © DYN & Remender

Diary Secrets #10 © STJ

	GD 2.0	VG 4.0	FN 6.0	VF 8.0	VF/NM 9.0	NM- 9.2

DEVASTATOR
Image Comics/Halloween: 1998 - No. 3 ($2.95, B&W, limited series)

1,2-Hudnall-s/Horn-c/a 3.00

DEVI (Shekhar Kapur's...)
Virgin Comics: July, 2006 - No. 20, Jun, 2008 ($2.99)

1-20: 1-Mukesh Singh-a/Siddharth Kotian-s. 2-Greg Horn-c 3.00
.../Witchblade (4/08, $2.99) Singh-a/Land-c; continued from Witchblade/Devi 3.00
... Vol. 1 TPB (5/07, $14.99) r/#1-5 and Story from Virgin Comics Preview #0 15.00
... Vol. 2 TPB (9/07, $14.99) r/#6-10; character and cover sketches 15.00

DEVIL CHEF
Dark Horse Comics: July, 1994 ($2.50, B&W, one-shot)

nn 3.00

DEVIL DINOSAUR
Marvel Comics Group: Apr, 1978 - No. 9, Dec, 1978

1-Kirby/Royer-a in all; all have Kirby-c 3 6 9 19 30 40
2-9: 4-7-UFO/sci. fic. 8-Dinoriders-c/sty 2 4 6 10 14 18
... By Jack Kirby Omnibus HC (2007, $29.99, dustjacket) r/#1-9; intro. by Brevoort 30.00

DEVIL DINOSAUR SPRING FLING
Marvel Comics: June, 1997 ($2.99. one-shot)

1-(48 pgs.) Moon-Boy-c/app. 4.00

DEVIL-DOG DUGAN (Tales of the Marines No. 4 on)
Atlas Comics (OPI): July, 1956 - No. 3, Nov, 1956

1-Severin-c 20 40 60 114 182 250
2-Iron Mike McGraw x-over; Severin-c 13 26 39 72 101 130
3 12 24 36 67 94 120

DEVIL DOGS
Street & Smith Publishers: 1942

1-Boy Rangers, U.S. Marines 41 82 123 256 428 600

DEVILERS
Dynamite Entertainment: 2014 - No. 7, 2015 ($2.99)

1-7-Fialkov-s/Triano-a/Jock-c 3.00

DEVILINA (Magazine)
Atlas/Seaboard: Feb, 1975 - No. 2, May, 1975 (B&W)

1-Art by Reese, Marcos; "The Tempest" adapt. 4 8 12 27 44 60
2 (Low printing) 4 8 12 28 47 65

DEVIL KIDS STARRING HOT STUFF
Harvey Publications (Illustrated Humor): July, 1962 - No. 107, Oct, 1981 (Giant-Size #41-55)

1 (12¢ cover price #1-#41-9/69) 28 56 84 202 451 700
2 10 20 30 69 147 225
3-10 (1/64) 8 16 24 51 96 140
11-20 5 10 15 33 57 80
21-30 4 8 12 25 40 55
31-40: 40-(6/69) 3 6 9 19 30 40
41-50: All 68 pg. Giants 3 6 9 21 33 45
51-55: All 52 pg. Giants 3 6 9 19 30 40
56-70 2 4 6 11 16 20
71-90 2 4 6 8 11 14
91-107 1 2 3 5 6 8

DEVIL'S DUE FREE COMIC BOOK DAY
Devil's Due Publ.: May, 2005 (Free Comic Book Day giveaway)

nn-Short stories of G.I. Joe, Defex and Darkstalkers; Darkstalkers flip cover 3.00

DEVIL'S FOOTPRINTS, THE
Dark Horse Comics: March, 2003 - No. 4, June, 2003 ($2.99, limited series)

1-4-Paul Lee-c/a; Scott Allie-s 3.00

DEVI / WITCHBLADE
Graphic India Pte, Ltd.: Jan, 2016 ($4.99, one-shot)

1-Ron Marz & Samit Basu-s/Eric & Rick Basuldua & Mukesh Singh-a; multiple covers 5.00

DEVOLUTION
Dynamite Entertainment: 2016 - No. 5, 2016 ($3.99)

1-5-Remender-s/Wayshak-a/Jae Lee-c 4.00

DEXTER (Character from the novels and Showtime series)
Marvel Comics: Sept, 2013 - No. 5, Jan, 2014 ($3.99, limited series)

1-5-Jeff Linsday-s/Dalibor Talajic-a/Mike Del Mundo-c 4.00

DEXTER COMICS
Dearfield Publ.: Summer, 1948 - No. 5, July, 1949

1-Teen-age humor 17 34 51 100 158 215
2-Junie Prom app. 12 24 36 69 97 125
3-5 10 20 30 58 79 100

DEXTER DOWN UNDER (Character from the novels and Showtime series)
Marvel Comics: Apr, 2014 - No. 5, Aug, 2014 ($3.99, limited series)

1-5-Jeff Linsday-s/Dalibor Talajic-a/Mike Del Mundo-c 4.00

DEXTER'S LABORATORY (Cartoon Network)
DC Comics: Sept, 1999 - No. 34, Apr, 2003 ($1.99/$2.25)

1 4.00
2-10: 2-McCracken-s 3.00
11-24, 26-34: 31-Begin $2.25-c. 32-34-Wray-c 3.00
25-(50¢-c) Tartakovsky-s/a; Action Hank-c/app. 3.00

DEXTER'S LABORATORY (Cartoon Network)
IDW Publishing: Apr, 2014 - No. 4, Jul, 2014 ($3.99)

1-4-Fridolfs-s/Jampole-a; three covers on each 4.00

DEXTER THE DEMON (Formerly Melvin The Monster)(See Cartoon Kids & Peter the Little Pest)
Atlas Comics (HPC): No. 7, Sept, 1957

7 11 22 33 62 86 110

DHAMPIRE: STILLBORN
DC Comics (Vertigo): 1996 ($5.95, one-shot, mature)

1-Nancy Collins script; Paul Lee-c/a 6.00

DIABLO
DC Comics: Jan, 2012 - No. 5, Oct, 2012 ($2.99, limited series)

1-5-Aaron Williams-s/Joseph Lacroix-a/c 3.00

DIABLO HOUSE
IDW Publishing: Jul, 2017 - Present ($3.99)

1-3-Horror anthology; Ted Adams-s/Santipérez-a 4.00

DIAL H (Dial H for HERO)(Also see Justice League #23.3)
DC Comics: Jul, 2012 - No. 15, Oct, 2013 ($2.99/$4.99)

1-14: 1-6-China Miéville-s/Mateus Santolouco-a/Brian Bolland-c. 1-Variant-c by Finch 3.00
15-($4.99) Mieville-s/Ponticelli-a/Bolland-c 5.00
#0 (11/12, $2.99) Origin of the dial; Miéville-s/Burchielli-a/Bolland-c 3.00

DIARY CONFESSIONS (Formerly Ideal Romance)
Stanmor/Key Publ.(Medal Comics): No. 9, May, 1955 - No. 14, Apr, 1955

9 12 24 36 69 97 125
10-14 10 20 30 54 72 90

DIARY LOVES (Formerly Love Diary #1; G. I. Sweethearts #32 on)
Quality Comics Group: No. 2, Nov, 1949 - No. 31, April, 1953

2-Ward-c/a, 9 pgs. 22 44 66 130 213 295
3 (1/50)-Photo-c begin, end #27? 13 26 39 74 105 135
4-Crandall-a 14 28 42 80 115 150
5-7,10 12 24 36 67 94 120
8,9-Ward-a 6,8 pgs. 8-Gustavson-a; Esther Williams photo-c
15 30 45 88 137 185
11,13,14,17-20 11 22 33 64 90 115
12,15,16-Ward-a 9,7,8 pgs. 15 30 45 84 127 170
21-Ward-a, 7 pgs. 14 28 42 81 118 155
22-31: 31-Whitney-a 11 22 33 62 86 110
NOTE: *Photo c-3-10, 12-28.*

DIARY OF HORROR
Avon Periodicals: December, 1952

1-Hollingsworth-c/a; bondage-c 81 162 243 518 884 1250

DIARY SECRETS (Formerly Teen-Age Diary Secrets)(See Giant Comics Ed.)
St. John Publishing Co.: No. 10, Feb, 1952 - No. 30, Sept, 1955

10-Baker-c/a most issues 68 136 204 435 743 1050
11-16,18,19: 12,13,15-Baker-c 61 122 183 390 670 950
17,20: Kubert-r/Hollywood Confessions #1. 17-r/Teen Age Romances #9
65 130 195 416 708 1000
21-30: 22,27-Signed stories by Estrada. 28-Last precode (3/55)
55 110 165 352 601 850
nn-(25¢ giant, nd (1950?)-Baker-c & rebound St. John comics
148 296 444 947 1624 2300

DICK COLE (Sport Thrills No. 11 on)(See Blue Bolt & Four Most #1)
Curtis Publ./Star Publications: Dec-Jan, 1948-49 - No. 10, June-July, 1950

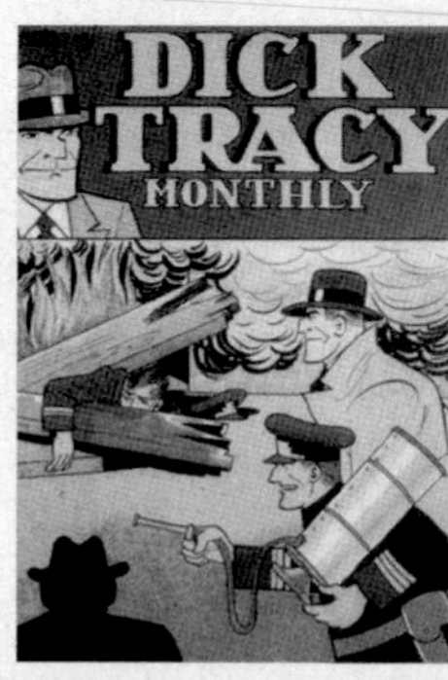

Dick Tracy #2 © NYNS

Die Hard: Year One #1 © 20th Century Fox

Die Kitty Die! #3 #413 © Parent & Ruiz

GD VG FN VF VF/NM NM-
2.0 4.0 6.0 8.0 9.0 9.2

1-Sgt. Spook; L. B. Cole-c; McWilliams-a; Curt Swan's 1st work
36 72 108 211 343 475
2,5 16 32 48 94 147 200
3,4,6-10: All-L.B. Cole-c. 10-Joe Louis story 22 44 66 132 216 300
Accepted Reprint #7(V1#6 on-c)(1950's)-Reprints #7; L.B. Cole-c
9 18 27 47 61 75
Accepted Reprint #9(nd)-(Reprints #9 & #8-c) 9 18 27 47 61 75
NOTE: *L. B. Cole c-1, 3, 4, 6-10. Al McWilliams a-6. Dick Cole in 1-9. Baseball c-10. Basketball c-9. Football c-8.*

DICKIE DARE
Eastern Color Printing Co.: 1941 - No. 4, 1942 (#3 on sale 6/15/42)
1-Caniff-a, bondage-c by Everett 63 126 189 403 689 975
2 30 60 90 177 289 400
3,4-Half Scorchy Smith by Noel Sickles who was very influential in Milton
Caniff's development 32 64 96 188 307 425

DICK POWELL (Also see A-1 Comics)
Magazine Enterprises: No. 22, 1949 (one shot)
A-1 22-Photo-c 22 44 66 132 216 300

DICK QUICK, ACE REPORTER (See Picture News #10)

DICKS
Caliber Comics: 1997 - No. 4, 1998 ($2.95, B&W)
1-4-Ennis-s/McCrea-c/a; r/Fleetway 3.00
TPB ('98, $12.95) r/series 13.00

DICK'S ADVENTURES
Dell Publishing Co.: No. 245, Sept, 1949
Four Color 245 6 12 18 37 66 95

DICK TRACY (See Famous Feature Stories, Harvey Comics Library, Limited Collectors' Ed., Mammoth Comics, Merry Christmas, The Original..., Popular Comics, Super Book No. 1, 7, 13, 25, Super Comics & Tastee-Freez)

DICK TRACY
David McKay Publications: May, 1937 - Jan, 1938
Feature Books nn - 100 pgs., partially reprinted as 4-Color No. 1 (appeared before Large Feature Comics, 1st Dick Tracy comic book) (Very Rare-five known copies; two incomplete) 1400 2800 4200 10,500 19,250 28,000
Feature Books 4 - Reprints nn issue w/new-c 155 310 465 992 1696 2400
Feature Books 6,9 107 214 321 680 1165 1650

DICK TRACY (...Monthly #1-24)
Dell Publishing Co.: 1939 - No. 24, Dec, 1949
Large Feature Comic 1 (1939) -Dick Tracy Meets The Blank
226 452 678 1446 2473 3500
Large Feature Comic 4,8 113 226 339 718 1234 1750
Large Feature Comic 11,13,15 103 206 309 659 1130 1600
Four Color 1(1939)('35-r) 1100 2200 3300 8360 15,930 23,500
Four Color 6(1940)('37-r)-(Scarce) 265 530 795 1694 2897 4100
Four Color 8(1940)('38-'39-r) 139 278 417 883 1517 2150
Large Feature Comic 3(1941, Series II) 103 206 309 659 1130 1600
Four Color 21('41)('38-r) 94 188 282 597 1024 1450
Four Color 34('43)('39-'40-r) 38 76 114 282 634 985
Four Color 56('44)('40-r) 34 68 102 247 554 860
Four Color 96('46)('40-r) 23 46 69 161 356 550
Four Color 133('47)('40-'41-r) 18 36 54 124 275 425
Four Color 163('47)('41-r) 16 32 48 110 243 375
1(1/48)('34-r) 42 84 126 311 706 1100
2,3 22 44 66 154 340 525
4-10 18 36 54 126 281 435
11-18: 13-Bondage-c 14 28 42 97 214 330
19-1st app. Sparkle Plenty, B.O. Plenty & Gravel Gertie in a 3-pg. strip not by Gould 15 30 45 103 227 350
20-1st app. Sam Catchem; c/a not by Gould 13 26 39 91 201 310
21-24-Only 2 pg. Gould-a in each 13 26 39 89 195 300
NOTE: *No. 19-24 have a 2 pg. biography of a famous villain illustrated by Gould: 19-Little Face; 20-Flattop; 21-Breathless Mahoney; 22-Measles; 23-Itchy; 24-The Brow.*

DICK TRACY (Continued from Dell series)(...Comics Monthly #25-140)
Harvey Publications: No. 25, Mar, 1950 - No. 145, April, 1961
25-Flat Top-c/story (also #26,27) 11 22 33 76 163 250
26-28,30: 28-Bondage-c. 28,29-The Brow-c/stories 9 18 27 61 123 185
29-1st app. Gravel Gertie in a Gould-r 10 20 30 69 147 225
31,32,34,35,37-40: 40-Intro/origin 2-way wrist radio (6/51)
8 16 24 52 99 145
33- "Measles the Teen-Age Dope Pusher" 9 18 27 61 123 185
36-1st app. B.O. Plenty in a Gould-r 9 18 27 61 123 185
41-50 7 14 21 46 86 125
51-56,58-80: 51-2pgs Powell-a 6 12 18 40 73 105
57-1st app. Sam Catchem in a Gould-r 7 14 21 46 86 125
81-99,101-140: 99-109-Painted-c 6 12 18 37 66 95
100, 141-145 (25¢)(titled "Dick Tracy") 6 12 18 40 73 105
NOTE: *Powell a(1-2pgs.)-43, 44, 104, 108, 109, 145. No. 110-120, 141-145 are all reprints from earlier issues.*

DICK TRACY ("Reuben Award" series)
Blackthorne Publishing: 12/84 - No. 24, 6/89 (1-12: $5.95; 13-24: $6.95, B&W, 76 pgs.)
1-8-1st printings; hard-c ed. ($14.95) 20.00
1-3-2nd printings, 1986; hard-c ed. 20.00
1-12-1st & 2nd printings; squarebound. thick-c 12.00
13-24 ($6.95): 21,22-Regular-c & stapled 14.00
NOTE: *Gould daily & Sunday strip-r in all. 1-12 r-12/31/45-4/5/49; 13-24 r-7/13/41-2/20/44.*

DICK TRACY (Disney)
WD Publications: 1990 - No. 3, 1990 (color) (Book 3 adapts 1990 movie)
Book One ($3.95, 52pgs.)-Kyle Baker-c/a 6.00
Book Two, Three ($5.95, 68pgs.)-Direct sale 6.00
Book Two, Three ($2.95, 68pgs.)-Newsstand 4.00

DICK TRACY ADVENTURES
Gladstone Publishing: May, 1991 ($4.95, 76 pgs.)
1-Reprints strips 2/1/42-4/18/42 5.00

DICK TRACY, EXPLOITS OF
Rosdon Books, Inc.: 1946 ($1.00, hard-c strip reprints)
1-Reprints the near complete case of "The Brow" from 6/12/44 to 9/24/44 (story starts a few weeks late) 25 50 75 147 241 335
with dust jacket... 39 78 117 240 395 550

DICK TRACY MONTHLY/WEEKLY
Blackthorne Publishing: May, 1986 - No. 99, 1989 ($2.00, B&W)
(Becomes Weekly #26 on)
1-60: Gould-r. 30,31-Mr. Crime app. 4.00
61-90 4.00
91-95 6.00
96-99-Low print 1 2 3 5 7 9
NOTE: *#1-10 reprint strips 3/10/40-7/13/41; #10(pg.8)-51 reprint strips 4/6/49-12/31/55; #52-99 reprint strips 12/26/56-4/26/64.*

DICK TRACY SPECIAL
Blackthorne Publ.: Jan, 1988 - No. 3, Aug. (no month), 1989 ($2.95, B&W)
1-3: 1-Origin D. Tracy; 4/strips 10/12/31-3/30/32 4.00

DICK TRACY: THE EARLY YEARS
Blackthorne Publishing: Aug, 1987 - No. 4, Aug (no month) 1989 ($6.95, B&W, 76 pgs.)
1-3: 1-4-r/strips 10/12/31(1st daily)-8/31/32 & Sunday strips 6/12/32-8/28/32; Big Boy apps. in #1-3 1 2 3 4 5 7
4 ($2.95, 52pgs.) 4.00

DICK TRACY UNPRINTED STORIES
Blackthorne Publishing: Sept, 1987 - No. 4, June, 1988 ($2.95, B&W)
1-4: Reprints strips 1/1/56-12/25/56 4.00

DICK TURPIN (See Legend of Young...)

DIE-CUT
Marvel Comics UK, Ltd: Nov, 1993 - No. 4, Feb, 1994 ($1.75, limited series)
1-4: 1-Die-cut-c; The Beast app. 3.00

DIE-CUT VS. G-FORCE
Marvel Comics UK, Ltd: Nov, 1993 - No. 2, Dec, 1993 ($2.75, limited series)
1,2-($2.75)-Gold foil-c on both 4.00

DIE HARD: YEAR ONE (Based on the John McClane character)
BOOM! Studios: Aug, 2009 - No. 8, Mar, 2010 ($3.99, limited series)
1-8-Chaykin-s; Officer McClane in 1976 NYC; multiple covers on each 4.00

DIE KITTY DIE!
Chapterhouse Comics: Oct, 2016 - Present ($3.99/$4.99)
1,3,4-($3.99) Fernando Ruiz-s/Dan Parent-a; Harvey-style spoof 4.00
2-($4.99) Bonus faux 1969 reprint; Li'l Satan app. 5.00
... Christmas Special 1 (12/07, $4.99) Christmas stories 5.00
... Summer Vacation 1 (7/17, $3.99) Parent, Ruiz & Lagace-a 4.00

DIE KITTY DIE! HOLLYWOOD OR BUST
Chapterhouse Comics: Jul, 2017 - No. 4, Sept, 2017 ($3.99/$4.99)
1,2-($3.99) Fernando Ruiz-s/Dan Parent-a 4.00
3,4-($4.99) 5.00

DIE, MONSTER, DIE (See Movie Classics)

Dilton's Strange Science #3 © ACP

Dinosaurs For Hire #5 © Tom Mason

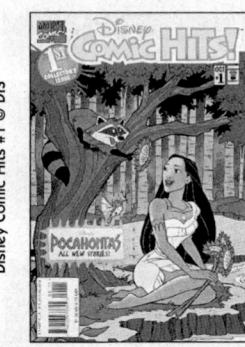

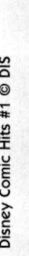

Disney Comic Hits #1 © DIS

	GD 2.0	VG 4.0	FN 6.0	VF 8.0	VF/NM 9.0	NM- 9.2

DIESEL (TYSON HESSE'S...)
Boom Entertainment (BOOM! Box): Sept, 2015 - No. 4, Dec, 2015 ($3.99, limited series)
1-4-Tyson Hesse-s/a in all. 1-Three covers 4.00

DIGIMON DIGITAL MONSTERS (TV)
Dark Horse Comics: May, 2000 - No. 12, Nov, 2000 ($2.95/$2.99)
1-12 3.00

DIGITEK
Marvel UK, Ltd: Dec, 1992 - No. 4, Mar, 1993 ($1.95/$2.25, mini-series)
1-4: 3-Deathlock-c/story 3.00

DILLY (Dilly Duncan from Daredevil Comics; see Boy Comics #57)
Lev Gleason Publications: May, 1953 - No. 3, Sept, 1953

	GD	VG	FN	VF	VF/NM	NM-
1-Teenage; Biro-c	9	18	27	47	61	75
2,3-Biro-c	7	14	21	35	43	50

DILTON'S STRANGE SCIENCE (See Pep Comics #78)
Archie Comics: May, 1989 - No. 5, May, 1990 (75¢/$1.00)
1-5 3.00

DIME COMICS
Newsbook Publ. Corp.: 1945; 1951

	GD	VG	FN	VF	VF/NM	NM-
1-(32 pgs.) Silver Streak/Green Dragon-c/sty; Japanese WWII-c by L. B. Cole (Rare)	194	388	582	1242	2121	3000
1(1951)	21	42	63	122	199	275

DINGBATS (See 1st Issue Special)

DING DONG
Compix/Magazine Enterprises: Summer?, 1946 - No. 5, 1947 (52 pgs.)

	GD	VG	FN	VF	VF/NM	NM-
1-Funny animal	39	78	117	231	378	525
2 (9/46)	17	34	51	100	158	215
3 (Wint '46-'47) - 5	14	28	42	82	121	160

DINKY DUCK (Paul Terry's...) (See Approved Comics, Blue Ribbon, Giant Comics Edition #5A & New Terrytoons)
St. John Publishing Co./Pines No. 16 on: Nov, 1951 - No. 16, Sept, 1955; No. 16, Fall, 1956; No. 17, May, 1957 - No. 19, Summer, 1958

	GD	VG	FN	VF	VF/NM	NM-
1-Funny animal	14	28	42	82	121	160
2	8	16	24	44	57	70
3-10	6	12	18	31	38	45
11-16(9/55)	6	12	18	28	34	40
16 (Fall, '56) - 19	5	10	15	23	28	32

DINKY DUCK & HASHIMOTO-SAN (See Deputy Dawg Presents...)

DINO (TV)(The Flintstones)
Charlton Publications: Aug, 1973 - No. 20, Jan, 1977 (Hanna-Barbera)

	GD	VG	FN	VF	VF/NM	NM-
1	3	6	9	19	30	40
2-10	2	4	6	10	14	18
11-20	2	4	6	8	10	12
Digest nn (w/Xerox Pub., 1974) (low print run)	2	4	6	11	16	20

DINO ISLAND
Mirage Studios: Feb, 1994 - No. 2, Mar, 1994 ($2.75, limited series)
1,2-By Jim Lawson 3.00

DINO RIDERS
Marvel Comics: Feb, 1989 - No. 3, 1989 ($1.00)
1-3: Based on toys 3.00

DINOSAUR REX
Upshot Graphics (Fantagraphics): 1986 - No. 3, 1986 ($2.00, limited series)
1-3 3.00

DINOSAURS, A CELEBRATION
Marvel Comics (Epic): Oct, 1992 - No. 4, Oct, 1992 ($4.95, lim. series, 52 pgs.)
1-4: 2-Bolton painted-c 5.00

DINOSAURS ATTACK! (Based on Topps trading card set)
IDW Publishing: Jul, 2013 - No. 5, Nov, 2013 ($3.99, limited series)
1-5: 1,2-Remastered version of 1991 graphic novel. 3-5-New continuation of story 4.00

DINOSAURS ATTACK! THE GRAPHIC NOVEL
Eclipse Comics: 1991 ($3.95, coated stock, stiff-c)
Book One- Based on Topps trading cards 5.00

DINOSAURS FOR HIRE
Malibu Comics: Feb, 1993 - No. 12, Feb, 1994 ($1.95/$2.50)
1-12: 1,10-Flip bk. 8-Bagged w/Skycap; Staton-c. 10-Flip book 3.00

DINOSAURS GRAPHIC NOVEL (TV)
Disney Comics: 1992 - No. 2, 1993 ($2.95, 52 pgs.)
1,2-Staton-a; based on Dinosaurs TV show 4.00

DINOSAURUS
Dell Publishing Co.: No. 1120, Aug, 1960

	GD	VG	FN	VF	VF/NM	NM-
Four Color 1120-Movie, painted-c	8	16	24	51	96	140

DIPPY DUCK
Atlas Comics (OPI): October, 1957

	GD	VG	FN	VF	VF/NM	NM-
1-Maneely-a; code approved	14	28	42	81	118	155

DIRECTORY TO A NONEXISTENT UNIVERSE
Eclipse Comics: Dec, 1987 ($2.00, B&W)
1 3.00

DIRK GENTLY'S HOLISTIC DETECTIVE AGENCY
IDW Publishing: May, 2015 - No. 5, Oct, 2015 ($3.99, limited series)
1-5: 1-Ryall-s/Kyriazis-a; multiple covers on each 4.00
...: A Spoon Too Short 1-5 (2/16 - No. 5, 6/16, $3.99) A.E. David-s/Kyriazis-a 4.00
...: The Salmon of Doubt 1-9 (10/16 - No. 9, 6/17, $3.99) A.E. David-s/Kyriazis-a 4.00

DIRTY DOZEN (See Movie Classics)

DIRTY PAIR (Manga)
Eclipse Comics: Dec, 1988 - No. 4, Apr, 1989 ($2.00, B&W, limited series)
1-4: Japanese manga with original stories 3.00
...: Start the Violence (Dark Horse, 9/99, $2.95) r/B&W stories in color from Dark Horse Presents #132-134; covers by Warren & Pearson 3.00

DIRTY PAIR: FATAL BUT NOT SERIOUS (Manga)
Dark Horse Comics: July, 1995 - No. 5, Nov, 1995 ($2.95, limited series)
1-5 3.00

DIRTY PAIR: RUN FROM THE FUTURE (Manga)
Dark Horse Comics: Jan, 2000 - No. 4, Mar, 2000 ($2.95, limited series)
1-4-Warren-s/c/a. Variant-c by Hughes(1), Stelfreeze(2), Timm(3), Ramos(4) 3.00

DIRTY PAIR: SIM HELL (Manga)
Dark Horse Comics: May, 1993 - No. 4, Aug, 1993 ($2.50, B&W, limited series)
1-4 3.00
...Remastered #1-4 (5/01 - 8/01) reprints in color, with pin-up gallery 3.00

DIRTY PAIR II (Manga)
Eclipse Comics: June, 1989 - No. 5, Mar, 1990 ($2.00, B&W, limited series)
1-5: 3-Cover is misnumbered as #1 3.00

DIRTY PAIR III, THE (A Plague of Angels) (Manga)
Eclipse Comics: Aug, 1990 - No. 5, Aug, 1991 ($2.00/$2.25, B&W, lim. series)
1-5 3.00

DISCIPLINE
Image Comics: Mar, 2016 - No. 6, Aug, 2016 ($2.99)
1-6-Peter Milligan-s/Leandro Fernández-a 3.00

DISNEY AFTERNOON, THE (TV)
Marvel Comics: Nov, 1994 - No. 10?, Aug, 1995 ($1.50)
1-10: 3-w/bound-in Power Ranger Barcode Card 3.00

DISNEY COMIC ALBUM
Disney Comics: 1990(no month, year) - No. 8, 1991 ($6.95/$7.95)
1,2 ($6.95): 1-Donald Duck and Gyro Gearloose by Barks(r). 2-Uncle Scrooge by Barks(r); Jr. Woodchucks app. 9.00
3-8: 3-Donald Duck-r/F.C. 308 by Barks; begin $7.95-c. 4-Mickey Mouse Meets the Phantom Blot; r/M.M Club Parade (censored 1956 version of story). 5-Chip 'n' Dale Rescue Rangers; new-a. 6-Uncle Scrooge. 7-Donald Duck in Too Many Pets; Barks-r(4) including F.C. #29. 8-Super Goof; r/S.G. #1, D.D. #102 9.00

DISNEY COMIC HITS
Marvel Comics: Oct, 1995 - No. 16, Jan, 1997 ($1.50/$2.50)
1-16: 4-Toy Story. 6-Aladdin. 7-Pocahontas. 10-The Hunchback of Notre Dame (Same story in Disney's The Hunchback of Notre Dame). 13-Aladdin and the Forty Thieves 4.00

DISNEY COMICS
Disney Comics: June, 1990

	GD	VG	FN	VF	VF/NM	NM-
Boxed set of #1 issues includes Donald Duck Advs., Ducktales, Chip 'n Dale Rescue Rangers, Roger Rabbit, Mickey Mouse Advs. & Goofy Advs.; limited to 10,000 sets	2	4	6	11	16	20

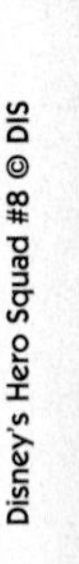
Disney Kingdoms: Figment 2 #3 © DIS

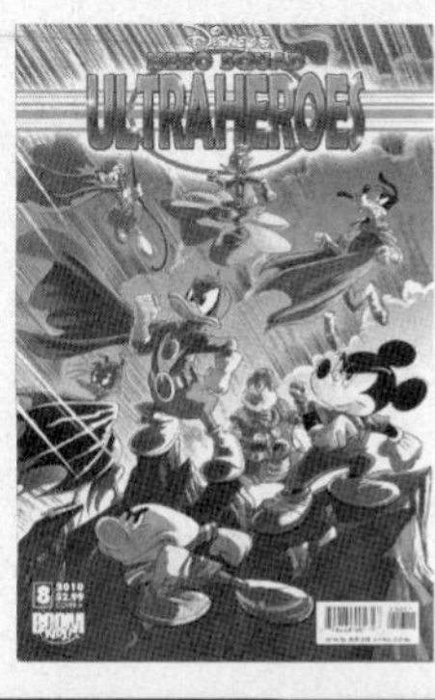

Disney's Hero Squad #8 © DIS

A Distant Soil #21 © Colleen Doran

GD 2.0 | VG 4.0 | FN 6.0 | VF 8.0 | VF/NM 9.0 | NM- 9.2

DISNEY GIANT HALLOWEEN HEX
IDW Publishing: Oct, 2016 ($6.99)
1-Halloween-themed reprints of U.S., Dutch and Italian stories; three covers 7.00

DISNEY KINGDOMS: FIGMENT 2 (Sequel to Figment series)
Marvel Comics: Nov, 2015 - No. 5, Mar, 2016 ($3.99)
1-5: 1-Jim Zub-s/Ramon Bachs-a/J. T. Christopher-c 4.00

DISNEY KINGDOMS: SEEKERS OF THE WEIRD
Marvel Comics: Mar, 2014 - No. 5, Jul, 2014 ($3.99)
1-5: 1-Seifert-s/Moline-a/Del Mundo-c. 3-Andrade-a 4.00

DISNEYLAND BIRTHDAY PARTY (Also see Dell Giants)
Gladstone Publishing Co.: Aug, 1985 ($2.50)
1-Reprints Dell Giant with new-photo-c 2 4 6 8 10 12
...Comics Digest #1-(Digest) 2 4 6 8 11 14

DISNEYLAND MAGAZINE
Fawcett Publications: Feb. 15, 1972 - ? (10-1/4"x12-5/8", 20 pgs, weekly)
1-One or two page painted art features on Dumbo, Snow White, Lady & the Tramp, the Aristocats, Brer Rabbit, Peter Pan, Cinderella, Jungle Book, Alice & Pinocchio. Most standard characters app. 3 6 9 16 23 30

DISNEYLAND, USA (See Dell Giant No. 30)

DISNEY MAGIC KINGDOM COMICS
IDW Publishing: May, 2016 - Present ($6.99, squarebound, quarterly)
1,2-Reprints inspired by the theme parks; Barks-a 7.00

DISNEY MOVIE BOOK
Walt Disney Productions (Gladstone): 1990 ($7.95, 8-1/2"x11", 52 pgs.) (w/pull-out poster)
1-Roger Rabbit in Tummy Trouble; from the cartoon film strips adapted to the comic format. Ron Dias-c 2 4 6 8 10 12

DISNEY'S ACTION CLUB
Acclaim Books: 1997 - No. 4 ($4.50, digest size)
1-4: 1-Hercules. 4-Mighty Ducks 4.50

DISNEY'S ALADDIN (Movie)
Marvel Comics: no date (Oct, 1994) - No. 11, 1995 ($1.50)
1-11 3.00

DISNEY'S BEAUTY AND THE BEAST (Movie)
Marvel Comics: Sept, 1994 - No. 13, 1995 ($1.50)
1-13 3.00

DISNEY'S BEAUTY AND THE BEAST HOLIDAY SPECIAL
Acclaim Books: 1997 ($4.50, digest size, one-shot)
1-Based on The Enchanted Christmas video 4.50

DISNEY'S COLOSSAL COMICS COLLECTION
Disney Comics: 1991 - No. 10, 1993 ($1.95, digest-size, 96/132 pgs.)
1-10: Ducktales, Talespin, Chip 'n Dale's Rescue Rangers. 4-r/Darkwing Duck #1-4. 6-Goofy begins. 8-Little Mermaid 5.00

DISNEY'S COMICS IN 3-D
Disney Comics: 1992 ($2.95, w/glasses, polybagged)
1-Infinity-c; Barks, Rosa, Gottfredson-r 5.00

DISNEY'S ENCHANTING STORIES
Acclaim Books: 1997 - No. 5 ($4.50, digest size)
1-5: 1-Hercules. 2-Pocahontas 4.50

DISNEY'S HERO SQUAD
BOOM! Studios: Jan, 2010 - No. 8, Aug, 2010 ($2.99)
1-8: 1-3-Phantom Blot app. 1-Back-up reprint of Super Goof #1 3.00

DISNEY'S NEW ADVENTURES OF BEAUTY AND THE BEAST (Also see Beauty and the Beast & Disney's Beauty and the Beast)
Disney Comics: 1992 - No. 2, 1992 ($1.50, limited series)
1,2-New stories based on movie 3.00

DISNEY'S POCAHONTAS (Movie)
Marvel Comics: 1995 ($4.95, one-shot)
1-Movie adaptation 1 2 3 4 5 7

DISNEY'S TALESPIN LIMITED SERIES: "TAKE OFF" (TV) (See Talespin)
W. D. Publications (Disney Comics): Jan, 1991 - No. 4, Apr, 1991 ($1.50, lim. series, 52 pgs.)
1-4: Based on animated series; 4 part origin 4.00

DISNEY'S TARZAN (Movie)
Dark Horse Comics: June, 1999 - No. 2, July, 1999 ($2.95, limited series)
1,2: Movie adaptation 3.00

DISNEY'S THE LION KING (Movie)
Marvel Comics: July, 1994 - No. 2, July, 1994 ($1.50, limited series)
1,2: 2-part movie adaptation 3.00
1-($2.50, 52 pgs.)-Complete story 5.00

DISNEY'S THE LITTLE MERMAID (Movie)
Marvel Comics: Sept, 1994 - No. 12, 1995 ($1.50)
1-12 4.00

DISNEY'S THE LITTLE MERMAID LIMITED SERIES (Movie)
Disney Comics: Feb, 1992 - No. 4, May, 1992 ($1.50, limited series)
1-4: Peter David scripts 4.00

DISNEY'S THE LITTLE MERMAID: UNDERWATER ENGAGEMENTS
Acclaim Books: 1997 ($4.50, digest size)
1-Flip book 4.50

DISNEY'S THE HUNCHBACK OF NOTRE DAME (Movie)(See Disney's Comic Hits #10)
Marvel Comics: July, 1996 ($4.95, squarebound, one-shot)
1-Movie adaptation. 1 2 3 4 5 7
NOTE: *A different edition of this series was sold at Wal-Mart stores with new covers depicting scenes from the 1989 feature film. Inside contents and price were identical.*

DISNEY'S THE PRINCE AND THE PAUPER
W. D. Publications: no date ($5.95, 68 pgs., squarebound)
nn-Movie adaptation 6.00

DISNEY'S THE THREE MUSKETEERS (Movie)
Marvel Comics: Jan, 1994 - No. 2, Feb, 1994 ($1.50, limited series)
1,2-Morrow-c; Spiegle-a; Movie adaptation 3.00

DISNEY'S TOY STORY (Movie)
Marvel Comics: Dec, 1995 ($4.95, one-shot)
nn-Adaptation of film 1 2 3 4 5 7

DISSONANCE
Image Comics (Top Cow): Jan, 2018 - Present ($3.99)
1-Basri-a 4.00

DISTANT SOIL, A (1st Series)
WaRP Graphics: Dec, 1983 - No. 9, Mar 1986 ($1.50, B&W)
1-Magazine size 6.00
2-9: 2-4 are magazine size 4.00
NOTE: Second printings exist of #1, 2, 3 & 6.

DISTANT SOIL, A
Donning (Star Blaze): Mar, 1989 ($12.95, trade paperback)
nn-new material 13.00

DISTANT SOIL, A (2nd Series)
Aria Press/Image Comics (Highbrow Entertainment) #15 on:
June, 1991 - Present ($1.75/$2.50/$2.95/$3.50/$3.95, B&W)
1-27: 13-$2.95-c begins. 14-Sketchbook. 15-(8/96)-1st Image issue 4.00
29-33,35,37-($3.95) 4.00
34-($4.95, 64 pages) includes sketchbook pages 5.00
36,38-($4.50) 36-Back-up story by Darnall & Doran. 38-Includes sketch pages 4.50
39-42-($3.50) 3.50
The Aria ('01, $16.95,TPB) r/#26-31 17.00
The Ascendant ('98, $18.95,TPB) r/#13-25 19.00
The Gathering ('97, $18.95,TPB) r/#1-13; intro. Neil Gaiman 19.00
Vol. 4: Coda (2005, $17.99, TPB) r/#32-38 18.00
NOTE: Four separate printings exist for #1 and are clearly marked. Second printings exist of #2-4 and are also clearly marked.

DISTANT SOIL, A: IMMIGRANT SONG
Donning (Star Blaze): Aug, 1987 ($6.95, trade paperback)
nn-new material 7.00

DISTRICT X (Also see X-Men titles) (Also see Mutopia X)
Marvel Comics: July, 2004 - No. 14, Aug, 2005 ($2.99)
1-14: 1-3-Bishop app.; Yardin-a/Hine-s 3.00
...Vol. 1: Mr. M (2005, $14.99) r/#1-6; sketch page by Yardin 15.00
...Vol. 2: Underground (2005, $19.99) r/#7-14; prologue from X-Men Unlimited #2 20.00

DIVER DAN (TV)
Dell Publishing Co.: Feb-Apr, 1962 - No. 2, June-Aug, 1962
Four Color 1254(#1), 2 5 10 15 31 53 75

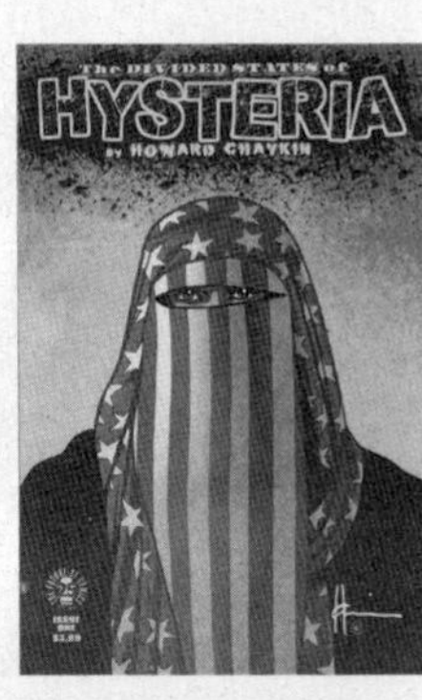

Divided States of Hysteria #1 © Howard Chaykin

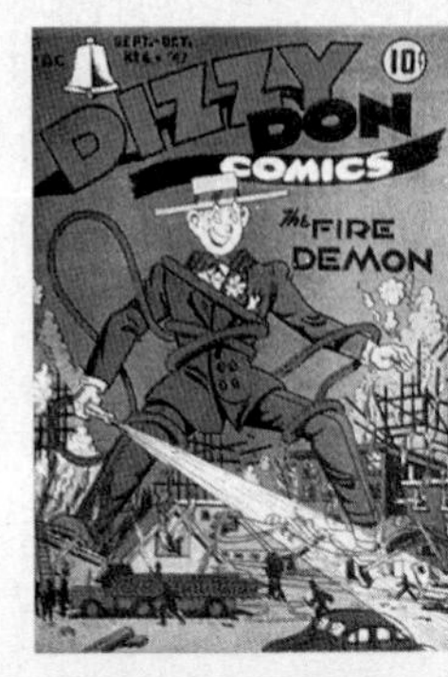

Dizzy Don Comics #4 © Howard Publ.

Doc Macabre #1 © Niles & Wrightson

	GD 2.0	VG 4.0	FN 6.0	VF 8.0	VF/NM 9.0	NM- 9.2

DIVERGENCE FCBD SPECIAL EDITION
DC Comics: Jun, 2015 (Free Comic Book Day giveaway)

1-Previews Batman #41, Superman #41, Justice League Darkseid War 3.00

DIVIDED STATES OF HYSTERIA
Image Comics: Jun, 2017 - No. 6, Nov, 2017 ($3.99)

1-6-Howard Chaykin-s/a 4.00

DIVINE RIGHT
Image Comics (WildStorm Prod.): Sept, 1997 - No. 12, Nov, 1999 ($2.50)

Preview 5.00
1,2: 1-Jim Lee-s/a(p)/c, 1-Variant-c by Charest 4.00
1-($3.50)-Voyager Pack w/Stormwatch preview 4.00
1-American Entertainment Ed. 6.00
2-Variant-c of Exotica & Blaze 5.00
3-Chromium-c by Jim Lee 5.00
3-12: 3-5-Fairchild & Lynch app. 4-American Entertainment Ed. 8-Two covers. 9-1st DC issue. 11,12-Divine Intervention pt. 1,4 3.00
5-Pacific Comicon Ed. 6.00
6-Glow in the dark variant-c, European Tour Edition 20.00
...Book One TPB (2002, $17.95) r/#1-7 18.00
...Book Two TPB (2002, $17.95) r/#8-12 & Divine Intervention Gen13, ...Wildcats 18.00
...Collected Edition #1-3 ($5.95, TPB) 1-r/#1,2. 2-r/#3,4. 3-r/#5,6 6.00
Divine Intervention/Gen 13 (11/99, $2.50) Part 3; D'Anda-a 3.00
Divine Intervention/Wildcats (11/99, $2.50) Part 2; D'Anda-a 3.00

DIVINITY
Valiant Entertainment: Feb, 2015 - No. 4, May, 2015 ($3.99, limited series)

1-4-Kindt-s/Hairsine-a 4.00
#0 (8/17, $3.99) Kindt-s/Guedes-a; bonus preview of Eternity #1 4.00

DIVINITY II
Valiant Entertainment: Apr, 2016 - No. 4, Jul, 2016 ($3.99, limited series)

1-4-Kindt-s/Hairsine-a; 1-Origin of Myshka 4.00

DIVINITY III: STALINVERSE
Valiant Entertainment: Dec, 2016 - No. 4, Mar, 2017 ($3.99, limited series)

1-4-Kindt-s/Hairsine-a 4.00
Divinity III: Aric, Son of the Revolution 1 (1/17, $3.99) Joe Harris-s/Cafu-a 4.00
Divinity III: Escape From Gulag 396 1 (3/17, $3.99) Eliot Rahal-s/Francis Portela-a 4.00
Divinity III: Komandar Bloodshot 1 (12/16, $3.99) Jeff Lemire-s/Clayton Crain-a 4.00
Divinity III: Shadowman and the Battle for New Stalingrad 1 (2/17, $3.99) Robert Gill-a 4.00

DIVISION 13 (See Comic's Greatest World)
Dark Horse Comics: Sept, 1994 - Jan, 1995 ($2.50, color)

1-4: Giffen story in all. 1-Art Adams-c 3.00

DIXIE DUGAN (See Big Shot, Columbia Comics & Feature Funnies)
McNaught Syndicate/Columbia/Publication Ent.: July, 1942 - No. 13, 1949
(Strip reprints in all)

	GD	VG	FN	VF	VF/NM	NM-
1-Joe Palooka x-over by Ham Fisher	30	60	90	177	289	400
2	16	32	48	94	147	200
3(1943)	14	28	42	76	108	140
4,5(1945-46)-Bo strip-r	10	20	30	58	79	100
6-13(1/47-49): 6-Paperdoll cut-outs	9	18	27	52	69	85

DIXIE DUGAN
Prize Publications (Headline): V3#1, Nov, 1951 - V4#4, Feb, 1954

	GD	VG	FN	VF	VF/NM	NM-
V3#1	11	22	33	60	83	105
2-4	8	16	24	40	50	60
V4#1-4(#5-8)	7	14	21	35	43	50

DIZZY DAMES
American Comics Group (B&M Distr. Co.): Sept-Oct, 1952 - No. 6, Jul-Aug, 1953

	GD	VG	FN	VF	VF/NM	NM-
1-Whitney-c	61	122	183	390	670	950
2	24	48	72	142	234	325
3-6	21	42	63	122	199	275

DIZZY DON COMICS
F. E. Howard Publications/Dizzy Don Ent. Ltd (Canada): 1942 - No. 22, Oct, 1946; No. 3, Apr, 1947 - No. 4, Sept./Oct., 1947 (Most B&W)

	GD	VG	FN	VF	VF/NM	NM-
1 (B&W)	52	104	156	328	552	775
2 (B&W)	36	72	108	211	343	475
4-21 (B&W)	32	64	96	188	307	425
22-Full color, 52 pgs.	36	72	108	211	343	475
3 (4/47), 4 (9-10/47)-Full color, 52 pgs.	36	72	108	211	343	475

DIZZY DUCK (Formerly Barnyard Comics)
Standard Comics: No. 32, Nov, 1950 - No. 39, Mar, 1952

	GD	VG	FN	VF	VF/NM	NM-
32-Funny animal	12	24	36	67	94	120
33-39	8	16	24	42	54	65

DJANGO UNCHAINED (Adaptation of the 2012 movie)
DC Comics (Vertigo): Feb, 2013 - No. 7, Oct, 2013 ($3.99, limited series)

1-Adaptation of Quentin Tarantino's script; Guéra-a; Tarantino foreword; sketch pages 20.00
1-Variant-c by Jim Lee 80.00
2-Cowan-c; bonus concept art and cover sketch art 8.00
2-Variant-c by Mark Chiarello 35.00
3-7: 5-Quitely-c. 7-Alex Ross-c 5.00

DJANGO / ZORRO (Django from the 2012 Taratino movie)
Dynamite Entertainment: 2014 - No. 7, 2015 ($3.99/$5.99, limited series)

1-6-Tarantino & Matt Wagner-s/Esteve Polls-a; multiple covers on each 4.00
7-($5.99) Covers by Jae Lee & Francesco Francavilla 6.00

DMZ
DC Comics (Vertigo): Jan, 2006 - No. 72, Feb, 2012 ($2.99)

1-Brian Wood-s/Riccardo Burchielli-a 4.00
1-(2008, no cover price) Convention Exclusive promotional edition 3.00
2-49,51-72: 2-10-Brian Wood-s/Riccardo Burchielli-a. 11-Donaldson-a. 12-Wood-s/a 3.00
50-($3.99) Short stories by various incl. Risso, Moon, Gibbons, Bermejo, Jim Lee 4.00
...: Blood in the Game TPB (2009, $12.99) r/#29-34; intro. by Greg Palast 13.00
...: Body of a Journalist TPB (2007, $12.99) r/#6-12; intro. by D. Randall Blythe 13.00
...: Collective Punishment TPB (2011, $14.99) r/#55-59 15.00
...: Friendly Fire TPB (2008, $12.99) r/#18-22; intro. by Sgt. John G. Ford 13.00
...: Hearts and Minds TPB (2010, $16.99) r/#42-49; intro. by Morgan Spurlock 17.00
...: M.I.A. TPB (2011, $14.99) r/#50-54 15.00
...: On the Ground TPB (2006, $9.99) r/#1-5; intro. by Brian Azzarello 10.00
...: Public Works TPB (2007, $12.99) r/#13-17; intro. by Cory Doctorow 13.00
...: The Hidden War TPB (2008, $12.99) r/#23-28 13.00
...: War Powers TPB (2009, $14.99) r/#35-41 15.00

DNAGENTS (The New DNAgents V2/1 on)(Also see Surge)
Eclipse Comics: March, 1983 - No. 24, July, 1985 ($1.50, Baxter paper)

1-Origin. 4.00
2-23: 4-Amber app. 8-Infinity-c 3.00

	GD	VG	FN	VF	VF/NM	NM-
24-Dave Stevens-c	1	2	3	5	6	8

... Industrial Strength Edition TPB (Image, 2008, $24.99) B&W r/#1-14; Evanier intro. 25.00

DOBERMAN (See Sgt. Bilko's Private...)

DOBERMAN
IDW Publishing (Darby Pop): Jul, 2014 - No. 5, Jan, 2015 ($3.99)

1-5-Marder, Rosell, & Lambert-s/McKinney-a 4.00

DOBIE GILLIS (See The Many Loves of...)

DOC FRANKENSTEIN
Burlyman Entertainment: Nov, 2004 - No. 6 ($3.50)

1-6-Wachowski brothers-s/Skroce-a 3.50

DOCK WALLOPER (Ed Burns' ...)
Virgin Comics: Nov, 2007 - No. 5, Jun, 2008 ($2.99)

1-5-Burns & Palmiotti-s/Siju Thomas-a; Prohibition time 3.00

DOC MACABRE
IDW Publishing: Dec, 2010 - No. 3, Feb, 2011 ($3.99)

1-3-Steve Niles-s/Bernie Wrightson-a/c 4.00

DOC SAMSON (Also see Incredible Hulk)
Marvel Comics: Jan, 1996 - No. 4, Apr, 1996 ($1.95, limited series)

1-4: 1-Hulk c/app. 2-She-Hulk-c/app. 3-Punisher-c/app. 4-Polaris-c/app. 3.00

DOC SAMSON (Incredible Hulk)
Marvel Comics: Mar, 2006 - No. 5, July, 2006 ($2.99, limited series)

1-5: 1-DiFilippo-s/Fiorentino-a. 3-Conner-c 3.00

DOC SAVAGE
Gold Key: Nov, 1966

	GD	VG	FN	VF	VF/NM	NM-
1-Adaptation of the Thousand-Headed Man; James Bama c-r/1964 Doc Savage paperback	11	22	33	77	166	255

DOC SAVAGE (Also see Giant-Size...)
Marvel Comics Group: Oct, 1972 - No. 8, Jan, 1974

	GD	VG	FN	VF	VF/NM	NM-
1	4	8	12	25	40	55
2,3-Steranko-c	3	6	9	16	23	30
4-8	2	4	6	9	13	16

Doc Savage (2013 series) #1 © Conde Nast

Doctor Aphra #3 © Lucasfilm

Doctor Fate (2015 series) #13 © DC

	GD 2.0	VG 4.0	FN 6.0	VF 8.0	VF/NM 9.0	NM- 9.2

...: The Man of Bronze TPB (DC Comics, 2010, $17.99) r/#1-8 — 18.00
NOTE: ***Gil Kane** c-5, 6. **Mooney** a-1i. No. 1, 2 adapts pulp story "The Man of Bronze"; No. 3, 4 adapts "Death in Silver"; No. 5, 6 adapts "The Monsters"; No. 7, 8 adapts "The Brand of The Werewolf".*

DOC SAVAGE (Magazine) (See Showcase Presents for reprint)
Marvel Comics Group: Aug, 1975 - No. 8, Spring, 1977 ($1.00, B&W)

1-Cover from movie poster; Ron Ely photo-c — 3 6 9 16 23 30
2-5: 3-Buscema-a. 5-Adams-a(1 pg.), Rogers-a(1 pg) — 2 4 6 9 13 16
6-8 — 2 4 6 10 14 18

DOC SAVAGE
DC Comics: Nov, 1987 - No. 4, Feb, 1988 ($1.75, limited series)

1-4: Dennis O'Neil-s/Adam & Andy Kubert-a/c in all — 4.00
...: The Silver Pyramid TPB (2009, $19.99) r/#1-4 — 20.00

DOC SAVAGE
DC Comics: Nov, 1988 - No. 24, Oct, 1990 ($1.75/$2.00: #13-24)

1-16,19-24 — 4.00
17,18-Shadow x-over — 5.00
Annual 1 (1989, $3.50, 68 pgs.) — 5.00

DOC SAVAGE (First Wave)
DC Comics: Jun, 2010 - No. 18, Nov, 2011 ($3.99/$2.99)

1-9: 1-4-Malmont-s/Porter-a/J.G. Jones-c. Justice Inc. back-up; S. Hampton-a — 4.00
1-6-Variant covers by Cassaday — 5.00
10-17-($2.99) 10,16,17-Winslade-a — 3.00

DOC SAVAGE
Dynamite Entertainment: 2013 - No. 8, 2014 ($3.99)

1-8: 1-Roberson-s/Evely-a; covers by Ross & Cassaday — 4.00
Annual 2014 ($5.99) Denton-s/Castro-a — 6.00
Special 2014: Woman of Bronze ($7.99, squarebound) Walker-s/Baal-a; Patricia Savage — 8.00

DOC SAVAGE COMICS (Also see Shadow Comics)
Street & Smith Publ.: May, 1940 - No. 20, Oct, 1943 (1st app. in Doc Savage pulp, 3/33)

1-Doc Savage, Cap Fury, Danny Garrett, Mark Mallory, The Whisperer, Captain Death, Billy the Kid, Sheriff Pete & Treasure Island begin; Norgil, the Magician app. — 595 1190 1785 4350 7675 11,000
2-Origin & 1st app. Ajax, the Sun Man; Danny Garrett, The Whisperer end; classic sci-fi cover — 232 464 696 1485 2543 3600
3 — 155 310 465 992 1696 2400
4-Treasure Island ends; Tuska-a — 123 246 369 787 1344 1900
5-Origin & 1st app. Astron, the Crocodile Queen, not in #9 & 11; Norgi the Magician app.; classic-c — 110 220 330 704 1202 1700
6-10: 6-Cap Fury ends; origin & only app. Red Falcon in Astron story. 8-Mark Mallory ends; Charlie McCarthy app. on-c plus true life story. 9-Supersnipe app. 10-Origin & only app. The Thunderbolt — 65 130 195 416 708 1000
11,12 — 54 108 162 343 574 825
V2#1-6,8(#13-18,20): 15-Origin of Ajax the Sun Man; Jack Benny on-c; Hitler app. 16-The Pulp Hero, The Avenger app.; Fanny Brice story. 17-Sun Man ends; Nick Carter begins; Duffy's Tavern part photo-c & story. 18-Huckleberry Finn part-c/story. 19-Henny Youngman part photo-c & life story. 20-Only all funny-c w/Huckleberry Finn — 50 100 150 315 533 750
V2#7-Classic Devil-c — 54 108 162 343 574 825

DOC SAVAGE: CURSE OF THE FIRE GOD
Dark Horse Comics: Sept, 1995 - No, 4, Dec, 1995 ($2.95, limited series)

1-4 — 3.00

DOC SAVAGE: THE MAN OF BRONZE
Skylark Pub: Mar, 1979, 68pgs. (B&W comic digest, 5-1/4x7-5/8")(low print)

15406-0: Whitman-a, 60 pgs., new comics — 4 8 12 23 37 50

DOC SAVAGE: THE MAN OF BRONZE
Millennium Publications: 1991 - No. 4, 1991 ($2.50, limited series)

1-4: 1-Bronze logo — 3.00
...: The Manual of Bronze 1 ($2.50, B&W, color, one-shot)-Unpublished proposed Doc Savage strip in color, B&W strip-r — 3.00

DOC SAVAGE: THE MAN OF BRONZE, DOOM DYNASTY
Millennium Publ.: 1992 (Says 1991) - No. 2, 1992 ($2.50, limited series)

1,2 — 3.00

DOC SAVAGE: THE MAN OF BRONZE - REPEL
Innovation Publishing: 1992 ($2.50)

1-Dave Dorman painted-c — 3.00

DOC SAVAGE: THE MAN OF BRONZE THE DEVIL'S THOUGHTS
Millennium Publ.: 1992 (Says 1991) - No. 3, 1992 ($2.50, limited series)

1-3 — 3.00

DOC SAVAGE: THE RING OF FIRE
Dynamite Entertainment: 2017 - No. 4, 2017 ($3.99, limited series)

1-4-Avallone-s/Acosta-a; multiple covers on each — 4.00

DOC SAVAGE: THE SPIDER'S WEB
Dynamite Entertainment: 2015 - No. 5, 2016 ($3.99, limited series)

1-5-Roberson-s/Razek-a. 1-Multiple covers — 4.00

DOC STEARN...MR. MONSTER (See Mr. Monster)

DR. ANTHONY KING, HOLLYWOOD LOVE DOCTOR
Minoan Publishing Corp./Harvey Publications No. 4: 1952(Jan) - No. 3, May, 1953; No. 4, May, 1954

1 — 18 36 54 105 165 225
2-4: 4-Powell-a — 11 22 33 60 83 105

DR. ANTHONY'S LOVE CLINIC (See Mr. Anthony's...)

DOCTOR APHRA (Star Wars)(Title changes to Star Wars: Doctor Aphra with #7) (See Darth Vader #3 for debut)
Marvel Comics: Feb, 2017 - No. 6, Jun, 2017 ($4.99/$3.99)

1-Gillen-s/Walker-a; back-up with Larroca-a; BT-1, Triple-Zero and Black Krrsantan app. — 5.00
2-6-($3.99) Walker-a — 4.00

DR. BOBBS
Dell Publishing Co.: No. 212, Jan, 1949

Four Color 212 — 6 12 18 40 73 105

DOCTOR DOOM AND THE MASTERS OF EVIL (All ages title)
Marvel Comics: Mar, 2009 - No. 4, Jun, 2009 ($2.99)

1-4: 1-Sinister Six app. 4-Magneto app. — 3.00

DR. DOOM'S REVENGE
Marvel Comics: 1989 (Came w/computer game from Paragon Software)

V1#1-Spider-Man & Captain America fight Dr. Doom — 3.00

DR. FATE (See 1st Issue Special, The Immortal..., Justice League, More Fun #55, & Showcase)

DOCTOR FATE
DC Comics: July, 1987 - No. 4, Oct, 1987 ($1.50, limited series, Baxter paper)

1-4: Giffen-c/a in all — 4.00

DOCTOR FATE
DC Comics: Winter, 1988-`89 - No. 41, June, 1992 ($1.25/$1.50 #5 on)

1,15: 15-Justice League app. — 4.00
2-14 — 3.00
16-41: 25-1st new Dr. Fate. 36-Original Dr. Fate returns — 3.00
Annual 1(1989, $2.95, 68 pgs.)-Sutton-a — 4.00

DOCTOR FATE
DC Comics: Oct, 2003 - No. 5, Feb, 2004 ($2.50, limited series)

1-5-Golden-s/Kramer-a — 3.00

DOCTOR FATE
DC Comics: Aug, 2015 - No. 18, Jan, 2017 ($2.99)

1-18: 1-Levitz-s/Liew-a; Khalid Nassour chosen as new Doctor. 12-15-Kent Nelson app. — 3.00

DR. FU MANCHU (See The Mask of...)
I.W. Enterprises: 1964

1-r/Avon's "Mask of Dr. Fu Manchu"; Wood-a — 6 12 18 41 76 110

DR. GIGGLES (See Dark Horse Presents #64-66)
Dark Horse Comics: Oct, 1992 - No. 2, Oct, 1992 ($2.50, limited series)

1,2-Based on movie — 3.00

DOCTOR GRAVES (Formerly The Many Ghosts of...)
Charlton Comics: No. 73, Sept, 1985 - No. 75, Jan, 1986

73-75-Low print run. 73,74-Ditko-a — 1 2 3 5 6 8
... Magic Book nn (Charlton Press/Xerox Education, 1977, 68 pgs., digest) Ditko-c/a; Staton-a — 4 8 12 23 37 50

DR. HORRIBLE (Based on Joss Whedon's internet feature)
Dark Horse Comics: Nov, 2009 ($3.50, one-shot)

1-Zack Whedon-s/Joëlle Jones-a; Captain Hammer pin-up by Gene Ha; 3 covers — 3.50
... and other Horrible Stories TPB (9/10, $9.99) r/#1 and 3 stories from MySpace DHP — 10.00

DR. JEKYLL AND MR. HYDE (See A Star Presentation & Supernatural Thrillers #4)

DR. KILDARE (TV)
Dell Publishing Co.: No. 1337, 4-6/62 - No. 9, 4-6/65 (All Richard Chamberlain photo-c)

Doctor Solar, Man of the Atom #14 © GK

Doctor Strange #171 © MAR

Doctor Strange (2015 series) #25 © MAR

GD 2.0 | VG 4.0 | FN 6.0 | VF 8.0 | VF/NM 9.0 | NM- 9.2

Four Color 1337(#1, 1962) 8 16 24 54 102 150
2-9 6 12 18 37 66 95

DR. MASTERS (See The Adventures of Young...)

DOCTOR MID-NITE (Also see All-American #25)
DC Comics: 1999 - No. 3, 1999 ($5.95, square-bound, limited series)

1-3-Matt Wagner-s/John K. Snyder III-painted art 6.00
TPB (2000, $19.95) r/series 20.00

DOCTOR OCTOPUS: NEGATIVE EXPOSURE
Marvel Comics: Dec, 2003 - No. 5, Apr, 2004 ($2.99, limited series)

1-5-Vaughan-s/Staz Johnson-a; Spider-Man app. 3.00
Spider-Man/Doctor Octopus: Negative Exposure TPB (2004, $13.99) r/series 14.00

DR. ROBOT SPECIAL
Dark Horse Comics: Apr, 2000 ($2.95, one-shot)

1-Bernie Mireault-s/a; some reprints from Madman Comics #12-15 3.00

DOCTOR SOLAR, MAN OF THE ATOM (See The Occult Files of Dr. Spektor #14 & Solar)
Gold Key/Whitman No. 28 on: 10/62 - No. 27, 4/69; No. 28, 4/81 - No. 31, 3/82 (1-27 have painted-c)

1-(#10000-210)-Origin/1st app. Dr. Solar (1st original Gold Key character)
42 84 126 311 706 1100
2-Prof. Harbinger begins 12 24 36 82 179 275
3,4 8 16 24 52 99 145
5-Intro. Man of the Atom in costume 9 18 27 57 111 165
6-10 5 10 15 35 63 90
11-14,16-20 4 8 12 28 47 65
15-Origin retold 5 10 15 30 50 70
21-23: 23-Last 12¢ issue 4 8 12 25 40 55
24-27 3 6 9 21 33 45
28-31: 29-Magnus Robot Fighter begins. 31-(3/82)The Sentinel app.
3 6 9 14 20 25
Hardcover Vol. One (Dark Horse Books, 2004, $49.95) r/#1-7; creator bios 50.00
Hardcover Vol. Two (Dark Horse Books, 6/05, $49.95) r/#8-14; Jim Shooter foreword 50.00
Hardcover Vol. Three (Dark Horse Books, 9/05, $49.95) r/#15-22; Mike Baron foreword 50.00
Hardcover Vol. Four (Dark Horse Books, 11/07, $49.95) r/#23-31 and The Occult Files of Dr. Spektor #14; Batton Lash foreword 50.00
NOTE: ***Frank Bolle** a-6-19, 29-31; c-29i, 30i. **Bob Fugitani** a-1-5. **Spiegle** a-29-31. **Al McWilliams** a-20-23.*

DOCTOR SOLAR, MAN OF THE ATOM
Valiant Comics: 1990 - No. 2, 1991 ($7.95, card stock-c, high quality, 96 pgs.)

1,2: Reprints Gold Key series 1 2 3 5 6 8

DOCTOR SOLAR, MAN OF THE ATOM
Dark Horse Comics: Jul, 2010 - No. 8, Sept, 2011 ($3.50)

1-(48 pgs.) Shooter-s/Calero-a; back-up reprint of origin/1st app. in D.S. #1 (1962) 4.00
2-8: 2-7-Roger Robinson-a 3.50
Free Comic Book Day Doctor Solar, Man of the Atom & Magnus, Robot Fighter (5/10, free) short story re-intros of Solar & Magnus; Shooter-s/Swanland-c; Calero & Reinhold-a 3.00

DOCTOR SPECTRUM (See Supreme Power)
Marvel Comics: Oct, 2004 - No. 6, Mar, 2005 ($2.99, limited series)

1-6-Origin; Sara Barnes-s/Travel Foreman-a 3.00
TPB (2005, $16.99) r/#1-6 17.00

DOCTOR SPEKTOR (See The Occult Files of..., & Spine-Tingling Tales)

DOCTOR SPEKTOR: MASTER OF THE OCCULT
Dynamite Entertainment: 2014 - No. 4, 2014 ($3.99)

1-4-Mark Waid-s; multiple covers on each 4.00

DOCTOR STAR AND THE KINGDOM OF LOST TOMORROW (Also see Black Hammer)
Dark Horse Comics: Mar, 2018 - Present ($3.99)

1-Lemire-s/Fiumara-a 4.00

DOCTOR STRANGE (Formerly Strange Tales #1-168) (Also see The Defenders, Giant-Size..., Marvel Fanfare, Marvel Graphic Novel, Marvel Premiere, Marvel Treasury Edition, Strange & Strange Tales, 2nd Series)
Marvel Comics Group: No. 169, Jun, 1968 - No. 183, Nov, 1969

169(#1)-Origin retold; continued from Strange Tales #167; Roy Thomas-s/Dan Adkins-a; panel swipe/M.D. #1-c 27 54 81 189 420 650
170-176: 170-vs. Nightmare. 171-173-vs. Dormammu. 172-1st Colan-a. 174-1st Sons of Satanish 5 10 15 35 63 90
177-New masked costume 8 16 24 54 102 150
178-181: 178-Black Knight app.; continues in Avengers #61. 179-r/Spider-Man & Dr. Strange story from Amazing Spider-Man Annual #2. 180-Nightmare & Eternity app.; photo montage-c. 181-Brunner-c(part-i), last 12¢ issue 5 10 15 33 57 80
182-Juggernaut app. 5 10 15 33 57 80
183-Intro. The Undying Ones; cont'd in Sub-Mariner #22; concludes in Incredible Hulk #126; Dr. Strange returns in Marvel Feature #1 (second story)
5 10 15 33 57 80

DOCTOR STRANGE (2nd series)(Follows from Marvel Premiere #14)
Marvel Comics Group: Jun, 1974 - No. 81, Feb, 1987

1-Englehart-s/Brunner-c/a; 1st Silver Dagger 10 20 30 64 132 200
2-Silver Dagger app.; Defenders-c 5 10 15 34 60 85
3-5: 3-Mostly reprints; r-Strange Tales #126-127; 1 pg. original art. 4-5-Silver Dagger app. 5-Last Brunner-a 3 6 9 17 26 35
6-10: 6-Dormammu app; Colan-a begins. 7-Dormammu app.; story x-over with Giant-Size Avengers #4. 8-Dormammu app.; continued from Giant-Size Avengers #4. 9-Dormammu app.; Umar revealed as Clea's mother. 10-Baron Mordo & Eternity app.
2 4 6 10 14 18
11-13,15-20: 13,15-17-(Regular 25¢ editions). 13-Nightmare app; slight x-over with Tomb of Dracula #44. 15,16-Strange vs. Satan. 17-1st Stygyro. 18-vs. Stygyro; last Englehart-s. 19-Wolfman-s begin; 1st Xander & the Creators. 20-vs. Xander & the Creators; slight x-over w/Annual #1 1 3 4 6 8 10
13,15-17-(30¢-c variants, limited distribution) 4 8 12 27 44 60
14-(5/76) (Regular 25¢ edition) Dracula app.; story continues from Tomb of Dracula #44 and leads into Tomb of Dracula #45 2 4 6 10 14 18
14-(30¢-c variant, limited distribution) 5 10 15 34 60 85
21-25,30,32-40: 21-Reprints origin from Dr. Strange #169. 22-1st Apalla, Queen of the Sun. 23-25-(Regular 30¢ editions). 23-Starlin layouts; last Wolfman-s. 24-Starlin-s. 25-Starlin-c/s. 30-1st full app. Dweller in Darkness. 32-vs. Dweller in Darkness; 1st Dream Weaver. 33-Dweller in Darkness & Dream Weaver app. 34-vs. Cyrus Black & Nightmare. 35-Captain America & Iron Man app; Black Knight statue app. 36-Ningal app. (from Chamber of Chills #3). 37-Ningal, Dweller in Darkness & D'Spayre app. 38-Claremont-s begin. 40-Baron Mordo app.; continues in Man-Thing Vol. 2 #4 6.00
23-25-(35¢-c variants, limited distribution)(6,8,10/77) 6 12 18 42 79 115
26-29,31: 26-Starlin-a (p); Ancient One & In-Betweener app. 27-vs. Stygyro; Roger Stern-s begin; Ancient One & In-Betweener app. 28-vs. In-Betweener; Brunner-c/a. 29-vs. Deathstalker; Nighthawk app; Brunner-c/a. 31-Sub-Mariner app. 6.00
41-57,63-77,79-81: 41-Continued from Man-Thing Vol. 2 #4; Man-Thing & Baron Mordo app. 46-Miller-c/p. 48,49-Brother Voodoo app; 48-Marshall Rogers-p begin. 49-Baron Mordo app. 50-vs. Baron Mordo. 51-Dormammu app. 52-Nightmare. 53-Fantastic Four & Rama-Tut app.; takes place during FF #19. 55-D'Spayre app; Golden-c/a. 56-Paul Smith-a; origin retold. 67-Hannibal King, Blade & Frank Drake app. 68,69-Black Knight app. 71-73 vs. Umar. 74-Secret Wars II x-over; Beyonder app. 75-Mignola-c; continued from FF #277; vs. Mephisto; last Stern-s. 79-1st Urthona. 80-1st Rintrah. 81-Last issue; Rintrah app; story continued in Strange Tales Vol. 2 #1 4.00
58-62: 58-Re-intro Hannibal King (cameo). 59-Hannibal King full app. 59-62-Dracula app. (Darkhold storyline). 61,62-Doctor Strange, Blade, Hannibal King & Frank Drake team-up to battle. Dracula. 62-Death of Dracula & Lilith 6.00
78-New costume; Cloak (from Cloak & Dagger) app. 1 2 3 5 6 8
Annual 1 (1976, 52 pgs.)-New Russell-a (35 pgs.) 3 6 9 14 20 25
....: From the Marvel Vault (4/11, $2.99) Stern-s/Vokes-a 3.00
.../Silver Dagger Special Edition 1 (3/83, $2.50)-r/#1,2,4,5; Wrightson-c 4.00
... Vs. Dracula TPB (2006, $19.99) r/#14,58-62 and Tomb of Dracula #44 20.00
...What Is It That Disturbs You, Stephen? #1 (10/97, $5.99, 48 pgs.) Russell-a/Andreyko & Russell-s, retelling of Annual #1 story 6.00
NOTE: ***Adkins** a-169, 170, 171i; c-169-171, 172i, 173. **Adams** a-4i. **Austin** a(i)-48-60, 66, 68, 70, 73; c(i)-38, 47-53, 55, 58-60, 70. **Brunner** a-1-5p; c-1-6, 22, 28-30, 33. **Colan** a(p)-172-178, 180-183, 6-18, 36-45, 47; c(p)-172, 174-183, 11-21, 23, 27, 35, 36, 47. **Ditko** a-179r, 3r. **Everett** c-183i. **Golden** a-46p, 55p; c-42-44, 46, 55p. **G. Kane** c(p)-8-10. **Miller** c-46p. **Nebres** a-20, 22, 23, 24i, 26i, 32i; c-32i, 34. **Rogers** a-48-53p; c-47p-53p. **Russell** a-34i, 46i, Annual 1. **B. Smith** c-179. **Paul Smith** a-54p, 56p, 65, 66p, 68p, 69, 71-73; c-56, 65, 66, 68, 71. **Starlin** a-23p, 26; c-25, 26. **Sutton** a-27-29p, 31i, 33, 34p. Painted c-62, 63.*

DOCTOR STRANGE (Volume 2)
Marvel Comics: Feb, 1999 - No. 4, May, 1999 ($2.99, limited series)

1-4: 1,2-Tony Harris-a/painted cover. 3,4-Chadwick-a 3.00

DOCTOR STRANGE (Follows Secret Wars event)
Marvel Comics: Dec, 2015 - No. 26, Dec, 2017 ($4.99/$3.99)

1-($4.99) Aaron-s/Bachalo-a; back-up with Nowlan-a 5.00
2-5,7-19-($3.99) Aaron-s/Bachalo-a. 7-10-The Last Days of Magic 4.00
6-($4.99) The Last Days of Magic 5.00
20-($4.99) Doctor Strange in Weirdworld; art by Bachalo & Nowlan; last Aaron-s 5.00
21-24,26: 21-24-Secret Empire tie-ins; Kingpin & Baron Mordo app.; Henrichon-a 4.00
25-($4.99) Barber-s/Nowlan-a/c 5.00

[Title switches to legacy numbering after #26 (12/17)]

381-386: 381-385-Walta-a; Loki as Sorceror Supreme. 383-385-The Sentry app. 386-Mephisto app.; Henrichon-a 4.00
#1.MU (4/17, $4.99) Monsters Unleashed tie-in; Chip Zdarsky-s/Julian Lopez-a 5.00
Annual 1 (11/16, $4.99) K. Immonen-s/Romero-a; Clea app. 5.00

Doctor Strange, Sorceror Supreme #42 © MAR

Doctor Tomorrow #6 © Acclaim

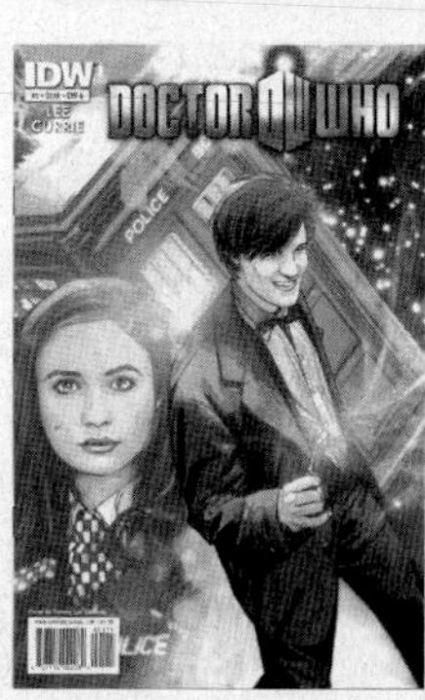

Doctor Who (2011 series) #1 © BBC

GD 2.0 | VG 4.0 | FN 6.0 | VF 8.0 | VF/NM 9.0 | NM- 9.2

...: Last Days of Magic 1 (6/16, $5.99) Story between #6 & 7; Doctor Voodoo & The Wu 6.00
...: Mystic Apprentice 1 (12/16, $3.99) New story w/Di Vito-a; r/Strange Tales #115, 110 4.00

DOCTOR STRANGE AND THE SORCERERS SUPREME (Prelude in Doctor Strange Annual #1)
Marvel Comics: Dec, 2016 - No. 12, Nov, 2017 ($3.99)

1-12: 1-9-Thompson-s/Rodriguez-a; The Ancient One, Wiccan & Merlin app. 5.00

DOCTOR STRANGE CLASSICS
Marvel Comics Group: Mar, 1984 - No. 4, June, 1984 ($1.50, Baxter paper)

1-4: Ditko-r; Byrne-c. 4-New Golden pin-up 4.00
NOTE: *Byrne c-1i, 2-4.*

DOCTOR STRANGE: DAMNATION
Marvel Comics: Apr, 2018 - Present ($3.99)

1,2-Spencer & Cates-s/Rod Reis-a; Las Vegas is restored; Mephisto app. 4.00

DOCTOR STRANGEFATE (See Marvel Versus DC #3 & DC Versus Marvel #4)
DC Comics (Amalgam): Apr, 1996 ($1.95)

1-Ron Marz script w/Jose Garcia-Lopez-(p) & Kevin Nowlan-(i). Access & Charles Xavier app. 3.00

DOCTOR STRANGE MASTER OF THE MYSTIC ARTS (See Fireside Book Series)

DOCTOR STRANGE/PUNISHER: MAGIC BULLETS
Marvel Comics: Feb, 2017 - No. 4, May, 2017 ($4.99, limited series)

1-4-Barber-s/Broccardo-a 5.00

DOCTOR STRANGE, SORCERER SUPREME
Marvel Comics (Midnight Sons imprint #60 on): Nov, 1988 - No. 90, June, 1996 ($1.25/$1.50/$1.75/$1.95, direct sales only, Mando paper)

1-Continued from Strange Tales Vol. 2 #19; Fantastic Four, Avengers, Spider-Man, Silver Surfer, Hulk, Daredevil app. (cameos); Dormammu app. 2 4 6 8 10 12
2-9: 2-Dormammu app. 3-New Defenders app. (Valkyrie, Andromeda, Interloper & Manslaughter.) 4-New Defenders becomes Dragoncircle; vs. Dragon of the Moon. 5-Roy & Dan Thomas-s & Guice-p begin; Rintrah app; vs. Baron Mordo. 6-1st Mephista (daughter of Mephisto); Satannish & Mephisto app; Rintrah appears as Howard the Duck this issue; origin of Baron Mordo Pt. 1 (in back-up). 7-Agamotto, Satannish, Mephisto app.; origin of Baron Mordo Pt. 2 (in back-up). 8-Mephisto vs. Satannish; origin of Baron Mordo Pt. 3 (in back-up). 9-History of Dr. Strange 5.00
10-12: 10-Re-intro Morbius w/new costume (11/89). 11-Acts of Vengeance x-over; vs. Hobgoblin; origin of Varnae (the first Vampire). 12-Acts of Vengeance x-over; vs. Enchantress & Executioner 3.00
13-14,16-25: 13-Acts of Vengeance x-over; Arkon & Enchantress app. 14-Origin Morbius. 16-vs. Baron Blood; Brother Voodoo app. also in back-up story (origin). 17-Morbius & Brother Voodoo app.; origin of Zombies in back-up. 18-Baron Blood & Varnae app. 19-Origin of the 1st Brother Voodoo in back-up. 20-Dormammu app. 21-24: Dormammu & Baron Mordo app.; last Guice-a. 25-Black Crow & Red Wolf app. 3.00
15,26,28: 15-Unauthorized Amy Grant photo-c. 26-Werewolf by Night app. 28-Ghost Rider story continued from Ghost Rider #12; published at the same time as Dr. Strange/Ghost Rider Special #1 (4/91) 3.00
27,29-30,34-40: 29-Baron Blood app. 30-Mephista, Mephisto & Satannish app. 34-36-Infinity Gauntlet x-overs. 34-Dr. Doom app. 35-Scarlet Witch & Thor app. 36-Continued from Infinity Gauntlet #6; Warlock app. 38-Scarecrow app. 40-vs. the Fear Lords; Daredevil app. 3.00
31-33,41: 31-Infinity Gauntlet x-over; continued from Infinity Gauntlet #1; Silver Surfer app. 32-vs. Silver Dagger; Warlock & Dr. Doom app; continued from Infinity Gauntlet #2. 33-Thanos app. 41-Wolverine app. 3.00
42-49: 42-47-Infinity War x-overs. 42-Galactus app.; continues in Silver Surfer #67. 43-Continued from Infinity War #2; Galactus vs. Agamotto. 44-Galactus, Silver Surfer & Juggernaut app. 45-Galactus, Silver Surfer & Death app. 46-Dr. Druid, Scarlet Witch & Agatha Harkness app. 3.00
50-($2.95, 52 pgs.)-Holo-grafx foil-c; Hulk, Ghost Rider & Silver Surfer app.; leads into new Secret Defenders series 4.00
51-61: 52,53-Nightmare & Morbius app. 54-56: Infinity Crusade x-overs. 54-Eternity app. 55-Goddess & Dormammu app.; last Thomas-s. 56-Baron Blood app. 59-Leads into Siege of Darkness Pt. 1 in Nightstalkers #14. 60-Spot varnish-c; Siege of Darkness Pt. 7; continued from Morbius #16; Midnight Sons app.; continued in Ghost Rider/Blaze: Spirits of Vengeance #17. 61-Siege of Darkness Pt. 15; new Dr. Strange begins (cameo, 1st app. 'Strange'; continued from Marvel Comics Presents #146; continued in Ghost Rider/Blaze Spirits of Vengeance #18 3.00
62-74: 62-Dr. Doom vs. Strange. 64,65-Sub-Mariner app. 65-Begin $1.95-c; bound-in card sheet. 66-Midnight Sons app.; continued in Dr. Strange Annual #4. 67-Clea returns; continued from Dr. Strange Annual #4. 69-Polaris & Forge app.; story takes place between X-Factor #105,106. 70,71-Hulk app. 72-Silver ink-c; Last Rites Pt. 1. 73-Last Rites Pt. 2.; Salom app. 74-Last Rites Pt. 3; Salom app. 3.00
75-($3.50) Foil-c; Last Rites Pt. 4; death of 'Strange' 5.00
75-($2.50) Reg-c 4.00
76-90: 76-New look Dr. Strange. 80-Warren Ellis-s begin; another new look for Dr. Strange. 81-Begins "Over the Edge" branding. 82-Last Ellis-s. 84-DeMatteis-s begin; Baron Mordo app. 85-Baron Mordo revealed to have cancer. 86-Baron Mordo app. 87-'Death' of Baron Mordo. 90-Last issue; Chthon app. 3.00
Annual 1 (See Doctor Strange 2nd series)
Annual 2 ('92, $2.25, 68 pgs.) Return of the Defenders Pt. 4; continued from Silver Surfer Annual #5; Hulk, Sub-Mariner, Silver Surfer app.; vs. Wild One 4.00
Annual 3 ('93, $2.95, 68 pgs.) Polybagged w/card; 1st Kyllian 4.00
Annual 4 ('94, $2.95, 68 pgs.) Story occurs between Doctor Strange #66-67 4.00
Ashcan (1995, 75¢) 3.00
.../Ghost Rider Special 1 (4/91, $1.50)-Same book as Doctor Strange, Sorceror Supreme #28 3.00
...Vs. Dracula 1 (3/94, $1.75, 52 pgs.)-r/Tomb of Dracula #44 & Dr. Strange #14 4.00
NOTE: *Colan c/a-19. **Golden** c-28. **Guice** a-5-16, 18, 20-24; c-5-12, 20-24.*

DOCTOR STRANGE: THE OATH
Marvel Comics: Dec, 2006 - No. 5, Apr, 2007 ($2.99, limited series)

1-5-Vaughan-s/Martin-a; Night Nurse app. 1-Origin re-told 3.00
1-Halloween Comic Fest 2015 (12/15, giveaway) r/#1 with logo on cover 3.00
TPB (2007, $13.99) r/#1-5; sketch pages and promotional art 14.00

DR. TOM BRENT, YOUNG INTERN
Charlton Publications: Feb, 1963 - No. 5, Oct, 1963

	GD	VG	FN	VF	VF/NM	NM-
1	3	6	9	16	23	30
2-5	2	4	6	11	16	20

DR. TOMORROW
Acclaim Comics (Valiant): Sept, 1997 - No. 12 ($2.50)

1-12: 1-Mignola-c 3.00

DR. VOLTZ (See Mighty Midget Comics)

DOCTOR VOODOO: AVENGER OF THE SUPERNATURAL
Marvel Comics: Dec, 2009 - No. 5, Apr, 2010 ($2.99, limited series)

1-5-Dr. Doom, Son of Satan & Ghost Rider app.; Palo-a 3.00
Doctor Voodoo: The Origin of Jericho Drumm (1/10, $4.99) r/Strange Tales #169,170 5.00

DR. WEIRD
Big Bang Comics: Oct, 1994 - No. 2, May, 1995 ($2.95, B&W)

1,2: 1-Frank Brunner-c 4.00
... Special (2/94, $3.95, B&W, 68 pgs.) Origin-r by Starlin; Starlin-c 4.00

DOCTOR WHO (Also see Marvel Premiere #57-60)
Marvel Comics Group: Oct, 1984 - No. 23, Aug, 1986 ($1.50, direct sales, Baxter paper)

1-British-r 2 4 6 8 11 14
2-15-British-r 5.00
16-23 6.00
Graphic Novel Voyager (1985, $8.95) color reprints of B&W comic pages from Doctor Who Magazine #88-99; Colin Baker afterword 15.00

DOCTOR WHO (Based on the 2005 TV series with David Tennant)
IDW Publishing: Jan, 2008 - No. 6, Jun, 2008 ($3.99)

1-6: 1-Nick Roche-a/Gary Russell-s; two covers 4.00

DOCTOR WHO (Based on the 2005 TV series with David Tennant)
IDW Publishing: Jul, 2009 - No. 16, Oct, 2010 ($3.99)

1-16-Grist-c on all. 3-5,13-16-Art by Matt Smith (not the actor) 4.00
... Annual 2010 (7/10, $7.99) short stories by various; Yates-c; cameo by 11th Doctor 8.00
...: Autopia (6/09, $3.99) Ostrander-s; Yates-a/c; variant photo-c 4.00
...: Black Death White Life (9/09, $3.99) Mandrake-a; Guy Davis- c; variant photo-c 4.00
...: Cold-Blooded War (8/09, $3.99) Salmon-a/c; variant photo-c 4.00
...: Room With a Déjà View (6/09, $3.99) Eric J-a; Mandrake-c; variant photo-c 4.00
...: The Whispering Gallery (2/09, $3.99) Moore & Reppion-s; Templesmith-a/2 covers 4.00
...: Time Machination (5/09, $3.99) Paul Grist-a/c; variant photo-c 4.00

DOCTOR WHO (Based on the 2010 TV series with Matt Smith)
IDW Publishing: Jan, 2011 - No. 12, Apr, 2012 ($3.99)

1-16: 1-Edwards & photo-c; Currie-a. 5-Buckingham-a. 12-Grist-a 4.00
Annual 2011 (8/11, $7.99) short stories by Fialkov, Shedd, Smith, McDaid and others 8.00
... Convention Special (7/11, no cover price, BBC America Shop Exclusive) The Doctor, Amy, and Rory at the San Diego Comic-Con; Matthew Dow Smith-s/Domingues-a 15.00
... 100 Page Spectacular 1 (7/12, $7.99) Short story reprints from various eras 8.00

DOCTOR WHO (Volume 3)(Based on the 2010 TV series with Matt Smith)
IDW Publishing: Sept, 2012 - No. 16, Dec, 2013 ($3.99)

1-16-Regular & photo-c on each: 1,2-Diggle-s/Buckingham-a. 3,4-Bond-a 4.00
...: 2016 Convention Exclusive (7/16, $10.00) Short stories of the various doctors 10.00
... Special 2012 (8/12, $7.99) Short stories by various incl. Wein, Diggle; Buckingham-c 8.00

Doctor Who: Ghost Stories #1 © BBC

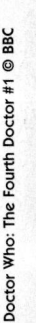

Doctor Who: The Fourth Doctor #1 © BBC

Doctor Who: The Tenth Doctor Year Two #6 © BBC

	GD 2.0	VG 4.0	FN 6.0	VF 8.0	VF/NM 9.0	NM- 9.2

... Special 2013 (12/13, $7.99) Cornell-s/Broxton-a; The Doctor visits the real world 8.00

DOCTOR WHO: A FAIRYTALE LIFE (Based on the 2010 TV series with Matt Smith)
IDW Publishing: Apr, 2011 - No. 4, Jul, 2011 ($3.99, limited series)

1-4: 1-Sturges-s/Yeates-a; covers by Buckingham & Mebberson. 3-Shearer-a 4.00

DR. WHO & THE DALEKS (See Movie Classics)

DOCTOR WHO CLASSICS
IDW Publishing: Nov, 2005 - Oct, 2013 ($3.99)

1-10: Reprints from Doctor Who Weekly (1979); art by Gibbons, Neary and others 4.00
Series 2 (12/08 - No. 12, 11/09, $3.99) 1-12 4.00
Series 3 (3/10 - No. 6, 8/10, $3.99) 1-6 4.00
Series 4 (2/12 - No. 6, 7/12, $3.99) 1-6: Colin Baker era 4.00
Series 5 (3/13 - No. 5, 10/13 $3.99) 1-5: Sylvester McCoy era 4.00
...: The Seventh Doctor (2/11, $3.99) 1-5: 1-Furman-s/Ridgway-a; Sylvester McCoy-era 4.00

DOCTOR WHO EVENT 2015: FOUR DOCTORS
Titan Comics: Sept, 2015 - No. 5, Oct, 2015 ($3.99, weekly limited series)

1-5-Paul Cornell-s/Neil Edwards-a; 10th, 11th, 12th and War Doctor app. 4.00

DOCTOR WHO EVENT 2016: SUPREMACY OF THE CYBERMEN
Titan Comics: Aug, 2016 - No. 5, Dec, 2016 ($3.99, limited series)

1-5-Mann & Scott-s; 9th, 10th, 11th, 12th Doctors app.; multiple covers on each 4.00

DOCTOR WHO: FREE COMIC BOOK DAY
Titan Comics: Jun, 2015; Jun, 2016; Jun, 2017 (giveaways)

1-Short stories with the 10th, 11th & 12th Doctors; Paul Cornell interview 3.00
2016 - (6/16) Short stories with the 9th, 10th, 11th & 12th Doctors 3.00
2017 - (6/17) 12th Doctor and Bill; flashbacks with the 9th, 10th, 11th Doctors 3.00

DOCTOR WHO: GHOST STORIES (Sequel to the 2016 Christmas episode with The Ghost)
IDW Publishing: May, 2017 - No. 4, Aug, 2017 ($3.99, limited series)

1-4-George Mann-s; Grant and Lucy app.; multiple covers on each. 3-Calero-a 4.00

DOCTOR WHO: PRISONERS OF TIME
IDW Publishing: Feb, 2013 - No. 12, Nov, 2013 ($3.99, limited series)

1-50th Anniversary series with each issue spotlighting one Doctor; Francavilla-c 6.00
1-12-Photo covers 5.00
2-12: Francavilla-c on all. 5-12-Dave Sim variant-c. 8-Langridge-a 4.00

DOCTOR WHO: SPECIAL (Also see Doctor Who: The Lost Dimension)
IDW Publishing: Nov, 2017 - No. 2, Nov, 2017 ($4.99)

1,2-The Lost Dimension x-over parts 5 & 7; River Song and the 4th Doctor app. 5.00

DOCTOR WHO: THE EIGHTH DOCTOR (Based on the Paul McGann version)
Titan Comics: Nov, 2015 - No. 5, Apr, 2016 ($3.99, limited series)

1-5: 1-Intro. Josephine; Vieceli-a; multiple covers on each 4.00

DOCTOR WHO: THE ELEVENTH DOCTOR (Based on the Matt Smith version)
Titan Comics: Aug, 2014 - No. 15, Sept, 2015 ($3.99)

1-15: 1-Intro. Alice; Fraser-a; multiple covers on each 4.00

DOCTOR WHO: THE ELEVENTH DOCTOR YEAR TWO (Matt Smith version)
Titan Comics: Oct, 2015 - No. 15, Dec, 2016 ($3.99)

1-15: 1-War Doctor & Abslom Daak app.; multiple covers on each 4.00

DOCTOR WHO: THE ELEVENTH DOCTOR YEAR THREE (Matt Smith version)
Titan Comics: Feb, 2017 - No. 13, Feb, 2018 ($3.99)

1-13: 1-The Doctor and Alice; Rob Williams-s; multiple covers on each. 10-Lost Dimension x-over part 4 4.00

DOCTOR WHO: THE FORGOTTEN (Based on the 2005 TV series with David Tennant)
IDW Publishing: Aug, 2008 - No. 6, Jan, 2009 ($3.99)

1-6: 1,2-Pia Guerra-a/Tony Lee-s; two covers 4.00

DOCTOR WHO: THE FOURTH DOCTOR (Based on the Tom Baker version)
Titan Comics: Apr, 2016 - No. 5, Oct, 2016 ($3.99)

1-5: Sarah Jane app.; Brian Williamson-a; multiple covers on each 4.00

DOCTOR WHO: THE LOST DIMENSION (Eight part x-over with 2017 Doctor Who titles)
Titan Comics: Sept, 2017 - Present ($3.99)

... Alpha (9/17, $3.99) Part one; multiple doctors and Capt. Jack app.; Stott-a 4.00
... Omega (11/17, $3.99) Concluding Part eight; multiple doctors and Jenny app. 4.00

DOCTOR WHO: THE NINTH DOCTOR (Based on the Christopher Eccleston version)
Titan Comics: Apr, 2015 - No. 5, Dec, 2015 ($3.99)

1-5: 1-Rose & Capt. Jack app.; Cavan Scott-s; multiple covers on each 4.00

DOCTOR WHO: THE NINTH DOCTOR ONGOING (Christopher Eccleston version)
Titan Comics: May, 2016 - No. 15, Sept, 2017 ($3.99)

1-15: 1-Rose & Capt. Jack app.; Cavan Scott-s; multiple covers on each 4.00
Doctor Who: The Ninth Special (Lost Dimension Part 2) (10/17, $3.99) Vastra app. 4.00

DOCTOR WHO: THE TENTH DOCTOR (Based on the David Tennant version)
Titan Comics: Aug, 2014 - No. 15, Sept, 2015 ($3.99)

1-15: 1-5-Casagrande-a; multiple covers on each. 1-Intro. Gabby. 6,7-Weeping Angels 4.00

DOCTOR WHO: THE TENTH DOCTOR YEAR TWO (David Tennant version)
Titan Comics: Oct, 2015 - No. 17, Jan, 2017 ($3.99)

1-17: 1-Abadzis-s/Carlini-a; multiple covers on each. 3-Captain Jack app. 4.00

DOCTOR WHO: THE TENTH DOCTOR YEAR THREE (David Tennant version)
Titan Comics: Feb, 2017 - No. 14, Mar, 2018 ($3.99)

1-14: 1-The Doctor & Gabby; Abadzis-s; multiple covers on each. 9-Lost Dimension x-over part 3 4.00

DOCTOR WHO: THE THIRD DOCTOR (Based on the Jon Pertwee version)
Titan Comics: Oct, 2016 - Present ($3.99)

1-5-Jo and The Brigadier app.; multiple covers on each 4.00

DOCTOR WHO: THE TWELFTH DOCTOR (Based on the Peter Capaldi version)
Titan Comics: Nov, 2014 - No. 15, Jan, 2016 ($3.99)

1-15: 1-The Doctor and Clara; Dave Taylor-a; multiple covers on each 4.00

DOCTOR WHO: THE TWELFTH DOCTOR YEAR TWO (Based on the Peter Capaldi version)
Titan Comics: Feb, 2016 - No. 15, Apr, 2017 ($3.99)

1-15: 1-The Doctor and Clara. 6-Intro. Hattie 4.00

DOCTOR WHO: THE TWELFTH DOCTOR YEAR THREE (The Peter Capaldi version)
Titan Comics: May, 2017 - Present ($3.99)

1-12: 5-Bill Potts comic debut. 8-Lost Dimension x-over part 6; 9th & 10th Doctors app. 4.00

DR. WONDER
Old Town Publishing: June, 1996 - No. 5 ($2.95, B&W)

1-5: 1-Intro & origin of Dr. Wonder; Dick Ayers-c/a; Irwin Hasen-a 3.00

DOCTOR ZERO
Marvel Comics (Epic Comics): Apr, 1988 - No. 8, Aug, 1989 ($1.25/$1.50)

1-8: 1-Sienkiewicz-c. 6,7-Spiegle-a 3.00
NOTE: ***Sienkiewicz** a-3i, 4i; c-1.*

DODGE CITY
BOOM! Studios (BOOM! Box): Mar, 2018 - Present ($3.99)

1-Trujillo-s/McGee-a 4.00

DO-DO (Funny Animal Circus Stories)
Nation-Wide Publishers: 1950 - No. 7, 1951 (5¢, 5x7-1/4" Miniature)

	GD	VG	FN	VF	VF/NM	NM-
1 (52 pgs.)	22	44	66	132	216	300
2-7	12	24	36	69	97	125

DODO & THE FROG, THE (Formerly Funny Stuff; also see It's Game Time #2)
National Periodical Publications: No. 80, 9-10/54 - No. 88, 1-2/56; No. 89, 8-9/56; No. 90, 10-11/56; No. 91, 9/57; No. 92, 11/57 (See Comic Cavalcade and Captain Carrot)

	GD	VG	FN	VF	VF/NM	NM-
80-1st app. Doodles Duck by Sheldon Mayer	20	40	60	114	182	250
81-91: Doodles Duck by Mayer in #81,83-90	11	22	33	62	86	110
92-(Scarce)-Doodles Duck by S. Mayer	18	36	54	105	165	225

DOGFACE DOOLEY
Magazine Enterprises: 1951 - No. 5, 1953

	GD	VG	FN	VF	VF/NM	NM-
1(A-1 40)	14	28	42	80	115	150
2(A-1 43), 3(A-1 49), 4(A-1 53)	10	20	30	58	79	100
5(A-1 64) Classic good girl-c	39	78	117	240	395	550
I.W. Reprint #1('64), Super Reprint #17	2	4	6	9	13	16

DOG MOON
DC Comics (Vertigo): 1996 ($6.95, one-shot)

1-Robert Hunter-scripts; Tim Truman-c/a. 7.00

DOG OF FLANDERS, A
Dell Publishing Co.: No. 1088, Mar, 1960

	GD	VG	FN	VF	VF/NM	NM-
Four Color 1088-Movie, photo-c	5	10	15	31	53	75

DOGPATCH (See Al Capp's... & Mammy Yokum)

DOGS OF WAR (Also see Warriors of Plasm #13)
Defiant: Apr, 1994 - No. 5, Aug, 1994 ($2.50)

1-5: 5-Schism x-over 3.00

DOGS-O-WAR
Crusade Comics: June, 1996 - No. 3, Jan, 1997 ($2.95, B&W, limited series)

1-3: 1,2-Photo-c 3.00

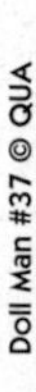
Doll Man #37 © QUA

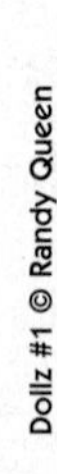
Dollz #1 © Randy Queen

Donald Duck Four Color #29 © DIS

GD 2.0 | VG 4.0 | FN 6.0 | VF 8.0 | VF/NM 9.0 | NM- 9.2

DOLLFACE & HER GANG (Betty Betz'...)
Dell Publishing Co.: No. 309, Jan, 1951

Four Color 309 6 12 18 38 69 100

DOLLHOUSE
Dark Horse Comics: Mar, 2011; Jul, 2011 - No. 5, Nov, 2011 ($3.50, limited series)

1-5-Richards-a; two covers on each 4.00
...: Epitaphs (3/11, $3.50) reprints story from DVD collection; covers by Noto & Morris 4.00

DOLLMAN (Movie)
Eternity Comics: Sept, 1991 - No. 4, Dec, 1991 ($2.50, limited series)

1-4: Adaptation of film 3.00

DOLL MAN QUARTERLY, THE (Doll Man #17 on; also see Feature Comics #27 & Freedom Fighters)
Quality Comics: Fall, 1941 - No. 7, Fall, '43; No. 8, Spr, '46 - No. 47, Oct, 1953

1-Dollman (by Cassone), Justin Wright begin 349 698 1047 2443 4272 6100
2-The Dragon begins; Crandall-a(5) 158 316 474 1003 1727 2450
3,4 97 194 291 621 1061 1500
5-Crandall-a 94 188 282 597 1024 1450
6,7(1943) 55 110 165 352 601 850
8(1946)-1st app. Torchy by Bill Ward 174 348 522 1114 1907 2700
9(Summer 1946) 55 110 165 352 601 850
10-20 42 84 126 265 445 625
21-26,28-30: 28-Vs. The Flame 39 78 117 240 395 550
27-Sci-fi bondage-c 42 84 126 265 445 625
31-(12/50)-Intro Elmo, the wonder dog (Dollman's faithful dog)
43 86 129 271 461 650
32-35,38,40: 32-34-Jeb Rivers app. 34-Crandall-a(p)
40 80 120 246 411 575
36-Giant shark-c 43 86 129 271 461 650
37-Origin & 1st app. Dollgirl; Dollgirl bondage-c 77 154 231 493 847 1200
39- "Narcotics...the Death Drug" c-/story 50 100 150 315 533 750
41-47 34 68 102 199 325 450
Super Reprint #11('64, r/#20),15(r/#23),17(r/#28): 15,17-Torchy app.; Andru/Esposito-c
3 6 9 20 30 40

NOTE: ***Ward*** *Torchy in 8, 9, 11, 12, 14-24, 27; by Fox-#26, 30, 35-47.* ***Crandall*** *a-2, 5, 10, 13 & Super #11, 17, 18.* ***Crandall/Cuidera*** *c-40-42.* ***Guardineer*** *a-3. Bondage c-27, 37, 38, 39.*

DOLLY
Ziff-Davis Publ. Co.: No. 10, July-Aug, 1951 (Funny animal)

10-Painted-c 11 22 33 62 86 110

DOLLY DILL
Marvel Comics/Newsstand Publ.: 1945

1 24 48 72 142 234 325

DOLLZ, THE
Image Comics: Apr, 2001 - No. 2, June, 2001 ($2.95)

1,2: 1-Four covers; Sniegoski & Green-s/Green-a 3.00

DOMINATION FACTOR
Marvel Comics: Nov, 1999 - 4.8, Feb, 2000 ($2.50, interconnected mini-series)

1.1, 2.3, 3.5, 4.7-Fantastic Four; Jurgens-s/a 3.00
1.2, 2.4, 3.6, 4.8-Avengers; Ordway-s/a 3.00

DOMINIC FORTUNE
Marvel Comics (MAX): Oct, 2009 - No. 4, Jan, 2010 ($3.99, limited series)

1-4-Howard Chaykin-s/a/c 4.00

DOMINION
Image Comics: Jan, 2003 - No. 2 ($2.95)

1,2-Keith Giffen-s/a 3.00

DOMINION (Manga)
Eclipse Comics: Dec, 1990 - No. 6., July, 1990 ($2.00, B&W, limited series)

1-6 3.00

DOMINION: CONFLICT 1 (Manga)
Dark Horse Comics: Mar, 1996 - No. 6, Aug, 1996 ($2.95, B&W, limited series)

1-6: Shirow-c/a/scripts 3.00

DOMINIQUE LAVEAU: VOODOO CHILD
DC Comics (Vertigo): May, 2012 - No. 7, Nov, 2012 ($2.99, limited series)

1-7-Selwyn Seyfu Hinds-s/Denys Cowan-a 3.00

DOMINO (See X-Force)
Marvel Comics: Jan, 1997 - No. 3, Mar, 1997 ($1.95, limited series)

1-3: 2-Deathstrike-c/app. 3.00

GD 2.0 | VG 4.0 | FN 6.0 | VF 8.0 | VF/NM 9.0 | NM- 9.2

DOMINO (See X-Force)
Marvel Comics: June, 2003 - No. 4, Aug, 2003 ($2.50, limited series)

1-4-Stelfreeze-c/a; Pruett-s. 3.00

DOMINO CHANCE
Chance Enterprises: May-June, 1982 - No. 9, May, 1985 (B&W)

1-9: 7-1st app. Gizmo, 2 pgs. 8-1st full Gizmo story. 1-Reprint, May, 1985 4.00

DONALD AND MICKEY
IDW Publishing: Aug, 2017 - No. 2, Nov, 2017 ($5.99)

1,2-Reprints from European stories; 2 covers on each 6.00

DONALD AND MICKEY IN DISNEYLAND (See Dell Giants)

DONALD AND SCROOGE
Disney Comics: 1992 ($8.95, squarebound, 100 pgs.)

nn-Don Rosa reprint special; r/U.S., D.D. Advs. 1 3 4 6 8 10
1-3 (1992, $1.50)-r/D.D. Advs. (Disney) #1,22,24 & U.S. #261-263,269 3.00

DONALD AND THE WHEEL (Disney)
Dell Publishing Co.: No. 1190, Nov, 1961

Four Color 1190-Movie, Barks-c 8 16 24 51 96 140

DONALD DUCK (See Adventures of Mickey Mouse, Cheerios, Donald & Mickey, Ducktales, Dynabrite Comics, Gladstone Comic Album, Mickey & Donald, Mickey Mouse Mag., Story Hour Series, Uncle Scrooge, Walt Disney's Comics & Stories, W. D.'s Donald Duck, Wheaties & Whitman Comic Books, Wise Little Hen, The)

DONALD DUCK
Whitman Publishing Co./Grosset & Dunlap/K.K.: 1935, 1936 (All pages on heavy linen-like finish cover stock in color;1st book ever devoted to Donald Duck; see Advs. of Mickey Mouse for 1st app.) (9-1/2x13")

978(1935)-16 pgs.; Illustrated text story book 206 412 618 1318 2259 3200
nn(1936)-36 pgs.plus hard cover & dust jacket. Story completely rewritten with B&W illos added. Mickey appears and his nephews are named Morty & Monty
Book only 194 388 582 1242 2121 3000
Dust jacket only.... 39 78 117 240 395 550

DONALD DUCK (Walt Disney's) (10¢)
Whitman/K.K. Publications: 1938 (8-1/2x11-1/2", B&W, cardboard-c)
(Has D. Duck with bubble pipe on-c)

nn-The first Donald Duck & Walt Disney comic book; 1936 & 1937 Sunday strip-r(in B&W); same format as the Feature Books; 1st strips with Huey, Dewey & Louie from 10/17/37
320 640 960 2240 3920 5600

DONALD DUCK (Walt Disney's...#262 on; see 4-Color listings for titles & Four Color No. 1109 for origin story)
Dell Publ. Co./Gold Key #85-216/Whitman #217-245/Gladstone #246 on: 1940 - No. 84, Sept-Nov, 1962; No. 85, Dec, 1962 - No. 245, July, 1984; No. 246, Oct, 1986 - No. 279, May, 1990; No. 280, Sept, 1993 - No. 307, Mar,1998

Four Color 4(1940)-Daily 1939 strip-r by Al Taliaferro
2100 4200 6300 15,750 28,875 42,000
Large Feature Comic 16(1/41?)-1940 Sunday strips-r in B&W
892 1784 2676 6512 11,506 16,500
Large Feature Comic 20('41)-Comic Paint Book, r-single panels from Large Feature #16 at top of each pg. to color; daily strip-r across bottom of each pg. (Rare)
1000 2000 3000 7500 13,500 19,500
Four Color 9('42)- "Finds Pirate Gold"; 64 pgs. by Carl Barks & Jack Hannah (pgs. 1,2,5,12-40 are by Barks, his 1st Donald Duck comic book art work; © 8/17/42)
1000 2000 3000 7600 13,800 20,000
Four Color 29(9/43)- "Mummy's Ring" by Barks; reprinted in Uncle Scrooge & Donald Duck #1('65), W. D. Comics Digest #44('73) & Donald Duck Advs. #14
800 1600 2400 5840 10,320 14,800
Four Color 62(1/45)- "Frozen Gold"; 52 pgs. by Barks, reprinted in The Best of W.D. Comics & Donald Duck Advs. #4 228 456 684 1881 4241 6600
Four Color 108(1946)- "Terror of the River"; 52 pgs. by Carl Barks; reprinted in Gladstone Comic Album #2 148 296 444 1221 2761 4300
Four Color 147(5/47)-in "Volcano Valley" by Barks 104 208 312 832 1866 2900
Four Color 159(8/47)-in "The Ghost of the Grotto";52 pgs. by Carl Barks; reprinted in Best of Uncle Scrooge & Donald Duck #1 ('66) & The Best of W.D. Comics & D.D. Advs. #9; two Barks stories 89 178 267 712 1606 2500
Four Color 178(12/47)-1st app. Uncle Scrooge by Carl Barks; reprinted in Gold Key Christmas Parade #3 & The Best of Walt Disney Comics 139 278 417 1112 2506 3900
Four Color 189(6/48)-by Carl Barks; reprinted in Best of Donald Duck & Uncle Scrooge #1('64) & D.D. Advs. #19 86 172 258 688 1544 2400
Four Color 199(10/48)-by Carl Barks; mentioned in Love and Death; r/in Gladstone Comic Album #5 86 172 258 688 1544 2400
Four Color 203(12/48)-by Barks; reprinted as Gold Key Christmas Parade #4
61 122 183 488 1094 1700

Donald Duck #27 © DIS

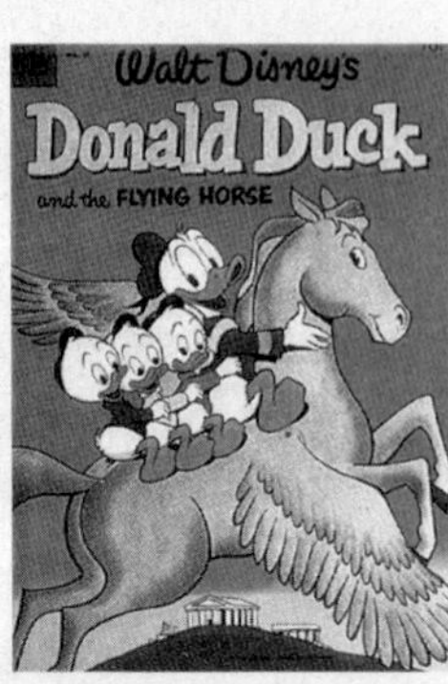

Donald Duck #269 © DIS

Donald Duck (2015 series) #19 © DIS

GD VG FN VF VF/NM NM-
2.0 4.0 6.0 8.0 9.0 9.2

Four Color 223(4/49)-by Barks; reprinted as Best of Donald Duck #1 & Donald Duck Advs. #3
79 158 237 632 1416 2200
Four Color 238(8/49)-in "Voodoo Hoodoo" by Barks 59 118 177 472 1061 1650
Four Color 256(12/49)-by Barks; reprinted in Best of Donald Duck & Uncle Scrooge #2('67), Gladstone Comic Album #16 & W.D. Comics Digest 44('73)
50 100 150 390 870 1350
Four Color 263(2/50)-Two Barks stories; r-in D.D. #278
47 94 141 367 821 1275
Four Color 275(5/50), 282(7/50), 291(9/50), 300(11/50)-All by Carl Barks; 275, 282 reprinted in W.D. Comics Digest #44('73). #275 r/in Gladstone Comic Album #10. #291 r/in D. Duck Advs. #16 46 92 138 359 805 1250
Four Color 308(1/51), 318(3/51)-by Barks; #318-reprinted in W.D. Comics Digest #34 & D.D. Advs. #2,19 45 90 135 333 754 1175
Four Color 328(5/51)-by Carl Barks 44 88 132 326 738 1150
Four Color 339(7-8/51), 379-2nd Uncle Scrooge-c; art not by Barks.
32 64 96 230 515 800
Four Color 348(9-10/51), 356,394-Barks-c only 23 46 69 161 356 550
Four Color 367(1-2/52)-by Barks; reprinted as Gold Key Christmas Parade #2 & #8
36 72 108 259 580 900
Four Color 408(7-8/52), 422(9-10/52)-All by Carl Barks. #408-r-in Best of Donald Duck & Uncle Scrooge #1('64) & Gladstone Comic Album #13
35 70 105 252 564 875
26(11-12/52)-In "Trick or Treat" (Barks-a, 36pgs.) 1st story r-in Walt Disney Digest #16 & Gladstone C.A. #23 34 68 102 245 548 850
27-30-Barks-c only 12 24 36 82 179 275
31-44,47-50 7 14 21 46 86 125
45-Barks-a (6 pgs.) 13 26 39 89 195 300
46- "Secret of Hondorica" by Barks, 24 pgs.; reprinted in Donald Duck #98 & 154
17 34 51 119 265 410
51-Barks-a,1/2 pg. 7 14 21 46 86 125
52- "Lost Peg-Leg Mine" by Barks, 10 pgs. 13 26 39 89 195 300
53,55-59 6 12 18 38 69 100
54- "Forbidden Valley" by Barks, 26 pgs. (10¢ & 15¢ versions exist)
14 28 42 98 217 335
60- "Donald Duck & the Titanic Ants" by Barks, 20 pgs. plus 6 more pgs.
14 28 42 98 217 335
61-67,69,70 5 10 15 34 60 85
68-Barks-a, 5 pgs. 9 18 27 62 126 190
71-Barks-r, 1/2 pg. 5 10 15 34 60 85
72-78,80,82-97,99,100: 96-Donald Duck Album 5 10 15 33 57 80
79,81-Barks-a, 1pg. 5 10 15 34 60 85
98-Reprints #46 (Barks) 5 10 15 34 60 85
101,103-111,113-135: 120-Last 12¢ issue. 134-Barks-r/#52 & WDC&S 194. 135-Barks-r/WDC&S 198, 19 pgs. 4 8 12 22 35 48
102-Super Goof. 112-1st Moby Duck 4 8 12 23 37 50
136-153,155,156,158: 149-20¢-c begin 3 6 9 14 20 26
154-Barks-r(#46) 3 6 9 16 24 32
157,159,160,164: 157-Barks-r(#45); 25¢-c begin. 159-Reprints/WDC&S #192 (10 pgs.). 160-Barks-r(#26). 164-Barks-r(#79) 3 6 9 14 20 26
161-163,165-173,175-187,189-191: 175-30¢-c begin. 187-Barks r/#68.
2 4 6 13 18 22
174,188: 174-r/4-Color #394. 3 6 9 14 19 24
175-177-Whitman variants 3 6 9 14 19 24
192-Barks-r(40 pgs.) from Donald Duck #60 & WDC&S #226,234 (52 pgs.)
3 6 9 15 22 28
193-200,202-207,209-211,213-216 2 4 6 9 13 16
201,208,212: 201-Barks-r/Christmas Parade #26, 16pgs. 208-Barks-r/#60 (6 pgs.). 212-Barks-r/WDC&S #130 2 4 6 9 13 16
217-219: 217 has 216 on-c. 219-Barks-r/WDC&S #106,107, 10 pgs. ea.
2 4 6 10 14 18
220,225-228: 228-Barks-r/F.C. #275 2 4 6 13 18 22
221,223,224: Scarce; only sold in pre-packs. 221(8/80), 223(11/80), 224(12/80)
5 10 15 35 63 90
222-(9-10/80)-(Very low distribution) 17 34 51 117 259 400
229-240: 229-Barks-r/F.C. #282. 230-Barks-r/ #52 & WDC&S #194. 236(2/82), 237(2-3/82), 238(3/82), 239(4/82), 240(5/82) 2 4 6 9 13 16
241-245: 241(4/83), 242(5/83), 243(3/84), 244(4/84), 245(7/84)(low print)
3 6 9 14 19 24
246-(1st Gladstone issue)-Barks-r/FC #422 3 6 9 15 21 26
247-249,251: 248,249-Barks-r/DD #54 & 26. 251-Barks-r/1945 Firestone
2 4 6 9 13 16
250-($1.50, 68 pgs.)-Barks-r/4-Color #9 2 4 6 10 14 18
252-277,280: 254-Barks-r/FC #328. 256-Barks-r/FC #147. 257-($1.50, 52 pgs.)-Barks-r/ Vacation Parade #1. 261-Barks-r/FC #300. 275-Kelly-r/FC #92. 280 (#1, 2nd Series)
1 2 3 5 6 8
278,279,286: 278,279 ($1.95, 68 pgs.): 278-Rosa-a; Barks-r/FC #263. 279-Rosa-c; Barks-r/MOC #4. 286-Rosa-a 1 2 3 5 7 9
281,282,284 1 2 3 4 5 7
283-Don Rosa-a, part-c & scripts 1 2 3 5 6 8
285,287-307 5.00
286 ($2.95, 68 pgs.)-Happy Birthday, Donald 6.00
Mini-Comic #1(1976)-(3-1/4x6-1/2"); r/D.D. #150 2 4 6 8 11 14

NOTE: *Carl Barks wrote all issues he illustrated, but #117, 126, 138 contain his script only. Issues 4-Color #189, 199, 203, 223, 238, 256, 263, 275, 282, 308, 348, 356, 367, 394, 408, 422, 26-30, 35, 44, 46, 52, 55, 57, 60, 65, 70-73, 77-80, 83, 101, 103, 105, 106, 111, 126, 246r, 266r, 268r, 271r, 275r, 278r(F.C. 263) all have* ***Barks*** *covers.* ***Barks*** *r-263-267, 269-278-282, 284, 285. #96 titled "Comic Album", #99-"Christmas Album". New art issues (not reprints)-106-46, 148-63, 167, 169, 170, 172, 173, 175, 178, 179, 196, 209, 223, 225, 236.* ***Taliaferro*** *daily newspaper strips #258-260, 264, 284, 285; Sunday strips #247, 280-283.*

DONALD DUCK (Numbering continues from Donald Duck and Friends #362)
BOOM! Studios (Kaboom!): No. 363, Feb, 2011 - No. 367, Jun, 2011 ($3.99)

363-367: 363-Barks reprints incl. "Mystery of the Loch". 364-Rosa-c 4.00

DONALD DUCK
IDW Publishing: May, 2015 - No. 21, Jun, 2017 ($3.99)

1-Legacy numbered #368; art by Scarpa and others; multiple covers 4.00
2-21-Reprints of Italian & Dutch stories; multiple covers on each. 8-Christmas issue 4.00
...'s Halloween Scream (10/15, Halloween giveaway) r/Donald Duck Advs. #7,8 (1990) 3.00

DONALD DUCK ADVENTURES (See Walt Disney's Donald Duck Adventures)

DONALD DUCK ALBUM (See Comic Album No. 1,3 & Duck Album)
Dell Publishing Co./Gold Key: 5-7/59 - F.C. No. 1239, 10-12/61; 1962; 8/63 - No. 2, Oct, 1963

Four Color 995 (#1) 7 14 21 44 82 120
Four Color 1099,1140,1239-Barks-c 7 14 21 44 82 120
Four Color 1182, 01204-207 (1962-Dell) 5 10 15 34 60 85
1(8/63-Gold Key)-Barks-c 5 10 15 34 60 85
2(10/63) 4 8 12 28 47 65

DONALD DUCK AND FRIENDS (Numbering continues from Walt Disney's ...)
BOOM! Studios: No. 347, Oct, 2009 - No. 362, Jan, 2011 ($2.99)

347-362: Two covers on most. Retitled "Donald Duck" with #363 3.00

DONALD DUCK AND THE BOYS (Also see Story Hour Series)
Whitman Publishing Co.: 1948 (5-1/4x5-1/2", 100pgs., hard-c; art & text)

845-(49) new illos by Barks based on his Donald Duck 10-pager in WDC&S #74, Expanded text not written by Barks; Cover not by Barks
50 100 150 350 600 850
(Prices vary widely on this book)

DONALD DUCK AND THE CHRISTMAS CAROL
Whitman Publishing Co.: 1960 (A Little Golden Book, 6-3/8"x7-5/8", 28 pgs.)

nn-Story book pencilled by Carl Barks with the intended title "Uncle Scrooge's Christmas Carol." Finished art adapted by Norman McGary. (Rare)-Reprinted in Uncle Scrooge in Color. 20 40 60 100 185 270

DONALD DUCK BEACH PARTY (Also see Dell Giants)
Gold Key: Sept, 1965 (12¢)

1(#10158-509)-Barks-r/WDC&S #45; painted-c 6 12 18 37 66 95

DONALD DUCK BOOK (See Story Hour Series)

DONALD DUCK COMICS DIGEST
Gladstone Publishing: Nov, 1986 - No. 5, July, 1987 ($1.25/$1.50, 96 pgs.)

1,3: 1-Barks-c/a-r 1 3 4 6 8 10
2,4,5: 4,5-$1.50-c 6.00

DONALD DUCK FUN BOOK (See Dell Giants)

DONALD DUCK IN DISNEYLAND (See Dell Giants)

DONALD DUCK MARCH OF COMICS (See March of Comics #4,20,41,56,69,263)

DONALD DUCK MERRY CHRISTMAS (See Dell Giant No. 53)

DONALD DUCK PICNIC PARTY (See Picnic Party listed under Dell Giants)

DONALD DUCK TELLS ABOUT KITES (See Kite Fun Book)

DONALD DUCK, THIS IS YOUR LIFE (Disney, TV)
Dell Publishing Co.: No. 1109, Aug-Oct, 1960

Four Color 1109-Gyro flashback to WDC&S #141; origin Donald Duck (1st told)
12 24 36 81 176 270

DONALD DUCK XMAS ALBUM (See regular Donald Duck No. 99)

DONALD IN MATHMAGIC LAND (Disney)
Dell Publishing Co.: No. 1051, Oct-Dec, 1959 - No. 1198, May-July, 1961

Donald Quest #1 © DIS

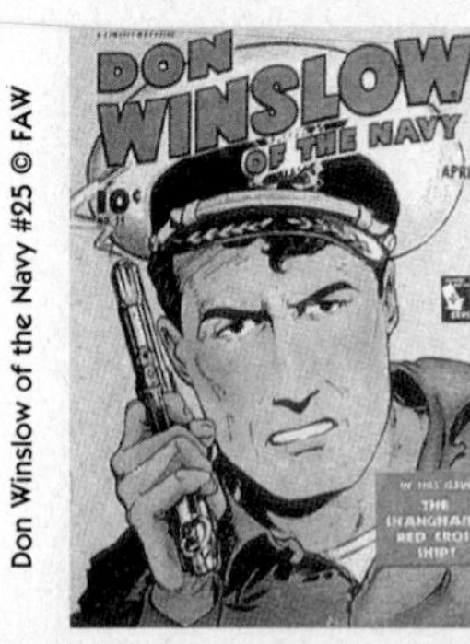

Don Winslow of the Navy #25 © FAW

Doom Patrol (2016 series) #4 © DC

GD 2.0 VG 4.0 FN 6.0 VF 8.0 VF/NM 9.0 NM- 9.2

Four Color 1051 (#1)-Movie 8 16 24 56 108 160
Four Color 1198-Reprint of above 6 12 18 37 66 95

DONALD QUEST (Donald Duck in parallel universe of Feudarnia)
IDW Publishing: Nov, 2016 - No. 5, Mar, 2017 ($3.99, limited series)
1-5-English version of Italian story; multiple covers on each. 1-Ambrosio-s/Freccero-a 4.00

DONATELLO, TEENAGE MUTANT NINJA TURTLE
Mirage Studios: Aug, 1986 ($1.50, B&W, one-shot, 44 pgs.)
1 2 4 6 11 16 20

DONDI
Dell Publishing Co.: No. 1176, Mar-May, 1961 - No. 1276, Dec, 1961
Four Color 1176 (#1)-Movie; origin, photo-c 6 12 18 37 66 95
Four Color 1276 4 8 12 28 47 65

DON FORTUNE MAGAZINE
Don Fortune Publishing Co.: Aug, 1946 - No. 6, Feb, 1947
1-Delecta of the Planets by C.C. Beck in all 30 60 90 177 289 400
2 15 30 45 85 130 175
3-6: 3-Bondage-c 14 28 42 76 108 140

DONG XOAI, VIETNAM 1965
DC Comics: 2010 ($19.95, B&W graphic novel)
SC-Joe Kubert-s/a/c; includes report of actual events that inspired the story 20.00

DONKEY KONG (See Blip #1)

DONNA MATRIX
Reactor, Inc.: Aug, 1993 ($2.95, 52 pgs.)
1-Computer generated-c/a by Mike Saenz; 3-D effects 4.00

DON NEWCOMBE
Fawcett Publications: 1950 (Baseball)
nn-Photo-c 54 108 162 343 574 825

DON ROSA'S COMICS AND STORIES
Fantagraphics Books (CX Comics): 1983 ($2.95)
1,2: 1-(68 pgs.) Reprints Rosa's The Pertwillaby Papers episodes #128-133.
2-(60 pgs.) Reprints episodes #134-138 2 4 6 11 16 20

DON SIMPSON'S BIZARRE HEROES (Also see Megaton Man)
Fiasco Comics: May, 1990 - No. 17, Sept, 1996 ($2.50/$2.95, B&W)
1-10,0,11-17: 0-Begin $2.95-c; r/Bizarre Heroes #1. 17-(9/96)-Indicia also reads Megaton Man #0; intro Megaton Man and the Fiascoverse to new readers 3.00

DON'T GIVE UP THE SHIP
Dell Publishing Co.: No. 1049, Aug, 1959
Four Color 1049-Movie, Jerry Lewis photo-c 9 18 27 58 114 170

DON WINSLOW OF THE NAVY
Merwil Publishing Co.: Apr, 1937 - No. 2, May, 1937 (96 pgs.)(A pulp/comic book cross; stapled spine)
V1#1-Has 16 pgs. comics in color. Captain Colorful & Jupiter Jones by Sheldon Mayer; complete Don Winslow novel 653 1306 1959 4900 - -
2-Sheldon Mayer-a 177 354 531 1325 - -

DON WINSLOW OF THE NAVY (See Crackajack Funnies, Famous Feature Stories, Popular Comics & Super Book #5,6)
Dell Publishing Co.: No. 2, Nov, 1939 - No. 22, 1941
Four Color 2 (#1)-Rare 226 452 678 1446 2473 3500
Four Color 22 52 104 156 328 552 775

DON WINSLOW OF THE NAVY (See TV Teens; Movie, Radio, TV) (Fightin' Navy No. 74 on)
Fawcett Publications/Charlton No. 70 on: 2/43 - #64, 12/48; #65, 1/51 - #69, 9/51; #70, 3/55 - #73, 9/55
1-(68 pgs.)-Captain Marvel on cover 123 246 369 787 1344 1900
2 45 90 135 284 480 675
3 37 74 111 222 361 500
4-6: 6-Flag-c 30 60 90 177 289 400
7-10: 8-Last 68 pg. issue? 22 44 66 132 216 300
11-20 19 38 57 111 176 240
21-40 16 32 48 94 147 200
41-43,45-64: 51,60-Singapore Sal (villain) app. 64-(12/48)
15 30 45 85 130 175
44-Classic spider-c 39 78 117 231 378 525
65(1/51)-Flying Saucer attack; photo-c 23 46 69 136 223 310
66 - 69(9/51): All photo-c. 66-sci-fi story 15 30 45 85 130 175
70(3/55)-73: 70-73 r-/#26,58 & 59 10 20 30 56 76 95

DOODLE JUMP (Based on the game app)
Dynamite Entertainment: 2014 - No. 6, 2015 ($3.99, limited series)
1-6-Steve Uy-a; multiple covers on each 4.00

DOOM
Marvel Comics: Oct, 2000 - No. 3, Dec, 2000 ($2.99, limited series)
1-3-Dr. Doom; Dixon-s/Manco-a 3.00

DOOMED (Also see Teen Titans #14 (2016))
DC Comics: Aug, 2015 - No. 6, Jan, 2016 ($2.99, limited series)
1-6: 1-Lobdell-s/Fernandez-a. 3-Alpha Centurion app. 4-6-Superman app. 3.00

DOOM FORCE SPECIAL
DC Comics: July, 1992 ($2.95, 68 pgs., one-shot, mature) (X-Force parody)
1-Morrison scripts; Simonson, Steacy, & others-a; Giffen/Mignola-c 4.00

DOOM PATROL, THE (Formerly My Greatest Adventure No. 1-85; see Brave and the Bold, DC Special Blue Ribbon Digest 19, Official... Index & Showcase No. 94-96)
National Periodical Publ.: No. 86, 3/64 - No. 121, 9-10/68; No. 122, 2/73 - No. 124, 6-7/73
86-1 pg. origin (#86-121 are 12¢ issues) 22 44 66 154 340 525
87-98: 88-Origin The Chief. 91-Intro. Mento 9 18 27 57 111 165
99-Intro. Beast Boy (later becomes the Changeling in New Teen Titans)
55 110 165 385 568 750
100-Origin Beast Boy; Robot-Maniac series begins (12/65)
11 22 33 72 154 235
101-110: 102-Challengers of the Unknown app. 104-Wedding issue. 105-Robot-Maniac series ends. 106-Negative Man begins (origin) 6 12 18 38 69 100
111-120 5 10 15 33 57 80
121-Death of Doom Patrol; Orlando-c. 11 22 33 75 160 245
122-124: All reprints 2 4 6 8 11 14

DOOM PATROL
DC Comics (Vertigo imprint #64 on): Oct, 1987 - No, 87, Feb, 1995 (75¢-$1.95, new format)
1-Wraparound-c; Lightle-a 6.00
2-18: 3-1st app. Lodestone. 4-1st app. Karma. 8,15,16-Art Adams-c(i). 18-Invasion tie-in 4.00
19-(2/89)-Grant Morrison scripts begin, ends #63; 1st app Crazy Jane; $1.50-c & new format begins. 1 2 3 5 6 8
20-30: 29-Superman app. 30-Night Breed fold-out 5.00
31-34,37-41,45-49,51-56,58-60: 39-World Without End preview 3.00
35-1st brief app. of Flex Mentallo 1 2 3 5 6 8
36-1st full app. of Flex Mentallo 1 2 3 5 7 9
42-44-Origin of Flex Mentallo 4.00
50,57 ($2.50, 52 pgs.) 4.00
61-87: 61,70-Photo-c. 73-Death cameo (2 panels) 3.00
...And Suicide Squad 1 (3/88, $1.50, 52 pgs.)-Wraparound-c 4.00
Annual 1 (1988, $1.50, 52 pgs.) 4.00
Annual 2 (1994, $3.95, 68 pgs.)-Children's Crusade tie-in. 4.00
...: Crawling From the Wreckage TPB (2004, $19.95) r/#19-25; Morrison-s 20.00
...: Down Paradise Way TPB (2005, $19.99) r/#35-41; Morrison-s 20.00
...: Magic Bus TPB (2007, $19.99) r/#51-57; Morrison-s; new Bolland-c 20.00
...: Musclebound TPB (2006, $19.99) r/#42-50; Morrison-s; new Bolland-c 20.00
...: Planet Love TPB (2008, $19.99) r/#58-63 & Doom Force Special #1; Morrison-s 20.00
...: The Painting That Ate Paris TPB (2004, $19.95) r/#26-34; Morrison-s 20.00
NOTE: *Bisley painted c-26-48, 55-58.* ***Bolland*** *c-64, 75.* ***Dringenberg*** *a-42(p).* ***Steacy*** *a-53.*

DOOM PATROL
DC Comics: Dec, 2001 - No. 22, Sept, 2003 ($2.50)
1-Intro. new team with Robotman; Tan Eng Huat-c/a; John Arcudi-s 4.00
2-22: 4,5-Metamorpho & Elongated Man app. 13,14-Fisher-a. 20-Geary-a 3.00

DOOM PATROL (see JLA #94-99)
DC Comics: Aug, 2004 - No. 18, Jan, 2006 ($2.50)
1-18-John Byrne-s/a. 1-Green Lantern, Batman app. 3.00

DOOM PATROL
DC Comics: Oct, 2009 - No. 22, Jul, 2011 ($3.99/$2.99)
1-7: 1-Giffen-s/Clark-a; back-up Metal Men feature w/Maguire-a. 1-Two covers. 4-5-Blackest Night. 6-Negative Man origin re-told 4.00
8-22-($2.99) 11,12-Ambush Bug app. 16-Giffen-a. 21-Robotman origin retold 3.00
...: Brotherhood TPB (2011, $17.99) r/#7-13 18.00
...: We Who Are About to Die TPB (2010, $14.99) r/#1-6; cover gallery; design art 15.00

DOOM PATROL
DC Comics (Young Animal): Nov, 2016 - Present ($3.99)
1-10: 1-Gerald Way-s/Nick Derington-a; main cover has peel-off gyro sticker. 8-Allred-a 4.00
1-Director's Cut (5/17, $5.99) Pencil/ink art; original script with thumbnails 6.00
.../ JLA Special 1 (4/18, $4.99) Part 5 of Milk Wars crossover; Eaglesham-a/Mann-c 5.00

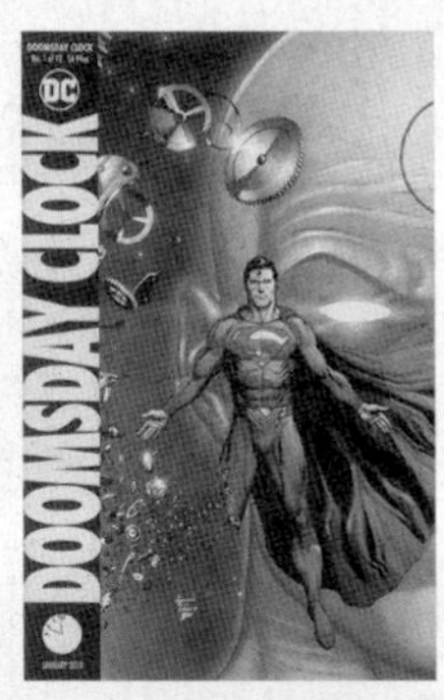

Doomsday Clock #1 © DC

Doomwar #5 © MAR

Double Comics 1941 © EP

	GD 2.0	VG 4.0	FN 6.0	VF 8.0	VF/NM 9.0	NM- 9.2

DOOM PATROL (See Tangent Comics/ Doom Patrol)

DOOMSDAY
DC Comics: 1995 ($3.95, one-shot)

1-Year One story by Jurgens, L. Simonson, Ordway, and Gil Kane; Superman app. 5.00

DOOMSDAY CLOCK (See Watchmen)
DC Comics: Jan, 2018 - No. 12 ($4.99, limited series)

1-Follows end of Watchmen; intro new Rorschach; Johns-s/Frank-a; 2 covers by Frank 5.00
1-($5.99) Lenticular cover 6.00
2-Two covers; Comedian returns; Nathaniel Dusk makes DCU return as fictional 1940s -'50s film noir detective 5.00

DOOMSDAY + 1 (Also see Charlton Bullseye)
Charlton Comics: July, 1975 - No. 6, June, 1976; No. 7, June, 1978 - No. 12, May, 1979

	GD	VG	FN	VF	VF/NM	NM-
1: #1-5 are 25¢ issues	3	6	9	16	24	32
2-6: 4-Intro Lor. 5-Ditko-a(1 pg.) 6-Begin 30¢-c	2	4	6	10	14	18

V3#7-12 (reprints #1-6) 6.00
5 (Modern Comics reprint, 1977) 6.00
NOTE: ***Byrne** c/a-1-12; Painted covers-2-7.*

DOOMSDAY.1
IDW Publishing: May, 2013 - No. 4, Aug, 2013 ($3.99)

1-4-John Byrne-s/a/c 4.00

DOOMSDAY SQUAD, THE
Fantagraphics Books: Aug, 1986 - No. 7, 1987 ($2.00)

1,2,4-7: Byrne-a in all. 1,2-New Byrne-c. 4-Neal Adams-c. 5-7-Gil Kane-c 4.00
3-Usagi Yojimbo app. (1st in color); new Byrne-c 6.00

DOOM'S IV
Image Comics (Extreme): July, 1994 - No.4, Oct, 1994 ($2.50, limited series)

1-4-Liefeld story 3.00
1,2-Two alternate Liefeld-c each, 4 covers form 1 picture 5.00

DOOM: THE EMPEROR RETURNS
Marvel Comics: Jan, 2002 - No. 3, Mar, 2002 ($2.50, limited series)

1-3-Dixon-s/Manco-a; Franklin Richards app. 3.00

DOOM 2099 (See Marvel Comics Presents #118 & 2099: World of Tomorrow)
Marvel Comics: Jan, 1993 - No. 44, Aug, 1996 ($1.25/$1.50/$1.95)

1-Metallic foil stamped-c 4.00
1-2nd printing 3.00
2-24,26-44: 4-Ron Lim-c(p). 17-bound-in trading card sheet. 40-Namor & Doctor Strange app. 41-Daredevil app., Namor-c/app. 44-Intro The Emissary; story contin'd in 2099: World of Tomorrow 3.00
18-Variant polybagged with Sega Sub-Terrania poster 4.00
25 ($2.25, 52 pgs.) 4.00
25 ($2.95, 52pgs.) Foil embossed cover 5.00
29 ($3.50)-acetate-c. 4.00

DOOMWAR
Marvel Comics: Apr, 2010 - No. 6, Sept, 2010 ($3.99, limited series)

1-6-Doctor Doom invades Wakanda; Black Panther & X-Men app.; Romita Jr.-c/Eaton-a 4.00

DOORWAY TO NIGHTMARE (See Cancelled Comic Cavalcade and Madame Xanadu)
DC Comics: Jan-Feb, 1978 - No. 5, Sept-Oct, 1978

	GD	VG	FN	VF	VF/NM	NM-
1-Madame Xanadu in all	3	6	9	14	20	25
2-5: 4-Craig-a	2	4	6	8	11	14

NOTE: ***Kaluta** covers on all. Merged into The Unexpected with No. 190.*

DOPEY DUCK COMICS (Wacky Duck No. 3) (See Super Funnies)
Timely Comics (NPP): Fall, 1945 - No. 2, Apr, 1946

	GD	VG	FN	VF	VF/NM	NM-
1-Casper Cat, Krazy Krow	41	82	123	256	428	600
2-Casper Cat, Krazy Krow	32	64	96	188	307	425

DORK
Slave Labor: June, 1993 - No. 11 ($2.50-$3.50, B&W, mature)

1-7,9-11: Evan Dorkin-c/a/scripts in all. 1(8/95),2(1/96)-(2nd printings). 1(3/97) (3rd printing). 1-Milk & Cheese app. 3-Eltingville Club starts. 6-Reprints 1st Eltingville Club app. from Instant Piano #1 3.00
8-($3.50) 4.00
Who's Laughing Now? TPB (2001, $11.95) reprints most of #1-5 12.00
The Collected Dork, Vol. 2: Circling the Drain (6/03, $13.95) r/most of #7-10 & other-s 14.00

DOROTHY & THE WIZARD IN OZ (Adaptation of the original 1908 L. Frank Baum book) (Also see Wonderful Wizard of Oz, Marvelous Land of Oz, and Ozma of Oz)
Marvel Comics: Nov, 2011 - No. 8, Aug, 2012 ($3.99, limited series)

1-8-Eric Shanower-a/Skottie Young-a/c 4.00

DOROTHY LAMOUR (Formerly Jungle Lil)(Stage, screen, radio)
Fox Feature Syndicate: No. 2, June, 1950 - No. 3, Aug, 1950

	GD	VG	FN	VF	VF/NM	NM-
2-Wood-a(3), photo-c	37	74	111	222	361	500
3-Wood-a(3), photo-c	30	60	90	177	289	400

DOROTHY OF OZ PREQUEL
IDW Publishing: Mar, 2012 - No. 4, Aug, 2012 ($3.99, limited series)

1-4-Tipton-s/Shedd-a 4.00

DOT DOTLAND (Formerly Little Dot Dotland)
Harvey Publications: No. 62, Sept, 1974 - No. 63, Nov, 1974

	GD	VG	FN	VF	VF/NM	NM-
62,63	2	4	6	11	16	20

DOTTY (...& Her Boy Friends)(Formerly Four Teeners; Glamorous Romances No. 41 on)
Ace Magazines (A. A. Wyn): No. 35, June, 1948 - No. 40, May, 1949

	GD	VG	FN	VF	VF/NM	NM-
35-Teen-age	12	24	36	67	94	120
36-40: 37-Transvestism story	9	18	27	47	61	75

DOTTY DRIPPLE (Horace & Dotty Dripple No. 25 on)
Magazine Ent.(Life's Romances)/Harvey No. 3 on: 1946 - No. 24, June, 1952 (Also see A-1 No. 1, 3-8, 10)

	GD	VG	FN	VF	VF/NM	NM-
1 (nd) (10¢)	14	28	42	82	121	160
2	9	18	27	50	65	80
3-10: 3,4-Powell-a	7	14	21	35	43	50
11-24	6	12	18	28	34	40

DOTTY DRIPPLE AND TAFFY
Dell Publishing Co.: No. 646, Sept, 1955 - No. 903, May, 1958

	GD	VG	FN	VF	VF/NM	NM-
Four Color 646 (#1)	6	12	18	37	66	95
Four Color 691,718,746,801,903	4	8	12	28	47	65

DOUBLE ACTION COMICS
National Periodical Publications: No. 2, Jan, 1940 (68 pgs., B&W)

	GD	VG	FN	VF	VF/NM	NM-
2-Contains original stories(?); pre-hero DC contents; same cover as Adventure No. 37. (seven known copies, four in high grade) (not an ashcan)	3500	7000	10,500	21,000	28,000	35,000

NOTE: *The cover to this book was probably reprinted from Adventure #37. #1 exists as an ash can copy with B&W cover; contains a coverless comic on inside with 1st & last page missing. There is proof of at least limited news-stand distribution. #2 cover proof only sold in 2005 for $4,000.*

DOUBLE COMICS
Elliot Publications: 1940 - 1944 (132 pgs.)

	GD	VG	FN	VF	VF/NM	NM-
1940 issues; Masked Marvel-c & The Mad Mong vs. The White Flash covers known	300	600	900	2040	3570	5100
1941 issues; Tornado Tim-c, Nordac-c, & Green Light covers known	206	412	618	1318	2259	3200
1942 issues	148	296	444	947	1624	2300
1943,1944 issues	126	252	378	806	1378	1950

NOTE: *Double Comics consisted of an almost endless combination of pairs of remaindered, unsold issues of comics representing most publishers and usually mixed publishers in the same book; e.g., a Captain America with a Silver Streak, or a Feature with a Detective, etc., could appear inside the same cover. The actual contents would have to determine its price. Prices listed are for average contents. Any containing rare origin or first issues are worth much more. Covers also vary in same year. Value would be approximately 50 percent of contents.*

DOUBLE-CROSS (See The Crusaders)

DOUBLE-DARE ADVENTURES
Harvey Publications: Dec, 1966 - No. 2, Mar, 1967 (35¢/25¢, 68 pgs.)

	GD	VG	FN	VF	VF/NM	NM-
1-Origin Bee-Man, Glowing Gladiator, & Magic-Master; Simon/Kirby-a	6	12	18	38	69	100
2-Torres-a; r/Alarming Adv. #3('63)	5	10	15	30	50	70

NOTE: ***Powell** a-1. **Simon/Sparling** c-1, 2.*

DOUBLE DRAGON
Marvel Comics: July, 1991 - No. 6, Dec, 1991 ($1.00, limited series)

1-6: Based on video game. 2-Art Adams-c 3.00

DOUBLE EDGE
Marvel Comics: Alpha, 1995; Omega, 1995 ($4.95, limited series)

Alpha ($4.95)- Punisher story, Nick Fury app. 5.00
Omega ($4.95)-Punisher, Daredevil, Ghost Rider app. Death of Nick Fury 5.00

DOUBLE IMAGE
Image Comics: Feb, 2001 - No. 5, July, 2001 ($2.95)

1-5: 1-Flip covers of Codeflesh (Casey-s/Adlard-a) and The Bod (Young-s). 2-Two covers. 5-"Trust in Me" begins; Chaudhary-a 3.00

DOUBLE LIFE OF PRIVATE STRONG, THE
Archie Publications/Radio Comics: June, 1959 - No. 2, Aug, 1959

1-Origin & re-intro The Shield; Simon & Kirby-c/a, their re-entry into the super-hero genre;

Down With Crime #7 © FAW

Dracula (2010 series) #4 © MAR

Dragon Age: Magekiller #1 © EA

GD VG FN VF VF/NM NM-
2.0 4.0 6.0 8.0 9.0 9.2

intro./1st app. The Fly; 1st S.A. super-hero for Archie Publ.
32 64 96 230 515 800
2-S&K-c/a; Tuska-a; The Fly app. (2nd or 3rd?) 18 36 54 124 275 425

DOUBLE TROUBLE
St. John Publishing Co.: Nov, 1957 - No. 2, Jan-Feb, 1958

1,2: Tuffy & Snuffy by Frank Johnson; dubbed "World's Funniest Kids"
7 14 21 35 43 50

DOUBLE TROUBLE WITH GOOBER
Dell Publishing Co.: No. 417, Aug, 1952 - No. 556, May, 1954

Four Color 417 5 10 15 33 57 80
Four Color 471,516,556 4 8 12 27 44 60

DOUBLE UP COMICS
Elliott Publications: 1941 (Pocket size, 192 pgs., 10¢)

1-Contains rebound copies of digest sized issues of Pocket Comics, Speed Comics, & Spitfire Comics; Japanese WWII-c 161 322 483 1030 1765 2500

DOVER & CLOVER (See All Funny & More Fun Comics #93)

DOVER BOYS (See Adventures of the...)

DOVER THE BIRD
Famous Funnies Publishing Co.: Spring, 1955

1-Funny animal; code approved 8 16 24 44 57 70

DOWN
Image Comics (Top Cow): Dec, 2005 - No. 4, Mar, 2006 ($2.99)

1-4-Warren Ellis-s. 1-Tony Harris-a/c. 2-4-Cully Hamner-a 3.00
Down & Top Cow's Best of Warren Ellis TPB (6/06, $15.99) r/#1-4 & Tales of the Witchblade #3,4; Ellis-s; script for Down #1 with Harris sketch pages 16.00

DOWN WITH CRIME
Fawcett Publications: Nov, 1952 - No. 7, Nov, 1953

1 37 74 111 222 361 500
2,4,5: 2,4-Powell-a in each. 5-Bondage-c 19 38 57 111 176 240
3-Used in **POP**, pg. 106; "H is for Heroin" drug story
21 42 63 126 206 285
6,7: 6-Used in **POP**, pg. 80 18 36 54 105 165 225

DO YOU BELIEVE IN NIGHTMARES?
St. John Publishing Co.: Nov, 1957 - No. 2, Jan, 1958

1-Mostly Ditko-c/a 61 122 183 390 670 950
2-Ayers-a 37 74 111 222 361 550

D.P. 7
Marvel Comics Group (New Universe): Nov, 1986 - No. 32, June, 1989

1-20, 3.00
21-32-Low print 4.00
Annual #1 (11/87)-Intro. The Witness 4.00
... Classic Vol. 1 TPB (2007, $24.99) r/#1-9; Mark Gruenwald-s/Paul Ryan-a in all 25.00
NOTE: ***Williamson*** *a-9i, 11i; c-9i.*

DRACULA (See Bram Stoker's Dracula, Giant-Size..., Little Dracula, Marvel Graphic Novel, Requiem for Dracula, Spider-Man Vs...., Stoker's..., Tomb of... & Wedding of...; also see Movie Classics under Universal Presents as well as Dracula)

DRACULA (See Movie Classics for #1)(Also see Frankenstein & Werewolf)
Dell Publ. Co.: No. 2, 11/66 - No. 4, 3/67; No. 6, 7/72 - No. 8, 7/73 (No #5)

2-Origin & 1st app. Dracula (11/66) (super hero) 4 8 12 28 47 65
3,4: 4-Intro. Fleeta ('67) 3 6 9 19 30 40
6-('72)-r/#2 w/origin 3 6 9 15 21 26
7,8-r/#3, #4 2 4 6 11 16 20

DRACULA (Magazine)
Warren Publishing Co.: 1979 (120 pgs., full color)

Book 1-Maroto art; Spanish material translated into English (mail order only)
6 12 18 37 66 95

DRACULA
Marvel Comics: Jul, 2010 - No. 4, Sept, 2010 ($3.99, limited series)

1-4-Colored reprint of Bram Stoker's Classic Dracula adapt. from Dracula Lives!, Legion of Monsters and Stoker's Dracula; Thomas-s/Giordano-a; J. Djurdjevic-c 4.00

DRACULA CHRONICLES
Topps Comics: Apr, 1995 - No. 3, June, 1995 ($2.50, limited series)

1-3-Linsner-c 3.00

DRACULA LIVES! (Magazine)(Also see Tomb of Dracula) (Reprinted in Stoker's Dracula)
Marvel Comics Group: 1973(no month) - No. 13, July, 1975 (75¢, B&W) (76 pgs.)

GD VG FN VF VF/NM NM-
2.0 4.0 6.0 8.0 9.0 9.2

1-Boris painted-c 8 16 24 52 99 145
2 (7/73)-1st time origin Dracula; Adams, Starlin-a 5 10 15 33 57 80
3-1st app. Robert E. Howard's Soloman Kane; Adams-c/a
5 10 15 31 53 75
4,5: 4-Ploog-a. 5(V2#1)-Bram Stoker's Classic Dracula adapt. begins
4 8 12 23 37 50
6-9: 6-8-Bram Stoker adapt. 9-Bondage-c 4 8 12 23 37 50
10 (1/75)-16 pg. Lilith solo (1st?) 4 8 12 27 44 60
11-13: 11-21 pg. Lilith solo sty. 12-31 pg. Dracula sty 4 8 12 23 37 50
Annual 1(Summer, 1975, $1.25, 92 pgs.)-Morrow painted-c; 6 Dracula stys.
25 pgs. Adams-a(r) 4 8 12 25 40 55
NOTE: ***N. Adams*** *a-2, 3i, 10i, Annual 1r(2, 3i).* ***Alcala*** *a-9.* ***Buscema*** *a-3p, 6p, Annual 1p.* ***Colan*** *a(p)-1, 2, 5, 6, 8.* ***Evans*** *a-7.* ***Gulacy*** *a-9.* ***Heath*** *a-1r, 13.* ***Pakula*** *a-6r. Sutton a-13.****Weiss*** *r-Annual 1p. 4* ***Dracula*** *stories each in 1, 609; 3* ***Dracula*** *stories each in 2, 4, 5,, 13.*

DRACULA: LORD OF THE UNDEAD
Marvel Comics: Dec, 1998 - No. 3, Dec, 1998 ($2.99, limited series)

1-3-Olliffe & Palmer-a 3.00

DRACULA: RETURN OF THE IMPALER
Slave Labor Graphics: July, 1993 - No. 4, Oct, 1994 ($2.95, limited series)

1-4 3.00

DRACULA'S REVENGE
IDW Publishing: Apr, 2004 - No. 3 ($3.99, limited series)

1,2-Forbeck-s/Kudranski-a 4.00

DRACULA: THE COMPANY OF MONSTERS
BOOM! Studios: Aug, 2010 - No. 12, Jul, 2011 ($3.99)

1-12: 1-5-Busiek & Gregory-s/Godlewski-a. 1-Two covers by Brereton and Salas 4.00

DRACULA VERSUS ZORRO
Topps Comics: Oct, 1993 - No. 2, Nov, 1993 ($2.95, limited series)

1,2: 1-Spot varnish & red foil-c. 2-Polybagged w/16 pg. Zorro #0 4.00

DRACULA VERSUS ZORRO
Dark Horse Comics: Sept, 1998 - No. 2, Oct, 1998 ($2.95, limited series)

1,2 3.00

DRACULA: VLAD THE IMPALER (Also see Bram Stoker's Dracula)
Topps Comics: Feb, 1993 - No. 3, Apr, 1993 ($2.95, limited series)

1-3-Polybagged with 3 trading cards each; Maroto-c/a 4.00

DRAFT, THE
Marvel Comics: 1988 ($3.50, one-shot, squarebound)

1-Sequel to "The Pitt" 4.00

DRAFTED: ONE HUNDRED DAYS
Devil's Due Publishing: June, 2009 ($5.99, one-shot)

1-Barack Obama on a post-galactic-war Earth; Powers-s 6.00

DRAG 'N' WHEELS (Formerly Top Eliminator)
Charlton Comics: No. 30, Sept, 1968 - No. 59, May, 1973

30 4 8 12 27 44 60
31-40-Scot Jackson begins 3 6 9 18 28 38
41-50 3 6 9 16 24 32
51-59: Scot Jackson 2 4 6 13 18 22
Modern Comics Reprint 58('78) 5.00

DRAGON, THE (Also see The Savage Dragon)
Image Comics (Highbrow Ent.): Mar, 1996 - No. 5, July, 1996 (99¢, lim. series)

1-5: Reprints Savage Dragon limited series w/new story & art. 5-Youngblood app; includes 5 pg. Savage Dragon story from 1984 3.00

DRAGON AGE (Based on the EA videogame)
IDW Publishing (EA Comics): Mar, 2010 - No. 6, Nov, 2010 ($3.99)

1-6-Orson Scott Card & Aaron Johnston-s; Ramos-c 4.00

DRAGON AGE: KNIGHT ERRANT (Based on the EA videogame)
Dark Horse Comics: May, 2017 - No. 5, Sept, 2017 ($3.99, limited series)

1-5-DeFilippis & Weir-s/Furukawa-a/Teng-c 4.00

DRAGON AGE: MAGEKILLER (Based on the EA videogame)
Dark Horse Comics: Dec, 2015 - No. 5, Apr, 2016 ($3.99, limited series)

1-3-Rucka-s/Carnero-a/Teng-c 4.00

DRAGON AGE: THOSE WHO SPEAK (Based on the EA videogame)
Dark Horse Comics: Aug, 2012 - No. 3, Nov, 2012 ($3.50, limited series)

1-3-Gaider-s/Hardin-a/Palumbo-c 3.50

DRAGON ARCHIVES, THE (Also see The Savage Dragon)

Dragonheart #2 © Universal Studios

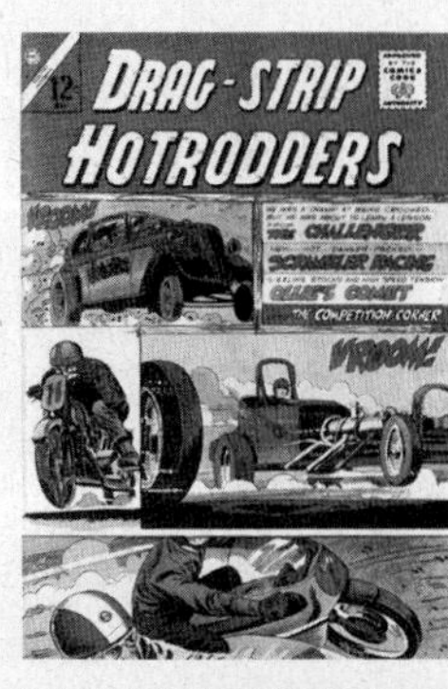

Dragstrip Hotrodders #9 © CC

Drax #11 © MAR

	GD 2.0	VG 4.0	FN 6.0	VF 8.0	VF/NM 9.0	NM- 9.2

Image Comics: Jun, 1998 - No. 4, Jan, 1999 ($2.95, B&W)

1-4: Reprints early Savage Dragon app. 3.00

DRAGON BALL
Viz Comics: Mar, 1998 - Part 6: #2, Feb, 2003($2.95, B&W, Manga reprints read right to left)

	GD	VG	FN	VF	VF/NM	NM-
Part 1: 1-Akira Toriyama-s/a	2	4	6	8	10	12
2-12						6.00
1-12 (2nd & 3rd printings)						4.00
Part 2: 1-15: 15-($3.50-c)						5.00
Part 3: 1-14						4.00
Part 4: 1-10						4.00
Part 5: 1-7						4.00
Part 6: 1,2						4.00

DRAGON BALL Z
Viz Comics: Mar, 1998 - Part 5: #10, Oct, 2002 ($2.95, B&W, Manga reprints read right to left)

	GD	VG	FN	VF	VF/NM	NM-
Part 1: 1-Akira Toriyama-s/a	2	4	6	8	10	12
2-9						6.00
1-9 (2nd & 3rd printings)						4.00
Part 2: 1-14						5.00
Part 3: 1-10						4.00
Part 4: 1-15						4.00
Part 5: 1-10						4.00

DRAGON, THE: BLOOD & GUTS (Also see The Savage Dragon)
Image Comics (Highbrow Entertainment): Mar, 1995 - No. 3, May, 1995 ($2.50, lim. series)

1-3: Jason Pearson-c/a/scripts 3.00

DRAGON CHIANG
Eclipse Books: 1991 ($3.95, B&W, squarebound, 52 pgs.)

nn-Timothy Truman-c/a(p) 4.00

DRAGONFLIGHT
Eclipse Books: Feb, 1991 - No. 3, 1991 ($4.95, 52 pgs.)

Book One - Three: Adapts 1968 novel 5.00

DRAGONFLY (See Americomics #4)
Americomics: Sum, 1985 - No. 8, 1986 ($1.75/$1.95)

1 4.00
2-8 3.00

DRAGONFORCE
Aircel Publishing: 1988 - No. 13, 1989 ($2.00)

1-Dale Keown-c/a/scripts in #1-12 4.00
2-13: 13-No Keown-a 3.00
...Chronicles Book 1-5 ($2.95, B&W, 60 pgs.): Dale Keown-r/Dragonring & Dragonforce 4.00

DRAGONHEART (Movie)
Topps Comics: May, 1996 - No. 2, June, 1996 ($2.95/$4.95, limited series)

1-($2.95, 24 pgs.)-Adaptation of the film; Hildebrandt Bros-c; Lim-a. 3.00
2-($4.95, 64 pgs.) 5.00

DRAGONLANCE (Also see TSR Worlds)
DC Comics: Dec, 1988 - No. 34, Sept, 1991 ($1.25/$1.50, Mando paper)

1-Based on TSR game 4.00
2-34: Based on TSR game. 30-32-Kaluta-c 3.00

DRAGONLANCE: CHRONICLES
Devil's Due Publ.: Aug, 2005 - No. 8, Mar, 2006 ($2.95)

1-8-Dabb-s/Kurth-a 3.00
...: Dragons of Autumn Twilight TPB (2006, $17.95) r/#1-8 18.00

DRAGONLANCE: CHRONICLES (Volume 2)
Devil's Due Publ.: July, 2006 - No. 4, Jan, 2007 ($4.95/$4.99, 48 pgs.)

1-4-Dragons of Winter Night; Dabb-s/Kurth-a 5.00
...: Dragons of Winter Night TPB (3/07, $18.99) r/#1-4; cover gallery 19.00

DRAGONLANCE: CHRONICLES (Volume 3)
Devil's Due Publ.: Mar, 2007 - No. 12, ($3.50)

1-11-Dragons of Spring Dawning; Dabb-s/Cope-a 3.50

DRAGONLANCE: THE LEGEND OF HUMA
Devil's Due Publ.: Jan, 2004 - No. 6, Oct, 2005 ($2.95)

1-6-Mike Miller & Rael-a 3.00

DRAGON LINES
Marvel Comics (Epic Comics/Heavy Hitters): May, 1993 - No. 4, Aug, 1993 ($1.95, limited series)

1-($2.50)-Embossed-c; Ron Lim-c/a in all 4.00
2-4 3.00

DRAGON LINES: WAY OF THE WARRIOR
Marvel Comics (Epic Comics/ Heavy Hitters): Nov, 1993 - No. 2, Jan, 1994 ($2.25, limited series)

1,2-Ron Lim-c/a(p) 3.00

DRAGONQUEST
Silverwolf Comics: Dec, 1986 - No. 2, 1987 ($1.50, B&W, 28 pgs.)

1,2-Tim Vigil-c/a in all 5.00

DRAGONRING
Aircel Publishing: 1986 - V2#15, 1988 ($1.70/$2.00, B&W/color)

1-6: 6-Last B&W issue, V2#1-15($2.00, color) 3.00

DRAGON'S CLAWS
Marvel UK, Ltd.: July, 1988 - No. 10, Apr, 1989 ($1.25/$1.50/$1.75, British)

1-10: 3-Death's Head 1 pg. strip on back-c (1st app.). 4-Silhouette of Death's Head on last pg. 5-1st full app. new Death's Head 3.00

DRAGON'S LAIR: SINGE'S REVENGE (Based on the Don Bluth video game)
CrossGen Comics: Sept, 2003 - No. 3 ($2.95, limited series)

1-3-Mangels-s/Laguna-a 3.00

DRAGONSLAYER (Movie)
Marvel Comics Group: October, 1981 - No. 2, Nov, 1981

1,2-Paramount Disney movie adaptation 4.00

DRAGOON WELLS MASSACRE
Dell Publishing Co.: No. 815, June, 1957

	GD	VG	FN	VF	VF/NM	NM-
Four Color 815-Movie, photo-c	7	14	21	46	86	125

DRAGSTRIP HOTRODDERS (World of Wheels No. 17 on)
Charlton Comics: Sum, 1963; No. 2, Jan, 1965 - No. 16, Aug, 1967

	GD	VG	FN	VF	VF/NM	NM-
1	6	12	18	41	76	110
2-5	4	8	12	25	40	55
6-16	3	6	9	21	33	45

DRAIN
Image Comics: Nov, 2006 - No. 6, Mar, 2008 ($2.99)

1-6: 1-Cebulski-s/Takeda-a; two covers by Takeda and Finch 3.00
Vol. 1 TPB (2008, $16.99) r/#1-6; cover gallery and Takeda sketch art gallery 17.00

DRAKUUN
Dark Horse Comics: Feb, 1997 - No. 25, Mar, 1999 ($2.95, B&W, manga)

1-25; 1-6- Johji Manabe-s/a in all. Rise of the Dragon Princess series. 7-12-Revenge of Gustav. 13-18-Shadow of the Warlock. 19-25-The Hidden War 3.00

DRAMA
Sirius: June, 1994 ($2.95, mature)

	GD	VG	FN	VF	VF/NM	NM-
1-1st full color Dawn app. in comics	1	3	4	6	8	10
1-Limited edition (1400 copies); signed & numbered; fingerprint authenticity	3	6	9	16	23	30

NOTE: *Dawn's 1st full color app. was a pin-up in Amazing Heroes' Swimsuit Special #5.*

DRAMA OF AMERICA, THE
Action Text: 1973 ($1.95, 224 pgs.)

	GD	VG	FN	VF	VF/NM	NM-
1- "Students' Supplement to History"	1	3	4	6	8	10

DRAWING ON YOUR NIGHTMARES
Dark Horse Comics: Oct, 2003 ($2.99, one-shot)

1-Short stories; The Goon, Criminal Macabre, Tales of the Vampires; Templesmith-c 3.00

DRAX (Guardians of the Galaxy)
Marvel Comics: Jan, 2016 - No. 11, Nov, 2016 ($3.99)

1-11-CM Punk & Cullen Bunn-s/Hepburn-a. 1-Guardians app. 4,5-Fin Fang Foom app. 4.00

DRAX THE DESTROYER (Guardians of the Galaxy)
Marvel Comics: Nov, 2005 - No. 4, Feb, 2006 ($2.99, limited series)

1-4-Giffen-s/Breitweiser-a 5.00
...: Earthfall TPB (2006, $10.99) r/#1-4; character design page 11.00

DREAD GODS
IDW Publishing: Jul, 2017 - Present ($3.99)

1-3-Marz-s/Raney-a 4.00

DREADLANDS (Also see Epic)
Marvel Comics (Epic Comics): 1992 - No. 4, 1992 ($3.95, lim. series, 52 pgs.)

1-4: Stiff-c 4.00

DREADSTAR (See Epic Illustrated #3 for 1st app. and Eclipse Graphic Album Series #5)

The Dreaming #24 © DC

Dream Police #12 © Studio JMS

Droopy #1 © Turner

GD 2.0 | VG 4.0 | FN 6.0 | VF 8.0 | VF/NM 9.0 | NM- 9.2

Marvel Comics (Epic Comics)/First Comics No. 27 on: Nov, 1982 - No. 64, Mar, 1991
1 2 4 6 8 10 12
2-5,8-49 4.00
6,7,51-64: 6,7-1st app. Interstellar Toybox; 8pgs. ea.; Wrightson-a. 51-64-Lower print run 5.00
50 6.00
Annual 1 (12/83)-r/The Price (Eclipse Graphic Album Series #5) 5.00

DREADSTAR
Malibu Comics (Bravura): Apr, 1994 - No. 6, Jan, 1995 ($2.50, limited series)
1-6-Peter David scripts: 1,2-Starlin-c 3.00
NOTE: *Issues 1-6 contain Bravura stamps.*

DREADSTAR AND COMPANY
Marvel Comics (Epic Comics): July, 1985 - No. 6, Dec, 1985
1-6: 1,3,6-New Starlin-a: 2-New Wrightson-c; reprints of Dreadstar series 3.00

DREAM BOOK OF LOVE (Also see A-1 Comics)
Magazine Enterprises: No. 106, June-July, 1954 - No. 123, Oct-Nov, 1954
A-1 106 (#1)-Powell, Bolle-a; Montgomery Clift, Donna Reed photo-c
19 38 57 111 176 240
A-1-114 (#2)-Guardineer, Bolle-a; Piper Laurie, Victor Mature photo-c
14 28 42 81 118 155
A-1 123 (#3)-Movie photo-c 14 28 42 76 108 140

DREAM BOOK OF ROMANCE (Also see A-1 Comics)
Magazine Enterprises: No. 92, 1954 - No. 124, Oct-Nov, 1954
A-1 92 (#5)-Guardineer-a; photo-c 17 34 51 100 158 215
A-1 101 (#6)(4-6/54)-Marlon Brando photo-c; Powell, Bolle, Guardineer-a
34 68 102 204 332 460
A-1 109,110,124: 109 (#7)(7-8/54)-Powell-a; movie photo-c. 110 (#8)(1/54)-Movie photo-c. 124 (#9)(10-11/54) 14 28 42 76 108 140

DREAMER, THE
Kitchen Sink Press: 1986 ($6.95, B&W, graphic novel)
nn-Will Eisner-s/a 15.00
DC Comics Reprint ($7.95, 6/00) 8.00

DREAMERY, THE
Eclipse Comics: Dec, 1986 - No. 14, Feb, 1989 ($2.00, B&W, Baxter paper)
1-14: 2-7-Alice In Wonderland adapt. 3.00

DREAMING, THE (See Sandman, 2nd Series)
DC Comics (Vertigo): June, 1996 - No. 60, May, 2001 ($2.50)
1-McKean-c on all.; LaBan scripts & Snejbjerg-a 4.00
2-30,32-60: 2,3-LaBan scripts & Snejbjerg-a. 4-7-Hogan scripts; Parkhouse-a. 8-Zulli-a. 9-11-Talbot-s/Taylor-a(p). 41-Previews Sandman: The Dream Hunters. 50-Hempel, Fegredo, McManus, Totleben-a 3.00
31-($3.95) Art by various 4.00
...Beyond The Shores of Night TPB ('97, $19.95) r/#1-8 20.00
...Special (7/98, $5.95, one-shot) Trial of Cain 6.00
...Through The Gates of Horn and Ivory TPB ('99, $19.95) r/#15-19,22-25 20.00

DREAMING EAGLES
AfterShock Comics: Dec, 2015 - No. 6, Jun, 2016 ($3.99)
1-6-Ennis-s/Coleby-a; Tuskegee Airmen in WWII 4.00

DREAM OF LOVE
I. W. Enterprises: 1958 (Reprints)
1,2,8: 1-r/Dream Book of Love #1; Bob Powell-a. 2-r/Great Lover's Romances #10. 8-Great Lover's Romances #1; also contains 2 Jon Juan stories by Siegel & Schomburg; Kinstler-c. 3 6 9 14 20 25
9-Kinstler-c; 1pg. John Wayne interview & Frazetta illo from John Wayne Adv. Comics #2
3 6 9 14 20 25

DREAM POLICE
Marvel Comics (Icon): Aug, 2005 ($3.99)
1-Straczynski-s/Deodato-a/c 4.00

DREAM POLICE
Image Comics (Joe's Comics): Apr, 2014 - No. 12, Sept, 2016 ($2.99)
1-12-Straczynski-s/Kotian-a 3.00

DREAMS OF THE DARKCHYLDE
Darkchylde Entertainment: Oct, 2000 - No. 6, Sept, 2001 ($2.95)
1-6-Randy Queen-s in all. 1-Brandon Peterson-c/a 3.00

DREAM TEAM (See Battlezones: Dream Team 2)
Malibu Comics (Ultraverse): July, 1995 ($4.95, one-shot)
1-Pin-ups teaming up Marvel & Ultraverse characters by various artists including Allred, Romita, Darrow, Balent, Quesada & Palmiotti 5.00

GD 2.0 | VG 4.0 | FN 6.0 | VF 8.0 | VF/NM 9.0 | NM- 9.2

DREAM THIEF
Dark Horse Comics: May, 2013 - No. 5, Sept, 2013 ($3.99, limited series)
1-5-Nitz-s/Smallwood-a. 1-Alex Ross-c. 2-Ryan Sook-c. 4-Dan Brereton-c 4.00

DREAM THIEF: ESCAPE
Dark Horse Comics: Jun, 2014 - No. 4, Sept, 2014 ($3.99, limited series)
1-4-Nitz-s/Smallwood-c. 1,2-Smallwood-a. 3,4-Galusha-a 4.00

DREAMWAVE PRODUCTIONS PREVIEW
Dreamwave Productions: May, 2002 ($1.00, one-shot)
nn-Previews Arkanium, Transformers: The War Within and other series 3.00

DRESDEN FILES (See Jim Butcher's...)

DRIFTER
Image Comics: Nov, 2014 - No. 19, Jun, 2017 ($3.50/$3.99)
1-19-Ivan Brandon-s/Nic Klein-a; multiple covers on each. 15-Start $3.99-c 4.00

DRIFT FENCE (See Zane Grey 4-Color 270)

DRIFT MARLO
Dell Publishing Co.: May-July, 1962 - No. 2, Oct-Dec, 1962 (Painted-c)
01-232-207 (#1) 5 10 15 30 50 70
2 (12-232-212) 4 8 12 27 44 60

DRISCOLL'S BOOK OF PIRATES
David McKay Publ. (Not reprints): 1934 (B&W, hardcover; 124 pgs, 7x9")
nn-"Pieces of Eight" strip by Montford Amory 26 52 78 154 252 350

DRIVER: CROSSING THE LINE (Based on the Ubisoft videogame)
DC Comics: Oct, 2011 ($2.99, one-shot)
1-David Lapham-s/Greg Scott-a/ Jock-c; bonus character design art 3.00

DROIDS (Based on Saturday morning cartoon) (Also see Dark Horse Comics)
Marvel Comics (Star Comics): April, 1986 - No. 8, June, 1987
1-R2D2 & C-3PO from Star Wars app. in all 2 4 6 13 18 22
2-8: 2,5,7,8-Williamson-a(i) 2 4 6 8 10 12
NOTE: ***Romita** a-3p. **Sinnott** a-3i.*

DRONES
IDW Publishing: Apr, 2015 - No. 5, Aug, 2015 ($3.99, limited series)
1-5-Chris Lewis-s/Bruno Oliveira-a 4.00

DROOPY (see Tom & Jerry #60)

DROOPY (Tex Avery's...)
Dark Horse Comics: Oct, 1995 - No. 3, Dec, 1995 ($2.50, limited series)
1-3: Characters created by Tex Avery; painted-c 3.00

DROPSIE AVENUE: THE NEIGHBORHOOD
Kitchen Sink Press: June, 1995 ($15.95/$24.95, B&W)
nn-Will Eisner (softcover) 18.00
nn-Will Eisner (hardcover) 30.00

DROWNED GIRL, THE
DC Comics (Piranha Press): 1990 ($5.95, 52 pgs, mature)
nn 6.00

DRUG WARS
Pioneer Comics: 1989 ($1.95)
1-Grell-c 3.00

DRUID
Marvel Comics: May, 1995 - No. 4, Aug, 1995 ($2.50, limited series)
1-4: Warren Ellis scripts. 3.00

DRUM BEAT
Dell Publishing Co.: No. 610, Jan, 1955
Four Color 610-Movie, Alan Ladd photo-c 8 16 24 55 105 155

DRUMS OF DOOM
United Features Syndicate: 1937 (25¢)(Indian)(Text w/color illos.)
nn-By Lt. F.A. Methot; Golden Thunder app.; Tip Top Comics ad in comic; nice-c
41 82 123 256 428 600

DRUNKEN FIST
Jademan Comics: Aug, 1988 - No. 54, Jan, 1993 ($1.50/$1.95, 68 pgs.)
1 5.00
2-50 4.00
51-54 4.00

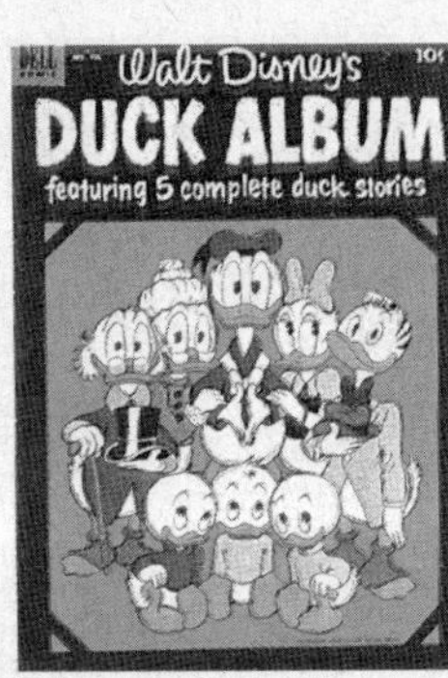

Duck Album Four Color #450 © DIS

Duck Tales (2011 series) #1 © DIS

Dungeons & Dragons #14 © WOTC

	GD 2.0	VG 4.0	FN 6.0	VF 8.0	VF/NM 9.0	NM- 9.2

DUCK ALBUM (See Donald Duck Album)
Dell Publishing Co.: No. 353, Oct, 1951 - No. 840, Sept, 1957

Four Color 353 (#1)-Barks-c; 1st Uncle Scrooge-c (also appears on back-c).
11 22 33 76 163 250
Four Color 450-Barks-c 8 16 24 54 102 150
Four Color 492,531,560,586,611,649,686, 7 14 21 46 86 125
Four Color 726,782,840 6 12 18 37 66 95

DUCK AVENGER
IDW Publishing: No. 0, Aug, 2016; Oct, 2016 - No. 5, Jun, 2017 ($4.99/$5.99/$6.99)

0-Reprints of Italian Donald Duck costumed super-hero stories 5.00
1,3-($5.99) Three covers. 1-(10/16) Red Raider app. 6.00
2-($4.99) Three covers; Xadhoom app. 5.00
4,5-($6.99) 7.00

DUCKMAN
Dark Horse Comics: Sept, 1990 ($1.95, B&W, one-shot)

1-Story & art by Everett Peck 4.00

DUCKMAN
Topps Comics: Nov, 1994 - No. 5, May, 1995; No. 0, Feb, 1996 ($2.50)

0 (2/96, $2.95, B&W)-r/Duckman #1 from Dark Horse Comics 3.00
1-5: 1-w/ coupon #A for Duckman trading card. 2-w/Duckman 1st season episode guide 3.00

DUCKMAN: THE MOB FROG SAGA
Topps Comics: Nov, 1994 - No. 3, Feb, 1995 ($2.50, limited series)

1-3: 1-w/coupon #B for Duckman trading card, S. Shaw!-c 3.00

DUCKTALES
Gladstone Publ.: Oct, 1988 - No. 13, May, 1990 (1,2,9-11: $1.50; 3-8: 95¢)

1-Barks-r 6.00
2-11: 2-7,9-11-Barks-r 4.00
12,13 ($1.95, 68 pgs.)-Barks-r; 12-r/F.C. #495 5.00
Disney Presents Carl Barks' Greatest DuckTales Stories Vol. 1 (Gemstone Publ., 2006, $10.95)
r/stories adapted for the animated TV series including "Back to the Klondike" 11.00
Disney Presents Carl Barks' Greatest DuckTales Stories Vol. 2 (Gemstone Publ., 2006, $10.95)
r/stories adapted for the animated TV series; "Robot Robbers" app. 11.00

DUCKTALES (TV)
Disney Comics: June, 1990 - No. 18, Nov, 1991 ($1.50)

1-All new stories; Marv Wolfman-s 4.00
2-18 3.00
Disney's DuckTales by Marv Wolfman: Scrooge's Quest TPB (Gemstone, 9/07, $15.99)
r/#1-7; intro. by Wolfman 16.00
Disney's DuckTales: The Gold Odyssey TPB (Gemstone, 10/08, $15.99) 16.00
The Movie nn (1990, $7.95, 68 pgs.)-Graphic novel adapting animated movie 8.00

DUCKTALES (TV)
Boom Entertainment (KABOOM!): May, 2011 - No. 4, Aug, 2011 ($3.99)

1-6: 1-4-Three covers on each; Spector-s/Massaroli-a. 5,6-Two covers; Crossover with Darkwing Duck #17,18 4.00

DUCKTALES (Based on the 2017 TV series)
IDW Publishing: No. 0, Jul, 2017; No. 1, Sept, 2017 - Present ($3.99)

0-6: 0,1-Caramagna-s; multiple covers 4.00

DUDLEY (Teen-age)
Feature/Prize Publications: Nov-Dec, 1949 - No. 3, Mar-Apr, 1950

1-By Boody Rogers 20 40 60 114 182 250
2,3 13 26 39 72 101 130

DUDLEY DO-RIGHT (TV)
Charlton Comics: Aug, 1970 - No. 7, Aug, 1971 (Jay Ward)

1 8 16 24 52 99 145
2-7 6 12 18 37 66 95

DUEL MASTERS (Based on a trading card game)
Dreamwave Productions: Nov, 2003 - No. 8, Sept, 2004 ($2.95)

1-8: 1-Bagged with card; Augustyn-s 3.00

DUKE NUKEM: GLORIOUS BASTARD (Based on the video game)
IDW Publishing: Jul, 2011 - No. 4, Nov, 2011 ($3.99)

1-4: 1-Three covers; Waltz-s/Xermanico-a 4.00

DUKE OF THE K-9 PATROL
Gold Key: Apr, 1963

1 (10052-304) 4 8 12 25 40 55

DUMBO (Disney; see Movie Comics, & Walt Disney Showcase #12)
Dell Publishing Co.: No. 17, 1941 - No. 668, Jan, 1958

Four Color 17 (#1)-Mickey Mouse, Donald Duck, Pluto app.
274 548 822 1740 2995 4250
Large Feature Comic 19 ('41)-Part-r 4-Color 17 307 614 921 1950 3350 4750
Four Color 234 ('49) 13 26 39 89 195 300
Four Color 668 (12/55)-1st of two printings. Dumbo on-c with starry sky. Same-c as #234
10 20 30 66 138 210
Four Color 668 (1/58)-2nd printing. Same cover altered with Timothy Mouse added. Same contents 7 14 21 44 82 120

DUMBO COMIC PAINT BOOK (See Dumbo, Large Feature Comic No. 19)

DUNC AND LOO (#1-3 titled "Around the Block with Dunc and Loo")
Dell Publishing Co.: Oct-Dec, 1961 - No. 8, Oct-Dec, 1963

1 5 10 15 35 63 90
2 4 8 12 27 44 60
3-8 3 6 9 21 33 45
NOTE: *Written by* ***John Stanley; Bill Williams*** *art.*

DUNE (Movie)
Marvel Comics: Apr, 1985 - No. 3, June, 1985

1-3-r/Marvel Super Special; movie adaptation 4.00

DUNGEONS & DRAGONS
IDW Publishing: No. 0, Aug, 2010 - No. 15, Jan, 2012 ($1.00/$3.99)

0-(8/10, $1.00) Five covers; previews D&D series and Dark Sun mini-series 3.00
1-15: 1-(11/10, $3.99) Di Vito-a/Rogers-s; two covers. 2-Two covers 4.00
Annual 2012: Eberron (3/12, $7.99) Crilley-s/Diaz & Rojo-a 8.00
... 100 Page Spectacular (1/12, $7.99) Reprints by various incl. Duursema & Morales 8.00

DUNGEONS & DRAGONS: CUTTER
IDW Publishing: Apr, 2013 - No. 5, Sept, 2013 ($3.99)

1-5-R.A. & Geno Salvatore-s/Baldeon-a; 2 covers on each 4.00

DUNGEONS & DRAGONS: FORGOTTEN REALMS
IDW Publishing: Apr, 2012 - No. 5, Sept, 2012 ($3.99, limited series)

1-5-Greenwood-s/Ferguson-a 4.00
... 100 Page Spectacular (4/12, $7.99) Reprints by various incl. Rags Morales 8.00

DUNGEONS & DRAGONS: FROST GIANT'S FURY
IDW Publishing: Dec, 2016 - No. 5, Apr, 2017 ($3.99, limited series)

1-5-Jim Zub-s/Netho Diaz-a 4.00

DUNGEONS & DRAGONS: LEGENDS OF BALDUR'S GATE
IDW Publishing: Oct, 2014 - No. 5, Feb, 2016 ($3.99, limited series)

1-5-Jim Zub-s/Max Dunbar-a 4.00
... #1 Greatest Hits Collection (4/16, $1.00) reprints #1 3.00

DUNGEONS & DRAGONS: SHADOWS OF THE VAMPIRE
IDW Publishing: Apr, 2016 - No. 5, Aug, 2016 ($4.99/$3.99, limited series)

1-($4.99) Jim Zub-s/Nelson Dániel-a; 4 covers 5.00
2-5-($3.99) Three covers on each 4.00

DUNGEONS & DRAGONS: THE LEGEND OF DRIZZT: NEVERWINTER TALES
IDW Publishing: Aug, 2011 - No. 5, Dec, 2011 ($3.99, limited series)

1-5-R.A. & Geno Salvatore-s/Agustin Padilla-a 4.00

DURANGO KID, THE (Also see Best of the West, Great Western & White Indian)
(Charles Starrett starred in Columbia's Durango Kid movies)
Magazine Enterprises: Oct-Nov, 1949 - No. 41, Oct-Nov, 1955 (All 36 pgs.)

1-Charles Starrett photo-c; Durango Kid & his horse Raider begin; Dan Brand & Tipi (origin) begin by Frazetta & continue through #16 74 148 222 470 810 1150
2-Starrett photo-c. 34 68 102 199 325 450
3-5-All have Starrett photo-c. 29 58 87 172 281 390
6-10: 7-Atomic weapon-c/story 16 32 48 94 147 200
11-16-Last Frazetta issue 14 28 42 80 115 150
17-Origin Durango Kid 16 32 48 94 147 200
18-30: 18-Fred Meagher-a on Dan Brand begins.19-Guardineer-c/a(3) begins, end #41. 23-Intro. The Red Scorpion 10 20 30 54 72 90
31-Red Scorpion returns 9 18 27 52 69 85
32-41-Bolle/Frazetta*ish*-a (Dan Brand; true in later issues?)
9 18 27 50 65 80
NOTE: *#6, 8, 14, 15 contain* ***Frazetta*** *art not reprinted in White Indian.* ***Ayers*** *c-18.* ***Guardineer*** *a(3)-19-41; c-19-41.* ***Fred Meagher*** *a-18-29 at least.*

DURANGO KID, THE
AC Comics: 1990 - #2, 1990 ($2.50,$2.75, half-color)

1,2: 1-Starrett photo front/back-c; Guardineer-r. 2-B&W)-Starrett photo-c; White Indian-r by Frazetta; Guardineer-r (50th anniversary of films) 3.00

DV8 #24 © WSP

Dynamic Comics #11 © CHES

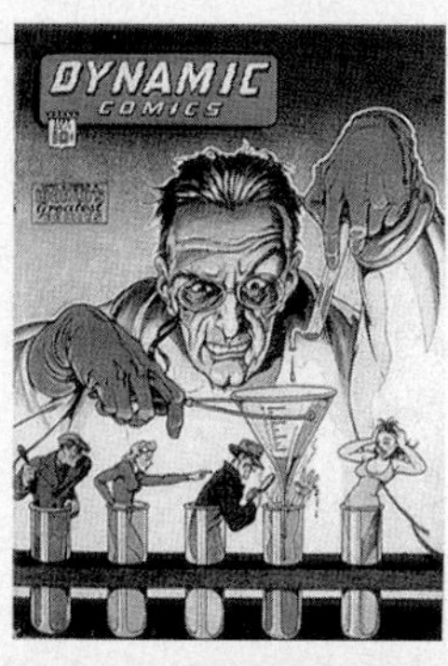

Dynamo #2 © TC

GD 2.0 | VG 4.0 | FN 6.0 | VF 8.0 | VF/NM 9.0 | NM- 9.2

DUSTCOVERS: THE COLLECTED SANDMAN COVERS 1989-1997
DC Comics (Vertigo): 1997 ($39.95, Hardcover)
Reprints Dave McKean's Sandman covers with Gaiman text 40.00
Softcover (1998, $24.95) 25.00

DUSTY STAR
Image Comics (Desperado Studios): No. 0, Apr, 1997 - No. 1 ($2.95, B&W)
0,1-Pruett-s/Robinson-a 3.00

DUSTY STAR
Image Comics (Desperado Publishing): June, 2006 ($3.50)
1-Pruett-s/Robinson-s/a 3.50

DV8 (See Gen 13)
Image Comics (WildStorm Productions): Aug, 1996 - No. 25, Dec, 1998;
DC Comics (WildStorm Prod.): No. 0, Apr, 1999 - No. 32, Nov, 1999 ($2.50)
1/2 6.00
1-Warren Ellis scripts & Humberto Ramos-c/a(p) 4.00
1-(7-variant covers, w/1 by Jim Lee) ...each 4.00
2-4: 3-No Ramos-a 3.00
5-32: 14-Regular-c, 14-Variant-c by Charest. 26-(5/99)-McGuinness-c 3.00
14-($3.50) Voyager Pack w/Danger Girl preview 5.00
0-(4/99, $2.95) Two covers (Rio and McGuinness) 3.00
Annual 1 (1/98, $2.95) 4.00
Annual 1999 ($3.50) Slipstream x-over with Gen13 4.00
Rave-(7/96, $1.75)-Ramos-c; pinups & interviews 3.00
...: Neighborhood Threat TPB (2002, $14.95) r/#1-6 & #1/2; Ellis intro.; Ramos-c 15.00

DV8: GODS AND MONSTERS
DC Comics (WildStorm): June, 2010 - No. 8, Jan, 2011 ($2.99, limited series)
1-8-Wood-s/Issacs-a 3.00
TPB (2011, $17.99) r/#1-8 18.00

DV8 VS. BLACK OPS
Image Comics (WildStorm): Oct, 1997 - No. 3, Dec, 1997 ($2.50, limited series)
1-3-Bury-s/Norton-a 3.00

DWIGHT D. EISENHOWER
Dell Publishing Co.: December, 1969
01-237-912 - Life story 4 8 12 28 47 65

DYNABRITE COMICS
Whitman Publishing Co.: 1978 - 1979 (69¢, 10x7-1/8", 48 pgs., cardboard-c)
(Blank inside covers)
11350 - Walt Disney's Mickey Mouse & the Beanstalk (4-C 157). 11350-1 - Mickey Mouse Album (4-C 1057, 1151,1246). 11351 - Mickey Mouse & His Sky Adventure (4-C 214, 343). 11354 - Goofy: A Gaggle of Giggles. 11354-1 - Super Goof Meets Super Thief. 11356 - (?). 11359 - Bugs Bunny-r. 11360 - Winnie the Pooh Fun and Fantasy (Disney-r).
each.... 2 4 6 10 14 18
11352 - Donald Duck (4-C 408, Donald Duck 45,52)-Barks-a. 11352-1 - Donald Duck (4-C 318, 10 pg. Barks/ WDC&S 125,128)-Barks-c(r). 11353 - Daisy Duck's Diary (4-C 1055,1150) Barks-a. 11355 - Uncle Scrooge (Barks-a/U.S. 12,33). 11355-1 - Uncle Scrooge (Barks-a/U.S. 13,16) - Barks-c(r). 11357 - Star Trek (r/-Star Trek 33,41). 11358 - Star Trek (r/-Star Trek 34,36). 11361 - Gyro Gearloose & the Disney Ducks (r/4-C 1047,1184)-Barks-c(r)
each.... 2 4 6 11 16 20

DYNAMIC ADVENTURES
I. W. Enterprises: No. 8, 1964 - No. 9, 1964
8-Kayo Kirby-r by Baker?/Fight Comics 53. 3 6 9 14 20 25
9-Reprints Avon's "Escape From Devil's Island"; Kinstler-c
3 6 9 16 23 30
nn (no date)-Reprints Risks Unlimited with Rip Carson, Senorita Rio; r/Fight #53
3 6 9 16 22 28

DYNAMIC CLASSICS (See Cancelled Comic Cavalcade)
DC Comics: Sept-Oct, 1978 (44 pgs.)
1-Neal Adams Batman, Simonson Manhunter-r 2 4 6 8 10 12

DYNAMIC COMICS (No #4-7)
Harry 'A' Chesler: Oct, 1941 - No. 3, Feb, 1942; No. 8, Mar, 1944 - No. 25, May, 1948
1-Origin Major Victory by Charles Sultan (reprinted in Major Victory #1), Dynamic Man & Hale the Magician; The Black Cobra only app.; Major Victory & Dynamic Man begin
252 504 756 1613 2757 3900
2-Origin Dynamic Boy & Lady Satan; intro. The Green Knight & sidekick Lance Cooper
155 310 465 992 1696 2400
3-1st small logo, resumes with #10 129 258 387 826 1413 2000
8-Classic-c; Dan Hastings, The Echo, The Master Key, Yankee Boy begin; Yankee Doodle Jones app.; hypo story 750 1500 2250 5000 8000 11,000

GD 2.0 | VG 4.0 | FN 6.0 | VF 8.0 | VF/NM 9.0 | NM- 9.2

9-Mr. E begins; Mac Raboy-c 123 246 369 787 1344 1900
10-Small logo begins 113 226 339 718 1234 1750
11-Classic-c 271 542 813 1734 2967 4200
12-16: 15-The Sky Chief app. 16-Marijuana story 77 154 231 493 847 1200
17(1/46)-Illustrated in **SOTI**, "The children told me what the man was going to do with the hot poker," but Wertham saw this in Crime Reporter #2
81 162 243 518 884 1250
18-Classic Airplanehead monster-c 77 154 231 493 847 1200
19-Classic puppeteer-c by Gattuso 77 154 231 493 847 1200
20-Bare-breasted woman-c 123 246 369 787 1344 1900
21-Dinosaur-c; new logo 55 110 165 352 601 850
22,25 48 96 144 302 514 725
23,24-(68 pgs.): 23-Yankee Girl app. 45 90 135 284 480 675
I.W. Reprint #1,8('64): 1-r/#23. 8-Exist? 3 6 9 17 26 35
NOTE: ***Kinstler** c-IW #1. **Tuska** art in many issues, #3, 9, 11, 12, 16, 19. Bondage c-16.*

DYNAMITE (Becomes Johnny Dynamite No. 10 on)
Comic Media/Allen Hardy Publ.: May, 1953 - No. 9, Sept, 1954
1-Pete Morisi-a; Don Heck-c; r-as Danger #6 41 82 123 256 428 600
2 22 44 66 132 216 300
3-Marijuana story; Johnny Dynamite (1st app.) begins by Pete Morisi(c/a); Heck text-a; man shot in face at close range 29 58 87 170 278 385
4-Injury-to-eye, prostitution; Morisi-c/a 26 52 78 154 252 350
5-9-Morisi-c/a in all. 7-Prostitute story & reprints 21 42 63 126 206 285

DYNAMO (Also see Tales of Thunder & T.H.U.N.D.E.R. Agents)
Tower Comics: Aug, 1966 - No. 4, June, 1967 (25¢)
1-Crandall/Wood, Ditko/Wood-a; Weed series begins; NoMan & Lightning cameos; Wood-c/a 8 16 24 54 105 150
2-4: Wood-c/a in all 5 10 15 34 60 85
NOTE: ***Adkins/Wood** a-2. **Ditko** a-4?. **Tuska** a-2, 3.*

DYNAMO 5 (See Noble Causes: Extended Family #2 for debut of Captain Dynamo)
Image Comics: Jan, 2007 - No. 25, Oct, 2009 ($3.50/$2.99)
1-Intro. the offspring of Captain Dynamo; Faerber-s/Asrar-a 8.00
2 5.00
3-7,11-24 : 5-Intro. Synergy. 13-Origin of Myriad. 21-Firebird app. 3.50
8-10-($2.99) 3.50
25-($4.99) Back-up short stories of team members 5.00
Annual #1 (4/08, $5.99) r/Captain Dynamo app. in Nobel Causes: Extended Family #2 and three new stories by Faerber & various; pin-up gallery 6.00
#0 (2/09, 99¢) short story leading into #20; text synopsis of story so far 3.00
...: Holiday Special 2010 (12/10, $3.99) Faerber-s/Takara-a 4.00
... Vol. 1: Post-Nuclear Family TPB (2007, $9.99) r/#1-7; Kirkman intro. 10.00
... Vol. 2: Moments of Truth TPB (2008, $14.99) r/#8-13 15.00

DYNAMO 5: SINS OF THE FATHER
Image Comics: Jun, 2010 - No. 5, Oct, 2010 ($3.99, limited series)
1-5-Faerber-s/Brilha-a. 2-4-Invincible app. 4.00

DYNAMO JOE (Also see First Adventures & Mars)
First Comics: May, 1986 - No. 15, Jan, 1988 (#12-15: $1.75)
1-15: 4-Cargonauts begin, Special 1(1/87)-Mostly-r/Mars 3.00

DYNOMUTT (TV)(See Scooby-Doo (3rd series))
Marvel Comics Group: Nov, 1977 - No. 6, Sept, 1978 (Hanna-Barbera)
1-The Blue Falcon, Scooby Doo in all 4 8 12 27 44 60
2-6-All newsstand only 3 6 9 17 26 35

EAGLE, THE (1st Series) (See Science Comics & Weird Comics #8)
Fox Feature Syndicate: July, 1941 - No. 4, Jan, 1942
1-The Eagle begins; Rex Dexter of Mars app. by Briefer; all issues feature German war covers 232 464 696 1485 2543 3600
2-The Spider Queen begins (origin) 142 284 426 909 1555 2200
3,4: 3-Joe Spook begins (origin) 135 270 405 864 1482 2100

EAGLE COMICS (2nd Series)
Rural Home Publ.: Feb-Mar, 1945 - No. 2, Apr-May, 1945
1-Aviation stories 84 168 252 538 919 1300
2-Lucky Aces 37 74 111 222 361 500
NOTE: ***L. B. Cole** c/a in each.*

EAGLE RESURGENT
American Mythology: 2016 ($4.99, B&W)
1-New story; Vokes-a/Herman-s; back-up reprint with art by Vokes & Rankin 5.00

EARTH 4 (Also see Urth 4)
Continuity Comics: Dec, 1993 - No. 4, Jan, 1994 ($2.50)

Earth 2 #1 © DC

East of West #22 © Hickman & Dragotta

Echo #16 © Terry Moore

GD 2.0 | VG 4.0 | FN 6.0 | VF 8.0 | VF/NM 9.0 | NM- 9.2

1-4: 1-3 all listed as Dec, 1993 in indicia 3.00

EARTH 4 DEATHWATCH 2000
Continuity Comics: Apr, 1993 - No. 3, Aug, 1993 ($2.50)
1-3 3.00

EARTH MAN ON VENUS (An...) (Also see Strange Planets)
Avon Periodicals: 1951
nn-Wood-a (26 pgs.); Fawcette-c 168 336 504 1075 1838 2600

EARTH 2
DC Comics: Jul, 2012 - No. 32, May, 2015 ($3.99/$2.99)
1-($3.99) James Robinson-s/Nicola Scott-a/Ivan Reis-c; 4.00
1-Variant-c by Hitch 6.00
2-15-($2.99) 2-New Flash. 3-New Green Lantern. 4-New Atom 3.00
15.1, 15.2 (11/13, $2.99, regular covers) 3.00
15.1 (11/13, $3.99, 3-D cover) "Desaad #1" on cover; Levitz-s/Cinar-a 5.00
15.2 (11/13, $3.99, 3-D cover) "Solomon Grundy #1" on cover; Kindt-s/Lopresti-a 5.00
16-24,26-30: 16-Superman returns. 17-Batman returns. 20-Jae Lee-c. 28-Lobo app. 3.00
25-($3.99) New Superman revealed 4.00
#0 (11/12, $2.99) Superman, Batman, Wonder Woman, Terry Sloan app.; Giorello-a 3.00
Annual 1 (7/13, $4.99) Robinson-s/Cafu-a; new Batman app. 5.00
Annual 2 (3/14, $4.99) Taylor-s/Rocha-a; origin of new Batman 5.00
...: Futures End 1 (11/14, $2.99, regular-c) Five years later; Barrows-a 3.00
...: Futures End 1 (11/14, $3.99, 3-D cover) 4.00

EARTH 2: SOCIETY
DC Comics: Aug, 2015 - No. 22, May, 2017 ($2.99)
1-22: 1-Johnny Sorrow app.; Dick Grayson as Batman. 4-Anarky app. 6-Intro. Hourman. 15-Tony Harris-a (8 pgs.) 3.00
Annual 1 (10/16, $4.99) Abnett-s/Redondo & Neves-a; The Ultra-Humanite app. 5.00

EARTH 2: WORLD'S END
DC Comics: Dec, 2014 - No. 26, Jun, 2015 ($2.99, weekly series)
1-25: 1-Prelude to Darkseid's first attack. 3,7,8,10-Constantine app. 3.00
26-($3.99) Andy Kubert-c; leads into Convergence #1 4.00

EARTHWORM JIM (TV, cartoon)
Marvel Comics: Dec, 1995 - No. 3, Feb, 1996 ($2.25)
1-3: Based on video game and toys 3.00

EARTH X
Marvel Comics: No. 0, Mar, 1999 - No. 12, Apr, 2000 ($3.99/$2.99, lim. series)
nn- (Wizard supplement) Alex Ross sketchbook; painted-c 6.00
Sketchbook (2/99) New sketches and previews 6.00
0-(3/99)-Prelude; Leon-a(p)/Ross-c 1 2 3 4 5 7
1-(4/99)-Leon-a(p)/Ross-c 1 2 3 4 5 7
1-2nd printing 4.00
2-12 4.00
#1/2 (Wizard) Nick Fury on cover; Reinhold-a 6.00
#X (6/00, $3.99) 4.00
... Trilogy Companion TPB (2008, $29.99) r/#1/2; artwork and content from the Earth X, Paradise X and Universe X series; gallery of variant covers and promotional art 30.00
HC (2005, $49.99) r/#0,1-12, #1/2, X; foreward by Joss Whedon; Ross sketch pages 50.00
TPB (12/00, $24.95) r/#0,1-12, X; foreward by Joss Whedon 25.00

EASTER BONNET SHOP (See March of Comics No. 29)

EASTER WITH MOTHER GOOSE
Dell Publishing Co.: No. 103, 1946 - No. 220, Mar, 1949
Four Color 103 (#1)-Walt Kelly-a 18 36 54 124 275 425
Four Color 140 ('47)-Kelly-a 14 28 42 94 207 320
Four Color 185 ('48), 220-Kelly-a 12 24 36 84 185 285

EAST MEETS WEST
Innovation Publishing: Apr, 1990 - No. 2, 1990 ($2.50, limited series, mature)
1,2: 1-Stevens part-i; Redondo-c(i). 2-Stevens-c(i); 1st app. Cheech & Chong in comics 3.00

EAST OF WEST
Image Comics: Mar, 2013 - Present ($3.50/$3.99)
1-Hickman-s/Dragotta-a 6.00
2-26-Hickman-s/Dragotta-a 3.50
27-36-($3.99) 4.00
... : The World (12/14, $3.99) Source book for characters, events, settings, timelines 4.00

EC ARCHIVES
Gemstone Publishing/Dark Horse Books: 2006 - Present ($49.95/$49.99, hardcover with dustjacket)
Crime SuspenStories Vol. 1 - Recolored reprints of #1-6; foreward by Max Allan Collins 50.00
Frontline Combat Vol. 1 - Recolored reprints of #1-6; foreward by Henry G. Franke III 50.00
Haunt of Fear Vol. 1 - Recolored reprints of #15-17,4-6; foreward by Robert Englund 50.00
Haunt of Fear Vol. 2 - Recolored reprints of #7-12; foreward by Tim Sullivan 50.00
Panic Vol. 1 - Recolored reprints of #1-6; foreward by Bob Fingerman 50.00
Shock SuspenStories Vol. 1 - Recolored reprints of #1-6; foreward by Steven Spielberg 50.00
Shock SuspenStories Vol. 2 - Recolored reprints of #7-12; foreward by Dean Kamen 50.00
Shock SuspenStories Vol. 3 - Recolored reprints of #13-18; foreward by Brian Bendis 50.00
Tales From the Crypt Vol. 1 - Recolored reprints of Crypt of Terror #17-19 and Tales From the Crypt #20-22; foreward by John Carpenter; Al Feldstein behind-the-scenes info 100.00
Tales From the Crypt Vol. 2 - Recolored reprints of #23-28; foreward by Joe Dante 50.00
Tales From the Crypt Vol. 3 - Recolored reprints of #29-34; foreward by Bob Overstreet 50.00
Tales From the Crypt Vol. 4 - (DH) Recolored reprints of #35-40; foreward by Russ Cochran 50.00
Tales From the Crypt Vol. 5 - (DH) Recolored reprints of #41-46; foreward by Bruce Campbell 50.00
Two-Fisted Tales Vol. 1 - Recolored reprints of #18-23; foreward by Stephen Geppi 50.00
Two-Fisted Tales Vol. 2 - Recolored reprints of #24-29; foreward by Rocco Versaci, Ph.D. 50.00
Two-Fisted Tales Vol. 3 - (DH) Recolored reprints of #30-35; foreward by Joe Kubert 50.00
Vault of Horror Vol. 1 - Recolored reprints of #12-17; foreward by R.L. Stine 50.00
Vault of Horror Vol. 2 - Recolored reprints of #18-23; foreward by John Landis 80.00
Vault of Horror Vol. 3 - (DH) Recolored reprints of #24-29; foreward by Mike Richardson 50.00
Vault of Horror Vol. 4 - (DH) Recolored reprints of #30-35; foreward by Jonathan Maberry 50.00
Weird Fantasy Vol. 1 - (DH) Recolored reprints of #13-17; foreward by Walt Simonson 50.00
Weird Science Vol. 1 - Recolored reprints of #1-6; foreward by George Lucas 75.00
Weird Science Vol. 2 - Recolored reprints of #7-12; foreward by Paul Levitz 50.00
Weird Science Vol. 3 - Recolored reprints of #13-18; foreward by Jerry Weist 50.00

E. C. CLASSIC REPRINTS
East Coast Comix Co.: May, 1973 - No. 12, 1976 (E.C. Comics reprinted in color minus ads)
1-The Crypt of Terror #1 (Tales from the Crypt #46) 2 4 6 11 16 20
2-12: 2-Weird Science #15('52). 3-Shock SuspenStories #12. 4-Haunt of Fear #12. 5-Weird Fantasy #13('52). 6-Crime SuspenStories #25. 7-Vault of Horror #26. 8-Shock SuspenStories #6. 9-Two-Fisted Tales #34. 10-Haunt of Fear #23. 11-Weird Science 12(#1). 12-Shock SuspenStories #2 2 4 6 8 11 14

EC CLASSICS
Russ Cochran: Aug, 1985 - No. 12, 1986? (High quality paper; each-r 8 stories in color) (#2-12 were resolicited in 1990)($4.95, 56 pgs., 8x11")
1-12: 1-Tales From the Crypt. 2-Weird Science. 3-Two-Fisted Tales (r/31); Frontline Combat (r/9). 4-Shock SuspenStories. 5-Weird Fantasy. 6-Vault of Horror. 7-Weird Science-Fantasy (r/23,24). 8-Crime SuspenStories (r/17,18). 9-Haunt of Fear (r/14,15). 10-Panic (r/1,2). 11-Tales From the Crypt (r/23,24). 12-Weird Science (r/20,22) 1 2 3 4 5 7

ECHO
Image Comics (Dreamwave Prod.): Mar, 2000 - No. 5, Sept, 2000 ($2.50)
1-5: 1-3-Pat Lee-c 3.00
0-(7/00) 3.00

ECHO
Abstract Studio: Mar, 2008 - No. 30, May, 2011 ($3.50)
1-Terry Moore-s/a/c 8.00
2-30 3.50
Terry Moore's Echo: Moon Lake TPB (2008, $15.95) r/#1-5; Moore sketch pages 16.00

ECHO OF FUTUREPAST
Pacific Comics/Continuity Com.: May, 1984 - No. 9, Jan, 1986 ($2.95, 52 pgs.)
1-9: Neal Adams-c/a in all? 6.00
NOTE: ***N. Adams*** *a-1-6,7i,9i; c-1-3, 5p,7i,8,9i.* ***Golden*** *a-1-6 (Bucky O'Hare); c-6.* ***Toth*** *a-6,7.*

ECLIPSE GRAPHIC ALBUM SERIES
Eclipse Comics: Oct, 1978 - 1989 (8-1/2x11") (B&W #1-5)
1-Sabre (10/78, B&W, 1st print.); Gulacy-a; 1st direct sale graphic novel 16.00
1-Sabre (2nd printing, 1/79) 8.00
1-Sabre (3rd printing, $5.95) 6.00
1-Sabre 30th Anniversary Edition (2008, $14.99, 9x6" HC) new McGregor & Gulacy intros. original script with sketch art 15.00
2,6,7: 2-Night Music (11/79, B&W)-Russell-a. 6-I Am Coyote (11/84, color)-Rogers-c/a. 7-The Rocketeer (2nd print, $7.95). 7-The Rocketeer (3rd print, 1991, $8.95) 10.00
3,4: 3-Detectives, Inc. (5/80, B&W, $6.95)-Rogers-a. 4-Stewart The Rat (1980, B&W) -G. Colan-a 10.00
5-The Price (10/81, B&W)-Starlin-a 20.00
7-The Rocketeer (9/85, color)-Dave Stevens-a (r/chapters 1-5)(see Pacific Presents & Starslayer); has 7 pgs. new-a 25.00
7-The Rocketeer, signed & limited HC 90.00
7-The Rocketeer, hardcover (1986, $19.95) 40.00
7-The Rocketeer, unsigned HC (3rd, $32.95) 33.00
8-Zorro In Old California ('86, color) 14.00
8,12-Hardcover 18.00

Eclipse Monthly #9 © ECL

Eclipso #4 © DC

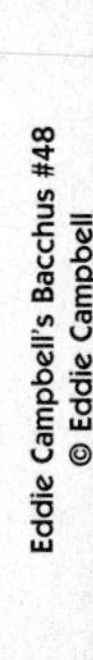
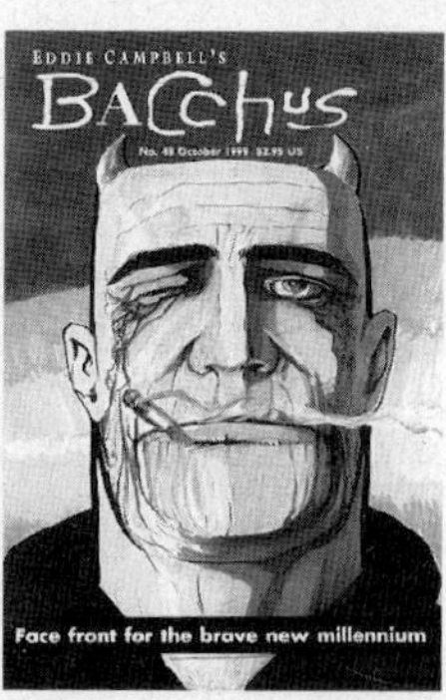

Eddie Campbell's Bacchus #48 © Eddie Campbell

	GD 2.0	VG 4.0	FN 6.0	VF 8.0	VF/NM 9.0	NM- 9.2

9,10: 9-Sacred And The Profane ('86)-Steacy-a. 10-Somerset Holmes ('86, $15.95)-Adults, soft-c 16.00
9,10,12-Hardcover ($24.95). 12-signed & #'d 25.00
11-Floyd Farland, Citizen of the Future ('87, $2.95, B&W) Chris Ware-s/a 15.00
12,28,31,35: 12-Silverheels ('87, $7.95, color). 28-Miracleman Book I ($5.95). 31-Pigeons From Hell by R. E. Howard (11/88). 35-Rael: Into The Shadow of the Sun ('88, $7.95)10.00
13-The Sisterhood of Steel ('87, $8.95, color) 10.00
14,16,18,20,23,24: 14-Samurai, Son of Death ('87, $4.95, B&W). 16,18,20,23-See Airfighters Classics #1-4. 24-Heartbreak ($4.95, B&W) 7.00
14 (2nd pr.),17,21: 14-Samurai, Son of Death ($3.95, 2nd printing). 17-Valkyrie, Prisoner of the Past SC ('88, $3.95, color). 21-XYR-Multiple ending comic ('88, $3.95, B&W) 6.00
15,22,27: 15-Twisted Tales (11/87, color)-Dave Stevens-c. 22-Alien Worlds #1 (5/88, $3.95, 52 pgs.)-Nudity. 27-Fast Fiction (She) ($5.95, B&W) 8.00
17-Valkyrie, Prisoner of the Past S&N Hardcover ('88, $19.95) 25.00
19-Scout: The Four Monsters ('88, $14.95, color)-r/Scout #1-7; soft-c 15.00
25,30,32-34: 25-Alex Toth's Zorro Vol. 1 ,2($10.95, B&W). 30-Brought To Light; Alan Moore scripts ('89). 32-Teenaged Dope Slaves and Reform School Girls. 33-Bogie. 34-Air Fighters Classics #5 12.00
29-Real Love: Best of Simon & Kirby Romance Comics (10/88, $12.95) 15.00
30,31: Limited hardcover ed. ($29.95). 31-signed 30.00
36-Dr. Watchstop: Adventures in Time and Space ('89, $8.95) 10.00

ECLIPSE MAGAZINE (Becomes Eclipse Monthly)
Eclipse Publishing: May, 1981 - No. 8, Jan, 1983 ($2.95, B&W, magazine)

1-8: 1-1st app. Cap'n Quick and a Foozle by Rogers, Ms. Tree by Beatty, and Dope by Trina Robbins. 2-1st app. I Am Coyote by Rogers. 7-1st app. Masked Man by Boyer 4.00
NOTE: ***Colan*** *a-3, 5, 8.* ***Golden*** *c/a-2.* ***Gulacy*** *a-6, c-1, 6.* ***Kaluta*** *c/a-5.* ***Mayerik*** *a-2, 3.* ***Rogers*** *a-1-8.* ***Starlin*** *a-1.* ***Sutton*** *a-6.*

ECLIPSE MONTHLY
Eclipse Comics: Aug, 1983 - No. 10, Jul, 1984 (Baxter paper, $2.00/$1.50/$1.75)

1-10: ($2.00, 52 pgs.)-Cap'n Quick and a Foozle by Rogers, Static by Ditko, Dope by Trina Robbins, Rio by Wildey, The Masked Man by Boyer begin. 3-Ragamuffins begins 4.00
NOTE: ***Boyer*** *c-6.* ***Ditko*** *a-1-3.* ***Rogers*** *a-1-4; c-2, 4, 7.* ***Wildey*** *a-1, 2, 5, 9, 10; c-5, 10.*

ECLIPSO (See Brave and the Bold #64, House of Secrets #61 & Phantom Stranger, 1987)
DC Comics: Nov, 1992 - No. 18, Apr, 1994 ($1.25)

1-18: 1-Giffen plots/breakdowns begin. 10-Darkseid app. Creeper in #3-6,9,11-13. 18-Spectre-c/s 3.00
Annual 1 (1993, $2.50, 68 pgs.)-Intro Prism 4.00
...: The Music of the Spheres TPB (2009, $19.99) r/stories from Countdown to Mystery #1-8 20.00

ECLIPSO: THE DARKNESS WITHIN
DC Comics: July, 1992 - No. 2, Oct, 1992 ($2.50, 68 pgs.)

1,2: 1-With purple gem attached to-c, 1-Without gem; Superman, Creeper app., 2-Concludes Eclipso storyline from annuals 4.00

EC SAMPLER - FREE COMIC BOOK DAY
Gemstone Publishing: May, 2008

Reprinted stories with restored color from Weird Science #6, Two-Fisted Tales #22, Crypt of Terror #17, Shock Suspenstories #6 3.00

E. C. 3-D CLASSICS (See Three Dimensional...)

ECTOKID (See Razorline)
Marvel Comics: Sept, 1993 - No. 9, May, 1994 ($1.75/$1.95)

1-($2.50)-Foil embossed-c; created by C. Barker 4.00
2-9: 2-Origin. 5-Saint Sinner x-over 3.00
...: Unleashed! 1 (10/94, $2.95, 52 pgs.) 4.00

ED "BIG DADDY" ROTH'S RATFINK COMIX (Also see Ratfink)
World of Fandom/ Ed Roth: 1991 - No. 3, 1991 ($2.50)

	GD	VG	FN	VF	VF/NM	NM-
1-3: Regular Ed., 1-Limited double cover	2	4	6	9	12	15

EDDIE CAMPBELL'S BACCHUS
Eddie Campbell Comics: May, 1995 - No. 60, May, 2001 ($2.95, B&W)

	GD	VG	FN	VF	VF/NM	NM-
1-Cerebus app.	1	2	3	5	6	8
1-2nd printing (5/97)						3.00
2-10: 9-Alex Ross back-c						5.00
11-60						3.00
Doing The Islands With Bacchus ('97, $17.95)						18.00
Earth, Water, Air & Fire ('98, $9.95)						10.00
King Bacchus ('99, $12.95)						13.00
The Eyeball Kid ('98, $8.50)						8.50

EDDIE STANKY (Baseball Hero)
Fawcett Publications: 1951 (New York Giants)

	GD	VG	FN	VF	VF/NM	NM-
nn-Photo-c	40	80	120	246	411	575

EDEN'S FALL (Characters from Postal, The Tithe, and Think Tank)
Image Comics (Top Cow): Aug, 2016 - Present ($3.99)

1-3-Matt Hawkins & Bryan Hill-s/Atilio Rojo-a 4.00

EDEN'S TRAIL
Marvel Comics: Jan, 2003 - No. 5, May 2003 ($2.99, unfinished lim. series, printed sideways)

1-5-Chuck Austen-s/Steve Uy-a 3.00

EDGAR ALLAN POE'S MORELLA AND THE MURDERS IN THE RUE MORGUE
Dark Horse Comics: Jun, 2015 ($3.99, one-shot)

1-Adaptation of Poe's poems; story and art by Richard Corben 4.00

EDGAR ALLAN POE'S THE CONQUEROR WORM
Dark Horse Comics: Nov, 2012 ($3.99, one-shot)

1-Adaptation of Poe's poem; story and art by Richard Corben; Corben sketch pages 4.00

EDGAR ALLAN POE'S THE FALL OF THE HOUSE OF USHER
Dark Horse Comics: May, 2013 - No. 2, Jun, 2013 ($3.99, limited series)

1,2-Adaptation of Poe's poem; story and art by Richard Corben; Corben sketch pages 4.00

EDGAR ALLAN POE'S - THE FALL OF THE HOUSE OF USHER AND OTHER TALES OF HORROR
Catlan Communications Pub.: Sept. 1985 (hardcover graphic novel)

nn-Reprints of Poe story issues from Warren comic mags; all Richard Corben-a; numbered edition of 350 signed by Corben; 60 pgs. 130.00
nn-Softcover edition 60.00

EDGAR ALLAN POE'S THE PREMATURE BURIAL
Dark Horse Comics: Apr, 2014 ($3.99, one-shot)

1-Adaptation of The Premature Burial and The Cask of Amontillado; Corben-s/a/c 4.00

EDGAR ALLAN POE'S THE RAVEN AND THE RED DEATH
Dark Horse Comics: Oct, 2013 ($3.99, one-shot)

1-Adaptation of The Raven and The Masque of the Red Death; Corben-s/a/c 4.00

EDGAR BERGEN PRESENTS CHARLIE McCARTHY
Whitman Publishing Co. (Charlie McCarthy Co.): No. 764, 1938 (36 pgs.; 15x10-1/2"; color)

	GD	VG	FN	VF	VF/NM	NM-
764	87	174	261	553	952	1350

EDGAR RICE BURROUGHS' TARZAN: A TALE OF MUGAMBI
Dark Horse Comics: 1995 ($2.95, one-shot)

1 3.00

EDGAR RICE BURROUGHS' TARZAN: IN THE LAND THAT TIME FORGOT AND THE POOL OF TIME
Dark Horse Comics: 1996 ($12.95, trade paperback)

nn-r/Russ Manning-a 13.00

EDGAR RICE BURROUGHS' TARZAN OF THE APES
Dark Horse Comics: May, 1999 ($12.95, trade paperback)

nn-reprints 13.00

EDGAR RICE BURROUGHS' TARZAN: THE LOST ADVENTURE
Dark Horse Comics: Jan, 1995 - No. 4, Apr, 1995 ($2.95, B&W, limited series)

1-4: ERB's last Tarzan story, adapted by Joe Lansdale 3.00
Hardcover (12/95, $19.95) 20.00
Limited Edition Hardcover ($99.95)-signed & numbered 100.00

EDGAR RICE BURROUGHS' TARZAN: THE RETURN OF TARZAN
Dark Horse Comics: May, 1997 - No. 3, July, 1997 ($2.95, limited series)

1-3 3.00

EDGAR RICE BURROUGHS' TARZAN: THE RIVERS OF BLOOD
Dark Horse Comics: Nov, 1999 - No. 4, Feb, 2000 ($2.95, limited series)

1-4-Kordey-c/a 3.00

EDGE
Malibu Comics (Bravura): July, 1994 - No. 3, Apr, 1995 ($2.50/$2.95, unfinished lim.series)

1,2-S. Grant-story & Gil Kane-c/a; w/Bravura stamp 3.00
3-($2.95-c) 3.00

EDGE (Re-titled as Vector starting with #13)
CrossGeneration Comics: May, 2002 - No. 12, Apr, 2003 ($9.95/$11.95/$7.95, TPB)

1-3: Reprints from various CrossGen titles 10.00
4-8-($11.95) 12.00
9-12-($7.95, 8-1/4" x 5-1/2") digest-sized reprints 8.00

EDGE OF CHAOS
Pacific Comics: July, 1983 - No. 3, Jan, 1984 (Limited series)

1-3-Morrow c/a; all contain nudity 3.00

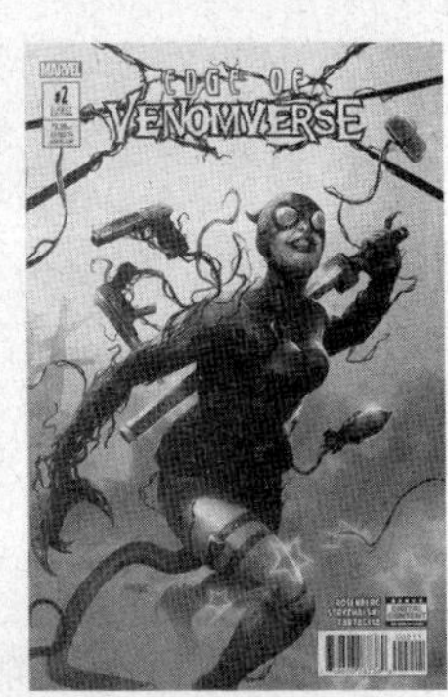

Edge of Venomverse #2 © MAR

Eerie #10 © AVON

Eerie #16 © WP

GD VG FN VF VF/NM NM-
2.0 4.0 6.0 8.0 9.0 9.2

EDGE OF DOOM (Horror anthology)
IDW Publishing: Oct, 2010 - No. 5, Mar, 2011 ($3.99)

1-5-Steve Niles-s/Kelley Jones-a 4.00

EDGE OF SPIDER-VERSE (See Amazing Spider-Man 2014 series #7-14)
Marvel Comics: Nov, 2014 - No. 5, Dec, 2014 ($3.99, limited series)

1,3-5: 1-Spider-Man Noir; Isanove-a. 3-Weaver-s/a. 5-Gerard Way-s 4.00
2-Gwen Stacy Spider-Woman 1st app.; Robbi Rodriguez-a/c 10.00

EDGE OF VENOMVERSE (Leads into Venomverse series)
Marvel Comics: Aug, 2017 - No. 5, Oct, 2017 ($3.99, limited series)

1-5: 1-Venom merges with X-23; Boschi-a. 2-Gwenpool/Venom; Daredevil app. 3-Ghost Rider. 4-Old Man Logan. 5-Deadpool; Stokoe-a 4.00

EDWARD SCISSORHANDS (Based on the movie)
IDW Publishing: Oct, 2014 - No. 10, Jul, 2015 ($3.99)

1-10-Kate Leth-s/Drew Rausch-a; multiple covers on each 4.00

ED WHEELAN'S JOKE BOOK STARRING FAT & SLAT (See Fat & Slat)

EERIE (Strange Worlds No. 18 on)
Avon Per.: No. 1, Jan, 1947; No. 1, May-June, 1951 - No. 17, Aug-Sept, 1954

1(1947)-1st supernatural comic; Kubert, Fugitani-a; bondage-c
703 1406 2109 5132 9066 13,000
1(1951)-Reprints story from 1947 #1 123 246 369 787 1344 1900
2-Wood-c/a; bondage-c 123 246 369 787 1344 1900
3-Wood-c; Kubert, Wood/Orlando-a 103 206 309 659 1130 1600
4,5-Wood-c 81 162 243 518 884 1250
6,8,13,14: 8-Kinstler-a; bondage-c; Phantom Witch Doctor story
48 96 144 302 514 725
7-Wood/Orlando-c; Kubert-a 61 122 183 390 670 950
9-Kubert-a; Check-c 52 104 156 328 552 775
10,11: 10-Kinstler-a. 11-Kinstlerish-a by McCann 52 104 156 328 552 775
12-Dracula story from novel, 25 pgs. 54 108 162 343 574 825
15-Reprints No. 1('51) minus-c(bondage) 39 78 117 231 378 525
16-Wood-a r-/No. 2 39 78 117 231 378 525
17-Wood/Orlando & Kubert-a; reprints #3 minus inside & outside Wood-c
39 78 117 231 378 525

NOTE: *Hollingsworth a-9-11; c-10, 11.*

EERIE
I. W. Enterprises: 1964

I.W. Reprint #1('64)-Wood-c(r); r-story/Spook #1 3 6 9 21 33 45
I.W. Reprint #2,6,8: 8-Dr. Drew by Grandenetti from Ghost #9
3 6 9 19 30 40
I.W. Reprint #9-r/Tales of Terror #1(Toby); Wood-c 4 8 12 23 37 50

EERIE (Magazine)(See Warren Presents)
Warren Publ. Co.: No. 1, Sept, 1965; No. 2, Mar, 1966 - No. 139, Feb, 1983

1-24 pgs., black & white, small size (5-1/4x7-1/4"), low distribution; cover from inside back cover of Creepy No. 2; stories reprinted from Creepy No. 7, 8. At least three different versions exist.
First Printing - B&W, 5-1/4" wide x 7-1/4" high, evenly trimmed. On page 18, panel 5, in the upper left-hand corner, the large rear view of a bald headed man blends into solid black and is unrecognizable. Overall printing quality is poor. 46 92 138 359 805 1250
Second Printing - B&W, 5-1/4x7-1/4", with uneven, untrimmed edges (if one of these were trimmed evenly, the size would be less than as indicated). The figure of the bald headed man on page 18, panel 5 is clear and discernible. The staples have a 1/4" blue stripe. 15 30 45 103 227 350
Other unauthorized reproductions for comparison's sake would be practically worthless. One known version was probably shot off a first printing copy with some loss of detail; the finer lines tend to disappear in this version which can be determined by looking at the lower right-hand corner of page one, first story. The roof of the house is shaded with straight lines. These lines are sharp and distinct on original, but broken on this version.

NOTE: ***The Overstreet Comic Book Price Guide** recommends that, before buying a 1st issue, you consult an expert.*

2-Frazetta-c; Toth-a; 1st app. host Cousin Eerie 10 20 30 70 150 230
3-Frazetta-c & half pg. ad (rerun in #4); Toth, Williamson, Ditko-a
9 18 27 58 114 170
4,6: 4-Frazetta-a (1/2 pg. ad) 6 12 18 38 69 100
5,7-Frazetta-c. Ditko-a in all 7 14 21 46 86 125
8-Frazetta-c; Ditko-a 8 16 24 52 99 145
9-11,25: 9,10-Neal Adams-a, Ditko-a. 11-Karloff Mummy adapt.-Wood-s/a. 25-Steranko-c
6 12 18 38 69 100
12-16,18-22,24,32-35,40,45: 12,13,20-Poe-s. 12-Bloch-s. 12,15-Jones-a. 13-Lovecraft-s. 14,16-Toth-a. 16,19,24-Stoker-s. 16,32,33,43-Corben-a. 34-Early Boris-c. 35-Early Brunner-a. 35,40-Early Ploog-a. 40-Frankenstein; Ploog-a (6/72, 6 months before Marvel's series) 4 8 12 28 47 65
17-(low distribution) 20 40 60 141 313 485
23-Frazetta-c; Adams-a(reprint) 10 20 30 64 132 200
26-31,36-38,43,44 4 8 12 25 40 55
39,41: 39-1st Dax the Warrior; Maroto-a. 41-(low distribution)
5 10 15 30 50 70
42,51: 42-('73 Annual, 84 pgs.) Spooktacular; Williamson-a. 51-('74 Annual, 76 pgs.) Color poster insert; Toth-a 4 8 12 28 47 65
46,48: 46-Dracula series by Sutton begins; 2pgs. Vampirella. 48-Begin "Mummy Walks" and "Curse of the Werewolf" series (both continue in #49,50,52,53)
4 8 12 25 40 55
47,49,50,52,53: 47-Lilith. 49-Marvin the Dead Thing. 50-Satanna, Daughter of Satan. 52-Hunter by Neary begins. 53-Adams-a 4 8 12 23 37 50
54,55-Color insert Spirit story by Eisner, reprints sections 12/21/47 & 6/16/46 54-Dr. Archaeus series begins 3 6 9 19 30 40
56,57,59,63,69,77,78: All have 8 pg. slick color insert. 56,57,77-Corben-a. 59-(100 pgs.) Summer Special, all Dax issue. 69-Summer Special, all Hunter issue, Neary-a. 78-All Mummy issue 3 6 9 19 30 40
58,60,62,68,72,: 8 pg. slick color insert & Wrightson-a in all. 58,60,62-Corben-a. 60-Summer Giant (9/74, $1.25) 1st Exterminator One; Wood-a. 62-Mummies Walk. 68-Summer Special (84 pgs.) 3 6 9 21 33 45
61,64-67,71: 61-Mummies Walk-s, Wood-a. 64-Corben-a. 64,65,67-Toth-a. 65,66-El Cid. 67-Hunter II. 71-Goblin-c/1st app. 3 6 9 17 26 35
70,73-75 3 6 9 14 20 26
76-1st app. Darklon the Mystic by Starlin-s/a 3 6 9 20 31 42
79,80-Origin Darklon the Mystic by Starlin 3 6 9 17 26 35
81,86,97: 81-Frazetta-c, King Kong; Corben-a. 86-(92 pgs.) All Corben issue. 97-Time Travel/ Dinosaur issue; Corben,Adams-a 3 6 9 16 23 30
82-Origin/1st app. The Rook 3 6 9 18 28 38
83,85,88,89,91-93,98,99: 98-Rook (31 pgs.). 99-1st Horizon Seekers.
2 4 6 10 14 18
84,87,90,96,100: 84,100-Starlin-a. 87-Hunter 3; Nino-a. 87,90-Corben-a. 96-Summer Special (92 pgs.). 100-(92 pgs.) Anniversary issue; Rook (30 pgs.)
2 4 6 13 18 22
94,95-The Rook & Vampirella team-up. 95-Vampirella-c; 1st MacTavish
3 6 9 16 24 32
101,106,112,115,118,120,121,128: 101-Return of Hunter II, Starlin-a. 106-Hard John Nuclear Hit Parade Special, Corben-a. 112-All Maroto issue, Luana-s. 115-All José Ortiz issues. 118-1st Haggarth. 120-1st Zud Kamish. 121-Hunter/Darklon. 128-Starlin-a, Hsu-a
2 4 6 10 14 18
102-105,107-111,113,114,116,117,119,122-124,126,127,129: 103-105,109-111-Gulacy-a. 104-Beast World. 2 4 6 9 13 16
125-(10/81, 84 pgs.) all Neal Adams issue 3 6 9 14 19 24
130-(76 pgs.) Vampirella-c/sty (54 pgs.); Pantha, Van Helsing, Huntress, Dax, Schreck, Hunter, Exterminator One, Rook app. 3 6 9 16 23 30
131-(Lower distr.); all Wood issue 3 6 9 14 20 26
132-134,136: 132-Rook returns. 133-All Ramon Torrents-a issue. 134,136-Color comic insert
2 4 6 10 14 18
135-(Lower distr., 10/82, 100 pgs.) All Ditko issue 3 6 9 14 20 26
137-139 (lower distr.):137-All Super-Hero issue. 138-Sherlock Holmes. 138,139-Color comic insert 2 4 6 13 18 22
Yearbook '70-Frazetta-c 5 10 15 33 57 80
Annual '71, '72-Reprints in both 4 8 12 25 40 55
... Archives - Volume One HC (Dark Horse, 3/09, $49.95, dustjacket) r/#1-5 50.00
... Archives - Volume Two HC (Dark Horse, 9/09, $49.95, dustjacket) r/#6-10; interview with Frank Frazetta from 1985 50.00

NOTE: *The above books contain art by many good artists:* ***N. Adams, Brunner, Corben, Craig (Taycee), Crandall, Ditko, Eisner, Evans, Jeff Jones, Krenkel, McWilliams, Morrow, Orlando, Ploog, Severin, Starlin, Torres, Toth, Williamson, Wood,*** *and* ***Wrightson****; covers by* ***Bode', Corben, Davis, Frazetta, Morrow,*** *and* ***Orlando. Frazetta*** *c-2, 3, 7, 8, 23. Annuals from 1973-on are included in regular numbering. 1970-74 Annuals are complete reprints. Annuals from 1975-on are in the format of the regular issues.*

EERIE
Dark Horse Comics: Jul, 2012 - Present ($2.99, B&W)

1-8-Sci-fi anthology by various. 2-Allred-a. 3-Wood-a(r). 4,6-Kelley Jones-a 3.00

EERIE ADVENTURES (Also see Weird Adventures)
Ziff-Davis Publ. Co.: Winter, 1951 (Painted-c)

1-Powell-a(2), McCann-a; used in **SOTI**; bondage-c; Krigstein back-c
90 180 270 576 988 1400

NOTE: *Title dropped due to similarity to Avon's Eerie & legal action.*

EERIE TALES (Magazine)
Hastings Associates: 1959 (Black & White)

1-Williamson, Torres, Tuska-a, Powell(2), & Morrow(2)-a
22 44 66 130 213 295

EERIE TALES
Super Comics: 1963-1964

Super Reprint No. 10,11,12,18: 10('63)-r/Spook #27. Purple Claw in #11,12 ('63); #12-r/Avon's Eerie #1('51)-Kida-r 3 6 9 16 24 32

Egypt #1 © Milligan & Dillon

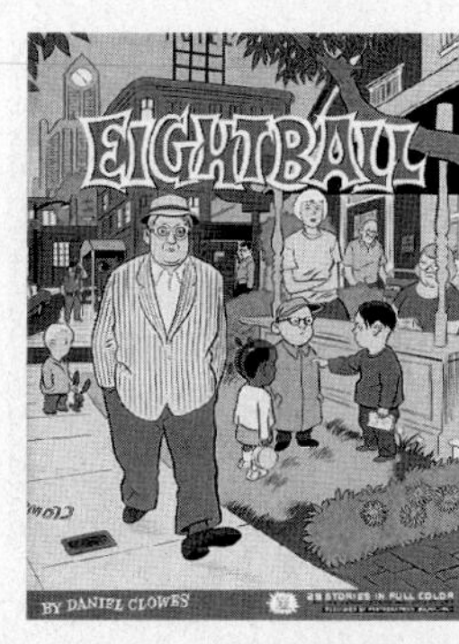

Eightball #22 © Dan Clowes

80 Page Giant #15 © DC

	GD 2.0	VG 4.0	FN 6.0	VF 8.0	VF/NM 9.0	NM- 9.2
15-Wolverton-a, Spacehawk-r/Blue Bolt Weird Tales #113; Disbrow-a	4	8	12	28	47	65

EFFIGY
DC Comics (Vertigo): Mar, 2015 - No. 7, Sept, 2015 ($2.99/$3.99)

	GD 2.0	VG 4.0	FN 6.0	VF 8.0	VF/NM 9.0	NM- 9.2
1-5: 1-Tim Seeley-s/Marley Zarcone-a						3.00
6,7-($3.99)						4.00

EGBERT
Arnold Publications/Quality Comics Group: Spring, 1946 - No. 20, Aug, 1950

	GD 2.0	VG 4.0	FN 6.0	VF 8.0	VF/NM 9.0	NM- 9.2
1-Funny animal; intro Egbert & The Count	21	42	63	126	206	285
2	12	24	36	67	94	120
3-10	9	18	27	52	69	85
11-20	8	16	24	42	54	65

EGYPT
DC Comics (Vertigo): Aug, 1995 - No.7, Feb, 1996 ($2.50, lim. series, mature)

	GD 2.0	VG 4.0	FN 6.0	VF 8.0	VF/NM 9.0	NM- 9.2
1-7: Milligan scripts in all.						3.00

EH! (...Dig This Crazy Comic) (From Here to Insanity No. 8 on)
Charlton Comics: Dec, 1953 - No. 7, Nov-Dec, 1954 (Satire)

	GD 2.0	VG 4.0	FN 6.0	VF 8.0	VF/NM 9.0	NM- 9.2
1-Davis-*ish*-c/a by Ayers, Wood-*ish*-a by Giordano; Atomic Mouse app.	41	82	123	250	418	585
2-Ayers-c/a	24	48	72	144	237	330
3,5,7	22	44	66	132	216	300
4,6: Sexual innuendo-c. 6-Ayers-a	27	54	81	158	259	360

EI8GT
Dark Horse Comics: Feb, 2015 - No. 5, Jun, 2015 ($3.50)

	GD 2.0	VG 4.0	FN 6.0	VF 8.0	VF/NM 9.0	NM- 9.2
1-Rafael Albuquerque-a/c; Mike Johnson-s						3.50

EIGHTBALL (Also see David Boring)
Fantagraphics Books: Oct, 1989 - Present ($2.75/$2.95/$3.95, semi-annually, mature)

	GD 2.0	VG 4.0	FN 6.0	VF 8.0	VF/NM 9.0	NM- 9.2
1 (1st printing) Daniel Clowes-s/a in all	10	20	30	64	132	200
2,3	3	6	9	14	19	24
4-8	2	4	6	8	11	14
9-19: 17-(8/96)	2	4	6	8	11	14
20-($4.50)	2	4	6	8	10	12
21-($4.95) Concludes David Boring 3-parter	2	4	6	8	10	12
22-($5.95) 29 short stories	2	4	6	8	10	12
23-($7.00, 9" x 12") The Death Ray	2	4	6	9	12	15
Twentieth Century Eightball (2002, $19.00) r/Clowes strips						20.00

EIGHTH WONDER, THE
Dark Horse Comics: Nov, 1997 ($2.95, one-shot)

	GD 2.0	VG 4.0	FN 6.0	VF 8.0	VF/NM 9.0	NM- 9.2
nn-Reprints stories from Dark Horse Presents #85-87						3.00

EIGHT IS ENOUGH KITE FUN BOOK (See Kite Fun Book 1979 in the Promotional Comics section)

EIGHT LEGGED FREAKS
DC Comics (WildStorm): 2002 ($6.95, one-shot, squarebound)

	GD 2.0	VG 4.0	FN 6.0	VF 8.0	VF/NM 9.0	NM- 9.2
nn-Adaptation of 2002 mutant spider movie; Joe Phillips-a; intro by Dean Devlin						7.00

1872 (Secret Wars tie-in)
Marvel Comics: Sept, 2015 - No. 4, Dec, 2015 ($3.99, limited series)

	GD 2.0	VG 4.0	FN 6.0	VF 8.0	VF/NM 9.0	NM- 9.2
1-4-Red Wolf in the western town of Timely in 1872. 4-Avengers of the West						4.00

80 PAGE GIANT (...Magazine No. 2-15)
National Periodical Publications: 8/64 - No. 15, 10/65; No. 16, 11/65 - No. 89, 7/71 (25¢)
(All reprints) (#1-56: 84 pgs.; #57-89: 68 pgs.)

	GD 2.0	VG 4.0	FN 6.0	VF 8.0	VF/NM 9.0	NM- 9.2
1-Superman Annual; originally planned as Superman Annual #9 (8/64)	34	68	102	245	548	850
2-Jimmy Olsen	18	36	54	125	276	430
3,4: 3-Lois Lane. 4-Flash-G.A.-r; Infantino-a	15	30	45	103	227	350
5-Batman; has Sunday newspaper strip; Catwoman-r; Batman's Life Story-r (25th anniversary special)	15	30	45	103	227	350
6-Superman	13	26	39	91	201	310
7-Sgt. Rock's Prize Battle Tales; Kubert-c/a	26	52	78	182	404	625
8-More Secret Origins-origins of JLA, Aquaman, Robin, Atom, & Superman; Infantino-a	26	52	78	182	404	625
9-15: 9-Flash (r/Flash #106,117,123 & Showcase #14); Infantino-a. 10-Superboy. 11-Superman; all Luthor issue. 12-Batman; has Sunday newspaper strip. 13-Jimmy Olsen. 14-Lois Lane. 15-Superman and Batman; Joker-c/story	12	24	36	82	179	275

Continued as part of regular series under each title in which that particular book came out, a Giant being published instead of the regular size. Issues No. 16 to No. 89 are listed for your information. See individual titles for prices. 16-JLA #39 (11/65), 17-Batman #176, 18-Superman #183, 19-Our Army at War #164, 20-Action #334, 21-Flash #160, 22-Superboy #129, 23-Superman #187, 24-Batman #182, 25-Jimmy Olsen #95, 26-Lois Lane #68, 27-Batman #185, 28-World's Finest #161, 29-JLA #48, 30-Batman #187, 31-Superman #193, 32-Our Army at War #177, 33-Action #347, 34-Flash #169, 35-Superboy #138, 36-Superman #197, 37-Batman #193, 38-Jimmy Olsen #104, 39-Lois Lane #77, 40-World's Finest #170, 41-JLA #58, 42-Superman #202, 43-Batman #198, 44-Our Army at War #190, 45-Action #360, 46-Flash #178, 47-Superboy #147, 48-Superman #207, 49-Batman #203, 50-Jimmy Olsen #113, 51-Lois Lane #86, 52-World's Finest #179, 53-JLA #67, 54-Superman #212, 55-Batman #208, 56-Our Army at War #203, 57-Action #373, 58-Flash #187, 59-Superboy #156, 60-Superman #217, 61-Batman #213, 62-Jimmy Olsen #122, 63-Lois Lane #95, 64-World's Finest #188, 65-JLA #76, 66-Superman #222, 67-Batman #218, 68-Our Army at War #216, 69-Adventure #390, 70-Flash #196, 71-Superboy #165, 72-Superman #227, 73-Batman #223, 74-Jimmy Olsen #131, 75-Lois Lane #104, 76-World's Finest #197, 77-JLA #85, 78-Superman #232, 79-Batman #228, 80-Our Army at War #229, 81-Adventure #403, 82-Flash #205, 83-Superboy #174, 84-Superman #239, 85-Batman #233, 86-Jimmy Olsen #140, 87-Lois Lane #113, 88-World's Finest #206, 89-JLA #93.

87TH PRECINCT (TV) (Based on the Ed McBain novels)
Dell Publishing Co.: Apr-June, 1962 - No. 2, July-Sept, 1962

	GD 2.0	VG 4.0	FN 6.0	VF 8.0	VF/NM 9.0	NM- 9.2
Four Color 1309(#1)-Krigstein-a	9	18	27	60	120	180
2-Photo-c	7	14	21	43	89	130

E IS FOR EXTINCTION (Secret Wars tie-in)
Marvel Comics: Aug, 2015 - No. 4, Nov, 2015 ($4.99/$3.99, limited series)

	GD 2.0	VG 4.0	FN 6.0	VF 8.0	VF/NM 9.0	NM- 9.2
1-($4.99) New X-Men in Mutopia; Burnham-s/Villalobos-a						5.00
2-4-($3.99) Cassandra Nova returns						4.00

EL BOMBO COMICS
Standard Comics/Frances M. McQueeny: 1946

	GD 2.0	VG 4.0	FN 6.0	VF 8.0	VF/NM 9.0	NM- 9.2
nn(1946), 1(no date)	17	34	51	100	158	215

EL CAZADOR
CrossGen Comics: Oct, 2003 - No. 6, Jun, 2004 ($2.95)

	GD 2.0	VG 4.0	FN 6.0	VF 8.0	VF/NM 9.0	NM- 9.2
1-Dixon-s/Epting-a						5.00
2-6: 5-Lady Death preview						3.00
...: The Bloody Ballad of Blackjack Tom 1 (4/04, $2.95, one-shot) Cariello-a						3.00

EL CID
Dell Publishing Co.: No. 1259, 1961

	GD 2.0	VG 4.0	FN 6.0	VF 8.0	VF/NM 9.0	NM- 9.2
Four Color 1259-Movie, photo-c	7	14	21	46	86	125

EL DIABLO (See All-Star Western #2 & Weird Western Tales #12)
DC Comics: Aug, 1989 - No. 16, Jan, 1991 ($1.50-$1.75, color)

	GD 2.0	VG 4.0	FN 6.0	VF 8.0	VF/NM 9.0	NM- 9.2
1 ($2.50, 52pgs.)-Masked hero						4.00
2-16						3.00

EL DIABLO
DC Comics (Vertigo): Mar, 2001 - No. 4, Jun, 2001 ($2.50, limited series)

	GD 2.0	VG 4.0	FN 6.0	VF 8.0	VF/NM 9.0	NM- 9.2
1-4-Azzarello-s/Zezelj-a/Sale-c						3.00
TPB (2008, $12.99) r/#1-4						13.00

EL DIABLO
DC Comics: Nov, 2008 - No. 6, Apr, 2009 ($2.99, limited series)

	GD 2.0	VG 4.0	FN 6.0	VF 8.0	VF/NM 9.0	NM- 9.2
1-6-Nitz-s/Hester-a/c. 4,5-Freedom Fighters app.						3.00

EL DORADO (See Movie Classics)

ELEANOR & THE EGRET
AfterShock Comics: Apr, 2017 - No. 5, Nov, 2017 ($3.99)

	GD 2.0	VG 4.0	FN 6.0	VF 8.0	VF/NM 9.0	NM- 9.2
1-5-John Layman-s/Sam Kieth-a/c						4.00

ELECTRIC ANT
Marvel Comics: Jun, 2010 - No. 5, Oct, 2010 ($3.99, Baxter paper)

	GD 2.0	VG 4.0	FN 6.0	VF 8.0	VF/NM 9.0	NM- 9.2
1-5-Based on a Philip K. Dick story; David Mack-s/Pascal Alixe-a; Paul Pope-c						4.00

ELECTRIC SUBLIME
IDW Publishing: Oct, 2016 - No. 4, Jan, 2017 ($3.99, limited series)

	GD 2.0	VG 4.0	FN 6.0	VF 8.0	VF/NM 9.0	NM- 9.2
1-4-W. Maxwell Prince-s/Martin Morazzo-a; two covers on each						4.00

ELECTRIC UNDERTOW (See Strikeforce Morituri: Electric Undertow)

ELECTRIC WARRIOR
DC Comics: May, 1986 - No. 18, Oct, 1987 ($1.50, Baxter paper)

	GD 2.0	VG 4.0	FN 6.0	VF 8.0	VF/NM 9.0	NM- 9.2
1-18						3.00

ELECTROPOLIS
Image Comics: May, 2001 - No. 4, Jan, 2003 ($2.95/$5.95)

	GD 2.0	VG 4.0	FN 6.0	VF 8.0	VF/NM 9.0	NM- 9.2
1-3-Dean Motter-s/a. 3-(12/01)						3.00
4-(1/03, $5.95, 72 pages) The Infernal Machine pts. 4-6						6.00

ELEKTRA (Also see Daredevil #319-325)
Marvel Comics: Mar, 1995 - No. 4, June, 1995 ($2.95, limited series)

	GD 2.0	VG 4.0	FN 6.0	VF 8.0	VF/NM 9.0	NM- 9.2
1-4-Embossed-c; Scott McDaniel-a						4.00

ELEKTRA (Also see Daredevil)
Marvel Comics: Nov, 1996 - No. 19, Jun, 1998 ($1.95)

	GD 2.0	VG 4.0	FN 6.0	VF 8.0	VF/NM 9.0	NM- 9.2
1-Peter Milligan scripts; Deodato-c/a						4.00
1-Variant-c						6.00

Elektra (2014 series) #2 © MAR

Elementals #6 © Bill Willingham

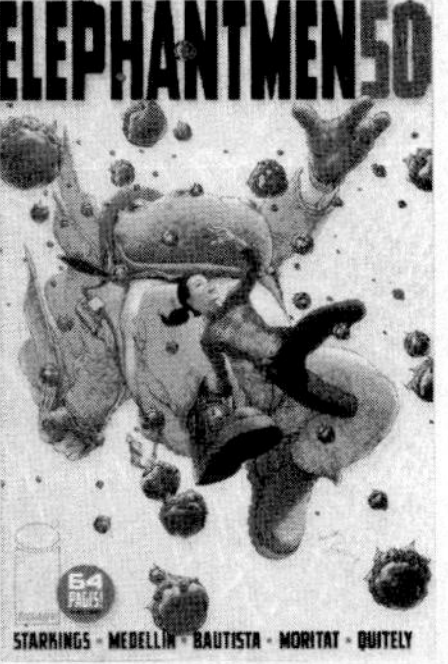

Elephantmen #50 © Active Images

GD 2.0 | VG 4.0 | FN 6.0 | VF 8.0 | VF/NM 9.0 | NM- 9.2

2-19: 4-Dr. Strange-c/app. 10-Logan-c/app. 3.00
#(-1) Flashback (7/97) Matt Murdock-c/app.; Deodato-c/a 3.00
.../Cyblade (Image, 3/97,$2.95) Devil's Reign pt. 7 3.00

ELEKTRA (Vol. 2) (Marvel Knights)
Marvel Comics: Sept, 2001 - No. 35, Jun, 2004 ($3.50/$2.99)

1-Bendis-s/Austen-a/Horn-c 4.00
2-6: 2-Two covers (Sienkiewicz and Horn) 3,4-Silver Samurai app. 3.00
3-Initial printing with panel of nudity; most copies pulped 40.00
7-35: 7-Rucka-s begin. 9,10,17-Bennett-a. 19-Meglia-a. 23-25-Chen-a; Sienkiewicz-c 3.00
...Vol. 1: Introspect TPB (2002, $16.99) r/#10-15; Marvel Knights: Double Shot #3 17.00
...Vol. 2: Everything Old is New Again TPB (2003, $16.99) r/#16-22 17.00
...Vol. 3: Relentless TPB (2004, $14.99) r/#23-28 15.00
...Vol. 4: Frenzy TPB (2004, $17.99) r/#29-35 18.00

ELEKTRA (All-New Marvel Now!)
Marvel Comics: Jun, 2014 - No. 11, May, 2015 ($3.99)

1-11: 1-Blackman-s/Del Mundo-a; multiple covers. 2,6,7-Lady Bullseye app. 4.00

ELEKTRA
Marvel Comics: Apr, 2017 - No. 5, Aug, 2017 ($3.99, limited series)

1-5: Matt Owens-s/Juann Cabal-a; Arcade app. 4.00

ELEKTRA & WOLVERINE: THE REDEEMER
Marvel Comics: Jan, 2002 - No. 3, Mar, 2002 ($5.95, square-bound, lim. series)

1-3-Greg Rucka-s/Yoshitaka Amano-a/c 6.00
HC (5/02, $29.95, with dustjacket) r/#1-3, interview with Greg Rucka 30.00

ELEKTRA: ASSASSIN (Also see Daredevil)
Marvel Comics (Epic Comics): Aug, 1986 - No. 8, June, 1987 (Limited series, mature)

1,8-Miller scripts in all; Sienkiewicz-c/a. 6.00
2-7 5.00
Signed & numbered hardcover (Graphitti Designs, $39.95, 2000 print run)- reprints 1-8 60.00
TPB (2000, $24.95) 25.00

ELEKTRA: GLIMPSE & ECHO
Marvel Comics: Sept, 2002 - No. 4, Dec, 2002 ($2.99, limited series)

1-4-Scott Morse-s/painted-a 3.00

ELEKTRA LIVES AGAIN (Also see Daredevil)
Marvel Comics (Epic Comics): 1990 ($24.95, oversize, hardcover, 76 pgs.)(Produced by Graphitti Designs)

nn-Frank Miller-c/a/scripts; Lynn Varley painted-a; Matt Murdock & Bullseye app. 40.00
2nd printing (9/02, $24.99) 25.00

ELEKTRA MEGAZINE
Marvel Comics: Nov, 1996 - No. 2, Dec, 1996 ($3.95, 96 pgs., reprints, limited series)

1,2: Reprints Frank Miller's Elektra stories in Daredevil 4.00

ELEKTRA SAGA, THE
Marvel Comics Group: Feb, 1984 - No. 4, June, 1984 ($2.00, limited series, Baxter paper)

1-4-r/Daredevil #168-190; Miller-c/a 5.00

ELEKTRA: THE HAND
Marvel Comics: Nov, 2004 - No. 5, Feb, 2005 ($2.99, limited series)

1-5-Gossett-a/Sienkiewicz-c/Yoshida-s; origin of the Hand in the 16th century 3.00

ELEKTRA: THE MOVIE
Marvel Comics: Feb, 2005 ($5.99)

1-Movie adaptation; McKeever-s/Perkins-a; photo-c 6.00
TPB (2005, $12.95) r/movie adaptation, Daredevil #168, 181 & Elektra #(-1) 13.00

ELEMENTALS, THE (See The Justice Machine & Morningstar Spec.)
Comico The Comic Co. : June, 1984 - No. 29, Sept, 1988; V2#1, Mar, 1989 - No. 28, 1994? ($1.50/$2.50, Baxter paper); V3#1, Dec, 1995 - No. 3 ($2.95)

1-Willingham-c/a, 1-8 5.00
2-29, V2#1-28: 9-Bissette-a(p). 10-Photo-c. V2#6-1st app. Strike Force America. 18-Prelude to Avalon mini-series. 27-Prequel to Strike Force America series 3.00
V3#1-3: 1-Daniel-a(p), bagged w/gaming card 3.00
Lingerie (5/96, $2.95) 3.00
Special 1,2 (3/86, 1/89)-1-Willingham-a(p) 3.00

ELEMENTALS: (Title series), **Comico**

--GHOST OF A CHANCE, 12/95 ($5.95)-graphic novel, nn-Ross-c. 6.00
--HOW THE WAR WAS WON, 6/96 - No. 2, 8/96 ($2.95) 1,2-Tony Daniel-a, & 1-Variant-c; no logo 3.00
--SEX SPECIAL, 1991 - No. 4, Feb, 1993 ($2.95, color) 2 covers for each 3.00
--SEX SPECIAL, 5/97 - No. 2, 6/97 ($2.95, B&W) 1-Tony Daniel, Jeff Moy-a, 2-Robb Phipps, Adam McDaniel-a 3.00
--SWIMSUIT SPECTACULAR 1996, 6/96 ($2.95), 1-pin-ups, 1-Variant-c; no logo 3.00
--THE VAMPIRE'S REVENGE, 6/96 - No. 2 8/96 ($2.95) 1,2-Willingham-s, 1-Variant-c; no logo 3.00

ELEPHANTMEN
Image Comics: July, 2006 - Present ($2.99/$3.50/$3.99) (Flip covers on most)

1-16: 1-Starkings-s/Moritat-a/Ladronn-c. 6-Campbell flip-c. 15-Sale flip-c 4.00
17-30-($3.50) 25-Flip book preview of Marineman 4.00
31-49,51-80-($3.99) 32-Conan/Red Sonja homage. 42-44-Dave Sim-a (5 pgs.) 4.00
50-($5.99) Flip book with reprint of #1; cover gallery 6.00
...: Man and Elephantman 1 (3/11, $3.99) Three covers 4.00
... Shots (5/15, $5.99) Reprints short stories from anthologies; art by Sim, Sale, & others 6.00
...: The Pilot (5/07, $2.99) short stories and pin-ups by various incl. Sale, Jim Lee, Jae Lee 4.00
...: War Toys (11/07 - No. 3, 4/08, $2.99) 1-3-Mappo war; Starkings-s/Moritat-a/Ladronn-c 4.00
... War Toys: Yvette (7/09, $3.50) Starkings-s/Moritat-a 4.00
Giant-Size Elephantmen 1 (10/11, $5.99) r/#31,32 & Man and Elephantman; Campbell-c 6.00

1111 (ELEVEN ELEVEN)
Crusade Entertainment: Oct, 1996 ($2.95, B&W, one-shot)

1-Wrightson-c/a 4.00

ELEVEN OR ONE
Sirius: Apr, 1995 ($2.95)

	GD 2.0	VG 4.0	FN 6.0	VF 8.0	VF/NM 9.0	NM- 9.2
1-Linsner-c/a	1	3	4	6	8	10
1-(6/96) 2nd printing						3.50

ELFLORD
Nightwind Productions: Jun, 1980 - Vol. 2 #1, 1982 (B&W, magazine-size)

	GD 2.0	VG 4.0	FN 6.0	VF 8.0	VF/NM 9.0	NM- 9.2
1-1st Barry Blair-s/c/a in comics; B&W-c; limited print run for all	10	20	30	64	132	200
2-5-B&W-c	5	10	15	31	53	75
6-14: 9-14-Color-c	4	8	12	27	44	60
Vol. 2 #1 (1982)	4	8	12	23	37	50

ELFLORD
Aircel Publ.: 1986 - No. 6, Oct, 1989 ($1.70, B&W); V2#1- V2#31, 1995 ($2.00)

1 4.00
2-4,V2#1-20,22-30: 4-6: Last B&W. V2#1-Color-a begin. 22-New cast. 25-Begin B&W 3.00
1,2-2nd printings 3.00
21-Double size ($4.95) 5.00

ELFLORD
Warp Graphics: Jan, 1997-No.4, Apr, 1997 ($2.95, B&W, mini-series)

1-4 3.00

ELFLORD (CUTS LOOSE) (Vol. 2)
Warp Graphics: Sept, 1997 - No. 7, Apr, 1998 ($2.95, B&W, mini-series)

1-7 3.00

ELFLORD: DRAGON'S EYE
Night Wynd Enterprises: 1993 ($2.50, B&W)

1 3.00

ELFLORD: THE RETURN
Mad Monkey Press: 1996 ($6.95, magazine size)

1 7.00

ELFQUEST (Also see Fantasy Quarterly & Warp Graphics Annual)
Warp Graphics, Inc.: No. 2, Aug, 1978 - No. 21, Feb, 1985 (All magazine size)
No. 1, Apr, 1979

NOTE: **Elfquest** was originally published as one of the stories in **Fantasy Quarterly** #1. When the publisher went out of business, the creative team, Wendy and Richard Pini, formed WaRP Graphics and continued the series, beginning with **Elfquest** #2. **Elfquest** #1, which reprinted the story from **Fantasy Quarterly**, was published about the same time **Elfquest** #4 was released. Thereafter, most issues were reprinted as demand warranted, until Marvel announced it would reprint the entire series under its Epic imprint (Aug., 1985).

	GD 2.0	VG 4.0	FN 6.0	VF 8.0	VF/NM 9.0	NM- 9.2
1(4/79)-Reprints Elfquest story from Fantasy Quarterly No. 1						
1st printing ($1.00-c)	6	12	18	41	76	110
2nd printing ($1.25-c)	2	4	6	9	12	15
3rd printings ($1.50-c)	1	2	3	5	6	8
4th printing; different-c ($1.50-c)						5.00
2(8/78) 1st printing ($1.00-c)	3	6	9	27	44	60
2nd printings ($1.25-c)						6.00
3rd & 4th printings ($1.50-c)(all 4th prints 1989)						5.00
3-5: 1st printings ($1.00-c)	3	6	9	16	23	30
6-9: 1st printings ($1.25-c)	3	6	9	14	20	25
2nd & 3rd printings ($1.50-c)						5.00
10-21: ($1.50-c); 16-8pg. preview of A Distant Soil	2	4	6	11	16	20

Elfquest New Blood #18 © Warp Graphics

Ella Cinders #3 © STJ

Elongated Man #4 © DC

	GD 2.0	VG 4.0	FN 6.0	VF 8.0	VF/NM 9.0	NM- 9.2

10-14: 2nd printings ($1.50) 5.00

ELFQUEST
Marvel Comics (Epic Comics): Aug, 1985 - No. 32, Mar, 1988
1-Reprints in color the Elfquest epic by Warp Graphics 5.00
2-32 4.00

ELFQUEST
DC Comics: 2003 - 2005
Archives Vol. 1 (2003, $49.95, HC) r/#1-5 50.00
Archives Vol. 2 (2005, $49.95, HC) r/#6-10 & Epic Illustrated #1 50.00
25th Anniversary Special (2003, $2.95) r/Elfquest #1 (Apr, 1979); interview w/Pinis 4.00

ELFQUEST (Title series), Warp Graphics
'89 - No. 4, '89 ($1.50, B&W) 1-4: R-original Elfquest series 4.00

ELFQUEST (Volume 2),**Warp Graphics:** V2#1, 5/96 - No. 33, 2/99 ($4.95/$2.95, B&W)
V2#1-31: 1,3,5,8,10,12,13,18,21,23,25-Wendy Pini-c 6.00
32,33-($2.95-c) 4.00

--BLOOD OF TEN CHIEFS, 7/93 - No. 20, 9/95 ($2.00/$2.50)
1-20-By Richard & Wendy Pini 4.00

--HIDDEN YEARS, 5/92 - No. 29, 3/96 ($2.00/$2.25)1-9,9 1/2, 10-29 4.00

--JINK, 11/94 - No. 12, 2/6 ($2.25/$2.50) 1-12-W. Pini/John Byrne-back-c 4.00

--KAHVI, 10/95 - No. 6,3/96 ($2.25, B&W) 1-6 4.00

--KINGS CROSS, 11/97 - No. 2, 12/97 ($2.95, B&W) 1,2 4.00

--KINGS OF THE BROKEN WHEEL, 6/90 - No. 9, 2/92 ($2.00, B&W) (3rd Elfquest saga)
1-9: By R. & W. Pini; 1-Color insert 5.00
1-2nd printing 4.00

--METAMORPHOSIS, 4/96 ($2.95, B&W) 1 4.00

--NEW BLOOD (...Summer Special on-c #1 only), 8/92 - No. 35, 1/96 ($2.00-$2.50, color/B&W) 1-($3.95, 68 pgs.,...Summer Special on-c)-Byrne-a/scripts (16 pgs.) 5.00
2-35: Barry Blair-a in all 4.00
1993 Summer Special ($3.95) Byrne-a/scripts 5.00

--SHARDS, 8/94 - No. 16, 3/96 ($2.25/$2.50) 1-16 4.00

--SIEGE AT BLUE MOUNTAIN, WaRP Graphics/Apple 3/87 - No. 8, 12/88 (1.75/ $1.95, B&W)
1-Staton-a(i) in all; 2nd Elfquest saga 1 2 3 5 6 8
1-3-2nd printing 4.00
2-8 5.00

--THE REBELS, 11/94 - No. 12, 3/96 ($2.25/$2.50, B&W/color) 1-12 4.00

--TWO-SPEAR, 10/95 - No. 5, 2/96 ($2.25, B&W) 1-5 4.00

--WAVE DANCERS, 12/93 - No. 6, 3/96, 1-6: 1-Foil-c & poster 4.00
Special 1 ($2.95) 4.00

--WORLDPOOL, 7/97 ($2.95, B&W) 1-Richard Pini-s/Barry Blair-a 4.00

ELFQUEST: THE DISCOVERY
DC Comics: Mar, 2006 - No. 4, Sept, 2006 ($3.99, limited series)
1-4-Wendy Pini-a/Wendy & Richard Pini-s 5.00
TPB (2006, $14.99) r/#1-4 15.00

ELFQUEST: THE FINAL QUEST
Dark Horse Comics: Oct, 2013; No. 1, Jan, 2014 - No. 24, Feb, 2018 ($3.50/$3.99)
1-14-Wendy Pini-a/Wendy & Richard Pini-s 3.50
15-24-($3.99) 4.00
... Special (10/13, $5.99) Wendy Pini-a/Wendy & Richard Pini-s; prologue to series 6.00

ELFQUEST: THE GRAND QUEST
DC Comics: 2004 - No. 14, 2006 ($9.95/$9.99, B&W, digest-size)
Vol. 1-6 ('04)1-r/Elfquest #1-5; new W. Pini-c. 2-r/#5-8. 3-r/#8-11. 4-r/#11-15. 5-r/#15-18 6-r/#18-20 10.00
Vol. 7-9 ('05) 1-r/Siege At Blue Mountain #1-3. 8-r/SABM #3-5. 9-r/SABM #6-8 10.00
Vol. 10-14 ('05) 10-r/Kings of the Broken Wheel #1-3. 11-KotBW #5-7 & Frazetta Fant. Ill. 12-r/Kings of the Broken Wheel #8&9. 13-r/Elfquest V2 #4-18. 14-r/Hidden Years #4-9 1/2 10.00

ELFQUEST: THE SEARCHER AND THE SWORD
DC Comics: 2004 ($24.95/$14.99, graphic novel)
HC (2004, $24.95, with dust jacket)-Wendy and Richard Pini-s/a/c 25.00
SC (2004, $14.99) 15.00

ELFQUEST: WOLFRIDER
DC Comics: 2003 - No. 2, 2003 ($9.95, digest-size)
Volume 1 ('03, $9.95, digest-size) r/Elfquest V2#19,21,23,25,27,29,31; Blood of Ten Chiefs #2; Hidden Years #5; New Blood Special #1; New Blood 1993 Special #1; new W. Pini-c 10.00
Volume 2 ('03, $9.95, digest-size) r/Elfquest V2#33; Blood of Ten Chiefs #10,11,19; Warp Graphics Annual #1 10.00

ELF-THING
Eclipse Comics: March, 1987 ($1.50, B&W, one-shot)
1 3.00

ELIMINATOR (Also see The Solution #16 & The Night Man #16)
Malibu Comics (Ultraverse): Apr, 1995 - No. 3, Jul, 1995 ($2.95/$2.50, lim. series)
0-Mike Zeck-a in all 3.00
1-3-($2.50): 1-1st app. Siren 3.00
1-($3.95)-Black cover edition 4.00

ELIMINATOR FULL COLOR SPECIAL
Eternity Comics: Oct, 1991 ($2.95, one-shot)
1-Dave Dorman painted-c 3.00

ELLA CINDERS (See Comics On Parade, Comics Revue #1,4, Famous Comics Cartoon Book, Giant Comics Editions, Sparkler Comics, Tip Top & Treasury of Comics)

ELLA CINDERS
United Features Syndicate: 1938 - 1940

	GD	VG	FN	VF	VF/NM	NM-
Single Series 3(1938)	43	86	129	271	461	650
Single Series 21(#2 on-c, #21 on inside), 28('40)	37	74	111	222	361	500

ELLA CINDERS
United Features Syndicate: Mar, 1948 - No. 5, Mar, 1949

	GD	VG	FN	VF	VF/NM	NM-
1-(#2 on cover)	15	30	45	90	140	190
2	11	22	33	60	83	105
3-5	9	18	27	47	61	75

ELLERY QUEEN
Superior Comics Ltd.: May, 1949 - No. 4, Nov, 1949

	GD	VG	FN	VF	VF/NM	NM-
1-Kamen-c; L.B. Cole-a; r-in Haunted Thrills	53	106	159	334	567	800
2-4: 3-Drug use stories(2)	39	78	117	240	395	550

NOTE: *Iger shop art in all issues.*

ELLERY QUEEN (TV)
Ziff-Davis Publishing Co.: 1-3/52 (Spring on-c) - No. 2, Summer/52 (Saunders painted-c)

	GD	VG	FN	VF	VF/NM	NM-
1-Saunders-c	47	94	141	296	498	700
2-Saunders bondage, torture-c	39	78	117	231	378	525

ELLERY QUEEN (Also see Crackajack Funnies No. 23)
Dell Publishing Co.: No. 1165, Mar-May, 1961 - No.1289, Apr, 1962

	GD	VG	FN	VF	VF/NM	NM-
Four Color 1165 (#1)	9	18	27	58	114	175
Four Color 1243 (11/61-1/62), 1289	7	14	21	48	89	130

ELMER FUDD (Also see Camp Comics, Daffy, Looney Tunes #1 & Super Book #10, 22)
Dell Publishing Co.: No. 470, May, 1953 - No. 1293, Mar-May, 1962

	GD	VG	FN	VF	VF/NM	NM-
Four Color 470 (#1)	10	20	30	64	132	200
Four Color 558,628,689('56)	6	12	18	38	69	100
Four Color 725,783,841,888,938,977,1032,1081,1131,1171,1222,1293('62)	5	10	15	33	57	80

ELMO COMICS
St. John Publishing Co.: Jan, 1948 (Daily strip-r)

	GD	VG	FN	VF	VF/NM	NM-
1-By Cecil Jensen	12	24	36	67	94	120

ELONGATED MAN (See Flash #112 & Justice League of America #105)
DC Comics: Jan, 1992 - No. 4, Apr, 1992 ($1.00, limited series)
1-4: 3-The Flash app. 3.00

ELRIC (Of Melnibone)(See First Comics Graphic Novel #6 & Marvel Graphic Novel #2)
Pacific Comics: Apr, 1983 - No. 6, Apr, 1984 ($1.50, Baxter paper)
1-6: Russell-c/a(i) in all 3.00

ELRIC
Topps Comics: 1996 ($2.95, one-shot)
0-One Life: Russell-c/a; adapts Neil Gaiman's short story "One Life--Furnished in Early Moorcock." 3.00

ELRIC, SAILOR ON THE SEAS OF FATE
First Comics: June, 1985 - No. 7, June, 1986 ($1.75, limited series)
1-7: Adapts Michael Moorcock's novel 3.00

ELRIC, STORMBRINGER
Dark Horse Comics/Topps Comics: 1997 - No. 7, 1997 ($2.95, limited series)
1-7: Russell-c/s/a; adapts Michael Moorcock's novel 3.00

ELRIC: THE BALANCE LOST
BOOM! Studios: Jul, 2011 - No. 12, Jun, 2012 ($3.99)
1-12: 1-Roberson-s/Biagini-a; four covers. 2-11-Three covers 4.00

Elsewhere #1 © Faerber & Kesgin

Elvira's House of Mystery #7 © DC

Emma #1 © MAR

GD 2.0 | VG 4.0 | FN 6.0 | VF 8.0 | VF/NM 9.0 | NM- 9.2

GD 2.0 | VG 4.0 | FN 6.0 | VF 8.0 | VF/NM 9.0 | NM- 9.2

ELRIC: THE BANE OF THE BLACK SWORD
First Comics: Aug, 1988 - No. 6, June, 1989 ($1.75/$1.95, limited series)
1-6: Adapts Michael Moorcock's novel 3.00

ELRIC: THE VANISHING TOWER
First Comics: Aug, 1987 - No. 6, June, 1988 ($1.75, limited series)
1-6: Adapts Michael Moorcock's novel 3.00

ELRIC: WEIRD OF THE WHITE WOLF
First Comics: Oct, 1986 - No. 5, June, 1987 ($1.75, limited series)
1-5: Adapts Michael Moorcock's novel 3.00

EL SALVADOR - A HOUSE DIVIDED
Eclipse Comics: March, 1989 ($2.50, B&W, Baxter paper, stiff-c, 52 pgs.)
1-Gives history of El Salvador 4.00

ELSEWHERE
Image Comics: Aug, 2017 - Present ($3.99)
1-5: 1-Jay Faerber-s/Sumeyye Kesgin-a; Amelia Earhart & DB Cooper app. 4.00

ELSEWHERE PRINCE, THE (Moebius' Airtight Garage)
Marvel Comics (Epic): May, 1990 - No. 6, Oct, 1990 ($1.95, limited series)
1-6: Moebius scripts & back-up-a in all 3.00

ELSEWORLDS 80-PAGE GIANT (See DC Comics Presents: ... for reprint)
DC Comics: Aug, 1999 ($5.95, one-shot)
1-Most copies destroyed by DC over content of the "Superman's Babysitter" story; some UK shipments sold before recall 12 24 36 83 182 280

ELSEWORLD'S FINEST
DC Comics: 1997 - No. 2, 1997 ($4.95, limited series)
1,2: Elseworld's story-Superman & Batman in the 1920's 5.00

ELSEWORLD'S FINEST: SUPERGIRL & BATGIRL
DC Comics: 1998 ($5.95, one-shot)
1-Haley-a 6.00

ELSIE THE COW
D. S. Publishing Co.: Oct-Nov, 1949 - No. 3, July-Aug, 1950
1-(36 pgs.) 29 58 87 174 285 395
2,3 20 40 60 115 185 255

ELSINORE
Alias Entertainment: Apr, 2005 - No. 5, Apr, 2006 (75¢/$2.99/$3.25)
1-5: 1-(75¢-c) Brian Denham-a/Kenneth Lillie-Paetz-s. 2-($2.99-c). 4-($3.25-c) 5-Sparacio-a 3.25

ELSON'S PRESENTS
DC Comics: 1981 (100 pgs., no cover price)
Series 1-6: Repackaged 1981 DC comics; 1-DC Comics Presents #29, Flash #303, Batman #331. 2-Superman #335, Ghosts #96, Justice League of America #186. 3-New Teen Titans #3, Secrets of Haunted House #32, Wonder Woman #275. 4-Secrets of the LSH #1, Brave & the Bold #170, New Adv. of Superboy #13. 5-LSH #271, Green Lantern #136, Super Friends #40. 6-Action #515, Mystery in Space #115, Detective #498 2 4 6 11 16 20

ELTINGVILLE CLUB, THE (Characters from Dork)
Dark Horse Comics: Apr, 2014 - No. 2, Aug, 2015 ($3.99, B&W, limited series)
1,2-Evan Dorkin-s/a 4.00
HC-(2/16, $19.99) Reprints #1,2 and stories from Dork, Instant Piano, DHP 20.00

ELVEN (Also see Prime)
Malibu Comics (Ultraverse): Oct, 1994 - No. 4, Feb, 1995 ($2.50, lim. series)
0 ($2.95)-Prime app. 3.00
1-4: 2,4-Prime app. 3-Primevil app. 3.00
1-Limited Foil Edition- no price on cover 4.00

ELVIRA MISTRESS OF THE DARK
Marvel Comics: Oct, 1988 ($2.00, B&W, magazine size)
1-Movie adaptation 5.00

ELVIRA MISTRESS OF THE DARK
Claypool Comics (Eclipse): May, 1993 - No. 166, Feb, 2007 ($2.50, B&W)
1-Austin-a(i). Spiegle-a 6.00
2-6: Spiegle-a 4.00
7-99,101-166-Photo-c: 3.00
100-(8/01) Kurt Busiek back-up-s; art by DeCarlo and others 4.00
TPB ($12.95) 13.00

ELVIRA'S HOUSE OF MYSTERY
DC Comics: Jan, 1986 - No. 11, Jan, 1987
1,11: 11-Dave Stevens-c 2 4 6 10 14 18
2-10: 9-Photo-c, Special 1 (3/87, $1.25) 6.00

ELVIS MANDIBLE, THE
DC Comics (Piranha Press): 1990 ($3.50, 52 pgs., B&W, mature)
nn 4.00

ELVIS PRESLEY (See Career Girl Romances #32, Go-Go, Howard Chaykin's American Flagg #10, Humbug #8, I Love You #60 & Young Lovers #18)

EL ZOMBO FANTASMA
Dark Horse Comics (Rocket Comics): Apr, 2004 - No. 3, June, 2004 ($2.99)
1-3-Wilkins-s&a/Munroe-s 3.00

E-MAN
Charlton Comics: Oct, 1973 - No. 10, Sept, 1975 (Painted-c No. 7-10)
1-Origin & 1st app. E-Man; Staton c/a in all 3 6 9 16 23 30
2-5: 2,4,5-Ditko-a. 3-Howard-a. 5-Miss Liberty Belle app. by Ditko 2 4 6 9 12 15
6-10: 6,7,9,10-Early Byrne-a (#6 is 1/75). 6-Disney parody. 8-Full-length story; Nova begins as E-Man's partner 2 4 6 11 16 20
1-4,9,10 (Modern Comics reprints, '77) 5.00
NOTE: *Killjoy app.-No. 2, 4. Liberty Belle app.-No. 5. Rog 2000 app.-No. 6, 7, 9, 10. Travis app.-No. 3.* ***Sutton*** *a-1.*

E-MAN
Comico: Sept, 1989 ($2.75, one-shot, no ads, high quality paper)
1-Staton-c/a; Michael Mauser story 3.00

E-MAN
Comico: V4#1, Jan, 1990 - No. 3, Mar, 1990 ($2.50, limited series)
1-3: Staton-c/a 3.00

E-MAN
Alpha Productions: Oct, 1993 ($2.75)
V5#1-Staton-c/a; 20th anniversary issue 3.00

E-MAN COMICS (Also see Michael Mauser & The Original E-Man)
First Comics: Apr, 1983 - No. 25, Aug, 1985 ($1.00/$1.25, direct sales only)
1-25: 2-X-Men satire. 3-X-Men/Phoenix satire. 6-Origin retold. 8-Cutey Bunny app. 10-Origin Nova Kane. 24-Origin Michael Mauser 3.00
NOTE: ***Staton*** *a-1-5, 6-25p; c-1-25.*

E-MAN RETURNS
Alpha Productions: 1994 ($2.75, B&W)
1-Joe Staton-c/a(p) 3.00

EMERALD CITY OF OZ, THE (Dorothy Gale from Wonderful Wizard of Oz)
Marvel Comics: Sept, 2013 - No. 5, Feb, 2014 ($3.99, limited series)
1-5-Eric Shanower-s/Skottie Young-a/c 4.00

EMERALD DAWN
DC Comics: 1991 ($4.95, trade paperback)
nn-Reprints Green Lantern: Emerald Dawn #1-6 1 2 3 5 6 8

EMERALD DAWN II (See Green Lantern...)

EMERGENCY (Magazine)
Charlton Comics: June, 1976 - No. 4, Jan, 1977 (B&W)
1-Neal Adams-c/a; Heath, Austin-a 4 8 12 23 37 50
2,3: 2-N. Adams-c. 3-N. Adams-a. 3 6 9 18 28 38
4-Alcala-a 3 6 9 14 20 25

EMERGENCY (TV)
Charlton Comics: June, 1976 - No. 4, Dec, 1976
1-Staton-c; early Byrne-a (22 pages) 3 6 9 19 30 40
2-4: 2-Staton-c. 2,3-Byrne text illos. 3 6 9 14 20 25

EMERGENCY DOCTOR
Charlton Comics: Summer, 1963 (one-shot)
1 3 6 9 19 30 40

EMIL & THE DETECTIVES (See Movie Comics)

EMISSARY (Jim Valentino's...)
Image Comics (Shadowline): May, 2006 - No. 6 ($3.50)
1-6: 1-Rand-s/Ferreyra-a. 4-6-Long-s 3.50

EMMA (Adaptation of the Jane Austen novel)
Marvel Comics: May, 2011 - No. 5, Sept, 2011 ($3.99)
1-5-Nancy Butler-s/Janet K. Lee-a 4.00

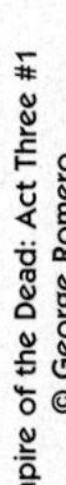
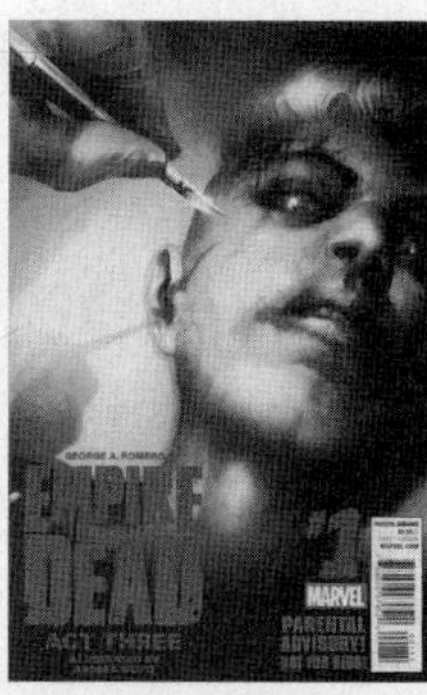
Empire of the Dead: Act Three #1 © George Romero

Empress #2 © Millar & Immonen

Enemy Ace: War Idyll SC © DC

GD 2.0 | VG 4.0 | FN 6.0 | VF 8.0 | VF/NM 9.0 | NM- 9.2

EMMA FROST
Marvel Comics: Aug, 2003 - No. 18, Feb, 2005 ($2.50/$2.99)
1-7-Emma in high school; Bollers-s/Green-a/Horn-c 3.00
8-18-($2.99) 3.00
... Vol. 1: Higher Learning TPB (2004, $7.99, digest size) r/#1-6 8.00
... Vol. 2: Mind Games TPB (2005, $7.99, digest size) r/#7-12 8.00
... Vol. 3: Bloom TPB (2005, $7.99, digest size) r/#13-18 8.00

EMMA PEEL & JOHN STEED (See The Avengers)

EMPEROR'S NEW CLOTHES, THE
Dell Publishing Co.: 1950 (10¢, 68 pgs., 1/2 size, oblong)
nn - (Surprise Books series) 6 12 18 31 38 45

EMPIRE
Image Comics (Gorilla): May, 2000 - No. 2, Sept, 2000 ($2.50)
DC Comics: No. 0, Aug, 2003; Sept, 2003 - No. 6, Feb, 2004 ($4.95/$2.50, limited series)
1,2: 1 (5/00)-Waid-s/Kitson-a; w/Crimson Plague prologue 3.00
0-(8/03) reprints #1,2 5.00
1-6: 1-(9/03) new Waid-s/Kitson-a/c 3.00
TPB (DC, 2004, $14.95) r/series; Kitson sketch pages; Waid intro. 15.00

EMPIRE OF THE DEAD: ACT ONE (George Romero's...)
Marvel Comics: Mar, 2014 - No. 5, Aug, 2014 ($3.99)
1-5-George Romero-s/Alex Maleev-a/c; zombies & vampires 4.00

EMPIRE OF THE DEAD: ACT TWO (George Romero's...)
Marvel Comics: Nov, 2014 - No. 5, Mar, 2015 ($3.99)
1-5-George Romero-s/Dalibor Talajic-a; zombies & vampires 4.00

EMPIRE OF THE DEAD: ACT THREE (George Romero's...)
Marvel Comics: Jun, 2015 - No. 5, Nov, 2015 ($3.99)
1-5-George Romero-s/Andrea Mutti-a; zombies & vampires 4.00

EMPIRE STRIKES BACK, THE (See Marvel Comics Super Special #16 & Marvel Special Edition)

EMPIRE: UPRISING
IDW Publishing: Apr, 2015 - No. 4, Jul, 2015 ($3.99)
1-4: Sequel to the 2003-2004 series; Waid-s/Kitson-a; two covers on each 4.00

EMPRESS
Marvel Comics (Icon): Jun, 2016 - No. 7, Jan, 2017 ($3.99/$5.99)
1-6-Millar-s/Immonen-a 4.00
7-($5.99) 6.00

EMPTY, THE
Image Comics: Feb, 2015 - No. 6, Sept, 2015 ($3.50/$3.99)
1-3-Jimmie Robinson-s/a 3.50
4-6-($3.99) 4.00

EMPTY LOVE STORIES
Slave Labor #1 & 2/Funny Valentine Press: Nov, 1994 - No. 2 ($2.95, B&W)
1,2: Steve Darnall scripts in all. 1-Alex Ross-c. 2-(8/96)-Mike Allred-c 4.00
1,2-2nd printing (Funny Valentine Press) 3.00
... 1999-Jeff Smith-c; Doran-a 3.00
..."Special" (2.95) Ty Templeton-c 3.00

EMPTY ZONE
Image Comics: Jun, 2015 - No. 10, Jul, 2016 ($3.50/$3.99)
1-8-Jason Shawn Alexander-s/a 3.50
9,10-($3.99) 4.00

ENCHANTED APPLES OF OZ, THE (See First Comics Graphic Novel #5)

ENCHANTED TIKI ROOM
Marvel Comics (Disney Kingdoms): Dec, 2016 - No. 5, Apr, 2017 ($3.99)
1-5-Jon Adams-s/Horacio Domingues-a 4.00

ENCHANTER
Eclipse Comics: Apr, 1987 - No. 3, Aug. 1987 ($2.00, B&W, limited series)
1-3 3.00

ENCHANTING LOVE
Kirby Publishing Co.: Oct, 1949 - No. 6, July, 1950 (All 52 pgs.)
1-Photo-c 21 42 63 124 202 285
2-Photo-c; Powell-a 14 28 42 76 108 140
3,4,6: 3-Jimmy Stewart photo-c. 4-Photo-c 13 26 39 74 105 135
5-Ingels-a, 9 pgs.; photo-c 18 36 54 107 169 230

ENCHANTMENT VISUALETTES (Magazine)
World Editions: Dec, 1949 - No. 5, Apr, 1950 (Painted c-1)
1-Contains two romance comic strips each 24 48 72 142 234 325
2 16 32 48 92 144 195
3-5 15 30 45 83 124 165

ENDER IN EXILE (Orson Scott Card's...)
Marvel Comics: Aug, 2010 - No. 5, Dec, 2010 ($3.99, limited series)
1-5-Sequel to Ender's Game; Johnston-s/Mhan-a/Fiumara-c 4.00

ENDER'S GAME: BATTLE SCHOOL
Marvel Comics: Dec, 2008 - No. 5, Jun, 2009 ($3.99, limited series)
1-5-Adaptation of Orson Scott Card novel Ender's Game; Yost-s/Ferry-a. 1-Two covers 4.00
Ender's Game: Mazer in Prison Special (4/10, $3.99) Johnston-s/Mhan-a 4.00
Ender's Game: Recruiting Valentine (8/09, $3.99) Timothy Green-a 4.00
Ender's Game: The League War (6/10, $3.99) Aaron Johnston-s/Timothy Green-a 4.00
Ender's Game: War of Gifts Special (2/10, $4.99) Timothy Green-a 5.00

ENDER'S GAME: COMMAND SCHOOL
Marvel Comics: Nov, 2009 - No. 5, Apr, 2010 ($3.99, limited series)
1-5-Adaptation of Orson Scott Card novel Ender's Game; Yost-s/Ferry-a 4.00

ENDER'S SHADOW: BATTLE SCHOOL
Marvel Comics: Feb, 2009 - No. 5, Jun, 2009 ($3.99, limited series)
1-5-Adaptation of O.S. Card novel Ender's Shadow; Carey-s/Fiumara-a. 1-Two covers 4.00

ENDER'S SHADOW: COMMAND SCHOOL
Marvel Comics: Nov, 2009 - No. 5, Apr, 2010 ($3.99, limited series)
1-5-Adaptation of O.S. Card novel Ender's Shadow; Carey-s/Fiumara-a 4.00

END LEAGUE, THE
Dark Horse Comics: Dec, 2007 - No. 9, Nov, 2009 ($2.99/$3.99)
1-8: 1-Broome-c/a; Remender-s. 5,6-Canete-a 3.00
9-($3.99) MacDonald-a/Canete-c 4.00

END OF NATIONS
DC Comics: Jan, 2012 - No. 4, Apr, 2012 ($2.99, limited series)
1-4-Based on the Trion Worlds videogame; Sanchez-s/Guichet-a/Sprouse-c 3.00

END TIMES OF BRAM AND BEN
Image Comics: Jan, 2013 - No. 4, Apr, 2013 ($2.99, limited series)
1-4: 1-Rapture parody; Asmus & Festante-s/Broo-a. 1-Mahfood-c 3.00

ENEMY ACE SPECIAL (Also see Our Army at War #151, Showcase #57, 58 & Star Spangled War Stories #138)
DC Comics: 1990 ($1.00, one-shot)
1-Kubert-r/Our Army #151,153; c-r/Showcase 57 5.00

ENEMY ACE: WAR IDYLL
DC Comics: 1990 (Graphic novel)
Hardcover-George Pratt-s/painted-a/c 30.00
Softcover (1991, $14.95) 15.00

ENEMY ACE: WAR IN HEAVEN
DC Comics: 2001 - No. 2, 2001 ($5.95, squarebound, limited series)
1,2-Ennis-s; Von Hammer in WW2. 1-Weston & Alamy-a. 2-Heath-a 6.00
TPB (2003, $14.95) r/#1,2 & Star Spangled War Stories #139; Jim Dietz-painted-c 15.00

ENGINEHEAD
DC Comics: June, 2004 - No. 6, Nov, 2004 ($2.50, limited series)
1-6-Joe Kelly-s/Ted McKeever-a/c. 6-Metal Men app. 3.00

ENIGMA
DC Comics (Vertigo): Mar, 1993 - No. 8, Oct, 1993 ($2.50, limited series)
1-8: Milligan scripts 3.00
Trade paperback ($19.95)-reprints 20.00

ENO AND PLUM (Also see Cud Comics)
Oni Press: Mar, 1998 ($2.95, B&W)
1-Terry LaBan-s/c/a 3.00

ENSIGN O'TOOLE (TV)
Dell Publishing Co.: Aug-Oct, 1963
1 3 6 9 19 30 40

ENSIGN PULVER (See Movie Classics)

ENTER THE HEROIC AGE
Marvel Comics: July, 2010 ($3.99, one-shot)
1-Short stories of Avengers Academy, Atlas, Black Widow, Thunderbolts; Hitch-c 4.00

EPIC
Marvel Comics (Epic Comics): 1992 - Book 4, 1992 ($4.95, lim. series, 52 pgs.)

Epic Illustrated #17 © MAR

ESPers V3 #3 © James Hudnall

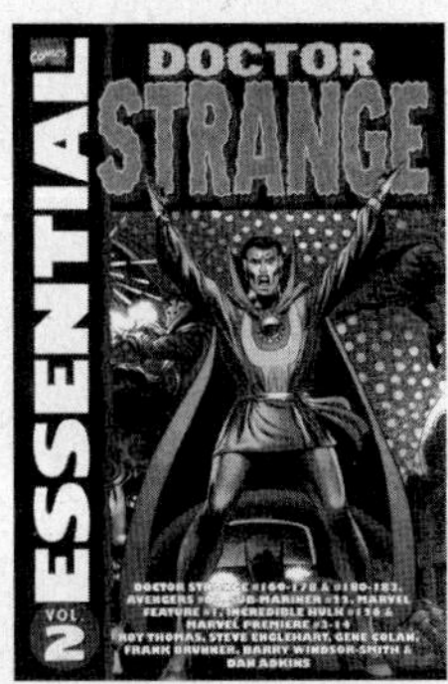

Essential Doctor Strange Vol. 2 © MAR

GD 2.0 | VG 4.0 | FN 6.0 | VF 8.0 | VF/NM 9.0 | NM- 9.2

Book One-Four: 2-Dorman painted-c 5.00
NOTE: *Alien Legion in #3. Cholly & Flytrap by* ***Burden****(scripts) &* ***Suydam****(art) in 3, 4. Dinosaurs in #4. Dreadlands in #1. Hellraiser in #1. Nightbreed in #2. Sleeze Brothers in #2. Stalkers in #1-4. Wild Cards in #1-4.*

EPIC ANTHOLOGY
Marvel Comics (Epic Comics): Apr, 2004 ($5.99)
1-Short stories by various; debut 2nd Sleepwalker by Kirkman-s 6.00

EPIC ILLUSTRATED (Magazine)
Marvel Comics Group: Spring, 1980 - No. 34, Feb, 1986 ($2.00/$2.50, B&W/color, mature)
1-Frazetta-c; Silver Surfer/Galactus-sty; Wendy Pini-s/a; Suydam-s/a; Metamorphosis Odyssey begins (thru #9) Starlin-a 3 6 9 16 24 32
2,4-10: 2-Bissette/Veitch-a; Goodwin-s. 4-Ellison 15 pg. story w/Steacy-a; Hempel-s/a; Veitch-s/a. 5-Hildebrandts-c/interview; Jusko-a; Vess-s/a. 6-Ellison-s (26 pgs). 7-Adams-s/a(16 pgs.); BWS interview. 8-Suydam-s/a; Vess-s/a. 9-Conrad-c. 10-Marada the She-Wolf-c/sty(21 pgs.) by Claremont/Bolton 1 3 4 6 8 10
3-1st app. Dreadstar 5 10 15 31 53 75
11-20: 11-Wood-a; Jusko-a. 12-Wolverton Spacehawk-r edited & recolored w/article on him; Muth-a. 13-Blade Runner preview by Williamson. 14-Elric of Melnibone by Russell; Revenge of the Jedi preview. 15-Vallejo-c & interview; 1st Dreadstar solo story (cont'd in Dreadstar #1). 16-B. Smith-c/a(2); Sim-s/a. 17-Starslammers preview. 18-Go Nagai; Williams-a. 19-Jabberwocky w/Hampton-a; Cheech Wizard-s. 20-The Sacred & the Profane begins by Ken Steacy; Elric by Gould; Williams-a 1 3 4 6 8 10
21-30: 21-Vess-s/a. 22-Frankenstein w/Wrightson-a. 26-Galactus series begins (thru #34); Cerebus the Aardvark story by Dave Sim. 27-Groo. 28-Cerebus. 29-1st Sheeva. 30-Cerebus; History of Dreadstar, Starlin-s/a; Williams-a; Vess-a 2 4 6 8 10 12
31-33: 31-Bolton-c/a. 32-Cerebus portfolio. 2 4 6 8 11 14
34-R.E.Howard tribute by Thomas-s/Plunkett-a; Moore-s/Veitch-a; Cerebus; Cholly & Flytrap w/Suydam-a; BWS-a 2 4 6 10 14 18
Sampler (early 1980 8 pg. preview giveaway) same cover as #1 with "Sampler" text 6.00
NOTE: **N. Adams** *a-7; c-6.* **Austin** *a-15-20i.* **Bode** *a-19, 23, 27r.* **Bolton** *a-7, 10-12, 15, 18, 22-25; c-10, 18, 22, 23.* **Boris** *c/a-15.* **Brunner** *c-12.* **Buscema** *a-1p, 9p, 11-13p.* **Byrne/Austin** *a-26-34.* **Chaykin** *a-2; c-8.* **Conrad** *a-2-5, 7-9, 25-34; c-17.* **Corben** *a-15; c-2.* **Frazetta** *c-1.* **Golden** *a-3r.* **Gulacy** *c/a-3.* **Jeff Jones** *c-25.* **Kaluta** *a-17r, 21, 24r, 26; c-4, 28.* **Nebres** *a-1.* **Reese** *a-12.* **Russell** *a-2-4, 9, 14, 33; c-14.* **Simonson** *a-17.* **B. Smith** *c/a-7, 16.* **Starlin** *a-1-9, 14, 15, 34.* **Steranko** *c-19.* **Williamson** *a-13, 27, 34.* **Wrightson** *a-13p, 22, 25, 27, 34; c-30.*

EPIC LITE
Marvel Comics (Epic Comics): Sept, 1991 ($3.95, 52 pgs., one-shot)
1-Bob the Alien, Normalman by Valentino 4.00

EPICURUS THE SAGE
DC Comics (Piranha Press): Vol. 1, 1991 - Vol. 2, 1991 ($9.95, 8-1/8x10-7/8")
Volume 1,2-Sam Kieth-c/a; Messner-Loebs-s 12.00
TPB (2003, $19.95) r/ #1,2, Fast Forward Rising the Sun; new story 20.00

EPILOGUE
IDW Publishing: Sept, 2008 - No. 4, Dec, 2008 ($3.99)
1-4-Steve Niles-s/Kyle Hotz-a/c 4.00

EQUILIBRIUM (Based on the 2002 movie)
American Mythology Prods.: 2016 - No. 3, 2017 ($3.99)
1-3-Pat Shand-s/Jason Craig-a; multiple covers 4.00
...: Deconstruction 1 (2017, $3.99) Moroney-s/Dela Cuesta-a 4.00
...: Gunkata Casebook 1 (2018, $3.99) Mell-s/Hilinski-a 4.00

ERADICATOR
DC Comics: Aug, 1996 - No. 3, Oct, 1996 ($1.75, limited series)
1-3: Superman app. 3.00

ERNIE COMICS (Formerly Andy Comics #21; All Love Romances #26 on)
Current Books/Ace Periodicals: No. 22, Sept, 1948 - No. 25, Mar, 1949
nn (9/48,11/48; #22,23)-Teenage humor 11 22 33 62 86 110
24,25 9 18 27 47 61 75

ESCAPADE IN FLORENCE (See Movie Comics)

ESCAPE FROM DEVIL'S ISLAND
Avon Periodicals: 1952
1-Kinstler-c; r/as Dynamic Adventures #9 43 86 129 271 461 650

ESCAPE FROM NEW YORK (Based on the Kurt Russell movie)
BOOM! Studios: Dec, 2014 - No. 16, Apr, 2016 ($3.99)
1-16: 1-8-Christopher Sebela-s/Diego Barreto-a; multiple covers on each. 9-16-Simic-a 4.00

ESCAPE FROM THE PLANET OF THE APES (See Power Record Comics)

ESCAPE TO WITCH MOUNTAIN (See Walt Disney Showcase No. 29)

ESCAPISTS, THE (See Michael Chabon Presents The Amazing Adventures of the Escapist)
Dark Horse Comics: July, 2006 - No. 6, Dec, 2006 ($1.00/$2.99, limited series)

GD 2.0 | VG 4.0 | FN 6.0 | VF 8.0 | VF/NM 9.0 | NM- 9.2

1-($1.00) Frank Miller-c; r/Vaughan story from Michael Chabon... #8 3.00
2-6($2.99) Vaughan-s/Rolston & Alexander-a. 2-James Jean-c. 3-Cassaday-c 3.00

ESPERS (Also see Interface)
Eclipse Comics: July, 1986 - No. 5, Apr, 1987 ($1.25/$1.75, Mando paper)
1-5-James Hudnall story & David Lloyd-a. 3.00

ESPERS
Halloween Comics: V2#1, 1996 - No. 6, 1997 ($2.95, B&W) (1st Halloween Comics series)
V2#1-6: James D. Hudnall scripts 3.00
Undertow TPB ('98, $14.95) r/#1-6 15.00

ESPERS
Image Comics: V3#1, 1997 - Present ($2.95, B&W, limited series)
V3#1-7: James D. Hudnall scripts 3.00
Black Magic TPB ('98, $14.95) r/#1-4 15.00

ESPIONAGE (TV)
Dell Publishing Co.: May-July, 1964
1 3 6 9 19 30 40

ESSENTIAL (Title series), **Marvel Comics**
--ANT-MAN, '02 (B&W- r) V1-Reprints app. from Tales To Astonish #27, #35-69; Kirby-c 15.00
--AVENGERS, '98 (B&W- r) V1-R-Avengers #1-24; new Immonen-c 15.00
V2(6/00)-Reprints Avengers #25-46, King-Size Special #1; Immonen-c 15.00
V3(3/01)-Reprints Avengers #47-68, Annual #2; Immonen-c 15.00
V4('04)-Reprints Avengers #69-97, Incredible Hulk #140; Neal Adams-c 17.00
V5('06)-Reprints Avengers #98-119, Daredevil #99, Defenders #8-11 17.00
V6('08)-Reprints Avengers #120-140, Giant Size #1-4, Capt. Marvel #33 & FF #150 17.00
--CAPTAIN AMERICA, '00 (B&W- r) V1-Reprints stories from Tales of Suspense #59-99, Captain America #100-102; new Romita & Milgrom-c 15.00
V2(1/02)-Reprints #103-126; Steranko-c 15.00
V3('06)-Reprints #127-153 17.00
V4('07)-Reprints #157-186 17.00
--CLASSIC X-MEN, '06 (B&W- r) (See Essential Uncanny X-Men for V1)
V2-($16.99) R-X-Men #25-53 & Avengers #53; Gil Kane-c 17.00
--CONAN, '00 (B&W- r) V1-R-Conan the Barbarian#1-25; new Buscema-c 15.00
--DAREDEVIL, '02 - V4 (B&W-r)
V1-R-Daredevil #1-25 15.00
V2-($16.99) R-Daredevil #26-48, Special #1, Fantastic Four #73 17.00
V3-($16.99) R-Daredevil #49-74, Iron Man #35-38 17.00
V4-($16.99) R-Daredevil #75-101, Avengers #111 17.00
--DAZZLER, '07 (B&W- r) V1-R/#1-21, X-Men #130-131, Amaz. Spider-Man #203 17.00
--DEFENDERS, '05 (B&W-r) V1-Reprints Doctor Strange #183, Sub-Mariner #22,34,35, Incredible Hulk #126, Marvel Feature #1-3, Defenders #1-14, Avengers #115-118 17.00
V2-($16.99) R- Defenders #15-30, Giant-Size Defenders #1-4, Marvel Two-In-One #6,7, Marvel Team-Up #33-35 and Marvel Treasury Edition #12 17.00
V3-($16.99) R- Defenders #31-60 and Annual #1 17.00
--DOCTOR STRANGE, '04 - V3 (B&W-r)
V1-($15.95) Reprints Strange Tales #110,111,114-168 17.00
V1 (2nd printing)-(2006, $16.99) Reprints Strange Tales #110,111,114-168 17.00
V2-($16.99) R-Doctor Strange #169-178,180-183; Avengers #61, Sub-Mariner #22 Marvel Feature #1, Incredible Hulk #126 and Marvel Premiere #3-14 17.00
V3-($16.99) R-Doctor Strange #1-29 & Annual #1;Tomb of Dracula #44,45 17.00
--FANTASTIC FOUR, '98 - V6 (B&W-r)
V1-Reprints FF #1-20, Annual #1; new Alan Davis-c; multiple printings exist 17.00
V2-Reprints FF #21-40, Annual #2; Davis and Farmer-c 15.00
V3-Reprints FF #41-63, Annual #3,4; Davis-c 15.00
V4-Reprints FF #64-83, Annual #5,6 17.00
V5-Reprints FF #84-110 17.00
V6-Reprints FF #111-137 17.00
--GHOST RIDER, '05 (B&W-r) V1-Reprints Marvel Spotlight #5-12, Ghost Rider #1-20 and Daredevil #138 17.00
V2-Reprints Ghost Rider #21-50 17.00
--GODZILLA, '06 (B&W-r) V1-Godzilla #1-24 20.00
--HOWARD THE DUCK, '02 (B&W- r) V1-Reprints #1-27, Annual #1; plus stories from Marvel Treasury Ed. #12, Man-Thing #1, Giant-Size Man-Thing #4,5, Fear #19; Bolland-c 15.00
--HULK, '99 (B&W-r) V1-R-Incred. Hulk #1-6, Tales To Astonish stories; new Timm-c 15.00
V2-Reprints Tales To Astonish #102-117, Annual #1 15.00
V3-Reprints Incredible Hulk #118-142, Capt. Marvel #20&21, Avengers #88 17.00
V4-Reprints Incredible Hulk #143-170 17.00
V5-Reprints Incredible Hulk #171-200, Annual #5 17.00

Essential Savage She-Hulk Vol. 1 © MAR

Essential Vertigo: The Sandman #31 © DC

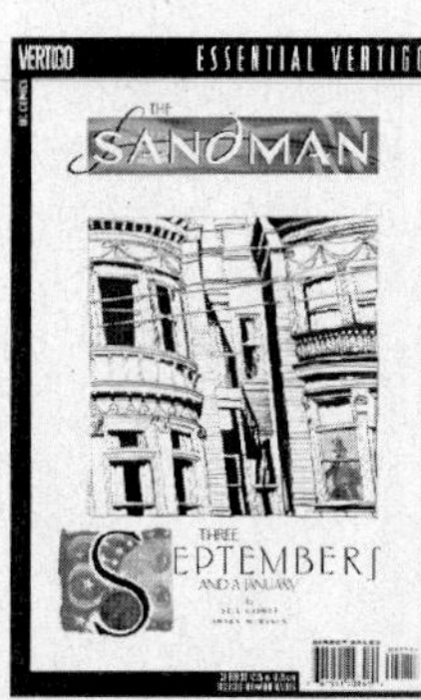

Eternal Empire #1 © Luna & Vaughn

GD VG FN VF VF/NM NM-
2.0 4.0 6.0 8.0 9.0 9.2

--**HUMAN TORCH,** '03 (B&W-r) V1-Strange Tales #101-134 & Ann. 2; Kirby-c 15.00
--**IRON MAN,** '00 - V3 (B&W-r)
V1-Reprints Tales Of Suspense #39-72; new Timm-c and back-c 15.00
V2-Reprints Tales Of Suspense #73-99, Tales To Astonish #82 & Iron Man #1-11 17.00
V3-Reprints Iron Man #12-38 & Daredevil #73 17.00
--**KILLRAVEN,** '05 (B&W-r) V1-Reprints Amazing Adventures V2 #18-39, Marvel Team-Up #45, Marvel Graphic Novel #7, Killraven #1 (2001) 17.00
--**LUKE CAGE, POWER MAN,** '05 (B&W-r) V1-Hero For Hire #1-16 & Power Man #17-27 17.00
V2-Reprints Power Man #28-49 & Annual #1 17.00
--**MAN-THING,** '06 (B&W-r) V1-Reprints Savage Tales #1, Astonishing Tales #12-13, Adventure Into Fear #10-19, Man-Thing #1-14, Giant-Size Man-Thing #1-2 & Monsters Unleashed #5,8,9 17.00
V2-R/Man-Thing #15-22 & #1-11 ('79 series), Giant-Size Man-Thing #3-5, Rampaging Hulk #7, Marvel Team-Up #68, Marvel Two-In-One #43 & Doctor Strange #41 17.00
--**MARVEL HORROR,** '06 (B&W-r) V1-R/#Ghost Rider #1-2, Marvel Spotlight #12-24, Son of Satan #1-8, Marvel Two-In-One #14, Marvel Team-Up #32,80,81, Vampire Tales #2-3, Haunt of Horror #2,4,5, Marvel Premiere #27, & Marvel Preview #7 17.00
--**MARVEL SAGA,** '08 (B&W-r) V1-R/#1-12 17.00
--**MARVEL TEAM-UP,** '02 - V2 (B&W-r) V1('02, '06)-R/#1-24 17.00
V2-R/#25-51 and Marvel Two-In-One #17 17.00
--**MARVEL TWO-IN-ONE,** '05 - V2 (B&W-r)
V1-Reprints Marvel Feature #11&12, Marvel Two-In-One #1-20,22-25 & Annual #1, Marvel Team-Up #47 and Fantastic Four Ann. #11 17.00
V2-R/#26-52 & Annual #2,3 17.00
--**MONSTER OF FRANKENSTEIN,** '04 (B&W-r) V1-Reprints Monster of Frankenstein #1-5, Frankenstein Monster #6-18, Giant-Size Werewolf #2, Monsters Unleashed #2,4-10 & Legion of Monsters #1 17.00
--**MOON KNIGHT,** '06 (B&W-r) V1-Reprints Moon Knight #1-10 and early apps. 17.00
V2-R/#11-30 17.00
--**MS. MARVEL,** '07 (B&W-r) V1-Reprints Ms. Marvel #1-23, Marvel Super-Heroes Magazine #10,11, and Avengers Annual #10 17.00
--**NOVA,** '06 (B&W-r) V1-Reprints Nova #1-25, AS-M #171, Marvel Two-In-One Ann. #3 17.00
--**OFFICIAL HANDBOOK OF THE MARVEL UNIVERSE,** '06 (B&W-r) V1-Reprints #1-15 profiling Abomination through Zzzax; dead and inactive characters; weapons & hardware; wraparound-c by Byrne 17.00
--**OFFICIAL HANDBOOK OF THE MARVEL UNIVERSE - DELUXE EDITION,** '06 (B&W-r)
V1-Reprints #1-7 profiling Abomination through Magneto; wraparound-c by Byrne 17.00
V2-Reprints #8-14 profiling Magus through Wolverine; wraparound-c by Byrne 17.00
V3-Reprints #15-20 profiling Wonder Man through Zzzax & Book of the Dead 17.00
--**OFFICIAL HANDBOOK OF THE MARVEL UNIVERSE - MASTER EDITION,** '08 (B&W-r)
V1-Reprints profiling Abomination through Gargoyle 17.00
V2-Reprints profiles 17.00
--**OFFICIAL HANDBOOK OF THE MARVEL UNIVERSE - UPDATE '89,** '06 (B&W-r)
V1-Reprints #1-8; wraparound-c by Frenz 17.00
--**PETER PARKER, THE SPECTACULAR SPIDER-MAN,** '05 (B&W-r) V1-Reprints #1-31 17.00
V2-Reprints #32-53 & Annual #1,2; Amazing Spider-Man Annual #13 17.00
V3-Reprints #54-74 & Annual #3; Frank Miller-c 17.00
--**POWER MAN AND IRON FIST,** '07 (B&W-r) V1-R/#50-72,74-75 17.00
--**PUNISHER,** '04, '06 - Present (B&W-r) V1-Reprints early app. in Amazing Spider-Man, Captain America, Daredevil, Marvel Preview and Punisher #1-5 (2 printings) 17.00
V2-Punisher #1-20, Annual #1 and Daredevil #257 17.00
V3-Punisher #21-40, Annual #2,3 17.00
--**RAMPAGING HULK,** '08 (B&W-r) V1-R/#1-9, The Hulk! #10-15 & Incredible Hulk #269 17.00
--**SAVAGE SHE-HULK,** '06 (B&W-r) V1-R/#1-25 17.00
--**SILVER SURFER,** '98 - Present (B&W-r)
V1-R-material from SS#1-18 and Fantastic Four Ann. #5 15.00
V2-R-SS#1(1982), SS#1-18 & Ann#1(1987), Epic Illustrated #1, Marvel Fanfare #51 17.00
--**SPIDER-MAN,** '96 - V8 (B&W-r)
V1-R-AF #15, Amaz. S-M #1-20, Ann. #1 (2 printings) 15.00
V2-R-Amaz. Spider-Man #21-43, Annual #2,3 15.00
V3-R-Amaz. Spider-Man #44-68 15.00
V4-R-Amaz. Spider-Man #69-89; Annual #4,5; new Timm-f&b-c 15.00
V5-R-Amaz. Spider-Man #90-113; new Romita-c 15.00
V6-R-Amaz. Spider-Man #114-137, Giant-Size Super-Heroes #1 G-S S-M #1,2 17.00
V7-R-Amaz. Spider-Man #138-160, Annual #10; Giant-Size Spider-Man #3-5 17.00
V8-R-Amaz. Spider-Man #161-185, Annual #11; G-S Spider-Man #6; Nova #12 17.00

GD VG FN VF VF/NM NM-
2.0 4.0 6.0 8.0 9.0 9.2

--**SPIDER-WOMAN,** '05 (B&W-r) V1-Reprints Marvel Spotlight #32, Marvel Two-In-One #29-33, Spider-Woman #1-25 17.00
V2-R-Spider-Woman #26-50, Marvel Team-Up #97 & Uncanny X-Men #148 17.00
--**SUPER-VILLAIN TEAM-UP,** '04 (B&W-r) V1-r/S-V T-U #1-14 & 16-17, Giant-Size S-V T-U #1,2; Avengers #154-156; Champions #16, & Astonishing Tales #1-8 17.00
--**TALES OF THE ZOMBIE,** '06 (B&W-r) V1-($16.99) r/#1-10 & Dracula Lives #1,2 17.00
--**THOR,** '01 (B&W-r) V1-R-Journey Into Mystery #83-112 15.00
V2-($16.99) R-Thor #113-136 & Annual #1,2 17.00
V3-($16.99) R-Thor #137-166 17.00
--**TOMB OF DRACULA,** '03 - V4 (B&W-r) V1-R-Tomb of Dracula #1-25, Werewolf By Night #15, Giant-Size Chillers #1 15.00
V2-($16.99) R-Tomb of Dracula #26-49, Giant-Size Dracula #2-5, Dr. Strange #14 17.00
V3-($16.99) R-Tomb of Dracula #50-70, Tomb of Dracula Magazine #1-4 17.00
V4-($16.99) R/Stories from Tomb of Dracula Magazine #2-6, Dracula Lives! #1-13, and Frankenstein Monster #7-9 17.00
--**UNCANNY X-MEN,** '99 (B&W reprints) (See Essential Classic X-Men for V2)
V1-Reprints X-Men (1st series) #1-24; Timm-c 15.00

ESSENTIAL VERTIGO: THE SANDMAN
DC Comics (Vertigo): Aug, 1996 - No. 32, Mar, 1999 ($1.95/$2.25, reprints)
1-13,15-31: Reprints Sandman, 2nd series 3.00
14-($2.95) 3.50
32-($4.50) Reprints Sandman Special #1 4.50

ESSENTIAL VERTIGO: SWAMP THING
DC Comics: Nov, 1996 - No. 24, Oct, 1998 ($1.95/$2.25,B&W, reprints)
1-11,13-24: 1-9-Reprints Alan Moore's Swamp Thing stories 3.00
12-($3.50) r/Annual #2 4.00

ESSENTIAL WEREWOLF BY NIGHT
Marvel Comics: 2005 - V2 (B&W reprints)
V1-($16.99) r/Marvel Spotlight #2-4, Werewolf By Night 1-23, Marvel Team-Up #12, Tomb of Dracula #18, Giant-Size Creatures #1 17.00
V2-R/#22-43, Giant-Size Werewolf #2-5 and Marvel Premiere #28 17.00

ESSENTIAL WOLVERINE
Marvel Comics: 1999 - V4 (B&W reprints)
V1-r/#1-23, V2-r/#24-47, V3-R/#48-69, V4-R/#70-90 17.00

ESSENTIAL X-FACTOR
Marvel Comics: 2005 - V2 (B&W reprints)
V1-($16.99) r/X-Factor #1-16 & Annual #1, Avengers #262, Fantastic Four #286, Thor #373&374 and Power Pack #27 17.00
V2-Reprints X-Factor #17-35 & Annual #2, Thor #378 17.00

ESSENTIAL X-MEN
Marvel Comics: 1996 - V8 (B&W reprints)
V1-V4: V1-R/Giant Size X-Men #1, X-Men #94-119. V2-R-X-Men #120-144. V3-R-Uncanny X-Men #145-161, Ann. #3-5. V4-Uncanny X-Men #162-179, Ann. #6 15.00
V5-($16.99) R/Uncanny X-Men #180-198, Ann. #7-8 17.00
V6-($16.99) R/Uncanny X-Men #199-213, Ann. #9, New Mutants Special Edition #1, X-Factor #9-11, New Mutants #46, Thor #373-374 and Power Pack #27 17.00
V7-($16.99) R/Uncanny X-Men #214-228, Ann. #10,11, and F.F. vs. The X-Men #1-4 17.00
V8-($16.99) R/Uncanny X-Men #229-243, Ann. #12 & X-Factor #36-39 17.00

ESTABLISHMENT, THE (Also see The Authority and The Monarchy)
DC Comics (WildStorm): Nov, 2001 - No. 13, Nov, 2002 ($2.50)
1-13-Edginton-s/Adlard-a 3.00

ETERNAL
BOOM! Studios: Dec, 2014 - No. 4, Apr, 2015 ($3.99)
1-4: 1-Harms-s/Valletta-a/Irving-c 4.00

ETERNAL, THE
Marvel Comics (MAX): Aug, 2003 - No. 6, Jan, 2004 ($2.99, mature)
1-6-Austen-s/Walker-a 3.00

ETERNAL BIBLE, THE
Authentic Publications: 1946 (Large size) (16 pgs. in color)

	GD 2.0	VG 4.0	FN 6.0	VF 8.0	VF/NM 9.0	NM- 9.2
1	16	32	48	94	147	200

ETERNAL EMPIRE
Image Comics: May, 2017 - Present ($3.99)
1-7-Sarah Vaughn & Jonathan Luna-s/Luna-a/c 4.00

ETERNALS, THE
Marvel Comics Group: July, 1976 - No. 19, Jan, 1978

Eternal Soulfire #5 © Aspen MLT

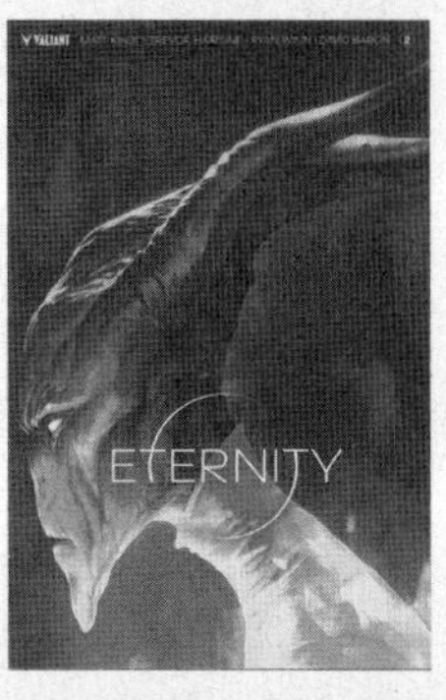

Eternity #2 © VAL

Everafter #1 © DC

	GD	VG	FN	VF	VF/NM	NM-
	2.0	4.0	6.0	8.0	9.0	9.2

1-(Regular 25¢ edition)-Origin & 1st app. Ikaris & The Eternals 3 6 9 21 33 45
1-(30¢-c variant, limited distribution) 5 10 15 34 60 85
2-(Reg. 25¢ edition)-1st app. Ajak & The Celestials 3 6 9 15 22 28
2-(30¢-c variant, limited distribution) 4 8 12 25 40 55
3-19: 3-1st app. Sersi. 5-1st app. Makarri, Domo, Zuras, & Thena. 14,15-Cosmic powered Hulk-c/story 2 4 6 8 10 12
12-16-(35¢-c variants, limited distribution) 6 12 18 41 76 110
Annual 1(10/77) 2 4 6 9 12 15
Eternals by Jack Kirby HC (2006, $75.00, dust jacket) r/#1-19 & Annual #1; intro by Royer; letter pages from #1,2,Annual #1; afterwords by Robert Greenberger 75.00
NOTE: *Kirby* c/a(p) in all.

ETERNALS, THE
Marvel Comics: Oct, 1985 - No. 12, Sept, 1986 (Maxi-series, mando paper)
1,12 (52 pgs.): 12-Williamson-a(i) 5.00
2-11 4.00

ETERNALS
Marvel Comics: Aug, 2006 - No. 7, Mar, 2007 ($3.99, limited series)
1-7-Neil Gaiman-s/John Romita Jr.-a/Rick Berry-c 4.00
1-7-Variant covers by Romita Jr. 4.00
1-Variant cover by Coipel 4.00
... Sketchbook (2006, $1.99, B&W) character sketches and sketch pages from #1 3.00
HC (2007, $29.99, dustjacket) r/#1-7; gallery of variant covers; sketches, Gaiman interview, Gaiman's original proposal; background essay on Kirby's Eternals 30.00

ETERNALS
Marvel Comics: Aug, 2008 - No. 9, May, 2009 ($2.99)
1-9: 1-6-Acuña-a/c; Knauf-s. 2,4-Iron Man app. 7,8-Nguyen-a; X-Men app. 3.00
Annual 1 (1/09, $3.99) Alixe-a/McGuinness-c; & reprint from Eternals #7 ('77) Kirby-s/a 4.00

ETERNAL SOULFIRE (Also see Soulfire)
Aspen MLT, Inc.: Jul, 2015 - No. 6, Feb, 2016 ($3.99, limited series)
1-6-Multiple covers on each. 1-Krul-s/Konat-a. 3-Tovar & Konat-a 4.00

ETERNALS: THE HEROD FACTOR
Marvel Comics: Nov, 1991 ($2.50, 68 pgs.)
1 4.00

ETERNAL WARRIOR (See Solar #10 & 11)
Valiant/Acclaim Comics (Valiant): Aug, 1992 - No. 50, Mar, 1996 ($2.25/$2.50)
1-Unity x-over; Miller-c; origin Eternal Warrior & Aram (Armstrong) 6.00
1-($2.25-c) Gold logo 2 4 6 13 18 22
1-Gold foil logo on embossed cover; no cover price 3 6 9 19 30 40
2,3,5-8: 2-Unity x-over; Simonson-c. 3-Archer & Armstrong x-over. 5-2nd full app. Bloodshot (12/92; see Rai #0). 6,7: 6-2nd app. Master Darque. 8-Flip book w/Archer & Armstrong #8 4.00
4-1st brief app. Bloodshot (last pg.); see Rai #0 for 1st full app.; Cowan-c 3 6 9 16 23 30
9-25,27-34: 9-1st Book of Geomancer. 14-16-Bloodshot app. 18-Doctor Mirage cameo. 19-Doctor Mirage app. 22-W/bound-in trading card. 25-Archer & Armstrong app.; cont'd from A&A #25 3.00
26-($2.75, 44 pgs.)-Flip book w/Archer & Armstrong 4.00
35-50: 35-Double-c; $2.50-c begins. 50-Geomancer app. 3.00
Special 1 (2/96, $2.50)-Wings of Justice; Art Holcomb script 3.00
Yearbook 1 (1993, $3.95), 2(1994, $3.95) 4.00

ETERNAL WARRIOR (Also see Wrath of the Eternal Warrior)
Valiant Entertainment: Sept, 2013 - No. 8, Apr, 2014 ($3.99)
1-8: 1-Pak-s/Hairsine-a; 2 covers. 2-Hairsine & Crain-a 4.00
...: Awakening 1 (5/17, $3.99) Venditti-s/Guedes-a 4.00

ETERNAL WARRIORS: BLACKWORKS
Acclaim Comics (Valiant Heroes): Mar, 1998 ($3.50, one-shot)
1 3.50

ETERNAL WARRIOR: DAYS OF STEEL
Valiant Entertainment: Nov, 2014 - No. 3, Jan, 2015 ($3.99)
1-3-Milligan-s/Nord-a 4.00

ETERNAL WARRIORS: DIGITAL ALCHEMY
Acclaim Comics (Valiant Heroes): Vol. 2, Sep, 1997 ($3.95, one-shot, 64 pgs.)
Vol. 2-Holcomb-s/Eaglesham-a(p) 4.00

ETERNAL WARRIORS: FIST AND STEEL
Acclaim Comics (Valiant): May, 1996 - No. 2, June, 1996 ($2.50, lim. series)
1,2: Geomancer app. in both. 1-Indicia reads "June." 2-Bo Hampton-a 3.00

	GD	VG	FN	VF	VF/NM	NM-
	2.0	4.0	6.0	8.0	9.0	9.2

ETERNAL WARRIORS: TIME AND TREACHERY
Acclaim Comics (Valiant Heroes): Vol. 1, Jun, 1997 ($3.95, one-shot, 48 pgs.)
Vol. 1-Reintro Aram, Archer, Ivar the Timewalker, & Gilad the Warmaster; 1st app. Shalla Redburn; Art Holcomb script 4.00

ETERNITY (Also see Divinity)
Valiant Entertainment: Oct, 2017 - No. 4, Jan, 2018 ($3.99, limited series)
1-4: 1-Kindt-s/Hairsine-a; 5 covers 4.00

ETERNITY SMITH
Renegade Press: Sept, 1986 - No. 5, May, 1987 ($1.25/$1.50, 36 pgs.)
1-5: 1st app. Eternity Smith. 5-Death of Jasmine 3.00

ETERNITY SMITH
Hero Comics: Sept, 1987 - No. 9, 1988 ($1.95)
V2#1-9: 8-Indigo begins 3.00

ETTA KETT
King Features Syndicate/Standard: No. 11, Dec, 1948 - No. 14, Sept, 1949
11-Teenage 14 28 42 80 115 150
12-14 10 20 30 58 79 100

ETHER
Dark Horse Comics: Nov, 2016 - Present ($3.99)
1-4-Matt Kindt-s/David Rubin-a 4.00

EVA: DAUGHTER OF THE DRAGON
Dynamite Entertainment: 2007 ($4.99, one-shot)
1-Two covers by Jo Chen and Edgar Salazar; Jerwa-s/Salazar-a 5.00

EVANGELINE (Also see Primer)
Comico/First Comics V2#1 on/Lodestone Publ.: 1984 - #2, 6/84; V2#1, 5/87 - V2#12, Mar, 1989 (Baxter paper)
1,2, V2#1 (5/87) - 12, Special #1 (1986, $2.00)-Lodestone Publ. 3.00

EVA THE IMP
Red Top Comic/Decker: 1957 - No. 2, Nov, 1957
1,2 5 10 14 22 26 30

EVEN MORE FUND COMICS (Benefit book for the Comic Book Legal Defense Fund) (Also see More Fund Comics)
Sky Dog Press: Sept, 2004 ($10.00, B&W, trade paperback)
nn-Anthology of short stories and pin-ups by various; Spider-Man-c by Cho 10.00

E.V.E. PROTOMECHA
Image Comics (Top Cow): Mar, 2000 - No. 6, Sept, 2000 ($2.50)
Preview ($5.95) Flip book w/Soul Saga preview 2 4 6 8 10 12
1-6: 1-Covers by Finch, Madureira, Garza. 2-Turner var-c 3.00
1-Another Universe variant-c 5.00
TPB (5/01, $17.95) r/#1-6 plus cover galley and sketch pages 18.00

EVERAFTER (See Fables)
DC Comics (Vertigo): Nov, 2016 - No. 12, Oct, 2017 ($3.99)
1-12: 1-Justus & Sturges-s/Travis Moore-a; Snow & Bigby app. 7-Buckingham-a 4.00

EVERQUEST: ... (Based on online role-playing game)
DC Comics (WildStorm): 2002 ($5.95, one-shots)
The Ruins of Kunark - Jim Lee & Dan Norton-a; McQuaid & Lee-s; Lee-c 6.00
Transformations - Philip Tan-a; Devin Grayson-s; Portacio-c 6.00

EVERYBODY'S COMICS (See Fox Giants)

EVERYMAN, THE
Marvel Comics (Epic Comics): Nov, 1991 ($4.50, one-shot, 52 pgs.)
1-Mike Allred-a 1 2 3 4 5 7

EVERYTHING HAPPENS TO HARVEY
National Periodical Publications: Sept-Oct, 1953 - No. 7, Sept-Oct, 1954
1 39 78 117 231 378 525
2 19 38 57 112 179 245
3-7 15 30 45 90 140 190

EVERYTHING'S ARCHIE
Archie Publications: May, 1969 - No. 157, Sept, 1991 (Giant issues No. 1-20)
1-(68 pages) 8 16 24 55 105 155
2-(68 pages) 4 8 12 28 47 65
3-5-(68 pages) 4 8 12 25 40 55
6-13-(68 pages) 3 6 9 17 26 35
14-31-(52 pages) 2 4 6 13 18 22
32 (7/74)-50 (8/76) 2 4 6 8 10 12

Eve: Valkyrie #1 © CCP

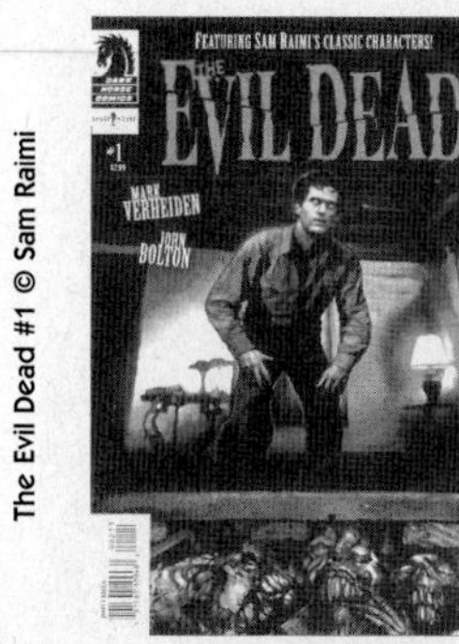

The Evil Dead #1 © Sam Raimi

Evil Ernie: Godeater #5 © DYN

GD VG FN VF VF/NM NM-
2.0 4.0 6.0 8.0 9.0 9.2

51-80 (12/79),100 (4/82) 1 2 3 5 6 8
81-99 6.00
101-103,105,106,108-120 5.00
104,107-Cheryl Blossom app. 1 2 3 4 5 7
121-156: 142,148-Gene Colan-a 4.00
157-Last issue 5.00

EVERYTHING'S DUCKY (Movie)
Dell Publishing Co.: No. 1251, 1961
Four Color 1251-Mickey Rooney & Buddy Hackett photo-c
5 10 15 34 60 85

EVE: VALKYRIE (Based on the video game)
Dark Horse Comics: Oct, 2015 - No. 4, Jan, 2016 ($3.99, limited series)
1-4-Brian Wood-s/Eduardo Francisco-a 4.00

EVIL DEAD, THE (Movie)
Dark Horse Comics: Jan, 2008 - No. 4, Apr, 2008 ($2.99, limited series)
1-4-Adaptation of the Sam Raimi/Bruce Campbell movie; Bolton painted-a/c 3.00

EVIL DEAD 2 (Movie)
Space Goat Productions: 2016 ($3.99, one-shots)
...: Revenge of Hitler 1 - Edginton-s/Watts-a 4.00
...: Revenge of Jack the Ripper 1 - Ball-s/Mauriz-a 4.00
...: Revenge of Krampus 1 - Edginton-s/Youkovich-a 4.00

EVIL DEAD 2: BEYOND DEAD BY DAWN (Movie)
Space Goat Productions: 2015 - No. 3 ($3.99, limited series)
1-3-Sequel to the Sam Raimi/Bruce Campbell movie; Hannah-s/Bagenda & Bazaldua-a 4.00

EVIL DEAD 2: CRADLE OF THE DAMNED (Movie)
Space Goat Productions: 2016 - Present ($3.99, limited series)
1-Hannah-s/Bagenda & Bazaldua-a 4.00

EVIL DEAD 2: DARK ONES RISING (Movie)
Space Goat Productions: 2016 - No. 3, 2016 ($3.99, limited series)
1-3-Sequel to the Sam Raimi/Bruce Campbell movie; Hannah-s/Valdes-a 4.00

EVIL DEAD 2: REVENGE OF EVIL ED (Movie)
Space Goat Productions: 2017 - Present ($3.99, limited series)
1-Edginton-s/Riccardi-a; Hitler, Rasputin, Bin Laden & Dracula app. 4.00

EVIL ERNIE
Eternity Comics: Dec, 1991 - No. 5, 1992 ($2.50, B&W, limited series)
1-1st app. Lady Death by Steven Hughes (12,000 print run); Lady Death app. in all issues
9 18 27 61 123 185
2-1st Lady Death-c (7,000 print run) 5 10 15 34 60 85
3-(7,000 print run) 4 8 12 28 47 65
4-(8,000 print run) 4 8 12 23 37 50
5 3 6 9 19 30 40
Special Edition 1 3 6 9 17 26 35
Youth Gone Wild! ($9.95, trade paperback)-r/#1-5 2 4 6 8 10 12
Youth Gone Wild! Director's Cut ($4.95)-Limited to 15,000, shows the making of the comic 6.00

EVIL ERNIE (Monthly series)
Chaos! Comics: July, 1998 - No. 10, Apr, 1999 ($2.95)
1-10-Pulido & Nutman-s/Brewer-a 3.00
1-($10.00) Premium Ed. 10.00
... Baddest Battles (1/97, $1.50) Pin-ups; 2 covers 3.00
... Pieces of Me (11/00, $2.95, B&W) Flashback story; Pulido-s/Beck-a 3.00
... Relentless (5/02, $4.99, B&W) Pulido-s/Beck, Bonk, & Brewer-a 5.00
... Returns (10/01, $3.99, B&W) Pulido-s/Beck-a 4.00

EVIL ERNIE
Dynamite Entertainment: 2012 - No. 6, 2013 ($3.99)
1-6: 1-Origin re-told; Snider-s/Craig-a; covers by Brereton, Seeley, Syaf & Bradshaw 4.00

EVIL ERNIE (Volume 2)
Dynamite Entertainment: 2014 - No. 6, 2015 ($3.99)
1-6-Tim & Steve Seeley-s/Rafael Lanhellas-a; multiple covers 4.00

EVIL ERNIE: DEPRAVED
Chaos! Comics: Jul, 1999 - No. 3, Sept, 1999 ($2.95, limited series)
1-3-Pulido-s/Brewer-a 3.00

EVIL ERNIE: DESTROYER
Chaos! Comics: Oct, 1997 - No. 9, Jun, 1998 ($2.95, limited series)
Preview ($2.50), 1-9-Flip cover 3.00

EVIL ERNIE: GODEATER

GD VG FN VF VF/NM NM-
2.0 4.0 6.0 8.0 9.0 9.2

Dynamite Entertainment: 2016 - No. 5, 2016 ($3.99)
1-5-Jordan-s/Worley-a; Davidsen-s/Razek-a; multiple covers 4.00

EVIL ERNIE: IN SANTA FE
Devil's Due Publ.: Sept, 2005 - No. 4, Mar, 2006 ($2.95, limited series)
1-4-Alan Grant-s/Tommy Castillo-a/Alex Horley-c 3.00

EVIL ERNIE: REVENGE
Chaos! Comics: Oct, 1994 - No. 4, Feb, 1995 ($2.95, limited series)
1-Glow-in-the-dark-c; Lady Death app. 1-3-flip book w. Kilzone Preview (series of 3) 5.00
1-Commemorative-(4000 print run) 1 3 4 6 8 10
2-4 4.00
Trade paperback (10/95, $12.95) 13.00

EVIL ERNIE: STRAIGHT TO HELL
Chaos! Comics: Oct, 1995 - No. 5, May, 1996 ($2.95, limited series)
1-5: 1-fold-out-c 4.00
1,3:1-($19.95) Chromium Ed. 3-Chastity Chase-c-(4000 printed) 20.00
Special Edition (10,000) 20.00

EVIL ERNIE: THE RESURRECTION
Chaos! Comics: 1993 - No. 4, 1994 (Limited series)
0 5.00
1 2 4 6 8 10 12
1A-Gold 3 6 9 16 23 30
2-4 1 2 3 5 6 8

EVIL ERNIE VS. THE MOVIE MONSTERS
Chaos! Comics: Mar, 1997 ($2.95, one-shot)
1 4.00
1-Variant-"Chaos-Scope•Terror Vision" card stock-c 6.00

EVIL ERNIE VS. THE SUPER HEROES
Chaos! Comics: Aug, 1995; Sept, 1998 ($2.95)
1-Lady Death poster 4.00
1-Foil-c variant (limited to 10,000) 2 4 6 11 16 20
1-Limited Edition (1000) 2 4 6 11 16 20
2-(9/98) Ernie vs. JLA and Marvel parodies 4.00

EVIL ERNIE: WAR OF THE DEAD
Chaos! Comics: Nov, 1999 - No. 3, Jan, 2000 ($2.95, limited series)
1-3-Pulido & Kaminski-s/Brewer-a. 3-End of Evil Ernie 3.00

EVIL EYE
Fantagraphics Books: June, 1998 - No. 12, Jun, 2004 ($2.95/$3.50/$3.95, B&W)
1-7-Richard Sala-s/a 4.00
8-10-($3.50) 4.00
11,12-($3.95) 4.00

EVO (Crossover from Tomb Raider #25 & Witchblade #60)
Image Comics (Top Cow): Feb, 2003 ($2.99, one-shot)
1-Silvestri-c/a(p); Endgame x-over pt. 3; Sara Pezzini & Lara Croft app. 3.00

EWOKS (Star Wars) (TV) (See Star Comics Magazine)
Marvel Comics (Star Comics): June, 1985 - No. 14, Jul, 1987 (75¢/$1.00)
1,10: 10-Williamson-a (From Star Wars) 3 6 9 17 26 35
2-9 2 4 6 8 11 14
11-14: 14-($1.00-c) 2 4 6 10 14 18

EXCALIBUR (Also see Marvel Comics Presents #31)
Marvel Comics: Apr, 1988; Oct, 1988 - No. 125, Oct, 1998 ($1.50/$1.75/$1.99)
Special Edition nn (The Sword is Drawn)(4/88, $3.25)-1st Excalibur comic
1 2 3 5 6 8
Special Edition nn (4/88)-no price on-c 2 4 6 8 10 12
Special Edition nn (2nd & 3rd print, 10/88, 12/89) 5.00
...The Sword is Drawn (Apr, 1992, $4.50) 5.00
1($1.50, 10/88)-X-Men spin-off; Nightcrawler, Shadowcat(Kitty Pryde), Capt. Britain, Phoenix & Meggan begin 6.00
2-4 5.00
5-10 4.00
11-49,51-70,72-74,76: 10,11-Rogers/Austin-a. 21-Intro Crusader X. 22-Iron Man x-over. 24-John Byrne app. in story. 26-Ron Lim-c/a. 27-B. Smith-a(p). 37-Dr. Doom & Iron Man app. 41-X-Men (Wolverine) app.; Cable cameo. 49-Neal Adams c-swipe. 52,57-X-Men (Cyclops, Wolverine) app. 53-Spider-Man-c/story. 58-X-Men (Wolverine, Gambit, Cyclops, etc.)-c/story. 61-Phoenix returns. 68-Starjammers-c/story 3.00
50-($2.75, 56 pgs.)-New logo 4.00
71-($3.95, 52 pgs.)-Hologram on-c; 30th anniversary 5.00
75-($3.50, 52 pgs.)-Holo-grafx foil-c 5.00

Excalibur #116 © MAR

Exciting Comics #11 © STD

Executive Assistant: Violet #1 © Aspen MLT

GD 2.0 | VG 4.0 | FN 6.0 | VF 8.0 | VF/NM 9.0 | NM- 9.2

75-($2.25, 52 pgs.)-Regular edition 4.00
77-81,83-86: 77-Begin $1.95-c; bound-in trading card sheet. 83-86-Deluxe Editions and Standard Editions. 86-1st app. Pete Wisdom 3.00
82-($2.50)-Newsstand edition 4.00
82-($3.50)-Enhanced edition 5.00
87-89,91-99,101-110: 87-Return from Age of Apocalypse. 92-Colossus-c/app. 94-Days of Future Tense 95-X-Man-c/app. 96-Sebastian Shaw & the Hellfire Club app. 99-Onslaught app. 101-Onslaught tie-in. 102-w/card insert. 103-Last Warren Ellis scripts; Belasco app. 104,105-Hitch & Neary-c/a. 109-Spiral-c/app. 3.00
90,100-($2.95)-double-sized. 100-Onslaught tie-in; wraparound-c 4.00
111-124: 111-Begin $1.99-c, wraparound-c. 119-Calafiore-a 3.00
125-($2.99) Wedding of Capt. Britain and Meggan 4.00
Annual 1,2 ('93, '94, 68 pgs.)-1st app. Khaos. 2-X-Men & Psylocke app. 4.00
#(-1) Flashback (7/97) 3.00
...Air Apparent nn (12/91, $4.95)-Simonson-c 6.00
...Mojo Mayhem nn (12/89, $4.50)-Art Adams/Austin-c/a 6.00
...: The Possession nn (7/91, $2.95, 52 pgs.) 4.00
...: XX Crossing (7/92, 5/92-inside, $2.50)-vs. The X-Men 4.00
...Classic Vol. 1: The Sword is Drawn TPB (2005, $19.99) r/#1-5 & Special Edition nn (The Sword is Drawn) 20.00
...Classic Vol. 2: Two-Edged Sword TPB (2006, $24.99) r/#6-11 25.00
...Classic Vol. 3: Cross-Time Caper Book 1 TPB (2007, $24.99) r/#12-20 25.00
...Classic Vol. 4: Cross-Time Caper Book 2 TPB (2007, $24.99) r/#21-28 25.00
...Classic Vol. 5 TPB (2008, $24.99) r/#29-34 & Marvel GN Excalibur: Weird War III 25.00

EXCALIBUR
Marvel Comics: Feb, 2001 - No. 4, May, 2001 ($2.99)

1-4-Return of Captain Britain; Raimondi-a 3.00

EXCALIBUR (X-Men Reloaded title) (Leads into House of M series, then New Excalibur)
Marvel Comics: July, 2004 - No. 14, July, 2005 ($2.99)

1-14: 1-Claremont-s/Lopresti-a/Park-c; Magneto returns. 6-11-Beast app. 13,14-Prelude to House of M; Dr. Strange app. 3.00
House of M Prelude: Excalibur TPB (2005, $11.99) r/#11-14 12.00
... Vol. 1: Forging the Sword (2004, $9.99) r/#1-4 10.00
... Vol. 2: Saturday Night Fever (2005, $14.99) r/#5-10 15.00

EXCITING COMICS
Nedor/Better Publications/Standard Comics: Apr, 1940 - No. 69, Sept, 1949

1-Origin & 1st app. The Mask, Jim Hatfield, Sgt. Bill King, Dan Williams begin; early Robot-c (see Smash #1) 481 962 1443 3511 6206 8900
2-The Sphinx begins; The Masked Rider app.; Son of the Gods begins, ends #8 245 490 735 1568 2684 3800
3-Classic Science Fiction Robot-c 232 464 696 1485 2543 3600
4-6: All have Sci-Fi covers by Max Plaisted 181 362 543 1158 1979 2800
7,8-Schomburg jungle covers 123 246 369 787 1344 1900
9-Origin/1st app. of The Black Terror & sidekick Tim, begin series (5/41) (Black Terror c-9-21,23-52,54,55) 1400 2800 4200 10,500 19,750 29,000
10-2nd app. Black Terror (6/41) 377 754 1131 2639 4620 6600
11-3rd app. Black Terror (7/41) 232 464 696 1485 2543 3600
12,13-Bondage covers 168 336 504 1075 1838 2600
14-Last Sphinx, Dan Williams 135 270 405 864 1482 2100
15-The Liberator begins (origin); WWII-c 174 348 522 1114 1907 2700
16,19,20: 20-The Mask ends 113 226 339 718 1234 1750
17,18-WWII-c 135 270 405 864 1482 2100
21,23,24 87 174 261 553 952 1350
22-Origin The Eaglet; The American Eagle begins 110 220 330 704 1202 1700
25-Robot-c 161 322 483 1030 1765 2500
26-Schomburg-c begin; Nazi WWII-c 206 412 618 1318 2259 3200
27,30-Japanese WWII-c 187 374 561 1197 2049 2900
28-(Scarce) Crime Crusader begins, ends #58; Nazi WWII-c 575 1150 1725 3450 5725 8000
29-Nazi WWII-c 187 374 561 1197 2049 2900
31,35,36-Japanese WWII-c. 35-Liberator ends, not in 31-33 155 310 465 992 1696 2400
32-34,37-Nazi WWII-c 155 310 465 992 1696 2400
38 Gangster-c 110 220 330 704 1202 1700
39-WWII-c; Nazis giving poison candy to kids on cover; origin Kara, Jungle Princess 950 1900 2850 5900 8950 12,000
40,41-Last WWII covers in this title; Japanese WWII-c 148 296 444 947 1624 2300
42-50: 42-The Scarab begins. 45-Schomburg Robot-c. 49-Last Kara, Jungle Princess. 50-Last American Eagle 77 154 231 493 847 1200
51-Miss Masque begins (1st app.) 103 206 309 659 1130 1600
52,54: 54-Miss Masque ends 71 142 213 454 777 1100

GD 2.0 | VG 4.0 | FN 6.0 | VF 8.0 | VF/NM 9.0 | NM- 9.2

53-Miss Masque-c 123 246 369 787 1344 1900
55-58: 55-Judy of the Jungle begins (origin), ends #69; 1 pg. Ingels-a; Judy of the Jungle c-56-66. 57,58-Airbrush-c 71 142 213 454 777 1100
59-Frazetta art in Caniff style; signed Frank Frazeta (one t), 9 pgs. 77 154 231 493 847 1200
60-66: 60-Rick Howard, the Mystery Rider begins. 66-Robinson/Meskin-a 68 136 204 435 743 1050
67-69-All western covers 24 48 72 142 234 325

NOTE: *Schomburg (Xela) c-26-68; airbrush c-57-66. Black Terror by **R. Moreira**-#65. **Roussos** a-62. Bondage-c 9, 12, 13, 20, 23, 25, 30, 59.*

EXCITING ROMANCES
Fawcett Publications: 1949 (nd); No. 2, Spring, 1950 - No. 5, 10/50; No. 6 (1951, nd); No. 7, 9/51 -No. 12, 1/53 (Photo-c on #1-3)

1,3: 1(1949). 3-Wood-a 14 28 42 82 121 160
2,4,5-(1950) 10 20 30 56 76 95
6-12 9 18 27 50 65 80

NOTE: ***Powell** a-8-10. **Marcus Swayze** a-5, 6, 9. Photo c-1-7, 10-12.*

EXCITING ROMANCE STORIES (See Fox Giants)

EXCITING WAR (Korean War)
Standard Comics (Better Publ.): No. 5, Sept, 1952 - No. 8, May, 1953; No. 9, Nov, 1953

5 14 28 42 82 121 160
6-Flame thrower/burning body-c 24 48 72 142 234 325
7,9 10 20 30 58 79 100
8-Toth-a 11 22 33 62 86 110

EXCITING X-PATROL
Marvel Comics (Amalgam): June, 1997 ($1.95, one-shot)

1-Barbara Kesel-s/Bryan Hitch-a 3.00

EX-CON
Dynamite Entertainment: 2014 - No. 5, 2015 ($2.99, limited series)

1-5-Swierczynski-s/Burns-a/Bradstreet-c 3.00

EXECUTIONER, THE (Don Pendleton's...)
IDW Publishing: Apr, 2008 - No. 5, Aug, 2008 ($3.99)

1-5-Mack Bolan origin re-told; Gallant-a/Wojtowicz-s 4.00

EXECUTIVE ASSISTANT: ASSASSINS
Aspen MLT: Jul, 2012 - No. 18, Feb, 2014 ($3.99)

1-18: 1-Five covers; Hernandez-s/Gunderson-a 4.00

EXECUTIVE ASSISTANT: IRIS (Also see All New Executive Assistant: Iris)
Aspen MLT: No. 0, Apr, 2009 - No. 6, Nov, 2010 ($2.50/$2.99)

0-($2.50) Wohl-s/Francisco-a; 3 covers 3.00
1-6-($2.99) Multiple covers on each 3.00
Annual 2015 (3/15, $5.99) Three stories by various; Benitez-c 6.00
... Sourcebook 1 (1/16, $4.99) Character profiles & storyline summaries 5.00

EXECUTIVE ASSISTANT: IRIS (Volume 2) (The Hit List Agenda x-over)
Aspen MLT: No. 0, Jul, 2011 - No. 5, Dec, 2011 ($2.50/$2.99/$3.50)

0-($2.50) Wohl-s/Francisco-a; sketch page art; 3 covers 3.00
1-4-($2.99) Multiple covers on each. 1-Francisco-a. 2-4-Odagawa-a 3.00
5-($3.50) Odagawa-a 3.50

EXECUTIVE ASSISTANT: IRIS (Volume 3) (See All New Executive Assistant: Iris for Vol. 4)
Aspen MLT: Dec, 2012 - No. 5, Sept, 2013 ($3.99)

1-5-Multiple covers on each. 1-Wohl-s/Lei-a 4.00

EXECUTIVE ASSISTANT: LOTUS (The Hit List Agenda x-over)
Aspen MLT: Aug, 2011 - No. 3, Oct, 2011 ($2.99, limited series)

1-3-Multiple covers on each. Hernandez-s/Nome-a 3.00

EXECUTIVE ASSISTANT: ORCHID (The Hit List Agenda x-over)
Aspen MLT: Aug, 2011 - No. 3, Oct, 2011 ($2.99, limited series)

1-3: 1-Lobdell-s/Gunnell-a; multiple covers 3.00

EXECUTIVE ASSISTANT: VIOLET (The Hit List Agenda x-over)
Aspen MLT: Aug, 2011 - No. 3, Oct, 2011 ($2.99, limited series)

1-3: 1-Andreyko-s/Mhan-a; multiple covers 3.00

EXILED (Part 1 of x-over with Journey Into Mystery #637,638 & New Mutants #42,43)
Marvel Comics: July, 2012 ($2.99, one-shot)

1-Thor, Loki and New Mutants app.; DiGiandomenico-a 3.00

EXILE ON THE PLANET OF THE APES
BOOM! Studios: Mar, 2012 - No. 4 ($3.99, limited series)

1-3-Bechko & Hardman-s/Laming-a 4.00

Exiles (2009 series) #5 © MAR

Ex Machina #33 © Vaughan & Harris

Exterminators #26 © Oliver & Moore

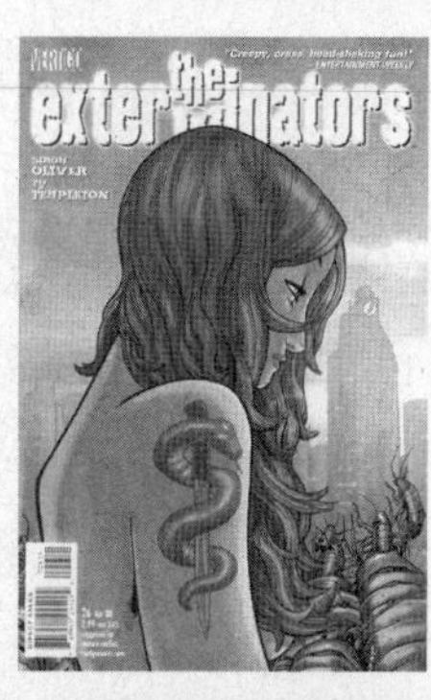

GD VG FN VF VF/NM NM-
2.0 4.0 6.0 8.0 9.0 9.2

EXILES (Also see Break-Thru)
Malibu Comics (Ultraverse): Aug, 1993 - No. 4, Nov, 1993 ($1.95)

1,2,4: 1,2-Bagged copies of each exist. 4-Team dies; story cont'd in Break-Thru #1 3.00
3-($2.50, 40 pgs.)-Rune flip-c/story by B. Smith (3 pgs.) 4.00
1-Holographic-c edition 1 2 3 5 6 8

EXILES (All New, The) (2nd Series) (Also see Black September)
Malibu Comics (Ultraverse): Sept, 1995 - V2#11, Aug, 1996 ($1.50)

Infinity (9/95, $1.50)-Intro new team including Marvel's Juggernaut & Reaper 3.00
Infinity (2000 signed), V2#1 (2000 signed) 1 3 4 6 8 10
V2 #1-(10/95, 64 pgs.)-Reprint of Ultraforce V2#1 follows lead story 4.00
V2#2-4,6-11: 2-1st app. Hellblade. 8-Intro Maxis. 11-Vs. Maxis; Ripfire app.; cont'd in Ultraforce #12 3.00
V2#5-($2.50) Juggernaut returns to the Marvel Universe. 4.00

EXILES (Also see X-Men titles) (Leads into New Exiles series)
Marvel Comics: Aug, 2001 - No. 100, Feb, 2008 ($2.99/$2.25)

1-($2.99) Blink and parallel world X-Men; Winick-s/McKone & McKenna-a 1 2 3 4 5 7
2-10-($2.25) 2-Two covers (McKone & JH Williams III). 5-Alpha Flight app. 4.00
11-24: 22-Blink leaves; Magik joins. 23,24-Walker-a; alternate Weapon-X app. 3.00
25-99: 25-Begin $2.99-c; Inhumans app.; Walker-a. 26-30-Austen-s. 33-Wolverine app. 35-37-Fantastic Four app. 37-Sunfire dies, Blink returns. 38-40-Hyperion app. 69-71-House of M. 77,78-Squadron Supreme app. 85,86-Multiple Wolverines. 90-Claremont-s begin; Psylocke app. 97-Shadowcat joins 3.00
100-($3.99) Last issue; Blink leaves; continues in Exiles (Days of Then and Now); r/#1 4.00
Annual 1 (2/07, $3.99) Bedard-s/Raney-a/c 4.00
Exiles #1 (Days of Then and Now) (3/08, $3.99) short stories by various 4.00

EXILES
Marvel Comics: Jun, 2009 - No. 6, Nov, 2009 ($2.99/$3.99)

1,6-($3.99) Blink and parallel world Scarlet Witch, Beast and others; Bullock-c 4.00
2-5-($2.99) 3.00

EXILES VS. THE X-MEN
Malibu Comics (Ultraverse): Oct, 1995 (one-shot)

0-Limited Super Premium Edition; signed w/certificate; gold foil logo, 0-Limited Premium Edition 1 3 4 6 8 10

EXIT STAGE LEFT: THE SNAGGLEPUSS CHRONICLES
DC Comics: Mar, 2018 - Present ($3.99)

1-3-Russell-s/Feehan-a; Snagglepuss as a 1950s playwright; Huckleberry Hound app. 4.00

EX MACHINA
DC Comics: Aug, 2004 - No. 50, Sept, 2010 ($2.95/$2.99)

1-Intro. Mitchell Hundred; Vaughan-s/Harris-a/c 4.00
1-Special Edition (6/10, $1.00) Reprints #1 with "What's Next?" logo on cover 3.00
2-49: 12-Intro. Automaton. 33-Mitchell meets the Pope 3.00
50-($4.99) Wraparound-c 5.00
...: The Deluxe Edition Book One HC (2008, $29.99, dustjacket) r/#1-11; Vaughan's original proposal, Harris sketch pages; Brad Meltzer intro. 30.00
...: The Deluxe Edition Book Two HC (2009, $29.99, dustjacket) r/#12-20; Special #1,2; script and pencil art for #20; Wachowski Bros. intro. 30.00
...: The Deluxe Edition Book Three HC (2010, $29.99, dustjacket) r/#21-29; Special #3 and Ex Machina: Inside the Machine 30.00
...: The Deluxe Edition Book Four HC (2010, $29.99, dustjacket) r/#30-40; cover gallery 30.00
...: The Deluxe Edition Book Five HC (2011, $29.99, dustjacket) r/#41-50; Special #4 30.00
...: Inside the Machine (4/07, $2.99) script pages and Harris art and cover process 3.00
...: Masquerade Special (#3) (10/07, $3.50) John Paul Leon-a; Harris-c 3.50
.. Special 1,2 (6/06 - No. 2, 8/06, $2.99) Sprouse-a; flashback to the Great Machine 3.00
.. Special 4 (5/09, $3.99) Leon-a; Great Machine flashback; covers by Harris & Leon 4.00
...: Dirty Tricks TPB (2009, $12.99) r/#35-39 and Masquerade Special #3 13.00
...: Ex Cathedra TPB (2008, $12.99) r/#30-34 13.00
...: March To War TPB (2006, $12.99) r/#17-20 and Special #1,2 13.00
...: Power Down TPB (2008, $12.99) r/#26-29 & ...: Inside the Machine 13.00
...: Ring Out the Old TPB (2010, $14.99) r/#40-44 and Special #4 15.00
...: Smoke Smoke TPB (2007, $12.99) r/#21-25 13.00
...: The First Hundred Days TPB ('05, $9.95) r/#1-5; photo reference and sketch pages 10.00
...: Tag TPB (2005, $12.99) r/#6-10; Harris sketch pages 13.00
...: Term Limits TPB (2010, $14.99) r/#45-50 15.00

EX-MUTANTS
Malibu Comics: Nov, 1992 - No. 18, Apr, 1994 ($1.95/$2.25/$2.50)

1-18: 1-Polybagged w/Skycap; prismatic cover 3.00

EXORCISTS (See The Crusaders)

EXOSQUAD (TV)

GD VG FN VF VF/NM NM-
2.0 4.0 6.0 8.0 9.0 9.2

Topps Comics: No. 0, Jan, 1994 ($1.00)

0-($1.00, 20 pgs.)-1st app.; Staton-a(p); wraparound-c 3.00

EXOTIC ROMANCES (Formerly True War Romances)
Quality Comics Group (Comic Magazines): No. 22, Oct, 1955 - No. 31, Nov, 1956

22 15 30 45 86 133 180
23-26,29 11 22 33 62 86 110
27,31-Baker-c/a 24 48 72 142 234 325
28,30-Baker-a 17 34 51 100 158 215

EXPENDABLES, THE (Movie)
Dynamite Entertainment: 2010 - No. 4, 2010 ($3.99, limited series)

1-4-Chuck Dixon-s/Esteve Polls-a/Lucio Parrillo-c; prelude to the 2010 movie 4.00

EXPLOITS OF DANIEL BOONE
Quality Comics Group: Nov, 1955 - No. 6, Oct, 1956

1-All have Cuidera-c(i) 20 40 60 114 182 250
2 (1/56) 14 28 42 82 121 160
3-6 13 26 39 74 105 135

EXPLOITS OF DICK TRACY (See Dick Tracy)

EXPLORER JOE
Ziff-Davis Comic Group (Approved Comics): Win, 1951 - No. 2, Oct-Nov, 1952

1-2: Saunders painted covers; 2-Krigstein-a 14 28 42 82 121 160

EXPLORERS OF THE UNKNOWN (See Archie Giant Series #587, 599)
Archie Comics: June, 1990 - No. 6, Apr, 1991 ($1.00)

1-6: Featuring Archie and the gang 3.00

EXPOSED (...True Crime Cases; ...Cases in the Crusade Against Crime #5-9)
D. S. Publishing Co.: Mar-Apr, 1948 - No. 9, July-Aug, 1949

1 36 72 108 211 343 475
2-Giggling killer story with excessive blood; two injury-to-eye panels; electrocution panel 39 78 117 240 395 550
3,8,9 17 34 51 98 154 210
4-Orlando-a 18 36 54 103 162 220
5-Breeze Lawson, Sky Sheriff by E. Good 18 36 54 103 162 220
6,7: 6-Ingels-a; used in **SOTI**, illo. "How to prepare an alibi" 7-Illo. in **SOTI**, "Diagram for housebreakers;" used by N.Y. Legis. Committee 39 78 117 240 395 550

EXTERMINATION
BOOM! Studios: Jun, 2012 - No. 8, Jan, 2013 ($1.00/$3.99)

1-($1.00) Nine covers; Spurrier-s/Jeffrey Edwards-a 3.00
2-8-($3.99) 4.00

EXTERMINATORS, THE
DC Comics (Vertigo): Mar, 2006 - No. 30, Aug, 2008 ($2.99)

1-30: Simon Oliver-s/Tony Moore-a in most. 11,12-Hawthorne-a 3.00
...: Bug Brothers TPB (2006, $9.99) r/#1-5; intro. by screenwriter Josh Olson 10.00
...: Bug Brothers Forever TPB (2008, $14.99) r/#24-30; intro. by Simon Oliver 15.00
...: Crossfire and Collateral TPB (2008, $14.99) r/#17-23 15.00
...: Insurgency TPB (2007, $12.99) r/#6-10 13.00
...: Lies of Our Fathers TPB (2007, $14.99) r/#11-16 15.00

EXTINCT!
New England Comics Press: Wint, 1991-92 - No. 2, Fall, 1992 ($3.50, B&W)

1,2-Reprints and background info of "perfectly awful" Golden Age stories 4.00

EXTINCTION EVENT
DC Comics (WildStorm): Sept, 2003 - No. 5, Jan, 2004 ($2.50, limited series)

1-5-Booth-a/Weinberg-s 3.00

EXTRA!
E. C. Comics: Mar-Apr, 1955 - No. 5, Nov-Dec, 1955

1-Not code approved 21 42 63 168 272 375
2-5 13 26 39 104 170 235

NOTE: *Craig, Crandall, Severin* art in all.

EXTRA!
Gemstone Publishing: Jan, 2000 - No. 5, May, 2000 ($2.50)

1-5-Reprints E.C. series 4.00

EXTRA COMICS
Magazine Enterprises: 1948 (25¢, 3 comics in one)

1-Giant; consisting of rebound ME comics. Two versions known; (1)-Funnyman by Siegel & Shuster, Space Ace, Undercover Girl, Red Fox by L.B. Cole, Trail Colt & (2)-All Funnyman 68 136 204 435 743 1050

EXTRAORDINARY X-MEN

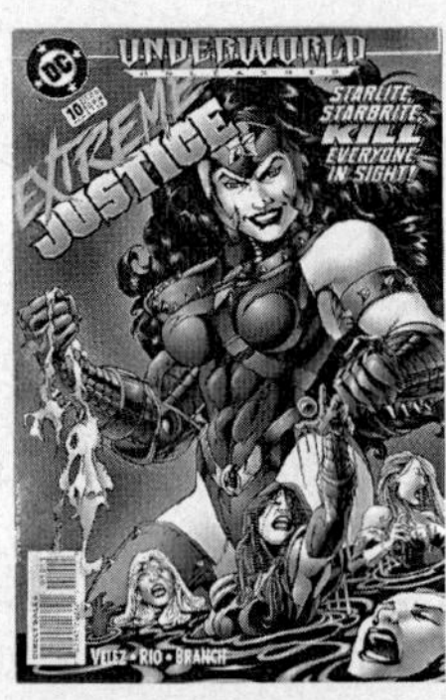

Extreme Justice #10 © DC

Fables #109 © Bill Willingham & DC

The Fade Out #4 © Basement Gang

GD 2.0 | VG 4.0 | FN 6.0 | VF 8.0 | VF/NM 9.0 | NM- 9.2

Marvel Comics: Jan, 2016 - No. 20, May, 2017 ($4.99/$3.99)

1-($4.99) Team of Old Man Logan, Storm, Jean Grey & others; Lemire-s/Ramos-a 5.00
2-7,9-20-($3.99) 2-Mister Sinister returns. 6,7,13-16-Ibanez-a. 9-12-Apocalypse Wars 4.00
8-($4.99) Apocalypse Wars x-over; Ramos-a; back-up story with Doctor Strange 5.00
Annual 1 (11/16, $4.99) Masters-s/Barberi-a; Montclare-s/Kämpe-a; Moon Girl app. 5.00

EXTREME
Image Comics (Extreme Studios): Aug, 1993 (Giveaway)

0 3.00

EXTREME DESTROYER
Image Comics (Extreme Studios): Jan, 1996 ($2.50)

Prologue 1-Polybagged w/card; Liefeld-c, Epilogue 1-Liefeld-c 3.00

EXTREME JUSTICE
DC Comics: No. 0, Jan, 1995 - No. 18, July, 1996 ($1.50/$1.75)

0-18 3.00

EXTREMELY YOUNGBLOOD
Image Comics (Extreme Studios): Sept, 1996 ($3.50, one-shot)

1 3.50

EXTREME SACRIFICE
Image Comics (Extreme Studios): Jan, 1995 ($2.50, limited series)

Prelude (#1)-Liefeld wraparound-c; polybagged w/ trading card 3.00
Epilogue (#2)-Liefeld wraparound-c; polybagged w/trading card 3.00
Trade paperback (6/95, $16.95)-Platt-a 17.00

EXTREME SUPER CHRISTMAS SPECIAL
Image Comics (Extreme Studios): Dec, 1994 ($2.95, one-shot)

1 3.00

EXTREMIST, THE
DC Comics (Vertigo): Sept, 1993 - No. 4, Dec, 1993 ($1.95, limited series)

1-4-Peter Milligan scripts; McKeever-c/a 3.00
1-Platinum Edition 5.00

EYE OF NEWT
Dark Horse Comics: Jun, 2014 - No. 4, Sept, 2014 ($3.99, limited series)

1-4-Michael Hague-s/a/c 4.00

EYE OF THE STORM
Rival Productions: Dec, 1994 - No. 7, June, 1995? ($2.95)

1-7: Computer generated comic 3.00

EYE OF THE STORM
DC Comics (WildStorm): Sept, 2003 ($4.95)

Annual 1-Short stories by various incl. Portacio, Johns, Coker, Pearson, Arcudi 5.00

FABLES
DC Comics (Vertigo): July, 2002 - Present ($2.50/$2.75/$2.99)

1-Willingham-s/Medina-a; two covers by Maleev & Jean 65.00
1: Special Edition (12/06, 25¢) r/#1 with preview of 1001 Nights of Snowfall 3.00
1: Special Edition (9/09, $1.00) r/#1 with preview of Peter & Max 3.00
1-Special Edition (8/10, $1.00) Reprints #1 with "What's Next?" logo on cover 3.00
1-Special Edition (3/16, $3.99) Reprints #1 with new cover by Dave McKean 4.00
2-Medina-a 15.00
3-5 10.00
6-37: 6-10-Buckingham-a. 11-Talbot-a. 18-Medley-a. 26-Preview of The Witching 5.00
6-RRP Edition wraparound variant-c; promotional giveaway for retailers (200 printed) 200.00
38-49,51-74,76-99,101-149: 38-Begin $2.75-c. 49-Begin $2.99-c. 57,58,76-Allred-a. 83-85-X-over with Jack of Fables & The Literals. 101-Shanower-a. 107-Terry Moore-a 113-Back-up art by Russell, Cannon, Hughes. 147-Terry Moore-a (3 pgs.) 3.00
50-($3.99) Wedding of Snow White and Bigby Wolf; preview of Jack of Fables series 5.00
75-($4.99) Geppetto surrenders; pin-up gallery by Powell, Nowlan, Cooke & others 5.00
100-(1/11, $9.99, squarebound) Buckingham-a; short stories art by Hughes & others 10.00
Animal Farm (2003, $12.95, TPB) r/#6-10; sketch pages by Buckingham & Jean 13.00
...: Arabian Nights (And Days) (2006, $14.99, TPB) r/#42-47 15.00
...: Homelands (2005, $14.99, TPB) r/#34-41 15.00
Legends in Exile (2002, $9.95, TPB) r/#1-5; new short story Willingham-s/a 15.00
...: March of the Wooden Soldiers (2004, $17.95, TPB) r/#19-21 & ...: The Last Castle 18.00
...: 1001 Nights of Snowfall HC (2006, $19.99) short stories by Willingham with art by various incl. Bolton, Kaluta, Jean, McPherson, Thompson, Vess, Wheatley, Buckingham 20.00
...: 1001 Nights of Snowfall (2008, $14.99, TPB) short stories with art by various 15.00
...: Rose Red (2011, $17.99, TPB) r/#94-100; Buckingham design and sketch pages 18.00
...: Sons of Empire (2007, $17.99, TPB) r/#52-59 18.00
...: Storybook Love (2004, $14.95, TPB) r/#11-18 15.00
...: The Dark Ages (2009, $17.99, TPB) r/#76-82 18.00
...: The Deluxe Edition Book One HC (2009, $29.99, DJ) r/#1-10; character sketch-a 30.00
...: The Deluxe Edition Book Two HC (2010, $29.99, DJ) r/#11-18 & ...: The Last Castle 30.00
...: The Good Prince (2008, $17.99, TPB) r/#60-69 18.00
...: The Great Fables Crossover (2010, $17.99, TPB) r/#83-85, Jack of Fables #33-35 and The Literals #1-3; sneak preview of Peter & Max: A Fables Novel 18.00
...: The Last Castle (2003, $5.95) Hamilton-a/Willingham-s; prequel to title 6.00
...: The Mean Seasons (2005, $14.99, TPB) r/#22,28-33 15.00
...: War and Pieces (2008, $17.99, TPB) r/#70-75; sketch and pin-up pages 18.00
...: Witches (2010, $17.99, TPB) r/#86-93 18.00
...: Wolves (2006, $17.99, TPB) r/#48-51; script to #50 18.00

FABLES: THE WOLF AMONG US (Based on the Telltale Games video game)
DC Comics (Vertigo): Mar, 2015 - No. 16, Jun, 2016 ($3.99, printing of digital first stories)

1-16-Prequel to Fables; Sturges & Justus-s 4.00

FACE, THE (Tony Trent, the Face No. 3 on) (See Big Shot Comics)
Columbia Comics Group: 1941 - No. 2, 1943

	GD 2.0	VG 4.0	FN 6.0	VF 8.0	VF/NM 9.0	NM- 9.2
1-The Face; Mart Bailey WWII-c	100	200	300	635	1093	1550
2-Bailey WWII-c	68	136	204	435	743	1050

FACES OF EVIL
DC Comics: Mar, 2009 ($2.99, series of one-shots)

...: Deathstroke 1 - Jeanty-a/Ladronn-c; Ravager app. 3.00
...: Kobra 1 - Jason Burr returns; Julian Lopez-a 3.00
...: Prometheus 1 - Gates-s/Dallacchio-a; origin re-told; Anima killed 3.00
...: Solomon Grundy 1 - Johns-s/Kolins-a; leads into Solomon Grundy mini-series 3.00

FACTOR X
Marvel Comics: Mar, 1995 - No. 4, July, 1995 ($1.95, limited series)

1-Age of Apocalypse 4.00
2-4 3.00

FACULTY FUNNIES
Archie Comics: June, 1989 - No. 5, May, 1990 (75¢/95¢ #2 on)

1-5: 1,2,4,5-The Awesome Foursome app. 3.00

FADE FROM GRACE
Beckett Comics: Aug, 2004 - No. 5, Mar, 2005 (99¢/$1.99)

1-(99¢) Jeff Amano-a/c; Gabriel Benson-s; origin of Fade 3.00
2-5-($1.99) 3.00
TPB (2005, $14.99) r/#1-5; cover gallery, afterword by David Mack 15.00

FADE OUT, THE
Image Comics: Aug, 2014 - No. 12, Jan, 2016 ($3.50/$3.99)

1-12-Ed Brubaker-s/Sean Phillips-a/c. 12-($3.99) 4.00

FAFHRD AND THE GREY MOUSER (Also see Sword of Sorcery & Wonder Woman #202)
Marvel Comics: Oct, 1990 - No. 4, 1991 ($4.50, 52 pgs., squarebound)

1-4: Mignola/Williamson-a; Chaykin scripts 5.00

FAGIN THE JEW
Doubleday: Oct, 2003 ($15.95, softcover graphic novel)

nn-Will Eisner-s/a; story of Fagin from Dickens' Oliver Twist 16.00

FAIREST (Characters from Fables)
DC Comics (Vertigo): May, 2012 - No. 33, Mar, 2015 ($2.99)

1-33: 1-6-Willingham-s/Jimenez-a. 1-Wraparound-c by Hughes & variant-c by Jimenez 3.00
...: In All The Land HC (2013, $24.99, dustjacket) New short stories by various; Hughes-c 25.00

FAIRY QUEST: OUTCASTS
BOOM! Studios: Nov, 2014 - No. 2, Dec, 2014 ($3.99, limited series)

1,2-Jenkins-s/Ramos-a/c 4.00

FAIRY QUEST: OUTLAWS
BOOM! Studios: Feb, 2013 - No. 2, Mar, 2013 ($3.99, limited series)

1,2-Jenkins-s/Ramos-a/c 4.00

FAIRY TALE PARADE (See Famous Fairy Tales)
Dell Publishing Co.: June-July, 1942 - No. 121, Oct, 1946 (Most by Walt Kelly)

	GD 2.0	VG 4.0	FN 6.0	VF 8.0	VF/NM 9.0	NM- 9.2
1-Kelly-a begins	86	172	258	688	1544	2400
2(8-9/42)	38	76	114	285	641	1000
3-5 (10-11/42 - 2-4/43)	29	58	87	196	441	685
6-9 (5-7/43 - 11-1/43-44)	22	44	66	154	340	525
Four Color 50('44), 69('45), 87('45)	21	42	63	147	324	500
Four Color 104, 114('46)-Last Kelly issue	16	32	48	112	249	385
Four Color 121('46)-Not by Kelly	10	20	30	69	147	225

NOTE: *#1-9, 4-Color #50, 69 have **Kelly** c/a; 4-Color #87, 104, 114-**Kelly** art only. #9 has a redrawn version of The Reluctant Dragon. This series contains all the classic fairy tales from Jack In The Beanstalk to Cinderella.*

FAIRY TALES

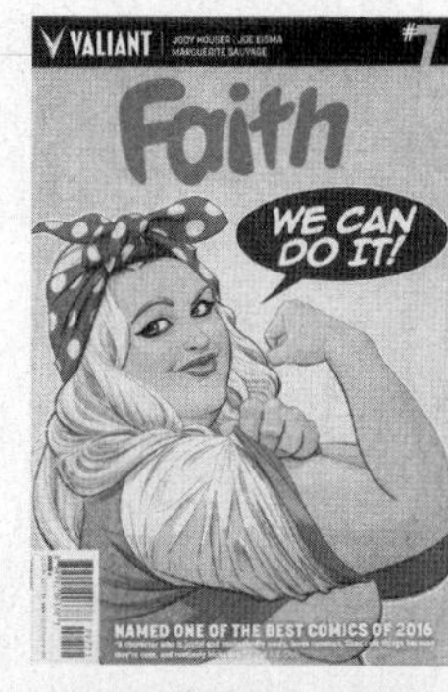

Faith #7 © VAL

Falcon (2017 series) #1 © MAR

Family Funnies #2 © KFS

GD 2.0 | VG 4.0 | FN 6.0 | VF 8.0 | VF/NM 9.0 | NM- 9.2

Ziff-Davis Publ. Co. (Approved Comics): No. 10, Apr-May, 1951 - No. 11, June-July, 1951
10,11-Painted-c 22 44 66 130 213 295

FAITH
DC Comics (Vertigo): Nov, 1999 - No. 5, Mar, 2000 ($2.50, limited series)
1-5-Ted McKeever-s/c/a 3.00

FAITH (Zephyr from Harbinger)
Valiant Entertainment: Jan, 2016 - No. 4, Apr, 2016 ($3.99, limited series)
1-4-Houser-s/Portela-a. 3,4-Torque app. 4.00

FAITH (Harbinger)
Valiant Entertainment: Jul, 2016 - No. 12, Jun, 2017 ($3.99)
1-12: 1-4-Houser-s/Pere Pérez-a. 5-Hillary Clinton app. 7-12-Eisma-a 4.00
Faith's Winter Wonderland Special 1 (12/17, $3.99) Sauvage-s/Portela & Kim-a 4.00

FAITH AND THE FUTURE FORCE (Harbinger)
Valiant Entertainment: Jul, 2017 - No. 4, Oct, 2017 ($3.99, limited series)
1-4-Houser-s. 1-Segovia & Kitson-a. 2-Kitson & Bernard-a. 3-Most Valiant heroes app. 4.00

FAITHFUL
Marvel Comics/Lovers' Magazine: Nov, 1949 - No. 2, Feb, 1950 (52 pgs.)
1,2-Photo-c 15 30 45 88 137 185

FAKER
DC Comics (Vertigo): Sept, 2007 - No. 6, Feb, 2008 ($2.99, limited series)
1-6-Mike Carey-s/Jock-a/c 3.00
TPB (2008, $14.99) r/#1-6; Jock sketch pages 15.00

FALCON (See Marvel Premiere #49, Avengers #181 & Captain America #117 & 133)
Marvel Comics Group: Nov, 1983 - No. 4, Feb, 1984 (Mini-series)
1-Paul Smith-c/a(p) 2 4 6 8 11 14
2-4: 2-Paul Smith-c/Mark Bright-a. 3-Kupperberg-c 6.00

FALCON (Marvel Legacy)
Marvel Comics: Dec, 2017 - Present ($3.99)
1-5-Sam Wilson back as the Falcon after Secret Empire; Barnes-s/Cassara-a 4.00

FALL AND RISE OF CAPTAIN ATOM, THE
DC Comics: Mar, 2017 - No. 6, Aug, 2017 ($2.99, limited series)
1-6-Bates-s/Conrad-a 3.00

FALLEN ANGEL
DC Comics: Sept, 2003 - No. 20, July, 2005 ($2.50/$2.95)
1-9-Peter David-s/David Lopez-a/Stelfreeze-c; intro. Lee 3.00
10-20: 10-Begin $2.95-c. 13,17-Kaluta-c. 20-Last issue; Pérez-c 3.00
TPB (2004, $12.95) r/#1-6; intro. by Harlan Ellison 13.00
Down to Earth TPB (2007, $14.99) r/#7-12 15.00

FALLEN ANGEL
IDW Publ.: Dec, 2005 - No. 33, Dec, 2008 ($3.99)
1-33: 1-14-Peter David-s/J.K Woodward-a. Retailer variant-c for each. 15-Donaldson-a. 17-Flip cover with Shi story; Tucci-a. 25-Wraparound-c; character gallery 4.00
... Reborn 1-4 (7/09 - No. 4, 10/09, $3.99) David-s/Woodward-a; Illyria (from Angel) app. 4.00
... Return of the Son 1-4 (1/11 - No. 4, 4/11, $3.99) David-s/Woodward-a; 4.00
...: To Serve in Heaven TPB (8/06, $19.99) r/#1-5; gallery of reg & variant covers 20.00

FALLEN ANGEL ON THE WORLD OF MAGIC: THE GATHERING
Acclaim (Armada): May, 1996 ($5.95, one-shot)
1-Nancy Collins story 6.00

FALLEN ANGELS
Marvel Comics Group: April, 1987 - No. 8, Nov, 1987 (Limited series)
1-8 4.00

FALLEN SON: THE DEATH OF CAPTAIN AMERICA
Marvel Comics: June, 2007 - No. 5, Aug, 2007 ($2.99, limited series)
1-5: Loeb-s in all. 1-Wolverine; Yu-a/c. 2-Avengers; McGuinness-a/c. 3-Captain America; Romita Jr.-a/c; Hawkeye app. 4-Spider-Man; Finch-c/a. 5-Cassaday-c/a 3.00
1-5-Variant covers by Turner 3.00
HC (2007, $19.99, dustjacket) r/#1-5 20.00
TPB (2008, $13.99) r/#1-5 14.00

FALLING IN LOVE
Arleigh Pub. Co./National Per. Pub.: Sept-Oct, 1955 - No. 143, Oct-Nov, 1973
1 47 94 141 296 498 700
2 26 52 78 154 252 350
3-10 17 34 51 98 154 210
11-20 15 30 45 84 127 170
21-40 13 26 39 72 101 130
41-47: 47-Last 10¢ issue 11 22 33 64 90 115
48-70 5 10 15 34 60 85
71-99,108: 108-Wood-a (4 pgs., 7/69) 4 8 12 25 40 55
100 (7/68) 4 8 12 27 44 60
101-107,109-124 3 6 9 16 23 30
134-143 3 6 9 14 19 24
125-133: 52 pgs. 3 6 9 21 33 45
NOTE: *Colan c/a-75, 81. 52 pgs.-#125-133.*

FALLING MAN, THE
Image Comics: Feb, 1998 ($2.95)
1-McCorkindale-s/Hester-a 3.00

FALL OF THE HOUSE OF USHER, THE (See A Corben Special & Spirit section 8/22/48)

FALL OF THE HULKS (Also see Hulk and Incredible Hulk)
Marvel Comics: Feb, 2010 - July, 2010 ($3.99, one-shots & limited series)
Alpha (2/10) Pelletier-a; The Leader, Dr. Doom, MODOK and The Thinker app. 4.00
Gamma (2/10) Romita Jr. -a; funeral for General Ross 4.00
Red Hulk (3/10 - No. 4, 6/10) 1-4: 1-A-Bomb app. 4.00
Savage She-Hulks (5/10 - No. 3, 7/10) 1-3: Cover tryptich by Campbell; Espin-a 4.00

FALL OF THE ROMAN EMPIRE (See Movie Comics)

FALL OUT TOY WORKS
Image Comics: Sept, 2009 - No. 5, Jun, 2010 ($3.99)
1-5-Co-created by Pete Wentz of the band Fall Out Boy; Basri-a. 5-Lau-c 4.00

FAMILY AFFAIR (TV)
Gold Key: Feb, 1970 - No. 4, Oct, 1970 (25¢)
1-With pull-out poster; photo-c 5 10 15 34 60 85
1-With poster missing 3 6 9 17 26 35
2-4-Photo-c 3 6 9 20 31 42

FAMILY DYNAMIC, THE
DC Comics: Oct, 2008 - No. 3, Dec, 2008 ($2.25)
1-3-J. Torres-s/Tim Levins-a 3.00

FAMILY FUNNIES
Parents' Magazine Institute: No. 9, Aug-Sept, 1946
9 6 12 18 28 34 40

FAMILY FUNNIES (Tiny Tot Funnies No. 9)
Harvey Publications: Sept, 1950 - No. 8, Apr, 1951
1-Mandrake (has over 30 King Feature strips) 10 20 30 58 79 100
2-Flash Gordon, 1 pg. 8 16 24 40 50 60
3-8: 4,5,7-Flash Gordon, 1 pg. 6 12 18 31 38 45

FAMILY GUY (TV)
Devil's Due Publ.: 2006 ($6.95)
nn-101 Ways to Kill Lois; 2-Peter Griffin's Guide to Parenting; 3-Books Don't Taste Very Good 7.00
... A Big Book o' Crap TPB (10/06, $16.95) r/nn,2,3 17.00

FAMILY MATTER
Kitchen Sink Press: 1998 ($24.95/$15.95, graphic novel)
Hardcover ($24.95) Will Eisner-s/a 25.00
Softcover ($15.95) 16.00

FAMOUS AUTHORS ILLUSTRATED (See Stories by...)

FAMOUS CRIMES
Fox Feature Syndicate/M.S. Dist. No. 51,52: June, 1948 - No. 19, Sept, 1950; No. 20, Aug, 1951; No. 51, 52, 1953
1-Blue Beetle app. & crime story-r/Phantom Lady #16 84 168 252 538 919 1300
2-Has woman dissolved in acid; lingerie-c/panels 57 114 171 362 619 875
3-Injury-to-eye story used in **SOTI**, pg. 112; has two electrocution stories 63 126 189 403 689 975
4-6 28 56 84 165 270 375
7- "Tarzan, the Wyoming Killer" (**SOTI**, pg. 44) 45 90 135 284 480 675
8-20: 17-Morisi-a. 20-Same cover as #15 21 42 63 122 199 275
51 (nd, 1953) 18 36 54 103 162 220
52 (Exist?) 18 36 54 103 162 220

FAMOUS FEATURE STORIES
Dell Publishing Co.: 1938 (7-1/2x11", 68 pgs.)
1-Tarzan, Terry & the Pirates, King of the Royal Mtd., Buck Jones, Dick Tracy, Smilin' Jack, Dan Dunn, Don Winslow, G-Man, Tailspin Tommy, Mutt & Jeff, Little Orphan Annie

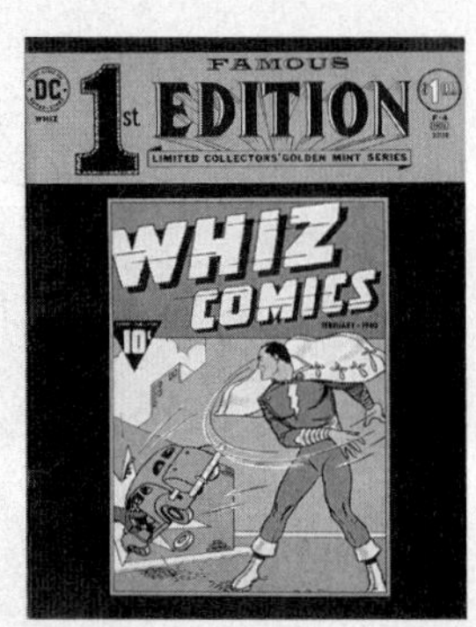

Famous First Edition F-4 © DC

Famous Funnies #1 © EAS

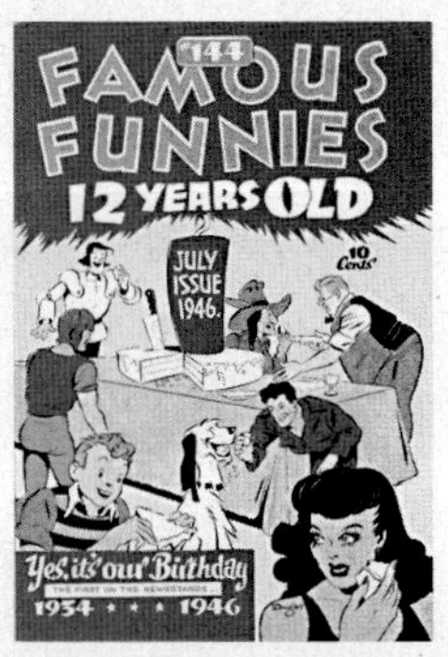

Famous Funnies #144 © EAS

GD VG FN VF VF/NM NM-
2.0 4.0 6.0 8.0 9.0 9.2

reprints - all illustrated text 65 130 195 416 708 1000

FAMOUS FIRST EDITION (See Limited Collectors' Edition)
National Periodical Publications/DC Comics: ($1.00, 10x13-1/2", 72 pgs.) (No.6-8, 68 pgs.) 1974 - No. 8, Aug-Sept, 1975; C-61, 1979
(Hardbound editions with dust jackets are from Lyle Stuart, Inc.)

C-26-Action Comics #1; gold ink outer-c 6 12 18 37 66 95
C-26-Hardbound edition w/dust jacket 15 30 45 105 233 360
C-28-Detective #27; silver ink outer-c 6 12 18 37 66 95
C-28-Hardbound edition w/dust jacket 15 30 45 105 233 360
C-30-Sensation #1(1974); bronze ink outer-c 5 10 15 30 50 70
C-30-Hardbound edition w/dust jacket 13 26 39 89 195 300
F-4-Whiz Comics #2(#1)(10-11/74)-Cover not identical to original (dropped "Gangway for Captain Marvel" from cover); gold ink on outer-c 5 10 15 30 50 70
F-4-Hardbound edition w/dust jacket 13 26 39 89 195 300
F-5-Batman #1(F-6 inside); silver ink on outer-c 5 10 15 33 57 80
F-5-Hardbound edition w/dust jacket (exist?) 13 26 39 89 195 300
V2#F-6-Wonder Woman #1 5 10 15 30 50 70
F-6-Wonder Woman #1 Hardbound w/dust jacket 13 26 39 89 195 300
F-7-All-Star Comics #3 5 10 15 30 50 70
F-8-Flash Comics #1(8-9/75) 5 10 15 30 50 70
V8#C-61-Superman #1(1979, $2.00) 4 8 12 27 44 60
V8#C-61 (Whitman variant) 4 8 12 28 47 65
V8#C-61 (Softcover in plain grey slipcase, edition of 250 copies) Each signed by Jerry Siegel and Joe Shuster at the bottom of the inside front cover 550.00

Warning: The above books are almost **exact** reprints of the originals that they represent except for the Giant-Size format. None of the originals are Giant-Size. The first five issues and C-61 were printed with two covers. Reprint information can be found on the outside cover, but not on the inside cover which was reprinted exactly like the original (inside and out).

FAMOUS FUNNIES
Eastern Color: 1934; July, 1934 - No. 218, July, 1955

A Carnival of Comics (See Promotional Comics section)

Series 1-(Very rare)(nd-early 1934)(68 pgs.) No publisher given (Eastern Color PrintingCo.); sold in chain stores for 10¢. 35,000 print run. Contains Sunday strip reprints of Mutt & Jeff, Reg'lar Fellers, Nipper, Hairbreadth Harry, Strange As It Seems, Joe Palooka, Dixie Dugan, The Nebbs, Keeping Up With the Jones, and others. Inside front and back covers and pages 1-16 of Famous Funnies Series 1, #s 49-64 reprinted from **Famous Funnies**, **A Carnival of Comics**, and most of pages 17-48 reprinted from **Funnies on Parade**.
7250 14,500 21,750 43,500 - -

No. 1 (Rare)(7/34-on stands 5/34) - Eastern Color Printing Co. First monthly newsstand comic book. Contains Sunday strip reprints of Toonerville Folks, Mutt & Jeff, Hairbreadth Harry, S'Matter Pop, Nipper, Dixie Dugan, The Bungle Family, Connie, Ben Webster, Tailspin Tommy, The Nebbs, Joe Palooka, & others.
3200 6400 9600 24,000 - -

2 (Rare, 9/34) 812 1624 2436 6100 - -
3-Buck Rogers Sunday strip-r by Rick Yager begins, ends #218; not in #191-208; 1st comic book app. of Buck Rogers; the number of the 1st strip reprinted is pg. 190, Series No. 1
947 1894 2841 7100 - -
4 333 666 999 2500 - -
5-1st Christmas-c on a newsstand comic 360 720 1080 2700 - -
6-10 240 480 720 1800 - -
11,12,18-Four pgs. of Buck Rogers in each issue, completes stories in Buck Rogers #1 which lacks these pages. 18-Two pgs. of Buck Rogers reprinted in Daisy Comics #1
110 220 330 699 1250 1800
13-17,19,20: 14-Has two Buck Rogers panels missing. 17-2nd Christmas-c on a newsstand comic (12/35) 79 158 237 474 937 1400
21,23-30: 27-(10/36)-War on Crime begins (4 pgs.); 1st true crime in comics (reprints); part photo-c. 29-X-Mas-c (12/36) 60 120 180 360 693 1025
22-Four pgs. of Buck Rogers needed to complete stories in Buck Rogers #1
68 136 204 432 791 1150
31,33,34,36,37,39,40: 33-Careers of Baby Face Nelson & John Dillinger traced
42 84 126 252 489 725
32-(3/37) 1st app. the Phantom Magician (costume hero) in Advs. of Patsy
50 100 150 318 559 800
35-Two pgs. Buck Rogers omitted in Buck Rogers #2
50 100 150 318 559 800
38-Full color portrait of Buck Rogers 44 88 132 264 507 750
41-60: 41,53-X-Mas-c. 55-Last bottom panel, pg. 4 in Buck Rogers redrawn in Buck Rogers #3 39 78 117 231 378 525
61,63,64,66,67,69,70 27 54 81 158 259 360
62,65,68,73-78-Two pgs. Kirby-a "Lightnin' & the Lone Rider". 65,77-X-Mas-c
29 58 87 170 278 385
71,79,80: 80-(3/41)-Buck Rogers story continues from Buck Rogers #5
22 44 66 132 216 300
72-Speed Spaulding begins by Marvin Bradley (artist), ends #88. This series was written by Edwin Balmer & Philip Wylie (later appeared as film & book "When Worlds Collide")
24 48 72 140 230 320

GD VG FN VF VF/NM NM-
2.0 4.0 6.0 8.0 9.0 9.2

81-Origin & 1st app. Invisible Scarlet O'Neil (4/41); strip begins #82, ends #167; 1st non-funny-c (Scarlet O'Neil) 30 60 90 177 289 400
82-Buck Rogers-c 32 64 96 188 307 425
83-87,90: 86-Connie vs. Monsters on the Moon-c (sci/fi). 87 has last Buck Rogers full page-r. 90-Bondage-c 20 40 60 117 189 260
88,89: 88-Buck Rogers in "Moon's End" by Calkins, 2 pgs.(not reprints). Beginning with #88, all Buck Rogers pgs. have rearranged panels. 89-Origin & 1st app. Fearless Flint, the Flint Man 22 44 66 130 213 295
91-93,95,96,98-99,101,103-110: 98-Hitler, Tojo and Mussolini on inside back-c. 101-Christmas cover. 105-Series 2 begins (Strip Page #1) 17 34 51 98 154 210
94-Buck Rogers in "Solar Holocaust" by Calkins, 3 pgs.(not reprints)
18 36 54 107 169 230
97-War Bond promotion, Buck Rogers by Calkins, 2 pgs.(not reprints)
18 36 54 107 169 230
100-1st comic to reach #100; 100th Anniversary cover features 11 major Famous Funnies characters, including Buck Rogers 23 46 69 136 223 310
102-Chief Wahoo vs. Hitler,Tojo & Mussolini-c (1/43) 81 162 243 518 884 1250
111-130 (5/45): 113-X-Mas-c 14 28 42 76 108 140
131-150 (1/47): 137-Strip page No. 110 omitted; Christmas-c. 144-(7/46) 12th Anniversary cover 12 24 36 69 97 125
151-162,164-168: 162-New Year's Eve-c 11 22 33 64 90 115
163-St. Valentine's Day-c (2/48) 12 24 36 69 97 125
169,170-Two text illos. by Al Williamson, his 1st comic book work
14 28 42 80 115 150
171-190: 171-Strip pgs. 227,229,230, Series 2 omitted. 172-Strip Pg. 232 omitted. 173-Christmas-c. 190-Buck Rogers ends with start of strip pg. 302, Series 2; Oaky Doaks-c/story 11 22 33 60 83 105
191-197,199,201,203,206-208: No Buck Rogers. 191-Barney Carr, Space detective begins, ends #192. 10 20 30 58 79 100
198,200,202,205-One pg. Frazetta ads; no B. Rogers 11 22 33 60 83 105
204-Used in **POP**, pg. 79,99; war-c begin, end #208 11 22 33 62 86 110
209-216: Frazetta-c. 209-Buck Rogers begins (12/53) with strip pg. 480, Series 2; 211-Buck Rogers ads by Anderson begins, ends #217. #215-Contains B. Rogers strip pg. 515-518, series 2 followed by pgs.179-181, Series 3 187 374 561 1197 2049 2900
217-Buck Rogers-c 16 32 48 94 147 200
218-Buck Rogers ends with pg. 199, Series 3; Wee Three-c/story
11 22 33 60 83 105

NOTE: ***Rick Yager*** *did the Buck Rogers Sunday strips reprinted in Famous Funnies. The Sundays were formerly done by Russ Keaton and Lt. Dick Calkins did the dailies, but would sometimes assist Yager on a panel or two from time to time. Strip No. 169 is Yager's first full Buck Rogers page. Yager did the strip until 1958 when* ***Murph Anderson*** *took over.* ***Tuska*** *art from 4/26/59 - 1965. Virtually every panel was rewritten for Famous Funnies. No identical to the original Sunday page. The Buck Rogers reprints run continuously through Famous Funnies issue No. 190 (Strip No. 302) with no break in story line. The story line has no continuity after No. 190. The Buck Rogers newspaper strips came out in four series: Series 1, 3/30/30 - 9/21/41 (No. 1 - 600); Series 2, 9/28/41 -10/21/51 (No 1 -525)(Strip No. 110-1/2 (1/2 pg.) published in only a few newspapers); Series 3, 10/28/51 -2/9/58 (No. 100-428)(No No.1-99); Series 4, 2/16/58 - 6/13/65 (No numbers, dates only).* ***Everett*** *c-85, 86.* ***Moulton*** *a-100. Chief Wahoo c 93, 97, 102, 116, 136, 139, 151. Dickie Dare c-83, 88. Fearless Flint c-89. Invisible Scarlet O'Neil c-81, 87, 95 121(part), 132. Scorchy Smith c-84, 90.*

FAMOUS FUNNIES
Super Comics: 1964

Super Reprint Nos. 15-18:17-r/Double Trouble #1. 18-Space Comics #?
2 4 6 9 12 15

FAMOUS GANGSTERS (Crime on the Waterfront No. 4)
Avon Periodicals/Realistic No. 3: Apr, 1951 - No. 3, Feb, 1952

1-3: 1-Capone, Dillinger; c-/Avon paperback #329. 2-Dillinger Machine Gun Killer; Wood-c/a (1 pg.); r/Saint #7 & retitled "Mike Strong". 3-Lucky Luciano & Murder, Inc; c-/Avon paperback #66 39 78 117 240 395 550

FAMOUS INDIAN TRIBES
Dell Publishing Co.: July-Sept, 1962; No. 2, July, 1972

12-264-209(#1) (The Sioux) 3 6 9 15 21 26
2(7/72)-Reprints above 1 3 4 6 8 10

FAMOUS STARS
Ziff-Davis Publ. Co.: Nov-Dec, 1950 - No. 6, Spring, 1952 (All have photo-c)

1-Shelley Winters, Susan Peters, Ava Gardner, Shirley Temple; Jimmy Stewart & Shelley Winters photo-c; Whitney-a 40 80 120 246 441 575
2-Betty Hutton, Bing Crosby, Colleen Townsend, Gloria Swanson; Betty Hutton photo-c; Everett-a(2) 29 58 87 170 278 385
3-Farley Granger, Judy Garland's ordeal (life story; she died 6/22/69 at the age of 47), Alan Ladd; Farley Granger photo-c; Whitney-a 36 72 108 211 343 475
4-Al Jolson, Bob Mitchum, Ella Raines, Richard Conte, Vic Damone; Jane Russell and Bob Mitchum photo-c; Crandall-a, 6pgs. 24 48 72 144 237 330
5-Liz Taylor, Betty Grable, Esther Williams, George Brent, Mario Lanza; Liz Taylor photo-c; Krigstein-a 53 106 159 334 567 800
6-Gene Kelly, Hedy Lamarr, June Allyson, William Boyd, Janet Leigh, Gary Cooper; Gene

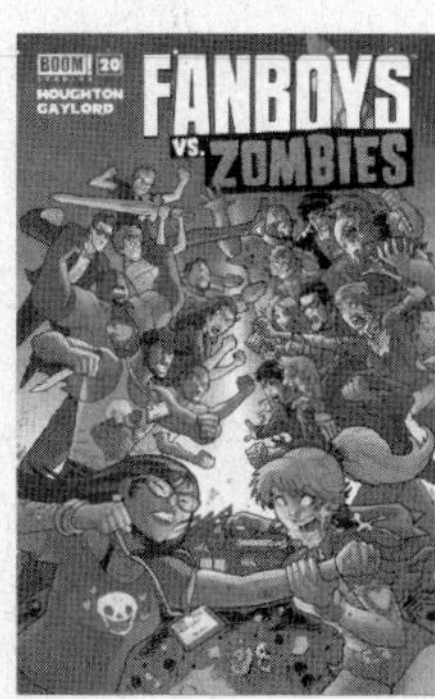

Fanboys vs. Zombies #20 © BOOM!

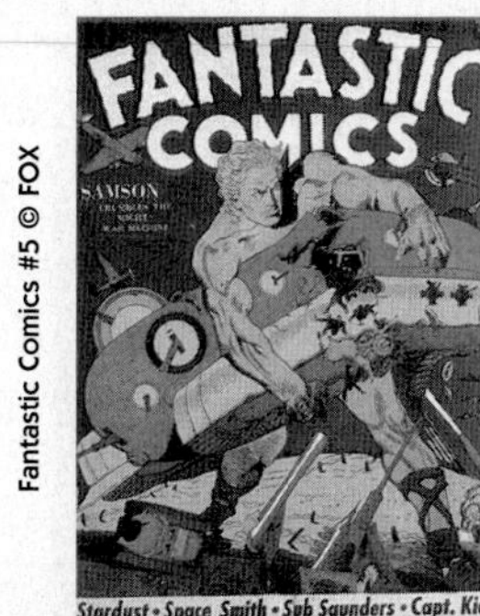

Fantastic Comics #5 © FOX

Fantastic Four #1 © MAR

	GD 2.0	VG 4.0	FN 6.0	VF 8.0	VF/NM 9.0	NM- 9.2
Kelly photo-c	22	44	66	132	216	300

FAMOUS STORIES (...Book No. 2)
Dell Publishing Co.: 1942 - No. 2, 1942

1,2: 1-Treasure Island. 2-Tom Sawyer 30 60 90 177 289 400

FAMOUS TV FUNDAY FUNNIES
Harvey Publications: Sept, 1961 (25¢ Giant)

1-Casper the Ghost, Baby Huey, Little Audrey 5 10 15 34 60 85

FAMOUS WESTERN BADMEN (Formerly Redskin)
Youthful Magazines: No. 13, Dec, 1952 - No. 15, Apr, 1953

13-Redskin story 15 30 45 88 137 185
14,15: 15-The Dalton Boys story 11 22 33 64 90 115

FAN BOY
DC Comics: Mar, 1999 - No. 6, Aug, 1999 ($2.50, limited series)

1-6: 1-Art by Aragonés and various in all. 2-Green Lantern-c/a by Gil Kane. 3-JLA. 4-Sgt. Rock art by Heath, Marie Severin. 5-Batman art by Sprang, Adams, Miller, Timm. 6-Wonder Woman; art by Rude, Grell 3.00
TPB (2001, $12.95) r/#1-6 13.00

FANBOYS VS. ZOMBIES
BOOM! Studios: Apr, 2012 - No. 20, Nov, 2013 ($1.00/$3.99)

1-($1.00) Eight covers; Humphries-s/Gaylord-a; zombies at San Diego Comic-Con 3.00
2-20-($3.99) 2-12-Multiple covers on each. 17-Bryan Turner-a 4.00

FANTASTIC (Formerly Captain Science; Beware No. 10 on)
Youthful Magazines: No. 8, Feb, 1952 - No. 9, Apr, 1952

8-Capt. Science by Harrison 47 94 141 296 498 700
9-Harrison-a; decapitation, shrunken head panels 39 78 117 231 378 525

FANTASTIC ADVENTURES
Super Comics: 1963 - 1964 (Reprints)

9,10,12,15,16,18: 9-r/? 10-r/He-Man #2(Toby). 11-Disbrow-a. 12-Unpublished Chesler material? 15-r/Spook #23. 16-r/Dark Shadows #2(Steinway); Briefer-a.18-r/Superior Stories #1 3 6 9 17 26 35
11-Wood-a; r/Blue Bolt #118 4 8 12 23 37 50
17-Baker-a(2) r/Seven Seas #6 4 8 12 23 37 50

FANTASTIC COMICS
Fox Feature Syndicate: Dec, 1939 - No. 23, Nov, 1941

1-Intro/origin Samson; Stardust, The Super Wizard, Sub Saunders (by Kiefer), Space Smith, Capt. Kidd begin 703 1406 2109 5132 9066 13,000
2-Powell text illos 326 652 978 2282 3991 5700
3-Classic Lou Fine Robot-c; Powell text illos 5500 11,000 16,500 24,200 32,100 40,000
4-Lou Fine-c 314 628 942 2198 3849 5500
5-Classic Lou Fine-c 423 846 1269 3046 5323 7600
6,7-Simon-c. 6-Bondage/torture-c 300 600 900 1920 3310 4700
8-Bondage/torture-c 206 412 618 1318 2259 3200
9,10: 9-Bondage-c. 10-Intro/origin David, Samson's aide 155 310 465 992 1696 2400
11-16,18-20: 11-Bondage/torture on a bed of nails-c. 16-Stardust ends 126 252 378 806 1378 1950
17,23: 17-1st app. Black Fury & sidekick Chuck; ends #23. 23-Origin The Gladiator 135 270 405 864 1482 2100
21-The Banshee begins(origin); ends #23; Hitler-c 271 542 813 1734 2967 4200
22-Hitler-c (likeness of Hitler as furnace on cover) 423 846 1269 3000 5250 7500
NOTE: *Lou Fine c-1-5. Tuska a-3-5, 8. Issue #11 has indicia to Mystery Men Comics #15. All issues feature Samson covers.*

FANTASTIC COMICS (Imagining of a 1941 issue by modern creators in Golden Age style)
Image Comics: No. 24, Jan, 2008 ($5.99, Golden Age sized, one-shot)

24-Samson, Yank Wilson, Stardust, Sub Saunders, Space Smith, Capt. Kidd app.; Larsen-c/a; art by Allred, Sienkiewicz, Yeates, Scioli, Hembeck, Ashley Wood & others 6.00

FANTASTIC COMICS (Fantastic Fears #1-9; Becomes Samson #12)
Ajax/Farrell Publ.: No. 10, Nov-Dec, 1954 - No. 11, Jan-Feb, 1955

10 (#1) 27 54 81 162 266 370
11-Robot-c 34 68 102 204 332 460

FANTASTIC FABLES
Silverwolf Comics: Feb, 1987 - No. 2, 1987 ($1.50, 28 pgs., B&W)

1,2: 1-Tim Vigil-a (6 pgs.). 2-Tim Vigil-a (7 pgs.) 4.00

FANTASTIC FEARS (Formerly Captain Jet) (Fantastic Comics #10 on)
Ajax/Farrell Publ.: No. 7, May, 1953 - No. 9, Sept-Oct, 1954

7(#1, 5/53)-Tales of Stalking Terror 61 122 183 390 670 950
8(#2, 7/53) 45 90 135 284 480 675
3,4 40 80 120 246 411 575
5-(1-2/54)-Ditko story (1st drawn) is written by Bruce Hamilton; r-in Weird V2#8 (1st pro work for Ditko but Daring Love #1 was published 1st) 174 348 522 1114 1907 2700
6-Decapitation-girl's head w/paper cutter (classic) 103 206 309 659 1130 1600
7(5-6/54), 9(9-10/54) 37 74 111 222 361 500
8(7-8/54)-Contains story intended for Jo-Jo; name changed to Kaza; decapitation story 39 78 117 231 378 525

FANTASTIC FIVE
Marvel Comics: Oct, 1999 - No. 5, Feb, 2000 ($1.99)

1-5: 1-M2 Universe; recaps origin; Ryan-a. 2-Two covers 3.00
Spider-Girl Presents Fantastic Five: In Search of Doom (2006, $7.99, digest) r/#1-5 8.00

FANTASTIC FIVE
Marvel Comics: Sept, 2007 - No. 5, Nov, 2007 ($2.99, limited series)

1-5-DeFalco-s/Lim-a; Dr. Doom returns vs. the future Fantastic Five 3.00
...: The Final Doom TPB (2007, $13.99) r/#1-5; cover sketches with inks 14.00

FANTASTIC FORCE
Marvel Comics: Nov, 1994 - No. 18, Apr, 1996 ($1.75)

1-($2.50)-Foil wraparound-c; intro Fantastic Force w/Huntara, Delvor, Psi-Lord & Vibraxas 4.00
2-18: 13-She-Hulk app. 3.00

FANTASTIC FORCE (See Fantastic Four #558, Nu-World heroes from 500 years in the future)
Marvel Comics: Jun, 2009 - No. 4, Sept, 2009 ($3.99/$2.99, limited series)

1-($3.99)-Ahearne-s/Kurth-a/Hitch-c; Fantastic Four app. 4.00
2-4-($2.99) 3,4-Ego the Living Planet app. 3.00

FANTASTIC FOUR (See America's Best TV..., Fireside Book Series, Giant-Size..., Giant Size Super-Stars, Marvel Age..., Marvel Collectors Item Classics, Marvel Knights 4, Marvel Milestone Edition, Marvel's Greatest, Marvel Treasury Edition, Marvel Triple Action, Official Marvel Index to..., Power Record Comics & Ultimate...)

FANTASTIC FOUR (See Volume Three for issues #500-611)
Marvel Comics Group: Nov, 1961 - No. 416, Sept, 1996 (Created by Stan Lee & Jack Kirby)

1-Origin & 1st app. The Fantastic Four (Reed Richards: Mr. Fantastic, Johnny Storm: The Human Torch, Sue Storm: The Invisible Girl, & Ben Grimm: The Thing–Marvel's 1st super-hero group since the G.A.; 1st app. S.A. Human Torch); origin/1st app. The Mole Man. 3000 6000 12,000 30,000 95,000 160,000
1-Golden Record Comic Set Reprint (1966)-cover not identical to original 22 44 66 154 340 525
with Golden Record 31 62 93 223 499 775
2-Vs. The Skrulls (last 10¢ issue); (should have a pin-up of The Thing which many copies are missing) 450 900 1350 3700 9350 15,000
3-Fantastic Four don costumes & establish Headquarters; brief 1pg. origin; intro. The Fantasti-Car; Human Torch drawn w/two left hands on-c 380 760 1140 3500 8750 14,000
4-1st S. A. Sub-Mariner app. (5/62) 450 900 1350 3700 9350 15,000
5-Origin & 1st app. Doctor Doom 700 1400 2500 6000 13,000 20,000
6-Sub-Mariner, Dr. Doom team up; 1st Marvel villain team-up (2nd S.A. Sub-Mariner app. 235 470 705 1939 4370 6800
7-10: 7-1st app. Kurrgo. 8-1st app. Puppet-Master & Alicia Masters. 9-3rd Sub-Mariner app. 10-Stan Lee & Jack Kirby app. in story 152 304 456 1254 2827 4300
11-Origin/1st app. The Impossible Man (2/63) 145 290 435 1196 2698 4200
12-Fantastic Four vs. The Hulk (1st meeting); 1st Hulk x-over & ties w/Amazing Spider-Man #1 as 1st Marvel x-over; (3/63) 340 680 1020 3100 8050 13,000
13-Intro. The Watcher; 1st app. The Red Ghost 125 250 375 1000 2250 3500
14,15,17,19: 14-Sub-Mariner x-over. 15-1st app. Mad Thinker. 19-Intro. Rama-Tut (Kang) 57 114 171 456 1028 1600
16-1st Ant-Man x-over (7/63); Wasp cameo 79 158 237 632 1416 2200
18-Origin/1st app. The Super Skrull 86 172 258 688 1544 2400
20-Origin/1st app. The Molecule Man 59 118 177 472 1061 1650
21-Intro. The Hate Monger; 1st Sgt. Fury x-over (12/63) 46 92 138 340 770 1200
22-24: 22-Sue Storm gains more powers 36 72 108 266 596 925
25-The Hulk vs. The Thing (their 1st battle); 3rd Avengers x-over (1st time w/Captain America)(cameo, 4/64); 2nd S.A. app. Cap (takes place between Avengers #4 & 5) 75 150 225 600 1350 2100
26-The Hulk vs. The Thing (continued); 4th Avengers x-over 64 128 192 512 1156 1800
27-1st Doctor Strange x-over (6/64) 42 84 126 311 706 1100
28-Early X-Men x-over (7/64); same date as X-Men #6 50 100 150 390 870 1350
29,30: 30-Intro. Diablo 27 54 81 194 435 675
31-35,37-40: 31-Early Avengers x-over (10/64). 33-1st app. Attuma; part photo-c. 35-Intro/1st app. Dragon Man. 39-Wood inks on Daredevil (early x-over) 22 44 66 154 340 525

Fantastic Four #52 © MAR

Fantastic Four #137 © MAR

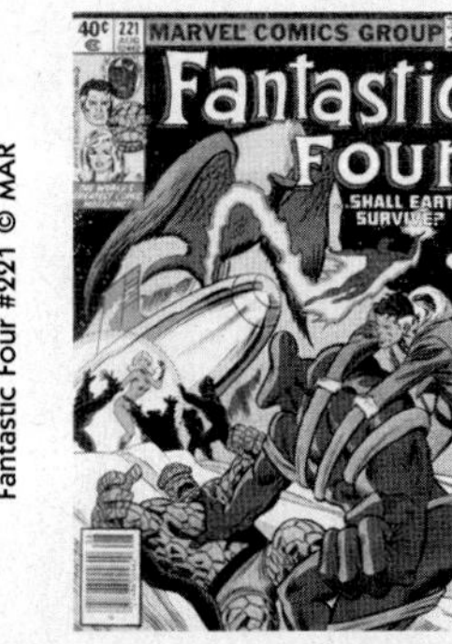

Fantastic Four #221 © MAR

	GD 2.0	VG 4.0	FN 6.0	VF 8.0	VF/NM 9.0	NM- 9.2
36-Intro/1st app. Madam Medusa & the Frightful Four (Sandman, Wizard, Paste Pot Pete)	50	100	150	390	870	1350
41-44: 41-43-Frightful Four app. 44-Intro. Gorgon	14	28	42	96	211	325
45-Intro/1st app. The Inhumans (c/story, 12/65); also see Incredible Hulk Special #1 & Thor #146, & 147	114	228	342	912	2056	3200
46-1st Black Bolt-c (Kirby) & 1st full app.	46	92	138	340	770	1200
47-3rd app. The Inhumans	19	38	57	131	291	450
48-Partial origin/1st app. The Silver Surfer & Galactus (3/66) by Lee & Kirby; Galactus brief app. in last panel; 1st of 3 part story	150	300	450	1200	2100	3000
49-2nd app./1st cover Silver Surfer & Galactus	54	108	162	432	966	1500
50-Silver Surfer battles Galactus; full S.S.-c	54	108	162	432	966	1500
51-Classic "This Man...This Monster" story	25	50	75	175	388	600
52-1st app. The Black Panther (7/66)	141	282	423	1142	2571	4000
53-Origin & 2nd app. The Black Panther; origin/1st app. of Klaw	22	44	66	154	340	525
54-Inhumans cameo	12	24	36	82	179	275
55-Thing battles Silver Surfer; 4th app. Silver Surfer	23	46	69	161	356	550
56-Silver Surfer cameo	12	24	36	82	179	275
57-60: Dr. Doom steals Silver Surfer's powers (also see Silver Surfer: Loftier Than Mortals). 59,60-Inhumans cameo	10	20	30	64	132	200
61-63,68-71: 61-Silver Surfer cameo; Sandman app. (new costume). 62-1st Blastaar; Sandman app. 63-Sandman & Blastaar team-up	8	16	24	54	102	150
64-1st Kree Sentry #459	9	18	27	59	117	175
65-1st app. Ronan the Accuser; 1st Kree Supreme Intelligence	15	30	45	103	227	350
66-Begin 2 part origin of Him (Warlock); does not app. (9/67)	22	44	66	154	340	525
66,67-2nd printings (1994)	2	4	6	11	16	20
67-Origin/1st brief app. Him (Warlock); 1 page; see Thor #165,166 for 1st full app.; white cover scarcer in true high grade	29	58	87	209	467	725
72-Silver Surfer-c/story (pre-dates Silver Surfer #1)	13	26	39	89	195	300
73-Spider-Man, D.D., Thor x-over; cont'd from Daredevil #38	10	20	30	69	147	225
74-77: Silver Surfer app.(#77 is same date/S.S. #1)	9	18	27	62	126	190
78-80: 78-Wizard app. 80-1st Tomazooma, the Living Totem	6	12	18	41	76	110
81,84-88: 81-Crystal joins & dons costume; vs. the Wizard. 84-87-Dr. Doom app. 88-Mole Man app.	6	12	18	40	73	105
82,83-Black Bolt & the Inhumans app.; vs. Maximus	6	12	18	41	80	125
89-98,101: 89-Mole Man app. 91-1st app. Kree disguised as 1930s era gangsters; 1st app. Torgo. 92-The Thing app. as a space gladiator. 93-Thing vs. Torgo. 94-intro Agatha Harkness; Frightful Four app. 95-1st app. the Monocle. 96-Mad-Thinker app. 98-Neil Armstrong Moon landing issue. 101-Last Kirby-a issue	6	12	18	37	66	95
99-Black Bolt & the Inhumans app.	6	12	18	40	73	105
100 (7/70) F.F. vs Thinker and Puppet-Master	9	18	27	62	126	190
102-104: 102-Romita Sr-a; 102-104-Sub-Mariner & Magneto app.	6	12	18	37	66	95
105,106,108,109,111: 108-Features Kirby & Buscema-a; Kirby material produced after issue #101, his last official issue before leaving Marvel. 109-Annihilus app. 111-Hulk cameo	5	10	15	35	63	90
107-Classic Thing transformation-c; 1st John Buscema-a on FF (2/71); 1st app. Janus	6	12	18	40	73	105
110-Initial version w/green Thing and blue faces and pink uniforms on-c	21	42	63	147	324	500
110-Corrected-c w/accurately colored faces and uniforms and orange Thing	6	12	18	38	69	100
112-Hulk Vs. Thing (7/71)	20	40	60	138	307	475
113-115: 113-1st app. The Overmind; Watcher app. 114-vs the Overmind. 115-Origin of the Overmind; plot by Stan Lee, Archie Goodwin script; last 15¢ issue	5	10	15	30	50	70
116 (52 pgs.) FF and Dr. Doom vs. the Overmind; the Stranger app.; Goodwin story	6	12	18	41	76	110
117-119: 117,118-Diablo app; Goodwin-s 119-Black Panther app. vs Klaw; 1st Roy Thomas FF story	4	8	12	28	47	65
120-1st app. Gabriel the Air-Walker (new herald of Galactus); Stan Lee story	5	10	15	31	53	75
121,123: 121-Silver Surfer vs. Gabriel; Galactus app. 123-Silver Surfer & Galactus app.	5	10	15	35	63	90
122-Silver Surfer & Galactus app; black cover, scarcer in higher grade	5	10	15	35	73	105
124,125,127,130,134-140: 125-Last Stan Lee-s. 127-Mole Man & Tyrannus app. 130-vs the new Frightful Four (Thundra; Sandman, Trapster and Wizard; Black Bolt & Inhumans app.). 134,135-Dragon Man app. 134-1st full Gerry Conway issue. 136-Shaper of Worlds app; Dragon Man cameo. 137-Shaper of Worlds app. 138-Return of the Miracle Man. 139-vs. Miracle Man. 140-Annihilus app.	4	8	12	23	37	50
126-Origin FF retold; cover swipe of FF #1; Roy Thomas scripts begin	4	8	12	27	44	60
128-Four page glossy insert of FF Friends & Foes; Mole Man app.	4	8	12	25	40	55
129,131-133: 1st app. Thundra (super-strong Femizon) joins new Frightful Four; Medusa app. 131-Black Bolt, Medusa, Crystal, Quicksilver app; New Frightful Four app; Ross Andru-a; Steranko-c. 132-Black Bolt & Inhumans app.; vs. Maximus; last Roy Thomas-s (returns in issue #158). 133-Thing vs Thundra battle issue; Ramona Fradon-a; Gerry Conway script	5	10	15	31	53	75
141-Franklin Richards 'depowered'; Annihilus app.; FF break-up; last Buscema-a	4	8	12	23	37	50
142-146,148-149: 142-1st Darkoth the Demon; Dr. Doom app; Kirbyish-a by Buckler begins. 143,144-vs. Dr. Doom. 145,146-vs. Ternak the Abominable Snowman. 148-vs. Wizard, Sandman, Trapster. 149-Sub-Mariner app.	3	6	9	21	33	45
147-Thing vs. Sub-Mariner-c/s	4	8	12	27	44	60
150-Crystal & Quicksilver's wedding; Avengers, Ultron-7 and Black Bolt & the Inhumans app; story continued from Avengers #127	5	10	15	31	53	75
151-154,158-160: 151-1st Mahkizmo the Nuclear Man; origin Thundra. 152,153-Thundra & Mahkizmo app. 154-Nick Fury app; part-r issue (Strange Tales #127). 158,159 vs. Xemu; Black Bolt & Inhumans app. 160-Arkon app.	3	6	9	15	22	28
155-157: Silver Surfer & Dr. Doom in all	3	6	9	19	30	40
161-163,168-171: 162,163-Arkon app. 168-Luke Cage, Power Man joins the FF (to replace the Thing). 169-Luke Cage app; 1st app. Thing exoskeleton. 170-Luke Cage leaves the FF; Puppet Master app. 171-1st Gorr the Golden Gorilla; Pérez-a	2	4	6	10	14	18
164,165: 164-Re-intro Marvel Boy (as the Crusader); 1st George Pérez-a on FF. 165-Origin of Marvel Boy & the Crusader; 1st app. Frankie Ray. Pérez-a; death of the Crusader (a new Marvel Boy appears in Captain America #217)	2	4	6	10	15	20
166,167-vs the Hulk; Pérez-a. 167-The Thing loses his powers	3	6	9	17	26	35
169-173-(30¢-c, limited distribution)(4-8/76)	4	8	12	27	44	60
172-175: 172-Galactus & High Evolutionary app. 175-Galactus vs. High Evolutionary; the Thing regains his powers	2	4	6	10	15	20
176-180: 176-Re-intro Impossible Man; Marvel artists app. 177-1st app. the Texas Twister & Captain Ultra; Impossible Man & Brute app. 178-179-Impossible Man, Tigra & Thundra app; Reed loses his stretching ability. 180-r/#101 by Kirby	2	4	6	10	14	18
181-199: 181-183-The Brute, Mad Thinker & Annihilus app; last Roy Thomas-s. 184-1st Eliminator; Len Wein-s begin. (co-plotter in #183-182) 185,186-New Salem Witches app.; part origin Agatha Harkness. 187,188-vs. Klaw & the Molecule Man. 189-G.A Human Torch app.; r-FF Annual #4. 190-1st Marv Wolfman FF. 191-FF break-up; Wolfman/Wein-s. 192-Last Pérez-a; Texas Twister app. 193,194-Diablo & Darkoth the Death Demon app. 195-Sub-Mariner app.; Wolfman begins as full plotter & scripter. 196-1st full app. of the clone of Dr. Doom. 197-vs. the Red Ghost; Reed regains his stretching ability. 198-vs Dr. Doom. 199-Origin & death of the clone of Doom; Dr. Doom app.	2	4	6	8	10	12
200-(11/78 52 pgs)-FF reunited vs. Dr. Doom	2	4	6	10	14	18
201-203,219,222-231: 202-vs. Quasimodo. 219-Sub-Mariner app.; Moench & Sienkiewicz 1st FF work. 222-Agatha Harkness & Gabriel the Devil Hunter app. 224-Contains unused alternate-c for #3 and pin-ups. 225-Thor & Odin app. 226-1st Samurai Destroyer. 229-1st Ebon-Seeker. 230-vs. Ebon Seeker; Avengers app. 231-1st Stygorr of the Negative Zone						6.00
204-1st Nova Corps (cameo); 1st app. Queen Adora of Xandar; 1st app. of Xandar; FF vs. the Skrulls	2	4	6	8	10	12
205-208: 205-1st full app. Nova Corps; Xandarian/Skrull war. 206-Nova app.; story continued from Nova #25; Sphinx app. 207-Spider-Man app. 208-Nova & and the New Champions app. (Powerhouse, Diamondhead, the Comet & Crimebuster); Sphinx app.	1	2	3	5	6	8
209-210,213,214: 209-1st Byrne-a on FF; 1st Herbie the Robot. 210-Galactus app. 213-Galactus vs. the Sphinx; Terrax app.	1	3	4	6	8	10
211-1st app. Terrax (new Herald of Galactus)	3	6	9	16	23	30
212-Byrne-a; Galactus vs. the High Evolutionary	2	4	8	9	12	15
215-218,220-221: Byrne-a in all. 215-Blastaar app; 1st app. the Futurist. 216-Blastaar & Futurist app; last Wolfman-s. 217-Early app. Dazzler (4/80); by Byrne; vs Herbie the Robot (destroyed). 218-Spider-Man app; vs. Frightful Four; continued from Spectacular Spider-Man #42. 220-1st Byrne story on FF; origin retold; Avengers and Vindicator app.	1	2	3	5	6	8
232-Byrne story & art begins (7/81); vs. Diablo; brief Dr. Strange app; re-intro Frankie Raye	1	2	3	5	6	8
233-235,237-241,245-249,251,253-256: 233-Hammerhead app. 234,235-Ego the Living Planet. 238-Origin & 1st app. of Frankie Raye's flame powers, joins the FF. The Thing is 'devolved' into an 'uglier' version. 239-1st app. Aunt Petunia. 240-Black Bolt & the Inhumans app;						

Fantastic Four #298 © MAR

Fantastic Four #360 © MAR

Fantastic Four #389 © MAR

GD VG FN VF VF/NM NM-
2.0 4.0 6.0 8.0 9.0 9.2

GD VG FN VF VF/NM NM-
2.0 4.0 6.0 8.0 9.0 9.2

Attilan (home of the Inhumans) relocated to the Moon. 241-Black Panther app. 245-Thing returns to his rocky-look. 246-Dr. Doom returns. 247-Doom and FF team-up vs. Prince Zorba; Doom regains rule of Latveria; 1st app. Kristoff. 248-Black Bolt & and the Inhumans app. 249-vs Gladiator (of the Sh'iar). 251-FF explore the Negative Zone; Annihillus app. 254-1st Mantracora. 255-Brief Daredevil app; Annihilus app. 256-FF return from the Negative Zone; vs Annihilus; Avengers, Galactus and Nova (Frankie Raye) app. 6.00

236-20th Anniversary issue (11/81, 68 pgs, $1.00)-brief origin FF; Byrne-c(p)/a; new Kirby-a; Marvel Super-Heroes & Stan Lee app. on cover; Dr. Doom and Puppet Master app.; 1st 'Liddleville' 1 2 3 5 6 8

242-vs. Terrax; Thor, Iron Man & Daredevil cameos 1 2 3 5 6 8

243-Classic Galactus-c by Byrne; Thor, Captain America, Dr. Strange, Spider-Man & Daredevil app. 2 4 6 9 12 15

244-Frankie Raye becomes Nova – the new Herald of Galactus 2 4 6 9 12 15

250,257-260: 250-(52 pgs)-Spider-Man x-over; Byrne-a; Skrulls impersonate New X-Men; Gladiator app. 257-Galactus devours the Skrull homeworld; Sue announces pregnancy; Vision & Scarlet Witch cameo. 258-Dr. Doom team-up with Terrax; Kristoff app. 259-Dr. Doom & Terrax. vs FF; Silver Surfer cameo. 260-Terrax, Silver Surfer & Sub-Mariner app.; 'death' of Dr. Doom 1 2 3 5 6 8

252-Reads sideways; Annihilus app. Contains skin 'Tattooz' decals (no 'Tattooz' were included in Canadian editions, also in Amazing Spider-Man #238)
with Tattooz 1 2 3 5 6 8
without Tattooz 6.00

261-262: The Trial of Reed Richards. 261-Silver Surfer & the Watcher app. 262-Origin Galactus; John Byrne writes himself into story; the Watcher, Odin, Eternity app. 6.00

263-285: 263-Mole Man app. Vision cameo. 264-vs Mole Man; swipes-c of FF #1. 265-Secret Wars x-over; She-Hulk replaces the Thing; Vision & Scarlet Witch app. 267-Dr. Octopus, Michael Morbius, Donald Blake & Bruce Banner app; Sue loses her baby. 268-Origin She-Hulk retold; Hulk and Dr. Octopus app. 269-1st app. Terminus; re-intro. Wyatt Wingfoot. 270-vs Terminus. 271-1st Gormuu (flashback story pre-FF #1). 272-1st app. Nathaniel Richards – the Warlord (Reed's father). 273-Nathaniel Richards app. 274-Spider-Man's alien costume app; (4th app. 1/85, 2 pgs.) the Thing app. on Battleword. 275-She-Hulk solo story. 276-Mephisto & Dr. Strange app. 277-Split story format - the Thing returns to Earth and battles Dire Wraiths; FF battle Mephisto; Dr. Strange app. 278-Origin Dr. Doom retold; Kristoff becomes new Dr. Doom. 279-Baxter Building destroyed by Kristoff; new Hate Monger app. 280-New Hate Monger & Psycho Man app.; 1st app. Sue as Malice. 281-New Hate Monger, Malice & Psycho Man app. 282-Power Pack cameo; Secret Wars II x-over; Psycho Man app.; infinity cover. 283,284-vs. Psycho Man. 285-Secret Wars II x-over; Beyonder app. 4.00

286-2nd app. X-Factor 2 4 6 8 10 12

287-295: 287-Return of Dr. Doom. 288-Secret Wars II x-over; Dr. Doom vs. the Beyonder. 289-Blastaar app; Basilisk killed by Scourge; Nick Fury app; Annihilus returns. 290-Blastaar, Annihilus & Nick Fury app. 291-Action Comics #1 cover swipe; Nick Fury app. 292-Hitler-c; Nick Fury app. 293-West Coast Avengers app; last Byrne-a. 294-Byrne plot only (last); Ordway-a; Roger Stern script. 295-Stern-s begin (over brief Byrne plot) 4.00

296-($1.50, 64-pgs)-Barry Smith-c/a (pgs 1-10); Shooter plot; Stan Lee script; Gammil, Frenz, Milgrom, John Buscema, Silvestri and Ordway-p; Sinnott & Colletta-inks; Mole Man app; the Thing returns to the FF 5.00

297-318,321-330: 297-Roger Stern-s begins; John Buscema-a returns. 299-Black costume Spider-Man app. 300-Wedding of Johnny Storm and 'Alicia'- see issue #358. 301-Wizard & Mad-Thinker app. 303-Thundra app. 304-Steve Englehart-s begins; vs. Quicksilver; the Thing becomes leader of the FF. 305-Quicksilver & Kristoff app ; Crystal rejoins FF; Dr. Doom app; leads into FF Annual #20. 306-v.s Diablo; Black Bolt & the Inhumans app; Captain America cameo; Ms. Marvel (Sharon Ventura) app. 307-Ms. Marvel joins the FF. vs. Diablo; Reed and Sue leave the FF. 308-1st Fasaud. 309-vs Fasaud; last Buscema-a. 310-Keith Pollard-a begins; 1st mutated Thing; Ms. Marvel becomes 'She-Thing'. 311-Black Panther & Dr. Doom app. 312-Dr. Doom, Black Panther & X-Factor app. 313-Mole Man app. 314-Belasco & Master Pandemonium app. 315-Master Pandemonium & Comet Man app; Morbius the Living Vampire cameo. 316-Ka-Zar & Shanna the She-Devil app.; origin of the Savage Land. 317-Comet Man app. 318-Molecule Man & Dr. Doom app. 322-Ron Lim guest-a; She-Hulk vs. Ms. Marvel; Dragon Man app; Aron the Renegade Watcher app. 322-Inferno x-over; Graviton, Aron & Dragon Man app. 323-Inferno x-over; Mantis & Kang app. 324-Kang, Mantis & Necrodamus app; Silver Surfer cameo. 325-Mantis, Kang & Silver Surfer app. 326-vs new Frightful Four (Wizard, Hydroman, Klaw and Titania); Reed & Sue return; the Thing becomes human; Englehart-s as 'John Harkness'. 327-vs Frightful Four; Aron the Renegade Watcher & Dragon Man app. 328-1st app. Aron's evil version of the FF; Frightful Four & Dragon Man app. 329-Evil FF vs. Mole Man; Aron app. 3.00

319,320: 319-(Double-size, 39 pgs); Secret Wars III; origin of the Beyonder; Dr. Doom, Molecule Man, Shaper of Worlds, Kubik app. 320-Grey Hulk vs. Thing; Dr. Doom app; x-over w/Incredible Hulk #350 6.00

331-346, 351-357,359,360: 331-Ultron app. in dream sequence; Aron the Renegade Watcher app. 333-Avengers & Dr. Strange app. Evil FF vs real FF; Aron the Renegade Watcher app. 334-Acts of Vengeance x-over; Simonson-s begin; Buckler-a; Thor & Captain America app. 335-Acts of Vengeance x-over; Apocalypse cameo. 336-Acts of Vengeance x-over. 337-Simonson-s and art begin; Thor & Iron Man join FF's mission. 338-Iron Man & Thor app. Death's Head app. Galactus cameo. 339-Thor vs. Gladiator; Galactus & the Black Celestial app. 340-Iron Man, Thor & Galactus app; death of the Black Celestial. 341-Thor, Iron Man & Galactus app. 342-Spider-Man cameo; no Simonson-s or art. 343-President Dan Quale app. 346-T.V.A (Time Variance Authority) app. 351-Kubik & Kosmos app; Mark Bagley-a. 352-Reed vs Dr. Doom; Kristof app; Justice Peace & the T.V.A app. 353,354-FF on trial by the T.V.A; Justice Peace and Mark Gruenwald (as Mr. Chairman) app; 354-Last Simonson issue. 355-vs. the Wrecker. 356-1st Tom Defalco-s & Paul Ryan-a (begin four-year run); Puppet Master & New Warriors app. 357-Alicia Masters revealed to be a Skrull (since issue #265); Puppet Master app. 3.00

347-Ghost Rider, Wolverine, Spider-Man, Hulk-c/stories thru #349; Arthur Adams-c/a(p) in each 5.00

347,348-Gold second printings 5.00

348-350: 348-349-Arthur Adams-c/a(p). 350-($1.50, 52 pgs)-The 'real' Dr. Doom returns; Kristoff app. Sharon Ventura becomes human again. Ben becomes the Thing again 5.00

358-(11/91, $2.25, 88 pgs)-30th anniversary issue; gives history of the FF; die-cut-c; Art Adams back-up story-a; origin of Lyja the Skrull as Alicia Masters; 1st app. Paibok the Power Skrull 5.00

361-368, 372-373: 361-Dr. Doom & the Yancy Street gang app. 362-Spider-Man app; 1st app. of the Innerverse. 363-1st app. Occulus. 364,365-vs. Occulus; 365-Sharon Ventura returns. 366-Infinity War x-over; Magus app; Paibok & Devos team-up. 367-Infinity War x-over; Magus app. numerous super-heroes app. 368-Infinity War x-over; Magus app. Human Torch vs. X-Men doppelgangers. 372-Spider-Man, Molecule Man, Puppet Master & Aron the Renegade Watcher app.; Silver Sable & the Wild Pack cameo; Devos, Paibok & Lyja app. 373-Human Torch vs. Silver Sable & the Wild Pack; Molecule Man vs. Aron the Rogue Watcher; Dr. Doom app. (steals the power of Aron) 3.00

369,370-Infinity War x-over. 369-Thanos & Warlock and the Infinity Watch app; Aron the Renegade Watcher app.; the Magus gains the Infinity Gauntlet. 370-Warlock vs. the Magus for the Infinity Gauntlet; 1st app. Lyja the Lazer-fist. 4.00

371-All-white embossed-c ($2.00); 1st new (revealing) Invisible Woman costume; Paibok, Devos & Lyja vs. Human Torch; Aron the Renegade Watcher app; Ms. Marvel (Sharon Ventura) rejoins the FF 4.00

371-All-red 2nd printing ($2.00) 3.00

374,375: 374-vs Wolverine, Dr. Strange, Ghost Rider, the Hulk and Spider-Man (as the Secret Defenders); Thing's face injured by Wolverine; Dr. Doom app; Black Bolt & the Inhumans cameo; Uatu the Watcher app. 375-($2.95, 52 pgs)-Holo-Grafx foil-c; Secret Defenders app.; Black Bolt & the Inhumans app; cosmic powered Dr. Doom app. Uatu app.; re-intro Nathaniel Richards (from issue #273); Lyja changes allegiance to the FF 4.00

376-($2.95)-Variant polybagged w/Dirt Magazine #4 and music tape; harder to find in true NM- 9.2 due to being packaged with a tape cassette 5.00

376-380,382-386: 376-Nathaniel Richards and Dr. Doom app; Franklin becomes an adult (Psi-Lord). 377-1st app. Huntara; origin Devos; Paibok, Dr. Doom & Klaw app. 378-vs. Devos, Paibok & Huntara; Avengers, Spider-Man & Daredevil app. 379-Devos, Paibok, Huntara & Dr. Doom app. 380-Dr. Doom app. 382-Contains a coupon from Kaybee Toys for an exclusive Ghost Rider issue; also has 16-pg Midnight Sons 'Siege of Darkness' insert; Devos vs. the Skrull Empire. 383-Paibok vs. Devos. 384-Scott Lang app. as Ant-Man; Psi-Lord vs. Invisible Woman. 385-Starblast x-over; Ant-Man & Sub-Mariner app.; continues in Namor the Sub-Mariner #48. 386-Starblast x-over; Ant-Man & Sub-Mariner app. 3.00

381-'Death' of Reed Richards (Mr. Fantastic) & Dr. Doom 4.00

387-Newstand ed. ($1.25) 3.00

387-($2.95)-Collectors Ed. w/die-cut foil-c; Ant-Man app; Invisible Woman returns to her regular costume 4.00

388-393,396,397: 388-Bound in trading card sheet; Ant-Man, Sub-Mariner & Avengers app; 1st app. the Dark Raider. 389-Ant-Man, Sub-Mariner and the Collector app. 390- Ant-Man & Sub-Mariner app. Galactus & Silver Surfer app. in flashback to FF #48-50. 391-Ant-Man, Sub-Mariner, Galactus & Silver Surfer app. 392-vs. the Dark Raider. 396-Power Rangers card insert. 397-Aron the Renegade Watcher & the Dark Raider app; return of Kristoff; Ant-Man app. 3.00

394-($2.95)-Collectors Edition-polybagged w/16-pg. Marvel; Action Hour book and acetate print; pink logo; Ant-Man, Wyatt Wingfoot & She-Hulk app. 4.00

394-(Newstand Edition-$1.50); white logo 3.00

395,398,399: 395-Wolverine-c/story; Ant-Man app. 398,399-($2.50)-Rainbow foil-c; Ant-Man, Uatu, Aron & the Dark Raider app. 4.00

400-($3.95, 64-pgs)-Rainbow foil-c; Stan Lee introduction; Celestials vs. the Watchers; Kristoff joins the FF. Ant-Man app.; Avengers & Spider-Man app. in back-up story; origin of the FF retold; Uatu vs. Aron (dies) 5.00

401-404: 401-Atlantis Rising x-over; Sub-Mariner & Thor app; Black Bolt cameo. 402-Atlantis Rising x-over; Sub-Mariner vs. Black Bolt; Thor vs. the FF. 404-1st brief app. Hyperstorm (arm only) 3.00

405-Overpower card insert; scarcer in higher grades due to card indentation; new Ant-Man costume; Zarko the Tomorrow Man app; 2nd app. Hyperstorm (cameo) 4.00

406-Return of Dr. Doom; Hyperstorm revealed, battles FF. 407-Return of Mr. Fantastic; x-over

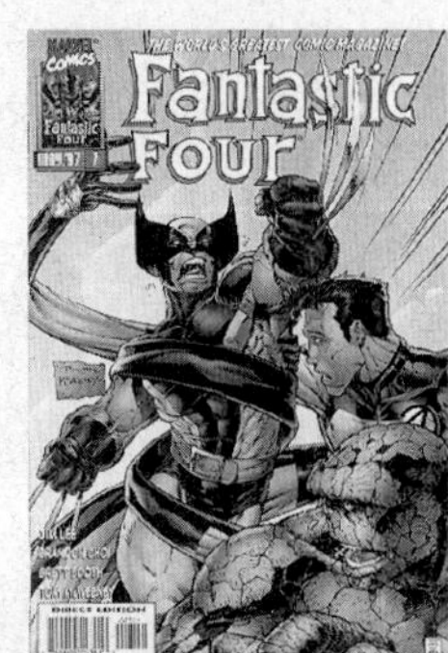
Fantastic Four V2 #7 © MAR

Fantastic Four V3 #55 © MAR

Fantastic Four #587 © MAR

	GD 2.0	VG 4.0	FN 6.0	VF 8.0	VF/NM 9.0	NM- 9.2

w/FF Unlimited #12; Hyperstorm app. 408-vs Hyperstorm; Dr. Doom app. 409-Dr. Doom & FF vs. Hyperstorm; Thing's facial injury cured (since #374). 410-Gorgon of the Inhumans app. 411-Black Bolt & the Inhumans app. 412-Mr. Fantastic vs. Sub-Mariner. 413-Silver Surfer cameo; x-over w/Doom 2099 #42; Doom 2099 & Hyperstorm app; Franklin returns to being a child (Psi-Lord since #376). 414-Galactus vs. Hyperstorm; last Paul Ryan-a (since #356) 4.00
415-Onslaught tie-in; Pacheco-a; Professor X & Avengers app.; Apocalypse cameo; story continued in X-Men #55 5.00
416-($2.50, 48 pgs)-Onslaught tie-in; Pacheco-a; Dr. Doom app; last issue; story continues in Onslaught Marvel Universe #1; Reed, Ben & Victor Von Doom app. in flashback in back-up story; Uatu the Watcher app. 6.00
#500-up (See Fantastic Four Vol. 3; series resumed original numbering after Vol. 3 #70)
Annual 1('63)-Origin of Sub-Mariner & 1st modern app. of Atlantis & the Atlanteans incl. Lady Dorma; FF origin retold; Spider-Man app. in detailed retelling of his app. from Amazing Spider-Man #1 70 140 210 555 1253 1950
Annual 2('64)-Dr. Doom origin & c/story; FF #5-r in 2nd story; Pharaoh Rama-Tut app. in 3rd story 38 76 114 285 641 1000
Annual 3('65)-Reed & Sue wed; r/#6,11 19 38 57 131 291 450
Special 4(11/66)-G.A. Torch x-over (1st S.A. app.) & origin retold; r/#25,26 (Hulk vs. Thing); Torch vs. Torch battle; Mad-Thinker app; 1st app Quasimodo 12 24 36 80 173 265
Special 5(11/67)-New art; Intro. Psycho-Man; early Black Panther, Inhumans & Silver Surfer (1st solo story); Black Bolt & the Inhumans app; Sue is revealed to be pregnant; Quasimodo app. 12 24 36 83 182 280
Special 6(11/68)-Intro. Annihilus; birth of Franklin Richards; new 48 pg. movie length epic; last non-reprint annual 17 34 51 117 259 400
Special 7(11/69)-all reprint issue; r/FF #1; r/origin of Dr. Doom from FF #5 & Dr. Doom story from FF Annual #2; Marvel staff photos seen in 'Because you Demanded it' featurette; new-c by Kirby 5 10 15 34 60 85
Special 8-10: All reprints. 8(12/70)-F.F. vs. Sub-Mariner plus gallery of F.F. foes. Special 9(12/71)-r/FF #43, Strange Tales #131 & FF Annual #3. Special 10('73)-r/FF Annual #3,4; new-c by John Buscema 3 6 9 21 33 45
Annual 11-14: 11-('76)-New story & art begins; alternate Earth versions of the Invaders app; story continues into Marvel Two-in-One Annual #1; Kirby-c. Annual 12 ('78)-Black Bolt & the Inhumans app; vs. the Sphinx. Annual 13 ('78)-vs the Mole Man; Daredevil app. Annual 14 ('79)-Pérez-a; Avengers cameo; Sandman & Salem's Seven app. 2 4 6 8 11 14
Annual 15-17: 15-(80, 68 pgs.); Perez-a; Captain Marvel & Dr. Doom app. Annual 16-('81)-Ditko-a/c; 1st Dragon lord. Annual 17-('83)-Byrne-c/a; Skrulls app. 6.00
Annual 18-23: 18-('84)-Minor x-over w/X-Men #137; Wolverine cameo; wedding of Black Bolt & Medusa; the Watcher app. Annual 19-('85)-vs the Skrulls; x-over w/Avengers Annual #14. Annual 20-('87)-Dr. Doom & Mephisto app; continued from FF #305. Annual 21-('88, 64 pgs.)-Square bound; Evolutionary War x-over; Black Bolt & the Inhumans app. Aron the Watcher app. (unnamed). Annual 22-('89, 64 pgs.)-Square bound; Atlantis Attacks x-over; Avengers & Dr. Strange app. Annual 23-('90, 64 pgs.)-Squarebound; 'Days of Future Present' Pt. 1; 1st Ahab; story continues in New Mutants Annual #6 (not X-Factor Annual #5 as noted); Dr. Doom app. in back-up feature; Byrne-c 4.00
Annual 24-27 (all square bound editions): Annual 24-('91, 64 pgs.); Korvac Quest Pt.1; Guardians of the Galaxy app; story continues in Thor Annual #16; Molecule Man & Super-Skrull app. in back-up features. Annual 25-('92, 64 pgs.)-Citizen Kang Pt.3; continued from Thor Annual #17; Avengers app.; story continues in Avengers Annual #21; Moondragon vs. Mantis solo story & Kang retrospective. Annual 26-('93, 64 pgs.)-Bagged w/card featuring a new character 'Wildstreak'; vs. Dreadface; Kubik & Kosmos app. in solo story featuring the Celestials. Annual 27-('94, 64 pgs.)-Justice Peace & the T.V.A (Time Variance Authority) app.; featuring the chairman (Mark Gruenwald); Molecule Man vs. Beyonder solo story 4.00
Best of the Fantastic Four Vol. 1 HC (2005, $29.99) oversized reprints of classic stories from FF#1,39,40,51,100,116,176,236,267, Ann.2, V3#56,60 and more; Brevoort intro. 30.00
Maximum Fantastic Four HC (2005, $49.99, dust jacket) r/Fantastic Four #1 with super-sized art; historical background from Walter Mosley and Mark Evanier; dust jacket unfolds to a poster: giant FF#1 cover on one side, gallery of interior pages on other 50.00
...: Monsters Unleashed nn (1992, $5.95)-r/F.F. #347-349 w/new Arthur Adams-c 1 2 3 5 6 8
...: Nobody Gets Out Alive (1994, $15.95) TPB r/ #387-392 16.00
... Omnibus Vol. 1 HC (2005, $99.99) r/#1-30 & Annual 1 plus letter pages; 3 intros. and a 1974 essay by Stan Lee; original plot synopsis for FF #1; essays and Kirby art 100.00
... Omnibus Vol. 2 HC (2007, $99.99) r/#31-60, Annual 2-4 and Not Brand Echh #1 plus letter pages and essays by Stan Lee, Reginald Hudlin, Roy Thomas and others 100.00
Special Edition 1(5/84)-r/Annual #1; Byrne-c/a 5.00
...: The Lost Adventure (4/08, $4.99) Lee & Kirby story partially used in flashback in FF #108 completed with additional art by Frenz & Sinnott; plus reprint of FF #108 5.00
... Visionaries: George Pérez Vol. 1 (2005, $19.99) r/#164-167,170,176-178,184-186 20.00
... Visionaries: George Pérez Vol. 2 (2006, $19.99) r/#187-188,191-192, Annual #14-15, Marvel Two-In-One #60 and back-up story from Adventures of the Thing #3 20.00

... Visionaries (11/01, $19.95) r/#232-240 by John Byrne 20.00
... Visionaries Vol. 2 (2004, $24.99) r/#241-250 by John Byrne 25.00
... Visionaries John Byrne Vol. 3 (2004, $24.99) r/#251-257; Annual #17; Avengers #233 and Thing #2 25.00
... Visionaries John Byrne Vol. 4 (2005, $24.99) r/#258-267; Alpha Flight #4 & Thing #10 25.00
... Visionaries John Byrne Vol. 5 (2005, $24.99) r/#268-275; Annual #18 & Thing #19 25.00
... Visionaries John Byrne Vol. 6 ('06, $24.99) r/#276-284; Secret Wars II #2 & Thing #23 25.00
... Visionaries John Byrne Vol. 7 ('07, $24.99) r/#285,286, Ann. #19, Avengers #263 & Ann. #14, and X-Factor #1 25.00
... Visionaries John Byrne Vol. 8 ('07, $24.99) r/#287-295 25.00
... Visionaries: Walter Simonson Vol. 1 (2007, $19.99) r/#334-341 20.00
NOTE: ***Arthur Adams*** *c/a-347-349p.* ***Austin*** *c(i)-232-236, 238, 240-242, 250i, 286i.* ***Buckler*** *c-151, 168.* ***John Buscema*** *a(p)-107, 108(w/****Kirby, Sinnott*** *&* ***Romita****),109-130, 132, 134-141, 160, 173-175, 202, 296-309p, Annual 11, 13; c(p)-107-122, 124-129, 133-139, 202, Annual 12p, Special 10.* ***Byrne*** *a-209-218p, 220p, 221p, 232-265, 266i, 267-273, 274-293p, Annual 17, 19; c-211-214p, 220p, 232-236p, 237, 238p, 239, 240-242p, 243-249, 250p, 251-267, 269-277, 278-281p, 283p, 284, 285, 286p, 288-293, Annual 17, 18.* ***Ditko*** *a-13i, 14i(w/****Kirby****-p), Annual 16.* ***G. Kane*** *c-145p, 146p, 150p, 160p.* ***Kirby*** *a-1-102p, 108p, 180r, 189r, 236p, Special 1-10; c-1-101, 164, 167, 171-177, 180, 181, 190, 200, Annual 11, Special 1-7, 9.* ***Marcos*** *a-Annual 14i.* ***Mooney*** *a-118i, 152i.* ***Perez*** *a(p)-164-167, 170-172, 176-178, 184-188, 191p, 192p. Annual 14p, 15p; c(p)-183-188, 191, 192, 194-197.* ***Simonson*** *a-337-341, 343, 344p, 345p, 346, 350p, 352-354; c-212, 334-341, 342p, 343-346, 350, 353, 354.* ***Steranko*** *c-130-132p.* ***Williamson*** *c-357i.*

FANTASTIC FOUR (Volume Two)
Marvel Comics: V2#1, Nov, 1996 - No. 13, Nov, 1997 ($2.95/$1.95/$1.99) (Produced by WildStorm Productions)

1-($2.95)-Reintro Fantastic Four; Jim Lee-c/a; Brandon Choi scripts; Mole Man app. 5.00
1-($2.95)-Variant-c 1 2 3 4 5 7
2-9: 2-Namor-c/app. 3-Avengers-c/app. 4-Two covers; Dr. Doom cameo 3.00
10,11,13: All $1.99-c. 13-"World War 3"-pt. 1, x-over w/Image 3.00
12-($2.99) "Heroes Reunited"-pt. 1 4.00
...: Heroes Reborn (7/00, $17.95, TPB) r/#1-6 18.00
Heroes Reborn: Fantastic Four (2006, $29.99, TPB) r/#1-12; Jim Lee intro.; pin-ups 30.00

FANTASTIC FOUR (Volume Three)
Marvel Comics: V3#1, Jan, 1998 - No. 588, Apr, 2011 ($2.99/$1.99/$2.25)
No. 600, Jan, 2012 - No. 611, Dec, 2012 (Issues #589-#599 do not exist, see FF series)

1-($2.99)-Heroes Return; Lobdell-s/Davis & Farmer-a 1 2 3 5 6 8
1-Alternate Heroes Return-c 1 3 4 6 8 10
2-4,12: 2-2-covers. 4-Claremont-s/Larroca-a begin; Silver Surfer c/app. 12-($2.99) Wraparound-c by Larroca 5.00
5-11: 6-Heroes For Hire app. 9-Spider-Man-c/app. 11-1st app. Ayesha 4.00
13-24: 13,14-Ronan-c/app. 3.00
25-($2.99) Dr. Doom returns 4.00
26-49: 27-Dr. Doom marries Sue. 30-Begin $2.25-c. 32,42-Namor-c/app. 35-Regular cover; Pacheco-s/a begins. 37-Super-Skrull-c/app. 38-New Baxter Building 3.00
35-($3.25) Variant foil enhanced-c; Pacheco-s/a begins 4.00
50-($3.99, 64 pgs.) BWS-c; Grummett, Pacheco, Rude, Udon-a 4.00
51-53,55-59: 51-53-Bagley-a(p)/Wieringo-c; Inhumans app. 55,56-Immonen-a 57-59-Warren-s/Grant-a 3.00
54-($3.50, 100 pgs.) Birth of Valeria; r/Annual #6 birth of Franklin 4.00
60-(9¢-c) Waid-s/Wieringo-a begin 3.00
60-($2.25 newsstand edition)(also see Promotional Comics section) 3.00
61-70: 62-64-FF vs. Modulus. 65,66-Buckingham-a. 68-70-Dr. Doom app. 3.00
(After #70 [Aug, 2003] numbering reverted back to original Vol. 1 with #500, Sept, 2003)
500-($3.50) Regular edition; concludes Dr. Doom app.; Dr. Strange app.; Rivera painted-c 4.00
500-($4.99) Director's Cut Edition; chromium-c by Wieringo; sketch and script pages 8.00
501-516: 501,502-Casey Jones-a. 503-508-Porter-a. 509-Wieringo-c/a resumes. 512,513-Spider-Man app. 514-516-Ha-c/Medina-a 3.00
517-537: 517-Begin $2.99-c. 519-523-Galactus app. 527-Straczynski-s begins. 537-Dr. Doom. 3.00
527-Variant Edition with different McKone-c 3.00
527-Wizard World Philadelphia Edition with B&W McKone sketch-c 3.00
536-Variant cover by Bryan Hitch 5.00
537-B&W variant cover 5.00
538-542-Civil War. 538-Don Blake reclaims Thor's hammer 4.00
543-45th Anniversary; Black Panther and Storm replace Reed and Sue; Granov-c 4.00
544-553: 544-546-Silver Surfer app.; Turner-c 3.00
554-568-Millar-s/Hitch-a/c. 558-561-Doctor Doom-c/app. 562-Funeral & proposal 3.00
554-Variant-c by Bianchi 6.00
554-Variant Skrull-c by Suydam 30.00
569-($3.99) Wraparound-c; Immonen-a; Dr. Doom app. 4.00
570-586: 570-572,575-578-Eaglesham-a. 574-Spider-Man app. 584-586-Galactus app. 3.00
587-(3/11, $3.99) Death of Human Torch; Epting-a; issue is in black polybag; Davis-c 4.00
587-Variant-c by Cassaday 10.00
588-($3.99) Last issue; Dragotta-a; preview of FF #1; back-up w/Spider-Man; Davis-c 4.00
589-599-**Do not exist**; story continues in FF series
600-(1/12, $7.99) Avengers app.; Human Torch returns, back-up short stories; Dell'Otto-c 8.00

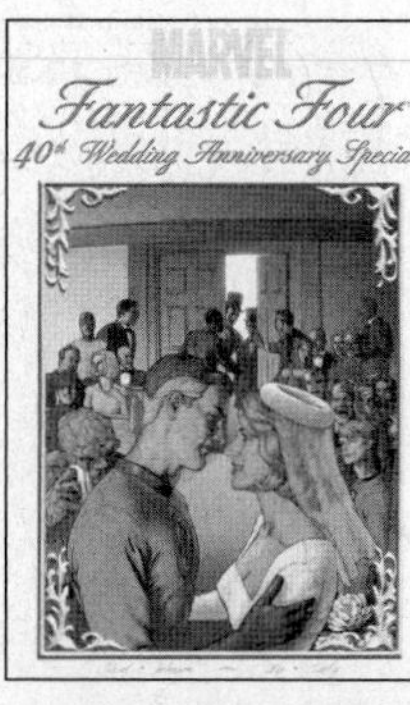

Fantastic Four: The Wedding Special #1 © MAR

Fantastic Four: Fireworks #1 © MAR

Fantastic Four 2099 #4 © MAR

	GD 2.0	VG 4.0	FN 6.0	VF 8.0	VF/NM 9.0	NM- 9.2

600-Variant-c by John Romita, Jr. 10.00
600-Variant-c by Art Adams 15.00
601-603,605,605.1, 606-611: 601-603-Johnny Storm & Avengers app. 602,603-Galactus app. 605.1-Alternate origin; Choi-a. 607,608-Black Panther app. 611-Doctor Doom app. 3.00
604-($3.99) Future Franklin and Valeria app. 4.00
...'98 Annual ($3.50) Immonen-a 4.00
...'99 Annual ($3.50) Ladronn-a 4.00
...'00 Annual ($3.50) Larocca-a; Marvel Girl back-up story 4.00
...'01 Annual ($2.99) Maguire-a; Thing back-up w/Yu-a 4.00
... Annual 32 (8/10, $4.99) Hitch-a/c 5.00
... Annual 33 (9/12, $4.99) Alan Davis-s/a/c; Dr. Strange & Clan Destine app. 5.00
... : A Death in the Family (7/06, $3.99, one-shot) Weeks-a/c; and r/F.F. #245 4.00
... By J. Michael Straczynski Vol. 1 (2005, $19.99, HC) r/#527-532 20.00
Civil War: Fantastic Four TPB (2007, $17.99) r/#538-543; 45th Anniversary Toasts 18.00
... Cosmic-Size Special 1 (2/09, $4.99) Cary Bates-s/Bing Cansino-a; r/F.F. #237 5.00
Fantastic 4th Voyage of Sinbad (9/01, $5.95) Claremont-s/Ferry-a 6.00
Flesh and Stone (8/01, $12.95, TPB) r/#35-39 13.00
... Giant-Size Adventures 1 (8/09, $3.99) Cifuentes & Coover-a; Egghead app. 4.00
... In...Ataque del M.O.D.O.K.! (11/10, $3.99) English & Spanish editions; Beland-s/Doe-a 4.00
... /Inhumans TPB (2007, $19.99) r/#51-54 and Inhumans ('00) #1-4 20.00
...: Isla De La Muerte! (2/08, $3.99) English & Spanish editions; Beland-s/Doe-a 4.00
... MGC #570 (7/11, $1.00) r/#570 with "Marvel's Greatest Comics" cover banner 3.00
... Presents: Franklin Richards 1 (11/05, $2.99) r/back-up stories from Power Pack #1-4 plus new 5 pg. story; Sumerak-s/Eliopoulos-a (Also see Franklin Richards) 3.00
...Special (2/06, $2.99) McDuffie-s/Casey Jones-a; dinner with Dr. Doom 3.00
...Tales Vol. 1 (2005, $7.99, digest) r/Marvel Age: FF Tales #1, Tales of the Thing #1-3, and Spider-Man Team-Up Special 8.00
...: The Last Stand (8/11, $4.99) r/#574, 587 & 588 (death of Johnny Storm) 5.00
...: The New Fantastic Four HC (2007, $19.99) r/#544-550; variant covers & sketch pgs. 20.00
...: The New Fantastic Four SC (2008, $15.99) r/#544-550; variant covers & sketch pgs. 16.00
... : The Wedding Special 1 (1/06, $5.00) 40th Anniversary new story & r/FF Annual #3 5.00
... Vol. 1 HC (2004, $29.99, dust jacket) oversized reprint /#60-70, 500-502; Mark Waid intro and series proposal; cover gallery 30.00
... Vol. 2 HC (2005, $29.99, d.j.) oversized r/#503-513; Waid intro.; deleted scenes 30.00
... Vol. 3 HC (2005, $29.99, d.j.) oversized r/#514-524; Waid commentaries; cover sketches 30.00
... Vol. 1: Imaginauts (2003, $17.99, TPB) r/#56,60-66; Mark Waid's series proposal 18.00
... Vol. 2: Unthinkable (2003, $17.99, TPB) r/#67-70,500-502; #500 Director's Cut extras 18.00
... Vol. 3: Authoritative Action (2004, $12.99, TPB) r/#503-508 13.00
... Vol. 4: Hereafter (2004, $11.99, TPB) r/#509-513 12.00
... Vol. 5: Disassembled (2004, $14.99, TPB) r/#514-519 15.00
... Vol. 6: Rising Storm (2005, $13.99, TPB) r/#520-524 14.00
...: The Beginning of the End TPB (2008, $14.99) r/#525,526,551-553 & Fantastic Four: Isla De La Muerte! one-shot 15.00
...: The Life Fantastic TPB (2006, $16.99) r/#533-535; The Wedding Special, Special (2/06) and A Death in the Family one-shots 17.00
Wizard #1/2 -Lim-a 10.00

FANTASTIC FOUR (Volume Four) (Marvel NOW!) (Also see FF)
Marvel Comics: Jan, 2013 - No. 16, Mar, 2014 ($2.99)

1-5-Fraction-s/Bagley-a/c 3.00
5AU-(5/13, $3.99) Age of Ultron tie-in; Fraction-s/Araújo-a/Bagley-c 4.00
6-15: 6,7-Blastaar app. 9,13-15-Dr. Doom app. 14,15-Ienco-a 3.00
16-($3.99) Fantastic Four vs. Doom, The Annihilating Conqueror; back-up w/Quinones-a 4.00

FANTASTIC FOUR (Volume Five) (All-New Marvel NOW!)
Marvel Comics: Apr, 2014 - No. 14, Feb, 2015; No. 642, Mar, 2015 - No. 645, Jun, 2015 ($3.99)

1-4-Robinson-s/Kirk-a. 3,4-Frightful Four app. 4.00
5-($4.99) Trial of the Fantastic Four; flashback-a by various incl. Starlin, Allred, Samnee 5.00
6-14: 6-8-Original Sin tie-in. 10,11-Scarlet Witch app. 11,12-Spider-Man app. 4.00
642-(3/15)-644: Heroes Reborn Avengers app. 643,644-Sleepwalker app. 4.00
645-($5.99) Psycho Man & the Frightful Four app.; Kirk-a; bonus back-up stories 6.00
Annual 1 (11/14, $4.99) Sue vs. Doctor Doom in Latveria; Grummett-a 5.00
100th Anniversary Special: Fantastic Four 1 (9/14, $3.99) Van Meter-s/Estep-a 4.00

FANTASTIC FOUR AND POWER PACK
Marvel Comics: Sept, 2007 - No. 4, Dec, 2007 ($2.99, limited series)

1-4-Gurihiru-a/Van Lente-s; the Wizard app. 3.00
...: Favorite Son TPB (2008, $7.99, digest size) r/#1-4 8.00

FANTASTIC FOUR: ATLANTIS RISING
Marvel Comics: June, 1995 - No. 2, July, 1995 ($3.95, limited series)

1,2: Acetate-c 5.00
Collector's Preview (5/95, $2.25, 52 pgs.) 4.00

FANTASTIC FOUR: BIG TOWN
Marvel Comics: Jan, 2001 - No. 4, Apr, 2001 ($2.99, limited series)

1-4:"What If?" story; McKone-a/Englehart-s 3.00

FANTASTIC FOUR: FIREWORKS
Marvel Comics: Jan, 1999 - No. 3, Mar, 1999 ($2.99, limited series)

1-3-Remix; Jeff Johnson-a 3.00

FANTASTIC FOUR: FIRST FAMILY
Marvel Comics: May, 2006 - No. 6, Oct, 2006 ($2.99, limited series)

1-6-Casey-s/Weston-a; flashback to the days after the accident 3.00
TPB (2006, $15.99) r/#1-6 16.00

FANTASTIC FOUR: FOES
Marvel Comics: Mar, 2005 - No. 6, Aug, 2005 ($2.99, limited series)

1-6-Kirkman-s/Rathburn-a. 1-Puppet Master app. 3-Super-Skrull app. 4-Mole Man app. 3.00
TPB (2005, $16.99) r/#1-6 17.00

FANTASTIC FOUR: HOUSE OF M (Reprinted in House of M: Fantastic Four/ Iron Man TPB)
Marvel Comics: Sept, 2005 - No. 3, Nov, 2005 ($2.99, limited series)

1-3: Fearsome Four, led by Doom; Scot Eaton-a 3.00

FANTASTIC FOUR INDEX (See Official...)

FANTASTIC FOUR/ IRON MAN: BIG IN JAPAN
Marvel Comics: Dec, 2005 - No. 4, Mar, 2006 ($3.50, limited series)

1-4-Seth Fisher-a/c; Zeb Wells-s; wraparound-c on each 3.50
TPB (2006, $12.99) r/#1-4 and Seth Fisher illustrated story from Spider-Man Unlimited #8 13.00

FANTASTIC FOUR: 1 2 3 4
Marvel Comics: Oct, 2001 - No. 4, Jan, 2002 ($2.99, limited series)

1-4-Morrison-s/Jae Lee-a. 2-4-Namor-c/app. 3.00
TPB (2002, $9.99) r/#1-4 10.00

FANTASTIC FOUR ROAST
Marvel Comics Group: May, 1982 (75¢, one-shot, direct sales)

1-Celebrates 20th anniversary of F.F.#1; X-Men, Ghost Rider & many others cameo; Golden, Miller, Buscema, Rogers, Byrne, Anderson art; Hembeck/Austin-c 5.00

FANTASTIC FOUR: THE END
Marvel Comics: Jan, 2007 - No. 6, May, 2007 ($2.99, limited series)

1-6-Alan Davis-s/a; last adventure of the future FF. 1-Dr. Doom-c/app. 3.00
Roughcut #1 ($3.99) B&W pencil art for full story and text script; B&W sketch cover 4.00
HC (2007, $19.99, dustjacket) r/#1-6 20.00
SC (2008, $14.99) r/#1-6 15.00

FANTASTIC FOUR: THE LEGEND
Marvel Comics: Oct, 1996 ($3.95, one-shot)

1-Tribute issue 4.00

FANTASTIC FOUR: THE MOVIE
Marvel Comics: Aug, 2005 ($4.99/$12.99, one-shot)

1-($4.99) Movie adaptation; Jurgens-a; behind the scenes feature; Doom origin; photo-c 5.00
TPB-($12.99) Movie adaptation, r/Fantastic Four #5 & 190, and FF Vol. 3 #60, photo-c 13.00

FANTASTIC FOUR: TRUE STORY
Marvel Comics: Sept, 2008 - No. 4, Jan, 2009 ($2.99, limited series)

1-4-Cornell-s/Domingues-a/Henrichon-c 3.00

FANTASTIC FOUR 2099
Marvel Comics: Jan, 1996 - No. 8, Aug, 1996 ($3.95/$1.95)

1-($3.95)-Chromium-c; X-Nation preview 4.00
2-8: 4-Spider-Man 2099-c/app. 5-Doctor Strange app. 7-Thibert-c 3.00
NOTE: *Williamson a-1i; c-1i.*

FANTASTIC FOUR UNLIMITED
Marvel Comics: Mar, 1993 - No. 12, Dec, 1995 ($3.95, 68 pgs.)

1-12: 1-Black Panther app. 4-Thing vs. Hulk. 5-Vs. The Frightful Four. 6-Vs. Namor. 7, 9-12-Wraparound-c 4.00

FANTASTIC FOUR UNPLUGGED
Marvel Comics: Sept, 1995 - No. 6, Aug 1996 (99¢, bi-monthly)

1-6 3.00

FANTASTIC FOUR - UNSTABLE MOLECULES
(Indicia for #1 reads STARTLING STORIES: ... ; #2 reads UNSTABLE MOLECULES)
Marvel Comics: Mar, 2003 - No. 4, June, 2003 ($2.99, limited series)

1-4-Guy Davis-c/a 3.00
Fantastic Four Legends Vol. 1 TPB (2003, $13.99) r/#1-4, origin from FF #1 (1963) 14.00
TPB (2005, $13.99) r/#1-4 14.00

FANTASTIC FOUR VS. X-MEN
Marvel Comics: Feb, 1987 - No. 4, June, 1987 (Limited series)

Fantastic Four: World's Greatest Comics Magazine #11 © MAR

Farscape #1 © Jim Henson Co.

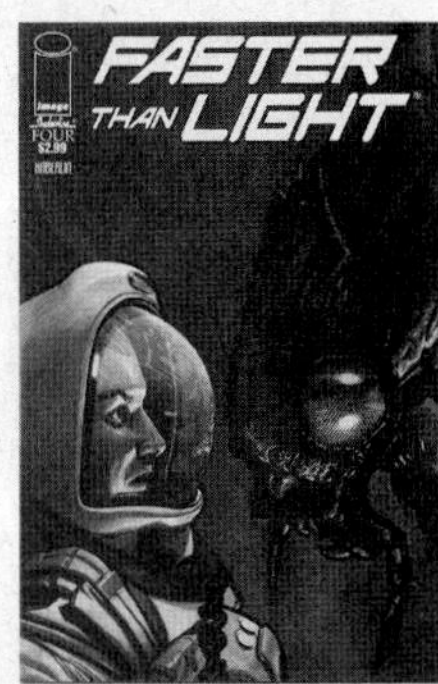

Faster Than Light #4 © Anomaly Prods.

GD VG FN VF VF/NM NM- 2.0 4.0 6.0 8.0 9.0 9.2

1-4: 4-Austin-a(i) 4.00

FANTASTIC FOUR: WORLD'S GREATEST COMICS MAGAZINE
Marvel Comics: Feb, 2001 - No. 12 (Limited series)

1-12: Homage to Lee & Kirby era of F.F.; s/a by Larsen & various. 5-Hulk-c/app. 10-Thor app. 3.00

FANTASTIC GIANTS (Formerly Konga #1-23)
Charlton Comics: V2#24, Sept, 1966 (25¢, 68 pgs.)

V2#24-Special Ditko issue; origin Konga & Gorgo reprinted plus two new Ditko stories 6 12 18 42 79 115

FANTASTIC TALES
I. W. Enterprises: 1958 (no date) (Reprint, one-shot)

1-Reprints Avon's "City of the Living Dead" 3 6 9 19 30 40

FANTASTIC VOYAGE (See Movie Comics)
Gold Key: Aug, 1969 - No. 2, Dec, 1969

1 (TV) 4 8 12 27 44 60
2-Cover has the text "Civilian Miniaturized Defense Force" in yellow bar at top; back cover has painted art 3 6 9 19 30 40
2-Variant cover has text "In This Issue Sweepstakes..." along top; ad on back-c 4 8 12 23 37 50

FANTASTIC VOYAGES OF SINDBAD, THE
Gold Key: Oct, 1965 - No. 2, June, 1967

1-Painted-c on both 6 12 18 38 69 100
2 5 10 15 30 50 70

FANTASTIC WORLDS
Standard Comics: No. 5, Sept, 1952 - No. 7, Jan, 1953

5-Toth, Anderson-a 39 78 117 231 378 525
6-Toth-c/a 31 62 93 182 296 410
7 23 46 69 136 223 310

FANTASY FEATURES
Americomics: 1987 - No. 2, 1987 ($1.75)

1,2 3.00

FANTASY ILLUSTRATED
New Media Publ.: Spring 1982 ($2.95, B&W magazine)

1-P. Craig Russell-c/a; art by Ditko, Sekowsky, Sutton; Englehart-s 1 2 3 4 5 7

FANTASY MASTERPIECES (Marvel Super Heroes No. 12 on)
Marvel Comics Group: Feb, 1966 - No. 11, Oct, 1967; V2#1, Dec, 1979 - No. 14, Jan, 1981

1-Photo of Stan Lee (12¢-c #1,2) 9 18 27 58 114 170
2-r/1st Fin Fang Foom from Strange Tales #89 5 10 15 35 63 90
3-8: 3-G.A. Capt. America-r begin, end #11; 1st 25¢ Giant; Colan-r. 3-6-Kirby-c(p). 4-Kirby-c(p)(i). 7-Begin G.A. Sub-Mariner, Torch-r/M. Mystery. 8-Torch battles the Sub-Mariner-r/Marvel Mystery #9 5 10 15 35 63 90
9-Origin Human Torch-r/Marvel Comics #1 6 12 18 37 66 95
10,11: 10-r/origin & 1st app. All Winners Squad from All Winners #19. 11-r/origin of Toro (H.T. #1) & Black Knight #1 5 10 15 34 60 85
V2#1(12/79, 75¢, 52 pgs.)-r/origin Silver Surfer from Silver Surfer #1 with editing plus reprints cover; J. Buscema-a 2 4 6 9 12 15
2-14-Reprints Silver Surfer #2-14 w/covers 6.00

NOTE: ***Buscema*** *c-V2#7-9(in part).* ***Ditko*** *r-1-3, 7, 9.* ***Everett*** *r-1,7-9.* ***Matt Fox*** *r-9i.* ***Kirby*** *r-1-11; c(p)-3, 4i, 5, 6.* ***Starlin*** *r-8-13. Some direct sale V2#14's had a 50¢ cover price. #3-11 contain Capt. America-r/Capt. America #3-10. #7-11 contain G.A.Human Torch & Sub-Mariner-r.*

FANTASY QUARTERLY (Also see Elfquest)
Independent Publishers Syndicate: Spring, 1978 (B&W)

1-1st app. Elfquest; Dave Sim-a (6 pgs.) 8 16 24 54 102 150

FANTOMAN (Formerly Amazing Adventure Funnies)
Centaur Publications: No. 2, Aug, 1940 - No. 4, Dec, 1940

2-The Fantom of the Fair, The Arrow, Little Dynamite-r begin; origin The Ermine by Filchock; Burgos, J. Cole, Ernst, Gustavson-a 155 310 465 992 1696 2400
3,4: Gustavson-r. 4-Red Blaze story 123 246 369 787 1344 1900

FANTOMEX MAX
Marvel Comics: Dec, 2013 - No. 4, Mar, 2014 ($3.99)

1-4-Hope-s/Crystal-a/Francavilla-c 4.00

FAREWELL MOONSHADOW (See Moonshadow)
DC Comics (Vertigo): Jan, 1997 ($7.95, one-shot)

nn-DeMatteis-s/Muth-c/a 8.00

FARGO KID (Formerly Justice Traps the Guilty)(See Feature Comics #47)
Prize Publications: V11#3(#1), June-July, 1958 - V11#5, Oct-Nov, 1958

V11#3(#1)-Origin Fargo Kid, Severin-c/a; Williamson-a(2); Heath-a 18 36 54 105 165 225
V11#4,5-Severin-c/a 13 26 39 74 105 135

FARMER'S DAUGHTER, THE
Stanhall Publ./Trojan Magazines: Feb-Mar, 1954 - No. 3, June-July, 1954; No. 4, Oct, 1954

1-Lingerie, nudity panel 116 232 348 742 1271 1800
2-4(Stanhall) 65 130 195 416 708 1000

FARSCAPE (Based on TV series)
BOOM! Studios: Nov, 2008 - No. 4, Feb, 2009 ($3.99)

1-4-O'Bannon-s/Patterson-a; multiple covers 4.00

FARSCAPE (Based on TV series)
BOOM! Studios: Nov, 2009 - No. 24, Oct, 2011 ($3.99)

1-24-O'Bannon-s/Sliney-a; multiple covers 4.00
...: D'Argo's Lament 1-4 (4/09 - No. 4, 7/09, $3.99) Edwards-a; three covers on each 4.00
...: D'Argo's Quest 1-4 (12/09 - No. 4, 3/10, $3.99) Cleveland-a; three covers on each 4.00
...: D'Argo's Trial 1-4 (8/09 - No. 4, 11/09, $3.99) Cleveland-a; multiple covers on each 4.00
...: Gone and Back 1-4 (7/09 - No. 4, 10/09, $3.99) Patterson-a; multiple covers on each 4.00
...: Scorpius 0-7 (4/10 - No. 7, 2010, $3.99) 0-3-Ruiz-a; multiple-c. 4-7-Purcell-a 4.00
...: Strange Detractors 1-4 (3/09 - No. 4, 6/09, $3.99) Sliney-a; three covers on each 4.00

FARSCAPE: WAR TORN (Based on TV series)
DC Comics (WildStorm): Apr, 2002 - No. 2, May, 2002 ($4.95, limited series)

1,2-Teranishi-a/Wolfman-s; photo-c 5.00

FASHION IN ACTION
Eclipse Comics: Aug, 1986 - Feb, 1987 (Baxter paper)

Summer Special 1 , Winter Special 1, each Snyder III-c/a 3.00

FASTBALL EXPRESS (Major League Baseball)
Ultimate Sports Force: 2000 ($3.95, one-shot)

1-Polybagged with poster; Johnson, Maddux, Park, Nomo, Clemens app. 4.00

FASTER THAN LIGHT
Image Comics (Shadowline): Sept, 2015 - Present ($2.99)

1-10-Brian Haberlin-s/a 3.00

FASTEST GUN ALIVE, THE (Movie)
Dell Publishing Co.: No. 741, Sept, 1956 (one-shot)

Four Color 741-Photo-c 7 14 21 44 82 120

FAST FICTION (...Action) (Stories by Famous Authors Illustrated #6 on)
Seaboard Publ./Famous Authors Ill.: Oct, 1949 - No. 5, Mar, 1950 (All have Kiefer-c)(48 pgs.)

1-Scarlet Pimpernel; Jim Lavery-c/a 29 58 87 170 278 385
2-Captain Blood; H. C. Kiefer-c/a 24 48 72 142 234 325
3-She, by Rider Haggard; Vincent Napoli-a 31 62 93 182 296 410
4-(1/50, 52 pgs.)-The 39 Steps; Lavery-c/a 19 38 57 112 176 240
5-Beau Geste; Kiefer-c/a 19 38 57 112 176 240

NOTE: ***Kiefer*** *a-2, 5; c-2, 3,5.* ***Lavery*** *c/a-1, 4.* ***Napoli*** *a-3.*

FAST FORWARD
DC Comics (Piranha Press): 1992 - No. 3, 1993 ($4.95, 68 pgs.)

1-3: 1-Morrison scripts; McKean-c/a. 3-Sam Kieth-a 5.00

FAST WILLIE JACKSON
Fitzgerald Periodicals, Inc.: Oct, 1976 - No. 7, 1977

1 4 8 12 28 47 65
2-7 3 6 9 16 23 30

FAT ALBERT (...& the Cosby Kids) (TV)
Gold Key: Mar, 1974 - No. 29, Feb, 1979

1 4 8 12 25 40 55
2-10 3 6 9 15 22 28
11-29 2 4 6 10 14 18

FATALE (Also see Powers That Be #1 & Shadow State #1,2)
Broadway Comics: Jan, 1996 - No. 6, Aug, 1996 ($2.50)

1-6: J.G. Jones-c/a in all, Preview Edition 1 (11/95, B&W) 3.00

FATALE
Image Comics: Jan, 2012 - No. 24, Jul, 2014 ($3.50)

1-Brubaker-s/Phillips-a/c 5.00
1-Variant-c of Demon with machine gun 8.00
1-Second through Fifth printings 4.00
2-23-Brubaker-s/Phillips-a/c in all 3.50

Fate #22 © DC

Fathom V5 #1 © Aspen MLT

Fatman, The Human Flying Saucer #1 © Milson

	GD 2.0	VG 4.0	FN 6.0	VF 8.0	VF/NM 9.0	NM- 9.2

24-($4.99) Story conclusion; bonus preview of The Fade Out series 5.00

FAT AND SLAT (Ed Wheelan) (Becomes Gunfighter No. 5 on)
E. C. Comics: Summer, 1947 - No. 4, Spring, 1948

1-Intro/origin Voltage, Man of Lightning; "Comics" McCormick, the World's No. 1 Comic Book Fan begins, ends #4 41 82 123 256 428 600
2-4: 4-Comics McCormick-c feature 29 58 87 170 278 385

FAT AND SLAT JOKE BOOK
All-American Comics (William H. Wise): Summer, 1944 (52 pgs., one-shot)

nn-by Ed Wheelan 34 68 102 199 325 450

FATE (See Hand of Fate & Thrill-O-Rama)

FATE
DC Comics: Oct, 1994 - No. 22, Sept, 1996 ($1.95/$2.25)

0,1-22: 8-Begin $2.25-c. 11-14-Alan Scott (Sentinel) app. 10,14-Zatanna app. 21-Phantom Stranger app. 22-Spectre app. 3.00

FATHER'S DAY
Dark Horse Comics: Oct, 2014 - No. 4, Jan, 2015 ($3.99, limited series)

1-4-Mike Richardson-s/Gabriel Guzmán-a 4.00

FATHOM
Comico: May, 1987 - No. 3, July, 1987 ($1.50, limited series)

1-3 3.00

FATHOM
Image Comics (Top Cow Prod.): Aug, 1998 - No. 14, May, 2002 ($2.50)

Preview 12.00
0-Wizard supplement 7.00
0-($6.95) DF Alternate 7.00
1/2 (Wizard) origin of Cannon; Turner-a 6.00
1/2 (3/03, $2.99) origin of Cannon 3.00
1-Turner-s/a; three covers; alternate story pages 6.00
1-Wizard World Ed. 9.00
2-14: 12-14-Witchblade app. 13,14-Tomb Raider app. 3.00
9-Green foil-c edition 15.00
9,12-Holofoil editions 18.00
12,13-DFE alternate-c 6.00
13,14-DFE Gold edition 8.00
14-DFE Blue 15.00
... Collected Edition 1 (3/99, $5.95) r/Preview & all three #1's 6.00
... Collected Edition 2-4 (3-12/99, $5.95) 2-r/#2,3. 3-r/#4,5. 4-r/#6,7 6.00
... Collected Edition 5 (4/00, $5.95) 5-r/#8,9 6.00
... Primer (6/11, $1.00) Comic style summary of Volume 1; text summaries of Vol. 2 & 3 3.00
... Swimsuit Special (5/99, $2.95) Pin-ups by various 3.00
... Swimsuit Special 2000 (12/00, $2.95) Pin-ups by various; Turner-c 3.00
Michael Turner's Fathom HC ('01, $39.95) r/#1-9, black-c w/silver foil 40.00
Michael Turner's Fathom SC ('01, $24.95) r/#1-9, new Turner-c 25.00
Michael Turner's Fathom The Definitive Edition ('08, $49.95) r/Preview, #0,1/2,1-14, Swimsuit Special 1999 & 2000; cover gallery; foreword by Geoff Johns 50.00

FATHOM (MICHAEL TURNER'S...) (Volume 2)
Aspen MLT, Inc.: No. 0, Apr, 2005 - No. 11, Dec, 2006 ($2.50/$2.99)

0-($2.50) Turnbull-a/Turner-c 3.00
1-11-($2.99) 1-Five covers. 2-Two covers. 4-Six covers 3.00
... Beginnings (2005, $1.99) Two covers; Turnbull-a 3.00
...: Killian's Vessel 1 (7/07, $2.99) 3 covers; Odagawa-a 3.00
... Prelude (6/05, $2.99) Seven covers; Garza-a 3.00

FATHOM (MICHAEL TURNER'S...) (Volume 3)
Aspen MLT, Inc.: No. 0, Jun, 2008 - No. 10, Feb, 2010 ($2.50/$2.99)

0-($2.50) Garza-a/c 3.00
1-10-($2.99) Garza-a; multiple covers on each 3.00

FATHOM (MICHAEL TURNER'S...) (Volume 4)
Aspen MLT, Inc.: No. 0, Jun, 2011 - No. 9, May, 2013 ($2.50/$2.99/$3.50)

0-($2.50) Lobdell-s/Konat-a/c; interview with Lobdell; sketch art 3.00
1-3-($2.99) 1-Five covers 3.00
4-9-($3.50) 3.50

FATHOM (MICHAEL TURNER'S...) (Volume 5)
Aspen MLT, Inc.: Jul, 2013 - No. 8, Sept, 2014 ($1.00/$3.99)

1-($1.00) Wohl-s/Konat-a; multiple covers 3.00
2-8-($3.99) Multiple covers on all 4.00
Annual 1 (6/14, $5.99) Turner-c; short stories by Turner, Wohl/Calero, Ruffino & others 6.00

FATHOM (ALL NEW MICHAEL TURNER'S...) (Volume 6)
Aspen MLT, Inc.: Feb, 2017 - No. 8, Sept, 2017 ($3.99)

1-8-Northcott-s/Renna-a; multiple covers 4.00

FATHOM BLUE (MICHAEL TURNER'S...)
Aspen MLT, Inc.: Jun, 2015 - No. 6, Dec, 2015 ($3.99, limited series)

1-6-Hernandez-s/Avella-a; multiple covers on all 4.00

FATHOM: BLUE DESCENT (MICHAEL TURNER'S...)
Aspen MLT, Inc.: Jun, 2010 - No. 4, Feb, 2012 ($2.50/$2.99, limited series)

0-($2.50) Scott Clark-a; covers by Clark & Benitez 3.00
1-4-($2.99) Alex Sanchez-a. 1-Covers by Clark & Finch 3.00

FATHOM: CANNON HAWKE (MICHAEL TURNER'S...)
Aspen MLT, Inc.: Nov, 2005 - No. 5, Feb, 2006 ($2.99)

1-5-To-a/Turner-c 3.00
... Prelude (11/05, $2.50) Turner-c 3.00

FATHOM: DAWN OF WAR (MICHAEL TURNER'S...)
Aspen MLT, Inc.: Oct, 2004 - No. 3, Dec, 2004 ($2.99, limited series)

0-Caldwell-a 3.00
1-3-Caldwell-a 3.00
...: Cannon Hawke #0 ('04, $2.50) Turner-c 3.00
... The Complete Saga Vol. 1 (2005, $9.99) r/series with cover gallery 10.00

FATHOM: KIANI (MICHAEL TURNER'S...)
Aspen MLT, Inc.: No. 0, Feb, 2007 - No. 4, Dec, 2007 ($2.99, limited series)

0-4-Marcus To-a. 1-Six covers 3.00
Vol. 2 (4/12, $2.50) 0-Four covers 3.00
Vol. 2 (5/12 - No. 4, 11/12, $3.50) 1-4-Hernandez-s/Nome-a; multiple covers on each 3.50
Vol. 3 (3/14 - No. 4, 6/14, $3.99) 1-4-Hernandez-s/Cafaro-a; multiple covers on each 4.00
Vol. 4 (2/15 - No. 4, 5/15, $3.99) 1-4-Hernandez-s/Cafaro-a; multiple covers on each 4.00

FATHOM: KILLIAN'S TIDE
Image Comics (Top Cow Prod.): Apr, 2001 - No. 4, Nov, 2001 ($2.95)

1-4-Caldwell-a(p); two covers by Caldwell and Turner. 2-Flip-book preview of Universe 3.00
1-DFE Blue, 1-Holographic logo 12.00
4-Foil-c 12.00

FATHOM: THE ELITE SAGA (MICHAEL TURNER'S...)
Aspen MLT, Inc.: Jun, 2013 - No. 5, Jul, 2013 ($3.99, weekly limited series)

1-5-Hernandez-s/Marion-a; multiple covers; leads into Fathom Volume 5 4.00

FATIMA...CHALLENGE TO THE WORLD (Also see Our Lady of Fatima)
Catechetical Guild: 1951, 36 pgs. (15¢)

nn (not same as 'Challenge to the World') 6 12 18 31 38 45

FATMAN, THE HUMAN FLYING SAUCER
Lightning Comics (Milson Publ. Co.): April, 1967 - No. 3, Aug-Sept, 1967 (68 pgs.) (Written by Otto Binder)

1-Origin/1st app. Fatman & Tinman by C.C. Beck; 1st app. Anti-Man; 2-pg. Fatman pin-up by Beck 6 12 18 37 66 95
2-C. C. Beck-a 4 8 12 27 44 60
3-(Scarce)-Beck-a 6 12 18 38 69 100

FAUNTLEROY COMICS (Super Duck Presents...)
Close-Up/Archie Publications: 1950; No. 2, 1951; No. 3, 1952

1-Super Duck-c/stories by Al Fagaly in all 11 22 33 60 83 105
2,3 7 14 21 35 43 50

FAUST
Northstar Publishing/Rebel Studios #7 on: 1989 - No 13, 1997 ($2.00/$2.25, B&W, mature themes)

1-Decapitation-c; Tim Vigil-c/a in all 3 6 9 14 19 24
1-2nd - 4th printings 4.00
2 2 4 6 8 10 12
2-2nd & 3rd printings, 3,5-2nd printing 4.00
3 1 3 4 6 8 10
4-10: 7-Begin Rebel Studios series 5.00
11-13-Scarce 2 4 6 8 10 12

FAWCETT MOTION PICTURE COMICS (See Motion Picture Comics)

FAWCETT MOVIE COMIC
Fawcett Publications: 1949 - No. 20, Dec, 1952 (All photo-c)

nn- "Dakota Lil"; George Montgomery & Rod Cameron (1949) 20 40 60 114 182 250
nn- "Copper Canyon"; Ray Milland & Hedy Lamarr (1950) 15 30 45 86 133 180
nn- "Destination Moon" (1950) 61 122 183 390 670 950

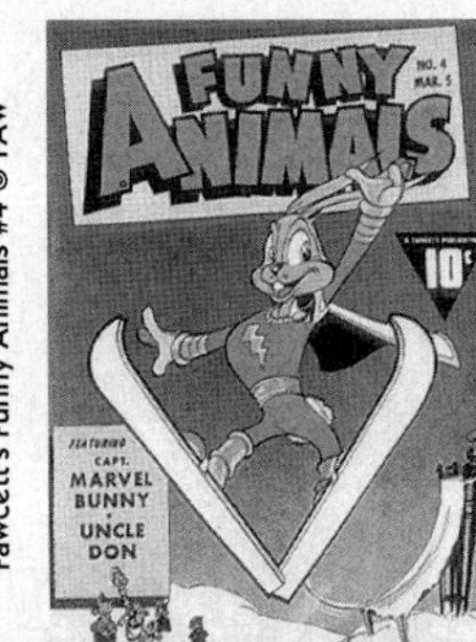

Fawcett's Funny Animals #4 © FAW

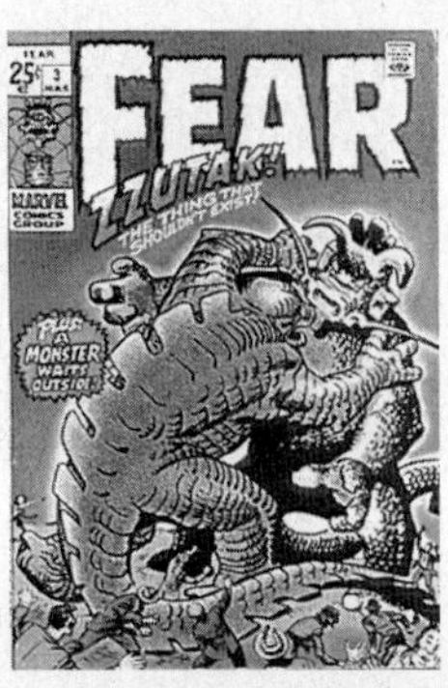

Fear #3 © MAR

Fear Itself #3 © MAR

	GD 2.0	VG 4.0	FN 6.0	VF 8.0	VF/NM 9.0	NM- 9.2
nn- "Montana"; Errol Flynn & Alexis Smith (1950)	15	30	45	86	133	180
nn- "Pioneer Marshal"; Monte Hale (1950)	15	30	45	86	133	180
nn- "Powder River Rustlers"; Rocky Lane (1950)	20	40	60	114	182	250
nn- "Singing Guns"; Vaughn Monroe, Ella Raines & Walter Brennan (1950)	14	28	42	82	121	160
7- "Gunmen of Abilene"; Rocky Lane; Bob Powell-a (1950)	16	32	48	92	144	195
8- "King of the Bullwhip"; Lash LaRue; Bob Powell-a (1950)	21	42	63	126	206	285
9- "The Old Frontier"; Monte Hale; Bob Powell-a (2/51; mis-dated 2/50)	15	30	45	90	140	190
10- "The Missourians"; Monte Hale (4/51)	15	30	45	90	140	190
11- "The Thundering Trail"; Lash LaRue (6/51)	19	38	57	111	176	240
12- "Rustlers on Horseback"; Rocky Lane (8/51)	15	30	45	90	140	190
13- "Warpath"; Edmond O'Brien & Forrest Tucker (10/51)	14	28	42	80	115	150
14- "Last Outpost"; Ronald Reagan (12/51)	32	64	96	188	307	425
15-(Scarce)- "The Man From Planet X"; Robert Clark; Schaffenberger-a (2/52)	245	490	735	1568	2684	3800
16- "Ten Tall Men"; Burt Lancaster	13	26	39	74	105	135
17- "Rose of Cimarron"; Jack Buetel & Mala Powers	10	20	30	58	79	100
18- "The Brigand"; Anthony Dexter & Anthony Quinn; Schaffenberger-a	10	20	30	58	79	100
19- "Carbine Williams"; James Stewart; Costanza-a; James Stewart photo-c	11	22	33	62	86	110
20- "Ivanhoe"; Robert Taylor & Liz Taylor photo-c	18	36	54	105	165	225

FAWCETT'S FUNNY ANIMALS (No. 1-26, 80-on titled "Funny Animals"; becomes Li'l Tomboy No. 92 on?)
Fawcett Publications/Charlton Comics No. 84 on: 12/42 - #79, 4/53; #80, 6/53 - #83, 12?/53; #84, 4/54 - #91, 2/56

	GD	VG	FN	VF	VF/NM	NM-
1-Capt. Marvel on cover; intro. Hoppy The Captain Marvel Bunny, cloned from Capt. Marvel; Billy the Kid & Willie the Worm begin	58	116	174	371	636	900
2-Xmas-c	36	72	108	211	343	475
3-5: 3(2/43)-Spirit of '43-c	25	50	75	150	245	340
6,7,9,10	15	30	45	88	137	185
8-Flag-c	16	32	48	92	144	195
11-20: 14-Cover is a 1944 calendar	12	24	36	69	97	125
21-40: 25-Xmas-c. 26-St. Valentine's Day-c	10	20	30	54	72	90
41-86,90,91	9	18	27	47	61	75
87-89(10-54-2/55)-Merry Mailman ish (TV/Radio)-part photo-c	10	20	30	54	72	90

NOTE: *Marvel Bunny in all issues to at least No. 68 (not in 49-54).*

FAZE ONE FAZERS
AC Comics: 1986 - No. 4, Sept, 1986 (Limited series)

1-4						3.00

F.B.I., THE
Dell Publishing Co.: Apr-June, 1965

1-Sinnott-a	3	6	9	19	30	40

F.B.I. STORY, THE (Movie)
Dell Publishing Co.: No. 1069, Jan-Mar, 1960

Four Color 1069-Toth-a; James Stewart photo-c	9	18	27	57	111	165

FBP: FEDERAL BUREAU OF PHYSICS (Titled Collider for issue #1)
DC Comics (Vertigo): Sept, 2013 - No. 24, Nov, 2015 ($2.99/$3.99)

Collider #1- Simon Oliver-s/Robbi Rodriguez-a/Nathan Fox-c						3.00
2-20: 2-(10/13)						3.00
21-24-($3.99)						4.00

FEAR (Adventure into...)
Marvel Comics Group: Nov, 1970 - No. 31, Dec, 1975

	GD	VG	FN	VF	VF/NM	NM-
1-Fantasy & Sci-Fi-r in early issues; 68 pg. Giant size; Kirby-a(r)	8	16	24	54	102	150
2-6: 2-4-(68 pgs.). 5,6-(52 pgs.) Kirby-a(r)	4	8	12	27	44	60
7-9-Kirby-a(r)	3	6	9	17	26	35
10-Man-Thing begins (10/72, 4th app.), ends #19; see Savage Tales #1 for 1st app.; 1st solo series; Chaykin/Morrow-c/a;	5	10	15	34	60	85
11,12: 11-N. Adams-c. 12-Starlin/Buckler-a	3	6	9	16	23	30
13,14,16-18: 17-Origin/1st app. Wundarr	3	6	9	14	20	26
15-1st full-length Man-Thing story (8/73)	3	6	9	16	24	32
19-Intro. Howard the Duck; Val Mayerik-a (12/73)	9	18	27	60	120	180
20-Morbius, the Living Vampire begins, ends #31; has history recap of Morbius with X-Men & Spider-Man	5	10	15	31	53	75
21-23,25	3	6	9	14	20	26
24-Blade-c/sty	3	6	9	21	33	45
26-31	2	4	6	10	14	18

NOTE: ***Bolle** a-13i. **Brunner** c-15-17. **Buckler** a-11p, 12i. **Chaykin** a-10i. **Colan** a-23r. **Craig** a-10p. **Ditko** a-6-8r. **Evans** a-30. **Everett** a-9, 10i, 21r. **Gulacy** a-20p. **Heath** a-12r. **Heck** a-8r, 13r. **Gil Kane** a-21p; c(p)-20, 21, 23-28, 31. **Kirby** a-1-9r. **Maneely** a-24r. **Mooney** a-11i, 26r. **Morrow** a-11i. **Paul Reinman** a-14r. **Robbins** a(p)-25-27, 31. **Russell** a-23p, 24p. **Severin** c-8. **Starlin** c-12p.*

FEAR AGENT
Image Comics (#1-11)/Dark Horse Comics.: Oct, 2005 - No. 32, Nov, 2011 ($2.99/$3.50)

1-11: 1-Remender-s/Moore-a. 5-Opeña-a begins. 11-Francavilla-a						3.00
... The Last Goodbye 1-4 (Dark Horse, 6/07 - No. 4, 9/07) (#12-15)						3.00
Tales of the Fear Agent: Twelve Steps in One (#16), 17-27						3.00
28-32-($3.50) Hawthorne & Moore-a/Moore-c						3.50
... Vol 1.: Re-Ignition TPB (2006, $9.99) r/#1-4						10.00
... Vol 2.: My War TPB (Dark Horse Books, 2007, $14.95) r/#5-10; Opeña sketch pages						15.00

FEARBOOK
Eclipse Comics: April, 1986 ($1.75, one-shot, mature)

1-Scholastic Mag-r; Bissette-a						4.00

FEAR EFFECT (Based on the video game)
Image Comics (Top Cow): May, 2000; March, 2001 ($2.95)

Retro Helix 1 (3/01), Special 1 (5/00)						3.00

FEAR IN THE NIGHT (See Complete Mystery No. 3)

FEAR ITSELF
Marvel Comics: Jun, 2011 - No. 7, Dec, 2011 ($3.99/$4.99, limited series)

1-6-Fraction-s/Immonen-a/McNiven-c. 3-Bucky apparently killed						4.00
1-Blank cover						4.00
7-($4.99) Thor perishes; previews of ...: The Fearless, Incredible Hulk #1, Defenders #1						5.00
7.1 Captain America (1/12, $3.99) Brubaker-s/Guice-a; Bucky's fate						4.00
7.2 Thor (1/12, $3.99) Fraction-s/Adam Kubert-a/c; Thor's funeral; Tanarus returns						4.00
7.3 Iron Man (1/12, $3.99) Fraction-s/Larroca-a/c; Odin app.						4.00
...: Black Widow (8/11, $3.99) Peter Nguyen-a; Peregrine app.						4.00
...: Book of the Skull (5/11, $3.99) prequel to series; WWII flashback, Red Skull app.						4.00
...: Fellowship of Fear (10/11, $3.99) profiles of hammer-wielders and fear thrivers						4.00
...: FF (9/11, $2.99) Reed & Sue vs. Ben Grimm; Grummett-a/Dell'Otto-c						3.00
...: Sin's Past (6/11, $4.99) r/Captain America #355-357; Sisters of Sin app.						5.00
... Spotlight (6/11, $3.99) Interviews with Fraction and Immonen; feature articles						4.00
...: The Monkey King (11/11, $2.99) Joshua Fialkov-s/Juan Doe-a						3.00
...: The Worthy (9/11, $3.99) Origins of the hammer wielders; s/a by various						4.00

FEAR ITSELF: DEADPOOL
Marvel Comics: Aug, 2011 - No. 3, Oct, 2011 ($2.99, limited series)

1-3-Hastings-s/Dazo-a						3.00

FEAR ITSELF: FEARSOME FOUR
Marvel Comics: Aug, 2011 - No. 4, Nov, 2011 ($2.99, limited series)

1-4-Art by Bisley and others; Man-Thing, She-Hulk & Howard the Duck app.						3.00

FEAR ITSELF: HULK VS. DRACULA
Marvel Comics: Nov, 2011 - No. 3, Dec, 2011 ($2.99, limited series)

1-3-Gischler-s/Stegman-a; Dell'Otto-c						3.00

FEAR ITSELF: SPIDER-MAN
Marvel Comics: Jul, 2011 - No. 3, Sept, 2011 ($2.99, limited series)

1-3-Yost-s/McKone-a; Vermin app.						3.00

FEAR ITSELF: THE DEEP
Marvel Comics: Aug, 2011 - No. 4, Nov, 2011 ($2.99, limited series)

1-4-Bunn-s/Garbett-a; Sub-Mariner vs. Attuma; Doctor Strange & Silver Surfer app.						3.00

FEAR ITSELF: THE FEARLESS (Follows Fear Itself #7)
Marvel Comics: Dec, 2011 - No. 12, Jun, 2012 ($2.99, limited series)

1-12: 1-Fate of the Hammers; Bagley & Pelletier-a; Art Adams-c. 7-Wolverine app.						3.00

FEAR ITSELF: THE HOME FRONT
Marvel Comics: Jun, 2011 - No. 7, Dec, 2011 ($3.99, limited series)

1-7-Short story anthology; Speedball w/Mayhew-a in all; Chaykin-a; Djurdjevic-c						4.00

FEAR ITSELF: UNCANNY X-FORCE
Marvel Comics: Sept, 2011 - No. 3, Nov, 2011 ($2.99, limited series)

1-3-Bianchi-a/c						3.00

FEAR ITSELF: WOLVERINE
Marvel Comics: Sept, 2011 - No. 3, Nov, 2011 ($2.99, limited series)

1-3-Boschi-a; Wolverine vs. S.T.R.I.K.E. 1-Acuña-c. 2,3-Molina-c						3.00

FEAR ITSELF: YOUTH IN REVOLT
Marvel Comics: Jul, 2011 - No. 6, Dec, 2011 ($2.99, limited series)

Fearless Defenders #9 © MAR

Feature Comics #125 © QUA

Feature Films #3 © DC

GD 2.0 | VG 4.0 | FN 6.0 | VF 8.0 | VF/NM 9.0 | NM- 9.2

GD 2.0 | VG 4.0 | FN 6.0 | VF 8.0 | VF/NM 9.0 | NM- 9.2

1-6-Firestar and The Initiative app.; McKeever-s/Norton-a 3.00

FEARLESS DEFENDERS (Marvel NOW!)
Marvel Comics: Apr, 2013 - No. 12, Feb, 2014 ($2.99/3.99)

1-4,5-7: 1-Valkyrie & Misty Knight team-up; Bunn-s/Sliney-a. 2-Dani Moonstar app. 3.00
4AU-(7/13, $3.99) Age of Ultron tie-in; Dr. Doom & Ares app. 4.00
8-12-($3.99) 4.00

FEARLESS FAGAN
Dell Publishing Co.: No. 441, Dec, 1952 (one-shot)

Four Color 441 5 10 15 31 53 75

FEATHERS
Archaia (BOOM! Studios): Jan, 2015 - No. 6, Jun, 2015 ($3.99, limited series)

1-6-Jorge Corona-s/a 4.00

FEATURE BOOK (Dell) (See Large Feature Comic)

FEATURE BOOKS (Newspaper-r, early issues)
David McKay Publications: May, 1937 - No. 57, 1948 (B&W)
(Full color, 68 pgs. begin #26 on)

Note: See individual alphabetical listings for prices

nn-Popeye & the Jeep (#1, 100 pgs.); reprinted as Feature Books #3(Very Rare; only 3 known copies, 1-VF, 2-in low grade)	nn-Dick Tracy (#1)-Reprinted as Feature Book #4 (100 pgs.) & in part as 4-Color #1 (Rare, less than 10 known copies)

NOTE: *Above books were advertised together with different covers from Feat. Books #3 & 4.*

1-King of the Royal Mtd. (#1)	2-Popeye (6/37) by Segar
3-Popeye (7/37) by Segar; same as nn issue but a new cover added	4-Dick Tracy (8/37)-Same as nn issue but a new cover added
5-Popeye (9/37) by Segar	6-Dick Tracy (10/37)
7-Little Orphan Annie (#1, 11/37) (Rare)-Reprints strips from 12/31/34 to 7/17/35	8-Secret Agent X-9 (12/37) -Not by Raymond
9-Dick Tracy (1/38)	10-Popeye (2/38)
11-Little Annie Rooney (#1, 3/38)	12-Blondie (#1) (4/38) (Rare)
13-Inspector Wade (5/38)	14-Popeye (6/38) by Segar
15-Barney Baxter (#1) (7/38)	16-Red Eagle (8/38)
17-Gangbusters (#1, 9/38) (1st app.)	18,19-Mandrake
20-Phantom (#1, 12/38)	21-Lone Ranger
22-Phantom	23-Mandrake
24-Lone Ranger (1941)	25-Flash Gordon (#1)-Reprints not by Raymond
26-Prince Valiant (1941)-Hal Foster-c/a; newspaper strips reprinted, pgs. 1-28,30-63; color & 68 pg. issues begin; Foster cover is only original comic book artwork by him	27-29,31,34-Blondie
30-Katzenjammer Kids (#1, 1942)	32,35,41,44-Katzenjammer Kids
33(nn)-Romance of Flying; World War II photos	36('43),38,40('44),42,43, 45,47-Blondie
37-Katzenjammer Kids; has photo & biog. of Harold H. Knerr (1883-1949) who took over strip from Rudolph Dirks in 1914	39-Phantom
46-Mandrake in the Fire World-(58 pgs.)	48-Maltese Falcon by Dashiell Hammett('46)
49,50-Perry Mason; based on Gardner novels	51,54-Rip Kirby; Raymond-c/s; origin-#51
52,55-Mandrake	53,56,57-Phantom

NOTE: *All Feature Books through #25 are over-sized 8-1/2x11-3/8" comics with color covers and black and white interiors. The covers are rough, heavy stock. The page counts, including covers, are as follows: nn, #3, 4-100 pgs.; #1, 2-52 pgs.; #5-25 are all 76 pgs. #33 was found in bound set from publisher. Reprints from 1980s exist.*

FEATURE COMICS (Formerly Feature Funnies)
Quality Comics Group: No. 21, June, 1939 - No. 144, May, 1950

21-The Clock, Jane Arden & Mickey Finn continue from Feature Funnies
61 122 183 390 670 950
22-26: 23-Charlie Chan begins (8/39, 1st app.) 45 90 135 284 480 675
26-(nn, nd)-Cover in one color, (10¢, 36 pgs.; issue No. blanked out. Two variations exist, each contain half of the regular #26) 47 94 141 296 498 700
27-(12/39, Rare)-Origin/1st app. Doll Man by Eisner (scripts) & Lou Fine (art); Doll Man begins, ends #139 676 1352 2028 4935 8718 12,500
28-(1/40, Rare)-2nd app. Doll Man by Lou Fine 239 478 717 1530 2615 3700
29-Clock-c 123 246 369 787 1344 1900
30-1st Doll Man-c 213 426 639 1363 2332 3300
31-Last Clock & Charlie Chan issue (4/40); Charlie Chan moves to Big Shot #1 following month (5/40) 81 162 243 518 884 1250
32,34,36: Dollman covers. 32-Rusty Ryan & Samar begin. 34-Captain Fortune app.
81 162 243 518 884 1250
33,35,37: 37-Last Fine Doll Man 50 100 150 315 533 750

NOTE: *A 15¢ Canadian version of Feature Comics #37, made in the US, exists.*

38,40-Dollman covers. 38-Origin the Ace of Space. 40-Bruce Blackburn in costume
57 114 171 362 619 875
39,41: 39-Origin The Destroying Demon, ends #40; X-Mas-c.
40 80 120 242 401 560
42,46,48,50-Dollman covers. 42-USA, the Spirit of Old Glory begins. 46-Intro. Boyville Brigadiers in Rusty Ryan. 48-USA ends 43 86 129 271 461 650
43,45,47,49: 47-Fargo Kid begins 30 60 90 177 289 400
44-Doll Man by Crandall begins, ends #63; Crandall-a(2)
55 110 165 352 601 850
51,53,55,57,59: 57-Spider Widow begins 22 44 66 128 209 290
52,54,56,58,60-Dollman covers. 56-Marijuana story in Swing Sisson strip. 60-Raven begins, ends #71 32 64 96 188 307 425
61,63,65,67 20 40 60 114 182 250
62,64,66,68-Dollman covers. 68-(5/43) 28 56 84 165 270 375
69,71-Phantom Lady x-over in Spider Widow 22 44 66 128 209 290
70-Dollman-c; Phantom Lady x-over 30 60 90 177 289 400
72,74,77-80,100-Dollman covers. 72-Spider Widow ends
23 46 69 136 223 310
73,75,76 17 34 51 98 154 210
81-99-All Dollman covers 19 38 57 111 176 240
101-144: 139-Last Doll Man & last Doll Man cover. 140-Intro. Stuntman Stetson (Stuntman Stetson c-140-144) 16 32 48 94 147 200

NOTE: ***Celardo** a-37-43. **Crandall** a-44-60, 62, 63-on(most). **Gustavson** a-(Rusty Ryan)- 32-134. **Powell** a-34, 64-73. The Clock c-25, 28, 29. Doll Man c-30, 32, 34, 36, 38, 40, 42, 44, 46, 48, 50, 52, 54, 56, 58, 60, 62, 64, 66, 68, 70, 72, 74, 77-139. Joe Palooka c-21, 24, 27.*

FEATURE FILMS
National Periodical Publ.: Mar-Apr, 1950 - No. 4, Sept-Oct, 1950 (All photo-c)

1- "Captain China" with John Payne, Gail Russell, Lon Chaney & Edgar Bergen
66 132 198 416 701 985
2- "Riding High" with Bing Crosby 69 138 207 435 735 1035
3- "The Eagle & the Hawk" with John Payne, Rhonda Fleming & D. O'Keefe
66 132 198 416 701 985
4- "Fancy Pants"; Bob Hope & Lucille Ball 72 144 216 454 770 1085

FEATURE FUNNIES (Feature Comics No. 21 on)(Earliest Quality Comics title)
Comic Favorites Inc./Quality Comics Group: Oct, 1937 - No. 20, May, 1939

1(V9#1-indicia)-Joe Palooka, Mickey Finn (1st app.), The Bungles, Jane Arden, Dixie Dugan (1st app.), Big Top, Ned Brant, Strange As It Seems, & Off the Record strip reprints begin
280 560 840 1540 2520 3500
2-The Hawk app. (11/37); Goldberg-c 113 226 339 718 1234 1750
3-Hawks of Seas begins by Eisner, ends #12; The Clock begins; Christmas-c
90 180 270 576 988 1400
4,5 65 130 195 416 708 1000
6-12: 11-Archie O'Toole by Bud Thomas begins, ends #22
50 100 150 315 533 750
13-Espionage, Starring Black X begins by Eisner, ends #20
54 108 162 343 574 825
14-20 40 80 120 246 411 575

NOTE: *Joe Palooka covers 1, 6, 9, 12, 15, 18.*

FEATURE PRESENTATION, A (Feature Presentations Magazine #6)
(Formerly Women in Love) (Also see Startling Terror Tales #11)
Fox Feature Syndicate: No. 5, April, 1950

5(#1)-Black Tarantula (scarce) 61 122 183 390 670 950

FEATURE PRESENTATIONS MAGAZINE (Formerly A Feature Presentation #5; becomes Feature Stories Magazine #3 on)
Fox Feature Syndicate: No. 6, July, 1950

6(#2)-Moby Dick; Wood-c 34 68 102 199 325 450

FEATURE STORIES MAGAZINE (Formerly Feature Presentations Mag. #6)
Fox Feature Syndicate: No. 3, Aug, 1950

3-Jungle Lil, Zegra stories; bondage-c 41 82 123 256 428 600

FEDERAL MEN COMICS
DC Comics: 1936

nn-Ashcan comic, not distributed to newsstands, only for in house use (no known sales)

FEDERAL MEN COMICS (See Adventure Comics #32, The Comics Magazine, New Adventure Comics, New Book of Comics, New Comics & Star Spangled Comics #91)
Gerard Publ. Co.: No. 2, 1945 (DC reprints from 1930's)

2-Siegel/Shuster-a; cover redrawn from Det. #9 39 78 117 231 378 525

FELICIA HARDY: THE BLACK CAT
Marvel Comics: July, 1994 - No. 4, Oct, 1994 ($1.50, limited series)

1-4: 1,4-Spider-Man app. 4.00

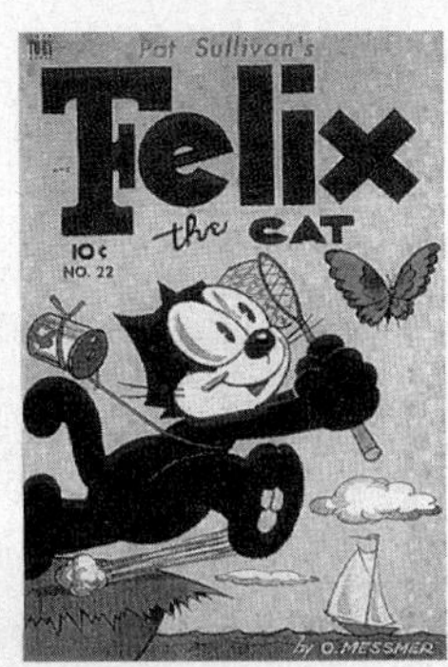

Felix the Cat #22 © KFS

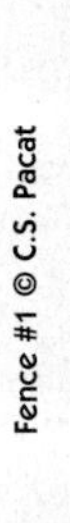

Fence #1 © C.S. Pacat

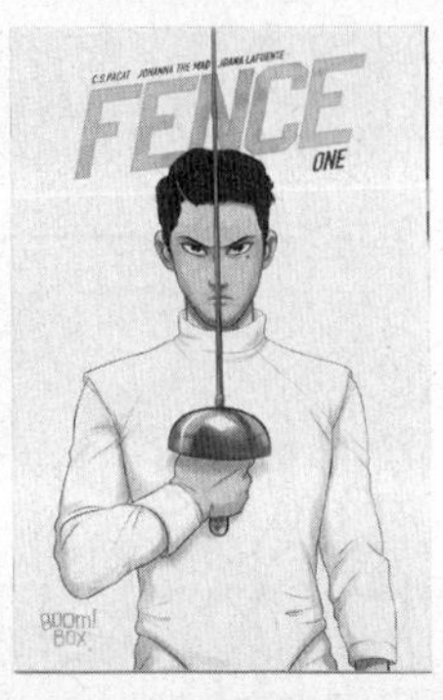

FF #1 © MAR

	GD 2.0	VG 4.0	FN 6.0	VF 8.0	VF/NM 9.0	NM- 9.2

FELIX'S NEPHEWS INKY & DINKY
Harvey Publications: Sept, 1957 - No. 7, Oct, 1958

	GD 2.0	VG 4.0	FN 6.0	VF 8.0	VF/NM 9.0	NM- 9.2
1-Cover shows Inky's left eye with 2 pupils	11	22	33	60	83	105
2-7	7	14	21	37	46	55

NOTE: *Messmer art in 1-6.* ***Oriolo*** *a-1-7.*

FELIX THE CAT (See Cat Tales 3-D, The Funnies, March of Comics #24,36,51, New Funnies & Popular Comics)
Dell Publ. No. 1-19/Toby No. 20-61/Harvey No. 62-118/Dell No. 1-12:
1943 - No. 118, Nov, 1961; Sept-Nov, 1962 - No. 12, July-Sept, 1965

	GD 2.0	VG 4.0	FN 6.0	VF 8.0	VF/NM 9.0	NM- 9.2
Four Color 15	77	154	231	616	1383	2150
Four Color 46('44)	39	78	117	289	657	1025
Four Color 77('45)	36	72	108	259	580	900
Four Color 119('46)-All new stories begin	32	64	96	230	515	800
Four Color 135('46)	21	42	63	147	324	500
Four Color 162(9/47)	16	32	48	110	243	375
1(2-3/48)(Dell)	26	52	78	182	404	625
2	12	24	36	81	176	270
3-5	9	18	27	62	126	190
6-19(2-3/51-Dell)	8	16	24	51	96	140
20-30,32,33,36,38-61(6/55)-All Messmer issues.(Toby): 28-(2/52)-Some copies have #29 on cover, #28 on inside (Rare in high grade)	14	28	42	96	211	325
31,34,35-No Messmer-a; Messmer-c only 31,34	8	16	24	51	96	140
37-(100 pgs., 25 ¢, 1/15/53, X-Mas-c, Toby; daily & Sunday-r (rare)	34	68	102	245	548	850
62(8/55)-80,100 (Harvey)	4	8	12	27	44	60
81-99	4	8	12	23	37	50
101-118(11/61): 101-117-Reprints. 118-All new-a	3	6	9	17	26	35
12-269-211(#1, 9-11/62)(Dell)-No Messmer	4	8	12	28	47	65
2-12(7-9/65)(Dell, TV)-No Messmer	4	8	12	23	37	50
3-D Comic Book 1(1953-One Shot, 25¢)-w/glasses	34	68	102	204	332	460
Summer Annual nn ('53, 25¢, 100 pgs., Toby)-Daily & Sunday-r	47	94	141	296	498	700
Winter Annual 2 ('54, 25¢, 100 pgs., Toby)-Daily & Sunday-r	43	86	129	271	461	650

(Special note: Despite the covers on Toby 37 and the Summer Annual above proclaiming "all new stories," they were actually reformatted newspaper strips)

NOTE: ***Otto Messmer*** *went to work for Universal Film as an animator in 1915 and then worked for the Pat Sullivan animation studio in 1916. He created a black cat in the cartoon short, Feline Follies in 1919 that became known as Felix in the early 1920s. The Felix Sunday strip began Aug. 14, 1923 and continued until Sept. 19, 1943 whjen* ***Messmer*** *took the character to Dell (Western Publishing) and began doing Felix comic books, first adapting strips to the comic format. The first all new Felix comic was Four Color #119 in 1946 (#4 in the Dell run). The daily Felix was begun on May 9, 1927 by another artist, but by the following year,* ***Messmer*** *did it too. King Features took the daily away from* ***Messmer*** *in 1954 and he began to do some of his most dynamic art for Toby Press. The daily was continued by* ***Joe Oriolo*** *who drew it until it was discontinued Jan. 9, 1967.* ***Oriolo*** *was* ***Messmer's*** *assistant for many years and inked some of* ***Messmer's*** *pencils through the Toby run, as well as doing some of the stories by himself. Though* ***Messmer*** *continued to work for Harvey, his contirubitons were limited, and no all* ***Messmer*** *stories appeared after the Toby run until some early Toby reprints were published in the 1990s Harvey revival of the title. 4-Color No. 15, 46, 77 and the Toby Annuals are all daily or Sunday newspaper reprints from the 1930's-1940's drawn by* ***Otto Messmer****. #101-r/#64; 102-r/#65; 103-r/#67; 104-117-r/#68-81.* ***Messmer****-a in all Dell/Toby/Harvey issues except #31, 34, 35, 97, 98, 100, 118.* ***Oriolo*** *a-20, 31-on.*

FELIX THE CAT (Also see The Nine Lives of...)
Harvey Comics/Gladstone: Sept, 1991 - No. 7, Jan, 1993 ($1.25/$1.50, bi-monthly)

1: 1950s-r/Toby issues by Messmer begins. 1-Inky and Dinky back-up story (produced by Gladstone) 4.00
2-7, Big Book, V2#1 (9/92, $1.95, 52 pgs.) 4.00

FELIX THE CAT AND FRIENDS
Felix Comics: 1992 - No. 5, 1993 ($1.95)

1-5: 1-Contains Felix trading cards 3.00

FELIX THE CAT & HIS FRIENDS (Pat Sullivan's...)
Toby Press: Dec, 1953 - No. 3, 1954 (Indicia title for #2&3 as listed)

	GD 2.0	VG 4.0	FN 6.0	VF 8.0	VF/NM 9.0	NM- 9.2
1 (Indicia title, "Felix and His Friends," #1 only)	30	60	90	177	289	400
2-3	18	36	54	107	169	230

FELIX THE CAT DIGEST MAGAZINE
Harvey Comics: July, 1992 ($1.75, digest-size, 98 pgs.)

1-Felix, Richie Rich stories 6.00

FELIX THE CAT KEEPS ON WALKIN'
Hamilton Comics: 1991 ($15.95, 8-1/2"x11", 132 pgs.)

nn-Reprints 15 Toby Press Felix the Cat and Felix and His Friends stories in new color 16.00

FELL
Image Comics: Sept, 2005 - No. 9, Jan, 2008 ($1.99)

1-9-Warren Ellis-s/Ben Templesmith-a 3.00
..., Vol. 1: Feral City TPB (2007, $14.99) r/#1-8 15.00

FELON
Image Comics (Minotaur Press): Nov, 2001 - No. 4, Apr, 2002 ($2.95, B&W)

1-4-Rucka-s/Clark-a/c 3.00

FEM FANTASTIQUE
AC Comics: Aug, 1988 ($1.95, B&W)

V2#1-By Bill Black; Bettie Page pin-up 4.00

FEMFORCE (Also see Untold Origin of the Femforce)
Americomics: Apr, 1985 - No. 109 (1.75-/2.95, B&W #16-56)

	GD 2.0	VG 4.0	FN 6.0	VF 8.0	VF/NM 9.0	NM- 9.2
1-Black-a in most; Nightveil, Ms. Victory begin	1	3	4	6	8	10
2-10						4.00
11-43: 25-Origin/1st app. new Ms. Victory. 28-Colt leaves. 29,30-Camilla-r by Mayo from Jungle Comics. 36-(2.95, 52 pgs.)						4.00
44,64: 44-W/mini-comic, Catman & Kitten #0. 64-Re-intro Black Phantom						5.00
45-49,51-63,65-99: 51-Photo-c from movie. 57-Begin color issues. 95-Photo-c						3.00
50 ($2.95, 52 pgs.)-Contains flexi-disc; origin retold; most AC characters app.						4.00
100-($3.95)						5.00
100-($6.90)-Polybagged	1	2	3	5	6	8
101-109-($4.95)						5.00
Special 1 (Fall, '84)(B&W, 52pgs.)-1st app. Ms. Victory, She-Cat, Blue Bulleteer, Rio Rita & Lady Luger						4.00
Bad Girl Backlash-(12/95, $5.00)						5.00
Frightbook 1 ('92, $2.95, B&W)-Halloween special, In the House of Horror 1 ('89, 2.50, B&W), Night of the Demon 1 ('90, 2.75, B&W), Out of the Asylum Special 1 ('87, B&W, $1.95), Pin-Up Portfolio						4.00
Pin-Up Portfolio (5 issues)						4.00

FEMFORCE UP CLOSE
AC Comics: Apr, 1992 - No. 11, 1995 ($2.75, quarterly)

1-11: 1-Stars Nightveil; inside f/c photo from Femforce movie. 2-Stars Stardust. 3-Stars Dragonfly. 4-Stars She-Cat 4.00

FENCE
BOOM! Studios (Boom! Box): Nov, 2017 - Present ($3.99)

1,2-C.S. Pacat-s/Johanna the Mad-a 4.00

FERDINAND THE BULL (See Mickey Mouse Magazine V4#3)(Walt Disney's)
Dell Publishing Co.: 1938 (10¢, large size (9-1/2" x 10"), some color w/rest B&W)

	GD 2.0	VG 4.0	FN 6.0	VF 8.0	VF/NM 9.0	NM- 9.2
nn	21	42	63	124	202	280

FERRET
Malibu Comics: Sept, 1992; May, 1993 - No. 10, Feb, 1994 ($1.95)

1-(1992, one-shot) 3.00
1-10: 1-Die-cut-c. 2-4-Collector's Ed. w/poster. 5-Polybagged w/Skycap 3.00
2-4-($1.95)-Newsstand Edition w/different-c 3.00

FERRYMAN
DC Comics (WildStorm): Early Dec, 2008 - No. 5, Mar, 2009 ($3.50)

1-5-Andreyko-s/Wayshak-a 3.50

FEVER RIDGE: A TALE OF MACARTHUR'S JUNGLE WAR
IDW Publishing: Feb, 2013 - No. 4, Oct, 2013 ($3.99)

1-4-Heimos-s/Runge-a/DeStefano-l; 1940s War stories on New Guinea 4.00

FF (Fantastic Four after Human Torch's death)
Marvel Comics: May, 2011 - No. 23, Dec, 2012 ($3.99)

1-Hickman-s/Epting-a; Spider-Man joins 4.00
1-Blank variant cover 4.00
1-Variant-c by Daniel Acuña 8.00
1-Variant-c by Stan Goldberg 6.00
2-23-($2.99) 2-Dr. Doom joins. 4,5-Kitson-a. 5-7-Black Bolt returns. 10,11-Avengers app. 3.00
...: Fifty Fantastic Years 1 (11/11, $4.99) Handbook format profiles of heroes and foes 5.00

FF (Marvel NOW!)
Marvel Comics: Jan, 2013 - No. 16, Mar, 2014 ($2.99)

1-15: 1-Fraction-s/Allred-a; new team forms (Ant-Man, She-Hulk, Medusa, Ms. Thing) 6,9-Quinones-a. 7,8,12-15-Dr. Doom app. 11-Impossible Man app. 3.00
16-($3.99) Ant-Man vs. Doom; back-up w/Quinones-a; Uatu & Silver Surfer app. 4.00

F5
Image Comics/Dark Horse: Jan, 2000 - No. 4, Oct, 2000 ($2.50/$2.95)

Preview (1/00, $2.50) Character bios and b&w pages; Daniel-s/a 3.00
1-($2.95, 48 pages) Tony Daniel-s/a 4.00
1-($20.00) Variant bikini-c 20.00
2-4-($2.50) 3.00
F5 Origin (Dark Horse Comics, 11/01, $2.99) w/cover gallery & sketches 3.00

Fiction Squad #1 © Fiction Squad

52 #6 © DC

Fight For Love nn © UFS

	GD 2.0	VG 4.0	FN 6.0	VF 8.0	VF/NM 9.0	NM- 9.2

FIBBER McGEE & MOLLY (Radio)(Also see A-1 Comics)
Magazine Enterprises: No. 25, 1949 (one-shot)

A-1 25 — 13 26 39 74 105 135

FICTION ILLUSTRATED
Byron Preiss Visual Publ./Pyramid: No. 1, Jan, 1975 - No. 4, Jan, 1977 ($1.00, #1,2 are digest size, 132 pgs.; #3,4 are graphic novels for mail order and specialty bookstores only)

1,2: 1-Schlomo Raven; Sutton-a. 2-Starfawn; Stephen Fabian-a. — 2 4 6 13 18 22
3-($1.00-c, 4 3/4 x 6 1/2" digest size) Chandler; new Steranko-a — 3 6 9 14 20 26
3-($4.95-c, 8 1/2 x 11" graphic novel; low print) same contents and indicia, but "Chandler" is the cover feature title — 5 10 15 31 53 75
4-($4.95-c, 8 1/2 x 11" graphic novel; low print) Son of Sherlock Holmes; Reese-a — 4 8 12 27 44 60

FICTION SQUAD
BOOM! Studios: Oct, 2014 - No. 6, Mar, 2015 ($3.99, limited series)

1-6-Jenkins-s/Bachs-a — 4.00

FIELD, THE
Image Comics: Apr, 2014 - No. 4, Sept, 2014 ($3.50, limited series)

1-4-Brisson-s/Roy-a — 3.50

FIERCE
Dark Horse Comics (Rocket Comics): July, 2004 - No. 4, Dec, 2004 ($2.99, limited series)

1-4-Jeremy Love-s/Robert Love-a — 3.00

15-LOVE
Marvel Comics: Aug, 2011 - No. 3, Oct, 2011 ($4.99, limited series)

1-3-Tennis academy story; Andi Watson-s/Tommy Ohtsuka-a/c; Sho Murase-c — 5.00

50 GIRLS 50
Image Comics: Jun, 2011 - No. 4, Sept, 2011 ($2.99, limited series)

1-4-Frank Cho-c; Cho & Murray-s/Medellin-a — 3.00

52 (Leads into Countdown series)
DC Comics: Week One, July, 2006 - Week Fifty-Two, Jul, 2007 ($2.50, weekly series)

1-Chronicles the year after Infinite Crisis; Johns, Morrison, Rucka & Waid-s; JG Jones-c — 4.00
2-10: 2-History of the DC Universe back-up thru #11. 6-1st app. The Great Ten. 7-Intro. Kate Kane. 10-Supernova — 3.00
11-Batwoman debut (single panel cameo in #9) — 4.00
12-52: 12-Isis gains powers; back-up 2 pg. origins begin. 15-Booster Gold killed. 17-Lobo returns. 30-Batman-c/Robin & Nightwing app. 37-Booster Gold returns. 38-The Question dies. 42-Ralph Dibny dies. 44-Isis dies. 48-Renee becomes The Question. 50-World War III. 51-Mister Mind evolves. 52-The Multiverse is re-formed; wraparound-c — 3.00
...: The Companion TPB (2007, $19.99) r/solo stories of series' prominent characters — 20.00
...: Volume One TPB (2007, $19.99) r/#1-13; sample of page development; cover gallery — 20.00
...: Volume Two TPB (2007, $19.99) r/#14-26; creator notes and sketches; cover gallery — 20.00
...: Volume Three TPB (2007, $19.99) r/#27-39; notes and sketches; cover gallery — 20.00
...: Volume Four TPB (2007, $19.99) r/#40-52; creator commentary; cover gallery — 20.00

52 AFTERMATH: THE FOUR HORSEMEN (Takes place during 52 Week Fifty)
DC Comics: Oct, 2007 - No. 6, Mar, 2008 ($2.99, limited series)

1-6-Giffen-s/Olliffe-a; Superman, Batman & Wonder Woman app. 2-4,6-Van Sciver-c — 3.00
TPB (2008, $19.99) r/#1-6 — 20.00

52/WWIII (Takes place during 52 Week Fifty)
DC Comics: Part One, Jun, 2007 - Part Four, Jun, 2007 ($2.50, 4 issues came out same day)

Part One - Part Four: Van Sciver-c; heroes vs. Black Adam. 3-Terra dies — 3.00
DC: World War III TPB (2007, $17.99) r/Part One - Four and 52 Week 50 — 18.00

55 DAYS AT PEKING (See Movie Comics)

FIGHT AGAINST CRIME (Fight Against the Guilty #22, 23)
Story Comics: May, 1951 - No. 21, Sept, 1954

1-True crime stories #1-4 — 54 108 162 343 574 825
2 — 32 64 96 192 314 435
3,5: 5-Frazetta-a, 1 pg.; content chan.ge to horror & suspense — 32 64 96 192 314 435
4-Drug story "Hopped Up Killers" — 34 68 102 204 332 460
6,7: 6-Used in **POP**, pgs. 83,84 — 31 62 93 182 296 410
8-Last crime format issue — 29 58 87 170 278 385

NOTE: *No. 9-21 contain violent, gruesome stories with blood, dismemberment, decapitation, E.C. style plot twists and several E.C. swipes. Bondage c-4, 6, 18, 19.*

9-11,13 — 55 110 165 352 601 850
12-Morphine drug story "The Big Dope" — 60 120 180 381 653 925
14-Tothish art by Ross Andru; electrocution-c — 65 130 195 416 708 1000
15-B&W & color illos in **POP** — 57 114 171 362 619 875
16-E.C. story swipe/Haunt of Fear #19; Tothish-a by Ross Andru; bondage-c — 65 130 195 416 708 1000
17-Wildey E.C. story swipe/Shock SuspenStories #9; knife through neck-c (1/54) — 77 154 231 493 847 1200
18,19: 19-Bondage/torture-c — 55 110 165 352 601 850
20-Decapitation cover; contains hanging, ax murder, blood & violence — 486 972 1458 3550 6275 9000
21-E.C. swipe — 47 94 141 296 498 700

NOTE: ***Cameron** a-4, 5, 8. **Hollingsworth** a-3-7, 9, 10, 13. **Wildey** a-6, 15, 16.*

FIGHT AGAINST THE GUILTY (Formerly Fight Against Crime)
Story Comics: No. 22, Dec, 1954 - No. 23, Mar, 1955

22-Toth styled art by Ross Andru; Ditko-a; E.C. story swipe; electrocution-c (Last pre-code) — 47 94 141 296 498 700
23-Hollingsworth-a — 31 62 93 184 300 415

FIGHT CLUB 2 (Sequel to the movie)(Also see Free Comic Book Day 2015)
Dark Horse Comics: May, 2015 - No. 10, Mar, 2016 ($3.99)

1-10-Chuck Palahniuk-s/Cameron Stewart-a — 4.00

FIGHT COMICS
Fiction House Magazines: Jan, 1940 - No. 83, 11/52; No. 84, Wint, 1952-53; No. 85, Spring, 1953; No. 86, Summer, 1954

1-Origin Spy Fighter, Starring Saber; Jack Dempsey life story; Shark Brodie & Chip Collins begin; Fine-c; Eisner-a — 389 778 1167 2723 4762 6800
2-Joe Louis life story; Fine/Eisner-c — 168 336 504 1075 1838 2600
3-Rip Regan, the Power Man begins (3/40); classic-c — 200 400 600 1280 2190 3100
4,5: 4-Fine-c — 123 246 369 787 1344 1900
6-10: 6,7-Powell-c — 110 220 330 704 1202 1700
11-14: Rip Regan ends — 103 206 309 659 1130 1600
15-1st app. Super American plus-c (10/41) — 135 270 405 864 1482 2100
16-Captain Fight begins (12/41); Spy Fighter ends — 116 232 348 742 1271 1800
17,18: Super American ends — 87 174 261 553 952 1350
19-Japanese WWII-c; Captain Fight ends; Senorita Rio begins (6/42, origin & 1st app.); Rip Carson, Chute Trooper begins — 97 194 291 621 1061 1500
20-Bondage/torture-c — 110 220 330 704 1202 1700
21-27,29,30: 21-24,26,27-Japanese WWII-c — 81 162 243 518 884 1250
28-Classic Japanese WWII torture-c — 123 246 369 787 1344 1900
31-Classic Japanese WWII decapitation-c — 326 652 978 2282 3991 5700
32-Tiger Girl begins (6/44, 1st app.?); Nazi WWII-c — 142 284 426 909 1555 2200
33,35-39,41,42: 42-Last WWII-c (2/46) — 66 132 198 419 722 1025
34-Classic Japanese WWII bondage-c — 110 220 330 704 1202 1700
40-Classic Nazi vulture bondage-c — 97 194 291 621 1061 1500
43,45-50: 48-Used in Love and Death by Legman. 49-Jungle-c begin, end #81 — 39 78 117 231 378 525
44-Classic bondage/torture-c; Capt. Fight returns — 71 142 213 454 777 1100
51-Origin Tiger Girl; Patsy Pin-Up app. — 41 82 123 250 418 585
52-60,62-64-Last Baker issue — 27 54 81 158 259 360
61-Origin Tiger Girl retold — 27 54 81 162 266 370
65-78: 78-Used in **POP**, pg. 99 — 22 44 66 132 216 300
79-The Space Rangers app. — 23 46 69 136 223 310
80-85: 81-Last jungle-c. 82-85-War-c/stories — 20 40 60 117 189 260
86-Two Tigerman stories by Evans-r/Rangers Comics #40,41; Moreira-r/Rangers Comics #45 — 20 40 60 117 189 260

NOTE: *Bondage covers, Lingerie, headlights panels are common. Captain Fight by **Kamen**-51-66. Kayo Kirby by **Baker**-#43-64, 67(not by Baker). Senorita Rio by **Kamen**-#57-64; by **Grandenetti**-#65, 66. Tiger Girl by **Baker**-#36-60, 62-64; **Eisner** c-1-3, 5, 10, 11. **Kamen** a-54?, 57? **Tuska** a-1, 5, 8, 10, 21, 29, 34. **Whitman** c-73-84. **Zolnerwich** c-16, 17, 22. Power Man c-5, 6, 9. Super American c-15-17. Tiger Girl c-49-81.*

FIGHT FOR LOVE
United Features Syndicate: 1952 (no month)

nn-Abbie & Slats newspaper-r — 10 20 30 54 72 90

FIGHT FOR TOMORROW
DC Comics (Vertigo): Nov, 2002 - No. 6, Apr, 2003 ($2.50, limited series)

1-6-Denys Cowan-a/Brian Wood-s. 1-Jim Lee-c. 5-Jo Chen-c — 3.00
TPB (2008, $14.99) r/#1-6 — 15.00

FIGHTING AIR FORCE (See United States Fighting Air Force)

FIGHTIN' AIR FORCE (Formerly Sherlock Holmes?; Never Again? War and Attack #54 on)
Charlton Comics: No. 3, Feb, 1956 - No. 53, Feb-Mar, 1966

V1#3 — 10 20 30 54 72 90
4-10 — 7 14 21 35 43 50
11(3/58, 68 pgs.) — 9 18 27 47 61 75
12 (100 pgs.)-U.S. Nukes Russia — 14 28 42 82 121 160

Fighting American (2017 series) #1 © S&K

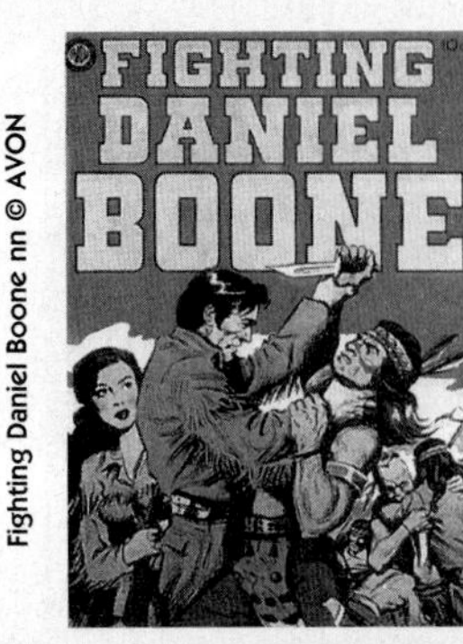

Fighting Daniel Boone nn © AVON

The Fighting Man Annual #1 © AJAX

	GD 2.0	VG 4.0	FN 6.0	VF 8.0	VF/NM 9.0	NM- 9.2
13-30: 13,24-Glanzman-a. 24-Glanzman-c. 27-Area 51, UFO story	3	6	9	19	30	40
31-53: 50-American Eagle begins	3	6	9	15	22	28

FIGHTING AMERICAN
Headline Publ./Prize (Crestwood): Apr-May, 1954 - No. 7, Apr-May, 1955

	GD	VG	FN	VF	VF/NM	NM-
1-Origin & 1st app. Fighting American & Speedboy (Capt. America & Bucky clones); S&K-c/a(3); 1st super hero satire series	200	400	600	1280	2190	3100
2-S&K-a(3)	97	194	291	621	1061	1500
3-5: 3,4-S&K-a(3). 5-S&K-a(2); Kirby/?-a	84	168	252	538	919	1300
6-Origin-r (4 pgs.) plus 2 pgs. by S&K	77	154	231	493	847	1200
7-Kirby-a	71	142	213	454	777	1100

NOTE: ***Simon & Kirby** covers on all. 6 is last pre-code issue.*

FIGHTING AMERICAN
Harvey Publications: Oct, 1966 (25¢)

	GD	VG	FN	VF	VF/NM	NM-
1-Origin Fighting American & Speedboy by S&K-r; S&K-c/a(3); 1 pg. Neal Adams ad	5	10	15	33	57	80

FIGHTING AMERICAN
DC Comics: Feb, 1994 - No. 6, 1994 ($1.50, limited series)

1-6 3.00

FIGHTING AMERICAN (Vol. 3)
Awesome Entertainment: Aug, 1997 - No. 2, Oct, 1997 ($2.50)

	GD	VG	FN	VF	VF/NM	NM-
Preview-Agent America (pre-lawsuit)	1	2	3	5	6	7
1-Four covers by Liefeld, Churchill, Platt, McGuinness						3.00
1-Platinum Edition, 1-Gold foil Edition						10.00
1-Comic Cavalcade Edition, 2-American Ent. Spice Ed.						4.00
2-Platt-c, 2-Liefeld variant-c						3.00

FIGHTING AMERICAN
Titan Comics: Oct, 2017 - No. 4, Jan, 2018 ($3.99)

1-4-Rennie-s/Mighten-a; multiple covers; Fighting American & Speedboy trapped in 2017 4.00

FIGHTING AMERICAN: DOGS OF WAR
Awesome-Hyperwerks: Sept, 1998 - No. 3, May, 1999 ($2.50)

Limited Convention Special (7/98, B&W) Platt-a 3.00
1-3-Starlin-s/Platt-a/c 3.00

FIGHTING AMERICAN: RULES OF THE GAME
Awesome Entertainment: Nov, 1997 - No. 3, Mar, 1998 ($2.50, lim. series)

1-3: 1-Loeb-s/McGuinness-a/c. 2-Flip book with Swat! preview 3.00
1-Liefeld SPICE variant-c, 1-Dynamic Forces Ed.; McGuinness-c 3.00
1-Liefeld Fighting American & cast variant-c 3.00

FIGHTING AMERICAN: THE TIES THAT BIND
Titan Comics: Apr, 2018 - Present ($3.99)

1-Rennie-s/Andie Tong-a; multiple covers 4.00

FIGHTIN' ARMY (Formerly Soldier and Marine Comics) (See Captain Willy Schultz)
Charlton Comics: No. 16, 1/56 - No. 127, 12/76; No. 128, 9/77 - No. 172, 11/84

	GD	VG	FN	VF	VF/NM	NM-
16	10	20	30	54	72	90
17-19,21-23,25-30	7	14	21	35	43	50
20-Ditko-a	9	18	27	50	65	80
24 (3/58, 68 pgs.)	9	18	27	47	61	75
31-45	3	6	9	18	28	38
46-50,52-60	3	6	9	16	23	30
51-Hitler-c	3	6	9	18	28	38
61-75	3	6	9	14	19	24
76-1st The Lonely War of Willy Schultz	3	6	9	17	26	35
77-80: 77-92-The Lonely War of Willy Schultz. 79-Devil Brigade	3	6	9	14	19	24
81-88,91,93-99: 82,83-Devil Brigade	2	4	6	10	14	18
89,90,92-Ditko-a	3	6	9	14	20	26
100	2	4	6	13	18	22
101-127	2	4	6	8	11	14
128-140	1	2	3	5	7	9
141-165	1	2	3	4	5	7
166-172-Low print run	1	2	3	5	6	8
108 (Modern Comics-1977)-Reprint						5.00

NOTE: ***Aparo** c-154. **Glanzman** a-77-88. **Montes/Bache** a-48, 49, 51, 69, 75, 76, 170r.*

FIGHTING CARAVANS (See Zane Grey 4-Color 632)

FIGHTING DANIEL BOONE
Avon Periodicals: 1953

	GD	VG	FN	VF	VF/NM	NM-
nn-Kinstler-c/a, 22 pgs.	21	42	63	122	199	275
I.W. Reprint #1-Reprints #1 above; Kinstler-c/a; Lawrence/Alascia-a	3	6	9	14	19	24

FIGHTING DAVY CROCKETT (Formerly Kit Carson)
Avon Periodicals: No. 9, Oct-Nov, 1955

	GD	VG	FN	VF	VF/NM	NM-
9-Kinstler-c	11	22	33	62	86	110

FIGHTIN' FIVE, THE (Formerly Space War) (Also see The Peacemaker)
Charlton Comics: July, 1964 - No. 41, Jan, 1967; No. 42, Oct, 1981 - No. 49, Dec, 1982

	GD	VG	FN	VF	VF/NM	NM-
V2#28-Origin/1st app. Fightin' Five; Montes/Bache-a	5	10	15	35	63	90
29-39-Montes/Bache-a in all	3	6	9	21	33	45
40-Peacemaker begins (1st app.)	6	12	18	37	66	95
41-Peacemaker (2nd app.); Montes/Bache-a	4	8	12	28	47	65
42-49: Reprints						5.00

FIGHTING FRONTS!
Harvey Publications: Aug, 1952 - No. 5, Jan, 1953

	GD	VG	FN	VF	VF/NM	NM-
1	10	20	30	54	72	90
2-Extreme violence; Nostrand/Powell-a	11	22	33	60	83	105
3-5: 3-Powell-a	7	14	21	37	46	55

FIGHTING INDIAN STORIES (See Midget Comics)

FIGHTING INDIANS OF THE WILD WEST!
Avon Periodicals: Mar, 1952 - No. 2, Nov, 1952

	GD	VG	FN	VF	VF/NM	NM-
1-Geronimo, Chief Crazy Horse, Chief Victorio, Black Hawk begin; Larsen-a; McCann-a(2)	20	40	60	120	195	270
2-Kinstler-c & inside-c only; Larsen, McCann-a	15	30	45	83	124	165
100 Pg. Annual (1952, 25¢)-Contains three comics rebound; Geronimo, Chief Crazy Horse, Chief Victorio; Kinstler-c	41	82	123	256	428	600

FIGHTING LEATHERNECKS
Toby Press: Feb, 1952 - No. 6, Dec, 1952

	GD	VG	FN	VF	VF/NM	NM-
1- "Duke's Diary"; full pg. pin-ups by Sparling	20	40	60	114	182	250
2-5: 2- "Duke's Diary" full pg. pin-ups. 3-5- "Gil's Gals"; full pg. pin-ups	11	22	33	62	86	110
6-(Same as No. 3-5?)	11	22	33	62	86	110

FIGHTING MAN, THE (War)
Ajax/Farrell Publications(Excellent Publ.): May, 1952 - No. 8, July, 1953

	GD	VG	FN	VF	VF/NM	NM-
1	17	34	51	98	154	210
2	11	22	33	64	90	115
3-8	9	18	27	52	69	85
Annual 1 (1952, 25¢, 100 pgs.)	37	74	111	222	361	500

FIGHTIN' MARINES (Formerly The Texan; also see Approved Comics)
St. John(Approved Comics)/Charlton Comics No. 14 on:
No. 15, 8/51 - No. 12, 3/53; No. 14, 5/55 - No. 132, 11/76; No. 133, 10/77 - No. 176, 9/84 (No #13?) (Korean War #1-3)

	GD	VG	FN	VF	VF/NM	NM-
15(#1)-Matt Baker c/a "Leatherneck Jack"; slightly large size; Fightin' Texan No. 16 & 17?	54	108	162	343	574	825
2-1st Canteen Kate by Baker; slightly large size; partial Baker-c	65	130	195	416	708	1000
3-9,11-Canteen Kate by Baker; Baker c-#2,3,5-11; 4-Partial Baker-c	39	78	117	231	378	525
10-Matt Baker-c	21	42	63	122	199	285
12-No Baker-a; Last St. John issue?	11	22	33	62	86	110
14 (5/55; 1st Charlton issue; formerly?)-Canteen Kate by Baker; all stories reprinted from #2	21	42	63	126	206	285
15-Baker-c	14	28	42	81	118	155
16,18-20-Not Baker-c. 16-Grey-tone-c	8	16	24	42	54	65
17-Canteen Kate by Baker	17	34	51	98	154	210
21-24	7	14	21	35	43	50
25-(68 pgs.)(3/58)-Check-a?	10	20	30	56	76	95
26-(100 pgs.)(8/58)-Check-a(5)	14	28	42	82	121	160
27-50	3	6	9	18	28	38
51-81: 78-Shotgun Harker & the Chicken series begin	3	6	9	15	22	28
82-85: 85-Last 12¢ issue	3	6	9	14	20	25
86-94: 94-Last 15¢ issue	2	4	6	10	14	18
95-100,122: 122-(1975) Pilot issue for "War" title (Fightin' Marines Presents War)	2	4	6	9	13	16
101-121	2	4	6	8	10	12
123-140: 132 Hitler-c	1	2	3	5	7	9
141-170						6.00
171-176-Low print run	1	2	3	5	6	8
120(Modern Comics reprint, 1977)						5.00

NOTE: *No. 14 & 16 (CC) reprint St. John issues; No. 16 reprints St. John insignia on cover. **Colan** a-3, 7. **Glanzman** c/a-92, 94. **Montes/Bache** a-48, 53, 55, 64, 65, 72-74, 77-83, 176r.*

Fighting War Stories #1 © MP

The Filth #1 © Morrison & Weston

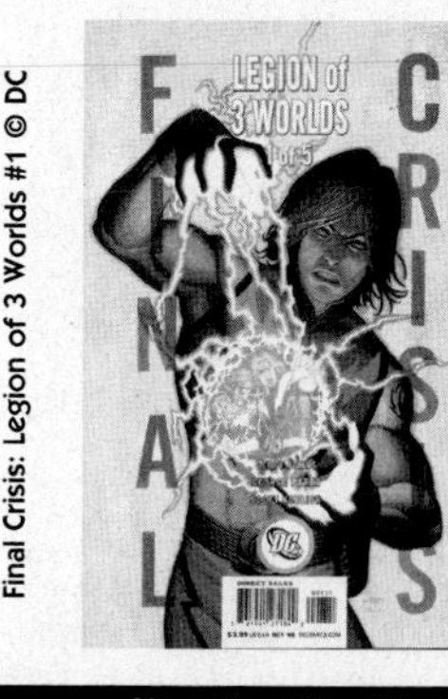

Final Crisis: Legion of 3 Worlds #1 © DC

	GD 2.0	VG 4.0	FN 6.0	VF 8.0	VF/NM 9.0	NM- 9.2

FIGHTING MARSHAL OF THE WILD WEST (See The Hawk)

FIGHTIN' NAVY (Formerly Don Winslow)
Charlton Comics: No. 74, 1/56 - No. 125, 4-5/66; No. 126, 8/83 - No. 133, 10/84

	GD	VG	FN	VF	VF/NM	NM-
74	5	10	15	34	60	85
75-81	4	8	12	23	37	50
82-Sam Glanzman-a (68 pg. Giant)	5	10	15	31	53	75
83-(100 pgs.)	6	12	18	41	76	110
84-99,101: 101-UFO-c/story	3	6	9	17	26	35
100	3	6	9	18	28	38
102-105,106-125('66)	3	6	9	14	21	26
126-133 (1984)-Low print run	1	2	3	5	6	8

NOTE: ***Montes/Bache** a-109. **Glanzman** a-82, 92, 96, 98, 100, 131r.*

FIGHTING PRINCE OF DONEGAL, THE (See Movie Comics)

FIGHTIN' TEXAN (Formerly The Texan & Fightin' Marines?)
St. John Publishing Co.: No. 16, Sept, 1952 - No. 17, Dec, 1952

	GD	VG	FN	VF	VF/NM	NM-
16,17: Tuska-a each. 17-Cameron-c/a	10	20	30	58	79	100

FIGHTING UNDERSEA COMMANDOS (See Undersea Fighting...)
Avon Periodicals: May, 1952 - No. 5, April, 1953 (U.S. Navy frogmen)

	GD	VG	FN	VF	VF/NM	NM-
1-Cover title is Undersea Fighting... #1 only	17	34	51	100	158	215
2	11	22	33	62	86	110
3-5: 1,3-Ravielli-c. 4-Kinstler-c	10	20	30	54	72	90

FIGHTING WAR STORIES
Men's Publications/Story Comics: Aug, 1952 - No. 5, 1953

	GD	VG	FN	VF	VF/NM	NM-
1	15	30	45	83	124	165
2-5	9	18	27	52	69	85

FIGHTING YANK (See America's Best Comics & Startling Comics)
Nedor/Better Publ./Standard: Sept, 1942 - No. 29, Aug, 1949

	GD	VG	FN	VF	VF/NM	NM-
1-The Fighting Yank begins; Mystico, the Wonder Man app; bondage-c	354	708	1062	2478	4339	6200
2	194	388	582	1242	2121	3000
3,4: Nazi WWII-c. 4-Schomburg-c begin	155	310	465	992	1696	2400
5,8,9: 5-Nazi-c. 8,9-Japan War-c	155	310	465	992	1696	2400
6-Classic Japanese WWII-c	258	516	774	1651	2826	4000
7-Classic Hitler special bomb-c; Grim Reaper app.	284	568	852	1818	3109	4400
10-Nazi bondage/torture/hypo-c	206	412	618	1318	2259	3200
11,14,15: 11-The Oracle app. 15-Bondage/torture-c	84	168	252	538	919	1300
12-Hirohito bondage Japanese WWII-c	168	336	504	1075	1838	2600
13-Last War-c (Japanese)	123	246	369	787	1344	1900
16-20: 18-The American Eagle app.	63	126	189	403	689	975
21-Kara, Jungle Princess app.; lingerie-c	161	322	483	1030	1765	2500
22-Schomburg Miss Masque dinosaur-c	97	194	291	621	1061	1500
23-Classic Schomburg hooded vigilante-c	187	374	561	1197	2049	2900
24-Miss Masque app.	65	130	195	416	708	1000
25-Robinson/Meskin-a; strangulation, lingerie panel; The Cavalier app.	63	126	189	403	689	975
26-29: All-Robinson/Meskin-a. 28-One pg. Williamson-a	52	104	156	328	552	775

NOTE: ***Schomburg (Xela)** c-4-29; airbrush-c 28, 29. Bondage c-1, 4, 8, 10, 11, 12, 15, 17.*

FIGHTMAN
Marvel Comics: June, 1993 ($2.00, one-shot, 52 pgs.)

	NM-
1	4.00

FIGHT THE ENEMY
Tower Comics: Aug, 1966 - No. 3, Mar, 1967 (25¢, 68 pgs.)

	GD	VG	FN	VF	VF/NM	NM-
1-Lucky 7 & Mike Manly begin	4	8	12	28	47	65
2-1st Boris Vallejo comic art; McWilliams-a	3	6	9	21	33	45
3-Wood-a (1/2 pg.); McWilliams, Bolle-a	3	6	9	21	33	45

FIGMENT (Disney Kingdoms) (See Disney Kingdoms: Figment 2 for sequel)
Marvel Comics: Aug, 2014 - No. 5, Dec, 2014 ($3.99, limited series)

	NM-
1-5-Jim Zub-s/Filipe Andrade-a	4.00

FILM FUNNIES
Marvel Comics (CPC): Nov, 1949 - No. 2, Feb, 1950 (52 pgs.)

	GD	VG	FN	VF	VF/NM	NM-
1-Krazy Krow, Wacky Duck	24	48	72	140	230	320
2-Wacky Duck	17	34	51	98	154	210

FILM STARS ROMANCES
Star Publications: Jan-Feb, 1950 - No. 3, May-June, 1950 (True life stories of movie stars)

	GD	VG	FN	VF	VF/NM	NM-
1-Rudy Valentino & Gregory Peck stories; L. B. Cole-c; lingerie panels	44	88	132	277	469	660
2-Liz Taylor/Robert Taylor photo-c & true life story	58	116	174	371	636	900
3-Douglas Fairbanks story; photo-c	27	54	81	158	259	360

FILTH, THE
DC Comics (Vertigo): Aug, 2002 - No. 13, Oct, 2003 ($2.95, limited series)

	NM-
1-13-Morrison-s/Weston & Erskine-a	3.00
TPB (2004, $19.95) r/#1-13	20.00

FINAL CRISIS
DC Comics: July, 2008 - No. 7, Mar, 2009 ($3.99, limited series)

	NM-
1-Grant Morrison-s/J.G. Jones-a/c; Martian Manhunter killed; 2 covers	4.00
1-Director's Cut (10/08, $4.99) B&W printing of #1 with creator commentary	5.00
2-7: 2-Barry Allen-c/cameo; intro Big Science Action; two covers. 6-Batman zapped	4.00
SC (2010, $19.99) r/#1-7, FC: Superman Beyond #1,2, FC: Submit & FC Sketchbook	20.00
...: Rage of the Red Lanterns (12/08, $3.99) Atrocitus app.; intro. Blue Lantern; 3 covers	4.00
...: Requiem (9/08, $3.99) History, death and funeral of the Martian Manhunter; 2 covers	4.00
...: Resist (12/08, $3.99) Checkmate app; Rucka & Trautman-s/Sook-a; 2 covers	4.00
...: Secret Files (2/09, $3.99) origin of Libra; Wein-s/Shasteen-a; JG Jones sketch-a	4.00
... Sketchbook (7/08, $2.99) Jones development sketches with Morrison commentary	3.00
...: Submit (12/08, $3.99) Black Lightning & Tattooed Man team up; Morrison-s; 2 covers	4.00

FINAL CRISIS: DANCE (Final Crisis Aftermath)
DC Comics: Jul, 2009 - No. 6, Dec, 2009 ($2.99, limited series)

	NM-
1-6-Super Young Team; Joe Casey-s/Chriscross-a/Stanley Lau-c	3.00
TPB (2009, $17.99) r/#1-6	18.00

FINAL CRISIS: ESCAPE (Final Crisis Aftermath)
DC Comics: Jul, 2009 - No. 6, Dec, 2009 ($2.99, limited series)

	NM-
1-6-Nemesis & Cameron Chase app.; Ivan Brandon-s/Marco Rudy-a/Scott Hampton-c	3.00
TPB (2010, $17.99) r/#1-6	18.00

FINAL CRISIS: INK (Final Crisis Aftermath)
DC Comics: Jul, 2009 - No. 6, Dec, 2009 ($2.99, limited series)

	NM-
1-6-The Tattooed Man; Eric Wallace-s/Fabrizio Florentino-a/Brian Stelfreeze-c	3.00
TPB (2010, $17.99) r/#1-6	18.00

FINAL CRISIS: LEGION OF THREE WORLDS
DC Comics: Oct, 2008 - No. 5, Sept, 2009 ($3.99, limited series)

	NM-
1-Johns-s/Pérez-a; R.J. Brande killed; Time Trapper app.; two covers on each issue	5.00
2-5-Three Legions meet; two covers. 3-Bart Allen returns. 4-Superboy (Conner) returns	4.00
HC (2009, $19.99) r/#1-5; variant covers	20.00
SC (2010, $14.99) r/#1-5; variant covers	15.00

FINAL CRISIS: REVELATIONS
DC Comics: Oct, 2008 - No. 5, Feb, 2009 ($3.99, limited series)

	NM-
1-5-Spectre and The Question; 2 covers on each. 1-Dr. Light killed; Rucka-s/Tan-a	4.00
HC (2009, $19.99, d.j.) r/#1-5; variant covers	20.00
SC (2010, $14.99) r/#1-5; variant covers	15.00

FINAL CRISIS: ROGUE'S REVENGE
DC Comics: Sept, 2008 - No. 3, Nov, 2008 ($3.99, limited series)

	NM-
1-3-Johns-s/Kolins-a; Flash's Rogues, Zoom and Inertia app.	4.00
HC (2009, $19.99, d.j.) r/#1-3 & Flash #182,197; variant covers	20.00
SC (2010, $14.99) r/#1-3 & Flash #182,197; variant covers	15.00

FINAL CRISIS: RUN (Final Crisis Aftermath)
DC Comics: Jul, 2009 - No. 6, Dec, 2009 ($2.99, limited series)

	NM-
1-6-The Human Flame on the run; Sturges-s/Williams-a/Kako-c	3.00
TPB (2010, $17.99) r/#1-6	18.00

FINAL CRISIS: SUPERMAN BEYOND
DC Comics: Oct, 2008 - No. 2, Mar, 2009 ($4.50, limited series)

	NM-
1,2-Morrison-s/Mahnke-a; parallel-Earth Supermen app.; 3-D pages and glasses	4.50

FINAL NIGHT, THE (See DC related titles and Parallax: Emerald Night)
DC Comics: Nov, 1996 - No. 4, Nov, 1996 ($1.95, weekly limited series)

	NM-
1-4: Kesel-s/Immonen-a(p) in all. 4-Parallax's final acts	4.00
Preview	3.00
TPB-(1998, $12.95) r/#1-4, Parallax: Emerald Night #1, and preview	13.00

FINALS (See Vertigo Resurrected:... for collected reprint)
DC Comics (Vertigo): Sept, 1999 - No. 4, Dec, 1999 ($2.95, limited series)

	NM-
1-4-Will Pfeifer-s/Jill Thompson-a	3.00

FINDING NEMO (Based on the Pixar movie)
BOOM! Studios: Jul, 2010 - No. 4, Oct, 2010 ($2.99, limited series)

	NM-
1-4-Michael Raicht & Brian Smith-s/Jake Myler-a.1-Three covers	3.00

FINDING NEMO: REEF RESCUE (Based on the Pixar movie)
BOOM! Studios: May, 2009 - No. 4, Aug, 2009 ($2.99, limited series)

Firehair Comics #10 © FH

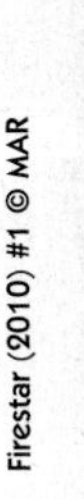

Firestar (2010) #1 © MAR

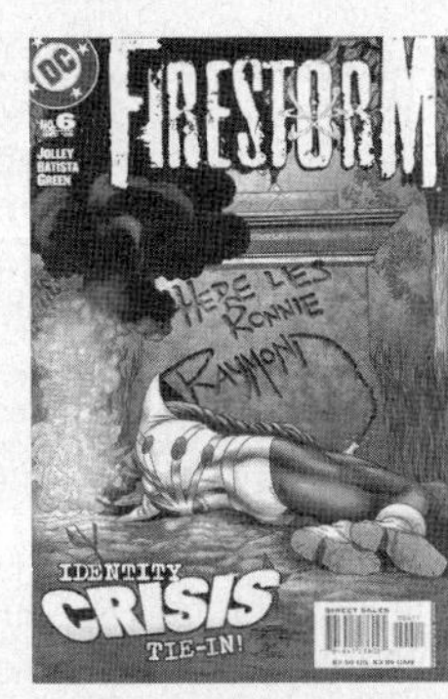

Firestorm (2004 series) #6 © DC

	GD 2.0	VG 4.0	FN 6.0	VF 8.0	VF/NM 9.0	NM- 9.2

1-4-Marie Croall-s/Erica Leigh Currey-a; 2 covers 3.00

FIN FANG FOUR RETURN!
Marvel Comics: Jul, 2009 ($3.99, one-shot)

1-Fin Fang Foom, Googam, Elektro, Gorgilla and Doc Samson app. 5.00

FIRE
Caliber Press: 1993 - No. 2, 1993 ($2.95, B&W, limited series, 52 pgs.)

1,2-Brian Michael Bendis-s/a 4.00
TPB (1999, 2001, $9.95) Restored reprints of series 10.00

FIREARM (Also see Codename: Firearm, Freex #15, Night Man #4 & Prime #10)
Malibu Comics (Ultraverse): Sept, 1993 - No. 18, Mar, 1995 ($1.95/$2.50)

0 ($14.95)-Came w/ video containing 1st half of story (comic contains 2nd half); 1st app. Duet 15.00
1,3-6: 1-James Robinson scripts begin; Cully Hamner-a; Chaykin-c; 1st app. Alec Swan. 3-Intro The Sportsmen; Chaykin-c. 4-Break-Thru x-over; Chaykin-c. 5-1st app. Ellen (Swan's girlfriend); 2 pg. origin of Prime. 6-Prime app. (story cont'd in Prime #10); Brereton-c 3.00
1-($2.50)-Newsstand edition polybagged w/card 3.50
1-Ultra Limited silver foil-c 1 2 3 5 6 8
2 ($2.50, 44 pgs.)-Hardcase app.;Chaykin-c; Rune flip-c/story by B. Smith (3 pgs.) 4.00
7-10,12-17: 12-The Rafferty Saga begins, ends #18; 1st app. Rafferty. 15-Night Man & Freex app. 17-Swan marries Ellen 3.00
11-($3.50, 68 pgs.)-Flip book w/Ultraverse Premiere #5 4.00
18-Death of Rafferty; Chaykin-c 4.00
NOTE: ***Brereton** c-6. **Chaykin** c-1-4, 14, 16, 18. **Hamner** a-1-4. **Herrera** a-12. **James Robinson** scripts-0-18.*

FIRE BALL XL5 (See Steve Zodiac & The ...)

FIREBIRDS (See Noble Causes)
Image Comics: Nov, 2004 ($5.95)

1-Faerber-s/Ponce-a/c; intro. Firebird 6.00

FIREBRAND (Also see Showcase '96 #4)
DC Comics: Feb, 1996 - No. 9, Oct, 1996 ($1.75)

1-9: Brian Augustyn scripts; Velluto-c/a in all. 9-Daredevil #319-c/swipe 3.00

FIREBREATHER
Image Comics: Jan, 2003 - No. 4, Apr, 2003 ($2.95)

1-4-Hester-s/Kuhn-a 3.00
...: The Iron Saint (12/04, $6.95, squarebound) Hester-s/Kuhn-a 7.00
TPB (7/04, $13.95) r/#1-4; foreword by Brad Meltzer; gallery and sketch pages 14.00

FIREBREATHER
Image Comics: Jun, 2008 - No. 4, Feb, 2009 ($2.99)

1-4-Hester-s/Kuhn-a 3.00

FIREBREATHER (Vol.3): HOLMGANG
Image Comics: Nov, 2010 - No. 4, ($3.99, limited series)

1,2-Hester-s/Kuhn-a 4.00

FIRE FROM HEAVEN
Image Comics (WildStorm Productions): Mar, 1996 ($2.50)

1,2-Moore-s 3.00

FIREHAIR COMICS (Formerly Pioneer West Romances #3-6; also see Rangers Comics)
Fiction House Magazines (Flying Stories): Winter/48-49; No. 2, Wint/49-50; No. 7, Spr/51 - No. 11, Spr/52

	GD	VG	FN	VF	VF/NM	NM-
1-Origin Firehair	36	72	108	211	343	475
2-Continues as Pioneer West Romances for #3-6	18	36	54	107	169	230
7-11	14	28	42	82	121	160
I.W. Reprint 8-(nd)-Kinstler-c; reprints Rangers #57; Dr. Drew story by Grandenetti	3	6	9	16	23	30

FIRESIDE BOOK SERIES (Hard and soft cover editions)
Simon and Schuster: 1974 - 1980 (130-260 pgs.), Square bound, color

		GD	VG	FN	VF	VF/NM	NM-
Amazing Spider-Man, The, 1979,	HC	7	14	21	48	89	130
130 pgs., $3.95, Bob Larkin-c	SC	5	10	15	33	57	80
America At War–The Best of DC War	HC	10	20	30	64	132	200
Comics, 1979, $6.95, 260 pgs, Kubert-c	SC	6	12	18	42	79	115
Best of Spidey Super Stories (Electric	HC	9	18	27	57	111	165
Company) 1978, $3.95,	SC	6	12	18	37	66	95
Bring On The Bad Guys (Origins of the	HC	7	14	21	46	86	125
Marvel Comics Villains) 1976, $6.95, 260 pgs.; Romita-c	SC	5	10	15	31	53	75
Captain America, Sentinel of Liberty,1979,	HC	7	14	21	48	89	130
130 pgs., $12.95, Cockrum-c	SC	5	10	15	33	57	80
Doctor Strange Master of the Mystic	HC	7	14	21	48	89	130
Arts, 1980, 130 pgs.	SC	5	10	15	33	57	80
Fantastic Four, The, 1979, 130 pgs.	HC	7	14	21	46	86	125
	SC	5	10	15	31	53	75
Heart Throbs–The Best of DC Romance	HC	13	26	39	86	188	290
Comics, 1979, 260 pgs., $6.95	SC	8	16	24	56	108	160
Incredible Hulk, The, 1978, 260 pgs.	HC	7	14	21	46	86	125
(8 1/4" x 11")	SC	5	10	15	31	53	75
Marvel's Greatest Superhero Battles,	HC	9	18	27	57	111	165
1978, 260 pgs., $6.95, Romita-c	SC	6	12	18	37	66	95
Mysteries in Space, 1980, $7,95,	HC	8	16	24	52	99	145
Anderson-c. r-DC sci/fi stories	SC	5	10	15	34	60	85
Origins of Marvel Comics, 1974, 260 pgs., $5.95. r-covers & origins of Fantastic Four, Hulk, Spider-Man, Thor,	HC	7	14	21	46	86	125
& Doctor Strange	SC	5	10	15	31	53	75
Silver Surfer, The, 1978, 130 pgs.,	HC	7	14	21	48	89	130
$4.95, Norem-c	SC	5	10	15	34	60	85
Son of Origins of Marvel Comics, 1975, 260 pgs., $6.95, Romita-c. Reprints covers & origins of X-Men, Iron Man,	HC	7	14	21	46	86	125
Avengers, Daredevil, Silver Surfer	SC	5	10	15	31	53	75
Superhero Women, The–Featuring the	HC	9	18	27	57	111	165
Fabulous Females of Marvel Comics, 1977, 260 pgs., $6.95, Romita-c	SC	6	12	18	37	66	95

Note: *Prices listed are for 1st printings. Later printings have lesser value.*

FIRESTAR
Marvel Comics Group: Mar, 1986 - No. 4, June, 1986 (75¢)(From Spider-Man TV series)

1,2: 1-X-Men & New Mutants app. 2-Wolverine-c (not real Wolverine?); Art Adams-a(p) 6.00
3,4: 3-Art Adams/Sienkiewicz-c. 4-B. Smith-c 4.00
X-Men: Firestar Digest (2006, $7.99, digest-size) r/#1-4; profile pages 8.00
1 (Jun, 2010, $3.99) Sean McKeever-s/Emma Rios-a 4.00

FIRESTONE (See Donald And Mickey Merry Christmas)

FIRESTORM (Also see The Fury of Firestorm, Cancelled Comic Cavalcade, DC Comics Presents, Flash #289, & Justice League of America #179)
DC Comics: March, 1978 - No. 5, Oct-Nov, 1978

	GD	VG	FN	VF	VF/NM	NM-
1-Origin & 1st app.	6	12	18	28	69	100
2,4,5: 2-Origin Multiplex. 4-1st app. Hyena	2	4	6	9	12	15
3-Origin & 1st app. Killer Frost (Crystal Frost)	4	8	12	25	40	55

...: The Nuclear Man TPB (2011, $17.99) r/#1-5 and stories from Flash #289-293, plus story from Cancelled Comic Cavalcade (uncolored) 18.00

FIRESTORM
DC Comics: July, 2004 - No. 35, June, 2007 ($2.50/$2.99)

1-24: 1-Intro. Jason Rusch; Jolley-s/ChrisCross-a. 6-Identity Crisis tie-in. 7-Bloodhound x-over. 8-Killer Frost returns. 9-Ronnie Raymond returns. 17-Villains United tie-in. 21-Infinite Crisis. 24-One Year Later; Killer Frost app. 3.00
25-35: 25-Begin $2.99-c; Mr. Freeze app. 33-35-Mister Miracle & Orion app. 3.00
...: Reborn TPB (2007, $14.99) r/#23-27 15.00

FIRESTORM, THE NUCLEAR MAN (Formerly Fury of Firestorm)
DC Comics: No. 65, Nov, 1987 - No. 100, Aug, 1990

65-99: 66-1st app. Zuggernaut; Firestorm vs. Green Lantern. 67,68-Millennium tie-ins. 71-Death of Capt. X. 83-1st new look 3.00
100-($2.95, 68 pgs.) 4.00
Annual 5 (10/87)-1st app. new Firestorm 4.00

FIRST, THE
CrossGeneration Comics: Jan, 2001 - No. 37, Jan, 2004 ($2.95)

1-3: 1-Barbara Kesel-s/Bart Sears & Andy Smith-a 5.00
4-10 4.00
11-37 3.00
Preview (11/00, free) 8 pg. intro 3.00
Two Houses Divided Vol. 1 TPB (11/01, $19.95) r/#1-7; new Moeller-c 20.00
Magnificent Tension Vol. 2 TPB (2002, $19.95) r/#8-13 20.00
Sinister Motives Vol. 3 TPB (2003, $15.95) r/#14-19 16.00
Vol. 4 Futile Endeavors (2003, $15.95) r/#20-25 16.00
Vol. 5 Liquid Alliances (2003, $15.95) r/#26-31 16.00
Vol. 6 Ragnarok (2004, $15.95) r/#32-37 16.00

FIRST ADVENTURES
First Comics: Dec, 1985 - No. 5, Apr, 1986 ($1.25)

1-5: Blaze Barlow, Whisper & Dynamo Joe in all 3.00

First Love Illustrated #29 © HARV

First Strike #1 © Hasbro

The Fix #3 © Spencer & Lieber

	GD 2.0	VG 4.0	FN 6.0	VF 8.0	VF/NM 9.0	NM- 9.2

FIRST AMERICANS, THE
Dell Publishing Co.: No. 843, Sept, 1957

Four Color 843-Marsh-a	8	16	24	51	96	140

FIRST BORN (See Witchblade and Darkness titles)
Image Comics (Top Cow): Aug, 2007 - No. 3 ($2.99, limited series)

... First Look (6/07, 99¢) Preview; The Darkness app.; Sejic-a; 2 covers (color & B&W) 3.00
1-3-($2.99) Two covers; Marz-s/Sejic-a. 3-Sara's baby is born 3.00
1-B&W variant Sejic cover 5.00
...: Aftermath (5/08, $3.99) short stories; Magdalena app.; two covers by Sook & Sejic 4.00

FIRST CHRISTMAS, THE (3-D)
Fiction House Magazines (Real Adv. Publ. Co.): 1953 (25¢, 8-1/4x10-1/4", oversize)(Came w/glasses)

nn-(Scarce)-Kelly Freas painted-c; Biblical theme, birth of Christ; Nativity-c	36	72	108	211	343	475

FIRST COMICS GRAPHIC NOVEL
First Comics: Jan, 1984 - No. 21? (52 pgs./176 pgs., high quality paper)

1,2: 1-Beowulf ($5.95)(both printings). 2-Time Beavers 10.00
3($11.95, 100 pgs.)-American Flagg! Hard Times (2nd printing exists) 15.00
4-Nexus ($6.95)-r/B&W 1-3 15.00
5,7: 5-The Enchanted Apples of Oz ($7.95, 52 pgs.)-Intro by Harlan Ellison (1986). 7-The Secret Island Of Oz ($7.95) 10.00
6-Elric of Melnibone ($14.95, 176 pgs.)-Reprints with new color 18.00
8,10,14,18: Teenage Mutant Ninja Turtles Book I -IV ($9.95, 132 pgs.)-8-r/TMNT #1-3 in color w/12 pgs. new-a; origin. 10-r/TMNT #4-6 in color. 14-r/TMNT #7,8 in color plus new 12 pg. story. 18-r/TMNT #10,11 plus 3 pg. fold-out 11.00
9-Time 2: The Epiphany by Chaykin (11/86, $7.95, 52 pgs. - indicia says #8) 15.00
11-Sailor On The Sea of Fate ($14.95) 16.00
nn-Time 2: The Satisfaction of Black Mariah (9/87) 10.00
12-American Flagg! Southern Comfort (10/87, $11.95) 15.00
13,16,17,21: 13-The Ice King Of Oz. 16-The Forgotten Forest of Oz ($8.95). 17-Mazinger (68 pgs., $8.95). 21-Elric, The Weird of the White Wolf; r/#1-5 10.00
15,19: 15-Hex Breaker: Badger ($7.95). 19-The Original Nexus Graphic Novel ($7.95, 104 pgs.)-Reprints First Comics Graphic Novel #4 12.00
20-American Flagg!: State of the Union ($11.95, 96 pgs.); r/A.F. #7-9 15.00
NOTE: *Most or all issues have been reprinted.*

1ST FOLIO (The Joe Kubert School Presents...)
Pacific Comics: Mar, 1984 ($1.50, one-shot)

1-Joe Kubert-c/a(2 pgs.); Adam & Andy Kubert-a 3.00

1ST ISSUE SPECIAL
National Periodical Publications: Apr, 1975 - No. 13, Apr, 1976 (Tryout series)

1,6: 1-Intro. Atlas; Kirby-c/a/script. 6-Dingbats	2	4	6	11	16	20
2,12: 2-Green Team (see Cancelled Comic Cavalcade). 12-Origin/1st app. "Blue" Starman (2nd app. in Starman, 2nd Series #3); Kubert-c	2	4	6	8	11	14
3-Metamorpho by Ramona Fradon	2	4	6	8	11	14
4,10,11: 4-Lady Cop. 10-The Outsiders. 11-Code Name: Assassin; Grell-c	1	3	4	6	8	10
5-Manhunter; Kirby-c/a/script	3	6	9	14	20	26
7,9: 7-The Creeper by Ditko (c/a). 9-Dr. Fate; Kubert-c/Simonson-a.	2	4	6	11	16	20
8-Origin/1st app. The Warlord; Grell-c/a (11/75)	5	10	15	31	53	75
13-Return of the New Gods; Darkseid app.; 1st new costume Orion; predates New Gods #12 by more than a year	3	6	9	19	30	40

FIRST KISS
Charlton Comics: Dec, 1957 - No. 40, Jan, 1965

V1#1	4	8	12	28	47	65
V1#2-10	3	6	9	18	28	38
11-40	3	6	9	14	19	24

FIRST LOVE ILLUSTRATED
Harvey Publications(Home Comics)(True Love): 2/49 - No. 9, 6/50; No. 10, 1/51 - No. 86, 3/58; No. 87, 9/58 - No. 88, 11/58; No. 89, 11/62, No. 90, 2/63

1-Powell-a(2)	20	40	60	114	182	250
2-Powell-a	12	24	36	69	97	125
3-"Was I Too Fat To Be Loved" story	15	30	45	83	124	165
4-10	9	18	27	52	69	85
11,12,14-30: 30-Lingerie panel	8	16	24	42	54	65
13-"I Joined a Teen-age Sex Club" story	12	24	36	69	97	125
31-34,37,39-49: 49-Last pre-code (2/55)	7	14	21	37	46	55
35-Used in **SOTI**, illo "The title of this comic book is First Love"	20	40	60	117	189	260
36-Communism story, "Love Slaves"	12	24	36	69	97	125
38-Nostrand-a	9	18	27	47	61	75
50-66,71-90	6	12	18	31	38	45
67-70-Kirby-c	8	16	24	42	54	65

NOTE: ***Disbrow** a-13. **Orlando** c-87. **Powell** a-1, 3-5, 7, 10, 11, 13-17, 19-24, 26-29, 33,35-41, 43, 45, 46, 50, 54, 55, 57, 58, 61-63, 65, 71-73, 76, 79r, 82, 84, 88.*

FIRST MEN IN THE MOON (See Movie Comics)

FIRST ROMANCE MAGAZINE
Home Comics(Harvey Publ.)/True Love: 8/49 - #6, 6/50; #7, 6/51 - #50, 2/58; #51, 9/58 - #52, 11/58

1	19	38	57	111	176	240
2	11	22	33	62	86	110
3-5	9	18	27	52	69	85
6-10,28: 28-Nostrand-a(Powell swipe)	8	16	24	42	54	65
11-20	7	14	21	37	46	55
21-27,29-32: 32-Last pre-code issue (2/55)	7	14	21	35	43	50
33-40,44-52	6	12	18	31	38	45
41-43-Kirby-c	8	16	24	42	54	65

NOTE: ***Powell** a-1-5, 8-10, 14, 18, 20-22, 24, 25, 28, 36, 46, 48, 51.*

FIRST STRIKE (Hasbro heroes)
IDW Publishing: Aug, 2017 - No. 6, Oct, 2017 ($3.99, limited series)

1-6-Transformers, G.I. Joe, Rom, Micronauts and MASK app.; multiple covers on each 4.00

FIRST TRIP TO THE MOON (See Space Adventures No. 20)

FIRST WAVE (Based on Sci-Fi Channel TV series)
Andromeda Entertainment: Dec, 2000 - No. 4, Jun, 2001 ($2.99)

1-4-Kuhoric-s/Parsons-a/Busch-c 3.00

FIRST WAVE (Also see Batman/Doc Savage Special #1)
DC Comics: May, 2010 - No. 6, Mar, 2011 ($3.99, limited series)

1-6-Batman, Doc Savage and The Spirit app.; Azzarello-s/Morales-a/JG Jones-c 4.00
... Special 1 (6/11, $3.99) Winslade-a/Jones-c 4.00
HC (2011, $29.99, dustjacket) r/#1-6 & Batman/Doc Savage Special #1; sketch art 30.00

FIRST X-MEN
Marvel Comics: Oct, 2012 - No. 5, Mar, 2013 ($3.99, limited series)

1-5: 1-Neal Adams-a/c; Adams & Gage-s; Wolverine & Sabretooth 1st meet Xavier 4.00

FISH POLICE (Inspector Gill of the...#2, 3)
Fishwrap Productions/Comico V2#5-17/Apple Comics #18 on: Dec, 1985 - No. 11, Nov, 1987 ($1.50, B&W); V2#5, April, 1988 - V2#17, May, 1989 ($1.75, color) No. 18, Aug, 1989 - No. 26, Dec, 1990 ($2.25, B&W)

1-11, 1(5/86),2-2nd print, V2#5-17-(Color): V2#5-11. 12-17, new-a, 18-26 ($2.25-c, B&W). 18-Origin Inspector Gill 3.00
Special 1($2.50, 7/87, Comico) 3.00
Graphic Novel: Hairballs (1987, $9.95, TPB) r/#1-4 in color 10.00

FISH POLICE
Marvel Comics: V2#1, Oct, 1992 - No. 6, Mar, 1993 ($1.25)

V2#1-6: 1-Hairballs Saga begins; r/#1 (1985) 3.00

FISTFUL OF BLOOD
IDW Publishing: Oct, 2015 - No. 4, Jan, 2016 ($4.99, limited series)

1-4-Eastman-s/Bisley-a; remastering of series from Heavy Metal magazine 5.00

5 CENT COMICS (Also see Whiz Comics)
Fawcett Publ.: Feb, 1940 (8 pgs., reg. size, B&W)

nn - 1st app. Dan Dare. Ashcan comic, not distributed to newsstands, only for in-house use. A CGC certified 9.6 copy sold for $10,800 in 2003, and a CGC 9.4 sold for $11,500 in 2005.

5 RONIN (Marvel characters in Samurai setting)
Marvel Comics: May, 2011 - No. 5, May, 2011 ($2.99, weekly limited series)

1-Wolverine. 2-Hulk. 3-Punisher. 4-Psylocke; Mack-c. 5-Deadpool 3.00

5-STAR SUPER-HERO SPECTACULAR (See DC Special Series No. 1)

FIVE WEAPONS
Image Comics: Feb, 2013 - No. 10, Jul, 2014 ($3.50)

1-10-Jimmie Robinson-s/a/c 3.50

FIX, THE
Image Comics: Apr, 2016 - No. 9, May, 2017 ($3.99)

1-11-Nick Spencer-s/Steve Lieber-a 4.00

FLAME, THE (See Big 3 & Wonderworld Comics)
Fox Feature Synd.: Sum, 1940 - No. 8, Jan, 1942 (#1,2: 68 pgs; #3-8: 44 pgs.)

1-Flame stories reprinted from Wonderworld #5-9; origin The Flame; Lou Fine-a (36 pgs.),	394	788	1182	2758	4829	6900

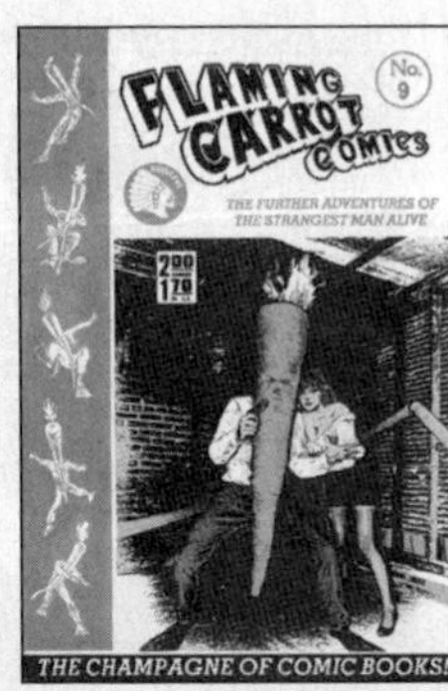

Flaming Carrot Comics #9 © Bob Burden

Flaming Love #5 © QUA

The Flash #165 © DC

GD 2.0 | VG 4.0 | FN 6.0 | VF 8.0 | VF/NM 9.0 | NM- 9.2

GD 2.0 | VG 4.0 | FN 6.0 | VF 8.0 | VF/NM 9.0 | NM- 9.2

2-Fine-a(2); Wing Turner by Tuska; r/Wonderworld #3,10
148 296 444 947 1624 2300
3-8: 3-Powell-a 110 220 330 704 1202 1700

FLAME, THE (Formerly Lone Eagle)
Ajax/Farrell Publications (Excellent Publ.): No. 5, Dec-Jan, 1954-55 - No. 3, April-May, 1955
5(#1)-1st app. new Flame 58 116 174 371 636 900
2,3 39 78 117 231 378 525

FLAMING CARROT COMICS (Also see Junior Carrot Patrol)
Killian Barracks Press: Summer-Fall, 1981 ($1.95, one shot) (Lg size, 8-1/2x11")
1-Bob Burden-c/a/scripts; serially #'ed to 6500 5 10 15 34 60 85

FLAMING CARROT COMICS (See Anything Goes, Cerebus, Teenage Mutant Ninja Turtles/Flaming Carrot Crossover & Visions)
Aardvark-Vanaheim/Renegade Press #6-17/Dark Horse #18-31:
May, 1984 - No. 5, Jan, 1985; No. 6, Mar, 1985 - No. 31, Oct, 1994 ($1.70/$2.00, B&W)
1-Bob Burden story/art 5 10 15 30 50 70
2 3 6 9 16 23 30
3 2 4 6 10 16 20
4-6 2 4 6 9 12 15
7-9 1 3 4 6 8 10
10-12 6.50
13-15 4.00
15-Variant without cover price 6.00
16-(6/87) 1st app. Mystery Men 1 2 3 5 6 8
17-20: 18-1st Dark Horse issue 4.00
21-23,25: 25-Contains trading cards; TMNT app. 3.00
24-(2.50, 52 pgs.)-10th anniversary issue 4.00
26-28: 26-Begin $2.25-c. 26,27-Teenage Mutant Ninja Turtles x-over. 27-McFarlane-c 3.00
29-31-(2.50-c) 3.00
Annual 1(1/97, $5.00) 5.00
... & Reid Fleming, World's Toughest Milkman (12/02, $3.99) listed as #32 in indicia 4.00
... :Fortune Favors the Bold (1998, $16.95, TPB) r/#19-24 17.00
... :Men of Mystery (7/97, $12.95, TPB) r/#1-3, + new material 13.00
... 's Greatest Hits (4/98, $17.95, TPB) r/#12-18, + new material 18.00
... :The Wild Shall Wild Remain (1997, $17.95, TPB) r/#4-11, + new s/a 18.00

FLAMING CARROT COMICS
Image Comics (Desperado): Dec, 2004 - 2006 ($2.95/$3.50, B&W)
1-3-Bob Burden story/art 3.00
4-($3.50-c) 3.50
... Special #1 (3/06, $3.50) All Photo comic 3.50
... Vol. 6 (2006, $14.99) r/1-4 & Special #1; intro. by Brian Bolland 15.00

FLAMING LOVE
Quality Comics Group (Comic Magazines): Dec, 1949 - No. 6, Oct, 1950 (Photo covers #2-6) (52 pgs.)
1-Ward-c/a (9 pgs.) 47 94 141 296 498 700
2 23 46 69 136 223 310
3-Ward-a (9 pgs.); Crandall-a 32 64 96 192 314 435
4-6: 4-Gustavson-a 20 40 60 117 189 260

FLAMING WESTERN ROMANCES (Formerly Target Western Romances)
Star Publications: No. 3, Mar-Apr, 1950
3-Robert Taylor, Arlene Dahl photo on-c with biographies inside; L. B. Cole-c
39 78 117 231 378 525

FLARE (Also see Champions for 1st app. & League of Champions)
Hero Comics/Hero Graphics Vol. 2 on: Nov, 1988 - No. 3, Jan, 1989 ($2.75, color, 52 pgs); V2#1, Nov, 1990 - No. 7, Nov, 1991 ($2.95/$3.50, color, mature, 52 pgs.);V2#8, Oct, 1992 - No. 16, Feb, 1994 ($3.50/$3.95, B&W, 36 pgs.)
V1#1-3, V2#1-16: 5-Eternity Smith returns. 6-Intro The Tigress 4.00
Annual 1(1992, $4.50, B&W, 52 pgs.)-Champions-r 4.50

FLARE ADVENTURES
Hero Graphics: Feb, 1992 - No. 12, 1993? ($3.50/$3.95)
1 (90¢, color, 20 pgs.) 4.00
2-12-Flip books w/Champions Classics 4.00

FLASH, THE (See Adventure Comics, The Brave and the Bold, Crisis On Infinite Earths, DC Comics Presents, DC Special, DC Special Series, DC Super-Stars, The Greatest Flash Stories Ever Told, Green Lantern, Impulse, JLA, Justice League of America, Showcase, Speed Force, Super Team Family, Titans & World's Finest)

FLASH, THE (1st Series)(Formerly Flash Comics)(See Showcase #4,8,13,14)
National Periodical Publ./DC: No. 105, Feb-Mar, 1959 - No. 350, Oct, 1985
105-(2-3/59)-Origin Flash(retold), & Mirror Master (1st app.)
645 1290 2250 8000 19,000 30,000
106-Origin Grodd & Pied Piper; Flash's 1st visit to Gorilla City; begin Grodd the Super Gorilla trilogy (Scarce) 276 552 828 2277 5139 8000
107-Grodd trilogy, part 2 129 258 387 1032 2316 3600
108-Grodd trilogy ends 107 214 321 856 1928 3000
109-2nd app. Mirror Master 89 178 267 712 1606 2500
110-Intro/origin Kid Flash who later becomes Flash in Crisis On Infinite Earths #12; begin Kid Flash trilogy, ends #112 (also in #114,116,118); 1st app. & origin of The Weather Wizard
224 448 672 1848 4174 6500
111-2nd Kid Flash tryout; Cloud Creatures 64 128 192 512 1156 1800
112-Origin & 1st app. Elongated Man (4-5/60); also apps. in #115,119,130
86 172 258 688 1544 2400
113-Origin & 1st app. Trickster 59 118 177 472 1061 1650
114-Captain Cold app. (see Showcase #8) 46 92 138 368 834 1300
115,116,118-120: 119-Elongated Man marries Sue Dearborn. 120-Flash & Kid Flash team-up for 1st time 38 76 114 285 641 1000
117-Origin & 1st app. Capt. Boomerang; 1st & only S.A. app. Winky Blinky & Noddy
46 92 138 368 834 1300
121,122: 122-Origin & 1st app. The Top 31 62 93 223 499 775
123-(9/61)-Re-intro. Golden Age Flash; origins of both Flashes; 1st mention of an Earth II where DC G. A. heroes live 241 482 723 1988 4494 7000
124-Last 10¢ issue 27 54 81 189 420 650
125-128,130: 127-Return of Grodd-c/story. 128-Origin & 1st app. Abra Kadabra. 130-(7/62)-1st Gauntlet of Super-Villains (Mirror Master, Capt. Cold, The Top, Capt. Boomerang & Trickster) 24 48 72 168 372 575
129-2nd G.A. Flash x-over; J.S.A. cameo in flashback (1st S.A. app. G.A. Green Lantern, Hawkman, Atom, Black Canary & Dr. Mid-Nite. Wonder Woman (1st S.A. app.?) appears)
27 54 81 194 435 675
131-134,136,138: 131-Early Green Lantern x-over (9/62). 136-1st Dexter Miles
17 34 51 117 259 400
135-1st app. of Kid Flash's yellow costume (3/63) 19 38 57 133 297 460
137-G.A. Flash x-over; J.S.A. cameo (1st S.A. app.)(1st real app. since 2-3/51); 1st S.A. app. Vandal Savage & Johnny Thunder; JSA team decides to re-form
38 76 114 281 628 975
139-Origin & 1st app. Prof. Zoom 133 266 400 850 1925 3000
140-Origin & 1st app. Heat Wave 18 36 54 124 275 425
141-146,148-150: 142-Trickster app. 12 24 36 84 185 285
147-2nd Prof. Zoom 17 34 51 117 259 400
151-Engagement of Barry Allen & Iris West; G.A. Flash vs. The Shade.
13 26 39 89 195 300
152-159: 159-Dr. Mid-Nite cameo 10 20 30 64 132 200
160-(80-Pg. Giant G-21); G.A. Flash & Johnny Quick-r
11 22 33 73 157 240
161-164,166,167: 167-New facts about Flash's origin 8 16 24 54 102 150
165-Barry Allen weds Iris West 8 16 24 56 108 160
168,170: 168-Green Lantern-c/app. 170-Dr. Mid-Nite, Dr. Fate, G.A. Flash x-over
8 16 24 54 102 150
169-(80-Pg. Giant G-34)-New facts about origin 9 18 27 57 111 165
171,172,174,176,177,179,180: 171-JLA, Green Lantern, Atom flashbacks. 174-Barry Allen reveals I.D. to wife. 179-(5/68)-Flash travels to Earth-Prime and meets DC editor Julie Schwartz; 1st unnamed app. Earth-Prime (See Justice League of America #123 for 1st named app. & 3rd app. overall) 7 14 21 46 86 125
173-G.A. Flash x-over 8 16 24 54 102 150
175-2nd Superman/Flash race (12/67) (See Superman #199 & World's Finest #198,199); JLA cameo; gold kryptonite used (on J'onn J'onzz impersonating Superman)
17 34 51 117 259 400
178-(80-Pg. Giant G-46) 8 16 24 52 99 145
181-186,188,189: 186-Re-intro. Sargon. 189-Last 12¢-c
5 10 15 34 60 85
187,196: (68-Pg. Giants G-58, G-70) 6 12 18 40 73 105
190-195,197-199: 198-Zatanna 1st solo story 4 8 12 27 44 60
200 5 10 15 30 50 70
201-204,206,207: 201-New G.A. Flash story. 206-Elongated Man begins
207-Last 15¢ issue 3 6 9 21 33 45
205-(68-Pg. Giant G-82) 6 12 18 41 76 110
208-213-(52 pg.): 211-G.A. Flash origin-r/#104; Roller Derby-c. 213-Reprints #137
4 8 12 25 40 55
214-DC 100 Page Super Spectacular DC-11; origin Metal Men-r/Showcase #37; never before published G.A. Flash story 8 16 24 54 102 150
215 (52 pgs.)-Flash-r/Showcase #4; G.A. Flash x-over, continued in #216
4 8 12 27 44 60
216,220: 220-1st app. Turtle since Showcase #4 3 6 9 17 26 35
217-219: Neal Adams-a in all. 217-Green Lantern/Green Arrow series begins (9/72); 2nd G.L. & G.A. team-up series (see Green Lantern #76). 219-Last Green Arrow
5 10 15 33 57 80

The Flash #305 © DC

The Flash (2nd series) #24 © DC

The Flash (2nd series) #233 © DC

	GD 2.0	VG 4.0	FN 6.0	VF 8.0	VF/NM 9.0	NM- 9.2

221-224,227,228,230,231: 222-G. Lantern x-over. 228-(7-8/74)-Flash writer Cary Bates travels to Earth-One & meets Flash, Iris Allen & Trickster; 2nd unnamed app. Earth-Prime (See Justice League of America #123 for 1st named app. & 3rd app. overall) 3 6 9 14 19 24
225-Professor Zoom-c/app. 5 10 15 33 57 80
226-Neal Adams-p 3 6 9 16 24 32
229,232-(100 pg. issues)-G.A. Flash-r & new-a. 229-G.A. Flash & Rag Doll app. in new story 4 8 12 28 47 65
233-Professor Zoom-c/app. 3 6 9 21 33 45
234-236,238-250: 235-Green Lantern x-over. 243-Death of The Top. 245-Origin The Floronic Man in Green Lantern back-up, ends #246. 246-Last Green Lantern. 247-Jay Garrick app. 250-Intro Golden Glider 2 4 6 10 14 18
237-Professor Zoom-c/app. 3 6 9 16 24 32
251-274: 256-Death of The Top retold. 265-267-(44 pgs.). 267-Origin of Flash's uniform. 270-Intro The Clown 2 4 6 8 10 12
268,273,274,278,283,286-(Whitman variants; low print run; no issue #s shown on covers) 2 4 6 8 11 14
275,276-Iris Allen dies 2 4 6 11 16 20
275,276-(Whitman variants; low print run; no issue #s shown on covers) 3 6 9 14 20 25
277-288,290: 286-Intro/origin Rainbow Raider 1 2 3 5 6 8
289-1st Pérez DC art (Firestorm); new Firestorm back-up series begins (9/80), ends #304 2 3 4 6 8 10
291-299,301-305: 291-1st app. Saber-Tooth (villain). 295-Gorilla Grodd-c/story. 298-Intro & origin new Shade. 301-Atomic bomb-c. 303-The Top returns. 304-Intro/origin Colonel Computron; 305-G.A. Flash x-over 6.00
300-(8/81, 52 pgs.)-25th Anniversary issue; Flash's origin and life story retold; wraparound-c by Infantino; no ads 1 2 3 5 6 8
306-313-Dr. Fate by Giffen. 309-Origin Flash retold 6.00
314-322,325-340: 318-323-Creeper back-ups. 328-Iris West Allen's death retold. 329-JLA app. 340-Trial of the Flash begins 5.00
323,324-Two part Flash vs. Flash story. 323-Creeper back-up. 324-Death of Reverse Flash (Professor Zoom) 3 6 9 18 28 38
341-349: 344-Origin Kid Flash 6.00
350-Double size ($1.25) Final issue 1 2 3 5 6 8
Annual 1 (10-12/63, 84 pgs.)-Origin Elongated Man & Kid Flash-r; origin Grodd; G.A. Flash-r 32 64 96 230 515 800
Annual 1 Replica Edition (2001, $6.95)-Reprints the entire 1963 Annual 7.00
...Chronicles SC Vol. 1 (2009, $14.99)-r/Showcase #4,8,13,14 and Flash #105,106 15.00
...Chronicles SC Vol. 2 (2010, $14.99)-r/Flash #107-112 15.00
The Flash Spectacular (See DC Special Series No. 11)
The Flash vs. The Rogues TPB (2009, $14.99) r/1st app. of classic rogues in Showcase #8 and Flash #105,106,110,113,117,122,140,155; new Van Sciver-c 15.00
The Life Story of the Flash (1997, $19.95, Hardcover) "Iris Allen's" chronicle of Barry Allen's life; comic panels w/additional text; Waid & Augustyn-s/ Kane & Staton-a/Orbik painted-c 20.00
The Life Story of the Flash (1998, $12.95, Softcover) New Orbik-c 13.00
NOTE: ***N. Adams*** *c-194, 195, 203, 204, 206-208, 211, 213, 215, 226p, 246.* ***M. Anderson*** *c-165, a(i)-195, 200-204, 206-208.* ***Austin*** *a-233i, 234i, 246i.* ***Buckler*** *a-271p, 272p; c(p)-247-250, 252, 253p, 255, 256p, 258, 262, 265-267, 269-271.* ***Giffen*** *a-306-313p; c-310p, 315.* ***Giordano*** *a-226i.* ***Sid Greene*** *a-167-174i, 229i(r).* ***Grell*** *a-237p, 238p, 240-243p; c-236.* ***Heck*** *a-198p.* ***Infantino/Anderson*** *a-135. c-135, 170-174, 192, 200, 201, 328-330.* ***Infantino/Giella*** *c-105-112, 163, 164, 166-168.* ***G. Kane*** *a-195p, 197-199p, 229r, 232r; c-197-199, 312p.* ***Kubert*** *a-108p, 215i(r); c-189-191.* ***Lopez*** *c-272.* ***Meskin*** *a-229r, 232r.* ***Perez*** *a-289-293p; c-293.* ***Starlin*** *a-294-296p.* ***Staton*** *c-263p, 264p. Green Lantern x-over-131, 143, 168, 171, 191.*

FLASH (2nd Series)(See Crisis on Infinite Earths #12 and All Flash #1)
DC Comics: June, 1987 - No. 230, Mar, 2006; No. 231, Oct, 2007 - No. 247, Feb, 2009

1-Guice-c/a begins; New Teen Titans app. 2 4 6 11 16 20
2-10: 3-Intro. Kilgore. 5-Intro. Speed McGee. 7-1st app. Blue Trinity. 8,9-Millennium tie-ins. 9-1st app. The Chunk 5.00
11-61: 12-Free extra 16 pg. Dr. Light story. 19-Free extra 16 pg. Flash story. 28-Capt. Cold app. 29-New Phantom Lady app. 40-Dr. Alchemy app. 50-($1.75, 52 pgs.) 4.00
62-78,80: 62-Flash: Year One begins, ends #65. 65-Last $1.00-c. 66-Aquaman app. 69,70-Green Lantern app. 70-Gorilla Grodd story ends. 73-Re-intro Barry Allen & begin saga ("Barry Allen's" true ID revealed in #78). 76-Re-intro of Max Mercury (Quality Comics' Quicksilver), not in uniform until #77. 80-($1.25-c) Regular Edition 4.00
79,80 ($2.50): 79-(68 pgs.) Barry Allen saga ends. 80-Foil-c 5.00
81-91,93,94,0,95-99,101: 81,82-Nightwing & Starfire app. 84-Razer app. 94-Zero Hour. 0-(10/94). 95-"Terminal Velocity" begins, ends #100. 96,98,99-Kobra app. 97-Origin Max Mercury; Chillblaine app. 4.00
92-1st Impulse 3 6 9 17 26 35
100 ($2.50)-Newstand edition; Kobra & JLA app. 4.00
100 ($3.50)-Foil-c edition; Kobra & JLA app. 5.00
102-131: 102-Mongul app.; begin-$1.75-c. 105-Mirror Master app. 107-Shazam app. 108-"Dead Heat" begins; 1st app. Savitar. 109-"Dead Heat" Pt. 2 (cont'd in Impulse #10). 110-"Dead Heat" Pt. 4 (cont'd in Impulse #11). 111-"Dead Heat" finale; Savitar disappears into the Speed Force; John Fox cameo (2nd app.). 112-"Race Against Time" begins, ends #118; re-intro John Fox. 113-Tornado Twins app. 119-Final Night x-over. 127-129-Rogue's Gallery & Neron. 128,129-JLA-app.130-Morrison & Millar-s begin 3.50
132-149: 135-GL & GA app. 138,140-Black Flash cameos. 141-1st full app. Black Flash. 142-Wally almost marries Linda; Waid-s return. 144-Cobalt Blue origin. 145-Chain Lightning begins. 147-Professor Zoom app. 149-Barry Allen app. 3.00
150-($2.95) Final showdown with Cobalt Blue 4.00
151-162: 151-Casey-s. 152-New Flash-c. 154-New Flash ID revealed. 159-Wally marries Linda. 162-Last Waid-s. 3.00
163-187,189-196,201-206: 163-Begin $2.25-c. 164-186-Bolland-c. 183-1st app of 2nd Trickster (Axel Walker). 196-Winslade-a. 201-Dose-a begins. 205-Batman-c/app. 3.00
188-($2.95) Mirror Master, Weather Wizard, Trickster app. 4.00
197-Origin of Zoom (Hunter Zolomon) (6/03) 4 8 12 25 40 55
198,199-Zoom app. 1 2 3 4 5 7
200-($3.50) Flash vs. Zoom; Barry Allen & Hal Jordan app.; wraparound-c 1 2 3 5 6 8
207-230: 207-211-Turner-c/Porter-a. 209-JLA app. 210-Nightwing app. 212-Origin Mirror Master. 214-216-Identity Crisis x-over. 219-Wonder Woman app. 220-Rogue War 224-Zoom & Prof. Zoom app. 225-Twins born; Barry Allen app.; last Johns-s 3.00
231-247: 231-(10/07) Waid-s/Acuña-a. 240-Grodd app.; "Dark Side Club" 3.00
#1,000,000 (11/98) 853rd Century x-over 3.00
Annual 1-7,9: 2-('87-'94,'96, 68 pgs), 3-Gives history of G.A.,S.A., & Modern Age Flash in text. 4-Armageddon 2001. 5-Eclipso-c/story. 7-Elseworlds story. 9-Legends of the Dead Earth story; J.H. Williams-a(p); Mick Gray-a(i) 4.00
Annual 8 (1995, $3.50)-Year One story 4.00
Annual 10 (1997, $3.95)-Pulp Heroes stories 4.00
Annual 11,12 ('98, '99)-11-Ghosts; Wrightson-c. 12-JLApe; Art Adams-c 4.00
Annual 13 ('00, $3.50) Planet DC; Alcatena-c/a 4.00
...: Blitz (2004, $19.95, TPB)-r/#192-200; Kolins-c 20.00
...: Blood Will Run (2002, 2008; $17.95, TPB)-r/#170-176, Secret Files #3, Iron Heights 18.00
...: Crossfire (2004, $17.95, TPB)-r/#183-191 & parts of Flash Secret Files #3 18.00
Dead Heat (2000, $14.95, TPB)-r/#108-111, Impulse #10,11 15.00
...80-Page Giant (8/98, $4.95) Flash family stories by Waid, Millar and others; Mhan-c 5.00
...80-Page Giant 2 (4/99, $4.95) Stories of Flash family, future Kid Flash, original Teen Titans and XS 5.00
...: Emergency Stop (2008, $12.99, TPB)-r/#130-135; Morrison & Millar-s 13.00
...: Ignition (2005, $14.95, TPB)-r/#201-206 15.00
...: Iron Heights (2001, $5.95)-Van Sciver-c/a; 1st app. of the prison; intro. Girder, Murmur, Double Down and Blacksmith 6.00
...: Mercury Falling (2009, $14.99, TPB)-r/Impulse #62-67 15.00
...: Our Worlds at War 1 (10/01, $2.95)-Jae Lee-c; Black Racer app. 3.00
...Plus 1 (1/1997, $2.95)-Nightwing-c/app. 4.00
Race Against Time (2001, $14.95, TPB)-r/#112-118 15.00
...: Rogues (2003, $14.95, TPB)-r/#177-182 15.00
...: Rogue War (2006, $17.99, TPB)-r/#1/2,212,218,220-225; cover gallery 18.00
...Secret Files 1 (11/97, $4.95) Origin-s & pin-ups 5.00
...Secret Files 2 (11/99, $4.95) Origin of Replicant 5.00
...Secret Files 3 (11/01; $4.95) Intro. Hunter Zolomon (who later becomes Zoom) 5.00
Special 1 (1990, $2.95, 84 pgs.)-50th anniversary issue; Kubert-c; 1st Flash story by Mark Waid; 1st app. John Fox (27th Century Flash) 5.00
Terminal Velocity (1996, $12.95, TPB)-r/#95-100. 13.00
...: The Greatest Stories Ever Told (2007, $19.99, TPB) reprints; Ross-c/Waid intro. 20.00
The Return of Barry Allen (1996, $12.95, TPB)-r/#74-79 13.00
The Secret of Barry Allen (2005, $19.99, TPB)-r/#207-211,213-217; Turner sketch page 20.00
...: The Wild Wests HC (2008, $24.99, dustjacket)-r/#231-237 25.00
...: Time Flies (2002, $5.95)-Seth Fisher-c/a; Rozum-s 6.00
TV Special 1 (1991, $3.95, 76 pgs.)-Photo-c plus behind the scenes photos of TV show; Saltares-a, Byrne scripts 5.00
Wizard #1/2 (2005) prelude to Rogue Wars; Justiano-a 10.00
....: Wonderland TPB (2007, $12.99, TPB)-r/#164-169 13.00
NOTE: ***Guice*** *a-1-9p, 11p, Annual 1p; c-1-9p, Annual 1p.* ***Perez*** *c-15-17, Annual 2i.* ***Charest*** *c/a-Annual 5p.*

FLASH, THE (Brightest Day)(Leads into Flashpoint series)
DC Comics: Jun, 2010 - No. 12, Jul, 2011 ($3.99/$2.99)

1-($3.99) Barry Allen vs. the 25th Century Rogues; Johns-s/Manapul-a/c 4.00
1-Variant-c by Tony Harris 10.00
2-12-($2.99) Capt. Boomerang app. 8-Reverse Flash origin retold 3.00
2-12-Variant covers. 2-Sook. 3-Horn. 4-Kolins. 5-Sook. 6-Garza. 7-Cooke 5.00
...: Secret Files and Origins 1 (5/10, $3.99) Johns-s/Kolins-a; profiles of the Rogues 4.00
...: The Dastardly Death of the Rogues HC (2011, $19.99, dj) r/#1-7 & Secret Files 20.00

FLASH (New DC 52)
DC Comics: Nov, 2011 - No. 52, Jul, 2016 ($2.99/$3.99)

1-Manapul & Buccellato-s; Manapul-a/c 1 3 4 6 8 10
1-Special Edition (12/14, $1.00) reprints #1 with Flash TV image above cover logo 3.00

The Flash (2011 series) #29 © DC

The Flash (2016 series) #22 © DC

Flash Comics #1 © DC

GD VG FN VF VF/NM NM-
2.0 4.0 6.0 8.0 9.0 9.2

2-24: 6,7-Captain Cold app. 8,9,13-17-Grodd app. 17-24-Reverse Flash app. 18-Takara-a. 21-Kid Flash app. 3.00
23.1, 23.2, 23.3 (11/13, $2.99, regular-c) 3.00
23.1 (11/13, $3.99, 3-D cover) "Grodd #1" on cover; Batista-a/Manapul-c
1 2 3 5 6 8
23.2 (11/13, $3.99, 3-D cover) "Reverse Flash #1" on cover; origin; Hepburn-a/Manapul-c
1 2 3 5 6 8
23.3 (11/13, $3.99, 3-D cover) "The Rogues #1" on cover; Zircher-a/Manapul-c
1 2 3 5 6 8
25-($3.99) Zero Year; Sprouse & Manapul-a; first meeting of Barry and Iris 4.00
26-39: 26-Googe-a. 27-Buccellato-s begin. 28-Deadman app. 3.00
40-49,51,52: 40-($3.99) Professor Zoom cameo. 41-47-Prof. Zoom app. 4.00
50-($4.99) The Rogues and The Riddler app.; back-up Kid Flash story 5.00
#0 (11/12, $2.99) Barry's childhood and origin re-told; Manapul-a/c 3.00
Annual #1 (10/12, $4.99) Continued from #12; origin of Glider; Kolins-a 5.00
Annual #2 (9/13, $4.99) Green Lantern app.; Basri-a 5.00
Annual #3 (6/14, $4.99) Intro. Wally West; Grodd app.; leads into Flash #31 5.00
Annual #4 (9/15, $4.99) Jensen-s/Dazo-a; background on Eobard Thawne; cont'd in #43 5.00
...: Futures End 1 (11/14, $2.99, reg.-c) Five years later; Wally West gains speed power 3.00
...: Futures End 1 (11/14, $3.99, 3-D cover) 4.00

FLASH, THE (DC Rebirth)
DC Comics: Aug, 2016 - Present ($2.99)

1-20: 1-3-Williamson-s/Di Giandomenico-a. 3-Intro Godspeed. 8-Wally becomes the new Kid Flash in costume. 9-Flash of Two Worlds cover swipe; both Wallys app. 10-12-The Shade app. 14-17-Rogues Reloaded 3.00
21,22-The Button x-over with Batman #21,22. 21-Flashpoint Thomas Wayne app.; Porter-a. 22-Reverse Flash app; Jay Garrick app.; leads into Doomsday Clock series 3.00
23,24,26-41: 23-Reverse Flash & Hal Jordan app. 28-Intro. Negative Flash. 33-Dark Nights: Metal tie-in. 36-Preview of Damage #1. 39-41-Grodd app. 3.00
25-($3.99) Reverse Flash origin re-told; art by Di Giandomenico, Sook & Googe 4.00
Annual 1 (3/18, $4.99) Porter & Duce-a; leads into Flash War in Flash #47 5.00
...: Rebirth (8/16) Williamson-s/Di Giandomenico-a; Wally West & Batman app. 3.00

FLASH, THE (See Tangent Comics/ The Flash)

FLASH AND GREEN LANTERN: THE BRAVE AND THE BOLD
DC Comics: Oct, 1999 - No. 6, Mar, 2000 ($2.50, limited series)

1-6-Waid & Peyer-s/Kitson-a. 4-Green Arrow app.; Grindberg-a(p) 3.00
TPB (2001, $12.95) r/#1-6 13.00

FLASH COMICS
DC Comics:. Dec. 1939

1-Ashcan comic, not distributed to newsstands, only for in-house use. Cover art is Adventure Comics #41 and interior from All-American Comics #8. A CGC certified 9.6 sold for $11,500 in 2004. A CGC certified 9.4 sold for $6,572.50 in 2008. A CGC certified 9.6 sold for $8,513 in 2013.

FLASH COMICS (Whiz Comics No. 2 on)
Fawcett Publications: Jan, 1940 (12 pgs., B&W, regular size)
(Not distributed to newsstands; printed for in-house use)

NOTE: ***Whiz Comics** #2 was preceded by two books, **Flash Comics** and **Thrill Comics**, both dated Jan, 1940, (12 pgs, B&W, regular size) and were not distributed. These two books are identical except for the title, and were sent out to major distributors as ad copies to promote sales. It is believed that the complete 68 page issue of Fawcett's **Flash** and **Thrill Comics** #1 was finished and ready for publication with the January date. Since DC Comics was also about to publish a book with the same date and title, Fawcett hurriedly printed up the black and white version of **Flash Comics** to secure copyright before DC. The inside covers are blank, with the covers and inside pages printed on a high quality uncoated paper stock.The eight page origin story of Captain Thunder is composed of pages 1-7 and 13 of the Captain Marvel story essentially as they appeared in the first issue of **Whiz Comics**. The balloon dialogue on page thirteen was relettered to tie the story into the end of page seven in **Flash** and **Thrill Comics** to produce a shorter version of the origin story for copyright purposes. Obviously, DC acquired the copyright and Fawcett dropped **Flash** as well as **Thrill** and came out with **Whiz Comics** a month later. Fawcett never used the cover to **Flash** and **Thrill** #1, designing a new cover for **Whiz Comics**. Fawcett also must have discovered that Captain Thunder had already been used by another publisher (Captain Terry Thunder by Fiction House). All references to Captain Thunder were relettered to Captain Marvel before appearing in **Whiz**.*

1-(nn on-c, #1 on inside)-Origin & 1st app. Captain Thunder. Cover by C.C. Beck. Eight copies of Flash and three copies of Thrill exist. All 3 copies of Thrill sold in 1986 for between $4,000-$10,000 each. A NM copy of Thrill sold in 1987 for $12,000. A VG copy of Thrill sold in 1987 for $9000 cash. A CGC certified 9.0 copy of the Flash Comics version sold for $10,117.50 in 2006. A CGC certified 9.4 copy of the Flash Comics version sold for $14,340 in 2008. A CGC certified 9.0 copy of the Thrill Comics version sold for $20,315 in 2008. A CGC certified 8.0 copy sold for $12,999 in 2012. A CGC certified 4.5 copy sold for $19,750 in 2017. A CGC certified 9.0 copy of Thrill Comics sold for $41,040 in 2017.

FLASH COMICS (The Flash No. 105 on) (Also see All-Flash)
National Periodical Publ./All-American: Jan, 1940 - No. 104, Feb, 1949

1-The Flash (origin/1st app.) by Harry Lampert, Hawkman (origin/1st app.) by Gardner Fox, The Whip, & Johnny Thunder (origin/1st app.) by Stan Asch; Cliff Cornwall by Moldoff, Flash Picture Novelets (later Minute Movies w/#12) begin; Moldoff (Shelly) cover; 1st app. Shiera Sanders who later becomes Hawkgirl, #24; reprinted in Famous First Edition (on sale 11/10/39); The Flash-c 16,425 32,850 49,000 120,000 175,000 230,000

1-Reprint, Oversize 13-1/2x10". **WARNING:** This comic is an exact reprint of the original except for its size. DC published it in 1974 with a second cover titling it as a Famous First Edition. There have been many reported cases of the outer cover being removed and the interior sold as the original edition. The reprint with the new outer cover removed is practically worthless. See Famous First Edition for value.

2-Rod Rian begins, ends #11; Hawkman-c 1375 2750 4125 8800 15,400 22,000
3-King Standish begins (1st app.), ends #41 (called The King #16-37,39-41); E.E. Hibbard-a begins on Flash 465 930 1395 3395 5998 8600
4-Moldoff (Shelly) Hawkman begins; The Whip-c 331 662 993 2317 4059 5800
5-The King-c 277 554 831 1759 3030 4300
6-2nd Flash-c (alternates w/Hawkman #6 on) 703 1406 2109 5132 9066 13,000
7-2nd Hawkman-c; 1st Moldoff Hawkman-c 622 1244 1866 4541 8021 11,500
8-New logo begins; classic Moldoff Flash-c 400 800 1200 2800 4900 7000
9,10: 9-Moldoff Hawkman-c; 10-Classic Moldoff Flash-c
411 822 1233 2877 5039 7200
11-13,15-20: 12-Les Watts begins; "Sparks" #16 on. 13-Has full page ad for All Star Comics #3. 17-Last Cliff Cornwall 258 516 774 1651 2826 4000
14-World War II cover 300 600 900 1950 3375 4800
21-Classic Hawkman-c 252 504 756 1613 2757 3900
22,23 232 464 696 1485 2543 3600
24-Shiera becomes Hawkgirl (12/41); see All-Star Comics #5 for 1st app.
265 530 795 1694 2897 4100
25-28,30: 28-Last Les Sparks. 152 304 456 965 1658 2350
29-Ghost Patrol begins (origin/1st app.), ends #104
165 330 495 1048 1799 2550
31-Classic Hawkman dragon-c 174 348 522 1114 1907 2700
32,34,35,37-40: 145 290 435 921 1586 2250
33-Classic Hawkman WWII-c; origin The Shade 290 580 870 1856 3178 4500
36-1st app. Rag Doll (see Flash #229) 155 310 465 992 1696 2400
41-50 129 258 387 826 1413 2000
51-61: 52-1st computer in comics, c/s (4/44). 59-Last Minute Movies. 61-Last Moldoff Hawkman 103 206 309 659 1130 1600
62-Hawkman by Kubert begins 126 252 378 806 1378 1950
63-66,68-85: 66,68-Hop Harrigan app. 70-Mutt & Jeff app. 80-Atom begins, ends #104
97 194 291 621 1061 1500
67-Hawkman dinosaur-c; Hop Harrigan app. 123 246 369 787 1344 1900
86-Intro. The Black Canary in Johnny Thunder (8/47); see All-Star #38.
2500 5000 7500 15,000 20,000 25,000
87,88,90: 87-Intro. The Foil. 88-Origin Ghost. 142 284 426 909 1555 2200
89-Intro villain The Thorn (scarce) 277 554 831 1759 3030 4300
91,93-99: 98-Atom & Hawkman don new costumes 148 296 444 947 1624 2300
92-1st solo Black Canary plus-c; rare in Mint due to black ink smearing on white-c
443 886 1329 3234 5717 8200
100 (10/48),103(Scarce)-52 pgs. each 300 600 900 1950 3375 4800
101,102(Scarce) 277 554 831 1759 3030 4300
104-Origin The Flash retold (Scarce) 811 1622 2433 5920 10,460 15,000

NOTE: ***Irwin Hasen** a-Wheaties Giveaway. c-97, Wheaties Giveaway. **E.E. Hibbard** c-6, 12, 20, 24, 26, 28, 30, 44, 46, 48, 50, 62, 66, 68, 69, 72, 74, 76, 78, 80, 82. **Infantino** a-86p, 90, 93-95, 99-104; c-90, 92, 93, 97, 99, 101, 103. **Kinstler** a-87, 89(Hawkman); c-87. **Chet Kozlak** c-77, 79, 81. **Krigstein** a-94. **Kubert** a-62-76, 83, 85, 86, 88-104; c-63, 65, 67, 70, 71, 73, 75, 83, 85, 86, 88, 89, 91, 94, 96, 98, 100, 104. **Moldoff** a-3; c-3, 7-11, 13-17, plus odd #'s 19-61. **Martin Naydell** c-52, 54, 56, 58, 60, 64, 84.*

FLASH DIGEST, THE (See DC Special Series #24)

FLASH GORDON (See Defenders Of The Earth, Eat Right to Work..., Giant Comic Album, King Classics, King Comics, March of Comics #118, 133, 142, The Phantom #18, Street Comix & Wow Comics, 1st series)

FLASH GORDON
Dell Publishing Co.: No. 25, 1941; No. 10, 1943 - No. 512, Nov, 1953

Feature Books 25 (#1)(1941))-r-not by Raymond 161 322 483 1030 1765 2500
Four Color 10(1942)-by Alex Raymond; reprints "The Ice Kingdom"
86 172 258 688 1544 2400
Four Color 84(1945)-by Alex Raymond; reprints "The Fiery Desert"
42 84 126 311 698 1085
Four Color 173 21 42 63 147 324 500
Four Color 190-Bondage-c; "The Adventures of the Flying Saucers"; 5th Flying Saucer story (6/48)- see The Spirit 9/28/47(1st), Shadow Comics V7#10 (2nd, 1/48), Captain Midnight #60 (3rd, 2/48) & Boy Commandos #26 (4th, 3-4/48)
25 50 75 175 388 600
Four Color 204,247 16 32 48 110 243 375
Four Color 424-Painted-c 11 22 33 76 163 250
2(5-7/53-Dell)-Painted-c; Evans-a? 9 18 27 60 120 180
Four Color 512-Painted-c 9 18 27 60 120 180

FLASH GORDON (See Tiny Tot Funnies)
Harvey Publications: Oct, 1950 - No. 4, April, 1951

Flash Gordon #1 © KFS

Flashpoint #5 © DC

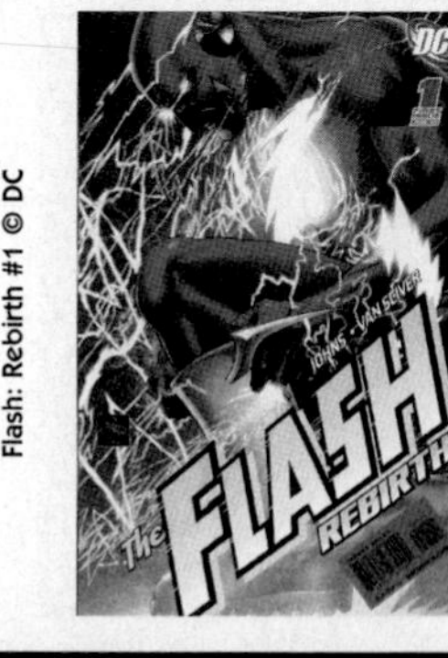

Flash: Rebirth #1 © DC

GD VG FN VF VF/NM NM-
2.0 4.0 6.0 8.0 9.0 9.2

1-Alex Raymond-a; bondage-c; reprints strips from 7/14/40 to 12/8/40 43 86 129 271 461 650
2-Alex Raymond-a; r/strips 12/15/40-4/27/41 28 56 84 165 270 375
3,4-Alex Raymond-a; 3-bondage-c; r/strips 5/4/41-9/21/41. 4-r/strips 10/24/37-3/27/38 27 54 81 158 259 360
5-(Rare)-Small size-5-1/2x8-1/2"; B&W; 32 pgs.; Distributed to some mail subscribers only 87 174 261 553 952 1350
(Also see All-New No. 15, Boy Explorers No. 2, and Stuntman No. 3)

FLASH GORDON
Gold Key: June, 1965

1 (1947 reprint)-Painted-c 7 14 21 48 89 130

FLASH GORDON (Also see Comics Reading Libraries in the Promotional Comics section)
King #1-11/Charlton #12-18/Gold Key #19-23/Whitman #28 on:
9/66 - #11, 12/67; #12, 2/69 - #18, 1/70; #19, 9/78 - #37, 3/82 (Painted covers No. 19-30, 34)

1-1st S.A. app Flash Gordon; Williamson c/a(2); E.C. swipe/Incredible S.F. #32; Mandrake story 7 14 21 49 92 135
1-Army giveaway(1968)("Complimentary" on cover)(Same as regular #1 minus Mandrake story & back-c) 4 8 12 28 47 65
2-8: 2-Bolle, Gil Kane-c; Mandrake story. 3-Williamson-c. 4-Secret Agent X-9 begins, Williamson-c/a(3). 5-Williamson-c/a(2). 6,8-Crandall-a. 7-Raboy-a (last in comics?). 8-Secret Agent X-9-r 4 8 12 28 47 65
9-13: 9,10-Raymond-r. 10-Buckler's 1st pro work (11/67). 11-Crandall-a. 12-Crandall-c/a. 13-Jeff Jones-a (15 pgs.) 4 8 12 27 44 60
14,15: 15-Last 12¢ issue 3 6 9 19 30 40
16,17: 17-Brick Bradford story 3 6 9 16 24 32
18-Kaluta-a (3rd pro work?)(see Teen Confessions) 3 6 9 21 33 45
19(9/78, G.K.), 20-26 2 4 6 8 10 12
27-29,34-37: 34-37-Movie adaptation 2 4 6 8 11 14
30 (10/80) (scarce, from Whitman 3-pack only, 40¢-c) 4 8 12 27 44 60
30 (7/81; re-issue, 50¢-c), 31-33-single issues 2 4 6 11 16 20
31-33 (Bagged 3-pack): Movie adaptation; Williamson-a. 60.00

NOTE: *Aparo a-8. Bolle a-21, 22. Boyette a-14-18. Briggs c-10. Buckler a-10. Crandall c-6. Estrada a-3. Gene Fawcette a-29, 30, 34, 37. McWilliams a-31-33, 36.*

FLASH GORDON
DC Comics: June, 1988 - No. 9, Holiday, 1988-'89 ($1.25, mini-series)

1-9: 1,5-Painted-c 4.00

FLASH GORDON
Marvel Comics: June, 1995 - No. 2, July, 1995 ($2.95, limited series)

1,2: Schultz scripts; Williamson-a 3.00

FLASH GORDON (The Mercy Wars)
Ardden Entertainment: Aug, 2008 - No. 6, Jul, 2009 ($3.99)

1-6: 1-Deneen-s/Green-a; two covers 4.00
...: The Mercy Wars #0 (4/09, $2.99) 3.00

FLASH GORDON
Dynamite Entertainment: 2014 ($3.99)

1-8: 1-Parker-s/Shaner-a; six covers. 2-8-Multiple covers on each 4.00
Annual 2014 ($7.99, squarebound) Short stories of the characters' pasts 8.00
Holiday Special 2014 ($5.99) Christmas-themed short stories by various 6.00

FLASH GORDON: INVASION OF THE RED SWORD
Ardden Entertainment: Jan, 2011 - No. 6, Nov, 2011 ($3.99)

1-6-Deneen-s/Garcia-a. 1-Two covers 4.00

FLASH GORDON: KINGS CROSS
Dynamite Entertainment: 2016 - No. 5, 2017 ($3.99)

1-5-Jeff Parker-s/Jesse Hamm-a; multiple covers on each; Mandrake & Phantom app. 4.00

FLASH GORDON THE MOVIE
Western Publishing Co.: 1980 (8-1/4 x 11", $1.95, 68 pgs.)

11294-Williamson-c/a; adapts movie 2 4 6 10 14 18
13743-Hardback edition 3 6 9 15 21 26

FLASH GORDON: ZEITGEIST
Dynamite Entertainment: 2011 - No. 10, 2013 ($1.00/$3.99)

1-($1.00) Flash, Dale and Zarkov head to Mongo; 4 covers by Ross, Renaud & others 3.00
2-10-($3.99) 2-8-Three covers. 9,10-Ross-c 4.00

FLASH/ GREEN LANTERN: FASTER FRIENDS (See Green Lantern/Flash...)
DC Comics: No. 2, 1997 ($4.95, continuation of Green Lantern/Flash: Faster Friends #1)

2-Waid/Augustyn-s 5.00

FLASHPOINT (Elseworlds Flash)
DC Comics: Dec, 1999 - No. 3, Feb, 2000 ($2.95, limited series)

1-3-Paralyzed Barry Allen; Breyfogle-a/McGreal-s 3.00

FLASHPOINT (Leads into DC New 52 relaunches)
DC Comics: Jul, 2011 - No. 5, Late Oct, 2011 ($3.99, limited series)

1-5-Johns-s/Andy Kubert-a; 2 covers on each. 2-4-Bonus design art. 5-New timeline 4.00
...: Abin Sur - The Green Lantern 1-3 (8/11 - No. 3, 10/11, $2.99) Massaferra-a/c 3.00
...: Batman Knight of Vengeance 1-3 (8/11 - No. 3, 10/11, $2.99) Risso-a/Johnson-c 5.00
...: Canterbury Cricket, The (8/11, $2.99, one-shot) Carlin-s/Morales-a 3.00
...: Citizen Cold 1-3 (8/11 - No. 3, 10/11, $2.99) Scott Kolins-s/a/c 3.00
...: Deadman and the Flying Grayson 1-3 (8/11 - No. 3, 10/11, $2.99) Chiang-c 3.00
...: Deathstroke & The Curse of the Ravager 1-3 (8/11 - No. 3, 10/11, $2.99) Bennett-a 3.00
...: Emperor Aquaman 1-3 (8/11 - No. 3, 10/11, $2.99) Bedard-s/Syaf-c 3.00
...: Frankenstein and the Creatures of the Unknown 1-3 (8/11 - No. 3, 10/11, $2.99) 3.00
...: Green Arrow Industries (8/11, $2.99, one-shot) Kalvachev-c 3.00
...: Grodd of War (8/11, $2.99, one-shot) Manapul-c 3.00
...: Hal Jordan 1-3 (8/11 - No. 3, 10/11, $2.99) 1-Oliver-a. 2,3-Richards-a 3.00
...: Kid Flash Lost 1-3 (8/11 - No. 3, 10/11, $2.99) Gates-s/Manapul-c; Brainiac app. 3.00
...: Legion of Doom 1-3 (8/11 - No. 3, 10/11, $2.99) Glass-s/Sepulveda-c 3.00
...: Lois Lane and the Resistance 1-3 (8/11 - No. 3, 10/11, $2.99) Abnett & Lanning-s 3.00
...: Outsider, The 1-3 (8/11 - No. 3, 10/11, $2.99) Robinson-s/Nowlan-c 3.00
...: Project Superman 1-3 (8/11 - No. 3, 10/11, $2.99) Gene Ha-c/a 3.00
...: Reverse Flash (8/11, $2.99, one-shot) Kolins-s/Gomez-a 5.00
...: Secret Seven 1-3 (8/11 - No. 3, 10/11, $2.99) Pérez-c on all. 1-Pérez-a. 3.00
...: Wonder Woman and The Furies 1-3 (8/11 - No. 3, 10/11, $2.99) Aquaman app. 3.00
...: World of Flashpoint 1-3 (8/11 - No. 3, 10/11, $2.99) Traci 13 app. 3.00

FLASH: REBIRTH
DC Comics: Jun, 2009 - No. 6, Apr, 2010 ($3.99/$2.99, limited series)

1-($3.99) Barry Allen's return; Johns-s/Van Sciver-a; Flash-c by Van Sciver 5.00
1-Variant Barry Allen-c by Van Sciver 10.00
1-Second thru fourth printings 4.00
1-Special Edition (8/10, $1.00) reprints #1 with "What's Next?" logo on cover 3.00
2-6-($2.99) 3-Max Mercury returns 3.00
2-6-Variant covers by Van Sciver 8.00
HC (2010, $19.99, dustjacket) r/#1-6; Johns original proposal; sketch art; cover gallery 20.00
SC (2011, $14.99) r/#1-6; Johns original proposal; sketch art; cover gallery 15.00

FLASH: SEASON ZERO (Based on the 2014 TV series)
DC Comics: Dec, 2014 - No. 12, Nov, 2015 ($2.99, printings of digital-first stories)

1-12-Photo-c on #1-8. 1-4,6-9-Hester-a. 5-Felicity Smoak app. 7-9-Intro. Suicide Squad 3.00

FLASH: THE FASTEST MAN ALIVE (3rd Series)(See Infinite Crisis)
DC Comics: Aug, 2006 - No. 13, Aug, 2007 ($2.99)

1-Bart Allen becomes the Flash; Lashley-a/Bilson & Demeo-s 3.00
1-Variant-c by Joe and Andy Kubert 5.00
2-12: 5-Cyborg app. 7-Inertia returns. 10-Zoom app. 3.00
13-Bart Allen dies; 2 covers 3.00
13-DC Nation Edition from the 2007 San Diego Comic-Con 8.00
...: Full Throttle TPB (2007, $12.99) r/#7-13, All-Flash #1, DCU Infinite Holiday Spec. story 13.00
...: Lightning in a Bottle TPB (2007, $12.99) r/#1-6 13.00

FLAT-TOP
Mazie Comics/Harvey Publ.(Magazine Publ.) No. 4 on: 11/53 - No. 3, 5/54; No. 4, 3/55 - No. 7, 9/55

1-Teenage; Flat-Top, Mazie, Mortie & Stevie begin 12 24 36 67 94 120
2,3 8 16 24 40 50 60
4-7 6 12 18 31 38 45

FLESH & BLOOD
Brainstorm Comics: Dec, 1995 ($2.95, B&W, mature)

1-Balent-c; foil-c. 3.00

FLESH AND BONES
Upshot Graphics (Fantagraphics Books): June, 1986 - No. 4, Dec, 1986 (Limited series)

1-4: Alan Moore scripts (r) & Dalgoda by Fujitake 3.00

FLESH CRAWLERS
Kitchen Sink Press: Aug, 1993 - No. 3, 1995 ($2.50, B&W, limited series, mature)

1-3 3.00

FLEX MENTALLO (Man of Muscle Mystery) (See Doom Patrol, 2nd Series)
DC Comics (Vertigo): Jun, 1996 - No. 4, Sept, 1996 ($2.50, lim. series, mature)

1-4: Grant Morrison scripts & Frank Quitely-c/a in all; banned from reprints due to Charles Atlas legal action 2 4 6 9 13 16

FLINCH (Horror anthology)
DC Comics (Vertigo): Jun, 1999 - No. 16, Jan, 2001 ($2.50)

1-16: 1-Art by Jim Lee, Quitely, and Corben. 5-Sale-c. 11-Timm-a 3.00

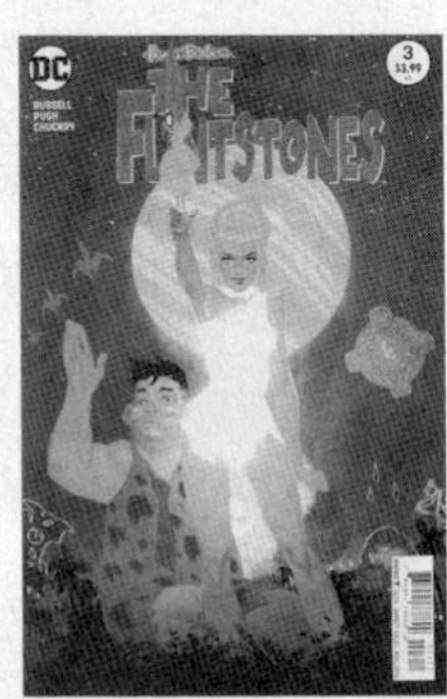

Flintstones (2016 series) #3 © H-B

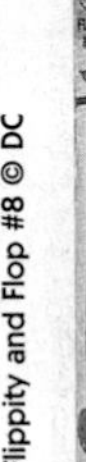

Flippity and Flop #8 © DC

Flyin' Jenny #2 © Pentagon

	GD 2.0	VG 4.0	FN 6.0	VF 8.0	VF/NM 9.0	NM- 9.2

FLINTSTONE KIDS, THE (TV) (See Star Comics Digest)
Star Comics/Marvel Comics #5 on: Aug, 1987 - No. 11, Apr, 1989

1 — 1 2 3 5 6 8
2-11 — 5.00

FLINTSTONES, THE (TV)(See Dell Giant #48 for No. 1)
Dell Publ. Co./Gold Key No. 7 (10/62) on: No. 2, Nov-Dec, 1961 - No. 60, Sept, 1970 (Hanna-Barbera)

2-2nd app. (TV show debuted on 9/30/60); 1st app. of Cave Kids; 15¢-c thru #5 — 9 18 27 61 123 185
3-6(7-8/62): 3-Perry Gunnite begins. 6-1st 12¢-c — 6 12 18 38 69 100
7 (10/62; 1st GK) — 6 12 18 42 79 115
8-10 — 5 10 15 33 57 80
11-1st app. Pebbles (6/63) — 8 16 24 51 96 140
12-15,17-20 — 4 8 12 28 47 65
16-1st app. Bamm-Bamm (1/64) — 8 16 24 54 102 150
21-23,25-30,33: 26,27-2nd & 3rd app. The Grusomes. 30-1st app. Martian Mopheads (10/65).
33-Meet Frankenstein & Dracula — 4 8 12 27 44 60
24-1st app. The Grusomes — 5 10 15 35 63 90
31,32,35-40: 31-Xmas-c. 36-Adaptation of "the Man Called Flintstone" movie. 39-Reprints — 4 8 12 23 37 50
34-1st app. The Great Gazoo — 5 10 15 35 63 90
41-60: 46-Last 12¢ issue — 3 6 9 20 31 42
At N. Y. World's Fair ('64)-J.W. Books (25¢)-1st printing; no date on-c (29¢ version exists, 2nd print?) Most H-B characters app.; including Yogi Bear, Top Cat, Snagglepuss and the Jetsons — 5 10 15 31 53 75
At N. Y. World's Fair (1965 on-c; re-issue; Warren Pub.)
NOTE: *Warehouse find in 1984.* — 2 4 6 10 14 18
Bigger & Boulder 1(#30013-211) (Gold Key Giant, 11/62, 25¢, 84 pgs.) — 7 14 21 46 86 125
Bigger & Boulder 2-(1966, 25¢)-Reprints B&B No. 1 — 4 8 12 23 37 50
...On the Rocks (9/61, $1.00, 6-1/4x9", cardboard-c, high quality paper,116 pgs.)
B&W new material — 8 16 24 54 102 150
...With Pebbles & Bamm Bamm (100 pgs., G.K.)-30028-511 (paper-c, 25¢) (11/65) — 6 12 18 38 69 100
NOTE: *(See Comic Album #16, Bamm-Bamm & Pebbles Flintstone, Dell Giant 48, Golden Comics Digest, March of Comics #229, 243, 271, 289, 299, 317, 327, 341, Pebbles Flintstone, Top Comics #2-4, and Whitman Comic Book.)*

FLINTSTONES, THE (TV)(...& Pebbles)
Charlton Comics: Nov, 1970 - No. 50, Feb, 1977 (Hanna-Barbera)

1 — 7 14 21 44 82 120
2 — 4 8 12 27 44 60
3-7,9,10 — 3 6 9 19 30 40
8- "Flintstones Summer Vacation" (Summer, 1971, 52 pgs.) — 5 10 15 31 53 75
11-20,36: 36-Mike Zeck illos (early work) — 3 6 9 16 23 30
21-35,38-41,43-45 — 3 6 9 14 19 24
37-Byrne text illos (early work; see Nightmare #20) — 3 6 9 16 23 30
42-Byrne-a (2 pgs.) — 3 6 9 16 23 30
46-50 — 2 4 6 13 18 22
Digest nn (1972, B&W, 100 pgs.) (low print run) — 3 6 9 19 30 40
(Also see Barney & Betty Rubble, Dino, The Great Gazoo, & Pebbles & Bamm-Bamm)

FLINTSTONES, THE (TV)(See Yogi Bear, 3rd series) (Newsstand sales only)
Marvel Comics Group: October, 1977 - No. 9, Feb, 1979 (Hanna-Barbera)

1,7-9: 1-(30¢-c). 7-9-Yogi Bear app. — 3 6 9 19 30 40
1-(35¢-c variant, limited distribution) — 8 16 24 54 102 150
2,3,5,6: Yogi Bear app. — 3 6 9 15 22 28
4-The Jetsons app. — 3 6 9 16 24 32

FLINTSTONES, THE (TV)
Harvey Comics: Sept, 1992 - No. 13, Jun, 1994 ($1.25/$1.50) (Hanna-Barbera)

V2#1-13 — 4.00
...Big Book 1,2 (11/92, 3/93; both $1.95, 52 pgs.) — 5.00
...Giant Size 1-3 (10/92, 4/93, 11/93; $2.25, 68 pgs.) — 5.00

FLINTSTONES, THE (TV)
Archie Publications: Sept, 1995 - No. 22, June, 1997 ($1.50)

1-22 — 3.00

FLINTSTONES, THE (TV)
DC Comics: Sept, 2016 - No. 12, Aug, 2017 ($3.99)

1-12: 1-6,8-12-Mark Russell-s/Steve Pugh-a; multiple covers. 2-Intro. Dino. 7-Leonardi-a; Great Gazoo app. 11-Jill Thompson-c. 11,12-Great Gazoo app. — 4.00

FLINTSTONES AND THE JETSONS, THE (TV)
DC Comics: Aug, 1997 - No. 21, May, 1999 ($1.75/$1.95/$1.99)

1 — 6.00
2-21: 19-Bizarro Elroy-c — 3.00

FLINTSTONES CHRISTMAS PARTY, THE (See The Funtastic World of Hanna-Barbera No. 1)

FLIP
Harvey Publications: April, 1954 - No. 2, June, 1954 (Satire)

1,2-Nostrand-a each. 2-Powell-a — 24 48 72 142 234 325

FLIPPER (TV)
Gold Key: Apr, 1966 - No. 3, Nov, 1967 (All have photo-c)

1 — 6 12 18 38 69 100
2,3 — 4 8 12 28 47 65

FLIPPITY & FLOP
National Per. Publ. (Signal Publ. Co.): 12-1/51-52 - No. 46, 8-10/59; No. 47, 9-11/60

1-Sam dog & his pets Flippity The Bird and Flop The Cat begin; Twiddle and Twaddle begin — 36 72 108 211 343 475
2 — 17 34 51 100 158 215
3-5 — 15 30 45 83 124 165
6-10 — 14 28 42 76 108 140
11-20: 20-Last precode (3/55) — 11 22 33 60 83 105
21-47 — 10 20 30 54 72 90

FLOATERS
Dark Horse Comics: Sept, 1993 - No. 5, Jan, 1994 ($2.50, B&W, lim. series)

1-5 — 3.00

FLOYD FARLAND (See Eclipse Graphic Album Series #11)

FLY, THE (Also see Adventures of..., Blue Ribbon Comics & Flyman)
Archie Enterprises, Inc.: May, 1983 - No. 9, Oct, 1984

1,2: 1-Mr. Justice app; origin Shield; Kirby-a; Steranko-c. 2-Ditko-a; Flygirl app. — 6.00
3-5: Ditko-a in all. 4,5-Ditko-c(p) — 5.00
6-9: Ditko-a in all. 6-8-Ditko-c(p) — 6.00
NOTE: *Ayers c-9.* ***Buckler*** *a-1, 2.* ***Kirby*** *a-1.* ***Nebres*** *c-3, 4, 5i, 6, 7i.* ***Steranko*** *c-1, 2.*

FLY, THE
Impact Comics (DC): Aug, 1991 - No. 17, Dec, 1992 ($1.00)

1 — 4.00
2-17: 4-Vs. The Black Hood. 9-Trading card inside — 3.00
Annual 1 ('92, $2.50, 68 pgs.)-Impact trading card — 4.00

FLYBOY (Flying Cadets)(Also see Approved Comics #5)
Ziff-Davis Publ. Co. (Approved): Spring, 1952 - No. 2, Oct-Nov, 1952

1-Saunders painted-c — 20 40 60 118 192 265
2-(10-11/52)-Saunders painted-c — 15 30 45 83 124 165

FLYING ACES (Aviation stories)
Key Publications: July, 1955 - No. 5, Mar, 1956

1 — 11 22 33 62 86 110
2-5: 2-Trapani-a — 7 14 21 37 46 55

FLYING A'S RANGE RIDER, THE (TV)(See Western Roundup under Dell Giants)
Dell Publishing Co.: #404, 6-7/52; #2, June-Aug, 1953 - #24, Aug, 1959 (All photo-c)

Four Color 404(#1)-Titled "The Range Rider" — 9 18 27 60 120 180
2 — 5 10 15 35 63 90
3-10 — 5 10 15 31 53 75
11-16,18-24 — 4 8 12 28 47 65
17-Toth-a — 5 10 15 33 57 80

FLYING CADET (WW II Plane Photos)
Flying Cadet Publ. Co.; Jan, 1943 - V2#8, Nov, 1944 (Half photos, half comics)

V1#1-Painted-c — 20 40 60 117 189 260
2-Photo-c, P-47 Thunderbolt — 13 26 39 72 101 130
3-9 (Two #6's, Sept. & Oct.): 4,5,6a,6b-Photo-c — 12 24 36 67 94 120
V2#1-7 (1/44-9/44)(#10-16): 1,2,4-7-Photo-c — 11 22 33 62 86 110
7 (#17 on cover)-Bare-breasted woman-c — 43 86 129 271 461 650

FLYING COLORS 10th ANNIVERSARY SPECIAL
Flying Colors Comics: Fall 1998 ($2.95, one-shot)

1-Dan Brereton-c; pin-ups by Jim Lee and Jeff Johnson — 3.00

FLYIN' JENNY
Pentagon Publ. Co./Leader Enterprises #2: 1946 - No. 2, 1947 (1945 strip-r)

nn-Marcus Swayze strip-r (entire insides) — 21 42 63 126 206 285
2-Baker-c; Swayze strip reprints — 42 84 126 265 445 625

FLYING MODELS

Flying Saucers #1 © AVON

Foolkiller (2017 series) #3 © MAR

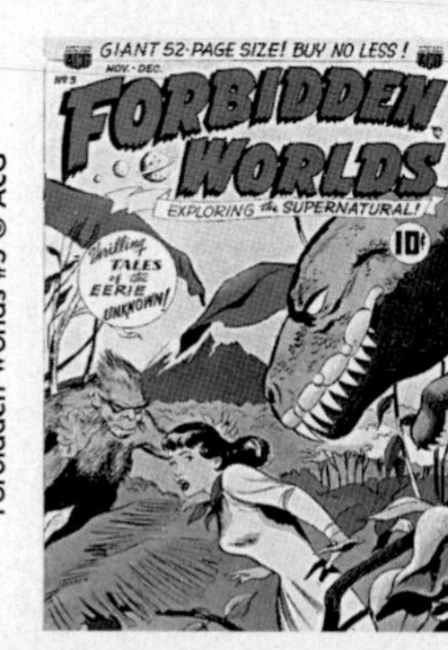

Forbidden Worlds #3 © ACG

GD VG FN VF VF/NM NM-
2.0 4.0 6.0 8.0 9.0 9.2

H-K Publ. (Health-Knowledge Publs.): V61#3, May, 1954 (5¢, 16 pgs.)
V61#3 (Rare) 10 20 30 54 72 90

FLYING NUN (TV)
Dell Publishing Co.: Feb, 1968 - No. 4, Nov, 1968
1-Sally Field photo-c 6 12 18 42 79 115
2-4: 2-Sally Field photo-c 4 8 12 27 44 60

FLYING NURSES (See Sue & Sally Smith...)

FLYING SAUCERS (See The Spirit 9/28/47(1st app.), Shadow Comics V7#10 (2nd, 1/48), Captain Midnight #60 (3rd, 2/48), Boy Commandos #26 (4th, 3-4/48) & Flash Gordon Four Color 190 (5th, 6/48))

FLYING SAUCERS (See Out of This World Adventures #2)
Avon Periodicals/Realistic: 1950; 1952; 1953
1(1950)-Wood-a, 21 pgs.; Fawcette-c 116 232 348 742 1271 1800
nn(1952)-Cover altered plus 2 pgs. of Wood-a not in original 58 116 174 371 636 900
nn(1953)-Reprints above (exist?) 58 116 174 371 636 900

FLYING SAUCERS (Comics)
Dell Publishing Co.: April, 1967 - No. 4, Nov, 1967; No. 5, Oct, 1969
1-(12¢-c) 5 10 15 31 53 75
2-5: 5-Has same cover as #1, but with 15¢ price 3 6 9 21 33 45

FLY MAN (Formerly Adventures of The Fly; Mighty Comics #40 on)
Mighty Comics Group (Radio Comics) (Archie): No. 32, July, 1965 - No. 39, Sept, 1966 (Also see Mighty Crusaders)
32,33-Comet, Shield, Black Hood, The Fly & Flygirl x-over. 33-Re-intro Wizard, Hangman (1st S.A. appearances) 5 10 15 34 60 85
34-39: 34-Shield begins. 35-Origin Black Hood. 36-Hangman x-over in Shield; re-intro. & origin of Web (1st S.A. app.). 37-Hangman, Wizard x-over in Flyman; last Shield issue. 38-Web story. 39-Steel Sterling (1st S.A. app.) 4 8 12 27 44 60

FLY, THE ; OUTBREAK (Sequel to the 1986 and 1989 movies)
IDW Publishing: Mar, 2015 - No. 5, Aug, 2015 ($3.99)
1-5-Martin Brundle's story continues; Brandon Seifert-s/Menton3-a; multiple covers 4.00

FOLLOW THE SUN (TV)
Dell Publishing Co.: May-July, 1962 - No. 2, Sept-Nov, 1962 (Photo-c)
01-280-207(No.1) 5 10 15 30 50 70
12-280-211(No.2) 4 8 12 27 44 60

FOODINI (TV)(The Great...; see Jingle Dingle & Pinhead &...)
Continental Publ. (Holyoke): March, 1950 - No. 4, Aug, 1950 (All have 52 pgs.)
1-Based on TV puppet show (very early TV comic) 23 46 69 136 223 310
2-Jingle Dingle begins 14 28 42 81 118 155
3,4 11 22 33 60 83 105

FOOEY (Magazine) (Satire)
Scoff Publishing Co.: Feb, 1961 - No. 4, May, 1961
1 5 10 15 31 53 75
2-4 3 6 9 21 33 45

FOOFUR (TV)
Marvel Comics (Star Comics)/Marvel No. 5 on: Aug, 1987 - No. 6, Jun, 1988
1-6 5.00

FOOLKILLER (Also see The Amazing Spider-Man #225, The Defenders #73, Man-Thing #3 & Omega the Unknown #8)
Marvel Comics: Oct, 1990 - No. 10, Oct, 1991 ($1.75, limited series)
1-10: 1-Origin 3rd Foolkiller; Greg Salinger app; DeZuniga-a(i) in 1-4. 8-Spider-Man x-over 3.00

FOOLKILLER
Marvel Comics: Dec, 2007 - No. 5, Jul, 2008 ($3.99, limited series)
1-5-Hurwitz-s/Medina-a. 2-Origin 4.00

FOOLKILLER
Marvel Comics: Jan, 2017 - No. 5, May, 2017 ($3.99, limited series)
1-5-Max Bemis-s/Dalibor Talajic-a. 4-Deadpool app. 5-The Hood app. 4.00

FOOLKILLER: WHITE ANGELS
Marvel Comics: Sept, 2008 - No. 5, Jan, 2009 ($3.99, limited series)
1-5-Hurwitz-s/Azaceta-a 4.00

FOOM (Friends Of Ol' Marvel)
Marvel Comics: 1973 - No. 22, 1979 (Marvel fan magazine)
1 8 16 24 54 102 150
2-Hulk-c by Steranko; Wolverine prototype 10 20 30 64 132 200
3,4 5 10 15 34 60 85
5-9,11: 5-Deathlok preview. 11-Kirby-a & interview 5 10 15 31 53 75
10-Article on new X-Men that came out before Giant-Size X-Men #1; new X-Men cover by Dave Cockrum 12 24 36 82 179 275
12-15: 11-Star-Lord preview. 12-Vision-c. 13-Daredevil-c. 14-Conan. 15-Howard the Duck; preview of Ms. Marvel & Capt. Britain 5 10 15 31 53 75
16-20: 16-Marvel bullpen. 17-Stan Lee issue. 19-Defenders 4 8 12 28 47 65
21-Star Wars 5 10 15 30 50 70
22-Spider-Man-c; low print run final issue 6 12 18 38 69 100

FOOTBALL THRILLS (See Tops In Adventure)
Ziff-Davis Publ. Co.: Fall-Winter, 1951-52 - No. 2, Fall, 1952 (Edited by "Red" Grange)
1-Powell a(2); Saunders painted-c; Red Grange, Jim Thorpe stories 27 54 81 158 259 360
2-Saunders painted-c 18 36 54 105 165 225

FOOT SOLDIERS, THE
Dark Horse Comics: Jan, 1996 - No. 4, Apr, 1996 ($2.95, limited series)
1-4: Krueger story & Avon Oeming-a. in all. 1-Alex Ross-c. 4-John K. Snyder, III-c 3.00

FOOT SOLDIERS, THE (Volume Two)
Image Comics: Sept, 1997 - No. 5, May, 1998 ($2.95, limited series)
1-5: 1-Yeowell-a. 2-McDaniel, Hester, Sienkiewicz, Giffen-a 3.00

FOR A NIGHT OF LOVE
Avon Periodicals: 1951
nn-Two stories adapted from the works of Emile Zola; Astarita, Ravielli-a; Kinstler-c 39 78 117 231 378 525

FORBIDDEN BRIDES OF THE FACELESS SLAVES IN THE SECRET HOUSE OF THE NIGHT OF DREAD DESIRE (Neil Gaiman's...)
Dark Horse Books: 2017 ($17.99, HC graphic novel)
HC-Neil Gaiman-s/Shane Oakley-a 18.00

FORBIDDEN KNOWLEDGE: ADVENTURE BEYOND THE DOORWAY TO SOULS WITH RADICAL DREAMER (Also see Radical Dreamer)
Mark's Giant Economy Size Comics: 1996 ($3.50, B&W, one-shot, 48 pgs.)
nn-Max Wrighter app.; Wheatley-c/a/script; painted infinity-c 4.00

FORBIDDEN LOVE
Quality Comics Group: Mar, 1950 - No. 4, Sept, 1950 (52 pgs.)
1-(Scarce)-Classic photo-c; Crandall-a 129 258 387 826 1413 2000
2-(Scarce)-Classic photo-c 87 174 261 553 952 1350
3-(Scarce)-Photo-c 68 136 204 435 743 1050
4-(Scarce)-Ward/Cuidera-a; photo-c 74 148 222 470 810 1150

FORBIDDEN LOVE (See Dark Mansion of...)

FORBIDDEN PLANET
Innovation Publishing: May, 1992 - No. 4, 1992 ($2.50, limited series)
1-4: Adapts movie; painted-c 3.00

FORBIDDEN TALES OF DARK MANSION (Formerly Dark Mansion of Forbidden Love #1-4)
National Periodical Publ.: No. 5, May-June, 1972 - No. 15, Feb-Mar, 1974
5-(52 pgs.) 5 10 15 35 63 90
6-15: 13-Kane/Howard-a 3 6 9 17 26 35
NOTE: ***N. Adams*** *c-9.* ***Alcala*** *a-9-11, 13.* ***Chaykin*** *a-7,15.* ***Evans*** *a-14.* ***Heck*** *a-5.* ***Kaluta*** *a-7i, 8-12; c-7, 8, 13.* ***G. Kane*** *a-13.* ***Kirby*** *a-6.* ***Nino*** *a-8, 12, 15.* ***Redondo*** *a-14.*

FORBIDDEN WORLDS
American Comics Group: 7-8/51 - No. 34, 10-11/54; No. 35, 8/55 - No. 145, 8/67 (No. 1-5: 52 pgs.; No. 6-8: 44 pgs.)
1-Williamson/Frazetta-a (10 pgs.) 184 368 552 1168 2009 2850
2 71 142 213 454 777 1100
3-Williamson/Wood-a (7 pgs.); Frazetta (1 panel) 74 148 222 470 810 1150
4 46 92 138 290 488 685
5-Krenkel/Williamson-a (8 pgs.) 55 110 165 352 601 850
6-Harrison/Williamson-a (8 pgs.) 50 100 150 315 533 750
7,8,10: 7-1st monthly issue 37 74 111 222 361 500
9-A-Bomb explosion story 39 78 117 234 385 535
11-20 26 52 78 154 252 350
21-33: 24-E.C. swipe by Landau 21 42 63 122 199 275
34(10-11/54)(Scarce)(becomes Young Heroes #35 on)-Last pre-code issue; A-Bomb explosion story 23 46 69 136 223 310
35(8/55)-Scarce 22 44 66 128 209 290
36-62 14 28 42 82 121 160
63,69,76,78-Williamson-a in all; w/Krenkel #69 15 30 45 83 124 165
64,66-68,70-72,74,75,77,79-85,87-90 11 22 33 60 83 105
65- "There's a New Moon Tonight" listed in #114 as holding 1st record fan mail response

Force Works #13 © MAR

Forever People #8 © DC

For Lovers Only #74 © CC

	GD 2.0	VG 4.0	FN 6.0	VF 8.0	VF/NM 9.0	NM- 9.2
	15	30	45	84	127	170
73-1st app. Herbie by Ogden Whitney	54	108	162	343	574	825
86-Flying saucer-c by Schaffenberger	12	24	36	67	94	120
91-93,95-100	5	10	15	34	60	85
94-Herbie (2nd app.)	11	22	33	77	166	255
101-109,111-113,115,117-120	4	8	12	28	44	60
110,116-Herbie app. 116-Herbie goes to Hell; Elizabeth Tayor-c	8	16	24	54	102	150
114-1st Herbie-c; contains list of editor's top 20 ACG stories	10	20	30	68	144	220
121-123	3	6	9	21	33	45
124,127-130: 124-Magic Agent app.	4	8	12	23	37	50
125-Magic Agent app.; intro. & origin Magicman series, ends #141; Herbie app.	5	10	15	31	53	75
126-Herbie app.	4	8	12	27	44	60
131-139: 133-Origin/1st app. Dragonia in Magicman (1-2/66); returns in #138. 136-Nemesis x-over in Magicman	3	6	9	21	33	45
140-Mark Midnight app. by Ditko	4	8	12	23	37	50
141-145	3	6	9	19	30	40

NOTE: ***Buscema*** *a-75, 79, 81, 82, 140r.* ***Cameron*** *a-5.* ***Disbrow*** *a-10.* ***Ditko*** *a-137p, 138, 140.* ***Landau*** *a-24, 27-29, 31-34, 48, 86r, 96, 143-45.* ***Lazarus*** *a-18, 23, 24, 57.* ***Moldoff*** *a-27, 31, 139r.* ***Reinman*** *a-93.* ***Whitney*** *a-70, 115, 116, 137; c-40, 46, 57, 60, 68, 70, 78, 79, 90, 93, 94, 100, 102, 103, 106-108, 114, 129.*

FORCE, THE (See The Crusaders)

FORCE MAJEURE: PRAIRIE BAY (Also see Wild Stars)
Little Rocket Publications: May, 2002 ($2.95, B&W)

1-Tierney-s/Gil-c/a — 3.00

FORCE OF BUDDHA'S PALM THE
Jademan Comics: Aug, 1988 - No. 55, Feb, 1993 ($1.50/$1.95, 68 pgs.)

1,55-Kung Fu stories in all — 5.00
2-54 — 4.00

FORCE WORKS
Marvel Comics: July, 1994 - No. 22, Apr, 1996 ($1.50)

1-($3.95)-Fold-out pop-up-c; Iron Man, Wonder Man, Spider-Woman, U.S. Agent & Scarlet Witch (new costume) — 4.00
2-11, 13-22: 5-Blue logo & pink logo versions. 9-Intro Dreamguard. 13-Avengers app. — 3.00
5-Pink logo ($2.95)-polybagged w/ 16pg. Marvel Action Hour Preview & acetate print — 4.00
12 ($2.50)-Flip book w/War Machine. — 4.00

FORD ROTUNDA CHRISTMAS BOOK (See Christmas at the Rotunda)

FOREIGN INTRIGUES (Formerly Johnny Dynamite; becomes Battlefield Action #16 on)
Charlton Comics: No. 14, 1956 - No. 15, Aug, 1956

14,15-Johnny Dynamite continues — 8 16 24 44 57 70

FOREMOST BOYS (See 4Most)

FOREVER DARLING (Movie)
Dell Publishing Co.: No. 681, Feb, 1956

Four Color 681-w/Lucille Ball & Desi Arnaz; photo-c — 10 20 30 66 138 210

FOREVER EVIL (See Justice League #23 (2013))
DC Comics: Nov, 2013 - No. 7, Jul, 2014 ($3.99, limited series)

1-Earth Three Crime Syndicate takes over; Nightwing unmasked; Johns-s/Finch-a — 4.00
1-Director's Cut 1 (12/13, $5.99) Pencil artwork with full script — 6.00
2-6: 2-Luthor dons the green battlesuit. 4-Sinestro returns — 4.00
7-($4.99) — 5.00
... Aftermath: Batman vs. Bane 1 (6/14, $3.99) Tomasi-s/Eaton-a — 4.00

FOREVER EVIL: A.R.G.U.S.
DC Comics: Dec, 2013 - No. 6, May, 2014 ($2.99, limited series)

1-6-Gates-s. Steve Trevor in search of missing heroes. 1,2-Deathstroke app. — 3.00

FOREVER EVIL: ARKHAM WAR
DC Comics: Dec, 2013 - No. 6, May, 2014 ($2.99, limited series)

1-6-Tomasi-s/Eaton-a; Bane and the Arkham inmates. 4-6-The Talons app. — 3.00

FOREVER EVIL: ROGUES REBELLION
DC Comics: Dec, 2013 - No. 6, May, 2014 ($2.99, limited series)

1-6-Buccellato-s/Hepburn-a/Shalvey-c. 2-Deathstorm & Power Ring app. 6-Grodd app. — 3.00

FOREVER MAELSTROM
DC Comics: Jan, 2003 - No. 6, Jun, 2003 ($2.95, limited series)

1-6-Chaykin & Tischman-s/Lucas & Barreto-a — 3.00

FOREVER PEOPLE, THE
National Periodical Publications: Feb-Mar, 1971 - No. 11, Oct-Nov, 1972 (Fourth World) (#1-3, 10-11 are 36 pgs; #4-9 are 52 pgs.)

	GD 2.0	VG 4.0	FN 6.0	VF 8.0	VF/NM 9.0	NM- 9.2
1-1st app. Forever People; Superman x-over; Kirby-c/a begins; 1st full app. Darkseid (3rd anywhere, 3 weeks before New Gods #1); Darkseid storyline begins, ends #8 (app. in 1-4,6,8; cameos in 5,11)	15	30	45	105	233	360
2-9: 4-G.A. reprints thru #9. 9,10-Deadman app.	4	8	12	25	40	55
10,11	3	6	9	19	30	40
Jack Kirby's Forever People TPB (1999, $14.95, B&W&Grey) r/#1-11 plus bonus cover gallery						15.00

NOTE: ***Kirby*** *c/a(p)-1-11; #4-9 contain Sandman reprints from Adventure #85, 84, 75, 80, 77, 74 in that order.*

FOREVER PEOPLE
DC Comics: Feb, 1988 - No. 6, July, 1988 ($1.25, limited series)

1-6 — 4.00

FORGE
CrossGeneration Comics: Feb, 2002 - No. 13, May, 2003 ($9.95/$11.95/$7.95, TPB)

1-3: Reprints from various CrossGen titles — 10.00
4-8-($11.95) — 12.00
9-13-($7.95, 8-1/4" x 5-1/2") digest-sized reprints — 8.00

FOR GIRLS ONLY
Bernard Baily Enterprises: 11/53 - No. 2, 6/54 (100 pgs., digest size, 25¢)

1-25% comic book, 75% articles, illos, games — 39 78 117 231 378 525
2-Eddie Fisher photo & story. — 30 60 90 177 289 400

FORGOTTEN FOREST OF OZ, THE (See First Comics Graphic Novel #16)

FORGOTTEN REALMS (Also see Avatar & TSR Worlds)
DC Comics: Sept, 1989 - No. 25, Sept, 1991 ($1.50/$1.75)

1, Annual 1 (1990, $2.95, 68 pgs.) — 4.00
2-25: Based on TSR role-playing game. 18-Avatar story — 3.00

FORGOTTEN REALMS (Based on Wizards of the Coast game)
Devil's Due Publ.: June, 2005 - No. 3, Aug, 2005 ($4.95)

1-3-Salvatore-s/Seeley-a — 5.00
...Exile (11/05 - No. 3, 1/06, $4.95) 1-3-Daab-s/Seeley-a. 1-Flip cover — 5.00
...: Legacy (2/08 - No. 3, 6/08, $5.50) 1-3-Daab-s/Atkins-a — 5.50
The Legend of Drizzt Book II: Exile (2006, $14.95, TPB) r/#1-3 — 15.00
...Sojourn (3/06 - No. 3, 6/06, $4.95) 1-3-Daab-s/Seeley-a — 5.00
...: Streams of Silver (12/06 - No. 3, $5.50) 1-3-Daab-s/Semeiks-a — 5.50
...The Crystal Shard (8/06 - No. 3, 12/06, $4.95) 1-3-Daab-s/Semeiks-a — 5.00
...The Halfling's Gem (8/07 - No. 3, 12/07, $5.50) 1-3-Daab-s/Seeley-a; two covers — 5.50

FORLORN RIVER (See Zane Grey Four Color 395)

FOR LOVERS ONLY (Formerly Hollywood Romances)
Charlton Comics: No. 60, Aug, 1971 - No. 87, Nov, 1976

60 — 3 6 9 19 30 40
61-80,82-87: 67-Morisi-a — 2 4 6 11 16 20
81-Psychedelic cover — 3 6 9 16 23 30

FORMERLY KNOWN AS THE JUSTICE LEAGUE
DC Comics: Sept, 2003 - No. 6, Feb, 2004 ($2.50, limited series)

1-Giffen & DeMatteis-s/Maguire-a; Booster Gold, Blue Beetle, Captain Atom, Mary Marvel, Fire, and Elongated Man app. — 4.00
2-6: 3,4-Roulette app. 6-JLA app. — 3.00
TPB (2004, $12.95) r/#1-6 — 13.00

FORMIC WARS: BURNING EARTH
Marvel Comics: Apr, 2011 - No. 7, Sept, 2011 ($3.99, limited series)

1-7-Prequel to Orson Scott Card's novel Ender's Game. 1-Covers by Larroca & Hitch — 4.00

FORMIC WARS: SILENT STRIKE (Follows Burning Earth limited series)
Marvel Comics: Feb, 2012 - No. 5, Jun, 2012 ($3.99, limited series)

1-5-Johnston-s/Caracuzzo-a/Camuncoli-c — 4.00

FORT: PROPHET OF THE UNEXPLAINED
Dark Horse Comics: June, 2002 - No. 4, Sept, 2002 ($2.99, B&W, limited series)

1-4-Peter Lenkov-s/Frazer Irving-c/a — 3.00
TPB (2003, $9.95) r/#1-4 — 10.00

FORTUNE AND GLORY
Oni Press: Dec, 1999 - No. 3, Apr, 2000 ($4.95, B&W, limited series)

1-3-Brian Michael Bendis in Hollywood — 5.00
TPB ($14.95) — 15.00

40 BIG PAGES OF MICKEY MOUSE
Whitman Publ. Co.: No. 945, Jan, 1936 (10-1/4x12-1/2", 44 pgs., cardboard-c)

945-Reprints Mickey Mouse Magazine #1, but with a different cover; ads were eliminated and some illustrated stories had expanded text. The book is 3/4" shorter than Mickey Mouse Mag. #1, but the reprints are same size (Rare) — 165 330 495 1048 1799 2550

Four Color Comics Series 1 #2 © DELL

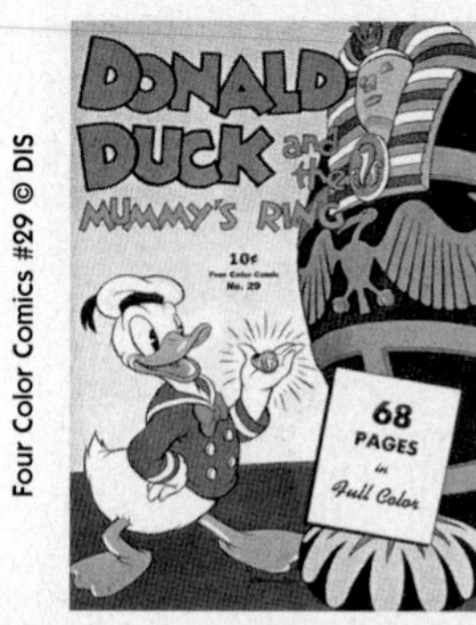

Four Color Comics #29 © DIS

Four Color Comics #30 © DIS

47 RONIN
Dark Horse Comics: Nov, 2012 - No. 5, Jul, 2013 ($3.99, limited series)

	GD 2.0	VG 4.0	FN 6.0	VF 8.0	VF/NM 9.0	NM- 9.2
1-5-Mike Richardson-s/Stan Sakai-a/c; 18th century samurai legend						4.00

FOR YOUR EYES ONLY (See James Bond...)

FOUNTAIN, THE (Companion graphic novel to the Darren Aronofsky film)
DC Comics (Vertigo): 2005 ($39.99, hardcover with dust jacket)

	GD 2.0	VG 4.0	FN 6.0	VF 8.0	VF/NM 9.0	NM- 9.2
1-Darren Aronofsky-s/Kent Williams-a						40.00

FOUR (Fantastic Four; See Marvel Knights 4 #28-30)

FOUR COLOR
Dell Publishing Co.: Sept?, 1939 - No. 1354, Apr-June, 1962
(Series I are all 68 pgs.)

NOTE: *Four Color only appears on issues #19-25, 1-99,101. Dell Publishing Co. filed these as Series I, #1-25, and Series II, #1-1354. Issues beginning with #710? were printed with and without ads on back cover. Issues without ads are worth more.*

SERIES I:

	GD 2.0	VG 4.0	FN 6.0	VF 8.0	VF/NM 9.0	NM- 9.2
1(nn)-Dick Tracy	1100	2200	3300	8360	15,930	23,500
2(nn)-Don Winslow of the Navy (#1) (Rare) (11/39?)	226	452	678	1446	2473	3500
3(nn)-Myra North (1/40)	103	206	309	659	1130	1600
4-Donald Duck by Al Taliaferro (1940)(Disney)(3/40?)	2100	4200	6300	15,750	28,875	42,000
(Prices vary widely on this book)						
5-Smilin' Jack (#1) (5/40?)	87	174	261	553	952	1350
6-Dick Tracy (Scarce)	265	530	795	1694	2897	4100
7-Gang Busters	60	120	180	381	653	925
8-Dick Tracy	139	278	417	883	1517	2150
9-Terry and the Pirates-r/Super #9-29	77	154	231	493	847	1200
10-Smilin' Jack	71	142	213	454	777	1100
11-Smitty (#1)	54	108	162	343	574	825
12-Little Orphan Annie; reprints strips from 12/19/37 to 6/4/38	65	130	195	416	708	1000
13-Walt Disney's Reluctant Dragon('41)-Contains 2 pgs. of photos from film; 2 pg. foreword to Fantasia by Leopold Stokowski; Donald Duck, Goofy, Baby Weems & Mickey Mouse (as the Sorcerer's Apprentice) app. (Disney)	226	452	678	1446	2473	3500
14-Moon Mullins (#1)	48	96	144	302	514	725
15-Tillie the Toiler (#1)	57	114	171	362	619	875
16-Mickey Mouse (#1) (Disney) by Gottfredson	1300	2600	3900	17,000	-	-
17-Walt Disney's Dumbo, the Flying Elephant (#1)(1941)-Mickey Mouse, Donald Duck, & Pluto app. (Disney)	274	548	822	1740	2995	4250
18-Jiggs and Maggie (#1)(1936-38-r)	53	106	159	334	567	800
19-Barney Google and Snuffy Smith (#1)-(1st issue with Four Color on the cover)	52	104	156	323	549	775
20-Tiny Tim	41	82	123	250	418	585
21-Dick Tracy	94	188	282	597	1024	1450
22-Don Winslow	52	104	156	328	552	775
23-Gang Busters	47	94	141	296	498	700
24-Captain Easy	54	108	162	346	591	835
25-Popeye (1942)	107	214	321	680	1165	1650

SERIES II:

	GD 2.0	VG 4.0	FN 6.0	VF 8.0	VF/NM 9.0	NM- 9.2
1-Little Joe (1942)	64	128	192	512	1156	1800
2-Harold Teen	32	64	96	230	515	800
3-Alley Oop (#1)	47	94	141	367	821	1275
4-Smilin' Jack	38	76	114	285	641	1000
5-Raggedy Ann and Andy (#1)	46	92	138	359	805	1250
6-Smitty	23	46	69	161	356	550
7-Smokey Stover (#1)	25	50	75	175	388	600
8-Tillie the Toiler	24	48	72	170	378	585
9-Donald Duck Finds Pirate Gold, by Carl Barks & Jack Hannah (Disney) (© 8/17/42)	1000	2000	3000	7600	13,800	20,000
10-Flash Gordon by Alex Raymond; reprinted from "The Ice Kingdom"	86	172	258	688	1544	2400
11-Wash Tubbs	26	52	78	182	404	625
12-Walt Disney's Bambi (#1)	46	92	138	340	770	1200
13-Mr. District Attorney (#1)-See The Funnies #35 for 1st app.	27	54	81	189	420	650
14-Smilin' Jack	30	60	90	216	483	750
15-Felix the Cat (#1)	77	154	231	616	1383	2150
16-Porky Pig (#1)(1942)- "Secret of the Haunted House"	93	186	279	744	1672	2600
17-Popeye	46	92	138	340	770	1200
18-Little Orphan Annie's Junior Commandos; Flag-c; reprints strips from 6/14/42 to 11/21/42	35	70	105	252	564	875
19-Walt Disney's Thumper Meets the Seven Dwarfs (Disney); reprinted in Silly Symphonies	44	88	132	326	738	1150
20-Barney Baxter	24	48	72	170	378	585
21-Oswald the Rabbit (#1)(1943)	38	76	114	285	641	1000
22-Tillie the Toiler	17	34	51	119	265	410
23-Raggedy Ann and Andy	32	64	96	230	515	800
24-Gang Busters	27	54	81	194	435	675
25-Andy Panda (#1) (Walter Lantz)	50	100	150	390	870	1350
26-Popeye	46	92	138	340	770	1200
27-Walt Disney's Mickey Mouse and the Seven Colored Terror	71	142	213	568	1284	2000
28-Wash Tubbs	17	34	51	117	259	400
29-Donald Duck and the Mummy's Ring, by Carl Barks (Disney) (9/43)	800	1600	2400	5840	10,320	14,800
30-Bambi's Children (1943)-Disney	40	80	120	296	673	1050
31-Moon Mullins	15	30	45	105	233	360
32-Smitty	15	30	45	103	227	350
33-Bugs Bunny "Public Nuisance #1"	111	222	333	888	1994	3100
34-Dick Tracy	38	76	114	282	634	985
35-Smokey Stover	15	30	45	103	227	350
36-Smilin' Jack	21	42	63	147	324	500
37-Bringing Up Father	18	36	54	124	275	425
38-Roy Rogers (#1, © 4/44)-1st western comic with photo-c (see Movie Comics #3)	152	304	456	1254	2827	4400
39-Oswald the Rabbit (1944)	27	54	81	189	420	650
40-Barney Google and Snuffy Smith	20	40	60	135	300	465
41-Mother Goose and Nursery Rhyme Comics (#1)-All by Walt Kelly	22	44	66	154	340	525
42-Tiny Tim (1934-r)	16	32	48	110	243	375
43-Popeye (1938-'42-r)	30	60	90	216	483	750
44-Terry and the Pirates (1938-r)	31	62	93	223	499	775
45-Raggedy Ann	25	50	75	175	388	600
46-Felix the Cat and the Haunted Castle	39	78	117	289	657	1025
47-Gene Autry (copyright 6/16/44)	35	70	105	252	564	875
48-Porky Pig of the Mounties by Carl Barks (7/44)	93	186	279	744	1672	2600
49-Snow White and the Seven Dwarfs (Disney)	46	92	138	368	834	1300
50-Fairy Tale Parade-Walt Kelly art (1944)	21	42	63	147	324	500
51-Bugs Bunny Finds the Lost Treasure	36	72	108	259	580	900
52-Little Orphan Annie; reprints strips from 6/18/38 to 11/19/38	24	48	72	170	378	585
53-Wash Tubbs	13	26	39	89	195	300
54-Andy Panda	25	50	75	175	388	600
55-Tillie the Toiler	13	26	39	86	188	290
56-Dick Tracy	34	68	102	247	554	860
57-Gene Autry	30	60	90	216	483	750
58-Smilin' Jack	21	42	63	147	324	500
59-Mother Goose and Nursery Rhyme Comics-Kelly-c/a	18	36	54	121	268	415
60-Tiny Folks Funnies	14	28	42	97	214	330
61-Santa Claus Funnies(11/44)-Kelly art	21	42	63	150	330	510
62-Donald Duck in Frozen Gold, by Carl Barks (Disney) (1/45)	228	456	684	1881	4241	6600
63-Roy Rogers; color photo-all 4 covers	38	76	114	285	641	1000
64-Smokey Stover	12	24	36	82	179	275
65-Smitty	12	24	36	84	185	285
66-Gene Autry	30	60	90	216	483	750
67-Oswald the Rabbit	16	32	48	110	243	375
68-Mother Goose and Nursery Rhyme Comics, by Walt Kelly	18	36	54	121	268	415
69-Fairy Tale Parade, by Walt Kelly	21	42	63	147	324	500
70-Popeye and Wimpy	22	44	66	154	340	525
71-Walt Disney's Three Caballeros, by Walt Kelly (© 4/45)-(Disney)	60	120	180	480	1078	1675
72-Raggedy Ann	20	40	60	141	313	485
73-The Gumps (#1)	11	22	33	76	163	250
74-Marge's Little Lulu (#1)	179	358	537	1477	3339	5200
75-Gene Autry and the Wildcat	23	46	69	164	362	560
76-Little Orphan Annie; reprints strips from 2/28/40 to 6/24/40	19	38	57	133	297	460
77-Felix the Cat	36	72	108	259	580	900
78-Porky Pig and the Bandit Twins	26	52	78	182	404	625
79-Walt Disney's Mickey Mouse in The Riddle of the Red Hat by Carl Barks (8/45)	89	178	267	712	1606	2500

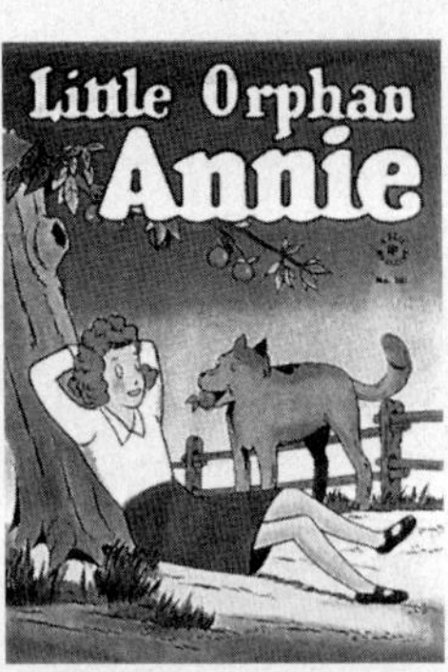

Four Color Comics #107 © NYNS

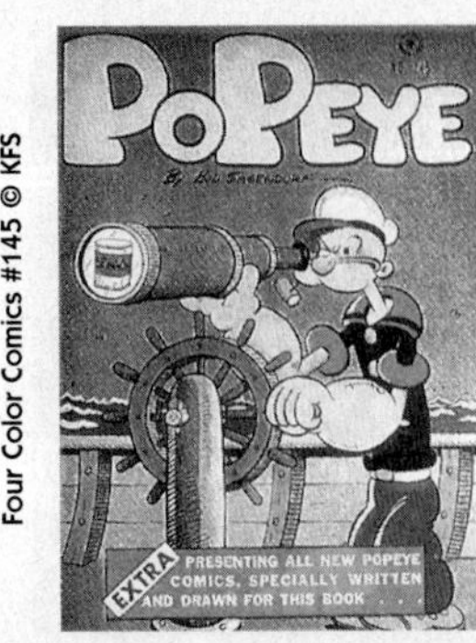

Four Color Comics #145 © KFS

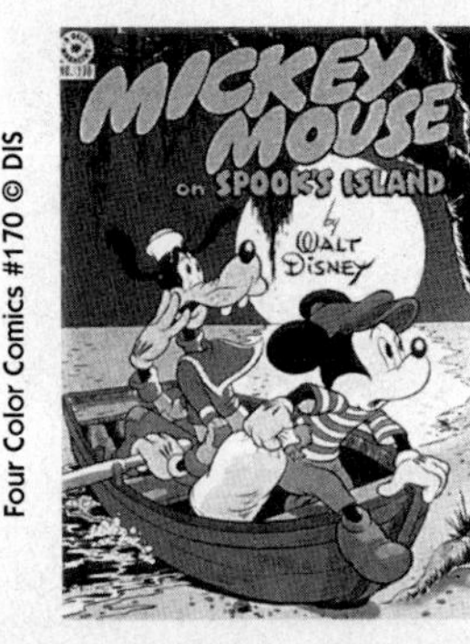

Four Color Comics #170 © DIS

	GD 2.0	VG 4.0	FN 6.0	VF 8.0	VF/NM 9.0	NM- 9.2
80-Smilin' Jack	13	26	39	89	195	300
81-Moon Mullins	10	20	30	66	138	210
82-Lone Ranger	38	76	114	281	628	975
83-Gene Autry in Outlaw Trail	23	46	69	164	362	560
84-Flash Gordon by Alex Raymond-Reprints from "The Fiery Desert"	42	84	126	311	698	1085
85-Andy Panda and the Mad Dog Mystery	15	30	45	103	227	350
86-Roy Rogers; photo-c	28	56	84	202	451	700
87-Fairy Tale Parade by Walt Kelly; Dan Noonan-c	21	42	63	147	324	500
88-Bugs Bunny's Great Adventure (Sci/fi)	23	46	69	156	348	540
89-Tillie the Toiler	13	26	39	86	188	290
90-Christmas with Mother Goose by Walt Kelly (11/45)	15	30	45	103	227	350
91-Santa Claus Funnies by Walt Kelly (11/45)	16	32	48	110	243	375
92-Walt Disney's The Wonderful Adventures Of Pinocchio (1945); Donald Duck by Kelly, 16 pgs. (Disney)	47	94	141	365	820	1275
93-Gene Autry in The Bandit of Black Rock	19	38	57	133	297	460
94-Winnie Winkle (1945)	12	24	36	79	170	260
95-Roy Rogers Comics; photo-c	28	56	84	202	451	700
96-Dick Tracy	23	46	69	161	356	550
97-Marge's Little Lulu (1946)	68	136	204	544	1222	1900
98-Lone Ranger, The	27	54	81	194	435	675
99-Smitty	10	20	30	66	138	210
100-Gene Autry Comics; 1st Gene Autry photo-c	22	44	66	155	345	535
101-Terry and the Pirates	20	40	60	135	300	465

NOTE: *No. 101 is last issue to carry "Four Color" logo on cover; all issues beginning with No. 100 are marked "...O. S." (One Shot) which can be found in the bottom left-hand panel on the first page; the numbers following "O. S." relate to the year/month issued.*

	GD 2.0	VG 4.0	FN 6.0	VF 8.0	VF/NM 9.0	NM- 9.2
102-Oswald the Rabbit-Walt Kelly art, 1 pg.	13	26	39	91	201	310
103-Easter with Mother Goose by Walt Kelly	18	36	54	124	275	425
104-Fairy Tale Parade by Walt Kelly	16	32	48	112	249	385
105-Albert the Alligator and Pogo Possum (#1) by Kelly (4/46)	54	108	162	432	966	1500
106-Tillie the Toiler (5/46)	10	20	30	64	132	200
107-Little Orphan Annie; reprints strips from 11/16/42 to 3/24/43	17	34	51	119	265	410
108-Donald Duck in The Terror of the River, by Carl Barks (Disney) (© 4/16/46)	148	296	444	1221	2761	4300
109-Roy Rogers Comics; photo-c	21	42	63	147	324	500
110-Marge's Little Lulu	41	82	123	303	689	1075
111-Captain Easy	12	24	36	82	179	275
112-Porky Pig's Adventure in Gopher Gulch	15	30	45	105	233	360
113-Popeye; all new Popeye stories begin	13	26	39	91	201	310
114-Fairy Tale Parade by Walt Kelly	16	32	48	112	249	385
115-Marge's Little Lulu	40	80	120	296	673	1050
116-Mickey Mouse and the House of Many Mysteries (Disney)	27	54	81	184	410	635
117-Roy Rogers Comics; photo-c	17	34	51	117	259	400
118-Lone Ranger, The	27	54	81	194	435	675
119-Felix the Cat; all new Felix stories begin	32	64	96	230	515	800
120-Marge's Little Lulu	35	70	105	252	564	875
121-Fairy Tale Parade-(not Kelly)	10	20	30	69	147	225
122-Henry (#1) (10/46)	15	30	45	103	227	350
123-Bugs Bunny's Dangerous Venture	15	30	45	105	233	360
124-Roy Rogers Comics; photo-c	17	34	51	117	259	400
125-Lone Ranger, The	19	38	57	131	291	450
126-Christmas with Mother Goose by Walt Kelly (1946)	11	22	33	76	163	250
127-Popeye	13	26	39	91	201	310
128-Santa Claus Funnies- "Santa & the Angel" by Gollub; "A Mouse in the House" by Kelly	13	26	39	91	201	310
129-Walt Disney's Uncle Remus and His Tales of Brer Rabbit (#1) (1946)-Adapted from Disney movie "Song of the South"	23	46	69	164	362	560
130-Andy Panda (Walter Lantz)	10	20	30	70	150	230
131-Marge's Little Lulu	35	70	105	252	564	875
132-Tillie the Toiler (1947)	10	20	30	64	132	200
133-Dick Tracy	18	36	54	124	275	425
134-Tarzan and the Devil Ogre; Marsh-c/a	56	112	168	448	999	1550
135-Felix the Cat	21	42	63	147	324	500
136-Lone Ranger, The	19	38	57	131	291	450
137-Roy Rogers Comics; photo-c	17	34	51	117	259	400
138-Smitty	9	18	27	59	117	175
139-Marge's Little Lulu (1947)	33	66	99	238	532	825
140-Easter with Mother Goose by Walt Kelly	14	28	42	94	207	320

	GD 2.0	VG 4.0	FN 6.0	VF 8.0	VF/NM 9.0	NM- 9.2
141-Mickey Mouse and the Submarine Pirates (Disney)	22	44	66	155	345	535
142-Bugs Bunny and the Haunted Mountain	15	30	45	105	233	360
143-Oswald the Rabbit & the Prehistoric Egg	9	18	27	59	117	175
144-Roy Rogers Comics (1947)-Photo-c	17	34	51	117	259	400
145-Popeye	13	26	39	91	201	310
146-Marge's Little Lulu	33	66	99	238	532	825
147-Donald Duck in Volcano Valley, by Carl Barks (Disney) (5/47)	104	208	312	832	1866	2900
148-Albert the Alligator and Pogo Possum by Walt Kelly (5/47)	38	76	114	285	641	1000
149-Smilin' Jack	9	18	27	62	126	190
150-Tillie the Toiler (6/47)	9	18	27	60	120	180
151-Lone Ranger, The	16	32	48	112	249	385
152-Little Orphan Annie; reprints strips from 1/2/44 to 5/6/44	12	24	36	79	170	260
153-Roy Rogers Comics; photo-c	15	30	45	105	233	360
154-Walter Lantz Andy Panda	10	20	30	70	150	230
155-Henry (7/47)	10	20	30	67	141	215
156-Porky Pig and the Phantom	11	22	33	75	160	245
157-Mickey Mouse & the Beanstalk (Disney)	22	44	66	155	345	535
158-Marge's Little Lulu	33	66	99	238	532	825
159-Donald Duck in the Ghost of the Grotto, by Carl Barks (Disney) (8/47)	89	178	267	712	1606	2500
160-Roy Rogers Comics; photo-c	15	30	45	105	233	360
161-Tarzan and the Fires Of Tohr; Marsh-c/a	46	92	138	340	770	1200
162-Felix the Cat (9/47)	16	32	48	110	243	375
163-Dick Tracy	16	32	48	110	243	375
164-Bugs Bunny Finds the Frozen Kingdom	15	30	45	105	233	360
165-Marge's Little Lulu	33	66	99	238	532	825
166-Roy Rogers Comics (52 pgs.)-Photo-c	15	30	45	105	233	360
167-Lone Ranger, The	16	32	48	112	249	385
168-Popeye (10/47)	13	26	39	91	201	310
169-Woody Woodpecker (#1)- "Manhunter in the North"; drug use story	18	36	54	128	284	440
170-Mickey Mouse on Spook's Island (11/47)(Disney)-reprinted in Mickey Mouse #103	19	38	57	133	297	460
171-Charlie McCarthy (#1) and the Twenty Thieves	25	50	75	175	388	600
172-Christmas with Mother Goose by Walt Kelly (11/47)	11	22	33	76	163	250
173-Flash Gordon	21	42	63	147	324	500
174-Winnie Winkle	8	16	24	54	102	150
175-Santa Claus Funnies by Walt Kelly (1947)	13	26	39	91	201	310
176-Tillie the Toiler (12/47)	9	18	27	60	120	180
177-Roy Rogers Comics-(36 pgs.); Photo-c	15	30	45	100	220	340
178-Donald Duck "Christmas on Bear Mountain" by Carl Barks; 1st app. Uncle Scrooge (Disney)(12/47)	139	278	417	1112	2506	3900
179-Uncle Wiggily (#1)-Walt Kelly-c	14	28	42	94	207	320
180-Ozark Ike (#1)	10	20	30	69	147	225
181-Walt Disney's Mickey Mouse in Jungle Magic	19	38	57	133	297	460
182-Porky Pig in Never-Never Land (2/48)	11	22	33	75	160	245
183-Oswald the Rabbit (Lantz)	9	18	27	59	117	175
184-Tillie the Toiler	9	18	27	60	120	180
185-Easter with Mother Goose by Walt Kelly (1948)	12	24	36	84	185	285
186-Walt Disney's Bambi (4/48)-Reprinted as Movie Classic Bambi #3 (1956)	14	28	42	96	211	325
187-Bugs Bunny and the Dreadful Dragon	11	22	33	76	163	250
188-Woody Woodpecker (Lantz, 5/48)	11	22	33	73	157	240
189-Donald Duck in The Old Castle's Secret, by Carl Barks (Disney) (6/48)	86	172	258	688	1544	2400
190-Flash Gordon (6/48); bondage-c; "The Adventures of the Flying Saucers"; 5th Flying Saucer story- see The Spirit 9/28/47(1st), Shadow Comics V7#10 (2nd, 1/48),Captain Midnight #60 (3rd, 2/48) & Boy Commandos #26 (4th, 3-4/48)	25	50	75	175	388	600
191-Porky Pig to the Rescue	11	22	33	75	160	245
192-The Brownies (#1)-by Walt Kelly (7/48)	13	26	39	89	195	300
193-M.G.M. Presents Tom and Jerry (#1)(1948)	24	48	72	168	372	575
194-Mickey Mouse in The World Under the Sea (Disney)-Reprinted in Mickey Mouse #101	19	38	57	133	297	460
195-Tillie the Toiler	8	16	24	51	96	140
196-Charlie McCarthy in The Haunted Hide-Out; part photo-c	16	32	48	108	239	370
197-Spirit of the Border (#1) (Zane Grey) (1948)	11	22	33	73	157	240
198-Andy Panda	10	20	30	70	150	230

Four Color Comics #252 © DIS

Four Color Comics #260 © WB

Four Color Comics #293 © Oskar Lebeck

	GD 2.0	VG 4.0	FN 6.0	VF 8.0	VF/NM 9.0	NM- 9.2
199-Donald Duck in Sheriff of Bullet Valley, by Carl Barks; Barks draws himself on wanted poster, last page; used in Love & Death (Disney) (10/48)	86	172	258	688	1544	2400
200-Bugs Bunny, Super Sleuth (10/48)	11	22	33	76	163	250
201-Christmas with Mother Goose by W. Kelly	10	20	30	64	132	200
202-Woody Woodpecker	8	16	24	56	108	160
203-Donald Duck in the Golden Christmas Tree, by Carl Barks (Disney) (12/48)	61	122	183	488	1094	1700
204-Flash Gordon (12/48)	16	32	48	110	243	375
205-Santa Claus Funnies by Walt Kelly	12	24	36	82	179	275
206-Little Orphan Annie; reprints strips from 11/10/40 to 1/11/41	8	16	24	52	99	145
207-King of the Royal Mounted (#1) (12/48)	13	26	39	86	188	290
208-Brer Rabbit Does It Again (Disney) (1/49)	10	20	30	66	138	210
209-Harold Teen	6	12	18	40	73	105
210-Tippie and Cap Stubbs	7	14	21	44	82	120
211-Little Beaver (#1)	9	18	27	61	123	185
212-Dr. Bobbs	6	12	18	40	73	105
213-Tillie the Toiler	8	16	24	51	96	140
214-Mickey Mouse and His Sky Adventure (2/49)(Disney)-Reprinted in Mickey Mouse #105	15	30	45	105	233	360
215-Sparkle Plenty (Dick Tracy-r by Gould)	10	20	30	69	147	225
216-Andy Panda and the Police Pup (Lantz)	8	16	24	55	105	155
217-Bugs Bunny in Court Jester	11	22	33	76	163	250
218-Three Little Pigs and the Wonderful Magic Lamp (Disney) (3/49)(#1)	10	20	30	66	138	210
219-Swee'pea	9	18	27	57	111	165
220-Easter with Mother Goose by Walt Kelly	12	24	36	84	185	285
221-Uncle Wiggily-Walt Kelly cover in part	9	18	27	58	114	170
222-West of the Pecos (Zane Grey)	7	14	21	46	86	125
223-Donald Duck "Lost in the Andes" by Carl Barks (Disney-4/49) (square egg story)	79	158	237	632	1416	2200
224-Little Iodine (#1), by Hatlo (4/49)	12	24	36	81	176	270
225-Oswald the Rabbit (Lantz)	7	14	21	46	86	125
226-Porky Pig and Spoofy, the Spook	9	18	27	61	123	185
227-Seven Dwarfs (Disney)	10	20	30	64	132	200
228-Mark of Zorro, The (#1) (1949)	20	40	60	138	307	475
229-Smokey Stover	6	12	18	42	79	115
230-Sunset Pass (Zane Grey)	7	14	21	46	86	125
231-Mickey Mouse and the Rajah's Treasure (Disney)	15	30	45	105	233	360
232-Woody Woodpecker (Lantz, 6/49)	8	16	24	56	108	160
233-Bugs Bunny, Sleepwalking Sleuth	11	22	33	76	163	250
234-Dumbo in Sky Voyage (Disney)	13	26	39	89	195	300
235-Tiny Tim	6	12	18	41	76	110
236-Heritage of the Desert (Zane Grey) (1949)	7	14	21	46	86	125
237-Tillie the Toiler	8	16	24	51	96	140
238-Donald Duck in Voodoo Hoodoo, by Carl Barks (Disney) (8/49)	59	118	177	472	1061	1650
239-Adventure Bound (8/49)	6	12	18	37	66	95
240-Andy Panda (Lantz)	8	16	24	55	105	155
241-Porky Pig, Mighty Hunter	9	18	27	61	123	185
242-Tippie and Cap Stubbs	5	10	15	31	53	75
243-Thumper Follows His Nose (Disney)	11	22	33	72	154	235
244-The Brownies by Walt Kelly	10	20	30	64	132	200
245-Dick's Adventures (9/49)	6	12	18	37	66	95
246-Thunder Mountain (Zane Grey)	5	10	15	35	63	90
247-Flash Gordon	16	32	48	110	243	375
248-Mickey Mouse and the Black Sorcerer (Disney)	15	30	45	105	233	360
249-Woody Woodpecker in the "Globetrotter" (10/49)	8	16	24	56	108	160
250-Bugs Bunny in Diamond Daze; used in **SOTI**, pg. 309	12	24	36	79	170	260
251-Hubert at Camp Moonbeam	9	18	27	61	123	185
252-Pinocchio (Disney)-not by Kelly; origin	11	22	33	72	154	235
253-Christmas with Mother Goose by W. Kelly	10	20	30	64	132	200
254-Santa Claus Funnies by Walt Kelly; Pogo & Albert story by Kelly (11/49)	12	24	36	82	179	275
255-The Ranger (Zane Grey) (1949)	5	10	15	35	63	90
256-Donald Duck in "Luck of the North" by Carl Barks (Disney) (12/49)-Shows #257 on inside	50	100	150	390	870	1350
257-Little Iodine	8	16	24	55	105	155
258-Andy Panda and the Balloon Race (Lantz)	8	16	24	55	105	155
259-Santa and the Angel (Gollub art-condensed from #128) & Santa at the Zoo (12/49) -two books in one	6	12	18	41	76	110

	GD 2.0	VG 4.0	FN 6.0	VF 8.0	VF/NM 9.0	NM- 9.2
260-Porky Pig, Hero of the Wild West (12/49)	9	18	27	61	123	185
261-Mickey Mouse and the Missing Key (Disney)	15	30	45	105	233	360
262-Raggedy Ann and Andy	9	18	27	57	111	165
263-Donald Duck in "Land of the Totem Poles" by Carl Barks (Disney) (2/50)-Has two Barks stories	47	94	141	367	821	1275
264-Woody Woodpecker in the Magic Lantern (Lantz)	8	16	24	56	108	160
265-King of the Royal Mounted (Zane Grey)	9	18	27	58	114	170
266-Bugs Bunny on the "Isle of Hercules" (2/50)-Reprinted in Best of Bugs Bunny #1	9	18	27	61	123	185
267-Little Beaver; Harmon-c/a	6	12	18	38	69	100
268-Mickey Mouse's Surprise Visitor (1950)(Disney)	14	28	42	98	217	335
269-Johnny Mack Brown (#1)-Photo-c	18	36	54	124	275	425
270-Drift Fence (Zane Grey) (3/50)	5	10	15	35	63	90
271-Porky Pig in Phantom of the Plains	9	18	27	61	123	185
272-Cinderella (Disney) (4/50)	12	24	36	82	179	275
273-Oswald the Rabbit (Lantz)	7	14	21	46	86	125
274-Bugs Bunny, Hare-brained Reporter	9	18	27	61	123	185
275-Donald Duck in "Ancient Persia" by Carl Barks (Disney) (5/50)	46	92	138	359	805	1250
276-Uncle Wiggily	7	14	21	49	92	135
277-Porky Pig in Desert Adventure (5/50)	9	18	27	61	123	185
278-(Wild) Bill Elliott Comics (#1)-Photo-c	12	24	36	79	170	260
279-Mickey Mouse and Pluto Battle the Giant Ants (Disney); reprinted in Mickey Mouse #102 & 245	12	24	36	79	170	260
280-Andy Panda in The Isle Of Mechanical Men (Lantz)	8	16	24	55	105	155
281-Bugs Bunny in The Great Circus Mystery	9	18	27	61	123	185
282-Donald Duck and the Pixilated Parrot by Carl Barks (Disney) (© 5/23/50)	46	92	138	359	805	1250
283-King of the Royal Mounted (7/50)	9	18	27	58	114	170
284-Porky Pig in The Kingdom of Nowhere	9	18	27	61	123	185
285-Bozo the Clown & His Minikin Circus (#1) (TV)	17	34	51	117	259	400
286-Mickey Mouse in The Uninvited Guest (Disney	12	24	36	79	170	260
287-Gene Autry's Champion in The Ghost Of Black Mountain; photo-c	11	22	33	76	163	250
288-Woody Woodpecker in Klondike Gold (Lantz)	8	16	24	56	108	160
289-Bugs Bunny in "Indian Trouble"	9	18	27	61	123	185
290-The Chief (#1) (8/50)	8	16	24	51	96	140
291-Donald Duck in "The Magic Hourglass" by Carl Barks (Disney) (9/50)	46	92	138	359	805	1250
292-The Cisco Kid Comics (#1)	21	42	63	147	324	500
293-The Brownies-Kelly-c/a	10	20	30	64	132	200
294-Little Beaver	6	12	18	38	69	100
295-Porky Pig in President Porky (9/50)	9	18	27	61	123	185
296-Mickey Mouse in Private Eye for Hire (Disney)	12	24	36	79	170	260
297-Andy Panda in The Haunted Inn (Lantz, 10/50)	8	16	24	55	105	155
298-Bugs Bunny in Sheik for a Day	9	18	27	61	123	185
299-Buck Jones & the Iron Horse Trail (#1)	12	24	36	83	182	280
300-Donald Duck in "Big-Top Bedlam" by Carl Barks (Disney) (11/50)	46	92	138	359	805	1250
301-The Mysterious Rider (Zane Grey)	5	10	15	35	63	90
302-Santa Claus Funnies (11/50)	8	16	24	51	96	140
303-Porky Pig in The Land of the Monstrous Flies	8	16	24	51	96	140
304-Mickey Mouse in Tom-Tom Island (Disney) (12/50)	11	22	33	72	154	235
305-Woody Woodpecker (Lantz)	6	12	18	41	76	110
306-Raggedy Ann	7	14	21	46	86	125
307-Bugs Bunny in Lumber Jack Rabbit	8	16	24	55	105	155
308-Donald Duck in "Dangerous Disguise" by Carl Barks (Disney) (1/51)	45	90	135	333	754	1175
309-Betty Betz' Dollface and Her Gang (1951)	6	12	18	38	69	100
310-King of the Royal Mounted (1/51)	7	14	21	46	86	125
311-Porky Pig in Midget Horses of Hidden Valley	8	16	24	51	96	140
312-Tonto (#1)	11	22	33	73	157	240
313-Mickey Mouse in The Mystery of the Double-Cross Ranch (#1) (Disney) (2/51)	11	22	33	72	154	235

Note: Beginning with the above comic in 1951 Dell/Western began adding #1 in small print on the covers of several long running titles with the evident intention of switching these titles to their own monthly numbers, but when the conversions were made, there was no connection. It is thought that the post office may have stepped in and decreed the sequences should commence as though the first four colors printed had each begun with number one, or the first issues sold by subscription. Since the regular series' numbers don't correctly match to the numbers of earlier issues published, it's not known whether or not the numbering was in error.

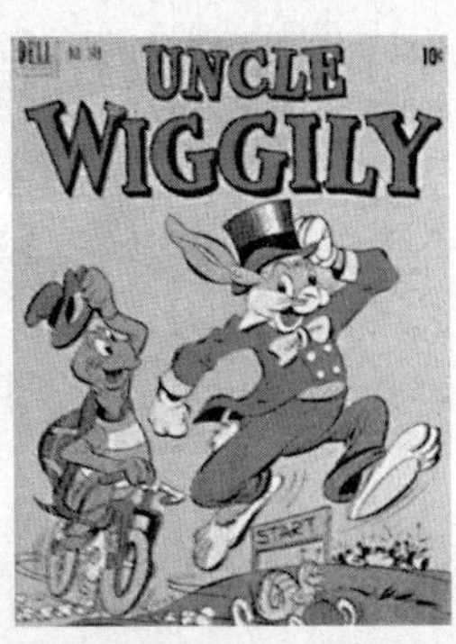

Four Color Comics #349 © HR Garis

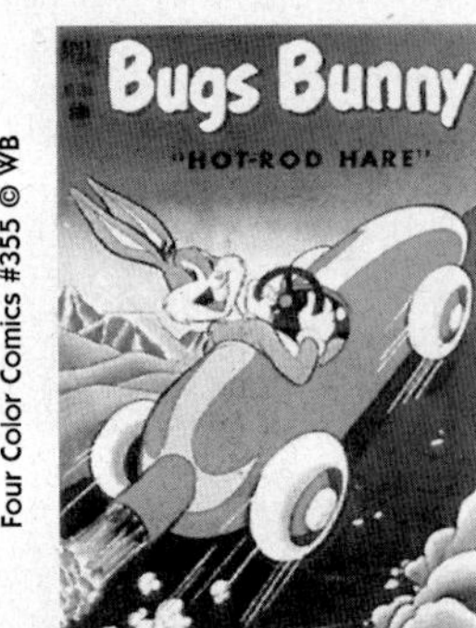

Four Color Comics #355 © WB

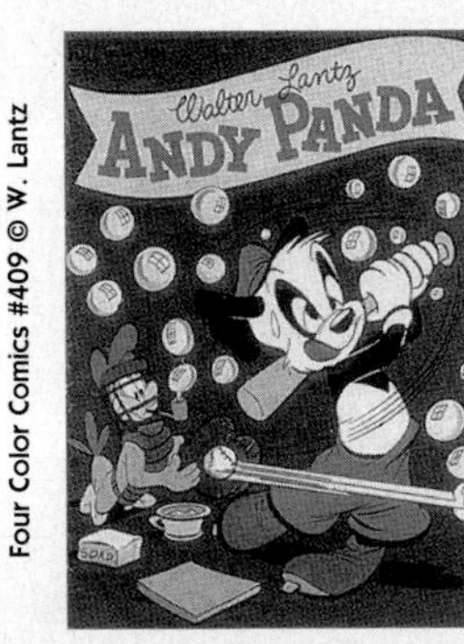

Four Color Comics #409 © W. Lantz

	GD 2.0	VG 4.0	FN 6.0	VF 8.0	VF/NM 9.0	NM- 9.2
314-Ambush (Zane Grey)	5	10	15	35	63	90
315-Oswald the Rabbit (Lantz)	6	12	18	40	73	105
316-Rex Allen (#1)-Photo-c; Marsh-a	13	26	39	86	188	290
317-Bugs Bunny in Hair Today Gone Tomorrow (#1)	8	16	24	55	105	155
318-Donald Duck in "No Such Varmint" by Carl Barks (#1)-Indicia shows #317 (Disney, © 1/23/51)	45	90	135	333	754	1175
319-Gene Autry's Champion; painted-c	6	12	18	41	76	110
320-Uncle Wiggily (#1)	7	14	21	49	92	135
321-Little Scouts (#1) (3/51)	6	12	18	37	66	95
322-Porky Pig in Roaring Rockets (#1 on-c)	8	16	24	51	96	140
323-Susie Q. Smith (#1) (3/51)	6	12	18	37	66	95
324-I Met a Handsome Cowboy (3/51)	7	14	21	49	92	135
325-Mickey Mouse in The Haunted Castle (#2) (Disney) (4/51)	11	22	33	72	154	235
326-Andy Panda (#1) (Lantz)	6	12	18	41	76	110
327-Bugs Bunny and the Rajah's Treasure (#2)	8	16	24	55	105	155
328-Donald Duck in Old California (#2) by Carl Barks-Peyote drug use issue (Disney) (5/51)	44	88	132	326	738	1150
329-Roy Roger's Trigger (#1)(5/51)-Painted-c	14	28	42	97	214	330
330-Porky Pig Meets the Bristled Bruiser (#2)	8	16	24	51	96	140
331-Alice in Wonderland (Disney) (1951)	15	30	45	103	227	350
332-Little Beaver	6	12	18	38	69	100
333-Wilderness Trek (Zane Grey) (5/51)	5	10	15	35	63	90
334-Mickey Mouse and Yukon Gold (Disney) (6/51)	11	22	33	72	154	235
335-Francis the Famous Talking Mule (#1, 6/51)-1st Dell non animated movie comic (all issues based on movie)	10	20	30	68	144	220
336-Woody Woodpecker (Lantz)	6	12	18	41	76	110
337-The Brownies-not by Walt Kelly	6	12	18	38	69	100
338-Bugs Bunny and the Rocking Horse Thieves	8	16	24	55	105	155
339-Donald Duck and the Magic Fountain-not by Carl Barks (Disney) (7-8/51)	32	64	96	230	515	800
340-King of the Royal Mounted (7/51)	7	14	21	46	86	125
341-Unbirthday Party with Alice in Wonderland (Disney) (7/51)	15	30	45	103	227	350
342-Porky Pig the Lucky Peppermint Mine; r/in Porky Pig #3	6	12	18	40	73	105
343-Mickey Mouse in The Ruby Eye of Homar-Guy-Am (Disney)-Reprinted in Mickey Mouse #104	9	18	27	62	126	190
344-Sergeant Preston from Challenge of The Yukon (#1) (TV)	12	24	36	81	176	270
345-Andy Panda in Scotland Yard (8-10/51) (Lantz)	6	12	18	41	76	110
346-Hideout (Zane Grey)	5	10	15	35	63	90
347-Bugs Bunny the Frigid Hare (8-9/51)	8	16	24	55	105	155
348-Donald Duck "The Crocodile Collector"; Barks-c only (Disney) (9-10/51)	23	46	69	161	356	550
349-Uncle Wiggily	6	12	18	41	76	110
350-Woody Woodpecker (Lantz)	6	12	18	41	76	110
351-Porky Pig & the Grand Canyon Giant (9-10/51)	6	12	18	40	73	105
352-Mickey Mouse in The Mystery of Painted Valley (Disney)	9	18	27	62	126	190
353-Duck Album (#1)-Barks-c (Disney)	11	22	33	76	163	250
354-Raggedy Ann & Andy	7	14	21	46	86	125
355-Bugs Bunny Hot-Rod Hare	8	16	24	55	105	155
356-Donald Duck in "Rags to Riches"; Barks-c only	23	46	69	161	356	550
357-Comeback (Zane Grey)	5	10	15	33	57	80
358-Andy Panda (Lantz) (11-1/52)	6	12	18	41	76	110
359-Frosty the Snowman (#1)	10	20	30	66	138	210
360-Porky Pig in Tree of Fortune (11-12/51)	6	12	18	40	73	105
361-Santa Claus Funnies	8	16	24	51	96	140
362-Mickey Mouse and the Smuggled Diamonds (Disney)	9	18	27	62	126	190
363-King of the Royal Mounted	6	12	18	40	73	105
364-Woody Woodpecker (Lantz)	6	12	18	37	66	95
365-The Brownies-not by Kelly	6	12	18	38	69	100
366-Bugs Bunny Uncle Buckskin Comes to Town (12-1/52)	8	16	24	55	105	155
367-Donald Duck in "A Christmas for Shacktown" by Carl Barks (Disney) (1-2/52)	36	72	108	259	580	900
368-Bob Clampett's Beany and Cecil (#1)	22	44	66	154	340	525
369-The Lone Ranger's Famous Horse Hi-Yo Silver (#1); Silver's origin	10	20	30	70	150	230
370-Porky Pig in Trouble in the Big Trees	6	12	18	40	73	105
371-Mickey Mouse in The Inca Idol Case (1952) (Disney)	9	18	27	62	126	190

	GD 2.0	VG 4.0	FN 6.0	VF 8.0	VF/NM 9.0	NM- 9.2
372-Riders of the Purple Sage (Zane Grey)	5	10	15	33	57	80
373-Sergeant Preston (TV)	8	16	24	54	102	150
374-Woody Woodpecker (Lantz)	6	12	18	37	66	95
375-John Carter of Mars (E. R. Burroughs)-Jesse Marsh-a; origin	30	60	90	216	483	750
376-Bugs Bunny, "The Magic Sneeze"	8	16	24	55	105	155
377-Susie Q. Smith	5	10	15	30	50	70
378-Tom Corbett, Space Cadet (#1) (TV)-McWilliams-a	16	32	48	112	249	385
379-Donald Duck in "Southern Hospitality"; 2nd Uncle Scrooge-c; not by Barks (Disney)	32	64	96	230	515	800
380-Raggedy Ann & Andy	7	14	21	46	86	125
381-Marge's Tubby (#1)	18	36	54	126	281	435
382-Snow White and the Seven Dwarfs (Disney)-origin; partial reprint of Four Color #49 (Movie)	10	20	30	69	147	225
383-Andy Panda (Lantz)	5	10	15	35	63	90
384-King of the Royal Mounted (3/52)(Zane Grey)	6	12	18	40	73	105
385-Porky Pig in The Isle of Missing Ships (3-4/52)	6	12	18	40	73	105
386-Uncle Scrooge (#1)-by Carl Barks (Disney) in "Only a Poor Old Man" (3/52)	179	358	537	1477	3839	6200
387-Mickey Mouse in High Tibet (Disney) (4-5/52)	9	18	27	62	126	190
388-Oswald the Rabbit (Lantz)	6	12	18	40	73	105
389-Andy Hardy Comics (#1)	6	12	18	37	66	95
390-Woody Woodpecker (Lantz)	6	12	18	37	66	95
391-Uncle Wiggily	6	12	18	41	76	110
392-Hi-Yo Silver	6	12	18	42	79	115
393-Bugs Bunny	8	16	24	55	105	155
394-Donald Duck in Malayalaya-Barks-c only (Disney)	23	46	69	161	356	550
395-Forlorn River(Zane Grey)-First Nevada (5/52)	5	10	15	33	57	80
396-Tales of the Texas Rangers(#1)(TV)-Photo-c	10	20	30	67	141	215
397-Sergeant Preston of the Yukon (TV) (5/52)	8	16	24	54	102	150
398-The Brownies-not by Kelly	6	12	18	38	69	100
399-Porky Pig in The Lost Gold Mine	6	12	18	40	73	105
400-Tom Corbett, Space Cadet (TV)-McWilliams-c/a	10	20	30	64	132	200
401-Mickey Mouse and Goofy's Mechanical Wizard (Disney) (6-7/52)	8	16	24	56	108	160
402-Mary Jane and Sniffles	8	16	24	54	102	150
403-Li'l Bad Wolf (Disney) (6/52)(#1)	8	16	24	52	99	145
404-The Range Rider (#1) (Flying A's...)(TV)-Photo-c	9	18	27	60	120	180
405-Woody Woodpecker (Lantz) (6-7/52)	6	12	18	37	66	95
406-Tweety and Sylvester (#1)	12	24	36	83	182	280
407-Bugs Bunny, Foreign-Legion Hare	7	14	21	48	89	130
408-Donald Duck and the Golden Helmet by Carl Barks (Disney) (7-8/52)	35	70	105	252	564	875
409-Andy Panda (7-9/52)	5	10	15	35	63	90
410-Porky Pig in The Water Wizard (7/52)	6	12	18	40	73	105
411-Mickey Mouse and the Old Sea Dog (Disney) (8-9/52)	8	16	24	56	108	160
412-Nevada (Zane Grey)	5	10	15	33	57	80
413-Robin Hood (Disney-Movie) (8/52)-Photo-c (1st Disney movie Four Color book)	9	18	27	60	120	180
414-Bob Clampett's Beany and Cecil (TV)	12	24	36	84	185	285
415-Rootie Kazootie (#1) (TV)	9	18	27	59	117	175
416-Woody Woodpecker (Lantz)	6	12	18	37	66	95
417-Double Trouble with Goober (#1) (8/52)	5	10	15	33	57	80
418-Rusty Riley, a Boy, a Horse, and a Dog (#1)-Frank Godwin-a (strip reprints) (8/52)	6	12	18	41	76	110
419-Sergeant Preston (TV)	8	16	24	54	102	150
420-Bugs Bunny in The Mysterious Buckaroo (8-9/52)	7	14	21	48	89	130
421-Tom Corbett, Space Cadet(TV)-McWilliams-a	10	20	30	64	132	200
422-Donald Duck and the Gilded Man, by Carl Barks (Disney) (9-10/52) (#423 on inside)	35	70	105	252	564	875
423-Rhubarb, Owner of the Brooklyn Ball Club (The Millionaire Cat) (#1)-Painted cover	7	14	21	44	82	120
424-Flash Gordon-Test Flight in Space (9/52)	11	22	33	76	163	250
425-Zorro, the Return of	11	22	33	72	154	235
426-Porky Pig in The Scalawag Leprechaun	6	12	18	40	73	105
427-Mickey Mouse and the Wonderful Whizzix (Disney) (10-11/52)-Reprinted in Mickey Mouse #100	8	16	24	56	108	160
428-Uncle Wiggily	5	10	15	34	63	90
429-Pluto in "Why Dogs Leave Home" (Disney) (10/52)(#1)	10	20	30	68	144	220
430-Marge's Tubby, the Shadow of a Man-Eater	11	22	33	73	157	240
431-Woody Woodpecker (10/52) (Lantz)	6	12	18	37	66	95

Four Color Comics #437 © ERB

Four Color Comics #521 © KFS

Four Color Comics #546 © DELL

	GD 2.0	VG 4.0	FN 6.0	VF 8.0	VF/NM 9.0	NM- 9.2
432-Bugs Bunny and the Rabbit Olympics	7	14	21	48	89	130
433-Wildfire (Zane Grey) (11-1/52-53)	5	10	15	33	57	80
434-Rin Tin Tin "In Dark Danger" (#1) (TV) (11/52)-Photo-c	14	28	42	97	214	330
435-Frosty the Snowman (11/52)	6	12	18	42	79	115
436-The Brownies-not by Kelly (11/52)	5	10	15	35	63	90
437-John Carter of Mars (E.R. Burroughs)-Marsh-a	16	32	48	112	249	385
438-Annie Oakley (#1) (TV)	13	26	39	89	195	300
439-Little Hiawatha (Disney) (12/52)j(#1)	7	14	21	46	86	125
440-Black Beauty (12/52)	5	10	15	34	60	85
441-Fearless Fagan	5	10	15	31	53	75
442-Peter Pan (Disney) (Movie)	10	20	30	67	141	215
443-Ben Bowie and His Mountain Men (#1)	9	18	27	61	123	185
444-Marge's Tubby	11	22	33	73	157	240
445-Charlie McCarthy	6	12	18	41	76	110
446-Captain Hook and Peter Pan (Disney)(Movie)(1/53)	9	18	27	59	117	175
447-Andy Hardy Comics	4	8	12	27	44	60
448-Bob Clampett's Beany and Cecil (TV)	12	24	36	84	185	285
449-Tappan's Burro (Zane Grey) (2-4/53)	5	10	15	33	57	80
450-Duck Album; Barks-c (Disney)	8	16	24	54	102	150
451-Rusty Riley-Frank Godwin-a (strip-r) (2/53)	5	10	15	30	50	70
452-Raggedy Ann & Andy (1953)	7	14	21	46	86	125
453-Susie Q. Smith (2/53)	5	10	15	30	50	70
454-Krazy Kat Comics; not by Herriman	6	12	18	37	66	95
455-Johnny Mack Brown Comics(3/53)-Photo-c	6	12	18	40	73	105
456-Uncle Scrooge Back to the Klondike (#2) by Barks (3/53) (Disney)	88	176	264	704	1802	2900
457-Daffy (#1)	12	24	36	81	176	270
458-Oswald the Rabbit (Lantz)	5	10	15	35	63	90
459-Rootie Kazootie (TV)	6	12	18	41	76	110
460-Buck Jones (4/53)	6	12	18	41	76	110
461-Marge's Tubby	10	20	30	68	144	220
462-Little Scouts	5	10	15	30	50	70
463-Petunia (4/53)	5	10	15	33	57	80
464-Bozo (4/53)	9	18	27	58	114	170
465-Francis the Famous Talking Mule	6	12	18	41	76	110
466-Rhubarb, the Millionaire Cat; painted-c	6	12	18	37	66	95
467-Desert Gold (Zane Grey) (5-7/53)	5	10	15	33	57	80
468-Goofy (#1) (Disney)	12	24	36	79	170	260
469-Beetle Bailey (#1) (5/53	13	26	39	86	188	290
470-Elmer Fudd	10	20	30	64	132	200
471-Double Trouble with Goober	4	8	12	27	44	60
472-Wild Bill Elliott (6/53)-Photo-c	5	10	15	35	63	90
473-Li'l Bad Wolf (Disney) (6/53)(#2)	5	10	15	34	60	85
474-Mary Jane and Sniffles	6	12	18	42	79	115
475-M.G.M.'s The Two Mouseketeers (#1)	9	18	27	57	111	165
476-Rin Tin Tin (TV)-Photo-c	9	18	27	57	111	165
477-Bob Clampett's Beany and Cecil (TV)	12	24	36	84	185	285
478-Charlie McCarthy	6	12	18	41	76	110
479-Queen of the West Dale Evans (#1)-Photo-c	16	32	48	110	243	375
480-Andy Hardy Comics	4	8	12	27	44	60
481-Annie Oakley And Tagg (TV)	9	18	27	59	117	175
482-Brownies-not by Kelly	5	10	15	35	63	90
483-Little Beaver (7/53)	5	10	15	34	60	85
484-River Feud (Zane Grey) (8-10/53)	5	10	15	33	57	80
485-The Little People-Walt Scott (#1)	8	16	24	51	96	140
486-Rusty Riley-Frank Godwin strip-r	5	10	15	30	50	70
487-Mowgli, the Jungle Book (Rudyard Kipling's)	6	12	18	42	79	115
488-John Carter of Mars (Burroughs)-Marsh-a; painted-c	16	32	48	112	249	385
489-Tweety and Sylvester	8	16	24	51	96	140
490-Jungle Jim (#1)	8	16	24	54	102	150
491-Silvertip (#1) (Max Brand)-Kinstler-a (8/53)	8	16	24	52	99	145
492-Duck Album (Disney)	7	14	21	46	86	125
493-Johnny Mack Brown; photo-c	6	12	18	40	73	105
494-The Little King (#1)	8	16	24	56	108	160
495-Uncle Scrooge (#3) (Disney)-by Carl Barks (9/53)	59	118	177	472	1186	1900
496-The Green Hornet; painted-c	24	48	72	168	372	575
497-Zorro (Sword of…)-Kinstler-a	11	22	33	76	163	250
498-Bugs Bunny's Album (9/53)	6	12	18	38	69	100
499-M.G.M.'s Spike and Tyke (#1) (9/53)	7	14	21	46	86	125
500-Buck Jones	6	12	18	41	76	110

	GD 2.0	VG 4.0	FN 6.0	VF 8.0	VF/NM 9.0	NM- 9.2
501-Francis the Famous Talking Mule	5	10	15	35	63	90
502-Rootie Kazootie (TV)	6	12	18	41	76	110
503-Uncle Wiggily (10/53)	5	10	15	34	63	90
504-Krazy Kat; not by Herriman	6	12	18	37	66	95
505-The Sword and the Rose (Disney) (10/53)(Movie)-Photo-c	8	16	24	52	99	145
506-The Little Scouts	5	10	15	30	50	70
507-Oswald the Rabbit (Lantz)	5	10	15	35	63	90
508-Bozo (10/53)	9	18	27	58	114	170
509-Pluto (Disney) (10/53)	6	12	18	42	79	115
510-Son of Black Beauty	5	10	15	31	53	75
511-Outlaw Trail (Zane Grey)-Kinstler-a	5	10	15	35	63	90
512-Flash Gordon (11/53)	9	18	27	60	120	180
513-Ben Bowie and His Mountain Men	5	10	15	34	60	85
514-Frosty the Snowman (11/53)	6	12	18	42	79	115
515-Andy Hardy	4	8	12	27	44	60
516-Double Trouble With Goober	4	8	12	27	44	60
517-Chip 'N' Dale (#1) (Disney)	11	22	33	73	157	240
518-Rivets (11/53)	5	10	15	30	50	70
519-Steve Canyon (#1)-Not by Milton Caniff	8	16	24	54	102	150
520-Wild Bill Elliott-Photo-c	5	10	15	35	63	90
521-Beetle Bailey (12/53)	7	14	21	49	92	135
522-The Brownies	5	10	15	35	63	90
523-Rin Tin Tin (TV)-Photo-c (12/53)	9	18	27	57	111	165
524-Tweety and Sylvester	8	16	24	51	96	140
525-Santa Claus Funnies	8	16	24	51	96	140
526-Napoleon	5	10	15	30	50	70
527-Charlie McCarthy	6	12	18	41	76	110
528-Queen of the West Dale Evans; photo-c	9	18	27	60	120	180
529-Little Beaver	5	10	15	34	60	85
530-Bob Clampett's Beany and Cecil (TV) (1/54)	12	24	36	84	185	285
531-Duck Album (Disney)	7	14	21	46	86	125
532-The Rustlers (Zane Grey) (2-4/54)	5	10	15	33	57	80
533-Raggedy Ann and Andy	7	14	21	46	86	125
534-Western Marshal (Ernest Haycox's)-Kinstler-a	6	12	18	38	69	100
535-I Love Lucy (#1) (TV) (2/54)-Photo-c	45	90	135	333	754	1175
536-Daffy (3/54)	7	14	21	49	92	135
537-Stormy, the Thoroughbred… (Disney-Movie) on top 2/3 of each page; Pluto story on bottom 1/3 of each page (2/54)	5	10	15	33	57	80
538-The Mask of Zorro; Kinstler-a	11	22	33	76	163	250
539-Ben and Me (Disney) (3/54)	5	10	15	30	50	70
540-Knights of the Round Table (3/54) (Movie)-Photo-c	6	12	18	41	76	110
541-Johnny Mack Brown; photo-c	6	12	18	40	73	105
542-Super Circus Featuring Mary Hartline (TV) (3/54)	7	14	21	46	86	125
543-Uncle Wiggily (3/54)	5	10	15	34	63	90
544-Rob Roy (Disney-Movie)-Manning-a; photo-c	7	14	21	49	92	135
545-The Wonderful Adventures of Pinocchio-Partial reprint of Four Color #92 (Disney-Movie)	8	16	24	51	96	140
546-Buck Jones	6	12	18	41	76	110
547-Francis the Famous Talking Mule	5	10	15	35	63	90
548-Krazy Kat; not by Herriman (4/54)	5	10	15	31	53	75
549-Oswald the Rabbit (Lantz)	5	10	15	35	63	90
550-The Little Scouts	5	10	15	30	50	70
551-Bozo (4/54)	9	18	27	58	114	170
552-Beetle Bailey	7	14	21	49	92	135
553-Susie Q. Smith	5	10	15	30	50	70
554-Rusty Riley (Frank Godwin strip-r)	5	10	15	30	50	70
555-Range War (Zane Grey)	5	10	15	33	57	80
556-Double Trouble With Goober (5/54)	4	8	12	27	44	60
557-Ben Bowie and His Mountain Men	5	10	15	34	60	85
558-Elmer Fudd (5/54)	6	12	18	38	69	100
559-I Love Lucy (#2) (TV)-Photo-c	27	54	81	189	420	650
560-Duck Album (Disney) (5/54)	7	14	21	46	86	125
561-Mr. Magoo (5/54)	9	18	27	58	114	170
562-Goofy (Disney)(#2)	7	14	21	46	86	125
563-Rhubarb, the Millionaire Cat (6/54)	6	12	18	37	66	95
564-Li'l Bad Wolf (Disney)(#3)	5	10	15	34	60	85
565-Jungle Jim	5	10	15	33	57	80
566-Son of Black Beauty	5	10	15	31	53	75
567-Prince Valiant (#1)-By Bob Fuje (Movie)-Photo-c	10	20	30	64	132	200
568-Gypsy Colt (Movie) (6/54)	5	10	15	35	63	90

Four Color Comics #590 © DIS

Four Color Comics #602 © Columbia

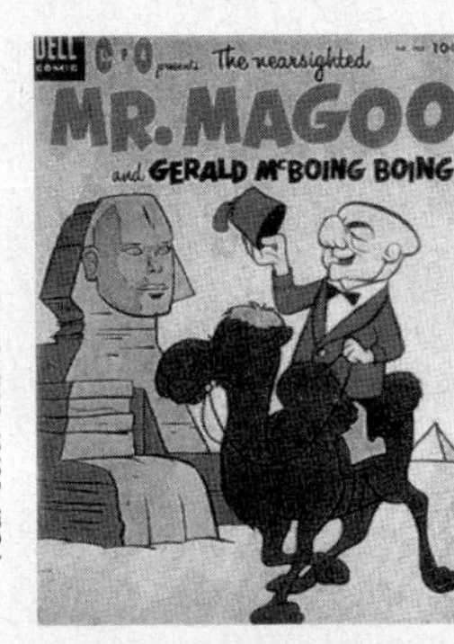

Four Color Comics #668 © DIS

	GD 2.0	VG 4.0	FN 6.0	VF 8.0	VF/NM 9.0	NM- 9.2
569-Priscilla's Pop	5	10	15	33	57	80
570-Bob Clampett's Beany and Cecil (TV)	12	24	36	84	185	285
571-Charlie McCarthy	6	12	18	41	76	110
572-Silvertip (Max Brand) (7/54); Kinstler-a	5	10	15	34	60	85
573-The Little People by Walt Scott	5	10	15	35	63	90
574-The Hand of Zorro; Kinstler-a	11	22	33	76	163	250
575-Annie Oakley and Tagg (TV)-Photo-c	9	18	27	59	117	175
576-Angel (#1) (8/54)	5	10	15	30	50	70
577-M.G.M.'s Spike and Tyke	5	10	15	35	63	90
578-Steve Canyon (8/54)	5	10	15	35	63	90
579-Francis the Famous Talking Mule	5	10	15	35	63	90
580-Six Gun Ranch (Luke Short-8/54)	5	10	15	33	57	80
581-Chip 'N' Dale (#2) (Disney)	6	12	18	42	79	115
582-Mowgli Jungle Book (Kipling) (8/54)	5	10	15	33	57	80
583-The Lost Wagon Train (Zane Grey)	5	10	15	33	57	80
584-Johnny Mack Brown-Photo-c	6	12	18	40	73	105
585-Bugs Bunny's Album	6	12	18	38	69	100
586-Duck Album (Disney)	7	14	21	46	86	125
587-The Little Scouts	5	10	15	30	50	70
588-King Richard and the Crusaders (Movie) (10/54) Matt Baker-a; photo-c	9	18	27	58	114	170
589-Buck Jones	6	12	18	41	76	110
590-Hansel and Gretel; partial photo-c	6	12	18	42	79	115
591-Western Marshal (Ernest Haycox's)-Kinstler-a	5	10	15	34	60	85
592-Super Circus (TV)	6	12	18	37	66	95
593-Oswald the Rabbit (Lantz)	5	10	15	35	63	90
594-Bozo (10/54)	9	18	27	58	114	170
595-Pluto (Disney)	6	12	18	37	66	95
596-Turok, Son of Stone (#1)	82	164	246	656	1478	2300
597-The Little King	5	10	15	34	60	85
598-Captain Davy Jones	6	12	18	37	66	95
599-Ben Bowie and His Mountain Men	5	10	15	34	60	85
600-Daisy Duck's Diary (#1) (Disney) (11/54)	8	16	24	51	96	140
601-Frosty the Snowman	6	12	18	42	79	115
602-Mr. Magoo and Gerald McBoing-Boing	9	18	27	58	114	170
603-M.G.M.'s The Two Mouseketeers	6	12	18	41	76	110
604-Shadow on the Trail (Zane Grey)	5	10	15	33	57	80
605-The Brownies-not by Kelly (12/54)	5	10	15	35	63	90
606-Sir Lancelot (not TV)	6	12	18	42	79	115
607-Santa Claus Funnies	8	16	24	51	96	140
608-Silvertip- "Valley of Vanishing Men" (Max Brand)-Kinstler-a	5	10	15	34	60	85
609-The Littlest Outlaw (Disney-Movie) (1/55)-Photo-c	6	12	18	41	76	110
610-Drum Beat (Movie); Alan Ladd photo-c	8	16	24	55	105	155
611-Duck Album (Disney)	7	14	21	46	86	125
612-Little Beaver (1/55)	5	10	15	33	57	80
613-Western Marshal (Ernest Haycox's) (2/55)-Kinstler-a	5	10	15	34	60	85
614-20,000 Leagues Under the Sea (Disney) (Movie) (2/55)-Painted-c	8	16	24	56	108	160
615-Daffy	7	14	21	49	92	135
616-To the Last Man (Zane Grey)	5	10	15	33	57	80
617-The Quest of Zorro	11	22	33	72	154	235
618-Johnny Mack Brown; photo-c	6	12	18	40	73	105
619-Krazy Kat; not by Herriman	5	10	15	31	53	75
620-Mowgli Jungle Book (Kipling)	5	10	15	33	57	80
621-Francis the Famous Talking Mule (4/55)	5	10	15	33	57	80
622-Beetle Bailey	7	14	21	49	92	135
623-Oswald the Rabbit (Lantz)	5	10	15	33	57	80
624-Treasure Island(Disney-Movie)(4/55)-Photo-c	7	14	21	48	89	130
625-Beaver Valley (Disney-Movie)	6	12	18	37	66	95
626-Ben Bowie and His Mountain Men	5	10	15	34	60	85
627-Goofy (Disney) (5/55)	7	14	21	46	86	125
628-Elmer Fudd	6	12	18	38	69	100
629-Lady and the Tramp with Jock (Disney)	8	16	24	51	96	140
630-Priscilla's Pop	5	10	15	33	57	80
631-Davy Crockett, Indian Fighter (#1) (Disney) (5/55) (TV)-Fess Parker photo-c	14	28	42	96	211	325
632-Fighting Caravans (Zane Grey)	5	10	15	33	57	80
633-The Little People by Walt Scott (6/55)	5	10	15	35	63	90
634-Lady and the Tramp Album (Disney) (6/55)	5	10	15	35	63	95
635-Bob Clampett's Beany and Cecil (TV)	12	24	36	84	185	285
636-Chip 'N' Dale (Disney)	6	12	18	42	79	115
637-Silvertip (Max Brand)-Kinstler-a	5	10	15	34	60	85
638-M.G.M.'s Spike and Tyke (8/55)	5	10	15	35	63	90
639-Davy Crockett at the Alamo (Disney) (7/55) (TV)-Fess Parker photo-c	11	22	33	76	163	260
640-Western Marshal(Ernest Haycox's)-Kinstler-a	5	10	15	34	60	85
641-Steve Canyon (1955)-by Caniff	5	10	15	35	63	90
642-M.G.M.'s The Two Mouseketeers	6	12	18	41	76	110
643-Wild Bill Elliott; photo-c	5	10	15	33	57	80
644-Sir Walter Raleigh (5/55)-Based on movie "The Virgin Queen"; photo-c	6	12	18	42	79	115
645-Johnny Mack Brown; photo-c	6	12	18	40	73	105
646-Dotty Dripple and Taffy (#1)	6	12	18	37	66	95
647-Bugs Bunny's Album (9/55)	6	12	18	38	69	100
648-Jace Pearson of the Texas Rangers (TV)-Photo-c	6	12	18	40	73	105
649-Duck Album (Disney)	7	14	21	46	86	125
650-Prince Valiant; by Bob Fuje	7	14	21	48	89	130
651-King Colt (Luke Short) (9/55)-Kinstler-a	5	10	15	33	57	80
652-Buck Jones	5	10	15	35	63	90
653-Smokey the Bear (#1) (10/55)	10	20	30	66	138	210
654-Pluto (Disney)	6	12	18	37	66	95
655-Francis the Famous Talking Mule	5	10	15	33	57	80
656-Turok, Son of Stone (#2) (10/55)	35	70	105	252	564	875
657-Ben Bowie and His Mountain Men	5	10	15	34	60	85
658-Goofy (Disney)	7	14	21	46	86	125
659-Daisy Duck's Diary (Disney)(#2)	6	12	18	40	73	105
660-Little Beaver	5	10	15	33	57	80
661-Frosty the Snowman	6	12	18	42	79	115
662-Zoo Parade (TV)-Marlin Perkins (11/55)	5	10	15	33	57	80
663-Winky Dink (TV)	8	16	24	51	96	140
664-Davy Crockett in the Great Keelboat Race (TV) (Disney) (11/55)-Fess Parker photo-c	11	22	33	75	160	245
665-The African Lion (Disney-Movie) (11/55)	5	10	15	34	60	85
666-Santa Claus Funnies	8	16	24	51	96	140
667-Silvertip and the Stolen Stallion (Max Brand) (12/55)-Kinstler-a	5	10	15	34	60	85
668-Dumbo (Disney) (12/55)-First of two printings. Dumbo on cover with starry sky. Reprints 4-Color #234?; same-c as #234	10	20	30	66	138	210
668-Dumbo (Disney) (1/58)-Second printing. Same cover altered, with Timothy Mouse added. Same contents as above	7	14	21	44	82	120
669-Robin Hood (Disney-Movie) (12/55)-Reprints #413 plus-c; photo-c	5	10	15	35	63	90
670-M.G.M's Mouse Musketeers (#1) (1/56)-Formerly the Two Mouseketeers	6	12	18	38	69	100
671-Davy Crockett and the River Pirates (TV) (Disney) (12/55)-Jesse Marsh-a; Fess Parker photo-c	11	22	33	75	160	245
672-Quentin Durward (1/56) (Movie)-Photo-c	6	12	18	42	79	115
673-Buffalo Bill, Jr. (#1) (TV)-James Arness photo-c	8	16	24	56	108	160
674-The Little Rascals (#1) (TV)	9	18	27	59	117	175
675-Steve Donovan, Western Marshal (#1) (TV)-Kinstler-a; photo-c	7	14	21	48	89	130
676-Will-Yum!	4	8	12	28	47	65
677-Little King	5	10	15	34	60	85
678-The Last Hunt (Movie)-Photo-c	6	12	18	42	79	115
679-Gunsmoke (#1) (TV)-Photo-c	16	32	48	112	249	385
680-Out Our Way with the Worry Wart (2/56)	5	10	15	30	50	70
681-Forever Darling (Movie) with Lucille Ball & Desi Arnaz (2/56)-; photo-c	10	20	30	66	138	210
682-The Sword & the Rose (Disney-Movie)-Reprint of #505; Renamed When Knighthood Was in Flower for the novel; photo-c	6	12	18	40	73	105
683-Hi and Lois (3/56)	5	10	15	34	60	85
684-Helen of Troy (Movie)-Buscema-a; photo-c	9	18	27	60	120	180
685-Johnny Mack Brown; photo-c	6	12	18	40	73	105
686-Duck Album (Disney)	7	14	21	46	86	125
687-The Indian Fighter (Movie)-Kirk Douglas photo-c	7	14	21	48	89	130
688-Alexander the Great (Movie) (5/56)-Buscema-a; photo-c	6	12	18	42	79	115
689-Elmer Fudd (3/56)	6	12	18	38	69	100
690-The Conqueror (Movie) - John Wayne photo-c	15	30	45	103	227	350
691-Dotty Dripple and Taffy	4	8	12	28	47	65
692-The Little People-Walt Scott	5	10	15	33	57	80
693-Song of the South (Disney) (1956)-Partial reprint of #129	7	14	21	49	92	135
694-Super Circus (TV)-Photo-c	6	12	18	37	66	95

Four Color Comics #717 © WB

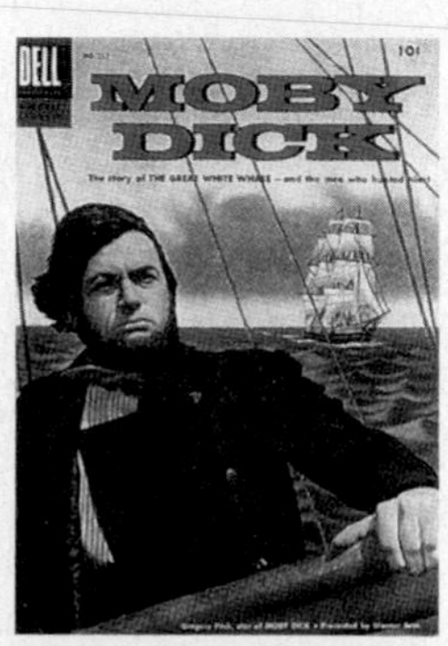

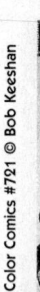

Four Color Comics #721 © Bob Keeshan

Four Color Comics #815 © DELL

	GD 2.0	VG 4.0	FN 6.0	VF 8.0	VF/NM 9.0	NM- 9.2
695-Little Beaver	5	10	15	33	57	80
696-Krazy Kat; not by Herriman (4/56)	5	10	15	31	53	75
697-Oswald the Rabbit (Lantz)	5	10	15	33	57	80
698-Francis the Famous Talking Mule (4/56)	5	10	15	33	57	80
699-Prince Valiant-by Bob Fuje	7	14	21	48	89	130
700-Water Birds and the Olympic Elk (Disney-Movie) (4/56)	5	10	15	33	57	80
701-Jiminy Cricket (#1) (Disney) (5/56)	8	16	24	51	96	140
702-The Goofy Success Story (Disney)	7	14	21	46	86	125
703-Scamp (#1) (Disney)	9	18	27	57	111	165
704-Priscilla's Pop (5/56)	5	10	15	33	57	80
705-Brave Eagle (#1) (TV)-Photo-c	6	12	18	42	79	115
706-Bongo and Lumpjaw (Disney) (6/56)	6	12	18	38	69	100
707-Corky and White Shadow (Disney) (5/56)-Mickey Mouse Club (TV); photo-c	6	12	18	42	79	115
708-Smokey the Bear	6	12	18	40	73	105
709-The Searchers (Movie) - John Wayne photo-c	24	48	72	168	372	575
710-Francis the Famous Talking Mule	5	10	15	33	57	80
711-M.G.M's Mouse Musketeers	5	10	15	31	53	75
712-The Great Locomotive Chase (Disney-Movie) (9/56)-Photo-c	6	12	18	42	79	115
713-The Animal World (Movie) (8/56)	5	10	15	31	53	75
714-Spin and Marty (#1) (TV) (Disney)-Mickey Mouse Club (6/56); photo-c	11	22	33	72	154	235
715-Timmy (8/56)	5	10	15	35	63	90
716-Man in Space (Disney)(A science feature from Tomorrowland)	7	14	21	49	92	135
717-Moby Dick (Movie)-Gregory Peck photo-c	7	14	21	49	92	135
718-Dotty Dripple and Taffy	4	8	12	28	47	65
719-Prince Valiant; by Bob Fuje (8/56)	7	14	21	48	89	130
720-Gunsmoke (TV)-James Arness photo-c	9	18	27	59	117	175
721-Captain Kangaroo (TV)-Photo-c	13	26	39	89	195	300
722-Johnny Mack Brown-Photo-c	6	12	18	40	73	105
723-Santiago (Movie)-Kinstler-a (9/56); Alan Ladd photo-c	8	16	24	56	108	160
724-Bugs Bunny's Album	5	10	15	34	60	85
725-Elmer Fudd (9/56)	5	10	15	33	57	80
726-Duck Album (Disney) (9/56)	6	12	18	37	66	95
727-The Nature of Things (TV) (Disney)-Jesse Marsh-a	5	10	15	33	57	80
728-M.G.M's Mouse Musketeers	5	10	15	31	53	75
729-Bob Son of Battle (11/56)	4	8	12	28	47	65
730-Smokey Stover	5	10	15	34	60	85
731-Silvertip and The Fighting Four (Max Brand)-Kinstler-a	5	10	15	34	60	85
732-Zorro, the Challenge of (10/56)	11	22	33	72	154	235
733-Buck Jones	5	10	15	35	63	90
734-Cheyenne (#1) (TV) (10/56)-Clint Walker photo-c	13	26	39	86	188	290
735-Crusader Rabbit (#1) (TV)	21	42	63	147	324	500
736-Pluto (Disney)	6	12	18	37	66	95
737-Steve Canyon-Caniff-a	5	10	15	35	63	90
738-Westward Ho, the Wagons (Disney-Movie)-Fess Parker photo-c	8	16	24	54	102	150
739-Bounty Guns (Luke Short)-Drucker-a	5	10	15	30	50	70
740-Chilly Willy (#1) (Walter Lantz)	8	16	24	51	96	140
741-The Fastest Gun Alive (Movie)(9/56)-Photo-c	7	14	21	44	82	120
742-Buffalo Bill, Jr. (TV)-Photo-c	5	10	15	35	63	90
743-Daisy Duck's Diary (Disney) (11/56)	6	12	18	40	73	105
744-Little Beaver	5	10	15	33	57	80
745-Francis the Famous Talking Mule	5	10	15	33	57	80
746-Dotty Dripple and Taffy	4	8	12	28	47	65
747-Goofy (Disney)	7	14	21	46	86	125
748-Frosty the Snowman (11/56)	5	10	15	35	63	90
749-Secrets of Life (Disney-Movie)-Photo-c	5	10	15	31	53	75
750-The Great Cat Family (Disney-TV/Movie)-Pinocchio & Alice app.	6	12	18	37	66	95
751-Our Miss Brooks (TV)-Photo-c	7	14	21	49	92	135
752-Mandrake, the Magician	10	20	30	66	138	210
753-Walt Scott's Little People (11/56)	5	10	15	33	57	80
754-Smokey the Bear	6	12	18	40	73	105
755-The Littlest Snowman (12/56)	5	10	15	35	63	90
756-Santa Claus Funnies	8	16	24	51	96	140
757-The True Story of Jesse James (Movie)-Photo-c	9	18	27	57	111	165
758-Bear Country (Disney-Movie)	5	10	15	34	60	85
759-Circus Boy (TV)-The Monkees' Mickey Dolenz photo-c (12/56)	12	24	36	81	176	270
760-The Hardy Boys (#1) (TV) (Disney)-Mickey Mouse Club; photo-c	9	18	27	62	126	190
761-Howdy Doody (TV) (1/57)	9	18	27	61	123	185
762-The Sharkfighters (Movie) (1/57); Buscema-a; photo-c	7	14	21	48	89	130
763-Grandma Duck's Farm Friends (#1) (Disney)	8	16	24	51	96	140
764-M.G.M's Mouse Musketeers	5	10	15	31	53	75
765-Will-Yum!	4	8	12	28	47	65
766-Buffalo Bill, Jr. (TV)-Photo-c	5	10	15	35	63	90
767-Spin and Marty (TV) (Disney)-Mickey Mouse Club (2/57)	8	16	24	56	108	160
768-Steve Donovan, Western Marshal (TV)-Kinstler-a; photo-c	6	12	18	38	69	100
769-Gunsmoke (TV)-James Arness photo-c	9	18	27	59	117	175
770-Brave Eagle (TV)-Photo-c	5	10	15	31	53	75
771-Brand of Empire (Luke Short)(3/57)-Drucker-a	5	10	15	30	50	70
772-Cheyenne (TV)-Clint Walker photo-c	8	16	24	51	96	140
773-The Brave One (Movie)-Photo-c	5	10	15	34	60	85
774-Hi and Lois (3/57)	4	8	12	28	47	65
775-Sir Lancelot and Brian (TV)-Buscema-a; photo-c	9	18	27	59	117	175
776-Johnny Mack Brown; photo-c	6	12	18	40	73	105
777-Scamp (Disney) (3/57)	6	12	18	40	73	105
778-The Little Rascals (TV)	6	12	18	38	69	100
779-Lee Hunter, Indian Fighter (3/57)	6	12	18	37	66	95
780-Captain Kangaroo (TV)-Photo-c	11	22	33	76	163	250
781-Fury (#1) (TV) (3/57)-Photo-c	7	14	21	49	92	135
782-Duck Album (Disney)	6	12	18	37	66	95
783-Elmer Fudd	5	10	15	33	57	80
784-Around the World in 80 Days (Movie) (2/57)-Photo-c	7	14	21	46	86	125
785-Circus Boy (TV) (4/57)-The Monkees' Mickey Dolenz photo-c	9	18	27	62	126	190
786-Cinderella (Disney) (3/57)-Partial-r of #272	6	12	18	41	76	110
787-Little Hiawatha (Disney) (4/57)(#2)	5	10	15	34	60	85
788-Prince Valiant; by Bob Fuje	7	14	21	44	82	120
789-Silvertip-Valley Thieves (Max Brand) (4/57)-Kinstler-a	5	10	15	34	60	85
790-The Wings of Eagles (Movie) (John Wayne)-Toth-a; John Wayne photo-c; 10¢ & 15¢ editions exist	12	24	36	83	182	280
791-The 77th Bengal Lancers (TV)-Photo-c	6	12	18	41	76	110
792-Oswald the Rabbit (Lantz)	5	10	15	33	57	80
793-Morty Meekle	5	10	15	30	50	70
794-The Count of Monte Cristo (5/57) (Movie)-Buscema-a	8	16	24	51	96	140
795-Jiminy Cricket (Disney)(#2)	6	12	18	38	69	100
796-Ludwig Bemelman's Madeleine and Genevieve	5	10	15	30	50	70
797-Gunsmoke (TV)-Photo-c	9	18	27	59	117	175
798-Buffalo Bill, Jr. (TV)-Photo-c	5	10	15	35	63	90
799-Priscilla's Pop	5	10	15	33	57	80
800-The Buccaneers (TV)-Photo-c	6	12	18	42	79	115
801-Dotty Dripple and Taffy	4	8	12	28	47	65
802-Goofy (Disney) (5/57)	7	14	21	46	86	125
803-Cheyenne (TV)-Clint Walker photo-c	8	16	24	51	96	140
804-Steve Canyon-Caniff-a (1957)	5	10	15	35	63	90
805-Crusader Rabbit (TV)	16	32	48	111	246	380
806-Scamp (Disney) (6/57)	6	12	18	40	73	105
807-Savage Range (Luke Short)-Drucker-a	5	10	15	30	50	70
808-Spin and Marty (TV)(Disney)-Mickey Mouse Club; photo-c	8	16	24	56	108	160
809-The Little People (Walt Scott)	5	10	15	33	57	80
810-Francis the Famous Talking Mule	5	10	15	31	53	75
811-Howdy Doody (TV) (7/57)	9	18	27	61	123	185
812-The Big Land (Movie); Alan Ladd photo-c	8	16	24	52	99	145
813-Circus Boy (TV)-The Monkees' Mickey Dolenz photo-c	9	18	27	62	126	190
814-Covered Wagons, Ho! (Disney)-Donald Duck (TV) (6/57); Mickey Mouse app.	5	10	15	34	60	85
815-Dragoon Wells Massacre (Movie)-photo-c	7	14	21	46	86	125
816-Brave Eagle (TV)-photo-c	5	10	15	31	53	75
817-Little Beaver	5	10	15	33	57	80
818-Smokey the Bear (6/57)	6	12	18	40	73	105

Four Color Comics #845 © Universal

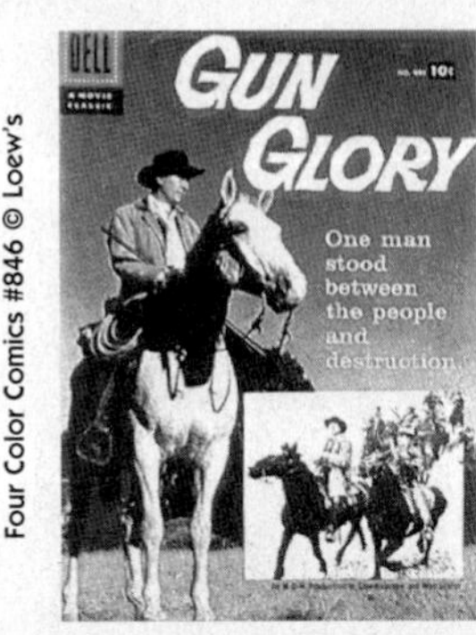

Four Color Comics #846 © Loew's

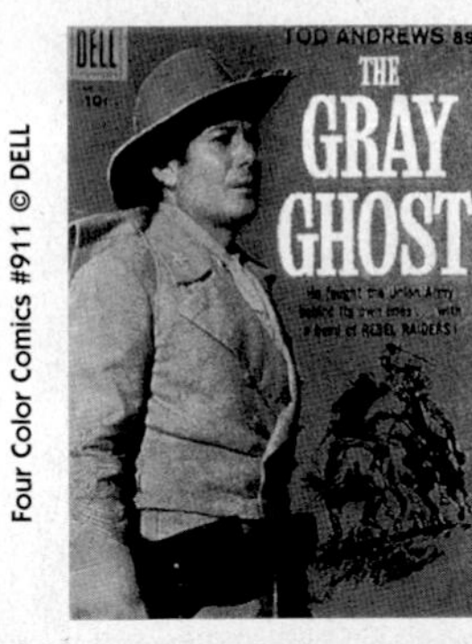

Four Color Comics #911 © DELL

	GD 2.0	VG 4.0	FN 6.0	VF 8.0	VF/NM 9.0	NM- 9.2
819-Mickey Mouse in Magicland (Disney) (7/57)	6	12	18	41	76	110
820-The Oklahoman (Movie)-Photo-c	8	16	24	54	102	150
821-Wringle Wrangle (Disney)-Based on movie "Westward Ho, the Wagons"; Marsh-a; Fess Parker photo-c	7	14	21	46	86	125
822-Paul Revere's Ride with Johnny Tremain (TV) (Disney)-Toth-a	7	14	21	49	92	135
823-Timmy	5	10	15	31	53	75
824-The Pride and the Passion (Movie) (8/57)-Frank Sinatra & Cary Grant photo-c	9	18	27	59	117	175
825-The Little Rascals (TV)	6	12	18	38	69	100
826-Spin and Marty and Annette (TV) (Disney)-Mickey Mouse Club; Annette Funicello photo-c	18	36	54	124	275	425
827-Smokey Stover (8/57)	5	10	15	34	60	85
828-Buffalo Bill, Jr. (TV)-Photo-c	5	10	15	35	63	90
829-Tales of the Pony Express (TV) (8/57)-Painted-c	5	10	15	35	63	90
830-The Hardy Boys (TV) (Disney)-Mickey Mouse Club (8/57); photo-c	8	16	24	54	102	150
831-No Sleep 'Til Dawn (Movie)-Karl Malden photo-c	6	12	18	42	79	115
832-Lolly and Pepper (#1)	6	12	18	37	66	95
833-Scamp (Disney) (9/57)	6	12	18	40	73	105
834-Johnny Mack Brown; photo-c	6	12	18	40	73	105
835-Silvertip-The False Rider (Max Brand)	5	10	15	34	60	85
836-Man in Flight (Disney) (TV) (9/57)	6	12	18	41	76	110
837-Cotton Woods, (All-American Athlete...)	5	10	15	30	50	70
838-Bugs Bunny's Life Story Album (9/57)	5	10	15	34	60	85
839-The Vigilantes (Movie)	7	14	21	46	86	125
840-Duck Album (Disney) (9/57)	6	12	18	37	66	95
841-Elmer Fudd	5	10	15	33	57	80
842-The Nature of Things (Disney-Movie) ('57)-Jesse Marsh-a (TV series)	5	10	15	33	57	80
843-The First Americans (Disney) (TV)-Marsh-a	8	16	24	51	96	140
844-Gunsmoke (TV)-Photo-c	9	18	27	59	117	175
845-The Land Unknown (Movie)-Alex Toth-a	10	20	30	68	144	220
846-Gun Glory (Movie)-by Alex Toth; photo-c	8	16	24	51	96	140
847-Perri (squirrels) (Disney-Movie)-Two different covers published	6	12	18	37	66	95
848-Marauder's Moon (Luke Short)	5	10	15	30	50	70
849-Prince Valiant; by Bob Fuje	7	14	21	44	82	120
850-Buck Jones	5	10	15	35	63	90
851-The Story of Mankind (Movie) (1/58)-Hedy Lamarr & Vincent Price photo-c	7	14	21	44	82	120
852-Chilly Willy (2/58) (Lantz)	5	10	15	34	60	85
853-Pluto (Disney) (10/57)	6	12	18	37	66	95
854-The Hunchback of Notre Dame (Movie)-Photo-c	11	22	33	73	157	240
855-Broken Arrow (TV)-Photo-c	6	12	18	37	66	95
856-Buffalo Bill, Jr. (TV)-Photo-c	5	10	15	35	63	90
857-The Goofy Adventure Story (Disney) (11/57)	7	14	21	46	86	125
858-Daisy Duck's Diary (Disney) (11/57)	5	10	15	35	63	90
859-Topper and Neil (TV) (11/57)	5	10	15	35	63	90
860-Wyatt Earp (#1) (TV)-Manning-a; photo-c	9	18	27	61	123	185
861-Frosty the Snowman	5	10	15	35	63	90
862-The Truth About Mother Goose (Disney-Movie) (11/57)	7	14	21	44	82	120
863-Francis the Famous Talking Mule	5	10	15	31	53	75
864-The Littlest Snowman	5	10	15	35	63	90
865-Andy Burnett (TV) (Disney) (12/57)-Photo-c	8	16	24	54	102	150
866-Mars and Beyond (Disney-TV)(A science feature from Tomorrowland)	7	14	21	49	92	135
867-Santa Claus Funnies	8	16	24	51	96	140
868-The Little People (12/57)	5	10	15	33	57	80
869-Old Yeller (Disney-Movie)-Photo-c	6	12	18	38	69	100
870-Little Beaver (1/58)	5	10	15	33	57	80
871-Curly Kayoe	5	10	15	30	50	70
872-Captain Kangaroo (TV)-Photo-c	11	22	33	76	163	250
873-Grandma Duck's Farm Friends (Disney)	6	12	18	37	66	95
874-Old Ironsides (Disney-Movie with Johnny Tremain) (1/58)	6	12	18	42	79	115
875-Trumpets West (Luke Short) (2/58)	5	10	15	30	50	70
876-Tales of Wells Fargo (#1)(TV)(2/58)-Photo-c	8	16	24	52	99	145
877-Frontier Doctor with Rex Allen (TV)-Alex Toth-a; Rex Allen photo-c	9	18	27	57	111	165
878-Peanuts (#1)-Schulz-c only (2/58)	79	158	237	632	1416	2200
879-Brave Eagle (TV) (2/58)-Photo-c	5	10	15	31	53	75
880-Steve Donovan, Western Marshal-Drucker-a (TV)-Photo-c	5	10	15	31	53	75
881-The Captain and the Kids (2/58)	5	10	15	30	50	70
882-Zorro (Disney)-1st Disney issue; by Alex Toth (TV) (2/58); photo-c	13	26	39	89	195	300
883-The Little Rascals (TV)	5	10	15	35	63	90
884-Hawkeye and the Last of the Mohicans (TV) (3/58); photo-c	7	14	21	44	82	120
885-Fury (TV) (3/58)-Photo-c	5	10	15	35	63	90
886-Bongo and Lumpjaw (Disney) (3/58)	4	8	12	28	47	65
887-The Hardy Boys (Disney) (TV)-Mickey Mouse Club (1/58)-Photo-c	8	16	24	54	102	150
888-Elmer Fudd (3/58)	5	10	15	33	57	80
889-Clint and Mac (Disney) (TV) (3/58)-Alex Toth-a; photo-c	10	20	30	64	132	200
890-Wyatt Earp (TV)-by Russ Manning; photo-c	7	14	21	44	82	120
891-Light in the Forest (Disney-Movie) (3/58)-Fess Parker photo-c	6	12	18	42	79	115
892-Maverick (#1) (TV) (4/58)-James Garner photo-c	18	36	54	126	281	435
893-Jim Bowie (TV)-Photo-c	6	12	18	41	76	110
894-Oswald the Rabbit (Lantz)	5	10	15	33	57	80
895-Wagon Train (#1) (TV) (3/58)-Photo-c	9	18	27	62	126	190
896-The Adventures of Tinker Bell (Disney)	9	18	27	59	117	175
897-Jiminy Cricket (Disney)	6	12	18	38	69	100
898-Silvertip (Max Brand)-Kinstler-a (5/58)	5	10	15	34	60	85
899-Goofy (Disney) (5/58)	5	10	15	35	63	90
900-Prince Valiant; by Bob Fuje	7	14	21	44	82	120
901-Little Hiawatha (Disney)	5	10	15	34	60	85
902-Will-Yum!	4	8	12	28	47	65
903-Dotty Dripple and Taffy	4	8	12	28	47	65
904-Lee Hunter, Indian Fighter	5	10	15	30	50	70
905-Annette (Disney) (TV) (5/58)-Mickey Mouse Club; Annette Funicello photo-c	21	42	63	147	324	500
906-Francis the Famous Talking Mule	5	10	15	31	53	75
907-Sugarfoot (#1) (TV)Toth-a; photo-c	10	20	30	67	141	215
908-The Little People and the Giant-Walt Scott (5/58)	5	10	15	33	57	80
909-Smitty	4	8	12	23	37	50
910-The Vikings (Movie)-Buscema-a; Kirk Douglas photo-c	8	16	24	54	102	150
911-The Gray Ghost (TV)-Photo-c	7	14	21	49	92	135
912-Leave It to Beaver (#1) (TV)-Photo-c	14	28	42	94	207	320
913-The Left-Handed Gun (Movie) (7/58); Paul Newman photo-c	9	18	27	57	111	165
914-No Time for Sergeants (Movie)-Andy Griffith photo-c; Toth-a	9	18	27	60	120	180
915-Casey Jones (TV)-Alan Hale photo-c	5	10	15	34	60	85
916-Red Ryder Ranch Comics (7/58)	4	8	12	28	47	65
917-The Life of Riley (TV)-Photo-c	9	18	27	62	126	190
918-Beep Beep, the Roadrunner (#1) (7/58)-Published with two different back covers	12	24	36	82	179	275
919-Boots and Saddles (#1) (TV)-Photo-c	7	14	21	48	89	130
920-Zorro (Disney) (TV) (6/58)Toth-a; photo-c	10	20	30	66	138	210
921-Wyatt Earp (TV)-Manning-a; photo-c	7	14	21	44	82	120
922-Johnny Mack Brown by Russ Manning; photo-c	6	12	18	41	76	110
923-Timmy	5	10	15	31	53	75
924-Colt .45 (#1) (TV) (8/58)-W. Preston photo-c	9	18	27	62	126	190
925-Last of the Fast Guns (Movie) (8/58)-Photo-c	6	12	18	41	76	110
926-Peter Pan (Disney)-Reprint of #442	5	10	15	34	60	85
927-Top Gun (Luke Short) Buscema-a	5	10	15	30	50	70
928-Sea Hunt (#1) (9/58) (TV)-Lloyd Bridges photo-c	10	20	30	66	138	210
929-Brave Eagle (TV)-Photo-c	5	10	15	31	53	75
930-Maverick (TV) (7/58)-James Garner photo-c	10	20	30	64	132	200
931-Have Gun, Will Travel (#1) (TV)-Photo-c	12	24	36	81	176	270
932-Smokey the Bear (His Life Story)	6	12	18	40	73	105
933-Zorro (Disney, 9/58) (TV)-Alex Toth-a; photo-c	10	20	30	66	138	210
934-Restless Gun (#1) (TV)-Photo-c	9	18	27	61	123	185
935-King of the Royal Mounted	5	10	15	31	53	75
936-The Little Rascals (TV)	5	10	15	35	63	90
937-Ruff and Reddy (#1) (9/58) (TV) (1st Hanna-Barbera comic book)	10	20	30	67	141	215
938-Elmer Fudd (9/58)	5	10	15	33	57	80
939-Steve Canyon - not by Caniff	5	10	15	35	63	90
940-Lolly and Pepper (10/58)	4	8	12	28	47	65

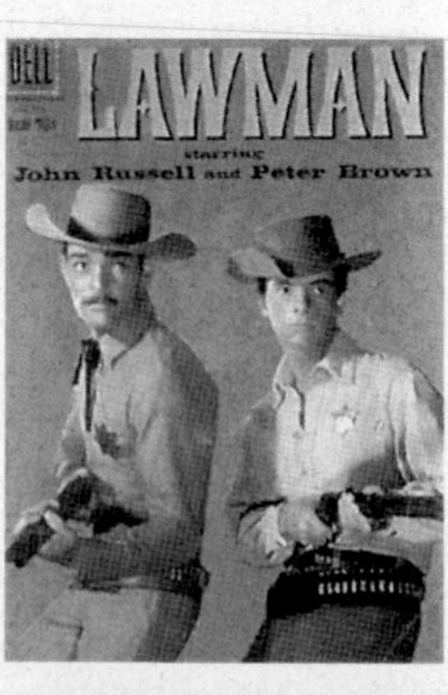

Four Color Comics #970 © WB

Four Color Comics #1006 © Oscar Films

Four Color Comics #1052 © Loew's

	GD 2.0	VG 4.0	FN 6.0	VF 8.0	VF/NM 9.0	NM- 9.2
941-Pluto (Disney) (10/58)	5	10	15	33	57	80
942-Pony Express (Tales of the ...) (TV)	5	10	15	31	53	75
943-White Wilderness (Disney-Movie) (10/58)	6	12	18	37	66	95
944-The 7th Voyage of Sinbad (Movie) (9/58)-Buscema-a; photo-c	11	22	33	73	157	240
945-Maverick (TV)-James Garner/Jack Kelly photo-c	10	20	30	64	132	200
946-The Big Country (Movie)-Photo-c	6	12	18	42	79	115
947-Broken Arrow (TV)-Photo-c (11/58)	5	10	15	31	53	75
948-Daisy Duck's Diary (Disney) (11/58)	5	10	15	35	63	90
949-High Adventure(Lowell Thomas')(TV)-Photo-c	5	10	15	34	60	85
950-Frosty the Snowman	5	10	15	35	63	90
951-The Lennon Sisters Life Story (TV)-Toth-a, 32 pgs.; photo-c	11	22	33	73	157	240
952-Goofy (Disney) (11/58)	5	10	15	35	63	90
953-Francis the Famous Talking Mule	5	10	15	31	53	75
954-Man in Space-Satellites (TV)	6	12	18	41	76	110
955-Hi and Lois (11/58)	4	8	12	28	47	65
956-Ricky Nelson (#1) (TV)-Photo-c	15	30	45	100	220	340
957-Buffalo Bee (#1) (TV)	8	16	24	52	99	145
958-Santa Claus Funnies	6	12	18	41	76	110
959-Christmas Stories-(Walt Scott's Little People) (1951-56 strip reprints)	5	10	15	33	57	80
960-Zorro (Disney) (TV) (12/58)-Toth art; photo-c	10	20	30	66	138	210
961-Jace Pearson's Tales of the Texas Rangers (TV)-Spiegle-a; photo-c	5	10	15	34	60	85
962-Maverick (TV) (1/59)-James Garner/Jack Kelly photo-c	10	20	30	64	132	200
963-Johnny Mack Brown; photo-c	6	12	18	40	73	105
964-The Hardy Boys (TV) (Disney) (1/59)-Mickey Mouse Club; photo-c	8	16	24	54	102	150
965-Grandma Duck's Farm Friends (Disney)(1/59)	5	10	15	34	60	85
966-Tonka (starring Sal Mineo; Disney-Movie)-Photo-c	8	16	24	54	102	150
967-Chilly Willy (2/59) (Lantz)	5	10	15	34	60	85
968-Tales of Wells Fargo (TV)-Photo-c	7	14	21	48	89	130
969-Peanuts (2/59)	27	54	81	194	435	675
970-Lawman (#1) (TV)-Photo-c	10	20	30	69	147	225
971-Wagon Train (TV)-Photo-c	6	12	18	41	76	110
972-Tom Thumb (Movie)-George Pal (1/59)	8	16	24	52	99	145
973-Sleeping Beauty and the Prince(Disney)(5/59)	10	20	30	69	147	225
974-The Little Rascals (TV) (3/59)	5	10	15	35	63	90
975-Fury (TV)-Photo-c	5	10	15	35	63	90
976-Zorro (Disney) (TV)-Toth-a; photo-c	10	20	30	66	138	210
977-Elmer Fudd (3/59)	5	10	15	33	57	80
978-Lolly and Pepper	4	8	12	28	47	65
979-Oswald the Rabbit (Lantz)	5	10	15	33	57	80
980-Maverick (TV) (4-6/59)-James Garner/Jack Kelly photo-c	10	20	30	64	132	200
981-Ruff and Reddy (TV) (Hanna-Barbera)	7	14	21	44	82	120
982-The New Adventures of Tinker Bell (TV) (Disney)	8	16	24	54	102	150
983-Have Gun, Will Travel (TV) (4-6/59)-Photo-c	9	18	27	60	120	180
984-Sleeping Beauty's Fairy Godmothers (Disney)	9	18	27	58	114	170
985-Shaggy Dog (Disney-Movie)-Photo-all four covers; Annette on back-c(5/59)	7	14	21	46	86	125
986-Restless Gun (TV)-Photo-c	7	14	21	46	86	125
987-Goofy (Disney) (7/59)	5	10	15	35	63	90
988-Little Hiawatha (Disney)	5	10	15	34	60	85
989-Jiminy Cricket (Disney) (5-7/59)	6	12	18	38	69	100
990-Huckleberry Hound (#1)(TV)(Hanna-Barbera); 1st app. Huck, Yogi Bear, & Pixie & Dixie & Mr. Jinks	16	32	48	110	243	375
991-Francis the Famous Talking Mule	5	10	15	31	53	75
992-Sugarfoot (TV)-Toth-a; photo-c	9	18	27	63	129	195
993-Jim Bowie (TV)-Photo-c	5	10	15	35	63	90
994-Sea Hunt (TV)-Lloyd Bridges photo-c	7	14	21	48	89	130
995-Donald Duck Album (Disney) (5-7/59)(#1)	7	14	21	44	82	120
996-Nevada (Zane Grey)	5	10	15	33	57	80
997-Walt Disney Presents-Tales of Texas John Slaughter (#1) (TV) (Disney)-Photo-c; photo of W. Disney inside-c	6	12	18	42	79	115
998-Ricky Nelson (TV)-Photo-c	15	30	45	100	220	340
999-Leave It to Beaver (TV)-Photo-c	12	24	36	80	173	265
1000-The Gray Ghost (TV) (6-8/59)-Photo-c	7	14	21	49	92	135
1001-Lowell Thomas' High Adventure (TV) (8-10/59)-Photo-c	5	10	15	33	57	80
1002-Buffalo Bee (TV)	6	12	18	40	73	105
1003-Zorro (TV) (Disney)-Toth-a; photo-c	10	20	30	66	138	210
1004-Colt .45 (TV) (6-8/59)-Photo-c	7	14	21	48	89	130
1005-Maverick (TV)-James Garner/Jack Kelly photo-c	10	20	30	64	132	200
1006-Hercules (Movie)-Buscema-a; photo-c	9	18	27	57	111	165
1007-John Paul Jones (Movie)-Robert Stack photo-c	6	12	18	37	66	95
1008-Beep Beep, the Road Runner (7-9/59)	8	16	24	51	96	140
1009-The Rifleman (#1) (TV)-Photo-c	21	42	63	147	324	500
1010-Grandma Duck's Farm Friends (Disney)-by Carl Barks	11	22	33	73	157	240
1011-Buckskin (#1) (TV)-Photo-c	7	14	21	44	82	120
1012-Last Train from Gun Hill (Movie) (7/59)-Photo-c	8	16	24	52	99	145
1013-Bat Masterson (#1) (TV) (8/59)-Gene Barry photo-c	10	20	30	67	141	215
1014-The Lennon Sisters (TV)-Toth-a; photo-c	10	20	30	69	147	225
1015-Peanuts-Schulz-c	27	54	81	194	435	675
1016-Smokey the Bear Nature Stories	5	10	15	31	53	75
1017-Chilly Willy (Lantz)	5	10	15	34	60	85
1018-Rio Bravo (Movie)(6/59)-John Wayne; Toth-a; John Wayne, Dean Martin & Ricky Nelson photo-c	24	48	72	170	378	585
1019-Wagon Train (TV)-Photo-c	6	12	18	41	76	110
1020-Jungle Jim-McWilliams-a	5	10	15	31	53	75
1021-Jace Pearson's Tales of the Texas Rangers (TV)-Photo-c	5	10	15	34	60	85
1022-Timmy	5	10	15	31	53	75
1023-Tales of Wells Fargo (TV)-Photo-c	7	14	21	48	89	130
1024-Darby O'Gill and the Little People (Disney-Movie)-Toth-a; photo-c	9	18	27	57	111	165
1025-Vacation in Disneyland (8-10/59)-Carl Barks-a(24pgs.) (Disney)	14	28	42	93	204	315
1026-Spin and Marty (TV) (Disney) (9-11/59)-Mickey Mouse Club; photo-c	7	14	21	44	82	120
1027-The Texan (#1)(TV)-Photo-c	8	16	24	52	99	145
1028-Rawhide (#1) (TV) (9-11/59)-Clint Eastwood photo-c; Tufts-a	22	44	66	154	340	525
1029-Boots and Saddles (TV) (9/59)-Photo-c	5	10	15	34	60	85
1030-Spanky and Alfalfa, the Little Rascals (TV)	5	10	15	35	63	90
1031-Fury (TV)-Photo-c	5	10	15	35	63	90
1032-Elmer Fudd	5	10	15	33	57	80
1033-Steve Canyon-not by Caniff; photo-c	5	10	15	35	63	90
1034-Nancy and Sluggo Summer Camp (9-11/59)	5	10	15	30	50	70
1035-Lawman (TV)-Photo-c	7	14	21	46	86	125
1036-The Big Circus (Movie)-Photo-c	6	12	18	40	73	105
1037-Zorro (Disney) (TV)-Tufts-a; Annette Funicello photo-c	12	24	36	81	176	270
1038-Ruff and Reddy (TV)(Hanna-Barbera)(1959)	7	14	21	44	82	120
1039-Pluto (Disney) (11-1/60)	5	10	15	33	57	80
1040-Quick Draw McGraw (#1) (TV) (Hanna-Barbera) (12-2/60)	12	24	36	83	182	280
1041-Sea Hunt (TV) (10-12/59)-Toth-a; Lloyd Bridges photo-c	7	14	21	48	89	130
1042-The Three Chipmunks (Alvin, Simon & Theodore) (#1) (TV) (10-12/59)	9	18	27	60	120	180
1043-The Three Stooges (#1)-Photo-c	22	44	66	155	345	535
1044-Have Gun, Will Travel (TV)-Photo-c	9	18	27	60	120	180
1045-Restless Gun (TV)-Photo-c	7	14	21	46	86	125
1046-Beep Beep, the Road Runner (11-1/60)	8	16	24	51	96	140
1047-Gyro Gearloose (#1) (Disney)-All Barks-c/a	15	30	45	103	227	350
1048-The Horse Soldiers (Movie) (John Wayne)-Sekowsky-a; painted cover featuring John Wayne	11	22	33	76	163	250
1049-Don't Give Up the Ship (Movie) (8/59)-Jerry Lewis photo-c	9	18	27	58	114	170
1050-Huckleberry Hound (TV) (Hanna-Barbera) (10-12/59)	10	20	30	67	141	215
1051-Donald in Mathmagic Land (Disney-Movie)	8	16	24	56	108	160
1052-Ben-Hur (Movie) (11/59)-Manning-a	9	18	27	61	123	185
1053-Goofy (Disney) (11-1/60)	5	10	15	35	63	90
1054-Huckleberry Hound Winter Fun (TV) (Hanna-Barbera) (12/59)	10	20	30	67	141	215
1055-Daisy Duck's Diary (Disney)-by Carl Barks (11-1/60)	8	16	24	56	108	160
1056-Yellowstone Kelly (Movie)-Clint Walker photo-c	5	10	15	35	63	90
1057-Mickey Mouse Album (Disney)	6	12	18	37	66	95

Four Color Comics #1066 © WB

Four Color Comics #1150 © DIS

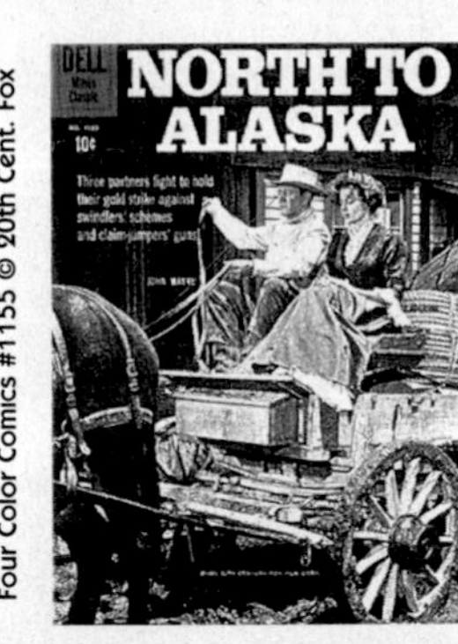

Four Color Comics #1155 © 20th Cent. Fox

	GD 2.0	VG 4.0	FN 6.0	VF 8.0	VF/NM 9.0	NM- 9.2
1058-Colt .45 (TV)-Photo-c	7	14	21	48	89	130
1059-Sugarfoot (TV)-Photo-c	7	14	21	49	92	135
1060-Journey to the Center of the Earth (Movie)-Pat Boone & James Mason photo-c	10	20	30	66	138	210
1061-Buffalo Bee (TV)	6	12	18	40	73	105
1062-Christmas Stories (Walt Scott's Little People strip-r)	5	10	15	33	57	80
1063-Santa Claus Funnies	6	12	18	41	76	110
1064-Bugs Bunny's Merry Christmas (12/59)	5	10	15	34	60	85
1065-Frosty the Snowman	5	10	15	35	63	90
1066-77 Sunset Strip (#1) (TV)-Toth-a (1-3/60)-Efrem Zimbalist, Jr. & Edd "Kookie" Byrnes photo-c	9	18	27	61	123	185
1067-Yogi Bear (#1) (TV) (Hanna-Barbera)	12	24	36	82	179	275
1068-Francis the Famous Talking Mule	5	10	15	31	53	75
1069-The FBI Story (Movie)-Toth-a; James Stewart photo on-c	9	18	27	57	111	165
1070-Solomon and Sheba (Movie)-Sekowsky-a; photo-c	9	18	27	57	111	165
1071-The Real McCoys (#1) (TV) (1-3/60)-Toth-a; Walter Brennan photo-c	8	16	24	51	96	140
1072-Blythe (Marge's)	5	10	15	34	60	85
1073-Grandma Duck's Farm Friends-Barks-c/a (Disney)	11	22	33	73	157	240
1074-Chilly Willy (Lantz)	5	10	15	34	60	85
1075-Tales of Wells Fargo (TV)-Photo-c	7	14	21	48	89	130
1076-The Rebel (#1) (TV)-Sekowsky-a; photo-c	9	18	27	63	129	195
1077-The Deputy (#1) (TV)-Buscema-a; Henry Fonda photo-c	10	20	30	64	132	200
1078-The Three Stooges (2-4/60)-Photo-c	11	22	33	73	157	240
1079-The Little Rascals (TV) (Spanky & Alfalfa)	5	10	15	35	63	90
1080-Fury (TV) (2-4/60)-Photo-c	5	10	15	35	63	90
1081-Elmer Fudd	5	10	15	33	57	80
1082-Spin and Marty (Disney) (TV)-Photo-c	7	14	21	44	82	120
1083-Men into Space (TV)-Anderson-a; photo-c	5	10	15	35	63	90
1084-Speedy Gonzales	6	12	18	41	76	110
1085-The Time Machine (H.G. Wells) (Movie) (3/60)-Alex Toth-a; Rod Taylor photo-c	12	24	36	84	185	285
1086-Lolly and Pepper	4	8	12	28	47	65
1087-Peter Gunn (TV)-Photo-c	7	14	21	49	92	135
1088-A Dog of Flanders (Movie)-Photo-c	5	10	15	31	53	75
1089-Restless Gun (TV)-Photo-c	7	14	21	46	86	125
1090-Francis the Famous Talking Mule	5	10	15	31	53	75
1091-Jacky's Diary (4-6/60)	5	10	15	33	57	80
1092-Toby Tyler (Disney-Movie)-Photo-c	6	12	18	38	69	100
1093-MacKenzie's Raiders (Movie/TV)-Richard Carlson photo-c from TV show	6	12	18	37	66	95
1094-Goofy (Disney)	5	10	15	35	63	90
1095-Gyro Gearloose (Disney)-All Barks-c/a	9	18	27	59	117	175
1096-The Texan (TV)-Rory Calhoun photo-c	7	14	21	46	86	125
1097-Rawhide (TV)-Manning-a; Clint Eastwood photo-c	13	26	39	89	195	300
1098-Sugarfoot (TV)-Photo-c	7	14	21	49	92	135
1099-Donald Duck Album (Disney) (5-7/60)-Barks-c	7	14	21	44	82	120
1100-Annette's Life Story (Disney-Movie) (5/60)-Annette Funicello photo-c	17	34	51	117	259	400
1101-Robert Louis Stevenson's Kidnapped (Disney-Movie) (5/60); photo-c	6	12	18	37	66	95
1102-Wanted: Dead or Alive (#1) (TV) (5-7/60); Steve McQueen photo-c	11	22	33	73	157	240
1103-Leave It to Beaver (TV)-Photo-c	12	24	36	80	173	265
1104-Yogi Bear Goes to College (TV) (Hanna-Barbera) (6-8/60)	8	16	24	54	102	150
1105-Gale Storm (Oh! Susanna) (TV)-Toth-a; photo-c	9	18	27	63	129	195
1106-77 Sunset Strip(TV)(6-8/60)-Toth-a; photo-c	7	14	21	49	92	135
1107-Buckskin (TV)-Photo-c	6	12	18	40	73	105
1108-The Troubleshooters (TV)-Keenan Wynn photo-c	6	12	18	37	66	95
1109-This Is Your Life, Donald Duck (Disney) (TV) (8-10/60)-Gyro flashback to WDC&S #141; origin Donald Duck (1st told)	12	24	36	81	176	270
1110-Bonanza (#1) (TV) (6-8/60)-Photo-c	30	60	90	216	483	750
1111-Shotgun Slade (TV)-Photo-c	6	12	18	37	66	95
1112-Pixie and Dixie and Mr. Jinks (#1) (TV) (Hanna-Barbera) (7-9/60)	7	14	21	49	92	135
1113-Tales of Wells Fargo (TV)-Photo-c	7	14	21	48	89	130
1114-Huckleberry Finn (Movie) (7/60)-Photo-c	6	12	18	37	66	95
1115-Ricky Nelson (TV)-Manning-a; photo-c	12	24	36	80	173	265
1116-Boots and Saddles (TV) (8/60)-Photo-c	5	10	15	34	60	85
1117-Boy and the Pirates (Movie)-Photo-c	6	12	18	37	66	95
1118-The Sword and the Dragon (Movie) (6/60)-Photo-c	7	14	21	48	89	130
1119-Smokey the Bear Nature Stories	5	10	15	31	53	75
1120-Dinosaurus (Movie)-Painted-c	8	16	24	51	96	140
1121-Hercules Unchained (Movie) (8/60)-Crandall/Evans-a	8	16	24	54	102	150
1122-Chilly Willy (Lantz)	5	10	15	34	60	85
1123-Tombstone Territory (TV)-Photo-c	7	14	21	49	92	135
1124-Whirlybirds (#1) (TV)-Photo-c	7	14	21	49	92	135
1125-Laramie (#1) (TV)-Photo-c; G. Kane/Heath-a	8	16	24	51	96	140
1126-Hotel Deparee - Sundance (TV) (8-10/60)-Earl Holliman photo-c	6	12	18	40	73	105
1127-The Three Stooges-Photo-c (8-10/60)	11	22	33	73	157	240
1128-Rocky and His Friends (#1) (TV) (Jay Ward) (8-10/60)	25	50	75	175	388	600
1129-Pollyanna (Disney-Movie)-Hayley Mills photo-c	7	14	21	49	92	135
1130-The Deputy (TV)-Buscema-a; Henry Fonda photo-c	8	16	24	54	102	150
1131-Elmer Fudd (9-11/60)	5	10	15	33	57	80
1132-Space Mouse (Lantz) (8-10/60)	5	10	15	33	57	80
1133-Fury (TV)-Photo-c	5	10	15	35	63	90
1134-Real McCoys (TV)-Toth-a; photo-c	8	16	24	51	96	140
1135-M.G.M.'s Mouse Musketeers (9-11/60)	4	8	12	28	47	65
1136-Jungle Cat (Disney-Movie)-Photo-c	6	12	18	37	66	95
1137-The Little Rascals (TV)	5	10	15	35	63	90
1138-The Rebel (TV)-Photo-c	8	16	24	52	99	145
1139-Spartacus (Movie) (11/60)-Buscema-a; Kirk Douglas photo-c	10	20	30	69	147	225
1140-Donald Duck Album (Disney)-Barks-c	7	14	21	44	82	120
1141-Huckleberry Hound for President (TV) (Hanna-Barbera) (10/60)	7	14	21	46	86	125
1142-Johnny Ringo (TV)-Photo-c	6	12	18	41	76	110
1143-Pluto (Disney) (11-1/61)	5	10	15	33	57	80
1144-The Story of Ruth (Movie)-Photo-c	8	16	24	54	102	150
1145-The Lost World (Movie)-Gil Kane-a; photo-c; 1 pg. Conan Doyle biography by Torres	9	18	27	57	111	165
1146-Restless Gun (TV)-Photo-c; Wildey-a	7	14	21	46	86	125
1147-Sugarfoot (TV)-Photo-c	7	14	21	49	92	135
1148-I Aim at the Stars-the Werner Von Braun Story (Movie) (11-1/61)-Photo-c	6	12	18	41	76	110
1149-Goofy (Disney) (11-1/61)	5	10	15	35	63	90
1150-Daisy Duck's Diary (Disney) (12-1/61) by Carl Barks	8	16	24	56	108	160
1151-Mickey Mouse Album (Disney) (11-1/61)	6	12	18	37	66	95
1152-Rocky and His Friends (TV) (Jay Ward) (12-2/61)	16	32	48	107	236	365
1153-Frosty the Snowman	5	10	15	35	63	90
1154-Santa Claus Funnies	6	12	18	41	76	110
1155-North to Alaska (Movie)-John Wayne photo-c	15	30	45	100	220	340
1156-Walt Disney Swiss Family Robinson (Movie) (12/60)-Photo-c	7	14	21	48	89	130
1157-Master of the World (Movie) (7/61)	7	14	21	48	89	130
1158-Three Worlds of Gulliver (2 issues exist with different covers) (Movie)-Photo-c	6	12	18	42	79	115
1159-77 Sunset Strip (TV)-Toth-a; photo-c	7	14	21	49	92	135
1160-Rawhide (TV)-Clint Eastwood photo-c	13	26	39	89	195	300
1161-Grandma Duck's Farm Friends (Disney) by Carl Barks (2-4/61)	11	22	33	73	157	240
1162-Yogi Bear Joins the Marines (TV) (Hanna-Barbera) (5-7/61)	8	16	24	54	102	150
1163-Daniel Boone (3-5/61); Marsh-a	5	10	15	35	63	90
1164-Wanted: Dead or Alive (TV)-Steve McQueen photo-c	8	16	24	56	108	160
1165-Ellery Queen (#1) (3-5/61)	9	18	27	58	114	175
1166-Rocky and His Friends (TV) (Jay Ward)	16	32	48	107	236	365
1167-Tales of Wells Fargo (TV)-Photo-c	7	14	21	44	82	120
1168-The Detectives (TV)-Robert Taylor photo-c	9	18	27	61	123	185
1169-New Adventures of Sherlock Holmes	12	24	36	79	170	260
1170-The Three Stooges (3-5/61)-Photo-c	11	22	33	73	157	240

Four Color Comics #1218 © DELL

Four Color Comics #1221 © CBS

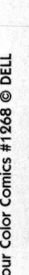

Four Color Comics #1268 © DELL

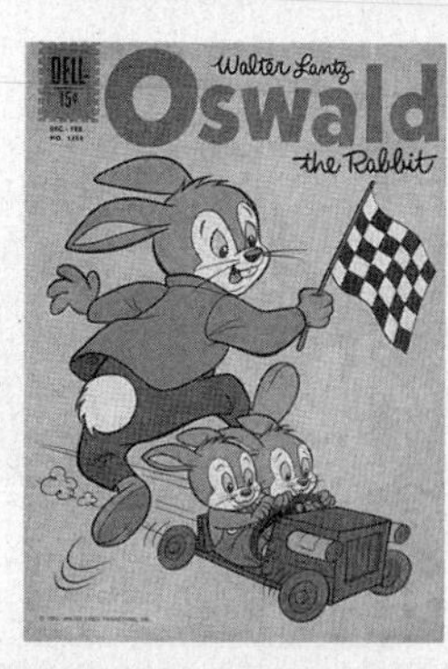

	GD 2.0	VG 4.0	FN 6.0	VF 8.0	VF/NM 9.0	NM- 9.2
1171-Elmer Fudd	5	10	15	33	57	80
1172-Fury (TV)-Photo-c	5	10	15	35	63	90
1173-The Twilight Zone (#1) (TV) (5/61)-Crandall/Evans-c/a; Crandall tribute to Ingles	18	36	54	128	284	440
1174-The Little Rascals (TV)	5	10	15	33	57	80
1175-M.G.M.'s Mouse Musketeers (3-5/61)	4	8	12	28	47	65
1176-Dondi (Movie)-Origin; photo-c	6	12	18	37	66	95
1177-Chilly Willy (Lantz) (4-6/61)	5	10	15	34	60	85
1178-Ten Who Dared (Disney-Movie) (12/60)-Painted-c; cast member photo on back-c	7	14	21	46	86	125
1179-The Swamp Fox (TV) (Disney)-Leslie Nielsen photo-c	8	16	24	54	102	150
1180-The Danny Thomas Show (TV)-Toth-a; photo-c	13	26	39	89	195	300
1181-Texas John Slaughter (TV) (Walt Disney Presents...) (4-6/61)-Photo-c	5	10	15	35	63	90
1182-Donald Duck Album (Disney) (5-7/61)	5	10	15	34	60	85
1183-101 Dalmatians (Disney-Movie) (3/61)	9	18	27	62	126	190
1184-Gyro Gearloose; All Barks-c/a (Disney) (5-7/61) Two variations exist	9	18	27	59	117	175
1185-Sweetie Pie	5	10	15	34	60	85
1186-Yak Yak (#1) by Jack Davis (2 versions - one minus 3-pg. Davis-c/a)	8	16	24	54	102	150
1187-The Three Stooges (6-8/61)-Photo-c	11	22	33	73	157	240
1188-Atlantis, the Lost Continent (Movie) (5/61)-Photo-c	9	18	27	60	120	180
1189-Greyfriars Bobby (Disney-Movie) (11/61)-Photo-c (scarce)	6	12	18	41	76	110
1190-Donald and the Wheel (Disney-Movie) (11/61); Barks-c	8	16	24	51	96	140
1191-Leave It to Beaver (TV)-Photo-c	12	24	36	80	173	265
1192-Ricky Nelson (TV)-Manning-a; photo-c	12	24	36	80	173	265
1193-The Real McCoys (TV) (6-8/61)-Photo-c	7	14	21	48	89	130
1194-Pepe (Movie) (4/61)-Photo-c	5	10	15	30	50	70
1195-National Velvet (#1) (TV)-Photo-c	6	12	18	41	76	110
1196-Pixie and Dixie and Mr. Jinks (TV) (Hanna-Barbera) (7-9/61)	5	10	15	35	63	90
1197-The Aquanauts (TV) (5-7/61)-Photo-c	6	12	18	41	76	110
1198-Donald in Mathmagic Land (Disney-Movie)-Reprint of #1051	6	12	18	37	66	95
1199-The Absent-Minded Professor (Disney-Movie) (4/61)-Photo-c	7	14	21	46	86	125
1199-Shaggy Dog & The Absent-Minded Professor (Disney-Movie) (8/67)-Photo-c	7	14	21	46	86	125
1200-Hennessey (TV) (8-10/61)-Gil Kane-a; photo-c	7	14	21	44	82	120
1201-Goofy (Disney) (8-10/61)	5	10	15	35	63	90
1202-Rawhide (TV)-Clint Eastwood photo-c	13	26	39	89	195	300
1203-Pinocchio (Disney) (3/62)	6	12	18	40	73	105
1204-Scamp (Disney)	4	8	12	27	44	60
1205-David and Goliath (Movie) (7/61)-Photo-c	6	12	18	42	79	115
1206-Lolly and Pepper (9-11/61)	4	8	12	28	47	65
1207-The Rebel (TV)-Sekowsky-a; photo-c	8	16	24	52	99	145
1208-Rocky and His Friends (Jay Ward) (TV)	16	32	48	107	236	365
1209-Sugarfoot (TV)-Photo-c (10-12/61)	7	14	21	49	92	135
1210-The Parent Trap (Disney-Movie) (8/61)-Hayley Mills photo-c	8	16	24	56	108	160
1211-77 Sunset Strip (TV)-Manning-a; photo-c	7	14	21	46	86	125
1212-Chilly Willy (Lantz) (7-9/61)	5	10	15	34	60	85
1213-Mysterious Island (Movie)-Photo-c	7	14	21	49	92	135
1214-Smokey the Bear	5	10	15	31	53	75
1215-Tales of Wells Fargo (TV) (10-12/61)-Photo-c	7	14	21	44	82	120
1216-Whirlybirds (TV)-Photo-c	7	14	21	46	86	125
1218-Fury (TV)-Photo-c	5	10	15	35	63	90
1219-The Detectives (TV)-Robert Taylor & Adam West photo-c	9	18	27	61	123	185
1220-Gunslinger (TV)-Photo-c	7	14	21	49	92	135
1221-Bonanza (TV) (9-11/61)-Photo-c	15	30	45	100	220	340
1222-Elmer Fudd (9-11/61)	5	10	15	33	57	80
1223-Laramie (TV)-Gil Kane-a; photo-c	6	12	18	37	66	95
1224-The Little Rascals (TV) (10-12/61)	5	10	15	33	57	80
1225-The Deputy (TV)-Henry Fonda photo-c	8	16	24	54	102	150
1226-Nikki, Wild Dog of the North (Disney-Movie) (9/61)-Photo-c	5	10	15	33	57	80
1227-Morgan the Pirate (Movie)-Photo-c	6	12	18	42	79	115
1229-Thief of Baghdad (Movie)-Crandall/Evans-a; photo-c	6	12	18	41	76	110
1230-Voyage to the Bottom of the Sea (#1) (Movie)-Photo insert on-c	10	20	30	64	132	200
1231-Danger Man (TV) (9-11/61)-Patrick McGoohan photo-c	10	20	30	66	138	210
1232-On the Double (Movie)	5	10	15	34	60	85
1233-Tammy Tell Me True (Movie) (1961)	6	12	18	38	69	100
1234-The Phantom Planet (Movie) (1961)	7	14	21	44	82	120
1235-Mister Magoo (#1) (12-2/62)	7	14	21	48	89	130
1235-Mister Magoo (3-5/65) 2nd printing; reprint of 12-2/62 issue	5	10	15	35	63	90
1236-King of Kings (Movie)-Photo-c	7	14	21	46	86	125
1237-The Untouchables (#1) (TV)-Not by Toth; photo-c	17	34	51	114	252	390
1238-Deputy Dawg (TV)	9	18	27	63	129	195
1239-Donald Duck Album (Disney) (10-12/61)-Barks-c	7	14	21	44	82	120
1240-The Detectives (TV)-Tufts-a; Robert Taylor photo-c	8	16	24	51	96	140
1241-Sweetie Pie	4	8	12	28	47	65
1242-King Leonardo and His Short Subjects (#1) (TV) (11-1/62)	10	20	30	67	141	215
1243-Ellery Queen	7	14	21	48	89	130
1244-Space Mouse (Lantz) (11-1/62)	5	10	15	33	57	80
1245-New Adventures of Sherlock Holmes	10	20	30	70	150	230
1246-Mickey Mouse Album (Disney)	6	12	18	37	66	95
1247-Daisy Duck's Diary (Disney) (12-2/62)	5	10	15	35	63	90
1248-Pluto (Disney)	5	10	15	33	57	80
1249-The Danny Thomas Show (TV)-Manning-a; photo-c	12	24	36	80	173	265
1250-The Four Horsemen of the Apocalypse (Movie)-Photo-c	6	12	18	41	76	110
1251-Everything's Ducky (Movie) (1961)	5	10	15	34	60	85
1252-The Andy Griffith Show (TV)-Photo-c; 1st show aired 10/3/60	36	72	108	266	596	925
1253-Space Man (#1) (1-3/62)	7	14	21	48	89	130
1254- "Diver Dan" (#1) (TV) (2-4/62)-Photo-c	5	10	15	31	53	75
1255-The Wonders of Aladdin (Movie) (1961)	6	12	18	40	73	105
1256-Kona, Monarch of Monster Isle (#1) (2-4/62)-Glanzman-a	9	18	27	61	123	185
1257-Car 54, Where Are You? (#1) (TV) (3-5/62)-Photo-c	8	16	24	54	102	150
1258-The Frogmen (#1)-Evans-a	8	16	24	54	102	150
1259-El Cid (Movie) (1961)-Photo-c	7	14	21	46	86	125
1260-The Horsemasters (TV, Movie) (Disney) (12-2/62)-Annette Funicello photo-c	10	20	30	69	147	225
1261-Rawhide (TV)-Clint Eastwood photo-c	13	26	39	89	195	300
1262-The Rebel (TV)-Photo-c	8	16	24	52	99	145
1263-77 Sunset Strip (TV) (12-2/62)-Manning-a; photo-c	7	14	21	46	86	125
1264-Pixie and Dixie and Mr. Jinks (TV) (Hanna-Barbera)	5	10	15	35	63	90
1265-The Real McCoys (TV)-Photo-c	7	14	21	48	89	130
1266-M.G.M.'s Spike and Tyke (12-2/62)	4	8	12	28	47	65
1267-Gyro Gearloose; Barks-c/a, 4 pgs. (Disney) (12-2/62)	7	14	21	48	89	130
1268-Oswald the Rabbit (Lantz)	5	10	15	33	57	80
1269-Rawhide (TV)-Clint Eastwood photo-c	13	26	39	89	195	300
1270-Bullwinkle and Rocky (#1) (TV) (Jay Ward) (3-5/62)	16	32	48	110	243	375
1271-Yogi Bear Birthday Party (TV) (Hanna-Barbera) (11/61) (Given away for 1 box top from Kellogg's Corn Flakes)	6	12	18	40	73	105
1272-Frosty the Snowman	5	10	15	35	63	90
1273-Hans Brinker (Disney-Movie)-Photo-c (2/62)	6	12	18	37	66	95
1274-Santa Claus Funnies (12/61)	6	12	18	41	76	110
1275-Rocky and His Friends (TV) (Jay Ward)	16	32	48	107	236	365
1276-Dondi	4	8	12	28	47	65
1278-King Leonardo and His Short Subjects (TV)	10	20	30	67	141	215
1279-Grandma Duck's Farm Friends (Disney)	5	10	15	34	60	85
1280-Hennesey (TV)-Photo-c	6	12	18	40	73	105
1281-Chilly Willy (Lantz) (4-6/62)	5	10	15	34	60	85
1282-Babes in Toyland (Disney-Movie) (1/62); Annette Funicello photo-c	12	24	36	83	182	280

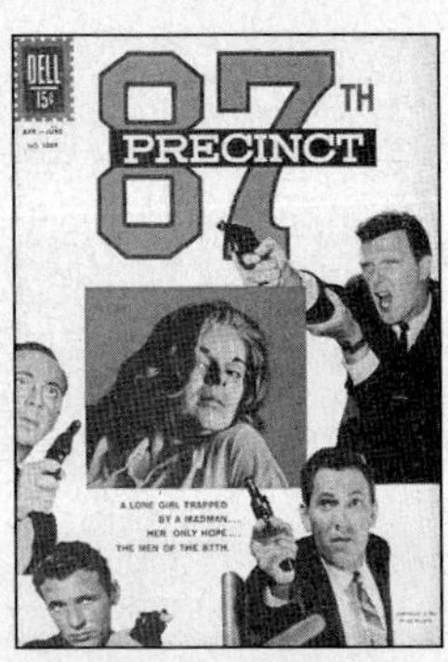

Four Color Comics #1309 © DELL

Four Favorites #14 © ACE

Four Points #1 © Aspen MLT

	GD 2.0	VG 4.0	FN 6.0	VF 8.0	VF/NM 9.0	NM- 9.2
1283-Bonanza (TV) (2-4/62)-Photo-c	15	30	45	100	220	340
1284-Laramie (TV)-Heath-a; photo-c	6	12	18	37	66	95
1285-Leave It to Beaver (TV)-Photo-c	12	24	36	80	173	265
1286-The Untouchables (TV)-Photo-c	12	24	36	80	173	265
1287-Man from Wells Fargo (TV)-Photo-c	6	12	18	37	66	95
1288-Twilight Zone (TV) (4/62)-Crandall/Evans-c/a	10	20	30	69	147	225
1289-Ellery Queen	7	14	21	48	89	130
1290-M.G.M.'s Mouse Musketeers	4	8	12	28	47	65
1291-77 Sunset Strip (TV)-Manning-a; photo-c	7	14	21	46	86	125
1293-Elmer Fudd (3-5/62)	5	10	15	33	57	80
1294-Ripcord (TV)	6	12	18	40	73	105
1295-Mister Ed, the Talking Horse (#1) (TV) (3-5/62)-Photo-c	11	22	33	73	157	240
1296-Fury (TV) (3-5/62)-Photo-c	5	10	15	35	63	90
1297-Spanky, Alfalfa and the Little Rascals (TV)	5	10	15	33	57	80
1298-The Hathaways (TV)-Photo-c	5	10	15	31	53	75
1299-Deputy Dawg (TV)	9	18	27	63	129	195
1300-The Comancheros (Movie) (1961)-John Wayne photo-c	14	28	42	94	207	320
1301-Adventures in Paradise (TV) (2-4/62)	6	12	18	37	66	95
1302-Johnny Jason, Teen Reporter (2-4/62)	4	8	12	23	37	50
1303-Lad: A Dog (Movie)-Photo-c	5	10	15	33	57	80
1304-Nellie the Nurse (3-5/62)-Stanley-a	8	16	24	51	96	140
1305-Mister Magoo (3-5/62)	7	14	21	48	89	130
1306-Target: The Corruptors (#1) (TV) (3-5/62)-Photo-c	5	10	15	33	57	80
1307-Margie (TV) (3-5/62)	6	12	18	41	76	110
1308-Tales of the Wizard of Oz (TV) (3-5/62)	11	22	33	76	163	250
1309-87th Precinct (#1) (TV) (4-6/62)-Krigstein-a; photo-c	9	18	27	60	120	180
1310-Huck and Yogi Winter Sports (TV) (Hanna-Barbera) (3/62)	8	16	24	51	96	140
1311-Rocky and His Friends (TV) (Jay Ward)	16	32	48	107	236	365
1312-National Velvet (TV)-Photo-c	4	8	12	27	44	60
1313-Moon Pilot (Disney-Movie)-Photo-c	6	12	18	40	73	105
1328-The Underwater City (Movie) (1961)-Evans-a; photo-c	6	12	18	42	79	115
1329-See Gyro Gearloose #01329-207						
1330-Brain Boy (#1)-Gil Kane-a	10	20	30	64	132	200
1332-Bachelor Father (TV)	7	14	21	44	82	120
1333-Short Ribs (4-6/62)	5	10	15	35	63	90
1335-Aggie Mack (4-6/62)	5	10	15	31	53	75
1336-On Stage; not by Leonard Starr	5	10	15	34	60	85
1337-Dr. Kildare (#1) (TV) (4-6/62)-Photo-c	8	16	24	54	102	150
1341-The Andy Griffith Show (TV) (4-6/62)-Photo-c	34	68	102	245	548	850
1348-Yak Yak (#2)-Jack Davis-c/a	7	14	21	46	86	125
1349-Yogi Bear Visits the U.N. (TV) (Hanna-Barbera) (1/62)-Photo-c	8	16	24	54	102	150
1350-Comanche (Disney-Movie)(1962)-Reprints 4-Color #966 (title change from "Tonka" to "Comanche") (4-6/62)-Sal Mineo photo-c	5	10	15	33	57	80
1354-Calvin & the Colonel (#1) (TV) (4-6/62)	8	16	24	54	102	150

NOTE: *Missing numbers probably do not exist.*

4-D MONKEY, THE (Adventures of... #? on)
Leung's Publications: 1988 - No. 11, 1990 ($1.80/$2.00, 52 pgs.)

1-11: 1-Karate Pig, Ninja Flounder & 4-D Monkey (48 pgs., centerfold is a Christmas card). 2-4 (52 pgs.) 4.00

FOUR FAVORITES (Crime Must Pay the Penalty No. 33 on)
Ace Magazines: Sept, 1941 - No. 32, Dec, 1947

	GD 2.0	VG 4.0	FN 6.0	VF 8.0	VF/NM 9.0	NM- 9.2
1-Vulcan, Lash Lightning (formerly Flash Lightning in Sure-Fire), Magno the Magnetic Man & The Raven begin; flag/Hitler-c	300	600	900	1950	3375	4800
2-The Black Ace only app.; WWII flag-c	135	270	405	864	1482	2100
3-Last Vulcan; V For Victory WWII-c	129	258	387	826	1413	2000
4,5: 4-The Raven & Vulcan end; Unknown Soldier begins (see Our Flag), ends #28. 5-Captain Courageous begins (5/42), ends #28 (moves over from Captain Courageous #6); not in #6. 5,6-Bondage/torture-c	129	258	387	826	1413	2000
6-8: 6-The Flag app.; Mr. Risk begins (7/42)	116	232	348	742	1271	1800
9-Kurtzman-a (Lash Lightning); robot-c	123	246	369	787	1344	1900
10-Classic Kurtzman-c/a (Magno & Davey)	181	362	543	1158	1979	2800
11-Kurtzman-a; Hitler, Mussolini, Hirohito-c; L.B. Cole-a; Unknown Soldier by Kurtzman	206	412	618	1318	2259	3200
12-L.B. Cole-a; Japanese WWII-c	116	232	348	742	1271	1800
13-L.B. Cole-c (his first cover?); WWII-c	123	246	369	787	1344	1900
14,16-18,20: 18,20-Palais-c/a	63	126	189	403	689	975
15-Japanese WWII-c	65	130	195	416	708	1000
19-Nazi WWII bondage-c	90	180	270	576	988	1400
21-No Unknown Soldier; The Unknown app.	57	114	171	362	619	875
22-27: 22-Captain Courageous drops costume. 23-Unknown Soldier drops costume. 25-29-Hap Hazard app. 26-Last Magno	52	104	156	328	552	775
28,29: Hap Hazard app. in all	39	78	117	231	378	525
30-32: 30-Funny-c begin (teen humor), end #32	19	38	57	111	176	240

NOTE: ***Dave Berg** c-5. **Jim Mooney** a-6; c-1-3. **Palais** a-18-20; c-18-25.*

FOUR HORSEMEN, THE (See The Crusaders)

FOUR HORSEMEN
DC Comics (Vertigo): Feb, 2000 - No. 4, May, 2000 ($2.50, limited series)

1-4-Esad Ribic-c/a; Robert Rodi-s 3.00

FOUR HORSEMEN OF THE APOCALYPSE, THE (Movie)
Dell Publishing Co.: No. 1250, Jan-Mar, 1962 (one-shot)

	GD 2.0	VG 4.0	FN 6.0	VF 8.0	VF/NM 9.0	NM- 9.2
Four Color 1250-Photo-c	6	12	18	41	76	110

4MOST (Foremost Boys No. 32-40; becomes Thrilling Crime Cases #41 on)
Novelty Publications/Star Publications No. 37-on:
Winter, 1941-42 - V8#5(#36), 9-10/49; #37, 11-12/49 - #40, 4-5/50

	GD 2.0	VG 4.0	FN 6.0	VF 8.0	VF/NM 9.0	NM- 9.2
V1#1-The Target by Sid Greene, The Cadet & Dick Cole begin with origins retold; produced by Funnies Inc.; quarterly issues begin, end V6#3; German WWII-c	219	438	657	1402	2401	3400
2-Last Target (Spr/42); WWII cover	74	148	222	470	810	1150
3-Dan'l Flannel begins; flag-c	52	104	156	328	552	775
4-1pg. Dr. Seuss (signed) (Aut/42); fish in the face-c	53	106	159	334	567	800
V2#1-3	28	56	84	165	270	375
4-Hitler, Tojo & Mussolini app. as pumpkins on-c	58	116	174	371	636	900
V3#1-4	20	40	60	114	182	250
V4#1-4: 2-Walter Johnson-c	15	30	45	83	124	165
V5#1-4: 1-The Target & Targeteers app.	14	28	42	76	108	140
V6#1-4	11	22	33	62	86	110
5-L. B. Cole-c	20	40	60	114	182	250
V7#1,3,5, V8#1, 37	11	22	33	60	83	105
2,4,6-L. B. Cole-c. 6-Last Dick Cole	20	40	60	114	182	250
V8#2,3,5-L. B. Cole-c/a	22	44	66	132	216	300
4-L. B. Cole-a	15	30	45	83	124	165
38-40: 38-Johnny Weismuller (Tarzan) life story & Jim Braddock (boxer) life story. 38-40-L.B. Cole-c. 40-Last White Rider	17	34	51	98	154	210
Accepted Reprint 38-40 (nd): 40-r/Johnny Weismuller life story; all have L.B. Cole-c	10	20	30	56	76	95

411
Marvel Comics: June, 2003 - No. 3 ($3.50, limited series)

1,2-Tributes to peacemakers; s/a by various. 1-Millar, Quitely, Mack, Winslade & others-s/a. 2-Harris, Phillips, Manco, Bruce Jones. 3.50

FOUR POINTS, THE
Aspen MLT Inc.: Apr, 2015 - No. 5, Aug, 2015 ($3.99)

1-5-Lobdell-s/Gunderson-a; multiple covers 4.00

FOUR-STAR BATTLE TALES
National Periodical Publications: Feb-Mar, 1973 - No. 5, Nov-Dec, 1973

	GD 2.0	VG 4.0	FN 6.0	VF 8.0	VF/NM 9.0	NM- 9.2
1-Reprints begin	3	6	9	16	24	32
2-5	2	4	6	11	16	20

NOTE: ***Drucker** r-1, 3-5. **Heath** r-2, 5; c-1. **Krigstein** r-5. **Kubert** r-4; c-2.*

FOUR STAR SPECTACULAR
National Periodical Publications: Mar-Apr, 1976 - No. 6, Jan-Feb, 1977

	GD 2.0	VG 4.0	FN 6.0	VF 8.0	VF/NM 9.0	NM- 9.2
1-Includes G.A. Flash story with new art	2	4	6	11	16	20
2-6: Reprints in all. 2-Infinity cover	2	4	6	8	10	12

NOTE: *All contain DC Superhero reprints. #1 has 68 pgs.; #2-6, 52 pgs.. #1, 4-Hawkman app.; #2-Kid Flash app.; #3-Green Lantern app; #2, 4, 5-Wonder Woman, Superboy app; #5-Green Arrow, Vigilante app; #6-Blackhawk G.A.-r.*

FOUR TEENERS (Formerly Crime Must Pay The Penalty; Dotty No. 35 on)
A. A. Wyn: No. 34, April, 1948 (52 pgs.)

	GD 2.0	VG 4.0	FN 6.0	VF 8.0	VF/NM 9.0	NM- 9.2
34-Teen-age comic; Dotty app.; Curly & Jerry continue from Four Favorites	13	26	39	74	105	135

4001 A.D. (See Valiant 2016 FCBD edition for prelude)
Valiant Entertainment: May, 2016 - No. 4, Aug, 2016 ($3.99, limited series)

1-4-Matt Kindt-s/Clayton Crain-a. 1-David Mack-a (3 pages) 4.00
...: Bloodshot 1 (6/16, $3.99) Lemire-s/Braithwaite-a; Bloodshot reforms in 4001 A.D. 4.00
...: Shadowman 1 (7/16, $3.99) Houser & Roberts-s/Gill-a 4.00

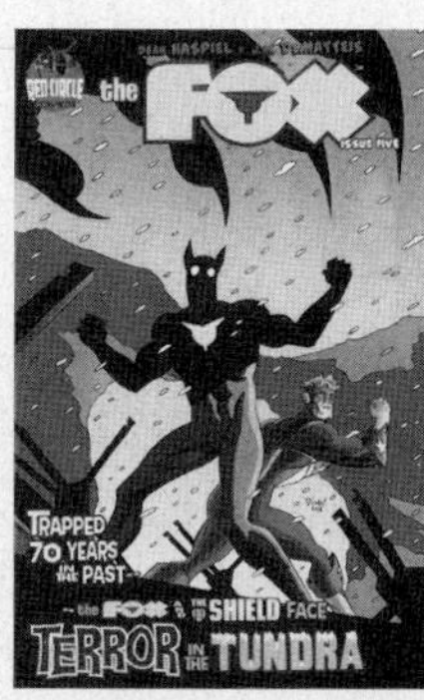

The Fox (2013 series) #5 © ACP

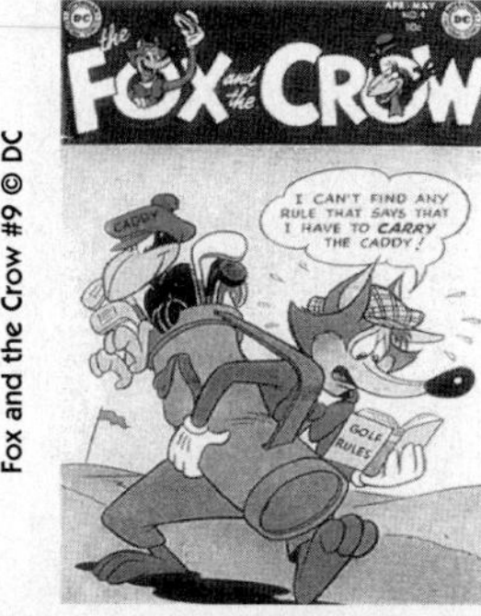

Fox and the Crow #9 © DC

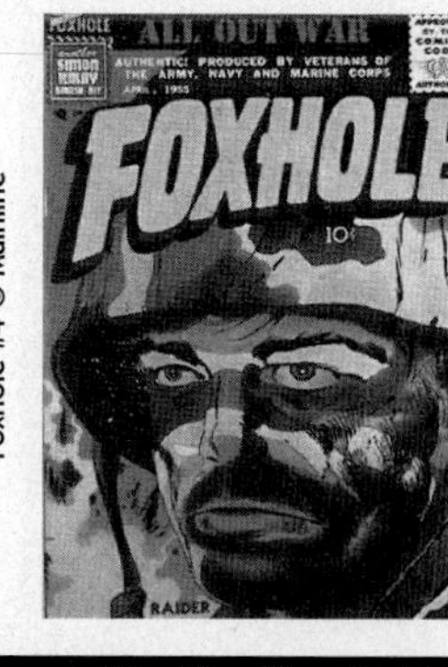

Foxhole #4 © Mainline

GD 2.0 | VG 4.0 | FN 6.0 | VF 8.0 | VF/NM 9.0 | NM- 9.2

...: War Mother 1 (8/16, $3.99) Van Lente-s/Giorello-a 4.00
...: X-O Manowar 1 (5/16, $3.99) Venditti-s/Henry-a; prelude to main series 4.00

FOURTH WORLD GALLERY, THE (Jack Kirby's...)
DC Comics: 1996 (9/96) ($3.50, one-shot)
nn-Pin-ups of Jack Kirby's Fourth World characters (New Gods, Forever People & Mister Miracle) by John Byrne, Rick Burchett, Dan Jurgens, Walt Simonson & others 4.00

FOUR WOMEN
DC Comics (Homage): Dec, 2001 - No. 5, Apr, 2002 ($2.95, limited series)
1-5-Sam Kieth-s/a 3.00
TPB (2002, $17.95) r/series; foreward by Kieth 18.00

FOX, THE
Archie Comic Publications (Red Circle Comics): Dec, 2013 - No. 5, Apr, 2014 ($2.99)
1-5-Dean Haspiel-a/Haspiel and Mark Waid-s. 1-Three covers. 2-Two covers 3.00

FOX, THE
Archie Comic Publications (Dark Circle Comics): Jun, 2015 - No. 5, Oct, 2015 ($3.99)
1-5-Dean Haspiel-a/Haspiel and Mark Waid-s; multiple covers on each 4.00

FOX AND THE CROW (Stanley & His Monster No. 109 on) (See Comic Cavalcade & Real Screen Comics)
National Periodical Publications: Dec-Jan, 1951-52 - No. 108, Feb-Mar, 1968
1 129 258 387 826 1413 2000
2(Scarce) 57 114 171 362 619 875
3-5 37 74 111 222 361 500
6-10 (6-7/53) 26 52 78 154 252 350
11-20 (10/54) 20 40 60 114 182 250
21-30: 22-Last precode issue (2/55) 15 30 45 83 124 165
31-40 12 24 36 69 97 125
41-60 6 12 18 37 66 95
61-80 5 10 15 31 53 75
81-94: 94-(11/65)-The Brat Finks begin 4 8 12 25 40 55
95-Stanley & His Monster begins (origin & 1st app) 5 10 15 33 57 80
96-99,101-108 3 6 9 19 30 40
100 (10-11/66) 3 6 9 21 33 45
NOTE: *Many later covers by* **Mort Drucker.**

FOX AND THE HOUND, THE (Disney)(Movie)
Whitman Publishing Co.: Aug, 1981 - No. 3, Oct, 1981
11292- Golden Press Graphic Novel 2 4 6 8 10 12
1-3-Based on animated movie 1 2 3 5 7 9

FOXFIRE (See The Phoenix Resurrection)
Malibu Comics (Ultraverse): Feb, 1996 - No. 4, May, 1996 ($1.50)
1-4: Sludge, Ultraforce app. 4-Punisher app. 3.00

FOX GIANTS (Also see Giant Comics Edition)
Fox Feature Syndicate: 1944 - 1950 (25¢, 132 - 196 pgs.)
Album of Crime nn(1949, 132p) 61 122 183 390 670 950
Album of Love nn(1949, 132p) 68 136 204 435 743 1050
All Famous Crime Stories nn('49, 132p) 61 122 183 390 670 950
All Good Comics 1(1944, 132p)(R.W. Voigt)-The Bouncer, Purple Tigress, Rick Evans, Puppeteer, Green Mask; Infinity-c 77 154 231 493 847 1200
All Great nn(1944, 132p)-Capt. Jack Terry, Rick Evans, Jaguar Man 53 106 159 334 567 800
All Great nn(Chicago Nite Life News)(1945, 132p)-Green Mask, Bouncer, Puppeteer, Rick Evans, Rocket Kelly 52 104 156 328 552 775
All-Great Confession Magazine nn(1949, 132p) 66 132 198 419 722 1025
All-Great Confessions nn(1949, 132p) 66 132 198 419 722 1025
All Great Crime Stories nn('49, 132p) 61 122 183 390 670 950
All Great Jungle Adventures nn('49, 132p) 77 154 231 493 847 1200
All Real Confession Magazine 3 (3/49, 132p) 65 130 195 416 708 1000
All Real Confession Magazine 4 (4/49, 132p) 65 130 195 416 708 1000
All Your Comics 1(1944, 132p)-The Puppeteer, Red Robbins, & Merciless the Sorcerer 54 108 162 343 574 825
Almanac Of Crime nn(1948, 148p)-Phantom Lady 69 138 207 442 759 1075
Almanac Of Crime 1(1950, 132p) 60 120 180 381 653 925
Book Of Love nn(1950, 132p) 63 126 189 403 689 975
Burning Romances 1(1949, 132p) 74 148 222 470 810 1150
Crimes Incorporated nn(1950, 132p) 57 114 171 362 619 875
Daring Love Stories nn(1950, 132p) 63 126 189 403 689 975
Everybody's Comics 1(1944, 50¢, 196p)-The Green Mask, The Puppeteer, The Bouncer, Rocket Kelly, Rick Evans 65 130 195 416 708 1000
Everybody's Comics 1(1946, 196p)-Green Lama, The Puppeteer 53 106 159 334 567 800
Everybody's Comics 1(1946, 196p)-Same as 1945 Ribtickler 41 82 123 256 428 600
Everybody's Comics nn(1947, 132p)-Jo-Jo, Purple Tigress, Cosmo Cat, Bronze Man 53 106 159 334 567 800
Exciting Romance Stories nn(1949, 132p) 66 132 198 419 722 1025
Famous Love nn(1950, 132p)-Photo-c 65 130 195 416 708 1000
Intimate Confessions nn(1950, 132p) 63 126 189 403 689 975
Journal Of Crime nn(1949, 132p) 61 122 183 390 670 950
Love Problems nn(1949, 132p) 66 132 198 419 722 1025
Love Thrills nn(1950, 132p) 63 126 189 403 689 975
March of Crime nn('48, 132p)-Female w/rifle-c 63 126 189 403 689 975
March of Crime nn('49, 132p)-Cop w/pistol-c 58 116 174 371 636 900
March of Crime nn(1949, 132p)-Coffin & man w/machine-gun-c 58 116 174 371 636 900
Revealing Love Stories nn(1950, 132p) 63 126 189 403 689 975
Ribtickler nn(1945, 50¢, 196p)-Chicago Nite Life News; Marvel Mutt, Cosmo Cat, Flash Rabbit, The Nebbs app. 48 96 144 302 514 725
Romantic Thrills nn(1950, 132p) 63 126 189 403 689 975
Secret Love Stories nn(1949, 132p) 66 132 198 419 722 1025
Strange Love nn(1950, 132p)-Photo-c 84 168 252 538 919 1300
Sweetheart Scandals nn(1950, 132p) 63 126 189 403 689 975
Teen-Age Love nn(1950, 132p) 63 126 189 403 689 975
Throbbing Love nn(1950, 132p)-Photo-c; used in **POP**, pg. 107 84 168 252 538 919 1300
Truth About Crime nn(1949, 132p) 61 122 183 390 670 950
Variety Comics 1(1946, 132p)-Blue Beetle, Jungle Jo 54 108 162 343 574 825
Variety Comics nn(1950, 132p)-Jungle Jo, My Secret Affair (w/Harrison/Wood-a), Crimes by Women & My Story 52 104 156 328 552 775
Western Roundup nn('50, 132p)-Hoot Gibson; Cody of the Pony Express app. 41 82 123 256 428 600
NOTE: *Each of the above usually contain four remaindered Fox books minus covers. Since these missing covers often had the first page of the first story, most Giants therefore are incomplete. Approximate values are listed. Books with appearances of Phantom Lady, Rulah, Jo-Jo, etc. could bring more.*

FOXHOLE (Becomes Never Again #8?)
Mainline/Charlton No. 5 on: 9-10/54 - No. 4, 3-4/55; No. 5, 7/55 - No. 7, 3/56
1-Classic Kirby-c 66 132 198 419 722 1025
2-Kirby-c/a(2); Kirby scripts based on his war time experiences 41 82 123 256 428 600
3-5-Simon/Kirby-c only 30 60 90 177 289 400
6-Kirby-c/a(2) 39 78 117 231 378 525
7-Simon & Kirby-c 16 32 48 94 147 200
Super Reprints #10,15-17: 10-r/? 15,16-r/United States Marines #5,8. 17-r/Monty Hall #? 2 4 6 11 16 20
11,12,18-r/Foxhole #1,2,3; Kirby-c 3 6 9 17 26 35
NOTE: **Kirby** *a(r)-Super #11, 12.* **Powell** *a(r)-Super #15, 16. Stories by actual veterans.*

FOXY FAGAN COMICS (Funny Animal)
Dearfield Publishing Co.: Dec, 1946 - No. 7, Summer, 1948
1-Foxy Fagan & Little Buck begin 14 28 42 81 118 155
2 9 18 27 47 61 75
3-7: 6-Rocket ship-c 8 16 24 42 54 65

FRACTION
DC Comics (Focus): June, 2004 - No. 6, Nov, 2004 ($2.50, limited series)
1-6-David Tischman-s/Timothy Green II-a 3.00
SC (2011, $17.99) r/#1-6; cover gallery 18.00

FRACTURED FAIRY TALES (TV)
Gold Key: Oct, 1962 (Jay Ward)
1 (10022-210)-From Bullwinkle TV show 9 18 27 60 120 180

FRAGGLE ROCK (TV)
Marvel Comics (Star Comics)/Marvel V2#1 on: Apr, 1985 - No. 8, Sept, 1986; V2#1, Apr, 1988 - No. 5, Aug, 1988
1-6 (75¢-c) 5.00
7,8 6.00
V2#1-5-($1.00): Reprints 1st series 3.00

FRAGGLE ROCK: JOURNEY TO THE EVERSPRING, (JIM HENSON'S...)
Archaia: Oct, 2014 - No. 4, Jan, 2015 ($3.99, limited series)
1-4-Kate Leth-s/Jake Myler-a. 1-Multiple covers 4.00

FRANCIS, BROTHER OF THE UNIVERSE
Marvel Comics Group: 1980 (75¢, 52 pgs., one-shot)
1-John Buscema/Marie Severin-a; story of Francis Bernadone, celebrating his 800th birthday

Frankenstein, Agent of S.H.A.D.E. #1 © DC

Frankenstein Comics #4 © PRIZE

Frankenstein Underground #1 © Mike Mignola

	GD 2.0	VG 4.0	FN 6.0	VF 8.0	VF/NM 9.0	NM- 9.2
in 1982						6.00

FRANCIS THE FAMOUS TALKING MULE (All based on movie)
Dell Publishing Co.: No. 335 (#1), June, 1951 - No. 1090, March, 1960

	GD 2.0	VG 4.0	FN 6.0	VF 8.0	VF/NM 9.0	NM- 9.2
Four Color 335 (#1)	10	20	30	68	144	220
Four Color 465	6	12	18	41	76	110
Four Color 501,547,579	5	10	15	35	63	90
Four Color 621,655,698,710,745	5	10	15	33	57	80
Four Color 810,863,906,953,991,1068,1090	5	10	15	31	53	75

FRANK
Nemesis Comics (Harvey): Apr (Mar inside), 1994 - No. 4, 1994 ($1.75/$2.50, limited series)

	GD 2.0	VG 4.0	FN 6.0	VF 8.0	VF/NM 9.0	NM- 9.2
1-4-($2.50, direct sale): 1-Foil-c Edition						3.50
1-4-($1.75)-Newsstand Editions; Cowan-a in all						3.00

FRANK
Fantagraphics Books: Sept, 1996 ($2.95, B&W)

	GD 2.0	VG 4.0	FN 6.0	VF 8.0	VF/NM 9.0	NM- 9.2
1-Woodring-c/a/scripts						3.00

FRANK BUCK (Formerly My True Love)
Fox Feature Syndicate: No. 70, May, 1950 - No. 3, Sept, 1950

	GD 2.0	VG 4.0	FN 6.0	VF 8.0	VF/NM 9.0	NM- 9.2
70-Wood a(p)(3 stories)-Photo-c	39	78	117	234	385	535
71-Wood-a (9 pgs.); photo/painted-c	20	40	60	118	192	265
3: 3-Photo/painted-c	15	30	45	85	130	175

NOTE: *Based on "Bring 'Em Back Alive" TV show.*

FRANKEN-CASTLE (See The Punisher, 2009 series)

FRANKENSTEIN (See Dracula, Movie Classics & Werewolf)
Dell Publishing Co.: Aug-Oct, 1964; No. 2, Sept, 1966 - No. 4, Mar, 1967

	GD 2.0	VG 4.0	FN 6.0	VF 8.0	VF/NM 9.0	NM- 9.2
1(12-283-410)(1964)(2nd printing; see Movie Classics for 1st printing)	5	10	15	35	63	90
2-Intro. & origin super-hero character (9/66)	5	10	15	30	50	70
3,4	4	8	12	23	37	50

FRANKENSTEIN (The Monster of...; also see Monsters Unleashed #2, Power Record Comics, Psycho & Silver Surfer #7)
Marvel Comics Group: Jan, 1973 - No. 18, Sept, 1975

	GD 2.0	VG 4.0	FN 6.0	VF 8.0	VF/NM 9.0	NM- 9.2
1-Ploog-c/a begins, ends #6	7	14	21	46	86	125
2	4	8	12	27	44	60
3-5	3	6	9	21	33	45
6,7,10: 7-Dracula cameo	3	6	9	17	26	35
8,9-Dracula c/sty. 9-Death of Dracula	4	8	12	28	47	65
11-17	3	6	9	15	22	28
18-Wrightson-c(i)	3	6	9	16	24	32

NOTE: ***Adkins** c-17i. **Buscema** a-7-10p. **Ditko** a-12r. **G. Kane** c-15p. **Orlando** a-8r. **Ploog** a-1-3, 4p, 5p, 6; c-1-6. **Wrightson** c-18i.*

FRANKENSTEIN (Mary Wollstonecraft Shelley's...; A Marvel Illustrated Novel)
Marvel Pub.: 1983 ($8.95, B&W, 196 pgs., 8x11" TPB)

	GD 2.0	VG 4.0	FN 6.0	VF 8.0	VF/NM 9.0	NM- 9.2
nn-Wrightson-a; 4 pg. intro. by Stephen King	5	10	15	30	50	70
Limited HC Edition						175.00

FRANKENSTEIN, AGENT OF S.H.A.D.E. (New DC 52)
DC Comics: Nov, 2011 - No. 16, Mar, 2013 ($2.99)

	GD 2.0	VG 4.0	FN 6.0	VF 8.0	VF/NM 9.0	NM- 9.2
1-16: 1-Lemire-s/Ponticelli-a/J.G. Jones-c; Ray Palmer & The Creature Commandos app. 5-Crossover with OMAC #5. 13-15-Rotworld						3.00
#0 (11/12, $2.99) Kindt-s/Ponticelli-a; Frankenstein's origin						3.00

FRANKENSTEIN ALIVE, ALIVE
IDW Publishing: May, 2012 - No. 4, Jan, 2018 ($3.99, B&W)

	GD 2.0	VG 4.0	FN 6.0	VF 8.0	VF/NM 9.0	NM- 9.2
1-3-Niles-s/Wrightson-a; interview with creators; excerpt from M.W. Shelley writings						4.00
4-($4.99) Art by Wrightson and Kelley Jones						5.00
... Reanimated Edition (4/14, $5.99) r/#1,2; silver foil cover logo						6.00
... Trio (1/18, $7.99) r/#1-3; silver foil cover logo						8.00

FRANKENSTEIN COMICS (Also See Prize Comics)
Prize Publ. (Crestwood/Feature): Sum, 1945 - V5#5(#33), Oct-Nov, 1954

	GD 2.0	VG 4.0	FN 6.0	VF 8.0	VF/NM 9.0	NM- 9.2
1-Frankenstein begins by Dick Briefer (origin); Frank Sinatra parody	300	600	900	2070	3635	5200
2	84	168	252	538	919	1300
3-5	65	130	195	416	708	1000
6-10: 7-S&K a(r)/Headline Comics. 8(7-8/47)-Superman satire	58	116	174	371	636	900
11-17(1-2/49)-11-Boris Karloff parody-c/story. 17-Last humor issue	52	104	156	328	552	775
18(3/52)-New origin, horror series begins	97	194	291	621	1061	1500
19,20(V3#4, 8-9/52)	65	130	195	416	708	1000
21(V3#5), 22(V3#6), 23(V4#1) - #28(V4#6)	58	116	174	371	636	900
29(V5#1) - #33(V5#5)	53	106	159	334	567	800

NOTE: ***Briefer** c/a-all. **Meskin** a-21, 29.*

FRANKENSTEIN/DRACULA WAR, THE
Topps Comics: Feb, 1995 - No. 3, May, 1995 ($2.50, limited series)

	GD 2.0	VG 4.0	FN 6.0	VF 8.0	VF/NM 9.0	NM- 9.2
1-3						3.00

FRANKENSTEIN, JR. (...& the Impossibles) (TV)
Gold Key: Jan, 1966 (Hanna-Barbera)

	GD 2.0	VG 4.0	FN 6.0	VF 8.0	VF/NM 9.0	NM- 9.2
1-Super hero (scarce)	10	20	30	66	138	210

FRANKENSTEIN MOBSTER
Image Comics: No. 0, Oct, 2003 - No. 7, Dec, 2004 ($2.95)

	GD 2.0	VG 4.0	FN 6.0	VF 8.0	VF/NM 9.0	NM- 9.2
0-7: 0-Two covers by Wheatley and Hughes; Wheatley-s/a. 1-Variant-c by Wieringo						3.00

FRANKENSTEIN: OR THE MODERN PROMETHEUS
Caliber Press: 1994 ($2.95, one-shot)

	GD 2.0	VG 4.0	FN 6.0	VF 8.0	VF/NM 9.0	NM- 9.2
1						3.00

FRANKENSTEIN UNDERGROUND (From Hellboy)
Dark Horse Comics: Mar, 2015 - No. 5, Jul, 2015 ($3.50, limited series)

	GD 2.0	VG 4.0	FN 6.0	VF 8.0	VF/NM 9.0	NM- 9.2
1-5-Mike Mignola-s/c; Ben Stenbeck-a						3.50

FRANK FRAZETTA FANTASY ILLUSTRATED (Magazine)
Quantum Cat Entertainment: Spring 1998 - No. 8 ($5.95, quarterly)

	GD 2.0	VG 4.0	FN 6.0	VF 8.0	VF/NM 9.0	NM- 9.2
1-Anthology; art by Corben, Horley, Jusko	1	2	3	4	5	7
1-Linsner variant-c						10.00
2-Battle Chasers by Madureira; Harris-a						8.00
2-Madureira Battle Chasers variant-c						12.00
3-8-Frazetta-c						6.00
3-Tony Daniel variant-c						15.00
5,6-Portacio variant-c, 7,8-Alex Nino variant-c						10.00
8-Alex Ross Chicago Comicon variant-c						10.00

FRANK FRAZETTA'S DEATH DEALER
Image Comics: Mar, 2007 - No. 6, Jan, 2008 ($3.99)

	GD 2.0	VG 4.0	FN 6.0	VF 8.0	VF/NM 9.0	NM- 9.2
1-6-Nat Jones-a; 3 covers (Frazetta, Jones, Jones sketch)						4.00

FRANK FRAZETTA'S...
Fantagraphics Books/Image Comics: one-shots

	GD 2.0	VG 4.0	FN 6.0	VF 8.0	VF/NM 9.0	NM- 9.2
... Creatures 1 (Image Comics, 7/08, $3.99) Bergting-a; covers by Frazetta & Bergting						4.00
... Dark Kingdom 1-4 (Image, 4/08 - No. 4, 1/10, $3.99) Vigil-a; covers by Frazetta & Vigil						4.00
... Dracula Meets the Wolfman 1 (Image, 8/08, $3.99) Francavilla-a; 2 covers						4.00
... Moon Maid 1 (Image, 1/09, $3.99) Tim Vigil-a; covers by Frazetta & Vigil						4.00
... Neanderthal 1 (Image, 4/09, $3.99) Fotos & Vigil-a; covers by Frazetta & Fotos						4.00
... Sorcerer 1 (Image, 8/09, $3.99) Medors-a; covers by Frazetta & Medors						4.00
... Swamp Demon 1 (Image, 7/08, $3.99) Medors-a; covers by Frazetta & Medors						4.00
... Thun'da Tales 1 (Fantagraphics Books, 1987, $2.00) Frazetta-r						6.00
... Untamed Love 1 (Fantagraphics Books, 11/87, $2.00) r/1950's romance comics						6.00

FRANKIE COMICS (...& Lana No. 13-15) (Formerly Movie Tunes; becomes Frankie Fuddle No. 16 on)
Marvel Comics (MgPC): No. 4, Wint, 1946-47 - No. 15, June, 1949

	GD 2.0	VG 4.0	FN 6.0	VF 8.0	VF/NM 9.0	NM- 9.2
4-Mitzi, Margie, Daisy app.	24	48	72	142	234	325
5-9	15	30	45	88	137	185
10-15: 13-Anti-Wertham editorial	14	28	42	81	118	155

FRANKIE DOODLE (See Sparkler, both series)
United Features Syndicate: No. 7, 1939

	GD 2.0	VG 4.0	FN 6.0	VF 8.0	VF/NM 9.0	NM- 9.2
Single Series 7	34	68	102	204	332	460

FRANKIE FUDDLE (Formerly Frankie & Lana)
Marvel Comics: No. 16, Aug, 1949 - No. 17, Nov, 1949

	GD 2.0	VG 4.0	FN 6.0	VF 8.0	VF/NM 9.0	NM- 9.2
16,17	14	28	42	80	115	150

FRANKLIN RICHARDS (Fantastic Four)
Marvel Comics: April, 2006 - Present ($2.99/$3.99, one-shots)

	GD 2.0	VG 4.0	FN 6.0	VF 8.0	VF/NM 9.0	NM- 9.2
...: April Fools (6/09, $3.99) Eliopoulos-s/a						4.00
...: Collected Chaos (2008, $8.99, digest) reprints various one-shots						9.00
...: Fall Football Fiasco (1/08, $2.99) Eliopoulos-a/Sumerak-s						3.00
...: Happy Franksgiving (1/07, $2.99) Thanksgiving stories by Eliopoulos-a/Sumerak-s						3.00
...: It's Dark Reigning Cats & Dogs (4/09, $3.99) Eliopoulos-s/a						4.00
...: Lab Brat (2007, $7.99, digest) reprints one-shots and Masked Marvel back-ups						8.00
...: March Madness (5/07, $2.99) More science gone wrong by Eliopoulos-a/Sumerak-s						3.00
...: Monster Mash (11/07, $2.99) Science mishaps by Eliopoulos-a/Sumerak-s						3.00
...: Not-So-Secret Invasion (7/08, $2.99) Skrull cover; The Wizard app.						3.00
... One Shot (4/06, $2.99) short stories by Eliopoulos-a/Sumerak-s						3.00
...: School's Out (4/09, $3.99) Eliopoulos-s/a; Katie Power app.						4.00
...: Sons of Geniuses (1/09, $3.99) parallel dimension alternate version hijinks						4.00

Freaks of the Heartland #1 © Niles & Ruth

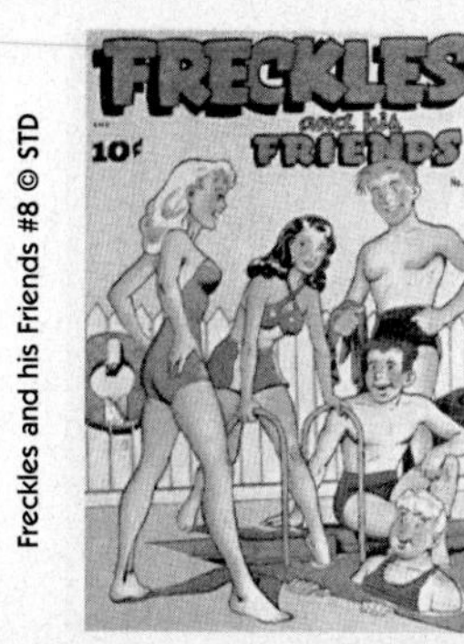
Freckles and his Friends #8 © STD

Freedom Fighters #2 © DC

	GD	VG	FN	VF	VF/NM	NM-
	2.0	4.0	6.0	8.0	9.0	9.2

...: Spring Break (5/08, $2.99) short stories by Eliopoulos-a/Sumerak-s 3.00
...: Summer Smackdown (10/08, $2.99) short stories by Eliopoulos-a/Sumerak-s 3.00
...: Super Summer Spectacular (9/06, $2.99) short stories by Eliopoulos-a/Sumerak-s 3.00
...: World Be Warned (8/07, $2.99) short stories by Eliopoulos-a/Sumerak-s; Hulk app. 3.00

FRANK LUTHER'S SILLY PILLY COMICS (See Jingle Dingle...)
Children's Comics (Maltex Cereal): 1950 (10¢)

1-Characters from radio, records, & TV 10 20 30 58 79 100
NOTE: *Also printed as a promotional comic for Maltex cereal.*

FRANK MERRIWELL AT YALE (Speed Demons No. 5 on?)
Charlton Comics: June, 1955 - No. 4, Jan, 1956 (Also see Shadow Comics)

1 7 14 21 37 46 55
2-4 5 10 15 24 30 35

FRANTIC (Magazine) (See Ratfink & Zany)
Pierce Publishing Co.: Oct, 1958 - V2#2, Apr, 1959 (Satire)

V1#1 15 30 45 85 130 175
2 10 20 30 58 79 100
V2#1,2: 1-Burgos-a, Severin-c/a; Powell-a? 9 18 27 50 65 80

FRAY (Also see Buffy the Vampire Slayer "season eight" #16-19)
Dark Horse Comics: June, 2001 - No. 8, July, 2003 ($2.99, limited series)

1-Joss Whedon-s/Moline & Owens-a 1 2 3 5 6 8
1-DF Gold edition 2 4 6 9 12 15
2-8: 6-(3/02). 7-(4/03) 4.00
TPB (11/03, $19.95) r/#1-8; intros by Whedon & Loeb; Moline sketch pages 20.00

FREAK FORCE (Also see Savage Dragon)
Image Comics (Highbrow Ent.): Dec, 1993 - No. 18, July, 1995 ($1.95/$2.50)

1-18-Superpatriot & Mighty Man in all; Erik Larsen scripts in all. 4-Vanguard app. 8-Begin $2.50-c. 9-Cyberforce-c & app. 13-Variant-c 3.00

FREAK FORCE (Also see Savage Dragon)
Image Comics: Apr, 1997 - No. 3, July, 1997 ($2.95)

1-3-Larsen-s 3.00

FREAK OUT, USA (See On the Scene Presents...)

FREAK SHOW
Image Comics (Desperado): 2006 ($5.99, B&W, one-shot)

nn-Bruce Jones-s/Bernie Wrightson-c/a 6.00

FREAKS OF THE HEARTLAND
Dark Horse Comics: Jan, 2004 - No. 6, Nov, 2004 ($2.99)

1-6-Steve Niles-s/Greg Ruth-a 3.00

FRECKLES AND HIS FRIENDS (See Crackajack Funnies, Famous Comics Cartoon Book, Honeybee Birdwhistle... & Red Ryder)

FRECKLES AND HIS FRIENDS
Standard Comics/Argo: No. 5, 11/47 - No. 12, 8/49; 11/55 - No. 4, 6/56

5-Reprints 12 24 36 69 97 125
6-12-Reprints. 7-9-Airbrush-c (by Schomburg?). 11-Lingerie panels
9 18 27 50 65 80
NOTE: *Some copies of No. 8 & 9 contain a printing oddity. The negatives were elongated in the engraving process, probably to conform to page dimensions on the filler pages. Those pages only look normal when viewed at a 45 degree angle.*
1(Argo,'55)-Reprints (NEA Service) 6 12 18 31 38 45
2-4 4 8 12 18 22 25

FREDDY (Formerly My Little Margie's Boy Friends) (Also see Blue Bird)
Charlton Comics: V2#12, June, 1958 - No. 47, Feb, 1965

V2#12-Teenage 3 6 9 21 33 45
13-15 3 6 9 15 22 28
16-47 2 4 6 11 16 20

FREDDY
Dell Publishing Co.: May-July, 1963 - No. 3, Oct-Dec, 1964

1 3 6 9 18 28 38
2,3 3 6 9 14 20 26

FREDDY KRUEGER'S A NIGHTMARE ON ELM STREET
Marvel Comics: Oct, 1989 - No. 2, Dec, 1989 ($2.25, B&W, movie adaptation, magazine)

1,2: Origin Freddy Krueger; Buckler/Alcala-a 2 4 6 10 14 18

FREDDY'S DEAD: THE FINAL NIGHTMARE
Innovation Publishing: Oct, 1991 - No. 3, Dec 1991 ($2.50, color mini-series, adapts movie)

1-3: Dismukes (film poster artist) painted-c 3.00

FREDDY VS. JASON VS. ASH (Freddy Krueger, Friday the 13th, Army of Darkness)
DC Comics (WildStorm): Early Jan, 2008 - No. 6, May, 2008 ($2.99, limited series)

	GD	VG	FN	VF	VF/NM	NM-
	2.0	4.0	6.0	8.0	9.0	9.2

1-Three covers by J. Scott Campbell; Kuhoric-s/Craig-a 5.00
1-Second printing with 3 covers combined sideways 4.00
2-6: 2-4-Eric Powell-c. 5,6-Richard Friend-c 4.00
2-4-Second printings with B&W covers 3.00
TPB (2008, $17.99) r/#1-6; creators' interview afterword 18.00

FREDDY VS. JASON VS. ASH: THE NIGHTMARE WARRIORS
DC Comics (WildStorm): Aug, 2009 - No. 6, Jan, 2010 ($3.99, limited series)

1-6-Katz & Kuhoric-s/Craig-a. 1-Suydam-c 4.00
TPB (2010, $17.99) r/#1-6; cover gallery 18.00

FRED HEMBECK DESTROYS THE MARVEL UNIVERSE
Marvel Comics: July, 1989 ($1.50, one-shot)

1-Punisher app.; Staton-i (5 pgs.) 4.00

FRED HEMBECK SELLS THE MARVEL UNIVERSE
Marvel Comics: Oct, 1990 ($1.25, one-shot)

1-Punisher, Wolverine parodies; Hembeck/Austin-c 4.00

FREE COMIC BOOK DAY
Various publishers

2013 (Avengers/Hulk)(Marvel, 5/13) Hulk and Avengers Assemble animated series 3.00
2014 (Guardians of the Galaxy)(Marvel, 5/14) r/#1; Thanos & Spider-Verse back-ups 3.00
2015 (Avengers)(Marvel, 6/15) All-New Avengers and Uncanny Humans 3.00
2015 (Dark Horse, 5/15) Previews Fight Club 2, The Goon, and The Strain 3.00
2015 (Secret Wars #1)(Marvel, 6/15) Prelude to Secret Wars series (#0 on cover); back-up with Avengers/Attack on Titan x-over; Alex Ross wraparound-c 3.00
2016 (Captain America #1)(Marvel, 5/16) Preview of Captain America: Steve Rogers #1 and Amazing Spider-Man "Dead No More" storyline 3.00
2016 (Dark Horse, 5/16) Previews Serenity, Hellboy and Aliens: Defiance 3.00
2017 (Dark Horse, 5/17) Avatar (movie) w/Doug Wheatley-a; Briggs Land story - Wood-s/Dell'Edera-a 3.00
2017 (Secret Empire)(Marvel, 7/17) 1-Spencer-s/Sorrentino-a/Brooks-c; Steve Rogers vs. the Avengers; back-up prelude to Peter Parker: The Spectacular Spider-Man #1; Zdarsky-s/Siqueira-a; Vulture app. 3.00
...: Dark Circle 1 (Archie Comic Pub., 6-7/15) Previews Black Hood, The Fox, The Shield 3.00
...: R.I.P.D. and The True Lives of the Fabulous Killjoys (Dark Horse, 5/13) Flipbook with Mass Effect 3.00

FREEDOM AGENT (Also see John Steele)
Gold Key: Apr, 1963 (12¢)

1 (10054-304)-Painted-c 4 8 12 25 40 55

FREEDOM FIGHTERS (See Justice League of America #107,108)
National Periodical Publ./DC Comics: Mar-Apr, 1976 - No. 15, July-Aug, 1978

1-Uncle Sam, The Ray, Black Condor, Doll Man, Human Bomb, & Phantom Lady begin (all former Quality characters) 3 6 9 16 23 30
2-9: 4,5-Wonder Woman x-over. 7-1st app. Crusaders 2 4 6 9 12 15
10-15: 10-Origin Doll Man; Cat-Man-c/story (4th app; 1st revival since Detective #325). 11-Origin The Ray. 12-Origin Firebrand. 13-Origin Black Condor. 14-Batgirl & Batwoman app. 15-Batgirl & Batwoman app.; origin Phantom Lady
2 4 6 9 13 16
NOTE: ***Buckler** c-5-11p, 13p, 14p.*

FREEDOM FIGHTERS (Also see "Uncle Sam and the Freedom Fighters")
DC Comics: Nov, 2010 - No. 9, Jul, 2011 ($2.99)

1-9-Travis Moore-a. 1-6-Dave Johnson-c 3.00

FREEDOM FORCE
Image Comics: Jan, 2005 - No. 6, June, 2005 ($2.95)

1-6-Eric Dieter-s/Tom Scioli-a 3.00

FREELANCERS
BOOM! Studios: Oct, 2012 - No. 6, Mar, 2013 ($1.00/$3.99)

1-($1.00) Brill-s/Covey-a; eight covers; back-up origin of Valerie & Cassie 3.00
2-6-($3.99) Multiple covers on each 4.00

FREEMIND
Future Comics: No. 0, Aug, 2002; Nov, 2002 - No. 7, June, 2003 ($3.50)

0-($2.25) Two covers by Giordano & Layton 3.00
1-7 ($3.50) 1-Two covers by Giordano & Layton; Giordano-a thru #3. 4,5-Leeke-a 3.50

FREEREALMS
DC Comics (WildStorm): Sept, 2009 - No. 12, Oct, 2010 ($3.99, limited series)

1-12-Based on the online game; Jon Buran-a 4.00
... Book One TPB (2010, $19.99) r/#1-6 20.00
... Book Two TPB (2010, $19.99) r/#7-12 20.00

FREEX

Friendly Neighborhood Spider-Man #1 © MAR

Fringe #1 © WB

Frisky Fables V3 #11 © NOVP

	GD	VG	FN	VF	VF/NM	NM-
	2.0	4.0	6.0	8.0	9.0	9.2

GD VG FN VF VF/NM NM- 2.0 4.0 6.0 8.0 9.0 9.2

Malibu Comics (Ultraverse): July, 1993 - No. 18, Mar, 1995 ($1.95)

1-3,5-14,16-18: 1-Polybagged w/trading card. 2-Some were polybagged w/card. 6-Nightman-c/story. 7-2 pg. origin Hardcase by Zeck. 17-Rune app. 3.00
1-Holographic-c edition 8.00
1-Ultra 5,000 limited silver ink-c 5.00
4-($2.50, 48 pgs.)-Rune flip-c/story by B. Smith (3 pgs.); 3 pg. Night Man preview 4.00
15 ($3.50)-w/Ultraverse Premiere #9 flip book; Alec Swan & Rafferty app. 4.00
Giant Size 1 (1994, $2.50)-Prime app. 4.00
NOTE: *Simonson c-1.*

FRENEMY OF THE STATE
Oni Press: May, 2010 - No. 5, Dec, 2011 ($3.99)

1-5-Rashida Jones, Christina Weir & Nunzio DeFilippis-s 4.00

FRENZY (Magazine) (Satire)
Picture Magazine: Apr, 1958 - No. 6, Mar, 1959

1-Painted-c 14 28 42 80 115 150
2-6 9 18 27 47 61 75

FRESHMEN
Image Comics: Jul, 2005 - No. 6, Mar, 2006 ($2.99)

1-Sterbakov-s/Kirk-a; co-created by Seth Green; covers by Pérez, Migliari, Linsner 3.00
2-6-Migliari-c 3.00
... Yearbook (1/06, $2.99) profile pages of characters; art by various incl. Chaykin, Kirk 3.00
... Vol. 1 (3/06, $16.99, TPB) r/#1-6 & Yearbook; cover gallery with concept art 17.00

FRESHMEN (Volume 2)
Image Comics: Nov, 2006 - No. 6, Aug, 2007 ($2.99)

1-6: 1-Sterbakov-s/Conrad-a; 4 covers 3.00
...: Summer Vacation Special (7/08, $4.99) Sterbakov-s; bonus pin-ups by various 5.00
... Vol. 2 Fundamentals of Fear (6/07, $16.99, TPB) r/#1-6; cover gallery, journals 17.00

FRIDAY FOSTER
Dell Publishing Co.: October, 1972

1 5 10 15 30 50 70

FRIDAY THE 13TH (Based on the horror movie franchise)
DC Comics (WildStorm): Feb, 2007 - No. 6, July, 2007 ($2.99, mature)

1-6: 1-Two covers by Sook and Bradstreet; Gray & Palmiotti-s 3.00
...: Abuser and The Abused (6/08, $3.50) Fialkov-s/Andy B. -a 3.50
...: Bad Land 1,2 (3/08 - No. 2, 4/08, $2.99) Marz-s/Huddleston-a/McKone-c 3.00
...: How I Spent My Summer Vacation 1,2 (11/07 - No. 2, 12/07, $2.99) Aaron-s/Archer-a 3.00
...: Pamela's Tale 1,2 (9/07 - No. 2, 10/07, $2.99) Andreyko-s/Moll-a/Nguyen-c 3.00

FRIENDLY GHOST, CASPER, THE (Becomes Casper... #254 on)
Harvey Publications: Aug, 1958 - No. 224, Oct, 1982; No. 225, Oct, 1986 - No. 253, June, 1990

1-Infinity-c 57 114 171 456 1028 1600
2 20 40 60 138 307 475
3-6: 6-X-Mas-c 10 20 30 66 138 210
7-10 8 16 24 56 108 160
11-20: 18-X-Mas-c 7 14 21 46 86 125
21-30 5 10 15 31 53 75
31-50 4 8 12 23 37 50
51-70,100: 54-X-Mas-c 3 6 9 19 30 40
71-99 3 6 9 16 23 30
101-131: 131-Last 12¢ issue 3 6 9 14 20 26
132-159 2 4 6 11 16 20
160-163: All 52 pg. Giants 3 6 9 14 20 26
164-199: 173,179,185-Cub Scout Specials 2 4 6 8 10 12
200 2 4 6 8 11 14
201-224 1 2 3 5 7 9
225-237: 230-X-mas-c. 232-Valentine's-c 5.00
238-253: 238-Begin $1.00-c. 238,244-Halloween-c. 243-Last new material 4.00

FRIENDLY NEIGHBORHOOD SPIDER-MAN
Marvel Comics: Dec, 2005 - No. 24, Nov, 2007 ($2.99)

1-Evolve or Die pt. 1; Peter David-s/Mike Wieringo-a; Morlun app. 4.00
1-Variant Wieringo-c with regular costume 5.00
2-4: 2-New Avengers app. 3-Spider-Man dies 3.00
2-4-var-c: 2-Bag-Head Fantastic Four costume. 3-Captain Universe. 4-Wrestler 5.00
5-10: 6-Red & gold costume. 8-10-Uncle Ben app. 3.00
11-23: 17-Black costume; Sandman app. 3.00
24-($3.99) "One More Day" part 2; Quesada-a; covers by Quesada & Djurdjevic 4.00
Annual 1 (7/07, $3.99) Origin of The Sandman; back-up w/Doran-a 4.00
... Vol. 1: Derailed (2006, $14.99) r/#5-10; Wieringo sketch pages 15.00
... Vol. 2: Mystery Date (2007, $13.99) r/#11-16 14.00

FRIENDS OF MAXX (Also see Maxx)
Image Comics (I Before E): Apr, 1996 - No. 3, Mar, 1997 ($2.95)

1-3: Sam Kieth-c/a/scripts. 1-Featuring Dude Japan 3.00

FRIGHT
Atlas/Seaboard Periodicals: June, 1975 (Aug. on inside)

1-Origin/1st app. The Son of Dracula; Frank Thorne-c/a 3 6 9 14 19 24

FRIGHT NIGHT
Now Comics: Oct, 1988 - No. 22, 1990 ($1.75)

1-22: 1,2 Adapts movie. 8, 9-Evil Ed horror photo-c from movie 3.00

FRIGHT NIGHT II
Now Comics: 1989 ($3.95, 52 pgs.)

1-Adapts movie sequel 4.00

FRINGE (Based on the 2008 FOX television series)
DC Comics (WildStorm): Oct, 2008 - No. 6, Aug, 2009 ($2.99, limited series)

1-6-Anthology by various. 1-Mandrake & Coleby-a 3.00
TPB (2009, $19.99) r/#1-6; intro. by TV series co-creators Kurtzman & Orci 20.00

FRINGE: TALES FROM THE FRINGE (Based on the 2008 FOX television series)
DC Comics (WildStorm): Aug, 2010 - No. 6, Jan, 2011 ($3.99, limited series)

1-6-Anthology by various; LaTorre-c. 1-Reg & photo-c 4.00
2-6-Variant covers from parallel world. 2-Death of Batman. 3-Superman/Dark Knight Returns. 4-Crisis #7 Supergirl holding dead Superman. 5-Justice League #1 w/Jonah Hex. 6-Red Lantern/Red Arrow #76 10.00
TPB (2011, $14.99) r/#1-6 with variant cover gallery and sketch art 15.00

FRISKY ANIMALS (Formerly Frisky Fables; Super Cat #56 on)
Star Publications: No. 44, Jan, 1951 - No. 55, Sept, 1953

44-Super Cat; L.B. Cole 21 42 63 122 199 275
45-Classic L. B. Cole-c 30 60 90 177 289 400
46-51,53-55: Super Cat. 54-Super Cat-c begin 19 38 57 112 179 245
52-L. B. Cole-c/a, 3 1/2 pgs.; X-Mas-c 20 40 60 117 189 260
NOTE: *All have* ***L. B. Cole****-c. No. 47-No Super Cat.* ***Disbrow*** *a-49, 52.* ***Fago*** *a-51.*

FRISKY ANIMALS ON PARADE (Formerly Parade Comics; becomes Superspook)
Ajax-Farrell Publ. (Four Star Comic Corp.): Sept, 1957 - No. 3, Dec-Jan, 1957-1958

1-L. B. Cole-c 17 34 51 100 158 215
2-No L. B. Cole-c 10 20 30 56 76 95
3-L. B. Cole-c 15 30 45 85 130 175

FRISKY FABLES (Frisky Animals No. 44 on)
Premium Group/Novelty Publ./Star Publ. V5#4 on: Spring, 1945 - No. 43, Oct, 1950

V1#1-Funny animal; Al Fago-c/a #1-38 23 46 69 138 227 315
2,3(Fall & Winter, 1945) 14 28 42 81 118 155
V2#1(#4, 4/46) - 9,11,12(#15, 3/47): 4-Flag-c 11 22 33 62 86 110
10-Christmas-c. 12-Valentine's-c 11 22 33 64 90 115
V3#1(#16, 4/47) - 12(#27, 3/48): 4-Flag-c. 7,9-Infinity-c. 10-X-Mas-c. 12-Washington crossing the Delaware parody-c 10 20 30 56 76 95
V4#1(#28, 4/48) - 7(#34, 2-3/49) 9 18 27 52 69 85
V5#1(#35, 4-5/49) - 4(#38, 10-11/49) 9 18 27 50 65 80
39-43-L. B. Cole-c; 40-Xmas-c 20 40 60 115 185 255
Accepted Reprint No. 43 (nd); L.B. Cole-c 10 20 30 56 76 95

FRITZI RITZ (See Comics On Parade, Single Series #5, 1(reprint), Tip Top & United Comics)

FRITZI RITZ (United Comics No. 8-26) (Also see Tip Topper for early Peanuts by Schulz)
United Features Synd./St. John No. 37-55/Dell No. 56 on:
1939; Fall, 1948; No. 3, 1949 - No. 7, 1949; No. 27, 3-4/53 - No. 36, 9-10/54; No. 37 - No. 55, 9-11/57; No. 56, 12-2/57-58 - No. 59, 9-11/58

Single Series #5 (1939) 39 78 117 240 395 550
nn(1948)-Special Fall issue; by Ernie Bushmiller 21 42 63 126 206 285
3(#1) 15 30 45 84 127 170
4-7(1949): 6-Abbie & Slats app. 11 22 33 62 86 110
27(1953)-33,37-50,57-59-Early Peanuts (1-4 pgs.) by Schulz. 29-Five pg. Abbie & Slats; 1 pg. Mamie by Russell Patterson. 38(9/55)-41(4/56)-Low print run 15 30 45 90 140 190
34-36,51-56: 36-1 pg. Mamie by Patterson 9 18 27 52 69 85
NOTE: *Abbie & Slats in #6,7, 27-31. Li'l Abner in #32-36.*

FROGMAN COMICS
Hillman Periodicals: Jan-Feb, 1952 - No. 11, May, 1953

1 17 34 51 100 158 215
2 11 22 33 62 86 110
3,4,6-11: 4-Meskin-a 9 18 27 52 69 85

From Hell #3 © Moore & Campbell

Frontier Fighters #4 © DC

Frozen #4 © DIS

	GD 2.0	VG 4.0	FN 6.0	VF 8.0	VF/NM 9.0	NM- 9.2
5-Krigstein-a	10	20	30	56	76	95

FROGMEN, THE
Dell Publishing Co.: No. 1258, Feb-Apr, 1962 - No. 11, Nov-Jan, 1964-65 (Painted-c)

	GD 2.0	VG 4.0	FN 6.0	VF 8.0	VF/NM 9.0	NM- 9.2
Four Color 1258(#1)-Evans-a	8	16	24	54	102	150
2,3-Evans-a; part Frazetta inks in #2,3	5	10	15	33	57	80
4,6-11	4	8	12	23	37	50
5-Toth-a	4	8	12	27	44	60

FROM BEYOND THE UNKNOWN
National Periodical Publications: 10-11/69 - No. 25, 11-12/73

	GD 2.0	VG 4.0	FN 6.0	VF 8.0	VF/NM 9.0	NM- 9.2
1	5	10	15	33	57	80
2-6	3	6	9	19	30	40
7-11: (64 pgs.) 7-Intro Col. Glenn Merrit	3	6	9	21	33	45
12-17: (52 pgs.) 13-Wood-a(i)(r). 17-Pres. Nixon-c	3	6	9	17	26	35
18-25: Star Rovers-r begin #18,19. Space Museum in #23-25	2	4	6	13	18	22

NOTE: ***N. Adams** c-3, 6, 8, 9. **Anderson** c-2, 4, 5, 10, 11i, 15-17, 22; reprints-3, 4, 6-8, 10, 11, 13-16, 24, 25. **Infantino** r-1-5, 7-19, 23-25; c-11p. **Kaluta** c-18, 19. **Gil Kane** a-9r. **Kubert** c-1, 7, 12-14. **Toth** a-2r. **Wood** a-13i. Photo c-22.*

FROM DUSK TILL DAWN (Movie)
Big Entertainment: 1996 ($4.95, one-shot)

	GD 2.0	VG 4.0	FN 6.0	VF 8.0	VF/NM 9.0	NM- 9.2
nn-Adaptation of the film; Brereton-c						5.00
nn-($9.95)Deluxe Ed. w/ new material						10.00

FROM HELL
Mad Love/Tundra Publishing/Kitchen Sink: 1991 - No. 11, Sept, 1998 (B&W)

	GD 2.0	VG 4.0	FN 6.0	VF 8.0	VF/NM 9.0	NM- 9.2
1-Alan Moore and Eddie Campbell's Jack The Ripper story collected from the Taboo anthology series	3	6	9	15	22	28
1-(2nd printing)	2	4	6	8	10	12
1-(3rd printing)	1	2	3	4	5	7
2	1	3	4	6	8	10
2-(2nd printing)						6.00
2-(3rd printing)						4.00
3-1st Kitchen Sink Press issue	1	3	4	6	8	10
3-(2nd printing)						5.00
4-10: 10-(8/96)	1	2	3	5	6	8
11-Dance of the Gull Catchers (9/98, $4.95) Epilogue	2	4	6	10	14	18
Tundra Publishing reprintings 1-5 ('92)	1	2	3	4	5	7
HC						125.00
HC Ltd. Edition of 1,000 (signed and numbered)						230.00
TPB-1st printing (11/99)						60.00
TPB-2nd printing (3/00)						50.00
TPB-3rd printing (11/00)						40.00
TPB-4th printing (7/01) Regular and movie covers						35.00
TPB-5th printing - Regular and movie covers						35.00

FROM HERE TO INSANITY (Satire) (Formerly Eh! #1-7) (See Frantic & Frenzy)
Charlton Comics: No. 8, Feb, 1955 - V3#1, 1956

	GD 2.0	VG 4.0	FN 6.0	VF 8.0	VF/NM 9.0	NM- 9.2
8	21	42	63	122	199	275
9	20	40	60	114	182	250
10-Ditko-c/a (3 pgs.)	30	60	90	177	289	400
11-All Kirby except 4 pgs.	39	78	117	240	395	550
12-(Mag. size) Marilyn Monroe, Jackie Gleason-c; all Kirby except 4 pgs.	41	82	123	256	428	600
V3#1(1956)-Ward-c/a(2) (signed McCartney); 5 pgs. Wolverton-a; 3 pgs. Ditko-a; magazine format (cover says "Crazy, Man, Crazy" and becomes Crazy, Man, Crazy with V2#2)	48	96	144	302	514	725

FROM THE PIT
Fantagor Press: 1994 ($4.95, one-shot, mature)

	GD 2.0	VG 4.0	FN 6.0	VF 8.0	VF/NM 9.0	NM- 9.2
1-R. Corben-a; HP Lovecraft back-up story	1	3	4	6	8	10

FRONTIER DOCTOR (TV)
Dell Publishing Co.: No. 877, Feb, 1958 (one-shot)

	GD 2.0	VG 4.0	FN 6.0	VF 8.0	VF/NM 9.0	NM- 9.2
Four Color 877-Toth-a, Rex Allen photo-c	9	18	27	57	111	165

FRONTIER FIGHTERS
National Periodical Publications: Sept-Oct, 1955 - No. 8, Nov-Dec, 1956

	GD 2.0	VG 4.0	FN 6.0	VF 8.0	VF/NM 9.0	NM- 9.2
1-Davy Crockett, Buffalo Bill (by Kubert), Kit Carson begin (Scarce)	55	110	165	352	601	850
2	37	74	111	222	361	500
3-8	34	68	102	199	325	450

NOTE: *Buffalo Bill by **Kubert** in all.*

FRONTIER ROMANCES
Avon Periodicals/I. W.: Nov-Dec, 1949 - No. 2, Feb-Mar, 1950 (Painted-c)

	GD 2.0	VG 4.0	FN 6.0	VF 8.0	VF/NM 9.0	NM- 9.2
1-Used in **SOTI**, pg. 180 (General reference) & illo. "Erotic spanking in a western comic book"	63	126	189	403	689	975
2 (Scarce)-Woodish-a by Stallman	42	84	126	265	445	625
I.W. Reprint #1-Reprints Avon's #1	3	6	9	21	33	45
I.W. Reprint #9-Reprints ?	3	6	9	15	22	28

FRONTIER SCOUT: DAN'L BOONE (Formerly Death Valley; The Masked Raider No. 14 on)
Charlton Comics: No. 10, Jan, 1956 - No. 13, Aug, 1956; V2#14, Mar, 1965

	GD 2.0	VG 4.0	FN 6.0	VF 8.0	VF/NM 9.0	NM- 9.2
10	10	20	30	54	72	90
11-13(1956)	6	12	18	31	38	45
V2#14(3/65)	3	6	9	15	22	28

FRONTIER TRAIL (The Rider No. 1-5)
Ajax/Farrell Publ.: No. 6, May, 1958

	GD 2.0	VG 4.0	FN 6.0	VF 8.0	VF/NM 9.0	NM- 9.2
6	6	12	18	28	34	40

FRONTIER WESTERN
Atlas Comics (PrPl): Feb, 1956 - No. 10, Aug, 1957

	GD 2.0	VG 4.0	FN 6.0	VF 8.0	VF/NM 9.0	NM- 9.2
1-The Pecos Kid rides	23	46	69	136	223	310
2,3,6-Williamson-a, 4 pgs. each	15	30	45	88	137	185
4,7,9,10: 10-Check-a	12	24	36	67	94	120
5-Crandall, Baker, Davis-a; Williamson text illos	15	30	45	83	124	165
8-Crandall, Morrow, & Wildey-a	12	24	36	69	97	125

NOTE: ***Baker** a-9. **Colan** a-2, 6. **Drucker** a-3, 4. **Heath** c-5. **Maneely** c/a-2, 7, 9. **Maurera** a-2. **Romita** a-7. **Severin** c-6, 8, 10. **Tuska** a-2. **Wildey** a-5, 8. Ringo Kid in No. 4.*

FRONTLINE COMBAT
E. C. Comics: July-Aug, 1951 - No. 15, Jan, 1954

	GD 2.0	VG 4.0	FN 6.0	VF 8.0	VF/NM 9.0	NM- 9.2
1-Severin/Kurtzman-a	86	172	258	688	1094	1500
2	43	86	129	344	547	750
3	33	66	99	264	420	575
4-Used in **SOTI**, pg. 257; contains "Airburst" by Kurtzman which is his personal all-time favorite story	33	66	99	264	420	575
5-John Severin and Bill Elder bios.	27	54	81	216	346	475
6-10: 6-Kurtzman bio. 9-Civil War issue	23	46	69	184	292	400
11-15: 11-Civil War issue	18	36	54	144	232	320

NOTE: ***Davis** a-in all; c-11, 12. **Evans** a-10-15. **Heath** a-1. **Kubert** a-14. **Kurtzman** a-1-5; c-1-9. **Severin** a-5-7, 9, 13, 15. **Severin/Elder** a-2-11; c-10. **Toth** a-8, 12. **Wood** a-1-4, 6-10, 12-15; c-13-15. Special issues: No. 7 (Iwo Jima), No. 9 (Civil War), No. 12 (Air Force).*

(Canadian reprints known; see Table of Contents.)

FRONTLINE COMBAT
Russ Cochran/Gemstone Publishing: Aug, 1995 - No. 14 ($2.00/$2.50)

	GD 2.0	VG 4.0	FN 6.0	VF 8.0	VF/NM 9.0	NM- 9.2
1-14-E.C. reprints in all						4.00

FRONT PAGE COMIC BOOK
Front Page Comics (Harvey): 1945

	GD 2.0	VG 4.0	FN 6.0	VF 8.0	VF/NM 9.0	NM- 9.2
1-Kubert-a; intro. & 1st app. Man in Black by Powell; Fuje-c	53	106	159	334	567	800

FROST AND FIRE (See DC Science Fiction Graphic Novel)

FROSTBITE
DC Comics (Vertigo): Nov, 2016 - Present ($3.99)

	GD 2.0	VG 4.0	FN 6.0	VF 8.0	VF/NM 9.0	NM- 9.2
1-6-Joshua Williamson-s/Jason Shawn Alexander-a						4.00

FROSTY THE SNOWMAN
Dell Publishing Co.: No. 359, Nov, 1951 - No. 1272, Dec-Feb?/1961-62

	GD 2.0	VG 4.0	FN 6.0	VF 8.0	VF/NM 9.0	NM- 9.2
Four Color 359 (#1)	10	20	30	66	138	210
Four Color 435,514,601,661	6	12	18	42	79	115
Four Color 748,861,950,1065,1153,1272	5	10	15	35	63	90

FROZEN (Disney movie)
Joe Books Ltd.: Jul, 2016 - No. 5 ($2.99)

	GD 2.0	VG 4.0	FN 6.0	VF 8.0	VF/NM 9.0	NM- 9.2
1-5-Georgia Ball-s/Benedetta Barone-a						3.00

FRUITMAN SPECIAL (See Bunny #2 for 1st app.)
Harvey Publications: Dec, 1969 (68 pgs.)

	GD 2.0	VG 4.0	FN 6.0	VF 8.0	VF/NM 9.0	NM- 9.2
1-Funny super hero	4	8	12	25	40	55

F-TROOP (TV)
Dell Publishing Co.: Aug, 1966 - No. 7, Aug, 1967 (All have photo-c)

	GD 2.0	VG 4.0	FN 6.0	VF 8.0	VF/NM 9.0	NM- 9.2
1	9	18	27	57	111	165
2-7	5	10	15	34	60	85

FUGITIVES FROM JUSTICE (True Crime Stories)
St. John Publishing Co.: Feb, 1952 - No. 5, Oct, 1952

	GD 2.0	VG 4.0	FN 6.0	VF 8.0	VF/NM 9.0	NM- 9.2
1	26	52	78	154	252	350
2-Matt Baker-r/Northwest Mounties #2; Vic Flint strip reprints begin	24	48	72	142	234	325

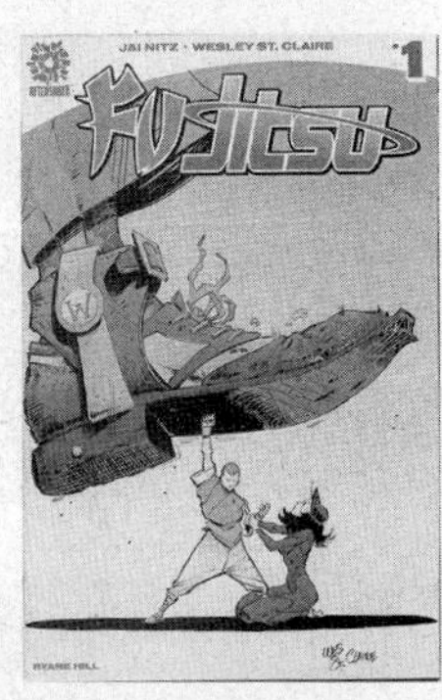

Fu Jitsu #1 © Nitz & St. Claire

Funky Phantom #12 © H-B

Funny Frolics #1 © MAR

	GD 2.0	VG 4.0	FN 6.0	VF 8.0	VF/NM 9.0	NM- 9.2

3-Reprints panel from Authentic Police Cases that was used in **SOTI** with changes; Tuska-a 23 46 69 138 227 315
4 14 28 42 81 118 155
5-Last Vic Flint-r; bondage-c 15 30 45 90 140 190

FUGITOID
Mirage Studios: 1985 (B&W, magazine size, one-shot)
1-Ties into Teenage Mutant Ninja Turtles #5 3 6 9 14 20 25

FU JITSU
AfterShock Comics: Sept, 2017 - No. 5, Feb, 2018 ($3.99)
1-5-Jai Nitz-s/Wesley St. Claire-a 4.00

FULL OF FUN
Red Top (Decker Publ.)(Farrell)/I. W. Enterprises: Aug, 1957 - No. 2, Nov, 1957; 1964
1(1957)-Funny animal; Dave Berg-a 7 14 21 37 46 55
2-Reprints Bingo, the Monkey Doodle Boy 5 10 15 22 26 30
8-I.W. Reprint('64) 2 4 6 9 12 15

FUN AT CHRISTMAS (See March of Comics No. 138)

FUN CLUB COMICS (See Interstate Theatres...)

FUN COMICS (Formerly Holiday Comics #1-8; Mighty Bear #13 on)
Star Publications: No. 9, Jan, 1953 - No. 12, Oct, 1953
9-(25¢ Giant)-L. B. Cole X-Mas-c; X-Mas issue 22 44 66 132 216 300
10-12-L. B. Cole-c. 12-Mighty Bear-c/story 18 36 54 105 165 225

FUNDAY FUNNIES (See Famous TV..., and Harvey Hits No. 35,40)

FUN-IN (TV)(Hanna-Barbera)
Gold Key: Feb, 1970 - No. 10, Jan, 1972; No. 11, 4/74 - No. 15, 12/74
1-Dastardly & Muttley in Their Flying Machines; Perils of Penelope Pitstop in #1-4; It's the Wolf in all 6 12 18 41 76 110
2-4,6-Cattanooga Cats in 2-4 3 6 9 21 33 45
5,7-Motormouse & Autocat, Dastardly & Muttley in both; It's the Wolf in #7 4 8 12 23 37 50
8,10-The Harlem Globetrotters, Dastardly & Muttley in #10 4 8 12 23 37 50
9-Where's Huddles?, Dastardly & Muttley, Motormouse & Autocat app. 4 8 12 23 37 50
11-Butch Cassidy 3 6 9 19 30 40
12-15: 12,15-Speed Buggy. 13-Hair Bear Bunch. 14-Inch High Private Eye 3 6 9 19 30 40

FUNKY PHANTOM, THE (TV)
Gold Key: Mar, 1972 - No. 13, Mar, 1975 (Hanna-Barbera)
1 5 10 15 31 53 75
2-5 3 6 9 18 28 38
6-13 3 6 9 15 22 28

FUNLAND
Ziff-Davis (Approved Comics): No date (1940s) (25¢)
nn-Contains games, puzzles, cut-outs, etc. 21 42 63 126 206 285

FUNLAND COMICS
Croyden Publishers: 1945
1-Funny animal 17 34 51 100 158 215

FUNNIES, THE (New Funnies No. 65 on)
Dell Publishing Co.: Oct, 1936 - No. 64, May, 1942
1-Tailspin Tommy, Mutt & Jeff, Alley Oop (1st app?), Capt. Easy (1st app.), Don Dixon begin 400 800 1200 2300 3650 5000
2 (11/36)-Scribbly by Mayer begins (see Popular Comics #6 for 1st app.) 180 360 540 1035 1643 2250
3 124 248 372 713 1132 1550
4,5: 4(1/37)-Christmas-c 92 184 276 529 840 1150
6-10 70 140 210 403 639 875
11-20: 16-Christmas-c 65 130 195 374 612 850
21-29: 25-Crime Busters by McWilliams(4pgs.) 52 104 156 299 475 650
30-John Carter of Mars (origin/1st app.) begins by Edgar Rice Burroughs; Jim Gary-a Warner Bros.' Bosko-c (4/39) 219 438 657 1402 2401 3400
31-34,36-44: 31,32-Gary-a. 33-John Coleman Burroughs art begins on John Carter. 34-Last funny-c. 40-John Carter of Mars-c 97 194 291 621 1061 1500
35-(9/39)-Mr. District Attorney begins; based on radio show; 1st cover app. John Carter of Mars 155 310 465 992 1696 2400
45-Origin/1st app. Phantasmo, the Master of the World (Dell's 1st super-hero, 7/40) & his sidekick Whizzer McGee 103 206 309 659 1130 1600
46-50: 46-The Black Knight begins, ends #62 58 116 174 371 636 900
51-56-Last ERB John Carter of Mars 47 94 141 296 498 700
57-Intro. & origin Captain Midnight (7/41) 366 732 1098 2562 4481 6400
58-60: 58-Captain Midnight-c begin, end #63 90 180 270 576 988 1400
61-Andy Panda begins by Walter Lantz; WWII-c 129 258 387 826 1413 2000
62,63: 63-Last Captain Midnight-c; bondage-c 71 142 213 454 777 1100
64-Format change; Oswald the Rabbit, Felix the Cat, Li'l Eight Ball app.; origin & 1st app. Woody Woodpecker in Oswald; last Capt. Midnight; Oswald, Andy Panda, Li'l Eight Ball-c 239 478 717 1530 2615 3700

NOTE: *Mayer c-26, 48.* ***McWilliams*** *art in many issues on "Rex King of the Deep". Alley Oop c-17, 20. Captain Midnight c-57(i/2), 58-63. John Carter c-35-37, 40. Phantasmo c-45-56, 57(1/2), 58-61(part). Rex King c-38, 39, 42. Tailspin Tommy c-41.*

FUNNIES ANNUAL, THE
Avon Periodicals: 1959 ($1.00, approx. 7x10", B&W; tabloid-size)
1-(Rare)-Features the best newspaper comic strips of the year: Archie, Snuffy Smith, Beetle Bailey, Henry, Blondie, Steve Canyon, Buz Sawyer, The Little King, Hi & Lois, Popeye, & others. Also has a chronological history of the comics from 2000 B.C. to 1959. 54 108 162 343 574 825

FUNNIES ON PARADE (See Promotional Comics section)

FUNNY ANIMALS (See Fawcett's Funny Animals)
Charlton Comics: Sept, 1984 - No. 2, Nov, 1984
1,2-Atomic Mouse-r; low print 6.00

FUNNYBONE (... The Laugh-Book of Comical Comics)
La Salle Publishing Co.: 1944 (25¢, 132 pgs.)
nn 34 68 102 199 325 450

FUNNY BOOK (...Magazine for Young Folks) (Hocus Pocus No. 9)
Parents' Magazine Press (Funny Book Publishing Corp.):
Dec, 1942 - No. 9, Aug-Sept, 1946 (Comics, stories, puzzles, games)
1-Funny animal; Alice In Wonderland app. 17 34 51 98 154 210
2-Gulliver in Giant-Land 11 22 33 62 86 110
3-9: 4-Advs. of Robin Hood. 9-Hocus-Pocus strip 10 20 30 54 72 90

FUNNY COMICS
Modern Store Publ.: 1955 (7¢, 5x7", 36 pgs.)
1-Funny animal 5 10 15 30 50 70

FUNNY COMIC TUNES (See Funny Tunes)

FUNNY FABLES
Decker Publications (Red Top Comics): Aug, 1957 - V2#2, Nov, 1957
V1#1 6 12 18 31 38 45
V1#2,V2#1,2: V1#2 (11/57)-Reissue of V1#1 5 10 14 20 24 28

FUNNY FILMS (Features funny animal characters from films)
American Comics Group(Michel Publ./Titan Publ.): Sept-Oct, 1949 - No. 29, May-June, 1954 (No. 1-4: 52 pgs.)
1-Puss An' Boots, Blunderbunny begin 18 36 54 107 169 230
2 11 22 33 62 86 110
3-10: 3-X-Mas-c 9 18 27 47 61 75
11-20 7 14 21 35 43 50
21-29 6 12 18 28 34 40

FUNNY FOLKS
DC Comics: Feb, 1946
nn-Ashcan comic, not distributed to newsstands, only for in house use (no known sales)

FUNNY FOLKS (Hollywood... on cover only No. 16-26; becomes Hollywood Funny Folks No. 27 on)
National Periodical Publ.: April-May, 1946 - No. 26, June-July, 1950 (52 pgs., #15 on)
1-Nutsy Squirrel begins (1st app.) by Rube Grossman; Grossman-a in most issues 41 82 123 250 418 585
2 20 40 60 118 192 265
3-5: 4-1st Nutsy Squirrel-c 15 30 45 86 133 180
6-10: 6,9-Nutsy Squirrel-c begin 11 22 33 62 86 110
11-26: 15-Begin 52 pg. issues (8-9/48) 10 20 30 54 72 90

NOTE: ***Sheldon Mayer*** *a-in some issues.* ***Post*** *a-18. Christmas c-12.*

FUNNY FROLICS
Timely/Marvel Comics (SPI): Summer, 1945 - No. 5, Dec, 1946
1-Sharpy Fox, Puffy Pig, Krazy Krow 31 62 93 184 300 415
2-(Fall 1945) 17 34 51 100 158 215
3,4: 3-(Spring 1946) 15 30 45 83 124 165
5-Kurtzman-a 15 30 45 86 133 180

FUNNY FUNNIES
Nedor Publishing Co.: April, 1943 (68 pgs.)

Funny Pages V2 #12 © CEN

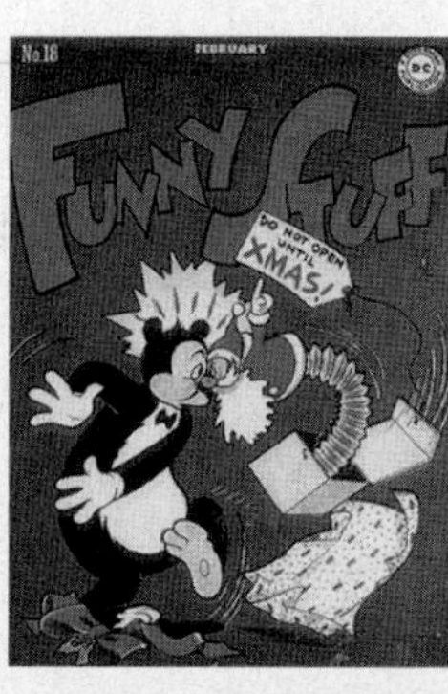

Funny Stuff #18 © DC

Furious #5 © Glass & Santos

GD 2.0 | VG 4.0 | FN 6.0 | VF 8.0 | VF/NM 9.0 | NM- 9.2

GD 2.0 | VG 4.0 | FN 6.0 | VF 8.0 | VF/NM 9.0 | NM- 9.2

1-Funny animals; Peter Porker app. 21 42 63 126 206 285

FUNNYMAN (Also see Cisco Kid Comics & Extra Comics)
Magazine Enterprises: Dec, 1947; No. 1, Jan, 1948 - No. 6, Aug, 1948

nn(12/47)-Prepublication B&W undistributed copy by Siegel & Shuster-(5-3/4x8"), 16 pgs.; Sold at auction in 1997 for $575.00
1-Siegel & Shuster-a in all; Dick Ayers 1st pro work (as assistant) on 1st few issues 50 100 150 315 533 750
2 32 64 96 188 307 425
3-6 28 56 84 165 270 375

FUNNY MOVIES (See 3-D Funny Movies)

FUNNY PAGES (Formerly The Comics Magazine)
Comics Magazine Co./Ultem Publ.(Chesler)/Centaur Publications: No. 6, Nov, 1936 - No. 42, Oct, 1940

V1#6 (nn, nd)-The Clock begins (2 pgs., 1st app.), ends #11; The Clock is the 1st masked comic book hero 400 800 1200 2800 4900 7000
7-11: 11-(6/37) 161 322 483 1030 1765 2500
V2#1-V2#5: V2#1 (9/37)(V2#2 on-c; V2#1 in indicia). V2#2 (10/37)(V2#3 on-c; V2#2 in indicia). V2#3(11/37) - 5 129 258 387 826 1413 2000
6(1st Centaur, 3/38) 135 270 405 864 1482 2100
7-9 123 246 369 787 1344 1900
10(Scarce, 9/38)-1st app. of The Arrow by Gustavson (Blue costume) 459 918 1377 3350 5925 8500
11,12 161 322 483 1030 1765 2500
V3#1-Bruce Wayne prototype in "Case of the Missing Heir," by Bob Kane, 3 months before app. Batman (See Det. Pic. Stories #5) 245 490 735 1568 2684 3800
2-6,8: 6,8-Last funny covers 155 310 465 992 1696 2400
7-1st Arrow-c (9/39) 432 864 1296 3154 5577 8000
9-Tarpe Mills jungle-c 168 336 504 1075 1838 2600
10-2nd Arrow-c (Rare) 423 846 1269 3000 5250 7500
V4#1(1/40, Arrow-c)-(Rare)-The Owl & The Phantom Rider app.; origin Mantoka, Maker of Magic by Jack Cole. Mad Ming begins, ends #42; Tarpe Mills-a 423 846 1269 3000 5250 7500
35-Classic Arrow-c (Scarce) 432 864 1296 3154 5577 8000
36-38-Mad Ming-c 258 516 774 1651 2826 4000
39-41-Arrow-c 300 600 900 2070 3635 5200
42 (Scarce,10/40)-Arrow-c 320 640 960 2240 3920 5600

NOTE: ***Biro** c-V2#9.* ***Burgos** c-V3#10.* ***Jack Cole** a-V2#3, 7, 8, 10, 11, V3#2, 6, 9, 10, V4#1, 37; c-V3#2, 4.* ***Eisner** a-V1#7, 8?, 10.* ***Ken Ernst** a-V1#7, 8.* ***Everett** a-V2#11 (illos).* ***Filchock** c-V2#10, V3#6.* ***Gill Fox** a-V2#11.* ***Sid Greene** a-39.* ***Guardineer** a-V2#2, 3, 5.* ***Gustavson** a-V2#5, 11, 12, V3#1-10, 35, 38-42; c-V3#7, 35, 39-42.* ***Bob Kane** a-V3#1.* ***McWilliams** a-V2#12, V3#1, 3-6.* ***Tarpe Mills** a-V3#8-10, V4#1; c-V3#9.* ***Ed Moore Jr.** a-V2#12.* ***Schwab** c-V3#1.* ***Bob Wood** a-V2#2, 3, 8, 11, V3#6, 9, 10; c-V2#6, 7. Arrow c-V3#7, 10, V4#1, 35, 40-42.*

FUNNY PICTURE STORIES (Comic Pages V3#4 on)
Comics Magazine Co./Centaur Publications: Nov, 1936 - V3#3, May, 1939

V1#1-The Clock begins (c-feature)(see Funny Pages for 1st app.) 443 886 1329 3234 5717 8200
2 219 438 657 1402 2401 3400
3-6(4/37): 4-Eisner-a 165 330 495 1048 1799 2550
7-(6/37) (Rare) Racial humor-c 411 822 1233 2877 5039 7200
V2#1 (9/37; V1#10 on-c; V2#1 in indicia)-Jack Strand begins 116 232 348 742 1271 1800
2 (10/37; V1#11 on-c; V2#2 in indicia) 116 232 348 742 1271 1800
3-5,7-11(11/38): 4-Christmas-c 106 212 318 673 1162 1650
6-(1st Centaur, 3/38) 116 232 348 742 1271 1800
V3#1(1/39)-3 103 206 309 659 1130 1600

NOTE: ***Biro** c-V2#1, 8, 9, 11.* ***Guardineer** a-V1#11; c-V2#6, V3#5.* ***Bob Wood** c/a-V1#11, V2#2; c-V2#3, 5.*

FUNNY STUFF (Becomes The Dodo & the Frog No. 80)
All-American/National Periodical Publications No. 7 on: Summer, 1944 - No. 79, July-Aug, 1954 (#1-7 are quarterly)

1-The Three Mouseketeers (ends #28) & The "Terrific Whatzit" begin; Sheldon Mayer-a; Grossman-a in most issues 92 184 276 584 1005 1425
2-Sheldon Mayer-a 43 86 129 271 461 650
3-5: 3-Flash parody. 5-All Mayer-a/scripts issue 32 64 96 188 307 425
6-10 10-(6/46) 20 40 60 117 189 260
11-17,19 15 30 45 90 140 190
18-The Dodo & the Frog (2/47, 1st app?) begin?; X-Mas-c 28 56 84 165 270 375
19-1st Dodo & the Frog-c (3/47) 20 40 60 114 182 250
20-2nd Dodo & the Frog-c (4/47) 14 28 42 82 121 160
21,23-30: 24-Infinity-c. 30-Christmas-c 11 22 33 62 86 110
22-Superman cameo 37 74 111 222 361 500
31-79: 62-Bo Bunny app. by Mayer. 70-Bo Bunny series begins 10 20 30 56 76 95

NOTE: ***Mayer** a-1-8, 55, ,57, 58, 61, 62, 64, 65, 68, 70, 72, 74-79; c-2, 5, 6, 8.*

FUNNY STUFF STOCKING STUFFER
DC Comics: Mar, 1985 ($1.25, 52 pgs.)

1-Almost every DC funny animal featured 4.00

FUNNY 3-D
Harvey Publications: December, 1953 (25¢, came with 2 pair of glasses)

1-Shows cover in 3-D on inside 11 22 33 64 90 115

FUNNY TUNES (Animated Funny Comic Tunes No. 16-22; Funny Comic Tunes No. 23, on covers only; Oscar No. 24 on)
U.S.A. Comics Magazine Corp. (Timely): No. 16, Summer, 1944 - No. 23, Fall, 1946

16-Silly Seal, Ziggy Pig, Krazy Krow begin 26 52 78 154 252 350
17 (Fall/44)-Becomes Gay Comics #18 on? 21 42 63 122 199 275
18-22: 21-Super Rabbit app. 20 40 60 114 182 250
23-Kurtzman-a 20 40 60 117 189 260

FUNNY TUNES (Becomes Space Comics #4 on)
Avon Periodicals: July, 1953 - No. 3, Dec-Jan, 1953-54

1-Space Mouse, Peter Rabbit, Merry Mouse, Spotty the Pup, Cicero the Cat begin; all continue in Space Comics 12 24 36 69 97 125
2,3 9 18 27 47 61 75

FUNNY WORLD
Marbak Press: 1947 - No. 3, 1948

1-The Berrys, The Toodles & other strip-r begin 9 18 27 50 65 80
2,3 6 12 18 31 38 45

FUNTASTIC WORLD OF HANNA-BARBERA, THE (TV)
Marvel Comics Group: Dec, 1977 - No. 3, June, 1978 ($1.25, oversized)

1-3: 1-The Flintstones Christmas Party(12/77). 2-Yogi Bear's Easter Parade(3/78). 3-Laff-a-lympics(6/78) 4 8 12 25 40 55

FUN TIME
Ace Periodicals: Spring, 1953; No. 2, Sum, 1953; No. 3(nn), Fall, 1953; No. 4, Wint, 1953-54

1-(25¢, 100 pgs.)-Funny animal 21 42 63 124 202 280
2-4 (All 25¢, 100 pgs.) 16 32 48 94 147 200

FUN WITH SANTA CLAUS (See March of Comics No. 11, 108, 325)

FURIOUS
Dark Horse Comics: Jan, 2014 - No. 5, May, 2014 ($3.99)

1-5-Glass-s/Santos-a 4.00

FURTHER ADVENTURES OF CYCLOPS AND PHOENIX (Also see Adventures of Cyclops and Phoenix, Uncanny X-Men & X-Men)
Marvel Comics: June, 1996 - No. 4, Sept, 1996 ($1.95, limited series)

1-4: Origin of Mr. Sinister; Milligan scripts; John Paul Leon-c/a(p). 2-4-Apocalypse app. 3.00
Trade Paperback (1997, $14.99) r/1-4 15.00

FURTHER ADVENTURES OF INDIANA JONES, THE (Movie) (Also see Indiana Jones and the Last Crusade & Indiana Jones and the Temple of Doom)
Marvel Comics Group: Jan, 1983 - No. 34, Mar, 1986

1-Byrne/Austin-a; Austin-c 1 2 3 5 6 8
2-34: 2-Byrne/Austin-c/a 4.00

NOTE: ***Austin** a-1i, 2i, 6i, 9i; c-1, 2i, 6i, 9i.* ***Byrne** a-1p, 2p; c-2p.* ***Chaykin** a-6p; c-6p, 8p-10p.* ***Ditko** a-21p, 25-28, 34.* ***Golden** c-24, 25.* ***Simonson** c-9. Painted c-14.*

FURTHER ADVENTURES OF NICK WILSON, THE
Image Comics: Jan, 2018 - Present ($3.99)

1,2-Gorodetsky & Andreyko-s/Sadowski-a 4.00

FURTHER ADVENTURES OF NYOKA, THE JUNGLE GIRL, THE (See Nyoka)
AC Comics: 1988 - No. 5, 1989 ($1.95, color; $2.25/$2.50, B&W)

1-5 : 1,2-Bill Black-a plus reprints. 3-Photo-c. 5-(B&W)-Reprints plus movie photos 3.00

FURY (Straight Arrow's Horse...) (See A-1 No. 119)

FURY (TV) (See March Of Comics #200)
Dell Publishing Co./Gold Key: No. 781, Mar, 1957 - Nov, 1962 (All photo-c)

Four Color 781 7 14 21 49 92 135
Four Color 885,975,1031,1080,1133,1172,1218,1296 5 10 15 35 63 90
01292-208(#1-'62), 10020-211(11/62-G.K.) 5 10 15 33 57 80

FURY
Marvel Comics: May, 1994 ($2.95, one-shot)

1-Iron Man, Red Skull, FF, Hatemonger, Logan app.; origin Nick Fury 3.00

FURY (Volume 3)
Marvel Comics (MAX): Nov, 2001 - No. 6, Apr, 2002 ($2.99, mature content)

Fury of Firestorm (2011 series) #14 © DC

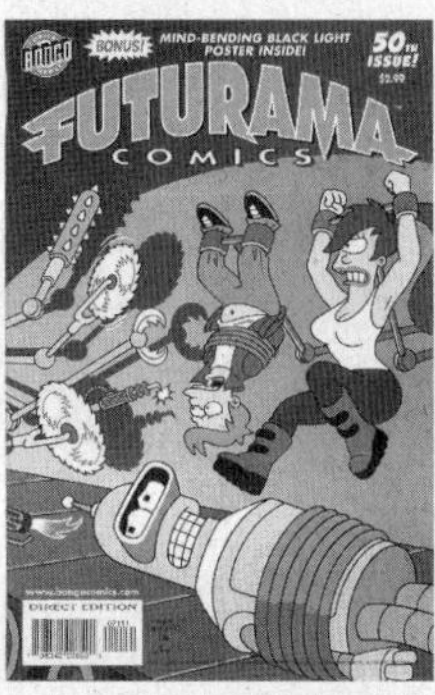

Futurama #50 © Bongo

Gabby #11 © QUA

	GD 2.0	VG 4.0	FN 6.0	VF 8.0	VF/NM 9.0	NM- 9.2

1-6-Ennis-s/Robertson-a 3.00

FURY/ AGENT 13
Marvel Comics: June, 1998 - No. 2, July, 1998 ($2.99, limited series)

1,2-Nick Fury returns 3.00

FURY MAX (Nick Fury)("My War Gone By" on cover)
Marvel Comics (MAX): Jul, 2012 - No. 13, Aug, 2013 ($3.99, mature content)

1-13: 1-Ennis-s/Parlov-a/Johnson-c; Nick Fury in 1954 Indochina. 7-9-Frank Castle app. 4.00

FURY OF FIRESTORM, THE (Becomes Firestorm The Nuclear Man on cover with #50, in indicia with #65) (Also see Firestorm)
DC Comics: June, 1982 - No. 64, Oct, 1987 (75¢ on)

1-Intro The Black Bison; brief origin 3 6 9 14 20 25
2-6,8-22,25-40,43-64: 4-JLA x-over. 6-Masters of the Universe preview insert. 17-1st app. Firehawk. 21-Death of Killer Frost. 22-Origin. 34-1st app./origin Killer Frost II. 39-Weasel's ID revealed. 48-Intro. Moonbow. 53-Origin & 1st app. Silver Shade. 55,56-Legends x-over. 58-1st app./origin new Parasite 4.00
7-1st app. Plastique 1 3 4 6 8 10
23-(5/84) 1st app. Felicity Smoak (Byte) 2 4 6 13 18 22
24-(6/84)-1st app. Bug (origin); origin Byte; 1st app. Blue Devil in a prevue pull-out 2 4 6 11 16 20
41,42-Crisis x-over. 41-Harbinger, Psycho Pirate-c/app. 5.00
61-Test cover variant; Superman logo 4 8 12 23 37 50
Annual 1-4: 1(1983), 2(1984), 3(1985), 4(1986) 5.00
NOTE: *Colan a-19p, Annual 4p.* ***Giffen*** *a-Annual 4p.* ***Gil Kane*** *c-30.* ***Nino*** *a-37.* ***Tuska*** *a-(p)-17, 18, 32, 45.*

FURY OF FIRESTORM: THE NUCLEAR MEN (New DC 52)
DC Comics: Nov, 2011 - No. 20, Jul, 2013 ($2.99)

1-18: 1-Van Sciver & Simone-s/Cinar-a/Van Sciver-c. 7,8-Van Sciver-a. 9-JLI app. 3.00
19,20-Killer Frost app. 5.00
#0 (11/12, #2.99) Cinar-a/c 3.00

FURY OF SHIELD
Marvel Comics: Apr, 1995 - No. 4, July, 1995 ($2.50/$1.95, limited series)

1 ($2.50)-Foil-c 4.00
2-4: 4-Bagged w/ decoder 3.00

FURY: PEACEMAKER
Marvel Comics: Apr, 2006 - No. 6, Sept, 2006 ($3.50, limited series)

1-6-Flashback to WW2; Ennis-s/Robertson-a. 1-Deodato-c. 2-Texeira-c. 5-Dillon-c 3.50
TPB (2006, $17.99) r/#1-6 18.00

FURY: S.H.I.E.L.D. 50TH ANNIVERSARY
Marvel Comics: Nov, 2015 ($3.99, one-shot)

1-Walker-s/Ferguson-a/Deodato-c; Nick Fury Jr. time travels to meet 1965 Nick Fury 4.00

FUSED
Image Comics: Mar, 2002 - No. 4, Jan, 2003 ($2.95)

1-4-Steve Niles-s. 1,2-Paul Lee-a. 3-Brad Rader-a. 4-Templesmith-a 3.00

FUSED
Dark Horse Comics: Dec, 2003 - No. 4, Mar, 2004 ($2.95)

1-4-Steve Niles-s/Josh Medors-a. 1-Powell-c 3.00

FUSION
Eclipse Comics: Jan, 1987 - No. 17, Oct, 1989 ($2.00, B&W, Baxter paper)

1-17: 11-The Weasel Patrol begins (1st app.?) 3.00

FUSION
Image Comics (Top Cow): May, 2009 - No. 3, Jul, 2009 ($2.99, limited series)

1-3-Avengers, Thunderbolts, Cyberforce and Hunter-Killer meet; Kirkham-a 3.00

FUTURAMA (TV)
Bongo Comics: 2000 - No. 81, 2016 ($2.50/$2.99/$3.99, bi-monthly)

1-Based on the FOX-TV animated series; Groening/Morrison-c 3 6 9 16 23 30
1-San Diego Comic-Con Premiere Edition 6 12 18 38 69 100
2-10: 8-CGC cover spoof; X-Men parody 2 4 6 8 10 12
11-30 6.00
31-81: 40,64-Santa app. 50-55-Poster included 4.00
Futurama Adventures TPB (2004, $14.95) r/#5-9 15.00
Futurama Conquers the Universe TPB (2007, $14.95) r/#10-13 15.00
Futurama-O-Rama TPB (2002, $12.95) r/#1-4; sketch pages of Fry's development 15.00
...: The Time Bender Trilogy TPB (2006, $14.95) r/#16-19; cover gallery 15.00

FUTURAMA/SIMPSONS INFINITELY SECRET CROSSOVER CRISIS (TV) (See Simpsons/ Futurama Crossover Crisis II for sequel)
Bongo Comics: 2002 - No. 2, 2002 ($2.50, limited series)

1-Evil Brain Spawns put Futurama crew into the Simpsons' Springfield 2 4 6 8 11 14
2 6.00

FUTURE COMICS
David McKay Publications: June, 1940 - No. 4, Sept, 1940

1-(6/40, 64 pgs.)-Origin The Phantom (1st in comics) (4 pgs.); The Lone Ranger (8 pgs.) & Saturn Against the Earth (4 pgs.) begin 300 600 900 2070 3635 5200
2 135 270 405 864 1482 2100
3,4 103 206 309 659 1130 1600

FUTURE COP L.A.P.D. (Electronic Arts video game) (Also see Promotional Comics section)
DC Comics (WildStorm): Jan, 1999 ($4.95, magazine sized)

1-Stories & art by various 5.00

FUTURE IMPERFECT (Secret Wars tie-in)
Marvel Comics: Aug, 2015 - No. 5, Nov, 2015 ($3.99, limited series)

1-5-Peter David-s/Greg Land-a; Maestro (Hulk) and The Thing (Thaddeus Ross) app. 4.00

FUTURE QUEST
DC Comics: Jul, 2016 - No. 12, Jul, 2017 ($3.99)

1-12: 1-Jonny Quest, Space Ghost, Birdman and Dr. Zin app.; Shaner & Rude-a. 8-Olivetti-a; The Impossibles app. 4.00

FUTURE QUEST PRESENTS
DC Comics: Oct, 2017 - Present ($3.99)

1-4: 1-3-Space Ghost and the Herculoids; Parker-s/Olivetti-a/c. 4-Galaxy Trio; Randall-a 4.00
5-7-Birdman; Hester-s/Rude-a; Mentok app. 4.00

FUTURE SHOCK
Image Comics: 2006 (Free Comic Book Day giveaway)

...: FCBD 2006 Edition; Spawn, Invincible, Savage Dragon & others short stories 3.00

FUTURE WORLD COMICS
George W. Dougherty: Summer, 1946 - No. 2, Fall, 1946

1,2: H. C. Kiefer-c; preview of the World of Tomorrow 30 60 90 177 289 400

FUTURE WORLD COMIX (Warren Presents...)
Warren Publications: Sept, 1978 (B&W magazine, 84 pgs.)

1-Corben, Maroto, Morrow, Nino, Sutton-a; Todd-c/a; contains nudity panels 2 4 6 8 11 14

FUTURIANS, THE (See Marvel Graphic Novel #9)
Lodestone Publishing/Eternity Comics: Sept, 1985 - No. 3, 1985 ($1.50)

1-3: Indicia title "Dave Cockrum's..." 3.00
Graphic Novel 1 ($9.95, Eternity)-r/#1-3, plus never published #4 issue 10.00

FX
IDW Publishing: Mar, 2008 - No. 6, Aug, 2008 ($3.99)

1-6-John Byrne-a/c; Wayne Osborne-s 4.00

G-8 (Listed at G-Eight)

GABBY (Formerly Ken Shannon) (Teen humor)
Quality Comics Group: No. 11, Jul, 1953; No. 2, Sep, 1953 - No. 9, Sep, 1954

11(#1)(7/53) 10 20 30 56 76 95
2 7 14 21 37 46 55
3-9 6 12 18 31 38 45

GABBY GOB (See Harvey Hits No. 85, 90, 94, 97, 100, 103, 106, 109)

GABBY HAYES ADVENTURE COMICS
Toby Press: Dec, 1953

1-Photo-c 15 30 45 90 140 190

GABBY HAYES WESTERN (Movie star)(See Monte Hale, Real Western Hero & Western Hero)
Fawcett Publications/Charlton Comics No. 51 on: Nov, 1948 - No. 50, Jan, 1953; No. 51, Dec, 1954 - No. 59, Jan, 1957

1-Gabby & his horse Corker begin; photo front/back-c begin 41 82 123 256 428 600
2 20 40 60 120 195 270
3-5 15 30 45 88 137 185
6-10: 9-Young Falcon begins 14 28 42 78 112 145
11-20: 19-Last photo back-c 11 22 33 64 90 115
21-49: 20,22,24,26,28,29-(52 pgs.) 9 18 27 52 69 85
50-(1/53)-Last Fawcett issue; last photo-c? 10 20 30 58 79 100
51-(12/54)-1st Charlton issue; photo-c 11 22 33 60 83 105
52-59(1955-57): 53,55-Photo-c. 58-Swayze-a 8 16 24 42 54 65

GAGS

Galaktikon #1 © Brenden Small

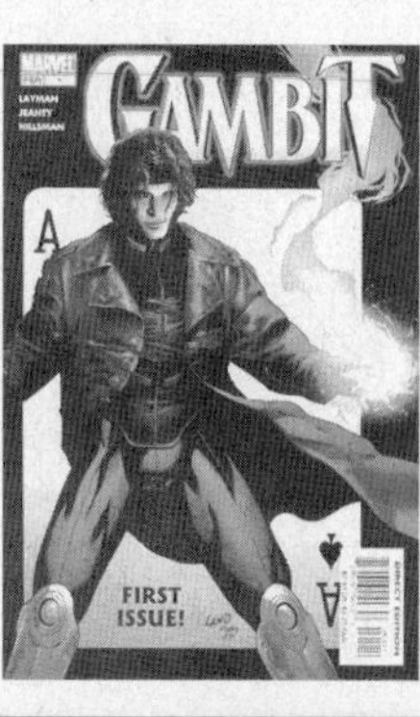

Gambit (2004 series) #1 © MAR

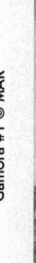

Gamora #1 © MAR

	GD 2.0	VG 4.0	FN 6.0	VF 8.0	VF/NM 9.0	NM- 9.2

United Features Synd./Triangle Publ. No. 9 on: Jul, 1937 - V3#10, Oct, 1944 (13-3/4x10-3/4")

1(7/37)-52 pgs.; 20 pgs. Grin & Bear It, Fellow Citizen	15	30	45	85	130	175
V1#9 (36 pgs.) (7/42)	9	18	27	52	69	85
V3#10	9	18	27	47	61	75

GALACTA: DAUGHTER OF GALACTUS
Marvel Comics: July, 2010 ($3.99, one-shot)

1-Adam Warren-s/Hector Sevilla-a; Warren & Sevilla-c : Wolverine and the FF app. 4.00

GALACTICA 1980 (Based on the Battlestar Galactica TV series)
Dynamite Entertainment: 2009 - No. 4, 2009 ($3.50)

1-4-Guggenheim-s/Razek-a 3.50

GALACTICA: THE NEW MILLENNIUM
Realm Press: Sept, 1999 ($2.99)

1-Stories by Shooter, Braden, Kuhoric 3.00

GALACTIC GUARDIANS
Marvel Comics: July, 1994 - No. 4, Oct, 1994 ($1.50, limited series)

1-4 3.00

GALACTIC WARS COMIX (Warren Presents... on cover)
Warren Publications: Dec, 1978 (B&W magazine, 84 pgs.)

nn-Wood, Williamson-r; Battlestar Galactica/Flash Gordon photo/text stories	2	4	6	8	11	14

GALACTUS THE DEVOURER
Marvel Comics: Sept, 1999 - No. 6, Mar, 2000 ($3.50/$2.50, limited series)

1-($3.50) L. Simonson-s/Muth & Sienkiewicz-a 4.00
2-5-($2.50) Buscema & Sienkiewicz-a 3.00
6-($3.50) Death of Galactus; Buscema & Sienkiewicz-a 4.00

GALAKTIKON
Albatross Funnybooks: 2017 - No. 6 ($3.99, limited series)

1-5-Brendon Small-s/Steve Mannion-a/Eric Powell-c 4.00

GALAXIA (Magazine)
Astral Publ.: 1981 ($2.50, B&W, 52 pgs.)

1-Buckler/Giordano-c; Texeira/Guice-a; 1st app. Astron, Sojourner, Bloodwing, Warlords; Buckler-s/a	2	4	6	9	13	16

GALAXY QUEST: GLOBAL WARNING! (Based on the 1999 movie)
IDW Publishing: Aug, 2008 - No. 5, Dec, 2008 ($3.99)

1-5-Lobdell-s/Kyriazis-a 4.00

GALAXY QUEST: THE JOURNEY CONTINUES (Based on the 1999 movie)
IDW Publishing: Jan, 2015 - No. 4, Apr, 2015 ($3.99)

1-4-Erik Burnham-s/Nacho Arranz-a 4.00

GALLANT MEN, THE (TV)
Gold Key: Oct, 1963 (Photo-c)

1(1008-310)-Manning-a	3	6	9	21	33	45

GALLEGHER, BOY REPORTER (Disney, TV)
Gold Key: May, 1965

1(10149-505)-Photo-c	3	6	9	17	26	35

GAMBIT (See X-Men #266 & X-Men Annual #14)
Marvel Comics: Dec, 1993 - No. 4, Mar, 1994 ($2.00, limited series)

1-($2.50)-Lee Weeks-c/a in all; gold foil stamped-c	2	4	6	11	16	20
1 (Gold)	3	6	9	19	30	40
2-4						6.00

GAMBIT
Marvel Comics: Sept, 1997 - No. 4, Dec, 1997 ($2.50, limited series)

1-4-Janson-a/Mackie & Kavanagh-s	1	2	3	5	6	8

GAMBIT
Marvel Comics: Feb, 1999 - No. 25, Feb, 2001 ($2.99/$1.99)

1-($2.99) Five covers; Nicieza-a/Skroce-a	1	2	3	5	6	8
2-11,13-16-($1.99): 2-Two covers (Skroce & Adam Kubert)						3.00
12-($2.99)						4.00
17-24: 17-Begin $2.25-c. 21-Mystique-c/app.						3.00
25-($2.99) Leads into "Gambit & Bishop"						4.00
...1999 Annual ($3.50) Nicieza-s/McDaniel-a						4.00
...2000 Annual ($3.50) Nicieza-s/Derenick & Smith-a						4.00

GAMBIT
Marvel Comics: Nov, 2004 - No. 12, Aug, 2005 ($2.99)

1-12: 1-Jeanty-a/Land-c/Layman-s. 5-Wolverine-c/app. 9-Brother Voodoo-c/app. 3.00
... and the Champions: From the Marvel Vault 1 (10/11, $2.99) George Tuska's last art 3.00
...: Hath No Fury TPB (2005, $14.99) r/#7-12 15.00
...: House of Cards TPB (2005, $14.99) r/#1-6; Land cover sketches; unused covers 15.00

GAMBIT
Marvel Comics: Oct, 2012 - No. 17, Nov, 2013 ($2.99)

1-17: 1-Asmus-s/Mann-a; covers by Mann & Bachalo. 6,7-Pete Wisdom app. 3.00

GAMBIT & BISHOP (... : Sons of the Atom on cover)
Marvel Comics: Feb, 2001 - No. 6, May, 2001 ($2.25, bi-weekly limited series)

Alpha (2/01) Prelude to series; Nord-a 3.00
1-6-Jeanty-a/Williams-c 3.00
Genesis (3/01, $3.50) reprints their first apps. and first meeting 4.00

GAMBIT AND THE X-TERNALS
Marvel Comics: Mar, 1995 - No. 4, July, 1995 ($1.95, limited series)

1-4-Age of Apocalypse 4.00

GAMEBOY (Super Mario covers on all)
Valiant: 1990 - No. 5 ($1.95, coated-c)

1-5: 3,4-Layton-c. 4-Morrow-a. 5-Layton-c(i)	2	4	6	8	10	12

GAMEKEEPER (Guy Ritchie's...)
Virgin Comics: Mar, 2007 - No. 5, Sept, 2007; Mar, 2008 - No. 5, Jul, 2008 ($2.99)

1-5-Andy Diggle-s/Mukesh Singh-a; 2 covers on each 3.00
1-Extended Edition (6/07, $2.99) r/#1 with script excerpt and sketch art 3.00
Series 2 (3/08 - No. 5, 7/08) 1-5-Parker-s/Randle-a 3.00
Vol. 1 TPB (10/07, $14.99) r/#1-5; script and sketch pages; Guy Ritchie intro. 15.00

GAME OF THRONES, A (George R.R. Martin's...) (Based on A Song of Ice and Fire)
Dynamite Entertainment: 2011 - No. 24, 2014 ($3.99)

1-Covers by Alex Ross and Mike Miller	2	4	6	11	16	20
2-24: 2-Covers by Alex Ross and Mike Miller						4.00

GAMERA
Dark Horse Comics: Aug, 1996 - No. 4, Nov, 1996 ($2.95, limited series)

1-4 3.00

GAMMARAUDERS
DC Comics: Jan, 1989 - No. 10, Dec, 1989 ($1.25/$1.50/$2.00)

1-10-Based on TSR game 3.00

GAMORA (Guardians of the Galaxy)
Marvel Comics: Feb, 2017 - Present ($3.99)

1-5-Perlman-s/Checchetto-a. 1,5-Thanos & Nebula app. 4.00

GAMORRA SWIMSUIT SPECIAL
Image Comics (WildStorm Productions): June, 1996 ($2.50, one-shot)

1-Campbell wraparound-c; pinups 3.00

GANDY GOOSE (Movies/TV)(See All Surprise, Giant Comics Edition #5A &10, Paul Terry's Comics & Terry-Toons)
St. John Publ. Co./Pines No. 5,6: Mar, 1953 - No. 5, Nov, 1953; No. 5, Fall, 1956 - No. 6, Sum/58

1-All St. John issues are pre-code	12	24	36	69	97	125
2	8	16	24	42	54	65
3-5(1953)(St. John)	7	14	21	35	43	50
5,6(1956-58)(Pines)-CBS Television Presents...	5	10	15	24	30	35

GANG BUSTERS (See Popular Comics #38)
David McKay/Dell Publishing Co.: 1938 - 1943

Feature Books 17(McKay)('38)-1st app.	77	154	231	493	847	1200
Large Feature Comic 10('39)-(Scarce)	77	154	231	493	847	1200
Large Feature Comic 17('41)	54	108	162	343	574	825
Four Color 7(1940)	60	120	180	381	653	925
Four Color 23('42)	47	94	141	296	498	700
Four Color 24('43)	27	54	81	194	435	675

GANG BUSTERS (Radio/TV)(Gangbusters #14 on)
National Periodical Publ.: Dec-Jan, 1947-48 - No. 67, Dec-Jan, 1958-59 (No. 1-23: 52 pgs.)

1	90	180	270	576	988	1400
2	41	82	123	256	428	600
3-5	28	56	84	165	270	375
6-10: 9-Dan Barry-a. 9,10-Photo-c	21	42	63	122	199	275
11-13-Photo-c	17	34	51	100	158	215
14,17-Frazetta-a, 8 pgs. each. 14-Photo-c	36	72	108	211	343	475
15,16,18-20,26: 26-Kirby-a	15	30	45	85	130	175
21-25,27-30	14	28	42	76	108	140

Gangland #2 © DC

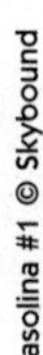
Gasolina #1 © Skybound

Gears of War #12 © Epic Games

	GD	VG	FN	VF	VF/NM	NM-
	2.0	4.0	6.0	8.0	9.0	9.2

31-44: 44-Last Pre-code (2-3/55) 12 24 36 67 94 120
45-67 10 20 30 54 72 90
NOTE: *Barry a-6, 8, 10. Drucker a-51. Moreira a-48, 50, 59. Roussos a-8.*

GANGLAND
DC Comics (Vertigo): Jun, 1998 - No. 4, Sept, 1998 ($2.95, limited series)
1-4: Crime anthology by various. 2-Corben-a 3.00
TPB-(2000, $12.95) r/#1-4; Bradstreet-c 13.00

GANGSTERS AND GUN MOLLS
Avon Per./Realistic Comics: Sept, 1951 - No. 4, June, 1952 (Painted c-1-3)
1-Wood-a, 1 pg; c-/Avon paperback #292 63 126 189 403 689 975
2-Check-a, 8 pgs.; Kamen-a; Bonnie Parker story 57 114 171 362 619 875
3-Marijuana mentioned; used in **POP**, pg. 84,85 48 96 144 302 514 725
4-Syd Shores-c 45 90 135 284 480 675

GANGSTERS CAN'T WIN
D. S. Publishing Co.: Feb-Mar, 1948 - No. 9, June-July, 1949 (All 52 pgs?)
1-True crime stories 41 82 123 250 418 585
2-Skull-c 29 58 87 170 278 385
3,5,6 21 42 63 122 199 275
4-Acid in face story 26 52 78 156 256 355
7-9 17 34 51 98 154 210
NOTE: *Ingles a-5, 6. McWilliams a-5, 7, 8. Reinman c-6.*

GANG WORLD
Standard Comics: No. 5, Nov, 1952 - No. 6, Jan, 1953
5-Bondage-c 20 40 60 120 195 270
6 15 30 45 85 130 175

GARBAGE PAIL KIDS COMIC BOOK (Based on the tranding cards)
IDW Publishing: Dec, 2014 - Feb, 2015 ($3.99, series of one-shots)
... Love Stinks (2/15) short stories by various incl. Haspiel, Wheeler, Bagge; 3 covers 4.00
... Puke-tacular (12/14) short stories by various incl. Bagge, Wray, Barta; 3 covers 4.00

GARFIELD (Newspaper/cartoon cat)(Also see Grumpy Cat)
Boom Entertainment (KaBOOM!): May, 2012 - No. 36, Apr, 2015 ($3.99)
1-24-Evanier-s. 1-Two covers by Barker. 8-Christmas-c. 13,20-Pet Force app. 4.00
1-4-First Appearance Variants by Jim Davis. 1-Garfield. 2-Odie. 3-Jon. 4-Nermal 10.00
25-($4.99) Covers by George Pérez and Barker; bonus pin-ups 5.00
26-36: 30-EC-style horror cover. 33-36-His 9 Lives 4.00
... 2016 Summer Special 1 (7/16, $7.99) Evanier & Nickel-s; Batman spoof 1 2 3 5 6 8
... Cheesy Holiday Special 1 (12/15, $4.99) Christmas stories; Evanier & Nickel-s 5.00
...: Pet Force Special 1 (8/13, $4.99) Cover swipe of Amazing Spider-Man #50 5.00
...: Pet Force 2014 Special (4/14, $4.99) The Pet Force multiverse; bonus sketch art 5.00

GARGOYLE (See The Defenders #94)
Marvel Comics Group: June, 1985 - No. 4, Sept, 1985 (75¢, limited series)
1-Wrightson-c; character from Defenders 5.00
2-4 4.00

GARGOYLES (TV cartoon)
Marvel Comics: Feb, 1995 - No. 11, Dec, 1995 ($2.50)
1-11: Based on animated series 3.00

GARRISON
DC Comics (WildStorm): Jun, 2010 - No. 6, Nov, 2010 ($2.99)
1-6-Mariotte-s/Francavilla-a/c 3.00

GARRISON'S GORILLAS (TV)
Dell Publishing Co.: Jan, 1968 - No. 4, Oct, 1968; No. 5, Oct, 1969 (Photo-c)
1 4 8 12 28 47 65
2-5: 5-Reprints #1 3 6 9 19 30 40

GARY GIANNI'S THE MONSTERMEN
Dark Horse Comics: Aug, 1999 ($2.95, one-shot)
1-Gianni-s/c/a; back-up Hellboy story by Mignola 4.00

GASM (Sci-Fi, Horror, Fantasy comics magazine)(Mature content)
Stories, Layouts & Press, Inc.: Nov, 1977 - nn (No. 5), Jun, 1978 (B&W/color)
1-Mark Wheatley-s/a; Gene Day-s/a; Workman-a 3 6 9 14 19 24
2 (12/77) Wheatley-a; Winnick-s/a; Workman-a 2 4 6 11 16 20
nn(#3, 2/78) Day-s/a; Wheatley-a; Workman-a 2 4 6 10 14 18
nn(#4, 4/78) Day-s/a; Wheatley-a; Corben-a 3 6 9 14 20 26
nn(#5, 6/78) Hempel-a; Howarth-a; Corben-a 3 6 9 15 22 28

GASOLINA
Image Comics (Skybound): Sept, 2017 - Present ($3.99)
1-6-Sean Mackiewicz-s/Niko Walter-a 4.00

GASOLINE ALLEY (Top Love Stories No. 3 on?)
Star Publications: Sept-Oct, 1950 - No. 2, Dec, 1950 (Newspaper-r)
1-Contains 1 pg. intro. history of the strip (The Life of Skeezix); reprints 15 scenes of highlights from 1921-1935, plus an adventure from 1935 and 1936 strips; a 2-pg. filler is included on the life of the creator Frank King, with photo of the cartoonist. 20 40 60 118 192 265
2-(1936-37 reprints)-L. B. Cole-c 22 44 66 132 216 300
(See Super Book No. 21)

GASP!
American Comics Group: Mar, 1967 - No. 4, Aug, 1967 (12¢)
1 5 10 15 31 53 75
2-4 3 6 9 21 33 45

GATECRASHER
Black Bull Entertainment: Mar, 2000 - No. 4, Jun, 2000 ($2.50, limited series)
1,2-Waid-s/Conner & Palmiotti-c/a; 1,2-variant-c by J.G. Jones 3.00
3,4: 3-Jusko var-c. 4-Linsner-c 3.00
... Ring of Fire TPB (11/00, $12.95) r/#1-4; Hughes-c; Ennis intro. 13.00

GATECRASHER (Regular series)
Black Bull Entertainment: Aug, 2000 - No. 6, Jan, 2001 ($2.50, limited series)
1-6-Waid-s/Conner & Palmiotti-c/a; 1-3-Variant-c by Fabry. 4-Hildebrandts variant-c. 5-Art Adams var-c. 6-Texeira var-c 3.00

GAY COMICS (Honeymoon No. 41)
Timely Comics/USA Comic Mag. Co. No. 18-24: Mar, 1944 (no month); No. 18, Fall, 1944 - No. 40, Oct, 1949
1-Wolverton's Powerhouse Pepper; Tessie the Typist begins; 1st app. Willie (one shot) 81 162 243 518 884 1250
18-(Formerly Funny Tunes #17?)-Wolverton-a 54 108 162 343 574 825
19-29: Wolverton-a in all. 21,24-6 pg., 7 pg. Powerhouse Pepper; additional 2 pg. story in 24). 23-7 pg Wolverton story & 2 two pg stories (total of 11pgs.).
24,29-Kurtzman-a (24-"Hey Look"(2)) 48 96 144 302 514 725
30,33,36,37-Kurtzman's "Hey Look" 24 48 72 142 234 325
31-Kurtzman's "Hey Look" (1), Giggles 'N' Grins (1-1/2) 24 48 72 142 234 325
32,35,38-40: 35-Nellie The Nurse begins? 22 44 66 130 213 295
34-Three Kurtzman's "Hey Look" 24 48 72 142 234 325

GAY COMICS (Also see Smile, Tickle, & Whee Comics)
Modern Store Publ.: 1955 (7¢, 5x7-1/4", 52 pgs.)
1 5 10 15 31 53 75

GAY PURR-EE (See Movie Comics)

GEARS OF WAR (Based on the video game)
DC Comics (WildStorm): Dec, 2008 - No. 24, Aug, 2012 ($3.99/$2.99)
1-15: 1-Liam Sharp-a/Joshua Ortega-s. 1-Two covers 4.00
16-24-($2.99) 16-Traviss-s/Gopez-a. 18-20-Mhan-a. 19-24-Prelude to Gears of War 3 3.00
... Reader (4/09, $3.99) r/#1 & 2 in flipbook 4.00
... Sourcebook (8/09, $3.99) character pin-ups by various; Platt-c 4.00
Book One HC (2009, $19.99, dustjacket) r/#1-6 & Sourcebook 20.00
Book One SC (2010, $14.99) r/#1-6 & Sourcebook 15.00
Book Two HC (2011, $24.99, dustjacket) r/#7-13 25.00

GEARS OF WAR: THE RISE OF RAAM (Based on the video game)
IDW Publishing: Jan, 2018 - Present ($3.99)
1,2-Kurtis Wiebe-s/Max Dunbar-a 4.00

GEAR STATION, THE
Image Comics: Mar, 2000 - No. 5, Nov, 2000 ($2.50)
1-Four covers by Ross, Turner, Pat Lee, Fraga 3.00
1-($6.95) DF Cover 7.00
2-5: 2-Two covers by Fraga and Art Adams 3.00

GEEK, THE (See Brother Power... & Vertigo Visions)

GEEKSVILLE (Also see 3 Geeks, The)
3 Finger Prints/ Image: Aug, 1999 - No. 6, Mar, 2001 ($2.75/$2.95, B&W)
1,2,4-6-The 3 Geeks by Koslowski; Innocent Bystander by Sassaman 3.00
3-Includes "Babes & Blades" mini-comic 5.00
0-(3/00) First Image issue 3.00
(Vol. 2) 1-4-($2.95) 3-Mini-comic insert by the Geeks. 4-Steve Borock app. 3.00

G-8 AND HIS BATTLE ACES (Based on pulps)
Gold Key: Oct, 1966
1 (10184-610)-Painted-c 4 8 12 25 40 55

Gene Autry Comics #8 © FAW

Generation Hope #4 © MAR

Generation X (2017 series) #3 © MAR

	GD 2.0	VG 4.0	FN 6.0	VF 8.0	VF/NM 9.0	NM- 9.2

G-8 AND HIS BATTLE ACES
Blazing Comics: 1991 ($1.50, one-shot)

1-Glanzman-a; Truman-c 3.00

NOTE: *Flip book format with "The Spider's Web" #1 on other side w/***Glanzman**-*a*, **Truman**-*c*.

GEM COMICS
Spotlight Publishers: Apr, 1945 (52 pgs)

	GD	VG	FN	VF	VF/NM	NM-
1-Little Mohee, Steve Strong app.; Jungle bondage-c	60	120	180	381	653	925

GEMINAR
Image Comics: July, 2000 ($4.95, B&W)

1-(72-Page Special) Terry Collins-s/Al Bigley-a 5.00

GEMINI BLOOD
DC Comics (Helix): Sept, 1996 - No. 9, May, 1997 ($2.25, limited series)

1-9: 5-Simonson-c 3.00

GEN ACTIVE
DC Comics (WildStorm): May, 2000 - No. 6, Aug, 2001 ($3.95)

1-6: 1-Covers by Campbell and Madureira; Gen 13 & DV8 app. 5-Mahfood-a; Quitely and Stelfreeze-c. 6-Portacio-a/c 4.00

GENE AUTRY (See March of Comics No. 25, 28, 39, 54, 78, 90, 104, 120, 135, 150 in the Promotional Comics section & Western Roundup under Dell Giants)

GENE AUTRY COMICS (Movie, Radio star; singing cowboy)
Fawcett Publications: Jan, 1942 (On sale 12/17/41) - No. 10, 1943 (68 pgs.) (Dell takes over with No. 11)

	GD	VG	FN	VF	VF/NM	NM-
1 (Scarce)-Gene Autry & his horse Champion begin; photo back-c	423	846	1269	3000	5250	7500
2-(1942)	90	180	270	576	988	1400
3-5: 3-(11/1/42)	50	100	150	315	533	750
6-10	41	82	123	256	428	600

GENE AUTRY COMICS (...& Champion No. 102 on)
Dell Publishing Co.: No. 11, 1943 - No. 121, Jan-Mar, 1959 (TV - later issues)

	GD	VG	FN	VF	VF/NM	NM-
11 (1943, 60 pgs.)-Continuation of Fawcett series; photo back-c; first Dell issue	32	64	96	230	515	800
12 (2/44, 60 pgs.)	28	56	84	202	451	700
Four Color 47 (1944, 60 pgs.)	35	70	105	252	564	875
Four Color 57 (11/44), 66 ('45)(52 pgs. each)	30	60	90	216	483	750
Four Color 75, 83 ('45, 36 pgs. each)	23	46	69	164	362	560
Four Color 93 ('45, 36 pgs.)	19	38	57	133	297	460
Four Color 100 ('46, 36 pgs.) First Gene Autry photo-c	22	44	66	155	345	535
1 (5-6/46, 52 pgs.)	33	66	99	238	532	825
2 (7-8/46)-Photo-c begin, end #111	14	28	42	96	211	325
3-5: 4-Intro Flapjack Hobbs	11	22	33	76	163	250
6-10	10	20	30	64	132	200
11-20: 20-Panhandle Pete begins	9	18	27	60	120	180
21-29 (36 pgs.)	8	16	24	52	99	145
30-40 (52 pgs.)	7	14	21	44	82	120
41-56 (52 pgs.)	6	12	18	38	69	100
57-66 (36 pgs.): 58-X-mas-c	5	10	15	34	60	85
67-80 (52 pgs.): 70-X-mas-c	5	10	15	34	60	85
81-90 (52 pgs.): 82-X-mas-c. 87-Blank inside-c	5	10	15	31	53	75
91-99 (36 pgs. No. 91-on). 94-X-mas-c	4	8	12	28	47	65
100	5	10	15	30	50	70
101-111-Last Gene Autry photo-c	4	8	12	27	44	60
112-121-All Champion painted-c, most by Savitt	4	8	12	25	40	55

NOTE: *Photo back covers 4-18, 20-45, 48-65.* ***Manning** a-118.* ***Jesse Marsh** art: 4-Color No. 66, 75, 93, 100, No. 1-25, 27-37, 39, 40.*

GENE AUTRY'S CHAMPION (TV)
Dell Publ. Co.: No. 287, 8/50; No. 319, 2/51; No. 3, 8-10/51 - No. 19, 8-10/55

	GD	VG	FN	VF	VF/NM	NM-
Four Color 287(#1)('50, 52 pgs.)-Photo-c	11	22	33	76	163	250
Four Color 319(#2, '51), 3: 2-Painted-c begin, most by Sam Savitt	6	12	18	41	76	110
4-19: 19-Last painted-c	4	8	12	28	47	65

GENE COLAN TRIBUTE BOOK (Produced for The Hero Initiative)
Marvel Comics: 2008 ($9.99, one-shot)

1-Spotlighted stories from Tales of Suspense #89,90, Doctor Strange #174 and others 10.00

GENE DOGS
Marvel Comics UK: Oct, 1993 - No. 4, Jan, 1994 ($1.75, limited series)

1-($2.75)-Polybagged w/4 trading cards 4.00
2-4: 2-Vs. Genetix 3.00

GENE POOL
IDW Publishing: Oct, 2003 ($6.99, squarebound)

nn-Wein & Wolfman-s/Cummings-a 7.00

GENERAL DOUGLAS MACARTHUR
Fox Feature Syndicate: 1951

	GD	VG	FN	VF	VF/NM	NM-
nn-True life story	20	40	60	114	182	250

GENERATION HEX
DC Comics (Amalgam): June, 1997 ($1.95, one-shot)

1-Milligan-s/ Pollina & Morales-a 3.00

GENERATION HOPE (See X-Men titles and Cable)
Marvel Comics: Jan, 2011 - No. 17, May, 2012 ($3.99/$2.99)

1-($3.99) Gillen-s/Espin-a; Coipel-c; back-up bio of Hope Summers 4.00
1-Variant-c by Greg Land 8.00
2-17-($2.99) 5,9-McKelvie-a. 10,11-Seeley-a. 11-X-Men: Schism tie-in 3.00

GENERATION M (Follows House of M x-over)
Marvel Comics: Jan, 2006 - No. 5, May, 2006 ($2.99, limited series)

1-5-Jenkins-s/Bachs-a. 1-Chamber app. 2-Jubilee app. 3-Blob-c. 4-Angel-c 3.00
Decimation: Generation M TPB (2006, $13.99) r/#1-5 14.00

GENERATION NEXT
Marvel Comics: Mar, 1995 - No. 4, June, 1995 ($1.95, limited series)

1-4-Age of Apocalypse; Scott Lobdell scripts & Chris Bachalo-c/a 3.00

GENERATIONS: (Team-ups of legacy characters after Secret Empire)
Marvel Comics: Oct, 2017 - Nov, 2017 ($4.99, series of one-shots)

... Banner Hulk & The Totally Awesome Hulk 1 (10/17) Pak-s/Buffagni-a 5.00
... Captain Marvel & Captain Mar-Vell 1 (11/17) Stohl-s/Schoonover-a; Annihilus app. 5.00
... Hawkeye & Hawkeye 1 (10/17) Thompson-s/Raffaele-a; Swordsman app. 5.00
... Iron Man & Ironheart 1 (11/17) Bendis-s; future Tony Stark as Sorceror Supreme app. 5.00
... Miles Morales Spider-Man & Peter Parker Spider-Man 1 (11/17) Bendis-s 5.00
... Ms. Marvel & Ms. Marvel 1 (11/17) Kamala meets younger Carol; Nightscream app. 5.00
... Phoenix & Jean Grey 1 (10/17) Bunn-s/Silva-a; Galactus app. 5.00
... Sam Wilson Captain America & Steve Rogers Captain America 1 (11/17) Spencer-s 5.00
... The Unworthy Thor & The Mighty Thor 1 (10/17) Aaron-s/Asrar-a; Apocalypse app. 5.00
... Wolverine & All-New Wolverine 1 (10/17) Taylor-s/Rosanas-a; Sabretooth app. 5.00

GENERATION X (See Gen [13]/ Generation X)
Marvel Comics: Oct, 1994 - No. 75, June, 2001 ($1.50/$1.95/$1.99/$2.25)

Collectors Preview ($1.75), "Ashcan" Edition 3.00
-1(7/97) Flashback story 3.00

	GD	VG	FN	VF	VF/NM	NM-
1/2 (San Diego giveaway)	2	4	6	8	10	12

1-($3.95)-Wraparound chromium-c; Scott Lobdell scripts & Chris Bachalo-a begins 6.00
2-($1.95)-Deluxe edition, Bachalo-a 4.00
3,4-($1.95)-Deluxe Edition; Bachalo-a 4.00
2-10: 2-4-Standard Edition. 5-Returns from "Age of Apocalypse," begin $1.95-c. 6-Bachalo-a(p) ends, returns #17. 7-Roger Cruz-a(p). 10-Omega Red-c/app. 3.00
11-24, 26-28: 13,14-Bishop-app. 17-Stan Lee app. (Stan Lee scripts own dialogue); Bachalo/Buckingham-a; Onslaught update. 18-Toad cameo. 20-Franklin Richards app; Howard the Duck cameo. 21-Howard the Duck app. 22-Nightmare app. 3.00
25-($2.99)-Wraparound-c. Black Tom, Howard the Duck app. 4.00
29-37: 29-Begin $1.99-c, "Operation Zero Tolerance". 33-Hama-s 3.00
38-49: 38-Dodson-a begins. 40-Penance ID revealed. 49-Maggott app. 3.00
50,57-($2.99): 50-Crossover w/X-Man #50 4.00
51-56, 58-62: 59-Avengers & Spider-Man app. 3.00
63-74: 63-Ellis-s begin. 64-Begin $2.25-c. 69-71-Art Adams-c 3.00
75-($2.99) Final issue; Chamber joins the X-Men; Lim-a 4.00
'95 Special-($3.95) 4.00
'96 Special-($2.95)-Wraparound-c; Jeff Johnson-c/a 4.00
'97 Special-($2.99)-Wraparound-c; 4.00
'98 Annual-($3.50)-vs. Dracula 4.00
'99 Annual-($3.50)-Monet leaves 4.00
75¢ Ashcan Edition 3.00
...Holiday Special 1 (2/99, $3.50) Pollina-a 4.00
...Underground Special 1 (5/98, $2.50, B&W) Mahfood-a 3.00

GENERATION X
Marvel Comics: Jul, 2017 - No. 9, Jan, 2018; No. 85, Feb, 2018 - No. 87, Apr, 2018 ($3.99)

1-9: 1-Strain-s/Pinna-a 4.00

[Title switches to legacy numbering after #9 (1/18)]

85-87: 85-(2/18) Monet app.; Dodson-c 4.00

GENERATION X/ GEN [13] (Also see Gen [13]/ Generation X)

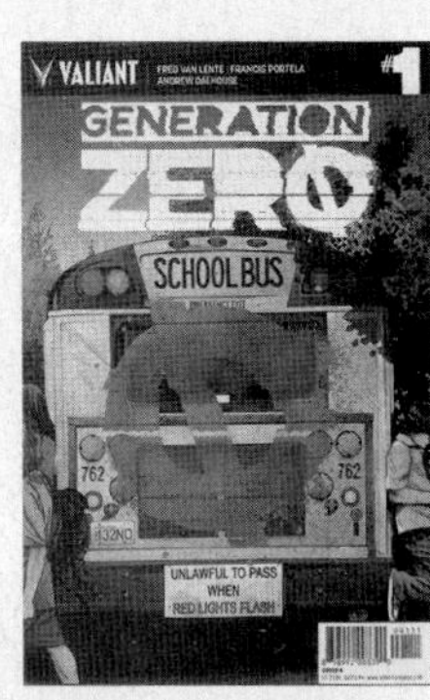

Generation Zero #1 © VAL

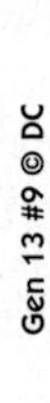

Gen 13 #9 © DC

Gen 13 (2nd series) #7 © WSP

	GD	VG	FN	VF	VF/NM	NM-
	2.0	4.0	6.0	8.0	9.0	9.2

Marvel Comics: 1997 ($3.99, one-shot)

1-Robinson-s/Larroca-a(p) 4.00

GENERATION ZERO (see Harbinger Wars)
Valiant Entertainment: Aug, 2016 - No. 9, Apr, 2017 ($3.99)

1-9: 1-Van Lente-s/Portela-a; multiple covers. 3-Archie-style art by Derek Charm 4.00

GENERIC COMIC, THE
Marvel Comics Group: Apr, 1984 (one-shot)

1 3.00

GENE RODDENBERRY'S LOST UNIVERSE
Tekno Comix: Apr, 1995 - No. 7, Oct, 1995 ($1.95)

1-7: 1-3-w/ bound-in game piece & trading card. 4-w/bound-in trading card 3.00

GENE RODDENBERRY'S XANDER IN LOST UNIVERSE
Tekno Comix: No. 0, Nov, 1995; No. 1, Dec, 1995 - No. 8, July, 1996 ($2.25)

0,1-8: 1-5-Jae Lee-c. 4-Polybagged. 8-Pt. 5 of The Big Bang x-over 3.00

GENESIS (See DC related titles)
DC Comics: Oct, 1997 - No. 4, Oct, 1997 ($1.95, weekly limited series)

1-4: Byrne-s/Wagner-a(p) in all. 3.00

GENESIS: THE #1 COLLECTION (WildStorm Archives)
WildStorm Productions: 1998 ($9.99, TPB, B&W)

nn-Reprints #1 issues of WildStorm titles and pin-ups 10.00

GENETIX
Marvel Comics UK: Oct, 1993 - No. 6, Mar, 1994 ($1.75, limited series)

1-($2.75)-Polybagged w/4 cards; Dark Guard app. 4.00
2-6: 2-Intro Tektos. 4-Vs. Gene Dogs 3.00

GENEXT (Next generation of X-Men)
Marvel Comics: July, 2008 - No. 5, Nov, 2008 ($3.99, limited series)

1-5: 1-Claremont-s/Scherberger-a; character profile pages 4.00

GENEXT: UNITED
Marvel Comics: July, 2009 - No. 5, Dec, 2009 ($3.99, limited series)

1-5: 1-Claremont-s/Meyers-a; Beast app. 4.00

GENIUS
Image Comics (Top Cow): Aug, 2014 - No. 5, Aug, 2014 ($3.99, limited series)

1-5-Bernardin & Freeman-s/Afua Richardson-a 4.00

GEN 12 (Also see Gen13 and Team 7)
Image Comics (WildStorm Productions): Feb, 1998 - No. 5, June, 1998 ($2.50, lim. series)

1-5: 1-Team 7 & Gen13 app.; wraparound-c 3.00

GEN 13 (Also see Wild C.A.T.S. #1 & Deathmate Black #2)
Image Comics (WildStorm Productions): Feb, 1994 - No. 5, July 1994 ($1.95, limited series)

0 (8/95, $2.50)-Ch. 1 w/Jim Lee-p; Ch. 4 w/Charest-p 4.00
1/2 1 2 3 4 5 7
1-($2.50)-Created by Jim Lee 1 3 4 6 8 10
1-2nd printing 3.00
1-"3-D" Edition (9/97, $4.95)-w/glasses 5.00
2-($2.50) 1 2 3 4 5 7
3-Pitt-c & story 4.00
4-Pitt-c & story; wraparound-c 4.00
5 4.00
5-Alternate Portacio-c; see Deathblow #5 6.00
...Collected Edition ('94, $12.95)-r/#1-5 13.00
...Rave ($1.50, 3/95)-wraparound-c 4.00
...: Who They Are And How They Came To Be... (2006, $14.99) r/#1-5; sketch gallery 15.00

NOTE: *Issues 1-4 contain coupons redeemable for the ashcan edition of Gen 13 #0. Price listed is for a complete book.*

GEN 13
Image Comics (WildStorm Productions): Mar, 1995 - No. 36, Dec, 1998;
DC Comics (WildStorm): No. 37, Mar, 1999 - No. 77, Jul, 2002 ($2.95/$2.50)

1-A (Charge)-Campbell/Garner-c 5.00
1-B (Thumbs Up)-Campbell/Garner-c 5.00
1-C-1-F,1-I-1-M: 1-C (Lil' GEN 13)-Art Adams-c. 1-D (Barbari-GEN)-Simon Bisley-c. 1-E (Your Friendly Neighborhood Grunge)-Cleary-c. 1-F (GEN 13 Goes Madison Ave.)-Golden-c. 1-I (That's the way we became GEN 13)-Campbell/Gibson-c. 1-J (All Dolled Up)-Campbell/McWeeney-c. 1-K (Verti-GEN)-Dunn-c. 1-L (Picto-Fiction). 1-M (Do it Yourself Cover) 1 2 3 4 5 7
1-G (Lin-GEN-re)-Michael Lopez-c 3 6 9 14 20 25
1-H (GEN-et Jackson)-Jason Pearson-c 2 4 6 8 10 12
1-Chromium-c by Campbell 4 8 12 27 44 60
1-Chromium-c by Jim Lee 5 10 15 33 57 80
1-"3-D" Edition (2/98, $4.95)-w/glasses 5.00
2 ($1.95, Newsstand)-WildStorm Rising Pt. 4; bound-in card 3.00
2-12: 2-($2.50, Direct Market)-WildStorm Rising Pt. 4, bound-in card. 6,7-Jim Lee-c/a(p). 9-Ramos-a. 10,11-Fire From Heaven Pt. 3. & Pt.9 4.00
11-($4.95)-Special European Tour Edition; chromium-c 2 4 6 10 14 18
13A,13B,13C-($1.30, 13 pgs.): 13A-Archie & Friends app. 13B-Bone-c/app.; Teenage Mutant Ninja Turtles, Madman, Spawn & Jim Lee app. 4.00
14-24: 20-Last Campbell-a 3.00
25-($3.50)-Two covers by Campbell and Charest 4.00
25-($3.50)-Voyager Pack w/Danger Girl preview 5.00
25-Foil-c 10.00
26-32,34: 26-Arcudi-s/Frank-a begins. 34-Back-up story by Art Adams 3.00
33-Flip book w/Planetary preview 4.00
35-49: 36,38,40-Two covers. 37-First DC issue. 41-Last Frank-a 3.00
50-($3.95) Two covers by Lee and Benes; art by various 4.00
51-76: 51-Moy-a; Fairchild loses her powers. 60-Warren-s/a. 66-Art by various incl. Campbell (3 pgs.). 70,75,76-Mays-a. 76-Original team dies 3.00
77-($3.50) Mays, Andrews, Warren-a 4.00
Annual 1 (1997, $2.95) Ellis-s/ Dillon-c/a. 4.00
Annual 1999 ($3.50, DC) Slipstream x-over w/ DV8 4.00
Annual 2000 ($3.50) Devil's Night x-over w/WildStorm titles; Bermejo-c 4.00
...: A Christmas Caper (1/00, $5.95, one-shot) McWeeney-s/a 6.00
... Archives (4/98, $12.99) B&W reprints of mini-series, #0,1/2,1-13ABC; includes cover gallery and sourcebook 13.00
...: Carny Folk (2/00, $3.50) Collect back-up stories 3.50
... European Vacation TPB ($6.95) r/#6,7 7.00
.../ Fantastic Four (2001, $5.95) Maguire-s/c/a(p) 6.00
...: Going West (6/99, $2.50, one-shot) Pruett-s 3.00
...: Grunge Saves the World (5/99, $5.95, one-shot) Altieri-c/a 6.00
... I Love New York TPB ($9.95) r/part #25, 26-29; Frank-c 10.00
... London, New York, Hell TPB ($6.95) r/Annual #1 & Bootleg Ann. #1 7.00
... Lost in Paradise TPB ($6.95) r/#3-5 7.00
.../ Maxx (12/95, $3.50, one-shot) Messner-Loebs-s, 1st Coker-c/a. 4.00
...: Meanwhile (2003, $17.95) r/#43,44,66-70; all Warren-s; art by various 18.00
...: Medicine Song (2001, $5.95) Brent Anderson-c/a(p)/Raab-s 6.00
... Science Friction (2001, $5.95) Haley & Lopresti-a 6.00
... Starting Over TPB ($14.95) r/#1-7 15.00
... Superhuman Like You TPB ($12.95) r/#60-65; Warren-c 13.00
... #13 A,B&C Collected Edition ($6.95, TPB) r/#13A,B&C 7.00
... 3-D Special (1997, $4.95, one-shot) Art Adams-s/a(p) 5.00
...: The Unreal World (7/96, $2.95, one-shot) Humberto Ramos-c/a 3.00
... We'll Take Manhattan TPB ($14.95) r/#45-50; new Benes-c 15.00
...: Wired (4/99, $2.50, one-shot) Richard Bennett-c/a 3.00
... Yearbook 1997 (6/97, $2.50) College-themed stories and pin-ups by various 3.00
...: 'Zine (12/96, $1.95, B&W, digest size) Campbell/Garner-c 3.00
Variant Collection-Four editions (all 13 variants w/Chromium variant-limited, signed) 100.00

GEN 13
DC Comics (WildStorm): No. 0, Sept, 2002 - No. 16, Feb, 2004 ($2.95)

0-(13¢-c) Intro. new team; includes previews of 21 Down & The Resistance 3.00
1-Claremont-s/Garza-c/a; Fairchild app. 3.00
2-16: 8-13-Bachs-a. 16-Original team returns 3.00
...: September Song TPB (2003, $19.95) r/#0-6; Garza sketch pages 20.00

GEN 13 (Volume 4)
DC Comics (WildStorm): Dec, 2006 - No. 39, Feb, 2011 ($2.99)

1-39: 1-Simone-s/Caldwell-a; re-intro the original team; Caldwell-c. 8-The Authority app. 3.00
1-Variant-c by J. Scott Campbell 5.00
...: Armageddon (1/08, $2.99) Gage-s/Meyers-a; future Gen13 app. 3.00
...: Best of a Bad Lot TPB (2007, $14.99) r/#1-6 15.00
...: 15 Minutes TPB (2008, $14.99) r/#14-20 15.00
...: Road Trip TPB (2008, $14.99) r/#7-13 15.00
...: World's End TPB (2009, $17.99) r/#21-26 18.00

GEN 13 BOOTLEG
Image Comics (WildStorm): Nov, 1996 - No. 20, Jul, 1998 ($2.50)

1-Alan Davis-a; alternate costumes-c 3.00
1-Team falling variant-c 4.00
2-7: 2-Alan Davis-a. 5,6-Terry Moore-s. 7-Robinson-s/Scott Hampton-a 3.00
8-10-Adam Warren-s/a 4.00
11-20: 11,12-Lopresti-s/a & Simonson-s. 13-Wieringo-s/a. 14-Mariotte-s/Phillips-a. 15,16-Strnad-s/Shaw-a. 18-Altieri-s/a(p)/c, 18-Variant-c by Bruce Timm 3.00
Annual 1 (2/98, $2.95) Ellis-s/Dillon-c/a 4.00

Georgie Comics #4 © MAR

Get Smart #5 © DELL

Ghost #4 © FH

	GD	VG	FN	VF	VF/NM	NM-
	2.0	4.0	6.0	8.0	9.0	9.2

... Grunge: The Movie (12/97, $9.95) r/#8-10, Warren-c 10.00
...Vol. 1 TPB (10/98, $11.95) r/#1-4 12.00

GEN [13]/ GENERATION X (Also see Generation X / Gen [13])
Image Comics (WildStorm Publications): July, 1997 ($2.95, one-shot)
1-Choi-s/ Art Adams-p/Garner-i. Variant covers by Adams/Garner and Campbell/McWeeney 3.00
1-($4.95) 3-D Edition w/glasses; Campbell-c 5.00

GEN [13] INTERACTIVE
Image Comics (WildStorm): Oct, 1997 - No. 3, Dec, 1997 ($2.50, lim. series)
1-3-Internet voting used to determine storyline 3.00
... Plus! (7/98, $11.95) r/series & 3-D Special (in 2-D) 12.00

GEN [13] : MAGICAL DRAMA QUEEN ROXY
Image Comics (WildStorm): Oct, 1998 - No. 3, Dec, 1998 ($3.50, lim. series)
1-3-Adam Warren-s/c/a; manga style, 2-Variant-c by Hiroyuki Utatane 3.50
1-($6.95) Dynamic Forces Ed. w/Variant Warren-c 7.00

GEN [13] /MONKEYMAN & O'BRIEN
Image Comics (WildStorm): Jun, 1998 - No. 2, July, 1998 ($2.50, lim. series)
1,2-Art Adams-s/a(p); 1-Two covers 3.00
1-($4.95) Chromium-c 5.00
1-($6.95) Dynamic Forces Ed. 7.00

GEN [13]: ORDINARY HEROES
Image Comics (WildStorm Publications): Feb, 1996 - No. 2, July, 1996 ($2.50, lim. series)
1,2-Adam Hughes-c/a/scripts 3.00
TPB (2004, $14.95) r/series, Gen13 Bootleg #1&2 and Wildstorm Thunderbook; new Hughes-c and art pages 15.00

GENTLE BEN (TV)
Dell Publishing Co.: Feb, 1968 - No. 5, Oct, 1969 (All photo-c)
1 4 8 12 25 40 55
2-5: 5-Reprints #1 3 6 9 16 23 30

GEOMANCER (Also see Eternal Warrior: Fist & Steel)
Valiant: Nov, 1994 - No. 8, June, 1995 ($3.75/$2.25)
1 ($3.75)-Chromium wraparound-c; Eternal Warrior app. 4.00
2-8 3.00

GEORGE OF THE JUNGLE (TV)(See America's Best TV Comics)
Gold Key: Feb, 1969 - No. 2, Oct, 1969 (Jay Ward)
1 8 16 24 56 108 160
2 5 10 15 35 63 90

GEORGE PAL'S PUPPETOONS (Funny animal puppets)
Fawcett Publications: Dec, 1945 - No. 18, Dec, 1947; No. 19, 1950
1-Captain Marvel-c 42 84 126 265 445 625
2 23 46 69 136 223 310
3-10 15 30 45 86 133 180
11-19 13 26 39 74 105 135

GEORGE PEREZ'S SIRENS
BOOM! Studios: Sept, 2014 - No. 6, Dec, 2016 ($3.99, limited series)
1-6-George Pérez-s/a; multiple covers 4.00

GEORGE R.R. MARTIN'S A CLASH OF KINGS (Based on A Song of Ice and Fire, Book 2)
Dynamite Entertainment: 2017 - Present ($3.99)
1-8: 1-Landry Walker-s/Mel Rubi-a; multiple covers 4.00

GEORGIE COMICS (...& Judy Comics #20-35?; see All Teen & Teen Comics)
Timely Comics/GPI No. 1-34: Spr, 1945 - No. 39, Oct, 1952 (#1-3 are quarterly)
1-Dave Berg-a 48 96 144 302 514 725
2 28 56 84 165 270 375
3-5,7,8(11/46) 21 42 63 126 206 285
6-Georgie visits Timely Comics 26 52 78 154 252 350
9,10-Kurtzman's "Hey Look" (1 & ?); Millie the Model & Margie app. 22 44 66 132 216 300
11,12: 11-Margie, Millie app. 18 36 54 107 169 230
13-Kurtzman's "Hey Look", 3 pgs. 19 38 57 111 176 240
14-Wolverton-a(1 pg.); Kurtzman's "Hey Look" 20 40 60 114 182 250
15,16,18-20 17 34 51 98 154 210
17,29-Kurtzman's "Hey Look", 1 pg. 18 36 54 107 169 230
21-24,27,28,30-39: 21-Anti-Wertham editorial. 33-38-Hy Rosen-c 16 32 48 94 147 200
25-Painted-c by classic pin-up artist Peter Driben 77 154 231 493 847 1200
26-Logo design swipe from Archie Comics 30 60 90 177 289 400

GERALD McBOING-BOING AND THE NEARSIGHTED MR. MAGOO (TV)
(Mr. Magoo No. 6 on)
Dell Publishing Co.: Aug-Oct, 1952 - No. 5, Aug-Oct, 1953
1 9 18 27 62 126 190
2-5 8 16 24 54 102 150

GERONIMO (See Fighting Indians of the Wild West!)
Avon Periodicals: 1950 - No. 4, Feb, 1952
1-Indian Fighter; Maneely-a; Texas Rangers-r/Cowpuncher #1; Fawcette-c 21 42 63 126 206 285
2-On the Warpath; Kit West app.; Kinstler-c/a 15 30 45 83 124 165
3-And His Apache Murderers; Kinstler-c/a(2); Kit West-r/Cowpuncher #6 15 30 45 83 124 165
4-Savage Raids of; Kinstler-c & inside front-c; Kinstlerish-a by McCann(3) 14 28 42 81 118 155

GERONIMO JONES
Charlton Comics: Sept, 1971 - No. 9, Jan, 1973
1 3 6 9 14 20 25
2-9 2 4 6 8 10 12
Modern Comics Reprint #7('78) 5.00

GETALONG GANG, THE (TV)
Marvel Comics (Star Comics): May, 1985 - No. 6, Mar, 1986
1-6: Saturday morning TV stars 5.00

GET JIRO!
DC Comics (Vertigo): 2012 ($24.99, hardcover graphic novel with dust jacket)
HC - Anthony Bourdain & Joel Rose-s/Langdon Foss-a 25.00
SC - (2013, $14.99) Anthony Bourdain & Joel Rose-s/Langdon Foss-a 15.00

GET JIRO: BLOOD AND SUSHI
DC Comics (Vertigo): 2015 ($22.99, hardcover graphic novel with dust jacket)
HC - Prequel to Get Jiro!; Anthony Bourdain & Joel Rose-s/Alé Garza-a/Dave Johnson-c 23.00

GET LOST
Mikeross Publications/New Comics: Feb-Mar, 1954 - No. 3, June-July, 1954 (Satire)
1-Andru/Esposito-a in all? 39 78 117 231 378 525
2-Andru/Esposito-c; has 4 pg. E.C. parody featuring "The Sewer Keeper" 26 52 78 154 252 350
3-John Wayne 'Hondo' parody 22 44 66 128 209 290
1,2 (10,12/87-New Comics)-B&W r-original 4.00

GET SMART (TV)
Dell Publ. Co.: June, 1966 - No. 8, Sept, 1967 (All have Don Adams photo-c)
1 9 18 27 59 117 175
2,3-Ditko-a 6 12 18 40 73 105
4-8: 8-Reprints #1 (cover and insides) 5 10 15 33 57 80

GHOST (...Comics #9)
Fiction House Magazines: 1951(Winter) - No. 11, Summer, 1954
1-Most covers by Whitman 129 258 387 826 1413 2000
2-Ghost Gallery & Werewolf Hunter stories; classic-c 116 232 348 742 1271 1800
3-9: 3,6,7,9-Bondage-c. 9-Abel, Discount-a 90 180 270 576 988 1400
10,11-Dr. Drew by Grandenetti in each, reprinted from Rangers; 11-Evans-r/ Rangers #39; Grandenetti-r/Rangers #49 58 116 174 371 636 900

GHOST (See Comic's Greatest World)
Dark Horse Comics: Apr, 1995 - No. 36, Apr, 1998 ($2.50/$2.95)
1-Adam Hughes-a 1 2 3 5 6 8
2,3-Hughes-a 4.00
4-24: 4-Barb Wire app. 5,6-Hughes-c. 12-Ghost/Hellboy preview. 15,21-X app. 18,19-Barb Wire app. 3.00
25-($3.50)-48 pgs. special 4.00
26-36: 26-Begin $2.95-c. 29-Flip book w/Timecop. 33-36-Jade Cathedral; Harris painted-c 3.00
Special 1 (7/94, $3.95, 48 pgs.) 1 2 3 4 5 7
Special 2 (6/98, $3.95) Barb Wire app. 4.00
... Black October (1/99, $14.95, trade paperback)-r/#6-9,26,27 15.00
... Nocturnes (1996, $9.95, trade paperback)-r/#1-3 & 5 10.00
... Omnibus Vol. 1 (10/08, $24.95, 9x6") r/#1-12; Special 1 and Decade of Dark Horse #2 25.00
... Stories (1995, $9.95, trade paperback)-r/Early Ghost app. 10.00

GHOST (Volume 2)
Dark Horse Comics: Sept, 1998 - No. 22, Aug, 2000 ($2.95)
1-22: 1-4-Ryan Benjamin-c/Zanier-a 3.00
Handbook (8/99, $2.95) guide to issues and characters 3.00

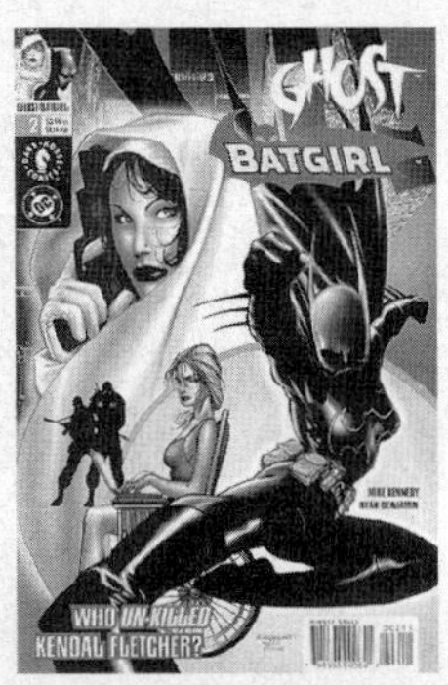

Ghost/Batgirl #2 © DH & DC

Ghostbusters: Answer the Call #1 © Columbia Picts

Ghostly Haunts #44 © CC

	GD 2.0	VG 4.0	FN 6.0	VF 8.0	VF/NM 9.0	NM- 9.2

Special 3 (12/98, $3.95) 4.00

GHOST (3rd series)
Dark Horse Comics: No. 0, Sept, 2012 - No. 4, Mar, 2013 ($2.99)
0-4-DeConnick-s/Noto-a. 0-Frison-c. 1,2-Covers by Noto & Alex Ross 3.00

GHOST (4th series)
Dark Horse Comics: Dec, 2013 - No. 12, Feb, 2015 ($2.99)
1-12: 1,2-DeConnick & Sebela-s/Sook-a/Dodson-c. 3,4-Borges-a 3.00

GHOST AND THE SHADOW
Dark Horse Comics: Dec, 1995 ($2.95, one-shot)
1-Moench scripts 3.00

GHOST/BATGIRL
Dark Horse Comics: Aug, 2000 - No. 4, Dec, 2000 ($2.95, limited series)
1-4-New Batgirl; Oracle & Bruce Wayne app.; Benjamin-c/a 3.00

GHOST/HELLBOY
Dark Horse Comics: May, 1996 - No. 2, June, 1996 ($2.50, limited series)
1,2: Mike Mignola-c/scripts & breakdowns; Scott Benefiel finished-a 4.00

GHOST BREAKERS (Also see Racket Squad in Action, Red Dragon & (CC) Sherlock Holmes Comics)
Street & Smith Publications: Sept, 1948 - No. 2, Dec, 1948 (52 pgs.)

	GD	VG	FN	VF	VF/NM	NM-
1-Powell-c/a(3); Dr. Neff (magician) app.	43	86	129	271	461	650
2-Powell-c/a(2); Maneely-a	37	74	111	218	354	490

GHOSTBUSTERS (TV) (Also, see Real...and Slimer)
First Comics: Feb, 1987 - No. 6, Aug, 1987 ($1.25)
1-6: Based on new animated TV series 4.00

GHOSTBUSTERS
IDW Publishing: Sept, 2011 - No. 16, Dec, 2012 ($3.99)
1-16-Burnham-s/Schoening-a; multiple covers 4.00
...: 100-Page Spooktacular (10/12, $7.99) reprints of IDW stories 8.00

GHOSTBUSTERS
IDW Publishing: (one-shots)
Annual 2017 (1/17, $7.99) Burnham-s/Schoening-a and short stories by various 8.00
Annual 2018 (2/18, $7.99) Burnham-s/Schoening-a; Ghostbusters: Crossing Over prelude 8.00
...: Con-Volution (6/10, $3.99) Josh Howard-a 4.00
...: Deviations (3/16, $4.99) What If.. Ghostbusters never crossed the streams 5.00
... Funko Universe One Shot (5/17, $4.99) Story with Funko Pop-styled characters 5.00
... Halloween Comicfest 2017 (10/17, giveaway) Burnham-s/Schoening-a 3.00
...: Tainted Love (2/10, $3.99) Salgood Sam-a 4.00
...: What in Samhain Just Happened? (10/10, $3.99) Peter David-s/Dan Schoening-a 4.00

GHOSTBUSTERS
IDW Publishing: Feb, 2013 - No. 20, Sept, 2014 ($3.99)
1-20-Janine & the female Ghostbuster crew; Burnham-s/Schoening-a; multiple covers 4.00
Annual 2015 (11/15, $7.99) Burnham-s/Schoening-a and bonus 1-pagers by various 8.00

GHOSTBUSTERS: ANSWER THE CALL
IDW Publishing: Oct, 2017 - Present ($3.99)
1-3-Female crew; Thompson-s/Howell-a 4.00

GHOSTBUSTERS: DISPLACED AGGRESSION
IDW Publishing: Sept, 2009 - No. 4, Dec, 2009 ($3.99)
1-3-Lobdell-s/Kyriazis-a 4.00
Hundred Penny Press: Ghostbusters: Displaced Aggression (3/11, $1.00) r/#1 3.00

GHOSTBUSTERS: GET REAL
IDW Publishing: Jun, 2015 - No. 4, Sept, 2015 ($3.99)
1-4-Burnham-s/Schoening-a; multiple-c; Real Ghostbusters meet comic Ghostbusters 4.00

GHOSTBUSTERS: INFESTATION (Zombie x-over with Star Trek, G.I. Joe & Transformers)
IDW Publishing: Mar, 2011 - No. 2, Mar, 2011 ($3.99, limited series)
1,2-Kyle Hotz-a; covers by Hotz and Snyder III 4.00

GHOSTBUSTERS: INTERNATIONAL
IDW Publishing: Jan, 2016 - No. 11, Nov, 2016 ($3.99)
1-11-Burnham-s/Schoening-a; 2 covers on each 4.00

GHOSTBUSTERS: LEGION (Movie)
88 MPH Studios: Feb, 2004 - No. 4, May, 2004 ($2.95/$3.50)
1-4-Steve Kurth-a/Andrew Dabb-s 3.00
1-3-($3.50) Brereton variant-c 3.50

GHOSTBUSTERS 101
IDW Publishing: Mar, 2017 - No. 6, Aug, 2017 ($3.99, limited series)
1-6-Burnham-s/Schoening-a; multiple covers on each; original and female teams meet 4.00

GHOSTBUSTERS: THE OTHER SIDE
IDW Publishing: Oct, 2008 - No. 4, Jan, 2009 ($3.99)
1-4-Champagne-s/Nguyen-a 4.00

GHOSTBUSTERS II
Now Comics: Oct, 1989 - No. 3, Dec, 1989 ($1.95, mini-series)
1-3: Movie Adaptation 3.00

GHOST CASTLE (See Tales of...)

GHOSTED
Image Comics (Skybound): Jul, 2013 - No. 20, May, 2015 ($2.99)
1-20: 1-Williamson-s/Sudzuka-a/Phillips-c. 6-10-Gianfelice-a. 16-Ryp-a 3.00

GHOST IN THE SHELL (Manga)
Dark Horse: Mar, 1995 - No. 8, Oct, 1995 ($3.95, B&W/color, lim. series)

	GD	VG	FN	VF	VF/NM	NM-
1	5	10	15	31	53	75
2	3	6	9	17	25	34
3	3	6	9	14	19	24
4-8	2	4	6	8	10	12

GHOST IN THE SHELL 2: MAN-MACHINE INTERFACE (Manga)
Dark Horse Comics: Jan, 2003 - No. 11, Dec, 2003 ($3.50, color/B&W, lim. series)
1-11-Masamune Shirow-s/a. 5-B&W 5.00

GHOSTLY HAUNTS (Formerly Ghost Manor)
Charlton Comics: #20, 9/71 - #53, 12/76; #54, 9/77 - #55, 10/77; #56, 1/78 - #58, 4/78

	GD	VG	FN	VF	VF/NM	NM-
20	3	6	9	21	33	45
21	2	4	6	13	18	22
22-25,27,31-34,36-Ditko-c/a. 27-Dr. Graves x-over. 32-New logo. 33-Back to old logo	3	6	9	15	22	28
26,29,30,35-Ditko-c	2	4	6	13	18	22
28,37-40-Ditko-a. 39-Origin & 1st app. Destiny Fox	2	4	6	11	16	20
41,42: 41-Sutton-c; Ditko-a. 42-Newton-c/a	2	4	6	13	18	22
43-46,48,50,52-Ditko-a	2	4	6	10	14	18
47,54,56-Ditko-c/a. 56-Ditko-a(r).	3	6	9	14	19	24
49,51,53,55,57	2	4	6	8	10	12
58 (4/78) Last issue	3	6	9	14	19	24
40,41(Modern Comics-r, 1977, 1978)						6.00

NOTE: ***Ditko** a-22-25, 27, 28, 31-34, 36-41, 43-48, 50, 52, 54, 56r; c-22-27, 29, 30, 33-36, 47, 54, 56. **Glanzman** a-20. **Howard** a-27, 30, 35, 40-43, 48, 54, 57. **Kim** a-38, 41, 57. **Larson** a-48, 50. **Newton** c/a-42. **Staton** a-32, 35; c-28, 46. **Sutton** c-33, 37, 39, 41.*

GHOSTLY TALES (Formerly Blue Beetle No. 50-54)
Charlton Comics: No. 55, 4-5/66 - No. 124, 12/76; No. 125, 9/77 - No. 169, 10/84

	GD	VG	FN	VF	VF/NM	NM-
55-Intro. & origin Dr. Graves; Ditko-a	9	18	27	61	123	185
56-58,60,61,70,71,72,75-Ditko-a. 70-Dr. Graves ends. 75-Last 12¢ issue	5	10	15	30	50	70
59,62-66,68	4	8	12	23	37	50
67,69,73-Ditko-c/a	5	10	15	33	57	80
74,91,98,119,123,124,127-130: 127,130-Sutton-a	2	4	6	13	18	22
76,79-82,85-Ditko-a	3	6	9	16	24	32
77,78,83,84,86-90,92-95,97,99-Ditko-c/a	4	8	12	23	37	50
96-Ditko-c	3	6	9	16	24	32
100-Ditko-c; Sutton-a	3	6	9	17	26	35
101,103-105-Ditko-a	3	6	9	14	19	24
102,109-Ditko-c/a	3	6	9	16	23	30
110,113-Sutton-c; Ditko-a	3	6	9	14	19	24
106-Ditko & Sutton-a; Sutton-c	3	6	9	14	19	24
107-Ditko, Wood, Sutton-a	3	6	9	14	20	26
108,116,117,126-Ditko-a	3	6	9	14	19	24
111,118,120-122,125-Ditko-c/a	3	6	9	16	23	30
112,114,115: 112,114-Ditko, Sutton-a. 114-Newton-a. 115-Newton, Ditko-a.	3	6	9	14	19	24
131-134,151,157,163-Ditko-c/a	2	4	6	13	18	22
135,142,145-150,153,154,156,158-160	1	2	3	5	7	9
136-141,143,144,152,155-Ditko-a	2	4	6	8	10	12
161,162,164-168-Lower print run. 162-Nudity panel	2	4	6	9	12	15
169 (10/84) Last issue; lower print run	2	4	6	11	16	20

NOTE: ***Aparo** a-65, 66, 68, 72, 137, 141r, 142r; c-71, 72, 74-76, 81, 146r, 149. **Ditko** a-55-58, 60, 61, 67, 69-73, 75-90, 92-95, 97, 99-118, 120-122, 125r, 126r, 131-141r, 143r, 144r, 146, 147, 149-152, 154-157, 159-161, 163; c-67, 69, 73, 77, 78, 83, 84, 86-90, 92-97, 99, 102, 109, 111, 118, 120-122, 125, 131-133, 147, 148, 151, 157-160, 163. **Glanzman** a-167. **Howard** a-95, 98, 99, 108, 117, 129, 131; c-98, 107, 120, 121, 161. **Larson** a-117, 119, 136, 159; c-136. **Morisi** a-83, 84, 86. **Newton** a-114; c-115(painted). **Palais** a-61. **Staton** a-161; c-117. **Sutton** a-106, 107, 111-114, 127, 130, 162; c-100, 106, 110, 113(painted). **Wood** a-107.*

Ghost Manor #18 © CC

Ghost Rider #30 © MAR

Ghost Rider V3 #6 © MAR

GD VG FN VF VF/NM NM-
2.0 4.0 6.0 8.0 9.0 9.2

GHOSTLY WEIRD STORIES (Formerly Blue Bolt Weird)
Star Publications: No. 120, Sept, 1953 - No. 124, Sept, 1954

120-Jo-Jo-r 65 130 195 416 708 1000

121-124: 121-Jo-Jo-r. 122-The Mask-r/Capt. Flight #5; Rulah-r; has 1pg. story 'Death and the Devil Pills'-r/Western Outlaws #17. 123-Jo-Jo; Disbrow-a(2). 124-Torpedo Man
58 116 174 371 636 900

NOTE: ***Disbrow** a-120-124. **L. B. Cole** covers-all issues (#122 is a sci-fi cover).*

GHOST MANOR (Ghostly Haunts No. 20 on)
Charlton Comics: July, 1968 - No. 19, July, 1971

1 8 16 24 51 96 140

2-7: 7-Last 12¢ issue 4 8 12 27 44 60

8-12,17: 17-Morisi-a 3 6 9 19 30 40

13,14,16-Ditko-a 4 8 12 22 35 48

15,18,19-Ditko-c/a 4 8 12 28 47 65

GHOST MANOR (2nd Series)
Charlton Comics: Oct, 1971-No. 32, Dec, 1976; No. 33, Sept, 1977-No. 77, 11/84

1 5 10 15 34 60 85

2,3,5-7,9-Ditko-c 3 6 9 17 26 35

4,10-Ditko-c/a 3 6 9 21 33 45

8-Wood, Ditko-a; Sutton-c 3 6 9 19 30 40

11,14-Ditko-c/a 3 6 9 16 24 32

12,17,27,30 2 4 6 9 13 16

13,15,16,23-26,29: 13-Ditko-a. 15,16-Ditko-c. 23-Sutton-a. 24-26,29-Ditko-a. 26-Early Zeck-a; Boyette-c 2 4 6 13 18 22

18-(3/74) Newton 1st pro art; Ditko-a; Sutton-c 3 6 9 15 22 28

19-21: 19-Newton, Sutton-a; nudity panels. 20-Ditko-a. 21-E-Man, Blue Beetle, Capt. Atom cameos; Ditko-a. 2 4 6 13 18 22

22-Newton-c/a; Ditko-a 3 6 9 14 19 24

25,28,31,37,38-Ditko-c/a: 28-Nudity panels 3 6 9 14 19 24

32-36,39,41,45,48-50,53: 34-Black Cat by Kim 2 4 6 8 10 12

40-Ditko-a; torture & drug use 2 4 6 13 18 22

42,43,46,47,51,52,60,62,69-Ditko-c/a 2 4 6 11 16 20

44,54,71-Ditko-a 2 4 6 8 11 14

55,56,58,59,61,63,65-68,70 1 2 3 5 7 9

57-Wood, Ditko, Howard-a 2 4 6 9 12 15

64-Ditko & Newton-a 2 4 6 8 11 14

71-76 (low print) 2 3 4 6 8 10

77-(11/84) Last issue Aparo-r/Space Adventures V3#60 (Paul Mann)
2 4 6 9 13 16

19 (Modern Comics reprint, 1977) 6.00

NOTE: ***Ditko** a-4, 8, 10, 11(2), 13, 14, 18, 20-22, 24-26, 28, 29, 31, 37r, 38r, 40r, 42-44r, 46r, 47, 51r, 52r, 54r, 57, 60, 62(4), 64r, 69, 71; c-2-7, 9-11, 14-16, 28, 31, 37, 38, 42, 43, 46, 47, 51, 52, 60, 62, 64. **Howard** a-4, 8, 12, 17, 19-21, 31, 41, 45, 57. **Newton** a-18-20, 22, 64; c-22. **Staton** a-13, 38, 44, 45. **Sutton** a-19, 23, 25, 45; c-8, 18.*

GHOST RACERS (Secret Wars Battleworld tie-in)
Marvel Comics: Aug, 2015 - No. 4, Nov, 2015 ($3.99, limited series)

1-4-Johnny Blaze, Danny Ketch, Robbie Reyes, Carter Slade app.; Francavilla-c 4.00

GHOST RIDER (See A-1 Comics, Best of the West, Black Phantom, Bobby Benson, Great Western, Red Mask & Tim Holt)
Magazine Enterprises: 1950 - No. 14, 1954

NOTE: *The character was inspired by Vaughn Monroe's "Ghost Riders in the Sky", and Disney's movie "The Headless Horseman".*

1(A-1 #27)-Origin Ghost Rider 116 232 348 742 1271 1800

2-5: 2(A-1 #29), 3(A-1 #31), 4(A-1 #34), 5(A-1 #37)-All Frazetta-c only
90 180 270 576 988 1400

6,7: 6(A-1 #44)-Loco weed story, 7(A-1 #51) 41 82 123 256 428 600

8,9: 8(A-1 #57)-Drug use story, 9(A-1 #69) 36 72 108 211 343 475

10(A-1 #71)-Vs. Frankenstein 39 78 117 231 378 525

11-14: 11(A-1 #75). 12(A-1 #80)-Bondage-c; one-eyed Devil-c. 13(A-1 #84). 14(A-1 #112) 32 64 96 188 307 425

NOTE: ***Dick Ayers** art in all; c-1, 6-14.*

GHOST RIDER, THE (See Night Rider & Western Gunfighters)
Marvel Comics Group: Feb, 1967 - No. 7, Nov, 1967 (Western hero)(12¢)

1-Origin & 1st app. Ghost Rider; Kid Colt-reprints begin
13 26 39 89 195 300

2 7 14 21 46 86 125

3-7: 6-Last Kid Colt-r; All Ayers-c/a(p) 6 12 18 41 76 110

GHOST RIDER (See The Champions, Marvel Spotlight #5, Marvel Team-Up #15, 58, Marvel Treasury Edition #18, Marvel Two-In-One #8, The Original Ghost Rider & The Original Ghost Rider Rides Again)
Marvel Comics Group: Sept, 1973 - No. 81, June, 1983 (Super-hero)

1-Johnny Blaze, the Ghost Rider begins; 1st brief app. Daimon Hellstrom (Son of Satan)
18 36 54 125 276 430

2-1st full app. Daimon Hellstrom; gives glimpse of costume (1 panel); story continues in Marvel Spotlight #12 8 16 24 51 96 140

3-5: 3-Ghost Rider gains power to make cycle of fire; Son of Satan app.
5 10 15 31 53 75

6-10: 10-Hulk on cover; reprints origin/1st app. from Marvel Spotlight #5; Ploog-a
3 6 9 21 33 45

11-16: 11-Hulk app. 3 6 9 14 20 25

17,19-(Reg. 25¢ editions)(4,8/76) 3 6 9 14 20 25

17,19-(30¢-c variants, limited distribution) 5 10 15 30 50 70

18-(Reg. 25¢ edition)(6/76). Spider-Man-c & app. 3 6 9 15 22 28

18-(30¢-c variant, limited distribution) 5 10 15 31 53 75

20-Daredevil x-over; ties into D.D. #138; Byrne-a 3 6 9 17 26 35

21-30: 22-1st app. Enforcer. 29,30-Vs. Dr. Strange 2 4 6 9 12 15

24-26-(35¢-c variants, limited distribution) 5 10 15 31 53 75

31-34,36-49: 40-Nuclear explosion-c 2 3 4 6 8 10

35-Death Race classic; Starlin-c/a/sty 2 4 6 10 14 18

50-Double size 2 4 6 10 14 18

51-76: 55-Werewolf by Night app. 68-Origin retold 6.00

77-80: 77-Origin retold. 80-Brief origin recap 1 2 3 5 6 8

81-Death of Ghost Rider (Demon leaves Blaze) 3 6 9 17 26 35

... Team Up TPB (2007, $15.99) r/#27, 50, Marvel Team-Up #91, Marvel Two-In-One #80, Avengers #214 and Marvel Premiere #28; Night Rider app.; cover gallery 16.00

NOTE: ***Anderson** c-64p. **Infantino** a(p)-43, 44, 51. **G. Kane** a-21p; c(p)-1, 2, 4, 5, 8, 9, 11-13, 19, 20, 24, 25. **Kirby** c-21-23. **Mooney** a-2-9p, 30i. **Nebres** c-26i. **Newton** a-23i. **Perez** c-26p. **Shores** a-2i. J. **Sparling** a-62p, 64p, 65p. **Starlin** a(p)-35. **Sutton** a-1p, 44i, 64i, 65i, 66, 67i. **Tuska** a-13p, 14p, 16p.*

GHOST RIDER (Volume 2) (Also see Doctor Strange/Ghost Rider Special, Marvel Comics Presents & Midnight Sons Unlimited)
Marvel Comics (Midnight Sons imprint #44 on): V2#1, May, 1990 - No. 93, Feb, 1998 ($1.50/$1.75/$1.95)

1-($1.95, 52 pgs.)-Origin/1st app. new Ghost Rider; Kingpin app.
3 6 9 14 20 25

1-2nd printing (not gold) 4.00

2-5: 3-Kingpin app. 5-Punisher app.; Jim Lee-c 5.00

5-Gold background 2nd printing 4.00

6-14,16-24,29,30,32-39: 6-Punisher app. 6,17-Spider-Man/Hobgoblin-c/story. 9-X-Factor app. 10-Reintro Johnny Blaze on the last pg. 11-Stroman-c/a(p). 12,13-Dr. Strange x-over cont'd in D.S. #28. 13-Painted-c. 14-Johnny Blaze vs. Ghost Rider; origin recap 1st Ghost Rider (Blaze). 18-Painted-c by Nelson. 29-Wolverine-c/story. 32-Dr. Strange x-over; Johnny Blaze app. 34-Williamson-a(i). 36-Daredevil app. 37-Archangel app. 3.00

15-Glow in the dark-c 6.00

25-27: 25-($2.75)-Double-size; contains pop-up scene insert. 26,27-X-Men x-over; Lee/Williams-c on both 4.00

28,31-($2.50, 52 pgs.)-Polybagged w/poster; part 1 & part 6 of Rise of the Midnight Sons storyline (see Ghost Rider/Blaze #1) 4.00

40-Outer-c is Darkhold envelope made of black parchment w/gold ink; Midnight Massacre; Demogoblin app. 4.00

41-48: 41-Lilith & Centurious app.; begin $1.75-c. 41-43-Neon ink-c. 43-Has free extra 16 pg. insert on Siege of Darkness. 44,45-Siege of Darkness parts 2 & 10. 44-Spot varnish-c. 46-Intro new Ghost Rider. 48-Spider-Man app. 3.00

49,51-60,62-74: 49-Begin $1.95-c; bound-in trading card sheet; Hulk app. 55-Werewolf by Night app. 65-Punisher app. 67,68-Gambit app. 68-Wolverine app. 73,74-Blaze, Vengeance app. 3.00

50,61: 50-($2.50, 52 pgs.)-Regular edition 4.00

50-($2.95, 52 pgs.)-Collectors Ed. die cut foil-c 5.00

75-89: 76-Vs. Vengeance. 77,78-Dr. Strange-app. 78-New costume 3.00

90-92 6.00

93-($2.99)-Last issue; Saltares & Texeira-a 2 4 6 8 10 12

(#94, see Ghost Rider Finale for unpublished story)

#(-1) Flashback (7/97) Saltares-a 3.00

Annual 1,2 ('93, '94, $2.95, 68 pgs.) 1-Bagged w/card 4.00

...And Cable 1 (9/92, $3.95, stiff-c, 68 pgs.)-Reprints Marvel Comics Presents #90-98 w/new Kieth-c 4.00

...:Crossroads (11/95, $3.95) Die cut cover; Nord-a 5.00

... Cycle of Vengeance 1 (3/12, $5.99) r/Marvel Spotlight #5, Ghost Rider (1990) #1 and Ghost Rider (2006) #1; Leinil Yu-c 6.00

... Finale (2007, $3.99) r/#93 and the story meant for the unpublished #94; Saltares-a 4.00

Highway to Hell (2001, $3.50) Reprints origin from Marvel Spotlight #5 3.50

...: Resurrected TPB (2001, $12.95) r/#1-7 13.00

NOTE: ***Andy & Joe Kubert** c/a-28-31. **Quesada** c-21. **Williamson** a(i)-33-35; c-33i.*

GHOST RIDER (Volume 3)
Marvel Comics: Aug, 2001 - No. 6, Jan, 2002 ($2.99, limited series)

1-6-Grayson-s/Kaniuga-a/c 3.00

...: The Hammer Lane TPB (6/02, $15.95) r/#1-6 16.00

Ghost Rider (2006 series) #33 © MAR

Ghost Rider 2099 #4 © MAR

Ghosts #76 © DC

	GD	VG	FN	VF	VF/NM	NM-
	2.0	4.0	6.0	8.0	9.0	9.2

GHOST RIDER
Marvel Comics: Nov, 2005 - No. 6, Apr, 2006 ($2.99, limited series)

1-6-Garth Ennis-s/Clayton Crain-a/c. 1-Origin retold 3.00
1 (Director's Cut) (2005, $3.99) r/#1 with Ennis pitch and script and Crain art process 4.00
...: Road to Damnation HC (2006, $19.99, dust jacket) r/#1-6; variant covers & concept-a 20.00
...: Road to Damnation SC (2007, $14.99) r/#1-6; variant covers & concept-a 15.00

GHOST RIDER
Marvel Comics: Sept, 2006 - No. 35, Jul, 2009 ($2.99)

1-11: 1-Daniel Way-s/Saltares & Texeira-a. 2-4-Dr. Strange app. 6,7-Corben-a 3.00
12-27,29-35: 12,13-World War Hulk; Saltares-a/Dell'Otto-c. 23-Danny Ketch returns 3.00
28-($3.99) Silvestri-c/Huat-a; back-up history of Danny Ketch 4.00
Annual 1 (1/08, $3.99) Ben Oliver-a/c/Stuart Moore-s 4.00
Annual 2 (10/08, $3.99) Spurrier-s/Robinson-a; r/Ghost Rider #35 (1979) 4.00
... Vol. 1: Vicious Cycle TPB (2007, $13.99) r/#1-5 14.00
... Vol. 2: The Life and Death of Johnny Blaze TPB (2007, $13.99) r/#6-11 14.00
... Vol. 3: Apocalypse Soon TPB (2008, $10.99) r/#12,13 & Annual #1 11.00
... Vol. 4: Revelations TPB (2008, $14.99) r/#14-19 15.00

GHOST RIDER
Marvel Comics: No. 0.1, Aug, 2011 - No. 9, May 2012 ($2.99/$3.99)

0.1-($2.99) Johnny Blaze gets rid of the Spirit of Vengeance; Matthew Clark-a 3.00
1-($3.99) Adam Kubert-c; Fear Itself tie-in; new female Ghost Rider; Mephisto app. 4.00
2-9: 2-4-($2.99) Fear Itself tie-in. 5-Garbett-a. 7,8-Hawkeye app. 3.00

GHOST RIDER (Robbie Reyes) (Also see All-New Ghost Rider)
Marvel Comics: Jan, 2017 - No. 5, May, 2017 ($3.99)

1-5-Felipe Smith-s; Hulk (Amadeus Cho) and X-23 app. 1-Intro. Pyston Nitro. 3-5-Silk app. 4.00

GHOST RIDER/BALLISTIC
Marvel Comics: Feb, 1997 ($2.95, one-shot)

1-Devil's Reign pt. 3 3.00

GHOST RIDER/BLAZE: SPIRITS OF VENGEANCE (Also see Blaze)
Marvel Comics (Midnight Sons imprint #17 on): Aug, 1992 - No. 23, June, 1994 ($1.75)

1-($2.75, 52 pgs.)-Polybagged w/poster; part 2 of Rise of the Midnight Sons storyline; Adam Kubert-c/a begins 4.00
2-11,14-21: 4-Art Adams & Joe Kubert-p. 5,6-Spirits of Venom parts 2 & 4 cont'd from Web of Spider-Man #95,96 w/Demogoblin. 14-17-Neon ink-c. 15-Intro Blaze's new costume & power. 17,18-Siege of Darkness parts 8 & 13. 17-Spot varnish-c 3.00
12-($2.95)-Glow-in-the-dark-c 4.00
13-($2.25)-Outer-c is Darkhold envelope made of black parchment w/gold ink; Midnight Massacre x-over 4.00
22,23: 22-Begin $1.95-c; bound-in trading card sheet 3.00
NOTE: *Adam & Joe Kubert c-7, 8. Adam Kubert/Steacy c-6. J. Kubert a-13p(6 pgs.)*

GHOST RIDER/CAPTAIN AMERICA: FEAR
Marvel Comics: Oct, 1992 ($5.95, 52 pgs.)

nn-Wraparound gatefold-c; Williamson inks 6.00

GHOST RIDER: DANNY KETCH
Marvel Comics: Dec, 2008 - No. 5, Apr, 2009 ($3.99, limited series)

1-5-Saltares-a 4.00

GHOST RIDER: HEAVEN'S ON FIRE
Marvel Comics: Oct, 2009 - No. 6, Mar, 2010 ($3.99, limited series)

1-6: 1-Jae Lee-c/Boschi-a/Aaron-s; Hellstorm app.; r/pages from Ghost Rider #1 ('73) 4.00

GHOST RIDER: TRAIL OF TEARS
Marvel Comics: Apr, 2007 - No. 6, Sept, 2007 ($2.99, limited series)

1-6-Garth Ennis-s/Clayton Crain-a/c; Civil War era tale 3.00
HC (2007, $19.99) r/series 20.00
SC (2008, $14.99) r/series 15.00

GHOST RIDER 2099
Marvel Comics: May, 1994 - No. 25, May, 1996 ($1.50/$1.95)

1 ($2.25)-Collector's Edition w/prismatic foil-c 4.00
1 ($1.50)-Regular Edition; bound-in trading card sheet 3.00
2-24: 7-Spider-Man 2099 app. 3.00
2-(Variant; polybagged with Sega Sub-Terrania poster) 5.00
25 ($2.95) 4.00

GHOST RIDER, WOLVERINE, PUNISHER: THE DARK DESIGN
Marvel Comics: Dec, 1994 ($5.95, one-shot)

nn-Gatefold-c 6.00

GHOST RIDER; WOLVERINE; PUNISHER: HEARTS OF DARKNESS
Marvel Comics: Dec, 1991 ($4.95, one-shot, 52 pgs.)

1-Double gatefold-c; John Romita, Jr.-c/a(p) 6.00

GHOSTS (See The World Around Us #24)

GHOSTS (Ghost No. 1)
National Periodical Publications/DC Comics: Sept-Oct, 1971 - No. 112, May, 1982 (No. 1-5: 52 pgs.)

	GD	VG	FN	VF	VF/NM	NM-
1-Aparo-a	12	24	36	82	179	275
2-Wood-a(i)	7	14	21	44	82	120
3-5-(52 pgs.)	6	12	18	38	69	100
6-10	4	8	12	27	44	60
11-20	3	6	9	14	20	25
21-39	2	4	6	9	13	16
40-(68 pgs.)	3	6	9	16	23	30
41-60	2	4	6	8	10	12
61-96	1	2	3	5	6	8
97-99-The Spectre vs. Dr. 13 by Aparo. 97,98-Spectre-c by Aparo.	2	4	6	10	14	18
100-Infinity-c	2	4	6	8	10	12
101-112	1	2	3	5	6	8

NOTE: ***B. Baily** a-77. **Buckler** c-99, 100. **J. Craig** a-108. **Ditko** a-77, 111. **Giffen** a-104p, 106p, 111p. **Glanzman** a-2. **Golden** a-88. **Infantino** a-8. **Kaluta** c-7, 93, 101. **Kubert** a-8; c-89, 105-108, 111. **Mayer** a-111. **McWilliams** a-99. **Win Mortimer** a-89, 91, 94. **Nasser/Netzer** a-97. **Newton** a-92p, 94p. **Nino** a-35, 37, 57. **Orlando** a-74i; c-80. **Redondo** a-8, 13, 45. **Sparling** a(p)-90, 93, 94. **Spiegle** a-103, 105. **Tuska** a-2i. Dr. 13, the Ghostbreaker back-ups in 95-99, 101.*

GHOSTS
DC Comics (Vertigo): Dec, 2012 ($7.99, one-shot)

1-Short stories by various incl. Johns, Lemire, Pope, Lapham; Joe Kubert's last work 8.00

GHOSTS SPECIAL (See DC Special Series No. 7)

GHOST STATION ZERO (See Codename: Baboushka)
Image Comics: Aug, 2017 - No. 4, Nov, 2017 ($3.99)

1-4-Johnston-s/Chankhamma-a 4.00

GHOST STORIES (See Amazing Ghost Stories)

GHOST STORIES
Dell Publ. Co.: Sept-Nov, 1962; No. 2, Apr-June, 1963 - No. 37, Oct, 1973

	GD	VG	FN	VF	VF/NM	NM-
12-295-211(#1)-Written by John Stanley	6	12	18	38	69	100
2	4	8	12	23	37	50
3-10: Two No. 6's exist with different c/a(12-295-406 & 12-295-503) #12-295-503 is actually #9 with indicia to #6	3	6	9	19	30	40
11-21: 21-Last 12¢ issue	3	6	9	16	23	30
22-37	2	4	6	13	18	22

NOTE: *#21-34, 36, 37 all reprint earlier issues.*

GHOST WHISPERER (Based on the CBS television series)
IDW Publishing: Mar, 2008 - No. 5, July, 2008 ($3.99)

1-5: 1-Two covers by Casagrande & Ho; Casagrande-a 4.00

GHOST WHISPERER: THE MUSE
IDW Publishing: Dec, 2008 - No. 4, Mar, 2009 ($3.99)

1-4-Two covers (photo & art) for each; Barbara Kesel-s/ Adriano Loyola-a 4.00

GHOUL, THE
IDW Publishing: Nov, 2009 - No. 3, Mar, 2010 ($3.99, limited series)

1-3-Niles-s/Wrightson-a 4.00

GHOUL TALES (Magazine)
Stanley Publications: Nov, 1970 - No. 5, July, 1971 (52 pgs.) (B&W)

	GD	VG	FN	VF	VF/NM	NM-
1-Aragon pre-code reprints; Mr. Mystery as host; bondage-c	8	16	24	54	102	150
2,3: 2-(1/71)Reprint/Climax #1. 3-(3/71)	5	10	15	30	50	70
4-(5/71)Reprints story "The Way to a Man's Heart" used in **SOTI**	5	10	15	33	57	80
5-ACG reprints	4	8	12	25	40	55

NOTE: *No. 1-4 contain pre-code Aragon reprints.*

GIANT BOY BOOK OF COMICS (Also see Boy Comics)
Newsbook Publications (Gleason): 1945 (240 pgs., hard-c)

	GD	VG	FN	VF	VF/NM	NM-
1-Crimebuster & Young Robin Hood; Biro-c	107	214	321	680	1165	1650

GIANT COMIC ALBUM
King Features Syndicate: 1972 (59¢, 11x14", 52 pgs., B&W, cardboard-c)

	GD	VG	FN	VF	VF/NM	NM-
Newspaper reprints: Barney Google, Little Iodine, Katzenjammer Kids, Henry, Beetle Bailey, Blondie, & Snuffy Smith each...	3	6	9	19	30	40
Flash Gordon ('68-69 Dan Barry)	4	8	12	25	40	55
Mandrake the Magician ('59 Falk), Popeye	4	8	12	23	37	50

GIANT COMICS

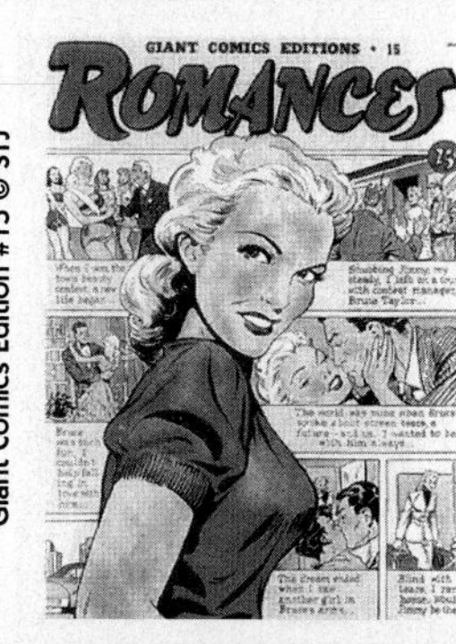

Giant Comics Edition #15 © STJ

Giant Days #19 © John Allison

Giant-Size Captain Marvel #1 © MAR

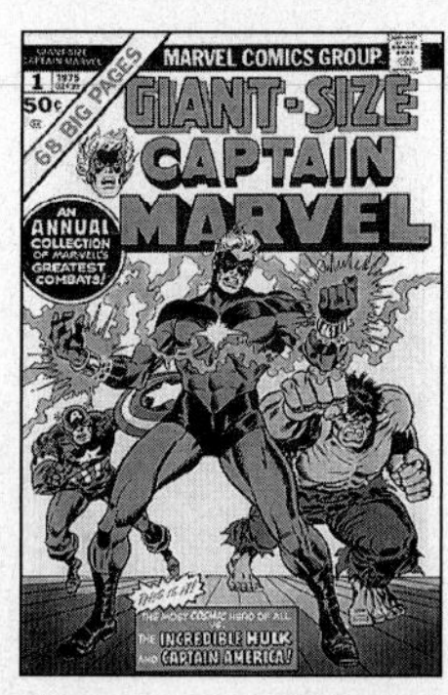

GD 2.0 | VG 4.0 | FN 6.0 | VF 8.0 | VF/NM 9.0 | NM- 9.2

Charlton Comics: Summer, 1957 - No. 3, Winter, 1957 (25¢, 96 pgs., not rebound material)
1-Atomic Mouse, Lil Genius, Lil Tomboy app. 26 52 78 154 252 350
2-(Fall '57) Romance 26 52 78 154 252 350
3-Christmas Book; Atomic Mouse, Atomic Rabbit, Li'l Genius, Li'l Tomboy & Atom the Cat stories 20 40 60 114 182 250

GIANT COMICS (See Wham-O Giant Comics)

GIANT COMICS EDITION (See Terry-Toons) (Also see Fox Giants)
St. John Publishing Co.: 1947 - No. 17, 1950 (25¢, 100-164 pgs.)
1-Mighty Mouse 61 122 183 390 670 950
2-Abbie & Slats 37 74 111 222 361 500
3-Terry-Toons Album; 100 pgs. 47 94 141 296 498 700
4-Crime comics; contains Red Seal No. 16, used & illo. in **SOTI** 81 162 243 518 884 1250
5-Police Case Book (4/49, 132 pgs.)-Contents varies; contains remaindered St. John books - some volumes contain 5 copies rather than 4, with 160 pages; Matt Baker-c 77 154 231 493 847 1200
5A-Terry-Toons Album (132 pgs.)-Mighty Mouse, Heckle & Jeckle, Gandy Goose & Dinky stories 42 84 126 265 445 625
6-Western Picture Stories; Baker-c/a(3); Tuska-a; The Sky Chief, Blue Monk, Ventrilo app., 132 pgs. 63 126 189 403 689 975
7-Contains a teen-age romance plus 3 Mopsy comics 77 154 231 493 847 1200
8-The Adventures of Mighty Mouse (10/49) 42 84 126 265 445 625
9-Romance and Confession Stories; Kubert-a(4); Baker-a; photo-c (132 pgs.) 168 336 504 1075 1838 2600
10-Terry-Toons Album (132 pgs.)-Mighty Mouse, Heckle & Jeckle, Gandy Goose stories 42 84 126 265 445 625
11-Western Picture Stories-Baker-c/a(4); The Sky Chief, Desperado, & Blue Monk app.; another version with Son of Sinbad by Kubert (132 pgs.) 63 126 189 403 689 975
12-Diary Secrets; Baker prostitute-c; 4 St. John romance comics; Baker-a 1167 2334 3500 7000 10,500 14,000
13-Romances; Baker, Kubert-a 161 322 483 1030 1765 2500
14-Mighty Mouse Album (132 pgs.) 41 82 123 256 428 600
15-Romances (4 love comics)-Baker-c 194 388 582 1242 2121 3000
16-Little Audrey; Abbott & Costello, Casper 58 116 174 371 636 900
17(nn)-Mighty Mouse Album (nn, no date, but did follow No. 16); 100 pgs. on cover but has 148 pgs. 41 82 123 256 428 600
NOTE: *The above books contain remaindered comics and contents could vary with each issue. No. 11, 12 have part photo magazine insides.*

GIANT COMICS EDITIONS
United Features Syndicate: 1940's (132 pgs.)
1-Abbie & Slats, Abbott & Costello, Jim Hardy, Ella Cinders, Iron Vic, Gordo, & Bill Bumlin 47 94 141 296 498 700
2-Jim Hardy, Ella Cinders, Elmo & Gordo 36 72 108 211 343 475
NOTE: *Above books contain rebound copies; contents can vary.*

GIANT DAYS
BOOM! Studios (BOOM! Box): Mar, 2015 - Present ($3.99)
1-24,26-36: 1-6-John Allison-s/Lissa Treiman-a/c. 7-36-Max Sarin-a 4.00
25-($4.99) Christmas story 5.00
... 2016 Holiday Special #1 (10/16, $7.99) Treiman-a/c; back-up w/Caanan Grall-a 8.00
... 2017 Holiday Special #1 (10/16, $7.99) St-Onge-a/c 8.00

GIANT GRAB BAG OF COMICS (See Archie All-Star Specials under Archie Comics)

GIANTKILLER
DC Comics: Aug, 1999 - No. 6, Jan, 2000 ($2.50, limited series)
1-6-Story and painted art by Dan Brereton 3.00
...A to Z: A Field Guide to Big Monsters (8/99) 3.00
...Vol. 1 TPB (Image Comics, 2006, $14.99) r/#1-6 & A-Z; gallery of concept art 15.00

GIANTKILLERS
IDW Publishing: No. 0, Nov, 2017 - Present ($3.99)
0-Bart Sears-s/a; Ron Marz-s/Tom Raney-a 4.00

GIANTS (See Thrilling True Story of the Baseball...)

GIANTS
Dark Horse Comics: Dec, 2017 - Present ($3.99)
1,2-Carlos & Miguel Valderrama-s/a 4.00

GIANT-SIZE ATOM
DC Comics: May, 2011 ($4.99, one-shot)
1-Gary Frank-c; Hawkman app.; Lemire-s/Asrar-a 5.00

GIANT-SIZE...
Marvel Comics Group: May, 1974 - Dec, 1975 (35/50¢, 52/68 pgs.)
(Some titles quarterly) (Scarce in strict NM or better due to defective cutting, gluing and binding; warping, splitting and off-center pages are common)
Avengers 1(8/74)-New-a plus G.A. H. Torch-r; 1st modern app. The Whizzer; 1st modern app. Miss America; 2nd app. Invaders; Kang, Rama-Tut, Mantis app. 6 12 18 37 66 95
Avengers 2,3,5: 2(11/74)-Death of the Swordsman; origin of Rama-Tut. 3(2/75). 5(12/75)-Reprints Avengers Special #1 4 8 12 25 40 55
Avengers 4 (6/75)-Vision marries Scarlet Witch. 5 10 15 35 63 90
Captain America 1(12/75)-r/stories T.O.S. 59-63 by Kirby (#63 reprints origin) 4 8 12 27 44 60
Captain Marvel 1(12/75)-r/Capt. Marvel #17, 20, 21 by Gil Kane (p) 4 8 12 22 35 48
Chillers 1(6/74, 52 pgs)-Curse of Dracula; origin/1st app. Lilith, Dracula's daughter; Heath-r, Colan-c/a(p); becomes Giant-Size Dracula #2 on 6 12 18 37 66 95
Chillers 1(2/75, 50¢, 68 pgs.)-Alcala-a 4 8 12 25 40 55
Chillers 2(5/75)-All-r; Everett-r from Advs. into Weird Worlds 3 6 9 18 28 38
Chillers 3(8/75)-Wrightson-c(new)/a(r); Colan, Kirby, Smith-r 4 8 12 23 37 50
Conan 1(9/74)-B. Smith-r/#3; start adaptation of Howard's "Hour of the Dragon" (ends #4); 1st app. Belit; new-a begins 4 8 12 25 40 55
Conan 2(12/74)-B. Smith-r/#5; Sutton-a(i)(#1 also); Buscema-c 3 6 9 18 28 38
Conan 3-5: 3(4/75)-B. Smith-r/#6; Sutton-a(i). 4(6/75)-B. Smith-r/#7. 5(1975)-B. Smith-r/#14,15; Kirby-c 3 6 9 16 24 32
Creatures 1(5/74, 52 pgs.)-Werewolf app; 1st app. Tigra (formerly Cat); Crandall-r; becomes Giant-Size Werewolf w/#2 7 14 21 44 82 120
Daredevil 1(1975)-Reprints Daredevil Annual #1 3 6 9 21 33 45
Defenders 1(7/74, 68-pgs.)-Dr. Strange, Hulk, Namor & Valkyrie app; continued from Defenders #12; mostly reprint stories, with a few pages of new material by Jim Starlin; Hulk-r from Incredible Hulk #3; Sub-Mariner-r from Sub-Mariner (Golden Age) #41; Dr. Strange-r from Strange Tales #145; Silver Surfer-r from Fantastic Four Annual #5 5 10 15 30 50 70
Defenders 2(10/74, 68-pgs.)-New G. Kane-c/a/p; Son of Satan app. vs. Asmodeus; Sub-Mariner-r from Young Men #25; Black Knight-r from Black Knight #4 (1955); Dr. Strange-r from Strange Tales #119 4 8 12 22 35 48
Defenders 3(1/75, 68-pgs.)-1st app. Korvac; Grandmaster vs. The Prime Mover; Daredevil app.; G.A. Sub-Mariner-r from Sub-Mariner #38; Dr. Strange-r from Strange Tales #120 6 12 18 41 76 110
Defenders 4(4/75, 68-pgs.)-Continued from Defenders #21; Yellowjacket & Wasp app; vs. Egghead, Squadron Sinister (Hyperion, Dr. Spectrum and the Whizzer; Sub-Mariner-r from Human Torch Comics #4 (technically 3rd issue); Dr. Strange-r from Strange Tales #121 3 6 9 21 33 45
Defenders 5(7/75, 68-pgs.)-Continued from Defenders #25; Guardians of the Galaxy app; (3rd app); continued from Marvel Two-in-One #5; story continued in Defenders #26; Nighthawk-r from Daredevil #62 3 6 9 21 33 45
Doc Savage 1(1975, 68 pgs.)-r/#1,2; Mooney-r 3 6 9 16 24 32
Doctor Strange 1(11/75)-Reprints stories from Strange Tales #164-168; Lawrence, Tuska-r 3 6 9 20 31 42
Dracula 2(9/74, 50¢)-Formerly Giant-Size Chillers 4 8 12 22 35 48
Dracula 3(12/74)-Fox-r/Uncanny Tales #6 3 6 9 20 31 42
Dracula 4(3/75)-Ditko-r(2) 3 6 9 20 31 42
Dracula 5(6/75)-1st Byrne art at Marvel 5 10 15 33 57 80
Fantastic Four 2,3: 2(8/74)-Formerly Giant-Size Super-Stars; Ditko-r. 2-Buscema-a. 3(11/74)-Buckler-a 4 8 12 25 40 55
Fantastic Four 4(2/75)-1st Madrox; Buscema-a 7 14 21 46 86 125
Fantastic Four 5,6: 5(5/75)-All-r; Kirby, G. Kane-r. 6(10/75)-All-r; Kirby-r 3 6 9 20 31 42
Hulk 1(1975) r/Hulk Special #1 4 8 12 22 35 48
Invaders 1(6/75, 50¢, 68 pgs.)-Origin; G.A. Sub-Mariner-r/Sub-Mariner #1; intro Master Man 4 8 12 27 44 60
Iron Man 1(1975)-Ditko reprint 4 8 12 28 47 65
Kid Colt 1-3: 1(1/75). 2(4/75). 3(7/75)-new Ayers-a 7 14 21 48 89 130
Man-Thing 1(8/74)-New Ploog-c/a (25 pgs.); Ditko-r/Amazing Adv. #11; Kirby-r/ Strange Tales Ann. #2 & T.O.S. #15; (#1-5 all have new Man-Thing stories, pre-hero-r & are 68 pgs.) 4 8 12 27 44 60
Man-Thing 2,3: 2(11/74)-Buscema-c/a(p); Kirby, Powell-r. 3(2/75)-Alcala-a; Ditko, Kirby, Sutton-r; Gil Kane-c 3 6 9 20 31 42
Man-Thing 4,5: 4(5/75)-Howard the Duck by Brunner-c/a; Ditko-r. 5(8/75)-Howard the Duck by Brunner (p); Dracula cameo in Howard the Duck; Buscema-a(p); Sutton-a(i); G. Kane-c 4 8 12 27 44 60
Marvel Triple Action 1,2: 1(5/75). 2(7/75) 3 6 9 16 24 32
Master of Kung Fu 1(9/74)-Russell-a; Yellow Claw-r in #1-4; Gulacy-a in #1,2

Giant-Size Spider-Woman #1 © MAR

G.I. Combat #12 © QUA

G.I. Combat #217 © DC

GD VG FN VF VF/NM NM-
2.0 4.0 6.0 8.0 9.0 9.2

4 8 12 25 40 55
Master of Kung Fu 2-4: 2-(12/74)-r/Yellow Claw #1. 3(3/75)-Gulacy-a; Kirby-a. 4(6/75)-Kirby-a
3 6 9 20 31 42
Power Man 1(1975) 3 6 9 18 28 38
Spider-Man 1(7/74)-Spider-Man /Human Torch-r by Kirby/Ditko; Byrne-r plus new-a (Dracula-c/story) 6 12 18 41 76 110
Spider-Man 2,3: 2(10/74)-Shang-Chi-c/app. 3(1/75)-Doc Savage-c/app.; Daredevil/ Spider-Man-r w/Ditko-a 4 8 12 27 44 60
Spider-Man 4(4/75)-3rd Punisher app.; Byrne, Ditko-r
10 20 30 66 138 210
Spider-Man 5,6: 5(7/75)-Man-Thing/Lizard-c. 6(9/75) 4 8 12 23 37 50
Super-Heroes Featuring Spider-Man 1(6/74, 35¢, 52 pgs.)-Spider-Man vs. Man-Wolf; Morbius, the Living Vampire app.; Ditko-r; G. Kane-a(p); Spidey villains app.
6 12 18 38 69 100
Super-Stars 1(5/74, 35¢, 52 pgs.)-Fantastic Four; Thing vs. Hulk; Kirbyish-c/a by Buckler/Sinnott; F.F. villains profiled; becomes Giant-Size Fantastic Four #2 on
6 12 18 37 66 95
Super-Villain Team-Up 1(3/75, 68 pgs.)-Craig-r(i) (Also see Fantastic Four #6 for 1st super-villain team-up) 3 6 9 20 31 42
Super-Villain Team-Up 2(6/75, 68 pgs.)-Dr. Doom, Sub-Mariner app.; Spider-Man-r from Amazing Spider-Man #8 by Ditko; Sekowsky-a(p) 3 6 9 17 26 35
Thor 1(7/75) 4 8 12 25 40 55
Werewolf 2(10/74, 68 pgs.)-Formerly Giant-Size Creatures; Ditko-r; Frankenstein app.
3 6 9 19 30 40
Werewolf 3,5: 3(1/75, 68 pgs.). 5(7/75, 68 pgs.) 3 6 9 19 30 40
Werewolf 4(4/75, 68 pgs.)-Morbius the Living Vampire app.
3 6 9 21 33 45
X-Men 1(Summer, 1975, 50¢, 68 pgs.)-1st app. new X-Men; intro. Nightcrawler, Storm, Colossus & Thunderbird; 2nd full app. Wolverine after Incredible Hulk #181
170 340 510 850 1275 1700
X-Men 2 (11/75)-N. Adams-r (51 pgs) 8 16 24 56 108 160
Giant Size Marvel TPB (2005, $24.99) reprints stories from Giant-Size Avengers #1, G-S Fantastic Four #4, G-S Defenders #4, G-S Super-Heroes #1, G-S Invaders #1, G-S X-Men #1 and Giant-Size Creatures #1 25.00

GIANT-SIZE...
Marvel Comics: 2005 - 2014 ($4.99/$3.99)

Astonishing X-Men 1 (7/08, $4.99) Concludes story from Astonishing X-Men #24; Whedon-s/ Cassaday-a/wraparound-c; Spider-Man, FF, Dr. Strange app.; variant cover gallery 5.00
Astonishing X-Men 1 (7/08, $4.99) Variant B&W cover 5.00
Avengers 1 (2/08, $4.99) new short stories and r/Avengers #58, 201; Hitch-c 5.00
Avengers/Invaders 1 ('08, $3.99) r/Avengers #71; Invaders #10, Ann. 1 & G-S #2 4.00
Hulk 1 (8/06, $4.99)-2 new stories; Planet Hulk (David-s/Santacruz-a) & Hulk vs. The Champions (Pak-s/Lopresti-a; r/Incredible Hulk: The End) 5.00
Incredible Hulk 1 (7/08, $3.99)-1 new story; r/Incredible Hulk Annual #7; Frank-c 4.00
Invaders 2 ('05, $4.99)-new Thomas-s/Weeks-a; r/Invaders #1&2 & All-Winners #1&2 5.00
Marvel Adventures The Avengers (9/07, $3.99) Agents of Atlas and Kang app.; Kirk-a: reprint of 1st Namora app. from Marvel Mystery Comics #82; reprint from Venus #1 4.00
Spider-Man (7/14, $4.99) origin retold, other short stories; Scherberger-c 5.00
Spider-Woman ('05, $4.99)-new Bendis-s/Mays-a; r/Marvel Spotlight #32 & S-W #1,37,38 5.00
Wolverine (12/06, $4.99)-new Lapham-s/Aja-a; r/X-Men #6,7 5.00
X-Men 3 ('05, $4.99)-new Whedon-s/N. Adams-a; r/team-ups; Cockrum & Cassaday-c 5.00

GIANT-SIZE LITTLE MARVEL: AVX (Secret Wars tie-in)
Marvel Comics: Aug, 2015 - No. 4, Nov, 2015 ($3.99, limited series)

1-4-Skottie Young-s/a; all ages kid-version Avengers vs. X-Men spoof. 4-GOTG app. 4.00

GIANT SPECTACULAR COMICS (See Archie All-Star Special under Archie Comics)

GIANT SUMMER FUN BOOK (See Terry-Toons...)

G. I. COMBAT
Quality Comics Group: Oct, 1952 - No. 43, Dec, 1956

1-Crandall-c; Cuidera a-1-43i 148 296 444 947 1624 2300
2 50 100 150 315 533 750
3-5,10-Crandall-c/a 43 86 129 271 461 650
6-Crandall-a 40 80 120 246 411 575
7-9 39 78 117 231 378 525
11-20 30 60 90 177 289 400
21-31,33,35-43: 41-1st S.A. issue 28 56 84 165 270 375
32-Nuclear attack-c/story "Atomic Rocket Assault" 37 74 111 222 361 500
34-Crandall-a 29 58 87 170 278 385

G. I. COMBAT (See DC Special Series #22)
National Periodical Publ./DC Comics: No. 44, Jan, 1957 - No. 288, Mar, 1987

44-Grey tone-c 89 178 267 712 1606 2500
45 38 76 114 281 628 975

GD VG FN VF VF/NM NM-
2.0 4.0 6.0 8.0 9.0 9.2

46-50 34 68 102 245 548 850
51-Grey tone-c 38 76 114 285 641 1000
52-54,59,60 28 56 84 202 451 700
55-Minor Sgt. Rock prototype by Finger 31 62 93 223 499 775
56-Sgt. Rock prototype by Kanigher/Kubert 42 84 126 311 706 1100
57,58-Pre-Sgt. Rock Easy Co. stories 34 68 102 245 548 850
61-65,70-73 22 44 66 154 340 525
66-Pre-Sgt. Rock Easy Co. story 31 62 93 223 499 775
67-1st Tank Killer 42 84 126 311 706 1100
68-(1/59) "The Rock" - Sgt. Rock prototype. Part of lead-up trio to 1st definitive Sgt. Rock. Character named Jimmy referred to as "The Rock" appears as a sergeant on the cover and as a private in the story. In reprint (Our Army at War #242) DC edits Jimmy's name out; also see Our Army at War #81-84 152 304 456 1254 2827 4400
69-Grey tone-c 36 72 108 266 596 925
74-American flag-c 26 52 78 182 404 625
75-80: 75-Grey tone-c begin, end #109 34 68 102 245 548 850
81,82,84-86-Grey tone-c 30 60 90 216 483 750
83-1st Big Al, Little Al, & Charlie Cigar; grey tone-c 38 76 114 285 641 1000
87-(4-5/61) 1st Haunted Tank; series begins; classic Heath washtone-c
179 358 537 1477 3339 5200
88-(6-7/61) 2nd Haunted Tank; Grey tone-c 46 92 138 368 834 1300
89,90: 90-Last 10¢ issue; Grey tone-c 29 58 87 209 467 725
91-(12/61-1/62)1st Haunted Tank-c; Grey tone-c 64 128 192 512 1156 1800
92-95,99-Grey tone-c. 94-Panel inspired a famous Roy Lichtenstein painting
25 50 75 175 388 600
96-98-Grey tone-c 19 38 57 131 291 450
100,108: 100-(6-7/63). 108-1st Sgt. Rock x-over; Grey tone-c
20 40 60 141 313 485
101-103,105-107-Grey tone-c 16 32 48 110 243 375
104,109-Grey tone-c 20 40 60 138 307 475
110-112,115-118,120 12 24 36 82 179 275
113-Grey tone-c 16 32 48 112 249 385
114-Origin Haunted Tank 36 72 108 259 580 900
119-Grey tone-c 15 30 45 105 233 360
121-136: 121-1st app. Sgt. Rock's father. 125-Sgt. Rock app. 136-Last 12¢ issue
8 16 24 56 108 160
137,139,140 5 10 15 35 63 90
138-Intro. The Losers (Capt. Storm, Gunner/Sarge, Johnny Cloud) in Haunted Tank (10-11/69)
12 24 36 80 173 265
141-143 4 8 12 25 40 55
144-148 (68 pgs.) 5 10 15 30 50 70
149,151-154 (52 pgs.): 151-Capt. Storm story. 151,153-Medal of Honor series by Maurer
4 8 12 25 40 55
150- (52 pgs.) Ice Cream Soldier story (tells how he got his name); Death of Haunted Tank-c/s
5 10 15 30 50 70
155-167,169,170 3 6 9 14 20 25
168-Neal Adams-c 3 6 9 17 26 35
171-194,196-199 2 4 6 11 16 20
195-(10/76) Haunted Tank meets War That Time Forgot; Dinosaur-c/s; Kubert-a
3 6 9 14 20 25
200-(3/77) Haunted Tank-c/s; Sgt. Rock and the Losers app.; Kubert-c
3 6 9 16 23 30
201,202 ($1.00 size) Neal Adams-c 3 6 9 16 23 30
203-210 ($1.00 size) 3 6 9 14 20 25
211-230 ($1.00 size) 2 4 6 11 16 20
231-259 ($1.00 size).232-Origin Kana the Ninja. 244-Death of Slim Stryker; 1st app. The Mercenaries. 246-(76 pgs., $1.50)-30th Anniversary issue. 257-Intro. Stuart's Raiders
2 4 6 9 13 16
260-281: 260-Begin $1.25, 52 pg. issues, end #281. 264-Intro Sgt. Bullet; origin Kana. 269-Intro. The Bravos of Vietnam. 274-Cameo of Monitor from Crisis on Infinite Earths
2 4 6 8 10 12
282-288 (75¢): 282-New advs. begin 1 2 3 5 7 9
NOTE: ***N. Adams*** *c-168, 201, 202.* ***Check*** *a-168, 173.* ***Drucker*** *a-48, 61, 63, 66, 71, 72, 76, 134, 140, 141, 144, 147, 148, 153.* ***Evans*** *a-135, 138, 158, 164, 166, 201, 202, 204, 205, 215, 256. Giffen a-267.* ***Glanzman*** *a-most issues.* ***Kubert/Heath*** *a-most issues;* ***Kubert*** *covers most issues.* ***Morrow*** *a-159-161(2 pgs.).* ***Redondo*** *a-189, 240i, 243i.* ***Sekowsky*** *a-162p.* ***Severin*** *a-147, 152, 154.* ***Simonson*** *c-169.* ***Thorne*** *a-152, 156.* ***Wildey*** *a-153. Johnny Cloud app.-112, 115, 120. Mlle. Marie app.-123, 132, 200. Sgt. Rock app.-111-113, 115, 120, 125, 141, 146, 147, 149, 200. USS Stevens by* ***Glanzman****-145, 150-153, 157.* ***Grandenetti*** *c-44-48.*

G. I. COMBAT
DC Comics: Nov, 2010 ($3.99, one-shot)

1-Haunted Tank and General J.E.B. Stuart app.; Sturges-s/Winslade-a/Darrow-c 4.00

G. I. COMBAT
DC Comics: Jul, 2012 - No. 7, Feb, 2013 ($3.99)

1-7: 1-War That Time Forgot; Olivetti-a; Unknown Soldier; Panosian-a; two covers 4.00

Gifts of the Night #1 © Bolton & Chadwick

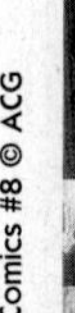
Giggle Comics #8 © ACG

G.I. Joe (2016 series) #1 © Hasbro

GD VG FN VF VF/NM NM-
2.0 4.0 6.0 8.0 9.0 9.2

#0 (11/12, $3.99) Unknown Soldiers through history; War That Time Forgot; Olivetti-a 4.00

GIDEON FALLS
Image Comics: Mar, 2018 - Present ($3.99)
1-Lemire-s/Sorrentino-a 4.00

GIDGET (TV)
Dell Publishing Co.: Apr, 1966 - No. 2, Dec, 1966
1-Sally Field photo-c 8 16 24 52 99 145
2 6 12 18 37 66 95

GIFT COMICS
Fawcett Publications: 1942 - No. 4, 1949 (50¢/25¢, 324 pgs./152 pgs.)
1-Captain Marvel, Bulletman, Golden Arrow, Ibis the Invincible, Mr. Scarlet, & Spy Smasher begin; not rebound, remaindered comics, printed at same time as originals; 50¢-c & 324 pgs. begin, end #3. 314 628 942 2198 3849 5500
2-Commando Yank, Phantom Eagle, others app. 200 400 600 1280 2190 3100
3-(50¢, 324 pgs.) 148 296 444 947 1624 2300
4-(25¢, 152 pgs.)-The Marvel Family, Captain Marvel, etc.; each issue can vary in contents 90 180 270 576 988 1400

GIFTS FROM SANTA (See March of Comics No. 137)

GIFTS OF THE NIGHT
DC Comics (Vertigo): Feb, 1999 - No. 4, May, 1999 ($2.95, limited series)
1-4-Bolton-c/a; Chadwick-s 3.00

GIGANTIC
Dark Horse Comics: Nov, 2008 - No. 5, Jan, 2010 ($3.50, limited series)
1-5-Remender-s/Nguyen-a; Earth as a reality show 3.50

GIGGLE COMICS (Spencer Spook No. 100) (Also see Ha Ha Comics)
Creston No.1-63/American Comics Group No. 64 on; Oct, 1943 - No. 99, Jan-Feb, 1955
1-Funny animal 42 84 126 265 445 625
2 21 42 63 126 206 285
3-5: Ken Hultgren-a begins? 16 32 48 92 144 195
6-9: 9-1st Superkatt (6/44) 14 28 42 81 118 155
10-Superkatt shoots Japanese plane & fights Nazi robot 15 30 45 85 130 175
11-20 12 24 36 69 97 125
21-40: 22-Spencer Spook 2nd app. 32-Patriotic-c. 37-X-Mas-c. 39-St. Valentine-c 11 22 33 62 86 110
41-54,56-59,62-99: Spencer Spook app. in many. 44-Mussel-Man app. (Superman parody). 45-Witch Hazel 1st app. 46-Bob Hope & Bing Crosby app. 49,69-X-Mas-c. 10 20 30 56 76 95
55,60,61-Milt Gross-a. 61-X-Mas-c 12 24 36 69 97 125

G-I IN BATTLE (G-I No. 1 only)
Ajax-Farrell Publ./Four Star: Aug, 1952 - No. 9, July, 1953; Mar, 1957 - No. 6, May, 1958
1 18 36 54 105 165 225
2 11 22 33 62 86 110
3-9 9 18 27 52 69 85
Annual 1(1952, 25¢, 100 pgs.) 31 62 93 182 296 410
1(1957-Ajax) 9 18 27 47 61 75
2-6 6 12 18 28 34 40

G. I. JANE
Stanhall/Merit No. 11: May, 1953 - No. 11, Mar, 1955 (Misdated 3/54)
1-PX Pete begins; Bill Williams-c/a 39 78 117 240 395 550
2-7(5/54) 34 68 102 199 325 450
8-10(12/54, Stanhall) 22 44 66 132 216 300
11 (3/55, Merit) 22 44 66 132 216 300

G. I. JOE (Also see Advs. of..., Showcase #53, 54 & The Yardbirds)
Ziff-Davis Publ. Co. (Korean War): No. 10, Feb/Mar, 1951; No. 11, Apr/May, 1951 - No. 51, Jun, 1957 (52 pgs.: #10-14, V2 #6-17?)
10(#1)-Saunders painted-c begin 21 42 63 122 199 275
11-14(#2-5, 10/51): 11-New logo. 12-New logo 14 28 42 78 112 145
V2#6(12/51)-17-(11/52; Last 52 pgs.?) 12 24 36 69 97 125
18-(25¢, 100 pg. Giant, 12-1/52-53) 28 56 84 165 270 375
19-30: 20-22,24,28-31-The Yardbirds app. 11 22 33 60 83 105
31-47,49-51 10 20 30 58 79 100
48-Atom bomb story 11 22 33 60 83 105
NOTE: ***Powell** a-V2#7, 8, 11. **Norman Saunders** painted c-10-14, V2#6-14, 26, 30, 31, 35, 38, 39. **Tuska** a-7. Bondage c-29, 35, 38.*

G. I. JOE (America's Movable Fighting Man)
Custom Comics: 1967 (5-1/8x8-3/8", 36 pgs.)
nn-Schaffenberger-a; based on Hasbro toy 3 6 9 21 33 45

G.I. JOE
Dark Horse Comics: Dec, 1995 - No. 4, Apr, 1996 ($1.95, limited series)
1-4: Mike W. Barr scripts. 1-Three Frank Miller covers with title logos in red, white and blue. 2-Breyfogle-c. 3-Simonson-c 4.00

G.I. JOE
Dark Horse Comics: V2#1, June, 1996 - V2#4, Sept, 1996 ($2.50)
V2#1-4: Mike W. Barr scripts. 4-Painted-c 4.00

G.I. JOE
Image Comics/Devil's Due Publishing: 2001 - No. 43, May, 2005 ($2.95)
1-Campbell-c; back-c painted by Beck; Blaylock-s 2 4 6 8 10 12
1-2nd printing with front & back covers switched 6.00
2,3 5.00
4-($3.50) 5.00
5-20,22-41: 6-SuperPatriot preview. 18-Brereton-c. 31-33-Wraith back-up; Caldwell-a 3.00
21-Silent issue; Zeck-a; two covers by Campbell and Zeck 4.00
42,43-($4.50)-Dawn of the Red Shadows; leads into G.I. Joe Vol. 2 4.50
...: Cobra Reborn (1/04, $4.95) Bradstreet-c/Jenkins-s 5.00
...: G.I. Joe Reborn (2/04, $4.95) Bradstreet-c/Bennett & Saltares-a 5.00
...: Malfunction (2003, $15.95) r/#11-15 16.00
... M. I. A. (2002, $4.95) r/#1&2; Beck back-c from #1 on cover 5.00
...: Players & Pawns (11/04, $12.95) r/#28-33; cover gallery 13.00
...: Reborn (2004, $9.95) r/Cobra Reborn & G.I. Joe Reborn 10.00
...: Reckonings (2002, $12.95) r/#6-9; Zeck-c 13.00
...: Reinstated (2002, $14.95) r/#1-4 15.00
...: The Return of Serpentor (9/04, $12.95) r/#16,22-25; cover gallery 13.00
...Vol. 8: The Rise of the Red Shadows (1/06, $14.95) r/#42,43 & prologue pgs. from #37-41 15.00

G.I. JOE (Volume 2) (Also see Snake Eyes: Declassified)
Devil's Due Publishing: No. 0, June, 2005 - No. 36, June, 2008 (25¢/$2.95/$3.50/$4.50)
0-(25¢-c) Casey-s/Caselli-a 3.00
1-4,7-19 ($2.95): 1-Four covers; Casey-s/Caselli-a. 4-R. Black-c 3.00
5,6-($4.50) 6-Wraparound-c 4.50
20-29,31-35-($3.50) 25-Wraparound-c World War III part 1 3.50
30,36-($5.50) 30-Double-sized World War III part 6. 36-Double-sized WW III part 12 5.50
...America's Elite Vol. 1: The Newest War TPB ('06, $14.95) r/#0-5; cover gallery 15.00
...America's Elite Vol. 2: The Ties That Bind TPB (8/06, $15.95) r/#6-12; cover gallery 16.00
...America's Elite Vol. 3: In Sheep's Clothing TPB (2007, $18.99) r/#13-18; cover gallery 19.00
...America's Elite Vol. 4: Truth and Consequences TPB (9/07, $18.99) r/#19-24; covers 19.00
... Data Desk Handbook (10/05, $2.95) character profile pages 3.00
... Data Desk Handbook A-M (10/07, $5.50) character profile pages 5.50
... Data Desk Handbook N-Z (11/07, $3.50) character profile pages 3.50
...: Scarlett: Declassified (7/06, $4.95) Scarlett's childhood and training; Noto-c/a 5.00
... Special Missions (2/06, $4.95) short stories and profile pages by various 5.00
... Special Missions Antarctica (12/06, $4.95) short stories and profile pages by various 5.00
... Special Missions Brazil (4/07, $5.50) short stories and profile pages by various 5.50
... Special Missions: The Enemy (9/07, $5.50) two stories and profile pages by various 5.50
... Special Missions Tokyo (9/06, $4.95) short stories and profile pages by various 5.00
...: The Hunt For Cobra Commander (5/06, 25¢) short story and character profiles 3.00

G.I. JOE
IDW Publishing: No. 0, Oct, 2008; No. 1, Jan, 2009 - No. 27, Feb, 2011 ($1.00/$3.99)
0-($1.00) Short stories by Dixon & Hama; creator interviews and character sketches 3.00
1-27-($3.99) 1-Dixon-s/Atkins-a; covers by Johnson, Atkins and Dell'Otto 4.00
...: Cobra Commander Tribute - 100-Page Spectacular 1 (4/11, $7.99) reprints 8.00
...: Special - Helix (8/09, $3.99) Reed-s/Suitor-a 4.00

G.I. JOE, VOLUME 2 (Prelude in G.I. Joe: Cobra Civil War #0) (Season 2 in indicia)
IDW Publishing: May, 2011 - No. 21, Jan, 2013 ($3.99)
1-21: 1-Dixon-s/Saltares-a; three covers by Howard. 9-Cobra Command Part 1 4.00

G.I. JOE VOLUME 3
IDW Publishing: Feb, 2013 - No. 15, Apr, 2014 ($3.99)
1-15-Van Lente-s/Kurth-a in most; multiple covers. 6-Igle-a. 12-15-Allor-s 4.00

G.I. JOE VOLUME 4
IDW Publishing: Sept, 2014 - No. 8, Apr, 2015 ($3.99)
1-4-The Fall of G.I. Joe; Karen Traviss-s/Steve Kurth-a; multiple covers 4.00

G.I. JOE (Follows the Revolution x-over)
IDW Publishing: Jan, 2017 - Present ($3.99)
1-9: 1-4-Reconstruction; Dreadnoks app.; Milonogiannis-a; multiple covers 4.00
... First Strike 1 (9/17, $3.99) Tie-in to First Strike x-over series; Kyriazis-a; 3 covers 4.00
...: Revolution 1 (10/16, $3.99) Tie-in to Revolution x-over; Sitterson-s/Milonogiannis-a 4.00

G.I. JOE AND THE TRANSFORMERS

G.I. Joe, A Real American Hero #247 © Hasbro

G.I. Joe: Infestation #2 © Hasbro

G.I. Joe: Reloaded #1 © Hasbro

GD 2.0 | VG 4.0 | FN 6.0 | VF 8.0 | VF/NM 9.0 | NM- 9.2

GD 2.0 | VG 4.0 | FN 6.0 | VF 8.0 | VF/NM 9.0 | NM- 9.2

Marvel Comics Group: Jan, 1987 - No. 4, Apr, 1987 (Limited series)

1 2 4 6 9 12 15
2-4 1 2 3 5 6 8

G.I. JOE, A REAL AMERICAN HERO (...Starring Snake-Eyes on-c #135 on)
Marvel Comics Group: June, 1982 - No. 155, Dec, 1994

1-Printed on Baxter paper; based on Hasbro toy 5 10 15 30 50 70
2-Printed on regular paper; 1st app. Kwinn 3 6 9 21 33 45
3-10: 6-1st app. Oktober Guard 3 6 9 14 20 25
11-20: 11-Intro Airborne. 13-1st Destro (cameo). 14-1st full app. Destro. 15-1st app. Major Blood. 16-1st app. Cover Girl and Trip-Wire 2 4 6 10 14 18
21-1st app. Storm Shadow; silent issue 5 10 15 35 63 90
22-1st app. Duke and Roadblock 2 4 6 11 16 20
23,24,28-30,60: 60-Todd McFarlane-a 2 3 4 6 8 10
25-1st full app. Zartan, 1st app of Cutter, Deep Six, Mutt and Junkyard, and The Dreadnoks 3 6 9 16 24 32
26,27-Origin Snake-Eyes parts 1 & 2 3 6 9 14 20 26
31-50: 31-1st Spirit Iron-Knife. 32-1st Blowtorch, Lady J, Recondo, Ripcord. 33-New headquarters. 40-1st app. of Shipwreck, Barbecue. 48-1st app. Sgt. Slaughter. 49-1st app. of Lift-Ticket, Slipstream, Leatherneck, Serpentor 6.00
51-59,61-90 5.00
91,92,94-99: 94-96-Snake Eyes Trilogy 6.00
93-Snake-Eyes' face first revealed 2 4 6 13 18 22
100,135-138: 135-138-($1.75)-Bagged w/trading card. 138-Transformers app. 2 4 6 9 13 16
101-134: 101-New Oktober Guard app. 110-1st Garney-a. 117- Debut G.I. Joe Ninja Force 2 3 4 6 8 10
139-142-New Transformers app. 2 4 6 13 18 22
143,145-149: 145-Intro. G.I. Joe Star Brigade 2 4 6 9 13 16
144-Origin Snake-Eyes 3 6 9 14 19 24
150-Low print thru #155 3 6 9 19 30 40
151-154: 152-30th Anniversary (of doll) issue, original G.I. Joe General Joseph Colton app. (also app. in #151) 3 6 9 18 28 38
155-Last issue 6 12 18 37 66 95
All 2nd printings 4.00
Special #1 (2/95, $1.50) r/#60 w/McFarlane-a. Cover swipe from Spider-Man #1 5 10 15 35 63 90
Special Treasury Edition (1982)-r/#1 3 6 9 19 30 40
Volume 1 TPB (4/02, $24.95) r/#1-10; new cover by Michael Golden 25.00
Volume 2 TPB (6/02, $24.95) r/#11-20; new cover by J. Scott Campbell 25.00
Volume 3 TPB (2002, $24.99) r/#21-30; new cover by J. Scott Campbell 25.00
Volume 4 TPB (2002, $25.99) r/#31-40; new cover by J. Scott Campbell 26.00
Volume 5 TPB (2002, $24.99) r/#42-50; new cover by J. Scott Campbell 25.00
Yearbook 1-4: (3/85-3/88)-r/#1; Golden-c. 2-Golden-c/a 5.00
NOTE: ***Garney** a(p)-110. **Golden** c-23, 29, 34, 36. **Heath** a-24. **Rogers** a(p)-75, 77-82, 84, 86; c-77.*

G. I. JOE, A REAL AMERICAN HERO
IDW Publishing: No. 156, Jul, 2010 - Present ($3.99)

156-199-Continuation of story from Marvel series #155 (1994); Hama-s 4.00
200-(3/14, $5.99) Multiple covers; bonus interview with artist SL Gallant 6.00
201-249: 201-214-Hama-s/Gallant-a. 213-Death of Snake Eyes. 216-218-Villanelli-a. 219-225-Cobra World Order 4.00
Annual 2012 (2/12, $7.99) Hama-s; Frenz, Wagner & Trimpe-a 8.00
...: Cobra World Order Prelude (10/15, $3.99) Starts seven-part bi-weekly event 4.00
Hundred Penny Press: G.I. Joe: Real American Hero #1 (3/11, $1.00) r/#1 (1982) 3.00

G. I. JOE, A REAL AMERICAN HERO VS. THE SIX MILLION DOLLAR MAN
IDW Publishing: Feb, 2018 - Present ($3.99)

1-Ferrier-s/Gallant-a; 5 covers 4.00

G.I. JOE: BATTLE FILES
Image Comics: 2002 - No. 3, 2002 ($5.95)

1-3-Profile pages of characters and history; Beck-c 6.00

G.I. JOE: COBRA (#5-on is continuation of G.I. Joe: Cobra II #4, not G.I. Joe: Cobra #4)
IDW Publishing: Mar, 2009 - No. 13, Feb, 2011 ($3.99)

1-4,5-13: 1-4-Gage & Costa-s/Fuso-a/covers by Chaykin & Fuso. 5-8-Carrera-a 4.00
Hundred Penny Press: G.I. Joe: Cobra #1 (4/11, $1.00) r/#1 with Chaykin-c 3.00
... Special (9/09, $3.99) Costa-s/Fuso-a 4.00
... Special 2 - Chameleon (9/10, $3.99) Costa-s/Fuso-a 4.00
... II (1/10 - No. 4, 4/10, $3.99) 1-4-Gage & Costa-s/Fuso-a/covers by Chaykin & Fuso 4.00

G.I. JOE: COBRA CIVIL WAR
IDW Publishing: No. 0, Apr, 2011 ($3.99)

0-Prelude to G.I. Joe, Cobra & Snake Eyes Civil War series; four covers 4.00
0-Muzzle Flash Edition (6/11, price not shown) r/#0 in B&W and partial color 4.00

G.I. JOE: COBRA VOLUME 2 (Prelude in G.I. Joe: Cobra Civil War #0)
IDW Publishing: May, 2011 - No. 9, Jan, 2012 ($3.99)(Re-named Cobra with #10)

1-9: Multiple covers on all. 1-4-Costa-s/Fuso-a 4.00

G. I. JOE COMICS MAGAZINE
Marvel Comics Group: Dec, 1986 - No. 13, 1988 ($1.50, digest-size)

1-G.I. Joe reprints 2 4 6 11 16 20
2-13: G.I. Joe-r 2 4 6 8 10 12

G.I. JOE DECLASSIFIED
Devil's Due Publishing: June, 2006 - No. 3 ($4.95, bi-monthly)

1-3-New "early" adventures of the team; Hama-s; Quinn & DeLandro-a; var-c for each 5.00
TPB (1/07, $18.99) r/#1-3; cover gallery 19.00

G.I. JOE: DEVIATIONS
IDW Publishing: Mar, 2016 ($4.99, one-shot)

1-Paul Allor-s/Corey Lewis-a; What If Cobra defeated G.I. Joe and ruled the world 5.00

G.I. JOE DREADNOKS: DECLASSIFIED
Devil's Due Publishing: Nov, 2006 - No. 3, Mar, 2007 ($4.95/$4.99/$5.50, bi-monthly)

1,2-Secret history of the team; Blaylock-s; var-c for each 5.00
3-($5.50) 5.50

G.I. JOE EUROPEAN MISSIONS (Action Force in indicia) (Series reprints Action Force)
Marvel Comics Ltd. (British): Jun, 1988 - No. 15, Dec, 1989 ($1.50/$1.75)

1,3-Snake Eyes & Storm Shadow-c/s 2 4 6 8 10 12
2,4-15 6.00

G.I. JOE: FRONT LINE
Image Comics: 2002 - No. 18, Dec, 2003 ($2.95)

1-18: 1-Jurgens-a/Hama-s. 1-Two covers by Dorman & Sharpe. 7,8-Harris-c 3.00
...Vol. 1 - The Mission That Never Was TPB (2003, $14.95) r/ #1-4; script pages 15.00
...Vol. 2 - Icebound TPB (3/04, $12.95) r/ #5-8 13.00
...Vol. 3 - History Repeating TPB (4/04, $9.95) r/#11-14 10.00
...Vol. 4 - One-Shots TPB (5/04, $15.95) r/#9,10,15-18 16.00

G.I. JOE: FUTURE NOIR SPECIAL
IDW Publishing: Nov, 2010 - No. 2, Dec, 2010 ($3.99, limited series, greytone art)

1,2-Schmidt-s/Bevilacqua-a 4.00

G. I. JOE: HEARTS & MINDS
IDW Publishing: May, 2010 - No. 5, Sept, 2010 ($3.99)

1-5: Short origin stories; Brooks-s; Chaykin & Fuso-a 4.00

G. I. JOE: INFESTATION (Zombie x-over with Star Trek, Ghostbusters & Transformers)
IDW Publishing: Mar, 2011 - No. 2, Mar, 2011 ($3.99, limited series)

1,2-Timpano-a; covers by Timpano and Snyder III 4.00

G.I. JOE: MASTER & APPRENTICE
Image Comics: May, 2004 - No. 4, Aug, 2004 ($2.95)

1-4-Caselli-a/Jerwa-s 3.00

G.I. JOE: MASTER & APPRENTICE 2
Image Comics: Feb, 2005 - No. 4, May, 2005 ($2.95, limited series)

1-4: Stevens & Vedder-a/Jerwa-s 3.00

G.I. JOE MOVIE PREQUEL...
IDW Publishing: Mar, 2009 - No. 4, June, 2009 ($3.99, limited series)

1-4-Two covers on each: 1-Duke. 2-Destro. 3-The Baroness. 4-SnakeEyes 4.00

G.I. JOE: OPERATION HISS
IDW Publishing: Feb, 2010 - No. 5, Jun, 2010 ($3.99, limited series)

1-5: 1-4-Reed-s/Padilla-a; covers by Corroney & Padilla. 5-Guglotta-a 4.00

G. I. JOE ORDER OF BATTLE, THE
Marvel Comics Group: Dec, 1986 - No. 4, Mar, 1987 (limited series)

1-4 6.00

G.I. JOE: ORIGINS
IDW Publishing: Feb, 2009 - No. 23, Jan, 2011 ($3.99)

1-23: 1-Origin of Snake Eyes; Hama-s. 12-Templesmith-a. 19-Benitez-a 4.00

G.I. JOE: RELOADED
Image Comics: Mar, 2004 -No. 14, Apr, 2005 ($2.95)

1-14: 1-3-Granov-c/Ney Rieber-s. 5,6-Rieber-s/Saltares-a. 8-Origin of the Baroness 3.00
Vol. 1 In the Name of Patriotism (11/04, $12.95) r/#1-6; cover gallery 13.00

G.I. JOE: RISE OF COBRA MOVIE ADAPTATION
IDW Publishing: July, 2009 - No. 4, July, 2009 ($3.99, weekly limited series)

1-4-Tipton-s/Maloney-a; two covers 4.00

Giles Season 11 #1 © 20th Century Fox

The Girl From U.N.C.L.E. #3 © GK

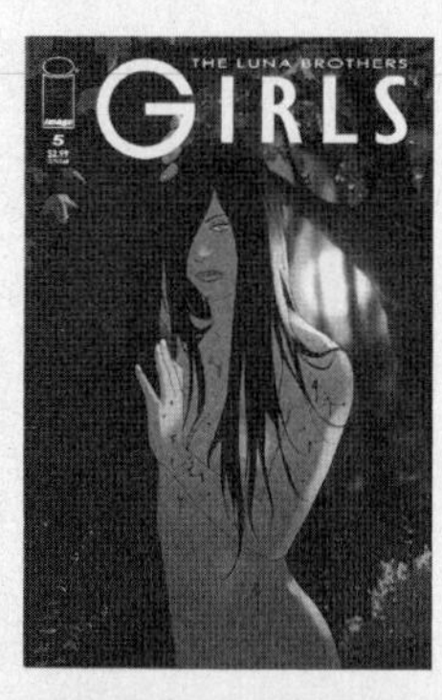

Girls #5 © Luna Brothers

	GD 2.0	VG 4.0	FN 6.0	VF 8.0	VF/NM 9.0	NM- 9.2

G.I. JOE SIGMA 6 (Based on the cartoon TV series)
Devil's Due Publishing: Dec, 2005 - No. 6, May, 2006 ($2.95, limited series)

1-6-Andrew Daab-s 3.00
TPB Vol. 1 (10/06, $10.95, 8-1/4" x 5-3/4") r/#1-6; cover gallery 11.00

G.I. JOE: SNAKE EYES
IDW Publishing: Oct, 2009 - No. 4, Jan, 2010 ($3.99, limited series)

1-4-Ray Park & Kevin VanHook-s/Lee Ferguson-a; two covers 4.00

G.I. JOE: SNAKE EYES, AGENT OF COBRA
IDW Publishing: Jan, 2015 - No. 5, May, 2015 ($3.99, limited series)

1-5-Costa-s/Villanelli-a 4.00

G.I. JOE: SNAKE EYES, VOLUME 2 (Continues as Snake Eyes #8)
IDW Publishing: May, 2011 - No. 7, Nov, 2011 ($3.99)

1-7: 1-Dixon-s/Atkins & Padilla-a; two covers 4.00

G. I. JOE SPECIAL MISSIONS (Indicia title: Special Missions)
Marvel Comics Group: Oct, 1986 - No. 28, Dec, 1989 ($1.00)

1-20 5.00
21-28 6.00

G. I. JOE: SPECIAL MISSIONS
IDW Publishing: Mar, 2013 - No. 14, Apr, 2014($3.99)

1-14: 1-4-Dixon-s/Gulacy-a; covers by Chen and Gulacy. 5-7-Rosado-a. 10-13-Gulacy-a 4.00

G. I. JOE: THE COBRA FILES
IDW Publishing: Apr, 2013 - No. 9, Dec, 2013 ($3.99)

1-9: 1-Costa-s/Fuso-a; multiple covers. 5,6-Dell'edera-a 4.00

G.I. JOE 2 MOVIE PREQUEL...
IDW Publishing: Feb, 2012 - No. 4, Apr, 2012 ($3.99, limited series)

1-4-Barber-s/Navarro & Rojo-a 4.00

G.I. JOE VS. THE TRANSFORMERS
Image Comics: Jun, 2003 - No. 6, Nov, 2003 ($2.95, limited series)

1-Blaylock-s/Mike Miller-a; three covers by Miller, Campbell & Andrews 4.00
1-2nd printing; black cover with logo; back-c by Campbell 3.00
2-6: 2-Two covers by Miller & Brooks 3.00
TPB (3/04, $15.95) r/series; sketch pages 16.00

G.I. JOE VS. THE TRANSFORMERS (Volume 2)
Devil's Due Publ.: Sept, 2004 - No. 4, Dec, 2004 ($4.95/$2.95, limited series)

1-($4.95) Three covers; Jolley-s/Su & Seeley-a 5.00
2-4-($2.95) Two covers by Su & Pollina 3.00
Vol. 2 TPB (4/05, $14.95) r/series; interview with creators; sketch pages and covers 15.00

G.I. JOE VS. THE TRANSFORMERS (Volume 3) THE ART OF WAR
Devil's Due Publ.: Mar, 2006 - No. 5, July, 2006 ($2.95, limited series)

1-5: 1-Three covers; Seeley-s/Ng-a 3.00
TPB (8/06, $14.95) r/series; cover gallery 15.00

G.I. JOE VS. THE TRANSFORMERS (Volume 4) BLACK HORIZON
Devil's Due Publ.: Jan, 2007 - No. 2, Feb, 2007 ($5.50, limited series)

1,2: 1-Three covers; Seeley-s/Wildman-a. 2-Two covers 5.50

G. I. JUNIORS (See Harvey Hits No. 86,91,95,98,101,104,107,110,112,114,116,118,120,122)

GILES SEASON 11 (From Buffy the Vampire Slayer)
DC Comics: Feb, 2018 ($3.95, limited series)

1-Whedon & Akexander-s/ Jan Lam-a 5.00

GILGAMESH II
DC Comics: 1989 - No. 4, 1989 ($3.95, limited series, prestige format, mature)

1-4: Starlin-c/a/scripts 5.00

GIL THORP
Dell Publishing Co.: May-July, 1963

	GD	VG	FN	VF	VF/NM	NM-
1-Caniff-*ish* art	4	8	12	23	37	50

GINGER
Archie Publications: 1951 - No. 10, Summer, 1954

	GD	VG	FN	VF	VF/NM	NM-
1-Teenage humor; headlights-c	41	82	123	256	428	600
2-(1952)	16	32	48	94	147	200
3-6: 6-(Sum/53)	15	30	45	86	133	180
7-10-Katy Keene app.	16	32	48	94	147	200

GINGER FOX (Also see The World of Ginger Fox)
Comico: Sept, 1988 - No. 4, Dec, 1988 ($1.75, limited series)

1-4: Part photo-c on all 3.00

GIRL
DC Comics (Vertigo Verite): Jul, 1996 - No. 3, 1996 ($2.50, lim. series, mature)

1-3: Peter Milligan scripts; Fegredo-c/a 3.00

GIRL COMICS (Becomes Girl Confessions No. 13 on)
Marvel/Atlas Comics(CnPC): Oct, 1949 - No. 12, Jan, 1952 (#1-4: 52 pgs.)

	GD	VG	FN	VF	VF/NM	NM-
1-Photo-c	29	58	87	172	281	390
2-Kubert-a; photo-c	16	32	48	92	144	195
3-Everett-a; Liz Taylor photo-c	39	78	117	231	378	525
4-11: 4-Photo-c. 10-12-Sol Brodsky-c	15	30	45	83	124	165
12-Krigstein-a; Al Hartley-c	15	30	45	85	130	175

GIRL COMICS
Marvel Comics: May, 2010 - No. 3, Sept, 2010 ($4.99, limited series)

1-3-Anthology of short stories by women creators. 1-Conner-c. 2-Thompson-c. 3-Chen-c 5.00

GIRL CONFESSIONS (Formerly Girl Comics)
Atlas Comics (CnPC/ZPC): No. 13, Mar, 1952 - No. 35, Aug, 1954

	GD	VG	FN	VF	VF/NM	NM-
13-Everett-a	15	30	45	90	140	190
14,15,19,20	14	28	42	78	112	145
16-18-Everett-a	15	30	45	83	124	165
21-35: Robinson-a	12	24	36	69	97	125

GIRL CRAZY
Dark Horse Comics: May, 1996 - No. 3, July, 1996 ($2.95, B&W, limited series)

1-3: Gilbert Hernandez-a/scripts. 3.00

GIRL FROM U.N.C.L.E., THE (TV) (Also see The Man From...)
Gold Key: Jan, 1967 - No. 5, Oct, 1967

	GD	VG	FN	VF	VF/NM	NM-
1-McWilliams-a; Stephanie Powers photo front/back-c & pin-ups (no ads, 12¢)	7	14	21	46	86	125
2-5-Leonard Swift-Courier No. 5. 4-Back-c pin-up	5	10	15	33	57	80

GIRLS
Image Comics: May, 2005 - No. 24, Apr, 2007 ($2.95/$2.99)

1-Luna Brothers-s/a/c 4.00
2-24 3.00
Image Firsts: Girls #1 (4/10, $1.00) r/#1 with "Image Firsts" cover logo 3.00
... Vol. 1: Conception TPB (2005, $14.99) r/#1-6 15.00
... Vol. 2: Emergence TPB (2006, $14.99) r/#7-12 15.00
... Vol. 3: Survival TPB (2006, $14.99) r/#13-18 15.00
... Vol. 4: Extinction TPB (2007, $14.99) r/#19-24 15.00

GIRLS' FUN & FASHION MAGAZINE (Formerly Polly Pigtails)
Parents' Magazine Institute: V5#44, Jan, 1950 - V5#48, Sept., 1950

	GD	VG	FN	VF	VF/NM	NM-
V5#44	8	16	24	40	50	60
45-48	6	12	18	28	34	40

GIRLS IN LOVE
Fawcett Publications: May, 1950 - No. 2, July, 1950

	GD	VG	FN	VF	VF/NM	NM-
1-Photo-c	12	24	36	69	97	125
2-Photo-c	10	20	30	54	72	90

GIRLS IN LOVE (Formerly G. I. Sweethearts No. 45)
Quality Comics Group: No. 46, Sept, 1955 - No. 57, Dec, 1956

	GD	VG	FN	VF	VF/NM	NM-
46	13	26	39	72	101	130
47-53,55,56	10	20	30	54	72	90
54- 'Commie' story	11	22	33	64	90	115
57-Matt Baker-c/a	15	30	45	90	140	190

GIRLS IN WHITE (See Harvey Comics Hits No. 58)

GIRLS' LIFE (Patsy Walker's Own Magazine For Girls!)
Atlas Comics (BFP): Jan, 1954 - No. 6, Nov, 1954

	GD	VG	FN	VF	VF/NM	NM-
1	20	40	60	117	189	260
2-Al Hartley-c	13	26	39	74	105	135
3-6	12	24	36	69	97	125

GIRLS' LOVE STORIES
National Comics(Signal Publ. No. 9-65/Arleigh No. 83-117): Aug-Sept, 1949 - No. 180, Nov-Dec, 1973 (No. 1-13: 52 pgs.)

	GD	VG	FN	VF	VF/NM	NM-
1-Toth, Kinstler-a, 8 pgs. each; photo-c	71	142	213	454	777	1100
2-Kinstler-a?	36	72	108	211	343	475
3-10: 1-9-Photo-c	24	48	72	142	234	325
11-20	19	38	57	112	179	245
21-33: 21-Kinstler-a. 33-Last pre-code (1-2/55)	14	28	42	82	121	160
34-50	11	22	33	62	86	110
51-70	10	20	30	56	76	95

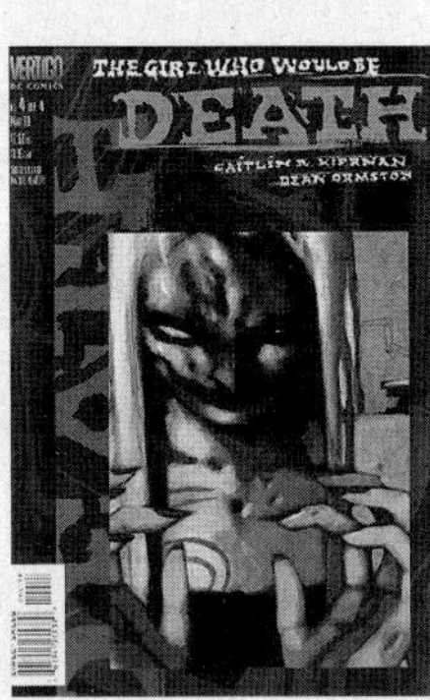

The Girl Who Would Be Death #4 © DC

Gizmo #1 © MS

Glory #4 © Rob Liefeld

	GD 2.0	VG 4.0	FN 6.0	VF 8.0	VF/NM 9.0	NM- 9.2
71-99: 83-Last 10¢ issue	5	10	15	31	53	75
100	5	10	15	33	57	80
101-146: 113-117-April O'Day app.	3	6	9	20	31	42
147-151- "Confessions" serial. 150-Wood-a	3	6	9	21	33	45
152-160,171-179	3	6	9	16	23	30
161-170 (52 pgs.)	4	8	12	22	35	48
180 Last issue	3	6	9	20	31	42
Ashcan (8-9/49) not distributed to newsstands (a FN/VF copy sold for $836.50 in 2012)						

GIRLS' ROMANCES
National Periodical Publ.(Signal Publ. No. 7-79/Arleigh No. 84): Feb-Mar, 1950 - No. 160, Oct, 1971 (No. 1-11: 52 pgs.)

	GD 2.0	VG 4.0	FN 6.0	VF 8.0	VF/NM 9.0	NM- 9.2
1-Photo-c	61	122	183	390	670	950
2-Photo-c; Toth-a	34	68	102	199	325	450
3-10: 3-6-Photo-c	23	46	69	136	223	310
11,12,14-20	16	32	48	94	147	200
13-Toth-c	17	34	51	98	154	210
21-31: 31-Last pre-code (2-3/55)	14	28	42	80	115	150
32-50	6	12	18	40	73	105
51-99: 78-Panel inspired a famous Roy Lichtenstein painting. 80-Last 10¢ issue	5	10	15	31	53	75
100	5	10	15	33	57	80
101-108,110-120: 105-Panel inspired a famous Roy Lichtenstein painting	3	6	9	20	31	42
109-Beatles-c/story	15	30	45	105	233	360
121-133,135-140	3	6	9	18	28	38
134-Neal Adams-c (splash pg. is same as-c)	5	10	15	33	57	80
141-158	3	6	9	16	23	30
159,160-52 pgs.	4	8	12	25	40	55

GIRL WHO KICKED THE HORNETS NEST, THE
DC Comics (Vertigo): 2015 ($29.99, HC graphic novel, dustjacket)

HC-Adaptation of the novel; Mina-s/Mutti & Fuso-a/Bermejo-c 30.00

GIRL WHO WOULD BE DEATH, THE
DC Comics (Vertigo): Dec, 1998 - No. 4, March, 1999 ($2.50, lim. series)

1-4-Kiernan-s/Ormston-a 3.00

GIRL WITH THE DRAGON TATTOO, THE
DC Comics (Vertigo): Book One, 2012; Book Two, 2013 ($19.99, HC graphic novels)

Book One HC-First part of the adaptation of the novel; Mina-s/Manco-a/Bermejo-c 20.00
Book Two HC-Second part of the adaptation; Mina-s/Manco-a/Bermejo-c 20.00

G. I. SWEETHEARTS (Formerly Diary Loves; Girls In Love #46 on)
Quality Comics Group: No. 32, June, 1953 - No. 45, May, 1955

	GD 2.0	VG 4.0	FN 6.0	VF 8.0	VF/NM 9.0	NM- 9.2
32	13	26	39	74	105	135
33-45: 44-Last pre-code (3/55)	10	20	30	54	72	90

G.I. TALES (Formerly Sgt. Barney Barker No. 1-3)
Atlas Comics (MCI): No. 4, Feb, 1957 - No. 6, July, 1957

	GD 2.0	VG 4.0	FN 6.0	VF 8.0	VF/NM 9.0	NM- 9.2
4-Severin-a(4)	13	26	39	74	105	135
5	10	20	30	54	72	90
6-Orlando, Powell, & Woodbridge-a	10	20	30	56	76	95

GIVE ME LIBERTY (Also see Dark Horse Presents Fifth Anniversary Special, Dark Horse Presents #100-4, Happy Birthday Martha Washington, Martha Washington Goes to War, Martha Washington Stranded In Space & San Diego Comicon Comics #2)
Dark Horse Comics: June, 1990 - No. 4, 1991 ($4.95, limited series, 52 pgs.)

1-4: 1st app. Martha Washington; Frank Miller scripts, Dave Gibbons-c/a in all 6.00

G. I. WAR BRIDES
Superior Publishers Ltd.: Apr, 1954 - No. 8, June, 1955

	GD 2.0	VG 4.0	FN 6.0	VF 8.0	VF/NM 9.0	NM- 9.2
1	15	30	45	84	127	170
2	10	20	30	56	76	95
3-8: 4-Kamenesque-a; lingerie panels	9	18	27	52	69	85

G. I. WAR TALES
National Periodical Publications: Mar-Apr, 1973 - No. 4, Oct-Nov, 1973

	GD 2.0	VG 4.0	FN 6.0	VF 8.0	VF/NM 9.0	NM- 9.2
1-Reprints in all; dinosaur-c/s	3	6	9	17	26	35
2-N. Adams-a(r)	2	4	6	13	18	22
3,4: 4-Krigstein-a(r)	2	4	6	11	16	20

NOTE: ***Drucker** a-3r, 4r. **Heath** a-4r. **Kubert** a-2, 3; c-4r.*

GIZMO (Also see Domino Chance)
Chance Ent.: May-June, 1985 (B&W, one-shot)

1 6.00

GIZMO
Mirage Studios: 1986 - No. 6, July, 1987 ($1.50, B&W)

1-6 4.00

G.L.A. (Great Lakes Avengers)(Also see GLX-Mas Special)
Marvel Comics: June, 2005 - No. 4, Sept, 2005 ($2.99, limited series)

1-4-Slott-s/Pelletier-a 3.00
...: Misassembled TPB (2005, $14.99) r/#1-4, West Coast Avengers #46 (1st app.) and Marvel Super-Heroes #8 (1st app. Squirrel Girl; Ditko-a) 15.00

GLADSTONE COMIC ALBUM
Gladstone: 1987 - No. 28, 1990 ($5.95/$9.95, 8-1/2x11")(All Mickey Mouse albums are by Gottfredson)

	GD 2.0	VG 4.0	FN 6.0	VF 8.0	VF/NM 9.0	NM- 9.2
1-10: 1-Uncle Scrooge; Barks-r; Beck-c. 2-Donald Duck; r/F.C. #108 by Barks. 3-Mickey Mouse-r by Gottfredson. 4-Uncle Scrooge; r/F.C. #456 by Barks w/unedited story. 5-Donald Duck Advs.; r/F.C. #199. 6-Uncle Scrooge-r by Barks. 7-Donald Duck-r by Barks. 8-Mickey Mouse-r. 9-Bambi; r/F.C. #186? 10-Donald Duck Advs.; r/F.C. #275	1	3	4	6	8	10
11-20: 11-Uncle Scrooge; r/U.S. #4. 12-Donald And Daisy; r/F.C. #1055, WDC&S. 13-Donald Duck Advs.; r/F.C. #408. 14-Uncle Scrooge; Barks-r/U.S #21. 15-Donald And Gladstone; Barks-r. 16-Donald Duck Advs.; r/F.C. #238. 17-Mickey Mouse strip-r (The World of Tomorrow, The Pirate Ghost Ship). 18-Donald Duck and the Junior Woodchucks; Barks-r. 19-Uncle Scrooge; r/U.S. #12; Rosa-c. 20-Uncle Scrooge; r/F.C. #386; Barks-c/a(r)	1	3	4	6	8	10
21-25: 21-Donald Duck Family; Barks-c/a(r). 22-Mickey Mouse strip-r. 23-Donald Duck; Barks-r/D.D. #26 w/unedited story. 24-Uncle Scrooge; Barks-r; Rosa-c. 25-D. Duck; Barks-c/a-r/F.C. #367	1	3	4	6	8	10
26-28: All have $9.95-c. 26-Mickey & Donald; Gottfredson-c/a(r). 27-Donald Duck; r/WDC&S by Barks; Barks painted-c. 28-Uncle Scrooge & Donald Duck; Rosa-c/a (4 stories)	1	3	4	6	8	10
Special 1-7: 1 ('89-'90, $9.95/13.95)-1-Donald Duck Finds Pirate Gold; r/F.C. #9. 2 ('89, $8.95)-Uncle Scrooge and Donald Duck; Barks-r/Uncle Scrooge #5; Rosa-c. 3 ('89, $8.95)-Mickey Mouse strip-r. 4 ('89, $11.95)-Uncle Scrooge; Rosa-c/a-r/Son of the Sun from U.S. #219 plus Barks-r/U.S. 5 ('90, $11.95)-Donald Duck Advs.; Barks-r/F.C. #282 & 422 plus Barks painted-c. 6 ('90, $12.95)-Uncle Scrooge; Barks-c/a-r/Uncle Scrooge. 7 ('90, $13.95)-Mickey Mouse; Gottfredson strip-r	2	4	6	9	11	14

GLADSTONE COMIC ALBUM (2nd Series)(Also see The Original Dick Tracy)
Gladstone Publishing: 1990 ($5.95, 8-1/2 x 11," stiff-c, 52 pgs.)

	GD 2.0	VG 4.0	FN 6.0	VF 8.0	VF/NM 9.0	NM- 9.2
1,2-The Original Dick Tracy. 2-Origin of the 2-way wrist radio						6.00
3-D Tracy Meets the Mole-r by Gould ($6.95).	1	2	3	5	6	8

GLAMOROUS ROMANCES (Formerly Dotty)
Ace Magazines (A. A. Wyn): No. 41, July, 1949 - No. 90, Oct, 1956 (Photo-c 68-90)

	GD 2.0	VG 4.0	FN 6.0	VF 8.0	VF/NM 9.0	NM- 9.2
41-Dotty app.	15	30	45	84	127	170
42-72,74-80: 44-Begin 52 pg. issues. 45,50-61-Painted-c. 80-Last pre-code (2/55)	11	22	33	62	86	110
73-L.B. Cole-r/All Love #27	11	22	33	64	90	115
81-90	10	20	30	56	76	95

GLAMOURPUSS
Aardvark-Vanaheim Inc.: Apr, 2008 - No. 26, Jul, 2012 ($3.00, B&W)

1-26: 1-Two covers; Dave Sim-s/a/c. 9,10-Gene Colan-c. 11-Heath-c. 19-Allred-c 3.00
1-Comics Industry Preview Edition (Diamond Dateline supplement) 4.00

GLOBAL FREQUENCY
DC Comics (WildStorm): Dec, 2002 - No. 12, Aug, 2004 ($2.95, limited series)

1-12-Warren Ellis-s. 1-Leach-a. 2-Fabry-a. 3-Dillon-a. 5-Muth-a. 7-Bisley-a. 12-Ha-a 3.00
1-RRP Edition variant-c; promotional giveaway for retailers (200 printed) 10.00
...: Detonation Radio TPB (2005, $14.95) r/#7-12 15.00
...: Planet Ablaze TPB (2003, $14.95) r/#1-6 15.00

GLORY
Image Comics (Extreme Studios)/Maximum Press: Mar, 1995 - No. 22, Apr, 1997 ($2.50)

0-Deodato-c/a, 1-(3/95)-Deodato-a 4.00
1A-Variant-c 5.00
2-11,13-22: 4-Variant-c by Quesada & Palmiotti. 5-Bagged w/Youngblood gaming card. 7,8-Deodato-c/a(p). 8-Babewatch x-over. 9-Cruz-c; Extreme Destroyer Pt. 5; polybagged w/card. 10-Angela-c/app. 11-Deodato-c. 3.00
12-($3.50)-Photo-c 4.00
... & Friends Christmas Special (12/95, $2.50) Deodato-c 3.00
... & Friends Lingerie Special (9/95, $2.95) Pin-ups w/photos; photo-c; variant-c exists 3.00
... /Angela: Angels in Hell (4/96, $2.50) Flip book w/Darkchylde #1 4.00
... /Avengelyne (10/95, $3.95) 1-Chromium-c, 1-Regular-c 4.00
Trade Paperback (1995, $9.95)-r/#1-4 10.00

GLORY (Continues numbering from the 1995-1997 series)
Image Comics: Feb, 2012 - No. 34, Apr, 2013 ($2.99/$3.99)

23-28-Joe Keatinge-s/Ross Campbell-a. 23-Supreme app. 3.00
29-34-($3.99) 4.00

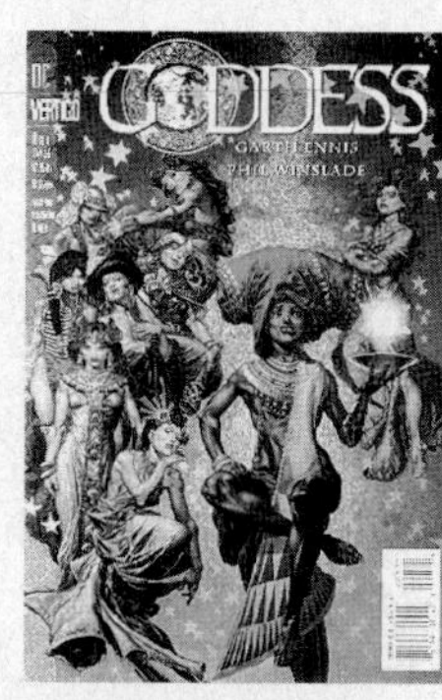

Goddess #8 © Ennis & Winslade

God is Dead #40 © Avatar

Godzilla #12 © Toho

	GD 2.0	VG 4.0	FN 6.0	VF 8.0	VF/NM 9.0	NM- 9.2

GD VG FN VF VF/NM NM- 2.0 4.0 6.0 8.0 9.0 9.2

GLORY
Awesome Comics: Mar, 1999 ($2.50)
0-Liefeld-c; story and sketch pages 3.00

GLORY (ALAN MOORE'S...)
Avatar Press: Dec, 2001 - No. 2 ($3.50)
Preview-(9/01, $1.99) B&W pages and cover art; Alan Moore-s 3.00
0-Four regular covers 3.50
1,2: 1-Alan Moore-s/Mychaels & Gebbie-a; nine covers by various. 2-Five covers 3.50

GLORY & FRIENDS BIKINI FEST
Image Comics (Extreme): Sept, 1995 - No. 2, Oct, 1995 ($2.50, limited series)
1,2: 1-Photo-c; centerfold photo; pin-ups 4.00

GLORY/CELESTINE: DARK ANGEL
Image Comics/Maximum Press (Extreme Studios): Sept, 1996 - No. 3, Nov, 1996 ($2.50)
1-3 3.00

GLX-MAS SPECIAL (Great Lakes Avengers)
Marvel Comics: Feb, 2006 ($3.99, one-shot)
1-Christmas themed stories by various incl. Haley, Templeton, Grist, Wieringo 4.00

G-MAN: CAPE CRISIS
Image Comics: Aug, 2009 - No. 5, Jan, 2010 ($2.99, limited series)
1-5-Chris Giarrusso-s/a; back-up short strips by various 3.00

GNOME MOBILE, THE (See Movie Comics)

GOBBLEDYGOOK
Mirage Studios: 1984 - No. 2, 1984 (B&W)(1st Mirage comics, published at same time)
1-(24 pgs.)-(distribution of approx. 50) Teenage Mutant Ninja Turtles app. on full page back-c ad; Teenage Mutant Ninja Turtles do not appear inside. 1st app of Fugitoid
214 428 642 1766 3983 6200
2-(24 pgs.)-Teenage Mutant Ninja Turtles on full page back-c ad
86 172 258 688 1544 2400
NOTE: *Counterfeit copies exist. Originals feature both black & white covers and interiors. Signed and numbered copies do not exist.*

GOBBLEDYGOOK
Mirage Studios: Dec, 1986 ($3.50, B&W, one-shot, 100 pgs.)
1-New 8 pg. TMNT story plus a Donatello/Michaelangelo 7 pg. story & a Gizmo story; Corben-i(r)/TMNT #7 2 4 6 11 16 20

GOBLIN, THE
Warren Publishing Co.: June, 1982 - No. 3, Dec, 1982 ($2.25, B&W magazine with 8 pg. color insert comic in all)
1-The Gremlin app. Philo Photon & the Troll Patrol, Micro-Buccaneers & Wizard Wormglow begin & app. in all. Tin Man app. Golden-a(p). Nebres-c/a in all
3 6 9 14 19 24
2,3: 2-1st Hobgoblin. 3-Tin Man app. 2 4 6 10 14 18
NOTE: ***Bermejo** a-1-3. **Elias** a-1-3. **Laxamana** a-1-3. **Nino** a-3.*

GOD COMPLEX
Image Comics: Dec, 2009 - No. 7, Jun, 2010 ($2.99)
1-7-Oeming & Berman-s/Broglia-a/Oeming-c 3.00

GOD COMPLEX: DOGMA
Image Comics (Top Cow): Oct, 2017 - Present ($3.99)
1-4-Jenkins-s/Prasetya-a 4.00

GODDAMNED, THE
Image Comics: Nov, 2015 - Present ($3.99)
1-5-Jason Aaron-s/r.m. Guéra-a; story of Cain and Noah 4.00

GODDESS
DC Comics (Vertigo): June, 1995 - No. 8, Jan, 1996 ($2.95, limited series)
1-Garth Ennis scripts; Phil Winslade-c/a in all 5.00
2-8 4.00

GODFATHERS, THE (See The Crusaders)

GOD HATES ASTRONAUTS
Image Comics: Sept, 2014 - No. 10, Jul, 2015 ($3.50)
1-10-Ryan Browne-s/a. 1-Covers by Browne & Darrow 3.50

GOD IS
Spire Christian Comics (Fleming H. Revell Co.): 1973, 1975 (35-49¢)
nn-(1973) By Al Hartley 3 6 9 14 19 24
nn-(1975) 2 4 6 10 14 18

GOD IS DEAD
Avatar Press: Aug, 2013 - No. 48, Feb, 2016 ($3.99)
1-24,26-46: 1-5-Hickman & Costa-s/Amorim-a 4.00
25,48-($5.99) 25-Costa-s/DiPascale, Nobile & Urdinola-a. 48-Last issue; cover gallery 6.00
...Book of Acts Alpha (7/14, $5.99) Short stories by Alan Moore and others 6.00
...Book of Acts Omega (7/14, $5.99) Short stories by various 6.00

GODLAND
Image Comics: July, 2005 - Finale, Dec, 2013 ($2.99)
1-15,17-35-Joe Casey-s; Kirby-esque art by Tom Scioli. 13-Var-c by Giffen & Larsen. 33-"Dogland" on cover 3.00
16-(60¢-c) Re-cap/origin issue 3.00
36-($3.99) 4.00
... Finale (12/13, $6.99) Final issue 7.00
Image Firsts: Godland #1 (9/10, $1.00) r/#1 with "Image Firsts" cover logo 3.00
...: Celestial Edition One HC (2007, $34.99) r/#1-12 and story from Image Holiday Special; intro. by Grant Morrison; cover gallery, developmental art and original story pitches 35.00

GOD OF WAR (Based on the Sony videogame)
DC Comics (WildStorm): May, 2010 - No. 6, Mar, 2011 ($3.99/$2.99, limited series)
1-6-Wolfman-s/Sorrentino-a/Park-c. 6-($2.99) 4.00
TPB (2011, $14.99) r/#1-6; cover gallery 15.00

GOD SAVE THE QUEEN
DC Comics (Vertigo): 2007 ($19.99, hardcover with dustjacket, graphic novel)
HC-Mike Carey-s/John Bolton-painted art 20.00
SC-(2008, $12.99) Different painted-c by Bolton 13.00

GOD'S COUNTRY (Also see Marvel Comics Presents)
Marvel Comics: 1994 ($6.95)
nn-P. Craig Russell-a; Colossus story; r/Marvel Comics Presents #10-17 7.00

GOD'S HEROES IN AMERICA
Catechetical Guild Educational Society: 1956 (nn) (25¢/35¢, 68 pgs.)
307 3 6 9 16 23 30

GOD'S SMUGGLER (Religious)
Spire Christian Comics/Fleming H. Revell Co.: 1972 (35¢/39¢/40¢)
1-Three variations exist 3 6 9 14 19 24

GODWHEEL
Malibu Comics (Ultraverse): No. 0, Jan, 1995 - No. 3, Feb, 1995 ($2.50, limited series)
0-3: 0-Flip-c. 1-1st app. Primevil; Thor cameo (1 panel). 3-Pérez-a in Ch. 3, Thor app. 3.00

GODZILLA (Movie)
Marvel Comics : August, 1977 - No. 24, July, 1979 (Based on movie series)
1-(Reg. 30¢ edition)-Moench-s/Trimpe-a/Mooney-i 4 8 12 25 40 55
1-(35¢-c variant, limited distribution) 11 22 33 76 163 250
2-(Reg. 30¢ edition)-Tuska-i. 2 4 6 11 16 20
2,3-(35¢-c variant, limited distribution) 9 18 27 59 117 175
3-(30¢-c) Champions app.(w/o Ghost Rider) 2 4 6 13 18 22
4-10: 4,5-Sutton-a 2 4 6 9 13 16
11-23: 14-Shield app. 20-F.F. app. 21,22-Devil Dinosaur app.
2 4 6 8 11 14
24-Last issue 2 4 6 10 14 18

GODZILLA (Movie)
Dark Horse Comics: May, 1988 - No. 6, 1988 ($1.95, B&W, limited series) (Based on movie series)
1 2 4 6 8 10 12
2-6 1 2 3 5 6 8
...Collection (1990, $10.95)-r/1-6 with new-c 14.00
...Color Special 1 (Sum, 1992, $3.50, color, 44 pgs.)-Arthur Adams wraparound-c/a & part scripts 1 2 3 5 6 8
...King Of The Monsters Special (8/87, $1.50)-Origin; Bissette-c/a
1 2 3 5 6 8
...Vs. Barkley nn (12/93, $2.95, color)-Dorman painted-c
1 2 3 5 6 8

GODZILLA (King of the Monsters) (Movie)
Dark Horse Comics: May, 1995 - No. 16, Sept, 1996 ($2.50) (Based on movies)
0-16: 0-r/Dark Horse Comics #10,11. 1-3-Kevin Maguire scripts. 3-8-Art Adams-c 5.00
...Vs. Hero Zero ($2.50) 5.00

GODZILLA
IDW Publishing: May, 2012 - May, 2013 ($3.99)
1-13: 1-5,7,8,10-Swierczynski-s/Gane-a; multiple covers on each. 6-Wachter-a 4.00
...: The IDW Era (5/14, $3.99) Plot synopses of mini-series and cover galleries 4.00

Go Girl! #4 © Trina Robbins

Go-Go #7 © CC

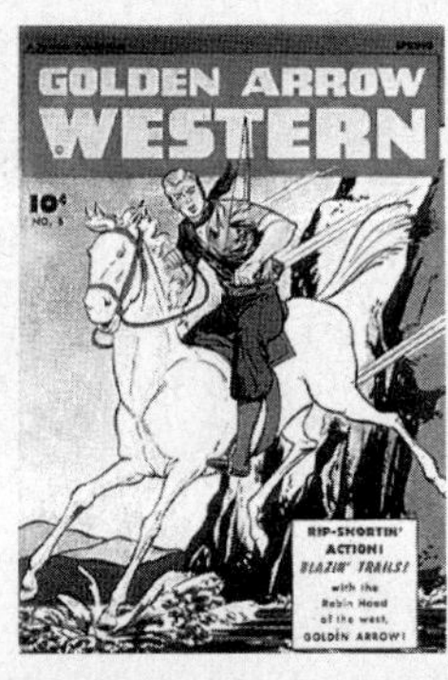

Golden Arrow Western #6 © FAW

	GD 2.0	VG 4.0	FN 6.0	VF 8.0	VF/NM 9.0	NM- 9.2

GODZILLA: CATACLYSM
IDW Publishing: Aug, 2014 - No. 5, Dec, 2014 ($3.99, limited series)
1-5-Bunn-s/Wachter-a; multiple covers on each 4.00

GODZILLA: GANGSTERS AND GOLIATHS
IDW Publishing: Jun, 2011 - No. 5, Oct, 2011 ($3.99, limited series)
1-5-Layman-s/Ponticelli-a; Mothra app. 1-Darrow-c 4.00

GODZILLA IN HELL
IDW Publishing: Jul, 2015 - No. 5, Nov, 2015 ($3.99, limited series)
1-5: Two covers on each. 1-Stokoe-s/a. 5-Wachter-s/a 4.00

GODZILLA: KINGDOM OF MONSTERS
IDW Publishing: Mar, 2011 - No. 12, Feb, 2012 ($3.99)
1-12: 1-Hester-a; covers by Ross & Powell. 2,3-Covers by Hester & Powell 4.00
...: 100 Cover Charity Spectacular (8/11, $7.99) Variant covers for Japan Disaster Relief 8.00

GODZILLA LEGENDS (Spotlight on other monsters)
IDW Publishing: Nov, 2011 - No. 5, Mar, 2012 ($3.99, limited series)
1-5-Art Adams-c. 1-Anguirus. 2-Rodan. 3-Titanosaurus. 4-Hedorah. 5-Kumonga 4.00

GODZILLA: OBLIVION
IDW Publishing: Mar, 2016 - No. 5, Jul, 2016 ($3.99, limited series)
1-5-Fialkov-s/Churilla-a; Mechagodzilla & Ghidorah app. 4.00

GODZILLA: RAGE ACROSS TIME
IDW Publishing: Aug, 2016 - No. 5, Nov, 2016 ($3.99, limited series)
1-5-Story & art by various 4.00

GODZILLA: RULERS OF EARTH
IDW Publishing: Jun, 2013 - No. 25, Jun, 2015 ($3.99, limited series)
1-24: 1-8-Chris Mowry-s/Matt Frank-a 4.00
25-($7.99) Mowry-s/Frank & Zornow-a 8.00

GODZILLA: THE HALF-CENTURY WAR
IDW Publishing: Aug, 2012 - No. 5, Feb, 2013 ($3.99, limited series)
1-5-James Stokoe-s/a 4.00

GOG (VILLAINS) (See Kingdom Come)
DC Comics: Feb, 1998 ($1.95, one-shot)
1-Waid-s/Ordway-a(p)/Pearson-c 3.00

GO GIRL!
Image Comics: Aug, 2000 - No. 5 ($3.50, B&W, quarterly)
1-5-Trina Robbins-s/Anne Timmons-a; pin-up gallery 3.50

GO-GO
Charlton Comics: June, 1966 - No. 9, Oct, 1967
1-Miss Bikini Luv begins; Rolling Stones, Beatles, Elvis, Sonny & Cher, Bob Dylan, Sinatra, parody; Herman's Hermits pin-ups; D'Agostino-c/a in #1-8 7 14 21 49 92 135
2-Ringo Starr, David McCallum & Beatles photos on cover; Beatles story and photos; Blooperman & parody of JLA heroes 7 14 21 49 92 135
3,4: 3-Blooperman, ends #6; 1 pg. Batman & Robin satire; full pg. photo pin-ups Lovin' Spoonful & The Byrds 5 10 15 31 53 75
5,7,9: 5 (2/67)-Super Hero & TV satire by Jim Aparo & Grass Green begins. 6-8-Aparo-a. 7-Photo of Brian Wilson of Beach Boys on-c & Beach Boys photo inside f/b-c. 9-Aparo-c/a 5 10 15 35 55 75
6-Parody of JLA & DC heroes vs. Marvel heroes; Aparo-a; Elvis parody; Petula Clark photo-c; first signed work by Jim Aparo 5 10 15 34 60 85
8-Monkees photo on-c & photo inside f/b-c 6 12 18 37 66 95

GO-GO AND ANIMAL (See Tippy's Friends...)

GOING STEADY (Formerly Teen-Age Temptations)
St. John Publ. Co.: No. 10, Dec, 1954 - No. 13, June, 1955; No. 14, Oct, 1955
10(1954)-Matt Baker-c/a 77 154 231 493 847 1200
11(2/55, last precode), 12(4/55)-Baker-c 60 120 180 381 653 925
13(6/55)-Baker-c/a 66 132 198 419 722 1025
14(10/55)-Matt Baker-c/a, 25 pgs. 90 180 270 576 988 1400

GOING STEADY (Formerly Personal Love)
Prize Publications/Headline: V3#3, Feb, 1960 - V3#6, Aug, 1960; V4#1, Sept-Oct, 1960
V3#3-6, V4#1 4 8 12 28 47 65

GOING STEADY WITH BETTY (Becomes Betty & Her Steady No. 2)
Avon Periodicals: Nov-Dec, 1949 (Teen-age)
1-Partial photo-c 36 72 108 211 343 475

GOLDEN AGE, THE (TPB also reprinted in 2005 as JSA: The Golden Age)
DC Comics (Elseworlds): 1993 - No. 4, 1994 ($4.95, limited series)
1-4: James Robinson scripts; Paul Smith-c/a; gold foil embossed-c 6.00
Trade Paperback (1995, $19.95) intro by Howard Chaykin 20.00

GOLDEN AGE SECRET FILES
DC Comics: Feb, 2001 ($4.95, one-shot)
1-Origins and profiles of JSA members and other G.A. heroes; Lark-c 5.00

GOLDEN ARROW (See Fawcett Miniatures, Mighty Midget & Whiz Comics)

GOLDEN ARROW (...Western No. 6)
Fawcett Publications: Spring, 1942 - No. 6, Spring, 1947 (68 pgs.)
1-Golden Arrow begins 47 94 141 296 498 700
2-(1943) 22 44 66 132 216 300
3-5: 3-(Win/45-46). 4-(Spr/46). 5-(Fall/46) 15 30 45 90 140 190
6-Krigstein-a 16 32 48 94 147 200
Ashcan (1942) not distributed to newsstands, only for in house use. A CGC certified 9.0 sold for $3,734.38 in 2008.

GOLDEN COMICS DIGEST
Gold Key: May, 1969 - No. 48, Jan, 1976
NOTE: *Whitman editions exist of many titles and are generally valued the same.*
1-Tom & Jerry, Woody Woodpecker, Bugs Bunny 5 10 15 33 57 80
2-Hanna-Barbera TV Fun Favorites; Space Ghost, Flintstones, Atom Ant, Jetsons, Yogi Bear, Banana Splits, others app. 6 12 18 41 76 110
3-Tom & Jerry, Woody Woodpecker 3 6 9 16 24 32
4-Tarzan; Manning & Marsh-a 4 8 12 28 47 65
5,8-Tom & Jerry, W. Woodpecker, Bugs Bunny 3 6 9 16 23 30
6-Bugs Bunny 3 6 9 16 23 30
7-Hanna-Barbera TV Fun Favorites 5 10 15 33 57 80
9-Tarzan 4 8 12 28 47 65
10,12-17: 10-Bugs Bunny. 12-Tom & Jerry, Bugs Bunny, W. Woodpecker Journey to the Sun. 13-Tom & Jerry. 14-Bugs Bunny Fun Packed Funnies. 15-Tom & Jerry, Woody Woodpecker, Bugs Bunny. 16-Woody Woodpecker Cartoon Special. 17-Bugs Bunny 3 6 9 16 23 30
11-Hanna-Barbera TV Fun Favorites 5 10 15 34 60 85
18-Tom & Jerry; Barney Bear-r by Barks 3 6 9 16 24 32
19-Little Lulu 4 8 12 25 40 55
20-22: 20-Woody Woodpecker Falltime Funtime. 21-Bugs Bunny Showtime. 22-Tom & Jerry Winter Wingding 3 6 9 16 23 30
23-Little Lulu & Tubby Fun Fling 4 8 12 25 40 55
24-26,28: 24-Woody Woodpecker Fun Festival. 25-Tom & Jerry. 26-Bugs Bunny Halloween Hulla-Boo-Loo; Dr. Spektor article, also #25. 28-Tom & Jerry 3 6 9 14 20 26
27-Little Lulu & Tubby in Hawaii 4 8 12 24 38 52
29-Little Lulu & Tubby 4 8 12 24 38 52
30-Bugs Bunny Vacation Funnies 3 6 9 14 20 26
31-Turok, Son of Stone; r/4-Color #596,656; c-r/#9 4 8 12 27 44 60
32-Woody Woodpecker Summer Fun 3 6 9 14 20 26
33,36: 33-Little Lulu & Tubby Halloween Fun; Dr. Spektor app. 36-Little Lulu & Her Friends 4 8 12 24 38 52
34,35,37-39: 34-Bugs Bunny Winter Funnies. 35-Tom & Jerry Snowtime Funtime. 37-Woody Woodpecker County Fair. 39-Bugs Bunny Summer Fun 3 6 9 14 20 26
38-The Pink Panther 3 6 9 16 24 32
40,43: 40-Little Lulu & Tubby Trick or Treat; all by Stanley. 43-Little Lulu in Paris 4 8 12 24 38 52
41,42,44,47: 41-Tom & Jerry Winter Carnival. 42-Bugs Bunny. 44-Woody Woodpecker Family Fun Festival. 47-Bugs Bunny 3 6 9 14 20 25
45-The Pink Panther 3 6 9 16 24 32
46-Little Lulu & Tubby 4 8 12 21 33 45
48-The Lone Ranger 3 6 9 17 26 35
NOTE: *#1-30, 164 pgs.; #31 on, 132 pgs..*

GOLDEN LAD
Spark/Fact & Fiction Publ.: July, 1945 - No. 5, June, 1946 (#4, 5: 52 pgs.)
1-Origin & 1st app. Golden Lad & Swift Arrow; Sandusky and the Senator begins 61 122 183 390 670 950
2-Mort Meskin-c/a 30 60 90 177 289 400
3,4-Mort Meskin-c/a 27 54 81 158 259 360
5-Origin & 1st app. Golden Girl; Shaman & Flame app. 34 68 102 199 325 450
NOTE: *All have **Robinson**, and **Roussos** art plus **Meskin** covers and art.*

GOLDEN LEGACY
Fitzgerald Publishing Co.: 1966 - 1972 (Black History) (25¢)
1-12,14-16: 1-Toussaint L'Ouverture (1966), 2-Harriet Tubman (1967), 3-Crispus Attucks &

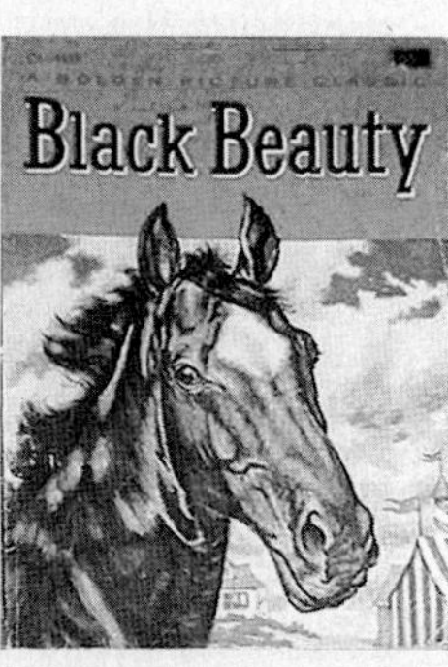

Golden Picture Classic CL-403 © S&S

Goldie Vance #9 © Larson & Williams

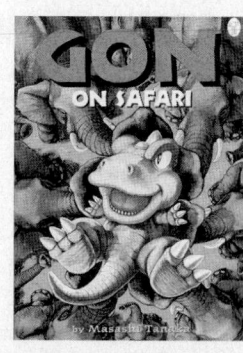

Gon on Safari © Kodansha Ltd.

	GD 2.0	VG 4.0	FN 6.0	VF 8.0	VF/NM 9.0	NM- 9.2

the Minutemen (1967), 4-Benjamin Banneker (1968), 5-Matthew Henson (1969), 6-Alexander Dumas & Family (1969), 7-Frederick Douglass, Part 1 (1969), 8-Frederick Douglass, Part 2 (1970), 9-Robert Smalls (1970), 10-J. Cinque & the Amistad Mutiny (1970), 11-Men in Action: White, Marshall J. Wilkins (1970), 12-Black Cowboys (1972), 14-The Life of Alexander Pushkin (1971), 15-Ancient African Kingdoms (1972), 16-Black Inventors (1972) each.... 4 8 12 23 37 50
13-The Life of Martin Luther King, Jr. (1972) 5 10 15 30 50 70
1-10,12,13,15,16(1976)-Reprints 2 4 6 9 12 15

GOLDEN LOVE STORIES (Formerly Golden West Love)
Kirby Publishing Co.: No. 4, April, 1950
4-Powell-a; Glenn Ford/Janet Leigh photo-c 17 34 51 98 154 210

GOLDEN PICTURE CLASSIC, A
Western Printing Co. (Simon & Shuster): 1956-1957 (Text stories w/illustrations in color; 100 pgs. each)
CL-401: Treasure Island 11 22 33 64 90 115
CL-402,403: 402: Tom Sawyer. 403: Black Beauty 10 20 30 54 72 90
CL-404, 405: CL-404: Little Women. CL-405: Heidi 10 20 30 54 72 90
CL-406: Ben Hur 8 16 24 44 57 70
CL-407: Around the World in 80 Days 8 16 24 44 57 70
CL-408: Sherlock Holmes 9 18 27 50 65 80
CL-409: The Three Musketeers 8 16 24 44 57 70
CL-410: The Merry Advs. of Robin Hood 8 16 24 44 57 70
CL-411,412: 411: Hans Brinker. 412: The Count of Monte Cristo 9 18 27 50 65 80
(Both soft & hardcover editions are valued the same)
NOTE: *Recent research has uncovered new information. Apparently #s 1-6 were issued in 1956 and #7-12 in 1957. But they can be found in five different series listings: CL-1 to CL-12 (softbound); CL-401 to CL-412 (also softbound); CL-101 to CL-112 (hardbound); plus two new series discoveries: A Golden Reading Adventure, publ. by Golden Press; edited down to 60 pages and reduced in size to 6x9"; only #s discovered so far are #381 (CL-4), #382 (CL-6) & #387 (CL-3). They have no reorder list and some have covers different from GPC. There have also been found British hardbound editions of GPC with dust jackets. Copies of all five listed series vary from scarce to very rare. Some editions of some series have not yet been found at all.*

GOLDEN PICTURE STORY BOOK
Racine Press (Western): Dec, 1961 (50¢, Treasury size, 52 pgs.) (All are scarce)
ST-1-Huckleberry Hound (TV); Hokey Wolf, Pixie & Dixie, Quick Draw McGraw, Snooper and Blabber, Augie Doggie app. 15 30 45 103 227 350
ST-2-Yogi Bear (TV); Snagglepuss, Yakky Doodle, Quick Draw McGraw, Snooper and Blabber, Augie Doggie app. 15 30 45 103 227 350
ST-3-Babes in Toyland (Walt Disney's...)-Annette Funicello photo-c 19 38 57 131 291 450
ST-4-(...of Disney Ducks)-Walt Disney's Wonderful World of Ducks (Donald Duck, Uncle Scrooge, Donald's Nephews, Grandma Duck, Ludwig Von Drake, & Gyro Gearloose stories) 19 38 57 131 291 450

GOLDEN RECORD COMIC (See Amazing Spider-Man #1, Avengers #4, Fantastic Four #1, Journey Into Mystery #83) (Also see Superman Record Comic and Batman Record Comic in the Promotional section)

GOLDEN STORY BOOKS
Western Printing Co. (Simon & Shuster): 1949-1950 (Heavy covers, digest size, 128 pgs.) (Illustrated text in color)
7-Walt Disney's Mystery in Disneyville, a book-length adventure starring Donald and Nephews, Mickey and Nephews, and with Minnie, Daisy and Goofy. Art by Dick Moores & Manuel Gonzales (scarce) 30 60 90 177 289 400
10-Bugs Bunny's Treasure Hunt, a book-length adventure starring Bugs & Porky Pig, with Petunia Pig & Nephew, Cicero. Art by Tom McKimson (scarce) 21 42 63 122 199 275
11,12 ('50): 11-M-G-M's Tom & Jerry. 12-Walt Disney's "So Dear My Heart" 20 40 60 114 182 250

GOLDEN WEST LOVE (Golden Love Stories No. 4)
Kirby Publishing Co.: Sept-Oct, 1949 - No. 3, Feb, 1950 (All 52 pgs.)
1-Powell-a in all; Roussos-a; painted-c 22 44 66 128 209 290
2,3: Photo-c 17 34 51 98 154 210

GOLDEN WEST RODEO TREASURY (See Dell Giants)

GOLDFISH (See A.K.A. Goldfish)

GOLDIE VANCE
Boom Entertainment (BOOM! Box): Apr, 2016 - No. 12, May, 2017 ($3.99)
1-12: 1-8-Hope Larson-s/Brittney Williams-a. 1-Five covers. 2-4-Two covers. 9-12-Hayes-a 4.00

GOLDILOCKS (See March of Comics No. 1)

GOLD KEY: ALLIANCE
Dynamite Entertainment: 2016 - No. 5, 2016 ($3.99, limited series)
1-5: 1-Team up of Magnus, Turok, Solar & Samson; Hester-s/Peeples-a 4.00

GOLD KEY CHAMPION
Gold Key: Mar, 1978 - No. 2, May, 1978 (50¢, 52 pgs.)
1,2: 1-Space Family Robinson; half-r. 2-Mighty Samson; half-r 1 3 4 6 8 10

GOLD KEY SPOTLIGHT
Gold Key: May, 1976 - No. 11, Feb, 1978
1-Tom, Dick & Harriet 2 4 6 8 11 14
2-11: 2-Wacky Advs. of Cracky. 3-Wacky Witch. 4-Tom, Dick & Harriet. 5-Wacky Advs. of Cracky. 6-Dagar the Invincible; Santos-a; origin Demonomicon. 7-Wacky Witch & Greta Ghost. 8-The Occult Files of Dr. Spektor, Simbar, Lu-sai; Santos-a. 9-Tragg. 10-O. G. Whiz. 11-Tom, Dick & Harriet 2 4 6 8 10 12

GOLD MEDAL COMICS
Cambridge House: 1945 (25¢, one-shot, 132 pgs.)
nn-Captain Truth by Fujitani as well as Stallman and Howie Post, Crime Detector, The Witch of Salem, Luckyman, others app. 39 78 117 231 378 525

GOMER PYLE (TV)
Gold Key: July, 1966 - No. 3, Oct, 1967
1-Photo front/back-c 9 18 27 59 117 175
2,3-Photo-c 5 10 15 35 63 90

GON
DC Comics (Paradox Press): July, 1996 - No. 4, Oct, 1996; No. 5, 1997 ($5.95, B&W, digest-size, limited series)
1-5: Misadventures of baby dinosaur; 1-Gon. 2-Gon Again. 3-Gon: Here Today, Gone Tomorrow. 4-Gon: Going, Going...Gon. 5-Gon Swimmin'. Tanaka-c/a/scripts in all 1 2 3 5 6 8

GON COLOR SPECTACULAR
DC Comics (Paradox Press): 1998 ($5.95, square-bound)
nn-Tanaka-c/a/scripts 1 2 3 5 6 8

GONERS
Image Comics: Oct, 2014 - No. 6, Mar, 2015 ($2.99)
1-6-Semahn-s/Corona-a 3.00

GON ON SAFARI
DC Comics (Paradox Press): 2000 ($7.95, B&W, digest-size)
nn-Tanaka-c/a/scripts 1 2 3 5 6 8

GON UNDERGROUND
DC Comics (Paradox Press): 1999 ($7.95, B&W, digest-size)
nn-Tanaka-c/a/scripts 1 2 3 5 6 8

GON WILD
DC Comics (Paradox Press): 1997 ($9.95, B&W, digest-size)
nn-Tanaka-c/a/scripts in all. (Rep. Gon #3,4) 1 3 4 6 8 10

GOODBYE, MR. CHIPS (See Movie Comics)

GOOD GIRL ART QUARTERLY
AC Comics: Summer, 1990 - No. 15, Spring, 1994, No. 19, 2001 (B&W/color, 52 pgs.)
1,3-15 ($3.50)-All have one new story (often FemForce) & rest reprints by Baker, Ward & other "good girl" artists 4.00
2 ($3.95), 19 (2001) FX Convention Exclusive 4.00

GOOD GIRL COMICS (Formerly Good Girl Art Quarterly)
AC Comics: No. 16, Summer, 1994 - No. 18, 1995 (B&W)
16-18 4.00

GOOD GUYS, THE
Defiant: Nov, 1993 - No. 9, July, 1994 ($2.50/$3.25/$3.50)
1-($3.50, 52 pgs.)-Glory x-over from Plasm 4.00
2,3,5-9: 3-Chasm app. 9-Pre-Schism issue 3.00
4-($3.25, 52 pgs.) Nudge sends Chasm to Plasm 4.00

GOOD, THE BAD AND THE UGLY, THE (Also see Man With No Name)
Dynamite Entertainment: 2009 - No. 8 ($3.50)
1-8: 1-Character from the 1966 Clint Eastwood movie; Dixon-s/Polls-a; three covers 3.50

GOOD TRIUMPHS OVER EVIL! (Also see Narrative Illustration)
M.C. Gaines: 1943 (12 pgs., 7-1/4"x10", B&W) (not a comic book) (Rare)
nn-A pamphlet, sequel to Narrative Illustration 155 310 465 992 1696 2400
NOTE: *Print, A Quarterly Journal of the Graphic Arts Vol. 3 No. 3 (64 pg. square bound) features 1st printing of Good Triumphs Over Evil! A VG copy sold for $350 in 2005.*

GOOFY (Disney)(See Dynabrite Comics, Mickey Mouse Magazine V4#7, Walt Disney Showcase #35 & Wheaties)

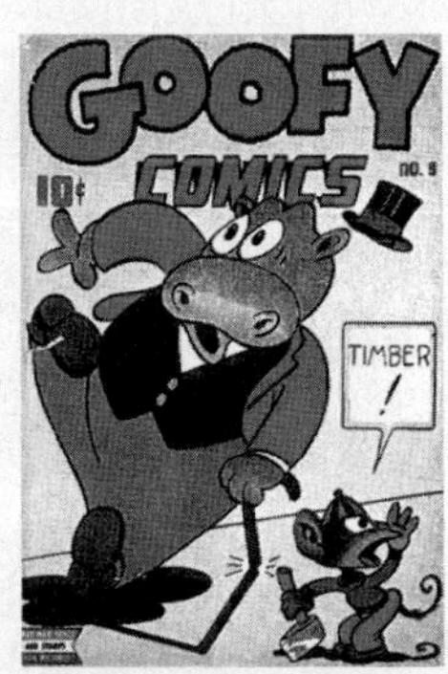

Goofy Comics #9 © STD

The Goon #32 © Eric Powell

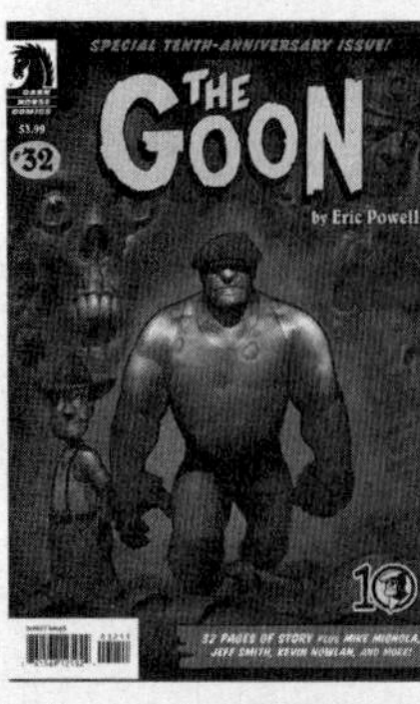

Gotham Academy #11 © DC

Dell Publishing Co.: No. 468, May, 1953 - Sept-Nov, 1962

	GD 2.0	VG 4.0	FN 6.0	VF 8.0	VF/NM 9.0	NM- 9.2
Four Color 468 (#1)	12	24	36	79	170	260
Four Color 562,627,658,702,747,802,857	7	14	21	46	86	125
Four Color 899,952,987,1053,1094,1149,1201	5	10	15	35	63	90
12-308-211(Dell, 9-11/62)	5	10	15	31	53	75

GOOFY ADVENTURES
Disney Comics: June, 1990 - No. 17, 1991 ($1.50)

1-17: Most new stories. 2-Joshua Quagmire-a w/free poster. 7-WDC&S-r plus new-a. 9-Gottfredson-r. 14-Super Goof story. 15-All Super Goof issue. 17-Gene Colan-a(p) 3.00

GOOFY ADVENTURE STORY (See Goofy No. 857)

GOOFY COMICS (Companion to Happy Comics)(Not Disney)
Nedor Publ. Co. No. 1-14/Standard No. 14-48: June, 1943 - No. 48, 1953 (Animated Cartoons)

	GD 2.0	VG 4.0	FN 6.0	VF 8.0	VF/NM 9.0	NM- 9.2
1-Funny animal; Oriolo-c	39	78	117	231	378	525
2	20	40	60	114	182	250
3-10	15	30	45	85	130	175
11-19	13	26	39	72	101	130
20-35-Frazetta text illos in all	14	28	42	78	112	145
36-48	11	22	33	60	83	105

GOOFY SUCCESS STORY (See Goofy No. 702)

GOON, THE
Avatar Press: Mar, 1999 - No. 3, July, 1999 ($3.00, B&W)

	GD 2.0	VG 4.0	FN 6.0	VF 8.0	VF/NM 9.0	NM- 9.2
1-Eric Powell-s/a	13	26	39	89	195	300
2	6	12	18	38	69	100
3	5	10	15	34	60	85
...: Rough Stuff (Albatross, 1/03, $15.95) r/Avatar Press series #1-3						20.00
...: Rough Stuff (Dark Horse, 2/04, $12.95) r/Avatar Press series #1-3 newly colored						15.00

GOON, THE (2nd series)
Albatross Exploding Funny Books: Oct, 2002 - No. 4, Feb, 2003 ($2.95)

	GD 2.0	VG 4.0	FN 6.0	VF 8.0	VF/NM 9.0	NM- 9.2
1-Eric Powell-s/a	5	10	15	34	60	85
2-4	3	6	9	14	20	25
...Color Special 1 (8/02)	3	6	9	16	23	30
...: Nothin' But Misery Vol. 1 (Dark Horse, 7/03, $15.95, TPB) - Reprints The Goon #1-4 (Albatross series), Color Special, and story from DHP #157						18.00

GOON, THE (3rd series) (Also see Dethklok Versus the Goon)
Dark Horse Comics: June, 2003 - No. 44, Nov, 2013 ($2.99/$3.50)

	GD 2.0	VG 4.0	FN 6.0	VF 8.0	VF/NM 9.0	NM- 9.2
1-Eric Powell-s/a in all	3	6	9	19	30	40
2-4	2	4	6	8	10	12
5-31: 7-Hellboy-c/app; framing seq. by Mignola 14-Two covers						4.00
32-($3.99, 3/09) Tenth Anniversary issue; with sketch pages and pin-ups						5.00
33-44-($3.50) 33-Silent issue. 35-Dorkin-s. 39-Gimmick issue. 41-43-Buckingham-a. 44-Spanish issue						3.50
... 25¢ Edition (9/05, 25¢)						3.00
...: Chinatown and the Mystery of Mr. Wicker HC (11/07, $19.95) original GN; Powell-s/a						20.00
...: Fancy Pants Edition HC (10/05, $24.95, dust jacket) r/#1,2 of 2nd series & #1,3,5,9 of 3rd series; Powell intro.; sketch pages and cover gallery						25.00
...: Heaps of Ruination (5/05, $12.95, TPB) r/#5-8; intro. by Frank Darabont						13.00
...: My Murderous Childhood (And Other Grievous Yarns) (5/04, $13.95, TPB) r/#1-4 and short story from Drawing on Your Nightmares one-shot; intro. by Frank Cho						14.00
...: One For One (8/10, $1.00) r/#1 with red cover frame						3.00
...: One For The Road (6/14, $3.50) Jack Davis-c; EC horror hosts app.						3.50
...: Theater Bizarre (10/15, $3.99) Prelude to The Lords of Misery; Zombo app.						4.00
...: Virtue and the Grim Consequences Thereof (2/06, $16.95) r/#9-13						17.00
...: Wicked Inclinations (12/06, $14.95) r/#14-18; intro. by Mike Allred						15.00

GOON NOIR, THE (Dwight T. Albatross's...)
Dark Horse Comics: Sept, 2006 - No. 3, Jan, 2007 ($2.99, B&W, limited series)

1-3-Anthology 1-Oswalt-s/Ploog-a; Sniegoski-s/Powell-a; Morrison-s/a; Niles-s/Sook-a 3.00

GOON: OCCASION OF REVENGE, THE
Dark Horse Comics: Jul, 2014 - No. 4, Dec, 2014 ($3.50, limited series)

1-4-Powell-s/a. 3-Origin of Kid Gargantuan 3.50

GOON: ONCE UPON A HARD TIME, THE
Dark Horse Comics: Feb, 2015 - No. 4, Oct, 2015 ($3.50, limited series)

1-4-Powell-s/a 3.50

GOOSE (Humor magazine)
Cousins Publ. (Fawcett): Sept, 1976 - No. 3, 1976 (75¢, 52 pgs., B&W)

	GD 2.0	VG 4.0	FN 6.0	VF 8.0	VF/NM 9.0	NM- 9.2
1-Nudity in all	3	6	9	16	23	30
2,3: 2-(10/76) Fonz-c/s; Lone Ranger story. 3-Wonder Woman, King Kong, Six Million Dollar Man stories	2	4	6	11	16	20

GOOSEBUMPS: MONSTERS AT MIDNIGHT
IDW Publishing: Oct, 2017 - Present ($3.99)

1-3-Lambert-s/Fenoglio-a 4.00

GORDO (See Comics Revue No. 5 & Giant Comics Edition)

GORGO (Based on M.G.M. movie) (See Return of...)
Charlton Comics: May, 1961 - No. 23, Sept, 1965

	GD 2.0	VG 4.0	FN 6.0	VF 8.0	VF/NM 9.0	NM- 9.2
1-Ditko-a, 22 pgs.	24	48	72	170	378	585
2,3-Ditko-c/a	13	26	39	86	188	290
4-Ditko-c	9	18	27	60	120	180
5-11,13-16: 11,13-16-Ditko-a. 11-Ditko-c	8	16	24	51	96	140
12,17-23: 12-Reptisaurus x-over. 17-23-Montes/Bache-a. 20-Giordano-c	5	10	15	35	63	90
Gorgo's Revenge('62)-Becomes Return of...	6	12	18	42	79	115

GORILLA MAN (From Agents of Atlas)
Marvel Comics: Sept, 2010 - No. 3, Nov, 2010 ($3.99, limited series)

1-3-Parker-s/Caracuzzo-a. 1-Johnson-c. 3-Dell'Otto-c 4.00

GOSPEL BLIMP, THE
Spire Christian Comics (Fleming H. Revell Co.): 1974, 1975 (35¢/39¢, 36 pgs.)

	GD 2.0	VG 4.0	FN 6.0	VF 8.0	VF/NM 9.0	NM- 9.2
nn-(1974)	3	6	9	14	19	24
nn-(1975)	2	4	6	9	13	16

GOTHAM ACADEMY
DC Comics: Dec, 2014 - No. 18, Jul, 2016 ($2.99)

	NM- 9.2
1-18: 1-Cloonan & Fletcher-s/Kerschl-a. 4-6-Killer Croc. 6,7-Damian Wayne app.	3.00
Annual 1 (10/16, $4.99) Art by Archer, Wildgoose, Dialynas, Msassyk; Blight app.	5.00
...: Endgame 1 (5/15, $2.99) Tie-in to Joker story in Batman titles	3.00

GOTHAM ACADEMY: SECOND SEMESTER
DC Comics: Nov, 2016 - No. 12, Oct, 2017 ($2.99)

1-12: 1-3-Cloonan, Fletcher & Kerschl-s/Archer-a. 4-Jon Lam-a. 11-Damian app. 3.00

GOTHAM BY GASLIGHT (A Tale of the Batman)(See Batman: Master of...)
DC Comics: 1989 ($3.95, one-shot, squarebound, 52 pgs.)

	GD 2.0	VG 4.0	FN 6.0	VF 8.0	VF/NM 9.0	NM- 9.2
nn-Mignola/Russell-a; intro by Robert Bloch	1	3	4	6	8	10

GOTHAM BY MIDNIGHT
DC Comics: Jan, 2015 - No. 12, Feb, 2016 ($2.99)

	NM- 9.2
1-12: 1-5-Fawkes-s/Templesmith-a/c. 4,5,7-11-The Spectre app. 6-12-Ferreyra-a	3.00
Annual 1 (9/15, $4.99) Fawkes-s/Duce-a; The Gentleman Ghost origin	5.00

GOTHAM CENTRAL
DC Comics: Early Feb, 2003 - No. 40, Apr, 2006 ($2.50)

	NM- 9.2
1-40-Stories of Gotham City Police. 1-Brubaker & Rucka-s/Lark-c/a. 10-Two-Face app. 13,15-Joker-c. 18-Huntress app. 27-Catwoman-c. 32-Poison Ivy app. 34-Teen Titans-c/app. 38-Crispus Allen killed (becomes The Spectre in Infinite Crisis #5)	3.00
... Special Edition 1 (11/14, $1.00) r/#1 with Gotham TV show banner on cover	3.00
... Book One: In the Line of Duty HC (2008, $29.99, dustjacket) r/#1-10; sketch pages	30.00
... Book One: In the Line of Duty SC (2008, $19.99) r/#1-10; sketch pages	20.00
... Book Two: Jokers and Madmen HC (2009, $29.99, dustjacket) r/#11-22	30.00
... Book Two: Jokers and Madmen SC (2011, $19.99) r/#11-22	20.00
... Book Three: On the Freak Beat HC (2010, $29.99, dustjacket) r/#23-31	30.00
... Book Four: Corrigan HC (2011, $29.99, dustjacket) r/#32-40	30.00
...: Dead Robin (2007, $17.99, TPB) r/#33-40; cover gallery	18.00
...: Half a Life (2005, $14.99, TPB) r/#6-10, Batman Chronicles #16 and Detective #747	15.00
...: In The Line of Duty (2004, $9.95, TPB) r/#1-5, cover gallery & sketch pages	10.00
...: The Quick and the Dead TPB (2006, $14.99) r/#23-25,28-31	15.00
...: Unresolved Targets (2006, $14.99, TPB) r/#12-15,19-22, cover gallery	15.00

GOTHAM CITY GARAGE
DC Comics: Dec, 2017 - Present ($2.99, printings of stories that first appeared online)

1-10: 1-Female heroes as a biker gang; Kelly & Lanzing-s/Ching-a/Albuquerque-c 3.00

GOTHAM CITY SIRENS (Batman: Reborn)
DC Comics: Aug, 2009 - No. 26, Oct, 2011 ($2.99)

	GD 2.0	VG 4.0	FN 6.0	VF 8.0	VF/NM 9.0	NM- 9.2
1-Catwoman, Harley Quinn and Poison Ivy; Dini-s/March-a/c	5	10	15	30	50	70
1-Variant-c by JG Jones	12	24	36	79	170	260
2-4	2	4	6	8	10	12
5-Full Harley Quinn cover	3	6	9	14	20	25
6-10	1	3	4	6	8	10
11-19	1	2	3	5	6	8
20,23-Joker, Harley Quinn cover	2	4	6	9	12	15
21-Full Harley Quinn cover	2	4	6	9	12	15

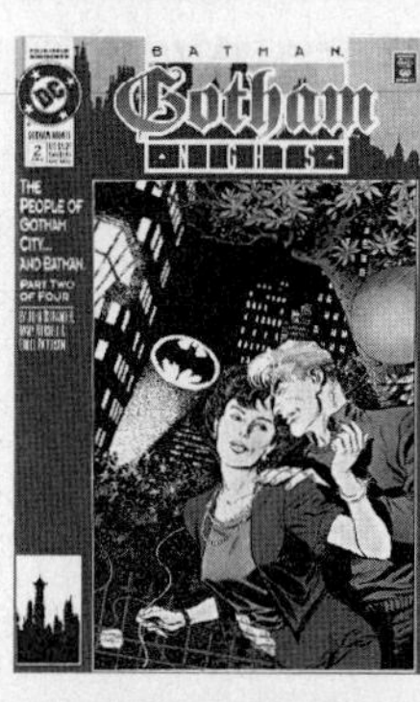

Gotham Nights #2 © DC

Grand Passion #5 © DYN & Robinson

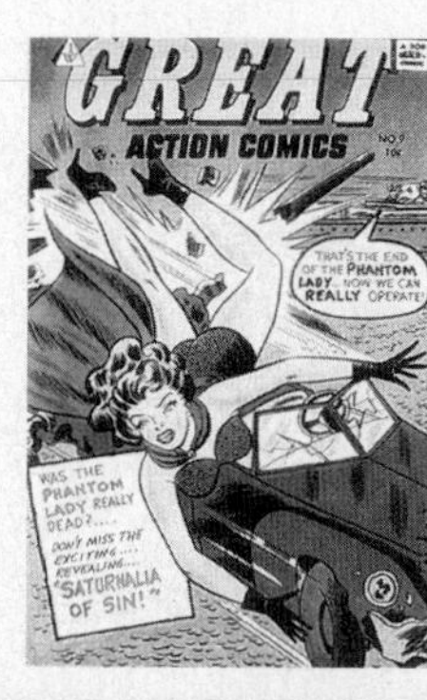

Great Action Comics #9 © IWE

GD 2.0 | VG 4.0 | FN 6.0 | VF 8.0 | VF/NM 9.0 | NM- 9.2

22,24-26 5.00
...: Song of the Sirens HC (2010, $19.99, dustjacket) r/#8-13 & Catwoman #83 20.00
...: Union HC (2010, $19.99, dustjacket) r/#1-7 20.00
...: Union SC (2011, $17.99) r/#1-7 18.00

GOTHAM GAZETTE (Battle For The Cowl crossover in Batman titles)
DC Comics: May, 2009; Jul, 2009 ($2.99, one-shots)

1-Short stories of Gotham without Batman; Nguyen, March, ChrisCross & others-a 3.00
...: Batman Alive? (7/09) Vicki Vale app.; Nguyen, March, ChrisCross & others-a 3.00

GOTHAM GIRLS
DC Comics: Oct, 2002 - No. 5, Feb, 2003 ($2.25, limited series)

1-Catwoman, Batgirl, Poison Ivy, Harley Quinn from animated series; Catwoman-c
2 4 6 11 16 20
2,4,5: 2-Poison Ivy-c. 4-Montoya-c. 5-Batgirl-c 2 4 6 8 11 14
3-Harley Quinn-c 4 8 12 23 37 50

GOTHAM NIGHTS (See Batman: Gotham Nights II)
DC Comics: Mar, 1992 - No. 4, June, 1992 ($1.25, limited series)

1-4: Featuring Batman 3.00

GOTHAM UNDERGROUND
DC Comics: Dec, 2007 - No. 9, Aug, 2008 ($2.99, limited series)

1-9-Nine covers interlock for single image; Tieri-s/Calafiore-a/c. 7,8-Vigilante app. 3.00
Batman: Gotham Underground TPB (2008, $19.99) r/#1-9; interlocked image cover 20.00

GOTHIC ROMANCES (Also see My Secrets)
Atlas/Seaboard Publ.: Dec, 1974 (75¢, B&W, magazine, 76 pgs.)

1-Text w/ illos by N. Adams, Chaykin, Heath (2 pgs. ea.); painted cover from Ravenwood Gothic paperback "The Conservatory"(scarce) 27 54 81 194 435 675

GOTHIC TALES OF LOVE (Magazine)
Marvel Comics: Apr, 1975 - No. 3, 1975 (B&W, 76 pgs.)

1-3-Painted-c/a (scarce) 27 54 81 194 435 675

GOVERNOR & J. J., THE (TV)
Gold Key: Feb, 1970 - No. 3, Aug, 1970 (Photo-c)

1 4 8 12 25 40 55
2,3 3 6 9 18 28 38

GRACKLE, THE
Acclaim Comics: Jan, 1997 - No. 4, Apr, 1997 ($2.95, B&W)

1-4: Mike Baron scripts & Paul Gulacy-c/a. 1-4-Doublecross 3.00

GRAFIK MUSIK
Caliber Press: Nov, 1990 - No. 4, Aug, 1991 ($3.50/$2.50)

1-($3.50, 48 pgs., color) Mike Allred-c/a/scripts-1st app. in color of Frank Einstein (Madman)
3 6 9 14 20 25
2-($2.50, 24 pgs., color) 2 4 6 9 12 15
3,4-($2.50, 24 pgs., B&W) 2 4 6 8 10 12

GRANDMA DUCK'S FARM FRIENDS(See Walt Disney's C&S 293 & Wheaties)
Dell Publishing Co.: No. 763, Jan, 1957 - No. 1279, Feb, 1962 (Disney)

Four Color 763 (#1) 8 16 24 51 96 140
Four Color 873 6 12 18 37 66 95
Four Color 965,1279 5 10 15 34 60 85
Four Color 1010,1073,1161-Barks-a; 1073,1161-Barks-c/a
11 22 33 73 157 240

GRAND PASSION
Dynamite Entertainment: 2016 - No. 5, 2017 ($3.99, limited series)

1-5-James Robinson-s/Tom Feister-a/John Cassaday-c 4.00

GRAND PRIX (Formerly Hot Rod Racers)
Charlton Comics: No. 16, Sept, 1967 - No. 31, May, 1970

16-Features Rick Roberts 3 6 9 21 33 45
17-20 3 6 9 17 26 35
21-31 3 6 9 16 23 30

GRAPHIQUE MUSIQUE
Slave Labor Graphics: Dec, 1989 - No. 3, May, 1990 ($2.95, 52 pgs.)

1-Mike Allred-c/a/scripts 3 6 9 19 30 40
2,3 3 6 9 16 23 30

GRASS KINGS
BOOM! Studios: Mar, 2017 - Present ($3.99)

1-12-Matt Kindt-s/Tyler Jenkins-a 4.00

GRAVESLINGER
Image Comics (Shadowline): Oct, 2007 - No. 4, Mar, 2008 ($3.50, limited series)

1-4-Denton & Mariotte-s/Cboins-a 3.50

GRAVE TALES
Hamilton Comics: Oct, 1991 - No. 3, Feb, 1992 ($3.95, B&W, mag., 52 pgs.)

1-Staton-c/a 2 3 4 6 8 10
2,3: 2-Staton-a; Morrow-c 1 2 3 5 6 8

GRAVEYARD SHIFT
Image Comics: Dec, 2014 - No. 4, Apr, 2015 ($3.50)

1-4: 1-Jay Faerber-s/Fran Bueno-a; wraparound-c 3.50

GRAVITY (Also see Beyond! limited series)
Marvel Comics: Aug, 2005 - No. 5, Dec, 2005 ($2.99, limited series)

1-5: 1-Intro. Gravity; McKeever-s/Norton-a. 2-Rhino-c/app. 5-Spider-Man app. 3.00
...: Big-City Super Hero (2005, $7.99, digest) r/#1-5 8.00

GRAY AREA, THE
Image Comics: Jun, 2004 - No. 3, Oct, 2004 ($5.95/$3.95, limited series)

1,3-($5.95) Romita, Jr.-a/Brunswick-s; sketch pages and script pages. 3-Pin-up pages 6.00
2-($3.95) 4.00
...Vol. 1: All Of This Can Be Yours (2005, $14.95) r/series & sketch,script & pin-up pages 15.00

GRAY GHOST, THE
Dell Publishing Co.: No. 911, July, 1958; No. 1000, June-Aug, 1959

Four Color 911 (#1), 1000-Photo-c each 7 14 21 49 92 135

GRAYSON (See Forever Evil) (Leads into Nightwing: Rebirth)
DC Comics: Sept, 2014 - No. 20, Jul, 2016 ($2.99/$3.99)

1-8-Dick Grayson as secret agent; Seeley & King-s/Janin-a. 1,2,6,7-Midnighter app. 3.00
9-20-($3.99): 10-Lex Luthor app. 12-Return to Gotham; Batgirl, Red Robin app. 15-"Robin War" tie-in 4.00
Annual 1 (2/15, $4.99) Mooney-a 5.00
Annual 2 (11/15, $4.99) Superman and Blockbuster app.; Alvaro Martinez-a 5.00
Annual 3 (8/16, $4.99) Harley Quinn, Constantine, Azrael, Simon Baz app. 5.00
...: Futures End 1 (11/14, $2.99, regular-c) Five years later; Mooney-a 3.00
...: Futures End 1 (11/14, $3.99, 3-D cover) 4.00

GREAT ACTION COMICS
I. W. Enterprises: 1958 (Reprints with new covers)

1-Captain Truth reprinted from Gold Medal #1 3 6 9 16 23 30
8,9-Reprints Phantom Lady #15 & 23 6 12 18 41 76 110

GREAT AMERICAN COMICS PRESENTS - THE SECRET VOICE
Peter George 4-Star Publ./American Features Syndicate: 1945 (10¢)

1-Anti-Nazi; "What Really Happened to Hitler" 65 130 195 416 708 1000

GREAT AMERICAN WESTERN, THE
AC Comics: 1987 - No. 4, 1990? ($1.75/$2.95/$3.50, B&W with some color)

1-4: 1-Western-r plus Bill Black-a. 2-Tribute to ME comics; Durango Kid photo-c 3-Tribute to Tom Mix plus Roy Rogers, Durango Kid; Billy the Kid-r by Severin; photo-c. 4- ($3.50, 52 pgs., 16 pgs. color)-Tribute to Lash LaRue; photo-c & interior photos; Fawcett-r 4.00
...Presents 1 (1991, $5.00) New Sunset Carson; film history 5.00

GREAT CAT FAMILY, THE (Disney-TV/Movie)
Dell Publishing Co.: No. 750, Nov, 1956 (one-shot)

Four Color 750-Pinocchio & Alice app. 6 12 18 37 66 95

GREAT COMICS
Great Comics Publications: Nov, 1941 - No. 3, Jan, 1942

1-Origin/1st app. The Great Zarro; Madame Strange & Guy Gorham, Wizard of Science & The Great Zarro begin 148 296 444 947 1624 2300
2-Buck Johnson, Jungle Explorer app.; X-Mas-c 74 148 222 470 810 1150
3-Futuro Takes Hitler to Hell-c/s; "The Lost City" movie story (starring William Boyd); continues in Choice Comics #3 (scarce) 1400 2800 4200 7000 10,500 14,000

GREAT COMICS
Novack Publishing Co./Jubilee Comics/Knockout/Barrel O' Fun: 1945

1-(Four publ. variations: Barrel O-Fun, Jubilee, Knockout & Novack)-The Defenders, Capt. Power app.; L. B. Cole-c 34 68 102 199 325 450
1-(Jubilee)-Same cover; Boogey Man, Satanas, & The Sorcerer & His Apprentice
29 58 87 174 285 395
1-(Barrel O' Fun)-L. B. Cole-c; Barrel O' Fun overprinted in indicia; Li'l Cactus, Cuckoo Sheriff (humorous) 22 44 66 130 213 295

GREAT DOGPATCH MYSTERY (See Mammy Yokum & the...)

GREATEST ADVENTURE, THE (Edgar Rice Burroughs characters)
Dynamite Entertainment: 2017 - No. 9, 2018 ($3.99)

1-9: 1-Tarzan & Jane, Korak, Jason Gridley, John Carter & Dejah Thoris app.; Razek-a 4.00

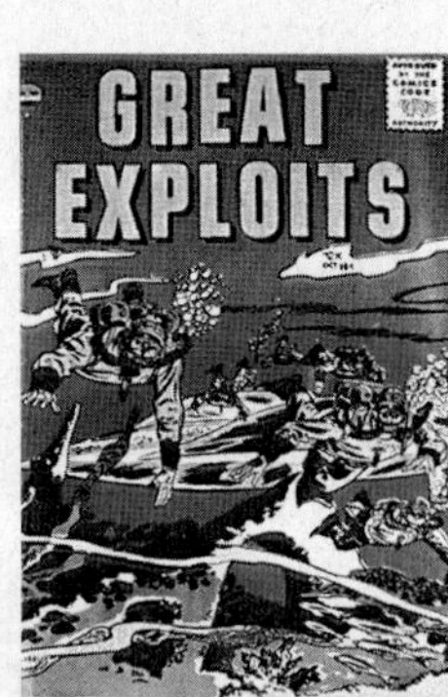
Great Exploits #1 © Decker Pub.

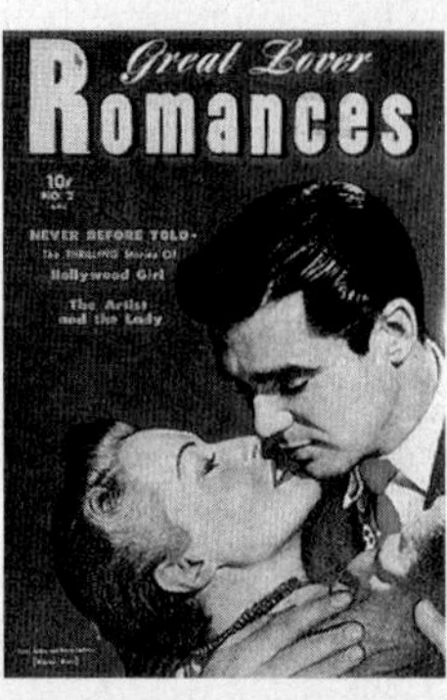
Great Lover Romances #2 © TOBY

Green Arrow #45 © DC

GD 2.0 VG 4.0 FN 6.0 VF 8.0 VF/NM 9.0 NM- 9.2

GREATEST AMERICAN HERO (Based on the 1981-1986 TV series)
Catastrophic Comics: Dec, 2008 - No. 3, May, 2009 ($3.50/$3.95)
1-3-Origin re-told; William Katt and others-s. 3-Obama-c/app. 4.00

GREATEST BATMAN STORIES EVER TOLD, THE
DC Comics
Hardcover ($24.95) 50.00
Softcover ($15.95) "Greatest DC Stories Vol. 2" on spine 20.00
Vol. 2 softcover (1992, $16.95) "Greatest DC Stories Vol. 7" on spine 20.00

GREATEST FLASH STORIES EVER TOLD, THE
DC Comics: 1991
nn-Hardcover ($29.95); Infantino-c 45.00
nn-Softcover ($14.95) 20.00

GREATEST GOLDEN AGE STORIES EVER TOLD, THE
DC Comics: 1990 ($24.95, hardcover)
nn-Ordway-c 60.00

GREATEST HITS
DC Comics (Vertigo): Dec, 2008 - No. 6, Apr, 2009 ($2.99, limited series)
1-6-Intro. The Mates superhero team in 1967 England; Tischman-s/Fabry-a/c 3.00

GREATEST JOKER STORIES EVER TOLD, THE (See Batman)
DC Comics: 1983
Hardcover ($19.95)-Kyle Baker painted-c 50.00
Softcover ($14.95) 20.00
Stacked Deck...Expanded Edition (1992, $29.95)-Longmeadow Press Publ. 35.00

GREATEST 1950s STORIES EVER TOLD, THE
DC Comics: 1990
Hardcover ($29.95)-Kubert-c 55.00
Softcover ($14.95) "Greatest DC Stories Vol. 5" on spine 22.00

GREATEST TEAM-UP STORIES EVER TOLD, THE
DC Comics: 1989
Hardcover ($24.95)-DeVries and Infantino painted-c 55.00
Softcover ($14.95) "Greatest DC Stories Vol. 4" on spine; Adams-c 22.00

GREATEST SUPERMAN STORIES EVER TOLD, THE
DC Comics: 1987
Hardcover ($24.95) 50.00
Softcover ($15.95) 22.00

GREAT EXPLOITS
Decker Publ./Red Top: Oct, 1957
1-Krigstein-a(2) (re-issue on cover); reprints Daring Advs. #6 by Approved Comics
6 12 18 31 38 45

GREAT FOODINI, THE (See Foodini)

GREAT GAZOO, THE (The Flintstones)(TV)
Charlton Comics: Aug, 1973 - No. 20, Jan, 1977 (Hanna-Barbera)
1 4 8 12 23 37 50
2-10 3 6 9 14 19 24
11-20 2 4 6 10 14 18

GREAT GRAPE APE, THE (TV)(See TV Stars #1)
Charlton Comics: Sept, 1976 - No. 2, Nov, 1976 (Hanna-Barbera)
1 3 6 9 21 33 45
2 3 6 9 14 20 25

GREAT GRIMMAX, THE
Defiant: Aug. 1994 (8 pgs.)
0-Hero Illustrated giveaway, Polgardy/Shooter story, J.G. Jones-c, Cockrum-a 3.00

GREAT LAKES AVENGERS (Also see G.L.A.)
Marvel Comics: Dec, 2016 - No. 7, Jun, 2017 ($3.99)
1-7: 1-Team reunites; Squirrel Girl cameo; Gorman-s/Robson-a. 7-Deadpool app. 4.00

GREAT LOCOMOTIVE CHASE, THE (Disney)
Dell Publishing Co.: No. 712, Sept, 1956 (one-shot)
Four Color 712-Movie, photo-c 6 12 18 42 79 115

GREAT LOVER ROMANCES (Young Lover Romances #4,5)
Toby Press: 3/51; #2, 1951(nd); #3, 1952 (nd); #6, Oct?, 1952 - No. 22, May, 1955 (Photo-c #1-5, 10 ,13, 15, 17) (no #4, 5)
1-Jon Juan story-r/Jon Juan #1 by Schomburg; Dr. Anthony King app.
23 46 69 138 227 315
2-Jon Juan, Dr. Anthony King app. 14 28 42 81 118 155
3,7,9-14,16-22: 10-Rita Hayworth photo-c. 17-Rita Hayworth & Aldo Ray photo-c
11 22 33 64 90 115
6-Kurtzman-a (10/52) 14 28 42 80 115 150
8-Five pgs. of "Pin-Up Pete" by Sparling 14 28 42 78 112 145
15-Liz Taylor photo-c (scarce) 50 100 150 315 533 750

GREAT RACE, THE (See Movie Classics)

GREAT SCOTT SHOE STORE (See Bulls-Eye)

GREAT SOCIETY COMIC BOOK, THE (Political parody)
Pocket Books Inc./Parallax Pub.: 1966 ($1.00, 36 pgs., 7"x10", one-shot)
nn-Super-LBJ-c/story; 60s politicians app. as super-heroes; Tallarico-a
3 6 9 17 26 35

GREAT TEN, THE (Characters from Final Crisis)
DC Comics: Jan, 2010 - No. 9, Sept, 2010 ($2.99, limited series)
1-9-Super team of China; Bedard-s/McDaniel-a/Stanley Lau-c 3.00

GREAT WEST (Magazine)
M. F. Enterprises: 1969 (B&W, 52 pgs.)
V1#1 2 4 6 10 14 18

GREAT WESTERN
Magazine Enterprises: No. 8, Jan-Mar, 1954 - No. 11, Oct-Dec, 1954
8(A-1 93)-Trail Colt by Guardineer; Powell Red Hawk-r/Straight Arrow begins, ends #11; Durango Kid story 18 36 54 103 162 220
9(A-1 105), 11(A-1 127)-Ghost Rider, Durango Kid app. in each. 9-Red Mask-c, but no app.
15 30 45 83 124 165
10(A-1 113)-The Calico Kid by Guardineer-r/Tim Holt #8; Straight Arrow, Durango Kid app.
12 24 36 69 97 125
I.W. Reprint #1,2 9: 1,2-r/Straight Arrow #36,42. 9-r/Straight Arrow #?
3 6 9 15 22 28
I.W. Reprint #8-Origin Ghost Rider(r/Tim Holt #11); Tim Holt app.; Bolle-a
3 6 9 16 24 32
NOTE: *Guardineer c-8. Powell a(r)-8-11 (from Straight Arrow).*

GREEK STREET
DC Comics (Vertigo): Sept, 2009 - No. 16, Dec, 2010 ($1.00/$2.99)
1-16: 1-($1.00) Milligan-s/Gianfelice-a. 2: Begin $2.99-c 3.00
...: Blood Calls For Blood SC (2010, $9.99) r/#1-5; Mike Carey intro.; sketch art 10.00
...: Cassandra Complex SC (2010, $14.99) r/#6-11 15.00

GREEN ARROW (See Action #440, Adventure, Brave & the Bold, DC Super Stars #17, Detective #521, Flash #217, Green Lantern #76, Justice League of America #4, Leading Comics, More Fun #73 (1st app.), Showcase '95 #9 & World's Finest Comics)

GREEN ARROW
DC Comics: May, 1983 - No. 4, Aug, 1983 (limited series)
1-Origin; Speedy cameo; Mike W. Barr scripts, Trevor Von Eeden-c/a
2 4 6 11 16 20
2-4 1 3 4 6 8 10

GREEN ARROW
DC Comics: Feb, 1988 - No. 137, Oct, 1998 ($1.00-$2.50) (Painted-c #1-3)
1-Mike Grell scripts begin, ends #80 2 4 6 9 12 15
2-49,51-74,76-86: 27,28-Warlord app. 35-38-Co-stars Black Canary; Bill Wray-i. 40-Grell-a. 47-Begin $1.50-c. 63-No longer has mature readers on-c. 63-66-Shado app. 81-Aparo-a begins, ends #100; Nuklon app. 82-Intro & death of Rival. 83-Huntress-c/story. 84, 85-Deathstroke app. 86-Catwoman-c/story w/Jim Balent layouts 4.00
50,75-($2.50, 52 pgs.): Anniversary issues. 75-Arsenal (Roy Harper) & Shado app. 5.00
0,87-96: 87-$1.95-c begins. 88-Guy Gardner, Martian Manhunter, & Wonder Woman-c/app.; Flash-c. 89-Anarky app. 90-(9/94)-Zero Hour tie-in. 0-(10/94)-1st app. Connor Hawke; Aparo-a(p). 91-(11/94). 93-1st app. Camorouge. 95-Hal Jordan cameo. 96-Intro new Force of July; Hal Jordan (Parallax) app; Oliver Queen learns that Connor Hawke is his son 3.00
97-99,102-109: 97-Begin $2.25-c; no Aparo-a. 97-99-Arsenal app. 102,103-Underworld Unleashed x-over. 104-GL(Kyle Rayner)-c/app. 105-Robin-c/app. 107-109-Thorn app. 109-Lois Lane cameo; Weeks-c. 3.00
100-($3.95)-Foil-c; Superman app. 1 3 4 6 8 10
101-Death of Oliver Queen; Superman app. 3 6 9 16 23 30
110,111-124: 110,111-GL x-over. 110-Intro Hatchet. 114-Final Night. 115-117-Black Canary & Oracle app. 3.00
125-($3.50, 48 pgs)-GL x-over cont. in GL #92 4.00
126-136: 126-Begin $2.50-c. 130-GL & Flash x-over. 132,133-JLA app. 134,135-Brotherhood of the Fist pts. 1,5. 136-Hal Jordan-c/app. 3.00
137-Last issue; Superman app.; last panel cameo of Oliver Queen
2 4 6 9 12 15
#1,000,000 (11/98) 853rd Century x-over 3.00
Annual 1-6 ('88-'94, 68 pgs.)-1-No Grell scripts. 2-No Grell scripts; recaps origin Green Arrow,

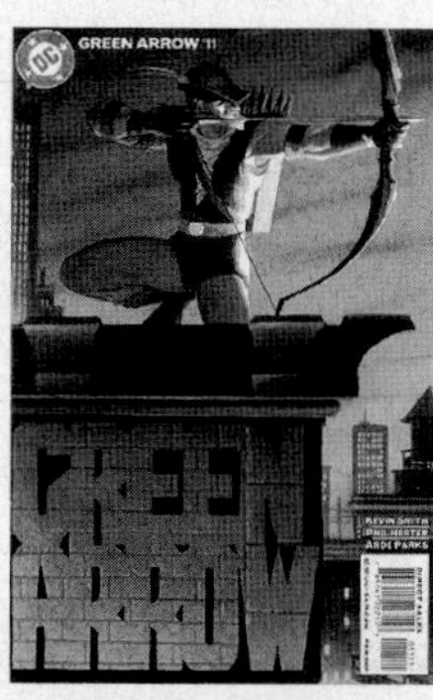

Green Arrow (2001 series) #11 © DC

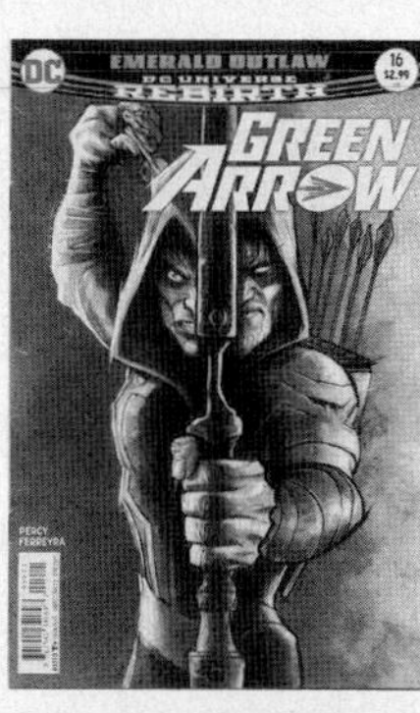

Green Arrow (2016 series) #16 © DC

Green Hornet #14 © Now

GD VG FN VF VF/NM NM-
2.0 4.0 6.0 8.0 9.0 9.2

GD VG FN VF VF/NM NM-
2.0 4.0 6.0 8.0 9.0 9.2

Speedy, Black Canary & others. 3-Bill Wray-a. 4-50th anniversary issue. 5-Batman, Eclipso app. 6-Bloodlines; Hook app. 4.00
Annual 7-('95, $3.95)-Year One story 4.00
NOTE: **Aparo** *a-0, 81-85, 86 (partial),87p, 88p, 91-95, 96i, 98-100p, 109p; c-81,98-100p.* **Austin** *c-96i.* **Balent** *layouts-86.* **Burchett** *c-91-95.* **Campanella** *a-100-108i, 110-113i; c-99i, 101-108i,110-113i.* **Denys Cowan** *a-39p, 41-43p, 47p, 48p, 60p; c-41-43.* **Damaggio** *a(p)-97p, 100-108p, 110-112p; c-97-99p, 101-108p, 110-113p.* **Mike Grell** *c-1-4, 10p, 11, 39, 40, 44, 45, 47-80, Annual 4, 5.* **Nasser/Netzer** *a-89, 96.* **Sienkiewicz** *a-109i.* **Springer** *a-67, 68.* **Weeks** *c-109.*

GREEN ARROW
DC Comics: Apr, 2001 - No. 75, Aug, 2007 ($2.50/$2.99)

1-Oliver Queen returns; Kevin Smith-s/Hester-a/Wagner-painted-c 2 4 6 10 14 18
1-2nd-4th printings 3.00
2-Batman cameo 1 2 3 4 5 7
2-2nd printing 3.00
3-5: 4-JLA app. 5.00
6-15: 7-Barry Allen & Hal Jordan app. 9,10-Stanley & his Monster app. 10-Oliver regains his soul. 12-Hawkman-c/app. 4.00
16-25: 16-Brad Meltzer-s begin; The Shade app. 18-Solomon Grundy-c/app. 19-JLA app. 22-Beatty-s; Count Vertigo app. 23-25-Green Lantern app.; Raab-s/Adlard-a 3.00
26-49: 26-Winick-s begin. 35-37-Riddler app. 43-Mia learns she's HIV+. 45-Mia becomes the new Speedy. 46-Teen Titans app. 49-The Outsiders app. 3.00
50-($3.50) Green Arrow's team and the Outsiders vs. The Riddler and Drakon 4.00
51-59: 51-Anarky app. 52-Zatanna-c/app. 55-59-Dr. Light app. 3.00
60-74: 60-One Year Later starts. 62-Begin $2.99-c; Deathstroke app. 69-Batman app. 3.00
75-($3.50) Ollie proposes to Dinah (see Black Canary mini-series); JLA app. 4.00
... By Jack Kirby (2001, $5.95) Collects Green Arrow stories by Kirby from the 1950s; introduction by Evanier 6.00
...: City Walls SC (2005, $17.95) r/#32, 34-39 18.00
...: Crawling Through the Wreckage SC (2007, $12.99) r/#60-65 13.00
...: Heading Into the Light SC (2006, $12.99) r/#52,54-59 13.00
...: Moving Targets SC (2006, $17.99) r/#40-50 18.00
...: Quiver HC (2002, $24.95) r/#1-10; Smith intro. 25.00
...: Quiver SC (2003, $17.95) r/#1-10; Smith intro. 18.00
...: Road to Jericho SC (2007, $17.99) r/#66-75 18.00
...Secret Files & Origins 1-(12/02, $4.95) Origin stories & profiles; Wagner-c 5.00
...: Sounds of Violence HC (2003, $19.95) r/#11-15; Hester intro. & sketch pages 20.00
...: Sounds of Violence SC (2003, $12.95) r/#11-15; Hester intro. & sketch pages 13.00
...: Straight Shooter SC (2004, $12.95) r/#26-31 13.00
...: The Archer's Quest HC (2003, $19.95) r/#16-21; pitch, script and sketch pages 20.00
...: The Archer's Quest SC (2004, $14.95) r/#16-21; pitch, script and sketch pages 15.00

GREEN ARROW (Brightest Day)
DC Comics: Aug, 2010 - No. 15, Oct, 2011 ($3.99/$2.99)

1-Oliver Queen in the Star City forest; Green Lantern app.; Neves-a/Cascioli-c 5.00
1-Variant-c by Van Sciver 8.00
2-15-($2.99) 2-Green Lantern app. 7-Mayhew-a. 8-11-The Demon app. 12-Swamp Thing 3.00
...: Into the Woods HC (2011, $22.99) r/#1-7; variant cover gallery 23.00

GREEN ARROW (DC New 52)
DC Comics: Nov, 2011 - No. 52, Jul, 2016 ($2.99)

1-Krul-s/Jurgens & Pérez-a/Wilkins-c 1 3 4 6 8 10
2-24: 4,5-Giffen-s. 13,14-Hawkman app. 17-24-Lemire-s/Sorrentino-a/c. 22-Count Vertigo app. 23,24-Richard Dragon app. 3.00
23.1 (11/13, $2.99, regular cover) "Count Vertigo #1" on cover; Sorrentino-a/c 3.00
23.1 (11/13, $3.99, 3-D cover) "Count Vertigo #1" on cover; Sorrentino-a/c 5.00
25-($3.99) Zero Year tie-in; Batman app.; back-up with Cowan-a 4.00
26-49: 26-31-Outsiders War; Lemire-s/Sorrentino-a/c. 35-40-Hitch-c; Felicity Smoak app. 3.00
50-($4.99) Kudranski-a; Deathstroke app. 5.00
51,52-Deathstroke app. 3.00
#0 (11/12) Origin story re-told; Nocenti-s/Williams II-a 3.00
Annual 1 (11/15, $4.99) Percy-s/Kudranski-a/Edwards-c 5.00
...: Futures End 1 (11/14, $2.99, regular-c) Five years later; Lemire-s/Sorrentino-a 3.00
...: Futures End 1 (11/14, $3.99, 3-D cover) 4.00

GREEN ARROW (DC Rebirth)
DC Comics: Aug, 2016 - Present ($2.99/$3.99)

1-24: 1,2-Percy-s/Schmidt-a; Black Canary & Shado app. 3-5-Ferreyra-a. 14-Malcolm Merlyn returns. 21-24-Cheshire app. 3.00
25-($3.99) Schmidt-a; Kate Spencer app.; Moira Queen returns 4.00
26-33: 26,27-Flash app. 27-Wonder Woman app. 28-Superman app. 29-Batman app. 30,31-Green Lantern app. 32-Dark Nights: Metal tie-in 3.00
34-38-($3.99) 4.00
Annual 1 (1/18, $4.99) Count Vertigo app.; Percy-s/Carlini-a 5.00
...: Rebirth 1 (8/16, $2.99) Percy-a/Schmidt-a; Black Canary app. 3.00

GREEN ARROW/BLACK CANARY (Titled Green Arrow for #30-32)
DC Comics: Dec, 2007 - No. 32, Jun, 2010 ($3.50/$2.99)

1-($3.50) Connor Hawke & Black Canary; follows Wedding Special; Winick-s/Chang-a 4.00
2-21-($2.99) 3-Two covers; Connor shot. 5-Dinah & Ollie's real wedding 3.00
22-30-($3.99) Back-up stories begin. 28-Origin of Cupid. 30-Blackest Night 4.00
30-Variant cover by Mike Grell 8.00
31-32-($2.99) Rise and Fall; Dallocchio-a 3.00
...: A League of Their Own TPB (2009, $17.99) r/#11-14 & G.A. Secret Files & Origins 18.00
...: Big Game TPB (2010, $19.99) r/#21-26 20.00
...: Enemies List TPB (2009, $17.99) r/#15-20 18.00
...: Family Business TPB (2008, $17.99) r/#5-10 18.00
...: Five Stages TPB (2010, $17.99) r/#27-30 18.00
...: Road To The Altar TPB (2008, $17.99) r/proposal pages from Green Arrow #75, Birds of Prey #109, Black Canary #1-4 and Black Canary Wedding Planner #1 18.00
...: The Wedding Album HC (2008, $19.99, dustjacket) r/#1-5 & Wedding Special #1 20.00
...: The Wedding Album SC (2009, $17.99) r/#1-5 & Wedding Special #1 18.00
... Wedding Special 1 (11/07, $3.99) Winick-s/Conner-a/c; Dinah & Ollie's "wedding" 5.00
... Wedding Special 1 (11/07, $3.99) 2nd printing with Ryan Sook variant-c 4.00

GREEN ARROW: THE LONG BOW HUNTERS
DC Comics: Aug, 1987 - No. 3, Oct, 1987 ($2.95, limited series, mature)

1-Grell-c/a in all 2 4 6 8 10 12
1,2-2nd printings 4.00
2,3 6.00
Trade paperback (1989, $12.95)-r/#1-3 15.00

GREEN ARROW: THE WONDER YEAR
DC Comics: Feb, 1993 - No. 4, May, 1993 ($1.75, limited series)

1-4: Mike Grell-a(p)/scripts & Gray Morrow-a(i) 4.00

GREEN ARROW: YEAR ONE
DC Comics: Early Sept, 2007 - No. 6, Late Nov, 2007 ($2.99, bi-weekly limited series)

1-6-Origin re-told; Diggle-s/Jock-a 3.00
1-Special Edition (12/14, $1.00) Reprints #1; Arrow TV show banner atop cover 3.00
HC (2008, $24.99) r/#1-6; intro. by Brian K. Vaughan; script and sketch pages 25.00
SC (2009, $14.99) r/#1-6; intro. by Brian K. Vaughan; script and sketch pages 15.00

GREEN BERET, THE (See Tales of...)

GREEN GIANT COMICS (Also see Colossus Comics)
Pelican Publ. (Funnies, Inc.): 1940 (No price on cover; distributed in New York City only)

1-Dr. Nerod, Green Giant, Black Arrow, Mundoo & Master Mystic app.; origin Colossus (Rare) 1400 2800 4200 10,000 20,000 30,000
NOTE: *The idea for this book came from George Kapitan. Printed by Moreau Publ. of Orange, N.J. as an experiment to see if they could profitably use the idle time of their 40-page Hoe color press. The experiment failed due to the difficulty of obtaining good quality color registration and Mr. Moreau believes the book never reached the stands. The book has no price or date which lends credence to this. Contains five pages reprinted from Motion Picture Funnies Weekly.*

GREEN GOBLIN
Marvel Comics: Oct, 1995 - No. 13, Oct, 1996 ($2.95/$1.95)

1-($2.95)-Scott McDaniel-c/a begins, ends #7; foil-c 4.00
2-13: 2-Begin $1.95-c. 4-Hobgoblin-c/app; Thing app. 6-Daredevil-c/app. 8-Robertson-a; McDaniel-c. 12,13-Onslaught x-over. 13-Green Goblin quits; Spider-Man app. 3.00

GREENHAVEN
Aircel Publishing: 1988 - No. 3, 1988 ($2.00, limited series, 28 pgs.)

1-3 3.00

GREEN HORNET, THE (TV)
Dell Publishing Co./Gold Key: Sept, 1953; Feb, 1967 - No. 3, Aug, 1967

Four Color 496-Painted-c. 24 48 72 168 372 575
1-Bruce Lee photo-c and back-c pin-up 18 36 54 121 268 415
2,3-Bruce Lee photo-c 10 20 30 70 150 230

GREEN HORNET, THE (Also see Kato of the... & Tales of the...)
Now Comics: Nov, 1989 - No. 14, Feb, 1991 ($1.75)
V2#1, Sept, 1991 - V2#40, Jan, 1995 ($1.95)

1 ($2.95, double-size)-Steranko painted-c; G.A. Green Hornet 6.00
1,2: 1-2nd printing ('90, $3.95)-New Butler-c 4.00
3-14: 5-Death of original ('30s) Green Hornet. 6-Dave Dorman painted-c. 11-Snyder-c 4.00
V2#1-11,13-21,24-26,28-30,32-37: 1-Butler painted-c. 9-Mayerik-c 3.00
12-($2.50)-Color Green Hornet button polybagged inside 4.00
22,23-($2.95)-Bagged w/color hologravure card 4.00
27-($2.95)-Newsstand ed. polybagged w/multi-dimensional card (1993 Anniversary Special on cover), 27-($2.95)-Direct Sale ed. polybagged w/multi-dimensional card; cover variations 4.00
31,38: 31-($2.50)-Polybagged w/trading card 4.00

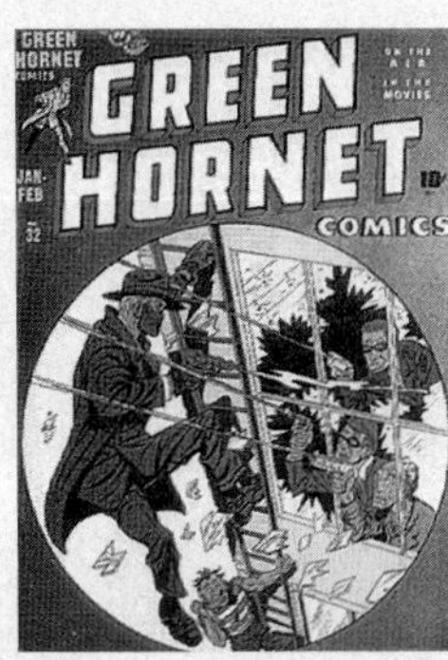

Green Hornet Comics #32 © HARV

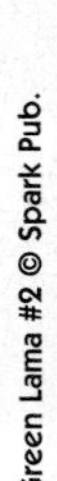
Green Lama #2 © Spark Pub.

Green Lantern #1 © DC

	GD 2.0	VG 4.0	FN 6.0	VF 8.0	VF/NM 9.0	NM- 9.2

39,40-Low print run 6.00
1-($2.50)-Polybagged w/button (same as #12) 4.00
2,3-($1.95)-Same as #13 & 14 3.00
Annual 1 (12/92, $2.50), Annual 1994 (10/94, $2.95) 4.00

GREEN HORNET (Becomes Green Hornet: Legacy with #34)
Dynamite Entertainment: 2010 - No. 33, 2013 ($3.99)

1-Kevin Smith-s/Jonathan Lau-a; multiple covers by Alex Ross, Cassaday, Campbell and Segovia 4.00
2-33-Multiple covers by Ross and others on each. 11-Hester-s begins 4.00
Annual 1 (2010, $5.99) Hester-s/Netzer & Rafael-a 6.00
Annual 2 (2012, $4.99) Hester-c/Rahner-s/Cliquet-a; back-up r/G.H. Comics #1 (1940) 5.00
... FCBD Edition; 5 previews of various new Green Hornet series; Cassaday-c 3.00

GREEN HORNET
Dynamite Entertainment: 2013 - No. 13, 2014 ($3.99)

1-13: 1-Set in 1941; Mark Waid-s/Daniel Indro-a; 2 covers by Alex Ross & Paolo Rivera 4.00

GREEN HORNET: AFTERMATH
Dynamite Entertainment: 2011 - No. 4, 2011 ($1.99/$3.99, limited series)

1-Nitz-s/Raynor-a; Green Hornet & Kato after the 2011 movie 3.00
2-4-($3.99) 4.00

GREEN HORNET: BLOOD TIES
Dynamite Entertainment: 2010 - No. 4, 2011 ($3.99)

1-4-Ande Parks-s/Johnny Desjardins-a; original Green Hornet & Kato 4.00

GREEN HORNET COMICS (...Racket Buster #44) (Radio, movies)
Helnit Publ. Co.(Holyoke) No. 1-6/Family Comics(Harvey) No. 7-on:
Dec, 1940 - No. 47, Sept, 1949 (See All New #13,14)(Early issues: 68 pgs.)

	GD	VG	FN	VF	VF/NM	NM-
1-1st app. Green Hornet & Kato; text origin of Green Hornet on inside front-c; intro the Black Beauty (Green Hornet's car); painted-c	815	1630	2445	5950	11,475	17,000
2-(3/41) Early issues based on radio adventures	277	554	831	1759	3030	4300
3	181	362	543	1158	1979	2800
4-6: 6-(8/41)	161	322	483	1030	1765	2500
7 (6/42)-1st app. of the Green Hornet villain The Murdering Clown; origin The Zebra & begins; Robin Hood, Spirit of '76, Blonde Bomber & Mighty Midgets begin; new logo	148	296	444	947	1624	2300
8-Classic horror bondage killer dwarf-c	181	362	543	1158	1979	2800
9-Kirby-c	181	362	543	1158	1979	2800
10-(12/42) Hornet vs. The Murdering Clown-c/sty	129	258	387	826	1413	2000
11-Mr. Q app.	116	232	348	742	1271	1800
12-1st WWII cover for this title; Mr. Q app.	123	246	369	787	1344	1900
13-1st Nazi-c; shows Hitler poster on-c	232	464	696	1485	2543	3600
14-Bondage-c; Mr. Q app.	110	220	330	704	1202	1700
15-Nazi WWII-c	119	238	357	762	1306	1850
16-Nazi WWII prisoner of war cable car cover	126	252	378	806	1378	1950
17-Nazi WWII-c	119	238	357	762	1306	1850
18,19-Japanese WWII-c	119	238	357	762	1306	1850
20-Classic Japanese WWII-c	126	252	378	806	1378	1950
21-23-Japanese WWII-c	87	174	261	553	952	1350
24-Classic Japanese poison rockets Sci-Fi-c	119	238	357	762	1306	1850
25,27,28,30	50	100	150	315	533	750
26-(9/45) Japanese WWII-c	53	106	159	334	567	800
29-Jerry Robinson skull-c	52	104	156	328	552	775
31-The Man in Black Called Fate begins (11-12/45, early app.)	53	106	159	334	567	800
32-36	36	72	108	216	351	485
37,38: Shock Gibson app. by Powell. 37-S&K Kid Adonis reprinted from Stuntman #3. 38-Kid Adonis app.	36	72	108	211	343	475
39-Stuntman story by S&K	39	78	117	236	388	540
40-47: 42-47-Kerry Drake in all. 45-Boy Explorers on-c only. 46- "Case of the Marijuana Racket" cover/story; Kerry Drake app.	27	54	81	160	263	365

NOTE: *Fuje a-23, 24, 26.* ***Henkle*** *c-7-9.* ***Kubert*** *a-20, 30.* ***Powell*** *a-7-10, 12, 14, 16-21, 30, 31(2), 32(3), 33, 34(3), 35, 36, 37(2), 38.* ***Robinson*** *a-27.* ***Schomburg*** *c-17-23. Kirbyish c-7, 15. Bondage c-8, 11, 14, 18, 26, 36.*

GREEN HORNET: DARK TOMORROW
Now Comics: Jun, 1993 - No. 3, Aug, 1993 ($2.50, limited series)

1-3: Future Green Hornet 3.00

GREEN HORNET: GOLDEN AGE RE-MASTERED
Dynamite Entertainment: 2010 - No. 8, 2011 ($3.99)

1-8-Re-colored reprints of 1940's Green Hornet Comics; new Rubenstein-c 4.00

GREEN HORNET: LEGACY (Numbering continues from Green Hornet 2010-2013 series)
Dynamite Entertainment: No. 34, 2013 - No. 42, 2013 ($3.99)

34-42: 34-Jai Nitz-s/Jethro Morales-a 4.00

	GD 2.0	VG 4.0	FN 6.0	VF 8.0	VF/NM 9.0	NM- 9.2

GREEN HORNET: PARALLEL LIVES
Dynamite Entertainment: 2010 - No. 5, 2010 ($3.99, limited series)

1-5-Jai Nitz-s/Nigel Raynor-a; semi-prequel to the 2011 movie; Kato's origin 4.00

GREEN HORNET: REIGN OF THE DEMON
Dynamite Entertainment: 2016 - No. 4, 2017 ($3.99, limited series)

1-4-David Liss-s/Kewber Baal-a 4.00

GREEN HORNET '66 MEETS THE SPIRIT: VOLUME 1
Dynamite Entertainment: 2017 - No. 5, 2017 ($3.99, limited series)

1-5-Fred VanLente-s/Bob Q-a; The Octopus app. 4.00

GREEN HORNET: SOLITARY SENTINEL, THE
Now Comics: Dec, 1992 - No. 3, 1993 ($2.50, limited series)

1-3 3.00

GREEN HORNET STRIKES!
Dynamite Entertainment: 2010 - No. 10, 2012 ($3.99, limited series)

1-10: 1-Matthews-s/Padilla-a/Cassaday-c; future Green Hornet 4.00

GREEN HORNET, VOLUME 2
Dynamite Entertainment: 2018 - Present ($3.99)

1-Amy Chu-s/German Erramouspe-a; new female Green Hornet 4.00

GREEN HORNET: YEAR ONE
Dynamite Entertainment: 2010 - No. 12, 2011 ($3.99, limited series)

1-12-Matt Wagner-s/Aaron Campbell-a; 1940s' Green Hornet & Kato. 1-5-Cassaday-c 4.00
...: Special 1 (2013, $4.99) Crosby-s/Menna-a/Chen-c 5.00

GREEN JET COMICS, THE (See Comic Books, Series 1 in the Promotional Comics section)

GREEN LAMA (Also see Comic Books, Series 1, Daring Adventures #17 & Prize Comics #7)
Spark Publications/Prize No. 7 on: Dec, 1944 - No. 8, Mar, 1946

	GD	VG	FN	VF	VF/NM	NM-
1-Intro. Lt. Hercules & The Boy Champions; Mac Raboy-c/a #1-8	135	270	405	864	1482	2100
2-Lt. Hercules borrows the Human Torch's powers for one panel	74	148	222	470	810	1150
3-5,8: 4-Dick Tracy take-off in Lt. Hercules story by H. L. Gold (science fiction writer); Japanese WWII-c; Emperor Hirohito app. 5-Nazi WWII-c; Hitler story; Lt. Hercules story; Little Orphan Annie, Smilin' Jack & Snuffy Smith take-off (5/45)	55	110	165	352	601	850
6-Classic Raboy swastika-c	77	154	231	493	847	1200
7-Christmas-c; Raboy craft tint-c/a (note: a small quantity of NM copies surfaced)	34	68	102	199	325	450

... Archives Featuring the Art of Mac Raboy Vol. 1 HC (Dark Horse Books, 4/08, $49.95) r/#1-4 including back-up features; foreward by Chuck Rozanski 50.00
... Archives Featuring the Art of Mac Raboy Vol. 2 HC (Dark Horse Books, 1/09, $49.95) r/#5-8; foreward by Chuck Rozanski 50.00

NOTE: ***Robinson*** *a-3-5, 8.* ***Roussos*** *a-8. Formerly a pulp hero who began in 1940.*

GREEN LANTERN (1st Series) (See All-American, All Flash Quarterly, All Star Comics, The Big All-American & Comic Cavalcade)
National Periodical Publications/All-American: Fall, 1941 - No. 38, May-June, 1949 (#1-18 are quarterly)

	GD	VG	FN	VF	VF/NM	NM-
1-Origin retold; classic Purcell-c	2775	5550	8325	22,200	40,600	74,000
2-1st book-length story	686	1372	2058	5008	8854	12,700
3-Classic German war-c by Mart Nodell	67	1340	2010	4891	8646	12,400
4-Green Lantern & Doiby Dickles join the Army	400	800	1200	2800	4900	7000
5-WWII-c	326	652	978	2282	3991	5700
6,8: 8-Hop Harrigan begins; classic-c	300	600	900	1920	3310	4700
7-Classic robot-c	303	606	909	2121	3711	5300
9	245	490	735	1568	2684	3800
10-Origin/1st app. Vandal Savage	300	600	900	2010	3505	5000
11,13-15	171	342	513	1086	1868	2650
12-Origin/1st app. Gambler	187	374	561	1197	2049	2900
16-Classic jungle-c (scarce in high grade)	190	380	570	1207	2079	2950
17,19,20	145	290	435	921	1586	2250
18-Christmas-c	190	380	570	1207	2079	2950
21-26	142	284	426	909	1555	2200
27-Origin/1st app. Sky Pirate	174	348	522	1114	1907	2700
28-1st Sportsmaster (Crusher Crock)	161	322	483	1030	1765	2500
29-All Harlequin issue; classic Harlequin-c	219	438	657	1402	2401	3400
30-Origin/1st app. Streak the Wonder Dog by Toth (2-3/48) (Rare)	423	846	1269	3046	5323	7600
31-Harlequin-c/app.	142	284	426	909	1555	2200
32-35: 35-Kubert-c. 35-38-New logo	126	252	378	806	1378	1950
36-38: 37-Sargon the Sorcerer app.	148	296	444	947	1624	2300

NOTE: *Book-length stories #2-7.* ***Mayer/Moldoff*** *c-9.* ***Mayer/Purcell*** *c-8.* ***Purcell*** *c-1.* ***Mart Nodell*** *c-2, 3, 7.* ***Paul***

Green Lantern (2nd series) #42 © DC

Green Lantern (2nd series) #99 © DC

Green Lantern (3rd series) #122 © DC

GD VG FN VF VF/NM NM-
2.0 4.0 6.0 8.0 9.0 9.2

Reinman c-11, 12, 15-22. ***Toth*** *a-28, 30, 31, 34-38; c-28, 30, 34p, 36-38p. Cover to #8 says Fall while the indicia says Summer Issue. Streak the Wonder Dog c-30 (w/Green Lantern), 34, 36, 38.*

GREEN LANTERN (See Action Comics Weekly, Adventure Comics, Brave & the Bold, Day of Judgment, DC Special, DC Special Series, Flash, Guy Gardner, Guy Gardner Reborn, JLA, JSA, Justice League of America, Parallax: Emerald Night, Showcase, Showcase '93 #12 & Tales of The…Corps)

GREEN LANTERN (2nd Series)(Green Lantern Corps #206 on) (See Showcase #22-24)
National Periodical Publ./DC Comics: Jul/Aug. 1960 - No. 89, Apr/May 1972; No. 90, Aug/Sept. 1976 - No. 205, Oct, 1986

1-(7-8/60)-Origin retold; Gil Kane-c/a continues; 1st app. Guardians of the Universe 450 900 1350 4200 10,850 17,500
2-1st Pieface 86 172 258 688 1544 2400
3-Contains readers poll 50 100 150 390 870 1350
4,5: 5-Origin/1st app. Hector Hammond 42 84 126 311 706 1100
6-Intro Tomar-Re the alien G.L. 41 82 123 303 689 1075
7-Origin/1st app. Sinestro (7-8/61) 82 164 246 656 1478 2300
8-1st 5700 A.D. story; grey tone-c 36 72 108 259 580 900
9-1st Sinestro-c; 1st Jordan Brothers; last 10¢-c 35 70 105 252 564 875
10 32 64 96 230 515 800
11,12 21 42 63 147 324 500
13-Flash x-over 32 64 96 230 515 800
14,15,17-20: 14-Origin/1st app. Sonar. 20-Flash x-over 17 34 51 117 259 400
16-Origin & 1st app. (Silver Age) Star Sapphire 36 72 108 266 596 925
21,22,25-28,30: 21-Origin & 1st app. Dr. Polaris 12 24 36 81 176 270
23-1st Tattooed Man 14 28 42 96 211 325
24-Origin & 1st app. Shark 21 42 63 147 324 500
29-JLA cameo; 1st Blackhand 15 30 45 103 227 350
31-39: 37-1st app. Evil Star (villain) 10 20 30 69 147 225
40-Origin of Infinite Earths (10/65); 2nd solo G.A. Green Lantern in Silver Age (see Showcase #55); origin The Guardians; Doiby Dickles app. 46 92 138 335 760 1185
41-44,46-50: 42-Zatanna x-over. 43-Flash x-over 9 18 27 60 120 180
45-2nd S.A. app. G.A. Green Lantern in title (6/66) 13 26 39 91 201 310
51,53-58 8 16 24 51 96 140
52-G.A. Green Lantern x-over; Sinestro app. 10 20 30 67 141 215
59-1st app. Guy Gardner (3/68) 28 56 84 202 451 700
60,62-69: 69-Wood inks; last 12¢ issue 6 12 18 38 69 100
61-G.A. Green Lantern x-over 7 14 21 46 86 125
70-75 5 10 15 34 60 85
76-(4/70)-Begin Green Lantern/Green Arrow series (by Neal Adams #76-89) ends #122 (see Flash #217 for 2nd series) 96 192 288 768 1734 2700
77 11 22 33 76 163 250
78-80 10 20 30 66 138 210
81-84: 82-Wrightson-i(1 pg.). 83-G.L. reveals i.d. to Carol Ferris. 84-N. Adams/Wrightson-a (22 pgs.); last 15¢-c; partial photo-c 9 18 27 59 117 175
85,86-(52 pgs.) Classic anti-drug covers/stories; Speedy as a heroin junkie. 86-G.A. Green Lantern-r; Toth-a 11 22 33 76 163 250
87-(52 pgs.) 1st app. John Stewart (12-1/71-72) (becomes 3rd Green Lantern in #182); 2nd app. Guy Gardner (cameo) 19 38 57 131 291 450
88-(2-3/72, 52 pgs.)-Unpubbed G.A. Green Lantern story; Green Lantern-r/Showcase #23. N. Adams-c/a (1 pg.) 8 16 24 51 96 140
89-(4-5/72, 52 pgs.)-G.A. Green Lantern-r; Green Lantern & Green Arrow move to Flash #217 (2nd team-up series) 8 16 24 56 108 160
90 (8-9/76)-Begin 3rd Green Lantern/Green Arrow team-up series; Mike Grell-c/a begins, ends #111 3 6 9 17 26 35
91-99 2 4 6 10 16 20
100-(1/78, Giant)-1st app. Air Wave II 3 6 9 16 23 30
101-107,111,113-115,117-119: 107-1st Tales of the G.L. Corps story 2 4 6 8 11 14
108-110-(44 pgs)-G.A. Green Lantern back-ups in each. 111-Origin retold; G.A. Green Lantern app. 2 4 6 10 14 18
112-G.A. Green Lantern origin retold 2 4 6 13 18 22
116-1st app. Guy Gardner as a G.L. (5/79) 4 8 12 27 44 60
116-Whitman variant; issue # on cover 5 10 15 31 53 75
117-119,121-(Whitman variants; low print run; none have issue # on cover) 2 4 6 10 14 18
120,121,123-140,142-150: 123-Last Green Lantern/Green Arrow team-up. 130-132-Tales of the G.L. Corps. 132-Adam Strange series begins, ends147. 136,137-1st app. Citadel; Space Ranger app. 142,143-Omega Men app.;Perez-c. 144-Omega Men cameo. 148-Tales of the G.L. Corps begins, ends #173. 150-Anniversary issue, 52 pgs.; no G.L. Corps 1 2 3 5 7 9
122-2nd app. Guy Gardner as Green Lantern; Flash & Hawkman brief app. 3 6 9 14 20 25
141-1st app. Omega Men (6/81) 3 6 9 16 24 32
151-180,183,184,186,187: 159-Origin Evil Star. 160,161-Omega Men app. 172-Gibbons-c/a begins. 175-No issue number shown on cover 6.00
181,182,185,188,191: 181-Hal Jordan resigns as G.L. 182-John Stewart becomes new G.L.; origin recap of Hal Jordan as G.L. 185-Origin new G.L. (John Stewart).188-I.D. revealed; 1st app. Mogo; Alan Moore back-up scripts. 191-Re-intro Star Sapphire (cameo) 1 2 3 5 6 8
189,190,193,196-199,202-205: 194,198-Crisis x-over. 199-Hal Jordan returns as a member of G.L. Corps (3 G.L.s now). 5.00
192-Re-intro & origin of Star Sapphire (1st full app.) 2 4 6 9 13 16
194-Hal Jordan/Guy Gardner battle; Guardians choose Guy Gardner to become new Green Lantern 1 2 3 5 6 8
195-Guy Gardner becomes Green Lantern; Crisis on Infinite Earths x-over 2 4 6 9 13 16
200-Double-size 6.00
201-Green Lantern Corps begins (is cover title, says premiere issue); intro. Kilowog 3 6 9 15 22 28
Annual 1 (Listed as Tales Of The Green Lantern Corps Annual 1)
Annual 2,3 (See Green Lantern Corps Annual #2,3) 5.00
Special 1 (1988), 2 (1989)-(Both $1.50, 52 pgs.) 5.00
... Chronicles TPB (2009, $14.99) r/Showcase #22-24 & Green Lantern #1-3 15.00
... Chronicles Vol. 2 TPB (2009, $14.99) r/Green Lantern #4-9 15.00
... Chronicles Vol. 3 TPB (2010, $14.99) r/Green Lantern #10-14 and Flash #131 15.00

NOTE: ***N. Adams*** *a-76, 77-87p, 89; c-63, 76-89.* ***M. Anderson*** *a-137i.* ***Austin*** *a-93i, 94i, 171i.* ***Chaykin*** *c-196.* ***Greene*** *a-39-49i, 58-63i; c-54-58i.* ***Grell*** *a-90-100, 106, 108-111; c-90-106, 108-112.* ***Heck*** *a-120-122p.* ***Infantino*** *a-137p, 145-147p, 151, 152p.* ***Gil Kane*** *a-1-49p, 50-57, 58-61p, 68-75p, 85p(r), 87p(r), 88p(r), 156, 177, 184p; c-1-52, 54-61p, 67-75, 123, 154, 156, 165-171, 177, 184.* ***Newton*** *a-148p, 149p, 181.* ***Perez*** *c-132p, 141-144.* ***Sekowsky*** *a-65p, 170p.* ***Simonson*** *c-200.* ***Sparling*** *a-63p.* ***Starlin*** *c-129, 133.* ***Staton*** *a-117p, 123-127p, 128, 129-131p, 132-139, 140p, 141-146, 147p, 148-150, 151-155p; c-107p, 117p, 135(i), 136p, 145p, 146, 147, 148-152p, 155p.* ***Toth*** *a-86r, 171p.* ***Tuska*** *a-166-168p, 170p.*

GD VG FN VF VF/NM NM-
2.0 4.0 6.0 8.0 9.0 9.2

GREEN LANTERN (3rd Series)
DC Comics: June, 1990 - No. 181, Nov, 2004 ($1.00/$1.25/$1.50/$1.75/$1.95/$1.99/$2.25)

1-Hal Jordan, John Stewart & Guy Gardner return; Batman & JLA app. 6.00
2-18,20-26: 9-12-Guy Gardner solo story. 13-(52 pgs.). 18-Guy Gardner solo story. 25-($1.75, 52 pgs.)-Hal Jordan/Guy Gardner battle 4.00
19-($1.75, 52 pgs.)-50th anniversary issue; Mart Nodell (original G.A. artist) part-p on G.A. Green Lantern; G. Kane-c 5.00
27-45,47: 30,31-Gorilla Grodd-c/story(see Flash #69). 38,39-Adam Strange-c/story. 42-Deathstroke-c/s. 47-Green Arrow x-over 4.00
46,48,49,50: 46-Superman app. cont'd in Superman #82. 48-Emerald Twilight part 1. 50-($2.95, 52 pgs.)-Glow-in-the-dark-c 6.00
0, 51-62: 51-1st app. New Green Lantern (Kyle Rayner) with new costume. 53-Superman-c/story. 55-(9/94)-Zero Hour. 0-(10/94). 56-(11/94) 4.00
63,64-Kyle Rayner vs. Hal Jordan. 4.00
65-80,82-92: 63-Begin $1.75-c. 65-New Titans app. 66,67-Flash app. 71-Batman & Robin app. 72-Shazam!-c/app. 73-Wonder Woman-c/app. 73-75-Adam Strange app. 76,77-Green Arrow x-over. 80-Final Night. 87-JLA app. 91-Genesis x-over. 92-Green Arrow x-over 3.00
81-(Regular Ed.)-Memorial for Hal Jordan (Parallax); most DC heroes app. 5.00
81-($3.95, Deluxe Edition)-Embossed prism-c 6.00
93-99: 93-Begin $1.95-c; Deadman app. 94-Superboy app. 95-Starlin-a(p). 98,99-Legion of Super-Heroes-c/app. 3.00
100-($2.95) Two covers (Jordan & Rayner); vs. Sinestro 6.00
101-106: 101-106-Hal Jordan-c/app. 103-JLA-c/app. 104-Green Arrow app. 105,106-Parallax app. 3.00
107-126: 107-Jade becomes a Green Lantern. 119-Hal Jordan/Spectre app. 125-JLA app. 3.00
127-149: 127-Begin $2.25-c. 129-Winick-s begin. 134-136-JLA-c/app. 143-Joker: Last Laugh; Lee-c. 145-Kyle becomes The Ion. 149-Superman-c/app. 3.00
150-($3.50) Jim Lee-c; Kyle becomes Green Lantern again; new costume 4.00
151-181: 151-155-Jim Lee-c: 154-Terry attacked. 155-Spectre-c/app. 162-164-Crossover with Green Arrow #23-25. 165-Raab-s begin. 169-Kilowog returns 3.00
#1,000,000 (11/98) 853rd Century x-over; Hitch & Neary-a/c 3.00
Annual 1-3: ('92-'94, 68 pgs.)-1-Eclipso app. 2 -Intro Nightblade. 3-Elseworlds story 4.00
Annual 4 (1995, $3.50)-Year One story 4.00
Annual 5,7,8 ('96, '98, '99, $2.95): 5-Legends of the Dead Earth. 7-Ghosts; Wrightson-c. 8-JLApe; Art Adams-c 4.00
Annual 6 (1997, $3.95)-Pulp Heroes story 5.00
Annual 9 (2000, $3.50) Planet DC 4.00
...80 Page Giant (12/98, $4.95) Stories by various 5.00
...80 Page Giant 2 (6/99, $4.95) Team-ups 5.00
...80 Page Giant 3 (8/00, $5.95) Darkseid vs. the GL Corps 6.00
...: 1001 Emerald Nights (2001, $6.95) Elseworlds; Guay-a/c; LaBan-s 7.00
...3-D #1 (12/98, $3.95) Jeanty-a 4.00
...: A New Dawn TPB (1998, $9.95)-r/#50-55 10.00
...: Baptism of Fire TPB (1999, $12.95)-r/#59,66,67,70-75 13.00
...: Brother's Keeper (2003, $12.95)-r/#151-155; Green Lantern Secret Files #3 13.00
...: Emerald Allies TPB (2000, $14.95)-r/GL/GA team-ups 15.00
...: Emerald Knights TPB (1998, $12.95)-r/Hal Jordan's return 13.00

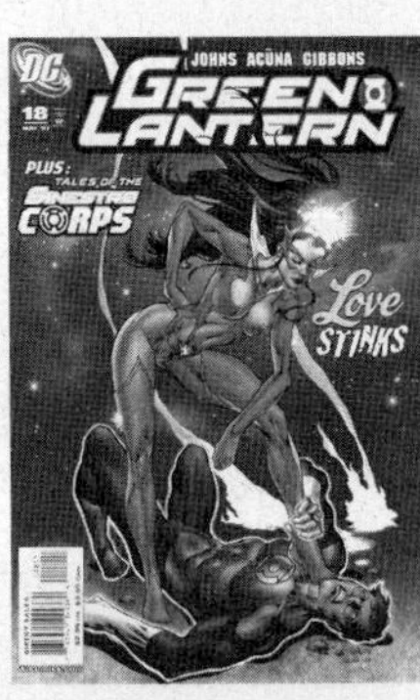

Green Lantern (2005 series) #18 © DC

Green Lantern (2005 series) #60 © DC

Green Lantern: Brightest Day; Blackest Night © DC

GD 2.0 | VG 4.0 | FN 6.0 | VF 8.0 | VF/NM 9.0 | NM- 9.2

GD 2.0 | VG 4.0 | FN 6.0 | VF 8.0 | VF/NM 9.0 | NM- 9.2

...: Emerald Twilight nn (1994, $5.95)-r/#48-50 6.00
...: Emerald Twilight/New Dawn TPB (2003, $19.95)-r/#48-55 20.00
...: Ganthet's Tale nn (1992, $5.95, 68 pgs.)-Silver foil logo; Niven scripts; Byrne-c/a 6.00
.../Green Arrow Vol. 1 (2004, $12.95) -r/GL #76-82; intro. by O'Neil 13.00
.../Green Arrow Vol. 2 (2004, $12.95) -r/GL #83-87,89 & Flash #217-219, 226; cover gallery with 1983-84 GL/GA covers #1-7; intro. by Giordano 13.00
.../Green Arrow Collection, Vol. 2-r/GL #84-87,89 & Flash #217-219 & GL/GA #5-7 by O'Neil/Adams/Wrightson 13.00
...: New Journey, Old Path TPB (2001, $12.95)-r/#129-136 13.00
... : Our Worlds at War (8/01, $2.95) Jae Lee-c; prelude to x-over 3.00
...: Passing The Torch (2004, $12.95, TPB) r/#156,158-161 & GL Secret Files #2 13.00
...Plus 1 (12/1996, $2.95)-The Ray & Polaris-c/app. 4.00
...Secret Files 1-3 (7/98-7/02, $4.95)1-Origin stories & profiles. 2-Grell-c 5.00
.../Superman: Legend of the Green Flame (2000, $5.95) 1988 unpub. Neil Gaiman story of Hal Jordan with new art by various; Frank Miller-c 6.00
...: The Power of Ion (2003, $14.95, TPB) r/#142-150 15.00
...The Road Back nn (1992, $8.95)-r/1-8 w/covers 9.00
...: Traitor TPB (2001, $12.95) r/Legends of the DCU #20,21,28,29,37,38 13.00
...: Willworld (2001, $24.95, HC) Seth Fisher-a/J.M. DeMatteis-s; Hal Jordan 25.00
...: Willworld (2003, $17.95, SC) Seth Fisher-a/J.M. DeMatteis-s; Hal Jordan 18.00
NOTE: ***Staton** a(p)-9-12; c-9-12.*

GREEN LANTERN (See Tangent Comics/ Green Lantern)

GREEN LANTERN (4th Series) (Follows Hal Jordan's return in Green Lantern: Rebirth)
DC Comics: July, 2005 - No. 67, Aug, 2011 ($3.50/$2.99)

1-($3.50) Two covers by Pacheco and Ross; Johns-s/Van Sciver and Pacheco-a 5.00
2-20-($2.99) 2-4-Manhunters app. 6-Bianchi-a. 7,8-Green Arrow app. 8-Bianchi-c. 9-Batman app.; two covers by Bianchi and Van Sciver. 10,11-Reis-a. 17-19-Star Sapphire returns. 18-Acuna-a; Sinestro Corps back-ups begin 3.00
8-Variant-c by Neal Adams 8.00
21-Sinestro Corps War pt. 2 5.00
21-2nd printing with variant green hued background-c 3.00
22-24: 22-Sinestro Corps War pt. 4; green hued-c. 23-Part 6. 24-Part 8 4.00
22,23-2nd printings. 22-Yellow hued-c. 23-B&W Hal Jordan with colored rings 3.00
25-($4.99) Sinestro Corps War conclusion; Ivan Reis-c 6.00
25-($4.99) Variant cover by Gary Frank; Sinestro Corps War conclusion 8.00
26-28,30-43: 26-Alpha Lanterns. 30-35-Childhood & origin re-told; Sinestro app. 41-Origin Larfleeze. 43-Prologue to Blackest Night, origin of Black Hand; Mahnke-a 3.00
29-Childhood & origin re-told 5.00
29-Special Edition (6/10, $1.00) reprints #29 with "What's Next?" logo on cover 3.00
29-Special Edition (2010 San Diego Comic-Con giveaway) reprints #29 with new Van Sciver cover and Geoff Johns intro on inside front cover 3.00
39-43-Variant covers: 39,40-Migliari. 41-42-Barrows 12.00
44-49,51,52-Blackest Night. 44-Flash app. 46-Sinestro vs. Mongul. 47-Black Lantern Abin Sur. 49-Art by Benes & Ordway; Atom and Mera app. 51-Nekron app. 3.00
44-49,51-Variant covers: 44-Tan. 45-Manapul. 46. Andy Kubert. 47-Benes. 48-Morales. 49-Migliari. 51-Horn. 52-Shane Davis 8.00
50-($3.99)-Black Lantern Spectre & Parallax app.; Mahnke-a/c 4.00
50-Variant-c by Jim Lee 12.00
53-67: 53-62-Brightest Day. 54,55-Lobo app. 58-60-Flash app. 60-Krona returns. 64-67-War of the Green Lanterns x-over. 67-Sinestro becomes a Green Lantern 3.00
FCBD 2011 Green Lantern Flashpoint Special Edition (6/11, giveaway) r/#30 and previews Flashpoint x-over; Andy Kubert-a 3.00
...: Larfleeze Christmas Special 1 (2/11, $3.99) Johns-s/Booth-a/Ha-c 4.00
.../Plastic Man: Weapons of Mass Deception (2/11, $4.99) Brent Anderson-a 5.00
...Secret Files and Origins 2005 (6/05, $4.99) Johns-s/Cooke & Van Sciver-a; profiles with art by various incl. Chaykin, Gibbons, Gleason, Igle; Pacheco-c 5.00
.../Sinestro Corps: Secret Files 1 (2/08, $4.99) Profiles of Green Lanterns and Corps info 5.00
...: Agent Orange HC (2009, $19.99) r/#38-42 & Blackest Night #0; sketch art 20.00
...: Agent Orange SC (2010, $14.99) r/#38-42 & Blackest Night #0; sketch art 15.00
Blackest Night: Green Lantern HC (2010, $24.99) r/#43-52; variant covers; sketch art 25.00
Blackest Night: Green Lantern SC (2011, $19.99) r/#43-52; variant covers; sketch art 20.00
...: Brightest Day HC (2011, $22.99) r/#53-62; variant cover gallery 23.00
...: In Brightest Day SC (2008, $19.99) r/stories selected by Geoff Johns w/commentary 20.00
...: No Fear HC (2006, $24.99) r/#1-6 & Secret Files and Origins 25.00
...: No Fear SC (2008, $12.99) r/#1-6 & Secret Files and Origins 13.00
...: Rage of the Red Lanterns HC (2009, $24.99) r/#26-28,36-38 & Final Crisis: Rage... 25.00
...: Rage of the Red Lanterns SC (2010, $14.99) r/#26-28,36-38 & Final Crisis: Rage... 15.00
...: Revenge of the Green Lanterns HC (2006, $19.99) r/#7-13; variant cover gallery 20.00
...: Revenge of the Green Lanterns SC (2008, $12.99) r/#7-13; variant cover gallery 13.00
...: Secret Origin HC (2008, $19.99) r/#29-35 20.00
...: Secret Origin (New Edition) HC (2010, $19.99) r/#29-35; intro. by Ryan Reynolds 20.00
...: Secret Origin SC (2008, $14.99) r/#29-35 15.00
...: Secret Origin (New Edition) SC (2011, $14.99) r/#29-35; intro. by Ryan Reynolds; photo-c of Reynolds from movie; movie preview photo gallery 15.00
... Super Spectacular (1/12, $7.99, magazine-size) r/Blackest Night #0,1, Green Lantern #76 from 1970 and Brave and the Bold #30 from 2009 8.00
...: Tales of the Sinestro Corps HC (2008, $29.99, d.j.) r/back-up stories from #18-20, Tales of the Sinestro Corps series, Green Lantern: Sinestro Corps Special and Sinestro Corps: Secret Files 30.00
...: Tales of the Sinestro Corps SC (2009, $14.99) same contents as HC 15.00
...: The Sinestro Corps War Vol. 1 HC (2008, $24.99, d.j.) r/#21-23, Green Lantern Corps #14-15 and Green Lantern: Sinestro Corps Special 25.00
...: The Sinestro Corps War Vol. 1 SC (2009, $14.99) same contents as HC 15.00
...: The Sinestro Corps War Vol. 2 HC (2008, $24.99, d.j.) r/#24,25, Green Lantern Corps #16-19; interview with the creators and sketch art 25.00
... - Wanted: Hal Jordan HC (2007, $19.99) r/#14-20 without Sinestro Corps back-ups 20.00
... - Wanted: Hal Jordan SC (2008, $14.99) r/#14-20 without Sinestro Corps back-ups 15.00

GREEN LANTERN (DC New 52)
DC Comics: Nov, 2011 - No. 52, Jul, 2016 ($2.99/$3.99)

1-19: 1-Sinestro as Green Lantern; Johns-s/Mahnke-a/Reis-c (1st & 2nd print). 6-Choi-a. 9-Origin of the Indigo tribe. 14-Justice League app. 17-19-Wrath of the First Lantern 3.00
1-9-Variant-c. 1-Capullo. 2-Finch. 3-Van Sciver. 4-Manapul. 5-Choi. 6-Reis. 8-Keown 4.00
8-Combo pack ($3.99) polybagged with digital code 4.00
20-($7.99, squarebound) Conclusion of "Wrath of the First Lantern"; last Johns-s 8.00
21-23: 21-Venditti-s/Tan-a begin 3.00
23.1, 23.2, 23.3, 23.4 (11/13, $2.99, regular covers) 3.00
23.1 (11/13, $3.99, 3-D cover) "Relic #1" on cover; origin of Relic; Morales-a 6.00
23.2 (11/13, $3.99, 3-D cover) "Mongul #1" on cover; origin; Starlin-s/Porter-a 5.00
23.3 (11/13, $3.99, 3-D cover) "Black Hand #1" on cover; Soule-s/Ponticelli-a 5.00
23.4 (11/13, $3.99, 3-D cover) "Sinestro #1" on cover; origin; Kindt-s/Eaglesham-a 5.00
24-27,29-34: 24-Lights Out pt. 1; Relic app.; Central Battery destroyed 3.00
28-Flip-book with Red Lanterns #28; Red Lantern Supergirl app. 3.00
35-40: 35-37-Godhead x-over; New Gods, Orion & Metron app. 36,37-Black Hand app. 3.00
41-49,51,52-($3.99) 42,43,45,46-Black Hand app. 43-Relic returns. 47-Parallax app. 4.00
50-($4.99) Parallax app.; Sienkiewicz-c 5.00
#0 (11/12, $2.99) Simon Baz becomes a Green Lantern; Mahnke-a 3.00
Annual 1 (10/12, $4.99) 1st print w/black-c; Rise of the Third Army prologue 5.00
Annual 2 (12/13, $4.99) Lights Out pt. 5; Sean Chen-a 5.00
Annual 3 (2/15, $4.99) Godhead conclusion; Van Sciver-c 5.00
Annual 4 (11/15, $4.99) Venditti-s/Alixe-a 5.00
...: Futures End 1 (11/14, $2.99, regular-c) Five years later; Relic app. 3.00
...: Futures End 1 (11/14, $3.99, 3-D cover) 4.00
.../New Gods: Godhead 1 (12/14, $4.99) Part 1 to Godhead x-over; Highfather app. 5.00

GREEN LANTERN ANNUAL NO. 1, 1963
DC Comics: 1998 ($4.95, one-shot)

1-Reprints Golden Age & Silver Age stories in 1963-style 80 pg. Giant format; new Gil Kane sketch art 5.00

GREEN LANTERN: BRIGHTEST DAY; BLACKEST NIGHT
DC Comics: 2002 ($5.95, squarebound, one-shot)

nn-Alan Scott vs. Solomon Grundy in 1944; Snyder III-c/a; Seagle-s 1 2 3 5 6 8

GREEN LANTERN: CIRCLE OF FIRE
DC Comics: Early Oct, 2000 - No. 2, Late Oct, 2000 (limited series)

1-($4.95) Intro. other Green Lanterns 5.00
2-($3.75) 4.00
Green Lantern (x-overs)- .../Adam Strange; .../Atom; .../Firestorm; ... /Green Lantern, Winick-s; .../Power Girl (all $2.50-c) 3.00
TPB (2002, $17.95) r/#1,2 & x-overs 18.00

GREEN LANTERN CORPS, THE (Formerly Green Lantern; see Tales of...)
DC Comics: No. 206, Nov, 1986 - No. 224, May, 1988

206-223: 212-John Stewart marries Katma Tui. 220,221-Millennium tie-ins 4.00
224-Double-size last issue 5.00
...Corps Annual 2,3- (12/86,8/87) 1-Formerly Tales of ...Annual #1; Alan Moore scripts. 3-Indicia says Green Lantern Annual #3; Moore scripts; Byrne-a 5.00
NOTE: ***Austin** a-Annual 3i. **Gil Kane** a-223, 224p; c-223, 224, Annual 2. **Russell** a-Annual 3i. **Staton** a-207-213p, 217p, 221p, 222p, Annual 3; c-207-213p, 217p, 221p, 222p. **Willingham** a-213p, 219p, 220p, 218p, 219p, Annual 2, 3p; c-218p, 219p.*

GREEN LANTERN CORPS
DC Comics: Aug, 2006 - No. 63, Oct, 2011 ($2.99)

1,14-19: 1-Gibbons-s. 14-19-Sinestro Corps War pts. 3,5,7,9,10, Epilogue 4.00
2-13: 2-6,10,11-Gibbons-s. 9-Darkseid app. 3.00
20-38: 20-Mongul app. 3.00
20-Second printing with sketch-c 3.00
34-38: 34-37-Variant covers by Migliari. 38-Fabry var-c 10.00
39-45-Blackest Night. 43-45-Red Lantern Guy Gardner 3.00

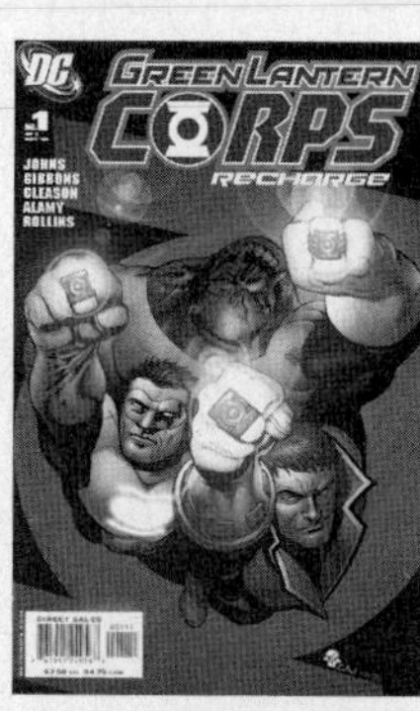

Green Lantern Corps: Recharge #1 © DC

Green Lantern: Rebirth #1 © DC

Green Lantern: The Animated Series #0 © DC

	GD	VG	FN	VF	VF/NM	NM-
	2.0	4.0	6.0	8.0	9.0	9.2

39-45-Variant covers: 39-Jusko. 40-Tucci. 41,42,44-Horn. 43-Ladronn. 45 Bolland 8.00
46,47-($3.99) 46-Blackest Night. 47-Brightest Day 4.00
48-61-($2.99) 48-Migliari-c; Ganthet joins the Corps. 49-52-Cyborg Superman app. 58-60-War of the Green Lanterns x-over. 60-Mogo destroyed 3.00
Blackest Night: Green Lantern Corps HC (2010, $24.99, d.j.) r/#39-47, cover gallery 25.00
Blackest Night: Green Lantern Corps SC (2011, $19.99) r/#39-47, cover gallery 20.00
...: Emerald Eclipse HC (2009, $24.99) r/#33-39; gallery of variant covers 25.00
...: Emerald Eclipse SC (2010, $14.99) r/#33-39; gallery of variant covers 15.00
...: Revolt of the Alpha-Lanterns HC (2011, $22.99) r/#21,22,48-52 23.00
...: Ring Quest TPB (2008, $14.99) r/#19,20,23-26 15.00
...: The Dark Side of Green TPB (2007, $12.99) r/#7-13 13.00
...: To Be a Lantern TPB (2007, $12.99) r/#1-6 13.00

GREEN LANTERN CORPS (DC New 52)
DC Comics: Nov, 2011 - No. 40, May, 2015 ($2.99)

1-23: 1-Tomasi-s/Pasarin-a/Mahnke-c; John Stewart & Guy Gardner. 4-6-Andy Kubert-c 3.00
24-39: 24-Lights Out pt. 2; Oa destroyed. 25-Year Zero. 35-37-Godhead x-over 3.00
40-($3.99) Chang-a 4.00
#0 (11/12, $2.99) Origin of Guy Gardner; Tomasi-s/Pasarin-a 3.00
Annual 1 (3/13, $4.99) Rise of the Third Army conclusion; Mogo returns 5.00
Annual 2 (3/14, $4.99) Villains United; Evil Star, Bolphunga, Kanjar Ro app. 5.00
...: Futures End 1 (11/14, $2.99, regular-c) Five years later; Indigo Tribe app. 3.00
...: Futures End 1 (11/14, $3.99, 3-D cover) 4.00

GREEN LANTERN CORPS: EDGE OF OBLIVION
DC Comics: Mar, 2016 - No. 6, Aug, 2016 ($2.99, limited series)

1-6: 1-3-Taylor-s/Van Sciver-a. 4,5-Syaf-a 3.00

GREEN LANTERN CORPS QUARTERLY
DC Comics: Summer, 1992 - No. 8, Spring, 1994 ($2.50/$2.95, 68 pgs.)

1-G.A. Green Lantern story; Staton-a(p) 5.00
2-8: 2-G.A. G.L.-c/story; Austin-c(i); Gulacy-a(p). 3-G.A. G.L. story. 4-Austin-i. 7-Painted-c; Tim Vigil-a. 8-Lobo-c/s 4.00

GREEN LANTERN CORPS: RECHARGE
DC Comics: Nov, 2005 - No. 5, Mar, 2006 ($3.50/$2.99, limited series)

1-($3.50) Kyle Rayner, Guy Gardner & Kilowog app.; Gleason-a 4.00
2-5-($2.99) 3.00
TPB (2006, $12.99) r/series 13.00

GREEN LANTERN: DRAGON LORD
DC Comics: 2001 - No. 3, 2001 ($4.95, squarebound, limited series)

1-3: A G.L. in ancient China; Moench-s/Gulacy-c/a 5.00

GREEN LANTERN: EMERALD DAWN (Also see Emerald Dawn)
DC Comics: Dec, 1989 - No. 6, May, 1990 ($1.00, limited series)

1-Origin retold; Giffen plots in all 6.00
2-6: 4-Re-intro. Tomar-Re 4.00

GREEN LANTERN: EMERALD DAWN II (Emerald Dawn II #1 & 2)
DC Comics: Apr, 1991 - No. 6, Sept, 1991 ($1.00, limited series)

1-6 3.00
TPB (2003, $12.95) r/#1-6; Alan Davis-c 13.00

GREEN LANTERN: EMERALD WARRIORS
DC Comics: Oct, 2010 - No. 13, Oct, 2011 ($3.99/$2.99)

1-5-($3.99) Guy Gardner's exploits; Migliari-c. 1-Bermejo variant-c. 2-5-Massaferra var-c 4.00
6-13-($2.99) 6,7-Covers by Migliari & Massaferra. 8-10-War of the Green Lanterns x-over 3.00

GREEN LANTERN: EVIL'S MIGHT (Elseworlds)
DC Comics: 2002 - No. 3 ($5.95, squarebound, limited series)

1-3-Kyle Rayner in 19th century NYC; Rogers-a; Chaykin & Tischman-s 6.00

GREEN LANTERN: FEAR ITSELF
DC Comics: 1999 (Graphic novel)

Hardcover ($24.95) Ron Marz-s/Brad Parker painted-a 25.00
Softcover ($14.95) 15.00

GREEN LANTERN/FLASH: FASTER FRIENDS (See Flash/Green Lantern...)
DC Comics: 1997 ($4.95, limited series)

1-Marz-s 5.00

GREEN LANTERN GALLERY
DC Comics: Dec, 1996 ($3.50, one-shot)

1-Wraparound-c; pin-ups by various 3.50

GREEN LANTERN/GREEN ARROW (Also see The Flash #217)
DC Comics: Oct, 1983 - No. 7, April, 1984 (52-60 pgs.)

1-7- r-Green Lantern #76-89 1 3 4 6 8 10

NOTE: ***Neal Adams** r-1-7; c-1-4. **Wrightson** r-4, 5.*

GREEN LANTERN • LEGACY: THE LAST WILL & TESTAMENT OF HAL JORDAN
DC Comics: 2002 ($24.95, hardcover graphic novel)

Hardcover-Anderson & Sienkiewicz-a/c; Kelly-s; Return of Oa 25.00
Softcover (2004, $17.95) 18.00

GREEN LANTERN: LOST ARMY
DC Comics: Aug, 2015 - No. 6, Jan, 2016 ($2.99)

1-6: 1-Bunn-s/Saiz-a; featuring John Stewart, Guy Gardner, Kilowog, Arisia, Krona 3.00

GREEN LANTERN: MOSAIC (Also see Cosmic Odyssey #2)
DC Comics: June, 1992 - No. 18, Nov, 1993 ($1.25)

1-18: Featuring John Stewart. 1-Painted-c by Cully Hamner 3.00

GREEN LANTERN MOVIE PREQUEL (2011 movie)
DC Comics: July, 2011; Oct, 2011 ($2.99, one-shots)

...: Abin Sur 1 - Green-s/Gleason-a; movie photo-c 3.00
...: Hal Jordan 1 - Johns & Berlanti-s/Ordway-a; movie photo-c; Sinestro & Tomar-Re app. 3.00
...: Kilowog 1 - Tomasi-s/Ferreira-a; movie photo-c 3.00
...: Sinestro 1 (10/11) - Johns-s/Tolibao, Richards & Ordway-a; movie photo-c 3.00
...: Tomar-Re 1 - Guggenheim-s/Richards-a; movie photo-c 3.00

GREEN LANTERN: NEW GUARDIANS (DC New 52)
DC Comics: Nov, 2011 - No. 40, May, 2015 ($2.99)

1-Bedard-s/Kirkham-a/c; Kyle origin flashback; Fatality app. 6.00
2-23: 13-16-Third Army. 21-Relic freed. 22,23-Kyle vs. Relic. 23-Blue Lanterns destroyed 3.00
24-34: 24-Lights Out pt. 3. 3.00
35-39: 35-37-Godhead x-over; Highfather app. 38,39-Oblivion returns 3.00
40-($3.99) Oblivion app.; the start of the White Lantern Corps 4.00
#0 (11/12, $2.99) Bedard-s/Kuder-a; Zamarons app. 3.00
Annual 1 (3/13, $4.99) Giffen-s/Kolins-a/c 5.00
Annual 2 (6/14, $4.99) Segovia-a; takes place between #30 & #31 5.00
...: Futures End 1 (11/14, $2.99, regular-c) Five years later; intro. Saysoran 3.00
...: Futures End 1 (11/14, $3.99, 3-D cover) 4.00

GREEN LANTERN: REBIRTH
DC Comics: Dec, 2004 - No. 6, May, 2005 ($2.95, limited series)

1-Johns-s/Van Sciver-a; Hal Jordan as The Spectre on-c 8.00
1-2nd printing; Hal Jordan as Green Lantern on-c 4.00
1-3rd printing; B&W-c version of 1st printing 3.00
1 Special Edition (9/09, $1.00) r/#1 with "After Watchmen" cover frame 3.00
2-Guy Gardner becomes a Green Lantern again; JLA app. 5.00
2-2nd & 3rd printings 3.00
3-6: 3-Sinestro returns. 4-6-JLA & JSA app. 3.00
HC (2005, $24.99, dust jacket) r/series & Wizard preview; intro. by Brad Meltzer 25.00
SC (2007, 2010, $14.99) r/series & Wizard preview; intro. by Brad Meltzer 15.00

GREEN LANTERNS (DC Rebirth) (Also see Hal Jordan and the Green Lantern Corps)
DC Comics: Aug, 2016 - Present ($2.99)

1-24: 1-Simon Baz and Jessica Cruz team up; Humphries-s/Rocha-a. 6-1st app. the Phantom Ring. 8-Dominators app.; Benes-a. 9-14-Phantom Lantern. 16,17-Batman app. 3.00
25-($3.99) Lanterns vs. Volthoom; Rocha-a 4.00
26-42: 28-31-The Ancient Lanterns app. 35-Intro. Singularity Jain. 35,36-Bolphunga app. 3.00
...: Rebirth 1 (8/16, $2.99) Van Sciver & Benes-a; Hal Jordan & Atrocitus app. 3.00

GREEN LANTERN/SENTINEL: HEART OF DARKNESS
DC Comics: Mar, 1998 - No. 3, May, 1998 ($1.95, limited series)

1-3-Marz-s/Pelletier-a 3.00

GREEN LANTERN/SILVER SURFER: UNHOLY ALLIANCES
DC Comics: 1995 ($4.95, one-shot)(Prelude to DC Versus Marvel)

nn-Hal Jordan app. 6.00

GREEN LANTERN SINESTRO CORPS SPECIAL (Continues in Green Lantern #21)
DC Comics: Aug, 2007 ($4.99, one-shot)

1-Kyle Rayner becomes Parallax; Cyborg Superman & Earth-Prime Superboy app.; Johns-s; Van Sciver-a/c; back-up story origin of Sinestro; Gibbons-a; Sinestro on cover 8.00
1-(2nd printing) Kyle Rayner as Parallax on cover 6.00
1-(3rd printing) Sinestro cover with muted colors 5.00

GREEN LANTERN/ SPACE GHOST SPECIAL
DC Comics: May, 2017 ($4.99, one-shot)

1-Tynion IV-s/Olivetti-a/c; back-up Ruff 'n' Ready re-intro. by Chaykin-s/a 5.00

GREEN LANTERN: THE ANIMATED SERIES (Based on the Cartoon Network series)
DC Comics: No. 0, Jan, 2012 - No. 14, Sept, 2013 ($2.99)

0-14: 0-Baltazar & Franco-s/Brizuela-a; Kilowog and Red Lanterns app. 13-Lobo app. 3.00

Green Mask #1 © FOX

Green Valley #7 © Skybound

Grendel: War Child #1 © Matt Wagner

	GD 2.0	VG 4.0	FN 6.0	VF 8.0	VF/NM 9.0	NM- 9.2

GREEN LANTERN: THE GREATEST STORIES EVER TOLD
DC Comics: 2006 ($19.99, TPB)
SC-Reprints Showcase #22; G.L. #1,31,74,87,172; ('90 series) #3, and others; Ross-c 20.00

GREEN LANTERN: THE NEW CORPS
DC Comics: 1999 - No. 2, 1999 ($4.95, limited series)
1,2-Kyle recruits new GLs; Eaton-a 5.00

GREEN LANTERN VS. ALIENS
Dark Horse Comics: Sept, 2000 - No. 4, Dec, 2000 ($2.95, limited series)
1-4: 1-Hal Jordan and GL Corps vs. Aliens; Leonardi-p. 2-4-Kyle Rayner 3.00

GREEN MASK, THE (See Mystery Men)
Summer, 1940 - No. 9, 2/42; No. 10, 8/44 - No. 11, 11/44;
Fox Feature Syndicate: V2#1, Spring, 1945 - No. 6, 10-11/46

	GD	VG	FN	VF	VF/NM	NM-
V1#1-Origin The Green Mask & Domino; reprints/Mystery Men #1-3,5-7; Lou Fine-c	300	600	900	1950	3375	4800
2-Zanzibar The Magician by Tuska	116	232	348	742	1271	1800
3-Powell-a; Marijuana story	87	174	261	553	952	1350
4-Navy Jones begins, ends #6	69	138	207	442	759	1075
5	57	114	171	362	619	875
6-The Nightbird begins, ends #9; Good Girl bondage/torture-c	116	232	348	742	1271	1800
7,9: 9(2/42)-Becomes The Bouncer #10(nn) on? & Green Mask #10 on	41	82	123	256	428	600
8-Classic Good Girl torture/bondage-c	129	258	387	826	1413	2000
10,11: 10-Origin One Round Hogan & Rocket Kelly	34	68	102	199	325	450
V2#1	25	50	75	150	245	340
2-6	20	40	60	118	192	265

GREEN PLANET, THE
Charlton Comics: 1962 (one-shot) (12¢)

	GD	VG	FN	VF	VF/NM	NM-
nn-Giordano-c; sci-fi	8	16	24	54	102	150

GREEN TEAM (See Cancelled Comic Cavalcade & 1st Issue Special)

GREEN TEAM: TEEN TRILLIONAIRES
DC Comics: Jul, 2013 - No. 8, Mar, 2014 ($2.99)
1-8-Baltazar & Franco-s/Guara-a. 1-3-Conner-c. 3-Deathstroke app. 8-Teen Titans app. 3.00
1-Variant-c by Chiang 3.00

GREEN VALLEY
Image Comics (Skybound): Oct, 2016 - No. 9, Jun, 2017 ($2.99/$3.99)
1-8-Max Landis-s/Giuseppe Camuncoli-a 3.00
9-($3.99) 4.00

GREEN WOMAN, THE
DC Comics (Vertigo): 2010 ($24.99, HC graphic novel)
HC-John Bolton-a/Peter Straub & Michael Easton-s 25.00

GREETINGS FROM SANTA (See March of Comics No. 48)

GRENDEL (Also see Primer #2, Mage and Comico Collection)
Comico: Mar, 1983 - No. 3, Feb, 1984 ($1.50, B&W)(#1 has indicia to Skrog #1)

	GD	VG	FN	VF	VF/NM	NM-
1-Origin Hunter Rose	9	18	27	62	126	190
2,3: 2-Origin Argent	7	14	21	46	86	125

GRENDEL
Comico: Oct, 1986 - No. 40, Feb, 1990 ($1.50/$1.95/$2.50, mature)

	GD	VG	FN	VF	VF/NM	NM-
1	1	2	3	5	7	9
1,2: 2nd printings						3.00
2,3,5-15: 13-15-Ken Steacy-c.						4.00
4,16: 4-Dave Stevens-c(i). 16-Re-intro Mage (series begins, ends #19)						6.00
17-40: 24-25,27-28,30-31-Snyder-c/a						3.00
Devil by the Deed (Graphic Novel, 10/86, $5.95, 52 pgs.)-r/Grendel back-ups/ Mage 6-14; Alan Moore intro.	1	3	4	6	8	10
Devil's Legacy ($14.95, 1988, Graphic Novel)	2	4	6	9	12	15
Devil's Vagary (10/87, B&W & red)-No price; included in Comico Collection	2	4	6	8	10	12

GRENDEL (Title series): **Dark Horse Comics**

--ARCHIVES, 5/07 ($14.95, HC) r/1st apps. in Primer #2 and Grendel #1-3; Wagner intro. 15.00

--BEHOLD THE DEVIL, No. 0, 7/07 - No. 8, 6/08 ($3.50/50¢, B&W&Red)
0-(50¢-c) Prelude to series; Matt Wagner-s/a; interview with Wagner 3.00
1-8-Matt Wagner-s/a/c in all 3.50

--BLACK, WHITE, AND RED, 11/98 - No. 4, 2/99 ($3.95, anthology)
1-Wagner-s in all. Art by Sale, Leon and others 5.00
2-4: 2-Mack, Chadwick-a. 3-Allred, Kristensen-a. 4-Pearson, Sprouse-a 4.00

--CLASSICS, 7/95 - 8/95 ($3.95, mature) 1,2-reprints; new Wagner-c 4.00

--CYCLE, 10/95 ($5.95) 1-nn-history of Grendel by M. Wagner & others 6.00

--DEVIL BY THE DEED, 7/93 ($3.95, varnish-c) 1-nn-M. Wagner-c/a/scripts; r/Grendel back-ups from Mage #6-14 6.00
Reprint (12/97, $3.95) w/pin-ups by various 4.00
Hardcover (2007, $12.95) reprint recolored to B&W&red; includes covers and intros from previously reprinted editions 13.00

--DEVIL CHILD, 6/99 - No. 2, 7/99 ($2.95, mature) 1,2-Sale & Kristiansen-a/Schutz-s 3.00

--DEVIL QUEST, 11/95 ($4.95) 1-nn-Prequel to Batman/Grendel II; M. Wagner story & art; r/back-up story from Grendel Tales series. 5.00

--DEVILS AND DEATHS, 10/94 - 11/94 ($2.95, mature) 1,2 3.00

: DEVIL'S LEGACY, 3/00 - No. 12, 2/01 ($2.95, reprints 1986 series, recolored)
1-12-Wagner-s/c; Pander Bros.-a 3.00

: DEVIL'S REIGN, 5/04 - No. 7, 12/04 ($3.50, repr. 1989 series #34-40, recolored)
1-7-Sale-c/a. 3.50

: GOD AND THE DEVIL, No. 0, 1/03 - No. 10, 12/03 ($3.50/$4.99, repr. 1986 series, recolored)
0-9: 0-Sale-c/a; r/#23. 1-9-Snyder-c 3.50
10-($4.99) Double-sized; Snyder-c 5.00

--RED, WHITE & BLACK, 9/02 - No. 4, 12/02 ($4.99, anthology)
1-4-Wagner-s in all. 1-Art by Thompson, Sakai, Mahfood and others. 2-Kelley Jones, Watson, Brereton, Hester & Parks-a. 3-Oeming, Noto, Cannon, Ashley Wood, Huddleston-a 4-Chiang, Dalrymple, Robertson, Snyder III and Zulli-a 5.00
TPB (2005, $19.95) r/#1-4; cover gallery, artist bios 20.00

--TALES: DEVIL'S CHOICES, 3/95 - 6/95 ($2.95, mature) 1-4 3.00

--TALES: FOUR DEVILS, ONE HELL, 8/93 - 1/94 ($2.95, mature)
1-6-Wagner painted-c 3.00
TPB (12/94, $17.95) r/#1-6 18.00

--TALES: HOMECOMING, 12/94 - 2/95 ($2.95, mature) 1-3 3.00

--TALES: THE DEVIL IN OUR MIDST, 5/94 - 9/95 ($2.95, mature) 1-5-Wagner painted-c 3.00

--TALES: THE DEVIL MAY CARE, 12/95 - No. 6, 5/96 ($2.95, mature)
1-6-Terry LaBan scripts. 5-Batman/Grendel II preview 3.00

--TALES: THE DEVIL'S APPRENTICE, 9/97 - No. 3, 11/97 ($2.95, mature)
1-3 3.00

--TALES: THE DEVIL'S HAMMER, 2/94 - No. 3, 4/94 ($2.95, mature)
1-3-Rob Walton-s/a; back-up stories by Wagner 3.00

: THE DEVIL INSIDE, 9/01 - No. 3, 11/01 ($2.99)
1-3-r/#13-15 with new Wagner-c 3.00

VS. THE SHADOW, 9/14 - No. 3, 11/14 ($5.99, squarebound)
Matt Wagner-s/a/c; Grendel time-travels to The Shadow's era 6.00

: WAR CHILD, 8/92 - No. 10, 6/93 ($2.50, lim. series, mature)
1-9: 1-4-Bisley painted-c; Wagner-i & scripts in all 3.00
10-($3.50, 52 pgs.) Wagner-c 4.00
Limited Edition Hardcover ($99.95) 100.00

GREYFRIARS BOBBY (Disney)(Movie)
Dell Publishing Co.: No. 1189, Nov, 1961 (one-shot)

	GD	VG	FN	VF	VF/NM	NM-
Four Color 1189-Photo-c	6	12	18	41	76	110

GREYLORE
Sirius: 12/85 - No. 5, Sept, 1986 ($1.50/$1.75, high quality paper)
1-5: Bo Hampton-a in all 3.00

GREYSHIRT: INDIGO SUNSET (Also see Tomorrow Stories)
America's Best Comics: Dec, 2001 - No. 6, Aug, 2002 ($3.50, limited series)
1-6-Veitch-s/a. 4-Back-up w/John Severin-a. 6-Cho-a 3.50
TPB (2002, $19.95) r/#1-6; preface by Alan Moore 20.00

GRIDIRON GIANTS
Ultimate Sports Ent.: 2000 - No. 2 ($3.95, cardstock covers)
1,2-NFL players Sanders, Marino, Plummer, T. Davis battle evil 4.00

GRIFFIN, THE
DC Comics: 1991 - No. 6, 1991 ($4.95, limited series, 52 pgs.)
Book 1-6: Matt Wagner painted-c 5.00

GRIFTER (Also see Team 7 & WildC.A.T.S)
Image Comics (WildStorm Prod.): May, 1995 - No. 10, Mar, 1996 ($1.95)
1 ($1.95, Newsstand)-WildStorm Rising Pt. 5 3.00
1-10:1 ($2.50, Direct)-WildStorm Rising Pt. 5, bound-in trading card 3.00

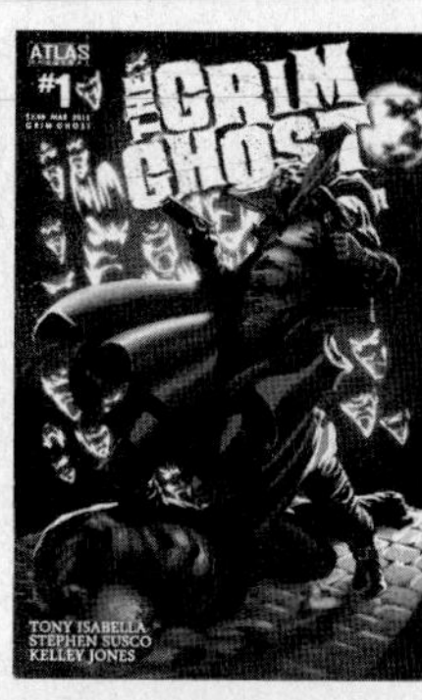

Grim Ghost (2011 series) #1 © Nemesis

Grimm Fairy Tales #123 © Zenescope

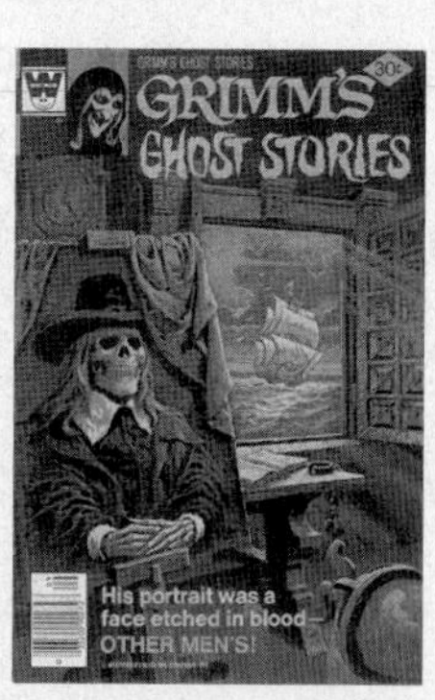

Grimm's Ghost Stories #40 © GK

...: One Shot (1/95, $4.95) Flip-c 5.00

GRIFTER
Image Comics (WildStorm Prod.): V2#1, July, 1996 - No. 14, Aug, 1997 ($2.50)

V2#1-14: Steven Grant scripts 3.00

GRIFTER (DC New 52)
DC Comics: Nov, 2011 - No. 16, Mar, 2013 ($2.99)

1-16: 1-Grifter in the new DC universe; Edmonson-s/Cafu-a/c. 4-Green Arrow app. 3.00
#0 (11/12, $2.99) Liefeld-s/c; Clark-a 3.00

GRIFTER & MIDNIGHTER
DC Comics (WildStorm Prod.): May, 2007 - No. 6, Oct, 2007 ($2.99, limited series)

1-6-Dixon-s/Benjamin-a/c. 1,3-The Authority app. 3.00
TPB (2008, $17.99) r/#1-6 18.00

GRIFTER AND THE MASK
Dark Horse Comics: Sept, 1996 - No. 2, Oct, 1996 ($2.50, limited series)
(1st Dark Horse Comics/Image x-over)

1,2: Steve Seagle scripts 3.00

GRIFTER/BADROCK (Also see WildC.A.T.S & Youngblood)
Image Comics (Extreme Studios): Oct, 1995 - No.2, Nov, 1995 ($2.50, unfinished lim. series)

1,2: 2-Flip book w/Badrock #2 3.00

GRIFTER/SHI
Image Comics (WildStorm Productions): Apr, 1996 - No. 2, May, 1996 ($2.95, limited series)

1,2: 1-Jim Lee-c/a(p); Travis Charest-a(p). 2-Billy Tucci-c/a(p); Travis Charest-a(p) 3.00

GRIM GHOST, THE
Atlas/Seaboard Publ.: Jan, 1975 - No. 3, July, 1975

1-3: Fleisher-s in all. 1-Origin. 2-Son of Satan; Colan-a. 3-Heath-c
2 4 6 13 18 22

GRIM GHOST
Ardden Entertainment (Atlas Comics): Mar, 2011 - No. 5 ($2.99)

1-5-Isabella & Susco-s/Kelley Jones-a. 1-Re-intro. Matthew Dunsinane 3.00
... Issue Zero - NY Comicon Edtion (10/10, $2.99) Qing Ping Mui-a; prequel to #1 3.00

GRIMJACK (Also see Demon Knight & Starslayer)
First Comics: Aug, 1984 - No. 81, Apr, 1991 ($1.00/$1.95/$2.25)

1-John Ostrander scripts & Tim Truman-c/a begins. 5.00
2-25: 20-Sutton-c/a begins. 22-Bolland-a. 3.00
26-2nd color Teenage Mutant Ninja Turtles 6.00
27-74,76-81 (Later issues $1.95, $2.25): 30-Dynamo Joe x-over; 31-Mandrake-c/a begins. 73,74-Kelley Jones-a 3.00
75-($5.95, 52 pgs.)-Fold-out map; coated stock 6.00
The Legend of Grimjack Vol. 1 (IDW Publishing, 2004, $19.99) r/Starslayer #10-18; 8 new pages & art 20.00
The Legend of Grimjack Vol. 2 (IDW, 2005, $19.99) r/#1-7; unpublished art 20.00
The Legend of Grimjack Vol. 3 (IDW, 2005, $19.99) r/#8-14; cover gallery 20.00
The Legend of Grimjack Vol. 4 (IDW, 2005, $24.99) r/#15-21; cover gallery 25.00
The Legend of Grimjack Vol. 5 (IDW, 5/06, $24.99) r/#22-30; cover gallery 25.00
The Legend of Grimjack Vol. 6 (IDW, 1/07, $24.99) r/#31-37; cover gallery 25.00
The Legend of Grimjack Vol. 7 (IDW, 4/07, $24.99) r/#38-46; covers; "Rough Trade" 25.00
NOTE: *Truman c/a-1-17.*

GRIMJACK CASEFILES
First Comics: Nov, 1990 - No. 5, Mar, 1991 ($1.95, limited series)

1-5 Reprints 1st stories from Starslayer #10 on 3.00

GRIMJACK: KILLER INSTINCT
IDW Publ.: Jan, 2005 - No. 6, June, 2005 ($3.99, limited series)

1-6-Ostrander-s/Truman-a 4.00

GRIMJACK: THE MANX CAT
IDW Publ.: Aug, 2009 - No. 6, Jan, 2010 ($3.99, limited series)

1-6-Ostrander-s/Truman-a 4.00

GRIMM (Based on the NBC TV series)
Dynamite Entertainment.: 2013 - No. 12, 2014 ($3.99)

1-11: 1-Two covers (Alex Ross & photo). 2-11-Pararillo & photo-c on each 4.00
12-($4.99) Gaffen & McVey-s/Rodolfo-a; Pararillo & photo-c 5.00
#0 (2013, Free Comic Book Day giveaway) Prequel to issue #1; Portacio-c 3.00
... Portland, WU (2014, $7.99) Gaffen & McVey-s/Govar-a/c 8.00
...: The Warlock 1-4 (2013 - No. 4, 2014, $3.99) Nitz-s/Malaga-a 4.00

GRIMM VOLUME 2 (Based on the NBC TV series)
Dynamite Entertainment.: 2016 - Present ($3.99)

1-5-Kittredge-s/Sanapo-a; two covers 4.00

GRIMM FAIRY TALES
Zenescope Entertainment: Jun, 2005 - No. 125, Aug, 2016 ($2.99/$3.99)

1-Al Rio-c; Little Red Riding Hood app.; multiple variant covers
5 10 15 35 63 90
2-Multiple variant covers 3 6 9 17 26 35
3-6-Multiple variant covers 2 4 6 10 14 18
7-12: Multiple covers on each 6.00
13-74,76-84,86-99,101,102: Multiple covers on each 3.00
75-(7/12, $5.99) Covers by Campbell, Sejic, Michaels and others 6.00
85-(5/13, $5.99) Unleashed part 2 6.00
100-(7/14, $5.99) Age of Darkness; covers by Neal Adams and others 6.00
103-124-($3.99) 4.00
125-(8/16, $9.99) Five covers 10.00
#0 Free Comic Book Day Special Edition (4/14, giveaway) Age of Darkness tie-in 3.00
2016 Annual (10/16, $5.99) Spotlight on Skylar; art by various; 4 covers 6.00
... Animated One Shot (10/12, $3.99) Schnepp-c; bonus design art 4.00
Grimm Tales of Terror 2016 Holiday Special (11/16, $5.99) 4 covers 6.00
... Halloween Special 1,2, 2013, 2014, 2015, 2016 (10/09, 10/10, 10/13, 10/14, 9/15, 10/16, $5.99) Multiple covers on each 6.00
... Holiday Edition (11/14, $5.99) The story of Krampus; multiple covers 6.00
... Presents Wounded Warriors (7/13, $6.99) Multiple military-themes covers 7.00
... The Dark Queen One Shot (1/14, $5.99) Sharma-a; 4 covers 6.00

GRIMM FAIRY TALES (Volume 2)
Zenescope Entertainment: Dec, 2016 - Present ($3.99)

1-12: 1-3-Brusha-s/Silva-a; multiple covers on each 4.00
... 2017 Halloween Special (10/17, $5.99) Short stories by various; 4 covers 6.00

GRIMM FAIRY TALES PRESENTS ALICE IN WONDERLAND
Zenescope Entertainment: Jan, 2012 - No. 6, May, 2012 ($2.99)

1-Multiple variant covers 3 6 9 14 19 24
2-6: Multiple covers on each 1 2 3 5 6 8

GRIMM FAIRY TALES MYTHS & LEGENDS
Zenescope Entertainment: Jan, 2011 - No. 25, Feb, 2013 ($2.99)

1-Campbell-c; multiple variant covers 2 4 6 8 10 12
2-5 5.00
6-24 3.00
25-(2/13, $5.99) Multiple variant covers 6.00

GRIMM FAIRY TALES PRESENTS WONDERLAND (Title changes to Wonderland with #43)
Zenescope Entertainment: Jul, 2012 - Finale, Sept, 2016 ($2.99)

1-Campbell-c; multiple variant covers 1 3 4 6 8 10
2,3 5.00
4-18 3.00
19-24,26-49-($3.99) 4.00
25-(7/14, $5.99) Multiple variant covers 6.00
50-(8/16, $5.99) Multiple variant covers 6.00
... Finale (9/16, $5.99) Last issue; 4 covers; Shand-s/Follini-a 6.00
Free Comic Book Day 2015 Special Edition (5/15, giveaway) Brescini-a 3.00

GRIMMISS ISLAND (Issue #1 titled Itty Bitty Comics #5: Grimmiss Island)
Dark Horse Comics: Mar, 2015 - No. 4, Jun, 2015 ($2.99, limited series)

1-4-All-ages humor story by Art Baltazar & Franco 3.00

GRIMM'S GHOST STORIES (See Dan Curtis)
Gold Key/Whitman No. 55 on: Jan, 1972 - No. 60, June, 1982 (Painted-c #1-42,44,46-56)

1 3 6 9 21 33 45
2-5,8: 5,8-Williamson-a 2 4 6 13 18 22
6,7,9,10 2 4 6 11 16 20
11-20 2 4 6 8 11 14
21-42,45-54: 32,34-Reprints. 45-Photo-c 1 3 4 6 8 10
43,44,55-60: 43,44-(52 pgs.). 43-Photo-c. 58(2/82). 59(4/82)-Williamson-a(r/#8). 60(6/82)
2 4 6 8 11 14
Mini-Comic No. 1 (3-1/4x6-1/2", 1976) 1 3 4 6 8 10
NOTE: *Reprints-#32?, 34?, 39, 43, 44, 47?, 53; 56-60(1/3).* ***Bolle*** *a-8, 17, 22-25, 27, 29(2), 33, 35, 41, 43r, 45(2), 48(2), 50, 52, 57.* ***Celardo*** *a-17, 26, 28p, 30, 31, 43(2), 45.* ***Lopez*** *a-24, 25.* ***McWilliams*** *a-33, 44r, 48, 54(2), 57, 58.* ***Win Mortimer*** *a-31, 33, 49, 51, 55, 56, 58(2), 59, 60.* ***Roussos*** *a-25, 30.* ***Sparling*** *a-23, 24, 28, 30, 31, 33, 43r, 44, 45, 51(2), 52, 56-58, 59(2), 60.* ***Spiegle*** *a-44.*

GRIN (The American Funny Book) (Satire)
APAG House Pubs: Nov, 1972 - No. 3, April, 1973 (Magazine, 52 pgs.)

1-Parodies-Godfather, All in the Family 3 6 9 16 24 32
2,3 2 4 6 11 16 20

GRIN & BEAR IT (See Gags)

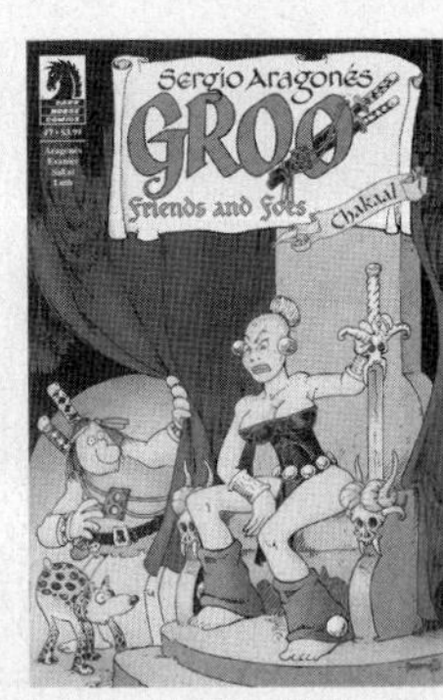

Groo: Friends and Foes #7 © Sergio Aragonés

Grumpy Cat / Garfield #2 © DYN

Guardians of Knowhere #1 © MAR

	GD	VG	FN	VF	VF/NM	NM-
	2.0	4.0	6.0	8.0	9.0	9.2

Dell Publishing Co.: No. 28, 1941
Large Feature Comic 28 19 38 57 112 179 245

GRINDHOUSE: DOORS OPEN AT MIDNIGHT
Dark Horse Comics: Oct, 2013 - No. 8, May, 2014 ($3.99)
1-8: 1-Francavilla-c/DeCampi-s. 1,2-Bee Vixens From Mars. 3,4-Prison Ship Antares 4.00

GRINDHOUSE: DRIVE IN, BLEED OUT
Dark Horse Comics: Nov, 2014 - No. 8, Aug, 2015 ($3.99)
1-8: 1,2-Slay Ride; DeCampi-s/Guéra-a. 7,8-Nebulina. 8-Manara-c 4.00

GRIPS (Extreme violence)
Silverwolf Comics: Sept, 1986 - No. 4, Dec, 1986 ($1.50, B&W, mature)
1-Tim Vigil-c/a in all 6.00
2-4 4.00

GRIP: THE STRANGE WORLD OF MEN
DC Comics (Vertigo): Jan, 2002 - No. 5, May, 2002 ($2.50, limited series)
1-4-Gilbert Hernandez-s/a 3.00

GRIT GRADY (See Holyoke One-Shot No. 1)

GROO (Also see Sergio Aragonés' Groo...)

GROO (Sergio Aragonés'...)
Image Comics: Dec, 1994 - No. 12, Dec, 1995 ($1.95)
1-12: 2-Indicia reads #1, Jan, 1995; Aragonés-c/a in all 4.00

GROO (Sergio Aragonés'...)
Dark Horse Comics: Jan, 1998 - No. 4, Apr, 1998 ($2.95)
1-4: Aragonés-c/a in all 4.00
...: One For One (9/10, $1.00) reprints #1 with red cover frame 3.00

GROO CHRONICLES, THE (Sergio Aragonés)
Marvel Comics (Epic Comics): June, 1989 - No. 6, Feb, 1990 ($3.50)
Book 1-6: Reprints early Pacific issues 5.00

GROO: FRAY OF THE GODS (Sergio Aragonés'...)
Dark Horse Comics: Jul, 2016 - No. 4, Jan, 2017 ($3.99, limited series)
1-4-Aragonés-c/a; Evanier-s 4.00

GROO: FRIENDS AND FOES (Sergio Aragonés'...)
Dark Horse Comics: Jan, 2015 - No. 12, Jan, 2016 ($3.99)
1-12-Aragonés-c/a in all; spotlights on various characters. 1-Spotlight on Captain Ahax 4.00

GROO: PLAY OF THE GODS (Sergio Aragonés'...)
Dark Horse Comics: Jul, 2017 - No. 4, Oct, 2017 ($3.99, limited series)
1-4-Aragonés-c/a; Evanier-s 4.00

GROO SPECIAL
Eclipse Comics: Oct, 1984 ($2.00, 52 pgs., Baxter paper)
1-Aragonés-c/a 3 6 9 15 22 28

GROOT (Guardians of the Galaxy)
Marvel Comics: Aug, 2015 - No. 6, Jan, 2016 ($3.99)
1-6: 1-Loveness-s/Kesinger-a; Rocket Raccoon app. 2-Flashback to Groot meeting Rocket. 3-Silver Surfer app. 4.00

GROO THE WANDERER (See Destroyer Duck #1 & Starslayer #5)
Pacific Comics: Dec, 1982 - No. 8, Apr, 1984
1-Aragonés-c/a(p)/Evanier-s in all; Aragonés bio. 3 6 9 16 24 32
2-5: 5-Deluxe paper (1.00-c) 2 4 6 9 13 16
6-8 2 4 6 10 14 18

GROO THE WANDERER (Sergio Aragonés'...) (See Marvel Graphic Novel #32)
Marvel Comics (Epic Comics): March, 1985 - No. 120, Jan, 1995
1-Aragonés-c/a in all 2 4 6 11 16 20
2-10 1 2 3 5 6 8
11-20,50-($1.50, double size) 5.00
21-49,51-99: 87-direct sale only, high quality paper 3.00
100-($2.95, 52 pgs.) 5.00
101-120 4.00
Groo Carnival, The (12/91, $8.95)-r/#9-12 11.00
Groo Garden, The (4/94, $10.95)-r/#25-28 11.00

GROO VS. CONAN (Sergio Aragonés'...)
Dark Horse Comics: Jul, 2014 - No. 4, Oct, 2014 ($3.50, limited series)
1-4: Aragonés & Evanier-s/Aragonés-c/a in all; Thomas Yeates on Conan art 3.50

GROOVY (Cartoon Comics - not CCA approved)
Marvel Comics Group: March, 1968 - No. 3, July, 1968
1-Monkees, Ringo Starr, Sonny & Cher, Mamas & Papas photos 8 16 24 55 105 155
2,3 6 12 18 37 66 95

GROSS POINT
DC Comics: Aug, 1997 - No. 14, Aug, 1998 ($2.50)
1-14: 1-Waid/Augustyn-s 3.00

GROUNDED
Image Comics: July, 2005 - No. 6, May, 2006 ($2.95/$2.99, limited series)
1-6-Mark Sable-s/Paul Azaceta-a. 1-Mike Oeming-c 3.00
Vol. 1: Powerless TPB (2006, $14.99) r/#1-6; sketch pages and creator bios 15.00

GRRL SCOUTS (Jim Mahfood's...) (Also see 40 oz. Collected)
Oni Press: Mar,1999 - No. 4, Dec, 1999 ($2.95, B&W, limited series)
1-4-Mahfood-s/c/a 3.00
TPB (2003, $12.95) r/#1-4; pin-ups by Warren, Winick, Allred, Fegredo and others 13.00

GRRL SCOUTS: MAGIC SOCKS
Image Comics: May, 2017 - No. 6, Oct, 2017 ($3.99, limited series)
1-6-Mahfood-s/c/a 4.00

GRRL SCOUTS: WORK SUCKS
Image Comics: Feb, 2003 - No. 4, May, 2003 ($2.95, B&W, limited series)
1-4-Mahfood-s/c/a 3.00
TPB (2004, $12.95) r/#1-4; pin-ups by Oeming, Dwyer, Tennapel and others 13.00

GRUMPY CAT
Dynamite Entertainment: 2015 - No. 3, 2015 ($3.99, limited series)
1-3-Short stories; Ben McCool & Ben Fisher-s/Steve Uy & Michelle Nguyen-a 4.00
..., Free Comic Book Day 2016 (giveaway) Short stories by various 3.00

GRUMPY CAT AND POKEY
Dynamite Entertainment: 2016 - No. 6, 2016 ($3.99, limited series)
1-6-Short stories. 1-McCool & Fisher-s/Uy, Haeser & Garbowska-a; multiple covers 4.00

GRUMPY CAT / GARFIELD
Dynamite Entertainment: 2017 - No. 3, 2017 ($3.99, limited series)
1-3-Mark Evanier-s/Steve Uy-a; multiple covers 4.00

GUADALCANAL DIARY (See American Library)

GUARDIAN ANGEL
Image Comics: May, 2002 - No. 2, July, 2002 ($2.95)
1,2-Peterson-s/Wiesenfeld-a 3.00

GUARDIANS
Marvel Comics: Sept, 2004 - No. 5, Dec, 2004 ($2.99, limited series)
1-5-Sumerak-s/Casey Jones-a 3.00

GUARDIANS OF INFINITY
Marvel Comics: Feb, 2016 - No. 8, Sept, 2016 ($4.99)
1-8-Guardians of the Galaxy & 31st century Guardians. 1-Back-up story with The Thing 5.00

GUARDIANS OF KNOWHERE (Secret Wars tie-in)
Marvel Comics: Sept, 2015 - No. 4, Nov, 2015 ($3.99, limited series)
1-4-Bendis-s/Deodato-a; Guardians of the Galaxy, Angela & Mantis app. 4.00
1-Variant Gwenom (Gwen/Venom) cover by Guillory 8.00

GUARDIANS OF METROPOLIS
DC Comics: Nov, 1995 - Feb, 1995 ($1.50, limited series)
1-4: 1-Superman & Granny Goodness app. 3.00

GUARDIANS OF THE GALAXY (Also see The Defenders #26, Marvel Presents #3, Marvel Super-Heroes #18, Marvel Two-In-One #5)
Marvel Comics: June, 1990 - No. 62, July, 1995 ($1.00/$1.25)
1-Valentino-c/a(p) begin; 1st app. Taserface 3 6 9 15 22 28
2-5: 2-Zeck-c(i). 5-McFarlane-c(i) 1 2 3 5 6 8
6-15: 7-Intro Malevolence (Mephisto's daughter); Perez-c(i). 8-Intro Rancor (descendant of Wolverine) in cameo. 9-1st full app. Rancor; Rob Liefeld-c(i). 10-Jim Lee-c(i). 13,14-1st app. Spirit of Vengeance (futuristic Ghost Rider). 14-Spirit of Vengeance vs. The Guardians. 15-Starlin-c(i) 4.00
16-($1.50, 52 pgs.)-Starlin-c(i) 5.00
17-24,26-38,40-47: 17-20-31st century Punishers storyline. 20-Last $1.00-c. 21-Rancor app. 22-Reintro Starhawk. 24-Silver Surfer-c/story; Ron Lim-c. 26-Origin retold. 27-28-Infinity War x-over; 27-Inhumans app. 43-Intro Wooden (son of Thor) 3.00
25-($2.50)-Prism foil-c; Silver Surfer/Galactus-c/s 5.00
25-($2.50)-Without foil-c; newsstand edition 4.00
39-($2.95, 52 pgs.)-Embossed & holo-grafx foil-c; Dr. Doom vs. Rancor 4.00
48,49,51-56: 48-bound-in trading card sheet 4.00

Guardians of the Galaxy #55 © MAR

Guardians of the Galaxy (2015 series) #6 © MAR

Guarding the Globe #5 © R. Kirkman

	GD	VG	FN	VF	VF/NM	NM-
	2.0	4.0	6.0	8.0	9.0	9.2

50-($2.00, 52 pgs.)-Newsstand edition 4.00
50-($2.95, 52 pgs.)-Collectors ed. w/foil embossed-c 5.00
57-61 1 2 3 5 6 8
62 2 4 6 9 12 15
Annual 1-4: ('91-'94, 68 pgs.)-1-Origin. 2-Spirit of Vengeance-c/story. 3,4-Bagged w/card 4.00

GUARDIANS OF THE GALAXY (See Annihilation series)
Marvel Comics: July, 2008 - No. 25, Jun, 2010 ($2.99)

1-Continued from Annihilation Conquest #6; origin of the new Guardians: Star-Lord, Drax, Warlock, Rocket Raccoon, Quasar (female version: Phyla-Vell) and Gamora; Mantis and Groot appear but not official members; Cosmo the talking dog and Nova (Richard Rider) app.; Abnett & Lanning-s/Pelletier-a 5 10 15 34 60 85
1-Second printing; variant-c 3 6 9 14 20 25
2,3: 2-Vance Astro (Major Victory) app.; full-size Groot on the cover but still growing (potted plant-size) in story. 3-Starhawk app; Guardians vs. the Universal Church of Truth 2 4 6 10 14 18
3-Variant cover 2 4 6 11 16 20
4,5-Secret Invasion x-overs; Skrulls app. 1 3 4 6 8 10
5-Monkey variant-c by Nic Klein 2 4 6 9 12 15
6-Secret Invasion x-over; Warlock, Gamora, Quasar and Star-Lord leave the team 1 3 4 6 8 10
7-Original Guardians app: Vance Astro, Charlie-27, Martinex & Yondu app; Groot, Mantis and Bug (from the Micronauts) join Rocket Raccoon, Vance Astro (Major Victory) and a re-grown Groot as the Guardians; Blastaar app. 2 4 6 8 10 12
7-Variant-c by Jim Valentino 2 4 6 11 16 20
8-War of Kings x-over; Blastaar & Ronan the Accuser app. 1 3 4 6 8 10
8-Variant-c; Thanos with the Infinity Gauntlet by Brandon Peterson 3 6 9 19 30 40
9,10; 9-War of Kings x-over; Star-Lord and Jack Flagg vs. Blastaar at the super-villain prison in the Negative Zone. 10-War of Kings x-over; Blastaar & Reed Richards app. Star-Lord reunited with the Guardians 1 3 4 6 8 10
11,12: 11-Drax and Quasar (Phyla-Vell) story; Maelstrom & Dragon of the Moon app. 12-Moondragon returns; Quasar (Wendell Vaughn) regains the Quantum-bands becomes Protector of the Universe; Maelstrom & Oblivion app; Phyla-Vell becomes new Avatar of Death 1 3 4 6 8 10
13-War of Kings x-over; Phyla-Vell changes name to 'Martyr'; Moondragon & Jack Flagg join the Guardians; Warlock, Drax & Gamora return to Guardians; Black Bolt & the Inhumans, Vulcan, ruler of the Shi'ar Empire and the Starjammers app.; story continues on War of Kings #3 2 4 6 8 10 12
14-17: 14-War of Kings x-over; Warlock vs. Vulcan; Guardians vs. the Inhumans. 15-War of Kings x-over; Guardians vs. the Sh'iar; Black Bolt & the Inhumans app. 16-War of Kings x-over; Star-Lord, Bug, Jack Flagg, Mantis & Cosmo vs. the Badoon; original Guardians: Martinex, Youndu, Charlie-27, Starhawk and Major Victory app. 17-War of Kings x-over; 'death' of Warlock & Martyr; return of the Magus 1 3 4 6 8 10
17-Variant 70th Anniversary Frame-c by Perkins 2 4 6 11 16 20
18-20: 18-Star-Lord, Mantis, Cosmo, Bug & Jack Flagg in alternate future 3000AD; Killraven & Hollywood (Wonder Man) app.; vs. the Martians; original Guardians app.; Starhawk, Charlie-27 & Nikki. 19-Kang app.; 'death' of Martyr & Warlock again; 'death' of Major Victory, Gamora, Cosmo & Mantis. 20-Realm of Kings x-over; Star-Lord, Groot, Rocket Raccoon, Bug, Jack Flagg, Drax & Moondragon appear as the Guardians 1 3 4 6 8 10
21-Realm of Kings x-over; brief appearance of the Cancerverse 2 4 6 8 10 12
22,23: 23-Realm of Kings x-over; the Magus returns. 23-Martyr, Gamora, Cosmo, Mantis & Major Victory return to life; Magus app. 2 4 6 9 12 15
23-Deadpool Variant-c by Alex Garner 3 6 9 17 26 35
24-Realm of Kings x-over; Thanos returns, kills Martyr; Maelstrom app. 3 6 9 14 20 25
25-Last issue; Guardians vs. Thanos; leads into Thanos Imperative #1 3 6 9 16 23 30
25-Variant-c by Skottie Young 2 4 6 11 16 20

GUARDIANS OF THE GALAXY (Marvel NOW!) (Also see the 2013 Nova series)
(See Incredible Hulk #271, Iron Man #55, Marvel Preview #4,7, Strange Tales #180 and Tales to Astonish #13 for 1st app. of 2014 movie characters)
Marvel Comics: No. 0.1, Apr, 2013; No. 1, May, 2013 - No. 27, Jul, 2015 ($3.99)

0.1-(4/13) Origin of Star-Lord; Bendis-s/McNiven-a 5.00
1-Bendis-s/McNiven-a; Iron Man app.; at least 15 variant covers exist 2 4 6 8 10 12
2-4: Iron Man app. 1 2 3 5 6 8
5-Angela & Thanos app. 5.00
6-13: 8,9-Infinity tie-in; Francavilla-a/c. 10-Maguire-a. 11-13-Trial of Jean Grey 4.00
14-($4.99) Venom and Captain Marvel app.; Bradshaw-a; Guardians of 3014 app. 5.00
15-24,26,27: 16,17-Angela app. 18-20-Original Sin tie-in; Thanos app. 23-Origin of the Symbiotes. 24-Black Vortex crossover 4.00
25-($4.99)-Black Vortex crossover; Kree homeworld destroyed 5.00
Annual 1 (2/15, $4.99) Bendis-s/Cho-a; Nick Fury, Dum Dum, Skrulls app. 5.00
...: Best Story Ever 1 (6/15, $3.99) Tim Seeley-s; Nebula & Thanos app. 4.00
...: Galaxy's Most Wanted 1 (9/14, $3.99) Rocket & Groot; DiVito-a; r/Thor #314 Drax app. 4.00
100th Anniversary Special: Guardians of the Galaxy (9/14, $3.99) Future Guardians 4.00
...: Tomorrow's Avengers 1 (9/13, $4.99) Short stories; art by various 5.00
Marvel's Guardians of the Galaxy Prelude 1,2 (6/14 - No. 2, 7/14, $2.99) 1-Gamora & Nebula app. 2-Rocket & Groot 3.00

GUARDIANS OF THE GALAXY
Marvel Comics: Dec, 2015 - No. 19, Jun, 2017 ($3.99)

1-18: 1-Rocket, Groot, Drax, Venom, The Thing and Kitty Pryde team; Bendis-s. 12,13-Civil War II tie-ins. 12-Avengers app. 14-Spider-Man app.; Maguire-a 4.00
19-($4.99) Thanos and Annihilus app.; Schiti, Noto, Pichelli, Bagley & others-a 5.00
1.MU (Monsters Unleashed) (5/17, $4.99) Baldeón-a/Walsh-c 5.00
... Dream On 1 (6/17, $3.99) Death's Head app.; r/1st Taserface from GOTG #1 (1990) 4.00
... Mission Breakout 1 (7/17, $4.99) Hastings-s/Salazar-a; The Collector app. 5.00

GUARDIANS OF THE GALAXY (Marvel Legacy)
Marvel Comics: No. 146, Jan, 2018 - Present ($3.99)

146-149: 146-Ant-Man joins; Nova Corps app.; Duggan-s/To-a 4.00
150-($4.99) Lenticular-c by Ross; Adam Warlock returns 5.00

GUARDIANS OF THE GALAXY ADAPTATION ("... Vol. 2 Prelude" on cover)
Marvel Comics: Mar, 2017 - No. 2, Apr, 2017 ($3.99, limited series)

1,2-Adaptation of the 2014 movie; Corona Pilgrim-s/Chris Allen-a 4.00

GUARDIANS OF THE GALAXY & X-MEN: THE BLACK VORTEX
Marvel Comics: Alpha, Apr, 2015 - Omega, Jun, 2015 ($4.99, bookends for crossover)

... Alpha (4/15) Part 1 of crossover; McGuinness-a 5.00
... Omega (6/15) Part 13 of crossover; Ronan app.; McGuinness-a 5.00

GUARDIANS OF THE GALAXY: MOTHER ENTROPY
Marvel Comics: Jul, 2017 - No. 5, Jul, 2017 ($3.99, weekly limited series)

1-5-Starlin-s/Alan Davis-a; Pip the Troll app. 4-Gladiator app. 4.00

GUARDIANS TEAM-UP
Marvel Comics: May, 2015 - No. 10, Oct, 2015 ($3.99)

1-10: 1-Bendis-s/Art Adams-a. 1,2-The Avengers & Nebula app. 3-Black Vortex crossover. 4-Gamora & She-Hulk. 7-Drax & Ant-Man. 9-Spider-Man & Star-Lord; Pulido-s/a. 10-Deadpool & Rocket 4.00

GUARDIANS OF THE GALAXY: TELLTALE GAMES (Based on the videogame)
Marvel Comics: Sept, 2017 - No. 5, Jan, 2018 ($3.99, limited series)

1-5: 1-Van Lente-s/Espin-a. 2-5-Cosmo app. 5-Thanos app. 4.00

GUARDIANS 3000
Marvel Comics: Dec, 2014 - No. 8, Jul, 2015 ($3.99)

1-8: 1-Abnett-s/Sandoval-a; Alex Ross-c; Guardians vs. Badoon in 3014 A.D. 1-6-Ross-c. 6-Guardians meet the 2015 Guardians 4.00

GUARDING THE GLOBE (See Invincible)
Image Comics: Aug, 2010 - No. 6, Oct, 2011 ($3.50)

1-6-Kirkman & Cereno-s/Getty-a. 1-Back-c swipe of Avengers #4 w/Obama 3.50

GUARDING THE GLOBE (2nd series) (See Invincible Universe)
Image Comics: Sept, 2012 - No. 6, Feb, 2013 ($2.99)

1-6: 1-Wraparound-c; Hester-s/Nauck-a 3.00

GUERRILLA WAR (Formerly Jungle War Stories)
Dell Publishing Co.: No. 12, July-Sept, 1965 - No. 14, Mar, 1966

12-14 3 6 9 15 22 28

GUIDEBOOK TO THE MARVEL CINEMATIC UNIVERSE
Marvel Comics: Dec, 2015 - Present ($3.99)

... - Marvel's Agents of S.H.I.E.L.D. Season One (8/16, $3.99) Profile pages 4.00
... - Marvel's Agents of S.H.I.E.L.D. Season Two/Marvel's Agent Carter Season One (12/16, $3.99) Flipbook with character profile pages; both covers by Marcos Martin 4.00
... - Marvel's Agents of S.H.I.E.L.D. Season Three/Marvel's Agent Carter Season Two (2/17, $3.99) Flipbook with character profile pages; covers by Del Mundo & Johnson 4.00
... - Marvel's Avengers: Age of Ultron (11/16, $3.99) Profile pages of characters 4.00
... - Marvel's Captain America: Civil War (3/17, $3.99) Profile pages 4.00
... - Marvel's Captain America: The First Avenger (3/16, $3.99) Profile pages 4.00
... - Marvel's Captain America: The Winter Soldier/Marvel's Ant-Man (7/16, $3.99) Flipbook 4.00
... - Marvel's Doctor Strange (5/17, $3.99) Profile pages of characters, weapons, locations 4.00
... - Marvel's Guardians of the Galaxy (9/16, $3.99) Profile pages of characters, locations 4.00
... - Marvel's Incredible Hulk/Marvel's Iron Man 2 (1/16, $3.99) Flipbook; profile pages 4.00

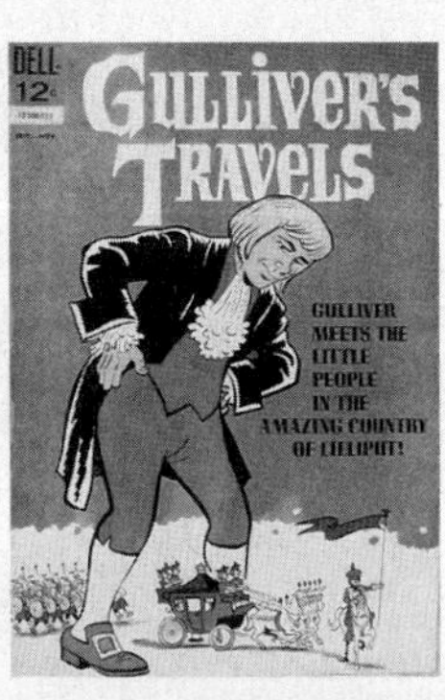

Gulliver's Travels #1 © DELL

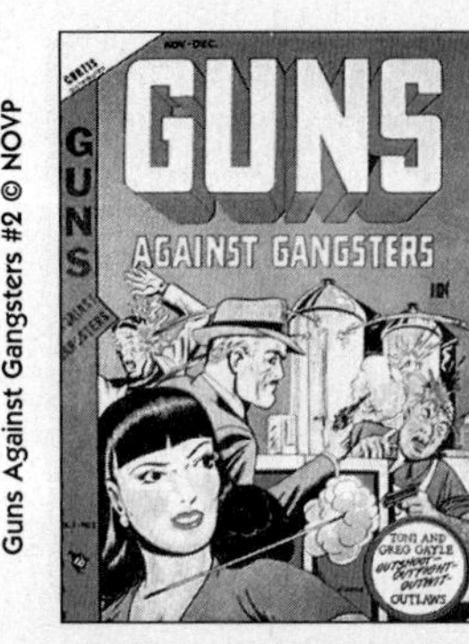

Guns Against Gangsters #2 © NOVP

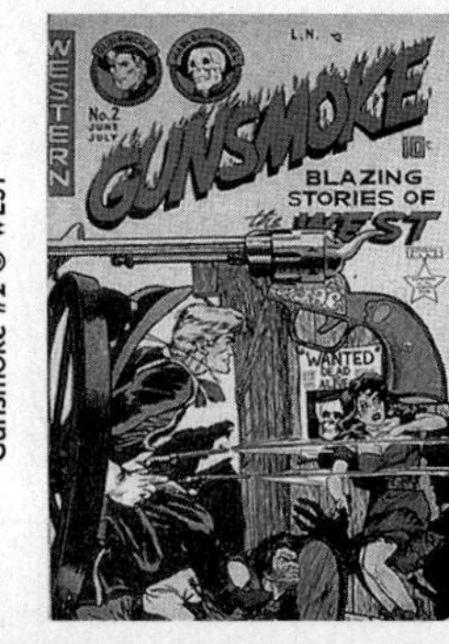

Gunsmoke #2 © WEST

	GD 2.0	VG 4.0	FN 6.0	VF 8.0	VF/NM 9.0	NM- 9.2

... - Marvel's Iron Man (12/15, $3.99) Profile pages of characters, weapons, locations 4.00
... - Marvel's Iron Man 3/Marvel's Thor: The Dark World (6/16, $3.99) Flipbook profiles 4.00
... - Marvel's The Avengers (4/16, $3.99) Profile pages of characters, weapons 4.00
... - Marvel's Thor (2/16, $3.99) Profile pages of characters, weapons, locations 4.00

GUILD, THE (Based on the web-series)
Dark Horse Comics: Mar, 2010 - No. 3, May, 2010 ($3.50, limited series)

1-3-Felicia Day-s/Jim Rugg-a; two covers on each 3.50
... Bladezz 1 (6/11, $3.50) Currie-a/Kerschl-c; variant-c by Dalrymple 3.50
... Clara 1 (9/11, $3.50) Chan-a/Chaykin-c; variant-c by Aronowitz 3.50
... Fawkes 1 (5/12, $3.50) Day & Wheaton-s/McKelvie-a; variant-c by Rios 3.50
... Tink 1 (3/11, $3.50) art by Donaldson, Warren, Seeley & others; variant-c by Bagge 3.50
... Vork 1 (12/10, $3.50) Robertson-a/c; variant-c by Hernandez 3.50
... Zaboo 1 (12/11, $3.50) Cloonan-a/Dorkin-c; variant-c by Jeanty 3.50

GUILTY (See Justice Traps the Guilty)

GULLIVER'S TRAVELS (See Dell Jr. Treasury No. 3)
Dell Publishing Co.: Sept-Nov, 1965

1 5 10 15 31 53 75

GUMBY
Wildcard Ink: July, 2006 - No. 3 ($3.99)

1-3-Bob Burden & Rick Geary-s&a 4.00

GUMBY'S SUMMER FUN SPECIAL
Comico: July, 1987 ($2.50)

1-Art Adams-c/a; B. Burden scripts 5.00

GUMBY'S WINTER FUN SPECIAL
Comico: Dec, 1988 ($2.50, 44 pgs.)

1-Art Adams-c/a 5.00

GUMPS, THE (See Merry Christmas..., Popular & Super Comics)
Dell Publ. Co./Bridgeport Herald Corp.: No. 73, 1945; Mar-Apr, 1947 - No. 5, Nov-Dec, 1947

Four Color 73 (Dell)(1945) 11 22 33 76 163 250
1 (3-4/47) 16 32 48 94 147 200
2-5 11 22 33 62 86 110

GUN CANDY (Also see The Ride)
Image Comics: July, 2005 - No. 2 ($5.99)

1,2-Stelfreeze-c/a; flip book with The Ride (1-Pearson-c. 2-Noto-c) 6.00

GUNFIGHTER (Fat & Slat #1-4) (Becomes Haunt of Fear #15 on)
E. C. Comics (Fables Publ. Co.): No. 5, Sum, 1948 - No. 14, Mar-Apr, 1950

5,6-Moon Girl in each 61 122 183 390 670 950
7-14: 13,14-Bondage-c 45 90 135 284 480 675

NOTE: ***Craig & H. C. Kiefer** art in most issues. **Craig** c-5, 6, 13, 14. **Feldstein/Craig** a-10. **Feldstein** a-7-11. **Harrison/Wood** a-13, 14. **Ingels** a-5-14; c-7-12.*

GUNFIGHTERS, THE
Super Comics (Reprints): 1963 - 1964

10-12,15,16,18: 10,11-r/Billy the Kid #s? 12-r/The Rider #5(Swift Arrow). 15-r/Straight Arrow #42; Powell-r. 16-r/Billy the Kid #?(Toby). 18-r/The Rider #3; Severin-c
2 4 6 10 14 18

GUNFIGHTERS, THE (Formerly Kid Montana)
Charlton Comics: No. 51, 10/66 - No. 52, 10/67; No. 53, 6/79 - No. 85, 7/84

51,52 2 4 6 11 16 20
53,54,56:53,54-Williamson/Torres-r/Six Gun Heroes #47,49. 56-Williamson/Severin-c; Severin-r/Sheriff of Tombstone #1 1 3 4 6 8 10
55,57-80 6.00
81-84-Lower print run 1 2 3 5 6 8
85-S&K-r/1955 Bullseye 1 3 4 6 8 10

GUNFIRE (See Deathstroke Annual #2 & Showcase 94 #1,2)
DC Comics: May, 1994 - No. 13, June, 1995 ($1.75/$2.25)

1-5,0,6-13: 2-Ricochet-c/story. 5-(9/94). 0-(10/94). 6-(11/94) 3.00

GUN GLORY (Movie)
Dell Publishing Co.: No. 846, Oct, 1957 (one-shot)

Four Color 846-Toth-a, photo-c. 8 16 24 51 96 140

GUNHAWK, THE (Formerly Whip Wilson)(See Wild Western)
Marvel Comics/Atlas (MCI): No. 12, Nov, 1950 - No. 18, Dec, 1951
(Also see Two-Gun Western #5)

12 20 40 60 118 192 265
13-18: 13-Tuska-a. 16-Colan-a. 18-Maneely-c 15 30 45 83 124 165

GUNHAWKS (Gunhawk No. 7)
Marvel Comics Group: Oct, 1972 - No. 7, October, 1973

1,6: 1-Reno Jones, Kid Cassidy; Shores-c/a(p). 6-Kid Cassidy dies
3 6 9 19 30 40
2-5,7: 7-Reno Jones solo 2 4 6 11 16 20

	GD 2.0	VG 4.0	FN 6.0	VF 8.0	VF/NM 9.0	NM- 9.2

GUNMASTER (Becomes Judo Master #89 on)
Charlton Comics: 9/64 - No. 4, 1965; No. 84, 7/65 - No. 88, 3-4/66; No. 89, 10/67

V1#1 3 6 9 21 33 45
2-4, V5#84-86: 84-Formerly Six-Gun Heroes 3 6 9 15 22 28
V5#87-89 2 4 6 11 16 20

NOTE: *Vol. 5 was originally cancelled with #88 (3-4/66). #89 on, became Judo Master, then later in 1967, Charlton issued #89 as a Gunmaster one-shot.*

GUN RUNNER
Marvel Comics UK: Oct, 1993 - No. 6, Mar, 1994 ($1.75, limited series)

1-($2.75)-Polybagged w/4 trading cards; Spirits of Vengeance app. 4.00
2-6: 2-Ghost Rider & Blaze app. 3.00

GUNS AGAINST GANGSTERS (True-To-Life Romances #8 on)
Curtis Publications/Novelty Press: Sept-Oct, 1948 - No. 6, July-Aug, 1949; V2#1, Sept-Oct, 1949

1-Toni & Greg Gayle begins by Schomburg; L.B. Cole-c
44 90 135 284 480 675
2-L.B. Cole-c 34 68 102 199 325 450
3-5 30 60 90 177 289 400
6-Giant shark and Toni Gayle-c by Cole 39 78 117 231 378 525
V2#1 29 58 87 170 278 385

NOTE: ***L. B. Cole** c-1-6, V2#1, 2; a-1, 2, 3(2), 4-6.*

GUNSLINGER
Dell Publishing Co.: No. 1220, Oct-Dec, 1961 (one-shot)

Four Color 1220-Photo-c 7 14 21 49 92 135

GUNSLINGER (Formerly Tex Dawson...)
Marvel Comics Group: No. 2, Apr, 1973 - No. 3, June, 1973

2,3 2 4 6 13 18 22

GUNSLINGERS
Marvel Comics: Feb, 2000 ($2.99)

1-Reprints stories of Two-Gun Kid, Rawhide Kid and Caleb Hammer 3.00

GUNSMITH CATS: (Title series), **Dark Horse Comics**

--BAD TRIP (Manga), 6/98 - No. 6, 11/98 ($2.95, B&W) 1-6 3.00
--BEAN BANDIT (Manga), 1/99 - No. 9 ($2.95, B&W, limited series) 1-9 3.00
--GOLDIE VS. MISTY (Manga), 11/97 - No. 7, 5/98 ($2.95, B&W) 1-7 3.00
--KIDNAPPED (Manga), 11/99 - No. 10, 8/00 ($2.95, B&W) 1-10 3.00
--MISTER V (Manga), 10/00 - No. 11, 8/01 ($3.50/$2.99), B&W) 1-11 3.50
--THE RETURN OF GRAY (Manga), 8/96 - No. 7, 2/97 ($2.95, B&W) 1-7 3.00
--SHADES OF GRAY (Manga), 5/97 - No. 5, 9/97 ($2.95, B&W) 1-5 3.00
--SPECIAL (Manga) Nov, 2001 ($2.99, B&W, one-shot) 3.00

GUNSMOKE (Blazing Stories of the West)
Western Comics (Youthful Magazines): Apr-May, 1949 - No. 16, Jan, 1952

1-Gunsmoke & Masked Marvel begin by Ingels; Ingels bondage-c
52 104 156 328 552 775
2-Ingels-c/a(2) 34 68 102 199 325 450
3-Ingels bondage-c/a 29 58 87 170 278 385
4-6: Ingels-c 23 46 69 136 223 310
7-10 15 30 45 88 137 185
11-16: 15,16-Western/horror stories 15 30 45 85 130 175

NOTE: ***Stallman** a-11, 14. **Wildey** a-15, 16.*

GUNSMOKE (TV)
Dell Publishing Co./Gold Key (All have James Arness photo-c): No. 679, Feb, 1956 - No. 27, Feb, 1969 - No. 6, Feb, 1970

Four Color 679(#1) 16 32 48 112 249 385
Four Color 720,769,797,844 (#2-5),6(11-1/57-58) 9 18 27 59 117 175
7,8,9,11,12-Williamson-a in all, 4 pgs. each 8 16 24 54 102 150
10-Williamson/Crandall-a, 4 pgs. 8 16 24 54 102 150
13-27 7 14 21 44 82 120
1 (Gold Key) 6 12 18 40 73 105
2-6('69-70) 4 8 12 23 37 50

GUNSMOKE TRAIL
Ajax-Farrell Publ./Four Star Comic Corp.: June, 1957 - No. 4, Dec, 1957

1 11 22 33 60 83 105

Guy Gardner: Warrior #33 © DC

GWAR: Orgasmageddon #1 © Slave Pit

Hack / Slash #5 © Hack / Slash Inc.

	GD 2.0	VG 4.0	FN 6.0	VF 8.0	VF/NM 9.0	NM- 9.2
2-4	7	14	21	35	43	50

GUNSMOKE WESTERN (Formerly Western Tales of Black Rider)
Atlas Comics No. 32-35(CPS/NPI); Marvel No. 36 on: No. 32, Dec, 1955 - No. 77, July, 1963

32-Baker & Drucker-a 25 50 75 150 245 340
33,35,36-Williamson-a in each: 5,6 & 4 pgs. plus Drucker-a #33. 33-Kinstler-a?
19 38 57 111 176 240
34-Baker-a, 4 pgs.; Severin-c 19 38 57 111 176 240
37-Davis-a(2); Williamson text illo 15 30 45 90 140 190
38,39: 39-Williamson text illo (unsigned) 14 28 42 82 121 160
40-Williamson/Mayo-a (4 pgs.) 15 30 45 84 127 170
41,42,45,46,48,49,52-54,57,58,60: 49,52-Kid from Texas story. 57-1st Two Gun Kid by Severin. 60-Sam Hawk app. in Kid Colt 13 26 39 74 105 135
43,44-Torres-a 13 26 39 74 105 135
47,51,59,61: 47,51,59-Kirby-a. 61-Crandall-a 14 28 42 80 115 150
50-Kirby, Crandall-a 15 30 45 84 127 170
55,56-Matt Baker-a 15 30 45 84 127 170
62-67,69,71-73,77-Kirby-a. 72-Origin Kid Colt 8 16 24 51 96 140
68,70,74-76: 68-(10¢-c) 7 14 21 46 86 125
68-(10¢ cover price blacked out, 12¢ printed on) 13 26 39 86 188 290

NOTE: ***Colan** a-35-37, 39, 72, 76. **Davis** a-37, 52, 54, 55; c-50, 54. **Ditko** a-66; c-56p. **Drucker** a-.32-34. **Heath** c-33. **Jack Keller** a-34, 35, 40, 51, 53, 55, 56, 60, 61, 65, 68, 69, 71, 72, 74, 75, 77; c-72. **Kirby** a-47, 50, 51, 59, 62(3), 63-67, 69, 71, 73, 77; c-56(w/**Ditko**), 57, 58, 60, 61(w/**Ayers**), 62, 63, 65, 66, 68, 69, 71-77. **Maneely** a-53; c-45. **Robinson** a-35. **Severin** a-35, 59-61; c-34, 35, 39, 42, 43. **Tuska** a-34. **Wildey** a-10, 37, 42, 56, 57. Kid Colt in all. Two-Gun Kid in No. 57, 59, 60-63. Wyatt Earp in No. 45, 48, 49, 51-56, 58.*

GUNS OF FACT & FICTION (Also see A-1 Comics)
Magazine Enterprises: No. 13, 1948 (one-shot)

A-1 13-Used in **SOTI**, pg. 19; Ingels & J. Craig-a 29 58 87 170 278 385

GUNS OF THE DRAGON
DC Comics: Oct, 1998 - No. 4, Jan, 1999 ($2.50, limited series)

1-4-DCU in the 1920's; Enemy Ace & Bat Lash app. 3.00

GUNWITCH, THE : OUTSKIRTS OF DOOM (See The Nocturnals)
Oni Press: June, 2001 - No. 3, Oct, 2001 ($2.95, B&W, limited series)

1-3-Brereton-s/painted-c/Naifeh-s 3.00

GUY GARDNER (Guy Gardner: Warrior #17 on)(Also see Green Lantern #59)
DC Comics: Oct, 1992 - No. 44, July, 1996 ($1.25/$1.50/$1.75)

1-Staton-c/a(p) begins 4.00
2-24,0,26-30: 6-Guy vs. Hal Jordan. 8-Vs. Lobo-c/story. 15-JLA x-over, begin $1.50-c. 18-Begin 4-part Emerald Fallout story; splash page x-over GL #50. 18-21-Vs. Hal Jordan. 24-(9/94)-Zero Hour. 0-(10/94) 3.00
25 (11/94, $2.50, 52 pgs.) 4.00
29 ($2.95)-Gatefold-c 4.00
29-Variant-c (Edward Hopper's Nighthawks) 3.00
31-44: 31-$1.75-c begins. 40-Gorilla Grodd-c/app. 44-Parallax-app. (1 pg.) 3.00
Annual 1 (1995, $3.50)-Year One story 4.00
Annual 2 (1996, $2.95)-Legends of the Dead Earth story 4.00

GUY GARDNER: COLLATERAL DAMAGE
DC Comics: 2006 - No. 2 ($5.99, square-bound, limited series)

1,2-Howard Chaykin-s/a 6.00

GUY GARDNER REBORN
DC Comics: 1992 - Book 3, 1992 ($4.95, limited series)

1-3: Staton-c/a(p). 1-Lobo-c/cameo. 2,3-Lobo-c/s 6.00

GWAR: ORGASMAGEDDON (Based on the band GWAR)
Dynamite Entertainment: 2017 - No. 4, 2017 ($3.99, limited series)

1-4-Matt Maguire & Matt Miner-s/Sawyer & Maguire-a; multiple covers 4.00

GWENPOOL (Also see Unbelievable Gwenpool)
Marvel Comics: Feb, 2016; Feb, 2017 ($5.99, one-shots)

... Holiday Special: Merry Mix-Up (2/17, $5.99) 1-Deadpool, Squirrel Girl, Punisher app. 6.00
... Special (2/16, $5.99) 1-Christmas-themed short stories; She-Hulk, Deadpool app. 6.00

GYPSY COLT
Dell Publishing Co.: No. 568, June, 1954 (one-shot)

Four Color 568-Movie 5 10 15 35 63 90

GYRO GEARLOOSE (See Dynabrite Comics, Walt Disney's C&S #140 & Walt Disney Showcase #18)
Dell Publishing Co.: No. 1047, Nov-Jan/1959-60 - May-July, 1962 (Disney)

Four Color 1047 (No. 1)-All Barks-c/a 15 30 45 103 227 350
Four Color 1095,1184-All by Carl Barks 9 18 27 59 117 175
Four Color 1267-Barks c/a, 4 pgs. 7 14 21 48 89 130
01329-207 (#1, 5-7/62)-Barks-c only (intended as 4-Color 1329?)

	GD 2.0	VG 4.0	FN 6.0	VF 8.0	VF/NM 9.0	NM- 9.2
	5	10	15	35	63	90

HACKER FILES, THE
DC Comics: Aug, 1992 - No. 12, July, 1993 ($1.95)

1-12: 1-Sutton-a(p) begins; computer generated-c 3.00

HACK/SLASH
Devil's Due Publishing: Apr. 2004 - No. 32, Mar, 2010 ($3.25/$4.95)

1-Seeley-s/Caselli-a/c 4 8 12 22 35 48
...: (The Series) 1-24,26-32 (5/07-No. 32, 3/10, $3.50) Flashack to Cassie's childhood and origin. 12-Milk & Cheese cameo. 15-Re-Animator app. 3.50
25-($5.50) Double sized issue; Baugh-a; two covers 5.50
...: Comic Book Carnage (3/05) Manfredi-a/Seeley-s; Robert Kirkman & Steve Niles app. 5.00
...: First Cut TPB (10/05, $14.95) r/one-shots with sketch pages, designs, interviews 15.00
...: Girls Gone Dead (10/04, $4.95) Manfredi-a/Seeley-s 5.00
...: Land of Lost Toys 1-3 (11/05 - No. 3, 1/06, $3.25) Crossland-a/Seeley-s 3.25
...: New Reader Halloween Treat #1 (10/08, $3.50) origin retold; Cassie's diary pages 3.50
...: The Final Revenge of Evil Ernie (6/05, $4.95) Salman-a/Seeley-s; two covers 5.00
...: Trailers (2/05, $3.25) short stories by Seeley; art by various; three covers 3.25
...: Slice Hard (12/05, $4.95) Seeley-s 5.00
...: Slice Hard Pre-Sliced 25¢ Special (2/06, 25¢) origin story by Seeley; sketch pages 3.00
...: Vs Chucky (3/07, $5.50) Seeley-s/Merhoff-a; 3 covers 5.50
...: Vol. 2 Death By Sequel TPB (1/07, $18.99) r/Land of Lost Toys #1-3, Trailers, Slice Hard 19.00
...: Vol. 3 Friday the 31st TPB (10/07, $18.99) r/The Series #1-4 & ... Vs Chucky 19.00

HACK/SLASH
Image Comics: Jun, 2010 - No. 25, Mar, 2013 ($3.50)

1-25: 1-(2/11, $3.50) Seeley-s/Leister-a. 5-Esquejo-c. 9-11-Bomb Queen app. 3.50
... Annual 2010: Murder Messiah (10/10, $5.99) Seeley-s/Morales-a 6.00
... Annual 2011: Hatchet/Slash (11/11, $5.99) 6.00
.../ Eva: Monster's Ball 1-4 (Dynamite Ent., 2011 - No. 4, 2011, $3.99) Jerwa-s/Razek-a 4.00
...: Me Without You (1/11, $3.50) Leister-a/Seeley-s; 2 covers 3.50
...: My First Maniac 1-4 (6/10- No. 4, 9/10) Leister-a/Seeley-s 3.50
.../ Nailbiter 1 (3/15, $4.99) Flip book with Nailbiter / Hack/Slash 1 5.00
...: Son of Samhain 1-5 (7/14- No. 5, 11/14) Laiso-a/Moreci & Seeley-s 3.50
...: Trailers #2 (11/10, $6.99) short stories; story & art by various; Seeley-c 7.00
Image Firsts: Hack/Slash #1 (10/10, $1.00) r/#1 (2004) with "Image Firsts" cover frame 3.00

HACK SLASH: RESURRECTION
Image Comics: Oct, 2017 - Present ($3.99)

1-5-Tini Howard-s/Celor-a. 3-Vlad returns 4.00

HACK/SLASH VS. VAMPIRELLA
Dynamite Entertainment: 2017 - No. 5, 2018 ($3.99)

1-5-Aldridge-s/Lobosco-a; multiple covers 4.00

HACKTIVIST
Archaia Black Label: Jan, 2014 - No. 4, Apr, 2014 ($3.99)

1-4-Kelly & Lanzing-s/To-a; created by Alyssa Milano 4.00
... Volume 2 (BOOM! Ent.; 7/15 - No. 6, 12/15, $3.99) 1-6-Kelly & Lanzing-s/To-a 4.00

HAGAR THE HORRIBLE (See Comics Reading Libraries in the Promotional Comics section)

HA HA COMICS (Teepee Tim No. 100 on; also see Giggle Comics)
Scope Mag.(Creston Publ.) No. 1-80/American Comics Group: Oct, 1943 - No. 99, Jan, 1955

1-Funny animal 41 82 123 250 418 585
2 21 42 63 126 206 285
3-5: Ken Hultgren-a begins? 15 30 45 90 140 190
6-10 14 28 42 80 115 150
11-20: 14-Infinity-c 12 24 36 69 97 125
21-40 11 22 33 60 83 105
41-43,45-94,97-99: 49,61-X-Mas-c 10 20 30 56 76 95
44-1st Tee-Pee Tim app.; begin series; Little Black Sambo app.
11 22 33 60 83 105
95,96-3-D effect-c/story 17 34 51 100 158 215

HAIL HYDRA (Secret Wars tie-in)
Marvel Comics: Sept, 2015 - No. 4, Jan, 2016 ($3.99, limited series)

1-4-Nomad (Ian Rogers) vs. Hydra; Remender-s/Boschi-a; Venom app. 4.00

HAIR BEAR BUNCH, THE (TV) (See Fun-In No. 13)
Gold Key: Feb, 1972 - No. 9, Feb, 1974 (Hanna-Barbera)

1 4 8 12 23 37 50
2-9 3 6 9 16 24 32

HALCYON
Image Comics: Nov, 2010 - No. 5, May, 2011 ($2.99)

Hal Jordan and the Green Lantern Corp #22 © DC

Halo: Blood Line #5 © MS

Hand of Fate #9 © ACE

	GD	VG	FN	VF	VF/NM	NM-
	2.0	4.0	6.0	8.0	9.0	9.2

GD VG FN VF VF/NM NM- 2.0 4.0 6.0 8.0 9.0 9.2

1-5-Guggenheim & Butters-s/Bodenheim-a 3.00

HALF PAST DANGER
IDW Publishing: May, 2013 - No. 6, Oct, 2013 ($3.99, limited series)

1-6: Dinosaurs and Nazis in 1943; Stephen Mooney-s/a/c 4.00

HALF PAST DANGER 2
IDW Publishing: Sept, 2017 - No. 5, Jan, 2018 ($3.99, limited series)

1-5-Nazis in 1943; Stephen Mooney-s/a/c 4.00

HAL JORDAN AND THE GREEN LANTERN CORPS (DC Rebirth) (Also see Green Lanterns)
DC Comics: Sept, 2016 - Present ($2.99)

1-24: 1-Venditti-s/Sandoval-a; Sinestro app.; GL Corps returns. 4,5,17,22-24-Van Sciver-a. 10-12-Larfleeze app. Kyle becomes a Green Lantern again 3.00
25-($3.99) Van Sciver-a 4.00
26-39: 26,27-Orion of the New Gods app. 30,31-Superman app. 32-Dark Nights: Metal. 37-39-Zod app. 3.00
...: Rebirth 1 (9/16, $2.99) Venditti-s/Van Sciver-a; Sinestro & Lyssa app. 3.00

HALLELUJAH TRAIL, THE (See Movie Classics)

HALL OF FAME FEATURING THE T.H.U.N.D.E.R. AGENTS
JC Productions(Archie Comics Group): May, 1983 - No. 3, Dec, 1983

1-3: Thunder Agents-r(Crandall, Kane, Tuska, Wood-a). 2-New Ditko-c 4.00

HALLOWEEN (Movie)
Chaos! Comics: Nov, 2000; Apr, 2001 ($2.95/$2.99, one-shots)

1-Brewer-a; Michael Myers childhood at the Sanitarium 3.00
...II: The Blackest Eyes (4/01, $2.99) Beck-a 3.00
...III: The Devil's Eyes (11/01, $2.99) Justiniano-a 3.00

HALLOWEEN (Halloween Nightdance on cover)(Movie)
Devils Due Publishing: Mar, 2008 - No. 4, May, 2008 ($3.50, limited series)

1-4-Seeley-a/Hutchinson-s; multiple covers on each 3.50
...: 30 Years of Terror (8/08, $5.50) short stories by various incl. Seeley 5.50

HALLOWEEN EVE
Image Comics: Oct, 2012 ($3.99, one-shot)

One-Shot - Brandon Montclare-s/Amy Reeder-a; two covers by Reeder 4.00

HALLOWEEN HORROR
Eclipse Comics: Oct, 1987 (Seduction of the Innocent #7)($1.75)

1-Pre-code horror-r 5.00

HALLOWEEN MEGAZINE
Marvel Comics: Dec, 1996 ($3.95, one-shot, 96 pgs.)

1-Reprints Tomb of Dracula 4.00

HALO GRAPHIC NOVEL (Based on video game)
Marvel Publishing Inc.: 2006 ($24.99, hardcover with dust jacket)

HC-Anthology set in the Halo universe; art by Bisley, Moebius and others; pin-up gallery by various incl. Darrow, Pratt, Williams and Van Fleet; Phil Hale painted-c 25.00

HALO: BLOOD LINE (Based on video game)
Marvel Comics: Feb, 2010 - No. 5, Jul, 2010 ($3.99, limited series)

1-5-Van Lente-s/Portela-a 4.00

HALO: ESCALATION (Based on video game)
Dark Horse Comics: Dec, 2013 - No. 24, Nov, 2015 ($3.99)

1-24: 1-4-Chris Schlerf-s/Sergio Ariño-a 4.00

HALO: FALL OF REACH - BOOT CAMP (Based on video game)
Marvel Comics: Nov, 2010 - No. 4, Apr, 2011 ($3.99, limited series)

1-4-Reed-s/Ruiz-a 4.00

HALO: FALL OF REACH - COVENANT (Based on video game)
Marvel Comics: Jun, 2011 - No. 4, Dec, 2011 ($3.99, limited series)

1-4-Reed-s/Ruiz-a 4.00

HALO: FALL OF REACH - INVASION (Based on video game)
Marvel Comics: Mar, 2012 - No. 4, Aug, 2012 ($3.99, limited series)

1-4-Reed-s/Ruiz-a 4.00

HALO: HELLJUMPER (Based on video game)
Marvel Comics: Sept, 2009 - No. 5, Jan, 2010 ($3.99, limited series)

1-5-Peter David-s/Eric Nguyen-a 4.00

HALO: INITIATION (Based on video game)
Dark Horse Comics: Aug, 2013 - No. 3, Oct, 2013 ($3.99, limited series)

1-3-Brian Reed-s/Marco Castiello-a 4.00

HALO: RISE OF ATRIOX (Based on video game)
Marvel Comics: Aug, 2017 - No. 5, Jan, 2018 ($3.99, limited series)

1-5: 1-Cullen Bunn-s/Eric Nguyen-a. 2-Houser-s/Gonzalez-a. 3-John Jackson Miller-s 4.00

HALO: UPRISING (Based on video game) (Also see Marvel Spotlight: Halo)
Marvel Comics: Oct, 2007 - No. 4, Jun, 2009 ($3.99, limited series)

1-4-Bendis-s/Maleev-a; takes place between the *Halo 2* and *Halo 3* video games 4.00

HALO JONES (See The Ballad of...)

HAMMER, THE
Dark Horse Comics: Oct, 1997 - No. 4, Jan, 1998 ($2.95, limited series)

1-4-Kelley Jones-s/c/a, ...: Uncle Alex (8/98, $2.95) 3.00

HAMMER, THE: THE OUTSIDER
Dark Horse Comics: Feb, 1999 - No. 3, Apr, 1999 ($2.95, limited series)

1-3-Kelley Jones-s/c/a 3.00

HAMMERLOCKE
DC Comics: Sept, 1992 - No. 9, May, 1993 ($1.75, limited series)

1-($2.50, 52 pgs.)-Chris Sprouse-c/a in all 4.00
2-9 3.00

HAMMER OF GOD (Also see Nexus)
First Comics: Feb, 1990 - No. 4, May, 1990 ($1.95, limited series)

1-4 3.00

HAMMER OF GOD: BUTCH
Dark Horse Comics: May, 1994 - No. 4, Aug, 1994 ($2.50, limited series)

1-3 3.00

HAMMER OF GOD: PENTATHLON
Dark Horse Comics: Jan, 1994 ($2.50, one shot)

1-Character from Nexus 3.00

HAMMER OF GOD: SWORD OF JUSTICE
First Comics: Feb 1991 - Mar 1991 ($4.95, lim. series, squarebound, 52 pgs.)

V2#1,2 5.00

HAMMER OF THE GODS
Insight Studio Groups: 2001 - No. 5, 2001 ($2.95, limited series)

1-Michael Oeming & Mark Wheatley-s/a; Frank Cho-c 6.00
1-(IDW, 7/11, $1.00) reprints #1 with "Hundred Penny Press" logo on Oeming cover 3.00
2-5: 3-Hughes-c. 5-Dave Johnson-c 3.00
The Color Saga (2002, $4.95) r/"Enemy of the Gods" internet strip 5.00
Mortal Enemy TPB (2002, $18.95) r/#1-5; intro. by Peter David; afterword by Raven 19.00

HAMMER OF THE GODS: HAMMER HITS CHINA
Image Comics: Feb, 2003 - No. 3, Sept, 2003 ($2.95, limited series)

1-3-Oeming & Wheatley-s/a; Oeming-c. 2-Frankenstein Mobster by Wheatley 3.00

HANDBOOK OF THE CONAN UNIVERSE, THE
Marvel Comics: June, 1985; Jan, 1986 ($1.25, one-shot)

1-(6/85) Kaluta-c (2 printings) 6.00
1-(1/86) Kaluta-c 6.00

	GD	VG	FN	VF	VF/NM	NM-
nn-(no date, circa '87-88, B&W, 36 pgs.) reprints '86 with changes; new painted cover	1	2	3	5	6	8

HAND OF FATE (Formerly Men Against Crime)
Ace Magazines: No. 8, Dec, 1951 - No. 25, Dec, 1954 (Weird/horror stories) (Two #25's)

	GD	VG	FN	VF	VF/NM	NM-
8-Surrealistic text story	53	106	159	334	567	800
9,10,21-Necronomicon sty; drug belladonna used	36	72	108	211	343	475
11-18,20,22,23	30	60	90	177	289	400
19-Bondage, hypo needle scenes	32	64	96	188	307	425
24-Electric chair-c	39	78	117	240	395	550
25a(11/54), 25b(12/54)-Both have Cameron-a	25	50	75	150	245	340

NOTE: ***Cameron** a-9, 10, 19-25a, 25b; c-13. **Sekowsky** a-8, 9, 13, 14.*

HAND OF FATE
Eclipse Comics: Feb, 1988 - No. 3, Apr, 1988 ($1.75/$2.00, Baxter paper)

1-3; 3-B&W 4.00

HANDS OF THE DRAGON
Seaboard Periodicals (Atlas): June, 1975

	GD	VG	FN	VF	VF/NM	NM-
1-Origin/1st app.; Craig-a(p)/Mooney inks	2	4	6	11	16	20

HANGMAN, THE
Archie Comic Publications: Dec, 2015 - No. 4, Dec, 2016 ($3.99)

1-4-Tieri-s/Ruiz-a; new Hangman recruited; multiple covers 4.00

HANGMAN COMICS (Special Comics No. 1; Black Hood No. 9 on)

Hangman Comics #3 © MLJ

Han Solo #2 © Lucasfilm

Hap Hazard Comics #1 © ACE

GD 2.0 | VG 4.0 | FN 6.0 | VF 8.0 | VF/NM 9.0 | NM- 9.2

(Also see Flyman, Mighty Comics, Mighty Crusaders & Pep Comics)
MLJ Magazines: No. 2, Spring, 1942 - No. 8, Fall, 1943

2-The Hangman, Boy Buddies begin 343 686 1029 2400 4200 6000
3-Beheading splash pg.; 1st Nazi war-c 320 640 960 2240 3920 5600
4-Classic Nazi WWII hunchback torture-c 300 600 900 2070 3635 5200
5-1st Japan war-c 245 490 735 1568 2684 3800
6-8: 8-2nd app. Super Duck (ties w/Jolly Jingles #11)
226 452 678 1446 2473 3500

NOTE: *Fuje a-7(3), 8(3); c-3. Reinman c/a-3. Bondage c-3. Sahle c-6.*

HANK
Pentagon Publishing Co.: 1946

nn-Coulton Waugh's newspaper reprint 10 20 30 54 72 90

HANK JOHNSON, AGENT OF HYDRA (Secret Wars tie-in)
Marvel Comics: Oct, 2015 ($3.99, one-shot)

1-Mandel-s/Walsh-a; Steranko cover swipe by Conner 4.00

HANNA-BARBERA (See Golden Comics Digest No. 2, 7, 11)

HANNA-BARBERA ALL-STARS
Archie Publications: Oct, 1995 - No. 4, Apr, 1996 ($1.50, bi-monthly)

1-4 4.00

HANNA-BARBERA BANDWAGON (TV)
Gold Key: Oct, 1962 - No. 3, Apr, 1963

1-Giant, 84 pgs. 1-Augie Doggie app.; 1st app. Lippy the Lion, Touché Turtle & Dum Dum, Wally Gator, Loopy de Loop, 10 20 30 69 147 225
2-Giant, 84 pgs.; Mr. & Mrs. J. Evil Scientist (1st app.) in Snagglepuss story; Yakky Doodle, Ruff and Reddy and others app. 8 16 24 51 96 140
3-Regular size; Mr. & Mrs. J. Evil Scientist app. (pre-#1), Snagglepuss, Wally Gator and others app. 6 12 18 40 73 105

HANNA-BARBERA GIANT SIZE
Harvey Comics: Oct, 1992 - No. 3 ($2.25, 68 pgs.)

V2#1-3:Flintstones, Yogi Bear, Magilla Gorilla, Huckleberry Hound, Quick Draw McGraw, Yakky Doodle & Chopper, Jetsons & others 6.00

HANNA-BARBERA HI-ADVENTURE HEROES (See Hi-Adventure...)

HANNA-BARBERA PARADE (TV)
Charlton Comics: Sept, 1971 - No. 10, Dec, 1972

1 6 12 18 41 76 110
2,4-10 4 8 12 25 40 55
3-(52 pgs.)- "Summer Picnic" 5 10 15 33 57 80

NOTE: *No. 4 (1/72) went on sale late in 1972 with the January 1973 issues.*

HANNA-BARBERA PRESENTS
Archie Publications: Nov, 1995 - No. 8 ($1.50, bi-monthly)

1-8: 1-Atom Ant & Secret Squirrel. 2-Wacky Races. 3-Yogi Bear. 4-Quick Draw McGraw & Magilla Gorilla. 5-A Pup Named Scooby-Doo. 6-Superstar Olympics. 7-Wacky Races. 8-Frankenstein Jr. & the Impossibles 4.00

HANNA-BARBERA SPOTLIGHT (See Spotlight)

HANNA-BARBERA SUPER TV HEROES (TV)
Gold Key: Apr, 1968 - No. 7, Oct, 1969 (Hanna-Barbera)

1-The Birdman, The Herculoids (ends #6; not in #3), Moby Dick, Young Samson & Goliath (ends #2,4), and The Mighty Mightor begin; Spiegle-a in all
11 22 33 76 163 250
2-The Galaxy Trio app.; Shazzan begins; 12¢ & 15¢ versions exist
8 16 24 56 108 160
3,6,7-The Space Ghost app. 8 16 24 51 96 140
4,5 7 14 21 44 82 120

NOTE: *Birdman in #1,2,4,5. Herculoids in #2,4-7. Mighty Mightor in #1,2,4-7. Moby Dick in all. Shazzan in #2-5. Young Samson & Goliath in #1,3.*

HANNA-BARBERA TV FUN FAVORITES (See Golden Comics Digest #2,7,11)

HANNA-BARBERA (TV STARS) (See TV Stars)

HANS BRINKER (Disney)
Dell Publishing Co.: No. 1273, Feb, 1962 (one-shot)

Four Color 1273-Movie, photo-c 6 12 18 37 66 95

HANS CHRISTIAN ANDERSEN
Ziff-Davis Publ. Co.: 1953 (100 pgs., Special Issue)

nn-Danny Kaye (movie)-Photo-c; fairy tales 18 36 54 105 165 225

HANSEL & GRETEL
Dell Publishing Co.: No. 590, Oct, 1954 (one-shot)

Four Color 590-Partial photo-c 6 12 18 42 79 115

HANSI, THE GIRL WHO LOVED THE SWASTIKA
Spire Christian Comics (Fleming H. Revell Co.): 1973, 1976 (39¢/49¢)

1973 edition with 39¢-c 9 18 27 59 117 175
1976 edition with 49¢-c 7 14 21 49 92 135

HAN SOLO (Star Wars)
Marvel Comics: Aug, 2016 - No. 5, Jan, 2017 ($3.99, limited series)

1-5-Marjorie Liu-s/Mark Brooks-a/Lee Bermejo-c; takes place between Episodes 4 & 5 4.00

HAP HAZARD COMICS (Real Love No. 25 on)
Ace Magazines (Readers' Research): Summer, 1944 - No. 24, Feb, 1949
(#1-6 are quarterly issues)

1 15 30 45 90 140 190
2 10 20 30 54 72 90
3-10 9 18 27 47 61 75
11-13,15-24 8 16 24 42 54 65
14-Feldstein-c (4/47) 10 20 30 56 76 95

HAP HOPPER (See Comics Revue No. 2)

HAPPIEST MILLIONAIRE, THE (See Movie Comics)

HAPPI TIM (See March of Comics No. 182)

HAPPY
Image Comics: Sept, 2012 - No. 4, Feb, 2013 ($2.99, limited series)

1-4-Grant Morrison-s/Darick Robertson-a. 1-Covers by Robertson & Allred 5.00

HAPPY BIRTHDAY MARTHA WASHINGTON (Also see Give Me Liberty, Martha Washington Goes To War, & Martha Washington Stranded In Space)
Dark Horse Comics: Mar, 1995 ($2.95, one-shot)

1-Miller script; Gibbons-c/a 3.00

HAPPY COMICS (Happy Rabbit No. 41 on)
Nedor Publ./Standard Comics (Animated Cartoons): Aug, 1943 - No. 40, Dec, 1950
(Companion to Goofy Comics)

1-Funny animal 36 72 108 211 343 475
2 19 38 57 109 172 235
3-10 14 28 42 81 118 155
11-19 12 24 36 69 97 125
20-31,34-37-Frazetta text illos in all (2 in #34&35, 3 in #27,28,30). 27-Al Fago-a
14 28 42 78 112 145
32-Frazetta-a, 7 pgs. plus 2 text illos; Roussos-a 23 46 69 136 223 310
33-Frazetta-a(2), 6 pgs. each (Scarce) 32 64 96 190 310 430
38-40 11 22 33 60 83 105

HAPPYDALE: DEVILS IN THE DESERT
DC Comics (Vertigo): 1999 - No. 2, 1999 ($6.95, limited series)

1,2-Andrew Dabb-s/Seth Fisher-a 7.00

HAPPY DAYS (TV)(See Kite Fun Book)
Gold Key: Mar, 1979 - No. 6, Feb, 1980

1-Photo-c of TV cast; 35¢-c 3 6 9 16 23 30
2-6-(40¢-c) 2 4 6 9 12 15

HAPPY HOLIDAY (See March of Comics No. 181)

HAPPY HOULIHANS (Saddle Justice No. 3 on; see Blackstone, The Magician Detective)
E. C. Comics: Fall, 1947 - No. 2, Winter, 1947-48

1-Origin Moon Girl (same date as Moon Girl #1) 65 130 195 416 708 1000
2 36 72 108 211 343 475

HAPPY JACK
Red Top (Decker): Aug, 1957 - No. 2, Nov, 1957

V1#1,2 5 10 15 22 26 30

HAPPY JACK HOWARD
Red Top (Farrell)/Decker: 1957

nn-Reprints Handy Andy story from E. C. Dandy Comics #5, renamed "Happy Jack"
5 10 15 22 26 30

HAPPY RABBIT (Formerly Happy Comics)
Standard Comics (Animated Cartoons): No. 41, Feb, 1951 - No. 48, Apr, 1952

41-Funny animal 10 20 30 54 72 90
42-48 8 16 24 42 54 65

HARBINGER (Also see Unity)
Valiant: Jan, 1992 - No. 41, June, 1995 ($1.95/$2.50)

0-Prequel to the series; available by redeeming coupons in #1-6; cover image has pink sky; title logo is blue 4 8 12 28 47 65

Harbinger #14 © VAL

Hardcase #21 © MAL

Harley Quinn #1 © DC

	GD 2.0	VG 4.0	FN 6.0	VF 8.0	VF/NM 9.0	NM- 9.2
0-(2nd printing) cover has blue sky & red logo	1	3	4	6	8	10
1-1st app.	7	14	21	48	89	130
2-4: 4-Low print run	2	4	6	13	18	22
5,6: 5-Solar app. 6-Torque dies	2	4	6	9	12	15
7-10: 8,9-Unity x-overs. 8-Miller-c. 9-Simonson-c. 10-1st app. H.A.R.D Corps (10/92)	1	2	3	5	6	8

11-24,26-41: 14-1st app. Stronghold. 18-Intro Screen. 19-1st app. Stunner. 22-Archer & Armstrong app. 24-Cover similar to #1. 26-Intro New Harbingers. 29-Bound-in trading card. 30-H.A.R.D. Corps app. 32-Eternal Warrior app. 33-Dr. Eclipse app. 4.00
25-($3.50, 52 pgs.)-Harada vs. Sting 5.00
...Files 1,2 (8/94,2/95 $2.50) 4.00
...: The Beginning HC (2007, $24.95) recolored reprints #0-7 and Story of Harada from coupons from #1-6; new "Origin of Harada" story by Shooter and Bob Hall 30.00
Trade paperback nn (11/92, $9.95)-Reprints #1-4 & comes polybagged with a copy of Harbinger #0 w/new-c. Price for TPB only 15.00
NOTE: *Issues 1-6 have coupons with origin of Harada and are redeemable for Harbinger #0.*

HARBINGER
Valiant Entertainment: Jun, 2012 - Present ($3.99)(#0 released between #8 & #9)
1-Dysart-s/Khari Evans-a; covers by Lozzi and Suayan (Pullbox variant) 4.00
1-Variant cover by Braithwaite 10.00
1-QR voice variant cover by Jelena Djurdjevic 40.00
2-24-Two covers on each (standard & pullbox). 2-Origin continues. 11-14-Harbinger Wars tie-in. 23-Flamingo dies 4.00
25-($4.99) Back-up story by Tiwary & Larosa; bonus features and cover gallery 5.00
#0 (2/13, $3.99) Origin of Harada; Suayan & Pere Pérez-a; covers by Crain & Suayan 4.00
#0-Variant gatefold-c by Lewis Larosa 15.00
... Bleeding Monk #0 (3/14, $3.99) Dysart-s; art by Evans, Suayan, Segovia & LaRosa 4.00
... Faith #0 (12/14, $3.99) Dysart-s; Robert Gill-a 4.00

HARBINGER: OMEGAS
Valiant Entertainment: Jul, 2014 - No. 3, Oct, 2014 ($3.99, limited series)
1-3-Dysart-s/Sandoval-a 4.00

HARBINGER RENEGADE
Valiant Entertainment: Nov, 2016 - No. 8, Oct, 2017; No. 0 Nov, 2017 ($3.99, limited series)
1-8: 1-Rafer Roberts-s/Darick Robertson-a; intro Alexander Solomon. 6-Ryp-a 4.00
#0-(11/17) Follows #8; Ryp-a; H.A.R.D. Corps app. 4.00

HARBINGER WARS
Valiant Entertainment: Apr, 2013 - No. 4, Jul, 2013 ($3.99, limited series)
1-4: 1-Dysart-s/Henry, Crain & Suayan-a; covers by Larosa & Henry (Pullbox) 4.00
1-Variant cover by Crain 10.00
1-Variant cover by Zircher 50.00

HARD BOILED
Dark Horse Comics: Sept, 1990 - No. 3, Mar, 1992 ($4.95/$5.95, 8 1/2x11", lim. series)

	GD	VG	FN	VF	VF/NM	NM-
1-Frank Miller-s/Darrow-c/a in all; sexually explicit & violent	2	4	6	11	16	20
2,3	2	4	6	8	10	12

TPB (5/93, $15.95) 20.00
Big Damn Hard Boiled (12/97, $29.95, B&W) r/#1-3 30.00

HARDCASE (See Break Thru, Flood Relief & Ultraforce, 1st Series)
Malibu Comics (Ultraverse): June, 1993 - No. 26, Aug, 1995 ($1.95/$2.50)
1-Intro Hardcase; Dave Gibbons-c; has coupon for Ultraverse Premiere #0; Jim Callahan-a(p) begin, ends #3 4.00
1-With coupon missing 2.00
1-Platinum Edition 6.00
1-Holographic Cover Edition; 1st full-c holograph tied w/Prime 1 & Strangers 1 8.00
1-Ultra Limited silver foil-c 6.00
2,3-Callahan-a, 2-($2.50)-Newsstand edition bagged w/trading card 3.00
4,6-15, 17-19: 4-Strangers app. 7-Break-Thru x-over. 8-Solution app. 9-Vs. Turf. 12-Silver foil logo, wraparound-c. 17-Prime app. 3.00
5-($2.50, 48 pgs.)-Rune flip-c/story by B. Smith (3 pgs.) 4.00
16 ($3.50, 68 pgs.)-Rune pin-up 4.00
20-26: 23-Loki app. 3.00
NOTE: *Perez a-8(2); c-20i.*

HARDCORE
Image Comics: May, 2012 ($2.99)
1-Kirkman-s/Stelfreeze-a/Silvestri-c 3.00

HARDCORE STATION
DC Comics: July, 1998 - No. 6, Dec, 1998 ($2.50, limited series)
1-6-Starlin-s/a(p). 3-Green Lantern-c/app. 5,6-JLA-c/app. 3.00

GD VG FN VF VF/NM NM-
2.0 4.0 6.0 8.0 9.0 9.2

H.A.R.D. CORPS, THE (See Harbinger #10)
Valiant: Dec, 1992 - No. 30, Feb, 1995 ($2.25) (Harbinger spin-off)
1-($2.50)-Gatefold-c by Jim Lee & Bob Layton 5.00
1-Gold variant 15.00
2-30: 5-Bloodshot-c/story cont'd from Bloodshot #3. 5-Variant edition; came w/Comic Defense System. 10-Turok app. 17-vs. Armorines. 18-Bound-in trading card. 20-Harbinger app. 3.00

HARD TIME
DC Comics (Focus): Apr, 2004 - No. 12, Mar, 2005 ($2.50)
1-12-Gerber-s/Hurtt-a; 1-Includes previews of other DC Focus series 3.00
...: 50 to Life (2004, $9.95, TPB) r/#1-6; cover gallery with sketches 10.00

HARD TIME: SEASON TWO
DC Comics: Feb, 2006 - No. 7, Aug, 2006 ($2.50/$2.99)
1-5-Gerber-s/Hurtt-a 3.00
6,7-($2.99) 7-Ethan paroled in 2053 3.00

HARDWARE
DC Comics (Milestone): Apr, 1993 - No. 50, Apr, 1997 ($1.50/$1.75/$2.50)
1-($2.95)-Collector's Edition polybagged w/poster & trading card (direct sale only) 4.00
1-Platinum Edition 6.00
1-15,17-19: 11-Shadow War x-over. 11,14-Simonson-c. 12-Buckler-a(p). 17-Worlds Collide Pt. 2. 18-Simonson-c; Worlds Collide Pt. 9. 15-1st Humberto Ramos DC work 3.00
16,25: 16-($2.50, 52 pgs.)-Newsstand Ed. 25-($2.95, 52 pgs.) 4.00
16,50-($3.95, 52 pgs.)-16-Collector's Edition w/gatefold 2nd cover by Byrne; new armor; Icon app. 5.00
20-24,26-49: 49-Moebius-c 3.00
...: The Man in the Machine TPB (2010, $19.99) r/#1-8 20.00

HARDY BOYS, THE (Disney
Dell Publ. Co.: No. 760, Dec, 1956 - No. 964, Jan, 1959 (Mickey Mouse Club)

	GD	VG	FN	VF	VF/NM	NM-
Four Color 760 (#1)-Photo-c	9	18	27	62	126	190
Four Color 830(8/57), 887(1/58), 964-Photo-c	8	16	24	54	102	150

HARDY BOYS, THE (TV)
Gold Key: Apr, 1970 - No. 4, Jan, 1971

	GD	VG	FN	VF	VF/NM	NM-
1	4	8	12	27	44	60
2-4	3	6	9	17	26	35

HARLAN ELLISON'S DREAM CORRIDOR
Dark Horse Comics: Mar, 1995 - No. 5, July, 1995 ($2.95, anthology)
1-5: Adaptation of Ellison stories. 1-4-Byrne-a. 4.00
Special (1/95, $4.95) 6.00
Trade paperback-(1996, $18.95, 192 pgs)-r/#1-5 & Special #1 19.00

HARLAN ELLISON'S DREAM CORRIDOR QUARTERLY
Dark Horse Comics: V2#1, Aug, 1996 ($5.95, anthology, squarebound)
V2#1-Adaptations of Ellison's stories w/new material; Neal Adams-a 6.00
Volume 2 TPB (3/07, $19.95) r/V2#1 and unpublished material incl. last Swan-a 20.00

HARLEM GLOBETROTTERS (TV) (See Fun-In No. 8, 10)
Gold Key: Apr, 1972 - No. 12, Jan, 1975 (Hanna-Barbera)

	GD	VG	FN	VF	VF/NM	NM-
1	4	8	12	25	40	55
2-5	3	6	9	15	22	28
6-12	2	4	6	13	18	22

NOTE: *#4, 8, and 12 contain 16 extra pages of advertising.*

HARLEQUIN ROMANCE
Dark Horse Comics: Nov, 2001 ($10.95, hardcover, one-shot)
nn-Neil Gaiman-s; painted-a/c by John Bolton 11.00

HARLEY & IVY MEET BETTY & VERONICA
DC Comics: Dec, 2017 - No. 6, May, 2018 ($3.99, limited series)
1-6: 1-Harvey & Ivy go to Riverdale; Dini & Andreyko-s/Braga-a. 1-Conner-c. 2-Zatanna app. 3,4-The Joker app. 4.00
1-Variant-c by Adam Hughes 4.00

HARLEY QUINN (See Batman Adventures #12 for 1st app.)(Also see Gotham City Sirens)
DC Comics: Dec, 2000 - No. 38, Jan, 2004 ($2.95/$2.25/$2.50)

	GD	VG	FN	VF	VF/NM	NM-
1-Joker and Poison Ivy app.; Terry & Rachel Dodson-a/c	4	8	12	28	47	65
2,3-($2.25): 2-Two-Face-c/app. 3-Slumber party	2	4	6	10	14	18
4-9,11-($2.25). 6,7-Riddler app.	1	2	3	5	6	8
10-Batgirl-c/s	2	4	6	10	14	18
12-($2.95) Batman app.	2	4	6	10	14	18
13,17-19: 13-Joker: Last Laugh. 17,18-Bizarro-c/app. 19-Superman-c	2	4	6	10	14	18

14-16,20-24,26-31,33-37: 23-Begin $2.50-c. 23,24-Martian Manhunter app.

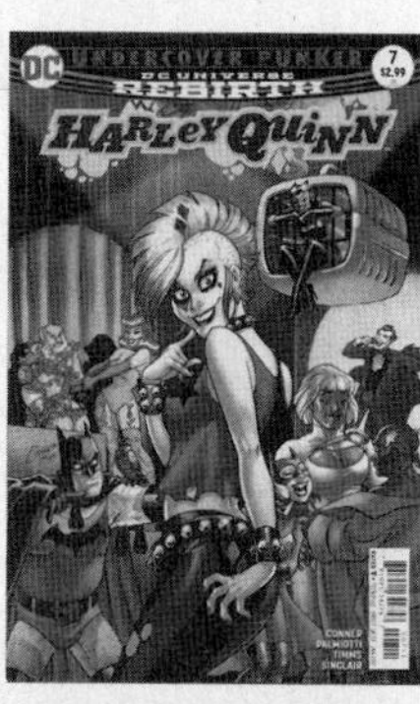

Harley Quinn (2016 series) #7 © DC

Harrow County #2 © Bunn & Crook

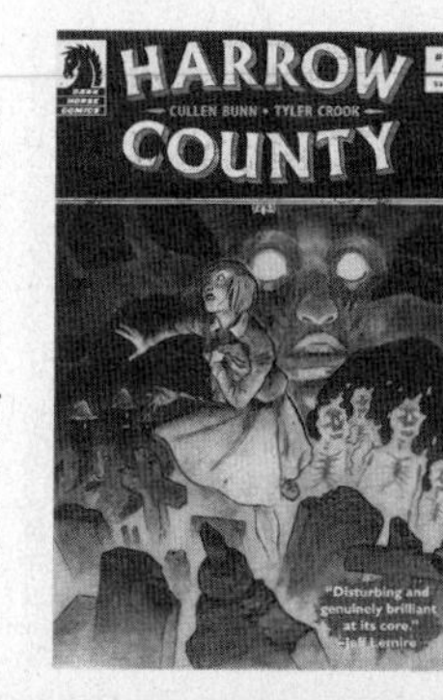

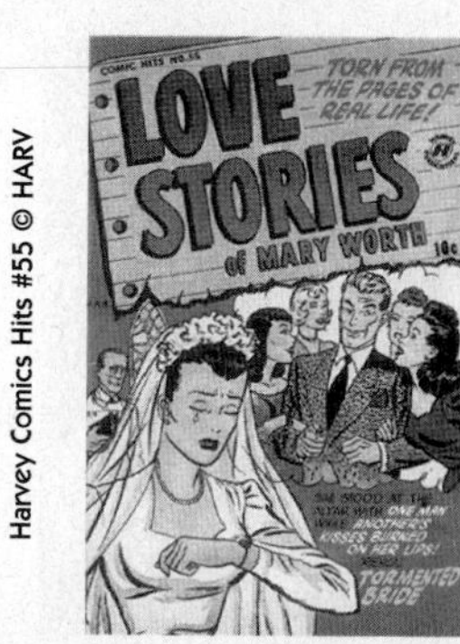

Harvey Comics Hits #55 © HARV

	GD 2.0	VG 4.0	FN 6.0	VF 8.0	VF/NM 9.0	NM- 9.2
	1	2	3	5	6	8
25-Classic Joker-c/s	3	6	9	15	22	28
32-Joker-c/app.	2	4	6	11	16	20
38-Last issue; Adlard-a/Morse-c	3	6	9	14	20	25
Harley & Ivy: Love on the Lam (2001, $5.95) Winick-s/Chiodo-c/a	3	6	9	14	19	24
...: Our Worlds at War (10/01, $2.95) Jae Lee-c; art by various	2	4	6	11	16	20

HARLEY QUINN (DC New 52)
DC Comics: No. 0, Jan, 2014 - No. 30, Sept, 2016 ($2.99/$3.99)

	GD	VG	FN	VF	VF/NM	NM-
0-Conner & Palmiotti-s; art by Conner & various; Conner-c	2	4	6	9	12	15
0-Variant-c by Stephane Roux	2	4	6	11	16	20
1-(2/14) Chad Hardin-a; Conner-c	3	6	9	14	19	24
1-Variant-c by Adam Hughes	12	24	36	82	179	275
1-Halloween Fest Special Edition (12/15, free) r/#1 with "Halloween ComicFest" logo						3.00
2-Poison Ivy app.	2	4	6	9	12	15
3-5: 4-Roux-a	1	2	3	5	6	8
6-16: 6,7-Poison Ivy app. 11-13-Power Girl app. 16-Intro. of The Gang of Harleys						4.00
17-30-($3.99) 17-19-Capt Strong app. 20,21-Deadshot app. 25-Joker app. 26-28-Red Tool app. 30-Charretier-a; Poison Ivy app.						4.00
Annual 1 (12/14, $5.99) Polybagged with "Rub 'N Smell" pages						6.00
... & The Suicide Squad April Fools' Special 1 (6/16, $4.99) Rob Williams-s/Jim Lee-a						5.00
...Director's Cut #0 (8/14, $4.99) With commentary by Conner & Palmiotti; cover gallery						5.00
...: Futures End 1 (11/14, $2.99, regular-c) Five years later; Joker app.						3.00
...: Futures End 1 (11/14, $3.99, 3-D cover)						4.00
... Holiday Special (2/15, $4.99) Christmas-themed stories; back-up Darwyn Cooke-a						5.00
... Invades Comic-Con International: San Diego 1 (9/14, $4.99) Wraparound-c						5.00
... Road Trip Special (11/15, $5.99) Harley, Catwoman & Poison Ivy road trip; Conner-c						6.00
... Valentine's Day Special (4/15, $4.99) Bruce Wayne and Poison Ivy app.						5.00

HARLEY QUINN (DC Rebirth)
DC Comics: Oct, 2016 - Present ($2.99)

	GD	VG	FN	VF	VF/NM	NM-
1-Conner & Palmiotti-s/Hardin-a; Poison Ivy & Red Tool app.						4.00
2-6: 4-Linsner-a. 6-Joker flashback w/Jill Thompson-a (4 pgs.)						3.00
7-24: 9-Kaluta-a (4 pgs.). 10-Linsner & Moritat-a. 15,16-Power Girl & Atlee app. 17-Back-up stories by Dini & Palmiotti-s/Blevins-a begin, thru #25; Joker app.						3.00
25-($3.99) Back-up story w/Joker continues in Harley Loves Joker #1						4.00
26-39: 27-Tieri-s/Carlini-a/Thompson-c. 29-Kaluta-a (5 pgs.) 34-Last Palmiotti & Conner-s. 35-39-Tieri-s. 36,37-Penguin app.						3.00
... Batman Day Special Edition (10/17, giveaway) r/#7; Joker app.						3.00
...: Be Careful What You Wish For Special Edition 1 (3/18, $4.99) Reprints story from Loot Crate edition plus 18 new pages; art by Conner, Hardin, Schmidt & Caldwell						5.00
... 25th Anniversary Special 1 (11/17, $4.99) Short stories by various incl. Dini, Conner, Palmiotti, Zdarsky, Quinones, Hardin; 2 covers by Conner & Dodson						5.00
Harley Quinn's Greatest Hits TPB (2016, $9.99) r/Batman Advs. #12 & other stories						10.00

HARLEY QUINN AND HER GANG OF HARLEYS
DC Comics: Jun, 2016 - No. 6, Nov, 2016 ($3.99, limited series)

	GD	VG	FN	VF	VF/NM	NM-
1-6-Palmiotti & Tieri-s/Mauricet-a/Conner-c; intro. Harley Sinn. 5-Origin of Harley Sinn						4.00

HARLEY QUINN AND POWER GIRL
DC Comics: Aug, 2015 - No. 6, Feb, 2016 ($3.99, limited series)

	GD	VG	FN	VF	VF/NM	NM-
1-6-Takes place during Harley Quinn #11-13; Vartox app.; Roux-a						4.00

HARLEY'S LITTLE BLACK BOOK (Harley Quinn team-up book)
DC Comics: Feb, 2016 - No. 6, May, 2017 ($4.99, bi-monthly)

	GD	VG	FN	VF	VF/NM	NM-
1-4,6: 1-Palmiotti & Conner-s; Wonder Woman app.; Conner-c. 2-Green Lantern app. 3-Zatanna app.; Linsner-a. 4-DC Bombshells app.; Tucci-a. 6-Lobo app.; Bisley-a						5.00
1-Polybagged variant-c by Campbell (3 versions: sketch, B&W, and color)	1	2	3	5	6	8
5-Neal Adams-a; homage to "Superman vs. Muhammad Ali"						5.00

HAROLD TEEN (See Popular Comics, & Super Comics)
Dell Publishing Co.: No. 2, 1942 - No. 209, Jan, 1949

	GD	VG	FN	VF	VF/NM	NM-
Four Color 2	32	64	96	230	515	800
Four Color 209	6	12	18	40	73	105

HARROW COUNTY
Dark Horse Comics: May, 2015 - Present ($3.99)

	GD	VG	FN	VF	VF/NM	NM-
1-28: 1-8-Cullen Bunn-s/Tyler Crook-a. 9,17-Carla Speed McNeil-a						4.00
1-Halloween ComicFest Edition (10/16, no price) r/#1						3.00

HARROWERS, THE (See Clive Barker's...)

HARSH REALM (Inspired 1999 TV series)
Harris Comics: 1993- No. 6, 1994 ($2.95, limited series)

	GD	VG	FN	VF	VF/NM	NM-
1-6: Painted-c. Hudnall-s/Paquette & Ridgway-a						4.00
TPB (2000, $14.95) r/series						15.00

HARVESTER, THE
Legendary Comics: Feb, 2015 - No. 6, Jul, 2015 ($3.99)

	GD	VG	FN	VF	VF/NM	NM-
1-6-Brandon Seifert-s/Eric Battle-a/c						4.00

HARVEY
Marvel Comics: Oct, 1970; No. 2, 12/70; No. 3, 6/72 - No. 6, 12/72

	GD	VG	FN	VF	VF/NM	NM-
1-Teenage	10	20	30	66	138	210
2-6	7	14	21	46	86	125

HARVEY COLLECTORS COMICS (Titled Richie Rich Collectors Comics on cover of #6-on)
Harvey Publ.: Sept, 1975 - No. 15, Jan, 1978; No. 16, Oct, 1979 (52 pgs.)

	GD	VG	FN	VF	VF/NM	NM-
1-Reprints Richie Rich #1,2	2	4	6	13	18	22
2-10: 7-Splash pg. shows cover to Friendly Ghost Casper #1	2	4	6	8	11	14
11-16: 16-Sad Sack-r	1	2	3	5	7	9

NOTE: *All reprints: Casper-#2, 7, Richie Rich-#1, 3, 5, 6, 8-15, Sad Sack-#16. Wendy-#4.*

HARVEY COMICS HITS (Formerly Joe Palooka #50)
Harvey Publications: No. 51, Oct, 1951 - No. 62, Apr, 1953

	GD	VG	FN	VF	VF/NM	NM-
51-The Phantom	37	74	111	222	361	500
52-Steve Canyon's Air Power(Air Force sponsored)	13	26	39	72	101	130
53-Mandrake the Magician	20	40	60	114	182	250
54-Tim Tyler's Tales of Jungle Terror	13	26	39	74	105	135
55-Love Stories of Mary Worth	11	22	33	64	90	115
56-The Phantom; bondage-c	27	54	81	162	266	370
57-Rip Kirby Exposes the Kidnap Racket; entire book by Alex Raymond	15	30	45	88	137	185
58-Girls in White (nurses stories)	12	24	36	67	94	120
59-Tales of the Invisible featuring Scarlet O'Neil	12	24	36	69	97	125
60-Paramount Animated Comics #1 (9/52) (3rd app. Baby Huey); 2nd Harvey app. Baby Huey & Casper the Friendly Ghost (1st in Little Audrey #25 (8/52)); 1st app. Herman & Catnip (c/story) & Buzzy the Crow	60	120	180	381	653	925
61-Casper the Friendly Ghost #6 (3rd Harvey Casper, 10/52)-Casper-c	53	106	159	334	567	800
62-Paramount Animated Comics #2; Herman & Catnip, Baby Huey & Buzzy the Crow	18	36	54	105	165	225

HARVEY COMICS LIBRARY
Harvey Publications: Apr, 1952 - No. 2, 1952

	GD	VG	FN	VF	VF/NM	NM-
1-Teen-Age Dope Slaves as exposed by Rex Morgan, M.D.; drug propaganda story; used in **SOTI**, pg. 27	300	600	900	2010	3505	5000
2-Dick Tracy Presents Sparkle Plenty in "Blackmail Terror"	20	40	60	114	182	250

HARVEY COMICS SPOTLIGHT
Harvey Comics: Sept, 1987 - No. 4, Mar, 1988 (75¢/$1.00)

	GD	VG	FN	VF	VF/NM	NM-
1-New material; begin 75¢, ends #3; Sad Sack						5.00
2-4: 2,4-All new material. 2-Baby Huey. 3-Little Dot; contains reprints w/5 pg. new story. 4-$1.00-c; Little Audrey						4.00

NOTE: No. 5 was advertised but not published.

HARVEY HITS (Also see Tastee-Freez Comics in the Promotional Comics section)
Harvey Publications: Sept, 1957 - No. 122, Nov, 1967

	GD	VG	FN	VF	VF/NM	NM-
1-The Phantom	27	54	81	194	435	675
2-Rags Rabbit (10/57)	5	10	15	35	63	90
3-Richie Rich (11/57)-r/Little Dot; 1st book devoted to Richie Rich; see Little Dot for 1st app.	145	290	435	1196	2698	4200
4-Little Dot's Uncles (12/57)	15	30	45	103	227	350
5-Stevie Mazie's Boy Friend (1/58)	4	8	12	28	47	65
6-The Phantom (2/58); 2pg. Powell-a	17	34	51	119	265	410
7-Wendy the Good Little Witch (3/58, pre-dates Wendy #1; 1st book devoted to Wendy)	46	92	138	340	770	1200
8-Sad Sack's Army Life; George Baker-c	8	16	24	52	99	145
9-Richie Rich's Golden Deeds; (2nd book devoted to Richie Rich) reprints Richie Rich story from Tastee-Freez #1	75	150	225	600	1350	2100
10-Little Lotta's Lunch Box	10	20	30	70	150	230
11-Little Audrey Summer Fun (7/58)	8	16	24	55	105	155
12-The Phantom; 2pg. Powell-a (8/58)	14	28	42	96	211	325
13-Little Dot's Uncles (9/58); Richie Rich 1pg.	10	20	30	67	141	215
14-Herman & Katnip (10/58, TV/movies)	4	8	12	28	47	65
15-The Phantom (12/58)-1 pg. origin	15	30	45	103	227	350
16-Wendy the Good Little Witch (1/59); Casper app.	12	24	36	79	170	260
17-Sad Sack's Army Life (2/59)	5	10	15	34	66	85
18-Buzzy & the Crow	4	8	12	25	40	55

Harvey Hits #107 © HARV

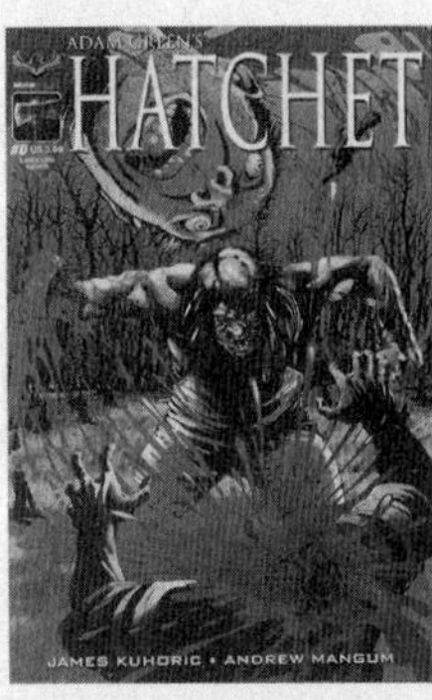

Hatchet #0 © ArieScope Picts.

Haunt #1 © TMP

	GD 2.0	VG 4.0	FN 6.0	VF 8.0	VF/NM 9.0	NM- 9.2
19-Little Audrey (4/59)	5	10	15	33	57	80
20-Casper & Spooky	7	14	21	44	82	120
21-Wendy the Witch	7	14	21	44	82	120
22-Sad Sack's Army Life	4	8	12	28	47	65
23-Wendy the Witch (8/59)	7	14	21	44	82	120
24-Little Dot's Uncles (9/59); Richie Rich 1pg.	8	16	24	54	102	150
25-Herman & Katnip (10/59)	3	6	9	21	33	45
26-The Phantom (11/59)	11	22	33	73	157	240
27-Wendy the Good Little Witch (12/59)	6	12	18	42	79	115
28-Sad Sack's Army Life (1/60)	4	8	12	25	40	55
29-Harvey-Toon (No.1)('60); Casper, Buzzy	5	10	15	31	53	75
30-Wendy the Witch (3/60)	7	14	21	44	82	120
31-Herman & Katnip (4/60)	3	6	9	19	30	40
32-Sad Sack's Army Life (5/60)	3	6	9	21	33	45
33-Wendy the Witch (6/60)	6	12	18	40	73	105
34-Harvey-Toon (7/60)	4	8	12	23	37	50
35-Funday Funnies (8/60)	3	6	9	19	30	40
36-The Phantom (1960)	10	20	30	70	150	230
37-Casper & Nightmare	5	10	15	34	60	85
38-Harvey-Toon	4	8	12	23	37	50
39-Sad Sack's Army Life (12/60)	3	6	9	20	31	42
40-Funday Funnies (1/61)	3	6	9	16	24	32
41-Herman & Katnip	3	6	9	16	24	32
42-Harvey-Toon (3/61)	3	6	9	18	28	38
43-Sad Sack's Army Life (4/61)	3	6	9	18	28	38
44-The Phantom (5/61)	10	20	30	67	141	215
45-Casper & Nightmare	4	8	12	28	47	65
46-Harvey-Toon (7/61)	3	6	9	16	24	32
47-Sad Sack's Army Life (8/61)	3	6	9	16	24	32
48-The Phantom (9/61)	10	20	30	67	141	215
49-Stumbo the Giant (1st app. in Hot Stuff)	8	16	24	56	108	160
50-Harvey-Toon (11/61)	3	6	9	16	23	30
51-Sad Sack's Army Life (12/61)	3	6	9	16	23	30
52-Casper & Nightmare	4	8	12	27	44	60
53-Harvey-Toons (2/62)	3	6	9	16	23	30
54-Stumbo the Giant	5	10	15	33	57	80
55-Sad Sack's Army Life (4/62)	3	6	9	16	23	30
56-Casper & Nightmare	4	8	12	25	40	55
57-Stumbo the Giant	5	10	15	31	53	75
58-Sad Sack's Army Life	3	6	9	16	23	30
59-Casper & Nightmare (7/62)	4	8	12	25	40	55
60-Stumbo the Giant (9/62)	5	10	15	31	53	75
61-Sad Sack's Army Life	3	6	9	15	22	28
62-Casper & Nightmare	4	8	12	22	35	48
63-Stumbo the Giant	4	8	12	27	44	60
64-Sad Sack's Army Life (1/63)	3	6	9	15	22	28
65-Casper & Nightmare	4	8	12	22	35	48
66-Stumbo The Giant (3/63)	4	8	12	27	44	60
67-Sad Sack's Army Life (4/63)	3	6	9	15	22	28
68-Casper & Nightmare	4	8	12	22	35	48
69-Stumbo the Giant (6/63)	4	8	12	27	44	60
70-Sad Sack's Army Life (7/63)	3	6	9	15	22	28
71-Casper & Nightmare (8/63)	3	6	9	20	31	42
72-Stumbo the Giant	4	8	12	27	44	60
73-Little Sad Sack (10/63)	3	6	9	15	22	28
74-Sad Sack's Muttsy... (11/63)	3	6	9	15	22	28
75-Casper & Nightmare	3	6	9	18	28	38
76-Little Sad Sack	3	6	9	15	22	28
77-Sad Sack's Muttsy...	3	6	9	15	22	28
78-Stumbo the Giant (3/64); JFK caricature	4	8	12	28	44	60
79-87: 79-Little Sad Sack (4/64). 80-Sad Sack's Muttsy... (5/64). 81-Little Sad Sack. 82-Sad Sack's Muttsy... 83-Little Sad Sack(8/64). 84-Sad Sack's Muttsy... 85-Gabby Gob (#1) (10/64). 86-G. I. Juniors (#1)(11/64). 87-Sad Sack's Muttsy... (12/64)	3	6	9	15	22	28
88-Stumbo the Giant (1/65)	4	8	12	27	44	60
89-122: 89-Sad Sack's Muttsy... 90-Gabby Gob. 91-G. I. Juniors. 92-Sad Sack's Muttsy... (5/65). 93-Sadie Sack (6/65). 94-Gabby Gob. 95-G. I. Juniors (8/65). 96-Sad Sack's Muttsy... (9/65). 97-Gabby Gob (10/65). 98-G. I. Juniors (11/65). 99-Sad Sack's Muttsy... (12/65). 100-Gabby Gob(1/66). 101-G. I. Juniors (2/66). 102-Sad Sack's Muttsy... (3/66). 103-Gabby Gob. 104- G. I. Juniors. 105-Sad Sack's Muttsy... 106-Gabby Gob (7/66). 107-G. I. Juniors (8/66). 108-Sad Sack's Muttsy...109-Gabby Gob. 110-G. I. Juniors (11/66). 111-Sad Sack's Muttsy... (12/66). 112-G. I. Juniors. 113-Sad Sack's Muttsy... 114-G. I. Juniors. 115-Sad Sack's Muttsy... 116-G. I. Juniors (5/67). 117-Sad Sack's Muttsy... 118-G. I. Juniors. 119-Sad Sack's Muttsy... (8/67). 120-G. I. Juniors (9/67). 121-Sad Sack's Muttsy... (10/67). 122-G. I. Juniors (11/67)	2	4	6	10	14	18

HARVEY HITS COMICS
Harvey Publications: Nov, 1986 - No. 6, Oct, 1987

	GD 2.0	VG 4.0	FN 6.0	VF 8.0	VF/NM 9.0	NM- 9.2
1-Little Lotta, Little Dot, Wendy & Baby Huey	1	2	3	4	5	7
2-6: 3-Xmas-c						4.50

HARVEY POP COMICS (Rock Happening) (Teen Humor)
Harvey Publications: Oct, 1968 - No. 2, Nov, 1969 (Both are 68 pg. Giants)

	GD 2.0	VG 4.0	FN 6.0	VF 8.0	VF/NM 9.0	NM- 9.2
1-The Cowsills	5	10	15	34	60	85
2-Bunny	5	10	15	31	53	75

HARVEY 3-D HITS (See Sad Sack)

HARVEY-TOON (...S) (See Harvey Hits No. 29, 34, 38, 42, 46, 50, 53)

HARVEY WISEGUYS (...Digest #? on)
Harvey Comics: Nov, 1987; #2, Nov, 1988; #3, Apr, 1989 - No. 4, Nov, 1989 (98 pgs., digest-size, $1.25/$1.75)

	GD 2.0	VG 4.0	FN 6.0	VF 8.0	VF/NM 9.0	NM- 9.2
1-Hot Stuff, Spooky, etc.	2	3	4	6	8	10
2-4: 2 (68 pgs.)	1	2	3	4	5	7

HASBRO HEROES SOURCEBOOK 2017
IDW Publishing: May, 2017 - No. 3, Jul, 2017 ($4.99, limited series)

1-3-Profile pages of characters from Transformers, G.I. Joe, Micronauts, Rom, M.A.S.K. 5.00

HASBRO TOYBOX QUARTERLY
IDW Publishing: Dec, 2017 ($5.99, one-shot)

1-Short stories of My Little Pony, Equestria Girls and Hanazuki by various; pin-ups 6.00

HATARI (See Movie Classics)

HATCHET (Based on the 2007 movie)
American Mythology Productions: No. 0, 2017 - No. 3, 2018 ($3.99)

0-3-Kuhoric-s/Mangum-a; Victor Crowley app. 4.00

HATE
Fantagraphics Books: Spr, 1990 - No. 30, 1998 ($2.50/$2.95, B&W/color)

	GD 2.0	VG 4.0	FN 6.0	VF 8.0	VF/NM 9.0	NM- 9.2
1	2	4	6	11	16	20
2-3	1	2	3	5	6	8
4-10						5.00
11-20: 16- color begins						4.00
21-29						3.00
30-($3.95) Last issue						4.00
Annual 1 (2/01, $3.95) Peter Bagge-s/a						5.00
Annual 2-9 (12/01-Present; $4.95) Peter Bagge-s/a						5.00
Buddy Bites the Bullet! (2001, $16.95) r/Buddy stories in color						17.00
Buddy Go Home! (1997, $16.95) r/Buddy stories in color						17.00
Hate-Ball Special Edition ($3.95, giveaway)-reprints						4.00
Hate Jamboree (10/98, $4.50) old & new cartoons						4.50

HATHAWAYS, THE (TV)
Dell Publishing Co.: No. 1298, Feb-Apr, 1962 (one-shot)

	GD 2.0	VG 4.0	FN 6.0	VF 8.0	VF/NM 9.0	NM- 9.2
Four Color 1298-Photo-c	5	10	15	31	53	75

HAUNT
Image Comics: Oct, 2009 - No. 28, Dec, 2012 ($2.99)

	GD 2.0	VG 4.0	FN 6.0	VF 8.0	VF/NM 9.0	NM- 9.2
1-McFarlane & Kirkman-s/Capullo & Ottley-a/McFarlane-a(i)/c; two variant-c						6.00
2-28: 2-Two covers. 13-($1.99). 19-Casey-s/Fox-a begins						3.00
Image Firsts: Haunt #1 (10/10, $1.00) r/#1 with "Image First" cover logo						3.00

HAUNTED (See This Magazine Is Haunted)

HAUNTED (Baron Weirwulf's Haunted Library on-c #21 on)
Charlton Comics: 9/71 - No. 30, 11/76; No. 31, 9/77 - No. 75, 9/84

	GD 2.0	VG 4.0	FN 6.0	VF 8.0	VF/NM 9.0	NM- 9.2
1-All Ditko issue	6	12	18	41	76	110
2-7-Ditko-c/a	3	6	9	21	33	45
8,12,28-Ditko-a	2	4	6	13	18	22
9,19	2	4	6	8	11	14
10,20,15,18: 10,20-Sutton-a. 15-Sutton-c	2	4	6	8	11	14
11,13,14,16-Ditko-c/a	3	6	9	16	23	30
17-Sutton-c/a; Newton-a	2	4	6	9	12	15
21-Newton-c/a; Sutton-a; 1st Baron Weirwulf	3	6	9	16	24	32
22-Newton-c/a; Sutton-a	2	4	6	9	13	16
23,24-Sutton-c; Ditko-a	2	4	6	9	13	16
25-27,29,32,33	1	3	4	6	8	10
30,41,47,49-52,60,74-Ditko-c/a: 51-Reprints #1	2	4	6	11	16	20
31,35,37,38-Sutton-a	1	3	4	6	8	10
34,36,39,40,42,57-Ditko-a	2	4	6	8	10	12

43-46,48,53-56,58,59,61-73: 59-Newton-a. 64-Sutton-c. 71-73-Low print

Haunted Tank #1 © DC

Haunted Thrills #2 © AJAX

The Haunt of Fear #8 © WMG

	GD 2.0	VG 4.0	FN 6.0	VF 8.0	VF/NM 9.0	NM- 9.2
	1	2	3	5	6	8
75-(9/84) Last issue; low print	2	4	6	9	13	16

NOTE: ***Aparo*** *c-45.* ***Ditko*** *a-1-8, 11-16, 18, 23, 24, 28, 30, 34r, 36r, 39-42r, 47r, 49-52r, 57, 60, 74. c-1-7, 11, 13, 14, 16, 30, 41, 47, 49-52, 74.* ***Howard*** *a-6, 9, 18, 22, 25, 32.* ***Kim*** *a-9, 19.* ***Morisi*** *a-13.* ***Newton*** *a-17, 21, 59r; c-21, 22(painted).* ***Staton*** *a-11, 12, 18, 21, 22, 30, 33, 35, 38; c-18, 33, 38.* ***Sutton*** *a-10, 17, 20-22, 31, 35, 37, 38; c-15, 17, 18, 23(painted), 24(painted), 27, 64r. #49 reprints Tales of the Mysterious Traveler #4.*

HAUNTED, THE
Chaos! Comics: Jan, 2002 - No. 4, Apr, 2002 ($2.99, limited series)

1-4-Peter David-s/Nat Jones-a 3.00
...: Gray Matters (7/02, $2.99) David-s/Jones-a 3.00

HAUNTED CITY
Aspen MLT: No. 0, Aug, 2011 - Present ($2.50)

0-($2.50)-Taylor & Johnson-s/Michael Ryan-a; four covers 3.00
1,2-($3.50) 1-Taylor & Johnson-s/Michael Ryan-a; four covers 3.50

HAUNTED LOVE
Charlton Comics: Apr, 1973 - No. 11, Sept, 1975

	GD	VG	FN	VF	VF/NM	NM-
1-Tom Sutton-a (16 pgs.)	5	10	15	34	60	85
2,3,6,7,10,11	3	6	9	17	26	35
4,5-Ditko-a	3	6	9	21	33	45
8,9-Newton-c	3	6	9	18	28	38
Modern Comics #1(1978)	2	3	4	6	8	10

NOTE: ***Howard*** *a-8i.* ***Kim*** *a-7-9.* ***Newton*** *c-8, 9.* ***Staton*** *a-1-6.* ***Sutton*** *a-1, 3-5, 10, 11.*

HAUNTED MANSION, THE (Disney Kingdoms)
Marvel Comics: May, 2016 - No. 5, Sept, 2016 ($3.99, limited series)

1-5-Joshua Williamson-s/Jorge Coelho-a/E.M. Gist-c 4.00
... No. 1 Halloween Comic Fest 2016 (giveaway, 12/16) r/#1 3.00

HAUNTED TANK, THE
DC Comics (Vertigo): Feb, 2009 - No. 5, June, 2009 ($2.99, limited series)

1-5-Marraffino-s/Flint-a. 1-Two covers by Flint and Joe Kubert 3.00
TPB (2010, $14.99) r/#1-5 15.00

HAUNTED THRILLS (Tales of Horror and Terror)
Ajax/Farrell Publications: June, 1952 - No. 18, Nov-Dec, 1954

	GD	VG	FN	VF	VF/NM	NM-
1-r/Ellery Queen #1	81	162	243	518	884	1250
2-L. B. Cole-a r-/Ellery Queen #1	48	96	144	302	514	725
3,4: 3-Drug use story	45	90	135	284	480	675
5-Classic skull-c	135	270	405	864	1482	2100
6-8,10,12: 7-Hitler story.	45	90	135	284	480	675
9-Classic decapitated heads-c	84	168	252	538	919	1300
11-Nazi death camp story	52	104	156	328	552	775
13-18: 14-Jesus Christ apps. in story by Webb. 15-Jo-Jo-r. 18-Lingerie panels; skull-c	42	84	126	265	445	625

NOTE: ***Kamenish*** *art in most issues.* ***Webb*** *a-12.*

HAUNT OF FEAR (Formerly Gunfighter)
E. C. Comics: No. 15, May-June, 1950 - No. 28, Nov-Dec, 1954

	GD	VG	FN	VF	VF/NM	NM-
15(#1, 1950)(Scarce)	326	652	978	2608	4154	5700
16-1st app. "The Witches Cauldron" & the Old Witch (by Kamen); begin series as hostess of Haunt of Fear (also see Yellowjacket #7-10)	137	274	411	1096	1748	2400
17-Origin of Crypt of Terror, Vault of Horror, & Haunt of Fear; used in **SOTI**, pg. 43; last pg. Ingels-a used by N.Y. Legis. Comm.; story "Monster Maker" based on Frankenstein. Old Witch by Feldstein	134	268	402	1072	1711	2350
4-Ingels becomes regular artist for Old Witch. 1st Vault Keeper & Crypt Keeper app. in HOF; begin series	86	172	258	688	1094	1500
5-Injury-to-eye panel, pg. 4 of Wood story	77	154	231	616	983	1350
6,7,9,10: 6-Crypt Keeper by Feldstein begins. 9-Crypt Keeper by Davis begins. 10-Ingels biog.	57	114	171	456	728	1000
8-Classic Feldstein Shrunken Head-c	80	160	240	640	1020	1400
11,12: Classic Ingels-c; 11-Kamen biog. 12-Feldstein biog.; "Poetic Justice" story adapted for the 1972 Tales From the Crypt film	53	106	159	424	675	925
13,15,16,20: 16-Ray Bradbury adaptation. 20-Feldstein-r/Vault of Horror #12	49	98	147	392	621	850
14-Origin Old Witch by Ingels; classic-Ingels-c	69	138	207	552	876	1200
17-Classic Ingels-c and "Horror We? How's Bayou?" story, considered ECs best horror story	69	138	207	552	876	1200
18-Old Witch-c; Ray Bradbury adaptation & biography	66	132	198	528	839	1150
19-Used in **SOTI**, ill. "A comic book baseball game" & Senate investigation on juvenile delinq. bondage/decapitation-c	56	112	168	448	712	975
21-27: 22-"Wish You Were Here" story adapted for the 1972 Tales From the Crypt film. 23-EC version of the Hansel and Gretel story; **SOTI**, pg. 241 discusses the original Grimm tale in relation to comics. 24-Used in Senate Investigative Report, pg.8. 26-Contains anti-censorship editorial, 'Are you a Red Dupe?' 27-Cannibalism story; Vault Keeper shown reading **SOTI**	36	72	108	288	457	625
28-Low distribution	51	102	153	408	654	900

NOTE: *(Canadian reprints known; see Table of Contents).* ***Craig*** *a-15-17, 5, 7, 10, 12, 13; c-15-17, 5-7.* ***Crandall*** *a-20, 21, 26, 27.* ***Davis*** *a-4-26, 28.* ***Evans*** *a-15-19, 22-25, 27.* ***Feldstein*** *a-15-17, 20; c-4, 8-10.* ***Ingels*** *a-16, 17, 4-28; c-11-28.* ***Kamen*** *a-16, 4, 6, 7, 9-11, 13-19, 21-28.* ***Krigstein*** *a-28.* ***Kurtzman*** *a-15(#1), 17(#3).* ***Orlando*** *a-9, 12.* ***Wood*** *a-15, 16, 4-6.*

HAUNT OF FEAR, THE
Gladstone Publishing: May, 1991 - No. 2, July, 1991 ($2.00, 68 pgs.)

1,2: 1-Ghastly Ingels-c(r); 2-Craig-c(r) 4.00

HAUNT OF FEAR
Russ Cochran/Gemstone Publ.: Sept, 1991 - No. 5, 1992 ($2.00, 68 pgs.); Nov, 1992 - No. 28, Aug, 1998 ($1.50/$2.00/$2.50)

1-28: 1-Ingels-c(r). 1-3-r/HOF #15-17 with original-c. 4,5-r/HOF #4,5 with original-c 4.00
Annual 1-5: 1- r/#1-5. 2- r/#6-10. 3- r/#11-15. 4- r/#16-20. 5- r/#21-25 14.00
Annual 6-r/#26-28 9.00

HAUNT OF HORROR, THE (Digest)
Marvel Comics: Jun, 1973 - No. 2, Aug, 1973 (164 pgs.; text and art)

	GD	VG	FN	VF	VF/NM	NM-
1-Morrow painted skull-c; stories by Ellison, Howard, and Leiber; Brunner-a	4	8	12	23	37	50
2-Kelly Freas painted bondage-c; stories by McCaffrey, Goulart, Leiber, Ellison; art by Simonson, Brunner, and Buscema	3	6	9	16	24	32

HAUNT OF HORROR, THE (Magazine)
Cadence Comics Publ. (Marvel): May, 1974 - No. 5, Jan, 1975 (75¢) (B&W)

	GD	VG	FN	VF	VF/NM	NM-
1,2: 2-Origin & 1st app. Gabriel the Devil Hunter; Satana begins	3	6	9	17	26	35
3-5: 4-Neal Adams-a. 5-Evans-a(2)	3	6	9	19	30	40

NOTE: ***Alcala*** *a-2.* ***Colan*** *a-2p.* ***Heath*** *r-1.* ***Krigstein*** *r-3.* ***Reese*** *a-1.* ***Simonson*** *a-1.*

HAUNT OF HORROR: EDGAR ALLAN POE
Marvel Comics (MAX): July, 2006 - No. 3, Sept, 2006 ($3.99, B&W, limited series)

1-3- Poe-inspired/adapted stories with Richard Corben-a 4.00
HC (2006, $19.99) r/series; cover sketches 20.00

HAUNT OF HORROR: LOVECRAFT
Marvel Comics (MAX): Aug, 2008 - No. 3, Oct, 2008 ($3.99, B&W, limited series)

1-3-Lovecraft-inspired/adapted stories with Richard Corben-a 4.00

HAVE GUN, WILL TRAVEL (TV)
Dell Publishing Co.: No. 931, 8/58 - No. 14, 7-9/62 (All Richard Boone photo-c)

	GD	VG	FN	VF	VF/NM	NM-
Four Color 931 (#1)	12	24	36	81	176	270
Four Color 983,1044 (#2,3)	9	18	27	60	120	180
4 (1-3/60) - 10	7	14	21	46	86	125
11-14	7	14	21	44	82	120

HAVEN: THE BROKEN CITY (See JLA/Haven: Arrival and JLA/Haven: Anathema)
DC Comics: Feb, 2002 - No. 9, Oct, 2002 ($2.50, limited series)

1-9-Olivetti-c/a: 1- JLA app. Series concludes in JLA/Haven: Anathema 3.00

HAVOK & WOLVERINE - MELTDOWN (See Marvel Comics Presents #24)
Marvel Comics (Epic Comics): Mar, 1989 - No. 4, Oct, 1989 ($3.50, mini-series, square-bound, mature)

1-4: Art by Kent Williams & Jon J. Muth; story by Walt & Louise Simonson 6.00

HAWAIIAN DICK (Also see Aloha, Hawaiian Dick)
Image Comics: Dec, 2002 - No. 3, Feb, 2003 ($2.95, limited series)

1-3-B. Clay Moore-s/Steven Griffin-a 3.00
...: Byrd of Paradise TPB (8/03, $14.95) r/#1-3, script & sketch pages 15.00

HAWAIIAN DICK: SCREAMING BLACK THUNDER
Image Comics: Nov, 2007 - No. 5, Oct, 2008 ($2.99, limited series)

1-5-B. Clay Moore-s/Scott Chantler-a 3.00

HAWAIIAN DICK: THE LAST RESORT
Image Comics: Aug, 2004 - No. 4, June, 2006 ($2.95/$2.99, limited series)

1-4-B. Clay Moore-s/Steven Griffin-a 3.00
Vol. 2 TPB (10/06, $14.99) r/#1-4 & the original series pitch 15.00

HAWAIIAN EYE (TV)
Gold Key: July, 1963 (Troy Donahue, Connie Stevens photo-c)

	GD	VG	FN	VF	VF/NM	NM-
1 (10073-307)	5	10	15	31	53	75

HAWAIIAN ILLUSTRATED LEGENDS SERIES
Hogarth Press: 1975 (B&W)(Cover printed w/blue, yellow, and green)

1-Kalelealuaka, the Mysterious Warrior 5.00

HAWK, THE (Also see Approved Comics #1, 7 & Tops In Adventure)

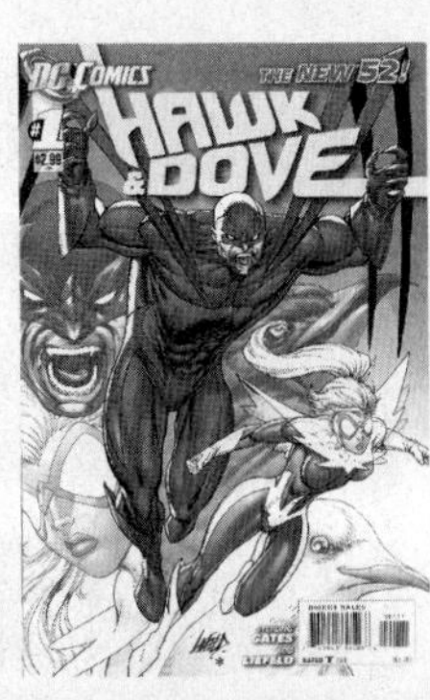

Hawk and Dove (2011 series) #1 © DC

Hawkeye (2017 series) #11 © MAR

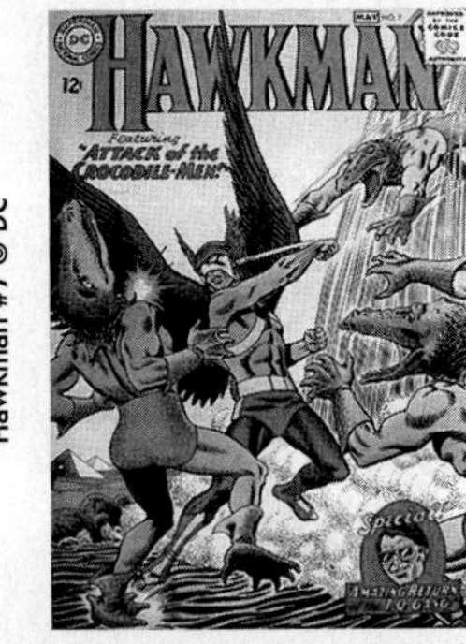

Hawkman #7 © DC

GD VG FN VF VF/NM NM-
2.0 4.0 6.0 8.0 9.0 9.2

Ziff-Davis/St. John Publ. Co. No. 4 on: Wint/51 - No. 3, 11-12/52; No. 4, 1-2/53; No. 8, 9/54 - No. 12, 5/55 (Painted c-1-4)(#5-7 don't exist)

1-Anderson-a 23 46 69 136 223 310
2 (Sum, '52)-Kubert, Infantino-a 14 28 42 81 118 155
3-4 12 24 36 67 94 120
8-12: 8(9/54)-Reprints #3 w/different-c by Baker. 9-Baker-c/a; Kubert-a(r)/#2. 10-Baker-c/a; r/one story from #2. 11-Baker-c; Buckskin Belle & The Texan app. 12-Baker-c/a; Buckskin Belle app. 18 36 54 105 165 225
3-D 1(11/53, 25¢)-Came w/glasses; Baker-c 36 72 108 211 343 475
NOTE: ***Baker** c-8-12. **Larsen** a-10. **Tuska** a-1, 9, 12. Painted c-1, 4, 7.*

HAWK AND THE DOVE, THE (See Showcase #75 & Teen Titans) (1st series)
National Periodical Publications: Aug-Sept, 1968 - No. 6, June-July, 1969

1-Ditko-c/a 7 14 21 48 89 130
2-6: 5-Teen Titans cameo 5 10 15 32 51 70
NOTE: ***Ditko** c/a-1, 2. **Gil Kane** a-3p, 4p, 5, 6p; c-3-6.*

HAWK AND DOVE (2nd Series)
DC Comics: Oct, 1988 - No. 5, Feb, 1989 ($1.00, limited series)

1-Rob Liefeld-c/a(p) in all; 1st app. Dawn Granger as Dove 4.00
2-5 3.00
Trade paperback ('93, $9.95)-Reprints #1-5 12.00

HAWK AND DOVE
DC Comics: June, 1989 - No. 28, Oct, 1991 ($1.00)

1-28 3.00
Annual 1,2 ('90, '91; $2.00) 1-Liefeld pin-up. 2-Armageddon 2001 x-over 4.00

HAWK AND DOVE
DC Comics: Nov, 1997 - No. 5, Mar, 1998 ($2.50, limited series)

1-5-Baron-s/Zachary & Giordano-a 3.00

HAWK AND DOVE (DC New 52)
DC Comics: Nov, 2011 - No. 8, Jun, 2012 ($2.99)

1-8: 1-Gates-s/Liefeld-a/c; Deadman app. 6-Batman & Robin app.; Liefeld-s/a/c 3.00

HAWK AND WINDBLADE (See Elflord)
Warp Graphics: Aug, 1997 - No.2, Sept, 1997 ($2.95, limited series)

1,2-Blair-s/Chan-c/a 3.00

HAWKEN: MELEE (Based on the computer game Hawken)
Archaia Black Label: Dec, 2013 - No. 5 ($3.99, limited series)

1,2: 1-Abnett-s/Dallocchio-a. 2-Jim Mahfood-s/a 4.00

HAWKEYE (See The Avengers #16 & Tales Of Suspense #57)
Marvel Comics Group: Sept, 1983 - No. 4, Dec, 1983 (limited series)

1-Mark Gruenwald-a/scripts in all; origin Hawkeye 2 4 6 11 16 20
2-4: 3-Origin Mockingbird. 4-Hawkeye & Mockingbird elope 1 3 4 6 8 10

HAWKEYE
Marvel Comics: Jan, 1994 - No. 4, Apr, 1994 ($1.75, limited series)

1-4 5.00

HAWKEYE (Volume 2)
Marvel Comics: Dec, 2003 - No. 8, Aug, 2004 ($2.99)

1-8: 1-6-Nicieza-s/Raffaele-a. 7,8-Bennett-a; Black Widow app. 4.00

HAWKEYE (Also see All-New Hawkeye)
Marvel Comics: Oct, 2012 - No. 22, Sept, 2015 ($2.99)

1-Fraction-s/Aja-a; Kate Bishop app. 3 6 9 15 22 28
2,3 1 3 4 6 8 10
4-8: 7-Lieber & Hamm-a 6.00
9-21: 10,12-Francavilla-a. 11-Dog issue. 16-Released before #15 4.00
22-($4.99) Aja-a 5.00
Annual 1 (9/13, $4.99) Pulido-a; Kate Bishop in L.A.; Madame Mask app. 5.00

HAWKEYE (Kate Bishop as Hawkeye)
Marvel Comics: Feb, 2017 - No. 16, May, 2018 ($3.99)

1-16: 1-5,7-11-Thompson-s/Romero-a. 5,6-Jessica Jones app. 4.00

HAWKEYE AND MOCKINGBIRD (Avengers) (Leads into Widowmaker mini-series)
Marvel Comics: Aug, 2010 - No. 6, Jan, 2011 ($3.99/$2.99)

1-($3.99) Heroic Age; Jim McCann-s/David Lopez-a; history of the characters 4.00
2-6-($2.99) Phantom Rider, Dominic Fortune & Crossfire app. 3.00

HAWKEYE & THE LAST OF THE MOHICANS (TV)
Dell Publishing Co.: No. 884, Mar, 1958 (one-shot)

Four Color 884-Lon Chaney Jr. photo-c 7 14 21 44 82 120

GD VG FN VF VF/NM NM-
2.0 4.0 6.0 8.0 9.0 9.2

HAWKEYE: BLINDSPOT (Avengers)
Marvel Comics: Apr, 2011 - No. 4, Jul, 2011 ($2.99, limited series)

1-4: 1-McCann-s/Diaz-a; Zemo app. 2-Diaz & Dragotta-a 3.00

HAWKEYE: EARTH'S MIGHTIEST MARKSMAN
Marvel Comics: Oct, 1998 ($2.99, one-shot)

1-Justice and Firestar app.; DeFalco-s 5.00

HAWKEYE VS. DEADPOOL
Marvel Comics: No. 0, Nov, 2014 - No. 4, Mar, 2015 ($4.99/$3.99, limited series)

0-($4.99) Duggan-s/Lolli-a; Black Cat app. 5.00
1-4-($3.99) 1-Covers by Harren & Pearson; Kate Bishop & Typhoid Mary app. 4.00

HAWKGIRL (Title continued from Hawkman #49, Apr, 2006)
DC Comics: No. 50, May, 2006 - No. 66, Sept, 2007 ($2.50/$2.99)

50-66: 50-Chaykin-a/Simonson-s begin; One Year Later. 52-Begin $2.99-c. 57,58-Bennett-a. 59-Blackfire app. 63-Batman app. 64-Superman app. 3.00
...: Hath-Set TPB (2008, $17.99) r/#61-66 18.00
...: Hawkman Returns TPB (2007, $17.99) r/#57-60 & JSA Classified #21,22 18.00
...: The Maw TPB (2007, $17.99) r/#50-56 18.00

HAWKMAN (See Atom & Hawkman, The Brave & the Bold, DC Comics Presents, Detective Comics, Flash Comics, Hawkworld, JSA, Justice League of America #31, Legend of the Hawkman, Mystery in Space, Savage Hawkman, Shadow War Of..., Showcase, & World's Finest #256)

HAWKMAN (1st Series) (Also see The Atom #7 & Brave & the Bold #34-36, 42-44, 51)
National Periodical Publications: Apr-May, 1964 - No. 27, Aug-Sept, 1968

1-(4-5/64)-Anderson-c/a begins, ends #21 54 108 162 432 966 1500
2 20 40 60 141 313 485
3,5: 5-2nd app. Shadow Thief 13 26 39 89 195 300
4-Origin & 1st app. Zatanna (10-11/64) 85 170 340 680 1290 1900
6 10 20 30 66 138 210
7 9 18 27 60 120 180
8-10: 9-Atom cameo; Hawkman & Atom learn each other's I.D.; 3rd app. Shadow Thief 8 16 24 54 102 150
11-15 6 12 18 40 73 105
16-27: 18-Adam Strange x-over (cameo #19). 25-G.A. Hawkman-r by Moldoff. 26-Kirby-a(r). 27-Kubert-c 5 10 15 33 57 80

HAWKMAN (2nd Series)
DC Comics: Aug, 1986 - No. 17, Dec, 1987

1-17: 10-Byrne-c, Special #1 (1986, $1.25) 4.00
Trade paperback (1989, $19.95)-r/Brave and the Bold #34-36,42-44 by Kubert; Kubert-c 20.00

HAWKMAN (4th Series)(See both Hawkworld limited & ongoing series)
DC Comics: Sept, 1993 - No. 33, July, 1996 ($1.75/$1.95/$2.25)

1-($2.50)-Gold foil embossed-c; storyline cont'd from Hawkworld ongoing series; new costume & powers. 4.00
2-13,0,14-33: 2-Green Lantern x-over. 3-Airstryke app. 4,6-Wonder Woman app. 13-(9/94)-Zero Hour. 0-(10/94). 14-(11/94). 15-Aquaman-c & app. 23-Wonder Woman app. 25-Kent Williams-c. 29,30-Chaykin-c. 32-Breyfogle-c 3.00
Annual 1 (1993, $2.50, 68 pgs.)-Bloodlines Earthplague 4.00
Annual 2 (1995, $3.95)-Year One story 4.00

HAWKMAN (Title continues as Hawkgirl #50-on) (See JSA #23 for return)
DC Comics: May, 2002 - No. 49, Apr, 2006 ($2.50)

1-Johns & Robinson-s/Morales-a 5.00
1-2nd printing 3.00
2-40: 2-4-Shadow Thief app. 5,6-Green Arrow-c/app. 8-Atom-c/app. 13-Van Sciver-a. 14-Gentleman Ghost app. 15-Hawkwoman app. 16-Byth returns. 23-25-Black Reign x-over with JSA #56-58. 26-Byrne-c/a. 29,30-Land-c. 37-Golden Eagle returns 3.00
41-49: 41-Hawkman killed. 43-Golden Eagle origin. 46-49-Adam Kubert-c 3.00
...: Allies & Enemies TPB (2004, $14.95) r/#7-14 & pages from Secret Files and Origins 15.00
...: Endless Flight TPB (2003, $12.95) r/#1-6 & Secret Files and Origins 13.00
...: Rise of the Golden Eagle TPB (2006, $17.99) r/#37-45 18.00
... Secret Files and Origins (10/02, $4.95) profiles and pin-ups by various 5.00
...: Special 1 (10/08, $3.50) Tie-in to Rann-Thanagar Holy War series; Starlin-s/a(p) 3.50
...: Wings of Fury TPB (2005, $17.99) r/#15-22 18.00

HAWKMAN: FOUND (See Dark Nights: Metal series and other tie-ins)
DC Comics: Feb, 2018 ($3.99, one-shot)

1-Lemire-s/Hitch-a; foil-c 4.00

HAWKMOON: THE JEWEL IN THE SKULL
First Comics: May, 1986 - No. 4, Nov, 1986 ($1.75, limited series, Baxter paper)

1-4: Adapts novel by Michael Moorcock 3.00

HAWKMOON: THE MAD GOD'S AMULET
First Comics: Jan, 1987 - No. 4, July, 1987 ($1.75, limited series, Baxter paper)

Headline Comics #29 © PRIZE

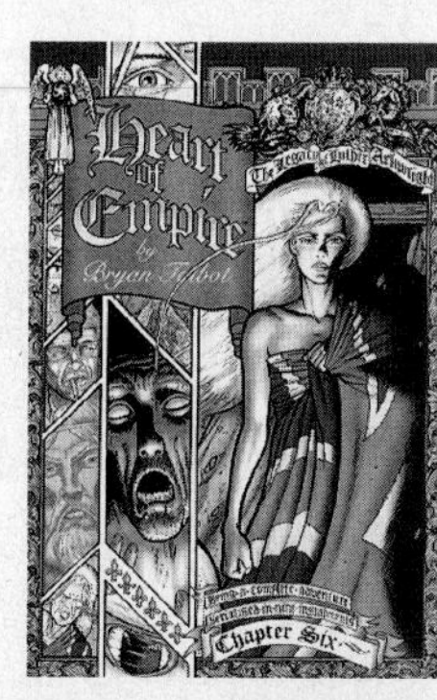

Heart of Empire #6 © Bryan Talbot

Heart Throbs #1 © DC

GD 2.0 | VG 4.0 | FN 6.0 | VF 8.0 | VF/NM 9.0 | NM- 9.2

1-4: Adapts novel by Michael Moorcock 3.00

HAWKMOON: THE RUNESTAFF
First Comics: Jun, 1988 -No. 4, Dec, 1988 ($1.75-$1.95, lim. series, Baxter paper)

1-4: ($1.75) Adapts novel by Michael Moorcock. 3,4 ($1.95) 3.00

HAWKMOON: THE SWORD OF DAWN
First Comics: Sept, 1987 - No. 4, Mar, 1988 ($1.75, lim. series, Baxter paper)

1-4: Dorman painted-c; adapts Moorcock novel 3.00

HAWKS OF THE SEAS (WILL EISNER'S...)
Dark Horse Comics: July, 2003 ($19.95, B&W, hardcover)

nn-Reprints 1937-1939 weekly Pirate serial by Will Eisner; Williamson intro. 20.00

HAWKWORLD
DC Comics: 1989 - No. 3, 1989 ($3.95, prestige format, limited series)

Book 1-3: 1-Tim Truman story & art in all; Hawkman dons new costume; reintro Byth 5.00
TPB (1991, $16.95) r/#1-3 17.00

HAWKWORLD (3rd Series)
DC Comics: June, 1990 - No. 32, Mar, 1993 ($1.50/$1.75)

1-Hawkman spin-off; story cont'd from limited series. 4.00
2-32: 15,16-War of the Gods x-over. 22-J'onn J'onzz app. 3.00
Annual 1-3 ('90-'92, $2.95, 68 pgs.), 2-2nd printing with silver ink-c 4.00
NOTE: *Truman a-30-32; c-27-32, Annual 1.*

HAYWIRE
DC Comics: Oct, 1988 - No. 13, Sept, 1989 ($1.25, mature)

1-13 3.00

HAZARD
Image Comics (WildStorm Prod.): June, 1996 - No. 7, Nov, 1996 ($1.75)

1-7: 1-Intro Hazard; Jeff Mariotte scripts begin; Jim Lee-c(p) 3.00

HEADLINE COMICS
DC Comics: Jan. 1942

nn - Ashcan comic, not distributed to newsstands, only for in-house use. Cover art is More Fun Comics #73, interior being Star Spangled Comics #2 (a FN copy sold for $2270.50 in 2012)

HEADLINE COMICS (...For the American Boy) (...Crime No. 32-39)
Prize Publ./American Boys' Comics: Feb, 1943 - No. 22, Nov-Dec, 1946; No. 23, 1947 - No. 77, Oct, 1956

	GD	VG	FN	VF	VF/NM	NM-
1-WWII-c/sty.; Junior Rangers-c/stories begin; Yank & Doodle x-over in Junior Rangers (Junior Rangers are Uncle Sam's nephews)	100	200	300	635	1093	1550
2-Japanese WWII-c; Junior Rangers "Nip the Nippons!"-c	60	120	180	381	653	925
3-Junior Rangers vs. Hitler sty.; 1st app. Invisible Boy; German WWII-c; used in **POP**, pg. 84 (scarce)	57	114	171	362	619	875
4-Junior Rangers vs. Hitler, Mussolini, Hirohito & Dr. Schmutz (1st app.); German WWII-c; (scarce)	54	108	162	343	574	825
5-7,9: 5-Junior Rangers invade Italy; WWII-c/sty. 6,7-Nazi WWII-c/sty. 7-1st app. Kinker Kinkaid (ends #12). 9-WWII Halloween-c/sty	53	106	159	334	567	800
8-Classic Hitler-c	1135	2270	3400	6800	9650	12,500
10-Hitler story	53	106	159	334	567	800
11-Classic Mad Japanese scientist WWII-c	129	258	387	826	1413	2000
12,13,15: 13,15-Blue Streak app.	25	50	75	150	245	340
14-Japanese WWII-c	29	58	87	170	278	385
16-Origin & 1st app. Atomic Man (11-12/45)	36	72	108	211	343	475
17,18-Atomic Man-c/sty.	25	50	75	150	245	340
19-Atomic Man-c/sty.; S&K-a	36	72	108	211	343	475
20,21: 21-Atomic Man ends (9-10/46)	20	40	60	117	189	260
22-Last Junior Rangers; Kiefer-c	19	38	57	109	172	235
23,24: (All S&K-a). 23-Valentine's Day Massacre story; content changes to true crime. 24-Dope-crazy killer story	34	68	102	206	336	465
25-35-S&K-c/a. 25-Powell-a	30	60	90	177	289	400
36-S&K-a; photo-c begin	25	50	75	150	245	340
37-1 pg. S&K, Severin-a; rare Kirby photo-c app.	42	84	126	265	445	625
38,40-Meskin-a	15	30	45	83	124	165
39,41-43,46-56: 41-J. Edgar Hoover 26th Anniversary Issue with photo on-c. 43,49-Meskin-a. 48-Meskin-c	14	28	42	78	112	145
44,45-S&K-c; Severin/Elder, Meskin-a	18	36	54	107	169	230
57-77: 70-Roller Derby-c. 72-Meskin-c/a(i)	12	24	36	69	97	125

NOTE: ***Hollingsworth** a-30. Photo c-36-43. **H. C. Kiefer** c-12-16, 22. Atomic Man c-17-19.*

HEAP, THE
Skywald Publications: Sept, 1971 (52 pgs.)

	GD	VG	FN	VF	VF/NM	NM-
1-Kinstler-r/Strange Worlds #8; new-s w/Sutton-a	5	10	15	30	50	70

GD 2.0 | VG 4.0 | FN 6.0 | VF 8.0 | VF/NM 9.0 | NM- 9.2

HEART AND SOUL
Mikeross Publications: April-May, 1954 - No. 2, June-July, 1954

	GD	VG	FN	VF	VF/NM	NM-
1,2	11	22	33	62	86	110

HEARTBREAKERS (Also see Dark Horse Presents)
Dark Horse Comics: Apr, 1996 - No. 4, July, 1996 ($2.95, limited series)

1-4: 1-With paper doll & pin-up. 2-Alex Ross pin-up. 3-Evan Dorkin pin-ups. 4-Brereton-c; Matt Wagner pin-up 3.00
...Superdigest (7/98, $9.95, digest-size) new stories 10.00

HEARTLAND (See Hellblazer)
DC Comics (Vertigo): Mar, 1997 ($4.95, one-shot, mature)

1-Garth Ennis-s/Steve Dillon-c/a 5.00

HEART OF EMPIRE
Dark Horse Comics: Apr, 1999 - No. 9, Dec, 1999 ($2.95, limited series)

1-9-Bryan Talbot-s/a 3.00

HEART OF THE BEAST, THE
DC Comics (Vertigo): 1994 ($19.95, hardcover, mature)

1-Dean Motter scripts 20.00

HEARTS OF DARKNESS (See Ghost Rider; Wolverine; Punisher: Hearts of...)

HEART THROBS (Love Stories No. 147 on)
Quality Comics/National Periodical #47(4-5/57) on (Arleigh #48-101): 8/49 - No. 8, 10/50; No. 9, 3/52 - No. 146, Oct, 1972

	GD	VG	FN	VF	VF/NM	NM-
1-Classic Ward-c, Gustavson-a, 9 pgs.	50	100	150	315	533	750
2-Ward-c/a (9 pgs); Gustavson-a	31	62	93	184	300	415
3-Gustavson-a	15	30	45	90	140	190
4,6,8-Ward-a, 8-9 pgs.	20	40	60	114	182	250
5,7	14	28	42	81	118	155
9-Robert Mitchum, Jane Russell photo-c	16	32	48	92	144	195
10,15-Ward-a	16	32	48	92	144	195
11-14,16-20: 12 (7/52)	13	26	39	72	101	130
21-Ward-c	15	30	45	88	137	185
22,23-Ward-a(p)	14	28	42	76	108	140
24-33: 33-Last pre-code (3/55)	12	24	36	69	97	125
34-39,41-44,46 (12/56; last Quality issue)	11	22	33	64	90	115
40-Ward-a; r-7 pgs./#21	12	24	36	69	97	125
45-Baker-a	7	14	21	48	89	130
47-(4-5/57; 1st DC issue)	20	40	60	138	307	475
48-60, 100	9	18	27	60	120	180
61-70	6	12	18	42	79	115
71-99: 74-Last 10 cent issue	6	12	18	38	69	100
101-The Beatles app. on-c	16	32	48	110	243	375
102-119: 102-123-(Serial)-Three Girls, Their Lives, Their Loves	4	8	12	28	47	65
120-(6-7/69) Neal Adams-c	5	10	15	30	50	70
121-132,143-146	3	6	9	21	33	45
133-142-(52 pgs.)	4	8	12	27	44	60

NOTE: ***Gustavson** a-8. **Tuska** a-128. Photo c-4, 5, 8-10, 15, 17.*

HEART THROBS - THE BEST OF DC ROMANCE COMICS (See Fireside Book Series)

HEART THROBS
DC Comics (Vertigo): Jan, 1999 - No. 4, Apr, 1999 ($2.95, lim. series)

1-4-Romance anthology. 1-Timm-c. 3-Corben-a 3.00

HEATHCLIFF (See Star Comics Magazine)
Marvel Comics (Star Comics)/Marvel Comics No. 23 on: Apr, 1985 - No. 56, Feb, 1991 (#16-on, $1.00)

	GD	VG	FN	VF	VF/NM	NM-
1-Post-a most issues	1	2	3	4	5	7

2-10,47: 47-Batman parody (Catman vs. the Soaker) 5.00
11-46,48-56: 43-X-Mas issue 4.00
Annual 1 ('87) 4.00

HEATHCLIFF'S FUNHOUSE
Marvel Comics (Star Comics)/Marvel No. 6 on: May, 1987 - No. 10, 1988

1 5.00
2-10 4.00

HEAVEN'S DEVILS
Image Comics: Sept, 2003 - No. 4, July, 2004 ($2.95/$3.50, B&W, limited series)

1-3-($2.95) Jai Nitz-s/Zach Howard-a 3.00
4-($3.50) Kevin Sharpe-a 3.50

HEAVY HITTERS
Marvel Comics (Epic Comics): 1993 ($3.75, 68 pgs.)

Heavy Vinyl #4 © Scheme Machine

Hedy Devine Comics #27 © MAR

Hellblazer #228 © DC

	GD 2.0	VG 4.0	FN 6.0	VF 8.0	VF/NM 9.0	NM- 9.2
1-Bound w/trading card; Lawdog, Feud, Alien Legion, Trouble With Girls, & Spyke						4.00

HEAVY LIQUID
DC Comics (Vertigo): Oct, 1999 - No. 5, Feb, 2000 ($5.95, limited series)

	GD	VG	FN	VF	VF/NM	NM-
1-5-Paul Pope-s/a; flip covers						6.00
TPB (2001, $29.95) r/#1-5						30.00
TPB (2009, $24.95) r/#1-5; development sketches and cover gallery; new cover						25.00
HC (2008, $39.99, dustjacket) r/#1-5; development sketches and cover gallery						40.00

HEAVY VINYL (Title changed from Hi-Fi Fight Club after #3)
Boom Entertainment (BOOM! Box): No. 4, Nov, 2017 ($3.99)

	GD	VG	FN	VF	VF/NM	NM-
4-Carly Usdin-s/Nina Vakueva-a						4.00

HECKLE AND JECKLE (Paul Terry's...)(See Blue Ribbon, Giant Comics Edition #5A & 10, Paul Terry's, Terry-Toons Comics)
St. John Publ. Co. No. 1-24/Pines No. 25 on: No. 3, 2/52 - No. 24, 10/55; No. 25, Fall/56 - No. 34, 6/59

	GD	VG	FN	VF	VF/NM	NM-
3(#1)-Funny animal	27	54	81	158	259	360
4(6/52), 5	14	28	42	80	115	150
6-10(4/53)	10	20	30	54	72	90
11-20	8	16	24	40	50	60
21-34: 25-Begin CBS Television Presents on-c	7	14	21	35	43	50

HECKLE AND JECKLE (TV) (See New Terrytoons)
Gold Key/Dell Publ. Co.: 11/62 - No. 4, 8/63; 5/66; No. 2, 10/66; No. 3, 8/67

	GD	VG	FN	VF	VF/NM	NM-
1 (11/62; Gold Key)	6	12	18	37	66	95
2-4	3	6	9	21	33	45
1 (5/66; Dell)	4	8	12	25	40	55
2,3	3	6	9	18	28	38

(See March of Comics No. 379, 472, 484)

HECKLE AND JECKLE 3-D
Spotlight Comics: 1987 - No. 2?, 1987 ($2.50)

	GD	VG	FN	VF	VF/NM	NM-
1,2						5.00

HECKLER, THE
DC Comics: Sept, 1992 - No. 6, Feb, 1993 ($1.25)

	GD	VG	FN	VF	VF/NM	NM-
1-6-T&M Bierbaum-s/Keith Giffen-c/a						3.00

HECTIC PLANET
Slave Labor Graphics 1998 ($12.95/$14.95)

	GD	VG	FN	VF	VF/NM	NM-
Book 1,2-r-Dorkin-s/a from Pirate Corp$ Vol. 1 & 2						15.00

HECTOR COMICS (The Keenest Teen in Town)
Key Publications: Nov, 1953 - No. 3, 1954

	GD	VG	FN	VF	VF/NM	NM-
1-Teen humor	9	18	27	47	61	75
2,3	6	12	18	29	36	42

HECTOR HEATHCOTE (TV)
Gold Key: Mar, 1964

	GD	VG	FN	VF	VF/NM	NM-
1 (10111-403)	6	12	18	40	73	105

HECTOR THE INSPECTOR (See Top Flight Comics)

HEDGE KNIGHT, THE
Image Comics: Aug, 2003 - No. 6, Apr, 2004 ($2.95, limited series)

	GD	VG	FN	VF	VF/NM	NM-
1-6-George R.R. Martin-s/Mike S. Miller-a. 1-Two covers by Kaluta and Miller						3.00
George R.R. Martin's The Hedge Knight HC (Marvel, 2006, $19.99) r/series; 2 covers						20.00
George R.R. Martin's The Hedge Knight SC (Marvel, 2007, $14.99) r/series						15.00
TPB (2004, $14.95) r/series plus new short story						15.00

HEDGE KNIGHT II: SWORN SWORD
Marvel Comics (Dabel Brothers): Jun, 2007 - No. 6, Jun, 2008 ($2.99, limited series)

	GD	VG	FN	VF	VF/NM	NM-
1-6-George R.R. Martin-s/Mike Miller-a. 1-Two covers by Yu & Miller, plus Miller B&W-c						3.00
... HC (2008, $19.99) r/series; 2 covers						20.00

HEDY DEVINE COMICS (Formerly All Winners #21? or Teen #22?(6/47); Hedy of Hollywood #36 on; also see Annie Oakley & Venus)
Marvel Comics (RCM): No. 22, Aug, 1947 - No. 35, Oct, 1949

	GD	VG	FN	VF	VF/NM	NM-
22-1st app. Hedy Devine (also see Joker #32)	71	142	213	454	777	1100
23,24,27-30: 23-Wolverton-a, 1 pg; Kurtzman's "Hey Look", 2 pgs. 24,27-30- "Hey Look" by Kurtzman, 1-3 pgs.	43	86	129	271	461	650
25-Classic "Hey Look" by Kurtzman, "Optical Illusion"	45	90	135	284	480	675
26- "Giggles 'n' Grins" by Kurtzman	39	78	117	231	378	525
31-34: 32-Anti-Wertham editorial	28	56	84	165	270	375
35-Four pgs. "Rusty" by Kurtzman	32	64	96	188	307	425

HEDY-MILLIE-TESSIE COMEDY (See Comedy Comics)

HEDY OF HOLLYWOOD (Formerly Hedy Devine Comics)
Marvel Comics (RCM)/Atlas #50: No. 36, Feb, 1950 - No. 50, Sept, 1952

	GD	VG	FN	VF	VF/NM	NM-
36(#1)	37	74	111	222	361	500
37-50	28	56	84	165	270	375

HEDY WOLFE (Also see Patsy & Hedy & Miss America Magazine V1#2)
Atlas Publishing Co. (Emgee): Aug, 1957

	GD	VG	FN	VF	VF/NM	NM-
1-Patsy Walker's rival; Al Hartley-c	30	60	90	177	289	400

HEE HAW (TV)
Charlton Press: July, 1970 - No. 7, Aug, 1971

	GD	VG	FN	VF	VF/NM	NM-
1	4	8	12	28	47	65
2-7	3	6	9	19	30	40

HEIDI (See Dell Jr. Treasury No. 6)

HEIDI SAHA (AN ILLUSTRATED HISTORY OF...)
Warren Publishing: 1973 (500 printed)

nn-Photo-c; an early Vampirella model for Warren (a FN/VF copy sold in 2011 for $776.75)

HELEN OF TROY (Movie)
Dell Publishing Co.: No. 684, Mar, 1956 (one-shot)

	GD	VG	FN	VF	VF/NM	NM-
Four Color 684-Buscema-a, photo-c	9	18	27	60	120	180

HELL
Dark Horse Comics: July, 2003 - No. 4, Mar, 2004 ($2.99, limited series)

	GD	VG	FN	VF	VF/NM	NM-
1-4-Augustyn-s/Demong-a/Meglia-c						3.00

HELLBLAZER (John Constantine) (See Saga of Swamp Thing #37 & 2013 Constantine title) (Also see Books of Magic limited series)
DC Comics (Vertigo #63 on): Jan, 1988 - No. 300, Apr, 2013 ($1.25-$2.99)

	GD	VG	FN	VF	VF/NM	NM-
1-(44 pgs.)-John Constantine; McKean-c thru #21; 1st app. Papa Midnite	4	8	12	27	44	60
1-Special Edition (7/10, $1.00) r/#1 with "What's Next?" cover logo						3.00
2-5	1	2	3	5	7	9
6-8,10: 10-Swamp Thing cameo						6.00
9,19: 9-X-over w/Swamp Thing #76. 19-Sandman app.	1	2	3	5	6	8
11-18,20						6.00
21-26,28-30: 22-Williams-c. 24-Contains bound-in Shocker movie poster. 25,26-Grant Morrison scripts.						5.00
27-Neil Gaiman scripts; Dave McKean-a; low print run	2	4	6	11	16	20
31-39: 36-Preview of World Without End.						4.00
40-($2.25, 52 pgs.)-Dave McKean-a & colors; preview of Kid Eternity						5.00
41-Ennis scripts begin; ends #83						5.00
42-49,51-74,76-99,101-119: 44,45-Sutton-a(i). 52-Glenn Fabry painted-c begin. 62-Special Death insert by McKean. 63-Silver metallic ink on-c. 77-Totleben-c. 84-Sean Phillips-c/a begins; Delano story. 85-88-Eddie Campbell story. 89-Paul Jenkins scripts begin						3.50
50,75,100,120: 50-($3.00, 52 pgs.). 75-($2.95, 52 pgs.). 100,120 ($3.50,48 pgs.)						4.00
121-199, 201-249, 251-274,276-299: 129-Ennis-s. 141-Bradstreet-a. 146-150-Corben-a. 151-Azzarello-s begin. 175-Carey-s begin; Dillon-a. 176-Begin $2.75-c. 182,183-Bermejo-a. 216-Mina-s begins. 220-Begin $2.99-c. 229-Carey-s/Leon-a. 234-Initial printing (white title logo) has missing text; corrected printing has lt. blue title logo. 265,266,271-274-Bisley-a. 268-271-Shade the Changing Man app.						3.00
200-($4.50) Carey-s/Dillon, Frusin, Manco-a						5.00
250-($3.99) Short stories by various; art by Lloyd, Phillips, Milligan; Bermejo-c						4.00
275-($4.99) Constantine's wedding; Bisley-c						5.00
300-($4.99) Last issue; Bisley-c						5.00
Annual 1 (1989, $2.95, 68 pgs.)-Bryan Talbot's 1st work in American comics						6.00
Annual 1 (Annual 2011 on cover, 2/12, $4.99)-Milligan-s/Bisley-a/c						5.00
Special 1 (1993, $3.95, 68 pgs.)-Ennis story; w/pin-ups.						5.00
...Black Flowers (2005, $14.99, TPB) r/#181-186						15.00
...Bloodlines (2007, $19.99, TPB) r/#47-50,52-55,59-61						20.00
...Damnation's Flame (1999, $16.95, TPB) r/#72-77						17.00
...Dangerous Habits (1997, $14.95, TPB) r/#41-46						15.00
...Fear and Loathing (1997, $14.95, TPB) r/#62-67						18.00
...Fear and Loathing (2nd printing, $17.95)						18.00
...: Freezes Over (2003, $14.95, TPB) r/#157-163						15.00
...Good Intentions (2002, $12.95, TPB) r/#151-156						13.00
...Hard Time (2001, $9.95, TPB) r/#146-150						10.00
...Haunting (2003, $12.95, TPB) r/#134-139						13.00
...Highwater (2004, $19.95, TPB) r/#164-174						20.00
John Constantine Hellblazer: All His Engines HC (2005, $24.95, with dustjacket) new graphic novel; Mike Carey-s/Leonardo Manco-a						25.00
John Constantine Hellblazer: All His Engines SC (2006, $14.99) new graphic novel						15.00
John Constantine Hellblazer: Bloody Carnations SC (2011, $19.99) r/#267-275						20.00

Hellblazer (2016 series) #13 © DC

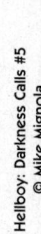

Hellboy: Darkness Calls #5 © Mike Mignola

Hellboy: Krampusnacht © Mike Mignola

GD	VG	FN	VF	VF/NM	NM-
2.0	4.0	6.0	8.0	9.0	9.2

John Constantine Hellblazer: Empathy is the Enemy SC (2006, $14.99) r/#216-222 15.00
John Constantine Hellblazer: Hooked SC (2010, $14.99) r/#256-260 15.00
John Constantine Hellblazer: India SC (2010, $14.99) r/#261-266 15.00
John Constantine Hellblazer: Joyride SC (2008, $14.99) r/#230-237 15.00
John Constantine Hellblazer: Pandemonium HC (2010, $24.99, with dustjacket) new graphic novel; Jamie Delano-s/Jock-a 25.00
John Constantine Hellblazer: Pandemonium SC (2011, $17.99) new graphic novel 18.00
John Constantine Hellblazer: Scab SC (2009, $14.99) r/#250-255 15.00
John Constantine Hellblazer: The Devil You Know SC (2007, $19.99) r/#10-13, Annual #1 and The Horrorist miniseries #1,2 20.00
John Constantine Hellblazer: The Family Man SC (2008, $19.99, TPB) r/#23,24,28-33 20.00
John Constantine Hellblazer: The Fear Machine SC (2008, $19.99, TPB) r/#14-22 20.00
John Constantine Hellblazer: The Red Right Hand SC (2007, $14.99) r/#223-228 15.00
John Const. Hellblazer: The Roots of Coincidence SC ('09, $14.99) r/#243,244,247-249 15.00
...Original Sins (1993, $19.95, TPB) r/#1-9 20.00
...Original Sins (2011, $19.99, TPB) r/#1-9 20.00
...Rake at the Gates of Hell (2003, $19.95, TPB) r/#78-83; Heartland #1 20.00
...: Rare Cuts (2005, $14.95, TPB) r/#11,25,26,35,56,84 & Vertigo Secret Files: Hellblazer 15.00
...: Reasons To Be Cheerful (2007, $14.99, TPB) r/#201-206 15.00
...: Red Sepulchre (2005, $12.99, TPB) r/#175-180 13.00
...: Setting Sun (2004, $12.95, TPB) r/#140-143 13.00
...: Son of Man (2004, $12.95, TPB) r/#129-133 13.00
...: Stations of the Cross (2006, $14.99, TPB) r/#194-200 15.00
...: Staring At The Wall (2005, $14.99, TPB) r/#187-193 15.00
...Tainted Love (1998, $16.95, TPB) r/#68-71, Vertigo Jam #1 and Hellblazer Special #1 17.00
NOTE: *Alcala a-8i, 9i, 18-22i. **Gaiman** scripts-27. **McKean** a-27,40; c-1-21. **Sutton** a-44i, 45i. **Talbot** a-Annual 1.*

HELLBLAZER (DC Rebirth)
DC Comics: Oct, 2016 - Present ($2.99, limited series)
1-8: 1-4-Simon Oliver-s/Moritat-a; Swamp Thing app. 5-7-Cassaday-c 3.00
9-19-($3.99): 9-12-Fabbri-a. 11,12-Lotay-c. 15-Justice League app. 4.00
...: Rebirth 1 (9/16, $2.99) Oliver-s/Moritat-a; Swamp Thing, Wonder Woman app. 3.00

HELLBLAZER: CITY OF DEMONS
DC Comics (Vertigo): Early Dec, 2010 - No. 5, Feb, 2011 ($2.99, limited series)
1-5-Si Spencer-s/Sean Murphy-a/c 3.00
TPB (2011, $14.99) r/#1-5 & story from Vertigo Winter's Edge #3 15.00

HELLBLAZER SPECIAL: BAD BLOOD
DC Comics (Vertigo): Sept, 2000 - No. 4, Dec, 2000 ($2.95, limited series)
1-4-Delano-s/Bond-a; Constantine in 2025 London 3.00

HELLBLAZER SPECIAL: CHAS
DC Comics (Vertigo): Sept, 2008 - No. 5, Jan, 2009 ($2.99, limited series)
1-5-Story of Constantine's cab driver; Oliver-s/Sudzuka-a/Fabry-c 3.00
... - The Knowledge TPB (2009, $14.99) r/#1-5 15.00

HELLBLAZER SPECIAL: LADY CONSTANTINE
DC Comics (Vertigo): Feb, 2003 - No. 4, May, 2003 ($2.95, limited series)
1-4-Story of Johanna Constantine in 1785; Diggle-s/Sudzuka-a/Noto-c 3.00

HELLBLAZER/THE BOOKS OF MAGIC
DC Comics (Vertigo): Dec, 1997 - No. 2, Jan, 1998 ($2.50, limited series)
1,2-John Constantine and Tim Hunter 3.00

HELLBOY (Also see Batman/Hellboy/Starman, Danger Unlimited #4, Dark Horse Presents, Gen[13] #13B, Ghost/Hellboy, John Byrne's Next Men, San Diego Comic Con #2, & Savage Dragon)

HELLBOY
Dark Horse Comics: Apr, 2008
... : Free Comic Book Day; Three short stories; Mignola-c; art by Fegredo, Davis, Azaceta 3.00

HELLBOY: ALMOST COLOSSUS
Dark Horse Comics (Legend): Jun, 1997 - No. 2, Jul, 1997 ($2.95, lim. series)
1,2-Mignola-s/a 5.00

HELLBOY AND THE B.P.R.D.
Dark Horse Comics: Dec, 2014 - No. 5, Apr, 2015 ($3.50, limited series)
1-5-Mignola & Arcudi-s/Maleev-a/c; Hellboy's first mission; set in 1952 3.50
...: 1953 - Beyond the Fences 1-3 (2/16 - No. 3, 4/16, $3.50) Paolo Rivera-a/c 3.50
...: 1953 - The Phantom Hand & The Kelpie (10/15, $3.50) Mignola-s/c; Stenbeck-a 3.50
...: 1953 - The Witch Tree & Rawhead and Bloody Bones (11/15, $3.50) Mignola-s/c; Stenbeck-a 3.50
...: 1953 - The Witch Tree & Rawhead and Bloody Bones, Halloween Comics Fest (10/17, giveaway) Mignola-s/c; Stenbeck-a 3.00
...: 1954 - Black Sun 1,2 (9/16 - No. 2, 10/16, $3.99) Stephen Green-a/c 4.00
...: 1954 - Ghost Moon 1,2 (3/17 - No. 2, 4/17, $3.99) Mignola & Roberson-s/Churilla-a 4.00
...: 1954 - The Unreasoning Beast (11/16, $3.99) Mignola & Roberson-s/Reynolds-a 4.00

GD VG FN VF VF/NM NM-
2.0 4.0 6.0 8.0 9.0 9.2

...: 1955 - Burning Season (2/18, $3.99) Mignola & Roberson-s/Rivera-a 4.00
...: 1955 - Occult Intelligence 1-3 (9/17 - No. 3, 11/17, $3.99) Churilla-a 4.00
...: 1955 - Secret Nature (8/16, $3.99) Mignola & Roberson-s/Martinbrough-a 4.00

HELLBOY/BEASTS OF BURDEN
Dark Horse Comics: Oct, 2010 ($3.50, one-shot)
... Sacrifice - Evan Dorkin & Mignola-s/Jill Thompson-a 3.50

HELLBOY: BEING HUMAN
Dark Horse Comics: May, 2011 ($3.50, one-shot)
nn-Mignola-s; Richard Corben-a/c; Roger app. 3.50

HELLBOY: BOX FULL OF EVIL
Dark Horse Comics: Aug, 1999 - No. 2, Sept, 1999 ($2.95, lim. series)
1,2-Mignola-s/a; back-up story w/ Matt Smith-a 4.00

HELLBOY: BUSTER OAKLEY GETS HIS WISH
Dark Horse Comics: Apr, 2011 ($3.50, one-shot)
nn-Mignola-s; Kevin Nowlan-a; two covers by Mignola & Nowlan 3.50

HELLBOY CHRISTMAS SPECIAL
Dark Horse Comics: Dec, 1997 ($3.95, one-shot)
nn-Christmas stories by Mignola, Gianni, Darrow, Purcell 6.00

HELLBOY: CONQUEROR WORM
Dark Horse Comics: May, 2001 - No. 4, Aug, 2001 ($2.99, limited series)
1-4-Mignola-s/a/c 4.00

HELLBOY: DARKNESS CALLS
Dark Horse Comics: Apr, 2007 - No. 6, Nov, 2007 ($2.99, limited series)
1-6-Mignola-s/Fegredo-a 3.00

HELLBOY: DOUBLE FEATURE OF EVIL
Dark Horse Comics: Nov, 2010 ($3.50, one-shot)
1-Mignola-s; Corben-a/c 3.50

HELLBOY: HOUSE OF THE LIVING DEAD
Dark Horse Comics: Nov, 2011 ($14.99, hardcover graphic novel)
1-Mignola-s; Corben-a/c; Hellboy and Lucha Libre 15.00

HELLBOY IN HELL (Follows Hellboy's death in Hellboy: The Fury)
Dark Horse Comics: Dec, 2012 - No. 10, Jun, 2016 ($2.99)
1-10-Mignola-s/a/c 3.00
1-Variant "Year in Monsters" cover 10.00

HELLBOY IN MEXICO
Dark Horse Comics: May, 2010 ($3.50, one-shot)
1-Mignola-s; Corben-a/c; Mexican wrestlers vs. monsters 3.50

HELLBOY: IN THE CHAPEL OF MOLOCH
Dark Horse Comics: Oct, 2008 ($2.99, one-shot)
nn-Mignola-s/a/c 3.00

HELLBOY: INTO THE SILENT SEA
Dark Horse Comics: Apr, 2017 ($14.99, HC graphic novel)
nn-Mignola-s/c; Gianni-a 15.00

HELLBOY, JR.
Dark Horse Comics: Oct, 1999 - No. 2, Nov, 1999 ($2.95, limited series)
1,2-Stories and art by various 4.00
TPB (1/04, $14.95) r/#1&2, Halloween; sketch pages; intro. by Steve Niles; Bill Wray-c 15.00

HELLBOY, JR., HALLOWEEN SPECIAL
Dark Horse Comics: Oct, 1997 ($3.95, one-shot)
nn-"Harvey" style renditions of Hellboy characters; Bill Wray, Mike Mignola & various-s/a; wraparound-c by Wray 5.00

HELLBOY: KRAMPUSNACHT
Dark Horse Comics: Dec, 2017 ($3.99, one-shot)
nn-Krampus app.; Mike Mignola-s/Adam Hughes-a; covers by Mignola & Hughes 4.00

HELLBOY: MAKOMA, OR A TALE TOLD...
Dark Horse Comics: Feb, 2006 - No. 2, Mar, 2006 ($2.99, lim. series)
1,2-Mignola-s/c; Mignola & Corben-a 3.00

HELLBOY PREMIERE EDITION
Dark Horse Comics (Wizard): 2004 (no price, one-shot)
nn- Two covers by Mignola & Davis; Mignola-s/a; BPRD story w/Arcudi-s/Davis-a 5.00
Wizard World Los Angeles-Movie photo-c; Mignola-s/a; BPRD story w/Arcudi-s/Davis-a 10.00

HELLBOY: SEED OF DESTRUCTION (First Hellboy series)

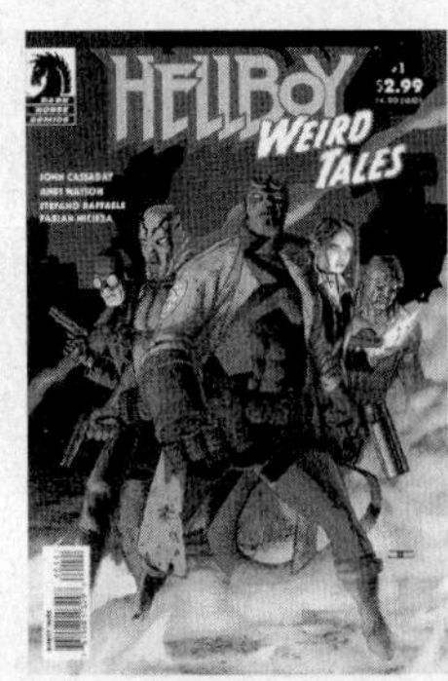

Hellboy: Weird Tales #1 © Mike Mignola

Hello Pal Comics #3 © HARV

Hellshock #4 © Jae Lee

GD 2.0 | VG 4.0 | FN 6.0 | VF 8.0 | VF/NM 9.0 | NM- 9.2

Dark Horse Comics (Legend): Mar, 1994 - No. 4, Jun, 1994 ($2.50, lim. series)

1-Mignola-c/a w/Byrne scripts; Monkeyman & O'Brien back-up story (origin) by Art Adams. 3 6 9 20 31 42
2-4: 2-1st app. Abe Sapien & Liz Sherman 1 3 4 6 8 10
Hellboy: One for One (8/10, $1.00) r/#1 Hellboy story with red cover frame 3.00
Trade paperback (1994, $17.95)-collects all four issues plus r/Hellboy's 1st app. in San Diego Comic Con #2 & pin-ups 18.00
Limited edition hardcover (1995, $99.95)-includes everything in trade paperback plus additional material. 100.00

HELLBOY STRANGE PLACES
Dark Horse Books: Apr, 2006 ($17.95, TPB)
SC - Reprints Hellboy: The Third Wish #1,2 and Hellboy: The Island #1,2; sketch pages 18.00

HELLBOY: THE BRIDE OF HELL
Dark Horse Comics: Dec, 2009 ($3.50, one-shot)
1-Mignola-s/c; Corben-a; preview of The Marquis: Inferno 3.50

HELLBOY: THE CHAINED COFFIN AND OTHERS
Dark Horse Comics (Legend): Aug, 1998 ($17.95, TPB)
nn-Mignola-c/a/s; reprints out-of-print one shots; pin-up gallery 18.00

HELLBOY: THE COMPANION
Dark Horse Books: May, 2008 ($14.95, 9"x6", TPB)
nn-Overview of Hellboy history, characters, stories, mythology; text with Mignola panels 15.00

HELLBOY: THE CORPSE
Dark Horse Comics: Mar, 2004 (25¢, one-shot)
nn-Mignola-c/a/scripts; reprints "The Corpse" serial from Capitol City's Advance Comics catalog; development sketches and photos of the Corpse from the Hellboy movie 3.00

HELLBOY: THE CORPSE AND THE IRON SHOES
Dark Horse Comics (Legend): Jan, 1996 ($2.95, one-shot)
nn-Mignola-c/a/scripts; reprints "The Corpse" serial w/new story 5.00

HELLBOY: THE CROOKED MAN
Dark Horse Comics: Jul, 2008 - No. 3, Sept, 2008 ($2.99, lim. series)
1-3-Mignola-s/Corben-a/c 3.00

HELLBOY: THE FURY
Dark Horse Comics: Jun, 2011 - No. 3, Aug, 2011 ($2.99, lim. series)
1-3-Mignola-s/c; Fegredo-a. 1-Variant-c by Fegredo. 3-Hellboy dies 3.00
3-Retailer Incentive Variant 30 60 90 150 225 300

HELLBOY: THE GOLDEN ARMY
Dark Horse Comics: Jan, 2008 (no cover price)
nn-Prelude to the 2008 movie; Del Toro & Mignola-s/Velasco-a; 3 photo covers 3.00

HELLBOY: THE ISLAND
Dark Horse Comics: June, 2005 - No. 2, July, 2005 ($2.99, lim. series)
1,2: Mignola-c/a & scripts 4.00

HELLBOY: THE MIDNIGHT CIRCUS
Dark Horse Books: Oct, 2013 ($14.99, hardcover graphic novel)
nn-Mignola-s/c; Fegredo-a; young Hellboy runs away from BPRD in 1948 15.00

HELLBOY: THE RIGHT HAND OF DOOM
Dark Horse Comics (Legend): Apr, 2000 ($17.95, TPB)
nn-Mignola-c/a/s; reprints 18.00

HELLBOY: THE SLEEPING AND THE DEAD
Dark Horse Comics: Dec, 2010 - No. 2, Feb, 2011 ($3.50, lim. series)
1,2-Mignola-s/Scott Hampton-a 3.50

HELLBOY: THE STORM
Dark Horse Comics: Jul, 2010 - No. 3, Sept, 2010 ($2.99, lim. series)
1-3-Mignola-s/Fegredo-a 3.00

HELLBOY: THE THIRD WISH
Dark Horse Comics (Maverick): July, 2002 - No. 2, Aug, 2002 ($2.99, limited series)
1,2-Mignola-c/a/s 4.00

HELLBOY THE TROLL WITCH AND OTHERS
Dark Horse Books: Nov, 2007 ($17.95, TPB)
SC - Reprints Hellboy: Makoma, Hellboy Premiere Edition and stories from Dark Horse Book of Hauntings, DHB of Witchcraft, DHB of the Dead, DHB of Monsters 18.00

HELLBOY: THE WILD HUNT
Dark Horse Comics: Dec, 2008 - No. 8, Nov, 2009 ($2.99, lim. series)
1-8: Mignola-c/s; Fegredo-a 3.00

HELLBOY: THE WOLVES OF ST. AUGUST
Dark Horse Comics (Legend): 1995 ($4.95, squarebound, one-shot)
nn-Mignola--c/a/scripts; r/Dark Horse Presents #88-91 with additional story 6.00

HELLBOY: WAKE THE DEVIL (Sequel to Seed of Destruction)
Dark Horse Comics (Legend): Jun, 1996 - No. 5, Oct, 1996 ($2.95, lim. series)
1-5: Mignola-c/a & scripts; The Monstermen back-up story by Gary Gianni 6.00
TPB (1997, $17.95) r/#1-5 18.00

HELLBOY: WEIRD TALES
Dark Horse Comics: Feb, 2003 - No. 8, Apr, 2004 ($2.99, limited series, anthology)
1-8-Hellboy stories from other creators. 1-Cassaday-c/s/a; Watson-s/a. 6-Cho-c 4.00
... Vol. 1 (2004, 17.95) r/#1-4 18.00
... Vol. 2 (2004, 17.95) r/#5-8 and Lobster Johnson serial from #1-8 18.00

HELLBOY WINTER SPECIAL
Dark Horse Comics: Jan, 2016; Jan, 2017 ($3.99, one-shots)
1-Short stories by Mignola, Sale, Oeming, Allie, Roberson and others; Sale-c 4.00
nn (1/17)-Short stories; Mignola & Roberson-s, Mitten, Grist & Fiumara-a; Fiumara-c 4.00

HELLCAT
Marvel Comics: Sept, 2000 - No. 3, Nov, 2000 ($2.99)
1-3-Englehart-s/Breyfogle-a; Hedy Wolfe app. 3.00

HELLCOP
Image Comics (Avalon Studios): Aug, 1998 - No. 4, Mar, 1999 ($2.50)
1-4: 1-(Oct. on-c) Casey-s 3.00

HELL ETERNAL
DC Comics (Vertigo Verité): 1998 ($6.95, squarebound, one-shot)
1-Delano-s/Phillips-a 7.00

HELLGATE: LONDON (Based on the video game)
Dark Horse Comics: No. 0, May 2006 - No. 3, Mar, 2007 ($2.99)
0-3-Edginton-s/Pugh-a/Briclot-c 3.00

HELLHOUNDS (...: Panzer Cops #3-6)
Dark Horse Comics: 1994 - No. 6, July, 1994 ($2.50, B&W, limited series)
1-6: 1-Hamner-c. 3-(4/94). 2-Joe Phillips-c 3.00

HELLHOUND, THE REDEMPTION QUEST
Marvel Comics (Epic Comics): Dec, 1993 - No. 4, Mar, 1994 ($2.25, lim. series, coated stock)
1-4 3.00

HELLO BUDDIES
Harvey Publications: 1953 (25¢, small size)
1 3 6 9 21 33 45

HELLO, I'M JOHNNY CASH
Spire Christian Comics (Fleming H. Revell Co.): 1976 (39¢/49¢)
nn-(39¢-c) 3 6 9 16 23 30
nn-(49¢-c) 2 4 6 11 16 20

HELL ON EARTH (See DC Science Fiction Graphic Novel)

HELLO PAL COMICS (Short Story Comics)
Harvey Publications: Jan, 1943 - No. 3, May, 1943 (Photo-c)
1-Rocketman & Rocketgirl begin; Yankee Doodle Jones app.; Mickey Rooney photo-c 65 130 195 416 708 1000
2-Charlie McCarthy photo-c (scarce) 56 112 168 349 595 840
3-Bob Hope photo-c (scarce) 60 120 180 384 660 935

HELLRAISER (See Clive Barker's...)

HELLRAISER/NIGHTBREED – JIHAD (Also see Clive Barker's...)
Epic Comics (Marvel Comics): 1991 - Book 2, 1991 ($4.50, 52 pgs.)
Book 1,2 5.00

HELL-RIDER (Motorcycle themed magazine)
Skywald Publications: Aug, 1971 - No. 2, Oct, 1971 (B&W, 68 pgs.)
1-Origin & 1st app.; Butterfly & the Wild Bunch begin; 1st Hell-Rider by Andru, Esposito and Friedrich 6 12 18 37 60 95
2-Andru, Ayers, Buckler, Shores-a 4 8 12 28 47 65
NOTE: *#3 advertised in Psycho #5 but did not come out.* ***Buckler*** *a-1, 2.* ***Rosenbaum*** *c-1,2.*

HELL'S ANGEL (Becomes Dark Angel #6 on)
Marvel Comics UK: July, 1992 - No. 5, Nov, 1993 ($1.75)
1-5: X-Men (Wolverine, Cyclops)-c/stories. 1-Origin. 3-Jim Lee cover swipe 3.00

HELLSHOCK

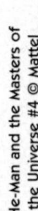

He-Man and the Masters of the Universe #4 © Mattel

Henry Aldrich Comics #3 © DELL

Heralds #4 © MAR

	GD 2.0	VG 4.0	FN 6.0	VF 8.0	VF/NM 9.0	NM- 9.2

Image Comics: July, 1994 - No. 4, Nov, 1994 ($1.95, limited series)
1-4-Jae Lee-c/a & scripts. 4-Variant-c. 3.00

HELLSHOCK
Image Comics: Jan, 1997 - No. 3, Jan, 1998 ($2.95/$2.50, limited series)
1-($2.95)-Jae Lee-c/s/a, Villarrubia-painted-a 4.00
2-($2.50) 3.00
Book 3: The Science of Faith (1/98, $2.50) Jae Lee-c/s/a, Villarrubia-painted-a 3.00
Vol. 1 HC (2006, $49.99) r/#1-3 re-colored, with unpublished 22 pg. conclusion; cover gallery and sketches; alternate opening art; intro. by Jim Lee 50.00

HELLSPAWN
Image Comics: Aug, 2000 - No. 16, Apr, 2003 ($2.50)
1-Bendis-s/Ashley Wood-c/a; Spawn and Clown app. 3.00
2-9: 6-Last Bendis-s; Mike Moran (Miracleman app.). 7-Niles-s 3.00
10-16-Templesmith-a 3.00
...: The Ashley Wood Collection Vol. 1 (4/06, $24.95, TPB) r/#1-10; sketch & cover gallery 25.00

HELLSTORM: PRINCE OF LIES (See Ghost Rider #1 & Marvel Spotlight #12)
Marvel Comics: Apr, 1993 - No. 21, Dec, 1994 ($2.00)
1-($2.95)-Parchment-c w/red thermographic ink 4.00
2-21: 14-Bound-in trading card sheet. 18-P. Craig Russell-c 3.00

HELLSTORM: SON OF SATAN
Marvel Comics (MAX): Dec, 2006 - No. 5, Apr, 2007 ($3.99, limited series)
1-5-Suydam-c/Irvine-s/Braun & Janson-a 4.00
... - Equinox TPB (2007, $17.99) r/#1-5; interviews with the creators 18.00

HELMET OF FATE, THE (Series of one-shots following Doctor Fate's helmet)
DC Comics: Mar, 2007 - May 2007 ($2.99, one-shots)
...: Black Alice (5/07) Simone-s/Rouleau-a/c 3.00
...: Detective Chimp (3/07) Willingham-s/McManus-a/Bolland-c 3.00
...: Ibis the Invincible (3/07) Williams-s/Winslade-a; the Ibistick returns 3.00
...: Sargon the Sorcerer (4/07) Niles-s/Scott Hampton-s; debut new Sargon 3.00
...: Zauriel (4/07) Gerber-s/Snejbjerg-a/Kaluta-c; leads into new Doctor Fate series 3.00
TPB (2007, $14.99) r/one-shots 15.00

HELP US! GREAT WARRIOR
BOOM! Studios (BOOM! Box): Feb, 2015 - No. 6, Jul, 2015 ($3.99)
1-6-Madeleine Flores-s/a 4.00

HE-MAN (See Masters Of The Universe)

HE-MAN (Also see Tops In Adventure)
Ziff-Davis Publ. Co. (Approved Comics): Fall, 1952
1-Kinstler painted-c; Powell-a 17 34 51 98 154 210

HE-MAN
Toby Press: May, 1954 - No. 2, July, 1954 (Painted-c by B. Safran)
1-Gorilla-c 15 30 45 88 137 185
2-Shark-c 15 30 45 85 130 175

HE-MAN AND THE MASTERS OF THE UNIVERSE
DC Comics: Sept, 2012 - No. 6, Mar, 2013 ($2.99)
1-6: 1-James Robinson-s/Philip Tan-a/c; Skeletor app. 5-Adam gets the sword 3.00

HE-MAN AND THE MASTERS OF THE UNIVERSE
DC Comics: Jun, 2013 - No. 19, Jan, 2015 ($2.99)
1-19: 1-Giffen-s/Mhan-a/Benes-c. 7,8-Abnett-s/Kayanan-a. 13-18-Origin of She-Ra 3.00

HE-MAN: THE ETERNITY WAR
DC Comics: Feb, 2015 - No. 15, Apr, 2016 ($2.99)
1-15: 1-Abnett-s/Mhan-a; Hordak invades; origin of Grayskull 3.00

HE-MAN / THUNDERCATS
DC Comics: Dec, 2016 - No. 6, May, 2017 ($3.99, limited series)
1-6-Freddie Williams II-a; Mumm-Ra & Skeletor app. 4.00

HENNESSEY (TV)
Dell Publishing Co.: No. 1200, Aug-Oct, 1961 - No. 1280, Mar-May, 1962
Four Color 1200-Gil Kane-a, photo-c 7 14 21 44 82 120
Four Color 1280-Photo-c 6 12 18 40 73 105

HENRY (Also see Little Annie Rooney)
David McKay Publications: 1935 (52 pgs.) (Daily B&W strip reprints)(10"x10" cardboard-c)
1-By Carl Anderson 40 80 120 246 411 575

HENRY (See King Comics & Magic Comics)
Dell Publishing Co.: No. 122, Oct, 1946 - No. 65, Apr-June, 1961
Four Color 122-All new stories begin 15 30 45 103 227 350
Four Color 155 (7/47), 1 (1-3/48)-All new stories 10 20 30 67 141 215
2 6 12 18 40 73 105
3-10 5 10 15 34 60 85
11-20: 20-Infinity-c 5 10 15 30 50 70
21-30 4 8 12 25 40 55
31-40 3 6 9 21 33 45
41-65 3 6 9 17 26 35

HENRY (See Giant Comic Album and March of Comics No. 43, 58, 84, 101, 112, 129, 147, 162, 178, 189)

HENRY ALDRICH COMICS (TV)
Dell Publishing Co.: Aug-Sept, 1950 - No. 22, Sept-Nov, 1954
1-Part series written by John Stanley; Bill Williams-a 9 18 27 60 120 180
2 5 10 15 35 63 90
3-5 5 10 15 31 53 75
6-10 4 8 12 27 44 60
11-22 4 8 12 23 37 50

HENRY BREWSTER
Country Wide (M.F. Ent.): Feb, 1966 - V2#7, Sept, 1967 (All 25¢ Giants)
1 3 6 9 19 30 40
2-6(12/66), V2#7-Powell-a in most 3 6 9 14 20 25

HEPCATS
Antarctic Press: Nov, 1996 - No. 12 ($2.95, B&W)
0-12-Martin Wagner-c/s/a: 0-color 3.00
0-($9.95) CD Edition 10.00

HERALDS
Marvel Comics: Aug, 2010 - No. 5, Aug, 2010 ($2.99, weelky limited series)
1-5-Kathryn Immonen-s/Zonjic & Harren-a; She-Hulk, Hellcat, Emma Frost, Photon app. 3.00

HERBIE (See Forbidden Worlds #73,94,110,114,116 & Unknown Worlds #20)
American Comics Group: April-May, 1964 - No. 23, Feb, 1967 (All 12¢)
1-Whitney-c/a in most issues 17 34 51 119 265 410
2-4 8 16 24 56 108 160
5-Beatles parody (10 pgs.), Dean Martin, Frank Sinatra app. (10-11/64) 9 18 27 61 123 185
6,7,9,10 7 14 21 48 89 130
8-Origin & 1st app. The Fat Fury 8 16 24 55 105 155
11-23: 14-Nemesis & Magicman app. 17-r/2nd Herbie from Forbidden Worlds #94. 23-r/1st Herbie from F.W. #73 6 12 18 37 66 95
... Archives Volume One HC (Dark Horse, 8/08, $49.95, dust jacket) r/earliest apps. in Forbidden Worlds, Unknown Worlds, and Herbie #1-5; Scott Shaw intro. 50.00

HERBIE
Dark Horse Comics: Oct, 1992 - No. 12, 1993 ($2.50, limited series)
1-Whitney-r plus new-c/a in all; Byrne-c/a & scripts 4.00
2-6: 3-Bob Burden-c/a. 4-Art Adams-c 3.00

HERBIE GOES TO MONTE CARLO, HERBIE RIDES AGAIN (See Walt Disney Showcase No. 24, 41)

HERC (Hercules from the Avengers)
Marvel Comics: Jun, 2011 - No. 10, Jan, 2012 ($2.99)
1-6, (6.1), 7-10: 1-Pak & Van Lente-s; Hobgoblin app. 3-6-Fear Itself tie-in. 6.1-Grell-a 7,8-Spider-Island tie-in; Herc gets Spider-powers. 10-Elektra app. 3.00

HERCULES (See Hit Comics #1-21, Journey Into Mystery Annual, Marvel Graphic Novel #37, Marvel Premiere #26 & The Mighty...)

HERCULES (See Charlton Classics)
Charlton Comics: Oct, 1967 - No. 13, Sept, 1969; Dec, 1968
1-Thane of Bagarth begins; Glanzman-a in all 4 8 12 27 44 60
2-13: 1-5,7-10-Aparo-a. 8-(12¢-c) 4 8 12 23 37 50
4-Magazine format (low distribution) 8 16 24 54 102 150
8-Magazine format (low distribution)(12/68, 35¢, B&W); new Hercules story plus-r story/#1; Thane-r/#1-3 5 10 15 33 57 80
Modern Comics reprint 10('77), 11('78) 6.00

HERCULES (Prince of Power) (Also see The Champions)
Marvel Comics Group: V1#1, Sept, 1982 - V1#4, Dec, 1982; V2#1, Mar, 1984 - V2#4, Jun, 1984 (color, both limited series)
1-4, V2#1-4: Layton-c/a. 4-Death of Zeus. 4.00
NOTE: *Layton a-1, 2, 3p, 4p, V2#1-4; c-1-4, V2#1-4.*

HERCULES
Marvel Comics: Jun, 2005 - No. 5, Sept, 2005 ($2.99, limited series)
1-5-Texeira-a/c; Tieri-s. 4-Capt. America, Wolverine and New Avengers app. 3.00
...: New Labors of Hercules TPB (2005, $13.99) r/#1-5 14.00

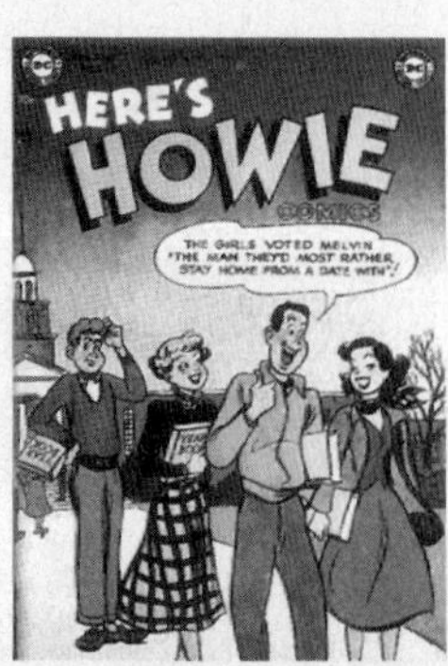

Here's Howie Comics #2 © DC

H-E-R-O #1 © DC

Hero Comics 2011 © IDW & Hero

	GD 2.0	VG 4.0	FN 6.0	VF 8.0	VF/NM 9.0	NM- 9.2

HERCULES
Marvel Comics: Jan, 2016 - Present ($3.99)
1-6: 1-Dan Abnett-s/Luke Ross-a; Gilgamesh app. 4.00

HERCULES: FALL OF AN AVENGER (Continues in Heroic Age: Prince of Power)
Marvel Comics: May, 2010 - No. 2, June, 2010 ($3.99, limited series)
1,2-Follows Hercules' demise in Incredible Hercules #141; Olivetti-c/a 4.00

HERCULES: HEART OF CHAOS
Marvel Comics: Aug, 1997 - No. 3, Oct, 1997 ($2.50, limited series)
1-3-DeFalco-s, Frenz-a 3.00

HERCULES: OFFICIAL COMICS MOVIE ADAPTION
Acclaim Books: 1997 ($4.50, digest size)
nn-Adaptation of the Disney animated movie 4.50

HERCULES: THE LEGENDARY JOURNEYS (TV)
Topps Comics: June, 1996 - No. 5, Oct, 1996 ($2.95)

	GD	VG	FN	VF	VF/NM	NM-
1-2: 1-Golden-c.						3.00
3-Xena-c/app.	1	2	3	4	5	7
3-Variant-c	2	4	6	9	12	15
4,5: Xena-c/app.						5.00

HERCULES UNBOUND
National Periodical Publications: Oct-Nov, 1975 - No. 12, Aug-Sept, 1977

	GD	VG	FN	VF	VF/NM	NM-
1-García-López-a/Wood-i begins	2	4	6	9	13	16
2-12: 2-6-García-López-a. 7-Adams ad. 10-Atomic Knights x-over	2	3	4	6	8	10

NOTE: ***Buckler*** *c-7p.* ***Layton*** *inks-No. 9, 10.* ***Simonson*** *a-7-10p, 11, 12; c- 8p, 9-12.* ***Wood*** *a-1-8i; c-7i, 8i.*

HERCULES (...Unchained #1121) (Movie)
Dell Publishing Co.: No. 1006, June-Aug, 1959 - No.1121, Aug, 1960

	GD	VG	FN	VF	VF/NM	NM-
Four Color 1006-Buscema-a, photo-c	9	18	27	57	111	165
Four Color 1121-Crandall/Evans-a	8	16	24	54	102	150

HERCULES: TWILIGHT OF A GOD
Marvel Comics: Aug, 2010 - No. 4, Nov, 2010 ($3.99, limited series)
1-4-Layton-s/a(i); Lim-a; Galactus app. 4.00

HERCULIAN
Image Comics: Mar, 2011 ($4.99, oversized, one-shot)
1-Golden Age style superhero stories and humor pages; Erik Larsen-s/a/c 5.00

HERE COMES SANTA (See March of Comics No. 30, 213, 340)

HERE'S HOWIE COMICS
National Periodical Publications: Jan-Feb, 1952 - No. 18, Nov-Dec, 1954

	GD	VG	FN	VF	VF/NM	NM-
1	36	72	108	216	351	485
2	19	38	57	109	172	235
3-5: 5-Howie in the Army issues begin (9-10/52)	15	30	45	85	130	175
6-10	14	28	42	80	115	150
11-18	14	28	42	76	108	140

Ashcan (1,2/51) not distributed to newsstands (a FN copy sold for $836.50 in 2012)

HERETIC, THE
Dark Horse (Blanc Noir): Nov, 1996 - No. 4, Mar, 1997 ($2.95, lim. series)
1-4:-w/back-up story 3.00

HERITAGE OF THE DESERT (See Zane Grey, 4-Color 236)

HERMAN & KATNIP (See Harvey Comics Hits #60 & 62, Harvey Hits #14,25,31,41 & Paramount Animated Comics #1)

HERMES VS. THE EYEBALL KID
Dark Horse Comics: Dec, 1994 - No. 3,Feb, 1995 ($2.95, B&W, limited series)
1-3: Eddie Campbell-c/a/scripts 3.00

H-E-R-O (Dial H For HERO)
DC Comics: Apr, 2003 - No. 22, Jan, 2005 ($2.50)
1-Will Pfeiffer-s/Kano-a/Van Fleet-c 3.50
2-22: 2-6-Kano-a. 7,8-Gleason-a. 12-14-Kirk-a. 15-22-Robby Reed app. 3.00
...: Double Feature (6/03, $4.95) r/#1&2 5.00
...: Powers and Abilities (2003, $9.95) r/#1-6; intro. by Geoff Johns 10.00

HERO (Warrior of the Mystic Realms)
Marvel Comics: May, 1990 - No. 6, Oct, 1990 ($1.50, limited series)
1-6: 1-Portacio-i 3.00

HERO ALLIANCE, THE
Sirius Comics: Dec, 1985 - No. 2, Sept, 1986 (B&W)
1,2: 2-($1.50), Special Edition 1 (7/86, color) 3.00

HERO ALLIANCE
Wonder Color Comics: May, 1987 ($1.95)
1-Ron Lim-a 3.00

HERO ALLIANCE
Innovation Publishing: V2#1, Sept, 1989 - V2#17, Nov, 1991 ($1.95, 28 pgs.)
V2#1-17: 1,2-Ron Lim-a 3.00
Annual 1 (1990, $2.75, 36 pgs.)-Paul Smith-c/a 3.00
Special 1 (1992, $2.50, 32 pgs.)-Stuart Immonen-a (10 pgs.) 3.00

HERO ALLIANCE: END OF THE GOLDEN AGE
Innovation Publ.: July, 1989 - No. 3, Aug, 1989 ($1.75, bi-weekly lim. series)
1-3: Bart Sears & Ron Lim-c/a; reprints & new-a 3.00

HEROBEAR AND THE KID
Boom Entertainment (KaBOOM!)
... 2013 Annual 1 (10/13, $3.99) Halloween-themed story 4.00
... 2016 Fall Special 1 (10/16, $5.99) Saving Time: Part Two 6.00
... Special (6/13, $3.99) Mike Kunkel-s/a/c 4.00
...: The Inheritance (8/13 - No. 5, 12/13, $3.99) 1-5-Mike Kunkel-s/a/c; origin re-told 4.00

HERO COMICS (Hero Initiative benefit book)
IDW Publishing: 2009 - Present ($3.99)
1-Short story anthology by various incl. Colan, Chaykin; covers by Wagner & Campbell 4.00
2011-Covers by Campbell & Hughes; Gaiman-s/Kieth-a; Chew & Elephantmen app. 4.00
2012-Cover by Campbell; TMNT by Eastman; art by Heath, Sim, Kupperberg, & others 4.00
2014-Covers by Campbell & Kieth; Sable by Grell; art by Kieth, Goldberg & others 4.00
...: A Hero Initiative Benefit Book SC (5/16, $19.99) reprints from previous editions 20.00

HEROES
Marvel Comics: Dec, 2001 ($3.50, magazine-size, one-shot)
1-Pin-up tributes to the rescue workers of the Sept. 11 tragedy; art and text by various; cover by Alex Ross 6.00
1-2nd and 3rd printings 4.00

HEROES (Also see Shadow Cabinet & Static)
DC Comics (Milestone): May, 1996 - No. 6, Nov, 1996 ($2.50, limited series)
1-6: 1-Intro Heroes (Iota, Donner, Blitzen, Starlight, Payback & Static) 3.00

HEROES (Based on the NBC TV series)
DC Comics (WildStorm): 2007; 2009 ($29.99, hardcover with dustjacket)
Vol. 1 - Collects 34 installments of the online graphic novel; art by various; two covers by Jim Lee and Alex Ross; intro. by Masi Oka; Jeph Loeb interview 30.00
Vol. 2 - (2009) Collects 46 installments of the online graphic novel; art by various incl. Gaydos, Grummett, Gunnell, Odagawa; two covers by Tim Sale and Gene Ha 30.00

HER-OES
Marvel Comics: Jun, 2010 - No. 4, Sept, 2010 ($2.99, limited series)
1-4-Randolph-s/Rousseau-a; Wasp, She-Hulk, Namora as teenagers 3.00

HEROES AGAINST HUNGER
DC Comics: 1986 ($1.50; one-shot for famine relief)
1-Superman, Batman app.; Neal Adams-c(p); includes many artists work; Jeff Jones assist (2 pg.) on B. Smith-a; Kirby-a 5.00

HEROES ALL CATHOLIC ACTION ILLUSTRATED
Heroes All Co.: 1943 - V6#5, Mar 10, 1948 (paper covers)

	GD	VG	FN	VF	VF/NM	NM-
V1#1-(16 pgs., 8x11")	24	48	72	142	234	325
V1#2-(16 pgs., 8x11")	19	38	57	111	176	240
V2#1(1/44)-3(3/44)-(16 pgs., 8x11")	15	30	45	94	147	200
V3#1(1/45)-10(12/45)-(16 pgs., 8x11")	15	30	45	85	130	175
V4#1-35 (12/20/46)-(16 pgs.)	14	28	42	80	115	150
V5#1(1/10/47)-8(2/28/47)-(16 pgs.), V5#9(3/7/47)-20(11/25/47)-(32 pgs.), V6#1(1/10/48)-5(3/10/48)-(32 pgs.)	12	24	36	69	97	125

HEROES ANONYMOUS
Bongo Comics: 2003 - No. 6, 2004 ($2.99, limited series)
1-6-($2.99)-Bill Morrison-c. 2-Guerra-a. 3-Pepoy-a 3.00

HEROES FOR HIRE
Marvel Comics: July, 1997 - No. 19, Jan, 1999 ($2.99/$1.99)
1-($2.99)-Wraparound cover 5.00
2-19: 2-Variant cover. 7-Thunderbolts app. 9-Punisher-c/app. 10,11-Deadpool-c/app. 18,19-Wolverine-c/app. 3.00
.../Quicksilver '98 Annual ($2.99) Siege of Wundagore pt.5 4.00

HEROES FOR HIRE
Marvel Comics: Oct, 2006 - No. 15, Dec, 2007 ($2.99)

Heroes For Hire (2011 series) #5 © MAR

Heroic Comics #3 © EAS

Hex #1 © DC

GD VG FN VF VF/NM NM-
2.0 4.0 6.0 8.0 9.0 9.2

1-5-Tucci-a/c; Black Cat, Shang-Chi, Tarantula, Humbug & Daughters of the Dragon app. 3.00
6-15: 6-8-Sparacio-c. 9,10-Golden-c. 11-13-World War Hulk x-over. 13-Takeda-c 3.00
... Vol. 1: Civil War (2007, $13.99) r/#1-5 14.00
... Vol. 2: Ahead of the Curve (2007, $13.99) r/#6-10 14.00
... Vol. 3: World War Hulk (2008, $13.99) r/#11-15 14.00

HEROES FOR HIRE
Marvel Comics: Feb, 2011 - No. 12, Nov, 2011 ($3.99/$2.99)

1-($3.99) Abnett & Lanning-s/Walker-a; back-up history of the various teams 4.00
2-12-($2.99) 2-Silver Sable & Ghost Rider app. 5-Punisher app. 9-11-Fear Itself tie-in 3.00

HEROES FOR HOPE STARRING THE X-MEN
Marvel Comics Group: Dec, 1985 ($1.50, one-shot, 52 pgs., proceeds donated to famine relief)

1-Stephen King scripts; Byrne, Miller, Corben-a; Wrightson/J. Jones-a (3 pgs.);
Art Adams-c; Starlin back-c 1 3 4 6 8 10

HEROES: GODSEND (Based on the NBC TV series)(Prelude to the 2015 revival)
Titan Comics: Apr, 2016 - No. 5, Aug, 2016 ($3.99, limited series)

1-5: 1-Origin of Farah Nazan; Roy Allan Martinez-a; multiple covers on each 4.00

HEROES, INC. PRESENTS CANNON
Wally Wood/CPL/Gang Publ.: 1969 - No. 2, 1976 (Sold at Army PXs)

nn-Ditko, Wood-a; Wood-c; Reese-a(p) 2 4 6 9 12 15
2-Wood-c; Ditko, Byrne, Wood-a; 8-1/2x10-1/2"; B&W; $2.00
3 6 9 16 23 30

NOTE: *First issue not distributed by publisher; 1,800 copies were stored and 900 copies were stolen from warehouse. Many copies have surfaced in recent years.*

HEROES OF THE WILD FRONTIER (Formerly Baffling Mysteries)
Ace Periodicals: No. 27, Jan, 1956 - No. 2, Apr, 1956

27(#1),2-Davy Crockett, Daniel Boone, Buffalo Bill 6 12 18 29 36 42

HEROES REBORN (one-shots)
Marvel Comics: Jan, 2000 ($1.99)

...:Ashema; ...:Doom; ...:Doomsday; ...:Masters of Evil; ...:Rebel; ...:Remnants;
...:Young Allies 3.00

HEROES REBORN: THE RETURN (Also see Avengers, Fantastic Four, Iron Man & Captain America titles for issues and TPBs)
Marvel Comics: Dec, 1997 - No. 4 ($2.50, weekly mini-series)

1-4-Avengers, Fantastic Four, Iron Man & Captain America rejoin regular Marvel Universe;
Peter David-s/Larocca-c/a 4.00
1-4-Variant-c for each 6.00
Wizard 1/2 1 2 3 5 7 9
Return of the Heroes TPB ('98, $14.95) r/#1-4 15.00

HEROES: VENGEANCE (Based on the NBC TV series)(Prelude to the 2015 revival)
Titan Comics: Nov, 2015 - No. 5, Mar, 2016 ($3.99, limited series)

1-5: 1-Origin of El Vengador; Rubine-a; multiple covers on each 4.00

HERO FOR HIRE (Power Man No. 17 on; also see Cage)
Marvel Comics Group: June, 1972 - No. 16, Dec, 1973

1-Origin & 1st app. Luke Cage; Tuska-a(p) 46 92 138 368 834 1300
2-Tuska-a(p) 6 12 18 42 79 115
3,4: 3-1st app. Mace. 4-1st app. Phil Fox of the Bugle
5 10 15 31 53 75
5-1st app. Black Mariah 5 10 15 33 57 80
6-10: 8,9-Dr. Doom app. 9-F.F. app. 10-1st app. Mr. Death
4 8 12 23 37 50
11-16: 14-Origin retold. 15-Everett Sub-Mariner-r('53). 16-Origin Stilletto; death of Rackham
3 6 9 19 30 40

HERO HOTLINE (1st app. in Action Comics Weekly #637)
DC Comics: April, 1989 - No. 6, Sept, 1989 ($1.75, limited series)

1-6: Super-hero humor; Schaffenberger-i 3.00

HEROIC ADVENTURES (See Adventures)

HEROIC AGE
Marvel Comics: Nov, 2010 ($3.99, limited series)

... Heroes 1 (11/10, $3.99) profile of heroes, bios, pros, cons, "power grid"; Raney-c 4.00
... Villains 1 (1/11, $3.99) profile of villains, bios, pros, cons, "power grid"; Jae Lee-c 4.00
... X-Men 1 (2/11, $3.99) profile of members in Steve Rogers journal entries,; Jae Lee-c 4.00

HEROIC AGE: PRINCE OF POWER (Continued from Hercules: Fall of an Avenger)
Marvel Comics: Jul, 2010 - No. 4, Oct, 2010 ($3.99, limited series)

1-4-Van Lente & Pak-s; Thor app.; leads into Chaos War #1 4.00

HEROIC COMICS (Reg'lar Fellers...#1-15; New Heroic #41 on)
Eastern Color Printing Co./Famous Funnies (Funnies, Inc. No. 1):
Aug, 1940 - No. 97, June, 1955

1-Hydroman (origin) by Bill Everett, The Purple Zombie (origin) & Mann of India
by Tarpe Mills begins (all 1st apps.) 239 478 717 1530 2615 3700
2 97 194 291 621 1061 1500
3,4 57 114 171 362 619 875
5,6 50 100 150 315 533 750
7-Origin & 1st app. Man O'Metal (1 pg.) 52 104 156 328 552 775
8-10: 10-Lingerie panels 39 78 117 234 385 535
11,13 37 74 111 222 361 500
12-Music Master (origin/1st app.) begins by Everett, ends No. 31; last Purple Zombie &
Mann of India 40 80 120 246 411 575
14,15-Hydroman x-over in Rainbow Boy. 14-Origin & 1st app. Rainbow Boy (super hero).
15-1st app. Downbeat 37 74 111 222 361 500
16-20: 16-New logo. 17-Rainbow Boy x-over in Hydroman. 19-Rainbow Boy x-over in
Hydroman & vice versa 26 52 78 154 252 350
21-30:25-Rainbow Boy x-over in Hydroman. 28-Last Man O'Metal. 29-Last Hydroman
20 40 60 114 182 250
31,34,38 9 18 27 50 65 80
32,36,37-Toth-a (3-4 pgs. each) 10 20 30 56 76 95
33,35-Toth-a (8 & 9 pgs.) 10 20 30 58 79 100
39-42-Toth, Ingels-a 10 20 30 58 79 100
43,46,47,49-Toth-a (2-4 pgs.). 47-Ingels-a 10 20 30 54 72 90
44,45,50-Toth-a (6-9 pgs.) 10 20 30 56 76 95
48,53,54 9 18 27 47 61 75
51-Williamson-a 10 20 30 56 76 95
52-Williamson-a (3 pg. story) 9 18 27 50 65 80
55-Toth-a 10 20 30 54 72 90
56-60: 60-Everett-a 9 18 27 50 65 80
61-Everett-a 9 18 27 47 61 75
62,64-Everett-c/a 10 20 30 54 72 90
63-Everett-c 9 18 27 52 69 85
65-Williamson/Frazetta-a; Evans-a (2 pgs.) 13 26 39 72 101 130
66,75,94-Frazetta-a (2 pgs. each) 9 18 27 52 69 85
67,73-Frazetta-a (4 pgs. each) 11 22 33 60 83 105
68,74,76-80,84,85,88-93,95-97: 95-Last pre-code 9 18 27 47 61 75
69,72-Frazetta-a (6 & 8 pgs. each); 1st (?) app. Frazetta Red Cross ad
13 26 39 72 101 130
70,71,86,87-Frazetta, 3-4 pgs. each; 1 pg. ad by Frazetta in #70
10 20 30 56 76 95
81,82-Frazetta art (1 pg. each): 81-1st (?) app. Frazetta Boy Scout ad (tied w/
Buster Crabbe #9 9 18 27 50 65 80
83-Frazetta-a (1/2 pg.) 9 18 27 50 65 80

NOTE: ***Evans** a-64, 65. **Everett** a-(Hydroman-c/a-No. 1-9), 44, 60-64; c-1-9, 62-64. **Harvey Fuller** c-28-35. **Sid Greene** a-38-43, 46. **Guardineer** a-42(3), 43, 44, 45(2), 49(3), 50, 60, 61(2), 65, 67(2) 70-72. **Ingels** c-41. **Kiefer** a-46, 48; c-19-22, 24, 44, 46, 48, 51-53, 65, 67-69, 71-74, 76, 77, 79, 80, 82, 85, 86, 88, 89, 94, 95. **Mort Lawrence** a-45. **Tarpe Mills** a-2(2), 3(2), 10. **Ed Moore** a-49, 52-54, 56-63, 65-69, 72-74, 76, 77. **H.G. Peter** a-58-74, 76, 77, 87. **Paul Reinman** a-49. **Rico** a-31. Captain Tootsie by **Beck**-31, 32. Painted-c #16 on. Hydroman c-1-11. Music Master c-12, 13, 15. Rainbow Boy c-14.*

HERO INITIATIVE: MIKE WIERINGO BOOK (Also see Hero Comics)
Marvel Comics: Aug, 2008 ($4.99)

1-The "What If" Fantastic Four story with Wieringo-a (7 pgs.) finished by other artists after
his passing; art by Davis, Immonen, Ramos, Kitson and others; written tributes 5.00

HERO WORSHIP
Avatar Press: Jun, 2012 - No. 6, Nov, 2012 ($3.99)

1-6: 1-Zak Penn & Scott Murphy-s/Michael DiPascale-a; 2 covers 4.00

HERO ZERO (Also see Comics' Greatest World & Godzilla Versus Hero Zero)
Dark Horse Comics: Sept, 1994 ($2.50)

0 3.00

HEX (Replaces Jonah Hex)
DC Comics: Sept, 1985 - No. 18, Feb, 1987 (Story cont'd from Jonah Hex # 92)

1-Hex in post-atomic war world; origin 2 4 6 8 10 12
2-10,14-18: 6-Origin Stiletta 1 2 3 4 5 7
11-13: All contain future Batman storyline. 13-Intro The Dogs of War (origin #15)
1 3 4 6 8 10

NOTE: ***Giffen** a(p)-15-18; c(p)-15,17,18. **Texeira** a-1, 2p, 3p, 5-7p, 9p, 11-14p; c(p)-1, 2, 4-7, 12.*

HEXBREAKER (See First Comics Graphic Novel #15)

HEXED
BOOM! Studios: Aug, 2014 - No. 12, Aug, 2015 ($3.99)

1-12: 1-Michael Alan Nelson-s/Dan Mora-s; 3 covers 4.00

HEY THERE, IT'S YOGI BEAR (See Movie Comics)

High Roads #2 © Leinil Yu

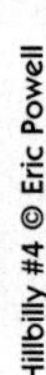

Hillbilly #4 © Eric Powell

Hi-School Romance #3 © HARV

HI-ADVENTURE HEROES (TV)
Gold Key: May, 1969 - No. 2, Aug, 1969 (Hanna-Barbera)

	GD 2.0	VG 4.0	FN 6.0	VF 8.0	VF/NM 9.0	NM- 9.2
1-Three Musketeers, Gulliver, Arabian Knights	5	10	15	30	50	70
2-Three Musketeers, Micro-Venture, Arabian Knights	4	8	12	27	44	60

HI AND LOIS
Dell Publishing Co.: No. 683, Mar, 1956 - No. 955, Nov, 1958

	GD 2.0	VG 4.0	FN 6.0	VF 8.0	VF/NM 9.0	NM- 9.2
Four Color 683 (#1)	5	10	15	34	60	85
Four Color 774(3/57),955	4	8	12	28	47	65

HI AND LOIS
Charlton Comics: Nov, 1969 - No. 11, July, 1971

	GD 2.0	VG 4.0	FN 6.0	VF 8.0	VF/NM 9.0	NM- 9.2
1	3	6	9	14	20	25
2-11	2	4	6	9	12	15

HICKORY (See All Humor Comics)
Quality Comics Group: Oct, 1949 - No. 6, Aug, 1950

	GD 2.0	VG 4.0	FN 6.0	VF 8.0	VF/NM 9.0	NM- 9.2
1-Sahl-c/a in all; Feldstein?-a	27	54	81	158	259	360
2	17	34	51	98	154	210
3-6-Good Girl covers	23	46	69	136	223	310

HIDDEN CREW, THE (See The United States Air Force Presents:...)

HIDE-OUT (See Zane Grey, Four Color No. 346)

HIDING PLACE, THE
Spire Christian Comics (Fleming H. Revell Co.): 1973 (39¢/49¢)

	GD 2.0	VG 4.0	FN 6.0	VF 8.0	VF/NM 9.0	NM- 9.2
nn	2	4	6	13	18	22

HI-FI FIGHT CLUB (Title changes to Heavy Vinyl for #4)
Boom Entertainment (BOOM! Box): Aug, 2017 - No. 3, Oct, 2017 ($3.99)

	GD 2.0	VG 4.0	FN 6.0	VF 8.0	VF/NM 9.0	NM- 9.2
1-3-Carly Usdin-s/Nina Vakueva-a						4.00

HIGH ADVENTURE
Red Top(Decker) Comics (Farrell): Oct, 1957

	GD 2.0	VG 4.0	FN 6.0	VF 8.0	VF/NM 9.0	NM- 9.2
1-Krigstein-r from Explorer Joe (re-issue on-c)	5	10	15	23	28	32

HIGH ADVENTURE (TV)
Dell Publishing Co.: No. 949, Nov, 1958 - No. 1001, Aug-Oct, 1959 (Lowell Thomas)

	GD 2.0	VG 4.0	FN 6.0	VF 8.0	VF/NM 9.0	NM- 9.2
Four Color 949 (#1)-Photo-c	5	10	15	34	60	85
Four Color 1001-Lowell Thomas'...(#2)	5	10	15	33	57	80

HIGH CHAPPARAL (TV)
Gold Key: Aug, 1968 (Photo-c)

	GD 2.0	VG 4.0	FN 6.0	VF 8.0	VF/NM 9.0	NM- 9.2
1 (10226-808)-Tufts-a	6	12	18	38	69	100

HIGHLANDER
Dynamite Entertainment: No. 0, 2006 - No. 12, 2007 (25¢/$2.99)

	GD 2.0	VG 4.0	FN 6.0	VF 8.0	VF/NM 9.0	NM- 9.2
0-(25¢-c) Takes place after the first movie; photo-c and Dell'Otto painted-c						3.00
1-12: 1-($2.99) Three covers; Moder-a/Jerwa & Oeming-s. 2-Three covers						3.00
... Origins: The Kurgan 1,2 (2009 - No. 2, 2009, $4.99) Three covers; Rafael-a						5.00
...: Way of the Sword (2007 - No. 4, 2008, $3.50) Two interlocking covers for each						3.50

HIGHLANDER: THE AMERICAN DREAM
IDW Publishing: Feb, 2017 - No. 5, Jun, 2017 ($3.99)

	GD 2.0	VG 4.0	FN 6.0	VF 8.0	VF/NM 9.0	NM- 9.2
1-5-Brian Ruckley-s/Andrea Mutti-a; multiple covers; MacLeod in 1985 New York						4.00

HIGH ROADS
DC Comics (Cliffhanger): June, 2002 - No. 6, Nov, 2002 ($2.95, limited series)

	GD 2.0	VG 4.0	FN 6.0	VF 8.0	VF/NM 9.0	NM- 9.2
1-6-Leinil Yu-c/a; Lobdell-s						3.00
TPB (2003, $14.95) r/#1-6; sketch pages						15.00

HIGH SCHOOL CONFIDENTIAL DIARY (Confidential Diary #12 on)
Charlton Comics: June, 1960 - No. 11, Mar, 1962

	GD 2.0	VG 4.0	FN 6.0	VF 8.0	VF/NM 9.0	NM- 9.2
1	4	8	12	27	44	60
2-11	3	6	9	17	26	35

HIGHWAYMEN
DC Comics (WildStorm): Aug, 2007 - No. 5, Dec, 2007 ($2.99)

	GD 2.0	VG 4.0	FN 6.0	VF 8.0	VF/NM 9.0	NM- 9.2
1-5-Bernardin & Freeman-s/Garbett-a						3.00
TPB (2008, $17.99) r/#1-5						18.00

HIGH WAYS, THE
IDW Publishing: Dec, 2012 - No. 4, Apr, 2013 ($3.99, limited series)

	GD 2.0	VG 4.0	FN 6.0	VF 8.0	VF/NM 9.0	NM- 9.2
1-4-John Byrne-s/a/c						4.00

HI HI PUFFY AMIYUMI (Based on Cartoon Network animated series)
DC Comics: Apr, 2006 - No. 3, June, 2006 ($2.25, limited series)

	GD 2.0	VG 4.0	FN 6.0	VF 8.0	VF/NM 9.0	NM- 9.2
1-3-Phil Moy-a						3.00

HI-HO COMICS
Four Star Publications: nd (2/46?) - No. 3, 1946

	GD 2.0	VG 4.0	FN 6.0	VF 8.0	VF/NM 9.0	NM- 9.2
1-Funny Animal; L. B. Cole-c	39	78	117	240	395	550
2,3: 2-L. B. Cole-c	22	44	66	132	216	300

HI-JINX (Teen-age Animal Funnies)
La Salle Publ. Co./B&I Publ. Co. (American Comics Group)/Creston: 1945; July-Aug, 1947 - No. 7, July-Aug, 1948

	GD 2.0	VG 4.0	FN 6.0	VF 8.0	VF/NM 9.0	NM- 9.2
nn-(© 1945, 25 cents, 132 Pgs.)(La Salle)	31	62	93	182	296	410
1-Teen-age, funny animal	20	40	60	117	189	260
2,3	14	28	42	80	115	150
4-7-Milt Gross. 4-X-Mas-c	20	40	60	114	182	250

HI-LITE COMICS
E. R. Ross Publishing Co.: Fall, 1945

	GD 2.0	VG 4.0	FN 6.0	VF 8.0	VF/NM 9.0	NM- 9.2
1-Miss Shady	22	44	66	132	216	300

HILLBILLY
Albatross Funnybooks: 2016 - No. 8, 2017 ($3.99)

	GD 2.0	VG 4.0	FN 6.0	VF 8.0	VF/NM 9.0	NM- 9.2
1-8-Eric Powell-s/c; Powell-a in #1-7. 2-The Buzzard app. 5-Back-up with Mannion-a. 8-Di Meo-a						4.00

HILLBILLY COMICS
Charlton Comics: Aug, 1955 - No. 4, July, 1956 (Satire)

	GD 2.0	VG 4.0	FN 6.0	VF 8.0	VF/NM 9.0	NM- 9.2
1-By Art Gates	13	26	39	72	101	130
2-4	9	18	27	50	65	80

HILLY ROSE'S SPACE ADVENTURES
Astro Comics: May, 1995 - No. 9 ($2.95, B&W)

	GD 2.0	VG 4.0	FN 6.0	VF 8.0	VF/NM 9.0	NM- 9.2
1	1	2	3	5	7	9
2-9						5.00
Trade Paperback (1996, $12.95)-r/#1-5						13.00

HINTERKIND
DC Comics (Vertigo): Dec, 2013 - No. 18, Jul, 2015 ($2.99)

	GD 2.0	VG 4.0	FN 6.0	VF 8.0	VF/NM 9.0	NM- 9.2
1-18: 1-Ian Edginton-s/Francesco Trifogli-a/Greg Tocchini-c						3.00

HIP FLASK (Also see Elephantmen)
Active Images/Image Comics

	GD 2.0	VG 4.0	FN 6.0	VF 8.0	VF/NM 9.0	NM- 9.2
...: Ouroborous (12/12, $4.99) Starkings-s/Ladronn-a						5.00
... Unnatural Selection (9/02, $2.99) Casey & Starkings-s/Ladronn-a; var.-c by Madureira, Campbell, Churchill						3.00

HIP-IT-TY HOP (See March of Comics No. 15)

HIRE, THE (BMWfilms.com's...)
Dark Horse Comics: July, 2004 - No. 6 ($2.99)

	GD 2.0	VG 4.0	FN 6.0	VF 8.0	VF/NM 9.0	NM- 9.2
1-4: 1-Matt Wagner-s/Wagner & Velasco-a. 2-Bruce Campbell-s/Plunkett-a. 3-Waid-s						3.00
TPB (4/06, $17.95) r/#1-4						18.00

HI-SCHOOL ROMANCE (...Romances No. 41 on)
Harvey Publ./True Love(Home Comics): Oct, 1949 - No. 5, June, 1950; No. 6, Dec, 1950 - No. 73, Mar, 1958; No. 74, Sept, 1958 - No. 75, Nov, 1958

	GD 2.0	VG 4.0	FN 6.0	VF 8.0	VF/NM 9.0	NM- 9.2
1-Photo-c	16	32	48	94	147	200
2-Photo-c	10	20	30	56	76	95
3-9: 3-5-Photo-c	9	18	27	47	61	75
10-Rape story	10	20	30	56	76	95
11-20	8	16	24	40	50	60
21-31	6	12	18	31	38	45
32- "Unholy passion" story	9	18	27	50	65	80
33-36: 36-Last pre-code (2/55)	6	12	18	29	36	42
37-53,59-72,74,75	5	10	15	24	30	35
54-58,73-Kirby-c	6	12	18	31	38	45

NOTE: ***Powell** a-1-3, 5, 8, 12-16, 18, 21-23, 25-27, 30-34, 36, 37, 39, 45-48, 50-52, 57, 58, 60, 64, 65, 67, 69.*

HI-SCHOOL ROMANCE DATE BOOK
Harvey Publications: Nov, 1962 - No. 3, Mar, 1963 (25¢ Giants)

	GD 2.0	VG 4.0	FN 6.0	VF 8.0	VF/NM 9.0	NM- 9.2
1-Powell, Baker-a	5	10	15	35	63	90
2,3	3	6	9	21	33	45

HIS NAME IS SAVAGE (Magazine format)
Adventure House Press: June, 1968 (35¢, 52 pgs.)

	GD 2.0	VG 4.0	FN 6.0	VF 8.0	VF/NM 9.0	NM- 9.2
1-Gil Kane-a	5	10	15	31	53	75

HI-SPOT COMICS (Red Ryder No. 1 & No. 3 on)
Hawley Publications: No. 2, Nov, 1940

	GD 2.0	VG 4.0	FN 6.0	VF 8.0	VF/NM 9.0	NM- 9.2
2-David Innes of Pellucidar; art by J. C. Burroughs; written by Edgar Rice Burroughs	168	336	504	1075	1838	2600

HISTORY OF THE DC UNIVERSE (Also see Crisis on Infinite Earths)

Hit Comics #6 © QUA

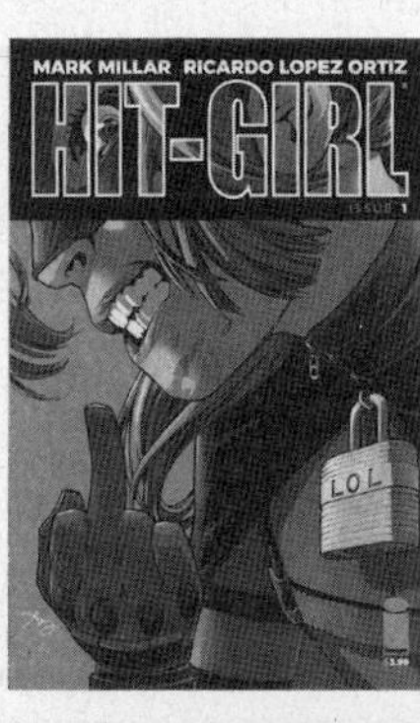

Hit-Girl (2018 series) #1 © Dave & Eggsy/JRJR

Holiday Comics #1 © DC

GD 2.0 VG 4.0 FN 6.0 VF 8.0 VF/NM 9.0 NM- 9.2

DC Comics: Sept, 1986 - No. 2, Nov, 1986 ($2.95, limited series)
1,2: 1-Perez-c/a 5.00
Limited Edition hardcover 4 8 12 26 41 55
Softcover (2002, $9.95) new Alex Ross wraparound-c 13.00
Softcover (2009, $12.99) Alex Ross wraparound-c 13.00

HISTORY OF VIOLENCE, A (Inspired the 2005 movie)
DC Comics (Paradox Press) 1997 ($9.95, B&W graphic novel)
nn-Paperback ($9.95) John Wagner-s/Vince Locke-a 18.00

HIT
BOOM! Studios: Sept, 2013 - No. 4, Dec, 2013 ($3.99, limited series)
1-4-Bryce Carlson-s/Vanesa R. Del Ray-a/Ryan Sook-c 4.00
...: 1957 (3/15 - No. 4, 7/15, $3.99) 1-4-Bryce Carlson-s/Vanesa R. Del Ray-a/c 4.00

HITCHHIKERS GUIDE TO THE GALAXY (See Life, the Universe and Everything & Restaurant at the End of the Universe)
DC Comics: 1993 - No. 3, 1993 ($4.95, limited series)
1-3: Adaptation of Douglas Adams book 5.00
TPB (1997, $14.95) r/#1-3 15.00

HIT COMICS
Quality Comics Group: July, 1940 - No. 65, July, 1950
1-Origin/1st app. Neon, the Unknown & Hercules; intro. The Red Bee; Bob & Swab, Blaze Barton, the Strange Twins, X-5 Super Agent, Casey Jones & Jack & Jill (ends #7) begin 811 1622 2433 5920 10,460 15,000
2-The Old Witch begins, ends #14 (scarce) 349 698 1047 2443 4272 6100
3-Casey Jones ends; transvestism story "Jack & Jill" 343 686 1029 2400 4200 6000
4-Super Agent (ends #17), & Betty Bates (ends #65) begin; X-5 ends 300 600 900 1980 3440 4900
5-Classic Lou Fine cover 865 1730 2595 6315 11,158 16,000
6,8-10: 10-Old Witch by Crandall (4 pgs.); 1st work in comics (4/41) 265 530 795 1694 2897 4100
7-Skull bondage-c 343 686 1029 2400 4200 6000
11-Classic cover 320 640 960 2240 3920 5600
12-16: 13-Blaze Barton ends 174 348 522 1114 1907 2700
17-Last Neon; Crandall Hercules in all; last Lou Fine-c; skeleton-c 239 478 717 1530 2615 3700
18-Origin & 1st app. Stormy Foster, the Great Defender (12/41); The Ghost of Flanders begins; Crandall-c 187 374 561 1197 2049 2900
19,20 135 270 405 864 1482 2100
21-24: 21-Last Hercules. 24-Last Red Bee & Strange Twins 123 246 369 787 1344 1900
25-Origin & 1st app. Kid Eternity and begins by Moldoff (12/42); 1st app. The Keeper (Kid Eternity's aide) 226 452 678 1446 2473 3500
26-Blackhawk x-over in Kid Eternity 110 220 330 704 1202 1700
27-29 52 104 156 328 552 775
30,31- "Bill the Magnificent" by Kurtzman, 11 pgs. in each 47 94 141 296 498 700
32-40: 32-Plastic Man x-over. 34-Last Stormy Foster 31 62 93 182 296 410
41-50 22 44 66 128 209 290
51-60-Last Kid Eternity 21 42 63 122 199 275
61-63-Crandall-c/a; 61-Jeb Rivers begins 21 42 63 126 206 285
64,65-Crandall-a 21 42 63 122 199 275
NOTE: ***Crandall** a-11-17(Hercules), 23, 24(Stormy Foster); c-18-20, 23, 24. **Fine** c-1-14, 16, 17(most). **Ward** c-33. Bondage c-7, 64. Hercules c-3, 10-17. Jeb Rivers c-61-65. Kid Eternity c-25-60 (w/Keeper-28-34, 36, 39-43, 45-55). Neon the Unknown c-2, 4, 8, 9. Red Bee c-1, 5-7. Stormy Foster c-18-24.*

HIT-GIRL (Also see Kick-Ass)
Marvel Comics (Icon): Aug, 2012 - No. 5, Apr, 2013 ($2.99, limited series)
1-Takes place between Kick-Ass & Kick Ass 2 series; Millar-s/Romita Jr.-a/c 5.00
2-5 3.00

HIT-GIRL (Also see Kick-Ass)
Image Comics: Feb, 2018 - Present ($3.99)
1-Millar-s/Ortiz-a 4.00

HITLER'S ASTROLOGER (See Marvel Graphic Novel #35)

HITMAN (Also see Bloodbath #2, Batman Chronicles #4, Demon #43-45 & Demon Annual #2)
DC Comics: May, 1996 - No. 60, Apr, 2001 ($2.25/$2.50)
1-Garth Ennis-s & John McCrea-c/a begin; Batman app. 2 4 6 10 14 18
2-Joker-c;Two Face, Mad Hatter, Batman app. 1 2 3 5 6 8
3-5: 3-Batman-c/app.; Joker app. 4-1st app. Nightfist 5.00
6-20: 8-Final Night x-over. 10-GL cameo. 11-20: 11,12-GL-c/app. 15-20-"Ace of Killers". 16-18-Catwoman app. 17-19-Demon-app. 4.00
21-59: 34-Superman-c/app. 3.00
60-($3.95) Final issue; includes pin-ups by various 4.00
#1,000,000 (11/98) Hitman goes to the 853rd Century 3.00
Annual 1 (1997, $3.95) Pulp Heroes 5.00
.../Lobo: That Stupid Bastich (7/00, $3.95) Ennis-s/Mahnke-a 4.00
TPB-(1997, $9.95) r/#1-3, Demon Ann. #2, Batman Chronicles #4 10.00
Ace of Killers TPB ('00/'11, $17.95/$17.99) r/#15-22 18.00
Local Heroes TPB ('99, $17.95) r/#9-14 & Annual #1 18.00
10,000 Bullets TPB ('98, $9.95) r/#4-8 10.00
Ten Thousand Bullets TPB ('10, $17.99) r/#4-8 & Annual #1; intro. by Kevin Smith 18.00
Who Dares Wins TPB ('01, $12.95) r/#23-28 13.00

HIT-MONKEY (See Deadpool)
Marvel Comics: Apr, 2010; Sept, 2010 - No. 3, Nov, 2010 ($3.99/$2.99)
1-(4/10, $3.99) Printing of story from Marvel Digital Comics; Frank Cho-c; origin revealed 4.00
1-3-Daniel Way-s/Talajic-a/Johnson-c; Bullseye app. 3.00

HI-YO SILVER (See Lone Ranger's Famous Horse... and The Lone Ranger; and March of Comics No. 215 in the Promotional Comics section)

HOBBIT, THE
Eclipse Comics: 1989 - No. 3, 1990 ($4.95, squarebound, 52 pgs.)
Book 1-3: Adapts novel; Wenzel-a 2 4 6 8 10 12
Book 1-Second printing 5.00
Graphic Novel (1990, Ballantine)-r/#1-3 25.00

HOCUS POCUS (See Funny Book #9)

HOGAN'S HEROES (TV) (Also see Wild!)
Dell Publishing Co.: June, 1966 - No. 8, Sept, 1967; No. 9, Oct, 1969
1: Photo-c on #1-7 7 14 21 48 89 130
2,3-Ditko-a(p) 5 10 15 33 57 80
4-9: 9-Reprints #1 4 8 12 28 47 65

HOKUM & HEX (See Razorline)
Marvel Comics (Razorline): Sept, 1993 - No. 9, May, 1994 ($1.75/$1.95)
1-($2.50)-Foil embossed-c; by Clive Barker 4.00
2-9: 5-Hyperkind x-over 3.00

HOLIDAY COMICS
Fawcett Publications: 1942 (25¢, 196 pgs.)
1-Contains three Fawcett comics plus two page portrait of Captain Marvel; Capt. Marvel, Jungle Girl #1, & Whiz. Not rebound, remaindered comics; printed at the same time as originals (scarce in high grade) 310 620 930 2170 4335 6500

HOLIDAY COMICS (Becomes Fun Comics #9-12)
Star Publications: Jan, 1951 - No. 8, Oct, 1952
1-Funny animal contents (Frisky Fables) in all; L. B. Cole X-Mas-c 37 74 111 222 361 500
2-Classic L. B. Cole-c 34 68 102 199 325 450
3-8: 5,8-X-Mas-c; all L.B. Cole-c 20 40 60 117 189 260
Accepted Reprint 4 (nd)-L.B. Cole-c 10 20 30 58 79 100

HOLIDAY DIGEST
Harvey Comics: 1988 ($1.25, digest-size)
1 1 2 3 5 7 9

HOLIDAY PARADE (Walt Disney's...)
W. D. Publications (Disney): Winter, 1990-91(no year given) - No. 2, Winter, 1990-91 ($2.95, 68 pgs.)
1-Reprints 1947 Firestone by Barks plus new-a 5.00
2-Barks-r plus other stories 4.00

HOLI-DAY SURPRISE (Formerly Summer Fun)
Charlton Comics: V2#55, Mar, 1967 (25¢ Giant)
V2#55 4 8 12 23 37 50

HOLLYWOOD COMICS
New Age Publishers: Winter, 1944 (52 pgs.)
1-Funny animal 20 40 60 117 189 260

HOLLYWOOD CONFESSIONS
St. John Publishing Co.: Oct, 1949 - No. 2, Dec, 1949
1-Kubert-c/a (entire book) 42 84 126 265 445 625
2-Kubert-c/a (entire book) (Scarce) 43 86 129 271 461 650

HOLLYWOOD DIARY
Quality Comics Group: Dec, 1949 - No. 5, July-Aug, 1950
1-No photo-c 28 56 84 165 270 375

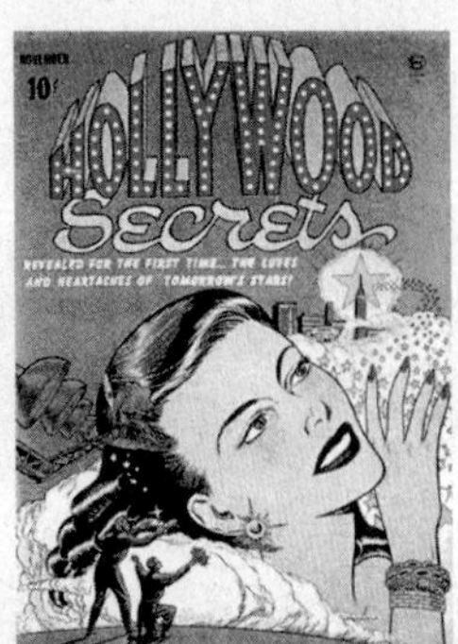

Hollywood Secrets #1 © QUA

Holyoke One-Shot #1 © HOKE

Homer, the Happy Ghost #1 © MAR

	GD 2.0	VG 4.0	FN 6.0	VF 8.0	VF/NM 9.0	NM- 9.2
2-Photo-c	18	36	54	103	162	220
3-5-Photo-c. 3-Betty Carlin photo-c. 5-June Allyson/Peter Lawford photo-c	15	30	45	90	140	190

HOLLYWOOD FILM STORIES
Feature Publications/Prize: April, 1950 - No. 4, Oct, 1950 (All photo-c; "Fumetti" type movie comic)

	GD 2.0	VG 4.0	FN 6.0	VF 8.0	VF/NM 9.0	NM- 9.2
1-June Allyson photo-c	22	44	66	128	209	290
2-4: 2-Lizabeth Scott photo-c. 3-Barbara Stanwick photo-c. 4-Betty Hutton photo-c	15	30	45	90	140	190

HOLLYWOOD FUNNY FOLKS (Formerly Funny Folks; Becomes Nutsy Squirrel #61 on)
National Periodical Publ.: No. 27, Aug-Sept, 1950 - No. 60, July-Aug, 1954

	GD 2.0	VG 4.0	FN 6.0	VF 8.0	VF/NM 9.0	NM- 9.2
27-Nutsy Squirrel continues	14	28	42	76	108	140
28-40	10	20	30	54	72	90
41-60	9	18	27	47	61	75

NOTE: ***Rube Grossman** a-most issues. **Sheldon Mayer** a-27-35, 37-40, 43-46, 48-51, 53, 56, 57, 60.*

HOLLYWOOD LOVE DOCTOR (See Doctor Anthony King...)

HOLLYWOOD PICTORIAL (...Romances on cover)
St. John Publishing Co.: No. 3, Jan, 1950

	GD 2.0	VG 4.0	FN 6.0	VF 8.0	VF/NM 9.0	NM- 9.2
3-Matt Baker-a; photo-c	39	78	117	231	378	525

(Becomes a movie magazine - Hollywood Pictorial Western with No. 4.)

HOLLYWOOD ROMANCES (Formerly Brides In Love; becomes For Lovers Only #60 on)
Charlton Comics: V2#46, 11/66; #47, 10/67; #48, 11/68;V3#49,11/69-V3#59, 6/71

	GD 2.0	VG 4.0	FN 6.0	VF 8.0	VF/NM 9.0	NM- 9.2
V2#46-Rolling Stones-c/story	8	16	24	56	108	160
V2#47-V3#59: 56- "Born to Heart Break" begins	3	6	9	14	19	24

HOLLYWOOD SECRETS
Quality Comics Group: Nov, 1949 - No. 6, Sept, 1950

	GD 2.0	VG 4.0	FN 6.0	VF 8.0	VF/NM 9.0	NM- 9.2
1-Ward-c/a (9 pgs.)	42	84	126	265	445	625
2-Crandall-a, Ward-c/a (9 pgs.)	31	62	93	184	300	415
3-6: All photo-c. 5-Lex Barker (Tarzan)-c	17	34	51	100	158	215
...of Romance, I.W. Reprint #9; r/#2 above w/Kinstler-c	2	4	6	11	16	20

HOLLYWOOD SUPERSTARS
Marvel Comics (Epic Comics): Nov, 1990 - No. 5, Apr, 1991 ($2.25)

	GD 2.0	VG 4.0	FN 6.0	VF 8.0	VF/NM 9.0	NM- 9.2
1-($2.95, 52 pgs.)-Spiegle-c/a in all; Aragonés-a, inside front-c plus 2-4 pgs.						4.00
2-5 ($2.25)						3.00

HOLO-MAN (See Power Record Comics)

HOLYOKE ONE-SHOT
Holyoke Publishing Co. (Tem Publ.): 1944 - No. 10, 1945 (All reprints)

	GD 2.0	VG 4.0	FN 6.0	VF 8.0	VF/NM 9.0	NM- 9.2
1,2: 1-Grit Grady (on cover only), Miss Victory, Alias X (origin)-All reprints from Captain Fearless. 2-Rusty Dugan (Corporal); Capt. Fearless (origin), Mr. Miracle (origin) app.	34	68	102	199	325	450
3-Miss Victory; r/Crash #4; Cat Man (origin), Solar Legion by Kirby app.; Miss Victory on cover only (1945)	50	100	150	315	533	750
4,6,8: 4-Mr. Miracle; The Blue Streak app.; reprints early Cat-Man story. 6-Capt. Fearless, Alias X, Capt. Stone (splash used as-c to #10); Diamond Jim & Rusty Dugan (splash from cover of #2). 8-Blue Streak, Strong Man (story matches cover to #7)-Crash reprints	28	56	84	165	270	375
5,7: 5-U.S. Border Patrol Comics (Sgt. Dick Carter of the...), Miss Victory (story matches cover to #3), Citizen Smith, & Mr. Miracle app. 7-Secret Agent Z-2, Strong Man, Blue Streak (story matches cover to #8); Reprints from Crash #2	29	58	87	172	281	390
9-Citizen Smith, The Blue Streak, Solar Legion by Kirby & Strongman, the Perfect Human app.; reprints from Crash #4 & 5; Citizen Smith on cover only-from story in #5 (1944-before #3)	32	64	96	188	307	425
10-Captain Stone; r/Crash; Solar Legion by S&K	32	64	96	188	307	425

HOLY TERROR
Legendary Comics: Sept, 2011 ($29.95, HC graphic novel, 12-1/4" wide x 9-1/4" tall)

	GD 2.0	VG 4.0	FN 6.0	VF 8.0	VF/NM 9.0	NM- 9.2
HC-Frank Miller-s/a/c; B&W art with spot color; The Fixer vs. Al-Qaeda in Empire City						30.00

HOME (Based on the DreamWorks movie)
Titan Comics: Aug, 2015 - No. 4, Nov, 2015 ($3.99)

	GD 2.0	VG 4.0	FN 6.0	VF 8.0	VF/NM 9.0	NM- 9.2
1-4: 1-Davison-s/Hebb-a						4.00

HOMECOMING
Aspen MLT: Aug, 2012 - No. 4, Sept, 2013 ($3.99)

	GD 2.0	VG 4.0	FN 6.0	VF 8.0	VF/NM 9.0	NM- 9.2
1-4: 1-Wohl-s/Laiso-a; covers by Michael Turner and Mike DeBalfo						4.00

HOMER COBB (See Adventures of...)

HOMER HOOPER
Atlas Comics: July, 1953 - No. 4, Dec, 1953

	GD 2.0	VG 4.0	FN 6.0	VF 8.0	VF/NM 9.0	NM- 9.2
1-Teenage humor	15	30	45	84	127	170
2-4	11	22	33	62	86	110

HOMER, THE HAPPY GHOST (See Adventures of...)
Atlas(ACI/PPI/WPI)/Marvel: 3/55 - No. 22, 11/58; V2#1, 11/69 - V2#4, 5/70

	GD 2.0	VG 4.0	FN 6.0	VF 8.0	VF/NM 9.0	NM- 9.2
V1#1-Dan DeCarlo-c/a begins, ends #22	36	72	108	211	343	475
2-1st code approved issue	19	38	57	111	176	240
3-10	18	36	54	105	165	225
11-20,22	16	32	48	94	147	200
21-Sci-fi cover	34	68	102	199	325	450
V2#1 (11/69)	11	22	33	76	163	250
2-4	7	14	21	46	86	125

HOME RUN (Also see A-1 Comics)
Magazine Enterprises: No. 89, 1953 (one-shot)

	GD 2.0	VG 4.0	FN 6.0	VF 8.0	VF/NM 9.0	NM- 9.2
A-1 89 (#3)-Powell-a; Stan Musial photo-c	17	34	51	98	154	210

HOMICIDE (Also see Dark Horse Presents)
Dark Horse Comics: Apr, 1990 ($1.95, B&W, one-shot)

	GD 2.0	VG 4.0	FN 6.0	VF 8.0	VF/NM 9.0	NM- 9.2
1-Detective story						3.00

HOMIES
Dynamite Entertainment: 2016 - No. 4, 2017 ($3.99)

	GD 2.0	VG 4.0	FN 6.0	VF 8.0	VF/NM 9.0	NM- 9.2
1-4-Gonzales & Serrano-s/Huerta-a						4.00

HONEYMOON (Formerly Gay Comics)
A Lover's Magazine(USA) (Marvel): No. 41, Jan, 1950

	GD 2.0	VG 4.0	FN 6.0	VF 8.0	VF/NM 9.0	NM- 9.2
41-Photo-c; article by Betty Grable	15	30	45	85	130	175

HONEYMOONERS, THE (TV)
Lodestone: Oct, 1986 ($1.50)

	GD 2.0	VG 4.0	FN 6.0	VF 8.0	VF/NM 9.0	NM- 9.2
1-Photo-c						6.00

HONEYMOONERS, THE (TV)
Triad Publications: Sept, 1987 - No. 13? ($2.00)

	GD 2.0	VG 4.0	FN 6.0	VF 8.0	VF/NM 9.0	NM- 9.2
1-13						5.00

HONEYMOON ROMANCE
Artful Publications (Canadian): Apr, 1950 - No. 2, July, 1950 (25¢, digest size)

	GD 2.0	VG 4.0	FN 6.0	VF 8.0	VF/NM 9.0	NM- 9.2
1,2-(Rare)	180	360	540	900	1350	1800

HONEY WEST (TV)
Gold Key: Sept, 1966 (Photo-c)

	GD 2.0	VG 4.0	FN 6.0	VF 8.0	VF/NM 9.0	NM- 9.2
1 (10186-609)	9	18	27	57	111	165

HONEY WEST (TV)
Moonstone: 2010 - No. 4 ($5.99/$3.99)

	GD 2.0	VG 4.0	FN 6.0	VF 8.0	VF/NM 9.0	NM- 9.2
1-($5.99) Trina Robbins-s/Cynthia Martin-a; two art covers & two photo covers						6.00
2-4-($3.99)						4.00

HONG KONG PHOOEY (TV)
Charlton Comics: June, 1975 - No. 9, Nov, 1976 (Hanna-Barbera)

	GD 2.0	VG 4.0	FN 6.0	VF 8.0	VF/NM 9.0	NM- 9.2
1	5	10	15	31	53	75
2	3	6	9	18	28	38
3-9	3	6	9	15	22	28

HONG ON THE RANGE
Image/Flypaper Press: Dec, 1997 - No. 3, Feb, 1998 ($2.50, lim. series)

	GD 2.0	VG 4.0	FN 6.0	VF 8.0	VF/NM 9.0	NM- 9.2
1-3: Wu-s/Lafferty-a						3.00

HOOD, THE
Marvel Comics (MAX): Jul, 2002 - No. 6, Dec, 2002 ($2.99, limited series)

	GD 2.0	VG 4.0	FN 6.0	VF 8.0	VF/NM 9.0	NM- 9.2
1-6-Vaughan-s/Hotz-c/a						3.00
Vol. 1 Blood From Stones HC (2007, $19.99, dustjacket) r/#1-6; production sketch art						20.00
Vol. 1 Blood From Stones TPB (2003, $14.99) r/#1-6						15.00

HOODED HORSEMAN, THE (Formerly Blazing West)
American Comics Group (Michel Publ.): No. 21, 1-2/52 - No. 27, 1-2/54; No. 18, 12-1/54-55 - No. 22, 8-9/55

	GD 2.0	VG 4.0	FN 6.0	VF 8.0	VF/NM 9.0	NM- 9.2
21(1-2/52)-Hooded Horseman, Injun Jones cont.	15	30	45	84	127	170
22	10	20	30	56	76	95
23,24,27(1-2/54)	9	18	27	50	65	80
25 (9-10/53)-Cowboy Sahib on cover only; Hooded Horseman i.d. revealed	9	18	27	52	69	85
26-Origin/1st app. Cowboy Sahib by L. Starr	11	22	33	62	86	110
18(12-1/54-55)(Formerly Out of the Night)	10	20	30	54	72	90
19,21,22: 19-Last precode (1-2/55)	8	16	24	44	57	70
20-Origin Johnny Injun	9	18	27	50	65	80

NOTE: ***Whitney** c/a-21('52), 20-22.*

Hopalong Cassidy #9 © FAW

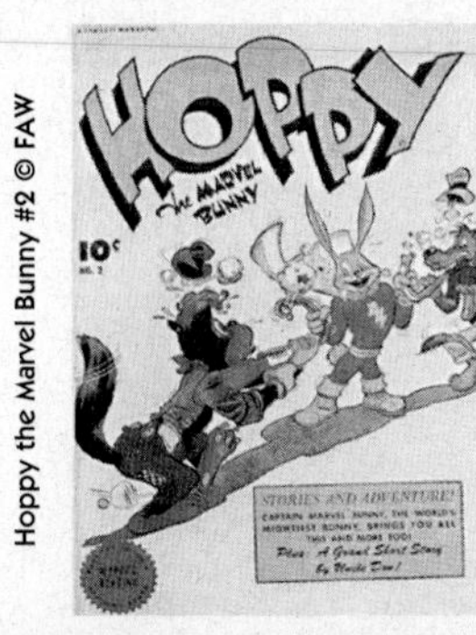

Hoppy the Marvel Bunny #2 © FAW

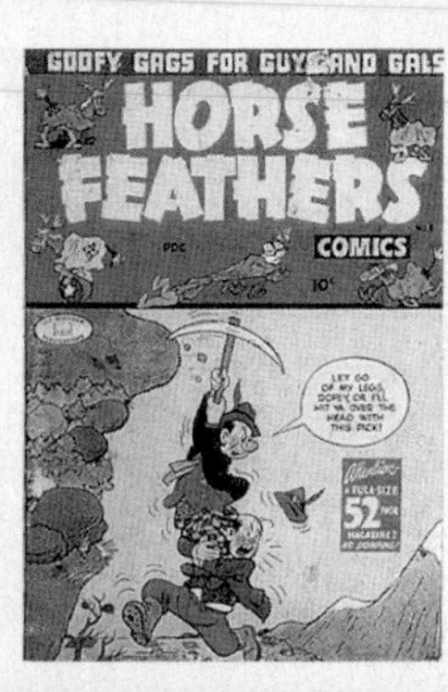

Horse Feathers Comics #1 © LEV

	GD 2.0	VG 4.0	FN 6.0	VF 8.0	VF/NM 9.0	NM- 9.2

HOODED MENACE, THE (Also see Daring Adventures)
Realistic/Avon Periodicals: 1951 (one-shot)

nn-Based on a band of hooded outlaws in the Pacific Northwest, 1900-1906; reprinted in Daring Advs. #15	61	122	183	390	670	950

HOODS UP (See the Promotional Comics section)

HOOK (Movie)
Marvel Comics: Early Feb, 1992 - No. 4, Late Mar, 1992 ($1.00, limited series)

1-4: Adapts movie; Vess-c; 1-Morrow-a(p)						3.00
nn (1991, $5.95, 84 pgs.)-Contains #1-4; Vess-c						6.00
1 (1991, $2.95, magazine, 84 pgs.)-Contains #1-4; Vess-c (same cover as nn issue)						4.00

HOOK JAW
Titan Comics: Jan, 2017 - No. 5, May, 2017 ($3.99)

1-5-Inspired by a 1976 British comic strip; Si Spurrier-s/Conor Boyle-a; multiple covers						4.00

HOOT GIBSON'S WESTERN ROUNDUP (See Western Roundup under Fox Giants)

HOOT GIBSON WESTERN (Formerly My Love Story)
Fox Feature Syndicate: No. 5, May, 1950 - No. 3, Sept, 1950

5,6(#1,2): 5-Photo-c. 6-Photo/painted-c	21	42	63	123	197	270
3-Wood-a; painted-c	22	44	66	131	211	290

HOPALONG CASSIDY (Also see Bill Boyd Western, Master Comics, Real Western Hero, Six Gun Heroes & Western Hero; Bill Boyd starred as Hopalong Cassidy in movies, radio & TV)
Fawcett Publications: Feb, 1943; No. 2, Summer, 1946 - No. 85, Nov, 1953

1 (1943, 68 pgs.)-H. Cassidy & his horse Topper begin (on sale 1/8/43)-Captain Marvel app. on-c	297	594	891	1900	3250	4600
2-(Sum, '46)	41	82	123	256	428	600
3,4: 3-(Fall, '46, 52 pgs. begin)	20	40	60	114	182	250
5- "Mad Barber" story mentioned in **SOTI**, pgs. 308,309; photo-c	19	38	57	111	176	240
6-10: 8-Photo-c	16	32	48	94	147	200
11-19: 11,13-19-Photo-c	14	28	42	80	115	150
20-29 (52 pgs.)-Painted/photo-c	12	24	36	69	97	125
30,31,33,34,37-39,41 (52 pgs.)-Painted-c	11	22	33	60	83	105
32,40 (36pgs.)-Painted-c	10	20	30	54	72	90
35,42,43,45-47,49-51,53,54,56 (52 pgs.)-Photo-c	10	20	30	56	76	95
36,44,48 (36 pgs.)-Photo-c	9	18	27	52	69	85
52,55,57-70 (36 pgs.)-Photo-c	9	18	27	47	61	75
71-84-Photo-c	8	16	24	42	54	65
85-Last Fawcett issue; photo-c	9	18	27	52	69	85

NOTE: *Line-drawn c-1-4, 6, 7, 9, 10, 12.*

... & The 5 Men of Evil (AC Comics, 1991, $12.95) r/newspaper strips and Fawcett story "Signature of Death"						13.00

HOPALONG CASSIDY
National Periodical Publications: No. 86, Feb, 1954 - No. 135, May-June, 1959 (All-36 pgs.)

86-Gene Colan-a begins, ends #117; photo covers continue	36	72	108	216	351	485
87	20	40	60	118	189	260
88-91: 91-1 pg. Superboy-sty (7/54)	15	30	45	83	124	165
92-99 (98 has #93 on-c; last precode issue, 2/55). 95-Reversed photo-c to #52. 98-Reversed photo-c to #61. 99-Reversed photo-c to #60	14	28	42	76	108	140
100-Same cover as #50	15	30	45	83	124	165
101-108: 105-Same photo-c as #54. 107-Same photo-c as #51. 108-Last photo-c	6	12	18	38	69	100
109-130: 118-Gil Kane-a begins. 123-Kubert-a (2 pgs.). 124-Grey tone-c	5	10	15	35	63	90
131-135	6	12	18	37	66	95

HOPELESS SAVAGES (Also see Too Much Hopeless Savages)
Oni Press: Aug, 2001 - No. 4, Nov, 2001 ($2.95, B&W, limited series)

1-4-Van Meter-s/Norrie-a/Clugston-Major-a/Watson-c						3.00
Free Comic Book Day giveaway (5/02) r/#1 with "Free Comic Book Day" banner on-c						3.00
TPB (2002, $13.95, 8" x 5.75") r/#1-4; plus color stories; Watson-c						14.00

HOPELESS SAVAGES: GROUND ZERO
Oni Press: June, 2002 - No. 4, Oct, 2002 ($2.95, B&W, limited series)

1-4-Van Meter-s/O'Malley-a/Dodson-c. 1-Watson-a						3.00
TPB (2003, $11.95, 8" x 5.75") r/#1-4; Dodson-c						12.00

HOPE SHIP
Dell Publishing Co.: June-Aug, 1963

1	3	6	9	15	22	28

HOPPY THE MARVEL BUNNY (See Fawcett's Funny Animals)
Fawcett Publications: Dec, 1945 - No. 15, Sept, 1947

1	28	56	84	165	270	375
2	14	28	42	82	121	160
3-15: 7-Xmas-c	12	24	36	67	94	120

HORACE & DOTTY DRIPPLE (Dotty Dripple No. 1-24)
Harvey Publications: No. 25, Aug, 1952 - No. 43, Oct, 1955

25-43	4	9	13	18	22	26

HORIZONTAL LIEUTENANT, THE (See Movie Classics)

HOROBI
Viz Premiere Comics: 1990 - No. 8, 1990 ($3.75, B&W, mature readers, 84 pgs.) V2#1, 1990 - No. 7, 1991 ($4.25, B&W, 68 pgs.)

1-8: Japanese manga, Part Two, #1-7						5.00

HORRIFIC (Terrific No. 14 on)
Artful/Comic Media/Harwell/Mystery: Sept, 1952 - No. 13, Sept, 1954

1	97	194	291	621	1061	1500
2	55	110	165	352	601	850
3-Bullet in head-c	187	374	561	1197	2049	2900
4,5,7,9,10: 4-Shrunken head-c. 7-Guillotine-c	52	104	156	328	552	775
6-Jack The Ripper story	53	106	159	334	567	800
8-Origin & 1st app. The Teller (E.C. parody)	53	106	159	334	567	800
11-13: 11-Swipe/Witches Tales #6,27; Devil-c	42	84	126	265	445	625

NOTE: ***Don Heck** a-8; c-3-13. **Hollingsworth** a-4. **Morisi** a-8. **Palais** a-5, 7-12.*

HORRORCIDE
IDW Publishing: Sept, 2004 ($6.99)

1-Steve Niles short stories; art by Templesmith, Medors and Chee						7.00

HORROR FROM THE TOMB (Mysterious Stories No. 2 on)
Premier Magazine Co.: Sept, 1954

1-Woodbridge/Torres, Check-a; The Keeper of the Graveyard is host	63	126	189	403	689	975

HORRORIST, THE (Also see Hellblazer)
DC Comics (Vertigo): Dec, 1995 - No. 2, Jan, 1996 ($5.95, lim. series, mature)

1,2: Jamie Delano scripts, David Lloyd-c/a; John Constantine (Hellblazer) app.						6.00

HORROR OF COLLIER COUNTY
Dark Horse Comics: Oct, 1999 - No. 5, Feb, 2000 ($2.95, B&W, limited series)

1-5-Rich Tommaso-s/a						3.00

HORRORS, THE (Formerly Startling Terror Tales #10)
Star Publications: No. 11, Jan, 1953 - No. 15, Apr, 1954

11-Horrors of War; Disbrow-a(2)	41	82	123	256	428	600
12-Horrors of War; color illo in **POP**	40	80	120	246	411	575
13-Horrors of Mystery; crime stories	39	78	117	240	395	550
14,15-Horrors of the Underworld; crime stories	40	80	120	246	411	575

NOTE: *All have **L. B. Cole** covers; a-12. **Hollingsworth** a-13. **Palais** a-13r.*

HORROR TALES (Magazine)
Eerie Publications: V1#7, 6/69 - V6#6, 12/74; V7#1, 2/75; V7#2, 5/76 - V8#5, 1977; V9#1-3, 8/78; V10#1(2/79) (V1-V6: 52 pgs.; V7, V8#2: 112 pgs.; V8#4 on: 68 pgs.) (No V5#3, V8#1,3)

V1#7	7	14	21	49	92	135
V1#8,9	5	10	15	34	60	85
V2#1-6('70), V3#1-6('71), V4#1-3,5-7('72)	5	10	15	31	53	75
V4#4-LSD story reprint/Weird V3#5	6	12	18	37	66	95
V5#1,2,4,5(6/73),5(10/73),6(12/73),V6#1-6('74),V7#1,2,4('76),V7#3('76)-Giant issue, V8#2,4,5('77)	5	10	15	31	53	75
V9#1-3(11/78, $1.50), V10#1(2/79)	5	10	15	33	57	80

NOTE: *Bondage-c-V6#1, 3, V7#2.*

HORSE FEATHERS COMICS
Lev Gleason Publ.: Nov, 1945 - No. 4, July(Summer on-c), 1948 (52 pgs.) (#2,3 are oversized)

1-Wolverton's Scoop Scuttle, 2 pgs.	19	38	57	111	176	240
2	11	22	33	60	83	105
3,4: 3-(5/48)	9	18	27	47	61	75

HORSEMAN
Crusade Comics/Kevlar Studios: Mar, 1996 - No. 3, Nov, 1997 ($2.95)

0-1st Kevlar Studios issue, 1-(3/96)-Crusade issue; Shi-c/app., 1-(11/96)-3-(11/97)-Kevlar Studios						3.00

HORSEMASTERS, THE (Disney)(TV, Movie)
Dell Publishing Co.: No. 1260, Dec-Feb, 1961/62

Four Color 1260-Annette Funicello photo-c	10	20	30	69	147	225

HORSE SOLDIERS, THE
Dell Publishing Co.: No. 1048, Nov-Jan, 1959/60 (John Wayne movie)

Hot Stuff, The Little Devil #1 © HARV

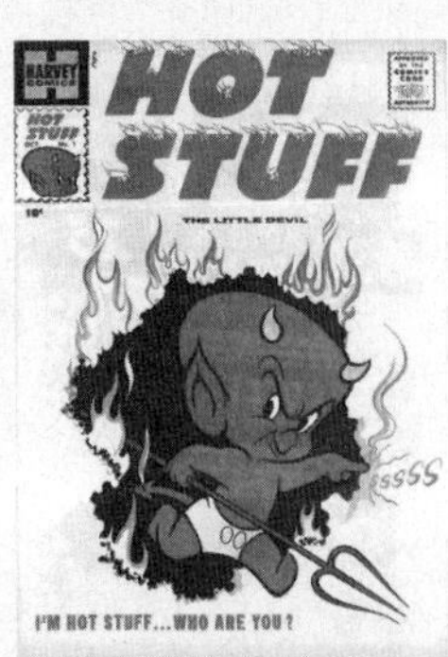

Hot Rod Comics #3 © FAW

Hourman #25 © DC

	GD 2.0	VG 4.0	FN 6.0	VF 8.0	VF/NM 9.0	NM- 9.2
Four Color 1048-Painted-c, Sekowsky-a	11	22	33	76	163	250

HORSE WITHOUT A HEAD, THE (See Movie Comics)

HOT DOG
Magazine Enterprises: June-July, 1954 - No. 4, Dec-Jan, 1954-55

	GD 2.0	VG 4.0	FN 6.0	VF 8.0	VF/NM 9.0	NM- 9.2
1(A-1 #107)	9	18	27	50	65	80
2,3(A-1 #115),4(A-1 #136)	7	14	21	35	43	50

HOT DOG (See Jughead's Pal, Hotdog)

HOTEL DEPAREE - SUNDANCE (TV)
Dell Publishing Co.: No. 1126, Aug-Oct, 1960 (one-shot)

	GD 2.0	VG 4.0	FN 6.0	VF 8.0	VF/NM 9.0	NM- 9.2
Four Color 1126-Earl Holliman photo-c	6	12	18	40	73	105

HOT ROD AND SPEEDWAY COMICS
Hillman Periodicals: Feb-Mar, 1952 - No. 5, Apr-May, 1953

	GD 2.0	VG 4.0	FN 6.0	VF 8.0	VF/NM 9.0	NM- 9.2
1	28	56	84	165	270	375
2-Krigstein-a	18	36	54	105	165	225
3-5	13	26	39	72	101	130

HOT ROD COMICS (...Featuring Clint Curtis) (See XMas Comics)
Fawcett Publications: Nov, 1951 (no month given) - V2#7, Feb, 1953

	GD 2.0	VG 4.0	FN 6.0	VF 8.0	VF/NM 9.0	NM- 9.2
nn (V1#1)-Powell-c/a in all	30	60	90	177	289	400
2 (4/52)	16	32	48	94	147	200
3-6, V2#7	13	26	39	74	105	135

HOT ROD KING (Also see Speed Smith the Hot Rod King)
Ziff-Davis Publ. Co.: Fall, 1952

	GD 2.0	VG 4.0	FN 6.0	VF 8.0	VF/NM 9.0	NM- 9.2
1-Giacoia-a; Saunders painted-c	29	58	87	174	285	395

HOT ROD RACERS (Grand Prix No. 16 on)
Charlton Comics: Dec, 1964 - No. 15, July, 1967

	GD 2.0	VG 4.0	FN 6.0	VF 8.0	VF/NM 9.0	NM- 9.2
1	7	14	21	49	92	135
2-5	5	10	15	30	50	70
6-15	4	8	12	23	37	50

HOT RODS AND RACING CARS
Charlton Comics (Motor Mag. No. 1): Nov, 1951 - No. 120, June, 1973

	GD 2.0	VG 4.0	FN 6.0	VF 8.0	VF/NM 9.0	NM- 9.2
1-Speed Davis begins; Indianapolis 500 story	31	62	93	184	300	415
2	16	32	48	92	144	195
3-10	12	24	36	67	94	120
11-20	10	20	30	54	72	90
21-33,36-40	8	16	24	44	57	70
34, 35 (? & 6/58, 68 pgs.)	11	22	33	60	83	105
41-60	7	14	21	37	46	55
61-80	3	6	9	19	30	40
81-100	3	6	9	16	23	30
101-120	3	6	9	14	19	24

HOT SHOT CHARLIE
Hillman Periodicals: 1947 (Lee Elias)

	GD 2.0	VG 4.0	FN 6.0	VF 8.0	VF/NM 9.0	NM- 9.2
1	14	28	42	82	121	160

HOT SHOTS: AVENGERS
Marvel Comics: Oct, 1995 ($2.95, one-shot)

	GD 2.0	VG 4.0	FN 6.0	VF 8.0	VF/NM 9.0	NM- 9.2
nn-pin-ups						3.00

HOTSPUR
Eclipse Comics: Jun, 1987 - No. 3, Sep, 1987 ($1.75, lim. series, Baxter paper)

	GD 2.0	VG 4.0	FN 6.0	VF 8.0	VF/NM 9.0	NM- 9.2
1-3						3.00

HOT STUFF (See Stumbo Tinytown)
Harvey Comics: V2#1, Sept, 1991 - No. 12, June, 1994 ($1.00)

	GD 2.0	VG 4.0	FN 6.0	VF 8.0	VF/NM 9.0	NM- 9.2
V2#1-Stumbo back-up story						5.00
2-12 ($1.50)						4.00
...Big Book 1 (11/92), 2 (6/93) (Both $1.95, 52 pgs.)						5.00

HOT STUFF CREEPY CAVES
Harvey Publications: Nov, 1974 - No. 7, Nov, 1975

	GD 2.0	VG 4.0	FN 6.0	VF 8.0	VF/NM 9.0	NM- 9.2
1	3	6	9	21	33	45
2-7	3	6	9	15	21	26

HOT STUFF DIGEST
Harvey Comics: July, 1992 - No. 5, Nov, 1993 ($1.75, digest-size)

	GD 2.0	VG 4.0	FN 6.0	VF 8.0	VF/NM 9.0	NM- 9.2
V2#1-Hot Stuff, Stumbo, Richie Rich stories						6.00
2-5						4.00

HOT STUFF GIANT SIZE
Harvey Comics: Oct, 1992 - No. 3, Oct, 1993 ($2.25, 68 pgs.)

	GD 2.0	VG 4.0	FN 6.0	VF 8.0	VF/NM 9.0	NM- 9.2
V2#1-Hot Stuff & Stumbo stories						5.00
2,3						4.00

HOT STUFF SIZZLERS
Harvey Publications: July, 1960 - No. 59, Mar, 1974; V2#1, Aug, 1992

	GD 2.0	VG 4.0	FN 6.0	VF 8.0	VF/NM 9.0	NM- 9.2
1- 84 pgs. begin, ends #5; Hot Stuff, Stumbo begin	14	28	42	96	211	325
2-5	7	14	21	49	92	135
6-10: 6-68 pgs. begin, ends #45	5	10	15	35	63	90
11-20	4	8	12	27	44	60
21-45	3	6	9	19	30	40
46-52: 52 pgs. begin	3	6	9	16	23	30
53-59	2	4	6	10	14	18
V2#1-(8/92, $1.25)-Stumbo back-up						5.00

HOT STUFF, THE LITTLE DEVIL (Also see Devil Kids & Harvey Hits)
Harvey Publications (Illustrated Humor): 10/57 - No. 141, 7/77; No. 142, 2/78 - No. 164, 8/82; No. 165, 10/86 - No. 171, 11/87; No. 172, 11/88; No. 173, Sept, 1990 - No. 177, 1/91

	GD 2.0	VG 4.0	FN 6.0	VF 8.0	VF/NM 9.0	NM- 9.2
1-1st app. Hot Stuff; UFO story	145	290	435	1196	2698	4200
2-Stumbo-like giant 1st app. (12/57)	34	68	102	245	548	850
3-Stumbo the Giant debut (2/58)	19	38	57	133	297	460
4,5	17	34	51	117	259	400
6-10	10	20	30	66	138	210
11-20	8	16	24	51	96	140
21-40	5	10	15	34	60	85
41-60	4	8	12	25	40	55
61-80	3	6	9	19	30	40
81-105	3	6	9	15	22	28
106-112: All 52 pg. Giants	3	6	9	17	26	35
113-125	2	4	6	9	12	15
126-141	1	2	3	5	7	9
142-177: 172-177-($1.00)						6.00
Harvey Comics Classics Vol. 3 TPB (Dark Horse Books, 3/08, $19.95) Reprints Hot Stuff's earliest appearances in this title and Devil Kids, mostly B&W with some color stories; history, early concept drawings; foreword by Mark Arnold						20.00

HOT WHEELS (TV)
National Periodical Publications: Mar-Apr, 1970 - No. 6, Jan-Feb, 1971

	GD 2.0	VG 4.0	FN 6.0	VF 8.0	VF/NM 9.0	NM- 9.2
1	10	20	30	64	132	200
2,4,5	5	10	15	34	60	85
3-Neal Adams-c	6	12	18	41	76	110
6-Neal Adams-c/a	7	14	21	49	92	135

NOTE: *Toth a-1p, 2-5; c-1p, 5.*

HOURMAN (Justice Society member, see Adventure Comics #48)

HOURMAN (See JLA and DC One Million)
DC Comics: Apr, 1999 - No. 25, Apr, 2001 ($2.50)

	GD 2.0	VG 4.0	FN 6.0	VF 8.0	VF/NM 9.0	NM- 9.2
1-25: 1-JLA app.; McDaniel-c. 2-Tomorrow Woman-c/app. 6,7-Amazo app. 11-13-Justice Legion A app. 16-Silver Age flashback. 18,19-JSA-c/app. 22-Harris-c/a. 24-Hourman Vs. Rex Tyler						3.00

HOUSE OF FUN
Dark Horse Comics: Dec, 2012 ($3.50)

	GD 2.0	VG 4.0	FN 6.0	VF 8.0	VF/NM 9.0	NM- 9.2
0-Reprints Evan Dorkin humor strips from Dark Horse Presents #10-12						3.50

HOUSE OF GOLD AND BONES
Dark Horse Comics: Apr, 2013 - No. 4, Jul, 2013 ($3.99, limited series)

	GD 2.0	VG 4.0	FN 6.0	VF 8.0	VF/NM 9.0	NM- 9.2
1-4-Corey Taylor-s/Richard Clark-a; 2 covers on each						4.00

HOUSE OF HEM
Marvel Comics: 2015 ($7.99, one-shot)

	GD 2.0	VG 4.0	FN 6.0	VF 8.0	VF/NM 9.0	NM- 9.2
1-Reprints Fred Hembeck's Marvel highlights incl. Fantastic Four Roast; wraparound-c						8.00

HOUSE OF M (Also see miniseries with Fantastic Four, Iron Man and Spider-Man)
Marvel Comics: Aug, 2005 - No. 8, Dec, 2005 ($2.99, limited series)

	GD 2.0	VG 4.0	FN 6.0	VF 8.0	VF/NM 9.0	NM- 9.2
1-Bendis-s/Coipel-a/Ribic-c; Scarlet Witch changes reality; Quesada variant-c						3.00
2-8-Variant covers for each. 3-Hawkeye returns						3.00
... MGC #1 (6/11, $1.00) r/#1 with "Marvel's Greatest Comics" logo on cover						3.00
Secrets Of The House Of M (2005, $3.99, one-shot) profile pages and background info						4.00
... Sketchbook (6/05) B&W preview sketches by Coipel, Davis, Hairsine, Quesada						3.00
TPB (2006, $24.99) r/#1-8 and The Pulse: House of M Special Edition newspaper						25.00
...: Fantastic Four/ Iron Man TPB (2006, $13.99) r/ both House of M mini-series						14.00
...: World of M Featuring Wolverine TPB (2006, $13.99) r/2005 x-over issues Wolverine #33-35, Black Panther #7, Captain America #10 and The Pulse #10						14.00
HC (2008, $29.99, oversized with d.j.) r/#1-8, The Pulse: House of M Special Edition newspaper and Secrets Of The House Of M one-shot; script pages; cover gallery						30.00

HOUSE OF M (Secret Wars tie-in)
Marvel Comics: Oct, 2015 - No. 4, Dec, 2015 ($3.99, limited series)

House of M (2015 series) #1 © MAR

House of Mystery #64 © DC

House of Secrets #14 © DC

	GD 2.0	VG 4.0	FN 6.0	VF 8.0	VF/NM 9.0	NM- 9.2
1-4: 1,2-Hopeless & Bunn-s/Failla-a; Magneto & the House of Magnus. 3,4-Anindito-a						4.00

HOUSE OF M: AVENGERS
Marvel Comics: Jan, 2008 - No. 5, Apr, 2008 ($2.99, limited series)

	GD 2.0	VG 4.0	FN 6.0	VF 8.0	VF/NM 9.0	NM- 9.2
1-5-Gage-s/Perkins-a; Luke Cage, Iron Fist, Hawkeye, Tigra, Misty Knight, Shang-Chi						3.00

HOUSE OF M: MASTERS OF EVIL
Marvel Comics: Oct, 2009 - No. 4, Jan, 2010 ($3.99, limited series)

	GD 2.0	VG 4.0	FN 6.0	VF 8.0	VF/NM 9.0	NM- 9.2
1-4-Gage-s/Garcia-a/Perkins-c; The Hood app.						4.00

HOUSE OF MYSTERY
DC Comics: Dec/Jan. 1951

nn - Ashcan comic, not distributed to newsstands, only for in-house use. Cover art is Danger Trail #3 with interior being Star Spangled Comics #109. A VG+ copy sold for $2,357.50 in 2002.

HOUSE OF MYSTERY (See Brave and the Bold #93, Elvira's House of Mystery, Limited Collectors' Edition & Super DC Giant)

HOUSE OF MYSTERY, THE
National Periodical Publications/DC Comics: Dec-Jan, 1951-52 - No. 321, Oct, 1983 (No. 194-203: 52 pgs.)

	GD 2.0	VG 4.0	FN 6.0	VF 8.0	VF/NM 9.0	NM- 9.2
1-DC's first horror comic	290	580	870	1856	3178	4500
2	129	258	387	826	1413	2000
3	76	152	228	486	831	1175
4,5	63	126	189	403	689	975
6-10	57	114	171	362	619	875
11-15	48	96	144	302	514	725
16(7/53)-25	39	78	117	240	395	550
26-35(2/55)-Last pre-code issue; 30-Woodish-a	33	66	99	194	317	440
36-50: 50-Text story of Orson Welles' War of the Worlds broadcast	17	34	51	117	259	400
51-60: 55-1st S.A. issue	15	30	45	100	220	340
61,63,65,66,69,70,72,76,79,85-Kirby-a	16	32	48	112	249	385
62,64,67,68,71,73-75,77,78,80-83,86-99: 92-Grey tone-c	14	28	42	94	207	320
84-Prototype of Negative Man (Doom Patrol)	19	38	57	131	291	450
100 (7/60)	14	28	42	93	204	315
101-116: 109-Toth, Kubert-a. 116-Last 10¢ issue	11	22	33	75	160	245
117-130: 117-Swipes-c to HOS #20. 120-Toth-a	10	20	30	64	132	200
131-142	9	18	27	58	114	170
143-J'onn J'onzz, Manhunter begins (6/64), ends #173; story continues from Detective #326; intro. Idol-Head of Diabolu	18	36	54	121	268	415
144	8	16	24	54	102	150
145-155,157-159: 149-Toth-a. 155-The Human Hurricane app. (12/65), Red Tornado prototype. 158-Origin Diabolu Idol-Head	5	10	15	35	63	90
156-Robby Reed begins (origin/1st app.), ends #173	7	14	21	48	89	130
160-(7/66)-Robby Reed becomes Plastic Man in this issue only; 1st S.A. app. Plastic Man; intro Marco Xavier (Martian Manhunter) & Vulture Crime Organization; ends #173	9	18	27	60	120	180
161-173: 169-Origin/1st app. Gem Girl	4	8	12	28	47	65
174-Mystery format begins.	15	30	45	101	223	345
175-1st app. Cain (House of Mystery host); Adams-c	13	26	39	87	191	295
176,177-Neal Adams-c	9	18	27	58	114	170
178-Neal Adams-c/a (2/69)	9	18	27	61	123	185
179-Neal Adams/Orlando, Wrightson-a (1st pro work, 3 pgs.); Adams-c	12	24	36	84	185	285
180,181,183: Wrightson-a (3,10, & 3 pgs.); Adams-c. 180-Last 12¢ issue; Kane/Wood-a(2). 183-Wood-a	8	16	24	56	108	160
182,184-Adams-c. 182-Toth-a. 184-Kane/Wood, Toth-a	6	12	18	41	76	110
185-Williamson/Kaluta-a; Howard-a (3 pgs.); Adams-c	7	14	21	44	82	120
186-N. Adams-c/a; Wrightson-a (10 pgs.)	9	18	27	59	117	175
187,190: Adams-c. 187-Toth-a. 190-Toth-a(r)	6	12	18	40	73	105
188-Wrightson-a (8 & 3pgs.); Adams-c	7	14	21	49	92	135
189,192,197: Adams-c on all. 189-Wood-a(i). 192-Last 15¢-c	6	12	18	40	73	105
191-Wrightson-a (8 & 3pgs.); Adams-c	7	14	21	49	92	135
193-Wrightson-c	6	12	18	40	73	105
194-Wrightson-c; 52 pgs begin, end #203; Toth,Kirby-a	8	16	24	51	96	140
195: Wrightson-c. Swamp creature story by Wrightson similar to Swamp Thing (10 pgs.)(10/71)	9	18	27	59	117	175
196,198	5	10	15	35	63	90
199-Adams-c; Wood-a(8pgs.); Kirby-a	6	12	18	42	79	115
200-(25¢, 52 pgs.)-One third-r (3/72)	6	12	18	41	76	110
201-203-(25¢, 52 pgs.)-One third-r	5	10	15	33	57	80
204-Wrightson-c/a, 9 pgs.	6	12	18	38	69	100
205,206,208,210,212,215,216,218	4	8	12	23	37	50
207-Wrightson-c/a; Starlin, Redondo-a	6	12	18	38	69	100
209,211,213,214,217,219-Wrightson-c	5	10	15	31	53	75
220,222,223	3	6	9	21	33	45
221-Wrighson/Kaluta-a(8 pgs.); Wrightson-c	5	10	15	35	63	90
224-229: 224-Wrightson-r from Spectre #9; Dillin/Adams-r from House of Secrets #82; begin 100 pg. issues; Phantom Stranger-r. 225,227-(100 pgs.): 225-Spectre app. 226-Wrightson/Redondo-a Phantom Stranger-r. 228-N. Adams inks; Wrightson-r. 229-Wrightson-a(r); Toth-r; last 100 pg. issue	5	10	15	35	63	90
230,232-235,237-250: 230-UFO-c	3	6	9	15	22	28
231-Classic Wrightson-c	5	10	15	34	60	85
236-Wrightson-c; Ditko-a(p); N. Adams-i	5	10	15	34	60	85
251-254-(84 pgs.)-Adams-c. 251-Wood-a	4	8	12	27	44	60
255,256-(84 pgs.)-Wrightson-c	4	8	12	27	44	60
257-259-(84 pgs.)	3	6	9	18	28	38
260-289: 282-(68 pgs.)-Has extra story "The Computers That Saved Metropolis" Radio Shack giveaway by Jim Starlin	2	4	6	8	10	12
290-1st "I, Vampire"	5	10	15	34	60	85
291-299: 291,293,295-299- "I, Vampire"	2	4	6	10	14	18
300,319-"I, Vampire"	2	4	6	11	16	20
301-318,320: 301-318-"I, Vampire"	2	4	6	10	14	18
321-Death of "I, Vampire"	3	6	9	16	23	30
Welcome to the House of Mystery (7/98, $5.95) reprints stories with new framing story by Gaiman and Aragonés						6.00

NOTE: ***Neal Adams** a-236i; c-175-192, 197, 199, 251-254. **Alcala** a-209, 217, 219, 224, 227. **M. Anderson** a-212; c/a-37. **Aparo** a-209. **Aragones** a-185, 186, 194, 196, 200, 202, 229, 251. **Baily** a-279p. **Cameron** a-76, 79. **Colan** a-202r. **Craig** a-263, 275, 295, 300. **Dillin/Adams** r-224. **Ditko** a-236p, 247, 254, 258, 276; c-277. **Drucker** a-37. **Evans** c-218. **Fradon** a-251. **Giffen** a-284. **Giunta** a-199, 227r. **Golden** a-257, 259. **Heath** a-194r; c-203. **Howard** a-182, 185, 187, 196, 229r, 247i, 254, 279i. **Kaluta** a-195, 200, 250r; c-200-202, 210, 212, 233, 260, 261, 263, 265, 267, 268, 273, 276, 284, 287, 288, 293-295, 300, 302, 304, 305, 309-319, 321. **Bob Kane** a-84. **Gil Kane** a-196p, 253p, 300p. **Kirby** a-194r, 199r; c-65, 76, 78, 79, 85. **Kubert** c-282, 283, 285, 286, 289-292, 297-299, 301, 303, 306-308. **Maneely** a-68, 227r. **Mayer** a-317p. **Meskin** a-52-144 (most), 195r, 224r, 229r; c-63, 66, 124, 127. **Mooney** a-24, 159, 160. **Moreira** a-3, 4, 20-50, 58, 59, 62, 68, 77, 79, 90, 108, 113, 123, 201r, 228; c-4-28, 44, 47, 50, 54, 59, 62, 64, 68, 70, 73. **Morrow** a-192, 196, 255, 320i. **Mortimer** a-204(3 pgs.). **Nasser** a-276. **Newton** a-259, 272. **Nino** a-204, 212, 213, 220, 224, 225, 245, 250, 252-256, 283. **Orlando** a-175(2 pgs.), 178, 240i; c-240, 258p, 262, 264p, 270p, 271, 272, 274, 275, 278, 296i. **Redondo** a-194, 195, 197, 202, 203, 207, 211, 214, 217, 219, 226, 227, 229, 235, 241, 287(layout), 302p, 303i, 308; c-229. **Reese** a-195, 200, 205i. **Rogers** a-254, 274, 277. **Roussos** a-65, 84, 224i. **Sekowsky** a-282p. **Sparling** a-203. **Starlin** a-207(2 pgs.), 282p; c-281. **Leonard Starr** a-9. **Staton** a-300p. **Sutton** a-189, 271, 290, 291, 293, 295, 297-299, 302, 303, 306-309, 310-313i, 314. **Tuska** a-293p, 294p, 316p. **Wrightson** c-193-195, 204, 207, 209, 211, 213, 214, 217, 219, 221, 231, 236, 255, 256; r-224.*

HOUSE OF MYSTERY
DC Comics (Vertigo): Jul, 2008 - No. 42, Dec, 2011 ($2.99)

	GD 2.0	VG 4.0	FN 6.0	VF 8.0	VF/NM 9.0	NM- 9.2
1-12,14-42: 1-Cain & Abel app.; Rossi-a/Weber-c. 9-Wrightson-a (6 pgs.). 16-Corben-a						3.00
1-Variant-c by Bernie Wrightson						5.00
13-Art by Neal Adams, Ralph Reese, Eric Powell, Sergio Aragonés						3.00
13-Variant-c by Neal Adams						5.00
... Halloween Annual #1 (12/09, $4.99) 1st app. I, Zombie in 7 pg. preview; short stories by various incl. Nowlan, Wagner, Willingham	3	6	9	14	20	25
... Halloween Annual #2 (12/10, $4.99) short stories by various incl. Carey, Allred, Gross						5.00
...: Love Stories for Dead People TPB (2009, $14.99) r/#6-10						15.00
...: Room and Boredom TPB (2008, $9.99) r/#1-5						10.00
...: Safe as Houses TPB (2011, $14.99) r/#26-30						15.00
...: The Beauty of Decay TPB (2010, $17.99) r/#16-20 & Halloween Annual #1						18.00
...: The Space Between TPB (2010, $14.99) r/#11-15; sketch pages						15.00
...: Under New Management TPB (2011, $14.99) r/#20-25						15.00

HOUSE OF NIGHT (Based on the series of novels by P.C. Cast and Kristin Cast)
Dark Horse Comics: Nov, 2011 - No. 5, Mar, 2012 ($1.00/$2.99, limited series)

	GD 2.0	VG 4.0	FN 6.0	VF 8.0	VF/NM 9.0	NM- 9.2
1-($1.00) Cast, Cast & Dalian-s/Joëlle Jones & Kerschl-a; Frison-c						3.00
1-($1.00) Variant-c by Steve Morris						4.00
2-5-($2.99) Jones-a; two covers by Jones & Ryan Hill on each						3.00

HOUSE OF PENANCE
Dark Horse Comics: Apr, 2016 - Present ($3.99)

	GD 2.0	VG 4.0	FN 6.0	VF 8.0	VF/NM 9.0	NM- 9.2
1-5: 1-Peter J. Tomasi-s/Ian Bertram-a						4.00

HOUSE OF SECRETS (Combined with The Unexpected after #154)
National Periodical Publications/DC Comics: 11-12/56 - No. 80, 9-10/66; No. 81, 8-9/69 - No. 140, 2-3/76; No. 141, 8-9/76 - No. 154, 10-11/78

	GD 2.0	VG 4.0	FN 6.0	VF 8.0	VF/NM 9.0	NM- 9.2
1-Drucker-a; Moreira-c	139	278	417	1112	2506	3900
2-Moreira-a	45	90	135	333	754	1175
3-Kirby-c/a	38	76	114	285	641	1000
4-Kirby-a	30	60	90	216	483	750
5-7	23	46	69	161	356	550
8-Kirby-a	24	48	72	168	372	575
9-11: 11-Lou Cameron-a (unsigned); Kirby-a	21	42	63	147	324	500
12-Kirby-c/a; Lou Cameron-a	22	44	66	154	340	525
13-15: 14-Flying saucer-c	16	32	48	108	239	370

House of Secrets #106 © DC

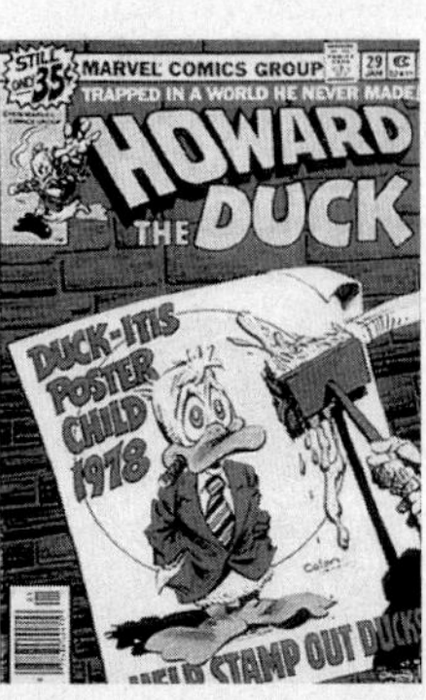

Howard the Duck #29 © MAR

Howard the Human #1 © MAR

	GD 2.0	VG 4.0	FN 6.0	VF 8.0	VF/NM 9.0	NM- 9.2
16-20	15	30	45	101	223	345
21,22,24-30	13	26	39	89	195	300
23-1st app. Mark Merlin & begin series (8/59)	14	28	42	96	211	335
31-50: 48-Toth-a. 50-Last 10¢ issue	11	22	33	77	166	255
51-60: 58-Origin Mark Merlin	9	18	27	59	117	175
61-First Eclipso (7-8/63) and begin series	50	100	150	400	900	1400
62	8	16	24	54	102	150
63-65-Toth-a on Eclipso (see Brave and the Bold #64)	6	12	18	41	76	110
66-1st Eclipso-c (also #67,70,78,79); Toth-a	8	16	24	56	108	160
67,73: 67-Toth-a on Eclipso. 73-Mark Merlin becomes Prince Ra-Man (1st app.)	6	12	18	41	76	110
68-72,74-80: 76-Prince Ra-Man vs. Eclipso. 80-Eclipso, Prince Ra-Man end	6	12	18	37	66	95
81-Mystery format begins; 1st app. Abel (House Of Secrets host); (cameo in DC Special #4)	16	32	48	110	243	375
82-84: 82-Neal Adams-c(i)	7	14	21	49	92	135
85,90: 85-N. Adams-a(i). 90-Buckler (early work)/N. Adams-a(i)	8	16	24	51	96	140
86,88,89,91	7	14	21	44	82	120
87-Wrightson & Kaluta-a	8	16	24	52	99	145
92-1st app. Swamp Thing-c/story (8 pgs.)(6-7/71) by Berni Wrightson(p) w/JeffJones/Kaluta/Weiss ink assists; classic-c	133	266	532	1064	1732	2400
93,94,96-(52 pgs.)-Wrightson-c. 94-Wrightson-a(i); 96-Wood-a	7	14	21	48	89	130
95,97,98-(52 pgs.)	5	10	15	35	63	90
99-Wrightson splash pg.	5	10	15	34	60	85
100-Classic Wrightson-c	8	16	24	51	96	140
101,102,104,105,108-111,113-120	3	6	9	19	30	40
103,106,107-Wrightson-c	5	10	15	33	57	80
112-Grey tone-c	4	8	12	23	37	50
121-133	2	4	6	11	16	20
134-Wrightson-a	3	6	9	17	26	35
135,136,139-Wrightson-a/c	3	6	9	20	31	42
137,138,141-153	2	4	6	8	10	12
140-1st solo origin of the Patchworkman (see Swamp Thing #3)	3	6	9	16	23	30
154 (10-11/78, 44 pgs.) Last issue	2	4	6	9	13	16

NOTE: ***Neal Adams** c-81, 82, 84-88, 90, 91. **Alcala** a-104-107. **Anderson** a-91. Aparo a-93, 97, 105. **B. Bailey** a-107. **Cameron** a-13, 15. **Colan** a-63. **Ditko** a-139p, 148. **Elias** a-58. **Evans** a-118. **Finlay** a-7r(Real Fact?). **Glanzman** a-91. **Golden** a-151. **Heath** a-31. **Heck** a-85. **Kaluta** a-87, 98, 99; c-98, 99, 101, 102, 105, 149, 151, 154. **Bob Kane** a-18, 21. **G. Kane** a-85p. **Kirby** c-3, 11, 12. **Kubert** a-39. **Meskin** a-2-68 (most), 94r; c-55-60. **Moreira** a-7, 8, 51, 54, 102-104, 106, 108, 113, 116, 118, 121, 123, 127; c-1, 2, 4-10, 13-20. **Morrow** a-86, 89, 90; c-89, 146-148. **Nino** a-101, 103, 106, 109, 115, 117, 126, 128, 131, 147, 153. **Redondo** a-95, 99, 102, 104p, 113, 116, 134, 136, 139, 140. **Reese** a-85. **Severin** a-91. **Starlin** c-150. **Sutton** a-154. **Toth** a-63-67, 83, 93r, 94r, 96r-98r, 123. **Tuska** a-90, 104. **Wrightson** a-134; c-92-94, 96, 100, 103, 106, 107, 135, 136, 139.*

HOUSE OF SECRETS
DC Comics (Vertigo): Oct, 1996 - No. 25, Dec, 1998 ($2.50) (Creator-owned series)

1-Steven Seagle-s/Kristiansen-c/a. 3.50
2-25: 5,7-Kristiansen-c/a. 6-Fegrado-a 3.00
TPB-(1997, $14.95) r/1-5 15.00

HOUSE OF SECRETS: FACADE
DC Comics (Vertigo): 2001 - No. 2, 2001 ($5.95, limited series)

1,2-Steven Seagle-s/Teddy Kristiansen-c/a. 6.00

HOUSE OF TERROR (3-D)
St. John Publishing Co.: Oct, 1953 (25¢, came w/glasses)

	GD 2.0	VG 4.0	FN 6.0	VF 8.0	VF/NM 9.0	NM- 9.2
1-Kubert, Baker-a	28	56	84	165	270	375

HOUSE OF YANG, THE (See Yang)
Charlton Comics: July, 1975 - No. 6, June, 1976; 1978

	GD 2.0	VG 4.0	FN 6.0	VF 8.0	VF/NM 9.0	NM- 9.2
1-Sanho Kim-a in all	2	4	6	13	18	22
2-6	2	4	6	8	10	12

Modern Comics #1,2(1978) 6.00

HOUSE ON THE BORDERLAND
DC Comics (Vertigo): 2000 ($29.95, hardcover, one-shot)

HC-Adaptation of William Hope Hodgson book; Corben-a 30.00
SC (2003, $19.95) 20.00

HOUSE II: THE SECOND STORY
Marvel Comics: Oct, 1987 (One-shot)

1-Adapts movie 4.00

HOWARD CHAYKIN'S AMERICAN FLAGG (See American Flagg!)
First Comics: V2#1, May, 1988 - V2#12, Apr, 1989 ($1.75/$1.95, Baxter paper)

V2#1-9,11,12-Chaykin-c(p) in all 3.00
10-Elvis Presley photo-c 4.00

HOWARD THE DUCK (See Bizarre Adventures #34, Crazy Magazine, Fear, Man-Thing, Marvel Treasury Edition & Sensational She-Hulk #14-17)
Marvel Comics Group: Jan, 1976 - No. 31, May, 1979; No. 32, Jan, 1986; No. 33, Sept, 1986

	GD 2.0	VG 4.0	FN 6.0	VF 8.0	VF/NM 9.0	NM- 9.2
1-Brunner-c/a; Spider-Man x-over (low distr.)	5	10	15	35	63	90
2-Brunner-c/a	2	4	6	11	16	20
3,4-(Regular 25¢ edition). 3-Buscema-a(p), (7/76)	2	4	6	8	11	14
3,4-(30¢-c, limited distribution)	3	6	9	21	33	45
5	2	4	6	8	11	14
6-11: 8-Howard The Duck for president. 9-1st Sgt. Preston Dudley of RCMP. 10-Spider-Man-c/sty	1	2	3	5	7	9
12-1st brief app. Kiss (3/77)	4	8	12	23	37	50
13-(30¢-c) 1st full app. Kiss (6/77); Daimon Hellstrom app. plus cameo of Howard as Son of Satan	4	8	12	27	44	60
13-(35¢-c, limited distribution)	10	20	30	64	132	200
14-32: 14-17-(Regular 30¢-c). 14-Howard as Son of Satan-c/story; Son of Satan app. 16-Album issue; 3 pgs. comics. 22,23-Man-Thing-c/stories; Star Wars parody. 30,32-P. Smith-a						6.00
14-17-(35¢-c, limited distribution)	6	12	18	38	69	100
33-Last issue; low print run	1	2	3	5	6	8
Annual 1(1977, 52 pgs.)-Mayerik-a	2	3	4	6	8	10

... Omnibus HC (2008, $99.99, dustjacket) r/#1-33 & Annual #1, Adventure Into Fear #19, Man-Thing #1, Giant-Size Man-Thing #4&5, Marvel Treasury Ed. #12, Marvel Team-Up #96 and FOOM #15; Gerber foreword; creator interviews; bonus art; 2 covers 100.00

NOTE: ***Austin** c-29i. **Bolland** c-33. **Brunner** a-1p, 2p; c-1, 2. **Buckler** c-3p. **Buscema** a-3p. **Colan** a(p)-4-15, 17-20, 24-27, 30, 31; c(p)-4-31, Annual 1p. **Leialoha** a-1-13i; c(i)-3-5, 8-11. **Mayerik** a-22, 23, 33. **Paul Smith** a-30p, 32. Man-Thing app. in #22, 23.*

HOWARD THE DUCK (Magazine)
Marvel Comics Group: Oct, 1979 - No. 9, Mar, 1981 (B&W, 68 pgs.)

	GD 2.0	VG 4.0	FN 6.0	VF 8.0	VF/NM 9.0	NM- 9.2
1-Art by Colan, Janson, Golden. Kidney Lady app.	2	4	6	9	12	15
2,3,5-9 (nudity in most): 2-Mayerick-c. 3-Xmas issue; Jack Davis-c; Duck World flashback. 5-Dracula app. 6-1st Street People back-up story. 7-Has pin-up by Byrne; Man-Thing-c/s (46 pgs.). 8-Batman parody w/Marshall Rogers-a; Dave Sim-a (1 pg.). 9-Marie Severin-a; John Pound painted-c						6.00
4-Beatles, John Lennon, Elvis, Kiss & Devo cameos; Hitler app.	2	4	6	9	12	15

NOTE: ***Buscema** a-4p. **Colan** a-1-5p, 7-9p. **Jack Davis** c-3. **Golden** a(p)-1, 5, 6(51pgs.). **Rogers** a-7, 8. **Simonson** a-7.*

HOWARD THE DUCK (Volume 2)
Marvel Comics: Mar, 2002 - No. 6, Aug, 2002 ($2.99)

1-Gerber-s/Winslade-a/Fabry-c 5.00
2-6: 2,4-6-Gerber-s/Winslade-a/Fabry-c. 3-Fabry-a/c 3.00
TPB (9/02, $14.99) r/#1-6 15.00

HOWARD THE DUCK (Volume 3)
Marvel Comics: Dec, 2007 - No. 4, Feb, 2008 ($2.99, limited series)

1-4-Templeton-s/Bobillo-a/c; She-Hulk app. 3.00
...: Media Duckling TPB (2008, $11.99) r/#1-4; Howard the Duck #1 (1/76) and pages from Civil War: Choosing Sides 12.00

HOWARD THE DUCK (Volume 4)
Marvel Comics: May 2015 - No. 5, Oct, 2015 ($3.99)

1-5-Zdarsky-s/Quinones-a. 1-Spider-Man app. 2-Guardians of the Galaxy app. 4.00

HOWARD THE DUCK (Volume 5)
Marvel Comics: Jan, 2016 - No. 11, Dec, 2016 ($4.99/$3.99)

1-3-($4.99): 1-Zdarsky-s/Quinones-a; back-up with Gwenpool in #1-3. 2-Fish-a 5.00
4-11-($3.99) 4,5-Silver Surfer, Galactus & the Guardians of the Galaxy app. 6-Squirrel Girl x-over. 7-Maguire-a. 8-Beverly app. 9-Lea Thompson app. 9-11-Mojo app. 4.00

HOWARD THE DUCK HOLIDAY SPECIAL
Marvel Comics: Feb, 1997 ($2.50, one-shot)

1-Wraparound-c; Hama-s 6.00

HOWARD THE DUCK: THE MOVIE
Marvel Comics Group: Dec, 1986 - No. 3, Feb, 1987 (Limited series)

1-3: Movie adaptation; r/Marvel Super Special 4.00

HOWARD THE HUMAN (Secret Wars tie-in)
Marvel Comics: Oct, 2015 ($3.99, one-shot)

1-Howard the Duck as human in an all-animal world; Skottie Young-s/Jim Mahfood-a 4.00

HOW BOYS AND GIRLS CAN HELP WIN THE WAR
The Parents' Magazine Institute: 1942 (10¢, one-shot)

	GD 2.0	VG 4.0	FN 6.0	VF 8.0	VF/NM 9.0	NM- 9.2
1-All proceeds used to buy war bonds	36	72	108	211	343	475

Howdy Doody #35 © DELL

Huckleberry Hound #17 © H-B

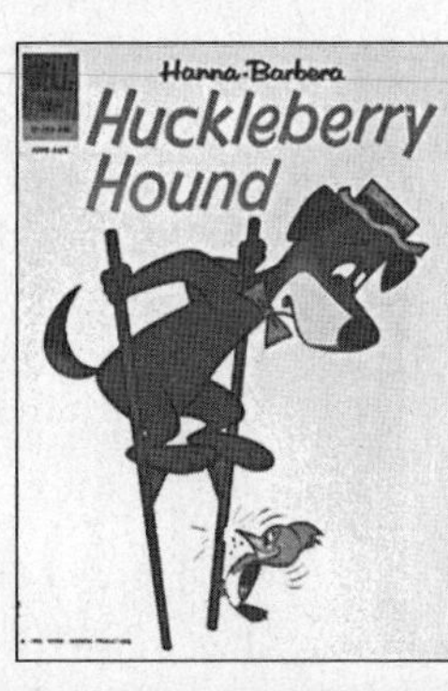

Hulk (2008 series) #40 © MAR

HOWDY DOODY (TV)(See Jackpot of Fun-- & Poll Parrot)(Some have stories by John Stanley)
Dell Publishing Co.: 1/50 - No. 38, 7-9/56; No. 761, 1/57; No. 811, 7/57

	GD 2.0	VG 4.0	FN 6.0	VF 8.0	VF/NM 9.0	NM- 9.2
1-(Scarce)-Photo-c; 1st TV comic	71	142	213	568	1284	2000
2-Photo-c	34	68	102	241	541	840
3-5: All photo-c	19	38	57	133	297	460
6-Used in **SOTI**, pg. 309; classic-c; painted covers begin	21	42	63	147	324	500
7-10	12	24	36	84	185	285
11-20: 13-X-Mas-c	10	20	30	70	150	230
21-38, Four Color 761,811	9	18	27	61	123	185

HOW IT BEGAN
United Features Syndicate: No. 15, 1939 (one-shot)

	GD 2.0	VG 4.0	FN 6.0	VF 8.0	VF/NM 9.0	NM- 9.2
Single Series 15	36	72	108	211	343	475

HOWLING COMMANDOS OF S.H.I.E.L.D.
Marvel Comics: Dec, 2015 - No. 6, May, 2016 ($3.99)

	GD 2.0	VG 4.0	FN 6.0	VF 8.0	VF/NM 9.0	NM- 9.2
1-6: 1-Barbiere-s/Schoonover-a; Dum Dum Dugan, Orrgo, Man-Thing, Hit-Monkey app.						4.00

HOW SANTA GOT HIS RED SUIT (See March of Comics No. 2)

HOW THE WEST WAS WON (See Movie Comics)

HOW TO DRAW FOR THE COMICS
Street and Smith: No date (1942?) (10¢, 64 pgs., B&W & color, no ads)

	GD 2.0	VG 4.0	FN 6.0	VF 8.0	VF/NM 9.0	NM- 9.2
nn-Art by Robert Winsor McCay (recreating his father's art), George Marcoux (Supersnipe artist), Vernon Greene (The Shadow artist), Jack Binder (with biog.), Thorton Fisher, Jon Small, & Jack Farr; has biographies of each artist	39	78	117	231	378	525

H. P. LOVECRAFT'S CTHULHU
Millennium Publications: Dec, 1991 - No. 3, May, 1992 ($2.50, limited series)

	GD 2.0	VG 4.0	FN 6.0	VF 8.0	VF/NM 9.0	NM- 9.2
1-3: 1-Contains trading cards on thin stock						3.00

H. R. PUFNSTUF (TV) (See March of Comics #360)
Gold Key: Oct, 1970 - No. 8, July, 1972

	GD 2.0	VG 4.0	FN 6.0	VF 8.0	VF/NM 9.0	NM- 9.2
1-Photo-c	10	20	30	64	132	200
2-8-Photo-c on all. 6-8-Both Gold Key and Whitman editions exist	7	14	21	46	86	125

HUBERT AT CAMP MOONBEAM
Dell Publishing Co.: No. 251, Oct, 1949 (one shot)

	GD 2.0	VG 4.0	FN 6.0	VF 8.0	VF/NM 9.0	NM- 9.2
Four Color 251	9	18	27	61	123	185

HUCK
Image Comics: Nov, 2015 - No. 6, Apr, 2016($3.50/$3.99)

	GD 2.0	VG 4.0	FN 6.0	VF 8.0	VF/NM 9.0	NM- 9.2
1-5-MIllar-s/Albuquerque-a; 2 covers on each						3.50
6-($3.99)						4.00

HUCK & YOGI JAMBOREE (TV)
Dell Publishing Co.: Mar, 1961 ($1.00, 6-1/4x9", 116 pgs., cardboard-c, high quality paper) (B&W original material)

	GD 2.0	VG 4.0	FN 6.0	VF 8.0	VF/NM 9.0	NM- 9.2
nn (scarce)	8	16	24	54	102	150

HUCK & YOGI WINTER SPORTS (TV)
Dell Publishing Co.: No. 1310, Mar, 1962 (Hanna-Barbera) (one-shot)

	GD 2.0	VG 4.0	FN 6.0	VF 8.0	VF/NM 9.0	NM- 9.2
Four Color 1310	8	16	24	51	96	140

HUCK FINN (See The New Adventures of... & Power Record Comics)

HUCKLEBERRY FINN (Movie)
Dell Publishing Co.: No. 1114, July, 1960

	GD 2.0	VG 4.0	FN 6.0	VF 8.0	VF/NM 9.0	NM- 9.2
Four Color 1114-Photo-c	6	12	18	37	66	95

HUCKLEBERRY HOUND (See Dell Giant #31,44, Golden Picture Story Book, Kite Fun Book, March of Comics #199, 214, 235, Spotlight #1 & Whitman Comic Books)

HUCKLEBERRY HOUND (TV)
Dell/Gold Key No. 18 (10/62) on: No. 990, 5-7/59 - No. 43, 10/70 (Hanna-Barbera)

	GD 2.0	VG 4.0	FN 6.0	VF 8.0	VF/NM 9.0	NM- 9.2
Four Color 990(#1)-1st app. Huckleberry Hound, Yogi Bear, & Pixie & Dixie & Mr. Jinks	16	32	48	110	243	375
Four Color 1050,1054 (12/59)	10	20	30	67	141	215
3(1-2/60) - 7 (9-10/60), Four Color 1141 (10/60)	7	14	21	46	86	125
8-10	6	12	18	37	66	95
11,13-17 (6-8/62)	5	10	15	30	50	70
12-1st Hokey Wolf & Ding-a-Ling	5	10	15	33	57	80
18,19 (84pgs.; 18-20 titled ...Chuckleberry Tales)	7	14	21	44	82	120
20-Titled Chuckleberry Tales	4	8	12	28	47	65
21-30: 28-30-Reprints	4	8	12	23	37	50
31-43: 31,32,35,37-43-Reprints	3	6	9	19	30	40

HUCKLEBERRY HOUND (TV)
Charlton Comics: Nov, 1970 - No. 8, Jan, 1972 (Hanna-Barbera)

	GD 2.0	VG 4.0	FN 6.0	VF 8.0	VF/NM 9.0	NM- 9.2
1	5	10	15	31	53	75
2-8	3	6	9	17	26	35

HUEY, DEWEY, & LOUIE (See Donald Duck, 1938 for 1st app. Also see Mickey Mouse Magazine V4#2, V5#7 & Walt Disney's Junior Woodchucks Limited Series)

HUEY, DEWEY, & LOUIE BACK TO SCHOOL (See Dell Giant #22, 35, 49 & Dell Giants)

HUEY, DEWEY, AND LOUIE JUNIOR WOODCHUCKS (Disney)
Gold Key No. 1-61/Whitman No. 62 on: Aug, 1966 - No. 81, July, 1984
(See Walt Disney's Comics & Stories #125)

	GD 2.0	VG 4.0	FN 6.0	VF 8.0	VF/NM 9.0	NM- 9.2
1	6	12	18	41	76	110
2,3(12/68)	4	8	12	23	37	50
4,5(4/70)-r/two WDC&S D.Duck stories by Barks	3	6	9	19	30	40
6-17	3	6	9	17	26	35
18,27-30	3	6	9	15	21	26
19-23,25-New storyboarded scripts by Barks, 13-25 pgs. per issue	3	6	9	18	28	38
24,26: 26-r/Barks Donald Duck WDC&S stories	3	6	9	16	23	30
31-57,60,61: 35,41-r/Barks J.W. scripts	2	4	6	8	11	14
58,59: 58-r/Barks Donald Duck WDC&S stories	2	4	6	9	13	16
62-64 (Whitman)	2	4	6	9	13	16
65-(9/80), 66 (Pre-pack? scarce)	4	8	12	25	40	55
67 (1/81),68	2	4	6	9	13	16
67-40¢ cover variant	4	8	12	17	21	24
69-74: 72(2/82), 73(2-3/82), 74(3/82)	2	4	6	8	11	14
75-81 (all #90183; pre-pack; nd, nd code; scarce): 75(4/83), 76(5/83), 77(7/83), 78(8/83), 79(4/84), 80(5/84), 81(7/84)	3	6	9	16	23	30

HUGGA BUNCH (TV)
Marvel Comics (Star Comics): Oct, 1986 - No. 6, Aug, 1987

	GD 2.0	VG 4.0	FN 6.0	VF 8.0	VF/NM 9.0	NM- 9.2
1-6						5.00

HULK (Magazine)(Formerly The Rampaging Hulk)(Also see The Incredible Hulk)
Marvel Comics: No. 10, Aug., 1978 - No. 27, June, 1981 ($1.50)

	GD 2.0	VG 4.0	FN 6.0	VF 8.0	VF/NM 9.0	NM- 9.2
10-18: 10-Bill Bixby interview. 11-Moon Knight begins. 12-15,17,18-Moon Knight stories. 12-Lou Ferrigno interview.	2	4	6	10	14	18
19-27: 20-Moon Knight story. 23-Last full color issue; Banner is attacked. 24-Part color, Lou Ferrigno interview. 25-Part color. 26,27-are B&W	2	4	6	9	12	15

NOTE: #10-20 have fragile spines which split easily. ***Alcala*** *a(i)-15, 17-20, 22, 24-27.* ***Buscema*** *a-23; c-26.* ***Chaykin*** *a-21-25.* ***Colan*** *a(p)-11, 19, 24-27.* ***Jusko*** *painted c-12.* ***Nebres*** *a-16.* ***Severin*** *a-19i. Moon Knight by* ***Sienkiewicz*** *in 13-15, 17, 18, 20.* ***Simonson*** *a-27; c-23. Dominic Fortune appears in #21-24.*

HULK (Becomes Incredible Hulk Vol. 2 with issue #12) (Also see Marvel Age Hulk)
Marvel Comics: Apr, 1999 - No. 11, Feb, 2000 ($2.99/$1.99)

	GD 2.0	VG 4.0	FN 6.0	VF 8.0	VF/NM 9.0	NM- 9.2
1-($2.99) Byrne-s/Garney-a						6.00
1-Variant-c	1	3	4	6	8	10
1-DFE Remarked-c						50.00
1-Gold foil variant						10.00
2-7-($1.99): 2-Two covers. 5-Art by Jurgens, Buscema & Texeira. 7-Avengers app.						4.00
8-Hulk battles Wolverine	1	2	3	5	6	8
9-11: 11-She-Hulk app.						3.00
1999 Annual ($3.50) Chapter One story; Byrne-s/Weeks-a						4.00
Hulk Vs. The Thing (12/99, $3.99, TPB) reprints their notable battles						4.00

HULK (Also see Fall of the Hulks and King-Size Hulk) (Becomes Red She-Hulk with #58)
Marvel Comics: Mar, 2008 - No. 57, Oct, 2012 ($2.99/$3.99)

	GD 2.0	VG 4.0	FN 6.0	VF 8.0	VF/NM 9.0	NM- 9.2
1-Red Hulk app.; Abomination killed; Loeb-s/McGuinness-a/c	2	4	6	9	12	15
1-Variant-c by Acuña						12.00
1-Variant-c with Incredible Hulk #1 cover swipe by McGuinness						40.00
1,2-2nd printings with wraparound McGuinness variant-c						3.00
2-22: 2-Iron Man app.; Rick Jones becomes the new Abomination. 4,6-Red Hulk vs. green Hulk; two covers (each Hulk); Thor app. 7-9-Art Adams & Cho-a (2 covers) 10-Defenders re-form. 14,15-X-Force, Elektra & Deadpool app. 15-Red She-Hulk app. 19-21-Fall of the Hulks x-over. 19-FF app. 22-World War Hulks						4.00
2-9: 2-Variant-c by Djurdjevic. 3-Var-c by Finch. 5-Var-c by Coipel. 6,7-Var-c by Turner 8-Var-c by Sal Buscema. 9-Two covers w/Hulks as Santa						6.00
23-($4.99) Origin of the Red Hulk; art by Sale, Romita, Deodato, Trimpe, Yu, others						5.00
24-31-($3.99): 24-World war Hulks. 25,26-Iron Man app. 26-Thor app.						4.00
30.1, 32-49 ($2.99): 34-Planet Red Hulk begins. 37-38-Fear Itself tie-in						3.00
50-($3.99) Haunted Hulk; Dr. Strange app.; back-up w/Brereton-a; Pagulayan-c						4.00
50-Variant covers by Art Adams, Humberto Ramos & Walt Simonson						10.00
51-57: 53-57-Eaglesham-a; Alpha Flight app.						3.00
... Family: Green Genes 1 (2/09, $4.99) new She-Hulk, Scorpion, Skaar & Mr. Fixit stories						5.00

Hulk (2017 series) #8 © MAR

Hulk 2099 #2 © MAR

Human Target (2010 series) #1 © DC

	GD 2.0	VG 4.0	FN 6.0	VF 8.0	VF/NM 9.0	NM- 9.2

... Let the Battle Begin 1 (5/10, $3.99) Snider-s/Kurth-a; Del Mundo-c; McGuinness-a 4.00
... MGC #1 (6/10, $1.00) r/#1 with "Marvel's Greatest Comics" logo on cover 3.00
... Monster-Size Special (12/08, $3.99) monster-themed stories by Niles, David & others 4.00
...: Raging Thunder 1 (8/08, $3.99) Hulk vs. Thundra; Breitweiser-a; r/FF #133; Land-c 4.00
Hulk-Sized Mini-Hulks ('11, $2.99) Red, Green & Blue Hulks all-ages humor; Giarrusso-a 3.00
... Vs. Fin Fang Foom (2/08, $3.99) new re-telling of first meeting; r/Strange Tales #89 4.00
... Vs. Hercules (6/08, $3.99) Djurdjevic-c; new story w/art by various; r/Tales To Ast. #79 4.00
...: Winter Guard (2/10, $3.99) Darkstar, Crimson Dynamo app. Steve Ellis-a/c 4.00
Hulk 100 Project (2008, $10.00, SC, charity book for the HERO Initiative) collection of 100 variant covers by Adams, Romita Sr. & Jr., Cho, McGuinness and more 10.00

HULK (Follows Indestructible Hulk series)
Marvel Comics: Jun, 2014 - No. 16, Jul, 2015 ($3.99)

1-15: 1-4-Waid-s/Bagley-a. 3,4-Avengers app. 5-Alex Ross-c. 6-15-Duggan-s. 13,14-Deadpool app. 14-15-Hulk vs. Red Hulk 4.00
16-($4.99) Avengers app.; Duggan-s/Bagley-a; leads into Secret Wars 5.00
Annual 1 (11/14, $4.99) Monty Nero-s; art by Luke Ross, Goddard & Laming 5.00

HULK (Jennifer Walters as Hulk; follows events of Civil War II)(Continues as She-Hulk #159)
Marvel Comics: Feb, 2017 - No. 11, Dec, 2017 ($3.99)

1-11: 1-6-Mariko Tamaki-s/Nico Leon-a. 3,11-Hellcat app. 4.00

HULK AND POWER PACK (All ages series)
Marvel Comics: May, 2007 - No. 4, Aug, 2007 ($2.99, limited series)

1-4-Sumerak-s. 1,2,4-Williams-a. 1-Absorbing Man app. 3-Kuhn-a; Abomination app. 3.00
...: Pack Smash! (2007, $6.99, digest) r/#1-4 7.00

HULK & THING: HARD KNOCKS
Marvel Comics: Nov, 2004 - No. 4, Feb, 2005 ($3.50, limited series)

1-4-Bruce Jones-s/Jae Lee-a/c 3.50
TPB (2005, $13.99) r/#1-4 and Giant-Size Super-Stars #1 14.00

HULK: BROKEN WORLDS
Marvel Comics: May, 2009 -No. 2, July, 2009 ($3.99, limited series)

1,2-Short stories of alternate world Hulks by various, incl. Trimpe, David, Warren 4.00

HULK CHRONICLES: WWH
Marvel Comics: Oct, 2008 - No. 6, Mar, 2009 ($4.99, limited series)

1-6-Reprints stories from World War Hulk x-over. 1-R/Inc. Hulk #106 & WWH Prologue 5.00

HULK: DESTRUCTION
Marvel Comics: Sept, 2005 - No. 4, Dec, 2005 ($2.99, limited series)

1-4-Origin of the Abomination; Peter David-s/Jim Muniz-a 3.00

HULKED-OUT HEROES
Marvel Comics: Jun, 2010 - No. 2, Jun, 2010 ($3.99, limited series)

1,2-World War Hulks tie-in; Deadpool app.; Ramos-a 4.00

HULK: FUTURE IMPERFECT
Marvel Comics: Jan, 1993 - No. 2, Dec, 1992 (In error) ($5.95, 52 pgs., squarebound, limited series)

1,2: Embossed-c; Peter David story & George Perez-c/a. 1-1st app. Maestro.
1 2 3 5 6 8

HULK: GRAY
Marvel Comics: Dec, 2003 - No. 6, Apr, 2004 ($3.50, limited series)

1-6-Hulk's origin & early days; Loeb-s/Sale-a/c 3.50
HC (2004, $21.99, with dust jacket) oversized r/#1-6 22.00
SC (2005, $19.99) r/#1-6 20.00

HULK: NIGHTMERICA
Marvel Comics: Aug, 2003 - No. 6, May, 2004 ($2.99, limited series)

1-6-Brian Ashmore painted-a/c 3.00

HULK/ PITT
Marvel Comics: 1997 ($5.99, one-shot)

1-David-s/Keown-c/a 6.00

HULK: SEASON ONE
Marvel Comics: 2012 ($24.99, hardcover graphic novel)

HC - Origin and early days; Van Lente-s/Fowler-a/Tedesco painted-c 25.00

HULK SMASH
Marvel Comics: Mar, 2001 - No. 2, Apr, 2001 ($2.99, limited series)

1,2-Ennis-s/McCrea & Janson-a/Nowlan painted-c 3.00

HULK SMASH AVENGERS
Marvel Comics: Jul, 2012 - No. 5, July, 2012 ($2.99, weekly limited series)

1-5-Hulk vs. Avengers from various points in Marvel History. 1-Frenz-a. 5-Oeming-a 3.00

HULK: THE MOVIE
Marvel Comics

...Adaptation (8/03, $3.50) Bruce Jones-s/Bagley-a/Keown-c 3.50
TPB (2003, $12.99) r/Adaptation, Ultimates #5, Inc. Hulk #34, Ult. Marvel Team-Up #2&3 13.00

HULK 2099
Marvel Comics: Dec, 1994 - No. 10, Sept, 1995 ($1.50/$1.95)

1-($2.50)-Green foil-c 4.00
2-10: 2-A. Kubert-c 3.00

HULK/WOLVERINE: 6 HOURS
Marvel Comics: Mar, 2003 - No. 4, May, 2003 ($2.99, limited series)

1-4-Bruce Jones-s/Scott Kolins-a; Bisley-c 3.00
Hulk Legends Vol. 1: Hulk/Wolverine: 6 Hours (2003, $13.99, TPB) r/#1-4 & 1st Wolverine app. from Incredible Hulk #181 14.00

HUMAN BOMB
DC Comics: Feb, 2013 - No. 4, May, 2013 ($2.99, limited series)

1-4: 1-Re-intro/origin; Gray & Palmiotti-s/Ordway-a/c 3.00

HUMAN DEFENSE CORPS
DC Comics: Jul, 2003 - No. 6, Dec, 2003 ($2.50, limited series)

1-6-Ty Templeton-s/Sauve, Jr & Vlasco-a. 1-Lois Lane app. 3.00

HUMAN FLY
I.W. Enterprises/Super: 1963 - 1964 (Reprints)

I.W. Reprint #1-Reprints Blue Beetle #44('46) 2 4 6 13 18 22
Super Reprint #10-R/Blue Beetle #46('47) 2 4 6 13 18 22

HUMAN FLY, THE
Marvel Comics Group: Sept, 1977 - No. 19, Mar, 1979

1-(Regular 30¢-c) Origin; Spider-Man x-over 2 4 6 13 18 22
1,2-(35¢-c, limited distribution) 5 10 15 33 57 80
2,9,19: 2-(Regular 30¢-c). 2-Ghost Rider app. 9-Daredevil x-over; Byrne-c(p). 19-Last issue
2 3 4 6 8 10
3-8,10-18 5.00
NOTE: ***Austin*** *c-4i, 9i.* ***Elias*** *a-1, 3p, 4p, 7p, 10-12p, 15p, 18p, 19p.* ***Layton*** *c-19.*

HUMANKIND
Image Comics (Top Cow): Sept, 2004 - No. 5, Mar, 2005 ($2.99, limited series)

1-5-Tony Daniel-a. 1-Three covers by Daniel, Silvestri, and Land 3.00

HUMAN RACE, THE
DC Comics: May, 2005 - No. 7, Nov, 2005 ($2.99, limited series)

1-7-Raab-s/Justiniano-a/c 3.00

HUMAN TARGET
DC Comics (Vertigo): Apr, 1999 - No. 4, July, 1999 ($2.95, limited series)

1-4-Milligan-s/Bradstreet-c/Biuković-a 3.00
1-Special Edition (6/10, $1.00) r/#1 with "What's Next?" logo on cover 3.00
TPB (2000, $12.95) new Bradstreet-c 13.00
...: Chance Meetings TPB (2010, $14.99) r/#1-4 and Human Target: Final Cut GN 15.00

HUMAN TARGET
DC Comics (Vertigo): Oct, 2003 - No. 21, June, 2005 ($2.95)

1-21: 1-5-Milligan-s/Pulido-a/c. 6-Chiang-a 3.00
...: Living in Amerika TPB (2004, $14.95) r/#6-10; Chiang sketch pages 15.00
...: Second Chances TPB (2011, $19.99) r/#1-10; Chiang sketch pages 20.00
...: Strike Zones TPB (2004, $9.95) r/#1-5 10.00

HUMAN TARGET (Based on the Fox TV series)
DC Comics: Apr, 2010 - No. 6, Sept, 2010 ($2.99, limited series)

1-6-Wein-s/Redondo-a; back-up stories by various. 1-Bermejo-c. 5-Sook-c 3.00
TPB (2010, $17.99) r/#1-6 18.00

HUMAN TARGET: FINAL CUT
DC Comics (Vertigo): 2002 ($29.95/$19.95, graphic novel)

Hardcover (2002, $29.95) Milligan-s/Pulido-a/c 30.00
Softcover (2003, $19.95) 20.00

HUMAN TARGET SPECIAL (TV)
DC Comics: Nov, 1991 ($2.00, 52 pgs., one-shot)

1 4.00

HUMAN TORCH, THE (Red Raven #1)(See All-Select, All Winners, Marvel Mystery, Men's Adventures, Mystic Comics (2nd series), Sub-Mariner, USA & Young Men)
Timely/Marvel Comics (TP 2,3/TCI 4-9/SePI 10/SnPC 11-25/CnPC 26-35/Atlas Comics (CPC 36-38)): No. 2, Fall, 1940 - No. 15, Spring, 1944; No. 16, Fall, 1944 - No. 35, Mar, 1949 (Becomes Love Tales #36 on); No. 36, April, 1954 - No. 38, Aug, 1954

Human Torch #10 © MAR

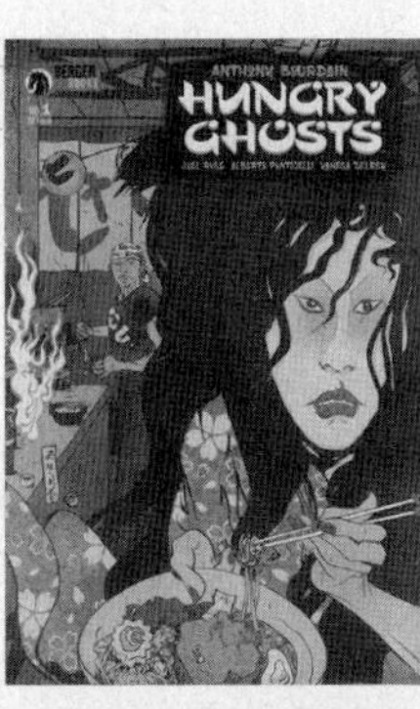

Hungry Ghosts #1 © Bourdain & Rose

Huntress (2011 series) #1 © DC

GD VG FN VF VF/NM NM-
2.0 4.0 6.0 8.0 9.0 9.2

2(#1)-Intro & Origin Toro; The Falcon, The Fiery Mask, Mantor the Magician, & Microman only app.; Human Torch by Burgos, Sub-Mariner by Everett begin (origin of each in text); WWII-c 2700 5400 8100 19,000 44,500 72,000
3(#2)-40 pg. H.T. story; H.T. & S.M. battle over who is best artist in text-Everett or Burgos 649 1298 1947 4738 8369 12,000
4(#3)-Origin The Patriot in text; last Everett Sub-Mariner; Sid Greene-a 503 1006 1509 3672 6486 9300
5(#4)-The Patriot app; Angel x-over in Sub-Mariner (Summer, 1941); 1st Nazi war-c this title; back-c ad for Young Allies #1 with diff. cover-a 429 858 1287 3132 5516 7900
5-Human Torch battles Sub-Mariner (Fall, '41); 60 pg. story 703 1406 2109 5132 9066 13,000
6-Schomburg hooded villain bondage-c 371 742 1113 2600 4550 6500
7-1st Japanese war-c 411 822 1233 2877 5039 7200
8-Human Torch battles Sub-Mariner; 52 pg. story; Wolverton-a, 1 pg.; Nazi WWII-c 514 1028 1542 3750 6625 9500
9-Classic Human Torch vs. Gen. Rommel, "The Desert Rat"; Nazi WWII-c 411 822 1233 2877 5039 7200
10-Human Torch battles Sub-Mariner, 45 pg. story; Wolverton-a, 1 pg.; Nazi WWII-c 423 846 1269 3088 5444 7800
11,14,15: 11-Nazi WWII-c. 14-Nazi WWII-c; 1st Atlas Globe logo (Winter, 1943-44; see All Winners #11 also) 320 640 960 2240 3920 5600
12-Classic Japanese WWII-c, Torch melts Japanese soldier's arm 919 1838 2757 6709 11,855 17,000
13-Classic Schomburg Japanese WWII bondage-c 354 708 1062 2478 4339 6200
16-20: 16-18,20-Japanese WWII-c. 19-Bondage-c. 20-Last War issue 252 504 756 1613 2757 3900
21,22,24-30: 27-2nd app. (1st-c) Asbestos Lady (see Capt. America Comics #63 for 1st app.) 187 374 561 1197 2049 2900
23 (Sum/46)-Becomes Junior Miss 24? Classic Schomburg Robot-c 284 568 852 1818 3109 4400
31,32: 31-Namora x-over in Sub-Mariner (also #30); last Toro. 32-Sungirl, Namora app.; Sungirl-c 171 342 513 1086 1868 2650
33-Capt. America x-over 174 348 522 1114 1907 2700
34-Sungirl solo 161 322 483 1030 1765 2500
35-Captain America & Sungirl app. (1949) 161 322 483 1030 1765 2500
36-38(1954)-Sub-Mariner in all 126 252 378 806 1378 1950

NOTE: ***Ayers*** *Human Torch in 36(3).* ***Brodsky*** *c-25, 31-33?, 37, 38,* ***Burgos*** *c-36.* ***Everett*** *a-1-3, 27, 28, 30, 37, 38.* ***Powell*** *a-36(Sub-Mariner).* ***Schomburg*** *c-1-3, 5-8, 10-23.* ***Sekowsky*** *c-28, 34?, 35?* ***Shores*** *c-24, 26, 27, 29, 30.* ***Mickey Spillane*** *text 4-6. Bondage c-2, 12, 19.*

HUMAN TORCH, THE (Also see Avengers West Coast, Fantastic Four, The Invaders, Saga of the Original... & Strange Tales #101)
Marvel Comics Group: Sept, 1974 - No. 8, Nov, 1975

1: 1-8-r/stories from Strange Tales #101-108 5 10 15 30 50 70
2-8: 1st H.T. title since G.A. 7-vs. Sub-Mariner 3 6 9 15 22 28

NOTE: *Golden Age & Silver Age Human Torch-r #1-8.* ***Ayers*** *r-6, 7.* ***Kirby/Ayers*** *r-1-5, 8.*

HUMAN TORCH (From the Fantastic Four)
Marvel Comics: June, 2003 - No. 12, Jun, 2004 ($2.50/$2.99)

1-7-Skottie Young-c/a; Karl Kesel-s 3.00
8-12-($2.99) 8,10-Dodd-a. 9-Young-a. 11-Porter-a. 12-Medina-a 3.00
... Vol. 1: Burn TPB (2005, $7.99, digest size) r/#1-6 8.00

HUMAN TORCH COMICS 70TH ANNIVERSARY SPECIAL
Marvel Comics: July, 2009 ($3.99, one-shot)

1-Covers by Granov and Martin; new story and r/1st app Toro from Human Torch #2 5.00

HUMBUG (Satire by Harvey Kurtzman)
Humbug Publications: Aug, 1957 - No. 9, May, 1958; No. 10, June, 1958; No. 11, Oct, 1958

1-Wood-a (intro pgs. only) 28 56 84 165 270 375
2 15 30 45 85 130 175
3-9: 8-Elvis in Jailbreak Rock 14 28 42 76 108 140
10,11-Magazine format. 10-Photo-c 15 30 45 90 140 190
Bound Volume(#1-9)(extremely rare) 65 130 195 416 708 1000

NOTE: ***Davis*** *a-1-11.* ***Elder*** *a-2-4, 6-9, 11.* ***Heath*** *a-2, 4-8, 10.* ***Jaffee*** *a-2, 4-9.* ***Kurtzman*** *a-11.*

HUMDINGER (Becomes White Rider and Super Horse #3 on?)
Novelty Press/Premium Group: May-June, 1946 - V2#2, July-Aug, 1947

1-Jerkwater Line, Mickey Starlight by Don Rico, Dink begin 37 74 111 222 361 500
2 16 32 48 94 147 200
3-6, V2#1,2 12 24 36 69 97 125

HUMONGOUS MAN
Alternative Press (Ikon Press): Sept, 1997 -No. 3 ($2.25, B&W)

1-3-Stepp & Harrison-c/s/a. 3.00

HUMOR (See All Humor Comics)

GD VG FN VF VF/NM NM-
2.0 4.0 6.0 8.0 9.0 9.2

HUMPHREY COMICS (Joe Palooka Presents...; also see Joe Palooka)
Harvey Publications: Oct, 1948 - No. 22, Apr, 1952

1-Joe Palooka's pal (r); (52 pgs.)-Powell-a 14 28 42 80 115 150
2,3: Powell-a 9 18 27 47 61 75
4-Boy Heroes app.; Powell-a 9 18 27 50 65 80
5-8,10: 5,6-Powell-a. 7-Little Dot app. 8 16 24 40 50 60
9-Origin Humphrey 9 18 27 47 61 75
11-22 7 14 21 37 46 55

HUNCHBACK OF NOTRE DAME, THE
Dell Publishing Co.: No. 854, Oct, 1957 (one shot)

Four Color 854-Movie, photo-c 11 22 33 73 157 240

HUNGER (See Age of Ultron and Cataclysm titles)
Marvel Comics: Sept, 2013 - No. 4, Dec, 2013 ($3.99, limited series)

1-4-Fialkov-s/Kirk-a/Granov-c; Galactus in the Ultimate Universe. 2-4-Silver Surfer app. 4.00
1-Variant-c by Neal Adams 18.00

HUNGER, THE
Speakeasy Comics: May, 2005 ($2.99)

1-Andy Bradshaw-s/a; Eric Powell-c 3.00

HUNGER DOGS, THE (See DC Graphic Novel #4)

HUNGRY GHOSTS
Dark Horse Comics (Berger Books): Jan, 2018 - No. 4 ($3.99)

1,2-Anthony Bourdain & Joel Rose-s. 1-Ponticelli & Del Rey-a. 2-Manco & Santolouco-a 4.00

HUNK
Charlton Comics: Aug, 1961 - No. 11, 1963

1 4 8 12 23 37 50
2-11 3 6 9 14 20 25

HUNT, THE
Image Comics (Shadowline): Jul, 2016 - No. 5, Dec, 2016 ($3.99)

1-5-Colin Lorimer-s/a 4.00

HUNTED (Formerly My Love Memoirs)
Fox Feature Syndicate: No. 13, July, 1950; No. 2, Sept, 1950

13(#1)-Used in **SOTI**, pg. 42 & illo. "Treating police contemptuously" (lower left); Hollingsworth bondage-c 43 86 129 271 461 650
2 21 42 63 122 199 275

HUNTER-KILLER
Image Comics (Top Cow): Nov, 2004 - No. 12, Mar, 2007 ($2.99)

0-(11/04, 25¢) Prelude with Silvestri sketch page and Waid afterword 3.00
1-12: 1-(3/05, $2.99) Waid-s/Silvestri-a; four covers. 2-Linsner variant-c 3.00
... Collected Edition Vol. 1 (9/05, $4.99) r/#0-3 5.00
...Dossier 1 (9/05, $2.99) character profiles with art by various; Migliari-c 3.00
... Volume 1 TPB (1/08, $24.99) r/#0-12; Dossier and Script Book; variant covers 25.00

HUNTER: THE AGE OF MAGIC (See Books of Magic)
DC Comics (Vertigo): Sept, 2001 - No. 25, Sept, 2003 ($2.50/$2.75)

1-25: Horrocks-s/Case-a. 1-8-Bolton-c. 14-Begin $2.75-c. 19-Bachalo-c 3.00

HUNTRESS, THE (See All-Star Comics #69, Batman Family, DC Super Stars #17, Detective #652, Infinity, Inc. #1 & Wonder Woman #271)
DC Comics: Apr, 1989 - No. 19, Oct, 1990 ($1.00, mature)

1-Staton-c/a(p) in all 5.00
2-19: 17-19-Batman-c/stories 3.00
...: Darknight Daughter TPB (2006, $19.99) r/origin & early apps. in DC Super Stars #17, Batman Family #18-20 & Wonder Woman #271-287,289,290,294,295; Bolland-c 20.00

HUNTRESS, THE
DC Comics: June, 1994 - No. 4, Sept, 1994 ($1.50, limited series)

1-4-Netzer-c/a: 2-Batman app. 3.00

HUNTRESS (Leads into 2012 World's Finest series)
DC Comics: Dec, 2011 - No. 6, May, 2012 ($2.99, limited series)

1-6-Levitz-s/To-a/March-c 3.00

HUNTRESS: YEAR ONE
DC Comics: Early July, 2008 - No. 6, Late Sept, 2008 ($2.99, limited series)

1-6-Origin re-told; Cliff Richards-a/Ivory Madison-s 3.00
TPB (2009, $17.99) r/#1-6; intro. by Paul Levitz 18.00

HURRICANE COMICS
Cambridge House: 1945 (52 pgs.)

1-(Humor, funny animal) 28 56 84 165 270 375

Hypernaturals #12 © BOOM!

I Am Groot #1 © MAR

Icon #17 © Milestone

	GD 2.0	VG 4.0	FN 6.0	VF 8.0	VF/NM 9.0	NM- 9.2

HUSK
Marvel Comics (Soleil): May, 2010 - No. 2, Jun, 2010 ($5.99, limited series)
1,2-English version of French comic; L'Homme-s/Boudoiron-a 6.00

HYBRIDS
Continunity Comics: Jan, 1994 ($2.50, one-shot)
1-Neal Adams-c(p) & part-a(i); embossed-c. 4.00

HYBRIDS DEATHWATCH 2000
Continuity Comics: Apr, 1993 - No. 3, Aug, 1993 ($2.50)
0-(Giveaway)-Foil-c; Neal Adams-c(i) & plots (also #1,2) 4.00
1-3: 1-Polybagged w/card; die-cut-c. 2-Thermal-c. 3-Polybagged w/card; indestructible-c; Adams plot 4.00

HYBRIDS ORIGIN
Continuity Comics: 1993 - No. 5, Jan, 1994 ($2.50)
1-5: 2,3-Neal Adams-c. 4,5-Valeria the She-Bat app. Adams-c(i) 4.00

HYDE
IDW Publ.: Oct, 2004 ($7.49, one-shot)
1-Steve Niles-s/Nick Stakal 7.50

HYDE-25
Harris Publications: Apr, 1995 ($2.95, one-shot)
0-Coupon for poster; r/Vampirella's 1st app. 3.00

HYDROMAN (See Heroic Comics)

HYPERION (Squadron Supreme)
Marvel Comics: May, 2016 - No. 6, Oct, 2016 ($3.99)
1-6: 1-4,6-Wendig-s/Virella-a. 5-Anindito-a. 5,6-Iron Man & Thundra app. 4.00*

HYPERKIND (See Razorline)
Marvel Comics: Sept, 1993 - No. 9, May, 1994 ($1.75/$1.95)
1-($2.50)-Foil embossed-c; by Clive Barker 4.00
2-9 3.00
...Unleashed 1 (8/94, $2.95, 52 pgs., one-shot) 4.00

HYPER MYSTERY COMICS
Hyper Publications: May, 1940 - No. 2, June, 1940 (68 pgs.)

	GD	VG	FN	VF	VF/NM	NM-
1-Hyper, the Phenomenal begins; Calkins-a	265	530	795	1694	2897	4100
2-H.G. Peter-a	148	296	444	947	1624	2300

HYPERNATURALS
BOOM! Studios: Jul, 2012 - No. 12, Jun, 2013 ($3.99)
1-12: 1-Abnett & Lanning-s/Walker & Guinaldo-a; at least eight covers. 2-Two printings 4.00
... Free Comic Book Day Edition (5/12) Prelude to issue #1 3.00

HYPERSONIC
Dark Horse Comics: Nov, 1997 - No. 4, Feb, 1998 ($2.95, limited series)
1-4: Abnett & White-s/Erskine-a 3.00

I AIM AT THE STARS (Movie)
Dell Publishing Co.: No. 1148, Nov-Jan/1960-61 (one-shot)

	GD	VG	FN	VF	VF/NM	NM-
Four Color 1148-The Werner Von Braun Sty-photo-c	6	12	18	41	76	110

I AM AN AVENGER (See Avengers, Young Avengers and Pet Avengers)
Marvel Comics: Nov, 2010 - No. 5, Mar, 2011 ($3.99, limited series)
1-5-Short stories by various. 1-Yu-c. 2-Land-c. 2-4-Mayhew-a. 3-Noto-c. 4-Acuña-c 4.00

I AM CAPTAIN AMERICA
Marvel Comics: Jan, 2012 ($3.99, one-shot)
1-Collection of Captain America-themed 70th Anniversary covers with artist profiles 4.00

I AM COYOTE (See Eclipse Graphic Album Series & Eclipse Magazine #2)

I AM GROOT (Guardians of the Galaxy)
Marvel Comics: Jul, 2017 - No. 5, Nov, 2017 ($3.99, limited series)
1-5-Hastings-s/Flaviano-a. 1,5-Guardians of the Galaxy app. 4.00

I AM LEGEND
Eclipse Books: 1991 - No. 4, 1991 ($5.95, B&W, squarebound, 68 pgs.)

	GD	VG	FN	VF	VF/NM	NM-
1-4: Based on 1954 novel by Richard Matheson	1	2	3	5	6	8

I AM LEGION (English version of French graphic novel Je Suis Légion)
Devils Due Publishing: Jan, 2009 - No. 6, July, 2009 ($3.50)
1-6-John Cassaday-a/Fabien Nury-s; two covers 3.50

IBIS, THE INVINCIBLE (See Fawcett Miniatures, Mighty Midget & Whiz)
Fawcett Publications: 1942 (Fall?); #2, Mar.,1943; #3, Wint, 1945 - #5, Fall, 1946; #6, Spring, 1948

	GD	VG	FN	VF	VF/NM	NM-
1-Origin Ibis; Raboy-c; on sale 1/2/43	271	542	813	1734	2967	4200
2-Bondage-c (on sale 2/5/43)	113	226	339	718	1234	1750
3-Wolverton-a #3-6 (4 pgs. each)	77	154	231	493	847	1200
4-6: 5-Bondage-c	53	106	159	334	567	800

NOTE: ***Mac Raboy** c(p)-3-5. **Schaffenberger** c-6.*

I-BOTS (See Isaac Asimov's I-BOTS)

ICE AGE ON THE WORLD OF MAGIC: THE GATHERING (See Magic The Gathering)

ICE KING OF OZ, THE (See First Comics Graphic Novel #13)

ICEMAN (Also see The Champions & X-Men #94)
Marvel Comics Group: Dec, 1984 - No. 4, June, 1985 (Limited series)
1,2,4: Zeck covers on all 4.00
3-The Defenders, Champions (Ghost Rider) & the original X-Men x-over 5.00

ICEMAN (X-Men)
Marvel Comics: Dec, 2001 - No. 4, Mar, 2002 ($2.50, limited series)
1-4-Abnett & Lanning-s/Kerschl-a 3.00

ICEMAN (X-Men)
Marvel Comics: Aug, 2017 - No. 11, May, 2018 ($3.99, limited series)
1-11: 1-Grace-s/Vitti-a. 2-Kitty Pryde app. 5-Juggernaut app. 4.00

ICEMAN AND ANGEL (X-Men)
Marvel Comics: May, 2011 ($2.99, one-shot)
1-Brian Clevinger-s/Juan Doe-a; Goom & Googam app. 3.00

ICON
DC Comics (Milestone): May, 1993 - No. 42, Feb, 1997($1.50/$1.75/$2.50)
1-($2.95)-Collector's Edition polybagged w/poster & trading card (direct sale only) 4.00
1-24,30-42: 9-Simonson-c. 15,16-Worlds Collide Pt. 4 & 11. 15-Superboy app. 16-Superman-c/story. 40-Vs. Blood Syndicate 3.00
25-($2.95, 52 pgs.) 4.00
... A Hero's Welcome SC (2009, $19.99) r/#1-8; intro. by Reginald Hudlin 20.00
...: Mothership Connection SC (2010, $24.99) r/#13,19-22,24-27,30 25.00

IDAHO
Dell Publishing Co.: June-Aug, 1963 - No. 8, July-Sept, 1965

	GD	VG	FN	VF	VF/NM	NM-
1	3	6	9	16	24	32
2-8: 5-7-Painted-c	2	4	6	9	13	16

IDEAL (... a Classical Comic) (2nd Series) (Love Romances No. 6 on)
Timely Comics: July, 1948 - No. 5, March, 1949 (Feature length stories)

	GD	VG	FN	VF	VF/NM	NM-
1-Antony & Cleopatra	37	74	111	222	361	500
2-The Corpses of Dr. Sacotti	31	62	93	186	303	420
3-Joan of Arc; used in **SOTI**, pg. 310 'Boer War'	29	58	87	172	281	390
4-Richard the Lion-hearted; titled "...the World's Greatest Comics"; The Witness story	40	80	120	246	411	575
5-Ideal Love & Romance; change to love; photo-c	20	40	60	117	189	260

IDEAL COMICS (1st Series) (Willie Comics No. 5 on)
Timely Comics (MgPC): Fall, 1944 - No. 4, Spring, 1946

	GD	VG	FN	VF	VF/NM	NM-
1-Funny animal; Super Rabbit in all	41	82	123	256	428	600
2	21	42	63	122	199	275
3,4	19	38	57	111	176	240

IDEAL LOVE & ROMANCE (See Ideal, A Classical Comic)

IDEAL ROMANCE (Formerly Tender Romance)
Key Publ.: No. 3, April, 1954 - No. 8, Feb, 1955 (Diary Confessions No. 9 on)

	GD	VG	FN	VF	VF/NM	NM-
3-Bernard Baily-c	11	22	33	62	86	110
4-8: 4-6-B. Baily-c	9	18	27	47	61	75

IDEALS (Secret Stories)
Ideals Publ., USA: 1981 (68 pgs, graphic novels, 7x10", stiff-c)

	GD	VG	FN	VF	VF/NM	NM-
Captain America - Star Spangled Super Hero	3	6	9	19	30	40
Fantastic Four - Cosmic Quartet	3	6	9	19	30	40
Incredible Hulk - Gamma Powered Goliath	3	6	9	19	30	40
Spider-Man - World Famous Wall Crawler	4	8	12	23	37	50

IDENTITY CRISIS
DC Comics: Aug, 2004 - No. 7, Feb, 2005 ($3.95, limited series)
1-Meltzer-s/Morales-a/Turner-c in all; Sue Dibny murdered 5.00
1-(Second printing) black-c with white sketch lines 5.00
1-(3rd & 4th) 3rd-Bloody broken photo glass image-c by Morales. 4th-Turner red-c 4.00
1-Diamond Retailer Summit Edition with sketch-c 30.00
1-Special Edition (6/09, $1.00) r/#1 with "After Watchmen" cover frame 3.00
2-7: 2-4-Deathstroke app. 5-Firestorm, Jack Drake, Capt. Boomerang killed 4.00
2-(Second printing) new Morales sketch-c 4.00

I Hate Fairyland #15 © Skottie Young

I Love Lucy FC #559 © Desilu

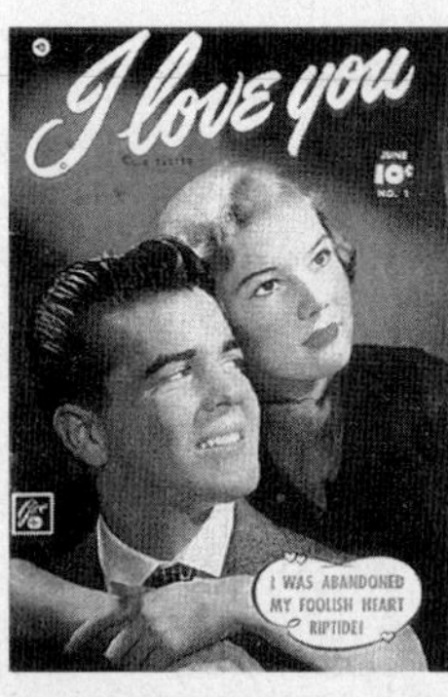

I Love You #1 © FAW

GD 2.0 | VG 4.0 | FN 6.0 | VF 8.0 | VF/NM 9.0 | NM- 9.2

Final printings for all issues with red background variant covers 4.00
HC (2005, $24.99, dust jacket) r/series; Director's Cut extras; cover gallery; Whedon intro.; 2 covers: Direct Market-c by Turner, Bookstore-c with Morales-a 25.00
SC (2006, $14.99) r/series; Director's Cut extras; cover gallery; Whedon intro 15.00

IDENTITY DISC
Marvel Comics: Aug, 2004 - No. 5, Dec, 2004 ($2.99, limited series)
1-5-Sabretooth, Bullseye, Sandman, Vulture, Deadpool, Juggernaut app.; Higgins-a 4.00
TPB (2004, $13.99) r/#1-5 14.00

IDES OF BLOOD
DC Comics (WildStorm): Oct, 2010 - No. 6, Mar, 2011 ($3.99/$2.99, limited series)
1-6-Stuart Paul-s/Christian Duce-a/Michael Geiger-c; Roman Empire vampires 4.00

I DIE AT MIDNIGHT (Vertigo V2K)
DC Comics (Vertigo): 2000 ($6.95, prestige format, one-shot)
1-Kyle Baker-s/a 7.00

IDOL
Marvel Comics (Epic Comics): 1992 - No. 3, 1992 ($2.95, mini-series, 52 pgs.)
Book 1-3 4.00

IDOLIZED
Aspen MLT: No. 0, Jun, 2012 - No. 5, Apr, 2013 ($2.50/$3.99)
0-($2.50) Schwartz-s/Gunnell-a; regular & photo covers; Superhero Idol background 3.00
1-5-($3.99) 1-Art Adams & photo covers; origin of Joule 4.00

I DREAM OF JEANNIE (TV)
Dell Publishing Co.: Apr, 1965 - No. 2, Dec, 1966 (Photo-c)
1-Barbara Eden photo-c, each 12 24 36 80 173 265
2 10 20 30 64 132 200

I FEEL SICK
Slave Labor Graphics: Aug, 1999 - No. 2, May, 2000 ($3.95, limited series)
1,2-Jhonen Vasquez-s/a 4.00

I HATE FAIRYLAND (Also see I Hate Image, FCBD Special)
Image Comics: Oct, 2015 - Present ($3.50/$3.99)
1-10-Skottie Young-s/a/c; each has variant cover with "F*** Fairyland" title 3.50
11-17-($3.99) 12-Lone Wolf & Cub homage-c. 13-Rankine-a 4.00
...: I Hate Image Special Edition (10/17, $5.99) r/I Hate Image FCBD Special with 4 new pages; bonus script and sketch art; 2 covers 6.00

I HATE GALLANT GIRL
Image Comics (Shadowline): Nov, 2008 - No. 3, Jan, 2009 ($3.50, limited series)
1-3-Kat Cahill-s/Seth Damoose-a 3.50

I HATE IMAGE, FCBD SPECIAL
Image Comics: May, 2017 (free giveaway)
1-Gert from I Hate Fairyland vs. Image characters from Walking Dead, Bitch Planet, Saga, Paper Girls, Chew, Spawn and others; Skottie Young-s/a/c 3.00

I (heart) MARVEL
Marvel Comics: Apr, 2006; May, 2006 ($2.99, one-shots)
...: Marvel AI 1 (4/06) Cebulski-s; manga art by various; Vision, Daredevil, Elektra app. 3.00
...: Masked Intentions 1 (5/06) Squirrel Girl, Speedball, Firestar, Justice app.; Nicieza-s 3.00
...: My Mutant Heart 1 (4/06) Wolverine, Cannonball, Doop app. 3.00
...: Outlaw Love 1 (4/06) Bullseye, The Answer, Ruby Thursday app.; Nicieza-s 3.00
...: Web of Romance 1 (4/06) Spider-Man, Mary Jane, The Avengers app. 3.00

ILLEGITIMATES, THE
IDW Publishing: Dec, 2013 - No. 6, May, 2014 ($3.99)
1-6: 1-Taran Killam & Marc Andreyko-a/Kevin Sharpe-a; covers by Ordway & Willingham 4.00

ILLUMUNATI
Marvel Comics: Jan, 2016 - No. 7, Jul, 2016 ($3.99)
1-7: 1-Williamson-s/Crystal-a; The Hood, Titania and others team. 4-Thor app. 4.00

ILLUMINATOR
Marvel Comics/Nelson Publ.: 1993 - No. 4, 1993 ($4.99/$2.95, 52 pgs.)
1,2-($4.99) Religious themed 5.00
3,4 4.00

ILLUSTRATED GAGS
United Features Syndicate: No. 16, 1940
Single Series 16 19 38 57 111 176 240

ILLUSTRATED LIBRARY OF..., AN (See Classics Illustrated Giants)

ILLUSTRATED STORIES OF THE OPERAS
Baily (Bernard) Publ. Co.: 1943 (16 pgs.; B&W) (25 cents) (covers are black,yellow & red, with scarcer editions having B&W with red)
nn-(Rare)(4 diff. issues)-Faust (part-r in Cisco Kid #1, 2 cover versions: 25¢ & no price) nn-Aida, nn-Carmen; Baily-a, nn-Rigoletto 71 142 213 454 777 1100

ILLUSTRATED STORY OF ROBIN HOOD & HIS MERRY MEN, THE (See Classics Giveaways, 12/44)

ILLUSTRATED TARZAN BOOK, THE (See Tarzan Book)

I LOVED (Formerly Rulah; Colossal Features Magazine No. 33 on)
Fox Feature Syndicate: No. 28, July, 1949 - No. 32, Mar, 1950
28 21 42 63 122 199 275
29-32 15 30 45 88 137 185

I LOVE LUCY
Eternity Comics : 6/90 - No. 6, 1990;V2#1, 11/90 - No. 6, 1991 ($2.95, B&W, mini-series)
1-6: Reprints 1950s comic strip; photo-c 4.00
Book II #1-6: Reprints comic strip; photo-c 4.00
...In Full Color 1 (1991, $5.95, 52 pgs.)-Reprints I Love Lucy Comics #4,5,8,16; photo-c with embossed logo (2 versions exist, one with pgs. 18 & 19 reversed, the other corrected) 1 2 3 5 6 8
...In 3-D 1 (1991, $3.95, w/glasses)-Reprints I Love Lucy Comics; photo-c; bagged 6.00

I LOVE LUCY COMICS (TV) (Also see The Lucy Show)
Dell Publishing Co.: No. 535, Feb, 1954 - No. 35, Apr-June, 1962 (Lucille Ball photo-c on all)
Four Color 535(#1) 45 90 135 333 754 1175
Four Color 559(#2, 5/54) 27 54 81 189 420 650
3 (8-10/54) - 5 16 32 48 108 239 370
6-10 12 24 36 84 185 285
11-20 10 20 30 66 138 210
21-35 9 18 27 57 111 165

I LOVE NEW YORK
Linsner.com: 2002 ($2.95, B&W, one-shot)
1-Linsner-s/a; benefit book for the Sept. 11 charities 3.00

I LOVE YOU
Fawcett Publications: June, 1950 (one-shot)
1-Photo-c 15 30 45 88 137 185

I LOVE YOU (Formerly In Love)
Charlton Comics: No. 7, 9/55 - No. 121, 12/76; No. 122, 3/79 - No. 130, 5/80
7-Kirby-c; Powell-a 8 16 24 54 102 150
8-10 5 10 15 30 50 70
11-16,18-20 4 8 12 27 44 60
17-(68 pg. Giant) 6 12 18 41 76 110
21-50: 26-No Torres-a 3 6 9 20 31 42
51-59 3 6 9 16 23 30
60-(1/66)-Elvis Presley line drawn c/story 14 28 42 96 211 325
61-85 2 4 6 11 16 20
86-90,92-98,100-110 2 4 6 8 10 12
91-(5/71) Ditko-a (5 pgs.) 2 4 6 13 18 22
99-David Cassidy pin-up 2 4 6 10 14 18
111-113,115-130 1 3 4 6 8 10
114-Psychedelic cover 3 6 9 17 26 35

I, LUSIPHUR (Becomes Poison Elves, 1st series #8 on)
Mulehide Graphics: 1991 - No. 7, 1992 (B&W, magazine size)
1-Drew Hayes-c/a/scripts 5 10 15 30 50 70
2,4,5 3 6 9 14 20 25
3-Low print run 4 8 12 27 44 60
6,7 2 4 6 8 11 14
Poison Elves: Requiem For An Elf (Sirius Ent., 6/96, $14.95, trade paperback) -Reprints I, Lusiphur #1,2 as text, and 3-6 15.00

I'M A COP
Magazine Enterprises: 1954 - No. 3, 1954
1(A-1 #111)-Powell-c/a in all 15 30 45 88 137 185
2(A-1 #126), 3(A-1 #128) 10 20 30 56 76 95

IMAGE COMICS HARDCOVER
Image Comics: 2005 ($24.99, hardcover with dust jacket)
Vol. 1-New Spawn by McFarlane-s/a; Savage Dragon origin by Larsen; CyberForce by Silvestri; ShadowHawk by Valentino; intro by Marder; Image timeline 25.00

IMAGE COMICS SUMMER SPECIAL
Image Comics: July, 2004 (Free Comic Book Day giveaway)
1-New short stories of Spawn, Invincible, Savage Dragon and Witchblade 3.00

IMAGE FIRST

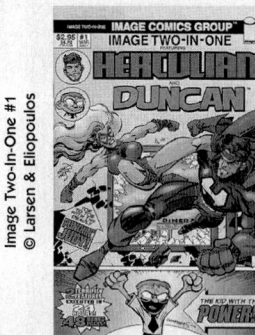

Image Two-In-One #1 © Larsen & Eliopoulos

Imaginary Fiends #1 © Seeley & Molnar

Impulse #9 © DC

GD 2.0 VG 4.0 FN 6.0 VF 8.0 VF/NM 9.0 NM- 9.2

Image Comics: 2005 ($6.99, TPB)

Vol. 1 (2005) r/Strange Girl #1, Sea of Red #1, The Walking Dead #1 and Girls #1 — 2 4 6 11 16 20

IMAGE GRAPHIC NOVEL
Image Int.: 1984 ($6.95)(Advertised as Pacific Comics Graphic Novel #1)

1-The Seven Samuroid; Brunner-c/a — 12.00

IMAGE HOLIDAY SPECIAL 2005
Image Comics: 2005 ($9.99, TPB)

nn-Holiday-themed short stories by various incl. Larsen, Kurtz, Kirkman, Valentino — 10.00

IMAGE INTRODUCES...
Image Comics: Oct, 2001 - June, 2002 ($2.95, anthology)

Believer #1-Schamberger-s/Thurman & Molder-a; Legend of Isis preview — 3.00
Cryptopia #1-Raab-s/Quinn-a — 3.00
Dog Soldiers #1-Hunter-s/Pachoumis-a — 3.00
Legend of Isis #1-Valdez-a — 3.00
Primate #1-Two covers; Beau Smith & Bernhardt-s/Byrd-a — 3.00

IMAGES OF A DISTANT SOIL
Image Comics: Feb, 1997 ($2.95, B&W, one-shot)

1-Sketches by various — 3.00

IMAGES OF SHADOWHAWK (Also see Shadowhawk)
Image Comics: Sept, 1993 - No. 3, 1994 ($1.95, limited series)

1-3: Keith Giffen-c/a; Trencher app. — 3.00

IMAGE 20 (FREE COMIC BOOK DAY 2012...)
Image Comics: May, 2012 (giveaway, one-shot)

nn-Previews of Revival, Guarding the Globe, It-Girl and the Atomics, Near Death — 3.00

IMAGE TWO-IN-ONE
Image Comics: Mar, 2001 ($2.95, 48 pgs., B&W, one-shot)

1-Two stories; 24 pages produced in 24 hrs. by Larsen and Eliopoulos — 4.00

IMAGE UNITED
Image Comics: No. 0, Mar, 2010; Nov, 2009 - No. 6 ($3.99, limited series)

0-(3/10, $2.99) Fortress and Savage Dragon app. — 3.00
1-3-($3.99) Image character crossover; Kirkman-s; art by Larsen, Liefeld, McFarlane, Portacio, Silvestri and Valentino; Spawn, Witchblade, Savage Dragon, Youngblood, Cyberforce and Shadowhawk app. Multiple covers on each — 4.00
1-Jim Lee variant-c — 8.00

IMAGE ZERO
Image Comics: 1993 (Received through mail w/coupons from Image books)

0-Savage Dragon, StormWatch, Shadowhawk, Strykeforce; 1st app. Troll; 1st app. McFarlane's Freak, Blotch, Sweat and Bludd — 5.00

IMAGINARIES, THE
Image Comics: Mar, 2005 - No. 4, June, 2005 ($2.95, limited series)

1-4-Mike S. Miller & Ben Avery-s; Miller & Titus-a — 3.00

IMAGINARY FIENDS
DC Comics (Vertigo): Jan, 2018 - Present ($3.99)

1-4-Tim Seeley-s/Stephen Molnar-a/Richard Pace-c — 4.00

IMAGINE AGENTS
BOOM! Studios: Oct, 2013 - No. 4, Jan, 2014 ($3.99, limited series)

1-4-Brian Joines-s/Bachan-a — 4.00

I'M DICKENS - HE'S FENSTER (TV)
Dell Publishing Co.: May-July, 1963 - No. 2, Aug-Oct, 1963 (Photo-c)

1 — 5 10 15 33 57 80
2 — 5 10 15 30 50 70

I MET A HANDSOME COWBOY
Dell Publishing Co.: No. 324, Mar, 1951

Four Color 324 — 7 14 21 49 92 135

IMMORTAL BROTHERS: THE TALE OF THE GREEN KNIGHT
Valiant Entertainment: Apr, 2017 ($4.99, one-shot)

1-Van Lente-s/Nord & Henry-a; Archer & Faith app.; bonus preview of Rapture — 5.00

IMMORTAL DOCTOR FATE, THE
DC Comics: Jan, 1985 - No. 3, Mar, 1985 ($1.25, limited series)

1-3: 1-Reprints; Simonson-c/a. 2-R/back-ups from Flash #306-313; Giffen-c/a(p) — 4.00

IMMORTAL IRON FIST, THE (Also see Iron Fist)
Marvel Comics: Jan, 2007 - No. 27, Aug, 2009 ($2.99/$3.99)

GD 2.0 VG 4.0 FN 6.0 VF 8.0 VF/NM 9.0 NM- 9.2

1-Brubaker & Fraction-s/Aja-c/a; origin retold; intro. Orson Randall — 1 3 4 6 8 10
1-Variant-c by Dell'Otto — 3 6 9 17 26 35
1-Director's Cut ($3.99) r/#1 and 8-page story from Civil War: Choosing Sides; script excerpt; character designs; sketch and inks art; cover variant and concepts — 4.00
2,3 — 1 2 3 5 6 8
4-13,15-26: 6,17-20-Flashback-a by Heath. 8-1st Immortal weapons. 21-Green-a — 3.00
14,27: 14-($3.99) Heroes For Hire app. 27-Last issue; 2 covers; Foreman & Lapham-a — 4.00
Annual 1 (11/07, $3.99) Brubaker & Fraction-s/Chaykin, Brereton & J. Djurdjevic-a — 4.00
... Orson Randall and the Death Queen of California (11/08, $3.99) art by Camuncoli — 4.00
... Orson Randall and the Green Mist of Death (4/08, $3.99) art by Heath and various — 4.00
...: The Origin of Danny Rand (2008, $3.99) r/Marvel Premiere #15-16 recolored — 4.00
... Vol. 1: The Last Iron Fist Story HC (2007, $19.99, dustjacket) r/#1-6, story from Civil War: Choosing Sides; sketch pages — 20.00
... Vol. 1: The Last Iron Fist Story SC (2007, $14.99) same content as HC — 15.00
... Vol. 2: The Seven Capital Cities HC (2008, $24.99, dustjacket) r/#8-14 & Annual #1 — 25.00

IMMORTALIS (See Mortigan Goth: Immortalis)

IMMORTAL II
Image Comics: Apr, 1997 - No. 5, Feb, 1998 ($2.50, B&W&Grey, limited series)

1-5: 1-B&W w/ color pull-out poster — 3.00

IMMORTAL WEAPONS (Also see Immortal Iron Fist)
Marvel Comics: Sept, 2009 - No. 5, Jan, 2010 ($3.99, limited series)

1-5: Back-up Iron Fist stories in all. 1-Origin of Fat Cobra. 2-Brereton-a — 4.00

IMPACT
E. C. Comics: Mar-Apr, 1955 - No. 5, Nov-Dec, 1955

1-Not code approved; classic Holocaust story — 23 46 69 184 292 400
1-Variant printed by Charlton. Title logo is white instead of yellow and print quality is inferior. Distributed to newsstands before being destroyed & reprinted (scarce) — 30 60 90 240 383 525
2 — 13 26 39 104 170 235
3-5: 4-Crandall-a — 11 22 33 88 144 200

NOTE: ***Crandall*** *a-1-4.* ***Davis*** *a-2-4; c-1-5.* ***Evans*** *a-1, 4, 5.* ***Ingels*** *a-in all.* ***Kamen*** *a-3.* ***Krigstein*** *a-1, 5.* ***Orlando*** *a-2, 5.*

IMPACT
Gemstone Publishing: Apr, 1999 - No. 5, Aug, 1999 ($2.50)

1-5-Reprints E.C. series — 4.00

IMPACT CHRISTMAS SPECIAL
DC Comics (Impact Comics): 1991 ($2.50, 68 pgs.)

1-Gift of the Magi by Infantino/Rogers; The Black Hood, The Fly, The Jaguar, & The Shield stories — 4.00

IMPERIAL
Image Comics: Aug, 2014 - No. 4, Nov, 2014 ($2.99, limited series)

1-4-Seagle-s/Dos Santos-a — 3.00

IMPERIAL GUARD
Marvel Comics: Jan, 1997 - No. 3, Mar, 1997 ($1.95, limited series)

1-3: Augustyn-s in all; 1-Wraparound-c — 3.00

IMPERIUM
Valiant Entertainment: Mar, 2015 - No. 16, May, 2016 ($3.99)

1-16: 1-4-Dysart-s/Braithwaite-a. 5-8-Eaton-a. 9-12-The Vine Imperative; Cafu-a — 4.00

IMPOSSIBLE MAN SUMMER VACATION SPECTACULAR, THE
Marvel Comics: Aug, 1990; No. 2, Sept, 1991 ($2.00, 68 pgs.) (See Fantastic Four#11)

1-Spider Man, Quasar, Dr. Strange, She-Hulk, Punisher & Dr. Doom stories; Barry Crain, Guice-a; Art Adams-c(i) — 4.00
2-Ka Zar & Thor app.; Cable Wolverine-c app. — 4.00

IMPULSE (See Flash #92, 2nd Series for 1st app.) (Also see Young Justice)
DC Comics: Apr, 1995 - No. 89, Oct, 2002 ($1.50/$1.75/$1.95/$2.25/$2.50)

1-Mark Waid scripts & Humberto Ramos-c/a(p) begin; brief retelling of origin — 6.00
2-12: 9-XS from Legion (Impulse's cousin) comes to the 20th Century, returns to the 30th Century in #12. 10-Dead Heat Pt. 3 (cont'd in Flash #110). 11-Dead Heat Pt. 4 (cont'd in Flash #111); Johnny Quick dies. — 4.00
13-25: 14-Trickster app. 17-Zatanna-c/app. 21-Legion-c/app. 22-Jesse Quick-c/app. 24-Origin; Flash app. 25-Last Ramos-a. — 3.00
26-55: 26-Rousseau-a begins. 28-1st new Arrowette (see World's Finest #113). 30-Genesis x-over. 47-Superman-c/app. 50-Batman & Joker-c/app. Van Sciver-a begins — 3.00
56-62: 56-Young Justice app. — 3.00
63-89: 63-Begin $2.50-c. 66-JLA,JSA-c/app. 68,69-Adam Strange, GL app. 77-Our Worlds at War x-over; Young Justice-c/app. 85-World Without Young Justice x-over pt. 2. — 3.00
#1,000,000 (11/98) John Fox app. — 3.00

Incognito #1 © Brubaker & Phillips

Incredible Hercules #113 © MAR

Incredible Hulk #141 © MAR

GD VG FN VF VF/NM NM-
2.0 4.0 6.0 8.0 9.0 9.2

Annual 1 (1996, $2.95)-Legends of the Dead Earth; Parobeck-a 4.00
Annual 2 (1997, $3.95)-Pulp Heroes stories; Orbik painted-c 4.00
.../Atom Double-Shot 1(2/98, $1.95) Jurgens-s/Mhan-a 3.00
...: Bart Saves the Universe (4/99, $5.95) JSA app. 6.00
...Plus (9/97, $2.95) w/Gross Out (Scare Tactics)-c/app. 4.00
...Reckless Youth (1997, $14.95, TPB) r/Flash #92-94, Impulse #1-6 15.00

INCAL, THE
Marvel Comics (Epic): Nov, 1988 - No. 3, Jan, 1989 ($10.95/$12.95, mature)
1-3: Moebius-c/a in all; sexual content 16.00

INCOGNEGRO
DC Comics (Vertigo): 2008 ($19.99, B&W, hardcover graphic novel with dustjacket)
HC-Mat Johnson-s/Warren Pleece-a 20.00

INCOGNEGRO: RENAISSANCE
Dark Horse Comics (Berger Books): Feb, 2018 - No. 5 ($3.99, B&W, limited series)
1,2-Mat Johnson-s/Warren Pleece-a 20.00

INCOGNITO
Marvel Comics (Icon): Dec, 2008 - No. 6, Aug, 2009 ($3.50/$3.99, limited series)
1-5-Brubaker-s/Phillips-a/c; pulp noir-style 3.50
6-($3.99) Bonus history of the Zeppelin pulps 4.00
...: Bad Influences (10/10 - No. 5, 4/11, $3.50) 1-5 Brubaker-s/Phillips-a/c 3.50

INCOMPLETE DEATH'S HEAD (Also see Death's Head)
Marvel Comics UK: Jan, 1993 - No. 12, Dec, 1993 ($1.75, limited series)
1-($2.95, 56 pgs.)-Die-cut cover 4.00
2-11: 2-Re-intro original Death's Head. 3-Original Death's Head vs. Dragon's Claws 3.00
12-($2.50, 52 pgs.)-She Hulk app. 4.00

INCORRUPTIBLE (Also see Irredeemable)
BOOM! Studios: Dec, 2000 - No. 30, May, 2012 ($3.99)
1-30: 1-Waid-s/Diaz-a; 3 covers 4.00
1-Artist Edition (12/11, $3.99) r/#1 in B&W with bonus sketch and design art 4.00

INCREDIBLE HERCULES (Continued from Incredible Hulk #112, Jan, 2008)
Marvel Comics: No. 113, Feb, 2008 - No. 141, Apr, 2010 ($2.99/$3.99)
113-125: 113-Ares and Wonder Man app.; Art Adams-c. 116-Romita Jr-c; Eternals app. 3.00
113-Variant-c by Pham 5.00
126-($3.99) Hercules origin retold; back-up story w/Miyazawa-a 4.00
127-137: 128-Dark Avengers app. 132-Replacement Thor. 136-Thor app. 3.00
138-141-($3.99) Assault on New Olympus; Avengers app. 4.00

INCREDIBLE HULK, THE (See Aurora, The Avengers #1, The Defenders #1, Giant-Size..., Hulk, Marvel Collectors Item Classics, Marvel Comics Presents #26, Marvel Fanfare, Marvel Treasury Edition, Power Record Comics, Rampaging Hulk, She-Hulk, 2099 Unlimited & World War Hulk)

INCREDIBLE HULK, THE
Marvel Comics: May, 1962 - No. 6, Mar, 1963; No. 102, Apr, 1968 - No. 474, Mar, 1999
1-Origin & 1st app. (skin is grey colored); Kirby pencils begin, end #5
4700 9400 16,700 49,800 157,400 265,000
2-1st green skinned Hulk; Kirby/Ditko-a 417 834 1251 3545 8023 12,500
3-Origin retold; 1st app. Ringmaster (9/62) 248 496 744 2046 4623 7200
4,5: 4-Brief origin retold 190 380 570 1568 3534 5500
6-(3/63) Intro. Teen Brigade; all Ditko-a 181 362 543 1493 3372 5250
102-(4/68) (Continued from Tales to Astonish #101)-Origin retold; Hulk in Asgard; Enchantress & Executioner app; Gary Friedrich-s begin 24 48 72 168 372 575
103-1st Space Parasite 10 20 30 64 132 200
104-Hulk vs. the Rhino 10 20 30 64 132 200
105-110: 105-1st Missing Link. 106-vs. Missing Link; Nick Fury & SHIELD app; Trimpe pencils begin (continues through issue #193). 107,108-vs. the Mandarin. 108-Nick Fury & SHIELD app.; Stan Lee-s (continues through issue #120). 109,110-Ka-Zar app.
7 14 21 46 86 125
111-117: 111-Ka-Zar app.; 1st Galaxy Master. 112-Origin of the Galaxy Master. 113-vs. Sandman. 114-Sandman & Mandarin vs. the Hulk. 115-117-vs. the Leader
5 10 15 33 57 80
118-Hulk vs. Sub-Mariner 6 12 18 42 79 115
119,120,123-125: 119-Maximus (of the Inhumans) app. 120-Last Stan Lee plot, Roy Thomas script; Maximus app. 123,124-vs. The Leader. 124-1st Sal Buscema-p (as a fill-in). 125-vs. the Absorbing Man 4 8 12 27 44 60
121-Roy Thomas-s begin; 1st app. and origin of the Glob
5 10 15 33 57 80
122-Hulk battles Thing (12/69); Fantastic Four app. 8 16 24 54 102 150
126-1st Barbara Norriss (becomes Valkyrie in Defenders #4); story continued from Sub-Mariner #22 (see Dr. Strange #183 for pt.1); Dr. Strange gives up being Sorcerer Supreme 5 10 15 35 63 90
127,129,130,132-139: 127-Tyrannus & the Mole Man app; 1st app. Mogol. 129-Leader revives the Glob. 130-(story continues from Captain Marvel #21); 132-HYDRA app. 134-1st Golem. 135-Kang & Phantom Eagle app. 136-1st Xeron the Starslayer; Abomination cameo. 137-Xeron app. Hulk vs. Abomination. 138-Sandman app. 139-Leader app; Hulk story continues in Avengers #88 3 6 9 21 33 45
128-Avengers app. 4 8 12 28 47 65
131-1st Jim Wilson; Iron Man app. 5 10 15 31 53 75
140-Writtem by Harlan Ellison; 1st Jarella (Hulk's love); story continues from Avengers #88; battles Psyklop 4 8 12 25 40 55
140-2nd printing 2 4 6 8 10 12
141-1st app. Doc Samson (7/71) 10 20 30 67 141 215
142-2nd Valkyrie app. (Samantha Parrington) (see Avengers #82 for 1st Marvel Valkyrie); Enchantress app. 5 10 15 30 50 70
143,144-Doctor Doom app. 3 6 9 19 30 40
145-(52-pgs)-Origin retold 4 8 12 28 47 65
146-151: 146,147-Richard Nixon & Yhe Leader app. 148-Jarella app. 149-1st app. The Inheritor. 150-Havok app. 151-Has minor Ant-Man app.
3 6 9 17 26 35
152,153: Hulk on trial; Daredevil, Fantastic Four, Avengers app.
3 6 9 19 30 40
154-Ant-Man app; story coincides with Ant-Man's re-intro in Marvel Feature #4; Hydra & the Chameleon app. 3 6 9 19 30 40
155-160: 155-1st Shaper of Worlds. 156-Jarella app. 157,158-the Leader & Rhino app. 158-Counter-Earth & the High Evolutionary app. 159-Steve Englehart-s begin; Hulk vs. Abomination. 160-vs. Tiger Shark app. 3 6 9 17 26 35
161-The Mimic dies; Beast app. 5 10 15 31 53 75
162-1st app. The Wendigo (4/73) Beast app. 8 16 24 54 102 150
163-165,170,173,174,179: 163-1st app. The Gremlin. 164-1st Capt. Omen & Colonel John D. Armbuster. 165-Capt. Omen app; 1st Aquon. 173,174-vs the Cobalt Man. 179-Return of the Missing Link; 1st Len Wein-s 3 6 9 15 22 28
166-169,171: 166-1st Zzzax; Hawkeye app.; story continues into Defenders #7. 167-Hulk vs. MODOK. 168-1st Harpy (transformed Betty Ross; also seen briefly in nudity panels) 169-1st Bi-Beast; MODOK and A.I.M app; Harpy transformed back into Betty. 171-vs. Abomination; last Englehart-s 3 6 9 16 24 32
172-X-Men cameo; origin Juggernaut retold 4 8 12 27 44 60
175-Black Bolt/Inhumans c/story 3 6 9 17 26 35
176-Hulk on Counter-Earth; Man-Beast app; Warlock cameo (2 panels only)
3 6 9 15 22 28
177-1st actual death of Warlock (last panel only); Man-Beast app.
4 8 12 27 44 60
178-Rebirth of Warlock (story continues in Strange Tales #178)
4 8 12 27 44 60
180-(10/74)-1st brief app. Wolverine (last pg.) 29 58 87 209 467 725
181-(11/74)-1st full Wolverine story; Trimpe-a 420 840 1260 2100 3150 4200
182-Wolverine cameo; see Giant-Size X-Men #1 for next app.; 1st Crackajack Jackson
12 24 36 80 173 265
183-192,194-196,199: 183-Zzzax app. 184-vs. Warlord Kraa. 185-Death of Col. Armbuster. 186-1st Devastator. 187-188-vs. the Gremlin, Nick Fury app. 189-Mole Man app. 190-1st Glorian; Shaper of Worlds app. 191-vs. the Toad Men; Glorian & Shaper of Worlds app. 194-vs. the Locust; 1st Sal Buscema-p (through #309). 195-Abomination & Hulk team-up. 196-Hulk vs. Abomination. 199-Hulk vs. SHIELD & Doc Samson; Nick Fury app.
2 4 6 10 14 20
193-vs. Doc Samson c/story; last regular Trimpe-p 2 4 6 10 18 25
197-Collector, Man-Thing & Glob app; Wrightson-c 3 6 9 19 30 40
198-Collector, Man-Thing & Glob app. 3 6 9 16 23 30
198,199, 201,202-(30¢-c variants, lim. distribution) 5 10 15 35 63 90
200-(25¢-c) Silver Surfer app. (illusion only); anniversary issue
3 6 9 21 33 40
200-(30¢-c variant, limited distribution)(6/76) 6 12 18 38 69 100
201-205,208-211,213,215-220: 201-Conan swipe-c/sty (vs. Bronak the Barbarian). 202-Jarella app.; Psyklop cameo. 203-Jarella app.; death of Psyklop. 204-Trimpe-p; alternate Hulk origin. 205-Death of Jarella; vs. the Crypto Man. 208-Absorbing Man app. 209-Hulk vs. Absorbing Man. 210,211-Hulk team-up with Dr. Druid vs. the Maha Yogi. 213-1st Quintronic Man. 215,216-vs. the second Bi-Beast. 218-Doc Samson vs. the Rhino (no Hulk in story). 219-220-vs. Captain Barracuda 2 4 6 8 10 12
206,207-Defenders app. 2 4 6 9 12 15
212,214: 212-1st app. The Constrictor. 214-Hulk vs. Jack of Hearts (1st app. outside of B&W magazines) 2 4 6 9 12 15
212-216-(35¢-c variant, limited distribution) 10 20 30 67 141 215
221-227,230-231: 221-Stingray app. 222-Last Wein-s; Jim Starlin co-plot and (p). 223-The Leader returns; Roger Stern-s begin. 224-225-vs. The Leader. 227-Original Avengers app. (in dream sequence) 1 2 3 5 7 9
228-1st female Moonstone (Karla Sofen) (10/78) 3 6 9 16 23 30
229-2nd app. new Moonstone 2 4 6 8 10 12
232,233: 232-Captain America x-over from Captain America #230; vs. Moonstone, Vamp and

Incredible Hulk #261 © MAR

Incredible Hulk #421 © MAR

Incredible Hulk #461 © MAR

'the Corporation'; Marvel Man (Quasar) app. 233-Marvel Man app. (Quasar)
1 3 4 6 8 10

234-(4/79)-Marvel Man formally changes his name to Quasar
3 6 9 16 23 30

235-249: 235-237-Machine Man app. 238-President Jimmy Carter app. 241-243-vs. Tyrannus. 243-Last Stern-s. 244-vs. It the Living Colossus. 245-1st Mantlo-s (through #313); 1st app. The Super-Mandroid (Col. Talbot); Captain Mar-Vell cameo. 246-Captain Mar-Vell app.; Hulk vs. Super-Mandroid. 247-Minor Captain Mar-Vell app. 248-vs. the Gardener. 249-Steve Ditko-p 1 2 3 5 6 8

250-Giant-Size (square-bound, 48-pgs)-Silver Surfer app.
3 6 9 14 19 24

251-254,256-270: 251-3-D Man app. 252,253-Woodgod app. 254-1st app. the U-Foes (evil versions of the Fantastic Four)256-1st Sabra (Israeli super-hero). 257-1st Arabian Knight. 258,259-Soviet Super-Soldiers, Red Guardian & the Presence app. 260-Death of Col. Talbot. 261-Absorbing Man app. 263-Landslide & Avalanche app. 264-Death of the Night Flyer; Corruptor app. 265-1st app. The Rangers (Firebird, Shooting Star, Night Rider, Red Wolf & Lobo, Texas Tornado); Corruptor app. 266-High Evolutionary app. 267-Glorian & the Shaper of Worlds app. 269-1st Marvel Universe app. of Bereet; 1st Hulk-Hunters (Amphibion, Torgo, Dark Crawler). 270-Hulk Hunters, Bereet & Galaxy Master app.
1 2 3 4 5 7

255-Hulk vs. Thor 1 3 4 6 8 10

271-(5/82)-2nd app. & 1st full app. Rocket Raccoon (see Marvel Preview #7 for debut)
10 20 30 64 132 200

272-3rd app Rocket Raccoon; Sasquatch & Wendigo app; Wolverine & Alpha Flight cameo in flashback; Bruce Banner's mind takes control of the Hulk
2 4 6 11 16 20

273-277,280-299: 273-Sasquatch app. 275-vs. Megalith; U-Foes app. 276,277-U-foes app. 280,281-The Leader returns. 282-She-Hulk app. 283,284-Avengers app; vs. the Leader. 285-Zzzax app. 287-290-MODOK & Abomination app. 292-Circus of Crime & Dragon Man app. 293-Fantastic Four app. (in a dream). 294,295-Boomerang app. 296-Rom app. 297-299-Dr. Strange & Nightmare app. 6.00

278,279-Most Marvel characters app. (Wolverine in both). 279-X-Men & Alpha Flight cameos 6.00

300-(11/84, 52 pgs)-Spider-Man app. in new black costume on-c & 2 pg. cameo; Hulk reverts to savagery; Thor, Daredevil, Power Man & Iron Fist, Human Torch app; Dr. Strange banishes the Hulk from Earth 2 4 6 8 10 12

301-313: 301-Hulk banished to the 'Crossroads' (through #313); Dr. Strange app. 302-Mignola-c. 304-U-Foes cameo; Mignola-c (through issue #309). 305-vs the U-Foes. 306-Return of Xeron the Starslayer. 307-Death of Xeron. 308-vs N'Garia demons. 309-Last Sal Buscema-a. 310-Blevins-a. 311-Mignola-c/a. 312-Secret Wars II x-over; Mignola-c/a; origin retold w/further details regarding physical abuse at the hands of his father. 313-Crossover w/Alpha Flight #29; Mignola-c/a 5.00

314-Byrne-c/a begins; ends #319; Hulk returns to Earth; vs. Doc Samson 6.00

315-319: 315-Hulk & Banner separated. 316-vs Hercules, Sub-Mariner, Wonder Man & Iron Man of the Avengers. 317-1st app. the new Hulkbusters; Hulk vs. Doc Samson. 318-Doc Samson vs. Hulkbusters. 319-Banner and Betty Ross wed 5.00

320,325,327-329: 320-Al Milgrom story & art begin. 325-vs. Zzzax. 327-Zzzax app. 328-1st Peter David-s. 329-1st app. The Outcasts 4.00

321-323: 321-Avengers vs. Hulk. 322-Avengers & West Coast Avengers app. 323-East & West Coast Avengers app. 6.00

324-Return of the Grey Hulk (Banner & Hulk rejoined) first since #1 (c-swipe of #1)
2 4 6 10 18 25

326-Grey vs. Green (Rick Jones) Hulk 1 3 4 6 8 10

330-1st McFarlane-c/p; last Milgrom-s; Thunderbolt Ross 'dies'
3 6 9 17 26 35

331-Peter David begins as regular plotter; McFarlane-p
3 6 9 16 23 30

332-Grey Hulk & Leader vs. Green Hulk (Rick Jones) 2 4 6 8 10 12

333-334,338-339: 338-1st app. Mercy. 339-The Leader app.
1 2 3 4 8 10

335-No McFarlane-a 6.00

336,337-X-Factor app. 1 3 4 6 8 10

340-Classic Hulk vs. Wolverine-c by McFarlane 5 10 15 31 53 75

341-344,346: 341-vs. The Man-Bull; McFarlane begins pencils and inks. 342-The Leader app. 343-1st app. Rock & Redeemer. 344-McFarlane (p) only; vs. The Leader, Rock & Redeemer; Betty revealed to be pregnant. 346-The Leader app. Last McFarlane-p (co-penciled with Erik Larsen) 1 2 3 4 8 12

345-($1.50, 52 pgs) vs. The Leader; Gamma-Bomb explosion; World thinks the Hulk is dead; McFarlane (p) only 3 6 9 14 20 25

347-349,351-366: 347-1st app. The Hulk as 'Mr. Fixit'; relocated to Las Vegas; 1st app. Marlo; Absorbing Man app. 348-vs. Absorbing Man. 349-Spider-Man app; Dr. Doom cameo. 351-How the Hulk survived the Gamma-Bomb is revealed. 355-Glorian app. 356-Glorian & Shaper of Worlds app. 359-Wolverine-c (illusion) by John Byrne. 360-Nightmare & D'spayre app; Betty loses her baby. 361-Iron Man app. 362-Werewolf by Night app. 363-Acts of Vengeance tie-in; Dr. Doom & Grey Gargoyle app. 364-vs Abomination; 1st app. Madman. 365-Fantastic Four app. 366-Leader & Madman app. 4.00

350-Hulk/Thing battle 1 2 3 5 6 8

367-1st Dale Keown-a on Hulk (3/90) Leader & Madman app.
1 2 3 5 6 8

368-371,373-375: 368-Sam Kieth-c/a; 1st app. Pantheon. 369-Keown-a (becomes regular artist through #398); vs. the Freedom Force. 370,371-Dr. Strange & Namor app. (Defenders reunion). 374,375-vs. the Super-Skrull. 5.00

372-Green Hulk returns 1 2 3 5 6 8

376-Green vs. Grey Hulk; 1st app. Agamemnon of the Pantheon
1 3 4 6 8 10

377-1st all new Hulk; fluorescent green background-c 1 2 3 6 8 10

377-2nd printing 2 4 6 8 10 12

377-3rd printing 8 16 24 54 102 150

378-392,394-399: 378,380,389-No Keown-a. 379-Contined from issue #377; new direction for the Hulk; 1st app. of Delphi, Ajax, Achilles, Paris & Hector of the Pantheon. 380-Doc Samson app. 381,382-Pantheon app. 383-Infinity Gauntlet x-over; Abomination app. 384-Infinity Gauntlet tie-in; Abomination app. 385-Infinity Gauntlet tie-in. 386,387-Sabra app. 388-1st app. Speedfreak. 390-X-Factor cameo. 391,392-X-Factor app.394-1st app. Trauma; no Keown-a. 395,396-Punisher app. 397-399; Leader & U-Foes app. 398-Last Keown-a. 3.00

393-($2.50, 72 pgs) 5.00

393-2nd print; silver-ink background 4.00

400-($2.50, 68-pgs)-Holo-grafx foil-c & r/TTA #63 4.00

400-2nd print; yellow logo 4.00

401-403,405-416: 401-U-Foes app. 402-Return of Doc Samson; Juggernaut & Red Skull app. 403-Gary Frank-a begins; Juggernaut & Red Skull app. 405-1st app. Piecemeal. 406-Captain America app. 407-vs. Piecemeal & Madman. 408-vs. Piecemeal & Madman; Motormouth & Killpower (Marvel UK characters) app. 409-vs. Madman; Motormouth & Killpower app. 410-Nick Fury & SHIELD app. 411-Pantheon vs. SHIELD; Nick Fury app. 412-Hulk & She-Hulk vs. Bi-Beast. 413-Trauma app; Pt. 1 (of 4) of the Troyjan War. 414-vs. Trauma; Silver Surfer app. 415-Silver Surfer & Starjammers app. 416-Final of the Troyjan War; death of Trauma. 3.00

404-Avengers vs. Juggernaut & the Hulk; Red Skull app. 4.00

417,419-424: 417-Begins $1.50-c; Rick Jones Bachelor party; many heroes from Avengers & Fantastic Four app; Hulk returns from "Future Imperfect". 419-No Frank-a. 420-Special AIDS awareness issue; death of Jim Wilson. 421-Hulk & the Pantheon in Asgard. 423-Hela app. 3.00

418-($2.50)-Collectors Edition w/Gatefold die-cut-c; the wedding of Rick Jones & Marlo; includes cameo apps. of various Marvel characters as well as DC"s Death & Peter David 4.00

418-($1.50, Regular Edition) 4.00

425-($2.25, 52 pgs); Last Frank-a; Liam Sharp-a begins; death of Achilles 4.00

425-($3.50, 52 pgs)-Holographic-c 5.00

426-433,441,442: 426-Nick Fury app. 427,428-Man-Thing app. 430-Speedfreak app. 431,432-Abomination app. 432-Last Sharp-a. 433-Punisher app; title becomes part of the 'Marvel Edge' titles (through #439) 441-She-Hulk-c/s; "Pulp Fiction" parody-c. 442-She-Hulk & Doc Samson team-up; no Hulk app. 3.00

434-Funeral for Nick Fury; Wolverine, Dr. Strange, Avengers app; Marvel Overpower card insert (harder to find above 9.2 due to card indentations) 4.00

435-($2.50)-Rhino app; excerpt from "What Savage Beast" 4.00

436-439: 436-"Ghosts of the Future" Pt.1 (of 5); Leader app. 439-Maestro app. 4.00

440-"Ghosts of the Future" Pt. 5; Hulk vs. Thor 5.00

443,446-448: 443-Begin $1.50-c; re-app. of Hulk. 446-w/card insert. 447-Begin Deodato-c/a 4.00

444,445: 444-Cable-c/app; Onslaught x-over. 445-Onslaught x-over; Avengers app. 5.00

447-Variant-c 4.00

449-1st app. Thunderbolts (1/97); Citizen V, Songbird, Mach-1, Techno, Atlas & Meteorite
3 6 9 16 24 32

450-($2.95)-Thunderbolts app. 2 stories; Heroes Reborn versions of Hulk, Dr. Strange, Mr. Fantastic & Iron Man app. 5.00

451-453, 458-470: 452-Heroes Reborn Hulk app. 453-Hulk vs. Heroes Reborn Hulk. 458-Mr. Hyde app. 459-Abomination app. 461-Maestro app. 463-Silver Surfer cameo. 464-Silver Surfer app. 465-Mr. Fantastic & Tony Stark app. 466-'Death' of Betty Banner. 467-Last Peter David issue. 468-Casey-s/Puilido-a begin. 469-Super-Adaptoid & Ringmaster app. 470-Ringmaster & the Circus of Crime app. 4.00

454-Wolverine & Ka-Zar app; Adam Kubert-a 5.00

455-Wolverine, Storm, Cannonball & Cyclops of the X-Men app.; Adam Kubert-a 5.00

456-Apocalypse enlists the Hulk as 'War'; Juggernaut app. 6.00

457-Hulk (as Horseman of the Apocalypse 'War' vs. Juggernaut. Apocalypse app.
1 2 3 4 6 8

471-473: 471-Circus of Crime app. 473-Watcher app; Abomination revealed as Betty's killer. 5.00

474-($2.99) Last issue; Abomination app; c-homage to issue #1

Incredible Hulk V2 #49 © MAR

Incredible Hulk (2011 series) #1 © MAR

Incredible Hulk #709 © MAR

GD 2.0 | VG 4.0 | FN 6.0 | VF 8.0 | VF/NM 9.0 | NM- 9.2

1 3 4 6 8 10
#(-1) Flashback (7/97) Kubert-a 3.00
Special 1 (10/68, 25¢, 68 pg.)-New 51 pg. story; Hulk battles the Inhumans (early app) 16 32 48 110 243 375
Special 2 (10/69, 25¢, 68 pg.)-Origin retold (from issue #3) r-TTA #62-66 6 12 18 38 69 100
Special 3,4: 3-(1/71, 25¢, 68 pg.)-r/TTA #70-74. 4-(1/72, 52 pg.)-r/TTA 75-77 & Not Brand Echh #5 4 8 12 23 37 50
Annual 5 (1976) 2nd app. Groot 5 10 15 34 60 85
Annual 6 (1977)-1st app. Paragon (later becomes Her, then later Ayesha); Dr. Strange app. 3 6 9 14 20 25
Annual 7 ('78)-Byrne/Layton-c/a; Iceman & Angel app; vs. the Mastermold 3 6 9 14 20 25
Annual 8 ('79)-Byrne/Stern-s; Hulk vs. Sasquatch 2 4 6 8 10 12
Annual 9,10: 9-('80)-Ditko-p. 10-('81)-Captain Universe app. 6.00
Annual 11 ('82)-Doc Samson back-up by Miller-(p)(5 pg); Spider-Man & Avengers app. 1 2 3 5 6 8
Annual 12-14: 12-('83)-Trimpe-a. 13-('84)-Story takes place at the 'Crossroads' (after Hulk was banished from Earth); takes place between Incredible Hulk #301-302. 14-Byrne-s; takes place between pages of Incredible Hulk #314 5.00
Annual 15-('86)-Zeck-c; Abomination & Tryannus app. 5.00
Annual 16-20: 16-('90, $2.00, 68 pgs. "Lifeform" Pt. 3; continued from Daredevil Annual #6, continued in Silver Surfer Annual #3; She-Hulk app. in back-up story. 17-('91, $2.00)-"Subterranean Wars" Pt. 2; continued from Avengers Annual #20; continued in Namor the Sub-Mariner Annual #1. 18-('92)-"Return of the Defenders" Pt.1; continued in Namor the Sub-Mariner Annual #1. 19-('93)-Bagged w/card; 1st app. Lazarus 4.00
...'97 ($2.99) Pollina-c 4.00
...And Wolverine 1 (10/86, $2.50)-r/1st app. (#180-181) 2 4 6 13 18 22
...: Beauty and the Behemoth ('98, $19.95, TPB) r/Bruce & Betty stories 20.00
...Ground Zero ('95, $12.95) r/#340-346 13.00
...Hercules Unleashed (10/96, $2.50) David-s/Deodato-c/a 4.00
... Omnibus Vol. 1 HC (2008, $99.99, dustjacket) r/#1-6 & 102, Tales To Astonish #59-101 bonus art, cover reprints; afterword by Peter David; Kirby cover from #1 140.00
... Omnibus Vol. 1 HC (2008, $99.99, dustjacket) Variant-c swipe of #1 by Alex Ross 110.00
.../Sub-Mariner '98 Annual ($2.99) 4.00
...Versus Quasimodo 1 (3/83, one-shot)-Based on Saturday morning cartoon 4.00
...Vs. Superman 1 (7/99, $5.95, one-shot)-painted-c by Rude 6.00
...Versus Venom 1 (4/94, $2.50, one-shot)-Embossed-c; red foil logo 4.00
... Visionaries: Peter David Vol. 1 (2005, $19.99) r/#331-339 written by Peter David 20.00
... Visionaries: Peter David Vol. 2 (2005, $19.99) r/#340-348 20.00
... Visionaries: Peter David Vol. 3 (2006, $19.99) r/#349-354, Web of Spider-Man #44, and Fantastic Four #320 20.00
... Visionaries: Peter David Vol. 4 (2007, $19.99) r/#355-363 and Marvel Comics Presents #26,45 20.00
... Visionaries: Peter David Vol. 5 (2008, $19.99) r/#364-372 and Annual #16 20.00
Wizard #1 Ace Edition - Reprints #1 with new Andy Kubert-c 14.00
Wizard #181 Ace Edition - Reprints #181 with new Chen-c 14.00
(Also see titles listed under **Hulk**)

NOTE: ***Adkins*** *a-111-116i.* ***Austin*** *a(i)-350, 351, 353, 354; c-302i, 350i.* ***Ayers*** *a-3-5i.* ***Buckler*** *a-Annual 5; c-252.* ***John Buscema*** *c-202p.* ***Byrne*** *a-314-319p; c-314-316, 318, 319, 359, Annual 14i.* ***Colan*** *c-363.* ***Ditko*** *a-2i, 6, 249, Annual 2r(5), 3r, 9p; c-2i, 6, 235, 249.* ***Everett*** *c-133i.* ***Golden*** *c-248, 251.* ***Kane*** *c(p)-193, 194, 196, 198.* ***Dale Keown*** *a(p)-367, 369-377, 379, 381-388, 390-393, 395-398; c-369-377p, 381, 382p, 384, 385, 386, 387p, 388, 390p, 391-393, 395p, 396, 397p, 398.* ***Kirby*** *a-1-5p, Special 2, 3p, Annual 5p; c-1-5, Annual 5.* ***McFarlane*** *a-330-334p, 336-339p, 340-343, 344-346p; c-330p, 340p, 341-343, 344p, 345, 346p.* ***Mignola*** *c-302, 305, 313.* ***Miller*** *c-258p, 261, 264, 268.* ***Mooney*** *a-230p, 287i, 288i.* ***Powell*** *a-Special 3r(2).* ***Romita*** *a-Annual 17p.* ***Severin*** *a(i)-108-110, 131-133, 141-151, 153-155; c(i)-109, 110, 132, 142, 144-155.* ***Simonson*** *c-283, 364-367.* ***Starlin*** *a-222p; c-217.* ***Staton*** *a(i)-187-189, 191-209.* ***Tuska*** *a-102i, 105i, 106i, 218p.* ***Williamson*** *a-310i; c-310i, 311i.* ***Wrightson*** *c-197.*

INCREDIBLE HULK (Vol. 2) (Formerly Hulk #1-11; becomes Incredible Hercules with #113) (Re-titled Incredible Hulks #612-on)(Also see World War Hulk)
Marvel Comics: No. 12, Mar, 2000 - No. 112, Jan, 2008 ($1.99-$3.50)
No. 600, Sept, 2009 - No. 625, Oct, 2011 ($3.99/$4.99)

12-Jenkins-s/Garney & McKone-a 4.00
13,14-($1.99) Garney & Buscema-a 3.00
15-24,26-32: 15-Begin $2.25-c. 21-Maximum Security x-over. 24-($1.99-c) 3.00
25-($2.99) Hulk vs. The Abomination; Romita Jr.-a 4.00
33-($3.50, 100 pgs.) new Bogdanove-a/Priest-s; reprints 4.00
34-Bruce Jones-s begin; Romita Jr.-a 5.00
35-49,51-54: 35-39-Jones-s/Romita Jr.-a. 40-43-Weeks-a. 44-49-Immonen-a 3.00
50-($3.50) Deodato-a begins; Abomination app. thru #54 4.00
55-74,77-91: 55(25¢-c) Absorbing Man returns; Fernandez-a. 60-65,70-72-Deodato-a. 66-69-Braithwaite-a. 71-74-Iron Man app. 77-($2.99-c) Peter David-s begin/Weeks-a. 80-Wolverine-c. 82-Jae Lee-c/a. 83-86-House of M x-over. 87-Scorpion app. 3.00
75,76-($3.50) The Leader app. 75-Robertson-a/Frank-c. 76-Braithwaite-a 4.00
92-Planet Hulk begins; Ladronn-c 5.00

GD 2.0 | VG 4.0 | FN 6.0 | VF 8.0 | VF/NM 9.0 | NM- 9.2

92-2nd printing with variant-c by Bryan Hitch 4.00
93-99,101-105 Planet Hulk; Ladronn-c 3.00
100-($3.99) Planet Hulk continues; back-up w/Frank-a; r/#152,153; Ladronn-c 5.00
100-($3.99) Green Hulk variant-c by Michael Turner 10.00
100-($3.99) Gray Hulk variant-c by Michael Turner 30.00
106-World War Hulk begins; Gary Frank-a/c 6.00
106-2nd printing with new cover of Hercules and Angel 3.00
107-112: 107-Hercules vs. Hulk. 108-Rick Jones app. 112-Art Adams-c 3.00
600-(9/09, $4.99) Covers by Ross, Sale and wraparound-c by McGuinness; back-up with Stan Lee-s; r/Hulk: Gray #1; cover gallery 5.00
601-611-($3.99): 601-605-Olivetti-a. 603-Wolverine app. 606-608-Fall of the Hulks 4.00
(Title becomes Incredible Hulks with #612, Nov, 2010)
612-621: 612-617-Dark Son. 618-620-Chaos War. 621-Hercules app. 4.00
622-634-($2.99) 623-625-Ka-Zar app.; Eaglesham-a. 626-629-Grummett-a 3.00
635-($3.99) Fin Fang Foom & Dr. Strange app.; Greg Pak interview 4.00
Annual 2000 ($3.50) Texeira-a/Jenkins-s; Avengers app. 4.00
Annual 2001 ($2.99) Thor-c/app.; Larsen-s/Williams III-c 4.00
Annual 1 (8/11, $3.99) Identity Wars; Spider-Man and Deadpool app.; Barrionuevo-a 4.00
... & The Human Torch: From the Marvel Vault 1 (8/11, $2.99) unpublished story w/Ditko-a 3.00
... : Boiling Point (Volume 2, 2002, $8.99, TPB) r/#40-43; Andrews-c 9.00
Dogs of War (6/01, $19.95, TPB) r/#12-20 20.00
House of M (2006, $13.99) r/House of M tie-in issues Incredible Hulk #83-87 14.00
Hulk: Planet Hulk HC (2007, $39.99, dustjacket) oversized r/#92-105, Planet Hulk: Gladiator Guidebook, stories from Amazing Fantasy (2004) #15 and Giant-Size Hulk #1 40.00
Hulk: Planet Hulk SC (2008, $34.99) same content as HC 35.00
Planet Hulk: Gladiator Guidebook (2006, $3.99) bios of combatants and planet history 4.00
...: Prelude to Planet Hulk (2006, $13.99, TPB) r/#88-91 & Official Handbook: Hulk 2004 14.00
...: Return of the Monster (7/02, $12.99, TPB) r/#34-39 13.00
...: The End (8/02, $5.95) David-s/Keown-a; Hulk in the far future 6.00
...: The End HC (2008, $19.99, dustjacket) r/The End and Hulk: Future Imperfect #1-2 20.00
...Volume 1 HC (2002, $29.99, oversized) r/#34-43 & Startling Stories: Banner #1-4 30.00
...Volume 2 HC (2003, $29.99, oversized) r/#44-54; sketch pages and cover gallery 30.00
Volume 3: Transfer of Power (2003, $12.99, TPB) r/#44-49 13.00
Volume 4: Abominable (2003, $11.99, TPB) r/#50-54; Abomination app.; Deodato-a 12.00
Volume 5: Hide in Plain Sight (2003, $11.99, TPB) r/#55-59; Fernandez-a 12.00
Volume 6: Split Decisions (2004, $12.99, TPB) r/#60-65; Deodato-a 13.00
Volume 7: Dead Like Me (2004, $12.99, TPB) r/#66-69 & Hulk Smash #1&2 13.00
Volume 8: Big Things (2004, $17.99, TPB) r/#70-76; Iron Man app. 18.00
Volume 9: Tempest Fugit (2005, $14.99, TPB) r/#77-82 15.00

INCREDIBLE HULK (Also see Indestructible Hulk)
Marvel Comics: Dec, 2011 - No. 15, Dec, 2012 ($3.99)

1-Aaron-s/Silvestri-a; bonus interview with Aaron; cover by Silvestri 4.00
1-Variant covers by Neal Adams, Whilce Portacio & Ladronn 8.00
2-7: 2-Silvestri, Portacio & Tan-a. 7-Hulk & Banner merge; Portacio-a 4.00
7.1-(7/12, $2.99) Palo-a/Komarck-c; Red She-Hulk app. 3.00
8-15: 8-Punisher app.; Dillon-a. 12-Wolverine & The Thing app. 4.00

INCREDIBLE HULK (Marvel Legacy)(Continued from Totally Awesome Hulk #23)
Marvel Comics: No. 709, Dec, 2017 - Present ($3.99)

709-713-"Return to Planet Hulk"; Hulk goes to Sakaar; Pak-s/Land-a 4.00

INCREDIBLE HULKS: ENIGMA FORCE
Marvel Comics: Nov, 2010 - No. 3, Jan, 2011 ($3.99, limited series)

1-3-Reed-s/Munera-a/Pagulayan-c; Bug app. 4.00

INCREDIBLE MR. LIMPET, THE (See Movie Classics)

INCREDIBLES, THE
Image Comics: Nov, 2004 - No. 4, Feb, 2005 ($2.99, limited series)

1-4-Adaptation of 2004 Pixar movie; Ricardo Curtis-a 3.00
TPB (2005, $12.95) r/#1-4; cover gallery 13.00

INCREDIBLES, THE (Pixar characters)
BOOM! Studios: No. 0, Jul, 2009 - No. 15, Oct, 2010 ($2.99)

0-15: 0-3-City of Incredibles; Waid & Walker-s. 0,1-Wagner-c. 8-15-Walker-s 3.00
...: Family Matters 1-4 (3/09 - No. 4, 6/09) Waid-s/Takara-a. 1-Five covers 3.00

INCREDIBLE SCIENCE FICTION (Formerly Weird Science-Fantasy)
E. C. Comics: No. 30, July-Aug, 1955 - No. 33, Jan-Feb, 1956

30-Davis-c begin, end #32 46 92 138 368 584 800
31-Williamson/Krenkel-a, Wood-a(2) 42 84 126 336 538 740
32-"Food For Thought" by Williamson/Krenkel 42 84 126 336 538 740
33-Classic Wood-c; "Judgment Day" story-r/Weird Fantasy #18; final issue & last E.C. comic book 49 98 147 392 621 850
NOTE: ***Davis*** *a-30, 32, 33; c-30-32.* ***Krigstein*** *a-in all.* ***Orlando*** *a-30, 32, 33.* ***Wood*** *a-30, 31, 33; c-33.*

INCREDIBLE SCIENCE FICTION (Formerly Weird Science-Fantasy)

Indestructible #8 © Darby Pop

Indian Chief #23 © DELL

Infamous Iron Man #11 © MAR

GD 2.0 VG 4.0 FN 6.0 VF 8.0 VF/NM 9.0 NM- 9.2

Russ Cochran/Gemstone Publ.: No. 8, Aug, 1994 - No. 11, May, 1995 ($2.00)
8-11: Reprints #30-33 of E.C. series 4.00

INDEPENDENCE DAY (Movie)
Marvel Comics: No. 0, June, 1996 - No. 2, Aug, 1996 ($1.95, limited series)
0-Special Edition; photo-c 5.00
0-2 3.00

INDEPENDENCE DAY (Movie)
Titan Comics: Mar, 2016 - No. 5, Jul, 2016 ($3.99, limited series)
1-5: 1-Victor Gischler-s/Steve Scott-a; four covers. 2-5-Two covers 4.00

INDESTRUCTIBLE
IDW (Darby Pop): Dec, 2013 - No. 10, Dec, 2014 ($3.99)
1-10: 1-Kline-s/Garron & Garcia-a 4.00
...: Stingray One Shot (5/15, $3.99) Marsick-s/Reguzzoni-a 4.00

INDESTRUCTIBLE HULK (Marvel NOW!)(Follows Incredible Hulk 2011-2012 series)
Marvel Comics: Jan, 2013 - No. 20, May, 2014 ($3.99)
1-Waid-s/Yu-a; Banner hired by SHIELD; Maria Hill app. 4.00
2-20: 2-Iron Man app. 4,5-Attuma app. 6-8-Thor app.; Simonson-a/c. 9,10-Daredevil app. 12-Two-Gun Kid, Kid Colt, and Rawhide Kid app. 17,18-Iron Man app. 4.00
Annual 1 (2/14, $4.99) Parker-s/Asrar-a; Iron Man app. 5.00
... Special 1 (12/13, $4.99) Original X-Men and Superior Spider-Man app. 5.00

INDIANA JONES (Title series), **Dark Horse Comics**
--ADVENTURES, 6/08 ($6.95, digest-sized) Vol. 1 - new all-ages adventures; Beavers-a 7.00
--AND THE ARMS OF GOLD, 2/94 - 5/94 ($2.50) 1-4 3.00
--AND THE FATE OF ATLANTIS, 3/91 - 9/91 ($2.50) 1-4-Dorman painted-c on all; contain trading cards (#1 has a 2nd printing, 10/91) 3.00
--AND THE GOLDEN FLEECE, 6/94 - 7/94 ($2.50) 1,2 3.00
--AND THE IRON PHOENIX, 12/94 - 3/95 ($2.50) 1-4 3.00

INDIANA JONES AND THE KINGDOM OF THE CRYSTAL SKULL
Dark Horse Comics: May, 2008 - No. 2, May, 2008 ($5.99, limited series, movie adaptation)
1,2-Luke Ross-a/John Jackson Miller-adapted-s; two covers by Struzan & Fleming 6.00
TPB (5/08, $12.95) r/#1,2; Struzan-c 13.00

INDIANA JONES AND THE LAST CRUSADE
Marvel Comics: 1989 - No. 4, 1989 ($1.00, limited series, movie adaptation)
1-4: Williamson-i assist 3.00
1-(1989, $2.95, B&W mag., 80 pgs.) 4.00
--AND THE SHRINE OF THE SEA DEVIL: Dark Horse, 9/94 ($2.50, one shot)
1-Gary Gianni-a 3.00
--AND THE SARGASSO PIRATES: Dark Horse, 12/95 - 3/96 ($2.50) 1-4: 1,2-Ross-c 3.00
--AND THE SPEAR OF DESTINY: Dark Horse, 4/95 - 8/95 ($2.50) 1-4 3.00
--AND THE TOMB OF THE GODS, 6/08 - No. 4, 3/09 ($2.99) 1-4: 1-Tony Harris-c 3.00
--THUNDER IN THE ORIENT: Dark Horse, 9/93 - '94 ($2.50)
1-6: Dan Barry story & art in all; 1-Dorman painted-c 3.00

INDIANA JONES AND THE TEMPLE OF DOOM
Marvel Comics Group: Sept, 1984 - No. 3, Nov, 1984 (Movie adaptation)
1-3-r/Marvel Super Special; Guice-a 5.00

INDIANA JONES OMNIBUS
Dark Horse Books: Feb, 2008; June 2008; Feb, 2009 ($24.95, digest-size)
Volume One - Reprints Indiana Jones and the Fate of Atlantis, Indiana Jones: Thunder in the Orient; and Indiana Jones and the Arms of Gold mini-series 25.00
Volume Two - Reprints I.J. and the Golden Fleece, I.J. and the Shrine of the Sea Devil, I.J. and the Iron Phoenix, I.J. and the Spear of Destiny, I.J. and the Sargasso Pirates 25.00
The Further Adventures Volume One - (2/09) r/Raiders of the Lost Ark #1-3 & The Further Adventures of Indiana Jones #1-12 25.00

INDIAN BRAVES (Baffling Mysteries No. 5 on)
Ace Magazines: March, 1951 - No. 4, Sept, 1951

	GD 2.0	VG 4.0	FN 6.0	VF 8.0	VF/NM 9.0	NM- 9.2
1-Green Arrowhead begins, apps. in all	20	40	60	114	182	250
2	10	20	30	56	76	95
3,4	9	18	27	47	61	75
I.W. Reprint #1 (nd)-r/Indian Braves #4	2	4	6	9	13	16

INDIAN CHIEF (White Eagle...) (Formerly The Chief, Four Color 290)
Dell Publ. Co.: No. 3, July-Sept, 1951 - No. 33, Jan-Mar, 1959 (All painted-c)

	GD 2.0	VG 4.0	FN 6.0	VF 8.0	VF/NM 9.0	NM- 9.2
3	5	10	15	33	57	80
4-11: 6-White Eagle app.	4	8	12	28	47	65
12-1st White Eagle (10-12/53)-Not same as earlier character	5	10	15	33	57	80
13-29	4	8	12	23	37	50
30-33-Buscema-a	4	8	12	25	40	55

INDIAN CHIEF (See March of Comics No. 94, 110, 127, 140, 159, 170, 187)

INDIAN FIGHTER, THE (Movie)
Dell Publishing Co.: No. 687, May, 1956 (one-shot)

	GD 2.0	VG 4.0	FN 6.0	VF 8.0	VF/NM 9.0	NM- 9.2
Four Color 687-Kirk Douglas photo-c	7	14	21	48	89	130

INDIAN FIGHTER
Youthful Magazines: May, 1950 - No. 11, Jan, 1952

	GD 2.0	VG 4.0	FN 6.0	VF 8.0	VF/NM 9.0	NM- 9.2
1	19	38	57	112	179	245
2-Wildey-a/c(bondage)	14	28	42	76	108	140
3-11: 3,4-Wildey-a. 6-Davy Crockett story	10	20	30	58	79	100

NOTE: ***Hollingsworth** a-5. **Walter Johnson** c-1, 3, 4, 6. **Palais** a-10. **Stallman** a-5-8. **Wildey** a-2-4; c-2, 5.*

INDIAN LEGENDS OF THE NIAGARA (See American Graphics)

INDIANS
Fiction House Magazines (Wings Publ. Co.): Spring, 1950 - No. 17, Spr, 1953 (1-8: 52 pgs.)

	GD 2.0	VG 4.0	FN 6.0	VF 8.0	VF/NM 9.0	NM- 9.2
1-Manzar The White Indian, Long Bow & Orphan of the Storm begin	30	60	90	177	289	400
2-Starlight begins	15	30	45	90	140	190
3-5: 5-17-Most-c by Whitman	14	28	42	81	118	155
6-10	13	26	39	72	101	130
11-17	11	22	33	64	90	115

INDIANS OF THE WILD WEST
I. W. Enterprises: Circa 1958? (no date) (Reprints)

	GD 2.0	VG 4.0	FN 6.0	VF 8.0	VF/NM 9.0	NM- 9.2
9-Kinstler-c; Whitman-a; r/Indians #?	2	4	6	10	14	18

INDIANS ON THE WARPATH
St. John Publishing Co.: No date (Late 40s, early 50s) (132 pgs.)

	GD 2.0	VG 4.0	FN 6.0	VF 8.0	VF/NM 9.0	NM- 9.2
nn-Matt Baker-c; contains St. John comics rebound. Many combinations possible	43	86	129	271	461	650

INDIAN TRIBES (See Famous Indian Tribes)

INDIAN WARRIORS (Formerly White Rider and Super Horse; becomes Western Crime Cases #9)
Star Publications: No. 7, June, 1951 - No. 8, Sept, 1951

	GD 2.0	VG 4.0	FN 6.0	VF 8.0	VF/NM 9.0	NM- 9.2
7-White Rider & Superhorse continue; "Last of the Mohicans" serial begins; L.B. Cole-c	19	38	57	109	172	235
8-L.B. Cole-c	17	34	51	100	158	215
3-D 1(12/53, 25¢)-Came w/glasses; L.B. Cole-c	34	68	102	199	325	450
Accepted Reprint(nn)(inside cover shows White Rider & Superhorse #11)-r/cover to #7; origin White Rider &...; L.B. Cole-c	8	16	24	40	50	60
Accepted Reprint #8 (nd); L.B. Cole-c (r-cover to #8)	8	16	24	40	50	60

INDOORS-OUTDOORS (See Wisco)

INDOOR SPORTS
National Specials Co.: nd (6x9", 64 pgs., B&W-r, hard-c)

	GD 2.0	VG 4.0	FN 6.0	VF 8.0	VF/NM 9.0	NM- 9.2
nn-By Tad	5	10	15	24	30	35

INDUSTRIAL GOTHIC
DC Comics (Vertigo): Dec, 1995 - No. 5, Apr, 1996 ($2.50, limited series)
1-5: Ted McKeever-c/a/scripts 3.00

INFAMOUS (Based on the Sony videogame)
DC Comics: Early May, 2011 - No. 6, Late July, 2011 ($2.99, limited series)
1-6: 1-William Harms-s/Eric Nguyen-a/Doug Mahnke-c. 3-6-Benes-c 3.00

INFAMOUS IRON MAN (Doctor Doom as Iron Man)
Marvel Comics: Dec, 2016 - No. 12, Nov, 2017 ($3.99)
1-12: 1-Bendis-s/Maleev-a; Diablo app. 1-9-The Thing app. 5-Doom's mother returns 4.00

INFERIOR FIVE, THE (Inferior 5 #11, 12) (See Showcase #62, 63, 65)
National Periodical Publications (#1-10: 12¢): 3-4/67 - No. 10, 9-10/68; No. 11, 8-9/72 - No. 12, 10-11/72

	GD 2.0	VG 4.0	FN 6.0	VF 8.0	VF/NM 9.0	NM- 9.2
1-(3-4/67)-Sekowsky-a(p); 4th app.	5	10	15	34	60	85
2-5: 2-Plastic Man, F.F. app. 4-Thor app.	3	6	9	19	30	40
6-9: 6-Stars DC staff	3	6	9	16	23	30
10-Superman x-over; F.F., Spider-Man & Sub-Mariner app.	3	6	9	19	30	40
11,12: Orlando-c/a; both r/Showcase #62,63	2	4	6	11	16	20

INFERNAL MAN-THING (Sequel to story in Man-Thing #12 [1974])
Marvel Comics: Sept, 2012 - No. 3, Oct, 2012 ($3.99, limited series)
1-3-Gerber-s; painted-a by Nowlan; Art Adams-c. 1,2-Bonus reprint of Man-Thing #12 4.00

INFERNO

Inferno #1 © DC

Infinity Countdown Prime #1 © MAR

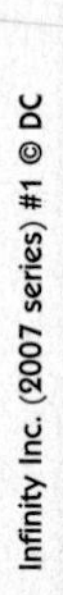

Infinity Inc. (2007 series) #1 © DC

GD VG FN VF VF/NM NM-
2.0 4.0 6.0 8.0 9.0 9.2

Caliber Comics: 1995 - No. 5 ($2.95, B&W)

1-5 3.00

INFERNO (See Legion of Super-Heroes)
DC Comics: Oct, 1997 - No. 4, Feb, 1998 ($2.50, limited series)

1-Immonen-s/c/a in all 4.00
2-4 3.00

INFERNO (Secret Wars tie-in)
Marvel Comics: Jul, 2015 - No. 5, Nov, 2015 ($3.99, limited series)

1-5-Hopeless-s/Garrón-a; Magik, Colossus, Nightcrawler, Madelyne Pryor app. 4.00

INFERNO: HELLBOUND
Image Comics (Top Cow): Jan, 2002 - No. 3 ($2.50/$2.99)

1,2: 1-Seven covers; Silvestri-a/Silvestri and Wohl-s 3.00
3-($2.99) Tan-a 3.00
#0 (7/02, $3.00) Tan-a 3.00
Wizard #0- Previews series; bagged with Wizard Top Cow Special mag 3.00

INFESTATION (Zombie crossover with G.I. Joe, Star Trek, Transformers and Ghostbusters)
IDW Publishing: Jan, 2011 - No. 2, Apr, 2011 ($3.99, limited series)

1,2-Abnett & Lanning-s/Messina-a; two covers by Messina & Snyder III 4.00
...: Outbreak 1-4 (6/11 - No. 4, 9/11, $3.99) Messina-a; Covert Vampiric Operations app. 4.00

INFESTATION 2 (IDW characters vs. H.P. Lovecraft's Elder Gods)
IDW Publishing: Jan, 2012 - No. 2, Apr, 2012 ($3.99, limited series)

1,2-Swierczynski-s/Messina-a; three covers by Garner, Ramondelli & Messina 4.00
...: Dungeons & Dragons 1,2 (2/12 - No. 2, 2/12, $3.99) 3 covers 4.00
...: G.I. Joe 1,2 (3/12 - No. 2, 3/12, $3.99) Raicht-s/De Landro-a; 3 covers 4.00
...: Team-Up 1 (2/12, $3.99) Ryall-s/Robinson-a; covers by Powell & Morrison 4.00
...: Teenage Mutant Ninja Turtles 1,2 (3/12 - No. 2, 3/12, $3.99) Mark Torres-a; 3 covers 4.00
...: 30 Days of Night 1 (4/12, $3.99) Swierczynski-s/Sayger-a; 3 covers 4.00
...: Transformers 1,2 (2/12 - No. 2, 2/12, $3.99) Dixon-s/Guidi-a; 3 covers 4.00

INFINITE, THE
Image Comics (SkyBound): Aug, 2011 - No. 4, Nov, 2011 ($2.99)

1-4: 1-Robert Kirkman-s/Rob Liefeld-a; at least 11 covers. 2-Six covers 3.00

INFINITE CRISIS
DC Comics: Dec, 2005 - No. 7, Jun, 2006 ($3.99, limited series)

1-Johns-s/Jimenez-a; two covers by Jim Lee and George Pérez 5.00
1-RRP Edition with Jim Lee sketch-c 100.00
2-7: 4-New Spectre; Earth-2 returns. 5-Earth-2 Lois dies; new Blue Beetle debut. 6-Superboy killed, new Earth formed. 7-Earth-2 Superman dies 4.00
HC (2006, $24.99, dustjacket) r/#1-7; DiDio intro.; sketch cover gallery; interview/commentary with Johns, Jimenez and editors; sketch art 25.00
... Companion TPB (2006, $14.99) r/Day of Vengeance: Infinite Crisis Special #1, Rann-Thanagar War: ICS #1, The Omac Project: ICS #1, Villains United: ICS #1 15.00
... Secret Files 2006 (4/06, $5.99) tie-in story with Earth-2 Lois and Superman, Earth-Prime Superboy and Alexander Luthor; art by various; profile pages 6.00

INFINITE CRISIS AFTERMATH (See Crisis Aftermath:...)

INFINITE CRISIS: FIGHT FOR THE MULTIVERSE (Based on the video game)
DC Comics: Sept, 2014 - No. 12, Aug, 2015 ($3.99, limited series)

1-12: 1-Abnett-s; art by various. 2-6-Polybagged 4.00

INFINITE LOOP
IDW Publishing: Apr, 2015 - No. 6, Sept, 2015 ($3.99)

1-6-Pierrick Colinet-s/Elsa Charretier-a 4.00

INFINITE LOOP, VOLUME 2
IDW Publishing: Sept, 2017 - No. 4, Dec, 2017 ($3.99)

1-4-Colinet & Charretier-s/Di Nicuolo-a 4.00

INFINITE VACATION
Image Comics (Shadowline): Jan, 2011 - No. 5, Jan, 2013 ($3.50/$5.99)

1-4-Nick Spencer-s/Christian Ward-a/c 3.50
5-($5.99) Conclusion; gatefold centerfold 6.00

INFINITY (Crossover with the Avengers titles)
Marvel Comics: Oct, 2013 - No. 6, Jan, 2014 ($4.99/$3.99/$5.99, limited series)

1-($4.99) Avengers, Inhumans and Thanos app.; Hickman-s/Cheung-a/Adam Kubert-c 5.00
2-5-($3.99) Opeña-a. 3-Terragen bomb triggered 4.00
6-($5.99) Cheung-a 6.00
Free Comic Book Day 2013 (Infinity) 1 (5/13, giveaway) Previews series; Cheung-a 3.00

INFINITY ABYSS (Also see Marvel Universe: The End)
Marvel Comics: Aug, 2002 - No. 6, Oct, 2002 ($2.99, limited series)

1-5-Starlin-s/a; Thanos, Captain Marvel, Spider-Man, Dr. Strange app. 4.00
6-($3.50) 4.00
Thanos Vol. 2: Infinity Abyss TPB (2003, $17.99) r/ #1-6 25.00

INFINITY COUNTDOWN
Marvel Comics: May, 2018 - No. 5 ($4.99, limited series with one-shots)

1-Duggan-s/Kuder-a; Guardians of the Galaxy app.; Groot restored 5.00
... Adam Warlock 1 (4/18, $4.99) Prelude to series; Duggan-s/Allred-a 5.00
... Prime 1 (4/18, $4.99) Duggan-s/Deodato-a; Wolverine, Magus, Ultron app. 5.00

INFINITY CRUSADE
Marvel Comics: June, 1993 - No. 6, Nov, 1993 ($3.50/$2.50, limited series, 52 pgs.)

1-6: By Jim Starlin & Ron Lim. 1-($3.50). 2-6-($2.99) 6.00

INFINITY ENTITY, THE (Concludes in Thanos: The Infinity Entity GN)
Marvel Comics: May, 2016 - No. 4, Jun, 2016 ($3.99, limited series)

1-4: Jim Starlin-s/Alan Davis-a. 1-Rebirth of Adam Warlock. 4-Mephisto app. 4.00

INFINITY GAUNTLET (The... #2 on; see Infinity Crusade, The Infinity War & Warlock & the Infinity Watch)
Marvel Comics: July, 1991 - No. 6, Dec, 1991 ($2.50, limited series)

1-Thanos-c/stories in all; Starlin scripts in all 3 6 9 21 33 45
2-6: 5,6-Ron Lim-c/a 2 4 6 10 14 18
TPB (4/99, $24.95) r/#1-6 30.00
NOTE: ***Lim*** *a-3p(part), 5p, 6p; c-5i, 6i.* ***Perez*** *a-1-3p, 4p(part); c-1(painted), 2-4, 5i, 6i.*

INFINITY GAUNTLET (Secret Wars tie-in)
Marvel Comics: Jul, 2015 - No. 5, Jan, 2016 ($3.99, limited series)

1-5-Duggan & Weaver-s/Weaver-a; Thanos & The Guardians of the Galaxy app. 4.00

INFINITY: HEIST (Tie-in to the Infinity crossover)
Marvel Comics: Nov, 2013 - No. 4, Feb, 2014 ($3.99, limited series)

1-4-Tieri-s/Barrionuevo-a; Spymaster, Titanium Man, Whirlwind app. 4.00

INFINITY, INC. (See All-Star Squadron #25)
DC Comics: Mar, 1984 - No. 53, Aug, 1988 ($1.25, Baxter paper, 36 pgs.)

1-Brainwave, Jr., Fury, The Huntress, Jade, Northwind, Nuklon, Obsidian, Power Girl, Silver Scarab & Star Spangled Kid begin 5.00
2-13,38-49,51-53: 2-Dr. Midnite, G.A. Flash, W. Woman, Dr. Fate, Hourman, Green Lantern, Wildcat app. 5-Nudity panels. 13-Re-intro Rose and Thorn. 46,47-Millennium tie-ins 3.00
14-Todd McFarlane-a (5/85, 2nd full story) 2 4 6 8 10 12
15-37-McFarlane-a (20,23,24: 5 pgs. only; 33: 2 pgs.); 18-24-Crisis x-over. 21-Intro new Hourman & Dr. Midnight. 26-New Wildcat app. 31-Star Spangled Kid becomes Skyman. 32-Green Fury becomes Green Flame. 33-Origin Obsidian. 35-1st modern app. G.A. Fury 4.00
50 ($2.50, 52 pgs.) 4.00
Annual 1,2: 1(12/85)-Crisis x-over. 2('88, $2.00), Special 1 ('87, $1.50) 4.00
...: The Generations Saga Volume One HC (2011, $39.99) r/#1-4, All-Star Squadron #25,26 & All-Star Squadron Annual #2 40.00
NOTE: ***Kubert*** *r-4.* ***McFarlane*** *a-14-37p, Annual 1p; c(p)-14-19, 22, 25, 26, 31-33, 37, Annual 1.* ***Newton*** *a-12p, 13p(last work 4/85).* ***Tuska*** *a-11p. JSA app. 3-10.*

INFINITY, INC. (See 52)
DC Comics: Nov, 2007 - No. 12, Oct, 2008 ($2.99)

1-12: 1-Milligan-s; Steel app. 3.00
...: Luthor's Monsters TPB (2008, $14.99) r/#1-5 15.00
...: The Bogeyman TPB (2008, $14.99) r/#6-10 15.00

INFINITY MAN AND THE FOREVER PEOPLE
DC Comics: Aug, 2014 - No. 9, May, 2015 ($2.99)

1-9: 1-DiDio-s/Giffen-a. 2,5,6-Grummett-a. 3-Starlin-a. 4-6-Guy Gardner app. 9-Giffen-a 3.00
...: Futures End 1 (11/14, $2.99, regular-c) Five years later; Philip Tan-a 3.00
...: Futures End 1 (11/14, $3.99, 3-D cover) 4.00

INFINITY: THE HUNT (Tie-in to the Infinity crossover)
Marvel Comics: Nov, 2013 - No. 4, Jan, 2014 ($3.99, limited series)

1-4-Kindt-s/Sanders-a; Avengers Academy, Wolverine & She-Hulk app. 4.00

INFINITY WAR, THE (Also see Infinity Gauntlet & Warlock and the Infinity...)
Marvel Comics: June, 1992 - No. 6, Nov, 1992 ($2.50, mini-series)

1-Starlin scripts, Lim-c/a(p), Thanos app. in all 1 3 4 6 8 10
2-6: All have wraparound gatefold covers 6.00
TPB (2006, $29.99) r/#1-6, Marvel Comics Presents #108-111, Warlock and the Infinity Watch #7-10; cover gallery and synopses of Infinity War crossovers 30.00

INFORMER, THE
Feature Television Productions: April, 1954 - No. 5, Dec, 1954

1-Sekowsky-a begins 14 28 42 78 112 145
2 9 18 27 47 61 75

Inhuman #10 © MAR

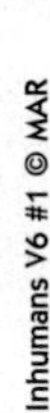

Inhumans V6 #1 © MAR

Insexts #13 © Marguerite Bennett

GD 2.0 | VG 4.0 | FN 6.0 | VF 8.0 | VF/NM 9.0 | NM- 9.2

3-5 8 16 24 42 54 65

IN HIS STEPS
Spire Christian Comics (Fleming H. Revell Co.): 1973, 1977 (39/49¢)
nn 2 4 6 11 16 20

INHUMAN (Also see Uncanny Inhumans)
Marvel Comics: Jun, 2014 - No. 14, Jun, 2015 ($3.99)
1-14: 1-3-Soule-s/Madureira-a; Medusa app. 4-7,9-11-Stegman-a. 10-Spider-Man app. 4.00
Annual 1 (7/15, $4.99) Soule-s/Stegman-a; continues from #14; Ms. Marvel app. 5.00
... Special 1 (6/15, $4.99) Crossover with Amaz. Spider-Man & All-New Capt. America 5.00

INHUMANITY
Marvel Comics: Feb, 2014 - No. 2, Mar, 2014 ($3.99)
1,2: 1-After the fall of Attilan, origin of the Inhumans retold; Fraction-s/Coipel-a 4.00
...: Superior Spider-Man 1 (3/14, $3.99) Gage-s/Hans-a/c 4.00
...: The Awakening 1,2 (2/14 - No. 2, 3/14, $3.99) Kindt-s/Davidson-a 4.00

INHUMANOIDS, THE (TV)
Marvel Comics (Star Comics): Jan, 1987 - No. 4, July 1987
1-4: Based on Hasbro toys 4.00

INHUMANS, THE (See Amazing Adventures, Fantastic Four #54 & Special #5, Incredible Hulk Special #1, Marvel Graphic Novel & Thor #146)
Marvel Comics Group: Oct, 1975 - No. 12, Aug, 1977
1: #1-4,6 are 25¢ issues 6 12 18 41 76 110
2-4-Peréz-a 3 6 9 14 20 25
5-12: 9-Reprints Amazing Adventures #1,2('70). 12-Hulk app. 2 4 6 10 14 18
4-(30¢-c variant, limited distribution)(4/76) Pérez-a 4 8 12 23 37 50
6-(30¢-c variant, limited distribution)(8/76) 4 8 12 23 37 50
11,12-(35¢-c variants, limited distribution) 6 12 18 38 69 100
Special 1(4/90, $1.50, 52 pgs.)-F.F. cameo 5.00
...: The Great Refuge (5/95, $2.95) 4.00
NOTE: ***Buckler** c-2-4p, 5. **Gil Kane** a-5-7p; c-1p, 7p, 8p. **Kirby** a-9r. **Mooney** a-11i. **Perez** a-1-4p, 8p.*

INHUMANS (Marvel Knights)
Marvel Comics: Nov, 1998 - No. 12, Oct, 1999 ($2.99, limited series)
1-Jae Lee-c/a; Paul Jenkins-s 3 6 9 14 20 25
1-($6.95) DF Edition; Jae Lee variant-c 3 6 9 19 30 40
2-Two covers by Lee and Darrow 6.00
3-12 4.00
TPB (10/00, $24.95) r/#1-12 25.00

INHUMANS (Volume 3)
Marvel Comics: Jun, 2000 - No. 4, Oct, 2000 ($2.99, limited series)
1-4-Ladronn-c/Pacheco & Marin-s. 1-3-Ladronn-a. 4-Lucas-a 3.00

INHUMANS (Volume 6)
Marvel Comics: Jun, 2003 - No. 12, Jun, 2004 ($2.50/$2.99)
1-12: 1-6-McKeever-s/Clark-a/JH Williams III-c. 7-Begin $2.99-c. 7,8-Teranishi-a 3.00
Vol. 1: Culture Shock (2005, $7.99, digest) r/#1-6; story pitch and sketch pages 8.00

INHUMANS: ATTILAN RISING (Secret Wars tie-in)
Marvel Comics: Jul, 2015 - No. 5, Nov, 2015 ($3.99, limited series)
1-5-Soule-s/Timms-a/Johnson-c 4.00

INHUMANS: JUDGMENT DAY
Marvel Comics: Mar, 2018 ($4.99, one-shot)
1-Follows from Royals #12; Al Ewing-s/Del Mundo & Libranda-a; Acuna-c 5.00

INHUMANS: ONCE AND FUTURE KINGS
Marvel Comics: Oct, 2017 - No. 5, Feb, 2018 ($3.99, limited series)
1-5: 1-Priest-s/Noto-a; young Black Bolt, Maximus & Medusa. 4-Spider-Man app. 4.00

INHUMANS PRIME
Marvel Comics: May, 2017 ($4.99, one-shot)
1-Follows IVX series; leads into Royals #1; Al Ewing-s/Ryan Sook & Chris Allen-a 5.00

INHUMANS 2099
Marvel Comics: Nov, 2004 ($2.99, one-shot)
1-Kirkman-s/Rathburn-a/Pat Lee-c 3.00

INHUMANS VS. X-MEN (See IVX)

INJECTION
Image Comics: May, 2015 - Present ($2.99/$3.99)
1-10-Warren Ellis-s/Declan Shalvey-a 3.00
11-15-($3.99) 4.00

INJUSTICE: GODS AMONG US (Based on the video game)
DC Comics: Mar, 2013 - No. 12, Feb, 2014 ($3.99)
1-Lois Lane dies; Joker app. 3 6 9 19 30 40
1-Variant-c 3 6 9 21 33 45
1-Second printing 6.00
2-Joker killed 10.00
3-12: 6-Nightwing dies 4.00
Annual 1 (1/14, $4.99) Harley Quinn & Lobo app.; Ryp-c 5.00

INJUSTICE (Gods Among Us:) **YEAR TWO** (Based on the video game)
DC Comics: Mar, 2014 - No. 12, Late Nov, 2014 ($2.99)
1-12: 1-6,9-12-Sinestro app. 7-11-Harley Quinn app. 3.00
Annual 1 (12/14, $4.99) Stories of Oracle, Green Lantern & Sinestro; Raapack-c 5.00

INJUSTICE: GODS AMONG US: YEAR THREE (Based on the video game)
DC Comics: Early Dec, 2014 - No. 12, Late May, 2015 ($2.99, printings of digital-first stories)
1-12: 1-Constantine joins the fight. 5-New Deadman app. 3.00
Annual 1 (6/15, $4.99) Prequel to Year Three; Constantine app.; Titans vs. Superman 5.00

INJUSTICE: GODS AMONG US: YEAR FOUR (Based on the video game)
DC Comics: Early Jul, 2015 - No. 12, Late Dec, 2015 ($2.99, printings of digital-first stories)
1-12: 1-The Olympus Gods join the fight. 10-Harley Quinn cover 3.00

INJUSTICE: GODS AMONG US: YEAR FIVE (Based on the video game)
DC Comics: Early Mar, 2016 - No. 20, Late Dec, 2016 ($2.99, printings of digital-first stories)
1-20: 1-Doomsday & Bane app. 6-Solomon Grundy app. 7-Damian becomes Nightwing. 12-Alfred killed by Zsasz. 18-Deathstroke app. 3.00
Annual 1 (1/17, $4.99) Harley Quinn app.; leads into Injustice: Ground Zero 5.00

INJUSTICE: GROUND ZERO (Follows Year Five)
DC Comics: Early Feb, 2016 - No. 12, Jul, 2017 ($2.99, printings of digital-first stories)
1-12: 1-Mhan & Derenick-a; Harley & Joker app. 12-Superman vs. Superman 3.00

INJUSTICE 2 (Follows Ground Zero)(Prequel to the Injustice 2 video game)
DC Comics: Early Jul, 2017 - Present ($2.99, printings of digital-first stories)
1-21 : 1-Taylor-s/Redondo-a; Harley joins the Suicide Squad. 3-Intro. Athanasia. 6-Intro/origin Supergirl 3.00
Annual 1 (1/18, $4.99) Origin of Wonder Woman; back-up with Harley Quinn; Mhan-a 5.00

INKY & DINKY (See Felix's Nephews...)

IN LOVE (...Magazine on-c; I Love You No. 7 on)
Mainline/Charlton No. 5 (5/55)-on: Aug-Sept, 1954 - No. 6, July, 1955 ('Adult Reading' on-c)
1-Simon & Kirby-a; book-length novel in all issues 53 106 159 334 567 800
2,3-S&K-a. 3-Last pre-code (12-1/54-55) 32 64 96 188 307 425
4-S&K-a.(Rare) 36 72 108 211 343 475
5-S&K-c only 20 40 60 114 182 250
6-No S&K-a 12 24 36 69 97 125

INNOVATION SPECTACULAR
Innovation Publishing: 1991 - No. 2, 1991 ($2.95, squarebound, 100 pgs.)
1,2: Contains rebound comics w/o covers 4.00

INNOVATION SUMMER FUN SPECIAL
Innovation Publishing: 1991 ($3.50, B&W/color, squarebound)
1-Contains rebound comics (Power Factory) 4.00

IN SEARCH OF THE CASTAWAYS (See Movie Comics)

INSEXTS
AfterShock Comics: Dec, 2015 - No. 13, Sept, 2017 ($3.99, mature)
1-13-Marguerite Bennett-s/Ariela Kristantina-a 4.00

INSIDE CRIME (Formerly My Intimate Affair)
Fox Feature Syndicate (Hero Books): No. 3, July, 1950 - No. 2, Sept, 1950
3-Wood-a (10 pgs.); L. B. Cole-c 34 68 102 199 325 450
2-Used in **SOTI**, pg. 182,183; r/Spook #24 24 48 72 142 234 325
nn (nd, M.S. Dist. Pub.) Wally Wood-c 11 22 33 62 86 110

INSPECTOR, THE (TV) (Also see The Pink Panther)
Gold Key: July, 1974 - No. 19, Feb, 1978
1 3 6 9 18 28 38
2-5 2 4 6 13 18 22
6-9 2 4 6 10 14 18
10-19: 11-Reprints 2 4 6 8 10 12

INSPECTOR, THE Volume 2 (The Pink Panther)
American Mythology: 2016 - Present ($3.99)
1-The Pink Files; new stories by Fridolfs & Gallagher; reprints 4.00

INSPECTOR GILL OF THE FISH POLICE (See Fish Police)

International Iron Man #5 © MAR

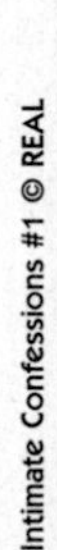

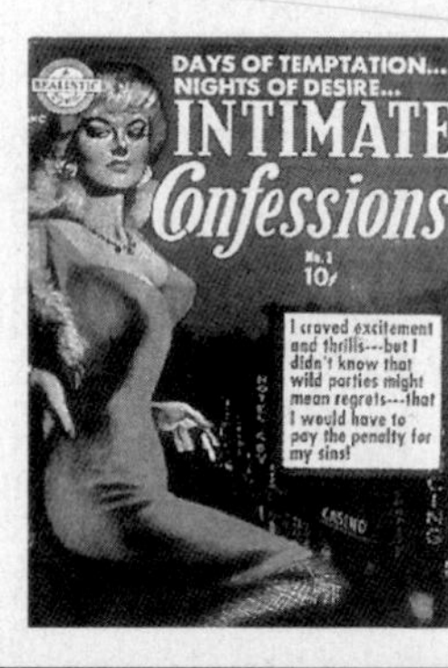

Intimate Confessions #1 © REAL

Invaders #10 © MAR

GD 2.0 | VG 4.0 | FN 6.0 | VF 8.0 | VF/NM 9.0 | NM- 9.2

INSPECTOR WADE
David McKay Publications: No. 13, May, 1938
Feature Books 13 — 34 68 102 204 332 460

INSTANT PIANO
Dark Horse Comics: Aug, 1994 - No. 4, Feb, 1995 ($3.95, B&W, bimonthly, mature)
1-4 — 4.00

INSUFFERABLE
IDW Publishing: May, 2015 - No. 8, Dec, 2015 ($3.99)
1-8-Waid-s/Krause-a — 4.00

INSUFFERABLE: HOME FIELD ADVANTAGE
IDW Publishing: Oct, 2016 - No. 4, Jan, 2017 ($3.99)
1-4-Waid-s/Krause-a — 4.00

INSUFFERABLE: ON THE ROAD
IDW Publishing: Feb, 2016 - No. 6, Jul, 2016 ($3.99)
1-6-Waid-s/Krause-a — 4.00

INSURGENT
DC Comics: Mar, 2013 - No. 3, May, 2013 ($2.99, limited series)
1-3-DeSanto & Farmer-s/Dallocchio-a — 3.00

INTERFACE
Marvel Comics (Epic Comics): Dec, 1989 - No. 8, Dec, 1990 ($1.95, mature, coated paper)
1-8: Cont. from 1st ESPers series; painted-c/a — 3.00
Espers: Interface TPB ('98, $16.95) r/#1-6 — 17.00

INTERNATIONAL COMICS (...Crime Patrol No. 6)
E. C. Comics: Spring, 1947 - No. 5, Nov-Dec, 1947
1-Schaffenberger-a begins, ends #4 — 81 162 243 518 884 1250
2 — 52 104 156 328 552 775
3-5 — 47 94 141 296 498 700

INTERNATIONAL CRIME PATROL (Formerly International Comics #1-5; becomes Crime Patrol No. 7 on)
E. C. Comics: No. 6, Spring, 1948
6-Moon Girl app. — 81 162 243 518 884 1250

INTERNATIONAL IRON MAN
Marvel Comics: May, 2016 - No. 7, Nov, 2016 ($3.99)
1-7-Bendis-s/Maleev-a. 1-4-Flashback to college years in London. 5-Intro. Amanda Armstrong. 6,7-Flashback to Stark's real parents meeting — 4.00

INTERSECT
Image Comics: Nov, 2014 - No. 6, Apr, 2015 ($3.50)
1-6-Ray Fawkes-s/a. 1-Lemire-c. 2-Kindt-c — 3.50

IN THE DAYS OF THE MOB (Magazine)
Hampshire Dist. Ltd. (National): Fall, 1971 (B&W)
1-Kirby-a; John Dillinger wanted poster inside (1/2 value if poster is missing) — 7 14 21 44 82 120

IN THE PRESENCE OF MINE ENEMIES
Spire Christian Comics/Fleming H. Revell Co.: 1973 (35/49¢)
nn — 2 4 6 10 14 18

IN THE SHADOW OF EDGAR ALLAN POE
DC Comics (Vertigo): 2002 (Graphic novel)
Hardcover (2002, $24.95) Fuqua-s/Phillips and Parke photo-a — 25.00
Softcover (2003, $17.95) — 18.00

INTIMATE
Charlton Comics: Dec, 1957 - No. 3, May, 1958
1 — 6 12 18 28 34 40
2,3 — 4 8 12 18 22 25

INTIMATE CONFESSIONS (See Fox Giants)

INTIMATE CONFESSIONS
Country Press Inc.: 1942
nn-Ashcan comic, not distributed to newsstands, only for in house use. A VF copy sold for $1,000 in 2007, and a VF+ copy sold for $1,525 in 2007.

INTIMATE CONFESSIONS
Realistic Comics: July-Aug, 1951 - No. 7, Aug, 1952; No. 8, Mar, 1953 (All painted-c)
1-Kinstler-a; c/Avon paperback #222 — 200 400 600 1280 2190 3100
2 — 47 94 141 296 498 700
3-c/Avon paperback #250; Kinstler-c/a — 48 96 144 302 514 725
4-8: 4-c/Avon paperback #304; Kinstler-c. 6-c/Avon paperback #120. 8-c/Avon paperback #375; Kinstler-a — 42 84 126 265 445 625

INTIMATE CONFESSIONS
I. W. Enterprises/Super Comics: 1964
I.W. Reprint #9,10, Super Reprint #10,12,18 — 2 4 6 13 18 22

INTIMATE LOVE
Standard Comics: No. 5, 1950 - No. 28, Aug, 1954
5-8: 6-8-Severin/Elder-a — 14 28 42 78 112 145
9 — 10 20 30 58 79 100
10-Jane Russell, Robert Mitchum photo-c — 15 30 45 90 140 190
11-18,20,23,25,27,28 — 10 20 30 56 76 95
19,21,22,24,26-Toth-a — 11 22 33 62 86 110
NOTE: *Celardo a-8, 10.* ***Colletta*** *a-23.* ***Moreira*** *a-13(2). Photo-c-6, 7, 10, 12, 14, 15, 18-20, 24, 26, 27.*

INTIMATES, THE
DC Comics (WildStorm): Jan, 2005 - No. 12, Dec, 2005 ($2.95/$2.99)
1-12: 1-Joe Casey-s/Jim Lee-c/Lee and Giuseppe Camuncoli-a — 3.00

INTIMATE SECRETS OF ROMANCE
Star Publications: Sept, 1953 - No. 2, Apr, 1954
1,2-L. B. Cole-c — 21 42 63 122 199 275

INTRIGUE
Quality Comics Group: Jan, 1955
1-Horror; Jack Cole reprint/Web of Evil — 37 74 111 222 361 500

INTRIGUE
Image Comics: Aug, 1999 - No. 3, Feb, 2000 ($2.50/$2.95)
1,2: 1-Two covers (Andrews, Wieringo); Shum-s/Andrews-a — 3.00
3-($2.95) — 3.00

INTRUDER
TSR, Inc.: 1990 - No. 10, 1991 ($2.95, 44 pgs.)
1-10 — 4.00

INVADERS, THE (TV)(Aliens From a Dying Planet)
Gold Key: Oct, 1967 - No. 4, Oct, 1968 (All have photo-c)
1-Spiegle-a in all — 8 16 24 54 102 150
2-4: 2-Pin-up on back-c. 3-Has variant 15¢-c with photo back-c — 5 10 15 35 63 90

INVADERS, THE (Also see The Avengers #71, Giant-Size Invaders, and All-New Invaders)
Marvel Comics Group: August, 1975 - No. 40, May, 1979; No. 41, Sept, 1979
1-Captain America & Bucky, Human Torch & Toro, & Sub-Mariner begin; cont'd. from Giant Size Invaders #1; #1-7 are 25¢ issues — 6 12 18 37 66 95
2-5: 2-1st app. Brain-Drain. 3-Battle issue; Cap vs. Namor vs. Torch; intro U-Man — 3 6 9 17 26 35
6-10: 6,7-(Regular 25¢ edition). 6-(7/76) Liberty Legion app. 7-Intro Baron Blood & intro/1st app. Union Jack; Human Torch origin retold. 8-Union Jack-c/story. 9-Origin Baron Blood. 10-G.A. Capt. America-r/C.A #22 — 2 4 6 11 16 20
6,7-(30¢-c variants, limited distribution) — 5 10 15 30 50 70
11-19: 11-Origin Spitfire; intro The Blue Bullet. 14-1st app. The Crusaders. 16-Re-intro The Destroyer. 17-Intro Warrior Woman. 18-Re-intro The Destroyer w/new origin. 19-Hitler-c/story — 2 4 6 8 11 14
17-19,21-(35¢-c variants, limited distribution) — 9 18 27 59 117 175
20-(Regular 30¢-c) Reprints origin/1st app. Sub-Mariner from Motion Picture Funnies Weekly with color added & brief write-up about MPFW; 1st app. new Union Jack II — 2 4 6 10 14 18
20-(35¢-c variant, limited distribution) — 10 20 30 69 147 225
21-(Regular 30¢ edition)-r/Marvel Mystery #10 (battle issue) — 2 4 6 9 13 16
22-30,34-40: 22-New origin Toro. 24-r/Marvel Mystery #17 (team-up issue; all-r). 25-All new-a begins. 28-Intro new Human Top & Golden Girl. 29-Intro Teutonic Knight. 34-Mighty Destroyer joins. 35-The Whizzer app. — 1 2 3 5 7 9
31-33: 31-Frankenstein-c/sty. 32,33-Thor app. — 2 4 6 8 11 14
41-Double size last issue — 3 6 9 14 19 24
Annual 1 (9/77)-Schomburg, Rico stories (new); Schomburg-c/a (1st for Marvel in 30 years); Avengers app.; re-intro The Shark & The Hyena — 5 10 15 31 53 75
... Classic Vol. 1 TPB (2007, $24.99) r/#1-9, Giant-Size Invaders #1 and Marvel Premiere #29,30; cover pencils and cover inks — 25.00
NOTE: ***Buckler*** *a-5.* ***Everett*** *r-20('39), 21(1940), 24, Annual 1.* ***Gil Kane*** *c(p)-13, 17, 18, 20-27.* ***Kirby*** *c(p)-3-12, 14-16, 32, 33.* ***Mooney*** *a-5i, 16, 22.* ***Robbins*** *a-1-4, 6-9, 10(3 pg.), 11-15, 17-21, 23, 25-28; c-28.*

INVADERS (See Namor, the Sub-Mariner #12)
Marvel Comics Group: May, 1993 - No. 4, Aug, 1993 ($1.75, limited series)
1-4 — 3.00

Invader Zim #6 © Viacom

Invincible #144 © Kirkman & Walker

Invincible Iron Man #593 © MAR

	GD 2.0	VG 4.0	FN 6.0	VF 8.0	VF/NM 9.0	NM- 9.2

INVADERS (2004 title - see New Invaders)

INVADERS FROM HOME
DC Comics (Piranha Press): 1990 - No. 6, 1990 ($2.50, mature)
1-6 3.00

INVADERS NOW! (See Avengers/Invaders and The Torch series)
Marvel Comics: Nov, 2010 - No. 5, Mar, 2011 ($3.99, limited series)
1-5-Alex Ross-c; Steve Rogers, Bucky, Human Torch & Toro, Sub-Mariner app. 4.00

INVADER ZIM
Oni Press: Jul, 2015 - Present ($3.99)
1-Jhonen Vasquez-s/Aaron Alexovich-a; multiple covers 4.00
2-28 4.00
... #1 Square One Edition (2/17, $1.00) r/#1 3.00

INVASION
DC Comics: Holiday, 1988-'89 - No. 3, Jan, 1989 ($2.95, lim. series, 84 pgs.)
1-3:1-McFarlane/Russell-a. 2-McFarlane/Russell & Giffen/Gordon-a 5.00
Invasion! TPB (2008, $24.99) r/#1-3 25.00

INVINCIBLE (Also see The Pact #4)
Image Comics: Jan, 2003 - No. 144, Feb, 2018 ($2.95/$2.99)

	GD	VG	FN	VF	VF/NM	NM-
1-Kirkman-s/Walker-a	11	22	33	76	163	250
2,3-Kirkman-s/Walker-a	4	8	12	23	37	50
4-8: 4-Preview of The Moth	2	4	6	10	14	18
9-14: 11-Origin of Omni-Man. 14-Cho-c	1	2	3	5	6	8

15-24,26-41,43-49: 33-Tie-in w/Marvel Team-Up #14 5.00
25-($4.95) Science Dog app.; back-up stories w/origins of Science Dog and teammates 6.00
42-($1.99) Includes re-cap of the entire series 5.00
50-(6/08, $4.99) Two covers; back-up origin of Cecil Stedman; Science Dog app. 6.00
51-59,61-74: 51-Jim Lee-c; new costumes. 57-Continues in Astounding Wolf-Man #11. 71-74-Viltrumite War 4.00
76-99,101-109,111-117: 89-Intro. Zandale. 97-Origin of Bulletproof. 112-Baby born 3.00
60-($3.99) Invincible War; Witchblade, Savage Dragon, Spawn, Youngblood app. 1 2 3 5 6 8
75-($5.99) Viltrumite War; Science Dog back-up; 2 covers 1 2 3 4 5 7
100-(1/13, $3.99) "The Death of Everyone" conclusion; multiple covers 5.00
110-Rape issue 6.00
118-141: 118-(25¢-c). 124-126-Reboot. 132-Oliver dies. 133-(25¢-c) Mark & Eve wedding 3.00
142-143-($3.99) 4.00
144-($5.99) Last issue; art by Ottley & Walker 6.00
#0-(4/05, 50¢) Origin of Invincible; Ottley-a 3.00
Image Firsts: Invincible #1 (4/10, $1.00) r/#1 with "Image Firsts" cover logo 3.00
Official Handbook of the Invincible Universe 1,2 (11/06, 1/07, $4.99) profile pages 5.00
Official Handbook of the Invincible Universe Vol. 1 (2007, $12.99) r/#1-2; sketch pages 13.00
... Presents Atom Eve 1,2 (12/07, 3/08, $2.99) origin of Atom Eve; Bellegarde-a 3.00
... Presents Atom Eve & Rex Splode 1-3 (10/09 - 2/10, $2.99) origin of Rex 3.00
... Returns (4/10, $3.99) Leads into Viltrumite War in #71; 4 covers 4.00
... Universe Primer 1 (5/08, $5.99) r/Invincible #1, Brit #1, Astounding Wolf-Man #1 6.00
The Complete Invincible Library Vol. 1 Slipcase HC (2006, $125.00) oversized r/#1-24, #0 and story from Image Comics Summer Special (FCBD 2004); sketch pages; script for #1 125.00
..., Ultimate Collection Vol. 1 HC (2005, $34.95) oversized r/#1-13; sketch pages 35.00
..., Ultimate Collection Vol. 2 HC (2006, $34.99) oversized r/#14-24, #0 and story from Image Comics Summer Special (FCBD 2004); sketch pages and script for #23; intro by Damon Lindelof; afterword by Robert Kirkman 35.00
..., Ultimate Collection Vol. 3 HC (2007, $34.95) oversized r/#25-35 & The Pact #4; sketch pages and script for #28; afterword by Robert Kirkman 35.00
..., Ultimate Collection Vol. 4 HC (2008, $34.99) oversized r/#36-47; sketch & script pgs. 35.00
Vol. 1: Family Matters TPB (8/03, $12.95) r/#1-4; intro. by Busiek; sketch pages 13.00
Vol. 2: Eight in Enough TPB (3/04, $12.95) r/#5-8; intro. by Larsen; sketch pages 13.00
Vol. 3: Perfect Strangers TPB (2004, $12.95) r/#9-12; intro. by Brevoort; sketch pages 13.00
Vol. 4: Head of the Class TPB (1/05, $14.95) r/#14-19; intro. by Waid; sketch pages 15.00
Vol. 5: The Facts of Life TPB (2005, $14.99) r/#0,20-24; intro. by Wieringo; sketch pages 15.00
Vol. 6: A Different World TPB (2006, $14.99) r/#25-30; intro. by Brubaker; sketch pages 15.00
Vol. 7: Three's Company TPB (2006, $14.99) r/#31-35 & The Pact #4; sketch pages 15.00
Vol. 8: My Favorite Martian TPB (2007, $14.99) r/#36-41; sketch pages 15.00
Vol. 9: Out of This World TPB (2008, $14.99) r/#42-47; sketch pages 15.00

INVINCIBLE FOUR OF KUNG FU & NINJA
Leung Publications: April, 1988 - No. 6, 1989 ($2.00)
1-($2.75) 4.00
2-6: 2-Begin $2.00-c 3.00

INVINCIBLE IRON MAN
Marvel Comics: July, 2008 - No. 33, Feb, 2011; No. 500, Mar, 2011 - No. 527, Dec, 2012 ($2.99/$3.99)
1-Fraction-s/Larroca-a; covers by Larroca & Quesada 4.00
1-Downey movie photo wraparound 5.00
1-Secret Movie Variant white-c with movie cast 30.00
2-18: 2-War Machine and Thor app. 7-Spider-Man app. 8-10-Dark Reign. 11-War Machine app.; Pepper gets her armor suit. 12-Namor app. 3.00
19,20-($3.99) 20-Stark Disassembled starts; back-up synopsis of recent storylines 4.00
21-24-Covers by Larocca and Zircher: 21-Thor & Capt. America app. 22-Dr. Strange app. 3.00
25-($3.99) Fraction-s/Larroca-a; new armor 4.00
26-31-($2.99) 29-New Rescue armor 3.00
32,33-($3.99)-War Machine app.; back-up w/McKelvie-a 4.00
(After #33, numbering reverts to original Vol. 1 as #500)
500-(3/11, $4.99) Two covers by Larroca; Mandarin & Spider-Man app.; cover gallery 5.00
500-Variant-c by Romita Jr. 10.00
500.1 (4/11, $2.99) History re-told; Fraction-s/Larroca-a/c 3.00
501-527-($3.99) 501-503-Doctor Octopus app. 503-Back-up w/Chaykin-a. 504-509-Fear Itself tie-in; Grey Gargoyle app. 517-New War Machine armor 4.00
Annual 1 (8/10, $4.99) Larroca-c; history of the Mandarin; Di Giandomenico-a 5.00
...MGC #1 (4/10, free) r/#1 with "Marvel's Greatest Comics" cover logo 3.00

INVINCIBLE IRON MAN
Marvel Comics: Dec, 2015 - No. 14, Dec, 2016 ($3.99)
1-6,8-14: 1-Bendis-s/Marquez-a; Doctor Doom & Madame Masque app. 6-14-Deodato-a. 8-Spider-Man app. 11-14-Civil War II tie-in 4.00
7-1st app. Riri Williams; Spider-Man app. 10.00

INVINCIBLE IRON MAN (Riri Williams as Ironheart)
Marvel Comics: Jan, 2017 - No. 11, Nov, 2017 ($3.99)
1-11: 1-Bendis-s/Caselli-a; Riri Williams childhood origin; Animax app. 4.00

INVINCIBLE IRON MAN (Marvel Legacy)(Also continued from Infamous Iron Man)
Marvel Comics: No. 593, Dec, 2017 - Present ($3.99)
593-597-Bendis-s/Caselli & Maleev-a; Ironheart & Doctor Doom app. 4.00

INVINCIBLE UNIVERSE (Characters from Invincible)
Image Comics: Apr, 2013 - No. 12, Apr, 2014 ($2.99)
1-12-Hester-s/Nauck-a. 1-Wraparound-c 3.00

INVISIBLE BOY (See Approved Comics)

INVISIBLE MAN, THE (See Superior Stories #1 & Supernatural Thrillers #2)

INVISIBLE PEOPLE
Kitchen Sink Press: 1992 (B&W, lim. series)
Book One: Sanctum; Book Two: "The Power": Will Eisner-s/a in all 4.00
Book Three: "Mortal Combat" 4.00
Hardcover ($34.95) 35.00
TPB (DC Comics, 9/00, $12.95) reprints series 13.00

INVISIBLE REPUBLIC
Image Comics: Feb, 2015 - Present ($2.99/$3.99)
1-10-Hardman & Bechko-s/Hardman-a 3.00
11-15-($3.99) 4.00

INVISIBLES, THE (1st Series)
DC Comics (Vertigo): Sept, 1994 - No. 25, Oct, 1996 ($1.95/$2.50, mature)
1-($2.95, 52 pgs.)-Intro King Mob, Ragged Robin, Boy, Lord Fanny & Dane (Jack Frost); Grant Morrison scripts in all 6.00
2-8: 4-Includes bound-in trading cards. 5-1st app. Orlando; brown paper-c 4.00
9-25: 10-Intro Jim Crow. 13-15-Origin Lord Fanny. 19-Origin King Mob; polybagged. 20-Origin Boy. 21-Mister Six revealed. 25-Intro Division X 3.00
Apocalipstick (2001, $19.95, TPB)-r/#9-16; Bolland-c 20.00
Entropy in the U.K. (2001, $19.95, TPB)-r/#17-25; Bolland-c 20.00
Say You Want A Revolution (1996, $17.50, TPB)-r/#1-8 18.00
NOTE: ***Buckingham** a-25p. **Rian Hughes** c-1, 5. **Phil Jimenez** a-17p-19p. **Paul Johnson** a-16, 21. **Sean Phillips** c-2-4, 6-25. **Weston** a-10p. **Yeowell** a-1p-4p, 22p-24p.*

INVISIBLES, THE (2nd Series)
DC Comics (Vertigo): V2#1, Feb, 1997 - No. 22, Feb, 1999 ($2.50, mature)
1-Intro Jolly Roger; Grant Morrison scripts, Phil Jimenez-a, & Brian Bolland-c begins 4.00
2-22: 9,14-Weston-a 3.00
Bloody Hell in America TPB ('98, $12.95) r/#1-4 13.00
Counting to None TPB ('99, $19.95) r/#5-13 20.00
Kissing Mr. Quimper TPB ('00, $19.95) r/#14-22 20.00

INVISIBLES, THE (3rd Series) (Issue #'s go in reverse from #12 to #1)
DC Comics (Vertigo): V3#12, Apr, 1999 - No. 1, June, 2000 ($2.95, mature)
1-12-Bolland-c; Morrison-s on all. 1-Quitely-a. 2-4-Art by various. 5-8-Phillips-a. 9-12-Phillip Bond-a. 3.00

Iron Fist (2017 series) #1 © MAR

Iron Fist: The Living Weapon #7 © MAR

Iron Man #100 © MAR

	GD 2.0	VG 4.0	FN 6.0	VF 8.0	VF/NM 9.0	NM- 9.2

The Invisible Kingdom TPB ('02, $19.95) r/#12-1; new Bolland-c 20.00

INVISIBLE SCARLET O'NEIL (Also see Famous Funnies #81 & Harvey Comics Hits #59)
Famous Funnies (Harvey): Dec, 1950 - No. 3, Apr, 1951 (2-3 pgs. of Powell-a in each issue.)

	GD	VG	FN	VF	VF/NM	NM-
1	16	32	48	92	144	195
2,3	12	24	36	69	97	125

ION (Green Lantern Kyle Rayner) (See Countdown)
DC Comics: Jun, 2006 - No. 12, May, 2007 ($2.99)

1-12: 1-Marz-s/Tocchini-a. 3-Mogo app. 9,10-Tangent Green Lantern app. 12-Monitor app. 3.00
...: The Torchbearer TPB (2007, $14.99) r/#1-6 15.00

I, PAPARAZZI
DC Comics (Vertigo): 2001 ($29.95, HC, digitally manipulated photographic art)

nn-Pat McGreal-s/Steven Parke-digital-a/Stephen John Phillips-photos 30.00

IRON AGE
Marvel Comics: Aug, 2011 - No. 3, Oct, 2011 ($4.99, limited series)

1-3-Iron Man time travels. 1-Avengers. 2-Fantastic Four. 3-Dazzler & X-Men 5.00
...: Alpha (8/11, $2.99) First part of the series; Dark Phoenix app.; Issacs-a 3.00
...: Omega (10/11, $2.99) Conclusion of the series; Olivetti-c/Issacs-a 3.00

IRON AND THE MAIDEN
Aspen MLT: Sept, 2007 - No. 4, Dec, 2007 ($3.99)

1-4: 1-Two covers by Manapul and Madureira/Matsuda; Jason Rubin-s 4.00
...: Brutes, Bims and the City (2/08, $2.99) character backgrounds/development art 3.00

IRON CORPORAL, THE (See Army War Heroes #22)
Charlton Comics: No. 23, Oct, 1985 - No. 25, Feb, 1986

23-25: Glanzman-a(r); low print 6.00

IRON FIST (See Immortal Iron Fist, Deadly Hands of Kung Fu, Marvel Premiere & Power Man)
Marvel Comics: Nov, 1975 - No. 15, Sept, 1977

	GD	VG	FN	VF	VF/NM	NM-
1-Iron Fist battles Iron Man (#1-6: 25¢)	9	18	27	59	117	175
2	4	8	12	27	44	60
3-10: 4-6-(Regular 25¢ edition)(4-6/76). 8-Origin retold	3	6	9	19	30	40
4-6-(30¢-c variant, limited distribution)	5	10	15	35	63	90
11,13: 13-(30¢-c)	3	6	9	16	24	32
12-Capt. America app.	4	8	12	23	37	50
13-(35¢-c variant, limited distribution)	14	28	42	96	211	325
14-1st app. Sabretooth (8/77)(see Power Man)	17	34	51	117	259	400
14-(35¢-c variant, limited distribution)	145	290	435	1196	2698	4200
15-(Regular 30¢ ed.) X-Men app., Byrne-a	6	12	18	41	76	110
15-(35¢-c variant, limited distribution)	46	92	138	368	834	1300

NOTE: *Adkins a-8p, 10i, 13i; c-8i.* ***Byrne*** *a-1-15p; c-8p, 15p.* ***G. Kane*** *c-4-6p.* ***McWilliams*** *a-1i.*

IRON FIST
Marvel Comics: Sept, 1996 - No. 2, Oct, 1996 ($1.50, limited series)

1,2 4.00

IRON FIST
Marvel Comics: Jul, 1998 - No. 3, Sept, 1998 ($2.50, limited series)

1-3: Jurgens-s/Guice-a 4.00

IRON FIST (Also see Immortal Iron Fist)
Marvel Comics: May, 2004 - No. 6, Oct, 2004 ($2.99)

1-6: 1-4,6-Kevin Lau-c/a. 5-Mays-c/a 4.00

IRON FIST
Marvel Comics: May, 2017 - No. 7, Nov, 2017; No. 73, Dec, 2017 - Present ($3.99)

1-7: 1-Brisson-s/Perkins-a. 4.00
[Title switches to legacy numbering after #7 (11/17)]
73-77-Sabretooth app. 4.00

IRON FIST: THE LIVING WEAPON
Marvel Comics: Jun, 2014 - No. 12, Jul, 2015 ($3.99)

1-12-Kaare Andrews-s/a/c; origin re-told in flashbacks 4.00

IRON FIST: WOLVERINE
Marvel Comics: Nov, 2000 - No. 4, Feb, 2001 ($2.99, limited series)

1-4-Igle-c/a; Kingpin app. 2-Iron Man app. 3,4-Capt. America app. 4.00

IRON GHOST
Image Comics: Apr, 2005 - No. 6, Mar, 2006 ($2.95/$2.99, limited series)

1-6-Chuck Dixon-s/Sergio Cariello-a; flip cover on each 3.00

IRONHAND OF ALMURIC (Robert E. Howard's...)
Dark Horse Comics: Aug, 1991 - No. 4, 1991 ($2.00, B&W, mini-series)

1-4: 1-Conrad painted-c 3.00

IRON HORSE (TV)
Dell Publishing Co.: March, 1967 - No. 2, June, 1967

	GD	VG	FN	VF	VF/NM	NM-
1-Dale Robertson photo covers on both	3	6	9	17	26	35
2	3	6	9	15	21	26

IRONJAW (Also see The Barbarians)
Atlas/Seaboard Publ.: Jan, 1975 - No. 4, July, 1975

	GD	VG	FN	VF	VF/NM	NM-
1,2-Neal Adams-c. 1-1st app. Iron Jaw; Sekowsky-a(p); Fleisher-s	3	6	9	14	20	25
3,4-Marcos. 4-Origin	2	4	6	9	13	16

IRON LANTERN
Marvel Comics (Amalgam): June, 1997 ($1.95, one-shot)

1-Kurt Busiek-s/Paul Smith & Al Williamson-a 3.00

IRON MAIDEN LEGACY OF THE BEAST
Heavy Metal Inc.: Oct, 2017 - No. 5 ($3.99, limited series)

1-Llexi Leon & Edginton-s/West-a/Casas-c; Eddie app. 4.00

IRON MAN (Also see The Avengers #1, Giant-Size..., Marvel Collectors Item Classics, Marvel Double Feature, Marvel Fanfare, Tales of Suspense #39 & Uncanny Tales #52)
Marvel Comics: May, 1968 - No. 332, Sept, 1996

	GD	VG	FN	VF	VF/NM	NM-
1-Origin; Colan-c/a(p); story continued from Iron Man & Sub-Mariner #1	120	240	360	700	1100	1500
2	13	26	39	89	195	300
3-Iron Man vs. The Freak	10	20	30	64	132	200
4,5: 4-Unicorn app.	9	18	27	57	111	165
6-10: 7,8-Gladiator app. 9-Iron Man battles green Hulk-like android. 9,10-The Mandarin app.	7	14	21	46	86	125
11-15: 10,11-Mandarin app. 13-1st app. Controller. 15-Last 12c issue; vs Unicorn and the Red Ghost	6	12	18	38	69	100
16,18-20: 16-Vs. Unicorn and the Red Ghost. 18-Avengers app. 19-Captain America app.	5	10	15	31	53	75
17-1st Madame Masque & Midas (Mordecai Midas)	6	12	18	38	69	100
21-24,26-30: 21-Crimson Dynamo app. 22-Death of Janice Cord; Crimson Dynamo app. 27-Intro Firebrand. 28-Controller app.	4	8	12	25	40	55
25-Iron Man battles Sub-Mariner	5	10	15	30	50	70
31-42: 33-1st app. Spymaster. 35-Daredevil & Nick Fury vs. Zodiak; x-over w/Daredevil #73. 36-Daredevil & Nick Fury vs Zodiak. 39-Avengers app. 42-Last 15c issue	3	6	9	21	33	45
43-Intro the Guardsman (25¢ Giant, 52 pgs); Giant-Man back-up (r) from TTA #52	5	10	15	35	63	90
44-46,48-53: 44-Capt. America app; back-up Ant-Man w/Andru-a. 46-The Guardsman dies. 48-Firebrand app. 49-Super-Adaptoid app. 50-Princess Python app. 53-1st Black Lama; Starlin part pencils	3	6	9	18	30	40
47-Origin retold; Barry Smith-a(p)	7	14	21	46	86	125
54-Iron Man battles Sub-Mariner; 1st app. Moondragon (1/73) as Madame MacEvil; Everett part-c	11	22	33	76	163	250
55-1st app. Thanos, Drax the Destroyer, Mentor, Starfox & Kronos (2/73); Starlin-c/a	120	240	360	700	1100	1500
56-Starlin-a	5	10	15	33	57	80
57-63: 57,58-Mandarin and Unicorn app. 59-Firebrand app. 60,61-Vs. the Masked Marauder. 62-Whiplash app. 63-Vs. Dr. Spectrum	3	6	9	16	24	32
64,65,67-70: 64,65-Dr. Spectrum app; origin is #65; Thor brief app. 67-Last 20c issue. 68-Sunfire, Mandarin and Unicorn app. 69,70-Mandarin, Yellow Claw & Ultimo app.	3	6	9	14	20	25
66-Iron Man vs. Thor.	4	8	12	27	44	60
71-84: 71-Yellow Claw & Black Lama app. 72-Black Lama app; Iron Man at the San Diego Comic Con. 73-Vs. Crimson Dynamo & Radioactive Man; Stark Industries renamed Stark International. 74-Modok vs. Mad-Thinker; Black Lama app in "War of the Super-Villains". 75-Black Lama & Yellow Claw app. 76-r/#9. 77-Conclusion of the "War of the Super-Villains"; Black Lama app. 80-Origin of Black Lama. 81-Black Lama & Firebrand app. 82,83-Red Ghost app.	2	4	6	10	14	18
85-89-(Regular 25¢ editions): 86-1st app. Blizzard. 87-Origin Blizzard. 88-Brief Thanos cameo. 89-Daredevil app.; last 25¢-c	2	4	6	10	14	18
85-89-(30¢-c variants, limited distribution)(4-8/76)	5	10	15	31	53	75
90-99: 90,91-Blood Brothers & Controller app. 92-Vs. Melter. 95-Ultimo app. 96-1st new Guardsman (Michael O' Brien). 98,99-Mandarin & Sunfire app.	2	4	6	9	12	15
99,101-103-(35¢-c variants, limited dist.)	11	22	33	73	157	240
100-(7/77)-Starlin-c; Iron Man vs. The Mandarin	4	8	12	25	40	55
100-(35¢-c variant, limited dist.)	21	42	63	147	324	500

101-117: 101-Intro DreadKnight; Frankenstein app. 103-Jack of Hearts app; guest stars through issue #113. 104-107-Vs. Midas. 109-1st app. New Crimson Dynamo; 1st app. Vanguard. 110-Origin Jack of Hearts retold; death of Count Nefaria. 113,114-Unicorn and

Iron Man #306 © MAR

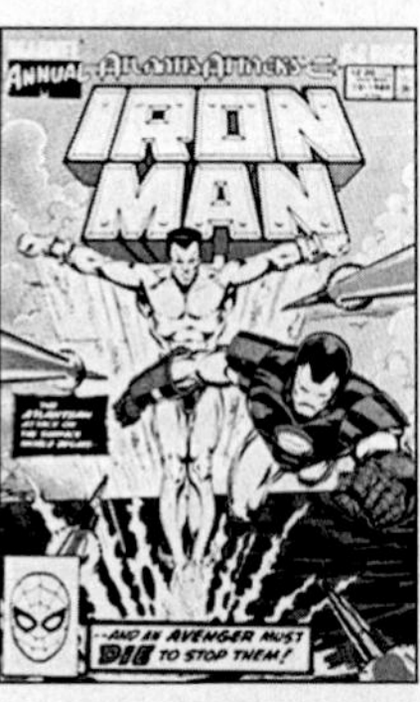

Iron Man Annual #10 © MAR

Iron Man V3 #55 © MAR

GD 2.0 | VG 4.0 | FN 6.0 | VF 8.0 | VF/NM 9.0 | NM- 9.2

Titanium Man app. 114,115-Avengers app; 1st John Romita Jr. pencils on Iron Man (10/78).
116-1st David Michelinie & Bob Layton issue 2 4 6 8 10 12
118-Byrne-a(p); 1st app. Jim Rhodes 5 10 15 30 50 70
119,122-124,127: 122-Origin. 123-128-Tony treated for alcohol problem. 123,124-Vs. Blizzard, Melter & Whiplash; Justin Hammer app. 127-Vs. Justin Hammer's "Super-Villain army" 2 4 6 11 16 20
120,121,126: 120,121-Sub-Mariner app. 126-Classic Tony becoming Iron Man-c 2 4 6 13 19 25
125-Avengers & Ant-Man (Scott Lang) app. 3 6 9 16 23 30
128-(11/79) Classic Tony Stark alcoholism cover 6 12 18 37 66 95
129,130,134-149: 134,135-Titanium Man app. 137-139-Spymaster app. 142-Intro. Space Armor. 143-1st app. Sunturion. 146 Backlash app. (formally Whiplash). 148-Captain America app. 149-Dr. Doom app. 1 2 3 5 7 9
131-133: 131,132-Hulk x-over. 133-Hulk/Ant Man-c 2 4 6 9 12 15
150-Double size; Dr. Doom; Merlin & Camelot 2 4 6 10 14 18
151-168: 151-Ant-Man (Scott Lang) app. 152-1st app stealth armor. 153-Living Laser app; last Layton co-plot (returns in #215). 154-Unicorn app. 156-Intro the Mauler; last Michelinie plot (returns in issue #215); last Romita Jr. art (p). 159-Paul Smith-a(p); Fantastic Four app. 160-Serpent Squad app. 161-Moon Knight app. 163-Intro. Obadiah Stane (hand only). 166-1st full app. Obadiah Stane. 167-Tony Stark alcohol problem resurfaces. 168-Machine Man app. 6.00
169-New Iron Man (Jim Rhodes replaces Tony Stark) 2 4 6 9 12 15
170,171 6.00
172-199: 172-Captain America x-over. 173-Stark International becomes Stane International. 179-Radioactive Man app. 180-181-Vs. Mandarin. 186-Intro. Vibro. 188-Brother Grimm app. 189-Intro. Termite. 190-Scarlet Witch app. 191-198-Tony Stark returns as original Iron Man. 191-192-Vibro app. 192-Tony Stark Iron Man vs. James Rhodes Iron Man. 193-West Coast Avengers app; unofficial 'Godzilla' app. 194-Intro. Scourge; kills the Enforcer. 195-West Coast Avengers & Shaman from Alpha Flight app. 197-Secret Wars II x-over; Byrne-c 5.00
200-(11/85, $1.25, 52 pgs.)-Tony Stark returns as new Iron Man (red & white armor) thru #230 2 4 6 8 10 12
201-213,215-224: 206-Hawkeye & Mockingbird app. 211-Vs. the Melter. 213-Intro. New Dominic Fortune. 215-Return of Michelinie/Layton creative team; James Rhodes app. (as Iron Man – also in #216). 219-Intro. The Ghost. 220-Spymaster & Ghost app. 221-Vs. Ghost. 222-Force app. 223-Intro. new Blizzard (Donald Gil). 224-Vs. Beetle, Backlash, Blizzard & Justin Hammer 4.00
214-Spider-Woman (Julia Carpenter) app. in new black costume (1/87) 6.00
225-(12/87, $1.25, 40 pgs)- Armor Wars begins; Ant-Man app. 1 3 4 6 8 10
226-227,229-230: Armor Wars in all. 226-West Coast Avengers app. 227-Beetle app.; Iron Man vs SHIELD Mandroids. 229-Vs. Crimson Dynamo & Titanium Man. 230-Armor Wars conclusion; vs Firepower 5.00
228-Armor Wars; Iron Man vs. Captain America (as the Captain) 6.00
231,234,247: 231-Intro. new Iron Man armor. 234-Spider-Man x-over. 247-Hulk x-over 5.00
232,233,235-243,245,246,248,249: 232-Barry Windsor Smith co-plot and (p). 233-Ant-Man app. 235,236-Vs. Grey Gargoyle. 238-Rhino & Capt. America app. 239,240-Vs. Justin Hammer. 241,242-Mandarin app. 243-Tony Stark loses use of legs. 249-Dr. Doom app. 3.00
244-($1.50, 52 pgs.)-New Armor makes him walk 4.00
250-($1.50, 52 pgs.)-Dr. Doom-c/story; Acts of Vengeance x-over; last Michelinie/Layton issue 4.00
251-274,276-281,283,285-287,289,292-299: 251,252-Acts of Vengeance x-over. 255-Intro new Crimson Dynamo (Valenyine Shatalov). 258-Byrne script & Romita Jr.-a(p) begins. 259-Armor Wars II begins; ends #266. 260-Vs. Living Laser. 261-264-Mandarin & Fin Fang Foom app. 266-Last Romita Jr.-a(p). 267,268-Origin expanded; Mandarin added to origin. 270-275-Dragon seed story w/Mandarin and Fin Fang Foom. 276-Black Widow app. 277-Last Byrne-s. 278-279-Operation Galactic Storm x-overs. 281-Intro. Masters of Silence; 1st cameo app. War Machine. 285,286-Beetle, Backlash & Blizzard app. 287-West Coast Avengers app. 287-Intro Atom Smasher. 289-Vs. Living Laser. 290-James Rhodes retains the War Machine armor. 292-Capt. America app. 295-Infinity Crusade x-over. 296,297-Omega Red app. 298,299-Return of Ultimo 3.00
275-($1.50, 52 pgs.) Mandarin & Fin Fang Foom app. 4.00
282-1st full app. War Machine (7/92) 4 8 12 23 37 50
284-Death of Iron Man (Tony Stark); James Rhodes becomes War Machine 6.00
288-($2.50, 52pg.)-Silver foil stamped-c; Iron Man's 350th app. in comics 5.00
290-($2.95, 52pg.)-Gold foil stamped-c; 30th ann. 5.00
291-Iron Man & War Machine team-up 5.00
300-($3.95, 68 pgs.)-Collector's Edition w/embossed foil-c; anniversary issue; War Machine-c/story 5.00
300-($2.50, 68 pgs.)-Newsstand Edition 4.00
301,303: 301-Venom cameo. 303-Captain America app. 4.00
302-Venom-c/story; Captain America app. 6.00
304-Thunderstrike app; begin $1.50-c; bound-in-trading card sheet 3 6 9 14 20 25
305-Hulk-c/story 2 4 6 10 14 18
306-309-Mandarin app. 309-War Machine app. 3.00
310-($2.95) Polybagged w/16 pg Marvel Action Hour preview & acetate print 6.00
310-($1.50) Regular edition; white logo; "Hands of the Mandarin" x-over w/Force Works and War Machine 4.00
311,312- "Hands of the Mandarin" x-over w/Force Works and War Machine. 312-w/bound-in Power Ranger card 4.00
313,315,316,318: 315-316-Black Widow app. 316-Crimson Dynamo & Titanium Man app. 5.00
314-Crossover w/Captain America; Henry Pym app. 6.00
317-($2.50)-Flip book; Black Widow app; death of Titanium Man; Hawkeye, War Machine & USAgent app. 6.00
319-Intro. new Iron Man armor; Force Works app; prologue to "The Crossing" story 6.00
320,321: 321-w/Overpower card insert 5.00
322-324-Avengers app; x-over w/Avengers and Force Works 5.00
325-($2.95)-Wraparound-c; Tony Stark Iron Man vs "Teen" Tony Iron Man; Avengers & Force Works x-over; continued in Avengers #395 5.00
326- "Teen" Tony app. as Iron Man thru #332; Avengers, Thor & Cap America x-over 6.00
327-330: 330-War Machine & Stockpile app; return of Morgan Stark 4.00
331-War Machine app; leads into the "Onslaught" x-over 5.00
332-(9/96) Onslaught x-over; last issue 6.00
Special 1 (8/70)-Sub-Mariner x-over; Everett-c 6 12 18 37 66 95
Special 2 (11/71, 52 pgs.)-r/TOS #81,82,91 (all-r) 3 6 9 19 30 40
Annual 3 (1976)-Man-Thing app. 3 6 9 14 20 25
King Size 4 (8/77)-The Champions (w/Ghost Rider) app.; Newton-a(i) 2 4 6 11 16 20
Annual 5 ('82) Black Panther & Mandarin app. 1 3 4 6 8 10
Annual 6-9: ('83-'86) 6-New Iron Man (J. Rhodes) app. 8-X-Factor app. 5.00
Annual 10 ('89) Atlantis Attacks x-over; P. Smith-a; Layton/Guice-a; Sub-Mariner app. 4.00
Annual 11-14 ('90-'93): 11-Terminus Factor pt. 2; origin of Mrs. Arbogast by Ditko (p&i). 12-1 pg. origin recap; Ant-Man back-up-s; Subterranean Wars Pt. 4. 13-Darkhawk & Avengers West Coast app.; Colan/Williamson-a. 14-Bagged w/card; 1st app. Face Thief 4.00
Annual 15 ('94)- Iron Man vs. the Controller 4.00
...: Armor Wars TPB (2007, $24.99) r/#225-232; Michelinie intro. 25.00
Manual 1 (1993, $1.75)-Operations handbook 3.00
Graphic Novel: Crash (1988, $12.95, Adults, 72 pgs.)-Computer generated art & color; violence & nudity 13.00
...Collector's Preview 1(11/94, $1.95)-wraparound-c; text & illos-no comics 3.00
...: Demon in a Bottle HC (2008, $24.99) r/#120-128; two covers 25.00
...: Demon in a Bottle TPB (2006, $24.99) r/#120-128 25.00
...: Many Armors of Iron Man (2008, $24.99) r/#47, 142-144, 152-153, 200, 218 25.00
...Vs. Dr. Doom (12/94, $12.95)-r/#149-150, 249,250. Julie Bell-c 13.00
...Vs. Dr. Doom: Doomquest HC (2008, $19.99, dustjacket)-r/#149-150, 249,250; new Michelinie intro.; bonus art 20.00
....: War Machine TPB (2008, $29.99) r/#280-291 30.00
The Invincible Iron Man Omnibus Vol. 1 HC (2008, $99.99, dustjacket) r/Iron Man stories from Tales of Suspense #39-83 & Tales To Astonish #82; 1992 intro. by Stan Lee; 1975 essay by Lee; 2008 essay by Layton; gallery of original art and covers; creator bios 100.00

NOTE: **Austin** *c-105i, 109-111i, 151i.* **Byrne** *a-118p; c-109p, 197, 253.* **Colan** *a-1p, 253, Special 1p(3); c-1p.* **Craig** *a-1i, 2-4, 5-13i, 14, 15-19i, 24p, 25p, 26-28i; c-2-4.* **Ditko** *a-160p.* **Everett** *c-29.* **Guice** *a-233-241p.* **G. Kane** *c(p)-52-54, 63, 67, 72-75, 77-79, 88, 98.* **Kirby** *a-Special 1p; 80p, 90, 92-95.* **Mooney** *a-40i, 43i, 47i.* **Perez** *c-103p.* **Simonson** *c-Annual 8.* **B. Smith** *a-232p, 243i; c-232.* **P. Smith** *a-159p, 245p, Annual 10p; c-159.* **Starlin** *a-53p(part), 55p, 56p; c-55p, 160, 163.* **Tuska** *a-5-13p, 15-23p, 24i, 32p, 38-46p, 48-54p, 57-61p, 63-69p, 70-72p, 78p, 86-92p, 95-106p, Annual 4p.* **Wood** *a-Special 1i.*

IRON MAN (The Invincible...) (Volume Two)
Marvel Comics: Nov, 1996 - No. 13, Nov, 1997 ($2.95/$1.95/$1.99)
(Produced by WildStorm Productions)

V2#1-3-Heroes Reborn begins; Scott Lobdell scripts & Whilce Portacio-c/a begin; new origin Iron Man & Hulk. 2-Hulk app. 3-Fantastic Four app. 4.00
1-Variant-c 5.00
4-11: 4-Two covers. 6-Fantastic Four app.; Industrial Revolution; Hulk app. 7-Return of Rebel. 11-($1.99) Dr. Doom-c/app. 3.00
12-($2.99) "Heroes Reunited"-pt. 3; Hulk-c/app. 4.00
13-($1.99) "World War 3"-pt. 3, x-over w/Image 3.00
Heroes Reborn: Iron Man (2006, $29.99, TPB) r/#1-12; Heroes Reborn #1/2; pin-ups 30.00

IRON MAN (The Invincible...) (Volume Three)
Marvel Comics: Feb, 1998 - No. 89, Dec, 2004 ($2.99/$1.99/$2.25)

V3#1-($2.99)-Follows Heroes Return; Busiek scripts & Chen-c/a begin; Deathsquad app. 6.00
1-Alternate Ed. 1 2 3 5 7 9
2-12: 2-Two covers. 6-Black Widow-c/app. 7-Warbird-c/app. 8-Black Widow app. 9-Mandarin returns 4.00
13-($2.99) battles the Controller 5.00
14-24: 14-Fantastic Four-c/app. 3.00
25-($2.99) Iron Man and Warbird battle Ultimo; Avengers app. 4.00
26-30-Quesada-s. 28-Whiplash killed. 29-Begin $2.25-c. 3.00
31-45,47-49,51-54: 35-Maximum Security x-over; FF-c/app. 41-Grant-a begins.

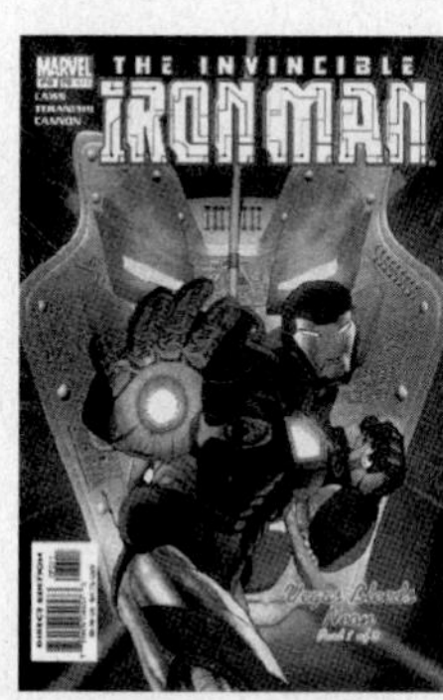

Iron Man V3 #70 © MAR

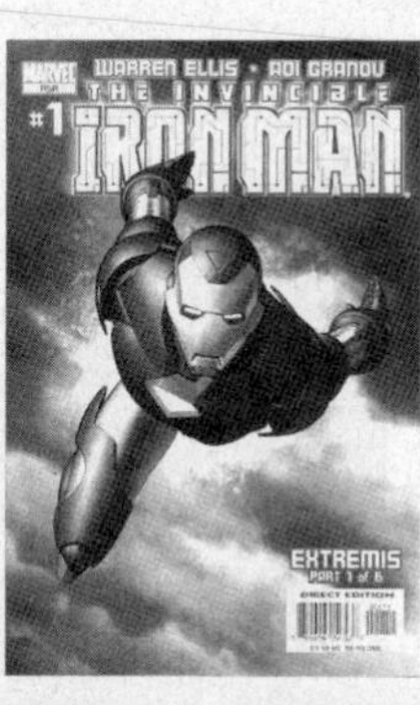

Iron Man (2005 series) #1 © MAR

Iron Man Noir #3 © MAR

GD 2.0 | VG 4.0 | FN 6.0 | VF 8.0 | VF/NM 9.0 | NM- 9.2

44-New armor debut. 48-Ultron-c/app. 3.00
46-($3.50, 100 pgs.) Sentient armor returns; r/V1#78,140,141 4.00
50-($3.50) Grell-s begin; Black Widow app. 4.00
55-($3.50) 400th issue; Asamiya-c; back-up story Stark reveals ID; Grell-a 4.00
56-66: 56-Reis-a. 57,58-Ryan-a. 59-61-Grell-c/a. 62,63-Ryan-a. 64-Davis-a; Thor-c/app. 3.00
67-89: 67-Begin $2.99-c; Gene Ha-c. 75-83-Granov-c. 84-Avengers Disassembled prologue
85-89-Avengers Disassembled. 85-88-Harris-a. 86-89-Pat Lee-c. 87-Rumiko killed 3.00
.../Captain America '98 Annual ($3.50) vs. Modok 4.00
1999, 2000 Annual ($3.50) 4.00
2001 Annual ($2.99) Claremont-s/Ryan-a 4.00
Avengers Disassembled: Iron Man TPB (2004, $14.99) r/#84-89 15.00
Mask in the Iron Man (5/01, $14.95, TPB) r/#26-30, #1/2 15.00

IRON MAN (The Invincible...)
Marvel Comics: Jan, 2005 - No. 35, Jan, 2009 ($3.50/$2.99)

1-($3.50-c) Warren Ellis-s/Adi Granov-c/a; start of Extremis storyline 5.00
2-6-($2.99): 5-Flashback to origin; Stark gets new abilities 4.00
7-14: 7-Knauf-s/Zircher-a. 13,14-Civil War 3.00
15-24,26,27,29-35: 15-Stark becomes Director of S.H.I.E.L.D. 19,20-World War Hulk.
33-Secret Invasion; War Machine app. 34,35-War Machine title logo 3.00
25,28-($3.99) 25-Includes movie preview & armor showcase. 28-Red & white armor 4.00
All-New Iron Manual (2/08, $4.99) Handbook-style guide to characters & armor suits 5.00
... By Design 1 (11/10, $3.99) Gallery of 2010 variant covers with artist commentary 4.00
.../Captain America: Casualities of War (2/07, $3.99) two covers; flashbacks 4.00
...: Director of S.H.I.E.L.D. Annual 1 (1/08, $3.99) Madame Hydra app.; Cheung-c 4.00
Free Comic Book Day 2010 (Iron Man: Supernova) #1 (5/10, 9-1/2" x 6-1/4") Nova app. 3.00
Free Comic Book Day 2010 (Iron Man/Thor) #1 (5/10, 9-1/2" x 6-1/4") Romita Jr.-a/c 3.00
...Golden Avenger 1 (11/08, $2.99) Santacruz-a; movie photo-c 3.00
.../Hulk/Fury 1 (2/09, $3.99) crossover of movie-version characters 4.00
Indomitable Iron Man (4/10, $3.99) B&W stories; Chaykin-s/a; Rosado-a; Parrillo-c 4.00
Iron Manual Mark 3 (6/10, $3.99) Handbook-format profiles of characters 4.00
...: Iron Protocols (12/09, $3.99) Olivetti-c/Nelson-a 4.00
...: Kiss and Kill (8/10, $3.99) Black Widow and Wolverine app. 4.00
Marvel Halloween Ashcan 2007 (8-1/2" x 5-3/8") updated origin; Michael Golden-c 3.00
...: Requiem (2009, $4.99) r/TOS #39, Iron Man #144 (1981); armor profiles 5.00
...: The End (1/09, $4.99) future Tony Stark retires; Michelinie-s/Chang & Layton-a 5.00
...: Titanium! 1 (12/10, $4.99) short stories by various; Yardin-c 5.00
Civil War: Iron Man TPB (2007, $11.99) r/#13,14, .../Captain America: Casualities of War,
and Civil War: The Confession 12.00
HC (2006, $19.99, dust jacket) r/#1-6 and Granov covers from Iron Man V3 #75-83 20.00
...: Director of S.H.I.E.L.D. TPB (2007, $14.99) r/#15-18; Strange Tales #135 (1965) and Iron
Man #129; profile pages for Iron Man and S.H.I.E.L.D.; creator interviews 15.00
...: Extremis SC (2007, $14.99) r/#1-6 and Granov covers from Iron Man V3 #75-83 15.00
...: Execute Program SC (2007, $14.99) r/#7-12; cover layouts and sketches 15.00

IRON MAN (Marvel Now!)(Leads into Superior Iron Man)
Marvel Comics: Jan, 2013 - No. 28, Aug, 2014 ($3.99)

1-28: 1-8-Gillen-s/Land-c/a. 5-Stark heads out to space. 9-17-Secret Origin of Tony Stark.
9-12-Eaglesham-a. 17-Arno Stark revealed. 23-26-Malekith app. 4.00
20.INH (3/12, $3.99) Inhumanity tie-in; origin The Exile; Padilla-a 4.00
Annual 1 (4/14, $4.99) Gillen-s/Martinez, Padilla & Marz-a 5.00
... Special 1 (9/14, $4.99) Cont'd from Uncanny X-Men Special #1; Ryan-s/Handoko-a 5.00

IRON MAN (The Armor Wars)
Marvel Comics: No. 258.1, Jul, 2013 - No. 258.4, Jul, 2013 ($3.99, weekly limited series)

258.1-258.4 - Set after Iron Man #258 (1990); Michelinie-s/Dave Ross & Bob Layton-a 4.00

IRON MAN AND POWER PACK
Marvel Comics: Jan, 2008 - No. 4, Apr, 2008 ($2.99, limited series)

1-4-Gurihiru-c/Sumerak-s; Puppet Master app.; Mini Marvels back-ups in each 3.00
...: Armored and Dangerous TPB (2008, $7.99, digest size) r/series 8.00

IRON MAN & SUB-MARINER
Marvel Comics Group: Apr, 1968 (12¢, one-shot) (Pre-dates Iron Man #1 & Sub-Mariner #1)

1-Iron Man story by Colan/Craig continued from Tales of Suspense #99 & continued in
Iron Man #1; Sub-Mariner story by Colan continued from Tales to Astonish #101 &
continued in Sub-Mariner #1; Colan/Everett-c 17 34 51 117 259 400

IRON MAN AND THE ARMOR WARS
Marvel Comics: Oct, 2009 - No. 4, Jan, 2010 ($2.99, limited series)

1-4-Rousseau-a; Crimson Dynamo & Omega Red app. 3.00

IRON MAN: ARMORED ADVENTURES
Marvel Comics: Sept, 2009 ($3.99, one-shot)

1-Based on the 2009 cartoon; Brizuela-a; Nick Fury & Living Laser app. 4.00

IRON MAN: BAD BLOOD
Marvel Comics: Sept, 2000 - No. 4, Dec, 2000 ($2.99, limited series)

1-4-Micheline-s/Layton-a 3.00

IRON MAN: ENTER THE MANDARIN
Marvel Comics: Nov, 2007 - No. 6, Apr, 2008 ($2.99, limited series)

1-6-Casey-s/Canete-a; retells first meeting 3.00
TPB (2008, $14.99) r/#1-6 15.00

IRON MAN: EXTREMIS DIRECTOR'S CUT
Marvel Comics: Jun, 2010 - No. 6, Sept, 2010 ($3.99, limited series)

1-6-Reprints Iron Man #1-6 (2005 series) with script pages and design art 4.00

IRON MAN: FATAL FRONTIER
Marvel Comics: 2014 ($34.99, hardcover)

HC - Printing of digital comic #1-13 and r/Iron Man Annual #1 (4/14) 35.00

IRON MAN: HOUSE OF M (Also see House of M and related x-overs)
(Reprinted in House of M: Fantastic Four/ Iron Man TPB)
Marvel Comics: Sept, 2005 - No. 3, Nov, 2005 ($2.99, limited series)

1-3-Pat Lee-a/c; Greg Pak-s 3.00

IRON MAN: HYPERVELOCITY
Marvel Comics: Mar, 2007 - No. 6, Aug, 2007 ($2.99, limited series)

1-6-Adam Warren-s/Brian Denham-a/c 3.00
TPB (2007, $14.99) r/#1-6; layout pages and armor design sketches 15.00

IRON MAN: I AM IRON MAN
Marvel Comics: Mar, 2010 - No. 2, Apr, 2010 ($3.99, limited series)

1,2-Adaptation of the first movie; Peter David-s/Sean Chen-a/Adi Granov-c 4.00

IRON MAN: INEVITABLE
Marvel Comics: Feb, 2006 - No. 6, July, 2006 ($2.99, limited series)

1-6-Joe Casey-s/Frazer Irving; Spymaster and the Living Laser app. 3.00
TPB (2006, $14.99) r/#1-6; cover sketches 15.00

IRON MAN: LEGACY
Marvel Comics: Jun, 2010 - No. 11, Apr, 2011 ($3.99/$2.99)

1-Van Lente-s/Kurth-a; Dr. Doom app.; back-up r/debut in Tales of Suspense #39 4.00
2-11-($2.99) 4-Titanium Man & Crimson Dynamo app. 6-The Pride app. 3.00

IRON MAN: LEGACY OF DOOM
Marvel Comics: Jun, 2008 - No. 4, Sept, 2008 ($2.99, limited series)

1-4-Michelinie-s/Lim & Layton-a; Dr. Doom app. 3.00

IRON MAN NOIR
Marvel Comics: Jun, 2010 - No. 4, Sept, 2010 ($3.99, limited series)

1-4-Pulp-style set in 1939; Snyder-s/Garcia-a 4.00

IRON MAN: RAPTURE
Marvel Comics: Jan, 2011 - No. 4, Feb, 2011 ($3.99, limited series)

1-4-Irvine-s/Medina-a/Bradstreet-c. 3,4-War Machine app. 4.00

IRON MAN: SEASON ONE
Marvel Comics: 2013 ($24.99, hardcover graphic novel)

HC - Origin story and early days; Chaykin-s/Parel-a/Tedesco painted-c 25.00

IRON MAN: THE COMING OF THE MELTER
Marvel Comics: Jul, 2013 ($3.99, one-shot)

1-Movie version; Ron Lim-a; back-up reprint of Iron Man #72 (1/75); 3 covers 4.00

IRON MAN: THE IRON AGE
Marvel Comics: Aug, 1998 - No. 2, Sept, 1998 ($5.99, limited series)

1,2-Busiek-s; flashback story from gold armor days 6.00

IRON MAN: THE LEGEND
Marvel Comics: Sept, 1996 ($3.95, one-shot)

1-Tribute issue 5.00

IRON MAN/ THOR
Marvel Comics: Jan, 2011 - No. 4, Apr, 2011 ($3.99, limited series)

1-4-Eaton-a; Crimson Dynamo & Diablo app. 4.00

IRON MAN 2: ... (Follows the first movie)
Marvel Comics: Jun, 2010 - Nov, 2010 ($3.99, limited series)

Agents of S.H.I.E.L.D. 1 (11/10, $3.99) Nick Fury, Agent Coulson & Black Widow app. 4.00
Public Identity (6/10 - No. 3, 7/10, $3.99) 1-3-Kitson & Lim-a/Granov-c 4.00
Spotlight (4/10, $3.99) Interviews with Granov, Guggenheim, Fraction, Ellis, Michelinie 4.00

IRON MAN 2 ADAPTATION, (MARVEL'S...)
Marvel Comics: Jan, 2013 - No. 2, Feb, 2013 ($2.99, limited series)

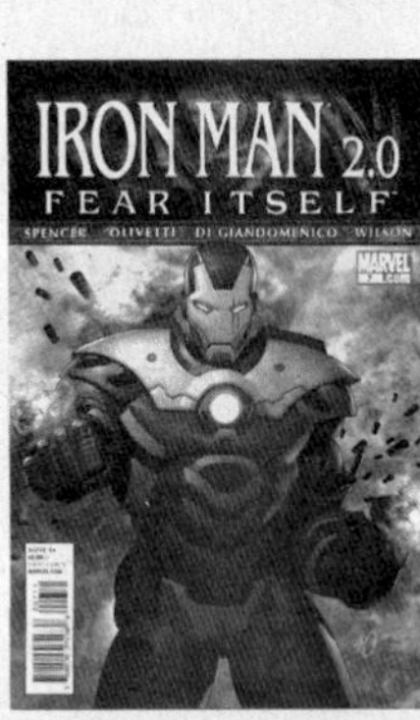

Iron Man 2.0 #7 © MAR

Irredeemable #37 © BOOM!

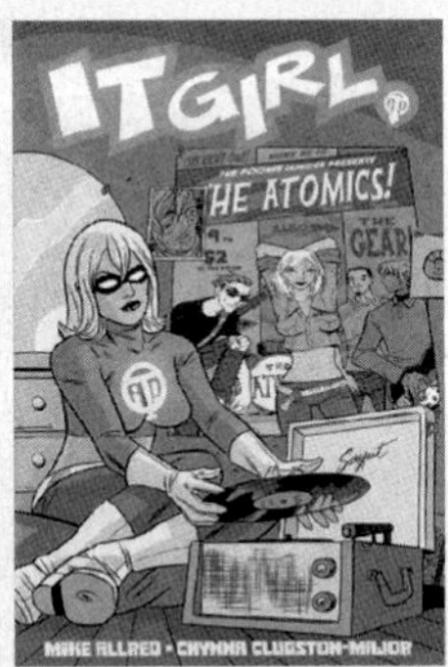

It Girl #1 © Mike Allred

	GD 2.0	VG 4.0	FN 6.0	VF 8.0	VF/NM 9.0	NM- 9.2
1,2-Photo-c; Rosanas-a						3.00

IRON MAN 2.0
Marvel Comics: Apr, 2011 - No. 12, Feb, 2012 ($3.99/$2.99)

	GD 2.0	VG 4.0	FN 6.0	VF 8.0	VF/NM 9.0	NM- 9.2
1-($3.99) Spencer-s/Kitson-c; back-up history of War Machine						4.00
1-Variant-c by Djurdjevic						6.00
2-7,(7.1),8-12-($2.99) 2,3-Kitson, Kano & Di Giandomenico-a. 5-7-Fear Itself tie-in						3.00
...: Modern Warfare 1 (10/11, $4.99) r/#1-3 with variant covers						5.00

IRON MAN 3 PRELUDE, (MARVEL'S...)
Marvel Comics: Mar, 2013 - No. 2, Apr, 2013 ($2.99, limited series)

	GD 2.0	VG 4.0	FN 6.0	VF 8.0	VF/NM 9.0	NM- 9.2
1,2-Photo-c; Gage-s/Kurth-a; War Machine app.						3.00

IRON MAN 2020 (Also see Machine Man limited series)
Marvel Comics: June, 1994 ($5.95, one-shot)

	GD 2.0	VG 4.0	FN 6.0	VF 8.0	VF/NM 9.0	NM- 9.2
nn						6.00

IRON MAN: VIVA LAS VEGAS
Marvel Comics: Jul, 2008 - No. 2 ($3.99, unfinished limited series)

	GD 2.0	VG 4.0	FN 6.0	VF 8.0	VF/NM 9.0	NM- 9.2
1,2-Jon Favreau-s/Adi Granov-a/c						4.00

IRON MAN VS WHIPLASH
Marvel Comics: Jan, 2010 - No. 4, Apr, 2010 ($3.99, limited series)

	GD 2.0	VG 4.0	FN 6.0	VF 8.0	VF/NM 9.0	NM- 9.2
1-4-Briones-a/Peterson-c; origin of new Whiplash						4.00

IRON MAN/X-O MANOWAR: HEAVY METAL (See X-O Manowar/Iron Man: In Heavy Metal)
Marvel Comics: Sept, 1996 ($2.50, one-shot) (1st Marvel/Valiant x-over)

	GD 2.0	VG 4.0	FN 6.0	VF 8.0	VF/NM 9.0	NM- 9.2
1-Pt. II of Iron Man/X-O Manowar x-over; Fabian Nicieza scripts; 1st app. Rand Banion						4.00

IRON MARSHALL
Jademan Comics: July, 1990 - No. 32, Feb, 1993 ($1.75, plastic coated-c)

	GD 2.0	VG 4.0	FN 6.0	VF 8.0	VF/NM 9.0	NM- 9.2
1,32: Kung Fu stories. 1-Poster centerfold						4.00
2-31-Kung Fu stories in all						3.00

IRON PATRIOT (Marvel Now!)
Marvel Comics: May, 2014 - No. 5, Sept, 2014 ($3.99)

	GD 2.0	VG 4.0	FN 6.0	VF 8.0	VF/NM 9.0	NM- 9.2
1-5-James Rhodes in the armor; Ales Kot-s/Garry Brown-a/c						4.00

IRON VIC (See Comics Revue No. 3 & Giant Comics Editions)
United Features Syndicate/St. John Publ. Co.: 1940

	GD 2.0	VG 4.0	FN 6.0	VF 8.0	VF/NM 9.0	NM- 9.2
Single Series 22	36	72	108	211	343	475

IRONWOLF
DC Comics: 1986 ($2.00, one shot)

	GD 2.0	VG 4.0	FN 6.0	VF 8.0	VF/NM 9.0	NM- 9.2
1-r/Weird Worlds #8-10; Chaykin story & art						4.00

IRONWOLF: FIRES OF THE REVOLUTION (See Weird Worlds #8-10)
DC Comics: 1992 ($29.95, hardcover)

	GD 2.0	VG 4.0	FN 6.0	VF 8.0	VF/NM 9.0	NM- 9.2
nn-Chaykin/Moore story, Mignola-a w/Russell inks.						30.00

IRREDEEMABLE (Also see Incorruptible)
BOOM! Studios: Apr, 2009 - No. 37, May, 2012 ($3.99)

	GD 2.0	VG 4.0	FN 6.0	VF 8.0	VF/NM 9.0	NM- 9.2
1-37: 1-Waid-s/Krause-a; 3 covers; Grant Morrison afterword. 2-32-Three covers						4.00
1-Artist Edition (12/11, $3.99) r/#1 in B&W with bonus sketch and design art						4.00
... Special 1 (4/10, $3.99) Art by Azaceta, Rios & Chaykin; three covers						4.00

IRREDEEMABLE ANT-MAN, THE
Marvel Comics: Dec, 2006 - No. 12, Nov, 2007 ($2.99)

	GD 2.0	VG 4.0	FN 6.0	VF 8.0	VF/NM 9.0	NM- 9.2
1-12-Kirkman-s/Hester-a/c; intro. Eric O'Grady as the new Ant-Man. 7-Ms. Marvel app. 10-World War Hulk x-over						3.00
... Vol. 1: Lowlife (2007, $9.99, digest) r/#1-6						10.00
... Vol. 2: Small-Minded (2007, $9.99, digest) r/#7-12						10.00

ISAAC ASIMOV'S I-BOTS
Tekno Comix: Dec, 1995 - No. 7, May, 1996 ($1.95)

	GD 2.0	VG 4.0	FN 6.0	VF 8.0	VF/NM 9.0	NM- 9.2
1-7: 1-6-Perez-c/a. 2-Chaykin variant-c exists. 3-Polybagged. 7-Lady Justice-c/app.						3.00

ISAAC ASIMOV'S I-BOTS
BIG Entertainment: V2#1, June, 1996 - No. 9, Feb, 1997 ($2.25)

	GD 2.0	VG 4.0	FN 6.0	VF 8.0	VF/NM 9.0	NM- 9.2
V2#1-9: 1-Lady Justice-c/app. 6-Gil Kane-c						3.00

ISIS (TV) (Also see Shazam)
National Per.l Publ./DC Comics: Oct-Nov, 1976 - No. 8, Dec-Jan, 1977-78

	GD 2.0	VG 4.0	FN 6.0	VF 8.0	VF/NM 9.0	NM- 9.2
1-Wood inks	3	6	9	16	23	30
2-8: 5-Isis new look. 7-Origin	2	3	4	6	8	10

ISLAND AT THE TOP OF THE WORLD (See Walt Disney Showcase #27)

ISLAND OF DR. MOREAU, THE (Movie)
Marvel Comics Group: Oct, 1977 (52 pgs.)

	GD 2.0	VG 4.0	FN 6.0	VF 8.0	VF/NM 9.0	NM- 9.2
1-Gil Kane-c	1	2	3	5	6	8

I SPY (TV)
Gold Key: Aug, 1966 - No. 6, Sept, 1968 (All have photo-c)

	GD 2.0	VG 4.0	FN 6.0	VF 8.0	VF/NM 9.0	NM- 9.2
1-Bill Cosby, Robert Culp photo covers	10	20	30	67	141	215
2-6: 3,4-McWilliams-a. 5-Last 12¢-c	6	12	18	38	69	100

IT! (See Astonishing Tales No. 21-24 & Supernatural Thrillers No. 1)

ITCHY & SCRATCHY COMICS (The Simpsons TV show)
Bongo Comics: 1993 - No. 3, 1993 ($1.95)

	GD 2.0	VG 4.0	FN 6.0	VF 8.0	VF/NM 9.0	NM- 9.2
1-3: 1-Bound-in jumbo poster. 3-w/decoder screen trading card	2	4	6	8	11	14
Holiday Special ('94, $1.95)	1	3	4	6	8	10

IT GIRL (Also see Atomics, and Madman Comics)
Oni Press: May, 2002 ($2.95, one-shot)

	GD 2.0	VG 4.0	FN 6.0	VF 8.0	VF/NM 9.0	NM- 9.2
1-Allred-s/Clugston-Major-c/a; Atomics and Madman app.						3.00

IT GIRL! AND THE ATOMICS (Also see Atomics, and Madman Comics)
Image Comics: Aug, 2012 - No. 12, Jul, 2013 ($2.99)

	GD 2.0	VG 4.0	FN 6.0	VF 8.0	VF/NM 9.0	NM- 9.2
1-12: 1-Rich-s/Norton-a/Allred-c. 2-Two covers (Allred & Cooke). 6-Clugston Flores-a						3.00

IT REALLY HAPPENED
William H. Wise No. 1,2/Standard (Visual Editions): 1944 - No. 11, Oct, 1947

	GD 2.0	VG 4.0	FN 6.0	VF 8.0	VF/NM 9.0	NM- 9.2
1-Kit Carson & Ben Franklin stories	26	52	78	154	252	350
2,3-Nazi WWII-c	15	30	45	85	130	175
4,6,9,11: 4-D-Day story. 6-Ernie Pyle WWII-c; Joan of Arc story. 9-Captain Kidd & Frank Buck stories	14	28	42	76	108	140
5-Lou Gehrig & Lewis Carroll stories	18	36	54	107	169	230
7-Teddy Roosevelt story	15	30	45	83	124	165
8-Story of Roy Rogers	17	34	51	98	154	210
10-Honus Wagner & Mark Twain stories	15	30	45	90	140	190

NOTE: ***Guardineer** a-7(2), 8(2), 10, 11. **Schomburg** c-1-7, 9-11.*

IT RHYMES WITH LUST (Also see Bold Stories & Candid Tales)
St. John Publishing Co.: 1950 (Digest size, 128 pgs., 25¢)

	GD 2.0	VG 4.0	FN 6.0	VF 8.0	VF/NM 9.0	NM- 9.2
nn (Rare)-Matt Baker & Ray Osrin-a	300	600	900	2010	3505	5000

IT'S A BIRD...
DC Comics: 2004 ($24.95, hardcover with dust jacket)

	GD 2.0	VG 4.0	FN 6.0	VF 8.0	VF/NM 9.0	NM- 9.2
HC-Semi-autobiographical story of Steven Seagle writing Superman; Kristiansen-a						25.00
SC-($17.95)						18.00

IT'S ABOUT TIME (TV)
Gold Key: Jan, 1967

	GD 2.0	VG 4.0	FN 6.0	VF 8.0	VF/NM 9.0	NM- 9.2
1 (10195-701)-Photo-c	4	8	12	27	44	60

IT'S A DUCK'S LIFE
Marvel Comics/Atlas(MMC): Feb, 1950 - No. 11, Feb, 1952

	GD 2.0	VG 4.0	FN 6.0	VF 8.0	VF/NM 9.0	NM- 9.2
1-Buck Duck, Super Rabbit begin	19	38	57	111	176	240
2	12	24	36	67	94	120
3-11	11	22	33	60	83	105

IT'S GAMETIME
National Periodical Publications: Sept-Oct, 1955 - No. 4, Mar-Apr, 1956

	GD 2.0	VG 4.0	FN 6.0	VF 8.0	VF/NM 9.0	NM- 9.2
1-(Scarce)-Infinity-c; Davy Crockett app. in puzzle	100	200	300	635	1093	1550
2,3 (Scarce): 2-Dodo & The Frog	69	138	207	442	759	1075
4 (Rare)	73	146	219	467	796	1125

IT'S LOVE, LOVE, LOVE
St. John Publishing Co.: Nov, 1957 - No. 2, Jan, 1958 (10¢)

	GD 2.0	VG 4.0	FN 6.0	VF 8.0	VF/NM 9.0	NM- 9.2
1,2	8	16	24	44	57	70

IT! THE TERROR FROM BEYOND SPACE
IDW Publishing: Jul, 2010 - No. 3, Sept, 2010 ($3.99, limited series)

	GD 2.0	VG 4.0	FN 6.0	VF 8.0	VF/NM 9.0	NM- 9.2
1-3-Naraghi-s/Dos Santos-a/Mannion-c						4.00

ITTY BITTY COMICS (Issue #5, see Grimmiss Island; title changes to Grimmiss Island)
Dark Horse Comics: Nov, 2014 - No. 4, Feb, 2015 ($2.99, limited series)

	GD 2.0	VG 4.0	FN 6.0	VF 8.0	VF/NM 9.0	NM- 9.2
1-4-All-ages humor stories of kid-version Mask by Art Baltazar & Franco						3.00

ITTY BITTY COMICS: THE MASK
Dark Horse Comics: Nov, 2014 - No. 4, Feb, 2015 ($2.99, limited series)

	GD 2.0	VG 4.0	FN 6.0	VF 8.0	VF/NM 9.0	NM- 9.2
1-4-All-ages humor stories of kid-version Mask by Art Baltazar & Franco						3.00

ITTY BITTY HELLBOY
Dark Horse Comics: Aug, 2013 - No. 5, Dec, 2013 ($2.99, limited series)

	GD 2.0	VG 4.0	FN 6.0	VF 8.0	VF/NM 9.0	NM- 9.2
1-5-All-ages humor stories of kid-version Hellboy characters by Art Baltazar & Franco						3.00

ITTY BITTY HELLBOY: THE SEARCH FOR THE WERE-JAGUAR

I, Vampire #1 © DC

Jack Armstrong #5 © PMI

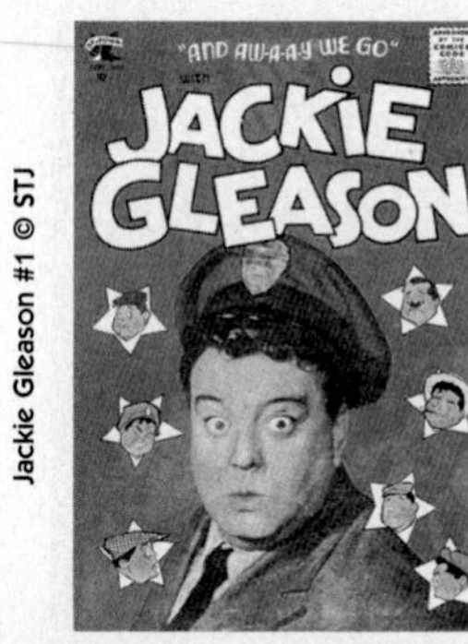

Jackie Gleason #1 © STJ

GD 2.0 | VG 4.0 | FN 6.0 | VF 8.0 | VF/NM 9.0 | NM- 9.2

Dark Horse Comics: Nov, 2015 - No. 4, Feb, 2016 ($2.99, limited series)

1-4-All-ages humor stories of kid-version Hellboy characters by Art Baltazar & Franco 3.00

I, VAMPIRE (DC New 52)
DC Comics: Nov, 2011 - No. 19, Jun, 2013 ($2.99)

1-19: 1-Fialkov-s/Sorrentino-a/Frison-c. 4-Constantine app. 5-7-Batman app. 7,8-Crossover with Justice League Dark #7,8. 12-Stormwatch app. 16-19-Constantine app. 3.00
#0-(11/12, $2.99) Origin of Andrew Bennett; Fialkov-s/Sorrentino-a/Crain-c 3.00

IVANHOE (See Fawcett Movie Comics No. 20)

IVANHOE
Dell Publishing Co.: July-Sept, 1963

1 (12-372-309) 3 6 9 20 31 42

IVAR, TIMEWALKER
Valiant Entertainment: Jan, 2015 - No. 12, Dec, 2015 ($3.99)

1-12: 1-4-Fred Van Lente-s/Clayton Henry-a. 5-8-Portela-a. 9-Pere Perez-a 4.00

IVX (Inhumans vs X-Men) (Also see Death of X)
Marvel Comics: No. 0, Jan, 2017 - No. 6, May, 2017 ($3.99/$4.99/$5.99)

0-($4.99) Soule-s/Rocafort-a; Beast, Medusa, Emma Frost, Magneto app. 5.00
1-($5.99) Soule & Lemire-s/Yu-a; multiple covers 6.00
2-5-($3.99) 2-Yu-a. 3-5-Garrón-a 4.00
6-($4.99) Yu-a; leads into Inhumans Prime #1, X-Men Prime #1 & Unc. Inhumans #20 5.00

IWO JIMA (See Spectacular Features Magazine)

IXTH GENERATION (See Ninth Generation)

I, ZOMBIE (Inspired the 2015 TV show)(See House of Mystery Halloween Annual #1 for 1st app.)
DC Comics (Vertigo): July, 2010 - No. 28, Oct, 2012 ($1.00/$2.99)

1-($1.00) Allred-a/Roberson-s; 2 covers by Allred & Cooke 3 6 9 16 23 30
2-28-($2.99) Allred-c/a in most. 12-Gilbert Hernandez-a. 18-Jay Stephens-a. 25-Rugg-a 3.00
... Special Edition 1 (5/15, $1.00) r/#1; new inteview with Allred 3.00
...: Dead to the World TPB (2011, $14.99) r/#1-5 & House of Mystery Hall. Ann. #1 15.00

JACE PEARSON OF THE TEXAS RANGERS (Radio/TV)(4-Color #396 is titled Tales of the Texas Rangers; ...'s Tales of ... #11-on)(See Western Roundup under Dell Giants)
Dell Publishing Co.: No. 396, 5/52 - No. 1021, 8-10/59 (No #10) (All-Photo-c)

Four Color 396 (#1) 10 20 30 67 141 215
2(5-7/53) - 9(2-4/55) 6 12 18 40 73 105
Four Color 648(#10, 9/55) 6 12 18 40 73 105
11(11-2/55-56) - 14,17-20(6-8/58) 5 10 15 33 57 80
15,16-Toth-a 5 10 15 34 60 85
Four Color 961,1021: 961-Spiegle-a 5 10 15 34 60 85
NOTE: *Joel McCrea photo c-1-9, F.C. 648 (starred on radio show only); Willard Parker photo c-11-on (starred on TV series).*

JACK ARMSTRONG (Radio)(See True Comics)
Parents' Institute: Nov, 1947 - No. 9, Sept, 1948; No. 10, Mar, 1949 - No. 13, Sept, 1949

nn (6/47) Ashcan edition; full color slick cover (a FN/VF sold for $485 in 2011)
1-(Scarce) (odd size) Cast intro. inside front-c; Vic Hardy's Crime Lab begins 48 96 144 302 514 725
2 21 42 63 122 199 275
3-5 15 30 45 88 137 185
6-13 14 28 42 80 115 150

JACK AVARICE IS THE COURIER
IDW Publishing: Nov, 2012 - No. 5, Nov, 2012 ($3.99, weekly limited series)

1-5-Chriss Madden-s/a/c 4.00

JACK CROSS
DC Comics: Oct, 2005 - No. 4, Jan, 2006 ($2.50)

1-4-Warren Ellis-s/Gary Erskine-a 3.00
DC Comics Presents: Jack Cross #1 (12/10, $7.99, squarebound) r/#1-4 8.00

JACKED
DC Comics (Vertigo): Jan, 2016 - No. 6, Jun, 2016 ($3.99)

1-6-Eric Kripke-s/John Higgins-a/Glenn Fabry-c 4.00

JACK HUNTER
Blackthorne Publishing: July, 1987 - No. 3 ($1.25)

1-3 3.00

JACKIE CHAN'S SPARTAN X
Topps Comics: May, 1997 - No. 3 ($2.95, limited series)

1-3-Michael Golden-s/a; variant photo-c 3.00

JACKIE CHAN'S SPARTAN X: HELL BENT HERO FOR HIRE
Image Comics (Little Eva Ink): Mar, 1998 - No. 3 ($2.95, B&W)

1-3-Michael Golden-s/a: 1-variant photo-c 3.00

JACKIE GLEASON (TV) (Also see The Honeymooners)
St. John Publishing Co.: Sept, 1955 - No. 4, Dec, 1955?

1(1955)(TV)-Photo-c 77 154 231 493 847 1200
2-4 50 100 150 315 533 750

JACKIE GLEASON AND THE HONEYMOONERS (TV)
National Periodical Publications: June-July, 1956 - No. 12, Apr-May, 1958

1-1st app. Ralph Kramden 135 270 405 864 1482 2100
2 65 130 195 416 708 1000
3-11: 8-Statue of Liberty-c 50 100 150 315 533 750
12 (Scarce) 69 138 207 442 759 1075

JACKIE JOKERS (Became Richie Rich &...)
Harvey Publications: March, 1973 - No. 4, Sept, 1973 (#5 was advertised, but not published)

1-1st app. 3 6 9 16 22 28
2-4: 2-President Nixon app. 2 4 6 8 11 14

JACKIE ROBINSON (Famous Plays of...) (Also see Negro Heroes #2 & Picture News #4)
Fawcett Publications: May, 1950 - No. 6, 1952 (Baseball hero) (All photo-c)

nn 97 194 291 621 1061 1500
2 55 110 165 352 601 850
3-6 47 94 141 296 498 700

JACK IN THE BOX (Formerly Yellowjacket Comics #1-10; becomes Cowboy Western Comics #17 on)
Frank Comunale/Charlton Comics No. 11 on: Feb, 1946; No. 11, Oct, 1946 - No. 16, Nov-Dec, 1947

1-Stitches, Marty Mouse & Nutsy McKrow 22 44 66 132 216 300
11-Yellowjacket (early Charlton comic) 24 48 72 142 234 325
12,14,15 15 30 45 85 130 175
13-Wolverton-a 23 46 69 136 223 310
16-12 pg. adapt. of Silas Marner; Kiefer-a 15 30 45 88 137 185

JACK KIRBY OMNIBUS, THE
DC Comics: 2011; 2013 ($49.99, hardcover with dustjacket)

Vol. 1 ('11) Recolored reprints of Kirby's DC work from 1946, 1957-1959; Evanier intro. 50.00
Vol. 2 ('13) Recolored reprints of Kirby's DC work from 1973-1987; Morrow intro. 50.00

JACK KIRBY'S FOURTH WORLD (See Mister Miracle & New Gods, 3rd Series)
DC Comics: Mar, 1997 - No. 20, Oct, 1998 ($1.95/$2.25)

1-20: 1-Byrne-a/scripts & Simonson-c begin; story cont'd from New Gods, 3rd Series #15; retells "The Pact" (New Gods, 1st Series #7); 1st brief DC app. Thor. 2-Thor vs. Big Barda; "Apokolips Then" back-up begins; Kirby-c/swipe (Thor #126) 8-Genesis x-over. 10-Simonson-s/a 13-Simonson back-up story. 20-Superman-c/app. 3.00

JACK KIRBY'S FOURTH WORLD OMNIBUS
DC Comics: 2007 - Vol. 4, 2008 ($49.99, hardcovers with dustjackets)

Vol. 1 ('07) Recolored reprints in chronological order of Superman's Pal, Jimmy Olsen #133-139, Forever People #1-3, New Gods #1-3, and Mister Miracle #1-3; Morrison intro, bonus art 50.00
Vol. 2 ('07) r/Jimmy Olsen #141-145, F.P. #4-6, N.G. #4-6 & M.M. #4-6; bonus art 50.00
Vol. 3 ('07) r/Jimmy Olsen #146-148, F.P. #7-10, N.G. #7-10 & M.M. #7-9; bonus art 50.00
Vol. 4 ('08) r/F.P. #11, M.M. #10-18, N.G. #11 & reprint series #6, & DC Graphic Novel #6 (The Hunger Dogs); Levitz intro.; Evanier afterword; character profile pages 50.00

JACK KIRBY'S GALACTIC BOUNTY HUNTERS
Marvel Comics (Icon): July, 2006 - No. 6, Nov, 2007 ($3.99)

1-6-Based on a Kirby concept; Mike Thibodeaux-a; Lisa Kirby, Thibodeaux and others-s 4.00
HC (2007, $24.99) r/series; pin-ups and supplemental art and interviews 25.00

JACK KIRBY'S SECRET CITY SAGA
Topps Comics (Kirbyverse): No. 0, Apr, 1993; No. 1, May, 1993 - No. 4, Aug, 1993 ($2.95, limited series)

0-(No cover price, 20 pgs.)-Simonson-c/a 3.00
0-Red embossed-c (limited ed.) 5.00
1-4-Bagged w/3 trading cards; Ditko-c/a: 1-Ditko/Art Adams-c. 2-Ditko/Byrne-c; has coupon for Pres. Clinton holo-foil trading card. 3-Dorman poster; has coupon for Gore holo-foil trading card. 4-Ditko/Perez-c 3.00
NOTE: *Issues #1-4 contain coupons redeemable for Kirbychrome version of #1*

JACK KIRBY'S SILVER STAR (Also see Silver Star)
Topps Comics (Kirbyverse): Oct, 1993 ($2.95)(Intended as a 4-issue limited series)

1-Silver ink-c; Austin-c/a(i); polybagged w/3 cards 3.00

JACK KIRBY'S TEENAGENTS (See Satan's Six)
Topps Comics (Kirbyverse): Aug, 1993 - No. 4, Nov, 1993 ($2.95, limited series)

Jack of Fables #10 © Bill Willingham & DC

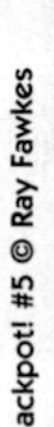
Jackpot! #5 © Ray Fawkes

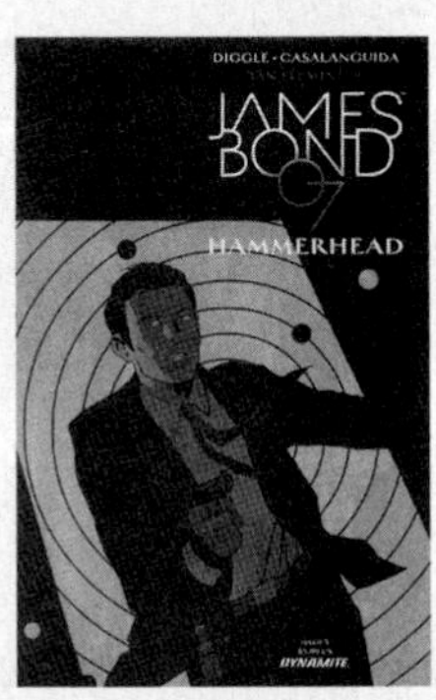

James Bond: Hammerhead #5 © Ian Fleming

GD VG FN VF VF/NM NM-
2.0 4.0 6.0 8.0 9.0 9.2

1-4: Bagged with/3 trading cards; Busiek-s/Austin-c(i): 3-Liberty Project app. 3.00

JACK KRAKEN
Dark Horse Comics: May, 2014 ($3.99, one-shot)
1-Tim Seeley-s; art by Ross Campbell & Jim Terry 4.00

JACK OF FABLES (See Fables)
DC Comics (Vertigo): Sept, 2006 - No. 50, Apr, 2011 ($2.99)
1-49: 1-Willingham & Sturges-s/Akins-a. 33-35-Crossover with Fables and The Literals 3.00
50-($4.99) Akins & Braun-a; Bolland-c 5.00
1-Special Edition (8/10, $1.00) r/#1 with "What's Next?" logo on cover 3.00
....: Americana TPB (2008, $14.99) r/#17-21 15.00
....: Jack of Hearts TPB (2007, $14.99) r/#6-11 15.00
....: The Bad Prince TPB (2008, $14.99) r/#12-16 15.00
....: The Big Book of War TPB (2009, $14.99) r/#28-32 15.00
....: The End TPB (2011, $17.99) r/#46-50 18.00
....: The Fulminate Blade TPB (2011, $14.99) r/#41-45 15.00
....: The (Nearly) Great Escape TPB (2007, $14.99) r/#1-5; Akins sketch pages 15.00
....: The New Adventures of Jack and Jack TPB (2010, $14.99) r/#36-40 15.00
....: Turning Pages TPB (2009, $14.99) r/#22-27 15.00

JACK OF HEARTS (Also see The Deadly Hands of Kung Fu #22 & Marvel Premiere #44)
Marvel Comics Group: Jan, 1984 - No. 4, Apr, 1984 (60¢, limited series)
1-4 4.00

JACKPOT!
AfterShock Comics: Apr, 2016 - No. 6, Jun, 2017 ($3.99)
1-6-Ray Fawkes-s/Brian Stelfreeze-c. 1-4-Marco Failla-a. 5,6-Georges Duarte-a 4.00

JACKPOT COMICS (Jolly Jingles #10 on)
MLJ Magazines: Spring, 1941 - No. 9, Spring, 1943
1-The Black Hood, Mr. Justice, Steel Sterling & Sgt. Boyle begin; Biro-c
331 662 993 2317 4059 5800
2-S. Cooper-c 161 322 483 1030 1765 2500
3-Hubbell-c 135 270 405 864 1482 2100
4-Archie begins; (his face appears on cover in small circle) (Win/41; on sale 12/41)-(also see Pep Comics #22); 1st app. Mrs. Grundy, the principal; Novick-c
3800 7600 11,400 21,700 28,350 35,000
5-Hitler, Tojo, Mussolini-c by Montana; 1st definitive Mr. Weatherbee; 1st brief app. Reggie in 1 panel 568 1136 1704 4146 7323 10,500
6-9: 6,7-Bondage-c by Novick. 8,9-Sahle-c 232 464 696 1485 2543 3600

JACK Q FROST (See Unearthly Spectaculars)

JACK STAFF (Vol. 2; previously published in Britain)
Image Comics: Feb, 2003 - No. 20, May, 2009 ($2.95/$3.50)
1-5-Paul Grist-s/a 3.50
6-20-($3.50) 6-Flashback to the WW2 Freedom Fighters 3.50
... Special 1 (1/08, $3.50) Molachi the Immortal app. 3.50
The Weird World of Jack Staff King Size Special 1 (7/07, $5.99, B&W) r/story serialized in Comics International magazine; afterword by Grist 6.00
Vol. 1: Everything Used to Be Black and White TPB (12/03, $19.95) r/British issues 20.00
Vol. 2: Soldiers TPB (2005, $15.95) r/#1-5; cover gallery 16.00
Vol. 3: Echoes of Tomorrow TPB (2006, $16.99) r/#6-12; cover gallery 17.00

JACK THE GIANT KILLER (See Movie Classics)

JACK THE GIANT KILLER (New Adventures of...)
Bimfort & Co.: Aug-Sept, 1953
V1#1-H. C. Kiefer-c/a 29 58 87 170 278 385

JACKY'S DIARY
Dell Publishing Co.: No. 1091, Apr-June, 1960 (one-shot)
Four Color 1091 5 10 15 33 57 80

JADEMAN COLLECTION
Jademan Comics: Dec, 1989 - No. 3, 1990 ($2.50, plastic coated-c, 68 pgs.)
1-3: 1-Wraparound-c w/fold-out poster 4.00

JADEMAN KUNG FU SPECIAL
Jademan Comics: 1988 ($1.50, 64 pgs.)
1 4.00

JADE WARRIORS (Mike Deodato's...)
Image Comics (Glass House Graphics): Nov, 1999 - No. 3, 2000 ($2.50)
1-3-Deodato-a 3.00
1-Variant-c 3.00

JAGUAR, THE (Also see The Adventures of...)
Impact Comics (DC): Aug, 1991 - No. 14, Oct, 1992 ($1.00)

GD VG FN VF VF/NM NM-
2.0 4.0 6.0 8.0 9.0 9.2

1-14: 4-The Black Hood x-over. 7-Sienkiewicz-c. 9-Contains Crusaders trading card 3.00
Annual 1 (1992, $2.50, 68 pgs.)-With trading card 4.00

JAGUAR GOD
Verotik: Mar, 1995 - No. 7, June, 1997 ($2.95, mature)
0 (2/96, $3.50)-Embossed Frazetta-c; Bisley-a; w/pin-ups. 5.00
1-Frazetta-c. 5.00
2-7: 2-Frazetta-c. 3-Bisley-c. 4-Emond-c. 7-($2.95)-Frazetta-c 4.00

JAKE THRASH
Aircel Publishing: 1988 - No. 3, 1988 ($2.00)
1-3 3.00

JAM, THE (...Urban Adventure)
Slave Labor Nos. 1-5/Dark Horse Comics Nos. 6-8/Caliber Comics No. 9 on: Nov, 1989 - No. 14, 1997 ($1.95/$2.50/$2.95, B&W)
1-14: Bernie Mireault-c/a/scripts. 6-1st Dark Horse issue. 9-1st Caliber issue 3.00

JAMBOREE COMICS
Round Publishing Co.: Feb, 1946(no month given) - No. 3, Apr, 1946
1-Funny animal 21 42 63 122 199 275
2,3 15 30 45 85 130 175

JAMES BOND
Dynamite Entertainment: 2015 - No. 12, 2016 ($3.99)
1-12-Warren Ellis-s/Jason Masters-a; multiple covers on each. 1-6-Vargr. 7-12-Eidolon 4.00
...: M (2018, $4.99) Shalvey-s/c; Holden-a 5.00
...: Moneypenny (2016, $4.99) Houser-s/Edgar-a/Lotay-c 5.00
...: Service (2017, $7.99) Kieron Gillen-s/Antonio Fuso-a/Jamie McKelvie-c 8.00
...: Solstice (2017, $4.99) Ibrahim Moustafa-s/a 5.00

JAMES BOND (Volume 2)
Dynamite Entertainment: 2017 - No. 6, 2017 ($3.99)
1-6-Black Box; Percy-s/Lobosco-a. 1-Five covers. 2-6-Multiple covers on each 4.00

JAMES BOND 007: A SILENT ARMAGEDDON
Dark Horse Comics/Acme Press: Mar, 1993 - Apr 1993 (limited series)
1,2 4.00

JAMES BOND 007: GOLDENEYE (Movie)
Topps Comics: Jan, 1996 ($2.95, unfinished limited series of 3)
1-Movie adaptation; Stelfreeze-c 3.00

JAMES BOND 007: SERPENT'S TOOTH
Dark Horse Comics/Acme Press: July 1992 - Aug 1992 ($4.95, limited series)
1-3-Paul Gulacy-c/a 5.00

JAMES BOND 007: SHATTERED HELIX
Dark Horse Comics: Jun 1994 - July 1994 ($2.50, limited series)
1,2 3.00

JAMES BOND 007: THE QUASIMODO GAMBIT
Dark Horse Comics: Jan 1995 - May 1995 ($3.95, limited series)
1-3 4.50

JAMES BOND: FELIX LEITER
Dynamite Entertainment: 2017 - No. 6, 2017 ($3.99)
1-6-James Robinson-s/Aaron Campbell-a 4.00

JAMES BOND FOR YOUR EYES ONLY
Marvel Comics Group: Oct, 1981 - No. 2, Nov, 1981
1,2-Movie adapt.; r/Marvel Super Special #19 6.00

JAMES BOND: HAMMERHEAD
Dynamite Entertainment: 2016 - No. 6, 2016 ($3.99)
1-6-Diggle-s/Casalanguida-a. 1-Three covers 4.00

JAMES BOND JR. (TV)
Marvel Comics: Jan, 1992 - No. 12, Dec, 1992 (#1: $1.00, #2-on: $1.25)
1-12: Based on animated TV show 3.00

JAMES BOND: KILL CHAIN
Dynamite Entertainment: 2017 - No. 6, 2017 ($3.99)
1-6-Diggle-s/Casalanguida-a. 1-Three covers. 2-Felix Leiter app. 4.00

JAMES BOND: LICENCE TO KILL (See Licence To Kill)

JAMES BOND: PERMISSION TO DIE
Eclipse Comics/ACME Press: 1989 - No. 3, 1991 ($3.95, lim. series, squarebound, 52 pgs.)
1-3: Mike Grell-c/a/scripts in all. 3-($4.95) 5.00

Jane Arden #1 © UFS

Jean Grey #1 © MAR

Jennifer Blood #27 © Spitfire

	GD 2.0	VG 4.0	FN 6.0	VF 8.0	VF/NM 9.0	NM- 9.2

JAMES BOND: THE BODY
Dynamite Entertainment: 2018 - Present ($3.99)

1,2: 1-Kot-s/Casalanguida-a. 2-Fuso-a — 4.00

JAM, THE: SUPER COOL COLOR INJECTED TURBO ADVENTURE #1 FROM HELL!
Comico: May, 1988 ($2.50, 44 pgs., one-shot)

1 — 4.00

JANE ARDEN (See Feature Funnies & Pageant of Comics)
St. John (United Features Syndicate): Mar, 1948 - No. 2, June, 1948

	GD	VG	FN	VF	VF/NM	NM-
1-Newspaper reprints	15	30	45	88	137	185
2	12	24	36	67	94	120

JANE WIEDLIN'S LADY ROBOTIKA
Image Comics: Jul, 2010 - No. 2, Aug, 2010 ($3.50, unfinished limited series)

1,2-Wiedlin & Bill Morrison-s. 1-Morrison & Rodriguez-a. 2-Moy-a — 3.50

JANN OF THE JUNGLE (Jungle Tales No. 1-7)
Atlas Comics (CSI): No. 8, Nov, 1955 - No. 17, June, 1957

	GD	VG	FN	VF	VF/NM	NM-
8(#1)	42	84	126	267	451	635
9,11-15	26	52	78	154	252	350
10-Williamson/Colletta-c	27	54	81	158	259	360
16,17-Williamson/Mayo-a(3), 5 pgs. each	27	54	81	162	266	370

NOTE: *Everett c-15-17.* ***Heck*** *a-8, 15, 17.* ***Maneely*** *c-11.* ***Shores*** *a-8.*

JASON & THE ARGOBOTS
Oni Press: Aug, 2002 - No. 4, Dec, 2002 ($2.95, B&W, limited series)

1-4-Torres-s/Norton-c/a — 3.00
Vol. 1 Birthquake TPB (6/03, $11.95, digest size) r/#1-4, Sunday comic strips — 12.00
Vol. 2 Machina Ex Deus TPB (9/03, $11.95, digest size) new story — 12.00

JASON & THE ARGONAUTS (See Movie Classics)

JASON GOES TO HELL: THE FINAL FRIDAY (Movie)
Topps Comics: July, 1993 - No. 3, Sept, 1993 ($2.95, limited series)

1-3: Adaptation of film. 1-Glow-in-the-dark-c — 3.00

JASON'S QUEST (See Showcase #88-90)

JASON VS. LEATHERFACE
Topps Comics: Oct, 1995 - No. 3, Jan, 1996 ($2.95, limited series)

1-3: Collins scripts; Bisley-c — 5.00

JAWS 2 (See Marvel Comics Super Special, A)

JAY & SILENT BOB (See Clerks, Oni Double Feature, and Tales From the Clerks)
Oni Press: July, 1998 - No. 4, Oct, 1999 ($2.95, B&W, limited series)

1-Kevin Smith-s/Fegredo-a; photo-c & Quesada/Palmiotti-c — 8.00
1-San Diego Comic Con variant covers (2 different covers, came packaged with action figures) — 10.00
1-2nd & 3rd printings, 2-4: 2-Allred-c. 3-Flip-c by Jaime Hernandez — 3.00
Chasing Dogma TPB (1999, $11.95) r/#1-4; Alanis Morissette intro. — 13.00
Chasing Dogma TPB (2001, $12.95) r/#1-4 in color; Morissette intro. — 13.00
Chasing Dogma HC (1999, $69.95, S&N) r/#1-4 in color; Morissette intro. — 70.00

JCP FEATURES
J.C. Productions (Archie): Feb, 1982-c; Dec, 1981-indicia ($2.00, one-shot, B&W magazine)

	GD	VG	FN	VF	VF/NM	NM-
1-T.H.U.N.D.E.R. Agents; Black Hood by Morrow & Neal Adams; Texeira-a; 2 pgs. S&K-a from Fly #1	2	4	6	8	10	12

JEAN GREY (X-Men) (Also see Phoenix Resurrection: The Return of Jean Grey)
Marvel Comics: Jul, 2017 - No. 11, Mar, 2018 ($3.99)

1-10: 1-Hopeless-s/Ibáñez-a. 4-Thor app. 6-Dr. Strange app. 7-Scarlet Witch app. — 4.00
11-($4.99) Follows Phoenix Resurrection #5; leads into X-Men: Red #1 — 5.00

JEANIE COMICS (Formerly All Surprise; Cowgirl Romances #28)
Marvel Comics/Atlas(CPC): No. 13, April, 1947 - No. 27, Oct, 1949

	GD	VG	FN	VF	VF/NM	NM-
13-Mitzi, Willie begin	34	68	102	199	325	450
14,15	22	44	66	132	216	300
16-Used in Love and Death by Legman; Kurtzman's "Hey Look"	26	52	78	154	252	350
17-19,21,22-Kurtzman's "Hey Look" (1-3 pgs. each)	20	40	60	114	182	250
20,23-27	18	36	54	105	165	225

JEEP COMICS (Also see G.I. Comics and Overseas Comics)
R. B. Leffingwell & Co.: Winter, 1944, No. 2, Spring, 1945 - No. 3, Mar-Apr, 1948

	GD	VG	FN	VF	VF/NM	NM-
1-Capt. Power, Criss Cross & Jeep & Peep (costumed) begin	76	152	228	486	831	1175
2- Jeep & Peep-c	47	94	141	296	498	700
3-L. B. Cole dinosaur-c	58	116	174	371	636	900

JEFF JORDAN, U.S. AGENT
D. S. Publishing Co.: Dec, 1947 - Jan, 1948

	GD	VG	FN	VF	VF/NM	NM-
1	18	36	54	107	169	230

JEFF STEINBERG: CHAMPION OF EARTH
Oni Press: Aug, 2016 - No. 6, Mar, 2017 ($4.99)

1-6: 1-Fialkov-s/Fleecs-a; covers by Fleecs & Burnham — 5.00

JEM & THE HOLOGRAMS
IDW Publishing: Mar, 2015 - No. 26, Apr, 2017 ($3.99)

1-25: 1-Origin re-told; multiple covers — 4.00
26-($4.99) Thompson-s/Lagace-a; previews Infinite x-over series; cover gallery — 5.00
Annual 2017 (1/17, $7.99) Thompson-s; art by Lagace and others; 2 covers — 8.00
... Holiday Special (12/15, $3.99) Mebberson-a — 4.00
IDW Greatest Hits: Jem and the Holograms #1 (7/16, $1.00) r/#1 — 3.00
... Valentine Special (2/16, $3.99) Thompson-s/Bartel-a — 4.00

JEM AND THE HOLOGRAMS: DIMENSIONS
IDW Publishing: Nov, 2017 - No. 4, Feb, 2018 ($3.99, limited series)

1-4-Anthology by various; multiple covers on each. 1-Leth-s/Ford-a — 4.00

JEM AND THE HOLOGRAMS: INFINITE
IDW Publishing: Jun, 2017 - No. 3, Aug, 2017 ($3.99, limited series)

1-3-Part 1,3,5 of the x-over with Jem and the Holograms: The Misfits: Infinite — 4.00

JEM AND THE HOLOGRAMS: THE MISFITS: INFINITE
IDW Publishing: Jun, 2017 - No. 3, Aug, 2017 ($3.99, limited series)

1-3-Part 2,4,6 of the x-over with Jem and the Holograms: Infinite — 4.00

JEMM, SON OF SATURN
DC Comics: Sept, 1984 - No. 12, Aug, 1985 (Maxi-series, mando paper)

1-12: 3-Origin. 4-Superman app. — 4.00

NOTE: ***Colan*** *a-1-12p; c-1-5, 7-12p.*

JEM: THE MISFITS (From Jem and the Holograms)
IDW Publishing: Dec, 2016 - No. 5, Apr, 2017 ($3.99)

1-5-Kelly Thompson-s/Jenn St-Onge-a — 4.00

JENNIFER BLOOD
Dynamite Entertainment: 2011 - No. 36, 2014 ($3.99)

1-36: 1-3-Garth Ennis-s/Adriano Batista-a; four covers on each. 4-The Ninjettes app. — 4.00
Annual 1 (2012, $4.99) Al Ewing-s/Igor Vitorino-a/Sean Chen-c; origin — 5.00

JENNIFER BLOOD: BORN AGAIN
Dynamite Entertainment: 2014 - No. 5, 2014 ($3.99)

1-5-Steven Grant-s/Kewber Baal-a/Stephen Segovia-c — 4.00

JENNIFER BLOOD: FIRST BLOOD
Dynamite Entertainment: 2011 - No. 6, 2013 ($3.99)

1-6-Mike Carroll-s/Igor Vitorino-a/Mike Mayhew-c; origin & training — 4.00

JENNIFER'S BODY (Based on the 2009 movie)
BOOM! Studios: Aug, 2009 ($24.99, hardcover graphic novel)

HC-Short stories of Jennifer and her victims; Spears-s/art by various; pin-up art — 25.00

JENNY FINN
Oni Press: June, 1999 - No. 2, Sept, 1999 ($2.95, B&W, unfinished lim. series)

1,2-Mignola & Nixey-s/Nixey-a/Mignola-c — 3.00
...: Doom (Atomeka, 2005, $6.99, TPB) r/#1 & 2 with new supplemental material — 7.00

JENNY SPARKS: THE SECRET HISTORY OF THE AUTHORITY
DC Comics (WildStorm): Aug, 2000 - No. 5, Mar, 2001 ($2.50, limited series)

	GD	VG	FN	VF	VF/NM	NM-
1-Millar-s/McCrea & Hodgkins-a/Hitch & Neary-c						4.00
1-Variant-c by McCrea	1	3	4	6	8	10
2-5: 2-Apollo & Midnighter. 3-Jack Hawksmoor. 4-Shen. 5-Engineer						3.00
TPB (2001, $14.95) r/#1-5; Ellis intro.						15.00

JERICHO (Based on the TV series)
Devil's Due Publishing/IDW Publishing: Oct, 2009 - Present ($3.99)

... Redux (IDW, 2/11, $7.99) r/Season 3: Civil War #1-3 — 8.00
... Season 3: Civil War 1-4: 1-Story by the show's writing staff — 4.00
... Season 4: 1-5: 1-(7/12) Photo-c & Bradstreet-c — 4.00

JERRY DRUMMER (Boy Heroes of the Revolutionary War) (Formerly Soldier & Marine V2#9)
Charlton Comics: V3#10, Apr, 1957 - V3#12, Oct, 1957

	GD	VG	FN	VF	VF/NM	NM-
V3#10-12: 11-Whitman-c/a	6	12	18	29	36	42

JERRY IGER'S... (All titles, Blackthorne/First)(Value: cover or less)

JERRY LEWIS (See The Adventures of...)

Jesse James #2 © AVON

Jessica Jones #13 © MAR

The Jetsons (2018 series) #1 © H-B

JERSEY GODS
Image Comics: Feb, 2009 - No. 12, May, 2010 ($3.50)

	GD 2.0	VG 4.0	FN 6.0	VF 8.0	VF/NM 9.0	NM- 9.2
1-11: 1-Brunswick-s/McDaid-a; two covers by McDaid and Allred						3.50
12-($4.99) Wraparound cover swipe of Superman #252 by Allred						5.00

JESSE JAMES (The True Story Of..., also seeThe Legend of...)
Dell Publishing Co.: No. 757, Dec, 1956 (one shot)

	GD 2.0	VG 4.0	FN 6.0	VF 8.0	VF/NM 9.0	NM- 9.2
Four Color 757-Movie, photo-c	9	18	27	57	111	165

JESSE JAMES (See Badmen of the West & Blazing Sixguns)
Avon Periodicals: 8/50 - No. 9, 11/52; No. 15, 10/53 - No. 29, 8-9/56

	GD 2.0	VG 4.0	FN 6.0	VF 8.0	VF/NM 9.0	NM- 9.2
1-Kubert Alabam-r/Cowpuncher #1	21	42	63	122	199	275
2-Kubert-a(3)	16	32	48	92	144	195
3-Kubert Alabam-r/Cowpuncher #2	15	30	45	88	137	185
4,9-No Kubert	11	22	33	62	86	110
5,6-Kubert Jesse James-a(3); 5-Wood-a(1pg.)	15	30	45	88	137	185
7-Kubert Jesse James-a(2)	14	28	42	82	121	160
8-Kinstler-a(3)	12	24	36	67	94	120
15-Kinstler-r/#3	10	20	30	58	79	100
16-Kinstler-r/#3 & story-r/Butch Cassidy #1	11	22	33	60	83	105
17-19,21: 17-Jesse James-r/#4; Kinstler-c idea from Kubert splash in #6. 18-Kubert Jesse James-r/#5. 19-Kubert Jesse James-r/#6. 21-Two Jesse James-r/#4, Kinstler-r/#4	10	20	30	56	76	95
20-Williamson/Frazetta-a; r/Chief Vic. Apache Massacre; Kubert Jesse James-r/#6; Kit West story by Larsen	16	32	48	92	144	195
22-29: 22,23-No Kubert. 24-New McCarty strip by Kinstler; Kinstler-r. 25-New McCarty Jesse James strip by Kinstler; Jesse James-r/#7,9. 26,27-New McCarty Jesse James strip plus a Kinstler/McCann Jesse James-r. 28-Reprints most of Red Mountain, Featuring Quantrells Raiders	10	20	30	56	76	95
Annual nn (1952; 25¢, 100 pgs.)- "...Brings Six-Gun Justice to the West"- 3 earlier issues rebound; Kubert, Kinstler-a(3)	34	68	102	199	325	450

NOTE: *Mostly reprints #10 on.* ***Fawcette*** *c-1, 2.* ***Kida*** *a-5.* ***Kinstler*** *a-3, 4, 7-9, 15r, 16r(2), 21-27; c-3, 4, 9, 17-27. Painted c-5-8. 22 has 2 stories r/Sheriff Bob Dixon's Chuck Wagon #1 with name changed to Sheriff Bob Trent.*

JESSE JAMES
Realistic Publications: July, 1953

	GD 2.0	VG 4.0	FN 6.0	VF 8.0	VF/NM 9.0	NM- 9.2
nn-Reprints Avon's #1; same-c, colors different	11	22	33	60	83	105

JESSICA JONES (Also see Alias)
Marvel Comics: Dec, 2016 - Present ($3.99)

	GD 2.0	VG 4.0	FN 6.0	VF 8.0	VF/NM 9.0	NM- 9.2
1-17-Bendis-s/Gaydos-a; Luke Cage app. 1-Misty Knight app. 13-17-Purple Man app.						4.00

JEST (Formerly Snap; becomes Kayo #12)
Harry 'A' Chesler: No. 10, 1944; No. 11, 1944

	GD 2.0	VG 4.0	FN 6.0	VF 8.0	VF/NM 9.0	NM- 9.2
10-Johnny Rebel & Yankee Boy app. in text	24	48	72	140	230	320
11-Little Nemo in Adventure Land	21	42	63	126	206	285

JESTER
Harry 'A' Chesler: No. 10, 1945

	GD 2.0	VG 4.0	FN 6.0	VF 8.0	VF/NM 9.0	NM- 9.2
10	20	40	60	120	195	270

JESUS
Spire Christian Comics (Fleming H. Revell Co.): 1979 (49¢)

	GD 2.0	VG 4.0	FN 6.0	VF 8.0	VF/NM 9.0	NM- 9.2
nn	2	4	6	11	16	20

JET (See Jet Powers)

JET (Crimson from Wildcore & Backlash)
DC Comics (WildStorm): Nov, 2000 - No. 4, Feb, 2001 ($2.50, limited series)

	GD 2.0	VG 4.0	FN 6.0	VF 8.0	VF/NM 9.0	NM- 9.2
1-4-Nguyen-a/Abnett & Lanning-s						3.00

JET ACES
Fiction House Magazines: 1952 - No. 4, 1953

	GD 2.0	VG 4.0	FN 6.0	VF 8.0	VF/NM 9.0	NM- 9.2
1- Sky Advs. of American War Aces (on sale 6/20/52)	20	40	60	117	189	260
2-4	13	26	39	72	101	130

JETCAT CLUBHOUSE (Also see Land of Nod, The)
Oni Press: Apr, 2001 - No. 3, Aug, 2001 ($3.25)

	GD 2.0	VG 4.0	FN 6.0	VF 8.0	VF/NM 9.0	NM- 9.2
1-3-Jay Stephens-s/a. 1-Wraparound-c						3.25
TPB (8/02, $10.95, 8 3/4" x 5 3/4") r/#1-3 & stories from Nickelodeon mag. & other						11.00

JET DREAM (...and Her Stunt-Girl Counterspies)(See The Man from Uncle #7)
Gold Key: June, 1968 (12¢)

	GD 2.0	VG 4.0	FN 6.0	VF 8.0	VF/NM 9.0	NM- 9.2
1-Painted-c	3	6	9	21	33	45

JET FIGHTERS (Korean War)
Standard Magazines: No. 5, Nov, 1952 - No. 7, Mar, 1953

	GD 2.0	VG 4.0	FN 6.0	VF 8.0	VF/NM 9.0	NM- 9.2
5,7-Toth-a. 5-Toth-c	15	30	45	84	127	170
6-Celardo-a	11	22	33	62	86	110

JET POWER
I.W. Enterprises: 1963

	GD 2.0	VG 4.0	FN 6.0	VF 8.0	VF/NM 9.0	NM- 9.2
I.W. Reprint 1,2-r/Jet Powers #1,2	3	6	9	16	24	32

JET POWERS (American Air Forces No. 5 on)
Magazine Enterprises: 1950 - No. 4, 1951

	GD 2.0	VG 4.0	FN 6.0	VF 8.0	VF/NM 9.0	NM- 9.2
1(A-1 #30)-Powell-c/a begins	39	78	117	231	378	525
2(A-1 #32) Classic Powell dinosaur-c/a	39	78	117	231	378	525
3(A-1 #35)-Williamson/Evans-a	41	82	123	250	418	585
4(A-1 #38)-Williamson/Wood-a; "The Rain of Sleep" drug story	41	82	123	250	418	585

JET PUP (See 3-D Features)

JETSONS, THE (TV) (See March of Comics #276, 330, 348 & Spotlight #3)
Gold Key: Jan, 1963 - No. 36, Oct, 1970 (Hanna-Barbera)

	GD 2.0	VG 4.0	FN 6.0	VF 8.0	VF/NM 9.0	NM- 9.2
1-1st comic book app.	24	48	72	171	378	585
2	10	20	30	66	138	210
3-10: 9-Flintstones x-over	8	16	24	51	96	140
11-22	6	12	18	40	73	105
23-36-Reprints: 23-(7/67)	4	8	12	27	44	60

JETSONS, THE (TV) (Also see Golden Comics Digest)
Charlton Comics: Nov, 1970 - No. 20, Dec, 1973 (Hanna-Barbera)

	GD 2.0	VG 4.0	FN 6.0	VF 8.0	VF/NM 9.0	NM- 9.2
1	8	16	24	56	108	160
2	4	8	12	28	47	65
3-10: Flintstones x-over	3	6	9	20	31	42
11-20	3	6	9	16	24	32
nn (1973, digest, 60¢, 100 pgs.) B&W one page gags	4	8	12	23	37	50

JETSONS, THE (TV)
Harvey Comics: V2#1, Sept, 1992 - No. 5, Nov, 1993 ($1.25/$1.50) (Hanna-Barbera)

	GD 2.0	VG 4.0	FN 6.0	VF 8.0	VF/NM 9.0	NM- 9.2
V2#1-5						5.00
...Big Book V2#1,2,3 ($1.95, 52 pgs.): 1-(11/92). 2-(4/93). 3-(7/93)						5.00
...Giant Size 1,2,3 ($2.25, 68 pgs): 1-(10/92). 2-(4/93). 3-(10/93)						5.00

JETSONS, THE (TV)
Archie Comics: Sept, 1995 - No. 8, Apr, 1996 ($1.50)

	GD 2.0	VG 4.0	FN 6.0	VF 8.0	VF/NM 9.0	NM- 9.2
1-8						3.00

JETSONS, THE (TV)
DC Comics: Jan, 2018 - No. 6 ($3.99, limited series)

	GD 2.0	VG 4.0	FN 6.0	VF 8.0	VF/NM 9.0	NM- 9.2
1-5: 1-Palmiotti-s/Brito-a; covers by Conner & Dave Johnson						4.00

JETTA OF THE 21ST CENTURY
Standard Comics: No. 5, Dec, 1952 - No. 7, Apr, 1953 (Teen-age Archie type)

	GD 2.0	VG 4.0	FN 6.0	VF 8.0	VF/NM 9.0	NM- 9.2
5-Dan DeCarlo-a	41	82	123	256	428	600
6-Robot-c	47	94	141	296	498	700
7	30	60	90	177	289	400
TPB (Airwave Publ., 2006, $9.99) B&W reprint of series; Bill Morrison intro./back-c						10.00

JEW GANGSTER
DC Comics: 2005 ($14.99, SC graphic novel)

	GD 2.0	VG 4.0	FN 6.0	VF 8.0	VF/NM 9.0	NM- 9.2
SC-Joe Kubert-s/a						15.00

JEZEBEL JADE (Hanna-Barbara)
Comico: Oct, 1988 - No. 3, Dec, 1988 ($2.00, mini-series)

	GD 2.0	VG 4.0	FN 6.0	VF 8.0	VF/NM 9.0	NM- 9.2
1-3: Johnny Quest spin-off; early Adam Kubert-a						3.00

JEZEBELLE (See Wildstorm 2000 Annuals)
DC Comics (WildStorm): Mar, 2001 - No. 6, Aug, 2001 ($2.50, limited series)

	GD 2.0	VG 4.0	FN 6.0	VF 8.0	VF/NM 9.0	NM- 9.2
1-6-Ben Raab-s/Steve Ellis-a						3.00

JIGGS & MAGGIE
Dell Publishing Co.: No. 18, 1941 (one shot)

	GD 2.0	VG 4.0	FN 6.0	VF 8.0	VF/NM 9.0	NM- 9.2
Four Color 18 (#1)-(1936-38-r)	53	106	159	334	567	800

JIGGS & MAGGIE
Standard Comics/Harvey Publications No. 22 on: No. 11, 1949 (June) - No. 21, 2/53; No. 22, 4/53 - No. 27, 2-3/54

	GD 2.0	VG 4.0	FN 6.0	VF 8.0	VF/NM 9.0	NM- 9.2
11	20	40	60	114	182	250
12-15,17-21	14	28	42	76	108	140
16-Wood text illos.	14	28	42	78	112	145
22-24-Little Dot app.	12	24	36	69	97	125
25,27	11	22	33	60	83	105
26-Four pgs. partially in 3-D	15	30	45	83	124	165

NOTE: *Sunday page reprints by McManus loosely blended into story continuity. Based on Bringing Up Father strip. Advertised on covers as "All New."*

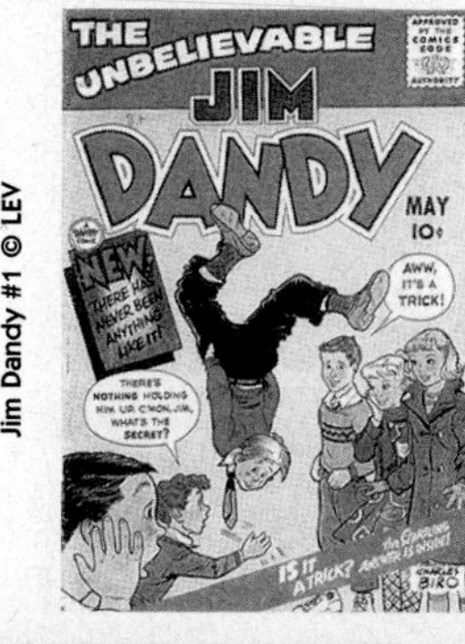

Jim Dandy #1 © LEV

Jimmy's Bastards #2 © Spitfire

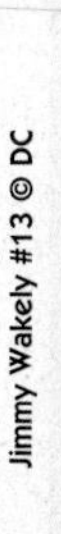
Jimmy Wakely #13 © DC

GD 2.0 VG 4.0 FN 6.0 VF 8.0 VF/NM 9.0 NM- 9.2

JIGSAW (Big Hero Adventures)
Harvey Publ. (Funday Funnies): Sept, 1966 - No. 2, Dec, 1966 (36 pgs.)
1-Origin & 1st app.; Crandall-a (5 pgs.) 3 6 9 21 33 45
2-Man From S.R.A.M. 3 6 9 15 22 28

JIGSAW OF DOOM (See Complete Mystery No. 2)

JIM BOWIE (Formerly Danger?; Black Jack No. 20 on)
Charlton Comics: No. 16, Mar, 1956 - No. 19, Apr, 1957
16 8 16 24 42 54 65
17-19: 18-Giordano-c 6 12 18 29 36 42

JIM BOWIE (TV, see Western Tales)
Dell Publishing Co.: No. 893, Mar, 1958 - No. 993, May-July, 1959
Four Color 893 (#1) 6 12 18 41 76 110
Four Color 993-Photo-c 5 10 15 35 63 90

JIM BUTCHER'S THE DRESDEN FILES: DOG MEN (Based on the Dresden Files novels)
Dynamite Entertainment: 2017 - No. 6, 2017 ($3.99, limited series)
1-6: 1-Jim Butcher & Mark Powers-s/Diego Galindo-a/c 4.00

JIM BUTCHER'S THE DRESDEN FILES: DOWN TOWN (Based on the Dresden Files novels)
Dynamite Entertainment: 2015 - No. 6, 2015 ($3.99, limited series)
1-6: 1-Jim Butcher & Mark Powers-s/Carlos Gomez-a/Stjepan Sejic-c 4.00

JIM BUTCHER'S THE DRESDEN FILES: FOOL MOON
Dynamite Entertainment: 2011 - No. 8, 2012 ($3.99, limited series)
1-8: 1-Jim Butcher & Mark Powers-s/Chase Conley-a/Brett Booth-c 4.00

JIM BUTCHER'S THE DRESDEN FILES: GHOUL GOBLIN
Dynamite Entertainment: 2012 - No. 6, 2013 ($3.99, limited series)
1-6: 1-Jim Butcher & Mark Powers-s/Joseph Cooper-a; Syaf-c 4.00

JIM BUTCHER'S THE DRESDEN FILES: STORM FRONT (Based on the Dresden Files novels)
Dabel Bros. Productions: Oct, 2008 (Nov. on-c) - No. 4, Apr, 2009 ($3.99, limited series)
1-4-Jim Butcher & Mark Powers-s/Ardian Syaf-a; covers by Syaf & Tsai 4.00
Vol. 2: 1,2 (7/09 - No. 4) 4.00

JIM BUTCHER'S THE DRESDEN FILES: WAR CRY
Dynamite Entertainment: 2014 - No. 5, 2014 ($3.99/$4.99, limited series)
1-4: 1-Jim Butcher & Mark Powers-s/Carlos Gomez-a; Sejic-c 4.00
5-($4.99) Wraparound-c by Sejic 5.00

JIM BUTCHER'S THE DRESDEN FILES: WELCOME TO THE JUNGLE
Dabel Bros. Productions: Mar, 2008 (Apr. on-c) - No. 4, Jul, 2008 ($3.99, limited series)
1-Jim Butcher-s/Ardian Syaf-a; Ardian Syaf-c 5.00
1-Variant-c by Chris McGrath 8.00
1-New York Comic-Con 2008 variant-c 15.00
1-Second printing 4.00
2-4-Two covers on each 4.00
HC (2008, $19.95, dustjacket) r/#1-4; Butcher intro.; concept art pages 20.00

JIM BUTCHER'S THE DRESDEN FILES: WILD CARD
Dynamite Entertainment: 2016 - No. 6, 2016 ($3.99, limited series)
1-6-Jim Butcher & Mark Powers-s/Carlos Gomez-a/c 4.00

JIM DANDY
Dandy Magazine (Lev Gleason): May, 1956 - No. 3, Sept, 1956 (Charles Biro)
1-Jim Dandy adventures w/Cup, an alien & his flying saucer (both invisible) from the planet Zikalug begins; ends #3. Biro-c. 1,2-Bammy Boozle app.
12 24 36 67 94 120
2,3: 2-Two pg. actual flying saucer reports 8 16 24 44 57 70

JIM HARDY (See Giant Comics Eds., Sparkler & Treasury of Comics #2 & 5)
United Features Syndicate/Spotlight Publ.: 1939; 1942; 1947 - No. 2, 1947
Single Series 6 ('39) 43 86 129 271 461 650
Single Series 27('42) 36 72 108 211 343 475
1('47)-Spotlight Publ. 15 30 45 85 130 175
2 10 20 30 54 72 90

JIM HARDY
Spotlight/United Features Synd.: 1944 (25¢, 132 pgs.) (Tip Top, Sparkler-r)
nn-Origin Mirror Man; Triple Terror app. 39 78 117 231 378 525

JIM HENSON'S LABYRINTH: CORONATION
BOOM! Studios (Archaia): Feb, 2018 - No. 12 ($3.99, limited series)
1-Spurrier-s/Bayliss-a/Staples-c; Jareth before becoming the Goblin King 4.00

JIM HENSON'S THE STORYTELLER: DRAGONS (Also see The Storyteller)
BOOM! Studios (Archaia): Dec, 2015 - No. 4, Mar, 2016 ($3.99, limited series)
1-4: 2-Pride-s/a 4.00

GD 2.0 VG 4.0 FN 6.0 VF 8.0 VF/NM 9.0 NM- 9.2

JIM HENSON'S THE STORYTELLER: WITCHES
BOOM! Studios (Archaia): Sept, 2014 - No. 4, Dec, 2014 ($3.99, limited series)
1-4: 1-Vidaurri-s/a. 2-Vanderklugt-s/a. 3-Matthew Dow Smith-s/a. 4-Stokely-s/a 4.00

JIMINY CRICKET (Disney,, see Mickey Mouse Mag. V5#3 & Walt Disney Showcase #37)
Dell Publishing Co.: No. 701, May, 1956 - No. 989, May-July, 1959
Four Color 701 8 16 24 51 96 140
Four Color 795, 897, 989 6 12 18 38 69 100

JIM LEE SKETCHBOOK
DC Comics (WildStorm): 2002 (no price, 16 pgs.)
nn-Various DC and WildStorm character sketches by Lee 8.00

JIMMY CORRIGAN (See Acme Novelty Library)

JIMMY DURANTE (Also see A-1 Comics)
Magazine Enterprises: No. 18, Oct, 1949 - No. 20, Winter 1949-50
A-1 18,20-Photo-c (scarce) 52 104 156 328 552 775

JIMMY OLSEN (See Superman's Pal...)

JIMMY OLSEN
DC Comics: May, 2011 ($5.99, one-shot)
1-Reprints back-up feature from Action Comics #893-896 plus new material; Conner-c 6.00

JIMMY OLSEN: ADVENTURES BY JACK KIRBY
DC Comics: 2003, 2004 ($19.95, TPB)
nn-(2003) Reprints Jack Kirby's early issues of Superman's Pal Jimmy Olsen #133-139,141; Mark Evanier intro.; cover by Kirby and Steve Rude 20.00
Vol. 2 (2004) Reprints #142-148; Evanier intro.; cover gallery and sketch pages 20.00

JIMMY'S BASTARDS
AfterShock Comics: Jun, 2017 - Present ($3.99)
1-6-Garth Ennis-s/Russ Braun-a/Dave Johnson-c; intro. Secret Agent Jimmy Regent 4.00

JIMMY WAKELY (Cowboy movie star)
National Per. Publ.: Sept-Oct, 1949 - No. 18, July-Aug, 1952 (1-13: 52pgs.)
1-Photo-c, 52 pgs. begin; Alex Toth-a; Kit Colby Girl Sheriff begins
42 84 126 265 445 625
2-Toth-a 18 36 54 107 169 230
3,4,6,7-Frazetta-a in all, 3 pgs. each; Toth-a in all. 7-Last photo-c. 4-Kurtzman "Pot-Shot Pete", 1 pg; Toth-a 21 42 63 122 199 275
5,8-15-Toth-a; 12,14-Kubert-a (3 & 2 pgs.) 16 32 48 94 147 200
16-18 15 30 45 83 124 165
NOTE: *Gil Kane c-10-18p.*

JIM RAY'S AVIATION SKETCH BOOK
Vital Publishers: Mar-Apr, 1946 - No. 2, May-June, 1946 (15¢)
1-Picture stories of planes and pilots; atomic explosion panel
39 78 117 231 378 525
2-Story of General "Nap" Arnold 25 50 75 147 241 335

JIM SOLAR (See Wisco/Klarer in the Promotional Comics section)

JINGLE BELLE (Paul Dini's...)
Oni Press/Top Cow: Nov, 1999 - No. 2, Dec, 1999 ($2.95, B&W, limited series)
1,2-Paul Dini-s. 2-Alex Ross flip-c 3.00
Jingle Belle: Dash Away All (12/03, $11.95, digest-size) Dini-s/Garibaldi-a 12.00
Jingle Belle: Gift-Wrapped (Top Cow, 12/11, $3.99) Dini-s/Gladden-a 4.00
Jingle Belle: Santa Claus vs. Frankenstein (Top Cow, 12/08, $2.99) Dini-s/Gladden-a 3.00
Jingle Belle's Cool Yule (11/02, $13.95,TPB) r/All-Star Holiday Hullabaloo, The Mighty Elves, and Jubilee; internet strips and a color section w/DeStefano-a 14.00
Paul Dini's Jingle Belle Jubilee (11/01, $2.95) Dini-s; art by Rolston, DeCarlo, Morrison and Bone; pin-ups by Thompson and Aragonés 3.00
Paul Dini's Jingle Belle's All-Star Holiday Hullabaloo (11/00, $4.95) stories by various including Dini, Aragonés, Jeff Smith, Bill Morrison; Frank Cho-c 5.00
Paul Dini's Jingle Belle: The Fight Before Christmas (12/05, $2.99) Dini-s/Bone & others-a 3.00
Paul Dini's Jingle Belle: The Mighty Elves (7/01, $2.95) Dini-s/Bone-a 3.00
Paul Dini's Jingle Belle Winter Wingding (11/02, $2.95) Dini-s/Clugston-Major-c 3.00
The Bakers Meet Jingle Belle (12/06, $2.99) Dini-s/Kyle Baker-a 3.00
TPB (10/00, $8.95) r/#1&2, and app. from Oni Double Feature #13 9.00

JINGLE BELLE (Paul Dini's...)
Dark Horse Comics: Nov, 2004 - No. 4, Apr, 2005 ($2.99, limited series)
1-4-Paul Dini-s/Jose Garibaldi-a 3.00
TPB (9/05, $12.95) r/#1-4 13.00

JINGLE BELLS (See March of Comics No. 65)

Jinx #5 © B. Bendis

JLA #16 © DC

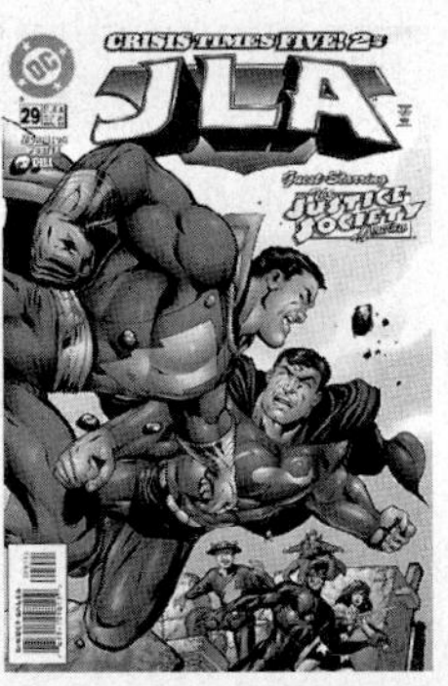

JLA #29 © DC

	GD 2.0	VG 4.0	FN 6.0	VF 8.0	VF/NM 9.0	NM- 9.2

JINGLE DINGLE CHRISTMAS STOCKING COMICS (See Foodini #2)
Stanhall Publications: V2#1, 1951 (no date listed) (25¢, 100 pgs.; giant-size) (Publ. annually)

	GD	VG	FN	VF	VF/NM	NM-
V2#1-Foodini & Pinhead, Silly Pilly plus games & puzzles	23	46	69	138	227	315

JINGLE JANGLE COMICS (Also see Puzzle Fun Comics)
Eastern Color Printing Co.: Feb, 1942 - No. 42, Dec, 1949

	GD	VG	FN	VF	VF/NM	NM-
1-Pie-Face Prince of Old Pretzleburg, Jingle Jangle Tales by George Carlson, Hortense, & Benny Bear begin	47	94	141	296	498	700
2-4: 2,3-No Pie-Face Prince. 4-Pie-Face Prince-c	21	42	63	122	199	275
5 (10/42)	19	38	57	111	176	240
6-10: 8-No Pie-Face Prince	15	30	45	85	130	175
11-15	12	24	36	69	97	125
16-30: 17,18-No Pie-Face Prince. 24,30-XMas-c	10	20	30	56	76	95
31-42: 36,42-Xmas-c	9	18	27	52	69	85

NOTE: ***George Carlson** a-(2) in all except No. 2, 3, 8; c-1-6. **Carlson** 1 pg. puzzles in 9, 10, 12-15, 18, 20. **Carlson** illustrated a series of Uncle Wiggily books in 1930's.*

JING PALS
Victory Publishing Corp.: Feb, 1946 - No. 4, Aug?, 1946 (Funny animal)

	GD	VG	FN	VF	VF/NM	NM-
1-Wishing Willie, Puggy Panda & Johnny Rabbit begin	17	34	51	100	158	215
2-4	11	22	33	62	86	110

JINKS, PIXIE, AND DIXIE (See Kite Fun Book & Whitman Comic Books)

JINX
Caliber Press: 1996 - No. 7, 1996 ($2.95, B&W, 32 pgs.)
1-7: Brian Michael Bendis-c/a/scripts. 2-Photo-c 3.00

JINX (Volume 2)
Image Comics: 1997 - No. 5, 1998 ($2.95, B&W, bi-monthly)
1-4: Brian Michael Bendis-c/a/scripts. 3.00
5-($3.95) Brereton-c 4.00
...Buried Treasures ('98, $3.95) short stories, ...Confessions ('98, $3.95) short stories, ...Pop Culture Hoo-Hah ('98, $3.95) humor shorts 4.00
TPB (1997, $10.95) r/Vol 1,#1-4 11.00
...: The Definitive Collection ('01, $24.95) remastered #1-5, sketch pages, art gallery, script excerpts, Mack intro. 25.00

JINX: TORSO
Image Comics: 1998 - No. 6, 1999 ($3.95/$4.95, B&W)
1-6-Based on Eliot Ness' pursuit of America's first serial killer; Brian Michael Bendis & Marc Andreyko-s/Bendis-a. 3-6-($4.95) 5.00
Softcover (2000, $24.95) r/#1-6; intro. by Greg Rucka; photo essay of the actual murders and police documents 25.00
Hardcover (2000, $49.95) signed & numbered 50.00

JIRNI
Aspen MLT: Apr, 2013 - No. 5, Oct, 2013 ($1.00/$3.99)
1-($1.00) J.T. Krul-s/Paolo Pantalena-a; multiple covers 3.00
2-5-($3.99) Multiple covers on each 4.00
Vol. 2 #1 (6/14, $3.99) Krul-s/Pantalena-a 4.00
Vol. 2 #1-5 (8/15 - No. 5, 12/15, $3.99) Krul-s/Marion-a; multiple covers on each 4.00

JLA (See Justice League of America and Justice Leagues)
DC Comics: Jan, 1997 - No. 125, Apr, 2006 ($1.95/$1.99/$2.25/$2.50)

	GD	VG	FN	VF	VF/NM	NM-
1-Morrison-s/Porter & Dell-a. The Hyperclan app.	2	4	6	9	12	15
2	1	3	4	6	8	10
3,4	1	2	3	5	7	9

5-Membership drive; Tomorrow Woman app. 6.00
6-9: 6-1st app. Zauriel. 8-Green Arrow joins. 6.00
10-21: 10-Rock of Ages begins. 11-Joker and Luthor-c/app. 12-Intro. Hourman from the 853rd century. 14-Darkseid app. 15-($2.95) Rock of Ages concludes; intro. Superman One Million. 16-New members join; Prometheus app. 17,20-Jorgensen-a. 18-21-Waid-s. 20,21-Adam Strange c/app. 5.00
22-40: 22-Begin $1.99-c; Sandman (Daniel) app. 23-1st app. Justice Legion A. 27-Amazo app. 28-31-JSA app. 35-Hal Jordan/Spectre app. 36-40-World War 3 3.00
41-($2.99) Conclusion of World War 3; last Morrison-s 4.00
42-49: 43-Waid-s; Ra's al Ghul app. 44-Begin $2.25-c. 46-Batman leaves. 47-Hitch & Neary-a begins; JLA battles Queen of Fables 3.00
50-($3.75) JLA vs. Dr. Destiny; art by Hitch & various 4.00
51-74: 52-55-Hitch-a. 59-Joker: Last Laugh. 61-68-Kelly-s/Mahnke-a. 69-73-Hunt for Aquaman; bi-monthly with alternating art by Mahnke and Guichet 3.00
75-(1/03, $3.95) leads into Aquaman (4th series) #1 4.00
76-93: 76-Firestorm app. 77-Banks-a. 79-Kanjar Ro app. 91-93-O'Neil-s/Huat-a 3.00
94-99-Byrne & Ordway-a/Claremont-s; Doom Patrol app. 3.00
100-($3.50) Intro. Vera Black; leads into Justice League Elite #1 4.00
101-125: 101-106-Austen-s/Garney-a/c. 107-114-Crime Syndicate app.; Busiek-s. 115-Begin $2.50-c; Johns & Heinberg-s; Secret Society of Super-Villains app. 3.00
#1,000,000 (11/98) 853rd Century x-over 3.00
Annual 1 (1997, $3.95) Pulp Heroes; Augustyn-s/Olivetti & Ha-a 4.00
Annual 2 (1998, $2.95) Ghosts; Wrightson-c 4.00
Annual 3 (1999, $2.95) JLApe; Art Adams-c 4.00
Annual 4 (2000, $3.50) Planet DC x-over; Steve Scott-c/a 4.00
... American Dreams (1998, $7.95, TPB) r/#5-9 8.00
...: Crisis of Conscience TPB (2006, $12.99) r/#115-119 13.00
.../ Cyberforce (DC/Top Cow, 2005, $5.99) Kelly-s/Mahnke-a/Silvestri-c 6.00
Divided We Fall (2001, $17.95, TPB) r/#47-54 18.00
...80-Page Giant 1 (7/98, $4.95) stories & art by various 6.00
...80-Page Giant 2 (11/99, $4.95) Green Arrow & Hawkman app. Hitch-c 6.00
...80-Page Giant 3 (10/00, $5.95) Pariah & Harbinger; intro. Moon Maiden 6.00
...Foreign Bodies (1999, $5.95, one-shot) Kobra app.; Semeiks-a 6.00
...Gallery (1997, $2.95) pin-ups by various; Quitely-c 3.00
...God & Monsters (2001, $6.95, one-shot) Benefiel-a/c 7.00
Golden Perfect (2003, $12.95, TPB) r/#61-65 13.00
.../ Haven: Anathema (2002, $6.95) Concludes the Haven: The Broken City series 7.00
.../ Haven: Arrival (2001, $6.95) Leads into the Haven: The Broken City series 7.00
...In Crisis Secret Files 1 (11/98, $4.95) recap of JLA in DC x-overs 5.00
...: Island of Dr. Moreau, The (2002, $6.95, one-shot) Elseworlds; Pugh-c/a; Thomas-s 7.00
.../ JSA Secret Files & Origins (1/03, $4.95) prelude to JLA/JSA: Virtue & Vice; short stories and pin-ups by various; Pacheco-c 5.00
.../ JSA: Virtue and Vice HC (2002, $24.95) Teams battle Despero & Johnny Sorrow; Goyer & Johns-s/Pacheco-a/c 25.00
.../ JSA: Virtue and Vice SC (2003, $17.95) 18.00
Justice For All (1999, $14.95, TPB) r/#24-33 15.00
New World Order (1997, $5.95, TPB) r/#1-4 6.00
...: Obsidian Age Book One, The (2003, $12.95) r/#66-71 13.00
...: Obsidian Age Book Two, The (2003, $12.95) r/#72-76 13.00
One Million (2004, $19.95, TPB) r/#DC One Million #1-4 and other #1,000,000 x-overs 20.00
...: Our Worlds at War (9/01, $2.95) Jae Lee-c; Aquaman presumed dead 3.00
...: Pain of the Gods (2005, $12.99) r/#101-106 13.00
...Primeval (1999, $5.95, one-shot) Abnett & Lanning-s/Olivetti-a 6.00
...: Riddle of the Beast HC (2001, $24.95) Grant-s/painted-a by various; Sweet-c 25.00
...: Riddle of the Beast SC (2003, $14.95) Grant-s/painted-a by various; Kaluta-c 15.00
Rock of Ages (1998, $9.95, TPB) r/#10-15 10.00
Rules of Engagement (2004, $12.95, TPB) r/#77-82 13.00
...: Seven Caskets (2000, $5.95, one-shot) Brereton-s/painted-c/a 6.00
...: Shogun of Steel (2002, $6.95, one-shot) Elseworlds; Justiniano-c/a 7.00
...Showcase 80-Page Giant (2/00, $4.95) Hitch-c 5.00
Strength in Numbers (1998, $12.95, TPB) r/#16-23, Secret Files #2 and Prometheus #1 13.00
...Superpower (1999, $5.95, one-shot) Arcudi-s/Eaton-a; Mark Antaeus joins 6.00
Syndicate Rules (2005, $17.99, TPB) r/#107-114, Secret Files #4 18.00
Terror Incognita (2002, $12.95, TPB) r/#55-60 13.00
...: The Deluxe Edition Vol. 1 HC (2008, $29.99, dustjacket) oversized r/#1-9 and JLA Secret Files #1 30.00
...: The Deluxe Edition Vol. 2 HC (2009, $29.99, dustjacket) oversized r/#10-17, JLA/Wildcats, and Prometheus #1 30.00
...: The Deluxe Edition Vol. 3 HC (2010, $29.99, dustjacket) oversized r/#22-26, 28-31 & #1,000,000 30.00
...: The Deluxe Edition Vol. 4 HC (2010, $34.99, dustjacket) oversized r/#34, 36-41, JLA Classified #1-3 and JLA: Earth 2 GN 35.00
The Tenth Circle (2004, $12.95, TPB) r/#94-99 13.00
...: The Greatest Stories Ever Told TPB (2006, $19.99) r/Justice League of America #19,71,122, 166-168,200, Justice League #1, JLA Secret Files #1 and JLA #61; Alex Ross-c 20.00
Tower of Babel (2001, $12.95, TPB) r/#42-46, Secret Files #3, 80-Page Giant #1 13.00
Trial By Fire (2004, $12.95, TPB) r/#84-89 13.00
...Vs. Predator (DC/Dark Horse, 2000, $5.95, one-shot) Nolan-c/a 6.00
...: Welcome to the Working Week (2003, $6.95, one-shot) Patton Oswalt-s 7.00
...: World War III (2000, $12.95, TPB) r/#34-41 13.00
...: World Without a Justice League (2006, $12.99, TPB) r/#120-125 13.00
...: Zatanna's Search (2003, $12.95, TPB) rep. Zatanna's early app. & origin; Bolland-c 13.00

JLA: ACT OF GOD
DC Comics: 2000 - No. 3, 2001 ($4.95, limited series)
1-3-Elseworlds; metahumans lose their powers; Moench-s/Dave Ross-a 5.00

JLA: AGE OF WONDER
DC Comics: 2003 - No. 2, 2003 ($5.95, limited series)
1,2-Elseworlds; Superman and the League of Science during the Industrial Revolution 6.00

JLA: A LEAGUE OF ONE
DC Comics: 2000 (Graphic novel)

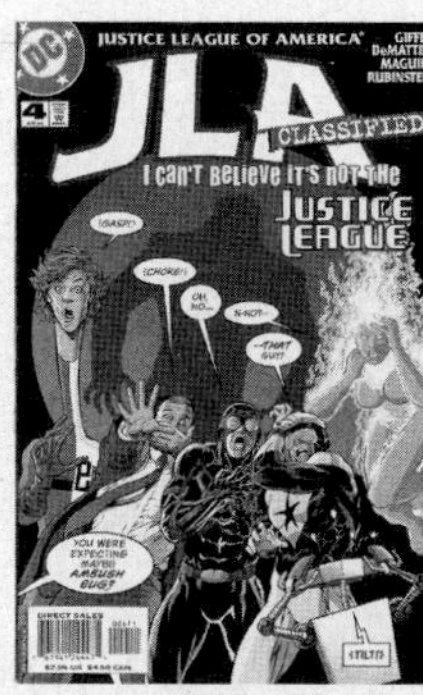

JLA: Classified #4 © DC

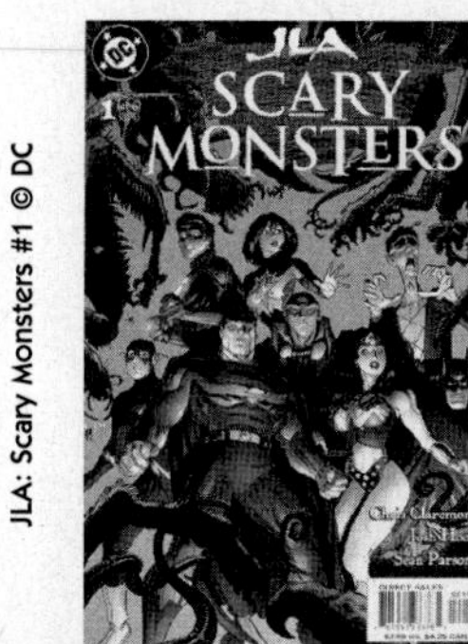

JLA: Scary Monsters #1 © DC

JLA: The Nail #1 © DC

	GD 2.0	VG 4.0	FN 6.0	VF 8.0	VF/NM 9.0	NM- 9.2

Hardcover ($24.95) Christopher Moeller-s/painted-a 25.00
Softcover (2002, $14.95) 15.00

JLA/AVENGERS (See Avengers/JLA for #2 & #4)
Marvel Comics: Sept, 2003; No. 3, Dec, 2003 ($5.95, limited series)

1-Busiek-s/Pérez-a; wraparound-c; Krona, Starro, Grandmaster, Terminus app. 6.00
3-Busiek-s/Pérez-a; wraparound-c; Phantom Stranger app. 6.00
SC (2008, $19.99) r/4-issue series; cover gallery; intros by Stan Lee & Julius Schwartz 20.00

JLA: BLACK BAPTISM
DC Comics: May, 2001 - No. 4, Aug, 2001 ($2.50, limited series)

1-4-Saiz-a(p)/Bradstreet-c; Zatanna app. 3.00

JLA: CLASSIFIED
DC Comics: Jan, 2005 - No. 54, May, 2008 ($2.95/$2.99)

1-3-Morrison-s/McGuinness-a/c; Ultramarines app. 3.00
4-9-"I Can't Believe It's Not The Justice League," Giffen & DeMatteis-s/Maguire-a 3.00
10-31,33-54: 10-15-New Maps of Hell; Ellis-s/Guice-a. 16-21-Garcia-Lopez-a. 22-25-Detroit League & Royal Flush Gang app.; Englehart-s. 26-28-Chaykin-s. 37-41-Kid Amazo. 50-54-Byrne-a/Middleston-c 3.00
32-($3.99) Dr. Destiny app.; Jurgens-a 4.00
I Can't Believe It's Not The Justice League TPB (2005, $12.99) r/#4-9 13.00
...: Kid Amazo TPB (2007, $12.99) r/#37-41 13.00
...: New Maps of Hell TPB (2006, $12.99) r/#10-15 13.00
...: That Was Now, This Is Then TPB (2008, $14.99) r/#50-54 15.00
...: The Hypothetical Woman TPB (2008, $12.99) r/#16-21 13.00
...: Ultramarine Corps TPB (2007, $14.99) r/#1-3, JLA/WildC.A.T.s #1 and JLA Secret Files 2004 #1 15.00

JLA CLASSIFIED: COLD STEEL
DC Comics: 2005 - No. 2, 2006 ($5.99, limited series, prestige format)

1,2-Chris Moeller-s/a; giant robot Justice League 6.00

JLA: CREATED EQUAL
DC Comics: 2000 - No. 2, 2000 ($5.95, limited series, prestige format)

1,2-Nicieza-s/Maguire-a; Elseworlds-Superman as the last man on Earth 6.00

JLA: DESTINY
DC Comics: 2002 - No. 4, 2002 ($5.95, prestige format, limited series)

1-4-Elseworlds; Arcudi-s/Mandrake-a 6.00

JLA / DOOM PATROL SPECIAL (Milk Wars DC/Young Animal crossover)
DC Comics: Mar, 2018 ($4.99, one-shot)

1-Part 1 of crossover; Orlando & Way-s/Aco-a/Quitely-c; Lord Manga Khan app. 5.00

JLA: EARTH 2
DC Comics: 2000 (Graphic novel)

Hardcover ($24.95) Morrison-s/Quitely-a; Crime Syndicate app. 25.00
Softcover ($14.95) 15.00

JLA: GATEKEEPER
DC Comics: 2001 - No. 3, 2001 ($4.95, prestige format, limited series)

1-3-Truman-s/a 5.00

JLA: HEAVEN'S LADDER
DC Comics: 2000 ($9.95, Treasury-size one-shot)

nn-Bryan Hitch & Paul Neary-c/a; Mark Waid-s 10.00

JLA/HITMAN (Justice League/Hitman in indicia)
DC Comics: Nov, 2007 - No. 2, Dec, 2007 ($3.99, limited series)

1,2-Ennis-s/McCrea-a; Bloodlines creatures return 4.00

JLA: INCARNATIONS
DC Comics: Jul, 2001 - No. 7, Feb, 2002 ($3.50, limited series)

1-7-Ostrander-s/Semeiks-a; different eras of the Justice League 4.00

JLA: LIBERTY AND JUSTICE
DC Comics: Nov, 2003 ($9.95, Treasury-size one-shot)

nn-Alex Ross-c/a; Paul Dini-s; story of the classic Justice League 10.00

JLA PARADISE LOST
DC Comics: Jan, 1998 - No. 3, Mar, 1998 ($1.95, limited series)

1-3-Millar-s/Olivetti-a 3.00

JLA: SCARY MONSTERS
DC Comics: May, 2003 - No. 6, Oct, 2003 ($2.50, limited series)

1-6-Claremont-s/Art Adams-c 3.00

JLA SECRET FILES
DC Comics: Sept, 1997 - 2004 ($4.95)

1-Standard Ed. w/origin-s & pin-ups 5.00
1-Collector's Ed. w/origin-s & pin-ups; cardstock-c 6.00
2,3: 2-(8/98) origin-s of JLA #16's newer members. 3-(12/00) 5.00
... 2004 (11/04) Justice League Elite app.; Mahnke & Byrne-a; Crime Syndicate app. 5.00

JLA: SECRET ORIGINS
DC Comics: Nov, 2002 ($7.95, Treasury-size one-shot)

nn-Alex Ross 2-page origins of Justice League members; text by Paul Dini 8.00

JLA: SECRET SOCIETY OF SUPER-HEROES
DC Comics: 2000 - No. 2, 2000 ($5.95, limited series, prestige format)

1,2-Elseworlds JLA; Chaykin and Tischman-s/McKone-a 6.00

JLA /SPECTRE: SOUL WAR
DC Comics: 2003 - No. 2, 2003 ($5.95, limited series, prestige format)

1,2-DeMatteis-s/Banks & Neary-a 6.00

JLA: THE NAIL (Elseworlds) (Also see Justice League of America: Another Nail)
DC Comics: Aug, 1998 - No. 3, Oct, 1998 ($4.95, prestige format)

1-3-JLA in a world without Superman; Alan Davis-s/a(p) 5.00
TPB ('98, $12.95) r/series w/new Davis-c 13.00

JLA / TITANS
DC Comics: Dec, 1998 - No. 3, Feb, 1999 ($2.95, limited series)

1-3-Grayson-s; P. Jimenez-c/a 3.00
...:The Technis Imperative ('99, $12.95, TPB) r/#1-3; Titans Secret Files 13.00

JLA: TOMORROW WOMAN (Girlfrenzy)
DC Comics: June, 1998 ($1.95, one-shot)

1-Peyer-s; story takes place during JLA #5 3.00

JLA / WILDC.A.T.S
DC Comics: 1997 ($5.95, one-shot, prestige format)

1-Morrison-s/Semeiks & Conrad-a 6.00

JLA /WITCHBLADE
DC Comics/Top Cow: 2000 ($5.95, prestige format, one-shot)

1-Pararillo-c/a 6.00

JLA / WORLD WITHOUT GROWN-UPS (See Young Justice)
DC Comics: Aug, 1998 - No. 2, Sept, 1998 ($4.95, prestige format)

1,2-JLA, Robin, Impulse & Superboy app.; Ramos & McKone-a 6.00
TPB ('98, $9.95) r/series & Young Justice: The Secret #1 10.00

JLA: YEAR ONE
DC Comics: Jan, 1998 - No. 12, Dec, 1998 ($2.95/$1.95, limited series)

1-($2.95)-Waid & Augustyn-s/Kitson-a 5.00
1-Platinum Edition 10.00
2-8-($1.95): 5-Doom Patrol-c/app. 7-Superman app. 4.00
9-12 3.00
TPB ('99,'09; $19.95/$19.99) r/#1-12; Busiek intro. 20.00

JLA-Z
DC Comics: Nov, 2003 - No. 3, Jan, 2004 ($2.50, limited series)

1-3-Pin-ups and info on current and former JLA members and villains; art by various 3.00

JLX
DC Comics (Amalgam): Apr, 1996 ($1.95, one-shot)

1-Mark Waid scripts 3.00

JLX UNLEASHED
DC Comics (Amalgam): June, 1997 ($1.95, one-shot)

1-Priest-s/ Oscar Jimenez & Rodriquez/a 3.00

JOAN OF ARC (Also see A-1 Comics, Classics Illustrated #78, and Ideal a Classical Comic)
Magazine Enterprises: No. 21, 1949 (one shot)

	GD	VG	FN	VF	VF/NM	NM-
A-1 21-Movie adaptation; Ingrid Bergman photo-covers & interior photos; Whitney-a	30	60	90	177	289	400

JOE COLLEGE
Hillman Periodicals: Fall, 1949 - No. 2, Wint, 1950 (Teen-age humor, 52 pgs.)

	GD	VG	FN	VF	VF/NM	NM-
1-Powell-a; Briefer-a	15	30	45	83	124	165
2-Powell-a	10	20	30	56	76	95

JOE FRANKENSTEIN
IDW Publishing: Feb, 2015 - No. 4, May, 2015 ($3.99)

1-4-Chuck Dixon & Graham Nolan-s/Graham Nolan-a 4.00

JOE GOLEM
Dark Horse Comics: Nov, 2015 - No. 5, Mar, 2016 ($3.50)

Joe Louis #1 © FAW

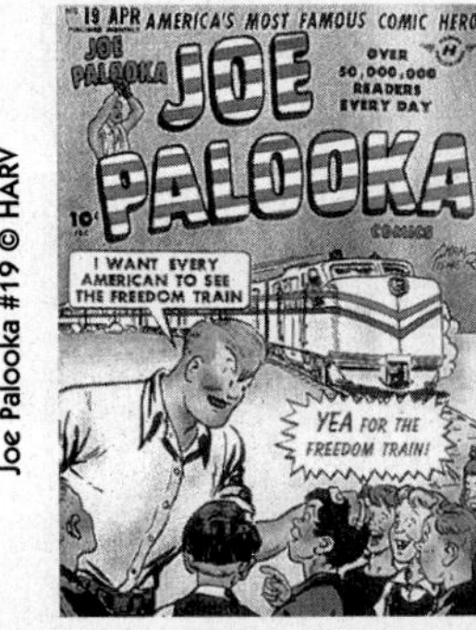

Joe Palooka #19 © HARV

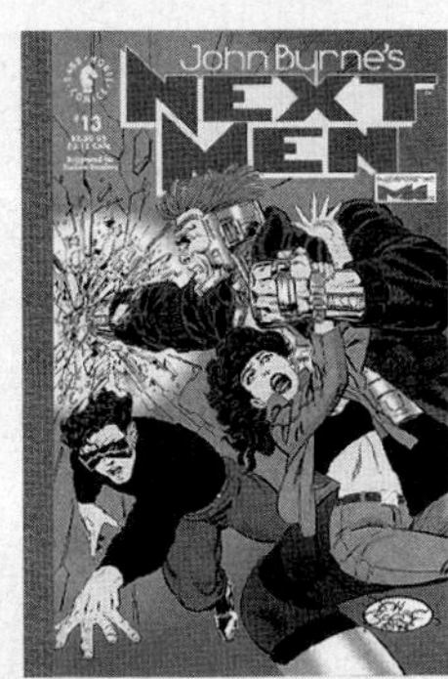

John Byrne's Next Men #13 © John Byrne

GD 2.0 | VG 4.0 | FN 6.0 | VF 8.0 | VF/NM 9.0 | NM- 9.2

1-5-Mignola & Golden-s/Reynolds-a 4.00

JOE GOLEM: THE OUTER DARK
Dark Horse Comics: May, 2017 - No. 5, Jan, 2018 ($3.99)
1-5-Mignola & Golden-s/Reynolds-a. 4,5-Titled Joe Golem: Flesh and Blood #1,2 4.00

JOE JINKS
United Features Syndicate: No. 12, 1939
Single Series 12 32 64 96 188 307 425

JOE KUBERT PRESENTS
DC Comics: Dec, 2012 - No. 6, May, 2013 ($4.99, limited series)
1-6: Anthology of short stories by Kubert, Buniak & Glanzman. 1-Hawkman app. 5.00

JOE LOUIS (See Fight Comics #2, Picture News #6 & True Comics #5)
Fawcett Publications: Sept, 1950 - No. 2, Nov, 1950 (Photo-c) (Boxing champ) (See Dick Cole #10)
1-Photo-c; life story 55 110 165 352 601 850
2-Photo-c 39 78 117 240 395 550

JOE PALOOKA (1st Series)(Also see Big Shot Comics, Columbia Comics & Feature Funnies)
Columbia Comic Corp. (Publication Enterprises): 1942 - No. 4, 1944
1-1st to portray American president; gov't permission required 129 258 387 826 1413 2000
2 (1943)-Hitler-c 103 206 309 659 1130 1600
3-Nazi Sub-c 48 96 144 302 514 725
4 39 78 117 231 378 525

JOE PALOOKA (2nd Series) (Battle Adv. #68-74; ...Advs. #75, 77-81, 83-85, 87; Champ of the Comics #76, 82, 86, 89-93) (See All-New)
Harvey Publications: Nov, 1945 - No. 118, Mar, 1961
1-By Ham Fisher 54 108 162 343 574 825
2 27 54 81 160 263 365
3,4,6,7-1st Flyin' Fool, ends #25 16 32 48 94 147 200
5-Boy Explorers by S&K (7-8/46) 21 42 63 122 199 275
8-10 14 28 42 80 115 150
11-14,16,18-20: 14-Black Cat text-s(2). 18-Powell-a.; Little Max app. 19-Freedom Train-c 11 22 33 64 90 115
15-Origin & 1st app. Humphrey (12/47); Super-heroine Atoma app. by Powell 15 30 45 90 140 190
17-Humphrey vs. Palooka-c/s; 1st app. Little Max 15 30 45 90 140 190
21-26,29,30: 22-Powell-a. 30-Nude female painting 10 20 30 56 76 95
27-Little Max app.; Howie Morenz-s 10 20 30 58 79 100
28-Babe Ruth 4 pg. sty. 10 20 30 58 79 100
31,39,51: 31-Dizzy Dean 4 pg. sty. 39-(12/49) Humphrey & Little Max begin; Sonny Baugh football-s; Sherlock Max-s. 51-Babe Ruth 2 pg. sty; Jake Lamotta 1/2 pg. sty 9 18 27 50 65 80
32-38,40-50,52-61: 35-Little Max-c/story(4 pgs.); Joe Louis 1 pg. sty. 36-Humphrey story. 41-Bing Crosby photo on-c. 44-Palooka marries Ann Howe. 50-(11/51)-Becomes Harvey Comics Hits #51 8 16 24 44 57 70
62-S&K Boy Explorers-r 9 18 27 50 65 80
63-65,73-80,100: 79-Story of 1st meeting with Ann 8 16 24 40 50 60
66,67-'Commie' torture story "Drug-Diet Horror" 13 26 39 72 101 130
68,70-72: 68,70-Joe vs. "Gooks"-c. 71-Bloody bayonets-c. 72-Tank-c 12 24 36 69 97 125
69-1st "Battle Adventures" issue; torture & bondage 14 28 42 76 108 140
81-99,101-115: 104,107-Humphrey & Little Max-s 7 14 21 37 46 55
116-S&K Boy Explorers-r (Giant, '60) 9 18 27 47 61 75
117-(84 pg. Giant) r/Commie issues #66,67; Powell-a 9 18 27 52 69 85
118-(84 pg. Giant) Jack Dempsey 2 pg. sty, Powell-a 9 18 27 47 61 75
...**Visits the Lost City** nn (1945)(One Shot)(50¢)-164 page continuous story strip reprint. Has biography & photo of Ham Fisher; possibly the single longest comic book story published in that era (159 pgs.?) (scarce) 239 478 717 1530 2615 3700
NOTE: ***Nostrand/Powell** a-73. **Powell** a-7, 8, 10, 12, 14, 17, 19, 26-45, 47-53, 70, 73 at least. Black Cat text stories #8, 12, 13, 19.*

JOE PALOOKA
IDW Publishing: Dec, 2012 - No. 6, May, 2013 ($3.99, limited series)
1-6: 1-Bullock-s/Peniche-a; Joe Palooka updated as a MMA fighter 4.00

JOE PSYCHO & MOO FROG
Goblin Studios: 1996 - No. 5, 1997 ($2.50, B&W)
1-5: 4-Two covers 3.00
...Full Color Extravagarbonzo ($2.95, color) 3.00

JOE THE BARBARIAN
DC Comics (Vertigo): Mar, 2010 - No. 8, May, 2011 ($1.00/$2.99/$3.99)
1-($1.00) Grant Morrison-s/Sean Murphy-a 3.00
2-7-($2.99) 3.00
8-($3.99) 4.00

JOE YANK (Korean War)
Standard Comics (Visual Editions): No. 5, Mar, 1952 - No. 16, 1954
5-Toth, Celardo, Tuska-a 11 22 33 64 90 115
6-Toth, Severin/Elder-a 11 22 33 60 83 105
7-Pinhead Perkins by Dan DeCarlo (in all?) 9 18 27 50 65 80
8-Toth-c 10 20 30 54 72 90
9-16: 9-Andru-c. 12-Andru-a 9 18 27 47 61 75

JOHN BOLTON'S HALLS OF HORROR
Eclipse Comics: June, 1985 - No. 2, June, 1985 ($1.75, limited series)
1,2-British-r; Bolton-c/a 4.00

JOHN BOLTON'S STRANGE WINK
Dark Horse Comics: Mar, 1998 - No. 3, May, 1998 ($2.95, B&W, limited series)
1-3-Anthology; Bolton-s/c/a 3.00

JOHN BYRNE'S NEXT MEN (See Dark Horse Presents #54)
Dark Horse Comics (Legend imprint #19 on): Jan, 1992 - No. 30, Dec, 1994 ($2.50, mature)
1-Silver foil embossed-c; Byrne-c/a/scripts in all 4.00
1-4: 1-2nd printing with gold ink logo 3.00
0-(2/92)-r/chapters 1-4 from DHP w/new Byrne-c 3.00
5-20,22-30: 7-10-MA #1-4 mini-series on flip side. 16-Origin of Mark IV. 17-Miller-c. 19-22-Faith storyline. 23-26-Power storyline. 27-30-Lies storyline Pt. 1-4 3.00
21-(12/93) 2nd Hellboy; cover and Hellboy pages by Mike Mignola; Byrne other pages (see San Diego Comic Con Comics #2 for 1st app.) 6 12 18 37 66 95
...Parallel, Book 2 ($16.95)-TPB; r/#7-12 17.00
...Fame, Book 3($16.95)-TPB r/#13-18 17.00
...Faith, Book 4($14.95)-TPB r/#19-22 15.00
NOTE: *Issues 1 through 6 contain certificates redeemable for an exclusive Next Men trading card set by Byrne. Prices are for complete books. **Cody** painted c-23-26. **Mignola** a-21(part); c-21.*

JOHN BYRNE'S NEXT MEN (Continues in Next Men: Aftermath #40)
IDW Publishing: Dec, 2010 - No. 9, Aug, 2011 ($3.99)
1-9-John Byrne-s/a/c in all. 1-Origin retold. 6,7-Abraham Lincoln app. 4.00

JOHN BYRNE'S 2112
Dark Horse Comics (Legend): Oct, 1991 ($9.95, TPB)
1-Byrne-c/a/s 10.00

JOHN CARTER OF MARS (See The Funnies & Tarzan #207)
Dell Publishing Co.: No. 375, Mar-May, 1952 - No. 488, Aug-Oct, 1953 (Edgar Rice Burroughs)
Four Color 375 (#1)-Origin; Jesse Marsh-a 30 60 90 216 483 750
Four Color 437, 488-Painted-c 16 32 48 112 249 385

JOHN CARTER OF MARS
Gold Key: Apr, 1964 - No. 3, Oct, 1964
1(10104-404)-r/4-Color #375; Jesse Marsh-a 6 12 18 42 79 115
2(407), 3(410)-r/4-Color #437 & 488; Marsh-a 5 10 15 31 53 75

JOHN CARTER OF MARS
House of Greystroke: 1970 (10-1/2x16-1/2", 72 pgs., B&W, paper-c)
1941-42 Sunday strip-r; John Coleman Burroughs-a 4 8 12 23 37 50

JOHN CARTER OF MARS: A PRINCESS OF MARS
Marvel Comics: Nov, 2011 - No. 5, Mar, 2012 ($2.99, limited series)
1-5: 1-Langridge-s/Andrade-a; covers by Young and Andrade. 2-4-Young-c 3.00

JOHN CARTER: THE END
Dynamite Entertainment: 2017 - No. 5, 2017 ($3.99)
1-5-Brian Wood-s/Alex Cox-a; multiple covers 4.00

JOHN CARTER: THE GODS OF MARS
Marvel Comics: May, 2012 - No. 5, Sept, 2012 ($3.99, limited series)
1-5-Sam Humphries-s/Ramón Pérez-a; Carter's 2nd trip to Mars 4.00

JOHN CARTER: THE WORLD OF MARS
Marvel Comics: Dec, 2011 - No. 4, Mar, 2012 ($3.99, limited series)
1-4-Movie prequel; Peter David-s/Luke Ross-a. 1-Ribic-c. 4-Olivetti-c 4.00

JOHN CARTER, WARLORD OF MARS (Also see Tarzan #207-209 and Weird Worlds)
Marvel Comics: June, 1977 - No. 28, Oct, 1979
1,18: 1-Origin. 18-Frank Miller-a(p)(1st publ. Marvel work) 3 6 9 17 26 35
1-(35¢-c variant, limited dist.) 9 18 27 59 117 175
2-5-(35¢-c variants, limited dist.) 6 12 18 38 69 100

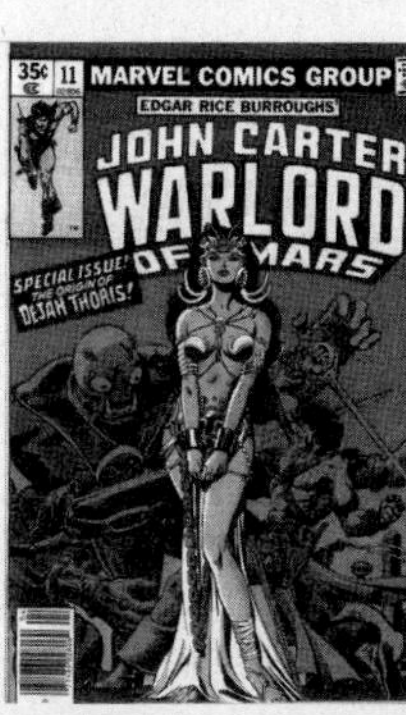

John Carter, Warlord of Mars #11 © ERB

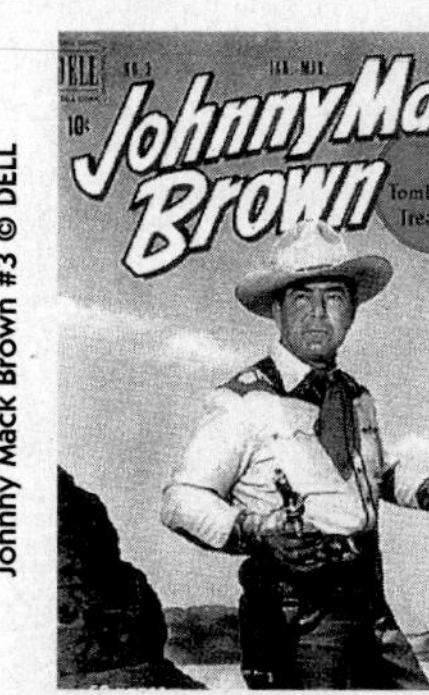

Johnny Mack Brown #3 © DELL

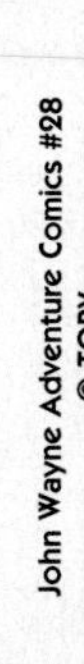
John Wayne Adventure Comics #28 © TOBY

	GD 2.0	VG 4.0	FN 6.0	VF 8.0	VF/NM 9.0	NM- 9.2
2-17,19-28: 11-Origin Dejah Thoris	1	3	4	6	8	10
Annuals 1-3: 1(1977). 2(1978). 3(1979)-All 52 pgs. with new book-length stories	1	3	4	6	8	10
Edgar Rice Burroughs' John Carter of Mars: Weird Worlds TPB (Dark Horse Books, Jan. 2011, $14.99) r/stories from Tarzan #207-209 and Weird Worlds #1-7; Marv Wolfman intro.						15.00

NOTE: ***Austin** c-24i. **Gil Kane** a-1-10p; c-1p, 2p, 3, 4-9p, 10, 15p, Annual 1p. **Layton** a-17i. **Miller** c-25, 26p. **Nebres** a-2-4i, 8-16i; c(i)-6-9, 11-22, 25, Annual 1. **Perez** c-24p. **Simonson** a-15p. **Sutton** a-7i.*

JOHN CARTER, WARLORD OF MARS
Dynamite Entertainment: 2014 - No. 14, 2015 ($3.99)

	GD	VG	FN	VF	VF/NM	NM-
1-14: 1-5-Marz-s/Malsuni-a; multiple covers on all						4.00
... 2015 Special ($4.99) Napton-s/Rodolfo-a/Parillo-c						5.00

JOHN CONSTANTINE - HELLBLAZER SPECIAL: PAPA MIDNITE
DC Comics (Vertigo): April, 2005 - No. 5, Aug, 2005 ($2.95/$2.99, limited series)

	GD	VG	FN	VF	VF/NM	NM-
1-5-Origin of Papa Midnite; Akins-a/Johnson-s						3.00

JOHN F. KENNEDY, CHAMPION OF FREEDOM
Worden & Childs: 1964 (no month) (25¢)

	GD	VG	FN	VF	VF/NM	NM-
nn-Photo-c	8	16	24	52	99	145

JOHN F. KENNEDY LIFE STORY
Dell Publishing Co.: Aug-Oct, 1964; Nov, 1965; June, 1966 (12¢)

	GD	VG	FN	VF	VF/NM	NM-
12-378-410-Photo-c	7	14	21	49	92	135
12-378-511 (reprint, 11/65)	3	6	9	21	33	45
12-378-606 (reprint, 6/66)	3	6	9	19	30	40

JOHN FORCE (See Magic Agent)

JOHN HIX SCRAP BOOK, THE
Eastern Color Printing Co. (McNaught Synd.): Late 1930's (no date) (10¢, 68 pgs., regular size)

	GD	VG	FN	VF	VF/NM	NM-
1-Strange As It Seems (resembles Single Series books)	41	82	123	256	428	600
2-Strange As It Seems	29	58	87	170	278	385

JOHN JAKES' MULLKON EMPIRE
Tekno Comix: Sept, 1995 - No. 6, Feb, 1996 ($1.95)

	GD	VG	FN	VF	VF/NM	NM-
1-6						3.00

JOHN LAW DETECTIVE (See Smash Comics #3)
Eclipse Comics: April, 1983 ($1.50, Baxter paper)

	GD	VG	FN	VF	VF/NM	NM-
1-Three Eisner stories originally drawn in 1948 for the never published John Law #1; original cover pencilled in 1948 & inked in 1982 by Eisner						4.00

JOHN McCAIN (See Presidential Material: John McCain)

JOHNNY APPLESEED (See Story Hour Series)

JOHNNY CASH (See Hello, I'm...)

JOHNNY DANGER (See Movie Comics, 1946)
Toby Press: 1950 (Based on movie serial)

	GD	VG	FN	VF	VF/NM	NM-
1-Photo-c; Sparling-a	23	46	69	136	223	310

JOHNNY DANGER PRIVATE DETECTIVE
Toby Press: Aug, 1954 (Reprinted in Danger #11 by Super)

	GD	VG	FN	VF	VF/NM	NM-
1-Photo-c; Opium den story	20	40	60	115	185	255

JOHNNY DYNAMITE (Formerly Dynamite #1-9; Foreign Intrigues #14 on)
Charlton Comics: No. 10, June, 1955 - No. 12, Oct, 1955

	GD	VG	FN	VF	VF/NM	NM-
10-12	14	28	42	76	108	140

JOHNNY DYNAMITE
Dark Horse Comics: Sept, 1994 - Dec, 1994 ($2.95, B&W & red, limited series)

	GD	VG	FN	VF	VF/NM	NM-
1-4: Max Allan Collins scripts in all; Terry Beatty-a						3.00
...: Underworld GN (AiT/Planet Lar, 3/03, $12.95, B&W) r/#1-4 in B&W without red						13.00

JOHNNY HAZARD
Best Books (Standard Comics) (King Features): No. 5, Aug, 1948 - No. 8, May, 1949; No. 35, date?

	GD	VG	FN	VF	VF/NM	NM-
5-Strip reprints by Frank Robbins (c/a)	19	38	57	109	172	235
6,8-Strip reprints by Frank Robbins	16	32	48	92	144	195
7,35: 7-New art, not Robbins	12	24	36	69	97	125

JOHNNY JASON (...Teen Reporter)
Dell Publishing Co.: Feb-Apr, 1962 - No. 2, June-Aug, 1962

	GD	VG	FN	VF	VF/NM	NM-
Four Color 1302, 2(01380-208)	4	8	12	23	37	50

JOHNNY LAW, SKY RANGER
Good Comics (Lev Gleason): Apr, 1955 - No. 3, Aug, 1955; No. 4, Nov, 1955

	GD	VG	FN	VF	VF/NM	NM-
1-Edmond Good-c/a	10	20	30	58	79	100
2-4	7	14	21	35	43	50

JOHNNY MACK BROWN (Western star; see Western Roundup under Dell Giants)
Dell Publishing Co.: No. 269, Mar, 1950 - No. 963, Feb, 1959 (All Photo-c)

	GD	VG	FN	VF	VF/NM	NM-
Four Color 269(#1)(3/50, 52pgs.)-Johnny Mack Brown & his horse Rebel begin; photo front/back-c begin; Marsh-a in #1-9	18	36	54	124	275	425
2(10-12/50, 52pgs.)	10	20	30	64	132	200
3(1-3/51, 52pgs.)	8	16	24	54	102	150
4-10 (9-11/52)(36pgs.), Four Color 455,493,541,584,618,645,685,722,776,834,963	6	12	18	40	73	105
Four Color 922-Manning-a	6	12	18	41	76	110

JOHNNY NEMO
Eclipse Comics: Sept, 1985 - No. 3, Feb, 1986 (Mini-series)

	GD	VG	FN	VF	VF/NM	NM-
1-3						4.00

JOHNNY PERIL (See Comic Cavalcade #15, Danger Trail #5, Sensation Comics #107 & Sensation Mystery)

JOHNNY RINGO (TV)
Dell Publishing Co.: No. 1142, Nov-Jan, 1960/61 (one shot)

	GD	VG	FN	VF	VF/NM	NM-
Four Color 1142-Photo-c	6	12	18	41	76	110

JOHNNY STARBOARD (See Wisco)

JOHNNY THE HOMICIDAL MANIAC (Also see Squee)
Slave Labor Graphics: Aug, 1995 - No. 7, Jan, 1997 ($2.95, B&W, lim. series)

	GD	VG	FN	VF	VF/NM	NM-
1-Jhonen Vasquez-c/s/a (1995)	6	12	18	41	76	110
1-Special Signed & numbered edition of 2,000 (1996)	3	6	9	17	26	35
2,3: 2-(11/95). 3-(2/96)	1	2	3	5	6	8
4-7: 4-(5-96). 5-(8/96)						4.00
Hardcover-($29.95) r/#1-7						35.00
TPB-($19.95)						25.00

JOHNNY THUNDER
National Periodical Publications: Feb-Mar, 1973 - No. 3, July-Aug, 1973

	GD	VG	FN	VF	VF/NM	NM-
1-Johnny Thunder & Nighthawk-r. in all	2	4	6	13	18	22
2,3: 2-Trigger Twins app.	2	4	6	8	11	14

NOTE: *All contain 1950s DC reprints from All-American Western. **Drucker** r-2, 3. **G. Kane** r-2, 3. **Moreira** r-1. **Toth** r-1, 3; c-1r, 3r. Also see All-American, All-Star Western, Flash Comics, Western Comics, World's Best & World's Finest.*

JOHN PAUL JONES
Dell Publishing Co.: No. 1007, July-Sept, 1959 (one-shot)

	GD	VG	FN	VF	VF/NM	NM-
Four Color 1007-Movie, Robert Stack photo-c	6	12	18	37	66	95

JOHN ROMITA JR. 30TH ANNIVERSARY SPECIAL
Marvel Comics: 2006 ($3.99, one-shot)

	GD	VG	FN	VF	VF/NM	NM-
nn-r/1st story in Amazing Spider-Man Annual #11; timeline, sketch pages, interviews						4.00

JOHN STEED & EMMA PEEL (See The Avengers, Gold Key series)

JOHN STEELE SECRET AGENT (Also see Freedom Agent)
Gold Key: Dec, 1964

	GD	VG	FN	VF	VF/NM	NM-
1-Freedom Agent	5	10	15	33	57	80

JOHN WAYNE ADVENTURE COMICS (Movie star; See Big Tex, Oxydol-Dreft, Tim McCoy, & With The Marines...#1)
Toby Press: Winter, 1949-50 - No. 31, May, 1955 (Photo-c: 1-12,17,25-on)

	GD	VG	FN	VF	VF/NM	NM-
1 (36pgs.)-Photo-c begin (1st time in comics on-c)	252	504	756	1613	2757	3900
2-4: 2-(4/50, 36pgs.)-Williamson/Frazetta-a(2) 6 & 2 pgs. (one story-r/Billy the Kid #1); photo back-c. 3-(36pgs.)-Williamson/Frazetta-a(2), 16 pgs. total; photo back-c. 4-(52pgs.)-Williamson/Frazetta-a(2), 16 pgs. total	82	164	246	528	902	1275
5 (52pgs.)-Kurtzman-a-(Alfred "L" Newman in Potshot Pete)	61	122	183	390	670	950
6 (52pgs.)-Williamson/Frazetta-a (10 pgs.); Kurtzman-a "Pot-Shot Pete", (5 pgs.); & "Genius Jones", (1 pg.)	73	146	219	467	796	1125
7 (52pgs.)-Williamson/Frazetta-a (10 pgs.)	63	126	189	403	689	975
8 (36pgs.)-Williamson/Frazetta-a(2) (12 & 9 pgs.)	76	152	228	486	831	1175
9-11: Photo western-c	43	86	129	268	454	640
12,14-Photo war-c. 12-Kurtzman-a(2 pg.) "Genius"	43	86	129	271	461	650
13,15: 13,15-Line-drawn-c begin, end #24	39	78	117	236	388	540
16-Williamson/Frazetta-r/Billy the Kid #1	40	80	120	248	414	580
17-Photo-c	40	80	120	248	414	580
18-Williamson/Frazetta-a (r/#4 & 8, 19 pgs.)	43	86	129	268	454	640
19-24: 23-Evans-a?	36	72	108	214	347	480
25-Photo-c resume; end #31; Williamson/Frazetta-r/Billy the Kid #3	43	86	129	268	454	640
26-28,30-Photo-c	39	78	117	236	388	540
29,31-Williamson/Frazetta-a in each (r/#4, 2)	41	82	123	256	428	600

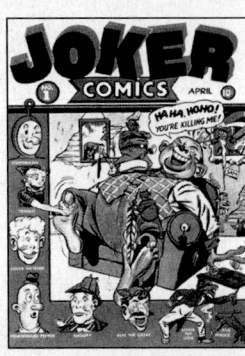

Jo-Jo Comics #17 © FOX

Joker Comics #1 © MAR

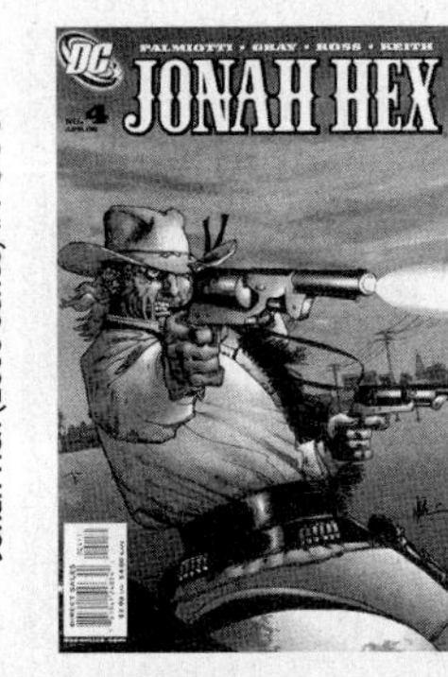

Jonah Hex (2006 series) #4 © DC

	GD 2.0	VG 4.0	FN 6.0	VF 8.0	VF/NM 9.0	NM- 9.2

NOTE: *Williamsonish art in later issues by **Gerald McCann.***

JOHN WICK (Based on the Keanu Reeves movies)
Dynamite Entertainment: 2017 - Present ($3.99)

1-Pak-s/Valletta-a; 4 covers 4.00

JO-JO COMICS (...Congo King #7-29; My Desire #30 on)(Also see Fantastic Fears and Jungle Jo)
Fox Feature Syndicate: 1945 - No. 29, July, 1949 (Two No.7's; no #13)

nn(1945)-Funny animal, humor 24 48 72 142 234 325
2(Sum,'46)-6(4-5/47): Funny animal. 2-Ten pg. Electro story (Fall/46)
15 30 45 90 140 190
7(7/47)-Jo-Jo, Congo King begins (1st app.); Bronze Man & Purple Tigress app. 97 194 291 621 1061 1500
7(#8) (9/47) 71 142 213 454 777 1100
8(#9) Classic Kamen mountain of skulls-c; Tanee begins
97 194 291 621 1061 1500
9,10(#10,11) 63 126 189 403 689 975
11,12(#12,13),14,16: 11,16-Kamen bondage-c 54 108 162 343 574 825
15-Cited by Dr. Wertham in 5/47 Saturday Review of Literature
55 110 165 352 601 850
17-Kamen bondage-c 71 142 213 454 777 1100
18-20 53 106 159 334 567 800
21-24,26-29: 21-Hollingsworth-a (4 pgs.; 23-1 pg.) 43 86 129 271 461 650
25-Bondage-c 90 180 270 576 988 1400
NOTE: *Many bondage-c/a by **Baker/Kamen/Feldstein/Good.** No. 7's have Princesses Gwenna, Geesa, Yolda, & Safra before settling down on Tanee.*

JOKEBOOK COMICS DIGEST ANNUAL (...Magazine No. 5 on)
Archie Publications: Oct, 1977 - No. 13, Oct, 1983 (Digest Size)

1(10/77)-Reprints; Neal Adams-a. 2 4 6 13 18 22
2(4/78)-5 2 4 6 9 12 15
6-13 1 3 4 6 8 10

JOKER
DC Comics: 2008 ($19.99, hardcover graphic novel with dustjacket)

HC-Joker is released from Arkham; Azzarello-s/Bermejo-a 20.00

JOKER, THE (See Batman #1, Batman: The Killing Joke, Brave & the Bold, Detective, Greatest Joker Stories & Justice League Annual #2)
National Periodical Publications: May, 1975 - No. 9, Sept-Oct, 1976

1-Two-Face app. 6 12 18 41 76 110
2-4: 3-The Creeper app. 4-Green Arrow-c/sty 4 8 12 23 37 50
5-9: 6-Sherlock Holmes-c/sty. 7-Lex Luthor-c/story. 8-Scarecrow-c/story. 9-Catwoman-c/story 3 6 9 19 30 40
...: The Greatest Stories Ever Told TPB (2008, $19.99) r/Batman #1 and other apps. 20.00

JOKER, THE (See Tangent Comics/ The Joker)

JOKER COMICS (Adventures Into Terror No. 43 on)
Timely/Marvel Comics No. 36 on (TCI/CDS): Apr, 1942 - No. 42, Aug, 1950

1-(Rare)-Powerhouse Pepper (1st app.) begins by Wolverton; Stuporman app. from Daring Comics 320 640 960 2240 3920 5600
2-Wolverton-a; 1st app. Tessie the Typist & begin series
129 258 387 826 1413 2000
3-5-Wolverton-a 77 154 231 493 847 1200
6-10-Wolverton-a. 6-Tessie-c begin 52 104 156 328 552 775
11-20-Wolverton-a 47 94 141 296 498 700
21,22,24-27,29,30-Wolverton cont'd. & Kurtzman's "Hey Look" in #23-27
41 82 123 256 428 600
23-1st "Hey Look" by Kurtzman; Wolverton-a 43 86 129 271 461 650
28,32,34,37-41: 28-Millie the Model begins. 32-Hedy begins. 41-Nellie the Nurse app.
22 44 66 132 216 300
31-Last Powerhouse Pepper; not in #28 39 78 117 231 378 525
33,35,36-Kurtzman's "Hey Look" 23 46 69 136 223 310
42-Only app. 'Patty Pinup,' clone of Millie the Model 23 46 69 136 223 310

JOKER: DEVIL'S ADVOCATE
DC Comics: 1996 ($24.95/$12.95, one-shot)

nn-(Hardcover)-Dixon scripts/Nolan & Hanna-a 30.00
nn-(Softcover) 15.00

JOKER: LAST LAUGH (See Batman: The Joker's Last Laugh for TPB)
DC Comics: Dec, 2001 - No. 6, Jan, 2002 ($2.95, weekly limited series)

1-6: 1,6-Bolland-c 3.00
...Secret Files (12/01, $5.95) Short stories by various; Simonson-c 6.00

JOKER / MASK
Dark Horse Comics: May, 2000 - No. 4, Aug, 2000 ($2.95, limited series)

1-4-Batman, Harley Quinn, Poison Ivy app. 2 4 6 9 12 15

JOKER'S ASYLUM
DC Comics: Sept, 2008 ($2.99, weekly limited series of one-shots)

...: Joker - Andy Kubert-c, Sanchez-a; ...: Penguin - Pearson-c/a; ...: Poison Ivy - Guillem March-c/a; ...: Scarecrow - Juan Doe-c/a; ...: Two-Face - Andy Clarke-c/a 3.00
Batman: The Joker's Asylum TPB (2008, $14.99) r/one-shots 15.00

JOKER'S ASYLUM II
DC Comics: Aug, 2010 ($2.99, weekly limited series of one-shots)

...: Clayface - Kelley Jones-c/a; ; ...: Killer Croc - Mattina-c; Mad Hatter - Giffen & Sienkiewicz-a, Sienkiewicz-c; ...: Riddler - Van Sciver-c 3.00
...: Harley Quinn - Quinones-a 2 4 6 11 16 20
Batman: The Joker's Asylum Volume 2 TPB (2011, $14.99) r/one-shots 15.00

JOLLY CHRISTMAS, A (See March of Comics No. 269)

JOLLY COMICS: Four Star Publishing Co.: 1947 (Advertised, not published)

JOLLY COMICS
No publisher: No date (1930s-40s)(10¢, cover is black/red ink on yellow paper, blank inside-c)

nn-Snuffy Smith & Katzenjamer Kids on-c only. Buck Rogers, Dickey Dare, Napoleon & others app. Reprints Ace Comics #8-c. A GD copy sold in 2014 for $358.50
219 438 657 1402 2401 3400

JOLLY JINGLES (Formerly Jackpot Comics)
MLJ Magazines: No. 10, Sum, 1943 - No. 16, Wint, 1944/45

10-Super Duck begins (origin & 1st app.); Woody The Woodpecker begins (not same as Lantz character) 60 120 180 381 653 925
11 (Fall, '43)-2nd Super Duck (see Hangman #8) 32 64 96 188 307 425
12-Hitler-c 90 180 270 576 988 1400
13-16: 13-Sahle-c. 15,16-Vigoda-c 22 44 66 132 216 300

JONAH HEX (See All-Star Western, Hex and Weird Western Tales)
National Periodical Pub./DC Comics: Mar-Apr, 1977 - No. 92, Aug, 1985

1-Garcia-Lopez-c/a 10 20 30 69 147 225
2-1st app. El Papagayo 6 12 18 38 69 100
3,4,9: 9-Wrightson-c. 5 10 15 33 57 80
5,6,10: 5-Rep 1st app. from All-Star Western #10 5 10 15 30 50 70
7,8-Explains Hex's face disfigurement (origin) 5 10 15 35 63 90
11-20: 12-Starlin-c 3 6 9 19 30 40
21-32: 23-Intro. Mei Ling. 31,32-Origin retold 2 4 6 13 18 22
33-50 2 4 6 8 11 14
51-80 1 2 3 5 7 9
81-91: 89-Mark Texeira-a. 91-Cover swipe from Superman #243 (hugging a mystery woman)
2 4 6 8 10 12
92-Story cont'd in Hex #1 3 6 9 19 30 40
NOTE: ***Ayers** a(p)-35-37, 40, 41, 44-53, 56, 58-82. **Buckler** a-11; c-11, 13-16. **Kubert** c-43-46. **Morrow** a-90-92; c-10. **Spiegle(Tothish)** a-34, 38, 40, 49, 52. **Texeira** a-89p. Batlash back-ups in 49, 52. El Diablo back-ups in 48, 56-60, 73-75. Scalphunter back-ups in 40, 41, 45-47.*

JONAH HEX (Also see All Star Western [2011 DC New 52 title])
DC Comics: Jan, 2006 - No. 70, Oct, 2011 ($2.99)

1-Justin Gray & Jimmy Palmiotti-s/Luke Ross-a/Quitely-c 5.00
1-Special Edition (7/10, $1.00) r/#1 with "What's Next?" logo on cover 3.00
2-49,51-70: 3-Bat Lash app. 10,16,17,19,20,22-Noto-a. 11-El Diablo app.; Beck-a. 13-15-Origin retold. 21,23,27,30,32,37,38,42,52,54,57,59,61,63,67-Bernet-a. 33-Darwyn Cooke-a/c. 34-Sparacio-a. 51-Giordano-c. 53-Tucci-c/a. 62-Risso-a 3.00
50-($3.99) Darwyn Cooke-a/c 4.00
...: Bullets Don't Lie TPB (2009, $14.99) r/#31-36 15.00
...: Counting Corpses TPB (2010, $14.99) r/#43,50-54 15.00
...: Face Full of Violence TPB (2006, $12.99) r/#1-6 13.00
...: Guns of Vengeance TPB (2007, $12.99) r/#7-12 13.00
...: Lead Poisoning TPB (2009, $14.99) r/#37-42 15.00
...: Luck Runs Out TPB (2008, $12.99) r/#25-30 13.00
...: No Way Back HC (2010, $19.99) new GN; Gray & Palmiotti-s/DeZuniga-a 20.00
...: No Way Back SC (2011, $14.99) new GN; Gray & Palmiotti-s/DeZuniga-a 15.00
...: Only the Good Die Young TPB (2008, $12.99) r/#19-24 13.00
...: Origins TPB (2007, $12.99) r/#13-18 13.00
...: Tall Tales TPB (2011, $14.99) r/#55-60 15.00
...: The Six Gun War TPB (2010, $14.99) r/#44-49 15.00
...: Welcome to Paradise TPB (2010, $17.99) r/debut in All-Star Western #10 plus early apps. in Weird Western Tales and Jonah Hex #2,4 (1977 series) 18.00

JONAH HEX AND OTHER WESTERN TALES (Blue Ribbon Digest)
DC Comics: Sept-Oct, 1979 - No. 3, Jan-Feb, 1980 (100 pgs.)

1-3: 1-Origin Scalphunter-r, Ayers/Evans, Neal Adams-a.; painted-c. 2-Weird Western Tales-r; Neal Adams, Toth, Aragonés-a. 3-Outlaw-r, Scalphunter-r; Gil Kane, Wildey-a
2 4 6 11 16 20

Jonesy #11 © Humphries & Boyle

Jon Sable, Freelance #19 © FC

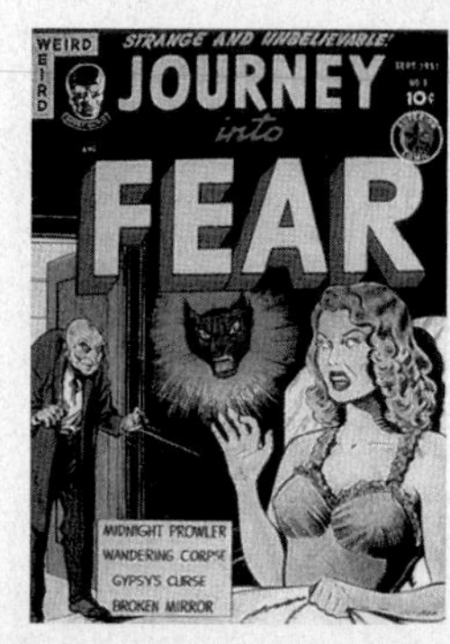

Journey Into Fear #3 © SUPR

JONAH HEX: RIDERS OF THE WORM AND SUCH
DC Comics (Vertigo): Mar, 1995 - No. 5, July, 1995 ($2.95, limited series)

	GD 2.0	VG 4.0	FN 6.0	VF 8.0	VF/NM 9.0	NM- 9.2
1-5-Lansdale story, Truman-a						4.00

JONAH HEX: SHADOWS WEST
DC Comics (Vertigo): Feb, 1999 - No. 3, Apr, 1999 ($2.95, limited series)

	GD 2.0	VG 4.0	FN 6.0	VF 8.0	VF/NM 9.0	NM- 9.2
1-3-Lansdale-s/Truman-a						4.00

JONAH HEX SPECTACULAR (See DC Special Series No. 16)

JONAH HEX: TWO-GUN MOJO
DC Comics (Vertigo): Aug, 1993 - No. 5, Dec, 1993 ($2.95, limited series)

	GD 2.0	VG 4.0	FN 6.0	VF 8.0	VF/NM 9.0	NM- 9.2
1-Lansdale scripts in all; Truman/Glanzman-a in all w/Truman-c						6.00
1-Platinum edition with no price on cover						20.00
2-5						4.00
TPB-(1994, $12.95) r/#1-5						13.00

JONAH HEX/ YOSEMITE SAM
DC Comics: Aug, 2017 ($4.99, one-shot)

	GD 2.0	VG 4.0	FN 6.0	VF 8.0	VF/NM 9.0	NM- 9.2
1-Palmiotti-s/Teixeira-a; Foghorn Leghorn app.						5.00

JONESY (Formerly Crack Western)
Comic Favorite/Quality Comics Group: No. 85, Aug, 1953; No. 2, Oct, 1953 - No. 8, Oct, 1954

	GD 2.0	VG 4.0	FN 6.0	VF 8.0	VF/NM 9.0	NM- 9.2
85(#1)-Teen-age humor	10	20	30	56	76	95
2	6	12	18	31	38	45
3-8	6	12	18	28	34	40

JONESY
BOOM! Studios (BOOM! Box): Feb, 2016 - No. 12, Apr, 2017 ($3.99, originally a 4-part series)

	GD 2.0	VG 4.0	FN 6.0	VF 8.0	VF/NM 9.0	NM- 9.2
1-12-Sam Humphries-s/Caitlin Rose Boyle-a. 1-Multiple covers						4.00

JON JUAN (Also see Great Lover Romances)
Toby Press: Spring, 1950

	GD 2.0	VG 4.0	FN 6.0	VF 8.0	VF/NM 9.0	NM- 9.2
1-All Schomburg-a (signed Al Reid on-c); written by Siegel; used in **SOTI**, pg. 38 (Scarce)	84	168	252	538	919	1300

JONNI THUNDER (...A.K.A. Thunderbolt)
DC Comics: Feb, 1985 - No. 4, Aug, 1985 (75¢, limited series)

	GD 2.0	VG 4.0	FN 6.0	VF 8.0	VF/NM 9.0	NM- 9.2
1-4: 1-Origin & 1st app.						4.00

JONNY DOUBLE
DC Comics (Vertigo): Sept, 1998 - No. 4, Dec, 1998 ($2.95, limited series)

	GD 2.0	VG 4.0	FN 6.0	VF 8.0	VF/NM 9.0	NM- 9.2
1-4-Azzarello-s						3.00
TPB (2002, $12.95) r/#1-4; Chiarello-c						13.00

JONNY QUEST (TV)
Gold Key: Dec, 1964 (Hanna-Barbera)

	GD 2.0	VG 4.0	FN 6.0	VF 8.0	VF/NM 9.0	NM- 9.2
1 (10139-412)	33	66	99	238	532	825

JONNY QUEST (TV)
Comico: June 1986 - No. 31, Dec, 1988 ($1.50/$1.75)(Hanna-Barbera)

	GD 2.0	VG 4.0	FN 6.0	VF 8.0	VF/NM 9.0	NM- 9.2
1,3,5: 3,5-Dave Stevens-c						6.00
2,4,6-31: 30-Adapts TV episode						4.00
Special 1(9/88, $1.75), 2(10/88, $1.75)						4.00

*NOTE: **M. Anderson** a-9. **Mooney** a-Special 1. **Pini** a-2. **Quagmire** a-31p. **Rude** a-1; c-2i. **Sienkiewicz** c-11. **Spiegle** a-7, 12, 21; c-21 **Staton** a-2i, 11p. **Steacy** c-8. **Stevens** a-4i; c-3,5. **Wildey** a-1, c-1, 7, 12. **Williamson** a-4i; c-4i.*

JONNY QUEST CLASSICS (TV)
Comico: May, 1987 - No. 3, July, 1987 ($2.00) (Hanna-Barbera)

	GD 2.0	VG 4.0	FN 6.0	VF 8.0	VF/NM 9.0	NM- 9.2
1-3: Wildey-c/a; 3-Based on TV episode						4.00

JON SABLE, FREELANCE (Also see Mike Grell's Sable & Sable)
First Comics: 6/83 - No. 56, 2/88 (#1-17, $1; #18-33, $1.25, #34-on, $1.75)

	GD 2.0	VG 4.0	FN 6.0	VF 8.0	VF/NM 9.0	NM- 9.2
1-Mike Grell-c/a/scripts						5.00
2-56: 3-5-Origin, parts 1-3. 6-Origin, part 4. 11-1st app. of Maggie the Cat. 14-Mando paper begins. 16-Maggie the Cat. app. 25-30-Shatter app. 34-Deluxe format begins ($1.75)						3.00
The Complete Jon Sable, Freelance: Vol. 1 (IDW, 2005, $19.99) r/#1-6						20.00
The Complete Jon Sable, Freelance: Vol. 2 (IDW, 2005, $19.99) r/#7-11						20.00
The Complete Jon Sable, Freelance: Vol. 3 (IDW, 2005, $19.99) r/#12-16						20.00
The Complete Jon Sable, Freelance: Vol. 4 (IDW, 2005, $19.99) r/#17-21						20.00

*NOTE: **Aragones** a-33; c-33(part). **Grell** a-1-43;c-1-52, 53p, 54-56.*

JON SABLE, FREELANCE
IDW Publ.: (Limited series)

	GD 2.0	VG 4.0	FN 6.0	VF 8.0	VF/NM 9.0	NM- 9.2
...: Ashes of Eden 1-5 (2009 - No. 5, 2/10, $3.99) Mike Grell-c/a/scripts						4.00
...: Bloodtrail 1-6 (4/05 - No. 6, 11/05, $3.99) Mike Grell-c/a/scripts						4.00
...: Bloodtrail TPB (4/06, $19.99) r/#1-6; cover gallery						20.00

JOSEPH & HIS BRETHREN (See The Living Bible)

JOSIE (She's... #1-16) (...& the Pussycats #45 on) (See Archie's Pals 'n' Gals #23 for 1st app.) (Also see Archie Giant Series Magazine #528, 540, 551, 562, 571, 584, 597, 610, 622)
Archie Publ./Radio Comics: Feb, 1963; No. 2, Aug, 1963 - No. 106, Oct, 1982

	GD 2.0	VG 4.0	FN 6.0	VF 8.0	VF/NM 9.0	NM- 9.2
1	46	92	138	340	770	1200
2	12	24	36	84	185	285
3-5	9	18	27	59	117	175
6-10: 6-(5/64) Book length Haunted Mansion-c/s. 7-(8/64) 1st app. Alexandra Cabot?	6	12	18	37	66	95
11-20	5	10	15	30	50	70
21, 23-30	4	8	12	25	40	55
22 (9/66)-Mighty Man & Mighty (Josie Girl) app.	4	8	12	28	47	65
31-44	3	6	9	20	31	42
45 (12/69)-Josie and the Pussycats begins (Hanna Barbera TV cartoon); 1st app. of the Pussycats	26	52	78	182	404	625
46-2nd app./1st cover Pussycats	10	20	30	66	138	210
47-3rd app. of the Pussycats	6	12	18	42	79	115
48,49-Pussycats band-c/s	7	14	21	46	86	125
50-J&P-c; go to Hollywood, meet Hanna & Barbera	8	16	24	51	96	140
51-54	3	6	9	20	31	42
55-74 (2/74)(52 pg. issues). 73-Pussycats band-c	3	6	9	20	31	42
75-90(8/76)	3	6	9	14	19	24
91-99	2	4	6	10	14	18
100 (10/79)	2	4	6	13	18	22
101-106: 103-Pussycats band-c	2	4	6	11	16	20

JOSIE & THE PUSSYCATS (TV)
Archie Comics: 1993 - No. 2, 1994 ($2.00, 52 pgs.)(Published annually)

	GD 2.0	VG 4.0	FN 6.0	VF 8.0	VF/NM 9.0	NM- 9.2
1,2-Bound-in pull-out poster in each. 2-(Spr/94)						5.00

JOSIE AND THE PUSSYCATS
Archie Comic Publications: Nov, 2016 - Present ($3.99)

	GD 2.0	VG 4.0	FN 6.0	VF 8.0	VF/NM 9.0	NM- 9.2
1-9: 1-Bennett & Deordio-s/Audrey Mok-a; multiple covers; back-up classic reprints. 5,6-Riverdale TV previews. 9-Shannon-a						4.00

JOURNAL OF CRIME (See Fox Giants)

JOURNEY
Aardvark-Vanaheim #1-14/Fantagraphics Books #15-on: 1983 - No. 14, Sept, 1984; No. 15, Apr, 1985 - No. 27, July, 1986 (B&W)

	GD 2.0	VG 4.0	FN 6.0	VF 8.0	VF/NM 9.0	NM- 9.2
1						4.00
2-27: 20-Sam Kieth-a						3.00

JOURNEY INTO FEAR
Superior-Dynamic Publications: May, 1951 - No. 21, Sept, 1954

	GD 2.0	VG 4.0	FN 6.0	VF 8.0	VF/NM 9.0	NM- 9.2
1-Baker-r(2)	81	162	243	518	884	1250
2	53	106	159	334	567	800
3,4	45	90	135	284	480	675
5-10,15: 15-Used in **SOTI**, pg. 389	39	78	117	240	395	550
11-14,16-21	39	78	117	231	378	525

*NOTE: Kamenish 'headlight'-a most issues. **Robinson** a-10.*

JOURNEY INTO MYSTERY (1st Series) (Thor Nos. 126-502)
Atlas(CPS No. 1-48/AMI No. 49-68/Marvel No. 69 (6/61) on): 6/52 - No. 48, 8/57; No. 49, 11/58 - No. 125, 2/66; 503, 11/96 - No. 521, June, 1998

	GD 2.0	VG 4.0	FN 6.0	VF 8.0	VF/NM 9.0	NM- 9.2
1-Weird/horror stories begin	1150	2300	3450	8000	12,000	16,000
2	226	452	678	1446	2473	3500
3,4	181	362	543	1158	1979	2800
5-11	168	336	504	1075	1838	2600
12-20,22: 15-Atomic explosion panel. 22-Davis*esque*-a; last pre-code issue (2/55)	108	216	324	686	1181	1675
21-Kubert-a; Tothish-a by Andru	113	226	339	718	1234	1750
23-32,35-38,40: 24-Torres?-a. 38-Ditko-a	81	162	243	518	884	1250
33-Williamson-a; Ditko-a (his 1st for Atlas?)	90	180	270	576	988	1400
34,39: 34-Krigstein-a. 39-1st S.A. issue; Wood-a	82	164	246	528	902	1275
41-Crandall-a; Frazetta*esque*-a by Morrow	40	80	120	296	673	1050
42,46,48: 42,48-Torres-a. 46-Torres & Krigstein-a	38	76	114	285	641	1000
43,44-Williamson/Mayo-a in both. 43-Invisible Woman prototype	42	84	126	311	706	1100
45,47	38	76	114	282	634	985
49-Matt Fox, Check-a	42	84	126	311	706	1100
50,52-54: Ditko/Kirby-a. 50-Davis-a. 54-Williamson-a	46	92	138	359	805	1250
51-Kirby/Wood-a	50	100	150	390	870	1350
55-61,63-65,67-69,71,72,74,75: 74-Contents change to Fantasy. 75-Last 10¢ issue	38	76	114	285	641	1000
62-Prototype ish. (The Hulk); 1st app. Xemnu (Titan) called "The Hulk"	79	158	237	632	1416	2200

Journey Into Mystery #95 © MAR

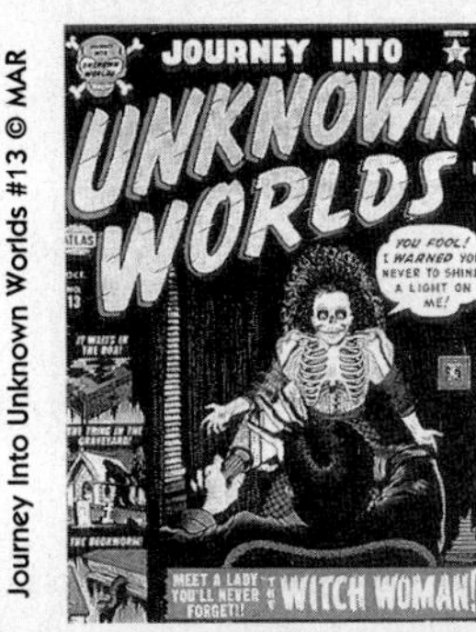

Journey Into Unknown Worlds #13 © MAR

JSA #23 © DC

GD VG FN VF VF/NM NM-
2.0 4.0 6.0 8.0 9.0 9.2
GD VG FN VF VF/NM NM-
2.0 4.0 6.0 8.0 9.0 9.2

66-Prototype ish. (The Hulk)-Return of Xemnu "The Hulk"
57 114 171 456 1028 1600
70-Prototype ish. (The Sandman)(7/61); similar to Spidey villain
42 84 126 311 706 1100
73-Story titled "The Spider" where a spider is exposed to radiation & gets powers of a human and shoots webbing; a reverse prototype of Spider-Man's origin
64 128 192 512 1156 1800
76,77,80,81: 80-Anti-communist propaganda story 33 66 99 238 532 825
76-(10¢ cover price blacked out, 12¢ printed on) 46 92 138 368 834 1300
78-The Sorceror (Dr. Strange prototype) app. (3/62) 46 92 138 340 770 1200
79-Prototype issue. (Mr. Hyde) 38 76 114 285 641 1000
82-Prototype ish. (Scorpion) 36 72 108 259 580 900
83-Origin & 1st app. The Mighty Thor by Kirby (8/62) and begin series; Thor-c also begin
1700 3400 5950 17,000 48,500 80,000
83-Reprint from the Golden Record Comic Set 18 36 54 122 271 420
With the record (1966) 26 52 78 183 407 630
84-2nd app. Thor 276 552 828 2277 5139 8000
85-1st app. Loki & Heimdall; 1st brief app. Odin (1 panel); 1st app. Asgard
259 518 777 2137 4819 7500
86-1st full app. Odin 96 192 288 768 1734 2700
87-89: 89-Origin Thor retold 82 164 246 656 1478 2300
90-No Kirby-a 61 122 183 488 1094 1700
91,92,94,96-Sinnott-a 46 92 138 359 805 1250
93,97-Kirby-a; Tales of Asgard series begins #97 (origin which concludes in #99); origin & 1st app. Lava Man. 97-1st app. Surtur (1 panel) 49 98 147 382 854 1325
95-Sinnott-a; Thor vs. Thor 54 108 162 432 966 1500
98,99-Kirby/Heck-a. 98-Origin/1st app. The Human Cobra. 99-1st app. Mr. Hyde; Surtur app.
37 74 111 274 612 950
100-Kirby/Heck-a; Thor battles Mr. Hyde 36 72 108 266 596 925
101,108: 101-(2/64)-2nd Avengers x-over (w/o Capt. America); see Tales Of Suspense #49 for 1st x-over. 108-(9/64)-Early Dr. Strange & Avengers x-over; ten extra pgs. Kirby-a
25 50 75 175 388 600
102-(3/64) 1st app. Sif, Balder and Hela 42 84 126 311 706 1100
103-1st app. Enchantress 68 136 204 544 1222 1900
104-107,110: 105-109-Ten extra pgs. Kirby-a in each. 107-1st app. Grey Gargoyle. 110,111-Two part battle vs. The Human Cobra & Mr. Hyde
24 48 72 168 372 575
109-Magneto-c & app. (1st x-over, 10/64) 45 90 135 333 754 1175
111,113: 113-Origin Loki 18 36 54 124 275 425
112-Thor Vs. Hulk (1/65); Origin Loki 57 114 171 456 1028 1600
114-Origin/1st app. Absorbing Man 28 56 84 202 451 700
115-Detailed origin of Loki 20 40 60 138 307 475
116,117,120-123,125 14 28 42 96 211 325
118-1st app. Destroyer 23 46 69 161 356 550
119-Intro Hogun, Fandral, Volstagg; 2nd Destroyer 20 40 60 138 307 475
124-Hercules-c/story 15 30 45 100 220 340
503-521: 503-(11/96, $1.50)-The Lost Gods begin; Tom DeFalco scripts & Deodato Studios-c/a. 505-Spider-Man-c/app. 509-Loki-c/app. 514-516-Shang-Chi 3.00
#(-1) Flashback (7/97) Tales of Asgard Donald Blake app. 3.00
Annual 1(1965, 25¢, 72 pgs.)-New Thor vs. Hercules(1st app.)-c/story (see Incredible Hulk #3); Kirby-c/a; r/#85,93,95,97 30 60 90 216 483 750
NOTE: ***Ayers*** *a-14, 39, 64i, 71i, 74i, 80i.* ***Bailey*** *a-43.* ***Briefer*** *a-5, 12.* ***Cameron*** *a-35.* ***Check*** *a-17.* ***Colan*** *a-23, 81; c-14.* ***Ditko*** *a-33, 38, 50-96; c-58, 67, 71, 88i.* ***Kirby/Ditko*** *a-50-83.* ***Everett*** *a-20, 48; c-4-7, 9, 36, 37, 39-42, 44, 45, 47.* ***Forte*** *a-19, 35, 40, 53.* ***Heath*** *a-4-6, 11, 14; c-1, 8, 11, 15, 51.* ***Heck*** *a-53, 73.* ***Kirby*** *a(p)-51, 52, 56, 57-60, 62-64, 66, 67, 69-89, 93, 97, 98, 100(w/****Heck****), 101-125; c-50-57, 59-66, 68-70, 72-82, 88(w/****Ditko****), 83 & 84(w/****Sinnott****), 85-96(w/****Ayers****), 97-125p.* ***Leiber/Fox*** *a-93, 98-102.* ***Maneely*** *c-20-22.* ***Morisi*** *a-42.* ***Morrow*** *a-41, 42.* ***Orlando*** *a-30, 45, 57.* ***Mac Pakula*** *(Tothish) a-9, 35, 41.* ***Powell*** *a-20, 27, 34.* ***Reinman*** *a-39, 70, 87, 92, 96i.* ***Robinson*** *a-9.* ***Roussos*** *a-39.* ***Robert Sale*** *a-14.* ***Severin*** *a-27; c-30.* ***Sinnott*** *a-41; c-50.* ***Tuska*** *a-11.* ***Wildey*** *a-16.*

JOURNEY INTO MYSTERY (Series and numbering continue from Thor #621)
Marvel Comics: No. 622, Jun, 2011 - No. 655, Oct, 2013 ($3.99/$2.99)

622-Reincarnated young Loki; Thor app.; Braithwaite-a; Hans-c 4.00
622-Variant covers by Art Adams and Lee Weeks 6.00
623-626, 626.1, 627-630-($2.99) Fear Itself tie-in. 628,629-Portacio-a 3.00
631-655: 631-Portacio-a; Aftermath. 632-Hellstrom app. 637,638-Exiled x-over with New Mutants #41-43. 642-644-Crossover with Mighty Thor #19-21. 646-Features Sif 3.00

JOURNEY INTO MYSTERY (2nd Series)
Marvel Comics: Oct, 1972 - No. 19, Oct, 1975

1-Robert Howard adaptation; Starlin/Ploog-a 4 8 12 28 47 65
2-5: 2,3,5-Bloch adapt. 4-H. P. Lovecraft adapt. 3 6 9 17 26 35
6-19: Reprints 3 6 9 16 23 30
NOTE: ***N. Adams*** *a-2i.* ***Ditko*** *r-7, 10, 12, 14, 15, 19; c-10.* ***Everett*** *r-9, 14.* ***G. Kane*** *a-1p, 2p; c-1-3p.* ***Kirby*** *r-7, 13, 15, 18, 19; c-7.* ***Mort Lawrence*** *r-2.* ***Maneely*** *r-3.* ***Orlando*** *r-16.* ***Reese*** *a-1, 2i.* ***Starlin*** *a-1p, 3p.* ***Torres*** *r-16.* ***Wildey*** *r-9, 14.*

JOURNEY INTO UNKNOWN WORLDS (Formerly Teen)
Atlas Comics (WFP): No. 36, Sept, 1950 - No. 38, Feb, 1951; No. 4, Apr, 1951 - No. 59, Aug, 1957

36(#1)-Science fiction/weird; "End Of The Earth" c/story
275 550 825 1750 3275 4800
37(#2)-Science fiction; "When Worlds Collide" c/story; Everett-c/a; Hitler story
123 246 369 787 1344 1900
38(#3)-Science fiction 103 206 309 659 1130 1600
4-6,8,10-Science fiction/weird 65 130 195 416 708 1000
7-Wolverton-a "Planet of Terror", 6 pgs; electric chair c-inset/story
103 206 309 659 1130 1600
9-Giant eyeball story 90 180 270 576 988 1400
11,12-Krigstein-a 50 100 150 315 533 750
13,16,17,20 43 86 129 271 461 650
14-Wolverton-a "One of Our Graveyards Is Missing", 4 pgs; Tuska-a
81 162 243 518 884 1250
15-Wolverton-a "They Crawl by Night", 5 pgs.; 2 pg. Maneely s/f story
81 162 243 518 884 1250
18,19-Matt Fox-a 50 100 150 315 533 750
21-33: 21-Decapitation-c. 24-Sci/fic story. 26-Atom bomb panel. 27-Sid Check-a. 33-Last pre-code (2/55) 39 78 117 236 388 540
34-Kubert, Torres-a 33 66 99 194 317 440
35-Torres-a 30 60 90 177 289 400
36-45,48,50,53,55,59: 43-Krigstein-a. 44-Davis-a. 45,55,59-Williamson-a in all; with Mayo #55,59. 55-Crandall-a. 48,53-Crandall-a (4 pgs. #48). 48-Check-a. 50-Davis, Crandall-a
29 58 87 170 278 385
46,47,49,52,54,56-58: 54-Torres-a 27 54 81 158 259 360
51-Ditko, Wood-a 31 62 93 182 296 410
NOTE: ***Ayers*** *a-24, 43,* ***Berg*** *a-38(#3), 43.* ***Lou Cameron*** *a-33.* ***Colan*** *a-37(#2), 6, 17, 19, 20, 23, 39.* ***Ditko*** *a-45, 51.* ***Drucker*** *a-35, 58.* ***Everett*** *a-37(#2), 11, 14, 41, 55, 56; c-37(#2), 11, 13, 14, 17, 22, 47, 48, 50, 53-55, 59.* ***Forte*** *a-49.* ***Fox*** *a-21i.* ***Heath*** *a-36(#1), 4, 6-8, 17, 20, 22, 36i; c-18.* ***Keller*** *a-15.* ***Mort Lawrence*** *a-38, 39.* ***Maneely*** *a-7, 8, 15, 16, 22, 49, 58; c-8, 19, 25, 52.* ***Morrow*** *a-48.* ***Orlando*** *a-44, 57.* ***Pakula*** *a-36.* ***Powell*** *a-42, 53, 54.* ***Reinman*** *a-8.* ***Rico*** *a-21.* ***Robert Sale*** *a-24, 49.* ***Sekowsky*** *a-4, 5, 9.* ***Severin*** *a-38, 51; c-38, 48i, 56.* ***Sinnott*** *a-9, 21, 24.* ***Tuska*** *a-38(#3), 14.* ***Wildey*** *a-25, 43, 44.*

JOURNEY TO STAR WARS: THE FORCE AWAKENS - SHATTERED EMPIRE
Marvel Comics: Nov, 2015 - No. 4, Dec, 2015 ($3.99, weekly limited series)

1-4-Rucka-s; takes place just after Episode 6 Battle of Endor; multiple covers on each 4.00

JOURNEY TO STAR WARS: THE LAST JEDI - CAPTAIN PHASMA
Marvel Comics: Nov, 2017 - No. 4, Dec, 2017 ($3.99, weekly limited series)

1-4-Checchetto-a/Renaud-c; takes place at the end of Episode 7 and just after 4.00

JOURNEY TO THE CENTER OF THE EARTH (Movie)
Dell Publishing Co.: No. 1060, Nov-Jan, 1959/60 (one-shot)

Four Color 1060-Pat Boone & James Mason photo-c 10 20 30 66 138 210

JOYRIDE
BOOM! Studios: Apr, 2016 - No. 12, Apr, 2017 ($3.99, originally planned as a 4-part series)

1-12-Jackson Lanzing & Collin Kelly-s/Marcus To-a. 1-Multiple covers 4.00

JSA (Justice Society of America) (Also see All Star Comics)
DC Comics: Aug, 1999 - No. 87, Sept, 2006 ($2.50/$2.99)

1-Robinson and Goyer-s; funeral of Wesley Dodds 2 4 6 8 10 12
2-5: 4-Return of Dr. Fate 6.00
6-24: 6-Black Adam-c/app. 11,12-Kobra. 16-20-JSA vs. Johnny Sorrow. 19,20-Spectre app. 22-Hawkgirl origin. 23-Hawkman returns 4.00
25-($3.75) Hawkman rejoins the JSA 1 2 3 5 7 9
26-36, 38-49: 27-Capt. Marvel app. 29-Joker: Last Laugh. 31,32-Snejbjerg-a. 33-Ultra-Humanite. 34-Intro. new Crimson Avenger and Hourman. 42-G.A. Mr. Terrific and the Freedom Fighters app. 46-Eclipso returns 3.00
37-($3.50) Johnny Thunder merges with the Thunderbolt; origin new Crimson Avenger 4.00
50-($3.95) Wraparound-c by Pacheco; Sentinel becomes Green Lantern again 4.00
51-74,76-82: 51-Kobra killed. 54-JLA app. 55-Ma Hunkle (Red Tornado) app. 56-58-Black Reign x-over with Hawkman #23-25. 64-Sand returns. 67-Identity Crisis tie-in; Gibbons-a. 68,69,72-81-Ross-c. 73,74-Day of Vengeance tie-in. 76-OMAC tie-in. 82-Infinite Crisis x-over; Levitz-s/Pérez-a 3.00
75-($2.99) Day of Vengeance tie-in; Alex Ross Spectre-c 4.00
83-87: One Year Later; Pérez-c. 83-85,87-Morales-a; Gentleman Ghost app. 85-Begin $2.99-c; Earth-2 Batman, Atom, Sandman, Mr. Terrific app. 86,87-Ordway-a. 3.00
Annual 1 (10/00, $3.50) Planet DC; intro. Nemesis 4.00
...: Black Reign TPB (2005, $12.99) r/#56-58, Hawkman #23-25; Watson cover gallery 13.00
...: Black Vengeance TPB (2006, $19.99) r/#66-75 20.00
...: Darkness Falls TPB (2002, $19.95) r/#6-15 20.00
...: Fair Play TPB (2003, $14.95) r/#26-31 & Secret Files #2 15.00
...: Ghost Stories TPB (2006, $14.99) r/#82-87 15.00
...: Justice Be Done TPB (2000, $14.95) r/Secret Files & #1-5 15.00
...: Lost TPB (2005, $19.99) r/#59-67 20.00

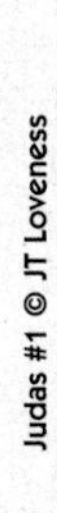
JSA: All Stars #7 © DC

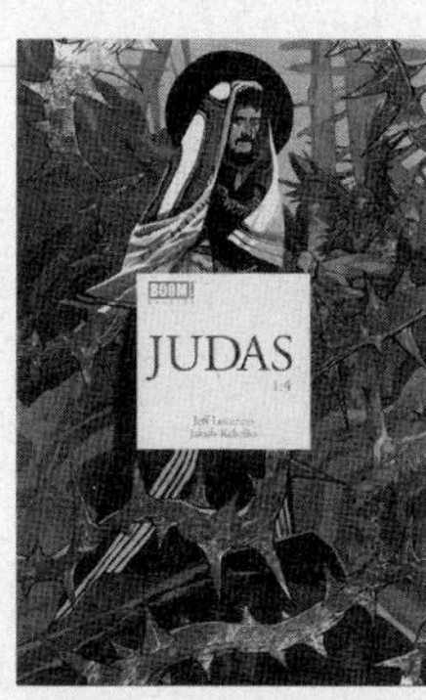

Judas #1 © JT Loveness

Judge Dredd (2015 series) #5 © Rebellion

GD 2.0 | VG 4.0 | FN 6.0 | VF 8.0 | VF/NM 9.0 | NM- 9.2

...: Mixed Signals TPB (2006, $14.99) r/#76-81 15.00
...: Our Worlds at War 1 (9/01, $2.95) Jae Lee-c; Saltares-a 3.00
... Presents Green Lantern TPB (2008, $14.99) r/JSA Classified #25,32,33 and Green Lantern: Brightest Day, Blackest Night 15.00
...: Princes of Darkness TPB (2005, $19.95) r/#46-55 20.00
...: Savage Times TPB (2004, $14.95) r/#39-45 15.00
... Secret Files 1 (8/99, $4.95) Origin stories and pin-ups; death of Wesley Dodds (G.A. Sandman); intro new Hawkgirl 5.00
... Secret Files 2 (9/01, $4.95) Short stories and profile pages 5.00
...: Stealing Thunder TPB (2003, $14.95) r/#32-38; JSA vs. The Ultra-Humanite 15.00
...: The Golden Age TPB (2005, $19.99) r/"The Golden Age" Elseworlds mini-series 20.00
...: The Return of Hawkman TPB (2002, $19.95) r/#16-26 & Secret Files #1 20.00

JSA: ALL STARS
DC Comics: July, 2003 - No. 8, Feb, 2004 ($2.50/$3.50, limited series, back-up stories in Golden Age style)

1-3,5,6,8-Goyer & Johns-s/Cassaday-c. 1-Velluto-a; intro. Legacy. 2-Hawkman by Loeb/Sale 3-Dr. Fate by Cooke. 5-Hourman by Chaykin. 6-Dr. Mid-nite by Azzarello/Risso 3.00
4-Starman by Robinson/Harris; 1st app. Courtney Whitmore as Stargirl 3.00
7-($3.50) Mr. Terrific back-up story by Chabon; Lark-a 4.00
TPB (2004, $14.95) r/#1-8 15.00

JSA: ALL STARS
DC Comics: Feb, 2010 - No. 18, Jul, 2011 ($3.99/$2.99)

1-13-Younger JSA members form team. 1-Covers by Williams and Sook 4.00
14-18-($2.99) 3.00
...: Constellations TPB (2010, $14.99) r/#1-6 and sketch art 15.00
...: Glory Days TPB (2011, $17.99) r/#7-13 18.00

JSA: CLASSIFIED (Issues #1-4 reprinted in Power Girl TPB)
DC Comics: Sept, 2005 - No. 39, Aug, 2008 ($2.50/$2.99)

1-(1st printing) Conner-c/a; origin of Power Girl 4.00
1-(1st printing) Adam Hughes variant-c 5.00
1-(2nd & 3rd printings) 2nd-Hughes B&W sketch-c. 3rd-Close-up of Conner-c 3.00
2-11: 2-LSH app. 4-Leads into Infinite Crisis #2. 5-7-Injustice Society app. 10-13-Vandal Savage origin retold; Gulacy-a/c 3.00
12-39: 12-Begin $2.99-c. 17,18-Bane app. 19,20-Morales-a. 21,22-Simonson-s/a 3.00
...: Honor Among Thieves TPB (2007, $14.99) r/#5-9 15.00

JSA LIBERTY FILES: THE WHISTLING SKULL
DC Comics: Feb, 2013 - No. 6, Jul, 2013 ($2.99, limited series)

1-6-Dr. Mid-Nite and Hourman in 1940; B. Clay Moore-s/Tony Harris-c/a 3.00

JSA STRANGE ADVENTURES
DC Comics: Oct, 2004 - No. 6, Mar, 2005 ($3.50, limited series)

1-6-Johnny Thunder as pulp writer; Kitson-a/Watson-c/ Kevin Anderson-s 3.50
TPB (2010, $14.99) r/#1-6 15.00

JSA: THE LIBERTY FILE (Elseworlds)
DC Comics: Feb, 2000 - No. 2, Mar, 2000 ($6.95, limited series)

1,2-Batman, Dr. Mid-Nite and Hourman vs. WW2 Joker; Tony Harris-c/a 7.00
JSA: The Liberty Files TPB (2004, $19.95) r/The Liberty File and The Unholy Three series 20.00

JSA: THE UNHOLY THREE (Elseworlds)(Sequel to JSA: The Liberty File)
DC Comics: 2003 - No. 2, 2003 ($6.95, limited series)

1,2-Batman, Superman and Hourman; Tony Harris-c/a 7.00

JSA VS. KOBRA
DC Comics: Aug, 2009 - No. 6, Jan, 2010 ($2.99, limited series)

1-6-Kramer-a/Ha-c; Jason Burr app. 3.00
TPB (2010, $14.99) r/#1-6; cover gallery 15.00

J2 (Also see A-Next and Juggernaut)
Marvel Comics: Oct, 1998 - No. 12, Sept, 1999 ($1.99)

1-12:1-Juggernaut's son; Lim-a. 2-Two covers; X-People app. 3-J2 battles the Hulk 3.00
Spider-Girl Presents Juggernaut Jr. Vol.1: Secrets & Lies (2006, $7.99, digest) r/#1-6 8.00

JUBILEE (X-Men)
Marvel Comics: Nov, 2004 - No. 6, Apr, 2005 ($2.99)

1-6: 1-Jubilee in a Los Angeles high school; Kirkman-s; Casey Jones-c 3.00

JUDAS
BOOM! Studios: Dec, 2017 - No. 4 ($3.99, limited series)

1,2-Judas' time with Jesus and in the Afterlife; Lucifer app.; Loveness-s/Rebelka-a 4.00

JUDAS COIN, THE
DC Comics: 2012 ($22.99, hardcover graphic novel with dust jacket)

HC-Walt Simonson-s/a/c; Batman, Two-Face, Golden Gladiator, Viking Prince, Captain Fear, Bat Lash, Manhunter 2070 app.; bonus sketch gallery 23.00

JUDENHASS
Aardvark-Vanaheim Press: 2008 ($4.00, B&W, squarebound)

nn-Dave Sim-writer/artist; The Shoah and Jewish persecution through history 4.00

JUDE, THE FORGOTTEN SAINT
Catechetical Guild Education Soc.: 1954 (16 pgs.; 8x11"; full color; paper-c)

nn 6 12 18 28 34 40

J.U.D.G.E.: THE SECRET RAGE
Image Comics: Mar, 2000 - No. 3, May, 2000 ($2.95)

1-3-Greg Horn-s/c/a 3.00

JUDGE COLT
Gold Key: Oct, 1969 - No. 4, Sept, 1970 (Painted cover)

1 3 6 9 16 23 30
2-4 2 4 6 9 13 16

JUDGE DREDD (...Classics #62 on; also see Batman - Judge Dredd, The Law of Dredd & 2000 A.D. Monthly)
Eagle Comics/IPC Magazines Ltd./Quality Comics #34-35, V2#1-37/ Fleetway #38 on: Nov, 1983 - No. 35, 1986; V2#1, Oct, 1986 - No. 77, 1993

1-Bolland-c/a 3 6 9 19 30 40
2-5 1 3 4 6 8 10
6-35 5.00
V2#1-('86)-New look begins 5.00
2-10 4.00
11-77: 20-Begin $1.50-c. 21/22, 23/24-Two issue numbers in one. 28-1st app. Megaman (super-hero). 39-Begin $1.75-c. 51-Begin $1.95-c. 53-Bolland-a. 57-Reprints 1st published Judge Dredd story 3.00
Special 1 5.00
NOTE: ***Bolland** a-1-6, 8, 10; c-1-10, 15. **Guice** c-V2#23/24, 26, 27.*

JUDGE DREDD (3rd Series)
DC Comics: Aug, 1994 - No. 18, Jan, 1996 ($1.95)

1-18: 12-Begin $2.25-c 3.00
nn ($5.95)-Movie adaptation, Sienkiewicz-c 6.00

JUDGE DREDD
IDW Publishing: Nov, 2012 - No. 30, May, 2015 ($3.99)

1-30: 1-Swierczynski-s; six covers 4.00

JUDGE DREDD
IDW Publishing: Dec, 2015 - No. 12, Nov, 2016 ($3.99)

1-12: 1-Farinas & Freitas-s/McDaid-a; multiple covers 4.00
Annual 1 (2/17; $7.99) Farinas & Freitas-s/McDaid-a; two covers 8.00
...: Cry of the Werewolf (3/17, $5.99) Reprint from 2000 AD; Steve Dillon-a/c; new pin-ups 6.00
...: Deviations (3/17, $4.99) McCrea-s/a; What If Dredd stayed a werewolf; bonus pin-ups 5.00
... Funko Universe (4/17, $4.99) Short stories w/characters styled like Pop! Vinyl figures 5.00

JUDGE DREDD: ANDERSON, PSI-DIVISION
IDW Publishing: Aug, 2014 - No. 4, Dec, 2014 ($3.99)

1-4-Matt Smith-s/Carl Critchlow-a; three covers on each 4.00

JUDGE DREDD CLASSICS (Reprints)
IDW Publishing: Jul, 2013 - Present ($3.99)

1-6-Wagner & Grant-s 4.00
Free Comic Book Day 2013 (5/13, free) Judge Death app.; Walter the Wobot back-ups 3.00
...: The Dark Judges 1-5 (1/15 - No. 5, 5/15, $3.99) Wagner & Grant-s/Bolland-a 4.00

JUDGE DREDD: LEGENDS OF THE LAW
DC Comics: Dec, 1994 - No. 13, Dec, 1995 ($1.95)

1-13: 1-5-Dorman-c 3.00

JUDGE DREDD: MEGA-CITY TWO
IDW Publishing: Jan, 2014 - No. 5, May, 2014 ($3.99)

1-5-Wolk-s/Farinas-a 4.00

JUDGE DREDD'S CRIME FILE
Eagle Comics: Aug, 1985 - No. 6, Feb, 1986 ($1.25, limited series)

1-6: 1-Byrne-a 5.00

JUDGE DREDD: THE BLESSED EARTH
IDW Publishing: Apr, 2017 - No. 8, Nov, 2017 ($3.99)

1-8-Farinas & Freitas-a; multiple covers on each 4.00

JUDGE DREDD: THE EARLY CASES
Eagle Comics: Feb, 1986 - No. 6, Jul, 1986 ($1.25, Mega-series, Mando paper)

1-6: 2000 A.D.-r 5.00

Judomaster #92 © CC

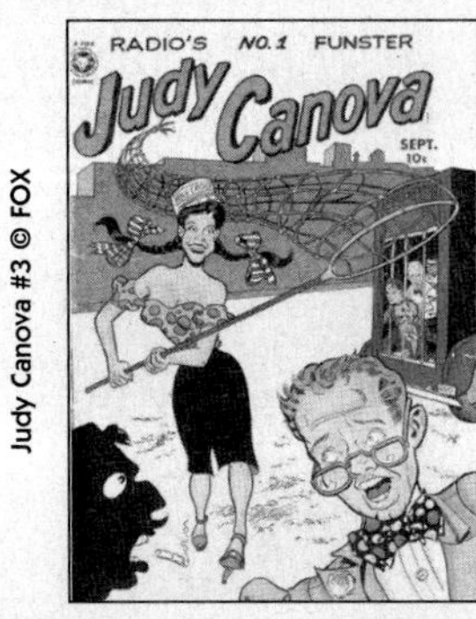

Judy Canova #3 © FOX

Jughead V3 #15 © ACP

JUDGE DREDD: THE JUDGE CHILD QUEST (Judge Child in indicia)
Eagle Comics: Aug, 1984 - No. 5, Oct, 1984 ($1.25, Lim. series, Baxter paper)

	GD 2.0	VG 4.0	FN 6.0	VF 8.0	VF/NM 9.0	NM- 9.2
1-5: 2000A.D.-r; Bolland-c/a						6.00

JUDGE DREDD: THE MEGAZINE
Fleetway/Quality: 1991 - No. 3 ($4.95, stiff-c, squarebound, 52 pgs.)

	GD 2.0	VG 4.0	FN 6.0	VF 8.0	VF/NM 9.0	NM- 9.2
1-3						5.00

JUDGE DREDD VS. ALIENS: INCUBUS
Dark Horse Comics: March, 2003 - No. 4, June, 2003 ($2.99, limited series)

	GD 2.0	VG 4.0	FN 6.0	VF 8.0	VF/NM 9.0	NM- 9.2
1-4-Flint-a/Wagner & Diggle-s						3.00

JUDGE DREDD: YEAR ONE
IDW Publishing: Mar, 2013 - No. 4, Jul, 2013 ($3.99)

	GD 2.0	VG 4.0	FN 6.0	VF 8.0	VF/NM 9.0	NM- 9.2
1-4-Matt Smith-s/Simon Coleby-a						4.00

JUDGE PARKER
Argo: Feb, 1956 - No. 2, 1956

	GD 2.0	VG 4.0	FN 6.0	VF 8.0	VF/NM 9.0	NM- 9.2
1-Newspaper strip reprints	7	14	21	35	43	50
2	5	10	15	24	30	35

JUDGMENT DAY
Awesome Entertainment: June, 1997 - No. 3, Oct, 1997 ($2.50, limited series)

	GD 2.0	VG 4.0	FN 6.0	VF 8.0	VF/NM 9.0	NM- 9.2
1-3: 1 Alpha-Moore-s/Liefeld-c/a(p) flashback art by various in all. 2 Omega. 3 Final Judgment. All have a variant cover by Dave Gibbons						3.00
...Aftermath-($3.50) Moore-s/Kane-a; Youngblood, Glory, New Men, Maximage, Allies and Spacehunter short stories. Also has a variant cover by Dave Gibbons						4.00
TPB (Checker Books, 2003, $16.95) r/series						17.00

JUDO JOE
Jay-Jay Corp.: Aug, 1953 - No. 3, Dec, 1953 (Judo lessons in each issue)

	GD 2.0	VG 4.0	FN 6.0	VF 8.0	VF/NM 9.0	NM- 9.2
1-Drug ring story	14	28	42	80	115	150
2,3: 3-Hypo needle story	9	18	27	52	69	85

JUDOMASTER (Gun Master #84-89) (Also see Crisis on Infinite Earths, Sarge Steel #6, Special War Series, & Thunderbolt)
Charlton Comics: No. 89, May-June, 1966 - No. 98, Dec, 1967 (Two No. 89's)

	GD 2.0	VG 4.0	FN 6.0	VF 8.0	VF/NM 9.0	NM- 9.2
89-3rd app. Judomaster	4	8	12	25	40	55
90-Origin of Thunderbolt	4	8	12	23	37	50
91-Sarge Steel begins	3	6	9	21	33	45
92-98: 93-Intro. Tiger	3	6	9	20	31	42
93,94,96,98 (Modern Comics reprint, 1977)						6.00

NOTE: *Morisi Thunderbolt #90. #91 has 1 pg. biography on writer/artist Frank McLaughlin.*

JUDY CANOVA (Formerly My Experience) (Stage, screen, radio)
Fox Feature Syndicate: No. 23, May, 1950 - No. 3, Sept, 1950

	GD 2.0	VG 4.0	FN 6.0	VF 8.0	VF/NM 9.0	NM- 9.2
23(#1)-Wood-c,a(p)?	26	52	78	154	252	350
24-Wood-a(p)	24	48	72	144	237	330
3-Wood-c; Wood/Orlando-a	27	54	81	158	259	360

JUDY GARLAND (See Famous Stars)

JUDY JOINS THE WAVES
Toby Press: 1951 (For U.S. Navy)

	GD 2.0	VG 4.0	FN 6.0	VF 8.0	VF/NM 9.0	NM- 9.2
nn	7	14	21	37	46	55

JUGGERNAUT (See X-Men)
Marvel Comics: Apr, 1997, Nov, 1999 ($2.99, one-shots)

	GD 2.0	VG 4.0	FN 6.0	VF 8.0	VF/NM 9.0	NM- 9.2
1-(4/97) Kelly-s/ Rouleau-a						3.00
1-(11/99) Casey-s; Eighth Day x-over; Thor, Iron Man, Spidey app.						3.00

JUGHEAD (Formerly Archie's Pal...)
Archie Publications: No. 127, Dec, 1965 - No. 352, June, 1987

	GD 2.0	VG 4.0	FN 6.0	VF 8.0	VF/NM 9.0	NM- 9.2
127-130: 129-LBJ on cover	3	6	9	17	26	35
131,133,135-160(9/68)	3	6	9	15	22	28
132,134: 132-Shield-c; The Fly & Black Hood app.; Shield cameo.						
134-Shield-c	4	8	12	27	44	60
161-180	2	4	6	13	18	22
181-199	2	4	6	9	13	16
200(1/'72)	2	4	6	11	16	20
201-240(5/75)	2	4	6	8	10	12
241-270(11/77)	1	2	3	5	7	9
271-299	1	2	3	4	5	7
300(5/80)-Anniversary issue; infinity-c	1	2	3	5	6	8
301-320(1/82)						5.00
321-324,326-352						4.00
325-(10/82) Cheryl Blossom app. (not on cover); same month as intro. (cover & story) in Archie's Girls, Betty & Veronica #320; Jason Blossom app.; DeCarlo-a	8	16	24	54	102	150

JUGHEAD (2nd Series)(Becomes Archie's Pal Jughead Comics #46 on)
Archie Enterprises: Aug, 1987 - No. 45, May, 1993 (.75/$1.00/$1.25)

	GD 2.0	VG 4.0	FN 6.0	VF 8.0	VF/NM 9.0	NM- 9.2
1	1	2	3	4	5	7
2-10						4.00
11-45: 4-X-Mas issue. 17-Colan-c/a						3.00

JUGHEAD (Volume 3)
Archie Comic Publications: Nov, 2015 - No. 16, Aug, 2017 ($3.99)

	GD 2.0	VG 4.0	FN 6.0	VF 8.0	VF/NM 9.0	NM- 9.2
1-16-Multiple covers and classic back-up reprints. 1-6-Chip Zdarsky-s/Erica Henderson-a. 5,6-Jughead as Captain Hero. 7-13-Derek Charm-a. 9-13-Ryan North-s; Sabrina app.						4.00

JUGHEAD AND ARCHIE DOUBLE DIGEST (Becomes Jughead & Archie Comics Digest)
Archie Comic Publ.: Jun, 2014 - Present ($3.99-$6.99, digest-size)

	GD 2.0	VG 4.0	FN 6.0	VF 8.0	VF/NM 9.0	NM- 9.2
1-3: 1-Reprints; That Wilkin Boy app.						4.00
4,7-9,11-14,16,19,26-($4.99)						5.00
5,10,15,21,23,25-($6.99, 320 pgs.) Titled Jughead & Archie Jumbo Comics Digest						7.00
6,17,18,20,22,24,27-($5.99, 192 pgs.) Titled Jughead & Archie Comics Annual. 24-Winter Annual						6.00

JUGHEAD & FRIENDS DIGEST MAGAZINE
Archie Publ.: June, 2005 - No. 38, Aug, 2010 ($2.39/$2.49/$2.69, digest-size)

	GD 2.0	VG 4.0	FN 6.0	VF 8.0	VF/NM 9.0	NM- 9.2
1-38: 1-That Wilkin Boy app.						3.00

JUGHEAD AS CAPTAIN HERO (See Archie as Pureheart the Powerful, Archie Giant Series Magazine #142 & Life With Archie)
Archie Publications: Oct, 1966 - No. 7, Nov, 1967

	GD 2.0	VG 4.0	FN 6.0	VF 8.0	VF/NM 9.0	NM- 9.2
1-Super hero parody	7	14	21	48	89	130
2	5	10	15	30	50	70
3-7	4	8	12	27	44	60

JUGHEAD COMICS. NIGHT AT GEPPI'S ENTERTAINMENT MUSEUM
Archie Comic Publ. Inc: 2008

	GD 2.0	VG 4.0	FN 6.0	VF 8.0	VF/NM 9.0	NM- 9.2
Free Comic Book Day giveaway - New story; Archie gang visits GEM; Steve Geppi app.						3.00

JUGHEAD JONES COMICS DIGEST, THE (...Magazine No. 10-64; Jughead Jones Digest Magazine #65)
Archie Publ.: June, 1977 - No. 100, May, 1996 ($1.35/$1.50/$1.75, digest-size, 128 pgs.)

	GD 2.0	VG 4.0	FN 6.0	VF 8.0	VF/NM 9.0	NM- 9.2
1-Neal Adams-a; Capt. Hero-r	3	6	9	20	31	42
2(9/77)-Neal Adams-a	3	6	9	15	22	28
3-6,8-10	2	4	6	11	16	20
7-Origin Jaguar-r; N. Adams-a.	2	4	6	13	18	22
11-20: 13-r/1957 Jughead's Folly	2	4	6	8	10	12
21-50	1	2	3	4	5	7
51-70						5.00
71-100						3.00

JUGHEAD'S BABY TALES
Archie Comics: Spring, 1994 - No. 2, Wint. 1994 ($2.00, 52 pgs.)

	GD 2.0	VG 4.0	FN 6.0	VF 8.0	VF/NM 9.0	NM- 9.2
1,2: 1-Bound-in pull-out poster						4.00

JUGHEAD'S DINER
Archie Comics: Apr, 1990 - No. 7, Apr, 1991 ($1.00)

	GD 2.0	VG 4.0	FN 6.0	VF 8.0	VF/NM 9.0	NM- 9.2
1						4.00
2-7						3.00

JUGHEAD'S DOUBLE DIGEST (...Magazine #5)
Archie Comics: Oct, 1989 - No. 200, Apr, 2014 ($2.25 - $3.99/$5.99)

	GD 2.0	VG 4.0	FN 6.0	VF 8.0	VF/NM 9.0	NM- 9.2
1	2	4	6	8	10	12
2-10: 2,5-Capt. Hero stories	1	2	3	5	6	8
11-25						5.00
26-195: 58-Begin $2.99-c. 66-Begin $3.19-c. 91-Begin $3.59-c. 138-Reprints entire Jughead #1 (1949). 139-142-"New Look" Jughead; Staton-a. 148-Begin $3.99-c						4.00
196-200-($5.99) Titled "Jughead's Double Double Digest"						6.00
Archie New Look Series Book 2, Jughead "The Matchmakers" TPB (2009, $10.95) r/new look series in #139-142; new cover by Staton & Milgrom						11.00

JUGHEAD'S EAT-OUT COMIC BOOK MAGAZINE (See Archie Giant Series Magazine No. 170)

JUGHEAD'S FANTASY
Archie Publications: Aug, 1960 - No. 3, Dec, 1960

	GD 2.0	VG 4.0	FN 6.0	VF 8.0	VF/NM 9.0	NM- 9.2
1	19	38	57	131	291	450
2	12	24	36	79	170	260
3	10	20	30	66	138	210

JUGHEAD'S FOLLY
Archie Publications (Close-Up): 1957 (36 pgs.)(one-shot)

	GD 2.0	VG 4.0	FN 6.0	VF 8.0	VF/NM 9.0	NM- 9.2
1-Jughead a la Elvis (Rare) (1st reference to Elvis in comics?)	71	142	213	454	777	1100

Jughead: The Hunger #2 © ACP

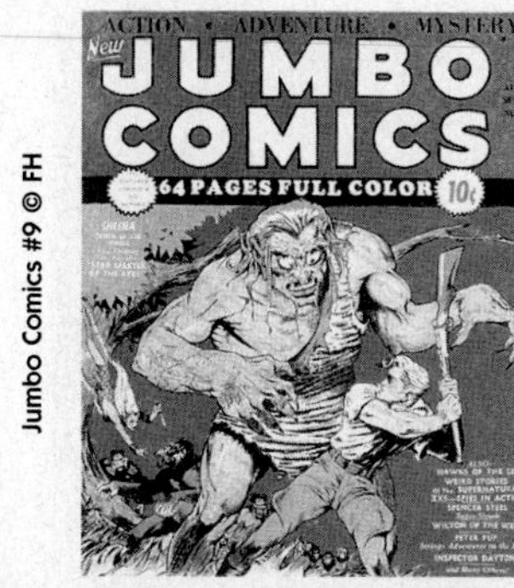

Jumbo Comics #9 © FH

Jungle Action #16 © MAR

	GD 2.0	VG 4.0	FN 6.0	VF 8.0	VF/NM 9.0	NM- 9.2

JUGHEAD'S JOKES
Archie Publications: Aug, 1967 - No. 78, Sept, 1982
(No. 1-8, 38 on: reg. size; No. 9-23: 68 pgs.; No. 24-37: 52 pgs.)

	GD 2.0	VG 4.0	FN 6.0	VF 8.0	VF/NM 9.0	NM- 9.2
1	6	12	18	38	69	100
2	4	8	12	25	40	55
3-8	3	6	9	16	24	32
9,10 (68 pgs.)	3	6	9	18	28	38
11-23(4/71) (68 pgs.)	3	6	9	16	23	30
24-37(1/74) (52 pgs.)	2	4	6	11	16	20
38-50(9/76)	1	3	4	6	8	10
51-78						6.00

JUGHEAD'S PAL HOT DOG (See Laugh #14 for 1st app.)
Archie Comics: Jan, 1990 - No. 5, Oct, 1990 ($1.00)

	GD 2.0	VG 4.0	FN 6.0	VF 8.0	VF/NM 9.0	NM- 9.2
1						4.00
2-5						3.00

JUGHEAD'S SOUL FOOD
Spire Christian Comics (Fleming H. Revell Co.): 1979 (49¢/59¢)

	GD 2.0	VG 4.0	FN 6.0	VF 8.0	VF/NM 9.0	NM- 9.2
nn-Low print run	3	6	9	15	22	28

JUGHEAD'S TIME POLICE
Archie Comics: July, 1990 - No. 6, May, 1991 ($1.00, bi-monthly)

	GD 2.0	VG 4.0	FN 6.0	VF 8.0	VF/NM 9.0	NM- 9.2
1						4.00
2-6: Colan a-3-6p; c-3-6						3.00

JUGHEAD: THE HUNGER
Archie Comic Publications: Dec, 2017 - Present ($3.99)

	GD 2.0	VG 4.0	FN 6.0	VF 8.0	VF/NM 9.0	NM- 9.2
1-4-Tieri-s/Pat & Tim Kennedy-a; Jughead as a werewolf. 2-4-Eisma-a (partial)						4.00
Jughead The Hunger, One-Shot (5/17, $4.99) Tieri-s/Walsh-a; prelude to issue #1						5.00

JUGHEAD WITH ARCHIE DIGEST (...Plus Betty & Veronica & Reggie Too No. 1,2; ...Magazine #33-?, 101-on; ...Comics Digest Mag.)
Archie Pub.: Mar, 1974 - No. 200, May, 2005 ($1.00-$2.39)

	GD 2.0	VG 4.0	FN 6.0	VF 8.0	VF/NM 9.0	NM- 9.2
1	5	10	15	31	53	75
2	3	6	9	21	33	45
3-10	3	6	9	17	26	35
11-13,15-17,19,20: Capt. Hero-r in #14-16; Capt. Pureheart #17,19	2	4	6	10	14	18
14,18,21,22-Pureheart the Powerful in #18,21,22	2	4	6	11	16	20
23-30: 29-The Shield-r. 30-The Fly-r	1	3	4	6	8	10
31-50,100	1	2	3	5	6	8
51-99	1	2	3	4	5	7
101-121						4.00
122-200: 156-Begin $2.19-c. 180-Begin $2.39-c						3.00

JUICE SQUEEZERS
Dark Horse Comics: Jan, 2014 - No. 4, Apr, 2014 ($3.99, limited series)

	GD 2.0	VG 4.0	FN 6.0	VF 8.0	VF/NM 9.0	NM- 9.2
1-4-David Lapham-s/a/c						4.00

JUKE BOX COMICS
Famous Funnies: Mar, 1948 - No. 6, Jan, 1949

	GD 2.0	VG 4.0	FN 6.0	VF 8.0	VF/NM 9.0	NM- 9.2
1-Toth-c/a; Hollingsworth-a	37	74	111	222	361	500
2-Transvestism story	22	44	66	132	216	300
3-6: 3-Peggy Lee story. 4-Jimmy Durante line drawn-c. 6-Features Desi Arnaz plus Arnaz line drawn-c	18	36	54	105	165	225

JUMBO COMICS (Created by S.M. Iger)
Fiction House Magazines (Real Adv. Publ. Co.): Sept, 1938 - No. 167, Mar, 1953 (No. 1-3: 68 pgs.; No. 4-8: 52 pgs.)(No. 1-8 oversized-10-1/2x14-1/2"; black & white)

	GD 2.0	VG 4.0	FN 6.0	VF 8.0	VF/NM 9.0	NM- 9.2
1-(Rare)-Sheena Queen of the Jungle(1st app.) by Meskin, Hawks of the Seas (The Hawk #10 on; see Feature Funnies #3) by Eisner, The Hunchback by Dick Briefer (ends #8), Wilton of the West (ends #24), Inspector Dayton (ends #67) & ZX-5 (ends #140) begin; 1st comic art by Jack Kirby (Count of Monte Cristo & Wilton of the West); Mickey Mouse appears (1 panel) with brief biography of Walt Disney; 1st app. Peter Pupp by Bob Kane. Note: Sheena was created by Iger for publication in England as a newspaper strip. The early issues of Jumbo contain Sheena strip-r; multiple panel-c 1,2,7	4000	8000	12,000	32,000	-	-
2-(Rare)-Origin Sheena. Diary of Dr. Hayward by Kirby (also #3) plus 2 other stories; contains strip from Universal Film featuring Edgar Bergen & Charlie McCarthy plus-c (preview of film)	1325	2650	3975	10,600	-	-
3-Last Kirby issue	950	1900	2850	7600	-	-
4-(Scarce)-Origin The Hawk by Eisner; Wilton of the West by Fine (ends #14)(1st comic work); Count of Monte Cristo by Fine (ends #15); The Diary of Dr. Hayward by Fine (cont'd #8,9)	900	1800	2700	7200	-	-
5-Christmas-c	825	1650	2475	6600	-	-
6-8-Last B&W issue. #8 was a 1939 N. Y. World's Fair Special Edition; Frank Buck's Jungleland story	725	1450	2175	5800	-	-
9-Stuart Taylor begins by Fine (ends #140); Fine-c; 1st color issue (8-9/39)-1st Sheena (jungle) cover; 8-1/4x10-1/4" (oversized in width only)	938	1876	2814	7500	-	-
10-Regular size 68 pg. issues begin; Sheena dons new costume w/origin costume; Stuart Taylor sci/fi-c; classic Lou Fine-c.	443	886	1329	3234	5717	8200
11-13: 12-The Hawk-c by Eisner. 13-Eisner-c	219	438	657	1402	2401	3400
14-Intro. Lightning (super-hero) on-c only	226	452	678	1446	2473	3500
15-1st Lightning story and begins, ends #41	155	310	465	992	1696	2400
16-Lightning-c	171	342	513	1086	1868	2650
17,18,20: 17-Lightning part-c	126	252	378	806	1378	1950
19-Classic Sheena Giant Ape-c by Powell	158	316	474	1003	1727	2450
21-30: 22-1st Tom, Dick & Harry; origin The Hawk retold. 25-Midnight the Black Stallion begins, ends #65	90	180	270	576	988	1400
31-(9/41)-1st app. Mars God of War in Stuart Taylor story (see Planet Comics #15.) (scarce)	290	580	870	1856	3178	4500
32-40: 35-Shows V2#11 (correct number does not appear)	71	142	213	454	777	1100
41-50: 42-Ghost Gallery begins, ends #167	47	94	141	296	498	700
51-60: 52-Last Tom, Dick & Harry	40	80	120	246	411	575
61-70: 68-Sky Girl begins, ends #130; not in #79	36	72	108	211	343	475
71-93,95-99: 89-ZX5 becomes a private eye.	28	56	84	165	270	375
94-Used in Love and Death by Legman	30	60	90	177	289	400
100	30	60	90	177	289	400
101-121	24	48	72	142	234	325
121-140,150-158: 155-Used in **POP**, pg. 98	22	44	66	128	209	290
141-149-Two Sheena stories. 141-Long Bow, Indian Boy begins, ends #160	22	44	66	132	216	300
159-163: Space Scouts serial in all. 160-Last jungle-c (6/52). 161-Ghost Gallery covers begin, end #167. 163-Suicide Smith app.	24	48	72	142	234	325
164-The Star Pirate begins, ends #165	32	64	96	188	307	425
165-167: 165,167-Space Rangers app.	30	60	90	177	289	400

NOTE: *Bondage covers, negligee panels, torture, etc. are common in this series. Hawks of the Seas, Inspector Dayton, Spies in Action, Sports Shorts, & Uncle Otto by Eisner, #1-7. Hawk by* ***Eisner****-#10-15.* ***Eisner*** *c-1-8, 12-14. 1pg. Patsy pin-ups in 92-97, 99-101. Sheena by* ***Meskin****-#1, 4; by* ***Powell****-#2, 3, 5-28;* ***Powell*** *c-14, 16, 17, 19.* ***Powell/Eisner*** *c-15. Sky Girl by* ***Matt Baker****-#69-78, 80-130. ZX-5 & Ghost Gallery by* ***Kamen****-#90-130.* ***Bailey*** *a-3-8.* ***Briefer*** *a-1-8, 10.* ***Fine*** *a-14; c-9-11.* ***Kamen*** *a-101, 105, 123, 132; c-105, 121-145.* ***Bob Kane*** *a-1-8.* ***Whitman*** *c-146-167(most). Jungle c-9, 13, 15, 17 on.*

JUMPER: JUMPSCARS
Oni Press: Jan, 2008 ($14.95, graphic novel)

	GD 2.0	VG 4.0	FN 6.0	VF 8.0	VF/NM 9.0	NM- 9.2
SC-Prelude to 2008 movie Jumper; Brian Hurtt-a/c						15.00

JUNGLE ACTION
Atlas Comics (IPC): Oct, 1954 - No. 6, Aug, 1955

	GD 2.0	VG 4.0	FN 6.0	VF 8.0	VF/NM 9.0	NM- 9.2
1-Leopard Girl begins by Al Hartley (#1,3); Jungle Boy by Forte; Maneely-a in all	50	100	150	315	533	750
2-(3-D effect cover)	42	84	126	265	445	625
3-6: 3-Last precode (2/55)	30	60	90	177	289	400

NOTE: ***Maneely*** *c-1, 2, 5, 6.* ***Romita*** *a-3, 6.* ***Shores*** *a-3, 6; c-3, 4?.*

JUNGLE ACTION (...& Black Panther #18-21?)
Marvel Comics Group: Oct, 1972 - No. 24, Nov, 1976

	GD 2.0	VG 4.0	FN 6.0	VF 8.0	VF/NM 9.0	NM- 9.2
1-Lorna, Jann-r (All reprints in 1-4)	4	8	12	23	37	50
2-4	3	6	9	14	20	25
5-Black Panther begins (r/Avengers #62)	12	24	36	82	179	275
6-New solo Black Panther stories begin; 1st app. Erik Killmonger	10	20	30	64	132	200
7,9,10: 9-Contains pull-out centerfold ad by Mark Jewelers	3	6	9	21	33	45
8-Origin Black Panther	5	10	15	34	60	85
11-20,23,24: 19-23-KKK x-over. 23-r/#22. 24-1st Wind Eagle; story contd in Marvel Premiere #51-#53	3	6	9	14	20	25
21,22-(Regular 25¢ edition)(5,7/76)	3	6	9	14	20	25
21,22-(30¢-c variant, limited distribution)	9	18	27	59	117	175

NOTE: ***Buckler*** *a-6-9p, 22; c-8p, 12p.* ***Buscema*** *a-5p; c-22.* ***Byrne*** *c-23.* ***Gil Kane*** *a-8p; c-2, 4, 10p, 11p, 13-17, 19, 24.* ***Kirby*** *c-18.* ***Maneely*** *r-1.* ***Russell*** *a-13i.* ***Starlin*** *c-3p.*

JUNGLE ADVENTURES
Super Comics: 1963 - 1964 (Reprints)

	GD 2.0	VG 4.0	FN 6.0	VF 8.0	VF/NM 9.0	NM- 9.2
10,12,15,17,18: 10-r/Terrors of the Jungle #4 & #10(Rulah). 12-r/Zoot #14(Rulah).15-r/Kaanga from Jungle #152 & Tiger Girl. 17-All Jo-Jo-r. 18-Reprints/White Princess of the Jungle #1; no Kinstler-a; origin of both White Princess & Cap'n Courage	3	6	9	18	28	38

JUNGLE ADVENTURES
Skywald Comics: Mar, 1971 - No. 3, June, 1971 (25¢, 52 pgs.) (Pre-code reprints & new-s)

1-Zangar origin; reprints of Jo-Jo, Blue Gorilla(origin)/White Princess #3,

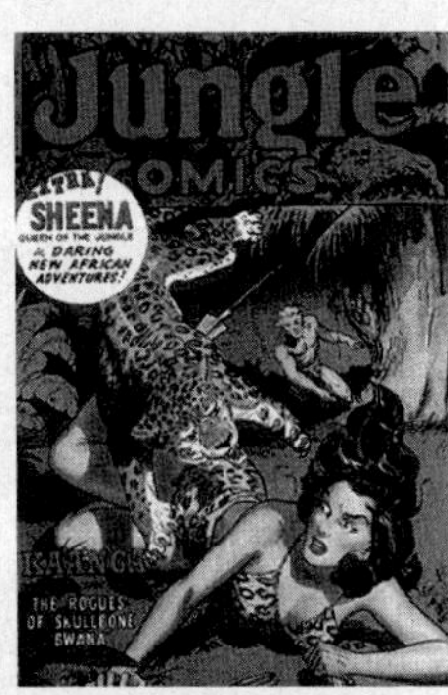
Jungle Comics #158 © FH

Jungle Jim #14 © STD

Jungle War Stories #8 © DELL

GD 2.0 | VG 4.0 | FN 6.0 | VF 8.0 | VF/NM 9.0 | NM- 9.2

Kinstler-r/White Princess #2 3 6 9 19 30 40
2,3: 2-Zangar, Sheena-r/Sheena #17 & Jumbo #162, Jo-Jo, origin Slave Girl-r. 3-Zangar, Jo-Jo, White Princess, Rulah-r 3 6 9 15 22 28

JUNGLE BOOK (See King Louie and Mowgli, Movie Comics, Mowgli..., Walt Disney Showcase #45 & Walt Disney's The Jungle Book)

JUNGLE CAT (Disney)
Dell Publishing Co.: No. 1136, Sept-Nov, 1960 (one shot)
Four Color 1136-Movie, photo-c 6 12 18 37 66 95

JUNGLE COMICS
Fiction House Magazines: 1/40 - No. 157, 3/53; No. 158, Spr, 1953 - No. 163, Summer, 1954
1-Origin The White Panther, Kaanga, Lord of the Jungle, Tabu, Wizard of the Jungle; Wambi, the Jungle Boy, Camilla & Capt. Terry Thunder begin (all 1st app.). Lou Fine-c 622 1244 1866 4541 8021 11,500
2-Fantomah, Mystery Woman of the Jungle begins, ends #51; The Red Panther begins, ends #26 213 426 639 1363 2332 3300
3,4 158 316 474 1003 1727 2450
5-Classic Eisner-c 187 374 561 1197 2049 2900
6-10: 7,8-Powell-c 94 188 282 597 1024 1450
11-Classic dinosaur-c 100 200 300 635 1093 1550
12-20: 13-Tuska-c 63 126 189 403 689 975
21-30: 25-Shows V2#1 (correct number does not appear). #27-New origin Fantomah, Daughter of the Pharoahs; Camilla dons new costume 52 104 156 328 557 785
31-40 41 82 123 250 418 585
41,43-50 37 74 111 222 361 500
42-Kaanga by Crandall, 12 pgs. 39 78 117 240 395 550
51-60 33 66 99 194 317 440
61-70: 67-Cover swipes Crandall splash pg. in #42 29 58 87 170 278 385
71-80: 79-New origin Tabu 25 50 75 147 241 335
81-97,99 24 48 72 140 230 320
98-Used in **SOTI**, pg. 185 & illo "In ordinary comic books, there are pictures within pictures for children who know how to look;" used by N.Y. Legis. Comm. 37 74 111 222 361 500
100 28 56 84 165 270 375
101-110: 104-In Camilla story, villain is Dr. Wertham 23 46 69 136 223 310
111-120: 118-Clyde Beatty app. 22 44 66 128 209 290
121-130 21 42 63 122 199 275
131-163: 135-Desert Panther begins in Terry Thunder (origin), not in #137; ends (dies) #138. 139-Last 52 pg. issue. 141-Last Tabu. 143,145-Used in **POP**, pg. 99. 151-Last Camilla & Terry Thunder. 152-Tiger Girl begins. 158-Last Wambi; Sheena app. 20 40 60 114 182 250
I.W. Reprint #1,9: 1-r/? 9-r/#151 3 6 9 16 24 32
NOTE: *Bondage covers, negligee panels, torture, etc. are common to this series. Camilla by* ***Fran Hopper****-#70-92; by* ***Baker****-#69, 100-113, 115, 116; by* ***Lubbers****-#97-99 by* ***Tuska****-#63, 65. Kaanga by* ***John Celardo****-#80-113; by* ***Larsen****-#71, 75-79; by* ***Moreira****-#58, 60, 61, 63-70, 72-74; by* ***Tuska****-#37, 62; by* ***Whitman****-#114-163. Tabu by* ***Larsen****-#59-75, 82-92; by* ***Whitman****-#93-115. Terry Thunder by* ***Hopper****-#71, 72; by* ***Celardo****-#78, 79; by* ***Lubbers****-#80-85. Tiger Girl-r by* ***Baker****-#152, 153, 155-157, 159. Wambi by* ***Baker****-#62-67, 74.* ***Astarita*** *c-45, 46.* ***Celardo*** *a-78; c-98-113.* ***Crandall*** *c-67 from splash pg.* ***Eisner*** *c-2, 5, 6.* ***Fine*** *c-1.* ***Larsen*** *a-65, 66, 71, 72, 74, 75, 79, 83, 84, 87-90.* ***Moreira*** *c-43, 44.* ***Morisi*** *a-51.* ***Powell*** *c-7, 8.* ***Sultan*** *c-3, 4.* ***Tuska*** *c-13.* ***Whitman*** *c-132-163(most).* ***Zolnerowich*** *c-11, 12, 18-41.*

JUNGLE COMICS
Blackthorne Publishing: May, 1988 - No. 4 ($2.00, B&W/color)
1-Dave Stevens-c; B. Jones scripts in all 2 4 6 13 18 22
2-4: 2-B&W-a begins 5.00

JUNGLE GIRL (See Lorna, the...)

JUNGLE GIRL (Nyoka, Jungle Girl No. 2 on)
Fawcett Publications: Fall, 1942 (one-shot)(No month listed)
1-Bondage-c; photo of Kay Aldridge who played Nyoka in movie serial app. on-c. Adaptation of the classic Republic movie serial Perils of Nyoka. 1st comic to devote entire contents to a movie serial adaptation 139 278 417 883 1517 2150

JUNGLE GIRL
Dynamite Entertainment: No. 0, 2007 - 2009 (25¢/$2.99/$3.50)
0-(25¢-c) Eight page preview; preview of Superpowers w/Alex Ross-a 3.00
1-5-Frank Cho-plot/cover; Batista-a/variant-c 3.00
... Season 2 ($3.50) 1-5-Two covers by Cho & Batista 3.50
... Season 3 ($3.99) 1-4-Cho-c/Jadson-a/Murray-s 4.00

JUNGLE GIRLS
AC Comics: 1989 - No. 16, 1993 (B&W)
1-16: 1-4,10,13-16-New story & "good girl" reprints. 5-9,11,12-All g.g. reprints (Baker, Powell, Lubbers, others) 3.00

JUNGLE JIM (Also see Ace Comics)
Standard Comics (Best Books): No. 11, Jan, 1949 - No. 20, Apr, 1951
11 13 26 39 74 105 135
12-20 9 18 27 52 69 85

JUNGLE JIM
Dell Publishing Co.: No. 490, 8/53 - No. 1020, 8-10/59 (Painted-c)
Four Color 490(#1) 8 16 24 54 102 150
Four Color 565(#2, 6/54) 5 10 15 33 57 80
3(10-12/54)-5 4 8 12 27 44 60
6-19(1-3/59) 4 8 12 25 40 55
Four Color 1020(#20) 5 10 15 31 53 75

JUNGLE JIM
King Features Syndicate: No. 5, Dec, 1967
5-Reprints Dell #5; Wood-c 2 4 6 10 14 18

JUNGLE JIM (Continued from Dell series)
Charlton Comics: No. 22, Feb, 1969 - No. 28, Feb, 1970 (#21 was an overseas edition only)
22-Dan Flagg begins; Ditko/Wood-a 3 6 9 20 31 42
23-26: 23-Last Dan Flagg; Howard-c. 24-Jungle People begin 3 6 9 15 21 26
27,28: 27-Ditko/Howard-a. 28-Ditko-a 3 6 9 16 24 32
NOTE: *Ditko cover of #22 reprints story panels*

JUNGLE JO
Fox Feature Syndicate (Hero Books): Mar, 1950 - No. 3, Sept, 1950
nn-Jo-Jo blanked out in titles of interior stories, leaving Congo King; came out after Jo-Jo #29 (intended as Jo-Jo #30?) 61 122 183 390 670 950
1-Tangi begins; part Wood-a 65 130 195 416 708 1000
2,3 48 96 144 302 514 725

JUNGLE LIL (Dorothy Lamour #2 on; also see Feature Stories Magazine)
Fox Feature Syndicate (Hero Books): April, 1950
1 52 104 156 328 552 775

JUNGLE TALES (Jann of the Jungle No. 8 on)
Atlas Comics (CSI): Sept, 1954 - No. 7, Sept, 1955
1-Jann of the Jungle 45 90 135 284 480 675
2-7: 3-Last precode (1/55) 34 68 102 199 325 450
NOTE: ***Heath*** *c-5.* ***Heck*** *a-6, 7.* ***Maneely*** *a-2; c-1, 3.* ***Shores*** *a-5-7; c-4, 6.* ***Tuska*** *a-2.*

JUNGLE TALES OF TARZAN
Charlton Comics: Dec, 1964 - No. 4, July, 1965
1 5 10 15 35 63 90
2-4 4 8 12 25 40 55
NOTE: ***Giordano*** *c-3p.* ***Glanzman*** *a-1-3.* ***Montes/Bache*** *a-4.*

JUNGLE TERROR (See Harvey Comics Hits No. 54)

JUNGLE THRILLS (Formerly Sports Thrills; Terrors of the Jungle #17 on)
Star Publications: No. 16, Feb, 1952; Dec, 1953; No. 7, 1954
16-Phantom Lady & Rulah story-reprint/All Top No. 15; used in **POP**, pg. 98,99; L. B. Cole-c 54 108 162 343 574 825
3-D 1(12/53, 25¢)-Came w/glasses; Jungle Lil & Jungle Jo appear; L. B. Cole-c 53 106 159 334 567 800
7-Titled 'Picture Scope Jungle Adventures;' (1954, 36 pgs, 15¢)-3-D effect c/stories; story & coloring book; Disbrow-a/script; L.B. Cole-c 53 106 159 334 567 800

JUNGLE TWINS, THE (Tono & Kono)
Gold Key/Whitman No. 18: Apr, 1972 - No. 17, Nov, 1975; No. 18, May, 1982
1-All painted covers 3 6 9 16 23 30
2-5 2 4 6 9 12 15
6-18: 18(Whitman, 5/82)-Reprints 1 3 4 6 8 10
NOTE: *UFO c/story No. 13. Painted-c No. 1-17.* ***Spiegle*** *c-18.*

JUNGLE WAR STORIES (Guerrilla War No. 12 on)
Dell Publishing Co.: July-Sept, 1962 - No. 11, Apr-June, 1965 (Painted-c)
01-384-209 (#1) 4 8 12 23 37 50
2-11 3 6 9 16 24 32

JUNIE PROM (Also see Dexter Comics)
Dearfield Publishing Co.: Winter, 1947-48 - No. 7, Aug, 1949
1-Teen-age 24 48 72 142 234 325
2 20 40 60 114 182 250
3-7 18 36 54 105 165 225

JUNIOR
Fantagraphics Books: June, 2000 - No. 5, Jan, 2001 ($2.95, B&W)
1-5-Peter Bagge-s/a 3.00

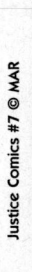

Junior Miss #34 © MAR

Jupiter's Legacy 2 #1 © Millar & Quitely

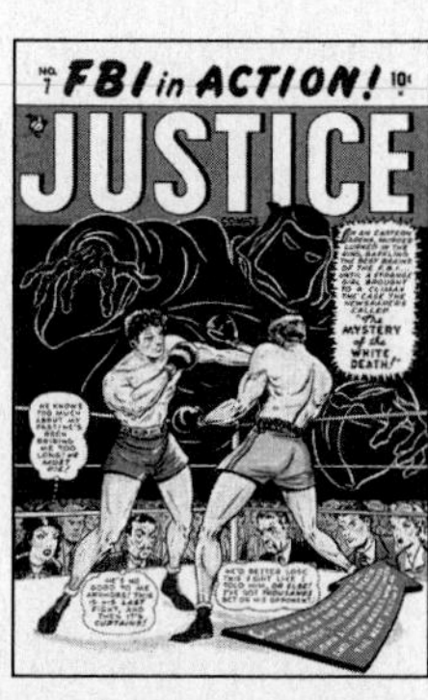

Justice Comics #7 © MAR

	GD 2.0	VG 4.0	FN 6.0	VF 8.0	VF/NM 9.0	NM- 9.2

JUNIOR CARROT PATROL (Jr. Carrot Patrol #2)
Dark Horse Comics: May, 1989; No. 2, Nov, 1990 ($2.00, B&W)

1,2-Flaming Carrot spin-off. 1-Bob Burden-c(i) 3.00

JUNIOR COMICS (Formerly Li'l Pan; becomes Western Outlaws with #17)
Fox Feature Syndicate: No. 9, Sept, 1947 - No. 16, July, 1948

	GD	VG	FN	VF	VF/NM	NM-
9-Feldstein-c/a; headlights-c	174	348	522	1114	1907	2700
10-16: 10-12,14-16-Feldstein-c/a; headlights-c	161	322	483	1030	1765	2500

JUNIOR FUNNIES (Formerly Tiny Tot Funnies No. 9)
Harvey Publ. (King Features Synd.): No. 10, Aug, 1951 - No. 13, Feb, 1952

	GD	VG	FN	VF	VF/NM	NM-
10-Partial reprints in all; Blondie, Dagwood, Daisy, Henry, Popeye, Felix, Katzenjammer Kids	6	12	18	28	34	40
11-13	5	10	15	24	30	35

JUNIOR HOPP COMICS
Stanmor Publ.: Feb, 1952 - No. 3, July, 1952

	GD	VG	FN	VF	VF/NM	NM-
1-Teenage humor	18	36	54	103	162	220
2,3: 3-Dave Berg-a	13	26	39	72	101	130

JUNIOR MEDICS OF AMERICA, THE
E. R. Squire & Sons: No. 1359, 1957 (15¢)

	GD	VG	FN	VF	VF/NM	NM-
1359	5	10	14	20	24	28

JUNIOR MISS
Timely/Marvel (CnPC): Wint, 1944; No. 24, Apr, 1947 - No. 39, Aug, 1950

	GD	VG	FN	VF	VF/NM	NM-
1-Frank Sinatra & June Allyson life story	41	82	123	256	428	600
24-Formerly The Human Torch #23?	21	42	63	122	199	275
25-38: 29,31,34-Cindy-c/stories (others?)	14	28	42	82	121	160
39-Kurtzman-a	15	30	45	88	137	185

NOTE: *Painted-c 35-37. 35, 37-all romance. 36, 38-mostly teen humor.* ***Louise Alston*** *c-36.*

JUNIOR PARTNERS (Formerly Oral Roberts' True Stories)
Oral Roberts Evangelistic Assn.: No. 120, Aug, 1959 - V3#12, Dec, 1961

	GD	VG	FN	VF	VF/NM	NM-
120(#1)	4	8	12	23	37	50
2(9/59)	3	6	9	16	24	32
3-12(7/60)	2	4	6	13	18	22
V2#1(8/60)-5(12/60)	2	4	6	9	13	16
V3#1(1/61)-12	2	4	6	8	10	12

JUNIOR TREASURY (See Dell Junior...)

JUNIOR WOODCHUCKS GUIDE (Walt Disney's...)
Danbury Press: 1973 (8-3/4"x5-3/4", 214 pgs., hardcover)

	GD	VG	FN	VF	VF/NM	NM-
nn-Illustrated text based on the long-standing J.W. Guide used by Donald Duck's nephews Huey, Dewey & Louie by Carl Barks. The guidebook was a popular plot device to enable the nephews to solve problems facing their uncle or Scrooge McDuck (scarce)	5	10	15	31	53	75

JUNIOR WOODCHUCKS LIMITED SERIES (Walt Disney's...)
W. D. Publications (Disney): July, 1991 - No. 4, Oct, 1991 ($1.50, limited series; new & reprint-a)

1-4: 1-The Beagle Boys app.; Barks-r 3.00

JUNIOR WOODCHUCKS (See Huey, Dewey & Louie...)

JUPITER'S CIRCLE (Prequel to Jupiter's Legacy)
Image Comics: Apr, 2015 - No. 6, Sept, 2015 ($3.50/$3.99)

1-6-Mark Millar-s/Frank Quitely-a/c. 1-Three covers. 1-3,6-Torres-a. 4,5-Gianfelice-a 4.00
Volume 2 (11/15 - No. 6, 5/16) 1-6-Covers by Quitely & Sienkiewicz. 1,2,6-Torres-a. 3-5-Spouse-a 4.00

JUPITER'S LEGACY
Image Comics: Apr, 2013 - No. 5, Jan, 2015 ($2.99/$4.99)

1-4-Mark Millar-s/Frank Quitely-a/c 3.00
1-Variant-c by Hitch 4.00
5-($4.99) Covers by Hitch and Fegredo; bonus pin-ups and cosplay photos 5.00
1-Studio Edition (12/13, $4.99) Quitely's B&W art and Millar's script; design art 5.00

JUPITER'S LEGACY 2
Image Comics: Jan, 2016 - No. 5, Jul, 2017 ($3.99)

1-5-Mark Millar-s/Frank Quitely-a/c 4.00

JURASSIC PARK
Topps Comics: June, 1993 - No. 4, Aug, 1993; No. 5, Oct, 1994 - No. 10, Feb, 1995

	GD	VG	FN	VF	VF/NM	NM-
1-($2.50)-Newsstand Edition; Kane/Perez-a in all; 1-4: movie adaptation						4.00
1-($2.95)-Collector's Ed.; polybagged w/3 cards						5.00
1-Amberchrome Edition w/no price or ads	1	2	3	5	6	8
2-4-($2.50)-Newsstand Edition						3.00
2,3-($2.95)-Collector's Ed.; polybagged w/3 cards						4.00
4-10: 4-($2.95)-Collector's Ed.; polybagged w/1 of 4 different action hologram trading card; Gil Kane/Pérez-a. 5-becomes Advs. of						3.00
Annual 1 ($3.95, 5/95)						4.00
Trade paperback (1993, $9.95)-r/#1-4; bagged w/#0						10.00

JURASSIC PARK
IDW Publishing: Jun, 2010 - No. 5, Oct, 2010 ($3.99, limited series)

1-5: Takes place 13 years after the first movie; Schreck-s. 1-Covers by Yeates & Miller 4.00

JURASSIC PARK: DANGEROUS GAMES
IDW Publishing: Sept, 2011 - No. 5, Jan, 2012 ($3.99, limited series)

1-5-Erik Bear-s/Jorge Jimenez-a, 1-Covers by Darrow & Zornow 4.00

JURASSIC PARK: RAPTOR
Topps Comics: Nov, 1993 - No. 2, Dec, 1993 ($2.95, limited series)

1,2: 1-Bagged w/3 trading cards & Zorro #0; Golden c-1,2 4.00

JURASSIC PARK: RAPTORS ATTACK
Topps Comics: Mar, 1994 - No. 4, June, 1994 ($2.50, limited series)

1-4-Michael Golden-c/frontispiece 3.00

JURASSIC PARK: RAPTORS HIJACK
Topps Comics: July, 1994 - No. 4, Oct, 1994 ($2.50, limited series)

1-4: Michael Golden-c/front piece 3.00

JURASSIC PARK: THE DEVILS IN THE DESERT
IDW Publishing: Jan, 2011 - No. 4, Apr, 2011 ($3.99, limited series)

1-4-John Byrne-s/a/c 4.00

JUST A PILGRIM
Black Bull Entertainment: May, 2001 - No. 5, Sept, 2001 ($2.99)

Limited Preview Edition (12/00, $7.00) Ennis & Ezquerra interviews 7.00
1-Ennis-s/Ezquerra-a; two covers by Texeira & JG Jones 3.00
2-5: 2-Fabry-c. 3-Nowlan-c. 4-Sienkiewicz-c 3.00
TPB (11/01, $12.99) r/#1-5; Waid intro. 13.00

JUST A PILGRIM: GARDEN OF EDEN
Black Bull Entertainment: May, 2002 - No. 4, Aug, 2002 ($2.99, limited series)

Limited Preview Ed. (1/02, $7.00) Ennis & Ezquerra interviews; Jones-c 7.00
1-4-Ennis-s/Ezquerra-a 3.00
TPB (11/02, $12.99) r/#1-4; Gareb Shamus intro. 13.00

JUSTICE
Marvel Comics Group (New Universe): Nov, 1986 - No. 32, June, 1989

1-32: 26-32-$1.50-c (low print run) 3.00

JUSTICE
DC Comics: Oct, 2005 - No. 12, Aug, 2007 ($2.99/$3.50/$3.99, bi-monthly maxi-series)

1-Classic Justice League vs. The Legion of Doom; Alex Ross & Doug Braithwaite-a; Jim Krueger-s; two covers by Ross; Ross sketch pages 5.00
1-2nd & 3rd printings 4.00
2-($3.50) 4.00
2 (2nd printing), 3-11-($3.50) 3.50
12-($3.99) Two covers (Heroes & Villains) 4.00
Absolute Justice HC (2009, $99.99, slipcased book with dustjacket) oversized r/#1-12; afterwords by creators; Ross sketch and design art; photo gallery of action figures 100.00
HC (2011, $39.99, dustjacket) r/#1-12 40.00
... Volume One HC (2006, $19.99, dustjacket) r/#1-4; Krueger intro.; sketch pages 20.00
... Volume One SC (2008, $14.99) r/#1-4; Krueger intro.; sketch pages 15.00
... Volume Two HC (2007, $19.99, dustjacket) r/#5-8; Krueger intro.; sketch pages 20.00
... Volume Two SC (2008, $14.99) r/#5-8; Krueger intro.; sketch pages 15.00
... Volume Three HC (2007, $19.99, dustjacket) r/#9-12; Ross intro.; sketch pages 20.00
... Volume Three SC (2007, $14.99) r/#9-12; Ross intro.; sketch pages 15.00

JUSTICE COMICS (Formerly Wacky Duck; Tales of Justice #53 on)
Marvel/Atlas Comics (NPP 7-9,4-19/CnPC 20-23/MjMC 24-38/Male 39-52:
No. 7, Fall/47 - No. 9, 6/48; No. 4, 8/48 - No. 52, 3/55

	GD	VG	FN	VF	VF/NM	NM-
7(#1, 1947)	36	72	108	211	343	475
8(#2)-Kurtzman-a "Giggles 'n' Grins" (3)	23	46	69	138	227	315
9(#3, 6/48)	20	40	60	118	192	265
4	18	36	54	107	169	230
5(9/48)-9: 8-Anti-Wertham editorial	16	32	48	92	144	195
10-15-Photo-c	14	28	42	81	118	155
16-30	14	28	42	76	108	140
31-40,42-52: 35-Gene Colan-a. 48-Last precode; Pakula & Tuska-a. 50-Ayers-a	13	26	39	72	101	130
41-Electrocution-c	20	40	60	117	189	260

NOTE: ***Hartley*** *a-48.* ***Heath*** *a-24.* ***Maneely*** *c-44, 52.* ***Pakula*** *a-43, 45, 47, 48.* ***Louis Ravielli*** *a-39, 47.* ***Robinson*** *a-22, 25, 41.* ***Sale*** *c-45.* ***Shores*** *c-7(#1), 8(#2)?* ***Tuska*** *a-41, 48.* ***Wildey*** *a-52.*

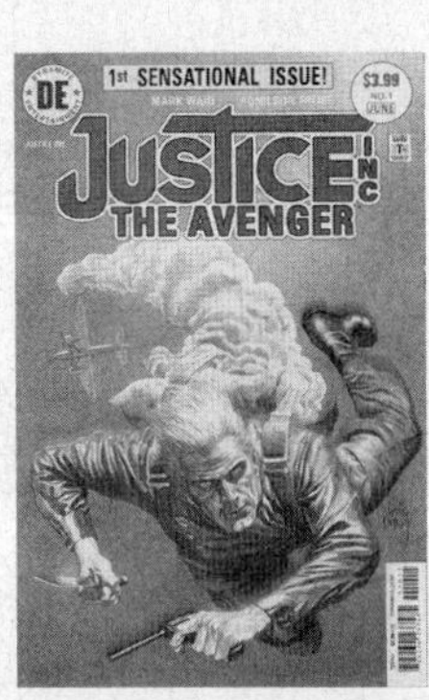

Justice, Inc.: The Avenger #1 © AMP

Justice League (2011 series) #42 © DC

Justice League (2016 series) #32 © DC

	GD 2.0	VG 4.0	FN 6.0	VF 8.0	VF/NM 9.0	NM- 9.2

JUSTICE: FOUR BALANCE
Marvel Comics: Sept, 1994 - No. 4, Dec, 1994 ($1.75, limited series)

1-4: 1-Thing & Firestar app. 3.00

JUSTICE, INC. (The Avenger) (Pulp)
National Periodical Publications: May-June, 1975 - No. 4, Nov-Dec, 1975

1-McWilliams-a, Kubert-c; origin 2 4 6 11 16 20
2-4: 2-4-Kirby-a(p), c-2,3p. 4-Kubert-c 2 4 6 11 16 20
NOTE: *Adapted from Kenneth Robeson novel, creator of Doc Savage.*

JUSTICE, INC. (Pulp)
DC Comics: 1989 - No. 2, 1989 ($3.95, 52 pgs., squarebound, mature)

1,2: Re-intro The Avenger; Andrew Helfer scripts & Kyle Baker-c/a 5.00

JUSTICE, INC. (Pulp)
Dynamite Entertainment: 2014 - No. 6, 2015 ($3.99/$5.99)

1-5-The Shadow, Doc Savage and The Avenger app; Uslan-s/Timpano-a; multiple covers 4.00
6-($5.99) Covers by Ross, Francavilla, Hardman and Syaf 6.00

JUSTICE, INC.: THE AVENGER (Pulp)
Dynamite Entertainment: 2015 - No. 6, 2015 ($3.99)

1-6: 1-Waid-s/Freire-a; multiple covers incl. 1975 series #1 cover swipe by Ross 4.00

JUSTICE, INC.: THE AVENGER VOLUME 1 (Pulp)
Dynamite Entertainment: 2017 - No. 4, 2017 ($3.99)

1-4-Higgins & Gentile-s/Shibao-a. 1-Covers by Mandrake & Shibao 4.00

JUSTICE LEAGUE (...International #7-25; ...America #26 on)
DC Comics: May, 1987 - No. 113, Aug, 1996 (Also see Legends #6)

1-Batman, Green Lantern (Guy Gardner), Blue Beetle, Mr. Miracle, Capt. Marvel & Martian Manhunter begin; 1st app. Maxwell Lord 2 4 6 11 16 20
2,3: 3-Regular-c (white background) 5.00
3-Limited-c (yellow background, Superman logo) 4 8 12 27 44 60
4-6,8-10: 4-Booster Gold joins. 5-Origin Gray Man; Batman vs. Guy Gardner; Creeper app. 9,10-Millennium x-over 4.00
7-($1.25, 52 pgs.)-Capt. Marvel & Dr. Fate resign; Capt. Atom & Rocket Red join 5.00
11-17,22,23,25-49,51-68,71-82: 16-Bruce Wayne-c/story. 31,32-J. L. Europe x-over. 58-Lobo app. 61-New team begins; swipes-c to J.L. of A. #1('60). 70-Newsstand version w/o outer-c. 71-Direct sales version w/black outer-c. 71-Newsstand version w/o outer-c. 80-Intro new Booster Gold. 82,83-Guy Gardner-c/stories 3.00
18-21,24,50: 18-21-Lobo app. 24-($1.50)-1st app. Justice League Europe. 50-($1.75, 52 pgs.) 4.00
69-Doomsday tie-in; takes place between Superman: The Man of Steel #18 & Superman #74 1 3 4 6 8 10
69,70-2nd printings 3.00
70-Funeral for a Friend part 1; red 3/4 outer-c 5.00
83-99,101-113: 92-(9/94)-Zero Hour x-over; Triumph app. 113-Green Lantern, Flash & Hawkman app. 3.00
100 ($3.95)-Foil-c; 52 pgs. 5.00
100 ($2.95)-Newsstand 4.00
#0-(10/94) Zero Hour (publ between #92 & #93); new team begins (Hawkman, Flash, Wonder Woman, Metamorpho, Nuklon, Crimson Fox, Obsidian & Fire) 3.00
Annual 1-8,10 ('87-'94, '96, 68 pgs.): 2-Joker-c/story; Batman cameo. 5-Armageddon 2001 x-over; Silver ink 2nd print. 7-Bloodlines x-over. 8-Elseworlds story. 10-Legends of the Dead Earth 4.00
Annual 9 (1995, $3.50)-Year One story 4.00
Special 1,2 ('90,'91, 52 pgs.): 1-Giffen plots. 2-Staton-a(p) 4.00
Spectacular 1 (1992, $1.50, 52 pgs.)-Intro new JLI & JLE teams; ties into JLI #61 & JLE #37; two interlocking covers by Jurgens 4.00
A New Beginning Trade Paperback (1989, $12.95)-r/#1-7 13.00
... International Vol. 1 HC (2008, $24.99) r/#1-7; new intro. by Giffen 25.00
... International Vol. 1 SC (2009, $17.99) r/#1-7; new intro. by Giffen 18.00
... International Vol. 2 HC (2008, $24.99) r/#8-13, Annual #1 and Suicide Squad #13 25.00
... International Vol. 2 SC (2009, $17.99) r/#8-13, Annual #1 and Suicide Squad #13 18.00
... International Vol. 3 SC (2009, $19.99) r/#14-22 20.00
... International Vol. 4 SC (2010, $17.99) r/#23-30 18.00
... International Vol. 5 SC (2011, $19.99) r/#Annual #2,3 & Justice League Europe #1-6 20.00
... International Vol. 6 SC (2011, $24.99) r/#31-35 & Justice League Europe #7-11 25.00
NOTE: ***Anderson** c-61i. **Austin** a-1i, 60i; c-1i. **Giffen** a-13; c-21p. **Guice** a-62i. **Maguire** a-1-12, 16-19, 22, 23. **Russell** a-Annual 1i; c-54i. **Willingham** a-30p, Annual 2.*

JUSTICE LEAGUE (DC New 52)
DC Comics: Oct, 2011 - No. 52, Aug, 2016 ($3.99)

1-Johns-s/Jim Lee-a/c; Batman, Green Lantern & Superman app.; orange background-c 2 4 6 11 16 20
1-Combo-Pack edition ($4.99) polybagged with digital download code; blue background-c 1 3 4 6 8 10
1-Variant-c by Finch 25.00
1-Second printing 25.00
2-11,13-23: 3-Wonder Woman & Aquaman arrive. 4-Darkseid arrives. 6-Pandora back-up. 7-Gene Ha-a; back-up Shazam origin begins; Frank-a. 8-D'Anda-a. 13,14-Cheetah app. 15-17-Throne of Atlantis. 22,23-Trinity War. 23-Crime Syndicate arrives 4.00
12-Superman/Wonder Woman kiss-c 4.00
23.1, 23.2, 23.3, 23.4 (11/13, $2.99, regular-c) 3.00
23.1 (11/13, $3.99, 3-D cover) "Darkseid #1" on cover; origin; Kaiyo app.; Reis-c 5.00
23.2 (11/13, $3.99, 3-D cover) "Lobo #1" on cover; Bennett-s/Oliver-a/Kuder-c 5.00
23.3 (11/13, $3.99, 3-D cover) "Dial E #1" on cover; Miéville-s; art by various 5.00
23.4 (11/13, $3.99, 3-D cover) "Secret Society #1" on cover; Owlman app.; Kudranski-a 5.00
24-29-Forever Evil. 24-Origin of Ultraman. 25-Origin of Owlman. 27-Cyborg upgraded. 28,29-Metal Men return 4.00
30-39: 30-Lex Luthor app.; intro Jessica Cruz. 31-33-Doom Patrol app. 33-Luthor joins. 35-Amazo virus unleashed; intro Lena Luthor 4.00
40-Darkseid War prologue, continues in DC's 2015 FCBD edition; intro. Grail (cameo) 4.00
41-($4.99) Darkseid War pt 1; Mister Miracle & the Anti-Monitor app.; intro Myrina Black 5.00
42-49-Darkseid War; Darkseid vs. the Anti-Monitor. 45,46-Manapul-a 4.00
48-Coloring Book variant-c by Kolins 4.00
50-($5.99) Conclusion to Darkseid War; Jessica Cruz becomes a Green Lantern 6.00
51,52: 51-Flashback with Robin; Pelletier-a. Lex Luthor as Superman; Grummett-a 4.00
#0-(11/12, $3.99) Origin of Shazam; back-up with Pandora 4.00
...: Darkseid War: Batman (12/15, $3.99) Pasarin-a; Batman on Mobius chair; Joe Chill app. 4.00
...: Darkseid War: Flash (1/16, $3.99) Merino-a; Flash vs. the Black Racer 4.00
...: Darkseid War: Green Lantern (1/16, $3.99) Shaner-a; Hal Jordan becomes God of Light 4.00
...: Darkseid War: Lex Luthor (2/16, $3.99) Dazo-a; The God of Apocalypse 4.00
...: Darkseid War: Shazam (1/16, $3.99) Kolins-a 4.00
...: Darkseid War Special (6/16, $3.99) Reis, Jimenez & Pelletier-a; Grail's origin 4.00
...: Darkseid War: Superman (1/16, $3.99) Dazo-a; The God of Steel 4.00
...: Futures End 1 (11/14, $2.99, regular-c) Cont'd from Justice League United: FE #1 3.00
...: Futures End 1 (11/14, $3.99, 3-D cover) 4.00
...: Trinity War Director's Cut 1 (10/13, $5.99) r/#22 pencil art and script 6.00

JUSTICE LEAGUE (DC Rebirth)
DC Comics: Sept, 2016 - Present ($2.99)

1-11: 1-Hitch-s/Daniel-a. 4-Merino-a. Clark & Derenick-a. 11-Amazo app. 3.00
1 Director's Cut (12/16, $5.99) r/#1 with B&W art; original script; variant cover gallery 6.00
12-24,26-40: 12,13: Justice League vs. Suicide Squad tie-ins. 12-Max Lord returns. 20,21-Hitch-a. 24-Mera app. 26-Intro. Justice League's children. 32,33-Dark Nights: Metal 3.00
25-($3.99) Hitch-s/Derenick-a; Mera app. 4.00
... Day Special Edition 1 (1/18, giveaway) r/Justice League #1 (2011) new Reis-c 3.00
...: Rebirth 1 (9/16, $2.99) Hitch-s/a; pre-New 52 Superman joins 3.00

JUSTICE LEAGUE ADVENTURES (Based on Cartoon Network series)
DC Comics: Jan, 2002 - No. 34, Oct, 2004 ($1.99/$2.25)

1-Timm & Ross-c 4.00
2-32: 3-Nicieza-s. 5-Starro app. 10-Begin $2.25-c. 14-Includes 16 pg. insert for VERB with Haberlin CG-art. 15,29-Amancio-a. 16-McCloud-s. 20-Psycho Pirate app. 25,26-Adam Strange-c/app. 28-Legion of Super-Heroes app. 30-Kamandi app. 3.00
Free Comic Book Day giveaway - (5/02) r/#1 with "Free Comic Book Day" banner on-c 3.00
TPB (2003, $9.95) r/#1,3,6,10-13; Timm/Ross-c from #1 10.00
...Vol. 1: The Magnificent Seven (2004, $6.95) digest-size reprints #3,6,10-12 7.00
...Vol. 2: Friends and Foes (2004, $6.95) digest-size reprints #13,14,16,19,20 7.00

JUSTICE LEAGUE: A MIDSUMMER'S NIGHTMARE
DC Comics: Sept, 1996 - No. 3, Nov, 1996 ($2.95, limited series, 38 pgs.)

1-3: Re-establishes Superman, Batman, Green Lantern, The Martian Manhunter, Flash, Aquaman & Wonder Woman as the Justice League; Mark Waid & Fabian Nicieza co-scripts; Jeff Johnson & Darick Robertson-a(p); Kevin Maguire-c 5.00
TPB-(1997, $8.95) r/1-3 9.00

JUSTICE LEAGUE: CRY FOR JUSTICE
DC Comics: Sept, 2009 - No. 7, Apr, 2010 ($3.99, limited series)

1-7-James Robinson-s/Mauro Cascioli-a/c. 1-Two covers; Congorilla origin 4.00
HC (2010, $24.99, d.j.) r/#1-7, Face of Evil: Prometheus 25.00
SC (2011, $19.99) r/#1-7, Face of Evil: Prometheus 20.00

JUSTICE LEAGUE DARK (DC New 52)
DC Comics: Nov, 2011 - No. 40, May, 2015 ($2.99/$3.99)

1-23: 1-Milligan-s; Deadman, Madame Xanadu, Zatanna, Shade, John Constantine app. 7,8-Crossover with I,Vampire #6,7. 7-Batgirl app. 9-Black Orchid joins. 11,12-Tim Hunter app. 13-Leads into J.L. Dark Annual #1. 19-21-Flash app. 22,23-Trinity War 3.00
23.1, 23.2 (11/13, $2.99, regular-c) 3.00
23.1 (11/13, $3.99, 3-D cover) "The Creeper #1" on cover; origin; Nocenti-s/Janin-c 5.00
23.2 (11/13, $3.99, 3-D cover) "Eclipso #1" on cover; origin; Tan-a/Janin-c 5.00

Justice League Elite #1 © DC

Justice League of America #4 © DC

Justice League of America #107 © DC

GD 2.0 · VG 4.0 · FN 6.0 · VF 8.0 · VF/NM 9.0 · NM- 9.2

24-40: 24-29-Forever Evil tie-ins. 40-Constantine returns 4.00
#0-(11/12, $2.99) Constantine and Zatanna's 1st meeting; Garbett-a/Sook-c 3.00
Annual #1 (12/12, $4.99) Continued from #13; Frankenstein & Amethyst app. 5.00
Annual #2 (12/14, $4.99) Janson-a/March-c; House of Wonders app. 5.00
...: Futures End 1 (11/14, $2.99, regular-c) Five years later; Etrigan app. 3.00
...: Futures End 1 (11/14, $3.99, 3-D cover) 4.00

JUSTICE LEAGUE ELITE (See JLA #100 and JLA Secret Files 2004)
DC Comics: Sept, 2004 - No. 12, Aug, 2005 ($2.50)

1-12-Flash, Green Arrow, Vera Black and others; Kelly-s/Mahnke-a. 5,6-JSA app. 3.00
JL Elite TPB (2005, $19.99) r/#1-4, Action #775, JLA #100, JLA Secret Files 2004 20.00
... Vol. 2 TPB (2007, $19.99) r/#5-12 20.00

JUSTICE LEAGUE EUROPE (Justice League International #51 on)
DC Comics: Apr, 1989 - No. 68, Sept., 1994 (75¢/ $1.00/$1.25/$1.50)

1-Giffen plots in all, breakdowns in #1-8,13-30; Justice League #1-c/swipe 4.00
2-10: 7-9-Batman app. 7,8-JLA x-over. 8,9-Superman app. 3.00
11-49: 12-Metal Men app. 20-22-Rogers-c/a(p). 33,34-Lobo vs. Despero. 37-New team begins; swipes-c to JLA #9; see JLA Spectacular 3.00
50-($2.50, 68 pgs.)-Battles Sonar 4.00
51-68: 68-Zero Hour x-over; Triumph joins Justice League Task Force (See JLTF #17) 3.00
Annual 1-5 ('90-'94, 68 pgs.)-1-Return of the Global Guardians; Giffen plots/breakdowns. 2-Armageddon 2001; Giffen-a(p); Rogers-a(p); Golden-a(i). 5-Elseworlds story 4.00
NOTE: *Phil Jimenez a-68p.* *Rogers c/a-20-22.* *Sears a-1-12, 14-19, 23-29; c-1-10, 12, 14-19, 23-29.*

JUSTICE LEAGUE: GENERATION LOST (Brightest Day)
DC Comics: Early July, 2010 - No. 24, Early Jun, 2011 ($2.99, bi-weekly limited series)

1-23: 1-Maxwell Lord's return; Winick & Giffen-s. 1-5,7-Harris-c. 13-Magog killed 3.00
24-($4.99) Wonder Woman vs. Omac Prime; Lopresti-a/Nguyen-c 5.00
... Volume One HC (2010, $39.99, dustjacket) r/#1-12; cover gallery 40.00

JUSTICE LEAGUE: GODS & MONSTERS (Tie-in to 2015 animated film)
DC Comics: Oct, 2015 - No. 3, Oct, 2015 ($3.99, weekly limited series)

1-3-DeMatteis & Timm-/Silas-a; alternate Superman, Batman & Wonder Woman 4.00
... - Batman 1 (9/15, $3.99) origin of the Kirk Langstrom Batman; Matthew Dow Smith-a 4.00
... - Superman 1 (9/15, $3.99) origin of the Hernan Guerra Superman; Moritat-a 4.00
... - Wonder Woman 1 (9/15, $3.99) origin of Bekka of New Genesis; Leonardi-a 4.00

JUSTICE LEAGUE INTERNATIONAL (See Justice League Europe)

JUSTICE LEAGUE INTERNATIONAL (DC New 52)
DC Comics: Nov, 2011 - No. 12, Oct, 2012 ($2.99)

1-12: 1-Jurgens-s/Lopresti-a/c; Batman, Booster Gold, Guy Gardner, Vixen, Fire, Ice. 8-Batwing joins; OMAC app. 3.00
Annual 1 (10/12, $4.99) Fabok-a/c; JLI vs. OMAC; Blue Beetle joins 5.00

JUSTICE LEAGUE OF AMERICA (See Brave & the Bold #28-30, Mystery In Space #75 & Official... Index) (See Crisis on Multiple Earths TPBs for reprints of JLA/JSA crossovers)
National Periodical Publ./DC Comics: Oct-Nov, 1960 - No. 261, Apr, 1987 (#91-99,139-157: 52 pgs.)

1-(10-11/60)-Origin & 1st app. Despero; Aquaman, Batman, Flash, Green Lantern, J'onn J'onzz, Superman & Wonder Woman continue from Brave and the Bold 550 1100 2200 7200 17,600 28,000
2 118 236 354 944 2122 3300
3-Origin/1st app. Kanjar Ro (see Mystery in Space #75)(scarce in high grade due to black-c) 111 222 333 888 1994 3100
4-Green Arrow joins JLA 71 142 213 568 1284 2000
5-Origin & 1st app. Dr. Destiny 56 112 168 448 999 1550
6-8,10: 6-Origin & 1st app. Prof. Amos Fortune. 7-(10-11/61)-Last 10¢ issue. 10-(3/62)-Origin & 1st app. Felix Faust; 1st app. Lord of Time 44 88 132 326 738 1150
9-(2/62)-Origin JLA (1st origin) 50 100 150 400 900 1400
11-15: 12-(6/62)-Origin & 1st app. Dr. Light. 13-(8/62)-Speedy app. 14-(9/62)-Atom joins JLA. 27 54 81 194 435 675
16-20: 17-Adam Strange flashback 23 46 69 164 362 560
21-(8/63)-"Crisis on Earth-One"; re-intro. of JSA in this title (see Flash #129) (1st S.A. app. Hourman & Dr. Fate) 46 92 138 340 770 1200
22- "Crisis on Earth-Two"; JSA x-over (story continued from #21) 35 70 105 252 564 875
23-28: 24-Adam Strange app. 27-Robin app. 16 32 48 112 249 385
29-"Crisis on Earth-Three"; JSA x-over; 1st app. Crime Syndicate of America (Ultraman, Owlman, Superwoman, Power Ring, Johnny Quick); 1st S.A. app. Starman 23 46 69 161 356 550
30-JSA x-over; Crime Syndicate app. 19 38 57 131 291 450
31-Hawkman joins JLA, Hawkgirl cameo (11/64) 13 26 39 91 201 310
32,34: 32-Intro & Origin Brain Storm. 34-Joker-c/sty 10 20 30 69 147 225
33,35,36,40,41: 40-3rd S.A. Penguin app. 41-Intro & origin The Key 10 20 30 66 138 210
37-39: 37,38-JSA x-over. 37-1st S.A. app. Mr. Terrific; Batman cameo. 38-"Crisis on Earth-A". 39-Giant G-16; r/B&B #28,30 & JLA #5 12 24 36 81 176 270
42-45: 42-Metamorpho app. 43-Intro. Royal Flush Gang 8 16 24 56 108 160
46-JSA x-over; 1st S.A. app. Sandman; 3rd S.A. app. of G.A. Spectre (8/66) 12 24 36 84 185 285
47-JSA x-over; 4th S.A. app of G.A. Spectre. 10 20 30 64 132 200
48-Giant G-29; r/JLA #2,3 & B&B #29 9 18 27 58 114 170
49-54,57,59,60: 51-Zatanna app. 7 14 21 46 86 125
55-Intro. Earth 2 Robin (1st G.A. Robin in S.A.) 9 18 27 61 123 185
56-JLA vs. JSA (1st G.A. Wonder Woman in S.A.) 8 16 24 54 102 150
58-Giant G-41; r/JLA #6,8,1 8 16 24 52 99 145
61-63,66,68-72: 69-Wonder Woman quits. 71-Manhunter leaves. 72-Last 12¢ issue 5 10 15 35 63 90
64-(8/68)-JSA story; origin/1st app. S.A. Red Tornado 8 16 24 54 102 150
65-JSA story continues 6 12 18 37 66 95
67-Giant G-53; r/JLA #4,14,31 8 16 24 51 96 140
73-1st S.A. app. of G.A. Superman 6 12 18 41 76 110
74-Black Canary joins; Larry Lance dies; 1st meeting of G.A. & S.A. Superman; Neal Adams-c 8 16 24 54 102 150
75-2nd app. Green Arrow in new costume (see Brave & the Bold #85) 32 64 96 230 515 800
76-Giant G-65 6 12 18 41 76 110
77-80: 78-Re-intro Vigilante (1st S.A. app?) 4 8 12 28 47 65
81-90: 82-1st S.A. app. of G.A. Batman (cameo). 83-Apparent death of The Spectre. 87-Zatanna app. 90-Last 15¢ issue 4 8 12 27 44 60
91,92: 91-1st meeting of the G.A. & S.A. Robin; begin 25¢, 52 pgs. issues, ends #99. 92-S.A. Robin tries on costume that is similar to that of G.A. Robin in All Star Comics #58 4 8 12 28 47 65
93-(Giant G-77,G-89; 68 pgs.) 6 12 18 38 69 100
94-1st app. Merlyn (Green Arrow villain); reprints 1st Sandman story (Adv. #40) & origin/1st app. Starman (Adv. #61); Deadman x-over; N. Adams-a (4 pgs.) 8 16 24 52 99 145
95,96: 95-Origin Dr. Fate & Dr. Midnight -r/ More Fun #67, All-American #25). 96-Origin Hourman (Adv. #48); Wildcat-r 5 10 15 30 50 70
97-99: 97-Origin JLA retold; Sargon, Starman-r. 98-G.A. Sargon, Starman-r. 99-G.A. Sandman, Atom-r; last 52 pg. issue 4 8 12 27 44 60
100-(8/72)-1st meeting of G.A. & S.A. W. Woman 6 12 18 38 69 100
101,102: JSA x-overs. 102-Red Tornado destroyed 4 8 12 27 44 60
103-106,109: 103-Rutland Vermont Halloween x-over; Phantom Stranger joins. 105-Elongated Man joins. 106-New Red Tornado joins. 109-Hawkman resigns 3 6 9 19 30 40
107,108-JSA x-over; 1st revival app. of G.A. Uncle Sam, Black Condor, The Ray, Dollman, Phantom Lady & The Human Bomb 4 8 12 27 44 60
110,112-116: All 100 pgs. 112-Amazo app; Crimson Avenger, Vigilante-r; origin Starman-r/ Adv. #81. 115-Martian Manhunter app. 5 10 15 31 53 75
111-JLA vs. Injustice Gang; intro. Libra (re-appears in 2008's Final Crisis); Shining Knight, Green Arrow-r 5 10 15 34 60 85
117-122,125-134: 117-Hawkman rejoins. 120,121-Adam Strange app. 125,126-Two-Face-app. 128-Wonder Woman rejoins. 129-Destruction of Red Tornado 3 6 9 16 23 30
123-(10/75),124: JLA/JSA x-over. DC editor Julie Schwartz & JLA writers Cary Bates & Elliot S! Maggin appear in story as themselves. 1st named app. Earth-Prime (3rd app. after Flash; 1st Series #179 & 228) 3 6 9 17 26 35
135-136: 135-137-G.A. Bulletman, Bulletgirl, Spy Smasher, Mr. Scarlet, Pinky & Ibis x-over, 1st appearances since G.A. 3 6 9 17 26 35
137-(12/76) Superman battles G.A. Captain Marvel 4 8 12 23 37 50
138-Adam Strange app. w/c by Neal Adams; 1st app. Green Lantern of the 73rd Century 3 6 9 19 30 40
139-157: 139-157-(52 pgs.): 139-Adam Strange app. 144-Origin retold; origin J'onn J'onzz. 145-Red Tornado resurrected. 147,148-Legion of Super-Heroes x-over 2 4 6 10 14 18
158-160-(44 pgs.) 2 4 6 8 11 14
158,160-162,169,171,172,173,176,179,181-(Whitman variants; low print run, none show issue # on cover) 2 4 6 10 14 18
161-165,169-182: 161-Zatanna joins & new costume. 171,172-JSA x-over. 171-Mr. Terrific murdered. 178-Cover similar to #1; J'onn J'onzz app. 179-Firestorm joins. 181-Green Arrow leaves JLA 1 2 3 5 6 8
166-168- "Identity Crisis (2004)" precursor; JSA app. vs. Secret Society of Super-Villains 3 6 9 16 23 30
166-168-Whitman variants (no issue # on covers) 4 8 12 23 37 50
183-185-JSA/New Gods/Darkseid/Mr. Miracle x-over 2 4 6 10 14 18
186-194,198,199: 192,193-Real origin Red Tornado. 193-1st app. All-Star Squadron

Justice League of America #228 © DC

Justice League of America (2013 series) #8 © DC

Justice League / Power Rangers #1 © DC & Saban

GD 2.0 | VG 4.0 | FN 6.0 | VF 8.0 | VF/NM 9.0 | NM- 9.2

as free 16 pg. insert 6.00
195-197-JSA app. vs. Secret Society of Super-Villains 1 2 3 5 6 8
200 ($1.50, Anniversary issue, 76 pgs.)-JLA origin retold; Green Arrow rejoins; Bolland, Aparo, Giordano, Gil Kane, Infantino, Kubert-a; Pérez-c/a 1 3 4 6 8 10
201-206,209-243,246-259: 203-Intro/origin new Royal Flush Gang. 219,220-True origin Black Canary. 228-Re-intro Martian Manhunter. 228-230-War of the Worlds storyline; JLA Satellite destroyed by Martians. 233-Story cont'd from Annual #2. 243-Aquaman leaves. 250-Batman rejoins. 253-Origin Despero. 258-Death of Vibe. 258-261-Legends x-over 5.00
207,208-JSA, JLA, & All-Star Squadron team-up 1 2 3 4 5 7
244,245-Crisis x-over 6.00
260-Death of Steel 1 2 3 4 5 7
261-Last issue 1 3 4 6 8 10
Annual 1-3 ('83-'85), 2-Intro new J.L.A. (Aquaman, Martian Manhunter, Steel, Gypsy, Vixen, Vibe, Elongated Man & Zatanna). 3-Crisis x-over 5.00
... Hereby Elects (2006, $14.99, TPB) reprints issues where new members joined; JLofA #4,75,105,106,146,161,173 &174; roster of various incarnations; Ordway-c 15.00
NOTE: ***Neal Adams** c-63, 66, 67, 70, 74, 79, 81, 82, 86-89, 91, 92, 94, 96-98, 138, 139. **M. Anderson** c-1-4, 6, 7, 10, 12-14. **Aparo** a-200. **Austin** a-200i. **Baily** a-96r. **Bolland** a-200. **Buckler** c-158, 163, 164. **Burnley** r-94, 98, 99. **Greene** a-46-61i, 64-73i, 110i(r). **Grell** c-117, 122. **Kaluta** c-154p. **Gil Kane** a-200. **Krigstein** a-96(r/Sensation #84). **Kubert** a-200; c-72, 73. **Nino** a-228i, 230i. **Orlando** c-151i. **Perez** a-184-186p, 192-197p, 200p; c-184p, 186, 192-195, 196p, 197p, 199, 200, 201p, 202, 203-205p, 207-209, 212-215, 217, 219, 220. **Reinman** r-97. **Roussos** a-62i. **Sekowsky** a-37, 38, 44-63p, 110-112p(r); c-46-48p, 51p. **Sekowsky/Anderson** c-5, 8, 9, 11, 15. **B. Smith** c-185i. **Starlin** c-178-180, 183, 185p. **Staton** a-244p; c-157p, 244p. **Toth** r-110. **Tuska** a-153, 228p, 241-243p. JSA x-overs-21, 22, 29, 30, 37, 38, 46, 47, 55, 56, 64, 65, 73, 74, 82, 83, 91, 92, 100, 101, 102, 107, 108, 110, 113, 115, 123, 124, 135-137, 147, 148, 159, 160, 171, 172, 183-185, 195-197, 207-209, 219, 220, 231, 232, 244.*

JUSTICE LEAGUE OF AMERICA
DC Comics: No. 0, Sept, 2006 - No. 60, Oct, 2011 ($2.99/$3.99)

0-Meltzer-s; history of the JLA; art by various incl. Lee, Giordano, Benes; Turner-c 5.00
0-Variant-c by Campbell 15.00
1-($3.99) Two interlocking covers by Benes; Benes-a 5.00
1-Variant-c by Turner 8.00
1-RRP Edition; sideways composite of both Benes covers 50.00
1-Second printing; Benes cover image between black bars 4.00
2-5-($2.99) Turner-c 4.00
2-5: Variant-c: 2-Jimenez. 3-Sprouse. 4-JG Jones. 5-Art Adams 5.00
6,7-($3.50) 6-JLA vs. Amazo; covers by Turner and Hughes. 7-Roster picked, new HQs; two Benes covers and Turner cover. 4.00
8-11,13-24,26-38-($2.99) 8-11-JLA/JSA team-up; covers by Turner & Jimenez. 10-Wally West returns. 13-Two covers. 13-15-Injustice Gang. 16-Tangent Flash. 20-Queen Bee app. 21-Libra app.; leads into Final Crisis #1. 35,36-Royal Flush Gang app. 38-Bagley-a begins 3.00
12-($3.50) Two Ross covers; origin retold with Wight-a; Benes-a 4.00
25-($3.99) McDuffie-s/art by various; Benes-c 4.00
39-49,51,52-($3.99) 39,40-Blackest Night. 41-New team; 2 covers. 44-48-Justice Society app. 44-Jade returns. 4.00
50-($4.99) Crime Syndicate app.; Bagley-a; wraparound-c by Van Sciver 5.00
50-Variant-c by Bagley, swipe of Quitely's JLA: Earth 2 cover 8.00
50-Variant-c by Jim Lee; swipe of Brave and the Bold #28 Starro cover 120.00
53-60-($2.99) 54-Booth-a; Eclipso returns. 55-Doomsday app. 3.00
... 80 Page Giant (11/09, $5.99) Anacleto-c; short stories by various; Ra's al Ghul app. 6.00
... 80 Page Giant 2011 (6/11, $5.99) Lau-c; chapters by various; JLA goes to Hell 6.00
Free Comic Book Day giveaway - (2007) r/#0 with "Free Comic Book Day" banner on-c 3.00
Justice League Wedding Special 1 (11/07, $3.99) McKone-a; Injustice League forms 4.00
...: Dark Things HC (2011, $24.99, dustjacket) r/#44-48 & J.S.A. #41,42 25.00
...: The Injustice Gang HC (2008, $19.99, dustjacket) r/#13-16; Wedding Special 20.00
...: The Lightning Saga HC (2008, $24.99, dustjacket) r/#0,8-12 & Justice Society of America #5,6; intro. by Patton Oswalt 25.00
...: The Lightning Saga SC (2008, $17.99) r/#0,8-12 & J.S.A. #5,6; intro. by Oswalt 18.00
...: Sanctuary SC (2009, $14.99) r/#17-21 15.00
...: Second Coming HC (2009, $19.99, dustjacket) r/#22-26 20.00
...: Second Coming SC (2010, $17.99) r/#22-26 18.00
...: Team History HC (2010, $19.99, dustjacket) r/#38-43 20.00
...: The Tornado's Path HC (2007, $24.99, dustjacket) r/#1-7; variant cover gallery; Lindelof intro.; commentary by Meltzer & Benes 25.00
...: The Tornado's Path SC (2008, $17.99) r/#1-7; variant cover gallery; Lindelof intro.; commentary by Meltzer & Benes 18.00
...: When Worlds Collide HC (2009, $24.99, dustjacket) r/#27,28,30-34 25.00
...: When Worlds Collide SC (2010, $14.99) r/#27,28,30-34 15.00

JUSTICE LEAGUE OF AMERICA (DC New 52)(Leads into Justice League United)
DC Comics: Apr, 2013 - No. 14, Jul, 2014 ($3.99)

1-14: 1-Johns-s/Finch-a/c; Green Arrow, Catwoman, Martian Manhunter, Katana & others team; variant covers with U.S. flag and each of the 50 state flags plus DC and Puerto Rico. 2-Covers by Finch and Ryp. 3-7: 3-5-Martian Manhunter back-up. 4,5-Shaggy Man app. 6,7-Trinity War. 8-14-Forever Evil. 10-Stargirl origin. 11,12-Despero app. 4.00
7.1, 7.2, 7.3, 7.4 (11/13, $2.99, regular-c) 3.00
7.1 (11/13, $3.99, 3-D cover) "Deadshot #1" on cover; origin; Kindt-s/Daniel-c 5.00
7.2 (11/13, $3.99, 3-D cover) "Killer Frost #1" on cover; origin; Gates-s/Santacruz-a 5.00
7.3 (11/13, $3.99, 3-D cover) "Shadow Thief #1" on cover; origin; Hardin-a/Daniel-c 5.00
7.4 (11/13, $3.99, 3-D cover) "Black Adam #1" on cover; Black Adam returns 5.00

JUSTICE LEAGUE OF AMERICA
DC Comics: Aug, 2015 - No. 10, Jan, 2017 ($5.99/$3.99)

1-($5.99) Bryan Hitch-s/a; the Parasite app. 6.00
2-10-($3.99) 2-4-Hitch-s/a. 5-Martian Manhunter spotlight; Kindt & Williams-s/Tan-a 4.00

JUSTICE LEAGUE OF AMERICA (DC Rebirth)
DC Comics: Apr, 2017 - Present ($2.99)

1-24: 1-Orlando-s/Reis-a; team of Batman, Black Canary, Lobo, Vixen, Killer Frost, The Atom & The Ray; Lord Havok app. 14-17-Ray Palmer app. 18-20-Prometheus app. 21-Intro new Aztek. 22-24-Queen of Fables app. 23,24-Promethea app. 3.00
25-($3.99) Lord Havok app. 4.00
Annual 1 (1/18, $4.99) Lobo & Black Canary team-up; Kelley Jones-a 5.00
...: Killer Frost - Rebirth 1 (3/17, $2.99) Orlando-s/Andolfo-a; Amanda Waller app. 3.00
...: Rebirth 1 (4/17, $2.99) Orlando-s/Reis-a; team assembles 3.00
...: The Atom - Rebirth 1 (3/17, $2.99) Orlando-s; Ryan Choi as the new Atom 3.00
...: The Ray - Rebirth 1 (3/17, $2.99) Orlando-s; Stephen Byrne-a; origin 3.00
...: Vixen - Rebirth 1 (3/17, $2.99) Orlando & Houser-s; Jamal Campbell-a; origin retold 3.00

JUSTICE LEAGUE OF AMERICA : ANOTHER NAIL (Elseworlds) (Also see JLA: The Nail)
DC Comics: 2004 - No. 3, 2004 ($5.95, prestige format)

1-3-Sequel to JLA: The Nail; Alan Davis-s/a(p) 6.00
TPB (2004, $12.95) r/series 13.00

JUSTICE LEAGUE OF AMERICA SUPER SPECTACULAR
DC Comics: 1999 ($5.95, mimics format of DC 100 Page Super Spectaculars)

1-Reprints Silver Age JLA and Golden Age JSA 6.00

JUSTICE LEAGUE OF AMERICA'S VIBE (DC New 52)
DC Comics: Apr, 2013 - No. 10, Feb, 2014 ($2.99)

1-10: 1,2-Johns & Kreisberg-s/Woods-a/Finch-c; origin. 5-Suicide Squad app. 3.00

JUSTICE LEAGUE OF AMERICA/ THE 99
DC Comics: Dec, 2010 - No. 6, May, 2011 ($3.99/$2/99, limited series)

1-3-($3.99) Derenick-a/Massaferra-c; JLA meets Teshkeel Comics characters 4.00
4-6-($2.99) Starro app. 3.00

JUSTICE LEAGUE/ POWER RANGERS
DC Comics: Mar, 2017 - No. 6, Nov, 2017 ($3.99, limited series)

1-6-Tom Taylor-s/Stephen Byrne-a; Lord Zedd app.; Power Rangers in JLA dimension 4.00

JUSTICE LEAGUE QUARTERLY (...International Quarterly #6 on)
DC Comics: Winter, 1990-91 - No. 17, Winter, 1994 ($2.95/$3.50, 84 pgs.)

1-12,14-17: 1-Intro The Conglomerate (Booster Gold, Praxis, Gypsy, Vapor, Echo, Maxi-Man, & Reverb); Justice League #1-c/swipe. 1,2-Keith Giffen plots/breakdowns. 3-Giffen plot; 72 pg. story. 4-Rogers/Russell-a in back-up. 5,6-Mark Waid scripts. 8,17-Global Guardians app. 4.00
13-Linsner-c 6.00
NOTE: ***Phil Jimenez** a-17p. **Sprouse** a-1p.*

JUSTICE LEAGUE: RISE AND FALL
DC Comics: 2010, 2011

Justice League: The Rise and Fall Special #1 (5/10, $3.99) Hunt for Green Arrow 4.00
HC-(2011, $24.99) Reprints Justice League of America #43, Justice League: The Rise and Fall Special #1, Green Arrow #31,32 and Justice League: The Rise of Arsenal #1-4 25.00

JUSTICE LEAGUES...
DC Comics: Mar, 2001 ($2.50, limited series)

JL?, Justice League of Amazons, Justice League of Atlantis, Justice League of Arkham, Justice League of Aliens, JLA: JLA split by the Advance Man; Perez-c in all; s&a by various 3.00

JUSTICE LEAGUE TASK FORCE
DC Comics: June, 1993 - No. 37, Aug, 1996 ($1.25/$1.50/$1.75)

1-16,0,17-37: Aquaman, Nightwing, Flash, J'onn J'onzz, & Gypsy form team. 5,6-Knight-quest tie-ins (new Batman cameo #5, 1 pg.). 15-Triumph cameo. 16-(9/94)-Zero Hour x-over; Triumph app. 0-(10/94). 17-(11/94)-Triumph becomes part of Justice League Task Force (See JLE #68). 26-Impulse app. 35-Warlord app. 37-Triumph quits team 3.00

JUSTICE LEAGUE: THE NEW FRONTIER SPECIAL (Also see DC: The New Frontier)
DC Comics: May, 2008 ($4.99, one-shot)

1-Short stories by Darwyn Cooke, J. Bone and Dave Bullock; bonus storyboards from the movie 5.00

Justice League United #16 © DC

Justice Society of America (2007 series) #11 © DC

Justice Traps the Guilty #1 © PRIZE

	GD 2.0	VG 4.0	FN 6.0	VF 8.0	VF/NM 9.0	NM- 9.2

JUSTICE LEAGUE: THE RISE OF ARSENAL (Follows Justice League: Cry For Justice)
DC Comics: May, 2010 - No. 4, Aug, 2010 ($3.99, limited series)

1-4-Horn-c/Borges-a/Krul-s. 2,3-Cheshire app. 4.00

JUSTICE LEAGUE 3000
DC Comics: Feb, 2014 - No. 15, May, 2015 ($2.99)

1-15-Justice League of the 31st century. 1-Giffen & DeMatteis-s/Porter-a/c. 10-Etrigan app. 11-Blue Beetle and Booster Gold cameo. 12-14-Blue Beetle and Booster Gold app. 14-Kamandi app.; Kuhn-a 14,15-Etrigan app. 15-Fire returns 3.00

JUSTICE LEAGUE 3001
DC Comics: Aug, 2015 - No. 12, Jul, 2016 ($2.99)

1-12: 1-Giffen & DeMatteis-s/Porter-a/c; Supergirl app. 4-Kolins-a. 5,6-Harley Quinn app. 3.00

JUSTICE LEAGUE UNITED (DC New 52)
DC Comics: No. 0, Jun, 2014 - No. 16, Feb, 2016 ($3.99)

0-16: 0-Lemire-s/McKone-a; Adam Strange, Lobo & Byth app. 3-Hawkman killed. 6-10-Legion of Super-Heroes app. 11-13,15-Harris-c. 13-15-Sgt Rock app. 4.00
Annual #1 (12/14, $4.99) Legion of Super-Heroes app.; continued in #6 5.00
...: Futures End 1 (11/14, $2.99, reg-c) 5 years later; 2-parter with Justice League: FE #1 3.00
...: Futures End 1 (11/14, $3.99, 3-D cover) 4.00

JUSTICE LEAGUE UNLIMITED (Based on Cartoon Network animated series)
DC Comics: Nov, 2004 - No. 46, Aug, 2008 ($2.25)

1-46: 1-Zatanna app. 2,23,42-Royal Flush Gang app. 4-Adam Strange app. 10-Creeper app. 17-Freedom Fighters app. 18-Space Cabby app. 27-Black Lightning app. 34-Zod app. 41-Harley Quinn-c/app. 3.00
Free Comic Book Day giveaway (5/06) r/#1 with "Free Comic Book Day" banner on-c 3.00
Jam Packed Action (2005, $7.99, digest) adaptations of two TV episodes 8.00
... Vol. 1: United They Stand (2005, $6.99, digest) r/#1-5 7.00
... Vol. 2: World's Greatest Heroes (2006, $6.99, digest) r/#6-10 7.00
... Vol. 3: Champions of Justice (2006, $6.99, digest) r/#11-15 7.00
...: Heroes (2009, $12.99, full-size) r/#23-29 13.00
...: The Ties That Bind (2008, $12.99, full-size) r/#16-22 13.00

JUSTICE LEAGUE VS. SUICIDE SQUAD (Leads into Justice League of America '17 series)
DC Comics: Feb, 2017 - No. 6, Mar, 2017 ($3.99, weekly limited series)

1-6: 1-Max Lord & Lobo app.; Fabok-a. 2-Daniel-a. 4-6-Eclipso app. 6-Porter-a 4.00

JUSTICE MACHINE, THE
Noble Comics: June, 1981 - No. 5, Nov, 1983 ($2.00, nos. 1-3 are mag. size)

	GD	VG	FN	VF	VF/NM	NM-
1-Byrne-c(p)	3	6	9	15	21	26
2-Austin-c(i)	2	4	6	9	12	15
3	1	3	4	6	8	10

4,5, Annual 1: Ann. 1-(1/84, 68 pgs.)(published by Texas Comics); 1st app. The Elementals; Golden-c(p); new Thunder Agents story (43 pgs.) 6.00

JUSTICE MACHINE (Also see The New Justice Machine)
Comico/Innovation Publishing: Jan, 1987 - No. 29, May 1989 ($1.50/$1.75)

1-29 3.00
Annual 1(6/89, $2.50, 36 pgs.)-Last Comico ish. 3.00
Summer Spectacular 1 ('89, $2.75)-Innovation Publ.; Byrne/Gustovich-c 3.00

JUSTICE MACHINE, THE
Innovation Publishing: 1990 - No. 4, 1990 ($1.95/$2.25, deluxe format, mature)

1-4: Gustovich-c/a in all 3.00

JUSTICE MACHINE FEATURING THE ELEMENTALS
Comico: May, 1986 - No. 4, Aug, 1986 ($1.50, limited series)

1-4 3.00

JUSTICE RIDERS
DC Comics: 1997 ($5.95, one-shot, prestige format)

1-Elseworlds; Dixon-s/Williams & Gray-a 6.00

JUSTICE SOCIETY
DC Comics: 2006; 2007 ($14.99, TPB)

Vol. 1 - Rep. from 1976 revival in All Star Comics #58-67 & DC Special #29; Bolland-c 15.00
Vol. 2 - R/All Star Comics #68-74 & Adventure Comics #461-466; new Bolland-c 15.00

JUSTICE SOCIETY OF AMERICA (See Adventure #461 & All-Star #3)
DC Comics: April, 1991 - No. 8, Nov, 1991 ($1.00, limited series)

1-8: 1-Flash. 2-Black Canary. 3-Green Lantern. 4-Hawkman. 5-Flash/Hawkman. 6-Green Lantern/Black Canary. 7-JSA 3.00

JUSTICE SOCIETY OF AMERICA (Also see Last Days of the... Special)
DC Comics: Aug, 1992 - No. 10, May, 1993 ($1.25)

1-10: 1-1st app. Jesse Quick 3.00

	GD 2.0	VG 4.0	FN 6.0	VF 8.0	VF/NM 9.0	NM- 9.2

JUSTICE SOCIETY OF AMERICA (Follows JSA series)
DC Comics: Feb, 2007 - No. 54, Oct, 2011 ($3.99/$2.99)

1-($3.99) New team selected; intro. Maxine Hunkle; Alex Ross-c 4.00
1-Variant-c by Eaglesham 6.00
2-22,24-49,51-54: 1-Covers by Ross & Eaglesham. 3,4-Vandal Savage app. 5,6-JLA/JSA team-up. 9-22-Kingdom Come Superman app.18-Magog app. 22-Superman returns to Kingdom Come Earth; Ross partial art. 23-25-Ordway-a. 26-Triptych cover by Ross. 33-Team splits. 34,35-Mordru app. 41,42-Justice League x-over. 52-54-Challengers of the Unknown app. 54-Darwyn Cooke-c 3.00
23-Black Adam-c/app. 6.00
50-($4.99) Degaton app.; art by Derenick, Chaykin, Williams II, and Pérez; Massafera-c 5.00
JSA Annual 1 (9/08, $3.99) Power Girl on Earth-2; Ross-c/Ordway-a 5.00
JSA Annual 2 (4/10, $4.99) All Star team app.; Magog quits; Williams-a 5.00
... 80 Page Giant (1/10, $5.99) short stories by various incl. Ordway, S. Hampton 6.00
... 80 Page Giant 2010 (12/10, $5.99) short stories by various 6.00
... 80 Page Giant 2011 (8/11, $5.99) short stories by various incl. Chaykin, Hampton 6.00
... Special (11/10, $4.99) Scott Kolins-s/a; spotlight on Magog 5.00
...: Axis of Evil SC (2010, $14.99) r/#34-40 15.00
...: Black Adam and Isis HC (2009, $19.99, d.j.) r/#23-28 20.00
...: Black Adam and Isis SC (2010, $14.99) r/#23-28 15.00
... Kingdom Come Special: Magog (1/09, $3.99) Pasarin-a; origin re-told; 2 covers 4.00
... Kingdom Come Special: Superman (1/09, $3.99) Lois' death re-told; Alex Ross-s/a/c; thumbnails, photo references, sketch art 4.00
... Kingdom Come Special: Superman (1/09, $3.99) Eaglesham variant cover 8.00
... Kingdom Come Special: The Kingdom (1/09, $3.99) Pasarin-a; 2 covers 4.00
...: The Bad Seed SC (2010, $14.99) r/#29-33 15.00
...: The Next Age SC (2008, $14.99) r/#1-4; Ross and Eaglesham sketch pages 15.00
...: Thy Kingdom Come Part One HC (2008, $19.99, d.j.) r/#7-12; Ross sketch pages 20.00
...: Thy Kingdom Come Part One SC (2009, $14.99) r/#7-12; Ross sketch pages 15.00
...: Thy Kingdom Come Part Two HC (2008, $24.99, d.j.) r/#13-18 & Annual #1; Ross sketch pages 25.00
...: Thy Kingdom Come Part Two SC (2009, $19.99) r/#13-18 & Ann. #1; Ross sketch-a 20.00
...: Thy Kingdom Come Part Three HC (2009, $24.99, d.j.) r/#19-22 & K.C. Specials - Superman, Magog and The Kingdom; Ross sketch pages 25.00
...: Thy Kingdom Come Part Three SC (2010, $19.99) same contents as HC 20.00

JUSTICE SOCIETY OF AMERICA 100-PAGE SUPER SPECTACULAR
DC Comics: 2000 ($6.95, mimics format of DC 100 Page Super Spectaculars)

1-"1975 Issue" reprints Flash team-up and Golden Age JSA 7.00

JUSTICE SOCIETY RETURNS, THE (See All Star Comics (1999) for related titles)
DC Comics: 2003 ($19.95, TPB)

TPB-Reprints 1999 JSA x-over from All-Star Comics #1,2 and related one-shots 20.00

JUSTICE TRAPS THE GUILTY (Fargo Kid V11#3 on)
Prize/Headline Publications: Oct-Nov, 1947 - V11#2(#92), Apr-May, 1958 (True FBI Cases)

	GD	VG	FN	VF	VF/NM	NM-
V2#1-S&K-c/a; electrocution-c	71	142	213	454	777	1100
2-S&K-c/a	37	74	111	222	361	500
3-5-S&K-c/a	34	68	102	204	332	460
6-S&K-c/a; Feldstein-a	36	72	108	216	351	485
7,9-S&K-c/a. 7-9-V2#1-3 in indicia; #7-9 on-c	31	62	93	182	296	410
8-Krigstein-a; S&K-c; electric chair-c	28	56	84	165	270	375
10-Krigstein-a; S&K-c/a	31	62	93	182	296	410
11,18,19-S&K-c	18	36	54	103	162	220
12,14-17,20-No S&K. 14-Severin/Elder-a (8pg.)	12	24	36	67	94	120
13-Used in **SOTI**, pg. 110-111	14	28	42	78	112	145
21,30-S&K-c/a	18	36	54	107	169	230
22,23-S&K-c	14	28	42	81	118	155
24-26,27,29,31-50: 32-Meskin story	11	22	33	62	86	110
28-Kirby-c	14	28	42	76	108	140
51-55,57,59-70	10	20	30	56	76	95
56-Ben Oda, Joe Simon, Joe Genola, Mort Meskin & Jack Kirby app. in police line-up on classic-c	21	42	63	122	199	275
58-Illo. in **SOTI**, "Treating police contemptuously" (top left); text on heroin	29	58	87	170	278	385
71-92: 76-Orlando-a	9	18	27	47	61	75

NOTE: ***Bailey*** *a-12, 13.* ***Elder*** *a-8.* ***Kirby*** *a-19p.* ***Meskin*** *a-22, 27, 63, 64; c-45, 46.* ***Robinson/Meskin*** *a-5, 19.* ***Severin*** *a-8, 11p. Photo c-12, 15-17.*

JUST IMAGINE STAN LEE WITH... (Stan Lee re-invents DC icons)
DC Comics: 2001 - 2002 ($5.95, prestige format, one-shots)
(Adam Hughes back-c on all)(Michael Uslan back-up stories in all, diff. artists)

Scott McDaniel Creating **Aquaman**- Back-up w/Fradon-a 6.00
Joe Kubert Creating **Batman**- Back-up w/Kaluta-a 6.00
Chris Bachalo Creating **Catwoman**- Back-up w/Cooke & Allred-a 6.00
John Cassaday Creating **Crisis**- no back-up story 6.00

Just Married #28 © CC

Kabuki V7 #6 © David Mack

The Kamandi Challenge #8 © DC

	GD 2.0	VG 4.0	FN 6.0	VF 8.0	VF/NM 9.0	NM- 9.2

Kevin Maguire Creating **The Flash**- Back-up w/Aragonés-a 6.00
Dave Gibbons Creating **Green Lantern**- Back-up w/Giordano-a 6.00
Jerry Ordway Creating **JLA** 6.00
John Byrne Creating **Robin**- Back-up w/John Severin-a 6.00
Walter Simonson Creating **Sandman**- Back-up w/Corben-a 6.00
Gary Frank Creating **Shazam!**- Back-up w/Kano-a 6.00
John Buscema Creating **Superman**- Back-up w/Kyle Baker-a 6.00
Jim Lee Creating **Wonder Woman**- Back-up w/Gene Colan-a 6.00
Secret Files and Origins #1 (3/02, $4.95) Crisis prologue; Jurgens-a 5.00
TPB -Just Imagine Stan Lee Creating the DC Universe: Book One (2002, $19.95) r/Batman, Wonder Woman, Superman, Green Lantern 20.00
TPB -Just Imagine Stan Lee Creating the DC Universe: Book Two (2003, $19.95) r/Flash, JLA, Secret Files and Origins, Robin, Shazam; sketch pages 20.00
TPB -Just Imagine Stan Lee Creating the DC Universe: Book Three (2004, $19.95) r/Aquaman, Catwoman, Sandman, Crisis; profile pages 20.00

JUST MARRIED
Charlton Comics: January, 1958 - No. 114, Dec, 1976

	GD	VG	FN	VF	VF/NM	NM-
1	6	12	18	38	69	100
2	3	6	9	21	33	45
3-10	3	6	9	17	26	35
11-30	3	6	9	14	20	26
31-50	2	4	6	11	16	20
51-70	2	4	6	9	13	16
71-78,80-89	2	4	6	8	11	14
79-Ditko-a (7 pages)	2	4	6	10	14	18
90-Susan Dey and David Cassidy full page poster	2	4	6	11	16	20
91-114	2	4	6	8	10	12

KA'A'NGA COMICS (...Jungle King)(See Jungle Comics)
Fiction House Magazines (Glen-Kel Publ. Co.): Spring, 1949 - No. 20, Summer, 1954

	GD	VG	FN	VF	VF/NM	NM-
1-Ka'a'nga, Lord of the Jungle begins	58	116	174	371	636	900
2 (Winter, '49-'50)	32	64	96	188	307	425
3,4	24	48	72	142	234	325
5-Camilla app.	23	46	69	136	223	310
6-10: 7-Tuska-a. 9-Tabu, Wizard of the Jungle app. 10-Used in **POP**, pg. 99	16	32	48	94	147	200
11-15: 15-Camilla-r by Baker/Jungle #106	14	28	42	80	115	150
16-Sheena app.	14	28	42	82	121	160
17-20	13	26	39	74	105	135
I.W. Reprint #1,8: 1-r/#18; Kinstler-c. 8-r/#10	3	6	9	14	20	25

NOTE: *Celardo c-1. Whitman c-8-20(most).*

KABOOM
Awesome Entertainment: Sept, 1997 - No. 3, Nov, 1997 ($2.50)
1-3: 1-Matsuda-a/Loeb-s; 4 covers exist (Matsuda, Sale, Pollina and McGuinness), 1-Dynamic Forces Edition, 2-Regular, 2-Alicia Watcher variant-c, 2-Gold logo variant-c, 3-Two covers by Liefeld & Matsuda, 3-Dynamic Forces Ed., Prelude Ed. 3.00
Prelude Gold Edition 4.00

KABOOM (2nd series)
Awesome Entertainment: July, 1999 - No. 3, Dec, 1999 ($2.50)
1-3: 1-Grant-a(p); at least 4 variant covers 3.00

KABOOM! SUMMER BLAST FREE COMIC BOOK DAY EDITION
Boom Entertainment (KaBOOM!): May 2013; May 2014 (free giveaways)
nn-(5/13) Short stories of Adventure Time, Regular Show, Herobear, Garfield, Peanuts 3.00
nn-(5/14) Adventure TIme, Regular Show, Steven Universe, Uncle Grandpa and others 3.00

KABUKI
Caliber: Nov, 1994 ($3.50, B&W, one-shot)

	GD	VG	FN	VF	VF/NM	NM-
nn-(Fear The Reaper) 1st app.; David Mack-c/a/s	1	2	3	5	6	8
Color Special (1/96, $2.95)-Mack-c/a/scripts; pin-ups by Tucci, Harris & Quesada						4.00
Gallery (8/95, $2.95)- pinups from Mack, Bradstreet, Paul Pope & others						3.00

KABUKI
Image Comics: Oct, 1997 - No. 9, Mar, 2000 ($2.95, color)

	GD	VG	FN	VF	VF/NM	NM-
1-David Mack-c/s/a						5.00
1-($10.00)-Dynamic Forces Edition	1	3	4	6	8	10
2-5						4.00
6-9						3.00
#1/2 (9/01, $2.95) r/Wizard 1/2; Eklipse Mag. article; bio						3.00
...Classics (2/99, $3.95) Reprints Fear the Reaper						4.00
...Classics 2 (3/99, $3.95) Reprints Dance of Dance						4.00
...Classics 3-5 (3-6/99, $4.95) Reprints Circle of Blood-Acts 1-3						5.00
...Classics 6-12 (7/99-3/00, $3.25) Various reprints						3.25
...Images (6/98, $4.95) r/#1 with new pin-ups						5.00
...Images 2 (1/99, $4.95) r/#1 with new pin-ups						5.00
...Metamorphosis TPB (10/00, $24.95) r/#1-9; Sienkiewicz intro.; 2nd printing exists						25.00
...Reflections 1-4 (7/98-5/02; $4.95) new story plus art techniques						5.00
... The Ghost Play (11/02, $2.95) new story plus interview						3.00

KABUKI
Marvel Comics (Icon): July, 2004 - Present ($2.99, color)
1-9: 1-David Mack-c/s/a in all; variant-c by Alex Maleev. 4-Variant-c by Adam Hughes. 6-Variant-c by Mignola. 8-Variant-c by Kent Williams. 9-Allred var-c 3.00
...: The Alchemy HC (2008, $29.99, dust jacket) oversized r/#1-9; bonus art & content 30.00
... Reflections 5-15 (7/05-10/09, $5.99) paintings & sketches of recent work; photos 6.00

KABUKI AGENTS (SCARAB)
Image Comics: Aug, 1999 - No. 8, Aug, 2001 ($2.95, B&W)
1-8-David Mack-s/Rick Mays-a 3.00
Lost in Translation HC (3/02, $29.95) r/#1-8; intro. by Paul Pope 30.00
Lost in Translation SC (3/02, $19.95) r/#1-8; intro. by Paul Pope 20.00

KABUKI: CIRCLE OF BLOOD
Caliber Press: Jan, 1995 - No. 6, Nov, 1995 ($2.95, B&W)
1-David Mack story/a in all 5.00
2-6: 3-#1 on inside indicia. 3.00
6-Variant-c 3.00
TPB ($16.95) r/#1-6, intro. by Steranko 17.00
TPB (1997, $17.95) Image Edition-r/#1-6, intro. by Steranko 18.00
TPB ($24.95) Deluxe Edition 25.00

KABUKI: DANCE OF DEATH
London Night Studios: Jan, 1995 ($3.00, B&W, one-shot)

	GD	VG	FN	VF	VF/NM	NM-
1-David Mack-c/a/scripts	1	2	3	5	6	8

KABUKI: DREAMS
Image Comics: Jan, 1998 ($4.95, TPB)
nn-Reprints Color Special & Dreams of the Dead 5.00

KABUKI: DREAMS OF THE DEAD
Caliber: July, 1996 ($2.95, one-shot)
nn-David Mack-c/a/scripts 3.00

KABUKI FAN EDITION
Gemstone Publ./Caliber: Feb, 1997 (mail-in offer, one-shot)
nn-David Mack-c/a/scripts 4.00

KABUKI: MASKS OF THE NOH
Caliber: May, 1996 - No. 4, Feb, 1997 ($2.95, limited series)
1-4: 1-Three-c (1A-Quesada, 1B-Buzz, &1C-Mack). 3-Terry Moore pin-up 3.00
TPB-(4/98, $10.95) r/#1-4; intro by Terry Moore 11.00

KABUKI: SKIN DEEP
Caliber Comics: Oct, 1996 - No. 3, May, 1997 ($2.95)
1-3:David Mack-c/a/scripts. 2-Two-c (1-Mack, 1-Ross) 3.00
TPB-(5/98, $9.95) r/#1-3; intro by Alex Ross 10.00

KAMANDI: AT EARTH'S END
DC Comics: June, 1993 - No. 6, Nov, 1993 ($1.75, limited series)
1-6: Elseworlds storyline 3.00

KAMANDI CHALLENGE, THE (Commemoration for Jack Kirby's 100th birthday)
DC Comics: Mar, 2017 - No. 12, Feb, 2018 ($4.99/$3.99, limited series)
1-($4.99) DiDio-s/Giffen-a; Abnett-s/Eaglesham-a; Timm-c 5.00
2-11-($3.99) 2-Neal Adams-a; Tomasi-s; covers by Adams & Rocafort. 3-Palmiotti-s/Conner-a. 8-Giffen-s/Rude-a; Jim Lee-c. 10-Shane Davis-a. 11-Simonson-a 4.00
12-($4.99) Gail Simone-s; art by Jill Thompson and Ryan Sook; afterword by Paul Levitz 5.00
... Special 1 (3/17, $7.99) r/#1,32 and unpubl'd #60,61 from Cancelled Comic Cavalcade 8.00

KAMANDI, THE LAST BOY ON EARTH (Also see Alarming Tales #1, Brave and the Bold #120 & 157, Cancelled Comic Cavalcade & Wednesday Comics)
National Periodical Publ./DC Comics: Oct-Nov, 1972 - No. 59, Sept-Oct, 1978

	GD	VG	FN	VF	VF/NM	NM-
1-Origin & 1st app. Kamandi; intro Ben Boxer	7	14	21	46	86	125
2,3	4	8	12	28	47	65
4,5: 4-Intro. Prince Tuftan of the Tigers	4	8	12	25	40	55
6-10	3	6	9	18	28	38
11-20	3	6	9	15	22	28
21-28,30,31,33-40: 24-Last 20¢ issue. 31-Intro Pyra.	2	4	6	13	18	22
29,32: 29-Superman x-over. 32-(68 pgs.)-r/origin from #1 plus one new story; 4 pg. biog. of Jack Kirby with B&W photos	3	6	9	14	20	26
41-57	2	4	6	10	14	18
58-Karate Kid x-over from LSH (see Karate Kid #15)	3	6	9	14	19	24

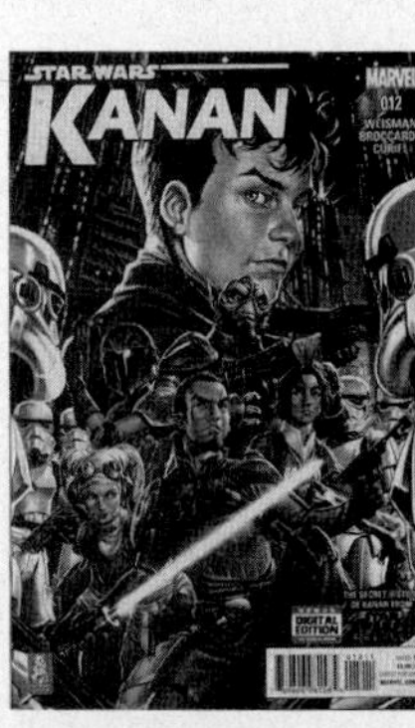

Kanan - The Last Padawan #12 © Lucasfilm

Kaptara #5 © Zdarsco & McLeod

Katy Keene #37 © ACP

GD 2.0 | VG 4.0 | FN 6.0 | VF 8.0 | VF/NM 9.0 | NM- 9.2

59-(44 pgs.)-Story cont'd in Brave and the Bold #157; The Return of Omac back-up by Starlin-c/a(p) cont'd in Warlord #37 3 6 9 16 23 30

NOTE: *Ayers a(p)-48-59 (most). Giffen a-44p, 45p. Kirby a-1-40p; c-1-33. Kubert c-34-41. Nasser a-45p, 46p. Starlin a-59p; c-57, 59p.*

KAMUI (Legend Of...#2 on)
Eclipse Comics/Viz Comics: May 12, 1987 - No. 37, Nov. 15, 1988 ($1.50, B&W, bi-weekly)

1-37: 1-3 have 2nd printings 3.00

KANAN - THE LAST PADAWAN (Star Wars)
Marvel Comics: Jun, 2015 - No. 12, May, 2016 ($3.99)

1-12: 1-Weisman-s/Larraz-a; takes place after Episode 3; flashbacks to the Clone Wars. 9-11-General Grievous app. 4.00

KANE & LYNCH (Based on the video games)
DC Comics (WildStorm): Oct, 2010 - No. 6, Apr, 2011 ($3.99/$2.99, limited series)

1-4-($3.99) Templesmith-c/Edginton-s/Mitten-a 4.00
5,6-($2.99) 3.00
TPB (2011, $17.99) r/#1-6; cover gallery 18.00

KAOS MOON (Also see Negative Burn #34)
Caliber Comics: 1996 - No. 4, 1997 ($2.95, B&W)

1-4-David Boller-s/a 3.00
3,4-Limited Alternate-c 4.00
3,4-Gold Alternate-c, Full Circle TPB ($5.95) r/#1,2 6.00

KAPTARA
Image Comics: Apr, 2015 - No. 5, Nov, 2015 ($3.50)

1-5-Chip Zdarsky-s/Kagan McLeod-a 3.50

KARATE KID (See Action, Adventure, Legion of Super-Heroes, & Superboy)
National Periodical Publications/DC Comics: Mar-Apr, 1976 - No. 15, July-Aug, 1978 (Legion of Super-Heroes spin-off)

1-Meets Iris Jacobs; Estrada/Staton-a 3 6 9 17 26 35
2-14: 2-Major Disaster app. 14-Robin x-over 2 3 4 6 8 10
15-Continued into Kamandi #58 2 4 6 11 16 20

NOTE: *Grell c-1-4, 7, 8, 5p, 6p, Staton a-1-9i. Legion x-over-No. 1, 2, 4, 6, 10, 12, 13. Princess Projectra x-over-#8, 9.*

KARNAK (Inhumans)
Marvel Comics: Dec, 2015 - No. 6, Apr, 2017 ($3.99)

1-6: 1,2-Warren Ellis-s/Gerardo Zaffino-a. 3-6-Roland Boschi-a 4.00

KATANA (DC New 52) (From Justice League Of America 2013 series)
DC Comics: Apr, 2013 - No. 10, Feb, 2014 ($2.99)

1-10: 1,2-Nocenti-s/Sanchez-a/Finch-c; origin. 2-Steve Trevor app. 3-6-Creeper app. 3.00

KATHY
Standard Comics: Sept, 1949 - No. 17, Sept, 1955

1-Teen-age 20 40 60 114 182 250
2-Schomburg-c 15 30 45 83 124 165
3-5 11 22 33 64 90 115
6-17: 17-Code approved 10 20 30 58 79 100

KATHY (The Teenage Tornado)
Atlas Comics/Marvel (ZPC): Oct, 1959 - No. 27, Feb, 1964 (most issues contain paper dolls and pin-up pages)

1-The Teen-age Tornado; Goldberg-c/a in all 26 52 78 154 252 350
2 15 30 45 85 130 175
3-15 14 28 42 82 121 160
16-23,25,27 12 24 36 69 97 125
24-(8/63) Frank Sinatra, Cary Grant, Ed Sullivan & Liz Taylor-c 17 34 51 98 154 210
26-(12/63) Kathy becomes a model; Millie app. 14 28 42 76 108 140

KAT KARSON
I. W. Enterprises: No date (Reprint)

1-Funny animals 2 4 6 10 12 15

KATO (Also see The Green Hornet)
Dynamite Entertainment: 2010 - No. 14, 2011 ($3.99)

1-14: 1-Kato and daughter origin; Garza-a/Parks-s. 2-10 Bernard-a 4.00
Annual 1 (2011, $4.99) Parks-s/Salazar-a 5.00

KATO OF THE GREEN HORNET (Also see The Green Hornet)
Now Comics: Nov, 1991 - No. 4, Feb, 1992 ($2.50, mini-series)

1-4: Brent Anderson-c/a 3.00

KATO OF THE GREEN HORNET II (Also see The Green Hornet)
Now Comics: Nov, 1992 - No. 2, Dec, 1993 ($2.50, mini-series)

1,2-Baron-s/Mayerik & Sherman-a 3.00

KATO ORIGINS (Also see The Green Hornet: Year One)
Dynamite Entertainment: 2010 - No. 11, 2011 ($3.99)

1-11-Kato in 1942; Jai Nitz-s/Colton Worley-a; covers by Worley & Francavilla 4.00

KATY KEENE (Also see Kasco Komics, Laugh, Pep, Suzie, & Wilbur)
Archie Publ./Close-Up/Radio Comics: 1949 - No. 4, 1951; No. 5, 3/52 - No. 62, Oct, 1961 (50-53-Adventures of...on-c) (Cut and missing pages are common)

1-Bill Woggon-c/a begins; swipes-c to Mopsy #1 232 464 696 1485 2543 3600
2-(1950) 71 142 213 454 777 1100
3-5: 3-(1951). 4-(1951). 5-(3/52) 55 110 165 352 601 850
6-10 40 80 120 246 411 575
11,13-21: 21-Last pre-code issue (3/55) 34 68 102 204 332 460
12-(Scarce) 40 80 120 246 411 575
22-40 23 46 69 138 227 315
41-60: 54-Wedding Album plus wedding pin-up 19 38 57 109 172 235
61-Sci-fi-c 24 48 72 142 234 325
62-Classic Robot-c 41 82 123 256 428 600
Annual 1('54, 25¢)-All new stories; last pre-code 57 114 171 362 619 875
Annual 2-6('55-59, 25¢)-All new stories 33 66 99 194 317 440
3-D 1(1953, 25¢, large size)-Came w/glasses 39 78 117 240 395 550
Charm 1(9/58)-Woggon-c/a; new stories, and cut-outs 30 60 90 180 293 400
Glamour 1(1957)-Puzzles, games, cut-outs 30 60 90 180 293 400
Spectacular 1('56) 32 64 96 188 307 425

NOTE: *Debby's Diary in #45, 47-49, 52, 57.*

KATY KEENE COMICS DIGEST MAGAZINE
Close-Up, Inc. (Archie Ent.): 1987 - No. 10, July, 1990 ($1.25/$1.35/$1.50, digest size)

1 2 4 6 10 14 18
2-10 1 3 4 6 8 10

NOTE: *Many used copies are cut-up inside.*

KATY KEENE FASHION BOOK MAGAZINE
Radio Comics/Archie Publications: 1955 - No. 13, Sum, '56 - N. 23, Wint, '58-59 (nn 3-10) (no #11,12)

1-Bill Woggon-c/a 57 114 171 362 619 875
2 31 62 93 186 303 420
13-18: 18-Photo Bill Woggon 24 48 72 140 230 320
19-23 20 40 60 117 189 260

KATY KEENE HOLIDAY FUN (See Archie Giant Series Magazine No. 7, 12)

KATY KEENE MODEL BEHAVIOR
Archie Comic Publications: 2008 ($10.95, TPB)

Vol. 1 - New story and reprinted apps./pin-ups from Archie & Friends #101-112 11.00

KATY KEENE PINUP PARADE
Radio Comics/Archie Publications: 1955 - No. 15, Summer, 1961 (25¢) (Cut-out & missing pages are common)

1-Cut-outs in all?; last pre-code issue 55 110 165 352 601 850
2-(1956) 31 62 93 186 303 420
3-5: 3-(1957). 5-(1959) 26 52 78 154 252 350
6-10,12-14: 8-Mad parody. 10-Bill Woggon photo 22 44 66 128 209 290
11-Story of how comics get CCA approved, narrated by Katy 28 56 84 165 270 375
15(Rare)-Photo artist & family 41 82 123 256 428 600

KATY KEENE SPECIAL (Katy Keene #7 on; see Laugh Comics Digest)
Archie Ent.: Sept, 1983 - No. 33, 1990 (Later issues published quarterly)

1-10: 1-Woggon-r; new Woggon-c. 3-Woggon-r 5.00
11-25: 12-Spider-Man parody 6.00
26-32-(Low print run) 1 2 3 5 7 9
33 2 4 6 8 10 12

KATZENJAMMER KIDS, THE (See Captain & the Kids & Giant Comic Album)
David McKay Publ./Standard No. 12-21(Spring/'50 - 53)/Harvey No. 22, 4/53 on: 1945-1946; Summer, 1947 - No. 27, Feb-Mar, 1954

Feature Books 30 21 42 63 122 199 275
Feature Books 32,35('45),41,44('46) 19 38 57 109 172 235
Feature Book 37-Has photos & biography of Harold Knerr 20 40 60 114 182 250
1(1947)-All new stories begin 20 40 60 114 182 250
2-5 12 24 36 69 97 125
6-11 10 20 30 56 76 95
12-14(Standard) 9 18 27 47 61 75
15-21(Standard) 8 16 24 44 57 70
22-25,27(Harvey): 22-24-Henry app. 7 14 21 35 43 50

Ka-Zar (2011 series) #1 © MAR

Keen Detective Funnies #9 © CEN

Ken Shannon #3 © QUA

GD 2.0 | VG 4.0 | FN 6.0 | VF 8.0 | VF/NM 9.0 | NM- 9.2

26-Half in 3-D 16 32 48 94 147 200

KAYO (Formerly Bullseye & Jest; becomes Carnival Comics)
Harry 'A' Chesler: No. 12, Mar, 1945

12-Green Knight, Capt. Glory, Little Nemo (not by McCay)
24 48 72 142 234 325

KA-ZAR (Also see Marvel Comics #1, Savage Tales #6 & X-Men #10)
Marvel Comics Group: Aug, 1970 - No. 3, Mar, 1971 (Giant-Size, 68 pgs.)

1-Reprints earlier Ka-Zar stories; Avengers x-over in Hercules; Daredevil, X-Men app.; hidden profanity-c 4 8 12 28 47 65
2,3-Daredevil-r. 2-r/Daredevil #13 w/Kirby layouts; Ka-Zar origin, Angel-r from X-Men by Tuska. 3-Romita & Heck-a (no Kirby) 3 6 9 17 26 35

NOTE: *Buscema r-2. Colan a-1p(r). Kirby c/a-1, 2. #1-Reprints X-Men #10 & Daredevil #24.*

KA-ZAR
Marvel Comics Group: Jan, 1974 - No. 20, Feb, 1977 (Regular Size)

1 3 6 9 15 22 28
2-10 2 4 6 8 10 12
11-14,16,18-20: 16-Only a 30 ¢ edition exists 1 2 3 5 6 8
15,17-(Regular 25¢ edition)(8/76) 1 2 3 5 6 8
15,17-(30¢-c variants, limited distribution) 3 6 9 19 30 40

NOTE: *Alcala a-6i, 8i. Brunner c-4. J. Buscema a-6-10p; c-1, 5, 7. Heath a-12. G. Kane c(p)-3, 5, 8-11, 15, 20. Kirby c-12p. Reinman a-1p.*

KA-ZAR (Volume 2)
Marvel Comics: May, 1997 - No. 20, Dec, 1998 ($1.95/$1.99)

1-Waid-s/Andy Kubert-c/a. thru #4 4.00
1-2nd printing; new cover 3.00
2,4: 2-Two-c 3.00
3-Alpha Flight #1 preview 4.00
5-13,15-20: 8-Includes Spider-Man Cybercomic CD-ROM. 9-11-Thanos app. 15-Priest-s/Martinez & Rodriguez-a begin; Punisher app. 3.00
14-($2.99) Last Waid/Kubert issue; flip book with 2nd story previewing new creative team of Priest-s/Martinez & Rodriguez-a 4.00
'97 Annual ($2.99)-Wraparound-c 4.00

KA-ZAR
Marvel Comics: Aug, 2011 - No. 5, Dec, 2011 ($2.99, limited series)

1-5-Jenkins-s/Alixe-a/c 3.00

KA-ZAR OF THE SAVAGE LAND
Marvel Comics: Feb, 1997 ($2.50, one-shot)

1-Wraparound-c 4.00

KA-ZAR: SIBLING RIVALRY
Marvel Comics: July, 1997 ($1.95, one-shot)

(# -1) Flashback story w/Alpha Flight #1 preview 3.00

KA-ZAR THE SAVAGE (See Marvel Fanfare)
Marvel Comics Group: Apr, 1981 - No. 34, Oct, 1984 (Regular size)(Mando paper #10 on)

1-Bruce Jones-s begin 5.00
2-20,24,27,28,30-34: 11-Origin Zabu. 12-One of two versions with panel missing on pg. 10. 20-Kraven the Hunter-c/story (also apps. in #21) 3.00
12-Version with panel on pg. 10 (1600 printed) 1 2 3 5 6 8
21-23, 25,26-Spider-Man app. 26-Photo-c. 4.00
29-Double size; Ka-Zar & Shanna wed 4.00

NOTE: *B. Anderson a-1-15p, 18, 19; c-1-17, 18p, 20(back). G. Kane a(back-up)-11, 12, 14.*

KEEN DETECTIVE FUNNIES (Formerly Detective Picture Stories?)
Centaur Publications: No. 8, July, 1938 - No. 24, Sept, 1940

V1#8-The Clock continues-r/Funny Picture Stories #1; Roy Crane-a (1st?)
354 708 1062 2478 4339 6200
9-Tex Martin by Eisner; The Gang Buster app. 290 580 870 1856 3178 4500
10,11: 11-Dean Denton story (begins?) 258 516 774 1651 2826 4000
V2#1,2-The Eye Sees by Frank Thomas begins; ends #23(Not in V2#3&5). 2-Jack Cole-a
142 284 426 909 1555 2200
3-6: 3-TNT Todd begins. 4-Gabby Flynn begins. 5,6-Dean Denton story
135 270 405 864 1482 2100
7-The Masked Marvel by Ben Thompson begins (7/39, 1st app.)(scarce)
300 600 900 2070 3635 5200
8-Nudist ranch panel w/four girls 155 310 465 992 1696 2400
9-11 123 246 369 787 1344 1900
12(12/39)-Origin The Eye Sees by Frank Thomas; death of Masked Marvel's sidekick ZL
161 322 483 1030 1765 2500
V3#1 116 232 348 742 1271 1800
18-Bondage/torture-c 155 310 465 992 1696 2400
19,21,22 116 232 348 742 1271 1800
20-Classic Eye Sees-c by Thomas 258 516 774 1651 2826 4000
23-Air Man begins (intro); Air Man-c 168 336 504 1075 1838 2600
24-(scarce) Air Man-c 194 388 582 1242 2121 3000

NOTE: *Burgos a-V2#2. Jack Cole a-V2#2. Eisner a-10, V2#6r. Ken Ernst a-V2#4-7, 9, 10, 19, 21; c-V2#4. Everett a-V2#6, 7, 9, 11, 12, 20. Guardineer a-V2#5, 66. Gustavson a-V2#4-6. Simon c-V3#1. Thompson c-V2#7, 9, 10, 22.*

KEEN KOMICS
Centaur Publications: V2#1, May, 1939 - V2#3, Nov, 1939

V2#1(Large size)-Dan Hastings (s/f), The Big Top, Bob Phantom the Magician, The Mad Goddess app. 290 580 870 1856 3178 4500
V2#2(Reg. size)-The Forbidden Idol of Machu Picchu; Cut Carson by Burgos begins
110 220 330 704 1202 1700
V2#3-Saddle Sniffl by Jack Cole, Circus Pays, Kings Revenge app.
97 194 291 621 1061 1500

NOTE: *Binder a-V2#2. Burgos a-V2#2, 3. Ken Ernst a-V2#3. Gustavson a-V2#2. Jack Cole a-V2#3.*

KEEN TEENS (Girls magazine)
Life's Romances Publ./Leader/Magazine Ent.: 1945; nn, 1946; No. 3, Feb-Mar, 1947 - No. 6, Aug-Sept, 1947

nn (#1)-14 pgs. Claire Voyant (cont'd. in other nn issue) movie photos, Dotty Dripple, Gertie O'Grady & Sissy; Van Johnson, Sinatra photo-c 47 94 141 296 498 700
nn (#2, 1946)-16 pgs. Claire Voyant & 16 pgs. movie photos
36 72 108 211 343 475
3-6: 4-Glenn Ford photo-c. 5-Perry Como-c 18 36 54 103 162 220

KELLYS, THE (Formerly Rusty Comics; Spy Cases No. 26 on)
Marvel Comics (HPC): No. 23, Jan, 1950 - No. 25, June, 1950 (52 pgs.)

23-Teenage 18 36 54 105 165 225
24,25: 24-Margie app. 14 28 42 76 108 140

KEN MAYNARD WESTERN (Movie star)(See Wow Comics, 1936)
Fawcett Publ.: Sept, 1950 - No. 8, Feb, 1952 (All 36 pgs; photo front/back-c)

1-Ken Maynard & his horse Tarzan begin 28 56 84 165 270 375
2 17 34 51 98 154 210
3-8: 6-Atomic bomb explosion panel 14 28 42 76 108 140

KENNEL BLOCK BLUES
BOOM! Studios: Feb, 2016 - No. 4, May, 2016 ($3.99, limited series)

1-4-Ryan Ferrier-s/Daniel Bayliss-a 4.00

KEN SHANNON (Becomes Gabby #11 on) (Also see Police Comics #103)
Quality Comics Group: Oct, 1951 - No. 10, Apr, 1953 (A private eye)

1-Crandall-a 47 94 141 296 498 700
2-Crandall c/a(2) 36 72 108 211 343 475
3-Horror-c; Crandall-a 40 80 120 246 411 575
4,5-Crandall-a 27 54 81 158 259 360
6-Crandall-c/a; "The Weird Vampire Mob"-c/s 42 84 126 265 445 625
7-"The Ugliest Man Alive"-c; Crandall-a 39 78 117 231 378 525
8,9: 8-Opium den drug use story 22 44 66 132 216 300
10-Crandall-c 23 46 69 136 223 310

NOTE: *Crandall/Cuidera c-1-10. Jack Cole a-1-9. #1-15 published after title change to Gabby.*

KEN STUART
Publication Enterprises: Jan, 1949 (Sea Adventures)

1-Frank Borth-c/a 12 24 36 67 94 120

KENT BLAKE OF THE SECRET SERVICE (Spy)
Marvel/Atlas Comics (20CC): May, 1951 - No. 14, July, 1953

1-Injury to eye, bondage, torture; Brodsky-c 28 56 84 165 270 375
2-Drug use w/hypo scenes; Brodsky-c 19 38 57 109 172 235
3-14: 8-R.Q. Sale-a (2 pgs.) 14 28 42 76 108 140

NOTE: *Heath c-5, 7, 8. Infantino c-12. Maneely c-3. Sinnott a-2(3). Tuska a-8(3pg.).*

KENTS, THE
DC Comics: Aug, 1997 - No. 12, July, 1998 ($2.50, limited series)

1-12-Ostrander-s/art by Truman and Bair (#1-8), Mandrake (#9-12) 3.00
TPB ($19.95) r/#1-12 20.00

KERRY DRAKE (Also see A-1 Comics)
Argo: Jan, 1956 - No. 2, March, 1956

1,2-Newspaper-r 8 16 24 44 57 70

KERRY DRAKE DETECTIVE CASES (...Racket Buster No. 32,33)
(Also see Chamber of Clues & Green Hornet Comics #42-47)
Life's Romances/Com/Magazine Ent. No.1-5/Harvey No.6 on: 1944 - No. 5, 1944; No. 6, Jan, 1948 - No. 33, Aug, 1952

nn(1944)(A-1 Comics)(slightly over-size) 32 64 96 190 310 430
2 20 40 60 114 182 250

Kevin Keller #1 © ACP

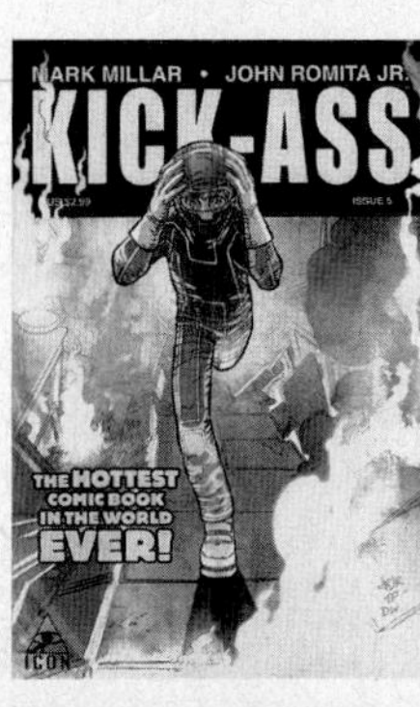

Kick-Ass #5 © Millar & Romita Jr.

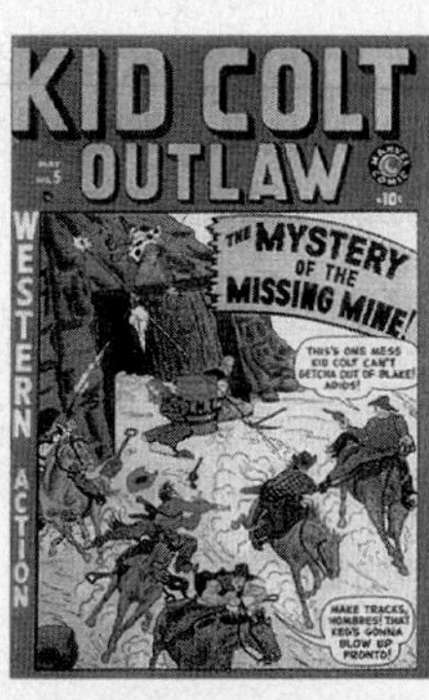

Kid Colt Outlaw #5 © MAR

	GD 2.0	VG 4.0	FN 6.0	VF 8.0	VF/NM 9.0	NM- 9.2
3-5(1944)	15	30	45	90	140	190
6,8(1948): Lady Crime by Powell. 8-Bondage-c	12	24	36	67	94	120
7-Kubert-a; biog of Andriola (artist)	13	26	39	74	105	135
9,10-Two-part marijuana story; Kerry smokes marijuana in #10	15	30	45	88	137	185
11-15	10	20	30	58	79	100
16-33	9	18	27	50	65	80

NOTE: *Andiola c-6-9.* ***Berg*** *a-5.* ***Powell*** *a-10-23, 28, 29.*

KEVIN KELLER (Also see Veronica #202 for 1st app. & #207-210 for first mini-series)
Archie Comics Publications: Apr, 2012 - No. 15, Nov, 2014 ($2.99)

	GD	VG	FN	VF	VF/NM	NM-
1-14-Two covers on each. 5-Action #1 swipe-c. 6-George Takei app.						3.00
15-($3.99) The Equalizer app.; 3 covers incl. Sensation #1 and X-Men #141 swipes						4.00

KEWPIES
Will Eisner Publications: Spring, 1949

	GD	VG	FN	VF	VF/NM	NM-
1-Feiffer-a; Kewpie Doll ad on back cover; used in **SOTI**, pg. 35	61	122	183	390	670	950

KEY COMICS
Consolidated Magazines: Jan, 1944 - No. 5, Aug, 1946

	GD	VG	FN	VF	VF/NM	NM-
1-The Key, Will-O-The-Wisp begin	52	104	156	328	552	775
2 (3/44)	28	56	84	165	270	375
3,4: 3 (Winter 45/46). 4-(5/46)-Origin John Quincy The Atom (begins); Walter Johnson c-3-5	24	48	72	142	234	325
5-4pg. Faust Opera adaptation; Kiefer-a; back-c advertises "Masterpieces Illustrated" by Lloyd Jacquet after he left Classic Comics (no copies of Masterpieces Illustrated known)	36	72	108	211	343	425

KEY OF Z
BOOM! Studios: Oct, 2011 - No. 4, Jan, 2012 ($3.99, limited series)

	GD	VG	FN	VF	VF/NM	NM-
1-4: 1-Claudio Sanchez & Chondra Echert-s/Aaron Kuder-a; covers by Fox & Moore						4.00

KEY RING COMICS
Dell Publishing Co.: 1941 (16 pgs.; two colors) (sold 5 for 10¢)

	GD	VG	FN	VF	VF/NM	NM-
1-Sky Hawk, 1-Features Sleepy Samson, 1-Origin Greg Gilday; r/War Comics #2	15	30	45	85	130	175
1-Radior (Super hero)	17	34	51	98	154	210
1-Viking Carter (WWII Nazi-c)	17	34	51	98	154	210

NOTE: *Each book has two holes in spine to put in binder.*

KICK-ASS
Marvel Comics (Icon): April, 2008 - No. 8, Mar, 2010 ($2.99)

	GD	VG	FN	VF	VF/NM	NM-
1-Mark Millar-s/John Romita Jr.-a/c						20.00
1-Red variant cover by McNiven						25.00
1-2nd printing						4.00
1-Director's Cut (8/08, $3.99) r/#1 with script and sketch pages; Millar afterword						5.00
2						8.00
3-8: 3-1st app. Hit-Girl. 5-Intro. Red Mist						4.00

NOTE: *Multiple printings exist for most issues.*

KICK-ASS
Image Comics: Feb, 2018 - Present ($3.99)

	GD	VG	FN	VF	VF/NM	NM-
1-Mark Millar-s/John Romita Jr.-a/c; intro. Patience Lee						4.00

KICK-ASS 2
Marvel Comics (Icon): Dec, 2010 - No. 7, May, 2012 ($2.99/$4.99)

	GD	VG	FN	VF	VF/NM	NM-
1-6-Mark Millar-s/John Romita Jr.-a/c. 1-Five printings						3.00
1-6-Variant covers. 1-Edwards. 2-Yu. 5-Photo & Hitch. 6-Photo-c						5.00
7-($4.99) Extra-sized finale; bonus preview of Secret Service #1						5.00
7-($4.99) Variant photo-c						7.00

KICK-ASS 3
Marvel Comics (Icon): Jul, 2013 - No. 8, Oct, 2014 ($2.99/$3.99/$4.99/$5.99)

	GD	VG	FN	VF	VF/NM	NM-
1-5-($2.99) Mark Millar-s/John Romita Jr.-a/c						3.00
1-5-Variant covers. 1-Hughes. 2-Fegredo. 3-Mack. 5-Bond						5.00
6-($4.99) Secret origin of Hit-Girl						5.00
7-($3.99)						4.00
8-($5.99)						6.00

KID CARROTS
St. John Publishing Co.: September, 1953

	GD	VG	FN	VF	VF/NM	NM-
1-Funny animal	10	20	30	56	76	95

KID COLT ONE-SHOT
Marvel Comics: Sept, 2009 ($3.99)

	GD	VG	FN	VF	VF/NM	NM-
1-DeFalco-s/Burchett-a/Luke Ross-c						4.00

KID COLT OUTLAW (Kid Colt #1-4; ...Outlaw #5-on)(Also see All Western Winners, Best Western, Black Rider, Giant-Size..., Two-Gun Kid, Two-Gun Western, Western Winners, Wild Western, Wisco)
Marvel Comics(LCC) 1-16; Atlas(LMC) 17-102; Marvel 103-on: 8/48 - No. 139, 3/68; No. 140, 11/69 - No. 229, 4/79

	GD	VG	FN	VF	VF/NM	NM-
1-Kid Colt & his horse Steel begin.	194	388	582	1242	2121	3000
2	84	168	252	538	919	1300
3-5: 4-Anti-Wertham editorial; Tex Taylor app. 5-Blaze Carson app.	61	122	183	390	670	950
6-8: 6-Tex Taylor app; 7-Nimo the Lion begins, ends #10	40	80	120	246	411	575
9,10 (52 pgs.)	40	80	120	246	411	575
11-Origin (10/50)	43	86	129	271	461	650
12-20	27	54	81	160	263	365
21-32	22	44	66	132	216	300
33-45: Black Rider in all	20	40	60	114	182	250
46,47,49,50	18	36	54	105	165	225
48-Kubert-a	19	38	57	109	172	235
51-53,55,56	16	32	48	94	147	200
54-Williamson/Maneely-c	17	34	51	98	154	210
57-60,66: 4-pg. Williamson-a in all	10	20	30	66	138	210
61-63,67-78,80-86: 70-Severin-c. 69,73-Maneely-c. 86-Kirby-a(r).	10	20	30	64	132	200
64,65-Crandall-a	10	20	30	66	138	210
79,87: 79-Origin retold. 87-Davis-a(r)	10	20	30	66	138	210
88,89-Williamson-a in both (4 pgs.). 89-Redrawn Matt Slade #2	10	20	30	66	138	210
90-99,101-106,108,109: 91-Kirby/Ayers-c. 95-Kirby/Ayers-c/story. 102-Last 10¢ issue	11	22	33	76	163	250
100	14	28	42	96	211	325
107-Only Kirby sci-fi cover of title	36	72	108	266	596	925
110-(5/63)-1st app. Iron Mask (Iron Man type villain)	14	28	42	96	211	325
111-113,115-120	8	16	24	56	108	160
114-(1/64)-2nd app. Iron Mask	10	20	30	66	138	210
121-129,133-139: 121-Rawhide Kid x-over. 125-Two-Gun Kid x-over. 139-Last 12¢ issue	5	10	15	35	63	90
130-132 (68 pgs.)-one new story each. 130-Origin	6	12	18	42	79	115
140-155: 140-Reprints begin (later issues mostly-r). 155-Last 15¢ issue	3	6	9	16	23	30
156-Giant; reprints (52 pgs.)	3	6	9	20	31	42
157-180,200: 170-Origin retold.	3	6	9	14	20	25
181-199	2	4	6	11	16	20
201-229: 201-New material w/Rawhide Kid app; Kane-c. 229-Rawhide Kid-r	2	4	6	10	14	18
205-209-(30¢-c variants, limited dist.)	10	20	30	64	132	200
218-220-(35¢-c variants, limited dist.)	19	38	57	131	291	450
...Album (no date; 1950's; Atlas Comics)-132 pgs.; cardboard cover, B&W stories; (Rare)	155	310	465	992	1696	2400

NOTE: ***Ayers*** *a-many.* ***Colan*** *a-52, 53, 84, 112, 114; c(p)-223, 228, 229.* ***Crandall*** *a-140r, 167r.* ***Everett*** *a-90, 137i, 225i(r).* ***Heath*** *a-8(2); c-34, 35, 39, 44, 46, 48, 49, 57, 64.* ***Heck*** *a-135, 139.* ***Jack Keller*** *a-25(2), 26-68(3-4), 73, 78, 84, 85, 88, 92, 94p, 98, 99, 101, 102, 106-108, 110-112, 114, 115, 117-127, 129, 130, 132, 140-150r.* ***Kirby*** *a-86r, 93, 96, 119, 176(part); c-87, 92-95, 97, 99-112, 114-117, 121-123, 197r; w/****Ditko*** *c-89.* ***Maneely*** *a-12, 68, 81; c-9, 17, 19, 40-43, 47, 52, 53, 62, 65, 68, 73, 78, 81, 142r, 150r.* ***Morrow*** *a-173r, 216r.* ***Rico*** *a-13, 18.* ***Severin*** *c-55, 58, 59, 84, 143, 148, 149i.* ***Shores*** *a-39, 41-43, 143r; c-1-10(most), 24.* ***Sutton*** *a-136, 137p, 225p(r).* ***Wildey*** *a-47, 54, 82, 144r.* ***Williamson*** *r-147, 170, 172, 216.* ***Woodbridge*** *a-64, 81. Black Rider in #33-45, 74, 86. Iron Mask in #110, 114, 121, 127. Sam Hawk in #80, 84, 101, 111, 121, 146, 174, 181, 188.*

KID COWBOY (Also see Approved Comics #4 & Boy Cowboy)
Ziff-Davis Publ./St. John (Approved Comics) #11,14: 1950 - No. 11, Wint, '52-'53; No. 13, April 1953; No. 14, June, 1954 (No #12) (Painted covers #1-10,13,14)

	GD	VG	FN	VF	VF/NM	NM-
1-Lucy Belle & Red Feather begin	20	40	60	117	189	260
2-Maneely-c	14	28	42	78	112	145
3-11,13,14: (#3, spr. '51). 5-Berg-a. 14-Code approved	13	26	39	72	101	130

KID DEATH & FLUFFY HALLOWEEN SPECIAL
Event Comics: Oct, 1997 ($2.95, B&W, one-shot)

	GD	VG	FN	VF	VF/NM	NM-
1-Variant-c by Cebollero & Quesada/Palmiotti						3.00

KID DEATH & FLUFFY SPRING BREAK SPECIAL
Event Comics: July, 1996 ($2.50, B&W, one-shot)

	GD	VG	FN	VF	VF/NM	NM-
1-Quesada & Palmiotti-c/scripts						3.00

KIDDIE KAPERS
Kiddie Kapers Co., 1945/Decker Publ. (Red Top-Farrell): 1945?(nd); Oct, 1957; 1963 - 1964

	GD	VG	FN	VF	VF/NM	NM-
1(nd, 1945-46?, 36 pgs.)-Infinity-c; funny animal	11	22	33	60	83	105
1(10/57)(Decker)-Little Bit-r from Kiddie Karnival	5	10	15	22	26	30

Kid Eternity #7 © DC

Kid Komics #8 © MAR

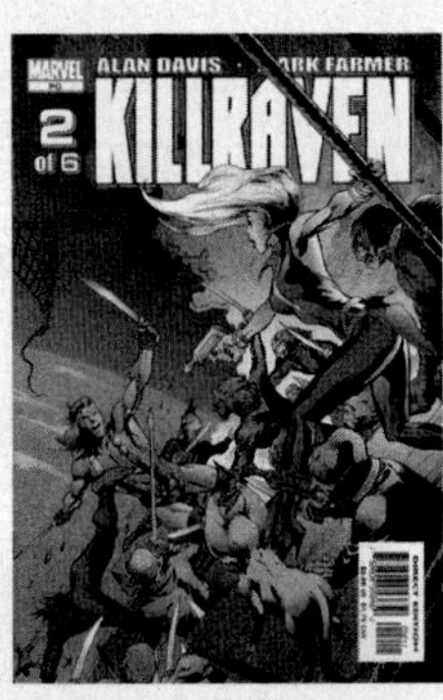

Killraven (2002 series) #2 © MAR

	GD 2.0	VG 4.0	FN 6.0	VF 8.0	VF/NM 9.0	NM- 9.2

Super Reprint #7, 10('63), 12, 14('63), 15,17('64), 18('64): 10, 14-r/Animal Adventures #1.
15-Animal Advs. #? 17-Cowboys 'N' Injuns #? 2 4 6 8 11 14

KIDDIE KARNIVAL
Ziff-Davis Publ. Co. (Approved Comics): 1952 (25¢, 100 pgs.) (One Shot)

nn-Rebound Little Bit #1,2; painted-c 36 72 108 216 351 485

KID ETERNITY (Becomes Buccaneers) (See Hit Comics)
Quality Comics Group: Spring, 1946 - No. 18, Nov, 1949

1 90 180 270 576 988 1400
2 39 78 117 240 395 550
3-Mac Raboy-a 40 80 120 246 411 575
4-10 25 50 75 147 241 335
11-18 19 38 57 112 179 245

KID ETERNITY
DC Comics: 1991 - No. 3, Nov, 1991 ($4.95, limited series)

1-3: Grant Morrison scripts/Duncan Fegredo-a/c 6.00
TPB (2006, $14.99) r/#1-3 15.00

KID ETERNITY
DC Comics (Vertigo): May, 1993 - No. 16, Sept, 1994 ($1.95, mature)

1-16: 1-Gold ink-c. 6-Photo-c. All Sean Phillips-c/a except #15 (Phillips-c/i only) 3.00

KID FROM DODGE CITY, THE
Atlas Comics (MMC): July, 1957 - No. 2, Sept, 1957

1-Don Heck-c 14 28 42 82 121 160
2-Everett-c 11 22 33 60 83 105

KID FROM TEXAS, THE (A Texas Ranger)
Atlas Comics (CSI): June, 1957 - No. 2, Aug, 1957

1-Powell-a; Severin-c 14 28 42 78 112 145
2 9 18 27 52 69 85

KID KOKO
I. W. Enterprises: 1958

Reprint #1,2-(r/M.E.'s Koko & Kola #4, 1947) 2 4 6 8 11 14

KID KOMICS (Kid Movie Komics No. 11)
Timely Comics (USA 1,2/FCI 3-10): Feb, 1943 - No. 10, Spring, 1946

1-Origin Captain Wonder & sidekick Tim Mullrooney, & Subbie; intro the Sea-Going Lad, Pinto Pete, & Trixie Trouble; Knuckles & Whitewash Jones (from Young Allies) app.; Wolverton-a (7 pgs.) 595 1190 1785 4350 7925 11,500
2-The Young Allies, Red Hawk, & Tommy Tyme begin; last Captain Wonder & Subbie; Schomburg Japanese WWII bondage-c 290 580 870 1856 3178 4500
3-The Vision, Daredevils & Red Hawk app. 194 388 582 1242 2121 3000
4-The Destroyer begins; Sub-Mariner app.; Red Hawk & Tommy Tyme end; classic Schomburg WWII human meat grinder-c 258 516 774 1651 2826 4000
5,6: 5-Tommy Tyme begins, ends #10 123 246 369 787 1344 1900
7-10: 7,10-The Whizzer app. Destroyer not in #7,8. 10-Last Destroyer, Young Allies & Whizzer 107 214 321 680 1165 1650

NOTE: ***Brodsky** c-5. **Schomburg** c-2-4, 6-10. **Shores** c-1. Captain Wonder c-1, 2. The Young Allies c-3-10.*

KID LOBOTOMY
IDW Publishing (Black Crown): Oct, 2017 - Present ($3.99)

1-5: 1-Milligan-s/Fowler-a; covers by Fowler & Quitely 4.00

KID MONTANA (Formerly Davy Crockett Frontier Fighter; The Gunfighters No. 51 on)
Charlton Comics: V2#9, Nov, 1957 - No. 50, Mar, 1965

V2#9 (#1) 4 8 12 27 44 60
10 3 6 9 19 30 40
11,12,14-20 3 6 9 15 22 28
13-Williamson-a 3 6 9 19 30 40
21-35: 25,31-Giordano-c. 32-Origin Kid Montana. 34-Geronimo-c/s. 35-Snow Monster-c/s 2 4 6 11 16 20
36-50: 36-Dinosaur-c/s. 37,48-Giordano-c 2 4 6 9 12 15

NOTE: *Title change to Montana Kid on cover only #44 & 45; remained Kid Montana on inside. **Chasal** a-29,30. **Giordano** c-25,31,37,48. **Giordano/Alascia** c-12. **Mastroserio** a-9,11,13,14,22; c-11,14. **Masulli/Mastroserio** c-13. **Montes/Bache** c-42. **Morisi** c-16,32-34,36?,40,41,44,46; a-13,15;16,31-50. **Nicholas/Alascia** a-44,48.*

KID MOVIE KOMICS (Formerly Kid Komics; Rusty Comics #12 on)
Timely Comics: No. 11, Summer, 1946

11-Silly Seal & Ziggy Pig; 2 pgs. Kurtzman "Hey Look" plus 6 pg. "Pigtales" story 31 62 93 184 300 415

KIDNAPPED (See Marvel Illustrated: Kidnapped)

KIDNAPPED (Robert Louis Stevenson's...also see Movie Comics)(Disney)
Dell Publishing Co.: No. 1101, May, 1960

Four Color 1101-Movie, photo-c 6 12 18 37 66 95

KIDNAP RACKET (See Harvey Comics Hits No. 57)

KID SLADE, GUNFIGHTER (Formerly Matt Slade...)
Atlas Comics (SPI): No. 5, Jan, 1957 - No. 8, July, 1957

5-Maneely, Roth, Severin-a in all; Maneely-c 14 28 42 82 121 160
6,8-Severin-c 10 20 30 56 76 95
7-Williamson/Mayo-a, 4 pgs.; Maneely-c 12 24 36 67 94 120

KID SUPREME (See Supreme)
Image Comics (Extreme Studios): Mar, 1996 - No. 3, July, 1996 ($2.50)

1-3: Fraga-a/scripts. 3-Glory-c/app. 3.00

KID TERRIFIC
Image Comics: Nov, 1998 ($2.95, B&W)

1-Snyder & Diliberto-s/a 3.00

KID ZOO COMICS
Street & Smith Publications: July, 1948 (52 pgs.)

1-Funny Animal 32 64 96 188 307 425

KILL ALL PARENTS
Image Comics: June, 2008 ($3.99, one-shot)

1-Marcelo Di Chiara-a/Mark Andrew Smith-s 4.00

KILLAPALOOZA
DC Comics (WildStorm): July, 2009 - No. 6, Dec, 2009 ($2.99, limited series)

1-6: 1-Beechen-s/Hairsine-a/c 3.00
TPB (2010, $19.99) r/#1-6 20.00

KILLER (...Tales By Timothy Truman)
Eclipse Comics: March, 1985 ($1.75, one-shot, Baxter paper)

1-Timothy Truman-c/a 3.00

KILLER INSTINCT (Video game)
Acclaim Comics: June, 1996 - No. 6 ($2.50, limited series)

1-6: 1-Bart Sears-a(p). 4-Special #1. 5-Special #2. 6-Special #3 3.00

KILLER INSTINCT (Video game)
Dynamite Entertainment: 2017 - No. 6, 2018 ($3.99, limited series)

1-5: 1,2-Ian Edginton-s/Cam Adams-a; multiple covers. 3-5-Ediano Silva-a 4.00

KILLERS, THE
Magazine Enterprises: 1947 - No. 2, 1948 (No month)

1-Mr. Zin, the Hatchet Killer; mentioned in **SOTI**, pgs. 179,180; used by N.Y. Legis. Comm.; L. B. Cole-c 148 296 444 947 1624 2300
2-(Scarce)-Hashish smoking story; "Dying, Dying, Dead" drug story; Whitney, Ingels-a; Whitney hanging-c 123 246 369 787 1344 1900

KILLING GIRL
Image Comics: Aug, 2007 - No. 5, Dec, 2007 ($2.99, limited series)

1-5: 1-Frank Espinosa-a/Glen Brunswick-s; covers by Espinosa and Frank Cho 3.00

KILLING JOKE, THE (See Batman: The Killing Joke under Batman one-shots)

KILL OR BE KILLED
Image Comics: Aug, 2016 - Present ($3.99)

1-15-Ed Brubaker-s/Sean Phillips-a 4.00

KILLPOWER: THE EARLY YEARS
Marvel Comics UK: Sept, 1993 - No. 4, Dec, 1993 ($1.75, mini-series)

1-($2.95)-Foil embossed-c 4.00
2-4: 2-Genetix app. 3-Punisher app. 3.00

KILLRAVEN (See Amazing Adventures #18 (5/73))
Marvel Comics: Feb, 2001 ($2.99, one-shot)

1-Linsner-s/a/c 3.00

KILLRAVEN
Marvel Comics: Dec, 2002 - No. 6, May, 2003 ($2.99, limited series)

1-6-Alan Davis-s/a(p)/Mark Farmer-i 3.00
HC (2007, $19.99) r/#1-6; cover gallery, pencil art; foreward by Alan Davis 20.00

KILLRAZOR
Image Comics (Top Cow Productions): Aug, 1995 ($2.50, one-shot)

1 3.00

KILL YOUR BOYFRIEND
DC Comics (Vertigo): June, 1995 ($4.95, one-shot)

1-Grant Morrison story 6.00
1 ($5.95, 1998) 2nd printing 6.00

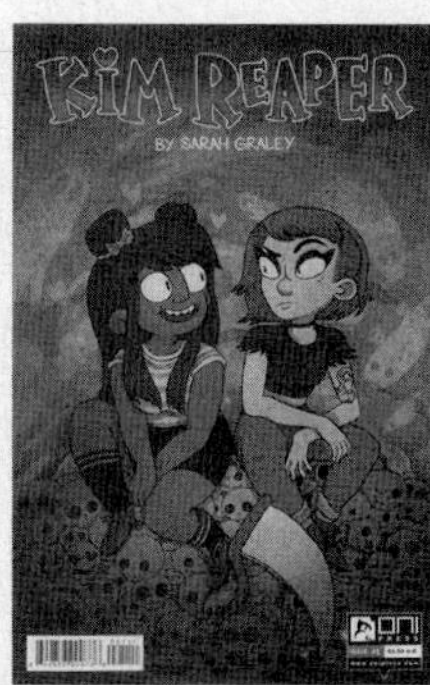

Kim Reaper #1 © Sarah Graley

King Comics #39 © KFS

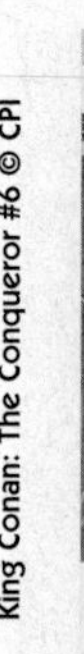
King Conan: The Conqueror #6 © CPI

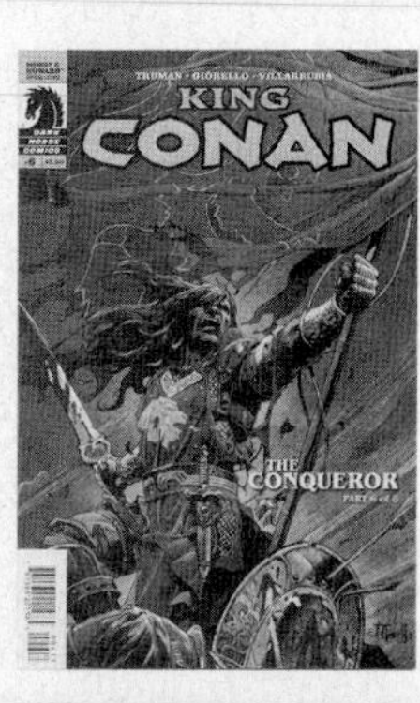

	GD 2.0	VG 4.0	FN 6.0	VF 8.0	VF/NM 9.0	NM- 9.2

KILROY (Volume 2)
Caliber Press: 1998 ($2.95, B&W)

1-Pruett-s 3.00

KILROY IS HERE
Caliber Press: 1995 ($2.95, B&W)

1-10 3.00

KILROYS, THE
B&I Publ. Co. No. 1-19/American Comics Group: June-July, 1947 - No. 54, June-July, 1955

	GD	VG	FN	VF	VF/NM	NM-
1	27	54	81	158	259	360
2	15	30	45	85	130	175
3-5: 5-Gross-a	14	28	42	80	115	150
6-10: 8-Milt Gross's Moronica (1st app.)	11	22	33	62	86	110
11-20: 14-Gross-a	10	20	30	56	76	95
21-30	9	18	27	52	69	85
31-47,50-54	9	18	27	47	61	75
48,49-(3-D effect-c/stories)	18	36	54	105	165	225

KILROY: THE SHORT STORIES
Caliber Press: 1995 ($2.95, B&W)

1 3.00

KIM REAPER
Oni Press: Apr, 2017 - No. 4, Jul, 2017 ($3.99, limited series)

1-4-Sarah Graley-s/a/c 4.00

KIN
Image Comics (Top Cow): Mar, 2000 - No. 6, Sept, 2000 ($2.95)

1-5-Gary Frank-s/c/a 3.00
1-($6.95) DF Alternate footprint cover 7.00
6-($3.95) 4.00
... Descent of Man TPB (2002, $19.95) r/ #1-6 20.00

KINDRED, THE
Image Comics (WildStorm Productions): Mar, 1994 - No. 4, July, 1995 ($1.95, lim. series)

1-($2.50)-Grifter & Backlash app. in all; bound-in trading card 4.00
2-4 3.00
2,3: 2-Variant-c. 3-Alternate-c by Portacio, see Deathblow #5 4.00
Trade paperback (2/95, $9.95) 10.00
NOTE: *Booth c/a-1-4. The first four issues contain coupons redeemable for a Jim Lee Grifter/Backlash print.*

KINDRED II, THE
DC Comics (WildStorm): Mar, 2002 - No. 4, June, 2002 ($2.50, limited series)

1-4-Booth-s/Booth & Regla-a 3.00

KINETIC
DC Comics (Focus): May, 2004 - No. 8, Dec, 2004 ($2.50)

1-8-Puckett-s/Pleece-a/c 3.00
TPB (2005, $9.99) r/#1-8; cover gallery and sketch pages 10.00

KING (Magazine)
Skywald Publ.: Mar, 1971 - No. 2, July, 1971

	GD	VG	FN	VF	VF/NM	NM-
1-Violence; semi-nudity; Boris Vallejo-a (2 pgs.)	5	10	15	31	53	75
2-Photo-c	3	6	9	21	33	45

KING ARTHUR AND THE KNIGHTS OF JUSTICE
Marvel Comics UK: Dec, 1993 - No. 3, Feb, 1994 ($1.25, limited series)

1-3: TV adaptation 3.00

KING CLASSICS
King Features : 1977 (36 pgs., cardboard-c) (Printed in Spain for U.S. distr.)

1-Connecticut Yankee, 2-Last of the Mohicans, 3-Moby Dick, 4-Robin Hood, 5-Swiss Family Robinson, 6-Robinson Crusoe, 7-Treasure Island, 8-20,000 Leagues, 9-Christmas Carol, 10-Huck Finn, 11-Around the World in 80 Days, 12-Davy Crockett, 13-Don Quixote, 14-Gold Bug, 15-Ivanhoe, 16-Three Musketeers, 17-Baron Munchausen, 18-Alice in Wonderland, 19-Black Arrow, 20-Five Weeks in a Balloon, 21-Great Expectations, 22-Gulliver's Travels, 23-Prince & Pauper, 24-Lawrence of Arabia (Originals, 1977-78)

	GD	VG	FN	VF	VF/NM	NM-
each....	2	4	6	10	14	18
Reprints (1979; HRN-24)	2	4	6	8	10	12

NOTE: *The first eight issues were not numbered. Issues No. 25-32 were advertised but not published. The 1977 originals have HRN 32a; the 1978 originals have HRN 32b.*

KING COLT (See Luke Short's Western Stories)

KING COMICS (Strip reprints)
David McKay Publications/Standard #156-on: 4/36 - No. 155, 11-12/49; No. 156, Spr/50 - No. 159, 2/52 (Winter on-c)

	GD	VG	FN	VF	VF/NM	NM-
1-1st app. Flash Gordon by Alex Raymond; Brick Bradford (1st app.), Popeye, Henry (1st app.) & Mandrake the Magician (1st app.) begin; Popeye-c begin	1450	2900	4350	11,600	-	-
2	360	720	1080	1980	2990	4000
3	245	490	735	1348	2074	2800
4	190	380	570	1045	1623	2200
5	140	280	420	770	1185	1600
6-10: 9-X-Mas-c	95	190	285	523	812	1100
11-20	75	150	225	413	619	825
21-30: 21-X-Mas-c	55	110	165	303	464	625
31-40: 33-Last Segar Popeye	45	90	135	248	399	550
41-50: 46-Text illos by Marge Buell contain characters similar to Lulu, Alvin & Tubby. 50-The Lone Ranger begins	36	72	108	211	343	475
51-60: 52-Barney Baxter begins?	34	68	102	199	325	450
61-The Phantom begins	34	68	102	204	332	460
62-80: 76-Flag-c. 79-Blondie begins	20	40	60	114	182	250
81-99	15	30	45	85	130	175
100	18	36	54	103	162	220
101-114: 114-Last Raymond issue (1 pg.); Flash Gordon by Austin Briggs begins, ends #155	14	28	42	76	108	140
115-145: 117-Phantom origin retold	10	20	30	56	76	95
146,147-Prince Valiant in both	9	18	27	50	65	80
148-155: 155-Flash Gordon ends (11-12/49)	9	18	27	50	65	80
156-159: 156-New logo begins (Standard)	9	18	27	47	61	75

NOTE: *Marge Buell text illos in No. 24-46 at least.*

KING CONAN (Conan The King No. 20 on)
Marvel Comics Group: Mar, 1980 - No. 19, Nov, 1983 (52 pgs.)

	GD	VG	FN	VF	VF/NM	NM-
1	2	4	6	10	14	18

2-19: 4-Death of Thoth Amon. 7-1st Paul Smith-a, 1 pg. pin-up (9/81) 5.00
NOTE: ***J. Buscema** a-1-9p, 17p; c(p)-1-5, 7-9, 14, 17. **Kaluta** c-19. **Nebres** a-17i, 18, 19i. **Severin** c-18. **Simonson** c-6.*

KING CONAN: THE CONQUEROR
Dark Horse Comics: Feb, 2014 - No. 6, Jul, 2014 ($3.50, limited series)

1-6-Truman-s/Giorello-a/c 3.50

KING CONAN: THE HOUR OF THE DRAGON
Dark Horse Comics: May, 2013 - No. 6, Oct, 2013 ($3.50, limited series)

1-6-Truman-s/Giorello-a/Parel-c 3.50

KING CONAN: THE PHOENIX ON THE SWORD
Dark Horse Comics: Jan, 2012 - No. 4, Apr, 2012 ($3.50, limited series)

1-4-Truman-s/Giorello-a/Robinson-c. 1-Variant-c by Parel 3.50

KING CONAN: THE SCARLET CITADEL
Dark Horse Comics: Feb, 2011 - No. 4, May, 2011 ($3.50, limited series)

1-4-Truman-s/Giorello-a/Robertson-c. 1-Variant-c by Parel 3.50

KING CONAN: WOLVES BEYOND THE BORDER
Dark Horse Comics: Dec, 2015 - No. 4, Mar, 2016 ($3.99, limited series)

1-4-Truman-s/Giorello-a/c. 1-Kull app. 4-Bran Mak Morn app. 4.00

KING DAVID
DC Comics (Vertigo): 2002 ($19.95, 8 1/2" x 11")

nn-Story of King David; Kyle Baker-s/a 20.00

KINGDOM, THE
DC Comics: Feb, 1999 - No. 2, Feb, 1999 ($2.95/$1.99, limited series)

1,2-Waid-s; sequel to Kingdom Come; introduces Hypertime 4.00
...: Kid Flash 1 (2/99, $1.99) Waid-s/Pararillo-a, ...: Nightstar 1 (2/99, $1.99) Waid-s/Haley-a, ...: Offspring 1 (2/99, $1.99) Waid-s/Quitely-a, ...: Planet Krypton 1 (2/99, $1.99) Waid-s/Kitson-a, ...: Son of the Bat 1 (2/99, $1.99) Waid-s/Apthorp-a 3.00

KINGDOM COME (Also see Justice Society of America #9-22)
DC Comics: 1996 - No. 4, 1996 ($4.95, painted limited series)

	GD	VG	FN	VF	VF/NM	NM-
1-Mark Waid scripts & Alex Ross-painted c/a in all; tells the last days of the DC Universe; 1st app. Magog	2	4	6	8	10	12
2-Superman forms new Justice League	1	2	3	5	6	8
3-Return of Captain Marvel	1	2	3	5	6	8
4-Final battle of Superman and Captain Marvel	1	3	4	6	8	10

Deluxe Slipcase Edition-($89.95) w/Revelations companion book, 12 new story pages, foil stamped covers, signed and numbered 120.00
Hardcover Edition-($29.95)-Includes 12 new story pages and artwork from Revelations, new cover artwork with gold foil inlay 40.00
Hardcover 2nd printing 30.00
Softcover Ed.-($14.95)-Includes 12 new story pgs. & artwork from Revelations, new c-artwork 20.00
Softcover Ed.-(2008, $17.99)-New wraparound gatefold cover by Ross 18.00

KING: FLASH GORDON
Dynamite Entertainment: 2015 - No. 4, 2015 ($3.99)

King of the Royal Mounted #8 © DELL

Kingpin (2017 series) #4 © MAR

King's Road #1 © Hogan & Winslade

	GD 2.0	VG 4.0	FN 6.0	VF 8.0	VF/NM 9.0	NM- 9.2

1-4: 1-Acker & Blacker-s/Ferguson-a/Cooke-c; variant-c by Liefeld. 2-Zdarsky-c 4.00

KING: JUNGLE JIM
Dynamite Entertainment: 2015 - No. 4, 2015 ($3.99)

1-4: 1-Tobin-s/Jarrell-a/Cooke-c; variant-c by Liefeld. 2-Zdarsky-c 4.00

KING KONG (See Movie Comics)

KING KONG: THE 8TH WONDER OF THE WORLD (Adaptation of 2005 movie)
Dark Horse Comics: Dec, 2005 ($3.99, planned limited series completed in TPB)

1-Photo-c; Dustin Weaver-a/Christian Gossett-s 4.00
TPB (11/06, $12.95) r/#1 and unpublished parts 2&3; photo-c; Dorman paintings 13.00

KING LEONARDO & HIS SHORT SUBJECTS (TV)
Dell Publishing Co./Gold Key: Nov-Jan, 1961-62 - No. 4, Sept, 1963

	GD	VG	FN	VF	VF/NM	NM-
Four Color 1242,1278	10	20	30	67	141	215
01390-207(5-7/62)(Dell)	8	16	24	52	99	145
1 (10/62)	9	18	27	60	120	180
2-4	7	14	21	48	89	130

KING LOUIE & MOWGLI (See Jungle Book under Movie Comics)
Gold Key: May, 1968 (Disney)

	GD	VG	FN	VF	VF/NM	NM-
1 (#10223-805)-Characters from Jungle Book	3	6	9	19	30	40

KING: MANDRAKE THE MAGICIAN
Dynamite Entertainment: 2015 - No. 4, 2015 ($3.99)

1-4: 1-Langridge-s/Treece-a/Cooke-c; variant-c by Liefeld. 2-Zdarsky-c 4.00

KING OF DIAMONDS (TV)
Dell Publishing Co.: July-Sept, 1962

	GD	VG	FN	VF	VF/NM	NM-
01-391-209-Photo-c	4	8	12	25	40	55

KING OF KINGS (Movie)
Dell Publishing Co.: No. 1236, Oct-Nov, 1961

	GD	VG	FN	VF	VF/NM	NM-
Four Color 1236-Photo-c	7	14	21	46	86	125

KING OF THE BAD MEN OF DEADWOOD
Avon Periodicals: 1950 (See Wild Bill Hickok #16)

	GD	VG	FN	VF	VF/NM	NM-
nn-Kinstler-c; Kamen/Feldstein-r/Cowpuncher #2	20	40	60	114	182	250

KING OF THE ROYAL MOUNTED (See Famous Feature Stories, King Comics, Red Ryder #3 & Super Book #2, 6)

KING OF THE ROYAL MOUNTED (Zane Grey's...)
David McKay/Dell Publishing Co.: No. 1, May, 1937; No. 9, 1940; No. 207, Dec, 1948 - No. 935, Sept-Nov, 1958

	GD	VG	FN	VF	VF/NM	NM-
Feature Books 1 (5/37)(McKay)	110	220	330	704	1202	1700
Large Feature Comic 9 (1940)	53	106	159	334	567	800
Four Color 207(#1, 12/48)	13	26	39	86	188	290
Four Color 265,283	9	18	27	58	114	170
Four Color 310,340	7	14	21	46	86	125
Four Color 363,384, 8(6-8/52)-10	6	12	18	40	73	105
11-20	5	10	15	31	53	75
21-28(3-5/58)	4	8	12	27	44	60
Four Color 935(9-11/58)	5	10	15	31	53	75

NOTE: *4-Color No. 207, 265, 283, 310, 340, 363, 384 are all newspaper reprints with **Jim Gary** art. No. 8 on are all Dell originals. Painted c-No. 9-on.*

KINGPIN
Marvel Comics: Nov, 1997 ($5.99, squarebound, one-shot)

nn-Spider-Man & Daredevil vs. Kingpin; Stan Lee-s/ John Romita Sr.-a 6.00

KINGPIN
Marvel Comics: Aug, 2003 - No. 7, Jan, 2004 ($2.50/$2.99, limited series)

1-6-Bruce Jones-s/Sean Phillips & Klaus Janson-a 3.00
7-($2.99) 3.00

KINGPIN
Marvel Comics: Apr, 2017 - No. 5, Aug, 2017 ($3.99, limited series)

1-Wilson Fisk goes legit; Matthew Rosenberg-s/Ben Torres-a. 2-5-Tombstone app. 4.00

KING: PRINCE VALIANT
Dynamite Entertainment: 2015 - No. 4, 2015 ($3.99)

1-4: 1-Cosby-s/Salasl-a/Cooke-c; variant-c by Liefeld. 2-Zdarsky-c 4.00

KING RICHARD & THE CRUSADERS
Dell Publishing Co.: No. 588, Oct, 1954

	GD	VG	FN	VF	VF/NM	NM-
Four Color 588-Movie, Matt Baker-a, photo-c	9	18	27	58	114	170

KING-SIZE CABLE SPECTACULAR (Takes place between Cable (2008 series) #6 & #7)
Marvel Comics: Nov, 2008 ($4.99, one-shot)

1-Lashley-a; Deadpool #1 preview; cover gallery of variants from 2008 series 5.00

KING-SIZE HULK (Takes place between Hulk (2008 series) #3 & #4)
Marvel Comics: July, 2008 ($4.99, one-shot)

1-Art Adams, Frank Cho, & Herb Trimpe-a; double-c by Cho & Adams; Red Hulk, She-Hulk & Wendigo app.; origin Abomination; r/Incr. Hulk #180,181 & Avengers #83 5.00

KING-SIZE SPIDER-MAN SUMMER SPECIAL
Marvel Comics: Oct, 2008 ($4.99, one-shot)

1-Short stories by various; Falcon app.; Burchett, Giarrusso & Coover-a 5.00

KINGSMEN: THE RED DIAMOND (Sequel to Secret Service)(Inspired Kingsmen movies)
Image Comics: Sept, 2017 - No. 6, Feb, 2018 ($3.99, limited series)

1-6-Rob Willliams-s/Simon Fraser-a. 1-Multiple covers 4.00

KINGS OF THE NIGHT
Dark Horse Comics: 1990 - No. 2, 1990 ($2.25, limited series)

1,2-Robert E. Howard adaptation; Bolton-c 3.00

KING SOLOMON'S MINES (Movie)
Avon Periodicals: 1951

	GD	VG	FN	VF	VF/NM	NM-
nn (#1 on 1st page)	45	90	135	284	480	675

KINGS QUEST
Dynamite Entertainment: 2016 - No. 5, 2016 ($3.99, limited series)

1-5-Flash Gordon, Mandrake, Prince Valiant, The Phantom team; multiple-c on each 4.00

KING'S ROAD
Dark Horse Comics: Feb, 2016 - No. 3, Apr, 2016 ($3.99, limited series)

1-3-Peter Hogan-s/Phil Winslade & Staz Johnson-a; Johnson-c 4.00

KINGS WATCH
Dynamite Entertainment: 2013 - No. 5, 2014 ($3.99)

1-5-Flash Gordon, Mandrake and The Phantom team up; Parker-s/Laming-a 4.00

KINGSWAY WEST
Dark Horse Comics: Aug, 2016 - No. 4, Feb, 2017 ($3.99)

1-4-Greg Pak-s/Mirko Colak-a/c 4.00

KING: THE PHANTOM
Dynamite Entertainment: 2015 - No. 4, 2015 ($3.99)

1-4: 1-Clevinger-s/Schoonover-a/Cooke-c; var-c by Liefeld; Mandrake app. 2-Zdarsky-c 4.00

KING TIGER
Dark Horse Comics: Aug, 2015 - No. 4, Nov, 2015 ($3.99, limited series)

1-4-Randy Stradley-s/Doug Wheatley-a/c 4.00

KIPLING, RUDYARD (See Mowgli, The Jungle Book)

KIRBY: GENESIS
Dynamite Entertainment: No. 0, 2011 - No. 8, 2012 ($1.00/$3.99)

0-($1.00) Busiek-s; art by Alex Ross & Jack Herbert; series preview, sketch-a 3.00
1-8-($3.99) Ross & Herbert-a. 1-Seven covers. 2-8-Covers by Ross & Sook 4.00

KIRBY: GENESIS - CAPTAIN VICTORY
Dynamite Entertainment: 2011 - No. 6, 2012 ($3.99)

1-6: 1-Origin retold; four covers; Sterling Gates-s/Wagner Reis-a 4.00

KIRBY: GENESIS - DRAGONSBANE
Dynamite Entertainment: 2012 - No. 4, 2013 ($3.99, unfinished limited series)

1-4-Rodi & Ross-s/Casas-a; covers by Ross and Herbert 4.00

KIRBY: GENESIS - SILVER STAR
Dynamite Entertainment: 2011 - No. 6, 2012 ($3.99)

1-6-Jai Nitz-s/Johnny Desjardins-a. 1-Four covers. 2-6-Three covers 4.00

KISS (See Crazy Magazine, Howard the Duck #12, 13, Marvel Comics Super Special #1, 5, Rock Fantasy Comics #10 & Rock N' Roll Comics #9)

KISS
Dark Horse Comics: June, 2002 - No. 13, Sept, 2003 ($2.99, limited series)

1-Photo-c and J. Scott Campbell-c; Casey-s 5.00
2-13: 2-Photo-c and J. Scott Campbell-c. 3-Photo-c and Leinil Yu-c 4.00
...: Men and Monsters TPB (9/03, $12.95) r/#7-10 13.00
...: Rediscovery TPB (2003, $9.95) r/#1-3 10.00
...: Return of the Phantom TPB (2003, $9.95) r/#4-6 10.00
...: Unholy War TPB (2004, $9.95) r/#11-13 10.00

KISS
IDW Publishing: June, 2012 - No. 8, Jan, 2013 ($3.99)

1-8-Multiple covers on each. 1,2-Ryall-s/Igle-a 4.00

KISS (2016 series) #3 © KISS Catalog

Kit Carson #7 © AVON

Klaws of the Panther #1 © MAR

	GD 2.0	VG 4.0	FN 6.0	VF 8.0	VF/NM 9.0	NM- 9.2

KISS (Volume 1)
Dynamite Entertainment: 2016 - No. 10, 2017 ($3.99)

1-10-Amy Chu-s/Kewber Baal-a; multiple covers 4.00
...: Forever (2017, $7.99, squarebound) Burnham-s/Daniel HDR-a/Cinar-c 8.00
...: The Demon 1-4 (2017, $3.99) prequel to 2016 series; Chu & Burnham-s/Casallos-a 4.00

KISS 4K
Platinum Studios Comics: May, 2007 - No. 6, Apr, 2008 ($3.99/$2.99)

1-Sprague-s/Crossley & Campos-a/Migliari-c 4.00
1-B&W sketch-c 6.00
1-Destroyer Edition ($50.00, 30"x18", edition of 5000) 50.00
2-6-($2.99) 3.00
KISSMAS (12/07, $4.99) Christmas-themed issue; re-cap of issues #1-4 5.00

KISSING CHAOS
Oni Press: Sept, 2001 - No. 8, Mar, 2002 ($2.25, B&W, 6" x 9", limited series)

1-8-Arthur Dela Cruz-s/a 3.00
...: Nine Lives (12/03, $2.99, regular comic-sized) 3.00
...: 1000 Words (7/03, $2.99, regular comic-sized) 3.00
TPB (9/02, $17.95) r/#1-8 18.00

KISSING CHAOS: NONSTOP BEAUTY
Oni Press: Oct, 2002 - No. 4, March, 2003 ($2.95, B&W, 6" x 9", limited series)

1-4-Arthur Dela Cruz-s/a 3.00
TPB (9/03, $11.95) r/#1-4 12.00

KISS KIDS
IDW Publishing: Aug, 2013 - No. 4, Nov, 2013 ($3.99, limited series)

1-4-Short stories of KISS members as grade-school kids; Ryall & Waltz-s 4.00

KISS KISS BANG BANG
CrossGen Comics: Feb, 2004 - No. 5, Jun, 2004 ($2.95)

1-5-Bedard-s/Perkins-a 3.00

KISS ME, SATAN
Dark Horse Comics: Sept, 2013 - No. 5, Jan, 2014 ($3.99, limited series)

1-5-Gischler-s/Ferreyra-a; Dave Johnson-c 4.00

KISS SOLO
IDW Publishing: Mar, 2013 - No. 4, Jun, 2013 ($3.99, limited series)

1-4-Multiple covers on each. 1-Ryall-s/Medina-a. 2-Waltz-s/Rodriguez-a 4.00

KISS THE ARMY OF DARKNESS
Dynamite Entertainment: 2018 - Present ($3.99)

1-Bowers & Sims-s/Coleman-a; multiple covers; KISS meets Ash 4.00

KISS: THE PSYCHO CIRCUS
Image Comics: Aug, 1997 - No. 31, June, 2000 ($1.95/$2.25/$2.50)

	GD	VG	FN	VF	VF/NM	NM-
1-Holguin-s/Medina-a(p)	1	3	4	6	8	10

1-2nd & 3rd printings 3.00
2 6.00
3,4: 4-Photo-c 5.00
5-8: 5-Begin $2.25-c 4.00
9-29 4.00
30,31: 30-Begin $2.50-c 4.00
Book 1 TPB ('98, $12.95) r/#1-6 13.00
Book 2 Destroyer TPB (8/99, $9.95) r/#10-13 10.00
Book 3 Whispered Scream TPB ('00, $9.95) r/#7-9,18 10.00
...Magazine 1 ($6.95) r/#1-3 plus interviews 7.00
...Magazine 2-5 ($4.95) 2-r/#4,5 plus interviews. 3-r/#6,7. 4-r/#8,9 5.00
Wizard Edition ('98, supplement) Bios, tour preview and interviews 3.00

KISS / VAMPIRELLA
Dynamite Entertainment: 2017 - No. 5, 2017 ($3.99)

1-5-Sebela-s/Martello-a; multiple covers; Vampirella meets KISS in 1974 4.00

KISSYFUR (TV)
DC Comics: 1989 (Sept.) ($2.00, 52 pgs., one-shot)

1-Based on Saturday morning cartoon 4.00

KIT CARSON (Formerly All True Detective Cases No. 4; Fighting Davy Crockett No. 9; see Blazing Sixguns & Frontier Fighters)
Avon Periodicals: 1950; No. 2, 8/51 - No. 3, 12/51; No. 5, 11-12/54 - No. 8, 9/55 (No #4)

	GD	VG	FN	VF	VF/NM	NM-
nn(#1) (1950)- "...Indian Scout" ; r-Cowboys 'N' Injuns #?	15	30	45	88	137	185
2(8/51)	12	24	36	67	94	120
3(12/51)- "...Fights the Comanche Raiders"	11	22	33	60	83	105
5-6,8(11-12/54-9/55): 5-Formerly All True Detective Cases (last pre-code); titled "...and the Trail of Doom"	10	20	30	56	76	95
7-McCann-a?	10	20	30	56	76	95
I.W. Reprint #10('63)-r/Kit Carson #1; Severin-c	2	4	6	11	16	20

NOTE: *Kinstler c-1-3, 5-8.*

KIT CARSON & THE BLACKFEET WARRIORS
Realistic: 1953

	GD	VG	FN	VF	VF/NM	NM-
nn-Reprint; Kinstler-c	10	20	30	58	79	100

KITCHEN, THE
DC Comics (Vertigo): Jan, 2015 - No. 8, Aug, 2015 ($2.99, limited series)

1-8-Masters-s/Doyle-a/Cloonan-c 3.00

KIT KARTER
Dell Publishing Co.: May-July, 1962

	GD	VG	FN	VF	VF/NM	NM-
1	3	6	9	18	28	38

KITTY
St. John Publishing Co.: Oct, 1948

	GD	VG	FN	VF	VF/NM	NM-
1-Teenage; Lily Renee-c/a	21	42	63	122	199	275

KITTY PRYDE, AGENT OF S.H.I.E.L.D. (Also see Excalibur and Mekanix)
Marvel Comics: Dec, 1997 - No. 3, Feb, 1998 ($2.50, limited series)

1-3-Hama-s 3.00

KITTY PRYDE AND WOLVERINE (Also see Uncanny X-Men & X-Men)
Marvel Comics Group: Nov, 1984 - No. 6, Apr, 1985 (Limited series)

1-6: Characters from X-Men 5.00
X-Men: Kitty Pryde and Wolverine HC (2008, $19.99) r/series 20.00

KLARER GIVEAWAYS (See Wisco in the Promotional Comics section)

KLARION (The Witchboy)
DC Comics: Dec, 2014 - No. 6, May, 2015 ($2.99)

1-6: 1-3-Nocenti-s/McCarthy-a. 4-Fiorentino-a 3.00

KLAUS
BOOM! Studios: Nov, 2015 - No. 7, Aug, 2016 ($3.99)

1-7: 1-Origin of Santa Claus; Grant Morrison-s/Dan Mora-a; multiple covers 4.00
... and the Crisis in Xmasville 1 (12/17, $7.99) Morrison-s/Mora-a; Snowmaiden app. 8.00
... and the Witch of Winter 1 (12/16, $7.99) Morrison-s/Mora-a; Geppetto app. 8.00

KLAWS OF THE PANTHER (Also see Black Panther)
Marvel Comics: Dec, 2010 - No. 4, Feb, 2011 ($3.99, limited series)

1-4-Maberry-s/Gugliotta-a/Del Mundo-c. 1-Ka-Zar & Shanna app. 3-Spider-Man app. 4.00

KNIGHT AND SQUIRE (Also see Batman #667-669)
DC Comics: Dec, 2010 - No. 6, May, 2011 ($2.99, limited series)

1-6-Cornell-s/Broxton-a. 1-Two covers by Paquette & Tucci. 5,6-Joker app. 3.00
TPB (2011, $14.99) r/#1-6; sketch and design art 15.00

KNIGHTHAWK
Acclaim Comics (Windjammer): Sept, 1995 - No. 6, Nov, 1995 ($2.50, lim. series)

1-6: 6-origin 3.00

KNIGHTMARE
Antarctic Press: July, 1994 - May, 1995 ($2.75, B&W, mature readers)

1-6 3.00

KNIGHTMARE
Image Comics (Extreme Studios): Feb, 1995 - No. 5, June, 1995 ($2.50)

0 ($3.50) 4.00
1-5: 4-Quesada & Palmiotti variant-c, 5-Flip book w/Warcry 3.00

KNIGHTS 4 (See Marvel Knights 4)

KNIGHTS OF PENDRAGON, THE (Also see Pendragon)
Marvel Comics Ltd.: July, 1990 - No. 18, Dec, 1991 ($1.95)

1-18: 1-Capt. Britain app. 2,8-Free poster inside. 9,10-Bolton-c. 11,18-Iron Man app. 3.00

KNIGHTS OF THE ROUND TABLE
Dell Publishing Co.: No. 540, Mar, 1954

	GD	VG	FN	VF	VF/NM	NM-
Four Color 540-Movie, photo-c	6	12	18	41	76	110

KNIGHTS OF THE ROUND TABLE
Pines Comics: No. 10, April, 1957

	GD	VG	FN	VF	VF/NM	NM-
10-Features Sir Lancelot	5	10	15	24	30	35

KNIGHTS OF THE ROUND TABLE
Dell Publishing Co.: Nov-Jan, 1963-64

	GD	VG	FN	VF	VF/NM	NM-
1 (12-397-401)-Painted-c	3	6	9	20	31	42

Kobra #1 © DC

Konga #2 © CC

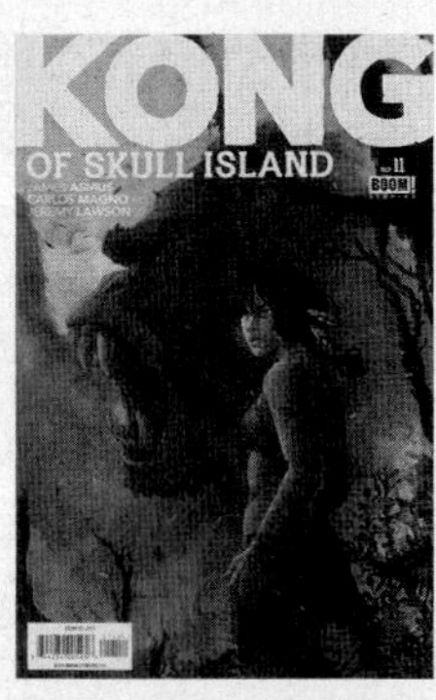

Kong of Skull Island #11 © Devito Artworks

KNIGHTSTRIKE (Also see Operation: Knightstrike)
Image Comics (Extreme Studios): Jan, 1996 ($2.50)

	GD 2.0	VG 4.0	FN 6.0	VF 8.0	VF/NM 9.0	NM- 9.2
1-Rob Liefeld & Eric Stephenson story; Extreme Destroyer Part 6.						3.00

KNIGHT WATCHMAN (See Big Bang Comics & Dr. Weird)
Image Comics: June, 1998 - No. 4, Oct, 1998 ($2.95/$3.50, B&W, lim. series)

	GD 2.0	VG 4.0	FN 6.0	VF 8.0	VF/NM 9.0	NM- 9.2
1-3-Ben Torres-c/a in all						3.00
4-($3.50)						3.50

KNIGHT WATCHMAN: GRAVEYARD SHIFT
Caliber Press: 1994 ($2.95, B&W)

	GD 2.0	VG 4.0	FN 6.0	VF 8.0	VF/NM 9.0	NM- 9.2
1,2-Ben Torres-a						3.00

KNOCK KNOCK (...Who's There?)
Dell Publ./Gerona Publications: No. 801, 1936 (52 pgs.) (8x9", B&W)

	GD 2.0	VG 4.0	FN 6.0	VF 8.0	VF/NM 9.0	NM- 9.2
801-Joke book; Bob Dunn-a	14	28	42	82	121	160

KNOCKOUT ADVENTURES
Fiction House Magazines: Winter, 1953-54

	GD 2.0	VG 4.0	FN 6.0	VF 8.0	VF/NM 9.0	NM- 9.2
1-Reprints Fight Comics #53 w/Rip Carson-c/s	14	28	42	76	108	140

KNUCKLES (Spin-off of Sonic the Hedgehog)
Archie Publications: Apr, 1997 - No. 32, Feb, 2000 ($1.50/$1.75/$1.79)

	GD 2.0	VG 4.0	FN 6.0	VF 8.0	VF/NM 9.0	NM- 9.2
1-32						4.00

KNUCKLES' CHAOTIX
Archie Publications: Jan, 1996 ($2.00, annual)

	GD 2.0	VG 4.0	FN 6.0	VF 8.0	VF/NM 9.0	NM- 9.2
1						5.00

KOBALT
DC Comics (Milestone): June, 1994 - No. 16, Sept, 1995 ($1.75/$2.50)

	GD 2.0	VG 4.0	FN 6.0	VF 8.0	VF/NM 9.0	NM- 9.2
1-16: 1-Byrne-c. 4-Intro Page. 16-Kent Williams-c						3.00

KOBRA (Unpublished #8 appears in DC Special Series No. 1)
National Periodical Publications: Feb-Mar, 1976 - No. 7, Mar-Apr, 1977

	GD 2.0	VG 4.0	FN 6.0	VF 8.0	VF/NM 9.0	NM- 9.2
1-1st app.; Kirby-a redrawn by Marcos; only 25¢-c	3	6	9	15	22	28
2-7: (All 30¢ issues) 3-Giffen-a	1	3	4	6	8	10
...: Resurrection TPB (2010, $19.99) r/#1, DC Special Series No. 1 and later apps. in Checkmate #23-25, Faces of Evil: Kobra #1 and various Who's Who issues						20.00

NOTE: ***Austin** a-3i. **Buckler** a-5p; c-5p. **Kubert** c-4. **Nasser** a-6p, 7; c-7.*

KOKEY KOALA (...and the Magic Button)
Toby Press: May, 1952

	GD 2.0	VG 4.0	FN 6.0	VF 8.0	VF/NM 9.0	NM- 9.2
1-Funny animal	15	30	45	84	127	170

KOKO AND KOLA (Also see A-1 Comics #16 & Tick Tock Tales)
Com/Magazine Enterprises: Fall, 1946 - No. 5, May, 1947; No. 6, 1950

	GD 2.0	VG 4.0	FN 6.0	VF 8.0	VF/NM 9.0	NM- 9.2
1-Funny animal	15	30	45	88	137	185
2-X-Mas-c	11	22	33	62	86	110
3-6: 6(A-1 28)	10	20	30	56	76	95

KO KOMICS
Gerona Publications: Oct, 1945 (scarce)

	GD 2.0	VG 4.0	FN 6.0	VF 8.0	VF/NM 9.0	NM- 9.2
1-The Duke of Darkness & The Menace (hero); Kirby-c	100	200	300	635	1093	1550

KOLCHAK: THE NIGHT STALKER (TV)
Moonstone: 2002 - Present ($6.50/$6.95)

	GD 2.0	VG 4.0	FN 6.0	VF 8.0	VF/NM 9.0	NM- 9.2
1-($6.50) Jeff Rice-s/Gordon Purcell-a						6.50
... Black & White & Read All Over (2005, $4.95) short stories by various; 2 covers						5.00
... Devil in the Details (2003, $6.95) Trevor Von Eeden-a						7.00
... Eve of Terror (2005, $5.95) Gentile-s/Figueroa-a/Beck-c						6.00
... Fever Pitch (2002, $6.95) Christopher Jones-a						7.00
... Get of Belial (2002, $6.95) Art Nichols-a						7.00
... Lambs to the Slaughter (2003, $6.95) Trevor Von Eeden-a						7.00
... Pain Most Human (2004, $6.95) Greg Scott-a						7.00
... Tales: The Frankenstein Agenda 1 (2007 - No. 3, $3.50) Michelinie-s						3.50
... Tales of the Night Stalker 1-7 (2003-Present, $3.50) two covers by Moore & Ulanski						3.50
TPB (2004, $17.95) r/#1, Get of Belial & Fever Pitch						18.00
Vol. 2: Terror Within TPB (2006, $16.95) r/Pain Most Human, Pain Without Tears & Devil in the Details						17.00

KOMIC KARTOONS
Timely Comics (EPC): Fall, 1945 - No. 2, Winter, 1945

	GD 2.0	VG 4.0	FN 6.0	VF 8.0	VF/NM 9.0	NM- 9.2
1,2-Andy Wolf, Bertie Mouse	31	62	93	186	303	420

KOMIK PAGES (Formerly Snap; becomes Bullseye #11)
Harry 'A' Chesler, Jr. (Our Army, Inc.): Apr, 1945 (All reprints)

	GD 2.0	VG 4.0	FN 6.0	VF 8.0	VF/NM 9.0	NM- 9.2
10(#1 on inside)-Land O' Nod by Rick Yager (2 pgs.), Animal Crackers, Foxy GrandPa, Tom, Dick & Mary, Cheerio Minstrels, Red Starr plus other 1-2 pg. strips; Cole-a	26	52	78	154	252	350

KONA (...Monarch of Monster Isle)
Dell Publishing Co.: Feb-Apr, 1962 - No. 21, Jan-Mar, 1967 (Painted-c)

	GD 2.0	VG 4.0	FN 6.0	VF 8.0	VF/NM 9.0	NM- 9.2
Four Color 1256 (#1)	9	18	27	61	123	185
2-10: 4-Anak begins. 6-Gil Kane-c	5	10	15	33	57	80
11-21	4	8	12	28	47	65

NOTE: ***Glanzman** a-all issues.*

KONGA (Fantastic Giants No. 24) (See Return of...)
Charlton Comics: 1960; No. 2, Aug, 1961 - No. 23, Nov, 1965

	GD 2.0	VG 4.0	FN 6.0	VF 8.0	VF/NM 9.0	NM- 9.2
1(1960)-Based on movie; Giordano-c	24	48	72	168	372	575
2-5: 2-Giordano-c; no Ditko-a	10	20	30	66	138	210
6-9-Ditko-c/a	9	18	27	58	114	170
10-15	8	16	24	54	102	150
16-23	5	10	15	35	63	90

NOTE: ***Ditko** a-1, 3-15; c-4, 6-9, 11. **Glanzman** a-12. **Montes** & **Bache** a-16-23.*

KONGA'S REVENGE (Formerly Return of...)
Charlton Comics: No. 2, Summer, 1963 - No. 3, Fall, 1964; Dec, 1968

	GD 2.0	VG 4.0	FN 6.0	VF 8.0	VF/NM 9.0	NM- 9.2
2,3: 2-Ditko-c/a	7	14	21	44	82	120
1(12/68)-Reprints Konga's Revenge #3	3	6	9	16	24	32

KONG: GODS OF SKULL ISLAND
BOOM! Studios: Oct, 2017 ($7.99, one-shot)

	GD 2.0	VG 4.0	FN 6.0	VF 8.0	VF/NM 9.0	NM- 9.2
1-Phillip Kennedy Johnson-s/Chad Lewis-a						8.00

KONG OF SKULL ISLAND
BOOM! Studios: Jul, 2016 - No. 12, Jun, 2017 ($3.99, limited series)

	GD 2.0	VG 4.0	FN 6.0	VF 8.0	VF/NM 9.0	NM- 9.2
1-12-James Asmus-s/Carlos Magno-a; multiple covers on each						4.00

KONG ON THE PLANET OF THE APES
BOOM! Studios: Nov, 2017 - No. 6 ($3.99, limited series)

	GD 2.0	VG 4.0	FN 6.0	VF 8.0	VF/NM 9.0	NM- 9.2
1-4-Ryan Ferrier-s/Carlos Magno-a; multiple covers on each						4.00

KONG THE UNTAMED
National Periodical Publications: June-July, 1975 - V2#5, Feb-Mar, 1976

	GD 2.0	VG 4.0	FN 6.0	VF 8.0	VF/NM 9.0	NM- 9.2
1-1st app. Kong; Wrightson-c; Alcala-a	2	4	6	13	18	22
2-Wrightson-c; Alcala-a	2	4	6	10	14	18
3-5: 3-Alcala-a	1	3	4	6	8	10

KOOKABURRA K
Marvel Comics (Soleil): 2009 - No. 3, 2010 ($5.99, limited series)

	GD 2.0	VG 4.0	FN 6.0	VF 8.0	VF/NM 9.0	NM- 9.2
1-3-Humbertos Ramos-a/c						6.00

KOOKIE
Dell Publishing Co.: Feb-Apr, 1962 - No. 2, May-July, 1962 (15 cents)

	GD 2.0	VG 4.0	FN 6.0	VF 8.0	VF/NM 9.0	NM- 9.2
1-Written by John Stanley; Bill Williams-a	7	14	21	46	86	125
2	6	12	18	41	76	110

KOOSH KINS
Archie Comics: Oct, 1991 - No. 3, Feb, 1992 ($1.00, bi-monthly, limited series)

	GD 2.0	VG 4.0	FN 6.0	VF 8.0	VF/NM 9.0	NM- 9.2
1-3						4.00

NOTE: *No. 4 was planned, but cancelled.*

KORAK, SON OF TARZAN (Edgar Rice Burroughs)(See Tarzan #139)
Gold Key: Jan, 1964 - No. 45, Jan, 1972 (Painted-c No. 1-?)

	GD 2.0	VG 4.0	FN 6.0	VF 8.0	VF/NM 9.0	NM- 9.2
1-Russ Manning-a	9	18	27	58	114	170
2-5-Russ Manning-a	5	10	15	33	57	80
6-11-Russ Manning-a	5	10	15	30	50	70
12-23: 12,13-Warren Tufts-a. 14-Jon of the Kalahari ends. 15-Mabu, Jungle Boy begins. 21-Manning-a. 23-Last 12¢ issue	4	8	12	27	44	60
24-30	3	6	9	21	33	45
31-45	3	6	9	17	26	35

KORAK, SON OF TARZAN (Tarzan Family #60 on; see Tarzan #230)
National Periodical Publications: V9#46, May-June, 1972 - V12#56, Feb-Mar, 1974; No. 57, May-June, 1975 - No. 59, Sept-Oct, 1975 (Edgar Rice Burroughs)

	GD 2.0	VG 4.0	FN 6.0	VF 8.0	VF/NM 9.0	NM- 9.2
46-(52 pgs.)-Carson of Venus begins (origin), ends #56; Pellucidar feature; Weiss-a	3	6	9	15	22	28
47-59: 49-Origin Korak retold	2	4	6	8	11	14

NOTE: *All have covers by **Joe Kubert**. **Manning** strip reprints-No. 57-59. **Murphy Anderson** a-52,56. **Michael Kaluta** a-46-56. **Frank Thorne** a-46-51.*

KORE
Image Comics: Apr, 2003 - No. 5, Sept, 2003 ($2.95)

	GD 2.0	VG 4.0	FN 6.0	VF 8.0	VF/NM 9.0	NM- 9.2
1-5: 1-Two covers by Capullo and Seeley; Seeley-a (p)						3.00

KORG: 70,000 B. C. (TV)

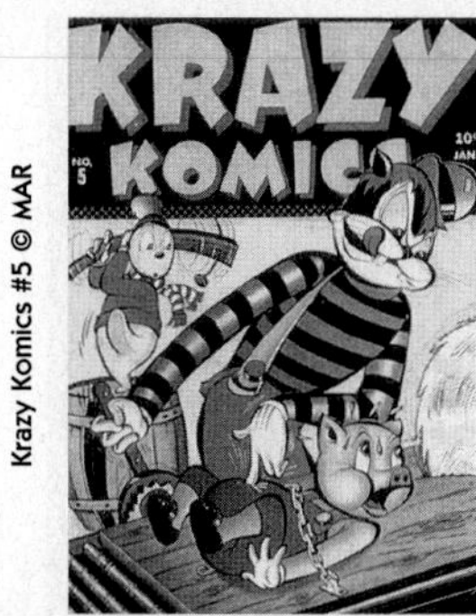

Krazy Komics #5 © MAR

Krypto the Superdog #5 © DC

Kull Eternal #1 © REHP

GD VG FN VF VF/NM NM-
2.0 4.0 6.0 8.0 9.0 9.2

Charlton Publications: May, 1975 - No. 9, Nov, 1976 (Hanna-Barbera)
1,2: 1-Boyette-c/a. 2-Painted-c; Byrne text illos 2 4 6 13 18 22
3-9 2 4 6 8 11 14

KORNER KID COMICS: Four Star Publications: 1947 (Advertised, not pub.)

KORVAC SAGA (Secret Wars tie-in)
Marvel Comics: Aug, 2015 - No. 4, Nov, 2015 ($3.99, limited series)
1-4-Guardians 3000, Avengers and Wonder Man app.; Abnett-s/Schmidt-a 4.00

KOSHCHEI THE DEATHLESS
Dark Horse Comics: Dec, 2017 - No. 6 ($3.99, limited series)
1-3-Mignola-s/c; Stenbeck-a. 1-Hellboy app. 4.00

KRAMPUS
Image Comics: Dec, 2013 - No. 5, May, 2014 ($2.99)
1-5-Sinterklaas' assistant; Joines-s/Kotz-a 3.00

KRAZY KAT
Holt: 1946 (Hardcover)
Reprints daily & Sunday strips by Herriman 55 110 165 352 601 850
dust jacket only 42 84 126 265 450 635

KRAZY KAT (See Ace Comics & March of Comics No. 72, 87)

KRAZY KAT COMICS (...& Ignatz the Mouse early issues)
Dell Publ. Co./Gold Key: May-June, 1951 - F.C. #696, Apr, 1956; Jan, 1964 (None by Herriman)
1(1951) 9 18 27 60 120 180
2-5 (#5, 8-10/52) 5 10 15 34 60 85
Four Color 454,504 6 12 18 37 66 95
Four Color 548,619,696 (4/56) 5 10 15 31 53 75
1(10098-401)(1/64-Gold Key)(TV) 4 8 12 25 40 55

KRAZY KOMICS (1st Series) (Cindy Comics No. 27 on) (Also see Ziggy Pig)
Timely Comics (USA No. 1-21/JPC No. 22-26): July, 1942 - No. 26, Spr, 1947
1-Toughy Tomcat, Ziggy Pig (by Jaffee) & Silly Seal begin
135 270 405 864 1482 2100
2 47 94 141 296 498 700
3-8,10 36 72 108 211 343 475
9-Hitler parody-c 65 130 195 416 708 1000
11,13,14 24 48 72 142 234 325
12-Timely's entire art staff drew themselves into a Creeper story
39 78 117 231 378 525
15-(8-9/44)-Has "Super Soldier" by Pfc. Stan Lee 25 50 75 150 245 340
16-24,26: 16-(10-11/44). 26-Super Rabbit-c/story 21 42 63 122 199 275
25-Wacky Duck-c/story & begin; Kurtzman-a (6pgs.) 25 50 75 150 245 340

KRAZY KOMICS (2nd Series)
Timely/Marvel Comics: Aug, 1948 - No. 2, Nov, 1948
1-Wolverton (10 pgs.) & Kurtzman (8 pgs.)-a; Eustice Hayseed begins (Li'l Abner swipe)
55 110 165 352 601 850
2-Wolverton-a (10 pgs.); Powerhouse Pepper cameo
39 78 117 240 395 550

KRAZY KROW (Also see Dopey Duck, Film Funnies, Funny Frolics & Movie Tunes)
Marvel Comics (ZPC): Summer, 1945 - No. 3, Wint, 1945/46
1 32 64 96 188 307 425
2,3 20 40 60 114 182 250
I.W. Reprint #1('57), 2('58), 7 2 4 6 11 16 20

KRAZYLIFE (Becomes Nutty Life #2)
Fox Feature Syndicate: 1945 (no month)
1-Funny animal 28 56 84 165 270 375

KREE/SKRULL WAR STARRING THE AVENGERS, THE
Marvel Comics: Sept, 1983 - No. 2, Oct, 1983 ($2.50, 68 pgs., Baxter paper)
1,2 6.00
NOTE: ***Neal Adams** p-1r, 2. **Buscema** a-1r, 2r. **Simonson** a-1p; c-1p.*

KROFFT SUPERSHOW (TV)
Gold Key: Apr, 1978 - No. 6, Jan, 1979
1-Photo-c 3 6 9 17 26 35
2-6: 6-Photo-c 3 6 9 14 19 24

KRULL
Marvel Comics Group: Nov, 1983 - No. 2, Dec, 1983
1,2-Adaptation of film; r/Marvel Super Special. 1-Photo-c from movie 4.00

KRUSTY COMICS (TV)(See Simpsons Comics)
Bongo Comics: 1995 - No. 3, 1995 ($2.25, limited series)
1-3 4.00

KRYPTON CHRONICLES
DC Comics: Sept, 1981 - No. 3, Nov, 1981
1-3: 1-Buckler-c(p) 4.00

KRYPTO THE SUPERDOG (TV)
DC Comics: Nov, 2006 - No. 6, Apr, 2007 ($2.25)
1-6-Based on Cartoon Network series. 1-Origin retold 3.00

KULL
Dark Horse Comics: Nov, 2008 - No. 6, May, 2009 ($2.99)
1-6: 1-Nelson-s/Conrad-a; two covers by Andy Brase and Joe Kubert 3.00

KULL AND THE BARBARIANS
Marvel Comics: May, 1975 - No. 3, Sept, 1975 ($1.00, B&W, magazine)
1-(84 pgs.) Andru/Wood-r/Kull #1; 2 pgs. Neal Adams; Gil Kane(p), Marie & John Severin-a(r); Krenkel text illo. 3 6 9 17 25 34
2,3: 2-(84 pgs.) Red Sonja by Chaykin begins; Solomon Kane by Weiss/Adams; Gil Kane-a; Solomon Kane pin-up by Wrightson. 3-(76 pgs.) Origin Red Sonja by Chaykin; Adams-a; Solomon Kane app. 3 6 9 15 22 28

KULL: ETERNAL
IDW Publsihing: Jun, 2017 - Present ($3.99)
1-2-Waltz-s/Pizzari-a; multiple covers on each; Kull travels through history 4.00

KULL: THE CAT AND THE SKULL
Dark Horse Comics: Oct, 2011 - No. 4, Jan, 2012 ($3.50, limited series)
1-4-Lapham-s/Guzman-a/Chen-c. 1-Variant-c by Hans 3.50

KULL THE CONQUEROR (...the Destroyer #11 on; see Conan #1, Creatures on the Loose #10, Marvel Preview, Monsters on the Prowl)
Marvel Comics Group: June, 1971 - No. 2, Sept, 1971; No. 3, July, 1972 - No. 15, Aug, 1974; No. 16, Aug, 1976 - No. 29, Oct, 1978
1-Andru/Wood-a; 2nd app. & origin Kull; 15¢ issue 6 12 18 37 66 95
2-5: 2-3rd Kull app. Last 15¢ iss. 3-13: 20¢ issues. 3-Thulsa Doom-c/app.
3 6 9 17 26 35
6-10: 7-Thulsa Doom-c/app 2 4 6 10 14 18
11-15: 11-15-Ploog-a. 14,15: 25¢ issues 2 4 6 8 11 14
16-(Regular 25¢ edition)(8/76) 2 3 4 6 8 10
16-(30¢-c variant, limited distribution) 3 6 9 17 26 35
17-29: 21-23-(Reg. 30¢ editions) 2 3 4 6 8 10
21-23-(35¢-c variants, limited distribution) 10 20 30 64 132 200
NOTE: *No. 1, 2, 7-9, 11 are based on Robert E. Howard stories. **Alcala** a-17p, 18-20i; c-24. **Ditko** a-12r, 15r. **Gil Kane** c-15p, 21. **Nebres** a-22i-27i; c-25i, 27i. **Ploog** c-11, 12p, 13. **Severin** a-2-9i; c-2-10i, 19. **Starlin** c-14.*

KULL THE CONQUEROR
Marvel Comics Group: Dec, 1982 - No. 2, Mar, 1983 (52 pgs., Baxter paper)
1,2: 1-Buscema-a(p) 4.00

KULL THE CONQUEROR (No. 9,10 titled "Kull")
Marvel Comics Group: 5/83 - No. 10, 6/85 (52 pgs., Baxter paper)
V3#1-10: Buscema-a in #1-3,5-10 4.00
NOTE: Bolton a-4. Golden painted c-3-8. Guice a-4p. Sienkiwicz a-4; c-2.

KULL: THE HATE WITCH
Dark Horse Comics: Nov, 2010 - No. 4, Feb, 2011 ($3.50)
1-4-Lapham-s/Guzman-a/Fleming-c 3.50

KUNG FU (See Deadly Hands of..., & Master of...)

KUNG FU FIGHTER (See Richard Dragon...)

KUNG FU PANDA
Titan Comics: Nov, 2015 -No. 4, Jan, 2016 ($3.99, limited series)
1-4-Simon Furman-s, 1,2-Lee Robinson-a 4.00

KUNG FU PANDA 2
Ape Entertainment: 2011 - No. 6, 2012 ($3.95/$3.99, limited series)
1-6-Short stories by various 4.00

KURT BUSIEK'S ASTRO CITY (Limited series) (Also see Astro City: Local Heroes)
Image Comics (Juke Box Productions): Aug, 1995 - No. 6, Jan, 1996 ($2.25)
1-Kurt Busiek scripts, Brent Anderson-a & Alex Ross front & back-c begins; 1st app. Samaritan & Honor Guard (Cleopatra, MHP, Beautie, The Black Rapier, Quarrel & N-Forcer) 2 4 6 101 14 18
2-6: 2-1st app. The Silver Agent, The Old Soldier, & the "original" Honor Guard (Max O'Millions, Starwoman, the "original" Cleopatra, the "original" N-Forcer, the Bouncing Beatnik, Leopardman & Kitkat). 3-1st app. Jack-in-the-Box & The Deacon. 4-1st app.

Kurt Busek's Astro City #4 © Jukebox

Lab Rats #3 © John Byrne

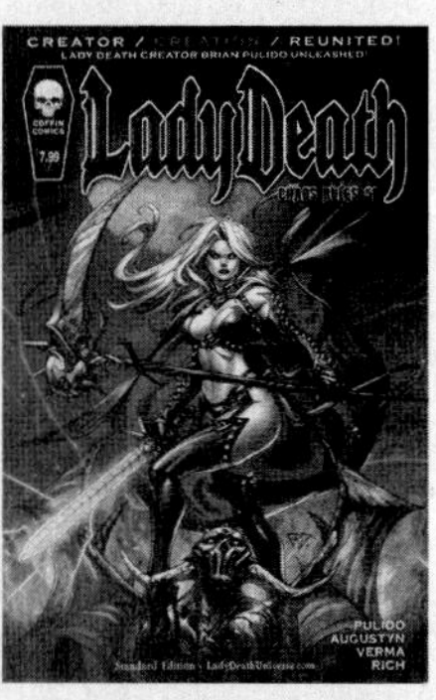

Lady Death: Chaos Rules #1 © Lady Death LLC

	GD 2.0	VG 4.0	FN 6.0	VF 8.0	VF/NM 9.0	NM- 9.2

Winged Victory (cameo), The Hanged Man & The First Family. 5-1st app. Crackerjack, The Astro City Irregulars, Nightingale & Sunbird. 6-Origin Samaritan; 1st full app. Winged Victory 1 3 4 6 8 10
Life In The Big City-(8/96, $19.95, trade paperback)-r/Image Comics limited series w/sketchbook & cover gallery; Ross-c 20.00
Life In The Big City-(8/96, $49.95, hardcover, 1000 print run)-r/Image Comics limited series w/sketchbook & cover gallery; Ross-c 50.00

KURT BUSIEK'S ASTRO CITY (1st Homage Comics series)
Image Comics (Homage Comics): V2#1, Sept, 1996 - No. 15, Dec, 1998;
DC Comics (Homage Comics): No. 16, Mar, 1999 - No. 22, Aug, 2000 ($2.50)

1/2-(10/96)-The Hanged Man story; 1st app. The All-American & Slugger, The Lamplighter, The Time-Keeper & Eterneon 1 3 4 6 8 10
1/2-(1/98) 2nd printing w/new cover 3.00
1- Kurt Busiek scripts, Alex Ross-c, Brent Anderson-p & Will Blyberg-i begin; intro The Gentleman, Thunderhead & Helia. 1 2 3 5 6 8
1-(12/97, $4.95) "3-D Edition" w/glasses 5.00
2-Origin The First Family; Astra story 1 2 3 4 5 7
3-5: 4-1st app. The Crossbreed, Ironhorse, Glue Gun & The Confessor (cameo) 6.00
6-10 5.00
11-22: 14-20-Steeljack story arc. 16-(3/99) First DC issue 3.00
TPB-($19.95) Ross-c, r/#4-9, #1/2 w/sketchbook 20.00
Family Album TPB ($19.95) r/#1-3,10-13 20.00
The Tarnished Angel HC ($29.95) r/#14-20; new Ross dust jacket; sketch pages by Anderson & Ross; cover gallery with reference photos 30.00
The Tarnished Angel SC ($19.95) r/#14-20; new Ross-c 20.00

LABMAN
Image Comics: Nov, 1996 ($3.50, one-shot)

1-Allred-c 4.00

LAB RATS
DC Comics: June, 2002 - No. 8, Jan, 2003 ($2.50)

1-8-John Byrne-s/a. 5,6-Superman app. 3.00

LABYRINTH
Marvel Comics Group: Nov, 1986 - No. 3, Jan, 1987 (Limited series)

1-3: David Bowie movie adaptation; r/Marvel Super Special #40 3 6 9 14 20 26

LABYRINTH (Jim Henson's...)
Boom Entertainment (Archaia): (one-shots)

... 30th Anniversary Special 1 (8/16, $9.99)-Short stories by various; multiple covers 10.00
... 2017 Special 1 (11/17, $7.99) Short stories by various incl. Katie Cook & Landridge 8.00

LA COSA NOSTROID (See Scud: The Disposible Assassin)
Fireman Press: Mar, 1996 - No. 9, 1998 ($2.95, B&W)

1-9-Dan Harmon-s/Rob Schrab-c/a 3.00

LAD: A DOG (Movie)
Dell Publishing Co.: 1961 - No. 2, July-Sept, 1962

Four Color 1303 5 10 15 33 57 80
2 4 8 12 23 37 50

LADY AND THE TRAMP (Disney, See Dell Giants & Movie Comics)
Dell Publishing Co.: No. 629, May, 1955 - No. 634, June, 1955

Four Color 629 (#1)-..with Jock 8 16 24 51 96 140
Four Color 634-...Album 5 10 15 35 63 95

LADY CASTLE
BOOM! Studios: Jan, 2017 - No. 4, May, 2017 ($3.99, limited series)

1-4: 1-Delilah Dawson-s/Ashley Woods-a. 2-4-Farrow-a 4.00

LADY COP (See 1st Issue Special)

LADY DEADPOOL
Marvel Comics: Sept, 2010 ($3.99, one-shot)

1-Land-c/Lashley-a 2 4 6 9 12 15

LADY DEATH (See Evil Ernie)
Chaos! Comics: Jan, 1994 - No. 3, Mar, 1994 ($2.75, limited series)

1/2-S. Hughes-c/a in all, 1/2 Velvet 1 2 3 4 5 7
1/2 Gold 1 3 4 6 8 10
1/2 Signed Limited Edition 2 4 6 8 10 12
1-($3.50)-Chromium-c 2 4 6 11 16 20
1-Commemorative 2 4 6 9 13 16
1-(9/96, $2.95) "Encore Presentation"; r/#1 3.00
2 1 2 3 5 6 8
3 5.00
... And Jade (4/02, $2.99) Augustyn-s/Reis-a 3.00
...And The Women of Chaos! Gallery #1 (11/96, $2.25) pin-ups by various 3.00
.../Bad Kitty (9/01, $2.99) Mota-c/a 3.00
.../Bedlam (6/02, $2.99) Augustyn-s/Reis-c 3.00
...By Steven Hughes (6/00, $2.95) Tribute issue to Steven Hughes 3.00
...By Steven Hughes Deluxe Edition(6/00, $15.95) 16.00
.../Chastity (1/02, $2.99) Mota-c/a; Augustyn-s 3.00
...Death Becomes Her #0 (11/97, $2.95) Hughes-c/a 3.00
...FAN Edition: All Hallow's Eve #1 (1/97, mail-in) 5.00
...In Lingerie #1 (8/95, $2.95) pin-ups, wraparound-c 3.00
...In Lingerie #1-Leather Edition (10,000) 12.00
...In Lingerie #1-Micro Premium Edition; Lady Demon-c (2,000) 35.00
...: Love Bites (3/01, $2.99) Kaminski-s/Luke Ross-a 3.00
.../Medieval Witchblade (8/01, $3.50) covers by Molenaar and Silvestri 3.50
.../Medieval Witchblade Preview Ed. (8/01, $1.99) Molenaar-c 3.00
...: Mischief Night (11/01, $2.99) Ostrander-s/Reis-a 3.00
...: Re-Imagined (7/02, $2.99) Gossett-c 3.00
...: River of Fear (4/01, $2.99) Bennett-a(p)/Cleavenger-c 3.00
...Swimsuit Special #1-($2.50)-Wraparound-c 3.00
...Swimsuit Special #1-Red velvet-c 14.00
...Swimsuit 2001 #1-(2/01, $2.99)-Reis-c; art by various 3.00
...: The Reckoning (7/94, $6.95)-r/#1-3 7.00
...: The Reckoning (8/95, $12.95)- new printing including Lady Death 1/2 & Swimsuit Special #1 13.00
.../Vampirella (3/99, $3.50) Hughes-c/a 3.50
.../Vampirella 2 (3/00, $3.50) Deodato-c/a 3.50
... Vs. Purgatori (12/99, $3.50) Deodato-a 3.50
... Vs. Vampirella Preview (2/00, $1.00) Deodato-a/c 3.00

LADY DEATH (Ongoing series)
Chaos! Comics: Feb, 1998 - No. 16, May, 1999 ($2.95)

1-16: 1-4: Pulido-s/Hughes-c/a. 5-8,13-16-Deodato-a. 9-11-Hughes-a 3.00
...Retribution (8/98, $2.95) Jadsen-a 3.00
...Retribution Premium Ed. 6.00

LADY DEATH
Boundless Comics: No. 0, Nov, 2010 - No. 26 ($3.99)

0-26-Pulido & Wolfer-s/Mueller-a on most; multiple covers on all. 25-Borstel-a 4.00
... Free Comic Book Day 2012 (5/12, free) "The Beginning" on cover; Mueller-a 3.00
... Origins Annual 1 (8/11, $4.99) Martin-a/Pulido-s 5.00
... Premiere (7/10, free) previews series; five covers 3.00

LADY DEATH...
Coffin Comics (One-shots)

... Chaos Rules 1 (5/16, $7.99) Pulido & Augustyn-s/Verma-a 8.00
... Merciless Onslaught 1 (8/17, $7.99) Pulido & Maclean-s/Verma-a; multiple covers 8.00
... Oblivion Kiss 1 (4/17, $7.99) Pulido & Maclean-s/Verma-a; multiple covers 8.00
... Revelations 1 (2/17, $3.99) Pin-up gallery of covers 4.00
... Zodiac 1 (12/16, $3.99) 12 pin-up images of the 12 zodiac signs by Nei Ruffino 4.00

LADY DEATH: ALIVE
Chaos! Comics: May, 2001 - No. 4, Aug, 2001 ($2.99, limited series)

1-4-Ivan Reis-a; Lady Death becomes mortal 3.00

LADY DEATH: A MEDIEVAL TALE (Brian Pulido's...)
CG Entertainment: Mar, 2003 - No. 12, Apr, 2004 ($2.95)

1-12: 1-Brian Pulido-s/Ivan Reis-a; Lady Death in the CrossGen Universe 3.00
Vol.1 TPB (2003, $9.95) digest-sized reprint of #1-6 10.00

LADY DEATH: APOCALYPSE
Boundless Comics: Jan, 2015 - No. 6, Jun, 2015 ($4.99)

1-6: 1-4-Wolfer-s/Borstel-a; multiple covers. 5,6-Wickline-s/Mueller-a 5.00
#0 (8/15, $6.99) Pulido-s/Valenzuela-a; bonus art gallery 7.00

LADY DEATH: DARK ALLIANCE
Chaos! Comics: July, 2002 - No. 5, ($2.99, limited series)

1-3-Reis-a/Ostrander-s 3.00

LADY DEATH: DARK MILLENNIUM
Chaos! Comics: Feb, 2000 - No. 3, Apr, 2000 ($2.95, limited series)

Preview (6/00, $5.00) 5.00
1-3-Ivan Reis-a 3.00

LADY DEATH: GODDESS RETURNS
Chaos! Comics: Jun, 2002 - No. 2, Aug, 2002 ($2.99, limited series)

1,2-Mota-a/Ostrander-s 3.00

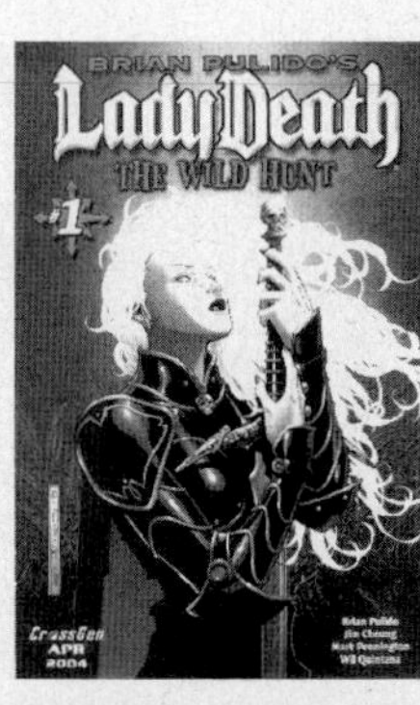

Lady Death: The Wild Hunt #1 © CRO

Lady Killer 2 #1 © Joëlle Jones

Lady Mechanika #5 © Joe Benitez

GD 2.0 | VG 4.0 | FN 6.0 | VF 8.0 | VF/NM 9.0 | NM- 9.2

LADY DEATH: HEARTBREAKER
Chaos! Comics: Mar, 2002 - No. 4, ($2.99, limited series)
1-Molenaar-a/Ostrander-s 3.00

LADY DEATH: JUDGEMENT WAR
Chaos! Comics: Nov, 1999 - No. 3, Jan, 2000 ($2.95, limited series)
Prelude (10/99) two covers 3.00
1-3-Ivan Reis-a 3.00

LADY DEATH: LAST RITES
Chaos! Comics: Oct, 2001 - No. 4, Feb, 2001 ($2.99, limited series)
1-4-Ivan Reis-a/Ostrander-s 3.00

LADY DEATH ORIGINS: CURSED
Boundless Comics: Mar, 2012 - No. 3, May, 2012 ($4.99/$3.99, limited series)
1-($4.99)-Pulido-s/Guzman-a; multiple covers 5.00
2,3-($3.99) 4.00

LADY DEATH: THE CRUCIBLE
Chaos! Comics: Nov, 1996 - No. 6, Oct, 1997 ($3.50/$2.95, limited series)
1/2 4.00
1/2 Cloth Edition 8.00
1-Wraparound silver foil embossed-c 4.00
2-6-($2.95) 3.00

LADY DEATH: THE GAUNTLET
Chaos! Comics: Apr, 2002 - No. 2, May, 2002 ($2.99, limited series)
1,2: 1-J. Scott Campbell-c/redesign of Lady Death's outfit; Mota-a 3.00

LADY DEATH: THE ODYSSEY
Chaos! Comics: Apr, 1996 - No. 4, Aug, 1996 ($3.50/$2.95)
1-($1.50)-Sneak Peek Preview 3.00
1-($1.50)-Sneak Peek Preview Micro Premium Edition (2500 print run) 2 4 6 8 10 12
1-($3.50)-Embossed, wraparound goil foil-c 5.00
1-Black Onyx Edition (200 print run) 5 10 15 33 57 80
1-($19.95)-Premium Edition (10,000 print run) 20.00
2-4-($2.95) 3.00

LADY DEATH: THE RAPTURE
Chaos! Comics: Jun, 1999 - No. 4, Sept, 1999 ($2.95, limited series)
1-4-Ivan Reis-c/a; Pulido-s 3.00

LADY DEATH: THE WILD HUNT (Brian Pulido's...)
CG Entertainment: Apr, 2004 - No. 2, May, 2005 ($2.95)
1-2: 1-Brian Pulido-s/Jim Cheung-a 3.00

LADY DEATH: TRIBULATION
Chaos! Comics: Dec, 2000 - No. 4, Mar, 2001 ($2.95, limited series)
1-4-Ivan Reis-a; Kaminski-s 3.00

LADY DEATH II: BETWEEN HEAVEN & HELL
Chaos! Comics: Mar, 1995 - No. 4, July, 1995 ($3.50, limited series)
1-Chromium wraparound-c; Evil Ernie cameo 5.00
1-Commemorative (4,000), 1-Black Velvet-c 2 4 6 10 14 18
1-Gold 1 3 4 6 8 10
1-"Refractor" edition (5,000) 2 4 6 11 16 20
2-4 3.50
4-Lady Demon variant-c 1 2 3 5 7 9
Trade paperback-($12.95)-r/#1-4 13.00

LADY DEMON
Chaos! Comics: Mar, 2000 - No. 3, May, 2000 ($2.95, limited series)
1-3-Kaminski-s/Brewer-a 3.00

LADY DEMON
Dynamite Entertainment: 2014 - No. 4, 2015 ($3.99)
1-4: 1-3-Gillespie-s/Andolfo-a; multiple covers. 1-Origin retold. 4-Ramirez-a 4.00

LADY FOR A NIGHT (See Cinema Comics Herald)

LADY JUSTICE (See Neil Gaiman's...)

LADY KILLER
Dark Horse Comics: Jan, 2015 - No. 5, May, 2015 ($3.50)
1-5-Joëlle Jones-a/Jones and Jamie Rich-s 3.50

LADY KILLER 2
Dark Horse Comics: Aug, 2016 - No. 5, Sept, 2017 ($3.99)
1-5-Joëlle Jones-s/a 4.00

LADY LUCK (Formerly Smash #1-85) (Also see Spirit Sections #1)
Quality Comics Group: No. 86, Dec, 1949 - No. 90, Aug, 1950
86(#1) 103 206 309 659 1130 1600
87-90 71 142 213 454 777 1100

LADY MECHANIKA
Aspen MLT: No. 0, Oct, 2010 - No. 5, Mar, 2015 ($2.50/$2.99)
0-Joe Benitez-s/a; two covers; Benitez interview and sketch pages 3.00
0-(Benitez Productions, 8/15, $1.00) 3.00
1-(1/11, $2.99) Multiple covers 10.00
2-5-Multiple covers on each. 5-($4.99) 5.00
... FCBD Vol. 1 Issue 1 (5/16, giveaway) r/#0; excerpt from mini-series 3.00

LADY MECHANIKA: LA DAMA DE LA MUERTE
Benitez Productions: Sept, 2016 - No. 3, Dec, 2016 ($3.99)
1-3-Joe Benitez-a/s; M.M. Chen-s; multiple covers on each 4.00

LADY MECHANIKA: THE CLOCKWORK ASSASSIN
Benitez Productions: Jul, 2017 - No. 3, Oct, 2017 ($3.99)
1-3-Joe Benitez-a/M.M. Chen-s; multiple covers on each 4.00

LADY MECHANIKA: THE LOST BOYS OF WEST ABBEY
Benitez Productions: May, 2016 - No. 2, Jun, 2016 ($3.99)
1,2-Joe Benitez-a/M.M. Chen-s; multiple covers on each 4.00

LADY MECHANIKA: THE TABLET OF DESTINIES
Benitez Productions: Apr, 2015 - No. 6, Oct, 2015 ($3.99)
1-6-Joe Benitez-s/a; multiple covers on each 4.00

LADY PENDRAGON
Maximum Press: Mar, 1996 ($2.50)
1-Matt Hawkins script 3.00

LADY PENDRAGON
Image Comics: Nov, 1998 - No. 3, Jan, 1999 ($2.50, mini-series)
Preview (6/98) Flip book w/ Deity preview 3.00
1-3: 1-Matt Hawkins-s/Stinsman-a 3.00
1-($6.95) DF Ed. with variant-c by Jusko 7.00
2-($4.95)Variant edition 5.00
0-(3/99) Origin; flip book 3.00

LADY PENDRAGON (Volume 3)
Image Comics: Apr, 1999 - No. 9, Mar, 2000 ($2.50, mini-series)
1,2,4-6,8-10: 1-Matt Hawkins-s/Stinsman-a. 2-Peterson-c 3.00
3-Flip book w/Alley Cat preview (1st app.) 4.00
7-($3.95) Flip book; Stinsman-a/Cleavenger painted-a 4.00
Gallery Edition (10/99, $2.95) pin-ups 3.00
...Merlin (1/00, $2.95) Stinsman-a 3.00
.../ More Than Mortal (5/99, $2.50) Scott-s/Norton-a; 2 covers by Norton & Finch 3.00
.../ More Than Mortal Preview (2/99) Diamond Dateline supplement 3.00
Pilot Season: Lady Pendragon (5/08, $3.99) Hawkins-s/Eru-a; wraparound-c by Struzan 4.00

LADY RAWHIDE
Topps Comics: July, 1995 - No. 5, Mar, 1996 ($2.95, bi-monthly, limited series)
1-5: Don McGregor scripts & Mayhew-a. in all. 2-Stelfreeze-c. 3-Hughes-c. 4-Golden-c. 5-Julie Bell-c. 3.00
It Can't Happen Here TPB (8/99, $16.95) r/#1-5 17.00
Mini Comic 1 (7/95) Maroto-a; Zorro app. 3.00
Special Edition 1 (6/95, $3.95)-Reprints 4.00

LADY RAWHIDE (Volume 2)
Topps Comics: Oct, 1996 - No. 5, June, 1997 ($2.95, limited series)
1-5: 1-Julie Bell-c. 3.00

LADY RAWHIDE (Volume 1)
Dynamite Entertainment: 2013 - No. 5, 2014 ($3.99)
1-5-Trautmann-s/Estevam-a/Linsner-c 4.00

LADY RAWHIDE / LADY ZORRO
Dynamite Entertainment: 2015 - No. 4, 2015 ($3.99, limited series)
1-4-Denton-s/Villegas-a. 1-Mayhew-c. 2-4-Chin-c 4.00

LADY RAWHIDE OTHER PEOPLE'S BLOOD (ZORRO'S ...)
Image Comics: Mar, 1999 - No. 5, July, 1999 ($2.95, B&W)
1-5-Reprints Lady Rawhide series in B&W 3.00

LADY SUPREME (See Asylum)(Also see Supreme & Kid Supreme)
Image Comics (Extreme): May, 1996 - No. 2, June, 1996 ($2.50, limited series)
1,2-Terry Moore -s: 1-Terry Moore-c. 2-Flip book w/Newmen preview 3.00

Lady Zorro (2014 series) #4 © Zorro Prods.

Lando #1 © Lucasfilm

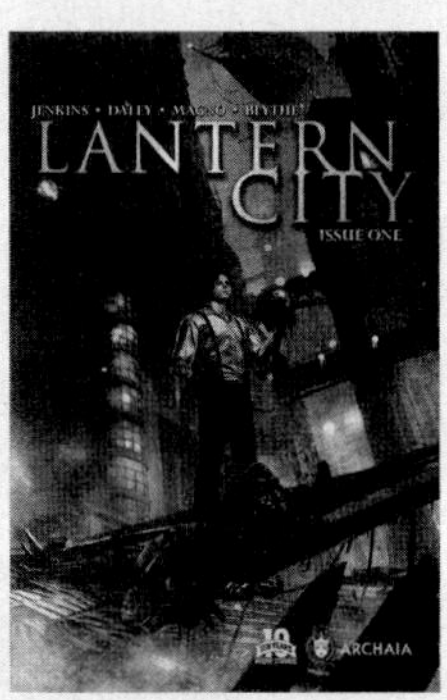

Lantern City #1 © Macrocosm Ent.

LADY ZORRO
Dynamite Entertainment: 2014 - No. 4, 2014 ($3.99, limited series)

	GD 2.0	VG 4.0	FN 6.0	VF 8.0	VF/NM 9.0	NM- 9.2
1-4-de Campi-s/Villegas-a/Linsner-c						4.00

LAFF-A-LYMPICS (TV)(See The Funtastic World of Hanna-Barbera)
Marvel Comics: Mar, 1978 - No. 13, Mar, 1979 (Newsstand sales only)

	GD 2.0	VG 4.0	FN 6.0	VF 8.0	VF/NM 9.0	NM- 9.2
1-Yogi Bear, Scooby Doo, Pixie & Dixie, etc.	3	6	9	19	30	40
2-8	3	6	9	14	19	24
9-13: 11-Jetsons x-over; 1 pg. illustrated bio of Mighty Mightor, Herculoids, Shazzan, Galaxy Trio & Space Ghost	3	6	9	16	23	30

LAFFY-DAFFY COMICS
Rural Home Publ. Co.: Feb, 1945 - No. 2, Mar, 1945

	GD 2.0	VG 4.0	FN 6.0	VF 8.0	VF/NM 9.0	NM- 9.2
1-Funny animal	14	28	42	76	108	140
2-Funny animal	11	22	33	62	86	110

LAKE OF FIRE
Image Comics: Aug, 2016 - No. 5, Dec, 2016 ($3.99)

	GD 2.0	VG 4.0	FN 6.0	VF 8.0	VF/NM 9.0	NM- 9.2
1-5-Nathan Fairbairn-s/Matt Smith-a						4.00

LA MUERTA...
Coffin Comics (One-shots)

	GD 2.0	VG 4.0	FN 6.0	VF 8.0	VF/NM 9.0	NM- 9.2
...: Descent 1 (7/16, $7.99) Maclean-s/Gomez-a; origin						8.00
...: Last Rites 1 (9/16, $7.99) Maclean-s/Gomez-a						8.00
...: Vengeance 1 (9/17, $7.99) Maclean-s/Gomez-a						8.00

LANA (Little Lana No. 8 on)
Marvel Comics (MjMC): Aug, 1948 - No. 7, Aug, 1949 (Also see Annie Oakley)

	GD 2.0	VG 4.0	FN 6.0	VF 8.0	VF/NM 9.0	NM- 9.2
1-Rusty, Millie begin	55	110	165	352	601	850
2-Kurtzman's "Hey Look" (1); last Rusty	28	56	84	165	270	375
3-7: 3-Nellie begins	21	42	63	122	199	275

LANCELOT & GUINEVERE (See Movie Classics)

LANCELOT LINK, SECRET CHIMP (TV)
Gold Key: Apr, 1971 - No. 8, Feb, 1973 (All photo-c)

	GD 2.0	VG 4.0	FN 6.0	VF 8.0	VF/NM 9.0	NM- 9.2
1	5	10	15	35	63	90
2-8	4	8	12	23	37	50

LANCELOT STRONG (See The Shield)

LANCE O'CASEY (See Mighty Midget & Whiz Comics)
Fawcett Publications: Spring, 1946 - No. 3, Fall, 1946; No. 4, Summer, 1948

	GD 2.0	VG 4.0	FN 6.0	VF 8.0	VF/NM 9.0	NM- 9.2
1-Captain Marvel app. on-c	26	52	78	154	252	350
2	16	32	48	94	147	200
3,4	14	28	42	80	115	150

NOTE: *The cover for the 1st issue was done in 1942 but was not published until 1946. The cover shows 68 pages but actually has only 36 pages.*

LANCER (TV)(Western)
Gold Key: Feb, 1969 - No. 3, Sept, 1969 (All photo-c)

	GD 2.0	VG 4.0	FN 6.0	VF 8.0	VF/NM 9.0	NM- 9.2
1	4	8	12	23	37	50
2,3	3	6	9	17	26	35

LANDO (Star Wars)
Marvel Comics: Sept, 2015 - No. 5, Dec, 2015 ($3.99, limited series)

	GD 2.0	VG 4.0	FN 6.0	VF 8.0	VF/NM 9.0	NM- 9.2
1-5-Soule-s/Maleev-a; Lobot & Emperor Palpatine app.						4.00

LAND OF NOD, THE
Dark Horse Comics: July, 1997 - No. 3, Feb, 1998 ($2.95, B&W)

	GD 2.0	VG 4.0	FN 6.0	VF 8.0	VF/NM 9.0	NM- 9.2
1-3-Jetcat; Jay Stephens-s/a						3.00

LAND OF OZ
Arrow Comics: 1998 - No. 9 ($2.95, B&W)

	GD 2.0	VG 4.0	FN 6.0	VF 8.0	VF/NM 9.0	NM- 9.2
1-9-Bishop-s/Bryan-s/a						3.00

LAND OF THE DEAD (George A. Romaro's...)
IDW Publishing: Aug, 2005 - No. 5 ($3.99, limited series)

	GD 2.0	VG 4.0	FN 6.0	VF 8.0	VF/NM 9.0	NM- 9.2
1-4-Adaptation of 2005 movie; Ryall-s/Rodriguez-a						4.00
TPB (3/06, $19.99) r/#1-5; cover gallery						20.00

LAND OF THE GIANTS (TV)
Gold Key: Nov, 1968 - No. 5, Sept, 1969 (All have photo-c)

	GD 2.0	VG 4.0	FN 6.0	VF 8.0	VF/NM 9.0	NM- 9.2
1	6	12	18	38	69	100
2-5	4	8	12	25	40	55

LAND OF THE LOST COMICS (Radio)
E. C. Comics: July-Aug, 1946 - No. 9, Spring, 1948

	GD 2.0	VG 4.0	FN 6.0	VF 8.0	VF/NM 9.0	NM- 9.2
1	41	82	123	256	428	600
2	26	52	78	154	252	350
3-9	22	44	66	132	216	300

LAND UNKNOWN, THE (Movie)
Dell Publishing Co.: No. 845, Sept, 1957

	GD 2.0	VG 4.0	FN 6.0	VF 8.0	VF/NM 9.0	NM- 9.2
Four Color 845-Alex Toth-a	10	20	30	68	144	220

LANTERN CITY (TV)
BOOM! Studios (Archaia): May, 2015 - No. 12, Apr, 2016 ($3.99)

	GD 2.0	VG 4.0	FN 6.0	VF 8.0	VF/NM 9.0	NM- 9.2
1-12: 1-Jenkins & Daley-s/Magno-a. 3-Daley & Scott-s						4.00

LA PACIFICA
DC Comics (Paradox Press): 1994/1995 ($4.95, B&W, limited series, digest size, mature)

	GD 2.0	VG 4.0	FN 6.0	VF 8.0	VF/NM 9.0	NM- 9.2
1-3						5.00

LARA CROFT AND THE FROZEN OMEN (Also see Tomb Raider titles)
Dark Horse Comics: Oct, 2015 - No. 5, Feb, 2016 ($3.99)

	GD 2.0	VG 4.0	FN 6.0	VF 8.0	VF/NM 9.0	NM- 9.2
1-5: 1-Corinna Bechko-s/Randy Green-a						4.00

LARAMIE (TV)
Dell Publishing Co.: Aug, 1960 - July, 1962 (All photo-c)

	GD 2.0	VG 4.0	FN 6.0	VF 8.0	VF/NM 9.0	NM- 9.2
Four Color 1125-Gil Kane/Heath-a	8	16	24	51	96	140
Four Color 1223,1284, 01-418-207 (7/62)	6	12	18	37	66	95

LAREDO (TV)
Gold Key: June, 1966

	GD 2.0	VG 4.0	FN 6.0	VF 8.0	VF/NM 9.0	NM- 9.2
1 (10179-606)-Photo-c	3	6	9	21	33	45

LARFLEEZE (Orange Lantern) (Story continued from back-ups in Threshold #1-5)
DC Comics: Aug, 2013 - No. 12, Aug, 2014 ($2.99)

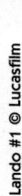

	GD 2.0	VG 4.0	FN 6.0	VF 8.0	VF/NM 9.0	NM- 9.2
1-12: 1-Giffen & DeMatteis-s/Kolins-a/Porter-c; origin told						3.00

LARGE FEATURE COMIC (Formerly called Black & White in previous guides)
Dell Publishing Co.: 1939 - No. 13, 1943

Note: See individual alphabetical listings for prices

1 (Series I)-Dick Tracy Meets the Blank
3-Heigh-Yo Silver! The Lone Ranger (text & ill.)(76 pgs.); also exists as a Whitman #710; based on radio
6-Terry & the Pirates & The Dragon Lady; reprints dailies from 1936
8-Dick Tracy the Racket Buster
9-King of the Royal Mounted (Zane Grey's...)
10-(Scarce)-Gang Busters (No. appears on inside front cover); first slick cover (based on radio program)
13-Dick Tracy and Scottie of Scotland Yard
15-Dick Tracy and the Kidnapped Princes
17-Gang Busters (1941)
18-Phantasmo (see The Funnies #45)
20-Donald Duck Comic Paint Book (rarer than #16) (Disney)
21,22: 21-Private Buck. 22-Nuts & Jolts
24-Popeye in "Thimble Theatre" by Segar
26-Smitty
28-Grin and Bear It
30-Tillie the Toiler
2-Winnie Winkle (#1)
3-Dick Tracy
4-Tiny Tim (#1)
6-Terry and the Pirates; Caniff-a
8-Bugs Bunny (#1)('42)
9-Bringing Up Father
10-Popeye (Thimble Theatre)
11-Barney Google and Snuffy Smith
13-(nn)-1001 Hours Of Fun; puzzles & games; by A. W. Nugent. This book was bound as #13 with Large Feature Comics in publisher's files
2-Terry and the Pirates (#1)
4-Dick Tracy Gets His Man
5-Tarzan of the Apes (#1) by Harold Foster (origin); reprints 1st Tarzan dailies from 1929
7-(Scarce, 52 pgs.)-Hi-Yo Silver the Lone Ranger to the Rescue; also exists as a Whitman #715, based on radio program
11-Dick Tracy Foils the Mad Doc Hump
12-Smilin' Jack; no number on-c
14-Smilin' Jack Helps G-Men Solve a Case!
16-Donald Duck; 1st app. Daisy Duck on back cover (6/41-Disney)
19-Dumbo Comic Paint Book (Disney); partial-r from 4-Color #17
23-The Nebbs
25-Smilin' Jack-1st issue to show title on-c
27-Terry and the Pirates; Caniff-c/a
29-Moon Mullins
1 (Series II)-Peter Rabbit by Harrison Cady; arrival date-3/27/42
5-Toots and Casper
7-Pluto Saves the Ship (#1) (Disney)-Written by Carl Barks, Jack Hannah, & Nick George (Barks' 1st comic book work)
12-Private Buck

NOTE: *The Black & White Feature Books are oversized 8-1/2x11-3/8" comics with color covers and black and white interiors. The first nine issues all have rough, heavy stock covers and, except for #7, all have 76 pages, including covers. #7 and #10-on all have 52 pages. Beginning with #10 the covers are slick and thin and, because of their size, are difficult to handle without damaging. For this reason, they are seldom found in fine to mint condition. The paper stock, unlike Wow #1 and Capt. Marvel #1, is itself not unstable ...just thin. Many issues were reprinted in the early 1980s, identical except for the copyright notice on the first page.*

LARRY DOBY, BASEBALL HERO

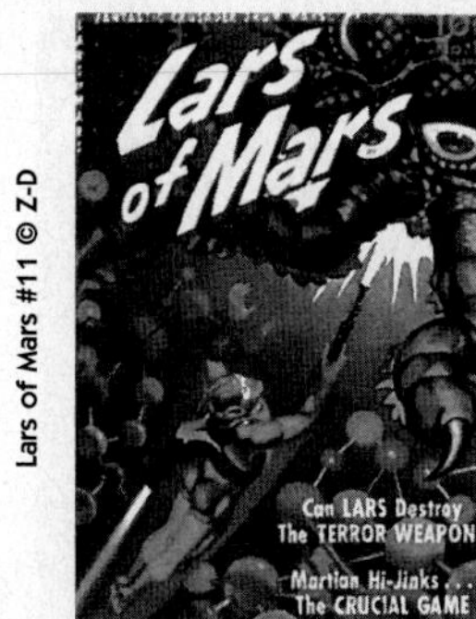

Lars of Mars #11 © Z-D

Lassie #37 © MGM

The Last Defenders #3 © MAR

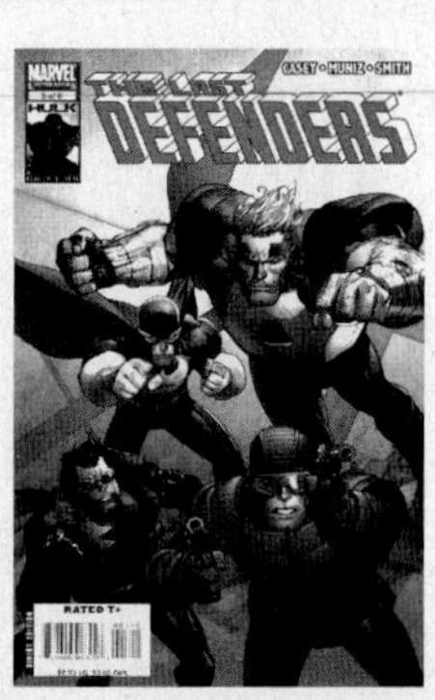

GD 2.0 | VG 4.0 | FN 6.0 | VF 8.0 | VF/NM 9.0 | NM- 9.2

Fawcett Publications: 1950 (Cleveland Indians)
nn-Bill Ward-a; photo-c 81 162 243 518 884 1250

LARRY HARMON'S LAUREL AND HARDY (...Comics)
National Periodical Publ.: July-Aug, 1972 (Digest advertised, not published)
1-Low print run 9 18 27 59 117 175

LARS OF MARS
Ziff-Davis Publishing Co.: No. 10, Apr-May, 1951 - No. 11, July-Aug, 1951 (Painted-c) (Created by Jerry Siegel, editor)
10-Origin; Anderson-a(3) in each; classic robot-c 110 220 330 704 1202 1700
11-Gene Colan-a; classic-c 87 174 261 553 952 1350

LARS OF MARS 3-D
Eclipse Comics: Apr, 1987 ($2.50)
1-r/Lars of Mars #10,11 in 3-D plus new story 5.00
2-D limited edition (B&W, 100 copies) 20.00

LASER ERASER & PRESSBUTTON (See Axel Pressbutton & Miracle Man 9)
Eclipse Comics: Nov, 1985 - No. 6, 1987 (95¢/$2.50, limited series)
1-6: 5,6-(95¢) 3.00
...In 3-D 1 (8/86, $2.50) 4.00
2-D 1 (B&W, limited to 100 copies signed & numbered) 20.00

LASH LARUE WESTERN (Movie star; King of the bullwhip)(See Fawcett Movie Comic, Motion Picture Comics & Six-Gun Heroes)
Fawcett Publications: Sum, 1949 - No. 46, Jan, 1954 (36 pgs., 1-6,9,13,16-on)
1-Lash & his horse Black Diamond begin; photo front/back-c begin
58 116 174 371 636 900
2(11/49) 28 56 84 165 270 375
3-5 21 42 63 126 206 285
6,9: 6-Last photo back-c; intro. Frontier Phantom (Lash's twin brother)
19 38 57 109 172 235
7,8,10 (52pgs.) 20 40 60 114 182 250
11,12,14,15 (52pgs.) 15 30 45 84 127 170
13,16-20 (36pgs.) 14 28 42 80 115 150
21-30: 21-The Frontier Phantom app. 12 24 36 69 97 125
31-45 11 22 33 60 83 105
46-Last Fawcett issue & photo-c 11 22 33 64 90 115

LASH LARUE WESTERN (Continues from Fawcett series)
Charlton Comics: No. 47, Mar-Apr, 1954 - No. 84, June, 1961
47-Photo-c 14 28 42 80 115 150
48 11 22 33 60 83 105
49-60, 67,68-(68 pgs.). 68-Check-a 9 18 27 52 69 85
61-66,69,70: 52-r/#8; 53-r/#22 9 18 27 47 61 75
71-83 8 16 24 40 50 60
84-Last issue 9 18 27 47 61 75

LASH LARUE WESTERN
AC Comics: 1990 ($3.50, 44 pgs) (24 pgs. of color, 16 pgs. of B&W)
1-Photo covers; r/Lash #6; r/old movie posters 4.00
Annual 1 (1990, $2.95, B&W, 44 pgs.)-Photo covers 4.00

LASSIE (TV)(M-G-M's... #1-36; see Kite Fun Book)
Dell Publ. Co./Gold Key No. 59 (10/62) on: June, 1950 - No. 70, July, 1969
1 (52 pgs.)-Photo-c; inside lists One Shot #282 in error
24 48 72 168 372 575
2-Painted-c begin 8 16 24 54 102 150
3-10 6 12 18 37 66 95
11-19: 12-Rocky Langford (Lassie's master) marries Gerry Lawrence. 15-1st app. Timbu
5 10 15 30 50 70
20-22-Matt Baker-a 5 10 15 33 57 80
23-38: 33-Robinson-a. 4 8 12 28 47 65
39-1st app. Timmy as Lassie picks up her TV family; photo-c
5 10 15 35 63 90
40-50-Photo-c on all 4 8 12 28 47 65
51-58-Photo-c on all 4 8 12 27 44 60
59 (10/62)-1st Gold Key 4 8 12 28 47 65
60-70: 63-Last Timmy (10/63). 64-r/#19. 65-Forest Ranger Corey Stuart begins, ends #69. 70-Forest Rangers Bob Ericson & Scott Turner app. (Lassie's new masters)
4 8 12 25 40 55
11193(1978, $1.95, 224 pgs., Golden Press)-Baker-r (92 pgs.)
4 8 12 25 40 55

NOTE: *Also see March of Comics #210, 217, 230, 254, 266, 278, 296, 308, 324,334, 346, 358, 370, 381, 394, 411, 432.*

LAST AMERICAN, THE
Marvel Comics (Epic): Dec, 1990 - No. 4, March, 1991 ($2.25, mini-series)
1-4: Alan Grant scripts 3.00

LAST AVENGERS STORY, THE (Last Avengers #1)
Marvel Comics: Nov, 1995 - No. 2, Dec, 1995 ($5.95, painted, limited series) (Alterniverse)
1,2: Peter David story; acetate-c in all. 1-New team (Hank Pym, Wasp, Human Torch, Cannonball, She-Hulk, Hotshot, Bombshell, Tommy Maximoff, Hawkeye & Mockingbird) forms to battle Ultron 59, Kang the Conqueror, The Grim Reaper & Oddball 6.00

LAST BATTLE, THE
Image Comics: Dec, 2011 ($7.99, square-bound, one-shot)
1-Facari-s/Brereton-painted art/c; Roman gladiator story; bonus Brereton sketch pages 8.00

LAST CHRISTMAS, THE
Image Comics: May, 2006 - No. 5, Oct, 2006 ($2.99, limited series)
1-5-Gerry Duggan & Brian Posehn-s/Rick Remender & Hilary Barta-a 3.00
TPB (2006, $14.99) r/#1-5; Patton Oswalt intro.; sketch pages and art 15.00

LAST CONTRACT, THE
BOOM! Studios: Jan, 2016 - No. 4, Apr, 2016 ($3.99, limited series)
1-4-Brisson-s/Estherren-a/c 4.00

LAST DAY IN VIETNAM
Dark Horse Books: July, 2000 ($10.95, graphic novel)
nn-Will Eisner-s/a/c 11.00

LAST DAYS OF ANIMAL MAN, THE
DC Comics: July, 2009 - No. 6, Dec, 2009 ($2.99, limited series)
1-6: 1-Conway-s/Batista-a/Bolland-c. 3,4-Starfire app. 5,6-Future Justice League app. 3.00
TPB (2010, $17.99) r/#1-6 18.00

LAST DAYS OF THE JUSTICE SOCIETY SPECIAL
DC Comics: 1986 ($2.50, one-shot, 68 pgs.)
1-62 pg. JSA story plus unpubbed G.A. pg. 2 4 6 8 10 12

LAST DEFENDERS, THE
Marvel Comics: May, 2008 - No. 6, Oct, 2008 ($2.99, limited series)
1-6-Nighthawk, She-Hulk, Colossus, and Blazing Skull; Muniz-a. 2-Deodato-c 3.00

LAST FANTASTIC FOUR STORY, THE
Marvel Comics: Oct, 2007 ($4.99, one-shot)
1-Stan Lee-s/John Romita, Jr.-a/c; Galactus app. 5.00

LAST GANG IN TOWN
DC Comics (Vertigo): Feb, 2016 - No. 6, Aug, 2016 ($3.99, limited series)
1-6: 1-Simon Oliver-s/Rufus Dayglo-a/Rob Davis-c 4.00

LAST GENERATION, THE
Black Tie Studios: 1986 - No. 5, 1989 ($1.95, B&W, high quality paper)
1-5 3.00
Book 1 (1989, $6.95)-By Caliber Press 7.00

LAST HERO STANDING (Characters from Spider-Girl's M2 universe)
Marvel Comics: Aug, 2005 - No. 5, Aug, 2005 ($2.99, weekly limited series)
1-5: 1-DeFalco-s/Olliffe-a. 4-Thor app. 5-Capt. America dies 3.00
TPB (2005, $13.99) r/#1-5 14.00

LAST HUNT, THE
Dell Publishing Co.: No. 678, Feb, 1956
Four Color 678-Movie, photo-c 6 12 18 42 79 115

LAST KISS
ACME Press (Eclipse): 1988 ($3.95, B&W, squarebound, 52 pgs.)
1-One story adapts E.A. Poe's The Black Cat 4.00

LAST OF THE COMANCHES (Movie) (See Wild Bill Hickok #28)
Avon Periodicals: 1953
nn-Kinstler-c/a, 21pgs.; Ravielli-a 19 38 57 109 172 240

LAST OF THE ERIES, THE (See American Graphics)

LAST OF THE FAST GUNS, THE
Dell Publishing Co.: No. 925, Aug, 1958
Four Color 925-Movie, photo-c 6 12 18 41 76 110

LAST OF THE MOHICANS (See King Classics & White Rider and...)

LAST OF THE VIKING HEROES, THE (Also see Silver Star #1)
Genesis West Comics: Mar, 1987 - No. 12 ($1.50/$1.95)
1-4,5A,5B,6-12: 4-Intro The Phantom Force, 1-Signed edition ($1.50), 5A-Kirby/Stevens-c. 5B,6 ($1.95). 7-Art Adams-c. 8-Kirby back-c. 4.00

The Last Phantom #6 © KFS

Laugh Comics #21 © ACP

Law Against Crime #1 © Essenkay

	GD 2.0	VG 4.0	FN 6.0	VF 8.0	VF/NM 9.0	NM- 9.2
Summer Special 1-3: 1-(1988)-Frazetta-c & illos. 2 (1990, $2.50)-A TMNT app. 3 (1991, $2.50)-Teenage Mutant Ninja Turtles						4.00
Summer Special 1-Signed edition (sold for $1.95)						4.00

NOTE: *Art Adams c-7.* ***Byrne*** *c-3.* ***Kirby*** *c-1p, 5p.* ***Perez*** *c-2i.* ***Stevens*** *c-5Ai.*

LAST ONE, THE
DC Comics (Vertigo): July, 1993 - No. 6, Dec, 1993 ($2.50, lim. series, mature)

	GD 2.0	VG 4.0	FN 6.0	VF 8.0	VF/NM 9.0	NM- 9.2
1-6						3.00

LAST PHANTOM, THE (Lee Falk's Phantom)
Dynamite Entertainment: 2010 - No. 12, 2012 ($3.99)

	GD 2.0	VG 4.0	FN 6.0	VF 8.0	VF/NM 9.0	NM- 9.2
1-12-Beatty-s/Ferigato-a; 1-Two covers by Alex Ross; Neves & Prado var. covers						4.00
Annual 1 (2011, $4.99) Beatty-s/Desjardins-a; two covers by Desjardins & Ross						5.00

LAST PLANET STANDING
Marvel Comics: July, 2006 - No. 5, Sept, 2006 ($2.99, limited series)

	GD 2.0	VG 4.0	FN 6.0	VF 8.0	VF/NM 9.0	NM- 9.2
1-5-Galactus threatens Spider-Girl & Fantastic Five's M2 Earth; Avengers app.; Olliffe-a						3.00
TPB (2006, $13.99) r/series						14.00

LAST SHOT
Image Comics: Aug, 2001 - No. 4, Mar, 2002 ($2.95, limited series)

	GD 2.0	VG 4.0	FN 6.0	VF 8.0	VF/NM 9.0	NM- 9.2
1-4: 1-Wraparound-c; by Studio XD						3.00
...: First Draw (5/01, $2.95) Introductory one-shot						3.00

LAST SONS OF AMERICA
BOOM! Studios: Nov, 2015 - No. 4, Apr, 2016 ($3.99, limited series)

	GD 2.0	VG 4.0	FN 6.0	VF 8.0	VF/NM 9.0	NM- 9.2
1-4-Phillip Johnson-s/Matthew Dow Smith-a						4.00

LAST STARFIGHTER, THE
Marvel Comics Group: Oct, 1984 - No. 3, Dec, 1984 (75¢, movie adaptation)

	GD 2.0	VG 4.0	FN 6.0	VF 8.0	VF/NM 9.0	NM- 9.2
1-3: r/Marvel Super Special; Guice-c						4.00

LAST TEMPTATION, THE
Marvel Comics: 1994 - No. 3, 1994 ($4.95, limited series)

	GD 2.0	VG 4.0	FN 6.0	VF 8.0	VF/NM 9.0	NM- 9.2
1-3-Alice Cooper story; Neil Gaiman scripts; McKean-c; Zulli-a: 1-Two covers						5.00
HC (Dark Horse Comics, 2005, $14.95) r/#1-3; Gaiman intro.						15.00

LAST TRAIN FROM GUN HILL
Dell Publishing Co.: No. 1012, July, 1959

	GD 2.0	VG 4.0	FN 6.0	VF 8.0	VF/NM 9.0	NM- 9.2
Four Color 1012-Movie, photo-c	8	16	24	52	99	145

LAST TRAIN TO DEADSVILLE: A CAL McDONALD MYSTERY (See Criminal Macabre)
Dark Horse Comics: May, 2004 - No. 4, Sept, 2004 ($2.99, limited series)

	GD 2.0	VG 4.0	FN 6.0	VF 8.0	VF/NM 9.0	NM- 9.2
1-4-Steve Niles-s/Kelley Jones-a/c						3.00
TPB (2005, $14.95) r/series						15.00

LATEST ADVENTURES OF FOXY GRANDPA (See Foxy Grandpa)

LATEST COMICS (Super Duper No. 3?)
Spotlight Publ./Palace Promotions (Jubilee): Mar, 1945 - No. 2, 1945?

	GD 2.0	VG 4.0	FN 6.0	VF 8.0	VF/NM 9.0	NM- 9.2
1-Super Duper	20	40	60	114	182	250
2-Bee-29 (nd); Jubilee in indicia blacked out	15	30	45	84	127	170

LAUGH
Archie Enterprises: June, 1987 - No. 29, Aug, 1991 (75¢/$1.00)

	GD 2.0	VG 4.0	FN 6.0	VF 8.0	VF/NM 9.0	NM- 9.2
V2#1						5.00
2-10,14,24: 5-X-Mas issue. 14-1st app. Hot Dog. 24-Re-intro Super Duck						4.00
11-13,15-23,25-29: 19-X-Mas issue						3.00

LAUGH COMICS (Teenage) (Formerly Black Hood #9-19) (Laugh #226 on)
Archie Publications (Close-Up): No. 20, Fall, 1946 - No. 400, Apr, 1987

	GD 2.0	VG 4.0	FN 6.0	VF 8.0	VF/NM 9.0	NM- 9.2
20-Archie begins; Katy Keene & Taffy begin by Woggon; Suzie & Wilbur also begin; Archie covers begin	161	322	483	1030	1765	2500
21-23,25	61	122	183	390	670	950
24- "Pipsy" by Kirby (6 pgs.)	63	126	189	403	689	975
26-30	41	82	123	250	418	585
31-40	32	64	96	192	314	435
41-60: 41,54-Debbi by Woggon	23	46	69	136	223	310
61-80: 67-Debbi by Woggon	15	30	45	88	137	185
81-99	8	16	24	55	105	155
100	9	18	27	57	111	165
101-105,110,112,114-126: 125-Debbi app.	6	12	18	40	73	105
106-109,111,113-Neal Adams-a (1 pg.) in each	6	12	18	41	76	110
127-144: Super-hero app. in all (see note)	7	14	21	46	86	125
145-(4/63) Josie by DeCarlo begins	7	14	21	46	86	125
146-149-early Josie app. by DeCarlo	5	10	15	33	57	80
150,162,163,165,167,169,170-No Josie	3	6	9	21	33	45
151-161,164,168-Josie app. by DeCarlo	4	8	12	27	44	60
166-Beatles-c (1/65)	6	12	18	42	79	115
171-180, 200 (12/67)	3	6	9	17	26	35
181-199	3	6	9	15	22	28
201-240(3/71)	2	4	6	11	16	20
241-280(7/74)	2	4	6	9	13	16
281-299	2	4	6	8	10	12
300(3/76)	2	4	6	8	11	14
301-340 (7/79)	1	2	3	5	7	9
341-370 (1/82)	1	2	3	4	5	7
371-379,385-399						5.00
380-Cheryl Blossom app.	2	4	6	9	12	15
381-384,400: 381-384-Katy Keene app.; by Woggon-381,382						6.00

NOTE: *The Fly app. in 128, 129, 132, 134, 138, 139. Flygirl app. in 136, 137, 143. Flyman app. in 137. The Jaguar app. in 127, 130, 131, 133, 135, 140-142, 144. Josie app. in 145-149, 151-161, 164, 168. Katy Keene app. in 20-125, 129, 130, 133. Horror/Sci-Fi covers on 128-135, 137, 139. Many issues contain paper dolls.* ***Al Fagaly*** *c-20-29.* ***Montana*** *c-33, 36, 37, 42.* ***Bill Vigoda*** *c-30, 50.*

LAUGH COMICS DIGEST (...Magazine #23-89; Laugh Digest Mag. #90 on)
Archie Publ. (Close-Up No. 1, 3 on): 8/74; No. 2, 9/75; No. 3, 3/76 - No. 200, Apr, 2005 (Digest-size) (Josie and Sabrina app. in most issues)

	GD 2.0	VG 4.0	FN 6.0	VF 8.0	VF/NM 9.0	NM- 9.2
1-Neal Adams-a	5	10	15	31	53	75
2,7,8,19-Neal Adams-a	3	6	9	19	30	40
3-6,9,10	3	6	9	15	22	28
11-18,20	2	4	6	11	16	20
21-40	2	4	6	9	13	16
41-60	1	3	4	6	8	10
61-80	1	2	3	5	6	8
81-99						5.00
100						6.00
101-138						4.00
139-200: 139-Begin $1.95-c. 148-Begin $1.99-c. 156-Begin $2.19-c. 180-Begin $2.39-c						3.00

NOTE: *Katy Keene in 23, 25, 27, 32-38, 40, 45-48, 50. The Fly-r in 19, 20. The Jaguar-r in 25, 27. Mr. Justice-r in 21. The Web-r in 23.*

LAUGH COMIX (Laugh Comics inside)(Formerly Top Notch Laugh; Suzie Comics No. 49 on)
MLJ Magazines: No. 46, Summer, 1944 - No. 48, Winter, 1944-45

	GD 2.0	VG 4.0	FN 6.0	VF 8.0	VF/NM 9.0	NM- 9.2
46-Wilbur & Suzie in all; Harry Sahle-c	36	72	108	211	343	475
47,48: 47-Sahle-c. 48-Bill Vigoda-c	24	48	72	142	234	325

LAUGH-IN MAGAZINE (TV)(Magazine)
Laufer Publ. Co.: Oct, 1968 - No. 12, Oct, 1969 (50¢) (Satire)

	GD 2.0	VG 4.0	FN 6.0	VF 8.0	VF/NM 9.0	NM- 9.2
V1#1	5	10	15	30	50	70
2-12	3	6	9	21	33	45

LAUREL & HARDY (See Larry Harmon's... & March of Comics No. 302, 314)

LAUREL AND HARDY (...Comics)
St. John Publ. Co.: 3/49 - No. 3, 9/49; No. 26, 11/55 - No. 28, 3/56 (No #4-25)

	GD 2.0	VG 4.0	FN 6.0	VF 8.0	VF/NM 9.0	NM- 9.2
1	87	174	261	553	952	1350
2	42	84	126	265	445	625
3	36	72	108	211	343	475
26-28 (Reprints)	17	34	51	98	154	210

LAUREL AND HARDY (TV)
Dell Publishing Co.: Oct, 1962 - No. 4, Sept-Nov, 1963

	GD 2.0	VG 4.0	FN 6.0	VF 8.0	VF/NM 9.0	NM- 9.2
12-423-210 (8-10/62)	6	12	18	41	76	110
2-4 (Dell)	4	8	12	28	47	65

LAUREL AND HARDY (Larry Harmon's...)
Gold Key: Jan, 1967 - No. 2, Oct, 1967

	GD 2.0	VG 4.0	FN 6.0	VF 8.0	VF/NM 9.0	NM- 9.2
1-Photo back-c	4	8	12	27	44	60
2	4	8	12	21	33	45

L.A.W., THE (LIVING ASSAULT WEAPONS)
DC Comics: Sept, 1999 - No. 6, Feb, 2000 ($2.50, limited series)

	GD 2.0	VG 4.0	FN 6.0	VF 8.0	VF/NM 9.0	NM- 9.2
1-6-Blue Beetle, Question, Judomaster, Capt. Atom app.; Giordano-a. 5-JLA app.						3.00

LAW AGAINST CRIME (Law-Crime on cover)
Essenkay Publishing Co.: April, 1948 - No. 3, Aug, 1948 (Real Stories from Police Files)

	GD 2.0	VG 4.0	FN 6.0	VF 8.0	VF/NM 9.0	NM- 9.2
1-(#1-3 are half funny animal, half crime stories)-L. B. Cole-c/a in all; electrocution-c	94	188	282	597	1024	1450
2-L. B. Cole-c/a	63	126	189	403	689	975
3-Used in **SOTI**, pg. 180,181 & illo "The wish to hurt or kill couples in lovers' lanes;" reprinted in All-Famous Crime #9	82	164	246	528	902	1275

LAW AND ORDER
Maximum Press: Sept, 1995 - No. 2, 1995 ($2.50, unfinished limited series)

	GD 2.0	VG 4.0	FN 6.0	VF 8.0	VF/NM 9.0	NM- 9.2
1,2						3.00

LAWBREAKERS (...Suspense Stories No. 10 on)
Law and Order Magazines (Charlton): Mar, 1951 - No. 9, Oct-Nov, 1952

Lazarus #17 © Rucka & Lark

Leading Comics #4 © DC

Leave It to Binky #9 © DC

	GD 2.0	VG 4.0	FN 6.0	VF 8.0	VF/NM 9.0	NM- 9.2
1	45	90	135	284	480	675
2	27	54	81	160	263	365
3,5,6,8,9: 6-Anti-Wertham editorial	22	44	66	132	216	300
4- "White Death" junkie story	32	64	96	192	314	435
7- "The Deadly Dopesters" drug story	32	64	96	192	314	435

LAWBREAKERS ALWAYS LOSE!
Marvel Comics (CBS): Spring, 1948 - No. 10, Oct, 1949

	GD 2.0	VG 4.0	FN 6.0	VF 8.0	VF/NM 9.0	NM- 9.2
1-2pg. Kurtzman-a, "Giggles 'n' Grins"	40	80	120	246	411	575
2	21	42	63	126	206	285
3-5: 4-Vampire story	17	34	51	100	158	215
6(2/49)-Has editorial defense against charges of Dr. Wertham	19	38	57	109	172	235
7-Used in **SOTI**, illo "Comic-book philosophy"	34	68	102	199	325	450
8-10: 9,10-Photo-c	15	30	45	88	137	185

NOTE: *Brodsky c-4, 5. Shores c-1-3, 6-8.*

LAWBREAKERS SUSPENSE STORIES (Formerly Lawbreakers; Strange Suspense Stories No. 16 on)
Capitol Stories/Charlton Comics: No. 10, Jan, 1953 - No. 15, Nov, 1953

	GD 2.0	VG 4.0	FN 6.0	VF 8.0	VF/NM 9.0	NM- 9.2
10	50	100	150	315	533	750
11 (3/53)-Severed tongues-c/story & woman negligee scene	300	600	900	1950	3375	4800
12-14: 13-Giordano-c begin, end #15	37	74	111	222	361	500
15-Acid-in-face-c/story; hands dissolved in acid story	77	154	231	493	847	1200

LAW-CRIME (See Law Against Crime)

LAWDOG
Marvel Comics (Epic Comics): May, 1993 - No. 10, Feb, 1993

	GD 2.0	VG 4.0	FN 6.0	VF 8.0	VF/NM 9.0	NM- 9.2
1-10						3.00

LAWDOG/GRIMROD: TERROR AT THE CROSSROADS
Marvel Comics (Epic Comics): Sept, 1993 ($3.50)

	GD 2.0	VG 4.0	FN 6.0	VF 8.0	VF/NM 9.0	NM- 9.2
1						4.00

LAWMAN (TV)
Dell Publishing Co.: No. 970, Feb, 1959 - No. 11, Apr-June, 1962 (All photo-c)

	GD 2.0	VG 4.0	FN 6.0	VF 8.0	VF/NM 9.0	NM- 9.2
Four Color 970(#1) John Russell, Peter Brown photo-c	10	20	30	69	147	225
Four Color 1035('60), 3(2-4/60)-Toth-a	7	14	21	46	86	125
4-11	6	12	18	37	66	95

LAW OF DREDD, THE (Also see Judge Dredd)
Quality Comics/Fleetway #8 on: 1989 - No. 33, 1992 ($1.50/$1.75)

	GD 2.0	VG 4.0	FN 6.0	VF 8.0	VF/NM 9.0	NM- 9.2
1-33: Bolland a-1-6,8,10-12,14(2 pg),15,19						3.00

LAWRENCE (See Movie Classics)

LAZARUS (Also see Lazarus: X +66)
Image Comics: Jun, 2013 - Present ($2.99/$3.50/$3.99)

	GD 2.0	VG 4.0	FN 6.0	VF 8.0	VF/NM 9.0	NM- 9.2
1-9-Rucka-s/Lark-a/c						3.50
10-21-($3.50) 19-Bonus preview of Black Magic #1						3.50
22-26-($3.99)						4.00
Image Firsts Lazarus #1 (11/15, $1.00) reprints #1; afterword by Rucka; Lark sketch art						3.00
... Sourcebook, Volume 1: Carlyle (4/16, $3.99) Dossier of politics, locations, weapons						4.00
... Sourcebook, Volume 2: Hock (5/17, $3.99) Dossier of politics, locations, weapons						4.00
... Sourcebook, Volume 3: Vassalovka (2/18, $3.99) Dossier of politics, locations						4.00

LAZARUS CHURCHYARD
Tundra Publishing: June, 1992 - No. 3, 1992 ($3.95/$4.50, 44 pgs., coated stock)

	GD 2.0	VG 4.0	FN 6.0	VF 8.0	VF/NM 9.0	NM- 9.2
1-3						5.00
The Final Cut (Image, 1/01, $14.95, TPB) Reprints Ellis/D'Israeli strips						15.00

LAZARUS FIVE
DC Comics: July, 2000 - No. 5, Nov, 2000 ($2.50, limited series)

	GD 2.0	VG 4.0	FN 6.0	VF 8.0	VF/NM 9.0	NM- 9.2
1-5-Harris-c/Abell-a(p)						3.00

LAZARUS: X +66 (Characters from Lazarus)
Image Comics: Jul, 2017 - No. 6, Feb, 2018 ($3.99, limited series)

	GD 2.0	VG 4.0	FN 6.0	VF 8.0	VF/NM 9.0	NM- 9.2
1-6: 1-Lieber-a; how Casey became a Dagger. 2-Chater-a. 5-Evely-a						4.00

LEADING COMICS
DC Comics: Jan. 1942

nn - Ashcan comic, not distributed to newsstands, only for in-house use. Cover art is Detective Comics #57, interior of Star Spangled Comics #2 (a FN+ copy sold for $1015.75 in 2012)

LEADING COMICS (...Screen Comics No. 42 on)
National Periodical Publications: Winter, 1941-42 - No. 41, Feb-Mar, 1950

	GD 2.0	VG 4.0	FN 6.0	VF 8.0	VF/NM 9.0	NM- 9.2
1-Origin The Seven Soldiers of Victory; Green Arrow & Speedy, Crimson Avenger, Shining Knight, The Vigilante, Star Spangled Kid & Stripesy begin; The Dummy (Vigilante villain) 1st app.; 1st Green Arrow-c	411	822	1233	2877	5039	7200
2-Meskin-a; Fred Ray-c	123	246	369	767	1344	1900
3	97	194	291	621	1061	1500
4,5	68	136	204	435	743	1050
6-10	52	104	156	328	552	775
11,12,14(Spring, 1945)	40	80	120	246	411	575
13-Classic robot-c	103	206	309	659	1130	1600
15-(Sum,'45)-Contents change to funny animal	26	52	78	154	252	350
16-22,24-30: 16-Nero Fox-c begin, end #22	14	28	42	80	115	150
23-1st app. Peter Porkchops by Otto Feuer & begins	26	52	78	154	252	350
31,32,34-41: 34-41-Leading Screen... on-c only	12	24	36	67	94	120
33-(Scarce)	20	40	60	114	182	250

NOTE: *Otto Feuer-a most #15-on; Rube Grossman-a most #15-on;c-15-41. Post a-23-37, 39, 41.*

LEADING MAN
Image Comics: June, 2006 - No. 5, Feb, 2007 ($3.50, limited series)

	GD 2.0	VG 4.0	FN 6.0	VF 8.0	VF/NM 9.0	NM- 9.2
1-5-B. Clay Moore-s/Jeremy Haun-a						3.50
TPB (2/07, $14.95) r/#1-5; sketch gallery						15.00

LEADING SCREEN COMICS (Formerly Leading Comics)
National Periodical Publ.: No. 42, Apr-May, 1950 - No. 77, Aug-Sept, 1955

	GD 2.0	VG 4.0	FN 6.0	VF 8.0	VF/NM 9.0	NM- 9.2
42-Peter Porkchops-c/stories continue	12	24	36	67	94	120
43-77	11	22	33	60	83	105

NOTE: *Grossman a-most. Mayer a-45-48, 50, 54-57, 60, 62-74, 75(3), 76, 77.*

LEAGUE OF CHAMPIONS, THE (Also see The Champions)
Hero Graphics: Dec, 1990 - No. 12, 1992 ($2.95, 52 pgs.)

	GD 2.0	VG 4.0	FN 6.0	VF 8.0	VF/NM 9.0	NM- 9.2
1-12: 1-Flare app. 2-Origin Malice						4.00

LEAGUE OF EXTRAORDINARY GENTLEMEN, THE
America's Best Comics: Mar, 1999 - No. 6, Sept, 2000 ($2.95, limited series)

	GD 2.0	VG 4.0	FN 6.0	VF 8.0	VF/NM 9.0	NM- 9.2
1-Alan Moore-s/Kevin O'Neill-a	2	4	6	11	16	20
1-DF Edition ($10.00) O'Neill-c	3	6	9	14	20	25
2,3						6.00
4-6: 5-Revised printing with "Amaze 'Whirling Spray' Syringe" parody ad						4.00
5-Initial printing recalled because of "Marvel Co. Syringe" parody ad	13	26	39	86	188	290
... Compendium 1,2: 1-r/#1,2. 2-r/#3,4						6.00
Hardcover (2000, $24.95) r/#1-6 plus cover gallery						25.00

LEAGUE OF EXTRAORDINARY GENTLEMEN, THE (Volume 2)
America's Best Comics: Sept, 2002 - No. 6, Nov, 2003 ($3.50, limited series)

	GD 2.0	VG 4.0	FN 6.0	VF 8.0	VF/NM 9.0	NM- 9.2
1-6-Alan Moore-s/Kevin O'Neill-a						5.00
... Bumper Compendium 1,2: 1-r/#1,2. 2-r/#3,4						6.00
... Black Dossier (HC, 2007, $29.99) new graphic novel; 3-D section with glasses; extras						30.00

LEAGUE OF EXTRAORDINARY GENTLEMEN
Top Shelf Productions/Knockabout Comics: 2009; 2011; 2012 ($7.95/$9.95, squarebound)

	GD 2.0	VG 4.0	FN 6.0	VF 8.0	VF/NM 9.0	NM- 9.2
... Century: 1910 (2009, $7.95) Alan Moore-s/Kevin O'Neill-a						8.00
... Century #2 "1969" (2011, $9.95) Alan Moore-s/Kevin O'Neill-a						10.00
... Century #3 "2009" (2012, $9.95) Alan Moore-s/Kevin O'Neill-a						10.00

LEAGUE OF JUSTICE
DC Comics (Elseworlds): 1996 - No. 2, 1996 ($5.95, 48 pgs., squarebound)

	GD 2.0	VG 4.0	FN 6.0	VF 8.0	VF/NM 9.0	NM- 9.2
1,2: Magic-based alternate DC Universe story; Giordano-i						6.00

LEATHERFACE
Arpad Publishing: May (April on-c), 1991 - No. 4, May, 1992 ($2.75, painted-c)

	GD 2.0	VG 4.0	FN 6.0	VF 8.0	VF/NM 9.0	NM- 9.2
1-4-Based on Texas Chainsaw movie; Dorman-c	1	2	3	5	7	9

LEATHERNECK THE MARINE (See Mighty Midget Comics)

LEAVE IT TO BEAVER (TV)
Dell Publishing Co.: No. 912, June, 1958; May-July, 1962 (All photo-c)

	GD 2.0	VG 4.0	FN 6.0	VF 8.0	VF/NM 9.0	NM- 9.2
Four Color 912	14	28	42	94	207	320
Four Color 999,1103,1191,1285, 01-428-207	12	24	36	80	173	265

LEAVE IT TO BINKY (Binky No. 72 on) (Super DC Giant) (No. 1-22: 52 pgs.)
National Periodical Publs.: 2-3/48 - #60, 10/58; #61, 6-7/68 - #71, 2-3/70 (Teen-age humor)

	GD 2.0	VG 4.0	FN 6.0	VF 8.0	VF/NM 9.0	NM- 9.2
1-Lucy wears Superman costume	43	86	129	271	461	650
2	21	42	63	126	206	285
3,4	15	30	45	88	137	185
5-Superman cameo	20	40	60	114	182	250
6-10	14	28	42	76	108	140
11-14,16-22: Last 52 pg. issue	12	24	36	67	94	120
15-Scribbly story by Mayer	14	28	42	76	108	140
23-28,30-45: 45-Last pre-code (2/55)	10	20	30	56	76	95

Leave It to Chance #3 © J&P

Legenderry Red Sonja #4 © Red Sonja LLC

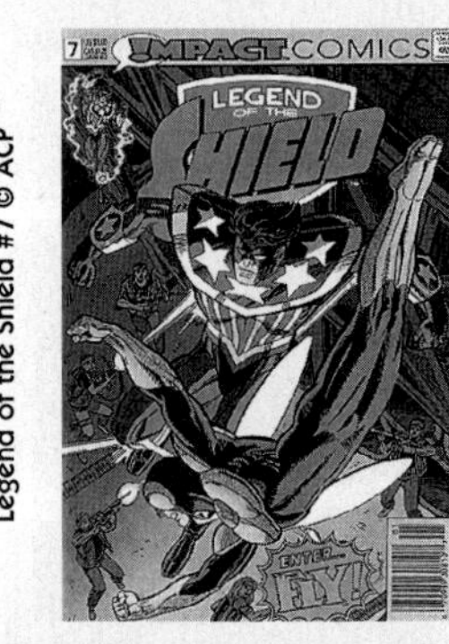

Legend of the Shield #7 © ACP

	GD 2.0	VG 4.0	FN 6.0	VF 8.0	VF/NM 9.0	NM- 9.2
29-Used in **POP**, pg. 78	10	20	30	58	79	100
46-60: 60-(10/58)	5	10	15	35	63	90
61 (6-7/68) 1950's reprints with art changes	5	10	15	34	60	85
62-69: 67-Last 12¢ issue	4	8	12	27	44	60
70-7pg. app. Bus Driver who looks like Ralph from Honeymooners	5	10	15	30	50	70
71-Last issue	4	8	12	28	47	65

NOTE: ***Aragones**-a-61, 62, 67. **Drucker** a-28. **Mayer** a-1, 2, 15. Created by **Mayer**.*

LEAVE IT TO CHANCE
Image Comics (Homage Comics): Sept, 1996 - No. 11, Sept, 1998; No. 13, July, 2002
DC Comics (Homage Comics): No. 12, Jun, 1999 ($2.50/$2.95/$4.95)

1-3: 1-Intro Chance Falconer & St. George; James Robinson scripts & Paul Smith-c/a 5.00
4-12: 12-(6/99) 3.00
13-(7/02, $4.95) includes sketch pages and pin-ups 5.00
Free Comic Book Day Edition (2003) - James Robinson-s/Paul Smith-a 3.00
Shaman's Rain TPB (1997, $9.95) r/#1-4 10.00
Shaman's Rain HC (2002, $14.95, over-sized 8 1/4" x 12") r/#1-4 15.00
Trick or Threat TPB (1997, $12.95) r/#5-8 13.00
Trick or Threat HC (2002, $14.95, over-sized 8 1/4" x 12") r/#5-8 15.00
Vol. 3: Monster Madness and Other Stories HC (2003, $14.95, 8 1/4" x 12") r/#9-11 15.00

LEAVING MEGALOPOLIS: SURVIVING MEGALOPOLIS
Dark Horse Comics: Jan, 2016 - No. 6, Sept, 2016 ($3.99)

1-6-Gail Simone-s/Jim Calafiore-a 4.00

LEE HUNTER, INDIAN FIGHTER
Dell Publishing Co.: No. 779, Mar, 1957; No. 904, May, 1958

	GD	VG	FN	VF	VF/NM	NM-
Four Color 779 (#1)	6	12	18	37	66	95
Four Color 904	5	10	15	30	50	70

LEFT-HANDED GUN, THE (Movie)
Dell Publishing Co.: No. 913, July, 1958

	GD	VG	FN	VF	VF/NM	NM-
Four Color 913-Paul Newman photo-c	9	18	27	57	111	165

LEGACY
Majestic Entertainment: Oct, 1993 - No. 2, Nov, 1993; No. 0, 1994 ($2.25)

1-2,0: 1-Glow-in-the-dark-c. 0-Platinum 3.00

LEGACY
Image Comics: May, 2003 - No. 4, Feb, 2004 ($2.95)

1-4: 1-Francisco-a/Treffiletti-s 3.00

LEGACY OF KAIN (Based on the Eidos video game)
Top Cow Productions: Oct, 1999; Jan, 2004 ($2.99)

...Defiance 1 (1/04, $2.99) Cha-c; Kirkham-a 3.00
...Soul Reaver 1 (10/99, Diamond Dateline supplement) Benitez-c 3.00

LEGACY OF LUTHER STRODE, THE (Also see Legend of Luther Strode)
Image Comics: Apr, 2015 - Present ($3.99/$3.50)

1-($3.99) Justin Jordan-s/Tradd Moore-a 4.00
2-6-($3.50) 3.50

LEGEND
DC Comics (WildStorm): Apr, 2005 - No. 4, July, 2005 ($5.95/$5.99, limited series)

1-4-Howard Chaykin-s/Russ Heath-a; inspired by Philip Wylie's novel "Gladiator" 6.00

LEGENDARY STAR-LORD (Guardians of the Galaxy)
Marvel Comics: Sept, 2014 - No. 12, Jul, 2015 ($3.99)

1-12: 1-Humphries-s/Medina-a. 4-Thanos app. 9-11-Black Vortex x-over 4.00

LEGENDARY TALESPINNERS
Dynamite Entertainment: 2010 - No. 3, 2010 ($3.99)

1-3-Kuhoric-s/Bond-a; two covers 4.00

LEGENDERRY: A STEAMPUNK ADVENTURE
Dynamite Entertainment: 2014 - No. 7, 2014 ($3.99)

1-7-Willingham-s/Davila-a/Benitez-c. 4.00

LEGENDERRY: GREEN HORNET
Dynamite Entertainment: 2015 - No. 5, 2015 ($3.99)

1-5-Gregory-s/Peeples-a; multiple covers 4.00

LEGENDERRY: RED SONJA
Dynamite Entertainment: 2015 - No. 5, 2015 ($3.99)

1-5: 1-Andreyko-s/Aneke-a; multiple covers; Steampunk Sonja; Bride of Frankenstein app. 4.00

LEGENDERRY: RED SONJA (Volume 2)
Dynamite Entertainment: 2018 - Present ($3.99)

1-Andreyko-s/Lima-a; multiple covers; Kulan Gath app. 4.00

LEGENDERRY: VAMPIRELLA
Dynamite Entertainment: 2015 - No. 5, 2015 ($3.99)

1-5-Avallone-s/Cabrera-a; Steampunk Vampirella 4.00

LEGEND OF CUSTER, THE (TV)
Dell Publishing Co.: Jan, 1968

	GD	VG	FN	VF	VF/NM	NM-
1-Wayne Maunder photo-c	3	6	9	17	26	35

LEGEND OF ISIS
Alias Entertainment: May, 2005 - No. 5 ($2.99)

1-5: 1-Three covers; Ottney-s/Fontana-a 3.00
...: Beginnings TPB (5/05, $9.99) Ottney-s 10.00

LEGEND OF JESSE JAMES, THE (TV)
Gold Key: Feb, 1966

	GD	VG	FN	VF	VF/NM	NM-
10172-602-Photo-c	3	6	9	17	26	35

LEGEND OF KAMUI, THE (See Kamui)

LEGEND OF LOBO, THE (See Movie Comics)

LEGEND OF LUTHER STRODE, THE (Sequel to Strange Talent of Luther Strode)
Image Comics: Dec, 2012 - No. 6, Aug, 2013 ($3.50, limited series)

1-5: Justin Jordan-s/Tradd Moore-a 3.50

LEGEND OF OZ: TIK-TOK AND THE KALIDAH
Aspen MLT: Apr, 2016 - No. 3, Jul, 2016 ($3.99)

1-3-Rob Anderson-s/Renato Rei-a. 1-Three covers. 2,3-Two covers 4.00

LEGEND OF OZ: THE WICKED WEST
Big Dog Press: Oct, 2011 - No. 6, Aug, 2012; Oct, 2012 - No. 18, May 2014 ($3.50)

1-6-Multiple covers on all 3.50
Vol. 2 1-18-Multiple covers on all 3.50

LEGEND OF OZ: THE WICKED WEST
Aspen MLT: Oct, 2015 - No. 6, Mar, 2016 ($3.99)

1-6-Reprints 2011 series 4.00

LEGEND OF SUPREME
Image Comics (Extreme): Dec, 1994 - No. 3, Feb, 1995 ($2.50, limited series)

1-3 3.00

LEGEND OF THE ELFLORD
DavDez Arts: July, 1998 - No. 2, Sept, 1998 ($2.95)

1,2-Barry Blair & Colin Chin-s/a 3.00

LEGEND OF THE HAWKMAN
DC Comics: 2000 - No. 3, 2000 ($4.95, limited series)

1-3-Raab-s/Lark-c/a 5.00

LEGEND OF THE SHADOW CLAN
Aspen MLT: Feb, 2013 - No. 5, Jul, 2013 ($1.00/$3.99)

1-($1.00) David Wohl-s/Cory Smith-a; mutiple covers 3.00
2-5-($3.99) 4.00

LEGEND OF THE SHIELD, THE
DC Comics (Impact Comics): July, 1991 - No. 16, Oct, 1992 ($1.00)

1-16: 6,7-The Fly x-over. 12-Contains trading card 4.00
Annual 1 (1992, $2.50, 68 pgs.)-Snyder-a; w/trading card 4.00

LEGEND OF WONDER WOMAN, THE
DC Comics: May, 1986 - No. 4, Aug, 1986 (75¢, limited series)

1-4 4.00

LEGEND OF WONDER WOMAN, THE (Printing of digital-first stories)
DC Comics: Mar, 2016 - No. 9, Oct, 2016 ($3.99)

1-9: Childhood/origin flashbacks of Diana; Renae de Liz-s/a. 2-Steve Trevor app. 4.00

LEGEND OF YOUNG DICK TURPIN, THE (Disney)(TV)
Gold Key: May, 1966

	GD	VG	FN	VF	VF/NM	NM-
1 (10176-605)-Photo/painted-c	3	6	9	17	26	35

LEGEND OF ZELDA, THE (Link: The Legend... in indicia)
Valiant Comics: 1990 - No. 4, 1990 ($1.95, coated stiff-c) V2#1, 1990 - No. 5, 1990 ($1.50)

	GD	VG	FN	VF	VF/NM	NM-
1-4: 4-Layton-c(i)	2	4	6	11	16	20
V2#1-5	1	3	4	6	8	10

LEGENDS
DC Comics: Nov, 1986 - No. 6, Apr, 1987 (75¢, limited series)

	GD	VG	FN	VF	VF/NM	NM-
1-Byrne-c/a(p) in all; 1st app. Amanda Waller and the new Captain Marvel	2	4	6	8	10	12

Legends of the Dark Knight #11 © DC

Legion (2018 series) #1 © MAR

Legion of Monsters: Satana #1 © MAR

GD 2.0 | VG 4.0 | FN 6.0 | VF 8.0 | VF/NM 9.0 | NM- 9.2

2,4,5 6.00
3-1st app. new Suicide Squad; death of Blockbuster 3 6 9 16 23 30
6-1st app. new Justice League 2 4 6 8 10 12

LEGENDS OF DANIEL BOONE, THE (...Frontier Scout)
National Periodical Publications: Oct-Nov, 1955 - No. 8, Dec-Jan, 1956-57

1 (Scarce)-Nick Cardy c-1-8 54 108 162 346 591 835
2 (Scarce) 40 80 120 246 411 575
3-8 (Scarce) 34 68 102 199 325 450

LEGENDS OF NASCAR, THE
Vortex Comics: Nov, 1990 - No. 14, 1992? (#1 3rd printing (1/91) says 2nd printing inside)

1-Bill Elliott biog.; Trimpe-a ($1.50) 5.00
1-2nd printing (11/90, $2.00) 3.00
1-3rd print; contains Maxx racecards ($3.00) 3.00
2-14: 2-Richard Petty. 3-Ken Schrader (7/91). 4-Bobby Allison; Spiegle-a(p); Adkins part-i. 5-Sterling Marlin. 6-Bill Elliott. 7-Junior Johnson; Spiegle-c/a. 8-Benny Parsons; Heck-a 3.00
1-13-Hologram cover versions. 2-Hologram shows Bill Elliott's car by mistake (all are numbered & limited) 5.00
2-Hologram corrected version 5.00
Christmas Special ($5.95) 6.00

LEGENDS OF RED SONJA
Dynamite Entertainment: 2013 - No. 5, 2014 ($3.99)

1-5-Short stories by various incl. Simone, Grayson; covers by Anacleto & Thorne 4.00

LEGENDS OF THE DARK CLAW
DC Comics (Amalgam): Apr, 1996 ($1.95)

1-Jim Balent-c/a 3.00

LEGENDS OF THE DARK KNIGHT (See Batman: ...)

LEGENDS OF THE DARK KNIGHT
DC Comics: Dec, 2012 - Present ($3.99, printings of stories first released online)

1-13: 1-Lindelof-s. 2-4-Joker app. 5-Hester-a 4.00
... 100 Page Super Spectacular 1-5 (2/14 - Present, quarterly, $9.99) 1-(2/14) 10.00

LEGENDS OF THE DC UNIVERSE
DC Comics: Feb, 1998 - No. 41, June, 2001 ($1.95/$1.99/$2.50)

1-13,15-21: 1-3-Superman; Robinson-s/Semeiks-a/Orbik-painted-c. 4,5-Wonder Woman; Deodato-a/Rude painted-c. 8-GL/GA, O'Neil-s. 10,11-Batgirl; Dodson-a. 12,13-Justice League. 15-17-Flash. 18-Kid Flash; Guice-a. 19-Impulse; prelude to JLApe Annuals. 20,21-Abin Sur 4.00
14-($3.95) Jimmy Olsen; Kirby-esque-c by Rude 5.00
22-27,30: 22,23-Superman; Rude-c/Ladronn-a. 26,27-Aquaman/Joker 3.00
28,29: Green Lantern & the Atom; Gil Kane-a; covers by Kane and Ross 3.00
31,32: 32-Begin $2.50-c; Wonder Woman; Texeira-c 3.00
33-36-Hal Jordan as The Spectre; DeMatteis-s/Zulli-a; Hale painted-c 3.00
37-41: 37,38-Kyle Rayner. 39-Superman. 40,41-Atom; Harris-c 3.00
... Crisis on Infinite Earths 1 (2/99, $4.95) Untold story during and after Crisis on Infinite Earths #4; Wolfman-s/Ryan-a/Orbik-c 5.00
... 80 Page Giant 1 (9/98, $4.95) Stories and art by various incl. Ditko, Perez, Gibbons, Mumy; Joe Kubert-c 5.00
... 80 Page Giant 2 (1/00, $4.95) Stories and art by various incl. Challengers by Art Adams; Sean Phillips-c 5.00
... 3-D Gallery (12/98, $2.95) Pin-ups w/glasses 3.00

LEGENDS OF THE LEGION (See Legion of Super-Heroes)
DC Comics: Feb, 1998 - No. 4, May, 1998 ($2.25, limited series)

1-4:1-Origin-s of Ultra Boy. 2-Spark. 3-Umbra. 4-Star Boy 3.00

LEGENDS OF THE STARGRAZERS (See Vanguard Illustrated #2)
Innovation Publishing: Aug, 1989 - No. 6, 1990 ($1.95, limited series, mature)

1-6: 1-Redondo part inks 3.00

LEGENDS OF THE WORLD'S FINEST (See World's Finest)
DC Comics: 1994 - No. 3, 1994 ($4.95, squarebound, limited series)

1-3: Simonson scripts; Brereton-c/a; embossed foil logos 6.00
TPB-(1995, $14.95) r/#1-3 15.00

LEGENDS OF TOMORROW
DC Comics: May, 2016 - Present ($7.99, squarebound)

1-6: Short stories of Firestorm, Metal Men, Metamorpho and Sugar & Spike. 6-Legion of Super-Heroes app. 8.00

LEGION (David Haller from X-Men)
Marvel Comics: Mar, 2018 - Present ($3.99)

1,2-MIlligan-s/Torres-a 4.00

L.E.G.I.O.N. (The # to right of title represents year of print)(Also see Lobo & R.E.B.E.L.S.)
DC Comics: Feb, 1989 - No. 70, Sept, 1994 ($1.50/$1.75)

1-Giffen plots/breakdowns in #1-12,28 5.00
2-22,24-47: 3-Lobo app. #3 on. 4-1st Lobo-c this title. 5-Lobo joins L.E.G.I.O.N. 13-Lar Gand app. 16-Lar Gand joins L.E.G.I.O.N., leaves #19. 31-Capt. Marvel app. 35-L.E.G.I.O.N. '92 begins 3.00
23,70-($2.50, 52 pgs.)-L.E.G.I.O.N. '91 begins. 70-Zero Hour 4.00
48,49,51-69: 48-Begin $1.75-c. 63-L.E.G.I.O.N. '94 begins; Superman x-over 3.00
50-($3.50, 68 pgs.) 4.00
Annual 1-5 ('90-94, 68 pgs.): 1-Lobo, Superman app. 2-Alan Grant scripts. 5-Elseworlds story; Lobo app. 4.00
NOTE: *Alan Grant scripts in #1-39, 51, Annual 1, 2.*

LEGION, THE (Continued from Legion Lost & Legion Worlds)
DC Comics: Dec, 2001 - No. 38, Oct, 2004 ($2.50)

1-Abnett & Lanning-s; Coipel & Lanning-c/a 4.00
2-24: 3-8-Ra's al Ghul app. 5-Snejbjerg-a. 9-DeStefano-a. 12-Legion vs. JLA. 16-Fatal Five app.; Walker-a 17,18-Ra's al Ghul app. 20-23-Universo app. 3.00
25-($3.95) Art by Harris, Cockrum, Rivoche; teenage Clark Kent app.; Harris-c 4.00
26-38-Superboy in classic costume. 26-30-Darkseid app. 31-Giffen-a. 35-38-Jurgens-a 3.00
...Secret Files 3003 (1/04, $4.95) Kirk-a, Harris-c/a; Superboy app. 5.00
...Foundations TPB (2004, $19.95) r/#25-30 & Secret Files 3003; Harris-c 20.00

LEGION LOST (Continued from Legion of Super-Heroes [4th series] #125)
DC Comics: May, 2000 - No. 12, Apr, 2001 ($2.50, limited series)

1-Abnett & Lanning-s. Coipel & Lanning-c/a 1 2 3 4 5 7
2-12-Abnett & Lanning-s. Coipel & Lanning-c/a in most. 4,9-Alixe-a 3.00
HC (2011, $39.99, dustjacket) r/#1-12 40.00

LEGION LOST (DC New 52)
DC Comics: Nov, 2011 - No. 16, Mar, 2013 ($2.99)

1-16: 1-Nicieza-s/Woods/a/c; Legionnaires trapped in the 21st century. 7,8-DeFalco-s. 8-Prelude to The Culling; Ravagers app. 9-The Culling x-over with Teen Titans. 14-16-Superboy & the Ravagers app. 3.00
#0 (11/12, $2.99) Origin of Timber Wolf; DeFalco-s/Woods-a 3.00

LEGIONNAIRES (See Legion of Super-Heroes #40, 41 & Showcase 95 #6)
DC Comics: Apr, 1992 - No. 81, Mar, 2000 ($1.25/$1.50/$2.25)

0-(10/94)-Zero Hour restart of Legion; released between #18 & #19 3.00
1-49,51-77: 1-(4/92)-Chris Sprouse-c/a; polybagged w/SkyBox trading card. 11-Kid Quantum joins. 18-(9/94)-Zero Hour. 19(11/94). 37-Valor (Lar Gand) becomes M'onel (5/96). 43-Legion tryouts; reintro Princess Projectra, Shadow Lass & others. 47-Forms one cover image with LSH #91. 60-Karate Kid & Kid Quantum join. 61-Silver Age & 70's Legion app. 76-Return of Wildfire. 79,80-Coipel-c/a; Legion vs. the Blight 3.00
50-($3.95) Pullout poster by Davis/Farmer 4.00
#1,000,000 (11/98) Sean Phillips-a 3.00
Annual 1,3 ('94,'96 $2.95)-1-Elseworlds-s. 3-Legends of the Dead Earth-s 4.00
Annual 2 (1995, $3.95)-Year One-s 4.50

LEGIONNAIRES THREE
DC Comics: Jan, 1986 - No. 4, May, 1986 (75¢, limited series)

1-4 4.00

LEGION OF MONSTERS (Also see Marvel Premiere #28 & Marvel Preview #8)
Marvel Comics Group: Sept, 1975 ($1.00, B&W, magazine, 76 pgs.)

1-Origin & 1st app. Legion of Monsters; Neal Adams-c; Morrow-a; origin & only app. The Manphibian; Frankenstein by Mayerik; Bram Stoker's Dracula adaptation; Reese-a; painted-c (#2 was advertised with Morbius & Satana, but was never published) 6 12 18 37 66 95

LEGION OF MONSTERS (One-shots)
Marvel Comics: Apr, 2007 - Sept, 2007 ($2.99)

... Man-Thing (5/07) Huston-s/Janson-a/Land-c; Simon Garth: Zombie by Ted McKeever 3.00
... Morbius (9/07) Cahill-s/Gaydos-a/Land-c; Dracula w/Finch-a/Cebulski-s 3.00
... Satana (8/07) Furth-s/Andrasofszky-a/Land-c; Living Mummy by Hickman 3.00
... Werewolf By Night (4/07) Carey-s/Land-a/c; Monster of Frankenstein by Skottie Young 3.00
HC (2007, $24.99, dustjacket) oversized r/series and classic stories; sketch pages 25.00

LEGION OF MONSTERS
Marvel Comics: Dec, 2011 - No. 4, Mar, 2012 ($3.99, limited series)

1-4-Hopeless-s/Doe-a/c; Morbius, Manphibian, Elsa Bloodstone app. 4.00

LEGION OF NIGHT, THE
Marvel Comics: Oct, 1991 - No. 2, Oct, 1991 ($4.95, 52 pgs.)

1,2-Whilce Portacio-c/a(p) 5.00

LEGION OF SUBSTITUTE HEROES SPECIAL (See Adventure Comics #306)
DC Comics: July, 1985 ($1.25, one-shot, 52 pgs.)

Legion of Super-Heroes #301 © DC

Legion of Super-Heroes (4th series) #100 © DC

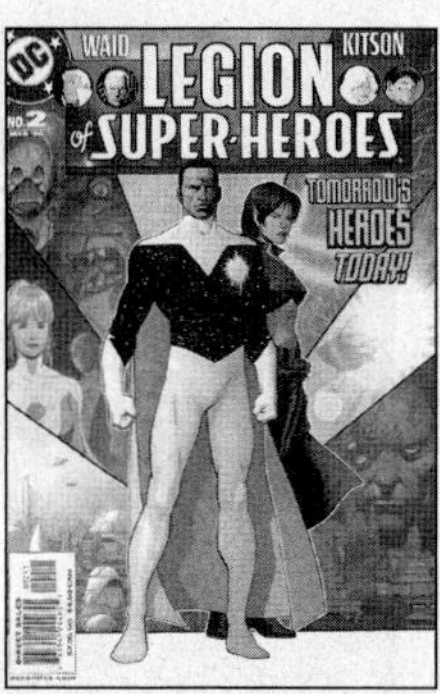

Legion of Super-Heroes (2005 series) #2 © DC

	GD	VG	FN	VF	VF/NM	NM-
	2.0	4.0	6.0	8.0	9.0	9.2

1-Giffen-c/a(p) 4.00

LEGION OF SUPER-HEROES (See Action Comics, Adventure, All New Collectors Edition, Legionnaires, Legends of the Legion, Limited Collectors Edition, Secrets of the..., Superboy & Superman)
National Periodical Publications: Feb, 1973 - No. 4, July-Aug, 1973

	GD	VG	FN	VF	VF/NM	NM-
1-Legion & Tommy Tomorrow reprints begin	3	6	9	19	30	40
2-4: 2-Forte-r. 3-r/Adv. #340. Action #240. 4-r/Adv. #341, Action #233; Mooney-r	2	4	6	11	16	20

LEGION OF SUPER-HEROES, THE (Formerly Superboy and...; Tales of The Legion #314 on)
DC Comics: No. 259, Jan, 1980 - No. 313, July, 1984

	GD	VG	FN	VF	VF/NM	NM-
259(#1)-Superboy leaves Legion	2	4	6	8	11	14
260-270,285-289: 265-Contains 28 pg. insert "Superman & the TRS-80 computer"; origin Tyroc; Tyroc leaves Legion						6.00
261,263,264,266-(Whitman variants; low print run; no cover #'s)	2	4	6	8	11	14
271-284: 272-Blok joins; origin; 20 pg. insert-Dial 'H' For Hero. 277-Intro. Reflecto. 280-Superboy re-joins Legion. 282-Origin Reflecto. 283-Origin Wildfire						6.00
290-294-Great Darkness saga. 294-Double size (52 pgs.)	1	2	3	5	7	9
295-299,301-313: 297-Origin retold. 298-Free 16 pg. Amethyst preview. 306-Brief origin Star Boy (Swan art). 311-Colan-a						4.00
300-(68 pgs., Mando paper)-Anniversary issue; has c/a by almost everyone at DC						5.00
Annual 1-3(82-84, 52 pgs.)-1-Giffen-c/a; 1st app./origin new Invisible Kid who joins Legion. 2-Karate Kid & Princess Projectra wed & resign						4.00
...The Great Darkness Saga (1989, $17.95, 196 pgs.)-r/LSH #287,290-294 & Annual #3; Giffen-c/a	2	4	6	10	14	18
...The Great Darkness Saga The Deluxe Edition HC (2010, $39.99, dj)-r/LSH #284-296 & Annual #1; new intro. by Levitz, script for #290, Giffen design sketches						40.00

NOTE: ***Aparo** c-282, 283, 300(part). **Austin** c-268i. **Buckler** c-273p, 274p, 276p. **Colan** a-311p. **Ditko** a(p)-267, 268, 272, 274, 276, 281. **Giffen** a-285-313p, Annual 1p; c-287p, 288p, 289, 290p, 291p, 292, 293, 294-299p, 300, 301-313p, Annual 1p, 2p. **Perez** c-268p, 277-280, 281p. **Starlin** a-265. **Staton** a-259p, 260p, 280. **Tuska** a-308p.*

LEGION OF SUPER-HEROES (3rd Series) (Reprinted in Tales of the Legion)
DC Comics: Aug, 1984 - No. 63, Aug, 1989 ($1.25/$1.75, deluxe format)

	GD	VG	FN	VF	VF/NM	NM-
1-Silver ink logo	1	2	3	5	6	8
2-36,39-44,46-49,51-62: 4-Death of Karate Kid. 5-Death of Nemesis Kid. 12-Cosmic Boy, Lightning Lad, & Saturn Girl resign. 14-Intro new members: Tellus, Sensor Girl, Quislet. 15-17-Crisis tie-ins. 18-Crisis x-over. 25-Sensor Girl i.d. revealed as Princess Projectra. 35-Saturn Girl rejoins. 42,43-Millennium tie-ins. 44-Origin Quislet						3.00
37,38-Death of Superboy	2	4	6	9	13	16
45,50: 45 ($2.95, 68 pgs.)-Anniversary ish. 50-Double size ($2.50-c)						4.00
63-Final issue						4.00
Annual 1-4 (10/85-'88, 52 pgs.)-1-Crisis tie-in						4.00
...: An Eye For An Eye TPB (2007, $17.99)-r/#1-6; intro by Paul Levitz; cover gallery						18.00
...: The More Things Change TPB (2008, $17.99)-r/#7-13; cover gallery						18.00

NOTE: ***Byrne** c-36p. **Giffen** a(p)-1, 2, 50-55, 57-63, Annual 1p, 2; c-1-5p, 54p, Annual 1. **Orlando** a-6p. **Steacy** c-45-50, Annual 3.*

LEGION OF SUPER-HEROES (4th Series)
DC Comics: Nov, 1989 - No. 125, Mar, 2000 ($1.75/$1.95/$2.25)

	GD	VG	FN	VF	VF/NM	NM-
0-(10/94)-Zero Hour restart of Legion; released between #61 & #62						3.00
1-Giffen-c/a(p)/scripts begin (4 pg.-a only #18)						6.00
2-20,26-49,51-53,55-58: 4-Mon-El (Lar Gand) destroys Time Trapper, changes reality. 5-Alt. reality story where Mordru rules all; Ferro Lad app. 6-1st app. of Laurel Gand (Lar Gand's cousin). 8-Origin. 13-Free poster by Giffen showing new costumes. 15-(2/91)-1st reference of Lar Gand as Valor. 17-Tornado Twins app. 26-New map of headquarters. 34-Six pg. preview of Timber Wolf mini-series. 40-Minor Legionnaires app. 41-(3/93)-SW6 Legion renamed Legionnaires w/new costumes and some new code-names						4.00
21-25: 21-24-Lobo & Darkseid storyline. 24-Cameo SW6 younger Legion duplicates. 25-SW6 Legion full intro.						5.00
50-($3.50, 68 pgs.)						5.00
54-($2.95)-Die-cut & foil stamped-c						5.00
59-99: 61-(9/94)-Zero Hour. 62-(11/94). 75-XS travels back to the 20th Century (cont'd in Impulse #9). 77-Origin of Brainiac 5. 81-Reintro Sun Boy. 85-Half of the Legion sent to the 20th century, Superman-c/app. 86-Final Night. 87-Deadman-c/app. 88-Impulse-c/app. Adventure Comics #247 cover swipe. 91-Forms one cover image with Legionnaires #47. 96-Wedding of Ultra Boy and Apparition. 99-Robin, Impulse, Superboy app.						3.00
100-($5.95, 96 pgs.)-Legionnaires return to the 30th Century; gatefold-c; 5 stories-art by Simonson, Davis and others	1	2	3	4	5	7
101-121: 101-Armstrong-a(p) begins. 105-Legion past & present vs. Time Trapper. 109-Moder-a. 110-Thunder joins. 114,115-Bizarro Legion. 120,121-Fatal Five.						3.00
122-124: 122,123-Coipel-c/a. 124-Coipel-c						4.00
125-Leads into "Legion Lost" maxi-series; Coipel-c						5.00
#1,000,000 (11/98) Giffen-a						3.00
Annual 1-5 (1990-1994, $3.50, 68 pgs.): 4-Bloodlines. 5-Elseworlds story						4.00
Annual 6 (1995,$3.95)-Year One story						4.00
Annual 7 (1996, $3.50, 48 pgs.)-Legends of the Dead Earth story; intro 75th Century Legion of Super-Heroes; Wildfire app.						4.00
Legion: Secret Files 1 (1/98, $4.95) Retold origin & pin-ups						5.00
Legion: Secret Files 2 (6/99, $4.95) Story and profile pages						5.00
The Beginning of Tomorrow TPB ('99, $17.95) r/post-Zero Hour reboot						18.00

NOTE: ***Giffen** a-1-24; breakdowns-26-32, 34-36; c-1-7, 8(part), 9-24. **Brandon Peterson** a(p)-15(1st for DC), 16, 18, Annual 2(54 pgs.); c-Annual 2p. **Swan/Anderson** c-8(part).*

LEGION OF SUPER-HEROES (5th Series) (Title becomes Supergirl and the Legion of Super-Heroes #16-36) (Intro. in Teen Titans/Legion Special)
DC Comics: Feb, 2005 - No. 15, Apr, 2006; No. 37, Feb, 2008 - No. 50, Mar, 2009 ($2.95/$2.99)

	NM-
1-15: 1-Waid-s/Kitson-a/c. 4-Kirk & Gibbons-a. 9-Jeanty-a. 15-Dawnstar, Tyroc, Blok-c	3.00
37-50: 37-Shooter-s/Manapul-a begin; two interlocking covers. 50-Wraparound cover	3.00
44-Variant-c by Neal Adams	5.00
... Death of a Dream TPB ('06, $14.99) r/#7-13	15.00
... Enemy Manifest HC ('09, $24.99, dustjacket) r/#45-50	25.00
... Enemy Manifest SC ('10, $14.99) r/#45-50	15.00
... Enemy Rising HC ('08, $19.99, dustjacket) r/#37-44	20.00
... Enemy Rising SC ('09, $14.99) r/#37-44	15.00
...: 1050 Years of the Future TPB ('08, $19.99) r/greatest tales of their 50 year history	20.00
... Teenage Revolution TPB ('05, $14.99) r/#1-6 & Teen Titans/Legion Spec.; sketch pages	15.00

LEGION OF SUPER-HEROES (6th Series)
DC Comics: Jul, 2010 - No. 16, Oct, 2011 ($3.99/$2.99)

	NM-
1-9: 1-Earth-Man app.; Titan destroyed; Levitz-s/Cinar-a/c. 6-Jimenez back-up-a	4.00
1-6-Variant covers by Jim Lee	8.00
10-16-($2.99) 12-16-Legion of Super-Villains app.	3.00
Annual 1 (2/11, $4.99) New Emerald Empress; Levitz-s/Giffen-a	5.00
...: The Choice HC (2011, $24.99, dustjacket) r/#1-6; variant-c gallery and Cinar art	25.00

LEGION OF SUPER-HEROES (DC New 52)(Also see Legion Lost)
DC Comics: Nov, 2011 - No. 23, Oct, 2013 ($2.99)

	NM-
1-23: 1-4-Levitz-s/Portela-a. 5-Simonson-c/a. 8-Lightle-a. 17-Giffen-a. 23-Maguire-a	3.00
#0 (11/12, $2.99) Story of Brainiac 5 joining the Legion; Levitz-s/Kolins-a	3.00

LEGION OF SUPER-HEROES/BUGS BUNNY SPECIAL
DC Comics: Aug, 2017 ($4.99, one-shot)

1-Humphries-s/Grummett-a/c; Bugs Bunny in the 31st century; Supergirl & Validus app. 5.00

LEGION OF SUPER-HEROES IN THE 31ST CENTURY (Based on the animated series)
DC Comics: June, 2007 - No. 20, Jan, 2009 ($2.25)

	NM-
1-20: 1-Chynna Clugston-a; Fatal Five app. 6-Green Lantern Corps app. 15-Impulse app.	3.00
1-(6/07) Free Comic Book Day giveaway	3.00
...: Tomorrow's Heroes (2008, $14.99) r/#1-7; cover gallery	15.00

LEGION OF SUPER-VILLAINS
DC Comics: May, 2011 ($4.99, one-shot)

1-Levitz-s/Portela-a; Saturn Queen, Lightning Lord, Sun-Killer, Micro Lad app. 5.00

LEGION: PROPHETS (Prelude to 2010 movie)
IDW Publishing: Nov, 2009 - No. 4, Dec, 2009 ($3.99, limited series)

1-4: Stewart & Waltz-s. 1-Muriel-a. 2-Holder-a. 3-Paronzini-a. 4-Gaydos-a 4.00

LEGION: SCIENCE POLICE (See Legion of Super-Heroes)
DC Comics: Aug, 1998 - No. 4, Nov, 1998 ($2.25, limited series)

1-4-Ryan-a 3.00

LEGION: SECRET ORIGIN (Legion of Super-Heroes)
DC Comics: Dec, 2011 - No. 6, May, 2012 ($2.99, limited series)

1-6-Levitz-s/Batista-a; formation of the Legion retold 3.00

LEGION WORLDS (Follows Legion Lost series)
DC Comics: Jun, 2001 - No. 6, Nov, 2001 ($3.95, limited series)

1-6-Abnett & Lanning-s; art by various. 5-Dillon-a. 6-Timber Wolf app. 4.00

LEMONADE KID, THE (See Bobby Benson's B-Bar-B Riders)
AC Comics: 1990 ($2.50, 28 pgs.)

1-Powell-c(r); Red Hawk-r by Powell; Lemonade Kid-r/Bobby Benson by Powell (2 stories) 3.00

LENNON SISTERS LIFE STORY, THE
Dell Publishing Co.: No. 951, Nov, 1958 - No. 1014, Aug, 1959

	GD	VG	FN	VF	VF/NM	NM-
Four Color 951 (#1)-Toth-a, 32pgs, photo-c	11	22	33	73	157	240
Four Color 1014-Toth-a, photo-c	10	20	30	69	147	225

LENORE
Slave Labor Graphics/Titan Comics: Feb, 1998 - Present ($2.95/$3.95, B&W, color #13-on)

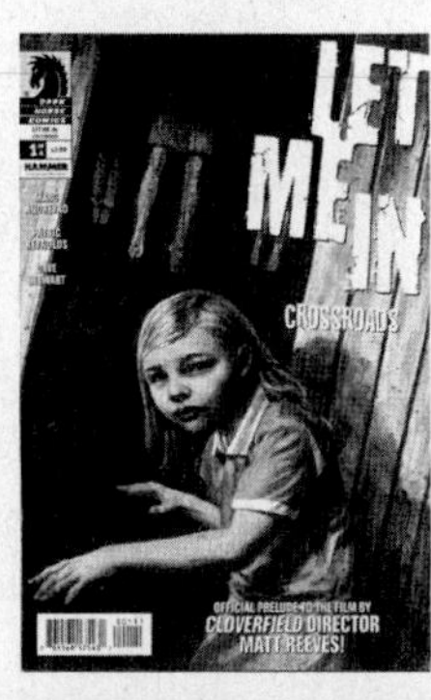

Let Me In: Crossroads #1 © Hammer LMI

Letter 44 #32 © Charles Soule

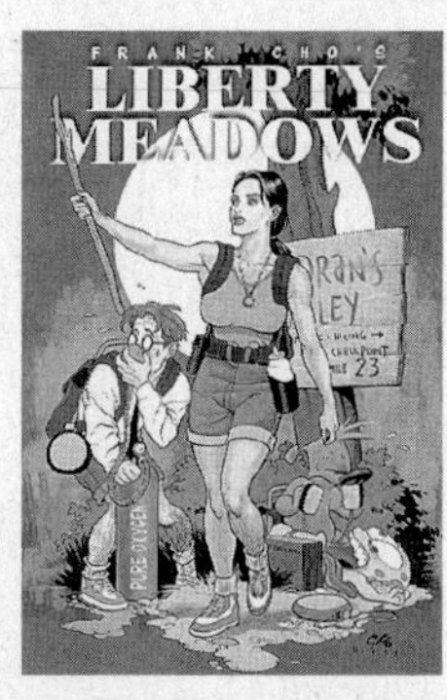

Liberty Meadows #3 © Creators Syndicate

GD VG FN VF VF/NM NM-
2.0 4.0 6.0 8.0 9.0 9.2

1-12: 1-Roman Dirge-s/a, 1,2-2nd printing 4.00
13-($3.95, color) 4.00
Vol. 2 (8/09 - Present) 1-11: 1-1st and 2nd printings; Lenore's origin 4.00
...: Cooties TPB (3/06, $13.95) r/#9-12; pin-ups by various 14.00
...: Noogies TPB ($11.95) r/#1-4 12.00
...: Pink Bellies HC (Titan, 3/15, $17.99) Vol. 2 #8-11 18.00
...: Purple Nurples HC (8/13, $17.95) Vol. 2 #4-7 18.00
...: Swirlies HC (8/12, $17.95) r/#13 & Vol. 2 #1-3 18.00
...: Wedgies TPB (2000, $13.95) r/#5-8 14.00

LEONARD NIMOY'S PRIMORTALS
Tekno Comix: Mar, 1995 - No. 15, May, 1996 ($1.95)

1-15: Concept by Leonard Nimoy & Isaac Asimov 1-3-w/bound-in game piece & trading card. 4-w/Teknophage Steel Edition coupon. 13,14-Art Adams-c. 15-Simonson-c 3.00

LEONARD NIMOY'S PRIMORTALS
BIG Entertainment: V2#0, June, 1996 - No. 8, Feb, 1997 ($2.25)

V2#0-8: 0-Includes Pt. 9 of "The Big Bang" x-over. 0,1-Simonson-c. 3-Kelley Jones-c 3.00

LEONARD NIMOY'S PRIMORTALS ORIGINS
Tekno Comix: Nov, 1995 - No. 2, Dec, 1995 ($2.95, limited series)

1,2: Nimoy scripts; Art Adams-c; polybagged 3.00

LEONARDO (Also see Teenage Mutant Ninja Turtles)
Mirage Studios: Dec, 1986 ($1.50, B&W, one-shot)

1 2 4 6 11 16 20

LEO THE LION
I. W. Enterprises: No date(1960s) (10¢)

1-Reprint 2 4 6 9 13 16

LEROY (Teen-age)
Standard Comics: Nov, 1949 - No. 6, Nov, 1950

1 18 36 54 107 169 230
2-Frazetta text illo. 12 24 36 67 94 120
3-6: 3-Lubbers-a 11 22 33 60 83 105

LETHAL (Also see Brigade)
Image Comics (Extreme Studios): Feb, 1996 ($2.50, unfinished limited series)

1-Marat Mychaels-c/a. 3.00

LETHAL FOES OF SPIDER-MAN (Sequel to Deadly Foes of Spider-Man)
Marvel Comics: Sept, 1993 - No. 4, Dec, 1993 ($1.75, limited series)

1-4 3.00

LETHARGIC LAD
Crusade Ent.: June, 1996 - No. 3, Sept, 1996 ($2.95, B&W, limited series)

1,2 3.00
3-Alex Ross-c/swipe (Kingdom Come) 4.00
...Jumbo Sized Annual #1 (Summer 2002, $3.99) prints comic stories from internet 4.00

LETHARGIC LAD ADVENTURES
Crusade Ent./Destination Ent.#3 on: Oct, 1997 - No. 12, Sept./Oct. 1999 ($2.95, B&W)

1-12-Hyland-s/a. 9-Alex Ross sketch page & back-c 3.00

LET ME IN: CROSSROADS (Based on the 2010 movie Let Me In)
Dark Horse Comics: Dec, 2010 - No. 4, Mar, 2011 ($3.99, limited series)

1-4-Prelude to the film; Andreyko-s/Reynolds-a/Phillips-c 4.00
1-4 Variant photo-c 8.00

LET'S PRETEND (CBS radio)
D. S. Publishing Co.: May-June, 1950 - No. 3, Sept-Oct, 1950

1 18 36 54 105 165 225
2,3 14 28 42 82 121 160

LET'S READ THE NEWSPAPER
Charlton Press: 1974

nn-Features Quincy by Ted Sheares 1 3 4 6 8 10

LET'S TAKE A TRIP (TV) (CBS Television Presents)
Pines Comics: Spring, 1958

1-Marv Levy-c/a 5 10 15 23 28 32

LETTER 44
Oni Press: Oct, 2013 - No. 35, Aug, 2017 ($1.00/$3.99)

1-($1.00)-Soule-a/Alberto Alburquerque-a 5.00
2-35-($3.99) 7-Joëlle Jones-a. 14-Drew Moss-a. 28-Gluskova-a 4.00
... #1 Square One Edition (2/17, $1.00) r/#1 3.00

LETTERS TO SANTA (See March of Comics No. 228)

GD VG FN VF VF/NM NM-
2.0 4.0 6.0 8.0 9.0 9.2

LEX LUTHOR: MAN OF STEEL
DC Comics: May, 2005 - No. 5, Sept, 2005 ($2.99, limited series)

1-5: 1-Azzarello-s/Bermejo-a/c in all. 3-Batman-c/app. 3.00
TPB (2005, $12.99) r/series 13.00
Luthor HC (2010, $19.99, d.j.) r/#1-5 with 10 new story pages; cover gallery & sketch-a 20.00

LEX LUTHOR: THE UNAUTHORIZED BIOGRAPHY
DC Comics: 1989 ($3.95, 52 pgs., one-shot, squarebound)

1-Painted-c; Clark Kent app. 6.00

LIBERTY COMICS (Miss Liberty No. 1)
Green Publishing Co.: No. 5, May, 1945 - No. 15, July, 1946 (MLJ & other-r)

5 (5/45)-The Prankster app; Starr-a 28 56 84 165 270 375
10-Hangman & Boy Buddies app.; reprints 3 Hangman stories, incl. Hangman #8
26 52 78 154 252 350
11 (V2#2, 1/46)-Wilbur in women's clothes 18 36 54 105 165 225
12 (V2#4)-Black Hood & Suzie app.; classic Skull-c 77 154 231 493 847 1200
14,15-Patty of Airliner; Starr-a in both 21 42 63 120 199 275

LIBERTY COMICS (The CBLDF Presents...)
Image Comics: July, 2008; Oct, 2009 ($3.99/$4.99, Comic Book Legal Defense Fund benefit)

1-Two covers by Campbell & Mignola; art by Cooke, Aragones, A. Adams & others 4.00
1-(12/08) Second printing with Thor-c by Simonson 4.00
2-(10/09, $4.99) two covers by Romita Jr. & Sale; art by Allred, Templesmith, Jim Lee 5.00
Liberty Annual 2010 (10/10, $4.99) Covers by Gibbons & Robertson 5.00
Liberty Annual 2011 (10/11, $4.99) Covers by Wagner & Cassaday 5.00
Liberty Annual 2012 (10/12, $4.99) Covers by Dodson & Bá; Walking Dead story 5.00
Liberty Annual 2013 (10/13, $4.99) Covers by Corben & Marquez 5.00
Liberty Annual 2014 (10/14, $4.99) Covers by Allred, Simonson, & Charm 5.00
Liberty Annual 2015 (10/15, $4.99) Covers by Fegredo, Fowler & Del Rey 5.00
Liberty Annual 2016 (11/16, $4.99) Stories by Guinan, Pope, Wimberly, Schkade & others 5.00

LIBERTY COMICS
Heroic Publishing: Sept, 2007 ($4.50)

1-Mark Sparacio-c 4.50

LIBERTY GIRL
Heroic Publishing: Aug, 2006 - No. 3, May, 2007 ($3.25/$2.99)

1-3-Mark Sparacio-c/a 3.25

LIBERTY GUARDS
Chicago Mail Order: No date (1946?)

nn-Reprints Man of War #1 with cover of Liberty Scouts #1; Gustavson-c
42 84 126 265 445 625

LIBERTY MEADOWS
Insight Studios Group/Image Comics #27 on: 1999 - No. 37 ($2.95, B&W)

1-Frank Cho-s/a; reprints newspaper strips 3 6 9 14 20 25
1-2nd & 3rd printings 1 2 3 4 5 7
2,3 2 4 6 8 11 14
4-10 1 2 3 4 5 7
11-25,27-37: 20-Adam Hughes-c. 22-Evil Brandy vs. Brandy. 27-1st Image issue, printed sideways 3.00
..., Cover Girl HC (Image, 2006, $24.99, with dustjacket) r/color covers of #1-19,21-37 along with B&W inked versions, sketches and pin-up art 25.00
...: Eden Book 1 SC (Image, 2002, $14.95) r/#1-9; sketch gallery 15.00
...: Eden Book 1 SC 2nd printing (Image, 2004, $19.95) r/#1-9; sketch gallery 20.00
...: Eden Book 1 HC (Image, 2003, $24.95, with dustjacket) r/#1-9; sketch gallery 25.00
...: Creature Comforts Book 2 HC (Image, 2004, $24.95, with d.j.) r/#10-18; sketch gallery 25.00
...: Creature Comforts Book 2 SC (Image, 12/04, $14.95) r/#10-18; sketch gallery 15.00
...Book 3: Summer of Love HC (Image, 12/04, $24.95) r/#19-27; sketch gallery 25.00
...Book 3: Summer of Love SC (Image, 7/05, $14.95) r/#19-27; sketch gallery 15.00
...Book 4: Cold, Cold Heart HC (Image, 9/05, $24.95) r/#28-36; sketch gallery 25.00
...Book 4: Cold, Cold Heart SC (Image, 2006, $14.99) r/#28-36; sketch gallery 15.00
Image Firsts: Liberty Meadows #1 (9/10, $1.00) r/#1 3.00
... Sourcebook (5/04, $4.95) character info and unpublished strips 5.00
... Wedding Album (#26) (2002, $2.95) 3.00

LIBERTY PROJECT, THE
Eclipse Comics: June, 1987 - No. 8, May, 1988 ($1.75, color, Baxter paper)

1-8: 6-Valkyrie app. 3.00

LIBERTY SCOUTS (See Liberty Guards & Man of War)
Centaur Publications: No. 2, June, 1941 - No. 3, Aug, 1941

2(#1)-Origin The Fire-Man, Man of War; Vapo-Man & Liberty Scouts begin; intro Liberty Scouts; Gustavson-c/a in both 155 310 465 992 1696 2400
3(#2)-Origin & 1st app. The Sentinel 103 206 309 659 1130 1600

Life of Captain Marvel #3 © MAR

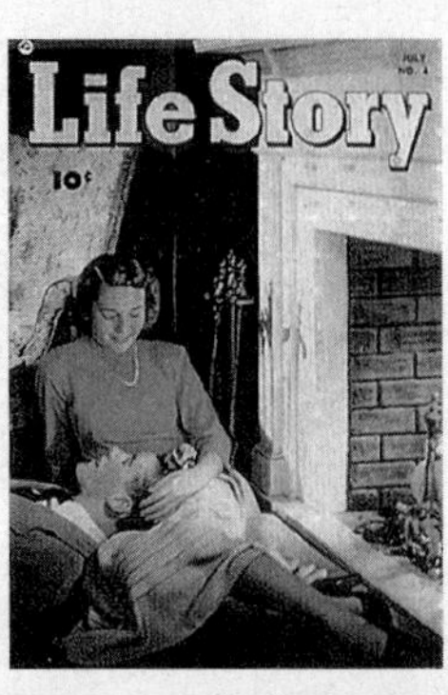

Life Story #4 © FAW

Life With Archie #1 © ACP

LIBRARIANS, THE (Based on the TV series)
Dynamite Entertainment: 2017 - No. 4, 2018 ($3.99)

	GD 2.0	VG 4.0	FN 6.0	VF 8.0	VF/NM 9.0	NM- 9.2
1-4-Pfeiffer-s/Buchemi-a; multiple covers						4.00

LICENCE TO KILL (James Bond 007) (Movie)
Eclipse Comics: 1989 ($7.95, slick paper, 52 pgs.)

	GD 2.0	VG 4.0	FN 6.0	VF 8.0	VF/NM 9.0	NM- 9.2
nn-Movie adaptation; Timothy Dalton photo-c	1	2	3	5	6	8
Limited Hardcover ($24.95)						25.00

LIDSVILLE (TV)
Gold Key: Oct, 1972 - No. 5, Oct, 1973

	GD 2.0	VG 4.0	FN 6.0	VF 8.0	VF/NM 9.0	NM- 9.2
1-Photo-c on all	5	10	15	31	53	75
2-5	3	6	9	21	33	45

LIEUTENANT, THE (TV)
Dell Publishing Co.: April-June, 1964

	GD 2.0	VG 4.0	FN 6.0	VF 8.0	VF/NM 9.0	NM- 9.2
1-Photo-c	3	6	9	17	26	35

LIEUTENANT BLUEBERRY (Also see Blueberry)
Marvel Comics (Epic Comics): 1991 - No. 3, 1991 (Graphic novel)

	GD 2.0	VG 4.0	FN 6.0	VF 8.0	VF/NM 9.0	NM- 9.2
1,2 ($8.95)-Moebius-a in all	2	4	6	11	16	20
3 ($14.95)	3	6	9	15	22	28

LT. ROBIN CRUSOE, U.S.N. (See Movie Comics & Walt Disney Showcase #26)

LIFE EATERS, THE
DC Comics (WildStorm): 2003 ($29.95, hardcover with dust jacket)

	GD 2.0	VG 4.0	FN 6.0	VF 8.0	VF/NM 9.0	NM- 9.2
HC-David Brin-s; Scott Hampton-painted-a/c; Norse Gods team with the Nazis						30.00
SC-(2004, $19.95)						20.00

LIFE OF CAPTAIN MARVEL, THE
Marvel Comics Group: Aug, 1985 - No. 5, Dec, 1985 ($2.00, Baxter paper)

	GD 2.0	VG 4.0	FN 6.0	VF 8.0	VF/NM 9.0	NM- 9.2
1-5: 1-All reprint Starlin issues of Iron Man #55, Capt. Marvel #25-34 plus Marvel Feature #12 (all with Thanos). 4-New Thanos back-c by Starlin						6.00

LIFE OF CHRIST, THE
Catechetical Guild Educational Society: No. 301, 1949 (35¢, 100 pgs.)

	GD 2.0	VG 4.0	FN 6.0	VF 8.0	VF/NM 9.0	NM- 9.2
301-Reprints from Topix(1949)-V5#11,12	9	18	27	52	69	85

LIFE OF CHRIST: THE CHRISTMAS STORY, THE
Marvel Comics/Nelson: Feb, 1993 ($2.99, slick stock)

	GD 2.0	VG 4.0	FN 6.0	VF 8.0	VF/NM 9.0	NM- 9.2
nn						5.00

LIFE OF CHRIST: THE EASTER STORY, THE
Marvel Comics/Nelson: 1993 ($2.99, slick stock)

	GD 2.0	VG 4.0	FN 6.0	VF 8.0	VF/NM 9.0	NM- 9.2
nn						5.00

LIFE OF CHRIST VISUALIZED
Standard Publishers: 1942 - No. 3, 1943

	GD 2.0	VG 4.0	FN 6.0	VF 8.0	VF/NM 9.0	NM- 9.2
1-3: All came in cardboard case, each...	9	18	27	50	65	80
Case only.....	10	20	30	54	72	90

LIFE OF CHRIST VISUALIZED
The Standard Publ. Co.: 1946? (48 pgs. in color)

	GD 2.0	VG 4.0	FN 6.0	VF 8.0	VF/NM 9.0	NM- 9.2
nn	7	14	21	37	46	55

LIFE OF ESTHER VISUALIZED
The Standard Publ. Co.: No. 2062, 1947 (48 pgs. in color)

	GD 2.0	VG 4.0	FN 6.0	VF 8.0	VF/NM 9.0	NM- 9.2
2062	7	14	21	37	46	55

LIFE OF JOSEPH VISUALIZED
The Standard Publ. Co.: No. 1054, 1946 (48 pgs. in color)

	GD 2.0	VG 4.0	FN 6.0	VF 8.0	VF/NM 9.0	NM- 9.2
1054	7	14	21	37	46	55

LIFE OF PAUL (See The Living Bible)

LIFE OF POPE JOHN PAUL II, THE
Marvel Comics Group: Jan, 1983 ($1.50/$1.75)

	GD 2.0	VG 4.0	FN 6.0	VF 8.0	VF/NM 9.0	NM- 9.2
1	2	4	6	8	10	12

LIFE OF RILEY, THE (TV)
Dell Publishing Co.: No. 917, July, 1958

	GD 2.0	VG 4.0	FN 6.0	VF 8.0	VF/NM 9.0	NM- 9.2
Four Color 917-William Bendix photo-c	9	18	27	62	126	190

LIFE ON ANOTHER PLANET
Kitchen Sink Press: 1978 (B&W, graphic novel, magazine size)

	GD 2.0	VG 4.0	FN 6.0	VF 8.0	VF/NM 9.0	NM- 9.2
nn-Will Eisner-s/a						20.00
Reprint (DC Comics, 5/00, $12.95)						13.00

LIFE'S LIKE THAT
Croyden Publ. Co.: 1945 (25¢, B&W, 68 pgs.)

	GD 2.0	VG 4.0	FN 6.0	VF 8.0	VF/NM 9.0	NM- 9.2
nn-Newspaper Sunday strip-r by Neher	7	14	21	35	43	50

LIFE STORIES OF AMERICAN PRESIDENTS (See Dell Giants)

LIFE STORY
Fawcett Publications: Apr, 1949 - V8#46, Jan, 1953; V8#47, Apr, 1953 (All have photo-c?)

	GD 2.0	VG 4.0	FN 6.0	VF 8.0	VF/NM 9.0	NM- 9.2
V1#1	17	34	51	98	154	210
2	11	22	33	60	83	105
3-6, V2#7-12 (3/50)	10	20	30	54	72	90
V3#13-Wood-a (4/50)	15	30	45	90	140	190
V3#14-18, V4#19-24, V5#25-30, V6#31-35	9	18	27	50	65	80
V6#36- "I sold drugs" on-c	14	28	42	82	121	160
V7#37,40-42, V8#44,45	9	18	27	47	61	75
V7#38, V8#43-Evans-a	9	18	27	50	65	80
V7#39-Drug Smuggling & Junkie story	12	24	36	69	97	125
V8#46,47 (Scarce)	10	20	30	56	76	100

NOTE: ***Powell*** *a-13, 23, 24, 26, 28, 30, 32, 39.* ***Marcus Swayze*** *a-1-3, 10-12, 15, 16, 20, 21, 23-25, 31, 35, 37, 40, 44, 46.*

LIFE, THE UNIVERSE AND EVERYTHING (See Hitchhikers Guide to the Galaxy & Restaurant at the End of the Universe)
DC Comics: 1996 - No. 3, 1996 ($6.95, squarebound, limited series)

	GD 2.0	VG 4.0	FN 6.0	VF 8.0	VF/NM 9.0	NM- 9.2
1-3: Adaptation of novel by Douglas Adams.	1	2	3	4	5	7

LIFE WITH ARCHIE
Archie Publications: Sept, 1958 - No. 286, Sept, 1991

	GD 2.0	VG 4.0	FN 6.0	VF 8.0	VF/NM 9.0	NM- 9.2
1	54	108	162	432	966	1500
2-(9/59)	21	42	63	147	324	500
3-5: 3-(7/60)	15	30	45	103	227	350
6-8,10	11	22	33	72	154	235
9,11-Horror/SciFi-c	14	28	42	96	211	325
12-20	7	14	21	48	89	130
21(7/63)-30	6	12	18	41	76	110
31-34,36-38,40,41	5	10	15	34	60	85
35,39-Horror/Sci-Fi-c	8	16	24	55	105	155
42-Pureheart begins (1st app.-c/s, 10/65)	11	22	33	76	163	250
43,44	6	12	18	38	69	100
45(1/66) 1st Man From R.I.V.E.R.D.A.L.E.	7	14	21	46	86	125
46-Origin Pureheart	6	12	18	40	73	105
47-49	5	10	15	33	57	80
50-United Three begin: Pureheart (Archie), Superteen (Betty), Captain Hero (Jughead)	7	14	21	44	82	120
51-59: 59-Pureheart ends	5	10	15	30	50	70
60-Archie band begins, ends #66	5	10	15	34	60	85
61-66: 61-Man From R.I.V.E.R.D.A.L.E.-c/s	4	8	12	25	40	55
67-80	3	6	9	17	26	35
81-99	3	6	9	16	23	30
100 (8/70), 113-Sabrina & Salem app.	3	6	9	19	30	40
101-112, 114-130(2/73), 139(11/73)-Archie Band c/s	2	4	6	11	16	20
131,134-138,140-146,148-161,164-170(6/76)	2	4	6	9	12	15
132,133,147,163-all horror-c/s	3	6	9	14	20	26
162-UFO c/s	3	6	9	14	19	24
171,173-175,177-184,186,189,191-194,196	2	3	4	6	8	10
172,185,197 : 172-(9/77)-Bi-Cent. spec. ish, 185-2nd 24th cent.-c/s, 197-Time machine/SF-c/s	2	4	6	8	10	12
176(12/76)-1st app. Capt. Archie of Starship Rivda, in 24th century c/s; 1st app. Stella the Robot	3	6	9	14	19	24
187,188,195,198,199-all horror-c/s	2	4	6	9	13	16
190-1st Dr. Doom-c/s	2	4	6	9	13	16
200 (12/78) Maltese Pigeon-s	2	4	6	8	11	14
201-203,205-237,239,240(1/84): 208-Reintro Veronica	1	2	3	5	6	8
204-Flying saucer-c/s	2	3	4	6	8	10
238-(9/83)-25th anniversary issue; Ol' Betsy (jalopy) replaced	1	2	3	5	7	9
241-278,280-285: 250-Comic book convention-s						5.00
279,286: 279-Intro Mustang Sally ($1.00, 7/90)						6.00

NOTE: ***Gene Colan*** *a-272-279, 285, 286. Horror/Sci-Fi-c 9, 11, 35, 39, 162.*

LIFE WITH ARCHIE (The Married Life) (Magazine)
Archie Publications: Sept, 2010 - No. 37, Sept, 2014 ($3.99, magazine-size)

	GD 2.0	VG 4.0	FN 6.0	VF 8.0	VF/NM 9.0	NM- 9.2
1-15,17-34: Continuation of Married Life stories from Archie #600-605; articles/interviews						4.00
16-Kevin Keller gay wedding						10.00
36-($4.99, comic-size) Death of Archie; 5 covers by Allred, Francavilla, Hughes, Ramon Perez & Staples	1	2	3	5	6	8
37-($4.99, comic-size) One Year Later aftermath; 5 covers by Chiang, Edwards, Alex Ross, Simonson & Thompson						5.00

...: The Death of Archie: A Life Celebrated Commemorative Issue (2014, $9.99) reprints #36

Lightning Comics Presents #1 © LC

Limited Collectors' Edition C-22 © ERB

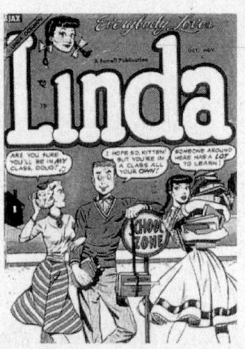

Linda #4 © AJAX

GD VG FN VF VF/NM NM-
2.0 4.0 6.0 8.0 9.0 9.2

& #37 in magazine size; afterword by Jon Goldwater; cover gallery w/artist quotes 10.00

LIFE WITH MILLIE (Formerly A Date With Millie) (Modeling With Millie #21 on)
Atlas/Marvel Comics Group: No. 8, Dec, 1960 - No. 20, Dec, 1962

8-Teenage 10 20 30 69 147 225
9-11 8 16 24 54 102 150
12-20 7 14 21 49 92 135

LIFE WITH SNARKY PARKER (TV)
Fox Feature Syndicate: Aug, 1950

1-Early TV comic; photo-c from TV puppet show 31 62 93 186 303 420

LIGHT AND DARKNESS WAR, THE
Marvel Comics (Epic Comics): Oct, 1988 - No. 6, Dec, 1989 ($1.95, lim. series)

1-6 3.00

LIGHT BRIGADE, THE
DC Comics: 2004 - No. 4, 2004 ($5.95, limited series)

1-4-Archangels in World War II; Tomasi-s/Snejbjerg-a 6.00
TPB (2005, 2009, $19.99) r/series; cover galery 20.00

LIGHT FANTASTIC, THE (Terry Pratchett's)
Innovation Publishing: June, 1992 - No. 4, Sept, 1992 ($2.50, mini-series)

1-4: Adapts 2nd novel in Discworld series 3.00

LIGHT IN THE FOREST (Disney)
Dell Publishing Co.: No. 891, Mar, 1958

Four Color 891-Movie, Fess Parker photo-c 6 12 18 42 79 115

LIGHTNING COMICS (Formerly Sure-Fire No. 1-3)
Ace Magazines: No. 4, Dec, 1940 - No. 13(V3#1), June, 1942

4-Characters continue from Sure-Fire 194 388 582 1242 2121 3000
5,6: 6-Dr. Nemesis begins 129 258 387 826 1413 2000
V2#1-6: 2- "Flash Lightning" becomes "Lash..." 103 206 309 659 1130 1600
V3#1-Intro. Lightning Girl & The Sword 103 206 309 659 1130 1600
NOTE: *Anderson a-V2#6. Mooney c-V1#5, 6, V2#1-6, V3#1. Bondage c-V2#6. Lightning-c on all.*

LIGHTNING COMICS PRESENTS
Lightning Comics: May, 1994 ($3.50)

1-Red foil-c distr. by Diamond Distr., 1-Black/yellow/blue-c distrib. by Capital Distr., 1-Red/yellow-c distributed by H. World, 1-Platinum 3.50

LI'L ... (These titles are listed under Little ...)

LILI
Image Comics: No. 0, 1999 ($4.95, B&W)

0-Bendis & Yanover-s 5.00

LILLITH (See Warrior Nun...)
Antarctic Press: Sept, 1996 - No. 3, Feb, 1997 ($2.95, limited series)

1-3: 1-Variant-c 3.00

LIMITED COLLECTORS' EDITION (See Famous First Edition, Marvel Treasury #28, Rudolph The Red-Nosed Reindeer, & Superman Vs. The Amazing Spider-Man; becomes All-New Collectors' Edition)
National Periodical Publications/DC Comics:
(#21-34,51-59: 84 pgs.; #35-41: 68 pgs.; #42-50: 60 pgs.)
C-21, Summer, 1973 - No. C-59, 1978 ($1.00) (10x13-1/2")

(Rudolph...C-20 (implied), 12/72)-See Rudolph The Red-Nosed Reindeer
C-21: Shazam (TV); r/Captain Marvel Jr. #11 by Raboy; C.C. Beck-c, biog. & photo 3 6 9 19 30 40
C-22: Tarzan; complete origin reprinted from #207-210; all Kubert-c/a; Joe Kubert biography & photo inside 3 6 9 16 24 32
C-23: House of Mystery; Wrightson, N. Adams/Orlando, G. Kane/Wood, Toth, Aragones, Sparling reprints 4 8 12 23 37 50
C-24: Rudolph The Red-Nosed Reindeer 6 12 18 38 69 100
C-25: Batman; Neal Adams-c/a(r); G.A. Joker-r; Batman/Enemy Ace-r; Novick-a(r); has photos from TV show 4 8 12 25 40 55
C-26: See Famous First Edition C-26 (same contents)
C-27,C-29,C-31: C-27: Shazam (TV); G.A. Capt. Marvel & Mary Marvel-r; Beck-r. C-29: Tarzan; reprints "Return of Tarzan" from #219-223 by Kubert; Kubert-c. C-31: Superman; origin-r; Giordano-a; photos of George Reeves from 1950s TV show on inside b/c; Burnley, Boring-r 3 6 9 16 23 30
C-32: Ghosts (new-a) 3 6 9 21 33 45
C-33: Rudolph The Red-Nosed Reindeer(new-a) 5 10 15 35 63 90
C-34: Christmas with the Super-Heroes; unpublished Angel & Ape story by Oksner & Wood; Batman & Teen Titans-r 3 6 9 16 23 30
C-35: Shazam (TV); photo cover features TV's Captain Marvel, Jackson Bostwick; Beck-r; TV photos inside b/c 3 6 9 15 22 28

GD VG FN VF VF/NM NM-
2.0 4.0 6.0 8.0 9.0 9.2

C-36: The Bible; all new adaptation beginning with Genesis by Kubert, Redondo & Mayer; Kubert-c 3 6 9 15 22 28
C-37: Batman; r-1946 Sundays; inside b/c photos of Batman TV show villains (all villain issue; r/G.A. Joker, Catwoman, Penguin, Two-Face, & Scarecrow stories plus 1946 Sundays-r) 3 6 9 17 26 35
C-38: Superman; 1 pg. N. Adams; part photo-c; photos from TV show on inside back-c 3 6 9 15 22 28
C-39: Secret Origins of Super-Villains; N. Adams-i(r); collection reprints 1950's Joker origin, Luthor origin from Adv. Comics #271, Captain Cold origin from Showcase #8 among others; G.A. Batman-r; Beck-r 3 6 9 15 22 28
C-40: Dick Tracy by Gould featuring Flattop; newspaper-r from 12/21/43 - 5/17/44; biog. of Chester Gould 3 6 9 15 22 28
C-41: Super Friends (TV); JLA-r(1965); Toth-c/a 3 6 9 16 23 30
C-42: Rudolph 4 8 12 27 44 60
C-43-C-47: C-43: Christmas with the Super-Heroes; Wrightson, S&K, Neal Adams-a. C-44: Batman; N. Adams-p(r) & G.A.-r; painted-c. C-45: More Secret Origins of Super-Villains; Flash-r/#105; G.A. Wonder Woman & Batman/Catwoman-r. C-46: Justice League of America(1963-r); 3 pgs. Toth-a C-47: Superman Salutes the Bicentennial (Tomahawk interior); 2 pgs. new-a 3 6 9 14 20 26
C-48,C-49: C-48: Superman Vs. The Flash (Superman/Flash race); swipes-c to Superman #199; r/Superman #199 & Flash #175; 6 pgs. Neal Adams-a. C-49: Superboy & the Legion of Super-Heroes 3 6 9 16 23 30
C-50: Rudolph The Red-Nosed Reindeer; contains poster attached at the centerfold with a cardstock flap (1/2 price if poster is missing) 4 8 12 27 44 60
C-51: Batman; Neal Adams-c/a 3 6 9 16 24 32
C-52,C-57: C-52: The Best of DC; Neal Adams-c/a; Toth, Kubert-a. C-57: Welcome Back, Kotter-r(TV)(5/78) includes unpublished #11 3 6 9 15 22 28
C-53 thru C-56, C-58, C-60 thru C-62 (See All-New Collectors' Edition)
C-59: Batman's Strangest Cases; N. Adams-r; Wrightson-r/Swamp Thing #7; N. Adams/Wrightson-c 3 6 9 15 22 28
NOTE: *All-r with exception of some special features and covers. **Aparo** a-52r; c-37. **Grell** c-49. **Infantino** a-25, 39, 44, 45, 52. **Bob Kane** r-25. **Robinson** r-25, 44. **Sprang** r-44. Issues #21-31, 35-39, 45, 48 have back cover cut-outs.*

LINDA (Everybody Loves...) (Phantom Lady No. 5 on)
Ajax-Farrell Publ. Co.: Apr-May, 1954 - No. 4, Oct-Nov, 1954

1-Kamenish-a 17 34 51 98 154 210
2-Lingerie panel 13 26 39 74 105 135
3,4 11 22 33 62 86 110

LINDA CARTER, STUDENT NURSE (Also see Night Nurse)
Atlas Comics (AMI): Sept, 1961 - No. 9, Jan, 1963

1-Al Hartley-c; 1st app. character who becomes Night Nurse in Daredevil V2 #58 (2004) 129 258 387 826 1413 2000
2-9 22 44 66 132 216 300

LINDA LARK
Dell Publishing Co.: Oct-Dec, 1961 - No. 8, Aug-Oct, 1963

1 3 6 9 18 28 38
2-8 3 6 9 14 19 24

LINE OF DEFENSE 3000AD (Based on the video game)
DC Comics: No. 0, 2012 (no price)

0-Brian Ching-a 3.00

LINUS, THE LIONHEARTED (TV)
Gold Key: Sept, 1965

1 (10155-509) 6 12 18 38 69 100

LION, THE (See Movie Comics)

LIONHEART
Awesome Comics: Sept, 1999 - No. 2, Dec, 1999 ($2.99/$2.50)

1-Ian Churchill-story/a, Jeph Loeb-s; Coven app. 3.50
2-Flip book w/Coven #4 3.00

LION OF SPARTA (See Movie Classics)

LIPPY THE LION AND HARDY HAR HAR (TV)
Gold Key: Mar, 1963 (12¢) (See Hanna-Barbera Band Wagon #1)

1 (10049-303) 7 14 21 46 86 125

LISA COMICS (TV)(See Simpsons Comics)
Bongo Comics: 1995 ($2.25)

1-Lisa in Wonderland 4.00

LITERALS, THE (See Fables and Jack of Fables)
DC Comics (Vertigo): June, 2009 - No. 3, Aug, 2009 ($2.99)

1-3-Crossover with Fables #83-85 and Jack of Fables #33-35; Buckingham-c/a 3.00

Li'l Abner #73 © TOBY

Little Archie #38 © ACP

Little Audrey #27 © HARV

	GD 2.0	VG 4.0	FN 6.0	VF 8.0	VF/NM 9.0	NM- 9.2

LI'L ABNER (See Comics on Parade, Sparkle, Sparkler Comics, Tip Top Comics & Tip Topper)
United Features Syndicate: 1939 - 1940

	GD	VG	FN	VF	VF/NM	NM-
Single Series 4 ('39)	89	178	267	565	970	1375
Single Series 18 ('40) (#18 on inside, #2 on-c)	65	130	195	416	708	1000

LI'L ABNER (Al Capp's; continued from Comics on Parade #58)
Harvey Publ. No. 61-69 (2/49)/Toby Press No. 70 on: No. 61, Dec, 1947 - No. 97, Jan, 1955
(See Oxydol-Dreft in Promotional Comics section)

	GD	VG	FN	VF	VF/NM	NM-
61(#1)-Wolverton & Powell-a	24	48	72	140	230	320
62-65: 63-The Wolf Girl app. 65-Powell-a	15	30	45	85	130	175
66,67,69,70	14	28	42	82	121	160
68-Full length Fearless Fosdick-c/story	15	30	45	88	137	185
71-74,76,80	13	26	39	74	105	135
75,77-79,86,91-All with Kurtzman art; 86-Sadie Hawkins Day. 91-r/#77	15	30	45	83	124	165
81-85,87-90,92-94,96,97: 83-Evil-Eye Fleegle & Double Whammy app. 88-Cousin Weakeyes goes hunting. 94-Six lessons from Adam Lazonga. 96-Football issue	12	24	36	69	97	125
95-Full length Fearless Fosdick story	14	28	42	76	108	140

LI'L ABNER
Toby Press: 1951

	GD	VG	FN	VF	VF/NM	NM-
1	18	36	54	103	162	220

LI'L ABNER'S DOGPATCH (See Al Capp's...)

LITTLE AL OF THE F.B.I.
Ziff-Davis Publications: No. 10, 1950 (no month) - No. 11, Apr-May, 1951 (Saunders painted-c)

	GD	VG	FN	VF	VF/NM	NM-
10(1950)	19	38	57	109	172	235
11(1951)	14	28	42	81	118	155

LITTLE AL OF THE SECRET SERVICE
Ziff-Davis Publications: No. 10, 7-8/51; No, 2, 9-10/51; No. 3, Winter, 1951 (Saunders painted-c)

	GD	VG	FN	VF	VF/NM	NM-
10(#1)	17	34	51	98	154	210
2,3	14	28	42	76	108	140

LITTLE AMBROSE
Archie Publications: September, 1958

	GD	VG	FN	VF	VF/NM	NM-
1-Bob Bolling-c	17	34	51	98	154	210

LITTLE ANGEL
Standard (Visual Editions)/Pines: No. 5, Sept, 1954; No. 6, Sept, 1955 - No. 16, Sept, 1959

	GD	VG	FN	VF	VF/NM	NM-
5-Last pre-code issue	8	16	24	42	54	65
6-16	6	12	18	28	34	40

LITTLE ANNIE ROONEY (Also see Henry)
David McKay Publ.: 1935 (25¢, B&W dailies, 48 pgs.)(10"x10", cardboard-c)

	GD	VG	FN	VF	VF/NM	NM-
Book 1-Daily strip-r by Darrell McClure	38	76	114	226	368	510

LITTLE ANNIE ROONEY (See King Comics & Treasury of Comics)
David McKay/St. John/Standard: 1938; Aug, 1948 - No. 3, Oct, 1948

	GD	VG	FN	VF	VF/NM	NM-
Feature Books 11 (McKay, 1938)	39	78	117	231	378	525
1 (St. John)	15	30	45	88	137	185
2,3	10	20	30	54	72	90

LITTLE ARCHIE (The Adventures of... #13-on) (See Archie Giant Series Mag. #527, 534, 538, 545, 549, 556, 560, 566, 570, 583, 594, 596, 607, 609, 619)
Archie Publications: 1956 - No. 180, Feb, 1983 (Giants No. 3-84)

	GD	VG	FN	VF	VF/NM	NM-
1-(Scarce)	118	236	354	944	2122	3300
2 (1957)	46	92	138	359	805	1050
3-5: 3-(1958)-Bob Bolling-c & giant issues begin	22	44	66	154	340	525
6-10	15	30	45	103	227	350
11-17,19,21 (84 pgs.)	11	22	33	73	157	240
18,20,22 (84 pgs.)-Horror/Sci-Fi-c	16	32	48	110	243	375
23-39 (68 pgs.)	7	14	21	46	86	125
40 (Fall/66)-Intro. Little Pureheart-c/s (68 pgs.)	8	16	24	51	96	140
41,44-Little Pureheart (68 pgs.)	6	12	18	37	66	95
42-Intro The Little Archies Band, ends #66 (68 pgs.)	6	12	18	40	73	105
43-1st Boy From R.I.V.E.R.D.A.L.E. (68 pgs.)	6	12	18	38	69	100
45-58 (68 pgs.)	5	10	15	31	53	75
59 (68 pgs.)-Little Sabrina begins	7	14	21	48	89	130
60-66 (68 pgs.)	4	8	12	27	44	60
67(9/71)-84: 84-Last 52pg. Giant-Size (2/74)	3	6	9	17	26	35
85-99	2	4	6	10	14	18
100	2	4	6	13	18	22
101-112,114-116,118-129	2	4	6	8	10	12
113,117,130: 113-Halloween Special issue(12/76). 117-Donny Osmond-c cameo 130-UFO cover (5/78)	2	4	6	9	13	16
131-150(1/80), 180(Last issue, 2/83)	1	2	3	5	7	9
151-179						5.00
...In Animal Land 1 (1957)	27	54	81	194	435	675
...In Animal Land 17 (Winter, 1957-58)-19 (Summer,1958)-Formerly Li'l Jinx	10	20	30	68	144	220
Archie Classics - The Adventures of Little Archie Vol. 1 TPB (2004, $10.95) reprints						11.00
Vol. 2 TPB (2008, $9.95) reprints plus new 22 pg. story with Bolling-s/a						10.00

NOTE: *Little Archie Band app. 42-66. Little Sabrina in 59-78,80-180*

LITTLE ARCHIE CHRISTMAS SPECIAL (See Archie Giant Series #581)

LITTLE ARCHIE COMICS DIGEST ANNUAL (...Magazine #5 on)
Archie Publications: 10/77 - No. 48, 5/91 (Digest-size, 128 pgs., later issues $1.35-$1.50)

	GD	VG	FN	VF	VF/NM	NM-
1(10/77)-Reprints	3	6	9	19	30	40
2(4/78,3(11/78)-Neal Adams-a. 3-The Fly-r by S&K	3	6	9	14	20	26
4(4/79) - 10	2	4	6	10	14	18
11-20	2	4	6	8	10	12
21-30: 28-Christmas-c	1	2	3	5	6	8
31-48: 40,46-Christmas-c						5.00

NOTE: *Little Archie, Little Jinx, Little Jughead & Little Sabrina in most issues.*

LITTLE ARCHIE DIGEST MAGAZINE
Archie Comics: July, 1991 - No. 21, Mar, 1998 ($1.50/$1.79/$1.89, digest size, bi-annual)

	GD	VG	FN	VF	VF/NM	NM-
V2#1						6.00
2-10						4.00
11-21						3.00

LITTLE ARCHIE MYSTERY
Archie Publications: Aug, 1963 - No. 2, Oct, 1963 (12¢ issues)

	GD	VG	FN	VF	VF/NM	NM-
1	15	30	45	103	227	350
2	8	16	24	52	99	145

LITTLE ARCHIE, ONE SHOT
Archie Comic Publications: May, 2017 ($4.99, one-shot)

	GD	VG	FN	VF	VF/NM	NM-
nn-Art Baltazar & Franco-s/a; 3 covers; Sabrina app.						5.00

LITTLE ASPIRIN (See Little Lenny & Wisco)
Marvel Comics (CnPC): July, 1949 - No. 3, Dec, 1949 (52 pgs.)

	GD	VG	FN	VF	VF/NM	NM-
1-Oscar app.; Kurtzman-a (4 pgs.)	20	40	60	117	189	260
2-Kurtzman-a (4 pgs.)	13	26	39	72	101	130
3-No Kurtzman-a	10	20	30	58	79	100

LITTLE AUDREY (Also see Playful...)
St. John Publ.: Apr, 1948 - No. 24, May, 1952

	GD	VG	FN	VF	VF/NM	NM-
1-1st app. Little Audrey	142	284	426	909	1555	2200
2	41	82	123	256	428	600
3-5	26	52	78	154	252	350
6-10	19	38	57	111	176	240
11-20: 16-X-Mas-c	14	28	42	82	121	160
21-24	13	26	39	74	105	135

LITTLE AUDREY (See Harvey Hits #11, 19)
Harvey Publications: No. 25, Aug, 1952 - No. 53, April, 1957

	GD	VG	FN	VF	VF/NM	NM-
25-(Paramount Pictures Famous Star... on-c); 1st Harvey Casper and Baby Huey (1 month earlier than Harvey Comic Hits #60(9/52))	26	52	78	182	404	625
26-30: 26-28-Casper app.	8	16	24	55	105	155
31-40: 32-35-Casper app.	6	12	18	40	73	105
41-53	5	10	15	31	53	75
...Clubhouse 1 (9/61, 68 pg. Giant)-New stories & reprints	8	16	24	52	99	145

LITTLE AUDREY
Harvey Comics: Aug, 1992 - No. 8, July, 1994 ($1.25/$1.50)

	GD	VG	FN	VF	VF/NM	NM-
V2#1						4.00
2-8						3.00

LITTLE AUDREY (...Yearbook)
St. John Publishing Co.: 1950 (50¢, 260 pgs.)

Contains 8 complete 1949 comics rebound; Casper, Alice in Wonderland, Little Audrey, Abbott & Costello, Pinocchio, Moon Mullins, Three Stooges (from Jubilee), Little Annie Rooney app. (Rare)

	GD	VG	FN	VF	VF/NM	NM-
	187	374	561	1197	2049	2900

(Also see All Good & Treasury of Comics)

NOTE: *This book contains remaindered St. John comics; many variations possible.*

LITTLE AUDREY & MELVIN (Audrey & Melvin No. 62)
Harvey Publications: May, 1962 - No. 61, Dec, 1973

	GD	VG	FN	VF	VF/NM	NM-
1	9	18	27	63	129	195
2-5	4	8	12	25	40	55

Li'l Depressed Boy #4 © S. Struble

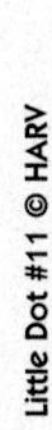
Little Dot #11 © HARV

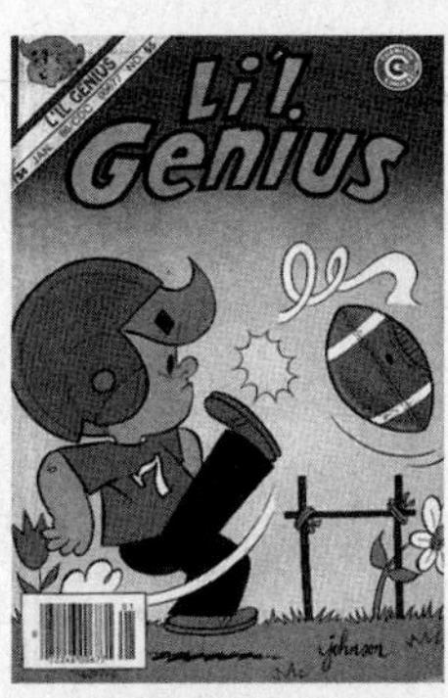
Li'l Genius #55 © CC

	GD 2.0	VG 4.0	FN 6.0	VF 8.0	VF/NM 9.0	NM- 9.2
6-10	3	6	9	21	33	45
11-20	3	6	9	16	23	30
21-40: 22-Richie Rich app.	2	4	6	13	18	22
41-50,55-61	2	4	6	9	13	16
51-54: All 52 pg. Giants	2	4	6	13	18	22

LITTLE AUDREY TV FUNTIME
Harvey Publ.: Sept, 1962 - No. 33, Oct, 1971 (#1-31: 68 pgs.; #32,33: 52 pgs.)

	GD 2.0	VG 4.0	FN 6.0	VF 8.0	VF/NM 9.0	NM- 9.2
1-Richie Rich app.	9	18	27	63	129	195
2,3: Richie Rich app.	4	8	12	27	44	60
4,5: 5-25¢ & 35¢ issues exist	4	8	12	23	37	50
6-10	3	6	9	17	26	35
11-20	3	6	9	14	19	24
21-33	2	4	6	11	16	20

LITTLE BAD WOLF (Disney; see Walt Disney's C&S #52, Walt Disney Showcase #21 & Wheaties)
Dell Publishing Co.: No. 403, June, 1952 - No. 564, June, 1954

	GD 2.0	VG 4.0	FN 6.0	VF 8.0	VF/NM 9.0	NM- 9.2
Four Color 403 (#1)	8	16	24	52	99	145
Four Color 473 (6/53), 564	5	10	15	34	60	85

LI'L BATTLESTAR GALACTICA (Classic 1978 TV series)
Dynamite Entertainment: 2014 ($3.99, one-shot)

	GD 2.0	VG 4.0	FN 6.0	VF 8.0	VF/NM 9.0	NM- 9.2
1-Kid version spoof by Franco & Art Baltazar; covers by Baltazar & Garbowska						4.00

LITTLE BEAVER
Dell Publishing Co.: No. 211, Jan, 1949 - No. 870, Jan, 1958 (All painted-c)

	GD 2.0	VG 4.0	FN 6.0	VF 8.0	VF/NM 9.0	NM- 9.2
Four Color 211('49)-All Harman-a	9	18	27	61	123	185
Four Color 267,294,332(5/51)	6	12	18	38	69	100
3(10-12/51)-8(1-3/53)	5	10	15	30	50	70
Four Color 483(8-10/53),529	5	10	15	34	60	85
Four Color 612,660,695,744,817,870	5	10	15	33	57	80

LI'L BIONIC KIDS (Six Million Dollar Man and Bionic Woman)
Dynamite Entertainment: 2014 ($3.99, one-shot)

	GD 2.0	VG 4.0	FN 6.0	VF 8.0	VF/NM 9.0	NM- 9.2
1-Kid version spoof; Bigfoot app.; Jerwa-s/McGinty-a; covers by Baltazar & Garbowska						4.00

LITTLE BIT
Jubilee/St. John Publishing Co.: Mar, 1949 - No. 2, June, 1949

	GD 2.0	VG 4.0	FN 6.0	VF 8.0	VF/NM 9.0	NM- 9.2
1-Kid humor	12	24	36	69	97	125
2	9	18	27	50	65	80

LI'L DEPRESSED BOY
Image Comics: Feb, 2011 - No. 16, Apr, 2013 ($2.99/$3.99)

	GD 2.0	VG 4.0	FN 6.0	VF 8.0	VF/NM 9.0	NM- 9.2
1-12-S. Steven Struble-s/Sina Grace-a. 5-Guillory-c. 6-Adlard-c. 10-Childish Gambino app.						3.00
13-16-($3.99)						4.00
Vol. 0 (12/11, $9.99) reprints earlier stories from webcomics & anthologies; various-a						10.00

LI'L DEPRESSED BOY: SUPPOSED TO BE THERE TOO
Image Comics: Oct, 2014 - No. 5, Jun, 2015 ($3.99)

	GD 2.0	VG 4.0	FN 6.0	VF 8.0	VF/NM 9.0	NM- 9.2
1-5-S. Steven Struble-s/Sina Grace-a						4.00

LITTLE DOT (See Humphrey, Li'l Max, Sad Sack, and Tastee-Freez Comics)
Harvey Publications: Sept, 1953 - No. 164, Apr, 1976

	GD 2.0	VG 4.0	FN 6.0	VF 8.0	VF/NM 9.0	NM- 9.2
1-Intro./1st app. Richie Rich & Little Lotta	730	1460	2190	5329	9415	13,500
2-1st app. Freckles & Pee Wee (Richie Rich's poor friends)	168	336	504	1075	1838	2600
3	97	194	291	621	1061	1500
4	87	174	261	553	952	1350
5-Origin dots on Little Dot's dress	90	180	270	576	988	1400
6-Richie Rich, Little Lotta, & Little Dot all on cover; 1st Richie Rich cover featured	200	400	600	1280	2190	3100
7-10: 9-Last pre-code issue (1/55)	63	126	189	403	689	975
11-20	36	72	108	211	343	475
21-30	18	36	54	105	165	225
31-40	14	28	42	80	115	150
41-50	11	22	33	62	86	110
51-60	9	18	27	52	69	85
61-80	4	8	12	27	44	60
81-100	3	6	9	19	30	40
101-141: 122-Richie Rich, Little Lotta, & Little Dot birthday-c. 134-Richie Rich, Little Lotta, Little Audrey & Little Dot lemonade-c	3	6	9	16	23	30
142-145: All 52 pg. Giants	3	6	9	17	26	35
146-164	2	4	6	11	16	20

NOTE: *Richie Rich & Little Lotta in all.*

LITTLE DOT
Harvey Comics: Sept, 1992 - No. 7, June, 1994 ($1.25/$1.50)

	GD 2.0	VG 4.0	FN 6.0	VF 8.0	VF/NM 9.0	NM- 9.2
V2#1-Little Dot, Little Lotta, Richie Rich in all						4.00
2-7 ($1.50)						3.00

LITTLE DOT DOTLAND (Dot Dotland No. 62, 63)
Harvey Publications: July, 1962 - No. 61, Dec, 1973

	GD 2.0	VG 4.0	FN 6.0	VF 8.0	VF/NM 9.0	NM- 9.2
1-Richie Rich begins	12	24	36	81	176	270
2,3	7	14	21	44	82	120
4,5	5	10	15	35	63	90
6-10	5	10	15	30	50	70
11-20	4	8	12	23	37	50
21-30	3	6	9	17	26	35
31-50	3	6	9	16	23	30
51-54: All 52 pg. Giants	3	6	9	17	26	35
55-61	2	4	6	11	16	20

LITTLE DOT'S UNCLES & AUNTS (See Harvey Hits No. 4, 13, 24)
Harvey Enterprises: Oct, 1961; No. 2, Aug, 1962 - No. 52, Apr, 1974

	GD 2.0	VG 4.0	FN 6.0	VF 8.0	VF/NM 9.0	NM- 9.2
1-Richie Rich begins; 68 pgs. begin	14	28	42	94	207	320
2,3	8	16	24	51	96	140
4,5	5	10	15	35	63	90
6-10	5	10	15	31	53	75
11-20	4	8	12	23	37	50
21-37: Last 68 pg. issue	3	6	9	18	28	38
38-52: All 52 pg. Giants	3	6	9	16	23	30

LITTLE DRACULA
Harvey Comics: Jan, 1992 - No. 3, May, 1992 ($1.25, quarterly, mini-series)

	GD 2.0	VG 4.0	FN 6.0	VF 8.0	VF/NM 9.0	NM- 9.2
1-3						3.00

LITTLE ENDLESS STORYBOOK, THE (See The Sandman titles and Delirium's Party)
DC Comics: 2001 ($5.95, Prestige format, one-shot)

	GD 2.0	VG 4.0	FN 6.0	VF 8.0	VF/NM 9.0	NM- 9.2
nn-Jill Thompson-s/painted-a/c; puppy Barnabas searches for Delirium						20.00
HC (2011, $14.99) r/story plus original character sketches and merchandise design						15.00

LI'L ERNIE (Evil Ernie)
Dynamite Entertainment: 2014 ($3.99, one-shot)

	GD 2.0	VG 4.0	FN 6.0	VF 8.0	VF/NM 9.0	NM- 9.2
1-Kid version spoof; Roger Langridge-s/a; covers by Baltazar & Garbowska						4.00

LITTLE EVA
St. John Publishing Co.: May, 1952 - No. 31, Nov, 1956

	GD 2.0	VG 4.0	FN 6.0	VF 8.0	VF/NM 9.0	NM- 9.2
1	19	38	57	111	176	240
2	12	24	36	67	94	120
3-5	10	20	30	54	72	90
6-10	9	18	27	47	61	75
11-31	8	16	24	42	54	65
3-D 1,2(10/53, 11/53, 25¢)-Both came w/glasses. 1-Infinity-c	18	36	54	107	169	230
I.W. Reprint #1-3,6-8: 1-r/Little Eva #28. 2-r/Little Eva #29. 3-r/Little Eva #24	2	4	6	8	11	14
Super Reprint #10,12('63),14,16,18('64): 18-r/Little Eva #25.	2	4	6	8	11	14

LI'L GENIUS (Formerly Super Brat; Summer Fun No. 54) (See Blue Bird & Giant Comics #3)
Charlton Comics: No. 6, 1954 - No. 52, 1/65; No. 53, 10/65; No. 54, 10/85 - No. 55, 1/86

	GD 2.0	VG 4.0	FN 6.0	VF 8.0	VF/NM 9.0	NM- 9.2
6 (#1)	11	22	33	62	86	110
7-10	7	14	21	37	46	55
11-1st app. Li'l Tomboy (10/56); same month as 1st issue of Li'l Tomboy (V14#92)	8	16	24	40	50	60
12-15,19,20	6	12	18	29	36	42
16,17-(68 pgs.)	8	16	24	40	50	60
18-(100 pgs., 10/58)	11	22	33	60	83	105
21-35: 34-Atomic bomb explosion	3	6	9	15	22	28
36-53	2	4	6	10	14	18
54,55 (Low print)						6.00

LI'L GHOST
St. John Publ. Co./Fago No. 1 on: 2/58; No. 2,1/59 - No. 3, Mar, 1959

	GD 2.0	VG 4.0	FN 6.0	VF 8.0	VF/NM 9.0	NM- 9.2
1(St. John)	11	22	33	62	86	110
2,3	7	14	21	37	46	55

LITTLE GIANT COMICS
Centaur Publications: 7/38 - No. 3, 10/38; No. 4, 2/39 (132 pgs.) (6-3/4x4-1/2")

	GD 2.0	VG 4.0	FN 6.0	VF 8.0	VF/NM 9.0	NM- 9.2
1-B&W with color-c; stories, puzzles, magic	226	452	678	1446	2473	3500
2,3-B&W with color-c	161	322	483	1030	1765	2500
4 (6-5/8x9-3/8")(68 pgs., B&W inside)	161	322	483	1030	1765	2500

NOTE: ***Filchock** c-2, 4. **Gustavson** a-1. **Pinajian** a-4. **Bob Wood** a-1.*

Little Giant Movie Funnies #1 © CEN

Little Lenny #1 © MAR

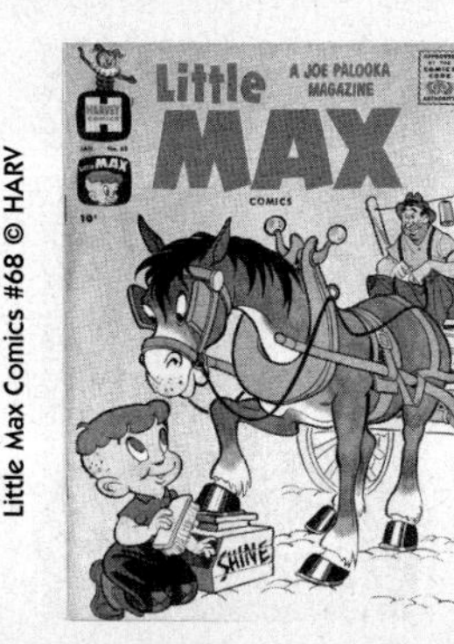

Little Max Comics #68 © HARV

	GD 2.0	VG 4.0	FN 6.0	VF 8.0	VF/NM 9.0	NM- 9.2

LITTLE GIANT DETECTIVE FUNNIES
Centaur Publ.: Oct, 1938; No. 4, Jan, 1939 (6-3/4x4-1/2", 132 pgs., B&W)

	GD	VG	FN	VF	VF/NM	NM-
1-B&W with color-c	226	452	678	1446	2473	3500
4(1/39, B&W; color-c; 68 pgs., 6-1/2x9-1/2")-Eisner-r	161	322	483	1030	1765	2500

LITTLE GIANT MOVIE FUNNIES
Centaur Publ.: Aug, 1938 - No. 2, Oct, 1938 (6-3/4x4-1/2", 132 pgs., B&W)

	GD	VG	FN	VF	VF/NM	NM-
1-Ed Wheelan's "Minute Movies" reprints	226	452	678	1446	2473	3500
2-Ed Wheelan's "Minute Movies" reprints	161	322	483	1030	1765	2500

LITTLE GROUCHO (...the Red-Headed Tornado; ...Grouchy No. 2)
Reston Publ. Co.: No. 16; Feb-Mar, 1955 - No. 2, June-July, 1955 (See Tippy Terry)

	GD	VG	FN	VF	VF/NM	NM-
16, 1 (2-3/55)	9	18	27	50	65	80
2(6-7/55)	7	14	21	35	43	50

LITTLE HIAWATHA (Disney; see Walt Disney's C&S #143)
Dell Publishing Co.: No. 439, Dec, 1952 - No. 988, May-July, 1959

	GD	VG	FN	VF	VF/NM	NM-
Four Color 439 (#1)	7	14	21	46	86	125
Four Color 787 (4/57), 901 (5/58), 988	5	10	15	34	60	85

LITTLE IKE
St. John Publishing Co.: April, 1953 - No. 4, Oct, 1953

	GD	VG	FN	VF	VF/NM	NM-
1-Kid humor	12	24	36	67	94	120
2	8	16	24	40	50	60
3,4	7	14	21	35	43	50

LITTLE IODINE (See Giant Comic Album)
Dell Publ. Co.: No. 224, 4/49 - No. 257, 1949: 3-5/50 - No. 56, 4-6/62 (1-4-52pgs.)

	GD	VG	FN	VF	VF/NM	NM-
Four Color 224-By Jimmy Hatlo	12	24	36	81	176	270
Four Color 257	8	16	24	55	105	155
1(3-5/50)	10	20	30	64	132	200
2-5	5	10	15	35	63	90
6-10	5	10	15	30	50	70
11-20	4	8	12	27	44	60
21-30: 27-Xmas-c	4	8	12	23	37	50
31-40	3	6	9	21	33	45
41-56	3	6	9	19	30	40

LITTLE JACK FROST
Avon Periodicals: 1951

	GD	VG	FN	VF	VF/NM	NM-
1	14	28	42	80	115	150

LI'L JINX (Little Archie in Animal Land #17) (Also see Pep Comics #62)
Archie Publications: No. 1(#11), Nov, 1956 - No. 16, Sept, 1957

	GD	VG	FN	VF	VF/NM	NM-
1(#11)-By Joe Edwards; "First Issue" on cover	17	34	51	98	154	210
12(1/57)-16	11	22	33	62	86	110

LI'L JINX (See Archie Giant Series Magazine No. 223)

LI'L JINX CHRISTMAS BAG (See Archie Giant Series Mag. No. 195, 206, 219)

LI'L JINX GIANT LAUGH-OUT (See Archie Giant Series Mag. No. 176, 185)
Archie Publications: No. 33, Sept, 1971 - No. 43, Nov, 1973 (52 pgs.)

	GD	VG	FN	VF	VF/NM	NM-
33-43 (52 pgs.)	2	4	6	13	18	22

LITTLE JOE (See Popular Comics & Super Comics)
Dell Publishing Co.: No. 1, 1942

	GD	VG	FN	VF	VF/NM	NM-
Four Color 1	64	128	192	512	1156	1800

LITTLE JOE
St. John Publishing Co.: Apr, 1953

	GD	VG	FN	VF	VF/NM	NM-
1	8	16	24	44	57	70

LI'L KIDS (Also see Li'l Pals)
Marvel Comics Group: 8/70 - No. 2, 10/70; No. 3, 11/71 - No. 12, 6/73

	GD	VG	FN	VF	VF/NM	NM-
1	8	16	24	54	102	150
2-9	4	8	12	28	47	65
10-12-Calvin app.	5	10	15	30	50	70

LITTLE KING
Dell Publishing Co.: No. 494, Aug, 1953 - No. 677, Feb, 1956

	GD	VG	FN	VF	VF/NM	NM-
Four Color 494 (#1)	8	16	24	56	108	160
Four Color 597, 677	5	10	15	34	60	85

LITTLE LANA (Formerly Lana)
Marvel Comics (MjMC): No. 8, Nov, 1949; No. 9, Mar, 1950

	GD	VG	FN	VF	VF/NM	NM-
8,9	18	36	54	107	169	230

LITTLE LENNY
Marvel Comics (CDS): June, 1949 - No. 3, Nov, 1949

	GD	VG	FN	VF	VF/NM	NM-
1-Little Aspirin app.	15	30	45	86	133	180
2,3	10	20	30	56	76	95

LITTLE LIZZIE
Marvel Comics (PrPI)/Atlas (OMC): 6/49 - No. 5, 4/50; 9/53 - No. 3, Jan, 1954

	GD	VG	FN	VF	VF/NM	NM-
1-Kid humor	17	34	51	100	158	215
2-5	11	22	33	60	83	105
1 (9/53, 2nd series by Atlas)-Howie Post-c	13	26	39	74	105	135
2,3	10	20	30	54	72	90

LITTLE LOTTA (See Harvey Hits No. 10)
Harvey Publications: 11/55 - No. 110, 11/73; No. 111, 9/74 - No. 120, 5/76
V2#1, Oct, 1992 - No. 4, July, 1993 ($1.25)

	GD	VG	FN	VF	VF/NM	NM-
1-Richie Rich (r) & Little Dot begin	53	106	159	413	932	1450
2,3	16	32	48	112	249	385
4,5	10	20	30	69	147	225
6-10	7	14	21	46	86	125
11-20	5	10	15	35	63	90
21-40	4	8	12	23	37	50
41-60	3	6	9	18	28	38
61-80: 62-1st app. Nurse Jenny	3	6	9	15	22	28
81-99	2	4	6	11	16	20
100-103: All 52 pg. Giants	3	6	9	14	19	24
104-120	2	4	6	8	10	12
V2#1-4 (1992-93)						4.00

NOTE: *No. 121 was advertised, but never released.*

LITTLE LOTTA FOODLAND
Harvey Publications: 9/63 - No. 14, 10/67; No. 15, 10/68 - No. 29, Oct, 1972

	GD	VG	FN	VF	VF/NM	NM-
1-Little Lotta, Little Dot, Richie Rich, 68 pgs. begin	11	22	33	73	157	240
2,3	6	12	18	38	69	100
4,5	5	10	15	30	50	70
6-10	4	8	12	23	37	50
11-20	3	6	9	16	23	30
21-26: 26-Last 68 pg. issue	3	6	9	14	20	25
27,28: Both 52 pgs.	2	4	6	11	16	20
29-(36 pgs.)	2	4	6	8	11	14

LITTLE LULU (Formerly Marge's Little Lulu)
Gold Key 207-257/Whitman 258 on: No. 207, Sept, 1972 - No. 268, Mar, 1984

	GD	VG	FN	VF	VF/NM	NM-
207,209,220-Stanley-r. 207-1st app. Henrietta	2	4	6	13	18	22
208,210-219: 208-1st app. Snobbly, Wilbur's butler	2	4	6	9	13	16
221-240,242-249, 250(r/#166), 251-254(r/#206)	2	4	6	8	10	12
241,263-Stanley-r	2	4	6	8	11	14
255-257(Gold Key): 256-r/#212	1	3	4	6	8	10
258,259,262(50¢-c),264(2/82),265(3/82) (Whitman)	2	4	6	11	16	20
260-(9/80)(Whitman pre-pack only - low distribution)	15	30	45	103	227	350
261-(11/80)(Whitman pre-pack only)	7	14	21	44	82	120
262-(1/81) Variant 40¢-c price error (reg. ed. 50¢-c)	3	6	9	15	22	28
266-268 (All #90028 on-c; no date, no date code; 3-pack): 266(7/83). 267(8/83). 268(3/84)-Stanley-r	3	6	9	17	26	35

LITTLE MARY MIXUP (See Comics On Parade)
United Features Syndicate: No. 10, 1939, - No. 26, 1940

	GD	VG	FN	VF	VF/NM	NM-
Single Series 10, 26	34	68	102	206	336	465

LITTLE MAX COMICS (Joe Palooka's Pal; see Joe Palooka)
Harvey Publications: Oct, 1949 - No. 73, Nov, 1961

	GD	VG	FN	VF	VF/NM	NM-
1-Infinity-c; Little Dot begins; Joe Palooka on-c	26	52	78	154	252	350
2-Little Dot app.; Joe Palooka on-c	14	28	42	82	121	160
3-Little Dot app.; Joe Palooka on-c	10	20	30	58	79	100
4-10: 5-Little Dot app., 1pg.	9	18	27	47	61	75
11-20	8	16	24	40	50	60
21-40: 23-Little Dot app. 38-r/#20	6	12	18	31	38	45
41-62,66	3	6	9	17	26	35
63-65,67-73-Include new five pg. Richie Rich stories. 70-73-Little Lotta app.	3	6	9	18	28	38

LI'L MENACE
Fago Magazine Co.: Dec, 1958 - No. 3, May, 1959

	GD	VG	FN	VF	VF/NM	NM-
1-Peter Rabbit app.	9	18	27	50	65	80
2-Peter Rabbit (Vincent Fago's)	7	14	21	35	43	50
3	6	12	18	28	34	40

LITTLE MERMAID, THE (Walt Disney's...; also see Disney's...)
W. D. Publications (Disney): 1990 (no date given)($5.95, no ads, 52 pgs.)

Little Miss Muffet #12 © STD

Little Roquefort Comics #1 © STJ

Littlest Pet Shop #5 © Hasbro

	GD 2.0	VG 4.0	FN 6.0	VF 8.0	VF/NM 9.0	NM- 9.2
nn-Adapts animated movie	1	2	3	4	5	7
nn-Comic version ($2.50)						4.00

LITTLE MERMAID, THE
Disney Comics: 1992 - No. 4, 1992 ($1.50, mini-series)

	GD	VG	FN	VF	VF/NM	NM-
1-4: Based on movie						4.00
1-4: 2nd printings sold at Wal-Mart w/different-c						4.00

LITTLE MISS MUFFET
Best Books (Standard Comics)/King Features Synd.: No. 11, Dec, 1948 - No. 13, March, 1949

	GD	VG	FN	VF	VF/NM	NM-
11-Strip reprints; Fanny Cory-c/a	10	20	30	58	79	100
12,13-Strip reprints; Fanny Cory-c/a	8	16	24	42	54	65

LITTLE MISS SUNBEAM COMICS
Magazine Enterprises/Quality Bakers of America: June-July, 1950 - No. 4, Dec-Jan, 1950-51

	GD	VG	FN	VF	VF/NM	NM-
1	18	36	54	103	162	220
2-4	11	22	33	60	83	105
...Advs. In Space ('55)	7	14	21	35	43	50

LITTLE MONSTERS, THE (See March of Comics #423, Three Stooges #17)
Gold Key: Nov, 1964 - No. 44, Feb, 1978

	GD	VG	FN	VF	VF/NM	NM-
1	5	10	15	33	57	80
2	3	6	9	19	30	40
3-10	3	6	9	16	24	32
11-20	3	6	9	15	21	26
21-30: 19-21-Reprints	2	4	6	11	16	20
31-44: 34-39,43-Reprints	2	4	6	8	11	14

LITTLE MONSTERS (Movie)
Now Comics: 1989 - No. 6, June, 1990 ($1.75)

	GD	VG	FN	VF	VF/NM	NM-
1-6: Photo-c from movie						3.00

LITTLE NEMO (See Cocomalt, Future Comics, Help, Jest, Kayo, Punch, Red Seal, & Superworld; most by Winsor McCay Jr., son of famous artist) (Other McCay books: see Little Sammy Sneeze & Dreams of the Rarebit Fiend)

LITTLE NEMO (...in Slumberland)
McCay Features/Nostalgia Press('69): 1945 (11x7-1/4", 28 pgs., B&W)

	GD	VG	FN	VF	VF/NM	NM-
1905 & 1911 reprints by Winsor McCay	10	20	30	56	76	95
1969-70 (Exact reprint)	2	4	6	9	12	15

LITTLE NEMO: RETURN TO SLUMBERLAND
IDW Publishing: Aug, 2014 - No. 4, Feb, 2015 ($3.99)

	GD	VG	FN	VF	VF/NM	NM-
1-4-New stories in McCay style; Shanower-s/Rodriguez-a in all. 1-Multiple covers						4.00

LITTLE ORPHAN ANNIE (See Annie, Famous Feature Stories, Marvel Super Special, Merry Christmas..., Popular Comics, Super Book #7, 11, 23 & Super Comics)

LITTLE ORPHAN ANNIE
David McKay Publ./Dell Publishing Co.: No. 7, 1937 - No. 3, Sept-Nov, 1948; No. 206, Dec, 1948

	GD	VG	FN	VF	VF/NM	NM-
Feature Books(McKay) 7-(1937) (Rare)	116	232	348	742	1271	1800
Four Color 12(1941)	65	130	195	416	708	1000
Four Color 18(1943)-Flag-c	35	70	105	252	564	875
Four Color 52(1944)	24	48	72	170	378	585
Four Color 76(1945)	19	38	57	133	297	460
Four Color 107(1946)	17	34	51	119	265	410
Four Color 152(1947)	12	24	36	79	170	260
1(3-5/48)-r/strips from 5/7/44 to 7/30/44	11	22	33	76	163	250
2-r/strips from 7/21/40 to 9/9/40	8	16	24	55	105	155
3-r/strips from 9/10/40 to 11/9/40	8	16	24	55	105	155
Four Color 206(12/48)	8	16	24	52	99	145

LI'L PALS (Also see Li'l Kids)
Marvel Comics Group: Sept, 1972 - No. 5, May, 1973

	GD	VG	FN	VF	VF/NM	NM-
1	7	14	21	52	99	145
2-5	5	10	15	30	50	70

LI'L PAN (Formerly Rocket Kelly; becomes Junior Comics with #9)(Also see Wotalife Comics)
Fox Feature Syndicate: No. 6, Dec-Jan, 1946-47 - No. 8, Apr-May, 1947

	GD	VG	FN	VF	VF/NM	NM-
6	14	28	42	76	108	140
7,8: 7-Atomic bomb story; robot-c	11	22	33	62	86	110

LITTLE PEOPLE (Also see Darby O'Gill & the...)
Dell Publishing Co.: No. 485, Aug-Oct, 1953 - No. 1062, Dec, 1959 (Walt Scott's)

	GD	VG	FN	VF	VF/NM	NM-
Four Color 485 (#1)	8	16	24	51	96	140
Four Color 573(7/54), 633(6/55)	5	10	15	35	63	90
Four Color 692(3/56),753(11/56),809(7/57),868(12/57),908(5/58),959(12/58),1062	5	10	15	33	57	80

LITTLE RASCALS
Dell Publishing Co.: No. 674, Jan, 1956 - No. 1297, Mar-May, 1962

	GD	VG	FN	VF	VF/NM	NM-
Four Color 674 (#1)	9	18	27	59	117	175
Four Color 778(3/57),825(8/57)	6	12	18	38	69	100
Four Color 883(3/58),936(9/58),974(3/59),1030(9/59),1079(2-4/60),1137(9-11/60)	5	10	15	35	63	90
Four Color 1174(3-5/61),1224(10-12/61),1297	5	10	15	33	57	80

LI'L RASCAL TWINS (Formerly Nature Boy)
Charlton Comics: No. 6, 1957 - No. 18, Jan, 1960

	GD	VG	FN	VF	VF/NM	NM-
6-Li'l Genius & Tomboy in all	6	12	18	29	36	42
7-18: 7-Timmy the Timid Ghost app.	4	8	12	18	22	25

LITTLE RED HOT: (CHANE OF FOOLS)
Image Comics: Feb, 1999 - No. 3, Apr, 1999 ($2.95/$3.50, B&W, limited series)

	GD	VG	FN	VF	VF/NM	NM-
1-3-Dawn Brown-s/a. 2,3-($3.50-c)						3.50
The Foolish Collection TPB ($12.95) r/#1-3						13.00

LITTLE RED HOT: BOUND
Image Comics: July, 2001 - No. 3, Nov, 2001 ($2.95, color, limited series)

	GD	VG	FN	VF	VF/NM	NM-
1-3-Dawn Brown-s/a.						3.00

LITTLE ROQUEFORT COMICS (See Paul Terry's Comics #105)
St. John Publishing Co.(all pre-code)/Pines No. 10: June, 1952 - No. 9, Oct, 1953; No. 10, Summer, 1958

	GD	VG	FN	VF	VF/NM	NM-
1-By Paul Terry; Funny Animal	12	24	36	69	97	125
2	8	16	24	42	54	65
3-10: 10-CBS Television Presents on-c	7	14	21	37	46	55

LITTLE SAD SACK (See Harvey Hits No. 73, 76, 79, 81, 83)
Harvey Publications: Oct, 1964 - No. 19, Nov, 1967

	GD	VG	FN	VF	VF/NM	NM-
1-Richie Rich app. on cover only	5	10	15	33	57	80
2-10	3	6	9	17	26	35
11-19	3	6	9	15	22	28

LITTLE SCOUTS
Dell Publishing Co.: No. 321, Mar, 1951 - No. 587, Oct, 1954

	GD	VG	FN	VF	VF/NM	NM-
Four Color 321 (#1, 3/51)	6	12	18	37	66	95
2(10-12/51) - 6(10-12/52)	4	8	12	25	40	55
Four Color 462,506,550,587	5	10	15	30	50	70

LITTLE SHOP OF HORRORS SPECIAL (Movie)
DC Comics: Feb, 1987 ($2.00, 68 pgs.)

	GD	VG	FN	VF	VF/NM	NM-
1-Colan-c/a						5.00

LI'L SONJA (Red Sonja)
Dynamite Entertainment: 2014 ($3.99, one-shot)

	GD	VG	FN	VF	VF/NM	NM-
1-Kid version spoof; Jim Zub-s/Joel Carroll-a; covers by Baltazar & Garbowska						4.00

LITTLE SPUNKY
I. W. Enterprises: No date (1958) (10¢)

	GD	VG	FN	VF	VF/NM	NM-
1-r/Frisky Fables #1	2	4	6	8	11	14

LITTLE STAR
Oni Press: Feb, 2005 - No. 6, Dec, 2005 ($2.99, B&W, limited series)

	GD	VG	FN	VF	VF/NM	NM-
1-6-Andi Watson-s/a						3.00
TPB (4/06, $19.95) r/#1-6						20.00

LITTLE STOOGES, THE (The Three Stooges' Sons)
Gold Key: Sept, 1972 - No. 7, Mar, 1974

	GD	VG	FN	VF	VF/NM	NM-
1-Norman Maurer cover/stories in all	3	6	9	18	28	38
2-7	2	4	6	13	18	22

LITTLEST OUTLAW (Disney)
Dell Publishing Co.: No. 609, Jan, 1955

	GD	VG	FN	VF	VF/NM	NM-
Four Color 609-Movie, photo-c	6	12	18	41	76	110

LITTLEST PET SHOP (Based on the Hasbro toys)
IDW Publishing: May, 2014 - No. 5, Sept, 2014 ($3.99)

	GD	VG	FN	VF	VF/NM	NM-
1-5: 1-Ball-s/Peña-a; multiple covers. 2-5-Two covers on each						4.00
... Spring Cleaning (4/15, $7.99) Four short stories; Ball-s; art by various						8.00

LITTLEST SNOWMAN, THE
Dell Publishing Co.: No. 755, 12/56; No. 864, 12/57; 12-2/1963-64

	GD	VG	FN	VF	VF/NM	NM-
Four Color 755,864, 1(1964)	5	10	15	35	63	90

LI'L TOMBOY (Formerly Fawcett's Funny Animals; see Giant Comics #3)
Charlton Comics: V14#92, Oct, 1956; No. 93, Mar, 1957 - No. 107, Feb, 1960

	GD	VG	FN	VF	VF/NM	NM-
V14#92-Ties as 1st app. with Li'l Genius #11	6	12	18	27	33	38

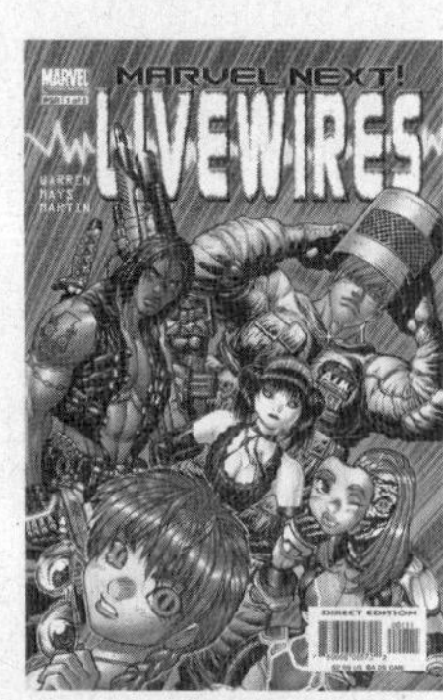

Livewires #1 © MAR

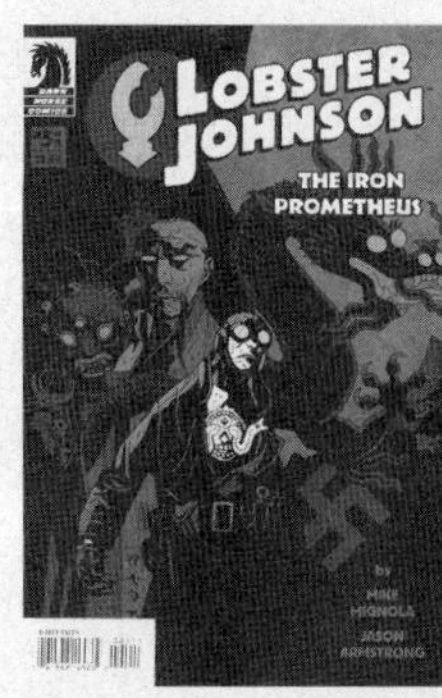

Lobster Johnson: The Iron Prometheus #5 © Mike Mignola

Locke & Key: Clockworks #5 © H&R

GD 2.0 | VG 4.0 | FN 6.0 | VF 8.0 | VF/NM 9.0 | NM- 9.2

93-107: 97-Atomic Bunny app. 5 10 14 20 24 28

LI'L VAMPI (Vampirella)
Dynamite Entertainment: 2014 ($3.99, one-shot)
1-Kid version spoof; Trautmann-s/Garbowska-a; covers by Baltazar & Garbowska 4.00

LI'L WILLIE COMICS (Formerly & becomes Willie Comics #22 on)
Marvel Comics (MgPC): No. 20, July, 1949 - No. 21, Sept, 1949
20,21: 20-Little Aspirin app. 16 32 48 94 147 200

LITTLE WOMEN (See Power Record Comics)

LIVE IT UP
Spire Christian Comics (Fleming H. Revell Co.): 1973, 1974,1976 (39-49 cents)
nn-1973 Edition 2 4 6 13 18 22
nn-1974,1976 Editions 2 4 6 8 11 14

LIVEWIRES
Marvel Comics: Apr, 2005 - No. 6, Sept, 2005 ($2.99, limited series)
1-6-Adam Warren-s/c; Rick Mays-a 3.00
...: Clockwork Thugs, Yo (2005, $7.99, digest) r/#1-6 8.00

LIVING BIBLE, THE
Living Bible Corp.: Fall, 1945 - No. 3, Spring, 1946
1-The Life of Paul; all have L. B. Cole-c 41 82 123 256 428 600
2-Joseph & His Brethren; Jonah & the Whale 30 60 90 177 289 400
3-Chaplains At War (classic-c) 42 84 126 267 451 635

LIVING WITH THE DEAD
Dark Horse Comics: Oct, 2007 - No. 3, Nov, 2007 ($2.99, limited series)
1-3-Zombies; Mike Richardson-s/Ben Stenbeck-a/Richard Corben-c 3.00

LOADED BIBLE
Image Comics: Apr, 2006; May, 2007; Feb, 2008 ($4.99)
...: Jesus vs. Vampires (4/06) Tim Seeley-s/Nate Bellegarde-a 5.00
...2: Blood of Christ (5/07) Seeley-s/Mike Norton-a. ...3: Communion (2/08) 5.00

LOBO
Dell Publishing Co.: Dec, 1965; No. 2, Oct, 1966
1-1st black character to have his own title 30 60 90 216 483 750
2 14 28 42 96 211 325

LOBO (Also see Action #650, Adventures of Superman, Demon (2nd series), Justice League, L.E.G.I.O.N., Mister Miracle, Omega Men #3 & Superman #41)
DC Comics: Nov, 1990 - No. 4, Feb, 1991 ($1.50, color, limited series)
1-(99¢)-Giffen plots/Breakdowns in all 1 3 4 6 8 10
1-2nd printing 4.00
2-4: 2-Legion '89 spin-off. 1-4 have Bisley painted covers & art 5.00
...: Blazing Chain of Love 1 (9/92, $1.50)-Denys Cowan-c/a; Alan Grant scripts, ...Convention Special 1 (1993, $1.75), ...: Portrait of a Victim 1 (1993, $1.75) 3.00
... Paramilitary Christmas Special 1 (1991, $2.39, 52 pgs.) Bisley-c/a 4.00
...: Portrait of a Bastich TPB (2008, $19.99) r/#1-4 & Lobo's Back #1-4 20.00

LOBO (Also see Showcase '95 #9)
DC Comics: Dec, 1993 - No. 64, Jul, 1999 ($1.75/$1.95/$2.25/$2.50, mature)
1 ($2.95)-Foil enhanced-c; Alan Grant scripts begin 4.00
2-9,0,10-64: 2-7-Alan Grant scripts. 9-(9/94). 0-(10/94)-Origin retold. 50-Lobo vs. the DCU. 58-Giffen-a 3.00
#1,000,000 (11/98) 853rd Century x-over 3.00
Annual 1 (1993, $3.50, 68 pgs.)-Bloodlines x-over 4.00
Annual 2 (1994, $3.50)-21 artists (20 listed on-c); Alan Grant script; Elseworlds story 4.00
Annual 3 (1995, $3.95)-Year One story 4.00
.../Authority: Holiday Hell TPB (2006, $17.99) r/Lobo Paramilitary Christmas Special; Authority/Lobo: Jingle Hell and Spring Break Massacre; WildStorm Winter Special 18.00
...Big Babe Spring Break Special (Spr, '95, $1.95)-Balent-a 3.00
...Bounty Hunting for Fun and Profit ('95)-Bisley-c 5.00
... Chained (5/97, $2.50)-Alan Grant story 3.00
.../Deadman: The Brave And The Bald (2/95, $3.50) 4.00
.../Demon: Helloween (12/96, $2.25)-Giarrano-a 3.00
...Fragtastic Voyage 1 ('97, $5.95)-Mejia painted-c/a 6.00
...Gallery (9/95, $3.50)-pin-ups. 3.50
...In the Chair 1 (8/94, $1.95, 36 pgs.), ...I Quit-(12/95, $2.25) 3.00
.../Judge Dredd ('95, $4.95). 5.00
...Lobocop 1 (2/94, $1.95)-Alan Grant scripts; painted-c 3.00

LOBO (Younger version from New 52 Justice League #23.2)
DC Comics: Dec, 2014 - No. 13, Feb, 2016 ($2.99)
1-13: 1-5-Bunn-s/Brown-a. 4-Superman app. 10,11-Sinestro app. 13-Hal Jordan app. 3.00
Annual 1 (9/15, $4.99) Bunn-s/Rocha-a; the Sinestro Corps app.; leads into Lobo #10 5.00

GD 2.0 | VG 4.0 | FN 6.0 | VF 8.0 | VF/NM 9.0 | NM- 9.2

LOBO: (Title Series), DC Comics
--A CONTRACT ON GAWD, 4/94 - 7/94 (mature) 1-4: Alan Grant scripts. 3-Groo cameo 3.00
--DEATH AND TAXES, 10/96 - No. 4, 1/97, 1-4-Giffen/Grant scripts 3.00
--GOES TO HOLLYWOOD, 8/96 ($2.25), 1-Grant scripts 3.00
--HIGHWAY TO HELL, 1/10 - No. 2, 2/10 ($6.99), 1,2-Scott Ian-s/Sam Kieth-a/c 7.00
TPB (2010, $19.99) r/#1,2; intro. by Scott Ian; Kieth B&W art pages 20.00
--INFANTICIDE, 10/92 - 1/93 ($1.50, mature), 1-4-Giffen-c/a; Grant scripts 3.00
--/ MASK, 2/97 - No. 2, 3/97 ($5.95), 1,2 6.00
--/ ROAD RUNNER, 8/17 ($4.99), 1-Bill Morrison-s/Kelley Jones-a/c; Wile E. Coyote app. 5.00
--'S BACK, 5/92 - No. 4, 11/92 ($1.50, mature), 1-4: 1-Has 3 outer covers. Bisley painted-c 1,2; a-1-3. 3-Sam Kieth-c; all have Giffen plots/breakdown & Grant scripts 4.00
Trade paperback (1993, $9.95)-r/1-4 10.00
--THE DUCK, 6/97 ($1.95), 1-A. Grant-s/V. Semeiks & R. Kryssing-a 3.00
--UNAMERICAN GLADIATORS, 6/93 - No. 4, 9/93 ($1.75, mature), 1-4-Mignola-c; Grant/Wagner scripts 4.00
--UNBOUND, 8/03 - No. 6, 5/04 ($2.95), 1-6-Giffen-s/Horley-c/a. 4-6-Ambush Bug app. 3.00

LOBSTER JOHNSON (One-shots) (See B.P.R.D. and Hellboy titles)
Dark Horse Comics
...: A Chain Forged in Life (7/15, $3.50) Mignola & Arcudi-s; Nixey & Nowlan-a 3.50
...: Caput Mortuum (9/12, $3.50) Mignola & Arcudi-s; Zonjic-c/a 3.50
...: Garden of Bones (1/17, $3.99) Mignola & Arcudi-s; Stephen Green-a/Zonjic-c 4.00
...: Mangekyo (8/17, $3.99) Mignola & Arcudi-s; Stenbeck-a/Zonjic-c 4.00
...: Satan Smells a Rat (5/13, $3.50) Mignola & Arcudi-s; Nowlan-c/a 3.50
...: The Forgotten Man (4/16, $3.50) Mignola & Arcudi-s; Snejbjerg-a/Zonjic-c 3.50
...: The Glass Mantis (12/15, $3.50) Mignola & Arcudi-s; Fejzula-a/Zonjic-c 3.50

LOBSTER JOHNSON: A SCENT OF LOTUS (See B.P.R.D. and Hellboy titles)
Dark Horse Comics: Jul, 2013 - No. 2, Aug, 2013 ($3.50, limited series)
1,2-Mignola & Arcudi-s; Fiumara-a/Zonjic-c 3.50

LOBSTER JOHNSON: GET THE LOBSTER
Dark Horse Comics: Feb, 2014 - No. 5, Aug, 2014 ($3.99, limited series)
1-5-Mignola & Arcudi-s; Zonjic-a/c 4.00

LOBSTER JOHNSON: METAL MONSTERS OF MIDTOWN
Dark Horse Comics: May, 2016 - No. 3, Jul, 2016 ($3.50/$3.99, limited series)
1-3-Mignola & Arcudi-s; Zonjic-a/c. 1-$3.50. 2,3-$3.99 4.00

LOBSTER JOHNSON: THE BURNING HAND
Dark Horse Comics: Jan, 2012 - No. 5, May, 2012 ($3.50, limited series)
1-5-Mignola & Arcudi-s; Zonjic-a. 1-Two covers by Dave Johnson & Mignola 3.50

LOBSTER JOHNSON: THE IRON PROMETHEUS
Dark Horse Comics: Sept, 2007 - No. 5, Jan, 2008 ($2.99, limited series)
1-Mignola-s/c; Armstrong-a 6.00
2-5-Mignola-s/c; Armstrong-a 4.00

LOBSTER JOHNSON: THE PIRATE'S GHOST
Dark Horse Comics: Mar, 2017 - No. 3, May, 2017 ($3.99, limited series)
1-3-Mignola & Arcudi-s; Zonjic-a/c 4.00

LOCKE & KEY
IDW Publ.: Feb, 2008 - No. 6, July, 2008 ($3.99, limited series)
1-Joe Hill-s/Gabriel Rodriguez-a 45.00
1-Second printing 5.00
2 10.00
3-6 5.00
...: Free Comic Book Day Edition (5/11) r/story from Crown of Shadows 3.00
...: Grindhouse (8/12, $3.99) EC-style; Hill-s/Rodriguez-a; bonus Guide to the Keyhouse 4.00
...: Guide to the Known Keys (1/12, $3.99) Key to the Moon; bonus Guide to the Keys 4.00
...: Welcome to Lovecraft Legacy Edition #1 (8/10, $1.00) r/#1; synopsis of later issues 3.00
...: Welcome to Lovecraft Special Edition #1 SC (9/09, $5.99) Hill-s/Rodriguez-a; script; back-up story with final art from Seth Fisher 6.00

LOCKE & KEY: ALPHA
IDW Publ.: Aug, 2013 - No. 2, Oct, 2013 ($7.99, limited series)
1,2-Series conclusion; Joe Hill-s/Gabriel Rodriguez-a 8.00

LOCKE & KEY: CLOCKWORKS
IDW Publ.: Jun, 2011 - No. 6, Apr, 2012 ($3.99, limited series)
1-6: 1-Hill-s/Rodriguez-a; set in 1776 4.00

LOCKE & KEY: CROWN OF SHADOWS
IDW Publ.: Nov, 2009 - No. 6, Apr, 2010 ($3.99, limited series)

Lockjaw #1 © MAR

Loki: Agent of Asgard #7 © MAR

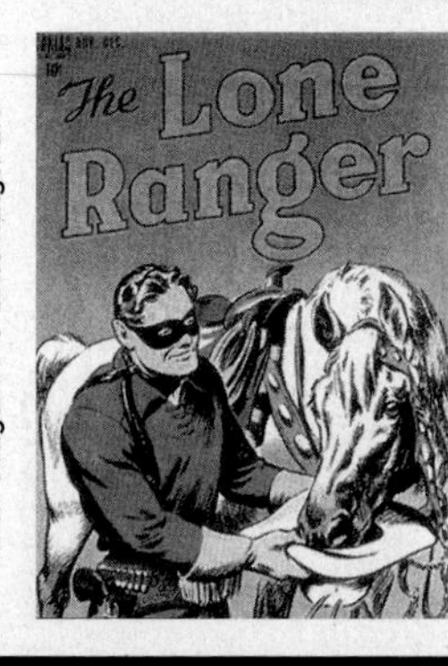

Lone Ranger #6 © Lone Ranger Inc.

	GD 2.0	VG 4.0	FN 6.0	VF 8.0	VF/NM 9.0	NM- 9.2

1-6-Joe Hill-s/Gabriel Rodriguez-a 4.00

LOCKE & KEY: HEAD GAMES
IDW Publ.: Jan, 2009 - No. 6, Jun, 2009 ($3.99, limited series)

1-6-Joe Hill-s/Gabriel Rodriguez-a. 3-EC style-c 4.00

LOCKE & KEY: KEYS TO THE KINGDOM
IDW Publ.: Sept, 2010 - No. 6, Mar, 2011 ($3.99, limited series)

1-6-Joe Hill-s/Gabriel Rodriguez-a 4.00

LOCKE & KEY: OMEGA
IDW Publ.: Nov, 2012 - No. 5, May, 2013 ($3.99, limited series)

1-5-Next to Final series; Joe Hill-s/Gabriel Rodriguez-a 4.00

LOCKE & KEY: SMALL WORLD
IDW Publ.: Dec, 2016 ($4.99, one-shot)

1-Set in early 1900s; Joe Hill-s/Gabriel Rodriguez-a; multiple covers 5.00

LOCKJAW (From the Inhumans)
Marvel Comics: Apr, 2018 - Present ($3.99)

1-Kibblesmith-s/Villa-a; D-Man and Ka-Zar app. 4.00

LOCKJAW AND THE PET AVENGERS (Also see Tails of the Pet Avengers)
Marvel Comics: July, 2009 - No. 4, Oct, 2009 ($2.99, limited series)

1-4-Lockheed, Frog Thor, Zabu, Lockjaw and Redwing team up; 2 covers on each 3.00

LOCKJAW AND THE PET AVENGERS UNLEASHED
Marvel Comics: May, 2010 - No. 4, Aug, 2010 ($2.99, limited series)

1-4-Eliopoulos-s/Guara-a; 2 covers on each 3.00

LOCO (Magazine) (Satire)
Satire Publications: Aug, 1958 - V1#3, Jan, 1959

	GD	VG	FN	VF	VF/NM	NM-
V1#1-Chic Stone-a	9	18	27	47	61	75
V1#2,3-Severin-a, 2 pgs. Davis; 3-Heath-a	7	14	21	35	43	50

LOGAN (Wolverine)
Marvel Comics: May, 2008 - No. 3, Jul, 2008 ($3.99, limited series)

1-3-Vaughan-s/Risso-a/c; regular & B&W editions for each 4.00

LOGAN: PATH OF THE WARLORD
Marvel Comics: Feb, 1996 ($5.95, one-shot)

1-John Paul Leon-a 6.00

LOGAN: SHADOW SOCIETY
Marvel Comics: 1996 ($5.95, one-shot)

1 6.00

LOGAN'S RUN
Marvel Comics Group: Jan, 1977 - No. 7, July, 1977

	GD	VG	FN	VF	VF/NM	NM-
1: 1-5-Based on novel & movie	2	4	6	9	12	15
2-5,7: 6,7-New stories adapted from novel	1	3	4	6	8	10
6-1st Thanos solo story (back-up) by Zeck (6/77)(See Iron Man #55 for debut)	4	8	12	27	44	60
6-(35¢-c variant, limited distribution)	13	26	39	89	195	300
7-(35¢-c variant, limited distribution)	10	20	30	64	132	200

NOTE: *Austin a-6i. Gulacy c-6. Kane c-7p. Perez a-1-5p; c-1-5p. Sutton a-6p, 7p.*

LOIS & CLARK, THE NEW ADVENTURES OF SUPERMAN
DC Comics: 1994 ($9.95, one-shot)

	GD	VG	FN	VF	VF/NM	NM-
1-r/Man of Steel #2, Superman Ann. 1, Superman #9 & 11, Action #600 & 655, Adventures of Superman #445, 462 & 466	1	3	4	6	8	10

LOIS LANE (Also see Daring New Adventures of Supergirl, Showcase #9,10 & Superman's Girlfriend...)
DC Comics: Aug, 1986 - No. 2, Sept, 1986 ($1.50, 52 pgs.)

1,2-Morrow-c/a in each 4.00

LOKI (Thor)(Also see Vote Loki)
Marvel Comics: Sept, 2004 - No. 4, Nov, 2004 ($3.50)

1-4-Rodi-s/Ribic-a/c 3.50
HC (2005, $17.99, with dustjacket) oversized r/#1-4; original proposal and sketch pages 18.00
SC (2007, $12.99) r/#1-4; original proposal and sketch pages 13.00

LOKI (Thor)
Marvel Comics: Dec, 2010 - No. 4, May, 2011 ($3.99, limited series)

1-4-Aguirre-Sacasa-s/Fiumara-a. 2-Balder dies 4.00

LOKI: AGENT OF ASGARD (Thor)
Marvel Comics: Apr, 2014 - No. 17, Oct, 2015 ($2.99/$3.99)

1-5: 1-Ewing-s/Garbett-a/Frison-c; Avengers app. 3.00
6-17-($3.99) 6-9-Axis tie-ins. 6,7-Doctor Doom app. 14-17-Secret Wars tie-ins 4.00

LOKI: RAGNAROK AND ROLL (not the character from Thor)
BOOM! Studios: Feb, 2014 - No. 4, Jun, 2014 ($3.99, limited series)

1,2-Esquivel-s/Gaylord-a/Ziritt-c 4.00

LOLA XOXO
Aspen MLT: Apr, 2014 - No. 6, Mar, 2015 ($3.99)

1-6-Siya Oum-s/a; multiple covers 4.00
The Art of Lolo XOXO 1 (9/16, $5.99) Siya Oum sketch pages and cover gallery 6.00

LOLA XOXO VOLUME 2
Aspen MLT: Jul, 2017 - No. 6, Jan, 2018 ($3.99)

1-6-Siya Oum-s/a; multiple covers 4.00

LOLA XOXO: WASTELAND MADAM
Aspen MLT: Apr, 2015 - No. 4, Feb, 2016 ($3.99)

1-4-Vince Hernandez-s/Siya Oum-a; multiple covers 4.00

LOLLY AND PEPPER
Dell Publishing Co.: No. 832, Sept, 1957 - July, 1962

	GD	VG	FN	VF	VF/NM	NM-
Four Color 832(#1)	6	12	18	37	66	95
Four Color 940,978,1086,1206	4	8	12	28	47	65
01-459-207 (7/62)	3	6	9	17	26	35

LOMAX (See Police Action)

LONDON'S DARK
Escape/Titan: 1989 ($8.95, B&W, graphic novel)

	GD	VG	FN	VF	VF/NM	NM-
nn-James Robinson script; Paul Johnson-c/a	1	2	3	5	7	9

LONE
Dark Horse Comics: Sept, 2003 - No. 6, Mar, 2004 ($2.99)

1-6-Stuart Moore-s/Jerome Opeña-a/Templesmith-c 3.00

LONE EAGLE (The Flame No. 5 on)
Ajax/Farrell Publications: Apr-May, 1954 - No. 4, Oct-Nov, 1954

	GD	VG	FN	VF	VF/NM	NM-
1	14	28	42	80	115	150
2-4: 3-Bondage-c	9	18	27	50	65	80

LONE GUNMEN, THE (From the X-Files)
Dark Horse Comics: June, 2001 ($2.99, one-shot)

1-Paul Lee-a; photo-c 3.00

LONELY HEART (Formerly Dear Lonely Hearts; Dear Heart #15 on)
Ajax/Farrell Publ. (Excellent Publ.): No. 9, Mar, 1955 - No. 14, Feb, 1956

	GD	VG	FN	VF	VF/NM	NM-
9-Kamen-*esque*-a; (Last precode)	14	28	42	81	118	155
10-14	10	20	30	54	72	90

LONE RANGER, THE (See Ace Comics, Aurora, Dell Giants, Future Comics, Golden Comics Digest #48, King Comics, Magic Comics & March of Comics #165, 174, 193, 208, 225, 238, 310, 322, 338, 350)

LONE RANGER, THE
Dell Publishing Co.: No. 3, 1939 - No. 167, Feb, 1947

	GD	VG	FN	VF	VF/NM	NM-
Large Feature Comic 3(1939)-Heigh-Yo Silver; text with illus. by Robert Weisman; also exists as a Whitman #710 (scarce)	277	554	831	1759	3030	4300
Large Feature Comic 7(1939)-Illustr. by Henry Vallely; Hi-Yo Silver the Lone Ranger to the Rescue; also exists as Whitman #715 (scarce)	258	516	774	1651	2826	4000
Feature Book 21(1940), 24(1941)	103	206	309	659	1130	1600
Four Color 82(1945)	38	76	114	281	628	975
Four Color 98(1945),118(1946)	27	54	81	194	435	675
Four Color 125(1946),136(1947)	19	38	57	131	291	450
Four Color 151,167(1947)	16	32	48	112	249	385

LONE RANGER, THE (Movie, radio & TV; Clayton Moore starred as Lone Ranger in the movies; No. 1-37: strip reprints)(See Dell Giants)
Dell Publishing Co.: Jan-Feb, 1948 - No. 145, May-July, 1962

	GD	VG	FN	VF	VF/NM	NM-
1 (36 pgs.)-The Lone Ranger, his horse Silver, companion Tonto & his horse Scout begin	64	128	192	512	1156	1800
2 (52 pgs. begin, end #41)	27	54	81	189	420	650
3-5	22	44	66	154	340	525
6,7,9,10	16	32	48	112	249	385
8-Origin retold; Indian back-c begin, end #35	19	38	57	131	291	450
11-20: 11- "Young Hawk" Indian boy serial begins, ends #145	12	24	36	80	173	265
21,22,24-31: 51-Reprint. 31-1st Mask logo	10	20	30	64	132	200
23-Origin retold	12	24	36	80	173	265
32-37: 32-Painted-c begin. 36-Animal photo back-c begin, end #49. 37-Last newspaper-r issue; new outfit; red shirt becomes blue; most known copies show the blue shirt on-c & inside	9	18	27	58	114	170

Lone Ranger (2006 series) #9 © Classic Media

Lone Rider #8 © Farrell

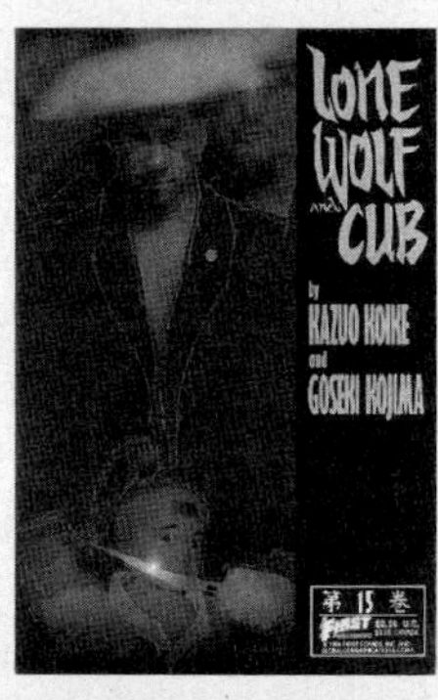

Lone Wolf and Cub #15 © FC

	GD 2.0	VG 4.0	FN 6.0	VF 8.0	VF/NM 9.0	NM- 9.2
37-Variant issue; Long Ranger wears a red shirt on-c and inside. A few copies of the red shirt outfit were printed before catching the mistake and changing the color to blue (rare)	16	32	48	110	243	375
38-41 (All 52 pgs.) 38-Paul S. Newman-s (wrote most of the stories #38-on)	8	16	24	54	102	150
42-50 (36 pgs.)	7	14	21	46	86	125
51-74 (52 pgs.): 56-One pg. origin story of Lone Ranger & Tonto. 71-Blank inside-c	6	12	18	42	79	115
75,77-99: 79-X-mas-c	6	12	18	40	73	105
76-Classic flag-c	6	12	18	42	79	115
100	7	14	21	46	86	125
101-111: Last painted-c	6	12	18	37	66	95
112-Clayton Moore photo-c begin, end #145	15	30	45	103	227	350
113-117: 117-10¢ &15¢-c exist	9	18	27	60	120	180
118-Origin Lone Ranger, Tonto, & Silver retold; Dan Reid origin; Special Silver anniversary issue	19	38	57	131	291	450
119-140: 139-Fran Striker-s	8	16	24	56	108	160
141-145	9	18	27	58	114	170

NOTE: ***Hank Hartman*** *painted c(signed)-65, 66, 70, 75, 82; unsigned-64?, 67-69?, 71, 72, 73?, 74?, 76-78, 80, 81, 83-91, 92?, 93-111.* ***Ernest Nordli*** *painted c(signed)-42, 50, 52, 53, 56, 59, 60; unsigned-39-41, 44-49, 51, 54, 55, 57, 58, 61-63?*

LONE RANGER, THE
Gold Key (Reprints in #13-20): 9/64 - No. 16, 12/69; No. 17, 11/72; No. 18, 9/74 - No. 28, 3/77

	GD 2.0	VG 4.0	FN 6.0	VF 8.0	VF/NM 9.0	NM- 9.2
1-Retells origin	5	10	15	35	63	90
2	3	6	9	21	33	45
3-10: Small Bear-r in #6-12. 10-Last 12¢ issue	3	6	9	19	30	40
11-17	3	6	9	15	22	28
18-28	2	4	6	11	16	20
Golden West 1(30029-610, 10/66)-Giant; r/most Golden West #3 including Clayton Moore photo front/back-c	6	12	18	38	69	100

LONE RANGER
Dynamite Entertainment: 2006 - No. 25, 2011 ($2.99/$3.50/$3.99)

	GD 2.0	VG 4.0	FN 6.0	VF 8.0	VF/NM 9.0	NM- 9.2
1-Retells origin; Carriello-a/Matthews-s; badge cover by Cassaday						4.00
1-Variant mask cover by Cassaday						5.00
1-Baltimore Comic-Con 2006 variant cover with masked face and horse silhouette						12.00
1-Directors' Cut ($4.99) r/#1 with comments at page bottoms, script and sketches						5.00
2-23: 2-Origin continues; Tonto app.						3.50
24-($3.99)						4.00
25-($4.99) Carriello-a						5.00
... and Tonto 1-4 (200-2010, $4.99) Cassaday-c						5.00
... Volume 1: Now and Forever TPB (2007, $19.99) r/#1-6; sketch pages						20.00

LONE RANGER, THE (Volume 2)
Dynamite Entertainment: 2012 - No. 25, 2014 ($3.99)

	GD 2.0	VG 4.0	FN 6.0	VF 8.0	VF/NM 9.0	NM- 9.2
1-25: 1-Parks-s/Polls-a; two covers by Ross & Francavilla. 2-21-Francavilla-c						4.00
Annual 2013 ($4.99) Denton-s/Triano-a/Worley-c						5.00

LONE RANGER AND TONTO, THE
Topps Comics: Aug, 1994 - No. 4, Nov, 1994 ($2.50, limited series)

	GD 2.0	VG 4.0	FN 6.0	VF 8.0	VF/NM 9.0	NM- 9.2
1-4: 3-Origin of Lone Ranger; Tonto leaves; Lansdale story, Truman-c/a in all.						3.00
1-4: Silver logo. 1-Signed by Lansdale and Truman						6.00
Trade paperback (1/95, $9.95)						10.00

LONE RANGER AND ZORRO: THE DEATH OF ZORRO, THE
Dynamite Entertainment: 2011 - No. 5, 2011 ($3.99, limited series)

	GD 2.0	VG 4.0	FN 6.0	VF 8.0	VF/NM 9.0	NM- 9.2
1-5: 1-Four covers by Alex Ross and others; Parks-s/Polls-a						4.00

LONE RANGER GREEN HORNET
Dynamite Entertainment: 2016 - No. 5, 2016 ($3.99, limited series)

	GD 2.0	VG 4.0	FN 6.0	VF 8.0	VF/NM 9.0	NM- 9.2
1-5-Uslan-s/Timpano-a. 3-Jesse Owens as the new Lone Ranger						4.00

LONE RANGER'S COMPANION TONTO, THE (TV)
Dell Publishing Co.: No. 312, Jan, 1951 - No. 33, Nov-Jan/58-59 (All painted-c)

	GD 2.0	VG 4.0	FN 6.0	VF 8.0	VF/NM 9.0	NM- 9.2
Four Color 312(#1, 1/51)	11	22	33	73	157	240
2(8-10/51),3: (#2 titled "Tonto")	6	12	18	41	76	110
4-10	5	10	15	35	63	90
11-20	5	10	15	31	53	75
21-33	4	8	12	28	47	65

NOTE: ***Ernest Nordli*** *painted c(signed)-2, 7; unsigned-3-6, 8-11, 12?, 13, 14, 18?, 22-24?*
See Aurora Comic Booklets.

LONE RANGER'S FAMOUS HORSE HI-YO SILVER, THE (TV)
Dell Publishing Co.: No. 369, Jan, 1952 - No. 36, Oct-Dec, 1960 (All painted-c, most by Sam Savitt) (Lone Ranger appears in most issues)

	GD 2.0	VG 4.0	FN 6.0	VF 8.0	VF/NM 9.0	NM- 9.2
Four Color 369(#1)-Silver's origin as told by The Lone Ranger	10	20	30	70	150	230
Four Color 392(#2, 4/52)	6	12	18	42	79	115
3(7-9/52)-10(4-6/52)	5	10	15	31	53	75
11-36	4	8	12	27	44	60

LONE RANGER, THE : SNAKE OF IRON
Dynamite Entertainment: 2012 - No. 4, 2013 ($3.99, limited series)

	GD 2.0	VG 4.0	FN 6.0	VF 8.0	VF/NM 9.0	NM- 9.2
1-4: 1-Dixon-s/Polls-a/Calero-c						4.00

LONE RANGER, THE : VINDICATED
Dynamite Entertainment: 2014 - No. 4, 2015 ($3.99, limited series)

	GD 2.0	VG 4.0	FN 6.0	VF 8.0	VF/NM 9.0	NM- 9.2
1-4-Justin Gray-s/Rey Villegas-a. 1-Cassaday-c. 2-4-Laming-c						4.00

LONE RIDER (Also see The Rider)
Superior Comics(Farrell Publ.): Apr, 1951 - No. 26, Jul, 1955 (#3-on: 36 pgs.)

	GD 2.0	VG 4.0	FN 6.0	VF 8.0	VF/NM 9.0	NM- 9.2
1 (52 pgs.)-The Lone Rider & his horse Lightnin' begin; Kamen-*ish*-a begins	32	64	96	192	314	435
2 (52 pgs.)-The Golden Arrow begins (origin)	20	40	60	120	195	220
3-6: 6-Last Golden Arrow	17	34	51	98	154	210
7-Golden Arrow becomes Swift Arrow; origin of his shield	20	40	60	120	195	220
8-Origin Swift Arrow	18	36	54	107	169	230
9,10	12	24	36	69	97	125
11-14	10	20	30	54	72	90
15-Golden Arrow origin-r from #2, changing name to Swift Arrow	10	20	30	58	79	100
16-20,22-26: 23-Apache Kid app.	9	18	27	50	65	80
21-3-D effect-c	16	32	48	94	147	200

LONERS, THE
Marvel Comics: June, 2007 - No. 6, Jan, 2008 ($2.99, limited series)

	GD 2.0	VG 4.0	FN 6.0	VF 8.0	VF/NM 9.0	NM- 9.2
1-6-Cebulski-s/Moline-a/Pearson-c; Lightspeed, Spider-Woman, Ricochet app.						3.00
...: The Secret Lives of Super Heroes TPB (2008, $14.99) r/#1-6; sketch pages						15.00

LONE WOLF AND CUB
First Comics: May, 1987 - No. 45, Apr, 1991 ($1.95-$3.25, B&W, deluxe size)

	GD 2.0	VG 4.0	FN 6.0	VF 8.0	VF/NM 9.0	NM- 9.2
1-Frank Miller-c & intro.; reprints manga series by Koike & Kojima	2	4	6	8	10	12
1-2nd print, 3rd print, 2-2nd print						4.00
2-12: 6-72 pgs. origin issue						6.00
13-38,40: 40-Ploog-c						4.00
39-($5.95, 120 pgs.)-Ploog-c	1	2	3	4	5	7
41-44: 41-($3.95, 84 pgs.)-Ploog-c. 42-Ploog-c						6.00
45-Last issue; low print	2	4	6	8	10	12
Deluxe Edition ($19.95, B&W)						20.00

NOTE: ***Sienkiewicz*** *c-13-24.* ***Matt Wagner*** *c-25-30.*

LONE WOLF AND CUB (Trade paperbacks)
Dark Horse Comics: Aug, 2000 - No. 28 ($9.95, B&W, 4" x 6", approx. 300 pgs.)

	GD 2.0	VG 4.0	FN 6.0	VF 8.0	VF/NM 9.0	NM- 9.2
1-Collects First Comics reprint series; Frank Miller-c						18.00
1-(2nd printing)						12.00
1-(3rd-5th printings)						10.00
2,3-(1st printings)						12.00
2,3-(2nd printings)						10.00
4-28						10.00

LONE WOLF 2100 (Also see Reveal)
Dark Horse Comics: May, 2002 - No. 11, Dec, 2003 ($2.99, color)

	GD 2.0	VG 4.0	FN 6.0	VF 8.0	VF/NM 9.0	NM- 9.2
1-New homage to Lone Wolf and Cub; Kennedy-s/Velasco-a						4.00
2-11						3.00
...: The Red File (1/03, $2.99) character and story background files						3.00
... Vol. 1 - Shadows on Saplings TPB (2003, $12.95, 6" x 9") r/#1-4						13.00
... Vol. 2 - The Language of Chaos TPB (2003, $12.95, 6" x 9") r/#5-8, Dirty Tricks short story from Reveal						13.00

LONE WOLF 2100: CHASE THE SETTING SUN
Dark Horse Comics: Jan, 2016 - No. 4, Apr, 2016 ($3.99, color)

	GD 2.0	VG 4.0	FN 6.0	VF 8.0	VF/NM 9.0	NM- 9.2
1-4-Heisserer-s/Sepulveda-a						4.00

LONG BOW (...Indian Boy)(See Indians & Jumbo Comics #141)
Fiction House Mag. (Real Adventures Publ.): 1951 - No. 8, Fall, 1952; No. 9, Spring, 1953

	GD 2.0	VG 4.0	FN 6.0	VF 8.0	VF/NM 9.0	NM- 9.2
1-Most covers by Maurice Whitman	18	36	54	107	169	230
2	11	22	33	62	86	110
3-9	10	20	30	56	76	95

LONG HOT SUMMER, THE
DC Comics (Milestone): Jul, 1995 - No. 3, Sept, 1995 ($2.95/$2.50, lim. series)

	GD 2.0	VG 4.0	FN 6.0	VF 8.0	VF/NM 9.0	NM- 9.2
1-3: 1-($2.95-c). 2,3-($2.50-c)						3.00

Looney Tunes #84 © WB

Looney Tunes and Merrie Melodies #1 © WB

Lords of Mars #1 © DYN

	GD 2.0	VG 4.0	FN 6.0	VF 8.0	VF/NM 9.0	NM- 9.2

LONG JOHN SILVER & THE PIRATES (Formerly Terry & the Pirates)
Charlton Comics: No. 30, Aug, 1956 - No. 32, March, 1957 (TV)

	GD	VG	FN	VF	VF/NM	NM-
30-32: Whitman-c	10	20	30	56	76	95

LONGSHOT (Also see X-Men, 2nd Series #10)
Marvel Comics: Sept, 1985 - No. 6, Feb, 1986 (60¢, limited series)

	GD	VG	FN	VF	VF/NM	NM-
1-Art Adams/Whilce Portacio-c/a in all	3	6	9	16	24	32
2-5: 4-Spider-Man app.	2	4	6	9	12	15
6-Double size	2	4	6	13	18	22
Trade Paperback (1989, $16.95)-r/#1-6						17.00

LONGSHOT
Marvel Comics: Feb, 1998 ($3.99, one-shot)

	GD	VG	FN	VF	VF/NM	NM-
1-DeMatteis-s/Zulli-a						4.00

LONGSHOT SAVES THE MARVEL UNIVERSE
Marvel Comics: Jan, 2014 - No. 4, Feb, 2014 ($2.99, limited series)

	GD	VG	FN	VF	VF/NM	NM-
1-4-Hastings-s/Camagni-a/Nakayama-c. 3,4-Superior Spider-Man app.						3.00

LOOKING GLASS WARS: HATTER M
Image Comics (Desperado): Dec, 2005 - No. 4, Nov, 2006 ($3.99)

	GD	VG	FN	VF	VF/NM	NM-
1-4-Templesmith-a/c						4.00

LOONEY TUNES (2nd Series) (TV)
Gold Key/Whitman: April, 1975 - No. 47, June, 1984

	GD	VG	FN	VF	VF/NM	NM-
1-Reprints	3	6	9	21	33	45
2-10: 2,4-reprints	2	4	6	13	18	22
11-20: 16-reprints	2	4	6	9	12	15
21-30	2	3	4	6	8	10
31,32,36-42(2/82)	1	2	3	5	6	8
33-(8/80)-35 (Whitman pre-pack only, scarce)	3	6	9	21	33	45
43(4/82),44(6/83) (low distribution)	2	4	6	9	13	16
45-47 (All #90296 on-c; nd, nd code, pre-pack) 45(8/83), 46(3/84), 47(6/84)	3	6	9	14	20	26

LOONEY TUNES (3rd Series) (TV)
DC Comics: Apr, 1994 - Present ($1.50/$1.75/$1.95/$1.99/$2.25/$2.50/$2.99)

	GD	VG	FN	VF	VF/NM	NM-
1-10,120: 1-Marvin Martian-c/sty; Bugs Bunny, Roadrunner, Daffy begin. 120-($2.95-C)						4.00
11-119,121-187: 23-34-($1.75-c). 35-43-($1.95-c). 44-Begin $1.99-c. 93-Begin $2.25-c. 100-Art by various incl. Kyle Baker, Marie Severin, Darwyn Cooke, Jill Thompson						3.00
188-241: 188-Begin $2.99-c; Scooby-Doo spoof. 193-Christmas-c. 237-Duck Dodgers						3.00
...Back In Action Movie Adaptation (12/03, $3.95) photo-c						4.00

LOONEY TUNES AND MERRIE MELODIES COMICS ("Looney Tunes" #166(8/55) on)
(Also see Porky's Duck Hunt)
Dell Publishing Co.: 1941 - No. 246, July-Sept, 1962

	GD	VG	FN	VF	VF/NM	NM-
1-Porky Pig, Bugs Bunny, Daffy Duck, Elmer Fudd, Mary Jane & Sniffles, Pat Patsy and Pete begin (1st comic book app. of each). Bugs Bunny story by Win Smith (early Mickey Mouse artist)	1150	2300	3450	8800	18,400	28,000
2 (11/41)	183	366	549	1510	3405	5300
3-Kandi the Cave Kid begins by Walt Kelly; also in #4-6,8,11,15	121	242	363	968	2184	3400
4-Kelly-a	121	242	363	968	2184	3400
5-Bugs Bunny The Super-Duper Rabbit story (1st funny animal super hero, 3/42; also see Coo Coo); Kelly-a	89	178	267	712	1606	2500
6,8: 8-Kelly-a	68	136	204	544	1222	1900
7,9,10: 9-Painted-c. 10-Flag-c	50	100	150	390	870	1350
11,15-Kelly-a; 15-Christmas-c	50	100	150	390	870	1350
12-14,16-19	37	74	111	274	612	950
20-25: Pat, Patsy & Pete by Walt Kelly in all. 20-War Bonds-c	30	60	90	219	490	760
26-30	23	46	69	161	356	550
31-40: 33-War Bonds-c. 39-Christmas-c	18	36	54	128	284	440
41-50: 45-War Bonds-c	14	28	42	96	211	325
51-60: 51-Christmas-c	11	22	33	76	163	250
61-80	8	16	24	56	108	160
81-99: 87,99-Christmas-c	7	14	21	49	92	135
100-New Year's-c	8	16	24	52	99	145
101-120	6	12	18	40	73	105
121-150: 124-New Year's-c. 133-Tattoo-c	5	10	15	35	63	90
151-200: 159-Christmas-c	5	10	15	33	57	80
201-240	5	10	15	31	53	75
241-246	5	10	15	33	57	80

LOONY SPORTS (Magazine)
3-Strikes Publishing Co.: Spring, 1975 (68 pgs.)

	GD	VG	FN	VF	VF/NM	NM-
1-Sports satire	2	4	6	8	11	14

LOOSE CANNON (Also see Action Comics Annual #5 & Showcase '94 #5)
DC Comics: June, 1995 - No. 4, Sept, 1995 ($1.75, limited series)

	GD	VG	FN	VF	VF/NM	NM-
1-4: Adam Pollina-a. 1-Superman app.						3.00

LOOY DOT DOPE
United Features Syndicate: No. 13, 1939

	GD	VG	FN	VF	VF/NM	NM-
Single Series 13	34	68	102	199	325	450

LORD JIM (See Movie Comics)

LORD OF THE JUNGLE
Dynamite Entertainment: 2012 - No. 15, 2013 ($1.00/$3.99)

	GD	VG	FN	VF	VF/NM	NM-
1-($1.00) Retelling of Tarzan's origin; Nelson-s/Castro-a; four covers						3.00
2-15-($3.99) 2-6-Three covers. 7-13-Two covers						4.00
Annual 1 (2012, $4.99) Rahner-s/Davila-a/Parrillo-c						5.00

LORD PUMPKIN
Malibu Comics (Ultraverse): Oct, 1994 ($2.50, one-shot)

	GD	VG	FN	VF	VF/NM	NM-
0-Two covers						3.00

LORD PUMPKIN/NECROMANTRA
Malibu Comics (Ultraverse): Apr, 1995 - No. 4, July, 1995 ($2.95, limited series, flip book)

	GD	VG	FN	VF	VF/NM	NM-
1-4						3.00

LORDS OF AVALON: KNIGHT OF DARKNESS
Marvel Comics: Jan, 2008 - No. 6, July, 2009 ($3.99, limited series)

	GD	VG	FN	VF	VF/NM	NM-
1-6-($3.99)-Kenyon & Furth-s; Ohtsuka-a/c						4.00

LORDS OF AVALON: SWORD OF DARKNESS
Marvel Comics: Apr, 2008 - No. 6, Sept, 2008 ($3.99/$2.99, limited series)

	GD	VG	FN	VF	VF/NM	NM-
1-($3.99)-Adaptation of Sherrilyn Kenyon's Arthurian fantasy; Ohtsuka-a/c						4.00
2-6-($2.99)						3.00
HC (2008, $19.99) r/#1-6; two covers						20.00

LORDS OF MARS
Dynamite Entertainment: 2013 - No. 6, 2014 ($3.99, limited series)

	GD	VG	FN	VF	VF/NM	NM-
1-6-Tarzan and Jane meet John Carter on Mars; Nelson-s/Castro-a; multiple covers						4.00

LORDS OF THE JUNGLE
Dynamite Entertainment: 2016 - No. 6, 2016 ($3.99, limited series)

	GD	VG	FN	VF	VF/NM	NM-
1-6-Tarzan and Sheena app.; Bechko-s/Castro-a; covers by Castro & Massafera						4.00

LORNA, RELIC WRANGLER
Image Comics: Mar, 2011 ($3.99, one-shot)

	GD	VG	FN	VF	VF/NM	NM-
1-Micah Harris-s; J. Bone-c						4.00

LORNA THE JUNGLE GIRL (...Jungle Queen #1-5)
Atlas Comics (NPI 1/OMC 2-11/NPI 12-26): July, 1953 - No. 26, Aug, 1957

	GD	VG	FN	VF	VF/NM	NM-
1-Origin & 1st app.	55	110	165	352	601	850
2-Intro. & 1st app. Greg Knight	30	60	90	177	289	400
3-5	26	52	78	154	252	350
6-11: 11-Last pre-code (1/55)	22	44	66	132	216	300
12-17,19-26: 14-Colletta & Maneely-c	20	40	60	118	192	265
18-Williamson/Colletta-c	21	42	63	122	199	275

NOTE: ***Brodsky*** *c-1-3, 5, 9.* ***Everett*** *c-21, 23-26.* ***Heath*** *c-6, 7.* ***Maneely*** *c-12, 15.* ***Romita*** *a-18, 20, 22, 24, 26.* ***Shores*** *a-14-16, 18, 24, 26; c-11, 13, 16.* ***Tuska*** *a-6.*

LOSERS (Inspired the 2010 movie)
DC Comics (Vertigo): Aug, 2003 - No. 32, Mar, 2006 ($2.95/$2.99)

	GD	VG	FN	VF	VF/NM	NM-
1-Andy Diggle-s/Jock-a						4.00
1-Special Edition (6/10, $1.00) r/#1 with "What's Next?" logo on cover						3.00
2-32: 15-Bagged with Sky Captain CD. 20-Oliver-a. 27-Wilson-a						3.00
...: Ante Up TPB (2004, $9.95) r/#1-6						10.00
...: Book Two TPB (2010, $24.99) r/#13-32; Ian Rankin intro.; preliminary art pages						25.00
...: Close Quarters TPB (2005, $14.99) r/#20-25						15.00
...: Double Down TPB (2004, $12.95) r/#7-12						13.00
...: Endgame TPB (2006, $14.99) r/#26-32						15.00
...: Trifecta TPB (2005, $14.99) r/#13-19						15.00
...: Volumes One and Two TPB (2010, $19.99) r/#1-12; new intro. by Diggle						20.00

LOSERS SPECIAL (See Our Fighting Forces #123)(Also see G.I. Combat & Our Fighting Forces)
DC Comics: Sept, 1985 ($1.25, one-shot)

	GD	VG	FN	VF	VF/NM	NM-
1-Capt. Storm, Gunner & Sarge; Crisis on Infinite Earths x-over						6.00

LOST, THE
Chaos! Comics: Dec, 1997 - No. 3 ($2.95, B&W, unfinished limited series)

	GD	VG	FN	VF	VF/NM	NM-
1-3-Andreyko-script: 1-Russell back-c						3.00

LOST BOYS, THE (Sequel to the 1987 vampire movie)

Lost in Space #1 © New Line

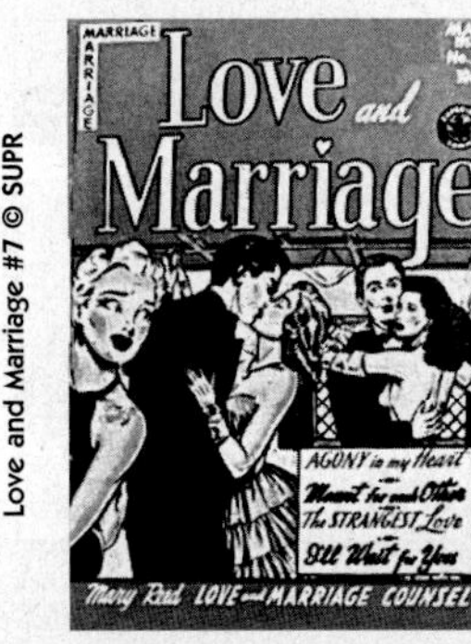

Love and Marriage #7 © SUPR

Love Classics #2 © MAR

DC Comics (Vertigo): Dec, 2016 - No. 6, May, 2017 ($3.99)

	GD 2.0	VG 4.0	FN 6.0	VF 8.0	VF/NM 9.0	NM- 9.2
1-6-Tim Seeley-s/Scott Godlewski-a/Tony Harris-c; Frog Bros. app.						4.00

LOST BOYS: REIGN OF FROGS (Based on the 1987 vampire movie)
DC Comics (WildStorm): Jul, 2008 - No. 4, Oct, 2008 ($3.50, limited series)

	GD 2.0	VG 4.0	FN 6.0	VF 8.0	VF/NM 9.0	NM- 9.2
1-4-Rodionoff-s/Gomez-a; Edgar Frog app.						3.50
TPB (2009, $12.99) r/#1-4						13.00

LOST CONTINENT
Eclipse Int'l: Sept, 1990 - No. 6, 1991 ($3.50, B&W, squarebound, 60 pgs.)

	GD 2.0	VG 4.0	FN 6.0	VF 8.0	VF/NM 9.0	NM- 9.2
1-6: Japanese story translated to English						4.00

LOST IN SPACE (Movie)
Dark Horse Comics: Apr, 1998 - No. 3, July, 1998 ($2.95, limited series)

	GD 2.0	VG 4.0	FN 6.0	VF 8.0	VF/NM 9.0	NM- 9.2
1-3-Continuation of 1998 movie; Erskine-c						3.00

LOST IN SPACE (TV)(Also see Space Family Robinson)
Innovation Publishing: Aug, 1991 - No. 12, Jan, 1993 ($2.50, limited series)

	GD 2.0	VG 4.0	FN 6.0	VF 8.0	VF/NM 9.0	NM- 9.2
1-12: Bill Mumy (Will Robinson) scripts in #1-9. 9-Perez-c						3.00
1,2-Special Ed.; r/#1,2 plus new art & new-c						3.00
Annual 1,2 (1991, 1992, $2.95, 52 pgs.)						4.00
....: Project Robinson (11/93, $2.50) 1st & only part of intended series						3.00

LOST IN SPACE: THE LOST ADVENTURES (IRWIN ALLEN'S...) (TV)
American Gothic Press: Mar, 2016 - No. 6, Nov, 2016 ($3.99, limited series)

	GD 2.0	VG 4.0	FN 6.0	VF 8.0	VF/NM 9.0	NM- 9.2
1-6-Adaptation of unused scripts. 1-3-The Curious Galactics. 4-6-Malice in Wonderland						4.00

LOST IN SPACE: VOYAGE TO THE BOTTOM OF THE SOUL
Innovation Publishing: No. 13, Aug, 1993 - No. 18, 1994 ($2.50, limited series)

	GD 2.0	VG 4.0	FN 6.0	VF 8.0	VF/NM 9.0	NM- 9.2
13(V1#1, $2.95)-Embossed silver logo edition; Bill Mumy scripts begin; painted-c						3.00
13(V1#1, $4.95)-Embossed gold logo edition bagged w/poster						5.00
14-18: Painted-c						3.00

NOTE: *Originally intended to be a 12 issue limited series.*

LOST ONES, THE
Image Comics: Mar, 2000 ($2.95)

	GD 2.0	VG 4.0	FN 6.0	VF 8.0	VF/NM 9.0	NM- 9.2
1-Ken Penders-s/a						3.00

LOST PLANET
Eclipse Comics: 5/87 - No. 5, 2/88; No. 6, 3/89 (Mini-series, Baxter paper)

	GD 2.0	VG 4.0	FN 6.0	VF 8.0	VF/NM 9.0	NM- 9.2
1-6-Bo Hampton-c/a in all						3.00

LOST WAGON TRAIN, THE (See Zane Grey Four Color 583)

LOST WORLD, THE
Dell Publishing Co.: No. 1145, Nov-Jan, 1960-61

	GD 2.0	VG 4.0	FN 6.0	VF 8.0	VF/NM 9.0	NM- 9.2
Four Color 1145-Movie, Gil Kane-a, photo-c; 1pg. Conan Doyle biography by Torres	9	18	27	57	111	165

LOST WORLD, THE (See Jurassic Park)
Topps Comics: May, 1997 - No. 4, Aug, 1997 ($2.95, limited series)

	GD 2.0	VG 4.0	FN 6.0	VF 8.0	VF/NM 9.0	NM- 9.2
1-4-Movie adaption						3.00

LOST WORLDS (Weird Tales of the Past and Future)
Standard Comics: No. 5, Oct, 1952 - No. 6, Dec, 1952

	GD 2.0	VG 4.0	FN 6.0	VF 8.0	VF/NM 9.0	NM- 9.2
5- "Alice in Terrorland" by Alex Toth; J. Katz-a	52	104	156	328	552	775
6-Toth-a	40	80	120	246	411	575

LOTS 'O' FUN COMICS
Robert Allen Co.: 1940s? (5¢, heavy stock, blue covers)

nn-Contents can vary; Felix, Planet Comics known; contents would determine value. Similar to Up-To-Date Comics. Remainders - re-packaged.

LOT 13
DC Comics: Dec, 2012 - No. 5, Apr, 2013 ($2.99, limited series)

	GD 2.0	VG 4.0	FN 6.0	VF 8.0	VF/NM 9.0	NM- 9.2
1-5-Niles-s/Fabry-a/c						3.00

LOU GEHRIG (See The Pride of the Yankees)

LOVE ADVENTURES (Actual Confessions #13)
Marvel (IPS)/Atlas Comics (MPI): Oct, 1949; No. 2, Jan, 1950; No. 3, Feb, 1951 - No. 12, Aug, 1952

	GD 2.0	VG 4.0	FN 6.0	VF 8.0	VF/NM 9.0	NM- 9.2
1-Photo-c	26	52	78	154	252	350
2-Powell-a; Tyrone Power, Gene Tierney photo-c	20	40	60	114	182	250
3-8,10-12: 8-Robinson-a	14	28	42	81	118	155
9-Everett-a	14	28	42	82	121	160

LOVE AND MARRIAGE
Superior Comics Ltd. (Canada): Mar, 1952 - No. 16, Sept, 1954

	GD 2.0	VG 4.0	FN 6.0	VF 8.0	VF/NM 9.0	NM- 9.2
1	21	42	63	122	199	275
2	13	26	39	72	101	130
3-10	11	22	33	64	90	115
11-16	10	20	30	56	76	95
I.W. Reprint #1,2,8,11,14: 8-r/Love and Marriage #3. 11-r/Love and Marriage #11	2	4	6	10	14	18
Super Reprint #10('63),15,17('64):15-Love and Marriage #?	2	4	6	10	14	18

NOTE: *All issues have **Kamenish** art.*

LOVE AND ROCKETS
Fantagraphics Books: 1981 - No. 50, May, 1996 ($2.95/$2.50/$4.95, B&W, mature)

	GD 2.0	VG 4.0	FN 6.0	VF 8.0	VF/NM 9.0	NM- 9.2
1-B&W-c (1981, $1.00; publ. by Hernandez Bros.)(800 printed)	10	20	30	64	132	200
1 (Fall '82; Fantagraphics, color-c)	4	8	12	27	44	60
1-2nd & 3rd printing, 2-11,29-31: 2nd printings						4.00
2	3	6	9	16	24	32
3-10	2	4	6	8	10	12
11-49: 30 ($2.95, 52 pgs.)						5.00
50-($4.95)						6.00

LOVE AND ROCKETS (Volume 2)
Fantagraphics Books: Spring, 2001 - Present ($3.95-$7.99, B&W, mature)

	GD 2.0	VG 4.0	FN 6.0	VF 8.0	VF/NM 9.0	NM- 9.2
1-9-Gilbert, Jaime and Mario Hernandez-s/a						5.00
10-($5.95)						6.00
11-19-($4.50)						4.50
20-($7.99)						8.00
...: Stories • Free Comic Book Day 2016 Edition (giveaway)						3.00

LOVE AND ROMANCE
Charlton Comics: Sept, 1971 - No. 24, Sept, 1975

	GD 2.0	VG 4.0	FN 6.0	VF 8.0	VF/NM 9.0	NM- 9.2
1	3	6	9	19	30	40
2-5,7-10	2	4	6	10	14	18
6-David Cassidy pin-up; grey-tone cover	3	6	9	14	19	24
11,13-24	2	4	6	8	10	12
12-Susan Dey poster	2	4	6	10	14	18

LOVE AT FIRST SIGHT
Ace Magazines (RAR Publ. Co./Periodical House): Oct, 1949 - No. 43, Nov, 1956 (Photo-c: 18-42)

	GD 2.0	VG 4.0	FN 6.0	VF 8.0	VF/NM 9.0	NM- 9.2
1-Painted-c	30	60	90	177	289	400
2-Painted-c	15	30	45	88	137	185
3-10: 4,7-Painted-c	14	28	42	82	121	160
11-20	14	28	42	78	112	145
21-33: 33-Last pre-code	13	26	39	74	105	135
34-43	11	22	33	64	90	115

LOVE BUG, THE (See Movie Comics)

LOVEBUNNY AND MR. HELL
Devil's Due Publ./Image Comics: 2002 - 2004 ($2.95, B&W, one-shots)

	GD 2.0	VG 4.0	FN 6.0	VF 8.0	VF/NM 9.0	NM- 9.2
1-Tim Seeley-s						3.00
...: A Day in the Lovelife (Image, 2003) Blaylock-a						3.00
...: Savage Love (Image, 2003) Seeley-s/a; Savage Dragon app.; Seeley & Larsen-c						3.00
TPB (4/04, $9.95, digest-sized) reprints						10.00

LOVE CLASSICS
A Lover's Magazine/Marvel: Nov, 1949 - No. 2, Feb, 1950 (Photo-c, 52 pgs.)

	GD 2.0	VG 4.0	FN 6.0	VF 8.0	VF/NM 9.0	NM- 9.2
1,2: 2-Virginia Mayo photo-c; 30 pg. story "I Turned Into a Small-Town Flirt"	22	44	66	132	216	300

LOVE CONFESSIONS
Quality Comics: Oct, 1949 - No. 54, Dec, 1956 (Photo-c: 3,4,6,7,9,11-18,21,24,25)

	GD 2.0	VG 4.0	FN 6.0	VF 8.0	VF/NM 9.0	NM- 9.2
1-Ward-c/a, 9 pgs; Gustavson-a	41	82	123	256	428	600
2-Gustavson-a; Ward-c	21	42	63	126	206	285
3	15	30	45	88	137	185
4-Crandall-a	16	32	48	94	147	200
5-Ward-a, 7 pgs.	18	36	54	103	162	220
6,7,9,11-13,15,16,18: 7-Van Johnson photo-c. 8-Robert Mitchum & Jane Russell photo-c	14	28	42	78	112	145
8,10-Ward-a (2 stories in #10)	17	34	51	98	154	210
14,17,19,22-Ward-a; 17-Faith Domerque photo-c	16	32	48	94	147	200
20-Ward-a(2)	17	34	51	98	154	210
21,23-28,30-38,40-42: Last precode, 4/55	12	24	36	69	97	125
29-Ward-a	15	30	45	86	133	180
39,53-Matt Baker-a	15	30	45	83	124	165
43,44,46,47,50-52,54: 47-Ward-c?	11	22	33	64	90	115
45,48-Ward-a	14	28	42	76	108	140
49-Baker-c/a	19	38	57	111	176	240

Loveless #24 © Azzarello & Frusin

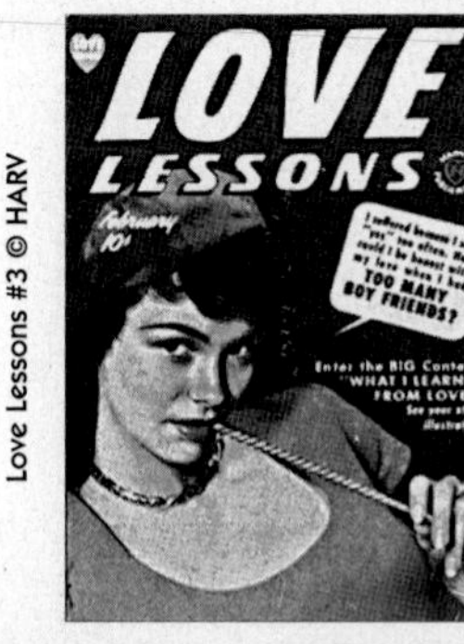

Love Lessons #3 © HARV

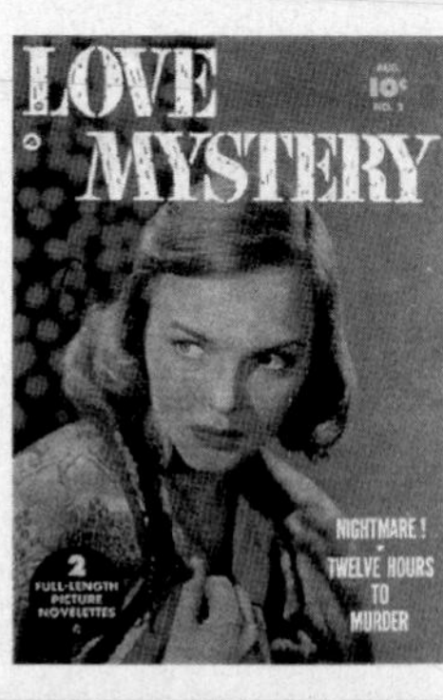

Love Mystery #2 © FAW

LOVECRAFT
DC Comics: 2003 (graphic novel)

	GD 2.0	VG 4.0	FN 6.0	VF 8.0	VF/NM 9.0	NM- 9.2
Hardcover ($24.95) Rodionoff & Giffen-s/Breccia-a; intro. by John Carpenter						25.00
Softcover ($17.95)						18.00

LOVE DIARY
Our Publishing Co./Toytown/Patches: July, 1949 - No. 48, Oct, 1955 (Photo-c: 1-24,27-29) (52 pgs. #1-11?)

	GD 2.0	VG 4.0	FN 6.0	VF 8.0	VF/NM 9.0	NM- 9.2
1-Krigstein-a	30	60	90	177	289	400
2,3-Krigstein & Mort Leav-a in each	18	36	54	107	169	230
4-8	15	30	45	84	127	170
9,10-Everett-a	15	30	45	86	133	180
11-15,17-20	14	28	42	81	118	155
16- Mort Leav-a, 3 pg. Baker-sty. Leav-a	15	30	45	83	124	165
21-30,32-48: 45-Leav-a. 47-Last precode(12/54)	14	28	42	78	112	145
31-John Buscema headlights-c	20	40	60	114	182	250

LOVE DIARY (Diary Loves #2 on; title change due to previously published title)
Quality Comics Group: Sept, 1949

	GD 2.0	VG 4.0	FN 6.0	VF 8.0	VF/NM 9.0	NM- 9.2
1-Ward-c/a, 9 pgs.	41	82	123	256	428	600

LOVE DIARY
Charlton Comics: July, 1958 - No. 102, Dec, 1976

	GD 2.0	VG 4.0	FN 6.0	VF 8.0	VF/NM 9.0	NM- 9.2
1	11	22	33	62	86	110
2	8	16	24	40	50	60
3-5,7-10: 10-Photo-c	7	14	21	35	43	50
6-Torres-a	7	14	21	37	46	55
11-20: 20-Photo-c	3	6	9	17	26	35
21-40	3	6	9	15	22	28
41-60	2	4	6	13	18	22
61-78,80,100-102	2	4	6	9	13	16
79-David Cassidy pin-up	2	4	6	13	18	22
81,83,84,86-99	2	4	6	8	10	12
82,85: 82-Partridge Family poster. 85-Danny poster	2	4	6	10	14	18

LOVE DOCTOR (See Dr. Anthony King...)

LOVE DRAMAS (True Secrets No. 3 on?)
Marvel Comics (IPS): Oct, 1949 - No. 2, Jan, 1950

	GD 2.0	VG 4.0	FN 6.0	VF 8.0	VF/NM 9.0	NM- 9.2
1-Jack Kamen-a; photo-c	25	50	75	150	245	340
2-Photo-c	17	34	51	100	158	215

LOVE EXPERIENCES (Challenge of the Unknown No. 6)
Ace Periodicals (A.A. Wyn/Periodical House): Oct, 1949 - No. 5, June, 1950; No. 6, Apr, 1951 - No. 38, June, 1956

	GD 2.0	VG 4.0	FN 6.0	VF 8.0	VF/NM 9.0	NM- 9.2
1-Painted-c	27	54	81	158	259	360
2	15	30	45	85	130	175
3-5: 5-Painted-c	14	28	42	81	118	155
6-10	14	28	42	76	108	140
11-30: 30-Last pre-code (2/55)	13	26	39	72	101	130
31-38: 38-Indicia date-6/56; c-date-8/56	11	22	33	64	90	115

NOTE: ***Anne Brewster** a-15. Photo c-4, 15-35, 38.*

LOVE FIGHTS
Oni Press: June, 2003 - No. 12, Aug, 2004 ($2.99, B&W)

	GD 2.0	VG 4.0	FN 6.0	VF 8.0	VF/NM 9.0	NM- 9.2
1-12-Andi Watson-s/a						3.00
Vol. 1 TPB (4/04, $14.95, digest-size) r/#1-6						15.00

LOVE IS LOVE
IDW Publishing/DC Comics: 2016 ($9.99, TPB)

	GD 2.0	VG 4.0	FN 6.0	VF 8.0	VF/NM 9.0	NM- 9.2
SC-Anthology to benefit the survivors of the Orlando Pulse shooting; Charretier-c						10.00

LOVE JOURNAL
Our Publishing Co.: No. 10, Oct, 1951 - No. 25, July, 1954

	GD 2.0	VG 4.0	FN 6.0	VF 8.0	VF/NM 9.0	NM- 9.2
10	26	52	78	154	252	350
11-15,17-25: 19-Mort Leav-a	16	32	48	92	144	195
16-Buscema headlight-c	19	38	54	111	176	240

LOVELAND
Mutual Mag./Eye Publ. (Marvel): Nov, 1949 - No. 2, Feb, 1950 (52 pgs.)

	GD 2.0	VG 4.0	FN 6.0	VF 8.0	VF/NM 9.0	NM- 9.2
1,2-Photo-c	18	36	54	105	165	225

LOVELESS
DC Comics: Dec, 2005 - No. 24, Jun, 2008 ($2.99)

	GD 2.0	VG 4.0	FN 6.0	VF 8.0	VF/NM 9.0	NM- 9.2
1-24: 1-Azzarello-s/Frusin-a. 6-8,15,22,23,24-Zezelj-a. 11,12,16-21-Dell'Edera-a						3.00
...: A Kin of Homecoming TPB (2006, $9.99) r/#1-5						10.00
...: Blackwater Falls TPB (2008, $19.99) r/#13-24						20.00
...: Thicker Than Blackwater TPB (2007, $14.99) r/#6-12						15.00

LOVE LESSONS
Harvey Comics/Key Publ. No. 5: Oct, 1949 - No. 5, June, 1950

	GD 2.0	VG 4.0	FN 6.0	VF 8.0	VF/NM 9.0	NM- 9.2
1-Metallic silver-c printed over the cancelled covers of Love Letters #1; indicia title is "Love Letters"	16	32	48	94	147	200
1-Non-metallic version	15	30	45	88	137	185
2-Powell-a; photo-c	9	18	27	52	69	85
3-5: 3,4-Photo-c	8	16	24	42	54	65

LOVE LETTERS (10/49, Harvey; advertised but never published; covers were printed before cancellation and were used as the cover to Love Lessons #1)

LOVE LETTERS (Love Secrets No. 32 on)
Quality Comics: 11/49 - #6, 9/50; #7, 3/51 - #31, 6/53; #32, 2/54 - #51, 12/56

	GD 2.0	VG 4.0	FN 6.0	VF 8.0	VF/NM 9.0	NM- 9.2
1-Ward-c, Gustavson-a	34	68	102	199	325	450
2-Ward-c, Gustavson-a	24	48	72	142	234	325
3-Gustavson-a	17	34	51	98	154	210
4-Ward-a, 9 pgs.; photo-c	20	40	60	120	195	270
5-8,10	14	28	42	76	108	140
9-One pg. Ward "Be Popular with the Opposite Sex"; Robert Mitchum photo-c	14	28	42	81	118	155
11-Ward-r/Broadway Romances #2 & retitled	14	28	42	81	118	155
12-15,18-20	12	24	36	69	97	125
16,17-Ward-a; 16-Anthony Quinn photo-c. 17-Jane Russell photo-c	16	32	48	94	147	200
21-29	12	24	36	67	94	120
30,31(6/53)-Ward-a	14	28	42	76	108	140
32(2/54)-39: 37-Ward-a. 38-Crandall-a. 39-Last precode (4/55)	11	22	33	62	86	110
40-48	10	20	30	56	76	95
49-51: 49,50-Baker-a. 51-Baker-c	15	30	45	88	137	185

NOTE: *Photo-c on most 3-28.*

LOVE LIFE
P. L. Publishing Co.: Nov, 1951

	GD 2.0	VG 4.0	FN 6.0	VF 8.0	VF/NM 9.0	NM- 9.2
1	14	28	42	82	121	160

LOVELORN (Confessions of the Lovelorn #52 on)
American Comics Group (Michel Publ./Regis Publ.): Aug-Sept, 1949 - No. 51, July, 1954 (No. 1-26: 52 pgs.)

	GD 2.0	VG 4.0	FN 6.0	VF 8.0	VF/NM 9.0	NM- 9.2
1	22	44	66	128	209	290
2	14	28	42	80	115	150
3-10	12	24	36	67	94	120
11-20,22-48: 18-Drucker-a(2 pgs.). 46-Lazarus-a	11	22	33	60	83	105
21-Prostitution story	15	30	45	84	127	170
49-51-Has 3-D effect-c/stories	19	38	57	112	179	245

LOVE MEMORIES
Fawcett Publications: 1949 (no month) - No. 4, July, 1950 (All photo-c)

	GD 2.0	VG 4.0	FN 6.0	VF 8.0	VF/NM 9.0	NM- 9.2
1	17	34	51	98	154	210
2-4: 2-(Win/49-50)	11	22	33	60	83	105

LOVE ME TENDERLOIN: A CAL McDONALD MYSTERY
Dark Horse Comics: Jan, 2004 ($2.99, one-shot)

	GD 2.0	VG 4.0	FN 6.0	VF 8.0	VF/NM 9.0	NM- 9.2
1-Niles-s/Templesmith-a/c						3.00

LOVE MYSTERY
Fawcett Publications: June, 1950 - No. 3, Oct, 1950 (All photo-c)

	GD 2.0	VG 4.0	FN 6.0	VF 8.0	VF/NM 9.0	NM- 9.2
1-George Evans-a	22	44	66	132	216	300
2,3-Evans-a. 3-Powell-a	16	32	48	96	151	205

LOVE PROBLEMS (See Fox Giants)

LOVE PROBLEMS AND ADVICE ILLUSTRATED (see True Love...)

LOVE ROMANCES (Formerly Ideal #5)
Timely/Marvel/Atlas(TCI No. 7-71/Male No. 72-106): No. 6, May, 1949 - No. 106, July, 1963

	GD 2.0	VG 4.0	FN 6.0	VF 8.0	VF/NM 9.0	NM- 9.2
6-Photo-c	25	50	75	150	245	340
7-Photo-c; Kamen-a	15	30	45	88	137	185
8-Kubert-a; photo-c	15	30	45	88	137	185
9-20: 9-12-Photo-c	15	30	45	83	124	165
21,24-Krigstein-a	15	30	45	84	127	170
22,23,25-35,37,39,40	14	28	42	81	118	155
36,38-Krigstein-a	14	28	42	82	121	160
41-44,46,47: Last precode (2/55)	14	28	42	80	115	150
45,57-Matt Baker-a	15	30	45	88	137	185
48,50-52,54-56,58-74	7	14	21	49	92	135
49,53-Toth-a, 6 & ? pgs.	8	16	24	52	99	145
75,77,82-Matt Baker-a	9	18	27	59	117	175

76,78-81,86,88-90,92-95: 80-Heath-c. 95-Last 10¢-c?

Love Scandals #1 © QUA

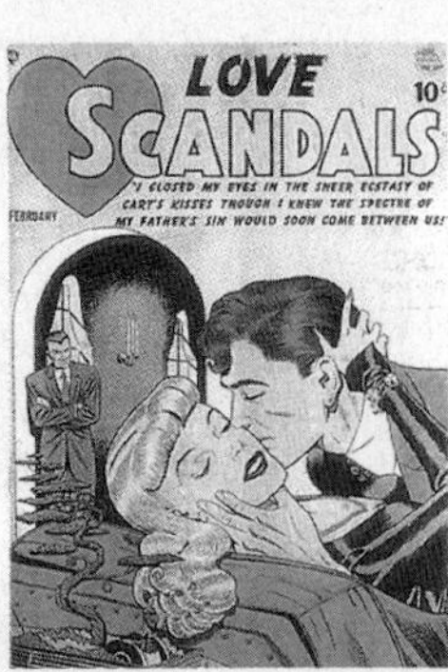

Low #10 © Remender & Tocchini

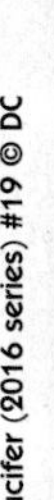
Lucifer (2016 series) #19 © DC

	GD 2.0	VG 4.0	FN 6.0	VF 8.0	VF/NM 9.0	NM- 9.2
	9	18	27	58	114	170
83,84,87,91,106-Kirby-c. 83-Severin-a	10	20	30	70	150	230
85,96,99-105-Kirby-c/a	12	24	36	83	182	280
97-10¢ cover price blacked out, 12¢ printed on cover; Kirby-c/a	20	40	60	138	307	475
98-Kirby-c/a	12	24	36	84	185	285

NOTE: ***Anne Brewster** a-67, 72. **Colletta** a-37, 40, 42, 44, 46, 67(2); c-42, 44, 46, 49, 54, 80. **Everett** c-70. **Hartley** c-20, 21, 30, 31. **Heath** a-87. **Kirby** c-80, 85, 88. **Robinson** a-29.*

LOVERS (Formerly Blonde Phantom)
Marvel Comics No. 23,24/Atlas No. 25 on (ANC): No. 23, May, 1949 - No. 86, Aug?, 1957

	GD 2.0	VG 4.0	FN 6.0	VF 8.0	VF/NM 9.0	NM- 9.2
23-Photo-c begin, end #29	25	50	75	150	245	340
24-Toth-*ish* plus Robinson-a	15	30	45	85	130	175
25,30-Kubert-a; 7, 10 pgs.	15	30	45	86	133	180
26-29,31-36,39,40: 35-Maneely-c	14	28	42	80	115	150
37,38-Krigstein-a	15	30	45	83	124	165
41-Everett-a(2)	15	30	45	83	124	165
42,44-65: 65-Last pre-code (1/55)	13	26	39	72	101	130
43-Frazetta 1 pg. ad	13	26	39	74	105	135
66,68-80,82-86	12	24	36	69	97	125
67-Toth-a	13	26	39	74	105	135
81-Baker-a	14	28	42	80	115	150

NOTE: ***Anne Brewster** a-86. **Colletta** a-54, 59, 62, 64, 65, 69, 85; c-61, 64, 65, 75. **Hartley** c-37, 53, 54. **Heath** a-61. **Maneely** a-57. **Powell** a-27, 30. **Robinson** a-42, 54, 56.*

LOVERS' LANE
Lev Gleason Publications: Oct, 1949 - No. 41, June, 1954 (No. 1-18: 52 pgs.)

	GD 2.0	VG 4.0	FN 6.0	VF 8.0	VF/NM 9.0	NM- 9.2
1-Biro-c	20	40	60	114	182	250
2-Biro-c	13	26	39	72	101	130
3-20: 3,4-Painted-c. 20-Frazetta 1 pg. ad	11	22	33	60	83	105
21-38,40,41	10	20	30	54	72	90
39-Story narrated by Frank Sinatra	13	26	39	72	101	130

NOTE: ***Briefer** a-6, 13, 21. **Esposito** a-5. **Fuje** a-4, 16; c-many. **Guardineer** a-1, 3. **Kinstler** c-41. **Sparling** a-3. **Tuska** a-6. Painted c-3-18. Photo c-19-22, 26-28.*

LOVE SCANDALS
Quality Comics: Feb, 1950 - No. 5, Oct, 1950 (Photo-c #2-5) (All 52 pgs.)

	GD 2.0	VG 4.0	FN 6.0	VF 8.0	VF/NM 9.0	NM- 9.2
1-Ward-c/a, 9 pgs.	34	68	102	204	332	460
2,3: 2-Gustavson-a	15	30	45	90	140	190
4-Ward-a, 18 pgs; Gil Fox-a	24	48	72	142	234	325
5-C. Cuidera-a; tomboy story "I Hated Being a Woman"	19	38	57	111	176	240

LOVE SECRETS
Marvel Comics(IPC): Oct, 1949 - No. 2, Jan, 1950 (52 pgs., photo-c)

	GD 2.0	VG 4.0	FN 6.0	VF 8.0	VF/NM 9.0	NM- 9.2
1	21	42	63	122	199	275
2	15	30	45	85	130	175

LOVE SECRETS (Formerly Love Letters #31)
Quality Comics Group: No. 32, Aug, 1953 - No. 56, Dec, 1956

	GD 2.0	VG 4.0	FN 6.0	VF 8.0	VF/NM 9.0	NM- 9.2
32	15	30	45	90	140	190
33,35-39	12	24	36	69	97	125
34-Ward-a	15	30	45	85	130	175
40-Matt Baker-c	15	30	45	88	137	185
41-43: 43-Last precode (3/55)	12	24	36	69	97	125
44,47-50,53,54	11	22	33	62	86	110
45-Ward-a	14	28	42	78	112	145
46-Ward-a; Baker-a	15	30	45	84	127	170
51,52-Ward(r). 52-r/Love Confessions #17	12	24	36	69	97	125
55,56: 55-Baker-a. 56-Baker-c	14	28	42	82	121	160

LOVE STORIES (See Top Love Stories)

LOVE STORIES (Formerly Heart Throbs)
National Periodical Publ.: No. 147, Nov, 1972 - No. 152, Oct-Nov, 1973

	GD 2.0	VG 4.0	FN 6.0	VF 8.0	VF/NM 9.0	NM- 9.2
147-152	3	6	9	14	20	26

LOVE STORIES OF MARY WORTH (See Harvey Comics Hits #55 & Mary Worth)
Harvey Publications: Sept, 1949 - No. 5, May, 1950

	GD 2.0	VG 4.0	FN 6.0	VF 8.0	VF/NM 9.0	NM- 9.2
1-1940's newspaper reprints-#1-4	9	18	27	50	65	80
2-5: 3-Kamen/Baker-a?	7	14	21	35	43	50

LOVE TALES (Formerly The Human Torch #35)
Marvel/Atlas Comics (ZPC No. 36-50/MMC No. 67-75): No. 36, 5/49 - No. 58, 8/52; No. 59, date? - No. 75, Sept, 1957

	GD 2.0	VG 4.0	FN 6.0	VF 8.0	VF/NM 9.0	NM- 9.2
36-Photo-c	24	48	72	140	230	320
37	14	28	42	82	121	160
38-44,46-50: 39-41-Photo-c. 48-Maneely-c	14	28	42	80	115	150
45,51,52,69: 45-Powell-a. 51,69-Everett-a. 52-Krigstein-a	14	28	42	81	118	155
53-60: 60-Last pre-code (2/55)	13	26	39	72	101	130
61-68,70-75: 75-Brewster, Cameron, Colletta-a	12	24	36	67	94	120

LOVE THRILLS (See Fox Giants)

LOVE TRAILS (Western romance)
A Lover's Magazine (CDS)(Marvel): Dec, 1949 - No. 2, Mar, 1950 (52 pgs.)

	GD 2.0	VG 4.0	FN 6.0	VF 8.0	VF/NM 9.0	NM- 9.2
1,2: 1-Photo-c	18	36	54	107	169	230

LOW
Image Comics: Aug, 2014 - No. 19, Aug, 2017 ($3.99/$3.50)

	NM- 9.2
1,11-19-($3.99) Remender-s/Tocchini-a	4.00
2-10-($3.50) Remender-s/Tocchini-a	3.50

LOWELL THOMAS' HIGH ADVENTURE (See High Adventure)

LT. (See Lieutenant)

LUCAS STAND
BOOM! Studios: Jun, 2016 - No. 6, Nov, 2016 ($3.99, limited series)

	NM- 9.2
1-6-Kurt Sutter & Caitlin Kittredge-s/Jesús Hervás-a. 1-Multiple covers	4.00

LUCAS STAND: INNER DEMONS
BOOM! Studios: Feb, 2018 - No. 4 ($3.99, limited series)

	NM- 9.2
1-Kurt Sutter & Caitlin Kittredge-s/Jesús Hervás-a	4.00

LUCIFER (See The Sandman #4)
DC Comics (Vertigo): Jun, 2000 - No. 75, Aug, 2006 ($2.50/$2.75)

	GD 2.0	VG 4.0	FN 6.0	VF 8.0	VF/NM 9.0	NM- 9.2
1-Carey-s/Weston-a/Fegredo-c	4	8	12	25	40	55
2,3-Carey-s/Weston-a/Fegredo-c	1	2	3	5	6	8
4-10: 4-Pleece-a. 5-Gross-a						4.00
11-49,51-73: 16-Moeller-c begin. 25,26-Death app. 45-Naifeh-a. 53-Kaluta-c begin. 62-Doran-a. 63-Begin $2.75-c						3.00
50-($3.50) P. Craig Russell-a; Mazikeen app.						4.00
74-($2.99) Kaluta-c						3.00
75-($3.99) Last issue; Lucifer's origins retold; Morpheus app.; Gross-a/Moeller-c						4.00
Preview-16 pg. flip book w/Swamp Thing Preview						3.00
Vertigo Essentials: Lucifer #1 Special Edition (3/16, $1.00) Flipbook with GN promos						3.00
...: A Dalliance With the Damned TPB ('02, $14.95) r/#14-20						15.00
...: Children and Monsters TPB ('01, $17.95) r/#5-13						18.00
...: Crux TPB (2006, $14.99) r/#55-61						15.00
...: Devil in the Gateway TPB ('01, $14.95) r/#1-4 & Sandman Presents:..#1-3						15.00
...: Evensong TPB (2007, $14.99) r/#70-75 & Lucifer: Nirvana one-shot						15.00
...: Exodus TPB (2005, $14.95) r/#42-44,46-49						15.00
...: Inferno TPB (2003, $14.95) r/#29-35						15.00
...: Mansions of the Silence TPB (2004, $14.95) r/#36-41						15.00
...: Morningstar TPB (2006, $14.99) r/#62-69						15.00
...: Nirvana (2002, $5.95) Carey-s/Muth-painted-c/a; Daniel app.						6.00
...: The Divine Comedy TPB (2003, $17.95) r/#21-28						18.00
...: The Wolf Beneath the Tree TPB (2005, $14.99) r/#45,50-54						15.00

LUCIFER (See The Sandman #4)
DC Comics (Vertigo): Feb, 2016 - No. 19, Aug, 2017 ($3.99)

	NM- 9.2
1-19: 1-Holly Black-s/Lee Garbett-a/Dave Johnson-c. 6-Stephanie Hans-a	4.00

LUCIFER'S HAMMER (Larry Niven & Jerry Pournelle's...)
Innovation Publishing: Nov, 1993 - No. 6, 1994 ($2.50, painted, limited series)

	NM- 9.2
1-6: Adaptatin of novel, painted-c & art	3.00

LUCKY COMICS
Consolidated Magazines: Jan, 1944; No. 2, Sum, 1945 - No. 5, Sum, 1946

	GD 2.0	VG 4.0	FN 6.0	VF 8.0	VF/NM 9.0	NM- 9.2
1-Lucky Starr & Bobbie begin	41	82	123	256	428	600
2-4	22	44	66	132	216	300
5-Devil-c by Walter Johnson	28	56	84	165	270	375

LUCKY DUCK
Standard Comics (Literary Ent.): No. 5, Jan, 1953 - No. 8, Sept, 1953

	GD 2.0	VG 4.0	FN 6.0	VF 8.0	VF/NM 9.0	NM- 9.2
5-Funny animal; Irving Spector-a	12	24	36	67	94	120
6-8-Irving Spector-a	10	20	30	56	76	95

NOTE: *Harvey Kurtzman tried to hire Spector for Mad #1.*

LUCKY "7" COMICS
Howard Publishers Ltd.: 1944 (No date listed)

	GD 2.0	VG 4.0	FN 6.0	VF 8.0	VF/NM 9.0	NM- 9.2
1-Pioneer, Sir Gallagher, Dick Royce, Congo Raider, Punch Powers; bondage-c	55	110	165	352	601	850

LUCKY STAR (Western)
Nation Wide Publ. Co.: 1950 - No. 7, 1951; No. 8, 1953 - No. 14, 1955 (5x7-1/4"; full color, 5¢)

	GD 2.0	VG 4.0	FN 6.0	VF 8.0	VF/NM 9.0	NM- 9.2
nn (#1)-(5¢, 52 pgs.)-Davis-a	20	40	60	120	195	270

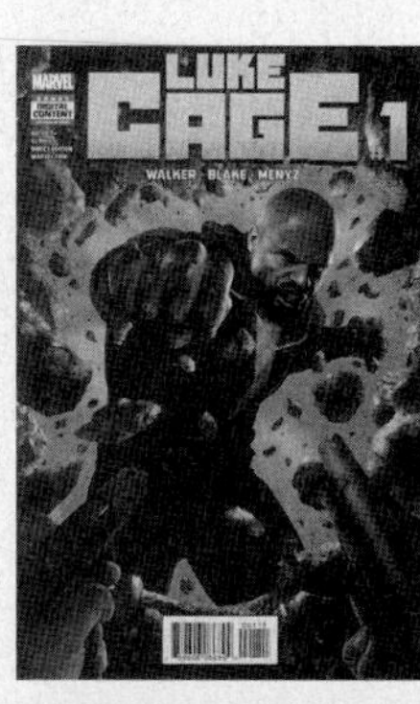

Luke Cage (2017 series) #1 © MAR

Lumberjanes #42 © BOOM!

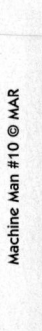

Machine Man #10 © MAR

	GD 2.0	VG 4.0	FN 6.0	VF 8.0	VF/NM 9.0	NM- 9.2

2,3-(5¢, 52 pgs.)-Davis-a 14 28 42 80 115 150
4-7-(5¢, 52 pgs.)-Davis-a 14 28 42 76 108 140
8-14-(36 pgs.)(Exist?) 14 28 42 76 108 140
Given away with Lucky Star Western Wear by the Juvenile Mfg. Co.
7 14 21 35 43 50

LUCY SHOW, THE (TV) (Also see I Love Lucy)
Gold Key: June, 1963 - No. 5, June, 1964 (Photo-c: 1,2)

1 11 22 33 72 154 235
2 6 12 18 41 76 110
3-5: Photo back c-1,2,4,5 6 12 18 37 66 95

LUCY, THE REAL GONE GAL (Meet Miss Pepper #5 on)
St. John Publishing Co.: June, 1953 - No. 4, Dec, 1953

1-Negligee panels 35 70 105 208 339 470
2 18 36 54 107 169 230
3,4: 3-Drucker-a 16 32 48 94 147 200

LUDWIG BEMELMAN'S MADELEINE & GENEVIEVE
Dell Publishing Co.: No. 796, May, 1957

Four Color 796 5 10 15 30 50 70

LUDWIG VON DRAKE (TV)(Disney)(See Walt Disney's C&S #256)
Dell Publishing Co.: Nov-Dec, 1961 - No. 4, June-Aug, 1962

1 6 12 18 38 69 100
2-4 5 10 15 30 50 70

LUFTWAFFE: 1946 (Volume 1)
Antarctic Press: July, 1996 - No. 4, Jan, 1997 ($2.95, B&W, limited series)

1-4-Ben Dunn & Ted Nomura-s/a, ...Special Ed. 3.00

LUFTWAFFE: 1946 (Volume 2)
Antarctic Press: Mar, 1997 - No. 18 ($2.95/$2.99, B&W, limited series)

1-18: 8-Reviews Tigers of Terra series 3.00
Annual 1 (4/98, $2.95)-Reprints early Nomura pages 4.00
...Color Special (4/98) 3.00
...Technical Manual 1,2 (2/98, 4/99) 4.00

LUGER
Eclipse Comics: Oct, 1986 - No. 3, Feb, 1987 ($1.75, miniseries, Baxter paper)

1-3: Bruce Jones scripts; Yeates-c/a 3.00

LUKE CAGE (Also see Cage & Hero for Hire)
Marvel Comics: Jul, 2017 - No. 5, Nov, 2017; No. 166, Dec, 2017 - No. 170, Apr, 2018 ($3.99)

1-5-Walker-s/Blake-a; Warhawk app. 4.00
[Title switches to legacy numbering after #5 (11/17)]
166-170: 166-Sanna-a; The Ringmaster app.; bonus origin re-cap w/Bagley-a 4.00

LUKE CAGE NOIR
Marvel Comics: Oct, 2009 - No. 4, Jan, 2010 ($3.99, limited series)

1-4-Glass & Benson-a/Martinbrough-a; covers by Bradstreet and Calero 4.00

LUKE SHORT'S WESTERN STORIES
Dell Publishing Co.: No. 580, Aug, 1954 - No. 927, Aug, 1958

Four Color 580(8/54), 651(9/55)-Kinstler-a 5 10 15 33 57 80
Four Color 739,771,807,848,875,927 5 10 15 30 50 70

LUMBERJANES
BOOM! Box: Apr, 2014 - Present ($3.99)

1-Noelle Stevenson & Grace Ellis-s/Brooke Allen-a; multiple covers 10.00
2 6.00
3-24,26-47 4.00
25-($4.99) Two covers by Allen & Wiedle; preview of Lumberjanes/Gotham Academy 5.00
...: Beyond Bay Leaf (10/15, $4.99) Faith Erin Hicks-s/Rosemary Valero-O'Connell-a 5.00
...: Faire and Square 2017 Special 1 (6/17, $7.99) Black-s/Julia-a; 3 covers 8.00
...: Making the Ghost of It 2016 Special 1 (5/16, $7.99) Wang-s/Norrie-a; Ganucheau-a 8.00

LUMBERJANES / GOTHAM ACADEMY
BOOM! Box: Jun, 2016 - No. 6, Nov, 2016 ($3.99)

1-6: 1-Chynna Clugston Flores-s/Rosemary Valero-O'Connell-a; multiple covers 4.00

LUNA MOON-HUNTER
WaterWalker Studios: Jul, 2012 - No. 2, Aug, 2012 ($5.95, limited series)

1,2-Rob Hughes-s/Jeff Slemons-a. 1-Posada-c. 2-Buzz-c 6.00
SC-($24.95, 180 pgs.) Painted-c by Buzz & Parrillo; art by Slemons, Buzz & LaRocque 25.00
HC-($49.95, limited edition of 1000) Signed by Hughes & Slemons; 2 bonus articles 50.00

LUNATIC FRINGE, THE
Innovation Publishing: July, 1989 - No. 2, 1989 ($1.75, deluxe format)

1,2 3.00

LUNATICKLE (Magazine) (Satire)
Whitstone Publ.: Feb, 1956 - No. 2, Apr, 1956

1,2-Kubert-a (scarce) 9 18 27 47 61 75

LUNATIK
Marvel Comics: Dec, 1995 - No. 3, Feb, 1996 ($1.95, limited series)

1-3 3.00

LURKERS, THE
IDW Publ.: Oct, 2004 - No. 4, Jan, 2005 ($3.99)

1-4-Niles-s/Casanova-a 4.00

LUST FOR LIFE
Slave Labor Graphics: Feb, 1997 - No. 4, Jan, 1998 ($2.95, B&W)

1-4: 1-Jeff Levin-s/a 3.00

LUTHOR (See Lex Luthor: Man of Steel)

LYCANTHROPE LEO
Viz Communications: 1994 - No. 7($2.95, B&W, limited series, 44 pgs.)

1-7 4.00

LYNCH (See Gen 13)
Image Comics (WildStorm Productions): May, 1997 ($2.50, one-shot)

1-Helmut-c/app. 3.00

LYNCH MOB
Chaos! Comics: June, 1994 - No. 4, Sept, 1994 ($2.50, limited series)

1-4 5.00
1-Special edition full foil-c 1 2 3 5 6 8

LYNDON B. JOHNSON
Dell Publishing Co.: Mar, 1965

12-445-503-Photo-c 3 6 9 19 30 40

M
Eclipse Books: 1990 - No. 4, 1991 ($4.95, painted, 52 pgs.)

1-Adapts movie; contains flexi-disc ($5.95) 6.00
2-4 5.00

MACE GRIFFIN BOUNTY HUNTER (Based on video game)
Image Comics (Top Cow): May, 2003 ($2.99, one-shot)

1-Nocon-a 3.00

MACGYVER: FUGITIVE GAUNTLET (Based on TV series)
Image Comics: Oct, 2012 - No. 5, Feb, 2013 ($3.50, limited series)

1-5-Lee Zlotoff & Tony Lee-s/Will Sliney-a 3.50

MACHETE (Based on the Robert Rodriguez movie)
IDW Publishing: No. 0, Sept, 2010 ($3.99)

0-Origin story; Rodriguez & Kaufman-s/Sayger-a; 3 covers 4.00

MACHINE, THE
Dark Horse Comics: Nov, 1994 - No. 4, Feb, 1995 ($2.50, limited series)

1-4 3.00

MACHINE MAN (Also see 2001, A Space Odyssey)
Marvel Comics Group: Apr, 1978 - No. 9, Dec, 1978; No. 10, Aug, 1979 - No. 19, Feb, 1981

1-Jack Kirby-c/a/scripts begin; end #9 3 6 9 20 31 42
2-9-Kirby-c/a/s. 9-(12/78) 2 4 6 9 12 15
10-17: 10-(8/79) Marv Wolfman scripts & Ditko-a begins
1 3 4 6 8 10
18-Wendigo, Alpha Flight-ties into X-Men #140 3 6 9 16 23 30
19-Intro/1st app. Jack O'Lantern (Macendale), later becomes 2nd Hobgoblin
3 6 9 16 24 32

NOTE: ***Austin*** *c-7i, 19i.* ***Buckler*** *c-17p, 18p.* ***Byrne*** *c-14p.* ***Ditko*** *a-10-19; c-10-13, 14i, 15, 16.* ***Kirby*** *a-1-9p; c-1-5, 7-9p.* ***Layton*** *c-7i.* ***Miller*** *c-19p.* ***Simonson*** *c-6.*

MACHINE MAN (Also see X-51)
Marvel Comics Group: Oct, 1984 - No. 4, Jan, 1985 (limited series)

1-4-Barry Smith-c/a(i) & colors in all; Jocasta app. 1-3-Trimpe-a(p). 2-1st app. Arno Stark (Iron Man 2020) 5.00
TPB (1988, $6.95) r/ #1-4; Barry Smith-c 10.00
.../Bastion '98 Annual ($2.99) wraparound-c 4.00

MACHINE MAN 2020
Marvel Comics: Aug, 1994 - No. 2, Sept, 1994 ($2.00, 52 pgs., limited series)

1,2: Reprints Machine Man limited series; Barry Windsor-Smith-c/i(r) 4.00

Mad #3 © EC Publ.

Mad #180 © EC Publ.

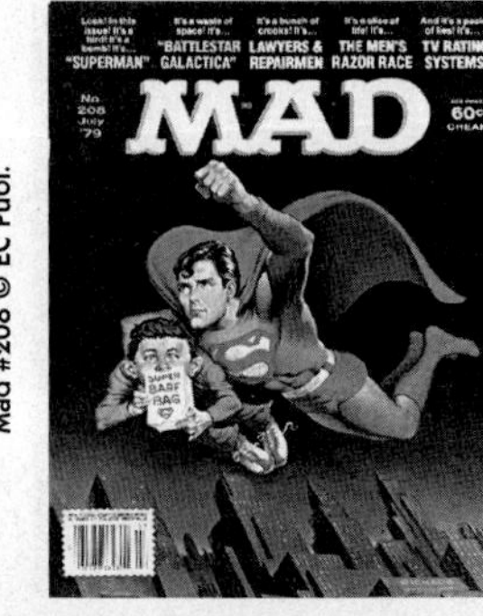

Mad #208 © EC Publ.

GD 2.0 | VG 4.0 | FN 6.0 | VF 8.0 | VF/NM 9.0 | NM- 9.2

GD 2.0 | VG 4.0 | FN 6.0 | VF 8.0 | VF/NM 9.0 | NM- 9.2

MACHINE TEEN
Marvel Comics: July, 2005 - No. 5, Nov, 2005 ($2.99, limited series)

1-5-Sumerak-s/Hawthorne-a. 1-James Jean-c 3.00
...: History (2005, $7.99, digest) r/#1-5 8.00

MACK BOLAN: THE EXECUTIONER (Don Pendleton's...)
Innovation Publishing: July, 1993 ($2.50)

1-3-($2.50) 3.00
1-($3.95)-Indestructible Cover Edition 4.00
1-($2.95)-Collector's Gold Edition; foil stamped 4.00
1-($3.50)-Double Cover Edition; red foil outer-c 4.00

MACKENZIE'S RAIDERS (Movie, TV)
Dell Publishing Co.: No. 1093, Apr-June, 1960

Four Color 1093-Richard Carlson photo-c from TV show 6 12 18 37 66 95

MACROSS (Becomes Robotech: The Macross Saga #2 on)
Comico: Dec, 1984 ($1.50)(Low print run)

1-Early manga app. 5 10 15 30 50 70

MACROSS II
Viz Select Comics: 1992 - No. 10, 1993 ($2.75, B&W, limited series)

1-10: Based on video series 4.00

MAD (Tales Calculated to Drive You...)
E. C. Comics (Educational Comics): Oct-Nov, 1952 - No. 550, Apr, 2018
(No. 24-on are magazine format) (Kurtzman editor No. 1-28, Feldstein No. 29 - No. ?)

1-Wood, Davis, Elder start as regulars 440 880 1320 3520 5610 7700
2-Dick Tracy cameo 114 228 342 912 1456 2000
3,4: 3-Stan Lee mentioned. 4-Reefer mention story "Flob Was a Slob" by Davis; Superman parody 83 166 249 664 1057 1450
5-W.M. Gaines biog. 166 332 498 1328 2114 2900
6-11: 6-Popeye cameo. 7,8- "Hey Look" reprints by Kurtzman. 11-Wolverton-a; Davis story was-r/Crime Suspenstories #12 w/new Kurtzman dialogue 60 120 180 480 765 1050
12-15: 12-Archie parody. 15,18-Pot Shot Pete-r by Kurtzman 48 96 144 384 612 840
16-23(5/55): 18-Alice in Wonderland by Jack Davis. 21-1st app. Alfred E. Neuman on-c in fake ad. 22-All by Elder plus photo-montages by Kurtzman. 23-Special cancel announcement 40 80 120 320 510 700
24(7/55)-1st magazine issue (25¢); Kurtzman logo & border on-c; 1st "What? Me Worry?" on-c; 2nd printing exists 94 188 282 752 1201 1650
25-Jaffee starts as regular writer 44 88 132 352 564 775
26,27: 27-Jaffee starts as story artist; new logo 39 78 117 312 499 685
28-Last issue edited by Kurtzman; (three cover variations exist with different wording on contents banner on lower right of cover; value of each the same) 37 74 111 222 361 500
29-Kamen-a; Don Martin starts as regular; Feldstein editing begins 36 72 108 216 351 485
30-1st A. E. Neuman cover by Mingo; last Elder-a; Bob Clarke starts as regular; Disneyland & Elvis Presley spoof 52 104 156 328 552 775
31-Freas starts as regular; last Davis-a until #99 32 64 96 192 314 435
32,33: 32-Orlando, Drucker, Woodbridge start as regulars; Wood back-c. 33-Orlando back-c 27 54 81 162 266 370
34-Berg starts as regular 22 44 66 132 216 300
35-Mingo wraparound-c; Crandall-a 22 44 66 132 216 300
36-40 (7/58): 39-Beall-c 18 36 54 105 165 225
41-50: 42-Danny Kaye-s. 44-Xmas-c. 47-49-Sid Caesar-s. 48-Uncle Sam-c. 50 (10/59)-Peter Gunn-s 15 30 45 90 140 190
51-59: 52-Xmas-c; 77 Sunset Strip. 53-Rifleman-s. 54-Jaffee-a begins. 55-Sid Caesar-s. 59-Strips of Superman, Flash Gordon, Donald Duck & others. 59-Halloween/Headless Horseman-c 14 28 42 80 115 150
60 (1/61)-JFK/Nixon flip-c; 1st Spy vs. Spy by Prohias, who starts as regular 15 30 45 86 133 180
61-70: 64-Rickard starts as regular. 65-JFK-s. 66-JFK-c. 68-Xmas-c by Martin. 70-Route 66-s 6 12 18 41 76 110
71-75,77-80 (7/63): 72-10th Anniv. special; 1/3 pg. strips of Superman, Tarzan & others. 73-Bonanza-s. 74-Dr. Kildare-s 5 10 15 31 53 75
76-Aragonés starts as regular 5 10 15 34 60 85
81-85: 81-Superman strip. 82-Castro-c. 85-Lincoln-c 4 8 12 28 47 65
86-1st Fold-in; commonly creased back covers makes these and later issues scarcer in NM 5 10 15 33 57 80
87,88 5 10 15 31 53 75
89,90: 89-One strip by Walt Kelly; Frankenstein-c; Fugitive-s. 90-Ringo back-c by Frazetta; Beatles app. 5 10 15 33 57 80
91,94,96,100: 94-King Kong-c. 96-Man From U.N.C.L.E. 100-(1/66)-Anniversary issue 4 8 12 28 47 65
92,93,95,97-99: 99-Davis-a resumes 4 8 12 27 44 60
101,104,106,108,114,115,119,121: 101-Infinity-c; Voyage to the Bottom of the Sea-s. 104-Lost in Space-s. 106-Tarzan back-c by Frazetta; 2 pg. Batman by Aragonés. 108-Hogan's Heroes by Davis. 114-Rat Patrol-s. 115-Star Trek. 119-Invaders (TV). 121-Beatles-c; Ringo pin-up; flip-c of Sik-Teen; Flying Nun-s 3 6 9 20 31 42
102,103,107,109-113,116-118,120(7/68): 118-Beatles cameo 3 6 9 18 28 38
105-Batman-c/s, TV show parody (9/66) 4 8 12 28 47 65
122,124,126,128,129,131-134,136,137,139,140: 122-Ronald Reagan photo inside; Drucker & Mingo-c. 126-Family Affair-s. 128-Last Orlando. 131-Reagan photo back-c. 132-Xmas-c. 133-John Wayne/True Grit. 136-Room 222 3 6 9 15 22 28
123-Four different covers 3 6 9 16 23 30
125,127,130,135,138: 125-2001 Space Odyssey; Hitler back-c. 127-Mod Squad-c/s. 130-Land of the Giants-s; Torres begins as reg. 135-Easy Rider-c by Davis. 138-Snoopy-c; MASH-s 3 6 9 16 24 32
141-149,151-156,158-165,167-170: 141-Hawaii Five-0. 147-All in the Family-s. 153-Dirty Harry-s. 155-Godfather-c/s. 156-Columbo-s. 159-Clockwork Orange-c/s. 161-Tarzan-s. 164-Kung Fu (TV)-s. 165-James Bond-s; Dean Martin-c. 169-Drucker-c; McCloud-s. 170-Exorcist-s 3 6 9 14 19 24
150-(4/72) Partridge Family-s 3 6 9 15 21 26
157-(3/73) Planet of the Apes-c/s 3 6 9 16 23 30
166-(4/74) Classic finger-c 3 6 9 16 23 30
171-185,187,189-192,194,195,198,199: 172-Six Million Dollar Man-s; Hitler back-c. 178-Godfather II-c/s. 180-Jaws-c/s (1/76). 182-Bob Jones starts as regular.185-Starsky & Hutch-s. 187-Fonz/Happy Days-c/s; Harry North starts as regular. 189-Travolta/Kotter-c/s. 190-John Wayne-c/s. 192-King Kong-c/s. 194-Rocky-c/s; Laverne & Shirley-s. 199-James Bond-s 2 4 6 10 14 18
186,188,197,200: 186-Star Trek-c/s. 188-Six Million Dollar Man/ Bionic Woman. 197-Spock-s; Star Wars-s. 200-Close Encounters 2 4 6 13 18 22
193,196: 193-Farrah/Charlie's Angels-c/s. 196-Star Wars-c/s 3 6 9 14 19 24
201,203,205,220: 201-Sat. Night Fever-c/s. 203-Star Wars. 205-Travolta/Grease. 220-Yoda-c, Empire Strikes Back-s 2 4 6 9 13 16
202,204,206,207,209,211-219,221-227,229,230: 204-Hulk TV show. 206-Tarzan. 208-Superman movie. 209-Mork & Mindy. 212-Spider-Man-s; Alien (movie)-s. 213-James Bond, Dracula, Rocky II-s 216-Star Trek. 219-Martin-c. 221-Shining-s. 223-Dallas-c/s. 225-Popeye. 226-Superman II. 229-James Bond. 230-Star Wars 1 3 4 6 8 10
208,228: 208-Superman movie-c/s; Battlestar Galactica-s. 228-Raiders of the Lost Ark-c/s 2 4 6 9 12 15
210-Lord of the Rings 2 4 6 9 13 16
231-235,237-241,243-249,251-260: 233-Pac-Man-c. 234-MASH-c/s. 235-Flip-c with Rocky III & Conan; Boris-a. 239-Mickey Mouse-c. 241-Knight Rider-s. 243-Superman III. 245- Last Rickard-a. 247-Seven Dwarfs-c. 253-Supergirl movie-s; Prince/Purple Rain-s. 254-Rock stars-s. 255-Reagan-c; Cosby-s. 256-Last issue edited by Feldstein; Dynasty, Bev. Hills Cop. 259-Rambo. 260-Back to the Future-c/s; Honeymooners-s 1 2 3 5 6 8
236,242,250: 236-E.T.-c/s;Star Trek II-s. 242-Star Wars/A-Team-c/s. 250-Temple of Doom-c/s; Tarzan-s 1 2 3 5 7 9
261-267,269-276,278-288,290-297: 261-Miami Vice. 262-Rocky IV-c/s, Leave It To Beaver-s. 263-Young Sherlock Holmes-s. 264-Hulk Hogan-c; Rambo-s. 267-Top Gun. 271-Star Trek IV-c/s. 272-ALF-c; Get Smart-s. 273-Pee Wee Herman-c/s. 274-Last Martin-a. 281-California Raisins-c. 282-Star Trek:TNG-s; ALF-s. 283-Rambo III-c/s. 284-Roger Rabbit-c/s. 285-Hulk Hogan-c. 287-3 pgs. Eisner-a. 291-TMNT-c; Indiana Jones-s. 292-Super Mario Bros.-c; Married with Children-s. 295-Back to the Future II. 297-Mike Tyson-c 1 2 3 4 5 7
268,277,289,298-300: 268-Aliens-c/s. 277-Michael Jackson-c/s; Robocop-s. 289-Batman movie parody. 298-Gremlins II-c/s; Robocop II. Batman-s. 299-Simpsons-c/story; Total Recall-s. 300(1/91) Casablanca-s, Dick Tracy-s, Wizard of Oz-s, Gone With The Wind-s 1 2 3 5 6 8
300-303 (1/91-6/91)-Special Hussein Asylum Editions; only distributed to the troops in the Middle East (see Mad Super Spec.) 2 4 6 13 18 22
301-310,312,313,315-320,322,324,326-334,337-349: 303-Home Alone-c/s. 305-Simpsons-s. 306-TMNT II movie. 308-Terminator II. 315-Tribute to William Gaines. 316-Photo-c. 319-Dracula-c/s. 320-Disney's Aladdin-s. 322-Batman Animated series. 327-Seinfeld-s; X-Men-s. 331-Flintstones-c/s. 332-O.J. Simpson-c/s; Simpsons app. in Lion King. 334-Frankenstein-c/s. 338-Judge Dredd-c by Frazetta. 341-Pocahontas-s. 345-Beatles app. (1 pg.) 347-Broken Arrow & Mission Impossible 5.00
311,314,321,323,325,335,336,350,354,358: 311-Addams Family-c/story, Home Improvement-s. 314-Batman Returns-c/story. 321-Star Trek DS9-c/s. 323-Jurassic Park-c/s. 325,336-Beavis & Butthead-c/s. 335-X-Files-s; Pulp Fiction-s; Interview with the Vampire-s. 336-Lois & Clark-s. 350-Polybagged w/CD Rom. 354-Star Wars; Beavis & Butthead-s. 358-X-Files 6.00

Mad About Millie #1 © MAR

Madame Xanadu #29 © DC

Madman Atomic Comics #14 © M. Allred

	GD 2.0	VG 4.0	FN 6.0	VF 8.0	VF/NM 9.0	NM- 9.2

351-353,355-357,359-500 5.00
501-550-($5.99) 6.00
Mad About Super Heroes (2002, $9.95) r/super hero app.; Alex Ross-c 10.00
NOTE: ***Aragones** c-210, 293. **Beall** c-39. **Davis** c-2, 27, 135, 139, 173, 178, 212, 213, 219, 246, 260, 296, 308. **Drucker** a-35-62; c-122, 169, 176, 225, 234, 264, 266, 274, 280, 285, 297, 299, 303, 314, 315, 321. **Elder** c-5, 259, 261, 268. **Elder/Kurtzman** a-258-274. **Jules Feiffer** a(r)-42. **Freas** c-40-59, 62-67, 69-70, 72, 74. **Heath** a-14, 27. **Jaffee** c-199, 217, 224, 258. **Kamen** a-29. **Krigstein** a-12, 17, 24, 26. **Kurtzman** c-1, 3, 4, 6-10, 13, 16, 18. **Martin** a-29-62; c-68, 165, 229. **Mingo** c-30-37, 61, 71, 75-80, 82-114, 117-124, 126, 129, 131, 133, 134, 136, 140, 143-148, 150-162, 164, 166-168, 171, 172, 174, 175, 177, 179, 181, 183, 185, 198, 206, 209, 211, 214, 218, 221, 222, 300. **John Severin** a-1-6, 9, 10. **Wolverton** c-11; a-11, 17, 29, 31, 36, 40, 82, 137. **Wood** a-1-21, 23-62; c-26, 28, 29. **Woodbridge** a-35-62. Issues 1-23 are 36 pgs.; 24-28 are 58 pgs.; 29 on are 52 pgs.*

MAD (See Mad Follies, ...Special, More Trash from..., and The Worst from...)

MAD ABOUT MILLIE (Also see Millie the Model)
Marvel Comics Group: April, 1969 - No. 16, Nov, 1970

1-Giant issue	9	18	27	63	129	195
2,3 (Giants)	6	12	18	40	73	105
4-10	5	10	15	31	53	75
11-16: 16-r	5	10	15	30	50	70
Annual 1(11/71, 52 pgs.)	5	10	15	31	53	75

MADAME FRANKENSTEIN
Image Comics: May, 2014 - No. 7, Nov, 2014 ($2.99, B&W, limited series)
1-7-Jamie Rich-s/Megan Levens-a/Joëlle Jones-c. 1-Variant-c by Mittens 3.00

MADAME MIRAGE
Image Comics (Top Cow): June, 2007 - No. 6, May, 2008 ($2.99)
1-6: 1-Paul Dini-s/Kenneth Rocafort-a; two covers by Horn and Rocafort 3.00
... First Look (5/07, 99¢) preview of series; Dini interview; cover gallery 3.00
Volume 1 TPB (7/08, $14.99) r/#1-6; cover gallery; cover and design sketches 15.00

MADAME XANADU
DC Comics: July, 1981 ($1.00, no ads, 36 pgs.)
1-Marshall Rogers-a (25 pgs.); Kaluta-c/a (2pgs.); pin-up 1 2 3 5 6 8

MADAME XANADU (Also see Doorway to Nightmare)
DC Comics (Vertigo): Aug, 2008 - No. 29, Jan, 2011 ($2.99)
1-Matt Wagner-s/Amy Reeder Hadley-a/c; Phantom Stranger app. 4.00
1,2-Variant covers. 1-Wagner. 2-Kaluta 5.00
2-29: 2-10-Amy Reeder Hadley-a/c; Phantom Stranger app. 6-Death (from The Sandman) app.; covers by Hadley & Quitely. 9-Zatara app. 10-Jim Corrigan becomes The Spectre. 11-15-Kaluta-a. 14,15-Sandman (Wesley Dodds) app. 16-18-Hadley-a; Det. Jones app. 3.00
...: Broken House of Cards TPB (2011, $17.99) r/#16-23 and story from House of Mystery Halloween Annual #1 18.00
...: Disenchanted TPB (2009, $12.99) r/#1-10; James Robinson intro.; Hadley sketch-a 13.00
...: Exodus TPB (2010, $12.99) r/#11-15; Chris Roberson intro. 13.00
...: Extra-Sensory TPB (2011, $17.99) r/#24-29 18.00

MADBALLS
Star Comics/Marvel Comics #9 on: Sept, 1986 - No. 3, Nov, 1986; No. 4, June, 1987 - No. 10, June, 1988
1-10: Based on toys. 9-Post-a 5.00

MAD DISCO
E.C. Comics: 1980 (one-shot, 36 pgs.)
1-Includes 30 minute flexi-disc of Mad disco music 2 4 6 11 16 20

MAD-DOG
Marvel Comics: May, 1993 - No. 6, Oct, 1993 ($1.25)
1-6-Flip book w/2nd story "created" by Bob Newhart's character from his TV show "Bob" set at a comic book company; actual s/a-Ty Templeton 3.00

MAD DOGS
Eclipse Comics: Feb, 1992 - No. 3, July, 1992 ($2.50, B&W, limited series)
1-3 3.00

MAD 84 (Mad Extra)
E.C. Comics: 1984 (84 pgs.)
1 1 3 4 6 8 10

MAD FOLLIES (Special)
E. C. Comics: 1963 - No. 7, 1969

nn(1963)-Paperback book covers	19	38	57	129	287	445
2(1964)-Calendar	15	30	45	100	220	340
3(1965)-Mischief Stickers	11	22	33	76	163	250
4(1966)-Mobile; Frazetta-r/back-c Mad #90	9	18	27	57	111	165
5,6: 5(1967)-Stencils. 6(1968)-Mischief Stickers	7	14	21	44	82	120
7(1969)-Nasty Cards	7	14	21	44	82	120

(If bonus is missing, issue is half price)
NOTE: ***Clarke** c-4. **Frazetta** r-4, 6 (1 pg. ea.). **Mingo** c-1-3. **Orlando** a-5.*

MAD HATTER, THE (Costumed Hero)
O. W. Comics Corp.: Jan-Feb, 1946; No. 2, Sept-Oct, 1946

1-Freddy the Firefly begins; Giunta-c/a	77	154	231	493	847	1200
2-Has ad for E.C.'s Animal Fables #1	41	82	123	256	428	600

MADHOUSE
Ajax/Farrell Publ. (Excellent Publ./4-Star): 3-4/54 - No. 4, 9-10/54; 6/57 - No. 4, Dec?, 1957

1(1954)	39	78	117	231	378	525
2,3	20	40	60	120	195	270
4-Surrealistic-c	27	54	81	162	266	370
1(1957, 2nd series)	15	30	45	90	140	190
2-4 (#4 exist?)	11	22	33	62	86	110

MAD HOUSE (Formerly Madhouse Glads; ...Comics #104? on)
Red Circle Productions/Archie Publications: No. 95, 9/74 - No. 97, 1/75; No. 98, 8/75 - No. 130, 10/82

95,96-Horror stories through #97; Morrow-c	2	4	6	11	16	20
97-Intro. Henry Hobson; Morrow-a/c, Thorne-a	2	4	6	10	14	18
98,99,101-120-Satire/humor stories. 110-Sabrina app.,1pg.	1	3	4	6	8	10
100	2	4	6	8	10	12
121-129	2	4	6	8	10	12
130	2	4	6	9	13	16
Annual 8(1970-71)-Formerly Madhouse Ma-ad Annual; Sabrina app. (6 pgs.)	4	8	12	27	44	60
Annual 9-12(1974-75): 11-Wood-a(r)	3	6	9	14	20	25
...Comics Digest 1('75-76) r/1st & 2nd Sabrina app.	2	4	6	10	14	18
2-8(8/82)(...Mag. #5 on)-Sabrina in many	2	4	6	8	11	14

NOTE: ***B. Jones** a-96. **McWilliams** a-97. **Wildey** a-95, 96. See Archie Comics Digest #1, 13.*

MADHOUSE GLADS (Formerly ...Ma-ad; Madhouse #95 on)
Archie Publ.: No. 73, May, 1970 - No. 94, Aug, 1974 (No. 78-92: 52 pgs.)

73-77,93,94: 74-1 pg. Sabrina	2	4	6	9	13	16
78-92 (52 pgs.)	2	4	6	11	16	20

MADHOUSE MA-AD (...Jokes #67-70; ...Freak-Out #71-74)
(Formerly Archie's Madhouse) (Becomes Madhouse Glads #73 on)
Archie Publications: No. 67, April, 1969 - No. 72, Jan, 1970

67-71: 70-1 pg. Sabrina	3	6	9	15	22	28
72-6 pgs. Sabrina	4	8	12	27	44	60
...Annual 7(1969-70)-Formerly Archie's Madhouse Annual; becomes Madhouse Annual; 6 pgs. Sabrina	4	8	12	28	47	65

MADMAN (See Creatures of the Id #1)
Tundra Publishing: Mar, 1992 - No. 3, 1992 ($3.95, duotone, high quality, lim. series, 52 pgs.)
1-Mike Allred-c/a in all 2 4 6 8 10 12
1-2nd printing 4.00
2,3 6.00

MADMAN ADVENTURES
Tundra Publishing: 1992 - No. 3, 1993 ($2.95, limited series)
1-Mike Allred-c/a in all 1 3 4 6 8 10
2,3 5.00
TPB (Oni Press, 2002, $14.95) r/#1-3 & first app. of Frank Einstein from Creatures of the Id in color; gallery pages 15.00

MADMAN ATOMIC COMICS (Also see The Atomics)
Image Comics: Apr, 2007 - Present ($2.99/$3.50)
1-12-Mike Allred-s/c/a. 1-Origin re-told; pin-ups by Rivoche and Powell. 3-Sale back-c 3.50
13-17-($3.50) Wraparound-c. 14-Back up w/Darwyn Cooke-a 3.50
All-New Giant-Size Super Ginchy Special (4/11, $5.99) Allred-s/a; back-ups/pin-ups 6.00
Madman In Your Face 3D Special (11/14, $9.99) Classic stories converted to 3D plus a new short story by Mike Allred and pin-ups by various; glasses included 10.00
... Vol. 1 (2008, $19.99) r/#1-7; bonus art; Jamie Rich intro. 20.00

MADMAN COMICS (Also see The Atomics)
Dark Horse Comics (Legend No. 2 on): Apr, 1994 - No. 20, Dec, 2000 ($2.95/$2.99)
1-Allred-c/a; F. Miller back-c. 1 2 3 5 6 8
2-3: 3-Alex Toth back-c. 5.00
4-11: 4-Dave Stevens back-c. 6,7-Miller/Darrow's Big Guy app. 6-Bruce Timm back-c. 7-Darrow back-c. 8-Origin?; Bagge back-c. 10-Allred/Ross-c; Ross back-c. 11-Frazetta back-c 4.00
12-16: 12-(4/99) 3.50
17-20: 17-The G-Men From Hell #1 on cover; Brereton back-c. 18-(#2). 19,20-($2.99-c). 20-Clowes back-c 3.50

Mad Super Special #108 © EC Publ.

Maestros #1 © Steve Skroce

Magdalena V4 #1 © TCOW

GD 2.0 | VG 4.0 | FN 6.0 | VF 8.0 | VF/NM 9.0 | NM- 9.2

... Boogaloo TPB (6/99, $8.95) r/Nexus Meets Madman & Madman/The Jam 9.00
... Gargantua! (2007, $125.00, HC with dustjacket) r/Madman#1-3, Madman Adventures #1-3, Madman Comics #1-20 and Madman King-Size Super Groovy Special; pin-ups 125.00
Image Firsts: Madman #1 (10/10, $1.00) r/#1 3.00
Ltd. Ed. Slipcover (1997, $99.95, signed and numbered) w/Vol.1 & Vol. 2. Vol.1- reprints #1-5; Vol. 2- reprints #6-10 100.00
The Complete Madman Comics: Vol. 2 (11/96, $17.95, TPB) r/#6-10 plus new material 18.00
Madman King-Size Super Groovy Special (Oni Press, 7/03, $6.95) new short stories by Allred, Derington, Krall and Weissman 7.00
Madman Picture Exhibition No. 1-4 (4-7/02, $3.95) pin-ups by various 4.00
Madman Picture Exhibition Limited Edition (10/02, $29.95) Hardcover collects MPE #1-4 30.00
... Volume 2 SC (2007, $17.99) r/#1-11; Erik Larsen intro. 18.00
... Volume 3 SC (2007, $17.99) r/#12-20 and story from King-Size Groovy; Allred intro. 18.00
Yearbook '95 (1996, $17.95, TPB)-r/#1-5, intro by Teller 18.00

MADMAN / THE JAM
Dark Horse Comics: Jul, 1998 - No. 2, Aug, 1998 ($2.95, mini-series)
1,2-Allred & Mireault-s/a 4.00

MAD MAX: FURY ROAD (Based on the 2015 movie)
DC Comics (Vertigo): Jul, 2015 - Oct, 2015 ($4.99, series of one-shots)
... :Furiosa (8/15, $4.99) Origin of Furiosa; Tristan Jones-a; Edwards-c 5.00
...: Max 1,2 (9/15, 10/15, $4.99) Recap of Max's history & prelude to movie 5.00
...: Nux & Immortan Joe (7/15, $4.99) Origins of Nux & Immortan Joe; Edwards-c 5.00

MAD MONSTER PARTY (See Movie Classics)

MADNESS IN MURDERWORLD
Marvel Comics: 1989 (Came with computer game from Paragon Software)
V1#1-Starring The X-Men 5.00

MADRAVEN HALLOWEEN SPECIAL
Hamilton Comics: Oct, 1995 ($2.95, one-shot)
nn-Morrow-a 3.00

MADROX (from X-Factor)
Marvel Comics (Marvel Knights): Nov, 2004 - No. 5, Mar, 2005 ($2.99)
1-5-Peter David-s/Pablo Raimondi-a; Strong Guy app. 3.00
...: Multiple Choice TPB (2005, $13.99) r/#1-5 14.00
X-Factor: Madrox - Multiple Choice HC (2008, $19.99) r/#1-5 20.00

MAD SPECIAL (...Super Special)
E. C. Publications, Inc.: Fall, 1970 - No. 141, Nov, 1999 (84 - 116 pgs.)
(If bonus is missing, issue is one half price)
Fall 1970(#1)-Bonus-Voodoo Doll; contains 17 pgs. new material 9 18 27 58 114 170
Spring 1971(#2)-Wall Nuts; 17 pgs. new material 5 10 15 33 57 80
3-Protest Stickers 5 10 15 33 57 80
4-8: 4-Mini Posters. 5-Mad Flag. 6-Mad Mischief Stickers. 7-Presidential candidate posters, Wild Shocking Message posters. 8-TV Guise 5 10 15 30 50 70
9(1972)-Contains Nostalgic Mad #1 (28 pgs.) 4 8 12 25 40 55
10-13: 10-Nonsense Stickers (Don Martin). 13-Sickie Stickers; 3 pgs. Wolverton-r/Mad #137. 11-Contains 33-1/3 RPM record. 12-Contains Nostalgic Mad #2 (36 pgs.); Davis, Wolverton-a 3 6 9 19 30 40
14,16-21,24: 4-Vital Message posters & Art Depreciation paintings. 16-Mad-hesive Stickers. 17-Don Martin posters. 20-Martin Stickers. 18-Contains Nostalgic Mad #4 (36 pgs.). 21,24-Contains Nostalgic Mad #5 (28 pgs.) & #6 (28 pgs.) 3 6 9 16 23 30
15-Contains Nostalgic Mad #3 (28 pgs.) 3 6 9 16 24 32
22,23,25,27-29,30: 22-Diplomas. 23-Martin Stickers. 25-Martin Posters. 27-Mad Shock-Sticks. 28-Contains Nostalgic Mad #7 (36 pgs.). 29-Mad Collectable-Connectables Posters. 30-The Movies 2 4 6 9 13 16
26-Has 33-1/3 RPM record 2 4 6 13 18 22
31,33-35,37-50 2 4 6 8 11 14
32-Contains Nostalgic Mad #8. 36-Has 96 pgs. of comic book & comic strip spoofs: titles "The Comics" on-c 2 4 6 9 13 16
51-70 1 3 4 6 8 10
71-88,90-100: 71-Batman parodies-r by Wood, Drucker. 72-Wolverton-c r-from 1st panel in Mad #11; Wolverton-s r/new dialogue. 83-All Star Trek spoof issue 1 2 3 5 6 8
76-(Fall, 1991)-Special Hussein Asylum Edition; distributed only to the troops in the Middle East (see Mad #300-303) 2 4 6 13 18 22
89-($3.95)-Polybaged w/1st of 3 Spy vs. Spy hologram trading cards (direct sale only issue) (other cards came w/card set) 1 3 4 6 8 10
101-141: 117-Sci-Fi parodies-r. 4.00
NOTE: *#28-30 have no number on cover.* **Freas** *c-76.* **Mingo** *c-9, 11, 15, 19, 23.*

MAE
Dark Horse Comics: May, 2016 - Present ($3.99)
1-Gene Ha-s/a/c; intro. by Bill Willingham; bonus pin-ups by Graham & Conner 5.00
2-6: 2-5-Gene Ha-s/a/c. 3-Bonus pin-up by Katie Cook. 6-Ha-s/Ganucheau-a 4.00

MAESTROS
Image Comics: Oct, 2017 - Present ($3.99)
1-5-Steve Skroce-s/a 4.00

MAGDALENA, THE (See The Darkness #15-18)
Image Comics (Top Cow): Apr, 2000 - No. 3, Jan, 2001 ($2.50)
Preview Special ('00, $4.95) Flip book w/Blood Legacy preview 5.00
1-Benitez-c/a; variant covers by Silvestri & Turner 3.00
2,3: 2-Two covers 3.00
.../Angelus #1/2 (11/01, $2.95) Benitez-c/Ching-a 3.00
...Blood Divine (2002, $9.95) r/#1-3 & #1/2; cover gallery 10.00
.../Vampirella (7/03, $2.99) Wohl-s/Benitez-a; two covers 3.00

MAGDALENA, THE (Volume 2)
Image Comics (Top Cow): Aug, 2003 - No. 4, Dec, 2003 ($2.99)
Preview (6/03) B&W preview; Wizard World East logo on cover 3.00
1-4-Holguin-s/Basaldua-a 3.00
1-Variant-c by Jim Silke benefitting ACTOR charity 5.00
TPB Volume 1 (12/06, $19.99) r/both series, Darkness #15-18 & Magdalena/Angelus 20.00
.../Daredevil (5/08, $3.99) Phil Hester-s/a; Hester & Sejic-c 4.00
.../Vampirella (12/04, $2.99) Kirkman-s/Manapul-a; two covers by Manapul and Bachalo 3.00
... Vs. Dracula Monster War 2005 (6/05, $2.99) four covers; Joyce Chin-a 3.00

MAGDALENA, THE (Volume 3)
Image Comics (Top Cow): Apr, 2010 - No. 12, May, 2012 ($3.99)
1-12: 1-Marz-s/Blake-a/Sook-c. 7,8-Keu Cha-a 4.00
... Seventh Sacrament 1 (12/14, $3.99) Tini Howard-s/Aileen Oracion-a 4.00

MAGDALENA (Volume 4)
Image Comics (Top Cow): Mar, 2017 - No. 4, Jun, 2017 ($3.99, limited series)
1-4-Howard & Cady-s/DiBari-a 4.00

MAGE (The Hero Discovered...; also see Grendel #16)
Comico: Feb, 1984 (no month) - No. 15, Dec, 1986 ($1.50, Mando paper)
1-Comico's 1st color comic 2 4 6 8 11 14
2-5: 3-Intro Edsel 6.00
6-Grendel begins (1st in color) 3 6 9 14 20 25
7-1st new Grendel story 2 4 6 8 10 12
8-14: 13-Grendel dies. 14-Grendel story ends 6.00
15-($2.95) Double size w/pullout poster 1 2 3 5 6 8
Image Firsts: Mage - The Hero Discovered #1 (10/10, $1.00) r/#1 w/"Image Firsts" logo 3.00
TPB Volume 1-4 (Image, $5.95) 1- r/#1,2. 2- r/#3,4. 3- r/#5,6. 4- r/#7,8 7.00
TPB Volume 5-7 (Image, $6.95) 5- r/#9,10. 6- r/#11,12. 7- r/#13,14 7.00
TPB Volume 8 (Image, 9/99, $7.50) r/#15 7.50
..., Vol. 1 TPB (Image, 2004, $29.99) r/#1-15; cover gallery, promo artwork, bonus art 30.00

MAGE (The Hero Defined) (Volume 2)
Image Comics: July, 1997 - No. 15, Oct, 1999 ($2.50)
0-(7/97, $5.00) American Ent. Ed. 5.00
1-14: Matt Wagner-c/s/a in all. 13-Three covers 3.00
1-"3-D Edition" (2/98, $4.95) w/glasses 5.00
15-($5.95) Acetate cover 6.00
Volume 1,2 TPB ('98,'99, $9.95) 1- r/#1-4. 2-r/#5-8 10.00
Volume 3 TPB ('00, $12.95) r/#9-12 13.00
Volume 4 TPB ('01, $14.95) r/#13-15 15.00
Hardcover Vol. 2 (2005, $49.95) r/#1-15; cover gallery, character design & sketch pages 50.00

MAGE, BOOK THREE: THE HERO DENIED
Image Comics: No. 0 July, 2017 - Present ($1.99/$3.99)
0-(7/17, $1.99) Return of Kevin Matchstick 3.00
1-6-Matt Wagner-c/s/a 3.00

MAGE KNIGHT: STOLEN DESTINY (Based on the fantasy game Mage Knight)
Idea + Design Works: Oct, 2002 - No. 5, Feb, 2003 ($3.50, limited series)
1-5: 1-J. Scott Campbell-c; Cabrera-a/Dezago-s, 2-Dave Johnson-c 3.50

MAGGIE AND HOPEY COLOR SPECIAL (See Love and Rockets)
Fantagraphics Books: May, 1997 ($3.50, one-shot)
1 4.00

MAGGIE THE CAT (Also see Jon Sable, Freelance #11 & Shaman's Tears #12)
Image Comics (Creative Fire Studio): Jan, 1996 - No. 2, Feb, 1996 ($2.50, unfinished limited series)
1,2: Mike Grell-c/a/scripts 3.00

Magic Comics #15 © KFS

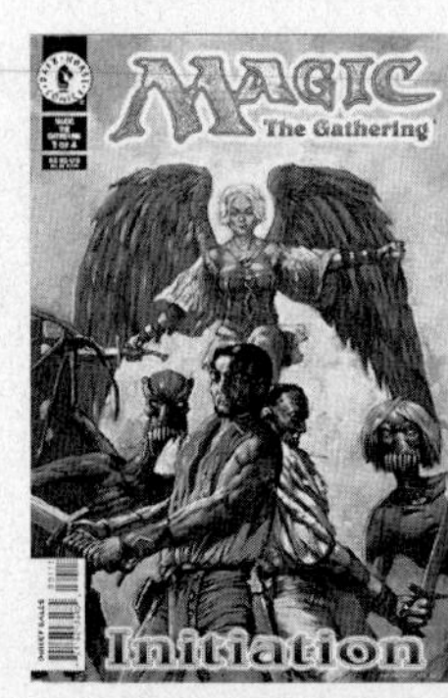

Magic the Gathering #1 © DH

Magneto: Dark Seduction #1 © MAR

	GD 2.0	VG 4.0	FN 6.0	VF 8.0	VF/NM 9.0	NM- 9.2

MAGICA DE SPELL (See Walt Disney Showcase #30)

MAGIC AGENT (See Forbidden Worlds & Unknown Worlds)
American Comics Group: Jan-Feb, 1962 - No. 3, May-June, 1962

	GD	VG	FN	VF	VF/NM	NM-
1-Origin & 1st app. John Force	4	8	12	27	44	60
2,3	3	6	9	19	30	40

MAGIC COMICS
David McKay Publications: Aug, 1939 - No. 123, Nov-Dec, 1949

	GD	VG	FN	VF	VF/NM	NM-
1-Mandrake the Magician, Henry, Popeye , Blondie, Barney Baxter, Secret Agent X-9 (not by Raymond), Bunky by Billy DeBeck & Thornton Burgess text stories illustrated by Harrison Cady begin; Henry covers begin	359	718	1077	2118	3659	5200
2	128	256	384	755	1303	1850
3	93	186	279	549	950	1350
4	76	152	228	448	774	1100
5	64	128	192	378	652	925
6-11: 8-11-Mandrake/Henry funny covers	50	100	150	315	533	750
12-16,18,20: 12-20,22-24-Serious Mandrake mystery covers	68	136	204	435	743	1050
17-The Lone Ranger begins (scarce)	90	180	270	576	988	1400
19-Classic robot-c (scarce)	155	310	465	992	1696	2400
21-Mandrake/Henry funny cover	39	78	117	240	395	550
22-24	50	100	150	315	533	750
25-1st Blondie-c	39	78	117	240	395	550
26-30: 26-Dagwood-c begin	30	60	90	177	289	400
31-40: 36-Flag-c	21	42	63	122	199	275
41-50	16	32	48	94	147	200
51-60	14	28	42	80	115	150
61-70	12	24	36	67	94	120
71-99, 107,108-Flash Gordon app; not by Raymond	10	20	30	54	72	90
100	11	22	33	60	83	105
101-106,109-123: 123-Last Dagwood-c	9	18	27	50	65	80

MAGIC FLUTE, THE (See Night Music #9-11)

MAGICIAN: APPRENTICE
Dabel Brothers/Marvel Comics (Dabel Brothers) #3 on: Mar, 2007 - No. 12, Dec, 2007 ($2.95/$2.99)

1-12-Adaptation of the Raymond E. Feist Riftwar Saga series 3.00
1,2-($5.95) 1-Wraparound variant-c by Maitz. 2-Wraparound variant-c by Booth 6.00
Collected Edition (10/06, $3.99) r/#1&2 4.00
Vol. 1 HC (2007, $19.99, dustjacket) r/#1-6; foreword by Feist 20.00
Vol. 1 SC (2007, $15.99) r/#1-6; foreword by Feist 16.00
Vol. 2 HC (2008, $19.99, dustjacket) r/#7-12 20.00

MAGIC PICKLE
Oni Press: Sept, 2001 - No. 4, Dec, 2001 ($2.95, limited series)

1-4-Scott Morse-s/a; Mahfood-a (2 pgs.) 3.00

MAGIC SWORD, THE (See Movie Classics)

MAGIC THE GATHERING (Title Series), **Acclaim Comics (Armada)**

...ANTIQUITIES WAR,11/95 - 2/96 ($2.50), 1-4-Paul Smith-a(p) 3.00
...ARABIAN NIGHTS, 12/95 - 1/96 ($2.50), 1,2 3.00
...COLLECTION ,'95 ($4.95), 1,2-polybagged 5.00
...CONVOCATIONS, '95 ($2.50), 1-nn-pin-ups 3.00
...ELDER DRAGONS ,'95 ($2.50), 1,2-Doug Wheatley-a 3.00
...FALLEN ANGEL ,'95 ($5.95), nn 6.00
...FALLEN EMPIRES ,9/95 - 10/95 ($2.75), 1,2 3.00
...Collection ($4.95)-polybagged 5.00
...HOMELANDS ,'95 ($5.95), nn-polybagged w/card; Hildebrandts-c 6.00
... ICE AGE (On The World of...) ,7/5 -11/95 ($2.50), 1-4: 1,2-bound-in Magic Card. 3,4-bound-in insert 3.00
...LEGEND OF JEDIT OJANEN, '96 ($2.50), 1,2 3.00
...NIGHTMARE, '95 ($2.50, one shot), 1 3.00
...THE SHADOW MAGE, 7/95 - 10/95 ($2.50), 1-4-bagged w/Magic The Gathering card 3.00
...Collection 1,2 (1995, $4.95)-Trade paperback; polybagged 5.00
...SHANDALAR ,'96 ($2.50), 1,2 3.00
...WAYFARER ,11/95 - 2/96 ($2.50), 1-5 3.00

MAGIC: THE GATHERING
IDW Publishing: Dec, 2011 - No. 4, Mar, 2012 ($3.99, limited series)

1-4-Forbeck-s/Cóccolo-a 4.00

MAGIC: THE GATHERING: GERRARD'S QUEST
Dark Horse Comics: Mar, 1998 - No. 4, June, 1998 ($2.95, limited series)

1-4: Grell-s/Mhan-a 3.00

MAGIC: THE GATHERING - PATH OF VENGEANCE
IDW Publishing: Oct, 2012 - No. 4, Feb, 2013 ($4.99, limited series, bagged with card)

1-4-Forbeck-s/Cóccolo-a 5.00

MAGIC: THE GATHERING - THEROS
IDW Publishing: Oct, 2013 - Present ($4.99, limited series, bagged with card)

1-5-Ciaramella-s/Cóccolo-a 5.00

MAGIC: THE GATHERING - THE SPELL THIEF
IDW Publishing: May, 2012 - No. 4, Aug, 2012 ($4.99, limited series, bagged with card)

1-4-Forbeck-s/Cóccolo-a 5.00

MAGIK (Illyana and Storm Limited Series)
Marvel Comics Group: Dec, 1983 - No. 4, Mar, 1984 (60¢, limited series)

1-4: 1-Characters from X-Men; Inferno begins; X-Men cameo (Buscema pencils in #1,2; c-1p. 2-4: 2-Nightcrawler app. & X-Men cameo 5.00

MAGIK (See Black Sun mini-series)
Marvel Comics: Dec, 2000 - No. 4, Mar, 2001 ($2.99, limited series)

1-4-Liam Sharp-a/Abnett & Lanning-s; Nightcrawler app. 3.00

MAGILLA GORILLA (TV) (See Kite Fun Book)
Gold Key: May, 1964 - No. 10, Dec, 1968 (Hanna-Barbera)

	GD	VG	FN	VF	VF/NM	NM-
1-1st comic app.	9	18	27	59	117	175
2-4: 3-Vs. Yogi Bear for President. 4-1st Punkin Puss & Mushmouse, Ricochet Rabbit & Droop-a-Long	5	10	15	33	57	80
5-10: 10-Reprints	4	8	12	28	47	65

MAGILLA GORILLA (TV)(See Spotlight #4)
Charlton Comics: Nov, 1970 - No. 5, July, 1971 (Hanna-Barbera)

	GD	VG	FN	VF	VF/NM	NM-
1	5	10	15	34	60	85
2-5	3	6	9	21	33	45

MAGNETIC MEN FEATURING MAGNETO
Marvel Comics (Amalgam): June, 1997 ($1.95, one-shot)

1-Tom Peyer-s/Barry Kitson & Dan Panosian-a 3.00

MAGNETO (See X-Men #1)
Marvel Comics: nd (Sept, 1993) (Giveaway) (one-shot)

0-Embossed foil-c by Sienkiewicz; r/Classic X-Men #19 & 12 by Bolton 5.00

MAGNETO
Marvel Comics: Nov, 1996 - No. 4, Feb, 1997 ($1.95, limited series)

1-4: Peter Milligan scripts & Kelley Jones-a(p) 3.00

MAGNETO
Marvel Comics: Mar, 2011 ($2.99, one-shot)

1-Howard Chaykin-s/a; Roger Cruz-c 3.00

MAGNETO
Marvel Comics: May, 2014 - No. 21, Oct, 2015 ($3.99)

1-21: 1-Bunn-s/Walta-a/Rivera-c. 9-12-AXIS tie-ins. 18-21-Secret Wars tie-ins 4.00

MAGNETO AND THE MAGNETIC MEN
Marvel Comics (Amalgam): Apr, 1996 ($1.95, one-shot)

1-Jeff Matsuda-a(p) 3.00

MAGNETO ASCENDANT
Marvel Comics: May, 1999 ($3.99, squarebound one-shot)

1-Reprints early Magneto appearances 4.00

MAGNETO: DARK SEDUCTION
Marvel Comics: Jun, 2000 - No. 4, Sept, 2000 ($2.99, limited series)

1-4: Nicieza-s/Cruz-a. 3,4-Avengers-c/app. 3.00

MAGNETO: NOT A HERO (X-Men Regenesis)
Marvel Comics: Jan, 2012 - No. 4, Apr, 2012 ($2.99, limited series)

1-4-Skottie Young-s/Clay Mann-a; Joseph returns 3.00

MAGNETO REX
Marvel Comics: Apr, 1999 - No. 3, July, 1999 ($2.50, limited series)

1-3-Rogue, Quicksilver app.; Peterson-a(p) 3.00

MAGNUS (Robot Fighter)(Volume 1)
Dynamite Entertainment: 2017 - No. 5, 2017 ($3.99)

1-5-Higgins-s/Fornés-a. 1,2-Turok back-up. 3-5-Doctor Spektor back-up 4.00

Magnus, Robot Fighter #17 © GK

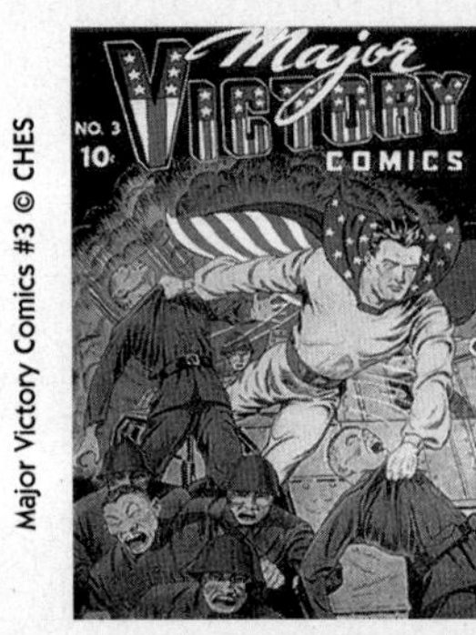

Major Victory Comics #3 © CHES

Man Called A-X #5 © MAL

	GD 2.0	VG 4.0	FN 6.0	VF 8.0	VF/NM 9.0	NM- 9.2

MAGNUS, ROBOT FIGHTER (...4000 A.D.)(See Doctor Solar)
Gold Key: Feb, 1963 - No. 46, Jan, 1977 (All painted covers except #5,30,31)

1-Origin & 1st app. Magnus; Aliens (1st app.) series begins — 54 108 162 432 966 1500
2,3 — 11 22 33 76 163 250
4-10: 10-Simonson fan club illo (5/65, 1st-a?) — 7 14 21 49 92 135
11-20 — 5 10 15 33 57 80
21,24-28: 28-Aliens ends — 4 8 12 25 40 55
22,23: 22-Origin-r/#1; last 12¢ issue — 4 8 12 27 44 60
29-46-Mostly reprints — 3 6 9 14 20 25
...: One For One (Dark Horse Comics, 9/10, $1.00) r/#1 — 3.00
Russ Manning's Magnus Robot Fighter - Vol. 1 HC (Dark Horse, 2004, $49.95) r/#1-7 — 70.00
Russ Manning's Magnus Robot Fighter - Vol. 2 HC (DH, 6/05, $49.95) r/#8-14; forward by Steve Rude — 50.00
Russ Manning's Magnus Robot Fighter - Vol. 3 HC (Dark Horse, 10/06, $49.95) r/#15-21 — 50.00
NOTE: ***Manning** a-1-22, 28-43(r). **Spiegle** a-23, 44r.*

MAGNUS ROBOT FIGHTER (Also see Vintage Magnus)
Valiant/Acclaim Comics: May, 1991 - No. 64, Feb, 1996 ($1.75/$1.95/$2.25/$2.50)

1-Nichols/Layton-c/a; 1-8 have trading cards — 2 4 6 10 14 18
2-4,6,8: 4-Rai cameo. 6-1st Solar x-over. — 1 3 4 6 8 10
5-Origin & 1st full app. Rai (10/91); #5-8 are in flip book format and back-c & half of book are Rai #1-4 mini-series — 3 6 9 16 23 30
7-Magnus vs. Rai-c/story; 1st X-O Armor — 2 4 6 11 16 20
0-Origin issue; Layton-a; ordered through mail w/coupons from 1st 8 issues plus 50¢; B. Smith trading card — 3 6 9 19 30 40
0-Sold thru comic shops without trading card — 3 6 9 14 19 24
9-11 — 6.00
12-(3.25, 44 pgs.)-Turok-c/story (1st app. in Valiant universe, 5/92); has 8 pg. Magnus story insert — 3 6 9 17 26 35
13-24,26-48: 14-1st app. Isak. 15,16-Unity x-overs. 15-Miller-c. 16-Birth of Magnus. 21-New direction & new logo.24-Story cont'd in Rai & the Future Force #9. 33-Timewalker app. 36-Bound-in trading cards. 37-Rai, Starwatchers & Psi-Lords app. 44-Bound-in sneak peek card — 4.00
21-Gold ink variant — 2 4 6 9 12 15
25-($2.95)-Embossed silver foil-c; new costume — 5.00
49-63 — 4.00
64-($2.50): 64-Magnus dies? — 2 4 6 9 12 15
...Invasion (1994, $9.95)-r/Rai #1-4 & Magnus #5-8 — 12.00
Magnus Steel Nation (1994, $9.95) r/#1-4 — 12.00
Yearbook (1994, $3.95, 52 pgs.) — 5.00
NOTE: ***Ditko/Reese** a-18. **Layton** a(i)-5; c-6-9i, 25; back(i)-5-8. **Reese** a(i)-22, 25, 28; c(i)-22, 24, 28. **Simonson** c-16. Prices for issues 1-8 are for trading cards and coupons intact.*

MAGNUS ROBOT FIGHTER
Acclaim Comics (Valiant Heroes): V2#1, May, 1997 - No. 18, Jun, 1998 ($2.50)

1-18: 1-Reintro Magnus; Donavon Wylie (X-O Manowar) cameo; Tom Peyer scripts & Mike McKone-c/a begin; painted variant-c exists — 3.00

MAGNUS ROBOT FIGHTER
Dark Horse Comics: Aug, 2010 - No. 4, May, 2011 ($3.50)

1-4: 1-Shooter-s/Reinhold-a; covers by Swanland & Reinhold; back-up r/#1 (1963) — 3.50

MAGNUS ROBOT FIGHTER
Dynamite Entertainment: 2014 - No. 12, 2015 ($3.99)

1-12: 1-8-Fred Van Lente-s/Cory Smith-a; multiple covers on each — 4.00
#0 (2014, $3.99) Takes place between #2 & #3; Roberto Castro-a — 4.00

MAGNUS ROBOT FIGHTER/NEXUS
Valiant/Dark Horse Comics: Dec, 1993 - No. 2, Apr, 1994 ($2.95, lim. series)

1,2: Steve Rude painted-c & pencils in all — 4.00

MAGOG (See Justice Society of America 2007 series)(Continues in Justice Society Special #1)
DC Comics: Nov, 2009 - No.12, Ot. 2010 ($2.99)

1-12: 1-Giffen-s/Porter-a/Fabry-c; variant-c by Porter. 7-Zatanna app. — 3.00
...: Lethal Force TPB (2010, $14.99) r/#1-5 — 15.00

MAID OF THE MIST (See American Graphics)

MAI, THE PSYCHIC GIRL
Eclipse Comics: May, 1987 - No. 28, July, 1989 ($1.50, B&W, bi-weekly, 44pgs.)

1-28, 1,2-2nd print — 4.00

MAJESTIC (Mr. Majestic from WildCATS)
DC Comics: Oct, 2004 - No. 4, Jan, 2005 ($2.95, limited series)

1-4-Kerschl-a/Abnett & Lanning-s. 1-Superman app.; Superman #1 cover swipe — 3.00
...: Strange New Visitor TPB (2005, $14.99) r/#1-4 & Action #811, Advs. of Superman #624 & Superman #201 — 15.00

MAJESTIC (Mr. Majestic from WildCATS)
DC Comics (WildStorm): Mar, 2005 - No. 17, July, 2006 ($2.95/$2.99)

1-17: 1-Googe-a/Abnett & Lanning-s; Superman app. 9-Jeanty-a; Zealot app. — 3.00
...: Meanwhile, Back on Earth... TPB (2006, $14.99) r/#8-12 — 15.00
...: The Final Cut TPB (2007, $14.99) r/#13-17 & story fro WildStorm Winter Special — 15.00
...: While You Were Out TPB (2006, $12.99) r/#1-7 — 13.00

MAJOR BUMMER
DC Comics: Aug, 1997 - No. 15, Oct, 1998 ($2.50)

1-15: 1-Origin and 1st app. Major Bummer — 3.00

MAJOR HOOPLE COMICS (See Crackajack Funnies)
Nedor Publications: nd (Jan, 1943)

1-Mary Worth, Phantom Soldier app. by Moldoff — 39 78 117 231 378 525

MAJOR VICTORY COMICS (Also see Dynamic Comics)
H. Clay Glover/Service Publ./Harry 'A' Chesler: 1944 - No. 3, Summer, 1945

1-Origin Major Victory (patriotic hero) by C. Sultan (reprint from Dynamic #1); 1st app. Spider Woman; Nazi WWII-c — 87 174 261 553 952 1350
2-Dynamic Boy app.; WWII-c — 55 110 165 352 601 850
3-Rocket Boy app.; WWII-c — 53 106 159 334 567 800

MALIBU ASHCAN: RAFFERTY (See Firearm #12)
Malibu Comics (Ultraverse): Nov, 1994 (99¢, B&W w/color-c; one-shot)

1-Previews "The Rafferty Saga" storyline in Firearm; Chaykin-c — 3.00

MALTESE FALCON
David McKay Publications: No. 48, 1946

Feature Books 48-by Dashiell Hammett — 97 194 291 621 1061 1500

MALU IN THE LAND OF ADVENTURE
I. W. Enterprises: 1964 (See White Princess of Jungle #2)

1-r/Avon's Slave Girl Comics #1; Severin-c — 5 10 15 30 50 70

MAMMOTH COMICS
Whitman Publishing Co.(K. K. Publ.): 1938 (84 pgs.) (B&W, 8-1/2x11-1/2")

1-Alley Oop, Terry & the Pirates, Dick Tracy, Little Orphan Annie, Wash Tubbs, Moon Mullins, Smilin' Jack, Tailspin Tommy, Don Winslow, Dan Dunn, Smokey Stover & other reprints (scarce) — 239 478 717 1530 2615 3700

MAN AGAINST TIME
Image Comics (Motown Machineworks): May, 1996 - No. 4, Aug, 1996 ($2.25, lim. series)

1-4: 1-Simonson-c. 2,3-Leon-c. 4-Barreto & Leon-c — 3.00

MAN-BAT (See Batman Family, Brave & the Bold, & Detective #400)
National Periodical Publ./DC Comics: Dec-Jan, 1975-76 - No. 2, Feb-Mar, 1976; Dec, 1984

1-Ditko-a(p); Aparo-c; Batman app.; 1st app. She-Bat?; 1st app. Baron Tyme — 3 6 9 16 23 30
2-Aparo-c — 2 4 6 10 14 18
1 (12/84)-N. Adams-r(3)/Det.(Vs. Batman on-c) — 6.00

MAN-BAT
DC Comics: Feb, 1996 - No. 3, Apr, 1996 ($2.25, limited series)

1-3: Dixon scripts in all. 2-Killer Croc-c/app. — 3.00

MAN-BAT
DC Comics: Jun, 2006 - No. 5, Oct, 2006 ($2.99, limited series)

1-5: Bruce Jones-s/Mike Huddleston-a/c. 1-Hush app. — 3.00

MAN CALLED A-X, THE
Malibu Comics (Bravura): Nov, 1994 - No. 4, Jun, 1995 ($2.95, limited series)

0-4: Marv Wolfman scripts & Shawn McManus-c/a. 0-(2/95). 1-"1A" on cover — 3.00

MAN CALLED A-X, THE
DC Comics: Oct, 1997 - No. 8, May, 1998 ($2.50)

1-8: Marv Wolfman scripts & Shawn McManus-c/a. — 3.00

MAN CALLED KEV, A (See The Authority)
DC Comics (WildStorm): Sept, 2006 - No. 5, Feb, 2007 ($2.99, limited series)

1-5-Ennis-s/Ezquerra-a/Fabry-c — 3.00
TPB (2007, $14.99) r/#1-5; cover gallery — 15.00

MAN COMICS
Marvel/Atlas Comics (NPI): Dec, 1949 - No. 28, Sept, 1953 (#1-6: 52 pgs.)

1-Tuska-a — 36 72 108 211 343 475
2-Tuska-a — 19 38 57 109 172 235
3-6 — 15 30 45 88 137 185
7,8 — 15 30 45 85 130 175
9-13,15: 9-Format changes to war — 15 30 45 85 130 175

Man Comics #16 © MAR

Man From U.N.C.L.E. #18 © GK

Manifest Destiny #22 © Skybound

GD VG FN VF VF/NM NM-
2.0 4.0 6.0 8.0 9.0 9.2

14-Henkel (3 pgs.); Pakula-a 15 30 45 86 153 180
16-21,23-28: 28-Crime issue (Bob Brant) 15 30 45 83 124 165
22-Krigstein-a, 5 pgs. 15 30 45 88 137 185

NOTE: ***Berg** a-14, 15, 19. **Colan** a-9, 13, 21, 23. **Everett** a-8, 22; c-22, 25. **Heath** a-11, 13, 16, 17, 21. **Henkel** a-7. Kubertish a-by **Bob Brown**-3. **Maneely** a-5, 11-13; c-5, 10, 11, 16. **Reinman** a-11. **Robinson** a-7, 10, 14. **Robert Sale** a-9, 11. **Sinnott** a-22, 23. **Tuska** a-14, 23.*

MANDRAKE THE MAGICIAN (See Defenders Of The Earth, 123, 46, 52, 55, Giant Comic Album, King Comics, Magic Comics, The Phantom #21, Tiny Tot Funnies & Wow Comics, '36)

MANDRAKE THE MAGICIAN (See Harvey Comics Hits #53)
David McKay Publ./Dell/King Comics (All 12¢): 1938 - 1948; Sept, 1966 - No. 10, Nov, 1967

Feature Books 18,19,23 (1938) 100 200 300 635 1093 1550
Feature Books 46 57 114 171 362 619 875
Feature Books 52,55 52 104 156 328 552 775
Four Color 752 (11/56) 10 20 30 66 138 210
1-Begin S.O.S. Phantom, ends #3 6 12 18 40 73 105
2-7,9: 4-Girl Phantom app. 5-Flying Saucer-c/story. 5,6-Brick Bradford app. 7-Origin Lothar. 9-Brick Bradford app. 4 8 12 23 37 50
8-Jeff Jones-a (4 pgs.) 4 8 12 25 40 55
10-Rip Kirby app.; Raymond-a (14 pgs.) 4 8 12 28 47 65

MANDRAKE THE MAGICIAN
Marvel Comics: Apr, 1995 - No. 2, May, 1995 ($2.95, unfinished limited series)

1,2: Mike Barr scripts 3.00

MAN-EATING COW (See Tick #7,8)
New England Comics: July, 1992 - No. 10, 1994? ($2.75, B&W, limited series)

1-10 3.00
Man-Eating Cow Bonanza (6/96, $4.95, 128 pgs.)-r/#1-4. 5.00

MAN FROM ATLANTIS (TV)
Marvel Comics: Feb, 1978 - No. 7, Aug, 1978

1-(84 pgs.)-Sutton-a(p), Buscema-c; origin & cast photos 2 4 6 8 12 15
2-7 6.00

MAN FROM PLANET X, THE
Planet X Productions: 1987 (no price; probably unlicensed)

1-Reprints Fawcett Movie Comic 3.00

MAN FROM U.N.C.L.E., THE (TV) (Also see The Girl From Uncle)
Gold Key: Feb, 1965 - No. 22, Apr, 1969 (All photo-c)

1 13 26 39 87 191 295
2-Photo back c-2-8 7 14 21 44 82 120
3-10: 7-Jet Dream begins (1st app., also see Jet Dream) (all new stories) 5 10 15 33 57 80
11-22: 19-Last 12¢ issue. 21,22-Reprint #10 & 7 5 10 15 30 50 70

MAN FROM U.N.C.L.E., THE (TV)
Entertainment Publishing: 1987 - No. 11 ($1.50/$1.75, B&W)

1-7 ($1.50), 8-11 ($1.75) 4.00

MAN FROM WELLS FARGO (TV)
Dell Publishing Co.: No. 1287, Feb-Apr, 1962 - May-July, 1962 (Photo-c)

Four Color 1287, #01-495-207 6 12 18 37 66 95

MANGA DARKCHYLDE (Also see Darkchylde titles)
Dark Horse Comics: Feb, 2005 - No. 5 ($2.99, limited series)

1,2-Randy Queen-s/a; manga-style pre-teen Ariel Chylde 3.00

MANGA SHI (See Tomoe)
Crusade Entertainment: Aug, 1996 ($2.95)

1-Printed back to front (manga-style) 3.00

MANGA SHI 2000
Crusade Entertainment: Feb, 1997 - No. 3, June, 1997 ($2.95, mini-series)

1-3: 1-Two covers 3.00

MANGA ZEN (Also see Zen Intergalactic Ninja)
Zen Comics (Fusion Studios): 1996 - No. 3, 1996 ($2.50, B&W)

1-3 3.00

MANGAZINE
Antarctic Press: Aug, 1985 - No. 5, Dec, 1986 (B&W)

1-5: 1-Soft paper-c 3.00

MANHATTAN PROJECTS, THE
Image Comics: Mar, 2012 - No. 25, Nov, 2014 ($3.50)

1-Hickman-s/Pitarra-a; intro. Robert and Joseph Oppenheimer 40.00
2 20.00
3 10.00
4-6 8.00
7-25: 10,15,19-Browne-a 4.00

MANHATTAN PROJECTS, THE : THE SUN BEYOND THE STARS
Image Comics: Mar, 2015 - No. 4, Feb, 2016 ($3.50)

1-4-Hickman-s/Pitarra-a 3.50

MANHUNT! (Becomes Red Fox #15 on)
Magazine Enterprises: 10/47 - No. 11, 8/48; #13,14, 1953 (no #12)

1-Red Fox by L. B. Cole, Undercover Girl by Whitney, Space Ace begin (1st app.); negligee panels 77 154 231 493 847 1200
2-Electrocution-c 103 206 309 659 1130 1600
3-6: 6-Bondage-c 47 94 141 296 498 700
7-10: 7-Space Ace ends. 8-Trail Colt begins (intro/1st app., 5/48) by Guardineer; Trail Colt-c. 10-G. Ingels-a 39 78 117 231 378 525
11(8/48)-Frazetta-a, 7 pgs.; The Duke, Scotland Yard begin 52 104 156 328 552 775
13(A-1 #63)-Frazetta, r-/Trail Colt #1, 7 pgs. 41 82 123 256 428 600
14(A-1 #77)-Bondage/hypo-c; last L. B. Cole Red Fox; Ingels-a 194 388 582 1242 2121 3000

NOTE: ***Guardineer** a-1-5; c-8. **Whitney** a-2-14; c-1-6, 10. Red Fox by **L. B. Cole**-#1-14. #15 was advertised but came out as Red Fox #15.*

MANHUNTER (See Adventure #58, 73, Brave & the Bold, Detective Comics, 1st Issue Special, House of Mystery #143 and Justice League of America)
DC Comics: 1984 ($2.50, 76 pgs; high quality paper)

1-Simonson-c/a(r)/Detective; Batman app. 5.00

MANHUNTER
DC Comics: July, 1988 - No. 24, Apr, 1990 ($1.00)

1-24: 8,9-Flash app. 9-Invasion. 17-Batman-c/sty 3.00

MANHUNTER
DC Comics: No. 0, Nov, 1994 - No. 12, Nov, 1995 ($1.95/$2.25)

0-12 3.00

MANHUNTER (Also see Batman: Streets of Gotham)
DC Comics: Oct, 2004 - No. 38, Mar, 2009 ($2.50/$2.99)

1-21: 1-Intro. Kate Spencer; Saiz-a/Jae Lee-c/Andreyko-s. 2,3 Shadow Thief app. 13,14-Omac x-over. 20-One Year Later 3.00
22-30: 22-Begin $2.99-c. 23-Sandra Knight app. 27-Chaykin-c. 28-Batman app. 3.00
31-38: 31-(8/08) Gaydos-a. 33,34-Suicide Squad app. 3.00
...: Forgotten (2009, $17.99) r/#31-38 18.00
...: Origins (2007, $17.99) r/#15-23 18.00
...: Street Justice (2005, $12.99) r/#1-5; Andreyko intro. 13.00
...: Trial By Fire (2007, $17.99) r/#6-14 18.00
...: Unleashed (2008, $17.99) r/#24-30 18.00

MANHUNTER: ...
DC Comics: 1979, 1999

The Complete Saga TPB (1979) Reprints stories from Detective Comics #437-443 by Goodwin and Simonson 40.00
The Special Edition TPB (1999, $9.95) r/stories from Detective Comics #437-443 12.00

MANHUNTER SPECIAL (Jack Kirby 100th Birthday tribute)
DC Comics: Oct, 2017 ($4.99, one-shot)

1-Paul Kirk Manhunter & Sandman and Sandy app.; Giffen-s/Buckingham-a; Demon back-up w/Rude-a; bonus Kirby reprint from Tales of the Unexpected #13; Bruce Timm-c 5.00

MANIFEST DESTINY
Image Comics (Skybound): Nov, 2013 - Present ($2.99/$3.99)

1-Lewis & Clark in 1804 American Frontier encountering zombies & other creatures; Chris Dingess-s/Matthew Roberts-a 3 6 9 16 24 32
2 1 3 4 6 8 10
3-30: 25-Back-up Sacagawea story 3.00
31-33-($3.99) 4.00

MANIFEST ETERNITY
DC Comics: Aug, 2006 - No. 6, Jan, 2007 ($2.99)

1-6-Lobdell-s/Nguyen-a/c 3.00

MAN IN BLACK (See Thrill-O-Rama) (Also see All New Comics, Front Page, Green Hornet #31, Strange Story & Tally-Ho Comics)
Harvey Publications: Sept, 1957 - No. 4, Mar, 1958

1-Bob Powell-c/a 18 36 54 105 165 225
2-4: Powell-c/a 14 28 42 80 115 150

MAN IN BLACK

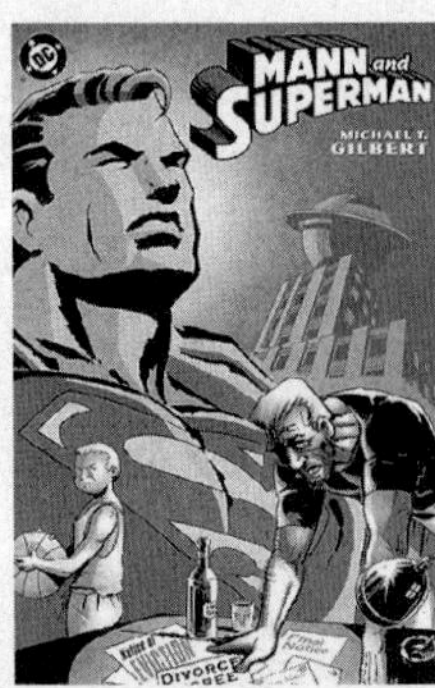

Mann and Superman © DC

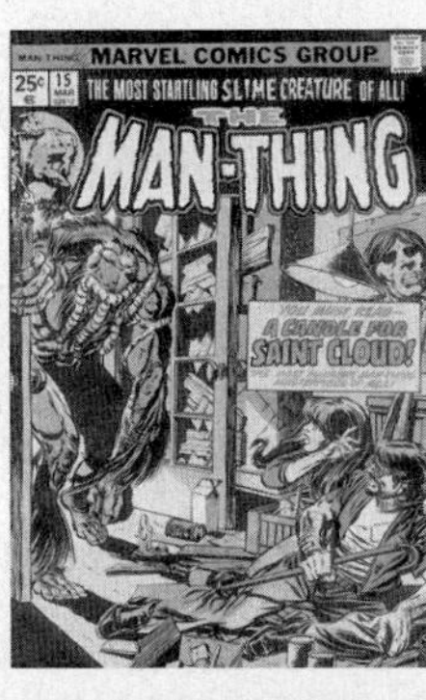

Man-Thing #15 © MAR

Mantra #12 © MAL

GD VG FN VF VF/NM NM-
2.0 4.0 6.0 8.0 9.0 9.2

Lorne-Harvey Publications (Recollections): 1990 - No. 2, July, 1991 (B&W)
1,2 4.00

MAN IN FLIGHT (Disney, TV)
Dell Publishing Co.: No. 836, Sept, 1957
Four Color 836 6 12 18 41 76 110

MAN IN SPACE (Disney, TV, see Dell Giant #27)
Dell Publishing Co.: No. 716, Aug, 1956 - No. 954, Nov, 1958
Four Color 716-A science feat. from Tomorrowland 7 14 21 49 92 135
Four Color 954-Satellites 6 12 18 41 76 110

MANKIND (WWF Wrestling)
Chaos Comics: Sept, 1999 ($2.95, one-shot)
1-Regular and photo-c 3.00
1-Premium Edition ($10.00) Dwayne Turner & Danny Miki-c 10.00

MANN AND SUPERMAN
DC Comics: 2000 ($5.95, prestige format, one-shot)
nn-Michael T. Gilbert-s/a 6.00

MAN OF STEEL, THE (Also see Superman: The Man of Steel)
DC Comics: 1986 (June release) - No. 6, 1986 (75¢, limited series)
1-6: 1-Silver logo; Byrne-c/a/scripts in all; origin, 1-Alternate-c for newsstand sales,1-Distr. to toy stores by So Much Fun, 2-6: 2-Intro. Lois Lane, Jimmy Olsen. 3-Intro/origin Magpie; Batman-c/story. 4-Intro. new Lex Luthor 1 2 3 5 6 8
1-6-Silver Editions (1993, $1.95)-r/1-6 3.00
...The Complete Saga nn (SC)-Contains #1-6, given away in contest; limited edition 4 8 12 28 47 65
NOTE: *Issues 1-6 were released between Action #583 (9/86) & Action #584 (1/87) plus Superman #423 (9/86) & Advs. of Superman #424 (1/87).*

MAN OF THE ATOM (See Solar, Man of the Atom Vol. 2)

MAN OF WAR (See Liberty Guards & Liberty Scouts)
Centaur Publications: Nov, 1941 - No. 2, Jan, 1942
1-The Fire-Man, Man of War, The Sentinel, Liberty Guards, & Vapo-Man begin; Gustavson-c/a; Flag-c 213 426 639 1363 2332 3300
2-Intro The Ferret; Gustavson-c/a 155 310 465 992 1696 2400

MAN OF WAR
Eclipse Comics: Aug, 1987 - No. 3, Feb, 1988 ($1.75, Baxter paper)
1-3: Bruce Jones scripts 3.00

MAN OF WAR (See The Protectors)
Malibu Comics: 1993 - No, 8, Feb, 1994 ($1.95/$2.50/$2.25)
1-5 ($1.95)-Newsstand Editions w/different-c 3.00
1-8: 1-5-Collector's Edi. w/poster. 6-8 ($2.25): 6-Polybagged w/Skycap. 8-Vs. Rocket Rangers 4.00

MAN O' MARS
Fiction House Magazines: 1953; 1964
1-Space Rangers; Whitman-c 90 180 270 576 988 1400
I.W. Reprint #1-r/Man O'Mars #1 & Star Pirate; Murphy Anderson-a 6 12 18 42 79 115

MANTECH ROBOT WARRIORS
Archie Enterprises, Inc.: Sept, 1984 - No. 4, Apr, 1985 (75¢)
1-4: Ayers-c/a(p). 1-Buckler-c(i) 4.00

MAN-THING (See Fear, Giant-Size..., Marvel Comics Presents, Marvel Fanfare, Monsters Unleashed, Power Record Comics & Savage Tales)
Marvel Comics Group: Jan, 1974 - No. 22, Oct, 1975; V2#1, Nov, 1979 - V2#11, July, 1981
1-Howard the Duck(2nd app.) cont'd/Fear #19 7 14 21 48 89 130
2 3 6 9 17 26 35
3-1st app. original Foolkiller 3 6 9 15 22 28
4-Origin Foolkiller; last app. 1st Foolkiller 3 6 9 14 20 26
5-11-Ploog-a. 11-Foolkiller cameo (flashback) 3 6 9 14 20 26
12-22: 19-1st app. Scavenger. 20-Spidey cameo. 21-Origin Scavenger, Man-Thing. 22-Howard the Duck cameo 2 4 6 9 13 16
V2#1(1979) 2 4 6 10 14 18
V2#2-11: 4-Dr. Strange-c/app. 11-Mayerik-a 6.00
NOTE: ***Alcala** a-14. **Brunner** c-1. **J. Buscema** a-12p, 13p, 16p. **Gil Kane** c-4p, 10p, 12-20p, 21. **Mooney** a-17, 18, 19p, 20-22, V2#1-3p. **Ploog** Man-Thing-5p, 6p, 7, 8, 9-11p; c-5, 6, 8, 9, 11. **Sutton** a-13i. No. 19 says #10 in indicia.*

MAN-THING (Volume Three, continues in Strange Tales #1 (9/98))
Marvel Comics: Dec, 1997 - No. 8, July, 1998 ($2.99)
1-8-DeMatteis-s/Sharp-a. 2-Two covers. 6-Howard the Duck-c/app. 3.00

GD VG FN VF VF/NM NM-
2.0 4.0 6.0 8.0 9.0 9.2

MAN-THING (Prequel to 2005 movie)
Marvel Comics: Sept, 2004 - No. 3, Nov, 2004 ($2.99, limited series)
1-3-Hans Rodionoff-s/Kyle Hotz-a 3.00
...: Whatever Knows Fear... (2005, $12.99, TPB) r/#1-3, Savage Tales #1, Adv. Into Fear #16 13.00

MAN-THING
Marvel Comics: May, 2017 - No. 5, Aug, 2017 ($3.99, limited series)
1-5-R.L. Stein-s/German Peralta-a; back-up horror short stories; Stein-s. 1-Origin re-told 4.00

MANTLE
Image Comics: May, 2015 - No. 5, Sept, 2015 ($3.99, limited series)
1-5-Brisson-s/Level-a 4.00

MANTRA
Malibu Comics (Ultraverse): July, 1993 - No. 24, Aug, 1995 ($1.95/$2.50)
1-Polybagged w/trading card & coupon 5.00
1-Newsstand edition w/o trading card or coupon 3.00
1-Full cover holographic edition 2 4 6 8 10 12
1-Ultra-limited silver foil-c 1 2 3 5 6 8
2,3,5-9,11-24: 2-($2.50-Newsstand edition bagged w/card. 3-Intro Warstrike & Kismet. 6-Break-Thru x-over. 7-Prime app.; origin Prototype by Jurgens/Austin (2 pgs.). 11-New costume. 17-Intro NecroMantra & Pinnacle; prelude to Godwheel 3.00
4-($2.50, 48 pgs.)-Rune flip-c/story by B. Smith (3 pgs.) 4.00
10-($3.50, 68 pgs.)-Flip-c w/Ultraverse Premiere #2 4.00
Giant Size 1 (7/94, $2.50, 44 pgs.) 4.00
...Spear of Destiny 1,2 (4/95, $2.50, 36pgs.) 3.00

MANTRA (2nd Series) (Also See Black September)
Malibu Comics (Ultraverse): Infinity, Sept, 1995 - No. 7, Apr, 1996 ($1.50)
Infinity (9/95, $1.50)-Black September x-over, Intro new Mantra 3.00
1-7: 1-(10/95). 5-Return of Eden (original Mantra). 6,7-Rush app. 3.00

MAN WITH NO NAME, THE (Based on the Clint Eastwood gunslinger character)
Dynamite Entertainment: 2008 - No. 11, 2009 ($3.50)
1-11: 1-Gage-s/Dias-a/Isanove-c. 7-Bernard-a 3.50

MAN WITH THE SCREAMING BRAIN (Based on screenplay by Bruce Campbell & David Goodman)
Dark Horse Comics: Apr, 2005 - No. 4, July, 2005 ($2.99, limited series)
1-4-Campbell & Goodman-s; Remender-a/c. 1-Variant-c by Noto. 3-Powell var-c. 4-Mignola var-c 3.00
TPB (11/05, $13.95) r/#1-4; David Goodman intro.; cover gallery 14.00

MAN WITH THE X-RAY EYES, THE (See X,... under Movie Comics)

MANY GHOSTS OF DR. GRAVES, THE (Doctor Graves #73 on)
Charlton Comics: 5/67 - No. 60, 12/76; No. 61, 9/77 - No. 62, 10/77; No. 63, 2/78 - No. 65, 4/78; No. 66, 6/81 - No. 72, 5/82
1-Ditko-a; Palais-a; early issues 12¢-c 8 16 24 52 99 145
2-6,8,10 3 6 9 19 30 40
7,9-Ditko-a 4 8 12 23 37 50
11-13,16-18-Ditko-c/a 3 6 9 19 30 40
14,19,23,25 2 4 6 10 14 18
15,20,21-Ditko-a 3 6 9 14 20 25
22,24,26,27,29-35,38,40-Ditko-c/a 3 6 9 15 22 28
28-Ditko-c 3 6 9 14 20 25
36,46,56,57,59,61,66,67,69,71 2 4 6 8 10 12
37,41,43,51,60-Ditko-a 2 4 6 9 13 16
39,58-Ditko-c. 39-Sutton-a. 58-Ditko-a 2 4 6 9 13 16
42,44,53-Sutton-c; Ditko-a. 42-Sutton-a 2 4 6 9 13 16
45-(5/74) 2nd Newton comic work (8 pgs.); new logo; Sutton-c 2 4 6 11 16 20
47-Newton, Sutton, Ditko-a 2 4 6 10 14 18
48-Ditko, Sutton-a 2 4 6 9 13 16
49-Newton-c/a; Sutton-a. 2 4 6 8 11 14
50-Sutton-a 2 4 6 8 10 12
52-Newton-c; Ditko-a 2 4 6 9 13 16
54-Early Byrne-c; Ditko-a 2 4 6 10 14 18
55-Ditko-c; Sutton-a 2 4 6 9 13 16
62-65,68-Ditko-c/a. 65-Sutton-a 2 4 6 11 16 20
70,72-Ditko-a 2 4 6 10 14 18
Modern Comics Reprint 12,25 (1978) 6.00
NOTE: ***Aparo** a-4, 5, 7, 8, 66r, 69r; c-8, 14, 19, 66r, 67r. **Byrne** c-54. **Ditko** a-1, 7, 9, 11-13, 15-18, 20-22, 24, 26, 27, 29, 30-35, 37, 38, 40-44, 47, 48, 51-54, 58, 60r-65r, 70, 72; c-11-13, 16-18, 22, 24, 26-35, 38, 40, 55, 58, 62-65. **Howard** a-38, 39, 45i, 65; c-48. **Kim** a-36, 46, 52. **Larson** a-58. **Morisi** a-13, 14, 23, 26. **Newton** a-45, 47p, 49p; c-49, 52. **Staton** a-36, 37, 41, 43. **Sutton** a-39, 42, 47-50, 55, 65; c-42, 44, 45; painted c-53. **Zeck** a-56, 59.*

MANY LOVES OF DOBIE GILLIS (TV)

Marc Spector: Moon Knight #34 © MAR

Marge's Little Lulu #44 © M. Buell

Marineman #4 © Ian Churchill

GD VG FN VF VF/NM NM-
2.0 4.0 6.0 8.0 9.0 9.2

National Periodical Publications: May-June, 1960 - No. 26, Oct, 1964
1-Most covers by Bob Oskner 25 50 75 175 388 600
2-5 14 28 42 96 211 325
6-10: 10-Last 10¢-c 10 20 30 69 147 225
11-26: 20-Drucker-a. 24-(3-4/64). 25-(9/64) 9 18 27 61 123 185

MANY WORLDS OF TESLA STRONG, THE (Also see Tom Strong)
America's Best Comics: July, 2003 ($5.95, one-shot)
1-Two covers by Timm & Art Adams; art by various incl. Campbell, Cho, Noto, Hughes 6.00

MARA
Image Comics: Dec, 2012 - No. 6, Oct, 2013 ($2.99)
1-6-Brian Wood-s/Ming Doyle-a 3.00

MARAUDER'S MOON (See Luke Short, Four Color #848)

MARCH OF COMICS (See Promotional Comics section)

MARCH OF CRIME (Formerly My Love Affair #1-6) (See Fox Giants)
Fox Feature Synd.: No. 7, July, 1950 - No. 2, Sept, 1950; No. 3, Sept, 1951
7(#1)(7/50)-True crime stories; Wood-a 44 88 132 277 469 660
2(9/50)-Wood-a (exceptional) 42 84 126 267 451 635
3(9/51) 23 46 69 136 223 310

MARCO POLO (Also see Classic Comics #27
Charlton Comics Group: 1962 (Movie classic)
nn (Scarce)-Glanzman-c/a (25 pgs.) 10 20 30 67 141 215

MARC SILVESTRI SKETCHBOOK
Image Comics (Top Cow): Jan, 2004 ($2.99, one-shot)
1-Character sketches, concept artwork, storyboards of Witchblade, Darkness & others 3.00

MARC SPECTOR: MOON KNIGHT (Also see Moon Knight)
Marvel Comics: June, 1989 - No. 60, Mar, 1994 ($1.50/$1.75, direct sales)
1 1 3 4 6 8 10
2-24,26-49,51-54,58,59: 4-Intro new Midnight. 8,9-Punisher app. 15-Silver Sable app. 19-21-Spider-Man & Punisher app. 32,33-Hobgoblin II (Macendale) & Spider-Man (in black costume) app. 35-38-Punisher story. 42-44-Infinity War x-over. 46-Demogoblin app. 51,53-Gambit app. 55-New look. 57-Spider-Man-c/story. 60-Moon Knight dies 3.00
25,50: 25-(52 pgs.)-Ghost Rider app. 50-(56 pgs.)-Special die-cut-c 4.00
55-New look; Platt-c/a 3 6 9 16 24 32
56,60-Platt-c/a 2 4 6 8 10 12
57-Spider-Man-c/app.; Platt-c/a 3 6 9 17 26 35
58,59-Platt-c 1 2 3 5 6 8
...: Divided We Fall ($4.95, 52 pgs.) 5.00
Special 1 (1992, $2.50) 4.00
NOTE: *Cowan c(p) 20-23. Guice c-20. Heath c/a-4. Platt-a 55-57,60; c-55-60.*

MARGARET O'BRIEN (See The Adventures of...)

MARGE'S LITTLE LULU (Continues as Little Lulu from #207 on)
Dell Publishing Co./Gold Key #165-206: No. 74, 6/45 - No. 164, 7-9/62; No. 165, 10/62 - No. 206, 8/72
Marjorie Henderson Buell, born in Philadelphia, Pa., in 1904, created Little Lulu, a cartoon character that appeared weekly in the Saturday Evening Post from Feb. 23, 1935 through Dec. 30, 1944. She was not responsible for any of the comic books. **John Stanley** did pencils only on all Little Lulu comics through at least #135 (1959). He did pencils and inks on Four Color #74 & 97. **Irving Tripp** began inking stories from #1 on, and remained the comic's illustrator throughout its entire run. **Stanley** did storyboards (layouts), pencils, and scripts in all cases and inking only on covers. His word balloons were written in cursive. **Tripp** and occasionally other artists at Western Publ. in Poughkeepsie, N.Y. blew up the pencilled pages, inked the blowups, and lettered them. **Arnold Drake** did storyboards, pencils and scripts starting with #197 (1970) on, amidst reprinted issues. **Buell** sold her rights exclusively to Western Publ. in Dec., 1971. The earlier issues had to be approved by **Buell** prior to publication.
Four Color 74('45)-Intro Lulu, Tubby & Alvin 179 358 537 1477 3339 5200
Four Color 97(2/46) 68 136 204 544 1222 1900
(Above two books are all John Stanley - cover, pencils, and inks.)
Four Color 110('46)-1st Alvin Story Telling Time; 1st app. Willy; variant cover exists
41 82 123 303 689 1075
Four Color 115-1st app. Boys' Clubhouse 40 80 120 296 673 1050
Four Color 120, 131: 120-1st app. Eddie 35 70 105 252 564 875
Four Color 139('47),146,158 33 66 99 238 532 825
Four Color 165 (10/47)-Smokes doll hair & has wild hallucinations. 1st Tubby detective story
33 66 99 238 532 825
1(1-2/48)-Lulu's Diary feature begins 71 142 213 568 1284 2000
2-1st app. Gloria; 1st app. Miss Feeny 31 62 93 223 499 775
3-5 27 54 81 194 435 675
6-10: 7-1st app. Annie; Xmas-c 21 42 63 150 330 510
11-20: 18-X-Mas-c. 19-1st app. Wilbur. 20-1st app. Mr. McNabbem
17 34 51 114 252 390
21-30: 26-r/F.C. 110. 30-Xmas-c 15 30 45 100 220 340
31-38,40: 35-1st Mumday story 12 24 36 81 176 270
39-Intro. Witch Hazel in "That Awful Witch Hazel" 12 24 36 82 179 275
41-60: 42-Xmas-c. 45-2nd Witch Hazel app. 49-Gives Stanley & others credit
10 20 30 69 147 225
61-80: 63-1st app. Chubby (Tubby's cousin). 68-1st app. Prof. Cleff. 78-Xmas-c. 80-Intro. Little Itch (2/55) 9 18 27 57 111 165
81-99: 90-Xmas-c 7 14 21 46 86 125
100 7 14 21 49 92 135
101-130: 123-1st app. Fifi 6 12 18 37 66 95
131-164: 135-Last Stanley-p 5 10 15 33 57 80
165-Giant; ...in Paris ('62) 9 18 27 61 123 185
166-Giant; ...Christmas Diary (1962 - '63) 9 18 27 61 123 185
167-169 4 8 12 28 47 65
170,172,175,176,178-196,198-200-Stanley-r. 182-1st app. Little Scarecrow Boy
3 6 9 17 26 35
171,173,174,177,197 3 6 9 16 23 30
201,203,206-Last issue to carry Marge's name 3 6 9 14 20 26
202,204,205-Stanley-r 3 6 9 16 23 30
...Summer Camp 1(8/67-G.K.-Giant) '57-58-r 5 10 15 35 63 90
...Trick 'N' Treat 1(12¢)(12/62-Gold Key) 6 12 18 40 73 105
Marge's Lulu and Tubby in Japan (15¢)(5-7/62) 01476-207
7 14 21 46 86 125
NOTE: *See Dell Giant Comics #23, 29, 36, 42, 50, & Dell Giants for annuals. All Giants not by Stanley from L.L. on Vacation (7/54) on. Irving Tripp a-#1-on. Christmas c-7, 18, 30, 42, 78, 90, 126, 166, 250. Summer Camp issues #173, 177, 181, 189, 197, 201, 206.*

MARGE'S LITTLE LULU (See Golden Comics Digest #19, 23, 27, 29, 33, 36, 40, 43, 46, & March of Comics #251, 267, 275, 293, 307, 323, 335, 349, 355, 369, 385, 406, 417, 427, 439, 456, 468, 475, 488)

MARGE'S TUBBY (Little Lulu)(See Dell Giants)
Dell Publishing Co./Gold Key: No. 381, Aug, 1952 - No. 49, Dec-Feb, 1961-62
Four Color 381(#1)-Stanley script; Irving Tripp-a 18 36 54 126 281 435
Four Color 430,444-Stanley-a 11 22 33 73 157 240
Four Color 461 (4/53)-1st Tubby & Men From Mars story; Stanley-a
10 20 30 68 144 220
5 (7-9/53)-Stanley-a 8 16 24 54 102 150
6-10 7 14 21 44 82 120
11-20 5 10 15 34 60 85
21-30 5 10 15 30 50 70
31-49 4 8 12 27 44 60
...& the Little Men From Mars No. 30020-410(10/64-G.K.)-25¢, 68 pgs.
7 14 21 44 82 120
NOTE: ***John Stanley** did all storyboards & scripts through at least #35 (1959). **Lloyd White** did all art except F.C. 381, 430, 444, 461 & #5.*

MARGIE (See My Little...)

MARGIE (TV)
Dell Publ. Co.: No. 1307, Mar-May, 1962 - No. 2, July-Sept, 1962 (Photo-c)
Four Color 1307(#1) 6 12 18 41 76 110
2 4 8 12 28 47 65

MARGIE COMICS (Formerly Comedy Comics; Reno Browne #50 on)
(Also see Cindy Comics & Teen Comics)
Marvel Comics (ACI): No. 35, Winter, 1946-47 - No. 49, Dec, 1949
35 30 60 90 177 289 400
36-38,42,45,47-49 16 32 48 94 147 200
39,41,43(2),44,46-Kurtzman's "Hey Look" 17 34 51 100 158 215
40-Three "Hey Looks", three "Giggles 'n' Grins" by Kurtzman
19 38 57 109 172 235

MARINEMAN (Ian Churchill's...)
Image Comics: Dec, 2010 - No. 6, Jun, 2011 ($3.99/$4.99)
1-5-Ian Churchill-s/a/c 4.00
6-($4.99) Origin revealed 5.00

MARINES (See Tell It to the...)

MARINES ATTACK
Charlton Comics: Aug, 1964 - No. 9, Feb-Mar, 1966
1-Glanzman-a begins 4 8 12 23 37 50
2-9: 8-1st Vietnam war-c/story 3 6 9 16 23 30

MARINES AT WAR (Formerly Tales of the Marines #4)
Atlas Comics (OPI): No. 5, Apr, 1957 - No. 7, Aug, 1957
5-7 15 30 45 83 124 165
NOTE: ***Colan** a-5. **Drucker** a-5. **Everett** a-5. **Maneely** a-5. **Orlando** a-7. **Severin** c-5.*

MARINES IN ACTION
Atlas News Co.: June, 1955 - No. 14, Sept, 1957
1-Rock Murdock, Boot Camp Brady begin 21 42 63 122 199 275

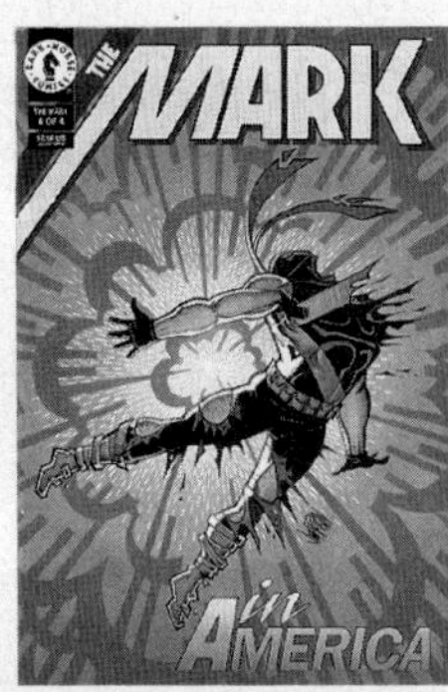

The Mark #4 © DH

The Marquis: Danse Macabre #2 © Guy Davis

Mars Attacks Baseball Special #1 © Topps

GD 2.0 | VG 4.0 | FN 6.0 | VF 8.0 | VF/NM 9.0 | NM- 9.2

2-14 15 30 45 83 124 165
NOTE: *Berg a-2, 8, 9, 11, 14. Heath c-2, 9. Maneely c-1, 3. Severin a-4; c-7-11, 14.*

MARINES IN BATTLE
Atlas Comics (ACI No. 1-12/WPI No. 13-25): Aug, 1954 - No. 25, Sept, 1958

1-Heath-c; Iron Mike McGraw by Heath; history of U.S. Marine Corps. begins
36 72 108 211 343 475
2-Heath-c 18 36 54 107 169 230
3-6,8-10: 4-Last precode (2/55); Romita-a 15 30 45 85 130 175
7-Kubert/Moskowitz-a (6 pgs.) 15 30 45 86 133 180
11-16,18-21,24 15 30 45 83 124 165
17-Williamson-a (3 pgs.) 15 30 45 88 137 185
22,25-Torres-a 15 30 45 83 124 165
23-Crandall-a; Mark Murdock app. 15 30 45 84 127 170
NOTE: *Berg a-22. G. Colan a-22, 23. Drucker a-6. Everett a-4, 15; c-21. Heath c-1, 2, 4. Maneely c-23, 24. Orlando a-14. Pakula a-6, 23. Powell a-16. Severin a-22; c-12. Sinnott a-23. Tuska a-15.*

MARINE WAR HEROES (Charlton Premiere #19 on)
Charlton Comics: Jan, 1964 - No. 18, Mar, 1967

1-Montes/Bache-c/a 4 8 12 23 37 50
2-16,18: 11-Vietnam sty w/VC tunnels & moles.14,18-Montes/Bache-a
3 6 9 16 23 30
17-Tojo's plan to bomb Pearl Harbor & 1st Atomic bomb blast on Japan
4 8 12 23 37 50

MARK, THE (Also see Mayhem)
Dark Horse Comics: Dec, 1993 - No. 4, Mar, 1994 ($2.50, limited series)

1-4 3.00

MARK HAZZARD: MERC
Marvel Comics Group: Nov, 1986 - No. 12, Oct, 1987 (75¢)

1-12: Morrow-a 3.00
Annual 1 (11/87, $1.25) 4.00

MARK OF CHARON (See Negation)
CG Entertainment: Apr, 2003 - No. 5, Aug, 2003 ($2.95, limited series)

1-5-Bedard-s/Bennett-a 3.00

MARK OF ZORRO (See Zorro, Four Color #228)

MARK 1 COMICS (Also see Shaloman)
Mark 1 Comics: Apr, 1988 - No. 3, Mar, 1989 ($1.50)

1-3: Early Shaloman app. 2-Origin 3.00

MARKSMAN, THE (Also see Champions)
Hero Comics: Jan, 1988 - No. 5, 1988 ($1.95)

1-5: 1-Rose begins. 1-3-Origin The Marksman 3.00
Annual 1 ('88, $2.75, 52 pgs.)-Champions app. 4.00

MARK TRAIL
Standard Magazines (Hall Syndicate)/Fawcett Publ. No. 5: Oct, 1955; No. 5, Summer, 1959

1(1955)-Sunday strip-r 7 14 21 37 46 55
5(1959) By Ed Dodd 5 10 15 22 26 30
...Adventure Book of Nature 1 (Summer, 1958, 25¢, Pines)-100 pg. Giant; Special Camp Issue; contains 78 Sunday strip-r by Ed Dodd 9 18 27 52 69 85

MARMADUKE MONK
I. W. Enterprises/Super Comics: No date; 1963 (10¢)

I.W. Reprint 1 (nd) 2 4 6 8 11 14
Super Reprint 14 (1963)-r/Monkeyshines Comics #? 2 4 6 8 10 12

MARMADUKE MOUSE
Quality Comics Group (Arnold Publ.): Spring, 1946 - No. 65, Dec, 1956 (Early issues: 52 pgs.)

1-Funny animal 20 40 60 114 182 250
2 12 24 36 69 97 125
3-10 10 20 30 56 76 95
11-30 8 16 24 42 54 65
31-65: Later issues are 36 pgs. 7 14 21 35 43 50
Super Reprint #14(1963) 2 4 6 9 12 15

MARQUIS, THE
Oni Press

...: A Sin of One ($2.99, 5/03) Guy Davis-s/a; Michael Gaydos-c 3.00
...: Intermezzo TPB ($11.95, 12/03) r/A Sin of One and Hell's Courtesan #1,2 12.00

MARQUIS, THE: DANSE MACABRE
Oni Press: May, 2000 - No. 5, Feb, 2001 ($2.95, B&W, limited series)

1-5-Guy Davis-s/a. 1-Wagner-c. 2-Mignola-c. 3-Vess-c. 5-K. Jones-c 3.00
TPB (8/2001, $18.95) r/1-5 & Les Preludes; Seagle intro. 19.00

GD 2.0 | VG 4.0 | FN 6.0 | VF 8.0 | VF/NM 9.0 | NM- 9.2

MARQUIS, THE: DEVIL'S REIGN: HELL'S COURTESAN
Oni Press: Feb, 2002 - No. 2, Apr, 2002 ($2.95, B&W, limited series)

1,2-Guy Davis-s/a 3.00

MARRIAGE OF HERCULES AND XENA, THE
Topps Comics: July, 1998 ($2.95, one-shot)

1-Photo-c; Lopresti-a; Alex Ross pin-up, 1-Alex Ross painted-c 3.00
1-Gold foil logo-c 5.00

MARRIED ... WITH CHILDREN (TV)(Based on Fox TV show)
Now Comics: June, 1990 - No. 7, Feb, 1991(12/90 inside) ($1.75)
V2#1, Sept, 1991 - No. 7, Apr, 1992 ($1.95)

1-7: 2-Photo-c, 1,2-2nd printing, V2#1-7: 1,4,6-Photo-c 3.00
...Buck's Tale (6/94, $1.95) 3.00
...1994 Annual nn (2/94, $2.50, 52 pgs.)-Flip book format 4.00
Special 1 (7/92, $1.95)-Kelly Bundy photo-c/poster 3.00

MARRIED ... WITH CHILDREN: KELLY BUNDY
Now Comics: Aug, 1992 - No. 3, Oct, 1992 ($1.95, limited series)

1-3: Kelly Bundy photo-c & poster in each 3.00

MARRIED ... WITH CHILDREN: QUANTUM QUARTET
Now Comics: Oct, 1993 - No. 4, 1994, ($1.95, limited series)

1-4: Fantastic Four parody 3.00

MARRIED ... WITH CHILDREN: 2099
Now Comics: June, 1993 - No. 3, Aug, 1993 ($1.95, limited series)

1-3 3.00

MARS
First Comics: Jan, 1984 - No. 12, Jan, 1985 ($1.00, Mando paper)

1-12: Marc Hempel & Mark Wheatley story & art. 2-The Black Flame begins. 10-Dynamo Joe begins 3.00
TPB (IDW Publ., 8/05, $39.99) r/#1-12, creator commentary; bonus art; new Hempel-c 40.00

MARS & BEYOND (Disney, TV)
Dell Publishing Co.: No. 866, Dec, 1957

Four Color 866-A Science feat. from Tomorrowland 7 14 21 49 92 135

MARS ATTACKS
Topps Comics: May, 1994 - No. 5, Sept, 1994 ($2.95, limited series)

1-5-Giffen story; flip books 2 4 6 8 10 12
Special Edition 2 4 6 9 12 15
Trade paperback (12/94, $12.95)-r/limited series plus new 8 pg. story 15.00

MARS ATTACKS
Topps Comics: V2#1, 8/95 - V2#3, 10/95; V2#4, 1/96 - No. 7, 5/96($2.95, bi-monthly #6 on)

V2#1-7: 1-Counterstrike storyline begins. 4-(1/96). 5-(1/96). 5,7-Brereton-c. 6-(3/96)-Simonson-c. 7-Story leads into Baseball Special #1 5.00
Baseball Special 1 (6/96, $2.95)-Bisley-c. 5.00

MARS ATTACKS
IDW Publishing: Jun, 2012 - No. 10, May, 2013 ($3.99, issues #6-10 polybagged with card)

1-10: 1-Layman-s/McCrea-a; 58 covers including all 54 cards from 1962 set 4.00
... #1 IDW's Greatest Hits Edition (3/16, $1.00) reprints #1 3.00
... Art Gallery (9/14, $3.99) Trading card style art by various 4.00
...: Classics Obliterated (6/13, $7.99) Spoofs of Moby Dick, Jeckll & Hyde, Robinson Crusoe 8.00
... KISS (1/13, $3.99) Ryall-s/Robinson-a; 2 variant-c with Judge Dredd & Star Slammers 4.00
... Popeye (1/13, $3.99) Beatty-a; 2 variant-c with Miss Fury & Opus 4.00
... The Holidays (10/12, $7.99) short stories for Halloween-Christmas; 5 covers 8.00
... The Real Ghostbusters (1/13, $3.99) Holder-a; 2 variant-c with Chew & Madman 4.00
... : The Transformers (1/13, $3.99) 2 variant-c with Spike & Strangers in Paradise 4.00
... Zombie vs. Robots (1/13, $3.99) Ryall-s; 2 variant-c with Rog-2000 & Cerebus 4.00

MARS ATTACKS FIRST BORN
IDW Publishing: May, 2014 - No. 4, Aug, 2014 ($3.99, limited series)

1-4-Chris Ryall-s/Sam Kieth-a; multiple covers on each 4.00

MARS ATTACKS HIGH SCHOOL
Topps Comics: May, 1997 - No. 2, Sept, 1997 ($2.95, B&W, limited series)

1,2-Stelfreeze-c 4.00

MARS ATTACKS JUDGE DREDD
IDW Publishing: Sept, 2013 - No. 4, Dec, 2013 ($3.99, limited series)

1-4-Al Ewing-s/John McCrea-a/Greg Staples-c 4.00

MARS ATTACKS IMAGE
Topps Comics: Dec, 1996 - No. 4, Mar, 1997 ($2.50, limited series)

1-4-Giffen-s/Smith & Sienkiewicz-a 4.00

Martian Manhunter (2015 series) #12 © DC

Marvel Adventures #15 © MAR

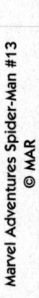

Marvel Adventures Spider-Man #13 © MAR

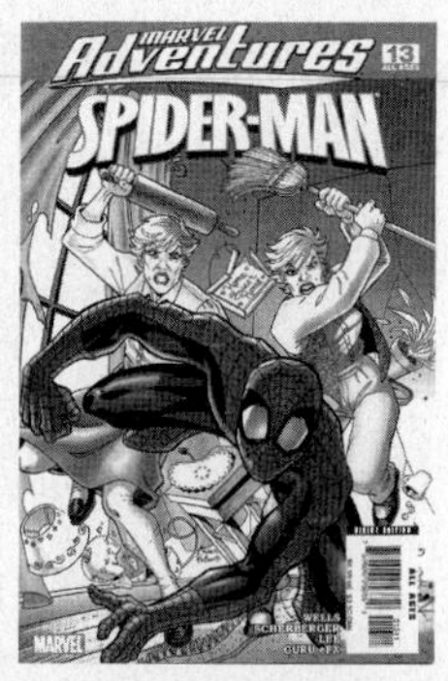

GD 2.0 | VG 4.0 | FN 6.0 | VF 8.0 | VF/NM 9.0 | NM- 9.2

MARS ATTACKS: OCCUPATION
IDW Publishing: Mar, 2016 - No. 5, Jul, 2016 ($3.99, limited series)
1-5-John Layman-s/Andy Kuhn-a; multiple covers 4.00

MARS ATTACKS THE SAVAGE DRAGON
Topps Comics: Dec, 1996 - No. 4, Mar, 1997 ($2.95, limited series)
1-4: 1-w/bound-in card 4.00

MARSHAL BLUEBERRY (See Blueberry)
Marvel Comics (Epic Comics): 1991 ($14.95, graphic novel)
1-Moebius-a 3 6 9 19 30 40

MARSHAL LAW (Also see Crime And Punishment: Marshall Law...)
Marvel Comics (Epic Comics): Oct, 1987 - No. 6, May, 1989 ($1.95, mature)
1-6 3.00

M.A.R.S. PATROL TOTAL WAR (Formerly Total War #1,2)
Gold Key: No. 3, Sept, 1966 - No. 10, Aug, 1969 (All-Painted-c except #7)
3-Wood-a; aliens invade USA 5 10 15 35 63 90
4-10 4 8 12 23 37 50
Wally Wood's M.A.R.S. Patrol Total War TPB (Dark Horse, 9/04, $12.95) r/#3 & Total War #1&2; foreward by Batton Lash; afterword by Dan Adkins 13.00

MARTHA WASHINGTON (Also see Dark Horse Presents Fifth Anniversary Special, Dark Horse Presents #100-4, Give Me Liberty, Happy Birthday Martha Washington & San Diego Comicon Comics #2)

MARTHA WASHINGTON... (one-shots)
Dark Horse Comics (Legend): ($2.95/$3.50, one-shots)
... Dies (7/07, $3.50) Miller-s/Gibbons-a; r/Miller's original outline for Give Me Liberty 4.00
... Stranded in Space (11/95, $2.95) Miller-s/Gibbons-a; Big Guy app. 5.00

MARTHA WASHINGTON GOES TO WAR
Dark Horse Comics (Legend): May, 1994 - No. 5, Sep, 1994 ($2.95, lim. series)
1-5-Miller scripts; Gibbons-c/a 5.00
TPB ($17.95) r/#1-5 18.00

MARTHA WASHINGTON SAVES THE WORLD
Dark Horse Comics: Dec, 1997 - No. 3, Feb, 1998 ($2.95/$3.95, lim. series)
1,2-Miller scripts; Gibbons-c/a in all 5.00
3-($3.95) 5.00

MARTHA WAYNE (See The Story of...)

MARTIAN MANHUNTER (See Detective Comics & Showcase '95 #9)
DC Comics: May, 1988 - No. 4, Aug,. 1988 ($1.25, limited series)
1-4: 1,4-Batman app. 2-Batman cameo 4.00
Special 1-(1996, $3.50) 4.00

MARTIAN MANHUNTER (See JLA)
DC Comics: No. 0, Oct, 1998 - No. 36, Nov, 2001 ($1.99)
0-(10/98) Origin retold; Ostrander-s/Mandrake-c/a 3.00
1-36: 1-(12/98). 6-9-JLA app. 18,19-JSA app. 24-Mahnke-a 3.00
#1,000,000 (11/98) 853rd Century x-over 3.00
Annual 1,2 (1998,1999; $2.95) 1-Ghosts; Wrightson-c. 2-JLApe 4.00

MARTIAN MANHUNTER (See DCU Brave New World)
DC Comics: Oct, 2006 - No. 8, May, 2007 ($2.99, limited series)
1-8-Lieberman-s/Barrionuevo-a/c 3.00
...: The Others Among Us TPB (2007, $19.99) r/#1-8 & story from DCU Brave New World 20.00

MARTIAN MANHUNTER
DC Comics: Aug, 2015 - No. 12, Jul, 2016 ($2.99)
1-12: 1-Rob Williams-s/Eddy Barrows-a. 1-3-JLA app. 10-Origin 3.00

MARTIAN MANHUNTER: AMERICAN SECRETS
DC Comics: 1992 - Book Three, 1992 ($4.95, limited series, prestige format)
1-3: Barreto-a 5.00

MARTIAN MANHUNTER/ MARVIN THE MARTIAN SPECIAL
DC Comics: Aug, 2017 ($4.99, one-shot)
1-Orlando & Barbiere-s/Lopresti-a; covers by Lopresti & DeStefano 5.00

MARTIN KANE (William Gargan as... Private Eye)(Stage/Screen/Radio/TV)
Fox Feature Syndicate (Hero Books): No. 4, June, 1950 - No. 2, Aug, 1950 (Formerly My Secret Affair)
4(#1)-True crime stories; Wood-c/a(2); used in **SOTI**, pg. 160; photo back-c
39 78 117 231 378 525
2-Wood/Orlando story, 5 pgs; Wood-a(2) 27 54 81 158 259 360

MARTIN LUTHER KING AND THE MONTGOMERY STORY (See Promotional Comics section)

MARTIN MYSTERY
Dark Horse (Bonelli Comics): Mar, 1999 - No. 6, Aug, 1999 ($4.95, B&W, digest size)
1-6-Reprints Italian series in English; Gibbons-c on #1-3 5.00

MARTY MOUSE
I. W. Enterprises: No date (1958?) (10¢)
1-Reprint 2 4 6 9 12 15

MARVEL ACTION HOUR FEATURING IRON MAN (TV cartoon)
Marvel Comics: Nov, 1994 - No. 8, June, 1995 ($1.50/$2.95)
1-8: Based on cartoon series 3.00
1 ($2.95)-Polybagged w/16 pg Marvel Action Hour Preview & acetate print 4.00

MARVEL ACTION HOUR FEATURING THE FANTASTIC FOUR (TV cartoon)
Marvel Comics: Nov, 1994 - No. 8, June, 1995 ($1.50/$2.95)
1-8: Based on cartoon series 3.00
1-($2.95)-Polybagged w/ 16 pg. Marvel Action Hour Preview & acetate print 4.00

MARVEL ACTION UNIVERSE (TV cartoon)
Marvel Comics: Jan, 1989 ($1.00, one-shot)
1-r/Spider-Man And His Amazing Friends 4.00

MARVEL ADVENTURES
Marvel Comics: Apr, 1997 - No. 18, Sept, 1998 ($1.50)
1-18-"Animated style": 1,4,7-Hulk-c/app. 2,11-Spider-Man. 3,8,15-X-Men. 5-Spider-Man & X-Men. 6-Spider-Man & Human Torch. 9,12-Fantastic Four. 10,16-Silver Surfer. 13-Spider-Man & Silver Surfer. 14-Hulk & Dr. Strange. 18-Capt. America 3.00

MARVEL ADVENTURES...
Marvel Comics: 2007, 2008 (Free Comic Book Day giveaways)
... Free Comic Book Day 2007 (6/07) 1-Iron Man, Hulk and Franklin Richards app. 3.00
... Free Comic Book Day 2008 - Iron Man, Hulk, Ant-Man and Spider-Man app. 3.00

MARVEL ADVENTURES FANTASTIC FOUR (All ages title)
Marvel Comics: No. 0, July, 2005 - No. 48, July, 2009 ($1.99/$2.50/$2.99)
0-($1.99) Movie version characters; Dr. Doom app.; Eaton-a 3.00
1-10-($2.50) 1-Skrulls app.; Pagulayan-a. 7-Namor app. 3.00
11-48-($2.99) 12,42-Dr. Doom app. 24-Namor app. 26,28-Silver Surfer app. 3.00
... Vol. 1: Family of Heroes (2005, $6.99, digest) r/#1-4 7.00
... Vol. 2: Fantastic Voyages (2006, $6.99, digest) r/#5-8 7.00
... Vol. 3: World's Greatest (2006, $6.99, digest) r/#9-12 7.00
... Vol. 4: Cosmic Threats (2006, $6.99, digest) r/#13-16 7.00
... Vol. 5: All 4 One, 4 For All (2007, $6.99, digest) r/#17-20 7.00
... Vol. 6: Monsters & Mysteries (2007, $6.99, digest) r/#21-24 7.00
... Vol. 7: The Silver Surfer (2007, $6.99, digest) r/#25-28 7.00
... Vol. 8: Monsters, Moles, Cowboys & Coupons (2008, $7.99, digest) r/#29-32 8.00

MARVEL ADVENTURES FLIP MAGAZINE (All ages title)
Marvel Comics: Aug, 2005 - No. 26, Sept, 2007 ($3.99/$4.99)
1-11: 1-10-Rep. Marvel Advs. Fantastic Four and Marvel Advs. Spider-Man in flip format 4.00
12-14-($4.99) Reprints Marvel Advs. Spider-Man & X-Men/Power Pack in flip format 5.00
15-26-Rep. Marvel Advs. Fantastic Four and Marvel Advs. Spider-Man in flip format 5.00

MARVEL ADVENTURES HULK (All ages title)
Marvel Comics: Sept, 2007 - No. 16, Dec, 2008 ($2.99)
1-16: 1-New version of Hulk's origin; Pagulayan-c. 2-Jamie Madrox app. 13-Mummies 3.00
... Vol. 1: Misunderstood Monster (2007, $6.99, digest) r/#1-4 7.00

MARVEL ADVENTURES IRON MAN (All ages title)
Marvel Comics: July, 2007 - No. 13, Jul, 2008 ($2.99)
1-13: 1-4-Michael Golden-c. 1-New version of Iron Man's origin. 2-Intro. the Mandarin 3.00
... Vol. 1: Heart of Steel (2007, $6.99, digest) r/#1-4 7.00
... Vol. 2: Iron Armory (2008, $7.99, digest) r/#5-8 8.00

MARVEL ADVENTURES SPIDER-MAN (All ages title)
Marvel Comics: May, 2005 - No. 61, May, 2010 ($2.50/$2.99)
1-13-Lee & Ditko stories retold with new art. 13-Conner-c 3.00
14-48: 14-Begin $2.99-c. 14-16-Conner-c. 22,23-Black costume. 35-Venom app. 3.00
50-($3.99) Sinister Six app.; back-up w/Sonny Liew-a 4.00
51-61: 53-Emma Frost becomes a regular; intro. Chat; Skottie Young-c begin 3.00
... Vol. 1 HC (2006, $19.99, with dustjacket) r/#1-8; plot for #7; sketch pages from #6,8 20.00
... Vol. 1: The Sinister Six (2005, $6.99, digest) r/#1-4 7.00
... Vol. 2: Power Struggle (2005, $6.99, digest) r/#5-8 7.00
... Vol. 3: Doom With a View (2006, $6.99, digest) r/#9-12 7.00
... Vol. 4: Concrete Jungle (2006, $6.99, digest) r/#13-16 7.00
... Vol. 5: Monsters on the Prowl (2007, $6.99, digest) r/#17-20 7.00
... Vol. 6: The Black Costume (2007, $6.99, digest) r/#21-24 7.00
... Vol. 7: Secret Identity (2007, $6.99, digest) r/#25-28 7.00
... Vol. 8: Forces of Nature (2008, $7.99, digest) r/#29-32 8.00

Marvel Adventures Super Heroes #2 © MAR

Marvel Age #41 © MAR

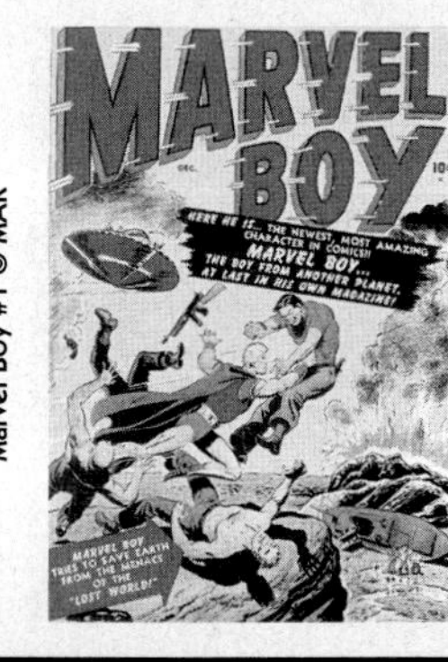

Marvel Boy #1 © MAR

	GD 2.0	VG 4.0	FN 6.0	VF 8.0	VF/NM 9.0	NM- 9.2

GD VG FN VF VF/NM NM-
2.0 4.0 6.0 8.0 9.0 9.2

... Vol. 9: Fiercest Foes (2008, $7.99, digest) r/#33-36 — 8.00

MARVEL ADVENTURES SPIDER-MAN (All ages title)
Marvel Comics: June, 2010 - No. 24, May, 2012 ($3.99/$2.99)

1-($3.99) Tobin-s; Franklin Richards back-up — 4.00
2-23-($2.99): 3,7-Wolverine app. 3,4-Bullseye app. 6-Doctor Octopus app. — 3.00

MARVEL ADVENTURES STARRING DAREDEVIL (...Adventure #3 on)
Marvel Comics Group: Dec, 1975 - No. 6, Oct, 1976

1 — 2 4 6 13 18 22
2-6-r/Daredevil #22-27 by Colan. 3-5-(25¢-c) — 1 3 4 6 8 10
3-5-(30¢-c variants, limited distribution)(4,6,8/76) — 5 10 15 33 57 80

MARVEL ADVENTURES SUPER HEROES (All ages title)
Marvel Comics: Sept, 2008 - No. 21, May, 2010 ($2.99)

1-21: 1-4: Spider-Man, Hulk and Iron Man team-ups. 1-Hercules app. 5-Dr. Strange app. 6-Ant-Man origin re-told. 7-Thor. 8,12-Capt. America. 17-Avengers begin — 3.00

MARVEL ADVENTURES SUPER HEROES (All ages title)
Marvel Comics: June, 2010 - No. 24, May, 2012 ($3.99/$2.99)

1-($3.99) Iron Man and Avengers vs. Magneto — 4.00
2-24-($2.99) 4-Deadpool app. 5-Rhino app. 11,12,22-Hulk app. 13,14,19-Thor — 3.00

MARVEL ADVENTURES THE AVENGERS (All ages title)
Marvel Comics: July, 2006 - No. 39, Oct, 2009 ($2.99)

1-39-Spider-Man, Wolverine, Hulk, Iron Man, Capt. America, Storm, Giant-Girl app. — 3.00
... Vol. 1: Heroes Assembled (2006, $6.99, digest) r/#1-4 — 7.00
... Vol. 2: Mischief (2007, $6.99, digest) r/#5-8 — 7.00
... Vol. 3: Bizarre Adventures (2007, $6.99, digest) r/#9-12 — 7.00
... Vol. 4: The Dream Team (2007, $6.99, digest) r/#13-15 & Giant-Size #1 — 7.00
... Vol. 5: Some Assembling Required (2008, $7.99, digest) r/#16-19 — 8.00

MARVEL ADVENTURES TWO-IN-ONE
Marvel Comics: Oct, 2007 - No. 18 ($4.99, bi-weekly)

1-18: 1-9-Reprints Marvel Adventures Spider-Man and Fantastic Four stories. 10-Hulk — 5.00

MARVEL AGE (The Official Marvel News Magazine)
(A low priced news Magazine in comic format to promote coming issues)
Marvel Publications: Apr, 1983 - No. 140, Sept, 1994

1-Saga of Crystar-c/s — 1 2 3 5 7 9
2-5 — 3.00
6,7,9,11,14,15 — 3.00
8-Stan Lee/Jim Shooter-c/interviews — 6.00
10-Star Wars-c, preview Spider-Man vs. Hobgoblin — 2 4 6 8 10 12
12-(3/84) 2 pg. preview/1st app. of Spider-Man in Alien Venom black costume, 2 months before Amazing Spider-Man #252 — 3 6 9 14 20 25
13,14 — 5.00
16-New Mutants-c/s — 1 2 3 5 6 8
17-24 — 3.00
25(4/85)-Rocket Raccoon-c/preview art one month before issue #1 — 1 3 4 6 8 10
26-37,39,40 — 3.00
38-He-Man & Masters of the Universe-c/preview — 1 3 4 6 8 10
41(8/86)-Classic Stan Lee-c/sty — 5 10 15 31 53 75
42-52,54-66 — 3.00
53-Girls of Marvel swimsuits-c — 6.00
67-Jim Lee-c, Wolverine/punisher/Sub-Mariner-c/s — 6.00
68-75,77-89 — 5.00
76-She-Hulk swimsuit-c by John Byrne — 1 2 3 5 6 8
90(7/90)-Spider-Man-c by Todd McFarlane; Jim Lee Interview — 2 4 6 9 12 15
91-Thanos and Silver Surfer-c — 2 4 6 8 10 12
92-94,96,98,100-103,105-137,139 — 3.00
95-Captain America 50th Anniversary-c/issue — 6.00
97(2/91)-Darkhawk-c/preview — 2 4 6 9 12 15
99(4/91)-Black Panther Returns-c — 1 2 3 5 6 8
104-Wolverine-c by Jim Lee — 6.00
138(7/94)-Deadpool, Cable-c — 2 4 6 9 12 15
140-Last issue — 7.00
Annual 1(9/85) — 6.00
Annual 2, 3(9/87) — 4.00
Annual 4(6/88)-1st app. Damage Control — 1 3 4 6 8 10

MARVEL AGE FANTASTIC FOUR (All ages title)
Marvel Comics: Jun, 2004 - No. 12, Mar, 2005 ($2.25)

1-12-Lee & Kirby stories retold with new art by various. 11-Impossible Man app. — 3.00
...Tales (4/05, $2.25) retells first meeting with the Black Panther; O'Hare & Lim-a — 3.00
Vol. 1: All For One TPB (2004, $5.99, digest size) r/#1-4 — 6.00
Vol. 2: Doom TPB (2004, $5.99, digest size) r/#5-8 — 6.00
Vol. 3: The Return of Doctor Doom TPB (2005, $5.99, digest size) r/#9-12 — 6.00

MARVEL AGE HULK (All ages title)
Marvel Comics: Nov, 2004 - No. 4, Feb, 2005 ($1.75)

1-3-Lee & Kirby stories retold with new art by various — 3.00
Vol. 1: Incredible TPB (2005, $5.99, digest size) r/#1-4 — 6.00
Vol. 2: Defenders (2008, $7.99, digest) r/#5-8 — 8.00

MARVEL AGE SPIDER-MAN (All ages title)
Marvel Comics: May, 2004 - No. 20, Mar, 2005 ($2.25)

1-20-Lee & Ditko stories retold with new art. 4-Doctor Doom app. 5-Lizard app. — 3.00
1-(Free Comic Book Day giveaway, 8/04) Spider-Man vs. The Vulture; Brooks-a — 3.00
Vol. 1 TPB (2004, $5.99, digest) 1-r/#1-4 — 6.00
Vol. 2: Everyday Hero TPB (2004, $5.99, digest) r/#5-8 — 6.00
Vol. 3: Swingtime TPB (2004, $5.99, digest) r/#9-12 — 6.00
Spidey Strikes Back TPB (2005, 5.99, digest) r/#17-20 — 6.00

MARVEL AGE SPIDER-MAN TEAM-UP (Marvel Adventures on cover)
Marvel Comics: June, 2005 (Free Comic Book Day giveaway)

1-Spider-Man meets the Fantastic Four — 3.00

MARVEL AGE TEAM-UP (All ages Spider-Man team-ups) (Also see Free Comic Book Day edition in the Promotional Comics section)
Marvel Comics: Nov, 2004 - No. 5, Apr, 2005 ($1.75)

1-5-Stories retold with new art by various. 1-Fantastic Four app. 3-Kitty Pryde app. — 3.00
... Vol. 1: A Little Help From My Friends (2005, $7.99, digest) r/#1-5 — 8.00

MARVEL AND DC PRESENT FEATURING THE UNCANNY X-MEN AND THE NEW TEEN TITANS
Marvel Comics/DC Comics: 1982 ($2.00, 68 pgs., one-shot, Baxter paper)

1-3rd app. Deathstroke the Terminator; Darkseid app.; Simonson/Austin-c/a — 3 6 9 16 23 30

MARVEL APES
Marvel Comics: Nov, 2008 - No. 4, Dec, 2008 ($3.99, limited series)

1-4: 1-Kesel-s/Bachs-a; back-up history story with Peyer-s/Kitson-a; two covers — 4.00
1-($10.00) Hero Initiative edition with Daredevil gorilla cover by Mike Wieringo — 10.00
#0-(2008, $3.99) r/Amazing Spider-Man #110,111; gallery of Marvel Apes variant covers — 4.00
...: Amazing Spider-Monkey Special 1 (6/09, $3.99) Sandmonk and the Apevengers app. — 4.00
...: Grunt Line 1 (7/09, $3.99) Kesel-s; Charles Darwin app. — 4.00
...: Speedball Special 1 (5/09, $3.99) Bachs & Hardin-a — 4.00

MARVEL ASSISTANT-SIZED SPECTACULAR
Marvel Comics: Jun, 2009 - No. 2, Jun, 2009 ($3.99, limited series)

1,2-Short stories by various incl. Isanove, Giarrusso, Nauck, Wyatt Cenak, Warren — 4.00

MARVEL ATLAS (Styled after the Official Marvel Handbooks)
Marvel Comics: 2007 - No. 2, 2008 ($3.99, limited series)

1,2-Profiles and maps of countries in the Marvel Universe — 4.00

MARVEL BOY (Astonishing #3 on; see Marvel Super Action #4)
Marvel Comics (MPC): Dec, 1950 - No. 2, Feb, 1951

1-Origin Marvel Boy by Russ Heath — 148 296 444 947 1624 2300
2-Everett-a; Washington DC under attack — 103 206 309 659 1130 1600

MARVEL BOY (Marvel Knights)
Marvel Comics: Aug, 2000 - No. 6, Mar, 2001 ($2.99, limited series)

1-Intro. Marvel Boy; Morrison-s/J.G. Jones-c/a — 4.00
1-DF Variant-c — 5.00
2-6 — 3.00
TPB (6/01, $15.95) — 16.00

MARVEL BOY: THE URANIAN (Agents of Atlas)
Marvel Comics: Mar, 2010 - No. 3, May, 2010 ($3.99, limited series)

1-3-Origin re-told; back-up reprints from 1950s; Heath & Everett-a — 4.00

MARVEL CHILLERS (Also see Giant-Size Chillers)
Marvel Comics Group: Oct, 1975 - No. 7, Oct, 1976 (All 25¢ issues)

1-Intro. Modred the Mystic, ends #2; Kane-c(p) — 3 6 9 16 24 32
2,4,5,7: 4-Kraven app. 5,6-Red Wolf app. 7-Kirby-c; Tuska-p — 2 4 6 9 12 15
3-Tigra, the Were-Woman begins (origin), ends #7 (see Giant-Size Creatures #1). Chaykin/Wrightson-c. — 5 10 15 31 53 75
4-6-(30¢-c variants, limited distribution)(4-8/76) — 4 8 12 27 44 60
6-Byrne-a(p); Buckler-c(p) — 2 4 6 11 16 20

NOTE: *Bolle a-1.* ***Buckler** c-2.* ***Kirby** c-7.*

Marvel Classics Comics #28 © MAR

Marvel Comics Digest #1 © MAR

Marvel Comics Presents #43 © MAR

GD VG FN VF VF/NM NM-
2.0 4.0 6.0 8.0 9.0 9.2

MARVEL CLASSICS COMICS SERIES FEATURING...
(Also see Pendulum Illustrated Classics)
Marvel Comics Group: 1976 - No. 36, Dec, 1978 (52 pgs., no ads)

1-Dr. Jekyll and Mr. Hyde 2 4 6 10 14 18
2-10,28: 28-1st Golden-c/a; Pit and the Pendulum 2 4 6 8 10 12
11-27,29-36 1 2 3 5 7 9

NOTE: ***Adkins** c-1i, 4i, 12i. **Alcala** a-34i; c-34. **Bolle** a-35. **Buscema** c-17p, 19p, 26p. **Golden** c/a-28. **Gil Kane** c-1-16p, 21p, 22p, 24p, 32p. **Nebres** a-5; c-24i. **Nino** a-2, 8, 12. **Redondo** a-1, 9. No. 1-12 were reprinted from Pendulum Illustrated Classics.*

MARVEL COLLECTIBLE CLASSICS: AVENGERS
Marvel Comics: 1998 ($10.00, reprints with chromium wraparound-c)

1-Reprints Avengers Vol.3, #1; Perez-c 3 6 9 16 23 30

MARVEL COLLECTIBLE CLASSICS: SPIDER-MAN
Marvel Comics: 1998 ($10.00, reprints with chromium wraparound-c)

1-Reprints Amazing Spider-Man #300; McFarlane-c 65 130 195 325 450 575
2-Reprints Spider-Man #1; McFarlane-c 22 44 66 110 155 200

MARVEL COLLECTIBLE CLASSICS: X-MEN
Marvel Comics: 1998 ($10.00, reprints with chromium wraparound-c)

1-Reprints (Uncanny) X-Men #1 & 2; Adam Kubert-c 3 6 9 17 26 35
2-6: 2-Reprints Uncanny X-Men #141 & 142; Byrne-c. 3-Reprints (Uncanny) X-Men #137; Larroca-c. 4-Reprints X-Men #25; Andy Kubert-c. 5-Reprints Giant Size X-Men #1; Gary Frank-c. 6-Reprints X-Men V2#1; Ramos-c 3 6 9 16 23 30

MARVEL COLLECTOR'S EDITION
Marvel Comics: 1992 (Ordered thru mail with Charleston Chew candy wrapper)

1-Flip-book format; Spider-Man, Silver Surfer, Wolverine (by Sam Kieth), & Ghost Rider stories; Wolverine back-c by Kieth 1 2 3 5 6 8

MARVEL COLLECTORS' ITEM CLASSICS (Marvel's Greatest #23 on)
Marvel Comics Group(ATF): Feb, 1965 - No. 22, Aug, 1969 (25¢, 68 pgs.)

1-Fantastic Four, Spider-Man, Thor, Hulk, Iron Man-r begin
12 24 36 84 185 285
2 (4/66) 6 12 18 42 79 115
3,4 5 10 15 35 63 90
5-10 5 10 15 33 57 80
11-22: 22-r/The Man in the Ant Hill/TTA #27 4 8 12 28 47 65

NOTE: *All reprints; **Ditko, Kirby** art in all.*

MARVEL COMICS (Marvel Mystery Comics #2 on)
Timely Comics (Funnies, Inc.): Oct, Nov, 1939

NOTE: The first issue was originally dated October 1939. Most copies have a black circle stamped over the date (on cover and inside) with "November" printed over it. However, some copies do not have the November overprint and could have a higher value. Most No. 1's have printing defects, i.e., tilted pages which caused trimming into the panels usually on right side and bottom. Covers exist with and without gloss finish.

1-Origin Sub-Mariner by Bill Everett(1st newsstand app.); 1st 8 pgs. were produced for Motion Picture Funnies Weekly #1 which was probably not distributed outside of advance copies; intro Human Torch by Carl Burgos, Kazar the Great (1st Tarzan clone), & Jungle Terror(only app.); intro. The Angel by Gustavson, The Masked Raider & his horse Lightning (ends #12); cover by sci/fi pulp illustrator Frank R. Paul
40,000 80,000 120,000 210,000 327,000 680,000

MARVEL COMICS
Marvel Comics: 1990 ($17.95, hardcover)

1-Reprint of entire Marvel Comics #1 3 6 9 16 23 30

MARVEL COMICS
Marvel Comics

... No. 1 Halloween Comic Fest 2014 (giveaway) Re-colored reprint of Human Torch and Sub-Mariner stories from Marvel Comics #1; cover swipe by Jelena Djurdjevic 3.00
... 70th Anniversary Special (10/09, $4.99) Re-colored reprint of entire Marvel Comics #1; cover swipe by Jelena Djurdjevic 6.00

MARVEL COMICS DIGEST (All-ages Marvel reprint stories printed by Archie Comics)
Archie Comics Publications: Jul, 2017 - Present ($6.99, digest-size)

1-5: 1-Spider-Man reprints. 2-Avengers. 3-Thor. 4-X-Men. 5-Avengers/Black Panther 7.00

MARVEL COMICS PRESENTS
Marvel Comics (Midnight Sons imprint #143 on): Early Sept, 1988 - No. 175, Feb, 1995 ($1.25/$1.50/$1.75, bi-weekly)

1-Wolverine by Buscema in #1-10 2 4 6 9 12 15
2-5 6.00
6-10: 6-Sub-Mariner app. 10-Colossus begins 4.00
11-18,20-47,51-71: 17-Cyclops begins. 24-Havok begins. 25-Origin/1st app. Nth Man. 26-Hulk begins by Rogers. 29-Quasar app. 31-Excalibur begins by Austin (i). 32-McFarlane-a(p). 33-Capt. America; Jim Lee-a. 37-Devil-Slayer app. 38-Wolverine begins by Buscema; Hulk app. 39-Spider-Man app. 46-Liefeld Wolverine-c. 51-53-Wolverine by Rob Liefeld. 54-61-Wolverine/Hulk story: 54-Werewolf by Night begins; The Shroud by Ditko. 58-Iron Man by Ditko. 59-Punisher. 62-Deathlok & Wolverine stories 63-Wolverine. 64-71-Wolverine/Ghost Rider 8-part story. 70-Liefeld Ghost Rider/ Wolverine-c 3.00
19-1st app. Damage Control 2 4 6 8 10 12
48-50-Wolverine & Spider-Man team-up by Erik Larsen-c/a. 48-Wasp app. 49,50-Savage Dragon prototype app. by Larsen. 50-Silver Surfer. 50-53-Comet Man; Mumy scripts 5.00
72-Begin 13-part Weapon-X story (Wolverine origin) by B. Windsor-Smith (prologue)
2 4 6 10 14 18
73-Weapon-X part 1; Black Knight, Sub-Mariner 1 2 3 5 6 8
74-84: 74-Weapon-X part 2; Black Knight, Sub-Mariner. 76-Death's Head story. 77-Mr. Fantastic story. 78-Iron Man by Steacy. 80,81-Capt. America by Ditko/Austin. 81-Daredevil by Rogers/Williamson. 82-Power Man. 83-Human Torch by Ditko(a&scripts); $1.00-c direct, $1.25 newsstand. 84-Last Weapon-X (24 pg. conclusion) 3.00
85-Begin 8-part Wolverine story by Sam Kieth (c/a); 1st Kieth-a on Wolverine; begin 8-part Beast story by Jae Lee(p) with Liefeld part pencils #85,86; 1st Jae Lee-a (assisted w/Liefeld, 1991) 4.00
86-90: 86-89-Wolverine, Beast stories continue. 90-Begin 8-part Ghost Rider & Cable story, ends #97; begin flip book format w/two-c 3.00
91-174: 93-Begin 6-part Wolverine story, ends #98. 98-Begin 2-part Ghost Rider story. 99-Spider-Man story. 100-Full-length Ghost Rider/Wolverine story by Sam Kieth w/Tim Vigil assists; anniversary issue, non flip-book. 101-Begin 6-part Ghost Rider/Dr. Strange story & begin 8-part Wolverine/Nightcrawler story by Colan/Williamson; Punisher story. 107-Begin 6-part Ghost Rider/Werewolf by Night story. 109-Begin 8 part Wolverine/Typhoid Mary story. 111-Iron Fist. 113-Begin 6-part Giant-Man & begin 6-part Ghost Rider/Iron Fist stories. 117-Preview of Ravage 2099 (1st app.); begin 6 part Wolverine/Venom story w/Kieth-a. 118-Preview of Doom 2099 (1st app.). 119-Begin Ghost Rider/Cloak & Dagger by Colan. 120,136,138-Spider-Man. 123-Begin 8-part Ghost Rider/Typhoid Mary story; begin 4-part She Hulk story; begin 8-part Wolverine/Lynx story. 125-Begin 6-part Iron Fist story. 130-Begin 6-part Ghost Rider/ Cage story. 136-Daredevil. 137-Begin 6-part Wolverine story & 6-part Ghost Rider story. 147-Begin 2-part Vengeance-c/story w/new Ghost Rider. 149-Vengeance-c/story w/new Ghost Rider. 150-Silver ink-c; begin 2-part Bloody Mary story w/Typhoid Mary,Wolverine, Daredevil, new Ghost Rider; intro Steel Raven. 152-Begin 4-part Wolverine, 4-part War Machine, 4-part Vengeance, 3-part Moon Knight stories; same date as War Machine #1. 143-146: Siege of Darkness parts 3,6,11,14; all have spot-varnished-c. 143-Ghost Rider/Scarlet Witch; intro new Werewolf. 144-Begin 2-part Morbius story. 145-Begin 2-part Nightstalkers story. 153-155-Bound-in Spider-Man trading card sheet. 172-Flip-book; intro new Lunatik, Giffen-c/a. 173-Flip-book; Lunatik story; Fabry-c/Giffen-a. 174-Lunatik story, Giffen-a 3.00
175-Flip-book with New Genix-c; Lunatik story, Giffen-a
2 4 6 10 14 18
...Colossus: God's Country (1994, $6.95) r/#10-17 1 2 3 4 5 7
...: Wolverine Vol. 1 TPB (2005, $12.99) r/Wolverine stories from #1-10 13.00
...: Wolverine Vol. 2 TPB (2006, $12.99) r/from #39-50 and Marvel Age Annual #4 13.00
...: Wolverine Vol. 3 TPB (2006, $12.99) r/from #51-61 13.00
...: Wolverine Vol. 4 TPB (2006, $12.99) r/from #62-71 13.00

NOTE: ***Austin** a-31-37i; c(i)-48, 50, 99, 122. **Buscema** a-1-10, 38-47; c-6. **Byrne** a-79; c-71. **Colan** a(p)-36, 37. **Colan/Williamson** a-101-108. **Ditko** a-7p, 10, 56p, 58, 80, 81, 83. **Guice** a-62. **Sam Kieth** a-85-92, 117-122; c-85-98, 99p, 100-108, 117, 118, 120-122; back c-109-113, 117. **Jae Lee** c-129(back). **Liefeld** a-51, 52, 53p(2), 85p; c-46, 70. **McFarlane** c-32. **Mooney** a-73. **Rogers** a-26, 38, 46i, 81p. **Russell** a-10-14,16,17i; c-4,19, 30,31i. **Saltares** a-8p(early), 38-45p. **Simonson** c-1. **B. Smith** a-72-84; c-72-84. **P. Smith** c-34. **Sparling** a-33. **Starlin** a-89i. **Staton** a-74. **Steacy** a-78. **Sutton** a-101-105. **Williamson** c-62i. Two Gun Kid by **Gil Kane** in #116, 122.*

MARVEL COMICS PRESENTS
Marvel Comics: Nov, 2007 - No. 12, Oct, 2008 ($3.99)

1-12-Short stories by various. 1-Wraparound-c by Campbell 4.00

MARVEL COMICS SUPER SPECIAL, A (Marvel Super Special #5 on)
Marvel Comics: Sept, 1977 - No. 41(?), Nov, 1986 (nn 7) ($1.50, magazine)

1-Kiss, 40 pgs. comics plus photos & features; John Buscema-a(p); also see Howard the Duck #12; ink contains real KISS blood; Dr. Doom, Spider-Man, Avengers, Fantastic Four, Mephisto app. 12 24 36 84 185 285
2-Conan (1978) 3 6 9 14 20 25
3-Close Encounters of the Third Kind (1978); Simonson-a
3 6 9 14 20 25
4-The Beatles Story (1978)-Perez/Janson-a; has photos & articles
6 12 18 42 79 115
5-Kiss (1978)-Includes poster 12 24 36 82 179 275
6-Jaws II (1978) 2 4 6 11 16 20
7-Sgt. Pepper; Beatles movie adaptation; withdrawn from U.S. distribution (French ed. exists)
8-Battlestar Galactica; tabloid size ($1.50, 1978); adapts TV show
2 4 6 13 18 20
8-Modern-r of tabloid size 2 4 6 10 14 18
8-Battlestar Galactica; publ. in regular magazine format; low distribution ($1.50, 8-1/2x11")
3 6 9 14 20 25

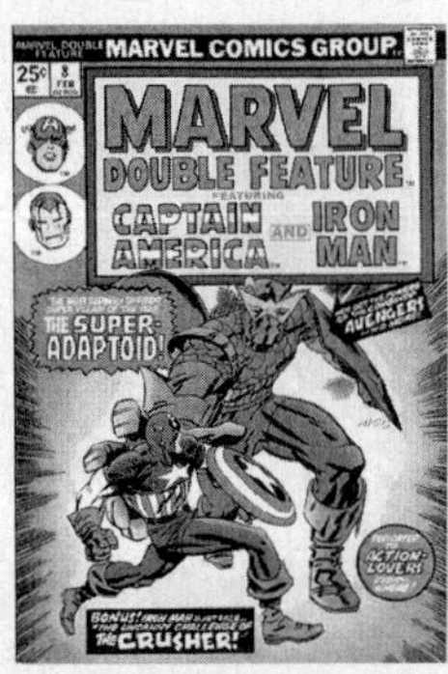

Marvel Double Feature #8 © MAR

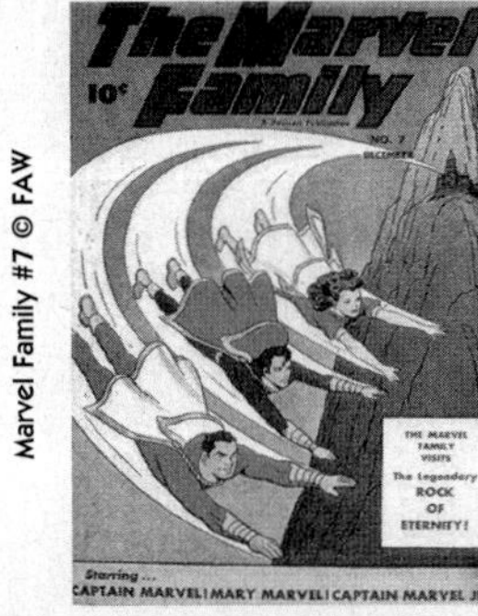

Marvel Family #7 © FAW

Marvel Fanfare #52 © MAR

GD VG FN VF VF/NM NM-
2.0 4.0 6.0 8.0 9.0 9.2

9-Conan 3 6 9 14 20 25
10-Star-Lord (1st color story) 5 10 15 30 50 70
11-13-Weirdworld begins #11; 25 copy special press run of each with gold seal and signed by artists (Proof quality), Spring-June, 1979 8 16 24 55 105 155
11-14: 11-13-Weirdworld (regular issues): 11-Fold-out centerfold. 14-Miller-c(p); adapts movie "Meteor." 1 3 4 6 8 10
15-Star Trek with photos & pin-ups ($1.50-c) 2 4 6 11 16 20
15-With $2.00 price; the price was changed at tail end of a 200,000 press run
3 6 9 14 20 25
16-Empire Strikes Back adaptation; Williamson-a 4 8 12 25 40 55
17-20 (Movie adaptations): 17-Xanadu. 18-Raiders of the Lost Ark. 19-For Your Eyes Only (James Bond). 20-Dragonslayer 6.00
21,23,25,26,28-30 (Movie adaptations): 21-Conan. 23-Annie. 25-Rock and Rule-w/photos; artwork is from movie. 26-Octopussy (James Bond). 28-Krull; photo-c. 29-Tarzan of the Apes (Greystoke movie). 30-Indiana Jones and the Temple of Doom
1 2 3 4 5 7
22-Blade Runner; Williamson-a/Steranko-c 4 8 12 27 44 60
24-The Dark Crystal 2 4 6 9 12 15
27-Return of the Jedi 2 4 6 10 14 18
31-39,41: 31-The Last Star Fighter. 32-The Muppets Take Manhattan. 33-Buckaroo Banzai. 34-Sheena. 35-Conan The Destroyer. 36-Dune. 37-2010. 38-Red Sonja. 39-Santa Claus:The Movie. 41-Howard The Duck
1 2 3 5 7 9
40-Labyrinth 3 6 9 21 33 45
NOTE: ***J. Buscema*** *a-1, 2, 9, 11-13, 18p, 21, 35, 40; c-11(part), 12.* ***Chaykin*** *a-9, 19p; c-18, 19.* ***Colan*** *a(p)-6, 10, 14.* ***Morrow*** *a-34; c-1i, 34.* ***Nebres*** *a-11.* ***Spiegle*** *a-29.* ***Stevens*** *a-27.* ***Williamson*** *a-27. #22-28 contain photos from movies.*

MARVEL COMICS: 2001
Marvel Comics: 2001 (no cover price, one-shot)
1-Previews new titles for Fall 2001; Wolverine-c 3.00

MARVEL DABEL BROTHERS SAMPLER
Marvel Comics: Dec, 2006 (no cover price, one-shot)
1-Profiles and sample pages of Anita Blake, Magician: Apprentice, Red Prophet, Ptolus 3.00

MARVEL DIVAS
Marvel Comics: Sept, 2009 - No. 4, Dec, 2009 ($3.99, limited series)
1-4-Black Cat, Firestar, Hellcat and Photon app. 1-Campbell-c 4.00

MARVEL DOUBLE FEATURE
Marvel Comics Group: Dec, 1973 - No. 21, Mar, 1977
1-Capt. America, Iron Man-r/T.O.S. begin 3 6 9 16 24 32
2-10: 3-Last 20¢ issue 2 4 6 8 10 12
11-17,20,21:17-Story-r/Iron Man & Sub-Mariner #1; last 25¢ issue
1 2 3 5 7 9
15-17-(30¢-c variants, limited distribution)(4,6,8/76) 3 6 9 21 33 45
18,19-Colan/Craig-r from Iron Man #1 in both 2 4 6 8 10 12
NOTE: ***Colan*** *r-1-19p.* ***Craig*** *r-17-19i.* ***G. Kane*** *r-15p; c-15p.* ***Kirby*** *r-1-16p, 20, 21; c-17-20.*

MARVEL DOUBLE SHOT
Marvel Comics: Jan, 2003 - No. 4, April, 2003 ($2.99, limited series)
1-4: 1-Hulk by Haynes; Thor w/Asamiya-a; Jusko-c. 2-Dr. Doom by Rivera; Simpsons-style Avengers by Bill Morrison 3.00

MARVEL FAMILY (Also see Captain Marvel Adventures No. 18)
Fawcett Publications: Dec, 1945 - No. 89, Jan, 1954
1-Origin Captain Marvel, Captain Marvel Jr., Mary Marvel, & Uncle Marvel retold; origin/1st app. Black Adam 900 1800 2700 6000 10,000 14,000
2-The 3 Lt. Marvels & Uncle Marvel app. 77 154 231 493 847 1200
3 54 108 162 346 591 835
4,5 45 90 135 284 480 675
6-10: 6-Classic portrait-c with Uncle Marvel. 7-Shazam app.
39 78 117 231 378 525
11-20 31 62 93 182 296 410
21-30 27 54 81 158 259 360
31-40 23 46 69 136 223 310
41-46,48-50 22 44 66 128 209 290
47-Flying Saucer-c/story (5/50) 29 58 87 170 278 385
51-76 20 40 60 120 195 270
77-Communist Threat-c 36 72 108 211 343 475
78,81-Used in **POP**, pg. 92,93. 23 46 69 136 223 310
79,80,82-88: 79-Horror satire-c 22 44 66 132 216 300
89-Last issue; last Fawcett Captain Marvel app. (low distribution)
36 72 108 211 343 475

MARVEL FANFARE (1st Series)
Marvel Comics Group: Mar, 1982 - No. 60, Jan, 1992 ($1.25/$2.25, slick paper, direct sales)

GD VG FN VF VF/NM NM-
2.0 4.0 6.0 8.0 9.0 9.2

1-Spider-Man/Angel team-up; 1st Paul Smith-a (1st full story; see King Conan #7); Daredevil app. (many copies were printed missing the centerfold)
2 4 6 8 10 12
2-Spider-Man, Ka-Zar, The Angel. F.F. origin retold 1 2 3 5 6 8
3,4-X-Men & Ka-Zar. 4-Deathlok, Spidey app. 6.00
5-14: 5-Dr. Strange, Capt. America. 6-Spider-Man, Scarlet Witch. 7-Incredible Hulk; D.D. back-up(also 15). 8-Dr. Strange; Wolf Boy begins. 9-Man-Thing. 10-13-Black Widow. 14-The Vision 4.00
15,24,33: 15-The Thing by Barry Smith, c/a. 24-Weirdworld; Wolverine back-up. 33-X-Men, Wolverine app.; Punisher pin-up 5.00
16-23,25-32,34-44,46-50: 16,17-Skywolf. 16-Sub-Mariner back-up. 17-Hulk back-up. 18-Capt. America by Miller. 19-Cloak and Dagger. 20-Thing/Dr. Strange. 21-Thing/Dr. Strange /Hulk. 22,23-Iron Man vs. Dr. Octopus. 25,26-Weirdworld. 27-Daredevil/Spider-Man. 28-Alpha Flight. 29-Hulk. 30-Moon Knight. 31,32-Captain America. 34-37-Warriors Three. 38-Moon Knight/Dazzler. 39-Moon Knight/Hawkeye. 40-Angel/Rogue & Storm. 41-Dr. Strange. 42-Spider-Man. 43-Sub-Mariner/Human Torch. 44-Iron Man vs. Dr. Doom by Ken Steacy. 46-Fantastic Four. 47-Hulk. 48-She-Hulk/Vision. 49-Dr. Strange/Nick Fury. 50-X-Factor 3.00
45-All pin-up issue by Steacy, Art Adams & others 5.00
51-($2.95, 52 pgs.)-Silver Surfer; Fantastic Four & Capt. Marvel app.; 51,52-Colan/Williamson back-up (Dr. Strange) 4.00
52,53,56-60: 52,53-Black Knight; 53-Iron Man back up. 56-59-Shanna the She-Devil. 58-Vision & Scarlet Witch back-up. 60-Black Panther/Rogue/Daredevil stories 3.00
54,55-Wolverine back-ups. 54-Black Knight. 55-Power Pack 4.00
... Vol. 1 TPB (2008, $24.99) r/#1-7 25.00
NOTE: ***Art Adams*** *c-13.* ***Austin*** *a-1i, 4i, 33i, 38i; c-8i, 33i.* ***Buscema*** *a-51p.* ***Byrne*** *a-1p, 29, 48; c-29.* ***Chiodo*** *painted c-56-59.* ***Colan*** *a-51p.* ***Cowan/Simonson*** *c/a-60.* ***Golden*** *a-1, 2, 4p, 47; c-1, 2, 47.* ***Infantino*** *c/a(p)-8.* ***Gil Kane*** *a-8-11p.* ***Miller*** *a-18; c-1(Back-c), 18.* ***Perez*** *a-10, 11p, 12, 13p; c-10-13p.* ***Rogers*** *a-5p; c-5p.* ***Russell*** *a-5i, 6i, 8-11i, 43i; c-5i, 6.* ***Paul Smith*** *a-1p, 4p, 32, 60; c-4p. Staton c/a-50(p).* ***Williamson*** *a-30i, 51i.*

MARVEL FANFARE (2nd Series)
Marvel Comics: Sept, 1996 - No. 6, Feb, 1997 (99¢)
1-6: 1-Capt. America & The Falcon-c/story; Deathlok app. 2-Wolverine & Hulk-c/app. 3-Ghost Rider & Spider-Man-c/app. 5-Longshot-c/app. 6-Sabretooth, Power Man, & Iron Fist-c/app 3.00

MARVEL FEATURE (See Marvel Two-In-One)
Marvel Comics Group: Dec, 1971 - No. 12, Nov, 1973 (1,2: 25¢, 52 pg. giants) (#1-3: quarterly)
1-Origin/1st app. The Defenders (Sub-Mariner, Hulk & Dr. Strange); see Sub-Mariner #34,35 for prequel; Dr. Strange solo story (predates Dr. Strange #1) plus 1950s Sub-Mariner-r; Neal Adams-c 20 40 60 141 313 485
2-2nd app. Defenders; 1950s Sub-Mariner-r. Rutland, Vermont Halloween x-over
9 18 27 58 114 170
3-Defenders ends 6 12 18 40 73 105
4-Re-intro Antman (1st app. since 1960s), begin series; brief origin; Spider-Man app.
8 16 24 54 102 150
5-7,9,10: 6-Wasp app. & begins team-ups. 9-Iron Man app. 10-Last Antman
3 6 9 21 33 45
8-Origin Antman & Wasp-r/TTA #44; Kirby-a 4 8 12 23 37 50
11-Thing vs. Hulk; 1st Thing solo book (9/73); origin Fantastic Four retold
7 14 21 49 92 135
12-Thing/Iron Man; early Thanos app.; occurs after Capt. Marvel #33; Starlin-a(p)
5 10 15 34 60 85
NOTE: ***Bolle*** *a-9i.* ***Everett*** *a-1i, 3i.* ***Hartley*** *r-10.* ***Kane*** *c-3p, 7p.* ***Russell*** *a-7-10p.* ***Starlin*** *a-8, 11, 12; c-8.*

MARVEL FEATURE (Also see Red Sonja)
Marvel Comics: Nov, 1975 - No. 7, Nov, 1976 (Story cont'd in Conan #68)
1-Red Sonja begins (pre-dates Red Sonja #1); adapts Howard short story; Adams-r/Savage Sword of Conan #1 3 6 9 17 26 35
2-6: Thorne-c/a in #2-7. 4,5-(Regular 25¢ edition)(5,7/76)
1 3 4 6 8 10
4,5-(30¢-c variants, limited distribution) 4 8 12 28 47 65
7-Red Sonja battles Conan 2 4 6 13 18 22

MARVEL FRONTIER COMICS UNLIMITED
Marvel Frontier Comics: Jan, 1994 ($2.95, 68 pgs.)
1-Dances with Demons, Immortalis, Children of the Voyager, Evil Eye, The Fallen stories 4.00

MARVEL FUMETTI BOOK
Marvel Comics Group: Apr, 1984 ($1.00, one-shot)
1-All photos; Stan Lee photo-c; Art Adams touch-ups 5.00

MARVEL FUN & GAMES
Marvel Comics Group: 1979/80 (color comic for kids)
1,11: 1-Games, puzzles, etc. 11-X-Men-c 2 4 6 8 10 12
2-10,12,13: (beware marked pages) 1 2 3 4 5 7

MARVEL GIRL

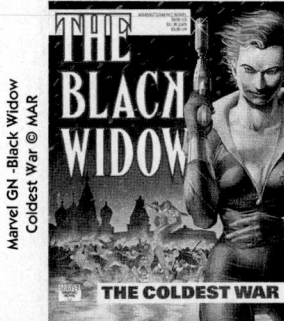

Marvel GN -Black Widow Coldest War © MAR

Marvel - Heroes & Legends 1997 © MAR

Marvel Illustrated: Treasure Island #4 © MAR

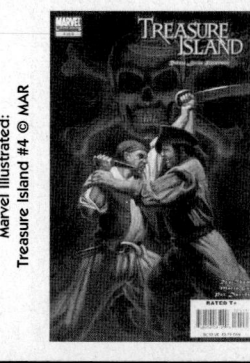

	GD 2.0	VG 4.0	FN 6.0	VF 8.0	VF/NM 9.0	NM- 9.2

Marvel Comics: Apr, 2011 ($2.99, one-shot)

1-Early X-Men days of Jean Grey; Fialkov-s/Plati-a/Cruz-c 3.00

MARVEL GRAPHIC NOVEL
Marvel Comics Group (Epic Comics): 1982 - No. 38, 1990? ($5.95/$6.95)

	GD 2.0	VG 4.0	FN 6.0	VF 8.0	VF/NM 9.0	NM- 9.2
1-Death of Captain Marvel (2nd Marvel graphic novel); Capt. Marvel battles Thanos by Jim Starlin (c/a/scripts)	5	10	15	34	60	85
1 (2nd & 3rd printings)	2	4	6	11	16	20
2-Elric: The Dreaming City	2	4	6	11	16	20
3-Dreadstar; Starlin-c/a, 52 pgs.	3	6	9	14	20	25
4-Origin/1st app. The New Mutants (1982)	7	14	21	49	92	135
4,5-2nd printings	2	4	6	10	14	18
5-X-Men; book-length story (1982)	4	8	12	23	37	50
6-15,20,25,30,31: 6-The Star Slammers. 7-Killraven. 8-Super Boxers; Byrne scripts. 9-The Futurians. 10-Heartburst. 11-Void Indigo. 12-Dazzler. 13-Starstruck. 14-The Swords Of The Swashbucklers. 15-The Raven Banner (a Tale of Asgard). 20-Greenberg the Vampire. 25-Alien Legion. 30-A Sailor's Story. 31-Wolfpack	2	4	6	8	10	12
16,17,21,29: 16-The Aladdin Effect (Storm, Tigra, Wasp, She-Hulk). 17-Revenge Of The Living Monolith (Spider-Man, Avengers, FF app.). 21-Marada the She-Wolf. 29-The Big Chance (Thing vs. Hulk)	2	4	6	9	12	15
18,19,26-28: 18-She Hulk. 19-Witch Queen of Acheron (Conan). 26-Dracula. 27-Avengers (Emperor Doom). 28-Conan the Reaver	2	4	6	10	14	18
22-24: 22-Amaz. Spider-Man in Hooky by Wrightson. 23-Dr. Strange. 24-Love and War (Daredevil); Miller scripts	3	6	9	14	19	24
32-Death of Groo	3	6	9	14	19	24
32-2nd printing ($5.95)	2	4	6	8	10	12
33,34,36,37: 33-Thor. 34-Predator & Prey (Cloak & Dagger). 36-Willow (movie adapt.). 37-Hercules	2	4	6	8	10	12
35-Hitler's Astrologer (The Shadow, $12.95, HC)	2	4	6	11	16	20
35-Soft-c reprint (1990, $10.95)	2	4	6	9	12	15
38-Silver Surfer (Judgement Day)($14.95, HC)	2	4	6	9	12	15
38-Soft-c reprint (1990, $10.95)	2	4	6	9	12	15
nn-Abslom Daak: Dalek Killer (1990, $8.95) Dr. Who	2	4	6	9	12	15
nn-Arena by Bruce Jones (1989, $5.95) Dinosaurs	2	4	6	8	10	12
nn- A-Team Storybook Comics Illustrated (1983) r/ A-Team mini-series #1-3	2	4	6	8	10	12
nn-Ax (1988, $5.95) Ernie Colan-s/a	2	4	6	8	10	12
nn-Black Widow Coldest War (4/90, $9.95)	2	4	6	9	12	15
nn-Chronicles of Genghis Grimtoad (1990, $8.95)-Alan Grant-s	2	4	6	8	10	12
nn-Conan the Barbarian in the Horn of Azoth (1990, $8.95)	2	4	6	8	11	16
nn-Conan of Isles ($8.95)	2	4	6	8	11	16
nn-Conan Ravagers of Time (1992, $9.95) Kull & Red Sonja app.	2	4	6	8	11	16
nn-Conan -The Skull of Set	2	4	6	8	11	16
nn-Doctor Strange and Doctor Doom Triumph and Torment (1989, $17.95, HC)	2	4	6	13	18	22
nn-Dreamwalker (1989, $6.95)-Morrow-a	2	4	6	8	10	12
nn-Excalibur Weird War III (1990, $9.95)	2	4	6	8	10	12
nn-G.I. Joe - The Trojan Gambit (1983, 68 pgs.)	2	4	6	9	12	15
nn-Harvey Kurtzman Strange Adventures (Epic, $19.95, HC) Aragonés, Crumb	3	6	9	14	20	25
nn-Hearts and Minds (1990, $8.95) Heath-a	2	4	6	8	10	12
nn-Inhumans (1988, $7.95)-Williamson-i	3	6	9	14	20	25
nn-Jhereg (Epic, 1990, $8.95)	2	4	6	8	10	12
nn-Kazar-Guns of the Savage Land (7/90, $8.95)	2	4	6	8	10	12
nn-Kull-The Vale of Shadow ('89, $6.95)	2	4	6	8	10	12
nn-Last of the Dragons (1988, $6.95) Austin-a(i)	2	4	6	8	10	12
nn-Nightraven: House of Cards (1991, $14.95)	2	4	6	10	14	18
nn-Nightraven: The Collected Stories (1990, $9.95) Bolton-r/British Hulk mag.; David Lloyd-c/a	2	4	6	8	10	12
nn-Original Adventures of Cholly and Flytrap (Epic, 1991, $9.95) Suydam-s/c/a	2	4	6	10	14	18
nn-Rick Mason Agent (1989, $9.95)	2	4	6	8	10	12
nn-Roger Rabbit In The Resurrection Of Doom (1989, $8.95)	2	4	6	9	12	15
nn-A Sailor's Story Book II: Winds, Dreams and Dragons ('86, $6.95, softcover) Glansman-s/c/a	2	4	6	8	10	12
nn-Squadron Supreme: Death of a Universe (1989, $9.95) Gruenwald-s; Ryan & Williamson-a	3	6	9	14	20	25
nn-Who Framed Roger Rabbit (1989, $6.95)	2	4	6	9	12	15

NOTE: ***Aragones** a-27, 32. **Buscema** a-38. **Byrne** c/a-18. **Heath** a-35i. **Kaluta** a-13, 35p; c-13. **Miller** a-24p. **Simonson** a-6; c-6. **Starlin** c/a-1,3. **Williamson** a-34. **Wrightson** c-29i.*

MARVEL HEARTBREAKERS
Marvel Comics: Apr, 2010 ($3.99, one-shot)

1-Romance short stories; Spider-Man, MJ & Gwen app.; Casagrande-a; Beast app. 4.00

MARVEL - HEROES & LEGENDS
Marvel Comics: Oct, 1996; 1997 ($2.95)

nn-Wraparound-c, ...1997 ($2.99) -Original Avengers story 3.00

MARVEL HEROES FLIP MAGAZINE
Marvel Comics: Aug, 2005 - No. 26, Sept, 2007 ($3.99/$4.99)

1-11-Reprints New Avengers and Captain America (2005 series) in flip format thru #13 4.00
12-26: 14-19-Reprints New Avengers and Young Avengers in flip format. 20-Ghost Rider 5.00

MARVEL HOLIDAY SPECIAL
Marvel Comics: No. 1, 1991 ($2.25, 84 pgs.) - Present

1-X-Men, Fantastic Four, Punisher, Thor, Capt. America, Ghost Rider, Capt. Ultra, Spidey stories; Art Adams-c/a 4.00
nn (1/93)-Wolverine, Thanos (by Starlin/Lim/Austin) 4.00
nn (1994)-Capt. America, X-Men, Silver Surfer 4.00
... 1996-Spider-Man by Waid & Olliffe; X-Men, Silver Surfer 4.00
... 2004-Spider-Man by DeFalco & Miyazawa; X-Men, Fantastic Four 4.00
... 2004 TPB ($15.99) r/M.H.S. 2004 & past Christmas-themed stories 16.00
1 (1/06, $3.99) new Christmas-themed stories by various; Immonen-c 4.00
... 2006 (2/07, $3.99) Fin Fang Foom, Hydra, AIM app.; gallery of past covers; Irving-c 4.00
... 2007 (2/08, $3.99) Spider-Man & Wolverine stories; Hembeck-a 4.00
... 2011 (2/12, $3.99) Seeley-c; Spider-Man, Wolverine, Nick Fury, The Thing app. 4.00
Marvel Holiday (2006, $7.99, digest) reprints from M.H.S. 2004, 2006 & TPB 8.00
Marvel Holiday Spectacular Magazine (2009, $9.99, magazine) reprints from M.H.S. '93, '94, & Amazing Spider-Man #166; and new material w/Doe, Semeiks & Nauck-a 10.00
NOTE: ***Art Adams** c-'93. **Golden** a-'93. **Perez** c-'94.*

MARVEL ILLUSTRATED...
Marvel Comics: 2007 ($2.99)

...Jungle Book - reprints from Marvel Fanfare #8-11; Gil Kane-s/a(p); P. Craig Russell-i 3.00

MARVEL ILLUSTRATED: KIDNAPPED (Title changes to Kidnapped with #5)
Marvel Comics: Jan, 2009 - No. 5, May, 2009 ($3.99, limited series)

1-5-Adaptation of the Stevenson novel; Roy Thomas-s/Mario Gully-a/Parel-c 4.00

MARVEL ILLUSTRATED: LAST OF THE MOHICANS
Marvel Comics: July, 2007 - No. 6, Dec, 2007 ($2.99, limited series)

1-6-Adaptation of the Cooper novel; Roy Thomas-s/Steve Kurth-a. 1-Jo Chen-c 3.00
HC (2008, $19.99) r/#1-6 20.00

MARVEL ILLUSTRATED: MOBY DICK
Marvel Comics: Apr, 2008 - No. 6, Sept, 2008 ($2.99, limited series)

1-6-Adaptation of the Melville novel; Roy Thomas-s/Alixe-a/Watson-c 3.00

MARVEL ILLUSTRATED: PICTURE OF DORIAN GRAY
Marvel Comics: Jan, 2008 - No. 6, July, 2008 ($2.99, limited series)

1-6-Adaptation of the Wilde novel; Roy Thomas-s/Fiumara-a. 1-Parel-c 3.00

MARVEL ILLUSTRATED: SWIMSUIT ISSUE (Also see Marvel Swimsuit Special)
Marvel Comics: 1991 ($3.95, magazine, 52 pgs.)

	GD 2.0	VG 4.0	FN 6.0	VF 8.0	VF/NM 9.0	NM- 9.2
V1#1-Parody of Sports Illustrated swimsuit issue; Mary Jane Parker centerfold pin-up by Jusko; 2nd print exists	2	4	6	8	10	12

MARVEL ILLUSTRATED: THE ILIAD
Marvel Comics: Feb, 2008 - No. 8, Sept, 2008 ($2.99, limited series)

1-8-Adaptation of Homer's Epic Poem; Roy Thomas-s/Sepulveda-a/Rivera-c 3.00

MARVEL ILLUSTRATED: THE MAN IN THE IRON MASK
Marvel Comics: Sept, 2007 - No. 6, Feb, 2008 ($2.99, limited series)

1-6-Adaptation of the Dumas novel; Roy Thomas-s/Hugo Petrus-a. 1-Djurdjevic-c 3.00
HC (2008, $19.99) r/#1-6 20.00

MARVEL ILLUSTRATED: THE ODYSSEY (Title changes to The Odyssey with #7)
Marvel Comics: Nov, 2008 - No. 8, June, 2009 ($3.99, limited series)

1-8-Adaptation of Homer's Epic Poem; Roy Thomas-s/Greg Tocchini-a/c 4.00

MARVEL ILLUSTRATED: THE THREE MUSKETEERS
Marvel Comics: Aug, 2008 - No. 6, Jan, 2009 ($3.99, limited series)

1-6-Adaptation of the Dumas novel; Roy Thomas-s/Hugo Petrus-a/Parel-c 4.00

MARVEL ILLUSTRATED: TREASURE ISLAND
Marvel Comics: Aug, 2007 - No. 6, Jan, 2008 ($2.99, limited series)

1-6-Adaptation of the Stevenson novel; Roy Thomas-s/Mario Gully-a/Greg Hildebrandt-c 3.00
HC (2008, $19.99) r/#1-6 20.00

MARVEL KNIGHTS (See Black Panther, Daredevil, Inhumans, & Punisher)

Marvel Knights #1 © MAR

Marvel Knights Spider-Man #5 © MAR

Marvel Legacy #1 © MAR

	GD	VG	FN	VF	VF/NM	NM-
	2.0	4.0	6.0	8.0	9.0	9.2

Marvel Comics: 1998 (Previews for upcoming series)

Sketchbook-Wizard suppl.; Quesada & Palmiotti-c 3.00
Tourbook-($2.99) Interviews and art previews 3.00

MARVEL KNIGHTS
Marvel Comics: July, 2000 - No. 15, Sept, 2001 ($2.99)

1-Daredevil, Punisher, Black Widow, Shang-Chi, Dagger app. 4.00
2-15: 2-Two covers by Barreto & Quesada 3.00
.../Marvel Boy Genesis Edition (6/00) Sketchbook preview 3.00
...: Millennial Visions (2/02, $3.99) Pin-ups by various; Harris-c 4.00

MARVEL KNIGHTS (Volume 2)
Marvel Comics: May, 2002 - No. 6, Oct, 2002 ($2.99)

1-6-Daredevil, Punisher, Black Widow app.; Ponticelli-a 3.00

MARVEL KNIGHTS: DOUBLE SHOT
Marvel Comics: June, 2002 - No. 4, Sept, 2002 ($2.99, limited series)

1-4: 1-Punisher by Ennis & Quesada; Daredevil by Haynes; Fabry-c 3.00

MARVEL KNIGHTS 4 (Fantastic Four) (Issues #1&2 are titled **Knights 4**) (#28-30 titled **Four**)
Marvel Comics: Apr, 2004 - No. 30, July, 2006 ($2.99)

1-30: 1-7-McNiven-c/a; Aguirre-Sacasa-a. 8,9-Namor app. 13-Cho-c. 14-Land-c. 21-Flashback meeting with Black Panther. 30-Namor app. 3.00
...Vol. 1: The Wolf at the Door (2004, $16.99, TPB) r/#1-7 17.00
...Vol. 2: The Stuff of Nightmares (2005, $13.99, TPB) r/#8-12 14.00
...Vol. 3: Divine Time (2005, $14.99, TPB) r/#13-18 15.00
...Vol. 4: Impossible Things Happen Every Day (2006, $14.99, TPB) r/#19-24 15.00
Fantastic Four: The Resurrection of Nicholas Scratch TPB (2006, $14.99) r/#25-30 15.00

MARVEL KNIGHTS: HULK
Marvel Comics: Feb, 2014 - No. 4, May, 2104 ($3.99, limited series)

1-4-Keatinge-s/Kowalski-a; Banner in Paris 4.00

MARVEL KNIGHTS MAGAZINE
Marvel Comics: May, 2001 - No. 6, Oct, 2001 ($3.99, magazine size)

1-6-Reprints of recent Daredevil, Punisher, Black Widow, Inhumans 4.00

MARVEL KNIGHTS SPIDER-MAN (Title continues in Sensational Spider-Man #23)
Marvel Comics: Jun, 2004 - No. 22, Mar, 2006 ($2.99)

1-Wraparound-c by Dodson; Millar-s/Dodson-a; Green Goblin app. 4.00
2-12: 2-Avengers app. 2,3-Vulture & Electro app. 5,8-Cho-c/a. 6-8-Venom app. 3.00
13-18-Reginald Hudlin-s/Billy Tan-a. 13,14,18-New Avengers app. 15-Punisher app. 3.00
19-22-The Other x-over pts. 2,5,8,11; Pat Lee-a 3.00
19-22-var-c: 19-Black costume. 20-Scarlet Spider. 21-Spider-Armor. 22-Peter Parker 5.00
... Vol. 1 HC (2005, $29.99, over-sized with d.j.) r/#1-12; Stan Lee intro.; Dodson & Cho sketch pages 30.00
... Vol. 1: Down Among the Dead Men (2004, $9.99, TPB) r/#1-4 10.00
... Vol. 2: Venomous (2005, $9.99, TPB) r/#5-8 10.00
... Vol. 3: The Last Stand (2005, $9.99, TPB) r/#9-12 10.00
... Vol. 4: Wild Blue Yonder (2005, $14.99, TPB) r/#13-18 15.00

MARVEL KNIGHTS: SPIDER-MAN
Marvel Comics: Dec, 2013 - No. 5, Apr, 2014 ($3.99, limited series)

1-5-Matt Kindt-s/Marco Rudy-a; Arcade app. 4.00

MARVEL KNIGHTS 2099
Marvel Comics: 2005 ($13.99, TPB)

nn-Reprints one shots: Daredevil 2099, Punisher 2099, Black Panther 2099, Inhumans 2099 and Mutant 2099; Pat Lee-c 14.00

MARVEL KNIGHTS: X-MEN
Marvel Comics: Jan, 2014 - No. 5, May, 2014 ($3.99, limited series)

1-4-Brahm Revel-s/Cris Peter-a; Sabretooth app. 4.00

MARVEL LEGACY
Marvel Comics: Nov, 2017 ($5.99, one-shot)

1-Leads into Marvel's Legacy title re-boot following Secret Empire; Aaron-s/Ribic & McNiven main art, plus art by various; wraparound gatefold front-c by Quesada 6.00

MARVEL LEGACY: ...
Marvel Comics: 2006, 2007 ($4.99, one-shots)

... The 1960s Handbook - Profiles of 1960s iconic and minor characters; info thru 1969 5.00
... The 1970s Handbook - Profiles of 1970s iconic and minor characters; info thru 1979 5.00
... The 1980s Handbook - Profiles of 1980s iconic and minor characters; info thru 1989 5.00
... The 1990s Handbook - Profiles of 1990s iconic and minor characters; Lim-c 5.00
...: The 1960s-1990s Handbook TPB (2007, $19.99) r/one-shots 20.00

MARVELMAN CLASSIC
Marvel Comics: 2010 ($34.99, B&W)

HC-(2010, $34.99) Reprints of 1950s British Marvelman stories; character history 35.00
... Primer (8/10, $3.99) Character history; Mick Anglo interview; Quesada-c 4.00

MARVELMAN FAMILY'S FINEST
Marvel Comics: 2010 - No. 6, Jan, 2011 ($3.99, B&W, limited series)

1-6-Reprints of 1950s Marvelman, Young Marvelman and Marvelman Family stories 4.00

MARVEL MANGAVERSE:... (one-shots)
Marvel Comics: March, 2002 ($2.25, manga-inspired one-shots)

Avengers Assemble! - Udon Studio-s/a 3.00
Eternity Twilight ($3.50) - Ben Dunn-s/a/wrap-around-c 4.00
Fantastic Four - Adam Warren-s/Keron Grant-a 3.00
Ghost Riders - Chuck Austen-s/a 3.00
Punisher - Peter David-s/Lea Hernandez-a 3.00
Spider-Man - Kaare Andrews-s/a 3.00
X-Men - C.B. Cebulski-s/Jeff Matsuda-a 3.00

MARVEL MANGAVERSE (Manga series)
Marvel Comics: June, 2002 - No. 6, Nov., 2002 ($2.25)

1-6: 1-Ben Dunn-s/a; intro. manga Captain Marvel 3.00
Vol. 1 TPB (2002, $24.95) r/one-shots 25.00
Vol. 2 TPB (2002, $12.99) r/#1-6 13.00
Vol. 3: Spider-Man-Legend of the Spider-Clan (2003, $11.99, TPB) r/series 12.00

MARVEL MASTERPIECES COLLECTION, THE
Marvel Comics: May, 1993 - No. 4, Aug, 1993 ($2.95, coated paper, lim. series)

1-4-Reprints Marvel Masterpieces trading cards w/ new Jusko paintings in each; Jusko painted-c/a 3.00

MARVEL MASTERPIECES 2 COLLECTION, THE
Marvel Comics: July, 1994 - No. 3, Sept, 1994 ($2.95, limited series)

1-3: 1-Kaluta-c; r/trading cards; new Steranko centerfold 3.00

MARVEL MILESTONE EDITION
Marvel Comics: 1991 - 1999 ($2.95, coated stock)(r/originals with original ads w/silver ink-c)

...: Amazing Fantasy #15 (3/92); ....:Hulk #181 (8/99, $2.99) 3 6 9 14 20 25
...: Amazing Spider-Man #1 (1/93), ...: Amazing Spider-Man #1 (1/93) variation- no price on-c, ...: Amazing Spider-Man #3 (3/95, $2.95), ...: Amazing Spider-Man #129 (11/92), ...: Avengers #1 (9/93), ...:Avengers #4 (3/95, $2.95), ...: Captain America #1 (3/95, $3.95), ...: Fantastic Four #1 (11/91), ...: Fantastic Four #5 (11/92), ...: Giant Size X-Men #1 (1991, $3.95, 68 pgs.), ...: Incredible Hulk #1 (3/92, says 3/91 by error), ...: Iron Man #55 (11/92), ...: Strange Tales-r/Dr. Strange stories from #110, 111, 114, & 115; ...: Tales of Suspense #39 (3/93), ...: X-Men #1-Reprints X-Men #1 (1991) 2 4 6 8 10 12
...: Amazing Spider-Man #149 (11/94, $2.95), ...: Avengers #16 (10/93), ...: X-Men #9 (10/93), ...:X-Men #28 (11/94, $2.95) 6.00
...: Iron Fist #14 (11/92) 1 3 4 6 8 10

MARVEL MILESTONES
Marvel Comics: 2005 - 2006 ($3.99, coated stock)(r/originals w/silver ink-c)

...: Beast & Kitty Pryde-r/from Amazing Adventures #11 & Uncanny X-Men #153 5.00
...: Black Panther, Storm & Ka-Zar-r/from Black Panther #26, Marvel Team-Up #100 and Marvel Mystery Comics #7 5.00
...: Blade, Man-Thing & Satana-r/from Tomb of Dracula #10, Adv. Into Fear #16 and Vampire Tales #2 5.00
...: Captain Britain, Psylocke & Sub-Mariner-r/from Spect. Spidey #114, Uncanny X-Men #213 and Human Torch #2 5.00
...: Doom, Sub-Mariner & Red Skull -r/from FF Ann. #2, Sub-Mariner Comics #1, Captain America Comics #1 5.00
...: Dragon Lord, Speedball and The Man in the Sky -r/from Marvel Spotlight #5, Speedball #1 and Amazing Adult Fantasy #14; Ditko-a on all 5.00
...: Dr. Strange, Silver Surfer, Sub-Mariner, & Hulk -r/from Marvel Premiere #3, FF Ann. #5, Marvel Comics #1, Incredible Hulk #3 5.00
...: Ghost Rider, Black Widow & Iceman -r/from Marvel Spotlight #5, Daredevil #81, X-Men #47 5.00
...: Iron Man, Ant-Man & Captain America -r/from TOS #39,40, TTA #27, Capt. America #1 5.00
...: Legion of Monsters, Spider-Man and Brother Voodoo -r/Marvel Premiere #28 & others 5.00
...: Millie the Model & Patsy Walker-r/from Millie the Model #100, Defenders #65 5.00
...: Onslaught -r/Onslaught: Marvel; wraparound-c 5.00
...: Rawhide Kid & Two-Gun Kid-r/Two-Gun Kid #60 and Rawhide Kid #17 5.00
...: Special: Bloodstone, X-51 & Captain Marvel II ($4.99) -r/from Marvel Presents #1, Machine Man #1, Amazing Spider-Man Ann. #19, and Bloodstone #1 6.00
...: Star Brand & Quasar -r/from Star Brand #1 & Quasar #1 5.00
...: Ultimate Spider-Man, Ult. X-Men, Microman & Mantor -r/from Ultimate Spider-Man #1/2, Ultimate X-Men #1/2 and Human Torch #2 5.00
...: Venom & Hercules -r/Marvel S-H Secret Wars #8, Journey Into Mystery Ann. #1 5.00
...: Wolverine, X-Men & Tuk: Caveboy -r/from Marvel Comics Presents #1, Uncanny X-Men

Marvel Monsters: Devil Dinosaur #1 © MAR

Marvel Mystery Comics #3 © MAR

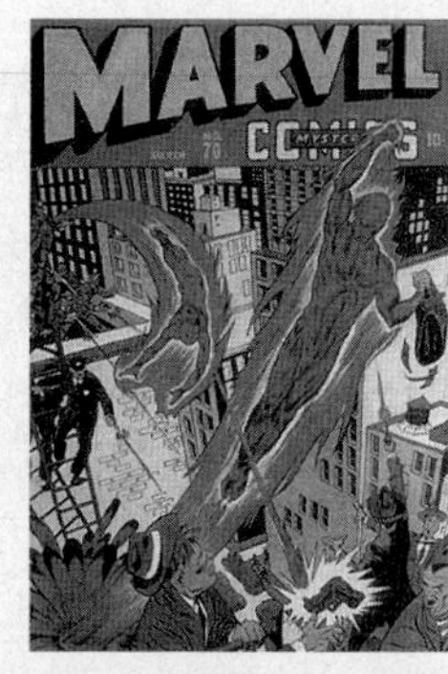

Marvel Mystery Comics #70 © MAR

	GD 2.0	VG 4.0	FN 6.0	VF 8.0	VF/NM 9.0	NM- 9.2

#201, Capt. America Comics #1,2 5.00
...: (Jim Lee and Chris Claremont) X-Men and the Starjammers Pt. 1 -r/Unc. X-Men #275 5.00
...: X-Men and the Starjammers Pt. 2 -r/Unc. X-Men #276,277 5.00

MARVEL MINI-BOOKS (See Promotional Comics section)

MARVEL MONSTERS:... (one-shots)
Marvel Comics: Dec, 2005 ($3.99)

...Devil Dinosaur 1 - Hulk app.; Eric Powell-c/a; Sniegoski-s; r/Journey Into Mystery #62 5.00
...Fin Fang Four 1 - FF app.; Powell-c; Langridge-s/Gray-a; r/Strange Tales #89 5.00
...From the Files of Ulysses Bloodstone 1 - Guide to classic Marvel monsters; Powell-c 5.00
...Monsters on the Prowl 1 - Niles-s/Fegredo-a/Powell-c; Thing, Hulk, Giant-Man & Beast app. 5.00
...Where Monsters Dwell 1 - Giffen-s/a; David-s/Pander-a; Parker-s/Braun-s; Powell-c 5.00
HC (2006, $20.99, dust jacket) r/one-shots 21.00

MARVEL MOVIE PREMIERE (Magazine)
Marvel Comics Group: Sept, 1975 (B&W, one-shot)

1-Burroughs' "The Land That Time Forgot" adapt. 2 4 6 9 13 16

MARVEL MOVIE SHOWCASE FEATURING STAR WARS
Marvel Comics Group: Nov, 1982 - No. 2, Dec, 1982 ($1.25, 68 pgs.)

1-Star Wars movie adaptation; reprints Star Wars #1-3 by Chaykin; reprints-c to Star Wars #1
4 8 12 25 40 55
2-Reprints Star Wars #4-6; Stevens-r 3 6 9 16 23 30

MARVEL MOVIE SPOTLIGHT FEATURING RAIDERS OF THE LOST ARK
Marvel Comics Group: Nov, 1982 ($1.25, 68 pgs.)

1-Edited-r/Raiders of the Lost Ark #1-3; Buscema-c/a(p); movie adapt. 6.00

MARVEL MUST HAVES (Reprints of recent sold-out issues)
Marvel Comics: Dec, 2001 - Present ($2.99/$3.99/$4.99)

1,2,4-6: 1-r/Wolverine: Origin #1, Startling Stories: Banner #1, Tangled Web #4 and Cable #97. 2-Amazing Spider-Man #36 and others. 4-Truth #1, Capt. America V4 #1, and The Ultimates #1. 5-r/Ultimate War #1, Ult. X-Men #26, Ult Spider-Man #33. 6-Ult. Spider-Man #33-36 4.00
3-r/Call of Duty: The Brotherhood #1 & Daredevil #32,33 3.00
Amazing Spider-Man #30-32; Incredible Hulk #34-36; The Ultimates #1-3; Ultimate Spider-Man #1-3; Ultimate X-Men #1-3; (New) X-Men #114-116 each.... 4.00
NYX #1-3 2 4 6 9 12 15
NYX #4-5 with sketch & cover gallery; Ultimates 2 #1-3 each... 5.00
Spider-Man and the Black Cat #1-3; preview of #4 5.00

MARVEL MYSTERY COMICS (Formerly Marvel Comics) (Becomes Marvel Tales No. 93 on)
Timely /Marvel Comics (TP #2-17/TCI #18-54/MCI #55-92): No. 2, Dec, 1939 - No. 92, June, 1949 (Some material from #8-10 reprinted in 2004's Marvel 65th Anniversary Special #1)

2-(Rare)-American Ace begins, ends #3; Human Torch (blue costume) by Burgos, Sub-Mariner by Everett continue; 2 pg. origin recap of Human Torch; Angel-c
3850 7700 11,550 29,000 64,500 100,000
3-New logo from Marvel pulp begins; 1st app. of television in comics? in Human Torch story (1/40); Angel-c 2700 5400 8100 20,000 40,000 60,000
4-Intro. Electro, the Marvel of the Age (ends #19), The Ferret, Mystery Detective (ends #9); 1st Sub-Mariner-c by Schomburg; 2nd German swastika on-c of a comic (2/40); one month after Top-Notch Comics #2 2900 5800 8700 21,500 43,250 65,000
5 Classic Schomburg Torch-c, his 1st ever (Scarce)
3600 7200 10,800 26,500 55,750 85,000
6-Angel-c; Gustavson Angel story 1025 2050 3075 7790 14,145 20,500
7-Sub-Mariner attacks N.Y. city & Torch joins police force setting up battle in #8-10. Classic Schomburg Torch-c, his 2nd ever 1225 2450 3675 8575 16,538 24,500
8-1st Human Torch & Sub-Mariner battle(6/40) 1500 3000 4500 11,200 24,100 37,000
9-(Scarce)-Human Torch & Sub-Mariner battle (cover/story); classic-c by Everett
5000 10,000 15,000 37,000 73,500 110,000
10-Human Torch & Sub-Mariner battle, conclusion, 1 pg.; Terry Vance, the Schoolboy Sleuth begins, ends #57 1300 2600 3900 9700 20,850 32,000
11-Schomburg Torch-c, his 3rd ever 503 1006 1509 3672 6486 9300
12-Classic Angel-c by Kirby 524 1048 1572 3825 6763 9700
13-Intro. of The Vision by S&K (11/40); Sub-Mariner dons new costume, ends #15; Schomburg's 4th Human Torch-c 757 1514 2271 5526 9763 14,000
14-16: 14-Shows-c to Human Torch #1 on-c (12/40). 15-S&K Vision, Gustavson Angel story
423 846 1269 3057 5379 7700
17-Human Torch/Sub-Mariner team-up by Burgos/Everett; Human Torch pin-up on back-c; shows-c to Human Torch #2 on-c 432 864 1296 3154 5577 8000
18-1st app. villain "The Cat's Paw" 400 800 1200 2800 4900 7000
19,20: 19-Origin Toro in text; shows-c to Sub-Mariner #1 on-c. 20-Origin The Angel in text
411 822 1233 2877 5039 7200
21-The Patriot begins, (intro. in Human Torch #4 (#3)); not in #46-48; Sub-Mariner pin-up on back-c; Gustavson Angel story (7/41) 423 846 1269 3000 5250 7500
22-25: 23-Last Gustavson Angel; origin The Vision in text. 24-Injury-to-eye story
406 812 1218 2842 4971 7100
26-29: 27-Ka-Zar ends; last S&K Vision who battles Satan. 28-Jimmy Jupiter in the Land of Nowhere begins, ends #48; Sub-Mariner vs. The Flying Dutchman
394 788 1182 2758 4829 6900
30-"Remember Pearl Harbor" Japanese war-c 486 972 1458 3550 6275 9000
31,32-"Remember Pearl Harbor" Japanese war-c. 31-Sub-Mariner by Everett ends, resumes #84. 32-1st app. The Boboes 394 788 1182 2758 4829 6900
33,35,36,38,39: 36-Nazi invasion of NYC cover. 39-WWII Nazi-c
377 754 1131 2639 4620 6600
34-Everett, Burgos, Martin Goodman, Funnies, Inc. office appear in story & battles Hitler; last Burgos Human Torch 389 778 1167 2723 4762 6800
37-Classic Hitler-c 423 846 1269 3000 5250 7500
40-Classic Zeppelin-c 975 1950 2919 7100 12,550 18,000
41-Hirohito & Tojo-c 420 840 1260 2940 5170 7400
42,43,47 366 732 1098 2562 4481 6400
44-Classic Super Plane-c 1000 2000 3000 7600 13,800 20,000
45-Red Skull, Nazi hooded Vigilante war-c 443 886 1329 3234 5717 8200
46-Classic Hitler-c 1250 2500 3750 9500 17,250 25,000
48-Last Vision; flag-c 377 754 1131 2639 4620 6600
49-Origin Miss America 377 754 1131 2639 4620 6600
50-Mary becomes Miss Patriot (origin) 349 698 1047 2443 4272 6100
51-60: 54-Bondage-c 300 600 900 1950 3375 4800
61,62,64-Last German war-c 277 554 831 1759 3030 4300
63-Classic Hitler War-c; The Villainess Cat-Woman only app.
432 864 1296 3154 5577 8000
65,66-Last Japanese War-c 277 554 831 1759 3030 4300
67-78: 74-Last Patriot. 75-Young Allies begin. 76-Ten Chapter Miss America serial begins, ends #85 161 322 483 1030 1765 2500
79-New cover format; Super Villains begin on cover; last Angel
181 362 543 1158 1979 2800
80-1st app. Capt. America in Marvel Comics 194 388 582 1242 2121 3000
81-Captain America app. 165 330 495 1048 1799 2550
82-Origin & 1st app. Namora (5/47); 1st Sub-Mariner/Namora team-up; Captain America app.
320 640 960 2240 3920 5600
83,85: 83-Last Young Allies. 85-Last Miss America; Blonde Phantom app.
155 310 465 992 1696 2400
84-Blonde Phantom begins (on-c of #84,88,89); Sub-Mariner by Everett begins; Captain America app.; Everett-c 200 400 600 1280 2190 3100
86-Blonde Phantom i.d. revealed; Captain America app.; last Bucky app.
158 316 474 1003 1727 2450
87-1st Capt. America/Golden Girl team-up; last Toro app. (8/48)
165 330 495 1048 1799 2550
88-Golden Girl, Namora, & Sun Girl (1st in Marvel Comics) x-over; Captain America, Blonde Phantom app. 168 336 504 1075 1838 2600
89-1st Human Torch/Sun Girl team-up; 1st Captain America solo; Blonde Phantom app.
161 322 483 1030 1765 2500
90,91: 90-Blonde Phantom un-masked; Captain America app. 91-Capt. America app.; Blonde Phantom & Sub-Mariner end; early Venus app. (4/49) (scarce)
219 438 657 1402 2401 3400
92-Feature story on the birth of the Human Torch and the death of Professor Horton (his creator); 1st app. The Witness in Marvel Comics; Captain America app. (scarce)
400 800 1200 2800 4900 7000
132 Pg. issue, B&W, 25¢ (1943-44)-printed in N. Y.; square binding, blank inside covers); has Marvel No. 33-c in color; contains Capt. America #18 & Marvel Mystery Comics #33; same contents as Captain America Annual 7100 14,200 21,800 44,000 - -
132 Pg. issue (with variant contents), B&W, 25¢ (1942-'43)- square binding, blank inside covers; has same Marvel No. 33-c in color but contains Capt. America #22 & Marvel Mystery Comics #41 instead 7100 14,200 21,800 44,000 - -

NOTE: ***Brodsky** c-49, 72, 86, 88-92. **Crandall** a-26i. **Everett** c-9, 27, 84. **Gabrielle** c-30-32. **Schomburg** c-3-11, 13-29, 33-36, 39-48, 50-59, 63-69, 74, 76, 132 pg. issue. **Shores** c-37, 38, 75p, 77, 78p, 79p, 80, 81p, 82-84, 85p, 87p. **Sekowsky** c-73. Bondage covers-3, 4, 7, 12, 28, 29, 49, 50, 52, 56, 57, 58, 59, 65. Angel c-2, 3, 8, 12. Remember Pearl Harbor issues-#30-32.*

MARVEL MYSTERY COMICS
Marvel Comics: Dec, 1999 ($3.95, reprints)

1-Reprints original 1940s stories; Schomburg-c from #74 5.00

MARVEL MYSTERY COMICS 70th ANNIVERARY SPECIAL
Marvel Comics: Jul, 2009 ($3.99, one-shot)

1-Rivera-c; new Sub-Mariner/Human Torch team-up set in 1941; reps. from #4 & 5 5.00

MARVEL MYSTERY HANDBOOK: 70th ANNIVERARY SPECIAL
Marvel Comics: 2009 ($4.99, one-shot)

1-Official Handbook-style profile pages of characters from Marvel's first year 5.00

MARVEL NEMESIS: THE IMPERFECTS (EA Games characters)
Marvel Comics: July, 2005 - No. 6, Dec, 2005 ($2.99, limited series)

Marvel No-Prize Book #1 © MAR

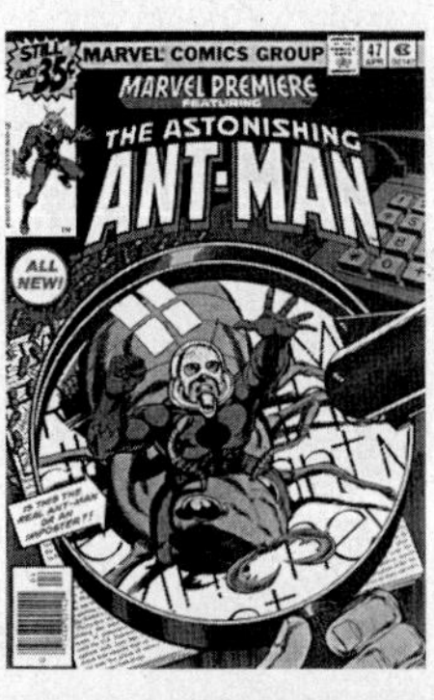

Marvel Premiere #47 © MAR

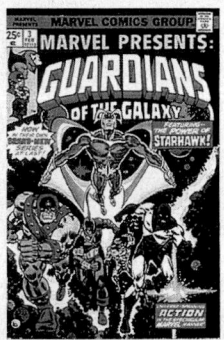

Marvel Presents #3 © MAR

GD VG FN VF VF/NM NM-
2.0 4.0 6.0 8.0 9.0 9.2

GD VG FN VF VF/NM NM-
2.0 4.0 6.0 8.0 9.0 9.2

1-6-Jae Lee-c/Greg Pak-s/Renato Arlem-a; Spider-Man, Thing, Wolverine, Elektra app 3.00
Digest (2005, $7.99) r/#1-6 8.00

MARVEL 1985
Marvel Comics: July, 2008 - No. 6, Dec, 2008 ($3.99, limited series)

1-6: 1-Marvel villains come to the real world; Millar-s/Edwards-a; three covers 4.00
HC (2009, $24.99) r/#1-6; intro. by Lindelof; Edwards production art 25.00

MARVEL NO-PRIZE BOOK, THE (The Official... on-c)
Marvel Comics Group: Jan, 1983 (one-shot, direct sales only)

1-Golden-c; Kirby-a 5.00

MARVEL NOW! POINT ONE
Marvel Comics: Dec, 2012 ($5.99, one-shot)

1-Short story lead-ins to new Marvel Now! series; Nick Fury, Nova, Star-Lord, Ant-Man & others app.; s/a by various; Granov-c and baby variant-c by Skottie Young 6.00

MARVEL: NOW WHAT?!
Marvel Comics: Dec, 2013 ($3.99, one-shot)

1-Short story spoofs; Doct. Octopus, X-Men, Avengers; s/a by various; Skottie Young-c 4.00

MARVELOUS ADVENTURES OF GUS BEEZER
Marvel Comics: May, 2003; Feb, 2004 ($2.99, one-shots)

...: Gus Beezer & Spider-Man 1 - (5/03) Gurihiru-a 3.00
...: Hulk 1 - (5/03) Simone-s/Lethcoe-a; She-Hulk app. 3.00
...: Spider-Man 1 - (5/03) Simone-s/Lethcoe-a; The Lizard & Dr. Doom app. 3.00
...: X-Men 1 - (5/03) Simone-s/Lethcoe-a 3.00

MARVELOUS LAND OF OZ (Sequel to Wonderful Wizard of Oz)
Marvel Comics: Jan, 2010 - No. 8, Sept, 2010 ($3.99, limited series)

1-8-Eric Shanower-a/Skottie Young-a/c. 1-Two covers by Young 4.00
1-Variant Pumpkinhead/Saw-Horse cover by McGuinness 6.00

MARVEL PETS HANDBOOK (Also see "Lockjaw and the Pet Avengers")
Marvel Comics: 2009 ($3.99, one-shot)

1-Official Handbook-style profile pages of animal characters 4.00

MARVEL PREMIERE
Marvel Comics Group: April, 1972 - No. 61, Aug, 1981 (A tryout book for new characters)

1-Origin Warlock (pre-#1) by Gil Kane/Adkins; origin Counter-Earth; Hulk & Thor cameo (#1-14 are 20¢-c) 14 28 42 96 211 325
2-Warlock ends; Kirby Yellow Claw-r 4 8 12 28 47 65
3-Dr. Strange series begins (pre #1, 7/72), Stan Lee-s/B. Smith-c/a(p) 9 18 27 57 111 165
4-Barry Smith-a; Roy Thomas brings the world of Robert E. Howard into the Marvel Universe (via serpent people) 4 8 12 25 40 55
5-9: 5-1st app. Sligguth; 1st mention of Shuma-Gorath. 6-Brunner-a; 1st N'Gabthoth (Shambler from the sea). 7-1st Dagoth; P. Craig Russell-a. 8-Starlin-(p). 9-Englehart-s; Brunner-a(p) begin 3 6 9 17 26 35
10-Death of the Ancient One; 1st app. Shuma-Gorath 3 6 9 21 33 45
11-14: 11-Three pages of original material; mostly reprint of origin from Strange Tales #115 with Ditko-a. 13-Baron Mordo app; 1st app. Cagliostro & Sise-Neg. 14-Sise-Neg & Shuma-Gorath app.14-Last Dr. Strange (3/74), gets own title 3 months later 3 6 9 14 20 25
15-Origin/1st app. Iron Fist (5/74), ends #25 25 50 75 175 388 600
16,25: 16-2nd app. Iron Fist; origin cont'd from #15; Hama's 1st Marvel-a. 25-1st Byrne Iron Fist (moves to own title next) 5 10 15 34 60 85
17,18,20,22-24: Iron Fist in all 3 6 9 21 33 45
19-1st app. Colleen Wing; Iron Fist app. 6 12 18 42 79 115
21-1st app. Misty Knight; Iron Fist app. 6 12 18 37 66 95
26-Hercules. 2 4 6 8 10 12
27-Satana 2 4 6 11 16 20
28-Legion of Monsters (Ghost Rider, Man-Thing, Morbius, Werewolf) 5 10 15 34 60 85
29-46: 29,30-The Liberty Legion. 29-1st modern app. Patriot. 31-1st app. Woodgod; last 25¢ issue. 32-1st app. Monark Starstalker. 33,34-1st color app. Solomon Kane (Robert E. Howard adaptation "Red Shadows".) 35-Origin/1st app. 3-D Man. 36,37-3-D Man. 38-1st Weirdworld. 39,40-Torpedo. 41-1st Seeker 3000! 42-Tigra. 43-Paladin. 44-Jack of Hearts (1st solo book, 10/78). 45,46-Man-Wolf 1 2 3 5 6 8
29-31-(30¢-c variants, limited distribution)(4,6,8/76) 4 8 12 25 40 55
36-38-(35¢-c variants, limited distribution)(6,8,10/77) 6 12 18 38 69 100
47-Origin/1st app. new Ant-Man (Scott Lang); Byrne-a 8 16 24 56 108 160
48-Ant-Man; Byrne-a 4 8 12 23 37 50
49-The Falcon (1st solo book, 8/79) 2 4 6 11 16 20
50-1st app. Alice Cooper; co-plotted by Alice 3 6 9 19 30 40
51-53-Black Panther vs. KKK 2 4 6 9 12 15
54-56: 54-1st Caleb Hammer. 55-Wonder Man. 56-1st color app. Dominic Fortune 6.00
57-Dr. Who (2nd U.S. app.-see Movie Classics) 3 6 9 19 30 40
58-60-Dr. Who 1 3 4 6 8 10
61-Star Lord 2 4 6 9 12 15

NOTE: ***N. Adams*** *(Crusty Bunkers) part inks-10, 12, 13.* ***Austin*** *a-50i, 56i; c-46i, 50i, 56i, 58.* ***Brunner*** *a-4i, 6p, 9-14p; c-9-14.* ***Byrne*** *a-47p, 48p.* ***Chaykin*** *a-32-34; c-32, 33, 56.* ***Giffen*** *a-31p, 44p; c-44.* ***Gil Kane*** *a(p)-1, 2, 15; c(p)-1, 2, 15, 16, 22-24, 27, 36, 37.* ***Kirby*** *c-26, 29-31, 35.* ***Layton*** *a-47i, 48i; c-47.* ***McWilliams*** *a-25i.* ***Miller*** *c-49p, 53p, 58p.* ***Nebres*** *a-44i; c-38i.* ***Nino*** *a-38i.* ***Perez*** *c/a-38p, 45p, 46p.* ***Ploog*** *a-38; c-5-7.* ***Russell*** *a-7p.* ***Simonson*** *a-60(2pgs.); c-57.* ***Starlin*** *a-8p; c-8.* ***Sutton*** *a-41, 43, 50p, 61; c-50p, 61. #57-60 publ'd w/two different prices on-c.*

MARVEL PRESENTS
Marvel Comics: October, 1975 - No. 12, Aug, 1977 (#1-6 are 25¢ issues)

1-Origin & 1st app. Bloodstone 3 6 9 15 22 28
2-Origin Bloodstone continued; Buckler-c 2 4 6 8 10 12
3-Guardians of the Galaxy (1st solo book, 2/76) begins, ends #12 5 10 15 31 53 75
4-7,9-12: 9,10-Origin Starhawk 2 4 6 8 10 12
4-6-(30¢-c variants, limited distribution)(4-8/76) 4 8 12 23 37 50
8-r/story from Silver Surfer #2 plus 4 pgs. new-a 2 4 6 11 16 20
11,12-(35¢-c variants, limited distribution)(6,8/77) 7 14 21 46 86 125

NOTE: ***Austin*** *a-6i.* ***Buscema*** *r-8p.* ***Chaykin*** *a-5p.* ***Kane*** *c-1p.* ***Starlin*** *layouts-10.*

MARVEL PREVIEW (Magazine) (Bizarre Adventures #25 on)
Marvel Comics: Feb (no month), 1975 - No. 24, Winter, 1980 (B&W) ($1.00)

1-Man-Gods From Beyond the Stars; Crusty Bunkers (Neal Adams)-a(i) & cover; Nino-a 3 6 9 19 30 40
2-1st origin The Punisher (see Amaz. Spider-Man #129 & Classic Punisher); 1st app. Dominic Fortune; Morrow-c 10 20 30 67 141 215
3,8,10: 3-Blade the Vampire Slayer. 8-Legion of Monsters; Morbius app. 10-Thor the Mighty; Starlin frontispiece 3 6 9 17 26 35
4-Star-Lord & Sword in the Star (origins & 1st app.); Morrow-c 16 32 48 112 249 385
5-Sherlock Holmes 3 6 9 14 19 24
6,9: 6-Sherlock Holmes; N. Adams frontispiece. 9-Man-God; origin Star Hawk, ends #20 2 4 6 11 16 20
7-(Summer/76) Debut of Rocket Raccoon (called Rocky Raccoon) in Sword in the Star story (see Incredible Hulk #271 (5/82) for next app.); Satana on cover 30 60 90 216 483 750
11,14,15,18-Star-Lord. 11-Byrne-a; Starlin frontispiece; 2 versions: with and w/o white Heinlein text at lower right corner of front-c; 1st app. Spartax. 14-Starlin painted-c. 18-Sienkiewicz-a; Veitch & Bissette-a 5 10 15 31 53 75
12,16,19,21,23: 12-Haunt of Horror. 16-Masters of Terror. 19-Kull. 21-Moon Knight (Spr/80)-Predates Moon Knight #1; The Shroud by Ditko. 23-Bizarre Advs.; Miller-a 2 4 6 8 10 12
13,17,20,22,24: 17-Blackmark by G. Kane (see Savage Sword of Conan #1-3). 20-Bizarre Advs. 22-King Arthur. 24-Debut Paradox 1 2 3 5 6 8

NOTE: ***N. Adams*** *(C. Bunkers) r-20i.* ***Buscema*** *a-22, 23.* ***Byrne*** *a-11.* ***Chaykin*** *a-20r; c-20 (new).* ***Colan*** *a-8, 16p(3), 18p, 23p; c-16p.* ***Elias*** *a-18.* ***Giffen*** *a-7.* ***Infantino*** *a-14p.* ***Kaluta*** *a-12; c-15.* ***Miller*** *a-23.* ***Morrow*** *a-8i; c-2-4.* ***Perez*** *a-20p.* ***Ploog*** *a-8.* ***Starlin*** *c-13, 14. Nudity in some issues.*

MARVEL RIOT
Marvel Comics: Dec, 1995 ($1.95, one-shot)

1-"Age of Apocalypse" spoof; Lobdell script 3.00

MARVEL ROMANCE
Marvel Comics: 2006 ($19.99, TPB)

nn-Reprints romance stories from 1960-1972; art by Kirby, Buscema, Colan, Romita 20.00

MARVEL ROMANCE REDUX (Humor stories using art reprinted from Marvel romance comics)
Marvel Comics: Apr, 2006 - Aug, 2006 ($2.99, one-shots)

...: But I Thought He Loved Me Too (4/06) art by Kirby, Colan, Buscema & Romita; Giffen-c 3.00
...: Guys & Dolls (5/06) art by Starlin, Heck, Colan & Buscema; Conner-c 3.00
...: I Should Have Been a Blonde (7/06) art by Brodsky Colletta & Colan; Cho-c 3.00
...: Love is a Four Letter Word (8/06) art by Kirby, Buscema, Colan & Heck; Land-c 3.00
...: Restraining Orders are For Other Girls (6/06) art by Giordano, Kirby; Baker-c 3.00
...: Another Kind of Love TPB (2007, $13.99) r/one-shots 14.00

MARVELS (Also see Marvels: Eye of the Camera)
Marvel Comics: Jan, 1994 - No. 4, Apr, 1994 ($5.95, painted lim. series)
No. 1 (2nd Printing), Apr, 1996 - No. 4 (2nd Printing), July, 1996 ($2.95)

1-4: Kurt Busiek scripts & Alex Ross painted-c/a in all; double-c w/acetate overlay 1 2 3 5 6 8
Marvel Classic Collectors Pack ($11.90)-Issues #1 & 2 boxed (1st printings). 2 4 6 9 13 16
0-(8/94, $2.95)-no acetate overlay. 5.00
1-4-(2nd printing): r/original limited series w/o acetate overlay 3.00
Hardcover (1994, $59.95)-r/#0-4; w/intros by Stan Lee, John Romita, Sr., Kurt Busiek &

Marvel Selects: Fantastic Four #1 © MAR

Marvel 1602 #2 © MAR

Marvel Spotlight #19 © MAR

	GD 2.0	VG 4.0	FN 6.0	VF 8.0	VF/NM 9.0	NM- 9.2

Scott McCloud. 60.00
...: 10th Anniversary Edition (2004, $49.99, hardcover w/dustjacket) r/#0-4; scripts and commentaries; Ross sketch pages, cover gallery, behind the scenes art 50.00
Trade paperback ($19.95) 20.00

MARVEL SAGA, THE
Marvel Comics Group: Dec, 1985 - No. 25, Dec, 1987

1-25 4.00

NOTE: ***Williamson*** *a(i)-9, 10; c(i)-7, 10-12, 14, 16.*

MARVEL'S ANT-MAN AND THE WASP PRELUDE (For the 2018 movie)
Marvel Comics: May, 2018 - No. 2, Jun, 2018 ($3.99, limited series)

1-Will Corona Pilgrim-s/Chris Allen-a; adaptation of Ant-Man movie 4.00

MARVEL'S ANT-MAN PRELUDE (For the 2015 movie)
Marvel Comics: Apr, 2015 - No. 2, May, 2015 ($2.99, limited series)

1,2-Will Corona Pilgrim-s/Sepulveda-a; photo-c on both; Agent Carter app. 3.00

MARVEL'S AVENGERS: INFINITY WAR PRELUDE (For the 2018 movie)
Marvel Comics: Mar, 2018 - No. 2, Apr, 2018 ($3.99, limited series)

1,2-Will Corona Pilgrim-s; photo-c on both. 1-Tigh Walker-a. 2-Jorge Fornés-a 4.00

MARVEL'S BLACK PANTHER PRELUDE (For the 2018 movie)
Marvel Comics: Dec, 2017 - No. 2, Jan, 2018 ($3.99, limited series)

1,2-Will Corona Pilgrim-s/Annapaola Martello-a; photo-c on both 4.00

MARVEL'S CAPTAIN AMERICA: CIVIL WAR PRELUDE (For the 2016 movie)
Marvel Comics: Feb, 2016 - No. 4, Mar, 2016 ($2.99, limited series)

1-4: 1,2-Adaptation of Iron Man 3 movie; Pilgrim-s/Kudranski-a. 3,4-Adapts Captain America: The Winter Soldier movie; Ferguson-a 3.00

MARVELS COMICS: ... (Marvel-type comics read in the Marvel Universe)
Marvel Comics: Jul, 2000 ($2.25, one-shots)

...Captain America #1 -Frenz & Sinnott-a; ...Daredevil #1 -Isabella-s/Newell-a; ...Fantastic Four #1 -Kesel-s/Paul Smith-a; Spider-Man #1 -Oliff-a; ...Thor #1 -Templeton-s/Aucoin-a 3.00
...X-Men #1 -Millar-s/ Sean Phillips & Duncan Fegredo-a 3.00
The History of Marvels Comics (no cover price)-Faux history; previews titles 3.00

MARVEL'S DOCTOR STRANGE PRELUDE (2016 movie)
Marvel Comics: Sept, 2016 - No. 2, Oct, 2016 ($3.99, limited series)

1,2-Corona Pilgrim-s/Fornés-a; photo-c 4.00

MARVEL SELECT FLIP MAGAZINE
Marvel Comics: Aug, 2005 - No. 24 ($3.99/$4.99)

1-11-Reprints Astonishing X-Men and New X-Men: Academy X in flip format 4.00
12-24-($4.99) Reprints recent X-Men mini-series in flip format 5.00

MARVEL SELECTS:
Marvel Comics: Jan, 2000 - No. 6, June, 2000 ($2.75/$2.99, reprints)

...Fantastic Four 1-6: Reprints F.F. #107-112; new Davis-c 3.00
...Spider-Man 1,2,4-6: Reprints AS-M #100,101,103,104,93; Wieringo-c 3.00
...Spider-Man 3 ($2.99): Reprints AS-M #102; new Wieringo-c 3.00

MARVEL 75TH ANNIVERSARY CELEBRATION
Marvel Comics: Dec, 2014 ($5.99, one-shot)

1-Short stories by various incl. Stan Lee, Timm, Bendis, Stan Goldberg; Rivera-c 6.00

MARVELS: EYE OF THE CAMERA (Sequel to Marvels)
Marvel Comics: Feb, 2009 - No. 6, Apr, 2010 ($3.99, limited series)

1-6-Kurt Busiek-s/Jay Anacleto-a; continuing story of photographer Phil Sheldon 4.00
1-6-B&W edition 4.00

MARVEL'S GREATEST COMICS (Marvel Collectors' Item Classics #1-22)
Marvel Comics Group: No. 23, Oct, 1969 - No. 96, Jan, 1981

	GD	VG	FN	VF	VF/NM	NM-
23-34 (Giants). Begin Fantastic Four-r/#30s?-116	3	6	9	17	26	35
35-37-Silver Surfer-r/Fantastic Four #48-50	2	4	6	9	12	15
38-50: 42-Silver Surfer-r/F.F.(others?)	1	2	3	5	7	9
51-70: 63,64-(25¢ editions)						6.00
63,64-(30¢-c variants, limited distribution)(5,7/76)	3	6	9	21	33	45
71-96: 71-73-(30¢ editions)						5.00
71-73-(35¢-c variants, limited distribution)(7,9-10/77)	5	10	15	34	60	85
...: Fantastic Four #52 (2006, $2.99) reprints entire comic with ads and letter column						6.00

NOTE: *Dr. Strange, Fantastic Four, Iron Man, Watcher-#23, 24. Capt. America, Dr. Strange, Iron Man, Fantastic Four-#25-28. Fantastic Four-#38-96.* ***Buscema*** *r-85-92; c-87-92r.* ***Ditko*** *r-23-28.* ***Kirby*** *r-23-82; c-75, 77p, 80p. #81 reprints Fantastic Four #100.*

MARVEL'S GREATEST SUPERHERO BATTLES (See Fireside Book Series)

MARVEL: SHADOWS AND LIGHT
Marvel Comics: Feb, 1997 ($2.95, B&W, one-shot)

1-Tony Daniel-c 3.00

MARVEL 1602
Marvel Comics: Nov, 2003 - No. 8, June, 2004 ($3.50/$3.99, limited series)

1-7-Neil Gaiman-s; Andy Kubert & Richard Isanove-a 3.50
8-($3.99) 4.00
... MGC #1 (7/10, $1.00) r/#1 with "Marvel's Greatest Comics" logo on cover 3.00
HC (2004, $24.99) r/series; script pages for #1, sketch pages and Gaiman afterword 25.00
SC (2005, $19.99) 20.00

MARVEL 1602: FANTASTICK FOUR
Marvel Comics: Nov, 2006 - No. 5, Mar, 2007s ($3.50, limited series)

1-5-Peter David-s/Pascal Alixe-a/Leinil Yu-c 3.50
TPB (2007, $14.99) r/#1-5; sketch page 15.00

MARVEL 1602: NEW WORLD
Marvel Comics: Oct, 2005 - No. 5, Jan, 2006 ($3.50, limited series)

1-5-Greg Pak-s/Greg Tocchini-a; "Hulk" and "Iron Man" app. 3.50
TPB (2006, $14.99) r/#1-5 15.00

MARVEL 65TH ANNIVERSARY SPECIAL
Marvel Comics: 2004 ($4.99, one-shot)

1-Reprints Sub-Mariner & Human Torch battle from Marvel Mystery Comics #8-10 6.00

MARVELS OF SCIENCE
Charlton Comics: March, 1946 - No. 4, June, 1946

	GD	VG	FN	VF	VF/NM	NM-
1-A-Bomb story	25	50	75	147	241	335
2-4	15	30	45	83	124	165

MARVEL SPECIAL EDITION FEATURING... (Also see Special Collectors' Ed.)
Marvel Comics Group: 1975 - 1978 (84 pgs.) (Oversized)

	GD	VG	FN	VF	VF/NM	NM-
1-The Spectacular Spider-Man ($1.50); r/Amazing Spider-Man #6,35, Annual 1; Ditko-a(r)	3	6	9	19	30	40
1,2-Star Wars ('77,'78) r/Star Wars #1-3 & #4-6; regular edition	2	4	6	11	16	20
1,2-Star Wars ('77,'78) Whitman variant	3	6	9	16	23	30
3-Star Wars ('78, $2.50, 116 pgs.); r/S. Wars #1-6; regular edition and Whitman variant exist	3	6	9	14	20	26
3-Close Encounters of the Third Kind (1978, $1.50, 56 pgs.)-Movie adaptation; Simonson-a(p)	2	4	6	10	14	18
V2#2(Spring, 1980, $2.00, oversized)- "Star Wars: The Empire Strikes Back"; r/Marvel Comics Super Special #16	3	6	9	16	23	30

NOTE: ***Chaykin*** *c/a(r)-1(1977), 2, 3.* ***Stevens*** *a(r)-2i, 3i.* ***Williamson*** *a(r)-V2#2.*

MARVEL SPECTACULAR
Marvel Comics Group: Aug, 1973 - No. 19, Nov, 1975

	GD	VG	FN	VF	VF/NM	NM-
1-Thor-r from mid-sixties begin by Kirby	3	6	9	14	20	25
2-19	1	3	4	6	8	10

MARVELS: PORTRAITS
Marvel Comics: Mar, 1995 - No. 4, June, 1995 ($2.95, limited series)

1-4: Different artists renditions of Marvel characters 3.00

MARVEL SPOTLIGHT (...& Son of Satan #19, 20, 23, 24)
Marvel Comics Group: Nov, 1971 - No. 33, Apr, 1977; V2#1, July, 1979 - V2#11, Mar, 1981
(A try-out book for new characters)

	GD	VG	FN	VF	VF/NM	NM-
1-Origin Red Wolf (western hero)(1st solo book, pre-#1); Wood inks, Neal Adams-c; only 15¢ issue	5	10	15	35	63	90
2-(25¢, 52 pgs.)-Venus-r by Everett; origin/1st app. Werewolf By Night (begins) by Ploog; N. Adams-c	18	36	54	126	281	435
3,4: 4-Werewolf By Night ends (6/72); gets own title 9/72	6	12	18	40	73	105
5-Origin/1st app. Ghost Rider (8/72) & begins	46	92	138	359	805	1250
6-8: 6-Origin G.R. retold. 8-Last Ploog issue	8	16	24	54	102	150
9-11-Last Ghost Rider (gets own title next mo.)	6	12	18	38	69	100
12-Origin & 2nd full app. The Son of Satan (10/73); story cont'd from Ghost Rider #2 & into #3; series begins, ends #24	5	10	15	31	53	75
13-24: 13-Partial origin Son of Satan. 14-Last 20¢ issue. 22-Ghost Rider-c & cameo (5 panels). 24-Last Son of Satan (10/75); gets own title 12/75	2	4	6	9	12	15
25,27,30,31: 27-(Regular 25¢-c), Sub-Mariner app. 30-The Warriors Three. 31-Nick Fury	1	2	3	5	6	8
26-Scarecrow	2	4	6	8	10	12
27-(30¢-c variant, limited distribution)	4	8	12	23	37	50
28-(Regular 25¢-c) 1st solo Moon Knight app.	7	14	21	46	86	125
28-(30¢-c variant, limited distribution)	14	28	42	96	211	325
29-(Regular 25¢-c) (8/76) Moon Knight app.; last 25¢ issue	3	6	9	19	30	40

Marvel Spotlight: Captain America © MAR

Marvel's Thor Ragnarok Prelude #1 © MAR

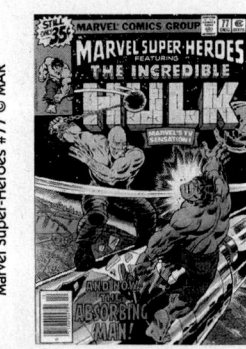

Marvel Super-Heroes #77 © MAR

GD VG FN VF VF/NM NM-
2.0 4.0 6.0 8.0 9.0 9.2

GD VG FN VF VF/NM NM-
2.0 4.0 6.0 8.0 9.0 9.2

29-(30¢-c variant, limited distribution) 7 14 21 44 82 120
32-1st app./partial origin Spider-Woman (2/77); Nick Fury app.
8 16 24 51 96 140
33-Deathlok; 1st app. Devil-Slayer 2 4 6 9 12 15
V2#1-Captain Marvel & Drax app. 2 4 6 8 10 12
1-Variant copy missing issue #1 on cover 3 6 9 19 30 40
2-5,9-11: 2-4-Captain Marvel. 2-Drax app. 4-Ditko-c/a. 5-Dragon Lord. 9-11-Captain Universe (see Micronauts #8) 6.00
6-Star-Lord origin 4 8 12 28 47 65
7-Star-Lord; Miller-c 4 8 12 23 37 50
8-Capt. Marvel; Miller-c/a(p) 2 4 6 8 10 12

NOTE: ***Austin*** *c-V2#2i, 8.* ***J. Buscema*** *c/a-30p.* ***Chaykin*** *a-31; c-26, 31.* ***Colan*** *a-18p, 19p.* ***Ditko*** *a-V2#4, 5, 9-11; c-V2#4, 9-11.* ***Kane*** *c-21p, 32p.* ***Kirby*** *c-29p.* ***McWilliams*** *a-20i.* ***Miller*** *a-V2#8p; c(p)-V2#2, 5, 7, 8.* ***Mooney*** *a-8i, 10i, 14p, 15, 16p, 17p, 24p, 27, 32i.* ***Nasser*** *a-33p.* ***Ploog*** *a-2-5, 6-8p; c-3-9.* ***Romita*** *c-13.* ***Sutton*** *a-9-11p, V2#6, 7. #29-25¢ & 30¢ issues exist.*

MARVEL SPOTLIGHT (Most issues spotlight one Marvel artist and one Marvel writer)
Marvel Comics: 2005 - Present ($2.99/$3.99)

...Brian Bendis/Mark Bagley; Daniel Way/Olivier Coipel; David Finch/Roberto Aguirre-Sacasa; Ed Brubaker/Billy Tan; John Cassaday/Sean McKeever; Joss Whedon/Michael Lark; Laurell K. Hamilton/George R.R. Martin; Neil Gaiman/Salvador Larroca; Robert Kirkman/Greg Land; Stan Lee/Jack Kirby; Warren Ellis/Jim Cheung each... 3.00
...Steve McNiven/Mark Millar - Civil War 10.00
...: Captain America (2009) interviews with Brubaker & Hitch; Reborn preview 3.00
...: Captain America Remembered (2007) character features; creator interviews 3.00
...: Civil War Aftermath (2007) Top 10 Moments, casualty list, previews of upcoming series 3.00
...: Dark Reign (2009) features on the Avengers, Fury and others; creator interview 4.00
...: Dark Tower (2007) previews the Stephen King adaptation; creator interviews 5.00
...: Deadpool (2009) character features; interviews with Kelly, Way, Medina & Benson 3.00
...: Fantastic Four and Silver Surfer (2007) character features; creator interviews 3.00
...: Ghost Rider (2007) character and movie features; creator interviews 3.00
...: Halo (2007) a World of Halo feature; Bendis & Maleev interviews 3.00
...: Heroes Reborn/Onslaught Reborn (2006) 3.00
...: Hulk Movie (2008) character and movie features; comic & movie creator interviews 3.00
...: Iron Man Movie (2008) character and movie features; Terrence Howard interview 3.00
...: Iron Man 2 (4/10) movie preview; Granov, Fraction interviews; Whiplash profile 4.00
...: Marvel Knights 10th Anniversary (2008) Quesada interview; series synopsies 3.00
...: Marvel Zombies/Mystic Arcana (2008) character features; creator interviews 3.00
...: Marvel Zombies Return (2009) character features; creator interviews 3.00
...: New Mutants (2009) character features; Claremont & McLeod interviews 3.00
...: Punisher Movie (2008) character and movie features; creator interviews 3.00
...: Secret Invasion (2008) features on the Skrulls; Bendis, Reed & Yu interviews 3.00
...: Secret Invasion Aftermath (2008) Skrull profiles; Bendis, Reed & Diggle interviews 4.00
...: Spider-Man (2007) character features; creator interviews; Ditko art showcase 3.00
...: Spider-Man - Brand New Day (2008) storyline features; Romitas interviews 3.00
...: Spider-Man-One More Day/Brand New Day (2008) storyline features; interviews 3.00
...: Summer Events (2009, $3.99) 2009 title previews; creator interviews 4.00
...: Thor (2007) character features; Straczynski interview; Romita Jr. art showcase 3.00
...: Ultimates 3 (2008) character features; Loeb & Madureira interviews 3.00
...: Ultimatum (2008) previews the limited series; Loeb & Bendis interviews 3.00
...: Uncanny X-Men 500 Issues Celebration (2008) creator interviews; timeline 3.00
...: War of Kings (2009) character features; Abnett, Lanning, Pelletier interviews 3.00
...: Wolverine (2009, $3.99) preview of 2009 Wolverine stories; creator interviews 4.00
...: World War Hulk (2007) character features; creator interviews; early art showcase 3.00
...: X-Men: Messiah Complex (2008) X-Men crossover features; creator interviews 3.00

MARVELS PROJECT, THE
Marvel Comics: Oct, 2009 - No. 8, July, 2010 ($3.99, limited series)

1-8-Emergence of Marvel heroes in 1939-40; Brubaker-s/Epting-a; Epting & McNiven-c 4.00
1-8-Variant covers by Parel 5.00

MARVEL'S SPIDER-MAN: HOMECOMING PRELUDE
Marvel Comics: May, 2017 - No. 2, Jun, 2017 ($3.99, limited series)

1,2-Adaptation from Captain America: Civil War movie; Pilgrim-s/Nauck-a; photo covers 4.00

MARVEL'S THE AVENGERS
Marvel Comics: Feb, 2015 - No. 2, Mar, 2015 ($2.99, limited series)

1,2-Adaptation of 2012 movie; Pilgrim-s/Bennett-a; photo covers 3.00

MARVEL'S THE AVENGERS: BLACK WIDOW STRIKES
Marvel Comics: Jul, 2012 - No. 3, Aug, 2012 ($2.99, limited series)

1-3-Prelude to 2012 movie; Van Lente-s. 1,3-Photo-c. 2-Granov-c 3.00

MARVEL'S THE AVENGERS PRELUDE
Marvel Comics: May, 2012 - No. 4, Jun, 2012 ($2.99, limited series)

1-4: 1-Prelude to 2012 movie; Luke Ross & Daniel HDR-a 3.00

MARVEL'S THE AVENGERS: THE AVENGERS INITIATIVE
Marvel Comics: Jul, 2012 ($2.99, one-shot)

1-Prelude to 2012 movie; Van Lente-s/Lim-a 3.00

MARVEL'S THOR: RAGNAROK PRELUDE
Marvel Comics: Sept, 2017 - No. 4, Oct, 2017 ($3.99, limited series)

1-4: 1,2-Adapts The Incredible Hulk movie. 3,4-Adapts Thor: The Dark World movie 4.00

MARVEL SUPER ACTION (Magazine)
Marvel Comics Group: Jan, 1976 (B&W, 76 pgs.)

1-2nd app. Dominic Fortune (see Marvel Preview); early Punisher app.; Weird World & The Huntress; Evans, Ploog-a 8 16 24 55 105 155

MARVEL SUPER ACTION
Marvel Comics Group: May, 1977 - No. 37, Nov, 1981

1-Reprints Capt. America #100 by Kirby 3 6 9 14 20 25
2-13: 2,3,5-13 reprint Capt. America #101,102,103-111. 4-Marvel Boy-r(origin)/M. Boy #1. 11-Origin-r. 12,13-Classic Steranko-c/a(r). 2 4 6 8 10 12
2,3-(35¢-c variants, limited distribution)(6,8/77) 9 18 27 61 123 185
14-20: r/Avengers #55,56, Annual 2, others 1 2 3 5 6 8
21-37: 30-r/Hulk #6 from U.K. 6.00

NOTE: ***Buscema*** *a(r)-14p, 15p; c-18-20, 22, 35r-37.* ***Everett*** *a-4.* ***Heath*** *a-4r.* ***Kirby*** *r-1-3, 5-11.* ***B. Smith*** *a-27r, 28r.* ***Steranko*** *a(r)-12p, 13p; c-12r, 13r.*

MARVEL SUPER HERO CONTEST OF CHAMPIONS
Marvel Comics Group: June, 1982 - No. 3, Aug, 1982 (Limited series)

1-Features nearly all Marvel characters currently appearing in their comics; 1st Marvel limited series 3 6 9 14 19 24
2,3 2 4 6 9 12 15

MARVEL SUPER HEROES
Marvel Comics Group: October, 1966 (25¢, 68 pgs.) (1st Marvel one-shot)

1-r/origin Daredevil from D.D. #1; r/Avengers #2; G.A. Sub-Mariner-r/Marvel Mystery #8 (Human Torch app.). Kirby-a 12 24 36 80 173 265

MARVEL SUPER-HEROES (Formerly Fantasy Masterpieces #1-11)
(Also see Giant-Size Super Heroes) (#12-20: 25¢, 68 pgs.)
Marvel Comics: No. 12, 12/67 - No. 31, 11/71; No. 32, 9/72 - No. 105, 1/82

12-Origin & 1st app. Capt. Marvel of the Kree; G.A. Human Torch, Destroyer, Capt. America, Black Knight, Sub-Mariner-r (#12-20 all contain new stories and reprints)
26 52 78 182 404 625
13-2nd app. Capt. Marvel; 1st app. of Carol Danvers (later becomes Ms. Marvel); Golden Age Black Knight, Human Torch, Vision, Capt. America, Sub-Mariner-r
57 114 171 456 1028 1600
14-Amazing Spider-Man (5/68, new-a by Andru/Everett); G.A. Sub-Mariner, Torch, Mercury (1st Kirby-a at Marvel), Black Knight, Capt. America reprints
10 20 30 65 135 200
15-Black Bolt cameo in Medusa (new-a); Black Knight, Sub-Mariner, Black Marvel, Capt. America-r 6 12 18 42 79 115
16,17: 16-Origin & 1st app. S. A. Phantom Eagle; G.A. Torch, Capt. America, Black Knight, Patriot, Sub-Mariner-r. 17-Origin Black Knight (new-a); G.A. Torch, Sub-Mariner-r; reprint from All-Winners Squad #21 (cover & story)
5 10 15 31 53 75
18-Origin/1st app. Guardians of the Galaxy (1/69); G.A. Sub-Mariner, All-Winners Squad-r
40 80 120 296 673 1050
19-Ka-Zar (new-a); G.A. Torch, Marvel Boy, Black Knight, Sub-Mariner reprints; Smith-c(p); Tuska-a(r) 4 8 12 27 44 60
20-Doctor Doom (5/69); r/Young Men #24 w/-c 6 12 18 37 66 95
21-31: All-r issues. 21-X-Men, Daredevil, Iron Man-r begin, end #31. 31-Last Giant issue
3 6 9 17 26 35
32-50: 32-Hulk/Sub-Mariner-r begin from TTA. 1 2 3 6 8 10
51-70,100: 56-r/origin Hulk/Inc. Hulk #102; Hulk-r begin
1 2 3 5 6 8
57,58-(30¢-c variants, limited distribution)(5,7/76) 4 8 12 28 47 65
65,66-(35¢-c variants, limited distribution)(7,9/77) 6 12 18 40 73 105
71-99,101-105 6.00

NOTE: ***Austin*** *a-104.* ***Colan*** *a(p)-12, 13, 15, 18; c-12, 13, 15, 18.* ***Everett*** *a-14i(new); r-14, 15i, 18, 19, 33; c-85(r). New* ***Kirby*** *c-22, 27, 54.* ***Maneely*** *r-14, 15, 19.* ***Severin*** *r-83-85i, 100-102; c-100-102r.* ***Starlin*** *c-47.* ***Tuska*** *a-19p. Black Knight-r by* ***Maneely*** *in 12-16, 19. Sub-Mariner-r by* ***Everett*** *in 12-20.*

MARVEL SUPER-HEROES
Marvel Comics: May, 1990 - V2#15, Oct, 1993 ($2.95/$2.50, quart., 68-84 pgs.)

1-Moon Knight, Hercules, Black Panther, Magik, Brother Voodoo, Speedball (by Ditko) & Hellcat; Hembeck-a 5.00
2,4,5,V2#3,6,7,9,13-15: 2-Summer Special(7/90); Rogue, Speedball (by Ditko), Iron Man, Falcon, Tigra & Daredevil. 4-Spider-Man/Nick Fury, Daredevil,Speedball, Wonder Man, Spitfire & Black Knight; Byrne-c. 5-Thor, Dr. Strange, Thing & She-Hulk; Speedball by Ditko(p). V2#3-Retells origin Capt. America w/new facts; Blue Shield, Capt. Marvel,

Marvel Super-Heroes Secret Wars #8 © MAR

Marvel Tales #96 © MAR

Marvel Tales #155 © MAR

	GD 2.0	VG 4.0	FN 6.0	VF 8.0	VF/NM 9.0	NM- 9.2
Speedball, Wasp; Hulk by Ditko/Rogers V2#6-9: 6,7-($2.25-c) X-Men, Cloak & Dagger, The Shroud (by Ditko) & Marvel Boy in each. 9-West Coast Avengers, Iron Man app.; Kieth-c(p). V2#13-15 ($2.75, 84 pgs.): 13-All Iron Man 30th anniversary. 15-Iron Man/Thor/Volstagg/Dr. Druid						4.00
V2#8-1st app. Squirrel Girl; X-Men, Namor & Iron Man (by Ditko); Larsen-c	5	10	15	30	50	70
V2#10-Ms. Marvel/Sabretooth-c/story (intended for Ms. Marvel #24; shows-c to #24); Namor, Vision, Scarlet Witch stories; $2.25-c	1	3	4	6	8	10
V2#11-Original Ghost Rider-c/story; Giant-Man, Ms. Marvel stories	2	4	6	8	10	12
V2#12-Dr. Strange, Falcon, Iron Man						4.00

MARVEL SUPER-HEROES MEGAZINE
Marvel Comics: Oct, 1994 - No. 6, Mar, 1995 ($2.95, 100 pgs.)

1-6: 1-r/FF #232, DD #159, Iron Man #115, Incred. Hulk #314						4.00

MARVEL SUPER-HEROES SECRET WARS (See Secret Wars II)
Marvel Comics Group: May, 1984 - No. 12, Apr, 1985 (limited series)

1	3	6	9	14	20	25
1-3-(2nd printings, sold in multi-packs)						4.00
2-6,9-11: 6-The Wasp dies	1	3	4	6	8	10
7,12: 7-Intro. new Spider-Woman. 12-($1.00, 52 pgs.)	2	4	6	9	12	15
8-Spider-Man's new black costume explained as alien costume (1st app. Venom as alien costume)	5	10	15	31	53	75
Secret Wars Omnibus HC (2008, $99.99, dustjacket) r/#1-12, Thor #383, She-Hulk (2004) #10 and What If? (1989) #4 & #114; photo gallery of related toys; pencil-a from #1						100.00

NOTE: ***Zeck** a-1-12; c-1,3,8-12. Additional artists (John Romita Sr., Art Adams and others) had uncredited art in #12.*

MARVEL SUPER HERO SPECTACULAR (All ages)
Marvel Comics: Dec, 2015 ($3.99, one-shot)

1-Avengers, Guardians of the Galaxy and Spider-Man app.; bonus puzzle pages						4.00

MARVEL SUPER HERO SQUAD (All ages)
Marvel Comics: Mar, 2009; Nov, 2009 - No. 4, Feb, 2010 ($3.99/$2.99)

1-4-Based on the animated series; back-up humor strips and pin-ups						3.00
...Hero Up! (3/09, $3.99) Collects humor strips from MarvelKids.com; 2 covers						4.00

MARVEL SUPER HERO SQUAD (All ages)
Marvel Comics: Mar, 2010 - No. 12, Feb, 2011 ($2.99)

1-12-Based on the animated series. 1-Wraparound-c						3.00
Super Hero Squad Spectacular 1 (4/11, $3.99) The Beyonder app.						4.00

MARVEL SUPER SPECIAL, A (See Marvel Comics Super...)

MARVEL SWIMSUIT SPECIAL (Also see Marvel Illustrated...)
Marvel Comics: 1992 - No. 4, 1995 ($3.95/$4.50, magazine, 52 pgs.)

1-4-Silvestri-c; pin-ups by diff. artists. 2-Jusko-c. 3-Hughes-c	1	3	4	6	8	10

MARVEL TAILS STARRING PETER PORKER THE SPECTACULAR SPIDER-HAM
(Also see Peter Porker...)
Marvel Comics Group: Nov, 1983 (one-shot)

1-Peter Porker, the Spectacular Spider-Ham, Captain Americat, Goose Rider, Hulk Bunny app.						4.00

MARVEL TALES (Formerly Marvel Mystery Comics #1-92)
Marvel/Atlas Comics (MCI): No. 93, Aug, 1949 - No. 159, Aug, 1957

	GD 2.0	VG 4.0	FN 6.0	VF 8.0	VF/NM 9.0	NM- 9.2
93-Horror/weird stories begin	258	516	774	1651	2826	4000
94-Everett-a	148	296	444	947	1624	2300
95-New logo	123	246	369	787	1344	1900
96,99,101,103,105	77	154	231	493	847	1200
97-Sun Girl, 2 pgs; Kirbyish-a; one story used in N.Y. State Legislative document	97	194	291	621	1061	1500
98,100: 98-Krigstein-a	74	148	222	470	810	1150
102-Wolverton-a "The End of the World", (6 pgs.)	94	188	282	597	1024	1450
104-Wolverton-a "Gateway to Horror", (6 pgs.)	97	194	291	621	1061	1500
106,107-Krigstein-a. 106-Decapitation story	60	120	180	381	653	925
108-120: 116-(7/53) Werewolf By Night story. 118-Hypo-c/panels in End of World story. 120-Jack Katz-a	54	108	162	343	574	825
121,123-131: 128-Flying Saucer-c. 131-Last precode (2/55)	43	86	129	271	461	650
122-Kubert-a	43	86	129	271	461	650
132,133,135-141,143,145	39	78	117	231	378	525
134-Krigstein, Kubert-a; flying saucer-c	40	80	120	246	411	575
142-Krigstein-a	39	78	117	231	378	525
144-Williamson/Krenkel-a, 3 pgs.	39	78	117	231	378	525
146,148-151,154-156,158: 150-1st S.A. issue. 156-Torres-a	33	66	99	194	317	440
147,152: 147-Ditko-a. 152-Wood, Morrow-a	35	70	105	208	339	470
153-Everett End of World c/story	39	78	117	240	395	550
157,159-Krigstein-a	34	68	102	199	325	450

NOTE: ***Andru** a-103. **Briefer** a-118. **Check** a-147. **Colan** a-102, 105, 107, 118, 120, 121, 127, 131. **Drucker** a-127, 135, 141, 146, 150. **Everett** a-98, 104, 106(2), 108(2), 131, 148, 151, 153, 155; c-107, 109, 111, 112, 114, 117, 127, 143, 147-151, 153, 155, 156. **Forte** a-119, 125, 130, 158. **Heath** a-110, 113, 118, 119; c-104-106, 110, 130. **Gil Kane** a-117. **Lawrence** a-130. **Maneely** a-111, 126, 129; c-108, 116, 120, 129, 152. **Mooney** a-114. **Morisi** a-153. **Morrow** a-150, 152, 156. **Orlando** a-149, 151, 157. **Pakula** a-119, 121, 133, 135, 144, 150, 152, 156. **Powell** a-136, 137, 150, 154. **Ravielli** a-117, 123. **Rico** a-97, 99. **Romita** a-108. **Sekowsky** a-96-98. **Shores** a-110; c-96. **Sinnott** a-105, 116, 144. **Tuska** a-114. **Whitney** a-107. **Wildey** a-126, 138.*

MARVEL TALES (...Annual #1,2; ...Starring Spider-Man #123 on)
Marvel Comics Group (NPP earlier issues): 1964 - No. 291, Nov, 1994 (No. 1-32: 72 pgs.)
(#1-3 have Canadian variants; back & inside-c are blank, same value)

	GD 2.0	VG 4.0	FN 6.0	VF 8.0	VF/NM 9.0	NM- 9.2
1-Reprints origins of Spider-Man/Amazing Fantasy #15, Hulk/Inc. Hulk#1, Ant-Man/T.T.A. #35, Giant Man/T.T.A. #49, Iron Man/T.O.S. #39,48, Thor/J.I.M. #83 & r/Sgt. Fury #1	33	66	99	238	532	825
2 ('65)-r/X-Men #1(origin), Avengers #1(origin), origin Dr. Strange-r/Strange Tales #115 & origin Hulk(Hulk #3)	10	20	30	66	138	210
3 (7/66)-Spider-Man, Strange Tales (H. Torch), Journey into Mystery (Thor), Tales to Astonish (Ant-Man)-r begin (r/Strange Tales #101)	6	12	18	40	73	105
4,5	5	10	15	30	50	70
6-8,10: 10-Reprints 1st Kraven/Amaz. S-M #15	3	6	9	21	33	45
9-r/Amazing Spider-Man #14 w/cover	4	8	12	25	40	55
11-33: 11-Spider-Man battles Daredevil-r/Amaz. Spider-Man #16. 13-Origin Marvel Boy-r from M. Boy #1. 22-Green Goblin-c/story-r/Amaz. Spider-Man #27. 30-New Angel story (x-over w/Ka-Zar #2,3). 32-Last 72 pg. iss. 33-(52 pgs.) Kraven-r	3	6	9	16	23	30
34-50: 34-Begin regular size issues	2	3	4	6	8	10
51-65	1	2	3	5	6	8
66-70-(Regular 25¢ editions)(4-8/76)	1	2	3	5	6	8
66-70-(30¢-c variants, limited distribution)	4	8	12	28	47	65
71-105: 75-Origin Spider-Man-r. 77-79-Drug issues-r/Amaz. Spider-Man #96-98. 98-Death of Gwen Stacy-r/Amaz. Spider-Man #121 (Green Goblin). 99-Death Green Goblin-r/Amaz. Spider-Man #122. 100-(52 pgs.)-New Hawkeye/Two Gun Kid story. 101-105-All Spider-Man-r						6.00
80-84-(35¢-c variants, limited distribution)(6-10/77)	6	12	18	37	66	95
106-r/1st Punisher-Amazing Spider-Man #129	2	4	6	9	12	15
107-136: 107-133-All Spider-Man-r. 111,112-r/Spider-Man #134,135 (Punisher). 113,114-r/Spider-Man #136,137(Green Goblin). 126-128-r/clone story from Amazing Spider-Man #149-151. 134-136-Dr. Strange-r begin; SpM stories continue. 134-Dr. Strange-r/Strange Tales #110						5.00
137-Origin-r Dr. Strange; shows original unprinted-c & origin Spider-Man/Amazing Fantasy #15	2	4	6	9	12	15
137-Nabisco giveaway	2	4	6	9	12	15
138-Reprints all Amazing Spider-Man #1; begin reprints of Spider-Man with covers similar to originals	1	3	4	6	8	10
139-144: r/Amazing Spider-Man #2-7						6.00
145-149,151-190,193-199: Spider-Man-r continue w/#8 on. 149-Contains skin "Tattooz" decals. 153-r/1st Kraven/Spider-Man #15. 155-r/2nd Green Goblin/Spider-Man #17. 161,164,165-Gr. Goblin-c/stories-r/Spider-Man #23,26,27. 178,179-Green Goblin-c/story-r/Spider-Man #39,40. 187,189-Kraven-r. 193-Byrne-r/Marvel Team-Up begin w/scripts						5.00
150,191,192,200: 150-($1.00, 52pgs.)-r/Spider-Man Annual #1(Kraven app.). 191-($1.50, 68 pgs.)-r/Spider-Man #96-98. 192-($1.25, 52 pgs.)-r/Spider-Man #121,122. 200-Double size ($1.25)-Miller-c & r/Annual #14						6.00
201-249,251,252,254-257: 208-Last Byrne-r. 210,211-r/Spidey #134,135. 212,213-r/Giant-Size Spidey #4. 213-r/1st solo Silver Surfer story/F.F. Annual #5. 214,215-r/Spidey #161,162. 222-Reprints origin Punisher/Spect. Spider-Man #83; last Punisher reprint. 209-Reprints 1st app. The Punisher/Amazing Spider-Man #129; Punisher reprints begin, end #222. 223-McFarlane-c begins, end #239. 233-Spider-Man/X-Men team-ups begin; r/X-Men #35. 234-r/Marvel Team-Up #4. 235,236-r/M. Team-Up Annual #1. 237,238-r/M. Team-Up #150. 239,240-r/M. Team-Up #38,90(Beast). 242-r/M.Team-Up #89. 243-r/M. Team-Up #117 (Wolverine). 251-r/Spider-Man #100 (Green Goblin-c/story). 252-r/1st app. Morbius/Amaz. Spider-Man #101. 254-r/M. Team-Up #15(Ghost Rider); new painted-c. 255,256-Spider-Man & Ghost Rider-r/Marvel Team-Up #58,91. 257-Hobgoblin-r begin (r/ASM #238)						3.00
250,253: 250-($1.50, 52 pgs.)-r/1st Karma/M. Team-Up #100. 253-($1.50, 52 pgs.) -r/Amaz. S-M #102						4.00
258-291: 258-261-r/A. Spider-Man #239,249-251(Hobgoblin). 262,263-r/Marv. Team-Up #53,54. 262-New X-Men vs. Sunstroke story. 263-New Woodgod origin story. 264,265-r/Amazing Spider-Man Annual 5. 266-273-Reprints alien costume stories/A. S-M 252-259. 277-r/1st Silver Sable/A. S-M 265. 283-r/A. S-M 275 (Hobgoblin). 284-r/A. S-M 276 (Hobgoblin)						3.00
285-variant w/Wonder-Con logo on c-no price-giveaway						3.00
286-($2.95)-p/bagged w/16 page insert & animation print						4.00

NOTE: *All contain reprints; some have new art. #89-97-r/Amazing Spider-Man #110-118; #98-136-r/#121-159; #137-150-r/Amazing Fantasy #15, #1-12 & Annual 1; #151-167-r/#13-28 & Annual 2; #168-186-r/#29-46. **Austin** a-100i; c-272i, 273i. **Byrne** a(r)-193-198p, 201-208p. **Ditko** a-1-30, 83, 100, 137-155. **G. Kane** a-71, 81, 98-101p,*

Marvel Team-Up #76 © MAR

Marvel Team-Up (2005 series) #1 © MAR

Marvel Treasury Edition #10 © MAR

249r; c-125-127p, 130p, 137-155. ***Sam Kieth*** *c-255, 262, 263.* ***Ron Lim*** *c-266p-281p, 283p-285p.* ***McFarlane*** *c-223-239.* ***Mooney*** *a-63, 95-97i, 103(i).* ***Nasser*** *a-100p.* ***Nebres*** *a-242i.* ***Perez*** *c-259-261.* ***Rogers*** *c-240, 241, 243-252.*

MARVEL TALES FLIP MAGAZINE
Marvel Comics: Sept, 2005 - No. 25, Sept, 2007 ($3.99/$4.99)

1-6-Reprints Amazing Spider-Man #30-up and Amazing Fantasy (2004) in flip format 4.00
7-10-Reprints Amazing Spider-Man #36-up and Runaways Vol. 2 in flip format 4.00
11-25-($4.99) Reprints Amazing Spider-Man #36-up and Runaways Vol. 2 in flip format 5.00

MARVEL TAROT, THE
Marvel Comics: 2007 ($3.99, one-shot)

1-Marvel characters featured in Tarot deck images; Djurdjevic-c 4.00

MARVEL TEAM-UP (See Marvel Treasury Edition #18 & Official Marvel Index To...)
(Replaced by Web of Spider-Man)
Marvel Comics Group: March, 1972 - No. 150, Feb, 1985
NOTE: *Spider-Man team-ups in all but Nos. 18, 23, 26, 29, 32, 35, 97, 104, 105, 137.*

1-Human Torch 13 26 39 87 191 295
2-Human Torch 5 10 15 35 63 90
3-Spider-Man/Human Torch vs. Morbius (part 1); 3rd app. of Morbius (7/72)
6 12 18 41 76 110
4-Spider-Man/X-Men vs. Morbius (part 2 of story); 4th app. of Morbius
6 12 18 41 76 110
5-10: 5-Vision. 6-Thing. 7-Thor. 8-The Cat (4/73, came out between The Cat #3 & 4). 9-Iron Man. 10-Human Torch 3 6 9 20 31 42
11-Inhumans 3 6 9 16 23 30
12-Werewolf (By Night) (8/73) 3 6 9 19 30 40
13,14,16-20: 13-Capt. America. 14-Sub-Mariner. 16-Capt. Marvel. 17-Mr. Fantastic. 18-Human Torch/Hulk. 19-Ka-Zar. 20-Black Panther; last 20¢ issue
2 4 6 13 18 22
15-1st Spider-Man/Ghost Rider team-up (11/73) 4 8 12 25 40 55
21,23-30: 21-Dr. Strange. 23-H-T/Iceman (X-Men cameo). 24-Brother Voodoo. 25-Daredevil. 26-H-T/Thor. 27-Hulk. 28-Hercules. 29-H-T/Iron Man. 30-Falcon
2 4 6 8 10 12
22-Hawkeye 3 6 9 14 19 24
31-45,47-50: 31-Iron Fist. 32-H-T/Son of Satan. 33-Nighthawk. 34-Valkyrie. 35-H-T/Dr. Strange. 36-Frankenstein. 37-Man-Wolf. 38-Beast. 39-H-T. 40-Sons of the Tiger/H-T. 41-Scarlet Witch. 42-The Vision. 43-Dr. Doom; retells origin. 44-Moondragon. 45-Killraven. 47-Thing. 48-Iron Man; last 25¢ issue. 49-Dr. Strange; Iron Man app. 50-Iron Man; Dr. Strange app.
1 2 3 5 6 8
44-48-(30¢-c variants, limited distribution)(4-8/76) 5 10 15 33 57 80
46-Spider-Man/Deathlok team-up 1 2 3 5 7 9
51,52,56,57: 51-Iron Man; Dr. Strange app. 52-Capt. America. 56-Daredevil. 57-Black Widow; 2nd app. Silver Samurai 1 2 3 4 5 7
53-Hulk; Woodgod & X-Men app., 1st Byrne-a on X-Men (1/77)
3 6 9 21 33 45
54,55,58-60: 54,59,60: 54-Hulk; Woodgod app. 59-Yellowjacket/The Wasp. 60-The Wasp (Byrne-a in all). 55-Warlock-c/story; Byrne-a. 58-Ghost Rider
2 3 4 6 8 10
58-62-(35¢-c variants, limited distribution)(6-10/77) 8 16 24 55 105 155
61-64,67-70: All Byrne-a; 61-H-T. 62-Ms. Marvel; last 30¢ issue. 63-Iron Fist. 64-Daughters of the Dragon. 67-Tigra; Kraven the Hunter app. 68-Man-Thing. 69-Havok (from X-Men). 70-Thor 1 2 3 5 7 9
65-Capt. Britain (1st U.S. app.) 4 8 12 27 44 60
66-Capt. Britain; 1st app. Arcade 3 6 9 14 19 24
71-74,76-78,80: 71-Falcon. 72-Iron Man. 73-Daredevil. 74-Not Ready for Prime Time Players (Belushi). 76-Dr. Strange. 77-Ms. Marvel. 78-Wonder Man. 80-Dr. Strange/Clea; last 35¢ issue 6.00
75,79,81: Byrne-a(p). 75-Power Man; Cage app. 79-Mary Jane Watson as Red Sonja; Clark Kent cameo (1 panel, 3/79). 81-Death of Satana
1 2 3 5 6 8
82-85,87-94,96-99: 82-Black Widow. 83-Nick Fury. 84-Shang-Chi. 89-Nightcrawler (X-Men). 91-Ghost Rider. 92-Hawkeye. 93-Werewolf by Night. 94-Spider-Man vs. The Shroud. 96-Howard the Duck; last 40¢ issue. 97-Spider-Woman/ Hulk. 98-Black Widow. 99-Machine Man. 85-Shang-Chi/Black Widow/Nick Fury. 87-Black Panther. 88-Invisible Girl. 90-Beast 5.00
86-Guardians of the Galaxy 2 4 6 8 10 12
95-Mockingbird (intro.); Nick Fury app. 4 8 12 28 47 65
100-(Double-size)-Spider-Man & Fantastic Four story with origin/1st app. Karma, one of the New Mutants; X-Men & Professor X cameo; Miller-c/a(p); Storm & Black Panther story; brief origins; Byrne-a(p) 2 4 6 9 12 15
101,102,104-116: 101-Nighthawk(Ditko-a). 102-Doc Samson. 104-Hulk/Ka-Zar. 105-Hulk/Power Man/Iron Fist. 106-Capt. America. 107-She-Hulk. 108-Paladin; Dazzler cameo. 109-Dazzler; Paladin app. 110-Iron Man. 111-Devil-Slayer. 112-King Kull; last 50¢ issue. 113-Quasar. 114-Falcon. 115-Thor. 116-Valkyrie 4.00

GD VG FN VF VF/NM NM-
2.0 4.0 6.0 8.0 9.0 9.2

103-Ant-Man 2 4 6 9 12 15
117-Wolverine-c/story 2 4 6 9 12 15
118-140,142-149: 118-Professor X; Wolverine app. (4 pgs.); X-Men cameo. 119-Gargoyle. 120-Dominic Fortune. 121-Human Torch. 122-Man-Thing. 123-Daredevil. 124-The Beast. 125-Tigra. 126-Hulk & Powerman/Son of Satan. 127-The Watcher. 128-Capt. America; Spider-Man/Capt. America photo-c. 129-The Vision. 130-Scarlet Witch. 131-Frogman. 132-Mr. Fantastic. 133-Fantastic Four. 134-Jack of Hearts. 135-Kitty Pryde; X-Men cameo. 136-Wonder Man. 137-Aunt May/Franklin Richards. 138-Sandman. 139-Nick Fury. 140-Black Widow. 142-Capt. Marvel. 143-Starfox. 144-Moon Knight. 145-Iron Man. 146-Nomad. 147-Human Torch; Spider-Man back to old costume. 148-Thor. 149-Cannonball 4.00
141-Daredevil; SpM/Black Widow app. (Spidey in new black costume; ties w/ Amazing Spider-Man #252 for 1st black costume) 4 8 12 27 44 60
150-X-Men ($1.00, double-size); B. Smith-c 1 2 3 5 6 8
Annual 1 (1976)-Spider-Man/X-Men (early app.) 4 8 12 23 37 50
Annual 2 (1979)-Spider-Man/Hulk 1 3 4 6 8 10
Annuals 3,4: 3 (1980)-Hulk/Power Man/Machine Man/Iron Fist; Miller-c(p). 4 (1981)-Spider-Man /Daredevil/Moon Knight/Power Man/Iron Fist; brief origins of each; Miller-c; Miller scripts on Daredevil 1 2 3 4 5 7
Annuals 5-7: 5 (1982)-SpM/The Thing/Scarlet Witch/Dr. Strange/Quasar. 6 (1983)-Spider-Man/ New Mutants (early app.), Cloak & Dagger. 7(1984)-Alpha Flight; Byrne-c(i) 6.00
NOTE: ***Art Adams*** *c-141p.* ***Austin*** *a-79i; c-76i, 79i, 96i, 101i, 112i, 130i.* ***Bolle*** *a-9i.* ***Byrne*** *a(p)-53-55, 59-70, 75, 79, 100; c-68p, 70p, 72p, 75, 76p, 79p, 129i, 133i.* ***Colan*** *a-87p.* ***Ditko*** *a-101.* ***Kane*** *a(p)-4-6, 13, 14, 16-19, 23; c(p)-4, 13, 14, 17-19, 23, 25, 26, 32-35, 37, 41, 44, 45, 47, 53, 54.* ***Miller*** *a-100p; c-95p, 99p, 100p, 102p, 106.* ***Mooney*** *a-2i, 7i, 8, 10p, 11p, 16i, 24-31p, 72, 93i, Annual 5i.* ***Nasser*** *a-89p; c-101p.* ***Simonson*** *c-99i, 148.* ***Paul Smith*** *c-131, 132.* ***Starlin*** *c-27.* ***Sutton*** *a-93p. "H-T" means Human Torch; "SpM" means Spider-Man; "S-M" means Sub-Mariner.*

MARVEL TEAM-UP (2nd Series)
Marvel Comics: Sept, 1997 - No. 11, July, 1998 ($1.99)

1-11: 1-Spider-Man team-ups begin, Generation x-app. 2-Hercules-c/app.; two covers. 3-Sandman. 4-Man-Thing. 7-Blade. 8-Namor team-ups begin, Dr. Strange app. 9-Capt. America. 10-Thing. 11-Iron Man 3.00

MARVEL TEAM-UP
Marvel Comics: Jan, 2005 - No. 25, Dec, 2006 ($2.25/$2.99)

1-7,9: 1,2-Spider-Man & Wolverine; Kirkman-s/Kolins-a. 5,6-X-23 app. 3.00
8,10-25 ($2.99-c) 10-Spider-Man & Daredevil. 12-Origin of Titannus. 14-Invincible app. 15-2nd app. of 2nd Sleepwalker 3.00
... Vol. 1: The Golden Child TPB (2005, $12.99) r/#1-6 13.00
... Vol. 2: Master of the Ring TPB (2005, $17.99) r/#7-13 18.00
... Vol. 3: League of Losers TPB (2006, $13.99) r/#14-18 14.00
... Vol. 4: Freedom Ring TPB (2007, $17.99) r/#19-25 18.00

MARVEL: THE LOST GENERATION
Marvel Comics: No. 12, Mar, 2000 - No. 1, Feb, 2001 ($2.99, issue #s go in reverse)

1-12-Stern-s/Byrne-s/a; untold story of The First Line. 5-Thor app. 3.00

MARVEL/ TOP COW CROSSOVERS
Image Comics (Top Cow): Nov, 2005 ($24.99, TPB)

Vol. 1-Reprints crossovers with Wolverine, Witchblade, Hulk, Darkness; Devil's Reign 25.00

MARVEL TREASURY EDITION
Marvel Comics Group/Whitman #17,18: 1974; #2, Dec, 1974 - #28, 1981 ($1.50/$2.50, 100 pgs., oversized, new-a &-r)(Also see Amazing Spider-Man, The, Marvel Spec. Ed. Feat.--, Savage Fists of Kung Fu, Superman Vs. , & 2001, A Space Odyssey)

1-Spectacular Spider-Man; story-r/Marvel Super-Heroes #14; Romita-c/a(r); G. Kane, Ditko-r; Green Goblin/Hulk-r 5 10 15 33 57 80
1-1,000 numbered copies signed by Stan Lee & John Romita on front-c & sold thru mail for $5.00; these were the 1st 1,000 copies off the press
11 22 33 72 154 235
2-10: 2-Fantastic Four-r/F.F. 6,11,48-50(Silver Surfer). 3-The Mighty Thor-r/Thor #125-130. 4-Conan the Barbarian; Barry Smith-c/a(r)/Conan #11. 5-The Hulk (origin-r/Hulk #3). 6-Dr. Strange. 7-Mighty Avengers. 8-Giant Superhero Holiday Grab-Bag; Spider-Man, Hulk, Nick Fury. 9-Giant; Super-hero Team-up. 10-Thor; r/Thor #154-157
3 6 9 17 26 35
11-20: 11-Fantastic Four. 12-Howard the Duck (r/#H. the Duck #1 & G.S. Man-Thing #4,5) plus new Defenders story. 13-Giant Super-Hero Holiday Grab-Bag. 14-The Sensational Spider-Man; r/1st Morbius from Amazing S-M #101,102 plus #100 & r/Not Brand Echh #6. 15-Conan; B. Smith, Neal Adams-i; r/Conan #24. 16-The Defenders (origin) & Valkyrie; r/Defenders #1,4,13,14. 17-Incredible Hulk; Blob, Havok, Rhino and The Leader app. 18-The Astonishing Spider-Man; r/Spider-Man's 1st team-ups with Iron Fist, The X-Men, Ghost Rider & Werewolf by Night; inside back-c has photos from 1978 Spider-Man TV show. 19-Conan the Barbarian. 20-Hulk 3 6 9 14 20 25
21-24,27: 21-Fantastic Four. 22-Spider-Man. 23-Conan. 24-Rampaging Hulk. 27-Spider-Man
3 6 9 14 20 25
25-Spider-Man vs. The Hulk new story 3 6 9 16 24 32

Marvel Triple Action #45 © MAR

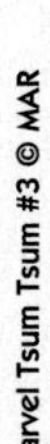

Marvel Tsum Tsum #3 © MAR

Marvel 2-In-One #1 © MAR

	GD 2.0	VG 4.0	FN 6.0	VF 8.0	VF/NM 9.0	NM- 9.2
26-The Hulk; 6 pg. new Wolverine/Hercules-s	3	6	9	16	23	30
28-Spider-Man/Superman; (origin of each)	5	10	15	31	53	75

NOTE: *Reprints-2, 3, 5, 7-9, 13, 14, 16, 17.* ***Neal Adams*** *a(i)-6, 15.* ***Brunner*** *a-6, 12; c-6.* ***Buscema*** *a-15, 19, 28; c-28.* ***Colan*** *a-6r; c-12p.* ***Ditko*** *a-1, 6.* ***Gil Kane*** *c-16p.* ***Kirby*** *a-1-3, 5, 7, 9-11; c-7.* ***Perez*** *a-26.* ***Romita*** *c-1, 5.* ***B. Smith*** *a-4, 15, 19; c-4, 19.*

MARVEL TREASURY OF OZ FEATURING THE MARVELOUS LAND OF OZ
Marvel Comics Group: 1975 ($1.50, oversized) (See MGM's Marvelous...)

1-Roy Thomas-s/Alfredo Alcala-a; Romita-c & bk-c	3	6	9	16	23	30

MARVEL TREASURY SPECIAL (Also see 2001: A Space Odyssey)
Marvel Comics Group: 1974; 1976 ($1.50, oversized, 84 pgs.)

Vol. 1-Spider-Man, Torch, Sub-Mariner, Avengers "Giant Superhero Holiday Grab-Bag"; Wood, Colan/Everett, plus 2 Kirby-r; reprints Hulk vs. Thing from Fantastic Four #25,26	3	6	9	16	24	32
Vol. 1-... Featuring Captain America's Bicentennial Battles (6/76)-Kirby-a; B. Smith inks, 11 pgs.	3	6	9	17	26	35

MARVEL TRIPLE ACTION (See Giant-Size...)
Marvel Comics Group: Feb, 1972 - No. 24, Mar, 1975; No. 25, Aug, 1975 - No. 47, Apr, 1979

1-(25¢ giant, 52 pgs.)-Dr. Doom, Silver Surfer, The Thing begin, end #4 ('66 reprints from Fantastic Four)	4	8	12	23	37	50
2-5	2	4	6	10	14	18
6-10	1	3	4	6	8	10
11-47: 45-r/X-Men #45. 46-r/Avengers #53(X-Men)	1	2	3	5	6	8
29,30-(30¢-c variants, limited distribution)(5,7/76)	4	8	12	23	37	50
36,37-(35¢-c variants, limited distribution)(7,9/77)	6	12	18	38	69	100

NOTE: *#5-44, 46, 47 reprint Avengers #11 thru ?. #40-r/Avengers #48(1st Black Knight).* ***Buscema*** *a(r)-35p, 36p, 38p, 39p, 41, 42, 43p, 44p, 46p, 47p.* ***Ditko*** *a-2r; c-47.* ***Kirby*** *a(r)-1-4p; c-9-19, 22, 24, 29.* ***Starlin*** *c-7.* ***Tuska*** *a(r)-40p, 43i, 46i, 47i. #2 through #17 are 20¢-c.*

MARVEL TRIPLE ACTION
Marvel Comics: May, 2009 - No. 2, Jun, 2009 ($5.99, limited series)

1,2-Reprints stories from Wolverine First Class, Marvel Adventures Avengers & Marvel Super Heroes 6.00

MARVEL TSUM TSUM
Marvel Comics: Oct, 2016 - No. 4, Jan, 2017 ($3.99, limited series)

1-4-Based on Japanese stackable plush toys. 1-Spider-Man and the Avengers app. 4.00

MARVEL TV: GALACTUS - THE REAL STORY
Marvel Comics: Apr, 2009 ($3.99, one-shot)

1-The "hoax" of Galactus, Tieri-s/Santacruz-a; r/Fantastic Four #50 4.00

MARVEL TWO-IN-ONE (...Featuring ... #82 on; also see The Thing)
Marvel Comics Group: January, 1974 - No. 100, June, 1983

1-Thing team-ups begin; Man-Thing	7	14	21	46	86	125
2,3: 2-Sub-Mariner; last 20¢ issue. 3-Daredevil	3	6	9	20	31	42
4,6: 4-Capt. America. 6-Dr. Strange (11/74)	3	6	9	15	22	28
5-Guardians of the Galaxy (9/74, 2nd app.)	4	8	12	25	40	55
7,9,10	2	4	6	10	14	18
8-Early Ghost Rider app. (3/75)	3	6	9	16	23	30
11-14,19,20: 13-Power Man. 14-Son of Satan (early app.)	1	3	4	6	8	10
15-18-(Regular 25¢ editions)(5-7/76) 17-Spider-Man	1	3	4	6	8	10
15-18-(30¢-c variants, limited distribution)	4	8	12	23	37	50
21-29: 27-Deathlok. 29-Master of Kung Fu; Spider-Woman cameo	1	2	3	5	6	8
28,29,31-(35¢-c variants, limited distribution)	5	10	15	31	53	75
30-2nd full app. Spider-Woman (see Marvel Spotlight #32 for 1st app.)	2	4	6	9	13	16
30-(35¢-c variant, limited distribution)(8/77)	8	16	24	51	96	140
31-33-Spider-Woman app.	1	3	4	6	8	10
34-40: 39-Vision	1	2	3	4	5	7
41,42,44,45,47-49: 42-Capt. America. 45-Capt. Marvel						6.00
43,50,53,55-Byrne-a(p). 53-Quasar(7/79, 2nd app.)	1	2	3	5	7	9
46-Thing battles Hulk-c/story	2	4	6	8	10	12
51-The Beast, Nick Fury, Ms. Marvel; Miller-a/c	1	2	3	5	7	9
52-Moon Knight app.; 1st app. Crossfire	2	4	6	8	10	12
54-Death of Deathlok; Byrne-a	2	4	6	10	14	18
56-60,64-68,70-74,76-79,81,82: 60-Intro. Impossible Woman. 68-Angel. 71-1st app. Maelstrom. 76-Iceman						4.00
61-63: 61-Starhawk (from Guardians); "The Coming of Her" storyline begins, ends #63; cover similar to F.F. #67 (Him-c). 62-Moondragon; Thanos & Warlock cameo in flashback; Starhawk app. 63-Warlock revived shortly; Starhawk & Moondragon app.	1	3	4	6	8	10
69-Guardians of the Galaxy	1	3	4	6	8	10
75-Avengers (52 pgs.)						5.00
80,90,100: 80-Ghost Rider. 90-Spider-Man. 100-Double size, Byrne-s						5.00
83-89,91-99: 83-Sasquatch. 84-Alpha Flight app. 93-Jocasta dies. 96-X-Men-c & cameo						4.00
Annual 1 (1976, 52 pgs.)-Thing/Liberty Legion; Kirby-c	2	4	6	10	14	18
Annual 2 (1977, 52 pgs.)-Thing/Spider-Man; 2nd death of Thanos; end of Thanos saga; Warlock app.; Starlin-c/a	6	12	18	38	69	100
Annual 3,4 (1978-79, 52 pgs.): 3-Nova. 4-Black Bolt	1	2	3	4	5	7
Annual 5-7 (1980-82, 52 pgs.): 5-Hulk. 6-1st app. American Eagle. 7-The Thing/Champion; Sasquatch, Colossus app.; X-Men cameo (1 pg.)						5.00

NOTE: ***Austin*** *c(i)-42, 54, 56, 58, 61, 63, 66.* ***John Buscema*** *a-30p, 45; c-30p.* ***Byrne*** *(p)-43, 50, 53-55; c-43, 53p, 56p, 98i, 99i.* ***Gil Kane*** *a-1p, 2p; c(p)-1-3, 9-11, 14, 28.* ***Kirby*** *c-12, 19p, 20, 25, 27.* ***Mooney*** *a-18i, 38i, 90i.* ***Nasser*** *a-70p.* ***Perez*** *a(p)-56-58, 60, 64, 65; c(p)-32, 33, 42, 50-52, 54, 55, 57, 58, 61-66, 70.* ***Roussos*** *a-Annual 1i.* ***Simonson*** *c-43i, 97p, Annual 6i.* ***Starlin*** *c-6, Annual 1.* ***Tuska*** *a-6p.*

MARVEL TWO-IN-ONE
Marvel Comics: Sept, 2007 - No. 17, Jan, 2009 ($4.99, 64 pgs.)

1-8,13-16-Reprints Marvel Adventures Avengers and X-Men: First Class stories 5.00
9-12,17-Reprints Marvel Adventures Iron Man and Avengers stories 5.00

MARVEL 2-IN-ONE
Marvel Comics: Feb, 2018 - Present ($3.99)

1-3: 1-Human Torch & The Thing team-up; Zdarsky-s/Cheung-a; Doctor Doom app. 4.00

MARVEL UNIVERSE (See Official Handbook Of The...)

MARVEL UNIVERSE (Title on variant covers for newsstand editions of some 2001 Marvel titles. See indicia for actual titles and issue numbers)

MARVEL UNIVERSE
Marvel Comics: June, 1998 - No. 7, Dec, 1998 ($2.99/$1.99)

1-($2.99)-Invaders stories from WW2; Stern-s 4.00
2-7-($1.99): 2-Two covers. 4-7-Monster Hunters; Manley-a/Stern-s 3.00

MARVEL UNIVERSE AVENGERS AND ULTIMATE SPIDER-MAN
Marvel Comics: 2012 (no price, Halloween giveaway)

1-Reprints from Marvel Universe Ultimate Spider-Man #1 & Avengers E.M.H #1 3.00

MARVEL UNIVERSE AVENGERS ASSEMBLE (Based on the Disney XD animated series) (Titled Avengers Assemble for #1,2)
Marvel Comics: Dec, 2013 - No. 12, Nov, 2014 ($3.99/$2.99)

1-($3.99) Red Skull app.; bonus Lego-style story 4.00
2-12-($2.99) 5-Dracula app. 7-Hyperion app. 12-Impossible Man app. 3.00

MARVEL UNIVERSE AVENGERS ASSEMBLE: CIVIL WAR
Marvel Comics: May, 2016 - No. 4, Aug, 2016 ($2.99)

1-4: 1,2,4-Ultron app. 3.00

MARVEL UNIVERSE AVENGERS ASSEMBLE SEASON TWO
Marvel Comics: Jan, 2015 - No. 16, Apr, 2016 ($3.99/$2.99)

1-($3.99) Red Skull & Thanos app. 4.00
2-16-($2.99) 2-Thanos & The Watcher app. 4-Winter Soldier app. 9-Ant-Man joins 3.00

MARVEL UNIVERSE AVENGERS: ULTRON REVOLUTION
Marvel Comics: Sept, 2016 - No. 12, Oct, 2017 ($2.99)

1-12-Ultron returns; A.I.M. app. 11-Ms. Marvel joins. 12-Captain Marvel app. 3.00

MARVEL UNIVERSE GUARDIANS OF THE GALAXY (Disney XD animated series)
Marvel Comics: Apr, 2015 - No. 4, Jul, 2015 ($2.99)

1-4: 1-Back-up story with Star-Lord origin 3.00

MARVEL UNIVERSE GUARDIANS OF THE GALAXY (Disney XD animated series)
Marvel Comics: Dec, 2015 - No. 23, Dec, 2017 ($3.99/$2.99)

1-($3.99) Cosmo & Korath app.; bonus Lego story 4.00
2-23-($2.99) 3-Fin Fang Foom app. 4-Grandmaster app. 13-Loki app. 20-Thanos app. 3.00

MARVEL UNIVERSE HULK: AGENTS OF S.M.A.S.H (Disney XD animated series)
Marvel Comics: Dec, 2013 - No. 4, Mar, 2014 ($2.99)

1-4: 1-Hulk, A-Bomb, She-Hulk, Red Hulk and Skaar team-up 3.00

MARVEL UNIVERSE: MILLENNIAL VISIONS
Marvel Comics: Feb, 2002 ($3.99, one-shot)

1-Pin-ups by various; wraparound-c by JH Williams & Gray 4.00

MARVEL UNIVERSE: THE END (Also see Infinity Abyss)
Marvel Comics: May, 2003 - No. 6, Aug, 2003 ($3.50/$2.99, limited series)

1-($3.50)-Thanos, X-Men, FF, Avengers, Spider-Man, Daredevil app.; Starlin-s/a(p) 4.00
2-6-($2.99) Akhenaten, Eternily, Living Tribunal app. 3.00
Thanos Vol. 3: Marvel Universe - The End (2003, $16.99) r/#1-6 17.00

MARVEL UNIVERSE ULTIMATE SPIDER-MAN (Based on the animated series)
Marvel Comics: Jun, 2012 - No. 31, Dec, 2014 ($2.99)

1-31: 1-Agent Coulson app. 13-Iron Man app. 16,19-Venom app. 29-Spider-Ham app. 3.00

Marvel Universe vs. Wolverine #1 © MAR

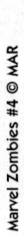

Marvel Zombies #4 © MAR

Marvel Zombies / Army of Darkness #1 © MAR & Sam Raimi

GD	VG	FN	VF	VF/NM	NM-
2.0	4.0	6.0	8.0	9.0	9.2

GD VG FN VF VF/NM NM-
2.0 4.0 6.0 8.0 9.0 9.2

MARVEL UNIVERSE ULTIMATE SPIDER-MAN: CONTEST OF CHAMPIONS
Marvel Comics: May, 2016 - No. 4, Aug, 2016 ($2.99, limited series)

1-4-The Collector & Grandmaster app. 1-Iron Man, Hulk & Kraven app. 3.00

MARVEL UNIVERSE ULTIMATE SPIDER-MAN SPIDER-VERSE
Marvel Comics: Jan, 2016 - No. 4, Apr, 2016 ($3.99/$2.99)

1-($3.99) 1-Spider-Man 2099 and Spider-Girl app. 4.00
2-4-($2.99) 3,4-Miles Morales app. 3.00

MARVEL UNIVERSE ULTIMATE SPIDER-MAN VS. THE SINISTER SIX
Marvel Comics: Sept, 2016 - No. 11, Sept, 2017 ($2.99)

1-11: 1,2-Doctor Octopus & Scarlet Spider app. 3-Dr. Strange app. 6-Venom app. 3.00

MARVEL UNIVERSE ULTIMATE SPIDER-MAN: WEB WARRIORS
Marvel Comics: Jan, 2015 - No. 12, Dec, 2015 ($3.99/$2.99)

1-($3.99) Captain America & Doctor Doom app.; back-up with Iron Spider 4.00
2-12-($2.99) 2-Hawkeye app. 3-Iron Man app. 8-Deadpool app. 12-Howling Commandos 3.00
.../Avengers Assemble Halloween ComicFest 2015 #1 (giveaway) reprints 3.00

MARVEL UNIVERSE VS. THE AVENGERS
Marvel Comics: Dec, 2012 - No. 4, Mar, 2013 ($3.99, limited series)

1-4-Avengers vs. Marvel Zombies; Maberry-s/Fernandez-a/Kuder-c 4.00

MARVEL UNIVERSE VS. THE PUNISHER
Marvel Comics: Oct, 2010 - No. 4, Nov, 2010 ($3.99, limited series)

1-4-Punisher vs. Marvel Zombies; Maberry-s/Parlov-a/c 4.00

MARVEL UNIVERSE VS. WOLVERINE
Marvel Comics: Aug, 2011 - No. 4, Nov, 2011 ($3.99, limited series)

1-4-Wolverine vs. Marvel Zombies; Maberry-s/Laurence Campbell-a/c 4.00

MARVEL UNLIMITED (Title on variant covers for newsstand editions of some 2001 Daredevil issues. See indicia for actual titles and issue numbers)

MARVEL VALENTINE SPECIAL
Marvel Comics: Mar, 1997 ($2.99, one-shot)

1-Valentine stories w/Spider-Man, Daredevil, Cyclops, Phoenix 3.00

MARVEL VERSUS DC (See DC Versus Marvel) (Also see Amazon, Assassins, Bruce Wayne: Agent of S.H.I.E.L.D., Bullets & Bracelets, Doctor Strangefate, JLX, Legend of the Dark Claw, Magneto & The Magnetic Men, Speed Demon, Spider-Boy, Super Soldier, & X-Patrol)
Marvel Comics: No. 2, 1996 - No. 3, 1996 ($3.95, limited series)

2,3: 2-Peter David script. 3-Ron Marz script; Dan Jurgens-a(p). 1st app. of Super Soldier, Spider-Boy, Dr. Doomsday, Doctor Strangefate, The Dark Claw, Nightcreeper, Amazon, Wraith & others. Storyline continues in Amalgam books. 5.00

MARVEL VISIONARIES
Marvel Comics: 2002 - 2007 (various prices, HC and TPB)

...: Chris Claremont (2005, $29.99) r/X-Men #137, Uncanny X-Men #153,205,268 & Ann. #12, Iron Fist #14, Wolverine #3, New Mutants #21 and other highlights 30.00
...: Gil Kane (8/02, $24.95) r/Amazing Spider-Man #99, Marvel Premiere #1,#15, TOA #76 & others; plus sketch pages and a cover gallery 25.00
...: Jack Kirby HC (2004, $29.99) r/career highlights- Red Raven Comics #1 (1st work), Captain America Comics #1, Avengers #4, Fantastic Four #48-50 and more 30.00
...: Jack Kirby Vol. 2 HC (2006, $34.99) r/career highlights- Captain America, Two-Gun Kid, Fantastic Four, Thor, Fin Fang Foom, Devil Dinosaur, romance and more 35.00
...: Jim Steranko (9/02, $14.95) r/Captain America #110,111,113; X-Men #50,51 and stories from Tower of Shadows #1 and Our Love Story #5; plus a cover gallery 15.00
...: John Buscema (2007, $34.99) r/career highlights-Avengers, Silver Surfer, Thor, FF, Hulk, Wolverine and others; Roy Thomas intro.; sketch pages and pin-up art 35.00
...: John Romita Jr. (2005, $29.99) r/various stories 1977-2002; debut in AS-M Ann. #11; Iron Man #128, AS-M V2 #36, issues of Hulk, Daredevil: The Man Without Fear, Punisher; sketch pages; intro. by John Romita Sr. 30.00
...: John Romita Sr. (2005, $29.99) r/various stories 1951-1997 including Young Men #24&26, Daredevil #16, ASM #39,42,50; sketch pages; intro. by John Romita Jr. 30.00
...: Roy Thomas (2006, $34.99) r/career highlights; intro. by Stan Lee 35.00
...: Steve Ditko (2005, $29.99) r/various stories 1961-1992; intro. by Blake Bell 30.00
...: Stan Lee HC (2005, $29.99) r/career highlights- Captain America Comics #3 (1st work), and various Spider-Man, FF, Thor, Daredevil stories; 1940-1995; Roy Thomas intro. 30.00

MARVEL WEDDINGS
Marvel Comics: 2005 ($19.99, TPB)

TPB-Reprints weddings of Peter & Mary Jane, Reed & Sue, Scott & Jean, and others 20.00

MARVEL WESTERNS: ...
Marvel Comics: 2006 ($3.99, one-shots)

... Kid Colt and the Arizona Girl 1 (9/06) 2 short stories & 3 Kirby/Ayers reps.; Powell-c 4.00
... Outlaw Files-Profiles and essays about Marvel western characters 4.00
... Strange Westerns Starring The Black Rider 1 (10/06) Englehart-s/Rogers-a & 2 Kirby Rawhide Kid reprints; Rogers-c 4.00
... The Two-Gun Kid 1 (8/06) 2 short stories & a Kirby/Ayers reprint; Powell-c 4.00
... Western Legends 1 (9/06) 2 short stories & r/Rawhide Kid origin by Kirby; Powell-c 4.00
HC (2006, $20.99, dustjacket) r/one-shots 21.00

MARVEL X-MEN COLLECTION, THE
Marvel Comics: Jan, 1994 - No. 3, Mar, 1994 ($2.95, limited series)

1-3-r/X-Men trading cards by Jim Lee 3.00

MARVEL - YEAR IN REVIEW (Magazine)
Marvel Comics: 1989 - No. 3, 1991 (52 pgs.)

1-3: 1-Spider-Man-c by McFarlane. 2-Capt. America-c. 3-X-Men/Wolverine-c 5.00

MARVEL: YOUR UNIVERSE
Marvel Comics: 2008; May, 2009 - No. 3, July, 2009 ($5.99)

1-3-Reprints of 5 recent comics (Ms. Marvel, Nova, Immortal Iron Fist & others) 6.00
...Saga (2008, no cover price) - Re-caps of crossovers (Secret War thru Secret Invasion) 3.00

MARVEL ZOMBIES (See Ultimate Fantastic Four #21-23, 30-32)
Marvel Comics: Feb, 2006 - No. 5, June, 2006 ($2.99, limited series)

1-Zombies vs. Magneto; Kirkman-s/Phillips-a/Suydam-c swipe of A.F. #15 38.00
1-(2nd-4th printings) Variant Suydam-c swipes of Spider-Man #1, Amazing Spider-Man #50 and Incredible Hulk #1 6.00
2-Avengers #4 cover swipe by Suydam 10.00
3-5: 3-Inc. Hulk #340 c-swipe. 4-X-Men #1 c-swipe. 5-AS-M Ann. #21 c-swipe 6.00
3-5-(2nd printings) 3-Daredevil #179 c-swipe. 4-AS-M #39 c-swipe. 5-Silver Surfer #1 4.00
...: Dead Days (7/07, $3.99) Early days of the plaque; Kirkman-s/Phillips-a/Suydam-c 5.00
...: Dead Days HC (2008, $29.99, oversized) r/Dead Days one-shot, Ultimate Fantastic Four #21-23, 30-32, and Black Panther #28-30 30.00
...: Evil Evolution (1/10, $4.99) Apes vs. Zombies; Marcos Martin-c 5.00
... Halloween (12/12, $3.99) Van Lente-s/Vitti-a/Francavilla-c 4.00
... MGC #1 (7/10, $1.00) r/#1 with "Marvel's Greatest Comics" logo on cover 3.00
...: The Book of Angels, Demons and Various Monstrosities (2007, $3.99) profile pages 5.00
...: The Covers HC (2007, $19.99, d.j.) Suydam's covers with originals and commentary 20.00
HC (2006, $19.99) r/#1-5; Kirkman foreword; cover gallery with variants 20.00

MARVEL ZOMBIES 2
Marvel Comics: Dec, 2007 - No. 5, Apr, 2008 ($2.99, limited series)

1-5-Kirkman-s/Phillips-a/Suydam zombie-fied cover swipes 5.00
HC (2008, $19.99) r/#1-5; cover swipe gallery 20.00

MARVEL ZOMBIES 3
Marvel Comics: Dec, 2008 - No. 4, Mar, 2009 ($3.99, limited series)

1-4-Van Lente-s/Walker-a/Land-c; Machine Man, Jocasta and Morbius app. 5.00

MARVEL ZOMBIES 4
Marvel Comics: Jun, 2009 - No. 4, Sept, 2009 ($3.99, limited series)

1-4-Van Lente-s/Walker-a/Land-c; Zombie Deadpool head app. 4.00

MARVEL ZOMBIES 5
Marvel Comics: Jun, 2010 - No. 5, Sept, 2010 ($3.99, limited series)

1-5-Van Lente-s; Machine Man and Howard the Duck app. 3-Kaluta-a 4.00

MARVEL ZOMBIES (Secret Wars tie-in)
Marvel Comics: Aug, 2015 - No. 4, Dec, 2015 ($3.99, limited series)

1-4-Spurrier-s/Walker-a; Elsa Bloodstone vs. zombies. 2,3-Deadpool app. 4.00

MARVEL ZOMBIES / ARMY OF DARKNESS
Marvel Comics/Dynamite Entertainment: May, 2007 - No. 5, Aug, 2007($2.99, limited series)

1-Zombies vs. Ash during the start of the plaque; Layman-s/Neves-a/Suydam-c 7.00
1-Second printing with Suydam zombie-fied Captain America Comics #1 cover swipe 4.00
2-5-Suydam zombie-fied cover swipes on all 5.00
HC (2007, $19.99) r/#1-5; cover gallery with variants and non-zombied original covers 20.00

MARVEL ZOMBIES CHRISTMAS CAROL ("Zombies Christmas Carol" on cover)
Marvel Comics: Aug, 2011 - No. 5, Oct, 2011 ($3.99, limited series)

1-5-Adaptation of the Dickens classic with zombies; Kaluta-c/Baldeon-a 4.00

MARVEL ZOMBIES DESTROY!
Marvel Comics: Jul, 2012 - No. 5, Sept, 2012 ($3.99, limited series)

1-5-Howard the Duck, Dum Dum Dugan vs. zombies; Del Mundo-c 4.00

MARVEL ZOMBIES RETURN
Marvel Comics: Nov, 2009 - No. 5, Nov, 2009 ($3.99, weekly limited series)

1-5-Suydam-c. 1-Zombie Spider-Man eats the Earth-Z Sinister Six; Dragotta-a. 4.00

MARVEL ZOMBIES SUPREME
Marvel Comics: May, 2011 - No. 5, Aug, 2011 ($3.99, limited series)

1-5-Zombies in Squadron Supreme dimension; Blanco-a/Komarck-c; Jack of Hearts app. 4.00

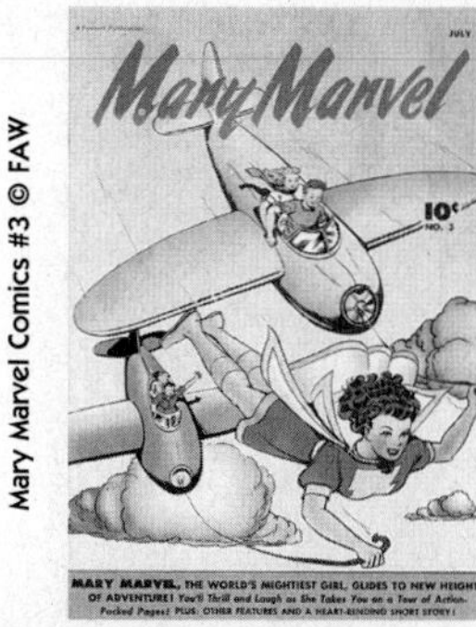

Mary Marvel Comics #3 © FAW

Masked Ranger #9 © Premier

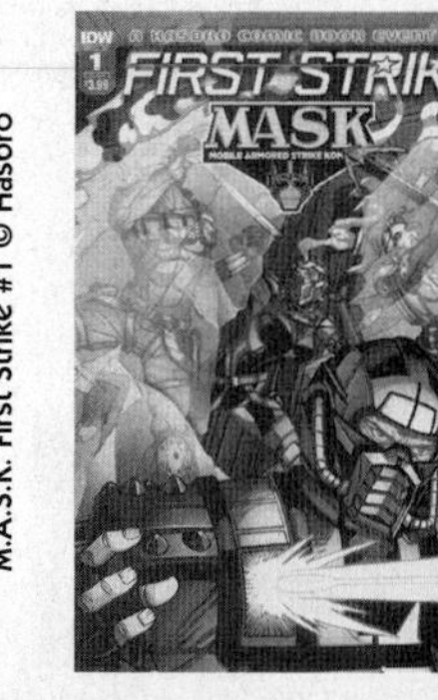

M.A.S.K. First Strike #1 © Hasbro

GD VG FN VF VF/NM NM-
2.0 4.0 6.0 8.0 9.0 9.2

GD VG FN VF VF/NM NM-
2.0 4.0 6.0 8.0 9.0 9.2

MARVILLE
Marvel Comics: Nov, 2002 - No. 7, Jul, 2003 ($2.25, limited series)
1-6-Satire on DC/AOL-Time-Warner; Jemas-a/Bright-a/Horn-c 3.00
1-($3.95) Variant foil cover by Udon Studios; bonus sketch pages and Jemas afterword 4.00
7-($2.99) Intro. to Epic Comics line with submission guidelines 3.00

MARVIN MOUSE
Atlas Comics (BPC): September, 1957
1-Everett-c/a; Maneely-a 17 34 51 98 154 210

MARY JANE (Spider-Man) (Also see Spider-Man Loves Mary Jane)
Marvel Comics: Aug, 2004 - No. 4, Nov, 2004 ($2.25, limited series)
1-4-Marvel Age series with teen-age MJ Watson; Miyazawa-c/a; McKeever-s 3.00
... Vol. 1: Circle of Friends (2004, $5.99, digest-size) r/#1-4 6.00

MARY JANE & SNIFFLES (See Looney Tunes)
Dell Publishing Co.: No. 402, June, 1952 - No. 474, June, 1953
Four Color 402 (#1) 8 16 24 54 102 150
Four Color 474 6 12 18 42 79 115

MARY JANE: HOMECOMING (Spider-Man)
Marvel Comics: May, 2005 - No. 4, Aug, 2005 ($2.99, limited series)
1-4-Teen-age MJ Watson in high school; Miyazawa-c/a; McKeever-s 3.00
... Vol. 2 (2005, $6.99, digest-size) r/#1-4 7.00

MARY MARVEL COMICS (Monte Hale #29 on) (Also see Captain Marvel #18, Marvel Family, Shazam, & Wow Comics)
Fawcett Publications: Dec, 1945 - No. 28, Sept, 1948
1-Captain Marvel introduces Mary on-c; intro/origin Georgia Sivana 161 322 483 1030 1765 2500
2 71 142 213 454 777 1100
3,4: 3-New logo 50 100 150 315 533 750
5-8: 8-Bulletgirl x-over; classic Christmas-c 40 80 120 246 411 575
9,10 37 74 111 222 361 500
11-20 27 54 81 158 259 360
21-28: 28-Western-c 24 48 72 140 230 320

MARY POPPINS (See Movie Comics & Walt Disney Showcase No. 17)

MARY SHELLEY'S FRANKENSTEIN
Topps Comics: Oct, 1994 - Jan, 1995 ($2.95, limited series)
1-4-polybagged w/3 trading cards 4.00
1-4 ($2.50)-Newstand ed. 3.00

MARY WORTH (See Harvey Comics Hits #55 & Love Stories of...)
Argo: March, 1956 (Also see Romantic Picture Novelettes)
1 8 16 24 42 54 65

MASK (TV)
DC Comics: Dec, 1985 - No. 4, Mar, 1986; Feb, 1987 - No. 9, Oct, 1987
1-4; 1-9 (2nd series)-Sat. morning TV show. 4.00

MASK, THE (Also see Mayhem)
Dark Horse Comics: Aug, 1991 - No. 4, Oct, 1991; No. 0, Dec, 1991 ($2.50, 36 pgs., limited series)
1-4: 1-1st app. Lt. Kellaway as The Mask (see Dark Horse Presents #10 for 1st app.) 5.00
0-(12/91, B&W, 56 pgs.)-r/Mayhem #1-4 4.00
...Omnibus Vol. 1 (8/08, $24.95) r/#1-4, Mask Returns and Mask Strikes Back series 25.00
...Omnibus Vol. 2 (4/09, $24.95) r/#1-4, The Hunt For Green October, World Tour, Southern Discomfort, Toys in the Attic series and short stories from DHP 25.00

...: HUNT FOR GREEN OCTOBER July, 1995 - Oct, 1995 ($2.50, lim. series)
1-4-Evan Dorkin scripts 3.00

.../ MARSHAL LAW Feb, 1998 - No. 2, Mar, 1998 ($2.95, lim. series)
1,2-Mills-s/O'Neill-a 3.00

...: OFFICIAL MOVIE ADAPTATION July, 1994 - Aug, 1994 ($2.50, lim. series)
1,2 3.00

... RETURNS Oct, 1992 - No. 4, Mar, 1993 ($2.50, limited series)
1-4 4.00

... SOUTHERN DISCOMFORT Mar, 1996 - No. 4, July, 1996 ($2.50, lim. series)
1-4 3.00

... STRIKES BACK Feb, 1995 - No. 5, Jun, 1995 ($2.50, limited series)
1-5 3.00

... SUMMER VACATION July, 1995 ($10.95, one shot, hard-c)
1-nn-Rick Geary-c/a 11.00

... TOYS IN THE ATTIC Aug, 1998 - No. 4, Nov, 1998 ($2.95, limited series)
1-4-Fingerman-s 3.00

... VIRTUAL SURREALITY July, 1997 ($2.95, one shot)
nn-Mignola, Aragonés, and others-s/a 3.00

... WORLD TOUR Dec, 1995 - No. 4, Mar, 1996 ($2.50, limited series)
1-4: 3-X & Ghost-c/app. 3.00

MASK COMICS
Rural Home Publ.: Feb-Mar, 1945 - No. 2, Apr-May, 1945; No. 2, Fall, 1945
1-Classic L. B. Cole Satan-c/a; Palais-a 423 846 1269 3000 5250 7500
2-(Scarce)-Classic L. B. Cole Satan-c; Black Rider, The Boy Magician, & The Collector app. 300 600 900 1920 3310 4700
2-(Fall, 1945)-No publ.-same as regular #2; L. B. Cole-c 245 490 735 1568 2684 3800

MASKED BANDIT, THE
Avon Periodicals: 1952
nn-Kinstler-a 20 40 60 114 182 250

MASKED MAN, THE
Eclipse Comics: 12/84 - #10, 4/86; #11, 10/87; #12, 4/88 ($1.75/$2.00, color/B&W #9 on, Baxter paper)
1-12: 1-Origin retold. 3-Origin Aphid-Man; begin $2.00-c 3.00

MASKED MARVEL (See Keen Detective Funnies)
Centaur Publications: Sept, 1940 - No. 3, Dec, 1940
1-The Masked Marvel begins 194 388 582 1242 2121 3000
2,3: 2-Gustavson, Tarpe Mills-a 135 270 405 864 1482 2100

MASKED RAIDER, THE (Billy The Kid #9 on; Frontier Scout, Daniel Boone #10-13) (Also see Blue Bird)
Charlton Comics: June, 1955 - No. 8, July, 1957; No. 14, Aug, 1958 - No. 30, June, 1961
1-Masked Raider & Talon the Golden Eagle begin; painted-c 14 28 42 78 112 145
2 9 18 27 47 61 75
3-8,15: 8-Billy The Kid app. 15-Williamson-a, 7 pgs. 7 14 21 35 43 50
14,16-30: 22-Rocky Lane app. 6 12 18 28 34 40

MASKED RANGER
Premier Magazines: Apr, 1954 - No. 9, Aug, 1955
1-The Masked Ranger, his horse Streak, & The Crimson Avenger (origin) begin, end #9; Woodbridge/Frazetta-a 42 84 126 265 445 625
2,3 16 32 48 94 147 200
4-8-All Woodbridge-a. 5-Jesse James by Woodbridge. 6-Billy The Kid by Woodbridge. 7-Wild Bill Hickok by Woodbridge. 8-Jim Bowie's Life Story 17 34 51 98 154 210
9-Torres-a; Wyatt Earp by Woodbridge; Says Death of Masked Ranger on-c 18 36 54 107 169 230
NOTE: *Check a-1. Woodbridge c/a-1, 4-9.*

M.A.S.K.: MOBILE ARMORED STRIKE KOMMAND (Hasbro toy)
IDW Publishing: Nov, 2016 - No. 10, Aug, 2017 ($3.99)
1-10: 1,2-Easton-s/Vargas-a. 3,6,7-Samu-a 4.00
Annual 2017 (2/17, $7.99, squarebound) Griffith-a; bonus character profiles 8.00
M.A.S.K. First Strike 1 (10/17, $3.99) G.I. Joe & Cobra app.; 3 covers; Kyriazis-a 4.00
...: Revolution 1 (9/16, $3.99) Easton-s/Vargas-a 4.00

MASK OF DR. FU MANCHU, THE (See Dr. Fu Manchu)
Avon Periodicals: 1951
1-Sax Rohmer adapt.; Wood-c/a (26 pgs.); Hollingsworth-a 123 246 369 787 1344 1900

MASK OF ZORRO, THE
Image Comics: Aug, 1998 - No. 4, Dec, 1998 ($2.95, limited series)
1-4-Movie adapt. Photo variant-c 3.00

MASKS
Dynamite Entertainment: 2012 - No. 8, 2013 ($3.99)
1-Team-up of the Shadow, Green Hornet, Spider; Alex Ross-a; multiple covers 5.00
2-8: 2-Miss Fury and Green Lama app.; Calero-a. 3-Black Terror app. 4.00

MASKS 2
Dynamite Entertainment: 2015 - No. 8, 2015 ($3.99)
1-8-Pulp hero team-up; Bunn-s/Casallos-a; multiple covers on each 4.00

MASKS: TOO HOT FOR TV!
DC Comics (WildStorm): Feb, 2004 ($4.95)
1-Short stories by various incl. Thompson, Brubaker, Mahnke, Conner; Fabry-c 5.00

MASQUE OF THE RED DEATH (See Movie Classics)

The Massive #30 © Brian Wood

Master Comics #96 © FAW

Master of Kung Fu #126 © MAR

GD 2.0 | VG 4.0 | FN 6.0 | VF 8.0 | VF/NM 9.0 | NM- 9.2

MASQUERADE (See Project Superpowers)
Dynamite Entertainment: 2009 - No. 4, 2009 ($3.50, limited series)

1-4-Alex Ross & Phil Hester-s/Carlos Paul-a; covers by Ross & others 3.50

MASS EFFECT: DISCOVERY (Based on the EA video game)
Dark Horse Comics: May, 2017 - No. 4, Oct, 2017 ($3.99, limited series)

1-4-Barlow-s/Guzmán-a 4.00

MASS EFFECT: EVOLUTION (2nd series based on the EA video game)
Dark Horse Comics: Jan, 2011 - No. 4, Apr, 2011 ($3.50, limited series)

1-4-Walters & Jackson Miller-s/Carnevale-c 3.50

MASS EFFECT: FOUNDATION (Based on the EA video game)
Dark Horse Comics: Jul, 2013 - No. 13, Jul, 2014 ($3.99, limited series)

1-13: 1-Walters-s/Francia-a. 2-4-Parker-a 4.00

MASS EFFECT: HOMEWORLDS (Based on the EA video game)
Dark Horse Comics: Apr, 2012 - No. 4, Aug, 2012 ($3.50, limited series)

1-4: 1-Walters-s/Francisco-a 3.50

MASS EFFECT: INVASION (3rd series based on the EA video game)
Dark Horse Comics: Oct, 2011 - No. 4, Jan, 2012 ($3.50, limited series)

1-4-Walters & Jackson Miller-s/Carnevale-c 3.50

MASS EFFECT: REDEMPTION (Based on the EA video game)
Dark Horse Comics: Jan, 2010 - No. 4, Apr, 2010 ($3.50, limited series)

1-4-Walters & Jackson Miller-s/Francia-a 3.50

MASSIVE, THE
Dark Horse Comics: Jun, 2012 - No. 30, Dec, 2014 ($3.50)

1-30: 1-Brian Wood-s/Kristian Donaldson-a. 4-9,25-30-Brown-a. 10-Erskine-a 3.50
...: Ninth Wave 1-6 ($3.99, 12/15 - No. 6, 5/16) Prequel to series; Wood-s/Brown-a 4.00

MASTER COMICS (Combined with Slam Bang Comics #7 on)
Fawcett Publications: Mar, 1940 - No. 133, Apr, 1953 (No. 1-6: oversized issues) (#1-3: 15¢, 52 pgs.; #4-6: 10¢, 36 pgs.; #7-Begin 68 pg. issues)

1-Origin & 1st app. Master Man; The Devil's Dagger, El Carim, Master of Magic, Rick O'Say, Morton Murch, White Rajah, Shipwreck Roberts, Frontier Marshal, Streak Sloan, Mr. Clue begin (all features end #6) 975 1950 2919 7100 12,550 18,000
2 (Rare) 300 600 900 1980 3440 4900
3-6: 6-Last Master Man (Rare) 239 478 717 1530 2615 3700
NOTE: *#1-6 rarely found in near mint or very fine condition due to large-size format.*
7-(10/40)-Bulletman, Zoro, the Mystery Man (ends #22), Lee Granger, Jungle King, & Buck Jones begin; only app. The War Bird & Mark Swift & the Time Retarder; Zoro, Lee Granger, Jungle King & Mark Swift all continue from Slam Bang; Bulletman moves from Nickel 300 600 900 1950 3375 4800
8-The Red Gaucho (ends #13), Captain Venture (ends #22) & The Planet Princess begin 161 322 483 1030 1765 2500
9,10: 10-Lee Granger ends 135 270 405 864 1482 2100
11-Origin & 1st app. Minute-Man (2/41) 277 554 831 1759 3030 4300
12 129 258 387 826 1413 2000
13-Origin & 1st app. Bulletgirl; Hitler-c 265 530 795 1694 2897 4100
14-16: 14-Companions Three begins, ends #31 116 232 348 742 1271 1800
17-20: 17-Raboy-a on Bulletman begins. 20-Captain Marvel cameo app. in Bulletman 110 220 330 704 1202 1700
21-(12/41; Scarce)-Captain Marvel & Bulletman team up against Capt. Nazi; origin & 1st app. Capt. Marvel Jr's most famous nemesis Captain Nazi who will cause creation of Capt. Marvel Jr. in Whiz #25. Part I of trilogy origin of Capt. Marvel Jr.; 1st Mac Raboy-c for Fawcett; Capt. Nazi-c 724 1448 2172 5285 9343 13,400
22-(1/42)-Captain Marvel Jr. moves over from Whiz #25 & teams up with Bulletman against Captain Nazi; part III of trilogy origin of Capt. Marvel Jr. & his 1st cover and adventure 632 1264 1896 4614 8157 11,700
23-Capt. Marvel Jr. c/stories begin (1st solo story); fights Capt. Nazi by himself. 300 600 900 2070 3635 5200
24,25 135 270 405 864 1482 2100
26,28,30-Captain Marvel Jr. vs. Capt. Nazi. 28-Liberty Bell-c. 30-Flag-c 129 258 387 826 1413 2000
27-Captain Marvel Jr. "V For Victory"-c; Capt. Nazi app. 168 336 504 1075 1838 2600
29-Hitler & Hirohito-c 245 490 735 1568 2684 3800
31,32,35: 32-Last El Carim & Buck Jones; intro Balbo, the Boy Magician in El Carim story; classic Eagle-c by Raboy 110 220 330 704 1202 1700
33-Capt. Marvel Jr. smashing swastika-c; Balbo, the Boy Magician (ends #47), Hopalong Cassidy (ends #49) begins 155 310 465 992 1696 2400
34-Capt. Marvel Jr. vs. Capt. Nazi-c/story; 1st mention of Capt. Nippon 135 270 405 864 1482 2100
36-Statue of Liberty-c 100 200 300 635 1093 1550
37-39 84 168 252 538 919 1300
40-Classic flag-c 142 284 426 909 1555 2200
41-(8/43)-Bulletman, Capt. Marvel Jr. & Bulletgirl x-over in Minute-Man; only app. Crime Crusaders Club (Capt. Marvel Jr., Minute-Man, Bulletman & Bulletgirl) 87 174 261 553 952 1350
42-47,49: 46-Hitler story. 47-Hitler becomes Corpl. Hitler Jr. 49-Last Minute-Man 54 108 162 343 574 825
48-Intro. Bulletboy; Capt. Marvel cameo in Minute-Man 57 114 171 362 619 875
50-Intro Radar & Nyoka the Jungle Girl & begin series (5/44); Radar also intro in Captain Marvel #35 (same date); Capt. Marvel x-over in Radar; origin Radar; Capt. Marvel & Capt. Marvel, Jr. introduce Radar on-c 54 108 162 346 591 835
51-58 31 62 93 182 296 410
59-62: Nyoka serial "Terrible Tiara" in all; 61-Capt. Marvel Jr. 1st meets Uncle Marvel 32 64 96 192 314 435
63-80 24 48 72 140 230 320
81,83-87,89-91,95-99: 88-Hopalong Cassidy begins (ends #94). 95-Tom Mix begins (cover only in #123, ends #133) 22 44 66 128 209 290
82,88,92-94-Krigstein-a 22 44 66 132 216 300
100 22 44 66 132 216 300
101-106-Last Bulletman (not in #104) 21 42 63 124 202 280
107-120: 118-Mary Marvel 20 40 60 120 195 270
121-131-(lower print run): 123-Tom Mix-c only 22 44 66 128 209 290
132-B&W and color illos in **POP**; last Nyoka 22 44 66 132 216 300
133-Bill Battle app. 28 56 84 165 270 375
NOTE: ***Mac Raboy** a-15-39, 40(part), 42, 58. c-21-49, 51, 52, 54, 56, 58, 68(part), 69(part). Bulletman c-7-11, 13(half), 15, 18(part), 19, 20, 21(w/Capt. Marvel & Capt. Nazi), 22(w/Capt. Marvel, Jr.). Capt. Marvel, Jr. c-23-133. Master Man c-1-6. Minute Man c-12, 13(half), 14, 16, 17, 18(part).*

MASTER DARQUE
Acclaim Comics (Valiant): Feb, 1998 ($3.95)

1-Manco-a/Christina Z.-s 4.00

MASTER DETECTIVE
Super Comics: 1964 (Reprints)

17-r/Criminals on the Loose V4 #2; r/Young King Cole #?; McWilliams-r 2 4 6 8 11 14

MASTER OF KUNG FU (Formerly Special Marvel Edition; see Deadly Hands of Kung Fu & Giant-Size...)
Marvel Comics Group: No. 17, April, 1974 - No. 125, June, 1983

17-Starlin-a; intro Black Jack Tarr; 3rd Shang-Chi (ties w/Deadly Hands #1) 4 8 12 27 44 60
18,20 3 6 9 16 23 30
19-Man-Thing-c/story 3 6 9 18 28 38
21-23,25-30 2 4 6 10 14 18
24-Starlin, Simonson-a 2 4 6 11 16 20
31-50: 33-1st Leiko Wu. 43-Last 25¢ issue 1 3 4 6 8 10
39-43-(30¢-c variants, limited distribution)(5-7/76) 5 10 15 33 57 80
51-75 6.00
53-57-(35¢-c variants, limited distribution)(6-10/77) 6 12 18 38 69 100
76-99 5.00
100,118,125-Double size 6.00
101-117,119-124 4.00
Annual 1(4/76)-Iron Fist app. 3 6 9 21 33 45
NOTE: ***Austin** c-63i, 74i. **Buscema** c-44p. **Gulacy** a(p)-18-20, 22, 25, 29-31, 33-35, 38, 39, 40(p&i), 42-50, 53r(#20); c-51, 55, 64, 67. **Gil Kane** c(p)-20, 38, 39, 42, 45, 59, 63. **Nebres** c-73i. **Starlin** a-17p, 24; c-54. **Sutton** a-42i. #53 reprints #20.*

MASTER OF KUNG FU (Secret Wars tie-in)
Marvel Comics: Jul, 2015 - No. 4, Oct, 2015 ($3.99, limited series)

1-4-Blackman-s/Talajic-a/Francavilla-c; Shang-Chi & Iron Fist app. 4.00

MASTER OF KUNG FU (Marvel Legacy)
Marvel Comics: No. 126, Jan, 2018 ($3.99, one-shot)

126-CM Punk-s/Talajic-a 4.00

MASTER OF KUNG-FU: BLEEDING BLACK
Marvel Comics: Feb, 1991 ($2.95, 84 pgs., one-shot)

1-The Return of Shang-Chi 4.00

MASTER OF KUNG-FU, SHANG-CHI:... (2002 series, see Shang Chi:...)

MASTER OF THE WORLD
Dell Publishing Co.: No. 1157, July, 1961

Four Color 1157-Movie based on Jules Verne's "Master of the World" and "Robur the Conqueror" novels; with Vincent Price & Charles Bronson 7 14 21 48 89 130

MASTERS OF TERROR (Magazine)

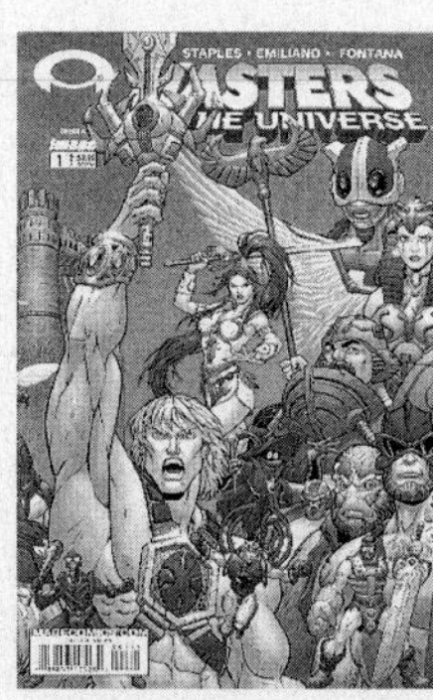

Masters of the Universe V2 #1 © Mattel

Mata Hari #1 © Beeby & Kristantina

Max Ride: First Flight #2 © James Patterson

	GD 2.0	VG 4.0	FN 6.0	VF 8.0	VF/NM 9.0	NM- 9.2

Marvel Comics Group: July, 1975 - No. 2, Sept, 1975 (B&W) (All reprints)
1-Brunner, Barry Smith-a; Morrow/Steranko-c; Starlin-a(p); Gil Kane-a
3 6 9 17 26 35
2-Reese, Kane, Mayerik-a; Adkins/Steranko-c 2 4 6 13 18 22

MASTERS OF THE UNIVERSE (See DC Comics Presents #47 for 1st app.)
DC Comics: Dec, 1982 - No. 3, Feb, 1983 (Mini-series)
1 3 6 9 16 23 30
2,3: 2-Origin He-Man & Ceril 2 4 6 10 14 18
NOTE: *Alcala a-1i,, 2i. Tuska a-1-3p; c-1-3p. #2 has 75 & 95 cent cover price.*

MASTERS OF THE UNIVERSE (Comic Album)
Western Publishing Co.: 1984 (8-1/2x11", $2.95, 64 pgs.)
11362-Based on Mattel toy & cartoon 2 4 6 11 16 20

MASTERS OF THE UNIVERSE
Star Comics/Marvel #7 on: May 1986 - No. 13, May, 1988 (75¢/$1.00)
1 3 6 9 16 23 30
2-11: 8-Begin $1.00-c 1 2 3 5 6 8
12-Death of He-Man (1st Marvel app.) 4 8 12 23 37 50
13-Return of He-Man & death of Skeletor 4 8 12 22 35 48
The Motion Picture (11/87, $2.00)-Tuska-p 2 4 6 9 12 15

MASTERS OF THE UNIVERSE
Image Comics: Nov, 2002 - No. 4, March, 2003 ($2.95, limited series)
1-($2.95) Two covers by Santalucia and Campbell; Santalucia-a 4.00
1-($5.95) Variant-c by Norem w/gold foil logo 6.00
2-4($2.95) 2-Two covers by Santalucia and Manapul. 3,4-Two covers 3.00
TPB (CrossGen, 2003, $9.95, 8-1/4" x 5-1/2") digest-sized reprints #1-4 10.00

MASTERS OF THE UNIVERSE (Volume 2)
Image Comics: March, 2003 - No. 6, Aug, 2003 ($2.95)
1-6-($2.95) 1-Santalucia-c. 2-Two covers by Santalucia & JJ Kirby 3.00
1-($5.95) Wraparound variant-c by Struzan w/silver foil logo 6.00
3,4-($5.95) Wraparound variant holofoil-c. 3-By Edwards 4-By Boris Vallejo & Julie Bell 6.00
Volume 2 Dark Reflections TPB (2004, $18.95) r/#1-6 19.00

MASTERS OF THE UNIVERSE (Volume 3)
MVCreations: Apr, 2004 - No. 8, Dec, 2004 ($2.95)
1-8: 1-Santalucia-c 3.00

MASTERS OF THE UNIVERSE...
CrossGen Comics
...Rise of the Snake-Men (Nov, 2003 - No. 3, $2.95) Meyers-a 3.00
...The Power of Fear (12/03, $2.95, one-shot) Santalucia-a 3.00

MASTERS OF THE UNIVERSE, ICONS OF EVIL
Image Comics/CrossGen Comics: 2003 ($4.95, one-shots)
...Beastman -(Image) Origin of Beast Man; Tony Moore-a 5.00
...Mer-Man -(CrossGen) 5.00
...Trapjaw -(CrossGen) 5.00
...Tri-Klops -(CrossGen) Walker-c 5.00
TPB (3/04, $18.95, MVCreations) r/one-shots; sketch pages 19.00

MASTERS OF THE UNIVERSE: ...
DC Comics: Dec, 2012; Mar, 2013; Jul, 2013 ($2.99, one-shots)
... Origin Of He-Man (3/13) Fialkov-s; Ben Oliver-a/c; Prince Adam finds the sword 3.00
... Origin Of Hordak (7/13) Giffen & Keene-s/Giffen-a/c 3.00
... The Origin Of Skeletor (12/12) Fialkov-s; Fraser Irving-a/c; Keldor becomes Skeletor 3.00

MASTERWORKS SERIES OF GREAT COMIC BOOK ARTISTS, THE
Sea Gate Dist./DC Comics: May, 1983 - No. 3, Dec, 1983 (Baxter paper)
1-3: 1,2-Shining Knight by Frazetta r-/Adventure. 2-Tomahawk by Frazetta-r. 3-Wrightson-c/a(r) 6.00

MATADOR
DC Comics (WildStorm): July, 2005 - No. 6, May, 2006 ($2.99, limited series)
1-6-Devin Grayson-s/Brian Stelfreeze-a/c 3.00

MATA HARI
Dark Horse Comics (Berger Books): Feb, 2018 - No. 5 ($3.99, limited series)
1-Beeby-s/Kristantina-a/c; story of the World War 1 spy 4.00

MATRIX COMICS, THE (Movie)
Burlyman Entertainment: 2003; 2004 ($21.95, trade paperback)
nn-Short stories by various incl. Wachowskis, Darrow, Gaiman, Sienkiewicz, Bagge 22.00
...Volume One Preview (7/03, no cover price) bios of creators; Chadwick-s/a 3.00
Volume 2-(2004) Short stories by various incl. Wachowskis, Sale, McKeever, Dorman 22.00

MATT SLADE GUNFIGHTER (Kid Slade Gunfighter #5 on; See Western Gunfighters)
Atlas Comics (SPI): May, 1956 - No. 4, Nov, 1956
1-Intro Matt & horse Eagle; Williamson/Torres-a 23 46 69 138 227 315
2-Williamson-a 15 30 45 88 137 185
3,4 13 26 39 72 101 130
NOTE: *Maneely a-1, 3, 4; c-1, 2, 4. Roth a-2-4. Severin a-1, 3, 4. Maneely c/a-1. Issue #s stamped on cover after printing.*

MAUS: A SURVIVOR'S TALE (First graphic novel to win a Pulitzer Prize)
Pantheon Books: 1986, 1991 (B&W)
Vol. 1-(...: My Father Bleeds History)(1986) Art Spiegelman-s/a; recounts stories of Spiegelman's father in 1930s-40s Nazi-occupied Poland; collects first six stories serialized in Raw Magazine from 1980-1985 30.00
Vol. 2-(...: And Here My Troubles Began)(1991) 25.00
Complete Maus Survivor's Tale -HC Vols. 1& 2 w/slipcase 35.00
Hardcover Vol. 1 (1991) 30.00
Hardcover Vol. 2 (1991) 30.00
TPB (1992, $14.00) Vols. 1& 2 18.00

MAVERICK (TV)
Dell Publishing Co.: No. 892, 4/58 - No. 19, 4-6/62 (All have photo-c)
Four Color 892 (#1)-James Garner photo-c begin 18 36 54 126 281 435
Four Color 930,945,962,980,1005 (6-8/59): 945-James Garner/Jack Kelly photo-c begin
10 20 30 64 132 200
7 (10-12/59) - 14: 11-Variant edition has "Time For Change" comic strip on back-c. 14-Last Garner/Kelly-c 8 16 24 54 102 150
15-18: Jack Kelly/Roger Moore photo-c 7 14 21 44 82 120
19-Jack Kelly photo-c (last issue) 7 14 21 46 86 125

MAVERICK (See X-Men)
Marvel Comics: Jan, 1997 ($2.95, one-shot)
1-Hama-s 4.00

MAVERICK (See X-Men)
Marvel Comics: Sept, 1997 - No. 12, Aug, 1998 ($2.99/$1.99)
1,12: 1-($2.99)-Wraparound-c. 12-($2.99) Battles Omega Red 4.00
2-11: 2-Two covers. 4-Wolverine app. 6,7-Sabretooth app. 3.00

MAVERICK MARSHAL
Charlton Comics: Nov, 1958 - No. 7, May, 1960
1 6 12 18 33 41 48
2-7 5 10 15 23 28 32

MAVERICKS
Daggar Comics Group: Jan, 1994 - No. 5, 1994 (#1-$2.75, #2-5-$2.50)
1-5: 1-Bronze. 1-Gold. 1-Silver 3.00

MAX BRAND (See Silvertip)

MAX HAMM FAIRY TALE DETECTIVE
Nite Owl Comix: 2002 - 2004 ($4.95, B&W, 6 1/2" x 8")
1-(2002) Frank Cammuso-s/a 5.00
Vol. 2 #1-3 (2003-2004) Frank Cammuso-s/a 5.00

MAXIMAGE
Image Comics (Extreme Studios): Dec, 1995 - No. 7, June 1996 ($2.50)
1-7: 1-Liefeld-c. 2-Extreme Destroyer Pt. 2; polybagged w/card. 4-Angela & Glory-c/app. 3.00

MAXIMO
Dreamwave Prods.: Jan, 2004 ($3.95, one-shot)
1-Based on the Capcom video game 4.00

MAXIMUM SECURITY (Crossover)
Marvel Comics: Oct, 2000 - No. 3, Jan, 2001 ($2.99)
1-3-Busiek-s/Ordway-a; Ronan the Accuser, Avengers app. 3.00
...Dangerous Planet 1: Busiek-s/Ordway-a; Ego, the Living Planet 3.00
Thor vs. Ego (11/00, $2.99) Reprints Thor #133,160,161; Kirby-a 3.00

MAX RIDE: FINAL FLIGHT (Based on the James Patterson novel Maximum Ride)
Marvel Comics: Nov, 2016 - No. 5, Mar, 2017 ($3.99, limited series)
1-5-Jody Houser-s/Marco Failla-a. 1-Two covers (Nakamura & Oum) 4.00

MAX RIDE: FIRST FLIGHT (Based on the James Patterson novel Maximum Ride)
Marvel Comics: Jun, 2015 - No. 5, Oct, 2015 ($3.99, limited series)
1-5-Marguerite Bennett-s/Alex Sanchez-a. 1-Three covers 4.00

MAX RIDE: ULTIMATE FLIGHT (Based on the James Patterson novel Maximum Ride)
Marvel Comics: Jan, 2016 - No. 5, May, 2016 ($3.99, limited series)
1-5-Jody Houser-s/RB Silva-a. 1-Two covers 4.00

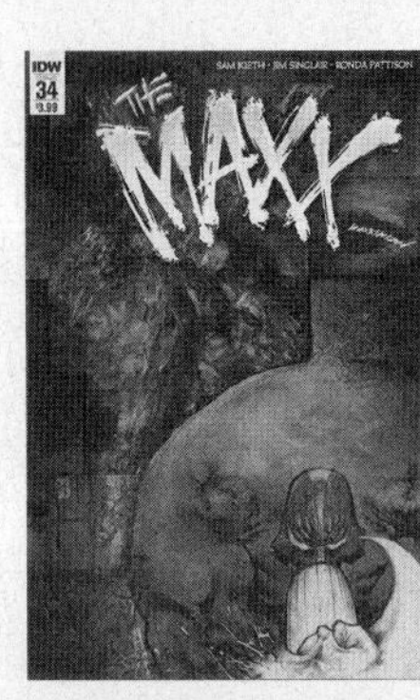

Maxx: Maxximized #34 © Sam Kieth

MD #3 © WMG

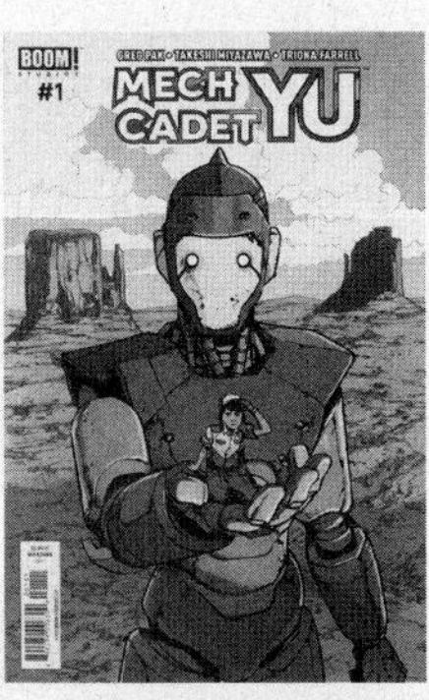

Mech Cadet Yu #1 © Pak & Miyazawa

MAXX (Also see Darker Image, Primer #5, & Friends of Maxx)
Image Comics (I Before E): Mar, 1993 - No. 35, Feb, 1998 ($1.95)

	GD 2.0	VG 4.0	FN 6.0	VF 8.0	VF/NM 9.0	NM- 9.2
1/2	1	3	4	6	8	10
1/2 (Gold)						20.00
1-Sam Kieth-c/a/scripts						5.00
1-Glow-in-the-dark variant	2	4	6	8	10	12
1-"3-D Edition" (1/98, $4.95) plus new back-up story						5.00
2-12: 6-Savage Dragon cameo(1 pg.). 7,8-Pitt-c & story						3.00
13-16						3.00
17-35: 21-Alan Moore-s						3.00
Volume 1 TPB (DC/WildStorm, 2003, $17.95) r/#1-6						18.00
Volume 2 TPB (DC/WildStorm, 2004, $17.95) r/#7-13						18.00
Volume 3 TPB (DC/WildStorm, 2004, $17.95) r/#14-20						18.00
Volume 4 TPB (DC/WildStorm, 2005, $17.95) r/#21-27						18.00
Volume 5 TPB (DC/WildStorm, 2005, $19.99) r/#28-35						20.00
Volume 6 TPB (DC/WildStorm, 2006, $19.99) r/Friends of Maxx #1-3 & The Maxx 3-D						20.00

MAXX: MAXXIMIZED
IDW Publishing: Nov, 2013 - No. 35, Sept, 2016 ($3.99)

1-35-Remastered, recolored reprint of the original Maxx issues — 4.00

MAYA (See Movie Classics)
Gold Key: Mar, 1968

	GD	VG	FN	VF	VF/NM	NM-
1 (10218-803)(TV) Photo-c	3	6	9	16	24	32

MAYDAY
Image Comics: Nov, 2016 - No. 5, May, 2017 ($3.99, limited series)

1-5-Alex de Campi-s/Tony Parker-a — 4.00

MAYHEM
Dark Horse Comics: May, 1989 - No. 4, Sept, 1989 ($2.50, B&W, 52 pgs.)

	GD	VG	FN	VF	VF/NM	NM-
1-Four part Stanley Ipkiss/Mask story begins; Mask-c	1	3	4	6	8	10
2-4: 2-Mask 1/2 back-c. 4-Mask-c	1	2	3	5	7	9

MAYHEM (Tyrese Gibson's...)
Image Comics: Aug, 2009 - No. 3, Oct, 2009 ($2.99, limited series)

1-3-Tyrese Gibson co-writer; Tone Rodriguez-a/c — 3.00

MAZE AGENCY, THE
Comico/Innovation Publ. #8 on: Dec, 1988 - No. 23, Aug, 1991 ($1.95-$2.50, color)

	NM-
1-23: 1-5,8,9,12-Adam Hughes-c/a. 9-Ellery Queen app. 7 ($2.50)-Last Comico issue	3.00
Annual 1 (1990, $2.75)-Ploog-c; Spirit tribute ish	4.00
Special 1 (1989, $2.75)-Staton-p (Innovation)	4.00
TPB (IDW Publ., 11/05, $24.99) r/#1-5	25.00

MAZE AGENCY, THE (Vol. 2)
Caliber Comics: July, 1997 - No. 3, 1998 ($2.95, B&W)

1-3: 1-Barr-s/Gonzales-a(p). 3-Hughes-c — 3.00

MAZE AGENCY, THE
IDW Publishing: Nov, 2005 - No. 3, Jan, 2006 ($3.99, limited series)

1-3-Barr-s/Padilla-a(p)/c — 4.00

MAZE RUNNER: THE SCORCH TRIALS (Based on the Maze Runner movies)
BOOM! Studios: Jun, 2015 ($14.99, squarebound SC)

...Official Graphic Novel Prelude - Short stories about the characters; s/a by various — 15.00

MAZIE (...& Her Friends) (See Flat-Top, Mortie, Stevie & Tastee-Freez)
Mazie Comics(Magazine Publ.)/Harvey Publ. No. 13-on: 1953 - #12, 1954; #13, 12/54 - #22, 9/56; #23, 9/57 - #28, 8/58

	GD	VG	FN	VF	VF/NM	NM-
1-(Teen-age)-Stevie's girlfriend	14	28	42	80	115	150
2	9	18	27	47	61	75
3-10	8	16	24	42	54	65
11-28	7	14	21	37	46	55

MAZIE
Nation Wide Publishers: 1950 - No. 7, 1951 (5¢) (5x7-1/4"-miniature)(52 pgs.)

	GD	VG	FN	VF	VF/NM	NM-
1-Teen-age	21	42	63	122	199	275
2-7	15	30	45	85	130	175

MAZINGER (See First Comics Graphic Novel #17)

'MAZING MAN
DC Comics: Jan, 1986 - No. 12, Dec, 1986

	NM-
1-11: 7,8-Hembeck-a	3.00
12-Dark Knight part-c by Miller	4.00
Special 1 ('87), 2 (4/88), 3 ('90)-All $2.00, 52pgs.	4.00

McCANDLESS & COMPANY
Mandalay Books/American Mythology

	NM-
...: Dead Razor (2001, $7.95) J.C. Vaughn-s/Busch & Sheehan-a; 3 covers	8.00
...: Insecurituces (American Myth., 10/16, $4.99) Vaughn-s/Gonzales-a/Oeming-c	5.00
Crime Scenes: A McCandless & Company Reader TPB (Spring 2006, $17.95) Vaughn-s	18.00

McHALE'S NAVY (TV) (See Movie Classics)
Dell Publ. Co.: May-July, 1963 - No. 3, Nov-Jan, 1963-64 (All have photo-c)

	GD	VG	FN	VF	VF/NM	NM-
1	6	12	18	38	69	100
2,3	5	10	15	30	50	70

McKEEVER & THE COLONEL (TV)
Dell Publishing Co.: Feb-Apr, 1963 - No. 3, Aug-Oct, 1963

	GD	VG	FN	VF	VF/NM	NM-
1-Photo-c	5	10	15	34	60	85
2,3-Photo-c	4	8	12	28	47	65

McLINTOCK (See Movie Comics)

MD
E. C. Comics: Apr-May, 1955 - No. 5, Dec-Jan, 1955-56

	GD	VG	FN	VF	VF/NM	NM-
1-Not approved by code; Craig-c	19	38	57	152	246	340
2-5	12	24	36	96	153	210

NOTE: *Crandall, Evans, Ingels, Orlando art in all issues; Craig c-1-5.*

MD
Russ Cochran/Gemstone Publishing: Sept, 1999 - No. 5, Jan, 2000 ($2.50)

	NM-
1-5-Reprints original EC series	4.00
Annual 1 (1999, $13.50) r/#1-5	14.00

MEASLES
Fantagraphics Books: Christmas 1998 - No. 8 ($2.95, B&W, quarterly)

1-8-Anthology: 1-Venus-s by Hernandez — 3.00

MECHA (Also see Mayhem)
Dark Horse Comics: June, 1987 - No. 6, 1988 ($1.50/$1.95, color/B&W)

1-6: 1,2 ($1.95, color), 3,4-($1.75, B&W), 5,6-($1.50, B&W) — 3.00

MECHANIC, THE
Image Comics: 1998 ($5.95, one-shot, squarebound)

	NM-
1-Chiodo-painted art; Peterson-s	6.00
1-($10.00) DF Alternate Cover Ed.	10.00

MECHANISM
Image Comics (Top Cow): Jul, 2016 - No. 5, Nov, 2016 ($3.99)

1-5-Raffaele Ienco-s/a — 4.00

MECHA SPECIAL
Dark Horse Comics: May, 1995 ($2.95, one-shot)

1 — 3.00

MECH CADET YU
BOOM! Studios: Aug, 2017 - Present ($3.99)

1-7-Greg Pak-s/Takeshi Miyazawa-a — 4.00

MECH DESTROYER
Image Comics: Apr, 2001 - No. 4, Sept, 2001 ($2.95, limited series)

1-4-Jae Kim-c/a; Robert Chong-s — 3.00

MEDAL FOR BOWZER, A (See Promotional Comics section)

MEDAL OF HONOR COMICS
A. S. Curtis: Spring, 1946

	GD	VG	FN	VF	VF/NM	NM-
1-War stories	15	30	45	90	140	190

MEDAL OF HONOR SPECIAL
Dark Horse Comics: 1994 ($2.50, one-shot)

1-Kubert-c/a (first story) — 3.00

MEDIA STARR
Innovation Publ.: July, 1989 - No. 3, Sept, 1989 ($1.95, mini-series, 28 pgs.)

1-3: Deluxe format — 3.00

MEDIEVAL SPAWN/WITCHBLADE
Image Comics (Top Cow Productions): May, 1996 - No. 3, June, 1996 ($2.95, limited series)

	NM-
1-3-Garth Ennis scripts in all	6.00
1-Platinum foil-c (500 copies from Pittsburgh Con)	35.00
1-Gold	10.00
1-ETM Exclusive Edition; gold foil logo	7.00
TPB ($9.95) r/#1-3	10.00

MEET ANGEL (Formerly Angel & the Ape)

Meet Miss Bliss #1 © MAR

Megaman #1 © Capcom

Menace #7 © MAR

GD VG FN VF VF/NM NM-
2.0 4.0 6.0 8.0 9.0 9.2

National Periodical Publications: No. 7, Nov-Dec, 1969
7-Wood-a(i) 3 6 9 19 30 40

MEET CORLISS ARCHER (Radio/Movie)(My Life #4 on)
Fox Feature Syndicate: Mar, 1948 - No. 3, July, 1948
1-(Teen-age)-Feldstein-c/a; headlight-c 116 232 348 742 1271 1800
2 58 116 174 371 636 900
3 54 108 162 343 574 825
NOTE: *No. 1-3 used in Seduction of the Innocent, pg. 39.*

MEET HERCULES (See Three Stooges)

MEET MERTON
Toby Press: Dec, 1953 - No. 4, June, 1954
1-(Teen-age)-Dave Berg-c/a 20 40 60 117 189 260
2-Dave Berg-c/a 13 26 39 72 101 130
3,4-Dave Berg-c/a 11 22 33 64 90 115
I.W. Reprint #9, Super Reprint #11('63), 18 2 4 6 8 11 14

MEET MISS BLISS (Becomes Stories Of Romance #5 on)
Atlas Comics (LMC): May, 1955 - No. 4, Nov, 1955
1-Al Hartley-c/a 24 48 72 142 234 325
2-4 15 30 45 88 137 185

MEET MISS PEPPER (Formerly Lucy, The Real Gone Gal)
St. John Publishing Co.: No. 5, April, 1954 - No. 6, June, 1954
5-Kubert/Maurer-a 32 64 96 188 307 425
6-Kubert/Maurer-a; Kubert-c 27 54 81 158 259 360

MEGACITY909
Devil's Due Publ.: Sept, 2004 - No. 8, Aug, 2005 ($2.95)
1-8-Kano Kang & Zack Suh-a 3.00

MEGA DRAGON & TIGER
Image Comics: Mar, 1999 - No. 5 ($2.95)
1-5-Tony Wong-s/a 3.00

MEGALITH (Megalith Deathwatch 2000 #1,2 of second series)
Continuity: 1989 - No. 9, Mar, 1992; No, 0, Apr, 1993 - No. 7, Jan, 1994
1-9-($2.00-c) 1-Neal Adams & Mark Texiera-c/Texiera & Nebres-a 3.00
2nd series: 0-(4/93)-Foil-c; no c-price, giveaway; Adams plot 3.00
1-7: 1-3-Bagged w/card: 1-Gatefold-c by Nebres; Adams plot. 2-Fold-out-c; Adams plot. 3-Indestructible-c. 4-7-Embossed-c: 4-Adams/Nebres-c; Adams part-i. 5-Sienkiewicz-i. 6-Adams part-i. 7-Adams-c(p); Adams plot 3.00

MEGAMAN
Dreamwave Productions: Sept, 2003 - No. 4, Dec, 2003 ($2.95)
1-4-Brian Augustyn-s/Mic Fong-a 3.00
1-($5.95) Chromium wraparound variant-c 6.00

MEGA MAN (Based on the Capcom video game character)
Archie Comics Publications: Jul, 2011 - Present ($2.99/$3.99)
1-39 1-Spaziante-a. 20-39-Multiple covers. 24-Worlds Collide x-over begins 3.00
40-49,51-55 ($3.99) Two covers on most. 51,52-Three covers 4.00
50-($4.99) Six covers; "Worlds Unite" Sonic/Mega Man x-over pt. 4 5.00
Free Comic Book Day Edition (2012, giveaway) Origin re-told 3.00
...: Worlds Unite Battles 1 (8/15, $3.99) Sonic/Mega Man x-over; 3 wraparound covers 4.00

MEGAMIND: BAD. BLUE. BRILLIANT (DreamWorks'...) (Based on the 2010 movie)
Ape Entertainment: 2010 - No. 4, 2011 ($3.95, limited series)
1-4: 1-High school flashback 4.00
nn-($6.95, 9x6") Prequel to the movie; Joe Kelly-s 7.00

MEGA MORPHS
Marvel Comics: Oct, 2005 - No. 4, Dec, 2005 ($2.99, limited series)
1-4-Giant robots based on action figures; McKeever-s; Kang-a 3.00
Digest (2006, $7.99) r/#1-4 plus mini-comics 8.00

MEGATON (A super hero)
Megaton Publ.: Nov, 1983; No. 2, Oct, 1985 - No. 8, Aug, 1987 (B&W)
1-($2.00, 68 pgs.)-Erik Larsen's 1st pro work; Vanguard by Larsen begins (1st app.), ends #4; 1st app. Megaton, Berzerker, & Ethrian; Guice-c/a(p); Gustovich-a(p) in #1,2
3 6 9 14 20 25
2-($2.00, 68 pgs.)-1st brief app. The Dragon (1 pg.) by Larsen (later The Savage Dragon in Image Comics); Guice-c/a(p) 2 4 6 9 12 15
3-(44 pgs.)-1st full app. Savage Dragon-c/story by Larsen; 1st comic book work by Angel Medina (pin-up) 4 8 12 23 37 50
4-(52 pgs.)-2nd full app. Savage Dragon by Larsen; 4,5-Wildman by Grass Green
2 4 6 8 10 12

GD VG FN VF VF/NM NM-
2.0 4.0 6.0 8.0 9.0 9.2

5-1st Liefeld published-a (inside f/c, 6/86) 1 2 3 5 7 9
6,7: 6-Larsen-c 1 2 3 4 5 7
8-1st Liefeld story-a (7 pg. super hero story) plus 1 pg. Youngblood ad
2 4 6 11 16 20
...Explosion (6/87, 16 pg. color giveaway)-1st app. Youngblood by Rob Liefeld (2 pg. spread); shows Megaton heroes 5 10 15 33 57 75
...Holiday Special 1 (1994, $2.95, color, 40 pgs., publ. by Entity Comics)-Gold foil logo; bagged w/Kelley Jones card; Vanguard, Megaton plus shows unpublished-c to 1987 Youngblood #1 by Liefeld/Ordway 5.00
NOTE: *Copies of Megaton Explosion were also released in early 1992 all signed by Rob Liefeld and were made available to retailers.*

MEGATON MAN (See Don Simpson's Bizarre Heroes)
Kitchen Sink Enterprises: Nov, 1984 - No. 10, 1986
1-10, 1-2nd printing (1989) 3.00
...Meets The Uncategorizable X-Thems 1 (4/89, $2.00) 3.00

MEGATON MAN: BOMB SHELL
Image Comics: Jul, 1999 - No. 2 ($2.95, B&W, mini-series)
1-Reprints stories from Megaton Man internet site 3.00

MEGATON MAN: HARD COPY
Image Comics: Feb, 1999 - No. 2, Apr, 1999 ($2.95, B&W, mini-series)
1,2-Reprints stories from Megaton Man internet site 3.00

MEGATON MAN VS. FORBIDDEN FRANKENSTEIN
Fiasco Comics: Apr, 1996 ($2.95, B&W, one-shot)
1-Intro The Tomb Team (Forbidden Frankenstein, Drekula, Bride of the Monster, & Moon Wolf). 3.00

MEK (See Reload/Mek flipbook for TPB reprint)
DC Comics (Homage): Jan, 2003 - No. 3, Mar, 2003 ($2.95, limited series)
1-3-Warren Ellis-s/Steve Rolston-a 3.00

MEKANIX (See X-Men titles) (See X-Treme X-Men Vol. 4 for TPB)
Marvel Comics: Dec, 2002 - No. 6, May, 2003 ($2.99, limited series)
1-6-Kitty Pryde in college; Claremont-s/Bobillo & Sosa-a 3.00

MEL ALLEN SPORTS COMICS (The Voice of the Yankees)
Standard Comics: No. 5, Nov, 1949; No. 6, June, 1950
5(#1 on inside)-Tuska-a 23 46 69 136 223 310
6(#2)-Lou Gehrig story 16 32 48 94 147 200

MELVIN MONSTER
Dell Publishing Co.: Apr-June, 1965 - No. 10, Oct, 1969
1-By John Stanley 6 12 18 40 73 105
2-10-All by Stanley. #10-r/#1 5 10 15 30 50 70

MELVIN THE MONSTER (See Peter, the Little Pest & Dexter The Demon #7)
Atlas Comics (HPC): July, 1956 - No. 6, July, 1957
1-Maneely-c/a 16 32 48 94 147 200
2-6: 4-Maneely-c/a 12 24 36 67 94 120

MENACE
Atlas Comics (HPC): Mar, 1953 - No. 11, May, 1954
1-Horror & sci/fi stories begin; Everett-c/a 174 348 522 1114 1907 2700
2-Post-atom bomb disaster by Everett; anti-Communist propaganda/torture scenes; Sinnott sci/fi story "Rocket to the Moon" 116 232 348 742 1271 1800
3,4,6-Everett-a. 4-Sci/fi story "Escape to the Moon". 6-Romita sci/fi story "Science Fiction"
84 168 252 538 919 1300
5-Origin & 1st app. The Zombie by Everett (reprinted in Tales of the Zombie #1)(7/53); 5-Sci/fi story "Rocket Ship" 155 310 465 992 1696 2400
7,8,10,11: 7-Frankenstein story. 8-End of world story; Heath 3-D art(3 pgs.). 10-H-Bomb panels 65 130 195 416 708 1000
9-Everett-a r-in Vampire Tales #1 90 180 270 576 988 1400
NOTE: ***Brodsky** c-7, 8, 11. **Colan** a-6; c-9. **Everett** a-1-6, 9; c-1-6. **Heath** a-1-8; c-10. **Katz** a-11. **Maneely** a-3-5, 7-9. **Powell** a-11. **Romita** a-3, 6, 8, 11. **Shelly** a-10. **Shores** a-7. **Sinnott** a-2, 7. **Tuska** a-1, 2, 5.*

MENACE
Awesome-Hyperwerks: Nov, 1998 ($2.50)
1-Jada Pinkett Smith-s/Fraga-a 3.00

MEN AGAINST CRIME (Formerly Mr. Risk; Hand of Fate #8 on)
Ace Magazines: No. 3, Feb, 1951 - No. 7, Oct, 1951
3-Mr. Risk app. 14 28 42 80 115 150
4-7: 4-Colan-a; entire book-r as Trapped! #4. 5-Meskin-a
10 20 30 56 76 95

MEN, GUNS, & CATTLE (See Classics Illustrated Special Issue)

Men in Action #3 © MAR

Mera: Queen of Atlantis #1 © DC

Merciless: The Rise of Ming #1 © KFS

	GD 2.0	VG 4.0	FN 6.0	VF 8.0	VF/NM 9.0	NM- 9.2

MEN IN ACTION (Battle Brady #10 on)
Atlas Comics (IPS): April, 1952 - No. 9, Dec, 1952 (War stories)

	GD	VG	FN	VF	VF/NM	NM-
1-Berg, Reinman-a	30	60	90	177	289	400
2,3: 3-Heath-c/a	16	32	48	92	144	195
4-6,8,9	15	30	45	85	130	175
7-Krigstein-a; Heath-c	16	32	48	92	144	195

NOTE: ***Brodsky** a-3; c-1, 4-6. **Maneely** a-4; c-5. **Pakula** a-1, 6. **Robinson** c-8. **Shores** c-9. **Sinnott** a-6.*

MEN IN ACTION
Ajax/Farrell Publications: Apr, 1957 - No. 6, Jun, 1958

	GD	VG	FN	VF	VF/NM	NM-
1	12	24	36	67	94	120
2	8	16	24	42	54	65
3-6	7	14	21	37	46	55

MEN IN BLACK, THE (1st series)
Aircel Comics (Malibu): Jan, 1990 - No. 3 Mar, 1990 ($2.25, B&W, lim. series)

	GD	VG	FN	VF	VF/NM	NM-
1-Cunningham-s/a in all	6	12	18	41	76	110
2,3	3	6	9	19	30	40
Graphic Novel (Jan, 1991) r/#1-3	3	6	9	16	23	30

MEN IN BLACK (2nd series)
Aircel Comics (Malibu): May, 1991 - No. 3, Jul, 1991 ($2.50, B&W, lim. series)

	GD	VG	FN	VF	VF/NM	NM-
1-Cunningham-s/a in all	3	6	9	19	30	40
2,3	2	4	6	11	16	20

MEN IN BLACK: FAR CRY
Marvel Comics: Aug, 1997 ($3.99, color, one-shot)

1-Cunningham-s 4.00

MEN IN BLACK: RETRIBUTION
Marvel Comics: Dec, 1997 ($3.99, color, one-shot)

1-Cunningham-s; continuation of the movie 4.00

MEN IN BLACK: THE MOVIE
Marvel Comics: Oct, 1997 ($3.99, one-shot, movie adaptation)

1-Cunningham-s 4.00

MEN INTO SPACE
Dell Publishing Co.: No. 1083, Feb-Apr, 1960

	GD	VG	FN	VF	VF/NM	NM-
Four Color 1083-Anderson-a, photo-c	5	10	15	35	63	90

MEN OF BATTLE (Also see New Men of Battle)
Catechetical Guild: V1#5, March, 1943 (Hardcover)

	GD	VG	FN	VF	VF/NM	NM-
V1#5-Topix reprints	6	12	18	28	34	40

MEN OF WAR
DC Comics, Inc.: August, 1977 - No. 26, March, 1980 (#9,10: 44 pgs.)

	GD	VG	FN	VF	VF/NM	NM-
1-Enemy Ace, Gravedigger (origin #1,2) begin	3	6	9	16	23	30
2-4,8-10,12-14,19,20: All Enemy Ace stories. 4-1st Dateline Frontline. 9-Unknown Soldier app.	2	4	6	10	14	18
5-7,11,15-18,21-25: 17-1st app. Rosa	2	4	6	8	11	14
26-Sgt. Rock & Easy Co.-c/s	3	6	9	14	19	24

NOTE: ***Chaykin** a-9, 10, 12-14, 19, 20. **Evans** c-25. **Kubert** c-2-23, 24p, 26.*

MEN OF WAR (DC New 52)
DC Comics: Nov, 2011 - No. 8, Jun, 2012 ($3.99)

1-8: 1-Sgt. Rock's grandson in modern times; Derenick-a; Navy Seals back-up; Winslade-a 6-Back-up w/Corben-a. 8-Frankenstein & G.I. Robot app. 4.00

MEN OF WRATH
Marvel Comics (ICON): Oct, 2014 - No. 5, Feb, 2015 ($3.50, limited series)

1-5-Jason Aaron-s/Ron Garney-a; two covers on each. 5-Alex Ross var-c 3.50

MEN'S ADVENTURES (Formerly True Adventures)
Marvel/Atlas Comics (CCC): No. 4, Aug, 1950 - No. 28, July, 1954

	GD	VG	FN	VF	VF/NM	NM-
4(#1)(52 pgs.)	39	78	117	231	378	525
5-Flying Saucer story	26	52	78	154	252	350
6-8: 7-Buried alive story. 8-Sci/fic story	24	48	72	140	230	320
9-20: All war format	18	36	54	105	165	225
21,22,24,26: All horror format	39	78	117	240	395	550
23-Crandall-a; Fox-a(i); horror format	40	80	120	246	411	575
25-Shrunken head-c	65	130	195	416	708	1000
27,28-Human Torch & Toro-c/stories; Captain America & Sub-Mariner stories in each (also see Young Men #24-28)	161	322	483	1030	1765	2500

NOTE: ***Ayers** a-20, 27(H. Torch). **Berg** a-15, 16. **Brodsky** c-4-9, 11, 12, 16-18, 24. **Burgos** c-27, 28 (Human Torch). **Colan** a-13, 14, 19. **Everett** a-10, 14, 22, 25, 28; c-14, 21-23. **Hartley** a-12. **Heath** a-8, 11, 24; c-13, 20, 26. **Lawrence** a-23; 27(Captain America). **Maneely** a-24; c-10, 15. **Mac Pakula** a-15, 25. **Post** a-23. **Powell** a-27(Sub-Mariner). **Reinman** a-10-12, 16. **Robinson** c-19. **Romita** a-22. **Sale** a-12-14. **Shores** c-25. **Sinnott** a-13, 21. **Tuska** a-24. Adventure-#4-8; War-#9-20; Weird/Horror-#21-26.*

MENZ INSANA
DC Comics (Vertigo): 1997 ($7.95, one-shot)

	GD	VG	FN	VF	VF/NM	NM-
nn-Fowler-s/Bolton painted art	1	2	3	5	6	8

MEPHISTO VS... (See Silver Surfer #3)
Marvel Comics Group: Apr, 1987 - No. 4, July, 1987 ($1.50, mini-series)

1-4: 1-Fantastic Four; Austin-i. 2-X-Factor. 3-X-Men. 4-Avengers 4.00

MERA: QUEEN OF ATLANTIS
DC Comics: Apr, 2018 - No. 6 ($3.99, limited series)

1-Abnett-s/Medina-a; origin retold; Ocean Master app. 4.00

MERC (See Mark Hazzard: Merc)

MERCENARIES (Based on the Pandemic video game)
Dynamite Entertainment: 2007 - No. 3, 2008 ($3.99, limited series)

1-3-Michael Turner-c; Brian Reed-s/Edgar Salazar-a 4.00

MERCHANTS OF DEATH
Acme Press (Eclipse): Jul, 1988 - No. 4, Nov, 1988 ($3.50, B&W/16 pgs. color, 44 pg. mag.)

1-4: 4-Toth-c 4.00

MERCILESS: THE RISE OF MING (Also see Flash Gordon: Zeitgeist)
Dynamite Entertainment: 2012 - No. 4, 2012 ($3.99, limited series)

1-4 Ming the Merciless' rise to power; Alex Ross-c; Beatty-c/Adrian-a 4.00

MERCY THOMPSON (Patricia Briggs'...)
Dynamite Entertainment: 2014 - No. 6, 2015 ($3.99, limited series)

1-6-Patricia Briggs & Rik Hoskin-s/Tom Garcia-a 4.00

MERIDIAN
CrossGeneration Comics: Jul, 2000 - No. 44, Apr, 2004 ($2.95)

1-44: Barbara Kesel-s	3.00
Flying Solo Vol. 1 TPB (2001, $19.95) r/#1-7; cover by Steve Rude	20.00
Going to Ground Vol. 2 TPB (2002, $19.95) r/#8-14	20.00
Taking the Skies Vol. 3 TPB (2002, $15.95) r/#15-20	16.00
Vol. 4: Coming Home (12/02, $15.95) r/#21-26	16.00
Vol. 5: Minister of Cadador (7/03, $15.95) r/#27-32	16.00
Vol. 6: Changing Course (1/04, $15.95) r/#33-38	16.00
Traveler Vol. 1-4 ($9.95): Digest-size reprints of TPBs	10.00

MERLIN JONES AS THE MONKEY'S UNCLE (See Movie Comics and The Misadventures of... under Movie Comics)

MERRILL'S MARAUDERS (See Movie Classics)

MERRY CHRISTMAS (See A Christmas Adventure, Donald Duck..., Dell Giant #39, & March of Comics #153 in the Promotional Comics section)

MERRY COMICS
Carlton Publishing Co.: Dec, 1945 (10¢)

	GD	VG	FN	VF	VF/NM	NM-
nn-Boogeyman app.	22	44	66	132	216	300

MERRY COMICS: Four Star Publications: 1947 (Advertised, not published)

MERRY-GO-ROUND COMICS
LaSalle Publ. Co./Croyden Publ./Rotary Litho.: 1944 (25¢, 132 pgs.); 1946; 9-10/47 - No. 2, 1948

	GD	VG	FN	VF	VF/NM	NM-
nn(1944)(LaSalle)-Funny animal; 29 new features	21	42	63	122	199	275
21 (Publisher?)	10	20	30	58	79	100
1(1946)(Croyden)-Al Fago-c; funny animal	13	26	39	74	105	135
V1#1,2(1947-48; 52 pgs.)(Rotary Litho. Co. Ltd., Canada); Ken Hultgren-a	10	20	30	58	79	100

MERRY MAILMAN (See Fawcett's Funny Animals #87-89)

MERRY MOUSE (Also see Funny Tunes & Space Comics)
Avon Periodicals: June, 1953 - No. 4, Jan-Feb, 1954

	GD	VG	FN	VF	VF/NM	NM-
1-1st app.; funny animal; Frank Carin-c/a	12	24	36	69	97	125
2-4	8	16	24	42	54	65

MERV PUMPKINHEAD, AGENT OF D.R.E.A.M. (See The Sandman)
DC Comics (Vertigo): 2000 ($5.95, one-shot)

1-Buckingham-a(p); Nowlan painted-c 6.00

META-4
First Comics: Feb, 1991 - No. 4, 1991 ($2.25)

1-($3.95, 52pgs.)	4.00
2-4	3.00

METAL GEAR SOLID (Based on the video game)
IDW Publ.: Sept, 2004 - No. 12, Aug, 2005 ($3.99)

1-12: 1-Two covers; Ashley Wood-a/Kris Oprisko-s 4.00

Metal Men #1 © DC

Metamorpho: Year One #6 © DC

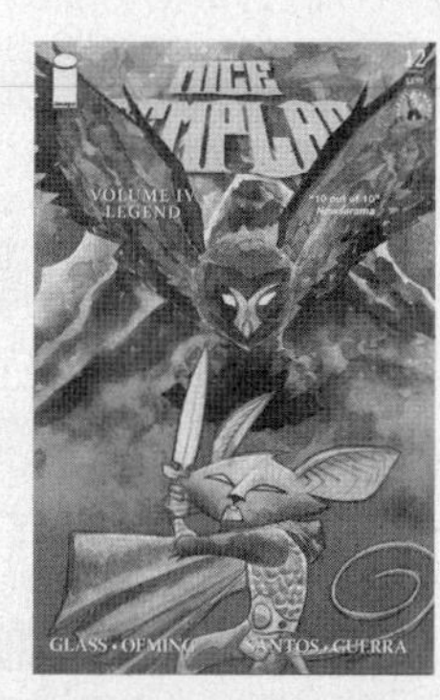

Mice Templar V4: Legend #12 © Glass & Oeming

GD 2.0 VG 4.0 FN 6.0 VF 8.0 VF/NM 9.0 NM- 9.2

1-Retailer edition with foil cover 15.00

METAL GEAR SOLID: SONS OF LIBERTY
IDW Publ.: Sept, 2005 - No. 12, Sept, 2007 ($3.99)

#0 (9/05) profile pages on characters; Ashley Wood-a 4.00
1-12: 1-Two covers; Ashley Wood-a/Alex Garner-s 4.00

METALLIX
Future Comics: Dec, 2002 - No. 6, June, 2003 ($3.50)

0-6-Ron Lim-a. 0-(6/03) Origin. 1-Layton-c 3.50
1-Collector's Edition with variant cover by Lim 3.50
1-Free Comic Book Day Edition (4/03) Layton-c 3.00

METAL MEN (See Brave & the Bold, DC Comics Presents, and Showcase #37-40)
National Periodical Publications/DC Comics: 4-5/63 - No. 41, 12-1/69-70; No. 42, 2-3/73 - No. 44, 7-8/73; No. 45, 4-5/76 - No. 56, 2-3/78

	GD	VG	FN	VF	VF/NM	NM-
1-(4-5/63)-5th app. Metal Men	56	112	168	448	999	1550
2	20	40	60	135	300	465
3-5	13	26	39	89	195	300
6-10	9	18	27	59	117	175
11-20: 12-Beatles cameo (2-3/65)	7	14	21	46	86	125
21-Batman, Robin & Flash x-over	6	12	18	37	66	95
22-26,28-30	5	10	15	34	60	85
27-Origin Metal Men retold	6	12	18	42	79	115
31-41(1968-70): 38-Last 12¢ issue. 41-Last 15¢	5	10	15	31	53	75
42-44(1973)-Reprints	2	4	6	10	14	18
45('76)-49-Simonson-a in all: 48,49-Re-intro Eclipso	2	4	6	10	14	18
50-56: 50-Part-r. 54,55-Green Lantern x-over	2	4	6	9	12	15

NOTE: ***Andru/Esposito** c-1-30. **Aparo** c-53-56. **Giordano** c-45, 46. **Kane/Esposito** a-30, 31; c-31. **Simonson** a-45-49; c-47-52. **Staton** a-50-56.*

METAL MEN (Also see Tangent Comics/ Metal Men)
DC Comics: Oct, 1993 - No. 4, Jan, 1994 ($1.25, mini-series)

1-($2.50)-Multi-colored foil-c 4.00
2-4: 2-Origin 3.00

METAL MEN (Also see 52)
DC Comics: Oct, 2007 - No. 8, Jul, 2008 ($2.99, limited series)

1-8-Duncan Rouleau-s/a; origin re-told. 3-Chemo returns 3.00
HC (2008, $24.99, dustjacket) r/#1-8; cover gallery and sketch pages 25.00
SC (2009, $14.99) r/#1-8; cover gallery and sketch pages 15.00

METAMORPHO (See Action Comics #413, Brave & the Bold #57,58, 1st Issue Special, & World's Finest #217)
National Periodical Publications: July-Aug, 1965 - No. 17, Mar-Apr, 1968 (All 12¢ issues)

	GD	VG	FN	VF	VF/NM	NM-
1-(7-8/65)-3rd app. Metamorpho	14	28	42	93	204	315
2,3	7	14	21	46	86	125
4-6,10:10-Origin & 1st app. Element Girl (1-2/67)	6	12	18	37	66	95
7-9	5	10	15	33	57	80
11-17: 17-Sparling-c/a	5	10	15	30	50	70

NOTE: ***Ramona Fradon** a-B&B 57, 58, 1-4. **Orlando** a-5, 6; c-5-9, 11. **Trapani** a(p)-7-16; i-16.*

METAMORPHO
DC Comics: Aug, 1993 - No. 4, Nov, 1993 ($1.50, mini-series)

1-4 3.00

METAMORPHO: YEAR ONE
DC Comics: Early Dec, 2007 - No. 6, Late Feb, 2008 ($2.99, limited series)

1-6-Origin re-told; Jurgens-s/Jurgens & Delperdang-a/Nowlan-c. 6-Justice League app. 3.00
TPB ('08, $14.99) r/#1-6 15.00

METAPHYSIQUE
Malibu Comics (Bravura): Apr, 1995 - No. 6, Oct, 1995 ($2.95, limited series)

1-6: Norm Breyfogle-c/a/scripts 3.00

METEOR COMICS
L. L. Baird (Croyden): Nov, 1945

	GD	VG	FN	VF	VF/NM	NM-
1-Captain Wizard, Impossible Man, Race Wilkins app.; origin Baldy Bean, Capt. Wizard's sidekick; bare-breasted mermaids story	53	106	159	334	567	800

METEOR MAN
Marvel Comics: Aug, 1993 - No. 6, Jan, 1994 ($1.25, limited series)

1-6: 1-Regular unbagged. 4-Night Thrasher-c/story. 6-Terry Austin-c(i) 3.00
1-Polybagged w/button & rap newspaper 4.00
...: The Movie (4/93 [7/93 on cover], $2.25) movie adaptation 3.00

METROPOL (See Ted McKeever's...)

METROPOL A.D. (See Ted McKeever's...)

METROPOLIS S.C.U. (Also see Showcase '96 #1)
DC Comics: Nov, 1995 - No. 4, Feb, 1996 ($1.50, limited series)

1-4:1-Superman-c & app. 3.00

MEZZ: GALACTIC TOUR 2494 (Also See Nexus)
Dark Horse Comics: May, 1994 ($2.50, one-shot)

1 3.00

MGM'S MARVELOUS WIZARD OF OZ (See Marvel Treasury of Oz)
Marvel Comics Group/National Periodical Publications: 1975 ($1.50, 84 pgs.; oversize)

	GD	VG	FN	VF	VF/NM	NM-
1-Adaptation of MGM's movie; J. Buscema-a	3	6	9	16	23	30

M.G.M'S MOUSE MUSKETEERS (Formerly M.G.M.'s The Two Mouseketeers)
Dell Publishing Co.: No. 670, Jan, 1956 - No. 1290, Mar-May, 1962

	GD	VG	FN	VF	VF/NM	NM-
Four Color 670 (#4)	6	12	18	38	69	100
Four Color 711,728,764	5	10	15	31	53	75
8 (4-6/57) - 21 (3-5/60)	4	8	12	27	44	60
Four Color 1135,1175,1290	4	8	12	28	47	65

M.G.M.'S SPIKE AND TYKE (also see Tom & Jerry #79)
Dell Publishing Co.: No. 499, Sept, 1953 - No. 1266, Dec-Feb, 1961-62

	GD	VG	FN	VF	VF/NM	NM-
Four Color 499 (#1)	7	14	21	46	86	125
Four Color 577,638	5	10	15	35	63	90
4(12-2/55-56)-10	4	8	12	27	44	60
11-24(12-2/60-61)	4	8	12	23	37	50
Four Color 1266	4	8	12	28	47	65

M.G.M.'S THE TWO MOUSKETEERS
Dell Publishing Co.: No. 475, June, 1953 - No. 642, July, 1955

	GD	VG	FN	VF	VF/NM	NM-
Four Color 475 (#1)	9	18	27	57	111	165
Four Color 603 (11/54), 642	6	12	18	41	76	110

MIAMI VICE REMIX
IDW Publishing (Lion Forge): Mar, 2015 - No. 5, Jul, 2015 ($3.99, limited series)

1-5-Joe Casey-s/Jim Mahfood-a; re-imagined Crockett & Tubbs 4.00

MICE TEMPLAR, THE
Image Comics: Sept, 2007 - No. 6, Oct, 2008 ($3.99/$2.99)

1-($3.99)-Bryan Glass-s/Michael Avon Oeming-a/c 4.00
2-6-($2.99) 3.00

MICE TEMPLAR, THE , VOLUME 2: DESTINY
Image Comics: July, 2009 - No. 9, May, 2010 ($3.99/$2.99/$4.99)

1,2-($3.99) 1-Bryan Glass-s/Oeming & Santos-a; 2 covers. 2-Santos-a 4.00
3-8-($2.99)-Santos-a; 2 covers by Oeming & Santos 3.00
9-($4.99) 5.00

MICE TEMPLAR, THE , VOLUME 3: A MIDWINTER NIGHT'S DREAM
Image Comics: Dec, 2010 - No. 8, Mar, 2012 ($3.99/$2.99)

1,8-($3.99) 1-Bryan Glass-s/Oeming & Santos-a; 2 covers 4.00
2-7-($2.99)-Santos-a; 2 covers by Oeming & Santos 3.00

MICE TEMPLAR, THE , VOLUME 4: LEGEND
Image Comics: Mar, 2013 - No. 14, Oct, 2014 ($3.99/$2.99/$4.99)

1-($3.99)-Bryan Glass-s/Victor Santos-a; 2 covers 4.00
2-7-($2.99)-Santos-a; 2 covers by Oeming & Santos 3.00
8-($4.99) 5.00
9-13-($3.99) 4.00
14-($5.99) Bonus back-up Hammer of the Gods by Oeming & Wheatley 6.00

MICE TEMPLAR, THE , VOLUME 5: NIGHT'S END
Image Comics: Mar, 2015 - No. 5, Sept, 2015 ($3.99/$5.99)

1,3,5-($3.99)-Bryan Glass-s/Victor Santos-a; 2 covers by Oeming & Santos 4.00
2,4-($5.99)-Bonus back-up Hammer of the Gods 6.00

MICHAELANGELO CHRISTMAS SPECIAL (See Teenage Mutant Ninja Turtles Christmas Special)

MICHAELANGELO, TEENAGE MUTANT NINJA TURTLE
Mirage Studios: 1986 (One shot) ($1.50, B&W)

	GD	VG	FN	VF	VF/NM	NM-
1-Christmas-c/story	3	6	9	16	23	30
1-2nd printing ('89, $1.75)-Reprint plus new-a						6.00

MICHAEL CHABON PRESENTS THE AMAZING ADVENTURES OF THE ESCAPIST
Dark Horse Comics: Feb, 2004 - No. 8, Nov, 2005 ($8.95, squarebound)

1-5,7,8-Short stories by Chabon and various incl. Chaykin, Starlin, Brereton, Baker 9.00
6-Includes 6 pg. Spirit & Escapist story (Will Eisner's last work); Spirit on cover 9.00
... Vol. 1 (5/04, $17.95, digest-size) r/#1&2; wraparound-c by Chris Ware 18.00
... Vol. 2 (11/04, $17.95, digest-size) r/#3&4; wraparound-c by Matt Kindt 18.00
... Vol. 3 (4/06, $14.95, digest-size) r/#5&6; Tim Sale-c 15.00

MICHAEL MOORCOCK'S ELRIC: THE MAKING OF A SORCEROR

Mickey Finn #5 © McNaught

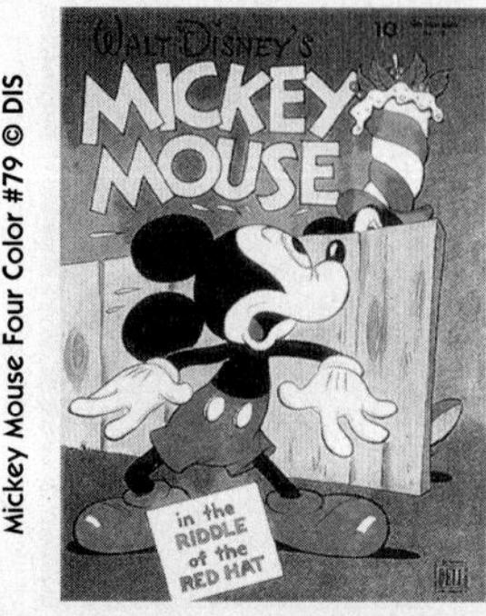

Mickey Mouse Four Color #79 © DIS

Mickey Mouse (and Friends) #306 © DIS

DC Comics: 2004 - No. 4, 2006 ($5.95, prestige format, limited series)

	GD 2.0	VG 4.0	FN 6.0	VF 8.0	VF/NM 9.0	NM- 9.2
1-4-Moorcock-s/Simonson-a						6.00
TPB (2007, $19.99) r/#1-4						20.00

MICHAEL MOORCOCK'S MULTIVERSE
DC Comics (Helix): Nov, 1997 - No. 12, Oct, 1998 ($2.50, limited series)

	GD 2.0	VG 4.0	FN 6.0	VF 8.0	VF/NM 9.0	NM- 9.2
1-12: Simonson, Reeve & Ridgway-a						3.00
TPB (1999, $19.95) r/#1-12						20.00

MICHAEL TURNER, A TRIBUTE TO...
Aspen MLT: 2008 ($8.99, squarebound)

	GD 2.0	VG 4.0	FN 6.0	VF 8.0	VF/NM 9.0	NM- 9.2
nn-Pin-ups and tributes from Turner's colleagues and friends; Turner & Ross-c						9.00

MICHAEL TURNER PRESENTS: ASPEN (See Aspen)

MICKEY AND DONALD (See Walt Disney's...)

MICKEY AND DONALD CHRISTMAS PARADE
IDW Publishing: Dec, 2015; Dec, 2016; Dec, 2017 ($5.99/$6.99, squaredbound)

	GD 2.0	VG 4.0	FN 6.0	VF 8.0	VF/NM 9.0	NM- 9.2
1,2-($5.99) English translations of Dutch, Italian and Swedish Disney Christmas stories						6.00
3-($6.99) English translations of Dutch & Italian Christmas stories; r/Four Color #62						7.00

MICKEY AND DONALD IN VACATIONLAND (See Dell Giant No. 47)

MICKEY & THE BEANSTALK (See Story Hour Series)

MICKEY & THE SLEUTH (See Walt Disney Showcase #38, 39, 42)

MICKEY FINN (Also see Big Shot Comics #74 & Feature Funnies)
Eastern Color 1-4/McNaught Synd. #5 on (Columbia)/Headline V3#2:
Nov?, 1942 - V3#2, May, 1952

	GD 2.0	VG 4.0	FN 6.0	VF 8.0	VF/NM 9.0	NM- 9.2
1	30	60	90	177	289	400
2	15	30	45	90	140	190
3-Charlie Chan story	12	24	36	69	97	125
4	10	20	30	56	76	95
5-10	9	18	27	47	61	75
11-15(1949): 12-Sparky Watts app.	8	16	24	40	50	60
V3#1,2(1952)	6	12	18	31	38	45

MICKEY MALONE
Hale Nass Corp.: 1936 (Color, punchout-c) (B&W-a on back)

	GD 2.0	VG 4.0	FN 6.0	VF 8.0	VF/NM 9.0	NM- 9.2
nn - 1pg. of comics	300	600	1200	-	-	-

MICKEY MANTLE (See Baseball's Greatest Heroes #1)

MICKEY MOUSE (See Adventures of Mickey Mouse, The Best of Walt Disney Comics, Cheerios giveaways, Donald and ..., Dynabrite Comics, 40 Big Pages..., Gladstone Comic Album, Merry Christmas From..., Walt Disney's Mickey and Donald, Walt Disney's Comics & Stories, Walt Disney's..., & Wheaties)

MICKEY MOUSE (...Secret Agent #107-109; Walt Disney's... #148-205?)
(See Dell Giants for annuals) (#204 exists from both G.K. & Whitman)
Dell Publ. Co./Gold Key #85-204/Whitman #204-218/Gladstone #219 on:
#16, 1941 - #84, 7-9/62; #85, 11/62 - #218, 6/84; #219, 10/86 - #256, 4/90

	GD 2.0	VG 4.0	FN 6.0	VF 8.0	VF/NM 9.0	NM- 9.2
Four Color 16(1941)-1st Mickey Mouse comic book; "...vs. the Phantom Blot" by Gottfredson	1300	2600	3900	17,000	-	-
Four Color 27(1943)- "7 Colored Terror"	71	142	213	568	1284	2000
Four Color 79(1945)-By Carl Barks (1 story)	89	178	267	712	1606	2500
Four Color 116(1946)	27	54	81	184	410	635
Four Color 141,157(1947)	22	44	66	155	345	535
Four Color 170,181,194('48)	19	38	57	133	297	460
Four Color 214('49),231,248,261	15	30	45	105	233	360
Four Color 268-Reprints/WDC&S #22-24 by Gottfredson ("Surprise Visitor")	14	28	42	98	217	335
Four Color 279,286,296	12	24	36	79	170	260
Four Color 304,313(#1),325(#2),334	11	22	33	72	154	235
Four Color 343,352,362,371,387	9	18	27	62	126	190
Four Color 401,411,427(10-11/52)	8	16	24	56	108	160
Four Color 819-Mickey Mouse in Magicland	6	12	18	41	76	110
Four Color 1057,1151,1246(1959-61)-Album; #1057 has 10¢ & 12¢ editions; back covers are different	6	12	18	37	66	95
28(12-1/52-53)-32,34	6	12	18	40	73	105
33-(Exists with 2 dates, 10-11/53 & 12-1/54)	6	12	18	40	73	105
35-50	5	10	15	35	63	90
51-73,75-80	5	10	15	31	53	75
74-Story swipe "The Rare Stamp Search" from 4-Color #422- "The Gilded Man"	5	10	15	33	57	80
81-105: 93,95-titled "Mickey Mouse Club Album". 100-105: Reprint 4-Color #427,194,279, 170,343,214 in that order	4	8	12	25	40	55
106-120	3	6	9	19	30	40
121-130	3	6	9	16	23	30
131-146	3	6	9	14	20	25
147,148: 147-Reprints "The Phantom Fires" from WDC&S #200-202.148-Reprints "The Mystery of Lonely Valley" from WDC&S #208-210	3	6	9	14	20	25
149-158	2	4	6	10	14	18
159-Reprints "The Sunken City" from WDC&S #205-207	2	4	6	10	14	18
160-178: 162-165,167-170-r	2	4	6	10	14	18
167-Whitman edition	2	4	6	10	14	18
179-(52 pgs.)	2	4	6	11	16	20
180-203: 200-r/Four Color #371	2	4	6	8	10	12
204-(Whitman or G.K.), 205,206	2	4	6	9	13	16
207(8/80), 209(pre-pack?)	6	12	18	38	69	100
208-(8-12/80)-Only distr. in Whitman 3-pack	10	20	30	68	144	220
210(2/81),211-214	2	4	6	9	13	16
215-218: 215(2/82), 216(4/82), 217(3/84), 218(misdated 8/82; actual date 7/84)	2	4	6	10	14	18
219-1st Gladstone issue; The Seven Ghosts serial-r begins by Gottfredson	2	4	6	11	16	20
220,221	2	3	4	6	8	10
222-225: 222-Editor-in Grief strip-r						5.00
226-230						5.00
231-243,246-254: 240-r/March of Comics #27. 245-r/F.C. #279. 250-r/F.C. #248						4.00
244 (1/89, $2.95, 100 pgs.)-Squarebound 60th anniversary issue; gives history of Mickey						5.00
245,255,256: 245-r/F.C. #279. 255,256-($1.95, 68 pgs.)						5.00

NOTE: *Reprints #195-197, 198(2/3), 199(1/3), 200-208, 211(1/2), 212, 213, 215(1/3), 216-on.* ***Gottfredson*** *Mickey Mouse serials in #219-239, 241-244, 246-249, 251-253, 255.*

	GD 2.0	VG 4.0	FN 6.0	VF 8.0	VF/NM 9.0	NM 9.2
Album 01-518-210(Dell), 1(10082-309)(9/63-Gold Key)	3	6	9	21	33	45
...Club 1(1/64-Gold Key)(TV)	4	8	12	22	35	48
Mini Comic 1(1976)(3-1/4x6-1/2")-Reprints 158	1	2	3	5	6	8
Surprise Party 1(30037-901, G.K.)(1/69)-40th Anniversary (see Walt Disney Showcase #47)	3	6	9	20	31	42
Surprise Party 1(1979)-r/1969 issue	1	2	3	5	6	8

MICKEY MOUSE (Continued from Mickey Mouse and Friends)
BOOM! Studios: No. 304, Jan, 2011 - No. 309, Jun, 2011 ($3.99)

	GD 2.0	VG 4.0	FN 6.0	VF 8.0	VF/NM 9.0	NM 9.2
304-309: 304-Peg-Leg Pete app. 309-Continues in Walt Disney's C&S #720						4.00

MICKEY MOUSE
IDW Publishing: Jun, 2015 - No. 21, Jun, 2017 ($3.99)

	GD 2.0	VG 4.0	FN 6.0	VF 8.0	VF/NM 9.0	NM 9.2
1-Legacy numbered #310; art by Cavazzano and others; multiple covers						4.00
2-21-Classic Disney and foreign reprints; multiple covers on each. 21-(Legacy #330)						4.00

MICKEY MOUSE ADVENTURES
Disney Comics: June, 1990 - No. 18, Nov, 1991 ($1.50)

	GD 2.0	VG 4.0	FN 6.0	VF 8.0	VF/NM 9.0	NM 9.2
1,8,9: 1-Bradbury, Murry-r/M.M. #45,73 plus new-a. 8-Byrne-c. 9-Fantasia 50th ann. issue w/new adapt. of movie						4.00
2-7,10-18: 2-Begin all new stories. 10-r/F.C. #214						3.00

MICKEY MOUSE AND FRIENDS (Continued from Walt Disney's Mickey Mouse and Friends)
(Title continues as Mickey Mouse #304-on)
BOOM! Studios: No. 296, Sept, 2009 - No. 303, Dec, 2010 ($2.99/$3.99)

	GD 2.0	VG 4.0	FN 6.0	VF 8.0	VF/NM 9.0	NM 9.2
296-299,301-303: 296-299-Wizards of Mickey stories. 301-Conclusion to story in #300						3.00
300-($3.99, 9/10) Petrucha-s/Pelaez-a; back-up Tanglefoot story w/Gottfredson-a						4.00
300 Deluxe Edition ($6.99) Variant cover by Daan Jippes						7.00

MICKEY MOUSE CLUB FUN BOOK
Golden Press: 1977 (1.95, 228 pgs.)(square bound)

	GD 2.0	VG 4.0	FN 6.0	VF 8.0	VF/NM 9.0	NM 9.2
11190-1950s-r; 20,000 Leagues, M. Mouse Silly Symphonys, The Reluctant Dragon, etc.	4	8	12	27	44	60

MICKEY MOUSE CLUB MAGAZINE (See Walt Disney...)

MICKEY MOUSE COMICS DIGEST
Gladstone: 1986 - No. 5, 1987 (96 pgs.)

	GD 2.0	VG 4.0	FN 6.0	VF 8.0	VF/NM 9.0	NM 9.2
1 ($1.25-c)	1	2	3	5	6	8
2-5: 3-5 ($1.50-c)						5.00

MICKEY MOUSE IN COLOR
Another Rainbow/Pantheon: 1988 (Deluxe, 13"x17", hard-c, $250.00)
(Trade, 9-7/8"x11-1/2", hard-c, $39.95)

	GD 2.0	VG 4.0	FN 6.0	VF 8.0	VF/NM 9.0	NM 9.2
Deluxe limited edition of 3,000 copies signed by Floyd Gottfredson and Carl Barks, designated as the "Official Mickey Mouse 60th Anniversary" book. Mickey Sunday and daily reprints, plus Barks "Riddle of the Red Hat" from Four Color #79. Comes with 45 r.p.m. record interview with Gottfredson and Barks. 240 pgs.	12	24	36	82	179	275
Deluxe, limited to 100 copies, as above, but with a unique colored pencil original drawing of Mickey Mouse by Carl Barks.						800.00
Pantheon trade edition, edited down & without Barks, 192 pgs.	3	6	9	19	30	40

Mickey Mouse Magazine V4 #2 © DIS

Mickey Spillane's Mike Danger #6 © Mickey Spillane

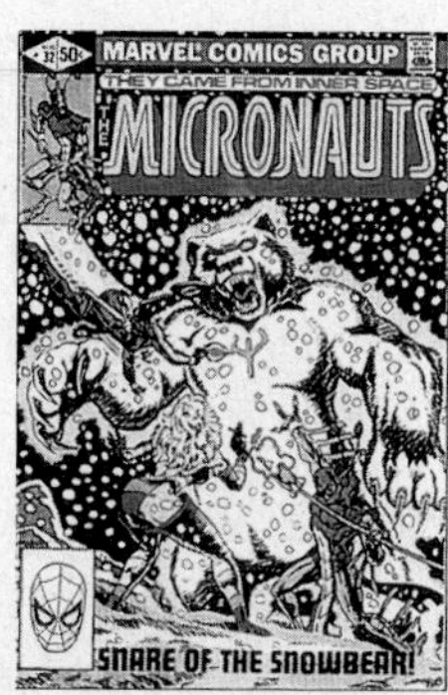

Micronauts #32 © Hasbro

	GD 2.0	VG 4.0	FN 6.0	VF 8.0	VF/NM 9.0	NM- 9.2

MICKEY MOUSE MAGAZINE (Becomes Walt Disney's Comics & Stories)(Also see 40 Big Pages of Mickey Mouse)
K. K. Publ./Western Publishing Co.: Summer, 1935 (June-Aug, indicia) - V5#12, Sept, 1940; V1#1-5, V3#11,12, V4#1-3 are 44 pgs; V2#3-100 pgs; V5#12-68 pgs; rest are 36 pgs.(No V3#1, V4#6)

V1#1 (Large size, 13-1/4x10-1/4"; 25¢)-Contains puzzles, games, cels, stories & comics of Disney characters. Promotional magazine for Disney cartoon movies and paraphernalia 1425 2850 4275 9200 19,000 -

Note: *Some copies were autographed by the editors & given away with all early one year subscriptions.*

2 (Size change, 11-1/2x8-1/2"; 10/35; 10¢)-High quality paper begins; Messmer-a 312 624 936 2650 - -
3,4: 3-Messmer-a 182 364 546 1550 - -
5-1st Donald Duck solo-c; 2nd cover app. ever; last 44 pg. & high quality paper issue 376 752 1128 3200 - -
6-9: 6-36 pg. issues begin; Donald becomes editor. 8-2nd Donald solo-c. 9-1st Mickey/Minnie-c 159 318 477 1350 - -
10-12, V2#1,2: 11-1st Pluto/Mickey-c; Donald fires himself and appoints Mickey as editor 147 294 441 1250 - -
V2#3-Special 100 pg. Christmas issue (25¢); Messmer-a; Donald becomes editor of Wise Quacks 471 942 1413 4000 - -
4-Mickey Mouse Comics & Roy Ranger (adventure strip) begin; both end V2#9; Messmer-a 129 258 387 1100 - -
5-9: 5-Ted True (adventure strip, ends V2#9) & Silly Symphony Comics (ends V3#3) begin. 6-1st solo Minnie-c. 6-9-Mickey Mouse Movies cut-out in each 60 120 180 381 653 925
10-1st full color issue; Mickey Mouse (by Gottfredson; ends V3#12) & Silly Symphony (ends V3#3) full color Sunday-r, Peter The Farm Detective (ends V5#8) & Ole Of The North (ends V3#3) begins 97 194 291 621 1061 1500
11-13: 12-Hiawatha-c & feature story 57 114 171 362 619 875
V3#2-Big Bad Wolf Halloween-c 65 130 195 416 708 1000
3 (12/37)-1st app. Snow White & The Seven Dwarfs (before release of movie) (possibly 1st in print); Mickey X-Mas-c 123 246 369 787 1344 1900
4 (1/38)-Snow White & The Seven Dwarfs serial begins (on stands before release of movie); Ducky Symphony (ends V3#11) begins 95 190 285 608 1042 1475
5-1st Snow White & Seven Dwarfs-c (St. Valentine's Day) 113 226 339 718 1234 1750
6-Snow White serial ends; Lonesome Ghosts app. (2 pp.) 68 136 204 435 743 1050
7-Seven Dwarfs Easter-c 61 122 183 390 670 950
8-10: 9-Dopey-c. 10-1st solo Goofy-c 52 104 156 328 552 775
11,12 (44 pgs; 8 more pgs. color added). 11-Mickey the Sheriff serial (ends V4#3) & Donald Duck strip-r (ends V3#12) begin. Color feature on Snow White's Forest Friends 55 110 165 352 601 850
V4#1 (10/38; 44 pgs.)-Brave Little Tailor-c/feature story, nominated for Academy Award; Bobby & Chip by Otto Messmer (ends V4#2) & The Practical Pig (ends V4#2) begin 55 110 165 352 601 850
2 (44 pgs.)-1st Huey, Dewey & Louie-c 60 120 180 381 653 925
3 (12/38, 44 pgs.)-Ferdinand The Bull-c/feature story, Academy Award winner; Mickey Mouse & The Whalers serial begins, ends V4#12 54 108 162 343 574 825
4-Spotty, Mother Pluto strip-r begin, end V4#8 52 104 156 328 552 775
5-St. Valentine's day-c. 1st Pluto solo-c 57 114 171 362 619 875
7 (3/39)-The Ugly Duckling-c/feature story, Academy Award winner 54 108 162 343 574 825
7 (4/39)-Goofy & Wilbur The Grasshopper classic-c/feature story from 1st Goofy solo cartoon movie; Timid Elmer begins, ends V5#5 57 114 171 362 619 875
8-Big Bad Wolf-c from Practical Pig movie poster; Practical Pig feature story 54 108 162 343 574 825
9-Donald Duck & Mickey Mouse Sunday-r begin; The Pointer feature story, nominated for Academy Award 54 108 162 343 574 825
10-Classic July 4th drum & fife-c; last Donald Sunday-r 77 154 231 493 847 1200
11-1st slick-c; last over-sized issue 53 106 159 334 567 800
12 (9/39; format change, 10-1/4x8-1/4")-1st full color, cover to cover issue; Donald's Penguin-c/feature story 58 116 174 371 636 900
V5#1-Black Pete-c; Officer Duck-c/feature story; Autograph Hound feature story; Robinson Crusoe serial begins 69 138 207 442 759 1075
2-Goofy-c; 1st brief app. Pinocchio 74 148 222 470 810 1150
3 (12/39)-Pinocchio Christmas-c (Before movie release). 1st app. Jiminy Cricket; Pinocchio serial begins 90 180 270 576 988 1400
4,5: 5-Jiminy Cricket-c; Pinocchio serial ends; Donald's Dog Laundry feature story 58 116 174 371 636 900
6,7: 6-Tugboat Mickey feature story; Rip Van Winkle feature begins, ends V5#8. 7-2nd Huey, Dewey & Louie-c 57 114 171 362 619 875
8-Last magazine size issue; 2nd solo Pluto-c; Figaro & Cleo feature story 58 116 174 371 636 900
9-11: 9 (6/40; change to comic book size)-Jiminy Cricket feature story; Donald-c & Sunday-r begin. 10-Special Independence Day issue. 11-Hawaiian Holiday & Mickey's Trailer feature stories; last 36 pg. issue 63 126 189 403 689 975
12 (Format change)-The transition issue (68 pgs.) becoming a comic book. With only a title change to follow, becomes Walt Disney's Comics & Stories #1 with the next issue 476 952 1428 3475 6138 8800

NOTE: ***Otto Messmer**-a is in many issues of the first two-three years. The following story titles and issues have gags created by **Carl Barks:** V4#3(12/38)-'Donald's Better Self' & 'Donald's Golf Game;' V4#4(1/39)-'Donald's Lucky Day;' V4#7(3/39)-'Hockey Champ;' V4#7(4/39)-'Donald's Cousin Gus;' V4#9(6/39)-'Sea Scouts;' V4#12(9/39)-'Donald's Penguin;' V5#9 (6/40)-'Donald's Vacation;' V5#10(7/40)-'Bone Trouble;' V5#12(9/40)-'Window Cleaners.'*

MICKEY MOUSE MAGAZINE (Russian Version)
May 16, 1991 (1st Russian printing of a modern comic book)

1-Bagged w/gold label commemoration in English 10.00

MICKEY MOUSE MARCH OF COMICS (See March of Comics #8,27,45,60,74)

MICKEY MOUSE SHORTS: SEASON ONE
IDW Publishing: Jul, 2016 - No. 4, Oct, 2016 ($3.99, limited series)

1-4-Adaptations of new Disney cartoon shorts 4.00

MICKEY MOUSE'S SUMMER VACATION (See Story Hour Series)

MICKEY MOUSE SUMMER FUN (See Dell Giants)

MICKEY SPILLANE'S MIKE DANGER
Tekno Comix: Sept, 1995 - No. 11, May, 1996 ($1.95)

1-11: 1-Frank Miller-c. 7-polybagged; Simonson-c. 8,9-Simonson-c 3.00

MICKEY SPILLANE'S MIKE DANGER
Big Entertainment: V2#1, June, 1996 - No. 10, Apr, 1997 ($2.25)

V2#1-10: Max Allan Collins scripts 3.00

MICKEY'S TWICE UPON A CHRISTMAS (Disney)
Gemstone Publishing: 2004 ($3.95, square-bound, one-shot)

nn-Christmas short stories with Mickey, Minnie, Donald, Uncle Scrooge, Goofy and others 4.00

MICROBOTS, THE
Gold Key: Dec, 1971 (one-shot)

1 (10271-112) Painted-c 3 6 9 15 22 28

MICRONAUTS (Toys)
Marvel Comics Group: Jan, 1979 - No. 59, Aug, 1984 (Mando paper #53 on)

1-Intro/1st app. Baron Karza 2 4 6 10 14 18
2-7,9,10,35,37,57: 7-Man-Thing app.9-1st app. Cilicia. 35-Double size; origin Microverse; intro Death Squad; Dr. Strange app. 37-Nightcrawler app.; X-Men cameo (2 pgs.). 57-(52 pgs.) 5.00
8-1st app. Capt. Universe (8/79) 3 6 9 19 30 40
11-34,36,38-56,58,59: 13-1st app. Jasmine. 15-Death of Microtron. 15-17-Fantastic Four app. 17-Death of Jasmine. 20-Ant-Man app. 21-Microverse series begins. 25-Origin Baron Karza. 25-29-Nick Fury app. 27-Death of Biotron. 34-Dr. Strange app. 38-First direct sale. 40-Fantastic Four app. 48-Early Guice-a begins. 59-Golden painted-c 4.00
Annual 1,2 (12/79,10/80)-Ditko-c/a 5.00

NOTE: *#38-on distributed only through comic shops.* ***N. Adams** c-7i. **Chaykin** a-13-18p. **Ditko** a-39p. **Giffen** a-36p, 37p(part). **Golden** a-1-12p; c-2-7p, 8-23, 24p, 38, 39, 59. **Guice** a-48-58p; c-49-58. **Gil Kane** a-38, 40-45p; c-40-45. **Layton** c-33-37. **Miller** c-31.*

MICRONAUTS (Micronauts: The New Voyages on cover)
Marvel Comics Group: Oct, 1984 - No. 20, May, 1986

V2#1-20 4.00

NOTE: ***Kelley Jones** a-1; c-1, 6. **Guice** a-4p; c-2p.*

MICRONAUTS
Image Comics: 2002 - No. 11, Sept, 2003 ($2.95)

2002 Convention Special (no cover price, B&W) previews series 3.00
1-11: 1-3-Hanson-a; Dave Johnson-c. 4-Su-a; 2 covers by Linsner & Hanson 3.00
...Vol. 1: Revolution (2003, $12.95, digest size) r/#1-5 13.00

MICRONAUTS (Volume 2)
Devil's Due Publishing: Mar, 2004 - No. 3, May, 2004 ($2.95)

1-3-Jolley-s/Broderick-a 3.00

MICRONAUTS
IDW Publishing: Apr, 2016 - No. 11, Mar, 2017 ($4.99/$3.99)

1-($4.99) Cullen Bunn-s/David Baldeón-a; multiple covers; Baron Karza app. 5.00
2-11-($3.99) Max Dunbar-a. 5-Revolution tie-in 4.00
Annual #1 (1/17, $7.99) Bunn-s/Ferreira-a; future Micronauts app. 8.00

Micronauts: Wrath of Karza #1 © Hasbro

Midnighter (2015 series) #9 © DC

Mighty Avengers #1 © MAR

	GD 2.0	VG 4.0	FN 6.0	VF 8.0	VF/NM 9.0	NM- 9.2

... First Strike 1 (9/17, $3.99) Rom app.; leads into Rom First Strike; Gage-s/Panda-a 4.00
...: Revolution 1 (9/16, $3.99) Tie-in w/Transformers, G.I. Joe, M.A.S.K.,Action Man, Rom 4.00

MICRONAUTS: KARZA
Image Comics: Feb, 2003 - No. 4, May, 2003 ($2.95)
1-4-Krueger-s/Kurth-a 3.00

MICRONAUTS SPECIAL EDITION
Marvel Comics Group: Dec, 1983 - No. 5, Apr, 1984 ($2.00, limited series, Baxter paper)
1-5: r-/original series 1-12; Guice-c(p)-all 4.00

MICRONAUTS: WRATH OF KARZA (Leads into First Strike #1)
IDW Publishing: Apr, 2017 - No. 5, Aug, 2017 ($3.99)
1-5-Cullen Bunn & Jimmy Johnston-s/Andrew Griffith-a; multiple covers 4.00

MIDGET COMICS (Fighting Indian Stories)
St. John Publishng Co.: Feb, 1950 - No. 2, Apr, 1950 (5-3/8x7-3/8", 68 pgs.)
1-Fighting Indian Stories; Matt Baker-c 33 66 99 194 317 440
2-Tex West, Cowboy Marshal (also in #1) 15 30 45 88 137 185

MIDNIGHT (See Smash Comics #18)

MIDNIGHT
Ajax/Farrell Publ. (Four Star Comic Corp.): Apr, 1957 - No. 6, June, 1958
1-Reprints from Voodoo & Strange Fantasy with some changes
18 36 54 105 165 225
2-6 12 24 36 69 97 125

MIDNIGHTER (See The Authority)
DC Comics (WildStorm): Jan, 2007 - No. 20, Aug, 2008 ($2.99)
1-20: 1-Ennis-s/Sprouse-a/c. 6-Fabry-a. 7-Vaughan-s. 8-Gage-s. 9-Stelfreeze-a 3.00
1-4-Variant covers. 1-Michael Golden. 2-Art Adams 3-Jason Pearson. 4-Glenn Fabry 4.00
...: Anthem TPB (2008, $14.99) r/#7,10-15 15.00
...: Armageddon (12/07, $2.99) Gage-s/Coleby-a/McKone-c 3.00
...: Assassin8 TPB (2009, $14.99) r/#16-20 15.00
...: Killing Machine TPB (2008, $14.99) r/#1-6 15.00

MIDNIGHTER (See The Authority)
DC Comics: Aug, 2015 - No. 12, Jul, 2016 ($2.99)
1-12: 1-Orlando-s/Aco-a. 3-5-Grayson app. 9-12-Harley Quinn & Suicide Squad app. 3.00

MIDNIGHTER AND APOLLO (The Authority)
DC Comics: Dec, 2016 - No. 6, May, 2017 ($3.99, limited series)
1-6-Orlando-s/Blanco-a. 1,2-Henry Bendix app. 2-6-Neron app. 4.00

MIDNIGHT MASS
DC Comics (Vertigo): Jun, 2002 - No. 8, Jan, 2003 ($2.50)
1-8-Rozum-s/Saiz & Palmiotti-a 3.00

MIDNIGHT MASS: HERE THERE BE MONSTERS
DC Comics (Vertigo): March, 2004 - No. 6, Aug, 2004 ($2.95, limited series)
1-6-Rozum-s/Paul Lee-a 3.00

MIDNIGHT MEN
Marvel Comics (Epic Comics/Heavy Hitters): June, 1993 - No. 4, Sept, 1993 ($2.50/$1.95, limited series)
1-($2.50)-Embossed-c; Chaykin-c/a & scripts in all 4.00
2-4 3.00

MIDNIGHT MYSTERY
American Comics Group: Jan-Feb, 1961 - No. 7, Oct, 1961
1-Sci/Fi story 8 16 24 51 96 140
2-7: 7-Gustavson-a 5 10 15 30 50 70
NOTE: *Reinman a-1, 3. Whitney a-1, 4-6; c-1-3, 5, 7.*

MIDNIGHT NATION
Image Comics (Top Cow): Oct, 2000 - No. 12, July, 2002 ($2.50/$2.95)
1-Straczynski-s/Frank-a; 2 covers 3.50
2-11: 9-Twin Towers cover 3.00
12-($2.95) Last issue 3.00
Wizard #1/2 (2001) Michael Zulli-a; two covers by Frank 3.00
Vol. 1 ('03, $29.99, TPB) r/#1-12 & Wizard #1/2; cover gallery; afterword by Straczynski 30.00

MIDNIGHT OF THE SOUL
Image Comics: Jun, 2016 - No. 5, Oct, 2016 ($3.50, limited series)
1-5-Howard Chaykin-s/a/c; set in 1950s New York City 3.50

MIDNIGHT SOCIETY: THE BLACK LAKE
Dark Horse Comics: Jun, 2015 - No. 4, Oct, 2015 ($3.99)
1-4-Drew Johnson-s/a/c 4.00

MIDNIGHT SONS UNLIMITED
Marvel Comics (Midnight Sons imprint #4 on): Apr, 1993 - No. 9, May, 1995 ($3.95, 68 pgs.)
1-9: Blaze, Darkhold (by Quesada #1), Ghost Rider, Morbius & Nightstalkers in all. 1-Painted-c. 3-Spider-Man app. 4-Siege of Darkness part 17; new Dr. Strange & new Ghost Rider app.; spot varnish-c 4.00
NOTE: *Sears a-2.*

MIDNIGHT TALES
Charlton Press: Dec, 1972 - No. 18, May, 1976
V1#1 3 6 9 16 23 30
2-10 2 4 6 10 14 18
11-18: 11-14-Newton-a(p) 2 4 6 8 11 14
12,17(Modern Comics reprint, 1977) 6.00
NOTE: *Adkins a-12i, 13i. Ditko a-12. Howard (Wood imitator) a-1-15, 17, 18; c-1-18. Don Newton a-11-14p. Staton a-1, 3-11, 13. Sutton a-3-10.*

MIGHTY, THE
DC Comics: Apr, 2009 - No. 12, Mar, 2010 ($2.99)
1-12: Tomasi & Champagne-s/Dave Johnson-c. 1-4-Snejbjerg-a. 5-12-Samnee-a 3.00
...: Volume 1 TPB (2009, $17.99) r/#1-6 18.00
...: Volume 2 TPB (2010, $17.99) r/#7-12 18.00

MIGHTY ATOM, THE (...& the Pixies #6) (Formerly The Pixies #1-5)
Magazine Enterprises: No. 6, 1949; Nov, 1957 - No. 6, Aug-Sept, 1958
6(1949-M.E.)-no month (1st Series) 7 14 21 35 43 50
1-6(2nd Series)-Pixies-r 4 8 12 18 22 25
I.W. Reprint #1(nd) 2 4 6 8 11 14

MIGHTY AVENGERS
Marvel Comics: May, 2007 - No. 36, Jun, 2010 ($3.99/$2.99)
1-($3.99) Iron Man, Ms. Marvel select new team; Bendis-s/Cho-a/c; Mole Man app. 5.00
2-20: 2-6-($2.99) Ultron returns. 7-15: 7-Bagley-a begins; Venom on-c. 9-11-Dr. Doom app. 12-20-Secret Invasion. 12,13-Maleev-a. 15-Romita Jr.-a. 16-Elektra. 20-Wasp funeral 3.00
21-($3.99) Dark Reign; Scarlet Witch returns; new team assembled; Pham-a 4.00
22-36: 25,26-Fantastic Four app. 35,36-Siege; Ultron returns 3.00
...: Most Wanted Files (2007, $3.99) profiles of members, accomplices & adversaries 4.00
... Vol. 1: The Ultron Initiative HC (2008, $19.99) r/#1-6; variant covers and sketch art 20.00
... Vol. 2: Venom Bomb HC (2008, $19.99) r/#7-11; B&W cover art 20.00

MIGHTY AVENGERS (Continues in Captain America and the Mighty Avengers)
Marvel Comics: Nov, 2013 - No. 14, Nov, 2014 ($3.99)
1-14: 1-Luke Cage, White Tiger, Power Man, Spectrum & Superior Spider-Man team; Land-a. 4-Falcon app. 5-She-Hulk app. 6-8-Schiti-a. 9-Ronin unmasked. 10-12-Original Sin 4.00

MIGHTY BEAR (Formerly Fun Comics; becomes Unsane #15)
Star Publ. No. 13,14/Ajax-Farrell (Four Star): No. 13, Jan, 1954 - No. 14, Mar, 1954; 9/57 - No. 3, 2/58
13,14-L. B. Cole-c 18 36 54 105 165 225
1-3('57-58)Four Star; becomes Mighty Ghost #4 7 14 21 37 46 55

MIGHTY CAPTAIN MARVEL, THE (Follows Civil War II)(Continues in Captain Marvel #125)
Marvel Comics: No. 0, Feb, 2017 - No. 9, Nov, 2017 ($3.99)
0-Stohl-s/Laiso-a; Alpha Flight app. 4.00
1-9: 1-(3/17) Stohl-s/Rosanas-a. 5-8-Secret Empire tie-ins 4.00

MIGHTY COMICS (...Presents) (Formerly Flyman)
Radio Comics (Archie): No. 40, Nov, 1966 - No. 50, Oct, 1967 (All 12¢ issues)
40-Web 5 10 15 30 50 70
41-50: 41-Shield, Black Hood. 42-Black Hood. 43-Shield, Web & Black Hood. 44-Black Hood, Steel Sterling & The Shield. 45-Shield & Hangman; origin Web retold. 46-Steel Sterling, Web & Black Hood. 47-Black Hood & Mr. Justice. 48-Shield & Hangman; Wizard x-over in Shield. 49-Steel Sterling & Fox; Black Hood x-over in Steel Sterling. 50-Black Hood & Web; Inferno x-over in Web 4 8 12 28 47 65
NOTE: *Paul Reinman a-40-50.*

MIGHTY CRUSADERS, THE (Also see Adventures of the Fly, The Crusaders & Fly Man)
Mighty Comics Group (Radio Comics): Nov, 1965 - No. 7, Oct, 1966 (All 12¢)
1-Origin The Shield 7 14 21 46 86 125
2-Origin Comet 4 8 12 28 47 65
3,5-7: 3-Origin Fly-Man. 5-Intro. Ultra-Men (Fox, Web, Capt. Flag) & Terrific Three (Jaguar, Mr. Justice, Steel Sterling). 7-Steel Sterling feature; origin Fly-Girl
4 8 12 27 44 60
4-1st S.A. app. Fireball, Inferno & Fox; Firefly, Web, Bob Phantom, Blackjack, Hangman, Zambini, Kardak, Steel Sterling, Mr. Justice, Wizard, Capt. Flag, Jaguar x-over
4 8 12 28 47 65
Volume 1: Origin of a Super Team TPB (2003, $12.95) r/#1 & Fly Man #31-33 13.00
NOTE: *Reinman a-6.*

MIGHTY CRUSADERS, THE (All New Advs. of...#2)

Mighty Crusaders #7 © ACP

Mighty Morphin Power Rangers #6 © SCGPR

Mighty Mouse #3 © Terry Toons

	GD 2.0	VG 4.0	FN 6.0	VF 8.0	VF/NM 9.0	NM- 9.2

Red Circle Prod./Archie Ent. No. 6 on: Mar, 1983 - No. 13, Sept, 1985 ($1.00, 36 pgs, Mando paper)

1-Origin Black Hood, The Fly, Fly Girl, The Shield, The Wizard, The Jaguar, Pvt. Strong & The Web. 1 2 3 4 5 7
2-10: 2-Mister Midnight begins. 4-Darkling replaces Shield. 5-Origin Jaguar, Shield begins. 7-Untold origin Jaguar. 10-Veitch-a 5.00
11-13-Lower print run 6.00
NOTE: *Buckler a-1-3, 4i, 5p, 7p, 8i, 9i; c-1-10p.*

MIGHTY CRUSADERS, THE (Also see The Shield, The Web and The Red Circle)
DC Comics: Sept, 2010 - No. 6, Feb, 2011 ($3.99, limited series)

1-6-The Shield, The Web, Fly-Girl, Inferno, War Eagle & The Comet team-up 4.00
... Special 1 (7/10, $4.99) Prequel to series; Pina-a/Lau-c 5.00

MIGHTY CRUSADERS, THE (Volume 3)
Archie Comic Publications (Dark Circle): Jan, 2018 - Present ($3.99)

1-3-The Shield, Jaguar, Firefly, Darkling, Steel Sterling, The Comet & The Web team-up 4.00

MIGHTY GHOST (Formerly Mighty Bear #1-3)
Ajax/Farrell Publ.: No. 4, June, 1958

4 7 14 21 37 46 55

MIGHTY HERCULES, THE (TV)
Gold Key: July, 1963 - No. 2, Nov, 1963

1 (10072-307) 11 22 33 77 166 255
2 (10072-311) 11 22 33 73 157 240

MIGHTY HEROES, THE (TV) (Funny)
Dell Publishing Co.: Mar, 1967 - No. 4, July, 1967

1-Also has a 1957 Heckle & Jeckle-r 10 20 30 64 132 200
2-4: 4-Has two 1958 Mighty Mouse-r 7 14 21 44 82 120

MIGHTY HEROES
Spotlight Comics: 1987 (B&W, one-shot)

1-Heckle & Jeckle backup 5.00

MIGHTY HEROES
Marvel Comics: Jan, 1998 ($2.99, one-shot)

1-Origin of the Mighty Heroes 3.00

MIGHTY LOVE
DC Comics: 2003 ($24.99/$17.95, graphic novel)

HC-($24.95) Howard Chaykin-s/a; intro. Skylark and the Iron Angel 25.00
SC-($17.95) 18.00

MIGHTY MAN (From Savage Dragon titles)
Image Comics: Dec, 2004 ($7.95, one-shot)

1-Reprints the serialized back-ups from Savage Dragon #109-118 8.00

MIGHTY MAN (From Savage Dragon)
Image Comics: Apr, 2017 ($3.99, one-shot)

1-Larsen-s/Koutsis-a; Superpatriot, Malcolm Dragon, Horridus, Barbaric, Ricochet app. 4.00

MIGHTY MARVEL TEAM-UP THRILLERS
Marvel Comics: 1983 ($5.95, trade paperback)

1-Reprints team-up stories 3 6 9 18 28 38

MIGHTY MARVEL WESTERN, THE
Marvel Comics Group (LMC earlier issues): Oct, 1968 - No. 46, Sept, 1976 (#1-14: 68 pgs.; #15,16: 52 pgs.)

1-Begin Kid Colt, Rawhide Kid, Two-Gun Kid-r 7 14 21 48 89 130
2-5: (2-14 are 68 pgs.) 4 8 12 27 44 60
6-16: (15,16 are 52 pgs.) 3 6 9 21 33 45
17-20 2 4 6 13 18 22
21-30,32,37: 24-Kid Colt-r end. 25-Matt Slade-r begin. 32-Origin-r/Rawhide Kid #23; Williamson-r/Kid Slade #7. 37-Williamson, Kirby-r/Two-Gun Kid 51
2 4 6 9 13 16
31,33-36,38-46: 31-Baker-r. 2 4 6 8 11 14
45-(30¢-c variant, limited distribution)(6/76) 8 16 24 56 108 160
NOTE: *Jack Davis a(r)-21-24. Keller r-1-13, 22. Kirby a(r)-1-3, 6, 9, 12-14, 16, 25-29, 32-38, 40, 41, 43-46; c-29. Maneely a(r)-22. Severin c-3i, 9. No Matt Slade-#43.*

MIGHTY MIDGET COMICS, THE (Miniature)
Samuel E. Lowe & Co.: No date; circa 1942-1943 (Sold 2 for 5¢, B&W and red, 36 pgs, approx. 5x4")

Bulletman #11(1943)-r/cover/Bulletman #3 16 32 48 94 147 200
Captain Marvel Adventures #11 16 32 48 94 147 200
Captain Marvel #11 (Same as above except for full color ad on back cover; this issue was glued to cover of Captain Marvel #20 and is not found in fine-mint condition)
340 680 1020 - - -
Captain Marvel Jr. #11 (Same-c as Master #27 16 32 48 94 147 200
Captain Marvel Jr. #11 (Same as above except for full color ad on back-c; this issue was glued to cover of Captain Marvel #21 and is not found in fine-mint condition)
340 680 1020 - - -
Golden Arrow #11 15 30 45 86 133 180
Golden Arrow #11 (Same as above except for full color ad on back-c; this issue was glued to cover of Captain Marvel #21 and is not found in fine-mint condition)
280 560 840 - - -
Ibis the Invincible #11(1942)-Origin; reprints cover to Ibis #1 (Predates Fawcett's Ibis the Invincible #1). 16 32 48 94 147 200
Spy Smasher #11(1942) 16 32 48 94 147 200
NOTE: *The above books came in a box called "box full of books" and was distributed with other Samuel Lowe puzzles, paper dolls, coloring books, etc. They are not titled Mighty Midget Comics. All have a war bond seal on back cover which is otherwise blank. These books came in a "Mighty Midget" flat cardboard counter display rack.*
Balbo, the Boy Magician #12 (1943)-1st book devoted entirely to character.
10 20 30 54 72 90
Bulletman #12 12 24 36 69 97 125
Commando Yank #12 (1943)-Only comic devoted entirely to character.
10 20 30 56 76 95
Dr. Voltz the Human Generator (1943)-Only comic devoted entirely to character.
10 20 30 54 72 90
Lance O'Casey #12 (1943)-1st comic devoted entirely to character (Predates Fawcett's Lance O'Casey #1). 10 20 30 54 72 90
Leatherneck the Marine (1943)-Only comic devoted entirely to character.
10 20 30 54 72 90
Minute Man #12 12 24 36 67 94 120
Mister "Q" (1943)-Only comic devoted entirely to character.
10 20 30 54 72 90
Mr. Scarlet and Pinky #12 (1943)-Only comic devoted entirely to character.
10 20 30 58 79 100
Pat Wilton and His Flying Fortress (1943)-1st comic devoted entirely to character. 10 20 30 54 72 90
The Phantom Eagle #12 (1943)-Only comic devoted entirely to character.
10 20 30 54 72 90
State Trooper Stops Crime (1943)-Only comic devoted entirely to character.
10 20 30 54 72 90
Tornado Tom (1943)-Origin, r/from Cyclone #1-3; only comic devoted entirely to character.
10 20 30 54 72 90

MIGHTY MORPHIN POWER RANGERS (Also see Saban's Mighty Morphin' Power Rangers)
BOOM! Studios: No. 0, Jan, 2016; Mar, 2016 - Present ($3.99)

0-Higgins-s/Prasetya-a; Rita Repulsa & Scorpina app.; multiple covers 4.00
1-24: 1-4,6-9,11-Higgins-s/Prasetya-a. 5-Silas-a. 10-Lam-a 4.00
2016 Annual 1 (8/16, $7.99) Short stories; art by Guillory, Terry Moore, Kochalka 8.00
2017 Annual 1 (5/17, $7.99) Short stories; art by Mora, Irving, Montes; 3 covers 8.00

MIGHTY MORPHIN POWER RANGERS: PINK
BOOM! Studios: Jun, 2016 - No. 6, Jan, 2017 ($3.99, limited series)

1-6-Fletcher & Thompson-s/DiNicuolo-a; multiple covers 4.00

MIGHTY MORPHIN' POWER RANGERS: THE MOVIE (Also see Saban's Mighty Morphin' Power Rangers)
Marvel Comics: Sept, 1995 ($3.95, one-shot)

nn-Adaptation of movie 5.00

MIGHTY MOUSE (See Adventures of..., Dell Giant #43, Giant Comics Edition, March of Comics #205, 237, 247, 257, 447, 459, 471, 483, Oxydol-Dreft, Paul Terry's, & Terry-Toons Comics)

MIGHTY MOUSE (1st Series)
Timely/Marvel Comics (20th Century Fox): Fall, 1946 - No. 4, Summer, 1947

1 200 400 600 1280 2190 3100
2 76 152 228 486 831 1175
3,4 48 96 144 302 514 725

MIGHTY MOUSE (2nd Series) (Paul Terry's... #62-71)
St. John Publishing Co./Pines No. 68 (3/56) on (TV issues #72 on):
Aug, 1947 - No. 67, 11/55; No. 68, 3/56 - No. 83, 6/59

5(#1) 61 122 183 390 670 950
6-10: 10-Over-sized issue 25 50 75 150 245 340
11-19 15 30 45 90 140 190
20 (11/50) - 25-(52 pg. editions) 14 28 42 76 108 140
20-25-(36 pg. editions) 12 24 36 67 94 120
26-37: 35-Flying saucer-c 11 22 33 62 86 110
38-45-(100 pgs.) 20 40 60 120 195 270
46-83: 62-64,67-Painted-c. 82-Infinity-c 10 20 30 58 79 100
Album nn (nd, 1952/53?, St. John)(100 pgs.)(Rebound issues w/new cover)

Mighty Mouse (2017 series) #1 © CBS

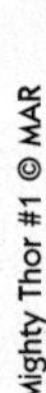

Mighty Thor #1 © MAR

Military Comics #6 © QUA

	GD 2.0	VG 4.0	FN 6.0	VF 8.0	VF/NM 9.0	NM- 9.2

	28	56	84	165	270	375
Album 1(10/52, 25¢, 100 pgs., St. John)-Gandy Goose app.	36	72	108	211	343	475
Album 2,3(11/52 & 12/52, St. John) (100 pgs.)	27	54	81	158	259	360
Fun Club Magazine 1(Fall, 1957-Pines, 25¢, 100 pgs.) (CBS TV)-Tom Terrific, Heckle & Jeckle, Dinky Duck, Gandy Goose	20	40	60	120	195	270
Fun Club Magazine 2-6(Winter, 1958-Pines)	12	24	36	67	94	120
3-D 1-(1st printing-9/53, 25¢)(St. John)-Came w/glasses; stiff covers; says World's First! on-c; 1st 3-D comic	29	58	87	170	278	385
3-D 1-(2nd printing-10/53, 25¢)-Came w/glasses; slick, glossy covers, slightly smaller	20	40	60	114	182	250
3-D 2,3(11/53, 12/53, 25¢)-(St. John)-With glasses	20	40	60	114	182	250

MIGHTY MOUSE (TV)(3rd Series)(Formerly Adventures of Mighty Mouse)
Gold Key/Dell Publ. Co. No. 166-on: No. 161, Oct, 1964 - No. 172, Oct, 1968

161(10/64)-165(9/65)-(Becomes Adventures of... No. 166 on)	4	8	12	28	47	65
166(3/66), 167(6/66)-172	3	6	9	20	31	42

MIGHTY MOUSE (TV)
Spotlight Comics: 1987 - No. 2, 1987 ($1.50, color)

1,2-New stories 4.00
...And Friends Holiday Special (11/87, $1.75) 4.00

MIGHTY MOUSE (TV)
Marvel Comics: Oct, 1990 - No. 10, July, 1991 ($1.00)(Based on Sat. cartoon)

1-10: 1-Dark Knight-c parody. 2-10: 3-Intro Bat-Bat; Byrne-c. 4,5-Crisis-c/story parodies w/Perez-c. 6-Spider-Man-c parody. 7-Origin Bat-Bat 3.00

MIGHTY MOUSE (TV)
Dynamite Entertainment: 2017 - No. 5, 2017 ($3.99)

1-5: 1-Multiple covers incl. Alex Ross & Neal Adams; Mighty Mouse in the real world 4.00

MIGHTY MOUSE ADVENTURE MAGAZINE
Spotlight Comics: 1987 ($2.00, B&W, 52 pgs., magazine size, one-shot)

1-Deputy Dawg, Heckle & Jeckle backup stories 5.00

MIGHTY MOUSE ADVENTURES (Adventures of... #2 on)
St. John Publishing Co.: November, 1951

1	40	80	120	246	411	575

MIGHTY MOUSE ADVENTURE STORIES (Paul Terry's... on-c only)
St. John Publishing Co.: 1953 (50¢, 384 pgs.)

nn-Rebound issues	57	114	171	362	619	875

MIGHTY MUTANIMALS (See Teenage Mutant Ninja Turtles Adventures #19)
May, 1991 - No. 3, July, 1991 ($1.00, limited series)
Archie Comics: Apr, 1992 - No. 8, June, 1993 ($1.25)

1-3: 1-Story cont'd from TMNT Advs. #19.	1	2	3	5	6	8
1-4 (1992)	1	2	3	5	6	8
5-8: 7-1st app. Merdude	2	4	6	8	10	12

MIGHTY SAMSON (Also see Gold Key Champion)
Gold Key/Whitman #32: July, 1964 - No. 20, Nov, 1969; No. 21, Aug, 1972; No. 22, Dec, 1973 - No. 31, Mar, 1976; No. 32, Aug, 1982 (Painted-c #1-31)

1-Origin/1st app.; Thorne-a begins	8	16	24	51	96	140
2-5	4	8	12	28	47	65
6-10: 7-Tom Morrow begins, ends #20	3	6	9	20	30	40
11-20	3	6	9	16	23	30
21-31: 21,22-r	2	4	6	11	16	20
32(Whitman, 8/82)-r	2	4	6	8	10	12

MIGHTY SAMSON
Dark Horse Comics: Dec, 2010 - No. 4, Oct, 2011 ($3.50)

1-4: 1-Origin retold; Shooter & Vaughn-s/Olliffe-a/Swanland-c; r/1st app. from 1964 3.50
1-Variant-c by Olliffe 4.00

MIGHTY THOR, THE (Continues in Thor; God of Thunder)
Marvel Comics: Jun, 2011 - No. 22, Dec, 2012 ($3.99)

1-Fraction-s/Coipel-a; Silver Surfer app.; bonus concept art from the movie 4.00
1-Variant-c by Charest 6.00
1-Variant-c by Simonson 10.00
2-22: 3-6-Galactus app. 7-Fear Itself tie-in; Odin's 1st battle vs. the Serpent. 8-Tanarus. 13-17-Simonson-c. 18-21-Alan Davis-a 4.00
12.1 (6/12, $2.99) Kitson-a/Coipel-c; flashbacks from Volstagg & Sif 3.00
Annual 1 (8/12, $4.99) Silver Surfer & Galactus app.; DeMatteis-s/Elson-a 5.00

MIGHTY THOR (Jane Foster as Thor)
Marvel Comics: Jan, 2016 - No. 23, Nov, 2017; No. 700, Dec, 2017 - Present ($4.99/$3.99)

1-($4.99) Tri-fold cover; Aaron-s/Dauterman-a; Loki app. 5.00
2-23-($3.99) 3-Multiple Lokis app. 12-Origin of Mjolnir; Frazer Irving-a. 14-Epting-a. 20-Volstagg becomes the War Thor 4.00

[Title switches to legacy numbering after #23 (11/17)]

700-(12/17, $5.99) Aaron-s; art by various incl. Dauterman, Simonson, Acuna, Coipel 6.00
701-704: 701-Mangog vs. War Thor; Harren-a. 703,704-Dauterman-a 4.00

MIKE BARNETT, MAN AGAINST CRIME (TV)
Fawcett Publications: Dec, 1951 - No. 6, Oct, 1952

1	21	42	63	122	199	275
2	14	28	42	78	112	145
3,4,6	11	22	33	64	90	115
5- "Market for Morphine" cover/story	15	30	45	90	140	190

MIKE DANGER (See Mickey Spillane's...)

MIKE DEODATO'S...
Caliber Comics: 1996, ($2.95, B&W)

...FALLOUT 3000 #1, **...JONAS** (mag. size) #1,**...PRIME CUTS** (mag. size) #1, **...PROTHEUS** #1,2, **...RAMTHAR** #1,**...RAZOR NIGHTS** #1 3.00

MIKE GRELL'S SABLE (Also see Jon Sable & Sable)
First Comics: Mar, 1990 - No. 10, Dec, 1990 ($1.75)

1-10: r/Jon Sable Freelance #1-10 by Grell 3.00

MIKE MIST MINUTE MIST-ERIES (See Ms. Tree/Mike Mist in 3-D)
Eclipse Comics: April, 1981 ($1.25, B&W, one-shot)

1 3.00

MIKE SHAYNE PRIVATE EYE
Dell Publishing Co.: Nov-Jan, 1962 - No. 3, Sept-Nov, 1962

1	4	8	12	23	37	50
2,3	3	6	9	16	24	32

MILES MORALES: ULTIMATE SPIDER-MAN
Marvel Comics: Jul, 2014 - No. 12, Jun, 2015 ($3.99)

1-11: 1-Bendis-s/Marquez-a; Peter Parker & Norman Osborn return. 11-Dr. Doom app. 4.00
12-Dr. Doom and the Ultimates app.; leads into Secret Wars #1 4.00

MILESTONE FOREVER
DC Comics: Apr, 2010 - No. 2, May, 2010 ($5.99, squarebound, limited series)

1,2-McDuffie-s/Leon & Bright-a; Icon, Blood Syndicate, Hardware and Static app. 6.00

MILITARY COMICS (Becomes Modern Comics #44 on)
Quality Comics Group: Aug, 1941 - No. 43, Oct, 1945

1-Origin/1st app. Blackhawk by C. Cuidera (Eisner scripts); Miss America, The Death Patrol by Jack Cole (also #2-7,27-30), & The Blue Tracer by Guardineer; X of the Underground, The Yankee Eagle, Q-Boat & Shot & Shell, Archie Atkins, Loops & Banks by Bud Ernest (Bob Powell)(ends #13) begin	459	918	1377	3350	5925	8500
2-Secret War News begins (by McWilliams #2-16); Cole-a; new uniform with yellow circle & hawk's head for Blackhawk	142	284	426	909	1555	2200
3-Origin/1st app. Chop Chop (9/41)	116	232	348	742	1271	1800
4	103	206	309	659	1130	1600
5-The Sniper begins; Miss America in costume #4-7	90	180	270	576	988	1400
6-9: 8-X of the Underground begins (ends #13). 9-The Phantom Clipper begins (ends #16)	71	142	213	454	777	1100
10-Classic Eisner-c	90	180	270	576	988	1400
11-Flag-c	68	136	204	435	743	1050
12-Blackhawk by Crandall begins, ends #22	71	142	213	454	777	1100
13-15: 14-Private Dogtag begins (ends #83)	58	116	174	371	636	900
16-20: 16-Blue Tracer ends. 17-P.T. Boat begins	53	106	159	334	567	800
21-31: 22-Last Crandall Blackhawk. 23-Shrunken head-c. 27-Death Patrol revived. 28-True story of Mussolini	47	94	141	296	498	700
32-43	41	82	123	256	428	600

NOTE: *Berg a-6.* ***Al Bryant*** *c-31-34, 38, 40-43.* ***J. Cole*** *a-1-3, 27-32.* ***Crandall*** *a-12-22; c-13-20.* ***Cuidera*** *c-2-9.* ***Eisner*** *c-1, 2(part), 9, 10.* ***Kotsky*** *c-21-29, 35, 37, 39.* ***McWilliams*** *a-2-16.* ***Powell*** *a-1-13.* ***Ward*** *Blackhawk-30, 31(15 pgs. each); c-30.*

MILK AND CHEESE (Also see Cerebus Bi-Weekly #20)
Slave Labor: 1991 - Present ($2.50, B&W)

1-Evan Dorkin story & art in all	4	8	12	28	47	65
1-2nd-6th printings						4.00
2-"Other #1"	3	6	9	16	24	32
2-reprint						3.00
3-"Third #1"	2	4	6	11	16	20
4-"Fourth #1", 5-"First Second Issue"	1	3	4	6	8	10
6,7: 6-"#666"						5.00

NOTE: *Multiple printings of all issues exist and are worth cover price unless listed here.*

Millennium (2015 series) #2 © 20th Century Fox

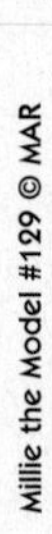

Millie the Model #129 © MAR

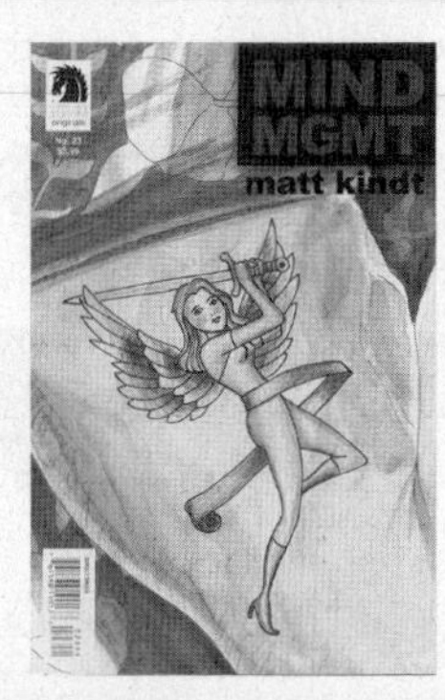

Mind Mgmt #23 © Matt Kindt

GD VG FN VF VF/NM NM-
2.0 4.0 6.0 8.0 9.0 9.2

GD VG FN VF VF/NM NM-
2.0 4.0 6.0 8.0 9.0 9.2

MILKMAN MURDERS, THE
Dark Horse Comics: Jun, 2004 - No. 4, Aug, 2004 ($2.99, limited series)

1-4-Casey-s/Parkhouse-a 3.00

MILLARWORLD (Mark Millar characters)
Image Comics: Jul, 2016; Sept, 2017 ($2.99)

...Annual 2016 1 (7/16) Short stories of Kick-Ass, Hit-Girl, Chrononauts and others 3.00
...Annual 2017 1 (9/17) Short stories of Kick-Ass, Superior, Huck, Nemesis and others 3.00

MILLENNIUM
DC Comics: Jan, 1988 - No. 8, Feb, 1988 (Weekly limited series)

1-Englehart-s/Staton c/a(p) 4.00
2-8 3.00
TPB (2008, $19.99) r/#1-8 20.00

MILLENNIUM (TV, spin-off from The X-Files)
IDW Publishing: Jan, 2015 - No. 5, May, 2015 ($3.99, limited series)

1-5: 1-Frank Black & Agent Mulder app.; Joe Harris-s/Colin Lorimer-a; three covers 4.00

MILLENNIUM EDITION:... (Reprints of classic DC issues, plus some WildStorm and non-DC issues with characters now published by DC)
DC Comics: Feb, 2000 - Feb, 2001 (gold foil cover stamps)

Action Comics #1, Adventure Comics #61, All Star Comics #3, All Star Comics #8, Batman #1, Detective Comics #1, Detective Comics #27, Detective Comics #38, Flash Comics #1, Military Comics #1, More Fun Comics #73, Police Comics #1, Sensation Comics #1, Superman #1, Whiz Comics #2, Wonder Woman #1 -($3.95-c) 5.00
Action Comics #252, Adventure Comics #247, Brave and the Bold #28, Brave and the Bold #85, Crisis on Infinte Earths #1, Detective #225, Detective #327, Detective #359, Detective #395, Flash #123, Gen13 #1, Green Lantern #76, House of Mystery #1, House of Secrets #92, JLA #1, Justice League #1, Mad #1, Man of Steel #1, Mysterious Suspense #1, New Gods, #1, New Teen Titans #1, Our Army at War #81, Plop! #1, Saga of the Swamp Thing #21, Shadow #1, Showcase #4, Showcase #9, Showcase #22, Superman #233, Superman (2nd) #75, Superman's Pal Jimmy Olsen #1, Watchmen #1, WildC.A.T.s #1, Wonder Woman (2nd) #1, World's Finest #71 -($2.50-c) 4.00
All-Star Western #10, Hellblazer #1, More Fun Comics #101, Preacher #1, Sandman #1, Spirit #1, Superboy #1, Superman #76, Young Romance #1-($2.95-c) 4.00
Batman: The Dark Knight Returns #1, Kingdom Come #1 -($5.95-c) 6.00
All Star Comics #3, Batman #1, Justice League #1: Chromium cover 12.00
Crisis on Infinite Earths #1 Chromium cover 20.00

MILLENNIUM FEVER
DC Comics (Vertigo): Oct, 1995 - No.4, Jan, 1996 ($2.50, limited series)

1-4: Duncan Fegredo-c/a 3.00

MILLENNIUM: THE GIRL WHO KICKED THE HORNET'S NEST
Titan Comics: Jan, 2018 - No. 2, Feb, 2018 ($5.99, limited series)

1,2-Adaptation of the Stieg Larsson novel; Runberg-s. 1-Homs-a. 2-Carot-a 6.00

MILLENNIUM: THE GIRL WHO PLAYED WITH FIRE
Titan Comics: Oct, 2017 - No. 2, Nov, 2017 ($5.99, limited series)

1,2-Adaptation of the Stieg Larsson novel; Runberg-s. 1-Gonzalez-a. 2-Carot-a 6.00

MILLENNIUM: THE GIRL WITH THE DRAGON TATTOO
Titan Comics: Jul, 2017 - No. 2, Aug, 2017 ($5.99, limited series)

1,2-Adaptation of the Stieg Larsson novel; Runberg-s/Homs-a 6.00

MILLENNIUM 2.5 A.D.
ACG Comics: No. 1, 2000 ($2.95)

1-Reprints 1934 Buck Rogers daily strips #1-48 3.00

MILLIE, THE LOVABLE MONSTER
Dell Publishing Co.: Sept-Nov, 1962 - No. 6, Jan, 1973

12-523-211-Bill Woggon c/a in all 5 10 15 31 53 75
2(8-10/63) 4 8 12 28 47 65
3(8-10/64) 4 8 12 25 40 55
4(7/72), 5(10/72), 6(1/73) 3 6 9 14 19 24

NOTE: ***Woggon** a-3-6; c-3-6. 4 reprints 1; 5 reprints 2; 6 reprints 3.*

MILLIE THE MODEL (See Comedy Comics, A Date With..., Joker Comics #28, Life With..., Mad About..., Marvel Mini-Books, Misty & Modeling With...)
Marvel/Atlas/Marvel Comics(CnPC #1)(SPI/Male/VPI):1945 - No. 207, Dec, 1973

1-Origin 300 600 900 2010 3505 5000
2 (10/46)-Millie becomes The Blonde Phantom to sell Blonde Phantom perfume; a pre-Blonde Phantom app. (see All-Select #11, Fall, 1946) 65 130 195 416 708 1000
3-8,10: 4-7-Willie app. 7-Willie smokes extra strong tobacco. 8,10-Kurtzman's "Hey Look". 8-Willie & Rusty app. 50 100 150 315 533 750
9-Powerhouse Pepper by Wolverton, 4 pgs. 53 106 159 334 567 800
11-Kurtzman-a, "Giggles 'n' Grins" 34 68 102 199 325 450
12,15,17,19,20: 12-Rusty & Hedy Devine app. 36 72 108 211 343 475
13,14,16,18: 13,14,16-Kurtzman's "Hey Look". 13-Hedy Devine app. 18-Dan DeCarlo-a begins 29 58 87 170 278 385
21-30 27 54 81 162 266 370
31-40 15 30 45 105 233 360
41-60 15 30 45 103 227 350
61-80 13 26 39 89 195 300
81-99: 93-Last DeCarlo issue? 10 20 30 66 138 210
100 10 20 30 69 147 225
101-106,108-130 6 12 18 40 73 105
107-Jack Kirby app. in story 6 12 18 42 79 115
131-134,136,138-153: 141-Groovy Gears-c/s 4 8 12 28 47 65
135-(2/66) 1st app. Groovy Gears 5 10 15 35 57 80
137-2nd app. Groovy Gears 5 10 15 30 50 70
154-New Millie begins (10/67) 6 12 18 38 69 100
155-190 4 8 12 28 47 65
191,193-199,201-206 4 8 12 25 40 55
192-(52 pgs.) 4 8 12 28 47 65
200,207(Last issue) 4 8 12 28 47 65
(Beware: cut-up pages are common in all Annuals)
Annual 1(1962)-Early Marvel annual (2nd?) 32 64 96 230 515 800
Annual 2(1963) 16 323 48 110 243 375
Annual 3-5 (1964-1966) 8 16 24 54 102 150
Annual 6-10(1967-11/71) 6 12 18 41 76 110
Queen-Size 11(9/74), 12(1975) 6 12 18 37 66 95

NOTE: ***Dan DeCarlo** a-18-93.*

MILLION DOLLAR DIGEST (Richie Rich... #23 on; also see Richie Rich...)
Harvey Publications: 11/86 - No. 7, 11/87; No. 8, 4/88 - No. 34, Nov, 1994 ($1.25/$1.75, digest size)

1 1 2 3 5 6 8
2-8: 8-(68 pgs.) 6.00
9-20: 9-Begin $1.75-c. 14-May not exist 1 2 3 4 5 7
21-34 1 3 4 6 8 10

MILT GROSS FUNNIES (Also see Picture News #1)
Milt Gross, Inc. (ACG?): Aug, 1947 - No. 2, Sept, 1947

1 27 54 81 158 259 360
2 18 36 54 107 169 230

MILTON THE MONSTER & FEARLESS FLY (TV)
Gold Key: May, 1966

1 (10175-605) 8 16 24 54 102 150

MINDFIELD
Aspen MLT: No. 0, May, 2010 - No. 6, Sept, 2011 ($2.50/$2.99)

0-($2.50) Krul-s/Konat-a; 3 covers 3.00
1-6-($2.99) Multiples covers on each 3.00

MIND MGMT
Dark Horse Comics: May, 2012 - No. 35, Jul, 2015 ($3.99)

1-Matt Kindt-s/a/c 30.00
2-6 10.00
7-35 4.00
#0 (11/12, $2.99) Prints background stories from Mind MGMT Secret Files digital site 3.00
New MGMT#1/Mind Mgmt #36 (8/15, $3.99) Series conclusion 4.00

MIND THE GAP
Image Comics: May, 2012 - No. 17, May, 2014 ($2.99)

1-17: 1-8,10-McCann-s/Esquejo-a/c. 9-McDaid-a. 11,12-Basri-a 3.00

MINIMUM CARNAGE
Marvel Comics: Dec, 2012 - Jan, 2013 ($3.99, limited series)

...: Alpha (12/12) Venom, Carnage and Scarlet Spider app.; Medina-a/Crain-c 4.00
...: Omega (1/13) The Enigma Force in the Microverse app. 4.00

MINIMUM WAGE
Fantagraphics Books: V1#1, July, 1995 ($9.95, B&W, graphic novel, mature)
V2#1, 1995 - 1997 ($2.95, B&W, mature)

V1#1-Bob Fingerman story & art 1 3 4 6 8 10
V2#1-9($2.95): Bob Fingerman story & art. 2-Kevin Nowlan back-c. 4-w/pin-ups. 5-Mignola back-c 3.00
Book Two TPB ('97, $12.95) r/V2#1-5 13.00

MINIMUM WAGE
Image Comics: Jan, 2014 - No. 6, Jun, 2014 ($3.50, B&W&Green, mature)

The Minx #1 © Milligan & Phillips

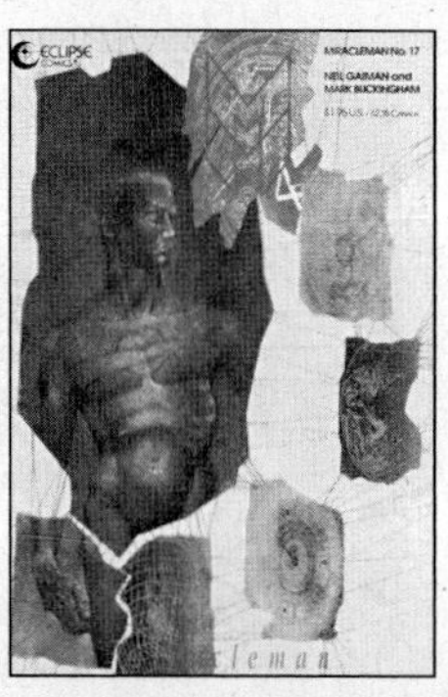

Miracleman #17 © ECL

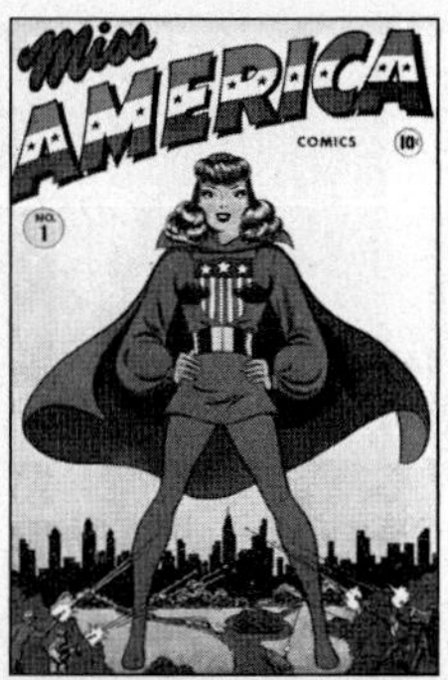

Miss America Comics #1 © MAR

GD 2.0 | VG 4.0 | FN 6.0 | VF 8.0 | VF/NM 9.0 | NM- 9.2

GD 2.0 | VG 4.0 | FN 6.0 | VF 8.0 | VF/NM 9.0 | NM- 9.2

1-6-Bob Fingerman story & art; story resumes in May 2000 3.50

MINIMUM WAGE: SO MANY BAD DECISIONS
Image Comics: May, 2015 - No. 6, Oct, 2015 ($3.99, B&W&Green/color pages, mature)

1-6-Bob Fingerman story & art. 3-Marc Maron app. 4.00

MINIONS (From Despicable Me movies)
Titan Comics: Jul, 2015 - No. 2, Aug, 2015 ($3.99, limited series)

1,2-Short stories and one-page gags; Ah-Koon-s/Collin-a 4.00

MINISTRY OF SPACE
Image Comics: Apr, 2001 - No. 3, Apr, 2004 ($2.95, limited series)

1-3-Warren Ellis-s/Chris Weston-a 3.00
...Vol. 1 Omnibus (3/04, $4.95) r/1&2 5.00
TPB (12/04, $12.95) r/series; sketch & design pages; intro by Mark Millar 13.00

MINKY WOODCOCK: THE GIRL WHO HANDCUFFED HOUDINI
Titan Comics: Nov, 2017 - Present ($3.99, limited series)

1-3-Cynthia Von Buhler-s/a. 1-Covers by Mack, McGinnis, Von Buhler & photo 4.00

MINOR MIRACLES
DC Comics: 2000 ($12.95, B&W, squarebound)

nn-Will Eisner-s/a 13.00

MINUTE MAN (See Master Comics & Mighty Midget Comics)
Fawcett Publications: Summer, 1941 - No. 3, Spring, 1942 (68 pgs.)

1 213 426 639 1363 2332 3300
2-Japanese invade NYC Statue of Liberty WWII-c 155 310 465 992 1696 2400
3 123 246 369 787 1344 1900

MINX, THE
DC Comics (Vertigo): Oct, 1998 - No. 8, May, 1999 ($2.50, limited series)

1-8-Milligan-s/Phillips-c/a 3.00

MIRACLE COMICS
Hillman Periodicals: Feb, 1940 - No. 4, Mar, 1941

1-Sky Wizard Master of Space, Dash Dixon, Man of Might, Pinkie Parker, Dusty Doyle, The Kid Cop, K-7, Secret Agent, The Scorpion, & Blandu, Jungle Queen begin; Masked Angel only app. (all 1st app.) 300 600 900 2010 3505 5000
2 168 336 504 1075 1838 2600
3,4: 3-Devil-c; Bill Colt, the Ghost Rider begins. 4-The Veiled Prophet & Bullet Bob (by Burnley) app. 135 270 405 864 1482 2100

MIRACLEMAN
Eclipse Comics: Aug, 1985 - No. 15, Nov, 1988; No. 16, Dec, 1989 - No. 24, Aug, 1993

1-r/British Marvelman series; Alan Moore scripts in #1-16 2 4 6 8 10 12
1-Gold variant (edition of 400, same as regular comic, but signed by Alan Moore, came with signed & #'d gold certificate of authenticity) 54 108 162 432 966 1500
1-Blue variant (edition of 600, comic came with signed blue certificate of authenticity) 34 68 102 245 548 850
2-8,10: 8-Airboy preview. 6,9,10-Origin Miracleman. 10-Snyder-c 1 2 3 5 6 8
9-Shows graphic scenes of childbirth 2 4 6 8 10 12
11-14(5/87-4/88) Totleben-a 2 4 6 11 16 20
15-($1.75-c, low print) end of Kid Miracleman 6 12 18 41 76 110
16-Last Alan Moore-s; 1st $1.95-c (low print) 3 6 9 16 24 32
17-22: 17-"The Golden Age" begins, ends #22. Dave McKean-c begins, end #22; Neil Gaiman scripts in #17-24 2 4 6 11 16 20
23-"The Silver Age" begins; Barry W. Smith-c 3 6 9 16 23 30
24-Last issue; Smith-c 3 6 9 19 30 40
3-D #1 (12/85) 2 4 6 8 10 12
3-D #1 Blue variant (edition of 99) 3 6 9 21 33 45
3-D #1 Gold variant (edition of 199) 3 6 9 16 23 30

NOTE: *Miracleman 3-D #1 (12/85) (2D edition) Interior is the same as the 3-D version except in non 3-D format. Indicia are the same for both versions of the book with only the non 3-D art distinguishing this book from the standard 3-D version. Standard 3-D edition has house ad mentioning the non 3-D edition. Two known copies exist, one in the Michigan State University Special Collection Department. (No known sales)*

Book One: A Dream of Flying (1988, $9.95, TPB) r/#1-5; Leach-c 25.00
Book One: A Dream of Flying-Hardcover (1988, $29.95) r/#1-5 70.00
Book Two: The Red King Syndrome (1990, $12.95, TPB) r/#6-10; Bolton-c 30.00
Book Two: The Red King Syndrome-Hardcover (1990, $30.95) r/#6-10 85.00
Book Three: Olympus (1990, $12.95, TPB) r/#11-16 130.00
Book Three: Olympus-Hardcover (1990, $30.95) r/#11-16 250.00
Book Four: The Golden Age (1992, $15.95, TPB) r/#17-22 30.00
Book Four: The Golden Age Hardcover (1992, $33.95) r/#17-22 50.00
Book Four: The Golden Age (1993, $12.99, TPB) new McKean-c 15.00

NOTE: *Eclipse archive copies exist for #4,5,8,17,23. Each has a small Miracleman image foil-stamped on the cover.* ***Chaykin*** *c-3.* ***Gulacy*** *c-7.* ***McKean*** *c-17-22.* ***B. Smith*** *c-23, 24.* ***Starlin*** *c-4.* ***Totleben*** *a-11-13; c-9, 11-13. Truman c-6.*

MIRACLEMAN
Marvel Comics: Mar, 2014 - No. 16, May, 2015 ($5.99/$4.99)

1-($5.99) Remastered reprints of Miracleman #1 and stories from Warrior #1&2; interview with Mick Anglo; reprints of 1950s Marvelman stories; Quesada-c 6.00
2-15: 2-($4.99) R/Warrior #3-5 and Kid Marvelman debut (1955) 5.00
16-($5.99) End of Book Three; bonus pencil art and design sketches 6.00
All-New Miracleman Annual 1 (2/15, $4.99) New stories; Morrison-s/Quesada-a and Milligan-s/Allred-a; bonus script and art pages 5.00

MIRACLEMAN: APOCRYPHA
Eclipse Comics: Nov, 1991 - No. 3, Feb, 1992 ($2.50, limited series)

1-3: 1-Stories by Neil Gaiman, Mark Buckingham, Alex Ross & others. 3-Stories by James Robinson, Kelley Jones, Matt Wagner, Neil Gaiman, Mark Buckingham & others 1 2 3 4 5 7
TPB (12/92, $15.95) r/#1-3; Buckingham-c 20.00

MIRACLEMAN BY GAIMAN & BUCKINGHAM (The Golden Age)
Marvel Comics: Nov, 2015 - No. 6, Mar, 2016 ($4.99)

1-6-Remastered reprints of Miracleman #17-22 with bonus script and art pages 5.00

MIRACLEMAN FAMILY
Eclipse Comics: May, 1988 - No. 2, Sept, 1988 ($1.95, lim. series, Baxter paper)

1,2: 2-Gulacy-c 5.00

MIRACLE OF THE WHITE STALLIONS, THE (See Movie Comics)

MIRROR'S EDGE (Based on the EA video game)
DC Comics (WildStorm): Dec, 2008 - No. 6, Jun, 2009 ($3.99, limited series)

1-6: 1-Origin of Faith; Rhianna Pratchett-s/Matthew Dow Smith-a 4.00
TPB (2009, $19.99) r/#1-6 20.00

MIRROR'S EDGE: EXORDIUM (Based on the EA video game)
Dark Horse Comics: Sept, 2015 - No. 6, Feb, 2016 ($3.99, limited series)

1-6: 1-Emgård-s/Häggström & Sammelin-a 4.00

MISADVENTURES OF ADAM WEST, THE
Bluewater Comics: Jul, 2011 - Feb, 2012 ($3.99)

1-4: 1-Two covers; co-created by Adam West 4.00
Second series 1-3 (1/12 - No. 3, 2/12) 4.00

MISADVENTURES OF MERLIN JONES, THE (See Movie Comics & Merlin Jones as the Monkey's Uncle under Movie Comics)

MISFIT CITY
BOOM! Studios (BOOM! Box): May, 2017 - No. 8, Dec, 2017 ($3.99)

1-8-Kirsten Smith & Kurt Lustgarten-s/Naomi Franquiz-a 4.00

MISPLACED
Image Comics: May, 2003 - No. 4, Dec, 2004 ($2.95)

1-4: 1-Three covers by Blaylock, Green and Clugston-Major; Blaylock-s/a 3.00
... @17 (12/04, $4.95) Nara from "Dead @17 " app.; Blaylock-s/a 5.00

MISS AMERICA COMICS (Miss America Magazine #2 on; also see Blonde Phantom & Marvel Mystery Comics)
Marvel Comics (20CC): 1944 (one-shot)

1-2 pgs. pin-ups 300 600 900 2010 3505 5000

MISS AMERICA COMICS 70th ANNIVERARY SPECIAL
Marvel Comics: Aug, 2009 ($3.99, one-shot)

1-Eaglesham-c; new Miss America & Whizzer story; reps. from All Winners #9-11 5.00

MISS AMERICA MAGAZINE (Formerly Miss America; Miss America #51 on)
Miss America Publ. Corp./Marvel/Atlas (MAP): V1#2, Nov, 1944 - No. 93, Nov, 1958

V1#2-Photo-c of teenage girl in Miss America costume; Miss America, Patsy Walker (intro.) comic stories plus movie reviews & stories; intro. Buzz Baxter & Hedy Wolfe; 1 pg. origin Miss America 300 600 900 1950 3375 4800
3-5-Miss America & Patsy Walker stories 97 194 291 621 1061 1500
6-Patsy Walker only 58 116 174 371 636 900
V2#1(4/45)-6(9/45)-Patsy Walker continues 22 44 66 132 216 300
V3#1(10/45)-6(4/46) 20 40 60 114 182 250
V4#1(5/46),2,5(9/46) 16 32 48 94 147 200
V4#3(7/46)-Liz Taylor photo-c 40 80 120 246 411 575
V4#4 (8/46; 68 pgs.), V4#6 (10/46; 92 pgs.) 15 30 45 85 130 175
V5#1(11/46)-6(4/47), V6#1(5/47)-3(7/47) 15 30 45 84 127 170
V7#1(8/47)-23(#56, 6/49) 14 28 42 82 121 160
V7#24(#57, 7/49)-Kamen-a (becomes Best Western #58 on?) 15 30 45 83 124 165
V7#25(8/49), 27-44(3/52), VII,nn(5/52) 14 28 42 81 118 155

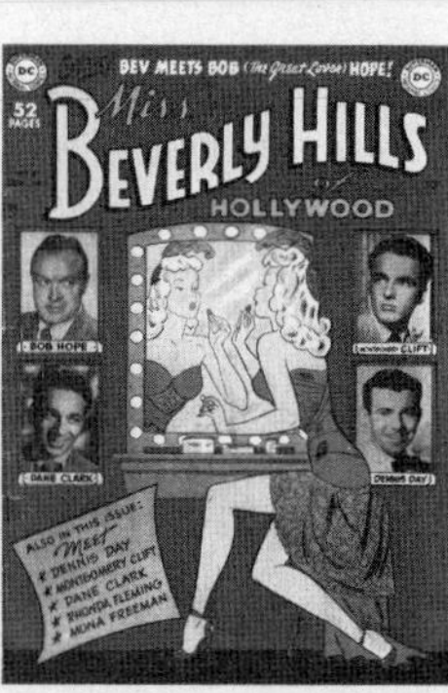

Miss Beverly Hills of Hollywood #5 © DC

Mr. District Attorney #17 © DC

Mister Miracle #1 © DC

	GD 2.0	VG 4.0	FN 6.0	VF 8.0	VF/NM 9.0	NM- 9.2
V7#26(9/49)-All comics	15	30	45	84	127	170
V1,nn(7/52)-V1,nn(1/53)(#46-49), V7#50(Spring '53), V1#51-V7?#54(7/53), 55-93	14	28	42	78	112	145

NOTE: *Photo-c #1, 4, V2#1, 4, 5, V3#5, V4#3, 4, 6, V7#15, 16, 24, 26, 34, 37, 38. Painted c-3.* **Powell** *a-V7#31.*

MISS BEVERLY HILLS OF HOLLYWOOD (See Adventures of Bob Hope)
National Periodical Publ.: Mar-Apr, 1949 - No. 9, July-Aug, 1950 (52 pgs.)

	GD 2.0	VG 4.0	FN 6.0	VF 8.0	VF/NM 9.0	NM- 9.2
1 (Meets Alan Ladd)	60	120	180	381	653	925
2-William Holden photo on-c	43	86	129	271	461	650
3-5: 2-9-Part photo-c. 5-Bob Hope photo on-c	39	78	117	236	388	540
6,7,9: 6-Lucille Ball photo on-c	36	72	108	214	347	480
8-Reagan photo on-c	40	80	120	244	402	560

NOTE: *Beverly meets Alan Ladd in #1, Eve Arden #2, Betty Hutton #4, Bob Hope #5.*

MISS CAIRO JONES
Croyden Publishers: 1945

	GD 2.0	VG 4.0	FN 6.0	VF 8.0	VF/NM 9.0	NM- 9.2
1-Bob Oksner daily newspaper-r (1st strip story); lingerie panels	24	48	72	140	230	320

MISS FURY
Adventure Comics: 1991 - No. 4, 1991 ($2.50, limited series)

	GD 2.0	VG 4.0	FN 6.0	VF 8.0	VF/NM 9.0	NM- 9.2
1-4: 1-Origin; granddaughter of original Miss Fury						3.00
1-Limited ed. ($4.95)						5.00

MISS FURY
Dynamite Entertainment: 2013 - No. 11, 2014 ($3.99)

	GD 2.0	VG 4.0	FN 6.0	VF 8.0	VF/NM 9.0	NM- 9.2
1-11: 1-Multiple covers on all; Herbert-a; origin						4.00

MISS FURY (VOLUME 2)
Dynamite Entertainment: 2016 - No. 5, 2016 ($3.99, limited series)

	GD 2.0	VG 4.0	FN 6.0	VF 8.0	VF/NM 9.0	NM- 9.2
1-5-Corinna Bechko-s/Jonathan Lau-a; covers by Lotay & Lau						4.00

MISS FURY COMICS (Newspaper strip reprints)
Timely Comics (NPI 1/CmPI 2/MPC 3-8): Winter, 1942-43 - No. 8, Winter, 1946 (Published twice a year)

	GD 2.0	VG 4.0	FN 6.0	VF 8.0	VF/NM 9.0	NM- 9.2
1-Origin Miss Fury by Tarpe' Mills (68 pgs.) in costume w/paper dolls with cut-out costumes	443	886	1329	3234	5717	8200
2-(60 pgs.)-In costume w/paper dolls; hooded Nazi-c	252	504	756	1613	2757	3900
3-(60 pgs.)-In costume w/paper dolls; Hitler-c	206	412	618	1318	2259	3200
4-(52 pgs.)-Classic Nazi WWII-c with giant swastika, Tojo & Hitler photo on wall; in costume, 2 pgs. w/paper dolls	174	348	522	1114	1907	2700
5-(52 pgs.)-In costume w/paper dolls; Japanese WWII-c	135	270	405	864	1482	2100
6-(52 pgs.)-Not in costume in inside stories, w/paper dolls	110	220	330	704	1202	1700
7,8-(36 pgs.)-In costume 1 pg. each; no paper dolls	89	178	267	565	970	1375

NOTE: ***Schomburg*** *c-1, 5, 6.*

MISS FURY DIGITAL FIRST
Dynamite Entertainment: 2013 - No. 2, 2013 ($3.99, limited series)

	GD 2.0	VG 4.0	FN 6.0	VF 8.0	VF/NM 9.0	NM- 9.2
1,2-Prints online stories. 1-Reis, Desjardins, Casas-a. 2-Casas-a						4.00

MISSION IMPOSSIBLE (TV) (Also see Wild!)
Dell Publ. Co.: May, 1967 - No. 4, Oct, 1968; No. 5, Oct, 1969 (All have photo-c)

	GD 2.0	VG 4.0	FN 6.0	VF 8.0	VF/NM 9.0	NM- 9.2
1	8	16	24	54	102	150
2-5: 5-Reprints #1	5	10	15	35	63	90

MISSION IMPOSSIBLE (Movie) (1st Paramount Comics book)
Marvel Comics (Paramount Comics): May, 1996 ($2.95, one-shot)

	GD 2.0	VG 4.0	FN 6.0	VF 8.0	VF/NM 9.0	NM- 9.2
1-Liefeld-c & back-up story						3.00

MISS LIBERTY (Becomes Liberty Comics)
Burten Publishing Co.: 1945 (MLJ reprints)

	GD 2.0	VG 4.0	FN 6.0	VF 8.0	VF/NM 9.0	NM- 9.2
1-The Shield & Dusty, The Wizard, & Roy, the Super Boy app.; r/Shield-Wizard #13	37	74	111	222	361	500

MISS MELODY LANE OF BROADWAY (See The Adventures of Bob Hope)
National Periodical Publ.: Feb-Mar, 1950 - No. 3, June-July, 1950 (52 pgs.)

	GD 2.0	VG 4.0	FN 6.0	VF 8.0	VF/NM 9.0	NM- 9.2
1-Movie stars photos app. on all-c.	65	130	195	416	708	1000
2,3: 3-Ed Sullivan photo on-c.	39	78	117	235	385	535

MISS PEACH
Dell Publishing Co.: Oct-Dec, 1963; 1969

	GD 2.0	VG 4.0	FN 6.0	VF 8.0	VF/NM 9.0	NM- 9.2
1-Jack Mendelsohn-a/script	7	14	21	44	82	120
...Tells You How to Grow (1969; 25¢)-Mel Lazarus-a; also given away (36 pgs.)	5	10	15	30	50	70

MISS PEPPER (See Meet Miss Pepper)

MISS SUNBEAM (See Little Miss...)

MISS VICTORY (See Captain Fearless #1,2, Holyoke One-Shot #3, Veri Best Sure Fire & Veri Best Sure Shot Comics)

MISTER AMERICA
Endeavor Comics: Apr, 1994 - No. 2, May, 1994 ($2.95, limited series)

	GD 2.0	VG 4.0	FN 6.0	VF 8.0	VF/NM 9.0	NM- 9.2
1,2						3.00

MR. & MRS. BEANS
United Features Syndicate: No. 11, 1939

	GD 2.0	VG 4.0	FN 6.0	VF 8.0	VF/NM 9.0	NM- 9.2
Single Series 11	34	68	102	204	332	460

MR. & MRS. J. EVIL SCIENTIST (TV)(See The Flintstones & Hanna-Barbera Band Wagon #3)
Gold Key: Nov, 1963 - No. 4, Sept, 1966 (Hanna-Barbera, all 12¢)

	GD 2.0	VG 4.0	FN 6.0	VF 8.0	VF/NM 9.0	NM- 9.2
1	6	12	18	37	66	95
2-4	4	8	12	23	37	50

MR. ANTHONY'S LOVE CLINIC (Based on radio show)
Hillman Periodicals: Nov, 1949 - No. 5, Apr-May, 1950 (52 pgs.)

	GD 2.0	VG 4.0	FN 6.0	VF 8.0	VF/NM 9.0	NM- 9.2
1-Photo-c on all	20	40	60	117	189	260
2	14	28	42	80	115	150
3-5	12	24	36	69	97	125

MISTER BLANK
Amaze Ink: No. 0, Jan, 1996 - No. 14, May, 2000 ($1.75/$2.95, B&W)

	GD 2.0	VG 4.0	FN 6.0	VF 8.0	VF/NM 9.0	NM- 9.2
0-($1.75, 16 pgs.) Origin of Mr. Blank						3.00
1-14-($2.95) Chris Hicks-s/a						3.00

MR. DISTRICT ATTORNEY (Radio/TV)
National Per. Publ.: Jan-Feb, 1948 - No. 67, Jan-Feb, 1959 (1-23: 52 pgs.)

	GD 2.0	VG 4.0	FN 6.0	VF 8.0	VF/NM 9.0	NM- 9.2
1-Howard Purcell c-5-23 (most)	90	180	270	576	988	1400
2	42	84	126	265	445	625
3-5	29	58	87	170	278	385
6-10: 8-Rise & fall of Lucky Lynn	22	44	66	132	216	300
11-20	17	34	51	98	154	210
21-43: 43-Last pre-code (1-2/55)	14	28	42	76	108	140
44-67: 55-UFO story	11	22	33	62	86	110

MR. DISTRICT ATTORNEY (SeeThe Funnies #35)
Dell Publishing Co.: No. 13, 1942

	GD 2.0	VG 4.0	FN 6.0	VF 8.0	VF/NM 9.0	NM- 9.2
Four Color 13-See The Funnies #35 for 1st app.	27	54	81	189	420	650

MISTER E (Also see Books of Magic limited series)
DC Comics: Jun, 1991- No. 4, Sept, 1991($1.75, limited series)

	GD 2.0	VG 4.0	FN 6.0	VF 8.0	VF/NM 9.0	NM- 9.2
1-4-Snyder III-c/a; follow-up to Books of Magic limited series						3.00

MISTER ED, THE TALKING HORSE (TV)
Dell Publishing Co./Gold Key: Mar-May, 1962 - No. 6, Feb, 1964 (All photo-c; photo back-c: 1-6)

	GD 2.0	VG 4.0	FN 6.0	VF 8.0	VF/NM 9.0	NM- 9.2
Four Color 1295	11	22	33	73	157	240
1(11/62) (Gold Key)-Photo-c	8	16	24	54	102	150
2-6: Photo-c	5	10	15	33	57	80

(See March of Comics #244, 260, 282, 290)

MR. GUM (From The Atomics)
Oni Press: April, 2003 ($2.99, one-shot)

	GD 2.0	VG 4.0	FN 6.0	VF 8.0	VF/NM 9.0	NM- 9.2
1-Mike Allred-s/J. Bone-a; Madman & The Atomics app.						3.00

MR. HERO, THE NEWMATIC MAN (See Neil Gaiman's...)

MR. MAGOO (TV) (The Nearsighted..., ...& Gerald McBoing Boing 1954 issues; formerly Gerald McBoing-Boing And ...)
Dell Publishing Co.: No. 6, Nov-Jan, 1953-54; 5/54 - 3-5/62; 9-11/63 - 3-5/65

	GD 2.0	VG 4.0	FN 6.0	VF 8.0	VF/NM 9.0	NM- 9.2
6	9	18	27	58	114	170
Four Color 561(5/54),602(11/54)	9	18	27	58	114	170
Four Color 1235(#1, 12-2/62),1305(#2, 3-5/62)	7	14	21	48	89	130
3(9-11/63) - 5	6	12	18	42	79	115
Four Color 1235(12-536-505)(3-5/65)-2nd Printing	5	10	15	35	63	90

MR. MAJESTIC (See WildC.A.T.S.)
DC Comics (WildStorm): Sept, 1999 - No. 9, May, 2000 ($2.50)

	GD 2.0	VG 4.0	FN 6.0	VF 8.0	VF/NM 9.0	NM- 9.2
1-9: 1-McGuinness-a/Casey & Holguin-s. 2-Two covers						3.00
TPB (2002, $14.95) r/#1-6 & Wildstorm Spotlight #1						15.00

MISTER MIRACLE (1st series) (See Cancelled Comic Cavalcade)
National Periodical Publications/DC Comics: 3-4/71 - V4#18, 2-3/74; V5#19, 9/77 - V6#25, 8-9/78; 1987 (Fourth World)

	GD 2.0	VG 4.0	FN 6.0	VF 8.0	VF/NM 9.0	NM- 9.2
1-1st app. Mr. Miracle (#1-3 are 15¢)	12	24	36	82	179	275
2,3: 2-Intro. Granny Goodness. 3-Last 15¢ issue	5	10	15	31	53	75

Mister Miracle (2017 series) #1 © DC

Mister Mystery #8 © Media Pub.

Mister Terrific #1 © DC

	GD	VG	FN	VF	VF/NM	NM-
	2.0	4.0	6.0	8.0	9.0	9.2

4-Intro. Barda; Boy Commandos-r begin; (52 pgs.) 4 8 12 28 47 65
5-8: All 52 pgs. 20 40 60 114 182 250
9-18: 9-Origin Mr. Miracle; Darkseid cameo. 15-Intro/1st app. Shilo Norman. 18-Barda & Scott Free wed; New Gods app. & Darkseid cameo; Last Kirby issue.
3 6 9 16 23 30
19-25 (1977-78) 2 4 6 8 10 12
Special 1(1987, $1.25, 52 pgs.) 1 2 3 5 6 8
Jack Kirby's Fourth World TPB ('01, $12.95) B&W&Grey-toned reprint of #11-18; Mark Evanier intro. 13.00
Jack Kirby's Mister Miracle TPB ('98, $12.95) B&W&Grey-toned reprint of #1-10; David Copperfield intro. 13.00
NOTE: ***Austin** a-19i. **Ditko** a-6r. **Golden** a-23-25p; c-25p. **Heath** a-24i, 25i; c-25i. **Kirby** a(p)/c-1-18. **Nasser** a-19i. **Rogers** a-19-22p; c-19, 20p, 21p, 22-24. 4-8 contain **Simon & Kirby** Boy Commandos reprints from Detective 82,76, Boy Commandos 1, 3 & Detective 64 in that order.*

MISTER MIRACLE (2nd Series) (See Justice League)
DC Comics: Jan, 1989 - No. 28, June, 1991 ($1.00/$1.25)
1-28: 13,14-Lobo app. 22-1st new Mr. Miracle w/new costume 3.00

MISTER MIRACLE (3rd Series)
DC Comics: Apr, 1996 - No. 7, Oct, 1996 ($1.95)
1-7: 2-Vs. JLA. 6-Simonson-c 3.00

MISTER MIRACLE (4th Series)
DC Comics: Oct, 2017 - No. 12 ($3.99, limited series)
1-Tom King-s/Mitch Gerads-a; covers by Derington & Gerads 20.00
1-Director's Cut (4/18, $5.99) r/#1 B&W art; bonus script 6.00
2-6-King-s/Gerads-a 5.00

MR. MIRACLE (See Capt. Fearless #1 & Holyoke One-Shot #4)

MR. MONSTER (1st Series)(Doc Stearn... #7 on; See Airboy-Mr. Monster Special, Dark Horse Presents, Super Duper Comics & Vanguard Illustrated #7)
Eclipse Comics: Jan, 1985 - No. 10, June, 1987 ($1.75, Baxter paper)
1,3: 1-1st story-r from Vanguard Ill. #7(1st app.). 3-Alan Moore scripts; Wolverton-r/Weird Mysteries #5. 5.00
2-Dave Stevens-c 1 3 4 6 8 10
4-10: 6-Ditko-r/Fantastic Fears #5 plus new Giffen-a. 10- "6-D" issue 4.00

MR. MONSTER
Dark Horse Comics: Feb, 1988 - No. 8, July, 1991 ($1.75, B&W)
1-7 3.00
8-($4.95, 60 pgs.)-Origins conclusion 5.00

MR. MONSTER ATTACKS! (Doc Stearn...)
Tundra Publ.: Aug, 1992 - No. 3, Oct, 1992 ($3.95, limited series, 32 pgs.)
1-3: Michael T. Gilbert-a/scripts; Gilbert/Dorman painted-c 4.00

MR. MONSTER PRESENTS (CRACK-A-BOOM!)
Caliber Comics: 1997 - No. 3, 1997 ($2.95, B&W&Red, limited series)
1-3: Michael T. Gilbert-a/scripts: 1-Wraparound-c 3.00

MR. MONSTER'S GAL FRIDAY...KELLY!
Image Comics: Jan, 2000 - No. 3, May, 2004 ($3.50, B&W)
1-3-Michael T. Gilbert-c; story & art by various. 3-Alan Moore-s 3.50

MR. MONSTER'S SUPER-DUPER SPECIAL
Eclipse Comics: May, 1986 - No. 8, July, 1987
1-(5/86)...3-D High Octane Horror #1 5.00
1-(5/86)...2-D version, 100 copies 2 4 6 11 16 20
2-(8/86)...High Octane Horror #1, 3-(9/86)...True Crime #1, 4-(11/86)...True Crime #2, 5-(1/87)...Hi-Voltage Super Science #1, 6-(3/87)...High Shock Schlock #1, 7-(5/87)...High Shock Schlock #2, 8-(7/87)...Weird Tales Of The Future #1 4.00
NOTE: ***Jack Cole** r-3, 4. **Evans** a-2r. **Kubert** a-1r. **Powell** a-5r. **Wolverton** a-2r, 7r, 8r.*

MR. MONSTER VS. GORZILLA
Image Comics: July, 1998 ($2.95, one-shot)
1-Michael T. Gilbert-a 3.00

MR. MONSTER: WORLDS WAR TWO
Atomeka Press: 2004 ($6.99, one-shot)
nn-Michael T. Gilbert-s/George Freeman-a; two covers by Horley & Dorman 7.00

MR. MUSCLES (Formerly Blue Beetle #18-21)
Charlton Comics: No. 22, Mar, 1956; No. 23, Aug, 1956
22,23 9 18 27 50 65 80

MR. MXYZPTLK (VILLAINS)
DC Comics: Feb, 1998 ($1.95, one-shot)
1-Grant-s/Morgan-a/Pearson-c 3.00

	GD	VG	FN	VF	VF/NM	NM-
	2.0	4.0	6.0	8.0	9.0	9.2

MISTER MYSTERY (Tales of Horror and Suspense)
Mr. Publ. (Media Publ.) No. 1-3/SPM Publ./Stanmore (Aragon): Sept, 1951 - No. 19, Oct, 1954
1-Kurtzman-*esque* horror story 129 258 387 826 1413 2000
2,3-Kurtzman-*esque* story. 3-Anti-Wertham edit. 71 142 213 454 777 1100
4-Bondage-c 97 194 291 621 1061 1500
5,8,10 71 142 213 454 777 1100
6-Classic torture-c 187 374 561 1197 2049 2900
7- "The Brain Bats of Venus" by Wolverton; partially re-used in Weird Tales of the Future #7
187 374 561 1197 2049 2900
9-Nostrand-a 71 142 213 454 777 1100
11-Wolverton "Robot Woman" story/Weird Mysteries #2, cut up, rewritten & partially redrawn
155 310 465 992 1696 2400
12-Classic injury to eye-c 377 754 1131 2639 4620 6600
13-16,19: 15- "Living Dead" junkie story. 16-Bondage-c. 19-Reprints
57 114 171 362 619 875
17-Severed heads-c 103 206 309 659 1130 1600
18- "Robot Woman" by Wolverton reprinted from Weird Mysteries #2; decapitation, bondage-c
116 232 348 742 1271 1800
NOTE: ***Andru** a-1, 2p, 3p. **Andru/Esposito** c-1-3. **Baily** c-10-18(most). **Mortellaro** c-5-7. Bondage c-7, 16. Some issues have graphic dismemberment scenes.*

MR. PEABODY AND SHERMAN (Based on the 2014 Dreamworks movie)
IDW Publishing: Nov, 2013 - No. 4, Jan, 2014 ($3.99)
1-4: 1-Fisch-s/Monlongo-a; 3 covers. 2-Three covers. 3,4-Two covers 4.00

MR. PUNCH
DC Comics (Vertigo): 1994 ($24.95, one-shot)
nn (Hard-c)-Gaiman scripts; McKean-c/a 40.00
nn (Soft-c) 18.00

MISTER Q (See Mighty Midget Comics & Our Flag Comics #5)

MR. RISK (Formerly All Romances; Men Against Crime #3 on)(Also see Our Flag Comics & Super-Mystery Comics)
Ace Magazines: No. 7, Oct, 1950; No. 2, Dec, 1950
7,2 14 28 42 78 112 145

MR. SCARLET & PINKY (See Mighty Midget Comics)

MR. T
APComics: May, 2005 ($3.50)
1-Chris Bunting-s/Neil Edwards-a 3.50

MR. T AND THE T-FORCE
Now Comics: June, 1993 - No. 10, May, 1994 ($1.95, color)
1-10-Newsstand editions: 1-7-polybagged with photo trading card in each. 1,2-Neal Adams-c/a(p). 3-Dave Dorman painted-c 3.00
1-10-Direct Sale editions polybagged w/line drawn trading cards. 1-Contains gold foil trading card by Neal Adams 3.00

MISTER TERRIFIC (DC New 52)(Leads into Earth 2 series)
DC Comics: Nov, 2011 - No. 8, Jun, 2012 ($2.99)
1-8: 1-Wallace-s/Gugliotta-a/JG Jones-c; origin re-told. 2-Intro. Brainstorm 3.00

MISTER UNIVERSE (Professional wrestler)
Mr. Publications Media Publ. (Stanmor, Aragon): July, 1951; No. 2, Oct, 1951 - No. 5, April, 1952
1 23 46 69 136 223 310
2- "Jungle That Time Forgot", (24 pg. story); Andru/Esposito-c
15 30 45 83 124 165
3-Marijuana story 15 30 45 83 124 165
4,5-"Goes to War" cover/stories (Korean War) 12 24 36 67 94 120

MISTER X (See Vortex)
Mr. Publications/Vortex Comics/Caliber V3#1 on: 6/84 - No. 14, 8/88 ($1.50/$2.25, direct sales, coated paper);V2#1, Apr, 1989 - V2#12, Mar, 1990 ($2.00/$2.50, B&W, newsprint) V3#1, 1996 - No. 4, 1996 ($2.95, B&W)
1-14: 11-Dave McKean story & art (6 pgs.) 4.00
V2 #1-12: 1-11 (Second Coming, B&W): 1-Four diff.-c. 10-Photo-c 3.00
V3 #1-4 3.00
Return of... ($11.95, graphic novel)-r/V1#1-4 12.00
Return of... ($34.95, hardcover limited edition)-r/1-4 35.00
Special (no date, 1990?) 3.00

MISTER X
Dark Horse Comics: Mar, 2013 ($2.99, one-shot)
...: Hard Candy (3/13) Dean Motter-s/a 3.00

MISTER X: CONDEMNED
Dark Horse Comics: Dec, 2008 - No. 4, Mar, 2009 ($3.50, limited series)

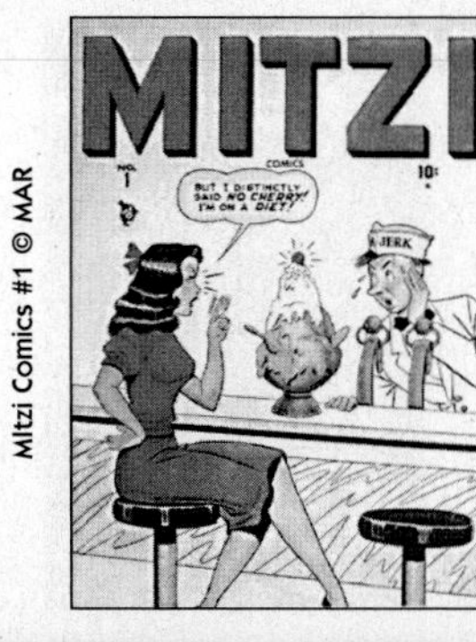

Mitzi Comics #1 © MAR

Mockingbird #1 © MAR

Mod Wheels #12 © GK

	GD 2.0	VG 4.0	FN 6.0	VF 8.0	VF/NM 9.0	NM- 9.2
1-4-Dean Motter-s/a						3.50
MISTER X: EVICTION						
Dark Horse Comics: May, 2013 - No. 3, Jul, 2013 ($3.99, limited series)						
1-3-Dean Motter-s/a						4.00
MISTER X: RAZED						
Dark Horse Comics: Feb, 2015 - No. 4, May, 2015 ($3.99, limited series)						
1-4-Dean Motter-s/a						4.00
MISTY						
Marvel Comics (Star Comics): Dec, 1985 - No. 6, May, 1986 (Limited series)						
1-6: Millie The Model's niece						4.00
MITZI COMICS (Becomes Mitzi's Boy Friend #2-7)(See All Teen)						
Timely Comics: Spring, 1948 (one-shot)						
1-Kurtzman's "Hey Look" plus 3 pgs. "Giggles 'n' Grins"	53	106	159	334	567	800
MITZI'S BOY FRIEND (Formerly Mitzi Comics; becomes Mitzi's Romances)						
Marvel Comics (TCI): No. 2, June, 1948 - No. 7, April, 1949						
2	26	52	78	154	252	350
3-7	19	38	57	111	176	240
MITZI'S ROMANCES (Formerly Mitzi's Boy Friend)						
Timely/Marvel Comics (TCI): No. 8, June, 1949 - No. 10, Dec, 1949						
8-Becomes True Life Tales #8 (10/49) on?	20	40	60	114	182	250
9,10: 10-Painted-c	17	34	51	98	154	210
MNEMOVORE						
DC Comics (Vertigo): Jun, 2005 - No. 6, Nov, 2005 ($2.99, limited series)						
1-6-Rodionoff & Fawkes-s/Huddleston-a/c						3.00
MOBY DICK (See Feature Presentations #6, King Classics, and Classic Comics #5)						
Dell Publishing Co.: No. 717, Aug, 1956						
Four Color 717-Movie, Gregory Peck photo-c	7	14	21	49	92	135
MOBY DUCK (See Donald Duck #112 & Walt Disney Showcase #2,11)						
Gold Key (Disney): Oct, 1967 - No. 11, Oct, 1970; No. 12, Jan, 1974 - No. 30, Feb, 1978						
1-Three Little Pigs app.	3	6	9	20	31	42
2-5: 2-Beagle Boys app. 5-Captain Hook app.	2	4	6	11	16	20
6-11: 6-Huey, Dewey & Louie app.	2	4	6	9	13	16
12-30: 21,30-r	1	3	4	6	8	10
MOCKINGBIRD (From S.H.I.E.L.D.)						
Marvel Comics: May, 2016 - No. 8, Dec, 2016 ($3.99)						
1-8: 1-4-Chelsea Cain-s/Kate Niemczyk-a/Joëlle Jones-c. 5-Moustafa-a. 6-Civil War II tie-in						4.00
... S.H.I.E.L.D. 50th Anniversary (11/15, $3.99) Joëlle Jones-a; back-up with Red Widow						4.00
MOCKING DEAD, THE						
Dynamite Entertainment: 2013 - No. 5, 2014 ($3.99, B&W, limited series)						
1-5: 1-Fred Van Lente-s/Max Dunbar-a						4.00
MODEL FUN (With Bobby Benson)						
Harle Publications: No. 2, Fall, 1954 - No. 5, July, 1955						
2-Bobby Benson	7	14	21	35	43	50
3-5-Bobby Benson	5	10	15	23	28	32
MODELING WITH MILLIE (Formerly Life With Millie)						
Atlas/Marvel Comics (Male Publ.): No. 21, Feb, 1963 - No. 54, June, 1967						
21	8	16	24	56	108	160
22-30	5	10	15	34	60	85
31-53	5	10	15	30	50	70
54-Last issue; Gears-c & 6 pg. story; Beatles swipe imitators; FF #63 comic appears in story; "Millie the Marvel" 6 pg. story as super-hero	5	10	15	33	57	80
MODELS, INC.						
Marvel Comics: Oct, 2009 - No. 4, Jan, 2010 ($3.99, limited series)						
1-4-Millie the Model, Patsy Walker, Mary Jane Watson app.; Land-c. 1-Tim Gunn app.						4.00
MODERN COMICS (Formerly Military Comics #1-43)						
Quality Comics Group: No. 44, Nov, 1945 - No. 102, Oct, 1950						
44-Blackhawk continues	54	108	162	343	574	825
45-52: 49-1st app. Fear, Lady Adventuress	38	76	114	228	369	510
53-Torchy by Ward begins (9/46)	42	84	126	265	445	625
54-60: 55-J. Cole-a	32	64	96	192	314	435
61-Classic-c	39	78	117	231	378	525
62-64,66-77,79,80: 73-J. Cole-a	31	62	93	182	296	410
65-Classic Grim Reaper Skull-c	61	122	183	390	670	950
78-1st app. Madame Butterfly	34	68	102	204	332	460
81-99,101: 82,83-One pg. J. Cole-a. 83-Last 52 pg. issue. 99-Blackhawks on the moon-c/story	31	62	93	182	296	410
100	32	64	96	192	314	435
102-(Scarce)-J. Cole-a; Spirit by Eisner app.	39	78	117	234	385	535

NOTE: ***Al Bryant** c-44-51, 54, 55, 66, 69. **Jack Cole** a-55, 73. **Crandall** Blackhawk-#46, 47, 50, 51, 54, 56, 58-60, 64, 67-70, 73, 74, 76-78, 80-83; c-60-65, 67, 68, 70-95. **Crandall/Cuidera** c-56-59, 96-102. **Gustavson** a-47, 49. **Ward** Blackhawk-#52, 53, 55 (15 pgs. each). Torchy in #53-102; by **Ward** only in #53-89(9/49); by **Gil Fox** #92, 93, 102.*

	GD 2.0	VG 4.0	FN 6.0	VF 8.0	VF/NM 9.0	NM- 9.2
MODERN LOVE						
E. C. Comics: June-July, 1949 - No. 8, Aug-Sept, 1950						
1-Feldstein, Ingels-a	106	212	318	673	1162	1650
2-Craig/Feldstein-c/s	74	148	222	470	810	1150
3	63	126	189	403	689	975
4-6 (Scarce): 4-Bra/panties panels	87	174	261	553	952	1350
7,8	63	126	189	403	689	975

NOTE: ***Craig** a-3. **Feldstein** a-in most issues; c-1, 2i, 3-8. **Harrison** a-4. **Iger** a-6-8. **Ingels** a-1, 2, 4-7. **Palais** a-5. **Wood** a-7. **Wood/Harrison** a-5-7. (Canadian reprints known; see Table of Contents.)*

	GD 2.0	VG 4.0	FN 6.0	VF 8.0	VF/NM 9.0	NM- 9.2
MODERN WARFARE 2: GHOST (Based on the videogame)						
DC Comics (WildStorm): Jan, 2010 - No. 6, Sept, 2010 ($3.99, limited series)						
1-6: 1-Two covers; Lapham-s/West-a						4.00
TPB (2010, $17.99) r/#1-6; cover sketches and sketch art						18.00
MOD LOVE						
Western Publishing Co.: 1967 (50¢, 36 pgs.)						
1-(Low print)	7	14	21	49	92	135
MODNIKS, THE						
Gold Key: Aug, 1967 - No. 2, Aug, 1970						
10206-708(#1)	3	6	9	21	33	45
2	3	6	9	15	22	28
M.O.D.O.K. ASSASSIN (Secret Wars tie-in)						
Marvel Comics: Jul, 2015 - No. 5, Nov, 2015 ($3.99, limited series)						
1-5-Yost-s/Pinna-a; Angela app. 1-Bullseye, Baron Mordo & Clea app.						4.00
M.O.D.O.K.: REIGN DELAY						
Marvel Comics: Nov, 2009 ($3.99, one-shot)						
1-M.O.D.O.K. cartoony humor stories from Marvel Digital Comics; Ryan Dunlavey-s/a						4.00
MOD SQUAD (TV)						
Dell Publishing Co.: Jan, 1969 - No. 3, Oct, 1969 - No. 8, April, 1971						
1-Photo-c	6	12	18	41	76	110
2-4: 2-4-Photo-c	4	8	12	27	44	60
5-8: 8-Photo-c; Reprints #2	4	8	12	23	37	50
MOD WHEELS						
Gold Key: Mar, 1971 - No. 19, Jan, 1976						
1	4	8	12	25	40	55
2-9	3	6	9	16	23	30
10-19: 11,15-Extra 16 pgs. ads	3	6	9	14	19	24
MOE & SHMOE COMICS						
O. S. Publ. Co.: Spring, 1948 - No. 2, Summer, 1948						
1	10	20	30	58	79	100
2	7	14	21	37	46	55
MOEBIUS (Graphic novel)						
Marvel Comics (Epic Comics): Oct, 1987 - No. 6, 1988; No. 7, 1990; No. 8, 1991 ($9.95, 8x11", mature)						
1,2,4-6,8: (#2, 2nd printing, $9.95)	3	6	9	17	26	35
3,7,0: 3-(1st & 2nd printings, $12.95). 0 (1990, $12.95)	3	6	9	19	30	40
Moebius I-Signed & #'d hard-c ($45.95, Graphitti Designs, 1,500 copies printed)-r/#1-3	7	14	21	46	86	125
MOEBIUS COMICS						
Caliber: May, 1996 - No. 6 ($2.95, B&W)						
1-6: Moebius-c/a. 1-William Stout-a						4.00
MOEBIUS: THE MAN FROM CIGURI						
Dark Horse Comics: 1996 ($7.95, digest-size)						
nn-Moebius-c/a	2	4	6	10	14	18
MOLLY MANTON'S ROMANCES (Romantic Affairs #3)						
Marvel Comics (SePI): Sept, 1949 - No. 2, Dec, 1949 (52 pgs.)						
1-Photo-c (becomes Blaze the Wonder Collie #2 (10/49) on? & Molly						

The Monkees #4 © Raybert Prods.

Monster Crime Comics #1 © HILL

Monster Pile-Up #1 © Image

	GD 2.0	VG 4.0	FN 6.0	VF 8.0	VF/NM 9.0	NM- 9.2
Manton's Romances #2	23	46	69	136	223	310
2-Titled "Romances of..."; photo-c	16	32	48	92	144	195

MOLLY O'DAY (Super Sleuth)
Avon Periodicals: February, 1945 (1st Avon comic)

1-Molly O'Day, The Enchanted Dagger by Tuska (r/Yankee #1), Capt'n Courage, Corporal Grant app. 71 142 213 454 777 1100

MOMENT OF SILENCE
Marvel Comics: Feb, 2002 ($3.50, one-shot)

1-Tributes to the heroes and victims of Sept. 11; s/a by various 3.50

MONARCHY, THE (Also see The Authority and StormWatch)
DC Comics (WildStorm): Apr, 2001 - No. 12, May, 2002 ($2.50)

1-12: 1-McCrea & Leach-a/Young-s 3.00
Bullets Over Babylon TPB (2001, $12.95) r/#1-4, Authority #21 13.00

MONKEES, THE (TV)(Also see Circus Boy, Groovy, Not Brand Echh #3, Teen-Age Talk, Teen Beam & Teen Beat)
Dell Publishing Co.: March, 1967 - No. 17, Oct, 1969

	GD	VG	FN	VF	VF/NM	NM-
1-Photo-c	9	18	27	62	126	190
2-17: All photo-c. 17-Reprints #1	6	12	18	37	66	95

MONKEY AND THE BEAR, THE
Atlas Comics (ZPC): Sept, 1953 - No. 3, Jan, 1954

	GD	VG	FN	VF	VF/NM	NM-
1-Howie Post-c/a in all; funny animal	13	26	39	74	105	135
2,3	9	18	27	52	69	85

MONKEYMAN AND O'BRIEN (Also see Dark Horse Presents #80, 100-5, Gen[13]/..., Hellboy: Seed of Destruction, & San Diego Comic Con #2)
Dark Horse Comics (Legend): Jul, 1996 - No. 3, Sept, 1996 ($2.95, lim. series)

1-3: New stories; Art Adams-c/a/scripts 4.00
nn-(2/96, $2.95)-r/back-up stories from Hellboy: Seed of Destruction; Adams-c/a/scripts 4.00

MONKEYSHINES COMICS
Ace Periodicals/Publishers Specialists/Current Books/Unity Publ.: Summer, 1944 - No. 27, July, 1949

	GD	VG	FN	VF	VF/NM	NM-
1-Funny animal	17	34	51	98	154	210
2-(Aut/44)	11	22	33	60	83	105
3-10: 3-(Win/44)	10	20	30	56	76	95
11-18,20-27: 23,24-Fago-c/a	9	18	27	47	61	75
19-Frazetta-a	10	20	30	56	76	95

MONKEY'S UNCLE, THE (See Merlin Jones As... under Movie Comics)

MONOLITH, THE
DC Comics: Apr, 2004 - No. 12, Mar, 2005 ($3.50/$2.95)

1-($3.50) Palmiotti & Gray-s/Winslade-a 3.50
2-12-($2.95): 6-8-Batman app.; Coker-a 3.00
...: Volume One HC (Image Comics, 2012, $17.99) r/#1-4; intro. by Jim Steranko 18.00

MONROES, THE (TV)
Dell Publishing Co.: Apr, 1967

	GD	VG	FN	VF	VF/NM	NM-
1-Photo-c	3	6	9	17	26	35

MONSTER
Fiction House Magazines: 1953 - No. 2, 1953

	GD	VG	FN	VF	VF/NM	NM-
1-Dr. Drew by Grandenetti; reprint from Rangers Comics #48; Whitman-c	71	142	213	454	777	1100
2-Whitman-c	48	96	144	302	514	725

MONSTER CRIME COMICS (Also see Crime Must Stop)
Hillman Periodicals: Oct, 1952 (15¢, 52 pgs.)

	GD	VG	FN	VF	VF/NM	NM-
1 (Scarce)	219	438	657	1402	2401	3400

MONSTER HOUSE (Companion to the 2006 movie)
IDW Publishing: June, 2006 ($7.99, one-shot)

nn-Two stories about Bones and Skull by Joshua Dysart and Simeon Wilkins 8.00

MONSTER HOWLS (Magazine)
Humor-Vision: December, 1966 (Satire) (35¢, 68 pgs.)

	GD	VG	FN	VF	VF/NM	NM-
1-John Severin-a	5	10	15	34	60	85

MONSTER HUNTERS
Charlton Comics: Aug, 1975 - No. 9, Jan, 1977; No. 10, Oct, 1977 - No. 18, Feb, 1979

	GD	VG	FN	VF	VF/NM	NM-
1-Howard-a; Newton-c; 1st Countess Von Bludd and Colonel Whiteshroud	3	6	9	17	26	35
2-Sutton-c/a; Ditko-a	3	6	9	14	19	24
3,4,5,7: 4-Sutton-c/a	2	4	6	9	12	15
6,8,10: 6,8,10-Ditko-a	2	4	6	10	14	18
9,11,12	1	3	4	6	8	10
13,15,18-Ditko-c/a. 18-Sutton-a	2	4	6	10	14	18
14-Special all-Ditko issue	3	6	9	16	24	32
16,17-Sutton-a	2	3	4	6	8	10
1,2 (Modern Comics reprints, 1977)						6.00

NOTE: *Ditko a-2, 6, 8, 10, 13-15r, 18r; c-13-15, 18.* ***Howard*** *a-1, 3, 17; r-13.* ***Morisi*** *a-1.* ***Staton*** *a-1, 13.* ***Sutton*** *a-2, 4; c-2, 4; r-16-18.* ***Zeck*** *a-4-9. Reprints in #12-18.*

MONSTER MADNESS (Magazine)
Marvel Comics: 1972 - No. 3, 1973 (60¢, B&W)

1-3: Stories by "Sinister" Stan Lee. 1-Frankenstein photo-c. 2-Son of Frankenstein photo-c. 3-Bride of Frankenstein photo-c 4 8 12 27 44 60

MONSTER MAN
Image Comics (Action Planet): Sept, 1997 ($2.95, B&W)

1-Mike Manley-c/s/a 3.00

MONSTER MASTERWORKS
Marvel Comics: 1989 ($12.95, TPB)

nn-Reprints 1960's monster stories; art by Kirby, Ditko, Ayers, Everett 20.00

MONSTER MATINEE
Chaos! Comics: Oct, 1997 - No. 3, Oct, 1997 ($2.50, limited series)

1-3: pin-ups 3.00

MONSTER MENACE
Marvel Comics: Dec, 1993 - No. 4, Mar, 1994 ($1.25, limited series)

1-4: Pre-code Atlas horror reprints. 6.00
NOTE: *Ditko-r & Kirby-r in all.*

MONSTER OF FRANKENSTEIN (See Frankenstein and Essential Monster of Frankenstein)

MONSTER PILE-UP
Image Comics: Aug, 2008 ($1.99)

1-New short stories of Astounding Wolf-Man, Firebreather, Perhapanauts, Proof 3.00

MONSTERS ATTACK (Magazine)
Globe Communications Corpse: Sept, 1989 - No. 5, Dec, 1990 (B&W)

	GD	VG	FN	VF	VF/NM	NM-
1-5-Ditko, Morrow, J. Severin-a. 5-Toth, Morrow-a	1	2	3	4	5	7

MONSTERS, INC. (Based on the Disney/Pixar movie)
BOOM! Studios: Jun, 2009 - No. 4, Nov, 2009 ($2.99, limited series)

...: Laugh Factory 1-4: 1,3-Three covers. 2,4-Two covers 3.00

MONSTERS, INC. (Based on the Disney/Pixar movie)
Marvel Worldwide Inc.: Feb, 2013 - No. 2 ($2.99, limited series)

1,2-Movie adaptation 3.00
...: A Perfect Date (2013, $2.99) 3.00
...: The Humanween Party (4/13, $2.99) 3.00

MONSTERS ON THE PROWL (Chamber of Darkness #1-8)
Marvel Comics Group (No. 13,14: 52 pgs.): No. 9, 2/71 - No. 27, 11/73; No. 28, 6/74 - No. 30, 10/74

	GD	VG	FN	VF	VF/NM	NM-
9-Barry Smith inks	5	10	15	31	53	75
10-12,15: 12-Last 15¢ issue	3	6	9	19	30	40
13,14-(52 pgs.)	4	8	12	22	35	48
16-(4/72)-King Kull 4th app.; Severin-c	4	8	12	22	35	48
17-30	3	6	9	16	24	32

NOTE: ***Ditko*** *r-9, 14, 16.* ***Kirby*** *r-10-17, 21, 23, 25, 27, 28, 30; c-9, 25.* ***Kirby/Ditko*** *r-14, 17-20, 22, 24, 26, 29.* ***Marie/John Severin*** *a-16(Kull). 9-13, 15 contain one new story. Woodish art by* ***Reese****-11. King Kull created by Robert E. Howard.*

MONSTERS TO LAUGH WITH (Magazine) (Becomes Monsters Unlimited #4)
Marvel Comics Group: 1964 - No. 3, 1965 (B&W)

	GD	VG	FN	VF	VF/NM	NM-
1-Humor by Stan Lee	7	14	21	46	86	125
2,3: 3-Frankenstein photo-c	5	10	15	31	53	75

MONSTERS UNLEASHED (Magazine)
Marvel Comics Group: July, 1973 - No. 11, Apr, 1975; Summer, 1975 (B&W)

	GD	VG	FN	VF	VF/NM	NM-
1-Soloman Kane sty; Werewolf app.	5	10	15	31	53	75
2-4: 2-The Frankenstein Monster begins, ends #10. 3-Neal Adams-c/a; The Man-Thing begins (origin-r); Son of Satan preview. 4-Werewolf app.	4	8	12	23	37	50
5-7: Werewolf in all. 5-Man-Thing. 7-Williamson-a(r)	3	6	9	17	26	35
8-11: 8-Man-Thing; N. Adams-r. 9-Man-Thing; Wendigo app. 10-Origin Tigra	3	6	9	18	28	38
Annual 1 (Summer,1975, 92 pgs.)-Kane-a	3	6	9	19	30	40

NOTE: ***Boris*** *c-2, 6.* ***Brunner*** *a-2; c-11.* ***J. Buscema*** *a-2p, 4p, 5p.* ***Colan*** *a-1, 4r.* ***Davis*** *a-3r.* ***Everett*** *a-2r.* ***G. Kane*** *a-3.* ***Krigstein*** *r-4.* ***Morrow*** *a-3; c-1.* ***Perez*** *a-8.* ***Ploog*** *a-6.* ***Reese*** *a-1, 2.* ***Tuska*** *a-3p.* ***Wildey*** *a-1r.*

MONSTERS UNLEASHED
Marvel Comics: Mar, 2017 - No. 5, May, 2017 ($4.99, limited series with tie-ins)

Monsters Unleashed (2017 series) #1 © MAR

Monte Hale Western #30 © FAW

Moon Girl and Devil Dinosaur #19 © MAR

GD VG FN VF VF/NM NM-
2.0 4.0 6.0 8.0 9.0 9.2

GD VG FN VF VF/NM NM-
2.0 4.0 6.0 8.0 9.0 9.2

1-5: 1-Cullen Bunn-s/Steve McNiven-a; Avengers, X-Men, Guardians of the Galaxy, Inhumans & Champions app. 2-Land-a. 3-Leinil Yu-a. 4-Larroca-a. 5-Adam Kubert-a 5.00

MONSTERS UNLEASHED (Ongoing series)
Marvel Comics: Jun, 2017 - Present ($3.99)

1-11: 1-Bunn-s/Baldeón-a; Elsa Bloodstone & Mole Man app. 7,8-Fin Fang Foom app. 4.00

MONSTERS UNLIMITED (Magazine) (Formerly Monsters To Laugh With)
Marvel Comics Group: No. 4, 1965 - No. 7, 1966 (B&W)

4-7: 4,7-Frankenstein photo-c 5 10 15 31 53 75

MONSTER WORLD
DC Comics (WildStorm): Jul, 2001 - No. 4, Oct, 2001 ($2.50, limited series)

1-4-Lobdell-s/Meglia-c/a 3.00

MONSTER WORLD
American Gothic Press: Dec, 2015 - No. 4, May, 2016 ($3.99)

1-4-Philip Kim & Steve Niles-s/Piotr Kowalski-a 4.00

MONSTRESS
Image Comics: Nov, 2015 - Present ($4.99/$3.99)

1-($4.99) Marjorie Liu-s/Sana Takeda-a 20.00
2 12.00
3,4 6.00
5-14-($3.99) 4.00

MONSTRO MECHANICA
AfterShock Comics: Dec, 2017 - Present ($3.99)

1-4-Paul Allor-s/Chris Evenhuis-a; Leonardo Da Vinci and his robot in 1472 4.00

MONTANA KID, THE (See Kid Montana)

MONTE HALE WESTERN (Movie star; Formerly Mary Marvel #1-28; also see Fawcett Movie Comic, Motion Picture Comics, Picture News #8, Real Western Hero, Six-Gun Heroes, Western Hero & XMas Comics)
Fawcett Publ./Charlton No. 83 on: No. 29, Oct, 1948 - No. 88, Jan, 1956

29-(#1, 52 pgs.)-Photo-c begin, end #82; Monte Hale & his horse Pardner begin
26 52 78 154 252 350
30-(52 pgs.)-Big Bow and Little Arrow begin, end #34; Captain Tootsie by Beck
14 28 42 80 115 150
31-36,38-40-(52 pgs.): 34-Gabby Hayes begins, ends #80. 39-Captain Tootsie by Beck
12 24 36 67 94 120
37,41,45,49-(36 pgs.) 10 20 30 54 72 90
42-44,46-48,50-(52 pgs.): 47-Big Bow & Little Arrow app.
10 20 30 58 79 100
51,52,54-56,58,59-(52 pgs.) 9 18 27 52 69 85
53,57-(36 pgs.): 53-Slim Pickens app. 8 16 24 44 57 70
60-81: 36 pgs. #60-on. 80-Gabby Hayes ends 8 16 24 42 54 65
82-Last Fawcett issue (6/53) 9 18 27 52 69 85
83-1st Charlton issue (2/55); B&W photo back-c begin. Gabby Hayes returns, ends #86
10 20 30 58 79 100
84 (4/55) 8 16 24 44 57 70
85-86 8 16 24 42 54 65
87,88: 87-Wolverton-r, 1/2 pg. 88-Last issue 8 16 24 44 57 70

NOTE: *Gil Kane a-33?, 34? Rocky Lane -1 pg. (Carnation ad)-38, 40, 41, 43, 44, 46, 55.*

MONTY HALL OF THE U.S. MARINES (See With the Marines…)
Toby Press: Aug, 1951 - No. 11, Apr, 1953

1 15 30 45 83 124 165
2 9 18 27 50 65 80
3-5 8 16 24 44 57 70
6-11 8 16 24 40 50 60

NOTE: *Full page pin-ups (Pin-Up Pete) by* ***Jack Sparling*** *in #1-9.*

MOON, A GIRL...ROMANCE, A (Becomes Weird Fantasy #13 on; formerly Moon Girl #1-8)
E. C. Comics: No. 9, Sept-Oct, 1949 - No. 12, Mar-Apr, 1950

9-Moon Girl cameo 103 206 309 659 1130 1600
10,11 90 180 270 576 988 1400
12-(Scarce) 100 200 300 635 1093 1550

NOTE: ***Feldstein, Ingels*** *art in all.* ***Feldstein*** *c-9-12.* ***Wood/Harrison*** *a-10-12. Canadian reprints known; see Table of Contents.*

MOON GIRL AND DEVIL DINOSAUR
Marvel Comics: Jan, 2016 - Present ($3.99)

1-28: 1-Reeder & Montclare-s/Bustos-a; intro. Lunella Lafayette. 4-Hulk app. 9-11-Ms. Marvel app. 14-Thing & Hulk (Cho) app. 15-Ironheart app. 19-Intro. Girl-Moon. 22,23-Ego the Living Planet app. 25-28-The Thing and Human Torch app. 4.00

MOON GIRL AND THE PRINCE (#1) (Moon Girl #2-6; Moon Girl Fights Crime #7, 8; becomes A Moon, A Girl, Romance #9 on)(Also see Animal Fables #7, Int. Crime Patrol #6, Happy Houlihans & Tales From The Crypt #22)
E. C. Comics: Fall, 1947 - No. 8, Summer, 1949

1-Origin Moon Girl (see Happy Houlihans #1). Intro Santana, Queen of the Underworld
142 284 426 909 1555 2200
2-Moon Girl battles Futureman 84 168 252 538 919 1300
3,4: 3-Santana, Queen of the Underworld returns. 4-Moon Girl vs. a vampire
77 154 231 493 847 1200
5-E.C.'s 1st horror story, "Zombie Terror" 206 412 618 1318 2259 3200
6-8 (Scarce): 7-Origin Star (Moongirl's sidekick) 90 180 270 576 988 1400

NOTE: ***Craig*** *a-2, 5; c-1, 2.* ***Moldoff*** *a-1-8; c-3-8 (Shelly).* ***Wheelan's*** *Fat and Slat app. in #3, 4, 6. #2 & #3 are 52 pgs., #4 on, 36 pgs. Canadian reprints known; (see Table of Contents.)*

MOON KNIGHT (Also see The Hulk, Marc Spector…, Marvel Preview #21, Marvel Spotlight & Werewolf by Night #32)
Marvel Comics Group: Nov, 1980 - No. 38, Jul, 1984 (Mando paper #33 on)

1-Origin resumed in #4 3 6 9 19 30 40
2-15,25,35: 4-Intro Midnight Man. 25-Double size. 35-($1.00, 52 pgs.)-X-Men app.; F.F. cameo 5.00
16-24,26-28,31-34,36-38: 16-The Thing app. 4.00
29,30-Werewolf By Night app. 6.00

NOTE: ***Austin*** *c-27i, 31i.* ***Cowan*** *a-16; c-16, 17.* ***Kaluta*** *c-36-38; back c-35.* ***Miller*** *c-9, 12p, 13p, 15p, 27p.* ***Ploog*** *back c-35.* ***Sienkiewicz*** *a-1-15, 17-20, 22-26, 28-30, 33i, 36(4), 37; c-1-5, 7, 8, 10, 11, 14-16, 18-26, 28-30, 31p, 33, 34.*

MOON KNIGHT
Marvel Comics Group: June, 1985 - V2#6, Dec, 1985

V2#1-Double size; new costume 5.00
V2#2-6: 6-Sienkiewicz painted-c 3.00

MOON KNIGHT
Marvel Comics: Jan, 1998 - No. 4, Apr, 1998 ($2.50, limited series)

1-4-Moench-s/Edwards-c/a 3.00

MOON KNIGHT (Volume 3)
Marvel Comics: Jan, 1999 - No. 4, Feb, 1999 ($2.99, limited series)

1-4-Moench-s/Texeira-a(p) 3.00

MOON KNIGHT (Fourth series) (Leads into Vengeance of the Moon Knight)
Marvel Comics: June, 2006 - No. 30, Jul, 2009 ($2.99)

1-Finch-a/c; Huston-s 4.00
1-B&W sketch variant-c 6.00
2-19,21-26: 7-Spider-Man app. 9,10-Punisher app. 13-Suydam-c begin. 23-25-Bullseye 3.00
20-($3.99) Deodato-a; back-up r/1st app. in Werewolf By Night #32,33 4.00
Annual 1 (1/08, $3.99) Swierczynski-s/Palo-a 4.00
... Saga (2009, free) synopsis of origin and major storylines 3.00
...: Silent Knight 1 (1/09, $3.99) Milligan-s/Laurence Campbell-a/Crain-c 4.00

MOON KNIGHT (Fifth series)
Marvel Comics: Jul, 2011 - No. 12, Jun, 2012 ($3.99, limited series)

1-Bendis-s/Maleev-a/c; Wolverine, Spider-Man and Capt. America "app." 4.00
2-12: 2-Echo returns. 3-Bullseye-c 4.00

MOON KNIGHT (Sixth series)
Marvel Comics: May, 2014 - No. 17, Sept, 2015 ($3.99)

1-17: 1-6-Ellis-s/Shalvey-a. 7-12-Wood-s/Smallwood-a. 13-17-Bunn 4.00

MOON KNIGHT (Seventh series)
Marvel Comics: Jun, 2016 - No. 14, Jul, 2017 ($4.99/$3.99)

1-($4.99)-Lemire-s/Smallwood-a 5.00
2-14-($3.99) 5-9-Art by Smallwood, Stokoe, Torres, and Francavilla 4.00

MOON KNIGHT (Marvel Legacy)
Marvel Comics: No. 188, Jan, 2018 - Present ($3.99)

188-192: 188-Bemis-s/Burrows-a 4.00

MOON KNIGHT: DIVIDED WE FALL
Marvel Comics: 1992 ($4.95, 52 pgs.)

nn-Denys Cowan-c/a(p) 5.00

MOON KNIGHT SPECIAL
Marvel Comics: Oct, 1992 ($2.50, 52 pgs.)

1-Shang Chi, Master of Kung Fu-c/story 4.00

MOON KNIGHT SPECIAL EDITION
Marvel Comics Group: Nov, 1983 - No. 3, Jan, 1984 ($2.00, limited series, Baxter paper)

1-3: Reprints from Hulk mag. by Sienkiewicz 4.00

MOON MULLINS (See Popular Comics, Super Book #3 & Super Comics)
Dell Publishing Co.: 1941 - 1945

Four Color 14(1941) 48 96 144 302 514 725

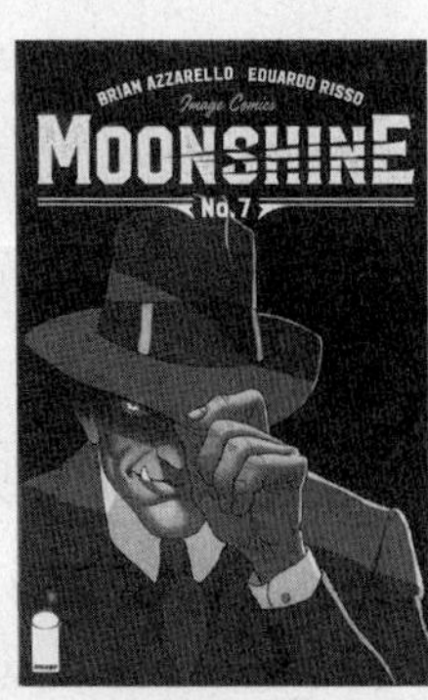

Moonshine #7 © Azzarello & Risso

Morbius: The Living Vampire #13 © MAR

More Fun Comics #48 © DC

	GD 2.0	VG 4.0	FN 6.0	VF 8.0	VF/NM 9.0	NM- 9.2
Large Feature Comic 29(1941)	36	72	108	216	351	485
Four Color 31(1943)	15	30	45	105	233	360
Four Color 81(1945)	10	20	30	66	138	210

MOON MULLINS
Michel Publ. (American Comics Group)#1-6/St. John #7,8: Dec-Jan, 1947-48 - No. 8, Mar-May, 1949 (52 pgs)

	GD 2.0	VG 4.0	FN 6.0	VF 8.0	VF/NM 9.0	NM- 9.2
1-Alternating Sunday & daily strip-r	24	48	72	142	234	325
2	15	30	45	84	127	170
3-8: 7,8-St. John Publ. 7,8-...Featuring Kayo on-c	14	28	42	82	121	160

NOTE: *Milt Gross a-2-6, 8. Frank Willard r-all.*

MOON PILOT
Dell Publishing Co.: No. 1313, Mar-May, 1962

	GD 2.0	VG 4.0	FN 6.0	VF 8.0	VF/NM 9.0	NM- 9.2
Four Color 1313-Movie, photo-c	6	12	18	40	73	105

MOONSHADOW (Also see Farewell, Moonshadow)
Marvel Comics (Epic Comics): 5/85 - #12, 2/87 ($1.50/$1.75, mature)
(1st fully painted comic book)

	GD 2.0	VG 4.0	FN 6.0	VF 8.0	VF/NM 9.0	NM- 9.2
1-Origin; J. M. DeMatteis scripts & Jon J. Muth painted-c/a.						6.00
2-12: 11-Origin						4.00
Trade paperback (1987?)-r/#1-12						14.00
Signed & #ed HC ($39.95, 1,200 copies)-r/#1-12	4	8	12	27	44	60

MOONSHADOW
DC Comics (Vertigo): Oct, 1994 - No. 12, Aug, 1995 ($2.25/$2.95)

	GD 2.0	VG 4.0	FN 6.0	VF 8.0	VF/NM 9.0	NM- 9.2
1-11: Reprints Epic series.						3.00
12 ($2.95)-w/expanded ending						4.00
The Complete Moonshadow TPB ('98, $39.95) r/#1-12 and Farewell Moonshadow; new Muth painted-c						40.00

MOONSHINE
Image Comics: Oct, 2016 - Present ($2.99/$3.99)

	GD 2.0	VG 4.0	FN 6.0	VF 8.0	VF/NM 9.0	NM- 9.2
1-6-Brian Azzarello-s/Eduardo Risso-a. 1-Covers by Risso & Frank Miller						3.00
7-($3.99) Azzarello-s/Risso-a						4.00

MOON-SPINNERS, THE (See Movie Comics)

MOONSTONE MONSTERS
Moonstone: 2003 - 2005 ($2.95, B&W)

	GD 2.0	VG 4.0	FN 6.0	VF 8.0	VF/NM 9.0	NM- 9.2
...: Demons ($2.95) - Short stories by various; Frenz-c						3.00
...: Ghosts ($2.95) - Short stories by various; Frenz-c						3.00
...: Sea Creatures ($2.95) - Short stories by various; Frenz-c						3.00
...: Witches ($2.95) - Short stories by various; Frenz-c						3.00
...: Zombies ($2.95) - Short stories by various; Frenz-c						3.00
Volume 1 (2004, $16.95, TPB) r/short stories from series; Wolak-c						17.00

MOONSTONE NOIR
Moonstone: 2003 - 2004 ($2.95/$4.95/$5.50, B&W)

	GD 2.0	VG 4.0	FN 6.0	VF 8.0	VF/NM 9.0	NM- 9.2
...: Bulldog Drummond (2004, $4.95) - Messner-Loebs-s/Barkley-a						5.00
...: Johnny Dollar ($4.95) - Gallaher-s/Theriault-a						5.00
...: Mr. Keen, Tracer of Lost Persons 1,2 ($2.95, limited series) - Ferguson-a						3.00
...: Mysterious Traveler (2003, $5.50) - Trevor Von Eeden-a/Joe Gentile-s						5.50
...: Mysterious Traveler Returns (2004, $4.95) - Trevor Von Eeden-a/Joe Gentile-s						5.00
...: The Lone Wolf ($4.95) - Jolley-s/Croall-a						5.00

MOPSY (See Pageant of Comics & TV Teens)
St. John Publ. Co.: Feb, 1948 - No. 19, Sept, 1953

	GD 2.0	VG 4.0	FN 6.0	VF 8.0	VF/NM 9.0	NM- 9.2
1-Part-r; reprints "Some Punkins" by Neher	39	78	117	240	395	550
2	15	30	45	88	137	185
3-10(1953): 8-Lingerie panels	15	30	45	84	127	170
11-19: 19-Lingerie-c	14	28	42	80	115	150

NOTE: *#1-7, 13, 18, 19 have paper dolls.*

MORBIUS REVISITED
Marvel Comic: Aug, 1993 - No. 5, Dec, 1993 ($1.95, mini-series)

	GD 2.0	VG 4.0	FN 6.0	VF 8.0	VF/NM 9.0	NM- 9.2
1-5-Reprints Fear #27-31						3.00

MORBIUS: THE LIVING VAMPIRE (Also see Amazing Spider-Man #101,102, Fear #20, Marvel Team-Up #3, 4, Midnight Sons Unl. & Vampire Tales)
Marvel Comics (Midnight Sons imprint #16 on): Sep, 1992 - No. 32, Apr, 1995 ($1.75/$1.95)

	GD 2.0	VG 4.0	FN 6.0	VF 8.0	VF/NM 9.0	NM- 9.2
1-($2.75, 52 pgs.)-Polybagged w/poster; Ghost Rider & Johnny Blaze x-over (part 3 of Rise of the Midnight Sons)						4.00
2-11,13-24,26-32: 3,4-Vs. Spider-Man-c/s.15-Ghost Rider app. 16-Spot varnish-c. 16,17-Siege of Darkness, parts 5 &13. 18-Deathlok app. 21-Bound-in Spider-Man trading card sheet; Spider-Man app.						3.00
12-($2.25)-Outer-c is a Darkhold envelope made of black parchment w/gold ink; Midnight Massacre x-over						4.00
25-($2.50, 52 pgs.)-Gold foil logo						4.00

MORBIUS: THE LIVING VAMPIRE (Marvel NOW!)
Marvel Comics: Mar, 2013 - No. 9, Nov, 2013 ($2.99)

	GD 2.0	VG 4.0	FN 6.0	VF 8.0	VF/NM 9.0	NM- 9.2
1-9: 1-Keatinge-s/Elson-a/Dell'Otto-c. 6,7-Superior Spider-Man app.						3.00

MORE FUN COMICS (Formerly New Fun Comics #1-6)
National Periodical Publs: No. 7, Jan, 1936 - No. 127, Nov-Dec, 1947 (No. 7,9-11: paper-c)

	GD 2.0	VG 4.0	FN 6.0	VF 8.0	VF/NM 9.0	NM- 9.2
7(1/36)-Oversized, paper-c; 1 pg. Kelly-a	1000	2000	3000	8000	-	-
8(2/36)-Oversized (10x12"), paper-c; 1 pg. Kelly-a; Sullivan-c	1000	2000	3000	8000	-	-
9(3-4/36)(Very rare, 1st standard-sized comic book with original material)-Last multiple panel-c	1375	2750	4125	11,000	-	-
10,11(7/36): 10-Last Henri Duval by Siegel & Shuster. 11-1st "Calling All Cars" by Siegel & Shuster; new classic logo begins	725	1450	2175	5800	-	-
12(8/36)-Slick-c begin	550	1100	1650	4400	-	-
V2#1(9/36, #13) 1 pg. Fred Astaire photo/bio	500	1000	1500	4000	-	-
2(10/36, #14)-Dr. Occult in costume (1st in color)(Superman prototype; 1st DC appearance) continues from The Comics Magazine, ends #17	2000	4000	6000	16,000	-	-
V2#3(11/36, #15), 17(V2#5)	825	1650	2475	6600	-	-
16(V2#4)-Cover numbering begins; ties with New Comics #11 as 1st DC Christmas-c; last Superman tryout issue	900	1800	2700	7200	-	-
18-20(V2#8, 5/37)	375	750	1125	3000	-	-
21(V2#9)-24(V2#12, 9/37)	245	490	735	1568	2684	3800
25(V3#1, 10/37)-27(V3#3, 12/37): 27-Xmas-c	245	490	735	1568	2684	3800
28-30: 30-1st non-funny cover	239	478	717	1530	2615	3700
31-Has ad for Action Comics #1	300	600	900	1920	3310	4700
32-35: 32-Last Dr. Occult	213	426	639	1363	2332	3300
36-40: 36-(10/38)-The Masked Ranger & sidekick Pedro begins; Ginger Snap by Bob Kane (2 pgs.; 1st-a?). 39-Xmas-c	200	400	600	1280	2190	3100
41-50: 41-Last Masked Ranger. 43-Beany (1 pg.) and Ginger Snap centerfold by Bob Kane	187	374	561	1197	2049	2900
51-The Spectre app. (in costume) in one panel ad at end of Buccaneer story	465	930	1395	3395	5998	8600
52-(2/40)-Origin/1st app. The Spectre (in costume splash panel only), part 1 by Bernard Baily (parts 1 & 2 written by Jerry Siegel; Spectre's costume changes color from purple & blue to green & grey; last Wing Brady; Spectre-c	10,500	21,000	31,500	73,500	126,750	190,000
53-Origin The Spectre (in costume at end of story), part 2; Capt. Desmo begins; Spectre-c	3300	6600	9900	23,000	54,500	86,000
54-The Spectre in costume; last King Carter; classic-Spectre-c	2000	4000	6000	14,000	27,500	41,000
55-(Scarce, 5/40)-Dr. Fate begins (1st app.); last Bulldog Martin; Spectre-c	2900	4000	6000	14,000	27,000	40,000
56-1st Dr. Fate-c (classic), origin continues. Congo Bill begins (6/40), 1st app.;	975	1950	2919	7100	12,550	18,000
57-60-All Spectre-c	486	972	1458	3550	6275	9000
61,65: 61-Classic Dr. Fate-c. 65-Classic Spectre-c	465	930	1395	3395	5998	8600
62-64,66: 63-Last Lt. Bob Neal. 64-Lance Larkin begins; all Spectre-c	343	686	1029	2400	4200	6000
67-(5/41)-Origin (1st) Dr. Fate; last Congo Bill & Biff Bronson (Congo Bill continues in Action Comics #37, 6/41)-Spectre-c	703	1406	2109	5132	9066	13,000
68-70: 68-Clip Carson begins. 70-Last Lance Larkin; all Dr. Fate-c	300	600	900	1950	3375	4800
71-Origin & 1st app. Johnny Quick by Mort Weisinger (9/41); classic sci/fi Dr. Fate-c	449	898	1347	3278	5789	8300
72-Dr. Fate's new helmet; last Sgt. Carey, Sgt. O'Malley & Captain Desmo; German submarine-c (Nazi war-c)	300	600	900	1920	3310	4700
73-Origin & 1st app. Aquaman (11/41) by Paul Norris; intro. Green Arrow & Speedy; Dr. Fate-c	10,500	21,000	31,500	68,250	94,125	120,000
74-2nd Aquaman; 1st Percival Popp, Supercop; Dr. Fate-c	676	1352	2028	4935	8718	12,500
75,76: 75-New origin Spectre; Nazi spy ring cover w/Hitler's photo. 76-Last Dr. Fate-c; Johnny Quick (by Meskin #76-97) begins, ends #107; last Clip Carson	300	600	900	1980	3440	4900
77-Green Arrow-c begin	232	464	696	1485	2543	3600
78-80	174	348	522	1114	1907	2700
81-83,85,88,90: 81-Last large logo. 82-1st small logo.	116	232	348	742	1271	1800
84-Green Arrow Japanese war-c	129	258	387	826	1413	2000
86,87-Johnny Quick-c. 87-Last Radio Squad	116	232	348	742	1271	1800
89-Origin Green Arrow & Speedy Team-up	135	270	405	864	1482	2100
91-97,99: 91-1st bi-monthly issue. 93-Dover & Clover begin (1st app., 9-10/43). 97-Kubert-a	87	174	261	553	952	1350
98-Last Dr. Fate (scarce)	100	200	300	635	1093	1550
100 (11-12/44)-Johnny Quick-c	97	194	291	621	1061	1500

More Than Mortal #5 © Sharon Scott

Morning Glories #1 © Spencer & Eisma

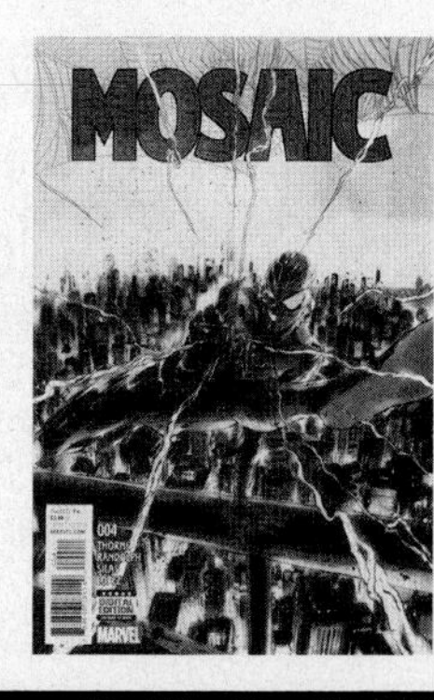

Mosaic #4 © MAR

	GD 2.0	VG 4.0	FN 6.0	VF 8.0	VF/NM 9.0	NM- 9.2
101-Origin & 1st app. Superboy (1-2/45)(not by Siegel & Shuster); last Spectre issue; Green Arrow-c	865	1730	2595	6315	11,158	16,000
102-2nd Superboy app; 1st Dover & Clover-c	152	304	456	965	1658	2350
103-3rd Superboy app; last Green Arrow-c	110	220	330	704	1202	1700
104-1st Superboy-c w/Dover & Clover	97	194	291	621	1061	1500
105,106-Superboy-c	86	172	258	546	936	1325
107-Last Johnny Quick & Superboy	84	168	252	538	919	1300
108-120: 108-Genius Jones begins; 1st c-app. (3-4/46; cont'd from Adventure Comics #102)	28	56	84	165	270	375
121-124,126: 121-123,126-Post funny animal (Jimminy & the Magic Book)-c	26	52	78	154	252	350
125-Superman c-app.w/Jimminy	97	194	291	621	1061	1500
127-(Scarce)-Post-c/a	43	86	129	271	461	650

NOTE: *All issues are scarce to rare. Cover features: The Spectre-#52-55, 57-60, 62-67. Dr. Fate-#56, 61, 68-76. The Green Arrow & Speedy-#77-85, 88-97, 99, 101 (w/Dover & Clover-#98, 103). Johnny Quick-#86, 87, 100. Dover & Clover-#102, (104, 106 w/Superboy), 107, 108(w/Genius Jones), 110, 112, 114, 117, 119. Genius Jones-#109, 111, 113, 115, 116, 118, 120.* **Baily** *a-45, 52-on; c-52-55, 57-60, 62-67.* **Al Capp** *a-45(signed Koppy).* **Ellsworth** *c-7.* **Creig Flessel** *c-30, 31, 35-48(most).* **Guardineer** *c-47, 49, 50.* **Kiefer** *a-20.* **Meskin** *c-86, 87, 100?* **Moldoff** *c-51.* **George Papp** *c-77-85.* **Post** *c-121-127.* **Vincent Sullivan** *c-8-28, 32-34.*

MORE FUND COMICS (Benefit book for the Comic Book Legal Defense Fund)
(Also see Even More Fund Comics)
Sky Dog Press: Sept, 2003 ($10.00, B&W, trade paperback)

nn-Anthology of short stories and pin-ups by various; Hulk-c by Pérez 10.00

MORE SEYMOUR (See Seymour My Son)
Archie Publications: Oct, 1963

	GD	VG	FN	VF	VF/NM	NM-
1-DeCarlo-a?	3	6	9	21	33	45

MORE THAN MORTAL (Also see Lady Pendragon/...)
Liar Comics: June, 1997 - No. 4, Apr, 1998 ($2.95, limited series)
Image Comics: No. 5, Dec, 1999 - No. 6, Mar, 2000 ($2.95)

1-Blue forest background-c, 1-Variant-c 4.00
1-White-c 6.00
1-2nd printing; purple sky cover 3.00
2-4: 3-Silvestri-c, 4-Two-c, one by Randy Queen 3.00
5,6: 5-1st Image Comics issue 3.00

MORE THAN MORTAL: OTHERWORLDS
Image Comics: July, 1999 - No. 4, Dec, 1999 ($2.95, limited series)

1-4-Firchow-a. 1-Two covers 3.00

MORE THAN MORTAL SAGAS
Liar Comics: Jun, 1998 - No. 3, Dec, 1998 ($2.95, limited series)

1,2-Painted art by Romano. 2-Two-c, one by Firchow 3.00
1-Variant-c by Linsner 5.00

MORE THAN MORTAL TRUTHS AND LEGENDS
Liar Comics: Aug, 1998 - No. 6, Apr, 1999 ($2.95)

1-6-Firchow-a(p) 3.00
1-Variant-c by Dan Norton 4.50

MORE TRASH FROM MAD (Annual)
E. C. Comics: 1958 - No. 12, 1969
(Note: Bonus missing = half price)

	GD	VG	FN	VF	VF/NM	NM-
nn(1958)-8 pgs. color Mad reprint from #20	16	32	48	112	249	385
2(1959)-Market Product Labels	11	22	33	76	163	250
3(1960)-Text book covers	10	20	30	69	147	225
4(1961)-Sing Along with Mad booklet	10	20	30	69	147	225
5(1962)-Window Stickers; r/from Mad #39	8	16	24	54	102	150
6(1963)-TV Guise booklet	8	16	24	54	102	150
7(1964)-Alfred E. Neuman commemorative stamps	7	14	21	44	82	120
8(1965)-Life size poster-Alfred E. Neuman	5	10	15	35	63	90
9-12: 9,10(1966-67)-Mischief Sticker. 11(1968)-Campaign poster & bumper sticker. 12(1969)-Pocket medals	5	10	15	35	63	90

NOTE: **Kelly Freas** *c-1, 2, 4.* **Mingo** *c-3, 5-9, 12.*

MORGAN THE PIRATE (Movie)
Dell Publishing Co.: No. 1227, Sept-Nov, 1961

	GD	VG	FN	VF	VF/NM	NM-
Four Color 1227-Photo-c	6	12	18	42	79	115

MORLOCKS
Marvel Comics: June, 2002 - No. 4, Sept, 2002 ($2.50, limited series)

1-4-Johns-s/Martinbrough-c/a. 1-1st app. Angel Dust 3.00

MORLOCK 2001
Atlas/Seaboard Publ.: Feb, 1975 - No. 3, July, 1975

	GD	VG	FN	VF	VF/NM	NM-
1,2: 1-(Super-hero)-Origin & 1st app.; Milgrom-c	2	4	6	11	16	20
3-Ditko/Wrightson-a; origin The Midnight Man & The Mystery Men	3	6	9	15	22	28

MORNING GLORIES
Image Comics: Aug, 2010 - Present ($3.99/$3.50/$2.99)

1-($3.99) Nick Spencer-s/Joe Eisma-a/Rodin Esquejo-c; group cover 10.00
1-Second-Fourth printings 4.00
2-($3.50) Regular cover and white background 2nd printing 5.00
3-6-Regular covers and white background 2nd printings 4.00
7-23-($2.99) 3.00
24,25,27,28-($3.99) 4.00
26-($1.00) Start of Season Two 3.00
29-48-($3.50) 3.50
49-($4.99) Spencer-s/Eisma-a 5.00
50-(7/16, $5.99) 6.00
...Vol. 1 TPB (2/11, $9.99) r/#1-6 10.00

MORNINGSTAR SPECIAL
Comico: Apr, 1990 ($2.50)

1-From the Elementals; Willingham-c/a/scripts 3.00

MORTAL KOMBAT
Malibu Comics: July, 1994 - No. 6, Dec, 1994 ($2.95)

1-6: 1-Two diff. covers exist 3.00
1-Limited edition gold foil embossed-c 4.00
0 (12/94), Special Edition 1 (11/94) 3.00
Tournament Edition I12/94, $3.95), II('95)($3.95) 4.00
...: **BARAKA** ,June, 1995 ($2.95, one-shot) #1; ...**BATTLEWAVE** ,2/95 - No. 6, 7/95 , #1-6; ...**GORO, PRINCE OF PAIN** ,9/94 - No. 3, 11/94, #1-3; ...**KITANA AND MILEENA** ,8/95 , ...**KUNG LAO** ,7/95 , #1; ... **RAYDON & KANO** ,3/95 - No. 3, 5/95, #1-3: ...(all $2.95-c) 3.00
...: **U.S. SPECIAL FORCES** ,1/95 - No. 2, ($3.50), #1,2 3.50

MORTAL KOMBAT X
DC Comics: Mar, 2015 - No. 12, Jan, 2016 ($3.99, printings of digital-first stories)

1-12: 1-Kittelsen-s/Soy-a/Reis-c. 9-12-Jae Lee-c 4.00

MORTIE (Mazie's Friend; also see Flat-Top)
Magazine Publishers: Dec, 1952 - No. 4, June, 1953?

	GD	VG	FN	VF	VF/NM	NM-
1	11	22	33	62	86	110
2-4	7	14	21	37	46	55

MORTIGAN GOTH: IMMORTALIS (See Marvel Frontier Comics Unlimited)
Marvel Comics: Sept, 1993 - No. 4, Mar, 1994 ($1.95, mini-series)

1-($2.95)-Foil-c 4.00
2-4 3.00

MORT THE DEAD TEENAGER
Marvel Comics: Nov, 1993 - No. 4, Mar, 1994 ($1.75, mini-series)

1-4 3.00

MORTY MEEKLE
Dell Publishing Co.: No. 793, May, 1957

	GD	VG	FN	VF	VF/NM	NM-
Four Color 793	5	10	15	30	50	70

MOSAIC
Marvel Comics: Dec, 2016 - No. 8, Jul, 2017 ($4.99/$3.99)

1-($4.99) Geoffrey Thorne-s/Khary Randolph-a; intro. Morris Sackett 5.00
2-8-($3.99) 3,4-Spider-Man app. 6-Inhumans app. 8-Diablo app. 4.00

MOSES & THE TEN COMMANDMENTS (See Dell Giants)

MOSTLY WANTED
DC Comics (WildStorm): Jul, 2000 - No. 4, Nov, 2000 ($2.50, limited series)

1-4-Lobdell-s/Flores-a 3.00

MOTEL HELL (Based on the 1980 movie)
IDW Publishing: Oct, 2010 - No. 3, Dec, 2010 ($3.99, limited series)

1-3-Matt Nixon-s/Chris Moreno-a. 1,2-Bradstreet-c. 3-Moreno-c 4.00

MOTH, THE
Dark Horse Comics: Apr, 2004 - No. 4, Aug, 2004 ($2.99)

1-4-Steve Rude-c/a; Gary Martin-s 3.00
... Special (3/04, $4.95) 5.00
TPB (5/05, $12.95) r/#1-4 and Special; gallery of extras 13.00

MOTH, THE
Rude Dude Productions: May 2008 (Free Comic Book Day giveaway)

... Special Edition - Steve Rude-s/a; sketch pages 3.00

MOTHER GOOSE AND NURSERY RHYME COMICS (See Christmas With Mother Goose)

Mother Panic #1 © DC

Motor Girl #3 © Terry Moore

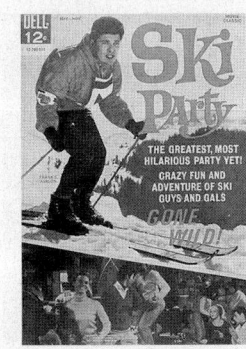

Movie Classics - Ski Party © DELL

	GD 2.0	VG 4.0	FN 6.0	VF 8.0	VF/NM 9.0	NM- 9.2
Dell Publishing Co.: No. 41, 1944 - No. 862, Nov, 1957						
Four Color 41-Walt Kelly-c/a	22	44	66	154	340	525
Four Color 59, 68-Kelly c/a	18	36	54	121	268	415
Four Color 862-The Truth About..., Movie (Disney)	7	14	21	44	82	120

MOTHERLANDS
DC Comics (Vertigo): Mar, 2018 - Present ($3.99)
1,2-Spurrier-s/Stott-a/Canete-c 4.00

MOTHER PANIC
DC Comics (Young Animal): Jan, 2017 - No. 12, Dec, 2017 ($3.99)
1-12: 1-Houser-s/Edwards-a; Batman cameo. 3-Batman & Batwoman app. 7-9-Leon-a 4.00
.../ Batman Special 1 (4/18, $4.99) Part 2 of Milk Wars crossover; Templeton-a/Quitely-c 5.00

MOTHER TERESA OF CALCUTTA
Marvel Comics Group: 1984

	GD 2.0	VG 4.0	FN 6.0	VF 8.0	VF/NM 9.0	NM- 9.2
1-(52 pgs.) No ads	1	3	4	6	8	10

MOTION PICTURE COMICS (See Fawcett Movie Comics)
Fawcett Publications: No. 101, 1950 - No. 114, Jan, 1953 (All-photo-c)

	GD 2.0	VG 4.0	FN 6.0	VF 8.0	VF/NM 9.0	NM- 9.2
101- "Vanishing Westerner"; Monte Hale (1950)	15	30	45	90	140	190
102- "Code of the Silver Sage"; Rocky Lane (1/51)	15	30	45	83	124	165
103- "Covered Wagon Raid"; Rocky Lane (3/51)	15	30	45	83	124	165
104- "Vigilante Hideout"; Rocky Lane (5/51)-Book length Powell-a	15	30	45	83	124	165
105- "Red Badge of Courage"; Audie Murphy; Bob Powell-a (7/51)	18	36	54	107	169	230
106- "The Texas Rangers"; George Montgomery (9/51)	15	30	45	83	124	165
107- "Frisco Tornado"; Rocky Lane (11/51)	14	28	42	80	115	150
108- "Mask of the Avenger"; John Derek	12	24	36	69	97	125
109- "Rough Rider of Durango"; Rocky Lane	14	28	42	80	115	150
110- "When Worlds Collide"; George Evans-a (5/52); Williamson & Evans drew themselves in story; (also see Famous Funnies No. 72-88)	77	154	231	493	847	1200
111- "The Vanishing Outpost"; Lash LaRue	15	30	45	90	140	190
112- "Brave Warrior"; Jon Hall & Jay Silverheels	12	24	36	67	94	120
113- "Walk East on Beacon"; George Murphy; Schaffenberger-a	10	20	30	54	72	90
114- "Cripple Creek"; George Montgomery (1/53)	10	20	30	58	79	100

MOTION PICTURE FUNNIES WEEKLY (See Promotional Comics section)

MOTOR CRUSH
Image Comics: Dec, 2016 - Present ($3.99)
1-10-Fletcher & Stewart-s/Tarr-a; covers by Tarr & Stewart. 6-Stewart-a 4.00

MOTOR GIRL
Abstract Studio: 2016 - No. 10, 2017 ($3.99, B&W)
1-10-Terry Moore-s/a/c 4.00

MOTORHEAD (See Comic's Greatest World)
Dark Horse Comics: Aug, 1995 - No. 6, Jan, 1996 ($2.50)
1-6: Bisley-c on all. 1-Predator app. 3.00
Special 1 (3/94, $3.95, 52pgs.)-Jae Lee-c; Barb Wire, The Machine & Wolf Gang app. 4.00

MOTORMOUTH (... & Killpower #7? on)
Marvel Comics UK: June, 1992 - No. 12, May, 1993 ($1.75)
1-13: 1,2-Nick Fury app. 3-Punisher-c/story. 5,6-Nick Fury & Punisher app. 6-Cable cameo. 7-9-Cable app. 3.00

MOUNTAIN MEN (See Ben Bowie)

MOUSE MUSKETEERS (See M.G.M.'s...)

MOUSE ON THE MOON, THE (See Movie Classics)

MOVEMENT, THE
DC Comics: Jul, 2013 - No. 12, Jul. 2014 ($2.99)
1-12: 1-Gail Simone-s/Freddie Williams-a/Amanda Conner-c. 2-4-Rainmaker app. 9,10-Batgirl app. 3.00

MOVIE CARTOONS
DC Comics: Dec, 1944 (cover only ashcan)
nn-Ashcan comic, not distributed to newsstands, only for in house use. Covers were produced, but not the rest of the book. A copy sold in 2006 for $500.

MOVIE CLASSICS
Dell Publishing Co.: Apr, 1956; May-Jul, 1962 - Dec, 1969
(Before 1963, most movie adaptations were part of the 4-Color series)
(Disney movie adaptations after 1970 are in Walt Disney Showcase)

	GD 2.0	VG 4.0	FN 6.0	VF 8.0	VF/NM 9.0	NM- 9.2
Around the World Under the Sea 12-030-612 (12/66)	3	6	9	19	30	40
Bambi 3(4/56)-Disney; r/4-Color #186	4	8	12	23	37	50
Battle of the Bulge 12-056-606 (6/66)	3	6	9	20	31	42
Beach Blanket Bingo 12-058-509	6	12	18	40	73	105
Bon Voyage 01-068-212 (12/62)-Disney; photo-c	3	6	9	21	33	45
Castilian, The 12-110-401	3	6	9	19	30	40
Cat, The 12-109-612 (12/66)	3	6	9	18	28	38
Cheyenne Autumn 12-112-506 (4-6/65)	5	10	15	31	53	75
Circus World, Samuel Bronston's 12-115-411; John Wayne app.; John Wayne photo-c	9	18	27	58	114	170
Countdown 12-150-710 (10/67)-James Caan photo-c	3	6	9	20	31	42
Creature, The 1 (12-142-302) (12-2/62-63)	9	18	27	58	114	170
Creature, The 12-142-410 (10/64)	5	10	15	30	50	70
David Ladd's Life Story 12-173-212 (10-12/62)-Photo-c	6	12	18	40	73	105
Die, Monster, Die 12-175-603 (3/66)-Photo-c	5	10	15	33	57	80
Dirty Dozen 12-180-710 (10/67)	4	8	12	27	44	60
Dr. Who & the Daleks 12-190-612 (12/66)-Peter Cushing photo-c; 1st U.S. app. of Dr. Who	21	43	63	147	324	500
Dracula 12-231-212 (10-12/62)	9	18	27	59	117	175
El Dorado 12-240-710 (10/67)-John Wayne; photo-c	10	20	30	69	147	225
Ensign Pulver 12-257-410 (8-10/64)	3	6	9	18	28	38
Frankenstein 12-283-305 (3-5/63)(see Frankenstein 8-10/64 for 2nd printing)	9	18	27	59	117	175
Great Race, The 12-299-603 (3/66)-Natallie Wood, Tony Curtis photo-c	4	8	12	27	44	60
Hallelujah Trail, The 12-307-602 (2/66) (Shows 1/66 inside); Burt Lancaster, Lee Remick photo-c	5	10	15	30	50	70
Hatari 12-340-301 (1/63)-John Wayne	7	14	21	44	82	120
Horizontal Lieutenant, The 01-348-210 (10/62)	3	6	9	18	28	38
Incredible Mr. Limpet, The 12-370-408; Don Knotts photo-c	5	10	15	30	50	70
Jack the Giant Killer 12-374-301 (1/63)	7	14	21	44	82	120
Jason & the Argonauts 12-376-310 (8-10/63)-Photo-c	8	16	24	56	108	160
Lancelot & Guinevere 12-416-310 (10/63)	5	10	15	30	50	70
Lawrence 12-426-308 (8/63)-Story of Lawrence of Arabia; movie ad on back-c; not exactly like movie	5	10	15	30	50	70
Lion of Sparta 12-439-301 (1/63)	3	6	9	21	33	45
Mad Monster Party 12-460-801 (9/67)-Based on Kurtzman's screenplay	8	16	24	54	102	150
Magic Sword, The 01-496-209 (9/62)	5	10	15	31	53	75
Masque of the Red Death 12-490-410 (8-10/64)-Vincent Price photo-c	5	10	15	35	63	90
Maya 12-495-612 (12/66)-Clint Walker & Jay North part photo-c	4	8	12	23	37	50
McHale's Navy 12-500-412 (10-12/64)	4	8	12	27	44	60
Merrill's Marauders 12-510-301 (1/63)-Photo-c	3	6	9	18	28	38
Mouse on the Moon, The 12-530-312 (10/12/63)-Photo-c	3	6	9	21	33	45
Mummy, The 12-537-211 (9-11/62) 2 versions with different back-c	9	18	27	60	120	180
Music Man, The 12-538-301 (1/63)	3	6	9	19	30	40
Naked Prey, The 12-545-612 (12/66)-Photo-c	5	10	15	31	53	75
Night of the Grizzly, The 12-558-612 (12/66)-Photo-c	3	6	9	21	33	45
None But the Brave 12-565-506 (4-6/65)	5	10	15	31	53	75
Operation Bikini 12-597-310 (10/63)-Photo-c	3	6	9	19	30	40
Operation Crossbow 12-590-512 (10-12/65)	3	6	9	19	30	40
Prince & the Pauper, The 01-654-207 (5-7/62)-Disney	3	6	9	21	33	45
Raven, The 12-680-309 (9/63)-Vincent Price photo-c	6	12	18	37	66	95
Ring of Bright Water 01-701-910 (10/69) (inside shows #12-701-909)	3	6	9	21	33	45
Runaway, The 12-707-412 (10-12/64)	3	6	9	18	28	38
Santa Claus Conquers the Martians #? (1964)-Photo-c	9	18	27	61	123	185
Santa Claus Conquers the Martians 12-725-603 (3/66, 12¢)-Reprints 1964 issue; photo-c	6	12	18	40	73	105
Another version given away with a Golden Record, SLP 170, nn, no price (3/66)-Complete with record	10	20	30	69	147	225
Six Black Horses 12-750-301 (1/63)-Photo-c	3	6	9	19	30	40
Ski Party 12-743-511 (9-11/65)-Frankie Avalon photo-c; photo inside-c; Adkins-a	4	8	12	28	47	65
Smoky 12-746-702 (2/67)	3	6	9	18	28	38

Movie Comics #2 © DC

Movie Comics #2 © FH

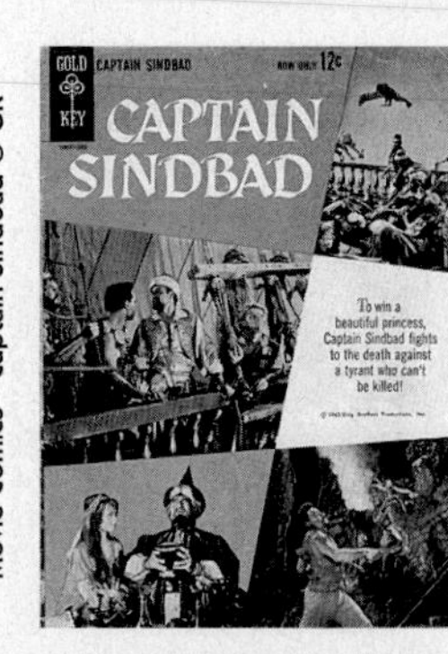

Movie Comics - Captain Sindbad © GK

GD 2.0 | VG 4.0 | FN 6.0 | VF 8.0 | VF/NM 9.0 | NM- 9.2

GD 2.0 | VG 4.0 | FN 6.0 | VF 8.0 | VF/NM 9.0 | NM- 9.2

Sons of Katie Elder 12-748-511 (9-11/65); John Wayne app.; photo-c
10 20 30 66 138 210
Tales of Terror 12-793-302 (2/63)-Evans-a 5 10 15 31 53 75
Three Stooges Meet Hercules 01-828-208 (8/62)-Photo-c
8 16 24 54 102 150
Tomb of Ligeia 12-830-506 (4-6/65) 5 10 15 31 53 75
Treasure Island 01-845-211 (7-9/62)-Disney; r/4-Color #624
3 6 9 19 30 40
Twice Told Tales (Nathaniel Hawthorne) 12-840-401 (11-1/63-64);
Vincent Price photo-c 5 10 15 33 57 80
Two on a Guillotine 12-850-506 (4-6/65) 3 6 9 21 33 45
Valley of Gwangi 01-880-912 (12/69) 8 16 24 52 99 145
War Gods of the Deep 12-900-509 (7-9/65) 3 6 9 19 30 40
War Wagon, The 12-533-709 (9/67); John Wayne app.
7 14 21 48 89 130
Who's Minding the Mint? 12-924-708 (8/67) 3 6 9 18 28 38
Wolfman, The 12-922-308 (6-8/63) 8 16 24 56 108 160
Wolfman, The 1(12-922-410)(8-10/64)-2nd printing; r/#12-922-308
4 8 12 22 35 48
Zulu 12-950-410 (8-10/64)-Photo-c 6 12 18 41 76 110

MOVIE COMICS (See Cinema Comics Herald & Fawcett Movie Comics)

MOVIE COMICS
National Periodical Publications/Picture Comics: April, 1939 - No. 6, Sept-Oct, 1939 (Most all photo-c)

1- "Gunga Din", "Son of Frankenstein", "The Great Man Votes", "Fisherman's Wharf", & "Scouts to the Rescue" part 1; Wheelan "Minute Movies" begin
366 732 1098 2562 4481 6400
2- "Stagecoach", "The Saint Strikes Back", "King of the Turf","Scouts to the Rescue" part 2, "Arizona Legion", Andy Devine photo-c 271 542 813 1734 2967 4200
3- "East Side of Heaven", "Mystery in the White Room", "Four Feathers", "Mexican Rose" with Gene Autry, "Spirit of Culver", "Many Secrets", "The Mikado" (1st Gene Autry photo cover) 200 400 600 1280 2190 3100
4- "Captain Fury", Gene Autry in "Blue Montana Skies", "Streets of N.Y." with Jackie Cooper, "Oregon Trail" part 1 with Johnny Mack Brown, "Big Town Czar" with Barton MacLane, & "Star Reporter" with Warren Hull 148 296 444 947 1624 2300
5- "The Man in the Iron Mask", "Five Came Back", "Wolf Call", "The Girl & the Gambler", "The House of Fear", "The Family Next Door", "Oregon Trail" part 2
161 322 483 1030 1765 2500
6- "The Phantom Creeps", "Chumps at Oxford", & "The Oregon Trail" part 3; 2nd Robot-c
232 464 696 1485 2543 3600

NOTE: *Above books contain many original movie stills with dialogue from movie scripts. All issues are scarce.*

MOVIE COMICS
Fiction House Magazines: Dec, 1946 - No. 4, 1947

1-Big Town (by Lubbers), Johnny Danger begin; Celardo-a; Mitzi of the Movies by Fran Hopper 41 82 123 256 428 600
2-(2/47)- "White Tie & Tails" with William Bendix; Mitzi of the Movies begins; Matt Baker-a 31 62 93 186 303 420
3-(6/47)-Andy Hardy starring Mickey Rooney 31 62 93 186 303 420
4-Mitzi In Hollywood by Matt Baker; Merton of the Movies with Red Skelton; Yvonne DeCarlo & George Brent in "Slave Girl" 39 78 117 231 378 525

MOVIE COMICS
Gold Key/Whitman: Oct, 1962 - 1984

Alice in Wonderland 10144-503 (3/65)-Disney; partial reprint of 4-Color #331
3 6 9 21 33 45
Alice In Wonderland #1 (Whitman pre-pack, 3/84) 2 4 6 10 14 18
Aristocats, The 1 (30045-103)(3/71)-Disney; with pull-out poster (25¢)
(No poster = half price) 6 12 18 40 73 105
Bambi 1 (10087-309)(9/63)-Disney; r/4-C #186 4 8 12 23 37 50
Bambi 2 (10087-607)(7/66)-Disney; r/4-C #186 3 6 9 19 30 40
Beneath the Planet of the Apes 30044-012 (12/70)-with pull-out poster; photo-c
(No poster = half price) 8 16 24 54 102 150
Big Red 10026-211 (11/62)-Disney; photo-c 3 6 9 19 30 40
Big Red 10026-503 (3/65)-Disney; reprints 10026-211; photo-c
3 6 9 16 23 30
Blackbeard's Ghost 10222-806 (6/68)-Disney 3 6 9 18 28 38
Bullwhip Griffin 10181-706 (6/67)-Disney; Spiegle-a; photo-c
3 6 9 21 33 45
Captain Sindbad 10077-309 (9/63)-Manning-a; photo-c
5 10 15 35 63 90
Chitty Chitty Bang Bang 1 (30038-902)(2/69)-with pull-out poster; Disney; photo-c
(No poster = half price) 6 12 18 37 66 95
Cinderella 10152-508 (8/65)-Disney; r/4-C #786 4 8 12 25 40 55
Darby O'Gill & the Little People 10251-001(1/70)-Disney; reprints 4-Color #1024 (Toth-a); photo-c 4 8 12 28 47 65
Dumbo 1 (10090-310)(10/63)-Disney; r/4-C #668 3 6 9 20 31 42
Emil & the Detectives 10120-502 (11/64)-Disney; photo-c & back-c photo pin-up
3 6 9 19 30 40
Escapade in Florence 1 (10043-301)(1/63)-Disney; starring Annette Funicello
7 14 21 44 82 120
Fall of the Roman Empire 10118-407 (7/64); Sophia Loren photo-c
4 8 12 23 37 50
Fantastic Voyage 10178-702 (2/67)-Wood/Adkins-a; photo-c
5 10 15 33 57 80
55 Days at Peking 10081-309 (9/63)-Photo-c 3 6 9 19 30 40
Fighting Prince of Donegal, The 10193-701 (1/67)-Disney
3 6 9 18 28 38
First Men in the Moon 10132-503 (3/65)-Fred Fredericks-a; photo-c
4 8 12 23 37 50
Gay Purr-ee 30017-301(1/63, 84 pgs.) 5 10 15 30 50 70
Gnome Mobile, The 10207-710 (10/67)-Disney; Walter Brennan photo-c & back-c photo pin-up
4 8 12 21 33 45
Goodbye, Mr. Chips 10246-006 (6/70)-Peter O'Toole photo-c
3 6 9 19 30 40
Happiest Millionaire, The 10221-804 (4/68)-Disney 3 6 9 21 33 45
Hey There, It's Yogi Bear 10122-409 (9/64)-Hanna-Barbera
6 12 18 37 66 95
Horse Without a Head, The 10109-401 (1/64)-Disney 3 6 9 18 28 38
How the West Was Won 10074-307 (7/63)-Based on the L'Amour novel; Tufts-a
4 8 12 27 44 60
In Search of the Castaways 10048-303 (3/63)-Disney; Hayley Mills photo-c
6 12 18 37 66 95
Jungle Book, The 1 (6022-801)(1/68-Whitman)-Disney; large size (10x13-1/2"); 59¢
6 12 18 37 66 95
Jungle Book, The 1 (30033-803)(3/68, 68 pgs.)-Disney; same contents as Whitman #1
4 8 12 23 37 50
Jungle Book, The 1 (6/78, $1.00 tabloid) 3 6 9 16 23 30
Jungle Book (7/84)-r/Giant; Whitman pre-pack 2 4 6 10 14 18
Kidnapped 10080-306 (6/63)-Disney; reprints 4-Color #1101; photo-c
3 6 9 19 30 40
King Kong 30036-809(9/68-68 pgs.)-painted-c 4 8 12 25 40 55
King Kong nn-Whitman Treasury($1.00, 68 pgs.,1968), same cover as Gold Key issue
5 10 15 31 53 75
King Kong 11299(#1-786, 10x13-1/4", 68 pgs., $1.00, 1978)
3 6 9 17 26 35
Lady and the Tramp 10042-301 (1/63)-Disney; r/4-Color #629
3 6 9 20 31 42
Lady and the Tramp 1 (1967-Giant; 25¢)-Disney; reprints part of Dell #1
5 10 15 31 53 75
Lady and the Tramp 2 (10042-203)(3/72)-Disney; r/4-Color #629
3 6 9 16 23 30
Legend of Lobo, The 1 (10059-303)(3/63)-Disney; photo-c
3 6 9 16 23 30
Lt. Robin Crusoe, U.S.N. 10191-610 (10/66)-Disney; Dick Van Dyke photo-c & back-c photo pin-up 3 6 9 17 26 35
Lion, The 10035-301 (1/63)-Photo-c 3 6 9 16 24 32
Lord Jim 10156-509 (9/65)-Photo-c 3 6 9 16 24 32
Love Bug, The 10237-906 (6/69)-Disney; Buddy Hackett photo-c
4 8 12 21 33 45
Mary Poppins 10136-501 (1/65)-Disney; photo-c 5 10 15 30 50 70
Mary Poppins 30023-501 (1/65-68 pgs.)-Disney; photo-c
6 12 18 41 76 110
McLintock 10110-403 (3/64); John Wayne app.; John Wayne & Maureen O'Hara photo-c
10 20 30 66 138 210
Merlin Jones as the Monkey's Uncle 10115-510 (10/65)-Disney; Annette Funicello front/back photo-c 5 10 15 34 60 85
Miracle of the White Stallions, The 10065-306 (6/63)-Disney
3 6 9 18 28 38
Misadventures of Merlin Jones, The 10115-405 (5/64)-Disney; Annette Funicello photo front/back-c 5 10 15 34 60 85
Moon-Spinners, The 10124-410 (10/64)-Disney; Hayley Mills photo-c
6 12 18 37 66 95
Mutiny on the Bounty 1 (10040-302)(2/63)-Marlon Brando photo-c
3 6 9 21 33 45
Nikki, Wild Dog of the North 10141-412 (12/64)-Disney; reprints 4-Color #1226
3 6 9 16 23 30
Old Yeller 10168-601 (1/66)-Disney; reprints 4-Color #869; photo-c

Movie Love #11 © FF

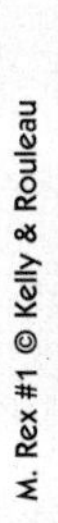
M. Rex #1 © Kelly & Rouleau

Ms. Marvel #14 © MAR

	GD 2.0	VG 4.0	FN 6.0	VF 8.0	VF/NM 9.0	NM- 9.2
	3	6	9	16	23	30
One Hundred & One Dalmations 1 (10247-002) (2/70)-Disney; reprints Four Color #1183	3	6	9	17	26	35
Peter Pan 1 (10086-309)(9/63)-Disney; reprints Four Color #442	3	6	9	20	31	42
Peter Pan 2 (10086-909)(9/69)-Disney; reprints Four Color #442	3	6	9	16	23	30
Peter Pan 1 (3/84)-r/4-Color #442; Whitman pre-pack	2	4	6	11	16	20
P.T. 109 10123-409 (9/64)-John F. Kennedy	4	8	12	28	47	65
Rio Conchos 10143-503(3/65)	3	6	9	21	33	45
Robin Hood 10163-506 (6/65)-Disney; reprints Four Color #413	3	6	9	16	24	32
Shaggy Dog & the Absent-Minded Professor 30032-708 (8/67-Giant, 68 pgs.) Disney; reprints 4-Color #985,1199	5	10	15	30	50	70
Sleeping Beauty 1 (30042-009)(9/70)-Disney; reprints Four Color #973; with pull-out poster (No poster = half price)	6	12	18	37	66	95
Snow White & the Seven Dwarfs 1 (10091-310)(10/63)-Disney; reprints Four Color #382	3	6	9	19	30	40
Snow White & the Seven Dwarfs 10091-709 (9/67)-Disney; reprints Four Color #382	3	6	9	16	23	30
Snow White & the Seven Dwarfs 90091-204 (2/84)-Reprints Four Color #382; Whitman pre-pack	2	4	6	11	16	20
Son of Flubber 1 (10057-304)(4/63)-Disney; sequel to "The Absent-Minded Professor"	3	6	9	21	33	45
Summer Magic 10076-309 (9/63)-Disney; Hayley Mills photo-c; Manning-a	6	12	18	37	66	95
Swiss Family Robinson 10236-904 (4/69)-Disney; reprints Four Color #1156; photo-c	3	6	9	17	26	35
Sword in the Stone, The 30019-402 (2/64-Giant, 68 pgs.)-Disney (see March of Comics #258 & Wart and the Wizard	6	12	18	37	66	95
That Darn Cat 10171-602 (2/66)-Disney; Hayley Mills photo-c	6	12	18	37	66	95
Those Magnificent Men in Their Flying Machines 10162-510 (10/65); photo-c	3	6	9	19	30	40
Three Stooges in Orbit 30016-211 (11/62-Giant, 32 pgs.)-All photos from movie; stiff-photo-c	8	16	24	56	108	160
Tiger Walks, A 10117-406 (6/64)-Disney; Torres?, Tufts-a; photo-c	4	8	12	23	37	50
Toby Tyler 10142-502 (2/65)-Disney; reprints Four Color #1092; photo-c	3	6	9	17	26	35
Treasure Island 1 (10200-703)(3/67)-Disney; reprints Four Color #624; photo-c	3	6	9	16	23	30
20,000 Leagues Under the Sea 1 (10095-312)(12/63)-Disney; reprints Four Color #614	3	6	9	17	26	35
Wonderful Adventures of Pinocchio, The 1 (10089-310)(10/63)-Disney; reprints Four Color #545 (see Wonderful Advs. of...)	3	6	9	20	31	42
Wonderful Adventures of Pinocchio, The 10089-109 (9/71)-Disney; reprints Four Color #545	3	6	9	16	23	30
Wonderful World of the Brothers Grimm 1 (10008-210)(10/62)	4	8	12	27	44	60
X, the Man with the X-Ray Eyes 10083-309 (9/63)-Ray Milland photo on-c	6	12	18	41	76	110
Yellow Submarine 35000-902 (2/69-Giant, 68 pgs.)-With pull-out poster; The Beatles cartoon movie; Paul S. Newman-s	24	48	72	168	372	575
Without poster	10	20	30	64	132	200

MOVIE FABLES
DC Comics: Dec, 1944 (cover only ashcan)

nn-Ashcan comic, not distributed to newsstands, only for in house use. Covers were produced, but not the rest of the book. A copy sold in 2006 for $500.

MOVIE GEMS
DC Comics: Dec, 1944 (cover only ashcan)

nn-Ashcan comic, not distributed to newsstands, only for in house use. Covers were produced, but not the rest of the book. A copy sold in 2006 for $500.

MOVIE LOVE (Also see Personal Love)
Famous Funnies: Feb, 1950 - No. 22, Aug, 1953 (All photo-c)

	GD	VG	FN	VF	VF/NM	NM-
1-Dick Powell, Evelyn Keyes, & Mickey Rooney photo-c	22	44	66	132	216	300
2-Myrna Loy photo-c	14	28	42	80	115	150
3-7,9: 6-Ricardo Montalban photo-c. 9-Gene Tierney, John Lund, Glenn Ford, & Rhonda Fleming photo-c.	14	28	42	76	108	140
8-Williamson/Frazetta-a, 6 pgs.	52	104	156	322	549	775
10-Frazetta-a, 6 pgs.	52	104	156	328	557	785
11,14-16: 14-Janet Leigh photo-c	13	26	39	74	105	135
12-Dean Martin & Jerry Lewis photo-c (12/51, pre-dates Advs. of Dean Martin & Jerry Lewis comic)	24	48	72	142	234	325
13-Ronald Reagan photo-c with 1 pg. biog.	32	64	96	188	307	425
17-Leslie Caron & Ralph Meeker photo-c; 1 pg. Frazetta ad	14	28	42	76	108	140
18-22: 19-John Derek photo-c. 20-Donald O'Connor & Debbie Reynolds photo-c. 21-Paul Henreid & Patricia Medina photo-c. 22-John Payne & Coleen Gray photo-c	13	26	39	72	101	130

NOTE: *Each issue has a full-length movie adaptation with photo covers.*

MOVIE MONSTERS (Magazine)
Atlas/Seaboard: Dec, 1974 - No. 4, Aug, 1975 (B&W; Film, photo & article magazine)

	GD	VG	FN	VF	VF/NM	NM-
1-(84 pages) Planet of the Apes, King Kong, Sindbad & Harryhausen, Christopher Lee Dracula, Star Trek, Werewolf, Creature from the Black Lagoon, Hammer's Mummy, Gorgo, & Exorcist	4	8	12	23	37	50
2-(2/1975) 2001: Planet of the Apes-c; 2001: A Space Odyssey; Doc Savage; Frankenstein; Rodan; One Million Years BC; (lower print run)	4	8	12	23	37	50
3-(4/1975) Phantom of the Opera-c; Wolfman, Godzilla, Boris Karloff, Batman, Forbidden Planet, Jack the Giant Killer	4	8	12	23	37	50
4-(8/1975) Thing, Flash Gordon, Lon Chaney Jr., Lost Worlds, Loch Ness Monster, Day the Earth Stood Still, Star Trek	4	8	12	23	37	50

MOVIE THRILLERS (Movie)
Magazine Enterprises: 1949

	GD	VG	FN	VF	VF/NM	NM-
1-Adaptation of "Rope of Sand" w/Burt Lancaster; Burt Lancaster photo-c	28	56	84	165	270	375

MOVIE TOWN ANIMAL ANTICS (Formerly Animal Antics; becomes Raccoon Kids #52 on)
National Periodical Publ.: No. 24, Jan-Feb, 1950 - No. 51, July-Aug, 1954

	GD	VG	FN	VF	VF/NM	NM-
24-Raccoon Kids continue	12	24	36	67	94	120
25-51	10	20	30	54	72	90

NOTE: ***Sheldon Mayer** a-28-33, 35, 37-41, 43, 44, 47, 49-51.*

MOVIE TUNES COMICS (Formerly Animated...; Frankie No. 4 on)
Marvel Comics (MgPC): No. 3, Fall, 1946

	GD	VG	FN	VF	VF/NM	NM-
3-Super Rabbit, Krazy Krow, Silly Seal & Ziggy Pig	20	40	60	114	182	250

MOWGLI JUNGLE BOOK (Rudyard Kipling's...)
Dell Publ. Co.: No. 487, Aug-Oct, 1953 - No. 620, Apr, 1955

	GD	VG	FN	VF	VF/NM	NM-
Four Color 487 (#1)	6	12	18	42	79	115
Four Color 582 (8/54), 620	5	10	15	33	57	80

MPH
Image Comics: May, 2014 - No. 5, Feb, 2015 ($2.99/$4.99)

	NM-
1-4-($2.99) Mark Millar-s/Duncan Fegredo-a; multiple covers on each	3.00
5-($4.99) Two covers	5.00

MR. (See Mister)

MRS. DEADPOOL AND THE HOWLING COMMANDOS (Secret Wars tie-in)
Marvel Comics: Aug, 2015 - No. 4, Nov, 2015 ($3.99, limited series)

	NM-
1-4-Duggan-s/Espin-a; Dracula and Ghost Deadpool app.	4.00

M. REX
Image Comics: July, 1999 - No. 2, Dec, 1999 ($2.95)

	NM-
Preview ($5.00) B&W pages and sketchbook; Rouleau-a	5.00
1,2-($2.95) 1-Joe Kelly-s/Rouleau-a/Anacleto-c. 2-Rouleau-c	3.00

MS. MARVEL (Also see The Avengers #183)
Marvel Comics Group: Jan, 1977 - No. 23, Apr, 1979

	GD	VG	FN	VF	VF/NM	NM-
1-1st app. Ms. Marvel; Scorpion app. in #1,2	9	18	27	57	111	165
2-Origin	3	6	9	16	23	30
3-10: 5-Vision app. 6-10-(Reg. 30¢-c). 9-1st Deathbird. 10-Last 30¢ issue	2	4	6	11	16	20
6-10-(35¢-c variants, limited dist.)(6/77)	13	26	39	89	195	300
11-15,19-22: 19-Capt. Marvel app. 20-New costume	2	4	6	9	12	15
16-1st brief app. Mystique (Raven Darkholme)	5	10	15	35	63	90
17-Brief app. Mystique, disguised as Nick Fury	4	8	12	27	44	60
18-1st full app. Mystique; Avengers x-over	8	16	24	54	102	150
23-Vance Astro (leader of the Guardians) app.	3	6	9	15	22	28

NOTE: ***Austin** c-14i, 16i, 17i, 22i. **Buscema** a-1-3p; c(p)-2, 4, 6, 7, 15. **Infantino** a-14p, 19p. **Gil Kane** c-8. **Mooney** a-4-8p, 13p, 15-18p. **Starlin** c-12.*

MS. MARVEL (Also see New Avengers)
Marvel Comics: May, 2006 - No. 50, Apr, 2010 ($2.99)

	GD	VG	FN	VF	VF/NM	NM-
1-Cho-c/Reed-s/De La Torre-a; Stilt-Man app.	2	4	6	10	14	18
1-Variant cover by Michael Turner	3	6	9	19	30	40
2-24: 4,5-Dr. Strange app. 6,7-Araña app.						3.00

Ms. Marvel (2014 series) #13 © MAR

Mucha Lucha #1 © WB

Munchkin #24 © SJG

	GD 2.0	VG 4.0	FN 6.0	VF 8.0	VF/NM 9.0	NM- 9.2
25-($3.99) Two covers by Horn and Dodson; Secret Invasion						4.00
26-49: 26-31-Secret Invasion. 34-Spider-Man app. 35-Dark Reign. 37-Carol explodes. 39,40,46,48,49-Takeda-a. 40-Deadpool app. 41-Carol returns. 47-Spider-Man app.						3.00
50-($3.99) Mystique and Captain Marvel app.; Takeda & Oliver-a						4.00
... Annual 1 (11/08, $3.99) Spider-Man app.; Horn-c						4.00
... Special (3/07, $2.99) Reed-s/Camuncoli-a/c						3.00
... Storyteller (1/09, $2.99) Reed-s/Camuncoli-a/c						3.00
... Vol. 1: Best of the Best HC (2006, $19.99) r/#1-5 & Giant-Size Ms. Marvel #1						20.00
... Vol. 1: Best of the Best SC (2007, $14.99) r/#1-5 & Giant-Size Ms. Marvel #1						15.00
... Vol. 2: Civil War HC (2007, $19.99) r/#6-10 & Ms. Marvel Special #1						20.00
... Vol. 2: Civil War SC (2007, $14.99) r/#6-10 & Ms. Marvel Special #1						15.00
... Vol. 3: Operation Lightning Storm HC (2007, $19.99) r/#11-17						20.00
... Vol. 4: Monster Smash HC (2008, $19.99) r/#18-24						20.00

MS. MARVEL (Kamala Khan)(See Captain Marvel [2012-2014] #14&17 for cameo 1st apps.)
Marvel Comics: Apr, 2014 - No. 19, Dec, 2015 ($2.99)

	GD	VG	FN	VF	VF/NM	NM-
1-Intro. Kamala Khan; G. Willow Wilson-s/Adrian Alphona-a; Pichelli-c	3	6	9	16	23	30
2-McKelvie-c	1	3	4	6	8	10
3-7: 3-5-Alphona-a. 3-McKelvie-c. 6,7-Wolverine app.; Wyatt-a						5.00
8-15: 8-11-Alphona-a. 9-Medusa app. 12-Loki app.; Bondoc-a. 13-15-Miyazawa-a						3.00
16-19-Secret Wars tie-ins; Captain Marvel app.; Alphona-a						3.00

MS. MARVEL (Kamala Khan)(Follows events of Secret Wars)
Marvel Comics: Jan, 2016 - Present ($4.99/$3.99)

	GD	VG	FN	VF	VF/NM	NM-
1-($4.99) Wilson-s/Miyazawa & Alphona-a; Chiang-c						5.00
2-11,13-27-($3.99) 2,3-Dr. Faustus app. 4-6-Nico Leon-a. 8-11-Civil War II tie-in.						4.00
12-($4.99) Andolfo-a; back-up Red Widow story						5.00

MS. MYSTIC
Pacific Comics: Oct, 1982 - No. 2, Feb, 1984 ($1.00/$1.50)

1,2: Neal Adams-c/a/script. 1-Origin; intro Erth, Ayre, Fyre & Watr 5.00

MS. MYSTIC
Continuity Comics: 1988 - No. 9, May, 1992 ($2.00)

1-9: 1,2-Reprint Pacific Comics issues 3.00

MS. MYSTIC
Continuity Comics: V2#1, Oct, 1993 - V2#4, Jan, 1994 ($2.50)

V2#1-4: 1-Adams-c(i)/part-i. 2-4-Embossed-c. 2-Nebres part-i. 3-Adams-c(i)/plot. 4-Adams-c(p)/plot 3.00

MS. MYSTIC DEATHWATCH 2000 (Ms. Mystic #3)
Continuity: May, 1993 - No. 3, Aug, 1993 ($2.50)

1-3-Bagged w/card; Adams plots 3.00

MS. TREE QUARTERLY / SPECIAL
DC Comics: Summer, 1990 -No. 10, 1992 ($3.95/$3.50, 84 pgs, mature)

1-10: 1-Midnight story; Batman text story, Grell-a. 2,3-Midnight stories; The Butcher text stories 4.00

NOTE: *Cowan c-2.* ***Grell*** *c-1, 6.* ***Infantino*** *a-8.*

MS. TREE'S THRILLING DETECTIVE ADVENTURES (Ms. Tree #4 on; also see The Best of Ms. Tree)(Baxter paper #4-9) (See Eclipse Magazine #1 for 1st app.)
Eclipse Comics/Aardvark-Vanaheim 10-18/Renegade Press 19 on:
2/83 - #9, 7/84; #10, 8/84 - #18, 5/85; #19, 6/85 - #50, 6/89

	GD	VG	FN	VF	VF/NM	NM-
1						4.00
2-49: 2-Schythe begins. 9-Last Eclipse & last color issue. 10,11-two-tone						3.00
50-Contains flexi-disc ($3.95, 52 pgs.)						4.00
Ms. Tree 3-D 1 (Renegade, 8/85)-With glasses; Mike Mist app.						3.00
Summer Special 1 (8/86)						3.00
1950s Three-Dimensional Crime (7/87, no glasses)-Johnny Dynamite in 3-D						3.00

NOTE: ***Miller*** *pin-up 1-4. Johnny Dynamite-r begin #36 by* ***Morisi.***

MS. VICTORY SPECIAL(Also see Capt. Paragon & Femforce)
Americomics: Jan, 1985 (nd)

1 3.00

MUCHA LUCHA (Based on Kids WB animated TV show)
DC Comics: Jun, 2003 - No. 3, Aug, 2003 ($2.25, limited series)

1-3-Rikochet, Buena Girl and The Flea app. 3.00

MUDMAN
Image Comics: Nov, 2011 - No. 6 ($3.50)

1-6-Paul Grist-s/a 3.50

MUGGSY MOUSE (Also see Tick Tock Tales)
Magazine Enterprises: 1951 - No. 3, 1951; No. 4, 1954 - No. 5, 1954; 1963

	GD	VG	FN	VF	VF/NM	NM-
1(A-1 #33)	13	26	39	74	105	135
2(A-1 #36)-Racist-c	18	36	54	105	165	225
3(A-1 #39), 4(A-1 #95), 5(A-1 #99)	9	18	27	47	61	75
Super Reprint #14(1963), I.W. Reprint #1,2 (nd)	2	4	6	8	11	14

MUGGY-DOO, BOY CAT
Stanhall Publ.: July, 1953 - No. 4, Jan, 1954

	GD	VG	FN	VF	VF/NM	NM-
1-Funny animal; Irving Spector-a	11	22	33	62	86	110
2-4	7	14	21	35	43	50
Super Reprint #12('63), 16('64)	2	4	6	8	11	14

MULAN: REVELATIONS
Dark Horse Comics: Jun, 2015 - No. 4, Nov, 2015 ($3.99)

1-4-Andreyko-s/Kaneshiro-a; Mulan in 2125 Shanghai 4.00

MULLKON EMPIRE (See John Jake's...)

MULTIVERSITY, THE
DC Comics: Oct, 2014 - No. 2, Jun, 2015 ($4.99/$5.99)

	NM-
1-($4.99) Morrison-s/Reis-a; Earth-23 Superman, Capt. Carrot, alternate Earth heroes gather	5.00
2-($5.99) Morrison-s/Reis-a/c	6.00
... 1&2 Director's Cut (2/16, $7.99, squarebound) reprints #1&2 with original B&W pencil art plus Morrison's original story proposals	8.00
...: Guidebook (3/15, $7.99) Legion of Sivanas, Kamandi app.; Multiverse map	8.00
...: Mastermen (4/15, $4.99) Earth-10 Overman & The Freedom Fighters; Jim Lee-a	5.00
...: Pax Americana 1 (1/15, $4.99) Earth-4 Charlton heroes; Quitely-a	5.00
...: Pax Americana Director's Cut 1 (7/15, $9.99) Quitely pencil art and Morrison's script excerpts; polybagged with large folded Multiverse map	10.00
...: The Just 1 (12/14, $4.99) Earth-16 Super-Sons and Justice League offspring; Oliver-a	5.00
...: The Society of Super-Heroes: Conquerors of the Counter-World 1 (11/14, $4.99) Earth-40 Dr. Fate, Green Lantern, Blackhawks, The Atom vs. Vandal Savage; Sprouse-a	5.00
...: Thunderworld Adventures 1 (2/15, $4.99) Earth-5 Shazam Family; Cam Stewart-c	5.00
...: Ultra Comics 1 (5/15, $4.99) Earth-33 Ultra; Mahnke-a	5.00

MUMMY, THE (See Universal Presents... under Dell Giants & Movie Classics)

MUMMY, THE: PALIMPSEST
Titan Comics (Hammer Comics): Dec, 2016 - No. 5, May, 2017 ($3.99)

1-5-Peter Milligan-s/Ronilson Freire-a 4.00

MUMMY, THE: THE RISE AND FALL OF XANGO'S AX (Based on the Brendan Fraser movies)
IDW Publishing: Apr, 2008 - No. 4, July, 2008 ($3.99, limited series)

1-4-Prequel to '08 movie The Mummy: Tomb of the Dragon Emperor; Stephen Mooney-a 4.00

MUNCHKIN
BOOM! Studios (BOOM! Box): Jan, 2015 - No. 25, Jan, 2017 ($3.99)

	NM-
1-24-Short stories of characters from the card game; each issue contains a card	4.00
25-($4.99) Covers by McGinty & Fridolfs	5.00
...: Deck the Dungeons (12/15, $4.99) Katie Cook-s/Mike Luckas-a; 2 covers	5.00

MUNDEN'S BAR ANNUAL
First Comics: Apr, 1988; 1989 ($2.95/$5.95)

	NM-
1-($2.95)-r/from Grimjack; Fish Police story; Ordway-c	3.00
2-($5.95)-Teenage Mutant Ninja Turtles app.	6.00

MUNSTERS, THE (TV)
Gold Key: Jan, 1965 - No. 16, Jan, 1968 (All photo-c)

	GD	VG	FN	VF	VF/NM	NM-
1 (10134-501)	21	42	63	147	324	500
2	10	20	30	68	144	220
3-5	9	18	27	57	111	165
6-16	8	16	24	52	99	145

MUNSTERS, THE (TV)
TV Comics!: Aug, 1997 - No. 4 ($2.95, B&W)

	NM-
1-4-All have photo-c	3.00
1,4-($7.95)-Variant-c	8.00
2-Variant-c w/Beverly Owens as Marilyn	3.00
Special Comic Con Ed. (7/97, $9.95)	10.00

MUPPET... (TV)
BOOM! Studios

	NM-
... King Arthur 1-4 (12/09 - No. 4, 3/10, $2.99) Benjamin & Storck-s/Alvarez-a; 2 covers	3.00
... Peter Pan 1-4 (8/09 - No. 4, 11/09, $2.99) Randolph-s/Mebberson-a; multiple covers	3.00
... Robin Hood 1-4 (4/09 - No. 4, 7/09, $2.99) Beedle-s/Villavert Jr.-a; multiple covers	3.00
... Sherlock Holmes 1-4 (8/10 - No. 4, 11/10, $2.99) Storck-s/Mebberson-a/c	3.00
... Snow White 1-4 (4/10 - No. 4, 7/10, $2.99) Snider & Storck-s/Paroline-a; 2 covers	3.00

MUPPET BABIES, THE (TV)(See Star Comics Magazine)
Marvel Comics (Star Comics)/Marvel #18 on: Aug, 1985 - No. 26, July, 1989
(Children's book)

The Muppet Show #10 © Muppet Studios

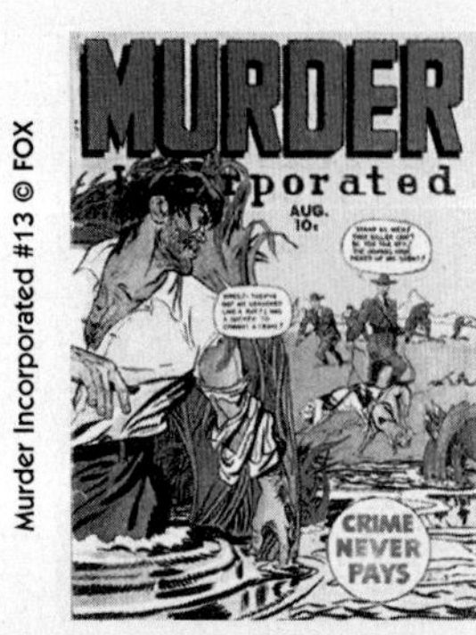

Murder Incorporated #13 © FOX

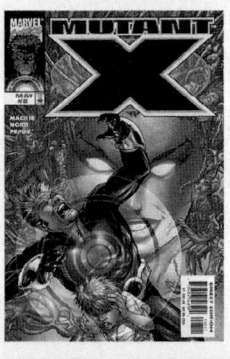

Mutant X #8 © MAR

GD VG FN VF VF/NM NM-
2.0 4.0 6.0 8.0 9.0 9.2

1-26 5.00

MUPPETS (The Four Seasons)
Marvel Worldwide: Sept, 2012 - No. 4, Dec, 2012 ($2.99, limited series)
1-4-Roger Landridge-s/a 3.00

MUPPET SHOW, THE (TV)
BOOM! Studios: Mar, 2009 - No. 4, Jun, 2009 ($2.99, limited series)
1-4-Roger Landridge-s/a; multiple covers 3.00
...: The Treasure of Peg Leg Wilson (7/09 - No. 4, 10/09) 1-4-Landridge-s/a; multiple-c 3.00

MUPPET SHOW COMIC BOOK, THE (TV)
BOOM! Studios: No. 0, Nov, 2009 - No. 11, Oct, 2010 ($2.99)
0-11: 0-3-Roger Landridge-s/a; multiple covers. 0-Paroline-a; Pigs in Space 3.00

MUPPETS TAKE MANHATTAN, THE
Marvel Comics (Star Comics): Nov, 1984 - No. 3, Jan, 1985
1-3-Movie adapt. r-/Marvel Super Special 4.00

MURCIELAGA, SHE-BAT
Heroic Publishing: Jan, 1993 - No. 2, 1993 (B&W)
1-($1.50, 28 pgs.) 3.00
2-($2.95, 36 pgs.)-Coated-c 3.00

MURDER CAN BE FUN
Slave Labor Graphics: Feb, 1996 - No. 12 ($2.95, B&W)
1-12: 1-Dorkin-c. 2-Vasquez-c. 3.00

MURDER INCORPORATED (My Private Life #16 on)
Fox Feature Syndicate: 1/48 - No. 15, 12/49; (2 No.9's); 6/50 - No. 3, 8/51
1 (1st Series); 1,2 have 'For Adults Only' on-c 68 136 204 435 743 1050
2-Electrocution story 47 94 141 296 498 700
3,5-7,9(4/49),10(5/49),11-15 33 66 99 194 317 440
4-Classic lingerie-c 55 110 165 352 601 850
8-Used in **SOTI**, pg. 160 36 72 108 211 343 475
9(3/49)-Possible use in **SOTI**, pg. 145; r/Blue Beetle #56('48)
32 64 96 188 307 425
5(#1, 6/50)(2nd Series)-Formerly My Desire #4; bondage-c.
25 50 75 150 245 340
2(8/50)-Morisi-a 22 44 66 132 216 300
3(8/51)-Used in **POP**, pg. 81; Rico-a; lingerie-c/panels
30 60 90 177 289 400

MURDERLAND
Image Comics: Aug, 2010 - No. 3, Nov, 2010 ($2.99)
1-3-Stephen Scott-s/David Haun-a 3.00

MURDER ME DEAD
El Capitán Books: July, 2000 - No. 9, Oct, 2001 ($2.95/$4.95, B&W)
1-8-David Lapham-s/a 3.00
9-($4.95) 5.00

MURDEROUS GANGSTERS
Avon Per./Realistic No. 3 on: Jul, 1951; No. 2, Dec, 1951 - No. 4, Jun, 1952
1-Pretty Boy Floyd, Leggs Diamond; 1 pg. Wood-a 71 142 213 454 777 1100
2-Baby-Face Nelson; 1 pg. Wood-a; classic painted-c
68 136 204 435 743 1050
3-Painted-c 40 80 120 246 411 575
4- "Murder by Needle" drug story; Mort Lawrence-a; Kinstler-c
42 84 126 265 445 625

MURDER MYSTERIES (Neil Gaiman's...)
Dark Horse Comics: 2002 ($13.95, HC, one-shot)
HC-Adapts Gaiman story; P. Craig Russell-script/art 14.00

MURDER TALES (Magazine)
World Famous Publications: V1#10, Nov, 1970 - V1#11, Jan, 1971 (52 pgs.)
V1#10-One pg. Frazetta ad 5 10 15 31 53 75
11-Guardineer-r; bondage-c 4 8 12 27 44 60

MUSHMOUSE AND PUNKIN PUSS (TV)
Gold Key: September, 1965 (Hanna-Barbera)
1 (10153-509) 7 14 21 49 92 135

MUSIC BOX (Jennifer Love Hewitt's...)
IDW Publishing: Nov, 2009 - No. 5, Apr, 2010 ($3.99, lim. series)
1-5-Anthology; Scott Lobdell-s/art by various. 1-Gaydos-a. 3-Archer-a 4.00

MUSIC MAN, THE (See Movie Classics)

GD VG FN VF VF/NM NM-
2.0 4.0 6.0 8.0 9.0 9.2

MUTANT CHRONICLES (Video game)
Acclaim Comics (Armada): May, 1996 - No. 4, Aug, 1996 ($2.95, lim. series)
1-4: Simon Bisley-c on all, Sourcebook (#5) 3.00

MUTANT EARTH (Stan Winston's...)
Image Comics: April, 2002 - No. 4, Jan, 2003 ($2.95)
1-4-Flip book w/Realm of the Claw 3.00
Trakk...His Adventures in Mutant Earth TPB (2003, $16.95) r/#1-4; Winston interview 17.00

MUTANT MISADVENTURES OF CLOAK AND DAGGER, THE
(Becomes Cloak and Dagger #14 on)
Marvel Comics: Oct, 1988 - No. 19, Aug, 1991 ($1.25/$1.50)
1-8,10-15: 1-X-Factor app. 10-Painted-c. 12-Dr. Doom app. 14-Begin new direction 3.00
9,16-19: 9-(52 pgs.) The Avengers x-over; painted-c. 16-18-Spider-Man x-over. 18-Infinity Gauntlet x-over; Thanos cameo; Ghost Rider app. 19-(52 pgs.) Origin Cloak & Dagger 4.00
NOTE: *Austin a-12i; c(i)-4, 12, 13; scripts-all.* ***Russell*** *a-2i.* ***Williamson*** *a-14i-16i; c-15i.*

MUTANTS & MISFITS
Silverline Comics (Solson): 1987 - No. 3, 1987 ($1.95)
1-3 3.00

MUTANTS VS. ULTRAS
Malibu Comics (Ultraverse): Nov, 1995 ($6.95, one-shot)
1-r/Exiles vs. X-Men, Night Man vs. Wolverine, Prime vs. Hulk 7.00

MUTANT, TEXAS: TALES OF SHERIFF IDA RED (Also see Jingle Belle)
Oni Press: May, 2002 - No. 4, Nov, 2002 ($2.95, B&W, limited series)
1-4-Paul Dini-s/J. Bone-c/a 3.00
TPB (2003, $11.95) r/#1-4; intro. by Joe Lansdale 12.00

MUTANT 2099
Marvel Comics (Marvel Knights): Nov, 2004 ($2.99, one-shot)
1-Kirkman-s/Pat Lee-c 3.00

MUTANT X (See X-Factor)
Marvel Comics: Nov, 1998 - No. 32, June, 2001 ($2.99/$1.99/$2.25)
1-($2.99) Alex Summers with alternate world's X-Men 4.00
2-11,13-19-($1.99): 2-Two covers. 5-Man-Spider-c/app. 3.00
12,25-($2.99): 12-Pin-up gallery by Kaluta, Romita, Byrne 4.00
20-24,26-32: 20-Begin $2.25-c. 28-31-Logan-c/app. 32-Last issue 3.00
Annual '99, '00 (5/99,'00, $3.50) '00-Doran-a(p) 4.00
Annual 2001 ($2.99) Story occurs between #31 & #32; Dracula app. 4.00

MUTANT X (Based on TV show)
Marvel Comics: May, 2002; June, 2002 ($3.50)
...: Dangerous Decisions (6/02) -Kuder-s/Immonen-a 3.50
...: Origin (5/02) -Tischman & Chaykin-s/Ferguson-a 3.50

MUTATIS
Marvel Comics (Epic Comics): 1992 - No. 3, 1992 ($2.25, mini-series)
1-3: Painted-c 3.00

MUTIES
Marvel Comics: Apr, 2002 - No. 6, Sept, 2002 ($2.50)
1-6: 1-Bollars-s/Ferguson-a. 2-Spaziante-a. 3-Haspiel-a. 4-Kanuiga-a 3.00

MUTINY (Stormy Tales of the Seven Seas)
Aragon Magazines: Oct, 1954 - No. 3, Feb, 1955
1 17 34 51 100 158 215
2,3: 2-Capt. Mutiny. 3-Bondage-c 14 28 42 78 112 145

MUTINY ON THE BOUNTY (See Classics Illustrated #100 & Movie Comics)

MUTOPIA X (Also see House of M and related titles)
Marvel Comics: Sept, 2005 - No. 5, Jan, 2006 ($2.99, limited series)
1-5-Medina-a/Hine-s 3.00
House of M: Mutopia X (2006, $13.99, TPB) r/series 14.00

MUTT AND JEFF (See All-American, All-Flash #18, Cicero's Cat, Comic Cavalcade, Famous Feature Stories, The Funnies, Popular & Xmas Comics)
All American/National 1-103(6/58)/Dell 104(10/58)-115 (10-12/59)/ Harvey 116(2/60)-148: Summer, 1939 (nd) - No. 148, Nov, 1965
1(nn)-Lost Wheels 200 400 600 1280 2190 3100
2(nn)-Charging Bull (Summer, 1940, nd; on sale 6/20/40)
87 174 261 553 952 1350
3(nn)-Bucking Broncos (Summer, 1941, nd) 58 116 174 371 636 900
4(Winter, '41), 5(Summer, '42) 54 108 162 343 574 825
6-10: 6-Includes Minute Man Answers the Call 32 64 96 188 307 425
11-20: 20-X-Mas-c 21 42 63 126 206 285

My Experience #19 © FOX

My Friend Irma #4 © MAR

My Greatest Adventure #9 © DC

	GD 2.0	VG 4.0	FN 6.0	VF 8.0	VF/NM 9.0	NM- 9.2
21-30	16	32	48	94	147	200
31-50: 32-X-Mas-c	14	28	42	82	121	160
51-75-Last Fisher issue. 53-Last 52 pgs.	12	24	36	67	94	120
76-99,101-103: 76-Last pre-code issue(1/55)	5	10	15	35	63	90
100	6	12	18	37	66	95
104-115,132-148	5	10	15	30	48	65
116-131-Richie Rich app.	5	10	15	32	51	70
...Jokes 1-3(8/60-61, Harvey)-84 pgs.; Richie Rich in all; Little Dot in #2,3; Lotta in #2	5	10	15	30	48	65
...New Jokes 1-4(10/63-11/65, Harvey)-68 pgs.; Richie Rich in #1-3; Stumbo in #1	4	8	12	24	37	50

NOTE: *Most all issues by* ***Al Smith****. Issues from 1963 on have* ***Fisher*** *reprints. Clarification: early issues signed by Fisher are mostly drawn by Smith.*

MY BROTHERS' KEEPER
Spire Christian Comics (Fleming H. Revell Co.): 1973 (35/49¢, 36 pgs.)

	GD	VG	FN	VF	VF/NM	NM-
nn	2	4	6	13	18	22

MY CONFESSIONS (My Confession #7&8; formerly Western True Crime; A Spectacular Feature Magazine #11)
Fox Feature Syndicate: No. 7, Aug, 1949 - No. 10, Jan-Feb, 1950

	GD	VG	FN	VF	VF/NM	NM-
7-Wood-a (10 pgs.)	61	122	183	390	670	950
8,9: 8-Harrison/Wood-a (19 pgs.). 9-Wood-a	36	72	108	216	351	485
10	21	42	63	126	206	285

MYCROFT HOLMES AND THE APOCALYPSE HANDBOOK
Titan Comics: Sept, 2016 - No. 5, Mar, 2017 ($3.99)

	GD	VG	FN	VF	VF/NM	NM-
1-5-Sherlock Holmes' older brother; Kareem Abdul-Jabbar & Raymond Obstfeld-s						4.00

MY DATE COMICS (Teen-age)
Hillman Periodicals: July, 1947 - V1#4, Jan, 1948 (2nd Romance comic; see Young Romance)

	GD	VG	FN	VF	VF/NM	NM-
1-S&K-c/a	43	86	129	271	461	650
2-4-S&K-c/a; Dan Barry-a	31	62	93	184	300	415

MY DESIRE (Formerly Jo-Jo Comics; becomes Murder, Inc. #5 on)
Fox Feature Syndicate: No. 30, Aug, 1949 - No. 4, April, 1950

	GD	VG	FN	VF	VF/NM	NM-
30 (#1)	28	56	84	165	270	375
31 (#2, 10/49),3(2/50),4	20	40	60	114	182	250
31 (Canadian edition)	12	24	36	69	97	125
32(12/49)-Wood-a	31	62	93	184	300	415

MY DIARY (Becomes My Friend Irma #3 on?)
Marvel Comics (A Lovers Mag.): Dec, 1949 - No. 2, Mar, 1950

	GD	VG	FN	VF	VF/NM	NM-
1,2-Photo-c	21	42	63	122	199	275

MY EXPERIENCE (Formerly All Top; becomes Judy Canova #23 on)
Fox Feature Syndicate: No. 19, Sept, 1949 - No. 22, Mar, 1950

	GD	VG	FN	VF	VF/NM	NM-
19,21: 19-Wood-a. 21-Wood-a(2)	34	68	102	199	325	450
20	18	36	54	107	169	230
22-Wood-a (9 pgs.)	31	62	93	182	296	410

MY FAITH IN FRANKIE
DC Comics (Vertigo): March, 2004 - No. 4, June, 2004 ($2.95, limited series)

	GD	VG	FN	VF	VF/NM	NM-
1-4-Mike Carey-s/Sonny Liew & Marc Hempel-a						3.00
TPB (2004, $6.95, digest-size) r/series in B&W; Dead Boy Detectives preview						7.00

MY FAVORITE MARTIAN (TV)
Gold Key: 1/64; No.2, 7/64 - No. 9, 10/66 (No. 1,3-9 have photo-c)

	GD	VG	FN	VF	VF/NM	NM-
1-Russ Manning-a	10	20	30	69	147	225
2	6	12	18	41	76	110
3-9	5	10	15	35	63	90

MY FRIEND IRMA (Radio/TV) (Formerly My Diary? and/or Western Life Romances?)
Marvel/Atlas Comics (BFP): No. 3, June, 1950 - No. 47, Dec, 1954; No. 48, Feb, 1955

	GD	VG	FN	VF	VF/NM	NM-
3-Dan DeCarlo-a in all; 52 pgs. begin, end ?	54	108	162	343	574	825
4-Kurtzman-a (10 pgs.)	30	60	90	177	289	400
5- "Egghead Doodle" by Kurtzman (4 pgs.)	21	42	63	126	206	285
6,8-10: 9-Paper dolls, 1 pg; Millie app. (5 pgs.)	17	34	51	98	154	210
7-One pg. Kurtzman-a	17	34	51	100	158	215
11-23: 23-One pg. Frazetta-a	14	28	42	81	118	155
24-48: 41,48-Stan Lee & Dan DeCarlo app.	14	28	42	76	108	140

MY GIRL PEARL
Atlas Comics: 4/55 - #4, 10/55; #5, 7/57 - #6, 9/57; #7, 8/60 - #11, ?/61

	GD	VG	FN	VF	VF/NM	NM-
1-Dan DeCarlo-c/a in #1-6	65	130	195	416	708	1000
2	30	60	90	177	289	400
3-6	22	44	66	132	216	300
7-11	10	20	30	64	132	200

MY GREATEST ADVENTURE (Doom Patrol #86 on)
National Periodical Publications: Jan-Feb, 1955 - No. 85, Feb, 1964

	GD 2.0	VG 4.0	FN 6.0	VF 8.0	VF/NM 9.0	NM- 9.2
1-Before CCA	141	282	423	1163	2632	4100
2	50	100	150	400	900	1400
3-5	36	72	108	266	596	925
6-10: 6-Science fiction format begins	29	58	87	209	467	725
11-14: 12-1st S.A. issue	23	46	69	156	348	540
15-17: Kirby-a in all	24	48	72	170	378	585
18-Kirby-c/a	27	54	81	185	415	645
19,23-25	19	38	57	133	297	460
20,21,28-Kirby-a	23	46	69	156	348	540
22-Space Ranger prototype (7-8/58)(see Showcase #15 for Space Ranger debut)	21	42	63	147	324	500
26,27,29,30	15	30	45	105	233	360
31-40	13	26	39	86	188	290
41,42,44-57,59	11	22	33	76	163	250
43-Kirby-a	12	24	36	80	173	265
58,60,61-Toth-a; Last 10¢ issue	11	22	33	77	166	255
62-76,78,79: 79-Promotes "Legion of the Strange" for next issue; renamed Doom Patrol for #80	9	18	27	63	129	195
77-Toth-a; Robotman prototype	10	20	30	65	135	205
80-(6/63)-Intro/origin Doom Patrol and begin series; origin & 1st app. Negative Man, Elasti-Girl & S.A. Robotman	125	250	375	1000	2750	3500
81,85-Toth-a	21	42	63	147	324	500
82-84	19	38	57	133	297	460

NOTE: ***Anderson*** *a-42.* ***Cameron*** *a-24.* ***Colan*** *a-77.* ***Meskin*** *a-25, 26, 32, 39, 45, 50, 56, 57, 61, 64, 70, 73, 74, 76, 79; c-76.* ***Moreira*** *a-11, 12, 15, 17, 20, 23, 25, 27, 37, 40-43, 46, 48, 55-57, 59, 60, 62-65, 67, 69, 70; c-1-4, 7-10.* ***Roussos*** *c/a-71-73.* ***Wildey*** *a-32.*

MY GREATEST ADVENTURE (Also see 2011 Weird Worlds series)
DC Comics: Dec, 2011 - No. 6, May, 2012 ($3.99, limited series)

	GD	VG	FN	VF	VF/NM	NM-
1-6-Short stories of Tanga, Robotman, and Garbage Man; Lopresti-s/a, Maguire-s/a						4.00

MY GREAT LOVE (Becomes Will Rogers Western #5)
Fox Feature Syndicate: Oct, 1949 - No. 4, Apr, 1950

	GD	VG	FN	VF	VF/NM	NM-
1	26	52	78	154	252	350
2-4	15	30	45	86	133	180

MY INTIMATE AFFAIR (Inside Crime #3)
Fox Feature Syndicate: Mar, 1950 - No. 2, May, 1950

	GD	VG	FN	VF	VF/NM	NM-
1	30	60	90	177	289	400
2	15	30	45	88	137	185

MY LIFE (Formerly Meet Corliss Archer)
Fox Feature Syndicate: No. 4, Sept, 1948 - No. 15, July, 1950

	GD	VG	FN	VF	VF/NM	NM-
4-Used in **SOTI**, pg. 39; Kamen/Feldstein-a	53	106	159	334	567	800
5-Kamen-a	34	68	102	199	325	450
6-Kamen/Feldstein-a	37	74	111	222	361	500
7-Wood-a; wash cover	39	78	117	231	378	525
8,9,11-15	19	38	57	111	176	240
10-Wood-a	29	58	87	172	281	390

MY LITTLE MARGIE (TV)
Charlton Comics: July, 1954 - No. 54, Nov, 1964

	GD	VG	FN	VF	VF/NM	NM-
1-Photo front/back-c	37	74	111	222	361	500
2-Photo front/back-c	19	38	57	109	172	235
3-7,10	12	24	36	69	97	125
8,9-Infinity-c	13	26	39	72	101	130
11-14: Part-photo-c (#13, 8/56). 14-UFO cover	10	20	30	58	79	100
15-19	10	20	30	54	72	90
20-(25¢, 100 pg. issue)	15	30	45	86	133	180
21-40: 40-Last 10¢ issue	5	10	15	30	50	70
41-53	4	8	12	27	44	60
54-(11/64) Beatles on cover; lead story spoofs the Beatle haircut craze of the 1960's; Beatles app. (scarce)	17	34	51	117	259	400

NOTE: *Doll cut-outs in 32, 33, 40, 45, 50.*

MY LITTLE MARGIE'S BOY FRIENDS (TV) (Freddy V2#12 on)
Charlton Comics: Aug, 1955 - No. 11, Apr?, 1958

	GD	VG	FN	VF	VF/NM	NM-
1-Has several Archie swipes	15	30	45	88	137	185
2	10	20	30	54	72	90
3-11	9	18	27	47	61	75

MY LITTLE MARGIE'S FASHIONS (TV)
Charlton Comics: Feb, 1959 - No. 5, Nov, 1959

	GD	VG	FN	VF	VF/NM	NM-
1	18	36	54	105	165	225
2-5	9	18	27	50	65	80

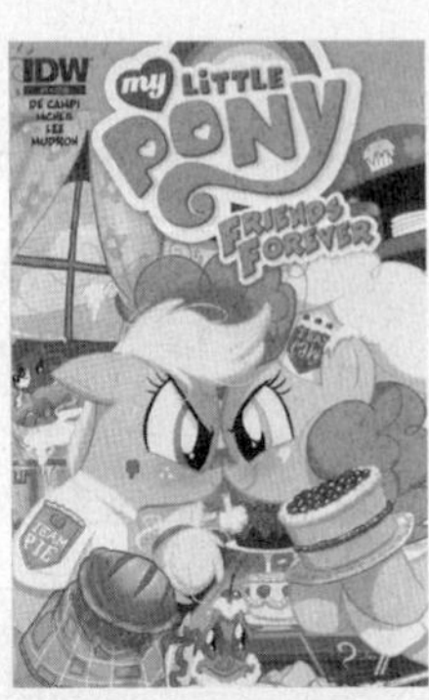

My Little Pony: Friends Forever #1 © Hasbro

My Love Secret #26 © FOX

My Only Love #9 © CC

MY LITTLE PHONY: A BRONY ADVENTURE
Dynamite Entertainment: 2014 ($5.99, one-shot)

	GD 2.0	VG 4.0	FN 6.0	VF 8.0	VF/NM 9.0	NM- 9.2
1-My Little Pony fandom parody; Moreci & Seeley-a/Haeser & Baal-a; 2 covers						6.00

MY LITTLE PONY
IDW Publishing

	GD 2.0	VG 4.0	FN 6.0	VF 8.0	VF/NM 9.0	NM- 9.2
... Annual #1: Equestria Girls (10/13, $7.99) Price & Fleecs-a; multiple covers						8.00
... Annual 2014 (9/14, $7.99) Anderson-s/Bates-a; two covers						8.00
... Annual 2017 (2/17, $7.99) Short stories by Whitley, Rice, Price & others; two covers						8.00
... Art Gallery (11/13, $3.99) Pin-ups by Sara Richard & others						4.00
... Cover Gallery (8/13, $3.99) Gallery of regular and variant covers						4.00
... Halloween Comicfest 2016 (10/16, giveaway) reprints Friends Forever #4						3.00
... Holiday Special (12/15, $3.99) Cook-s/Hickey, Garbowska, Price, Cook-a; 3 covers						4.00
... Holiday Special 2017 (12/17, $4.99) Asmus-s/Hickey-a; 3 covers						5.00

MY LITTLE PONY: FIENDS FOREVER
IDW Publishing: Apr, 2015 - No. 5, May, 2015 ($3.99, weekly mini-series)

	GD 2.0	VG 4.0	FN 6.0	VF 8.0	VF/NM 9.0	NM- 9.2
1-5-Spotlight on Equestria's villains. 1-Whitley-s/Hickey-a. 3-Garbowska-a						4.00

MY LITTLE PONY: FRIENDS FOREVER
IDW Publishing: Jan, 2014 - No. 38, Mar, 2017 ($3.99)

	GD 2.0	VG 4.0	FN 6.0	VF 8.0	VF/NM 9.0	NM- 9.2
1-38: 1-de Campi-s/McNeil-a; multiple covers. 3,6,10,13,14,21,27,30,34,37-Garbowska-a. 8-Katie Cook-s						4.00
... - Halloween Fest 2014 (10/14, giveaway) reprints #2						3.00

MY LITTLE PONY: FRIENDSHIP IS MAGIC
IDW Publishing: Nov, 2012 - Present ($3.99)

	GD 2.0	VG 4.0	FN 6.0	VF 8.0	VF/NM 9.0	NM- 9.2
1-Katie Cook-s/Andy Price-a; 7 covers						5.00
1-Subscription variant cover by Jill Thompson						5.00
2-49,51-63-Multiple covers on each. 18,19-Interlocking covers						4.00
50-($5.99) Anderson-s/Price-a; Whitley-s/Fosgitt-a						6.00
... #1 Greatest Hits (8/16, $1.00) reprints #1						3.00
... #1 Hundred Penny Press (2/14, $1.00) reprints #1						3.00
... Deviations 1 (3/17, $4.99) Cook-s/Garbowska-a; 3 covers; Prince Blueblood app.						5.00

MY LITTLE PONY: LEGENDS OF MAGIC
IDW Publishing: Apr, 2017 - Present ($3.99)

	GD 2.0	VG 4.0	FN 6.0	VF 8.0	VF/NM 9.0	NM- 9.2
1-11: 1-6-Whitley-s/Hickey-a. 7-11-Fleecs-a						4.00

MY LITTLE PONY MICRO-SERIES
IDW Publishing: Feb, 2013 - No. 10, Dec, 2013 ($3.99)

	GD 2.0	VG 4.0	FN 6.0	VF 8.0	VF/NM 9.0	NM- 9.2
1-Twilight Sparkle - Zahler-s/a						5.00
2-10: 2-Rainbow Dash. 3-Rarity. 4-Fluttershy						4.00

MY LITTLE PONY: THE MOVIE PREQUEL
IDW Publishing: Jun, 2017 - No. 4, Sept, 2017 ($3.99, limited series)

	GD 2.0	VG 4.0	FN 6.0	VF 8.0	VF/NM 9.0	NM- 9.2
1-4-Ted Anderson-s/Andy Price-a; The Storm King app.						4.00

MY LOVE (Becomes Two Gun Western #5 (11/50) on?)
Marvel Comics (CLDS): July, 1949 - No. 4, Apr, 1950 (All photo-c)

	GD 2.0	VG 4.0	FN 6.0	VF 8.0	VF/NM 9.0	NM- 9.2
1	22	44	66	132	216	300
2,3	15	30	45	88	137	185
4-Bettie Page photo-c (see Cupid #2)	50	100	150	315	533	750

MY LOVE
Marvel Comics Group: Sept, 1969 - No. 39, Mar, 1976

	GD 2.0	VG 4.0	FN 6.0	VF 8.0	VF/NM 9.0	NM- 9.2
1	9	18	27	59	117	175
2-9: 4-6-Colan-a	5	10	15	33	57	80
10-Williamson-r/My Own Romance #71; Kirby-a	5	10	15	34	60	85
11-13,15-19	4	8	12	27	44	60
14-(52 pgs.)-Woodstock-c/sty; Morrow-c/a; Kirby/Colletta-r	8	16	24	54	102	150
20-Starlin-a	4	8	12	28	47	65
21,22,24-27,29-38: 38-Reprints	4	8	12	23	37	50
23-Steranko-r/Our Love Story #5	4	8	12	27	44	60
28-Kirby-a	4	8	12	25	40	55
39-Last issue; reprints	4	8	12	27	44	60
Special 1 (12/71)(52 pgs.)	5	10	15	34	60	85

NOTE: ***John Buscema** a-1-7, 10, 18-21, 22r(2), 24r, 25r, 29r, 34r, 36r, 37r, Spec. (r)(4); c-13, 15, 25, 27, Spec. **Colan** a-4, 5, 6, 8, 9, 16, 17, 20, 21, 22, 24r, 27r, 30r, 35r, 39r. **Colan/Everett** a-13, 15, 16, 27(r/#13). **Kirby** a-(r)-10, 14, 26, 28. **Romita** a-1-3, 19, 20, 25, 34, 38; c-1-3, 15.*

MY LOVE AFFAIR (March of Crime #7 on)
Fox Feature Syndicate: July, 1949 - No. 6, May, 1950

	GD 2.0	VG 4.0	FN 6.0	VF 8.0	VF/NM 9.0	NM- 9.2
1	30	60	90	177	289	400
2	15	30	45	88	137	185
3-6-Wood-a. 5-(3/50)-Becomes Love Stories #6	28	56	84	165	270	375

MY LOVE LIFE (Formerly Zegra)
Fox Feature Synd.: No. 6, June, 1949 - No. 13, Aug, 1950; No. 13, Sept, 1951

	GD 2.0	VG 4.0	FN 6.0	VF 8.0	VF/NM 9.0	NM- 9.2
6-Kamenish-a	25	50	75	150	245	340
7-13	15	30	45	88	137	185
13 (9/51)(Formerly My Story #12)	15	30	45	83	124	165

MY LOVE MEMOIRS (Formerly Women Outlaws; Hunted #13 on)
Fox Feature Syndicate: No. 9, Nov, 1949 - No. 12, May, 1950

	GD 2.0	VG 4.0	FN 6.0	VF 8.0	VF/NM 9.0	NM- 9.2
9,11,12-Wood-a	27	54	81	162	266	370
10	15	30	45	86	133	180

MY LOVE SECRET (Formerly Phantom Lady; Animal Crackers #31)
Fox Feature Syndicate/M. S. Distr.: No. 24, June, 1949 - No. 30, June, 1950; No. 53, 1954

	GD 2.0	VG 4.0	FN 6.0	VF 8.0	VF/NM 9.0	NM- 9.2
24-Kamen/Feldstein-a	29	58	87	170	278	385
25-Possible caricature of Wood on-c?	18	36	54	107	169	230
26,28-Wood-a	27	54	81	162	266	370
27,29,30: 30-Photo-c	16	32	48	96	151	205
53-(Reprint, M.S. Distr.) 1954? nd given; formerly Western Thrillers; becomes Crimes by Women #54; photo-c	11	22	33	60	83	105

MY LOVE STORY (Hoot Gibson Western #5 on)
Fox Feature Syndicate: Sept, 1949 - No. 4, Mar, 1950

	GD 2.0	VG 4.0	FN 6.0	VF 8.0	VF/NM 9.0	NM- 9.2
1	25	50	75	150	245	340
2	15	30	45	86	133	180
3,4-Wood-a	27	54	81	162	266	370

MY LOVE STORY
Atlas Comics (GPS): April, 1956 - No. 9, Aug, 1957

	GD 2.0	VG 4.0	FN 6.0	VF 8.0	VF/NM 9.0	NM- 9.2
1	18	36	54	107	169	230
2	12	24	36	67	94	120
3,7: Matt Baker-a. 7-Toth-a	15	30	45	84	127	170
4-6,8,9	11	22	33	62	86	110

NOTE: ***Brewster** a-3. **Colletta** a-1(2), 3, 4(2), 5; c-3.*

MYLO XYLOTO COMICS
Bongo Comics: 2013 - No. 6, 2013 ($3.99, limited series)

	GD 2.0	VG 4.0	FN 6.0	VF 8.0	VF/NM 9.0	NM- 9.2
1-6-Mark Osborne & Coldplay-s/Fuentes-a						4.00

MY NAME IS BRUCE
Dark Horse Comics: Sept, 2008 ($3.50, one-shot)

	GD 2.0	VG 4.0	FN 6.0	VF 8.0	VF/NM 9.0	NM- 9.2
nn-Adaptation of the Bruce Campbell movie; Cliff Richards-a/Bart Sears-c						3.50

MY NAME IS HOLOCAUST
DC Comics: May, 1995 - No. 5, Sept, 1995 ($2.50, limited series)

	GD 2.0	VG 4.0	FN 6.0	VF 8.0	VF/NM 9.0	NM- 9.2
1-5						3.00

MY ONLY LOVE
Charlton Comics: July, 1975 - No. 9, Nov, 1976

	GD 2.0	VG 4.0	FN 6.0	VF 8.0	VF/NM 9.0	NM- 9.2
1	3	6	9	14	19	24
2,4-9	2	4	6	9	13	16
3-Toth-a	2	4	6	11	16	20

MY OWN ROMANCE (Formerly My Romance; Teen-Age Romance #77 on)
Marvel/Atlas (MjPC/RCM No. 4-59/ZPC No. 60-76): No. 4, Mar, 1949 - No. 76, July, 1960

	GD 2.0	VG 4.0	FN 6.0	VF 8.0	VF/NM 9.0	NM- 9.2
4-Photo-c	22	44	66	132	216	300
5-10: 5,6,8-10-Photo-c	14	28	42	82	121	160
11-20: 14-Powell-a	14	28	42	78	112	145
21-42,55: 42-Last precode (2/55). 55-Toth-a	13	26	39	74	105	135
43-54,56-60	7	14	21	44	82	120
61-70,72,73,75,76	6	12	18	41	76	110
71-Williamson-a	7	14	21	46	86	125
74-Kirby-a	7	14	21	46	86	125

NOTE: ***Brewster** a-59. **Colletta** a-45(2), 48, 50, 55, 57(2), 59; c-58i, 59, 61. **Everett** a-25; c-58p. **Kirby** c-71, 75, 76. **Maneely** c-18. **Morisi** a-18. **Orlando** a-61. **Romita** a-36. **Tuska** a-10.*

MY PAL DIZZY (See Comic Books, Series I)

MY PAST (...Confessions) (Formerly Western Thrillers)
Fox Feature Syndicate: No. 7, Aug, 1949 - No. 11, Apr, 1950 (Crimes Inc. #12)

	GD 2.0	VG 4.0	FN 6.0	VF 8.0	VF/NM 9.0	NM- 9.2
7	27	54	81	58	259	360
8-10	15	30	45	86	133	180
11-Wood-a	27	54	81	162	266	370

MY PERSONAL PROBLEM
Ajax/Farrell/Steinway Comic: 11/55; No. 2, 2/56; No. 3, 9/56 - No. 4, 11/56; 10/57 - No. 3, 5/58

	GD 2.0	VG 4.0	FN 6.0	VF 8.0	VF/NM 9.0	NM- 9.2
1	11	22	33	64	90	115
2-4	8	16	24	42	54	65
1-3('57-'58)-Steinway	7	14	21	35	43	50

MY PRIVATE LIFE (Formerly Murder, Inc.; becomes Pedro #18)

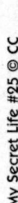

My Secret Life #25 © CC

Mysteries #4 © SUPR

Mysterious Adventures #2 © Story

	GD 2.0	VG 4.0	FN 6.0	VF 8.0	VF/NM 9.0	NM- 9.2

Fox Feature Syndicate: No. 16, Feb, 1950 - No. 17, April, 1950

16,17	18	36	54	105	165	225

MYRA NORTH (See The Comics, Crackajack Funnies & Red Ryder)
Dell Publishing Co.: No. 3, Jan, 1940

Four Color 3	103	206	309	659	1130	1600

MY REAL LOVE
Standard Comics: No. 5, June, 1952 (Photo-c)

5-Toth-a, 3 pgs.; Tuska, Cardy, Vern Greene-a	15	30	45	88	137	185

MY ROMANCE (Becomes My Own Romance #4 on)
Marvel Comics (RCM): Sept, 1948 - No. 3, Jan, 1949

1	25	50	75	150	245	340
2,3: 2-Anti-Wertham editorial (11/48)	15	30	45	90	140	190

MY ROMANTIC ADVENTURES (Formerly Romantic Adventures)
American Comics Group: No. 68, 8/56 - No. 115, 12/60; No. 116, 7/61 - No. 138, 3/64

68	9	18	27	47	61	75
69-85	7	14	21	35	43	50
86-Three pg. Williamson-a (2/58)	8	16	24	44	57	70
87-100	3	6	9	19	30	40
101-138	3	6	9	16	23	30

NOTE: ***Whitney*** *art in most issues.*

MY SECRET (Becomes Our Secret #4 on)
Superior Comics, Ltd.: Aug, 1949 - No. 3, Oct, 1949

1	20	40	60	120	195	270
2,3	15	30	45	85	130	175

MY SECRET AFFAIR (Becomes Martin Kane #4)
Hero Book (Fox Feature Syndicate): Dec, 1949 - No. 3, April, 1950

1-Harrison/Wood-a (10 pgs.)	36	72	108	211	343	475
2,3-Wood-a	29	58	87	172	281	390

MY SECRET CONFESSION
Sterling Comics: September, 1955

1-Sekowsky-a	11	22	33	62	86	110

MY SECRET LIFE (Formerly Western Outlaws; Romeo Tubbs #26 on)
Fox Feature Syndicate: No. 22, July, 1949 - No. 27, July, 1950; No. 27, 9/51

22	21	42	63	122	199	275
23,26-Wood-a, 6 pgs.	29	58	87	170	278	385
24,25,27	16	32	48	92	144	195
27 (9/51)	15	30	45	83	124	165

NOTE: *The title was changed to Romeo Tubbs after #25 even though #26 & 27 did come out.*

MY SECRET LIFE (Formerly Young Lovers; Sue & Sally Smith #48)
Charlton Comics: No. 19, Aug, 1957 - No. 47, Sept, 1962

19	4	8	12	25	40	55
20-35	3	6	9	16	23	30
36-47: 44-Last 10¢ issue. 47-1st app. Sue & Sally Smith	3	6	9	14	20	26

MY SECRET MARRIAGE
Superior Comics, Ltd.: May, 1953 - No. 24, July, 1956 (Canadian)

1	20	40	60	114	182	250
2	11	22	33	64	90	115
3-24	10	20	30	58	79	100
I.W. Reprint #9	2	4	6	8	11	14

NOTE: *Many issues contain* ***Kamen-ish*** *art.*

MY SECRET ROMANCE (Becomes A Star Presentation #3)
Hero Book (Fox Feature Syndicate): Jan, 1950 - No. 2, March, 1950

1	24	48	72	142	234	325
2-Wood-a	28	56	84	165	270	375

MY SECRETS (Magazine) (Also see Gothic Romances)
Atlas/Seaboard: Feb, 1975 (B&W, 68 pgs.)

Vol. 1 #1	15	30	45	105	233	360

MY SECRET STORY (Formerly Captain Kidd #25; Sabu #30 on)
Fox Feature Syndicate: No. 26, Oct, 1949 - No. 29, April, 1950

26	20	40	60	120	195	270
27-29	15	30	45	86	133	180

MYSPACE DARK HORSE PRESENTS
Dark Horse Books: Sept, 2008 - Feb, 2011 ($19.95/$19.99, TPB)

Vol. 1 - Short stories previously appearing on Dark Horse's MySpace.com webpage; s/a by various incl. Whedon, Bá, Bagge, Mignola, Moon, Nord, Trimpe, Warren, Way	20.00
Vol. 2 - Collects stories from online #7-12; s/a by Way, Niles, Dorkin, Hotz & others	20.00
Vol. 3 - Collects stories from online #13-19; s/a by Mignola, Cloonan & others	20.00
Vol. 4 - Collects stories from online #20-24; s/a by Whedon, Chen & others	20.00
Vol. 5 - Collects stories from online #25-30; s/a by Thompson, Aragonés & others	20.00
Vol. 6 - Collects stories from online #31-36; s/a by Sakai, Dorkin & others	20.00

MYSTERIES (...Weird & Strange)
Superior/Dynamic Publ. (Randall Publ. Ltd.): May, 1953 - No. 11, Jan, 1955

1-All horror stories	53	106	159	334	567	800
2-A-Bomb blast story	34	68	102	199	325	450
3-11: 10-Kamenish-c/a reprinted from Strange Mysteries #2; cover is from a panel in Strange Mysteries #2	30	60	90	177	289	400

MYSTERIES IN SPACE (See Fireside Book Series)

MYSTERIES OF SCOTLAND YARD (Also see A-1 Comics)
Magazine Enterprises: No. 121, 1954 (one shot)

A-1 121-Reprinted from Manhunt (5 stories)	16	32	48	94	147	200

MYSTERIES OF UNEXPLORED WORLDS (See Blue Bird)(Becomes Son of Vulcan V2#49 on)
Charlton Comics: Aug, 1956; No. 2, Jan, 1957 - No. 48, Sept, 1965

1	39	78	117	231	378	525
2-No Ditko	18	36	54	105	165	225
3,4,8,9 Ditko-a. 3-Diko c/a (4). 4-Ditko c/a (2).	31	62	93	184	300	415
5,6,10,11: 5,6-Ditko-c/a (all). 10-Ditko-c/a(4). 11-Ditko-c/a(3); signed J. Kotdi	32	64	96	192	314	435
7-(2/58, 68 pgs.) 4 stories w/Ditko-a	36	72	108	211	343	475
12-Ditko sty (3); Baker story "The Charm Bracelet"	31	62	93	182	296	410
13-18,20	10	20	30	58	79	100
19,21-24,26-Ditko-a	23	46	69	136	223	310
25,27-30: 28-Communist A-bomb story w/Khrushchev	5	10	15	31	53	75
31-45: 43-Atomic bomb panel	4	8	12	25	40	55
46(5/65)-Son of Vulcan begins (origin/1st app.)	4	8	12	27	44	60
47,48	4	8	12	21	33	45

NOTE: ***Ditko*** *c-3-6, 10, 11, 19, 21-24. Covers to #19, 21-24 reprint story panels.*

MYSTERIOUS ADVENTURES
Story Comics: Mar, 1951 - No. 24, Mar, 1955; No. 25, Aug, 1955

1-All horror stories	97	194	291	621	1061	1500
2-(6/51)	52	104	156	328	552	775
3,4,6,10	48	96	144	302	514	725
5-Severed heads/bondage-c	54	108	162	343	574	825
7-Dagger in eye panel; dismemberment stories	58	116	174	371	636	900
8-Eyeball story	60	120	180	381	653	925
9-Extreme violence (8/52)	54	108	162	343	574	825
11-(12/52)-Used in **SOTI**, pg. 84	52	104	156	328	552	775
12,14: 14-E.C. Old Witch swipe	48	96	144	302	514	725
13-Classic skull-c	100	200	300	635	1093	1550
15-21: 18-Used in Senate Investigative report, pgs. 5,6; E.C. swipe/TFTC #35; The Coffin-Keeper & Corpse (hosts). 20-Electric chair-c; used by Wertham in the Senate hearings. 21-Bondage/beheading-c; extreme violence	77	154	231	493	847	1200
22- "Cinderella" parody	52	104	156	328	552	775
23-Disbrow-a (6 pgs.); E.C. swipe "The Mystery Keeper's Tale" (host) and "Mother Ghoul's Nursery Tale"	47	94	141	296	498	700
24,25	39	78	117	240	395	550

NOTE: ***Tothish*** *art by* ***Ross Andru****-#22, 23.* ***Bache*** *a-8.* ***Cameron*** *a-5-7.* ***Harrison*** *a-12.* ***Hollingsworth*** *a-3-8, 12.* ***Schaffenberger*** *a-24, 25.* ***Wildey*** *a-15, 17.*

MYSTERIOUS ISLAND (Also see Classic Comics #34)
Dell Publishing Co.: No. 1213, July-Sept, 1961

Four Color 1213-Movie, photo-c	7	14	21	49	92	135

MYSTERIOUS ISLE
Dell Publishing Co.: Nov-Jan, 1963/64 (Jules Verne)

1-Painted-c	3	6	9	21	33	45

MYSTERIOUS RIDER, THE (See Zane Grey, 4-Color 301)

MYSTERIOUS STORIES (Formerly Horror From the Tomb #1)
Premier Magazines: No. 2, Dec-Jan, 1954-1955 - No. 7, Dec, 1955

2-Woodbridge-c; last pre-code issue	53	106	159	334	567	800
3-Woodbridge-c/a	39	78	117	231	378	525
4-7: 5-Cinderella parody. 6-Woodbridge-c	36	72	108	211	343	475

NOTE: ***Hollingsworth*** *a-2, 4.*

MYSTERIOUS STRANGER

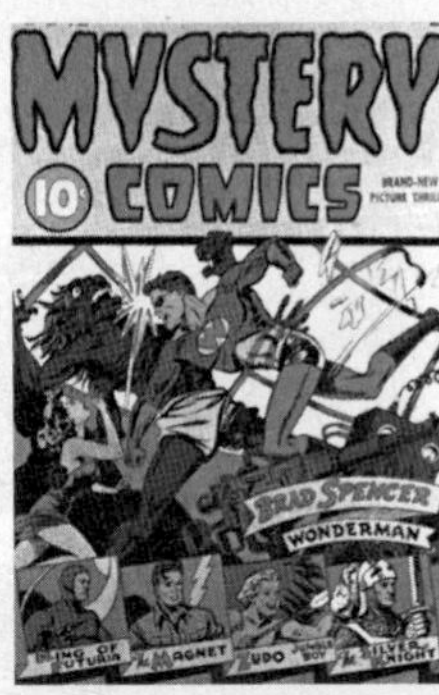

Mystery Comics #7 © WHW

Mystery in Space #24 © DC

Mystery Men Comics #2 © FOX

	GD	VG	FN	VF	VF/NM	NM-
	2.0	4.0	6.0	8.0	9.0	9.2

GD VG FN VF VF/NM NM- 2.0 4.0 6.0 8.0 9.0 9.2

DC Comics: Aug/Sept. 1952

nn-Ashcan comic, not distributed to newsstands, only for in-house use. Cover art is All Star Western #60 with interior being Sensation Comics #100. A FN/VF copy sold for $2,357.50 in 2002.

MYSTERIOUS SUSPENSE (Also see Blue Beetle #1 (1967))
Charlton Comics: Oct, 1968 (12¢)

1-Return of the Question by Ditko (c/a) 6 12 18 42 79 115

MYSTERIOUS TRAVELER (See Tales of the...)

MYSTERIOUS TRAVELER COMICS (Radio)
Trans-World Publications: Nov, 1948

1-Powell-c/a(2); Poe adaptation, "Tell Tale Heart" 68 136 204 435 743 1050

MYSTERIUS
DC Comics (WildStorm): Mar, 2009 - No. 6, Aug, 2009 ($2.99, limited series)

1-6-Jeff Parker-a/Tom Fowler-a 3.00
TPB (2010, $17.99) r/#1-6 18.00

MYSTERY COMICS
William H. Wise & Co.: 1944 - No. 4, 1944 (No months given)

1-The Magnet, The Silver Knight, Brad Spencer, Wonderman, Dick Devins, King of Futuria, & Zudo the Jungle Boy begin (all 1st app.); Schomburg-c on all
174 348 522 1114 1907 2700
2-Bondage-c 110 220 330 704 1202 1700
3,4: 3-Lance Lewis, Space Detective begins (1st app.); Robot-c. 4-(V2#1 inside); KKK-c
103 206 309 659 1130 1600

MYSTERY COMICS DIGEST
Gold Key/Whitman?: Mar, 1972 - No. 26, Oct, 1975

1-Ripley's Believe It or Not; reprint of Ripley's #1 origin Ra-Ka-Tep the Mummy; Wood-a
4 8 12 26 41 55
2-9: 2-Boris Karloff Tales of Mystery; Wood-a; 1st app. Werewolf Count Wulfstein. 3-Twilight Zone (TV); Crandall, Toth & George Evans-a; 1st app. Tragg & Simbar the Lion Lord; (2) Crandall/Frazetta-r/Twilight Zone #1 4-Ripley's Believe It or Not; 1st app. Baron Tibor, the Vampire. 5-Boris Karloff Tales of Mystery; 1st app. Dr. Spektor. 6-Twilight Zone (TV); 1st app. U.S. Marshal Reid & Sir Duane; Evans-r. 7-Ripley's Believe It or Not; origin The Lurker in the Swamp; 1st app. Duroc. 8-Boris Karloff Tales of Mystery; McWilliams-r; Orlando-r. 9-Twilight Zone (TV); Williamson, Crandall, McWilliams-a; 2nd Tragg app.;Torres, Evans, Heck/Tuska-r 3 6 9 20 30 40
10-26: 10,13-Ripley's Believe It or Not: 13-Orlando-r. 11,14-Boris Karloff Tales of Mystery. 14-1st app. Xorkon. 12,15-Twilight Zone (TV). 16,19,22,25-Ripley's Believe It or Not. 17-Boris Karloff Tales of Mystery; Williamson-r; Orlando-r. 18,21,24-Twilight Zone (TV). 20,23,26-Boris Karloff Tales of Mystery 3 6 9 16 23 30
NOTE: *Dr. Spektor app.-#5, 10-12, 21. Durak app.-#15. Duroc app.-#14 (later called Durak). King George 1st app.-#8.*

MYSTERY GIRL
Dark Horse Comics: Dec, 2015 - No. 4, Mar, 2016 ($3.99)

1-4-Tobin-s/Albuquerque-a 4.00

MYSTERY IN SPACE (Also see Fireside Book Series and Pulp Fiction Library: ...)
National Periodical Pub.: 4-5/51 - No. 110, 9/66; No. 111, 9/80 - No. 117, 3/81 (#1-3: 52 pgs.)

1-Frazetta-a, 8 pgs.; Knights of the Galaxy begins, ends #8
252 504 756 2079 4690 7300
2 89 178 267 712 1606 2500
3 63 126 187 504 1127 1750
4,5 50 100 150 400 900 1400
6-10: 7-Toth-a 40 80 120 296 673 1050
11-15 33 66 99 240 538 835
16-18,20-25: Interplanetary Insurance feature by Infantino in all. 21-1st app. Space Cabbie. 24-Last pre-code issue 30 60 90 211 473 735
19-Virgil Finlay-a 31 62 93 225 505 785
26-40: 26-Space Cabbie feature begins. 34-1st S.A. issue. 36,40-Grey-tone-c
23 46 69 164 362 560
41-52: 45,46-Grey-tone-c. 47-Space Cabbie ends 17 34 51 119 265 410
53-Adam Strange begins (8/59, 10pg. sty); robot-c 155 310 465 1279 2890 4500
54 43 86 129 318 722 1125
55-Grey tone-c 41 82 123 304 690 1075
56-60: 59-Kane/Anderson-a 23 46 69 164 362 560
61-71: 61-1st app. Adam Strange foe Ulthoon. 62-1st app. A.S. foe Mortan. 63-Origin Vandor. 66-Star Rovers begin (1st app.). 68-1st app. Dust Devils (6/61). 69-1st Mailbag. 70-2nd app. Dust Devils. 71-Last 10¢ issue 18 36 54 128 284 440
72-74,76-80 13 26 39 86 188 290
75-JLA x-over in Adam Strange (5/62)(sequel to J.L.A. #3, 2nd app. of Kanjar Ro)
22 44 66 152 336 520
81-86 10 20 30 64 132 200
87-(11/63)-Adam Strange/Hawkman double feat begins; 3rd Hawkman tryout series
15 30 45 100 220 340
88-Adam Strange & Hawkman stories 13 26 39 89 195 300
89-Adam Strange & Hawkman stories 13 26 39 86 188 290
90-Book-length Adam Strange & Hawkman story; 1st team-up (3/64); Hawkman moves to own title next month; classic-c 15 30 45 100 220 340
91-102: 91-End Infantino art on Adam Strange; double-length Adam Strange story. 92-Space Ranger begins (6/64), ends #103. 92-94,96,98-Space Ranger-c. 94,98-Adam Strange/ Space Ranger team-up. 102-Adam Strange ends (no Space Ranger)
7 14 21 44 82 120
103-Origin Ultra, the Multi-Alien; last Space Ranger 5 10 15 35 63 90
104-110: 110-(9/66)-Last 12¢ issue 5 10 15 30 50 70
V17#111(9/80)-117: 117-Newton-a(3 pgs.) 2 4 6 8 11 14
NOTE: ***Anderson** a-2, 4, 8-10, 12-17, 19, 45-48, 51, 57, 59i, 61-64, 70, 76, 87-91; c-9, 10, 15-25, 87, 89, 105-108, 110. **Aparo** a-111. **Austin** a-112i. **Bolland** a-115. **Craig** a-114, 116. **Ditko** a-111, 114-116. **Drucker** a-13, 14. **Elias** a-98, 102, 103. **Golden** a-113p. **Sid Greene** a-78, 91. **Infantino** a-1-8, 11, 14-25, 27-46, 48, 49, 51, 53-91, 103, 117; c-60-86, 88, 90, 91, 105, 107. **Gil Kane** a-14p, 15p, 18p, 19p, 26p, 29-59p(most), 100-102; c-52, 101. **Kubert** a-113; c-111-115. **Moreira** c-27, 28. **Rogers** a-111. **Sekowsky** a-52. **Simon & Kirby** a-4(2 pgs.). **Spiegle** a-111, 114. **Starlin** c-116. **Sutton** a-112. **Tuska** a-115p, 117p.*

MYSTERY IN SPACE
DC Comics: Nov, 2006 - No. 8, Jul, 2007 ($3.99, limited series)

1-8: 1-Captain Comet's rebirth; Starlin-s/Shane Davis-a; The Weird by Starlin 4.00
1-Variant cover by Neal Adams 10.00
Volume One TPB (2007, $17.99) r/#1-5 18.00
Volume Two TPB (2007, $17.99) r/#6-8 and The Weird from #1-4 18.00

MYSTERY IN SPACE
DC Comics (Vertigo): Jul, 2012 ($7.99, one-shot)

1-Short sci-fi stories by various incl. Kaluta, Allred, Baker, Diggle, Gianfelice; Sook-c 8.00

MYSTERY MEN
Marvel Comics: Aug, 2011 - No. 5, Nov, 2011 ($2.99, limited series)

1-5-Zircher-a/c; Liss-s; Pulp-era characters in 1932 3.00

MYSTERY MEN COMICS
Fox Feature Syndicate: Aug, 1939 - No. 31, Feb, 1942

1-Intro. & 1st app. The Blue Beetle, The Green Mask, Rex Dexter of Mars by Briefer, Zanzibar by Tuska, Lt. Drake, D-13-Secret Agent by Powell, Chen Chang, Wing Turner, & Captain Denny Scott 1450 2900 4350 10,500 18,750 27,000
2-Robot & sci/fi-c (2nd Robot-c w/Movie #6) 423 846 1269 3067 5384 7700
3 (10/39)-Classic Lou Fine-c 649 1298 1947 4738 8369 12,000
4,5: 4-Capt. Savage begins (11/39) 343 686 1029 2400 4200 6000
6-Tuska-c 300 600 900 2010 3505 5000
7-1st Blue Beetle-c app. 354 708 1062 2478 4339 6200
8-Lou Fine bondage-c 326 652 978 2282 3991 5700
9-The Moth begins; Lou Fine-c 232 464 696 1485 2543 3600
10-Wing Turner by Kirby; Simon bondage-c 258 516 774 1651 2826 4000
11,12: Both Joe Simon-c. 11-Intro. Domino 226 452 678 1446 2473 3500
13-Intro. Lynx & sidekick Blackie (8/40) 155 310 465 992 1696 2400
14-18 142 284 426 909 1555 2200
19-Intro. & 1st app. Miss X (ends #21) 155 310 465 992 1696 2400
20-31: 26-The Wraith begins 135 270 405 864 1482 2100
NOTE: ***Briefer** a-1-15, 20, 24; c-9. **Cuidera** a-22. **Lou Fine** c-1-5,8,9. **Powell** a-1-15, 24. **Simon** c-10-12. **Tuska** a-1-16, 22, 24, 27; c-6. Bondage-c 1, 3, 7, 8, 10, 25, 27-29, 31. Blue Beetle c-7, 8, 10-31. D-13 Secret Agent c-6. Green Mask c-1, 3-5. Rex Dexter of Mars c-2, 9.*

MYSTERY MEN MOVIE ADAPTION
Dark Horse Comics: July, 1999 - No. 2, Aug, 1999 ($2.95, mini-series)

1,2-Fingerman-s; photo-c 3.00

MYSTERY PLAY, THE
DC Comics (Vertigo): 1994 ($19.95, one-shot)

nn-Hardcover-Morrison-s/Muth-painted art 25.00
Softcover ($9.95)-New Muth cover 10.00

MYSTERY SOCIETY
IDW Publishing: May, 2010 - No. 5, Oct, 2010 ($3.99, limited series)

1-5-Niles-s/Staples-a 4.00
... Special (3/13, $3.99) Niles-s/Ritchie-a/c 4.00

MYSTERY TALES
Atlas Comics (20CC): Mar, 1952 - No. 54, Aug, 1957

1-Horror/weird stories in all 187 374 561 1197 2049 2900
2-Krigstein-a 106 212 318 673 1162 1650
3-10: 6-A-Bomb panel. 10-Story similar to "The Assassin" from Shock SuspenStories
87 174 261 553 952 1350
11,13-21: 14-Maneely s/f story. 20-Electric chair issue. 21-Matt Fox-a; decapitation story 58 116 174 371 636 900

Mystic (2011 series) #1 © DIS

Mystic Comics #9 © MAR

Mystik U #1 © DC

GD 2.0 | VG 4.0 | FN 6.0 | VF 8.0 | VF/NM 9.0 | NM- 9.2

12,22: 12-Matt Fox-a. 22-Forte/Matt Fox-c; a(i) 61 122 183 390 670 950
23-26 (2/55)-Last precode issue 53 106 159 334 567 800
27,29-35,37,38,41-43,48,49: 43-Morisi story contains Frazetta art swipes from Untamed Love
42 84 126 265 445 625
28,36,39,40,45: 28-Jack Katz-a. 36,39-Krigstein-a. 40,45-Ditko-a (#45 is 3 pgs. only)
42 84 126 267 451 635
44-Labyrinth-c/s; Williamson/Krenkel-a 50 100 150 315 533 750
46,51-Williamson/Krenkel-a. 46-Crandall text illos 43 86 129 271 461 650
47-Crandall, Ditko, Powell-a 43 86 129 271 461 650
50,52,53: 50-Torres, Morrow-a 42 84 126 265 445 625
54-Crandall, Check-a 42 84 126 267 451 635

NOTE: ***Ayers** a-18, 49, 52. **Berg** a-17, 51. **Colan** a-1, 3, 18, 35, 43. **Colletta** a-18. **Drucker** a-41. **Everett** a-2, 29, 33, 35, 41; c-8-11, 14, 38, 39, 41, 43, 44, 46, 48-51, 53. **Fass** a-16. **Forte** a-21, 22, 45, 46. **Matt Fox** a-12?, 21, 22; c-22. **Heath** a-3; c-3, 15, 17, 26. **Heck** a-25. **Kinstler** a-15. **Mort Lawrence** a-26, 32, 34. **Maneely** a-1, 9, 14, 22; c-12, 23, 24, 27. **Mooney** a-3, 40. **Morisi** a-43, 49, 52. **Morrow** a-50. **Orlando** a-51. **Pakula** a-16. **Powell** a-21, 29, 37, 38, 47. **Reinman** a-1, 14, 17. **Robinson** a-7p, 42. **Romita** a-37. **Roussos** a-4, 44. **R.Q. Sale** a-45, 46, 49. **Severin** c-52. **Shores** a-17, 45. **Tuska** a-10, 12, 14. **Whitney** a-2. **Wildey** a-37.*

MYSTERY TALES
Super Comics: 1964

Super Reprint #16,17('64): 16-r/Tales of Horror #2. 17-r/Eerie #14(Avon),
18-Kubert-r/Strange Terrors #4 3 6 9 14 20 25

MYSTERY TRAIL
DC Comics: Feb/Mar 1950

nn - Ashcan comic, not distributed to newsstands, only for in-house use. Cover art is Danger Trail #3 with interior being Star Spangled Comics #109. A FN/VF copy sold for $2,357.50 in 2002.

MYSTIC (3rd Series)
Marvel/Atlas Comics (CLDS 1/CSI 2-21/OMC 22-35/CSI 35-61): March, 1951 - No. 61, Aug, 1957

1-Atom bomb panels; horror/weird stories in all 139 278 417 883 1517 2150
2 68 136 204 435 743 1050
3-Eyes torn out 60 120 180 381 653 925
4- "The Devil Birds" by Wolverton (6 pgs.) 97 194 291 621 1061 1500
5,7-10 48 96 144 302 514 725
6- "The Eye of Doom" by Wolverton (7 pgs.) 97 194 291 621 1061 1500
11-17,19,20: 16-Bondage/torture c/story 42 84 126 265 445 625
18-Classic Everett skeleton-c 97 194 291 621 1061 1500
21-25,27-36-Last precode (3/55). 25-E.C. swipe 39 78 117 231 378 525
26-Atomic War story; severed head story/cover 45 90 135 284 480 675
37-51,53-56,61 32 64 96 188 307 425
52-Wood-a; Crandall-a? 34 68 102 199 325 450
57-Story "Trapped in the Ant-Hill" (1957) is very similar to "The Man in the Ant Hill" in TTA #27
43 86 129 271 461 650
58,59-Krigstein-a 33 66 99 194 317 440
60-Williamson/Mayo-a (4 pgs.) 34 68 102 199 325 450

NOTE: ***Andru** a-23, 25. **Ayers** a-35, 53; c-8. **Berg** a-49. **Cameron** a-49, 51. **Check** a-31, 60. **Colan** a-3, 7, 12, 21, 37, 60. **Colletta** a-29. **Drucker** a-46, 52, 56. **Everett** a-8, 9, 17, 40, 44, 57; c-13, 18, 21, 42, 47, 49, 51-55, 57-59, 61. **Forte** a-35, 52, 58. **Fox** a-24i. **Al Hartley** a-35. **Heath** a-10; c-10, 20, 22, 23, 25, 30. **Infantino** a-12. **Kane** a-8, 24p. **Jack Katz** a-31, 33. **Mort Law.rence** a-19, 37. **Maneely** a-22, 24, 58; c-7, 15, 28, 29, 31. **Moldoff** a-29. **Morisi** a-48, 49, 52. **Morrow** a-51. **Orlando** a-57, 61. **Pakula** a-52, 57, 59. **Powell** a-52, 54-56. **Robinson** a-5. **Romita** a-11, 15. **R.Q. Sale** a-35, 53, 58. **Sekowsky** a-1, 2, 4, 5. **Severin** c-56, 60. **Tuska** a-15. **Whitney** a-33. **Wildey** a-28, 30. **Ed Win** a-17, 20. Canadian reprints known-title 'Startling.'*

MYSTIC (Also see CrossGen Chronicles)
CrossGeneration Comics: Jul, 2000 - No. 43, Jan, 2004 ($2.95)

1-43: 1-Marz-s/Peterson & Dell-a. 15-Cameos by DC & Marvel characters 3.00

MYSTIC (CrossGen characters)
Marvel Comics: Oct, 2011 - No. 4, Jan, 2012 ($2.99, limited series)

1-4-G. Willow Wilson-s/David López-a/Amanda Conner-c 3.00

MYSTICAL TALES
Atlas Comics (CCC 1/EPI 2-8): June, 1956 - No. 8, Aug, 1957

1-Everett-c/a 61 122 183 390 670 950
2-4: 2-Berg-a. 3,4-Crandall-a. 36 72 108 211 343 475
5-Williamson-a (4 pgs.) 37 74 111 222 361 500
6-Torres, Krigstein-a 34 68 102 204 332 460
7-Bolle, Forte, Torres, Orlando-a 33 66 99 196 321 445
8-Krigstein, Check-a 34 68 102 204 332 460

NOTE: ***Ayers** a-6. **Everett** a-1; c-1-4, 6, 7. **Orlando** a-1, 2, 7. **Pakula** a-3. **Powell** a-1, 4. **Sale** a-5. **Sinnott** a-6.*

MYSTIC ARCANA
Marvel Comics: Aug, 2007 - Jan, 2008 ($2.99)

1-Magik on-c; art by Scott and Nguyen; Ian McNee and Dani Moonstar app. 3.00
(#2)...: Black Knight 1 (9/07, $2.99) Djurdjevic-c/Grummett & Hanna-a; origin retold 3.00
3-("Scarlet Witch" on cover)(10/07, $2.99) Djurdjevic-c/Santacruz-a; childhood 3.00
(#4)...: Sister Grimm 1 (1/08, $2.99) Nico Minoru from Runaways; Djurdjevic-c/Noto-a 3.00
...: The Book of Marvel Magic ('07, $3.99) Official Handbook profiles of the magic-related 4.00
HC (2007, $24.99, d.j.) r/series and ...: The Book of Marvel Magic 25.00

MYSTIC COMICS (1st Series)
Timely Comics (TPI 1-5/TCI 8-10): March, 1940 - No. 10, Aug, 1942

1-Origin The Blue Blaze, The Dynamic Man, & Flexo the Rubber Robot; Zephyr Jones, 3X's & Deep Sea Demon app.; The Magician begins (all 1st app.);
c-from Spider pulp V18#1, 6/39 1500 3000 4500 12,000 25,500 39,000
2-The Invisible Man & Master Mind Excello begin; Space Rangers, Zara of the Jungle,
Taxi Taylor app. (scarce) 730 1460 2190 5329 9415 13,500
3-Origin Hercules, who last appears in #4 470 940 1410 3431 6066 8700
4-Origin The Thin Man & The Black Widow; Merzak the Mystic app.; last Flexo, Dynamic Man, Invisible Man & Blue Blaze (some issues have date sticker on cover; others have July w/August overprint in silver color); Roosevelt assassination-c
703 1406 2109 5132 9066 13,000
5-(3/41)-Origin The Black Marvel, The Blazing Skull, The Sub-Earth Man, Super Slave & The Terror; The Moon Man & Black Widow app.; 5-German war-c begin, end #10
423 846 1269 3046 5323 7600
6-(10/41)-Origin The Challenger & The Destroyer (1st app.?; also see All-Winners #2,
Fall, 1941) 541 1082 1623 3950 6975 10,000
7-The Witness begins (12/41, origin & 1st app.); origin Davey & the Demon; last Black Widow; Hitler opens his trunk of terror-c by Simon & Kirby (classic-c)
757 1514 2271 5526 9763 14,000
8,10: 8-Classic Destroyer WWII Nazi bondage/torture-c. 10-Father Time, World of Wonder,
& Red Skeleton app.; last Challenger & Terror 541 1082 1623 3950 6975 10,000
9-Gary Gaunt app.; last Black Marvel, Mystic & Blazing Skull; Hitler-c
676 1352 2028 4935 8718 12,500

NOTE: ***Gabrielle** c-8-10. **Rico** a-9(2). **Schomburg** a-1-4; c-1-6. **Sekowsky** a-9. **Sekowsky/Klein** a-8 (Challenger). Bondage c-1, 2, 9.*

MYSTIC COMICS (2nd Series)
Timely Comics (ANC): Oct, 1944 - No. 3, Win, 1944-45; No. 4, Mar, 1945

1-The Angel, The Destroyer, The Human Torch, Terry Vance the Schoolboy Sleuth,
& Tommy Tyme begin 300 600 900 1935 3343 4750
2-(Fall/44)-Last Human Torch & Terry Vance; bondage/hypo-c
187 374 561 1197 2049 2900
3-Last Angel (two stories) & Tommy Tyme 148 296 444 947 1624 2300
4-The Young Allies-c & app.; Schomburg-c 142 284 426 909 1555 2200

MYSTIC COMICS 70th ANNIVERARY SPECIAL
Marvel Comics: Oct, 2009 ($3.99, one-shot)

1-New story of The Vision; r/G.A. Vision app. from Marvel Myst. Comics #13 & 16 5.00

MYSTIC HANDS OF DR. STRANGE
Marvel Comics: May, 2010 ($3.99, B&W, one-shot)

1-Short stories; art by Irving, Brunner, McKeever & Marcos Martin; Parrillo-c 4.00

MYSTIK U
DC Comics: Jan, 2018 - Present ($5.99)

1,2: 1-Teenage Zatanna, Enchantress at magic college; intro. Plop; Kwitney-s/Norton-a 6.00

MYSTIQUE (See X-Men titles)
Marvel Comics: June, 2003 - No. 24, Apr, 2005 ($2.99)

1-24: 1-6-Linsner-c/Vaughan-s/Lucas-a. 7-Ryan-a begins. 8-Horn-c. 9-24-Mayhew-c
23-Wolverine & Rogue app. 3.00
... Vol. 1: Drop Dead Gorgeous TPB (2004, $14.99) r/#1-6 15.00
... Vol. 2: Tinker, Tailor, Mutant, Spy TPB (2004, $17.99) r/#7-13 18.00
... Vol. 3: Unnatural TPB (2004, $13.99) r/#14-18 14.00

MYSTIQUE & SABRETOOTH (Sabretooth and Mystique on-c)
Marvel Comics: Dec, 1996 - No. 4, Mar, 1997 ($1.95, limited series)

1-4: Characters from X-Men 3.00

MY STORY (...True Romances in Pictures #5,6; becomes My Love Life #13) (Formerly Zago)
Hero Books (Fox Feature Syndicate): No. 5, May, 1949 - No. 12, Aug, 1950

5-Kamen/Feldstein-a 34 68 102 199 325 450
6-8,11,12: 12-Photo-c 18 36 54 103 162 220
9,10-Wood-a 27 54 81 162 266 370

MYTHIC
Image Comics: May, 2015 - Present ($1.99/$2.99/$3.99)

1-3: 1-($1.99) Phil Hester-s/John McCrea-a. 2,3-($2.99) 3.00
4-8-($3.99) 4.00

MYTHOS
Marvel Comics: Mar, 2006 - Dec, 2007 ($3.99)

1-Retelling of X-Men #1 with painted-a by Paolo Rivera; Paul Jenkins-s 4.00

The Nail #1 © DH & Rob Zombie

The 'Nam #65 © MAR

Namor, The Sub-Mariner #24 © MAR

	GD 2.0	VG 4.0	FN 6.0	VF 8.0	VF/NM 9.0	NM- 9.2
...: Captain America 1 (8/08) Retelling of origin; painted-a by Rivera; Jenkins-s						4.00
...: Fantastic Four 1 (12/07) Retelling of Fantastic Four #1; painted-a by Rivera; Jenkins-s						4.00
...: Ghost Rider 1 (3/07) Retelling of Marvel Spotlight #5; painted-a by Rivera; Jenkins-s						4.00
...: Hulk 1 (10/06) Retelling of Incredible Hulk #1; painted-a by Rivera; Jenkins-s						4.00
...: Spider-Man 1 (8/07) Retelling of Amazing Fantasy #15; painted-a by Rivera; Jenkins-s						4.00

MYTHOS: THE FINAL TOUR
DC Comics/Vertigo: Dec, 1996 - No. 3, Feb, 1997 ($5.95, limited series)

1-3: 1-Ney Rieber-s/Amaro-a. 2-Snejbjerg-a; Constantine-app. 3-Kristiansen-a; Black Orchid-app. 6.00

MYTHSTALKERS
Image Comics: Mar, 2003 - No. 8, Mar, 2004 ($2.95)

1-8-Jiro-a 3.00

MY TRUE LOVE (Formerly Western Killers #64; Frank Buck #70 on)
Fox Feature Syndicate: No. 65, July, 1949 - No. 69, March, 1950

	GD	VG	FN	VF	VF/NM	NM-
65	26	52	78	154	252	350
66,68,69: 69-Morisi-a	18	36	54	103	162	220
67-Wood-a	27	54	81	162	266	370

NAIL, THE
Dark Horse Comics: June, 2004 - No. 4, Oct, 2004 ($2.99, limited series)

1-4-Rob Zombie & Steve Niles-s/Nat Jones-a/Simon Bisley-c 3.00
TPB (2005, $12.95) r/series 13.00

NAILBITER
Image Comics: May, 2014 - No. 30, Mar, 2017 ($2.99)

1-29: 1-Williamson-s/Henderson-a. 7-Brian Bendis appears as a character. 13-Archie style cover 3.00
30-($3.99) Final issue 4.00
.../ Hack/Slash 1 (3/15, $4.99) Flip book with Hack/Slash / Nailbiter 1 5.00

NAKED BRAIN (Marc Hempel's...)
Insight Studios Group: 2002 - No. 3, 2002 ($2.95, B&W, limited series)

1-3-Marc Hempel cartoons and sketches; Tug & Buster app. 3.00

NAKED PREY, THE (See Movie Classics)

'NAM, THE (See Savage Tales #1, 2nd series & Punisher Invades...)
Marvel Comics Group: Dec, 1986 - No. 84, Sept, 1993

	GD	VG	FN	VF	VF/NM	NM-
1-Golden a(p)/c begins, ends #13	1	3	4	6	8	10
1 (2nd printing)						3.00
2-7,9-25,27-66,70-74: 7-Golden-a (2 pgs.). 32-Death R. Kennedy. 52,53-Frank Castle (The Punisher) app. 52,53-Gold 2nd printings. 58-Silver logo. 65-Heath-c/a. 70-Lomax scripts begin						3.00
8-1st app. Fudd Verzyl, Tunnel Rat	1	3	4	6	8	10
26-2nd app. Fudd Verzyl, Tunnel Rat						4.00
67-69-Punisher 3 part story						4.00
75-($2.25, 52 pgs.)						6.00
76-84						3.00
Trade Paperback 1,2: 1-r/#1-4. 2-r/#5-8	1	2	3	5	6	8
TPB ('99, $14.95) r/#1-4; recolored						15.00

'NAM MAGAZINE, THE
Marvel Comics: Aug, 1988 - No. 10, May, 1989 ($2.00, B&W, 52pgs.)

1-10: Each issue reprints 2 issues of the comic 4.00

NAMELESS
Image Comics: Feb, 2015 - No. 6, Dec, 2015 ($2.99)

1-6-Morrison-s/Burnham-a 3.00

NAMELESS, THE
Image Comics: May, 1997 - No. 5, Sept, 1997 ($2.95, B&W)

1-5: Pruett/Hester-s/a 3.00
...: The Director's Cut TPB (2006, $15.99) r/#1-5; original proposal by Pruett 16.00

NAMES, THE
DC Comics (Vertigo): Nov, 2014 - No. 9, Jul, 2015 ($2.99, limited series)

1-9-Peter Milligan-s/Leandro Fernandez-a 3.00

NAMESAKE
BOOM! Studios: Nov, 2016 - No. 4, Feb, 2017 ($3.99, limited series)

1-4-Orlando-s/Rebelka-a 4.00

NAMES OF MAGIC, THE (Also see Books of Magic)
DC Comics (Vertigo): Feb, 2001 - No. 5, June, 2001 ($2.50, limited series)

1-5: Bolton painted-c on all; Case-a; leads into Hunter: The Age of Magic 3.00
TPB (2002, $14.95) r/#1-5 15.00

NAME OF THE GAME, THE
DC Comics: 2001 ($29.95, graphic novel)

Hardcover ($29.95) Will Eisner-s/a 30.00

NAMOR (Volume 2)
Marvel Comics: June, 2003 - No. 12, May, 2004 (25¢/$2.25/$2.99)

1-(25¢-c)Young Namor in the 1920s; Larroca-c/a 3.00
2-6-($2.25) Larroca-a 3.00
7-12-($2.99): 7-Olliffe-a begins 3.00

NAMORA (See Marvel Mystery Comics #82 & Sub-Mariner Comics)
Marvel Comics (PrPl): Fall, 1948 - No. 3, Dec, 1948

	GD	VG	FN	VF	VF/NM	NM-
1-Sub-Mariner x-over in Namora; Namora by Everett(2), Sub-Mariner by Rico (10 pgs.)	300	600	900	2070	3635	5200
2-The Blonde Phantom & Sub-Mariner story; Everett-a	219	438	657	1402	2401	3400
3-(Scarce)-Sub-Mariner app.; Everett-a	245	490	735	1568	2684	3800

NAMORA (See Agents of Atlas)
Marvel Comics: Aug, 2010 ($3.99, one-shot)

1-Parker-s/Pichelli-a 4.00

NAMOR: THE FIRST MUTANT (Curse of the Mutants x-over with X-Men titles)
Marvel Comics: Oct, 2010 - No. 11, Aug, 2011 ($3.99/$2.99)

1-($3.99) Olivetti-a/Stuart Moore-s/Jae Lee-c; back-up retelling of origin and history 4.00
2-11-($2.99) 2-Emma Frost app. 5-Mayhew-c. 6-10-Noto-c 3.00
... Annual 1 (7/11, $3.99) Part 3 of "Escape From the Negative Zone" x-over; Fiumara-a 4.00

NAMOR, THE SUB-MARINER (See Prince Namor & Sub-Mariner)
Marvel Comics: Apr, 1990 - No. 62, May, 1995 ($1.00/$1.25/$1.50)

	GD	VG	FN	VF	VF/NM	NM-
1-Byrne-c/a/scripts in 1-25 (scripts only #26-32)	1	2	3	5	6	8
2-5: 5-Iron Man app.						4.00
6-11,13-23,25,27-36,38-49,51-62: 16-Re-intro Iron Fist (8-cameo only). 18-Punisher cameo (1 panel); 21-23,25-Wolverine cameos. 22,23-Iron Fist app. 28-Iron Fist-c/story. 31-Dr. Doom-c/story. 33,34-Iron Fist cameo. 35-New Tiger Shark-c/story. 48-The Thing app.						3.00
12,24: 12-(52pgs.)-Re-intro. The Invaders. 24-Namor vs. Wolverine						4.00
26-Namor w/new costume; 1st Jae Lee-c/a this title (5/92) & begins						5.00
37-Aqua holografx foil-c						4.00
50-($1.75, 52 pgs.)-Newsstand ed.; w/bound-in S-M trading card sheet (both versions)						4.00
50-($2.95, 52 pgs.)-Collector edition w/foil-c						5.00
Annual 1-4 ('91-94, 68 pgs.): 1-3 pg. origin recap. 2-Return/Defenders. 3-Bagged w/card. 4-Painted-c						4.00

NOTE: *Jae Lee a-26-30p, 31-37, 38p, 39, 40; c-26-40.*

'NAMWOLF
Albatross Funnybooks: 2017 - No. 4, 2017 ($3.99, limited series)

1-4-Fabian Rangel Jr.-s/Logan Faerber-a; werewolf in 1970 Viet Nam 4.00

NANCY AND SLUGGO (See Comics On Parade & Sparkle Comics)
United Features Syndicate: No. 16, 1949 - No. 23, 1954

	GD	VG	FN	VF	VF/NM	NM-
16(#1)	10	20	30	58	79	100
17-23	8	16	24	40	50	60

NANCY & SLUGGO (Nancy #146-173; formerly Sparkler Comics)
St. John/Dell #146-187/Gold Key #188 on: No. 121, Apr, 1955-No. 192, Oct, 1963

	GD	VG	FN	VF	VF/NM	NM-
121(4/55)(St. John)	10	20	30	54	72	90
122-145(7/57)(St. John)	8	16	24	44	57	70
146(9/57)-Peanuts begins, ends #192 (Dell)	8	16	24	56	108	160
147-161 (Dell) Peanuts in all	8	16	24	51	86	120
162-165,177-180-John Stanley-a	7	14	21	44	82	120
166-176-Oona & Her Haunted House series; Stanley-a	7	14	21	49	92	135
181-187(3-5/62)(Dell)	5	10	15	35	63	90
188(10/62)-192 (Gold Key)	5	10	15	35	63	90
Four Color 1034(9-11/59)-Summer Camp	5	10	15	30	50	70

(See Dell Giant #34, 45 & Dell Giants)

NANCY DREW AND THE HARDY BOYS: THE BIG LIE
Dynamite Entertainment: 2017 - No. 6, 2017 ($3.99, limited series)

1-6-Anthony Del Col-s/Werther Dell'Edera-a; multiple-c on each; Bobbsey twins app. 4.00

NANNY AND THE PROFESSOR (TV)
Dell Publishing Co.: Aug, 1970 - No. 2, Oct, 1970 (Photo-c)

	GD	VG	FN	VF	VF/NM	NM-
1-(01-546-008)	5	10	15	30	50	70
2	4	8	12	25	40	55

NAPOLEON

Nathaniel Dusk II #3 © DC

National Comics #29 © QUA

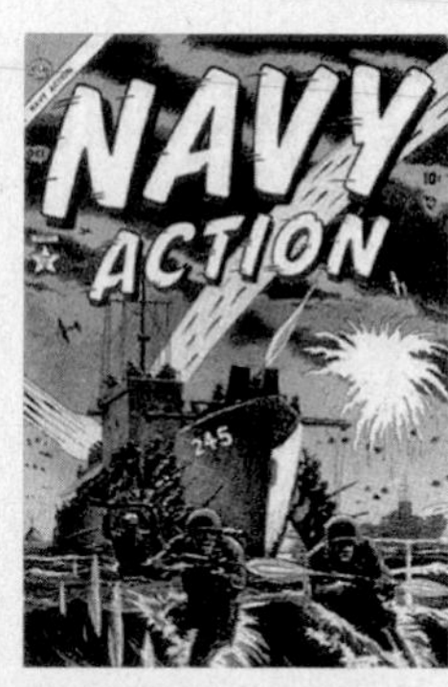

Navy Action #2 © MAR

	GD 2.0	VG 4.0	FN 6.0	VF 8.0	VF/NM 9.0	NM- 9.2

Dell Publishing Co.: No. 526, Dec, 1953

Four Color 526	5	10	15	30	50	70

NAPOLEON & SAMANTHA (See Walt Disney Showcase No. 10)

NAPOLEON & UNCLE ELBY (See Clifford McBride's...)
Eastern Color Printing Co.: July, 1942 (68 pgs.) (One Shot)

1	43	86	129	271	461	650
1945-American Book-Strafford Press (128 pgs.) (8x10-1/2"; B&W reprints; hardcover)	15	30	45	83	124	165

NARRATIVE ILLUSTRATION, THE STORY OF THE COMICS (Also see Good Triumphs Over Evil!)
M.C. Gaines: Summer, 1942 (32 pgs., 7-1/4"x10", B&W w/color inserts)

nn-16 pgs. text with illustrations of ancient art, strips and comic covers; 4 pg. WWII War Bond promo, "The Minute Man Answers the Call" color comic drawn by Shelly and a special 8-page color comic insert of "The Story of Saul" (from Picture Stories from the Bible #10 or soon to appear in PS #10) or "Noah and His Ark" or "The Story of Ruth". Insert has special title page indicating it was part of a Sunday newspaper supplement insert series that had already run in a New England "Sunday Herald." Another version exists with insert from Picture Stories from the Bible #7.
(very rare) Estimated value... 1500.00

NOTE: ***Print, A Quarterly Journal of the Graphic Arts** Vol. 3 No. 2 (88 pg., square bound) features the 1st printing of Narrative Illustration, The Story of The Comics. A VG+ copy sold for $750 in 2005.*

NASCAR HEROES
Starbridge Media: 2007 - No. 3 ($3.95)

1-3: 1-Origin of fictional racer Jimmy Dash. 3-Origin of the Daytona 500; DeStefano-s 4.00
nn-(2008, Free Comic Book Day giveaway) The Mystery of Driver Z 3.00

NASH (WCW Wrestling)
Image Comics: July, 1999 - No. 2, July, 1999 ($2.95)

1,2-Regular and photo-c 3.00
1-($6.95) Photo-split-cover Edition 7.00

NATHANIEL DUSK
DC Comics: Feb, 1984 - No. 4, May, 1984 ($1.25, mini-series, direct sales, Baxter paper)

1-4: 1-Intro/origin; Gene Colan-c/a in all 3.00

NATHANIEL DUSK II
DC Comics: Oct, 1985 - No. 4, Jan, 1986 ($2.00, mini-series, Baxter paper)

1-4: Gene Colan-c/a in all 3.00

NATIONAL COMICS
Quality Comics Group: July, 1940 - No. 75, Nov, 1949

	GD	VG	FN	VF	VF/NM	NM-
1-Uncle Sam begins (1st app.); origin sidekick Buddy by Eisner; origin Wonder Boy & Kid Dixon; Merlin the Magician (ends #45); Cyclone, Kid Patrol, Sally O'Neil Policewoman, Pen Miller (by Klaus Nordling; ends #22), Prop Powers (ends #26), & Paul Bunyan (ends #22) begin	670	1340	2010	4891	8646	12,400
2	277	454	831	1759	3030	4300
3-Last Eisner Uncle Sam	206	412	618	1318	2259	3200
4-Last Cyclone	155	310	465	992	1696	2400
5-(11/40)-Quicksilver begins (1st app.; 3rd w/lightning speed?; re-intro'd by DC in 1993 as Max Mercury in Flash #76, 2nd series); origin Uncle Sam; bondage-c	184	368	552	1168	2009	2850
6,8-11: 8-Jack & Jill begins (ends #22). 9-Flag-c	148	296	444	947	1624	2300
7-Classic Lou Fine-c	343	686	1029	2400	4200	6000
12-15-Lou Fine-a	116	232	348	742	1271	1800
16-Classic skeleton-c; Lou Fine-a	194	388	582	1242	2121	3000
17,19-22: 21-Classic Nazi swastika cover. 22-Last Pen Miller (moves to Crack #23)	90	180	270	576	988	1400
18-(12/41)-Shows Asians attacking Pearl Harbor; on stands one month before actual event	194	388	582	1242	2121	3000
23-The Unknown & Destroyer 171 begin	90	180	270	576	988	1400
24-Japanese War-c	94	188	282	597	1024	1450
25-30: 25-Nazi drug usage/hypodermic needle in story. 26-Wonder Boy ends. 27- G-2 the Unknown begins (ends #46). 29-Origin The Unknown	63	126	189	403	689	975
31-33: 33-Chic Carter begins (ends #47)	58	116	174	371	636	900
34-37,40: 35-Last Kid Patrol	53	106	159	334	567	800
38-Hitler, Tojo, Mussolini-c	97	194	291	621	1061	1500
39-Hitler-c	100	200	300	635	1093	1550
41-Classic Uncle Sam American Eagle WWII-c	50	100	150	315	533	750
42-The Barker begins (1st app?, 5/44); The Barker covers begin	41	82	123	256	428	600
43-50: 48-Origin The Whistler	28	56	84	165	270	375
51-Sally O'Neil by Ward, 8 pgs. (12/45)	30	60	90	117	289	400
52-60	20	40	60	118	192	265
61-67: 67-Format change; Quicksilver app.	15	30	45	90	140	190
68-75: The Barker ends	15	30	45	83	124	165

NOTE: ***Cole** Quicksilver-13; Barker-43; c-43, 46, 47, 49-51. **Crandall** Uncle Sam-11-13 (with **Fine**), 25, 26; c-24-26, 30-33, 43. **Crandall** Paul Bunyan-10-13. **Fine** Uncle Sam-13 (w/**Crandall**), 17, 18; c-1-14, 16, 18, 21. **Gill Fox** c-69-74. **Guardineer** Quicksilver-27, 35. **Gustavson** Quicksilver-14-26. **McWilliams** a-23-28, 55, 57. Uncle Sam c-1-41. Barker c-42-75.*

NATIONAL COMICS (Also see All Star Comics 1999 crossover titles)
DC Comics: May, 1999 ($1.99, one-shot)

1-Golden Age Flash and Mr. Terrific; Waid-s/Lopresti-a 3.00

NATIONAL COMICS
DC Comics: Sept, 2012 ($3.99, one-shots)

... Eternity 1 (9/12) Re-intro of Kid Eternity; Lemire-s/Hamner-a/c 4.00
... Looker 1 (10/12) Vampire supermodel; Edginton-s/Mike S. Miller-a/March-c 4.00
... Madame X 1 (12/12) Rob Williams-s/Trevor Hairsine-a/Fiona Staples-c 4.00
... Rose & Thorn 1 (11/12) Taylor-s/Googe-a/Sook-c 4.00

NATIONAL CRUMB, THE (Magazine-Size)
Mayfair Publications: August, 1975 (52 pgs., B&W) (Satire)

1-Grandenetti-c/a, Ayers-a	2	4	6	11	16	20

NATIONAL VELVET (TV)
Dell Publishing Co./Gold Key: May-July, 1961 - No. 2, Mar, 1963 (All photo-c)

Four Color 1195 (#1)	6	12	18	41	76	110
Four Color 1312, 01-556-207, 12-556-210 (Dell)	4	8	12	27	44	60
1,2: 1(12/62) (Gold Key). 2(3/63)	4	8	12	27	44	60

NATION OF SNITCHES
Piranha Press (DC): 1990 ($4.95, color, 52 pgs.)

nn 5.00

NATION X (X-Men on the Utopia island)
Marvel Comics: Feb, 2010 - No. 4, May, 2010 ($3.99, limited series)

1-4-Short stories by various. 1,4-Allred-a. 2-Choi, Cloonan-a. 4-Doop app. 4.00
...: X-Factor (3/10, $3.99) David-s/DeLandro-a 4.00

NATURE BOY (Formerly Danny Blaze; Li'l Rascal Twins #6 on)
Charlton Comics: No. 3, March, 1956 - No. 5, Feb, 1957

3-1st app./origin; Blue Beetle story (last Golden Age app.); Buscema-c/a	22	44	66	132	216	300
4,5	16	32	48	94	147	200

NOTE: ***John Buscema** a-3, 4p, 5; c-3. **Powell** a-4.*

NATURE OF THINGS (Disney, TV/Movie)
Dell Publishing Co.: No. 727, Sept, 1956 - No. 842, Sept, 1957

Four Color 727 (#1), 842-Jesse Marsh-a	5	10	15	33	57	80

NAUSICAA OF THE VALLEY OF WIND
Viz Comics: 1988 - No. 7, 1989; 1989 - No. 4, 1990 ($2.50, B&W, 68pgs.)

Book 1-7: 1-Contains Moebius poster 5.00
Part II, Book 1-4 ($2.95) 5.00

NAVY ACTION (Sailor Sweeney #12-14)
Atlas Comics (CDS): Aug, 1954 - No. 11, Apr, 1956; No. 15, 1/57 - No. 18, 8/57

1-Powell-a	41	82	123	256	428	600
2-Lawrence-a; RQ Sale-a	22	44	66	132	216	300
3-11: 4-Last precode (2/55)	20	40	60	114	182	250
15-18	18	36	54	105	165	225

NOTE: ***Berg** a-7, 9. **Colan** a-8. **Drucker** a-7, 17. **Everett** a-3, 7, 16; c-16, 17. **Heath** c-1, 2, 5, 6. **Maneely** a-5, 7, 8, 18; c-9, 11. **Pakula** a-2, 3, 9. **Reinman** a-17.*

NAVY COMBAT
Atlas Comics (MPI): June, 1955 - No. 20, Oct, 1958

1-Torpedo Taylor begins by Don Heck; Heath-c	39	78	117	231	378	525
2	20	40	60	120	195	270
3-10	19	38	57	109	172	235
11,13-16,18-20: 14-Torres-a	17	34	51	98	154	210
12-Crandall-a	18	36	54	103	162	220
17-Williamson-a, 4 pgs.; Torres-a	18	36	54	103	162	220

NOTE: ***Ayers** a-15. **Berg** a-10, 11. **Colan** a-11. **Drucker** a-7. **Everett** a-3, 20; c-8 & 9 w/**Tuska**, 10, 13-16. **Forte** a-15, 18. **Heck** a-11(2), 15, 19. **Maneely** c-1, 5, 6, 11, 17. **Morisi** a-8. **Pakula** a-7, 18. **Powell** a-20. **Reinman** a-18.*

NAVY HEROES
Almanac Publishing Co.: 1945

1-Heavy in propaganda	16	32	48	94	147	200

NAVY PATROL
Key Publications: May, 1955 - No. 4, Nov, 1955

Necessary Evil #1 © Williamson & Harris

Negative Burn #50 © Caliber

Neil Gaiman's Neverwhere #4 © Neil Gaiman

	GD 2.0	VG 4.0	FN 6.0	VF 8.0	VF/NM 9.0	NM- 9.2
1	10	20	30	56	76	95
2-4	8	16	24	40	50	60

NAVY TALES
Atlas Comics (CDS): Jan, 1957 - No. 4, July, 1957

1-Everett-c; Berg, Powell-a	36	72	108	211	343	475
2-Williamson/Mayo-a(5 pgs); Crandall-a	21	42	63	122	199	275
3,4-Reinman-a; Severin-c. 4-Crandall-a	17	34	51	100	158	215

NOTE: ***Colan** a-4. **Maneely** c-2. **Reinman** a-2-4. **Sinnott** a-4.*

NAVY TASK FORCE
Stanmor Publications/Aragon Mag. No. 4-8: Feb, 1954 - No. 8, April, 1956

1	12	24	36	67	94	120
2	8	16	24	44	57	70
3-8: 8-r/Navy Patrol #1; defeat of the Japanese Navy	8	16	24	40	50	60

NAVY WAR HEROES
Charlton Comics: Jan, 1964 - No. 7, Mar-Apr, 1965

1	4	8	12	23	37	50
2-7	3	6	9	15	22	28

NAZA (Stone Age Warrior)
Dell Publishing Co.: Nov-Jan, 1963-64 - No. 9, March, 1966

12-555-401 (#1)-Painted-c	5	10	15	33	57	80
2-9: 2-4-Painted-c	4	8	12	23	37	50

NEBBS, THE (Also see Crackajack Funnies)
Dell Publishing Co./Croydon Publishing Co.: 1941; 1945

Large Feature Comic 23(1941)	22	44	66	132	216	300
1(1945, 36 pgs.)-Reprints	14	28	42	76	108	140

NECESSARY EVIL
Desperado Publishing: Oct, 2007 - No. 9, Nov, 2008 ($3.99)

1-9: 1-Joshua Williamson-s/Marcus Harris-a/Dustin Nguyen-c 4.00

NECROMANCER
Image Comics (Top Cow): Sept, 2005 - No. 6, July 2006 ($2.99)

1-6: 1-Manapul-a/Ortega-s; three covers by Manapul, Horn & Bachalo 3.00
... Pilot Season Vol. 1 #1 (11/07, $2.99) Ortega-s/Meyers-a/Manapul-c 3.00

NECROMANCER: THE GRAPHIC NOVEL
Marvel Comics (Epic Comics): 1989 ($8.95)

nn 9.00

NECROWAR
Dreamwave Productions: July, 2003 - No. 3, Sept, 2003 ($2.95)

1-3-Furman-s/Granov-digital art 3.00

NEGATION
CrossGeneration Comics: Dec, 2001 - No. 27, Mar, 2004 ($2.95)

Prequel (12/01) 3.00
1-27: 1-(1/02) Pelletier-a/Bedard & Waid-s 3.00
... Lawbringer (11/02, $2.95) Nebres-a 3.00
Vol. 1: Bohica! (10/02, $19.95, TPB) r/ Prequel & #1-6 20.00
Vol. 2: Baptism of Fire (5/03, $15.95, TPB) r/#7-12 16.00
Vol. 3: Hounded (12/03, $15.95, TPB) r/#13-18 16.00

NEGATION WAR
CrossGeneration Comics: Apr, 2004 - No. 6 ($2.95)

1-4-Bedard-s/Pelletier-a 3.00

NEGATIVE BURN
Caliber: 1993 - No. 50, 1997 ($2.95, B&W, anthology)

1,2,4-12,14-47: Anthology by various including Bolland, Burden, Doran, Gaiman, Moebius, Moore, & Pope 4.00
3,13: 3-Bone story. 13-Strangers in Paradise story 2 4 6 8 10 12
48,49-($4.95) 5.00
50-($6.95, 96 pgs.)-Gaiman, Robinson, Bolland 7.00
...Summer Special 2005 (Image, 2005, $9.99) new short stories by various 10.00
...: The Best From 1993-1998 (Image, 1/05, $19.95) r/short stories by various 20.00
...Winter Special 2005 (Image, 2005, $9.95) new short stories by various 10.00

NEGATIVE BURN
Image Comics (Desperado): May, 2006 - No. 21 ($5.99, B&W, anthology)

1-21: 1-Art by Bolland, Powell, Luna, Smith, Hester. 2-Milk & Cheese by Dorkin 6.00

NEGRO (See All-Negro)

NEGRO HEROES (Calling All Girls, Real Heroes, & True Comics reprints)
Parents' Magazine Institute: Spring, 1947 - No. 2, Summer, 1948

1	161	322	483	1030	1765	2500
2-Jackie Robinson-c/story	161	322	483	1030	1765	2500

NEGRO ROMANCE (Negro Romances #4)
Fawcett Publications: June, 1950 - No. 3, Oct, 1950 (All photo-c)

1-Evans-a (scarce)	226	452	678	1446	2473	3500
2,3 (scarce)	187	374	561	1197	2049	2900

NEGRO ROMANCES (Formerly Negro Romance; Romantic Secrets #5 on)
Charlton Comics: No. 4, May, 1955

4-Reprints Fawcett #2 (scarce)	187	374	561	1197	2049	2900

NEIL GAIMAN AND CHARLES VESS' STARDUST
DC Comics (Vertigo): 1997 - No. 4, 1998 ($5.95/$6.95, square-bound, lim. series)

1-4: Gaiman text with Vess paintings in all 7.00
Hardcover (1998, $29.95) r/series with new sketches 35.00
Softcover (1999, $19.95) oversized; new Vess-c 20.00

NEIL GAIMAN'S LADY JUSTICE
Tekno Comix: Sept, 1995 - No. 11, May, 1996 ($1.95/$2.25)

1-11: 1-Sienkiewicz-c; pin-ups. 1-5-Brereton-c. 7-Polybagged. 11-The Big Bang Pt. 7 3.00
Free Comic Book Day (Super Genius, 2015, giveaway) r/#1 3.00

NEIL GAIMAN'S LADY JUSTICE
BIG Entertainment: V2#1, June, 1996 - No. 9, Feb, 1997 ($2.25)

V2#1-9: Dan Brereton-c on all. 6-8-Dan Brereton script 3.00

NEIL GAIMAN'S MIDNIGHT DAYS
DC Comics (Vertigo): 1999 ($17.95, trade paperback)

nn-Reprints Gaiman's short stories; new Swamp Thing w/ Bissette-a 18.00

NEIL GAIMAN'S MR. HERO-THE NEWMATIC MAN
Tekno Comix: Mar, 1995 - No. 17, May, 1996 ($1.95/$2.25)

1-17: 1-Intro Mr. Hero & Teknophage; bound-in game piece and trading card. 4-w/Steel edition Neil Gaiman's Teknophage #1 coupon. 13-Polybagged 3.00

NEIL GAIMAN'S MR. HERO-THE NEWMATIC MAN
BIG Entertainment: V2#1, June, 1996 ($2.25)

V2#1-Teknophage destroys Mr. Hero; includes The Big Bang Pt. 10 3.00

NEIL GAIMAN'S NEVERWHERE
DC Comics (Vertigo): Aug, 2005 - No. 9, Sept, 2006 ($2.99, limited series)

1-9-Adaptation of Gaiman novel; Carey-s/Fabry-a/c 3.00
TPB (2007, $19.99) r/series; intro. by Carey 20.00

NEIL GAIMAN'S PHAGE-SHADOWDEATH
BIG Entertainment: June, 1996 - No. 6, Nov, 1996 ($2.25, limited series)

1-6: Bryan Talbot-c & scripts in all. 1-1st app. Orlando Holmes 3.00

NEIL GAIMAN'S TEKNOPHAGE
Tekno Comix: Aug, 1995 - No. 10, Mar, 1996 ($1.95/$2.25)

1-6-Rick Veitch scripts & Bryan Talbot-c/a. 3.00
1-Steel Edition 4.00
7-10: Paul Jenkins scripts in all. 8-polybagged 3.00

NEIL GAIMAN'S WHEEL OF WORLDS
Tekno Comix: Apr, 1995 - No. 1, May, 1996 ($2.95/$3.25)

0-1st app. Lady Justice; 48 pgs.; bound-in poster 5.00
0-Regular edition 4.00
1 ($3.25, 5/96)-Bruce Jones scripts; Lady Justice & Teknophage app.; CGI photo-c 4.00

NEIL THE HORSE (See Charlton Bullseye #2)
Aardvark-Vanaheim #1-10/Renegade Press #11 on: 2/83 - No. 10, 12/84; No. 11, 4/85 - #15, 1985 (B&W)

1($1.40) 4.00
1-2nd print 3.00
2-12: 11-w/paperdolls 3.00
13-15: Double size ($3.00). 13-w/paperdolls. 15 is a flip book(2-c) 4.00

NEIL YOUNG'S GREENDALE
DC Comics (Vertigo): 2010 ($19.99, hardcover graphic novel)

HC-Story based on the Neil Young album; Dysart-s/Chiang-a; intro. by Neil Young 20.00

NELLIE THE NURSE (Also see Gay Comics & Joker Comics)
Marvel/Atlas Comics (SPI/LMC): 1945 - No. 36, Oct, 1952; 1957

1-(1945)	103	206	309	659	1130	1600
2-(Spring/46)	39	78	117	240	395	550
3,4: 3-New logo (9/46)	30	60	90	177	289	400

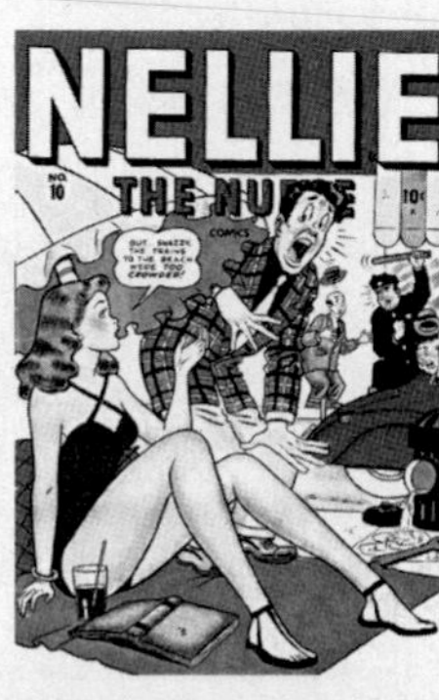

Nellie the Nurse #10 © MAR

The Nevermen #1 © DH

New Adventure Comics #24 © DC

	GD 2.0	VG 4.0	FN 6.0	VF 8.0	VF/NM 9.0	NM- 9.2
5-Kurtzman's "Hey Look" (3); Georgie app.	31	62	93	182	296	410
6-8,10: 7,8-Georgie app. 10-Millie app.	25	50	75	150	245	340
9-Wolverton-a (1 pg.); Mille the Model app.	26	52	78	154	252	350
11,14-16,18-Kurtzman's "Hey Look"	26	52	78	156	256	355
12- "Giggles 'n' Grins" by Kurtzman	25	50	75	150	245	340
13,17,19,20: 17-Annie Oakley app.	21	42	63	124	202	280
21-30: 28-Mr. Nexdoor-r (3 pgs.) by Kurtzman/Rusty #22	19	38	57	109	172	235
31-36: 36-Post-c	17	34	51	98	154	210
1('57)-Leading Mag. (Atlas)-Everett-a, 20 pgs	30	60	90	177	289	400

NELLIE THE NURSE
Dell Publishing Co.: No. 1304, Mar-May, 1962

	GD	VG	FN	VF	VF/NM	NM-
Four Color 1304-Stanley-a	8	16	24	51	96	140

NEMESIS (Millar & McNiven's...)
Marvel Comics (Icon): May, 2010 - No. 4, Feb, 2011 ($2.99)

	NM-
1-4-Millar-s/McNiven-a	3.00
1,2-Variant covers: 1-Yu. 2-Cassaday	8.00

NEMESIS ARCHIVES (Listed with Adventures Into the Unknown)

NEMESIS: THE IMPOSTERS
DC Comics: May, 2010 - No. 4, Aug, 2010 ($2.99, limited series)

	NM-
1-4-Richards-a/Luvisi-c. 1-Joker app. 2-4-Batman app.	3.00

NEMESIS THE WARLOCK (Also see Spellbinders)
Eagle Comics: Sept, 1984 - No. 7, Mar, 1985 (limited series, Baxter paper)

	NM-
1-7: 2000 A.D. reprints	3.00

NEMESIS THE WARLOCK
Quality Comics/Fleetway Quality #2 on: 1989 - No. 19, 1991 ($1.95, B&W)

	NM-
1-19	3.00

NEMO (The League of Extraordinary Gentlemen)
Top Shelf Productions: ($14.95, hardcover, one-shots)

	NM-
...: Heart of Ice HC (2/13) Alan Moore-s/Kevin O'Neill-a	15.00
...: River of Ghosts HC (2015) Alan Moore-s/Kevin O'Neill-a	15.00
...: Roses of Berlin HC (3/14) Alan Moore-s/Kevin O'Neill-a	15.00

NEON JOE, WEREWOLF HUNTER (Based on Adult Swim TV series)
DC Comics: 2015 (no price, one-shot)

	NM-
nn - Origin of Neon Joe; Glaser-s/Mandrake & Duursema-a/Panosian-c	3.00

NEUTRO
Dell Publishing Co.: Jan, 1967

	GD	VG	FN	VF	VF/NM	NM-
1-Jack Sparling-c/a (super hero); UFO-s	4	8	12	27	44	60

NEVADA (See Zane Grey's Four Color 412, 996 & Zane Grey's Stories of the West #1)

NEVADA (Also see Vertigo Winter's Edge #1)
DC Comics (Vertigo): May, 1998 - No. 6, Oct, 1998 ($2.50, limited series)

	NM-
1-6-Gerber-s/Winslade-c/a	3.00
TPB-(1999, $14.95) r/#1-6 & Vertigo Winter's Edge preview	15.00

NEVER AGAIN (War stories; becomes Soldier & Marine V2#9)
Charlton Comics: Aug, 1955; No. 8, July, 1956 (No #2-7)

	GD	VG	FN	VF	VF/NM	NM-
1-WWII	11	22	33	62	86	110
8-(Formerly Foxhole?)	7	14	21	37	46	55

NEVERBOY
Dark Horse Comics: Mar, 2015 - No. 6, Aug, 2015 ($3.99)

	NM-
1-6-Shaun Simon-s/Tyler Jenkins-a	4.00

NEVERMEN, THE (See Dark Horse Presents #148-150)
Dark Horse Comics: May, 2000 - No. 4, Aug, 2000 ($2.95, limited series)

	NM-
1-4-Phil Amara-s/Guy Davis-a	3.00

NEVERMEN, THE: STREETS OF BLOOD
Dark Horse Comics: Jan, 2003 - No. 3, Apr, 2003 ($2.99, limited series)

	NM-
1-3-Phil Amara-s/Guy Davis-a	3.00
TPB (7/03, $9.95) r/#1-3; Paul Jenkins intro.; Davis sketch pages	10.00

NEW ADVENTURE COMICS (Formerly New Comics; becomes Adventure Comics #32 on; V1#12 indicia says NEW COMICS #12)
National Periodical Publications: V1#12, Jan, 1937 - No. 31, Oct, 1938

	GD	VG	FN	VF	VF/NM	NM-
V1#12-Federal Men by Siegel & Shuster continues; Jor-L mentioned; Whitney Ellsworth-c begin, end #14	663	1326	1989	5300	–	–
V2#1(2/37, #13)-(Rare)	663	1326	1989	5300	–	–
V2#2 (#14)	563	1126	1689	4500	–	–
15(V2#3)-20(V2#8): 15-1st Adventure logo; Creig Flessel-c begin, end #31. 16-1st non-funny cover. 17-Nadir, Master of Magic begins, ends #30	431	864	1293	2371	3986	5600
21(V2#9),22(V2#10, 2/37): 22-X-Mas-c	377	754	1131	2074	3487	4900
23-25,28-31	346	692	1038	1903	3202	4500
26(5/38) (rare) has house ad for Action Comics #1 showing B&W image of cover (early published image of Superman)(prices vary widely on this book)	4800	9600	14,400	35,000	–	–
27(6/38) has house ad for Action Comics #1 showing B&W image of cover (rare) (early published image of Superman)	1575	3150	4725	9000	13,500	18,000

NEW ADVENTURES OF ABRAHAM LINCOLN, THE
Image Comics (Homage): 1998 ($19.95, one-shot)

	NM-
1-Scott McCloud-s/computer art	20.00

NEW ADVENTURES OF CHARLIE CHAN, THE (TV)
National Periodical Publications: May-June, 1958 - No. 6, Mar-Apr, 1959

	GD	VG	FN	VF	VF/NM	NM-
1 (Scarce)-John Broome-s/Sid Greene-a in all	94	188	282	597	1024	1450
2 (Scarce)	58	116	174	371	636	900
3-6 (Scarce)-Greene/Giella-a	52	104	156	328	552	775

NEW ADVENTURES OF CHOLLY AND FLYTRAP, THE
Epic Comics: Dec, 1990 - No. 3, Feb, 1991 ($4.95, limited series)

	NM-
1-3-Arthur Suydam-s/a/c; painted covers	5.00

NEW ADVENTURES OF HUCK FINN, THE (TV)
Gold Key: December, 1968 (Hanna-Barbera)

	GD	VG	FN	VF	VF/NM	NM-
1- "The Curse of Thut"; part photo-c	3	6	9	21	33	45

NEW ADVENTURES OF PINOCCHIO (TV)
Dell Publishing Co.: Oct-Dec, 1962 - No. 3, Sept-Nov, 1963

	GD	VG	FN	VF	VF/NM	NM-
12-562-212(#1)	7	14	21	48	89	130
2,3	6	12	18	38	69	100

NEW ADVENTURES OF ROBIN HOOD (See Robin Hood)

NEW ADVENTURES OF SHERLOCK HOLMES (Also see Sherlock Holmes)
Dell Publishing Co.: No. 1169, Mar-May, 1961 - No. 1245, Nov-Jan, 1961/62

	GD	VG	FN	VF	VF/NM	NM-
Four Color 1169(#1)	12	24	36	79	170	260
Four Color 1245	10	20	30	70	150	230

NEW ADVENTURES OF SPEED RACER
Now Comics: Dec, 1993 - No. 7, 1994? ($1.95)

	NM-
1-7	3.00
0-(Premiere)-3-D cover	3.00

NEW ADVENTURES OF SUPERBOY, THE (Also see Superboy)
DC Comics: Jan, 1980 - No. 54, June, 1984

	GD	VG	FN	VF	VF/NM	NM-
1	1	3	4	6	8	10
2-6,8-10						4.00
11-49,51-54: 11-Superboy gets new power. 14-Lex Luthor app. 15-Superboy gets new parents. 28-Dial "H" For Hero begins, ends #49. 45-47-1st app. Sunburst. 48-Begin 75¢-c.						3.00
1,2,5,6,8 (Whitman variants; low print run; no issue # shown on cover)	3	6	9	14	20	25
7,50: 7-Has extra story "The Computers That Saved Metropolis" by Starlin (Radio Shack giveaway w/indicia). 50-Legion app.						5.00

NOTE: ***Buckler** a-9p; c-36p. **Giffen** a-50; c-50. 40i. **Gil Kane** c-32p, 33p, 35, 39, 41-49. **Miller** c-51. **Starlin** a-7. Krypto back-ups in 17, 22. Superbaby in 11, 14, 19, 24.*

NEW ADVENTURES OF THE PHANTOM BLOT, THE (See The Phantom Blot)

NEW AMERICA
Eclipse Comics: Nov, 1987 - No. 4, Feb, 1988 ($1.75, Baxter paper)

	NM-
1-4: Scout limited series	3.00

NEW ARCHIES, THE (TV)
Archie Comic Publications: Oct, 1987 - No. 22, May, 1990 (75¢)

	NM-
1	5.00
2-10: 3-Xmas issue	4.00
11-22: 17-22 (95¢-$1.00): 21-Xmas issue	3.00

NEW ARCHIES DIGEST (TV)(...Comics Digest Magazine #4?-10; ...Digest Magazine #11 on)
Archie Comics: May, 1988 - No. 14, July, 1991 ($1.35/$1.50, quarterly)

	NM-
1	6.00
2-14: 6-Begin $1.50-c	3.50

NEW AVENGERS, THE (Also see Promotional section for military giveaway)
Marvel Comics: Jan, 2005 - No. 64, Jun, 2010 ($2.25/$2.50/$2.99/$3.99)

1-Bendis-s/Finch-a; Spider-Man app.; re-intro The Sentry; 4 covers by McNiven, Quesada

New Avengers (2010 series) #1 © MAR

New Comics #1 © DC

New 52: Future's End #21 © DC

GD VG FN VF VF/NM NM-
2.0 4.0 6.0 8.0 9.0 9.2

& Finch; variants from #1-6 combine for one team image 5.00
1-Director's Cut ($3.99) includes alternate covers, script, villain gallery 4.00
1-MGC (6/10 $1.00) r/#1 with "Marvel's Greatest Comics" cover logo 3.00
2-20: 2-6-Finch-a. 4-1st app. Maria Hill. 5-Wolverine app. 7-10-Origin of the Sentry; McNiven-a. 11-Debut of Ronin. 14,15-Cho-c/a. 17-20-Deodato-a 3.00
21-48: 21-26-Civil War. 21-Chaykin-a/c. 26-Maleev-a. 27-31-Yu-a; Echo & "Elektra" app. 33-37-The Hood app. 38-Gaydos-a. 39-Mack-a. 40-47-Secret Invasion 3.00
49-($3.99) Dark Reign 4.00
50-($4.99) Dark Reign; Tan, Hitch, McNiven, Yu, Horn & others-a; Tan wraparound-c 5.00
50-($4.99) Adam Kubert variant-c 6.00
51-64-($3.99) Dark Reign. 51,52-Tan & Bachalo-a. 54-Brother Voodoo becomes Sorceror Supreme. 56-Wrecking Crew app. 61-64-Siege; Steve Rogers app. 4.00
51-54-Variant covers by Bachalo 7.00
56,57-Variant covers. 56-70th Anniversary frame. 57-Super Hero Squad 6.00
Annual 1 (6/06, $3.99) Wedding of Luke Cage and Jessica Jones; Bendis-s/Coipel-a 4.00
Annual 2 (2/08, $3.99) Avengers vs. The Hood's gang; Bendis-s/Pagulayan-a 4.00
Annual 3 (2/10, $4.99) Mayhew-c/a; Dark Avengers app.; Siege preview 5.00
... Finale (6/10, $4.99) Follows Siege #4; Bendis-s/Hitch-a/c; Count Nefaria app. 5.00
...: Illuminati (5/06, $3.99) Bendis-s/Maleev-a; leads into Planet Hulk; Civil War preview 4.00
... Most Wanted Files (2006, $3.99) profile pages of Avenger villains 4.00
... Volume 1 HC (2007, $29.99) oversized r/#1-10, ... Most Wanted Files, and ... Guest Starring the Fantastic Four (militiary giveaway); new intro. by Bendis; script & sketch pages 30.00
... Volume 2 HC (2008, $29.99) oversized r/#11-20, ... Annual #1, and story from Giant-Size Spider-Woman; variant covers & sketch pages 30.00

NEW AVENGERS (The Heroic Age)
Marvel Comics: Aug, 2010 - No. 34, Jan, 2013 ($3.99)

1-Bendis-s/Immonen-a/c; Luke Cage forms new team; back-up text Avengers history 4.00
1-Variant-c by Djurdjevic 6.00
2-16: Hellstrom & Doctor Voodoo app.; back-up text Avengers history. 6-Doctor Voodoo killed. 9-13-Nick Fury flashback w/Chaykin-a. 10-Intro. Avengers 1959. 14-16-Fear Itself. 16-Daredevil joins 4.00
16.1 (11/11, $2.99) Neal Adams-a/c; Bendis-s; Norman Osborn app. 3.00
17-23-($3.99) 17-Norman Osborn attacks; Iron Man app.; Deodato-a 4.00
24-33: 24-30-Avengers vs. X-Men tie-in. 26,27-DaVinci app. 31-Gaydos-a. 32-Pacheco-a 4.00
34-($4.99) Dr. Strange become Sorcerer Supreme again; Deodato-a; gallery of Bendis-era Avengers covers 5.00
Annual 1 (11/11, $4.99) Dell'Otto-a; Wonder Man app.; continues in Avengers Annual #1 5.00

NEW AVENGERS (Marvel NOW!)
Marvel Comics: Mar, 2013 - No. 33, Jun, 2015 ($3.99)

1-7: 1-Hickman-s/Epting-a; Black Panther and the Illuminati. 4-Galactus app. 4.00
8-23: 8-12-Infinity tie-ins; Deodato-a. 13-Inhumanity; Bianchi-a. 17-21-Great Society app. 4.00
24-($4.99) Doctor Doom, Thanos and the Cabal app. 5.00
25-32: 27-Kudranski-a. 28,32-Deodato-a 4.00
33-($4.99) Doctor Doom & Molecule Man app.; leads into Secret Wars x-over; Deodato-a 5.00
Annual 1 (8/14, $4.99) Spotlight on Doctor Strange; Marco Rudy-a 5.00

NEW AVENGERS (Follows events of Secret Wars)(See U.S.Avengers)
Marvel Comics: Dec, 2015 - No. 18, Jan, 2017 ($3.99)

1-18: 1-Ewing-s/Sandoval-a; Squirrel Girl app. 5,6-Avengers of 20XX app. 8-10-Standoff tie-in; Marcus To-a. 12-17-Civil War II tie-in. 12-16-Interlocking covers 4.00

NEW AVENGERS: ILLUMINATI (Also see Civil War and Secret Invasion)
Marvel Comics: Feb, 2007 - No. 5, Jan, 2008 ($2.99, limited series)

1-5-Bendis & Reed-s/Cheung-a. 3-Origin of The Beyonder. 5-Secret Invasion 3.00
HC (2008, $19.99, dustjacket) r/#1-5; cover sketch art 20.00
SC (2008, $14.99) r/#1-5; cover sketch art 15.00

NEW AVENGERS: LUKE CAGE
Marvel Comics: Jun, 2010 - No. 3, Aug, 2010 ($3.99, limited series)

1-3-Arcudi-s/Canete-a; Spider-Man & Ronin app. 4.00

NEW AVENGERS: THE REUNION
Marvel Comics: May, 2009 - No. 4, Aug, 2009 ($3.99, limited series)

1-4-Mockingbird and Ronin (Hawkeye); McCann-s/López-a/Jo Chen-c 4.00

NEW AVENGERS/TRANSFORMERS
Marvel Comics: Sept, 2007 - No. 4, Dec, 2007 ($2.99, limited series)

1-4-Kirkham-a; Capt. America app. 1-Cheung-c. 2-Pearson-c 3.00
TPB (2008, $10.99) r/#1-4 11.00

NEW AVENGERS: ULTRON FOREVER
Marvel Comics: Jun, 2015 ($4.99)(Continues in Uncanny Avengers: Ultron Forever)

1-Part 2 of 3-part crossover with Avengers and Uncanny Avengers; Ewing-s/Alan Davis-a; team-up of past, present and future Avengers vs. Ultron 5.00

NEW BOOK OF COMICS (Also see Big Book Of Fun)
National Periodical Publ.: 1937; No. 2, Spring, 1938 (100 pgs. each) (Reprints)

1(Rare)-1st regular size comic annual; 2nd DC annual; contains r/New Comics #1-4 & More Fun #9; r/Federal Men (8 pgs.), Henri Duval (1 pg.), & Dr. Occult in costume (1 pg.) by Siegel & Shuster; Moldoff, Sheldon Mayer (15 pgs.)-a
1850 3700 5550 12,000 21,000 30,000
2-Contains-r/More Fun #15 & 16; r/Dr. Occult in costume (a Superman prototype), & Calling All Cars (4 pgs.) by Siegel & Shuster 950 1900 2850 6175 11,088 16,000

NEW COMICS (New Adventure #12 on)
National Periodical Publ.: 12/35 - No. 11, 12/36 (No. 1-6: paper cover) (No. 1-5: 84 pgs.)

V1#1-Billy the Kid, Sagebrush 'n' Cactus, Jibby Jones, Needles, The Vikings, Sir Loin of Beef, Now-When I Was a Boy, & other 1-2 pg. strips; 2 pgs. Kelly art(1st)-(Gulliver's Travels); Sheldon Mayer-a(1st)(2 2pg. strips); Vincent Sullivan-c(1st)
2349 4698 7047 14,800 – –
2-1st app. Federal Men by Siegel & Shuster & begins (also see The Comics Magazine #2); Mayer, Kelly-a (Rare)(1/36) 1317 2634 3951 8300 – –
3-6: 3,4-Sheldon Mayer-a which continues in The Comics Magazine #1. 3-Vincent Sullivan-c. 4-Dickens' "A Tale of Two Cities" adaptation begins. 5-Junior Federal Men Club; Kiefer-a. 6- "She" adaptation begins 760 1520 2280 5700 – –
7-10 493 986 1479 3600 – –
11-Ties with More Fun #16 as DC's 1st Christmas-c 547 1094 1641 4100 – –

NOTE: *#1-6 rarely occur in mint condition.* ***Whitney Ellsworth*** *c-4-11.*

NEW CRUSADERS (Rise of the Heroes)
Archie Comics (Red Circle Comics): Oct, 2012 - Present ($2.99)

1-6-The Shield and the offspring of the Mighty Crusaders 3.00

NEW DEADWARDIANS, THE
DC Comics (Vertigo): May, 2012 - No. 8, Dec, 2012 ($2.99, limited series)

1-8-Abnett-s/Culbard-a 3.00

NEW DEFENDERS (See Defenders)

NEW DNAGENTS, THE (Formerly DNAgents)
Eclipse Comics: V2#1, Oct, 1985 - V2#17, Mar, 1987 (Whole #s 25-40; Mando paper)

V2#1-17: 1-Origin recap. 7-Begin 95 cent-c. 9,10-Airboy preview 3.00
3-D 1 (1/86, $2.25) 3.00
2-D 1 (1/86)-Limited ed. (100 copies) 10.00

NEW DYNAMIX
DC Comics (WildStorm): May, 2008 - No. 5, Sept, 2008 ($2.99, limited series)

1-5-Warner-s/J.J. Kirby-a/c. 1-Variant-c by Jim Lee. 1-Convention Ed. with Lee-c 3.00

NEW ETERNALS: APOCALYPSE NOW (Also see Eternals, The)
Marvel Comics: Feb, 2000 ($3.99, one-shot)

1-Bennett & Hanna-a; Ladronn-c 4.00

NEW EXCALIBUR
Marvel Comics: Jan, 2006 - No. 24, Dec, 2007 ($2.99)

1-24: 1-Claremont-s/Ryan-a; Dazzler app. 3-Juggernaut app. 4-Lionheart app. 3.00
... Vol. 1: Defenders of the Realm TPB (2006, $17.99) r/#1-7 18.00
... Vol. 2: Last Days of Camelot TPB (2007, $19.99) r/#8-15 20.00
... Vol. 3: Battle for Eternity TPB (2007, $24.99) r/#16-24; sketch pages 25.00

NEW EXILES (Continued from Exiles #100 and Exiles - Days of Then and Now)
Marvel Comics: Mar, 2008 - No. 18, Apr, 2009 ($2.99)

1-18: 1-Claremont-s/Grummett-a; 2 covers by Land & Golden; new team 3.00
1-2nd printing with Grummett-c 3.00
Annual 1 (2/09, $3.99) Claremont-s/Grummett-a 4.00

NEW 52: FUTURE'S END
DC Comics: No 0, Jun, 2014 - No. 48, Jun, 2015 ($2.99, weekly limited series)

... FCBD Special Edition #0 (6/14, giveaway) Part 1; 35 years in the future 3.00
1-36: 1-Set 5 years in the future; Azzarello, Lemire, Jurgens & Giffen-s. 29-New Firestorm. 33-Kid Deathstroke-c. 44-Brainiac steals New York (Convergence) 3.00

NEWFORCE (Also see Newmen)
Image Comics (Extreme Studios): Jan, 1996-No. 4, Apr, 1996 ($2.50, lim. series)

1-4: 1-"Extreme Destroyer" Pt. 8; polybagged w/gaming card. 4-Newforce disbands 3.00

NEW FUN COMICS (More Fun #7 on; see Big Book of Fun Comics)
National Periodical Publications: Feb, 1935 - No. 6, Oct, 1935 (10x15", No. 1-4,: slick-c) (No. 1-5: 36 pgs; 40 pgs. No. 6)

V1#1 (1st DC comic); 1st app. Oswald The Rabbit; Jack Woods (cowboy) begins
8429 16,858 25,287 59,000 – –
2(3/35)-(Very Rare) 4000 8000 12,000 28,000 – –
3-5(8/35): 3-Don Drake on the Planet Soro-c/story (sci/fi, 4/35); early (maybe 1st) DC letter column. 5-Soft-c 2643 5286 7929 18,500 – –
6(10/35)-1st Dr. Occult by Siegel & Shuster (Leger & Reuths); last "New Fun" title.

New Funnies #67 © DELL

New Gods #10 © DC

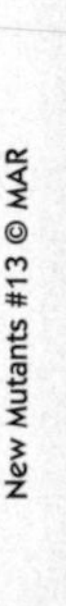
New Mutants #13 © MAR

GD VG FN VF VF/NM NM-
2.0 4.0 6.0 8.0 9.0 9.2

GD VG FN VF VF/NM NM-
2.0 4.0 6.0 8.0 9.0 9.2

"New Comics" #1 begins in Dec. which is reason for title change to More Fun; Henri Duval (ends #10) by Siegel & Shuster begins; paper-c
4286 8572 12,858 30,000 – –

NEW FUNNIES (The Funnies #1-64; Walter Lantz...#109 on; New TV... #259, 260, 272, 273; TV Funnies #261-271)
Dell Publishing Co.: No. 65, July, 1942 - No. 288, Mar-Apr, 1962

65(#1)-Andy Panda in a world of real people, Raggedy Ann & Andy, Oswald the Rabbit (with Woody Woodpecker x-overs), Li'l Eight Ball & Peter Rabbit begin; Bugs Bunny and Elmer app. 93 186 279 744 1672 2600
66-70: 66-Felix the Cat begins. 67-Billy & Bonny Bee by Frank Thomas begins. 69-Kelly-a (2 pgs.); The Brownies begin (not by Kelly); Halloween-c
31 62 93 223 499 775
71-75: 71-Christmas-c. 72-Kelly illos. 75-Brownies by Kelly?
21 42 63 146 311 475
76-Andy Panda (Carl Barks & Pabian-a); Woody Woodpecker x-over in Oswald ends
50 100 150 400 900 1400
77,78: 77-Kelly-c. 78-Andy Panda in a world with real people ends
15 30 45 103 227 350
79-81 10 20 30 69 147 225
82-Brownies by Kelly begins 11 22 33 73 157 240
83-85-Brownies by Kelly in ea. 83-X-mas-c; Homer Pigeon begins. 85-Woody Woodpecker, 1 pg. strip begins 11 22 33 72 154 235
86-90: 87-Woody Woodpecker stories begin 9 18 27 57 111 165
91-99 8 16 24 51 96 140
100 (6/45) 8 16 24 54 102 150
101-120: 119-X-Mas-c 7 14 21 46 86 125
121-150: 131,143-X-Mas-c 6 12 18 40 73 105
151-200: 155-X-Mas-c. 167-X-Mas-c. 182-Origin & 1st app. Knothead & Splinter. 191-X-Mas-c 5 10 15 35 63 90
201-240 5 10 15 35 57 80
241-288: 270,271-Walter Lantz c-app. 281-1st story swipes/WDC&S #100
5 10 15 30 50 70

NOTE: *Early issues written by* ***John Stanley.***

NEW GODS, THE (1st Series)(New Gods #12 on)(See Adventure #459, DC Graphic Novel #4, 1st Issue Special #13 & Super-Team Family)
National Periodical Publications/DC Comics: 2-3/71 - V2#11, 10-11/72; V3#12, 7/77 - V3#19, 7-8/78 (Fourth World)

1-Intro/1st app. Orion; 4th app. Darkseid (cameo; 3 weeks after Forever People #1) (#1-3 are 15¢ issues) 10 20 30 64 132 200
2-Darkseid-c/story (2nd full app., 4-5/71) 6 12 18 37 66 95
3-1st app. Black Racer; last 15¢ issue 4 8 12 27 44 60
4-6,8,9: (25¢, 52 pg. giants): 4-Darkseid cameo; origin Manhunter-r. 5,8-Young Gods feature. 9-1st app. Forager 4 8 12 23 37 50
7-1st app. Steppenwolf (2-3/72); Darkseid app.; origin Orion; 1st origin of all New Gods as a group; Young Gods feature 12 24 36 80 173 265
10,11: 11-Last Kirby issue. 3 6 9 19 30 40
12-19: Darkseid storyline w/minor apps. 12-New costume Orion (see 1st Issue Special #13 for 1st new costume). 19-Story continued in Adventure Comics #459,460
2 4 6 8 10 12
Jack Kirby's New Gods TPB ('98, $11.95, B&W&Grey) r/#1-11 plus cover gallery of original series and "84 reprints 12.00

NOTE: *#4-9(25¢, 52 pgs.) contain Manhunter-r by* ***Simon*** *&* ***Kirby*** *from Adventure #73, 74, 75, 76, 77, 78 with covers in that order.* ***Adkins*** *i-12-14, 17-19.* ***Buckler*** *a(p)-15.* ***Kirby*** *c/a-1-11p.* ***Newton*** *a(p)-12-14, 16-19.* ***Starlin*** *c-17.* ***Staton*** *c-19p.*

NEW GODS (Also see DC Graphic Novel #4)
DC Comics: June, 1984 - No. 6, Nov, 1984 ($2.00, Baxter paper)

1-5: New Kirby-c; r/New Gods #1-10. 5.00
6-Reprints New Gods #11 w/48 pgs of new Kirby story & art; leads into DC Graphic Novel #4
2 4 6 8 10 12

NEW GODS (2nd Series)
DC Comics: Feb, 1989 - No. 28, Aug, 1991 ($1.50)

1-28: 1,5-28-Evanier-s. 2-4-Starlin-s. 13-History of New Gods 20th anniv. 3.00

NEW GODS (3rd Series) (Becomes Jack Kirby's Fourth World) (Also see Showcase '94 #1 & Showcase '95 #7)
DC Comics: Oct, 1995 - No. 15, Feb, 1997 ($1.95)

1-11,13-15: 9-Giffen-a(p). 10,11-Superman app. 13-Takion, Mr. Miracle & Big Barda app. 13-15-Byrne-a(p)/scripts & Simonson-c. 15-Apokolips merged w/ New Genesis; story cont'd in Jack Kirby's Fourth World 3.00
12-(11/96, 99¢)-Byrne-a(p)/scripts & Simonson-c begin; Takion cameo; indicia reads October 1996 3.00
...Secret Files 1 (9/98, $4.95) Origin-s 5.00

NEW GODS SPECIAL, THE (Jack Kirby's 100th Birthday tribute)
DC Comics: Oct, 2017 ($4.99, one-shot)

1-Spotlight on Orion; Shane Davis-s/a; back-up by Walt Simonson-s/a; short reprints 5.00

NEW GUARDIANS, THE
DC Comics: Sept, 1988 - No. 12, Sept, 1989 ($1.25)

1-($2.00, 52 pgs)-Staton-c/a in #1-9 4.00
2-12 3.00

NEW HEROIC (See Heroic)

NEW INVADERS (Titled Invaders for #0 & #1) (See Avengers V3#83,84)
Marvel Comics: No. 0, Aug, 2004 - No. 9, June, 2005 ($2.99)

0-9-Roster of U.S. Agent, Sub-Mariner, Blazing Skull and others. 0-Avengers app. 3.00

NEW JUSTICE MACHINE, THE (Also see The Justice Machine)
Innovation Publishing: 1989 - No. 3, 1989 ($1.95, limited series)

1-3 3.00

NEW KIDS ON THE BLOCK, THE (Also see Richie Rich and...)
Harvey Comics: Dec, 1990 - No. 8, Dec, 1991 ($1.25)

1-8 4.00
...**Back Stage Pass** 1(12/90) - 7(11/91) **Chillin'** 1(12/90) - 7(12/91): 1-Photo-c ...**Comic Tour** '90/91 1 (12/90) - 7(12/91) **Digest** 1(1/91) - 5(1/92) **Hanging Tough** 1 (2/91) **Magic Summer Tour** 1 (Fall/90) **Magic Summer Tour** nn (Fall/90, sold at concerts) **Step By Step** 1 (Fall/90, one-shot) **Valentine Girl** 1 (Fall/90, one-shot)-Photo-c 4.00

NEW LINE CINEMA'S TALES OF HORROR (Anthology)
DC Comics (WildStorm): Nov, 2007 ($2.99, one-shot)

1-Freddy Krueger and Leatherface app.; Darick Robertson-c 3.00

NEW LOVE (See Love & Rockets)
Fantagraphics Books: Aug, 1996 - No. 6, Dec, 1997 ($2.95, B&W, lim. series)

1-6: Gilbert Hernandez-s/a 3.00

NEWMAN
Image Comics (Extreme Studios): Jan, 1996 - No. 4, Apr, 1996 ($2.50, lim. series)

1-4: 1-Extreme Destroyer Pt. 3; polybagged w/card. 4-Shadowhunt tie-in; Eddie Collins becomes new Shadowhawk 3.00

NEW MANGVERSE (Also see Marvel Mangaverse)
Marvel Comics: Mar, 2006 - No. 5, July, 2006 ($2.99, lim. series)

1-5: Cebulski-s/Ohtsuka-a; The Hand and Elektra app. 3.00
...: The Rings of Fate (2006, $7.99, digest) r/#1-5 8.00

NEWMEN (becomes The Adventures Of The...#22)
Image Comics (Extreme Studios): Apr, 1994 - No. 20, Nov, 1995; No. 21, Nov, 1996 ($1.95/$2.50)

1-21: 1-5: Matsuda-c/a. 10-Polybagged w/trading card. 11-Polybagged. 20-Has a variant-c; Babewatch! x-over. 21-(11/96)-Series relaunch; Chris Sprouse-a begins; pin-up. 16-Has a variant-c by Quesada & Palmiotti 3.00
TPB-(1996, $12.95) r/#1-4 w/pin-ups 13.00

NEW MEN OF BATTLE, THE
Catechetical Guild: 1949 (nn) (Carboard-c)

nn(V8#1-3,5,6)-192 pgs.; contains 6 issues of Topix rebound
10 20 30 54 72 90
nn(V8#7-V8#11)-160 pgs.; contains 5 iss. of Topix 9 18 27 50 65 80

NEW MGMT (See Mind MGMT)

NEW MUTANTS, THE (See Marvel Graphic Novel #4 for 1st app.)(Also see X-Force & Uncanny X-Men #167)
Marvel Comics Group: Mar, 1983 - No. 100, Apr, 1991

1-Claremont-s/McLeod-a 3 6 9 14 20 25
2-10: 3,4-Ties into X-Men #167. 10-1st app. Magma 5.00
11-15,17,19,20: 13-Kitty Pryde app. 4.00
16-1st app. Warpath (w/out costume); see Uncanny X-Men #193
2 4 6 13 18 22
18-Intro. new Warlock 2 4 6 9 12 15
21-Double size; origin new Warlock; newsstand version has cover price written in by Sienkiewicz 5.00
22-24,27-30: 23-25-Cloak & Dagger app. 4.00
25-1st brief app. Legion (David Haller) 3 6 9 16 23 30
26-1st full Legion app. 3 6 9 19 30 40
31-49,51-58: 35-Magneto intro'd as new headmaster. 43-Portacio-i. 58-Contains pull-out mutant registration form 4.00
50,73: 50-Double size. 73-(52 pgs.). 5.00
59-61: Fall of The Mutants series. 60-(52 pgs.) 5.00

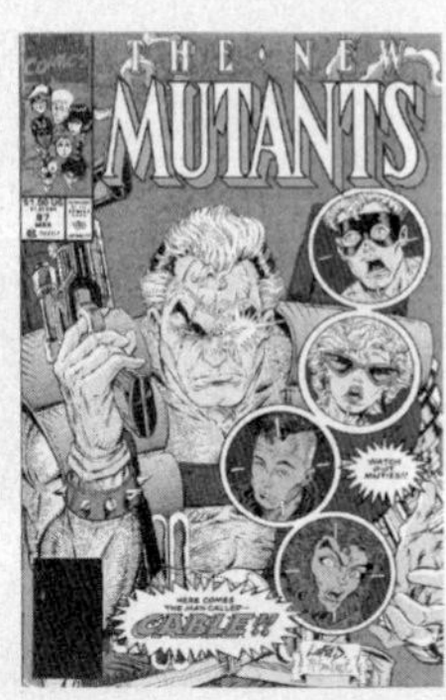

New Mutants #87 © MAR

New Suicide Squad #4 © DC

New Teen Titans #10 © DC

GD 2.0 | VG 4.0 | FN 6.0 | VF 8.0 | VF/NM 9.0 | NM- 9.2

62-72,74-85: 68-Intro Spyder. 63-X-Men & Wolverine clones app. 76-X-Factor & X-Terminator app. 85-Liefeld-c begin 4.00
86-Rob Liefeld-a begins; McFarlane-c(i) swiped from Ditko splash pg.; 1st brief app. Cable (last page teaser) 3 6 9 14 20 25
87-1st full app. Cable (3/90) 9 18 27 59 117 175
87-2nd printing; gold metallic ink-c ($1.00) 3 6 9 14 19 24
88-2nd app. Cable 2 4 6 8 10 12
92-No Liefeld-a; Liefeld-c 5.00
89,90,91,93-97,99: 89-3rd app. Cable. 90-New costumes. 90,91-Sabretooth app. 93,94-Cable vs. Wolverine. 95-97-X-Tinction Agenda x-over. 95-Death of new Warlock. 97-Wolverine & Cable-c, but no app. 99-1st app. of Feral (of X-Force); 2nd app. Shatterstar (cameo); Byrne-c/swipe (X-Men, 1st Series #138) 6.00
95,100-Gold 2nd printing. 100-Silver ink 3rd printing 6.00
98-1st app. Deadpool, Gideon & Domino (2/91); Liefeld-c/a 14 28 42 93 204 315
100-(52 pgs.)-1st brief app. X-Force; 1st full app. of Shatterstar 3 6 9 14 20 25
Annual 1 (1984) 1 3 4 6 8 10
Annual 2 (1986, $1.25)-1st Psylocke 4 8 12 27 44 60
Annual 3,4,6,7 ('87, '88,'90,'91, 68 pgs.): 4-Evolutionary War x-over. 6-1st new costumes by Liefeld (3 pgs.); 1st brief app. Shatterstar (of X-Force). 7-Liefeld pin-up only; X-Terminators back-up story; 2nd app. X-Force (cont'd in New Warriors Annual #1) 5.00
Annual 5 (1989, $2.00, 68 pgs.)-Atlantis Attacks; 1st Liefeld-a on New Mutants 6.00
... Classic Vol. 1 TPB (2006, $24.99) r/#1-7, Marvel Graphic Novel #4, Uncanny X-Men #167 25.00
... Classic Vol. 2 TPB (2007, $24.99) r/#8-17 25.00
... Classic Vol. 3 TPB (2008, $24.99) r/#18-25 & Annual #1 25.00
Special 1-Special Edition ('85, 68 pgs.)-Ties in w/X-Men Alpha Flight limited series; cont'd in X-Men Annual #9; Art Adams/Austin-a 2 4 6 8 10 12
Summer Special 1(Sum/90, $2.95, 84 pgs.) 5.00
NOTE: ***Art Adams*** *c-38, 39.* ***Austin*** *c-57i.* ***Byrne*** *c/a-75p.* ***Liefeld*** *a-86-91p, 93-96p, 98-100, Annual 5p, 6(3 pgs.); c-85-91p, 92, 93p, 94, 95, 96p, 97-100, Annual 5, 6p.* ***McFarlane*** *c-85-89i, 93i.* ***Portacio*** *a(i)-43.* ***Russell*** *a-48i.* ***Sienkiewicz*** *a-18-31, 35-38i; c-17-31, 35i, 37i, Annual 1.* ***Simonson*** *c-11p.* ***B. Smith*** *c-36, 40-48.* ***Williamson*** *a(i)-69, 71-73, 78-80, 82, 83; c(i)-69, 72, 73, 78i.*

NEW MUTANTS (Continues as New X-Men (Academy X))
Marvel Comics: July, 2003 - No. 13, June, 2004 ($2.50/$2.99)
1-13: 1-6-Josh Middleton-c. 7-11-Bachalo-c. 8-Begin $2.99 3.00
... Vol. 1: Back To School TPB (2005, $16.99) r/#1-6; new Middleton-c 17.00

NEW MUTANTS
Marvel Comics: July, 2009 - No. 50, Dec, 2012 ($3.99/$2.99)
1-($3.99) Neves-a; Legion app.; covers by Ross, Adam Kubert, McLeod, Benjamin 4.00
2-24-($2.99) 2-10-Adam Kubert-c. 11-Siege; Dodson-c. 12-14-Second Coming 3.00
25-($3.99) Fernandez-a; wraparound-c by Djurdjevic; Nate Grey returns 4.00
26-50: 29-32-Fear Itself tie-in. 33-Regenesis. 34-Blink returns. 42,43-Exiled x-over with Exiled #1 & Journey Into Mystery #637,638 3.00
... Saga (2009, giveaway) New Mutants character profiles and story synopsies; Neves-c 3.00

NEW MUTANTS FOREVER
Marvel Comics: Oct, 2010 - No. 5, Feb, 2011 ($3.99, limited series)
1-5-Claremont-s/Rio & McLeod-a; Red Skull app. 1-Back-up history of New Mutants 4.00

NEW MUTANTS, THE: TRUTH OR DEATH
Marvel Comics: Nov, 1997 - No. 3, Jan, 1998 ($2.50, limited series)
1-3-Raab-s/Chang-a(p) 3.00

NEW PEOPLE, THE (TV)
Dell Publishing Co.: Jan, 1970 - No. 2, May, 1970
1 3 6 9 16 24 32
2-Photo-c 3 6 9 15 21 26

NEW ROMANCER
DC Comics (Vertigo): Feb, 2016 - No. 6, Jul, 2016 ($3.99, limited series)
1-6-Milligan-s/Parson-a; Lord Byron & Casanova in present day 4.00

NEW ROMANCES
Standard Comics: No. 5, May, 1951 - No. 21, May, 1954
5-Photo-c 20 40 60 114 182 250
6-9: 6-Barbara Bel Geddes, Richard Basehart "Fourteen Hours" photo-c. 7-Ray Milland & Joan Fontaine photo-c. 9-Photo-c from '50s movie 14 28 42 76 108 140
10,14,16,17-Toth-a 14 28 42 80 115 150
11-Toth-a; Liz Taylor, Montgomery Clift photo-c 36 72 108 216 351 485
12,13,15,18-21 12 24 36 69 97 125
NOTE: ***Celardo*** *a-9.* ***Moreira*** *a-6.* ***Tuska*** *a-7, 20. Photo c-5-16.*

NEWSBOY LEGION AND THE BOY COMMANDOS SPECIAL, THE (Jack Kirby's 100th Birthday tribute)

GD 2.0 | VG 4.0 | FN 6.0 | VF 8.0 | VF/NM 9.0 | NM- 9.2

DC Comics: Oct, 2017 ($4.99, one-shot)
1-Howard Chaykin-s/a/c; reprint from Star Spangled Comics #29; Simon-s/Kirby-a 5.00

NEWSBOY LEGION BY JOE SIMON AND JACK KIRBY, THE
DC Comics: 2010 ($49.99, hardcover with dustjacket)
Vol. 1 - Reprints apps. in Star Spangled Comics #7-32; new intro. by Joe Simon 50.00

NEW SHADOWHAWK, THE (Also see Shadowhawk & Shadowhunt)
Image Comics (Shadowline Ink): June, 1995 - No. 7, Mar, 1996 ($2.50)
1-7: Kurt Busiek scripts in all 3.00

NEW STATESMEN, THE
Fleetway Publications (Quality Comics): 1989 - No. 5, 1990 ($3.95, limited series, mature readers, 52pgs.)
1-5: Futuristic; squarebound; 3-Photo-c 4.00

NEWSTRALIA
Innovation Publ.: July, 1989 - No. 5, 1989 ($1.75, color)(#2 on, $2.25, B&W)
1-5: 1,2: Timothy Truman-c/a; Gustovich-i 3.00

NEW SUICIDE SQUAD (DC New 52)
DC Comics: Sept, 2014 - No. 22, Sept, 2016 ($2.99)
1-New team of Harley Quinn, Joker's Daughter, Black Manta, Deathstroke, Deadshot 3 6 9 17 26 35
2,3 1 2 3 5 6 8
4-10 4.00
11-22: 22-Cliquet-a 3.00
Annual 1 (11/15, $4.99) Continues story from #12; Briones-a 5.00
...: Futures End 1 (11/14, $2.99, regular-c) Five years later; Coelho-a 3.00
...: Futures End 1 (11/14, $3.99, 3-D cover) 4.00

NEW SUPER-MAN (DC Rebirth)(See Batman/Superman #32 for 1st app.)
DC Comics: Sept, 2016 - No. 19, Mar, 2018 ($2.99/$3.99)
1-9: 1-Kong Kenan as China's Superman; origin; Gene Luen Yang-s/Bogdanovic-a. 7-9-Master I-Ching app. 8-Ching Lung (from Detective Comics #1) app. 9-Luthor app. 3.00
10-19-($3.99) 10-Superman app. 15-Suicide Squad app. 17,18-Justice League app. 4.00

NEW SUPER-MAN & THE JUSTICE LEAGUE OF CHINA
DC Comics: No. 20, Apr, 2018 - Present ($3.99)
20-Yang-s/Peeples-a 4.00

NEW TALENT SHOWCASE (Talent Showcase #16 on)
DC Comics: Jan, 1984 - No. 19, Oct, 1985 (Direct sales only)
1-19: Features new strips & artists. 18-Williamson-c(i) 3.00

NEW TALENT SHOWCASE
DC Comics: Jan, 2017 ($7.99, one-shot)
1-Janson-c; short stories by various; Wonder Woman, Harley Quinn, Deadman app. 8.00
... 2017 #1 (1/18, $7.99) Short stories by various; Wonder Woman, Red Hood, Duke, Katana, Deadshot, Poison Ivy and Dr. Fate app. 8.00

NEW TEEN TITANS, THE (See DC Comics Presents #26, Marvel and DC Present & Teen Titans; Tales of the Teen Titans #41 on)
DC Comics: Nov, 1980 - No. 40, Mar, 1984
1-Robin, Kid Flash, Wonder Girl, The Changeling (1st app.), Starfire, The Raven, Cyborg begin; partial origin 5 10 15 30 50 70
2-1st app. Deathstroke the Terminator 9 18 27 59 117 175
3-9: 3-Origin Starfire; Intro The Fearsome Five. 4-Origin continues; J.L.A. app. 6-Origin Raven. 7-Cyborg origin. 8-Origin Kid Flash retold. 9-Minor app. Deathstroke on last pg. 2 4 6 8 11 14
10-2nd app. Deathstroke the Terminator (see Marvel & DC Present for 3rd app.); origin Changeling retold 2 4 6 11 16 20
11-20: 13-Return of Madame Rouge & Capt. Zahl; Robotman revived. 14-Return of Mento; origin Doom Patrol. 15-Death of Madame Rouge & Capt. Zahl; intro. new Brotherhood of Evil. 16-1st app. Captain Carrot (free 16 pg. preview). 18-Return of Starfire. 19-Hawkman teams-up 1 2 3 4 5 7
21-Intro Night Force in free 16 pg. insert; intro Brother Blood 2 4 6 8 10 12
22-25,27-33,35-40: 22-1st app. Bethany Snow. 23-1st app. Vigilante (not in costume), & Blackfire; bondage-c. 24-Omega Men app. 25-Omega Men cameo; free 16 pg. preview Masters of the Universe. 27-Free 16 pg. preview Atari Force. 29-The New Brotherhood of Evil & Speedy app. 30-Terra joins the Titans. 37-Batman & The Outsiders x-over. 38-Origin Wonder Girl. 39-Last Dick Grayson as Robin; Kid Flash quits 5.00
26-1st app. Terra 2 4 6 8 10 12
34-4th app. Deathstroke the Terminator 2 4 6 8 10 12
Annual 1(11/82)-Omega Men app. 1 3 4 6 8 10
Annual V2#2(9/83)-1st app. Vigilante in costume; 1st app. Lyla

New Thunderbolts #1 © MAR

New Titans #114 © DC

New Warriors (2014 series) #1 © MAR

	GD 2.0	VG 4.0	FN 6.0	VF 8.0	VF/NM 9.0	NM- 9.2
	3	6	9	17	26	35

Annual 3 (See Tales of the Teen Titans Annual #3)
...: Games GN (2011, $24.99, HC) Wolfman-s/Pérez-a/c; original GN started in 1988, finished in 2011; '80s NTT roster; afterword by Pérez; Wolfman's original plot 25.00
...: Games GN (2013, $16.99, SC) same contents as HC 17.00
...: Terra Incognito TPB (2006, $19.99) r/#26,28-34 & Annual #2 20.00
...: The Judas Contract TPB (2003, $19.95) r/#39,40 plus Tales of the Teen Titans #41-44 & Annual #3 20.00
...: Who is Donna Troy? TPB (2005, $19.99) r/#38,Tales of the Teen Titans #50, New Titans #50-55 and Teen Titans/Outsiders Secret Files 2003 20.00
NOTE: ***Pérez*** *a-1-4p, 6-34p, 37-40p, Annual 1p, 2p; c-1-12, 13-17p, 18-21, 22p, 23p, 24-37, 38, 39(painted), 40, Annual 1, 2.*

NEW TEEN TITANS, THE (Becomes The New Titans #50 on)
DC Comics: Aug, 1984 - No. 49, Nov, 1988 ($1.25/$1.75; deluxe format)

1-New storyline; Pérez-c/a begins 2 4 6 8 10 12
2,3: 2-Re-intro Lilith 6.00
4-10: 5-Death of Trigon. 7-9-Origin Lilith. 8-Intro Kole. 10-Kole joins 5.00
11-49: 13,14-Crisis x-over. 20-Robin (Jason Todd) joins; original Teen Titans return. 38-Infinity, Inc. x-over. 47-Origin of all Titans; Titans (East & West) pin-up by Pérez 4.00
Annual 1-4 (9/85-'88): 1-Intro. Vanguard. 2-Byrne c/a(p); origin Brother Blood; intro new Dr. Light. 3-Intro. Danny Chase. 4-Pérez-c 4.00
...: The Terror of Trigon TPB (2003, $17.95) r/#1-5; new cover by Phil Jimenez 18.00
NOTE: ***Buckler*** *c-10.* ***Kelley Jones*** *a-47, Annual 4.* ***Erik Larsen*** *a-33.* ***Orlando*** *c-33p.* ***Perez*** *a-1-5; c-1-7, 19-23, 43.* ***Steacy*** *c-47.*

NEW TERRYTOONS (TV)
Dell Publishing Co./Gold Key: 6-8/60 - No. 8, 3-5/62; 10/62 - No. 54, 1/79

	GD 2.0	VG 4.0	FN 6.0	VF 8.0	VF/NM 9.0	NM- 9.2
1(1960-Dell)-Deputy Dawg, Dinky Duck & Hashimoto-San begin (1st app. of each)	10	20	30	64	132	200
2-8(1962)	6	12	18	41	76	110
1(30010-210)(10/62-Gold Key, 84 pgs.)-Heckle & Jeckle begins	9	18	27	58	114	170
2(30010-301)-84 pgs.	7	14	21	49	92	135
3-5	4	8	12	27	44	60
6-10	4	8	12	21	33	45
11-20	3	6	9	15	22	28
21-30	2	4	6	9	13	16
31-43	1	3	4	6	8	10
44-54: Mighty Mouse-c/s in all	2	4	6	8	11	14

NOTE: *Reprints: #4-12, 38, 40, 47. (See March of Comics #379, 393, 412, 435)*

NEW TESTAMENT STORIES VISUALIZED
Standard Publishing Co.: 1946 - 1947

"New Testament Heroes–Acts of Apostles Visualized, Book I"
"New Testament Heroes–Acts of Apostles Visualized, Book II"
"Parables Jesus Told" Set.... 17 34 51 98 154 210
NOTE: *All three are contained in a cardboard case, illustrated on front and info about the set.*

NEW THUNDERBOLTS (Continues in Thunderbolts #100)
Marvel Comics: Jan, 2005 - No. 18, Apr, 2006 ($2.99)

1-18: 1-Grummett-a/Nicieza-s. 1-Captain Marvel app. 2-Namor app. 4-Wolverine app. 3.00
... Vol. 1: One Step Forward (2005, $14.99) r/#1-6 15.00
... Vol. 2: Modern Marvels (2005, $14.99) r/#7-12 15.00
... Vol. 3: Right of Power (2006, $17.99) r/#13-18 & Thunderbolts #100 18.00

NEW TITANS, THE (Formerly The New Teen Titans)
DC Comics: No. 50, Dec, 1988 - No. 130, Feb, 1996 ($1.75/$2.25)

50-Perez-c/a begins; new origin Wonder Girl 6.00
51-59: 50-55-Painted-c. 55-Nightwing (Dick Grayson) forces Danny Chase to resign; Batman app. in flashback, Wonder Girl becomes Troia 4.00
60,61: 60-A Lonely Place of Dying Part 2 continues from Batman #440; new Robin tie-in; Timothy Drake app. 61-A Lonely Place of Dying Part 4 4.00
62-70,72-99,101-124,126-130: 62-65: Deathstroke the Terminator app. 65-Tim Drake (Robin) app. 70-1st Deathstroke solo cover/sty. 72-79-Deathstroke in all: 74-Intro. Pantha. 79-Terra brought back to life; 1 panel cameo Team Titans (1st app.). Deathstroke in #80-84,86. 80-2nd full app. Team Titans. 83,84-Deathstroke kills his son, Jericho. 85-Team Titans app. 86-Deathstroke vs. Nightwing-c/story; last Deathstroke app. 87-New costume Nightwing. 90-92-Parts 2,5,8 Total Chaos (Team Titans). 99-1st app. Arsenal. 115-(11/94) 3.00
71-(44 pgs.)-10th anniversary issue; Deathstroke cameo 4.00
100-($3.50, 52 pgs.)-Holo-grafx foil-c 4.00
125 (3.50)-wraparound-c 4.00
#0-(10/94) Zero Hour, released between #114 & 115 3.00
Annual 5-10 ('89-'94, 68 pgs.. 7-Armageddon 2001 x-over; 1st full app. Teen (Team) Titans (new group). 8-Deathstroke app.; Eclipso app. (minor). 10-Elseworlds story 4.00
Annual 11 (1995, $3.95)-Year One story 4.00

NOTE: ***Perez*** *a-50-55p, 57,60p, 58,59,61(layouts); c-50-61, 62-67i, Annual 5i; co-plots-66.*

NEW TV FUNNIES (See New Funnies)

NEW TWO-FISTED TALES, THE
Dark Horse Comics/Byron Preiss: 1993 ($4.95, limited series, 52 pgs.)

1-Kurtzman-r & new-a 5.00
NOTE: ***Eisner*** *c-1i.* ***Kurtzman*** *c-1p, 2.*

NEWUNIVERSAL
Marvel Comics: Feb, 2007 - No. 6, July, 2007 ($2.99)

1-6-Warren Ellis-s/Salvador Larroca-a. 1,2-Variant covers by Ribic 3.00
...: 1959 (9/08, $3.99) Aftermath of the White Event of 1953; Tony Stark app. 4.00
...: Conqueror (10/08, $3.99) The White Event of 2689 B.C.; Eric Nguyen-a 4.00
... : Everything Went White HC (2007, $19.99) r/#1-6; sketch pages 20.00
... : Everything Went White SC (2008, $14.99) r/#1-6; sketch pages 15.00

NEWUNIVERSAL: SHOCKFRONT
Marvel Comics: Jul, 2008 - Present ($2.99)

1,2-Warren Ellis-s/Steve Kurth-a 3.00

NEW WARRIORS, THE (See Thor #411,412)
Marvel Comics: July, 1990 - No. 75, 1996 ($1.00/$1.25/$1.50)

1-Williamson-i; Bagley-c/a(p) in #1-13, (1st printing has red cover) 2 4 6 10 14 18
1-Gold 2nd printing (7/91) 4.00
2-5: 1,3-Guice-c(i). 2-Williamson-c/a(i). 4.00
6-24,26-49,51-75: 7-Punisher cameo (last pg.). 8,9-Punisher app. 14-Darkhawk & Namor x-over. 17-Fantastic Four & Silver Surfer x-over. 19-Gideon (of X-Force) app. 28-Intro Turbo & Cardinal. 31-Cannonball & Warpath app. 42-Nova vs. Firelord. 46-Photo-c. 47-Bound-in S-M trading card sheet. 52-12 pg. ad insert. 62-Scarlet Spider-c/app. 70-Spider-Man-c/app. 72-Avengers-c/app. 3.00
25-($2.50, 52 pgs.)-Die-cut cover 4.00
40,60: 40-($2.25)-Gold foil collector's edition 4.00
50-($2.95, 52 pgs.)-Glow in the dark-c 4.00
Annual 1-4('91-'94,68 pgs.)-1-Origins all members; 3rd app. X-Force (cont'd from New Mutants Ann. #7 & cont'd in X-Men Ann. #15); x-over before X-Force #1; Bagley-c/a(p); Williamson-i. 3-Bagged w/card 4.00

NEW WARRIORS, THE
Marvel Comics: Oct, 1999 - No. 10, July, 2000 ($2.99/$2.50)

0-Wizard supplement; short story and preview sketchbook 3.00
1-($2.99) 4.00
2-10: 2-Two covers. 5-Generation X app. 9-Iron Man-c 3.00

NEW WARRIORS (See Civil War #1)
Marvel Comics: Aug, 2005 - No. 6, Feb, 2006 ($2.99, limited series)

1-6-Scottie Young-a 3.00
...: Reality Check TPB (2006, $14.99) r/#1-6 15.00

NEW WARRIORS (The Initiative)
Marvel Comics: Aug, 2007 - No. 20, Mar, 2009 ($2.99)

1-19: 1-Medina-a; new team is formed. 2-Jubilee app. 14-16-Secret Invasion 3.00
20-($3.99) 4.00
...: Defiant TPB (2008, $14.99) r/#1-6 15.00

NEW WARRIORS (All-New Marvel Now)
Marvel Comics: Apr, 2014 - No. 12, Jan, 2015 ($3.99)

1-12: 1-Nova, Speedball, Justice, Sun Girl, Scarlet Spider team; Yost-s/To-a 4.00

NEW WAVE, THE
Eclipse Comics: 6/10/86 - No. 13, 3/87 (#1-8: bi-weekly, 20pgs; #9-13: monthly)

1-13:1-Origin, concludes #5. 6-Origin Megabyte. 8,9-The Heap returns. 13-Snyder-c 3.00
...Versus the Volunteers 3-D #1,2(4/87): 1-Snyder-c 3.00

NEW WEST, THE
Black Bull Comics: Mar, 2005 - No. 2, Jun, 2005 ($4.99, limited series)

1,2-Phil Noto-a/c; Jimmy Palmiotti-s 5.00

NEW WORLD (See Comic Books, series I)

NEW WORLDS
Caliber: 1996 - No. 6 ($2.95/$3.95, 80 pgs., B&W, anthology)

1-6: 1-Mister X & other stories 4.00

NEW X-MEN (See X-Men 2nd series #114-156)

NEW X-MEN (Academy X) (Continued from New Mutants)
Marvel Comics: July, 2004 - No. 46, Mar, 2008 ($2.99)

1-46: 1,2-Green-c/a. 16-19-House of M. 20,21-Decimation. 40-Endangered Species back-ups begin. 44-46-Messiah Complex x-over; Ramos-a 3.00

New York Five #1 © Wood & Kelly

New York World's Fair Comics #2 © DC

Nexus #24 © FC

GD 2.0 VG 4.0 FN 6.0 VF 8.0 VF/NM 9.0 NM- 9.2

GD 2.0 VG 4.0 FN 6.0 VF 8.0 VF/NM 9.0 NM- 9.2

Yearbook 1 (12/05, $3.99) new story and profile pages 4.00
...: Childhood's End Vol. 1 TPB (2006, $10.99) r/#20-23 11.00
...: Childhood's End Vol. 2 TPB (2006, $10.99) r/#24-27 11.00
...: Childhood's End Vol. 3 TPB (2006, $10.99) r/#28-32 11.00
...: Childhood's End Vol. 4 TPB (2007, $10.99) r/#33-36 11.00
...: Childhood's End Vol. 5 TPB (2007, $17.99) r/#37-43 18.00
House of M: New X-Men TPB (2006, $13.99) r/#16-19 and selections from Secrets Of The House of M one-shot 14.00
... Vol. 1: Choosing Sides TPB (2004, $14.99) r/#1-6 15.00
... Vol. 2: Haunted TPB (2005, $14.99) r/#7-12 15.00
... Vol. 3: X-Posed TPB (2006, $14.99) r/#12-15 & Yearbook Special 15.00

NEW X-MEN: HELLIONS
Marvel Comics: July, 2005 - No. 4, Oct, 2005 ($2.99, limited series)

1-4-Henry-a/Weir & DeFilippis-s 3.00
TPB (2006, $9.99) r/#1-4 10.00

NEW YORK FIVE, THE
DC Comics (Vertigo): Mar, 2011 - No. 4, Jun, 2011 ($2.99, B&W, limited series)

1-4-Brian Wood-s/Ryan Kelly-a 3.00

NEW YORK GIANTS (See Thrilling True Story of the Baseball Giants)

NEW YORK STATE JOINT LEGISLATIVE COMMITTEE TO STUDY THE PUBLICATION OF COMICS, THE
N.Y. State Legislative Document: 1951, 1955

This document was referenced by Wertham for **Seduction of the Innocent.** Contains numerous repros from comics showing violence, sadism, torture, and sex. 1955 version (196p, No. 37, 2/23/55) - Sold for $180 in 1986.

NEW YORK, THE BIG CITY
Kitchen Sink Press: 1986 ($10.95, B&W); **DC Comics:** July, 2000 ($12.95, B&W)

nn-(1986, $10.95) Will Eisner-s/a 25.00
nn-(2000, $12.95) new printing 13.00

NEW YORK WORLD'S FAIR (Also see Big Book of Fun & New Book of Fun)
National Periodical Publ.: 1939, 1940 (100 pgs.; cardboard covers)
(DC's 4th & 5th annuals)

1939-Scoop Scanlon, Superman (blond haired Superman on-c), Sandman, Zatara, Slam Bradley, Ginger Snap by Bob Kane begin; 1st published app. The Sandman (see Adventure #40 for his 1st drawn story); Vincent Sullivan-c; cover background by Guardineer 1800 3600 5400 13,000 31,000 –
1940-Batman, Hourman, Johnny Thunderbolt, Red, White & Blue & Hanko (by Creig Flessel) app.; Superman, Batman & Robin-c (1st time they all appear together); early Robin app.; 1st Burnley-c/a (per Burnley) 950 1900 2850 7000 16,500 –

NOTE: *The 1939 edition was published 4/29/39 and released 4/30/39, the day the fair opened, at 25¢, and was first sold only at the fair. Since all other comics were 10¢, it didn't sell. Remaining copies were advertised beginning in the August issues of most DC comics for 25¢, but soon the price was dropped to 15¢. Everyone that sent a quarter through the mail for it received a free Superman #1 or a #2 to make up the dime difference. 15¢ stickers were placed over the 25¢ price. Four variations on the 15¢ stickers are known. The 1940 edition was published 5/11/40 and was priced at 15¢. It was a precursor to World's Best #1.*

NEW YORK: YEAR ZERO
Eclipse Comics: July, 1988 - No. 4, Oct, 1988 ($2.00, B&W, limited series)

1-4 3.00

NEXT, THE
DC Comics: Sept, 2006 - No. 6, Feb, 2007 ($2.99, limited series)

1-6-Tad Williams-s/Dietrich Smith-a; Superman app. 3.00

NEXT MEN (See John Byrne's...)

NEXT MEN: AFTERMATH (Continued from John Byrne's Next Men 2010-2011 series)
IDW Publishing: No. 40, Feb, 2012 - No. 44, Jun, 2012 ($3.99)

40-44-John Byrne-s/a/c 4.00

NEXT NEXUS, THE
First Comics: Jan, 1989 - No. 4, April, 1989 ($1.95, limited series, Baxter paper)

1-4: Mike Baron scripts & Steve Rude-c/a. 3.00
TPB (10/89, $9.95) r/series 10.00

NEXTWAVE: AGENTS OF H.A.T.E
Marvel Comics: Mar, 2006 - No. 12, Mar, 2007 ($2.99)

1-12-Warren Ellis-s/Stuart Immonen-a. 2-Fin Fang Foom app. 12-Devil Dinosaur app. 3.00
Vol. 1 - This Is What They Want HC (2006, $19.99) r/#1-6; Ellis original pitch 20.00
Vol. 1 - This Is What They Want SC (2007, $14.99) r/#1-6; Ellis original pitch 15.00
Vol. 2 - I Kick Your Face HC (2007, $19.99) r/#7-12 20.00
Vol. 2 - I Kick Your Face SC (2008, $14.99) r/#7-12 15.00

NEXUS (See First Comics Graphic Novel #4, 19 & The Next Nexus)
Capital Comics/First Comics No. 7 on: June, 1981 - No. 6, Mar, 1984; No. 7, Apr, 1985 - No. 80?, May, 1991 (Direct sales only, 36 pgs.; V2#1('83)-printed on Baxter paper)

1-B&W version; mag. size; w/double size poster 3 6 9 17 26 35
1-B&W 1981 limited edition; 500 copies printed and signed; same as above except this version has a 2-pg. poster & a pencil sketch on paperboard by Steve Rude 6 12 18 38 69 100
2-B&W, magazine size 2 4 6 11 16 20
3-B&W, magazine size; Brunner back-c; contains 33-1/3 rpm record ($2.95 price) 2 4 6 9 13 16
V2#1-Color version 5.00
2-49,51-80: 2-Nexus' origin begins. 67-Snyder-c/a 3.00
50-($3.50, 52 pgs.) 4.00
Hardcover Volume One (Dark Horse Books, 11/05, $49.95) r/#1-3 & V2 #1-4; creator bios 50.00
HC Volume Two (Dark Horse Books, 3/06, $49.95) r/V2 #5-11; creator bios 50.00
HC Volume Three (Dark Horse Books, 5/06, $49.95) r/V2 #12-18; Marz forward 50.00
HC Volume Four (Dark Horse Books, 8/06, $49.95) r/V2 #19-25; Powell forward 50.00
HC Volume Five (Dark Horse Books, 2/07, $49.95) r/V2 #26-32; Brubaker forward 50.00
HC Volume Six (Dark Horse Books, 2/07, $49.95) r/V2 #33-39; Evanier forward 50.00
HC Volume Seven (Dark Horse Books, 2/08, $49.95) r/V2 #40-46; Brunning forward 50.00
HC Volume Eight (Dark Horse Books, 1/09, $49.95) r/V2 #47-52 and The Next Nexus #1; interview with original publishers John Davis and Milton Griepp 50.00
HC Volume Nine (Dark Horse Books, 8/09, $49.95) r/V2 #53-57 & The Next Nexus #2-4 50.00

NOTE: ***Bissette*** *c-V2#29.* ***Giffen*** *c/a-V2#23.* ***Gulacy*** *c-1 (B&W), 2(B&W).* ***Mignola*** *c/a-V2#28.* ***Rude*** *c-3(B&W), V2#1-22, 24-27, 33-36, 39-42, 45-48, 50, 58-60, 75; a-1-3, V2#1-7, 8-16p, 18-22p, 24-27p, 33-36p, 39-42p, 45-48p, 50, 58, 59p, 60.* ***Paul Smith*** *a-V2#37, 38, 43, 44, 51-55p; c-V2#37, 38, 43, 44, 51-55.*

NEXUS
Rude Dude Productions: No. 99, July, 2007 - No. 102, Jun, 2009 ($2.99)

99-Mike Baron scripts & Steve Rude-c/a 3.00
100-($4.99) Part 2 of Space Opera; back-up feature: History of Nexus 5.00
101/102-(6/09, $4.95) Combined issue 5.00
..., Free Comic Book Day 2007 - Excerpts from previous issues and preview of #99 3.00
... Greatest Hits (8/07, $1.99) same content as Free Comic Book Day 2007 3.00
...: The Origin (11/07, $3.99) reprints the 7/96 one-shot 4.00

NEXUS: ALIEN JUSTICE
Dark Horse Comics: Dec, 1992 - No. 3, Feb, 1993 ($3.95, limited series)

1-3: Mike Baron scripts & Steve Rude-c/a 4.00

NEXUS: EXECUTIONER'S SONG
Dark Horse Comics: June, 1996 - No. 4, Sept, 1996 ($2.95, limited series)

1-4: Mike Baron scripts & Steve Rude-c/a 3.00

NEXUS FILES
First Comics: 1989 ($4.50, color/16pgs. B&W, one-shot, squarebound, 52 pgs.)

1-New Rude-a; info on Nexus 4.50

NEXUS: GOD CON
Dark Horse Comics: Apr, 1997 - No. 2, May, 1997 ($2.95, limited series)

1,2-Baron-s/Rude-c/a 3.00

NEXUS LEGENDS
First Comics: May, 1989 - No. 23, Mar, 1991 ($1.50, Baxter paper)

1-23: R/1-3(Capital) & early First Comics issues w/new Rude covers #1-6,9,10 3.00

NEXUS MEETS MADMAN (...Special)
Dark Horse Comics: May, 1996 ($2.95, one-shot)

nn-Mike Baron & Mike Allred scripts, Steve Rude-c/a. 3.00

NEXUS: NIGHTMARE IN BLUE
Dark Horse Comics: July, 1997 - No. 4, Oct, 1997 ($2.95, limited series)

1-4: 1,2,4-Adam Hughes-c 3.00

NEXUS: THE LIBERATOR
Dark Horse Comics: Aug, 1992 - No. 4, Nov, 1992 ($2.95, limited series)

1-4 3.00

NEXUS: THE ORIGIN
Dark Horse Comics: July, 1996 ($3.95, one-shot)

nn-Mike Baron- scripts, Steve Rude-c/a. 4.00

NEXUS: THE WAGES OF SIN
Dark Horse Comics: Mar, 1995 - No. 4, June, 1995 ($2.95, limited series)

1-4 3.00

NFL RUSH ZONE: SEASON OF THE GUARDIANS
Action Lab Comics: Feb, 2013 - No. 4 ($3.99)

1-4: 1-Matt Ryan & Roddy White app. 4.00
Free Comic Book Day edition (2013, giveaway) 3.00

NFL SUPERPRO
Marvel Comics: Oct, 1991 - No. 12, Sept, 1992 ($1.00)

Nickel Comics #1 © FAW

Nick Fury (2017 series) #1 © MAR

Nightcrawler (2014 series) #12 © MAR

GD 2.0 | VG 4.0 | FN 6.0 | VF 8.0 | VF/NM 9.0 | NM- 9.2

1-12: 1-Spider-Man-c/app. 3.00
Special Edition (9/91, $2.00) Jusko painted-c 4.00
Super Bowl Edition (3/91, squarebound) Jusko painted-c 4.00

NICKEL COMICS
Dell Publishing Co.: 1938 (Pocket size - 7-1/2x5-1/2")(68 pgs.)

1- "Bobby & Chip" by Otto Messmer, Felix the Cat artist. Contains some English reprints
86 172 258 546 936 1325

NICKEL COMICS
Fawcett Publications: Feb 1940

nn - Ashcan comic, not distributed to newsstands, only for in-house use. A CGC certified 9.6 copy sold for $7,200 in 2003. In 2008, a CGC certified 8.5 sold for $2,390 and an uncertified Near Mint copy sold for $3,100.

NICKEL COMICS
Fawcett Publications: May, 1940 - No. 8, Aug, 1940 (36 pgs.; Bi-Weekly; 5¢)

	GD	VG	FN	VF	VF/NM	NM-
1-Origin/1st app. Bulletman	394	788	1182	2758	4829	6900
2	119	238	357	762	1306	1850
3	87	174	261	553	952	1350
4-The Red Gaucho begins	73	146	219	467	796	1125
5-7	71	142	213	454	777	1100
8-World's Fair-c; Bulletman moved to Master Comics #7 in October (scarce)	90	180	270	576	988	1400

NOTE: *Beck c-5-8. Jack Binder c-1-4. Bondage c-5. Bulletman c-1-8.*

NICK FURY
Marvel Comics: Jun, 2017 - No. 6, Nov, 2017 ($3.99, limited series)

1-6-James Robinson-s/Aco-a; Nick Fury Jr. vs. Hydra; Frankie Noble app. 4.00

NICK FURY, AGENT OF SHIELD (See Fury, Marvel Spotlight #31 & Shield)
Marvel Comics Group: 6/68 - No. 15, 11/69; No. 16, 11/70 - No. 18, 3/71

	GD	VG	FN	VF	VF/NM	NM-
1	14	28	42	96	211	325
2-4: 4-Origin retold	8	16	24	51	96	140
5-Classic-c	8	16	24	56	108	160
6,7: 7-Salvador Dali painting swipe	7	14	21	46	86	125
8-11,13: 9-Hate Monger begins, ends #11. 10-Smith layouts/pencil. 11-Smith-c. 13-1st app. Super-Patriot; last 12¢ issue	4	8	12	28	47	65
12-Smith-c/a	5	10	15	30	50	70
14-Begin 15¢ issues	4	8	12	25	40	55
15-1st app. & death of Bullseye-c/story(11/69); Nick Fury shot & killed; last 15¢ issue	7	14	21	48	89	130
16-18-(25¢, 52 pgs.)-r/Str. Tales #135-143	3	6	9	20	31	42

TPB (May 2000, $19.95) r/ Strange Tales #150-168 20.00
...: Who is Scorpio? TPB (11/00, $12.95) r/#1-3,5; Steranko-c 13.00
NOTE: *Adkins a-3i. Craig a-10i. Sid Greene a-12i. Kirby a-16-18r. Springer a-4, 6, 7, 8p, 9, 10p, 11; c-8, 9. Steranko a(p)-1-3, 5; c-1-7.*

NICK FURY AGENT OF SHIELD (Also see Strange Tales #135)
Marvel Comics: Dec, 1983 - No. 2, Jan, 1984 (2.00, 52 pgs., Baxter paper)

1,2-r/Nick Fury #1-4; new Steranko-c 1 2 3 5 6 8

NICK FURY, AGENT OF S.H.I.E.L.D.
Marvel Comics: Sept, 1989 - No. 47, May, 1993 ($1.50/$1.75)

V2#1 5.00
2-26,30-47: 10-Capt. America app. 13-Return of The Yellow Claw. 15-Fantastic Four app. 30,31-Deathlok app. 36-Cage app. 37-Woodgod c/story. 38-41-Flashes back to pre-Shield days after WWII. 44-Capt. America-c/s. 45-Viper-c/s. 46-Gideon x-over 3.00
27-29-Wolverine-c/stories 4.00
NOTE: *Alan Grant scripts-11. Guice a(p)-20-23, 25, 26; c-20-28.*

NICK FURY'S HOWLING COMMANDOS
Marvel Comics: Dec, 2005 - No. 6, May, 2006 ($2.99)

1-6: 1-Giffen-s/Francisco-a 3.00
1-Director's Cut ($3.99) r/#1 with original script and sketch design pages 4.00

NICK FURY VS. S.H.I.E.L.D.
Marvel Comics: June, 1988 - No. 6, Nov, 1988 ($3.50, 52 pgs, deluxe format)

1,2: 1-Steranko-c. 2-(Low print run) Sienkiewicz-c 6.00
3-6 5.00

NICK HALIDAY (Thrill of the Sea)
Argo: May, 1956

1-Daily & Sunday strip-r by Petree 9 18 27 52 69 85

NIGHT AND THE ENEMY (Graphic Novel)
Comico: 1988 (8-1/2x11") ($11.95, color, 80 pgs.)

1-Harlan Ellison scripts/Ken Steacy-c/a; r/Epic Illustrated & new-a (1st & 2nd printings) 12.00
1-Limited edition ($39.95) 40.00

NIGHT BEFORE CHRISTMAS, THE (See March of Comics No. 152 in the Promotional Comics section)

NIGHT BEFORE CHRISTMASK, THE
Dark Horse Comics: Nov, 1994 ($9.95, one-shot)

nn-Hardcover book; The Mask; Rick Geary-c/a 10.00

NIGHTBREED (See Clive Barker's Nightbreed)

NIGHT CLUB
Image Comics: Apr, 2005 - No. 4, Dec, 2006 ($2.95/$2.99, limited series)

1-4: 1-Mike Baron-s/Mike Norton-a 3.00

NIGHTCRAWLER (X-Men)
Marvel Comics Group: Nov, 1985 - No. 4, Feb, 1986 (Mini-series from X-Men)

1-4: 1-Cockrum-c/a 6.00

NIGHTCRAWLER (Volume 2)
Marvel Comics: Feb, 2002 - No. 4, May, 2002 ($2.50, limited series)

1-4-Matt Smith-a 3.00

NIGHTCRAWLER
Marvel Comics: Nov, 2004 - No. 12, Jan, 2006 ($2.99)

1-12: 1-6-Robertson-a/Land-c. 2-Magik app. 8-Wolverine app. 10-Man-Thing app. 3.00
...: The Devil Inside TPB (2005, $14.99) r/#1-6 15.00
...: The Winding Way TPB (2006, $14.99) r/#7-12 15.00

NIGHTCRAWLER
Marvel Comics: Jun, 2014 - No. 12, May, 2015 ($3.99)

1-12: 1-Claremont-s/Nauck-a. 7-Death of Wolverine tie-in 4.00

NIGHTFALL: THE BLACK CHRONICLES
DC Comics (Homage): Dec, 1999 - No. 3, Feb, 2000 ($2.95, limited series)

1-3-Coker-a/Gilmore-s 3.00

NIGHT FORCE, THE (See New Teen Titans #21)
DC Comics: Aug, 1982 - No. 14, Sept, 1983 (60¢)

1 4.00
2-14: 13-Origin Baron Winter. 14-Nudity panels 3.00
NOTE: *Colan c/a-1-14p. Giordano c-1i, 2i, 4i, 5i, 7i, 12i.*

NIGHT FORCE
DC Comics: Dec, 1996 - No. 12, Nov, 1997 ($2.25)

1-12: 1-3-Wolfman-s/Anderson-a(p). 8-"Convergence" part 2 3.00

NIGHT FORCE
DC Comics: May, 2012 - No. 7, Nov, 2012 ($2.99, limited series)

1-7-Wolfman-s/Mandrake-a/Manco-c 3.00

NIGHT GLIDER
Topps Comics (Kirbyverse): April, 1993 ($2.95, one-shot)

1-Kirby c-1, Heck-a; polybagged w/Kirbychrome trading card 4.00

NIGHTHAWK
Marvel Comics: Sept, 1998 - No. 3, Nov, 1998 ($2.99, mini-series)

1-3-Krueger-s; Daredevil app. 3.00

NIGHTHAWK (From Squadron Supreme)
Marvel Comics: Jul, 2016 - No. 6, Dec, 2016 ($3.99)

1-6: 1-Walker-s/Villalobos-a/Cowan-c. 3-Morazzo-a 4.00

NIGHTINGALE, THE
Henry H. Stansbury Once-Upon-A-Time Press, Inc.: 1948 (10¢, 7-1/4x10-1/4", 14 pgs., 1/2 B&W)

(Very Rare)-Low distribution; distributed to Westchester County & Bronx, N.Y. only; used in **Seduction of the Innocent**, pg. 312,313 as the 1st and only "good" comic book ever published. Ill. by Dong Kingman; 1,500 words of text, printed on high quality paper & no word balloons. Copyright registered 10/22/48, distributed week of 12/5/48. Only 5000 copies printed, 6 currently known to still exist. (By Hans Christian Andersen)
Estimated value........ 275.00

NIGHT MAN, THE (See Sludge #1)
Malibu Comics (Ultraverse): Oct, 1993 - No. 23, Aug, 1995 ($1.95/$2.50)

1-($2.50, 48 pgs.)-Rune flip-c/story by B. Smith (3 pgs.) 4.00
1-Ultra-Limited silver foil-c 8.00
2-15, 17: 3-Break-Thru x-over; Freex app. 4-Origin Firearm (2 pgs.) by Chaykin. 6-TNTNT app. 8-1st app. Teknight 3.00
16 ($3.50)-flip book (Ultraverse Premiere #11) 4.00
...:The Pilgrim Conundrum Saga (1/95, $3.95, 68 pgs.)-Strangers app. 4.00
18-23: 22-Loki-c/app. 3.00
Infinity ($1.50) 3.00
...Vs. Wolverine #0-Kelley Jones-c; mail in offer 1 3 4 6 8 10
NOTE: *Zeck a-16.*

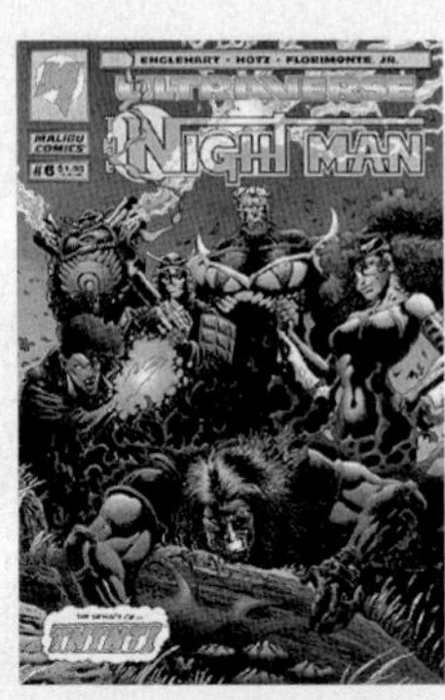

Night Man #6 © MAL

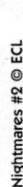

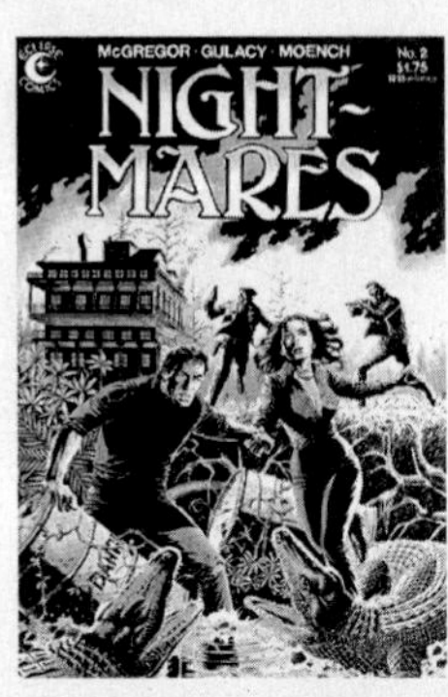

Nightmares #2 © ECL

Night Nurse #1 © MAR

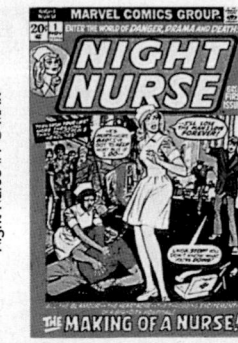

	GD	VG	FN	VF	VF/NM	NM-
	2.0	4.0	6.0	8.0	9.0	9.2

GD VG FN VF VF/NM NM- 2.0 4.0 6.0 8.0 9.0 9.2

NIGHT MAN, THE
Malibu Comics (Ultraverse): Sept, 1995 - No.4, Dec, 1995 ($1.50, lim. series)

1-4: Post Black September storyline 3.00

NIGHT MAN, THE /GAMBIT
Malibu Comics (Ultraverse): Mar, 1996 - No. 3, May, 1996 ($1.95, lim. series)

0-Limited Premium Edition 4.00
1-3: David Quinn scripts in all. 3-Rhiannon discovered to be The Night Man's mother 3.00

NIGHTMARE
Ziff-Davis (Approved Comics)/St. John No. 3: Summer, 1952 - No. 3, Winter, 1952, 53 (Painted-c)

1-1 pg. Kinstler-a; Tuska-a(2) 68 136 204 435 743 1050
2-Kinstler-a-Poe's "Pit & the Pendulum" 47 94 141 296 498 700
3-Kinstler-a 42 84 126 265 445 625

NIGHTMARE (Weird Horrors #1-9) (Amazing Ghost Stories #14 on)
St. John Publishing Co.: No. 10, Dec, 1953 - No. 13, Aug, 1954

10-Reprints Ziff-Davis Weird Thrillers #2 w/new Kubert-c plus 2 pgs. Kinstler-a; Anderson, Colan & Toth-a 61 122 183 390 670 950
11-Krigstein-a; painted-c; Poe adapt., "Hop Frog" 47 94 141 296 498 700
12-Kubert bondage-c; adaptation of Poe's "The Black Cat"; Cannibalism story 45 90 135 284 480 675
13-Reprints Z-D Weird Thrillers #3 with new cover; Powell-a(2), Tuska-a; Baker-c 39 78 117 240 395 550

NIGHTMARE (Magazine) (Also see Psycho)
Skywald Publishing Corp.: Dec, 1970 - No. 23, Feb, 1975 (B&W, 68 pgs.)

1-Everett-a; Heck-a; Shores-a 10 20 30 66 138 210
2-5,8,9: 2,4-Decapitation story. 5-Nazi-s; Boris Karloff 4 pg. photo/text-s. 8-Features E.C. movie "Tales From the Crypt"; reprints some E.C. comics panels. 9-Wrightson-a; bondage-c; 1st Lovecraft Saggoth Chronicles/Cthulhu 6 12 18 37 66 95
6-Kaluta-a; Jeff Jones-c, photo & interview; 1st Living Gargoyle; Love Witch-s w/nudity; Boris Karloff-s 6 12 18 40 73 105
7 5 10 15 33 57 80
10-Wrightson-a (1 pg.); Princess of Earth-c/s; Edward & Mina Sartyros, the Human Gargoyles series continues from Psycho #8 6 12 18 38 69 100
11-19: 12-Excessive gore, severed heads. 13-Lovecraft-s. 15-Dracula-c/s. 17-Vampires issue; Autobiography of a Vampire series begins 4 8 12 28 47 65
20-John Byrne's 1st artwork (2 pgs.)(8/74); severed head-c; Hitler app. 8 16 24 54 102 150
21-23: 21-(1974 Summer Special)-Kaluta-a. 22-Tomb of Horror issue. 23-(1975 Winter Special) 5 10 15 31 53 75
Annual 1(1972)-Squarebound; B. Jones-a 5 10 15 31 53 75
Winter Special 1(1973)-All new material 4 8 12 28 47 65
Yearbook nn(1974)-B. Jones, Reese, Wildey-a 4 8 12 28 47 65

NOTE: ***Adkins** a-5. **Boris** c-2, 3, 5 (#4 is not by Boris). **Buckler** a-3, 15. **Byrne** a-20p. **Everett** a-1, 2, 4, 5, 12. **Jeff Jones** a-6, 21r(Psycho #6); c-6. **Katz** a-3, 5, 21. **Reese** a-4, 5. **Wildey** a-4, 5, 6, 21, '74 Yearbook. **Wrightson** a-9, 10.*

NIGHTMARE (Alex Nino's)
Innovation Publishing: 1989 ($1.95)

1-Alex Nino-a 3.00

NIGHTMARE
Marvel Comics: Dec, 1994 - No. 4, Mar, 1995 ($1.95, limited series)

1-4 3.00

NIGHTMARE & CASPER (See Harvey Hits #71) (Casper & Nightmare #6 on) (See Casper The Friendly Ghost #19)
Harvey Publications: Aug, 1963 - No. 5, Aug, 1964 (25¢)

1-All reprints? 7 14 21 46 86 125
2-5: All reprints? 5 10 15 30 50 70

NIGHTMARE ON ELM STREET, A (Also see Freddy Krueger's...)
DC Comics (WildStorm): Dec, 2006 - Present ($2.99)

1-8: 1-Two covers by Harris & Bradstreet; Dixon-s/West-a 3.00

NIGHTMARES (See Do You Believe in Nightmares)

NIGHTMARES
Eclipse Comics: May, 1985 - No. 2, May, 1985 ($1.75, Baxter paper)

1,2 3.00

NIGHTMARE THEATER
Chaos! Comics: Nov, 1997 - No. 4, Nov, 1997 ($2.50, mini-series)

1-4-Horror stories by various; Wrightson-a 3.00

NIGHTMASK
Marvel Comics Group: Nov, 1986 - No. 12, Oct, 1987

1-12 3.00

NIGHT MASTER
Silverwolf: Feb, 1987 ($1.50, B&W)

1-Tim Vigil-c/a 3.00

NIGHTMASTER (See Shadowpact)
DC Comics: Jan, 2011 ($2.99, one-shot)

1-Wrightson-c/Beechen-s/Dwyer-a; Shadowpact app. 3.00

NIGHT MUSIC (See Eclipse Graphic Album Series, The Magic Flute)
Eclipse Comics: Dec, 1984 - No. 11, 1990 ($1.75/$3.95/$4.95, Baxter paper)

1-7: 3-Russell's Jungle Book adapt. 4,5-Pelleas And Melisande (double titled) 6-Salomé (double titled). 7-Red Dog #1 3.00
8-($3.95) Ariane and Bluebeard 4.00
9-11-($4.95) The Magic Flute; Russell adapt. 5.00

NIGHT NURSE (Also see Linda Carter, Student Nurse)
Marvel Comics Group: Nov, 1972 - No. 4, May, 1973

1 22 44 66 154 340 525
2-4 9 18 27 63 129 195

NIGHT NURSE
Marvel Comics: Jul, 2015 ($7.99, one-shot)

1-Reprints 1972 series #1-4 and Daredevil V2 #80; Siya Oum-c 8.00

NIGHT OF MYSTERY
Avon Periodicals: 1953 (no month) (one-shot)

nn-1 pg. Kinstler-a, Hollingsworth-c 68 136 204 435 743 1050

NIGHT OF THE GRIZZLY, THE (See Movie Classics)

NIGHT OF THE LIVING DEADPOOL
Marvel Comics: Mar, 2014 - No. 4, May, 2014 ($3.99, limited series)

1-4-Bunn-s/Rosanas-a; Deadpool in a zombie apocalypse 4.00

NIGHTRAVEN (See Marvel Graphic Novel)

NIGHT RIDER (Western)
Marvel Comics Group: Oct, 1974 - No. 6, Aug, 1975

1: 1-6 reprint Ghost Rider #1-6 (#1-origin) 3 6 9 21 33 45
2-6 3 6 9 14 19 24

NIGHT'S CHILDREN: THE VAMPIRE
Millenium: July, 1995 - No. 2, Aug, 1995 ($2.95, B&W)

1,2: Wendy Snow-Lang story & art 3.00

NIGHTSIDE
Marvel Comics: Dec, 2001 - No. 4, Mar, 2002 ($2.99)

1-4: 1-Weinberg-s/Derenick-a; intro Sydney Taine 3.00

NIGHTS INTO DREAMS (Based on video game)
Archie Comics: Feb, 1998 -No. 6, Oct, 1998 ($1.75, limited series)

1-6 3.00

NIGHTSTALKERS (Also see Midnight Sons Unlimited)
Marvel Comics (Midnight Sons #14 on): Nov, 1992 - No. 18, Apr, 1994 ($1.75)

1-($2.75, 52 pgs.)-Polybagged w/poster; part 5 of Rise of the Midnight Sons storyline; Garney/Palmer-c/a begins; Hannibal King, Blade & Frank Drake begin 4.00
2-9,11-18: 5-Punisher app. 7-Ghost Rider app. 8,9-Morbius app. 14-Spot varnish-c. 14,15-Siege of Darkness Pts 1 & 9 3.00
10-($2.25)-Outer-c is a Darkhold envelope made of black parchment w/gold ink; Midnight Massacre part 1 4.00

NIGHT TERRORS,THE
Chanting Monks Studios: 2000 ($2.75, B&W)

1-Bernie Wrightson-c; short stories, one by Wrightson-s/a 3.00

NIGHT THRASHER (Also see The New Warriors)
Marvel Comics: Aug, 1993 - No. 21, Apr, 1995 ($1.75/$1.95)

1-($2.95, 52 pgs.)-Red holo-grafx foil-c; origin 4.00
2-21: 2-Intro Tantrum. 3-Gideon (of X-Force) app. 10-Bound-in trading card sheet; Iron Man app. 15-Hulk app. 3.00

NIGHT THRASHER: FOUR CONTROL
Marvel Comics: Oct, 1992 - No. 4, Jan, 1993 ($2.00, limited series)

1-4: 2-Intro Tantrum. 3-Gideon (of X-Force) app. 3.00

NIGHT TRIBES
DC Comics (WildStorm): July, 1999 ($4.95, one-shot)

Nightwing #41 © DC

Nightwing (2016 series) #16 © DC

Nightworld #1 © McGovern & Leandri

GD 2.0 | VG 4.0 | FN 6.0 | VF 8.0 | VF/NM 9.0 | NM- 9.2

1-Golden & Sniegoski-s/Chin-a 5.00

NIGHTVEIL (Also see Femforce)
Americomics/AC Comics: Nov, 1984 - No. 7, 1987 ($1.75)

1-7 3.00
...'s Cauldron Of Horror 1 (1989, B&W)-Kubert, Powell, Wood-r plus new Nightveil story 3.00
...'s Cauldron Of Horror 2 (1990, $2.95, B&W)-Pre-code horror-r by Kubert & Powell 3.00
...'s Cauldron Of Horror 3 (1991) 3.00
Special 1 ('88, $1.95)-Kaluta-c 3.00
One Shot ('96, $5.95)-Flip book w/ Colt 6.00

NIGHTWATCH
Marvel Comics: Apr, 1994 - No. 12, Mar, 1995 ($1.50)

1-($2.95)-Collectors edition; foil-c; Ron Lim-c/a begins; Spider-Man app. 4.00
1-12-Regular edition. 2-Bound-in S-M trading card sheet; 5,6-Venom-c & app. 7,11-Cardiac app. 3.00

NIGHTWING (Also see New Teen Titans, New Titans, Showcase '93 #11,12, Tales of the New Teen Titans & Teen Titans Spotlight)
DC Comics: Sept, 1995 - No. 4, Dec, 1995 ($2.25, limited series)

1-Dennis O'Neil story/Greg Land-a in all 2 4 6 8 10 12
2-4 4.00
...: Alfred's Return (7/95, $3.50) Giordano-a 4.00
...Ties That Bind (1997, $12.95, TPB) r/mini-series & Alfred's Return 13.00

NIGHTWING
DC Comics: Oct, 1996 - No. 153, Apr, 2009 ($1.95/$1.99/$2.25/$2.50/$2.99)

1-Chuck Dixon scripts & Scott McDaniel-c/a 3 6 9 19 30 40
2,3 1 2 3 5 6 8
4-10: 6-Robin-c/app. 5.00
11-20: 13-15-Batman app. 19,20-Cataclysm pts. 2,11 4.00
21-49,51-64: 23-Green Arrow app. 26-29-Huntress-c/app. 30-Superman-c/app. 35-39-No Man's Land. 41-Land/Geraci-a begins. 46-Begin $2.25-c. 47-Texiera-c. 52-Catwoman-c/app. 54-Shrike app. 3.00
50-($3.50) Nightwing battles Torque 4.00
65-74,76-99: 65,66-Bruce Wayne: Murderer x-over pt. 3,9. 68,69: B.W.: Fugitive pt. 6,9. 70-Last Dixon-s. 71-Devin Grayson-s begin. 81-Batgirl vs. Deathstroke. 93-Blockbuster killed. 94-Copperhead app. 96-Bagged w/CD. 96-98-War Games 3.00
75-(1/03, $2.95) Intro. Tarantula 4.00
100-(2/05, $2.95) Tarantula app. 4.00
101-117: 101-Year One begins. 103-Jason Todd & Deadman app. 107-110-Hester-a. 109-Begin $2.50-c. 109,110-Villains United tie-ins. 112-Deathstroke app. 3.00
118-149,151-153: 118-One Year Later; Jason Todd as 2nd Nightwing. 120-Begin $2.99-c. 138,139-Resurrection of Ra's al Ghul x-over. 138-2nd printing. 147-Two-Face app. 3.00
150-($3.99) Batman R.I.P. x-over; Nightwing vs. Two-Face; Tan-c 4.00
#1,000,000 (11/98) teams with future Batman 3.00
Annual 1(1997, $3.95) Pulp Heroes 4.00
Annual 2 (6/07, $3.99) Dick Grayson and Barbara Gordon's shared history 4.00
...Eighty Page Giant 1 (12/00, $5.95) Intro. of Hella; Dixon-s/Haley-c 6.00
...: Big Guns (2004, $14.95, TPB) r/#47-50; Secret Files 1, Eighty Page Giant 1 15.00
...: Brothers in Blood (2007, $14.99, TPB) r/#118-124 15.00
...: A Darker Shade of Justice (2001, $19.95, TPB) r/#30-39, Secret Files #1 20.00
...: Freefall (2008, $17.99, TPB) r/#140-146 18.00
...: A Knight in Blüdhaven (1998, $14.95, TPB) r/#1-8 15.00
...: Love and Bullets (2000, $17.95, TPB) r/#1/2, 19,21,22,24-29 18.00
...: Love and War (2007, $14.99, TPB) r/#125-132 15.00
...: On the Razor's Edge (2005, $14.99, TPB) r/#52,54-60 15.00
...: Our Worlds at War (9/01, $2.95) Jae Lee-c 3.00
...: Renegade TPB (2006, $17.95) r/#112-117 18.00
...: Rough Justice (1999, $17.95, TPB) r/#9-18 18.00
Secret Files 1 (10/99, $4.95) Origin-s and pin-ups 5.00
...: The Great Leap (2009, $19.99) r/#147-153 20.00
...: The Hunt for Oracle (2003, $14.95, TPB) r/#41-46 & Birds of Prey #20,21 15.00
...: The Lost Year (2008, $14.99) r/#133-137 & Annual #2 15.00
...: The Target (2001, $5.95) McDaniel-c/a 6.00
Wizard 1/2 (Mail offer) 5.00
...: Year One (2005, $14.99) r/#101-106 15.00

NIGHTWING (DC New 52)(Leads into Grayson series)
DC Comics: Nov, 2011 - No. 30, Jul, 2014 ($2.99)

1-Dick Grayson in black/red costume; Higgins-s/Barrows-a/c 20.00
1-2nd printing with red background-c 10.00
2-7,10-14: 2-4-Batgirl app. 13,14-Lady Shiva app. 14-Joker cameo 4.00
8,9: 8-Night of the Owls prelude. 9-Night of the Owls x-over 5.00
15-Die-cut cover with Joker mask; Death of the Family tie-in 5.00
16-18: 16-Death of the Family tie-in. 18-Requiem; Tony Zucco returns 4.00
19-24,26-29: 19-24-Prankster app. 26,27-Mad Hatter app. 28,29-Mr. Zsasz app. 3.00
25-($3.99) Zero Year flashback to Haly's Circus days; Higgins-s/Conrad & Richards-a 4.00
30-($3.99) Aftermath of Forever Evil series; Grayson joins Spyral 4.00
#0-(11/12, $2.99) Origin re-told/updated; Lady Shiva app.; DeFalco-s/Barrows-a 4.00
Annual #1 (12/13, $4.99) Batgirl Wanted! tie-in; Firefly app. 5.00

NIGHTWING (DC Rebirth)
DC Comics: Sept, 2016 - Present ($2.99)

1-24: 1-Seeley-s/Fernandez-a. 1-Intro. Raptor. 5,6-Night of the Monster Men x-over. 17-20-Deathwing & Prof. Pyg app. 21-Flash (Wally) app. 22-24-Blockbuster app. 3.00
25-($3.99) Blockbuster & Tiger Shark app. 4.00
26-40: 26-28-Huntress app. 29-Dark Nights: Metal tie-in 3.00
...: Rebirth (9/16, $2.99) Seeley-s/Paquette-a; Damian app.; back in Nightwing costume 3.00

NIGHTWING (See Tangent Comics/ Nightwing)

NIGHTWING AND HUNTRESS
DC Comics: May, 1998 - No. 4, Aug, 1998 ($1.95, limited series)

1-4-Grayson-s/Land & Sienkiewicz-a 3.00
TPB (2003, $9.95) r/#1/4; cover gallery 10.00

NIGHTWINGS (See DC Science Fiction Graphic Novel)

NIGHTWING: THE NEW ORDER
DC Comics: Oct, 2017 - No. 6, Mar, 2018 ($3.99, limited series)

1-6-Higgins-s/McCarthy-a; future Nightwing in 2040. 4,5-Titans app. 5-Superman app. 4.00

NIGHTWORLD
Image Comics: Aug, 2014 - No. 4, Nov, 2014 ($3.99, limited series)

1-4-McGovern-s/Leandri-a/c 4.00

NIKKI, WILD DOG OF THE NORTH (Disney, see Movie Comics)
Dell Publishing Co.: No. 1226, Sept, 1961

Four Color 1226-Movie, photo-c 5 10 15 33 57 80

9-11 - ARTISTS RESPOND
Dark Horse Comics: 2002 ($9.95, TPB, proceeds donated to charities)

Volume 1-Short stories about the September 11 tragedies by various Dark Horse, Chaos! and Image writers and artists; Eric Drooker-c 10.00

9-11: EMERGENCY RELIEF
Alternative Comics: 2002 ($14.95, TPB, proceeds donated to the Red Cross)

nn-Short stories by various inc. Pekar, Eisner, Hester, Oeming, Noto; Cho-c 15.00

9-11 - THE WORLD'S FINEST COMIC BOOK WRITERS AND ARTISTS TELL STORIES TO REMEMBER
DC Comics: 2002 ($9.95, TPB, proceeds donated to charities)

Volume 2-Short stories about the September 11 tragedies by various DC, MAD, and WildStorm writers and artists ; Alex Ross-c 10.00

NINE RINGS OF WU-TANG
Image Comics: July, 1999 - No. 5, July, 2000 ($2.95)

Preview (7/99, $5.00, B&W) 5.00
1-5: 1-(11/99, $2.95) Clayton Henry-a 3.00
Tower Records Variant-c 5.00
Wizard #0 Prelude 3.00
TPB (1/01, $19.95) r/#1-5, Preview & Prelude; sketchbook & cover gallery 20.00

1963
Image Comics (Shadowline Ink): Apr, 1993 - No. 6, Oct, 1993 ($1.95, lim. series)

1-6: Alan Moore scripts; Veitch, Bissette & Gibbons-a(p) 3.00
1-Gold 4.00
*NOTE: **Bissette** a-2-4; **Gibbons** a-1i, 2i, 6i; c-2.*

1984 (Magazine) (1994 #11 on)
Warren Publishing Co.: June, 1978 - No. 10, Jan, 1980 ($1.50, B&W with color inserts, mature content with nudity; 84 pgs. except #4 has 92 pgs.)

1-Nino-a in all; Mutant World begins by Corben 3 6 9 14 19 24
2-10: 4-Rex Havoc begins. 7-1st Ghita of Alizarr by Thorne. 9-1st Starfire 2 4 6 9 13 16
NOTE: ***Alcala** a-1-3,5,7i. **Corben** a-1-8; c-1,2. **Nebres** a-1-8,10. **Thorne** a-7,8,10. **Wood** a-1,2,5i.*

1994 (Formerly 1984) (Magazine)
Warren Publishing Co.: No. 11, Feb, 1980 - No. 29, Feb, 1983 (B&W with color; mature; #11-(84 pgs.); #12-16,18-21,24-(76 pgs.); #17,22,23,25-29-(68 pgs.)

11,17,18,20,22,23,29: 11,17-8 pgs. color insert. 18-Giger-c. 20-1st Diana Jacklighter Manhuntress by Maroto. 22-1st Sigmund Pavlov by Nino; 1st Ariel Hart by Hsu. 23-All Nino issue 2 4 6 8 11 14
12-16,19,21,24-28: 21-1st app. Angel by Nebres. 27-The Warhawks return 1 3 4 6 8 10

Ninjak (2015 series) #17 © VAL

Noble Causes #4 © Jay Faerber

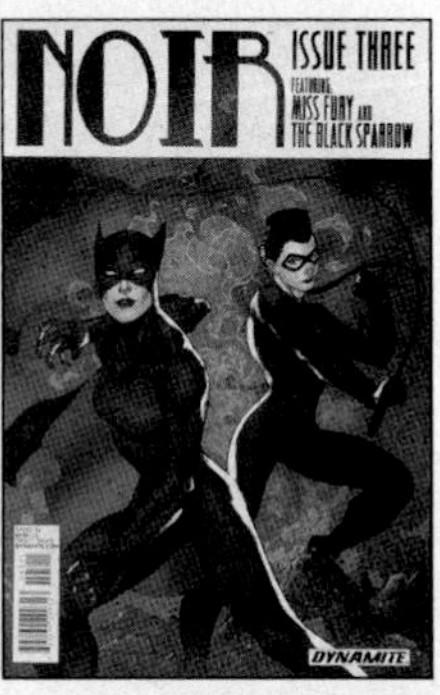

Noir #3 © DYN

GD VG FN VF VF/NM NM-
2.0 4.0 6.0 8.0 9.0 9.2

NOTE: *Corben c-26. Maroto a-20, 21, 24-28. Nebres a-11-13, 15, 16, 18, 21, 22, 25, 28. Nino a-11-19, 20(2), 21, 25, 26, 28; c-21. Redondo c-20. Thorne a-11-14, 17-21, 24-26, 28, 29.*

NINJA BOY
DC Comics (WildStorm): Oct, 2001 - No. 6, Mar, 2002 ($3.50/$2.95)

1-($3.50) Ale Garza-a/c 3.50
2-6-($2.95) 3.00
...: Faded Dreams TPB (2003, $14.95) r/#1-6; sketch pages 15.00

NINJA HIGH SCHOOL (1st series)
Antarctic Press: 1986 - No. 3, Aug, 1987 (B&W)

1-Ben Dunn-s/c/a; early Manga series 2 4 6 9 12 15
2,3 1 3 4 6 8 10

NINJAK (See Bloodshot #6, 7 & Deathmate)
Valiant/Acclaim Comics (Valiant) No. 16 on: Feb, 1994 - No. 26, Nov. 1995 ($2.25/$2.50)

1 ($3.50)-Chromium-c; Quesada-c/a(p) in #1-3 6.00
1-Gold 2 4 6 11 16 20
2-13: 3-Batman, Spawn & Random (from X-Factor) app. as costumes at party (cameo). 4-w/bound-in trading card. 5,6-X-O app. 4.00
0,00,14-26: 14-(4/95)-Begin $2.50-c. 0-(6/95, $2.50). 00-(6/95, $2.50) 3.00
... Black Water HC (2013, $24.99) r/#1-6, #0, #00; bonus Quesada sketch-a 25.00
Yearbook 1 (1994, $3.95) 4.00

NINJAK
Acclaim Comics (Valiant Heroes): V2#1, Mar, 1997 -No. 12, Feb, 1998 ($2.50)

V2#1-12: 1-Intro new Ninjak; 1st app. Brutakon; Kurt Busiek scripts begin; painted variant-c exists. 2-1st app. Karnivor & Zeer. 3-1st app. Gigantik, Shurikai, & Nixie. 4-Origin; 1st app. Yasuiti Motomiya; intro The Dark Dozen; Colin King cameo. 9-Copycat-c 3.00

NINJAK (See Rapture)
Valiant Entertainment: Mar, 2015 - No. 27, May, 2017 ($3.99)

1-27-Multiple covers on each: 1-Kindt-s/Guice and Mann-a. 4-Origin of Roku; Ryp-a 4.00

NINJA•K
Valiant Entertainment: No. 0, Sept, 2017; No. 1, Nov, 2017 - Present ($3.99)

0-Kindt-s/Portela-a; recaps origin 4.00
1-4-Gage-s/Giorello-a. 1-History of Ninja-A in 1917 4.00

NINJAK VS. THE VALIANT UNIVERSE
Valiant Entertainment: Jan, 2018 - No. 4 ($3.99, limited series)

1,2-Rahal-s/Bennett-a 4.00

NINJA SCROLL
DC Comics (WildStorm): Nov, 2006 - No. 12, Oct, 2007 ($2.99)

1-12: 1-J. Torres-s/Michael Chang Ting Yu-a/c. 11-Puckett-s/Meyers-a 3.00
1-3-Variant covers by Jim Lee 5.00
TPB (2007, $19.99) r/#1-3,5-7 20.00

NINJETTES (See Jennifer Blood #4)
Dynamite Entertainment: 2012 - No. 6, 2012 ($3.99, limited series)

1-6-Origin of the team; Ewing-s/Casallos-a. 6-Jennifer Blood app. 4.00

NINTENDO COMICS SYSTEM (Also see Adv. of Super Mario Brothers)
Valiant Comics: Feb, 1990 - No. 9, Oct, 1991 ($4.95, card stock-c, 68 pgs.)

1-9: 1-Featuring Game Boy, Super Mario, Clappwall. 3-Layton-c. 5-8-Super Mario Bros. 9-Dr. Mario 1st app. 2 4 6 8 10 12

(Ninth) **IXTH GENERATION** (See Aphrodite IX & Poseidon IX)
Image Comics (Top Cow): Jan, 2015 - No. 8, Mar, 2016 ($3.99)

1-8: 1-4-Hawkins-s/Sejic-a; Aphrodite IX app. 5-7-Atilio Rojo-a 4.00
... Hidden Files 1 (4/15, $3.99) Short story and guide to the cities; Hawkins-s/Rojo-a 4.00

NOAH (Adaptation of the 2014 movie)
Image Comics: Mar, 2014 (HC, $29.99, 8-3/4" x 11-1/2")

HC-Darren Aronofsky & Ari Handel-s/Niko Henrichon-a 30.00

NOAH'S ARK
Spire Christian Comics/Fleming H. Revell Co.: 1973,1975 (35/49¢)

nn-By Al Hartley 2 4 6 11 16 20

NOBLE CAUSES
Image Comics: July, 2001; Jan, 2002 - No. 4, May, 2002 ($2.95)

...First Impressions (7/01) Intro. the Noble family; Faerber-s 3.00
1-4: 1-(1/02) Back-up-s with Conner-a. 2-Igle back-up-a. 2-4-Two covers 3.00
...: Extended Family (5/03, $6.95) short stories by various 7.00
...: Extended Family 2 (6/04, $7.95) short stories by various 8.00
Vol. 1: In Sickness and in Health (2003, $12.95) r/#1-4 & ...First Impresssions 13.00

NOBLE CAUSES (Volume 3)
Image Comics: July, 2004 - No. 40, Mar, 2009 ($3.50)

1-24,26-40-Faerber-s. 1-Two covers. 2-Venture app. 5-Invincible app. 3.50
25-($4.99) Art by various; Randolph-c 5.00
Vol. 4: Blood and Water (2005, $14.95) r/#1-6 15.00
Vol. 5: Betrayals (2006, $14.99) r/#7-12 & The Pact V2 #2 15.00
Vol. 6: Hidden Agendas (2006, $15.99) r/#13-18 and Image Holiday Spec. 2005 story 16.00
Vol. 7: Powerless (2007, $15.99) r/#19-25; Wieringo sketch page 16.00

NOBLE CAUSES: DISTANT RELATIVES
Image Comics: Jul, 2003 - No. 4, Oct, 2003 ($2.95, B&W, limited series)

1-4-Faerber-s/Richardson & Ponce-a 3.00
Vol. 3: Distant Relatives (1/05, $12.95) r/#1-4; intro. by Joe Casey 13.00

NOBLE CAUSES: FAMILY SECRETS
Image Comics: Oct, 2002 - No. 4, Jan, 2003 ($2.95, limited series)

1,2,4-Faerber-s/Oeming-c. 1-Variant cover by Walker. 2-Valentino var-c. 4-Hester var-c 3.00
3-1st app. of Invincible (cameo & Valentino var-c) 3 6 9 15 23 30
3-1st app. of Invincible (cameo); regular Oeming-c 1 3 4 6 9 12
Vol. 2: Family Secrets (2004, $12.95) r/#1-4; sketch pages 13.00

NOBODY (Amado, Cho & Adlard's...)
Oni Press: Nov, 1998 - No. 4, Feb, 1999 ($2.95, B&W, mini-series)

1-4 3.00

NOCTURNALS, THE
Malibu Comics (Bravura): Jan, 1995 - No. 6, Aug, 1995 ($2.95, limited series)

1-6: Dan Brereton painted-c/a & scripts 3.00
1-Glow-in-the-Dark premium edition 5.00

NOCTURNALS, THE
Dark Horse Comics/Image Comics/Oni Press: one-shots and trade paperbacks

Black Planet TPB (Oni Press, 1998, $19.95) r/#1-6 (Malibu Comics series) 20.00
Black Planet and Other Stories HC (Olympian Publ.; 7/07, $39.95) r/Black Planet & Witching Hour contents; cover & sketch gallery with Brereton interviews 40.00
Carnival of Beasts (Image, 7/08, $6.99) short stories; Brereton-s/Brereton & others-a 7.00
Sinister Path (Big Wow! Art, 2017) original GN; Brereton-s/a 16.00
Troll Bridge (Oni Press, 2000, $4.95, B&W & orange) Brereton-s/painted-c; art by Brereton, Chin, Art Adams, Sakai, Timm, Warren, Thompson, Purcell, Stephens and others 5.00
Unhallowed Eve TPB (Oni Press, 10/02, $9.95) r/Witching Hour & Troll Bridge one-shots 10.00
Witching Hour (Dark Horse, 5/98, $4.95) Brereton-s/a; reprints DHP stories + 8 new pgs. 5.00

NOCTURNALS: THE DARK FOREVER
Oni Press: Jul, 2001 -No. 3, Feb, 2002 ($2.95, limited series)

1-3-Brereton-s/painted-a/c 3.00
TPB (5/02, $9.95) r/#1-3; afterword & pin-ups by Alex Ross 10.00

NOCTURNE
Marvel Comics: June, 1995 - No. 4, Sept. 1995 ($1.50, limited series)

1-4 3.00

NO ESCAPE (Movie)
Marvel Comics: June, 1994 - No. 3, Aug, 1994 ($1.50)

1-3: Based on movie 3.00

NO HONOR
Image Comics (Top Cow): Feb, 2001 - No. 4, July, 2001 ($2.50)

Preview (12/00, B&W) Silvestri-c 3.00
1-4-Avery-s/Crain-a 3.00
TPB (8/03, $12.99) r/#1-4; intro. by Straczynski 13.00

NOIR
Dynamite Entertainment: 2013 - No. 5, 2014 ($3.99, limited series)

1-5: 1-Miss Fury, Black Sparrow & The Shadow app.; Gischler-s/Mutti-a 4.00

NOMAD (See Captain America #180)
Marvel Comics: Nov, 1990 - No. 4, Feb, 1991 ($1.50, limited series)

1-4: 1,4-Captain America app. 3.00

NOMAD
Marvel Comics: V2#1, May, 1992 - No. 25, May, 1994 ($1.75)

V2#1-25: 1-Has gatefold-c w/map/wanted poster. 4-Deadpool x-over. 5-Punisher vs. Nomad-c/story. 6-Punisher & Daredevil-c/story cont'd in Punisher War Journal #48. 7-Gambit-c/story. 10-Red Wolf app. 21-Man-Thing-c/story. 25-Bound-in trading card sheet 3.00

NOMAD: GIRL WITHOUT A WORLD (Rikki Barnes from Captain America V2 Heroes Reborn)
Marvel Comics: Nov, 2009 - No. 4, Feb, 2010 ($3.99, limited series)

1-4-McKeever-s. 2-Falcon app. 4-Young Avengers app. 4.00

NOMAN (See Thunder Agents)

Normals #1 © Adam Glass

Northanger Abbey #1 © MAR

Nova #4 © MAR

GD 2.0 | VG 4.0 | FN 6.0 | VF 8.0 | VF/NM 9.0 | NM- 9.2

Tower Comics: Nov, 1966 - No. 2, March, 1967 (25¢, 68 pgs.)
1-Wood/Williamson-c; Lightning begins; Dynamo cameo; Kane-a(p) & Whitney-a 8 16 24 54 102 150
2-Wood-c only; Dynamo x-over; Whitney-a 5 10 15 34 60 85

NO MERCY
Image Comics: Apr, 2015 - No. 14, Mar, 2017 ($2.99/$3.99)
1-4-Alex de Campi-s/Carla Speed McNeil-a 3.00
5-14-($3.99) 6-EC-style cover 4.00

NONE BUT THE BRAVE (See Movie Classics)

NON-HUMANS
Image Comics: Oct, 2012 - No. 4, Jul, 2013 ($2.99)
1-4-Brunswick-s/Portacio-a/c 3.00

NOODNIK COMICS (See Pinky the Egghead)
Comic Media/Mystery/Biltmore: Dec, 1953; No. 2, Feb, 1954 - No. 5, Aug, 1954
3-D(1953, 25¢; Comic Media)(#1)-Came w/glasses 31 62 93 182 296 410
2-5 11 22 33 60 83 105

NORMALMAN (See Cerebus the Aardvark #55, 56)
Aardvark-Vanaheim/Renegade Press #6 on: Jan, 1984 - No. 12, Dec, 1985 ($1.70/$2.00)
1-12: 1-Jim Valentino-c/a in all. 6-12 ($2.00, B&W); 10-Cerebus cameo; Sim-a (2 pgs.) 3.00
...- Megaton Man Special 1 (Image Comics, 8/94, $2.50) 3.00
...3-D 1 (Annual, 1986, $2.25) 3.00
...Twentieth Anniversary Special (7/04, $2.95) 3.00

NORMALS
AfterShock Comics: May, 2017 - No. 6, Oct, 2017 ($3.99, limited series)
1-6-Adam Glass-s/Dennis Calero-a 4.00

NORMANDY GOLD
Titan Comics: Jul, 2017 - Present ($3.99)
1-3-Megan Abbott & Alison Gaylin-s/Steve Scott-a; multiple covers 4.00

NORTHANGER ABBEY (Adaptation of the Jane Austen novel)
Marvel Comics: Jan, 2012 - No. 5, May, 2012 ($3.99, mini-series)
1-5-Nancy Butler-s/Janet K. Lee-a/Julian Tedesco-c 4.00

NORTH AVENUE IRREGULARS (See Walt Disney Showcase #49)

NORTH 40
DC Comics (WildStorm): Sept, 2009 - No. 6, Feb, 2010 ($2.99)
1-6-Aaron Williams-s/Fiona Staples-a 3.00
TPB (2010, $17.99) r/#1-6 18.00

NORTHGUARD (See Captain Canuck)
Chapterhouse Comics Group: Aug, 2016 - No. 4, Nov, 2017 ($3.99)
1-4: 1,2-Falcone-s/Salas-a 4.00
Season 2 1,2 (9/17 - Present) Falcone & Feldman-s/Watson-a 4.00

NORTHLANDERS
DC Comics (Vertigo): Feb, 2008 - No. 50, Jun, 2012 ($2.99)
1-50: 1-Vikings in 980 A.D.; Wood-s/Gianfelice-a; covers by Carnivale. 35-Cloonan-a 3.00
1-3-Variant covers. 1-Adam Kubert. 2-Andy Kubert. 3-Dave Gibbons 5.00
...: Blood in the Snow TPB (2010, $14.99) r/#9,10,17-20 15.00
...: Metal and Other Stories TPB (2011, $17.99) r/#29-36 18.00
...: Sven the Returned TPB (2008, $9.99) r/#1-8; cover gallery 10.00
...: The Cross + The Hammer TPB (2009, $14.99) r/#11-16 15.00
...: The Plague Widow TPB (2010, $16.99) r/#21-28 17.00

NORTHSTAR
Marvel Comics: Apr, 1994 - No. 4, July, 1994 ($1.75, mini-series)
1-4: Character from Alpha Flight 3.00

NORTH TO ALASKA
Dell Publishing Co.: No. 1155, Dec, 1960
Four Color 1155-Movie, John Wayne photo-c 15 30 45 100 220 340

NORTHWEST MOUNTIES (Also see Approved Comics #12)
Jubilee Publications/St. John: Oct, 1948 - No. 4, July, 1949
1-Rose of the Yukon by Matt Baker; Walter Johnson-a; Lubbers-c 52 104 156 328 552 775
2-Baker-a; Lubbers-c. Ventrilo app. 40 80 120 246 411 575
3-Bondage-c, Baker-a; Sky Chief, K-9 app. 41 82 123 256 428 600
4-Baker-c/a(2 pgs.); Blue Monk & The Desperado app. 45 90 135 284 480 675

NOSFERATU WARS

GD 2.0 | VG 4.0 | FN 6.0 | VF 8.0 | VF/NM 9.0 | NM- 9.2

Dark Horse Comics: Mar, 2014 ($3.99, one-shot)
1-Reprints serial story from Dark Horse Presents #26-29; Niles-s/Menton3-a 4.00

NO SLEEP 'TIL DAWN
Dell Publishing Co.: No. 831, Aug, 1957
Four Color 831-Movie, Karl Malden photo-c 6 12 18 42 79 115

NOSTALGIA ILLUSTRATED
Marvel Comics: Nov, 1974 - V2#8, Aug, 1975 (B&W, 76 pgs.)
V1#1 3 6 9 21 33 45
V1#2, V2#1-8 3 6 9 15 22 28

NOT BRAND ECHH (Brand Echh #1-4; See Crazy, 1973)
Marvel Comics Group (LMC): Aug, 1967 - No. 13, May, 1969; No. 14, Jan, 2018
(1st Marvel parody book)
1: 1-8 are 12¢ issues 7 14 21 48 89 130
2-8: 3-Origin Thor, Hulk & Capt. America; Monkees, Alfred E. Neuman cameo. 4-X-Men app. 5-Origin/intro. Forbush Man. 7-Origin Fantastical-4 & Stuporman. 8-Beatles cameo; X-Men satire; last 12¢-c 4 8 12 25 40 55
9-13 (25¢, 68 pgs., all Giants) 9-Beatles cameo. 10-All-r; The Old Witch, Crypt Keeper & Vault Keeper cameos. 12,13-Beatles cameo 5 10 15 30 50 70
14-(1/18, $3.99) Forbush Man app.; s/a by Zdarsky, Spencer & others; Nakamura-c 4.00
NOTE: ***Colan** a(p)-4, 5, 8, 9, 13. **Everett** a-1i. **Kirby** a(p)-1, 3, 5-7, 10r; c-1p. **J. Severin** a-1; c-3, 6-8, 11. **M. Severin** a-1-13; c-2, 9, 10, 12, 13. **Sutton** a-3, 4, 5i, 6i, 8, 9, 10r, 11-13; c-5. Archie satire in #9. Avengers satire in #8, 12.*

NOTHING CAN STOP THE JUGGERNAUT
Marvel Comics: 1989 ($3.95)
1-r/Amazing Spider-Man #229 & 230 5.00

NO TIME FOR SERGEANTS (TV)
Dell Publ. Co.: No. 914, July, 1958; Feb-Apr, 1965 - No. 3, Aug-Oct, 1965
Four Color 914 (Movie)-Toth-a; Andy Griffith photo-c 9 18 27 60 120 180
1(2-4/65) (TV): Photo-c 5 10 15 34 60 85
2,3 (TV): Photo-c 4 8 12 28 47 65

NOVA (The Man Called... No. 22-25)(See New Warriors)
Marvel Comics Group: Sept, 1976 - No. 25, May, 1979
1-Origin/1st app. Nova (Richard Rider) Marv Wolfman-s; John Buscema-a 6 12 18 42 79 115
2,3: 2-1st app. Condor & Powerhouse. 3-1st app. Diamondhead; Sal Buscema-p begin 2 4 6 9 12 15
4,12: 4-Thor x-over; 1st app. The Corrupter; Kirby-c. 12-Spider-Man x-over w/Amazing Spider-Man #171 2 4 6 10 14 18
5-11: 5-Nova vs. Tyrannus; Kirby-c; Marvel Bullpen app (incl. Stan Lee) 6-1st app. The Sphinx & Megaman. 7-Sphinx, Condor, Powerhouse & Diamondhead app. 8-Origin Megaman. 9-Megaman app. 10-Sphinx, Condor, Powerhouse & Diamondhead app. 11-vs. Sphinx 1 3 4 6 8 10
10,11-(35¢-c variants, limited distribution)(6,7/77) 8 16 24 56 108 160
12-(35¢-c variant, limited distribution)(8/77) 10 20 30 64 132 200
13,14-(Regular 30¢ editions)(9/77) 13-Intro Crime-Buster; Sandman app. 14-vs. Sandman 1 2 3 5 6 8
13,14-(35¢-c variants, limited distribution) 8 16 24 56 108 160
15-24: 15-Infantino-a begins. 16-18-vs. Yellow Claw; Nick Fury and SHIELD app. 19-Wally West (Kid Flash) cameo; 1st app Blackout. 20-1st Project X (Sherlock Holmes robot). 21-Richard reveals his Nova I.D to parents; vs Corrupter. 22-1st app the Comet (in costume). 23-Dr. Sun app. (origin) from Tomb of Dracula; Sphinx cameo. 24-Origin Powerhouse, Diamondhead, Crime-Buster, Comet Man, Sphinx & Dr. Sun app. 1 2 3 5 6 8
25-Last issue; Powerhouse, Diamondhead, Crime-Buster, Comet Man, Sphinx & Dr. Sun app. story continues in Fantastic Four #204-214 2 4 6 11 16 20
NOTE: ***Austin** c-21i, 23i. **John Buscema** a(p)-1-3, 8, 21; c-1p, 2, 15. **Infantino** a(p)-15-20, 22-25; c-17-20, 21p, 23p, 24p. **Kirby** c-4p, 5, 7. **Nebres** c-25i. **Simonson** a-23i.*

NOVA
Marvel Comics: Jan, 1994 - June, 1995 ($1.75/$1.95) (Started as 4-part mini-series)
1-($2.95, 52 pgs.)-Collector's Edition w/gold foil-c; new Nova costume; Nicieza-s/Marrinan-a; continued from New Warriors #42; re-intro Richard Rider's supporting cast – Ginger Jaye, Bernie Dillon & Roger 'Caps' Cooper; origin & history recap; vs. Gladiator of the Shi'ar Imperial Guard; Queen Adora app. 6.00
1-($2.25, 52 pgs.)-Newsstand Edition w/o foil-c 4.00
2-5: 2-1st app. Tailhook; Speedball app. 3-vs. Spider-Man; Corrupter app; 1st app Nova 00. 4-Vs. Nova 00; contains Rock Video Monthly insert (centerfold). 5-Re-intro Condor; Sphinx cameo; leads into New Warriors #47; contains centerfold insert for Marvel 'Masterprints' 3.00
6,7: 6-'Time and Time Again', pt.3; story continued from Night Thrasher #11; Rage & Firestar solo stories; continues in New Warriors #48. 7- 'Time and Time Again' pt.6; continued from

Nova (2007 series) #28 © MAR

Nova (2017 series) #1 © MAR

Nth Man The Ultimate Ninja #9 © MAR

GD 2.0 VG 4.0 FN 6.0 VF 8.0 VF/NM 9.0 NM- 9.2

GD 2.0 VG 4.0 FN 6.0 VF 8.0 VF/NM 9.0 NM- 9.2

Night Thrasher #12; Rage & Firestar solo stories; Cloak and Dagger app; continues in New Warriors #49; last Nicieza-s 4.00

8-12: 8-1st app. Shatterforce. 9-Vs. Shatterforce. 10-Vs. Diamondhead & Rhino; New Warriors and Corrupter app. 11-She-Hulk, the Thing & Ant-Man guest star; Nick Fury cameo; contains two inserts – a Marvel Subscription offer and a centerfold insert for a personalized X-Men/Captain Universe comic. 12-Vs. Nova 00; Nick Fury, Black Bolt & the Inhumans app. 13-'Deathstorm' T-Minus 3; Firestar, Night Thrasher & Nick Fury app. 14-'Deathstorm' T-Minus 2; Nova 00, Darkhawk & the New Warriors app. 15-'Deathstorm' T-Minus 1; 1st app. Kraa (brother of Zorr from Nova #1, 1976) 3.00

16-18: 16-'Deathstorm' conclusion; vs. Kraa; Nova-Corps app; death of Nova 00. 17-vs. Supernova (Garthan Saal); Richard is stripped of his rank; Queen Adora app. 18-Last issue; Richard Rider de-powered; Supernova becomes Nova-Prime; Dire Wraith Queen app; story continues in New Warriors #60 6.00

NOVA
Marvel Comics: May, 1999 - No. 7, Nov, 1999 ($2.99/$1.99)

1-($2.99, 38 pgs.) –Larsen-s/Bennett-a; wraparound-c by Larsen; origin retold; Nebula app; reveals her father to be Zorr (from issue #1, 1976); She-Hulk, Spider-Man, Speedball, Namorita app. 5.00

2-6: 2-Two covers; vs. Diamondhead; Captain America app.; Namorita's skin returns to normal. 3-Savage Dragon app.; (as a Skrull); New Warriors, Thor, Fantastic Four & the Condor app.; return of the Sphinx. 4-vs. Condor; Fantastic Four app; Red Raven cameo. 5-Spider-Man app. 6-vs. the Sphinx; Venom cameo 3.00

7-Last issue; Red Raven & Bi-Beast app. vs. Venom 4.00

NOVA (See Secret Avengers and The Thanos Imperative)
Marvel Comics: June, 2007 - No. 36, Jun, 2010 ($2.99)

1-Abnett/Lanning-s; Chen-a; Granov-c; continued from Annihilation #6; brief Iron Man app. 3 6 9 16 23 30

2-The Initiative x-over; Nova returns to Earth; vs. Diamondhead; Iron Man & the Thunderbolts (Penance, Radioactive Man, Venom & Moonstone) app. 1 3 4 6 8 10

3-The Initiative x-over; vs. the Thunderbolts; Iron Man app.; Nova leaves Earth 1 2 3 5 6 8

4-7,9: Annihilation Conquest x-overs. 4-Phalanx and Gamora app. 5-Nova infected with the Phalanx virus; Gamora app. 6-Gamora-c by Granov; Drax app. 7-Gamora and Drax app; last Chen-a. 9-Cosmo, Gamora and Drax app. 7.00

8-1st app. Cosmo - the Russian telepathic dog; 1st app. Knowhere – a space station formed out of the severed head of a Celestial (as seen in the GOTG movie); 1st app. of the Luminals; 1st Wellington Alves-a; brief Peter Quill (Star-Lord) app. 3 6 9 16 23 30

10-14: 10-Nova and Gamora solo story; Drax app.; leads into Nova Annual #1. 11-Gamora, Drax & Warlock of the New Mutants app; Pelletier-a begins. 12-Warlock of the New Mutants app. Nova, Gamora & Drax cured of the Phalanx virus; leads into Annihilation Conquest #6. 13-Galactus & Silver Surfer app.; contains 5-pg preview of the new Eternals series; Alves-a. 14-Galactus app.; Nova vs. Silver Surfer. 15-Galactus & Silver Surfer app. 6.00

16-18: Secret Invasion x-over. 16-Super-Skrull app.; Nova returns to Earth. 17-Team up w/Darkhawk at Project Pegasus vs. the Skrulls; Quasar (Wendell Vaughn) returns. 18-Quasar & Darkhawk app; vs. the Skrulls; return of the Nova Corps 5.00

18-Zombie 1:10 variant-c by Wellington Alves 6.00

19-Darkhawk app.; Robbie Rider joins the Nova-Corps; Serpent Society app. 20-New Warriors flashback; Justice & Firestar app; Ego the Living Planet app. 21-Fantastic Four app; Ego the Living Planet becomes new base for the Nova Corps; Nova's powers are taken away. 22-Quasar app.; Andrea Divito-a begins 4.00

20-Villain 'Sphinx' variant-c by Mike Deodato Jr. 1 2 3 5 6 8

23-28: War of Kings x-over. 23-Richard Rider dons the Quantum Bands – becomes the new Quasar. 24-Gladiator & the Shi'ar Imperial Guard app. 25-Richard regains his Nova powers; Wendell Vaughn (Quasar) regains the Quantum Bands; Emperor Vulcan app. 26-Lord Ravenous app. 27-Blastaar & Lord Ravenous app. 28-War of Kings ends; Robbie Rider officially joins the Nova Corps. Quasar app. 6.00

25-'Dirty Dancing' 1980s decade 1:10 variant by Alina Urusov 5.00

28-Marvel Comics 70th Anniversary frame variant 6.00

29,30: 'Starstalker' parts 1-2. 29-1st Marvel Universe app. of Monark Starstalker (previously from Marvel Premiere #32). 30-vs. Ego the Living Planet 3.00

31-Darkhawk app. 5.00

32-34: Realm of Kings x-over; 32,33-Reed Richards, Black Bolt, Darkhawk, Namorita & the Sphinx app. 33-Moonstone, Man-Wolf, Bloodstone, Basilisk app. 34-'Death' of Black Bolt; Nova vs. Moonstone, Reed Richards vs. Bloodstone, Namorita vs. Man-Wolf, Darkhawk vs. Gyre the Raptor; contains 6 pg. preview of the New Ultimates series 1 2 3 5 6 8

34-Deadpool variant-c 2 4 6 8 12 15

35-Realm of Kings x-over; Reed Richards, Darkhawk, Namorita vs. Sphinx; Namorita brought back to current continuity 1 3 4 6 8 10

36-Last issue; Darkhawk & Quasar app.; leads into Thanos Imperative Ignition 2 4 6 8 12 15

Annual #1 (4/08, $3.99); Slightly altered origin retold; Annihilation Conquest tie-in; Quasar app.; takes place between Nova issues #10-11 1 2 3 5 6 8

...: Origin of Richard Rider (2009, $4.99) origin retold from Nova #1 & 4 ('76) 5.00

... Vol. 1: Annihilation - Conquest TPB (2007, $17.99) r/#1-7; cover sketches 18.00

NOVA (Marvel NOW!)
Marvel Comics: Apr, 2013 - No. 31, Jul, 2015 ($3.99)

1-Loeb-s/McGuinness-a/c; Rocket Raccoon & Gamora app.; multiple variant covers 6.00

2-9: 2,3-Rocket Raccoon & Gamora app. 7-Superior Spider-Man app. 8,9-Infinity tie-in 4.00

10-($4.99) "Issue #100"; Speedball & Justice app.; cover gallery 5.00

11-24,26-31: 12-16-Beta Ray Bill app. 18-20-Original Sin tie-in. 19,20-Rocket Raccoon app. 23,24-Axis tie-in. 28-Black Vortex crossover 4.00

25-($4.99) Axis tie-in; Sam joins the Avengers 5.00

Annual 1 (5/15, $4.99) The Hulk app.; Duggan-s/Baldeon-a 5.00

... Special 1 (10/14, $4.99) Part 3 of x-over with Iron Man & Uncanny X-Men 5.00

NOVA
Marvel Comics: Jan, 2016 - No. 11, Nov, 2016 ($3.99)

1-11: 1-Sean Ryan-s/Cory Smith-a. 3,4-Ms. Marvel & Spider-Man (Miles) app. 8,9-Civil War II tie-in. 10,11-Richard Rider returns 4.00

NOVA
Marvel Comics: Feb, 2017 - No. 7, Aug, 2017 ($3.99)

1-7: 1-Ramón Pérez-a; Richard Rider & Ego app. 4-Gamora app. 4.00

NOW AGE ILLUSTRATED (See Pendulum Illustrated Classics)

NOW AGE BOOKS ILLUSTRATED (See Pendulum Illustrated Classics)

NOWHERE MAN
Dynamite Entertainment: 2011 - No. 4, 2011 ($3.99)

1-4-Marc Guggenheim-s/Jeevan J. Kang-a 4.00

NOWHERE MEN
Image Comics: Nov, 2012 - No. 11, Sept, 2016 ($2.99)

1-Stephenson-s/Bellegarde-a 15.00
1-2nd thru 5th printings 4.00
2 6.00
3-11 4.00

NO WORLD
Aspen MLT: Apr, 2017 - No. 6, Oct, 2017 ($3.99, limited series)

1-6-Lobdell-s/Gunderson-a; multiple covers on each 4.00

NTH MAN THE ULTIMATE NINJA (See Marvel Comics Presents #25)
Marvel Comics: Aug, 1989 - No. 16, Sept, 1990 ($1.00)

1-16-Ninja mercenary. 8-Dale Keown's 1st Marvel work (1/90, pencils) 3.00

NUCLEUS (Also see Cerebus)
Heiro-Graphic Publications: May, 1979 ($1.50, B&W, adult fanzine)

1-Contains "Demonhorn" by Dave Sim; early app. of Cerebus The Aardvark (4 pg. story) 5 10 15 34 60 85

NUKLA
Dell Publishing Co.: Oct-Dec, 1965 - No. 4, Sept, 1966

1-Origin & 1st app. Nukla (super hero) 4 8 12 28 47 65
2,3 3 6 9 19 30 40
4-Ditko-a, c(p) 4 8 12 23 37 50

NUMBER OF THE BEAST
DC Comics (WildStorm): June, 2008 - No. 8, Sept, 2008 ($2.99, limited series)

1-8-Beatty-s/Sprouse-a/c. 1-Variant-c by Mahnke. 6-The Authority app. 3.00

TPB (2008, $19.99) r/#1-8; character dossiers 20.00

NURSE BETSY CRANE (Formerly Teen Secret Diary) (Also see Registered Nurse for reprints)
Charlton Comics: V2#12, Aug, 1961 - V2#27, Mar, 1964 (See Soap Opera Romances)

V2#12-27 3 6 9 19 30 40

NURSE HELEN GRANT (See The Romances of...)

NURSE LINDA LARK (See Linda Lark)

NURSERY RHYMES
Ziff-Davis Publ. Co. (Approved Comics): No. 10, July-Aug, 1951 - No. 2, Winter, 1951 (Painted-c)

10 (#1), 2: 10-Howie Post-a 19 38 57 111 176 240

NURSES, THE (TV)
Gold Key: April, 1963 - No. 3, Oct, 1963 (Photo-c: #1,2)

1 4 8 12 27 44 60

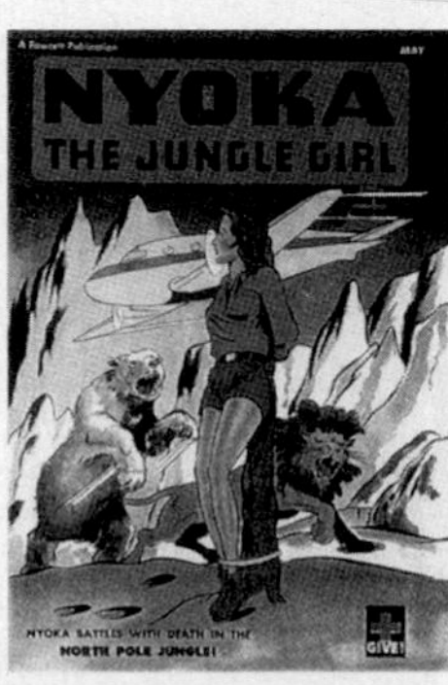

Nyoka, The Jungle Girl #7 © FAW

NYX #3 © MAR

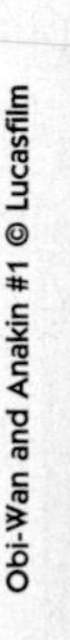
Obi-Wan and Anakin #1 © Lucasfilm

	GD 2.0	VG 4.0	FN 6.0	VF 8.0	VF/NM 9.0	NM- 9.2
2,3	3	6	9	17	26	35

NUTS! (Satire)
Premiere Comics Group: March, 1954 - No. 5, Nov, 1954

	GD	VG	FN	VF	VF/NM	NM-
1-Hollingsworth-a	36	72	108	211	343	475
2,4,5: 5-Capt. Marvel parody	22	44	66	132	216	300
3-Drug "reefers" mentioned; Marilyn Monroe & Joe DiMaggio parody-c	24	48	72	142	234	325

NUTS (Magazine) (Satire)
Health Knowledge: Feb, 1958 - No. 2, April, 1958

	GD	VG	FN	VF	VF/NM	NM-
1	10	20	30	54	72	90
2	7	14	21	37	46	55

NUTS & JOLTS
Dell Publishing Co.: No. 22, 1941

	GD	VG	FN	VF	VF/NM	NM-
Large Feature Comic 22	20	40	60	117	189	260

NUTSY SQUIRREL (Formerly Hollywood Funny Folks)(See Comic Cavalcade)
National Periodical Publications: #61, 9-10/54 - #69, 1-2/56; #70, 8-9/56 - #71, 10-11/56; #72, 11/57

	GD	VG	FN	VF	VF/NM	NM-
61-Mayer-a; Grossman-a in all	14	28	42	76	108	140
62-72: Mayer a-62,65,67-72	10	20	30	54	72	90

NUTTY COMICS
Fawcett Publications: Winter, 1946

	GD	VG	FN	VF	VF/NM	NM-
1-Capt. Kidd story; 1 pg. Wolverton-a	14	28	42	80	115	150

NUTTY COMICS
Home Comics (Harvey Publications): 1945; No. 4, May-June, 1946 - No. 8, June-July, 1947 (No #2,3)

	GD	VG	FN	VF	VF/NM	NM-
nn-Helpful Hank, Bozo Bear & others (funny animal)	9	18	27	50	65	80
4	7	14	21	37	46	55
5-Rags Rabbit begins(1st app.); infinity-c	8	16	24	44	57	70
6-8	6	12	18	31	38	45

NUTTY LIFE (Formerly Krazy Life #1; becomes Wotalife Comics #3 on)
Fox Feature Syndicate: No. 2, Summer, 1946

	GD	VG	FN	VF	VF/NM	NM-
2	21	42	63	126	206	285

NYOKA, THE JUNGLE GIRL (Formerly Jungle Girl; see The Further Adventures of..., Master Comics #50 & XMas Comics)
Fawcett Publications: No. 2, Winter, 1945 - No. 77, June, 1953 (Movie serial)

	GD	VG	FN	VF	VF/NM	NM-
2	68	136	204	435	743	1050
3	36	72	108	216	351	485
4,5	31	62	93	182	296	410
6-11,13,14,16-18-Krigstein-a: 17-Sam Spade ad by Lou Fine	20	40	60	118	192	265
12,15,19,20	19	38	57	111	176	240
21-30: 25-Clayton Moore photo-c?	14	28	42	78	112	145
31-40	11	22	33	64	90	115
41-50	10	20	30	58	79	100
51-60	9	18	27	52	69	85
61-77	9	18	27	47	61	75

NOTE: *Photo-c from movies 25, 30-70, 72, 75-77. Bondage c-4, 5, 7, 8, 14, 24.*

NYOKA, THE JUNGLE GIRL (Formerly Zoo Funnies; Space Adventures #23 on)
Charlton Comics: No. 14, Nov, 1955 - No. 22, Nov, 1957

	GD	VG	FN	VF	VF/NM	NM-
14	11	22	33	64	90	115
15-22	10	20	30	54	72	90

NYX (Also see X-23 title)
Marvel Comics: Nov, 2003 - No. 7, Oct, 2005 ($2.99)

	GD	VG	FN	VF	VF/NM	NM-
1,2: 1-Quesada-s/Middleton-a/c; intro. Kiden Nixon	2	4	6	8	11	14
3-1st app. X-23	15	30	45	105	233	360
4-2nd app X-23	4	8	12	23	37	50
5,6-Teranishi-a	2	4	6	8	11	14
7-($3.99) Teranishi-a	1	3	4	6	8	10
NYX X-23 (2005, $34.99, oversized with d.j.) r/X-23 #1-6 & NYX #1-7; intro by Craig Kyle; sketch pages, development art and unused covers						45.00
...: Wannabe TPB (2006, $19.99) r/#1-7; development art and unused covers						20.00

NYX: NO WAY HOME
Marvel Comics: Oct, 2008 - No. 6, Apr, 2009 ($3.99)

	NM-
1-6: 1-Andrasofszky-a/Liu-s/Urusov-c; sketch pages, character and cover design art	5.00

OAKLAND PRESS FUNNYBOOK, THE
The Oakland Press: 9/17/78 - 4/13/80 (16 pgs.) (Weekly)
Full color in comic book form; changes to tabloid size 4/20/80-on
Contains Tarzan by Manning, Marmaduke, Bugs Bunny, etc. (low distribution); 9/23/79 - 4/13/80 contain Buck Rogers by Gray Morrow & Jim Lawrence 3.00

OAKY DOAKS (See Famous Funnies #190)
Eastern Color Printing Co.: July, 1942 (One Shot)

	GD	VG	FN	VF	VF/NM	NM-
1	34	68	102	204	332	460

OBERGEIST: RAGNAROK HIGHWAY
Image Comics (Top Cow/Minotaur): May, 2001 - No. 6, Nov, 2001 ($2.95, limited series)

	NM-
Preview ('01, B&W, 16 pgs.) Harris painted-c	3.00
1-6-Harris-c/a/Jolley-s. 1-Three covers	3.00
... :The Directors' Cut (2002, $19.95, TPB) r/#1-6; Bruce Campbell intro.	20.00
... :The Empty Locket (3/02, $2.95, B&W) Harris & Snyder-a	3.00

OBIE
Store Comics: 1953 (6¢)

	GD	VG	FN	VF	VF/NM	NM-
1	8	16	24	40	50	60

OBI-WAN AND ANAKIN (Star Wars)
Marvel Comics: Mar, 2016 - No. 5, Jul, 2016 ($3.99)

	NM-
1-5-Takes place a few years after Episode One; Soule-s/Checchetto-a/c	4.00

OBJECTIVE FIVE
Image Comics: July, 2000 - No. 6, Jan, 2001 ($2.95)

	NM-
1-6-Lizalde-a	3.00

OBLIVION
Comico: Aug, 1995 - No. 3, May, 1996 ($2.50)

	NM-
1-3: 1-Art Adams-c. 2-(1/96)-Bagged w/gaming card. 3-(5/96)-Darrow-c	3.00

OBLIVION SONG
Image Comics: Mar, 2018 - Present ($3.99)

	NM-
1-Kirkman-s/De Felici-a	4.00

OBNOXIO THE CLOWN (Character from Crazy Magazine)
Marvel Comics Group: April, 1983 (one-shot)

	NM-
1-Vs. the X-Men	5.00

OCCULT CRIMES TASKFORCE
Image Comics: July, 2006 - No. 4, May, 2007 ($2.99, limited series)

	NM-
1-4-Rosario Dawson & David Atchison-s/Tony Shasteen-a	3.00
... Vol. 1 TPB (2007, $14.99) r/#1-4; sketch and cover development art	15.00

OCCULTIST, THE
Dark Horse Comics: Dec, 2010 ($3.50, one-shot)

	NM-
1-Richardson & Seeley-s/Drujiniu-a/Morris-c	3.50

OCCULTIST, THE
Dark Horse Comics: Nov, 2011 - No. 3, Jan, 2012 ($3.50, limited series)

	NM-
1-3-Seeley-s/Drujiniu-a/Morris-c. 1-Variant-c by Frison	3.50

OCCULTIST, THE
Dark Horse Comics: Oct, 2013 - No. 5, Feb, 2014 ($3.50, limited series)

	NM-
1-5-Seeley-s/Norton-a/Morris-c. 1-Variant-c by Rivera	3.50

OCCULT FILES OF DR. SPEKTOR, THE
Gold Key/Whitman No. 25: Apr, 1973 - No. 24, Feb, 1977; No. 25, May, 1982 (Painted-c #1-24)

	GD	VG	FN	VF	VF/NM	NM-
1-1st app. Lakota; Baron Tibor begins	5	10	15	33	57	80
2-5: 3-Mummy-c/s. 5-Jekyll & Hyde-c/s	3	6	9	19	30	40
6-10: 6,9-Frankenstein. 8,9-Dracula c/s. 9-Jekyll & Hyde c/s. 9,10-Mummy-c/s	3	6	9	15	22	28
11-13,15-17,19-22,24: 11-1st app. Spektor as Werewolf. 11-13-Werewolf-c/s. 12,16-Frankenstein c/s. 17-Zombie/Voodoo-c. 19-Sea monster-c/s. 20-Mummy-s. 21-Swamp monster-c/s. 24-Dragon-c/s	2	4	6	11	16	20
14-Dr. Solar app.	3	6	9	16	24	32
18,23-Dr. Solar cameo	2	4	6	13	18	22
22-Return of the Owl-c/s	2	4	6	13	18	22
25(Whitman, 5/82)-r/#1 with line drawn-c	2	4	6	9	13	16

NOTE: *Also see Dan Curtis, Golden Comics Digest 33, Gold Key Spotlight, Mystery Comics Digest 5, & Spine Tingling Tales.*

OCCUPY AVENGERS (Follows Civil War II)
Marvel Comics: Jan, 2017 - No. 9, Sept, 2017 ($3.99)

	NM-
1-4-Hawkeye and Red Wolf team; Pacheco-a. 3,4-Nighthawk & Nick Fury LMD app. 8,9-Secret Empire tie-ins. 9-Leads into Secret Empire #7	4.00

OCCUPY COMICS
Black Mask Studios: 2013 - No. 3, 2013 ($3.50)

	NM-
1-3-Short stories and essays about the Occupy movement; s/a by various. 1-Allred-c	3.50

ODY-C #9 © Milkfed & Ward

Odyssey of the Amazons #2 © DC

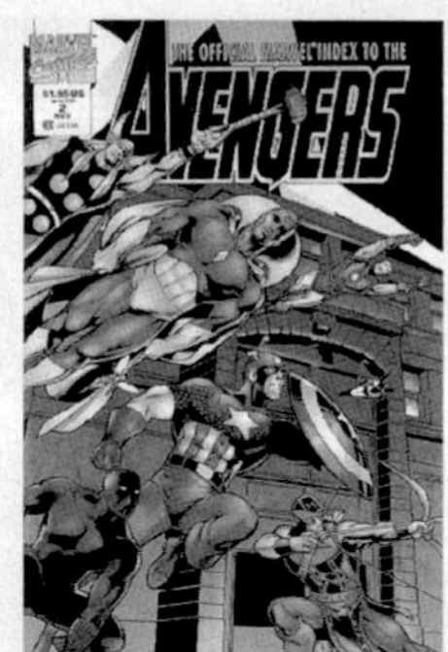

Official Marvel Index to The Avengers #2 © MAR

GD 2.0 | VG 4.0 | FN 6.0 | VF 8.0 | VF/NM 9.0 | NM- 9.2

OCEAN
DC Comics (WildStorm): Dec, 2005 - No. 6, Sept, 2006 ($2.95/$2.99/$3.99, limited series)

1-5-Warren Ellis-s/Chris Sprouse-a 3.00
6-($3.99) Conclusion 4.00

OCTOBER FACTION, THE
IDW Publishing: Oct, 2014 - No. 18, Jul, 2016 ($3.99)

1-18-Steve Niles-s/Damien Worm-a/c 4.00

OCTOBER FACTION, THE: DEADLY SEASON
IDW Publishing: Oct, 2016 - No. 5, Feb, 2017 ($3.99)

1-5-Steve Niles-s/Damien Worm-a/c 4.00

OCTOBER FACTION: SUPERNATURAL DREAMS
IDW Publishing: Mar, 2018 - Present ($3.99)

1-Steve Niles-s/Damien Worm-a/c 4.00

ODDLY NORMAL
Image Comics: Sept, 2014 - No. 10, Sept, 2015 ($2.99)

1-10-Otis Frampton-s/a 3.00

ODELL'S ADVENTURES IN 3-D (See Adventures in 3-D)

ODY-C
Image Comics: Nov, 2014 - Present ($3.99)

1-12: 1-Matt Fraction-s/Christian Ward-a; 8-page gatefold 4.00

ODYSSEY, THE (See Marvel Illustrated: The Odyssey)

ODYSSEY OF THE AMAZONS
DC Comics: Mar, 2017 - No. 6, Aug, 2017 ($3.99, limited series)

1-6-Early history of the Amazons; Kevin Grevioux-s/Ryan Benjamin-a 4.00

OFFCASTES
Marvel Comics (Epic Comics/Heavy Hitters): July, 1993 - No. 3, Sept, 1993 ($1.95, limited series)

1-3: Mike Vosburg-c/a/scripts in all 3.00

OFFICIAL CRISIS ON INFINITE EARTHS INDEX, THE
Independent Comics Group (Eclipse): Mar, 1986 ($1.75)

1 5.00

OFFICIAL CRISIS ON INFINITE EARTHS CROSSOVER INDEX, THE
Independent Comics Group (Eclipse): July, 1986 ($1.75)

1-Pérez-c. 5.00

OFFICIAL DOOM PATROL INDEX, THE
Independent Comics Group (Eclipse): Feb, 1986 - No. 2, Mar, 1986 ($1.50, limited series)

1,2: Byrne-c. 4.00

OFFICIAL HANDBOOK OF THE CONAN UNIVERSE (See Handbook of...)

OFFICIAL HANDBOOK OF THE MARVEL UNIVERSE, THE
Marvel Comics Group: Jan, 1983 - No. 15, May, 1984 (Limited series)

1-Lists Marvel heroes & villains (letter A) 6.00
2-15: 2 (B-C, 3-(C-D). 4-(D-G). 5-(H-J), 6-(K-L). 7-(M). 8-(N-P); Punisher-c. 9-(Q-S), 10-(S). 11-(S-U). 12-(V-Z); Wolverine-c. 13,14-Book of the Dead. 15-Weaponry catalogue 5.00

NOTE: *Bolland a-8. Byrne c/a(p)-1-14; c-15p. Grell a-6, 9. Kirby a-1, 3. Layton a-2, 5, 7. Mignola a-3, 4, 5, 6, 8, 12. Miller a-4-6, 8, 10. Nebres a-3, 4, 8. Redondo a-3, 4, 8, 13, 14. Simonson a-1, 4, 6-13. Paul Smith a-1-12. Starlin a-5, 7, 8, 10, 13, 14. Steranko a-8p. Zeck-2-14.*

OFFICIAL HANDBOOK OF THE MARVEL UNIVERSE, THE
Marvel Comics Group: Dec, 1985 - No. 20, Feb, 1988 ($1.50, maxi-series)

V2#1-Byrne-c 5.00
2-20: 2,3-Byrne-c 4.00
Trade paperback Vol. 1-10 ($6.95) 1 3 4 6 8 10

NOTE: *Art Adams a-7, 8, 11, 12, 14. Bolland a-8, 10, 13. Buckler a-1, 3, 5, 10. Buscema a-1, 5, 8, 9, 10, 13, 14. Byrne a-1-14; c-1-11. Ditko a-1, 2, 4, 6, 7, 11, 13. a-7, 11. Mignola a-2, 4, 9, 11, 13. Miller a-2, 4, 12. Simonson a-1, 2, 4-13, 15. Paul Smith a-1-5, 7-12, 14. Starlin a-6, 8, 9, 12, 16. Zeck a-1-4, 6, 7, 9-14, 16.*

OFFICIAL HANDBOOK OF THE MARVEL UNIVERSE, THE
Marvel Comics: July, 1989 - No. 8, Mid-Dec, 1990 ($1.50, lim. series, 52 pgs.)

V3#1-8: 1-McFarlane-a (2 pgs.) 4.00

OFFICIAL HANDBOOK OF THE MARVEL UNIVERSE, THE (Also see Spider-Man)
Marvel Comics: 2004 - Present ($3.99, one-shots)

...: Alternate Universes 2005 - Profile pages of 1602, MC2, 2099, Earth X, Mangaverse, Days of Future Past, Squadron Supreme, Spider-Ham's Larval Earth and others 4.00
...: Avengers 2004 - Profile pages; art by various; lists of character origins and 1st apps. 4.00
...: Avengers 2005 - Profile pages and info for New Avengers, Young Avengers & others 4.00
...: Book of the Dead 2004 - Profile pages of deceased Marvel characters; art by various; 4.00
...: Daredevil 2004 - Profile pages; art by various; lists of character origins and 1st apps. 4.00
...: Fantastic Four 2005 - Profile pages of members, friends & enemies 4.00
...: Golden Age 2005 - Profile pages; art by various; lists of character origins and 1st apps. 4.00
...: Horror 2005 - Profile pages; art by various; lists of character origins and 1st apps. 4.00
...: Hulk 2004 - Profile pages; art by various; lists of character origins and 1st apps. 4.00
...: Marvel Knights 2005 - Profile pages of characters from Marvel Knights line 4.00
...: Spider-Man 2004 - Profile pages; art by various; lists of character origins and 1st apps. 4.00
...: Spider-Man 2005 - Profile pages of Spidey's friends and foes, emphasizing the recent 4.00
...: Wolverine 2004 - Profile pages; art by various; lists of character origins and 1st apps. 4.00
...: Teams 2005 - Profile pages of Avengers, X-Men and other teams 4.00
...: Women of Marvel 2005 - Profile pages; art by various; Greg Land-c 4.00
...: X-Men 2004 - Profile pages; art by various; lists of character origins and 1st apps. 4.00
...: X-Men 2005 - Profile pages; art by various; lists of character origins and 1st apps. 4.00
...: X-Men - The Age of Apocalypse 2005 - Profile pages of characters plus Exiles 4.00

OFFICIAL HANDBOOK OF THE MARVEL UNIVERSE A-Z UPDATE
Marvel Comics: Apr, 2010 - No. 5, 2010 ($3.99, limited series)

1-5-Profile pages; Andrasofszky-c 4.00

OFFICIAL HANDBOOK OF THE ULTIMATE MARVEL UNIVERSE, THE
Marvel Comics: 2005 ($3.99, one-shots)

... 2005: The Fantastic Four and Spider-Man - Profile pages; art by various 4.00
... The Ultimates and X-Men 2005 - Profile pages; art by various; Bagley-c 4.00

OFFICIAL HAWKMAN INDEX, THE
Independent Comics Group: Nov, 1986 - No. 2, Dec, 1986 ($2.00)

1,2 4.00

OFFICIAL INDEX TO THE MARVEL UNIVERSE (Also see "Avengers, Thor...")
Marvel Comics: 2009 - No. 14, April, 2010 ($3.99)

1-14-Each issue has chronological synopsies, creator credits, character lists for 40-50 issues of apps. for Iron Man, Spider-Man and the X-Men starting with 1st apps. in issue #1 4.00

OFFICIAL JUSTICE LEAGUE OF AMERICA INDEX, THE
Independent Comics Group (Eclipse): April, 1986 - No. 8, Mar, 1987 ($2.00, Baxter paper)

1-8: 1,2-Perez-c. 6.00

OFFICIAL LEGION OF SUPER-HEROES INDEX, THE
Independent Comics Group (Eclipse): Dec, 1986 - No. 5, 1987 ($2.00, limited series) (No Official in Title #2 on)

1-5: 4-Mooney-c 6.00

OFFICIAL MARVEL INDEX TO MARVEL TEAM-UP
Marvel Comics Group: Jan, 1986 - No. 6, 1987 ($1.25, limited series)

1-6 4.00

OFFICIAL MARVEL INDEX TO THE AMAZING SPIDER-MAN
Marvel Comics Group: Apr, 1985 - No. 9, Dec, 1985 ($1.25, limited series)

1 ($1.00)-Byrne-c. 5.00
2-9: 5,6,8,9-Punisher-c. 4.00

OFFICIAL MARVEL INDEX TO THE AVENGERS, THE
Marvel Comics: Jun, 1987 - No. 7, Aug, 1988 ($2.95, limited series)

1-7 5.00

OFFICIAL MARVEL INDEX TO THE AVENGERS, THE
Marvel Comics: V2#1, Oct, 1994 - V2#6, 1995 ($1.95, limited series)

V2#1-#6 4.00

OFFICIAL MARVEL INDEX TO THE FANTASTIC FOUR
Marvel Comics Group: Dec, 1985 - No. 12, Jan, 1987 ($1.25, limited series)

1-12: 1-Byrne-c. 1,2-Kirby back-c (unpub. art) 4.00

OFFICIAL MARVEL INDEX TO THE X-MEN, THE
Marvel Comics: May, 1987 - No. 7, July, 1988 ($2.95, limited series)

1-7 5.00

OFFICIAL MARVEL INDEX TO THE X-MEN, THE
Marvel Comics: V2#1, Apr, 1994 - V2#5, 1994 ($1.95, limited series)

V2#1-5: 1-Covers X-Men #1-51. 2-Covers #52-122,Special #1,2,Giant-Size #1,2. 3-Byrne-c; covers #123-177, Annuals 3-7, Spec. Ed. #1. 4-Covers Uncanny X-Men #178-234, Annuals 8-12. 5-Covers #235-287, Annuals 13-15 4.00

OFFICIAL SOUPY SALES COMIC (See Soupy Sales)

OFFICIAL TEEN TITANS INDEX, THE
Indep. Comics Group (Eclipse): Aug, 1985 - No. 5, 1986 ($1.50, lim. series)

1-5 4.00

OFFICIAL TRUE CRIME CASES (Formerly Sub-Mariner #23; All-True Crime Cases #26 on)
Marvel Comics (OCI): No. 24, Fall, 1947 - No. 25, Winter, 1947-48

Oh My Goddess pt. 3 #11 © Fujishima

The Old Guard #2 © Rucka & Fernandez

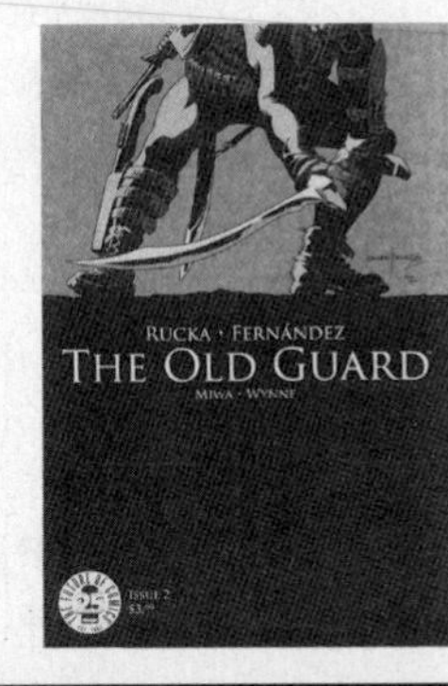

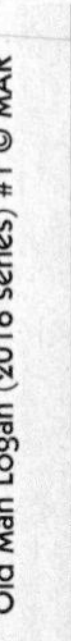
Old Man Logan (2016 series) #1 © MAR

	GD 2.0	VG 4.0	FN 6.0	VF 8.0	VF/NM 9.0	NM- 9.2
24(#1)-Burgos-a; Syd Shores-c	26	52	78	154	252	350
25-Syd Shores-c; Kurtzman's "Hey Look"	20	40	60	114	182	250
OF SUCH IS THE KINGDOM						
George A. Pflaum: 1955 (15¢, 36 pgs.)						
nn-Reprints from 1951 Treasure Chest	4	7	10	14	17	20
O.G. WHIZ (See Gold Key Spotlight #10)						
Gold Key: 2/71 - No. 6, 5/72; No. 7, 5/78 - No. 11, 1/79 (No. 7: 52 pgs.)						
1-John Stanley script	5	10	15	31	53	75
2-John Stanley script	4	8	12	23	37	50
3-6(1972)	3	6	9	17	26	35
7-11(1978-79)-Part-r: 9-Tubby issue	2	4	6	9	12	15
OH, BROTHER! (Teen Comedy)						
Stanhall Publ.: Jan, 1953 - No. 5, Oct, 1953						
1-By Bill Williams	15	30	45	86	133	180
2-5	11	22	33	62	86	110
OH MY GODDESS! (Manga)						
Dark Horse Comics: Aug, 1994 - No. 112 ($2.50-$3.99, B&W)						
1-6-Kosuke Fujishima-s/a in all						3.00
... **PART II** 2/95 - No. 9, 9/95 ($2.50, B&W, lim.series) #1-9						3.00
... **PART III** 11/95 - No. 11, 9/96 ($2.95, B&W, lim. series) #1-11						3.00
... **PART IV** 12/96 - No. 8, 7/97 ($2.95, B&W, lim. series) #1-8						3.00
... **PART V** 9/97 - No. 12, 8/98 ($2.95, B&W, lim. series)						
1,2,5,8: 5-Ninja Master pt. 1						3.00
3,4,6,7,10-12-($3.95, 48 pgs.) 10-Fallen Angel. 11-Play The Game						4.00
9-($3.50) "It's Lonely At The Top"						3.50
... **PART VI** 10/98 - No. 5, 3/99 ($3.50/$2.95, B&W, lim. series)						
1-($3.50)						3.50
2-6-($2.95)-6-Super Urd one-shot						3.00
... **PART VII** 5/99 - No. 8, 12/99 ($2.95, B&W, lim. series) #1-3						3.00
4-8-($3.50)						3.50
... **PART VIII** 1/00 - No. 6, 6/00 ($3.50, B&W, lim. series) #1-3,5,7						3.50
4-($2.95) "Hail To The Chief" begins						3.00
... **PART IX** 7/00 - No. 7, 1/01 ($3.50/$2.99) #1-4: 3-Queen Sayoko						3.50
5-7-($2.99)						3.00
... **PART X** 2/01 - No. 5, 6/01 ($3.50) #1-5						3.50
... **PART XI** 10/01 - No. 10, 3/02 ($3.50) #1,2,7,8						3.50
3-6,9-($2.99) Mystery Child						3.00
10-($3.99)						4.00
(Series adapts new numbering) 88-90-($3.50) Learning to Love						3.50
91-94,96-103,105,107-110: 91-94 ($2.99) Traveler. 96-98-The Phantom Racer						3.00
95,104,106-($3.50) 95-Traveler pt. 5						3.50
111,112-($3.99)						4.00
OH SUSANNA (TV)						
Dell Publishing Co.: No. 1105, June-Aug, 1960 (Gale Storm)						
Four Color 1105-Toth-a, photo-c	9	18	27	63	129	195
OKAY COMICS						
United Features Syndicate: July, 1940						
1-Captain & the Kids & Hawkshaw the Detective reprints	47	94	141	296	498	700
O.K. COMICS						
Hit Publications: May, 1940 (ashcan)						
nn-Ashcan comic, not distributed to newsstands, only for in house use. A CGC certified 8.0 copy sold in 2003 for $1,000.						
O.K. COMICS						
United Features Syndicate/Hit Publications: July, 1940 - No. 2, Oct, 1940						
1-Little Giant (w/super powers), Phantom Knight, Sunset Smith, & The Teller Twins begin	81	162	243	518	884	1250
2 (Rare)-Origin Mister Mist by Chas. Quinlan	84	168	252	538	919	1300
OKLAHOMA KID						
Ajax/Farrell Publ.: June, 1957 - No. 4, 1958						
1	11	22	33	62	86	110
2-4	7	14	21	37	46	55
OKLAHOMAN, THE						
Dell Publishing Co.: No. 820, July, 1957						
Four Color 820-Movie, photo-c	8	16	24	54	102	150
OKTANE						
Dark Horse Comics: Aug, 1995 - Nov, 1995 ($2.50, color, limited series)						

	GD 2.0	VG 4.0	FN 6.0	VF 8.0	VF/NM 9.0	NM- 9.2
1-4-Gene Ha-a						3.00
OKTOBERFEST COMICS						
Now & Then Publ.: Fall 1976 (75¢, Canadian, B&W, one-shot)						
1-Dave Sim-s/a; Gene Day-a; 1st app. Uncle Hans & Natter P. Bombast; The Beavers sty; 1st Cap'n Riverrat, Sim-s/Day-a	3	6	9	16	23	30
OLD GLORY COMICS						
DC Comics: 1941						
nn - Ashcan comic, not distributed to newsstands, only for in-house use. Cover art is Flash Comics #12 with interior being Action Comics #37						(no known sales)
OLD GUARD, THE						
Image Comics: Feb, 2017 - No. 5, Jun, 2017 ($3.99)						
1-5-Greg Rucka-s/Leandro Fernández-a						4.00
OLD IRONSIDES (Disney)						
Dell Publishing Co.: No. 874, Jan, 1958						
Four Color 874-Movie w/Johnny Tremain	6	12	18	42	79	115
OLD MAN HAWKEYE						
Marvel Comics: Mar, 2018 - Present ($3.99)						
1,2-Sacks-s/Checchetto-a; takes place 5 years before the original Old Man Logan						4.00
OLD MAN LOGAN (Secret Wars tie-in)						
Marvel Comics: Jul, 2015 - No. 5, Dec, 2015 ($4.99/$3.99, limited series)						
1-($4.99) Bendis-s/Sorrentino-a; future Logan from Wolverine V3 #66; Emma Frost app.						5.00
2-5-($3.99) 2-Sabretooth app. 3-Apocalypse app. 5-X-Men app.						4.00
OLD MAN LOGAN (Follows Secret Wars)						
Marvel Comics: Mar, 2016 - Present ($4.99/$3.99)						
1-($4.99) Lemire-s/Sorrentino-a; future Logan in current Marvel Universe						5.00
2-35-($3.99) 2-Amadeus Cho Hulk app. 4-Steve Rogers app. 7-Lady Deathstrike app. 14,15-Dracula app.; Andrade-a. 21-24-Past Lives. 25-30-Maestro app. 25-32-Deodato-a 31-35-Scarlet Samurai						4.00
OLD YELLER (Disney, see Movie Comics, and Walt Disney Showcase #25)						
Dell Publishing Co.: No. 869, Jan, 1958						
Four Color 869-Movie, photo-c	6	12	18	38	69	100
OMAC (One Man Army; ...Corps. #4 on; also see Kamandi #59 & Warlord) (See Cancelled Comic Cavalcade)						
National Periodical Publications: Sept-Oct, 1974 - No. 8, Nov-Dec, 1975						
1-Origin	5	10	15	33	57	80
2-8: 8-2 pg. Neal Adams ad	3	6	9	17	26	35
Jack Kirby's Omac: One Man Army Corps HC (2008, $24.99, d.j.) r/#1-8; Evanier intro.						25.00
NOTE: *Kirby a-1-8p; c-1-7p. Kubert c-8.*						
OMAC (See DCU Brave New World)						
DC Comics: Sept, 2006 - No. 8, Apr, 2007 ($2.99, limited series)						
1-8: 1-Bruce Jones-s/Renato Guedes-a. 1-3-Firestorm & Cyborg app. 8-Superman app.						3.00
O.M.A.C. (DC New 52)						
DC Comics: Nov, 2011 - No. 8, Jun, 2012 ($2.99)						
1-8: 1-DiDio-s/Giffen-a/c; Dubbilex and Brother Eye app. 2-Max Lord & Sarge Steel app. 5-Crossover with Frankenstein, Agent of SHADE #5. 6-Kolins-a						3.00
OMAC: ONE MAN ARMY CORPS						
DC Comics: 1991 - No. 4, 1991 ($3.95, B&W, mini-series, mature, 52 pgs.)						
Book One - Four: John Byrne-c/a & scripts						5.00
OMAC PROJECT, THE						
DC Comics: June, 2005 - No. 6, Nov, 2005 ($2.50, limited series)						
1-6-Prelude to Infinite Crisis x-over; Rucka-s/Saiz-a						3.00
...: Infinite Crisis Special 1 (5/06, $4.99) Rucka-s/Saiz-a; follows destruction of satellite						5.00
TPB (2005, $14.99) r/#1-6, Countdown to Infinite Crisis, Wonder Woman #219						15.00
O'MALLEY AND THE ALLEY CATS						
Gold Key: April, 1971 - No. 9, Jan, 1974 (Disney)						
1	3	6	9	16	23	30
2-9	2	4	6	9	13	16
OMEGA ELITE						
Blackthorne Publishing: 1987 ($1.25)						
1-Starlin-c						3.00
OMEGA FLIGHT						
Marvel Comics: Jun, 2007 - No. 5, Oct, 2007 ($2.99, limited series)						
1-Oeming-s/Kolins-a; Wrecking Crew app.						4.00
1-Second printing with Sasquatch variant-c						3.00

The Omega Men (2015 series) #12 © DC

100 Bullets #86 © Azzarello & Risso & DC

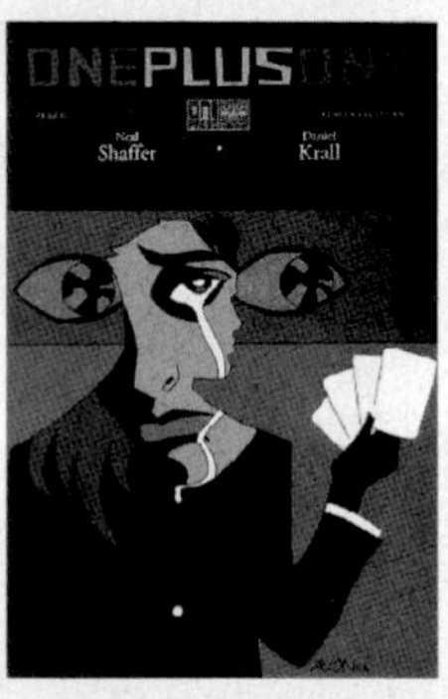

One Plus One #3 © Shaffer & Krall

GD 2.0 | VG 4.0 | FN 6.0 | VF 8.0 | VF/NM 9.0 | NM- 9.2

2-5: 5-Beta Ray Bill app. 3.00
...: Alpha to Omega TPB ('07, $13.99) r/#1-5, USAgent story/Civil War: Choosing Sides 14.00

OMEGA MEN, THE (See Green Lantern #141)
DC Comics: Dec, 1982 - No. 38, May, 1986 ($1.00/$1.25/$1.50; Baxter paper)

1,20: 20-2nd full Lobo story 5.00
2,4-9,11-19,21-25,28-30,32,33,36,38: 2-Origin Broot. 5,9-2nd & 3rd app. Lobo (cameo, 2 pgs. each). 7-Origin The Citadel. 19-Lobo cameo. 30-Intro new Primus 3.00
3-1st app. Lobo (5 pgs.)(6/83); Lobo-c 4 8 12 28 47 65
10-1st full Lobo story 1 2 3 5 6 8
26,27,31,34,35: 26,27-Alan Moore scripts. 31-Crisis x-over. 34,35-Teen Titans x-over 4.00
37-1st solo Lobo story (8 pg. back-up by Giffen) 6.00
Annual 1(11/84, 52 pgs.), 2(11/85) 4.00
NOTE: ***Giffen** c/a-1-6p. **Morrow** a-24r. **Nino** c/a-16, 21; a-Annual 1i.*

OMEGA MEN, THE
DC Comics: Dec, 2006 - No. 6, May, 2007 ($2.99, limited series)

1-6: 1-Superman, Wonder Girl, Green Lantern app.; Flint-a/Gabrych-s 3.00

OMEGA MEN, THE
DC Comics: Aug, 2015 - No. 12, Jul, 2016 ($2.99)

1-12: 1-Tom King-s/Barnaby Bagenda-a; Kyle Rayner app. 4-Cypress-a 3.00

OMEGA THE UNKNOWN
Marvel Comics Group: March, 1976 - No. 10, Oct, 1977

1-1st app. Omega 3 6 9 16 23 30
2,3-(Regular 25¢ editions). 2-Hulk-c/story. 3-Electro-c/story. 2 3 4 6 8 10
2,3-(30¢-c variants, limited distribution) 3 6 9 19 30 40
4-10: 8-1st brief app. 2nd Foolkiller (Greg Salinger), 1 panel only. 9,10-(Reg. 30¢ editions). 9-1st full app. 2nd Foolkiller 1 2 3 5 6 8
9,10-(35¢-c variants, limited distribution) 6 12 18 38 69 100
... Classic TPB (2005, $29.99) r/#1-10 30.00
NOTE: ***Kane** c(p)-3, 5, 8, 9. **Mooney** a-1-3, 4p, 5, 6p, 7, 8i, 9, 10.*

OMEGA: THE UNKNOWN
Marvel Comics: Dec, 2007 - No. 10, Sept, 2008 ($2.99, limited series)

1-10-Jonathan Lethem-s/Farel Dalrymple-a 3.00

OMEN
Northstar Publishing: 1989 - No. 3, 1989 ($2.00, B&W, mature)

1-Tim Vigil-c/a in all 1 2 3 5 7 9
1, (2nd printing) 3.00
2,3 6.00

OMEN, THE
Chaos! Comics: May, 1998 - No. 5, Sept, 1998 ($2.95, limited series)

1-5: 1-Six covers, ...: Vexed (10/98, $2.95) Chaos! characters appear 3.00

OMNI MEN
Blackthorne Publishing: 1987 - No. 3, 1987 ($1.25)

1-3 3.00
Graphic Novel (1989, $3.50) 4.00

ONCE UPON A TIME: OUT OF THE PAST (TV)
Marvel Comics: 2015 ($24.99, hardcover with dustjacket)

HC-Sequel to Shadow of the Queen HC; Bechko & Vazquez-s; Stacy Lee-c 25.00

ONCE UPON A TIME: SHADOW OF THE QUEEN (TV)
Marvel Comics: 2013 ($19.99, hardcover with dustjacket)

HC-Regina and the Huntsman; Bechko-s; art by Del Mundo, Lolos, Henderson, & Kaluta 20.00

ONE, THE
Marvel Comics (Epic Comics): July, 1985 - No. 6, Feb, 1986 (Limited series, mature)

1-6: Post nuclear holocaust super-hero. 2-Intro The Other 3.00

ONE-ARM SWORDSMAN, THE
Victory Prod./Lueng's Publ. #4 on: 1987 - No. 12, 1990 ($2.75/$1.80, 52 pgs.)

1-3 ($2.75) 4.00
4-12: 4-6-$1.80-c. 7-12-$2.00-c 4.00

ONE-HIT WONDER
Image Comics: Feb, 2014 - No. 5, Apr, 2015 ($3.50)

1-5: 1-4-Sapolsky-s/Olivetti-a/c. 5-Thompson & Fiorelli-a/Roux-a 3.50

ONE HUNDRED AND ONE DALMATIANS (Disney, see Cartoon Tales, Movie Comics, and Walt Disney Showcase #9, 51)
Dell Publishing Co.: No. 1183, Mar, 1961

Four Color 1183-Movie 9 18 27 62 126 190

101 DALMATIONS (Movie)
Disney Comics: 1991 (52 pgs., graphic novel)

nn-($4.95, direct sales)-r/movie adaptation & more 5.00
1-($2.95, newsstand edition) 3.00

101 WAYS TO END THE CLONE SAGA (See Spider-Man)
Marvel Comics: Jan, 1997 ($2.50, one-shot)

1 3.00

100 BULLETS
DC Comics (Vertigo): Aug, 1999 - No. 100, Jun, 2009 ($2.50/$2.75/$2.99)

1-Azzarello-s/Risso-a/Dave Johnson-c 3 6 9 21 33 45
2-5 6.00
6-49,51-61: 26-Series summary; art by various. 45-Preview of Losers 4.00
50-($3.50) History of the Trust 5.00
62-71: 62-Begin $2.75-c. 64-Preview of Loveless 3.00
72-99: 72-Begin $2.99-c 3.00
100-($4.99) Final issue 6.00
...#1/Crime Line Sampler Flip-Book (9/09, $1.00) r/#1 with previews of upcoming GNs 3.00
...: A Foregone Tomorrow TPB (2002, $17.95) r/#20-30 18.00
...: Decayed TPB (2006, $14.99) r/#68-75; Darwyn Cooke intro. 15.00
...: First Shot, Last Call TPB (2000, $9.95) r/#1-5, Vertigo Winter's Edge #3 10.00
...: Hang Up on the Hang Low TPB (2001, $9.95) r/#15-19; Jim Lee intro. 10.00
...: Once Upon a Crime TPB (2007, $12.99) r/#76-83 13.00
...: Samurai TPB (2003, $12.95) r/#43-49 13.00
...: Six Feet Under the Gun TPB (2003, $12.95) r/#37-42 13.00
...: Split Second Chance TPB (2001, $14.95) r/#6-14 15.00
...: Strychnine Lives TPB (2006, $14.99) r/#59-67; Manuel Ramos intro. 15.00
...: The Counterfifth Detective TPB (2003, $12.95) r/#31-36 13.00
...: The Hard Way TPB (2005, $14.99) r/#50-58 15.00
...: Wilt TPB (2009, $19.99) r/#89-100; Azzarello intro. 20.00

100 BULLETS: BROTHER LONO
DC Comics (Vertigo): Aug, 2013 - No. 8, Apr, 2014 ($3.99/$2.99, limited series)

1-($3.99) Azzarello-s/Risso-a/Dave Johnson-c 4.00
2-8-($2.99) Azzarello-s/Risso-a/Dave Johnson-c on all 3.00

100 GREATEST MARVELS OF ALL TIME
Marvel Comics: Dec, 2001 ($7.50/$3.50, limited series)

1-5-Reprints top #6-#25 stories voted by poll for Marvel's 40th ann. 7.50
6-($3.50) (#5 on-c) Reprints X-Men (2nd series) #1 4.00
7-($3.50) (#4 on-c) Reprints Giant-Size X-Men #1 4.00
8-($3.50) (#3 on-c) Reprints (Uncanny) X-Men #137 (Death of Jean Grey) 4.00
9-($3.50) (#2 on-c) Reprints Fantastic Four #1 4.00
10-($3.50) (#1 on-c) Reprints Amazing Fantasy #15 (1st app. Spider-Man) 4.00

100 PAGES OF COMICS
Dell Publishing Co.: 1937 (Stiff covers, square binding)

101(Found on back cover)-Alley Oop, Wash Tubbs, Capt. Easy, Og Son of Fire, Apple Mary, Tom Mix, Dan Dunn, Tailspin Tommy, Doctor Doom 161 322 483 1030 1765 2500

100 PAGE SUPER SPECTACULAR (See DC 100 Page Super Spectacular)

100%
DC Comics (Vertigo): Aug, 2002 - No. 5, July, 2003 ($5.95, B&W, limited series)

1-5-Paul Pope-s/a 6.00
HC (2009, $39.99, dustjacket) r/#1-5; sketch pages and background info 40.00
TPB (2005, $24.99) r/#1-5; sketch pages and background info 25.00
TPB (2009, $29.99) r/#1-5; sketch pages and background info 30.00

100% TRUE?
DC Comics (Paradox Press): Summer 1996 - No. 2 ($4.95, B&W)

1,2-Reprints stories from various Paradox Press books. 5.00

$1,000,000 DUCK (See Walt Disney Showcase #5)

ONE MILLION YEARS AGO (Tor #2 on)
St. John Publishing Co.: Sept, 1953

1-Origin & 1st app. Tor; Kubert-c/a; Kubert photo inside front cover 21 42 63 126 206 285

ONE MONTH TO LIVE ("Heroic Age: ..." in indicia)
Marvel Comics: Nov, 2010 - No. 5, Nov, 2010 ($2.99, weekly limited series)

1-5-Remender-s; Spider-Man and the Fantastic Four app. 3.00

ONE PLUS ONE
Oni Press: Sept, 2002 - No. 5, March, 2003 ($2.95, B&W, limited series)

1-5-Shaffer-s/Krall-a 3.00

Onslaught Unleashed #2 © MAR

Operation Peril #11 © ACG

Optimus Prime #8 © Hasbro

GD VG FN VF VF/NM NM-
2.0 4.0 6.0 8.0 9.0 9.2

TPB (9/03, $14.95, digest-size) r/#1-5 & story from Oni Press Color Special 2002 15.00

ONE SHOT (See Four Color...)

1001 HOURS OF FUN
Dell Publishing Co.: No. 13, 1943

Large Feature Comic 13 (nn)-Puzzles & games; by A.W. Nugent. This book was bound as #13 w/Large Feature Comics in publisher's files 34 68 102 199 325 450

ONE TRICK RIP OFF, THE (See Dark Horse Presents)

ONI (Adaption of video game)
Dark Horse Comics: Feb, 2001 - No. 3, Apr, 2001 ($2.99, limited series)

1-3-Sunny Lee-a(p) 3.00

ONIBA: SWORDS OF THE DEMON
Aspen MLT: No. 0, Oct, 2015 ($2.50)

0-Hernandez-s/Pantalena-a; two covers 3.00

ONI DOUBLE FEATURE (See Clerks: The Comic Book and Jay & Silent Bob)
Oni Press: Jan, 1998 - No. 13, Sept, 1999 ($2.95, B&W)

1-Jay & Silent Bob; Kevin Smith-s/Matt Wagner-a 1 3 4 6 8 10
1-2nd printing 3.00
2-11,13: 2,3-Paul Pope-s/a. 3,4-Nixey-s/a. 4,5-Sienkewicz-s/a. 6,7-Gaiman-s. 9-Bagge-c. 13-All Paul Dini-s; Jingle Belle 3.00
12-Jay & Silent Bob as Bluntman & Chronic; Smith-s/Allred-a 5.00

ONI PRESS COLOR SPECIAL
Oni Press: Jun, 2001; Jul, 2002 ($5.95, annual)

...2001-Oeming "Who Killed Madman?" cover; stories & art by various 6.00
...2002-Allred wraparound-c; stories & art by various 6.00

ONSLAUGHT: EPILOGUE
Marvel Comics: Feb, 1997 ($2.95, one-shot)

1-Hama-s/Green-a; Xavier-c; Bastion-app. 4.00

ONSLAUGHT: MARVEL
Marvel Comics: Oct, 1996 ($3.95, one-shot)

1-Conclusion to Onslaught x-over; wraparound-c 1 2 3 4 5 7

ONSLAUGHT REBORN
Marvel Comics: Jan, 2007 - No. 5, Feb, 2008 ($2.99, limited series)

1-5-Loeb-s/Liefeld-a; female Bucky app. 2-Variant-c by Joe Madureira. 3-McGuiness var-c. 4-Campbell var-c. 5-Bianchi var-c; female Bucky goes to regular Marvel Universe 3.00
1-Variant-c by Michael Turner 4.00
HC (2008, $19.99) r/#1-5; sketch pages; foreword by Liefeld 20.00

ONSLAUGHT UNLEASHED
Marvel Comics: Apr, 2011 - No. 4, Jul, 2011 ($3.99, limited series)

1-4-McKeever-s/Andrade-a/Ramos-c; Secret Avengers & Young Allies app. 4.00

ONSLAUGHT: X-MEN
Marvel Comics: Aug, 1996 ($3.95, one-shot)

1-Waid & Lobdell script; Fantastic Four & Avengers app.; Xavier as Onslaught 5.00
1-Variant-c 2 4 6 11 16 20

ON STAGE
Dell Publishing Co.: No. 1336, Apr-June, 1962

Four Color 1336-Not by Leonard Starr 5 10 15 34 60 85

ON THE DOUBLE (Movie)
Dell Publishing Co.: No. 1232, Sept-Nov, 1961

Four Color 1232 5 10 15 34 60 85

ON THE ROAD TO PERDITION (Movie)
DC Comics (Paradox Press): 2003 - Book 3, 2004 ($7.95, 8"x5 1/2", B&W, limited series)

...: Oasis, Book 1-Max Allan Collins-s/José Luis García-López-a/David Beck-c 8.00
...: Sanctuary, Book 2-Max Allan Collins-s/Steve Lieber-a/José Luis García-López-c 8.00
...: Detour, Book 3-Max Allan Collins-s/José Luis García-López-a/Steve Lieber-c/a(i) 8.00
Road to Perdition 2: On the Road (2004, $14.95) r/series; Collins intro. 15.00

ON THE ROAD WITH ANDRAE CROUCH
Spire Christian Comics (Fleming H. Revell): 1973, 1974 (39¢)

nn-1973 Edition 2 4 6 13 18 22
nn-1974 Edition 2 4 6 9 13 16

ON THE SCENE PRESENTS:...
Warren Publishing Co.: Oct, 1966 - No. 2, 1967 (B&W magazine, two #1 issues)

#1 "Super Heroes" (68 pgs.) Batman 1966 movie photo-c/s; has articles/photos/comic art from serials on Superman, Flash Gordon, Capt. America, Capt. Marvel and The Phantom 4 8 12 28 47 65
#1 "Freak Out, USA" (Fall/1966, 60 pgs.) (lower print run) articles on musicians like Zappa, Jefferson Airplane, Supremes 5 10 15 30 50 70
#2 "Freak Out, USA" (2/67, 52 pgs.) Beatles, Country Joe, Doors/Jim Morrison, Bee Gees 5 10 15 30 50 70

ON THE SPOT (Pretty Boy Floyd...)
Fawcett Publications: Fall, 1948

nn-Pretty Boy Floyd photo on-c; bondage-c 36 72 108 211 343 475

ONYX
IDW Publishing: Jul, 2015 - No. 4, Oct, 2015 ($3.99)

1-4-Gabriel Rodriguez & Chris Ryall-s&a. 1-Three covers 4.00

ONYX OVERLORD
Marvel Comics (Epic): Oct, 1992 - No. 4, Jan, 1993 ($2.75, mini-series)

1-4: Moebius scripts 3.00

OPEN SPACE
Marvel Comics: Mid-Dec, 1989 - No. 4, Aug, 1990 ($4.95, bi-monthly, 68 pgs.)

1-4: 1-Bill Wray-a; Freas-c 5.00
0-(1999) Wizard supplement; unpubl. early Alex Ross-a; new Ross-c 3.00

OPERATION BIKINI (See Movie Classics)

OPERATION: BROKEN WINGS, 1936
BOOM! Studios: Nov, 2011 - No. 3, Jan, 2012 ($3.99, limited series)

1-3-Hanna-s/Hairsine-a; English translation of French comic 4.00

OPERATION BUCHAREST (See The Crusaders)

OPERATION CROSSBOW (See Movie Classics)

OPERATION: KNIGHTSTRIKE (See Knightstrike)
Image Comics (Extreme Studios): May, 1995 - No.3, July, 1995 ($2.50)

1-3 3.00

OPERATION PERIL
American Comics Group (Michel Publ.): Oct-Nov, 1950 - No. 16, Apr-May, 1953 (#1-5: 52 pgs.)

1-Time Travelers, Danny Danger (by Leonard Starr) & Typhoon Tyler (by Ogden Whitney) begin 41 82 123 250 418 585
2-War-c 23 46 69 136 223 310
3-War-c; horror story 21 42 63 126 206 285
4,5-Sci/fi-c/story 23 46 69 136 223 310
6-10: 6,8,9,10-Sci/fi-c. 6-Tank vs. T-Rex-c. 7-Sabretooth-c 21 42 63 122 199 275
11,12-War-c; last Time Travelers 14 28 42 80 115 150
13-16: All war format 10 20 30 56 76 95

NOTE: *Starr a-2, 5. Whitney a-1, 2, 5-10, 12; c-1, 3, 5, 8, 9.*

OPERATION: S.I.N.
Marvel Comics: Mar, 2015 - No. 5, Jul, 2015 ($3.99, limited series)

1-5-Peggy Carter & Howard Stark in 1952; Kathryn Immonen-s/Rich Ellis-a 4.00

OPERATION: STORMBREAKER
Acclaim Comics (Valiant Heroes): Aug, 1997 ($3.95, one-shot)

1-Waid/Augustyn-s, Braithwaite-a 4.00

OPTIC NERVE
Drawn and Quarterly: Apr, 1995 - Present ($2.95-$3.95, bi-annual)

1-7: Adrian Tomine-c/a/scripts in all 3.00
8-11: 8-($3.50). 9-11-($3.95) 4.00
12,13-($5.95) Half front-c. 12-Amber Sweet story 6.00
14-($6.95) Half front-c 7.00
32 Stories-($9.95, trade paperback)-r/Optic Nerve mini-comics 10.00
32 Stories-($29.95, hardcover)-r/Optic Nerve mini-comics; signed & numbered 30.00

OPTIMUS PRIME (Transformers)
IDW Publishing: Nov, 2016 - Present ($3.99)

1-16-Follows Revolution x-over. 1-3-Barber-s/Zama-a; multiple covers on each. 4-Milne-a 4.00
Annual 2018 (2/18, $7.99) Barber-s/Tramontano & Griffith-a 8.00
... First Strike 1 (9/17, $3.99) Barber-s/Guidi & Wycough-a; part of Hasbro x-over 4.00

ORACLE: THE CURE
DC Comics: May, 2009 - No. 3, Jul, 2009 ($2.99, limited series)

1-3-Guillem March-c; Calculator app. 3.00
TPB (2010, $17.99) r/#1-3 and Birds of Prey #126,127 18.00

ORAL ROBERTS' TRUE STORIES (Junior Partners #120 on)
TelePix Publ. (Oral Roberts' Evangelistic Assoc./Healing Waters): 1956 (no month) - No. 119, 7/59 (15¢)(No. 102: 25¢)

V1#1(1956)-(Not code approved)- "The Miracle Touch"

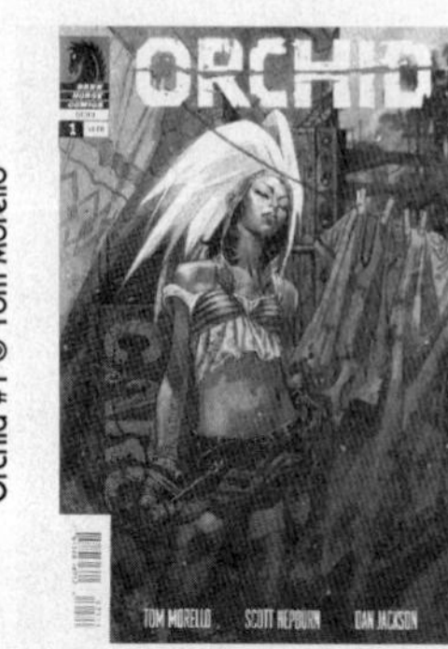

Orchid #1 © Tom Morello

Original Sin #8 © MAR

Origin II #5 © MAR

	GD	VG	FN	VF	VF/NM	NM-
	2.0	4.0	6.0	8.0	9.0	9.2
	19	38	57	109	172	235
102-(Only issue approved by code, 10/56) "Now I See"	13	26	39	74	105	135
103-119: 115-(114 on inside)	10	20	30	54	72	90

NOTE: *Also see Happiness & Healing For You.*

ORANGE BIRD, THE
Walt Disney Educational Media Co.: No date (1980) (36 pgs.; in color; slick cover)

nn-Included with educational kit on foods, ...in Nutrition Adventures nn (1980) ...and the Nutrition Know-How Revue nn (1983) 3.00

ORB (Magazine)
Orb Publishing: 1974 - No. 6, Mar/Apr 1976 (B&W/color)

	GD	VG	FN	VF	VF/NM	NM-
1-1st app. Northern Light & Kadaver, both series begin	5	10	15	30	50	70
2,3 (72 pgs.)	3	6	9	16	23	30
4-6 (60 pgs.): 4,5-origin Northern Light	2	4	6	10	14	18

NOTE: ***Allison** a-1-3. **Gene Day** a-1-6. **P. Hsu** a-4-6. **Steacy** s/a-3,4.*

ORBIT
Eclipse Books: 1990 - No. 3, 1990 ($4.95, 52 pgs., squarebound)

1-3: Reprints from Isaac Asimov's Science Fiction Magazine; 1-Dave Stevens-c, Bolton-a. 3-Bolton-c/a, Yeates-a 5.00

ORBITER
DC Comics (Vertigo): 2003 ($24.95, hardcover with dust jacket)

HC-Warren Ellis-s/Colleen Doran-a 25.00
SC-(2004, $17.95) Warren Ellis-s/Colleen Doran-a 18.00

ORCHID
Dark Horse Comics: Oct, 2011 - No. 12, Jan, 2013 ($1.00/$3.50)

1-Tom Morello-s/Scott Hepburn-a; covers by Carnevale & Fairey 3.00
2-12-($3.50) Carnevale-c 3.50

ORDER, THE (cont'd from Defenders V2#12)
Marvel Comics: Apr, 2002 - No. 6, Sept, 2002 ($2.25, limited series)

1-6: 1-Haley-a/Duffy & Busiek-s. 3-Avengers-c/app. 4-Jurgens-a 3.00

ORDER, THE (The Initiative following Civil War)
Marvel Comics: Sept, 2007 - No. 10, Jun, 2008 ($2.99)

1-10-California's Initiative team; Fraction-s/Kitson-a/c 3.00
... Vol. 1: The Next Right Thing TPB (2008, $14.99) r/#1-7 15.00

ORIENTAL HEROES
Jademan Comics: Aug, 1988 - No. 55, Feb, 1993 ($1.50/$1.95, 68 pgs.)

1,55 5.00
2-54 4.00

ORIGINAL ADVENTURES OF CHOLLY & FLYTRAP, THE
Image Comics: Feb, 2006 - No. 2, June, 2006 ($5.99, limited series)

1,2-Arthur Suydam-s/a; interview with Suydam and art pages 6.00

ORIGINAL ASTRO BOY, THE
Now Comics: Sept, 1987 - No. 20, Jun, 1989 ($1.50/$1.75)

1-20-All have Ken Steacy painted-c/a 4.00

ORIGINAL BLACK CAT, THE
Recollections: Oct. 6, 1988 - No. 9, 1992 ($2.00, limited series)

1-9: Elias-r; 1-Bondage-c. 2-Murphy Anderson-c 4.00

ORIGINAL DICK TRACY, THE
Gladstone Publishing: Sept, 1990 - No. 5, 1991 ($1.95, bi-monthly, 68pgs.)

1-5: 1-Vs. Pruneface. 2-& the Evil influence; begin $2.00-c 4.00
NOTE: *#1 reprints strips 7/16/43 - 9/30/43. #2 reprints strips 12/1/46 - 2/2/47. #3 reprints 8/31/46 - 11/14/46. #4 reprints 9/17/45 - 12/23/45. #5 reprints 6/10/46 - 8/28/46.*

ORIGINAL DOCTOR SOLAR, MAN OF THE ATOM, THE
Valiant: Apr, 1995 ($2.95, one-shot)

1-Reprints Doctor Solar, Man of the Atom #1,5; Bob Fugitani-r; Paul Smith-c; afterword by Seaborn Adamson 4.00

ORIGINAL E-MAN AND MICHAEL MAUSER, THE
First Comics: Oct, 1985 - No. 7, April, 1986 ($1.75/$2.00, Baxter paper)

1-6: 1-Has r-/Charlton's E-Man, Vengeance Squad. 2-Shows #4 in indicia by mistake 3.00
7-($2.00, 44 pgs.)-Staton-a 4.00

ORIGINAL GHOST RIDER, THE
Marvel Comics: July, 1992 - No. 20, Feb, 1994 ($1.75)

1-20: 1-7-r/Marvel Spotlight #5-11 by Ploog w/new-c. 3-New Phantom Rider (former Night Rider) back-ups begin by Ayers. 4-Quesada-c(p). 8-Ploog-c. 8,9-r/Ghost Rider #1,2. 10-r/Marvel Spotlight #12. 11-18,20-r/Ghost Rider #3-12. 19-r/Marvel Two-in-One #8 3.00

ORIGINAL GHOST RIDER RIDES AGAIN, THE
Marvel Comics: July, 1991 - No. 7, Jan, 1992, ($1.50, limited series, 52 pgs.)

1-7: 1-r/Ghost Rider #68(origin),69 w/covers. 2-7: R/ G.R. #70-81 w/covers 4.00

ORIGINAL MAGNUS ROBOT FIGHTER, THE
Valiant: Apr, 1995 ($2.95, one-shot)

1-Reprints Magnus, Robot Fighter 4000 #2; Russ Manning-r; Rick Leonardi-c; afterword by Seaborn Adamson 4.00

ORIGINAL NEXUS GRAPHIC NOVEL (See First Comics Graphic Novel #19)

ORIGINALS, THE
DC Comics (Vertigo): 2004 ($24.95/$17.99, B&W graphic novel)

HC (2004, $24.95) Dave Gibbons-s/a 25.00
SC (2005, $17.99) 18.00

ORIGINAL SHIELD, THE
Archie Enterprises, Inc.: Apr, 1984 - No. 4, Oct, 1984

1-4: 1,2-Origin Shield; Ayers p-1-4, Nebres c-1,2 5.00

ORIGINAL SIN
Marvel Comics: No. 0, Jun, 2014 - No. 8, Nov, 2014 ($4.99/$3.99, limited series)

0-($4.99) Origin of the Watcher re-told; Nova (Sam Alexander) app.; Waid-s/Cheung-a 5.00
1-($4.99) The Watcher is murdered; Aaron-s/Deodato-a 5.00
2-7-($3.99) 5-Nick Fury's origin. 7-Thor loses use of his hammer 4.00
8-($4.99) Murderer revealed; new Watcher begins 5.00
Annual 1 (12/14, $4.99) Fury and Howard Stark in 1958; Cisic-a/Tedesco-c 5.00
#3.1 - #3.4 (Hulk vs. Iron Man) ($3.99, 8/14 - 10/14) Flashback to the Gamma bomb 4.00
#5.1 - #5.5 (Thor & Loki: The Tenth Realm) ($3.99, 9/14 - 11/14) Angela revealed as Thor's sister; Aaron & Ewing-s 4.00

ORIGINAL SINS (Secrets from the Watcher's Eyes unleashed in Original Sin #3)
Marvel Comics: Aug, 2014 - No. 5, Oct, 2014 ($3.99, limited series)

1-5-Short stories; Young Avengers in all issue; The Hood apps. 1-Deathlok prelude. 5-Secret of Dum Dum Dugan 4.00

ORIGINAL SWAMP THING SAGA, THE (See DC Special Series #2, 14, 17, 20)

ORIGINAL TUROK, SON OF STONE, THE
Valiant: Apr, 1995 - No. 2, May, 1995 ($2.95, limited series)

1,2: 1-Reprints Turok, Son of Stone #24,25,42; Alberto Gioletti-r; Rags Morales-c; afterword by Seaborn Adamson. 2-Reprints Turok, Son of Stone #24,33; Gioletti-r; McKone-c 4.00

ORIGIN OF GALACTUS (See Fantastic Four #48-50)
Marvel Comics: Feb, 1996 ($2.50, one-shot)

1-Lee & Kirby reprints w/pin-ups 4.00

ORIGIN OF THE DEFIANT UNIVERSE, THE
Defiant Comics: Feb, 1994 ($1.50, 20 pgs., one-shot)

1-David Lapham, Adam Pollina & Alan Weiss-a; Weiss-c 5.00
NOTE: *The comic was originally published as Defiant Genesis and was distributed at the 1994 Philadelphia ComicCon.*

ORIGINS OF MARVEL COMICS (Also see Fireside Book Series)
Marvel Comics: July, 2010 ($3.99, one-shot)

1-Single page origins of prominent Marvel characters; text and art by various 4.00
...: X-Men (11/10, $3.99) single page origins of X-Men and other mutants; s/a-various 4.00

ORIGIN II (Sequel to Wolverine: The Origin)
Marvel Comics: Feb, 2014 - No. 5, Jun, 2014 ($4.99/$3.99, limited series)

1-($4.99) Gillen-s/Adam Kubert-a/c; acetate overlay on cover; set in 1907 5.00
2-5-($3.99) Sabretooth app. 4.00

ORION (Manga)
Dark Horse Comics: Sept, 1992 - No. 6, July, 1993 ($2.95/$3.95, B&W, bimonthly, lim. series)

1-6:1,2,6-Squarebound): 1-Masamune Shirow-c/a/s in all 4.00

ORION (See New Gods)
DC Comics: June, 2000 - No. 25, June, 2002 ($2.50)

1-14-Simonson-s/a. 3-Back-up story w/Miller-a. 4-Gibbons-a back-up. 7-Chaykin back-up. 8-Loeb/Liefeld back-up. 10-A. Adams back-up-a 12-Jim Lee back-up-a. 13-JLA-c/app.; Byrne-a 3.00
15-($3.95) Black Racer app.; back-up story w/J.P. Leon-a 4.00
16-24-Simonson-s/a: 19-Joker: Last Laugh x-over 3.00
25-($3.95) Last issue; Mister Miracle-c/app. 4.00
The Gates of Apocalypse (2001, $12.95, TPB) r/#1-5 & various short-s 13.00

ORORO: BEFORE THE STORM (Storm from X-Men)
Marvel Comics: Aug, 2005 - No. 4, Nov, 2005 ($2.99, limited series)

Orphan Black: Deviations #1 © OBP

Oscar Comics #6 © MAR

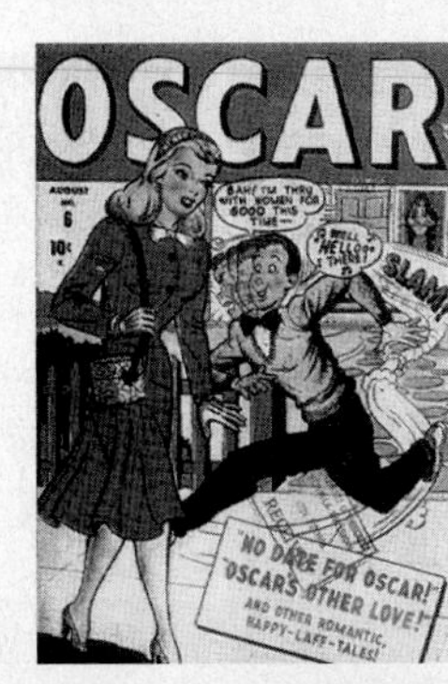

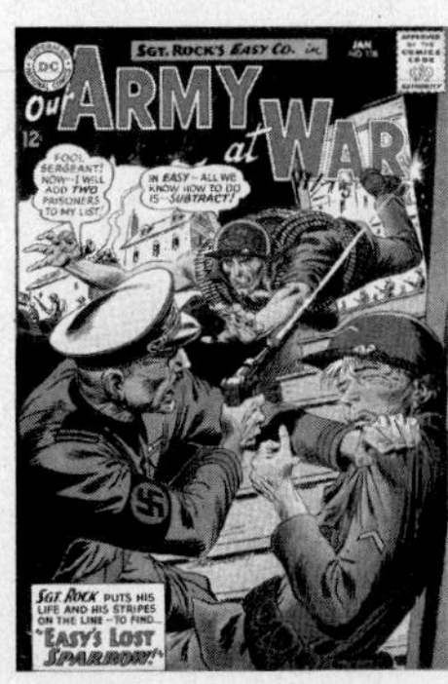

Our Army at War #138 © DC

	GD 2.0	VG 4.0	FN 6.0	VF 8.0	VF/NM 9.0	NM- 9.2

1-4-Barberi-a/Sumerak-s; young Storm in Egypt 3.00
... Digest (2006, $6.99) r/#1-4 7.00

ORPHAN BLACK (Based on the BBC TV show)
IDW Publishing: Feb, 2015 - No. 5, Jun, 2015 ($3.99)

1-6: Multiple covers on all. 1-Kudranski-a; spotlight on Sarah. 2-Spotlight on Helena. 3-Alison. 4-Cosima. 5-Rachel 4.00

ORPHAN BLACK: DEVIATIONS
IDW Publishing: Mar, 2017 - No. 6, Aug, 2017 ($4.99/$3.99)

1-($4.99) Kennedy-s/Nichols-a; what if Beth wasn't hit by the train; multiple covers 5.00
2-6-($3.99) Kennedy-s/Nichols-a 4.00

ORPHAN BLACK: HELSINKI
IDW Publishing: Nov, 2015 - No. 5, Mar, 2016 ($3.99)

1-5: Multiple covers on all. 1-Alan Quah-a 4.00

OSBORN (Green Goblin)
Marvel Comics: Jan, 2011 - No. 5, Jun, 2011 ($3.99, limited series)

1-5-Deconnick-s/Rios-a/Oliver-c 4.00

OSBORN JOURNALS (See Spider-Man titles)
Marvel Comics: Feb, 1997 ($2.95, one-shot)

1-Hotz-c/a 3.00

OSCAR COMICS (Formerly Funny Tunes; Awful...#11 & 12) (Also see Cindy Comics)
Marvel Comics: No. 24, Spring, 1947 - No. 10, Apr, 1949; No. 13, Oct, 1949

24(#1, Spring, 1947) 28 56 84 165 270 375
25(#2, Sum, 1947)-Wolverton-a plus Kurtzman's "Hey Look"
29 58 87 170 278 385
26(#3)-Same as regular #3 except #26 was printed over in black ink with #3 appearing on-c below the over print 19 38 57 111 176 240
3-9,13: 8-Margie app. 19 38 57 111 176 240
10-Kurtzman's "Hey Look" 21 42 63 122 199 275

OSWALD THE RABBIT (Also see New Fun Comics #1)
Dell Publishing Co.: No. 21, 1943 - No. 1268, 12-2/61-62 (Walter Lantz)

Four Color 21(1943) 38 76 114 285 641 1000
Four Color 39(1943) 27 54 81 189 420 650
Four Color 67(1944) 16 32 48 110 243 375
Four Color 102(1946)-Kelly-a, 1 pg. 13 26 39 91 201 310
Four Color 143,183 9 18 27 59 117 175
Four Color 225,273 7 14 21 46 86 125
Four Color 315,388 6 12 18 40 73 105
Four Color 458,507,549,593 5 10 15 35 63 90
Four Color 623,697,792,894,979,1268 5 10 15 33 57 80

OSWALD THE RABBIT (See The Funnies, March of Comics #7, 38, 53, 67, 81, 95, 111, 126, 141, 156, 171, 186, New Funnies & Super Book #8, 20)

OTHER DEAD, THE
IDW Publishing: Sept, 2013 - No. 6, Feb, 2014 ($3.99)

1-6-Zombie animals; Ortega-s/Mui-a. 1-Variant-c by Dorman. 2-6-Pres. Obama app. 4.00

OTHER SIDE, THE
DC Comics (Vertigo): Dec, 2006 - No. 5, Apr, 2007 ($2.99, limited series)

1-5-Soldiers from both sides of the Vietnam War; Aaron-s/Stewart-a/c 3.00
TPB (2007, $12.99) r/#1-5; sketch pages, Stewart's travelogue to Saigon 13.00

OTHERWORLD
DC Comics (Vertigo): May, 2005 - No. 7, Nov, 2005 ($2.99)

1-7-Phil Jimenez-s/a(p) 3.00
...: Book One TPB (2006, $19.99) r/#1-7; cover gallery 20.00

OUR ARMY AT WAR (Becomes Sgt. Rock #302 on; also see Army At War)
National Periodical Publications: Aug, 1952 - No. 301, Feb, 1977

1 235 470 705 1939 4370 6800
2 100 200 300 800 1800 2800
3,4: 4-Krigstein-a 77 154 231 616 1383 2150
5-7 56 112 168 448 999 1550
8-11,14-Krigstein-a 53 106 159 416 933 1450
12,15-20 46 92 138 350 788 1225
13-Krigstein-c/a; flag-c 54 108 162 432 966 1500
21-31: Last precode (2/55) 33 66 99 238 532 825
32-40 29 58 87 209 467 725
41-60: 51-1st S.A. issue. 57,60-Grey tone-c 26 52 78 182 404 625
61-70: 61-(8/57) Pre-Sgt. Rock Easy Co.-c/s. 67-Minor Sgt. Rock prototype
24 48 72 168 372 575
71-80 22 44 66 154 340 525
81-(4/59) "The Rock of Easy" - Sgt. Rock prototype. Part of lead-up trio to 1st definitive Sgt. Rock. Story features a character named "Sgt. Rocky" as a "4th grade rate" sergeant (three stripes/chevrons) who is referred to as "The Rock of Easy". Editor also promises more stories of "...Rock-like Sergeant". Andru & Esposito-a/Haney-s
350 700 1050 2975 6738 10,500
82-(5/59) "Hold up Easy"- 1st app. of a Sgt. Rock. Part of lead-up trio to 1st definitive Sgt. Rock. Character named Sgt. Rock appears in a supporting "motivator" role as a "4th grade rate" sergeant (three stripes/chevrons) in six panels in six page story; Haney-s/Drucker-a 132 264 396 1056 2378 3700
83-(6/59) "The Rock and Wall" - 1st true appearance of Sgt. Rock. Sgt. Rock finally introduced as a Master Sergeant (three chevrons and three rockers) and is main character of story. 1st specific narration that defines the "Rock of Easy" as Sgt. Rock. 1st actual "Sgt. Rock" collaboration between creators Robert Kanigher and Joe Kubert
850 1700 2550 7200 16,600 26,000
84-(7/59) "Laughter on Snakehead Hill" - 2nd appearance of Sgt. Rock. Story advances true Sgt. Rock continuity in 13-page title story featuring Sgt. Rock and Easy Co.; Kanigher-s/Novick-a/Kubert-c 71 142 213 568 1284 2000
85-Origin & 1st app. Ice Cream Soldier 68 136 204 544 1222 1900
86,87-Early Sgt. Rock; Kubert-a 53 106 159 416 933 1450
88-1st Sgt. Rock-c; Kubert-c/a 68 136 204 544 1222 1900
89-"No Shot From Easy!" story; Heath-c 44 88 132 326 738 1150
90-Kubert-c/a; How Rock got his stripes 73 146 219 584 1317 2050
91-All-Sgt. Rock issue; Grandenetti-c/Kubert-a 121 242 363 968 2184 3400
92,94,96-99: 97-Regular Kubert-c begin 33 66 99 238 532 825
93-1st Zack Nolan 36 72 108 266 596 925
95-1st app. Bulldozer 41 82 123 303 689 1075
100 46 92 138 357 805 1250
101,108,113: 101-1st app. Buster. 113-1st app. Wildman & Jackie Johnson
27 54 81 189 420 650
102-104,106,107,109,110,114,116-120: 104-Nurse Jane-c/s. 109-Pre Easy Co. Sgt. Rock-s. 118-Sunny injured 24 48 72 168 372 575
105-1st app. Junior 30 60 90 216 483 750
111-1st app. Wee Willie & Sunny 33 66 99 238 532 825
112-Classic Easy Co. roster-c 70 140 210 560 1255 1950
115-Rock revealed as orphan; 1st x-over Mlle. Marie. 1st Sgt. Rock's battle family
29 58 87 209 467 725
121-125 16 32 48 112 249 385
126-1st app. Canary; grey tone-c 25 50 75 175 388 600
127-2nd all-Sgt. Rock issue; 1st app. Little Sure Shot 27 54 81 189 420 650
128-Training & origin Sgt. Rock; 1st Sgt. Krupp 38 76 114 285 641 1000
129-139: 138-1st Sparrow. 141-1st Shaker 15 30 45 103 227 350
140-3rd all-Sgt. Rock issue 17 34 51 117 259 400
141-150: 147,148-Rock becomes a General 11 22 33 76 163 250
151-Intro. Enemy Ace by Kubert (2/65), black-c 44 88 132 326 738 1150
152-4th all-Sgt. Rock issue 14 28 42 96 211 325
153-2nd app. Enemy Ace (4/65) 20 40 60 138 307 475
154,156,157,159-161,165-167: 157-2 pg. centerfold spread pin-up as part of story. 159-1st Nurse Wendy Winston-c/s. 165-2nd Iron Major 10 20 30 64 132 200
155-3rd app. Enemy Ace (6/65)(see Showcase) 14 28 42 96 211 325
158-Book-length Sgt. Rock story; origin & 1st app. Iron Major(9/65), formerly Iron Captain; flashback to death of Rock's brother Josh 11 22 33 72 154 235
162,163-Viking Prince x-over in Sgt. Rock 10 20 30 69 147 225
164-Giant G-19 15 30 45 103 227 350
168-1st Unknown Soldier app.; referenced in Star-Spangled War Stories #157; (Sgt. Rock x-over) (6/66) 19 38 57 131 291 450
169,170 8 16 24 56 108 160
171-176,178-181: 171-1st Mad Emperor 8 16 24 51 96 140
177-(80 pg. Giant G-32) 10 20 30 64 132 200
182,183,186-Neal Adams-a. 186-Origin retold 9 18 27 57 111 165
184-Wee Willie dies 9 18 27 61 123 185
185,187,188,193-195,197-199 6 12 18 41 76 110
189,191,192,196: 189-Intro. The Teen-age Underground Fighters of Unit 3. 196-Hitler cameo
6 12 18 42 79 115
190-(80 pg. Giant G-44) 8 16 24 54 102 150
200-12 pg. Rock story told in verse; Evans-a 7 14 21 44 82 120
201,202,204-207: 201-Krigstein-r/#14. 204,205-All reprints; no Sgt. Rock. 207-Last 12¢ cover
5 10 15 34 60 85
203-(80 pg. Giant G-56)-All-r, Sgt. Rock story 7 14 21 48 89 130
208-215 4 8 12 27 44 60
216,229-(80 pg. Giants G-68, G-80): 216-Has G-58 on-c by mistake
6 12 18 40 73 105
217-219: 218-1st U.S.S. Stevens 4 8 12 25 40 55
220-Classic dinosaur/Sgt. Rock-c/s 4 8 12 28 47 65
221-228,230-234: 231-Intro/death Rock's brother. 234-Last 15¢ issue

Our Fighting Forces #96 © DC

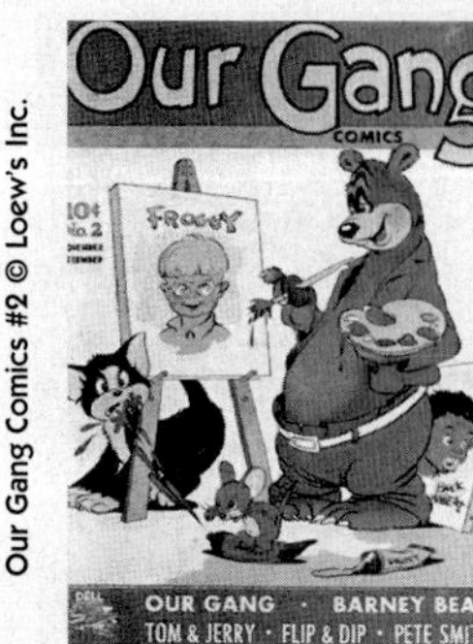

Our Gang Comics #2 © Loew's Inc.

Our Love Story #1 © MAR

	GD 2.0	VG 4.0	FN 6.0	VF 8.0	VF/NM 9.0	NM- 9.2
	3	6	9	21	33	45
235-239,241: 52 pg. Giants	4	8	12	27	44	60
240-Neal Adams-a; 52 pg. Giant	5	10	15	31	53	75
242-Also listed as DC 100 Page Super Spectacular #9	9	18	27	58	114	170
243-246: (All 52 pgs.) 244-No Adams-a	4	8	12	25	40	55
247-250,254-268,270: 247-Joan of Arc	3	6	9	15	22	28
251-253-Return of Iron Major	3	6	9	16	24	32
269,275-(100 pgs.)	5	10	15	31	53	75
271,272,274,276-279	3	6	9	14	19	24
273-Crucifixion-c	3	6	9	16	24	32
280-(68 pgs.)-200th app. Sgt. Rock; reprints Our Army at War #81,83	4	8	12	22	35	48
281-299,301: 295-Bicentennial cover	2	4	6	13	18	22
300-Sgt. Rock's-s by Kubert (2/77)	3	6	9	15	22	28

NOTE: ***Alcala** a-251. **Drucker** a-27, 67, 68, 79, 82, 83, 96, 164, 177, 203, 212, 243r, 244, 269r, 275r, 280r. **Evans** a-165-175, 200, 266, 269, 270, 274, 276, 278, 280. **Glanzman** a-218, 220, 222, 223, 225, 227, 230-232, 238-241, 244, 247, 248, 256-259, 261, 265-267, 271, 282, 283, 298. **Grandenetti** c-91,120. **Grell** a-287. **Heath** a-50, 164, & most 176-281. **Kubert** a-38, 59, 67, 68 & most issues from 83-165, 171, 233, 236, 267, 275, 300; c-84, 280. **Maurer** a-233, 237, 239, 240, 45, 280, 284, 288, 290, 291, 295. **Severin** a-236, 252, 265, 267, 269r, 272. **Toth** a-235, 241, 254. **Wildey** a-283-285, 287p. **Wood** a-249.*

OUR ARMY AT WAR
DC Comics: Nov, 2010 ($3.99, one-shot)

	GD 2.0	VG 4.0	FN 6.0	VF 8.0	VF/NM 9.0	NM- 9.2
1-Joe Kubert-c; Mike Marts-s/Victor Ibáñez-a						4.00
TPB (2011, $14.99) r/#1 and other 2010 war one-shots Weird War Tales #1, Our Fighting Forces #1, G.I. Combat #1 and Star-Spangled War Stories #1						15.00

OUR FIGHTING FORCES
National Per. Publ./DC Comics: Oct-Nov, 1954 - No. 181, Sept-Oct, 1978

	GD 2.0	VG 4.0	FN 6.0	VF 8.0	VF/NM 9.0	NM- 9.2
1-Grandenetti-c/a	139	278	417	1112	2506	3900
2	50	100	150	400	900	1400
3-Kubert-c; last precode issue (3/55)	44	88	132	326	738	1150
4,5	36	72	108	266	596	925
6-9: 7-1st S.A. issue	31	62	93	223	479	735
10-Wood-a	31	62	93	223	499	775
11-19	25	50	75	175	388	600
20-Grey tone-c (4/57)	33	66	99	238	532	825
21-30	20	40	60	141	313	485
31-40	18	36	54	122	271	420
41-Unknown Soldier tryout	22	44	66	154	340	525
42-44	17	34	51	117	259	400
45-1st app. of Gunner & Sarge, app. thru #94	56	112	168	448	999	1550
46	25	50	75	175	388	600
47	18	36	54	124	275	425
48,50	15	30	45	103	227	350
49-1st Pooch	26	52	78	182	404	625
51-Grey tone-c	24	48	72	168	372	575
52-64: 64-Last 10¢ issue	12	24	36	82	179	275
65-70: 66-Panel inspired a famous Roy Lichtenstein painting	10	20	30	64	132	200
71-Classic grey tone-c; Pooch fires machine gun; panel inspired a famous Roy Lichtenstein painting	22	44	66	154	340	525
72-80	8	16	24	56	108	160
81-90	7	14	21	44	82	120
91-98: 95-Devil-Dog begins, ends #98.	6	12	18	37	66	95
99-Capt. Hunter begins, ends #106	6	12	18	41	76	110
100	6	12	18	38	69	100
101-105,107-120: 116-Mlle. Marie app. 120-Last 12¢ issue	5	10	15	30	50	70
106-Hunters Hellcats begin	5	10	15	31	53	75
121,122: 121-Intro. Heller	4	8	12	27	44	60
123-The Losers (Capt. Storm, Gunner & Sarge, Johnny Cloud) begin	9	18	27	57	111	165
124-132: 132-Last 15¢ issue	4	8	12	23	37	50
133-137 (Giants). 134-Toth-a	4	8	12	27	44	60
138-145,147-150	3	6	9	16	23	30
146-Classic "Burma Sky" story; Toth-a/Goodwin-s	3	6	9	17	26	35
151-162-Kirby a(p)	3	6	9	18	28	38
163-180	3	6	9	14	19	24
181-Last issue	3	6	9	16	23	30
... (War One-Shot) 1 (11/10, $3.99) The Losers app.; B. Clay Moore-s/Chad Hardin-a						4.00

NOTE: ***N. Adams** c-147. **Drucker** a-28, 37, 39, 42-44, 49, 53, 133r. **Evans** a-149, 164-174, 177-181. **Glanzman** a-125-128, 132, 134, 138-141, 143, 144. **Heath** a-2, 16, 18, 28, 41, 44, 49, 50, 59, 64, 114, 135-138r; c-51. **Kirby** a-151-162p; c-152-159. **Kubert** c/a in many issues. **Maurer** a-135. **Redondo** a-166. **Severin** a-123-130, 131i, 132-150.*

OUR FIGHTING MEN IN ACTION (See Men In Action)

OUR FLAG COMICS
Ace Magazines: Aug, 1941 - No. 5, April, 1942

	GD 2.0	VG 4.0	FN 6.0	VF 8.0	VF/NM 9.0	NM- 9.2
1-Captain Victory, The Unknown Soldier (intro.) & The Three Cheers begin	277	554	831	1759	3030	4300
2-Origin The Flag (patriotic hero); 1st app?	161	322	483	1030	1765	2500
3-5: 5-Intro & 1st app. Mr. Risk	148	296	426	909	1555	2300

NOTE: ***Anderson** a-1, 4. **Mooney** a-1, 2; c-2.*

OUR GANG COMICS (With Tom & Jerry #39-59; becomes Tom & Jerry #60 on; based on film characters)
Dell Publishing Co.: Sept-Oct, 1942 - No. 59, June, 1949

	GD 2.0	VG 4.0	FN 6.0	VF 8.0	VF/NM 9.0	NM- 9.2
1-Our Gang & Barney Bear by Kelly, Tom & Jerry, Pete Smith, Flip & Dip, The Milky Way begin (all 1st app.)	96	192	288	768	1734	2700
2-Benny Burro begins (#2 by Kelly)	37	74	111	274	612	950
3-5	22	44	66	154	340	525
6-Bumbazine & Albert only app. by Kelly	29	58	87	209	467	725
7-No Kelly story	16	32	48	110	243	375
8-Benny Burro begins by Barks	38	76	114	281	628	975
9-Barks-a(2): Benny Burro & Happy Hound; no Kelly story	34	68	102	242	541	840
10-Benny Burro by Barks	25	50	75	175	388	600
11-1st Barney Bear & Benny Burro by Barks (5-6/44); Happy Hound by Barks	34	68	102	242	541	840
12-20	16	32	48	107	236	365
21-30: 30-X-Mas-c	11	22	33	77	166	255
31-36-Last Barks issue	9	18	27	63	129	195
37-40	7	14	21	44	82	120
41-50	6	12	18	38	69	100
51-57	5	10	15	35	63	90
58,59-No Kelly art or Our Gang stories	5	10	15	33	57	80
Our Gang Volume 1 (Fantagraphics Books, 2006, $12.95, TPB) r/Our Gang stories written and by Walt Kelly from #1-8; Leonard Maltin intro.; Jeff Smith-c						13.00
Our Gang Volume 2 (Fantagraphics Books, 2007, $12.95, TPB) r/Our Gang stories written and by Walt Kelly from #9-15; Steve Thompson intro.; Jeff Smith-c						13.00
Our Gang Volume 3 (Fantagraphics Books, 2008, $14.99, TPB) r/Our Gang stories written and by Walt Kelly from #16-23; Steve Thompson intro.; Jeff Smith-c						15.00

NOTE: ***Barks** art in part only. **Barks** did not write Barney Bear stories #30-34. (See March of Comics #3, 26). Early issues have photo back-c.*

OUR LADY OF FATIMA (Also see Fatima...)
Catechetical Guild Educational Society: 3/11/55 (15¢) (36 pgs.)

	GD 2.0	VG 4.0	FN 6.0	VF 8.0	VF/NM 9.0	NM- 9.2
395	6	12	18	28	34	40

OUR LOVE (True Secrets #3 on? or Romantic Affairs #3 on?)
Marvel Comics (SPC): Sept, 1949 - No. 2, Jan, 1950

	GD 2.0	VG 4.0	FN 6.0	VF 8.0	VF/NM 9.0	NM- 9.2
1-Photo-c	26	52	78	154	252	350
2-Photo-c	15	30	45	88	137	185

OUR LOVE STORY
Marvel Comics Group: Oct, 1969 - No. 38, Feb, 1976

	GD 2.0	VG 4.0	FN 6.0	VF 8.0	VF/NM 9.0	NM- 9.2
1	10	20	30	64	132	200
2-4,6-8,10,11	5	10	15	33	57	80
5-Steranko-a	11	22	33	72	154	235
9,12-Kirby-a	5	10	15	34	60	85
13-(10/71, 52 pgs.)	6	12	18	37	66	95
14-New story by Gary Fredrich & Tarpe' Mills	5	10	15	33	57	80
15-20,27:27-Colan/Everett-a(r?); Kirby/Colletta-r	4	8	12	25	40	55
21-26,28-37	4	8	12	23	37	50
38-Last issue	4	8	12	27	44	60

NOTE: ***J. Buscema** a-1-3, 5-7, 9, 13r, 16r, 19r(2), 21r, 22r(2), 23r, 34r, 35r; c-11, 13, 16, 22, 23, 24, 27, 35. **Colan** a-3-6, 21r(#6), 22r, 23r(#3), 24r(#4), 27; c-19. **Katz** a-17. **Maneely** a-13r. **Romita** a-13r; c-1, 2, 4-6. **Weiss** a-16, 17, 29r(#17).*

OUR MEN AT WAR
DC Comics: Aug/Sept 1952

nn - Ashcan comic, not distributed to newsstands, only for in-house use. Cover art is All Star Western #60, interior being Detective Comics #181 (a FN/VF copy sold for $1195 in 2012)

OUR MISS BROOKS
Dell Publishing Co.: No. 751, Nov, 1956

	GD 2.0	VG 4.0	FN 6.0	VF 8.0	VF/NM 9.0	NM- 9.2
Four Color 751-Photo-c	7	14	21	49	92	135

OUR SECRET (Exciting Love Stories)(Formerly My Secret)
Superior Comics Ltd.: No. 4, Nov, 1949 - No. 8, Jun, 1950

	GD 2.0	VG 4.0	FN 6.0	VF 8.0	VF/NM 9.0	NM- 9.2
4-Kamen-a; spanking scene	23	46	69	138	227	315
5,6,8	14	28	42	82	121	160

Outcast By Kirkman & Azaceta #19 © R. Kirkman

Outlaw Nation #3 © Delano & Sudzuka

Out of the Shadows #6 © STD

GD 2.0 | VG 4.0 | FN 6.0 | VF 8.0 | VF/NM 9.0 | NM- 9.2

7-Contains 9 pg. story intended for unpublished Ellery Queen #5; lingerie panels
15 30 45 84 127 170

OUTBREED 999
Blackout Comics: May, 1994 - No. 6, 1994 ($2.95)
1-6: 4-1st app. of Extreme Violet in 7 pg. backup story 3.00

OUTCAST, THE
Valiant: Dec, 1995 ($2.50, one-shot)
1-Breyfogle-a. 3.00

OUTCAST BY KIRKMAN & AZACETA
Image Comics: Jun, 2014 - Present ($2.99/$3.99)
1-Kirkman-s/Azaceta-a/c 10.00
2 5.00
3-33: 25-(25¢-c) 4.00

OUTCASTS
DC Comics: Oct, 1987 - No. 12, Sept, 1988 ($1.75, limited series)
1-12: John Wagner & Alan Grant scripts in all 3.00

OUTER LIMITS, THE (TV)
Dell Publishing Co.: Jan-Mar, 1964 - No. 18, Oct, 1969 (Most painted-c)
1 11 22 33 75 160 245
2-5 6 12 18 41 76 110
6-10 5 10 15 35 63 90
11-18: 17-Reprints #1. 18-r/#2 5 10 15 31 53 75

OUTER SPACE (Formerly This Magazine Is Haunted, 2nd Series)
Charlton Comics: No. 17, May, 1958 - No. 25, Dec, 1959; Nov, 1968
17-Williamson/Wood-a 14 28 42 80 115 150
18-20-Ditko-a 23 46 69 136 223 310
21-Ditko-c 20 40 60 114 182 250
22-25 14 28 42 80 115 150
V2#1(11/68)-Ditko-a, Boyette-c 5 10 15 31 53 75

OUT FOR BLOOD
Dark Horse: Sept, 1999 - No. 4, Dec, 1999 ($2.95, B&W, limited series)
1-4-Kelley Jones-c; Erskine-a 3.00

OUTLANDERS (Manga)
Dark Horse Comics: Dec, 1988 - No. 33, Sept,1991 ($2.00-$2.50, B&W, 44 pgs.)
1-33: Japanese Sci-fi manga 4.00

OUTLAW (See Return of the...)

OUTLAW FIGHTERS
Atlas Comics (IPC): Aug, 1954 - No. 5, Apr, 1955
1-Tuska-a 15 30 45 88 137 185
2-5: 5-Heath-c/a, 7 pgs. 11 22 33 62 86 110
NOTE: *Colan a-4. Hartley a-3. Heath c/a-5. Maneely c-2, 4. Pakula a-2. Reinman a-2, 4. Tuska a-1-3.*

OUTLAW KID, THE (1st Series; see Wild Western)
Atlas Comics (CCC No. 1-11/EPI No. 12-29): Sept, 1954 - No. 19, Sept, 1957
1-Origin; The Outlaw Kid & his horse Thunder begin; Black Rider app.
36 72 108 211 343 475
2-Black Rider app. 15 30 45 90 140 190
3-7,9: 3-Wildey-a(3) 14 28 42 80 115 150
8-Williamson/Woodbridge-a, 4 pgs. 14 28 42 82 121 160
10-Williamson-a 14 28 42 82 121 160
11-17,19: 13-Baker text illo. 15-Williamson text illo (unsigned)
11 22 33 62 86 110
18-Williamson/Mayo-a 12 24 36 67 94 120
NOTE: *Berg a-4, 7, 13. Maneely c-1-3, 5-8, 11-13, 15, 16, 18. Pakula a-3. Severin c-10, 17, 19. Shores a-1. Wildey a-1(3), 2-8, 10, 11, 12(4), 13(4), 15-19(4 each); c-4.*

OUTLAW KID, THE (2nd Series)
Marvel Comics Group: Aug, 1970 - No. 30, Oct, 1975
1-Reprints; 1-Orlando-r, Wildey-r(3) 3 6 9 19 30 40
2,3,9: 2-Reprints. 3,9-Williamson-a(r) 2 4 6 13 18 22
4-7: 7-Last 15¢ issue 2 4 6 11 16 20
8-Double size (52 pgs.); Crandall-r 3 6 9 16 24 32
10-Origin 3 6 9 19 30 40
11-20: new-a in #10-16 2 4 6 13 18 22
21-30: 27-Origin-r/#10 2 4 6 13 13 16
NOTE: *Ayers a-10, 27r. Berg a-7, 25r. Everett a-2(2 pgs.). Gil Kane c-10, 11, 15, 27r, 28. Roussos a-10i, 27i(r). Severin c-1, 9, 20, 25. Wildey r-1-4, 6-9, 19-22, 25, 26. Williamson a-28r. Woodbridge/Williamson a-9r.*

OUTLAW NATION
DC Comics (Vertigo): Nov, 2000 - No. 19, May, 2002 ($2.50)
1-19-Fabry painted-c/Delano-s/Sudzuka-a 3.00
TPB (Image Comics, 11/06, $15.99) B&W reprint of #1-19; Delano intro. 16.00

OUTLAW PRINCE, THE
Dark Horse Books: 2011 ($12.99, SC, 80 pgs.)
SC-Adaptation of ERB's The Outlaw of Torn; Rob Hughes-s/Thomas Yeates painted-a; origin/1st app. Norman of Torn; intro. & death of Lady Maud 13.00
Deluxe HC Limited Edition ($49.99, 112 pgs.) Bonus 2 articles (approx. 200 signed) 50.00

OUTLAWS
D. S. Publishing Co.: Feb-Mar, 1948 - No. 9, June-July, 1949
1-Violent & suggestive stories 36 72 108 211 343 475
2-Ingels-a; Baker-a 36 72 108 211 343 475
3,5,6: 3-Not Frazetta. 5-Sky Sheriff by Good app. 6-McWilliams-a
17 34 51 98 154 210
4-Orlando-a 18 36 54 103 162 220
7,8-Ingels-a in each 24 48 72 142 234 325
9-(Scarce)-Frazetta-a (7 pgs.) 48 96 144 302 514 725
NOTE: *Another #3 was printed in Canada with **Frazetta** art "Prairie Jinx," 7 pgs.*

OUTLAWS, THE (Formerly Western Crime Cases)
Star Publishing Co.: No. 10, May, 1952 - No. 13, Sep, 1953; No. 14, Apr, 1954
10-L.B. Cole-c 22 44 66 132 216 300
11-14-L.B. Cole-c. 14-Reprints Western Thrillers #4 (Fox) w/new L.B. Cole-c; Kamen, Feldstein-r 18 36 54 103 162 220

OUTLAWS
DC Comics: Sept, 1991 - No. 8, Apr, 1992 ($1.95, limited series)
1-8: Post-apocalyptic Robin Hood. 3.00

OUTLAWS OF THE WEST (Formerly Cody of the Pony Express #10)
Charlton Comics: No. 11, 7/57 - No. 81, 5/70; No. 82, 7/79 - No. 88, 4/80
11 8 16 24 44 57 70
12,13,15-17,19,20 6 12 18 27 33 38
14-(68 pgs., 2/58) 9 18 27 50 65 80
18-Ditko-a 10 20 30 56 76 95
21-30 3 6 9 16 23 30
31-50: 34-Gunmaster app. 2 4 6 13 18 22
51-63,65,67-70: 54-Kid Montana app. 2 4 6 10 14 18
64,66: 64-Captain Doom begins (1st app.). 68-Kid Montana series begins
2 4 6 13 18 22
71-79: 73-Origin & 1st app. The Sharp Shooter, last app. #74. 75-Last Capt. Doom 2 4 6 9 12 15
80,81-Ditko-a 2 4 6 13 18 22
82-88 6.00
64,79(Modern Comics-r, 1977, '78) 6.00

OUTLAWS OF THE WILD WEST
Avon Periodicals: 1952 (25¢, 132 pgs.) (4 rebound comics)
1-Wood back-c; Kubert-a (3 Jesse James-r) 39 78 117 240 395 550

OUTLAW TRAIL (See Zane Grey 4-Color 511)

OUT OF SANTA'S BAG (See March of Comics #10 in the Promotional Comics section)

OUT OF THE NIGHT (The Hooded Horseman #18 on)
Amer. Comics Group (Creston/Scope): Feb-Mar, 1952 - No. 17, Oct-Nov, 1954
1-Williamson/LeDoux-a (9 pgs.); ACG's 1st editor's page
87 174 261 553 952 1350
2-Williamson-a (5 pgs.) 55 110 165 352 601 850
3,5-10: 9-Sci/Fic story 36 72 108 211 343 475
4-Williamson-a (7 pgs.) 45 90 135 284 480 675
11-17: 13-Nostrand-a? 17-E.C. Wood swipe 28 56 84 165 270 375
NOTE: *Landau a-14, 16, 17. Shelly a-12.*

OUT OF THE SHADOWS
Standard Comics/Visual Editions: No. 5, July, 1952 - No. 14, Aug, 1954
5-Toth-p; Moreira, Tuska-a; Roussos-c 61 122 183 390 670 950
6-Toth/Celardo-a; Katz-a(2) 43 86 129 271 461 650
7,9: 7-Jack Katz-c/a(2). 9-Crandall-a(2) 39 78 117 240 395 550
8-Katz shrunken head-c 82 164 246 528 902 1275
10-Spider-c; Sekowsky-a 41 82 123 256 428 600
11-Toth-a, 2 pgs.; Katz-a; Andru-c 39 78 117 240 395 550
12-Toth/Peppe-a(2); Katz-a 45 90 135 284 480 675
13-Cannabalism story; Sekowsky-a; Roussos-c 47 94 141 296 498 700
14-Toth-a 39 78 117 240 395 550

OUT OF THE VORTEX (Comics' Greatest World:... #1-4)
Dark Horse Comics: Oct., 1993 - No. 12, Oct, 1994 ($2.00, limited series)

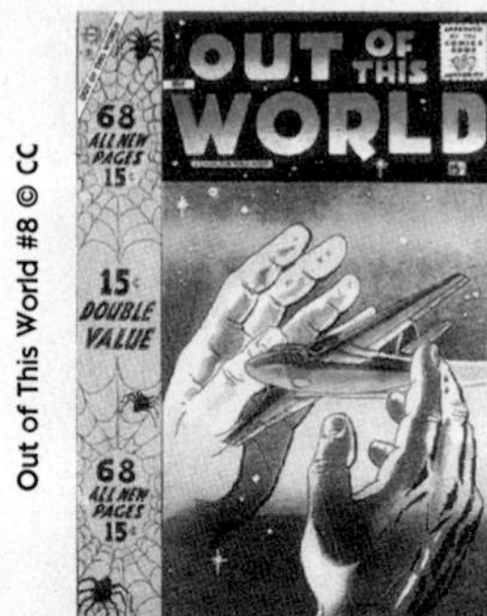

Out of This World #8 © CC

Outsiders (2009 series) #29 © DC

OZARK IKE
HOLD IT!

Ozark Ike #15 © KFS

	GD 2.0	VG 4.0	FN 6.0	VF 8.0	VF/NM 9.0	NM- 9.2

1-12: 1-Foil logo. 4-Dorman-c(p). 6-Hero Zero x-over. 12-$2.50-c 3.00
NOTE: *Art Adams c-7. Golden c-8. Mignola c-2. Simonson c-3. Zeck c-10.*

OUT OF THIS WORLD
Charlton Comics: Aug, 1956 - No. 16, Dec, 1959

	GD	VG	FN	VF	VF/NM	NM-
1	34	68	102	199	325	450
2	17	34	51	98	154	210
3-6-Ditko-c/a (3) each	36	72	108	211	343	475
7-(2/58, 15¢, 68 pgs.)-Ditko-c/a(4)	39	78	117	231	378	525
8-(5/58, 15¢, 68 pgs.)-Ditko-a(2)	36	72	108	214	347	480
9,10,12,16-Ditko-a	26	52	78	154	252	350
11-Ditko c/a (3)	33	66	99	194	317	440
13,15	14	28	42	81	118	155
14-Matt Baker-a, 7 pg. story	15	30	45	84	127	170

NOTE: *Ditko c-3-12, 16. Reinman a-10.*

OUT OF THIS WORLD
Avon Periodicals: June, 1950; Aug, 1950

	GD	VG	FN	VF	VF/NM	NM-
1-Kubert-a(2) (one reprinted/Eerie #1, 1947) plus Crom the Barbarian by Gardner Fox & John Giunta (origin); Fawcette-c	135	270	405	864	1482	2100
1-(8/50) Reprint; no month on cover	77	154	231	493	847	1200

OUT OF THIS WORLD ADVENTURES
Avon Periodicals: July, 1950 - No. 2, Apr, 1951 (25¢ sci-fi pulp magazine with 32-page color comic insert)

	GD	VG	FN	VF	VF/NM	NM-
1-Kubert-a(2); Crom the Barbarian by Fox & Giunta; text stories by Cummings, Van Vogt, del Rey, Chandler	90	180	270	576	988	1400
2-Kubert-a plus The Spider God of Akka by Gardner Fox & John Giunta pulp magazine w/comic insert; Wood-a (21 pgs.); mentioned in **SOTI**, page 120	58	116	174	371	636	900

OUT OUR WAY WITH WORRY WART
Dell Publishing Co.: No. 680, Feb, 1956

	GD	VG	FN	VF	VF/NM	NM-
Four Color 680	5	10	15	30	50	70

OUTPOSTS
Blackthorne Publishing: June, 1987 - No. 4, 1987 ($1.25)

1-4: 1-Kaluta-c(p) 3.00

OUTSIDERS, THE
DC Comics: Nov, 1985 - No. 28, Feb, 1988

1 4.00
2-28: 18-26-Batman returns. 21-Intro. Strike Force Kobra; 1st app. Clayface IV. 22-E.C. parody; Orlando-a. 21- 25-Atomic Knight app. 27,28-Millennium tie-ins 3.00
Annual 1 (12/86, $2.50), Special 1 (7/87, $1.50) 4.00
NOTE: *Aparo a-1-7, 9-14, 17-22, 25, 26; c-1-7, 9-14, 17, 19-26. Byrne a-11. Bolland a-6, 18; c-16. Ditko a-13p. Erik Larsen a-24, 27 28; c-27, 28. Morrow a-12.*

OUTSIDERS
DC Comics: Nov, 1993 - No. 24, Nov, 1995 ($1.75/$1.95/$2.25)

1-11,0,12-24: 1-Alpha; Travis Charest-c. 1-Omega; Travis Charest-c. 5-Atomic Knight app. 8-New Batman-c/story. 11-(9/94)-Zero Hour. 0-(10/94).12-(11/94). 21-Darkseid cameo. 22-New Gods app. 3.00

OUTSIDERS (See Titans/Young Justice: Graduation Day)(Leads into Batman and the Outsiders)
DC Comics: Aug, 2003 - No. 50, Nov, 2007 ($2.50/$2.99)

1-Nightwing, Arsenal, Metamorpho app.; Winick-s/Raney-a 5.00
2-Joker and Grodd app. 4.00
3-33: 3-Joker-c. 5,6-ChrisCross-a. 8-Huntress app. 9,10-Capt. Marvel Jr. app. 24,25-X-over with Teen Titans. 26,27-Batman & old Outsiders 3.00
34-50: 34-One Year Later. 36-Begin $2.99-c. 37-Superman app. 44-Red Hood app. 3.00
Annual 1 (6/07, $3.99) McDaniel-a; Black LIghtning app. 4.00
.../Checkmate: Checkout TPB (2008, $14.99) r/#47-49 & Checkmate #13-15 15.00
... Double Feature (10/03, $4.95) r/#1,2 5.00
...: Crisis Intervention TPB (2006, $12.99) r/#29-33 13.00
...: Looking For Trouble TPB (2004, $12.95) r/#1-7 & Teen Titans/Outsiders Secret Files & Origins 2003; intro. by Winick 13.00
...: Pay As You Go TPB (2007, $14.99) r/#42-46 & Annual #1 15.00
...: Sum of All Evil TPB (2004, $14.95) r/#8-15 15.00
...: The Good Fight TPB (2006, $14.99) r/#34-41 15.00
...: Wanted TPB (2005, $14.99) r/#16-23 15.00

OUTSIDERS, THE (See Batman and the Outsiders for #1-14 and #40)
DC Comics: No. 15, Apr, 2009 - No. 39, Jun, 2011 ($2.99)

15-23,26-39: 15-Alfred assembles a new team; Garbett-a. 17-19-Deathstroke app. 3.00
24,25-($3.99) Blackest Night; Terra rises as a Black Lantern 4.00
...: The Deep TPB (2009, $14.99) r/#15-20 & Batman and the Outsiders Special #1 15.00
...: The Great Divide TPB (2011, $17.99) r/#32-40; cover gallery 18.00
...: The Hunt TPB (2010, $14.99) r/#21-25 15.00
...: The Road to Hell TPB (2010, $14.99) r/#26-31 15.00

OUTSIDERS: FIVE OF A KIND (Bridges Outsiders #49 & 50)
DC Comics: Oct, 2007 ($2.99, weekly limited series)

...Katana/Shazam! (part 2 of 5) - Barr-s/Sharpe-a 3.00
...Metamorpho/Aquaman (part 4 of 5) - Wilson-s/Middleton-a 3.00
...Nightwing/Captain Boomerang (part 1 of 5) - DeFilippis & Weir-s/Willams-a 3.00
...Thunder/Martian Manhunter (part 3 of 5) - Bedard-s/Turnbull-a; Grayven app. 3.00
...Wonder Woman/Grace (part 5 of 5) - Andreyko-s/Richards-a 3.00
TPB (2008, $14.99) r/series & Outsiders #50 15.00

OUT THERE
DC Comics(Cliffhanger): July, 2001 - No. 18, Aug, 2003 ($2.50/$2.95)

1-Humberto Ramos-c/a; Brian Augustyn-s 3.00
1-Variant-c by Carlos Meglia 4.00
2-18: 3-Variant-c by Bruce Timm. 9-Begin $2.95-c 3.00
...: The Evil Within TPB (2002, $12.95) r/#1-6; Ramos sketch pages 13.00

OVERKILL: WITCHBLADE/ ALIENS/ DARKNESS/ PREDATOR
Image Comics/Dark Horse Comics: Dec, 2000 - No. 2, 2001 ($5.95)

1,2-Jenkins-s/Lansing, Ching & Benitez-a 6.00

OVERTAKEN
Aspen/MLT: Aug, 2013 - No. 5, Jan, 2018 ($1.00/$3.99)

1-5-Mastromauro-s/Lorenzana-a; multiple covers on each. 1-($1.00-c). 2-(3/16) 4.00

OVER THE EDGE
Marvel Comics: Nov, 1995 - No. 10, Aug, 1996 (99¢)

1-10: 1,6,10-Daredevil-c/story. 2,7-Dr. Strange-c/story. 3-Hulk-c/story. 4,9-Ghost Rider-c/story. 5-Punisher-c/story. 8-Elektra-c/story 3.00

OVER THE GARDEN WALL (Based on the Cartoon Network mini-series)
Boom Entertainment (KaBOOM!): Aug, 2015 - No. 4, Nov, 2015 ($3.99, limited series)

1-4-Pat McHale-s/Jim Campbell-a; multiple covers on each 4.00
Special 1 (11/14, $4.99)-Prequel to the Cartoon Network mini-series; McHale-s/Campbell-a 5.00

OVER THE GARDEN WALL ONGOING (Based on the Cartoon Network mini-series)
Boom Entertainment (KaBOOM!): Apr, 2016 - No. 20, Nov, 2018 ($3.99, limited series)

1-20: 1-4-Two stories in each; Campbell-s/Burgos-a & Levari-s/McGee-a; multiple covers 4.00
... 2017 Special 1 (9/17, $7.99) Three stories; covers by Mercado & Derek Kim 8.00

OWL, THE (See Crackajack Funnies #25, Popular Comics #72 and Occult Files of Dr. Spektor #22)
Gold Key: April, 1967; No. 2, April, 1968

	GD	VG	FN	VF	VF/NM	NM-
1-Written by Jerry Siegel; '40s super hero	5	10	15	34	60	85
2	4	8	12	28	47	65

OWL, THE (See Project Superpowers)
Dynamite Entertainment: 2013 - No. 4, 2013 ($3.99, limited series)

1-4-Golden Age hero in modern times; Krul-s/H.K. Michael-a; covers by Ross & Syaf 4.00

OZ (See First Comics Graphic Novel, Marvel Treaury Of Oz & MGM's Marvelous...)

OZ
Caliber Press: 1994 - 1997 ($2.95, B&W)

0-20: 0-Released between #10 & #11 3.00
1 ($5.95)-Limited Edition; double-c 6.00
...Specials: Freedom Fighters. Lion. Scarecrow. Tin Man 3.00

OZARK IKE
Dell Publishing Co./Standard Comics B11 on: Feb, 1948; Nov, 1948 - No. 24, Dec, 1951; No. 25, Sept, 1952

	GD	VG	FN	VF	VF/NM	NM-
Four Color 180(1948-Dell)	10	20	30	69	147	225
B11, B12, 13-15	12	24	36	69	97	125
16-25	11	22	33	60	83	105

OZ: DAEMONSTORM
Caliber Press: 1997 ($3.95, B&W, one-shot)

1 4.00

OZMA OF OZ (Dorothy Gale from Wonderful Wizard of Oz)
Marvel Comics: Jan, 2011 - No. 8, Sept, 2011 ($3.99, limited series)

1-6-Eric Shanower-s/Skottie Young-a/c 4.00
Oz Primer (5/11, $3.99) creator interviews and character profiles 4.00

OZ: ROMANCE IN RAGS
Caliber Press: 1996 ($2.95, B&W, limited series)

1-3, ..Special 3.00

Pacific Rim: Aftermath #1 © Legendary

Painkiller Jane #0 © Q&P

Panic #3 © WMG

GD 2.0 | VG 4.0 | FN 6.0 | VF 8.0 | VF/NM 9.0 | NM- 9.2

OZ SQUAD
Brave New Worlds/Patchwork Press: 1992 - No. 4, 1994 ($2.50/$2.75, B&W)
1-4-Patchwork Press 3.00

OZ SQUAD
Patchwork Press: Dec, 1995 - No. 10, 1996 ($3.95/$2.95, B&W)
1-($3.95) 4.00
2-10 3.00

OZ: STRAW AND SORCERY
Caliber Press: 1997 ($2.95, B&W, limited series)
1-3 3.00

OZ-WONDERLAND WARS, THE
DC Comics: Jan, 1986 - No. 3, March, 1986 (Mini-series)(Giants)
1-3-Capt. Carrot app.; funny animals 4.00

OZZIE & BABS (TV Teens #14 on)
Fawcett Publications: Dec, 1947 - No. 13, Fall, 1949
1-Teen-age 14 28 42 81 118 155
2 9 18 27 50 65 80
3-13 8 16 24 42 54 65

OZZIE AND HARRIET (The Adventures of... on cover) (Radio)
National Periodical Publications: Oct-Nov, 1949 - No. 5, June-July, 1950
1-Photo-c 103 206 309 659 1130 1600
2 48 96 144 302 514 725
3-5 40 80 120 246 411 575

OZZY OSBOURNE (Todd McFarlane Presents)
Image Comics (Todd McFarlane Prod.): June, 1999 ($4.95, magazine-sized)
1-Bio, interview and comic story; Ormston painted-a; Ashley Wood-c 5.00

PACIFIC COMICS GRAPHIC NOVEL (See Image Graphic Novel)

PACIFIC PRESENTS (Also see Starslayer #2, 3)
Pacific Comics: Oct, 1982 - No. 2, Apr, 1983; No. 3, Mar, 1984 - No. 4, Jun, 1984
1-Chapter 3 of The Rocketeer; Stevens-c/a; Bettie Page model
2 4 6 11 16 20
2-Chapter 4 of The Rocketeer (4th app.); nudity; Stevens-c/a
2 4 6 10 14 18
3,4: 3-1st app. Vanity 3.00
NOTE: *Conrad a-3, 4; c-3.* ***Ditko*** *a-1-3; c-1(1/2).* ***Dave Stevens*** *a-1, 2; c-1(1/2), 2.*

PACIFIC RIM: AFTERMATH
Legendary Comics: Jan, 2018 - Present ($3.99)
1,2-Cavan Scott-s 4.00

PACIFIC RIM: TALES FROM THE DRIFT
Legendary Comics: Nov, 2015 - No. 4, Apr, 2016 ($3.99)
1-4-Beachum & Fialkov-s/Marz-a 4.00

PACIFIC RIM: TALES FROM YEAR ZERO
Legendary Comics: Jun, 2013 ($24.99, HC graphic novel)
HC - Prequel to the 2013 movie; Beacham-s/Alex Ross-c; art by various 25.00

PACT, THE
Image Comics: Feb, 1994 - No. 3, June, 1994 ($1.95, limited series)
1-3: Valentino co-scripts & layouts 3.00

PACT, THE
Image Comics: Apr, 2005 - No. 4, Jan, 2006 ($2.99/$2.95)
1-4: Invincible, Shadowhawk, Firebreather & Zephyr team-up. 1-Valentino-s/a 3.00

PAGEANT OF COMICS (See Jane Arden & Mopsy)
Archer St. John: Sept, 1947 - No. 2, Oct, 1947
1-Mopsy strip-r 20 40 60 117 189 260
2-Jane Arden strip-r 13 26 39 72 101 130

PAINKILLER JANE
Event Comics: June, 1997 - No. 5, Nov, 1997 ($3.95/$2.95)
1-Augustyn/Waid-s/Leonardi/Palmiotti-a, variant-c 4.00
2-5: Two covers (Quesada, Leonardi) 3.00
0-(1/99, $3.95) Retells origin; two covers 4.00
Essential Painkiller Jane TPB (2007, $19.99) r/#0-5; cover gallery and pin-ups 20.00

PAINKILLER JANE
Dynamite Entertainment: 2006 - No. 3, 2006 ($2.99)
1-3-Quesada & Palmiotti-s/Moder-a. 1-Four covers by Q&P, Moder, Tan and Conner 3.00
Volume #1 TPB (2007, $9.99) r/#1-3; cover gallery and Palmiotti interview 10.00

PAINKILLER JANE
Dynamite Entertainment: No. 0, 2007 - No. 5, 2007 ($3.50)
0-(25¢) Quesada & Palmiotti-s/Moder-a 3.00
1-5-($3.50) 1-Continued from #0; 5 covers. 4,5-Crossover with Terminator 2 #6,7 3.50
Volume #2 TPB (2007, $11.99) r/#0-3; cover gallery 12.00

PAINKILLER JANE / DARKCHYLDE
Event Comics: Oct, 1998 ($2.95, one-shot)
Preview-($6.95) DF Edition, 1-($6.95) DF Edition 7.00
1-Three covers; J.G. Jones-a 3.00

PAINKILLER JANE / HELLBOY
Event Comics: Aug, 1998 ($2.95, one-shot)
1-Leonardi & Palmiotti-a 3.00

PAINKILLER JANE: THE PRICE OF FREEDOM
Marvel Comics (ICON): Nov, 2013 - No. 4, Jan, 2014 ($3.99/$2.99, limited series)
1-($3.99) Palmiotti-s/Santacruz & Lotfi-a; covers by Amanda Conner & Dave Johnson 4.00
2-4-($2.99) Santacruz-a/Conner-c 3.00

PAINKILLER JANE: THE 22 BRIDES
Marvel Comics (ICON): May, 2014 - No. 3, Oct, 2014 ($4.99/$3.99, limited series)
1-($4.99) Palmiotti-s/Santacruz & Fernandez-a; covers by Christian & Conner 5.00
2,3-($3.99) Santacruz-a2-Photo-c. 3-Conner-c 4.00

PAINKILLER JANE VS. THE DARKNESS
Event Comics: Apr, 1997 ($2.95, one-shot)
1-Ennis-s; four variant-c (Conner, Hildebrandts, Quesada, Silvestri) 3.50

PAKLIS
Image Comics: May, 2017 - Present ($5.99/$3.99/$4.99)
1,2,5-($5.99) Serialized anthology by Dustin Weaver-s/a/c 6.00
3-($3.99) Dustin Weaver-s/a/c 4.00
4-($4.99) Dustin Weaver-s/a/c 5.00

PANCHO VILLA
Avon Periodicals: 1950
nn-Kinstler-c 27 54 81 158 259 360

PANHANDLE PETE AND JENNIFER (TV) (See Gene Autry #20)
J. Charles Laue Publishing Co.: July, 1951 - No. 3, Nov, 1951
1 11 22 33 62 86 110
2,3: 2-Interior photo-cvrs 8 16 24 42 54 65

PANIC (Companion to Mad)
E. C. Comics (Tiny Tot Comics): Feb-Mar, 1954 - No. 12, Dec-Jan, 1955-56
1-Used in Senate Investigation hearings; Elder draws entire E. C. staff; Santa Claus & Mickey Spillane parody 43 86 129 344 542 750
2-Atomic bomb-c 20 40 60 160 255 350
3,4: 3-Senate Subcommittee parody; Davis draws Gaines, Feldstein & Kelly, 1 pg.; Old King Cole smokes marijuana. 4-Infinity-c; John Wayne parody
16 32 48 128 207 285
5-11: 8-Last pre-code issue (5/55). 9-Superman, Smilin' Jack & Dick Tracy app. on-c; has photo of Walter Winchell on-c. 11-Wheedies cereal box-c
15 30 45 120 193 265
12 (Low distribution; thousands were destroyed) 21 42 63 168 264 360
NOTE: ***Davis*** *a-1-12; c-12.* ***Elder*** *a-1-12.* ***Feldstein*** *c-1-3, 5.* ***Kamen*** *a-1.* ***Orlando*** *a-1-9.* ***Wolverton*** *c-4, panel-3.* ***Wood*** *a-2-9, 11, 12.*

PANIC (Magazine) (Satire)
Panic Publ.: July, 1958 - No. 6, July, 1959; V2#10, Dec, 1965 - V2#12, 1966
1 14 28 42 76 108 140
2-6 9 18 27 50 65 80
V2#10-12: Reprints earlier issues 3 6 9 17 26 35
NOTE: ***Davis*** *a-3(2 pgs.), 4, 5, 10; c-10.* ***Elder*** *a-5.* ***Powell*** *a-V2#10, 11.* ***Torres*** *a-1-5.* ***Tuska*** *a-V2#11.*

PANIC
Gemstone Publishing: March, 1997 - No. 12, Dec, 1999 ($2.50, quarterly)
1-12: E.C. reprints 4.00

PANTHA (See Vampirella-The New Monthly #16,17)

PANTHA (Also see Prophecy)
Dynamite Entertainment: 2012 - No. 6, 2013 ($3.99)
1-6: 1-Jerwa-s/Rodrix-a; covers by Sean Chen & Texiera. 2-6-Texiera-c 4.00

PANTHA: HAUNTED PASSION (Also see Vampirella Monthly #0)
Harris Comics: May, 1997 ($2.95, B&W, one-shot)
1-r/Vampirella #30,31 3.00

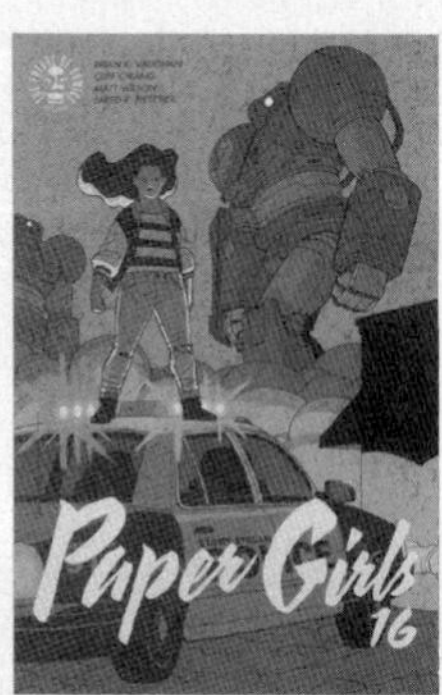

Paper Girls #16 © BKV & Chiang

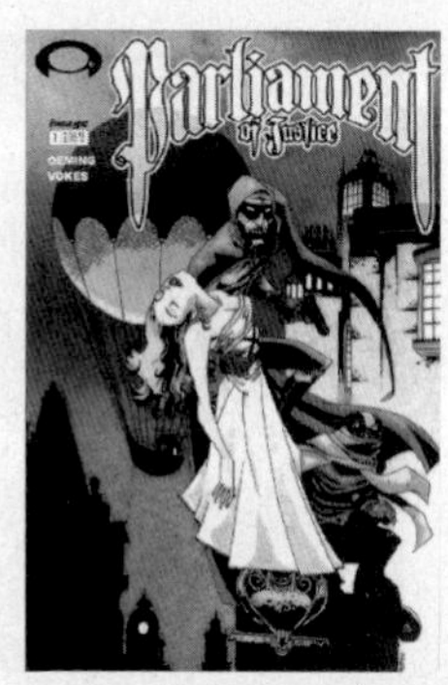

Parliament of Justice #1 © Oeming & Vokes

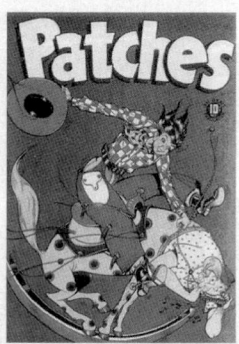

Patches #3 © Patches Pub.

GD 2.0 | VG 4.0 | FN 6.0 | VF 8.0 | VF/NM 9.0 | NM- 9.2

PANTHEON
IDW Publishing: Apr, 2010 - No. 5, Aug, 2010 ($3.99)
1-5-Andreyko-s/Molnar-a; co-created by Michael Chiklis 4.00

PAPA MIDNITE (See John Constantine - Hellblazer Special:...)

PAPER GIRLS
Image Comics: Oct, 2015 - Present ($2.99)
1-20-Brian K. Vaughn-s/Cliff Chiang-a 3.00

PARADE (See Hanna-Barbera...)

PARADE COMICS (See Frisky Animals on Parade)

PARADE OF PLEASURE
Derric Verschoyle Ltd., London, England: 1954 (192 pgs.) (Hardback book)
By Geoffrey Wagner. Contains section devoted to the censorship of American comic books with illustrations in color and black and white. (Also see **Seduction of the Innocent**).
Distributed in USA by Library Publishers, N. Y. 142 284 426 568 709 850
with dust jacket.... 267 534 801 1068 1334 1600

PARADISE TOO!
Abstract Studios: 2000 - No. 14, 2003 ($2.95, B&W)
1-14-Terry Moore's unpublished newspaper strips and sketches 3.00
Complete Paradise Too TPB (2010, $29.95) r/#1-14 with bonus material 30.00
...: Checking For Weirdos TPB (4/03, $14.95) r/#8-12 15.00
...: Drunk Ducks! TPB (7/02, $15.95) r/#1-7 16.00

PARADISE X (Also see Earth X and Universe X)
Marvel Comics: Apr, 2002 - No. 12, Aug, 2003 ($4.50/$2.99)
0-Ross-c; Braithwaite-a 4.50
1-12-($2.99) Ross-c; Braithwaite-a. 7-Punisher on-c. 10-Kingpin on-c 3.00
...:A (10/03, $2.99) Braithwaite-a; Ross-c 3.00
...:Devils (11/02, $4.50) Sadowski-a; Ross-c 4.50
...:Ragnarok 1,2 (3/02, 4/03; $2.99) Yeates-a; Ross-c 3.00
...:X (11/03, $2.99) Braithwaite-a; Ross-c; conclusion of story 3.00
...:Xen (7/02, $4.50) Yeowell & Sienkiewicz-a; Ross-c 4.50
Earth X Vol. 4: Paradise X Book 1 (2003, $29.99, TPB) r/#0,1-5, ...: Xen; Heralds #1-3 30.00
Vol. 5: Paradise X Book 2 (2004, $29.99, TPB) r/#6-12, Ragnarok #1&2; Devils, A & X 30.00

PARADISE X: HERALDS (Also see Earth X and Universe X)
Marvel Comics: Dec, 2001 - No. 3, Feb, 2002 ($3.50)
1-3-Prelude to Paradise X series; Ross-c; Pugh-a 3.50
Special Edition (Wizard preview) Ross-c 3.00

PARADOX
Dark Visions Publ: June, 1994 - No. 2, Aug, 1994 ($2.95, B&W, mature)
1,2: 1-Linsner-c. 2-Boris-c. 3.00

PARALLAX: EMERALD NIGHT (See Final Night)
DC Comics: Nov, 1996 ($2.95, one-shot, 48 pgs.)
1-Final Night tie-in; Green Lantern (Kyle Rayner) app. 4.00

PARAMOUNT ANIMATED COMICS (See Harvey Comics Hits #60, 62)
Harvey Publications: No. 3, Jun, 1953 - No. 22, Jul, 1956
3-Baby Huey, Herman & Katnip, Buzzy the Crow begin
29 58 87 170 278 385
4-6 15 30 45 83 124 165
7-Baby Huey becomes permanent cover feature; cover title becomes Baby Huey with #9
25 50 75 147 241 335
8-10: 9-Infinity-c 13 26 39 72 101 130
11-22 10 20 30 56 76 95

PARENT TRAP, THE (Disney)
Dell Publishing Co.: No. 1210, Oct-Dec, 1961
Four Color 1210-Movie, Hayley Mills photo-c 8 16 24 56 108 160

PARIAH (Aron Warner's...)
Dark Horse Comics: Feb, 2014 - No. 8, Sept, 2014 ($3.99)
1-8-Aron Warner & Philip Gelatt-s/Brett Weldele-a 4.00

PARLIAMENT OF JUSTICE
Image Comics: Mar, 2003 ($5.95, B&W, one-shot, square-bound)
1-Michael Avon Oeming-c/s; Neil Vokes-a 6.00

PARODY
Armour Publishing: Mar, 1977 - No. 3, Aug, 1977 (B&W humor magazine)
1 3 6 9 14 19 24
2,3: 2-King Kong, Happy Days. 3-Charlie's Angels, Rocky
2 4 6 10 14 18

PAROLE BREAKERS
Avon Periodicals/Realistic #2 on: Dec, 1951 - No. 3, July, 1952
1(#2 on inside)-r-c/Avon paperback #283 (painted-c)
57 114 171 362 619 875
2-Kubert-a; r-c/Avon paperback #114 (photo-c) 42 84 126 265 445 625
3-Kinstler-c 39 78 117 231 378 525

PARTRIDGE FAMILY, THE (TV)(Also see David Cassidy)
Charlton Comics: Mar, 1971 - No. 21, Dec, 1973
1-(2 versions: B&W photo-c & tinted color photo-c) 6 12 18 41 76 110
2-4,6-10 4 8 12 25 40 55
5-Partridge Family Summer Special (52 pgs.); The Shadow, Lone Ranger, Charlie McCarthy, Flash Gordon, Hopalong Cassidy, Gene Autry & others app.
7 14 21 46 86 125
11-21 3 6 9 21 33 45

PARTS OF A HOLE
Caliber Press: 1991 ($2.50, B&W)
1-Short stories & cartoons by Brian Michael Bendis 3.00

PARTS UNKNOWN
Eclipse Comics/FX: July, 1992 - No. 4, Oct, 1992 ($2.50, B&W, mature)
1-4: All contain FX gaming cards 3.00

PARTS UNKNOWN
Image Comics: May, 2000 - Sept, 2000 ($2.95, B&W)
...: Killing Attractions 1 (5/00) Beau Smith-s/Brad Gorby-a 3.00
...: Hostile Takeover 1-4 (6-9/00) 3.00

PASSION, THE
Catechetical Guild: No. 394, 1955
394 7 14 21 37 46 55

PASSOVER (See Avengelyne)
Maximum Press: Dec, 1996 ($2.99, one-shot)
1 3.00

PAST AWAYS
Dark Horse Comics: Mar, 2015 - No. 9, Mar, 2016 ($3.99)
1-9: 1-Matt Kindt-s/Scott Kolins-a; two covers by Kolins & Kindt 4.00

PAT BOONE (TV)(Also see Superman's Girlfriend Lois Lane #9)
National Per. Publ.: Sept-Oct, 1959 - No. 5, May-Jun, 1960 (All have photo-c)
1 42 84 126 265 445 625
2-5: 3-Fabian, Connie Francis & Paul Anka photos on-c. 4-Previews "Journey To The Center Of The Earth". 4-Johnny Mathis & Bobby Darin photos on-c. 5-Dick Clark & Frankie Avalon photos on-c 34 68 102 199 325 450

PATCHES
Rural Home/Patches Publ. (Orbit): Mar-Apr, 1945 - No. 11, Nov, 1947
1-L. B. Cole-c 42 84 126 265 445 625
2 17 34 51 98 154 210
3,4,6,8-11: 6-Henry Aldrich story. 8-Smiley Burnette-c/s (6/47); pre-dates Smiley Burnette #1. 9-Mr. District Attorney story (radio). Leav/Keigstein-a (16 pgs.). 9-11-Leav-c. 10-Jack Carson (radio) c/story; Leav-c. 11-Red Skelton story 15 30 45 90 140 190
5-Danny Kaye-c/story; L.B. Cole-c. 20 40 60 120 195 270
7-Hopalong Cassidy-c/story 19 38 57 109 172 235

PATH, THE (Also see Negation War)
CrossGeneration Comics: Apr, 2002 - No. 23, Apr, 2004 ($2.95)
1-23: 1-Ron Marz-s/Bart Sears-a. 13-Matthew Smith-a begins 3.00

PATHFINDER (Based on the Pathfinder roleplaying game)
Dynamite Entertainment: 2012 - No. 12, 2013 ($3.99)
1-12: 1-Jim Zub-s/Andrew Huerta-a; four covers. 2-12-Multiple covers on each 4.00
... Special 2013 ($4.99, 40 pgs.) Jim Zub-s/Kevin Stokes-a 5.00

PATHFINDER: CITY OF SECRETS (Based on the Pathfinder roleplaying game)
Dynamite Entertainment: 2014 - No. 6, 2014 ($4.99)
1-6-Zub-s/Oliveira-a; Bound-in poster; multiple covers on each 5.00

PATHFINDER: GOBLINS! (Based on the Pathfinder roleplaying game)
Dynamite Entertainment: 2013 - No. 5, 2013 ($3.99)
1-5: Short stories by various; multiple covers on each 4.00

PATHFINDER: HOLLOW MOUNTAIN (Based on the Pathfinder roleplaying game)
Dynamite Entertainment: 2015 - No. 6, 2016 ($4.99)
1-6: 1-Sutter-s/Garcia-a; multiple covers 5.00

Patsy & Hedy #17 © MAR

Patsy Walker, A.K.A. Hellcat #2 © MAR

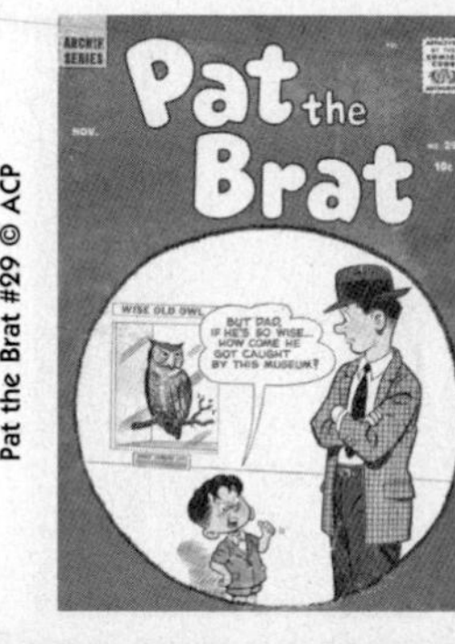

Pat the Brat #29 © ACP

	GD 2.0	VG 4.0	FN 6.0	VF 8.0	VF/NM 9.0	NM- 9.2

PATHFINDER: ORIGINS (Based on the Pathfinder roleplaying game)
Dynamite Entertainment: 2015 - No. 6, 2015 ($4.99)

1-6: 1-Spotlight on Valeros; multiple-c. 2-Kyra. 3-Seoni. 4-Merisiel. 5-Harsk. 6-Ezren						5.00

PATHFINDER: RUNESCARS (Based on the Pathfinder roleplaying game)
Dynamite Entertainment: 2017 - No. 5, 2017 ($3.99/$4.99)

1-($3.99) Schneider-s/Silva-a; multiple covers						4.00
2-5-($4.99) 2,4,5-Sutter-s. 3,5-Schneider-s						5.00

PATHFINDER: WORLDSCAPE (Based on the Pathfinder roleplaying game)
Dynamite Entertainment: 2016 - No. 6, 2017 ($4.99)

1-6-Red Sonja, John Carter and Tarzan app.; Jonathan Lau-a						5.00

PATHWAYS TO FANTASY
Pacific Comics: July, 1984

1-Barry Smith-c/a; Jeff Jones-a (4 pgs.)						4.00

PATORUZU (See Adventures of...)

PATRIOTS, THE
DC Comics (WildStorm): Jan, 2000 - No. 10, Oct, 2000 ($2.50)

1-10-Choi and Peterson-s/Ryan-a						3.00

PATSY & HEDY (Teenage)(Also see Hedy Wolfe)
Atlas Comics/Marvel (GPI/Male): Feb, 1952 - No. 110, Feb, 1967

1-Patsy Walker & Hedy Wolfe; Al Jaffee-c	58	116	174	371	636	900
2	22	44	66	132	216	300
3-10: 3,7,8,9-Al Jaffee-c	20	40	60	114	182	250
11-20: 17,19,20-Al Jaffee-c	16	32	48	94	147	200
21-40	15	30	45	85	130	175
41-50	8	16	24	51	96	140
51-60	7	14	21	48	89	130
61-80,100: 88-Lingerie panel	6	12	18	41	76	110
81-87,89-99,101-110	6	12	18	38	69	100
Annual 1(1963)-Early Marvel annual	10	20	30	66	138	210

PATSY & HER PALS (Teenage)
Atlas Comics (PPI): May, 1953 - No. 29, Aug, 1957

1-Patsy Walker	39	78	117	240	395	550
2	19	38	57	111	176	240
3-10	16	32	48	92	144	195
11-29: 24-Everett-c	14	28	42	82	121	160

PATSY WALKER (See All Teen, A Date With Patsy, Girls' Life, Miss America Magazine, Patsy & Hedy, Patsy & Her Pals & Teen Comics)
Marvel/Atlas Comics (BPC): 1945 (no month) - No. 124, Dec, 1965

1-Teenage	300	600	900	2010	3505	5000
2	43	86	129	271	461	650
3,4,6-10	36	72	108	211	343	475
5-Injury-to-eye-c	39	78	117	231	378	525
11,12,15,16,18	22	44	66	132	216	300
13,14,17,19-22-Kurtzman's "Hey Look"	23	46	69	136	223	310
23,24	20	40	60	117	189	260
25-Rusty by Kurtzman; painted-c	23	46	69	136	223	310
26-29,31: 26-31: 52 pgs.	18	36	54	103	162	220
30(52 pgs.)-Egghead Doodle by Kurtzman (1 pg.)	18	36	54	107	169	230
32-57: Last precode (3/55)	16	32	48	94	147	200
58-80,100	8	16	24	56	108	160
81-98: 92,98-Millie x-over	8	16	24	51	96	140
99-Linda Carter x-over	11	22	33	76	163	250
101-124	6	12	18	41	76	110
Fashion Parade 1(1966, 68 pgs.) (Beware cut-out & marked pages)	9	18	27	61	123	185

NOTE: *Painted c-25-28. Anti-Wertham editorial in #21. Georgie app. in #8, 11, 17. Millie app. in #10, 92, 98. Mitzi app. in #11. Rusty app. in #12, 25. Willie app. in #12.* ***Al Jaffee*** *c-44, 47, 49, 51, 57, 58.*

PATSY WALKER, A.K.A. HELLCAT
Marvel Comics: Feb, 2016 - No. 17, Jun, 2017 ($3.99)

1-17: 1-Kate Leth-s/Brittney Williams-a; She-Hulk and Tom Hale app. 2-Hedy Wolfe app. 6-Natasha Allegri-a. 6,7-Jessica Jones app. 8-Civil War II tie-in						4.00

PATSY WALKER: HELLCAT
Marvel Comics: Sept, 2008 - No. 5, Feb, 2009 ($2.99, limited series)

1-5-Lafuente-a/Kathryn Immonen-s/Stuart Immonen-c; Hellcat joins The Initiative						3.00

PAT THE BRAT (Adventures of Pipsqueak #34 on)
Archie Publications (Radio): June, 1953; Summer, 1955 - No. 4, 5/56; No. 15, 7/56 - No. 33, 7/59

nn(6/53)	16	32	48	94	147	210
1(Summer, 1955)	15	30	45	88	137	185
2-4-(5/56) (#5-14 not published). 3-Early Bolling-a	9	18	27	52	69	85
15-(7/56)-33: 18-Early Bolling-a	5	10	15	30	50	70

PAT THE BRAT COMICS DIGEST MAGAZINE
Archie Publications: October, 1980 (95¢)

1-Li'l Jinx & Super Duck app.	2	4	6	9	13	16

PATTY CAKE
Permanent Press: Mar, 1995 - No. 9, Jul, 1996 ($2.95, B&W)

1-9: Scott Roberts-s/a						3.00

PATTY CAKE
Caliber Press (Tapestry): Oct, 1996 - No. 3, Apr, 1997 ($2.95, B&W)

1-3: Scott Roberts-s/a, ...Christmas (12/96)						3.00

PATTY CAKE & FRIENDS
Slave Labor Graphics: Nov, 1997 - Nov, 2000 ($2.95, B&W)

Here There Be Monsters (10/97), 1-14: Scott Roberts-s/a						3.00
Volume 2 #1 (11/00, $4.95)						5.00

PATTY POWERS (Formerly Della Vision #3)
Atlas Comics: No. 4, Oct, 1955 - No. 7, Oct, 1956

4	17	34	51	98	154	210
5-7	14	28	42	80	115	150

PAT WILTON (See Mighty Midget Comics)

PAUL
Spire Christian Comics (Fleming H. Revell Co.): 1978 (49¢)

nn	2	4	6	10	14	18

PAULINE PERIL (See The Close Shaves of...)

PAUL REVERE'S RIDE (TV, Disney, see Walt Disney Showcase #34)
Dell Publishing Co.: No. 822, July, 1957

Four Color 822-w/Johnny Tremain, Toth-a	7	14	21	49	92	135

PAUL TERRY (See Heckle and Jeckle)

PAUL TERRY'S ADVENTURES OF MIGHTY MOUSE (See Adventures of...)

PAUL TERRY'S COMICS (Formerly Terry-Toons Comics; becomes Adventures of Mighty Mouse No. 126 on)
St. John Publishing Co.: No. 85, Mar, 1951 - No. 125, May, 1955

85,86-Same as Terry-Toons #85, & 86 with only a title change; published at same time?; Mighty Mouse, Heckle & Jeckle & Gandy Goose continue from Terry-Toons	13	26	39	72	101	130
87-99	10	20	30	54	72	90
100	10	20	30	58	79	100
101-104,107-125: 121,122,125-Painted-c	9	18	27	52	69	85
105,106-Giant Comics Edition (25¢, 100 pgs.) (9/53 & ?). 105-Little Roquefort-c/story	19	38	57	111	176	240

PAUL TERRY'S MIGHTY MOUSE (See Mighty Mouse)

PAUL TERRY'S MIGHTY MOUSE ADVENTURE STORIES (See Mighty Mouse Adventure Stories)

PAUL THE SAMURAI (See The Tick #4)
New England Comics: July, 1992 - No. 6, July, 1993 ($2.75, B&W)

1-6						3.00

PAWNEE BILL
Story Comics (Youthful Magazines?): Feb, 1951 - No. 3, July, 1951

1-Bat Masterson, Wyatt Earp app.	14	28	42	82	121	160
2,3: 3-Origin Golden Warrior; Cameron-a	9	18	27	50	65	80

PAYBACKS, THE
Dark Horse Comics: Sept, 2015 - No. 4, Dec, 2015 ($3.99)

1-4: 1-Cates & Rahal-s/Shaw-a						4.00

PAY-OFF (This Is the..., ...Crime, ...Detective Stories)
D. S. Publishing Co.: July-Aug, 1948 - No. 5, Mar-Apr, 1949 (52 pgs.)

1-True Crime Cases #1,2	32	64	96	192	314	435
2	18	36	54	105	165	225
3-5-Thrilling Detective Stories	15	30	45	86	133	180

PEACEMAKER, THE (Also see Fightin' Five)
Charlton Comics: V3#1, Mar, 1967 - No. 5, Nov, 1967 (All 12¢ cover price)

1-Fightin' Five begins	5	10	15	33	57	80
2,3,5	3	6	9	20	31	42
4-Origin The Peacemaker	4	8	12	25	40	55

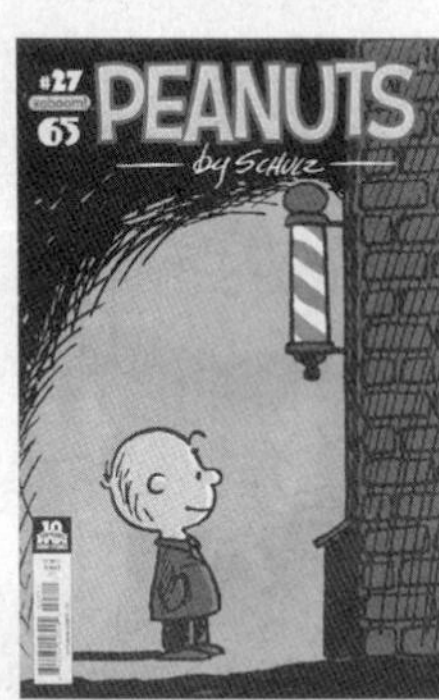

Peanuts V2 #27 © Peanuts WW

Pedro #1 © FOX

Penny #1 © AVON

	GD 2.0	VG 4.0	FN 6.0	VF 8.0	VF/NM 9.0	NM- 9.2
1,2(Modern Comics reprint, 1978)						6.00

PEACEMAKER (Also see Crisis On Infinite Earths & Showcase '93 #7,9,10)
DC Comics: Jan, 1988 - No. 4, Apr, 1988 ($1.25, limited series)

	GD 2.0	VG 4.0	FN 6.0	VF 8.0	VF/NM 9.0	NM- 9.2
1-4						4.00

PEANUTS (Charlie Brown) (See Tip Top #173 and United Comics #21 for Peanuts 1st comic book app.)(Also see Fritzi Ritz, Nancy & Sluggo, Sparkle & Sparkler, Tip Top, Tip Topper & United Comics)
United Features Syndicate/Dell Publishing Co./Gold Key: 1953-54; No. 878, 2/58 - No. 13, 5-7/62; 5/63 - No. 4, 2/64

	GD 2.0	VG 4.0	FN 6.0	VF 8.0	VF/NM 9.0	NM- 9.2
1(U.F.S.)(1953-54)-Reprints United Features' Strange As It Seems, Willie, Ferdnand (scarce)	757	1514	2271	5526	9763	14,000
Four Color 878(#1) (Dell) Schulz-s/a, with assistance from Dale Hale and Jim Sasseville thru #4	79	158	237	632	1416	2200
Four Color 969,1015('59)	27	54	81	194	435	675
4(2-4/60) Schulz-s/a; one story by Anthony Pocrnich, Schulz's assistant cartoonist	15	30	45	103	227	350
5-13-Schulz-c only; s/a by Pocrnich	13	26	39	89	195	300
1(Gold Key, 5/63)	28	56	84	202	451	700
2-4	12	24	36	79	170	260

PEANUTS (Charlie Brown)
BOOM! Entertainment: No. 0, Nov, 2011 - No. 4, Apr, 2012; V2 No. 1, Aug, 2012 - No. 32, Apr, 2016 ($1.00/$3.99)

	GD 2.0	VG 4.0	FN 6.0	VF 8.0	VF/NM 9.0	NM- 9.2
0-(11/11, $1.00) New short stories and Sunday page reprints						3.00
1-4: 1-(1/12, $3.99) New short stories and Sunday page reprints; Snoopy sled cover						4.00
1-4-Variant-c with first appearance image. 1-Charlie Brown. 2-Lucy. 3-Linus. 4-Snoopy						6.00
(Volume 2)						
1-32: 1-(8/12, "#1 of 4" on-c)						4.00
1-12-Variant-c with first appearance image. 1-Schroeder. 2-Pig-Pen. 4-Woodstock						10.00
... Free Comic Book Day Edition (5/12) Giveaway flip book with Adventure Time						3.00
...: Friends Forever 2016 Special (7/16, $7.99) New and classic short stories						8.00
Happiness is a Warm Blanket, Charlie Brown HC (Boom Entertainment, 3/2011, $19.99) adaptation of new animated special						20.00
It's Tokyo, Charlie Brown (10/12, $13.99, squarebound GN) Vicki Scott-s/a; bonus art						14.00
...: The Snoopy Special 1 (11/15, $4.99) New and classic Snoopy short stories						5.00
...: Where Beagles Dare! GN (9/15, $9.99, SC) Jason Cooper-s/Vicki Scott-a						10.00

PEANUTS HALLOWEEN
Fantagraphics Books: Sept, 2008 (8-1/2" x 5-3/8" ashcan giveaway)

	GD 2.0	VG 4.0	FN 6.0	VF 8.0	VF/NM 9.0	NM- 9.2
nn-Halloween themed reprints in color and B&W						2.00

PEBBLES & BAMM BAMM (TV) (See Cave Kids #7, 12)
Charlton Comics: Jan, 1972 - No. 36, Dec, 1976 (Hanna-Barbera)

	GD 2.0	VG 4.0	FN 6.0	VF 8.0	VF/NM 9.0	NM- 9.2
1-From the Flintstones; "Teen Age..." on cover	4	8	12	28	47	65
2-10	3	6	9	16	24	32
11-20	2	4	6	13	18	22
21-36	2	4	6	9	13	16
nn (1973, digest, 100 pgs.) B&W one page gags	3	6	9	17	26	35

PEBBLES & BAMM BAMM (TV)
Harvey Comics: Nov, 1993 - No. 3, Mar, 1994 ($1.50) (Hanna-Barbera)

	GD 2.0	VG 4.0	FN 6.0	VF 8.0	VF/NM 9.0	NM- 9.2
V2#1-3						3.00
...Giant Size 1 (10/93, $2.25, 68 pgs.)("Summer Special" on-c)						4.00

PEBBLES FLINTSTONE (TV) (See The Flintstones #11)
Gold Key: Sept, 1963 (Hanna-Barbera)

	GD 2.0	VG 4.0	FN 6.0	VF 8.0	VF/NM 9.0	NM- 9.2
1 (10088-309)-Early Pebbles app.	8	16	24	52	99	145

PEDRO (Formerly My Private Life #17; also see Romeo Tubbs)
Fox Feature Syndicate: No. 18, June, 1950 - No. 2, Aug, 1950?

	GD 2.0	VG 4.0	FN 6.0	VF 8.0	VF/NM 9.0	NM- 9.2
18(#1)-Wood-c/a(p)	24	48	72	144	237	330
2-Wood-a?	16	32	48	94	147	200

PEE-WEE PIXIES (See The Pixies)

PELLEAS AND MELISANDE (See Night Music #4, 5)

PENALTY (See Crime Must Pay the...)

PENANCE: RELENTLESS (See Civil War, Thunderbolts and related titles)
Marvel Comics: Nov, 2007 - No. 5 ($2.99)

	GD 2.0	VG 4.0	FN 6.0	VF 8.0	VF/NM 9.0	NM- 9.2
1-5-Speedball/Penance; Jenkins-s/Gulacy-a. 3-Wolverine app.						3.00
TPB (2008, $13.99) r/#1-5						14.00

PENDRAGON (Knights of... #5 on; also see Knights of...)
Marvel Comics UK, Ltd.: July, 1992 - No. 15, Sept, 1993 ($1.75)

	GD 2.0	VG 4.0	FN 6.0	VF 8.0	VF/NM 9.0	NM- 9.2
1-15: 1-4-Iron Man app. 6-8-Spider-Man app.						3.00

PENDULUM ILLUSTRATED BIOGRAPHIES
Pendulum Press: 1979 (B&W)

19-355x-George Washington/Thomas Jefferson, 19-3495-Charles Lindbergh/Amelia Earhart, 19-3509-Harry Houdini/Walt Disney, 19-3517-Davy Crockett/Daniel Boone-Redondo-a, 19-3525-Elvis Presley/Beatles, 19-3533-Benjamin Franklin/Martin Luther King Jr, 19-3541-Abraham Lincoln/Franklin D. Roosevelt, 19-3568-Marie Curie/Albert Einstein-Redondo-a, 19-3576-Thomas Edison/Alexander Graham Bell-Redondo-a, 19-3584-Vince Lombardi/Pele, 19-3592-Babe Ruth/Jackie Robinson, 19-3606-Jim Thorpe/Althea Gibson

	GD 2.0	VG 4.0	FN 6.0	VF 8.0	VF/NM 9.0	NM- 9.2
Softback						5.00
Hardback	1	2	3	4	5	7

PENDULUM ILLUSTRATED CLASSICS (Now Age Illustrated)
Pendulum Press: 1973 - 1978 (75¢, 62pp, B&W, 5-3/8x8")
(Also see Marvel Classics)

64-100x(1973)-Dracula-Redondo art, 64-131x-The Invisible Man-Nino art, 64-0968-Dr. Jekyll and Mr. Hyde-Redondo art, 64-1005-Black Beauty, 64-1010-Call of the Wild, 64-1020-Frankenstein, 64-1025-Hucklebury Finn, 64-1030-Moby Dick-Nino-a, 64-1040-Red Badge of Courage, 64-1045-The Time Machine-Nino-a, 64-1050-Tom Sawyer, 64-1055-Twenty Thousand Leagues Under the Sea, 64-1069-Treasure Island, 64-1328(1974)-Kidnapped, 64-1336-Three Musketeers-Nino art, 64-1344-A Tale of Two Cities, 64-1352-Journey to the Center of the Earth, 64-1360-The War of the Worlds-Nino-a, 64-1379-The Greatest Advs. of Sherlock Holmes-Redondo art, 64-1387-Mysterious Island, 64-1395-Hunchback of Notre Dame, 64-1409-Helen Keller-story of my life, 64-1417-Scarlet Letter, 64-1425-Gulliver's Travels, 64-2618(1977)-Around the World in Eighty Days, 64-2626-Captains Courageous, 64-2634-Connecticut Yankee, 64-2642-The Hound of the Baskervilles, 64-2650-The House of Seven Gables, 64-2669-Jane Eyre, 64-2677-The Last of the Mohicans, 64-2685-The Best of O'Henry, 64-2693-The Best of Poe-Redondo-a, 64-2707-Two Years Before the Mast, 64-2715-White Fang, 64-2723-Wuthering Heights, 64-3126(1978)-Ben Hur-Redondo art, 64-3134-A Christmas Carol, 64-3142-The Food of the Gods, 64-3150-Ivanhoe, 64-3169-The Man in the Iron Mask, 64-3177-The Prince and the Pauper, 64-3185-The Prisoner of Zenda, 64-3193-The Return of the Native, 64-3207-Robinson Crusoe, 64-3215-The Scarlet Pimpernel, 64-3223-The Sea Wolf, 64-3231-The Swiss Family Robinson, 64-3851-Billy Budd, 64-386x-Crime and Punishment, 64-3878-Don Quixote, 64-3886-Great Expectations, 64-3894-Heidi, 64-3908-The Iliad, 64-3916-Lord Jim, 64-3924-The Mutiny on Board H.M.S. Bounty, 64-3932-The Odyssey, 64-3940-Oliver Twist, 64-3959-Pride and Prejudice, 64-3967-The Turn of the Screw

	GD 2.0	VG 4.0	FN 6.0	VF 8.0	VF/NM 9.0	NM- 9.2
Softback						6.00
Hardback	1	2	3	5	6	8

NOTE: *All of the above books can be ordered from the publisher; some were reprinted as Marvel Classic Comics #1-12. In 1972 there was another brief series of 12 titles which contained Classics Ill. artwork. They were entitled* ***Now Age Books*** *Illustrated, but can be easily distinguished from later series by the small Classics Illustrated logo at the top of the front cover. The format is the same as the later series. The 48 pg. C.I. art was stretched out to make 62 pgs. After Twin Circle Publ. terminated the Classics Ill. series in 1971, they made a one year contract with Pendulum Press to print these twelve titles of C.I. art. Pendulum was unhappy with the contract, and at the end of 1972 began their own art series, utilizing the talents of the Filipino artist group. One detail which makes this rather confusing is that when they redid the art in 1973, they gave it the same identifying no. as the 1972 series. All 12 of the 1972 C.I. editions have new covers, taken from internal art panels. In spite of their recent age, all of the 1972 C.I. series are very rare. Mint copies would fetch at least $50. Here is a list of the 1972 series, with C.I. title no. counterpart:*

64-1005 (CI#60-A2) 64-1010 (CI#91) 64-1015 (CI-Jr #503) 64-1020 (CI#26)
64-1025 (CI#19-A2) 64-1030 (CI#5-A2) 64-1035 (CI#169) 64-1040 (CI#98)
64-1045 (CI#133) 64-1050 (CI#50-A2) 64-1055 (CI#47) 64-1060 (CI-Jr#535)

PENDULUM ILLUSTRATED ORIGINALS
Pendulum Press: 1979 (In color)

	GD 2.0	VG 4.0	FN 6.0	VF 8.0	VF/NM 9.0	NM- 9.2
94-4254-Solarman: The Beginning (See Solarman)						6.00

PENDULUM'S ILLUSTRATED STORIES
Pendulum Press: 1990 - No. 72, 1990? (No cover price ($4.95), squarebound, 68 pgs.)

	GD 2.0	VG 4.0	FN 6.0	VF 8.0	VF/NM 9.0	NM- 9.2
1-72: Reprints Pendulum Ill. Classics series						5.00

PENGUIN: PAIN & PREJUDICE (Batman)
DC Comics: Dec, 2011 - No. 5, Apr, 2012 ($2.99, limited series)

	GD 2.0	VG 4.0	FN 6.0	VF 8.0	VF/NM 9.0	NM- 9.2
1-5-Hurwitz-s/Kudranski-a/c; Penguin's childhood and rise to power						3.00

PENGUINS OF MADAGASCAR (Based on the DreamWorks movie and TV series)
Ape Entertainment: 2010 - No. 4, 2011 ($3.95, limited series)

	GD 2.0	VG 4.0	FN 6.0	VF 8.0	VF/NM 9.0	NM- 9.2
1-4-Skipper, Kowalski, Private and Rico app.						4.00

PENGUINS OF MADAGASCAR (Based on the DreamWorks movie and TV series)
Titan Comics: Dec, 2014 - No. 4, Mar, 2015 ($3.99, limited series)

	GD 2.0	VG 4.0	FN 6.0	VF 8.0	VF/NM 9.0	NM- 9.2
1-4-Skipper, Kowalski, Private and Rico app.						4.00

PENNY
Avon Comics: 1947 - No. 6, Sept-Oct, 1949 (Newspaper reprints)

	GD 2.0	VG 4.0	FN 6.0	VF 8.0	VF/NM 9.0	NM- 9.2
1-Photo & biography of creator	32	64	96	188	307	425
2-5	15	30	45	88	137	185
6-Perry Como photo on-c	16	32	48	92	144	195

PENNY CENTURY (See Love and Rockets)
Fantagraphics Books: Dec, 1997 - No. 7, Jul, 2000 ($2.95, B&W, mini-series)

	GD 2.0	VG 4.0	FN 6.0	VF 8.0	VF/NM 9.0	NM- 9.2
1-7-Jaime Hernandez-s/a						3.00

PENNY DORA AND THE WISHING BOX
Image Comics: Nov, 2014 - No. 5, Jun, 2015 ($2.99)

	GD 2.0	VG 4.0	FN 6.0	VF 8.0	VF/NM 9.0	NM- 9.2
1-5-Michael Stock-s/Sina Grace-a						3.00

PENNY DREADFUL (Based on the Showtime TV series)

Penny Dreadful V2 #1 © Showtime

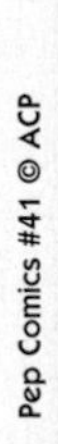
Pep Comics #41 © ACP

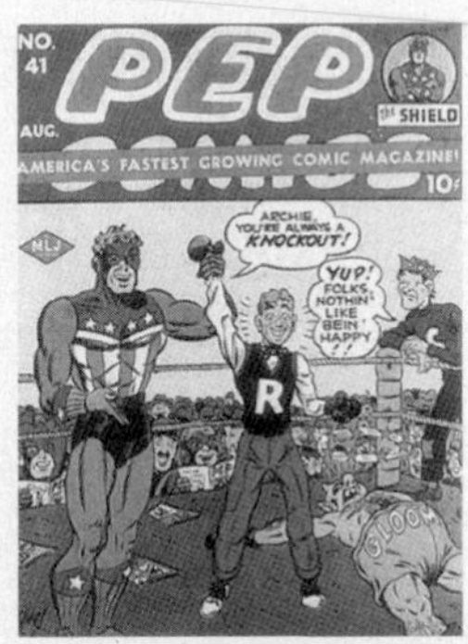

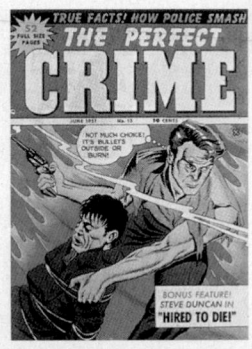

Perfect Crime #13 © Cross Pub.

	GD 2.0	VG 4.0	FN 6.0	VF 8.0	VF/NM 9.0	NM- 9.2

Titan Comics: Jun, 2016 - No. 5, Nov, 2016 ($3.99)

1-5: 1-Wilson-Cairns-s/De Martinis-a; multiple covers 4.00

PENNY DREADFUL (Volume 2) (Based on the Showtime TV series)
Titan Comics: May, 2017 - Present ($3.99)

1-($4.99)-Chris King-s/Jesús Hervás-a; multiple covers 5.00
2-8-($3.99) 4.00

PEP COMICS (See Archie Giant Series #576, 589, 601, 614, 624)
MLJ Magazines/Archie Publications No. 56 (3/46) on: Jan, 1940 - No. 411, Mar, 1987

1-Intro. The Shield (1st patriotic hero) by Irving Novick; origin & 1st app. The Comet by Jack Cole, The Queen of Diamonds & Kayo Ward; The Rocket, The Press Guardian (The Falcon #1 only), Sergeant Boyle, Fu Chang, & Bentley of of Scotland Yard; Robot-c; Shield-c begin
975 1950 2919 7100 12,550 18,000
2-Origin The Rocket 314 628 942 2198 3849 5500
3 252 504 756 1613 2757 3900
4-Wizard cameo; early robot-s 226 452 678 1446 2473 3500
5-Wizard cameo in Shield story 226 452 678 1446 2473 3500
6-10: 8-Last Cole Comet; no Cole-a in #6,7 181 362 543 1158 1979 2800
11-Dusty, Shield's sidekick begins (1st app.); last Press Guardian, Fu Chang
194 388 582 1242 2121 3000
12-Origin & 1st app. Fireball (2/41); last Rocket & Queen of Diamonds; Danny in Wonderland begins 213 426 639 1363 2332 3300
13-15: 15-Bondage-c 161 322 483 1030 1765 2500
16-Origin Madam Satan; blood drainage-c 252 504 756 1613 2757 3900
17-Origin/1st app. The Hangman (7/41); death of The Comet; Comet is revealed as Hangman's brother 514 1028 1542 3750 6625 9500
18,19,21: 19-WWII Nazi-c. 21-Last Madam Satan 161 322 483 1030 1765 2500
20-Classic Nazi swastika-c; last Fireball 343 686 1029 2400 4200 6000
22-Intro. & 1st app. Archie, Betty, & Jughead (12/41); (on sale 10/41)(also see Jackpot)
27,000 54,000 81,000 180,000 265,000 350,000
23-Statue of Liberty-c (1/42; on sale 11/41) 2275 4550 6825 13,650 19,325 25,000
24-Coach Kleats app. (unnamed until Archie #94); bondage/torture-c
757 1514 2271 5526 9763 14,000
25-1st app. Archie's jalopy; 1st skinny Mr. Weatherbee prototype
486 972 1458 3550 6275 9000
26-1st app. Veronica Lodge (4/42); "Remember Pearl Harbor!" cover caption
975 1950 2919 7100 12,550 18,000
27-Bill of Rights-c 400 800 1200 2800 4900 7000
28-Classic swastika/Hangman-c 383 766 1149 2681 4691 6700
29,30: 29-Origin Shield retold; 30-Capt. Commando begins; bondage/torture-c; 1st Miss Grundy (definitive version); see Jackpot #4 354 708 1062 2478 4339 6200
31-33,35: 31-MLJ offices & artists are visited in Sgt. Boyle story; 1st app. Mr. Lodge. 32-Shield dons new costume. 33-Pre-Moose tryout (see Jughead #1)
309 618 927 2163 3782 5400
34-Classic Bondage/Hypo-c 2275 4550 6825 13,650 19,325 25,000
36-1st full Archie-c in Pep (2/43) w/Shield & Hangman (see Jackpot #4 where Archie's face appears in a small circle) 1650 3300 4950 11,500 19,250 27,000
37-40 252 504 756 1613 2757 3900
41-Archie-c begin 314 628 942 2198 3849 5500
42-45 200 400 600 1280 2190 3100
46,47,49,50: 47-Last Hangman issue; infinity-c 174 348 522 1114 1907 2700
48-Black Hood begins (5/44); ends #51,59,60; Archie fish-c
219 438 657 1402 2401 3400
51-60: 52-Suzie begins; 1st Mr Weatherbee-c. 56-Last Capt. Commando. 59-Black Hood not in costume; lingerie panels; Archie dresses as his aunt; Suzie ends. 60-Katy Keene begins(3/47), ends #154 84 168 252 538 919 1300
61-65-Last Shield. 62-1st app. Li'l Jinx (7/47) 68 136 204 435 743 1050
66-80: 66-G-Man Club becomes Archie Club (2/48); Nevada Jones by Bill Woggon. 76-Katy Keene story. 78-1st app. Dilton 39 78 117 240 395 550
81-99 24 48 72 140 230 320
100 30 60 90 177 289 400
101-130 16 32 48 92 144 195
131(2/59)-137 7 14 21 44 82 120
138-140-Neal Adams-a (1 pg.) in each 7 14 21 46 86 125
141-149(9/61) 6 12 18 37 66 95
150-160-Super-heroes app. in each (see note). 150 (10/61?)-2nd or 3rd app. The Jaguar? 151-154,156-158-Horror/Sci/Fi-c. 157-Li'l Jinx. 159-Both 12¢ and 15¢ covers exist
8 16 24 52 99 145
161(3/63) 3rd Josie app.; early Josie stories w/DeCarlo-a begin (see Note for others)
5 10 15 35 63 90
162-167,169-180 4 8 12 28 47 65
168,200: 168-(1/64)-Jaguar app. 200-(12/66) 5 10 15 30 50 70
181(5/65)-199: 187-Pureheart try-out story. 192-UFO-c. 198-Giantman-c(only)
3 6 9 21 33 45
201-217,219-226,228-240(4/70): 224-(12/68) 1st app. Archie's pet, Hot Dog (later becomes Jughead's pet) 3 6 9 16 23 30
218,227-Archies Band-c only 3 6 9 17 26 35
241-270(10/72) 2 4 6 13 18 22
271-297,299 2 4 6 9 12 15
298, 300: 298-Josie and the Pussycats-c. 300(4/75) 2 4 6 13 18 22
301-340(8/78) 1 3 4 6 8 10
341-382 1 2 3 4 5 7
383(4/82),393(3/84): 383-Marvelous Maureen begins (Sci/fi). 393-Thunderbunny begins
1 2 3 5 6 8
384-392,394,395,397-399,401-410 5.00
396-Early Cheryl Blossom-c 2 4 6 9 12 15
400(5/85),411: 400-Story featuring Archie staff (DeCarlo-a)
1 2 3 4 5 7

NOTE: ***Biro** a-2, 4, 5. **Jack Cole** a-1-5, 8. **Al Fagaly** c-55-72. **Fuje** a-39, 45, 47; c-34. **Meskin** a-2, 4, 5, 11(2). **Montana** c-30, 32, 33, 36, 73-87(most). **Novick** c-1-28, 29(w/**Schomburg**), 31i. **Harry Sahle** c-35, 39-50. **Schomburg** c-38. **Bob Wood** a-2, 4-6, 11. The Fly app. in 151, 154, 160. Flygirl app. in 153, 155, 156, 158. Jaguar app. in 150, 152, 157, 159, 168. Josie by **DeCarlo** in 161-166, 168-171, 173, 175-177, 179, 181. Katy Keene by **Bill Woggon** in 73-126. Bondage c-7, 12, 13, 15, 18, 21, 31, 32. Cover features: Shield #1-16; Shield/Hangman #17-27, 29-41; Hangman #28. Archie #36, 41-on.*

PEP COMICS FEATURING BETTY AND VERONICA
Archie Comic Publications: May, 2011 (Giveaway)

Free Comic Book Day Edition - Little Archie flashback 3.00

PEPE
Dell Publishing Co.: No. 1194, Apr, 1961

Four Color 1194-Movie, photo-c 5 10 15 30 50 70

PERFECT CRIME, THE
Cross Publications: Oct, 1949 - No. 33, May, 1953 (#2-14, 52 pgs.)

1-Powell-a(2) 45 90 135 284 480 675
2 (4/50) 26 52 78 154 252 350
3-10: 7-Steve Duncan begins, ends #30. 10-Flag-c 22 44 66 132 216 300
11-Used in **SOTI**, pg. 159 25 50 75 147 241 335
12-14 21 42 63 124 202 280
15- "The Most Terrible Menace" 2 pg. drug editorial (8/51)
23 46 69 136 223 310
16,17,19-25,27-29,31-33 18 36 54 107 169 230
18-Drug cover, heroin drug propaganda story, plus 2 pg. anti-drug editorial (11/51)
40 80 120 246 411 575
26-Drug-c with hypodermic needle; drug propaganda story (7/52)
40 80 120 246 411 575
30-Strangulation cover (11/52) 39 78 117 240 395 550

NOTE: ***Powell** a-No. 1, 2, 4. **Wildey** a-1, 5. Bondage c-11.*

PERFECT LOVE
Ziff-Davis(Approved Comics)/St. John No. 9 on: #10, 8-9/51 (cover date; 5-6/51 indicia date); #2, 10-11/51 - #10, 12/53

10(#1)(8-9/51)-Painted-c 28 56 84 165 270 375
2(10-11/51) 19 38 57 109 172 235
3,5-7: 3-Painted-c. 5-Photo-c 15 30 45 90 140 190
4,8 (Fall, 1952)-Kinstler-a; last Z-D issue 15 30 45 90 140 190
9,10 (10/53, 12/53, St. John): 9-Painted-c. 10-Photo-c
15 30 45 86 133 180

PERHAPANAUTS, THE
Dark Horse Comics: Nov, 2005 - No. 4, Feb, 2006 ($2.99, limited series)

1-4-Todd Dezago-s/Craig Rousseau-a/c 3.00
... Annual #1 (2/08, $3.50) Two covers by Rousseau and Allred 3.50
...: Danger Down Under! 1-5 (11/12 - No. 5, 6/13, $3.50) Two covers on each 3.50
... Halloween Spooktacular 1 (10/09, $3.50) Hembeck, Rousseau and others-a 3.50
,,, - Molly's Story (2/10, $3.50) Copland-a 3.50
(2nd series) (4/08 - No. 6, $3.50) 1-6: 1-Two covers by Art Adams and Rousseau 3.50

PERHAPANAUTS: SECOND CHANCES, THE
Dark Horse Comics: Oct, 2006 - No. 4, Jan, 2007 ($2.99, limited series)

1-4-Todd Dezago-s/Craig Rousseau-a/c 3.00

PERRI (Disney)
Dell Publishing Co.: No. 847, Jan, 1958

Four Color 847-Movie, w/2 diff-c publ. 6 12 18 37 66 95

PERRY MASON
David McKay Publications: No. 49, 1946 - No. 50, 1946

Feature Books 49, 50-Based on Gardner novels 40 80 120 244 402 560

PERRY MASON MYSTERY MAGAZINE (TV)
Dell Publishing Co.: June-Aug, 1964 - No. 2, Oct-Dec, 1964

Personal Love #14 © FF

Peter Panda #9 © DC

Peter Parker: The Spectacular Spider-Man #1 © MAR

	GD 2.0	VG 4.0	FN 6.0	VF 8.0	VF/NM 9.0	NM- 9.2

1-Raymond Burr painted-c 7 14 21 46 86 125
2-Raymond Burr photo-c 5 10 15 34 60 85

PERSONAL LOVE (Also see Movie Love)
Famous Funnies: Jan, 1950 - No. 33, June, 1955

1-Photo-c 24 48 72 140 230 320
2-Kathryn Grayson & Mario Lanza photo-c 15 30 45 83 124 165
3-7,10: 7-Robert Walker & Joanne Dru photo-c. 10-Loretta Young & Joseph Cotton photo-c
14 28 42 80 115 150
8,9: 8-Esther Williams & Howard Keel photo-c. 9-Debra Paget & Louis Jourdan photo-c
14 28 42 81 118 155
11-Toth-a; Glenn Ford & Gene Tierney photo-c 15 30 45 86 133 180
12,16,17-One pg. Frazetta each. 17-Rock Hudson & Yvonne DeCarlo photo-c
14 28 42 81 118 155
13-15,18-23: 12-Jane Greer & William Lundigan photo-c. 14-Kirk Douglas photo-c. 15-Dale Robertson & Joanne Dru photo-c. 18-Gregory Peck & Susan Hayworth photo-c. 19-Anthony Quinn & Suzan Ball photo-c. 20-Robert Wagner & Kathleen Crowley photo-c. 21-Roberta Peters & Byron Palmer photo-c. 22-Dale Robertson photo-c. 23-Rhonda Fleming-c 14 28 42 76 108 140
24,27,28-Frazetta-a in each (8,8&6 pgs.). 27-Rhonda Fleming & Fernando Lamas photo-c. 28-Mitzi Gaynor photo-c 54 108 162 343 574 825
25-Frazetta-a (tribute to Bettie Page, 7 pg. story); Tyrone Power/Terry Moore photo-c from "King of the Khyber Rifles" 81 162 243 518 884 1250
26,29,30,33: 26-Constance Smith & Byron Palmer photo-c. 29-Charlton Heston & Nicol Morey photo-c. 30-Johnny Ray & Mitzi Gaynor photo-c. 33-Dana Andrews & Piper Laurie photo-c
14 28 42 76 108 140
31-Marlon Brando & Jean Simmons photo-c; last pre-code (2/55)
16 32 48 94 147 200
32-Classic Frazetta-a (8 pgs.); Kirk Douglas & Bella Darvi photo-c
77 154 231 493 847 1200

NOTE: *All have photo-c. Many feature movie stars.* ***Everett*** *a-5, 9, 10, 24.*

PERSONAL LOVE (Going Steady V3#3 on)
Prize Publ. (Headline): V1#1, Sept, 1957 - V3#2, Nov-Dec, 1959

V1#1 14 28 42 80 115 150
2 9 18 27 52 69 85
3-6(7-8/58) 8 16 24 44 57 70
V2#1(9-10/58)-V2#6(7-8/59) 8 16 24 40 50 60
V3#1-Wood?/Orlando-a 8 16 24 42 54 65
2 7 14 21 37 46 55

PESTILENCE
AfterShock Comics: May, 2017 - No. 6, Jan, 2018 ($3.99)

1-6-Tieri-s/Okunev-a/Bradstreet-c; Crusaders and zombies in the year 1347 4.00

PETER CANNON - THUNDERBOLT (See Crisis on Infinite Earths)(Also see Thunderbolt)
DC Comics: Sept, 1992 - No. 12, Aug, 1993 ($1.25)

1-12 3.00

PETER CANNON: THUNDERBOLT
Dynamite Entertainment: 2012 - No. 13, 2013 ($3.99)

1-10: 1-Darnell & Ross-s/Lau-a; back-up unpublished '80s Thunderbolt story; Pete Morisi-s/a. 1-3-Four covers on each. 4-7-Covers by Ross & Segovia 4.00

PETER COTTONTAIL
Key Publications: Jan, 1954; Feb, 1954 - No. 2, Mar, 1954 (Says 3/53 in error)

1(1/54)-Not 3-D 9 18 27 52 69 85
1(2/54)-(3-D, 25¢)-Came w/glasses; written by Bruce Hamilton
21 42 63 122 199 275
2-Reprints 3-D #1 but not in 3-D 6 12 18 31 38 45

PETER GUNN (TV)
Dell Publishing Co.: No. 1087, Apr-June, 1960

Four Color 1087-Photo-c 7 14 21 49 92 135

PETE ROSE: HIS INCREDIBLE BASEBALL CAREER
Masstar Creations Inc.: 1995

1-John Tartaglione-a 4.00

PETER PAN (Disney) (See Hook, Movie Classics & Comics, New Adventures of... & Walt Disney Showcase #36)
Dell Publishing Co.: No. 442, Dec, 1952 - No. 926, Aug, 1958

Four Color 442 (#1)-Movie 10 20 30 67 141 215
Four Color 926-Reprint of 442 5 10 15 34 60 85

PETER PAN
Disney Comics: 1991 ($5.95, graphic novel, 68 pgs.)(Celebrates video release)

nn-r/Peter Pan Treasure Chest from 1953 7.00

PETER PANDA
National Periodical Publications: Aug-Sept, 1953 - No. 31, Aug-Sept, 1958

1-Grossman-c/a in all 58 116 174 371 636 900
2 30 60 90 177 289 400
3,4,6-8,10 24 48 72 140 230 320
5-Classic-c (scarce) 100 200 300 635 1093 1550
9-Robot-c 37 74 111 222 361 500
11-31 18 36 54 103 162 220

PETER PAN RECORDS (See Power Records)

PETER PAN TREASURE CHEST (See Dell Giants)

PETER PANZERFAUST
Image Comics (Shadowline): Feb, 2012 - No. 25, Dec, 2016 ($3.50/$3.99)

1-Kurtis Wiebe-s/Tyler Jenkins-a/c; Peter Pan-type character in WWII Europe
5 10 15 31 53 75
1-Second printing 2 4 6 11 16 20
2 2 4 6 9 12 15
3 2 4 6 8 10 12
4-8 5.00
9-1st full app. Kapitan Haken 6.00
10-24 4.00
25-Last issue; bonus preview of Rat Queens v2 5.00

PETER PARKER (See The Spectacular Spider-Man)

PETER PARKER
Marvel Comics: May, 2010 - No. 5, Sept, 2010 ($3.99/$2.99)

1-($3.99) Prints material from Marvel Digital Comics; Olliffe-a; back-up w/Hembeck-s/a 4.00
2-5-($2.99): 2-4-Olliffe-a. 3-Braithwaite-c. 5-Nauck-a; Thing app. 3.00

PETER PARKER: SPIDER-MAN
Marvel Comics: Jan, 1999 - No. 57, Aug, 2003 ($2.99/$1.99/$2.25)

1-Mackie-s/Romita Jr.-a; wraparound-c 1 2 3 5 6 8
1-($6.95) DF Edition w/variant-c by the Romitas 2 4 6 8 10 12
2-11,13-17-($1.99): 2-Two covers; Thor app. 3-Iceman-c/app. 4-Marrow-c/app. 5-Spider-Woman app. 7,8-Blade app. 9,10-Venom app. 11-Iron Man & Thor-c/app. 3.00
12-($2.99) Sinister Six and Venom app. 4.00
18-24,26-43: 18-Begin $2.25-c. 20-Jenkins-s/Buckingham-a start. 23-Intro Typeface. 24-Maximum Security x-over. 29-Rescue of MJ. 30-Ramos-c. 42,43-Mahfood-a 3.00
25-($2.99) Two covers; Spider-Man & Green Goblin 4.00
44-47-Humberto Ramos-c/a; Green Goblin-c/app. 3.00
48,49,51-57: 48,49-Buckingham-c/a. 51,52-Herrera-a. 56,57-Kieth-a; Sandman returns 3.00
50-($3.50) Buckingham-c/a 4.00
#156.1 (10/12, $2.99, 50th Anniversary one-shot) Stern-s/De La Torre-a/Romita Jr.-c 3.00
...'99 Annual (8/99, $3.50) Man-Thing app. 4.00
...'00 Annual ($3.50) Bounty app.; Joe Bennett-a; Black Cat back-up story 4.00
...'01 Annual ($2.99) Avery-s 4.00
...: A Day in the Life TPB (5/01, $14.95) r/#20-22,26; Webspinners #10-12 15.00
...: One Small Break TPB (2002, $16.95) r/#27,28,30-34; Andrews-c 17.00
Spider-Man: Return of the Goblin TPB (2002, $8.99) r/#44-47; Ramos-c 9.00
...Vol. 4: Trials & Tribulations TPB (2003, $11.99) r/#35,37,48-50; Cho-c 12.00

PETER PARKER: THE SPECTACULAR SPIDER-MAN
Marvel Comics: Aug, 2017 - No. 6, Jan, 2018; No. 297, Feb, 2018 - Present ($4.99/$3.99)

1-($4.99) Zdarsky-s/Adam Kubert-a; Johnny Storm app.; back-up w/Black Widow app. 5.00
2-6-($3.99) 3,4-Kingpin app. 6-Walsh-a 4.00
[Title switches to legacy numbering after #6 (1/18)]
297-299-Kubert-a. 298,299-Black Panther app. 4.00
300-($5.99) Black Panther, Human Torch, Ironheart app.; bonus cover gallery 6.00

PETER PAT
United Features Syndicate: No. 8, 1939

Single Series 8 36 72 108 216 351 485

PETER PAUL'S 4 IN 1 JUMBO COMIC BOOK
Capitol Stories (Charlton): No date (1953)

1-Contains 4 comics bound; Space Adventures, Space Western, Crime & Justice, Racket Squad in Action 42 84 126 265 445 625

PETER PIG
Standard Comics: No. 5, May, 1953 - No. 6, Aug, 1953

5,6 7 14 21 35 43 50

PETER PORKCHOPS (See Leading Comics #23) (Also see Capt. Carrot)
National Periodical Publications: 11-12/49 - No. 61, 9-11/59; No. 62, 10-12/60 (1-11: 52 pgs.)

1 34 68 102 199 325 450
2 15 30 45 90 140 190

Peter Rabbit #4 © AVON

The Phantom #7 © KFS

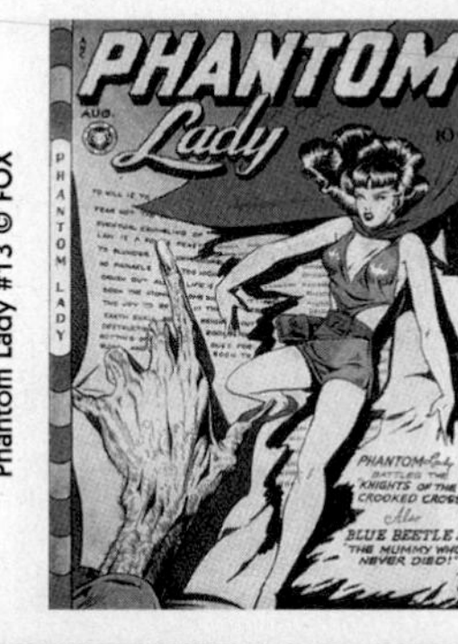

Phantom Lady #13 © FOX

GD VG FN VF VF/NM NM-
2.0 4.0 6.0 8.0 9.0 9.2

3-10: 6- "Peter Rockets to Mars!" c/story 13 26 39 74 105 135
11-30 10 20 30 56 76 95
31-62 9 18 27 47 61 75
NOTE: *Otto Feuer a-all. Rube Grossman-a most issues. Sheldon Mayer a-30-38, 40-44, 46-52, 61.*

PETER PORKER, THE SPECTACULAR SPIDER-HAM
Star Comics (Marvel): May, 1985 - No. 17, Sept, 1987 (Also see Marvel Tails)
1-Michael Golden-c 5.00
2-17: 12-Origin/1st app. Bizarro Phil. 13-Halloween issue 4.00
NOTE: *Back-up features: 2-X-Bugs. 3-Iron Mouse. 4-Croctor Strange. 5-Thrr, Dog of Thunder.*

PETER POTAMUS (TV)
Gold Key: Jan, 1965 (Hanna-Barbera)
1-1st app. Peter Potamus & So-So, Breezly & Sneezly
9 18 27 58 114 170

PETER RABBIT (See New Funnies #65 & Space Comics)
Dell Publishing Co.: No. 1, 1942
Large Feature Comic 1 76 152 228 486 831 1175

PETER RABBIT (Adventures of...; New Advs. of... #9 on)(Also see Funny Tunes & Space Comics)
Avon Periodicals: 1947 - No. 34, Aug-Sept, 1956
1(1947)-Reprints 1943-44 Sunday strips; contains a biography & drawing of Cady
37 74 111 222 361 500
2 (4/48) 24 48 72 144 237 330
3 ('48) - 6(7/49)-Last Cady issue 21 42 63 126 206 285
7-10(1950-8/51): 9-New logo 11 22 33 64 90 115
11(11/51)-34('56)-Avon's character 10 20 30 54 72 90
...Easter Parade (1952, 25¢, 132 pgs.) 21 42 63 124 202 280
...Jumbo Book (1954-Giant Size, 25¢)-Jesse James by Kinstler (6 pgs.);
space ship-c 25 50 75 150 245 340

PETER RABBIT 3-D
Eternity Comics: April, 1990 ($2.95, with glasses; sealed in plastic bag)
1-By Harrison Cady (reprints) 3.00

PETER, THE LITTLE PEST (#4 titled Petey)
Marvel Comics Group: Nov, 1969 - No. 4, May, 1970
1 6 12 18 42 79 115
2-4-r-Dexter the Demon & Melvin the Monster 5 10 15 30 50 70

PETE'S DRAGON (See Walt Disney Showcase #43)

PETE THE PANIC
Stanmor Publications: November, 1955
nn-Code approved 8 16 24 40 50 60

PETEY (See Peter, the Little Pest)

PETTICOAT JUNCTION (TV, inspired Green Acres)
Dell Publ. Co.: Oct-Dec, 1964 - No. 5, Oct-Dec, 1965 (#1-3, 5 have photo-c)
1 6 12 18 40 73 105
2-5 5 10 15 30 50 70

PETUNIA (Also see Looney Tunes and Porky Pig)
Dell Publishing Co.: No. 463, Apr, 1953
Four Color 463 5 10 15 33 57 80

PHAGE (See Neil Gaiman's Teknophage & Neil Gaiman's Phage-Shadowdeath)

PHANTACEA
McPherson Publishing Co.: Sept, 1977 - No. 6, Summer, 1980 (B&W)
1-Early Dave Sim-a (32 pgs.) 4 8 12 28 47 65
2-Dave Sim-a(10 pgs.) 3 6 9 14 19 24
3-6: 3-Flip-c w/Damnation Bridge. 4-Gene Day-a 2 4 6 10 14 18

PHANTASMO (See The Funnies #45)
Dell Publishing Co.: No. 18, 1941
Large Feature Comic 18 41 82 123 256 428 600

PHANTOM, THE
David McKay Publishing Co.: 1939 - 1949
Feature Books 20 161 322 483 1030 1765 2500
Feature Books 22 87 174 261 553 952 1350
Feature Books 39 66 132 198 419 722 1025
Feature Books 53,56,57 52 104 156 328 552 775

PHANTOM, THE (See Ace Comics, Defenders Of The Earth, Eat Right to Work and Win, Future Comics, Harvey Comics Hits #51,56, Harvey Hits #1, 6, 12, 15, 26, 36, 44, 48, & King Comics)

PHANTOM, THE (nn (#29)-Published overseas only) (Also see Comics Reading Libraries in the Promotional Comics section)
Gold Key(#1-17)/King(#18-28)/Charlton(#30 on): Nov, 1962 - No. 17, Jul, 1966; No. 18, Sept, 1966 - No. 28, Dec, 1967; No. 30, Feb, 1969 - No. 74, Jan, 1977
1-Origin revealed on inside-c & back-c 22 44 66 154 340 525
2-King, Queen & Jack begins, ends #11 10 20 30 67 141 215
3-5 8 16 24 56 108 160
6-10 7 14 21 44 82 120
11-17: 12-Track Hunter begins 6 12 18 37 66 95
18-Flash Gordon begins; Wood-a 5 10 15 30 50 70
19-24: 20-Flash Gordon ends (both by Gil Kane). 21-Mandrake begins. 20,24-
Girl Phantom app. 4 8 12 27 44 60
25-28: 25-Jeff Jones-a(4 pgs.); 1 pg. Williamson ad. 26-Brick Bradford app.
28-Brick Bradford app. 3 6 9 21 33 45
30-33: 33-Last 12¢ issue 3 6 9 16 24 32
34-40: 36,39-Ditko-a 3 6 9 16 23 30
41-66,72: 46-Intro. The Piranha. 51-Grey tone-c. 62-Bolle-c
3 6 9 14 19 24
67-Origin retold; Newton-c/a; Humphrey Bogart, Lauren Bacall & Peter Lorre app.
3 6 9 16 24 32
68,70,71,73-Newton-c/a 2 4 6 13 18 22
69-Newton-c only 2 4 6 13 18 22
74-Classic flag-c by Newton; Newton-a; 3 6 9 16 23 30
NOTE: *Aparo a-31-34, 36-38; c-31-38, 60, 61. Painted c-1-17.*

PHANTOM, THE
DC Comics: May, 1988 - No. 4, Aug, 1988 ($1.25, mini-series)
1-4: Orlando-c/a in all 4.00

PHANTOM, THE
DC Comics: Mar, 1989 - No. 13, Mar, 1990 ($1.50)
1-13: 1-Brief origin 4.00

PHANTOM, THE
Wolf Publishing: 1992 - No. 8, 1993 ($2.25)
1-8 3.00

PHANTOM, THE
Moonstone: 2003 - No. 26, Dec, 2008 ($3.50/$3.99)
1-26: 1-Cassaday-c/Raab-s/Quinn-a 4.00
... Annual #1 (2007, $6.50) Blevins-c; stroy and art by various incl. Nolan 6.50
... - Captain Action 1 (2010, $3.99) covers by Thibert, Sparacio, and Gilbert 4.00

PHANTOM, THE
Hermes Press: 2014 - Present ($3.99)
1-4: 1-Peter David-s/Sal Velluto-a; four covers 4.00

PHANTOM BLOT, THE (#1 titled New Adventures of...)
Gold Key: Oct, 1964 - No. 7, Nov, 1966 (Disney)
1 (Meets The Mysterious Mr. X) 6 12 18 38 69 100
2-1st Super Goof 5 10 15 33 57 80
3-7 3 6 9 21 33 45

PHANTOM EAGLE (See Mighty Midget, Marvel Super Heroes #16 & Wow #6)

PHANTOM FORCE
Image Comics/Genesis West #0, 3-7: 12/93 - #2, 1994; #0, 3/94; #3, 5/94 - #8, 10/94 ($2.50/$3.50, limited series)
0 (3/94, $2.50)-Kirby/Jim Lee-c; Kirby-p pgs. 1,5,24-29. 4.00
1 (12/93, $2.50)-Polybagged w/trading card; Kirby/Liefeld-c; Kirby plots/pencils w/inks by Liefeld, McFarlane, Jim Lee, Silvestri, Larsen, Williams, Ordway & Miki 4.00
2 ($3.50)-Kirby-a(p); Kirby/Larson-c 5.00
3-8: 3-(5/94, $2.50)-Kirby/McFarlane-c 4-(5/94)-Kirby-c(p). 5-(6/94) 4.00

PHANTOM GUARD
Image Comics (WildStorm Productions): Oct, 1997 - No. 6, Mar, 1998 ($2.50)
1-6: 1-Two covers 3.00
1-($3.50)-Voyager Pack w/Wildcore preview 4.00

PHANTOM JACK
Image Comics: Mar, 2004 - No. 5, July, 2004 ($2.95)
1-5-Mike San Giacomo-s/Mitchell Breitweiser-a. 4-Initial printings with errors exist 3.00
The Collected Edition (Speakeasy Comics, 2005, $17.99) r/series; Bendis intro 18.00

PHANTOM LADY (1st Series) (My Love Secret #24 on) (Also see All Top, Daring Adventures, Freedom Fighters, Jungle Thrills, & Wonder Boy)
Fox Feature Syndicate: No. 13, Aug, 1947 - No. 23, Apr, 1949
13(#1)-Phantom Lady by Matt Baker begins (see Police Comics #1 for 1st app.); Blue Beetle
story 486 972 1458 3550 6275 9000

Phantom Stranger #3 © DC

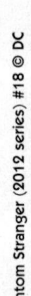

Phantom Stranger (2012 series) #18 © DC

Phoenix Resurrection: The Return of Jean Grey #2 © MAR

GD VG FN VF VF/NM NM-
2.0 4.0 6.0 8.0 9.0 9.2

14-16: 14(#2)-Not Baker-c. 15-P.L. injected with experimental drug. 16-Negligee-c, panels; true crime stories begin 300 600 900 1980 3440 4900
17-Classic bondage cover; used in **SOTI**, illo "Sexual stimulation by combining 'headlights' with the sadist's dream of tying up a woman" 1450 2900 4350 11,000 20,500 30,000
18,19 271 542 813 1734 2967 4200
20-22 232 464 696 1485 2543 3600
23-Classic bondage-c 568 1136 1704 4146 7323 10,500
NOTE: ***Matt Baker** a-in all; c-13, 15-21. **Kamen** a-22, 23.*

PHANTOM LADY (2nd Series) (See Terrific Comics) (Formerly Linda)
Ajax/Farrell Publ.: V1#5, Dec-Jan, 1954/1955 - No. 4, June, 1955
V1#5(#1)-By Matt Baker 161 322 483 1030 1765 2500
V1#2-Last pre-code 110 220 330 704 1202 1700
3,4-Red Rocket. 3-Heroin story 90 180 270 576 988 1400

PHANTOM LADY
Verotik Publications: 1994 ($9.95)
1-Reprints G. A. stories from Phantom Lady and All Top Comics; Adam Hughes-c 12.00

PHANTOM LADY
DC Comics: Oct, 2012 - No. 4, Jan, 2013 ($2.99, limited series)
1-4-Gray and Palmiotti-s/Staggs-a. 1-Re-intro with Doll Man; Conner-c 3.00

PHANTOM PLANET, THE
Dell Publishing Co.: No. 1234, 1961
Four Color 1234-Movie 7 14 21 44 82 120

PHANTOM STRANGER, THE (1st Series)(See Saga of Swamp Thing)
National Periodical Publications: Aug-Sept, 1952 - No. 6, June-July, 1953
1(Scarce)-1st app. 400 800 1200 2800 4900 7000
2 (Scarce) 245 490 735 1568 2684 3800
3-6 (Scarce) 239 478 717 1530 2615 3700
Ashcan (8,9/52) Not distributed to newsstands, only for in house use (no known sales)

PHANTOM STRANGER, THE (2nd Series) (See Showcase #80) (See Showcase Presents for B&W reprints)
National Periodical Publs.: May-June, 1969 - No. 41, Feb-Mar, 1976; No. 42, Mar, 2010
1-2nd S.A. app. P. Stranger; only 12¢ issue 11 22 33 73 157 240
2,3 6 12 18 38 69 100
4-1st new look Phantom Stranger; N. Adams-a 6 12 18 41 76 110
5-7 5 10 15 31 53 75
8-14: 14-Last 15¢ issue 4 8 12 23 37 50
15-19: All 25¢ giants (52 pgs.) 4 8 12 25 40 55
20-Dark Circle begins, ends #24. 3 6 9 16 24 32
21,22 3 6 9 14 20 25
23-Spawn of Frankenstein begins by Kaluta 4 8 12 25 40 55
24,25,27-30-Last Spawn of Frankenstein 3 6 9 19 30 40
26- Book-length story featuring Phantom Stranger, Dr. 13 & Spawn of Frankenstein 3 6 9 21 33 45
31-The Black Orchid begins (6-7/74). 3 6 9 18 28 38
32,34-38: 34-Last 20¢ issue (#35 on are 25¢) 2 4 6 13 18 22
33,39-41: 33-Deadman-c/story. 39-41-Deadman app. 3 6 9 14 20 25
42-(3/10, $2.99) Blackest Night one-shot; Syaf-a; Spectre, Deadman and Blue Devil app. 3.00
NOTE: ***N. Adams** a-4; c-3-19. **Anderson** a-4, 5i. **Aparo** a-7-17, 19-26; c-20-24, 33-41. **B. Bailey** a-27-30. **DeZuniga** a-12-16, 18, 19, 21, 22, 31, 34. **Grell** a-33. **Kaluta** a-23-25; c-26. **Meskin** r-15, 16, 18, 19. **Redondo** a-32, 35, 36. **Sparling** a-20. **Starr** a-17r. **Toth** a-15r. Black Orchid by **Carrilo**-38-41. Dr. 13 solo in-13, 18, 19, 20, 21, 34. Frankenstein by **Kaluta**-23-25; by **Baily**-27-30. No Black Orchid-33, 34, 37.*

PHANTOM STRANGER (See Justice League of America #103)
DC Comics: Oct, 1987 - No. 4, Jan, 1988 (75¢, limited series)
1-4-Mignola/Russell-c/a & Eclipso app. in all. 3,4-Eclipso-c 5.00

PHANTOM STRANGER (See intro. in DC Comics - The New 52 FCBD Special Edition) (Title changes to Trinity of Sin: The Phantom Stranger with #9 (Aug, 2013))
DC Comics: No. 0, Nov, 2012 - No. 22, Oct, 2015 ($2.99)
0-22: 0-Origin retold; Spectre app.; DiDio-s/Anderson-a. 2-Pandora app. 4,5-Jae Lee-c; Justice League Dark app. 6,7-Gene Ha-a/c; The Question app. 11-Trinity War. 12-17-Forever Evil tie-in. 18-Superman app. 20-The Spectre app. 3.00
...: Future's End (11/14, $3.99) 3-D lenticular cover; five years later; Winslade-a 4.00
...: Future's End (11/14, $2.99) regular cover; five years later 3.00

PHANTOM STRANGER (See Vertigo Visions-The Phantom Stranger)

PHANTOM: THE GHOST WHO WALKS
Marvel Comics: Feb, 1995 - No. 3, Apr, 1995 ($2.95, limited series)
1-3 4.00

PHANTOM: THE GHOST WHO WALKS
Moonstone: 2003 ($16.95, TPB)
nn-Three new stories by Raab, Goulart, Collins, Blanco and others; Klauba painted-c 17.00

PHANTOM 2040 (TV cartoon)
Marvel Comics: May, 1995 - No. 4, Aug, 1995 ($1.50)
1-4-Based on animated series; Ditko-a(p) in all 4.00

PHANTOM WITCH DOCTOR (Also see Durango Kid #8 & Eerie #8)
Avon Periodicals: 1952
1-Kinstler-c/a (7 pgs.) 77 154 231 493 847 1200

PHANTOM ZONE, THE (See Adventure #283 & Superboy #100, 104)
DC Comics: January, 1982 - No. 4, April, 1982
1-4-Superman app. in all. 2-4: Batman, Green Lantern, Supergirl, Wonder Woman app. 4.00
NOTE: ***Colan** a-1-4p; c-1-4p. **Giordano** c-1-4i.*

PHAZE
Eclipse Comics: Apr, 1988 - No. 2, Oct, 1988 ($2.25)
1,2: 1-Sienkiewicz-c. 2-Gulacy painted-c 3.00

PHIL RIZZUTO (Baseball Hero)(See Sport Thrills, Accepted reprint)
Fawcett Publications: 1951 (New York Yankees)
nn-Photo-c 71 142 213 454 777 1100

PHOENIX
Atlas/Seaboard Publ.: Jan, 1975 - No. 4, Oct, 1975
1-Origin; Rovin-s/Amendola-a 2 4 6 11 16 20
2-4: 3-Origin & only app. The Dark Avenger. 4-New origin/costume The Protector (formerly Phoenix) 2 4 6 9 13 16
NOTE: ***Infantino** appears in #1, 2. **Austin** a-3i. **Thorne** c-3.*

PHOENIX
Ardden Entertainment (Atlas Comics): Mar, 2011 - No. 6, May, 2012 ($2.99)
1-6-Krueger & Deneen-s/Zachary-a; origin re-told 3.00
... Issue Zero - NY Comicon Edtion (10/10, $2.99) Dorien-a; origin prequel to #1 3.00

PHOENIX (...The Untold Story)
Marvel Comics Group: April, 1984 ($2.00, one-shot)
1-Byrne/Austin-r/X-Men #137 with original unpublished ending 2 4 6 8 10 12

PHOENIX RESURRECTION, THE
Malibu Comics (Ultraverse): 1995 - 1996 ($3.95)
Genesis #1 (12/95)-X-Men app; wraparound-c, Revelations #1 (12/95)-X-Men app; wraparound-c, Aftermath #1 (1/96)-X-Men app. 5.00
0-($1.95)-r/series 3.00
0-American Entertainment Ed. 4.00

PHOENIX RESURRECTION: THE RETURN OF JEAN GREY
Marvel Comics: Feb, 2018 - No. 5 ($4.99/$3.99, limited series)
1,5-($4.99) Yu-a. 5-Leads into Jean Grey #11 and X-Men Red #1 5.00
2-4-($3.99) 2-Pacheco-a. 3-Bennett-a. 4-Rosanas-a 4.00

PHOENIX WITHOUT ASHES
IDW Publishing: Aug, 2010 - No. 4, Nov, 2010 ($3.99, limited series)
1-4-Harlan Ellison-s/Alan Robinson-a 4.00

PHONOGRAM
Image Comics: Aug, 2006 - No. 6, May, 2007 ($3.50, limited series)
1-Gillen-s/McKelvie-a 15.00
2-6 5.00

PHONOGRAM: THE SINGLES CLUB (Volume 2)
Image Comics: Dec, 2008 - No. 7, Feb, 2010 ($3.50, limited series)
1-7-Gillen-s/McKelvie-a. 5-Recalled for bar-code error 4.00

PHONOGRAM (Volume 3)(The Immaterial Girl)
Image Comics: Aug, 2015 - No. 6, Jan, 2016 ($3.99, limited series)
1-6-Gillen-s/McKelvie-a 4.00

PICNIC PARTY (See Dell Giants)

PICTORIAL CONFESSIONS (Pictorial Romances #4 on)
St. John Publishing Co.: Sept, 1949 - No. 3, Dec, 1949
1-Baker-c/a(3) 65 130 195 416 708 1000
2-Baker-a; photo-c 39 78 117 231 378 525
3-Kubert, Baker-a; part Kubert-c 40 80 120 246 411 575

PICTORIAL LOVE STORIES (Formerly Tim McCoy)
Charlton Comics: No. 22, Oct, 1949 - No. 26, July, 1950 (all photo-c)
22-26: All have "Me-Dan Cupid". 25-Fred Astaire-c 21 42 63 122 199 275

Pictorial Romances #9 © STJ

Picture News #8 © 299 LSC

Pigs #3 © Cosby & McCool

GD 2.0 | VG 4.0 | FN 6.0 | VF 8.0 | VF/NM 9.0 | NM- 9.2

PICTORIAL LOVE STORIES
St. John Publishing Co.: October, 1952

1-Baker-c 42 84 126 265 445 625

PICTORIAL ROMANCES (Formerly Pictorial Confessions)
St. John Publ. Co.: No. 4, Jan, 1950; No. 5, Jan, 1951 - No. 24, Mar, 1954

4-Baker-a; photo-c 47 94 141 296 498 700
5,10-All Matt Baker issues. 5-Reprints all stories from #4 w/new Baker-c
52 104 156 328 552 775
6-9,12,13,15,16-Baker-c, 2-3 stories 50 100 150 315 533 750
11-Baker-c/a(3); Kubert-r/Hollywood Confessions #1
52 104 156 328 552 775
14,21-24: Baker-c/a each. 21,24-Each has signed story by Estrada
54 108 162 343 574 825
17-20(7/53, 25¢, 100 pgs.): Baker-c/a; each has two signed stories by Estrada
100 200 300 635 1093 1550

NOTE: ***Matt Baker** art in most issues. **Estrada** a-17-20(2), 21, 24.*

PICTURE CRIMES
David McKay Publ.: June, 1937

1-Story in photo panels (a GD+ copy sold in 2012 for $478 and a certified 5.5 copy sold for $2051 in 2017)

PICTURE NEWS
Lafayette Street Corp.: Jan, 1946 - No. 10, Jan-Feb, 1947

1-Milt Gross begins, ends No. 6; 4 pg. Kirby-a; A-Bomb-c/story
48 96 144 302 514 725
2-Atomic explosion panels; Frank Sinatra/Perry Como story
25 50 75 150 245 340
3-Atomic explosion panels; Frank Sinatra, June Allyson, Benny Goodman stories 22 44 66 132 216 300
4-Atomic explosion panels; "Caesar and Cleopatra" movie adapt. w/Claude Raines & Vivian Leigh; Jackie Robinson story 25 50 75 147 241 335
5-7: 5-Hank Greenberg story; Atomic explosion panel. 6-Joe Louis-c/story
20 40 60 114 182 250
8,10: 8-Monte Hale story (9-10/46; 1st?). 10-Dick Quick; A-Bomb story; Krigstein, Gross-a
20 40 60 117 189 260
9-A-Bomb story; "Crooked Mile" movie adaptation; Joe DiMaggio story.
22 44 66 128 209 290

PICTURE PARADE (Picture Progress #5 on)
Gilberton Company (Also see A Christmas Adventure): Sept, 1953 - V1#4, Dec, 1953 (28 pgs.)

V1#1-Andy's Atomic Adventures; A-bomb blast-c; (Teachers version distributed to schools exists) 20 40 60 117 189 260
2-Around the World with the United Nations 12 24 36 69 97 125
3-Adventures of the Lost One(The American Indian), 4-A Christmas Adventure (r-under same title in 1969) 12 24 36 69 97 125

PICTURE PROGRESS (Formerly Picture Parade)
Gilberton Corp.: V1#5, Jan, 1954 - V3#2, Oct, 1955 (28-36 pgs.)

V1#5-9,V2#1-9: 5-News in Review 1953. 6-The Birth of America. 7-The Four Seasons. 8-Paul Revere's Ride. 9-The Hawaiian Islands(5/54). V2#1-The Story of Flight(9/54). 2-Vote for Crazy River (The Meaning of Elections). 3-Louis Pasteur. 4-The Star Spangled Banner. 5-News in Review 1954. 6-Alaska: The Great Land. 7-Life in the Circus. 8-The Time of the Cave Man. 9-Summer Fun(5/55)
9 18 27 50 65 80
V3#1,2: 1-The Man Who Discovered America. 2-The Lewis & Clark Expedition
9 18 27 47 61 75

PICTURE SCOPE JUNGLE ADVENTURES (See Jungle Thrills)

PICTURE STORIES FROM AMERICAN HISTORY
National/All-American/E. C. Comics: 1945 - No. 4, Sum, 1947 (#1,2: 10¢, 56 pgs.; #3,4: 15¢, 52 pgs.)

1 30 60 90 177 289 400
2-4 24 48 72 140 230 320

PICTURE STORIES FROM SCIENCE
E.C. Comics: Spring, 1947 - No. 2, Fall, 1947

1-(15¢) 30 60 90 177 289 400
2-(10¢) 24 48 72 140 230 320

PICTURE STORIES FROM THE BIBLE (See Narrative Illustration, the Story of the Comics by M.C. Gaines)
National/All-American/E.C. Comics: 1942 - No. 4, Fall, 1943; 1944-46

1-4('42-Fall, '43)-Old Testament (DC) 24 48 72 142 234 325
Complete Old Testament Edition, (12/43-DC, 50¢, 232 pgs.);-1st printing; contains #1-4; 2nd - 8th (1/47) printings exist; later printings by E.C. some with 65¢-c
32 64 96 192 314 435
Complete Old Testament Edition (1945-publ. by Bible Pictures Ltd.)-232 pgs., hardbound, in color with dust jacket 32 64 96 192 314 435

NOTE: *Both Old and New Testaments published in England by Bible Pictures Ltd. in hardback, 1943, in color, 376 pgs. (2 vols.: O.T. 232 pgs. & N.T. 144 pgs.), and were also published by Scarf Press in 1979 (Old Test., $9.95) and in 1980 (New Test., $7.95)*

1-3(New Test.; 1944-46, DC)-52 pgs. ea. 20 40 60 114 182 250
The Complete Life of Christ Edition (1945, 25¢, 96 pgs.)-Contains #1&2 of the New Testament Edition 32 64 96 192 314 435
1,2(Old Testament-r in comic book form)(E.C., 1946; 52 pgs.)
20 40 60 114 182 250
1(DC),2(AA),3(EC)(New Testament-r in comic book form)(E.C., 1946; 52 pgs.)
20 40 60 114 182 250
Complete New Testament Edition (1945-E.C., 40¢, 144 pgs.)-Contains #1-3
1946 printing has 50¢-c 32 64 96 192 314 435

NOTE: *Another British series entitled **The Bible Illustrated** from 1947 has recently been discovered, with the same internal artwork. This eight edition series (5-OT, 3-NT) is of particular interest to Classics Ill. collectors because it exactly copied the C.I. logo format. The British publisher was Thorpe & Porter, who in 1951 began publishing the British Classics Ill. series. All editions of The Bible Ill. have new British painted covers. While this market is still new, and not all editions have as yet been found, current market value is about the same as the first U.S. editions of Picture Stories From The Bible.*

PICTURE STORIES FROM WORLD HISTORY
E.C. Comics: Spring, 1947 - No. 2, Summer, 1947 (52, 48 pgs.)

1-(15¢) 30 60 90 177 289 400
2-(10¢) 24 48 72 140 230 320

PIGS
Image Comics: Sept, 2011 - No. 8, Aug, 2012 ($2.99)

1-8: 1-Cosby & McCool-s/Tamura-a/Jock-c. 3-Conner-c. 5-Gibbons-c. 7-Ramos-c 3.00

PILGRIM, THE
IDW Publishing: Apr, 2010 - No. 2, Jun, 2010 ($3.99, limited series)

1,2-Mike Grell-a/c; Mark Ryan-s 4.00

PILOT SEASON...
Image Comics (Top Cow): 2008 - 2011 ($1.00/$2.99/$3.99, one-shots)

...: Asset (9/10, $3.99) Sablik-s/Marquez-a/Frison-c 4.00
...: City of Refuge (10/11, $3.99) Foehl-s/Calero-a/c 4.00
...: Crosshair (10/10, $3.99) Katz-s/Jefferson-a/Silvestri-c 4.00
...: Declassified (10/09, $1.00) Preview of one-shots with covers, script and sketch pgs. 3.00
...: Demonic (1/10, $2.99) Kirkman-s/Benitez-a; two covers by Silvestri 3.00
...: Fleshdigger (10/11, $3.99) Denton & Keene-s; Sanchez-a; Francavilla-c 4.00
...: Forever (10/10, $3.99) Inglesby-s/Nachlik-a/Hutomo-c 4.00
...: Murdered (11/09, $2.99) Kirkman-s/Blake-a; two covers by Silvestri 3.00
...: 7 Days From Hell (10/10, $3.99) Noto-a/Hill & Levin-s/Stelfreeze-c 4.00
...: Stellar (7/10, $2.99) Kirkman-s/Chang-a/Silvestri-c 3.00
...: The Beauty (10/11, $3.99) Haun & Hurley-s/Haun-a/c (becomes a 2015 series) 10.00
...: The Test (10/10, $3.99) Fialkov-s/Ekedal-a/Hutomo-c 4.00
...: 39 Minutes (9/10, $3.99) Harms-s/Lando-a/Albuquerque-c 4.00
...: Twilight Guardian (5/08, $3.99) Hickman-s 4.00

PINHEAD
Marvel Comics (Epic Comics): Dec, 1993 - No. 6, May, 1994 ($2.50)

1-($2.95)-Embossed foil-c by Kelley Jones; Intro Pinhead & Disciples (Snakeoil, Hangman, Fan Dancer & Dixie) 4.00
2-6 3.00

PINHEAD & FOODINI (TV)(Also see Foodini & Jingle Dingle Christmas...)
Fawcett Publications: July, 1951 - No. 4, Jan, 1952 (Early TV comic)

1-(52 pgs.)-Photo-c; based on TV puppet show 32 64 96 188 307 425
2,3-Photo-c 16 32 48 94 147 200
4 14 28 42 80 115 150

PINHEAD VS. MARSHALL LAW (Law in Hell)
Marvel Comics (Epic): Nov, 1993 - No. 2, Dec, 1993 ($2.95, lim. series)

1,2: 1-Embossed red foil-c. 2-Embossed silver foil-c 4.00

PINK DUST
Kitchen Sink Press: 1998 ($3.50, B&W, mature)

1-J. O'Barr-s/a 3.50

PINK PANTHER, THE (TV)(See The Inspector & Kite Fun Book)
Gold Key #1-70/Whitman #71-87: April, 1971 - No. 87, Mar, 1984

1-The Inspector begins 5 10 15 35 63 90
2-5 3 6 9 17 26 35
6-10 3 6 9 14 19 24
11-30: Warren Tufts-a #16-on 2 4 6 9 13 16

Pink Panther #44 © GK

Pioneer West Romances #5 © FH

Pitt #6 © Dale Keown

	GD 2.0	VG 4.0	FN 6.0	VF 8.0	VF/NM 9.0	NM- 9.2
31-60	2	4	6	8	11	14
61-70	1	2	3	5	7	9
71-74,81-83: 81(2/82), 82(3/82), 83(4/82)	2	4	6	8	10	12
75(8/80)-77 (Whitman pre-pack) (scarce)	4	8	12	27	44	60
78(1/81)-80 (Whitman pre-pack) (not as scarce)	2	4	6	11	16	20
78 (1/81, 40¢-c) Cover price error variant	3	6	9	15	22	28
84-87(All #90266 on-c, no date or date code): 84(6/83), 85(8/83), 87(3/84)	3	6	9	14	20	26
Mini-comic No. 1(1976)(3-1/4x6-1/2")	1	3	4	6	8	10

NOTE: *Pink Panther began as a movie cartoon. (See Golden Comics Digest #38, 45 and March of Comics #376, 384, 390, 409, 418, 429, 441, 449, 461, 473, 486); #37, 72, 80-85 contain reprints.*

PINK PANTHER SUPER SPECIAL (TV)
Harvey Comics: Oct, 1993 ($2.25, 68 pgs.)

V2#1-The Inspector & Wendy Witch stories also 4.00

PINK PANTHER, THE
Harvey Comics: Nov, 1993 - No. 9, July, 1994 ($1.50)

V2#1-9 3.00

PINK PANTHER, THE (Volume 3)
American Mythology Productions: 2016 - Present ($3.99)

1-4-New and classic short stories by various; multiple covers on each. 4-Trick or Pink 4.00
... Anniversary Special 1 (2017, $3.99) New short stories and reprints; 3 covers 4.00
...: Cartoon Hour Special 1,2 (2017, $4.99) Short stories by various; 3 covers 5.00
...: Snow Day (2017, $3.99) New short stories by S.A. Check and reprint; 3 covers 4.00
... Super-Pink Special 1 (2017, $3.99) New short stories and reprint; 3 covers 4.00

PINKY & THE BRAIN (See Animaniacs)
DC Comics: July, 1996 - No. 27, Nov, 1998 ($1.75/$1.95/$1.99)

1-27, ...Christmas Special (1/96, $1.50) 3.00

PINKY LEE (See Adventures of...)

PINKY THE EGGHEAD
I.W./Super Comics: 1963 (Reprints from Noodnik)

	GD	VG	FN	VF	VF/NM	NM-
I.W. Reprint #1,2(nd)	2	4	6	8	11	14
Super Reprint #14-r/Noodnik Comics #4	2	4	6	8	11	14

PINOCCHIO (See 4-Color #92, 252, 545, 1203, Mickey Mouse Mag. V5#3, Movie Comics under Wonderful Advs. of..., New Advs. of..., Thrilling Comics #2, Walt Disney Showcase, Walt Disney's..., Wonderful Advs. of..., & World's Greatest Stories #2)
Dell Publishing Co.: No. 92, 1945 - No. 1203, Mar, 1962 (Disney)

	GD	VG	FN	VF	VF/NM	NM-
Four Color 92-The Wonderful Adventures of...; 16 pg. Donald Duck story ; entire book by Kelly	47	94	141	365	820	1275
Four Color 252 (10/49)-Origin, not by Kelly	11	22	33	72	154	235
Four Color 545 (3/54)-The Wonderful Advs. of...; part-r of 4-Color #92; Disney-movie	8	16	24	51	96	140
Four Color 1203 (3/62)	6	12	18	40	73	105

PINOCCHIO AND THE EMPEROR OF THE NIGHT
Marvel Comics: Mar, 1988 ($1.25, 52 pgs.)

1-Adapts film 4.00

PINOCCHIO LEARNS ABOUT KITES (See Kite Fun Book)

PIN-UP PETE (Also see Great Lover Romances & Monty Hall...)
Toby Press: 1952

	GD	VG	FN	VF	VF/NM	NM-
1-Jack Sparling pin-ups	22	44	66	128	209	290

PIONEER MARSHAL (See Fawcett Movie Comics)

PIONEER PICTURE STORIES
Street & Smith Publications: Dec, 1941 - No. 9, Dec, 1943

	GD	VG	FN	VF	VF/NM	NM-
1-The Legless Air Ace begins; WWII-c	52	104	156	328	552	775
2 -True life story of Errol Flynn	24	48	72	142	234	325
3-5,7-9	21	42	63	122	199	275
6-Classic Japanese WWII "Remember Pearl Harbor"-c	77	154	231	493	847	1200

PIONEER WEST ROMANCES (Firehair #1,2,7-11)
Fiction House Magazines: No. 3, Spring, 1950 - No. 6, Winter, 1950-51

	GD	VG	FN	VF	VF/NM	NM-
3-(52 pgs.)-Firehair continues	19	38	57	109	172	235
4-6	19	38	57	109	172	235

PIPSQUEAK (See The Adventures of...)

PIRACY
E. C. Comics: Oct-Nov, 1954 - No. 7, Oct-Nov, 1955

	GD	VG	FN	VF	VF/NM	NM-
1-Williamson/Torres-a	31	62	93	248	399	550
2-Williamson/Torres-a	21	42	63	168	264	360
3-7: 5-7-Comics Code symbol on cover	16	32	48	128	202	275

NOTE: *Crandall a-in all; c-2-4.* ***Davis*** *a-1, 2, 6.* ***Evans*** *a-3-7; c-7.* ***Ingels*** *a-3-7.* ***Krigstein*** *a-3-5, 7; c-5, 6.* ***Wood*** *a-1, 2; c-1.*

PIRACY
Gemstone Publishing: March, 1998 - No. 7, Sept, 1998 ($2.50)

1-7: E.C. reprints 4.00
Annual 1 ($10.95) Collects #1-4 11.00
Annual 2 ($7.95) Collects #5-7 8.00

PIRANA (See The Phantom #46 & Thrill-O-Rama #2, 3)

PIRATE CORP$, THE (See Hectic Planet)
Eternity Comics/Slave Labor Graphics: 1987 - No. 4, 1988 ($1.95)

1-4: 1,2-Color. 3,4-B&W 3.00
Special 1 ('89, B&W)-Slave Labor Publ. 3.00

PIRATE CORP$, THE (Volume 2)
Slave Labor Graphics: 1989 - No. 6, 1992 ($1.95)

1-6-Dorkin-s/a 3.00

PIRATE OF THE GULF, THE (See Superior Stories #2)

PIRATES COMICS
Hillman Periodicals: Feb-Mar, 1950 - No. 4, Aug-Sept, 1950 (All 52 pgs.)

	GD	VG	FN	VF	VF/NM	NM-
1	27	54	81	158	259	360
2-Dave Berg-a	17	34	51	98	154	210
3,4-Berg-a	15	30	45	88	137	185

PIRATES OF CONEY ISLAND, THE
Image Comics: Oct, 2006 - No. 8 ($2.99)

1-6-Rick Spears-s/Vasilis Lolos-a; two covers. 2-Cloonan var-c 3.00

PIRATES OF DARK WATER, THE (Hanna Barbera)
Marvel Comics: Nov, 1991 - No. 9, Aug, 1992 ($1.95)

1-9: 9-Vess-c 3.00

PISCES
Image Comics: Apr, 2015 - No. 3, Jul, 2015 ($3.50/$3.99, unfinished series)

1-3-Kurtis Wiebe-s/Johnnie Christmas-a 4.00

P.I.'S: MICHAEL MAUSER AND MS. TREE, THE
First Comics: Jan, 1985 - No. 3, May, 1985 ($1.25, limited series)

1-3: Staton-c/a(p) 3.00

PITT, THE (Also see The Draft & The War)
Marvel Comics: Mar, 1988 ($3.25, 52 pgs., one-shot)

1-Ties into Starbrand, D.P.7 4.00

PITT (See Youngblood #4 & Gen 13 #3,#4)
Image Comics #1-9/Full Bleed #1/2,10-on: Jan, 1993 - No. 20 ($1.95, intended as a four part limited series)

1/2-(12/95)-1st Full Bleed issue 4.00
1-Dale Keown-c/a. 1-1st app. The Pitt 5.00
2-13: All Dale Keown-c/a. 3 (Low distribution). 10 (1/96)-Indicia reads "January 1995" 3.00
14-20: 14-Begin $2.50-c, pullout poster 3.00
TPB-(1997, $9.95) r/#1/2, 1-4 12.00
TPB 2-(1999, $11.95) r/#5-9 12.00

PITT CREW
Full Bleed Studios: Aug, 1998 - No. 5, Dec, 1999 ($2.50)

1-5: 1-Richard Pace-s/Ken Lashley-a. 2-4-Scott Lee-a 3.00

PITT IN THE BLOOD
Full Bleed Studios: Aug, 1996 ($2.50, one-shot)

nn-Richard Pace-a/script 3.00

PIXIE & DIXIE & MR. JINKS (TV)(See Jinks, Pixie, and Dixie & Whitman Comic Books)
Dell Publishing Co./Gold Key: July-Sept, 1960 - Feb, 1963 (Hanna-Barbera)

	GD	VG	FN	VF	VF/NM	NM-
Four Color 1112	7	14	21	49	92	135
Four Color 1196,1264, 01-631-207 (Dell, 7/62)	5	10	15	35	63	90
1(2/63-Gold Key)	6	12	18	37	66	95

PIXIE PUZZLE ROCKET TO ADVENTURELAND
Avon Periodicals: Nov, 1952

	GD	VG	FN	VF	VF/NM	NM-
1	21	42	63	122	199	275

PIXIES, THE (Advs. of...)(The Mighty Atom and ...#6 on)(See A-1 Comics #16)
Magazine Enterprises: Winter, 1946 - No. 4, Fall?, 1947; No. 5, 1948

	GD	VG	FN	VF	VF/NM	NM-
1-Mighty Atom	11	22	33	62	86	110
2-5-Mighty Atom	7	14	21	37	46	55

Planetary #27 © WSP

Planet Comics #1 © FH

Planet of the Apes / Green Lantern #1 © 20th Century Fox & DC

GD 2.0 VG 4.0 FN 6.0 VF 8.0 VF/NM 9.0 NM- 9.2

I.W. Reprint #1(1958), 8-(Pee-Wee Pixies), 10-I.W. on cover, Super on inside
2 4 6 8 11 14

PIZZAZZ
Marvel Comics: Oct, 1977 - No. 16, Jan, 1979 (slick-color kids mag. w/puzzles, games, comics)

1-Star Wars photo-c/article; origin Tarzan; KISS photos/article; Iron-On bonus; 2 pg. pin-up calendars thru #8 3 6 9 21 33 45
2-Spider-Man-c; Beatles pin-up calendar 2 4 6 13 18 22
3-8: 3-Close Encounters-s; Bradbury-s. 4-Alice Cooper, Travolta; Charlie's Angels/Fonz/Hulk/ Spider-Man-c. 5-Star Trek quiz. 6-Asimov-s. 7-James Bond; Spock/Darth Vader-c.
8-TV Spider-Man photo-c/article 2 4 6 11 16 20
9-14: 9-Shaun Cassidy-c. 10-Sgt. Pepper-c/s. 12-Battlestar Galactica-s; Spider-Man app.
13-TV Hulk-c/s. 14-Meatloaf-c/s 2 4 6 10 14 18
15,16: 15-Battlestar Galactica-s. 16-Movie Superman photo-c/s, Hulk.
2 4 6 11 16 20

NOTE: ***Star Wars*** *comics in all (1-6:Chaykin-a, 7-9: DeZuniga-a, 10-13:Simonson/Janson-a. 14-16:Cockrum-a).* ***Tarzan*** *comics, 1pg.-#1-8. 1pg. "Hey Look" by Kurtzman #12-16.*

PLANETARY (See Preview in flip book Gen13 #33)
DC Comics (WildStorm Prod.): Apr, 1999 - No. 27, Dec, 2009 ($2.50/$2.95/$2.99)

1-Ellis-s/Cassaday-a/c 2 4 6 8 11 14
1-Special Edition (6/09, $1.00) r/#1 with "After Watchmen" cover frame 3.00
2-5 6.00
6-10 5.00
11-15: 12-Fourth Man revealed 4.00
16-26: 16-Begin $2.95-c. 23-Origin of The Drummer 3.00
27-($3.99) Wraparound gatefold-c 4.00
...: All Over the World and Other Stories (2000, $14.95) r/#1-6 & Preview 15.00
...: All Over the World and Other Stories-Hardcover (2000, $24.95) r/#1-6 & Preview; with dustjacket 25.00
.../Batman: Night on Earth 1 (8/03, $5.95) Ellis-s/Cassaday-a 6.00
...: Crossing Worlds (2004, $14.95) r/Batman, JLA, and The Authority x-overs 15.00
.../JLA: Terra Occulta (11/02, $5.95) Elseworlds; Ellis-s/Ordway-a 6.00
...: Leaving the 20th Century -HC (2004, $24.95) r/#13-18 25.00
...: Leaving the 20th Century -SC (2004, $14.99) r/#13-18 15.00
...: Spacetime Archaeology -HC (2010, $24.99) r/#19-27 25.00
...: Spacetime Archaeology -SC (2010, $17.99) r/#19-27 18.00
.../The Authority: Ruling the World (8/00, $5.95) Ellis-s/Phil Jimenez-a 6.00
...: The Fourth Man -Hardcover (2001, $24.95) r/#7-12 25.00
...: The Planetary Reader (8/03, $5.95) r/#13-15 6.00

PLANETARY BRIGADE (Also see Hero Squared)
BOOM! Studios: Feb, 2006 - No. 2, Mar, 2006 ($2.99)

1-3-Giffen & DeMatteis-s/art by various; Haley-c 3.00
... Origins 1-3 (10/06-4/07, $3.99) Giffen & DeMatteis-s/Julia Bax-a 4.00

PLANET COMICS
Fiction House Magazines: 1/40 - No. 62, 9/49; No. 63, Wint, 1949-50; No. 64, Spring, 1950; No. 65, 1951(nd); No. 66-68, 1952(nd); No. 69, Wint, 1952-53; No. 70-72, 1953(nd); No. 73, Winter, 1953-54

1-Origin Auro, Lord of Jupiter by Briefer (ends #61); Flint Baker & The Red Comet begin; Eisner/Fine-c 1275 2550 3825 9500 18,250 27,000
2-Lou Fine-c (Scarce) 622 1244 1866 4540 8020 11,500
3-Eisner-c 394 788 1182 2758 4829 6900
4-Gale Allen and the Girl Squadron begins 337 674 1011 2359 4130 5900
5,6-(Scarce): 5-Eisner/Fine-c 366 732 1098 2562 4481 6400
7-12: 8-Robot-c. 12-The Star Pirate begins 290 580 870 1856 3178 4500
13,14: 13-Reff Ryan begins 252 504 756 1613 2757 3900
15-(Scarce)-Mars, God of War begins (11/41); see Jumbo Comics #31 for 1st app.
757 1514 2271 5526 9763 14,000
16-20,22 181 362 543 1158 1979 2800
21-The Lost World & Hunt Bowman begin 187 374 561 1197 2049 2900
23-26: 26-Space Rangers begin (9/43), end #71 161 322 483 1030 1765 2500
27-30 129 258 387 826 1413 2000
31-35: 33-Origin Star Pirates Wonder Boots, reprinted in #52. 35-Mysta of the Moon begins, ends #62 116 232 348 742 1271 1800
36-45: 38-1st Mysta of the Moon-c. 41-New origin of "Auro, Lord of Jupiter". 42-Last Gale Allen. 43-Futura begins 103 206 309 659 1130 1600
46-60: 48-Robot-c. 53-Used in **SOTI**, pg. 32 84 168 252 538 919 1300
61-68,70: 64,70-Robot-c. 65-70-All partial-r of earlier issues. 70-r/stories from #41
68 136 204 435 743 1050
69-Used in **POP**, pgs. 101,102 69 138 207 442 759 1075
71-73-No series stories. 71-Space Rangers strip 60 120 180 381 653 925
I.W. Reprint 1,8,9: 1(nd)-r/#70; cover-r from Attack on Planet Mars. 8 (r/#72), 9-r/#73
8 16 24 56 108 160

NOTE: ***Anderson*** *a-33-38, 40-51 (Star Pirate), 58.* ***Matt Baker*** *a-53-59 (Mysta of the Moon).* ***Celardo*** *c-12.* ***Bill Discount*** *a-71 (Space Rangers).* ***Elias*** *c-70.* ***Evans*** *a-46-49 (Auro, Lord of Jupiter), 50-64 (Lost World).* ***Fine*** *c-2, 5.* ***Hopper*** *a-31, 35 (Gale Allen), 41, 42, 48, 49 (Mysta of the Moon).* ***Ingels*** *a-24-31 (Lost World), 56-61 (Auro, Lord of Jupiter).* ***Lubbers*** *a-44-47 (Space Rangers); c-40, 41.* ***Moreira*** *a-43, 44 (Mysta of the Moon).* ***Renee*** *a-40-49 (Lost World); c-33, 35, 39.* ***Tuska*** *a-30 (Star Pirate).* ***M. Whitman*** *a-50-52 (Mysta of the Moon), 53-58 (Star Pirate); c-71-73.* ***Starr*** *a-59.* ***Zolnerwich*** *c-10. 13-25. Bondage c-53.*

PLANET COMICS
Pacific Comics: 1984 ($5.95)

1-Reprints Planet Comics #1(1940) 1 2 3 5 6 8

PLANET COMICS
Blackthorne Publishing: Apr, 1988 - No. 3 ($2.00, color/B&W #3)

1-New stories; Dave Stevens-c 3 6 9 16 23 30
2,3: New stories 6.00

PLANET HULK (See Incredible Hulk and Giant-Size Hulk #1 (2006))

PLANET HULK (Secret Wars tie-in)
Marvel Comics: Jul, 2015 - No. 5, Nov, 2015 ($4.99/$3.99, limited series)

1-($4.99) Humphries-s/Laming-a; Steve Rogers app.; back-up Pak-s//Miyazawa-a 5.00
2-5-($3.99) Doc Green & Devil Dinosaur app. 4.00

PLANET OF THE APES (Magazine) (Also see Adventures on the... & Power Record Comics)
Marvel Comics Group: Aug, 1974 - No. 29, Feb, 1977 (B&W) (Based on movies)

1-Ploog-a 4 8 12 27 44 60
2-Ploog-a 3 6 9 16 24 32
3-10 3 6 9 14 20 26
11-20 3 6 9 15 22 28
21-28 (low distribution) 3 6 9 19 30 40
29 (low distribution) 5 10 15 33 57 80

NOTE: ***Alcala*** *a-7-11, 17-22, 24.* ***Ploog*** *a-1-4, 6, 8, 11, 13, 14, 19.* ***Sutton*** *a-11, 12, 15, 17, 19, 20, 23, 24, 29.* ***Tuska*** *a-1-6.*

PLANET OF THE APES
Adventure Comics: Apr, 1990 - No. 24, 1992 ($2.50, B&W)

1-New movie tie-in; comes w/outer-c (3 colors) 4.00
1-Limited serial numbered edition ($5.00) 1 2 3 5 6 8
1-2nd printing (no outer-c, $2.50) 3.00
2-24 3.00
Annual 1 ($3.50) 4.00
...Urchak's Folly 1-4 ($2.50, mini-series) 3.00

PLANET OF THE APES (The Human War)
Dark Horse Comics: Jun, 2001 - No. 3, Aug, 2001 ($2.99, limited series)

1-3-Follows the 2001 movie; Edginton-s 3.00

PLANET OF THE APES
Dark Horse Comics: Sept, 2001 - No. 6, Feb, 2002 ($2.99, ongoing series)

1-6: 1-3-Edginton-s. 1-Photo & Wagner covers. 2-Plunkett & photo-c 3.00

PLANET OF THE APES
BOOM! Studios: Apr, 2011 - No. 15, Jun, 2012 ($3.99)

1-4,6-15-Takes place 1200 years before Taylor's arrival; Magno-a; three covers 4.00
5-($1.00) Three covers 3.00
Annual 1 (8/12, $4.99) Short stories by various; six covers 5.00
Giant 1 (9/13, $4.99) Gregory-s/Barreto-a 5.00
Special 1 (2/13, $4.99) Continued from #15; Diego Barreto-a 5.00
Spectacular 1 (7/13, $4.99) Gregory-s/Barreto-a 5.00

PLANET OF THE APES: CATACLYSM
BOOM! Studios: Sept, 2012 - No. 12, Aug, 2013 ($3.99)

1-12-Takes place 8 years before Taylor's arrival; Couceiro-a. 1-Multiple covers 4.00

PLANET OF THE APES/ GREEN LANTERN
BOOM! Studios: Feb, 2017 - No. 6, Jul, 2017 ($3.99, limited series)

1-6-Bagenda-a; Hal Jordan & Sinestro on the POTA; Cornelius app.; multiple covers 4.00

PLANET OF THE APES: URSUS
BOOM! Studios: Jan, 2018 - No. 6 ($3.99)

1,2-Spotlight on General Ursus; Walker-s/Mooneyham-a 4.00

PLANET OF VAMPIRES
Seaboard Publications (Atlas): Feb, 1975 - No. 3, July, 1975

1-Neal Adams-c(i); 1st Broderick-c/a(p); Hama-s 3 6 9 16 23 30
2,3: 2-Neal Adams-c. 3-Heath-c/a 2 4 6 11 16 20

PLANET TERRY
Marvel Comics (Star Comics)/Marvel: April, 1985 - No. 12, March, 1986 (Children's comic)

1-12 5.00
1-Variant with "Star Chase" game on last page & inside back-c 15.00

Plastic Man #1 © DC

Plop! #13 © DC

Poe Dameron #7 © Lucasfilm

GD 2.0 | VG 4.0 | FN 6.0 | VF 8.0 | VF/NM 9.0 | NM- 9.2

PLANTS VS. ZOMBIES (Based on the Electronic Arts game)
Dark Horse Comics: Jun, 2015 - No. 12, Jun, 2016 ($2.99)

1-12: 1-3-Bully For You; Tobin-s/Chan-a. 4-6-Grown Sweet Home. 7-9-Petal to the Metal 3.00
...: Garden Warfare 1-3 (10/15 - No. 3, 12/15, $2.99) Tobin-s/Chabot-a 3.00

PLASM (See Warriors of Plasm)
Defiant: June, 1993

0-Came bound into Diamond Previews V3#6 (6/93); price is for complete Previews with comic still attached 5.00
0-Comic only removed from Previews 3.00

PLASMER
Marvel Comics UK: Nov, 1993 - No. 4, Feb, 1994 ($1.95, limited series)

1-($2.50)-Polybagged w/4 trading cards 4.00
2-4: Capt. America & Silver Surfer app. 3.00

PLASTIC FORKS
Marvel Comis (Epic Comics): 1990 - No. 5, 1990 ($4.95, 68 pgs., limited series, mature)

Book 1-5: Squarebound 5.00

PLASTIC MAN (Also see Police Comics & Smash Comics #17)
Vital Publ. No. 1,2/Quality Comics No. 3 on: Sum, 1943 - No. 64, Nov, 1956

nn(#1)- "In The Game of Death"; Skull-c; Jack Cole-c/a begins; ends-#64? 459 918 1377 3350 5925 8500
nn(#2, 2/44)- "The Gay Nineties Nightmare" 181 362 543 1158 1979 2800
3 (Spr, '46) 118 236 354 749 1287 1825
4 (Sum, '46) 89 178 267 565 970 1375
5 (Aut, '46) 73 146 219 467 796 1125
6-10 60 120 180 381 653 925
11-15,17-20 53 106 159 334 567 800
16-Classic-c 61 122 183 390 670 950
21-30: 26-Last non-r issue? 41 82 123 256 428 600
31-40: 40-Used in POP, pg. 91 34 68 102 199 325 450
41-64: 53-Last precode issue. 54-Robot-c. 64-Sci-fi-c 28 56 84 165 270 375
Super Reprint 11,16,18: 11('63)-r/#16. 16-r/#18 & #21; Cole-a. 18('64)-Spirit-r by Eisner from Police #95 4 8 12 24 37 50
NOTE: ***Cole** r-44, 49, 56, 58, 59 at least. **Cuidera** c-32-64i.*

PLASTIC MAN (See DC Special #15 & House of Mystery #160)
National Periodical Publications/DC Comics: 11-12/66 - No. 10, 5-6/68; V4#11, 2-3/76 - No. 20, 10-11/77

1-Real 1st app. Silver Age Plastic Man (House of Mystery #160 is actually tryout); Gil Kane-c/a; 12¢ issues begin 10 20 30 69 147 225
2-5: 4-Infantino-c; Mortimer-a 5 10 15 31 53 75
6-10('68): 7-G.A. Plastic Man & Woozy Winks (1st S.A. app.) app.; origin retold. 10-Sparling-a; last 12¢ issue 4 8 12 27 44 60
V4#11('76)-20: 11-20-Fradon-p. 17-Origin retold 2 4 6 8 11 14
...80-Page Giant (2003, $6.95) reprints origin and other stories in 80-Pg. Giant format 7.00
...Special 1 (8/99, $3.95) 4.00

PLASTIC MAN
DC Comics: Nov, 1988 - No. 4, Feb, 1989 ($1.00, mini-series)

1-4: 1-Origin; Woozy Winks app. 4.00

PLASTIC MAN
DC Comics: Feb, 2004 - No. 20, Mar, 2006 ($2.95/$2.99)

1-20-Kyle Baker-s/a in most. 1-Retells origin. 7,12-Scott Morse-s/a. 8-JLA cameo 3.00
...: On the Lam TPB (2004, $14.95) r/#1-6 15.00
...: Rubber Bandits TPB (2005, $14.99) r/#8-11,13,14 15.00

PLASTRON CAFE
Mirage Studios: Dec, 1992 - No. 4, July, 1993 ($2.25, B&W)

1-4: 1-Teenage Mutant Ninja Turtles app.; Kelly Freas-c. 2-Hildebrandt painted-c. 4-Spaced & Alien Fire stories 3.00

PLAYFUL LITTLE AUDREY (TV)(Also see Little Audrey #25)
Harvey Publications: 6/57 - No. 110, 11/73; No. 111, 8/74 - No. 121, 4/76

1 28 56 84 202 451 700
2 11 22 33 76 163 250
3-5 8 16 24 54 102 150
6-10 6 12 18 40 73 105
11-20 5 10 15 31 53 75
21-40 4 8 12 25 40 55
41-60 3 6 9 19 30 40
61-84: 84-Last 12¢ issue 3 6 9 15 22 28
85-99 2 4 6 11 16 20
100-52 pg. Giant 3 6 9 16 23 30
101-103: 52 pg. Giants 3 6 9 14 20 25
104-121 1 3 4 6 8 10
...In 3-D (Spring, 1988, $2.25, Blackthorne #66) 4.00

PLOP! (Also see The Best of DC #60,63 digests)
National Periodical Publications: Sept-Oct, 1973 - No. 24, Nov-Dec, 1976

1-Sergio Aragonés-a begins; Wrightson-a 4 8 12 23 37 50
2-4,6-20 3 6 9 14 20 26
5-Wrightson-a 3 6 9 15 22 28
21-24 (52 pgs.). 23-No Aragonés-a; Lord of the Rings parody with Wally Wood-s/a 3 6 9 16 23 30
NOTE: ***Alcala** a-1-3. **Anderson** a-5. **Aragonés** a-1-22, 24. **Ditko** a-16p. **Evans** a-1. **Mayer** a-1. **Orlando** a-21, 22; c-21. **Sekowsky** a-5, 6p. **Toth** a-11. **Wolverton** r-4, 22-24(1 pg.ea.); c-1-12, 14, 17, 18. **Wood** a-14, 16i, 18-24; c-13, 15, 16, 19.*

PLUTO (See Cheerios Premiums, Four Color #537, Mickey Mouse Magazine, Walt Disney Showcase #4, 7, 13, 20, 23, 33 & Wheaties)
Dell Publ. Co.: No. 7, 1942; No. 429, 10/52 - No. 1248, 11-1/61-62 (Disney)

Large Feature Comic 7(1942)-Written by Carl Barks, Jack Hannah, & Nick George (Barks' 1st comic book work) 206 412 618 1318 2259 3200
Four Color 429 (#1) 10 20 30 68 144 220
Four Color 509 6 12 18 42 79 115
Four Color 595,654,736,853 6 12 18 37 66 95
Four Color 941,1039,1143,1248 5 10 15 33 57 80

PLUTONA
Image Comics: Sept, 2015 - No. 5 ($2.99)

1-4-Lemire-s/Lenox-a 3.00

POCKET CLASSICS
Academic Inc. Publications: 1984 (B&W, 4 1/4" x 6 3/4", 68 pages)

C1(Black Beauty. C2(The Call of the Wild). C3(Dr. Jekyll and Mr. Hyde). C4(Dracula). C5(Frankenstein). C6(Huckleberry Finn). C7(Moby Dick). C8(The Red Badge of Courage). C9(The Time Machine). C10(Tom Sawyer). C11(Treasure Island). C12(20,000 Leagues Under the Sea). C13(The Great Adventures of Sherlock Holmes). C14(Gulliver's Travels). C15(The Hunchback of Notre Dame). C16(The Invisible Man). C17(Journey to the Center of the Earth). C18(Kidnapped). C19(The Mysterious Island). C20(The Scarlet Letter). C21(The Story of My Life). C22(A Tale of Two Cities). C23(The Three Musketeers). C24(The War of the Worlds). C25(Around the World in Eighty Days). C26(Captains Courageous). C27 (A Connecticut Yankee in King Arthur's Court). C28(Sherlock Holmes - The Hound of the Baskervilles). C29(The House of the Seven Gables). C30(Jane Eyre). C31(The Last of the Mohicans). C32(The Best of O. Henry). C33(The Best of Poe). C34(Two Years Before the Mast). C35(White Fang). C36(Wuthering Heights). C37(Ben Hur). C38(A Christmas Carol). C39(The Food of the Gods). C40(Ivanhoe). C41(The Man in the Iron Mask). C42(The Prince and the Pauper). C43(The Prisoner of Zenda). C44(The Return of the Native). C45(Robinson Crusoe). C46(The Scarlet Pimpernel). C47(The Sea Wolf). C48(The Swiss Family Robinson). C49(Billy Budd). C50(Crime and Punishment). C51(Don Quixote). C52(Great Expectations). C53(Heidi). C54(The Illiad). C55(Lord Jim). C56(The Mutiny on Board H.M.S. Bounty). C57(The Odyssey). C58(Oliver Twist). C59(Pride and Prejudice). C60(The Turn of the Screw) each... 8.00

Shakespeare Series:
S1(As You Like It). S2(Hamlet). S3(Julius Caesar). S4(King Lear). S5(Macbeth). S6(The Merchant of Venice). S7(A Midsummer Night's Dream). S8(Othello). S9(Romeo and Juliet). S10(The Taming of the Shrew). S11(The Tempest). S12(Twelfth Night) each... 9.00

POCKET COMICS (Also see Double Up)
Harvey Publications: Aug, 1941 - No. 4, Jan, 1942 (Pocket size; 100 pgs.)
(Tied with Spitfire Comics #1 for earliest Harvey comic)

1-Origin & 1st app. The Black Cat, Cadet Blakey the Spirit of '76, The Red Blazer, The Phantom, Sphinx, & The Zebra; Phantom Ranger, British Agent #99, Spin Hawkins, Satan, Lord of Evil begin (1st app. of each); classic Simon horror cover showing an army battling a gigantic monster with the Statue of Liberty in its claws; Simon-c/a in #1-3 271 542 813 1734 2967 4200
2 (9/41)-Black Cat & Nazi WWII-c by Simon 181 362 543 1158 1979 2800
3,4-Black Cat & Nazi WWII-c. 3-Simon-c 174 348 522 1114 1907 2700

POE DAMERON (Star Wars) (Title changes to Star Wars: Poe Dameron with #13)
Marvel Comics: Jun, 2016 - No. 12, May, 2017 ($4.99/$3.99)

1-($4.99) Soule-s/Noto-a/c; prelude to The Force Awakens; back-up w/Eliopoulos-a 5.00
2-6,8-12-($3.99) Black Squadron app. 4.00
7-($4.99) Anzueta-a; Leia cameo 5.00

POGO PARADE (See Dell Giants)

POGO POSSUM (Also see Animal Comics & Special Delivery)
Dell Publishing Co.: No. 105, 4/46 - No. 148, 5/47; 10-12/49 - No. 16, 4-6/54

Four Color 105(1946)-Kelly-c/a 54 108 162 432 966 1500

Point One #1 © MAR

Poison Elves #80 © Sirius

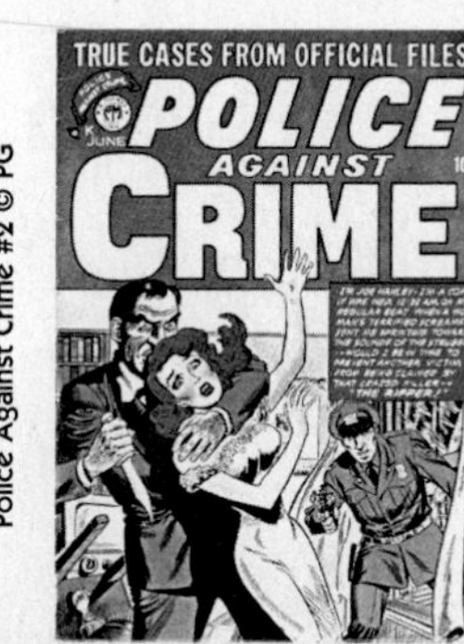

Police Against Crime #2 © PG

	GD 2.0	VG 4.0	FN 6.0	VF 8.0	VF/NM 9.0	NM- 9.2
Four Color 148-Kelly-c/a	38	76	114	285	641	1000
1-(10-12/49)-Kelly-c/a in all	36	72	108	259	580	900
2	22	44	66	154	340	525
3-5	15	30	45	105	233	360
6-10: 10-Infinity-c	13	26	39	91	201	310
11-16: 11-X-Mas-c	10	20	30	69	147	225

NOTE: *#1-4, 9-13: 52 pgs.; #5-8, 14-16: 36 pgs.*

POINT BLANK (See Wildcats)
DC Comics (WildStorm): Oct, 2002 - No. 5, Feb, 2003 ($2.95, limited series)

1-5-Brubaker-s/Wilson-a/Bisley-c. 1-Variant-c by Wilson; Grifter and John Lynch app. 3.00
TPB (2003, $14.95), (2009, $14.99) r/#1-5; afterword by Brubaker 15.00

POINT ONE
Marvel Comics: Jan, 2012 ($5.99, one-shot)

1-Short story preludes to Marvel's event storylines for 2012; s/a by various 6.00

POISON ELVES (Formerly I, Lusiphur)
Mulehide Graphics: No. 8, 1993- No. 20, 1995 (B&W, magazine/comic size, mature readers)

	GD	VG	FN	VF	VF/NM	NM-
8-Drew Hayes-c/a/scripts.	2	4	6	8	10	12
9-11: 11-1st comic size issue	2	4	6	8	10	12
12,14,16	1	2	3	5	6	8
13,15-(low print)	2	4	6	8	11	14
15-2nd print						4.00
17-20	1	2	3	5	6	8
...Desert of the Third Sin-(1997, $14.95, TPB)-r/#13-18						15.00
...Patrons-($4.95, TPB)-r/#19,20						5.00
...Traumatic Dogs-(1996, $14.95,TPB)-Reprints I, Lusiphur #7, Poison Elves #8-12						15.00

POISON ELVES (See I, Lusiphur)
Sirius Entertainment: June, 1995 - No. 79, Sept, 2004 ; No. 80, Nov, 2007 ($2.50/$2.95, B&W, mature readers)

	GD	VG	FN	VF	VF/NM	NM-
1-Linsner-c; Drew Hayes-a/scripts in all.						6.00
1-2nd print						3.00
2-25: 12-Purple Marauder-c/app.						3.00
26-45, 47-49						3.00
46,50-79: 61-Fillbäch Brothers-s/a. 74-Art by Crilley (3 pgs.)						3.00
80-($3.50) Tribute issue to Drew Hayes; sketchbook and notebook art with commentary						3.50
... Baptism By Fire-(2003, $19.95, TPB)-r/#48-59						20.00
... Color Special #1 (12/98, $2.95)						5.00
... Companion (12/02, $3.50) Back-story and character bios						3.50
... : Dark Wars TPB Vol. 1 (2005, $15.95) r/#60,62-68						16.00
... FAN Edition #1 mail-in offer; Drew Hayes-c/s/a	1	2	3	5	6	8
... Rogues-(2002, $15.95, TPB)-r/#40-47						16.00
...Salvation-(2001, $19.95, TPB)-r/#26-39						20.00
...Sanctuary-(1999, $14.95, TPB)-r/#1-12						15.00

POISON ELVES
Ape Entertainment: 2013 - Present ($2.99, B&W)

1-3: 1-Horan-s/Montos-a; Davidsen-s/Ritchie-a; 3 covers by Robertson, Montos & Moore 3.00

POISON ELVES: DOMINION
Sirius Entertainment: Sept, 2005 - No. 6, Sept, 2006 ($3.50, B&W, limited series)

1-6-Keith Davidsen-s/Scott Lewis-a 3.50

POISON ELVES: HYENA
Sirius Entertainment: Sept, 2004 - No. 4, Feb, 2005 ($2.95, B&W, limited series)

1-4-Keith Davidsen-s/Scott Lewis-a 3.00
Ventures TPB Vol. 1: The Hyena Collection (2006, $14.95) r/#1-4 & 2 short stories 15.00

POISON ELVES: LOST TALES
Sirius Entertainment: Jan, 2006 - No. 11 ($2.95, B&W, limited series)

1-11-Aaron Bordner-a; Bordner & Davidsen-s 3.00

POISON ELVES: LUSIPHUR & LIRILITH
Sirius Entertainment: 2001 - No. 4, 2001 ($2.95, B&W, limited series)

1-4-Drew Hayes-s/Jason Alexander-a 3.00
TPB (2002, $11.95) r/#1-4 12.00

POISON ELVES: PARINTACHIN
Sirius Entertainment: 2001 - No. 3, 2002 ($2.95, B&W, limited series)

1-3-Drew Hayes-c/Fillbäch Brothers-s/a 3.00
TPB (2003, $8.95) r/#1-3 9.00

POISON ELVES VENTURES
Sirius Entertainment: May, 2005 - No. 4, Apr, 2006 ($3.50, B&W, limited series)

... #1: Cassanova; ...#2: Lynn; ...#3: The Purple Marauder; #4: Jace - Bordner-a 3.50

POISON IVY: CYCLE OF LIFE AND DEATH
DC Comics: Mar, 2016 - No. 6 ($2.99, limited series)

1-6: 1-Amy Chu-s/Clay Mann-a; covers by Mann & Dodson; Harley Quinn app. 3.00

POKÉMON (TV) (Also see Magical Pokémon Journey)
Viz Comics: Nov, 1998 - 2000 ($3.25/$3.50, B&W)

	GD	VG	FN	VF	VF/NM	NM-
...Part 1: The Electric Tale of Pikachu						
1-Toshiro Ono-s/a	2	4	6	8	10	12
1-4 (2nd through current printings)						4.00
2						6.00
3,4						5.00
TPB ($12.95)						13.00
...Part 2: Pikachu Strikes Back						
1						6.00
2-4						5.00
TPB						13.00
...Part 3: Electric Pikachu Boogaloo						
1						6.00
2-4 ($2.95-c)						5.00
TPB						13.00
...Part 4: Surf's Up Pikachu						
1,3,4						5.00
2 ($2.95-c)						5.00
TPB						13.00

NOTE: Multiple printings exist for most issues

POKÉMON ADVENTURES
Viz Comics: Sept, 1999 - No. 4 ($5.95, B&W, magazine-size)

1-4-Includes stickers bound in 6.00

POKÉMON ADVENTURES
Viz Comics: 2000 - 2002 ($2.95/$4.95, B&W)

Part 2 (2/00-7/00) 1-6-Includes stickers bound in 5.00
Part 3 (8/00-2/01) 1-7 5.00
Part 4 (3/00-6/01) 1-4 5.00
Part 5 (7/01-10/01) 1-4 5.00
Part 6: 1-4, Part 7 1-5 5.00

POKÉMON: THE FIRST MOVIE
Viz Comics: 1999 ($3.95)

Mewtwo Strikes Back 1-4 5.00
Pikachu's Vacation 5.00

POKÉMON: THE MOVIE 2000
Viz Comics: 2000 ($3.95)

1-Official movie adaption 5.00
Pikachu's Rescue Adventure 5.00
....:The Power of One (mini-series) 1-3 5.00

POLARITY
BOOM! Studios: Apr, 2013 - No. 4 ($3.99, limited series)

1-4: 1-Bemis-s/Coelho-a; 3 covers 4.00

POLICE ACADEMY (TV)
Marvel Comics: Nov, 1989 - No. 6, Feb, 1990 ($1.00)

1-6: Based on TV cartoon; Post-c/a(p) in all 4.00

POLICE ACTION
Atlas News Co.: Jan, 1954 - No. 7, Nov, 1954

	GD	VG	FN	VF	VF/NM	NM-
1-Violent-a by Robert Q. Sale	30	60	90	177	289	400
2	15	30	45	88	137	185
3-7: 7-Powell-a	15	30	45	83	124	165

NOTE: ***Ayers** a-4, 5. **Colan** a-1. **Forte** a-1, 2. **Mort Lawrence** a-5. **Maneely** a-3; c-1, 5. **Reinman** a-6, 7.*

POLICE ACTION
Atlas/Seaboard Publ.: Feb, 1975 - No. 3, June, 1975

	GD	VG	FN	VF	VF/NM	NM-
1-3: 1-Lomax, N.Y.P.D., Luke Malone begin; McWilliams-a. 2-Origin Luke Malone, Manhunter; Ploog-a	2	4	6	10	14	18

NOTE: ***Ploog** art in all. **Sekowsky/McWilliams** a-1-3. **Thorne** c-3.*

POLICE AGAINST CRIME
Premiere Magazines: April, 1954 - No. 9, Aug, 1955

	GD	VG	FN	VF	VF/NM	NM-
1-Disbrow-a; extreme violence (man's face slashed with knife); Hollingsworth-a	45	90	135	284	480	675
2-Hollingsworth-a	25	50	75	150	245	340
3-9	21	42	63	126	206	285

POLICE BADGE #479 (Formerly Spy Thrillers #1-4)
Atlas Comics (PrPl): No. 5, Sept, 1955

Police Comics #18 © QUA

Polly Pigtails #2 © PMI

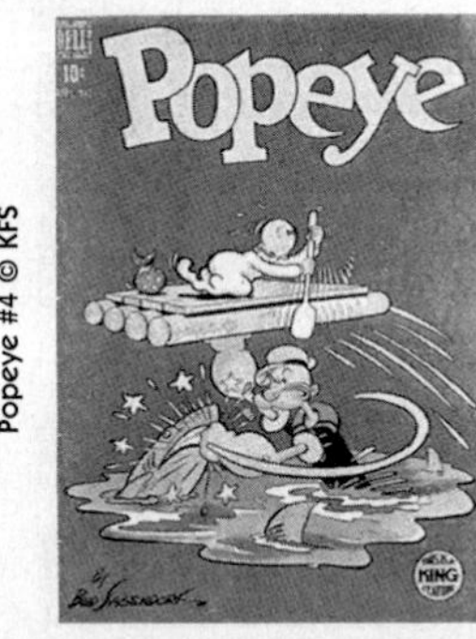

Popeye #4 © KFS

GD VG FN VF VF/NM NM-
2.0 4.0 6.0 8.0 9.0 9.2

GD VG FN VF VF/NM NM-
2.0 4.0 6.0 8.0 9.0 9.2

5-Maneely-c/a (6 pgs.); Heck-a 14 28 42 81 118 155

POLICE CASE BOOK (See Giant Comics Editions)

POLICE CASES (See Authentic... & Record Book of...)

POLICE COMICS
Quality Comics Group (Comic Magazines): Aug, 1941 - No. 127, Oct, 1953

1-Origin/1st app. Plastic Man by Jack Cole (r-in DC Special #15), The Human Bomb by Gustavson, & No. 711; intro. The Firebrand by Reed Crandall, The Mouthpiece by Guardineer, Phantom Lady, & The Sword; Chic Carter by Eisner app.; Firebrand-c 1-4 1000 2000 3000 7400 13,200 19,000
2-Plastic Man smuggles opium 320 640 960 2240 3920 5600
3 245 490 735 1568 2684 3800
4 210 420 630 1334 2292 3250
5-Plastic Man covers begin, end #102; Plastic Man forced to smoke marijuana 349 698 1047 2443 4272 6100
6,7 177 354 531 1124 1937 2750
8-Manhunter begins (origin/1st app.) (3/42) 200 400 600 1280 2190 3100
9,10 139 278 417 883 1517 2150
11-The Spirit strip reprints begin by Eisner (origin-strip #1); 1st comic book app. The Spirit & 1st cover app. (9/42) 389 778 1167 2723 4762 6800
12-Intro. Ebony 184 368 552 1168 2009 2850
13-Intro. Woozy Winks; last Firebrand 194 388 582 1242 2121 3000
14-19: 15-Last No. 711; Destiny begins 77 154 231 493 847 1200
20-The Raven x-over in Phantom Lady; features Jack Cole himself 77 154 231 493 847 1200
21,22: 21-Raven & Spider Widow x-over in Phantom Lady (cameo in #22) 65 130 195 416 708 1000
23-30: 23-Last Phantom Lady. 24-26-Flatfoot Burns by Kurtzman in all 58 116 174 371 636 900
31-41: 37-1st app. Candy by Sahle & begins (12/44). 41-Last Spirit-r by Eisner 50 100 150 315 533 750
42,43-Spirit-r by Eisner/Fine 41 82 123 256 428 600
44-Fine Spirit-r begin, end #88,90,92 41 82 123 256 428 600
45-50: 50-(#50 on-c, #49 on inside, 1/46) 36 72 108 214 347 480
51-60: 58-Last Human Bomb 30 60 90 177 289 400
61-88,90,92: 63-(Some issues have #65 printed on cover, but #63 on inside) Kurtzman-a, 6 pgs. 90,92-Spirit by Fine 25 50 75 150 245 340
89,91,93-No Spirit stories 23 46 69 136 223 310
94-99,101,102: Spirit by Eisner in all; 101-Last Manhunter. 102-Last Spirit & Plastic Man by Jack Cole 32 64 96 192 314 435
100 39 78 117 231 378 525
103-Content change to crime; Ken Shannon & T-Man begin (1st app. of each, 12/50) 37 74 111 222 361 500
104-112,114-127: Crandall-a most issues (not in 104,105,122,125-127). 109-Atomic bomb story. 112-Crandall-a 22 44 66 132 216 300
113-Crandall-c/a(2), 9 pgs. each 25 50 75 147 241 335

NOTE: *Most Spirit stories signed by Eisner are not by him; all are reprints.* **Crandall** *Firebrand-1-8. Spirit by* **Eisner** *1-41, 94-102; by* **Eisner/Fine**-*42, 43; by* **Fine**-*44-88, 90, 92. 103, 109.* **Al Bryant** *c-33, 34.* **Cole** *c-17-32, 35-102(most).* **Crandall** *c-13, 14.* **Crandall/Cuidera** *c-105-127.* **Eisner** *c-4i.* **Gill Fox** *c-1-3, 4p, 5-12, 15. Bondage c-103, 109, 125.*

POLICE LINE-UP
Avon Periodicals/Realistic Comics #3,4: Aug, 1951 - No. 4, July, 1952 (Painted-c #1-3)

1-Wood-a, 1 pg. plus part-c; spanking panel-r/Saint #5 47 94 141 296 498 700
2-Classic story "The Religious Murder Cult", drugs, perversion; r/Saint #5; c-r/Avon paperback #329 37 74 111 222 361 500
3,4: 3-Kubert-a(r?)/part-c; Kinstler-a (inside-c only) 26 52 78 154 252 350

POLICE TRAP (Public Defender In Action #7 on)
Mainline #1-4/Charlton #5,6: 8-9/54 - No. 4, 2-3/55; No. 5, 7/55 - No. 6, 9/55

1-S&K covers-all issues; Meskin-a; Kirby scripts 39 78 117 231 378 525
2-4 22 44 66 128 209 290
5,6-S&K-c/a 27 54 81 162 266 370

POLICE TRAP
Super Comics: No. 11, 1963; No. 16-18, 1964

Reprint #11,16-18: 11-r/Police Trap #3. 16-r/Justice Traps the Guilty #? 17-r/Inside Crime #3 & r/Justice Traps The Guilty #83; 18-r/Inside Crime #3 2 4 6 9 13 16

POLLY & HER PALS (See Comic Monthly #1)

POLLY & THE PIRATES
Oni Press: Sept, 2005 - No. 6, June, 2006 ($2.99, B&W, limited series)

1-6-Ted Naifeh-s/a; Polly is shanghaied by the pirate ship Titania 3.00
TPB (7/06, $11.95, digest) r/#1-6 12.00

POLLYANNA (Disney)
Dell Publishing Co.: No. 1129, Aug-Oct, 1960

Four Color 1129-Movie, Hayley Mills photo-c 7 14 21 49 92 135

POLLY PIGTAILS (Girls' Fun & Fashion Magazine #44 on)
Parents' Magazine Institute/Polly Pigtails: Jan, 1946 - V4#43, Oct-Nov, 1949

1-Infinity-c; photo-c 21 42 63 122 199 275
2-Photo-c 13 26 39 74 105 135
3-5: 3,4-Photo-c 11 22 33 62 86 110
6-10: 7-Photo-c 10 20 30 54 72 90
11-30: 22-Photo-c 9 18 27 47 61 75
31-43: 38-Natalie Wood photo-c 8 16 24 40 50 60

PONY EXPRESS (See Tales of the...)

PONYTAIL (Teen-age)
Dell Publishing Co./Charlton No. 13 on: 7-9/62 - No. 12, 10-12/65; No. 13, 11/69 - No. 20, 1/71

12-641-209(#1) 4 8 12 23 37 50
2-12 3 6 9 17 26 35
13-20 3 6 9 14 19 24

POP
Dark Horse Comics: Aug, 2014 - No. 4, Nov, 2014 ($3.99, limited series)

1-4-Curt Pires-s/Jason Copland-a 4.00

POP COMICS
Modern Store Publ.: 1955 (36 pgs.; 5x7"; in color) (7¢)

1-Funny animal 8 16 24 42 54 65

POPEYE (See Comic Album #7, 11, 15, Comics Reading Libraries *in the Promotional Comics section*, Eat Right to Work and Win, Giant Comic Album, King Comics, Kite Fun Book, Magic Comics, March of Comics #37,52, 66, 80, 96, 117, 134, 148, 157, 169, 194, 246, 264, 274, 294, 453, 465, 477 & Wow Comics, 1st series)

POPEYE
David McKay Publications: 1937 - 1939 (All by Segar)

Feature Books nn (100 pgs.) (Very Rare) 1000 2000 3000 7400 13,200 19,000
Feature Books 2 (52 pgs.) 139 278 417 1015 1583 2150
Feature Books 3 (100 pgs.)-r/nn issue with new-c 107 214 321 680 1165 1650
Feature Books 5,10 (76 pgs.) 97 194 291 621 1061 1500
Feature Books 14 (76 pgs.) (Scarce) 110 220 330 704 1202 1700

POPEYE (Strip reprints through 4-Color #70)
Dell #1-65/Gold Key #66-80/King #81-92/Charlton #94-138/Gold Key #139-155/Whitman #156 on: 1941 - 1947; #1, 2-4/48 - #65, 7-9/62; #66, 10/62 - #80, 5/66; #81, 8/66 - #92, 12/67; #94, 2/69 - #138, 1/77; #139, 5/78 - #171, 6/84 (no #93,160,161)

Large Feature Comic 24('41)-Half by Segar 94 188 282 597 1024 1450
Four Color 25('41)-by Segar 107 214 321 680 1165 1650
Large Feature Comic 10('43) 69 138 207 442 759 1075
Four Color 17('43),26('43)-by Segar 46 92 138 340 770 1200
Four Color 43('44) 30 60 90 216 483 750
Four Color 70('45)-Title: ...& Wimpy 22 44 66 154 340 525
Four Color 113('46-original strips begin),127,145('47),168 13 26 39 91 201 310
1(2-4/48)(Dell)-All new stories continue 30 60 90 216 483 750
2 14 28 42 98 217 335
3-10: 5-Popeye on moon w/rocket-c 11 22 33 76 163 250
11-20 9 18 27 60 120 180
21-40,46: 46-Origin Swee' Pee 8 16 24 51 96 140
41-45,47-50 6 12 18 40 73 105
51-60 5 10 15 35 63 90
61-65 (Last Dell issue) 5 10 15 31 53 75
66(10/62),67-Both 84 pgs. (Gold Key) 6 12 18 40 73 105
68-80 4 8 12 25 40 55
81-92,94-97 (no #93): 97-Last 12¢ issue 3 6 9 20 31 42
98,99,101-107,109-138: 123-Wimpy beats Neil Armstrong to the moon. 130-1st app. Superstuff 3 6 9 14 19 24
100 3 6 9 17 26 35
108-Traces Popeye's origin from 1929 3 6 9 15 22 28
139-155: 144-50th Anniversary issue 2 4 6 8 10 12
156,157,162-167(Whitman)(no #160,161).167(3/82) 2 4 6 10 14 18
158(9/80),159(11/80)-pre-pack only 5 10 15 33 57 80
168-171:(All #90069 on-c; pre-pack) 168(6/83). 169(#168 on-c)(8/83). 170(3/84). 171(6/84) 3 6 9 17 26 35

NOTE: *Reprints-#145, 147, 149, 151, 153, 155, 157, 163-168(1/3), 170.*

POPEYE
Harvey Comics: Nov, 1993 - No. 7, Aug, 1994 ($1.50)

Popeye (2012 series) #5 © KFS

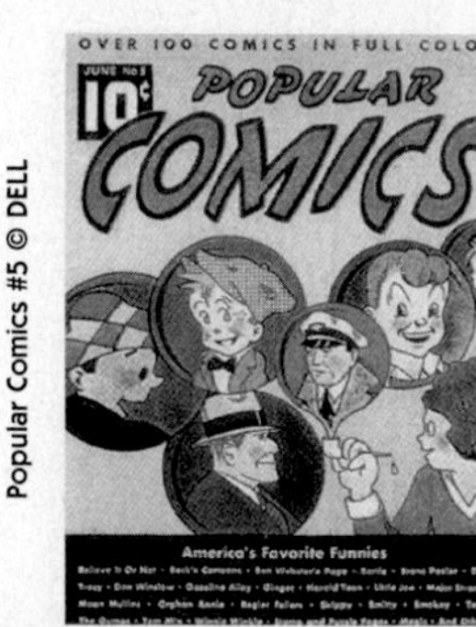

Popular Comics #5 © DELL

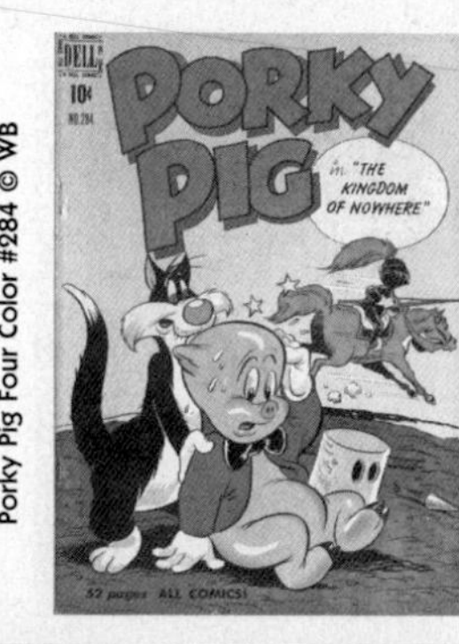

Porky Pig Four Color #284 © WB

	GD 2.0	VG 4.0	FN 6.0	VF 8.0	VF/NM 9.0	NM- 9.2
V2#1-7						3.00
...Summer Special V2#1-(10/93, $2.25, 68 pgs.)-Sagendorf-r & others						4.00

POPEYE
IDW Publishing: Apr, 2012 - No. 12, Apr, 2013 ($3.99)

	GD 2.0	VG 4.0	FN 6.0	VF 8.0	VF/NM 9.0	NM- 9.2
1-12-New stories in classic style; Langridge-s. 1-Action #1 cover swipe. 12-Barney Google and Spark Plug app.						4.00

POPEYE (CLASSIC...)
IDW Publishing: Aug, 2012 - Present ($3.99/$4.99)

	GD 2.0	VG 4.0	FN 6.0	VF 8.0	VF/NM 9.0	NM- 9.2
1-43-Reprints of Bud Sagendorf's classic stories						4.00
44-65-($4.99)						5.00

POPEYE SPECIAL
Ocean Comics: Summer, 1987 - No. 2, Sept, 1988 ($1.75/$2.00)

	GD 2.0	VG 4.0	FN 6.0	VF 8.0	VF/NM 9.0	NM- 9.2
1,2: 1-Origin						4.00

POPPLES (TV, movie)
Star Comics (Marvel): Dec, 1986 - No. 4, Jun, 1987

	GD 2.0	VG 4.0	FN 6.0	VF 8.0	VF/NM 9.0	NM- 9.2
1-4-Based on toys						5.00

POPPO OF THE POPCORN THEATRE
Fuller Publishing Co. (Publishers Weekly): 10/29/55 - No. 13, 1956 (weekly)

	GD 2.0	VG 4.0	FN 6.0	VF 8.0	VF/NM 9.0	NM- 9.2
1	10	20	30	54	72	90
2-5	7	14	21	37	46	55
6-13	6	12	18	31	38	45

NOTE: *By* ***Charles Biro.*** *10¢ cover, given away by supermarkets such as IGA.*

POP-POP COMICS
R. B. Leffingwell Co.: No date (Circa 1945) (52 pgs.)

	GD 2.0	VG 4.0	FN 6.0	VF 8.0	VF/NM 9.0	NM- 9.2
1-Funny animal	15	30	45	88	137	185

POPULAR COMICS
Dell Publishing Co.: Feb, 1936 - No. 145, July-Sept, 1948

	GD 2.0	VG 4.0	FN 6.0	VF 8.0	VF/NM 9.0	NM- 9.2
1-Dick Tracy (1st comic book app.), Little Orphan Annie, Terry & the Pirates, Gasoline Alley, Don Winslow (1st app.), Harold Teen, Little Joe, Skippy, Moon Mullins, Mutt & Jeff, Tailspin Tommy, Smitty, Smokey Stover, Winnie Winkle & The Gumps begin (all strip-r)	929	1858	2787	6500	-	-
2	271	542	813	1900	-	-
3	207	414	621	1450	-	-
4-6(7/36): 5-Tom Mix begins. 6-1st app. Scribbly	164	328	492	1150	-	-
7-10: 8,9-Scribbly & Reglar Fellers app.	132	264	396	925	-	-
11-20: 12-X-Mas-c	83	166	249	477	739	1000
21-27: 27-Last Terry & the Pirates, Little Orphan Annie, & Dick Tracy	63	126	189	362	556	750
28-37: 28-Gene Autry app. 31,32-Tim McCoy app. 35-Christmas-c; Tex Ritter app.	49	98	147	282	434	585
38-43: Tarzan in text only. 38-(4/39)-Gang Busters (Radio, 2nd app.) & Zane Grey's Tex Thorne begins? 43-The Masked Pilot app.; 1st non-funny-c?	47	94	141	270	415	560
44,45: 45-Hurricane Kid-c	40	80	140	230	365	500
46-Origin/1st app. Martan, the Marvel Man(12/39)	50	100	175	288	457	625
47-49-Martan, the Marvel Man-c	44	88	154	253	402	550
50-Gang Busters-c	38	76	133	219	347	475
51-Origin The Voice (The Invisible Detective) strip begins (5/40)	40	80	140	230	365	500
52-Classic Martan blasting robots-c/sty	62	124	217	357	566	775
53-56: 55-End of World story	36	72	126	207	329	450
57-59-Martan, the Marvel Man-c	42	84	147	242	371	525
60-Origin/1st app. Professor Supermind and Son (2/41)	40	80	140	230	365	500
61-64,66-Professor Supermind-c. 63-Smilin' Jack begins	34	68	119	196	311	425
65-Classic Professor Supermind WWII-c	42	84	147	242	371	525
67-71	23	46	69	136	223	310
72-The Owl & Terry & the Pirates begin (2/42); Smokey Stover reprints begin	42	84	126	242	371	500
73-75	29	58	87	167	259	350
76-78-Capt. Midnight in all (see The Funnies #57)	40	80	120	230	358	485
79-85-Last Owl	27	54	81	155	238	320
86-99: 86-Japanese WWII-c. 98-Felix the Cat, Smokey Stover-r begin	18	36	54	104	157	210
100	20	40	60	115	175	235
101-130	10	20	30	58	89	120
131-145: 142-Last Terry & the Pirates	9	18	27	52	79	105

NOTE: *Martan, the Marvel Man c-47-49, 52, 57-59. Professor Supermind c-60-63, 64(1/2), 65, 66. The Voice c-53.*

POPULAR FAIRY TALES (See March of Comics #6, 18)

POPULAR ROMANCE
Better-Standard Publications: No. 5, Dec, 1949 - No. 29, July, 1954

	GD 2.0	VG 4.0	FN 6.0	VF 8.0	VF/NM 9.0	NM- 9.2
5	18	36	54	105	165	225
6-9: 7-Palais-a; lingerie panels	14	28	42	80	115	150
10-Wood-a (2 pgs.)	15	30	45	85	130	175
11,12,14-16,18-21,28,29	13	26	39	72	101	130
13,17-Severin/Elder-a (3&8 pgs.)	14	28	42	76	108	140
22-27-Toth-a	14	28	42	81	118	155

NOTE: *All have photo-c.* ***Tuska*** *art in most issues.*

POPULAR TEEN-AGERS (Secrets of Love) (School Day Romances #1-4)
Star Publications: No. 5, Sept, 1950 - No. 23, Nov, 1954

	GD 2.0	VG 4.0	FN 6.0	VF 8.0	VF/NM 9.0	NM- 9.2
5-Toni Gay, Midge Martin & Eve Adams continue from School Day Romances; Ginger Bunn (formerly Ginger Snapp & becomes Honey Bunn #6 on) begins; all features end #8	42	84	126	265	445	625
6-8 (7/51)-Honey Bunn begins; all have L. B. Cole-c; 6-Negligee panels	39	78	117	231	378	525
9-(...Romances; 1st romance issue, 10/51)	34	68	102	199	325	450
10-(...Secrets of Love thru #23)	32	64	96	188	307	425
11,16,18,19,22,23	28	56	84	165	270	375
12,13,17,20,21-Disbrow-a	30	60	90	177	289	400
14-Harrison/Wood-a	37	74	111	222	361	500
15-Wood?, Disbrow-a	32	64	96	188	307	425
Accepted Reprint 5,6 (nd); L.B. Cole-c	9	18	27	52	69	85

NOTE: *All have* ***L. B. Cole*** *covers.*

PORKY PIG (See Bugs Bunny &..., Kite Fun Book, Looney Tunes, March of Comics #42, 57, 71, 89, 99, 113, 130, 143, 164, 175, 192, 209, 218, 367, and Super Book #6, 18, 30)

PORKY PIG (...& Bugs Bunny #40-69)
Dell Publishing Co./Gold Key No. 1-93/Whitman No. 94 on: No. 16, 1942 - No. 81, Mar-Apr, 1962; Jan, 1965 - No. 109, June, 1984

	GD 2.0	VG 4.0	FN 6.0	VF 8.0	VF/NM 9.0	NM- 9.2
Four Color 16(#1, 1942)	93	186	279	744	1672	2600
Four Color 48(1944)-Carl Barks-a	93	186	279	744	1672	2600
Four Color 78(1945)	26	52	78	182	404	625
Four Color 112(7/46)	15	30	45	105	233	360
Four Color 156,182,191('49)	11	22	33	75	160	245
Four Color 226,241('49),260,271,277,284,295	9	18	27	61	123	185
Four Color 303,311,322,330: 322-Sci/fi-c/story	8	16	24	51	96	140
Four Color 342,351,360,370,385,399,410,426	6	12	18	40	73	105
25 (11-12/52)-30	5	10	15	33	57	80
31-40	5	10	15	30	50	70
41-60	4	8	12	25	40	55
61-81(3-4/62)	3	6	9	21	33	45
1(1/65-Gold Key)(2nd Series)	5	10	15	31	53	75
2,4,5-r/4-Color 226,284 & 271 in that order	3	6	9	19	30	40
3,6-10: 3-r/Four Color #342	3	6	9	16	24	32
11-30	3	6	9	14	19	24
31-54	2	4	6	10	14	18
55-70	2	4	6	8	11	14
71-93(Gold Key)	2	3	4	6	8	10
94-96	2	4	6	8	10	12
97(9/80),98-pre-pack only (99 known not to exist)	4	8	12	27	44	60
100	2	4	6	10	14	18
101-105: 104(2/82). 105(4/82)	2	4	6	8	11	14
106-109 (All #90140 on-c, no date or date code): 106(7/83), 107(8/83), 108(2/84), 109(6/84) low print run	3	6	9	14	20	26

NOTE: *Reprints-#1-8, 9-35(2/3); 36-46(1/4-1/2), 58, 67, 69-74, 76, 78, 102-109(1/3-1/2).*

PORKY PIG'S DUCK HUNT
Saalfield Publishing Co.: 1938 (12pgs.)(large size)(heavy linen-like paper)

	GD 2.0	VG 4.0	FN 6.0	VF 8.0	VF/NM 9.0	NM- 9.2
2178-1st app. Porky Pig & Daffy Duck by Leon Schlesinger. Illustrated text story book written in verse. 1st book ever devoted to these characters. (see Looney Tunes #1 for their 1st comic book app.)	74	148	222	470	810	1150

PORTAL BOUND
Aspen MLT: No. 0, Feb, 2018 - Present ($1.50/$3.99)

	GD 2.0	VG 4.0	FN 6.0	VF 8.0	VF/NM 9.0	NM- 9.2
0-($1.50) Roslan & Carrasco-s/Arizmendi-a; 2 covers; bonus character sketches						3.00

PORTENT, THE
Image Comics: Feb, 2006 - No. 4, Aug, 2006 ($2.99)

	GD 2.0	VG 4.0	FN 6.0	VF 8.0	VF/NM 9.0	NM- 9.2
1-4-Peter Bergting-s/a						3.00
Vol. 1: Duende TPB (2006, 12.99) r/#1-4; pin-up art; intro. by Kaluta						13.00

PORTIA PRINZ OF THE GLAMAZONS
Eclipse Comics: Dec, 1986 - No. 6, Oct, 1987 ($2.00, B&W, Baxter paper)

	GD 2.0	VG 4.0	FN 6.0	VF 8.0	VF/NM 9.0	NM- 9.2
1-6						3.00

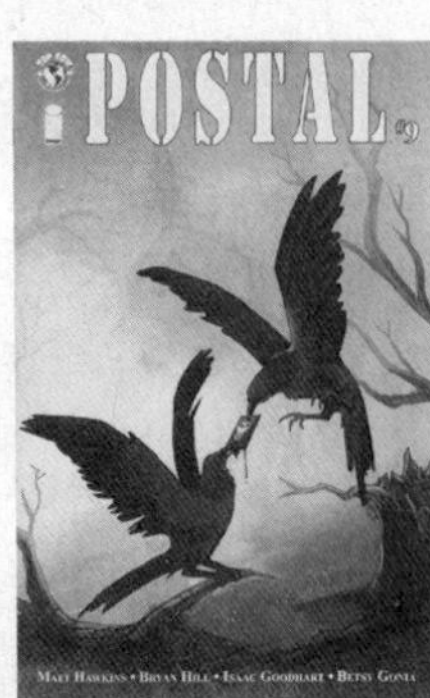

Postal #9 © Hawkins & TCOW

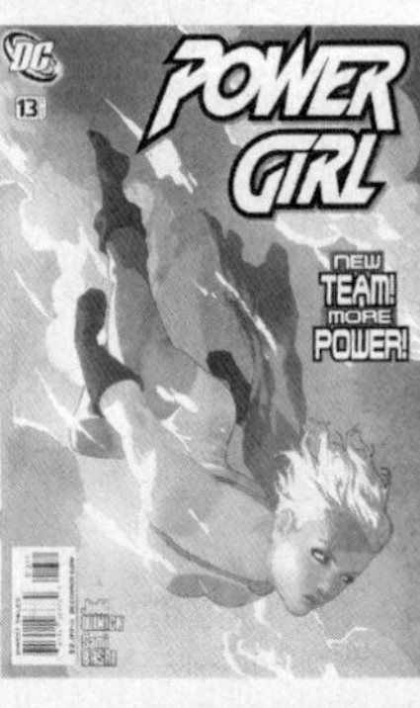

Power Girl #13 © DC

Power Man & Iron Fist #59 © MAR

GD 2.0 | VG 4.0 | FN 6.0 | VF 8.0 | VF/NM 9.0 | NM- 9.2

GD 2.0 | VG 4.0 | FN 6.0 | VF 8.0 | VF/NM 9.0 | NM- 9.2

POSEIDON IX (Also see Aphrodite IX and (Ninth) IX Generation)
Image Comics (Top Cow): Sept, 2015 ($3.99, one-shot)
1-Howard-s/Sevy-a; story continues in IX Generation #5 4.00

POSSESSED, THE
DC Comics (Cliffhanger): Sept, 2003 - No. 6, March, 2004 ($2.95, limited series)
1-6-Johns & Grimminger-s/Sharp-a 3.00
TPB (2004, $14.95) r/#1-6; promo art and sketch pages 15.00

POSTAL (Also see Eden's Fall)
Image Comics (Top Cow): Feb, 2015 - Present ($3.99)
1-24: 1-Matt Hawkins & Bryan Hill-s/Issac Goodheart-a 4.00
25-($5.99) Matt Hawkins & Bryan Hill-s/Issac Goodheart-a 6.00
...: Dossier 1 (11/15, $3.99) Ryan Cady-a; background on Eden and character profiles 4.00
...: Mark 1 (2/18, $3.99) Spotlight on Mark; Ienco-a 4.00

POST GAZETTE (See Meet the New... in the Promotional Comics section)

POWDER RIVER RUSTLERS (See Fawcett Movie Comics)

POWER & GLORY (See American Flagg! & Howard Chaykin's American Flagg!
Malibu Comics (Bravura): Feb, 1994 - No. 4, May, 1994 ($2.50, limited series, mature)
1A, 1B-By Howard Chaykin; w/Bravura stamp 3.00
1-Newsstand ed. (polybagged w/children's warning on bag), Gold ed., Silver-foil ed., Blue-foil ed.(print run of 10,000), Serigraph ed. (print run of 3,000)($2.95)-Howard Chaykin-c/a begin 4.00
2-4-Contains Bravura stamp 3.00
Holiday Special (Win '94, $2.95) 3.00

POWER COMICS
Holyoke Publ. Co./Narrative Publ.: 1944 - No. 4, 1945
1-L. B. Cole-c 200 400 600 1280 2190 3100
2-Hitler, Hirohito-c (scarce) 219 438 657 1402 2401 3400
3-Classic L.B. Cole-c; Dr. Mephisto begins? 213 426 639 1363 2332 3300
4-L.B. Cole-c; Miss Espionage app. #3,4; Leav-a 148 296 444 947 1624 2300

POWER COMICS
Power Comics Co.: 1977 - No. 5, Dec, 1977 (B&W)
1- "A Boy And His Aardvark" by Dave Sim; first Dave Sim aardvark (not Cerebus) 3 6 9 17 26 35
1-Reprint (3/77, black-c) 1 2 3 5 6 8
2-Cobalt Blue by Gustovich 1 3 4 6 8 10
3-5: 3-Nightwitch. 4-Northern Light. 5-Bluebird 1 3 4 6 8 10

POWER COMICS
Eclipse Comics (Acme Press): Mar, 1988 - No. 4, Sept, 1988 ($2.00, B&W, mini-series)
1-4: Bolland, Gibbons-r in all 3.00

POWER COMPANY, THE
DC Comics: Apr, 2002 - No. 18, Sep, 2003 ($2.50/$2.75)
1-6-Busiek-s/Grummett-a. 6-Green Arrow & Black Canary-c/app. 3.00
7-18: 7:Begin $2.75-c. 8,9-Green Arrow app. 11-Firestorm joins. 15-Batman app. 3.00
...Bork (3/02) Busiek-s/Dwyer-a; Batman & Flash (Barry Allen) app. 3.00
...Josiah Power (3/02) Busiek-s/Giffen-a; Superman app. 3.00
...Manhunter (3/02) Busiek-s/Jurgens-a; Nightwing app. 3.00
...Sapphire (3/02) Busiek-s/Bagley-a; JLA & Kobra app. 3.00
...Skyrocket (3/02) Busiek-s/Staton-a; Green Lantern (Hal Jordan) app. 3.00
...Striker Z (3/02) Busiek-s/Bachs-a; Superboy app. 3.00
...Witchfire (3/02) Busiek-s/Haley-a; Wonder Woman app. 3.00

POWER CUBED
Dark Horse Comics: Sept, 2015 - No. 4, Jan, 2016 ($3.99, limited series)
1-4-Aaron Lopresti-s/a 4.00

POWER FACTOR
Wonder Color Comics #1/Pied Piper #2: May, 1987 - No. 2, 1987 ($1.95)
1,2: Super team. 2-Infantino-c 3.00

POWER FACTOR
Innovation Publishing: Oct, 1990 - No. 3, 1991 ($1.95/$2.25)
1-3: 1-R-/1st story + new-a, 2-r/2nd story + new-a. 3-Infantino-a 3.00

POWER GIRL (See All-Star #58, Infinity, Inc., JSA Classified, Showcase #97-99)
DC Comics: June, 1988 - No. 4, Sept, 1988 ($1.00, color, limited series)
1 2 4 6 10 14 18
2-4 5.00
TPB (2006, $14.99) r/Showcase #97-99; Secret Origins #11; JSA Classified #1-4 and pages from JSA #32,39; cover gallery 15.00

POWER GIRL
DC Comics: Jul, 2009 - No. 27, Oct, 2011 ($2.99)
1-Amanda Conner-a; covers by Conner and Hughes; Ultra-Humanite app. 3 6 9 16 23 30
2-Conner-a; covers by Conner and Hughes 2 4 6 9 12 15
3-10: 3-6-Covers by Conner and March 5.00
11-26: 13-23-Winick-s/Basri-a. 20,21-Crossover with Justice League: Generation Lost #18-22 23-Zatanna app. 24,25-Batman app.; Prasetya-a 4.00
27-Cyclone app. 3 6 9 20 31 42
...: Aliens and Apes SC (2010, $17.99) r/#7-12 18.00
...: A New Beginning SC (2010, $17.99) r/#1-6; gallery of variant covers 18.00
...: Bomb Squad SC (2011, $14.99) r/#13-18 15.00

POWERHOUSE PEPPER COMICS (See Gay Comics, Joker Comics & Tessie the Typist)
Marvel Comics (20CC): No. 1, 1943; No. 2, May, 1948 - No. 5, Nov, 1948
1-(60 pgs.)-Wolverton-a in all; c-2,3 232 464 696 1485 2543 3600
2 100 200 300 635 1093 1550
3,4 94 188 282 597 1024 1450
5-(Scarce) 107 214 321 680 1165 1650

POWERLESS
Marvel Comics: Aug, 2004 - No. 6, Jan, 2005 ($2.99, limited series)
1-6-Peter Parker, Matt Murdock and Logan without powers; Gaydos-a 3.00
TPB (2005, $14.99) r/series; sketch page by Gaydos 15.00

POWER LINE
Marvel Comics (Epic Comics): May, 1988 - No. 8, Sept, 1989 ($1.25/$1.50)
1-8: 2-Williamson-i. 3-Dr. Zero app. 4-7-Morrow-a. 8-Williamson-i 3.00

POWER LINES
Image Comics: Mar, 2016 - No. 3 ($3.50/$3.99)
1-3-Jimmie Robinson-s/a. 1-($3.50-c). 2-Begin $3.99-c 4.00

POWER LORDS
DC Comics: Dec, 1983 - No. 3, Feb, 1984 (Limited series, Mando paper)
1-3: Based on Revell toys 4.00

POWER MAN (Formerly Hero for Hire; ...& Iron Fist #50 on; see Cage & Giant-Size...)
Marvel Comics Group: No. 17, Feb, 1974 - No. 125, Sept, 1986
17-Luke Cage continues; Iron Man app. 4 8 12 28 47 65
18,20: 18-Last 20¢ issue; intro. Wrecking Crew 3 6 9 16 23 30
19-1st app. Cottonmouth 4 8 12 27 44 60
21-23,25-30 2 4 6 9 12 15
24-Intro. Black Goliath 6 12 18 41 76 110
30-(30¢-c variant, limited distribution)(4/76) 4 8 12 25 40 55
31-46: 31-Part Neal Adams-i. 34-Last 25¢ issue. 36-r/Hero For Hire #12. 41-1st app. Thunderbolt. 45-Starlin-c. 1 3 4 6 8 10
31-34-(30¢-c variants, limited distribution)(5-8/76) 4 8 12 25 40 55
44-46-(35¢-c variants, limited distribution)(6-8/77) 8 16 24 56 108 160
47-Barry Smith-a 2 4 6 8 10 12
47-(35¢-c variant, limited distribution)(10/77) 8 16 24 56 108 160
48-Power Man/Iron Fist 1st meet; Byrne-a(p) 5 10 15 35 63 90
49-Byrne-a(p) 3 6 9 15 22 28
50-Iron Fist joins Cage; Byrne-a(p) 5 10 15 30 50 70
51-56,58-65,67-77: 58-Intro El Aguila. 75-Double size. 77-Daredevil app. 6.00
57-New X-Men app. (6/79) 4 8 12 25 40 55
66-2nd app. Sabretooth (see Iron Fist #14) 5 10 15 35 63 90
78,84: 78-3rd app. Sabretooth (cameo under cloak). 84-4th app. Sabretooth 4 8 12 25 40 55
79-83,85-99,101-124: 87-Moon Knight app. 109-The Reaper app. 4.00
100-Double size; Origin K'un L'un 1 2 3 5 6 8
125-Double size; Death of Iron Fist 2 4 6 9 12 15
Annual 1(1976)-Punisher cameo in flashback 3 6 9 14 20 25

NOTE: ***Austin*** *c-102i.* ***Byrne*** *a-48-50; c-102, 104, 106, 107, 112-116.* ***Kane*** *c(p)-24, 25, 28, 48.* ***Miller*** *a-68, 76(2 pgs.); c-66-68, 70-74, 80i.* ***Mooney*** *a-38i, 53i, 55i.* ***Nebres*** *a-76p.* ***Nino*** *a-42i, 43i.* ***Perez*** *a-27.* ***B. Smith*** *a-47i.* ***Tuska*** *a(p)-17, 20, 24, 26, 28, 29, 36, 47. Painted c-75, 100.*

POWER MAN AND IRON FIST
Marvel Comics: Apr, 2011 - No. 5, Jul, 2011 ($2.99, limited series)
1-5-Van Lente-s/Alves-a; Victor Alvarez as Power Man 3.00

POWER MAN AND IRON FIST
Marvel Comics: Apr, 2016 - No. 15, Jun, 2017 ($3.99)
1-15: 1-Luke Cage and Danny Rand; David Walker-s/Sanford Greene-a; Tombstone app. 6-9-Civil War II tie-in 4.00
...: Sweet Christmas Annual 1 (2/17, $4.99) Walker-s/Hepburn-a; Daimon Hellstrom app. 5.00

POWER OF PRIME
Malibu Comics (Ultraverse): July, 1995 - No. 4, Nov, 1995 ($2.50, lim. series)

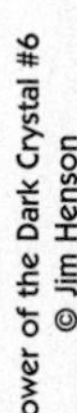
Power of the Dark Crystal #6 © Jim Henson

Powerpuff Girls #24 © Cartoon Network

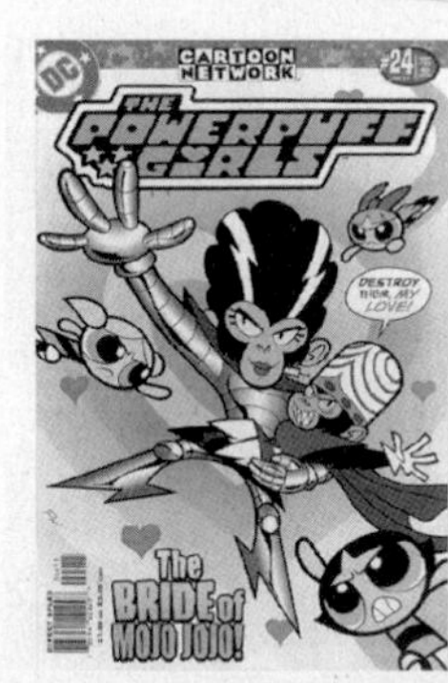

Powers #7 © Bendis & Oeming

GD VG FN VF VF/NM NM-
2.0 4.0 6.0 8.0 9.0 9.2

1-4 3.00

POWER OF SHAZAM!, THE (See SHAZAM!)
DC Comics: 1994 (Painted graphic novel) (Prequel to new series)
Hardcover-($19.95)-New origin of Shazam!; Ordway painted-c/a & script 3 6 9 14 20 25
Softcover-($7.50), Softcover-($9.95)-New-c. 2 4 6 8 10 12

POWER OF SHAZAM!, THE
DC Comics: Mar, 1995 - No. 47, Mar, 1999; No. 48, Mar, 2010 ($1.50/$1.75/$1.95/$2.50)
1-Jerry Ordway scripts begin 1 2 3 5 6 8
2-20: 4-Begin $1.75-c. 6:Re-intro of Capt. Nazi. 8-Re-intro of Spy Smasher, Bulletman & Minuteman; Swan-a (7 pgs.). 11-Re-intro of Ibis, Swan-a(2 pgs.). 14-Gil Kane-a(p). 20-Superman-c/app.; "Final Night" 3.00
21-47: 21-Plastic Man-c/app. 22-Batman-c/app. 24-Spy Smasher WWII story. 35,36-X-over w/Starman #39,40. 38-41-Mr. Mind. 43-Bulletman app. 45-JLA-c/app. 3.00
48-(3/10, $2.99) Blackest Night one-shot; Osiris rises as a Black Lantern; Kramer-a 3.00
#1,000,000 (11/98) 853rd Century x-over; Ordway-c/s/a 3.00
Annual 1 (1996, $2.95)-Legends of the Dead Earth story; Jerry Ordway-c; Mike Manley-a 4.00

POWER OF STRONGMAN, THE (Also see Strongman)
AC Comics: 1989 ($2.95)
1-Powell G.A.-r 3.00

POWER OF THE ATOM (See Secret Origins #29)
DC Comics: Aug, 1988 - No. 18, Nov, 1989 ($1.00)
1-18: 6-Chronos returns; Byrne-p. 9-JLI app. 3.00

POWER OF THE DARK CRYSTAL (Jim Henson)
BOOM! Studios (Archaia): Feb, 2017 - No. 12 ($3.99)
1-11-Simon Spurrier-s/Kelly & Nichole Matthews-a; multiple covers 4.00

POWER PACHYDERMS
Marvel Comics: Sept, 1989 ($1.25, one-shot)
1-Elephant super-heroes; parody of X-Men, Elektra, & 3 Stooges 3.00

POWER PACK
Marvel Comics Group: Aug, 1984 - No. 62, Feb, 1991
1-($1.00, 52 pgs.)-Origin & 1st app. Power Pack 5.00
2-18,20-26,28,30-45,47-62 3.00
19-(52 pgs.)-Cloak & Dagger, Wolverine app. 4.00
27-Mutant massacre; Wolverine & Sabretooth app. 5.00
29,46: 29-Spider-Man & Hobgoblin app. 46-Punisher app. 4.00
Graphic Novel: Power Pack & Cloak & Dagger: Shelter From the Storm ('89, SC, $7.95) Velluto/Farmer-a 10.00
...Holiday Special 1 (2/92, $2.25, 68 pgs.) 4.00
NOTE: ***Austin** scripts-53. **Mignola** c-20. **Morrow** a-51. **Spiegle** a-55i. **Williamson** a(i)-43, 50, 52.*

POWER PACK (Volume 2)
Marvel Comics: Aug, 2000 - No. 4, Nov, 2000 ($2.99, limited series)
1-4-Doran & Austin-c/a 3.00

POWER PACK
Marvel Comics: June, 2005 - No. 4, Aug, 2005 ($2.99, limited series)
1-4-Sumerak-s/Gurihiru-a; back-up Franklin Richards story. 3-Fantastic Four app. 3.00
... Digest (2006, $6.99) r/#1-4 7.00

POWER PACK (Marvel Legacy)
Marvel Comics: No. 63, Jan, 2018 ($3.99, one-shot)
63-Devin Grayson-s/Marika Cresta-a 4.00

POWER PACK: DAY ONE
Marvel Comics: May, 2008 - No. 4, Aug, 2008($2.99, limited series)
1-4-Van Lente-s/Gurihiru-a; origin retold; Coover-a back-ups. 1-Fantastic Four cameo 3.00

POWERPUFF GIRLS, THE (Also see Cartoon Network Starring... #1)
DC Comics: May, 2000 - No. 70, Mar, 2006 ($1.99/$2.25)
1 1 3 4 6 8 10
2-10 5.00
11-55,57-70: 25-Pin-ups by Allred, Byrne, Baker, Mignola, Hernandez, Warren 4.00
56-($2.95) Bonus pages; Mojo Jojo-c 5.00
...Double Whammy (12/00, $3.95) r/#1,2 & a Dexter's Lab story 5.00
...Movie: The Comic (9/02, $2.95) Movie adaptation; Phil Moy & Chris Cook-a 4.00

POWERPUFF GIRLS
IDW Publishing: Sept, 2013 - No. 10, Jun, 2014 ($3.99)
1-10: 1-Five covers; Troy Little-s/a; Mojo Jojo app. 2-10-Multiple covers on each 4.00

POWERPUFF GIRLS (Based on the 2016 TV reboot)
IDW Publishing: Jul, 2016 - Present ($3.99)

GD VG FN VF VF/NM NM-
2.0 4.0 6.0 8.0 9.0 9.2

1-6: 1-4-Derek Charm-a; multiple covers on each. 1-Mojo Jojo app. 4.00

POWERPUFF GIRLS: BUREAU OF BAD
IDW Publishing: Nov, 2017 - No. 3, Jan, 2018 ($3.99, limited series)
1-3-Mancini & Goldman-s/Murphy-a; multiple covers on each 4.00

POWERPUFF GIRLS: SUPER SMASH-UP!
IDW Publishing: Jan, 2015 - No. 5, May, 2015 ($3.99, limited series)
1-5-Dexter's Laboratory's Dexter & Dee-Dee app.; multiple covers on each 4.00

POWERPUFF GIRLS: THE TIME TIE
IDW Publishing: May, 2017 - No. 3, Jul, 2017 ($3.99, limited series)
1-3-Mancini & Goldman-s/Murphy-a; multiple covers on each 4.00

POWER RANGERS ZEO (TV)(Saban's...)(Also see Saban's Mighty Morphin Power Rangers)
Image Comics (Extreme Studios): Aug, 1996 ($2.50)
1-Based on TV show 4.00

POWER RECORD COMICS (Named Peter Pan Record Comics for #33-47)
Marvel Comics/Power Records: 1974 - 1978 ($1.49, 7x10" comics, 20 pgs. with 45 R.P.M. record) (Clipped corners - reduce value 20%) (Comic alone - 50%; record alone - 50%) (Some copies significantly warped by shrinkwrapping - reduce value 20%) (PR22, PR23, PR38, PR43, PR44 do not exist)
PR10-Spider-Man-r/from #124,125; Man-Wolf app. PR18-Planet of the Apes-r. PR19-Escape From the Planet of the Apes-r. PR20-Beneath the Planet of the Apes-r. PR21-Battle for the Planet of the Apes-r. PR24-Spider-Man II-New-a begins. PR27-Batman "Stacked Cards"; N. Adams-a(p). PR30-Batman "Robin Meets Man-Bat"; N. Adams-r/Det.(7 pgs.).
With record; each... 5 10 15 35 63 90
PR11-Incredible Hulk-r/#171. PR12-Captain America-r/#168. PR13-Fantastic Four-r/#126. PR14-Frankenstein-Ploog-r/#1. PR15-Tomb of Dracula-Colan-r/#2. PR16-Man-Thing-Ploog-r/#5. PR17-Werewolf By Night-Ploog-r/Marvel Spotlight #2. PR28-Superman "Alien Creatures". PR29-Space: 1999 "Breakaway". PR31-Conan-N. Adams-a; reprinted in Conan #116. PR32-Space: 1999 "Return to the Beginning". PR33-Superman-G.A. origin, Buckler-a(p). PR34-Superman. PR35-Wonder Woman-Buckler-a(p)
With record; each... 5 10 15 31 53 75
PR11, PR24-(1981 Peter Pan records re-issues) PR11-New Abomination & Rhino-c
With record; each... 5 10 15 33 57 80
PR25-Star Trek "Passage to Moauv". PR26-Star Trek "Crier in Emptiness." PR36-Holo-Man. PR37-Robin Hood. PR39-Huckleberry Finn. PR40-Davy Crockett. PR41-Robinson Crusoe. PR42-20,000 Leagues Under the Sea. PR47-Little Women
With record; each... 4 8 12 28 47 65
PR25, PR26 (Peter Pan records re-issues with photo covers). PR45-Star Trek "Dinosaur Planet". PR46-Star Trek "The Robot Masters" 4 8 12 28 47 65
NOTE: *Peter Pan re-issues exist for #25-32 and are valued the same.*

POWERS
Image Comics: 2000 - No. 37, Feb, 2004 ($2.95)
1-Bendis-s/Oeming-a; murder of Retro Girl 3 6 9 16 23 30
2-6: 6-End of Retro Girl arc. 1 3 4 6 8 10
7-14: 7-Warren Ellis app. 12-14-Death of Olympia 4.00
15-37: 31-36-Origin of the Powers 3.00
Annual 1 (2001, $3.95) 4.00
...: Anarchy TPB (11/03, $14.95) r/#21-24; interviews, sketchbook, cover gallery 15.00
...Coloring/Activity Book (2001, $1.50, B&W, 8 x 10.5") Oeming-a 3.00
... Firsts 1 (6/15, $1.00) r/#1 3.00
...: Forever TPB (2005, $19.95) r/#31-37; script for #31, sketchbook, cover gallery 20.00
...: Little Deaths TPB (2002, $19.95) r/#7,12-14, Ann. #1, Coloring/Activity Book; sketch pages, cover gallery 20.00
...: Roleplay TPB (2001, $13.95) r/#8-11; sketchbook, cover gallery 14.00
... Scriptbook (2001, $19.95) scripts for #1-11; Oeming sketches 20.00
...: Supergroup TPB (2003, $19.95) r/#15-20; sketchbook, cover gallery 20.00
...: The Definitive Collection Vol. 1 HC (2006, $29.99, dust jacket) r/#1-11 & Coloring/Activity Book, script for #1, sketch pages and covers, interviews, letter column highlights 30.00
...: The Definitive Collection Vol. 2 HC (2009, $29.99, dust jacket) r/#12-24 & Annual #1; cover gallery; 1st Bendis/Oeming Jinx story; interviews, letter column highlights 30.00
..: Who Killed Retro Girl TPB (2000, $21.95) r/#1-6; sketchbook, cover gallery, and promotional strips from Comic Shop News 22.00

POWERS
Marvel Comics (Icon): Jul, 2004 - No. 30, Sept, 2008 ($2.95/$3.95)
1-11,13-24-Bendis-s/Oeming-a. 14-Cover price error 3.00
12-($3.95, 64 pages) 2 covers; Bendis & Oeming interview 4.00
25-30-($3.95, 40 pages) 25-Two covers; Bendis interview 4.00
Annual 2008 (5/08, $4.95) Bendis-s/Oeming-a; interview with Brubaker, Simone, others 5.00
...: Legends TPB (2005, $17.95) r/#1-6; sketchbook, cover gallery 18.00

Powers: Bureau #7 © Bendis & Oeming

Preacher #34 © Ennis & Dillon

Predator: Hunters #2 © 20th Century Fox

	GD	VG	FN	VF	VF/NM	NM-
	2.0	4.0	6.0	8.0	9.0	9.2

...: Psychotic TPB (1/06, $19.95) r/#7-12; Bendis & Oeming interview, cover gallery 20.00
...: Cosmic TPB (10/07, $19.95) r/#13-18; script and sketch pages 20.00
...: Secret Identity TPB (12/07, $19.95) r/#19-24; script pages 20.00

POWERS (Volume 3)
Marvel Comics (Icon): Nov, 2009 - No. 11, Jul, 2012 ($3.95)
1-11-Bendis-s/Oeming-a 4.00

POWERS (Volume 5)
Marvel Comics (Icon): Jan, 2015 - No. 8, Apr, 2017 ($3.99)
1-8-Bendis-s/Oeming-a. 1-Bonus photo spread of TV show cast 4.00

POWERS: BUREAU (Follows Volume 3)
Marvel Comics (Icon): Feb, 2013 - No. 12, Nov, 2014 ($3.95)
1-12-Bendis-s/Oeming-a 4.00

POWERS THAT BE (Becomes Star Seed No.7 on)
Broadway Comics: Nov, 1995 - No. 6, June, 1996 ($2.50)
1-6: 1-Intro of Fatale & Star Seed. 6-Begin $2.95-c. 3.00
Preview Editions 1-3 (9/95 - 11/95, B&W) 3.00

POWER UP
BOOM! Studios: Jul, 2015 - No. 6, Dec, 2015 ($3.99)
1-6-Katie Leth-s/Matt Cummings-a. 1-Multiple covers 4.00

POW MAGAZINE (Bob Sproul's) (Satire Magazine)
Humor-Vision: Aug, 1966 - No. 3, Feb, 1967 (30¢)

	GD	VG	FN	VF	VF/NM	NM-
1,2: 2-Jones-a	4	8	12	28	47	65
3-Wrightson-a	5	10	15	34	60	85

PREACHER
DC Comics (Vertigo): Apr, 1995 - No. 66, Oct, 2000 ($2.50, mature)

	GD	VG	FN	VF	VF/NM	NM-
nn-Preview	10	20	30	69	147	225
1 ($2.95)-Ennis scripts, Dillon-a & Fabry-c in all; 1st app. Jesse, Tulip, & Cassidy	10	20	30	69	147	225
1-Retailer Incentive Edition (5/16, $3.99) r/#1 with new cover by Steve Dillon						4.00
1-Special Edition (6/09, $1.00) r/#1 with "After Watchmen" cover frame						4.00
2-1st app. Saint of Killers.	4	8	12	28	47	65
3	3	6	9	20	31	42
4,5	3	6	9	16	23	30
6-10	2	4	6	10	14	18
11,12,14,15: 12-Polybagged w/videogame w/Ennis text	1	3	4	6	8	10
13-Hunters storyline begins; ends #17; 1st app. Herr Starr	3	6	9	21	33	45
16-20: 19-Saint of Killers app.; begin "Crusaders", ends #24						6.00
21-25: 21-24-Saint of Killers app. 25-Origin of Cassidy.						4.00
26-49,52-64: 52-Tulip origin						3.00
50-($3.75) Pin-ups by Jim Lee, Bradstreet, Quesada and Palmiotti						4.00
51-Includes preview of 100 Bullets; Tulip origin	1	3	4	6	8	10
65,66-($3.75) 65-Almost everyone dies. 66-Final issue	1	3	4	6	8	10

Alamo (2001, $17.95, TPB) r/#59-66; Fabry-c 18.00
All Hell's a-Coming (2000, $17.95, TPB)-r/#51-58, ...:Tall in the Saddle 18.00
... Book One HC (2009, $39.99, d.j.) r/#1-12; new Ennis intro.; pin-ups from #50,66 40.00
... Book Two HC (2010, $39.99, d.j.) r/#13-26; new Stuart Moore intro. 40.00
... Book Three HC (2010, $39.99, d.j.) r/#27-33, ...Special: Saint of Killers #1-4 & ...Special: Cassidy: Blood & Whiskey #1; new Ennis intro. 40.00
... Book Four HC (2011, $39.99, d.j.) r/#34-40, ...Special: One Man's War, ...Special: The Story of You-Know-Who, & ...Special: The Good Old Boys; new Dillon intro. 40.00
...: Dead or Alive HC (2000, $29.95) Gallery of Glenn Fabry's cover paintings for every Preacher issue; commentary by Fabry & Ennis 30.00
...: Dead or Alive SC (2003, $19.95) 20.00
Dixie Fried (1998, $14.95, TPB)-r/#27-33, Special: Cassidy 15.00
Gone To Texas (1996, $14.95, TPB)-r/#1-7; Fabry-c 15.00
Proud Americans (1997, $14.95, TPB)-r/#18-26; Fabry-c 15.00
Salvation (1999, $14.95, TPB)-r/#41-50; Fabry-c 15.00
Until the End of the World (1996, $14.95, TPB)-r/#8-17; Fabry-c 15.00
War in the Sun (1999, $14.95, TPB)-r/#34-40 15.00

PREACHER SPECIAL: CASSIDY: BLOOD & WHISKEY
DC Comics (Vertigo): 1998 ($5.95, one-shot)
1-Ennis-scripts/Fabry-c/Dillon-a 6.00

PREACHER SPECIAL: ONE MAN'S WAR
DC Comics (Vertigo): Mar, 1998 ($4.95, one-shot)
1-Ennis-scripts/Fabry-c /Snejbjerg-a 5.00

	GD	VG	FN	VF	VF/NM	NM-
	2.0	4.0	6.0	8.0	9.0	9.2

PREACHER SPECIAL: SAINT OF KILLERS
DC Comics (Vertigo): Aug, 1996 - No. 4, Nov, 1996 ($2.50, lim. series, mature)
1-4: Ennis-scripts/Fabry-c. 1,2-Pugh-a. 3,4-Ezquerra-a 4.00
1-Signed & numbered 20.00

PREACHER SPECIAL: THE GOOD OLD BOYS
DC Comics (Vertigo): Aug, 1997 ($4.95, one-shot, mature)
1-Ennis-scripts/Fabry-c /Esquerra-a 5.00

PREACHER SPECIAL: THE STORY OF YOU-KNOW-WHO
DC Comics (Vertigo): Dec, 1996 ($4.95, one-shot, mature)
1-Ennis-scripts/Fabry-c/Case-a 5.00

PREACHER: TALL IN THE SADDLE
DC Comics (Vertigo): 2000 ($5.95, one-shot)
1-Ennis-scripts/Fabry-c/Dillon-a; early romance of Tulip and Jesse 6.00

PRECINCT, THE
Dynamite Entertainment: 2015 - No. 5, 2016 ($3.99)
1-5-Barbarie-s/Zamora-a. 1-Covers by Benitez & Robertson 4.00

PREDATOR (Also see Aliens Vs. ..., Batman vs. ..., Dark Horse Comics, & Dark Horse Presents)
Dark Horse Comics: June, 1989 - No. 4, Mar, 1990 ($2.25, limited series)

	GD	VG	FN	VF	VF/NM	NM-
1-Based on movie; 1st app. Predator	3	6	9	21	33	45
1-2nd printing	1	3	4	6	8	10
2	2	4	6	8	10	12
3,4	1	2	3	5	6	8

Trade paperback (1990, $12.95)-r/#1-4 15.00
... Omnibus Volume 1 (8/07, $24.95, 6" x 9") r/#1-4, ... Cold War, ... Dark River, ...Bloody Sands of Time mini-series and stories from Dark Horse Comics #1,2,4-7,10-12 25.00
... Omnibus Volume 2 (2/08, $24.95, 6" x 9") r/ ... Big Game, ... Race War, ...Invaders From The, Fourth Dimension mini-series and stories from Dark Horse Comics #16-18,20,21; Dark Horse Presents #46 and A Decade of Dark Horse 25.00
... Omnibus Volume 3 (6/08, $24.95, 6" x 9") r/ ... Bad Blood, ... Kindred, ...Hell and Hot Water, ... Strange Roux mini-series and stories from Dark Horse Comics #12-14 and Dark Horse Presents #119 & 124 25.00

PREDATOR
Dark Horse Comics: June, 2009 - No. 4, Jan, 2010 ($3.50, limited series)
1-4-Arcudi-s/Saltares-a/Swanland-c; variant-c by Warner 3.50

PREDATOR: (title series) **Dark Horse Comics**
--BAD BLOOD, 12/93 - No. 4, 1994 ($2.50) 1-4 4.00
--BIG GAME, 3/91 - No. 4, 6/91 ($2.50) 1-4: 1-3-Contain 2 Dark Horse trading cards 4.00
--BLOODY SANDS OF TIME, 2/92 - No. 2, 2/92 ($2.50) 1,2-Dan Barry-c/a(p)/scripts 4.00
--CAPTIVE, 4/98 ($2.95, one-shot) 1 4.00
--COLD WAR, 9/91 - No. 4, 12/91 ($2.50) 1-4: All have painted-c 4.00
--DARK RIVER, 7/96 - No.4, 10/96 ($2.95)1-4: Miran Kim-c 4.00
--HELL & HOT WATER, 4/97 - No. 3, 6/97 ($2.95) 1-3 4.00
--HELL COME A WALKIN', 2/98 - No. 2, 3/98 ($2.95) 1,2-In the Civil War 4.00
--HOMEWORLD, 3/99 - No. 4, 6/99 ($2.95) 1-4 4.00
--HUNTERS, 5/17 - No. 5, Aug, 2017 ($3.99) 1-5-Warner-s/Velasco-a/Doug Wheatley-c 4.00
--INVADERS FROM THE FOURTH DIMENSION, 7/94 ($3.95, one-shot, 52 pgs.) 1 4.00
--JUNGLE TALES. 3/95 ($2.95) 1-r/Dark Horse Comics 4.00
--KINDRED, 12/96 - No. 4, 3/97 ($2.50) 1-4 4.00
--NEMESIS, 12/97 - No. 2, 1/98 ($2.95) 1,2-Predator in Victorian England; Taggart-c 4.00
--PRIMAL, 7/97 - No. 2, 8/97 ($2.95) 1,2 4.00
--RACE WAR (See Dark Horse Presents #67), 2/93 - No. 4,10/93 ($2.50, color) 1-4,0: 1-4-Dorman painted-c #1-4, 0(4/93) 4.00
--STRANGE ROUX, 11/96 ($2.95, one-shot) 1 4.00
--XENOGENESIS (Also see Aliens Xenogenesis), 8/99 - No. 4, 11/99 ($2.95) 1,2-Edginton-s 4.00

PREDATOR: FIRE AND STONE (Crossover with Aliens, AvP, and Prometheus)
Dark Horse Comics: Oct, 2014 - No. 4, Jan, 2015 ($3.50, limited series)
1-4-Williamson-s/Mooneyham-a 3.50

PREDATOR: LIFE AND DEATH (Continues in Prometheus: Life and Death)
Dark Horse Comics: Mar, 2016 - No. 4, Jun, 2016 ($3.99, limited series)
1-4-Abnett-s/Thies-a 4.00

PREDATORS (Based on the 2010 movie)

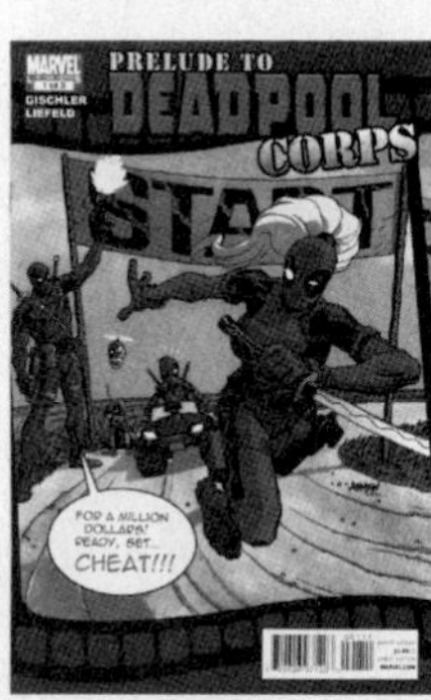

Prelude to Deadpool Corps #1 © MAR

Pride & Prejudice #1 © MAR

Princess Leia #4 © Lucasfilm

	GD 2.0	VG 4.0	FN 6.0	VF 8.0	VF/NM 9.0	NM- 9.2

Dark Horse Comics: Jun, 2010 - No. 4, Jun, 2010 ($2.99, weekly limited series)
1-4-Prequel to the 2010 movie; stories by Andreyko and Lapham; Paul Lee-c 3.00
... Film Adaptation (7/10, $6.99) Tobin-s/Drujiniu-s/photo-c 7.00
...: Preserve the Game (7/10, $3.50) Sequel to the movie; Lapham-s/Jefferson-a 3.50

PREDATOR 2
Dark Horse Comics: Feb, 1991 - No. 2, June, 1991 ($2.50, limited series)
1,2: 1-Adapts movie; both w/trading cards & photo-c 4.00

PREDATOR VS. JUDGE DREDD
Dark Horse Comics: Oct, 1997 - No. 3 ($2.50, limited series)
1-3-Wagner-s/Alcatena-a/Bolland-c 4.00

PREDATOR VS. JUDGE DREDD VS. ALIENS
Dark Horse Comics/IDW: Jul, 2016 - No. 4, Jun, 2017 ($3.99, limited series)
1-4-Layman-s/Mooneyham-a/Fabry-c 4.00

PREDATOR VS. MAGNUS ROBOT FIGHTER
Dark Horse/Valiant: Oct, 1992 - No. 2, 1993 ($2.95, limited series)
(1st Dark Horse/Valiant x-over)
1,2: (Reg.)-Barry Smith-c; Lee Weeks-a. 2-w/trading cards 4.00
1 (Platinum edition, 11/92)-Barry Smith-c 10.00

PREHISTORIC WORLD (See Classics Illustrated Special Issue)

PRELUDE TO DEADPOOL CORPS (Leads into Deadpool Corps #1)
Marvel Comics: May, 2010 - No. 5, May, 2010 ($3.99/$2.99, weekly limited series)
1-($3.99) Deadpool & Lady Deadpool vs. alternate dimension Capt. America; Liefeld-a 4.00
2-5-($2.99) Alternate reality Deadpools team-up; Dave Johnson interlocking covers 3.00

PRELUDE TO INFINITE CRISIS
DC Comics: 2005 ($5.99, squarebound)
nn-Reprints stories and panels with commentary leading into Infinite Crisis series 6.00

PREMIERE (See Charlton Premiere)

PRESIDENTIAL MATERIAL
IDW Publishing: Oct, 2008 ($3.99/$7.99)
...: Barack Obama - Biography of the candidate; Mariotte-s/Morgan-a/Campbell-c 4.00
...: John McCain - Biography of the candidate; Helfer-s/Thompson-a/Campbell-c 4.00
Flipbook ($7.99) Both issues in flipbook format 8.00

PRESTO KID, THE (See Red Mask)

PRETTY BOY FLOYD (See On the Spot)

PRETTY DEADLY
Image Comics: Oct, 2013 - Present ($3.50)
1-10-DeConnick-s/Rios-a/c 3.50

PREZ (See Cancelled Comic Cavalcade, Sandman #54 & Supergirl #10)
National Periodical Publications: Aug-Sept, 1973 - No. 4, Feb-Mar, 1974
1-Origin; Joe Simon scripts 3 6 9 17 26 35
2-4 2 4 6 13 18 22

PREZ
DC Comics: Aug, 2015 - No. 6, Feb, 2016 ($2.99)
1-6: 1-Intro. Beth Ross; Mark Russell-s/Ben Caldwell-a 3.00

PRICE, THE (See Eclipse Graphic Album Series)

PRIDE & JOY
DC Comics (Vertigo): July, 1997 - No. 4, Oct, 1997 ($2.50, limited series)
1-4-Ennis-s 3.00
TPB (2004, $14.95) r/#1-4 15.00

PRIDE & PREJUDICE
Marvel Comics: June, 2009 - No. 5, Oct, 2009 ($3.99, limited series)
1-5-Adaptation of the Jane Austen novel; Nancy Butler-s/Hugo Petrus-a 4.00

PRIDE AND THE PASSION, THE
Dell Publishing Co.: No. 824, Aug, 1957
Four Color 824-Movie, Frank Sinatra & Cary Grant photo-c
9 18 27 59 117 175

PRIDE OF BAGHDAD
DC Comics (Vertigo): 2006 ($19.99, hardcover with dustjacket)
HC-A pride of lions escaping from the Baghdad zoo in 2003; Vaughan-s/Henrichon-a 20.00
SC-(2007, $12.99) 13.00

PRIDE OF THE YANKEES, THE (See Real Heroes & Sport Comics)
Magazine Enterprises: 1949 (The Life of Lou Gehrig)
nn-Photo-c; Ogden Whitney-a 84 168 252 538 919 1300

PRIEST (Also see Asylum)
Maximum Press: Aug, 1996 - No. 2, Oct, 1996 ($2.99)
1,2 3.00

PRIMAL FORCE
DC Comics: No. 0, Oct, 1994 - No. 14, Dec, 1995 ($1.95/$2.25)
0-14: 0- Teams Red Tornado, Golem, Jack O'Lantern, Meridian & Silver Dragon.
9-begin $2.25-c 3.00

PRIMAL MAN (See The Crusaders)

PRIMAL RAGE
Sirius Entertainment: 1996 ($2.95)
1-Dark One-c; based of video game 3.00

PRIME (See Break-Thru, Flood Relief & Ultraforce)
Malibu Comics (Ultraverse): June, 1993 - No. 26, Aug, 1995 ($1.95/$2.50)
1-1st app. Prime; has coupon for Ultraverse Premiere #0 4.00
1-With coupon missing 2.00
1-Full cover holographic edition; 1st of kind w/Hardcase #1 & Strangers #1 10.00
1-Ultra 5,000 edition w/silver ink-c 6.00
2-4,6-11,14-26: 2-Polybagged w/card & coupon for U. Premiere #0. 3,4-Prototype app.
4-Direct sale w/o card.4-($2.50)-Newsstand ed. polybagged w/card.
6-Bill & Chelsea Clinton app.115-Intro Papa Verite; Pérez-c/a. 16-Intro Turbo Charge 3.00
5-($2.50, 48 pgs.)-Rune flip-c/story part B by Barry Smith; see Sludge #1 for 1st app. Rune;
3-pg. Night Man preview 4.00
12-($3.50, 68 pgs.)-Flip book w/Ultraverse Premiere #3; silver foil logo 4.00
13-($2.95, 52 pgs.)-Variant covers 4.00
...: Gross and Disgusting 1 (10/94, $3.95)-Boris-c; "Annual" on cover, published monthly
in indicia 4.00
...Month "Ashcan" (8/94, 75¢)-Boris-c 3.00
... Time: A Prime Collection (1994, $9.95)-r/1-4 10.00
...Vs. The Incredible Hulk (1995)-mail away limited edition 10.00
...Vs. The Incredible Hulk Premium edition 10.00
...Vs. The Incredible Hulk Super Premium edition 15.00
NOTE: *Perez a-15; c-15, 16.*

PRIME (Also see Black September)
Malibu Comics (Ultraverse): Infinity, Sept, 1995 - V2#15, Dec, 1996 ($1.50)
Infinity, V2#1-15: Post Black September storyline. 6-8-Solitaire app. 9-Breyfogle-c/a.
10-12-Ramos-c. 15-Lord Pumpkin app. 3.00
Infinity Signed Edition (2,000 printed) 1 2 3 5 6 8

PRIME/CAPTAIN AMERICA
Malibu Comics: Mar, 1996 ($3.95, one-shot)
1-Norm Breyfogle-a 5.00

PRIME8: CREATION
Two Morrows Publishing: July, 2001 ($3.95, B&W)
1-Neal Adams-c 4.00

PRIMER (Comico...)
Comico: Oct (no month), 1982 - No. 6, Feb, 1984 (B&W)
1 (52 pgs.) 2 4 6 13 18 22
2-1st app. Grendel & Argent by Wagner 10 20 30 66 138 210
3,4 2 4 6 9 12 15
5-1st Sam Kieth art in comics ('83) & 1st The Maxx 6 12 18 37 66 95
6-Intro & 1st app. Evangeline 2 4 6 13 18 22

PRIMORTALS (Leonard Nimoy's...)

PRIMUS (TV)
Charlton Comics: Feb, 1972 - No. 7, Oct, 1972
1-Staton-a in all 2 4 6 11 16 20
2-7: 6-Drug propaganda story 2 4 6 8 11 14

PRINCE NAMOR, THE SUB-MARINER (Also see Namor ...)
Marvel Comics Group: Sept, 1984 - No. 4, Dec, 1984 (Limited-series)
1-4 5.00

PRINCE OF PERSIA: BEFORE THE SANDSTORM (Based on the 2010 movie)
Dynamite Entertainment: 2010 - No. 4, 2010 ($3.99, limited series)
1-4-Art by Fowler and various. 1-Chang-a. 2-Lopez-a. 3-Edwards-a 5.00

PRINCESS LEIA (Star Wars)
Marvel Comics: May, 2015 - No. 5, Sept, 2015 ($3.99)
1-5-Mark Waid-s/Terry Dodson-a; story follows the ending of Episode IV 4.00

PRINCESS SALLY (Video game)

Prince Valiant #4 © KFS

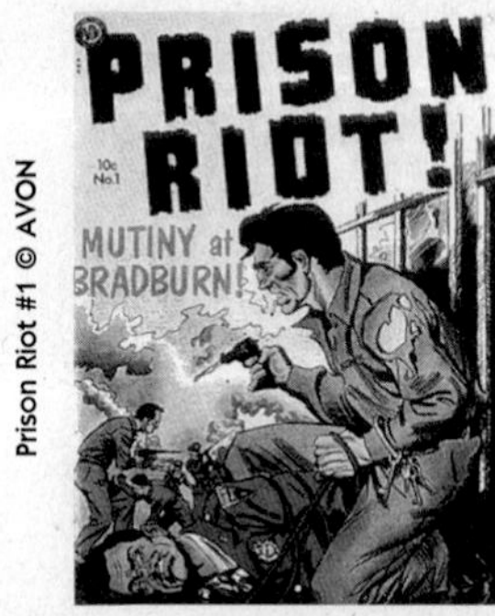

Prison Riot #1 © AVON

Prize Comics #29 © PRIZE

GD VG FN VF VF/NM NM-
2.0 4.0 6.0 8.0 9.0 9.2

GD VG FN VF VF/NM NM-
2.0 4.0 6.0 8.0 9.0 9.2

Archie Publications: Apr, 1995 - No. 3, June, 1995 ($1.50, limited series)
1-3: Spin-off from Sonic the Hedgehog 4.00

PRINCESS UGG
Oni Press: Jun, 2014 - No. 8, Mar, 2015 ($3.99)
1-8-Ted Naifeh-s/a 4.00

PRINCE VALIANT (See Ace Comics, Comics Reading Libraries *in the Promotional Comics section*, & King Comics #146, 147)
David McKay Publ./Dell: No. 26, 1941; No. 67, June, 1954 - No. 900, May, 1958
Feature Books 26 ('41)-Harold Foster-c/a; newspaper strips reprinted, pgs. 1-28,30-63; color & 68 pgs; Foster cover is only original comic book artwork by him 170 340 510 1080 1815 2550
Four Color 567 (6/54)(#1)-By Bob Fuje-Movie, photo-c 10 20 30 64 132 200
Four Color 650 (9/55), 699 (4/56), 719 (8/56),-Fuje-a 7 14 21 48 89 130
Four Color 788 (4/57), 849 (1/58), 900-Fuje-a 7 14 21 44 82 120

PRINCE VALIANT
Marvel Comics: Dec, 1994 - No. 4, Mar, 1995 ($3.95, limited series)
1-4: Kaluta-c in all 4.00

PRINCE VANDAL
Triumphant Comics: Nov, 1993 - Apr?, 1994 ($2.50)
1-6: 1,2-Triumphant Unleashed x-over 3.00

PRIORITY: WHITE HEAT
AC Comics: 1986 - No. 2, 1986 ($1.75, mini-series)
1,2-Bill Black-a 3.00

PRISCILLA'S POP
Dell Publishing Co.: No. 569, June, 1954 - No. 799, May, 1957
Four Color 569 (#1), 630 (5/55), 704 (5/56),799 5 10 15 33 57 80

PRISON BARS (See Behind...)

PRISON BREAK!
Avon Per./Realistic No. 3 on: Sept, 1951 - No. 5, Sept, 1952 (Painted c-3)
1-Wood-c & 1 pg.; has-r/Saint #7 retitled Michael Strong Private Eye 58 116 174 371 636 900
2-Wood-c; Kubert-a; Kinstler inside front-c 45 90 135 284 480 675
3-Orlando, Check-a; c-/Avon paperback #179 36 72 108 211 343 475
4,5: 4-Kinstler-c & inside f/c; Lawrence, Lazarus-a. 5-Kinstler-c; Infantino-a 32 64 96 188 307 425

PRISONER, THE (TV)
DC Comics: 1988 - No. 4, 1989 ($3.50, squarebound, mini-series)
1-4 (Books a-d) 5.00

PRISON RIOT
Avon Periodicals: 1952
1-Marijuana Murders-1 pg. text; Kinstler-c; 2 Kubert illos on text pages 42 84 126 265 445 625

PRISON TO PRAISE
Logos International: 1974 (35¢) (Religious, Christian)
nn-True Story of Merlin R. Carothers 2 4 6 13 18 22

PRIVATE BUCK
Dell Publishing Co./Rand McNally: No. 21, 1941 - No. 12, 1942 (4-1/2" x 5-1/2", 1942)
Large Feature Comic 21 (#1)(1941)(Series I), 22 (1941)(Series I), 12 (1942)(Series II) 20 40 60 114 182 250
382-Rand McNally, one panel per page; small size 10 20 30 58 79 100

PRIVATE EYE (Cover title: Rocky Jorden...#6-8)
Atlas Comics (MCI): Jan, 1951 - No. 8, March, 1952
1-Cover title: Crime Cases... #1-5 25 50 75 150 245 340
2,3-Tuska c/a(3) 15 30 45 83 124 165
4-8 13 26 39 74 105 135
NOTE: ***Henkel** a-6(3), 7; c-7. **Sinnott** a-6.*

PRIVATE EYE (See Mike Shayne...)

PRIVATE SECRETARY
Dell Publishing Co.: Dec-Feb, 1962-63 - No. 2, Mar-May, 1963
1 4 8 12 22 35 48
2 3 6 9 17 26 35

PRIVATE STRONG (See The Double Life of...)

PRIZE COMICS (...Western #69 on) (Also see Treasure Comics)
Prize Publications: March, 1940 - No. 68, Feb-Mar, 1948
1-Origin Power Nelson, The Futureman & Jupiter, Master Magician; Ted O'Neil, Secret Agent M-11, Jaxon of the Jungle, Bucky Brady & Storm Curtis begin (1st app. of each) 326 652 978 2282 3991 5700
2-The Black Owl begins (1st app.) 219 438 657 1402 2401 3400
3-Classic sci-fi-c 206 412 618 1318 2259 3200
4-Classic robot-c 258 516 774 1651 2826 4000
5-Dr. Dekkar, Master of Monsters app. 161 322 483 1030 1765 2500
6-Classic sci-fi-c; Dr. Dekkar app. 187 374 561 1197 2049 2900
7-(Scarce)-1st app. The Green Lama (12/40); Black Owl by S&K; origin/1st app. Dr. Frost & Frankenstein; Capt. Gallant, The Great Voodini & Twist Turner begin; 757 1514 2271 5526 9763 14,000
8,9-Black Owl & Ted O'Neil by S&K 174 348 522 1114 1907 2700
10-12,14,15: 11-Origin Bulldog Denny. 14-War-c 135 270 405 864 1482 2100
13-Yank & Doodle begin (8/41, origin/1st app.) 168 336 504 1075 1838 2600
16-19: 16-Spike Mason begins 123 246 369 787 1344 1900
20-(Rare) Frankenstein, Black Owl, Green Lama, Yank and Doodle WWII parade-c 354 708 1062 2478 4339 6200
21,25,27,28,31-All WWII covers 103 206 309 659 1130 1600
22-24,26: 22-Statue of Liberty Japanese attack war-c. 23-Uncle Sam patriotic war-c. 24-Lincoln statue patriotic-c. 26-Liberty Bell-c 135 270 405 864 1482 2100
29,30,32 87 174 261 553 952 1350
33-Classic bondage/torture-c 174 348 522 1114 1907 2700
34-Origin Airmale, Yank & Doodle; The Black Owl joins army, Yank & Doodle's father assumes Black Owl's role 65 130 195 416 708 1000
35-36,38-39: 35-Flying Fist & Bingo begin 55 110 165 352 601 850
37-Intro. Stampy, Airmale's sidekick; Hitler-c 258 516 774 1651 2826 4000
40-Nazi WWII-c 58 116 174 371 636 900
41-45,47-50: 45-Yank & Doodle learn Black Owl's I.D. (their father). 48-Prince Ra begins 50 100 150 315 533 750
46-Classic Zombie Horror-c/story 110 220 330 704 1202 1700
51-62,64,67,68: 53-Transvestism story. 55-No Frankenstein. 57-X-Mas-c. 64-Black Owl retires 36 72 108 211 343 475
63-Simon & Kirby c/a 39 78 117 240 395 550
65,66-Frankenstein-c by Briefer 41 82 123 256 428 600
NOTE: ***Briefer** a 7-on; c-65, 66. **J. Binder** a-16; c-21-29. **Guardineer** a-62. **Kiefer** c-62. **Palais** c-68. **Simon & Kirby** c-63, 75, 83.*

PRIZE COMICS WESTERN (Formerly Prize Comics #1-68)
Prize Publications (Feature): No. 69(V7#2), Apr-May, 1948 - No. 119, Nov-Dec, 1956 (No. 69-84: 52 pgs.)
69(V7#2) 15 30 45 90 140 190
70-75: 74-Kurtzman-a (8 pgs.) 14 28 42 81 118 155
76-Randolph Scott photo-c; "Canadian Pacific" movie adaptation 15 30 45 83 124 165
77-Photo-c; Severin/Elder, Mart Bailey-a; "Streets of Laredo" movie adaptation 14 28 42 80 115 150
78-Photo-c; S&K-a, 10 pgs.; Severin, Mart Bailey-a; "Bullet Code", & "Roughshod" movie adaptations 18 36 54 103 162 220
79-Photo-c; Kurtzman-a, 8 pgs.; Severin/Elder, Severin, Mart Bailey-a; "Stage To Chino" movie adaptation w/George O'Brien 18 36 54 103 162 220
80-82-Photo-c; 80,81-Severin/Elder-a(2). 82-1st app. The Preacher by Mart Bailey; Severin/Elder-a(3) 14 28 42 82 121 160
83,84 13 26 39 72 101 130
85-1st app. American Eagle by John Severin & begins (V9#6, 1-2/51) 20 40 60 120 195 270
86,101-105, 109-Severin/Williamson-a 14 28 42 78 112 145
87-99,110,111-Severin/Elder-a(2-3) each 14 28 42 81 110 155
100 15 30 45 85 124 165
106-108,112 10 20 30 56 76 95
113-Williamson/Severin-a(2)/Frazetta? 14 28 42 81 118 155
114-119: Drifter series in all; by Mort Meskin #114-118 9 18 27 52 69 85
NOTE: ***Fass** a-81. **Severin & Elder** c-84-99. **Severin** a-72, 75, 77-79, 83-86, 96, 97, 100-105; c-92,100-109(most), 110-119. **Simon & Kirby** c-75, 83.*

PRIZE MYSTERY
Key Publications: May, 1955 - No. 3, Sept, 1955
1 13 26 39 72 101 130
2,3 9 18 27 50 65 80

PRO, THE
Image Comics: July, 2002 ($5.95, squarebound, one-shot)
1-Ennis-s/Conner & Palmiotti-a; prostitute gets super-powers 8.00
1-Second printing with different cover 6.00
Hardcover Edition (10/04, $14.95) oversized reprint plus new 8 pg. story; sketch pages 15.00

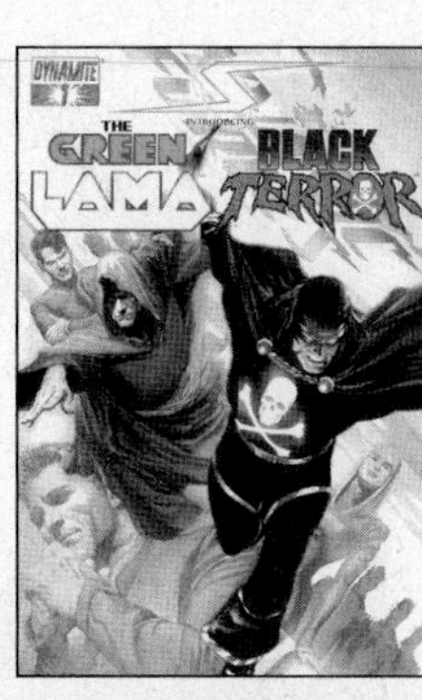

Project Superpowers #1 © SPH

Promethea #32 © ABC

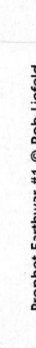

Prophet Earthwar #1 © Rob Liefeld

GD 2.0 | VG 4.0 | FN 6.0 | VF 8.0 | VF/NM 9.0 | NM- 9.2

PROFESSIONAL FOOTBALL (See Charlton Sport Library)

PROFESSOR COFFIN
Charlton Comics: No. 19, Oct, 1985 - No. 21, Feb, 1986
19-21: Wayne Howard-a(r); low print run 1 2 3 5 6 8

PROFESSOR OM
Innovation Publishing: May, 1990 - No. 2, 1990 ($2.50, limited series)
1,2-East Meets West spin-off 3.00

PROFESSOR XAVIER AND THE X-MEN (Also see X-Men, 1st series)
Marvel Comics: Nov, 1995 - No. 18 (99¢)
1-18: Stories featuring the Original X-Men. 2-vs. The Blob. 5-Vs. the Original Brotherhood of Evil Mutants. 10-Vs. The Avengers 3.00

PROGRAMME, THE
DC Comics (WildStorm): Sept, 2007 - No. 12, Aug, 2008 ($2.99, limited series)
1-12: 1-Milligan-s/C.P. Smith-a; covers by Smith & Van Sciver 3.00
Book One TPB (2008, $17.99) r/#1-6; cover sketches 18.00
Book Two TPB (2008, $17.99) r/#7-12; cover sketches 18.00

PROJECT A-KO (Manga)
Malibu Comics: Mar, 1994 - No. 4, June, 1994 ($2.95)
1-4-Based on anime film 3.00

PROJECT A-KO 2 (Manga)
CPM Comics: May, 1995 - No. 3, Aug, 1995 ($2.95, limited series)
1-3 3.00

PROJECT A-KO VERSUS THE UNIVERSE (Manga)
CPM Comics: Oct, 1995 - No. 5, June, 1996 ($2.95, limited series, bi-monthly)
1-5 3.00

PROJECT BLACK SKY
Dark Horse Comics
... Sampler (10/14, $4.99) 1-Reprints The Occultist (2013) #1, Brain Boy (2013) #0, Ghost (2013) #1, Blackout #1 5.00
Free Comic Book Day: Project Black Sky (5/14, giveaway) Capt. Midnight & Brain Boy app. 3.00

PROJECT SUPERPOWERS
Dynamite Entertainment: 2008 - No. 7, 2008 ($1.00/$3.50/$2.99)
0-($1.00) Two connecting covers by Alex Ross; re-intro of Golden Age heroes 3.00
0-($1.00) Variant cover by Michael Turner 5.00
1-($3.50) Covers by Ross and Turner; Jim Krueger-s/Carlos Paul-a 3.50
2-7-($2.99) 3.00
... Chapter One HC (2008, $29.99, dustjacket) r/#0-7; Ross sketch pages; layout art 30.00

PROJECT SUPERPOWERS: BLACKCROSS
Dynamite Entertainment: 2015 - No. 6, 2015 ($3.99)
1-6-Warren Ellis-s/Colton Worley-a; multiple covers on each 4.00

PROJECT SUPERPOWERS: CHAPTER TWO
Dynamite Entertainment: 2009 - No. 12, 2010 ($1.00/$2.99)
... Chapter Two Prelude (2008, $1.00) Ross sketch pages and mini-series previews 3.00
0-($1.00) Three connecting covers by Alex Ross; The Inheritors assemble 3.00
1-12-($2.99) 1-Krueger & Ross-s/Salazar-a; Ross sketch pages; 2 Ross covers 3.00
... X-Mas Carol (2010, $5.99) Berkenkotter-a/Ross-c 6.00

PROJECT SUPERPOWERS: HERO KILLERS
Dynamite Entertainment: 2017 - No. 5, 2017 ($3.99)
1-5-Browne-s/Woods-a. 1-Black Terror killed 4.00

PROJECT SUPERPOWERS: MEET THE BAD GUYS
Dynamite Entertainment: 2009 - No. 4, 2009 ($2.99)
1-4: Ross & Casey-s. 1-Bloodlust. 2-The Revolutionary. 3-Dagon. 4-Supremacy 3.00

PROMETHEA
America's Best Comics: Aug, 1999 - No. 32, Apr, 2005 ($3.50/$2.95)
1-Alan Moore-s/Williams III & Gray-a; Alex Ross painted-c 4.00
1-Variant-c by Williams III & Gray 4.00
2-31-($2.95): 7-Villarrubia photo-a. 10-"Sex, Stars & Serpents". 26-28-Tom Strong app. 27-Cover swipe of Superman vs. Spider-Man treasury ed. 3.00
32-($3.95) Final issue; pages can be cut & assembled into a 2-sided poster 2 4 6 9 12 15
32-Limited edition of 1000; variant issue printed as 2-sided poster, signed by Moore and Williams; each came with a 48 page book of Promethea covers 120.00
Book 1 Hardcover ($24.95, dust jacket) r/#1-6 25.00
Book 1 TPB ($14.95) r/#1-6 15.00
Book 2 Hardcover ($24.95, dust jacket) r/#7-12 25.00
Book 2 TPB ($14.95) r/#7-12 15.00
Book 3 Hardcover ($24.95, dust jacket) r/#13-18 25.00
Book 3 TPB ($14.95) r/#13-18 15.00
Book 4 Hardcover ($24.95, dust jacket) r/#19-25 25.00
Book 4 TPB ($14.99) r/#19-25 15.00
Book 5 Hardcover ($24.95, d.j.) r/#26-32; includes 2-sided poster image from #32 25.00
Book 5 TPB ($14.99) r/#26-32; includes 2-sided poster image from #32 15.00

PROMETHEUS: FIRE AND STONE (Crossover with Aliens, AvP, and Predator)
Dark Horse Comics: Sept, 2014 - No. 4, Dec, 2014 ($3.50, limited series)
1-4-Tobin-s/Ferreyra-a 3.50
... – Omega (2/15, $4.99) DeConnick-s/Alessio-a; finale to the crossover 4.00

PROMETHEUS: LIFE AND DEATH (Continues in Aliens: Life and Death)
Dark Horse Comics: Jun, 2016 - No. 4, Sept, 2016 ($3.99, limited series)
1-4-Abnett-s/Mutti-a 4.00
... – Final Conflict (4/17, $5.99) Abnett-s/Thies-a; finale of Life and Death x-over 6.00

PROMETHEUS (VILLAINS) (Leads into JLA #16,17)
DC Comics: Feb, 1998 ($1.95, one-shot)
1-Origin & 1st app.; Morrison-s/Pearson-c 3.00

PROPELLERMAN
Dark Horse Comics: Jan, 1993 - No. 8, Mar, 1994 ($2.95, limited series)
1-8: 2,4,8-Contain 2 trading cards 3.00

PROPHECY
Dynamite Entertainment: 2012 - No. 7, 2013 ($3.99, limited series)
1-7: 1-Marz-s/Geovani-a; Vampirella,Red Sonja, Dracula & Pantha app. 4-Ash app. 4.00

PROPHET (See Youngblood #2)
Image Comics (Extreme Studios): Oct, 1993 - No. 10, 1995 ($1.95)
1-($2.50)-Liefeld/Panosian-c/a; 1st app. Mary McCormick; Liefeld scripts in 1-4; #1-3 contain coupons for Prophet #0 4.00
1-Gold foil embossed-c edition rationed to dealers 6.00
2-10: 2-Liefeld-c(p). 3-1st app. Judas. 4-1st app. Omen; Black and White Pt. 3 by Thibert. 4-Alternate-c by Stephen Platt. 5,6-Platt-c/a. 7-(9/94, $2.50)-Platt-c/a. 8-Bloodstrike app. 10-Polybagged w/trading card; Platt-c. 3.00
0-(7/94, $2.50)-San Diego Comic Con ed. (2200 copies) 4.00

PROPHET
Image Comics (Extreme Studios): V2#1, Aug, 1995 - No. 8 ($3.50)
V2#1-8: Dixon scripts in all. 1-4-Platt-a. 1-Boris-c; F. Miller variant-c. 4-Newmen app. 5,6-Wraparound-c 3.50
Annual 1 (9/95, $2.50)-Bagged w/Youngblood gaming card; Quesada-c 3.00
Babewatch Special 1 (12/95, $2.50)-Babewatch tie-in 3.00
1995 San Diego Edition-B&W preview of V2#1. 3.00
TPB-(1996, $12.95) r/#1-7 13.00

PROPHET (Volume 3)
Awesome Comics: Mar, 2000 ($2.99)
1-Flip-c by Jim Lee and Liefeld 3.00

PROPHET
Image Comics: No. 21, Jan, 2012 - No. 45, Jul, 2014 ($2.99/$3.99)
21-27-($2.99): 21-Two covers; Graham-s 3.00
28-45-($3.99): 29-Dalrymple-a 4.00

PROPHET/CABLE
Image Comics (Extreme): Jan, 1997 - No. 2, Mar, 1997 ($3.50, limited series)
1,2-Liefeld-c/a: 2-#1 listed on cover 4.00

PROPHET/CHAPEL: SUPER SOLDIERS
Image Comics (Extreme): May, 1996 - No. 2, June, 1996 ($2.50, limited series)
1,2: 1-Two covers exist 3.00
1-San Diego Edition; B&W-c 3.00

PROPHET EARTHWAR
Image Comics: Jan, 2016 - No. 6, Nov, 2016 ($3.99)
1-6: 1-Graham & Roy-s/Milonogiannis & Roy-a 4.00

PROPHET: STRIKEFILE
Image Comics: Sept, 2014 - No. 2, Nov, 2015 ($3.99)
1,2-Short stories and profile pages by various 4.00

PROPOSITION PLAYER
DC Comics (Vertigo): Dec, 1999 - No. 6, May, 2000 ($2.50, limited series)
1-6-Willingham-s/Guinan-a/Bolton-c 3.00
TPB (2003, $14.95) r/#1-6; intro. by James McManus 15.00

Protectors Inc. #7 © JMS Studios

Psycho #7 © Skywald

Public Relations #1 © 1First Comics

	GD 2.0	VG 4.0	FN 6.0	VF 8.0	VF/NM 9.0	NM- 9.2

PROTECTORS (Also see The Ferret)
Malibu Comics: Sept, 1992 - No. 20, May, 1994 ($1.95-$2.95)

1-20 ($2.50, direct sale)-With poster & diff-c: 1-Origin; has 3/4 outer-c. 3-Polybagged w/Skycap						3.50
1-12 ($1.95, newsstand)-Without poster						3.00

PROTECTORS, INC.
Image Comics: Nov, 2013 - No. 10, Nov, 2014 ($2.99)

1-10-Straczynski-s/Purcell-a; multiple covers on #1-7						3.00

PROTOTYPE (Also see Flood Relief & Ultraforce)
Malibu Comics (Ultraverse): Aug, 1993 - No. 18, Feb, 1995 ($1.95/$2.50)

1-Holo-c	1	2	3	5	6	8
1-Ultra Limited silver foil-c						6.00
1,3: 3-($2.50, 48 pgs.)-Rune flip-c/story by B. Smith (3 pgs.)						4.00
2,4-12,14-18: 4-Intro Wrath. 5-Break-Thru & Strangers x-over. 6-Arena cameo. 7,8-Arena-c/story. 12-(7/94). 14 (10/94)						3.00
13 (8/94, $3.50)-Flip book (Ultraverse Premiere #6)						4.00
#0-(8/94, $2.50, 44 pgs.)						4.00
Giant Size 1 (10/94, $2.50, 44 pgs.)						4.00

PROTOTYPE (Based on the Activision video game)
DC Comics (WildStorm): Jun, 2009 - No. 6, Nov, 2009 ($3.99, limited series)

1-6-Darick Robertson-c/a						4.00
TPB (2010, $19.99) r/#1-6						20.00

PROWLER (Also see Clone Conspiracy and Amazing Spider-Man)
Marvel Comics: Dec, 2016 - May, 2017 ($3.99)

1-6-Sean Ryan-s/Javier Saltares-a. 6-Spider-Man app.						4.00

PRUDENCE & CAUTION (Also see Dogs of War & Warriors of Plasm)
Defiant: May, 1994 - No. 2, June, 1994 ($3.50/$2.50)(Spanish versions exist)

1-($3.50, 52 pgs.)-Chris Claremont scripts in all						4.00
2-($2.50)						3.00

PRYDE AND WISDOM (Also see Excalibur)
Marvel Comics: Sept, 1996 - No. 3, Nov, 1996 ($1.95, limited series)

1-3: Warren Ellis scripts; Terry Dodson & Karl Story-c/a						3.00

PSI-FORCE
Marvel Comics Group: Nov, 1986 - No. 32, June, 1989 (75¢/$1.50)

1-25: 11-13-Williamson-i						3.00
26-32						3.00
Annual 1 (10/87)						4.00
... Classic Vol. 1 TPB (2008, $24.99) r/#1-9						25.00

PSI-JUDGE ANDERSON
Fleetway Publications (Quality): 1989 - No. 15, 1990 ($1.95, B&W)

1-15						4.00

PSI-LORDS
Valiant: Sept, 1994 - No. 10, June, 1995 ($2.25)

1-($3.50)-Chromium wraparound-c						5.00
1-Gold						8.00
2-10: 3-Chaos Effect Epsilon Pt. 2						3.00

PSYBA-RATS (Also see Showcase '94 #3,4)
DC Comics: Apr, 1995-No. 3, June, 1995 ($2.50, limited series)

1-3						3.00

PSYCHO (Magazine) (Also see Nightmare)
Skywald Publ. Corp.: Jan, 1971 - No. 24, Mar, 1975 (68 pgs.; B&W)

1-All reprints	8	16	24	54	102	150
2-Origin & 1st app. The Heap, series begins	6	12	18	37	68	95
3-Frankenstein series by Adkins begins	5	10	15	35	63	90
4-7,9,10: 4-7-Squarebound. 4-1st Out of Chaos/Satan-c/s	5	10	15	33	57	80
8-(Squarebound)1st app. Edward & Mina Sartyros, the Human Gargoyles	5	10	15	35	63	90
11-17: 13-Cannabalism; 3 pgs of Christopher Lee as Dracula photos	4	8	12	27	44	60
18-Injury to eye-c	5	10	15	31	53	75
19-Origin Dracula.	4	8	12	28	47	65
20-Severed Head-c	5	10	15	33	57	80
21-24: 22-1974 Fall Special; Reese, Wildey-a(r). 24-1975 Winter Special; Dave Sim scripts (1st pro work)	5	10	15	30	50	70
Annual 1 (1972)(68 pgs.) Dracula & the Heap app.	5	10	15	30	50	70
Yearbook (1974-nn)-Everett, Reese-a	4	8	12	27	44	60

NOTE: *Boris c-3, 5. Buckler a-2, 4, 5. Gene Day a-21, 23, 24. Everett a-3-6. B. Jones a-4. Jeff Jones a-6, 7, 9; c-12. Kaluta a-13. Katz/Buckler a-3. Kim a-24. Morrow a-1. Reese a-5. Dave Sim s-24. Sutton a-3. Wildey a-5.*

PSYCHO, THE
DC Comics: 1991 - No. 3, 1991 ($4.95, squarebound, limited series)

1-3-Hudnall-s/Brereton painted-a/c						5.00
TPB (Image Comics, 2006, $17.99) r/series; Brereton sketch pages; Hudnall afterword						18.00

PSYCHOANALYSIS
E. C. Comics: Mar-Apr, 1955 - No. 4, Sept-Oct, 1955

1-All Kamen-c/a; not approved by code	24	48	72	192	309	425
2-4-Kamen-c/a in all	15	30	45	120	193	265

PSYCHOANALYSIS
Gemstone Publishing: Oct, 1999 - No. 4, Jan, 2000 ($2.50)

1-4-Reprints E.C. series						4.00
Annual 1 (2000, $10.95) r/#1-4						11.00

PSYCHOBLAST
First Comics: Nov, 1987 - No. 9, July, 1988 ($1.75)

1-9						3.00

PSYCHO BONKERS
Aspen MLT: May, 2015 - No. 4, Sept, 2015 ($3.99)

1-4-Vince Hernandez-s/Adam Archer-a						4.00

PSYCHONAUTS
Marvel Comics (Epic Comics): Oct, 1993 - No. 4, Jan, 1994 ($4.95, lim. series)

1-4: American/Japanese co-produced comic						5.00

PSYLOCKE
Marvel Comics: Jan, 2010 - No. 4, Apr, 2010 ($3.99, limited series)

1-Finch-c/Yost-s/Tolibao-a in all	4	8	12	23	37	50
2	2	4	6	10	14	18
3,4-Wolverine app.	2	4	6	8	10	12

PSYLOCKE & ARCHANGEL CRIMSON DAWN
Marvel Comics: Aug, 1997 - No. 4, Nov, 1997 ($2.50, limited series)

1-4-Raab-s/Larroca-a(p)						4.00

PTOLUS: CITY BY THE SPIRE
Dabel Brothers Productions/Marvel Comics (Dabel Brothers) #2 on: June, 2006 - No. 6, Mar, 2007 ($2.99)

1-(1st printing, Dabel) Adaptation of the Monte Cook novel; Cook-s						4.00
1-(2nd printing, Marvel), 2-6						3.00
Monte Cooke's Ptolus: City By the Spire TPB (2007, $14.99) r/#1-6						15.00

P.T. 109 (See Movie Comics)

PUBLIC DEFENDER IN ACTION (Formerly Police Trap)
Charlton Comics: No. 7, Mar, 1956 - No. 12, Oct, 1957

7	12	24	36	69	97	125
8-12	9	18	27	47	61	75

PUBLIC ENEMIES
D. S. Publishing Co.: 1948 - No. 9, June-July, 1949

1-True Crime Stories	36	72	108	211	343	475
2-Used in **SOTI**, pg. 95	28	56	84	165	270	375
3-5: 5-Arrival date of 10/1/48	19	38	57	111	176	240
6,8,9	18	36	54	107	169	230
7-McWilliams-a; injury to eye panel	19	38	57	111	176	240

PUBLIC RELATIONS
Devil's Due/1First Comics: 2015 - Present ($3.99)

1-13: 1-3-Sturges & Justus-s/Hahn-a; Annie Wu-c						4.00

PUBO
Dark Horse Comics: Dec, 2002 - No. 3, Mar, 2003 ($3.50, B&W, limited series)

1-3-Leland Purvis-s/a						3.50

PUDGY PIG
Charlton Comics: Sept, 1958 - No. 2, Nov, 1958

1,2	3	6	9	17	26	35

PUFFED
Image Comics: Jul, 2003 - No. 3, Sept, 2003 ($2.95, B&W)

1-3-Layman-s/Crosland-a. 1-Two covers by Crosland & Quitely						3.00

PULP FANTASTIC (Vertigo V2K)
DC Comics (Vertigo): Feb, 2000 - No. 3, Apr, 2000 ($2.50, limited series)

The Pulse #1 © MAR

Punch Comics #21 © CHES

Punisher V2 #37 © MAR

GD 2.0 | VG 4.0 | FN 6.0 | VF 8.0 | VF/NM 9.0 | NM- 9.2

1-3-Chaykin & Tischman-s/Burchett-a 3.00

PULP FICTION LIBRARY: MYSTERY IN SPACE
DC Comics: 1999 ($19.95, TPB)

nn-Reprints classic sci-fi stories from Mystery in Space, Strange Adventures, Real Fact Comics and My Greatest Adventure 20.00

PULSE, THE (Also see Alias and Deadline)
Marvel Comics: Apr, 2004 - No. 14, May, 2006 ($2.99)

1-Jessica Jones, Ben Urich, Kat Farrell app.; Bendis-s/Bagley-a 5.00
2-14: 2-5-Bendis-s/Bagley-a. 3-5-Green Goblin app. 6,7-Brent Anderson-a 9-Wolverine app. 10-House of M. 11-14-Gaydos-a 3.00
...: House of M Special (9/05, 50¢) tabloid newspaper format; Mayhew- "photos" 3.00
Vol. 1: Thin Air (2004, $13.99) r/#1-5, gallery of cover layouts and sketches 14.00
Vol. 2: Secret War (2005, $11.99) r/#6-9 12.00
Vol. 3: Fear (2006, $14.99) r/#11-14 and New Avengers Annual #1 15.00

PUMA BLUES
Aardvark One International/Mirage Studios #21 on: 1986 - No. 26, 1990 ($1.70-$1.75, B&W)

1-19, 21-26: 1-1st & 2nd printings. 25,26-$1.75-c 3.00
20 ($2.25)-By Alan Moore, Miller, Grell, others 5.00
Trade Paperback (12/88, $14.95) 15.00

PUMPKINHEAD (Movie)
Dynamite Entertainment: 2018 - Present ($3.99)

1-Cullen Bunn-s/Blacky Shepherd-a; 3 covers 4.00

PUMPKINHEAD: THE RITES OF EXORCISM (Movie)
Dark Horse Comics: 1993 - No. 2, 1993 ($2.50, limited series)

1,2: Based on movie; painted-c by McManus 3.00

PUNCH & JUDY COMICS
Hillman Per.: 1944; No. 2, Fall, 1944 - V3#2, 12/47; V3#3, 6/51 - V3#9, 12/51

	GD	VG	FN	VF	VF/NM	NM-
V1#1-(60 pgs.)	28	56	84	165	270	375
2	15	30	45	84	127	170
3-12(7/46)	13	26	39	74	105	135
V2#1(8/49),3-9	10	20	30	56	76	95
V2#2,10-12, V3#1-Kirby-a(2) each	22	44	66	130	213	295
V3#2-Kirby-a	20	40	60	117	189	260
3-9	9	18	27	52	69	85

PUNCH COMICS
Harry 'A' Chesler: 12/41; #2, 2/42; #9, 7/44 - #19, 10/46; #20, 7/47 - #23, 1/48

	GD	VG	FN	VF	VF/NM	NM-
1-Mr. E, The Sky Chief, Hale the Magician, Kitty Kelly begin	194	388	582	1242	2121	3000
2-Captain Glory app.	119	238	357	762	1306	1850
9-Rocketman & Rocket Girl & The Master Key begin; classic-c	300	600	900	1920	3310	4700
10-Sky Chief app.; J. Cole-a; Master Key-r/Scoop #3	77	154	231	493	847	1200
11-Origin Master Key-r/Scoop #1; Sky Chief, Little Nemo app.; Jack Cole-a; Fine-*ish* art by Sultan	81	162	243	518	884	1250
12-Rocket Boy & Capt. Glory app; classic Skull-c	2900	5800	8700	16,000	24,000	32,000
13-Cover has list of 4 Chesler artists' names on tombstone	110	220	330	704	1202	1700
14,15,21: 21-Hypo needle story	77	154	231	493	847	1200
16,17-Gag-c	40	80	120	246	411	575
18-Bondage-c; hypodermic panels	81	162	243	518	884	1250
19-Giant bloody hands-c	155	310	465	992	1696	2400
20-Unique cover with bare-breasted women. Rocket Girl-c	174	348	522	1114	1907	2700
22,23-Little Nemo-not by McCay. 22-Intro Baxter (teenage)(68 pgs.)	26	52	78	154	252	350

PUNCHY AND THE BLACK CROW
Charlton Comics: No. 10, Oct, 1985 - No. 12, Feb, 1986

10-12: Al Fago funny animal-r; low print run 6.00

PUNISHER (See Amazing Spider-Man #129, Blood and Glory, Born, Captain America #241, Classic Punisher, Daredevil #182-184, 257, Daredevil and the..., Ghost Rider V2#5, 6, Marc Spector #8 & 9, Marvel Preview #2, Marvel Super Action, Marvel Tales, Power Pack #46, Spectacular Spider-Man #81-83, 140, 141, 143 & new Strange Tales #13 & 14)

PUNISHER (The...)
Marvel Comics Group: Jan, 1986 - No. 5, May, 1986 (Limited series)

	GD	VG	FN	VF	VF/NM	NM-
1-Double size	5	10	15	31	53	75
2	3	6	9	16	23	30
3-5	2	4	6	11	16	20

Trade Paperback (1988)-r/#1-5 16.00

Circle of Blood TPB (8/01, $15.95) Zeck-c 16.00
Circle of Blood HC (2008, $19.99) two covers 20.00
NOTE: ***Zeck*** *a-1-4; c-1-5.*

PUNISHER (The...) (Volume 2)
Marvel Comics: July, 1987 - No. 104, July, 1995

	GD	VG	FN	VF	VF/NM	NM-
1	3	6	9	19	30	40
2-9: 8-Portacio/Williams-c/a begins, ends #18. 9-Scarcer, low dist.						6.00
10-Daredevil app; ties in w/Daredevil #257	2	4	6	13	18	22

11-25,50: 13-18-Kingpin app. 19-Stroman-c/a. 20-Portacio-c(p). 24-1st app. Shadowmasters. 25,50:($1.50,52 pgs.). 25-Shadowmasters app. 4.00
26-49,51-74,76-85,87-89: 57-Photo-c; came w/outer-c (newsstand ed. w/o outer-c). 59-Punisher is severely cut & has skin grafts (has black skin). 60-62-Luke Cage app. 62-Punisher back to white skin. 68-Tarantula-c/story. 85-Prequel to Suicide Run Pt. 0. 87,88-Suicide Run Pt. 6 & 9 3.00
75-($2.75, 52 pgs.)-Embossed silver foil-c 4.00
86-($2.95, 52 pgs.)-Embossed & foil stamped-c; Suicide Run part 3 4.00
90-99: 90-bound-in cards. 99-Cringe app. 3.00
100,104: 100-($2.95, 68 pgs.). 104-Last issue 4.00
100-($3.95, 68 pgs.)-Foil cover 5.00
101-103: 102-Bullseye 3.50
"Ashcan" edition (75¢)-Joe Kubert-c 3.00
Annual 1-7 ('88-'94, 68 pgs.) 1-Evolutionary War x-over. 2-Atlantis Attacks x-over; Jim Lee-a(p) (back-up story, 6 pgs.); Moon Knight app. 4-Golden-c(p). 6-Bagged w/card. 4.00
...: A Man Named Frank (1994, $6.95, TPB) 7.00
...and Wolverine in African Saga nn (1989, $5.95, 52 pgs.)-Reprints Punisher War Journal #6 & 7; Jim Lee-c/a(r) 6.00
... Assassin Guild ('88, $6.95, graphic novel) 10.00
Back to School Special 1-3 (11/92-10/94, $2.95, 68 pgs.) 4.00
.../Batman: Deadly Knights (10/94, $4.95) 6.00
.../Black Widow: Spinning Doomsday's Web (1992, $9.95, graphic novel) 12.00
...Bloodlines nn (1991, $5.95, 68 pgs.) 6.00
...: Die Hard in the Big Easy nn ('92, $4.95, 52 pgs.) 6.00
...: Empty Quarter nn ('94, $6.95) 7.00
...G-Force nn (1992, $4.95, 52 pgs.)-Painted-c 6.00
...Holiday Special 1-3 (1/93-1/95,, 52 pgs.,68pgs.)-1-Foil-c 4.00
...Intruder Graphic Novel (1989, $14.95, hardcover) 20.00
...Intruder Graphic Novel (1991, $9.95, softcover) 12.00
...Invades the 'Nam: Final Invasion nn (2/94, $6.95)-J. Kubert-c & chapter break art; reprints The 'Nam #84 & unpublished #85,86 10.00
...Kingdom Gone Graphic Novel (1990, $16.95, hardcover) 20.00
...Meets Archie (8/94, $3.95, 52 pgs.)-Die cut-c; no ads; same contents as Archie Meets The Punisher 5.00
...Movie Special 1 (6/90, $5.95, squarebound, 68 pgs.) painted-c; Brent Anderson-a; contents intended for a 3 issue series which was advertised but not published 6.00
...: No Escape nn (1990, $4.95, 52 pgs.)-New-a 6.00
...Return to Big Nothing Graphic Novel (Epic, 1989, $16.95, hardcover) 25.00
...Return to Big Nothing Graphic Novel (Marvel, 1989, $12.95, softcover) 15.00
...The Prize nn (1990, $4.95, 68 pgs.)-New-a 6.00
Summer Special 1-4(8/91-7/94, 52 pgs.):1-No ads. 2-Bisley-c; Austin-a(i). 3-No ads 4.00
NOTE: ***Austin*** *c(i)-47, 48.* ***Cowan*** *c-39.* ***Golden*** *c-50, 85, 86, 100.* ***Heath*** *a-26, 27, 89, 90, 91; c-26, 27.* ***Quesada*** *c-56p, 62p.* ***Sienkiewicz*** *c-Back to School 1.* ***Stroman*** *a-76p(9 pgs.).* ***Williamson*** *a(i)-25, 60-62i, 64-70, 74, Annual 5; c(i)-62, 65-68.*

PUNISHER (Also see Double Edge)
Marvel Comics: Nov, 1995 - No. 18, Apr, 1997 ($2.95/$1.95/$1.50)

1 ($2.95)-Ostrander scripts begin; foil-c. 4.00
2-18: 7-Vs. S.H.I.E.L.D. 11-"Onslaught." 12-17-X-Cutioner-c/app. 17-Daredevil, Spider-Man-c/app. 3.00

PUNISHER (Marvel Knights)
Marvel Comics: Nov, 1998 - No. 4, Feb, 1999 ($2.99, limited series)

1-4: 1-Wrightson-a; Wrightson & Jusko-c 3.00
1-($6.95) DF Edition; Jae Lee variant-c 7.00

PUNISHER (Marvel Knights) (Volume 3)
Marvel Comics: Apr, 2000 - No. 12, Mar, 2001 ($2.99, limited series)

	GD	VG	FN	VF	VF/NM	NM-
1-Ennis-s/Dillon & Palmiotti-a/Bradstreet-c	1	3	4	6	8	10
1-Bradstreet white variant-c	2	4	6	8	10	12
1-($6.95) DF Edition; Jurgens & Ordway variant-c	2	4	6	9	12	15

2-Two covers by Bradstreet & Dillon 3.00
3-($3.99) Bagged with Marvel Knights Genesis Edition; Daredevil app. 4.00
4-12: 9-11-The Russian app. 3.00
HC (6/02, $34.95) r/#1-12, Punisher Kills the Marvel Universe, and Marvel Knights Double Shot #1 35.00
... By Garth Ennis Omnibus (2008, $99.99) oversized r/#1-12, #1-7 & #13-37 of 2001 series,

The Punisher (2004 series) #69 © MAR

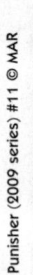

The Punisher (2009 series) #11 © MAR

PunisherMax #1 © MAR

	GD 2.0	VG 4.0	FN 6.0	VF 8.0	VF/NM 9.0	NM- 9.2

Punisher Kills the Marvel Universe, and Marvel Knights Double Shot #1; extras 100.00
.../Painkiller Jane (1/01, $3.50) Jusko-c; Ennis-s/Jusko and Dave Ross-a(p) 3.50
...: Welcome Back Frank TPB (4/01, $19.95) r/#1-12 20.00

PUNISHER (Marvel Knights) (Volume 4)
Marvel Comics: Aug, 2001 - No. 37, Feb, 2004 ($2.99)

1-Ennis-s/Dillon & Palmiotti-a/Bradstreet-c; The Russian app. 4.00
2-Two covers (Dillon & Bradstreet) Spider-Man-c/app. 3.00
3-37: 3-7-Ennis-s/Dillon-a. 9-12-Peyer-s/Gutierrez-a. 13,14-Ennis-s/Dilllon-a. 16,17-Wolverine app.; Robertson-a. 18-23,32-Dillon-a. 24-27-Mandrake-a. 27-Elektra app. 33-37-Spider-Man, Daredevil, & Wolverine app. 36,37-Hulk app. 3.00
...Army of One TPB (2/02, $15.95) r/#1-7; Bradstreet-c 16.00
Vol. 2 HC (2003, $29.95) r/#1-7,13-18; intro. by Mike Millar 30.00
Vol. 3 HC (2004, $29.95) r/#19-27; script pages for #19 30.00
Vol. 3: Business as Usual TPB (2003, $14.99) r/#13-18; Bradstreet-c 15.00
Vol. 4: Full Auto TPB (2003, $17.99) r/#20-26; Bradstreet-c 18.00
Vol. 5: Streets of Laredo TPB (2003, $17.99) r/#19,27-32 18.00
Vol. 6: Confederacy of Dunces TPB (2004, $13.99) r/#33-37 14.00

PUNISHER (Marvel MAX)(Title becomes "Punisher: Frank Castle MAX" with #66)
Marvel Comics: Mar, 2004 - No. 75, Dec, 2009 ($2.99/$3.99)

1-49,51-60: 1-Ennis-s/LaRosa-a/Bradstreet-c; flashback to his family's murder; Micro app. 6-Micro killed. 7-12,19-25-Fernandez-a. 13-18-Braithwaite-a. 31-36-Barracuda. 43-49-Medina-a. 51-54-Barracuda app. 60-Last Ennis-s/Bradstreet-c 3.00
50-($3.99) Barracuda returns; Chaykin-a 4.00
61-65-Gregg Hurwitz-s/Dave Johnson-c/Laurence Campbell-a 3.00
66-73-($3.99) 66-70-Six Hours to Kill; Swierczynski-s. 71-73-Parlov-a 4.00
74,75-($4.99) 74-Parlov-a. 75-Short stories; art by Lashley, Coker, Parlov & others 5.00
Annual (11/07, $3.99) Mike Benson-s/Laurence Campbell-a 4.00
...: Bloody Valentine (4/06, $3.99) Palmiotti & Gray-s/Gulacy & Palmiotti-a; Gulacy-c 4.00
...: Force of Nature (4/08, $4.99) Swierczynski-s/Lacombe-a/Deodato-c 5.00
...: MAX MGC #1 (5/10, $1.00) reprints #1 with "Marvel's Greatest Comics" cover logo 3.00
...: MAX: Naked Kill (8/09, $3.99) Campbell-a/Bradstreet-c 4.00
...: MAX Special: Little Black Book (8/08, $3.99) Gischler-s/Palo-a/Johnson-c 4.00
...: MAX X-Mas Special (2/09, $3.99) Aaron-s/Boschi-a/Bachalo-c 4.00
...: Red X-Mas (2/05, $3.99) Palmiotti & Gray-s/Texeira & Palmiotti-a; Texeira-c 4.00
...: Silent Night (2/06, $3.99) Diggle-s/Hotz-a/Deodato-c 4.00
...: The Cell (7/05, $4.99) Ennis-s/LaRosa-a/Bradstreet-c 5.00
...: The Tyger (2/06, $4.99) Ennis-s/Severin-a/Bradstreet-c; Castle's childhood 5.00
...: Very Special Holidays TPB ('06, $12.99) r/Red X-Mas, Bloody Valentine and Silent Night 13.00
...: X-Mas Special (1/07, $3.99) Stuart Moore-s/CP Smith-a 4.00
... MAX: From First to Last HC (2006, $19.99) r/The Tyger, The Cell and The End 1-shots 20.00
... MAX Vol. 1 (2005, $29.99) oversized r/#1-12; gallery of Fernandez art from #7 shown from layout to colored pages 30.00
... MAX Vol. 2 (2006, $29.99) oversized r/#13-24; gallery of Fernandez pencil art 30.00
... MAX Vol. 3 (2007, $29.99) oversized r/#25-36; gallery of Fernandez & Parlov art 30.00
... MAX Vol. 4 (2008, $29.99) oversized r/#37-49; gallery of Fernandez & Medina art 30.00
Vol. 1: In the Beginning TPB (2004, $14.99) r/#1-6 15.00
Vol. 2: Kitchen Irish TPB (2004, $14.99) r/#7-12 15.00
Vol. 3: Mother Russia TPB (2005, $14.99) r/#13-18 15.00
Vol. 4: Up is Down and Black is White TPB (2005, $14.99) r/#19-24 15.00
Vol. 5: The Slavers TPB (2006, $15.99) r/#25-30; Fernandez pencil pages 16.00
Vol. 6: Barracuda TPB (2006, $15.99) r/#31-36; Parlov sketch page 16.00
Vol. 7: Man of Stone TPB (2007, $15.99) r/#37-42 16.00
Vol. 8: Widowmaker TPB (2007, $17.99) r/#43-49 18.00
Vol. 9: Long Cold Dark TPB (2008, $15.99) r/#50-54 16.00

PUNISHER (Frank Castle in the Marvel Universe after Secret Invasion)
(Title changes to Franken-Castle for #17-21)
Marvel Comics: Mar, 2009 - No. 21, Nov, 2010 ($3.99/$2.99)

1-($3.99) Dark Reign; Sentry app.; Remender-s/Opena-a; character history; 2 covers 4.00
2-5,710($2.99) 2-7-The Hood app. 4-Microchip returns. 5-Daredevil #183 cover swipe 3.00
6-($3.99) Huat-a/McKone-c; profile pages of resurrected villains 4.00
11-Follows Dark Reign: The List - Punisher; Franken-Castle begins; Tony Moore-a 4.00
12-16-Franken-Castle continues; Legion of Monsters app. 14-Brereton & Moore-a 3.00
Franken-Castle 17-20: 19, 20-Wolverine & Daken app. 3.00
Franken-Castle 21-($3.99) Brereton-a/c; Legion of Monsters app.; Frank gets body back 4.00
Annual 1 (11/09, $3.99) Pearson-a/c; Spider-Man app. 4.00
...: Franken-Castle - The Birth of the Monster 1 (7/10, $4.99) r/#11 & Dark Reign: The List 5.00

PUNISHER (Frank Castle in the Marvel Universe)(Continues in Punisher: War Zone [2012])
Marvel Comics: Oct, 2011 - No. 16, Nov, 2012 ($3.99/$2.99)

1-($3.99) Rucka-s/Checchetto-a/Hitch-c 4.00
1-Variant-c by Sal Buscema 6.00
1-Variant-c by Neal Adams 10.00
2-16-($2.99): 2,3-Vulture app. 10-Spider-Man & Daredevil app. 3.00

..., Moon Knight & Daredevil: The Big Shots (10/11, $3.99) Previews new series for Punisher, Moon Knight & Daredevil; creator interviews and production art 4.00

PUNISHER, THE
Marvel Comics: Apr, 2014 - No. 20, Sept, 2015 ($3.99)

1-20: 1-Edmonson-s/Gerads-a; Howling Commandos app. 2-6-Electro app. 16,17-Captain America (Falcon) app. 19,20-Secret Wars tie-ins 4.00

PUNISHER, THE
Marvel Comics: Jul, 2016 - No. 17, Dec, 2017; No. 218, Jan, 2018 - Present ($3.99)

1-17: 1-Becky Cloonan-s/Steve Dillon-a. 7-Steve Dillon's last work. 8-12-Horak-a. 13-Anka-a 14-17-Horak-a 4.00

[Title switches to legacy numbering after #11 (11/17)]

218-221-Castle gets the War Machine armor; Vilanova-a 4.00
Annual 1 (12/16, $4.99) Gerry Conway-s/Felix Ruiz-a 5.00

PUNISHER AND WOLVERINE: DAMAGING EVIDENCE (See Wolverine and...)

PUNISHER ARMORY, THE
Marvel Comics: 7/90 ($1.50); No. 2, 6/91; No. 3, 4/92 - 10/94($1.75/$2.00)

1-10: 1-r/weapons pgs. from War Journal. 1,2-Jim Lee-c. 3-10-All new material. 3-Jusko painted-c 4.00

PUNISHER: IN THE BLOOD (Marvel Universe Frank Castle)
Marvel Comics: Jan, 2011 - No. 5, May, 2011 ($3.99, limited series)

1-5-Remender-s/Boschi-a; Jigsaw & Microchip app. 4.00

PUNISHER KILLS THE MARVEL UNIVERSE
Marvel Comics: Nov, 1995 ($5.95, one-shot)

1-Garth Ennis script/Doug Braithwaite-a 4 8 12 23 37 50
1-2nd printing (3/00) Steve Dillon-c 6.00
1-3rd printing (2008, $4.99) original 1995 cover 5.00

PUNISHER MAGAZINE, THE
Marvel Comics: Oct, 1989 - No. 16, Nov, 1990 ($2.25, B&W, Magazine, 52 pgs.)

1-16: 1-r/Punisher #1('86). 2,3-r/Punisher 2-5. 4-16: 4-7-r/Punisher V2#1-8. 4-Chiodo-c. 8-r/Punisher #10 & Daredevil #257; Portacio & Lee-r. 14-r/Punisher War Journal #1,2 w/new Lee-c. 16-r/Punisher W. J. #3,8 4.00

NOTE: ***Chiodo** painted c-4, 7, 16.* ***Jusko** painted c-6, 8.* ***Jim Lee** r-8, 14-16; c-14.* ***Portacio/Williams** r-7-12.*

PUNISHERMAX
Marvel Comics (MAX): Jan, 2010 - No. 22, Apr, 2012 ($3.99)

1-22-Aaron-s/Dillon-a/Johnson-c. 1-5-Rise of the Kingpin. 6-11-Bullseye. 17-20-Elektra app. 21-Castle dies. 22-Afterword by Aaron 4.00
...: Butterfly (5/10, $4.99) Valerie D'Orazio-s/Laurence Campbell-a/c 5.00
...: Get Castle (3/10, $4.99) Rob Williams-s/Laurence Campbell-a/Bradstreet-c 5.00
...: Happy Ending (10/10, $3.99) Milligan-s/Ryp-a/c 4.00
...: Hot Rods of Death (11/10, $4.99) Huston-s/Martinbrough-a/Bradstreet-c 5.00
...: Tiny Ugly World (12/10, $4.99) Lapham-s/Talajic-a/Bradstreet-c 5.00

PUNISHER MAX: THE PLATOON (Titled Punisher: The Platoon for #3-6)
Marvel Comics: Dec, 2017 - No. 6, Apr, 2018 ($3.99, limited series)

1-6-Ennis-s/Parlov-a; Castle's first tour of Vietnam 4.00

PUNISHER: NIGHTMARE
Marvel Comics: Mar, 2013 - No. 5, Mar, 2013 ($3.99, weekly limited series)

1-5-Texeira-a/c; Gimple-s 4.00

PUNISHER NOIR
Marvel Comics: Oct, 2009 - No. 4, Jan, 2010 ($3.99, limited series)

1-4-Pulp-style set in 1935; Tieri-s/Azaceta-a 4.00

PUNISHER: OFFICIAL MOVIE ADAPTATION
Marvel Comics: May, 2004 - No. 3, May, 2004 ($2.99, limited series)

1-3-Photo-c of Thomas Jane; Milligan-s/Olliffe-a 3.00

PUNISHER: ORIGIN OF MICRO CHIP, THE
Marvel Comics: July, 1993 - No. 2, Aug, 1993 ($1.75, limited series)

1,2 4.00

PUNISHER: P.O.V.
Marvel Comics: 1991 - No. 4, 1991 ($4.95, painted, limited series, 52 pgs.)

1-4: Starlin scripts & Wrightson painted-c/a in all. 2-Nick Fury app. 6.00

PUNISHER PRESENTS: BARRACUDA MAX
Marvel Comics (MAX): Apr, 2007 - No. 5, Aug, 2007 ($3.99, limited series)

1-5-Ennis-s/Parlov-a/c 4.00
SC (2007, $17.99) r/series; sketch pages 18.00

PUNISHER: THE END
Marvel Comics: June, 2004 ($4.50, one-shot)

Punisher 2099 #20 © MAR

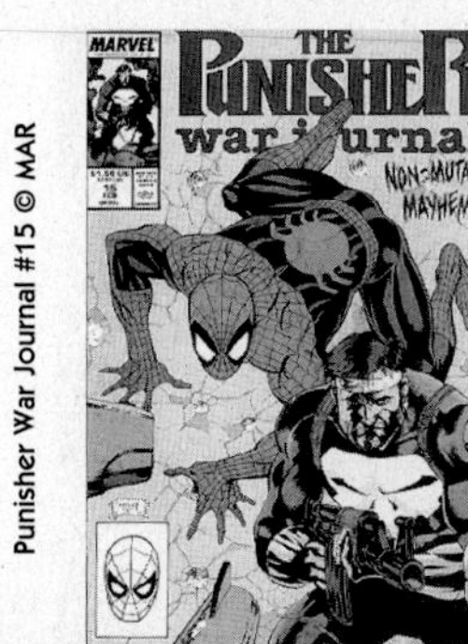

Punisher War Journal #15 © MAR

Punks Not Dead #1 © Barnett & Simmonds

GD VG FN VF VF/NM NM-
2.0 4.0 6.0 8.0 9.0 9.2

1-Ennis-s/Corben-a/c 4.50

PUNISHER: THE GHOSTS OF INNOCENTS
Marvel Comics: Jan, 1993 - No. 2, Jan, 1993 ($5.95, 52 pgs.)
1,2-Starlin scripts 6.00

PUNISHER: THE MOVIE
Marvel Comics: 2004 ($12.99,TPB)
nn-Reprints Amazing Spider-Man #129; Official Movie Adaptation and Punisher V3 #1 13.00

PUNISHER: THE PLATOON (See Punisher MAX: The Platoon)

PUNISHER: THE TRIAL OF THE PUNISHER
Marvel Comics: Nov, 2013 - No. 2, Dec, 2013 ($3.99, limited series)
1-Guggenheim-s/Yu-a/c. 2-Suayan-a; Matt Murdock app. 4.00

PUNISHER 2099 (See Punisher War Journal #50)
Marvel Comics: Feb, 1993 - No. 34, Nov, 1995 ($1.25/$1.50/$1.95)
1-Foil stamped-c 4.00
1-(Second printing) 3.00
2-24,26-34: 13-Spider-Man 2099 x-over; Ron Lim-c(p). 16-bound-in card sheet 3.00
25 ($2.95, 52 pgs.)-Deluxe edition; embossed foil-cover 5.00
25 ($2.25, 52 pgs.) 4.00
(Marvel Knights) #1 (11/04, $2.99) Kirkman-s/Mhan-a/Pat Lee-c 3.00

PUNISHER VS. BULLSEYE
Marvel Comics: Jan, 2006 - No. 5, May, 2006 ($2.99, limited series)
1-5-Daniel Way-s/Steve Dillon-a 3.00
TPB (2006, $13.99) r/#1-5; cover sketch pages 14.00

PUNISHER VS. DAREDEVIL
Marvel Comics: Jun, 2000 ($3.50, one-shot)
1-Reprints Daredevil #183,#184 & #257 4.00

PUNISHER WAR JOURNAL, THE
Marvel Comics: Nov, 1988 - No. 80, July, 1995 ($1.50/$1.75/$1.95)
1-Origin The Punisher; Matt Murdock cameo; Jim Lee inks begin 2 4 6 9 12 15
2-7: 2,3-Daredevil x-over; Jim Lee-c(i). 4-Jim Lee c/a begins. 6-Two part Wolverine story begins. 7-Wolverine-c, story ends 4.00
8-49,51-60,62,63,65: 13-16,20-22: No Jim Lee-a. 13-Lee-c only. 13-15-Heath-i. 14,15-Spider-Man x-over. 19-Last Jim Lee-c/a.29,30-Ghost Rider app. 31-Andy & Joe Kubert art. 36-Photo-c. 47,48-Nomad/Daredevil-c/stories; see Nomad. 57,58-Daredevil & Ghost Rider-c/stories. 62,63-Suicide Run Pt. 4 & 7 3.00
50,61,64($2.95, 52 pgs.): 50-Preview of Punisher 2099 (1st app.); embossed-c. 61-Embossed foil cover; Suicide Run Pt. 1. 64-Die-cut-c; Suicide Run Pt. 10 4.00
64-($2.25, 52 pgs.)-Regular cover edition 4.00
66-74,76-80: 66-Bound-in card sheet 3.00
75 ($2.50, 52 pgs.) 4.00
NOTE: ***Golden*** *c-25-30, 40, 61, 62.* ***Jusko*** *painted c-31, 32.* ***Jim Lee*** *a-1i-3i, 4p-13p, 17p-19p; c-2i, 3i, 4p-15p, 17p, 18p, 19p. Painted c-40.*

PUNISHER WAR JOURNAL (Frank Castle back in the regular Marvel Universe)
Marvel Comics: Jan, 2007 - No. 26, Feb, 2009 ($2.99)
1-Civil War tie-in; Spider-Man app; Fraction-s/Olivetti-a 5.00
1-B&W edition (11/06) 5.00
2-5: 2,3-Civil War tie-in. 4-Deodato-a 4.00
6-11,13-24,26: 6-10-Punisher dons Captain America-*esque* outfit. 7-Two covers. 11-Winter Soldier app. 16-23-Chaykin-a. 18-23-Jigsaw app. 24-Secret Invasion 3.00
12,25-($3.99) 12-World War Hulk x-over; Fraction-s/Olivetti-a. 25-Secret Invasion 4.00
... Annual 1 (1/09, $3.99) Spurrier-s/Dell'edera-a 4.00
... Vol. 1: Civil War HC (2007, $19.99) r/#1-4 and #1 B&W edition; Olivetti sketch pages 20.00
... Vol. 1: Civil War SC (2007, $14.99) r/#1-4 and #1 B&W edition; Olivetti sketch pages 15.00
... Vol. 2: Goin' Out West HC (2007, $24.99) r/#5-11; Olivetti sketch page 25.00
... Vol. 2: Goin' Out West SC (2008, $17.99) r/#5-11; Olivetti sketch page 18.00
... Vol. 3: Hunter Hunted HC (2008, $19.99) r/#12-17 20.00

PUNISHER: WAR ZONE, THE
Marvel Comics: Mar, 1992 - No. 41, July, 1995 ($1.75/$1.95)
1-($2.25, 40 pgs.)-Die cut-c; Romita, Jr.-c/a begins 6.00
2-22,24,26,27-41: 8-Last Romita, Jr.-c/a. 19-Wolverine app. 24-Suicide Run Pt. 5. 27-Bound-in card sheet. 31-36-Joe Kubert-a 3.00
23-($2.95, 52 pgs.)-Embossed foil-c; Suicide Run part 2; Buscema-a(part) 4.00
25-($2.25, 52 pgs.)-Suicide Run part 8; painted-c 4.00
Annual 1,2 ('93, 94, $2.95, 68 pgs.)-1-Bagged w/card; John Buscema-a 4.00
...: River Of Blood TPB (2006, $15.99) r/#31-36; Joe Kubert-a 16.00
NOTE: ***Golden*** *c-23.* ***Romita, Jr.*** *c/a-1-8.*

PUNISHER: WAR ZONE

GD VG FN VF VF/NM NM-
2.0 4.0 6.0 8.0 9.0 9.2

Marvel Comics: Feb, 2009 - No. 6, Mar, 2009 ($3.99, weekly limited series)
1-6-Ennis-s/Dillon-a/c; return of Ma Gnucci 4.00
1-Variant cover by John Romita, Jr. 6.00

PUNISHER: WAR ZONE (Follows Punisher 2011-2012 series)
Marvel Comics: Dec, 2012 - No. 5, Apr, 2013 ($3.99, limited series)
1-5: Rucka-s; Spider-Man and The Avengers app. 4.00

PUNISHER: YEAR ONE
Marvel Comics: Dec, 1994 - No. 4, Apr, 1995 ($2.50, limited series)
1-4 3.00

PUNK MAMBO
Valiant Entertainment: No. 0, Nov, 2014 ($3.99, one-shot)
0-Milligan-s/Gill-a; bonus preview of The Valiant #1 4.00

PUNK ROCK JESUS
DC Comics (Vertigo): Sept, 2012 - No. 6, Feb, 2013 ($2.99, B&W, limited series)
1-6-Sean Murphy-s/a/c; cloning of Jesus 3.00

PUNKS NOT DEAD
IDW Publishing (Black Crown): Feb, 2018 - Present ($3.99)
1-Barnett-s/Simmonds-a; 3 covers 4.00

PUNX
Acclaim (Valiant): Nov, 1995 - No. 3, Jan, 1996 ($2.50, unfinished lim. series)
1-3: Giffen story & art in all. 2-Satirizes Scott McCloud's Understanding Comics 3.00
(Manga) Special 1 (3/96, $2.50)-Giffen scripts 3.00

PUPPET COMICS
George W. Dougherty Co.: Spring, 1946 - No. 2, Summer, 1946
1-Funny animal in both 23 46 69 138 227 315
2 15 30 45 88 137 185

PUPPETOONS (See George Pal's...)

PUREHEART (See Archie as...)

PURGATORI
Chaos! Comics: Prelude #-1, 5/96 ($1.50, 16 pgs.); 1996 - No. 3 Dec, 1996 ($3.50/$2.95, limited series)
Prelude #-1-Pulido story; Balent-c/a; contains sketches & interviews 3.00
0-(2/01, $2.99) Prelude to "Love Bites"; Rio-c/a 3.00
1/2 (12/00, $2.95) Al Rio-c/a 3.00
1-($3.50)-Wraparound cover; red foil embossed-c; Jim Balent-a 5.00
1-($19.95)-Premium Edition (1000 print run) 20.00
2-($3.00)-Wraparound-c 3.00
2-Variant-c 5.00
...: Heartbreaker 1 (3/02, $2.99) Jolley-s 3.00
...: Love Bites 1 (3/01, $2.99) Turnbull-a/Kaminski-s 3.00
...: Mischief Night 1 (11/01, $2.99) 3.00
...: Re-Imagined 1 (7/02, $2.99) Jolley-s/Neves-a 3.00
...The Dracula Gambit-($2.95) 3.00
...The Dracula Gambit Sketchbook-($2.95) 3.00
...The Vampire's Myth 1-($19.95) Premium Ed. (10,000) 20.00
...Vs. Chastity (7/00, $2.95) Two versions (Alpha and Omega) with different endings; Rio-a 3.00
...Vs. Lady Death (1/01, $2.95) Kaminski-s 3.00
...Vs. Vampirella (4/00, $2.95) Zanier-a; Chastity app. 3.00

PURGATORI
Chaos! Comics: Oct, 1998 - No. 7, Apr, 1999 ($2.95)
1-7-Quinn-s/Rio-c/a. 2-Lady Death-c 3.00

PURGATORI
Dynamite Entertainment: 2014 - Present ($3.99)
1-5: 1-Gillespie-s; multiple covers. 2-4-Jade app. 4.00

PURGATORI: DARKEST HOUR
Chaos! Comics: Sept, 2001 - No. 2, Oct, 2001 ($2.99, limited series)
1,2 3.00

PURGATORI: EMPIRE
Chaos! Comics: May, 2000 - No. 3, July, 2000 ($2.95, limited series)
1-3-Cleavenger-c 3.00

PURGATORI: GODDESS RISING
Chaos! Comics: July, 1999 - No. 4, Oct, 1999 ($2.95, limited series)
1-4-Deodato-c/a 3.00

PURGATORI: GOD HUNTER

The Purple Claw #2 © TOBY

Puzzle Fun Comics #1 © GWD

Quantum & Woody #18 © ACC

	GD 2.0	VG 4.0	FN 6.0	VF 8.0	VF/NM 9.0	NM- 9.2

Chaos! Comics: Apr, 2002 - No. 2, May, 2002 ($2.99, limited series)

1,2-Molenaar-a/Jolley-s 3.00

PURGATORI: GOD KILLER
Chaos! Comics: Jun, 2002 - No. 2, July, 2002 ($2.99, limited series)

1,2-Molenaar-a/Jolley-s 3.00

PURGATORI: THE HUNTED
Chaos! Comics: Jun, 2001 - No. 2, Aug, 2001 ($2.99, limited series)

1,2 3.00

PURPLE CLAW, THE (Also see Tales of Horror)
Minoan Publishing Co./Toby Press: Jan, 1953 - No. 3, May, 1953

1-Origin; horror/weird stories in all 41 82 123 256 428 600
2,3: 1-3 r-in Tales of Horror #9-11 28 56 84 165 270 375
I.W. Reprint #8-Reprints #1 3 6 9 16 23 30

PUSH (Based on the 2009 movie)
DC Comics (WildStorm): Early Jan, 2009 - No. 6, Apr, 2009 ($3.50, limited series)

1-6-Movie prequel; Bruno Redondo-a. 1-Jock-c 3.50
TPB (2009, $19.99) r/#1-6 20.00

PUSSYCAT (Magazine)
Marvel Comics Group: Oct, 1968 (B&W reprints from Men's magazines)

1-(Scarce)-Ward, Everett, Wood-a; Everett-c 36 72 108 259 580 900

PUZZLE FUN COMICS (Also see Jingle Jangle)
George W. Dougherty Co.: Spring, 1946 - No. 2, Summer, 1946 (52 pgs.)

1-Gustavson-a 27 54 81 158 259 360
2 17 34 51 98 154 210

NOTE: *#1 & 2('46) each contain a* ***George Carlson*** *cover plus a 6 pg. story "Alec in Fumbleland"; also many puzzles in each.*

PvP (Player vs. Player)
Image Comics: Mar, 2003 - No. 45, Mar, 2010 ($2.95/$2.99/$3.50, B&W, reads sideways)

1-34,36-Scott Kurtz-s/a in all. 1,16-Frank Cho-c. 11-Savage Dragon-c/app. 14-Invincible app. 19-Jonathan Luna-c. 25-Cho-a (2 pgs.) 3.00
35,37-45 ($3.50): 45-Brandy from Liberty Meadows app. 3.50
#0 (7/05, 50¢) Secret Origin of Skull 3.00
...: At Large TPB (7/04, $11.95) r/#1-6 12.00
... Vol. 2: Reloaded TPB (12/04, $11.95) r/#7-12 12.00
... Vol. 3: Rides Again TPB (2005, $11.99) r/#13-18 12.00
... Vol. 4: PVP Goes Bananas TPB (2007, $12.99) r/#19-24 13.00
... Vol. 5: PVP Treks On TPB (2008, $14.99) r/#25-31 15.00
...: The Dork Ages TPB (2/04, $11.95) r/#1-6 from Dork Storm Press 12.00

Q2: THE RETURN OF QUANTUM & WOODY
Valiant Entertainment: Oct, 2014 - No. 5, Feb, 2015 ($3.99, limited series)

1-5: 1-Priest-s/Bright-a; multiple covers 4.00

QUACK!
Star Reach Productions: July, 1976 - No. 6, 1977? ($1.25, B&W)

1-Brunner-c/a on Duckaneer (Howard the Duck clone); Dave Stevens, Gilbert, Shaw-a 2 4 6 10 14 18
1-2nd printing (10/76) 5.00
2-6: 2-Newton the Rabbit Wonder by Aragonés/Leialoha; Gilbert, Shaw-a; Leialoha-c. 3-The Beavers by Dave Sim begin, end #5; Gilbert, Shaw-a; Sim/Leialoha-c. 6-Brunner-a (Duckeneer); Gilbert-a 2 4 6 8 10 12

QUADRANT
Quadrant Publications: 1983 - No. 8, 1986 (B&W, nudity, adults)

1-Peter Hsu-c/a in all 2 4 6 11 16 20
2-8 2 4 6 8 10 12

QUAKE CHAMPIONS (Based on the Bethesda Soltworks videogame)
Titan Comics: Sept, 2017 - Present ($3.99)

1-Ram V-s/Alan Quah-a; bonus character profiles; multiple covers 4.00

QUAKE: S.H.I.E.L.D. 50TH ANNIVERSARY
Marvel Comics: Nov, 2015 ($3.99, one-shot)

1-Spotlight on Daisy Johnson; Daniel Johnson-a/Nakayama-c; Avengers app. 4.00

QUANTUM & WOODY
Acclaim Comics: June, 1997 - No. 17, No. 32 (9/99), No. 18 - No. 21, Feb, 2000 ($2.50)

1-17: 1-1st app.; two covers. 6-Copycat-c. 9-Troublemakers app. 3.00
32-(9/99); 18-(10/99),19-21 3.00
The Director's Cut TPB ('97, $7.95) r/#1-4 plus extra pages 8.00

QUANTUM & WOODY
Valiant Entertainment: Jul, 2013 - No. 12, Jul, 2014 ($3.99)

1-12: 1-Asmus-s/Fowler-a; covers by Ryan Sook & Marcos Martin; origin re-told 4.00
#0 -(3/14, $3.99) Story of the goat; Asmus-s/Fowler-a/c 4.00
... Valiant-Sized #1 (12/14, $4.99) Thomas Edison app. 5.00

QUANTUM AND WOODY!
Valiant Entertainment: Dec, 2017 - Present ($3.99)

1-3: 1-Daniel Kibblesmith-s/Kano-a. 3-Portela-a 4.00

QUANTUM & WOODY: MUST DIE
Valiant Entertainment: Jan, 2015 - No. 4, Apr, 2015 ($3.99, limited series)

1-4: 1-James Asmus-s/Steve Lieber-a; multiple covers on each 4.00

QUANTUM LEAP (TV) (See A Nightmare on Elm Street)
Innovation Publishing: Sept, 1991 - No. 12, Jun, 1993 ($2.50, painted-c)

1-12: Based on TV show; all have painted-c. 8-Has photo gallery 4.00
Special Edition 1 (10/92)-r/#1 w/8 extra pgs. of photos & articles 4.00
Time and Space Special 1 (#13) ($2.95)-Foil logo 4.00

QUANTUM TUNNELER, THE
Revolution Studio: Oct, 2001 (no cover price, one-shot)

1-Prequel to "The One" movie; Clayton Henry-a 3.00

QUARANTINE ZONE
DC Comics: Apr, 2016 ($22.99, HC graphic novel)

HC - Daniel Wilson-s/Fernando Pasarin-a 23.00

QUASAR (See Avengers #302, Captain America #217, Incredible Hulk #234, Marvel Team-Up #113 & Marvel Two-in-One #53)
Marvel Comics: Oct, 1989 - No. 60, Jul, 1994 ($1.00/$1.25, Direct sales #17 on)

1-Gruenwald-s/Paul Ryan-c/a begin; Origin of Wendell Vaughn from Marvel Man to Quasar; Marvel Boy & Fantastic Four app. 6.00
2-6: 2-Origin of the Quantum-Bands; Deathurge & Eon app; Quasar becomes 'Protector of the Universe'. 3-Human Torch app. 4-Aquarian app. 5,6-Acts of Vengeance tie-in. 5-Absorbing Man & Loki app. 6-Red Ghost, Living Laser, Uatu the Watcher app; Venom cameo (2pgs); last Ryan-a(p) 3.00
7-Spider-Man & Quasar vs. Terminus 4.00
8-14,18: 8-Secret Wars x-over; Mike Manley-a begins. 9-Modam (female Modok) app. 10-Dr. Minerva app. 11-Excalibur & Mordred app; first Moondragon as 'H.D Steckley'. 12-Eternals app.; death of Quasar's father (Gilbert). 13-Squadron Supreme & Overmind app. 14-McFarlane-c; Squadron Supreme, Overmind app. 18-1st app. Origin & Unbeing; new Quasar costume; 1st Greg Capullo-a 3.00
15,16: 15-Mignola-c; Squadron Supreme, Overmind, the Stranger & the Watchers app. 16-($1.50, 52 pgs.) Squadron Supreme, Overmind, Stranger & the Watchers app. 4.00
17-Features Marvel's speedsters: Quicksilver, Makkari, Captain Marvel (Monica Rambeau), Speed Demon, Black Racer, Super Sabre & the Runner; Flash parody 'Buried Alien' 5.00
19-(2/91)-Re-intro Jack of Hearts & Maelstrom (neither one seen since 1984); Dr. Strange app. 6.00
20,21: 20-Fantastic Four & the Presence app. 21-Maelstrom revealed as the 'Cosmic Assassin' 5.00
22,23,27,29: 22-Quasar dies; Deathurge app. 'H.D Steckley' revealed to be Moondragon. 23-Ghost Rider app. 27-Original Marvel Boy app. 29-Kismet (Her) app; Vanity Fair Demi Moore pregnancy parody-c 3.00
24-Brief Infinity Gauntlet reference; Thanos & Mephisto app.; vs. Maelstrom; 1st app. Infinity (the female aspect of Eternity) 1 2 3 5 6 8
25-($1.50)-New costume Quasar (returns to life); Eternity, Infinity, Oblivion, Death, Celestials, Galactus, Watchers app.; 'death' of Maelstrom 4.00
26-Infinity Gauntlet tie-in; Thanos & Moondragon app. 5.00
28,30-33: 28-Kismet (Her) app.; Avengers; Warlock, Moondragon, Jack of Hearts app. 30-What If..? issue; Watcher, Thanos, Maelstrom app. 31-Quasar in the New Universe; gains the power of the Starbrand. 32-Operation Galactic Storm Pt. 3; continued from Avengers West Coast #80; Shi'ar Imperial Guard app.; 1st app. Korath the Pursuer. 33-Operation Galactic Storm Pt.10; continued from Avengers West Coast #81; story continues in Wonder Man #8 (#32-34 same as Special #1-3) 4.00
34-39,41-49,51-53: 34-Operation Galactic Storm Pt. 17; continued from Captain America #400; continued in Avengers West Coast #82. 35-Operation Galactic Storm aftermath; Quasar quits the Avengers. 38-Infinity War x-over; Quasar & the Avengers vs. Warlock, Thanos & the Infinity Watch; last Capullo-a. 39-Infinity War x-over; Thanos & Deathurge app. 41-Avengers app. 42-Punisher app. 43-Quasar returns to life. 47,48-Thunderstrike app. 49-Kismet app. 51,52: 52-Squadron Supreme app. 53-Warlock & the Infinity Watch app. 3.00
40,50: 40-Infinity War x-over; Quasar uses the Ultimate Nullifier and dies; Thanos app. 50-($2.95, 52 pgs.)-Holo-grafix foil-c Silver Surfer, Man-Thing, Ren & Stimpy app. 4.00
54,55: 53-Warlock & the Infinity Watch app. 54-Starblast tie-in; continued from Starblast #1; Hyperion vs. Gladiator. 55-Starblast tie-in; continued from Starblast #2; Black Bolt app; continued in Starblast #3 4.00

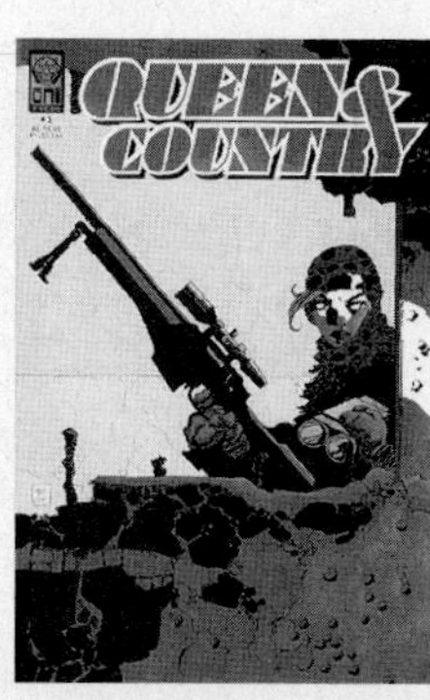

Queen & Country #1 © Greg Rucka

Queen Sonja #35 © RS LLC

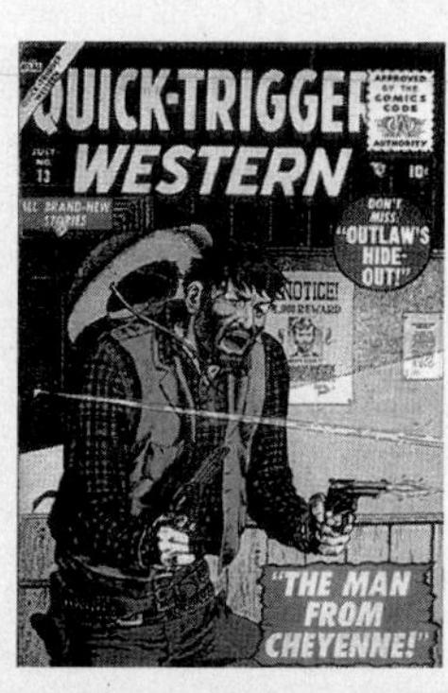

Quick Trigger Western #13 © MAR

GD 2.0 | VG 4.0 | FN 6.0 | VF 8.0 | VF/NM 9.0 | NM- 9.2

56-57: 56-Starblast tie-in; continued from Starblast #4; New Universe app.; continued in Starblast #4. 57-Living Tribunal & the New Universe app. 5.00
58,59: 58-w/bound-in card sheet; Makkari wins the Galactic Race; DC Comics Flash (as Fastforward) app. 59-Thanos & Starfox app. 6.00
60-Last issue; Avengers, New Warriors & Fantastic Four app; Quasar leaves Earth 1 2 3 5 6 8
Special #1-3 ($1.25, newsstand)-Same as #32-34 3.00

QUEEN & COUNTRY (See Whiteout)
Oni Press: Mar, 2001 - No. 32, Aug, 2007 ($2.95/$2.99, B&W)

1-Rucka-s in all. Rolston-a/Sale-c 1 2 3 4 5 7
2-5: 2-4-Rolston-a/Sale-c. 5-Snyder-c/Hurtt-a 4.00
6-24,26-32: 6,7-Snyder-c/Hurtt-a. 13-15-Alexander-a. 16-20-McNeil-a. 21-24-Hawthorne-a 26-28-Norton-a 3.00
25-($5.99) Rolston-a 6.00
Free Comic Book Day giveaway (5/02) r/#1 with "Free Comic Book Day" banner on-c 3.00
Operation: Blackwall (10/03, $8.95, TPB) r/#13-15; John Rogers intro. 9.00
Operation: Broken Ground (2002, $11.95, TPB) r/#1-4; Ellis intro. 12.00
Operation: Crystal Ball (1/03, $14.95, TPB) r/#8-12; Judd Winick intro. 15.00
Operation: Dandelion HC (8/04, $25.00) r/#21-24; Jamie S. Rich intro. 25.00
Operation: Dandelion (8/04, $11.95, TPB) r/#21-24; Jamie S. Rich intro. 12.00
Operation: Morningstar (9/02, $8.95, TPB) r/#5-7; Stuart Moore intro. 9.00
Operation: Storm Front (3/04, $14.95, TPB) r/#16-20; Geoff Johns intro. 15.00

QUEEN & COUNTRY: DECLASSIFIED
Oni Press: Nov, 2002 - No. 3, Jan, 2003 ($2.95, B&W, limited series)

1-3-Rucka-s/Hurtt-a/Morse-c 3.00
TPB (7/03, $8.95) r/#1-3; intro. by Micah Wright 9.00

QUEEN & COUNTRY: DECLASSIFIED (Volume 2)
Oni Press: Jan, 2005 - No. 3, Feb, 2006 ($2.95/$2.99, B&W, limited series)

1-3-Rucka-s/Burchett-a/c 3.00
TPB (3/06, $8.95) r/#1-3 9.00

QUEEN & COUNTRY: DECLASSIFIED (Volume 3)
Oni Press: Jun, 2005 - No. 3, Aug, 2005 ($2.95, B&W, limited series)

1-3- "Sons & Daughters;" Johnston-s/Mitten-a/c 3.00
TPB (3/06, $8.95) r/#1-3 9.00

QUEEN OF THE WEST, DALE EVANS (TV)(See Dale Evans Comics, Roy Rogers & Western Roundup under Dell Giants)
Dell Publ. Co.: No. 479, 7/53 - No. 22, 1-3/59 (All photo-c; photo back c-4-8,15)

Four Color 479(#1, '53) 16 32 48 110 243 375
Four Color 528(#2, '54) 9 18 27 60 120 180
3,4: 3(4-6/54)-Toth-a. 4-Toth, Manning-a 7 14 21 46 86 125
5-10-Manning-a. 5-Marsh-a 6 12 18 40 73 105
11,19,21-No Manning 21-Tufts-a 5 10 15 31 53 75
12-18,20,22-Manning-a 5 10 15 34 60 85

QUEEN SONJA (See Red Sonja)
Dynamite Entertainment: 2009 - No. 35, 2013 ($2.99/$3.99)

1-10: 1-Rubi-a/Ortega-s; 3 covers; back-up r/Marvel Feature #1 4.00
11-35-($3.99) 16-Thulsa Doom returns 4.00

QUENTIN DURWARD
Dell Publishing Co.: No. 672, Jan, 1956

Four Color 672-Movie, photo-c 6 12 18 42 79 115

QUESTAR ILLUSTRATED SCIENCE FICTION CLASSICS
Golden Press: 1977 (224 pgs.) ($1.95)

11197-Stories by Asimov, Sturgeon, Silverberg & Niven; Starstream-r 3 6 9 20 30 40

QUEST FOR CAMELOT
DC Comics: July, 1998 ($4.95)

1-Movie adaption 5.00

QUEST FOR DREAMS LOST (Also see Word Warriors)
Literacy Volunteers of Chicago: July 4, 1987 ($2.00, B&W, 52 pgs.)(Proceeds donated to help fight illiteracy)

1-Teenage Mutant Ninja Turtles by Eastman/Laird, Trollords, Silent Invasion, The Realm, Wordsmith, Reacto Man, Eb'nn, Aniverse 4.00

QUESTION, THE (See Americomics, Blue Beetle (1967), Charlton Bullseye & Mysterious Suspense)

QUESTION, THE (Also see Showcase '95 #3)
DC Comics: Feb, 1987 - No. 36, Mar, 1990; No. 37, Mar, 2010 ($1.50)

1-36: Denny O'Neil scripts in all 3.00
37-(3/10, $2.99) Blackest Night one-shot; Victor Sage rises; Shiva app.; Cowan-a 3.00
Annual 1 (1988, $2.50) 4.00
Annual 2 (1989, $3.50) 4.00
...: Epitaph For a Hero TPB (2008, $19.99) r/#13-18 20.00
...: Peacemaker TPB (2010, $19.99) r/#31-36 20.00
...: Pipeline TPB (2011, $14.99) r/stories from Detective Comics #854-865; sketch-a 15.00
...: Poisoned Ground TPB (2008, $19.99) r/#7-12 20.00
...: Riddles TPB (2009, $19.99) r/#25-30 20.00
...: Welcome to Oz TPB (2009, $19.99) r/#19-24 20.00
...: Zen and Violence TPB (2007, $19.99) r/#1-6 20.00

QUESTION, THE (Also see Crime Bible and 52)
DC Comics: Jan, 2005 - No. 6, Jun, 2005 ($2.95, limited series)

1-6-Rick Veitch-s/Tommy Lee Edwards-a. 4,6-Superman app. 3.00

QUESTION QUARTERLY, THE
DC Comics: Summer, 1990 - No. 5, Spring, 1992 ($2.50/$2.95, 52pgs.)

1-5 4.00
NOTE: *Cowan a-1, 2, 4, 5; c-1-3, 5.* ***Mignola*** *a-5i.* ***Quesada*** *a-3-5.*

QUESTION RETURNS, THE
DC Comics: Feb, 1997 ($3.50, one-shot)

1-Brereton-c 4.00

QUESTPROBE
Marvel Comics: 8/84; No. 2, 1/85; No. 3, 11/85 (lim. series)

1-3: 1-The Hulk app. by Romita. 2-Spider-Man; Mooney-a(i). 3-Human Torch & Thing 4.00

QUICK DRAW McGRAW (TV) (Hanna-Barbera)(See Whitman Comic Books)
Dell Publishing Co./Gold Key No. 12 on: No. 1040, 12-2/59-60 - No. 11, 7-9/62; No. 12, 11/62; No. 13, 2/63; No. 14, 4/63; No. 15, 6/69 (1st show aired 9/29/59)

Four Color 1040(#1) 1st app. Quick Draw & Baba Looey, Augie Doggie & Doggie Daddy and Snooper & Blabber 12 24 36 83 182 280
2(4-6/60)-4,6: 2-Augie Doggie & Snooper & Blabber stories (8 pgs. each); pre-dates both of their #1 issues. 4-Augie Doggie & Snooper & Blabber stories. 5 10 15 35 63 90
5-1st Snagglepuss app.; last 10¢ issue 6 12 18 38 69 100
7-11 5 10 15 30 50 70
12,13-Title change to ...Fun-Type Roundup (84pgs.) 6 12 18 38 69 100
14,15: 15-Reprints 4 8 12 27 44 60

QUICK DRAW McGRAW (TV)(See Spotlight #2)
Charlton Comics: Nov, 1970 - No. 8, Jan, 1972 (Hanna-Barbera)

1 5 10 15 30 50 70
2-8 3 6 9 18 28 38

QUICKSILVER (See Avengers)
Marvel Comics: Nov, 1997 - No. 13, Nov, 1998 ($2.99/$1.99)

1-($2.99)-Peyer-s/Casey Jones-a; wraparound-c 4.00
2-11: 2-Two covers-variant by Golden. 4-6-Inhumans app. 3.00
12-($2.99) Siege of Wundagore pt. 4 4.00
13-Magneto-c/app.; last issue 3.00

QUICK-TRIGGER WESTERN (...Action #12; Cowboy Action #5-11)
Atlas Comics (ACI #12/WPI #13-19): No. 12, May, 1956 - No. 19, Sept, 1957

12-Baker-a 20 40 60 120 195 270
13-Williamson-a, 5 pgs. 18 36 54 103 162 220
14-Everett, Crandall, Torres-a; Heath-c 16 32 48 94 147 200
15,16: 15-Torres, Crandall-a. 16-Orlando, Kirby-a 15 30 45 84 127 170
17,18: 18-Baker-a 15 30 45 83 124 165
19 13 26 39 74 105 135
NOTE: ***Ayers*** *a-17.* ***Colan*** *a-16.* ***Maneely*** *a-15, 17; c-15, 18.* ***Morrow*** *a-18.* ***Powell*** *a-14.* ***Severin*** *a-19; c-12, 13, 16, 17, 19.* ***Shores*** *a-16.* ***Tuska*** *a-17.*

QUINCY (See Comics Reading Libraries in the Promotional Comics section)

QUITTER, THE
DC Comics (Vertigo): 2005 ($19.99, B&W graphic novel)

HC ($19.99) Autobiography of Harvey Pekar; Pekar-s/Daen Haspiel-a 20.00
SC (2006, $12.99) 13.00

RACCOON KIDS, THE (Formerly Movietown Animal Antics)
National Periodical Publications (Arleigh No. 63,64): No. 52, Sept-Oct, 1954 - No. 62, Oct-Nov, 1956; No. 63, Sept, 1957; No. 64, Nov, 1957

52-Doodles Duck by Mayer 15 30 45 83 124 165
53-64: 53-62-Doodles Duck by Mayer 11 22 33 62 86 110
NOTE: ***Otto Feuer****-a most issues.* ***Rube Grossman****-a most issues.*

RACE FOR THE MOON
Harvey Publications: Mar, 1958 - No. 3, Nov, 1958

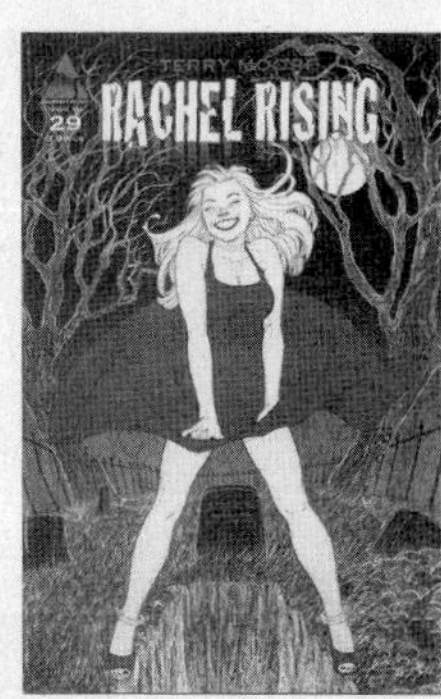

Rachel Rising #29 © Terry Moore

Radioactive Man #9 © Bongo

Ragman (2017 series) #1 © DC

	GD 2.0	VG 4.0	FN 6.0	VF 8.0	VF/NM 9.0	NM- 9.2

1-Powell-a(5); 1/2-pg. S&K-a; cover redrawn from Galaxy Science Fiction pulp (5/53)

	18	36	54	107	169	230
2-Kirby/Williamson-c(r)/a(3); Kirby-p 7 more stys	27	54	81	158	259	360
3-Kirby/Williamson-c/a(4); Kirby-p 6 more stys	30	60	90	177	289	400

RACER-X
Now Comics: 8/88 - No. 11, 8/89; V2#1, 9/89 - V2#10, 1990 ($1.75)

0-Deluxe ($3.50) 5.00
1 (9/88) - 11, V2#1-10 4.00

RACER X (See Speed Racer)
DC Comics (WildStorm): Oct, 2000 - No. 3, Dec, 2000 ($2.95, limited series)

1-3: 1-Tommy Yune-s/Jo Chen-a; 2 covers by Yune. 2,3-Kabala app. 4.00

RACHEL RISING
Abstract Studio: 2011 - No. 42, 2016 ($3.99, B&W)

1-Terry Moore-s/a/c; back cover by Fabio Moon; green background on cover 80.00
1-(2nd printing) Red background on cover 35.00
1-(3rd printing) Red background on cover 35.00
2 35.00
3-6 10.00
7-42: 42-Final issue 4.00
Halloween ComicFest Edition (2014, giveaway) Reprints #1 with orange bkgd on cover 5.00

RACING PETTYS
STP Corp.: 1980 ($2.50, 68 pgs., 10 1/8" x 13 1/4")

1-Bob Kane-a. Kane bio on inside back-c.	2	4	6	8	10	12

RACK & PAIN
Dark Horse Comics: Mar, 1994 - No. 4, June, 1994 ($2.50, limited series)

1-4: Brian Pulido scripts in all. 1-Greg Capullo-c 3.00

RACK & PAIN: KILLERS
Chaos! Comics: Sept, 1996 - No. 4, Jan, 1997 ($2.95, limited series)

1-4: Reprints Dark Horse series; Jae Lee-c 3.00

RACKET SQUAD IN ACTION
Capitol Stories/Charlton Comics: May-June, 1952 - No. 29, Mar, 1958

1	34	68	102	199	325	450
2-4,6: 3,4,6-Dr. Neff, Ghost Breaker app.	18	36	54	103	162	220
5-Dr. Neff, Ghost Breaker app; headlights-c	48	96	144	302	514	725
7-10: 10-Explosion-c	15	30	45	90	140	190
11-Ditko-c/a	39	78	117	231	378	525
12-Ditko explosion-c (classic); Shuster-a(2)	63	126	189	403	689	975
13-Shuster-c(p)/a.	14	28	42	81	118	155
14-Marijuana story "Shakedown"; Giordano-c	19	38	57	111	176	240
15-28: 15,20,22,23-Giordano-c	13	26	39	74	105	135
29-(15¢, 68 pgs.)	15	30	45	85	130	175

RADIANT LOVE (Formerly Daring Love #1)
Gilmor Magazines: No. 2, Dec, 1953 - No. 6, Aug, 1954

2	21	42	63	126	206	285
3-6	15	30	45	90	140	190

RADICAL DREAMER
Blackball Comics: No. 0, May, 1994 - No. 4, Nov, 1994 ($1.99, bi-monthly) (1st poster format comic)

0-4: 0-2-($1.99, poster format): 0-1st app. Max Wrighter. 3,4-($2.50-c) 3.00

RADICAL DREAMER
Mark's Giant Economy Size Comics: V2#1, June, 1995 - V2#6, Feb, 1996 ($2.95, B&W, limited series)

V2#1-6 3.00
Prime (5/96, $2.95) 3.00
Dreams Cannot Die!-(1996, $20.00, softcover)-Collects V1#0-4 & V2#1-6; intro by Kurt Busiek; afterward by Mark Waid 20.00
Dreams Cannot Die!-(1996, $60.00, hardcover)-Signed & limited edition; collects V1#0-4 & V2#1-6; intro by Kurt Busiek; afterward by Mark Waid 60.00

RADIOACTIVE MAN (Simpsons TV show)
Bongo Comics: 1993 - No. 6, 1994 ($1.95/$2.25, limited series)

1-($2.95)-Glow-in-the-dark-c; bound-in jumbo poster; origin Radioactive Man;

(cover dated Nov. 1952)	1	3	4	6	8	10

2-6: 2-Says #88 on-c & inside & dated May 1962; cover parody of Atlas Kirby monster-c; Superior Squad app.; origin Fallout Boy. 3-($1.95)-Cover "dated" Aug 1972 #216. 4-($2.25)-Cover "dated" Oct 1980 #412; w/trading card. 5-Cover "dated" Jan 1986 #679; w/trading card. 6-(Jan 1995 #1000) 4.00
Colossal #1-($4.95) 7.00
#4 (2001, $2.50) Faux 1953 issue; Murphy Anderson-i (6 pgs.) 3.00
#100 (2000, $2.50) Comic Book Guy-c/app.; faux 1963 issue inside 3.00
#136 (2001, $2.50) Dan DeCarlo-c/a 3.00
#222 (2001, $2.50) Batton Lash-s; Radioactive Man in 1972-style 3.00
#575 (2002, $2.50) Chaykin-c; Radioactive Man in 1984-style 3.00
1963-106 (2002, $2.50) Radioactive Man in 1960s Gold Key-style; Groening-c 3.00
#7 Bongo Super Heroes Starring... (2003, $2.50) Marvel Silver Age-style Superior Squad 3.00
#8 Official Movie Adaptation (2004, $2.99) starring Rainier Wolfcastle and Milhouse 3.00
#9 (#197 on-c) (2004, $2.50) Kirby-esque New Gods spoof; Golden Age Radio Man app. 3.00

RADIO FUNNIES
DC Comics: Mar. 1939; undated variant

nn-(3/39) Ashcan comic, not distributed to newsstands, only for in-house use. Cover art is Adventure Comics #39 with interior being Detective Comics #19 (no known sales)
nn - Ashcan comic. No date. Cover art is Detective #26 with interior from Detective #17; one copy, graded at GD/VG, sold at auction for $4481.25 in Nov, 2009. Another copy graded at GD/VG sold at auction for $3346 in Feb, 2010.

RAGAMUFFINS
Eclipse Comics: Jan, 1985 ($1.75, one shot)

1-Eclipse Magazine-r, w/color; Colan-a 3.00

RAGE (Based on the id video game)
Dark Horse Comics: Jun, 2011 - No. 3, Aug, 2011 ($3.50, limited series)

1-3-Nelson-s/Mutti-a/Fabry-c. 1-Variant-c by Martiniere 3.50

RAGEMOOR
Dark Horse Comics: Mar, 2012 - No. 4, Jun, 2012 ($3.50, B&W, limited series)

1-4-Richard Corben-a/c; Jan Strnad-s 3.50

RAGGEDY ANN AND ANDY (See Dell Giants, March of Comics #23 & New Funnies)
Dell Publishing Co.: No. 5, 1942 - No. 533, 2/54; 10-12/64 - No. 4, 3/66

Four Color 5(1942)	46	92	138	359	805	1250
Four Color 23(1943)	32	64	96	230	515	800
Four Color 45(1943)	25	50	75	175	388	600
Four Color 72(1945)	20	40	60	141	313	485
1(6/46)-Billy & Bonnie Bee by Frank Thomas	29	58	87	209	467	725
2,3: 3-Egbert Elephant by Dan Noonan begins	15	30	45	100	220	340
4-Kelly-a, 16 pgs.	15	30	45	105	233	360
5,6,8-10	12	24	36	80	173	265
7-Little Black Sambo, Black Mumbo & Black Jumbo only app; Christmas-c						
	14	28	42	94	207	320
11-20	10	20	30	64	132	200
21-Alice In Wonderland cover/story	12	24	36	80	173	265
22-27,29-39(8/49), Four Color 262 (1/50): 34-"...In Candyland"						
	9	18	27	57	111	165
28-Kelly-c	9	18	27	59	117	175
Four Color 306,354,380,452,533	7	14	21	46	86	125
1(10-12/64-Dell)	4	8	12	23	37	50
2,3(10-12/65), 4(3/66)	3	6	9	16	23	30

NOTE: ***Kelly** art ("Animal Mother Goose")-#1-34, 36, 37; c-28. Peterkin Pottle by **John Stanley** in 32-38.*

RAGGEDY ANN AND ANDY
Gold Key: Dec, 1971 - No. 6, Sept, 1973

1	3	6	9	18	28	38
2-6	3	6	9	15	21	26

RAGGEDY ANN & THE CAMEL WITH THE WRINKLED KNEES (See Dell Jr. Treasury #8)

RAGMAN (See Batman Family #20, The Brave & The Bold #196 & Cancelled Comic Cavalcade)
National Per. Publ./DC Comics No. 5: Aug-Sept, 1976 - No. 5, Jun-Jul, 1977

1-Origin & 1st app.	3	6	9	16	24	32
2-5: 2-Origin ends; Kubert-c. 4-Drug use story	2	4	6	8	10	12

NOTE: ***Kubert** a-4, 5; c-1-5. **Redondo** studios a-1-4.*

RAGMAN (2nd Series)
DC Comics: Oct, 1991 - No. 8, May, 1992 ($1.50, limited series)

1-8: 1-Giffen plots/breakdowns. 3-Origin. 8-Batman-c/story 3.00

RAGMAN (3rd Series)
DC Comics: Dec, 2017 - No. 6 ($2.99, limited series)

1-5-Ray Fawkes-s/Inaki Miranda-a/Guillem March-c; new origin. 3-5-Etrigan app. 3.00

RAGMAN: CRY OF THE DEAD
DC Comics: Aug, 1993 - No. 6, Jan, 1994 ($1.75, limited series)

1-6: Joe Kubert-c 3.00

RAGMAN: SUIT OF SOULS

Ragnarok #3 © Walt Simonson

The Rampaging Hulk #6 © MAR

Rangers Comics #44 © FH

GD VG FN VF VF/NM NM-
2.0 4.0 6.0 8.0 9.0 9.2

DC Comics: Dec, 2010 ($3.99, one-shot)
1-Gage-s/Segovia-a/Saiz-c; origin retold 4.00

RAGNAROK
IDW Publishing: Jul, 2014 - No. 12, Feb, 2017 ($3.99/$4.99)
1-7-Walt Simonson-s/a; two covers on each 4.00
8-12-($4.99) 5.00

RAGS RABBIT (Formerly Babe Ruth Sports #10 or Little Max #10?; also see Harvey Hits #2, Harvey Wiseguys & Tastee Freez)
Harvey Publications: No. 11, June, 1951 - No. 18, March, 1954 (Written & drawn for little folks)
11-(See Nutty Comics #5 for 1st app.) 6 12 18 31 38 45
12-18 5 10 15 24 30 35

RAI (Rai and the Future Force #9-23) (See Magnus #5-8)
Valiant: Mar, 1992 - No. 0, Oct, 1992; No. 9, May, 1993 - No. 33, Jun, 1995 ($1.95/$2.25)
1-Valiant's 1st original character 2 4 6 11 16 20
2-5: 4-Low print run 2 4 6 9 12 15
6-10: 6,7-Unity x-overs. 7-Death of Rai. 9-($2.50)-Gatefold-c; story cont'd from Magnus #24; Magnus, Eternal Warrior & X-O app. 6.00
11-33: 15-Manowar Armor app. 17-19-Magnus x-over. 21-1st app. The Starwatchers (cameo); trading card. 22-Death of Rai. 26-Chaos Effect Epsilon Pt. 3 4.00
#0-(11/92)-Origin/1st app. new Rai (Rising Spirit) & 1st full app. & partial origin Bloodshot; also see Eternal Warrior #4; tells future of all characters
3 6 9 14 20 25
NOTE: ***Layton** c-2i, 9i. **Miller** c-6. **Simonson** c-7.*

RAI
Valiant Entertainment: May, 2014 - No. 16, Aug, 2016 ($3.99)
1-16: 1-Kindt-s/Crain-a; Rai in Japan in the year 4001. 15,16-4001 AD tie-ins 4.00
...: The History of the Valiant Universe 1 (6/17, $3.99) Roberts-s/Portela-a; 2 covers 4.00

RAIDERS OF THE LOST ARK (Movie)
Marvel Comics Group: Sept, 1981 - No. 3, Nov, 1981 (Movie adaptation)
1-r/Marvel Comics Super Special #18 2 4 6 9 12 15
2,3 1 2 3 5 6 8
NOTE: ***Buscema** a(p)-1-3; c(p)-1. **Simonson** a-3i; scripts-1-3.*

RAINBOW BRITE AND THE STAR STEALER
DC Comics: 1985
nn-Movie adaptation 2 4 6 8 10 12

RAISE THE DEAD
Dynamite Entertainment: 2007 - No. 4, Aug, 2007 ($3.50)
1-4-Arthur Suydam-c/Leah Moore & John Reppion-s/Petrus-a; Phillips var-c on all 4.00
... Vol. 1 HC (2007, $19.99) r/#1-4; script, interview & sketch pages; cover gallery 20.00

RAISE THE DEAD 2
Dynamite Entertainment: 2010 - No. 4, 2011 ($3.99)
1-4-Leah Moore & John Reppion-s/Vilanova-a 4.00

RALPH KINER, HOME RUN KING
Fawcett Publications: 1950 (Pittsburgh Pirates)
nn-Photo-c; life story 60 120 180 381 658 935

RALPH SNART ADVENTURES
Now Comics: June, 1986 - V2#9, 1987; V3#1 - #26, Feb, 1991; V4#1, 1992 - #4, 1992
1-3, V2#1-7,V3#1-23,25,26:1-($1.00, B&W)-1(B&W),V2#1(11/86), B&W), 8,9-color. V3#1(9/88)-Color begins 3.00
V3#24-($2.50)-3-D issue, V4#1-3-Direct sale versions w/cards 3.00
V4#1-3-Newsstand versions w/random cards 3.00
Book 1 1 2 3 5 6 8
3-D Special (11/92, $3.50)-Complete 12-card set w/3-D glasses 4.00

RAMAR OF THE JUNGLE (TV)
Toby Press No. 1/Charlton No. 2 on: 1954 (no month); No. 2, Sept, 1955 - No. 5, Sept, 1956
1-Jon Hall photo-c; last pre-code issue 24 48 72 142 234 325
2-5: 2-Jon Hall photo-c 17 34 51 98 154 210

RAMAYAN 3392 A.D.
Virgin Comics: Sept, 2006 - No. 8, Aug, 2008 ($2.99)
1-8: 1-Alex Ross-c; re-imagining of the Indian myth of Ramayana; poster of cover inside 3.00
... Reloaded (8/07 - No. 7, 7/08, $2.99) 1-7: 1-Two covers by Kang and Oeming 3.00
... Reloaded Guidebook (4/08, $2.99) Profiles of characters and weapons 3.00

RAMM
Megaton Comics: May, 1987 - No. 2, Sept, 1987 ($1.50, B&W)
1,2-Both have 1 pg. Youngblood ad by Liefeld 3.00

RAMPAGING HULK (The Hulk #10 on; also see Marvel Treasury Edition)
Marvel Comics Group: Jan, 1977 - No. 9, June, 1978 ($1.00, B&W magazine)
1-Bloodstone story w/Buscema & Nebres-a. Origin re-cap w/Simonson-a; Gargoyle, UFO story; Ken Barr-c 3 6 9 20 31 42
2-Old X-Men app; origin old w/Simonson-a & new X-Men in text w/Cockrum illos; Bloodstone story w/Brown & Nebres-a 3 6 9 15 22 28
3-9: 3-Iron Man app.; Norem-c. 4-Gallery of villains w/Giffen-a. 5,6-Hulk vs. Sub-Mariner. 7-Man-Thing story. 8-Original Avengers app. 9-Thor vs. Hulk battle; Shanna the She-Devil story w/DeZuniga-a 2 4 6 13 18 22
NOTE: ***Alcala** a-1-3i, 5i, 8i. **Buscema** a-1. **Giffen** a-4. **Nino** a-4i. **Simonson** a-1-3p. **Starlin** a-4(w/**Nino**), 7; c-4, 5, 7.*

RAMPAGING HULK
Marvel Comics: Aug, 1998 - No. 6, Jan, 1999 ($2.99/$1.99)
1-($2.99) Flashback stories of Savage Hulk; Leonardi-a 4.00
2-6-($1.99): 2-Two covers 3.00

RAMPAGING WOLVERINE
Marvel Comics: June, 2009 ($3.99, B&W, one-shot)
1-Short stories by Fialkov, Luque, Ted McKeever, Yost, Santolouco, Firth, Nelson 4.00

RANDOLPH SCOTT (Movie star)(See Crack Western #67, Prize Comics Western #76, Western Hearts #8, Western Love #1 & Western Winners #7)

RANGE BUSTERS
Fox Feature Syndicate: Sept, 1950 (One shot)
1 (Exist?) 20 40 60 117 189 260

RANGE BUSTERS (Formerly Cowboy Love?; Wyatt Earp, Frontier Marshall #11 on)
Charlton Comics: No. 8, May, 1955 - No. 10, Sept, 1955
8 8 16 24 42 54 65
9,10 6 12 18 28 34 40

RANGELAND LOVE
Atlas Comics (CDS): Dec, 1949 - No. 2, Mar, 1950 (52 pgs.)
1-Robert Taylor & Arlene Dahl photo-c 20 40 60 114 182 250
2-Photo-c 15 30 45 84 127 170

RANGER, THE (See Zane Grey, Four Color #255)

RANGE RIDER, THE (TV)(See Flying A's...)

RANGE ROMANCES
Comic Magazines (Quality Comics): Dec, 1949 - No. 5, Aug, 1950 (#5: 52 pg)
1-Gustavson-c/a 27 54 81 158 259 360
2-Crandall-c/a 26 52 78 154 252 350
3-Crandall, Gustavson-a; photo-c 22 44 66 132 216 300
4-Crandall-a; photo-c 20 40 60 117 189 260
5-Gustavson-a; Crandall-a(p); photo-c 20 40 60 117 189 260

RANGERS COMICS (...of Freedom #1-7)
Fiction House Magazines: 10/41 - No. 67, 10/52; No. 68, Fall, 1952; No. 69, Winter, 1952-53 (Flying stories)
1-Intro. Ranger Girl & The Rangers of Freedom; ends #7, cover app. only #5
541 1082 1623 3950 6975 10,000
2 206 412 618 1318 2259 3200
3 148 296 444 947 1624 2300
4,5 103 206 309 659 1130 1600
6-10-All Japanese war covers. 8-U.S. Rangers begin
84 168 252 538 919 1300
11,12-Commando Rangers app. 77 154 231 493 847 1200
13-Commando Ranger begins-not same as Commando Rangers; Nazi war-c
84 168 252 538 919 1300
14-Classic Japanese bondage/torture WWII-c 100 200 300 635 1093 1550
15-20: 15,17,19-Japanese war-c. 18-Nazi war-c 65 130 195 416 708 1000
21-Intro/origin Firehair (begins, 2/45) 84 168 252 538 919 1300
22-25,27,29-Japanese war-c. 23-Kazanda begins, ends #28
50 100 150 315 533 750
26-Classic Japanese WWII good girl-c 84 168 252 538 919 1300
28,30: 28-Tiger Man begins (origin/1st app., 4/46), ends #46. 30-Crusoe Island begins, ends #40 40 80 120 246 411 575
31-40: 33-Hypodermic panels 36 72 108 211 343 475
41-46: 41-Last Werewolf Hunter 26 52 78 154 252 350
47-56- "Eisnerish" Dr. Drew by Grandenetti. 48-Last Glory Forbes. 53-Last 52 pg. issue. 55-Last Sky Rangers 24 48 72 142 234 325
57-60-Straight run of Dr. Drew by Grandenetti 18 36 54 105 165 225
61-69: 64-Suicide Smith begins. 63-Used in **POP**, pgs. 85, 99. 67-Space Rangers begin, end #69 15 30 45 90 140 190
NOTE: *Bondage, discipline covers, lingerie panels are common. Crusoe Island by **Larsen**-#30-36. Firehair by*

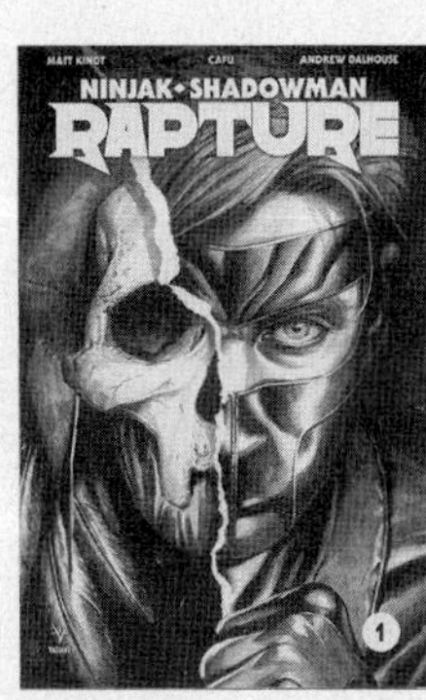

Rapture #1 © VAL

Rat Queens #14 © Wiebe & Upchurch

Rawhide Kid #2 © MAR

GD VG FN VF VF/NM NM-
2.0 4.0 6.0 8.0 9.0 9.2

GD VG FN VF VF/NM NM-
2.0 4.0 6.0 8.0 9.0 9.2

***Lubbers**-#30-49. Glory Forbes by **Baker**-#36-45, 47; by **Whitman**-#34, 35. I Confess in #41-53. Jan of the Jungle in #42-58. King of the Congo in #49-53. Tiger Man by **Celardo**-#30-39. **M. Anderson** a-30? **Baker** a-36-38, 42, 44. **John Celardo** a-34, 36-39. **Lee Elias** a-21-28. **Evans** a-19, 38-46, 48-52. **Hopper** a-25, 26. **Ingels** a-13-16. **Larsen** a-34. **Bob Lubbers** a-30-38, 40-44; c-40-45. **Moreira** a-41-47. **Tuska** a-16, 17, 19, 22. **M. Whitman** c-61-66. **Zolnerwich** c-1-17.*

RANGO (TV)
Dell Publishing Co.: Aug, 1967

1-Photo-c of comedian Tim Conway 4 8 12 28 47 65

RANN-THANAGAR HOLY WAR (Also see Hawkman Special #1)
DC Comics: July, 2008 - No. 8, Feb, 2009 ($3.50, limited series)

1-8-Adam Strange & Hawkman app.; Starlin-s/Lim-a. 1-Two covers by Starlin & Lim 3.50
Volume One TPB (2009, $19.99) r/#1-4 & Hawkman Special #1 20.00
Volume Two TPB (2009, $19.99) r/#5-8 & Adam Strange Special #1 20.00

RANN-THANAGAR WAR (See Adam Strange 2004 mini-series)(Prelude to Infinite Crisis)
DC Comics: July, 2005 - No. 6, Dec, 2005 ($2.50, limited series)

1-6-Adam Strange, Hawkman and Green Lantern (Kyle Rayner) app.; Gibbons-s/Reis-a 3.00
...: Infinite Crisis Special (4/06, $4.99) Kyle Rayner becomes Ion again; Jade dies 5.00
TPB (2005, $12.99) r/#1-6; cover gallery; new Bolland-c 13.00

RAPHAEL (See Teenage Mutant Ninja Turtles)
Mirage Studios: 1985 ($1.50, 7-1/2x11", B&W w/2 color cover, one-shot)

1-1st Turtles one-shot spin-off; contains 1st drawing of the Turtles as a group from 1983
8 16 24 51 96 140
1-2nd printing (11/87); new-c & 8 pgs. art 2 4 6 8 11 14

RAPHAEL BAD MOON RISING (See Teenage Mutant Ninja Turtles)
Mirage Publishing: July, 2007 - No. 4, Oct, 2007 ($3.25, B&W, limited series)

1-4-Continued from Tales of the TMNT #7; Lawson-a 3.25

RAPTURE
Dark Horse Comics: May, 2009 - No. 6, Jan, 2010 ($2.99, limited series)

1-6-Taki Soma & Michael Avon Oeming-s/a/c. 1-Maleev var-c. 2-Mack var-c 3.00

RAPTURE
Valiant Entertainment: May, 2017 - No. 4, Aug, 2017 ($3.99)

1-4-Kindt-s/Cafu-a; Ninjak, Shadowman & Punk Mambo app. 4-Ryp-a; preview of Eternity 4.00

RASCALS IN PARADISE
Dark Horse Comics: Aug, 1994 - No. 3, Dec, 1994 ($3.95, magazine size)

1-3-Jim Silke-a/story 4.00
Trade paperback-($16.95)-r/#1-3 17.00

RASL
Cartoon Books: Mar, 2008 - No. 15, Jul, 2012 ($3.50/$4.99, B&W)

1-14-Jeff Smith-s/a/c 3.50
15-($4.99) Conclusion 5.00

RASPUTIN: VOICE OF THE DRAGON
Dark Horse Comics: Nov, 2017 - No. 5, Mar, 2018 ($3.99, limited series)

1-5-Mignola & Roberson-s/Mittens-a; Rasputin in 1941 Nazi Germany 4.00

RATCHET & CLANK (Based on the Sony videogame)
DC Comics (WildStorm thru #4): Nov, 2010 - No. 6, Apr, 2011 ($3.99/$2.99, limited series)

1-4-Fixman-s/Archer-a 4.00
5,6-($2.99) 3.00
TPB (2011, $17.99) r/#1-6 18.00

RATFINK (See Frantic and Zany)
Canrom, Inc.: Oct, 1964

1-Woodbridge-a 9 18 27 61 123 185

RAT GOD
Dark Horse Comics: Feb, 2015 - No. 5, Jun, 2015 ($3.99, limited series)

1-5-Richard Corben-s/a/c 4.00

RAT PATROL, THE (TV) (Also see Wild!)
Dell Publishing Co.: Mar, 1967 - No. 5, Nov, 1967; No. 6, Oct, 1969

1-Christopher George photo-c 6 12 18 40 73 105
2-6: 3-6-Photo-c 4 8 12 27 44 60

RAT QUEENS
Image Comics (Shadowline): Sept, 2013 - No. 16, May, 2016 ($3.50/$3.99)

1-Kurtis Wiebe-s/Roc Upchurch-a/c 1 3 4 6 8 10
1-Variant-c by Fiona Staples 40.00
2-10: 2-8-Two covers on each. 9,10-Sejic-a. 9-Frison-c 3.50
11-16-($3.99) Fowler-a 4.00
... Special: Braga #1 (1/15, $3.50) Wiebe-s/Tess Fowler-a; origin of Braga the Orc 3.50

RAT QUEENS (Volume 2)
Image Comics (Shadowline): Mar, 2017 - Present ($3.99)

1-8-Kurtis Wiebe-s/Owen Gieni-a/c 4.00
... Special: Orc Dave 1 (9/17, $3.99) Staples-c; Dave's 1st meeting with the Queens 4.00

RAVAGERS, THE (See Teen Titans and Superboy New 52 series)
DC Comics: Jul, 2012 - No. 12, Jul, 2013 ($2.99)

1-12: 1-Fairchild, Beast Boy, Terra, Thunder, Lightning, Ridge team; Churchill-a 3.00
#0 (11/12, $2.99) Churchill-a; origin of Beast Boy & Terra 3.00

RAVAGE 2099 (See Marvel Comics Presents #117)
Marvel Comics: Dec, 1992 - No. 33, Aug, 1995($1.25/$1.50)

1-($1.75)-Gold foil stamped-c; Stan Lee scripts 4.00
1-($1.75)-2nd printing 3.00
2-24,26-33: 5-Last Ryan-c. 6-Last Ryan-a. 14-Punisher 2099 x-over. 15-Ron Lim-c(p). 18-Bound-in card sheet 3.00
25 ($2.25, 52 pgs.) 4.00
25 ($2.95, 52 pgs.)-Silver foil embossed-c 5.00

RAVEN (See DC Special: Raven and Teen Titans titles)

RAVEN (From Teen Titans)
DC Comics: Nov, 2016 - No. 6, Apr, 2017 ($2.99, limited series)

1-6: 1-3-Wolfman-s/Borges-a. 4-6-Neves-a 3.00

RAVEN, THE (See Movie Classics)

RAVEN CHRONICLES
Caliber (New Worlds): 1995 - No. 16 ($2.95, B&W)

1-16: 10-Flip book w/Wordsmith #6. 15-Flip book w/High Caliber #4 3.00

RAVEN: DAUGHTER OF DARKNESS (From Teen Titans)
DC Comics: Mar, 2018 - No. 12 ($3.99, limited series)

1,2-Wolfman-s/Mhan-a; Baron Winters app. 4.00

RAVENS AND RAINBOWS
Pacific Comics: Dec, 1983 (Baxter paper)(Reprints fanzine work in color)

1-Jeff Jones-c/a(r); nudity scenes 3.00

RAWHIDE (TV)
Dell Publishing Co./Gold Key: Sept-Nov, 1959 - June-Aug, 1962; July, 1963 - No. 2, Jan, 1964

Four Color 1028 (#1) 22 44 66 154 340 525
Four Color 1097,1160,1202,1261,1269 13 26 39 89 195 300
01-684-208 (8/62, Dell) 10 20 30 70 150 230
1(10071-307) (7/63, Gold Key) 10 20 30 70 150 230
2-(12¢) 10 20 30 64 132 200
NOTE: *All have Clint Eastwood photo-c. **Tufts** a-1028.*

RAWHIDE KID
Atlas/Marvel Comics (CnPC No. 1-16/AMI No. 17-30): Mar, 1955 - No. 16, Sept, 1957; No. 17, Aug, 1960 - No. 151, May, 1979

1-Rawhide Kid, his horse Apache & sidekick Randy begin; Wyatt Earp app.; #1 was not code approved; Maneely splash pg. 194 388 582 1242 2121 3000
2 52 104 156 328 552 775
3-5 40 80 120 246 411 575
6-10: 7-Williamson-a (4 pgs.) 34 68 102 199 325 450
11-16: 16-Torres-a 28 56 84 165 270 375
17-Origin by Jack Kirby; Kirby-a begins 290 580 870 1856 3178 4500
18-21,24-30 26 52 78 182 404 625
22-Monster-c/story by Kirby/Ayers 32 64 96 230 515 800
23-Origin retold by Jack Kirby 46 92 138 340 770 1200
31-35,40: 31,32-Kirby-a. 33-35-Davis-a. 34-Kirby-a. 35-Intro & death of The Raven. 40-Two-Gun Kid x-over. 14 28 42 96 211 325
36,37,39,41,42-No Kirby. 42-1st Larry Lieber issue 11 22 33 73 157 240
38-Red Raven-c/story; Kirby-c (2/64); Colan-a 15 30 45 103 227 350
43-Kirby-a (beware: pin-up often missing) 14 28 42 94 207 320
44,46: 46-Toth-a. 46-Doc Holliday-c/s 10 20 30 64 132 200
45-Origin retold, 17 pgs. 12 24 36 81 176 270
47-49,51-60 7 14 21 44 82 120
50-Kid Colt x-over; vs. Rawhide Kid 7 14 21 48 89 130
61-70: 64-Kid Colt story. 66-Two-Gun Kid story. 67-Kid Colt story. 70-Last 12¢ issue
5 10 15 33 57 80
71-78,80-83,85 3 6 9 20 31 42
79,84,86,95: 79-Williamson-a(r). 84,86: Kirby-a. 86-Origin-r; Williamson-r/Ringo Kid #13 (4 pgs.) 3 6 9 21 33 45
87-91: 90-Kid Colt app. 91-Last 15¢ issue 3 6 9 18 28 38
92,93 (52 pg.Giants). 92-Kirby-a 4 8 12 25 40 55
94,96-99 3 6 9 16 24 32

Rawhide Kid (2003 series) #5 © MAR

The Ray (2012 series) #1 © DC

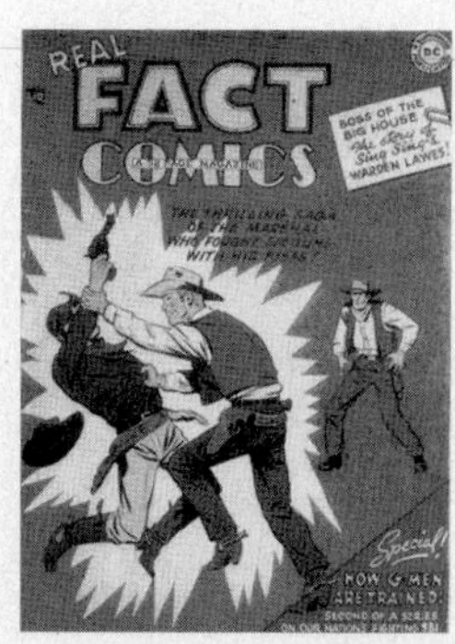

Real Fact Comics #12 © DC

GD VG FN VF VF/NM NM-
2.0 4.0 6.0 8.0 9.0 9.2

100 (6/72)-Origin retold & expanded 3 6 9 21 33 45
101-120: 115-Last new story 3 6 9 14 19 24
121-151 2 4 6 10 14 18
133,134-(30¢-c variants, limited distribution)(5,7/76) 6 12 18 42 79 115
140,141-(35¢-c variants, limited distribution)(7,9/77) 14 28 42 96 211 325
Special 1(9/71, 25¢, 68 pgs.)-All Kirby/Ayers-r 5 10 15 31 53 75
NOTE: ***Ayers** a-13, 14, 16, 29, 37-39, 61. **Colan** a-5, 35, 37, 38; c-145p, 148p, 149p. **Davis** a-125r. **Everett** a-54i, 65, 66, 88, 96i, 148i(r). **Gulacy** c-147. **Heath** c-4. **G. Kane** c-101, 144. **Keller** a-5, 39, 41, 144r. **Kirby** a-17-32, 34, 42, 43, 84, 86, 92, 109r, 112r, 116r, 117r, 137r, Spec. 1; c-17-35, 37, 38, 40, 41, 43-47, 137r. **Maneely** c-1-3, 5, 6, 14. **Morisi** a-13. **Morrow/Williamson** r-111. **Roussos** r-146i, 147i, 149-151i. **Severin** a-16; c-8, 13. **Sutton** a-61, 93. **Torres** a-99r. **Tuska** a-14. **Wildey** r-146-151(Outlaw Kid). **Williamson** r-79, 86, 95.*

RAWHIDE KID
Marvel Comics Group: Aug, 1985 - No. 4, Nov, 1985 (Mini-series)

1-4 5.00

RAWHIDE KID
Marvel Comics (MAX): Apr, 2003 - No. 5, June, 2003 ($2.99, limited series)

1-John Severin-a/Ron Zimmerman-s; Dave Johnson-c 3.00
2-5: 3-Dodson-c. 4-Darwyn Cooke-c. 5-J. Scott Campbell-c 3.00
Vol. 1: Slap Leather TPB (2003, $12.99) r/#1-5 13.00

RAWHIDE KID (The Sensational Seven)
Marvel Comics: Aug, 2010 - No. 4, Nov, 2010 ($3.99, limited series)

1-4-Chaykin-a/Zimmerman-s. 1-Cassaday-c. 2-Dave Johnson-c. 4-Suydam-c 4.00

RAY, THE (See Freedom Fighters & Smash Comics #14)
DC Comics: Feb, 1992 - No. 6, July, 1992 ($1.00, mini-series)

1-Sienkiewicz-c; Joe Quesada-a(p) in 1-5 5.00
2-6: 3-6-Quesada-c(p). 6-Quesada layouts only 3.00
...In a Blaze of Power (1994, $12.95)-r/#1-6 w/new Quesada-c 13.00

RAY, THE
DC Comics: May, 1994 - No. 28, Oct, 1996 ($1.75/$1.95/$2.25)

1-Quesada-c(p); Superboy app. 3.00
1-($2.95)-Collectors Edition w/diff. Quesada-c; embossed foil-c 4.00
2-5,0,6-24,26-28: 2-Quesada-c(p); Superboy app. 5-(9/94). 0-(10/94) 3.00
25-($3.50)-Future Flash (Bart Allen)-c/app; double size 4.00
Annual 1 ($3.95, 68 pgs.)-Superman app. 4.00

RAY, THE
DC Comics: Feb, 2012 - No. 4, May, 2012 ($2.99, limited series)

1-4: 1-Igle-a/Palmiotti & Gray-s; origin of the new Ray; intro. Lucien Gates 3.00

RAY BRADBURY COMICS
Topps Comics: Feb, 1993 - V4#1, June, 1994 ($2.95)

1-5-Polybagged w/3 trading cards each. 1-All dinosaur issue; Corben-a; Williamson/Torres/Krenkel-r/Weird Science-Fantasy #25. 3-All dinosaur issue; Steacy painted-c; Stout-a 3.00
Special Edition 1 (1994, $2.95)-The Illustrated Man 3.00
...Special: Tales of Horror #1 ($2.50), ...Trilogy of Terror V3#1 (5/94, $2.50), ...Martian Chronicles V4#1 (6/94, $2.50)-Steranko-c 3.00
NOTE: ***Kelley Jones** a-Trilogy of Terror V3#1. **Kaluta** a-Martian Chronicles V4#1. **Kurtzman/Matt Wagner** c-2. **McKean** c-4. **Mignola** a-4. **Wood** a-Trilogy of Terror V3#1r.*

RAZORLINE
Marvel Comics: Sept, 1993 (75¢, one-shot)

1-Clive Barker super-heroes: Ectokid, Hokum & Hex, Hyperkind & Saint Sinner 3.00

RAZOR'S EDGE, THE
DC Comics (WildStorm): Dec, 2004 - No. 5, Apr, 2005 ($2.95)

1-5-Warblade; Bisley-c/a; Ridley-s 3.00

REAL ADVENTURE COMICS (Action Adventure #2 on)
Gillmor Magazines: Apr, 1955

1 10 20 30 58 79 100

REAL ADVENTURES OF JONNY QUEST, THE
Dark Horse Comics: Sept, 1996 - No. 12, Sept, 1997 ($2.95)

1-12 3.00

REAL CLUE CRIME STORIES (Formerly Clue Comics)
Hillman Periodicals: V2#4, June, 1947 - V8#3, May, 1953

V2#4(#1)-S&K c/a(3); Dan Barry-a 49 98 147 309 522 735
5-7-S&K c/a(3-4). 7-Iron Lady app. 39 78 117 240 395 550
8-12 14 28 42 81 118 155
V3#1-8,10-12, V4#1-3,5-8,11,12 13 26 39 72 101 130
V3#9-Used in **SOTI**, pg. 102 15 30 45 83 124 165
V4#4-S&K-a 15 30 45 84 127 170
V4#9,10-Krigstein-a 13 26 39 74 105 135
V5#1-5,7,8,10,12 10 20 30 56 76 95
6,9,11(1/54)-Krigstein-a 11 22 33 60 83 105
V6#1-5,8,9,11 9 18 27 52 69 85
6,7,10,12-Krigstein-a. 10-Bondage-c 11 22 33 60 83 105
V7#1-3,5-11, V8#1-3: V7#6-1 pg. Frazetta ad "Prayer" - 1st app.? 10 20 30 56 76 95
4,12-Krigstein-a 11 22 33 60 83 105
NOTE: ***Barry** a-9, 10; c-V2#8. **Briefer** a-V6#6. **Fuje** a- V2#7(2), 8, 11. **Infantino** a-V2#8; c-V2#11. **Lawrence** a-V3#8, V5#7. **Powell** a-V4#11, 12. V5#4, 5, 7 are 68 pgs.*

REAL EXPERIENCES (Formerly Tiny Tessie)
Atlas Comics (20CC): No. 25, Jan, 1950

25-Virginia Mayo photo-c from movie "Red Light" 15 30 45 83 124 165

REAL FACT COMICS
National Periodical Publications: Mar-Apr, 1946 - No. 21, July-Aug, 1949

1-S&K-c/a; Harry Houdini story; Just Imagine begins (not by Finlay); Fred Ray-a 47 94 141 296 498 700
2-S&K-a; Rin-Tin-Tin & P. T. Barnum stories 28 56 84 165 270 375
3-H.G. Wells, Lon Chaney stories; early DC letter column (New Fun Comics #3 from 1935 may be the 1st) 26 52 78 154 252 350
4-Virgil Finlay-a on 'Just Imagine' begins, ends #12 (2 pgs. each); Jimmy Stewart & Jack London stories; Joe DiMaggio 1 pg. biography 29 58 87 172 281 390
5-Batman/Robin-c taken from cover of Batman #9; 5 pg. story about creation of Batman & Robin; Tom Mix story 155 310 465 992 1696 2400
6-Origin & 1st app. Tommy Tomorrow by Weisinger and Sherman (1-2/47); Flag-c; 1st writing by Harlan Ellison (letter column, non-professional); "First Man to Reach Mars" epic-c/story 84 168 252 538 919 1300
7-(No. 6 on inside)-Roussos-a; D. Fairbanks sty. 15 30 45 94 147 200
8-2nd app. Tommy Tomorrow by Finlay (5-6/47) 48 96 144 302 514 725
9-S&K-a; Glenn Miller, Indianapolis 500 stories 21 42 63 122 199 275
10-Vigilante by Meskin (based on movie serial); 4 pg. Finlay s/f story 20 40 60 118 192 265
11,12: 11-Annie Oakley, G-Men stories; Kinstler-a 14 28 42 82 121 160
13-Dale Evans and Tommy Tomorrow-c/stories 37 74 111 222 361 500
14,17,18: 14-Will Rogers story 14 28 42 80 115 150
15-Nuclear explosion part-c ("Last War on Earth" story); Clyde Beatty story 15 30 45 94 147 200
16-Tommy Tomorrow app.; 1st Planeteers? 36 72 108 211 343 475
19-Sir Arthur Conan Doyle story 15 30 45 83 124 165
20-Kubert-a, 4 pgs; Daniel Boone story 15 30 45 88 137 185
21-Kubert-a, 2 pgs; Kit Carson story 14 28 42 80 115 150
Ashcan (2/46) nn-Not distributed to newsstands, only for in house use. Covers were produced, but not the rest of the book. A copy sold in 2008 for $500.
NOTE: ***Barry** c-16. **Virgil Finlay** c-6, 8. **Meskin** c-10. **Roussos** a-1-4, 6.*

REAL FUNNIES
Nedor Publishing Co.: Jan, 1943 - No. 3, June, 1943

1-Funny animal, humor; Black Terrier app. (clone of The Black Terror) 34 68 102 206 336 465
2,3 18 36 54 105 165 225

REAL GHOSTBUSTERS, THE (Also see Slimer)
Now Comics: Aug, 1988 - No. 28, Feb, 1991 ($1.75/$1.95)

1-Based on Ghostbusters movie 2 4 6 11 16 20
2 1 2 3 5 6 8
3-28 4.00

REAL HEROES
Image Comics: Mar, 2014 - No. 4, Nov, 2014 ($3.99)

1-3-Bryan Hitch-s/a 4.00
4-($4.99) 5.00

REAL HEROES COMICS
Parents' Magazine Institute: Sept, 1941 - No. 16, Oct, 1946

1-Roosevelt-c/story 32 64 96 188 307 425
2-J. Edgar Hoover-c/story 15 30 45 83 124 165
3-5,7-10: 4-Churchill, Roosevelt stories 14 28 42 76 108 140
6-Lou Gehrig-c/story 19 38 57 112 179 245
11-16: 13-Kiefer-a 10 20 30 54 72 90

REALISTIC ROMANCES
Realistic Comics/Avon Periodicals: July-Aug, 1951 - No. 17, Aug-Sept, 1954 (No #9-14)

1-Kinstler-a; c-/Avon paperback #211 40 80 120 246 411 575
2 21 42 63 126 206 285
3,4 21 42 63 122 199 275
5,8-Kinstler-a 21 42 63 124 202 280
6-c-/Diversey Prize Novels #6; Kinstler-a 21 42 63 126 206 285

Real Life Comics #26 © PM

The Realm #4 © Peck & Haun

Real Screen Comics #29 © DC

	GD 2.0	VG 4.0	FN 6.0	VF 8.0	VF/NM 9.0	NM- 9.2
7-Evans-a?; c-/Avon paperback #360	21	42	63	126	206	285
15,17: 17-Kinstler-c	20	40	60	118	192	265
16-Kinstler marijuana story-r/Romantic Love #6	21	42	63	124	202	280
I.W. Reprint #1,8,9: #1-r/Realistic Romances #4; Astarita-a. 9-r/Women To Love #1	3	6	9	14	20	25

NOTE: ***Astarita** a-2-4, 7, 8, 17. Photo c-1, 2. Painted c-3, 4.*

REALITY CHECK
Image Comics: Sept, 2013 - No. 4, Dec, 2013 ($2.99)

1-4-Brunswick-s/Bogdanovic-a 3.00

REAL LIFE COMICS
Nedor/Better/Standard Publ./Pictorial Magazine No. 13: Sept, 1941 - No. 59, Sept, 1952

	GD	VG	FN	VF	VF/NM	NM-
1-Uncle Sam-c/story; Daniel Boone story	76	152	228	486	831	1175
2-Woodrow Wilson-c/story	39	78	117	231	378	525
3-Classic Schomburg Hitler-c with "Emperor of Hate" emblazoned in blood behind him. Cover shows world at war, concentration camps and Nazis killing civilians; Hitler 10 pg. bio	757	1514	2271	5526	9763	14,000
4,5: 4-Story of American flag "Old Glory"	32	64	96	188	307	425
6-10: 6-Wild Bill Hickok story	28	56	84	165	270	375
11-14,16-20: 17-Albert Einstein story	22	44	66	132	216	300
15-Japanese WWII-c by Schomburg	27	54	81	162	266	370
21-23,25,26,28-30: 29-A-Bomb story. 28-Japanese WWII-c	20	40	60	117	189	260
24-Story of Baseball (Babe Ruth); Japanese WWII-c	27	54	81	160	263	365
27-Schomburg A-Bomb-c; story of A-Bomb	25	50	75	150	245	340
31-33,35,36,42-44,48,49: 32-Frank Sinatra story. 49-Baseball issue	17	34	51	98	154	210
34,37-41,45-47: 34-Jimmy Stewart story. 37-Story of motion pictures; Bing Crosby story. 38-Jane Froman story. 39- "1,000,000 A.D." story. 40-Bob Feller. 41-Jimmie Foxx story ("Jimmy" on-c); "Home Run" Baker story. 45-Story of Olympic games; Burl Ives & Kit Carson story. 46-Douglas Fairbanks Jr. & Sr. story. 47-George Gershwin story	18	36	54	103	162	220
50-Frazetta-a (5 pgs.)	31	62	93	182	296	410
51-Jules Verne "Journey to the Moon" by Evans; Severin/Elder-a	22	44	66	128	209	290
52-Frazetta-a (4 pgs.); Severin/Elder-a(2); Evans-a	34	68	102	199	325	450
53-57-Severin/Elder-a. 54-Bat Masterson-c/story	18	36	54	103	162	220
58-Severin/Elder-a(2)	18	36	54	105	165	225
59-1 pg. Frazetta; Severin/Elder-a	18	36	54	105	165	225

NOTE: ***Guardineer** a-40(2), 44. **Meskin** a-52. **Roussos** a-50. **Schomburg** c-1-5, 7, 11, 13-21, 23, 24, 26-28, 30-32-40, 42, 44-50, 54, 55. **Tuska** a-53. Photo-c 5, 6.*

REAL LIFE SECRETS (Real Secrets #2 on)
Ace Periodicals: Sept, 1949 (one-shot)

1-Painted-c 17 34 51 100 158 215

REAL LIFE STORY OF FESS PARKER (Magazine)
Dell Publishing Co.: 1955

1 8 16 24 54 102 150

REAL LIFE TALES OF SUSPENSE (See Suspense)

REAL LOVE (Formerly Hap Hazard)
Ace Periodicals (A. A. Wyn): No. 25, April, 1949 - No. 76, Nov, 1956

	GD	VG	FN	VF	VF/NM	NM-
25	18	36	54	107	169	230
26	14	28	42	80	115	150
27-L. B. Cole-a	15	30	45	83	124	165
28-35	13	26	39	74	105	135
36-66: 66-Last pre-code (2/55)	12	24	36	69	97	125
67-76	11	22	33	62	86	110

NOTE: *Photo c-50-76. Painted c-46.*

REALM, THE
Arrow Comics/WeeBee Comics #13/Caliber Press #14 on: Feb, 1986 - No. 21, 1991 (B&W)

1-3,5-21 3.00
4-1st app. Deadworld (9/86) 4.00
Book 1 ($4.95, B&W) 5.00

REALM, THE
Image Comics: Sept, 2017 - Present ($3.99)

1-5-Seth Peck & Jeremy Haun-s/a. 1-Covers by Haun & Tony Moore 4.00

REAL McCOYS, THE (TV)
Dell Publ. Co.: No. 1071, 1-3/60 - 5-7/1962 (All have Walter Brennan photo-c)

	GD	VG	FN	VF	VF/NM	NM-
Four Color 1071,1134-Toth-a in both	8	16	24	51	96	140
Four Color 1193,1265	7	14	21	48	89	130
01-689-207 (5-7/62)	6	12	18	42	79	115

REALM OF KINGS (Also see Guardians of the Galaxy and Nova)
Marvel Comics: Jan, 2010 ($3.99, one-shot)

1-Abnett & Lanning-s/Manco & Asrar-a; Guardians of the Galaxy app. 4.00

REALM OF KINGS: IMPERIAL GUARD
Marvel Comics: Jan, 2010 - No. 5, May, 2010 ($3.99, limited series)

1-5-Abnett & Lanning-s/Walker-a; Starjammers app. 4.00

REALM OF KINGS: INHUMANS
Marvel Comics: Jan, 2010 - No. 5, May, 2010 ($3.99, limited series)

1-5-Abnett & Lanning-s/Raimondi-a; Mighty Avengers app. 4.00

REALM OF KINGS: SON OF HULK
Marvel Comics: Apr, 2010 - No. 4, July, 2010 ($3.99, limited series)

1-4-Reed-s/Munera-a; leads into Incredible Hulk #609 4.00

REALM OF THE CLAW (Also see Mutant Earth as part of a flipbook)
Image Comics: Oct, 2003 - No. 2 ($2.95)

0-(7/03, $5.95) Convention Special; cover has gold-foil title logo 6.00
1,2-Two covers by Yardin 3.00
Vol. 1 TPB (2006, $16.99) r/series; concept art & sketch pages 17.00

REAL SCREEN COMICS (#1 titled Real Screen Funnies; TV Screen Cartoons #129-138)
National Periodical Publications: Spring, 1945 - No. 128, May-June, 1959 (#1-40: 52 pgs.)

	GD	VG	FN	VF	VF/NM	NM-
1-The Fox & the Crow, Flippity & Flop, Tito & His Burrito begin	116	232	348	742	1271	1800
2	48	96	144	302	514	725
3-5	32	64	96	188	307	425
6-10 (2-3/47)	21	42	63	122	199	275
11-20 (10-11/48): 13-The Crow x-over in Flippity & Flop	16	32	48	94	147	200
21-30 (6-7/50)	14	28	42	76	108	140
31-50	11	22	33	60	83	105
51-99	10	20	30	54	72	90
100	10	20	30	56	76	95
101-128	8	16	24	44	57	70

REAL SCREEN FUNNIES
DC Comics: Spring 1945

1-Ashcan comic, not distributed to newsstands, only for in-house use. Cover art is Real Screen Funnies #1 with interior being Detective Comics #92. Only ashcan cover to be produced using the regular production first issue art and only using the color yellow. A copy sold in 2008 for $3,000. A FN/VF copy sold for $1314.50 in 2012.

REAL SECRETS (Formerly Real Life Secrets)
Ace Periodicals: No. 2, Nov, 1950 - No. 5, May, 1950

	GD	VG	FN	VF	VF/NM	NM-
2-Painted-c	14	28	42	80	115	150
3-5: 3-Photo-c	11	22	33	62	86	110

REAL SPORTS COMICS (All Sports Comics #2 on)
Hillman Periodicals: Oct-Nov, 1948 (52 pgs.)

1-Powell-a (12 pgs.) 41 82 123 250 418 585

REAL WAR STORIES
Eclipse Comics: July, 1987; No. 2, Jan, 1991 ($2.00, 52 pgs.)

1-Bolland-a(p), Bissette-a, Totleben-a(i); Alan Moore scripts (2nd printing exists, 2/88) 5.00
2-($4.95) 5.00

REAL WESTERN HERO (Formerly Wow #1-69; Western Hero #76 on)
Fawcett Publications: No. 70, Sept, 1948 - No. 75, Feb, 1949 (All 52 pgs.)

	GD	VG	FN	VF	VF/NM	NM-
70(#1)-Tom Mix, Monte Hale, Hopalong Cassidy, Young Falcon begin	22	44	66	132	216	300
71-75: 71-Gabby Hayes begins. 71,72-Captain Tootsie by Beck. 75-Big Bow and Little Arrow app.	15	30	45	85	130	175

NOTE: *Painted/photo c-70-73; painted c-74, 75.*

REAL WEST ROMANCES
Crestwood Publishing Co./Prize Publ.: 4-5/49 - V1#6, 3/50; V2#1, Apr-May, 1950 (All 52 pgs. & photo-c)

	GD	VG	FN	VF	VF/NM	NM-
V1#1-S&K-a(p)	27	54	81	158	259	360
2-Gail Davis and Rocky Shahan photo-c	14	28	42	81	118	155
3-Kirby-a(p) only	15	30	45	83	124	165
4-S&K-a; Whip Wilson, Reno Browne photo-c	19	38	57	112	179	245
5-Audie Murphy, Gale Storm photo-c; S&K-a	17	34	51	100	158	215
6-Produced by S&K, no S&K-a; Robert Preston & Cathy Downs photo-c	14	28	42	76	108	140
V2#1-Kirby-a(p)	14	28	42	76	108	140

Rebels: These Free and Independent States #7 © Brian Wood

Reborn #1 © Millarworld & Capullo

Red Dragon Comics #5 © C-N

GD 2.0 | VG 4.0 | FN 6.0 | VF 8.0 | VF/NM 9.0 | NM- 9.2

NOTE: *Meskin a-V1#5, 6. Severin/Elder a-V1#3-6, V2#1. Meskin a-V1#6. Leonard Starr a-1-3. Photo-c V1#1-6, V2#1.*

REALWORLDS :...
DC Comics: 2000 ($5.95, one-shots, prestige format)

Batman - Marshall Rogers-a/Golden & Sniegoski-s; Justice League of America -Dematteis-s/Barr-painted art; Superman - Vance-s/García-López & Rubenstein-a; Wonder Woman - Hanson & Neuwirth-s/Sam-a 6.00

REANIMATOR (Based on the 1985 horror movie)
Dynamite Entertainment: 2015 - No. 4, 2015 ($3.99, mini-series)

1-4-Further exploits of Herbert West; Davidsen-s/Valiente-a; four covers on each 4.00

RE-ANIMATOR IN FULL COLOR
Adventure Comics: Oct, 1991 - No. 3, 1992 ($2.95, mini-series)

1-3: Adapts horror movie. 1-Dorman painted-c 3.00

REAP THE WILD WIND (See Cinema Comics Herald)

REBEL, THE (TV)(Nick Adams as Johnny Yuma)
Dell Publishing Co.: No. 1076, Feb-Apr, 1960 - No. 1262, Dec-Feb, 1961-62

Four Color 1076 (#1)-Sekowsky-a, photo-c 9 18 27 63 129 195
Four Color 1138 (9-11/60), 1207 (9-11/61), 1262-Photo-c
8 16 24 52 99 145

REBELS (Also see Rebels: These Free And Independent States)
Dark Horse Comics: Apr, 2015 - No. 10, Jan, 2016 ($3.99)

1-Set in Revolutionary War 1775 Vermont; Brian Wood-s/Andrea Mutti-a/Tula Lotay-c 5.00
2-10: 4-General Washington app. 4.00

R.E.B.E.L.S.
DC Comics: Apr, 2009 - No. 28, Jul, 2011 ($2.99)

1-9,12-28: 1-Bedard-s/Clarke-a; Vril Dox returns; Supergirl app.; 2 covers. 15-Starfire app. 19-28-Lobo app. 3.00
10,11-($3.99) Blackest Night x-over; Vril Dox joins the Sinestro Corps 4.00
Annual 1 (12/09, $4.99) Origin on Starro the Conqueror; Despero app. 5.00
...: Sons of Brainiac TPB (2011, $14.99) r/#15-20 15.00
...: Strange Companions TPB (2010, $14.99) r/#7-9 & Annual #1 15.00
...: The Coming of Starro TPB (2010, $17.99) r/#1-6 18.00
...: The Son and the Stars TPB (2010, $17.99) r/#10-14 18.00

R.E.B.E.L.S. '94 (Becomes R.E.B.E.L.S. '95 & R.E.B.E.L.S. '96)
DC Comics: No. 0, Oct, 1994 - No. 17, Mar, 1996 ($1.95/$2.25)

0-17: 8-$2.25-c begins. 15-R.E.B.E.L.S '96 begins. 3.00

REBELS: THESE FREE AND INDEPENDENT STATES
Dark Horse Comics: Mar, 2017 - No. 8, Oct, 2017 ($3.99)

1-8: 1-5-Birth of the U.S. Navy in 1794; Brian Wood-s/Andrea Mutti-a 4.00

REBORN
Image Comics: Oct, 2016 - No. 6, Jun, 2017 ($3.99)

1-Mark Millar-s/Greg Capullo-a 5.00
2-5 4.00
6-($5.99) Bonus sketch pages and creator interview 6.00

RECORD BOOK OF FAMOUS POLICE CASES
St. John Publishing Co.: 1949 (25¢, 132 pgs.)

nn-Kubert-a(3); r/Son of Sinbad; Baker-c 55 110 165 352 601 850

RED (Inspired the 2010 Bruce Willis movie)
DC Comics (Homage): Sept, 2003 - No. 3, Feb, 2004 ($2.95, limited series)

1-3-Warren Ellis-s/Cully Hamner-a/c 5.00
Red/Tokyo Storm Warning TPB (2004, $14.95) Flip book r/both series 15.00
Red: Eyes Only (2/11, $4.99) comic prequel; Hamner-s/a/c 5.00
Red: Frank (11/10, $3.99) movie prequel; Noveck-s/Masters-a/Hamner & photo-c 4.00
Red: Joe (11/10, $3.99) movie prequel; Wagner-s/Redondo-a/Hamner & photo-c 4.00
Red: Marvin (11/10, $3.99) movie prequel; Hoeber-s/Olmos-a/Hamner & photo-c 4.00
Red: Victoria (11/10, $3.99) movie prequel; Hoeber-s/Hahn-a/Hamner & photo-c 4.00
...: Better R.E.D. Than Dead TPB (2011, $14.99) r/movie prequel issues; sketch-a 15.00

RED ARROW
P. L. Publishing Co.: May-June, 1951 - No. 3, Oct, 1951

1-Bondage-c 15 30 45 85 130 175
2,3 10 20 30 58 79 100

RED BAND COMICS
Enwil Associates: Nov, 1944, No. 2, Jan, 1945 - No. 4, May, 1945

1-Bogeyman-c/intro. (The Spirit swipe) 47 94 141 296 498 700
2-Origin Bogeyman & Santanas; c-reprint/#1 34 68 102 199 325 450
3,4-Captain Wizard app. in both (1st app.); each has identical contents/cover
32 64 96 188 307 425

REDBLADE
Dark Horse Comics: Apr, 1993 - No. 3, July, 1993 ($2.50, mini-series)

1-3: 1-Double gatefold-c 3.00

RED CIRCLE, THE (Re-introduction of characters from MLJ/Archie publications)
DC Comics: Oct, 2009 ($2.99, series of one-shots)

...Inferno 1 - Hangman app.; Straczynski-s/Greg Scott-a 5.00
...The Hangman 1 - Origin retold; Straczynski-s/Derenick & Sienkiewicz-a 5.00
...The Shield 1 - Origin retold; Straczynski-s/McDaniel-a 5.00
...The Web 1 - Straczynski-s/Robinson-a 5.00

RED CIRCLE COMICS (Also see Blazing Comics & Blue Circle Comics)
Rural Home Publications (Enwil): Jan, 1945 - No. 4, April, 1945

1-The Prankster & Red Riot begin 74 148 222 470 810 1150
2-Starr-a; The Judge (costumed hero) app. 39 78 117 231 378 525
3,4-Starr-c/a. 3-The Prankster not in costume 31 62 93 184 300 415
4-(Dated 4/45)-Leftover covers to #4 were later restapled over early 1950s coverless comics; variations in the coverless comics used are endless; Woman Outlaws, Dorothy Lamour, Crime Does Not Pay, Sabu, Diary Loves, Love Confessions & Young Love V3#3 known
21 42 63 126 206 285

RED CIRCLE SORCERY (Chilling Adventures in Sorcery #1-5)
Red Circle Prod. (Archie): No. 6, Apr, 1974 - No. 11, Feb, 1975 (All 25¢ iss.)

6,8,9,11: 6-Early Chaykin-a. 7-Pino-a. 8-Only app. The Cobra
2 4 6 9 13 16
7-Bruce Jones-a with Wrightson, Kaluta, Jeff Jones 3 6 9 14 19 24
10-Wood-a(i) 2 4 6 10 14 18

NOTE: *Chaykin a-6, 10. McWilliams a-10(2 & 3 pgs.). Mooney a-11p. Morrow a-6-8, 9(text illos), 10, 11i; c-6-11. Thorne a-8, 10. Toth a-8, 9.*

RED CITY
Image Comics: Jun, 2014 - No. 4, Sept, 2014 ($2.99)

1-4-Corey-s. 1,2-Dos Santos-a. 3,4-Diecidue-a 3.00

RED DOG (See Night Music #7)

RED DRAGON
Comico: June, 1996 ($2.95)

1-Bisley-c 3.00

RED DRAGON COMICS (1st Series) (Formerly Trail Blazers; see Super Magician V5#7, 8)
Street & Smith Publications: No. 5, Jan, 1943 - No. 9, Jan, 1944

5-Origin Red Rover, the Crimson Crimebuster; Rex King, Man of Adventure, Captain Jack Commando, & The Minute Man begin; text origin Red Dragon; Binder-c
97 194 291 621 1061 1500
6-Origin The Black Crusader & Red Dragon (3/43); 1st story app. Red Dragon & 1st cover (classic-c) 258 516 774 1651 2826 4000
7-Classic Japanese exploding soldier WWII-c 343 686 1029 2400 4200 6000
8-The Red Knight app. 61 122 183 390 670 950
9-Origin Chuck Magnon, Immortal Man 61 122 183 390 670 950

RED DRAGON COMICS (2nd Series)(See Super Magician V2#8)
Street & Smith Publications: Nov, 1947 - No. 6, Jan, 1949; No. 7, July, 1949

1-Red Dragon begins; Elliman, Nigel app.; Edd Cartier-c/a
119 238 357 762 1306 1850
2-Cartier-c 60 120 180 381 653 925
3-1st app. Dr. Neff Ghost Breaker by Powell; Elliman, Nigel app.
47 94 141 296 498 700
4-Cartier c/a 61 122 183 390 670 950
5-7 37 74 111 222 361 500

NOTE: *Maneely a-5, 7. Powell a-2-7; c-3, 5, 7.*

RED EAGLE
David McKay Publications: No. 16, Aug, 1938

Feature Books 16 34 68 102 206 336 465

REDEYE (See Comics Reading Libraries in the Promotional Comics section)

RED FOX (Formerly Manhunt! #1-14; also see Extra Comics)
Magazine Enterprises: No. 15, 1954

15(A-1 #108)-Undercover Girl story; L.B. Cole-c/a (Red Fox); r-from Manhunt; Powell-a
19 38 57 109 172 235

RED GOOSE COMIC SELECTIONS (See Comic Selections)

RED HAWK (See A-1 Comics, Bobby Benson's ..#14-16 & Straight Arrow #2)
Magazine Enterprises: No. 90, 1953

11-(A-1 Comics #90)-Powell-c/a 13 26 39 72 101 130

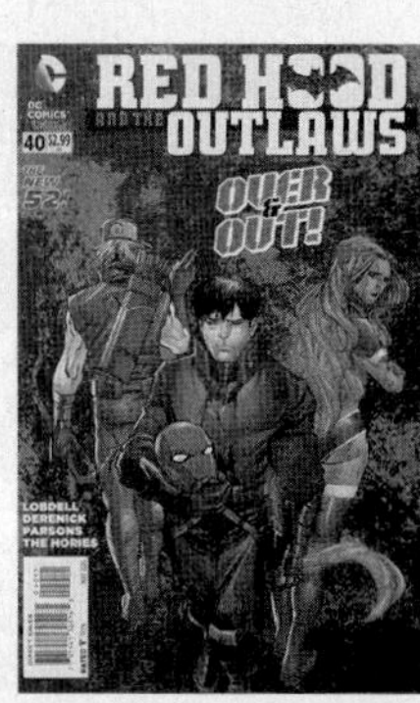

Red Hood and the Outlaws #40 © DC

Red Robin #11 © DC

Red Ryder Comics #3 © L/S

GD VG FN VF VF/NM NM-
2.0 4.0 6.0 8.0 9.0 9.2

GD VG FN VF VF/NM NM-
2.0 4.0 6.0 8.0 9.0 9.2

RED HERRING
DC Comics (WildStorm): Oct, 2009 - No. 6, Mar, 2010 ($2.99, limited series)
1-6-Tischman-s/Bond-a 3.00

RED HOOD AND THE OUTLAWS (DC New 52)
DC Comics: Nov, 2011 - No. 40, May, 2015 ($2.99)
1-Jason Todd, Starfire, Roy Harper team; Lobdell-s/Rocafort-a/c
2 4 6 8 10 12
2-4 6.00
5-8 4.00
9-Night of the Owls tie-in; Mr. Freeze vs. Talon 5.00
10-14 3.00
15-(2/13) Death of the Family tie-in; die-cut cover; Joker app. 5.00
16-18: 16,17-Death of the Family tie-in 4.00
19-24,26-40: 24,26,27-Ra's al Ghul app. 30,31-Lobo app. 37-Arsenal's origin 3.00
25-($3.99) Zero Year tie-in; Talia and the Red Hood Gang app.; Haun-a 4.00
#0-(11/12, $2.99) Jason Todd's origin re-told; Joker app. 6.00
Annual 1 (7/13, $4.99) Takes place between #20 & 21; Green Arrow app.; Barrionuevo-a 5.00
Annual 2 (2/15, $4.99) Christmas-themed; Derenick-a 5.00
...: Futures End 1 (11/14, $2.99, regular-c) Five years later; Lobdell-s/Kolins-a 3.00
...: Futures End 1 (11/14, $3.99, 3-D cover) 4.00

RED HOOD AND THE OUTLAWS (DC Rebirth)
DC Comics: Oct, 2016 - Present ($2.99/$3.99)
1-8: 1-Jason Todd, Artemis & Bizarro team; Lobdell-s/Soy-a; Blask Mask app. 3.00
9-19-($3.99) 12-Solomon Grundy app. 13-Lex Luthor app. 16,17-Harley Quinn app. 18-The Creeper app. 4.00
Annual 1 (10/17, $4.99) Nightwing & KGBeast app.; Kirkham-a/c 5.00
...: Rebirth (9/16, $2.99) Jason Todd origin re-told; Batman app. 3.00

RED HOOD / ARSENAL
DC Comics: Aug, 2015 - No. 13, Aug, 2016 ($2.99)
1-13: 1-Jason Todd & Roy Harper team; Lobdell-s/Medri. 3-5-Batman (Gordon) app. 6-13-Joker's Daughter app. 7-"Robin War" tie-in. 13-Bonus flashback 1st meeting 3.00

RED HOOD: THE LOST DAYS
DC Comics: Aug, 2010 - No. 6, Jan, 2011 ($2.99, limited series)
1-6-The Return of Jason Todd; Winick-s/Raimondi-a/Tucci-c. 6-Joker & Hush app. 4.00
TPB (2011, $14.99) r/#1-6 15.00

RED LANTERNS (DC New 52)
DC Comics: Nov, 2011 - No. 40, May, 2015 ($2.99)
1-34: 1-Milligan-s/Benes-a/c; Atrocitus, Dex-Starr & Bleez app. 6-8,11-Guy Gardner app. 10-Stormwatch app. 13-15-Rise of the Third Army. 17-First Lantern app. 24-Lights Out pt. 4. 28-Flipbook with Green Lantern #28; Supergirl app. 29-Superman app. 3.00
35-40: 35-37-Godhead x-over; Simon Baz app. 3.00
#0-(11/12, $2.99) Origin of Atrocitus, the 1st Red Lantern; Syaf-a 3.00
Annual 1 (9/14, $4.99) Story occurs between #33 & 34; Batman cameo 5.00
...: Futures End 1 (11/14, $2.99, regular-c) Five years later; Soule-s/Calafiore-a 3.00
...: Futures End 1 (11/14, $3.99, 3-D cover) 4.00

RED MASK (Formerly Tim Holt; see Best Comics, Blazing Six-Guns)
Magazine Enterprises No. 42-53/Sussex No. 54 (M.E. on-c): No. 42, June-July, 1954 - No. 53, May, 1956; No. 54, Sept, 1957
42-Ghost Rider by Ayers continues, ends #50; Black Phantom continues; 3-D effect c/stories begin 21 42 63 122 199 275
43- 3-D effect-c/stories 19 38 57 109 172 235
44-52: 3-D effect stories only. 47-Last pre-code issue. 50-Last Ghost Rider. 51-The Presto Kid begins by Ayers (1st app.); Presto Kid-c begins; last 3-D effect story.
52-Origin The Presto Kid 17 34 51 98 154 210
53,54-Last Black Phantom; last Presto Kid-c 15 30 45 83 124 165
I.W. Reprint #1 (r-/#52). 2 (nd, r/#51 w/diff.-c). 3, 8 (nd; Kinstler-c); 8-r/Red Mask #52
3 6 9 16 22 28

NOTE: ***Ayers** art on Ghost Rider & Presto Kid. **Bolle** art in all (Red Mask); c-43, 44, 49. **Guardineer** a-52. Black Phantom in #42-44, 47-50, 53, 54.*

REDMASK OF THE RIO GRANDE
AC Comics: 1990 ($2.50, 28pgs.)(Has photos of movie posters)
1-Bolle-c/a(r); photo inside-c 3.00

RED MENACE
DC Comics (WildStorm): Jan, 2007 - No. 6, Jun, 2007 ($2.99, limited series)
1-6-Ordway-a/c; Bilson, DeMeo & Brody-s 3.00
TPB (2007, $17.99) r/series, sketch pages & variant covers 18.00

RED MOUNTAIN FEATURING QUANTRELL'S RAIDERS (Movie)(Also see Jesse James #28)
Avon Periodicals: 1952
nn-Alan Ladd; Kinstler-c 34 68 102 199 325 450

RED ONE
Image Comics: Mar, 2015 - No. 4 ($2.99)
1-4-Xavier Dorison-s/Terry Dodson-a/c 3.00

RED PROPHET: THE TALES OF ALVIN MAKER
Dabel Brothers Prods./Marvel Comics (Dabel Brothers): Mar, 2006 - No. 12, Mar, 2008 ($2.99)
1-12-Adaptation of Orson Scott Card novel. 1-Miguel Montenegro-a 3.00
... Vol. 1 HC (2007, $19.99, dustjacket) r/#1-6 20.00
... Vol. 1 SC (2007, $15.99) r/#1-6 16.00
... Vol. 2 HC (2008, $19.99, dustjacket) r/#7-12 20.00

"RED" RABBIT COMICS
Dearfield Comic/J. Charles Laue Publ. Co.: Jan, 1947 - No. 22, Aug-Sep, 1951
1 16 32 48 92 144 195
2 10 20 30 58 79 100
3-10 9 18 27 52 69 85
11-17,19-22 8 16 24 44 57 70
18-Flying Saucer-c (1/51) 10 20 30 56 76 95

RED RAVEN COMICS (Human Torch #2 on)(Also see X-Men #44 & Sub-Mariner #26, 2nd series)
Timely Comics: August, 1940
1-Jack Kirby-c (his 1st signed work); origin & 1st app. Red Raven; Comet Pierce & Mercury by Kirby, The Human Top & The Eternal Brain; intro. Magar, the Mystic & only app.
2000 4000 6000 15,000 27,500 40,000

RED ROBIN (Batman: Reborn)
DC Comics: Aug, 2009 - No. 26, Oct, 2011 ($2.99)
1-26-Tim (Drake) Wayne in the Kingdom Come costume; Bachs-a. 1-Two covers 3.00

RED ROCKET 7
Dark Horse Comics: Aug, 1997 - No. 7, June, 1998 ($3.95, square format, limited series)
1-7-Mike Allred-c/s/a 4.00

RED RYDER COMICS (Hi Spot #2)(Movies, radio)(See Crackajack Funnies & Super Book of Comics)
Hawley Publ. No. 1/Dell Publishing Co.(K.K.) No. 3 on: 9/40; No. 3, 8/41 - No. 5, 12/41; No. 6, 4/42 - No. 151, 4-6/57 (Beware of almost identical reprints of #1 made in the late 1980s)
1-Red Ryder, his horse Thunder, Little Beaver & his horse Papoose strip reprints begin by Fred Harman; 1st meeting of Red & Little Beaver; Harman line-drawn-c #1-85
252 504 756 1613 2757 3900
3-(Scarce)-Alley Oop, Capt. Easy, Dan Dunn, Freckles & His Friends, King of the Royal Mtd., Myra North strip-r begin 50 100 150 400 900 1400
4-6: 6-1st Dell issue (4/42) 25 50 75 175 388 600
7-10 21 42 63 147 324 500
11-20 15 30 45 103 227 350
21-32-Last Alley Oop, Dan Dunn, Capt. Easy, Freckles
10 20 30 69 147 225
33-40 (52 pgs.): 40-Photo back-c begin, end #57 9 18 27 58 114 170
41 (52 pgs.)-Rocky Lane photo back-c 9 18 27 60 120 180
42-46 (52 pgs.): 46-Last Red Ryder strip-r 7 14 21 49 92 135
47-53 (52 pgs.): 47-New stories on Red Ryder begin. 49,52-Harmon photo back-c
6 12 18 41 76 110
54-92: 54-73 (36 pgs.). 59-Harmon photo back-c. 73-Last King of the Royal Mtd; strip-r by Jim Gary. 74-85 (52 pgs.)-Harman line-drawn-c. 86-92 (52 pgs.)-Harman painted-c
6 12 18 37 66 95
93-99,101-106: 94-96 (36 pgs.)-Harman painted-c. 97,98,(36 pgs.)-Harman line-drawn-c. 99,101-106 (36 pgs.)-Jim Bannon Photo-c 5 10 15 33 57 80
100 (36 pgs.)-Bannon photo-c 5 10 15 34 60 85
107-118 (52 pgs.)-Harman line-drawn-c 5 10 15 31 53 75
119-129 (52 pgs.): 119-Painted-c begin, not by Harman, end #151
5 10 15 30 50 70
130-151 (36 pgs.): 145-Title change to Red Ryder Ranch Magazine
149-Title change to Red Ryder Ranch Comics 4 8 12 28 47 65
Four Color 916 (7/58) 4 8 12 28 47 65

NOTE: ***Fred Harman** a-1-99; c-1-98, 107-118. Don Red Barry, Allan Rocky Lane, Wild Bill Elliott & Jim Bannon starred as Red Ryder in the movies. Robert Blake starred as Little Beaver.*

RED RYDER PAINT BOOK
Whitman Publishing Co.: 1941 (8-1/2x11-1/2", 148 pgs.)
nn-Reprints 1940 daily strips 76 152 228 479 810 1140

RED SEAL COMICS (Formerly Carnival Comics, and/or Spotlight Comics?)
Harry 'A' Chesler/Superior Publ. No. 19 on: No. 14, 10/45 - No. 18, 10/46; No. 19, 6/47 - No. 22, 12/47

Red She-Hulk #58 © MAR

Red Sonja (Volume 2) #16 © Red Sonja LLC

Red Star #9 © Christian Gossett

	GD 2.0	VG 4.0	FN 6.0	VF 8.0	VF/NM 9.0	NM- 9.2
14-The Black Dwarf begins (continued from Spotlight?); Little Nemo app; bondage/hypo-c; Tuska-a	100	200	300	635	1093	1550
15-Torture story; funny-c	41	82	123	256	428	600
16-Used in **SOTI**, pg. 181, illo "Outside the forbidden pages of de Sade, you find draining a girl's blood only in children's comics;" drug club story r-later in Crime Reporter #1; Veiled Avenger & Barry Kuda app; Tuska-a; funny-c	63	126	189	403	689	975
17,18,20: Lady Satan, Yankee Girl & Sky Chief app; 17-Tuska-a	66	122	183	390	670	950
19-No Black Dwarf (on-c only); Zor, El Tigre app.	60	120	180	381	653	925
21-Lady Satan & Black Dwarf app.	37	74	111	222	361	500
22-Zor, Rocketman app. (68 pgs.)	37	74	111	222	361	500

RED SHE-HULK (Title continues from Hulk (2008 series) #57)
Marvel Comics: No. 58, Dec, 2012 - No. 67, Sept, 2013 ($2.99)

58-67-Betty Ross character; Pagulayan-a/c. 59,60-Avengers app. 66-Man-Thing app. 3.00

REDSKIN (Thrilling Indian Stories)(Famous Western Badmen #13 on)
Youthful Magazines: Sept, 1950 - No. 12, Oct, 1952

	GD	VG	FN	VF	VF/NM	NM-
1-Walter Johnson-a (7 pgs.)	20	40	60	118	192	265
2	14	28	42	78	112	145
3-12: 3-Daniel Boone story. 6-Geronimo story	11	22	33	64	90	115

NOTE: *Walter Johnson c-3, 4.* ***Palais*** *a-11.* ***Wildey*** *a-5, 11. Bondage c-6, 12.*

RED SKULL
Marvel Comics: Sept, 2011 - No. 5, Jan, 2012 ($2.99, limited series)

1-5-Pak-s/Colak-a/Aja-c; Red Skull's childhood and origin 3.00

RED SKULL (Secret Wars Battleworld tie-in)
Marvel Comics: Sept, 2015 - No. 3, Nov, 2015 ($3.99, limited series)

1-3-Joshua Williamson-s/Luca Pizzari-a; Crossbones, Magneto & Bucky app. 4.00

RED SONJA (Also see Conan #23, Kull & The Barbarians, Marvel Feature & Savage Sword Of Conan #1)
Marvel Comics Group: 1/77 - No. 15, 5/79; V1#1, 2/83 - V2#2, 3/83; V3#1, 8/83 - V3#4, 2/84; V3#5, 1/85 - V3#13, 5/86

	GD	VG	FN	VF	VF/NM	NM-
1-Created by Robert E. Howard	4	8	12	23	37	50
2-10: 5-Last 30¢ issue	2	4	6	8	10	12
4,5-(35¢-c variants, limited distribution)(7,9/77)	8	16	24	56	108	160
11-15, V2#1,V2#2: 14-Last 35¢ issue	1	3	4	6	8	10
V3#1 ($1.00, 52 pgs.)	1	3	4	6	8	10
V3#2-13: #2-4 ($1.00, 52 pgs.)						5.00

NOTE: ***Brunner*** *c-12-14.* ***J. Buscema*** *a(p)-12, 13, 15; c-V#1.* ***Nebres*** *a-V3#3i(part).* ***N. Redondo*** *a-8i, V3#2i, 3i.* ***Simonson*** *a-V3#1.* ***Thorne*** *c/a-1-11.*

RED SONJA (Continues in Queen Sonja) (Also see Classic Red Sonja)
Dynamite Entertainment: No. 0, Apr, 2005 - No. 80, 2013 (25¢/$2.99/$3.99)

0-(4/05, 25¢) Greg Land-c/Mel Rubi-a/Oeming & Carey-s 4.00
1-(6/05, $2.99) Five covers by Ross, Linsner, Cassaday, Turner, Rivera; Rubi-a 10.00
2-46-Multiple covers on all. 29-Sonja dies. 34-Sonja reborn 3.00
5-RRP Edition with Red Foil logo and Isanove-a 15.00
50-('10, $4.99) new stories and reprints; Marcos, Chin, Desjardins-a; 4 covers 5.00
51-79-($3.99): 51-56-Geovani-a; multiple covers on each 4.00
80-($4.99) Red Sonja vs. Dracula; bonus interview with Gail Simone 5.00
Annual #1 (2007, $3.50) Oeming-s/Sadowski-a; Red Sonja Comics Chronology 4.00
Annual #2 (2009, $3.99) Gage-s/Marcos-a; wraparound Prado-c & Marcos-c 4.00
Annual #3 (2010, $5.99) Brereton-s/c/a; Batista-a 6.00
Annual #4 (2013, $4.99) Beatty-s/Mena-a 5.00
... Blue (2011, $4.99) Brett-s/Geovani-a; covers by Geovani & Rubi 5.00
... Break the Skin (2011, $4.99) Winslade-c/Van Meter-s/Salazar-a 5.00
... Cover Showcase Vol. 1 (2007, $5.99) gallery of variant covers; Cho sketches 6.00
... Deluge (2011, $4.99) Brereton-s/c; Bolson-a/var-c; reprint from Conan #48 ('74) 5.00
Giant Size Red Sonja #1 (2007, $4.99) Chaykin-c; new story and reprints and pin-ups 5.00
Giant Size Red Sonja #2 (2008, $4.99) Segovia-c; new story and reprints and pin-ups 5.00
... Goes East ($4.99) three covers; Joe Ng-a 5.00
...: Monster Isle ($4.99) two covers; Pablo Marcos-a/Roy Thomas-s 5.00
... One More Day ($4.99) two covers; Liam Sharp-a 5.00
... Raven ('12, $4.99) Antonio-a/Martin-c; bonus pin-up gallery 5.00
...: Revenge of the Gods 1-5 (2011 - No. 5, 2011, $3.99) Sampare-a/Lieberman-s 4.00
... Vacant Shell ($4.99) two covers; Remender-s/Renaud-a 5.00
...: Wrath of the Gods 1-5 (2010 - No. 5, 2010, $3.99) Geovani-a 4.00
The Adventures of Red Sonja TPB (2005, $19.99) r/Marvel Feature #1-7 20.00
The Adventures of Red Sonja Vol. 2 TPB (2007, $19.99) r/#1-7 of '77 Marvel series 20.00
... Vol. 1 TPB (2006, $19.99) r/#0-6; gallery of covers and variants; creators interview 20.00
... Vol. 2 Arrowsmith TPB (2007, $19.99) r/#7-12; gallery of covers and variants 20.00
... Vol. 3 The Rise of Gath TPB (2007, $19.99) r/#13-18; gallery of covers and variants 20.00
... Vol. 4 Animals & More TPB (2007, $24.99) r/#19-24; gallery of covers and variants 25.00

RED SONJA (Volume 2)
Dynamite Entertainment: 2013 - No. 18, 2015 ($3.99)

1-18: 1-Gail Simone-s/Walter Geovani-a; six covers. 2-18-Multiple covers 4.00
#0 (2014, $3.99) Simone-s/Salonga-a/Hardman-c 4.00
#100 (2015, $7.99) Five short stories by various incl. Simone, Oeming, Marcos; 5 covers 8.00
#1973 (2015, $7.99) Five short stories by various incl. Simone, Bunn, Thomas & others 8.00
...: and Cub (2014, $4.99) Nancy Collins-s/Fritz Casas-a/J.M. Linsner-c 5.00
...: Berserker (2014, $4.99) Jim Zub-s/Jonathan Lau-a/Jeffrey Cruz-c 5.00
...: Sanctuary (2014, $4.99) Mason-s/Salonga-a/Davila-c; includes full script 5.00

RED SONJA (Volume 3)
Dynamite Entertainment: 2016 - No. 6, 2016 ($3.99)

1-6: 1-Marguerite Bennett-s/Aneke-a; multiple covers 4.00

RED SONJA (Volume 4)
Dynamite Entertainment: No. 0, 2016 - Present ($3.99)

0-(25¢) Sonja transported to present day New York City; Amy Chu-s/Carlos Gomez-a 3.00
1-13-($3.99) Amy Chu-s/Carlos Gomez-a; multiple covers 4.00

RED SONJA: ATLANTIS RISES
Dynamite Entertainment: 2012 - No. 4, 2012 ($3.99, limited series)

1-4-Lieberman-s/Dunbar-a/Parrillo-c 4.00

RED SONJA/CLAW: THE DEVIL'S HANDS (See Claw the Unconquered)
DC Comics (WildStorm)/Dynamite Ent.: May, 2006 - No. 4, Aug, 2006 ($2.99, limited series)

1-4-Covers by Jim Lee & Dell'Otto; Andy Smith-a 1-Alex Ross var-c. 2-Dell'Otto var-c. 3-Bermejo var-c. 4-Andy Smith var-c 3.00
TPB (2007, $12.99) r/#1-4; cover gallery 13.00

RED SONJA/ CONAN
Dynamite Entertainment: 2015 - No. 4, 2015 ($3.99, limited series)

1-4-Gischler-s/Castro-a; multiple covers 4.00

RED SONJA: SCAVENGER HUNT
Marvel Comics: Dec, 1995 ($2.95, one-shot)

1 4.00

RED SONJA: THE BLACK TOWER
Dynamite Entertainment: 2014 - No. 4, 2015 ($3.99, limited series)

1-4-Tieri-s/Razek-a/Conner-c 4.00

RED SONJA: THE MOVIE
Marvel Comics Group: Nov, 1985 - No. 2, Dec, 1985 (Limited series)

1,2-Movie adapt-r/Marvel Super Spec. #38 4.00

RED SONJA: UNCHAINED
Dynamite Entertainment: 2013 - No. 4, 2013 ($3.99, limited series)

1-4-Follows the Red Sonja: Blue one-shot; Jadsen-a 4.00

RED SONJA: VULTURE'S CIRCLE
Dynamite Entertainment: 2015 - No. 5, 2015 ($3.99, limited series)

1-5-Collins & Lieberman-s/Casas-a; three covers on each 4.00

RED SONJA VS. THULSA DOOM
Dynamite Entertainment: 2005 - No. 4, 2006 ($3.50)

1-4-Conrad-a; Conrad & Dell'Otto covers 3.50
..., Volume 1 TPB (2006, $14.99) r/series; cover gallery 15.00

RED STAR, THE
Image Comics/Archangel Studios: June, 2000 - No. 9, June, 2002 ($2.95)

1-Christian Gossett-s/a(p) 4.00
2-9: 9-Beck-c 3.00
#(7.5) Reprints Wizard #1/2 story with new pages 3.00
Annual 1 (Archangel Studios, 11/02, $3.50) "Run Makita Run" 4.00
TPB (4/01, $24.95, 9x12") oversized r/#1-4; intro. by Bendis 25.00
Nokgorka TPB (8/02, $24.95, 9x12") oversized r/#6-9; w/sketch pages 25.00
Wizard 1/2 (mail order) 10.00

RED STAR, THE (Volume 2)
CrossGen #1,2/Archangel Studios #3 on: Feb, 2003 - No. 5, July, 2004 ($2.95/$2.99)

1-5-Christian Gossett-s/a(p) 3.00
Prison of Souls TPB (8/04, $24.95, 9x12") oversized r/#1-5; w/sketch pages 25.00

RED STAR, THE: SWORD OF LIES
Archangel Studios: Aug, 2006 ($4.50)

1-Christian Gossett-s/a(p); origin of the Red Star team 4.50

RED TEAM
Dynamite Entertainment: 2013 - No. 7, 2014 ($3.99)

1-7: 1-Ennis-s/Cermak-a; covers by Chaykin & Sook 4.00

Red Wolf (2016 series) #4 © MAR

Re-Gex #1 © A-H

Regular Show #24 © CN

	GD 2.0	VG 4.0	FN 6.0	VF 8.0	VF/NM 9.0	NM- 9.2

RED TEAM, VOLUME 2: DOUBLE TAP, CENTER MASS
Dynamite Entertainment: 2016 - No. 9, 2017 ($3.99)

1-8: 1-Ennis-s/Cermak-a/Panosian-c 4.00
9-($4.99) 5.00

RED THORN
DC Comics (Vertigo): Jan, 2016 - No. 13, Feb, 2017 ($3.99)

1-13: 1-6-David Baillie-s/Meghan Hetrick-a. 7-Steve Pugh-a 4.00

RED TORNADO (See All-American #20 & Justice League of America #64)
DC Comics: July, 1985 - No. 4, Oct, 1985 (Limited series)

1-4: Kurt Busiek scripts in all. 1-3-Superman & Batman cameos 4.00

RED TORNADO
DC Comics: Nov, 2009 - No. 6, Apr, 2010 ($2.99, limited series)

1-6: 1-3-Benes-c. 5,6-Vixen app. 3.00
...: Family Reunion TPB (2010, $17.99) r/#1-6 18.00

RED WARRIOR
Marvel/Atlas Comics (TCI): Jan, 1951 - No. 6, Dec, 1951

	GD 2.0	VG 4.0	FN 6.0	VF 8.0	VF/NM 9.0	NM- 9.2
1-Red Warrior & his horse White Wing; Tuska-a	20	40	60	114	182	250
2-Tuska-c	12	24	36	69	97	125
3-6: 4-Origin White Wing. 6-Maneely-c	10	20	30	58	79	100

RED, WHITE & BLUE COMICS
DC Comics: 1941

nn - Ashcan comic, not distributed to newsstands, only for in-house use. Cover art is All-American Comics #20 with interior being Flash Comics #17 (no known sales)

RED WING
Image Comics: Jul, 2011 - No. 4, Oct, 2011 ($3.50, limited series)

1-4-Hickman-s/Pitarra-a 3.50

RED WOLF (See Avengers #80 & Marvel Spotlight #1)
Marvel Comics Group: May, 1972 - No. 9, Sept, 1973

	GD 2.0	VG 4.0	FN 6.0	VF 8.0	VF/NM 9.0	NM- 9.2
1-(Western hero); Gil Kane/Severin-c; Shores-a	4	8	12	25	40	55
2-9: 2-Kane-c; Shores-a. 6-Tuska-r in back-up. 7-Red Wolf as super hero begins. 9-Origin sidekick, Lobo (wolf)	3	6	9	16	23	30

RED WOLF (From the Secret Wars tie-in series 1872)
Marvel Comics: Feb, 2016 - No. 6, Jul, 2016 ($3.99)

1-6: 1-Edmondson-s/Talajic-a. 2-Red Wolf in the present 4.00

REESE'S PIECES
Eclipse Comics: Oct, 1985 - No.2, Oct, 1985 ($1.75, Baxter paper)

1,2-B&W-r in color 3.00

REFORM SCHOOL GIRL!
Realistic Comics: 1951

	GD 2.0	VG 4.0	FN 6.0	VF 8.0	VF/NM 9.0	NM- 9.2
nn-Used in **SOTI**, pg. 358, & cover ill. with caption "Comic books are supposed to be like fairy tales"; classic photo-c	1100	2200	3300	8400	15,200	22,000

(Prices vary widely on this book)

NOTE: *The cover and title originated from a digest-sized book published by Diversey Publishing Co. of Chicago in 1948. The original book "House of Fury", Doubleday, came out in 1941. The girl's real name which appears on the cover of the digest and comic is Marty Collins, Canadian model and ice skating star who posed for this special color photograph for the Diversey novel.*

REGENTS ILLUSTRATED CLASSICS
Prentice Hall Regents, Englewood Cliffs, NJ 07632: 1981 (Plus more recent reprintings) (48 pgs., B&W-a with 14 pgs. of teaching helps)

NOTE: *This series contains Classics Ill. art, and was produced from the same illegal source as* ***Cassette Books.*** *But when Twin Circle sued to stop the sale of the Cassette Books, they decided to permit this series to continue. This series was produced as a teaching aid. The 20 title series is divided into four levels based upon number of basic words used therein. There is also a teacher's manual for each level. All of the titles are still available from the publisher for about $5 each retail. The number to call for mail order purchases is (201)767-5937. Almost all of the issues have new covers taken from some interior art panel. Here is a list of the series by Regents ident. no. and the Classics Ill. counterpart.*

16770(CI#24-A2)18333(CI#3-A2)21668(CI#13-A2)32224(CI#21)33051(CI#26)35788(CI#84)37153(CI#16)44460(CI#19-A2)44808(CI#18-A2)52395(CI#4-A2)58627(CI#5-A2)60067(CI#30)68405(CI#23A1)70302(CI#29)78192(CI#7-A2)78193(CI#10-A2)79679(CI#85)92046(CI#1-A2)93062(CI#64)93512(CI#25)

RE: GEX
Awesome-Hyperwerks: Jul, 1998 - No. 0, Dec, 1998; ($2.50)

Preview (7/98) Wizard Con Edition 3.00
0-(12/98) Loeb-s/Liefeld-a/Pat Lee-c, 1-(9/98) Loeb-s/Liefeld-a/c 3.00

REGGIE (Formerly Archie's Rival...; Reggie & Me #19 on)
Archie Publications: No. 15, Sept, 1963 - No. 18, Nov, 1965

	GD 2.0	VG 4.0	FN 6.0	VF 8.0	VF/NM 9.0	NM- 9.2
15(9/63), 16(10/64), 17(8/65), 18(11/65)	5	10	15	31	53	75

NOTE: *Cover title No. 15 & 16 is Archie's Rival Reggie.*

REGGIE AND ME (Formerly Reggie)
Archie Publ.: No. 19, Aug, 1966 - No. 126, Sept, 1980 (No. 50-68: 52 pgs.)

	GD 2.0	VG 4.0	FN 6.0	VF 8.0	VF/NM 9.0	NM- 9.2
19-Evilheart app.	4	8	12	25	40	55
20-23-Evilheart app.; with Pureheart #22	3	6	9	20	31	42
24-40(3/70)	3	6	9	15	22	28
41-49(7/71)	2	4	6	11	16	20
50(9/71)-68 (1/74, 52 pgs.)	3	6	9	14	19	24
69-99	2	4	6	8	10	12
100(10/77)	2	4	6	9	12	15
101-126	1	2	3	5	7	9

REGGIE AND ME (Volume 2)
Archie Comic Publications: Jan, 2017 - No. 5, ($3.99)

1-5-Multiple covers and classic back-up reprints in#1,2. Tom DeFalco-s/Sandy Jarrell-a 4.00

REGGIE'S JOKES (See Reggie's Wise Guy Jokes)

REGGIE'S REVENGE!
Archie Comic Publications, Inc.: Spring, 1994 - No. 3 ($2.00, 52 pgs.) (Published semi-annually)

1-Bound-in pull-out poster 5.00
2,3 4.00

REGGIE'S WISE GUY JOKES
Archie Publications: Aug, 1968 - No. 55, 1980 (#5-28 are Giants)

	GD 2.0	VG 4.0	FN 6.0	VF 8.0	VF/NM 9.0	NM- 9.2
1	4	8	12	27	44	60
2-4	3	6	9	14	20	26
5-16 (1/71)(68 pg. Giants)	3	6	9	16	24	32
17-28 (52 pg. Giants)	2	4	6	13	18	22
29-40(1/77)	1	3	4	6	8	10
41-55	1	2	3	5	6	8

REGISTERED NURSE
Charlton Comics: Summer, 1963

	GD 2.0	VG 4.0	FN 6.0	VF 8.0	VF/NM 9.0	NM- 9.2
1-r/Nurse Betsy Crane & Cynthia Doyle	3	6	9	21	33	45

REG'LAR FELLERS
Visual Editions (Standard): No. 5, Nov, 1947 - No. 6, Mar, 1948

	GD 2.0	VG 4.0	FN 6.0	VF 8.0	VF/NM 9.0	NM- 9.2
5,6	9	18	27	50	65	80

REG'LAR FELLERS HEROIC (See Heroic Comics)

REGRESSION
Image Comics: May, 2017 - Present ($3.99)

1-7-Bunn-s/Luckert-a 4.00

REGULAR SHOW (Based on Cartoon Network series)
Boom Entertainment (kaBOOM!): Apr, 2013 - No. 40, Oct, 2016 ($3.99)

1-40-Multiple covers on all 4.00
2014 Annual 1 (6/14, $4.99) Four short stories by various; three covers 5.00
2015 Special 1 (3/15, $4.99) Four short stories by various; two covers 5.00
2017 Special 1 (4/17, $7.99) Six short stories by various; two covers 8.00
2018 Special 1 (2/18, $7.99) Four short stories; McCreery-s; art by various 8.00

REGULAR SHOW: SKIPS (Based on Cartoon Network series)
Boom Entertainment (kaBOOM!): Nov, 2013 - No. 6, Apr, 2014 ($3.99)

1-6-Mad Rupert-s/a; multiple covers on all 4.00

REID FLEMING, WORLD'S TOUGHEST MILKMAN
Eclipse Comics/ Deep Sea Comics: 1980; 8/86; V2#1, 12/86 - V2#3, 12/88; V2#4, 11/89; V2#5, 11/90 - V2#9, 4/98 (B&W)

1-(1980, self-published) David Boswell-s/a 5.00
1-2nd, 4th & 5th printings ($2.50); (3rd print, large size, 8/86, $2.50) 3.00
V2#1 (10/86, regular size, $2.00), 1-2nd print, 3rd print ($2.00, 2/89) 3.00
2-9 , V2#2-2nd & 3rd printings, V2#4-2nd printing, V2#5 ($2.00), V2#6 (Deep Sea, r/V2#5) 7-9-New stories 3.00

REIGN IN HELL
DC Comics: Sept, 2008 - No. 8, Apr, 2009 ($3.50, limited series)

1-8-Neron, Shadowpact app.; Giffen-s; Dr. Occult back-up w/Segovia-a. 1-Two covers 3.50
TPB (2009, $19.99) r/#1-8 20.00

REIGN OF THE ZODIAC
DC Comics: Oct, 2003 - No. 8, May, 2004 ($2.75)

1-8: 1-6,8-Giffen-s/Doran-a/Harris-c. 7-Byrd-a 3.00

RELATIVE HEROES
DC Comics: Mar, 2000 - No. 6, Aug, 2000 ($2.50, limited series)

1-6-Grayson-s/Guichet & Sowd-a. 6-Superman-c/app. 3.00

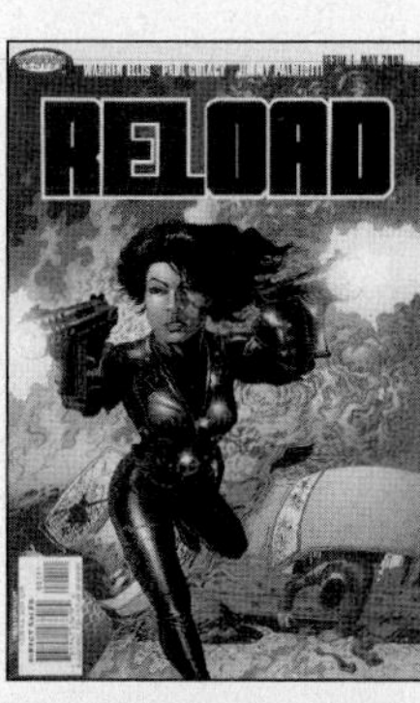

Reload #1 © Ellis, Gulacy, & Palmiotti

The Resistance #1 © WSP

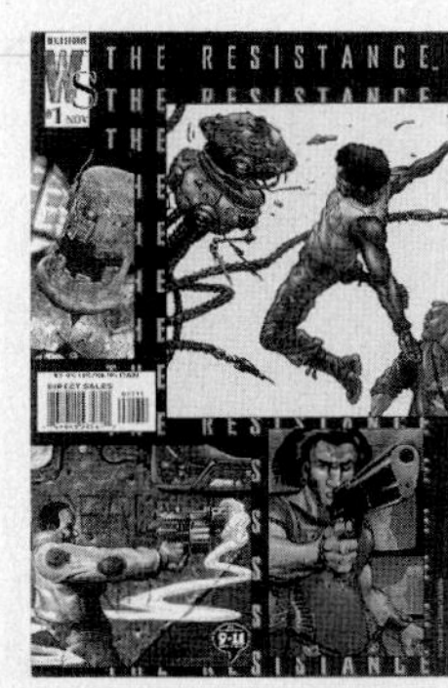

Resurrection Man #10 © DC

	GD 2.0	VG 4.0	FN 6.0	VF 8.0	VF/NM 9.0	NM- 9.2

RELOAD
DC Comics (Homage): May, 2003 - No. 3, Sept, 2003 ($2.95, limited series)

1-3-Warren Ellis-s/Paul Gulacy & Jimmy Palmiotti-a — 3.00
.../Mek TPB (2004, $14.95, flip book) r/Reload #1-3 & Mek #1-3 — 15.00

RELUCTANT DRAGON, THE (Walt Disney's...)
Dell Publishing Co.: No. 13, 1940

Four Color 13-Contains 2 pgs. of photos from film; 2 pg. foreword to Fantasia by Leopold Stokowski; Donald Duck, Goofy, Baby Weems & Mickey Mouse (as the Sorcerer's Apprentice) app. — 226 452 678 1446 2473 3500

REMAINS
IDW Publishing: May, 2004 - No. 5, Sept, 2004 ($3.99)

1-5-Steve Niles-s/Kieron Dwyer-a — 4.00

REMARKABLE WORLDS OF PROFESSOR PHINEAS B. FUDDLE, THE
DC Comics (Paradox Press): 2000 - No. 4, 2000 ($5.95, limited series)

1-4-Boaz Yakin-s/Erez Yakin-a — 6.00
TPB (2001, $19.95) r/series — 20.00

REMEMBER PEARL HARBOR
Street & Smith Publications: 1942 (68 pgs.) (Illustrated story of the battle)

nn-Uncle Sam-c; Jack Binder-a — 84 168 252 538 919 1300

REN & STIMPY SHOW, THE (TV) (Nickelodeon cartoon characters)
Marvel Comics: Dec, 1992 - No. 44, July, 1996 ($1.75/$1.95)

1-($2.25)-Polybagged w/scratch & sniff Ren or Stimpy air fowler (equal numbers of each were made) — 1 3 4 6 8 10
1-2nd & 3rd printing; different dialogue on-c — 4.00
2-6: 4-Muddy Mudskipper back-up. 5-Bill Wray painted-c. 6-Spider-Man vs. Powdered Toast Man — 5.00
7-17: 12-1st solo back-up story w/Tank & Brenner — 4.00
18-44: 18-Powered Toast Man app. — 4.00
25 ($2.95) Deluxe edition w/die cut cover — 5.00
...Don't Try This at Home (3/94, $12.95, TPB)-r/#9-12 — 13.00
...Eenteractive Special ('95, $2.95) — 4.00
...Holiday Special 1994 (2/95, $2.95, 52 pgs.) — 4.00
...Mini Comic (1995) — 5.00
...Pick of the Litter nn (1993, $12.95, TPB)-r/#1-4 — 13.00
...Radio Daze (11/95, $1.95) — 4.00
...Running Joke nn (1993, $12.95, TPB)-r/#1-4 plus new-a — 13.00
...Seeck Little Monkeys (1/95, $12.95)-r/#17-20 — 13.00
...Special 2 (7/94, $2.95, 52 pgs.), ...Special 3 (10/94, $2.95, 52 pgs.)-Choose adventure, ...Special: Around the World in a Daze ($2.95), ...Special: Four Swerks (1/95, $2.95, 52 pgs.)-FF #1 cover swipe; cover reads "Four Swerks w/5 pg. coloring book.", ...Special: Powdered Toast Man 1 (4/94, $2.95, 52 pgs.), ...Special: Powdered Toast Man's Cereal Serial (4/95, $2.95), ...Special: Sports (10/95, $2.95) — 4.00
...Tastes Like Chicken nn (11/93,$12.95,TPB)-r/#5-8 — 13.00
...Your Pals (1994, $12.95, TPB)-r/#13-16 — 13.00

RENATO JONES: THE ONE %
Image Comics: May, 2016 - No. 5, Oct, 2016 ($3.99)

1-5-Kaare Andrews-s/a/c — 4.00
Renato Jones, Season 2: Freelancer (5/17 - No. 5, 11/17, $3.99) 1-5-Andrews-s/a/c — 4.00

RENFIELD
Caliber Press: 1994 - No. 3, 1995 ($2.95, B&W, limited series)

1-3 — 3.00

RENO BROWNE, HOLLYWOOD'S GREATEST COWGIRL (Formerly Margie Comics; Apache Kid #53 on; also see Western Hearts, Western Life Romances & Western Love)
Marvel Comics (MPC): No. 50, April, 1950 - No. 52, Sept, 1950 (52 pgs.)

50-Reno Browne photo-c on all — 30 60 90 177 289 400
51,52 — 26 52 78 154 252 350

REPLICA
AfterShock Comics: Dec, 2015 - No. 5, Apr, 2016 ($3.99)

1-5-Paul Jenkins-s/Andy Clarke-a — 4.00

REPTILICUS (Becomes Reptisaurus #3 on)
Charlton Comics: Aug, 1961 - No. 2, Oct, 1961

1 (Movie) — 21 42 63 147 324 500
2 — 11 22 33 72 154 235

REPTISAURUS (Reptilicus #1,2)
Charlton Comics: V2#3, Jan, 1962 - No. 8, Dec, 1962; Summer, 1963

V2#3-8: 3-Flying saucer-c/s. 8-Montes/Bache-c/a — 5 10 15 35 63 90
Special Edition 1 (Summer, 1963) — 5 10 15 34 60 85

REQUIEM FOR DRACULA
Marvel Comics: Feb, 1993 ($2.00, 52 pgs.)

nn-r/Tomb of Dracula #69,70 by Gene Colan — 4.00

RESCUE (Pepper Potts in Iron Man armor)
Marvel Comics: July, 2010 ($3.99, one-shot)

1-DeConnick-s/Mutti-a/Foreman-c — 4.00

RESCUERS, THE (See Walt Disney Showcase #40)

RESIDENT ALIEN
Dark Horse Comics: No. 0, Apr, 2012 - No. 3, Jul, 2012 ($3.50, limited series)

0-3-Hogan-s/Parkhouse-a: 0-Reprints chapters from Dark Horse Presents #4-6 — 3.50

RESIDENT ALIEN: THE MAN WITH NO NAME
Dark Horse Comics: Sept, 2016 - No. 4, Dec, 2016 ($3.99, limited series)

1-4-Hogan-s/Parkhouse-a — 4.00

RESIDENT ALIEN: THE SAM HAIN MYSTERY
Dark Horse Comics: No. 0, Apr, 2015 - No. 3, Jul, 2015 ($3.99, limited series)

0-3-Hogan-s/Parkhouse-a: 0-Reprints chapters from Dark Horse Presents V3 #1-3 — 4.00

RESIDENT ALIEN: THE SUICIDE BLONDE
Dark Horse Comics: No. 0, Aug, 2013 - No. 3, Nov, 2013 ($3.99, limited series)

0-3-Hogan-s/Parkhouse-a: 0-Reprints chapters from Dark Horse Presents #18-20 — 4.00

RESIDENT EVIL (Based on video game)
Image Comics (WildStorm): Mar, 1998 - No. 5 ($4.95, quarterly magazine)

1 — 3 6 9 17 26 35
2-5 — 2 4 6 11 16 20
...Code: Veronica 1-4 (2002, $14.95) English reprint of Japanese comics — 15.00
...Collection One ('99, $14.95, TPB) r/#1-4 — 15.00

RESIDENT EVIL (Volume 2)
DC Comics (WildStorm): May, 2009 - No. 6, Feb, 2011 ($3.99)

1-6: 1,2-Liam Sharpe-a. 1-Two covers — 4.00
...: Volume 2 TPB (2011, $19.99) r/#1-6 — 20.00

RESIDENT EVIL: FIRE AND ICE
DC Comics (WildStorm): Dec, 2000 - No. 4, May, 2001 ($2.50, limited series)

1-4-Bermejo-c — 4.00
TPB (2009, $24.99) r/#1-4 plus short stories from Resident Evil magazine — 25.00

RESISTANCE (Based on the video game)
DC Comics (WildStorm): Early Mar, 2009 - No. 6, Jul, 2009 ($3.99, limited series)

1-6-Ramón Pérez-a/C.P. Smith-c — 4.00
TPB (2010, $19.99) r/#1-6 — 20.00

RESISTANCE, THE
DC Comics (WildStorm): Nov, 2002 - No. 8, June, 2003 ($2.95)

1-8-Palmiotti & Gray-s/Santacruz-a — 3.00

REST (Milo Ventimiglia Presents...)
Devil's Due Publ.: No. 0, Aug, 2008 - No. 2 (99¢/$3.50)

0-(99¢) Prelude to series; Powers-s/McManus-a — 3.00
1,2-($3.50) 1-Two covers (Tim Sale art & Milo Ventimiglia photo) — 3.50

RESTAURANT AT THE END OF THE UNIVERSE, THE (See Hitchhiker's Guide to the Galaxy & Life, the Universe & Everything)
DC Comics: 1994 - No. 3, 1994 ($6.95, limited series)

1-3 — 7.00

RESTLESS GUN (TV)
Dell Publishing Co.: No. 934, Sept, 1958 - No. 1146, Nov-Jan, 1960-61

Four Color 934 (#1)-Photo-c — 9 18 27 61 123 185
Four Color 986 (5/59), 1045 (11-1/60), 1089 (3/60), 1146-Wildey-a; all photo-c — 7 14 21 46 86 125

RESURRECTIONISTS
Dark Horse Comics: Nov, 2014 - No. 4, Feb, 2015 ($3.50)

1-4-Van Lente-s/Rosenzweig-a — 3.50

RESURRECTION MAN
DC Comics: May, 1997 - No. 27, Aug, 1999 ($2.50)

1-Lenticular disc on cover — 5.00
2-5: 2-JLA app. — 4.00
6-27: 6-Genesis-x-over. 7-Batman app. 10-Hitman-c/app. 16,17-Supergirl x-over. 18-Deadman & Phantom Stranger-c/app. 21-JLA-c/app. — 3.00
#1,000,000 (11/98) 853rd Century x-over — 3.00

Return of the Outlaw #1 © Minoan

Revival #41 © Seeley & Norton

Rex Allen Comics #10 © DELL

	GD 2.0	VG 4.0	FN 6.0	VF 8.0	VF/NM 9.0	NM- 9.2

RESURRECTION MAN (DC New 52)
DC Comics: Nov, 2011 - No. 12, Oct, 2012; No. 0, Nov, 2012 ($2.99)

1-12: 1-Abnett & Lanning-s/Dagnino-a/Reis-c; Body Doubles app. 9-Suicide Squad app. 3.00
#0 (11/12) Origin of Mitch Shelley and the Body Doubles; Bachs-a/Francavilla-c 3.00

RETIEF (Keith Laumer's)
Adventure Comics (Malibu): Dec, 1989 - Vol. 2, No.6, ($2.25, B&W)

1-6,Vol. 2, #1-6,Vol. 3 (...of The CDT) #1-6 3.00
...and The Warlords #1-6, ...: Diplomatic Immunity #1 (4/91), ...: Giant Killer #1 (9/91), ...: Crime & Punishment #1 (11/91) 3.00

RETROVIRUS
Image Comics: Nov, 2012 ($12.99, hardcover GN)

HC-Gray & Palmiotti-s/Fernandez-a/Conner-c 13.00

RETURN FROM WITCH MOUNTAIN (See Walt Disney Showcase #44)

RETURNING, THE
BOOM! Studios: Mar, 2014 - No. 4, Jun, 2014 ($3.99, limited series)

1-4-Jason Starr-s/Andrea Mutti-a/Frazer Irving-c 4.00

RETURN OF ALISON DARE: LITTLE MISS ADVENTURES, THE (Also see Alison Dare: Little Miss Adventures)
Oni Press: Apr, 2001 - No. 3, Sept, 2001 ($2.95, B&W, limited series)

1-3-J. Torres-s/J.Bone-c/a 3.00

RETURN OF GORGO, THE (Formerly Gorgo's Revenge)
Charlton Comics: No. 2, Aug, 1963; No. 3, Fall, 1964 (12¢)

	GD	VG	FN	VF	VF/NM	NM-
2,3-Ditko-c/a; based on M.G.M. movie	7	14	21	49	92	135

RETURN OF KONGA, THE (Konga's Revenge #2 on)
Charlton Comics: 1962

	GD	VG	FN	VF	VF/NM	NM-
nn	7	14	21	49	92	135

RETURN OF MEGATON MAN
Kitchen Sink Press: July, 1988 - No. 3, 1988 ($2.00, limited series)

1-3: Simpson-c/a 3.00

RETURN OF THE GREMLINS (The Roald Dahl characters)
Dark Horse Comics: Mar, 2008 - No. 3, May, 2008 ($2.99, limited series)

1-3-Richardson-s/Yeagle-a. 1-Back-up reprint of intro. from 1943. 2-Back-up reprints of three Gremlin Gus 2-pagers from 1943. 3-Back-up reprints 3.00

RETURN OF THE LIVING DEADPOOL
Marvel Comics: Apr, 2015 - No. 4, Jul, 2015 ($3.99, limited series)

1-4-Cullen Bunn-s/Nik Virella-a 6.00

RETURN OF THE OUTLAW
Toby Press (Minoan): Feb, 1953 - No. 11, 1955

	GD	VG	FN	VF	VF/NM	NM-
1-Billy the Kid	10	20	30	58	79	100
2	7	14	21	37	46	55
3-11	7	14	21	35	43	50

RETURN TO JURASSIC PARK
Topps Comics: Apr, 1995 - No. 9, Feb, 1996 ($2.50/$2.95)

1-9: 3-Begin $2.95-c. 9-Artists' Jam issue 3.00

RETURN TO THE AMALGAM AGE OF COMICS: THE MARVEL COMICS COLLECTION
Marvel Comics: 1997 ($12.95, TPB)

nn-Reprints Amalgam one-shots: Challengers of the Fantastic #1, The Exciting X-Patrol #1, Iron Lantern #1, The Magnetic Men Featuring Magneto #1, Spider-Boy Team-Up #1 & Thorion of the New Asgods #1 13.00

REVEAL
Dark Horse Comics: Nov, 2002 ($6.95, squarebound)

1-Short stories of Dark Horse characters by various; Lone Wolf 2100, Buffy, Spyboy app. 7.00

REVEALING LOVE STORIES (See Fox Giants)

REVEALING ROMANCES
Ace Magazines: Sept, 1949 - No. 6, Aug, 1950

	GD	VG	FN	VF	VF/NM	NM-
1	18	36	54	107	169	230
2	12	24	36	67	94	120
3-6	11	22	33	60	83	105

REVELATIONS
Dark Horse Comics: Aug, 2005 - No. 6, Jan, 2006 ($2.99, limited series)

1-6-Paul Jenkins-s/Humberto Ramos-a/c 3.00
1-6-(BOOM! Studios, 1/14 - No. 6, 6/14, $3.99) reprints original series 4.00

REVENGE
Image Comics: Feb, 2014 - No. 4, Jun, 2014 ($2.99)

1-4-Jonathan Ross-s/Ian Churchill-a 3.00

REVENGE OF THE PROWLER (Also see The Prowler)
Eclipse Comics: Feb, 1988 - No. 4, June, 1988 ($1.75/$1.95)

1,3,4: 1-$1.75. 3,4-$1.95-c; Snyder III-a(p) 3.00
2 ($2.50)-Contains flexi-disc 4.00

REVISIONIST, THE
AfterShock Comics: Jun, 2016 - No. 6, Nov, 2016 ($3.99)

1-6: 1-Frank Barbiere-s/Garry Brown-a 4.00

REVIVAL
Image Comics: Jul, 2012 - No. 47, Feb, 2017 ($2.99/$3.99)

1-Tim Seeley-s/Mike Norton-a/Jenny Frison-c 12.00
1-Variant-c by Craig Thompson 18.00
1-Second-fourth printings 4.00
2-26 3.00
27-47-($3.99) 4.00

REVOLUTION
IDW Publishing: Sept, 2016 - No. 5, Nov, 2016 ($3.99, limited series)

1-5-Barber & Bunn-s/Ossio-a; multiple covers on each; G.I. Joe, Transformers, Rom, Micronauts, and M.A.S.K. app. 2-5-Bonus character profile pages 4.00

REVOLUTIONARIES (Follows the Revolution x-over)
IDW Publishing: Dec, 2016 - No. 8, Jul, 2017 ($3.99)

1-7: 1,2-Barber-s/Ossio-a; multiple covers on each; G.I. Joe, Transformers, Rom app. 4.00
8-($4.99) Barber-s/Ossio & Joseph-a 5.00

REVOLUTIONARY WAR
Marvel Comics: Mar, 2014 - May, 2014 ($3.99)

...: Alpha 1 (3/14) Part 1; Lanning & Cowsill-s/Elson-a; Capt. Britain & Pete Wisdom app. 4.00
...: Dark Angel 1 (3/14) Part 2; Gillen-s/Dietrich Smith-a; Mephisto app. 4.00
...: Death's Head II 1 (4/14) Part 4; Lanning & Cowsill-s/Roche-a 4.00
...: Knights of Pendragon 1 (3/14) Part 3; Williams-s/Sliney-a; Union Jack app. 4.00
...: Motormouth 1 (5/14) Part 6; Dakin-s/Cliquet-a; Killpower app. 4.00
...: Omega 1 (5/14) Part 8; conclusion; Lanning & Cowsill-s/Elson-a 4.00
...: Supersoldiers 1 (4/14) Part 5; Williams-s/Brent Anderson-a 4.00
...: Warheads 1 (5/14) Part 7; Lanning & Cowsill-s/Erskine-a 4.00

REVOLUTION: AW YEAH!
IDW Publishing: Feb, 2017 - No. 3, Jul, 2017 ($3.99, limited series)

1-3-All ages x-over of Rom, Transformers, G.I. Joe, Micronauts; Art Baltazar-s/a 4.00

REVOLUTION ON THE PLANET OF THE APES
Mr. Comics: Dec, 2005 - No. 6, Aug, 2006 ($3.95)

1-6: 1,2-Salgood Sam-a 4.00

REX ALLEN COMICS (Movie star)(Also see Four Color #877 & Western Roundup under Dell Giants)
Dell Publ. Co.: No. 316, Feb, 1951 - No. 31, Dec-Feb, 1958-59 (All-photo-c)

	GD	VG	FN	VF	VF/NM	NM-
Four Color 316(#1)(52 pgs.)-Rex Allen & his horse Koko begin; Marsh-a	13	26	39	86	188	290
2 (9-11/51, 36 pgs.)	8	16	24	55	105	150
3-10	6	12	18	38	69	100
11-20	5	10	15	34	60	85
21-23,25-31	5	10	15	31	53	75
24-Toth-a	5	10	15	34	60	85

NOTE: ***Manning*** *a-20, 27-30. Photo back-c F.C. #316, 2-12, 20, 21.*

REX DEXTER OF MARS (See Mystery Men Comics)
Fox Feature Syndicate: Fall, 1940 (68 pgs.)

	GD	VG	FN	VF	VF/NM	NM-
1-Rex Dexter, Patty O'Day, & Zanzibar (Tuska-a) app.; Briefer-c/a	252	504	756	1613	2757	3900

REX HART (Formerly Blaze Carson; Whip Wilson #9 on)
Timely/Marvel Comics (USA): No. 6, Aug, 1949 - No. 8, Feb, 1950 (All photo-c)

	GD	VG	FN	VF	VF/NM	NM-
6-Rex Hart & his horse Warrior begin; Black Rider app; Captain Tootsie by Beck; Heath-a	26	52	78	154	252	350
7,8: 18 pg. Thriller in each. 7-Heath-a. 8-Blaze the Wonder Collie app. in text	18	36	54	105	165	225

REX MORGAN, M.D. (Also see Harvey Comics Library)
Argo Publ.: Dec, 1955 - No. 3, Apr?, 1956

	GD	VG	FN	VF	VF/NM	NM-
1-r/Rex Morgan daily newspaper strips & daily panel-r of "These Women" by D'Alessio & "Timeout" by Jeff Keate	14	28	42	82	121	160
2,3	10	20	30	58	79	100

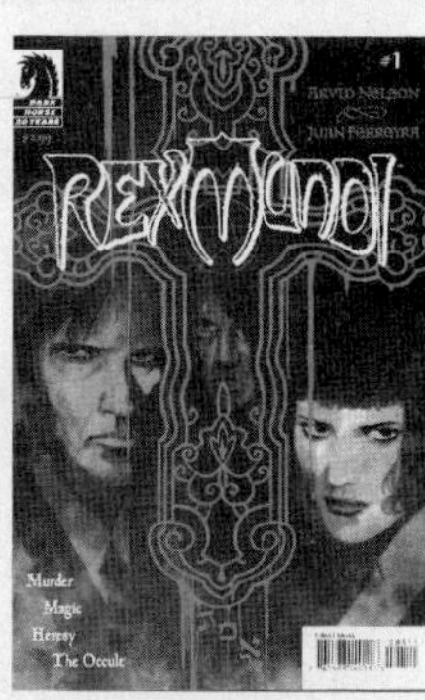

Rex Mundi V2 #1 © Arvid Nelson

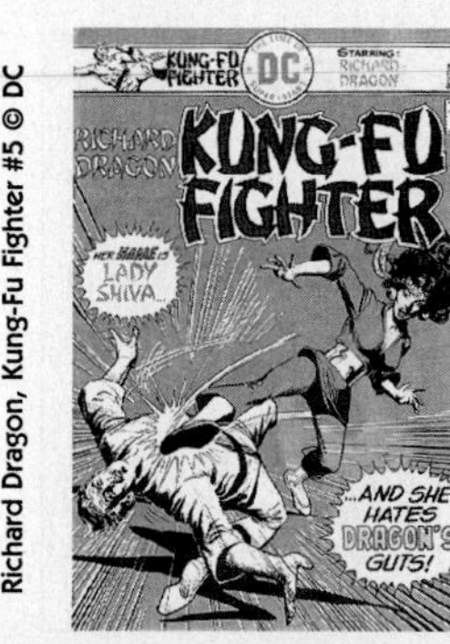

Richard Dragon, Kung-Fu Fighter #5 © DC

Richie Rich #154 © HARV

	GD 2.0	VG 4.0	FN 6.0	VF 8.0	VF/NM 9.0	NM- 9.2

REX MUNDI (Latin for "King of the World")
Image Comics: No. 0, Aug, 2002 - No. 18, Apr, 2006 ($2.95/$2.99)

0-18-Arvid Nelson-s. 0-13-Eric Johnson-a. 14,15-Jim DiBartolo-a. 18-Ramos-c 3.00
Vol. 1: The Guardian of the Temple TPB (1/04, $14.95) r/#0-5 15.00
Book 1: The Guardian of the Temple TPB (Dark Horse, 11/06, $16.95) r/#0-5 & Brother Matthew web comic; Dysart intro. 17.00
Vol. 2: The River Underground TPB (4/05, $14.95) r/#6-11 15.00
Book 2: The River Underground (Dark Horse, 2006, $16.95) r/#6-11 17.00
Vol. 3: The Lost Kings TPB (Dark Horse, 9/06, $16.95) r/#12-17 17.00
Book Four: Crowd and Sword TPB (Dark Horse, 12/07, $16.95) r/#18 plus V2 #1-5 and story from Dark Horse Book of Monsters 17.00

REX MUNDI (Volume 2)
Dark Horse Comics: July, 2006 - No. 19, Aug, 2009 ($2.99)

1-19-Arvid Nelson-s. 1-JH Williams-c. 16-Chen-c. 18-Linsner-c 3.00
Book Five: The Valley at the End of the World TPB (11/08, $17.95) r/#6-12 18.00

REX THE WONDER DOG (See The Adventures of...)

REYN
Image Comics: Jan, 2015 - No. 10, Nov, 2015 ($2.99)

1-10-Symons-s/Stockman-a 3.00

RHUBARB, THE MILLIONAIRE CAT
Dell Publishing Co.: No. 423, Sept-Oct, 1952 - No. 563, June, 1954

Four Color 423 (#1) 7 14 21 44 82 120
Four Color 466(5/53),563 6 12 18 37 66 95

RIB
Dilemma Productions: Oct, 1995 - April, 1996 ($1.95, B&W)

Ashcan, 1 3.00

RIB
Bookmark Productions: 1996 ($2.95, B&W)

1-Sakai-c; Andrew Ford-s/a 3.00

RIB
Caliber Comics: May, 1997 - No. 5, 1998 ($2.95, B&W)

1-5: 1-"Beginnings" pts. 1 & 2 3.00

RIBIT! (Red Sonja imitation)
Comico: Jan, 1989 - No. 4, April?, 1989 ($1.95, limited series)

1-4: Frank Thorne-c/a/scripts 3.00

RIBTICKLER (Also see Fox Giants)
Fox Feature Synd./Green Publ. (1957)/Norlen (1959): 1945, No. 2, 1946, No. 3, Jul-Aug, 1946 - No. 9, Jul-Aug, 1947; 1957; 1959

1-Funny animal 21 42 63 122 199 275
2-(1946) 13 26 39 72 101 130
3-9: 3,5,7-Cosmo Cat app. 11 22 33 62 86 110
3,7,8 (Green Publ.-1957), 3,7,8 (Norlen Mag.-1959) 3 6 9 16 23 30

RICHARD DRAGON
DC Comics: July, 2004 - No. 12, Jun, 2005 ($2.50)

1-12: 1-Dixon-s/McDaniel-a/c; Ben Turner app. 2,3-Nightwing app. 4-6,11,12-Lady Shiva 3.00

RICHARD DRAGON, KUNG-FU FIGHTER (See The Batman Chronicles #5, Brave & the Bold, & The Question)
National Periodical Publ./DC Comics: Apr-May, 1975 - No. 18, Nov-Dec, 1977

1-Intro Richard Dragon, Ben Stanley & O-Sensei; 1st app. Barney Ling; adaptation of Jim Dennis novel "Dragon's Fists" begins, ends #4 3 6 9 19 30 40
2,3: 2-Intro Carolyn Woosan; Starlin/Weiss-c/a; bondage-c. 3-Kirby-a(p); Giordano bondage-c 2 4 6 9 12 15
4,6-8-Wood inks. 4-Carolyn Woosan dies 2 4 6 8 10 12
5-1st app. Lady Shiva; Wood inks 6 12 18 38 69 100
9-13,15-17: 9-Ben Stanley becomes Ben Turner; intro Preying Mantis. 16-1st app. Prof Ojo. 1 3 4 6 8 10
14-"Spirit of Bruce Lee" 3 6 9 14 20 26
18-1st app. Ben Turner as The Bronze Tiger 2 4 6 9 12 15

NOTE: ***Buckler*** *a-14. c-15, 18.* ***Chua*** *c-13.* ***Estrada*** *a-9, 13-18.* ***Estrada/Abel*** *a-10-12.* ***Estrada/Wood*** *a-4-8.* ***Giordano*** *c-1, 3-11.* ***Weiss*** *a-2(partial) c-2i.*

RICHARD THE LION-HEARTED (See Ideal a Classical Comic)

RICHIE RICH (See Harvey Collectors Comics, Harvey Hits, Little Dot, Little Lotta, Little Sad Sack, Million Dollar Digest, Mutt & Jeff, Super Richie & 3-D Dolly; also Tastee-Freez Comics in the Promotional Comics section)

RICHIE RICH (...the Poor Little Rich Boy) (See Harvey Hits #3, 9)
Harvey Publ.: Nov, 1960 - #218, Oct, 1982; #219, Oct, 1986 - #254, Jan, 1991

1-(See Little Dot #1 for 1st app.) 317 634 951 2695 6098 9500
2 86 172 258 688 1544 2400
3-5 46 92 138 340 770 1200
6-10: 8-Christmas-c 27 54 81 189 420 650
11-20 16 32 48 112 249 385
21-30 11 22 33 76 163 250
31-40 9 18 27 61 123 185
41-50: 42(2/66)-X-mas-c 7 14 21 49 92 135
51-55,57-60: 59-Buck, prototype of Dollar the Dog 5 10 15 35 63 90
56-1st app. Super Richie 6 12 18 41 76 110
61-64,66-80: 71-Nixon & Robert Kennedy caricatures; outer space-c 4 8 12 28 47 65
65-Buck the Dog (Dollar prototype) on cover 6 12 18 37 66 95
81-99 3 6 9 21 33 45
100(12/70)-1st app. Irona the robot maid 4 8 12 25 40 55
101-111,117-120 3 6 9 14 20 26
112-116: All 52 pg. Giants 3 6 9 16 24 32
121-140: 137-1st app. Mr. Cheepers and Professor Keenbean 2 4 6 9 13 16
141-160: 145-Infinity-c. 155-3rd app. The Money Monster 2 4 6 8 10 12
161-180 1 3 4 6 8 10
181-199 1 2 3 5 6 8
200 1 3 4 6 8 10
201-218: 210-Stone-Age Riches app 1 2 3 4 5 7
219-254: 237-Last original material 6.00
Harvey Comics Classics Vol. 2 TPB (Dark Horse Books, 10/07, $19.95) Reprints Richie Rich's early appearances in this title, Little Dot and Richie Rich Success Stories, mostly B&W with some color stories; history and interview with Ernie Colón 20.00

RICHIE RICH
Harvey Comics: Mar, 1991 - No. 28, Nov, 1994 ($1.00, bi-monthly)

1-28: Reprints best of Richie Rich 3.00
Giant Size 1-4 (10/91-10/93, $2.25, 68 pgs.) 4.00

RICHIE RICH ADVENTURE DIGEST MAGAZINE
Harvey Comics: 1992 - No. 7, Sept, 1994 ($1.25, quarterly, digest-size)

1-7 4.00

RICHIE RICH AND...
Harvey Comics: Oct, 1987 - No. 11, May, 1990 ($1.00)

1-Professor Keenbean 4.00
2-11: 2-Casper. 3-Dollar the Dog. 4-Cadbury. 5 Mayda Munny. 6-Irona. 7-Little Dot. 8-Professor Keenbean. 9-Little Audrey. 10-Mayda Munny. 11-Cadbury 3.00

RICHIE RICH AND BILLY BELLHOPS
Harvey Publications: Oct, 1977 (52 pgs., one-shot)

1 2 4 6 11 16 20

RICHIE RICH AND CADBURY
Harvey Publ.: 10/77; #2, 9/78 - #23, 7/82; #24, 7/90 - #29, 1/91 (1-10: 52pgs.)

1-(52 pg. Giant) 2 4 6 11 16 20
2-10-(52 pg. Giant) 2 4 6 8 10 12
11-23 6.00
24-29: 24-Begin $1.00-c 4.00

RICHIE RICH AND CASPER
Harvey Publications: Aug, 1974 - No. 45, Sept, 1982

1 3 6 9 19 30 40
2-5 2 4 6 13 18 22
6-10: 10-Xmas-c 2 4 6 9 13 16
11-20 1 3 4 6 8 10
21-45: 22-Xmas-c 6.00

RICHIE RICH AND DOLLAR THE DOG (See Richie Rich #65)
Harvey Publications: Sept, 1977 - No. 24, Aug, 1982 (#1-10: 52 pgs.)

1-(52 pg. Giant) 2 4 6 11 16 20
2-10-(52 pg. Giant) 2 4 6 8 10 12
11-24 6.00

RICHIE RICH AND DOT
Harvey Publications: Oct, 1974 (one-shot)

1 3 6 9 15 22 28

RICHIE RICH AND GLORIA
Harvey Publications: Sept, 1977 - No. 25, Sept, 1982 (#1-11: 52 pgs.)

1-(52 pg. Giant) 2 4 6 11 16 20
2-11-(52 pg. Giant) 2 4 6 8 10 12
12-25 6.00

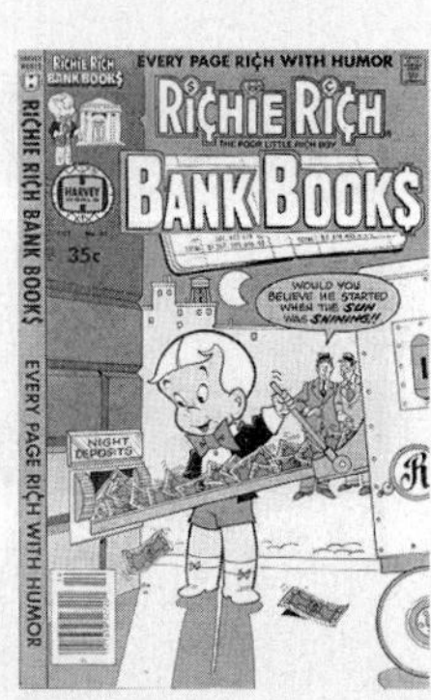

Richie Rich Bank Books #37 © HARV

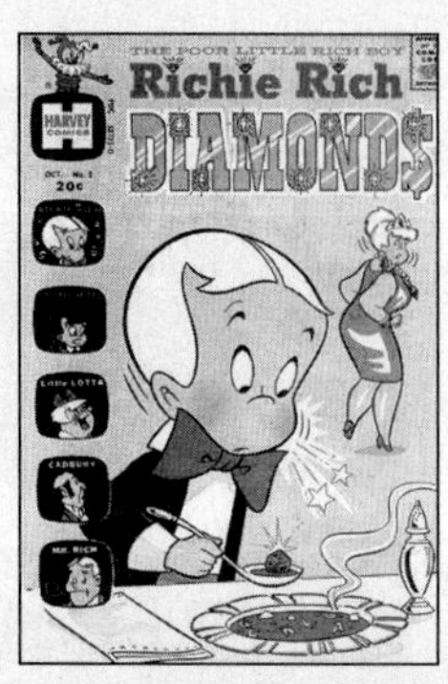

Richie Rich Diamonds #2 © HARV

Richie Rich Fortunes #26 © HARV

RICHIE RICH AND HIS GIRLFRIENDS
Harvey Publications: April, 1979 - No. 16, Dec, 1982

	GD 2.0	VG 4.0	FN 6.0	VF 8.0	VF/NM 9.0	NM- 9.2
1-(52 pg. Giant)	2	4	6	9	13	16
2-(52 pg. Giant)	1	3	4	6	8	10
3-10	1	2	3	5	6	8
11-16						6.00

RICHIE RICH AND HIS MEAN COUSIN REGGIE
Harvey Publications: April, 1979 - No. 3, 1980 (50¢) (#1,2: 52 pgs.)

	GD 2.0	VG 4.0	FN 6.0	VF 8.0	VF/NM 9.0	NM- 9.2
1	2	4	6	9	13	16
2-3:	1	3	4	6	8	10

NOTE: *No. 4 was advertised, but never released.*

RICHIE RICH AND JACKIE JOKERS (Also see Jackie Jokers)
Harvey Publications: Nov, 1973 - No. 48, Dec, 1982

	GD 2.0	VG 4.0	FN 6.0	VF 8.0	VF/NM 9.0	NM- 9.2
1: 52 pg. Giant; contains material from unpublished Jackie Jokers #5	4	8	12	23	37	50
2,3-(52 pg. Giants). 2-R.R. & Jackie 1st meet	3	6	9	15	22	28
4,5	2	4	6	13	18	22
6-10	2	4	6	9	13	16
11-20,26: 11-1st app. Kool Katz. 26-Star Wars parody	1	3	4	6	8	10
21-25,27-40	1	2	3	4	5	7
41-48						6.00

RICHIE RICH AND PROFESSOR KEENBEAN
Harvey Comics: Sept, 1990 - No. 2, Nov, 1990 ($1.00)

	GD 2.0	VG 4.0	FN 6.0	VF 8.0	VF/NM 9.0	NM- 9.2
1,2						3.00

RICHIE RICH AND THE NEW KIDS ON THE BLOCK
Harvey Publications: Feb, 1991 - No. 3, June, 1991 ($1.25, bi-monthly)

	GD 2.0	VG 4.0	FN 6.0	VF 8.0	VF/NM 9.0	NM- 9.2
1-3: 1,2-New Richie Rich stories						4.00

RICHIE RICH AND TIMMY TIME
Harvey Publications: Sept, 1977 (50¢, 52 pgs, one-shot)

	GD 2.0	VG 4.0	FN 6.0	VF 8.0	VF/NM 9.0	NM- 9.2
1	2	4	6	11	16	20

RICHIE RICH BANK BOOK
Harvey Publications: Oct, 1972 - No. 59, Sept, 1982

	GD 2.0	VG 4.0	FN 6.0	VF 8.0	VF/NM 9.0	NM- 9.2
1	4	8	12	28	47	65
2-5: 2-2nd app. The Money Monster	3	6	9	16	23	30
6-10	2	4	6	11	16	20
11-20: 18-Super Richie app.	2	4	6	8	10	12
21-30	1	2	3	5	7	9
31-40	1	2	3	4	5	7
41-59						6.00

RICHIE RICH BEST OF THE YEARS
Harvey Publications: Oct, 1977 - No. 6, June, 1980 (128 pgs., digest-size)

	GD 2.0	VG 4.0	FN 6.0	VF 8.0	VF/NM 9.0	NM- 9.2
1(10/77)-Reprints	2	4	6	9	12	15
2-6(11/79-6/80, 95¢). #2(10/78)-Rep.. #3(6/79, 75¢)	1	2	3	5	7	9

RICHIE RICH BIG BOOK
Harvey Publications: Nov, 1992 - No. 2, May, 1993 ($1.50, 52 pgs.)

	GD 2.0	VG 4.0	FN 6.0	VF 8.0	VF/NM 9.0	NM- 9.2
1,2						4.00

RICHIE RICH BIG BUCKS
Harvey Publications: Apr, 1991 - No. 8, July, 1992 ($1.00, bi-monthly)

	GD 2.0	VG 4.0	FN 6.0	VF 8.0	VF/NM 9.0	NM- 9.2
1-8						3.00

RICHIE RICH BILLIONS
Harvey Publications: Oct, 1974 - No. 48, Oct, 1982 (#1-33: 52 pgs.)

	GD 2.0	VG 4.0	FN 6.0	VF 8.0	VF/NM 9.0	NM- 9.2
1	3	6	9	21	33	45
2-5: 2-Christmas issue	3	6	9	14	20	25
6-10	2	4	6	10	14	18
11-20	2	4	6	8	10	12
21-33	1	2	3	5	6	8
34-48: 35-Onion app.						6.00

RICHIE RICH CASH
Harvey Publications: Sept, 1974 - No. 47, Aug, 1982

	GD 2.0	VG 4.0	FN 6.0	VF 8.0	VF/NM 9.0	NM- 9.2
1-1st app. Dr. N-R-Gee	3	6	9	19	30	40
2-5	2	4	6	13	18	22
6-10	2	4	6	9	13	16
11-20	1	3	4	6	8	10
21-30	1	2	3	4	5	7
31-47: 33-Dr. Blemish app.						6.00

RICHIE RICH CASH MONEY
Harvey Comics: May, 1992 - No. 2, Aug, 1992 ($1.25)

	GD 2.0	VG 4.0	FN 6.0	VF 8.0	VF/NM 9.0	NM- 9.2
1,2						3.00

RICHIE RICH, CASPER AND WENDY - NATIONAL LEAGUE
Harvey Comics: June, 1976 (50¢)

	GD 2.0	VG 4.0	FN 6.0	VF 8.0	VF/NM 9.0	NM- 9.2
1-Newsstand version of the baseball giveaway	2	4	6	13	18	22

RICHIE RICH COLLECTORS COMICS (See Harvey Collectors Comics)

RICHIE RICH DIAMONDS
Harvey Publications: Aug, 1972 - No. 59, Aug, 1982 (#1, 23-45: 52 pgs.)

	GD 2.0	VG 4.0	FN 6.0	VF 8.0	VF/NM 9.0	NM- 9.2
1-(52 pg. Giant)	5	10	15	30	50	70
2-5	3	6	9	16	23	30
6-10	2	4	6	11	16	20
11-22	2	4	6	8	10	12
23-30-(52 pg. Giants)	2	4	6	8	11	14
31-45: 39-r/Origin Little Dot	1	2	3	5	7	9
46-50	1	2	3	4	5	7
51-59						6.00

RICHIE RICH DIGEST MAGAZINE
Harvey Publications: Oct, 1986 - No. 42, Oct, 1994 ($1.25/$1.75, digest-size)

	GD 2.0	VG 4.0	FN 6.0	VF 8.0	VF/NM 9.0	NM- 9.2
1	1	2	3	5	6	8
2-10						5.00
11-20						4.00
21-42						4.00

RICHIE RICH DIGEST STORIES (...Magazine #?-on)
Harvey Publications: Oct, 1977 - No., 17, Oct, 1982 (75¢/95¢, digest-size)

	GD 2.0	VG 4.0	FN 6.0	VF 8.0	VF/NM 9.0	NM- 9.2
1-Reprints	2	4	6	9	12	15
2-10: Reprints	1	2	3	5	7	9
11-17: Reprints						6.00

RICHIE RICH DIGEST WINNERS
Harvey Publications: Dec, 1977 - No. 16, Sept, 1982 (75¢/95¢, 132 pgs., digest-size)

	GD 2.0	VG 4.0	FN 6.0	VF 8.0	VF/NM 9.0	NM- 9.2
1	2	4	6	9	12	15
2-5	1	2	3	5	7	9
6-16						6.00

RICHIE RICH DOLLARS & CENTS
Harvey Publications: Aug, 1963 - No. 109, Aug, 1982 (#1-43: 68 pgs.; 44-60, 71-94: 52 pgs.)

	GD 2.0	VG 4.0	FN 6.0	VF 8.0	VF/NM 9.0	NM- 9.2
1: (#1-64 are all reprint issues)	18	36	54	124	275	425
2	9	18	27	62	126	190
3-5: 5-r/1st app. of R.R. from Little Dot #1	8	16	24	54	102	150
6-10	6	12	18	40	73	105
11-20	4	8	12	28	47	65
21-30: 25-r/1st app. Nurse Jenny (Little Lotta #62)	3	6	9	21	33	45
31-43: 43-Last 68 pg. issue	3	6	9	17	26	35
44-60: All 52 pgs.	3	6	9	14	19	25
61-71	1	3	4	6	8	10
72-94: All 52 pgs.	2	4	6	8	10	12
95-99,101-109						6.00
100-Anniversary issue	1	2	3	5	7	9

RICHIE RICH FORTUNES
Harvey Publications: Sept, 1971 - No. 63, July, 1982 (#1-15: 52 pgs.)

	GD 2.0	VG 4.0	FN 6.0	VF 8.0	VF/NM 9.0	NM- 9.2
1	5	10	15	34	60	85
2-5	3	6	9	19	30	40
6-10	2	4	6	13	18	22
11-15: 11-r/1st app. The Onion	2	4	6	9	12	15
16-30	1	2	3	5	7	9
31-40	1	2	3	4	5	7
41-63: 62-Onion app.						6.00

RICHIE RICH GEMS
Harvey Publications: Sept, 1974 - No. 43, Sept, 1982

	GD 2.0	VG 4.0	FN 6.0	VF 8.0	VF/NM 9.0	NM- 9.2
1	3	6	9	19	30	40
2-5	2	4	6	13	18	22
6-10	2	4	6	9	13	16
11-20	1	3	4	6	8	10
21-30	1	2	3	4	5	7
31-43: 36-Dr. Blemish, Onion app. 38-1st app. Stone-Age Riches						6.00
44-48 (Ape Entertainment, 2011-2012, $3.99) new stories w/Colon-a & reprints						4.00
... Special Collection (Ape Entertainment, 2012, $6.99) r/Valentine & Winter Specials						7.00
... Valentines Special (Ape Entertainment, 2012, $3.99) new story w/Colon-a & reprints						4.00
... Winter Special (Ape Entertainment, 2011, $3.99) new story w/Colon-a & reprints						4.00

RICHIE RICH GOLD AND SILVER
Harvey Publications: Sept, 1975 - No. 42, Oct, 1982 (#1-27: 52 pgs.)

	GD 2.0	VG 4.0	FN 6.0	VF 8.0	VF/NM 9.0	NM- 9.2
1	3	6	9	17	26	35

Richie Rich Millions #10 © HARV

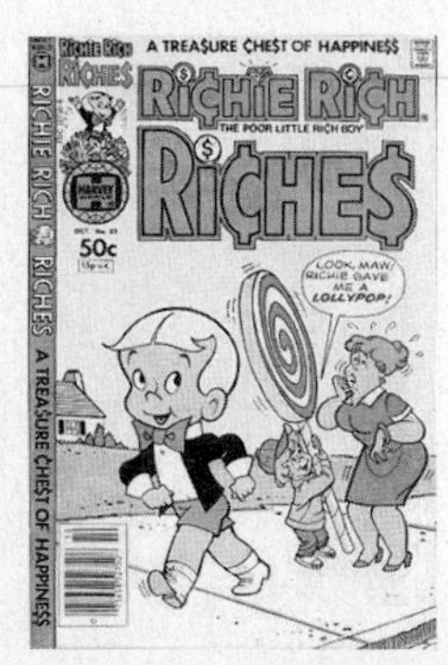

Richie Rich Riches #55 © HARV

Richie Rich Zillionz #1 © HARV

	GD 2.0	VG 4.0	FN 6.0	VF 8.0	VF/NM 9.0	NM- 9.2
2-5	2	4	6	11	16	20
6-10	2	4	6	8	11	14
11-27	1	2	3	5	7	9
28-42: 34-Stone-Age Riches app.						6.00

RICHIE RICH GOLD NUGGETS DIGEST
Harvey Publications: Dec., 1990 - No. 4, June, 1991 ($1.75, digest-size)

	GD 2.0	VG 4.0	FN 6.0	VF 8.0	VF/NM 9.0	NM- 9.2
1-4						4.00

RICHIE RICH HOLIDAY DIGEST MAGAZINE (...Digest #4)
Harvey Publications: Jan, 1980 - #3, Jan, 1982; #4, 3/88; #5, 2/89 (annual)

	GD 2.0	VG 4.0	FN 6.0	VF 8.0	VF/NM 9.0	NM- 9.2
1-X-Mas-c	1	3	4	6	8	10
2-5: 2,3: All X-Mas-c. 4-(3/88, $1.25), 5-(2/89, $1.75)	1	2	3	4	5	7

RICHIE RICH INVENTIONS
Harvey Publications: Oct, 1977 - No. 26, Oct, 1982 (#1-11: 52 pgs.)

	GD 2.0	VG 4.0	FN 6.0	VF 8.0	VF/NM 9.0	NM- 9.2
1	2	4	6	11	16	20
2-5	2	4	6	8	10	12
6-11	1	2	3	5	6	8
12-26						6.00

RICHIE RICH JACKPOTS
Harvey Publications: Oct, 1972 - No. 58, Aug, 1982 (#41-43: 52 pgs.)

	GD 2.0	VG 4.0	FN 6.0	VF 8.0	VF/NM 9.0	NM- 9.2
1-Debut of Cousin Jackpots	4	8	12	28	47	65
2-5	3	6	9	16	23	30
6-10	2	4	6	11	16	20
11-15,17-20	2	4	6	8	10	12
16-Super Richie app.	2	4	6	9	12	15
21-30	1	2	3	5	7	9
31-40,44-50: 37-Caricatures of Frank Sinatra, Dean Martin, Sammy Davis, Jr. 45-Dr. Blemish app.	1	2	3	4	5	7
41-43 (52 pgs.)	1	3	4	6	8	10
51-58						6.00

RICHIE RICH MILLION DOLLAR DIGEST (...Magazine #?-on)(See Million Dollar Digest)
Harvey Publications: Oct, 1980 - No. 10, Oct, 1982 ($1.50)

	GD 2.0	VG 4.0	FN 6.0	VF 8.0	VF/NM 9.0	NM- 9.2
1	1	3	4	6	8	10
2-10						7.00

RICHIE RICH MILLIONS
Harvey Publ.: 9/61; #2, 9/62 - #113, 10/82 (#1-48: 68 pgs.; 49-64, 85-97: 52 pgs.)

	GD 2.0	VG 4.0	FN 6.0	VF 8.0	VF/NM 9.0	NM- 9.2
1: (#1-3 are all reprint issues)	22	44	66	154	340	525
2	10	20	30	68	144	220
3-5: All other giants are new & reprints. 5-1st 15 pg. Richie Rich story	8	16	24	56	108	160
6-10	7	14	21	49	92	135
11-20	5	10	15	35	63	90
21-30	4	8	12	27	44	60
31-48: 31-1st app. The Onion. 48-Last 68 pg. Giant	3	6	9	19	30	40
49-64: 52 pg. Giants	3	6	9	14	20	25
65-67,69-73,75-84	2	4	6	8	10	12
68-1st Super Richie-c (11/74)	2	4	6	13	18	22
74-1st app. Mr. Woody; Super Richie app.	2	4	6	8	11	14
85-97: 52 pg. Giants	2	4	6	8	11	14
98,99	1	2	3	4	5	7
100	1	2	3	5	7	9
101-113						6.00

RICHIE RICH MONEY WORLD
Harvey Publications: Sept, 1972 - No. 59, Sept, 1982

	GD 2.0	VG 4.0	FN 6.0	VF 8.0	VF/NM 9.0	NM- 9.2
1-(52 pg. Giant)-1st app. Mayda Munny	5	10	15	33	57	80
2-Super Richie app.	3	6	9	17	26	35
3-5	3	6	9	16	23	30
6-10: 9,10-Richie Rich mistakenly named Little Lotta on covers	2	4	6	11	16	20
11-20: 16,20-Dr. N-R-Gee	2	4	6	8	10	12
21-30	1	2	3	5	7	9
31-50	1	2	3	4	5	7
51-59						6.00
Digest 1 (2/91, $1.75)						5.00
2-8 (12/93, $1.75)						3.00

RICHIE RICH PROFITS
Harvey Publications: Oct, 1974 - No. 47, Sept, 1982

	GD 2.0	VG 4.0	FN 6.0	VF 8.0	VF/NM 9.0	NM- 9.2
1	3	6	9	19	30	40
2-5	2	4	6	13	18	22
6-10: 10-Origin of Dr. N-R-Gee	2	4	6	9	13	16
11-20: 15-Christmas-c	1	3	4	6	8	10
21-30	1	2	3	4	5	7
31-47						6.00

RICHIE RICH RELICS
Harvey Comics: Jan, 1988 - No.4, Feb, 1989 (75¢/$1.00, reprints)

	GD 2.0	VG 4.0	FN 6.0	VF 8.0	VF/NM 9.0	NM- 9.2
1-4						3.00

RICHIE RICH RICHES
Harvey Publications: July, 1972 - No. 59, Aug, 1982 (#1, 2, 41-45: 52 pgs.)

	GD 2.0	VG 4.0	FN 6.0	VF 8.0	VF/NM 9.0	NM- 9.2
1-(52 pg. Giant)-1st app. The Money Monster	5	10	15	33	57	80
2-(52 pg. Giant)	3	6	9	19	30	40
3-5	3	6	9	16	23	30
6-10: 7-1st app. Aunt Novo	2	4	6	11	16	20
11-20: 17-Super Richie app. (3/75)	2	4	6	8	10	12
21-40	1	2	3	5	6	8
41-45: 52 pg. Giants	1	3	4	6	8	10
46-59: 56-Dr. Blemish app.						6.00

RICHIE RICH: RICH RESCUE
Ape Entertainment: 2011 - No. 4, 2011 ($3.95, limited series)

	GD 2.0	VG 4.0	FN 6.0	VF 8.0	VF/NM 9.0	NM- 9.2
1-6-New short stories by various incl. Ernie Colon; Jack Lawrence-c						4.00
FCBD Edition (2011, giveaway) Flip book with Kung Fu Panda						3.00

RICHIE RICH SUCCESS STORIES
Harvey Publications: Nov, 1964 - No. 105, Sept, 1982 (#1-38: 68 pgs., 39-55, 67-90: 52 pgs.)

	GD 2.0	VG 4.0	FN 6.0	VF 8.0	VF/NM 9.0	NM- 9.2
1	17	34	51	117	259	400
2	9	18	27	57	111	165
3-5	8	16	24	51	96	140
6-10	5	10	15	35	63	90
11-20	5	10	15	31	53	75
21-30: 27-1st Penny Van Dough (8/69)	4	8	12	23	37	50
31-38: 38-Last 68 pg. Giant	3	6	9	19	30	40
39-55-(52 pgs.): 44-Super Richie app.	3	6	9	14	20	25
56-66	2	4	6	8	10	12
67-90: 52 pgs.	2	4	6	8	11	14
91-99,101-105: 91-Onion app. 101-Dr. Blemish app.						6.00
100	1	2	3	5	7	9

RICHIE RICH SUMMER BONANZA
Harvey Comics: Oct, 1991 ($1.95, one-shot, 68 pgs.)

	GD 2.0	VG 4.0	FN 6.0	VF 8.0	VF/NM 9.0	NM- 9.2
1-Richie Rich, Little Dot, Little Lotta						4.00

RICHIE RICH TREASURE CHEST DIGEST (...Magazine #3)
Harvey Publications: Apr, 1982 - No. 3, Aug, 1982 (95¢, Digest Mag.)
(#4 advertised but not publ.)

	GD 2.0	VG 4.0	FN 6.0	VF 8.0	VF/NM 9.0	NM- 9.2
1	1	3	4	6	8	10
2,3	1	2	3	4	5	7

RICHIE RICH VACATION DIGEST
Harvey Comics: Oct, 1991; Oct, 1992; Oct, 1993 ($1.75, digest-size)

	GD 2.0	VG 4.0	FN 6.0	VF 8.0	VF/NM 9.0	NM- 9.2
1-(10/91), 1-(10/92), 1-(10/93)						4.00

RICHIE RICH VACATIONS DIGEST
Harvey Publ.: 11/77; No. 2, 10/78 - No. 7, 10/81; No. 8, 8/82; No. 9, 10/82 (Digest, 132 pgs.)

	GD 2.0	VG 4.0	FN 6.0	VF 8.0	VF/NM 9.0	NM- 9.2
1-Reprints	2	4	6	9	12	15
2-6	1	2	3	5	7	9
7-9						6.00

RICHIE RICH VAULT OF MYSTERY
Harvey Publications: Nov, 1974 - No. 47, Sept, 1982

	GD 2.0	VG 4.0	FN 6.0	VF 8.0	VF/NM 9.0	NM- 9.2
1	3	6	9	19	30	40
2-5: 5-The Condor app.	2	4	6	13	18	22
6-10	2	4	6	9	13	16
11-20	1	3	4	6	8	10
21-30	1	2	3	4	5	7
31-47						6.00

RICHIE RICH ZILLIONZ
Harvey Publ.: Oct, 1976 - No. 33, Sept, 1982 (#1-4: 68 pgs.; #5-18: 52 pgs.)

	GD 2.0	VG 4.0	FN 6.0	VF 8.0	VF/NM 9.0	NM- 9.2
1	3	6	9	17	26	35
2-4: 4-Last 68 pg. Giant	2	4	6	11	16	20
5-10	2	4	6	8	10	12
11-18: 18-Last 52 pg. Giant	1	2	3	5	6	8
19-33						6.00

RICH JOHNSTON'S... (Parody of the Avengers movie characters)
BOOM! Studios: Apr, 2012 ($3.99, series of one-shots)

Rick and Morty #16 © CN

Rima, The Jungle Girl #4 © DC

Riot #1 © MAR

	GD 2.0	VG 4.0	FN 6.0	VF 8.0	VF/NM 9.0	NM- 9.2

GD VG FN VF VF/NM NM- 2.0 4.0 6.0 8.0 9.0 9.2

... Captain American Idol 1 - Rich Johnston-s/Chris Haley-a 4.00
... Iron Muslim 1 - Rich Johnston-s/Bryan Turner-a; Demon in a Bottle cover swipe 4.00
... Scienthorlogy 1 - Rich Johnston-s/Michael Netzer-a 4.00
... The Avengefuls 1 - Rich Johnston-s/Joshua Covey; two printings 4.00

RICK AND MORTY (Based on the Adult Swim animated series)
Oni Press: Apr, 2015 - Present ($3.99)
1-Zac Gorman-s/CJ Cannon-a; multiple covers 5 10 15 34 60 85
2,3 2 4 6 11 16 20
4-35 4.00
... Free Comic Book Day 2017 (5/17, giveaway) r/#1; preview of Pocket Like You Stole It 3.00
... Presents: The Vindicators 1 (3/18, $4.99) Cannon-a; Pickle Rick app. 5.00

RICK AND MORTY: LIL' POOPY SUPERSTAR (Adult Swim)
Oni Press: Jul, 2016 - No. 5, Nov, 2016 ($3.99, limited series)
1-5-Sarah Graley-s/a; multiple covers 4.00

RICK AND MORTY: POCKET LIKE YOU STOLE IT (Adult Swim)
Oni Press: Jul, 2017 - No. 5, Nov, 2017 ($3.99, limited series)
1-5-Tim Howard-s/Marc Ellerby-a; multiple covers 4.00

RICKY
Standard Comics (Visual Editions): No. 5, Sept, 1953
5-Teenage humor 8 16 24 44 57 70

RICKY NELSON (TV)(See Sweethearts V2#42)
Dell Publishing Co.: No. 956, Dec, 1958 - No. 1192, June, 1961 (All photo-c)
Four Color 956,998 15 30 45 100 220 340
Four Color 1115,1192: 1192-Manning-a 12 24 36 80 173 265

RIDE, THE (Also see Gun Candy flip-book)
Image Comics: June, 2004 - No. 2, July, 2004 ($2.95, B&W, anthology)
1,2: Hughes-c/Wagner-s. 1-Hamner & Stelfreeze-a. 2-Jeanty & Pearson-a 3.00
... Die Valkyrie 1-3 (6/07 - No. 3, 2/08, $2.99) Stelfreeze-a/Wagner-s/Pearson-c 3.00
... Foreign Parts 1 (1/05, $2.95) Dixon-s/Haynes-a; Marz-s/Brunner-a; Pearson-c 3.00
... Halloween Special: The Key to Survival (10/07, $3.50) Tomm Coker-s/a 3.50
... Savannah 1 (4/07, $4.99) s/a by students of Savannah College of Art 5.00
... 2 For the Road 1 (10/04, $2.95) Dixon-s/Hamner & Gregory-a/Johnson-c 3.00
Vol. 1 TPB (2005, $9.99) r/#1,2, Foreign Parts, 2 For the Road; Chaykin intro. 10.00
Vol. 2 TPB (2005, $15.99) r/Gun Candy #1,2 & Die Valkyrie #1-3; sketch pages 16.00

RIDER, THE (Frontier Trail #6; also see Blazing Sixguns I.W. Reprint #10, 11)
Ajax/Farrell Publ. (Four Star Comic Corp.): Mar, 1957 - No. 5, 1958
1-Swift Arrow, Lone Rider begin 13 26 39 72 101 130
2-5 8 16 24 42 54 65

RIDERS OF THE PURPLE SAGE (See Zane Grey & Four Color #372)

RIFLEMAN, THE (TV)
Dell Publ. Co./Gold Key No. 13 on: No. 1009, 7-9/59 - No. 12, 7-9/62; No. 13, 11/62 - No. 20, 10/64
Four Color 1009 (#1) 21 42 63 147 324 500
2 (1-3/60) 10 20 30 65 135 200
3-Toth-a (4 pgs.); variant edition has back-c with "Something Special" comic strip
10 20 30 65 135 200
4-9: 6-Toth-a (4 pgs.) 9 18 27 59 117 175
10-Classic-c 28 56 84 202 451 700
11-20 7 14 21 46 86 125
NOTE: ***Warren Tufts** a-2-9. All have Chuck Connors & Johnny Crawford photo-c. Photo back c-13-15.*

RIFTWAR
Marvel Comics: July, 2009 - No. 5, Dec, 2009 ($3.99, limited series)
1-5-Adaptation of Raymond E. Feist novel; Glass-s/Stegman-a 4.00

RIMA, THE JUNGLE GIRL
National Periodical Publications: Apr-May, 1974 - No. 7, Apr-May, 1975
1-Origin, part 1 (#1-5: 20¢; 6,7: 25¢) 3 6 9 14 19 24
2-7: 2-4-Origin, parts 2-4. 7-Origin & only app. Space Marshal
2 3 4 6 8 10
NOTE: ***Kubert** c-1-7. **Nino** a-1-7. **Redondo** a-1-7.*

RING OF BRIGHT WATER (See Movie Classics)

RING OF THE NIBELUNG, THE
DC Comics: 1989 - No. 4, 1990 ($4.95, squarebound, 52 pgs., mature readers)
1-4: Adapts Wagner cycle of operas, Gil Kane-c/a 5.00

RING OF THE NIBELUNG, THE
Dark Horse Comics: Feb, 2000 - Sept, 2001 ($2.95/$2.99/$5.99, limited series)
Vol. 1 (The Rhinegold) 1-4: Adapts Wagner; P. Craig Russell-s/a 3.00
Vol. 2,3: Vol. 2 (The Valkyrie) 1-3: 1-(8/00). Vol. 3 (Siegfried) 1-3: 1-(12/00) 3.00
Vol. 4 (The Twilight of the Gods) 1-3: 1-(6/01) 3.00
4-(9/01, $5.99, 64 pgs.) Conclusion with sketch pages 6.00

RINGO KID, THE (2nd Series)
Marvel Comics Group: Jan, 1970 - No. 23, Nov, 1973; No. 24, Nov, 1975 - No. 30, Nov, 1976
1-Williamson-a r-from #10, 1956. 3 6 9 21 33 45
2-11: 2-Severin-c. 11-Last 15¢ issue 2 4 6 11 16 20
12 (52 pg. Giant) 3 6 9 16 23 30
13-20: 13-Wildey-r. 20-Williamson-r/#1 2 4 6 9 13 16
21-30 2 4 6 8 10 12
27,28-(30¢-c variant, limited distribution)(5,7/76) 12 24 36 79 170 260

RINGO KID WESTERN, THE (1st Series) (See Wild Western & Western Trails)
Atlas Comics (HPC)/Marvel Comics: Aug, 1954 - No. 21, Sept, 1957
1-Origin; The Ringo Kid begins 37 74 111 222 361 500
2-Black Rider app.; origin/1st app. Ringo's Horse Arab
19 38 57 111 176 240
3-5 14 28 42 82 121 160
6-8-Severin-a(3) each 15 30 45 84 127 170
9,11,12,14-21: 12-Orlando-a (4 pgs.) 13 26 39 72 101 130
10,13-Williamson-a (4 pgs.) 14 28 42 76 108 140
NOTE: ***Berg** a-8. **Maneely** a-1-5, 15, 16(text illos only), 17(4), 18, 20, 21; c-1-6, 8, 13, 15-18, 20. **J. Severin** c-10, 11. **Sinnott** a-1. **Wildey** a-16-18.*

RINGSIDE
Image Comics: Nov, 2015 - No. 12, Oct, 2017 ($3.99)
1-14-Keatinge-s/Barber-a 4.00

RINSE, THE
BOOM! Studios: Sept, 2011 - No. 4, Dec, 2011 ($1.00/$3.99)
1-($1.00)-Phillips-s/Laming-a 3.00
2-4-($3.99) 4.00

RIN TIN TIN (See March of Comics #163,180,195)

RIN TIN TIN (TV) (...& Rusty #21 on; see Western Roundup under Dell Giants)
Dell Publishing Co./Gold Key: Nov, 1952 - No. 38, May-July, 1961; Nov, 1963 (All Photo-c)
Four Color 434 (#1) 14 28 42 97 214 330
Four Color 476,523 9 18 27 57 111 165
4(3-5/54)-10 6 12 18 40 73 105
11-17,19,20 6 12 18 37 66 95
18-(4-5/57) 1st app. of Rusty and the Cavalry of Fort Apache; photo-c
7 14 21 46 86 125
21-38: 36-Toth-a (4 pgs.) 5 10 15 31 53 75
... & Rusty 1 (11/63-Gold Key) 5 10 15 33 57 80

RIO (Also see Eclipse Monthly)
Comico: June, 1987 ($8.95, 64 pgs.)
1-Wildey-c/a 9.00

RIO AT BAY
Dark Horse Comics: July, 1992 - No. 2, Aug, 1992 ($2.95, limited series)
1,2-Wildey-c/a 3.00

RIO BRAVO (Movie) (See 4-Color #1018)
Dell Publishing Co.: June, 1959
Four Color 1018-Toth-a; John Wayne, Dean Martin, & Ricky Nelson photo-c.
24 48 72 170 378 585

RIO CONCHOS (See Movie Comics)

RIOT (Satire)
Atlas Comics (ACI No. 1-5/WPI No. 6): Apr, 1954 - No. 3, Aug, 1954; No. 4, Feb, 1956 - No. 6, June, 1956
1-Russ Heath-a 43 86 129 271 461 650
2-Li'l Abner satire by Post 29 58 87 170 278 385
3-Last precode (8/54) 25 50 75 150 245 340
4-Infinity-c; Marilyn Monroe "7 Year Itch" movie satire; Mad Rip-off ads
32 64 96 190 310 430
5-Marilyn Monroe, John Wayne parody; part photo-c
33 66 99 194 317 440
6-Lorna of the Jungle satire by Everett; Dennis the Menace satire-c/story; part photo-c 25 50 75 150 245 340
NOTE: ***Berg** a-3. **Burgos** c-1, 2. **Colan** a-1. **Everett** a-4, 6. **Heath** a-1. **Maneely** a-1, 2, 4-6; c-3, 4, 6. **Post** a-1-4. **Reinman** a-2. **Severin** a-4-6.*

RIOT GEAR
Triumphant Comics: Sept, 1993 - No. 11, July, 1994 ($2.50, serially numbered)
1-11: 1-2nd app. Riot Gear. 2-1st app. Rabin. 3,4-Triumphant Unleashed x-over.

Rip Hunter Time Master #22 © DC

Rise of the Black Panther #1 © MAR

Riverdale #1 © ACP

	GD 2.0	VG 4.0	FN 6.0	VF 8.0	VF/NM 9.0	NM- 9.2

3-1st app. Surzar. 4-Death of Captain Tich 3.00
Violent Past 1,2: 1-(2/94, $2.50) 3.00

R.I.P.
TSR, Inc.:1990 - No. 8, 1991 ($2.95, 44 pgs.)
1-8-Based on TSR game 4.00

RIPCLAW (See Cyberforce)
Image Comics (Top Cow Prod.): Apr, 1995 - No. 3, June, 1995 (Limited series)
1/2-Gold, 1/2-San Diego ed., 1/2-Chicago ed. 1 3 4 6 8 10
1-3: Brandon Peterson-a(p) 3.00
Special 1 (10/95, $2.50) 3.00

RIPCLAW
Image Comics (Top Cow Prod.): V2#1, Dec, 1995 - No. 6, June, 1996 ($2.50)
V2#1-6: 5-Medieval Spawn/Witchblade Preview 3.00
...: Pilot Season 1 (2007, $2.99) Jason Aaron-s/Jorge Lucas-a/Tony Moore-c 3.00

RIPCORD (TV)
Dell Publishing Co.: Mar-May, 1962
Four Color 1294 6 12 18 40 73 105

R.I.P.D.
Dark Horse Comics: Oct, 1999 - No. 4, Jan, 2000 ($2.95, limited series)
1-4 3.00
TPB (2003, $12.95) r/#1-4 13.00

R.I.P.D.: CITY OF THE DAMNED
Dark Horse Comics: Nov, 2012 - No. 4, Mar, 2013 ($3.50, limited series)
1-4-Barlow-s/Parker-a/Wilkins-c 3.50

RIP HUNTER TIME MASTER (See Showcase #20, 21, 25, 26 & Time Masters)
National Periodical Publications: Mar-Apr, 1961 - No. 29, Nov-Dec, 1965
1-(3-4/61) 61 122 183 488 1094 1700
2 25 50 75 175 388 600
3-5: 5-Last 10¢ issue 15 30 45 105 232 360
6,7-Toth-a in each 10 20 30 70 150 230
8-15 8 16 24 54 102 150
16-19 6 12 18 41 76 110
20-Hitler-c/s 8 16 24 54 102 150
21-28 6 12 18 37 66 95
29-Gil Kane-c 11 22 33 64 90 115

RIP IN TIME (Also see Teenage Mutant Ninja Turtles #5-7)
Fantagor Press: Aug, 1986 - No.5, 1987 ($1.50, B&W)
1-5: Corben-c/a in all 4.00

RIP KIRBY (Also see Harvey Comics Hits #57, & Street Comix)
David McKay Publications: 1948
Feature Books 51,54: Raymond-c; 51-Origin 37 74 111 222 361 500

RIPLEY'S BELIEVE IT OR NOT! (See Ace Comics, All-American Comics, Mystery Comics Digest #1, 4, 7, 10, 13, 16, 19, 22, 25)

RIPLEY'S BELIEVE IT OR NOT!
Harvey Publications: Sept, 1953 - No. 4, March, 1954
1-Powell-a 16 32 48 94 147 200
2-4 10 20 30 54 72 90

RIPLEY'S BELIEVE IT OR NOT! (Continuation of Ripleys'...True Ghost Stories & Ripley's...True War Stories)
Gold Key: No. 4, April, 1967 - No. 94, Feb, 1980
4-Shrunken head photo-c; McWilliams-a 4 8 12 23 37 50
5-Subtitled "True War Stories"; Evans-a; 1st Jeff Jones-a in comics? (2 pgs.)
4 8 12 23 37 50
6-10: 6-McWilliams-a. 10-Evans-a(2) 3 6 9 19 30 40
11-20: 15-Evans-a 3 6 9 16 23 30
21-30 2 4 6 13 18 22
31-38,40-60 2 4 6 9 13 16
39-Crandall-a 2 4 6 10 14 18
61-73 1 3 4 6 8 10
74,77-83-(52 pgs.) 2 4 6 9 13 16
75,76,84-94 1 2 3 5 6 8
Story Digest Mag. 1(6/70)-4-3/4x6-1/2", 148pp. 5 10 15 31 53 75
NOTE: *Evanish art by Luiz Dominguez #22-25, 27, 30, 31, 40.* ***Jeff Jones*** *a-5(2 pgs.).* ***McWilliams*** *a-65, 66, 70, 89.* ***Orlando*** *a-8.* ***Sparling*** *c-68. Reprints-74, 77-84, 87 (part); 91, 93 (all).* ***Williamson, Wood*** *a-80r/#1.*

RIPLEY'S BELIEVE IT OR NOT!
Dark Horse Comics: May, 2002 - No. 3, Oct, 2002 ($2.99, B&W, unfinished limited series)
1-3-Nord-c/a. 1-Stories of Amelia Earhart & D.B. Cooper 3.00

RIPLEY'S BELIEVE IT OR NOT! TRUE GHOST STORIES (Along with Ripley's...True War Stories, the three issues together precede the 1967 series that starts its numbering with #4) (Also see Dan Curtis)
Gold Key: June, 1965 - No. 2, Oct, 1966
1-Williamson, Wood & Evans-a; photo-c 7 14 21 44 82 120
2-Orlando, McWilliams-a; photo-c 4 8 12 27 44 60
Mini-Comic 1(1976-3-1/4x6-1/2") 2 4 6 8 11 14
11186(1977)-Golden Press; ($1.95, 224 pgs.)-All-r 4 8 12 23 37 50
11401(3/79)-Golden Press; ($1.00, 96 pgs.)-All-r 3 6 9 15 21 26

RIPLEY'S BELIEVE IT OR NOT! TRUE WAR STORIES (Along with Ripley's...True Ghost Stories, the three issues together precede the 1967 series that starts its numbering with #4)
Gold Key: Nov, 1965 (Aug, 1965 in indicia)
1-No Williamson-a 4 8 12 27 44 60

RIPLEY'S BELIEVE IT OR NOT! TRUE WEIRD
Ripley Enterprises: June, 1966 - No. 2, Aug, 1966 (B&W Magazine)
1,2-Comic stories & text 3 6 9 17 26 35

RISE OF APOCALYPSE
Marvel Comics: Oct, 1996 - No. 4, Jan, 1997 ($1.95, limited series)
1-Adam Pollina-c/a in all 1 3 4 6 8 10
2-4 5.00

RISE OF THE BLACK FLAME
Dark Horse Comics: Sept, 2016 - No. 5, Jan, 2017 ($3.99, limited series)
1-5-Mignola & Roberson-s/Mitten-a/Laurence Campbell-c 4.00

RISE OF THE BLACK PANTHER
Marvel Comics: Mar, 2018 - No. 6 ($3.99, limited series)
1-3: 1-Origin of T'Challa; Narcisse-s/Renaud-a/Stelfreeze-c; Klaw app. 2-Namor app. 4.00

RISE OF THE MAGI
Image Comics (Top Cow): No. 0, May, 2014 - No. 5 ($3.50)
0 (5/14, Free Comic Book Day giveaway) Silvestri-s/c; bonus character & concept art 3.00
1-5: 1-(6/14) Silvestri-s/Kesgin-a; four covers 3.50

RISING STARS
Image Comics (Top Cow): Mar, 1999 - No. 24, Mar, 2005 ($2.50/$2.99)
Preview-(3/99, $5.00) Straczynski-s 6.00
0-(6/00, $2.50) Gary Frank-a/c 3.00
1/2-(8/01, $2.95) Anderson-c; art & sketch pages by Zanier 3.00
1-Four covers; Keu Cha-c/a 5.00
1-($10.00) Gold Editions-four covers 10.00
1-($50.00) Holofoil-c 50.00
2-7: 5-7-Zanier & Lashley-a(p) 4.00
8-23: 8-13-Zanier & Lashley-a(p). 14-Immonen-a. 15-Flip book B&W preview of Universe.
15-23-Brent Anderson-a 3.00
24-($3.99) Series finale; Anderson-a/c 4.00
Born In Fire TPB (11/00, $19.95) r/#1-8; foreword by Neil Gaiman 20.00
Power TPB (2002, $19.95) r/#9-16 20.00
Prelude-(10/00, $2.95) Cha-a/Lashley-c 3.00
...: Visitations (2002, $8.99) r/#0, 1/2, Preview; new Anderson-c; cover gallery 9.00
Vol. 3: Fire and Ash TPB (2005, $19.99) r/#17-24; design pages & cover gallery 20.00
Vol. 4 TPB (2006, $19.99) r/Rising Stars Bright #1-3 and Voices of the Dead #1-6 20.00
Vol. 5 TPB (2007, $16.99) r/Rising Stars: Untouchable #1-5 and ...: Visitations 17.00
Wizard #0-(3/99) Wizard supplement; Straczynski-s 3.00
Wizard #1/2 5.00

RISING STARS BRIGHT
Image Comics (Top Cow): Mar, 2003 - No. 3, May, 2003 ($2.99, limited series)
1-3-Avery-s/Jurgens & Gorder-a/Beck-c 3.00

RISING STARS: UNTOUCHABLE
Image Comics (Top Cow): Mar, 2006 - No. 5, July, 2006 ($2.99, limited series)
1-5-Avery-s/Anderson-a 3.00

RISING STARS: VOICES OF THE DEAD
Image Comics (Top Cow): June, 2005 - No. 6, Dec, 2005 ($2.99, limited series)
1-6-Avery-s/Staz Johnson-a 3.00

RIVERDALE (Based on the 2017 TV series)
Archie Comic Publications: Apr, 2017; May, 2017 - Present ($3.99)
1-10: 1-4-Eisma-a. 5,8,9-Pitilla-a. 6-History of Pop's 4.00
... One-Shot (4/17, $4.99) Short story prologues to the TV series; multiple covers 4.00

RIVERDALE DIGEST (Tie-in to 2017 TV series)
Archie Comic Publications: Jun, 2017 - Present ($5.99/$6.99)

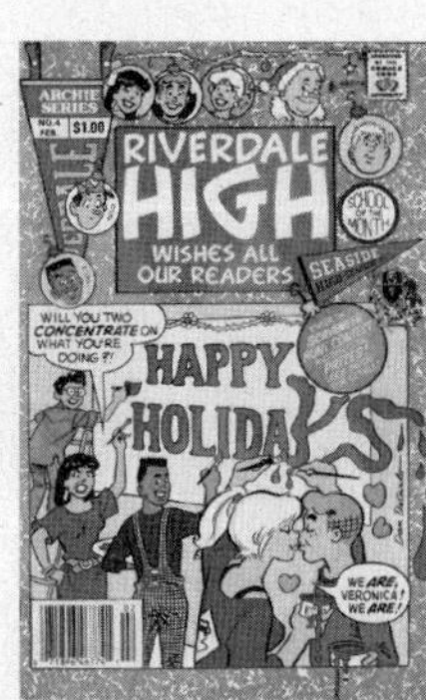

Riverdale High #4 © ACP

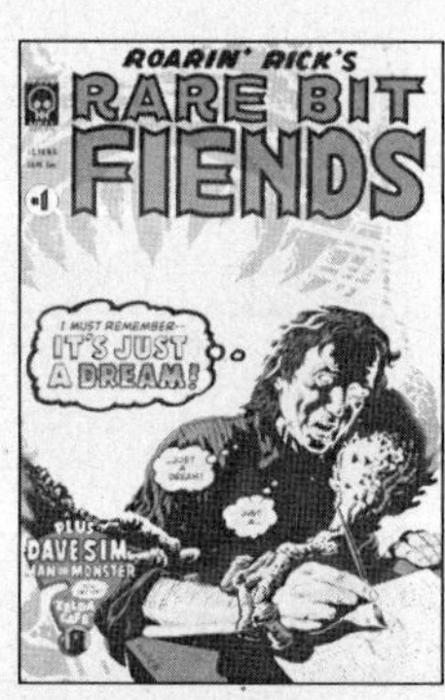

Roarin' Rick's Rare Bit Fiends #1 © Rick Veitch

Robin #159 © DC

GD 2.0 | VG 4.0 | FN 6.0 | VF 8.0 | VF/NM 9.0 | NM- 9.2

1,2-($5.99): 1-Reprints of first issues of recent 2015-2017 Archie series; Francavilla TV cast-c. 2-Reprints of early 2015-2017 issues and classic reprints 6.00
3-7-($6.99)-Reprints of early 2015-2017 issues and classic reprints 7.00

RIVERDALE HIGH (Archie's... #7,8)
Archie Comics: Aug, 1990 - No. 8, Oct, 1991 ($1.00, bi-monthly)
1 4.00
2-8 3.00

RIVER FEUD (See Zane Grey & Four Color #484)

RIVETS
Dell Publishing Co.: No. 518, Nov, 1953
Four Color 518 5 10 15 30 50 70

RIVETS (A dog)
Argo Publ.: Jan, 1956 - No. 3, May, 1956
1-Reprints Sunday & daily newspaper strips 6 12 18 31 38 45
2,3 5 10 15 22 26 30

ROACHMILL
Blackthorne Publ.: Dec, 1986 - No. 6, Oct, 1987 ($1.75, B&W)
1-6 3.00

ROACHMILL
Dark Horse Comics: May, 1988 - No. 10, Dec, 1990 ($1.75, B&W)
1-10: 10-Contains trading cards 3.00

ROAD RUNNER (See Beep Beep, the...)

ROAD TO OZ (Adaptation of the L. Frank Baum book)
Marvel Comics: Nov, 2012 - No. 6, May, 2013 ($3.99, limited series)
1-6-Eric Shanower-s/Skottie Young-a/c 4.00

ROAD TO PERDITION (Inspired the 2002 Tom Hanks/Paul Newman movie)
(Also see On the Road to Perdition)
DC Comics/Paradox Press: 1998, 2002 ($13.95, B&W paperback graphic novel)
nn-(1st printing) Max Allan Collins-s/Richard Piers Rayner-a 30.00
2nd & 3rd printings (2002, $13.95) 14.00
Movie photo cover edition (2002) 14.00

ROADTRIP
Oni Press: Aug, 2000 ($2.95, B&W, one-shot)
1-Reprints Judd Winick's back-up stories from Oni Double Feature #9,10 3.00

ROADWAYS
Cult Press: May, 1994 ($2.75, B&W, limited series)
1 3.00

ROARIN' RICK'S RARE BIT FIENDS
King Hell Press: July, 1994 - No. 21, Aug, 1996 ($2.95, B&W, mature)
1-21: Rick Veitch-c/a/scripts in all. 20-(5/96). 21-(8/96)-Reads Subtleman #1 on cover 3.00
Rabid Eye: The Dream Art of Rick Veitch ($14.95, B&W, TPB)-r/#1-8 & the appendix from #12 15.00
Pocket Universe (6/96, $14.95, B&W, TPB)-Reprints 15.00

ROBERT E. HOWARD'S CONAN THE BARBARIAN
Marvel Comics: 1983 ($2.50, 68 pgs., Baxter paper)
1-r/Savage Tales #2,3 by Smith, c-r/Conan #21 by Smith. 5.00

ROBERT LOUIS STEVENSON'S KIDNAPPED (See Kidnapped)

ROBIN (See Aurora, Birds of Prey, Detective Comics #38, New Teen Titans, Robin II, Robin III, Robin 3000, Star Spangled Comics #65, Teen Titans & Young Justice)

ROBIN (See Batman #457)
DC Comics: Jan, 1991 - No. 5, May, 1991 ($1.00, limited series)
1-Free poster by N. Adams; Bolland-c on all 6.00
1-2nd & 3rd printings (without poster) 3.00
2-5 4.00
2-2nd printing 3.00
Annual 1,2 (1992-93, $2.50, 68 pgs.): 1-Grant/Wagner scripts; Sam Kieth-c. 2-Intro Razorsharp; Jim Balent-c(p) 4.00

ROBIN (See Detective #668) (Also see Red Robin)
DC Comics: Nov, 1993 - No. 183, Apr, 2009 ($1.50/$1.95/$1.99/$2.25/$2.50/$2.99)
1-($2.95)-Collector's edition w/foil embossed-c; 1st app. Robin's car, The Redbird; Azrael as Batman app. 6.00
1-Newsstand ed. 3.00
0,2-49,51-66-Regular editions: 3-5-The Spoiler app. 6-The Huntress-c/story cont'd from Showcase '94 #5. 7-Knightquest: The Conclusion w/new Batman (Azrael) vs. Bruce Wayne. 8-KnightsEnd Pt. 5. 9-KnightsEnd Aftermath; Batman-c & app. 10-(9/94)-Zero Hour. 0-(10/94). 11-(11/94). 25-Green Arrow-c/app. 26-Batman app. 27-Contagion Pt. 3; Catwoman-c/app; Penguin & Azrael app. 28-Contagion Pt. 11. 29-Penguin app. 31-Wildcat-c/app. 32-Legacy Pt. 3. 33-Legacy Pt. 7. 35-Final Night. 46-Genesis. 52,53-Cataclysm pt. 7, conclusion. 55-Green Arrow app. 62-64-Flash-c/app. 3.50
14 ($2.50)-Embossed-c; Troika Pt. 4 4.00
50-($2.95)-Lady Shiva & King Snake app. 4.00
67-74,76-97: 67-72-No Man's Land. 79-Green Arrow app. 86-Pander Bros.-a 3.00
75-($2.95) 4.00
98,99-Bruce Wayne: Murderer x-over pt. 6, 11 3.00
100-($3.50) Last Dixon-s 4.00
101-174: 101-Young Justice x-over. 106-Kevin Lau-c. 121,122-Willingham-s/Mays-a. 125-Tim Drake quits. 126-Spoiler becomes the new Robin. 129-131-War Games. 132-Robin moves to Bludhaven, Batgirl app. 138-Begin $2.50-c. 139-McDaniel-a begins. 146-147-Teen Titans app. 148-One Year Later; new costume. 150-Begin $2.99-c. 152,153-Boomerang app. 168,169-Resurrection of Ra's al Ghul x-over. 174 Spoiler unmasked 3.00
175-183: 175,176-Batman R.I.P. x-over. 180-Robin vs. Red Robin 3.00
#1,000,000 (11/98) 853rd Century x-over 3.00
Annual 3-5: 3-(1994, $2.95)-Elseworlds story. 4-(1995, $2.95)-Year One story. 5-(1996, $2.95)-Legends of the Dead Earth story 4.00
Annual 6 (1997, $3.95)-Pulp Heroes story. 4.00
Annual 7 (12/07, $3.99)-Pearson-c/a; prelude to Resurrection of Ra's al Ghul x-over 4.00
.../Argent 1 (2/98, $1.95) Argent (Teen Titans) app. 3.00
.../Batgirl: Fresh Blood TPB (2005, $12.99) r/#132,133 & Batgirl #58,59 13.00
...: Days of Fire and Madness (2006, $12.99, TPB) r/#140-145 13.00
...Eighty-Page Giant 1 (9/00, $5.95) Chuck Dixon-s/Diego Barreto-a 6.00
...: Flying Solo (2000, $12.95, TPB) r/#1-6, Showcase '94 #5,6 13.00
...Plus 1 (12/96, $2.95) Impulse-c/app.; Waid-s 4.00
...Plus 2 (12/97, $2.95) Fang (Scare Tactics) app. 4.00
...: Search For a Hero (2009, $19.99, TPB) r/#175-183; cover gallery 20.00
.../Spoiler Special 1 (8/08, $3.99) Follows Spoiler's return in Robin #174; Dixon-s 4.00
...: Teenage Wasteland (2007, $17.99, TPB) r/#154-162 18.00
...: The Big Leagues (2008, $12.99, TPB) r/#163-167 13.00
...: Unmasked (2004, $12.95, TPB) r/#121-125; Pearson-c 13.00
...: Violent Tendencies (2008, $17.99, TPB) r/#170-174 & Robin/Spoiler Special 1 18.00
...: Wanted (2007, $12.99, TPB) r/#148-153 13.00

ROBIN: A HERO REBORN
DC Comics: 1991 ($4.95, squarebound, trade paperback)
nn-r/Batman #455-457 & Robin #1-5; Bolland-c 2 4 6 8 10 12

ROBIN HOOD (See The Advs. of..., Brave and the Bold, Classic Comics #7, Classics Giveaways (12/44), Four Color #413, 669, King Classics, Movie Comics & Power Record Comics) (...& His Merry Men, The Illustrated Story of...)

ROBIN HOOD (Disney)
Dell Publishing Co.: No. 413, Aug, 1952; No. 669, Dec, 1955
Four Color 413-(1st Disney movie Four Color book)(8/52)-Photo-c 9 18 27 60 120 180
Four Color 669 (12/55)-Reprints #413 plus photo-c 5 10 15 35 63 90

ROBIN HOOD (Adventures of... #6-8)
Magazine Enterprises (Sussex Pub. Co.): No. 52, Nov, 1955 - No. 5, Mar, 1957
52 (#1)-Origin Robin Hood & Sir Gallant of the Round Table 15 30 45 85 130 175
53 (#2), 3-5 12 24 36 67 94 120
I.W. Reprint #1,2,9: 1-r/#3. 2-r/#4. 9-r/#52 (1963) 2 4 6 9 13 16
Super Reprint #10,15: 10-r/#53. 15-r/#5 2 4 6 9 13 16
NOTE: *Bolle a-in all; c-52.*

ROBIN HOOD (Not Disney)
Dell Publishing Co.: May-July, 1963 (one-shot)
1 3 6 9 16 23 30

ROBIN HOOD (Disney) (Also see Best of Walt Disney)
Western Publishing Co.: 1973 ($1.50, 8-1/2x11", 52 pgs., cardboard-c)
96151- "Robin Hood", based on movie, 96152- "The Mystery of Sherwood Forest", 96153- "In King Richard's Service", 96154- "The Wizard's Ring" each.... 3 6 9 15 22 28

ROBIN HOOD
Eclipse Comics: July, 1991 - No. 3, Dec, 1991 ($2.50, limited series)
1-3: Timothy Truman layouts 3.00

ROBIN HOOD AND HIS MERRY MEN (Formerly Danger & Adventure)
Charlton Comics: No. 28, Apr, 1956 - No. 38, Aug, 1958
28 10 20 30 54 72 90
29-37 8 16 24 42 54 65
38-Ditko-a (5 pgs.); Rocke-c 14 28 42 76 108 140

Robin Hood Tales #9 © DC

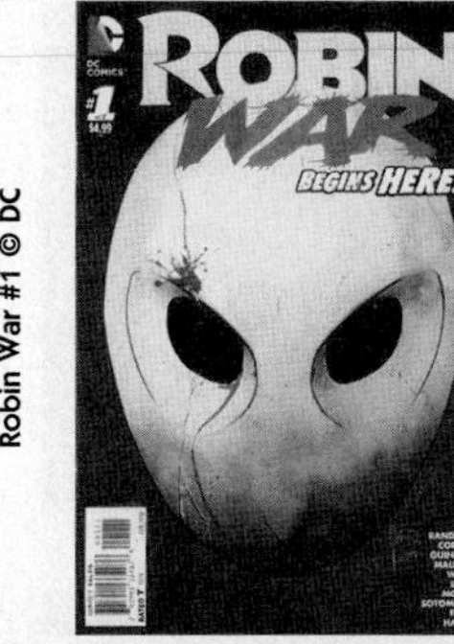

Robin War #1 © DC

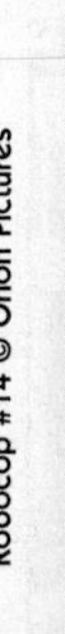
Robocop #14 © Orion Pictures

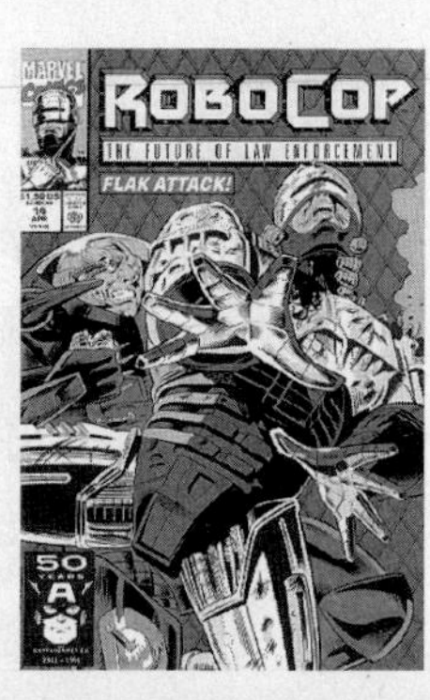

GD 2.0 | VG 4.0 | FN 6.0 | VF 8.0 | VF/NM 9.0 | NM- 9.2

ROBIN HOOD TALES (Published by National Periodical #7 on)
Quality Comics Group (Comic Magazines): Feb, 1956 - No. 6, Nov-Dec, 1956

1-All have Baker/Cuidera-c 32 64 96 188 307 425
2-6-Matt Baker-a 30 60 90 177 289 400

ROBIN HOOD TALES (Cont'd from Quality series)(See Brave & the Bold #5)
National Periodical Publ.: No. 7, Jan-Feb, 1957 - No. 14, Mar-Apr, 1958

7-All have Andru/Esposito-c 36 72 108 211 343 475
8-14 30 60 90 177 289 400

ROBIN RISES: OMEGA (See Batman & Robin #33-37)
DC Comics: Sept, 2014; Feb, 2015 ($4.99, one-shots)

Alpha 1 (2/15)-Tomasi-s/Andy Kubert-a/c; Damien returns; Talia app. 5.00
Omega 1 (9/14)-Tomasi-s/Andy Kubert-a/c; Ra's al Ghul and Justice League app. 5.00

ROBINSON CRUSOE (See King Classics & Power Record Comics)
Dell Publishing Co.: Nov-Jan, 1963-64

1 3 6 9 15 21 26

ROBIN: SON OF BATMAN (Damian Wayne)
DC Comics: Aug, 2015 - No. 13, Aug, 2016 ($3.99)

1-13: 1-Gleason-s/a. 4-Deathstroke app. 5-Damian vs. Talia. 7-"Robin War" tie-in 4.00

ROBIN II (The Joker's Wild)
DC Comics: Oct, 1991 - No. 4, Dec, 1991 ($1.50, mini-series)

1-(Direct sales, $1.50)-With 4 diff.-c; same hologram on each 5.00
1-(Newsstand, $1.00)-No hologram; 1 version 3.00
1-Collector's set ($10.00)-Contains all 5 versions bagged with hologram trading card inside 18.00
2-(Direct sales, $1.50)-With 3 different-c 4.00
2-4-(Newsstand, $1.00)-1 version of each 3.00
2-Collector's set ($8.00)-Contains all 4 versions bagged with hologram trading card inside 12.00
3-(Direct sale, $1.50)-With 2 different-c 4.00
3-Collector's set ($6.00)-Contains all 3 versions bagged with hologram trading card inside 10.00
4-(Direct sales, $1.50)-Only one version 4.00
4-Collector's set ($4.00)-Contains both versions bagged with Bat-Signal hologram trading card 6.00
Multi-pack (All four issues w/hologram sticker) 14.00
Deluxe Complete Set ($30.00)-Contains all 14 versions of #1-4 plus a new hologram trading card; numbered & limited to 25,000; comes with slipcase & 2 acid free backing boards 45.00

ROBIN III: CRY OF THE HUNTRESS
DC Comics: Dec, 1992 - No. 6, Mar, 1993 (Limited series)

1-6 ($2.50, collector's ed.)-Polybagged w/movement enhanced-c plus mini-poster of newsstand-c by Zeck 4.00
1-6 ($1.25, newsstand ed.): All have Zeck-c 3.00

ROBIN 3000
DC Comics (Elseworlds): 1992 - No. 2, 1992 ($4.95, mini-series, 52 pgs.)

1,2-Foil logo; Russell-c/a 6.00

ROBIN WAR (Crossover with Grayson, Robin: Son of Batman, and We Are Robin)
DC Comics: Feb, 2016 - No. 2, Mar, 2016 ($4.99)

1,2-Tom King-s; art by various; The Court of Owls app. 5.00

ROBIN: YEAR ONE
DC Comics: 2000 - No. 4, 2001 ($4.95, square-bound, limited series)

1-4: Earliest days of Robin's career; Javier Pulido-c/a. 2,4-Two-Face app. 6.00
TPB (2002, 2008, $14.95/$14.99, 2 printings) r/#1-4 15.00

ROBOCOP
Marvel Comics: Oct, 1987 ($2.00, B&W, magazine, one-shot)

1-Movie adaptation 1 3 4 6 8 10

ROBOCOP (Also see Dark Horse Comics)
Marvel Comics: Mar, 1990 - No. 23, Jan, 1992 ($1.50)

1-Based on movie 1 3 4 6 8 10
2-23 3.00
nn (7/90, $4.95, 52 pgs.)-r/B&W magazine in color; adapts 1st movie 5.00

ROBOCOP
Dynamite Entertainment: 2010 - No. 6, 2010 ($3.50, limited series)

1-6-Follows the events of the first film; Neves-a 3.50

ROBOCOP
BOOM! Studios: Jul, 2014 - No. 12, Jun, 2015 ($3.99)

1-12: 1-8-Williamson-s/Magno-a. 1-Multiple covers. 9,10-Aragon-a 4.00

ROBOCOP (FRANK MILLER'S...)
Avatar Press: July, 2003 - No. 9, Jan, 2006 ($3.50/$3.99, limited series)

1-9-Frank Miller-s/Juan Ryp-a. 1-Three covers by Miller, Ryp, and Barrows. 2-Two covers 4.00
Free Comic Book Day Edition (4/03) Previews Robocop & Stargate SG•1; Busch-c 3.00

ROBOCOP (Tie-ins to the 2014 movie)
BOOM! Studios: Feb, 2014 ($3.99)

...: Beta (2/14) Brisson-s/Laiso-a 4.00
...: Hominem Ex Machina (2/14) Moreci-s/Copland-a 4.00
...: Memento Mori (2/14) Barbiere-s/Vieira-a 4.00
...: To Live and Die in Detroit (2/14) Joe Harris-s/Piotr Kowalski-a 4.00

ROBOCOP: LAST STAND
BOOM! Studios: Aug, 2013 - No. 8, Mar, 2014 ($3.99, limited series)

1-8: 1-Miller & Grant-s/Oztekin-a 4.00

ROBOCOP: MORTAL COILS
Dark Horse Comics: Sept, 1993 - No. 4, Dec, 1993 ($2.50, limited series)

1-4: 1,2-Cago painted-c 3.00

ROBOCOP: PRIME SUSPECT
Dark Horse Comics: Oct, 1992 - No. 4, Jan, 1993 ($2.50, limited series)

1-4: 1,3-Nelson painted-c. 2,4-Bolton painted-c. 3.00

ROBOCOP: ROAD TRIP
Dynamite Entertainment: 2012 - No. 4, 2012 ($3.99, limited series)

1-4-De Zarate-a 4.00

ROBOCOP: ROULETTE
Dark Horse Comics: Dec, 1993 - No. 4, 1994 ($2.50, limited series)

1-4: 1,3-Nelson painted-c. 2,4-Bolton painted-c 3.00

ROBOCOP 2
Marvel Comics: Aug, 1990 ($2.25, B&W, magazine, 68 pgs.)

1-Adapts movie sequel scripted by Frank Miller; Bagley-a 4.00

ROBOCOP 2
Marvel Comics: Aug, 1990; Late Aug, 1990 - #3, Late Sept, 1990 ($1.00, limited series)

nn-(8/90, $4.95, 68 pgs., color)-Same contents as B&W magazine 5.00
1: #1-3 reprint no number issue 3.00
2,3: 2-Guice-c(i) 3.00

ROBOCOP 3
Dark Horse Comics: July, 1993 - No. 3, Nov, 1993 ($2.50, limited series)

1-3: Nelson painted-c; Nguyen-a(p) 3.00

ROBOCOP VERSUS THE TERMINATOR
Dark Horse Comics: Sept, 1992 - No. 4, 1992 (Dec.) ($2.50, limited series)

1-4: Miller scripts & Simonson-c/a in all 4.00
1-Platinum Edition 10.00
NOTE: *All contain a different Robocop cardboard cut-out stand-up.*

ROBO DOJO
DC Comics (WildStorm): Apr, 2002 - No. 6, Sept, 2002 ($2.95, limited series)

1-6-Wolfman-s 3.00

ROBO-HUNTER (Also see Sam Slade...)
Eagle Comics: Apr, 1984 - No. 5, 1984 ($1.00)

1-5-2000 A.D. 4.00

R.O.B.O.T. BATTALION 2050
Eclipse Comics: Mar, 1988 ($2.00, B&W, one-shot)

1 3.00

ROBOT COMICS
Renegade Press: No. 0, June, 1987 ($2.00, B&W, one-shot)

0-Bob Burden story & art 3.00

ROBOTECH
Antarctic Press: Mar, 1997 - No. 11, Nov, 1998 ($2.95)

1-11, Annual 1 (4/98, $2.95) 4.00
...Class Reunion (12/98, $3.95, B&W) 4.00
...Escape (5/98, $2.95, B&W), ...Final Fire (12/98, $2.95, B&W) 4.00

ROBOTECH
DC Comics (WildStorm): No. 0, Feb, 2003 - No. 6, Jul, 2003 ($2.50/$2.95, limited series)

0-Tommy Yune-s; art by Jim Lee, Garza, Bermejo and others; pin-up pages by various 3.00
1-6 ($2.95)-Long Vo-a 3.00

Robotech Masters #12 © Harmony

Rocket #4 © MAR

Rocketeer Adventures #3 © Rocketeer Trust

GD 2.0 | VG 4.0 | FN 6.0 | VF 8.0 | VF/NM 9.0 | NM- 9.2

...: From the Stars (2003, $9.95, digest-size) r/#0-6 & Sourcebook 10.00
... Sourcebook (3/03, $2.95) pin-ups and info on characters and mecha; art by various 3.00

ROBOTECH
Titan Comics: Aug, 2017 - Present ($3.99)
1-7-Brian Wood-s/Marco Turini-a; multiple covers on each 4.00

ROBOTECH: COVERT-OPS
Antarctic Press: Aug, 1998 - No. 2, Sept, 1998 ($2.95, B&W, limited series)
1,2-Gregory Lane-s/a 4.00

ROBOTECH DEFENDERS
DC Comics: Mar, 1985 - No. 2, Apr, 1985 (Mini-series)
1,2 4.00

ROBOTECH IN 3-D (TV)
Comico: Aug, 1987 ($2.50)
1-Steacy painted-c 5.00

ROBOTECH: INVASION
DC Comics (WildStorm): Feb, 2004 - No. 5, July, 2004 ($2.95, limited series)
1-5-Faerber & Yune-s/Miyazawa & Dogan-a 3.00

ROBOTECH: LOVE AND WAR
DC Comics (WildStorm): Aug, 2003 - No. 6, Jan, 2004 ($2.95, limited series)
1-6-Long Vo & Charles Park-a/Faerber & Yune-s. 2-Variant-c by Warren 3.00

ROBOTECH MASTERS (TV)
Comico: July, 1985 - No. 23, Apr, 1988 ($1.50)
1 6.00
2-23 4.00

ROBOTECH: PRELUDE TO THE SHADOW CHRONICLES
DC Comics (WildStorm): Dec, 2005 - No. 5, Mar, 2006 ($3.50, limited series)
1-5-Yune-s/Dogan & Udon Studios-a 3.50
TPB (2010, $17.99) r/#1-5; production art 18.00

ROBOTECH: SENTINELS - RUBICON
Antarctic Press: July, 1998 ($2.95, B&W)
1 4.00

ROBOTECH SPECIAL
Comico: May, 1988 ($2.50, one-shot, 44 pgs.)
1-Steacy wraparound-c; partial photo-c 5.00

ROBOTECH THE GRAPHIC NOVEL
Comico: Aug, 1986 ($5.95, 8-1/2x11", 52 pgs.)
1-Origin SDF-1; intro T.R. Edwards, Steacy-c/a 15.00
1-Second printing (12/86) 10.00

ROBOTECH: THE MACROSS SAGA (TV)(Formerly Macross)
Comico: No. 2, Feb, 1985 - No. 36, Feb, 1989 ($1.50)
2 1 2 3 5 6 8
3-10 5.00
11-36: 12,17-Ken Steacy painted-c. 26-Begin $1.75-c. 35,36-($1.95) 4.00
Volume 1-4 TPB (WildStorm, 2003, $14.95, 5-3/4" x 8-1/4")1-Reprints #2-6 & Macross #1. 2- r/#7-12. 3-r/#13-18. 4-r/#19-24 15.00

ROBOTECH: THE NEW GENERATION
Comico: July, 1985 - No. 25, July, 1988
1 6.00
2-25 4.00

ROBOTECH: VERMILION
Antarctic Press: Mar, 1997 - No. 4, ($2.95, B&W, limited series)
1-4 4.00

ROBOTECH / VOLTRON
Dynamite Entertainment: 2013 - No. 5, 2014 ($3.99, limited series)
1-5-Tommy Yune-s 4.00

ROBOTECH: WINGS OF GIBRALTAR
Antarctic Press: Aug, 1998 - No. 2, Sept, 1998 ($2.95, B&W, limited series)
1,2-Lee Duhig-s/a 4.00

ROBOTIX
Marvel Comics: Feb, 1986 (75¢, one-shot)
1-Based on toy 4.00

ROBOTMEN OF THE LOST PLANET (Also see Space Thrillers)
Avon Periodicals: 1952 (Also see Strange Worlds #19)
1-McCann-a (3 pgs.); Fawcette-a 168 336 504 1075 1838 2600

ROB ROY
Dell Publishing Co.: 1954 (Disney-Movie)
Four Color 544-Manning-a, photo-c 7 14 21 49 92 135

ROCK, THE (WWF Wrestling)
Chaos! Comics: June, 2001 ($2.99, one-shot)
1-Photo-c; Grant-s/Neves-a 4.00

ROCK & ROLL HIGH SCHOOL
Roger Corman's Cosmic Comics: Oct, 1995 ($2.50)
1-Bob Fingerman scripts 3.00

ROCK AND ROLLO (Formerly TV Teens)
Charlton Comics: V2#14, Oct, 1957 - No. 19, Sept, 1958
V2#14-19 6 12 18 31 38 45

ROCK COMICS
Landgraphic Publ.: Jul/Aug, 1979 ($1.25, tabloid size, 28 pgs.)
1-N. Adams-c; Thor (not Marvel's) story by Adams 3 6 9 14 20 25

ROCKET (Rocket Raccoon from Guardians of the Galaxy)
Marvel Comics: Jul, 2017 - No. 6, Dec, 2017 ($3.99, limited series)
1-6: 1-Ewing-s/Gorham-a/Mayhew-c. 4-Deadpool app. 4.00

ROCKET COMICS
Hillman Periodicals: Mar, 1940 - No. 3, May, 1940
1-Rocket Riley, Red Roberts the Electro Man (origin), The Phantom Ranger, The Steel Shark, The Defender, Buzzard Barnes and his Sky Devils, Lefty Larson, & The Defender, the Man with a Thousand Faces begin (1st app. of each); all have Rocket Riley-c 300 600 900 1980 3440 4900
2,3: 2-Jack Cole-a 194 388 582 1242 2121 3000

ROCKET COMICS: IGNITE
Dark Horse Comics: Apr, 2003 (Free Comic Book Day giveaway)
1-Previews Dark Horse series Syn, Lone, and Go Boy 7 3.00

ROCKETEER, THE (See Eclipse Graphic Album Series, Pacific Presents & Starslayer)

ROCKETEER ADVENTURE MAGAZINE, THE
Comico/Dark Horse Comics No. 3: July, 1988 ($2.00); No. 2, July, 1989 ($2.75); No. 3, Jan, 1995 ($2.95)
1-(7/88, $2.00)-Dave Stevens-c/a in all; Kaluta back-up-a; 1st app. Jonas (character based on The Shadow) 2 4 6 8 10 12
2-(7/89, $2.75)-Stevens/Dorman painted-c 1 3 4 6 8 10
3-(1/95, $2.95)-Includes pinups by Stevens, Gulacy, Plunkett, & Mignola 5.00
Volume 2-(9/96, $9.95, magazine size TPB)-Reprints #1-3 10.00

ROCKETEER ADVENTURES
IDW Publishing: May, 2011 - No. 4, Aug, 2011 ($3.99, limited series)
1-4-Anthology of new stories by various; covers by Alex Ross and Dave Stevens 4.00
The Rocketeer: The Best of Rocketeer Adventures: Funko Edition 1 (1/18, $4.99) r/stories from series; art by Cassaday, Ha, Kaluta, Sakai, & Weston; Funko fig cover 5.00

ROCKETEER ADVENTURES VOLUME 2
IDW Publishing: Mar, 2012 - No. 4, Jun, 2012 ($3.99, limited series)
1-4-Anthology by various; covers by Darwyn Cooke and Stevens. 1-Sakai-a. 4-Simonson & Byrne-a 4.00

ROCKETEER AT WAR, THE
IDW Publishing: Dec, 2015 - No. 4, Apr, 2016 ($4.99, limited series)
1-4-Guggenheim-s; covers by Bullock & Bradshaw. 1,2-Bullock-a. 3,4-J. Bone-a 5.00

ROCKETEER: CARGO OF DOOM
IDW Publishing: Aug, 2012 - No. 4, Nov, 2012 ($3.99, limited series)
1-4-Waid-s/Samnee-a/c; variant-c by Stevens on all 4.00

ROCKETEER: HOLLYWOOD HORROR
IDW Publishing: Feb, 2013 - No. 4, May, 2013 ($3.99, limited series)
1-4-Langridge-s/Bone-a/Simonson-c; variant-c on all 4.00

ROCKETEER JETPACK TREASURY EDITION
IDW Publishing: Nov, 2011 ($9.99, oversized 13" x 9-3/4" format)
1-Recolored r/Starslayer #1-3, Pacific Presents #1,2 & Rocketeer Special Edition 10.00

ROCKETEER SPECIAL EDITION, THE
Eclipse Comics: Nov, 1984 ($1.50, Baxter paper)(Chapter 5 of Rocketeer serial)
1-Stevens-c/a; Kaluta back-c; pin-ups inside 2 4 6 13 18 22
NOTE: *Originally intended to be published in Pacific Presents.*

Rocket Kelly #1 © FOX

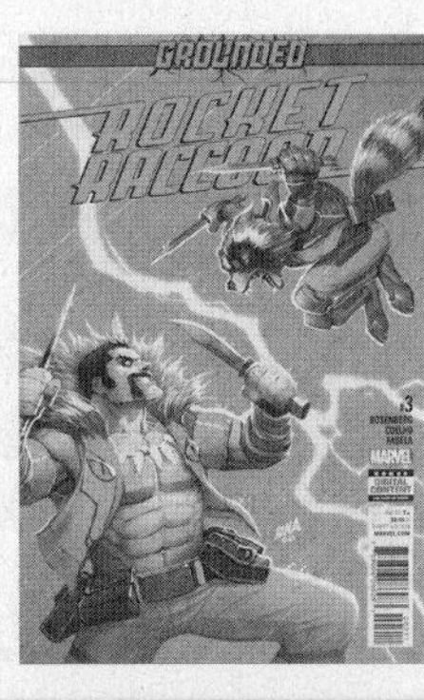

Rocket Raccoon (2017 series) #3 © MAR

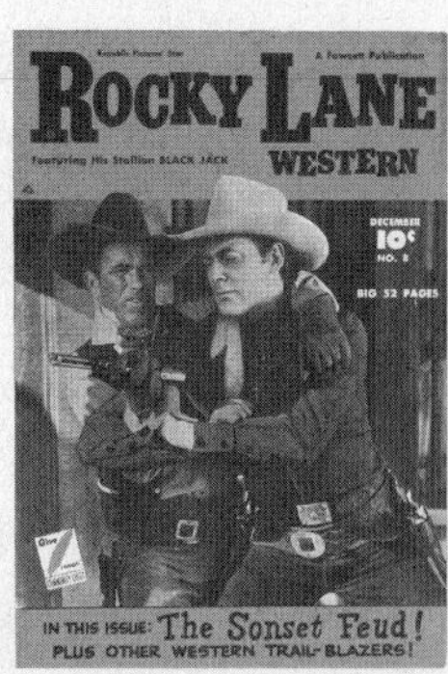

Rocky Lane Western #8 © FAW

GD VG FN VF VF/NM NM-
2.0 4.0 6.0 8.0 9.0 9.2

ROCKETEER, THE: THE COMPLETE ADVENTURES
IDW Publishing: Oct, 2009 ($29.99/$75.00, hardcover)

HC-Reprints of Dave Stevens' Rocketeer stories in Starslayer #1-3, Pacific Presents #1,2, Rocketeer Special Edition and Rocketeer Adventure Magazine #1-3; all re-colored 30.00
... Deluxe Edition ($75.00, 8"x12" slipcased HC) larger size reprints of HC content plus 100 bonus pages of sketch art, layouts, design work; intro. by Thomas Jane 110.00
... Deluxe Edition 2nd printing ($75.00, oversized slipcased HC) 75.00

ROCKETEER, THE: THE OFFICIAL MOVIE ADAPTATION
W. D. Publications (Disney): 1991

nn-($5.95, 68 pgs.)-Squarebound deluxe edition 6.00
nn-($2.95, 68 pgs.)-Stapled regular edition 4.00
3-D Comic Book (1991, $7.98, 52 pgs.) 8.00

ROCKETEER/THE SPIRIT: PULP FRICTION
IDW Publishing: Jul, 2013 - No. 4, Dec, 2013 ($3.99, limited series)

1-4: 1-Waid-s/Paul Smith-a; covers by Smith & Darwyn Cooke. 2-Wallace-a. 3,4-Bone-a 4.00

ROCKET GIRL
Image Comics: Oct, 2013 - No. 10, Oct, 2017 ($3.50/$3.99)

1-10-Brandon Montclare-a/Amy Reeder-a/c. 6-Begin $3.99 4.00

ROCKET KELLY (See The Bouncer, Green Mask #10); becomes Li'l Pan #6)
Fox Feature Syndicate: 1944; Fall, 1945 - No. 5, Oct-Nov, 1946

nn (1944), 1 (Fall, 1945) 41 82 123 256 428 600
2-The Puppeteer app. (costumed hero) 29 58 87 172 281 390
3-5: 5-(#5 on cover, #4 inside) 26 52 78 154 252 350

ROCKETMAN (Strange Fantasy #2 on) (See Hello Pal & Scoop Comics)
Ajax/Farrell Publications: June, 1952 (Strange Stories of the Future)

1-Rocketman & Cosmo 47 94 141 296 498 700

ROCKET RACCOON (Also see Marvel Preview #7 and Incredible Hulk #271)
Marvel Comics: May, 1985 - No. 4, Aug, 1985 (color, limited series)

1-Mignola-a/Mantlo-s in all 4 8 12 28 47 65
2-4 2 4 6 11 16 20
...: Tales From Half-World 1 (10/13, $7.99) r/#1-4; new cover by McNiven 8.00

ROCKET RACCOON (Guardians of the Galaxy)
Marvel Comics: Sept, 2014 - No. 11, Jul, 2015 ($3.99)

1-Skottie Young-s/a; Groot app. 5.00
2-11-Skottie Young-s. 7,8-Andrade-a 4.00
Free Comic Book Day 2014 (5/14, giveaway) Archer-a; Groot and Wal-rus app. 3.00

ROCKET RACCOON (Guardians of the Galaxy)
Marvel Comics: Feb, 2017 - No. 5, Jun, 2017 ($3.99)

1-5-Rosenberg-s/Coelho-a. 1-Johnny Storm app. 2-5-Kraven app. 4.00

ROCKET RACCOON & GROOT (Guardians of the Galaxy)
Marvel Comics: Mar, 2016 - No. 10, Nov, 2016 ($3.99)

1-10: 1-6-Skottie Young-s. 1-3-Filipe Andrade-a. 8-10-Gwenpool app. 4.00

ROCKET SHIP X
Fox Feature Syndicate: September, 1951; 1952

1 65 130 195 416 708 1000
1952 (nn, nd, no publ.)-Edited 1951-c (exist?) 39 78 117 240 395 550

ROCKET TO ADVENTURE LAND (See Pixie Puzzle...)

ROCKET TO THE MOON
Avon Periodicals: 1951

nn-Orlando-c/a; adapts Otis Adelbert Kline's "Maza of the Moon"
168 336 504 1075 1838 2600

ROCK FANTASY COMICS
Rock Fantasy Comics: Dec, 1989 - No. 16?, 1991 ($2.25/$3.00, B&W)(No cover price)

1-Pink Floyd part 1 5.00
1-2nd printing ($3.00-c) 3.00
2,3: 2-Rolling Stones #1. 3-Led Zeppelin #1 4.00
2,3: 2nd printings ($3.00-c, 1/90 & 2/90) 3.00
4-Stevie Nicks Not published
5-Monstrosities of Rock #1; photo back-c 4.00
5-2nd printing ($3.00, 3/90 indicia, 2/90-c) 3.00
6-9,11-15,17,18: 6-Guns n' Roses #1 (1st & 2nd printings, 3/90)-Begin $3.00-c. 7-Sex Pistols #1. 8-Alice Cooper; not published. 9-Van Halen #1; photo back-c. 11-Jimi Hendrix #1; wraparound-c 3.00
10-Kiss #1; photo back-c 2 4 6 8 10 12
16-($5.00, 68 pgs.)-The Great Gig in the Sky(Floyd) 5.00

ROCK HAPPENING (See Bunny and Harvey Pop Comics:...)

ROCK N' ROLL COMICS
DC Comics: Dec./Jan 1956 (ashcan)

nn-Ashcan comic, not distributed to newsstands, only for in house use (no known sales)

ROCK N' ROLL COMICS
Revolutionary Comics: Jun, 1989 - No. 65 ($1.50/$1.95/$2.50, B&W/col. #15 on)

1-Guns N' Roses 1 3 4 6 8 10
1-2nd thru 7th printings. 7th printing (full color w/new-c/a) 3.00
2-Metallica 1 3 4 6 8 10
2-2nd thru 6th printings (6th in color) 3.00
3-Bon Jovi (no reprints) 1 2 3 5 6 8
4-8,10-65: 4-Motley Crue(2nd printing only, 1st destroyed). 5-Def Leppard (2 printings). 6-Rolling Stones(4 printings). 7-The Who (3 printings). 8-Skid Row; not published. 10-Warrant/Whitesnake(2 printings; 1st has 2 diff.-c). 11-Aerosmith (2 printings?). 12-New Kids on the Block(2 printings). 12-3rd printing; rewritten & titled NKOTB Hate Book. 13-Led Zeppelin. 14-Sex Pistols. 15-Poison; 1st color issue. 16-Van Halen. 17-Madonna. 18-Alice Cooper. 19-Public Enemy/2 Live Crew. 20-Queensryche/Tesla. 21-Prince? 22-AC/DC; begin $2.50-c. 23-Living Colour. 26-Michael Jackson. 29-Ozzy. 45,46-Grateful Dead. 49-Rush. 50,51-Bob Dylan. 56-David Bowie 5.00
9-Kiss 2 4 6 8 10 12
9-2nd & 3rd printings 3.00

NOTE: *Most issues were reprinted except #3. Later reprints are in color. #8 was not released.*

ROCKO'S MODERN LIFE (TV) (Nickelodeon cartoon)
Marvel Comics: June, 1994 - No. 7, Dec, 1994 ($1.95)

1-7 3.00

ROCKO'S MODERN LIFE (TV) (Nickelodeon cartoon)
BOOM! Studios (kaboom!): Dec, 2017 - Present ($3.99)

1-3-Ferrier-s/McGinty-a; multiple covers 4.00

ROCKSTARS
Image Comics: Dec, 2016 - Present ($3.99)

1-8-Joe Harris-s/Megan Hutchison-a 4.00

ROCKY AND BULLWINKLE (TV)
IDW Publishing: Mar, 2014 - No. 4, Jun, 2014 ($3.99)

1-4-Evanier-s/Langridge-a; bonus Dudley Do-Right short story in each; two covers 4.00

ROCKY AND BULLWINKLE SHOW, THE (TV)
American Mythology: 2017 - Present ($3.99)

1,2: 1-New short stories and reprints from Bullwinkle #1&2; three covers 4.00

ROCKY AND HIS FIENDISH FRIENDS (TV)(Bullwinkle)
Gold Key: Oct, 1962 - No. 5, Sept, 1963 (Jay Ward)

1 (25¢, 80 pgs.) 13 26 39 86 188 290
2,3 (25¢, 80 pgs.) 9 18 27 62 126 190
4,5 (Regular size, 12¢) 7 14 21 46 86 125

ROCKY AND HIS FRIENDS (See Kite Fun Book & March of Comics #216 in the Promotional Comics section)

ROCKY AND HIS FRIENDS (TV)
Dell Publishing Co.: No. 1128, 8-10/60 - No.1311,1962 (Jay Ward)

Four Color 1128 (#1) (8-10/60) 25 50 75 175 388 600
Four Color 1152 (12-2/61), 1166, 1208, 1275, 1311('62)
16 32 48 107 236 365

ROCKY HORROR PICTURE SHOW THE COMIC BOOK, THE
Caliber Press: Jul, 1990 - No. 3, Jan, 1991 ($2.95, mini-series, 52 pgs.)

1-3: 1-Adapts cult film plus photos, etc., 1-2nd printing
1 3 4 6 8 10
...Collection ($4.95) 2 4 6 8 10 12

ROCKY JONES SPACE RANGER (See Space Adventures #15-18)

ROCKY JORDEN PRIVATE EYE (See Private Eye)

ROCKY LANE WESTERN (Allan Rocky Lane starred in Republic movies & TV for a short time as Allan Lane, Red Ryder & Rocky Lane) (See Black Jack Fawcett Movie Comics, Motion Picture Comics & Six-Gun Heroes)
Fawcett Publications/Charlton No. 56 on: May, 1949 - No. 87, Nov, 1959

1 (36 pgs.)-Rocky, his stallion Black Jack, & Slim Pickens begin; photo-c begin, end #57; photo back-c 55 110 165 352 601 850
2 (36 pgs.)-Last photo back-c 22 44 66 132 216 300
3-5 (52 pgs.): 4-Captain Tootsie by Beck 17 34 51 98 154 210
6,10 (36 pgs.): 10-Complete western novelette "Badman's Reward"
14 28 42 76 108 140
7-9 (52 pgs.) 14 28 42 82 121 160

Rod Cameron Western #8 © FAW

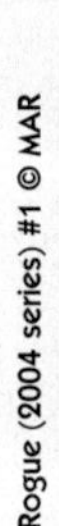
Rogue (2004 series) #1 © MAR

Rom #27 © Parker Brothers

	GD 2.0	VG 4.0	FN 6.0	VF 8.0	VF/NM 9.0	NM- 9.2

11-13,15-17,19,20 (52 pgs.): 15-Black Jack's Hitching Post begins, ends #25.
20-Last Slim Pickens 12 24 36 67 94 120
14,18 (36 pgs.) 10 20 30 58 79 100
21,23,24 (52 pgs.): 21-Dee Dickens begins, ends #55,57,65-68
10 20 30 58 79 100
22,25-28,30 (36 pgs. begin) 10 20 30 54 72 90
29-Classic complete novel "The Land of Missing Men" with hidden land of ancient temple ruins (r-in #65) 14 28 42 76 108 140
31-40 9 18 27 52 69 85
41-54 9 18 27 47 61 75
55-Last Fawcett issue (1/54) 9 18 27 52 69 85
56-1st Charlton issue (2/54)-Photo-c 14 28 42 82 121 160
57,60-Photo-c 10 20 30 54 72 90
58,59,61-64,66-78,80-86: 59-61-Young Falcon app. 64-Slim Pickens app.
66-68: Reprints #30,31,32 8 16 24 44 57 70
65-r/#29, "The Land of Missing Men" 9 18 27 50 65 80
79-Giant Edition (68 pgs.) 10 20 30 58 79 100
87-Last issue 9 18 27 52 69 85
NOTE: *Complete novels in #10, 14, 18, 22, 25, 30-32, 36, 38, 39, 49. Captain Tootsie in #4, 12, 20. Big Bow and Little Arrow in #11, 28, 63. Black Jack's Hitching Post in #15-25, 64, 73.*

ROCKY LANE WESTERN
AC Comics: 1989 ($2.50, B&W, one-shot?)
1-Photo-c; Giordano reprints 4.00
Annual 1 (1991, $2.95, B&W, 44 pgs.)-photo front/back & inside-c; reprints 4.00

ROD CAMERON WESTERN (Movie star)
Fawcett Publications: Feb, 1950 - No. 20, Apr, 1953
1-Rod Cameron, his horse War Paint, & Sam The Sheriff begin; photo front/back-c begin
30 60 90 177 289 400
2 15 30 45 86 133 180
3-Novel length story "The Mystery of the Seven Cities of Cibola"
14 28 42 82 121 160
4-10: 9-Last photo back-c 12 24 36 69 97 125
11-19 10 20 30 58 79 100
20-Last issue & photo-c 11 22 33 62 86 110
NOTE: *Novel length stories in No. 1-8, 12-14.*

RODEO RYAN (See A-1 Comics #8)

ROGAN GOSH
DC Comics (Vertigo): 1994 ($6.95, one-shot)
nn-Peter Milligan scripts 7.00

ROGER DODGER (Also in Exciting Comics #57 on)
Standard Comics: No. 5, Aug, 1952
5-Teen-age 8 16 24 44 57 70

ROGER RABBIT (Also see Marvel Graphic Novel)
Disney Comics: June, 1990 - No. 18, Nov, 1991 ($1.50)
1-18-All new stories 4.00
In 3-D 1 (1992, $2.50)-Sold at Wal-Mart?; w/glasses 1 2 3 5 6 8

ROGER RABBIT'S TOONTOWN
Disney Comics: Aug, 1991 - No. 5, Dec, 1991 ($1.50)
1-5 3.00

ROGER ZELAZNY'S AMBER: THE GUNS OF AVALON
DC Comics: 1996 - No. 3, 1996 ($6.95, limited series)
1-3: Based on novel 7.00

ROG 2000
Pacific Comics: June, 1982 ($2.95, 44 pgs., B&W, one-shot, magazine)
nn-Byrne-c/a (r) 2 4 6 8 10 12
2nd printing (7/82) 1 2 3 4 5 7

ROGUE (From X-Men)
Marvel Comics: Jan, 1995 - No. 4, Apr, 1995 ($2.95, limited series)
1-4: 1-Gold foil logo 4.00
TPB-($12.95) r/#1-4 13.00

ROGUE (Volume 2)
Marvel Comics: Sept, 2001 - No. 4, Dec, 2001 ($2.50, limited series)
1-4-Julie Bell painted-c/Lopresti-a; Rogue's early days with X-Men 3.00

ROGUE (From X-Men)
Marvel Comics: Sept, 2004 - No. 12, Aug, 2005 ($2.99)
1-12: 1-Richards-a. 4-Gambit app. 11-Sunfire dies, Rogue absorbs his powers 3.00
...: Going Rogue TPB (2005, $14.99) r/#1-6 15.00
...: Forget-Me-Not TPB (2006, $14.99) r/#7-12 15.00

ROGUE & GAMBIT
Marvel Comics: Mar, 2018 - Present ($3.99)
1-3-Kelly Thompson-s/Pere Pérez-a 4.00

ROGUE ANGEL: TELLER OF TALL TALES (Based on the Alex Archer novels)
IDW Publishing: Feb, 2008 - No. 5, Jun, 2008 ($3.99)
1-5-Annja Creed adventures; Barbara-Kesel-s/Renae De Liz-a 4.00

ROGUES GALLERY
DC Comics: 1996 ($3.50, one-shot)
1-Pinups of DC villains by various artists 4.00

ROGUE TROOPER
IDW Publishing: Feb, 2014 - No. 4, May, 2014 ($3.99)
1-4-Ruckley-s/Ponticelli-a/Fabry-c 4.00

ROGUE TROOPER CLASSICS
IDW Publishing: May, 2014 - No. 8, Dec, 2014 ($3.99)
1-8-Newly colored reprints of strips from 2000 AD magazine. 1-4-Gibbons-a 4.00

ROGUES, THE (VILLAINS) (See The Flash)
DC Comics: Feb, 1998 ($1.95, one-shot)
1-Augustyn-s/Pearson-c 3.00

ROKKIN
DC Comics (WildStorm): Sept, 2006 - No. 6, Feb, 2007 ($2.99, limited series)
1-6-Hartnell-s/Bradshaw-a 3.00

ROLLING STONES: VOODOO LOUNGE
Marvel Comics: 1995 ($6.95, Prestige format, one-shot)
nn-Dave McKean-script/design/art 7.00

ROLY POLY COMIC BOOK
Green Publishing Co.: 1945 - No. 15, 1946 (MLJ reprints)
1-(No number on cover or indicia, "1945 issue" on cover) Red Rube & Steel Sterling begin; Sahle-c 37 74 111 222 361 500
6-The Blue Circle & The Steel Fist app. 25 50 75 150 245 340
10-Origin Red Rube retold; Steel Sterling story (Zip #41)
29 58 87 170 278 385
11,12: The Black Hood app. in both 30 60 90 177 289 400
14-Classic decapitation-c; the Black Hood app. 300 600 900 1950 3375 4800
15-The Blue Circle & The Steel Fist app.; cover exact swipe from Fox Blue Beetle #1
37 74 111 222 361 500

ROM (Based on the Parker Brothers toy)
Marvel Comics Group: Dec, 1979 - No. 75, Feb, 1986
1-Origin/1st app. 5 10 15 31 53 75
2-16,19-23,28-30: 5-Dr. Strange. 13-Saga of the Space Knights begins. 19-X-Men cameo.
23-Powerman & Iron Fist app. 1 2 3 5 6 8
17,18-X-Men app. 2 4 6 9 12 15
24-27: 24-F.F. cameo; Skrulls, Nova & The New Champions app. 25-Double size.
26,27-Galactus app. 1 2 3 5 7 9
31-49,51-60: 31,32-Brotherhood of Evil Mutants app. 32-X-Men cameo. 34,35-Sub-Mariner app. 41,42-Dr. Strange app. 56,57-Alpha Flight app. 58,59-Ant-Man app. 6.00
50-Skrulls app. (52 pgs.) Pin-ups by Konkle, Austin 1 2 3 4 5 7
61-74: 65-West Coast Avengers & Beta Ray Bill app. 65,66-X-Men app. 6.00
75-Last issue 2 4 6 9 12 15
Annual 1-4: (1982-85, 52 pgs.) 6.00
NOTE: ***Austin** c-3i, 18i, 61i. **Byrne** a-74i; c-56, 57, 74. **Ditko** a-59-75p, Annual 4. **Golden** c-7-12, 19. **Guice** a-61i; c-55, 58, 60p, 70p. **Layton** a-59i, 72i; c-15, 59i, 69. **Miller** c-2p?, 3p, 17p, 18p. **Russell** a(i)-64, 65, 67, 69, 71, 75; c-64, 65i, 66, 71i, 75. **Severin** c-41p. **Sienkiewicz** a-53i; c-46, 47, 52-54, 68, 71p, Annual 2. **Simonson** c-18. **P. Smith** c-59p. **Starlin** c-67. **Zeck** c-50.*

ROM (Based on the Parker Brothers toy) (Also see Rom & The Micronauts)
IDW Publishing: Jul, 2016 - No. 14, Aug, 2017 ($4.99/$3.99)
1-($4.99) Ryall & Gage-s/Messina-a 5.00
2-14-($3.99) 2-4-Revolution tie-in. 2-G.I. Joe app. 5-Transformers app. 4.00
Annual 2017 (1/17, $7.99) Origin of Rom; Ryall & Gage-s/Messina-a 8.00
... First Strike 1 (10/17, $3.99) Part of the Hasbro character x-over; Gage-s/Panda-a 4.00
FCBD 2016 Edition #0 - (5/16, giveaway) Prelude to series; Action Man flip book 3.00
...: Revolution (9/16, $3.99) Revolution x-over; Ryall-s/Gage-a; multiple covers 4.00

ROMANCE (See True Stories of...)

ROMANCE AND CONFESSION STORIES (See Giant Comics Edition)
St. John Publishing Co.: No date (1949) (25¢, 100 pgs.)
1-Baker-c/a; remaindered St. John love comics 97 194 291 621 1061 1500

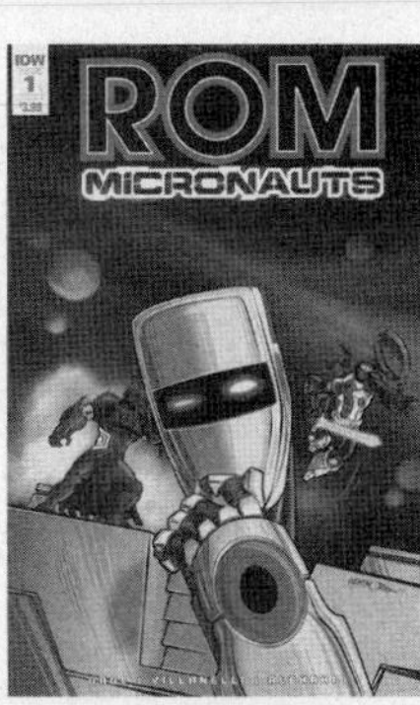

Rom & the Micronauts #1 © Hasbro

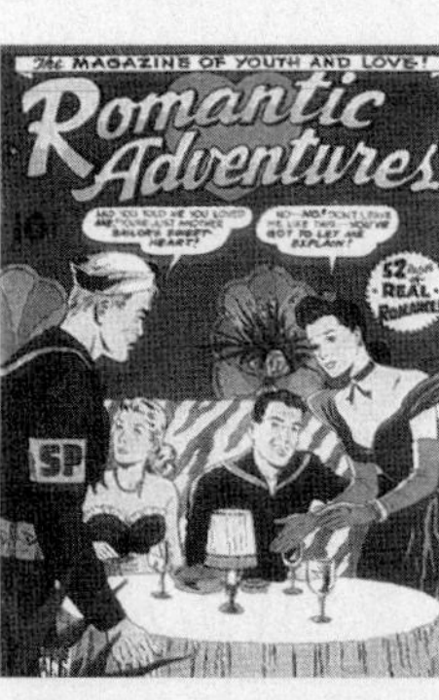

Romantic Adventures #3 © ACG

Romantic Story #16 © FAW

ROMANCE DIARY
Marvel Comics (CDS)(CLDS): Dec, 1949 - No. 2, Mar, 1950

	GD 2.0	VG 4.0	FN 6.0	VF 8.0	VF/NM 9.0	NM- 9.2
1,2-Photo-c	19	38	57	112	179	245

ROMANCE OF FLYING, THE
David McKay Publications: 1942

	GD 2.0	VG 4.0	FN 6.0	VF 8.0	VF/NM 9.0	NM- 9.2
Feature Books 33 (nn)-WW II photos	18	36	54	105	165	225

ROMANCES OF MOLLY MANTON (See Molly Manton)

ROMANCES OF NURSE HELEN GRANT, THE
Atlas Comics (VPI): Aug, 1957

	GD 2.0	VG 4.0	FN 6.0	VF 8.0	VF/NM 9.0	NM- 9.2
1	16	32	48	94	147	200

ROMANCES OF THE WEST (Becomes Romantic Affairs #3?)
Marvel Comics (SPC): Nov, 1949 - No. 2, Mar, 1950 (52 pgs.)

	GD 2.0	VG 4.0	FN 6.0	VF 8.0	VF/NM 9.0	NM- 9.2
1-Movie photo-c of Yvonne DeCarlo & Howard Duff (Calamity Jane & Sam Bass)	27	54	81	158	259	360
2-Photo-c	17	34	51	98	154	210

ROMANCE STORIES OF TRUE LOVE (Formerly True Love Problems & Advice Illustrated)
Harvey Publications: No. 45, 5/57 - No. 50, 3/58; No. 51, 9/58 - No. 52, 11/58

	GD 2.0	VG 4.0	FN 6.0	VF 8.0	VF/NM 9.0	NM- 9.2
45-51: 45,46,48-50-Powell-a	6	12	18	31	38	45
52-Matt Baker-a	9	18	27	47	61	75

ROMANCE TALES (Formerly Western Winners #6?)
Marvel Comics (CDS): No. 7, Oct, 1949 - No. 9, April, 1950 (7-9: photo-c)

	GD 2.0	VG 4.0	FN 6.0	VF 8.0	VF/NM 9.0	NM- 9.2
7	18	36	54	105	165	225
8,9: 8-Everett-a	14	28	42	76	108	140

ROMANCE TRAIL
National Periodical Publications: July-Aug, 1949 - No. 6, May-June, 1950
(All photo-c & 52 pgs.)

	GD 2.0	VG 4.0	FN 6.0	VF 8.0	VF/NM 9.0	NM- 9.2
1-Kinstler, Toth-a; Jimmy Wakely photo-c	57	114	171	362	619	875
2-Kinstler-a; Jim Bannon photo-c	32	64	96	188	307	425
3-Tex Williams photo-c; Kinstler, Toth-a	34	68	102	199	325	450
4-Jim Bannon as Red Ryder photo-c; Toth-a	24	48	72	144	237	330
5,6: Photo-c on both. 5-Kinstler-a	22	44	66	132	216	300

ROM & THE MICRONAUTS (Based on the Parker Brothers toys)
IDW Publishing: Dec, 2017 - Present ($3.99)

	GD 2.0	VG 4.0	FN 6.0	VF 8.0	VF/NM 9.0	NM- 9.2
1,2-Gage-s/Villanelli-a; multiple covers; Baron Karza app.						4.00

ROMAN HOLIDAYS, THE (TV)
Gold Key: Feb, 1973 - No. 4, Nov, 1973 (Hanna-Barbera)

	GD 2.0	VG 4.0	FN 6.0	VF 8.0	VF/NM 9.0	NM- 9.2
1	4	8	12	27	44	60
2-4	3	6	9	17	26	35

ROMANTIC ADVENTURES (My... #49-67, covers only)
American Comics Group (B&I Publ. Co.): Mar-Apr, 1949 - No. 67, July, 1956 (Becomes My... #68 on)

	GD 2.0	VG 4.0	FN 6.0	VF 8.0	VF/NM 9.0	NM- 9.2
1	23	46	69	138	227	315
2	14	28	42	82	121	160
3-10	12	24	36	67	94	120
11-20 (4/52)	10	20	30	58	79	100
21-45,51,52: 52-Last Pre-code (2/55)	10	20	30	54	72	90
46-49-3-D effect-c/stories (TrueVision)	15	30	45	85	130	175
50-Classic cover/story "Love of A Lunatic"	61	122	183	390	670	950
53-67	9	18	27	50	65	80

NOTE: *#1-23, 52 pgs.* ***Shelly*** *a-40. Whitney c/art in many issues.*

ROMANTIC AFFAIRS (Formerly Molly Manton's Romances #2 and/or Romances of the West #2 and/or Our Love #2?)
Marvel Comics (SPC): No. 3, Mar, 1950

	GD 2.0	VG 4.0	FN 6.0	VF 8.0	VF/NM 9.0	NM- 9.2
3-Photo-c from Molly Manton's Romances #2	14	28	42	80	115	150

ROMANTIC CONFESSIONS
Hillman Periodicals: Oct, 1949 - V3#1, Apr-May, 1953

	GD 2.0	VG 4.0	FN 6.0	VF 8.0	VF/NM 9.0	NM- 9.2
V1#1-McWilliams-a	22	44	66	128	209	290
2-Briefer-a; negligee panels	14	28	42	80	115	150
3-12	13	26	39	72	101	130
V2#1,2,4-8,10-12: 2-McWilliams-a	11	22	33	64	90	115
3-Krigstein-a	13	26	39	72	101	130
9-One pg. Frazetta ad	11	22	33	64	90	115
V3#1	11	22	33	62	86	110

ROMANTIC HEARTS
Story Comics/Master/Merit Pubs.: Mar, 1951 - No. 10, Oct, 1952; July, 1953 - No. 12, July, 1955

	GD 2.0	VG 4.0	FN 6.0	VF 8.0	VF/NM 9.0	NM- 9.2
1(3/51) (1st Series)	19	38	57	111	176	240
2	12	24	36	69	97	125
3-10: Cameron-a	11	22	33	64	90	115
1(7/53) (2nd Series)-Some say #11 on-c	14	28	42	82	121	160
2	11	22	33	62	86	110
3-12	10	20	30	56	76	95

ROMANTIC LOVE
Avon Periodicals/Realistic (No #14-19): 9-10/49 - #3, 1-2/50; #4, 2-3/51 - #13, 10/52; #20, 3-4/54 - #23, 9-10/54

	GD 2.0	VG 4.0	FN 6.0	VF 8.0	VF/NM 9.0	NM- 9.2
1-c-/Avon paperback #252	41	82	123	256	428	600
2-5: 3-c-/paperback Novel Library #12. 4-c-/paperback Diversey Prize Novel #5. 5-c-/paperback Novel Library #34	26	52	78	154	252	350
6- "Thrill Crazy" marijuana story; c-/Avon paperback #207; Kinstler-a	39	78	117	231	378	525
7,8: 8-Astarita-a(2)	25	50	75	150	245	340
9-c-/paperback Novel Library #41; Kinstler-a; headlights-c	39	78	117	231	378	525
10-12: 10-c-/Avon paperback #212. 11-c-/paperback Novel Library #17; Kinstler-a. 12-c-/paperback Novel Library #13	27	54	81	160	263	365
13,21-23: 22,23-Kinstler-c	25	50	75	150	245	340
20-Kinstler-c/a	26	52	78	154	252	350
nn(1-3/53)(Realistic-r)	17	34	51	98	154	210

NOTE: ***Astarita*** *a-7, 10, 11, 21. Painted c-1-3, 5, 7-11, 13. Photo c-4, 6.*

ROMANTIC LOVE
Quality Comics Group: 1963-1964

	GD 2.0	VG 4.0	FN 6.0	VF 8.0	VF/NM 9.0	NM- 9.2
I.W. Reprint #2,3,8,11: 2-r/Romantic Love #2	2	4	6	11	16	20

ROMANTIC MARRIAGE (Cinderella Love #25 on)
Ziff-Davis/St. John No. 18 on (#1-8: 52 pgs.): #1-3 (1950, no months); #4, 5-6/51 - #17, 9/52; #18, 9/53 - #24, 9/54

	GD 2.0	VG 4.0	FN 6.0	VF 8.0	VF/NM 9.0	NM- 9.2
1-Photo-c; Cary Grant/Betsy Drake photo back-c.	28	56	84	165	270	375
2-Painted-c; Anderson-a (also #15)	19	38	57	109	172	235
3-9: 3,4,8,9-Painted-c; 5-7-Photo-c	17	34	51	98	154	210
10-Unusual format; front-c is a painted-c; back-c is a photo-c complete with logo, price, etc.	28	56	84	165	270	375
11-17 13-Photo-c. 15-Signed story by Anderson. 17-(9/52)-Last Z-D issue	15	30	45	88	137	185
18-22: 20-Photo-c	15	30	45	88	137	185
23-Baker-c; all stories are reprinted from #15	41	82	123	256	428	600
24-Baker-c	81	162	243	518	884	1250

ROMANTIC PICTURE NOVELETTES
Magazine Enterprises: 1946

	GD 2.0	VG 4.0	FN 6.0	VF 8.0	VF/NM 9.0	NM- 9.2
1-Mary Worth-r; Creig Flessel-c	19	38	57	111	176	240

ROMANTIC SECRETS (Becomes Time For Love)
Fawcett/Charlton Comics No. 5 (10/55) on: Sept, 1949 - No. 39, 4/53; No. 5, 10/55 - No. 52, 11/64 (#1-39: photo-c)

	GD 2.0	VG 4.0	FN 6.0	VF 8.0	VF/NM 9.0	NM- 9.2
1-(52 pg. issues begin, end #?)	18	36	54	103	162	220
2,3	11	22	33	62	86	110
4,9-Evans-a	12	24	36	67	94	120
5-8,10(9/50)	9	18	27	52	69	85
11-23	9	18	27	47	61	75
24-Evans-a	9	18	27	52	69	85
25-39('53)	8	16	24	44	57	70
5 (Charlton, 2nd Series)(10/55, formerly Negro Romances #4)	10	20	30	58	79	100
6-10	8	16	24	44	57	70
11-20	4	8	12	22	35	48
21-35	3	6	9	19	30	40
36-52('64)	3	6	9	16	23	30

NOTE: ***Bailey*** *a-20.* ***Powell*** *a(1st series)-5, 7, 10, 12, 16, 17, 20, 26, 29, 33, 34, 36, 37.* ***Sekowsky*** *a-26.* ***Swayze*** *a(1st series)-16, 18, 19, 23, 26-28, 31, 32, 39.*

ROMANTIC STORY (Cowboy Love #28 on)
Fawcett/Charlton Comics No. 23 on: 11/49 - #22, Sum, 1953; #23, 5/54 - #27, 12/54; #28, 8/55 - #130, 11/73

	GD 2.0	VG 4.0	FN 6.0	VF 8.0	VF/NM 9.0	NM- 9.2
1-Photo-c begin, end #24; 52 pgs. begins	18	36	54	103	162	220
2	11	22	33	62	86	110
3-5	10	20	30	54	72	90
6-14	9	18	27	50	65	80
15-Evans-a	10	20	30	54	72	90
16-22(Sum, '53; last Fawcett issue). 21-Toth-a?	8	16	24	42	54	65
23-39: 26,29-Wood swipes	7	14	21	37	46	55
40-(100 pgs.)	11	22	33	64	90	115

Ronald McDonald #4 © McDonald's

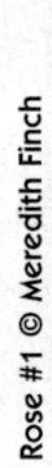

Rose #1 © Meredith Finch

Rose and Thorn #1 © DC

	GD 2.0	VG 4.0	FN 6.0	VF 8.0	VF/NM 9.0	NM- 9.2
41-50	3	6	9	20	31	42
51-80: 57-Hypo needle story	3	6	9	16	23	30
81-99	2	4	6	10	14	18
100	2	4	6	13	28	22
101-130: 120-Bobby Sherman pin-up	2	4	6	9	12	15

NOTE: ***Jim Aparo** a-94. **Powell** a-7, 8, 16, 20, 30. **Marcus Swayze** a-2, 12, 20, 32.*

ROMANTIC THRILLS (See Fox Giants)

ROMANTIC WESTERN
Fawcett Publications: Winter, 1949 - No. 3, June, 1950 (All Photo-c)

	GD 2.0	VG 4.0	FN 6.0	VF 8.0	VF/NM 9.0	NM- 9.2
1	22	44	66	128	209	290
2-(Spr/50)-Williamson, McWilliams-a	20	40	60	114	182	250
3	15	30	45	85	130	175

ROMEO TUBBS (...That Lovable Teenager; formerly My Secret Life)
Fox Features Syndicate/Green Publ. Co. No. 27: No. 26, 5/50 - No. 28, 7/50; No. 1, 1950; No. 27, 12/52

	GD 2.0	VG 4.0	FN 6.0	VF 8.0	VF/NM 9.0	NM- 9.2
26-Teen-age	13	26	39	74	105	135
28 (7/50)	11	22	33	64	90	115
27 (12/52)-Contains Pedro on inside; Wood-a (exist?)	15	30	45	90	140	190

ROMULUS
Image Comics: Oct, 2016 - No. 4, May, 2017 ($3.99)

1-4-Bryan Hill-s/Nelson Blake II-a 4.00

ROM VS. TRANSFORMERS: SHINING ARMOR
IDW Publishing: Jul, 2017 - No. 5, Nov, 2017 ($3.99, limited series)

1-5-Barber & Gage-s/Milne-a 4.00

RONALD McDONALD (TV)
Charlton Press: Sept, 1970 - No. 4, March, 1971

	GD 2.0	VG 4.0	FN 6.0	VF 8.0	VF/NM 9.0	NM- 9.2
1-Bill Yates-a in all	7	14	21	48	89	130
2-4: 2 & 3 both dated Jan, 1971	5	10	15	30	50	70
V2#1-4-Special reprint for McDonald systems; new cover art on each; "Not for resale" on cover	5	10	15	34	60	85

RONIN
DC Comics: July, 1983 - No. 6, Aug, 1984 ($2.50, limited series, 52 pgs.)

	GD 2.0	VG 4.0	FN 6.0	VF 8.0	VF/NM 9.0	NM- 9.2
1-5-Frank Miller-c/a/scripts in all	2	4	6	8	11	14
6-Scarcer; has fold-out poster.	2	4	6	11	16	20
Trade paperback (1987, $12.95)-Reprints #1-6						18.00

RONNA
Knight Press: Apr, 1997 ($2.95, B&W, one-shot)

1-Beau Smith-s 3.00

ROOK (See Eerie Magazine & Warren Presents: The Rook)
Warren Publications: Oct, 1979 - No. 14, April, 1982 (B&W magazine)

	GD 2.0	VG 4.0	FN 6.0	VF 8.0	VF/NM 9.0	NM- 9.2
1-Nino-a/Corben-c; with 8 pg. color insert	3	6	9	16	23	30
2-4,6,7: 2-Voltar by Alcala begins. 3,4-Toth-a	2	4	6	9	13	16
5,8-14: 11-Zorro-s. 12-14-Eagle by Severin	2	4	6	9	13	16

ROOK
Harris Comics: No. 0, Jun, 1995 - No. 4, 1995 ($2.95)

0-4: 0-short stories (3) w/preview. 4-Brereton-c. 3.00

ROOK, THE
Dark Horse Comics: Oct, 2015 - No. 4, Jan, 2016 ($3.99)

1-4-Steven Grant-s/Paul Gulacy-a/c 4.00

ROOKIE COP (Formerly Crime and Justice?)
Charlton Comics: No. 27, Nov, 1955 - No. 33, Aug, 1957

	GD 2.0	VG 4.0	FN 6.0	VF 8.0	VF/NM 9.0	NM- 9.2
27	9	18	27	52	69	85
28-33	7	14	21	35	43	50

ROOM 222 (TV)
Dell Publishing Co.: Jan, 1970; No. 2, May, 1970 - No. 4, Jan, 1971

	GD 2.0	VG 4.0	FN 6.0	VF 8.0	VF/NM 9.0	NM- 9.2
1	5	10	15	34	60	85
2-4-Photo-c. 3-Marijuana story. 4 r/#1	4	8	12	23	37	50

ROOTIE KAZOOTIE (TV)(See 3-D-ell)
Dell Publishing Co.: No. 415, Aug, 1952 - No. 6, Oct-Dec, 1954

	GD 2.0	VG 4.0	FN 6.0	VF 8.0	VF/NM 9.0	NM- 9.2
Four Color 415 (#1)	9	18	27	59	117	175
Four Color 459,502(#2,3), 4(4-6/54)-6	6	12	18	41	76	110

ROOTS OF THE SWAMP THING
DC Comics: July, 1986 - No.5, Nov, 1986 ($2.00, Baxter paper, 52 pgs.)

1-5: r/Swamp Thing #1-10 by Wrightson & House of Mystery-r. 1-new Wrightson-c (2-5 reprinted covers). 5.00

ROSE (See Bone)
Cartoon Books: Nov, 2000 - No. 3, Feb, 2002 ($5.95, lim. series, square-bound)

	NM- 9.2
1-3-Prequel to Bone; Jeff Smith-s/Charles Vess painted-a/c	6.00
HC (2001, $29.95) r/#1-3; new Vess cover painting	30.00
SC (2002, $19.95) r/#1-3; new Vess cover painting	20.00
1-($6.00)-Blood & Glory Edition	6.00

ROSE
Image Comics: Apr, 2017 - Present ($3.99)

1-8-Meredith Finch-s/Ig Guara-a 4.00

ROSE AND THORN
DC Comics: Feb, 2004 - No. 6, July, 2004 ($2.95, limited series)

1-6-Simone-s/Melo-a/Hughes-c 3.00

ROSWELL: LITTLE GREEN MAN (See Simpsons Comics #19-22)
Bongo Comics: 1996 - No. 6 ($2.95, quarterly)

	NM- 9.2
1-6	4.00
...Walks Among Us ('97, $12.95, TPB) r/ #1-3 & Simpsons flip books	13.00

ROUGH RIDERS
AfterShock Comics: Apr, 2016 - No. 7, Nov, 2016 ($3.99)

	NM- 9.2
1-7: 1-Teddy Roosevelt, Annie Oakley, Houdini, Jack Johnson, Thomas Edison team	4.00
... Nation 1 (11/16, $3.99) Dossier of other Rough Rider teams; art by various	4.00

ROUGH RIDERS: RIDERS ON THE STORM
AfterShock Comics: Feb, 2017 - No. 6, Sept, 2017 ($3.99)

1-6-Glass-s/Olliffe-a; Monk Eastman joins team 4.00

ROUND TABLE OF AMERICA: PERSONALITY CRISIS (See Big Bang Comics)
Image Comics: Aug, 2005 ($3.50, one-shot)

1-Carlos Rodriguez-a/Pedro Angosto-s 3.50

ROUNDUP (...Western Crime Stories)
D. S. Publishing Co.: July-Aug, 1948 - No. 5, Mar-Apr, 1949 (All 52 pgs.)

	GD 2.0	VG 4.0	FN 6.0	VF 8.0	VF/NM 9.0	NM- 9.2
1-Kiefer-a	20	40	60	114	182	250
2-5: 2-Marijuana drug mention story	15	30	45	85	130	175

ROUTE 666
CrossGeneration Comics: July, 2002 - No. 22, Jun, 2004 ($2.95)

1-22-Bedard-s/Moline-a in most. 5-Richards-a. 15-McCrea-a 3.00

ROWANS RUIN
BOOM! Studios: Oct, 2015 - No. 4, Jan, 2016 ($3.99, limited series)

1-4-Mike Carey-s/Mike Perkins-a. 1-Multiple covers 4.00

ROYAL CITY
Image Comics: Mar, 2017 - Present ($4.99/$3.99)

	NM- 9.2
1-($4.99) Jeff Lemire-s/a	5.00
2-10-($3.99)	4.00

ROYAL ROY
Marvel Comics (Star Comics): May, 1985 - No.6, Mar, 1986 (Children's book)

1-6 4.00

ROYALS (The Inhumans) (Leads into Inhumans: Judgment Day)
Marvel Comics: Jun, 2017 - No. 12, Feb, 2018 ($3.99)

1-12: 1-Ewing-s/Meyers-a; Marvel Boy app. 2-Maximus returns. 4,5-Ronan app. 4.00

ROYALS, THE: MASTERS OF WAR
DC Comics (Vertigo): Apr, 2014 - No. 6, Sept, 2014 ($2.99, limited series)

1-6-Rob Williams-s/Simon Coleby-a/c; super-powered Royal families during WWII 3.00

ROY CAMPANELLA, BASEBALL HERO
Fawcett Publications: 1950 (Brooklyn Dodgers)

	GD 2.0	VG 4.0	FN 6.0	VF 8.0	VF/NM 9.0	NM- 9.2
nn-Photo-c; life story	62	124	186	394	677	960

ROY ROGERS (See March of Comics #17, 35, 47, 62, 68, 73, 77, 86, 91, 100, 105, 116, 121, 131, 136, 146, 151, 161, 167, 176, 191, 206, 221, 236, 250)

ROY ROGERS AND TRIGGER
Gold Key: Apr, 1967

	GD 2.0	VG 4.0	FN 6.0	VF 8.0	VF/NM 9.0	NM- 9.2
1-Photo-c; reprints	4	8	12	27	44	60

ROY ROGERS ANNUAL
Wilson Publ. Co., Toronto/Dell: 1947 ("Giant Edition" on-c)(132 pgs., 50¢)

nn-Seven known copies. Front and back cover art are from Roy Rogers #2. Stories reprinted from Roy Rogers #2, Four Color #137 and Four Color #153. (A copy in VG/FN was sold in 1986 for $400, in 1996 for $1200 & in 2000 for $1500; a FN+ sold for $1,650;

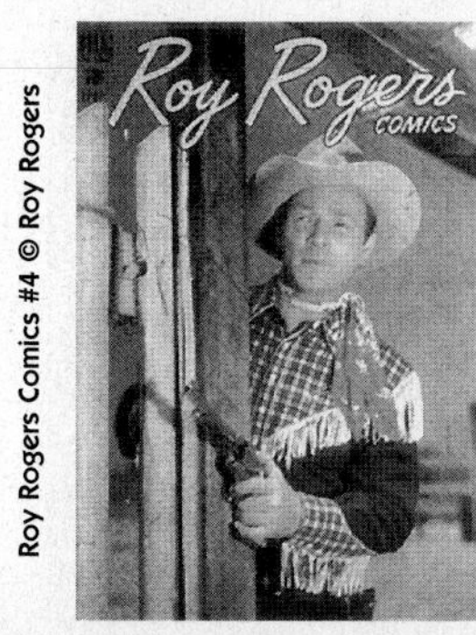

Roy Rogers Comics #4 © Roy Rogers

The Ruff & Reddy Show #2 © H-B

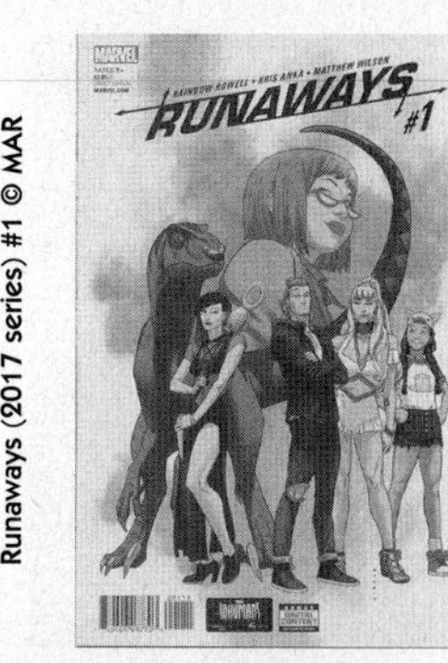

Runaways (2017 series) #1 © MAR

GD VG FN VF VF/NM NM-
2.0 4.0 6.0 8.0 9.0 9.2

a GD sold for $448 in 2008, a FN sold for $717 in 2009 and a FR sold for $156 in 2015.)

ROY ROGERS COMICS (See Western Roundup under Dell Giants)
Dell Publishing Co.: No. 38, 4/44 - No. 177, 12/47 (#38-166: 52 pgs.)

Four Color 38 (1944)-49 pg. story; photo front/back-c on all 4-Color issues (1st western comic with photo-c) 152 304 456 1254 2827 4400
Four Color 63 (1945)-Color photos on all four-c 38 76 114 285 641 1000
Four Color 86,95 (1945) 28 56 84 202 451 700
Four Color 109 (1946) 21 42 63 147 324 500
Four Color 117,124,137,144 17 34 51 117 259 400
Four Color 153,160,166: 166-48 pg. story 15 30 45 105 233 360
Four Color 177 (36 pgs.)-32 pg. story 15 30 45 100 220 340
HC (Dark Horse Books, 8/08, $49.95) r/Four Color #38,63,86,95,109; Roy Rogers Jr intro. 50.00

ROY ROGERS COMICS (...& Trigger #92(8/55)-on)(Roy starred in Republic movies, radio & TV) (Singing cowboy) (Also see Dale Evans, It Really Happened #8, Queen of the West Dale Evans, & Roy Rogers' Trigger)
Dell Publishing Co.: Jan, 1948 - No. 145, Sept-Oct, 1961 (#1-19: 36 pgs.)

1-Roy, his horse Trigger, & Chuck Wagon Charley's Tales begin; photo-c begin, end #145 60 122 183 488 1094 1700
2 20 40 60 138 307 475
3-5 14 28 42 96 211 325
6-10 12 24 36 80 173 265
11-19: 19-Chuckwagon Charley's Tales ends 10 20 30 68 144 220
20 (52 pgs.)-Trigger feature begins, ends #46 10 20 30 69 147 225
21-30 (52 pgs.) 9 18 27 60 120 180
31-46 (52 pgs.): 37-X-Mas-c 8 16 24 51 96 140
47-56 (36 pgs.): 47-Chuck Wagon Charley's Tales returns, ends #133. 49-X-mas-c. 55-Last photo back-c 6 12 18 40 73 105
57 (52 pgs.)-Heroin drug propaganda story 6 12 18 41 76 110
58-70 (52 pgs.): 58-Heroin drug use/dealing story. 61-X-Mas-c 6 12 18 40 73 105
71-80 (52 pgs.): 73-X-Mas-c 5 10 15 35 63 90
81-91 (36 pgs. #81-on): 85-X-Mas-c 5 10 15 34 60 85
92-99,101-110,112-118: 92-Title changed to Roy Rogers and Trigger (8/55) 5 10 15 33 57 80
100-Trigger feature returns, ends #131 6 12 18 37 66 95
111,119-124-Toth-a 6 12 18 38 69 100
125-131: 125-Toth-a (1 pg.) 5 10 15 31 53 75
132-144-Manning-a. 132-1st Dale Evans-sty by Russ Manning. 138,144-Dale Evans featured 5 10 15 34 60 85
145-Last issue 6 12 18 40 73 105
NOTE: *Buscema a-74-108(2 stories each). Manning a-123, 124, 132-144. Marsh a-110. Photo back-c No. 1-9, 11-35, 38-55.*

ROY ROGERS' TRIGGER
Dell Publishing Co.: No. 329, May, 1951 - No. 17, June-Aug, 1955

Four Color 329 (#1)-Painted-c 14 28 42 97 214 330
2 (9-11/51)-Photo-c 10 20 30 64 132 200
3-5: 3-Painted-c begin, end #17, most by S. Savitt 6 12 18 38 69 100
6-17: Title merges with Roy Rogers after #17 5 10 15 31 53 75

ROY ROGERS WESTERN CLASSICS
AC Comics: 1989 -No. 4 ($2.95/$3.95, 44pgs.) (24 pgs. color, 16 pgs. B&W)

1-4: 1-Dale Evans-r by Manning, Trigger-r by Buscema; photo covers & interior photos by Roy & Dale. 2-Buscema-r (3); photo-c & B&W photos inside. 3-Dale Evans-r by Manning; Trigger-r by Buscema plus other Buscema-r; photo-c 4.00

RUDOLPH, THE RED-NOSED REINDEER
National Per. Publ.: 1950 - No. 13, Winter, 1962-63 (Issues are not numbered)

1950 issue (#1); Grossman-c/a in all 30 60 90 177 289 400
1951-53 issues (3 total) 19 38 57 111 176 240
1954/55, 55/56, 56/57 17 34 51 98 154 210
1957/58, 58/59, 59/60, 60/61, 61/62 9 18 27 63 129 195
1962/63 (rare)(84 pgs.)(shows "Annual" in indicia) 18 36 54 124 275 425
NOTE: *13 total issues published. Has games & puzzles also.*

RUDOLPH, THE RED-NOSED REINDEER (Also see Limited Collectors' Edition C-20, C-24, C-33, C-42, C-50; and All-New Collectors' Edition C-53 & C-60)
National Per. Publ.: Christmas 1972 (Treasury-size)

nn-Precursor to Limited Collectors' Edition title (scarce) (implied to be Lim. Coll .Ed. C-20) 19 38 57 131 291 450

RUFF AND REDDY (TV)
Dell Publ. Co.: No. 937, 9/58 - No. 12, 1-3/62 (Hanna-Barbera)(#9 on: 15¢)

Four Color 937(#1)(1st Hanna-Barbera comic book) 10 20 30 67 141 215
Four Color 981,1038 7 14 21 44 82 120
4(1-3/60)-12: 8-Last 10¢ issue 6 12 18 38 69 100

RUFF & REDDY SHOW, THE
DC Comics: Dec, 2017 - No. 6 ($3.99, limited series)

1-5-Ruff & Ready in the real world; Chaykin-s/Mac Rey-a; 2 covers (Chaykin & Rey) 4.00

RUGGED ACTION (Strange Stories of Suspense #5 on)
Atlas Comics (CSI): Dec, 1954 - No. 4, June, 1955

1-Brodsky-c 17 34 51 98 154 210
2-4: 2-Last precode (2/55) 13 26 39 74 105 135
NOTE: *Ayers a-2, 3. Maneely c-2, 3. Severin a-2.*

RUGRATS (TV) (Nickelodeon cartoon)
BOOM! Studios (kaboom!): Oct, 2017 - Present ($3.99)

1-5: 1-3,5-Box Brown-s/Lisa DuBois-a; multiple covers 4.00

RUINS
Marvel Comics (Alterniverse): July, 1995 - No. 2, Sept, 1995 ($5.00, painted, limited series)

1,2: Phil Sheldon from Marvels; Warren Ellis scripts; acetate-c 6.00
Reprint (2009, $4.99) r/#1,2; cover gallery 5.00

RULAH JUNGLE GODDESS (Formerly Zoot; I Loved #28 on) (Also see All Top Comics & Terrors of the Jungle)
Fox Feature Syndicate: No. 17, Aug, 1948 - No. 27, June, 1949

17 142 284 426 909 1555 2200
18-Classic girl-fight interior splash 87 174 261 553 952 1350
19,20 84 168 252 538 919 1300
21-Used in **SOTI**, pg. 388,389 87 174 261 553 952 1350
22-Used in **SOTI**, pg. 22,23 84 168 252 538 919 1300
23-27 65 130 195 416 708 1000
NOTE: *Kamen c-17-19, 21, 22.*

RUNAWAY, THE (See Movie Classics)

RUNAWAYS
Marvel Comics: July, 2003 - No. 18, Nov, 2004 ($2.95/$2.25/$2.99)

1-($2.95) Vaughan-s/Alphona-a/Jo Chen-c 4.00
2-9-($2.50) 3.00
10-18-($2.99) 11,12-Miyazawa-a; Cloak and Dagger app. 16-The mole revealed 3.00
Hardcover (2005, $34.99) oversized r/#1-18; proposal & sketch pages; Vaughan intro. 35.00
Marvel Age Runaways Vol. 1: Pride and Joy (2004, $7.99, digest size) r/#1-6 8.00
...Vol. 2: Teenage Wasteland (2004, $7.99, digest size) r/#7-12 8.00
...Vol. 3: The Good Die Young (2004, $7.99, digest size) r/#13-18 8.00

RUNAWAYS (Also see X-Men/Runaways 2006 FCBD Edition)
Marvel Comics: Apr, 2005 - No. 30, Aug, 2008 ($2.99)

1-24: 1-6-Vaughan-s/Alphona-a/Jo Chen-c. 7,8-Miyazawa-a/Bachalo-c. 11-Spider-Man app. 12-New Avengers app. 18-Gert killed 3.00
25-30-Joss Whedon-s/Michael Ryan-a. 25-Punisher app. 3.00
...: Dead End Kids HC (2008, $19.99) r/#25-30 20.00
... Saga (2007, $3.99) re-caps the 2 series thru #24; 4 new pages w/Ramos-a; Ramos-c 4.00
Hardcover (2006, $24.99) oversized r/#1-12 & X-Men/Runaways; script & sketch pages 25.00
Hardcover Vol. 3 (2007, $24.99) oversized r/#13-24; sketch pages 25.00
...Vol. 4: True Believers (2006, $7.99, digest size) r/#1-6 8.00
...Vol. 5: Escape To New York (2006, $7.99, digest size) r/#7-12 8.00
...Vol. 6: Parental Guidance (2006, $7.99, digest size) r/#13-18 8.00

RUNAWAYS (3rd series)
Marvel Comics: Oct, 2008 - No. 14, Nov, 2009 ($2.99/$3.99)

1-9,11-14: 1-6-Terry Moore-s/Humberto Ramos-a/c. 7-9-Miyazawa-a 3.00
10-($3.99) Wolverine & the X-Men app.; Yost & Asmus-s; Pichelli & Rios-a; Lafuente-c 4.00

RUNAWAYS (Secret Wars Battleworld tie-in)
Marvel Comics: Aug, 2015 - No. 4, Nov, 2015 ($3.99, limited series)

1-4-Noelle Stevenson-s/Sanford Greene-a 4.00

RUNAWAYS
Marvel Comics: Nov, 2017 - Present ($3.99)

1-6: 1-Gert revived; Rowell-s/Anka-a 4.00
... Halloween Comic Fest 2017 1 (12/17, giveaway) r/#1 (2003) first app. 3.00

RUN BABY RUN
Logos International: 1974 (39¢, Christian religious)

nn-By Tony Tallarico from Nicky Cruz's book 2 4 6 11 16 20

RUN, BUDDY, RUN (TV)
Gold Key: June, 1967 (Photo-c)

1 (10204-706) 3 6 9 17 26 35

RUNE (See Curse of Rune, Sludge & all other Ultraverse titles for previews)

Ruse #4 © CRO

Rusty, Boy Detective #2 © LEV

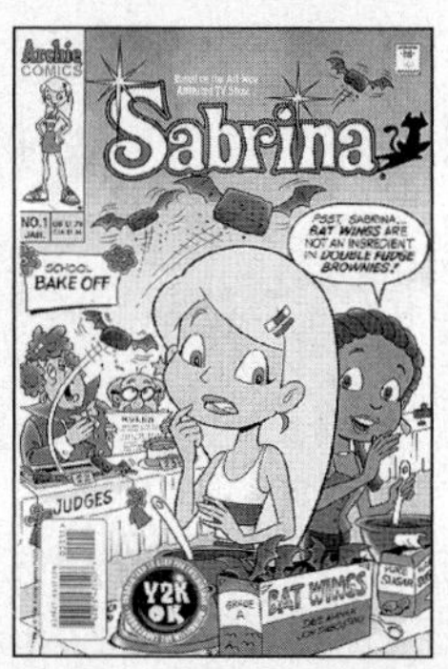

Sabrina V2 #1 © ACP

GD VG FN VF VF/NM NM-
2.0 4.0 6.0 8.0 9.0 9.2

Malibu Comics (Ultraverse): 1994 - No. 9, Apr, 1995 ($1.95)

0-Obtained by sending coupons from 11 comics; came w/Solution #0, poster, temporary tattoo, card 1 2 3 5 6 8
1,2,4-9: 1-Barry Windsor-Smith-c/a/stories begin, ends #6. 5-1st app. of Gemini. 6-Prime & Mantra app. 3.00
1-(1/94)-"Ashcan" edition flip book w/Wrath #1 3.00
1-Ultra 5000 Limited silver foil edition 6.00
3-(3/94, $3.50, 68 pgs.)-Flip book w/Ultraverse Premiere #1 4.00
Giant Size 1 ($2.50, 44 pgs.)-B.Smith story & art. 4.00

RUNE (2nd Series)(Formerly Curse of Rune)(See Ultraverse Unlimited #1)
Malibu Comics (Ultraverse): Infinity, Sept, 1995 - V2#7, Apr, 1996 ($1.50)

Infinity, V2#1-7: Infinity-Black September tie-in; black-c & painted-c exist. 1,3-7-Marvel's Adam Warlock app; regular & painted-c exist. 2-Flip book w/ "Phoenix Resurrection" Pt. 6 3.00
...Vs. Venom 1 (12/95, $3.95) 4.00

RUNE: HEARTS OF DARKNESS
Malibu Comics (Ultraverse): Sept, 1996 - No. 3, Nov, 1996 ($1.50, lim. series)

1-3: Moench scripts & Kyle Hotz-c/a; flip books w/6 pg. Rune story by the Pander Bros. 3.00

RUNE/SILVER SURFER
Marvel Comics/Malibu Comics (Ultraverse): Apr, 1995 ($5.95/$2.95, one-shot)

1 ($5.95, direct market)-BWS-c 6.00
1 ($2.95, newstand)-BWS-c 3.00
1-Collector's limited edition 6.00

RUNLOVEKILL
Image Comics: Apr, 2015 - No. 8 ($2.99, limited series)

1-4: 1-Tsuei-s/Canete-a 3.00

RUSE (Also see Archard's Agents)
CrossGeneration Comics: Nov, 2001 - No. 26, Jan, 2004 ($2.95)

1-Waid-s/Guice & Perkins-a 5.00
2-26: 6-Jeff Johnson-a. 11,15-Paul Ryan-a. 12-Last Waid-s 3.00
Enter the Detective Vol. 1 TPB (2002, $15.95) r/#1-6; Guice-c 16.00
...: The Silent Partner Vol. 2 (3/03, $15.95, TPB) r/#7-12 16.00
...: Criminal Intent Vol. 3 ('03, $15.95, TPB) r/#13-18 16.00
Traveler 1,2 ($9.95): Digest-size editions of the TPBs 10.00

RUSE
Marvel Comics: May, 2011 - No. 4 ($2.99, limited series)

1-4-Waid-s/Guice-c. 1,3,4-Pierfederici-a 3.00

RUSH CITY
DC Comics: Sept, 2006 - No. 6, May, 2007 ($2.99, limited series)

1-6: 1-Dixon-s/Green-a/Jock-c. 2,3-Black Canary app. 3.00

RUSTLERS, THE (See Zane Grey Four Color 532)

RUSTY, BOY DETECTIVE
Good Comics/Lev Gleason: Mar-April, 1955 - No. 5, Nov, 1955

1-Bob Wood, Carl Hubbell-a begins 9 18 27 52 69 85
2-5 7 14 21 37 46 55

RUSTY COMICS (Formerly Kid Movie Comics; Rusty and Her Family #21, 22; The Kelleys #23 on; see Millie The Model)
Marvel Comics (HPC): No. 12, Apr, 1947 - No. 22, Sept, 1949

12-Mitzi app. 30 60 90 177 289 400
13 18 36 54 103 162 220
14-Wolverton's Powerhouse Pepper (4 pgs.) plus Kurtzman's "Hey Look" 27 54 81 158 259 360
15-17-Kurtzman's "Hey Look" 20 40 60 117 189 260
18,19 16 32 48 94 147 200
20-Kurtzman-a (5 pgs.) 20 40 60 120 195 270
21,22-Kurtzman-a (17 & 22 pgs.) 26 52 78 154 252 350

RUSTY DUGAN (See Holyoke One-Shot #2)

RUSTY RILEY
Dell Publishing Co.: No. 418, Aug, 1952 - No. 554, April, 1954 (Frank Godwin strip reprints)

Four Color 418 (...a Boy, a Horse, and a Dog #1) 6 12 18 41 76 110
Four Color 451(2/53), 486 ('53), 554 5 10 15 30 50 70

RUULE
Beckett Comics: Dec, 2003 - No. 5, Apr, 2004 ($2.99)

1-5-David Mack-c/Mike Hawthorne-a 3.00

RUULE: KISS & TELL
Beckett Comics: Jun, 2004 - No. 8 ($1.99)

1-8: 1-Amano-s/c; Rousseau-a. 4-Maleev-c 3.00
TPB (2005, $19.99) r/#1-8 20.00

RYDER OF THE STORM
Radical Comics: Oct, 2010 - No. 3, Apr, 2011 ($4.99, limited series)

1-3-David Hine-s/Wayne Nichols-a 5.00

SAARI ("The Jungle Goddess")
P. L. Publishing Co.: November, 1951

1 53 106 159 334 567 800

SABAN POWERHOUSE (TV)
Acclaim Books: 1997 ($4.50, digest size)

1,2-Power Rangers, BeetleBorgs, and others 4.50

SABAN PRESENTS POWER RANGERS TURBO VS. BEETLEBORGS METALLIX (TV)
Acclaim Books: 1997 ($4.50, digest size, one-shot)

nn 4.50

SABAN'S GO GO POWER RANGERS
BOOM! Studios: Jul, 2017 - Present ($3.99)

1-7: 1-Parrott-s/Mora-a; multiple covers; retells 1st meeting with Rita Repulsa 4.00

SABAN'S MIGHTY MORPHIN POWER RANGERS
Hamilton Comics: Dec, 1994 - No. 6, May, 1995 ($1.95, limited series)

1-6: 1-w/bound-in Power Ranger Barcode Card 4.00

SABAN'S MIGHTY MORPHIN POWER RANGERS (TV)
Marvel Comics: 1995 - No. 8, 1996 ($1.75)

1-8 4.00

SABAN'S POWER RANGERS: AFTERSHOCK
BOOM! Studios: Mar, 2017 ($14.99, SC)

SC - Sequel to the 2017 movie; Parrott-s/Werneck-a; movie photo-c 15.00

SABLE (Formerly Jon Sable, Freelance; also see Mike Grell's...)
First Comics: Mar, 1988 - No. 27, May, 1990 ($1.75/$1.95)

1-27: 10-Begin $1.95-c 3.00

SABLE & FORTUNE (Also see Silver Sable and the Wild Pack)
Marvel Comics: Mar, 2006 - No. 4, June, 2006 ($2.99, limited series)

1-4-John Burns-a/Brendan Cahill-s 3.00

SABRE (See Eclipse Graphic Album Series)
Eclipse Comics: Aug, 1982 - No. 14, Aug, 1985 (Baxter paper #4 on)

1-14: 1-Sabre & Morrigan Tales begin. 4-6-Incredible Seven origin 3.00

SABRETOOTH (See Iron Fist, Power Man, X-Factor #10 & X-Men)
Marvel Comics: Aug, 1993 - No. 4, Nov, 1993 ($2.95, lim. series, coated paper)

1-4: 1-Die-cut-c. 3-Wolverine app. 5.00
...Special 1 "In the Red Zone" (1995, $4.95) Chromium wraparound-c 6.00
V2 #1 (1/98, $5.95, one-shot) Wildchild app. 6.00
Trade paperback (12/94, $12.95) r/#1-4 13.00

SABRETOOTH
Marvel Comics: Dec, 2004 - No. 4, Feb, 2005 ($2.99, limited series)

1-4-Sears-a. 3,4-Wendigo app. 3.00
...: Open Season TPB (2005, $9.99) r/#1-4 10.00

SABRETOOTH AND MYSTIQUE (See Mystique and Sabretooth)

SABRETOOTH CLASSIC
Marvel Comics: May, 1994 - No. 15, July, 1995 ($1.50)

1-15: 1-3-r/Power Man & Iron Fist #66,78,84. 4-r/Spec. S-M #116. 9-Uncanny X-Men #212, 10-r/Uncanny X-Men #213. 11-r/ Daredevil #238. 12-r/Classic X-Men #10 3.00

SABRETOOTH: MARY SHELLEY OVERDRIVE
Marvel Comics: Aug, 2002 - No. 4, Nov, 2002 ($2.99, limited series)

1-4-Jolley-s; Harris-c 3.00

SABRINA (Volume 2) (Based on animated series)
Archie Publications: Jan, 2000 - No. 104, Sept, 2009 ($1.79/$1.99/$2.19/$2.25/$2.50)

1-Teen-age Witch magically reverted to 12 years old 1 3 4 6 8 10
2-10: 4-Begin $1.99-c 4.00
11-104: 38-Sabrina aged back to 16 years old. 39-Begin $2.19-c. 58-Manga-style begins; Tania Del Rio-a. 67-Josie and the Pussycats app. 101-Young Salem; begin $2.50-c 3.00
... And The Archies (2004, 8 1/2"x 5 1/2", Diamond Comic Dist. Halloween giveaway) - Tania Del Rio-s/a; manga-style; Josie and the Pussycats app. 3.00

SABRINA'S CHRISTMAS MAGIC (See Archie Giant Series Magazine #196, 207, 220, 231, 243, 455, 467, 479, 491, 503, 515)

Sabu, "Elephant Boy" #1 © FOX

Sacred Creatures #1 © Raimondi & Janson

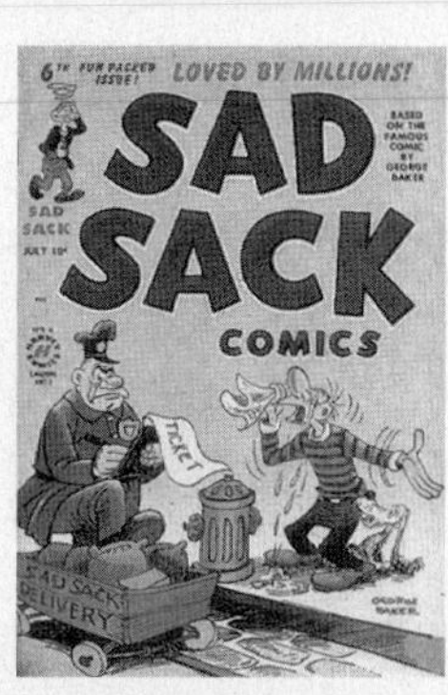

Sad Sack Comics #6 © HARV

	GD 2.0	VG 4.0	FN 6.0	VF 8.0	VF/NM 9.0	NM- 9.2

SABRINA'S HALLOWEEN SPOOOKTACULAR
Archie Publications: 1993 - 1995 ($2.00, 52 pgs.)

1-Neon orange ink-c; bound-in poster 1 3 4 6 8 10
2,3-Titled "Sabrina's Holiday Spectacular" 6.00

SABRINA, THE TEEN-AGE WITCH (TV)(See Archie Giant Series, Archie's Madhouse 22, Archie's TV..., Chilling Advs. In Sorcery, Little Archie #59)
Archie Publications: April, 1971 - No. 77, Jan, 1983 (52 pg.Giants No. 1-17)

1-52 pgs. begin, end #17 14 28 42 96 211 325
2-Archie's group x-over 8 16 24 56 108 160
3-5: 3,4-Archie's Group x-over 6 12 18 37 66 95
6-10 5 10 15 31 53 75
11-17(2/74) 4 8 12 25 40 55
18-30 3 6 9 18 28 38
31-40(8/77) 3 6 9 14 20 26
41-60(6/80) 2 4 6 10 14 18
61-70 2 4 6 8 11 14
71-76-low print run 2 4 6 11 16 20
77-Last issue; low print run 3 6 9 14 20 26

SABRINA, THE TEEN-AGE WITCH
Archie Publications: 1996 ($1.50, 32 pgs., one-shot)

1-Updated origin 1 3 4 6 8 10

SABRINA, THE TEEN-AGE WITCH (Continues in Sabrina, Vol. 2)
Archie Publications: May, 1997 - No. 32, Dec, 1999 ($1.50/$1.75/$1.79)

1-Photo-c with Melissa Joan Hart 1 3 4 6 8 10
2-10: 9-Begin $1.75-c 6.00
11-20 5.00
21-32: 24-Begin $1.79-c. 28-Sonic the Hedgehog-c/app. 4.00

SABU, "ELEPHANT BOY" (Movie; formerly My Secret Story)
Fox Feature Syndicate: No. 30, June, 1950 - No. 2, Aug, 1950

30(#1)-Wood-a; photo-c from movie 27 54 81 158 259 360
2-Photo-c from movie; Kamen-a 20 40 60 114 182 250

SACHS & VIOLENS
Marvel Comics (Epic Comics): Nov, 1993 - No. 4, July, 1994 ($2.25, limited series, mature)

1-($2.75)-Embossed-c w/bound-in trading card 3.00
1-($3.50)-Platinum edition (1 for each 10 ordered) 4.00
2-4: Perez-c/a; bound-in trading card: 2-(5/94) 3.00
TPB (DC, 2006, $14.99) r/series; intro. by Peter David; creator bios. 15.00

SACRAMENTS, THE
Catechetical Guild Educational Society: Oct, 1955 (35¢)

30304 7 14 21 35 43 50

SACRED AND THE PROFANE, THE (See Eclipse Graphic Album Series #9 & Epic Illustrated #20)

SACRED CREATURES
Image Comics: Jul, 2017 - Present ($4.99/$3.99)

1,4,5-($4.99) Pablo Raimondi & Klaus Janson-s/Raimondi-a. 4,5-Janson partial-a 5.00
2,3-($3.99) 4.00

SADDLE JUSTICE (Happy Houlihans #1,2) (Saddle Romances #9 on)
E. C. Comics: No. 3, Spring, 1948 - No. 8, Sept-Oct, 1949

3-The 1st E.C. by Bill Gaines to break away from M. C. Gaines' old Educational Comics format. Craig, Feldstein, H. C. Kiefer, & Stan Asch-a; mentioned in Love and Death 63 126 189 403 689 975
4-1st Graham Ingels-a for E.C. 54 108 162 343 574 825
5-8-Ingels-a in all 51 102 153 318 539 760

NOTE: ***Craig** and **Feldstein** art in most issues. Canadian reprints known; see Table of Contents. **Craig** c-3, 4. **Ingels** c-5-8. #4 contains a biography of **Craig**.*

SADDLE ROMANCES (Saddle Justice #3-8; Weird Science #12 on)
E. C. Comics: No. 9, Nov-Dec, 1949 - No. 11, Mar-Apr, 1950

9,11: 9-Ingels-c/a. 11-Ingels-a; Feldstein-c 54 108 162 340 575 810
10-Wally Wood's 1st work at E. C.; Ingels-a; Feldstein-c 54 108 162 346 591 835

NOTE: *Canadian reprints known; see Table of Contents. **Wood/Harrison** a-10, 11.*

SADIE SACK (See Harvey Hits #93)

SAD SACK AND THE SARGE
Harvey Publications: Sept, 1957 - No. 155, June, 1982

1 12 24 36 79 170 260
2 7 14 21 46 86 125
3-10 5 10 15 35 63 90
11-20 5 10 15 30 50 70
21-30 3 6 9 19 30 40
31-50 3 6 9 14 20 25
51-70 2 4 6 9 13 16
71-90,97-99 1 3 4 6 8 10
91-96: All 52 pg. Giants 2 4 6 9 13 16
100 2 4 6 8 10 12
101-120 1 2 3 4 5 7
121-155 5.00

NOTE: ***George Baker** covers on numerous issues.*

SAD SACK COMICS (See Harvey Collector's Comics #16, Little Sad Sack, Tastee Freez Comics #4 & True Comics #55 for 1st app.)
Harvey Publications/Lorne-Harvey Publications (Recollections) #288 0n: Sept, 1949 - No. 287, Oct, 1982; No. 288, 1992 - No. 291, 1993

1-Infinity-c; Little Dot begins (1st app.); civilian issues begin, end #21; based on comic strip (first app. in True Comics #55) 139 278 417 1112 2506 3900
2-Flying Fool by Powell 31 62 93 223 499 775
3 17 34 51 117 259 400
4-10 12 24 36 79 170 260
11-21 8 16 24 54 102 150
22-("Back In The Army Again" on covers #22-36); "The Specialist" story about Sad Sack's return to Army 9 18 27 59 117 175
23-30 5 10 15 34 60 85
31-50 4 8 12 28 47 65
51-80,100: 62-"The Specialist" reprinted 3 6 9 21 33 45
81-99 3 6 9 16 23 30
101-140 3 6 9 14 19 24
141-170,200 2 4 6 11 16 20
171-199 2 4 6 9 13 16
201-207: 207-Last 12¢ issue 2 4 6 8 11 14
208-222 1 3 4 6 8 10
223-228 (25¢ Giants, 52 pgs.) 2 4 6 8 11 14
229-250 1 3 4 6 8 10
251-285 6.00
286,287-Limited distribution 1 2 3 5 7 9
288,289 ($2.75, 1992): 289-50th anniversary issue 6.00
290,291 ($1.00, 1993, B&W) 3.00
3-D 1 (1/54, 25¢)-Came with 2 pairs of glasses; titled "Harvey 3-D Hits" 14 28 42 93 204 315
...At Home for the Holidays 1 (1993, no-c price)-Publ. by Lorne-Harvey' X-Mas issue 4.00

NOTE: *The Sad Sack Comics comic book was a spin-off from a Sunday Newspaper strip launched through John Wheeler's Bell Syndicate. The previous Sunday page and the first 21 comics depicted the Sad Sack in civvies. Unpopularity caused the Sunday page to be discontinued in the early '50s. Meanwhile Sad Sack returned to the Army, by popular demand, in issue No. 22, remaining there ever since. Incidentally, relatively few of the first 21 issues were ever collected and remain scarce due to this. **George Baker** covers on numerous issues.*

SAD SACK FUN AROUND THE WORLD
Harvey Publications: 1974 (no month)

1-About Great Britain 2 4 6 11 16 20

SAD SACK GOES HOME
Harvey Publications: 1951 (16 pgs. in color, no cover price)

nn-By George Baker 5 10 15 31 53 75

SAD SACK LAUGH SPECIAL
Harvey Publications: Winter, 1958-59 - No. 93, Feb, 1977 (#1-9: 84 pgs.; #10-60: 68 pgs.; #61-76: 52 pgs.)

1-Giant 25¢ issues begin 9 18 27 60 120 180
2 5 10 15 35 63 90
3-10 5 10 15 30 50 70
11-30 4 8 12 25 40 55
31-60: 31-Hi-Fi Tweeter app. 60-Last 68 pg. Giant 3 6 9 16 23 30
61-76-(All 52 pg. issues) 2 4 6 10 14 18
77-93 1 2 3 5 6 8

SAD SACK NAVY, GOBS 'N' GALS
Harvey Publications: Aug, 1972 - No. 8, Oct, 1973

1: 52 pg. Giant 3 6 9 16 23 30
2-8 2 4 6 9 12 15

SAD SACK'S ARMY LIFE (See Harvey Hits #8, 17, 22, 28, 32, 39, 43, 47, 51, 55, 58, 61, 64, 67, 70)

SAD SACK'S ARMY LIFE (...Parade #1-57, ...Today #58 on)
Harvey Publications: Oct, 1963 - No. 60, Nov, 1975; No. 61, May, 1976

1-(68 pg. issues begin) 7 14 21 44 82 120
2-10 4 8 12 27 44 60
11-20 3 6 9 19 30 40
21-34: Last 68 pg. issue 3 6 9 16 23 30

Sad Sack's Funny Friends #1 © HARV

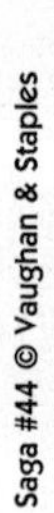
Saga #44 © Vaughan & Staples

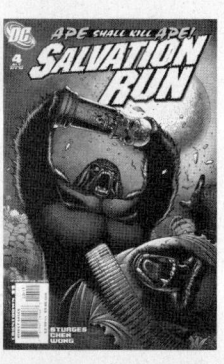

Salvation Run #4 © DC

	GD 2.0	VG 4.0	FN 6.0	VF 8.0	VF/NM 9.0	NM- 9.2
35-51: All 52 pgs.	2	4	6	10	14	18
52-61	1	3	4	6	8	10

SAD SACK'S FUNNY FRIENDS (See Harvey Hits #75)
Harvey Publications: Dec, 1955 - No. 75, Oct, 1969

	GD 2.0	VG 4.0	FN 6.0	VF 8.0	VF/NM 9.0	NM- 9.2
1	9	18	27	60	120	180
2-10	5	10	15	35	63	90
11-20	4	8	12	23	37	50
21-30	3	6	9	17	26	35
31-50	3	6	9	14	20	25
51-75	2	4	6	9	13	16

SAD SACK'S MUTTSY (See Harvey Hits #74, 77, 80, 82, 84, 87, 89, 92, 96, 99, 102, 105, 108, 111, 113, 115, 117, 119, 121)

SAD SACK USA (...Vacation #8)
Harvey Publications: Nov, 1972 - No. 7, Nov, 1973; No. 8, Oct, 1974

	GD 2.0	VG 4.0	FN 6.0	VF 8.0	VF/NM 9.0	NM- 9.2
1	3	6	9	14	20	25
2-8	2	4	6	8	10	12

SAD SACK WITH SARGE & SADIE
Harvey Publications: Sept, 1972 - No. 8, Nov, 1973

	GD 2.0	VG 4.0	FN 6.0	VF 8.0	VF/NM 9.0	NM- 9.2
1-(52 pg. Giant)	3	6	9	14	20	25
2-8	2	4	6	8	10	12

SAD SAD SACK WORLD
Harvey Publ.: Oct, 1964 - No. 46, Dec, 1973 (#1-31: 68 pgs.; #32-38: 52 pgs.)

	GD 2.0	VG 4.0	FN 6.0	VF 8.0	VF/NM 9.0	NM- 9.2
1	6	12	18	41	76	110
2-10	4	8	12	25	40	55
11-20	3	6	9	19	30	40
21-31: 31-Last 68 pg. issue	3	6	9	16	23	30
32-39-(All 52 pgs)	2	4	6	10	14	18
40-46	1	3	4	6	8	10

SAFEST PLACE IN THE WORLD, THE
Dark Horse Comics: 1993 ($2.50, one-shot)

	GD 2.0	VG 4.0	FN 6.0	VF 8.0	VF/NM 9.0	NM- 9.2
1-Steve Ditko-c/a/scripts						4.00

SAFETY-BELT MAN
Sirius Entertainment: June, 1994 - No. 6, 1995 ($2.50, B&W)

	GD 2.0	VG 4.0	FN 6.0	VF 8.0	VF/NM 9.0	NM- 9.2
1-6: 1-Horan-s/Dark One-a/Sprouse-c. 2,3-Warren-c. 4-Linsner back-up story. 5,6-Crilley-a						3.00

SAFETY-BELT MAN ALL HELL
Sirius Entertainment: June, 1996 - No. 6, Mar, 1997 ($2.95, color)

	GD 2.0	VG 4.0	FN 6.0	VF 8.0	VF/NM 9.0	NM- 9.2
1-6-Horan-s/Fillbach Bros.-a						3.00

SAGA
Image Comics: Mar, 2012 - Present ($2.99)

	GD 2.0	VG 4.0	FN 6.0	VF 8.0	VF/NM 9.0	NM- 9.2
1-Brian K. Vaughan-s/Fiona Staples-a/c; 1st app. Alana, Marko, Hazel, The Will, and Lying Cat	8	16	24	54	102	150
1-Second printing	2	4	6	13	18	22
2-1st app. The Stalk	3	6	9	17	26	35
3-5: 3-1st app. Izabel	3	6	9	14	20	25
6,7,9-12						6.00
8-1st app. Gwendolyn	2	4	6	11	16	20
13-49: 19-Intro. Ginny. 24-Lying Cat returns. 25,37-Wraparound-c. 43-(25¢-c)						4.00

SAGA OF BIG RED, THE
Omaha World-Herald: Sept, 1976 ($1.25) (In color)

	GD 2.0	VG 4.0	FN 6.0	VF 8.0	VF/NM 9.0	NM- 9.2
nn-by Win Mumma; story of the Nebraska Cornhuskers (sports)						6.00

SAGA OF CRYSTAR, CRYSTAL WARRIOR, THE
Marvel Comics: May, 1983 - No. 11, Feb, 1985 (Remco toy tie-in)

	GD 2.0	VG 4.0	FN 6.0	VF 8.0	VF/NM 9.0	NM- 9.2
1,6: 1-(Baxter paper). 6-Nightcrawler app; Golden-c						5.00
2-5,7-11: 3-Dr. Strange app. 3-11-Golden-c (painted-4,5). 11-Alpha Flight app.						4.00

SAGA OF RA'S AL GHUL, THE
DC Comics: Jan, 1988 - No. 4, Apr, 1988 ($2.50, limited series)

	GD 2.0	VG 4.0	FN 6.0	VF 8.0	VF/NM 9.0	NM- 9.2
1-4-r/N. Adams Batman						6.00

SAGA OF SABAN'S MIGHTY MORPHIN POWER RANGERS (Also see Saban's Mighty Morphin Power Rangers)
Hamilton Comics: 1995 - No. 4, 1995 ($1.95, limited series)

	GD 2.0	VG 4.0	FN 6.0	VF 8.0	VF/NM 9.0	NM- 9.2
1-4						4.00

SAGA OF SEVEN SUNS, THE : VEILED ALLIANCES
DC Comics (WildStorm): 2004 ($24.95, hardcover graphic novel with dustjacket)

	GD 2.0	VG 4.0	FN 6.0	VF 8.0	VF/NM 9.0	NM- 9.2
HC-Kevin J. Anderson-s/Robert Teranishi-a						25.00
SC-(2004, $17.95)						18.00

SAGA OF THE ORIGINAL HUMAN TORCH
Marvel Comics: Apr, 1990 - No. 4, July, 1990 ($1.50, limited series)

	GD 2.0	VG 4.0	FN 6.0	VF 8.0	VF/NM 9.0	NM- 9.2
1-4: 1-Origin; Buckler-c/a(p). 3-Hitler-c						4.00

SAGA OF THE SUB-MARINER, THE
Marvel Comics: Nov, 1988 - No. 12, Oct, 1989 ($1.25/$1.50 #5 on, maxi-series)

	GD 2.0	VG 4.0	FN 6.0	VF 8.0	VF/NM 9.0	NM- 9.2
1-12: 9-Original X-Men app.						4.00

SAGA OF THE SWAMP THING, THE (See Swamp Thing)

SAILOR MOON (Manga)
Mixx Entertainment Inc.: 1998 - No. 25 ($2.95)

	GD 2.0	VG 4.0	FN 6.0	VF 8.0	VF/NM 9.0	NM- 9.2
1	3	6	9	14	20	25
1-(San Diego edition)	3	6	9	16	23	30
2-5	2	4	6	9	12	15
6-10	1	3	4	6	8	10
11-25	1	2	3	4	5	7
26-35						5.00
... Rini's Moon Stick 1						15.00

SAILOR ON THE SEA OF FATE (See First Comics Graphic Novel #11)

SAILOR SWEENEY (Navy Action #1-11, 15 on)
Atlas Comics (CDS): No. 12, July, 1956 - No. 14, Nov, 1956

	GD 2.0	VG 4.0	FN 6.0	VF 8.0	VF/NM 9.0	NM- 9.2
12-14: 12-Shores-a. 13,14-Severin-c	22	44	66	132	216	300

SAINT, THE (Also see Movie Comics(DC) #2 & Silver Streak #18)
Avon Periodicals: Aug, 1947 - No. 12, Mar, 1952

	GD 2.0	VG 4.0	FN 6.0	VF 8.0	VF/NM 9.0	NM- 9.2
1-Kamen bondage-c/a	135	270	405	864	1482	2100
2	53	106	159	334	567	800
3,5	47	94	141	296	498	700
4-Lingerie panels, black background, Good Girl art-c	54	108	162	343	574	825
6-Miss Fury app. by Tarpe Mills (14 pgs.)	71	142	213	454	777	1100
7-c-/Avon paperback #118	40	80	120	246	411	575
8,9(12/50): Saint strip-r in #8-12; 9-Kinstler-c	39	78	117	231	378	525
10-Wood-a, 1 pg; c-/Avon paperback #289	39	78	117	231	378	525
11	34	68	102	199	325	450
12-c-/Avon paperback #123	36	72	108	211	343	475

NOTE: *Lucky Dale, Girl Detective in #1,2,4,6.* ***Hollingsworth*** *a-4, 6. Painted-c 7, 8, 10-12.*

SAINT ANGEL
Image Comics: Mar, 2000 - No. 4, Mar, 2001 ($2.95/$3.95)

	GD 2.0	VG 4.0	FN 6.0	VF 8.0	VF/NM 9.0	NM- 9.2
0-Altstaetter & Napton-s/Altstaetter-a						3.00
1-4-($3.95) Flip book w/Deity. 1-(6/00). 2-(10/00)						4.00

ST. GEORGE
Marvel Comics (Epic Comics): June, 1988 - No.8, Oct, 1989 ($1.25,/$1.50)

	GD 2.0	VG 4.0	FN 6.0	VF 8.0	VF/NM 9.0	NM- 9.2
1-8: Sienkiewicz-c. 3-begin $1.50-c						3.00

SAINT GERMAINE
Caliber Comics: 1997 - No. 8, 1998 ($2.95)

	GD 2.0	VG 4.0	FN 6.0	VF 8.0	VF/NM 9.0	NM- 9.2
1-8: 1,5-Alternate covers						3.00

ST. SWITHIN'S DAY
Trident Comics: Apr, 1990 ($2.50, one-shot)

	GD 2.0	VG 4.0	FN 6.0	VF 8.0	VF/NM 9.0	NM- 9.2
1-Grant Morrison scripts						3.00

ST. SWITHIN'S DAY
Oni Press: Mar, 1998 ($2.95, B&W, one-shot)

	GD 2.0	VG 4.0	FN 6.0	VF 8.0	VF/NM 9.0	NM- 9.2
1-Grant Morrison-s/Paul Grist-a						3.00

SALOMÉ (See Night Music #6)

SALVATION RUN
DC Comics: Jan, 2008 - No. 7, Jul, 2008 ($2.99/$3.50, limited series)

	GD 2.0	VG 4.0	FN 6.0	VF 8.0	VF/NM 9.0	NM- 9.2
1-6-DC villains banished to an alien planet; Willingham-s/Chen-a/c. 1-Var-c by Corroney						3.00
7-($3.50) Luthor cover by Chen						3.50
7-($3.50) Variant Joker cover by Neal Adams	3	6	9	21	33	45

SAM AND MAX, FREELANCE POLICE SPECIAL
Fishwrap Prod./Comico: 1987 ($1.75, B&W); Jan, 1989 ($2.75, 44 pgs.)

	GD 2.0	VG 4.0	FN 6.0	VF 8.0	VF/NM 9.0	NM- 9.2
1 ($1.75, B&W, Fishwrap)						4.00
2 ($2.75, color, Comico)						4.00

SAM AND TWITCH (See Spawn and Case Files:...)
Image Comics (Todd McFarlane Prod.): Aug, 1999 - No. 26, Feb, 2004 ($2.50)

	GD 2.0	VG 4.0	FN 6.0	VF 8.0	VF/NM 9.0	NM- 9.2
1-26: 1-19-Bendis-s. 1-14-Medina-a. 15-19-Maleev-a. 20-24-McFarlane-s/Maleev-a						3.00
Book One: Udaku (2000, $21.95, TPB) B&W reprint of #1-8						22.00
...: The Brian Michael Bendis Collection Vol. 1 (2/06, $24.95) r/#1-9 in color; sketch pages						25.00

Samson #3 © FOX

Samurai Jack: Quantum Jack #1 © CN

Sandman #34 © DC

GD VG FN VF VF/NM NM-
2.0 4.0 6.0 8.0 9.0 9.2

...: The Brian Michael Bendis Collection Vol. 2 (6/07, $24.95) r/#10-19; cover gallery 25.00

SAM AND TWITCH: THE WRITER
Image Comics (Todd McFarlane Prod.): May, 2010 - No. 4, Jun, 2010 ($2.99)
1-4-Blengino-s/Erbetta-a/c 3.00

SAMARITAN VERITAS
Image Comics: May, 2017 - No. 3, Jul, 2017 ($3.99)
1-3-Hawkins-s/Rojo-a 4.00

SAM HILL PRIVATE EYE
Close-Up (Archie): 1950 - No. 7, 1951
1 21 42 63 122 199 275
2 13 26 39 72 101 130
3-7 10 20 30 56 76 95

SAMSON (1st Series) (Captain Aero #7 on; see Big 3 Comics)
Fox Feature Syndicate: Fall, 1940 - No. 6, Sept, 1941 (See Fantastic Comics)
1-Samson begins, ends #6; Powell-a, signed 'Rensie;' Wing Turner by Tuska app; Fine-c?
194 388 582 1242 2121 3000
2-Dr. Fung by Powell; Fine-c? 90 180 270 576 988 1400
3-Navy Jones app.; Joe Simon-c 68 136 204 435 743 1050
4-Yarko the Great, Master Magician begins 61 122 183 390 670 950
5,6: 5-WWII Nazi-c. 6-Origin The Topper 53 106 159 334 567 800

SAMSON (2nd Series) (Formerly Fantastic Comics #10, 11)
Ajax/Farrell Publications (Four Star): No. 12, April, 1955 - No. 14, Aug, 1955
12-Wonder Boy 33 66 99 194 317 440
13,14: 13-Wonder Boy, Rocket Man 29 58 87 170 278 385

SAMSON (See Mighty Samson)

SAMSON & DELILAH (See A Spectacular Feature Magazine)

SAMUEL BRONSTON'S CIRCUS WORLD (See Circus World under Movie Classics)

SAMURAI (Also see Eclipse Graphic Album Series #14)
Aircel Publications: 1985 - No. 23, 1987 ($1.70, B&W)
1, 14-16-Dale Keown-a 4.00
1-(reprinted),2-12,17-23: 2 (reprinted issue exists) 3.00
13-Dale Keown's 1st published artwork (1987) 6.00

SAMURAI
Warp Graphics: May, 1997 ($2.95, B&W)
1 3.00

SAMURAI: BROTHERS IN ARMS
Titan Comics: Oct, 2016 - Present ($3.99)
1-6-Genet-a/DiGiorgio-s; English version of French comic 4.00

SAMURAI CAT
Marvel Comics (Epic Comics): June, 1991 - No. 3, Sept, 1991 ($2.25, limited series)
1-3: 3-Darth Vader-c/story parody 3.00

SAMURAI: HEAVEN & EARTH
Dark Horse Comics: Dec, 2004 - No. 5, Dec, 2005 ($2.99)
1-5-Luke Ross-a/Ron Marz-s 3.00
TPB (4/06, $14.95) r/#1-5; sketch pages and cover and pin-up gallery 15.00

SAMURAI: HEAVEN & EARTH (Volume 2)
Dark Horse Comics: Nov, 2006 - No. 5, June, 2007 ($2.99)
1-5-Luke Ross-a/Ron Marz-s 3.00
TPB (10/07, $14.95) r/#1-5; sketch pages and cover and pin-up gallery 15.00

SAMURAI JACK (TV)
IDW Publishing: Oct, 2013 - No. 20, May, 2015 ($3.99)
1-20: 1-5-Jim Zub-s/Andy Suriano-a; multiple covers on each 4.00
... Special - Director's Cut (2/14, $7.99) Reprints '02 DC issue; commentary by Bill Wray 8.00

SAMURAI JACK: QUANTUM JACK (TV)
IDW Publishing: Sept, 2017 - Present ($3.99)
1-4-Rangel, Jr.-s/Johnson-Cadwell-a; multiple covers 4.00

SAMURAI JACK SPECIAL (TV)
DC Comics: Sept, 2002 ($3.95, one-shot)
1-Adaptation of pilot episode with origin story; Tartakovsky-s/Naylor & Wray-a 4.00

SAMURAI: LEGEND
Marvel Comics (Soleil): 2008 - No. 4, 2009 ($5.99)
1-4-Genet-a/DiGiorgio-s; English version of French comic; preview of other titles 6.00

SAMUREE
Continuity Comics: May, 1987 - No. 9, Jan, 1991
1-9 3.00

SAMUREE
Continuity Comics: V2#1, May, 1993 - V2#4, Jan,1994 ($2.50)
V2#1-4-Embossed-c: 2,4-Adams plot, Nebres-i. 3-Nino-c(i) 3.00

SAMUREE
Acclaim Comics (Windjammer): Oct, 1995 - No. 2, Nov,1995 ($2.50, lim. series)
1,2 3.00

SAN DIEGO COMIC CON COMICS
Dark Horse Comics: 1992 - No.4, 1995 (B&W, promo comic for the San Diego Comic Con)
1-(1992)-Includes various characters published from Dark Horse including Concrete, The Mask, RoboCop and others; 1st app. of Sprint from John Byrne's Next Men; art by Quesada, Byrne, Rude, Burden, Moebius & others; pin-ups by Rude, Dorkin, Allred & others; Chadwick-c 2 4 6 8 10 12
2-(1993)-Intro of Legend imprint; 1st app. of John Byrne's Danger Unlimited, Mike Mignola's Hellboy (also see John Byrne's Next Men #21), Art Adams' Monkeyman & O'Brien; contains stories featuring Concrete, Sin City, Martha Washington & others; Grendel, Madman, & Big Guy pin-ups; Don Martin-c 6 12 18 42 79 115
3-(1994)-Contains stories featuring Barb Wire, The Mask, The Dirty Pair, & Grendel by Matt Wagner; contains pin-ups of Ghost, Predator & Rascals In Paradise; The Mask-c
1 2 3 5 6 8
4-(1995)-Contains Sin City story by Miller (3pg.), Star Wars, The Mask, Tarzan, Foot Soldiers; Sin City & Star Wars flip-c 1 2 3 5 6 8

SANDMAN, THE (1st Series) (Also see Adventure Comics #40, New York World's Fair, Sandman Special (2017) and World's Finest #3)
National Periodical Publ.: Winter, 1974; No. 2, Apr-May, 1975 - No. 6, Dec-Jan, 1975-76
1-1st app. Bronze Age Sandman by Simon & Kirby (last S&K collaboration)
6 12 18 41 76 110
2-6: 6-Kirby/Wood-c/a 3 6 9 21 33 45
The Sandman By Joe Simon & Jack Kirby HC (2009, $39.99, d.j.) r/Sandman app. from World's Finest #6,7, Adventure Comics #72-102 and Sandman #1; Morrow intro. 40.00
NOTE: *Kirby a-1p, 4-6p; c-1-5, 6p.*

SANDMAN (2nd Series) (See Books of Magic, Vertigo Jam & Vertigo Preview)
DC Comics (Vertigo imprint #47 on): Jan, 1989 - No. 75, Mar, 1996 ($1.50-$2.50, mature)
1 ($2.00, 52 pgs.)-1st app. Modern Age Sandman (Morpheus); Neil Gaiman scripts begin; Sam Kieth-a(p) in #1-5; Wesley Dodds (G.A. Sandman) cameo.
6 12 18 37 66 95
2-Cain & Abel app. (from HOM & HOS) 3 6 9 16 23 30
3,5: 3-John Constantine app. 2 4 6 13 18 22
4-1st app. Lucifer Morningstar; The Demon app. 4 8 12 27 44 60
6,7 2 4 6 8 11 14
8-Death-c/story (1st app.)-Regular ed. has Jeanette Kahn publishorial & American Cancer Society ad w/no indicia on inside front-c 4 8 12 25 40 55
8-Limited ed. (600+ copies?); has Karen Berger editorial and next issue teaser on inside covers (has indicia) 19 38 57 131 291 450
9-14: 10-Has explaination about #8 mixup; has bound-in Shocker movie poster.
14-(52 pgs.)-Bound-in Nightbreed fold-out 2 4 6 8 10 12
15-20: 16-Photo-c. 17,18-Kelley Jones-a. 19-Vess-a 1 2 3 5 6 8
18-Error version w/1st 3 panels on pg. 1 in blue ink 10 20 30 64 132 200
19-Error version w/pages 18 & 20 facing each other 2 4 6 10 14 18
21,23-27: Seasons of Mist storyline. 22-World Without End preview. 24-Kelley Jones/Russell-a 6.00
22-1st Daniel (Later becomes new Sandman) 2 4 6 9 12 15
28-30 5.00
31-49,51-74: 36-(52 pgs.). 41,44-48-Metallic ink on-c. 48-Cerebus appears as a doll. 54-Re-intro Prez; Death app.; Belushi, Nixon & Wildcat cameos. 57-Metallic ink on c. 65-w/bound-in trading card. 69-Death of Sandman. 70-73-Zulli-a. 74-Jon J. Muth-a. 4.00
50-($2.95, 52 pgs.)-Black-c w/metallic ink by McKean; Russell-a; McFarlane pin-up 5.00
50-($2.95)-Signed & limited (5,000) Treasury Edition with sketch of Neil Gaiman
2 4 6 9 12 15
50-Platinum 20.00
75-($3.95)-Vess-a. 5.00
Special 1 (1991, $3.50, 68 pgs.)-Glow-in-the-dark-c 5.00
Absolute Sandman Special Edition #1 (2006, 50¢) sampling from HC; recolored r/#1 3.00
Absolute Sandman Volume One (2006, $99.00, slipcased hardcover) recolored r/#1-20; Gaiman's original proposal; script and pencils from #19; character sketch gallery 100.00
Absolute Sandman Volume Two (2007, $99.00, slipcased hardcover) recolored r/#21-39; r/A Gallery of Dreams one-shot; bonus stories, scripts and pencil art 100.00
Absolute Sandman Volume Three (2008, $99.00, slipcased hardcover) recolored r/#40-56; & Special #1; bonus galleries, scripts and pencil art; Jill Thompson intro. 100.00
Absolute Sandman Volume Four (2008, $99.00, slipcased hardcover) recolored r/#57-75;

Sandman Mystery Theater #3 © DC

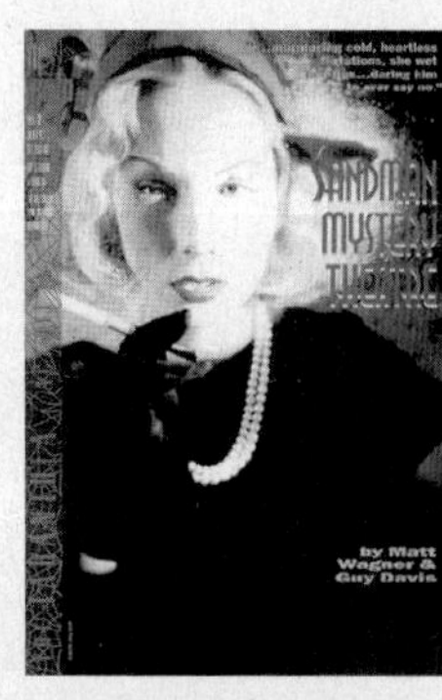

Sandman Special #1 © DC

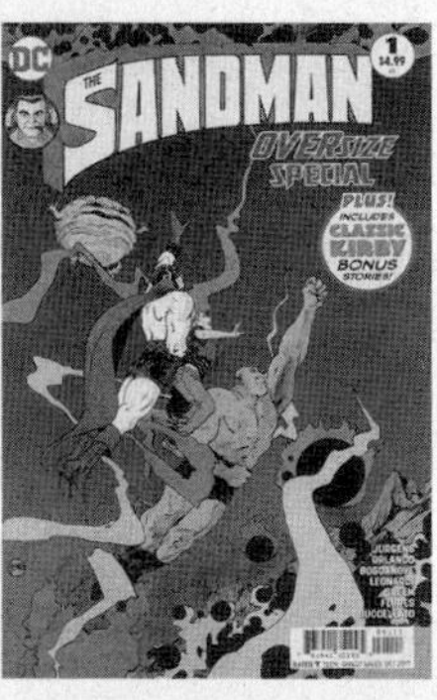

Santa Claus Funnies nn © DELL

	GD 2.0	VG 4.0	FN 6.0	VF 8.0	VF/NM 9.0	NM- 9.2

scripts & sketch pages for #57 & 75; gallery of Dreaming memorabilia; Berger intro. 100.00
...: A Gallery of Dreams ($2.95)-Intro by N. Gaiman 4.00
...: Preludes & Nocturnes ($29.95, HC)-r/#1-8. 30.00
...: The Doll's House (1990, $29.95, HC)-r/#8-16. 30.00
...: Dream Country ($29.95, HC)-r/#17-20. 30.00
...: Season of Mists ($29.95, Leatherbound HC)-r/#21-28. 50.00
...: A Game of You ($29.95, HC)-r/32-37, ...: Fables and Reflections ($29.95, HC)-r/Vertigo Preview #1, Sandman Special #1, #29-31, #38-40 & #50. ...: Brief Lives ($29.95, HC)-r/#41-49. ...: World's End ($29.95, HC)-r/#51-56 30.00
...: The Kindly Ones (1996, $34.95, HC)-r/#57-69 & Vertigo Jam #1 35.00
...: The Wake ($29.95, HC)-r/#70-75. 30.00

NOTE: *A new set of hardcover printings with new covers was introduced in 1998-99. Multiple printings exist of softcover collections. Recolored (from the Absolute HC) softcover editions were released in 2010.* **Bachalo** *a-12;* **Kelley Jones** *a-17, 18, 22, 23, 26, 27.* **Vess** *a-19, 75.*

SANDMAN: ENDLESS NIGHTS
DC Comics (Vertigo): 2003 ($24.95, hardcover, with dust jacket)

HC-Neil Gaiman stories of Morpheus and the Endless illustrated by Fabry, Manara, Prado, Quitely, Russell, Sienkiewicz, and Storey; McKean-c 25.00
...Special (11/03, $2.95) Previews hardcover; Dream story w/Prado-a; McKean-c 4.00
SC (2004, $17.95) 18.00

SANDMAN MIDNIGHT THEATRE
DC Comics (Vertigo): Sept, 1995 ($6.95, squarebound, one-shot)

nn-Modern Age Sandman (Morpheus) meets G.A. Sandman; Gaiman & Wagner story; McKean-c; Kristiansen-a 7.00

SANDMAN MYSTERY THEATRE (Also see Sandman (2nd Series) #1)
DC Comics (Vertigo): Apr, 1993 - No. 70, Feb, 1999 ($1.95/$2.25/$2.50)

1-G.A. Sandman advs. begin; Matt Wagner scripts begin 5.00
2-49,51-70: 5-Neon ink logo. 29-32-Hourman app. 38-Ted Knight (G.A. Starman) app. 42-Jim Corrigan (Spectre) app. 45-48-Blackhawk app. 3.00
50-($3.50, 48 pgs.) w/bonus story of S.A. Sandman, Torres-a 4.00
Annual 1 (10/94, $3.95, 68 pgs.)-Alex Ross, Bolton & others-a 5.00
...: Dr. Death and the Night of the Butcher (2007, $19.99) r/#21-28 20.00
...: The Blackhawk and The Return of the Scarlet Ghost (2010, $19.99) r/#45-52 20.00
...: The Face and the Brute (2004, $19.95) r/#5-12 20.00
...: The Hourman and The Python (2008, $19.99) r/#29-36 20.00
...: The Mist and The Phantom of the Fair (2009, $19.99) r/#37-44 20.00
...: The Scorpion (2006, $12.99) r/#17-20 13.00
...: The Tarantula (1995, $14.95) r/#1-4 15.00
...: The Vamp (2005, $12.99) r/#13-16 13.00

SANDMAN MYSTERY THEATRE (2nd Series)
DC Comics (Vertigo): Feb, 2007 - No. 5, Jun, 2007 ($2.99, limited series)

1-5-Wesley Dodds and Dian in 1997; Rieber-s/Nguyen-a 3.00

SANDMAN: OVERTURE
DC Comics (Vertigo): Dec, 2013 - No. 6, Nov, 2015 ($4.99/$3.99, limited series)

1-($4.99) Prelude to Sandman #1 ('89); Gaiman-s/JH Williams III-a/c; var-c by McKean 5.00
2-6-($3.99) Gaiman-s/JH Williams III-a/c 4.00
... Special Edition 1 (1/14, $5.99) B&W version of #1 with creator interviews; bonus info 6.00
... Special Edition 2-6 ($4.99) B&W versions with creator interviews; bonus info. 6-(12/15) 5.00

SANDMAN PRESENTS...
DC Comics (Vertigo)

Taller Tales TPB (2003, $19.95) r/S.P: The Thessaliad #1-4; Merv Pumpkinhead, Agent...; The Dreaming #55; S.P. Everything You Always...; new McKean-c; intro by Willingham 20.00

SANDMAN PRESENTS: BAST
DC Comics (Vertigo): Mar, 2003 - No. 3, May, 2003 ($2.95, limited series)

1-3-Kiernan-s/Bennett-a/McKean-c 3.00

SANDMAN PRESENTS: DEADBOY DETECTIVES (See Sandman #21-28)
DC Comics (Vertigo): Aug, 2001 - No. 4, Nov, 2001 ($2.50, limited series)

1-4:Talbot-a/McKean-c/Brubaker-s 3.00
TPB (2008, $12.99) r/#1-4 13.00

SANDMAN PRESENTS: EVERYTHING YOU ALWAYS WANTED TO KNOW ABOUT DREAMS...BUT WERE AFRAID TO ASK
DC Comics (Vertigo): Jul, 2001 ($3.95, one-shot)

1-Short stories by Willingham; art by various; McKean-c 4.00

SANDMAN PRESENTS: LOVE STREET
DC Comics (Vertigo): Jul, 1999 - No. 3, Sept, 1999 ($2.95, limited series)

1-3: Teenage Hellblazer in 1968 London; Zulli-a 3.00

SANDMAN PRESENTS: LUCIFER
DC Comics (Vertigo): Mar, 1999 - No. 3, May, 1999 ($2.95, limited series)

	GD 2.0	VG 4.0	FN 6.0	VF 8.0	VF/NM 9.0	NM- 9.2
1-Scott Hampton painted-c/a in all	1	2	3	5	6	8
2,3						4.00

SANDMAN PRESENTS: PETREFAX
DC Comics (Vertigo): Mar, 2000 - No. 4, Jun, 2000 ($2.95, limited series)

1-4-Carey-s/Leialoha-a 3.00

SANDMAN PRESENTS: THE CORINTHIAN
DC Comics (Vertigo): Dec, 2001 - No. 3, Feb, 2002 ($2.95, limited series)

1-3-Macan-s/Zezelj-a/McKean-c 3.00

SANDMAN PRESENTS, THE: THE FURIES
DC Comics (Vertigo): 2002 ($24.95, one-shot)

Hardcover-Mike Carey-s/John Bolton-painted art; Lyta Hall's reunion with Daniel 30.00
Softcover-(2003, $17.95) 18.00

SANDMAN PRESENTS, THE: THESSALY: WITCH FOR HIRE
DC Comics (Vertigo): Apr, 2004 - No. 4, July, 2004 ($2.95, limited series)

1-4-Willingham-s/McManus-a/McPherson-c 3.00
TPB-(2005, $12.99) r/#1-4 13.00

SANDMAN PRESENTS, THE: THE THESSALIAD
DC Comics (Vertigo): Mar, 2002 - No. 4, Jun, 2002 ($2.95, limited series)

1-4-Willingham-s/McManus-a/McKean-c 3.00

SANDMAN SPECIAL, THE (Jack Kirby 100th Birthday tribute)
DC Comics: Oct, 2017 ($4.99, one-shot)

1-Jurgens-s/Bogdanove-a and Orlando-s/Leonardi-a; Brute & Glob app.; Paul Pope-c 5.00

SANDMAN, THE: THE DREAM HUNTERS
DC Comics (Vertigo): Oct, 1999 ($29.95/$19.95, one-shot graphic novel)

Hardcover-Neil Gaiman-s/Yoshitaka Amano-painted art 30.00
Softcover-(2000, $19.95) new Amano-c 20.00

SANDMAN, THE: THE DREAM HUNTERS
DC Comics (Vertigo): Jan, 2009 - No. 4, Apr, 2009 ($2.99, limited series)

1-4-Adaptation of the Gaiman/Amano GN by P. Craig Russell-s/a; 2 covers on each 3.00
HC (2009, $24.99) afterwords by Gaiman, Russell, Berger; cover gallery & sketch art 25.00
SC (2010, $19.99) afterwords by Gaiman, Russell, Berger; cover gallery & sketch art 20.00

SANDS OF THE SOUTH PACIFIC
Toby Press: Jan, 1953

	GD 2.0	VG 4.0	FN 6.0	VF 8.0	VF/NM 9.0	NM- 9.2
1	23	46	69	138	227	315

SANTA AND HIS REINDEER (See March of Comics #166)

SANTA AND THE ANGEL (See Dell Junior Treasury #7)
Dell Publishing Co.: Dec, 1949 (Combined w/Santa at the Zoo) (Gollub-a condensed from FC#128)

	GD 2.0	VG 4.0	FN 6.0	VF 8.0	VF/NM 9.0	NM- 9.2
Four Color 259	6	12	18	41	76	110

SANTA AT THE ZOO (See Santa And The Angel)

SANTA CLAUS AROUND THE WORLD (See March of Comics #241 in Promotional Comics section)

SANTA CLAUS CONQUERS THE MARTIANS (See Movie Classics)

SANTA CLAUS FUNNIES (Also see Dell Giants)
Dell Publishing Co.: Dec?, 1942 - No. 1274, Dec, 1961

	GD 2.0	VG 4.0	FN 6.0	VF 8.0	VF/NM 9.0	NM- 9.2
nn(#1)(1942)-Kelly-a	35	70	105	252	564	875
2(12/43)-Kelly-a	23	46	69	161	356	550
Four Color 61(1944)-Kelly-a	21	42	63	150	330	510
Four Color 91(1945)-Kelly-a	16	32	48	110	243	375
Four Color 128('46),175('47)-Kelly-a	13	26	39	91	201	310
Four Color 205,254-Kelly-a	12	24	36	82	179	275
Four Color 302,361,525,607,666,756,867	8	16	24	51	96	140
Four Color 958,1063,1154,1274	6	12	18	41	76	110

NOTE: *Most issues contain only one Kelly story.*

SANTA CLAUS PARADE
Ziff-Davis (Approved Comics)/St. John Publishing Co.: 1951; No. 2, Dec, 1952; No. 3, Jan, 1955 (25¢)

	GD 2.0	VG 4.0	FN 6.0	VF 8.0	VF/NM 9.0	NM- 9.2
nn(1951-Ziff-Davis)-116 pgs. (Xmas Special 1,2)	36	72	108	211	343	475
2(12/52-Ziff-Davis)-100 pgs.; Dave Berg-a	28	56	84	165	270	375
V1#3(1/55-St. John)-100 pgs.; reprints-c/#1	21	42	63	126	206	285

SANTA CLAUS' WORKSHOP (See March of Comics #50,168 in Promotional Comics section)

SANTA IS COMING (See March of Comics #197 in Promotional Comics section)

SANTA IS HERE (See March of Comics #49 in Promotional Comics section)

SANTA'S BUSY CORNER (See March of Comics #31 in Promotional Comics section)

SANTA'S CANDY KITCHEN (See March of Comics #14 in Promotional Comics section)

Sarge Snorkel #3 © CC

Saucer State #4 © Cornell & Kelly

Savage Dragon #225 © Erik Larsen

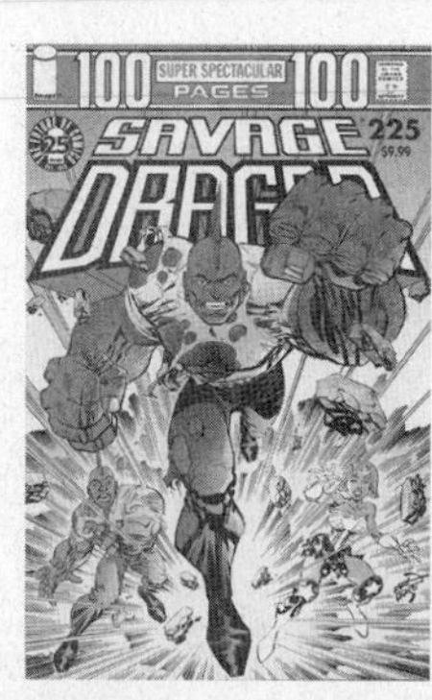

GD VG FN VF VF/NM NM-
2.0 4.0 6.0 8.0 9.0 9.2

GD VG FN VF VF/NM NM-
2.0 4.0 6.0 8.0 9.0 9.2

SANTA'S CHRISTMAS BOOK (See March of Comics #123 in Promotional Comics section)

SANTA'S CHRISTMAS COMICS
Standard Comics (Best Books): Dec, 1952 (100 pgs.)
nn-Supermouse, Dizzy Duck, Happy Rabbit, etc. 23 46 69 138 227 315

SANTA'S CHRISTMAS LIST (See March of Comics #255 in Promotional Comics section)

SANTA'S HELPERS (See March of Comics #64, 106, 198 in Promotional Comics section)

SANTA'S LITTLE HELPERS (See March of Comics #270 in Promotional Comics section)

SANTA'S SHOW (See March of Comics #311 in Promotional Comics section)

SANTA'S SLEIGH (See March of Comics #298 in Promotional Comics section)

SANTA'S SURPRISE (See March of Comics #13 in Promotional Comics section)

SANTA'S TINKER TOTS
Charlton Comics: 1958
1-Based on "The Tinker Tots Keep Christmas" 5 10 15 34 60 85

SANTA'S TOYLAND (See March of Comics #242 in Promotional Comics section)

SANTA'S TOYS (See March of Comics #12 in Promotional Comics section)

SANTA'S VISIT (See March of Comics #283 in Promotional Comics section)

SANTA THE BARBARIAN
Maximum Press: Dec, 1996 ($2.99, one-shot)
1-Fraga/Mhan-s/a 3.00

SANTERIA: THE GODDESS KISS
Aspen MLT: Mar, 2016 - No. 5, Nov, 2017 ($3.99, limited series)
1-5-Wohl-s/Cafaro-a 4.00

SANTIAGO (Movie)
Dell Publishing Co.: Sept, 1956 (Alan Ladd photo-c)
Four Color 723-Kinstler-a 8 16 24 56 108 160

SARGE SNORKEL (Beetle Bailey)
Charlton Comics: Oct, 1973 - No. 17, Dec, 1976
1 2 4 6 11 16 20
2-10 2 4 6 8 10 12
11-17 1 2 3 5 7 9

SARGE STEEL (Becomes Secret Agent #9 on; also see Judomaster)
Charlton Comics: Dec, 1964 - No. 8, Mar-Apr, 1966 (All 12¢ issues)
1-Origin & 1st app. 4 8 12 23 37 50
2-5,7,8 3 6 9 16 23 30
6-2nd app. Judomaster 3 6 9 19 30 40

SATAN'S SIX
Topps Comics (Kirbyverse): Apr, 1993 - No. 4, July, 1993 ($2.95, lim. series)
1-4: 1-Polybagged w/Kirbychrome trading card; Kirby/McFarlane-c plus 8 pgs. Kirby-a(p); has coupon for Kirbychrome ed. of Secret City Saga #0. 2-4-Polybagged w/3 cards. 4-Teenagents preview 4.00
NOTE: *Ditko a-1. Miller a-1.*

SATAN'S SIX: HELLSPAWN
Topps Comics (Kirbyverse): June, 1994 - No. 3, July, 1994 ($2.50, limited series)
1-3: 1-(6/94)-Indicia incorrectly shows "Vol 1 #2". 2-(6/94) 3.00

SATELLITE FALLING
IDW Publishing: May, 2016 - No. 5, May, 2017 ($3.99)
1-5-Steve Horton-s/Stephen Thompson-a 4.00

SATELLITE SAM
Image Comics: Jul, 2013 - No. 15, Jul, 2015 ($3.50, B&W, mature)
1-15-Matt Fraction-s/Howard Chaykin-a/c 3.50

SAUCER COUNTRY
DC Comics (Vertigo): May, 2012 - No. 14, Jun, 2013 ($2.99)
1-14: 1-Cornell-s/Kelly-a. 6-Broxton-a. 11-Colak-a 3.00

SAUCER STATE (Sequel to Saucer Country)
IDW Publishing: May, 2017 - Present ($3.99)
1-6-Cornell-s/Kelly-a 4.00

SAURIANS: UNNATURAL SELECTION (See Sigil)
CrossGeneration Comics: Feb, 2002 - No. 2, Mar, 2002 ($2.95, limited series)
1,2-Waid-s/DiVito-a 3.00

SAVAGE
Image Comics (Shadowline): Oct, 2008 - No. 4, Jan, 2009 ($3.50, limited series)
1-4-Mayhew-c/a; Niles and Frank-s 3.50

SAVAGE
Valiant Entertainment: Nov, 2016 - No. 4 ($3.99, limited series)
1-4-B. Clay Moore-s/Larosa & Henry-a 4.00

SAVAGE AXE OF ARES
Marvel Comics: June, 2010 ($3.99, B&W, one-shot)
1-B&W short stories by Hurwitz, Palo, McKeever, Swierczynski, Manco and others 4.00

SAVAGE COMBAT TALES
Atlas/Seaboard Publ.: Feb, 1975 - No. 3, July, 1975
1,3: 1-Sgt. Stryker's Death Squad begins (origin); Goodwin-s 2 4 6 9 13 16
2-Toth-a; only app. War Hawk; Goodwin-s 2 4 6 10 14 18
NOTE: *Buckler c-3. McWilliams a-1-3; c-1. Sparling a-1, 3.*

SAVAGE DRAGON, THE (See Megaton #3 & 4)
Image Comics (Highbrow Entertainment): July, 1992 - No. 3, Dec, 1992 ($1.95, lim. series)
1-Erik Larsen-c/a/scripts & bound-in poster in all; 4 cover color variations w/4 different posters; 1st Highbrow Entertainment title 1 2 3 5 6 8
2-Intro SuperPatriot-c/story (10/92) 4.00
3-Contains coupon for Image Comics #0 4.00
3-With coupon missing 2.00
...Vs. Savage Megaton Man 1 (3/93, $1.95)-Larsen & Simpson-c/a. 4.00
TPB-('93, $9.95) r/#1-3 10.00

SAVAGE DRAGON, THE
Image Comics (Highbrow Entertainment): June, 1993 - Present ($1.95/$2.50/$2.99/$3.50)
1-Erik Larsen-c/a/scripts 6.00
2-($2.95, 52 pgs.)-Teenage Mutant Ninja Turtles-c/story; flip book features Vanguard #0 (See Megaton for 1st app.); 1st app. Supreme 4.00
3-30: 3-7: Erik Larsen-c/a/scripts. 3-Mighty Man back-up story w/Austin-a(i). 4-Flip book w/Ricochet. 5-Mighty Man flip-c & back-up plus poster. 6-Jae Lee poster. 7-Vanguard poster. 8-Deadly Duo poster by Larsen. 13A (10/94)-Jim Lee-c/a; 1st app. Max Cash (Condition Red). 13B (6/95)-Larsen story. 15-Dragon poster by Larsen. 22-TMNT-c/a; Bisley pin-up. 27-"Wondercon Exclusive" new-c. 28-Maxx-c/app. 29-Wildstar-c/app. 30-Spawn app. 3.50
25 ($3.95)-variant-c exists. 4.00
31-49,51-71: 31-God vs. The Devil; alternate version exists w/o expletives (has "God Is Good" inside Image logo) 33-Birth of Dragon/Rapture's baby. 34,35-Hellboy-c/app. 51-Origin of She-Dragon. 70-Ann Stevens killed 3.50
50-($5.95, 100 pgs.) Kaboom and Mighty Man app.; Matsuda back-c; pin-ups by McFarlane, Simonson, Capullo and others 6.00
72-74: 72-Begin $2.95-c 3.50
75-($5.95) 6.00
76-99,101-106,108-114,116-124,126-127,129-131,133-136,138: 76-New direction starts. 83,84-Madman-c/app. 84-Atomics app. 97-Dragon returns home; Mighty Man app. 134-Bomb Queen app. 3.50
100-($8.95) Larsen-s/a; inked by various incl. Sienkiewicz, Timm, Austin, Simonson, Royer; plus pin-ups by Timm, Silvestri, Miller, Cho, Art Adams, Pacheco 9.00
107-($3.95) Firebreather, Invincible, Major Damage-c/app.; flip book w/Major Damage 4.00
115-($7.95, 100 pgs.) Wraparound-c; Freak Force app.; Larsen & Englert-a 8.00
125-($4.99, 64 pgs.) new story, The Fly, & various Mr. Glum reprints 5.00
128-Wesley and the villains from Wanted app.; J.G. Jones-c 4.00
132-($6.99, 80 pgs.) new story with Larsen-a; back-up story with Fosco-a 7.00
137-(8/08) Madman & Amazing Joy Buzzards-c/app. 1 3 4 6 8 10
137-(8/08) Variant cover with Barack Obama endorsed by Savage Dragon; yellow bkgrd 7 14 21 48 89 130
137-(8/08) 2nd printing of variant cover with Barack Obama and red background 1 3 4 6 8 10
137-3rd & 4th printings: 3rd-Blue background. 4th-Purple background 6.00
139-144,146-149,151-174,176-183: 139-Start $3.50-c; Invincible app. 140,141-Witchblade, Spawn app. 148-Also a FCBD edition.155-160-Dragon War. 160-163-Flip book 3.50
145-Obama-c/app. 1 2 3 5 6 8
150-($5.99, 100 pgs.) back up r/Daredevil's origin from Daredevil #18 (1943) 6.00
175-($3.99, 48 pgs.) Darklord app.; Vanguard back-c and back-up story 4.00
184-199,201-224 ($3.99) 184,186-188-The Claw app. 190-Regular & digest-size versions. 209-Malcolm's wedding. 217-Spawn app. 4.00
200-(12/14, $8.99, 100 pgs., squarebound) Back-up story w/Trimpe-a; Burnhum-a 9.00
225-(7/17, $9.99, 100 pgs., squarebound) Death of Savage Dragon; back-up by various 10.00
226-232: 226-Donald Trump on cover. 227-Malcolm & family move to Toronto 4.00
#0-(7/06, $1.95) reprints origin story from 2005 Image Comics Hardcover 3.50
...Archives Vol. 1 (12/06, $19.99) B&W rep. 1st mini-series #1-3 & #1-21 20.00
...Archives Vol. 2 (2007, $19.99) B&W rep. #22-50; roster pages of Dragon's fellow cops 20.00
...Companion (7/02, $2.95) guide to issues #1-100, character backgrounds 3.50
...Endgame (2/04, $15.95, TPB) r/#47-52 16.00
The Fallen (11/97, $12.95, TPB) r/#7-11, ...Possessed (9/98, $12.95, TPB) r/#12-16,

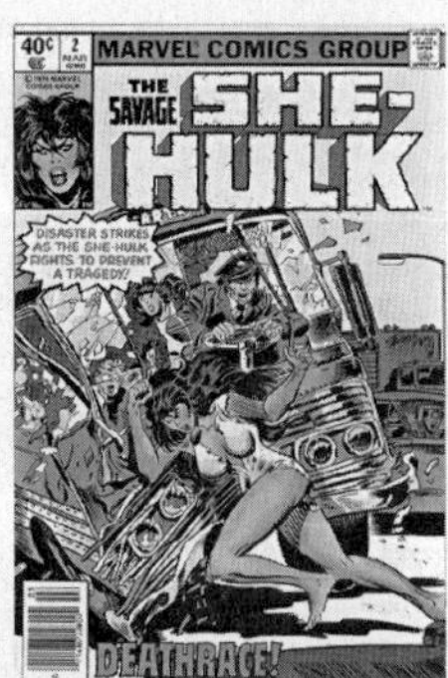

Savage She-Hulk #2 © MAR

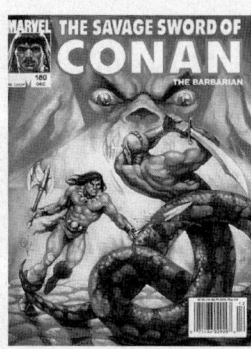

Savage Sword of Conan #180 © CPI

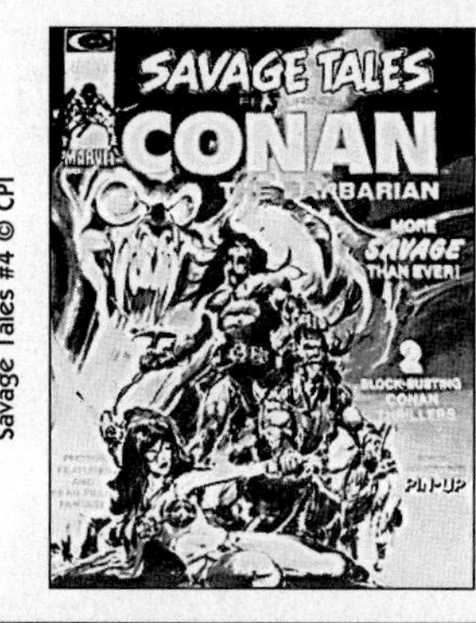

Savage Tales #4 © CPI

	GD 2.0	VG 4.0	FN 6.0	VF 8.0	VF/NM 9.0	NM- 9.2

...Revenge (1998, $12.95, TPB) r/#17-21 13.00
...Gang War (4/00, $16.95, TPB) r/#22-26 17.00
.../Hellboy (10/02, $5.95) r/#34 & #35; Mignola-c 6.00
Image Firsts: Savage Dragon #1 (4/10, $1.00) reprints #1 3.00
... Legacy FCBD 1 (5/15, giveaway) Story later re-worked for issue #211 3.00
...Team-Ups (10/98, $19.95, TPB) r/team-ups 20.00
...: Terminated HC (2/03, $28.95) r/#34-40 & #1/2 29.00
...: This Savage World HC (2002, $24.95) r/#76-81; intro. by Larsen 25.00
...: This Savage World SC (2003, $15.95) r/#76-81; intro. by Larsen 16.00
...: Worlds at War SC (2004, $16.95) r/#41-46; intro. by Larsen; sketch pages 17.00

SAVAGE DRAGON ARCHIVES (Also see Dragon Archives, The)

SAVAGE DRAGONBERT: FULL FRONTAL NERDITY
Image Comics: Oct, 2002 ($5.95, B&W, one-shot)
1-Reprints of the Savage Dragon/Dilbert spoof strips 6.00

SAVAGE DRAGON/DESTROYER DUCK, THE
Image Comics/ Highbrow Entertainment: Nov, 1996 ($3.95, one-shot)
1 4.00

SAVAGE DRAGON: GOD WAR
Image Comics: July, 2004 - No. 4, Oct, 2005 ($2.95, limited series)
1-4-Kirkman-s/Englert-a 3.50

SAVAGE DRAGON/MARSHALL LAW
Image Comics: July, 1997 - No. 2, Aug, 1997 ($2.95, B&W, limited series)
1,2-Pat Mills-s, Kevin O'Neill-a 3.50

SAVAGE DRAGON: SEX & VIOLENCE
Image Comics: Aug, 1997 - No. 2, Sept, 1997 ($2.50, limited series)
1,2-T&M Bierbaum-s, Mays, Lupka, Adam Hughes-a 3.50

SAVAGE DRAGON/TEENAGE MUTANT NINJA TURTLES CROSSOVER
Mirage Studios: Sept, 1993 ($2.75, one-shot)
1-Erik Larsen-c(i) only 4.00

SAVAGE DRAGON: THE RED HORIZON
Image Comics/ Highbrow Entertainment: Feb, 1997 - No. 3 ($2.50, lim. series)
1-3 3.50

SAVAGE FISTS OF KUNG FU
Marvel Comics Group: 1975 (Marvel Treasury)
1-Iron Fist, Shang Chi, Sons of Tiger; Adams, Starlin-a 3 6 9 17 26 35

SAVAGE HAWKMAN, THE (DC New 52)
DC Comics: Nov, 2011 - No. 20, Jun, 2013 ($2.99)
1-20: 1-Tony Daniel-s/Philip Tan-a/c; Carter Hall bonds with the Nth metal 3.00
#0-(11/12, $2.99) Origin story of Katar Hol on Thanagar; Bennett-a/c 3.00

SAVAGE HULK, THE (Also see Incredible Hulk)
Marvel Comics: Jan, 1996 ($6.95, one-shot)
1-Bisley-c; David, Lobdell, Wagner, Loeb, Gibbons, Messner-Loebs scripts; McKone, Kieth, Ramos & Sale-a 7.00

SAVAGE HULK
Marvel Comics: Aug, 2014 - No. 6, Jan, 2015 ($3.99, limited series)
1-6: 1-4-Alan Davis-s/a; follows story from X-Men #66 ('70) Silver Age X-Men & The Leader app. 2-Abomination app. 5,6-Bechko-s/Hardman-a; Dr. Strange app. 4.00

SAVAGE RAIDS OF GERONIMO (See Geronimo #4)

SAVAGE RANGE (See Luke Short, Four Color 807)

SAVAGE RED SONJA: QUEEN OF THE FROZEN WASTES
Dynamite Entertainment: 2006 - No. 4, 2006 ($3.50, limited series)
1-4: 1-Three covers by Cho, Texeira & Homs; Cho & Murray-s/Homs-a 3.50
TPB (2007, $14.99) r/series; cover gallery and sketch pages 15.00

SAVAGE RETURN OF DRACULA
Marvel Comics: 1992 ($2.00, 52 pgs.)
1-r/Tomb of Dracula #1,2 by Gene Colan 4.00

SAVAGE SHE-HULK, THE (See The Avengers, Marvel Graphic Novel #18 & The Sensational She-Hulk)
Marvel Comics Group: Feb, 1980 - No. 25, Feb, 1982
1-Origin & 1st app. She-Hulk 5 10 15 30 50 70
2-5,25: 25-(52 pgs.) 1 3 4 6 8 10
6-24: 6-She-Hulk vs. Iron Man. 8-Vs. Man-Thing 6.00
NOTE: ***Austin** a-25i; c-23i-25i. **J. Buscema** a-1p; c-1, 2p. **Golden** c-8-11.*

SAVAGE SHE-HULK (Titled All New Savage She Hulk for #3,4)
Marvel Comics: Jun, 2009 - No. 4, Sept, 2009 ($3.99, limited series)
1-4-Lyra, daughter of the Hulk; She-Hulk & Dark Avengers app. 2-Campbell-c 4.00

SAVAGE SKULLKICKERS (See Skullkickers #20)

SAVAGE SWORD (ROBERT E. HOWARD'S...)
Dark Horse Comics: Dec, 2010 - No. 9 ($7.99, squarebound)
1-9-Short stories by various incl. Roy Thomas, Barry-Windsor-Smith; Conan app. 8.00

SAVAGE SWORD OF CONAN (The... #41 on; ...The Barbarian #175 on)
Marvel Comics Group: Aug, 1974 - No. 235, July, 1995 ($1.00/$1.25/$2.25, B&W magazine, mature)
1-Smith-r; J. Buscema/N. Adams/Krenkel-a; origin Blackmark by Gil Kane (part 1, ends #3); Blackmark's 1st app. in magazine form-r/from paperback) & Red Sonja (3rd app.) 9 18 27 62 126 190
2-Neal Adams-c; Chaykin/N. Adams-a 5 10 15 34 60 85
3-Severin/B. Smith-a; N. Adams-a 4 8 12 28 47 65
4-Neal Adams/Kane-a(r) 3 6 9 21 33 45
5-10: 5-Jeff Jones frontispiece (r) 3 6 9 17 26 35
11-20 2 4 6 13 18 22
21-30 2 4 6 10 14 18
31-50: 34-3 pg. preview of Conan newspaper strip. 35-Cover similar to Savage Tales #1. 45-Red Sonja returns; begin $1.25-c 2 4 6 8 11 14
51-99: 63-Toth frontispiece. 65-Kane-a w/Chaykin/Miller/Simonson/Sherman finishes. 70-Article on movie. 83-Red Sonja-r by Neal Adams from #1 1 2 3 5 7 9
100 1 3 4 6 8 10
101-176: 163-Begin $2.25-c. 169-King Kull story. 171-Soloman Kane by Williamson (i). 172-Red Sonja story 6.00
177-199: 179,187,192-Red Sonja app. 190-193-4 part King Kull story. 196-King Kull story 5.00
200-220: 200-New Buscema-a; Robert E. Howard app. with Conan in story. 202-King Kull story. 204-60th anniversary (1932-92). 211-Rafael Kayanan's 1st Conan-a. 214-Sequel to Red Nails by Howard 6.00
221-230 2 4 6 8 10 12
231-234 2 4 6 11 16 20
235-Last issue 4 8 12 27 44 60
Special 1(1975, B&W)-B. Smith-r/Conan #10,13 3 6 9 16 24 32
Volume 1 TPB (Dark Horse Books, 12/07, $17.95, B&W) r/#1-10 and selected stories from Savage Tales #1-5 with covers 18.00
Volume 2 TPB (Dark Horse Books, 3/08, $17.95, B&W) r/#11-24 18.00
Volume 3 TPB (Dark Horse Books, 5/08, $19.95, B&W) r/#25-36 and selected pin-ups 20.00
Volume 4 TPB (Dark Horse Books, 9/08, $19.95, B&W) r/#37-48 and selected pin-ups 20.00
Volume 5 TPB (Dark Horse Books, 2/09, $19.95, B&W) r/#49-60 and selected pin-ups 20.00
NOTE: ***N. Adams** a-14p, 60, 83p(r). **Alcala** a-2 ,4, 7, 12, 15-20, 23, 24, 28, 59, 67, 69, 75, 76i, 80i, 82i, 83i, 89, 180i, 184i, 187i, 189i, 216p. **Austin** a-78i. **Boris** painted c-1, 4, 5, 7, 9, 10, 12, 15. **Brunner** a-30; c-8, 30. **Buscema** a-1-5, 7, 10-12, 15-24, 26-28, 31, 32, 36-43, 45, 47-58p, 60-67p, 70, 71-74p, 76-81p, 87-96p, 98, 99-101p, 190-204p; painted c-40. **Chaykin** c-31. **Chiodo** painted c-71, 76, 79, 81, 84, 85, 178. **Conrad** c-215, 217. **Corben** a-4, 16, 29. **Finlay** a-16. **Golden** a-98, 101; c-98, 101, 105, 106, 117, 124, 150. **Kaluta** a-11, 18; c-3, 91, 93. **Gil Kane** a-2, 3, 8, 13r, 29, 47, 64, 65, 67, 85p, 86p. **Rafael Kayanan** a-211-213, 215, 217. **Krenkel** a-9, 11, 14, 16, 24. **Morrow** a-7. **Nebres** a-93i, 101i, 107, 114. **Newton** a-6. **Nino** c/a-6. **Redondo** painted c-48-50, 52, 56, 57, 85i, 90, 96i. **Marie & John Severin** a-Special 1. **Simonson** a-7, 8, 12, 15-17. **Barry Smith** a-7, 16, 24, 82r, Special 1r. **Starlin** c-26. **Toth** a-64. **Williamson** a(i)-162, 171, 186. No. 8 , 10 & 16 contain a Robert E. Howard Conan adaptation.*

SAVAGE TALES (...Featuring Conan #4 on)(Magazine)
Marvel Comics Group: May, 1971; No. 2, 10/73; No. 3, 2/74 - No. 12, Summer, 1975 (B&W)
1-Origin/1st app. The Man-Thing by Morrow; Conan the Barbarian by Barry Smith (1st Conan x-over outside his own title); Femizons by Romita-r/in #3; Ka-Zar story by Buscema 19 38 57 131 291 450
2-B. Smith, Brunner, Morrow, Williamson-a; Wrightson King Kull reprint/ Creatures on the Loose #10 5 10 15 35 63 90
3-B. Smith, Brunner, Steranko, Williamson-a 5 10 15 30 50 70
4,5-N. Adams-c; last Conan (Smith-r/#4) plus Kane/N. Adams-a. 5-Brak the Barbarian begins, ends #8 4 8 12 27 44 60
6-Ka-Zar begins; Williamson-r; N. Adams-c 3 6 9 19 30 40
7-N. Adams-i 3 6 9 15 22 28
8,9,11: 8-Shanna, the She-Devil app. thru #10; Williamson-r 3 6 9 14 20 26
10-Neal Adams-a(i), Williamson-r 3 6 9 15 22 28
...Featuring Ka-Zar Annual 1 (Summer, '75, B&W)(#12 on inside)-Ka-Zar origin by Gil Kane; B. Smith-r/Astonishing Tales 3 6 9 16 24 32
NOTE: ***Boris** c-7, 10. **Buscema** a-5r, 6p, 8p; c-2. **Colan** a-1p. **Fabian** c-8. **Golden** a-1, 4; c-1. **Heath** a-10p, 11p. **Kaluta** c-9. **Maneely** r-2, 4(The Crusader in both). **Morrow** a-1, 2, Annual 1. **Reese** a-2. **Severin** a-1-7. **Starlin** a-5. Robert E. Howard adaptations-1-4.*

SAVAGE TALES (Volume 2)
Marvel Comics Group: Oct, 1985 - No. 8, Dec, 1986 ($1.50, B&W, magazine, mature)

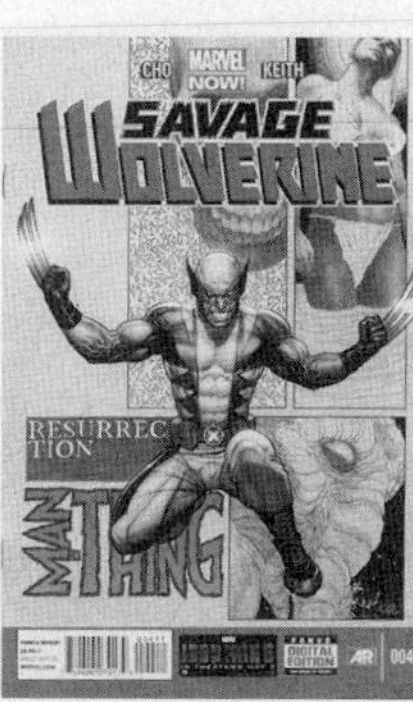

Savage Wolverine #4 © MAR

Scalped #56 © Jason Aaron

Scarlet Witch (2016 series) #6 © MAR

	GD 2.0	VG 4.0	FN 6.0	VF 8.0	VF/NM 9.0	NM- 9.2
1-1st app. The Nam; Golden, Morrow-a (indicia incorrectly lists this as Volume 1)						6.00
2-8: 2,7-Morrow-a. 4-2nd Nam story; Golden-a						4.00

SAVAGE TALES
Dynamite Entertainment: 2007 - No. 10, 2008 ($4.99)

1-10: 1-Anthology; Red Sonja app.; three covers — 5.00

SAVAGE THINGS
DC Comics (Vertigo): May, 2017 - Present ($3.99)

1-7-Justin Jordan-s/Ibrahim Moustafa-a/J.P. Leon-c — 4.00

SAVAGE WOLVERINE
Marvel Comics: Mar, 2013 - No. 23, Nov, 2014 ($3.99)

1-5-Frank Cho-s/a/c; Shanna & Amadeus Cho app. — 4.00
1-Variant-c by Skottie Young — 8.00
6-23: 6-8-Wells-s/Madureira-a/c; Elektra, Kingpin & Spider-Man app. 9-11-Jock-s/a. 14-17-Isanove-s/a. 19-Simone-s. 21,22-WWI; Quinones-a/Nowlan-c — 4.00

SAVANT GARDE (Also see WildC.A.T.S...)
Image Comics/WildStorm Productions: Mar, 1997 - No. 7, Sept, 1997 ($2.50)

1-7 — 3.00

SAVED BY THE BELL (TV)
Harvey Comics: Mar, 1992 - No. 5, May, 1993 ($1.25, limited series)

1-5, Holiday Special (3/92), Special 1 (9/92, $1.50)-photo-c, Summer Break 1 (10/92) — 3.00

SAVIOR
Image Comics/Todd McFarlane Productions: Apr, 2015 - No. 8, Nov, 2015 ($2.99)

1-8-Todd McFarlane & Brian Holguin-s/Clayton Crain-a/c — 3.00

SAW: REBIRTH (Based on 2004 movie Saw)
IDW Publ.: Oct, 2005 ($3.99, one-shot)

1-Guedes-a — 4.00

SCALPED
DC Comics (Vertigo): Mar, 2007 - No. 60, Oct, 2012 ($2.99, limited series)

	GD	VG	FN	VF	VF/NM	NM-
1-Aaron-s/Guera-a/Jock-c	4	8	12	28	47	65
1-Special Edition (7/10, $1.00) r/#1 with "What's Next?" cover frame						3.00
2-5	1	2	3	5	6	8
6-20: 12-Leon-a						4.00
21-60: 50-Bonus pin-ups by various						3.00
...: Casino Blood TPB (2008, $14.99) r/#6-11; intro. by Garth Ennis						15.00
...: Dead Mothers TPB (2008, $17.99) r/#12-18						18.00
...: High Lonesome TPB (2009, $14.99) r/#25-29; intro. by Jason Starr						15.00
...: Indian Country TPB (2007, $9.99) r/#1-5; intro. by Brian K. Vaughan						10.00
...: Rez Blues (2011, $17.99) r/#35-42						18.00
...: The Gnawing (2010, $14.99) r/#30-34; intro. by Matt Fraction						15.00
...: The Gravel in Your Guts (2009, $14.99) r/#19-24; intro. by Ed Brubaker						15.00

SCAMP (Walt Disney)(See Walt Disney's Comics & Stories #204)
Dell Publ. Co./Gold Key: No. 703, 5/56 - No. 1204, 8-10/61; 11/67 - No. 45, 1/79

	GD	VG	FN	VF	VF/NM	NM-
Four Color 703(#1)	9	18	27	57	111	165
Four Color 777,806('57),833	6	12	18	40	73	105
5(3-5/58)-10(6-8/59)	5	10	15	31	53	75
11-16(12-2/60-61), Four Color 1204(1961)	4	8	12	27	44	60
1(12/67-Gold Key)-Reprints begin	4	8	12	25	40	55
2(3/69)-10	2	4	6	13	18	22
11-20	2	4	6	8	11	14
21-45	1	2	3	4	5	7

NOTE: *New stories-#20(in part), 22-25, 27, 29-31, 34, 36-40, 42-45. New covers-#11, 12, 14, 15, 17-25, 27, 29-31, 34, 36-38.*

SCARAB
DC Comics (Vertigo): Nov, 1993 - No. 8, June, 1994 ($1.95, limited series)

1-8-Glenn Fabry painted-c: 1-Silver ink-c. 2-Phantom Stranger app. — 3.00

SCARECROW OF ROMNEY MARSH, THE (See W. Disney Showcase #53)
Gold Key: April, 1964 - No. 3, Oct, 1965 (Disney TV Show)

	GD	VG	FN	VF	VF/NM	NM-
10112-404 (#1)	6	12	18	37	66	95
2,3	4	8	12	27	44	60

SCARECROW (VILLAINS) (See Batman)
DC Comics: Feb, 1998 ($1.95, one-shot)

1-Fegredo-a/Milligan-s/Pearson-c — 3.00

SCARE TACTICS
DC Comics: Dec, 1996 - No. 12, Mar, 1998 ($2.25)

1-12: 1-1st app. — 3.00

SCAR FACE (See The Crusaders)

SCARFACE: SCARRED FOR LIFE (Based on the 1983 movie)
IDW Publishing: Dec, 2006 - No. 5, Apr, 2007 ($3.99, limited series)

1-5-Tony Montana survives his shooting; Layman-s/Crosland-a — 4.00
Scarface: Devil in Disguise (7/07 - No. 4, 10/07, $3.99) Alberto Dose-a — 4.00

SCARLET
Marvel Comics (ICON): July, 2010 - Present ($3.95)

1-10-Bendis-s/Maleev-a. 1-Second printing exists. 8-(5/16) — 4.00
1-5-Variant covers. 1-Deodato & Lafuente. 2-Oeming & Mack. 3,4-Oeming. 5-Bendis — 6.00

SCARLET O'NEIL (See Harvey Comics Hits #59 & Invisible...)

SCARLET SPIDER
Marvel Comics: Nov, 1995 - No. 2, Jan, 1996 ($1.95, limited series)

1,2: Replaces Spider-Man title — 3.00

SCARLET SPIDER
Marvel Comics: Mar, 2012 - No. 25, Feb, 2014 ($3.99/$2.99)

1-Kaine following "Spider Island"; Yost-s/Stegman-a; 2 covers by Stegman — 4.00
2-12, 12.1, 13-24-($2.99) 10,11-Carnage & Venom app. 17-19-Wolverine app. — 3.00
25-($3.99) Last issue; Yost-s/Baldeon-a — 4.00

SCARLET SPIDERS (Tie-in for Spider-Verse in Amazing Spider-Man [2014] #9-15)
Marvel Comics: Jan, 2015 - No. 3, Mar, 2015 ($3.99, limited series)

1-3-Kaine, Ben Reilly and Jessica Drew app.; Costa-s/Diaz-a — 4.00

SCARLET SPIDER UNLIMITED
Marvel Comics: Nov, 1995 ($3.95, one-shot)

1-Replaces Spider-Man Unlimited title — 4.00

SCARLETT COUTURE
Titan Comics: May, 2015 - No. 4, Aug, 2015 ($3.99)

1-4-Des Taylor-s/a — 4.00

SCARLETT'S STRIKE FORCE (G.I. Joe)
IDW Publishing: Dec, 2017 - Present ($3.99, limited series)

1-3-Sitterson-s/Daniel-a; Cobra Commander app. — 4.00

SCARLET WITCH (See Avengers #16, Vision &... & X-Men #4)
Marvel Comics: Jan, 1994 - No. 4, Apr, 1994 ($1.75, limited series)

1-4 — 3.00

SCARLET WITCH
Marvel Comics: Feb, 2016 - No. 15, Apr, 2017 ($3.99)

1-15: 1-3: 1-Robinson-s/Del Rey-a; Agatha Harkness app. 3-Dillon-a. 7-Wu-a. 9-Civil War II tie-in; Quicksilver app.; Joelle Jones-a — 4.00

SCARY GODMOTHER (Hardcover story books)
Sirius: 1997 - 2002 ($19.95, HC with dust jackets, one-shots)

Volume 1 (9/97) Jill Thompson-s/a; first app. of Scary Godmother — 20.00
Vol. 2 - The Revenge of Jimmy (9/98, $19.95) — 20.00
Vol. 3 - The Mystery Date (10/99, $19.95) — 20.00
Vol. 4 - The Boo Flu (9/02, $19.95) — 20.00

SCARY GODMOTHER
Sirius: 2001 - No. 6, 2002 ($2.95, B&W, limited series)

1-6-Jill Thompson-s/a — 3.00
...: Activity Book (12/00, $2.95, B&W) Jill Thompson-s/a — 3.00
...: Bloody Valentine Special (2/98, $3.95, B&W) Jill Thompson-s/a; pin-ups by Ross, Mignola, Russell — 4.00
...: Ghoul's Out For Summer (2002,$14.95, B&W) r/#1-6 — 15.00
...: Holiday Spooktakular (11/98, $2.95, B&W) Jill Thompson-s/a; pin-ups by Brereton, LaBan, Dorkin, Fingerman — 3.00

SCARY GODMOTHER: WILD ABOUT HARRY
Sirius: 2000 - No. 3 ($2.95, B&W, limited series)

1-3-Jill Thompson-s/a — 3.00
TPB (2001, $9.95) r/series — 10.00

SCARY TALES
Charlton Comics: 8/75 - #9, 1/77; #10, 9/77 - #20, 6/79; #21, 8/80 - #46, 10/84

	GD	VG	FN	VF	VF/NM	NM-
1-Origin/1st app. Countess Von Bludd, not in #2	3	6	9	21	33	45
2,4,6,9,10: 4,9-Sutton-c/a. 4-Man-Thing copy	2	4	6	11	16	20
3-Sutton painted-c; Ditko-a	3	6	9	14	20	25
5,11-Ditko-c/a.	3	6	9	16	23	30
7,8-Ditko-a	2	4	6	13	18	22
12,15,16,19,21,39-Ditko-a	2	4	6	11	16	20
13,17,20	2	4	6	9	12	15
14,18,30,32-Ditko-c/a	3	6	9	14	20	25

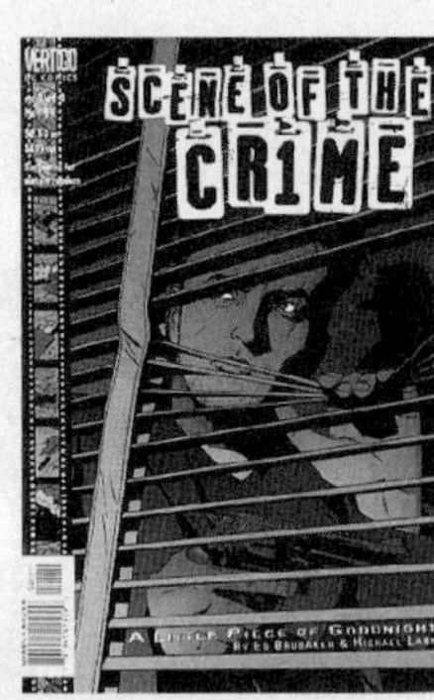

Scene of the Crime #1 © Brubaker & Lark

Scion #22 © CRO

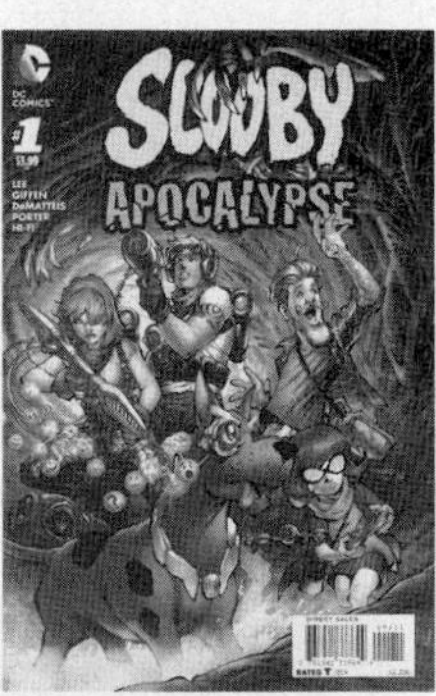

Scooby Apocalypse #1 © H-B

GD VG FN VF VF/NM NM-
2.0 4.0 6.0 8.0 9.0 9.2

22-29,33-37,39,40: 37,38,40-New-a. 39-All Ditko reprints and cover 2 4 6 8 10 12
31,38: 31-Newton-c/a. 38-Mr. Jigsaw app. 2 4 6 8 10 12
41-45-New-a. 41-Ditko-a(3). 42-45-(Low print) 2 4 6 9 12 15
46-Reprints (Low print) 2 4 6 11 16 20
1(Modern Comics reprint, 1977) 1 3 4 6 8 10

NOTE: ***Adkins*** *a-31i; c-31i.* ***Ditko*** *a-3, 5, 7, 8(2), 11, 12, 14-16r, 18(3)r, 19r, 21r, 30r, 32, 39r, 41(3); c-5, 11, 14, 18, 30, 32.* ***Newton*** *a-31p; c-31p.* ***Powell*** *a-18r.* ***Staton*** *a-1(2 pgs.), 4, 20r; c-1, 20.* ***Sutton*** *a-4, 9; c-4, 9.* ***Zeck*** *a-9.*

SCATTERBRAIN
Dark Horse Comics: Jun, 1998 - No. 4, Sept, 1998 ($2.95, limited series)
1-4-Humor anthology by Aragonés, Dorkin, Stevens and others 3.00

SCAVENGERS
Quality Comics: Feb, 1988 - No. 14, 1989 ($1.25/$1.50)
1-14: 9-13-Guice-c 3.00

SCAVENGERS
Triumphant Comics: 1993(nd, July) - No. 11, May, 1994 ($2.50, serially numbered)
1-9,0,10,11: 5,6-Triumphant Unleashed x-over. 9-(3/94). 0-Retail ed. (3/94, $2.50, 36 pgs.). 0-Giveaway edition (3/94, 20 pgs.). 0-Coupon redemption edition. 10-(4/94) 3.00

SCENE OF THE CRIME (Also see Vertigo: Winter's Edge #2)
DC Comics (Vertigo): May, 1999 - No. 4, Aug, 1999 ($2.50, limited series)
1-4-Brubaker-s/Lark-a 3.00
...: A Little Piece of Goodnight TPB ('00, $12.95) r/#1-4; Winter's Edge #2 13.00

SCHOOL DAY ROMANCES (...of Teen-Agers #4; Popular Teen-Agers #5 on)
Star Publications: Nov-Dec, 1949 - No. 4, May-June, 1950 (Teenage)
1-Toni Gayle (later Toni Gay), Ginger Snapp, Midge Martin & Eve Adams begin 39 78 117 231 378 525
2,3: 3-Jane Powell photo on-c & true life story 29 58 87 170 278 385
4-Ronald Reagan photo on-c; L.B. Cole-c 40 80 120 246 411 575

NOTE: *All have* ***L. B. Cole*** *covers.*

SCHWINN BICYCLE BOOK (...Bike Thrills, 1959)
Schwinn Bicycle Co.: 1949; 1952; 1959 (10¢)
1949 6 12 18 31 38 45
1952-Believe It or Not facts; comic format; 36 pgs. 5 10 15 22 26 30
1959 4 7 10 14 17 20

SCIENCE COMICS (1st Series)
Fox Feature Syndicate: Feb, 1940 - No. 8, Sept, 1940
1-Origin Dynamo (1st app., called Electro in #1), The Eagle (1st app.), & Navy Jones; Marga, The Panther Woman (1st app.), Cosmic Carson & Perisphere Payne, Dr. Doom begin; bondage/hypo-c; Electro-c 730 1460 2190 5329 9415 13,500
2-Classic Lou Fine Dynamo-c 411 822 1233 2877 5039 7200
3-Classic Lou Fine Dynamo-c 343 686 1029 2400 4200 6000
4-Kirby-a; Cosmic Carson-c by Joe Simon 343 686 1029 2400 4200 6000
5-8: 5,8-Eagle-c. 6,7-Dynamo-c 206 412 618 1318 2259 3200

NOTE: *Cosmic Carson by* ***Tuska****-#1-3; by* ***Kirby****-#4.* ***Lou Fine*** *c-1-3 only.*

SCIENCE COMICS (2nd Series)
Humor Publications (Ace Magazines?): Jan, 1946 - No. 5, 1946
1-Palais-c/a in #1-3; A-Bomb-c 26 52 78 154 252 350
2 15 30 45 84 127 170
3-Feldstein-a (6 pgs.); Palais-c 19 38 57 111 176 240
4,5: 4-Palais-c 12 24 36 69 97 125

SCIENCE COMICS
Ziff-Davis Publ. Co.: May, 1947 (8 pgs. in color)
nn-Could be ordered by mail for 10¢; like the nn Amazing Adventures (1950) & Boy Cowboy (1950); used to test the market 48 96 114 302 514 725

SCIENCE COMICS (True Science Illustrated)
Export Publication Ent., Toronto, Canada: Mar, 1951 (Distr. in U.S. by Kable News Co.)
1-Science Adventure stories plus some true science features; man on moon story 18 36 54 105 165 225

SCIENCE DOG SPECIAL (Also see Invincible)
Image Comics: Aug, 2010; No. 2, May, 2011 ($3.50)
1,2: 1-Kirkman-s/Walker-a/c; leads into Invincible #75 3.50

SCIENCE FICTION SPACE ADVENTURES (See Space Adventures)

SCION (Also see CrossGen Chronicles)
CrossGeneration Comics: July, 2000 - No. 43, Apr, 2004 ($2.95)
1-43: 1-Marz-s/Cheung-a 3.00

SCI-SPY
DC Comics (Vertigo): Apr, 2002 - No. 6, Sept, 2002 ($2.50, limited series)
1-6-Moench-s/Gulacy-c/a 3.00

SCI-TECH
DC Comics (WildStorm): Sept, 1999 - No. 4, Dec, 1999 ($2.50, limited series)
1-4-Benes-a/Choi & Peterson-s 3.00

SCOOBY APOCALYPSE (Scooby Doo)
DC Comics: Jul, 2016 - Present ($3.99)
1-22: 1-Giffen & DeMatteis-s/Porter-a; covers by Jim Lee and various; team's 1st meeting 4-Intro. Scrappy-Doo. 6-Velma's origin. 7-Eaglesham-a. 9-18-Scrappy-Doo app. 16-22-Secret Squirrel back-up 4.00
.../Hanna-Barbera Halloween Comics Fest Special Edition 1 (12/16, giveaway) previews Scooby Apocalypse, Future Quest, The Flintstones, and Wacky Races 3.00

SCOOBY DOO (TV)(...Where are you? #1-16,26; ...Mystery Comics #17-25, 27 on) (See March Of Comics #356, 368, 382, 391 in the Promotional Comics section)
Gold Key: Mar, 1970 - No. 30, Feb, 1975 (Hanna-Barbera)
1 125 250 375 1000 1750 2500
2-5 16 32 48 108 239 370
6-10 11 22 33 73 157 240
11-20: 11-Tufts-a 8 16 24 54 102 150
21-30: 28-Whitman edition 7 14 21 44 82 120

SCOOBY DOO (TV)
Charlton Comics: Apr, 1975 - No. 11, Dec, 1976 (Hanna-Barbera)
1 10 20 30 66 138 210
2-5 6 12 18 42 79 115
6-11 5 10 15 35 63 90
nn-(1976, digest, 68 pgs., B&W) 5 10 15 30 50 70

SCOOBY-DOO (TV)(Newsstand sales only) (See Dynamutt & Laff-A-Lympics)
Marvel Comics Group: Oct, 1977 - No. 9, Feb, 1979 (Hanna-Barbera)
1-Dyno-Mutt begins 5 10 15 34 60 85
1-(35¢-c variant, limited distribution)(10/77) 10 20 30 70 150 230
2-5 3 6 9 19 30 40
6-9 3 6 9 21 33 45

SCOOBY-DOO (TV)
Harvey Comics: Sept, 1992 - No. 3, May, 1993 ($1.25)
V2#1-3: 3-(Low print and scarce) 2 4 6 10 14 18
Big Book 1,2 (11/92, 4/93, $1.95, 52 pgs.) 2 4 6 8 10 12
Giant Size 1,2 (10/92, 3/93, $2.25, 68 pgs.) 2 4 6 8 10 12

SCOOBY DOO (TV)
Archie Comics: Oct, 1995 -No. 21, June, 1997 ($1.50)
1 2 4 6 11 16 20
2-21: 12-Cover by Scooby Doo creative designer Iwao Takamoto 6.00

SCOOBY DOO (TV)
DC Comics: Aug, 1997 - No. 159, Oct, 2010 ($1.75/$1.95/$1.99/$2.25/$2.50/$2.99)
1 1 3 4 6 8 10
2-10: 5-Begin-$1.95-c 5.00
11-45: 14-Begin $1.99-c 4.00
46-89,91-157: 63-Begin $2.25-c. 75-With 2 Garbage Pail Kids stickers. 100-Wray-c 3.00
90,158,159: 90-($2.95) Bonus stories. 158,159-($2.99-c) 4.00
...Spooky Spectacular 1 (10/99, $3.95) Comic Convention story 4.00
...Spooky Spectacular 2000 (10/00, $3.95) 4.00
...Spooky Summer Special 2001 (8/01, $3.95) Staton-a 4.00
...Super Scarefest (8/02, $3.95) r/#20,25,30-32 4.00

SCOOBY-DOO TEAM-UP (TV)
DC Comics: Jan, 2014 - Present ($2.99)
1-11,13-20,22-35: 1-Batman & Robin app.; Man-Bat app. 2-Ace the Bat-Hound app. 3-Bat-Mite app. 4-Teen Titans Go! 6-Super Friends & Legion of Doom app. 7-Flintstones. 8-Jetsons. 10-Jonny Quest. 13-Spectre, Deadman & Phantom Stranger. 27-Plastic Man. 28-Jonah Hex app. 31-The Atom. 33-Legion of Super-Heroes. 34-Birds of Prey 3.00
12-Harley Quinn, Poison Ivy, Catwoman & Batgirl app. 5.00
21-Harley Quinn, Joker, Batman, Robin & Batgirl app. 3.00
... FCBD Special Edition 1 (6/15, giveaway) flipbook with Teen Titans Go! 3.00
... Halloween Special Edition (12/14, giveaway) r/#1 3.00

SCOOBY-DOO: WHERE ARE YOU? (TV)
DC Comics: Nov, 2010 - Present ($2.99)
1-90: 32-KISS spoof 3.00

SCOOP COMICS (Becomes Yankee Comics #4-7, a digest sized cartoon book; then after #8 it becomes Snap #9)

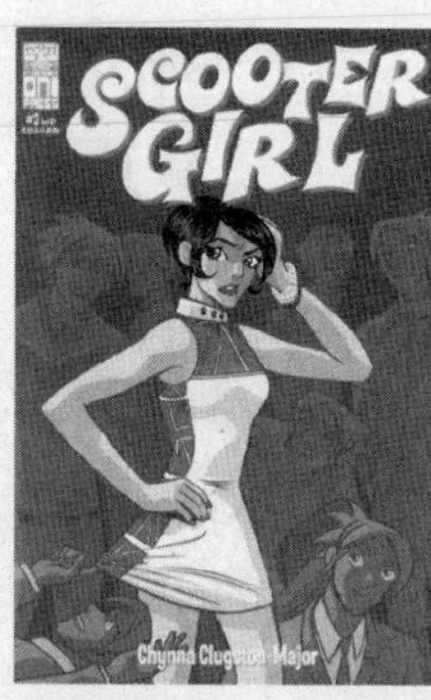

Scooter Girl #3 © Chynna Clugston-Major

Scream #1 © Skywald

Scribbly #9 © DC

	GD 2.0	VG 4.0	FN 6.0	VF 8.0	VF/NM 9.0	NM- 9.2

Harry 'A' Chesler (Holyoke): November, 1941 - No. 3, Mar, 1943; No. 8, 1944

1-Intro. Rocketman & Rocketgirl & begins; origin The Master Key & begins; Dan Hastings begins; Charles Sultan-c/a	155	310	465	992	1696	2400
2-Rocket Boy begins; injury to eye story (reprinted in Spotlight #3); classic-c	271	542	813	1734	2967	4200
3-Injury to eye story-r from #2; Rocket Boy	97	194	291	621	1061	1500
8-Formerly Yankee Comics; becomes Snap	58	116	174	371	636	900

SCOOTER (See Swing With...)

SCOOTER COMICS
Rucker Publ. Ltd. (Canadian): Apr, 1946

1-Teen-age/funny animal	20	40	60	117	189	260

SCOOTER GIRL
Oni Press: May, 2003 - No. 6, Feb, 2004 ($2.99, B&W, limited series)

1-6-Chynna Clugston-Major-s/a 3.00
TPB (5/04, $14.95, digest size) r/series; sketch pages 15.00

SCORPION
Atlas/Seaboard Publ.: Feb, 1975 - No. 3, July, 1975

1-Intro.; bondage-c by Chaykin	3	6	9	15	22	28
2-Chaykin-a w/Wrightson, Kaluta, Simonson assists(p)	3	6	9	15	22	28
3-Jim Craig-c/a	2	4	6	11	16	20

NOTE: ***Chaykin** a-1, 2; c-1. **Colon** c-2. **Craig** c/a-3.*

SCORPION KING, THE (Movie)
Dark Horse Comics: March, 2002 - No. 2, Apr, 2002 ($2.99, limited series)

1,2-Photo-c of the Rock; Richards-a 3.00

SCORPIO ROSE
Eclipse Comics: Jan, 1983 - No. 2, Oct, 1983 ($1.25, Baxter paper)

1,2: Dr. Orient back-up story begins. 2-origin. 4.00

SCOTLAND YARD (Inspector Farnsworth of)(Texas Rangers in Action #5 on?)
Charlton Comics Group: June, 1955 - No. 4, Mar, 1956

1-Tothish-a	14	28	42	82	121	160
2-4: 2-Tothish-a	10	20	30	54	72	90

SCOTT PILGRIM, ... (Inspired the 2010 movie)
Oni Press: Jul, 2004 - Vol. 6, Jul, 2010 ($11.99, B&W, 7-1/2" x 5", multiple printings exist)

Scott Pilgrim's Precious Little Life (Vol. 1) Bryan Lee O'Malley-s/a in all 12.00
Scott Pilgrim Vs. The World (Vol. 2), S.P. & The Infinite Sadness (Vol. 3), S.P. Gets it Together (Vol. 4), S.P. Vs. The Universe (Vol. 5), Scott Pilgrim's Finest Hour (Vol. 6) each 12.00
Free Scott Pilgrim #1 (Free Comic Book Day Edition, 2006) 15.00
Full-Colour Odds & Ends 2008 12.00

SCOURGE, THE
Aspen MLT: No. 0, Aug, 2010 - No. 6, Dec, 2011 ($2.50/$2.99)

0-($2.50) Lobdell-s/Battle-a; multiple covers 3.00
1-6-($2.99) Lobdell-s/Battle-a; multiple covers 3.00

SCOURGE OF THE GODS
Marvel Comics (Soleil): 2009 - No. 3, 2009 ($5.99, limited series)

1-3-Mangin-s/Gajic-a; English version of French comic 6.00
...: The Fall 1-3 (2009 - No. 3, 2009) 6.00

SCOUT (See Eclipse Graphic Album #16, New America & Swords of Texas)
(Becomes Scout: War Shaman)
Eclipse Comics: Dec, 1985 - No. 24, Oct, 1987($1.75/$1.25, Baxter paper)

1-15,17,18,20-24: 19-Airboy preview. 10-Bissette-a. 11-Monday, the Eliminator begins. 15-Swords of Texas 3.00
16,19: 16-Scout 3-D Special ($2.50), 16-Scout 2-D Limited Edition, 19-contains flexidisk ($2.50) 4.00
...Handbook 1 (8/87, $1.75, B&W) 3.00
Mount Fire (1989, $14.95, TPB) r/#8-14 15.00

SCOUT: WAR SHAMAN (Formerly Scout)
Eclipse Comics: Mar, 1988 - No. 16, Dec, 1989 ($1.95)

1-16 3.00

SCRATCH
DC Comics: Aug, 2004 - No. 5, Dec, 2004 ($2.50, limited series)

1-5-Sam Kieth-s/a/c; Batman app. 3.00

SCREAM (...Comics) (Andy Comics #20 on)
Humor Publications/Current Books(Ace Magazines): Autumn, 1944 - No. 19, Apr, 1948

1-Teenage humor	20	40	60	114	182	250
2	13	26	39	72	101	130
3-16: 11-Racist humor (Indians). 16-Intro. Lily-Belle	11	22	33	62	86	110
17,19	10	20	30	56	76	95
18-Hypo needle story	11	22	33	62	86	110

SCREAM (Magazine)
Skywald Publ. Corp.: Aug, 1973 - No. 11, Feb, 1975 (68 pgs., B&W) (Painted-c on all)

1-Nosferatu-c/1st app. (series thru #11); Morrow-a. Cthulhu/Necronomicon-s	8	16	24	52	99	145
2,3: 2-(10/73) Lady Satan 1st app. & series begins; Edgar Allan Poe adaptations begin (thru #11); Phantom of the Opera-s. 3-(12/73) Origin Lady Satan	5	10	15	33	57	80
4-1st Cannibal Werewolf and 1st Lunatic Mummy	4	8	12	28	50	70
5,7,8: 5,7-Frankenstein app. 8-Buckler-a; Werewolf-s; Slither-Slime Man-s	4	8	12	28	50	70
6, 9,10: 6-(6/74) Saga of The Victims/ I Am Horror, classic GGA Hewetson series begins (thru #11); Frankenstein 2073-s. 9-Severed head-c; Marcos-a. 9,10-Werewolf-s. 10-Dracula-c/s	5	10	15	31	53	75
11- (1975 Winter Special) "Mr. Poe and the Raven" story	5	10	15	33	57	80

NOTE: ***Buckler** a-8. **Hewetson** s-1-11. **Marcos** a-9. **Miralles** c-2. **Morrow** a-1. **Poe** s-2-11. **Segrelles** a-7; c-1.*

SCREEN CARTOONS
DC Comics: Dec, 1944 (cover only ashcan)

nn-Ashcan comic, not distributed to newsstands, only for in house use. Covers were produced, but not the rest of the book. A copy sold in 2006 for $400 and in 2008 for $500.

SCREEN COMICS
DC Comics: Dec, 1944 (cover only ashcan)

nn-Ashcan comic, not distributed to newsstands, only for in house use. Covers were produced, but not the rest of the book. A copy sold in 2006 for $400, in 2008 for $500 and in 2013 for $500.

SCREEN FABLES
DC Comics: Dec, 1944 (cover only ashcan)

nn-Ashcan comic, not distributed to newsstands, only for in house use. Covers were produced, but not the rest of the book. A copy sold in 2006 for $400 and in 2008 for $500.

SCREEN FUNNIES
DC Comics: Dec, 1944 (cover only ashcan)

nn-Ashcan comic, not distributed to newsstands, only for in house use. Covers were produced, but not the rest of the book. A copy sold in 2006 for $400 and in 2008 for $500.

SCREEN GEMS
DC Comics: Dec, 1944 (cover only ashcan)

nn-Ashcan comic, not distributed to newsstands, only for in house use. Covers were produced, but not the rest of the book. A copy sold in 2010 for $891 and a VF copy sold for $775.

SCREWBALL SQUIRREL
Dark Horse Comics: July, 1995 - No. 3, Sept, 1995 ($2.50, limited series)

1-3: Characters created by Tex Avery 3.00

SCRIBBLENAUTS UNMASKED: A CRISIS OF IMAGINATION (Based on the video game)
DC Comics: Mar, 2014 - No. 7, Sept, 2014 ($2.99)

1-7: 1-The Bat Family, the Joker and Phantom Stranger app. 3-The Anti-Monitor app. 3.00

SCRIBBLY (See All-American Comics, Buzzy, The Funnies, Leave It To Binky & Popular Comics)
National Periodical Publ.: 8-9/48 - No. 13, 8-9/50; No. 14, 10-11/51 - No. 15, 12-1/51-52

1-Sheldon Mayer-c/a in all; 52 pgs. begin	90	180	270	576	988	1400
2	57	114	171	362	619	875
3-5	47	94	141	296	498	700
6-10	37	74	111	222	361	500
11-15: 13-Last 52 pgs.	32	64	96	188	307	425

SCUD: TALES FROM THE VENDING MACHINE
Fireman Press: 1998 - No. 5 ($2.50, B&W)

1-5: 1-Kaniuga-a. 2-Ruben Martinez-a 3.00

SCUD: THE DISPOSABLE ASSASSIN
Fireman Press: Feb, 1994 - No. 20, 1997 ($2.95, B&W)
Image Comics: No. 21, Feb, 2008 - No. 24, May, 2008 ($3.50, B&W)

1	5	10	15	33	57	80
1-2nd printing in color						5.00
2	2	4	6	9	12	15
3						6.00
4-20						3.00
21-24: 21-(2/08, $3.50) Ashley Wood-c. 22-Mahfood-c						3.50
Heavy 3PO ($12.95, TPB) r/#1-4						13.00
Programmed For Damage ($14.95, TPB) r/#5-9						15.00
Solid Gold Bomb ($17.95, TPB) r/#10-15						18.00

Sea Devils #10 © DC

Second Sight #1 © David Hine

Secret Avengers #26 © MAR

GD 2.0 | VG 4.0 | FN 6.0 | VF 8.0 | VF/NM 9.0 | NM- 9.2

GD 2.0 | VG 4.0 | FN 6.0 | VF 8.0 | VF/NM 9.0 | NM- 9.2

SEA DEVILS (See Showcase #27-29)
National Periodical Publications: Sept-Oct, 1961 - No. 35, May-June, 1967

	GD	VG	FN	VF	VF/NM	NM-
1-(9-10/61)	59	118	177	472	1061	1650
2-Last 10¢ issue; grey-tone-c	27	54	81	194	435	675
3-Begin 12¢ issues thru #35; grey-tone-c	18	36	54	124	275	425
4,5-Grey-tone-c	15	30	45	105	233	360
6-10	10	20	30	69	147	225
11,12,14-20: 12-Grey-tone-c	8	16	24	54	102	150
13-Kubert, Colan-a; Joe Kubert app. in story	8	16	24	55	105	155
21-35: 22-Intro. International Sea Devils; origin & 1st app. Capt. X & Man Fish. 33,35-Grey-tone-c	6	12	18	40	73	105

NOTE: ***Heath** a-Showcase 27-29, 1-10; c-Showcase 27-29, 1-10, 14-16. **Moldoff** a-16i.*

SEA DEVILS (See Tangent Comics/ Sea Devils)

SEADRAGON (Also see the Epsilion Wave)
Elite Comics: May, 1986 - No. 8, 1987 ($1.75)

1-8: 1-1st & 2nd printings exist 3.00

SEAGUY
DC Comics (Vertigo): July, 2004 - No. 3, Sept, 2004 ($2.95, limited series)

1-3-Grant Morrison-s/Cameron Stewart-a/c 3.00
TPB (2005, $9.95) r/#1-3 10.00

SEAGUY: THE SLAVES OF MICKEY EYE
DC Comics (Vertigo): Jun, 2009 - No. 3, Aug, 2009 ($3.99, limited series)

1-3-Grant Morrison-s/Cameron Stewart-a/c 4.00

SEA HOUND, THE (Captain Silver's Log Of The...)
Avon Periodicals: 1945 (no month) - No. 2, Sept-Oct, 1945

	GD	VG	FN	VF	VF/NM	NM-
nn (#1)-29 pg. novel length sty-"The Esmeralda's Treasure"	18	36	54	105	165	225
2	13	26	39	74	105	135

SEA HOUND, THE (Radio)
Capt. Silver Syndicate: No. 3, July, 1949 - No. 4, Sept, 1949

	GD	VG	FN	VF	VF/NM	NM-
3,4	10	20	30	54	72	90

SEA HUNT (TV)
Dell Publishing Co.: No. 928, 8/58 - No. 1041, 10-12/59; No. 4, 1-3/60 - No. 13, 4-6/62 (All have Lloyd Bridges photo-c)

	GD	VG	FN	VF	VF/NM	NM-
Four Color 928(#1)	10	20	30	66	138	210
Four Color 994(#2), 4-13: Manning-a #4-6,8-11,13	7	14	21	48	89	130
Four Color 1041(#3)-Toth-a	7	14	21	48	89	130

SEA OF RED
Image Comics: Mar, 2005 - No. 13, Nov, 2006 ($2.95/$2.99/$3.50)

1-12-Vampirates at sea; Remender & Dwyer-s/Dwyer & Sam-a 3.00
13-($3.50) 3.50
Vol. 1: No Grave But The Sea (9/05, $8.95) r/#1-4 9.00
Vol. 2: No Quarter (2006, $11.99) r/#5-8 12.00
Vol. 3: The Deadlights (2006, $14.99) r/#9-13 15.00

SEAQUEST (TV)
Nemesis Comics: Mar, 1994 ($2.25)

1-Has 2 diff-c stocks (slick & cardboard); Alcala-i 3.00

SEARCHERS, THE (Movie)
Dell Publishing Co.: No. 709, 1956

	GD	VG	FN	VF	VF/NM	NM-
Four Color 709-John Wayne photo-c	24	48	72	168	372	575

SEARCHERS, THE
Caliber Comics: 1996 - No. 4, 1996 ($2.95, B&W)

1-4 3.00

SEARCHERS, THE : APOSTLE OF MERCY
Caliber Comics: 1997 - No. 2, 1997 ($2.95/$3.95, B&W)

1-($2.95) 3.00
2-($3.95) 4.00

SEARCH FOR LOVE
American Comics Group: Feb-Mar, 1950 - No. 2, Apr-May, 1950 (52 pgs.)

	GD	VG	FN	VF	VF/NM	NM-
1	15	30	45	83	124	165
2	10	20	30	58	79	100

SEARS (See Merry Christmas From...)

SEASON'S GREETINGS
Hallmark (King Features): 1935 (6-1/4x5-1/4", 24 pgs. in color)

nn-Cover features Mickey Mouse, Popeye, Jiggs & Skippy. "The Night Before Christmas" told one panel per page, each panel by a famous artist featuring their character. Art by Alex Raymond, Gottfredson, Swinnerton, Segar, Chic Young, Milt Gross, Sullivan (Messmer), Herriman, McManus, Percy Crosby & others (22 artists in all)
Estimated value... 950.00

SEBASTIAN O
DC Comics (Vertigo): May, 1993 - No. 3, July, 1993 ($1.95, limited series)

1-3-Grant Morrison scripts; Steve Yeowell-a 3.00
TPB (2004, $9.95) r/#1-3; intro. chronology by Morrison 10.00

SECOND LIFE OF DOCTOR MIRAGE, THE (See Shadowman #16)
Valiant: Nov, 1993 - No. 18, May, 1995 ($2.50)

1-18: 1-With bound-in poster. 5-Shadowman x-over. 7-Bound-in trading card 3.00
1-Gold ink logo edition; no price on-c 6.00

SECOND SIGHT
AfterShock Comics: Feb, 2016 - Present ($3.99)

1-6-David Hine-s/Alberto Ponticelli-a 4.00

SECRET AGENT (Formerly Sarge Steel)
Charlton Comics: V2#9, Oct, 1966; V2#10, Oct, 1967

	GD	VG	FN	VF	VF/NM	NM-
V2#9-Sarge Steel part-r begins	3	6	9	16	24	32
10-Tiffany Sinn, CIA app. (from Career Girl Romances #39); Aparo-a	3	6	9	14	19	24

SECRET AGENT (TV) (See Four Color #1231)
Gold Key: Nov, 1966; No. 2, Jan, 1968

	GD	VG	FN	VF	VF/NM	NM-
1-John Drake photo-c	7	14	21	49	92	135
2-Photo-c	5	10	15	35	63	90

SECRET AGENT X-9 (See Flash Gordon #4 by King)
David McKay Publ.: 1934 (Book 1: 84 pgs.; Book 2: 124 pgs.) (8x7-1/2")

	GD	VG	FN	VF	VF/NM	NM-
Book 1-Contains reprints of the first 13 weeks of the strip by Alex Raymond; complete except for 2 dailies	47	94	141	296	498	700
Book 2-Contains reprints immediately following contents of Book 1, for 20 weeks by Alex Raymond; complete except for two dailies. Note: Raymond mis-dated the last five strips from 6/34, and while the dating sequence is confusing, the continuity is correct	40	80	120	246	411	575

SECRET AGENT X-9 (See Magic Comics)
Dell Publishing Co.: Dec, 1937 (Not by Raymond)

	GD	VG	FN	VF	VF/NM	NM-
Feature Books 8	52	104	156	328	552	775

SECRET AGENT Z-2 (See Holyoke One-Shot No. 7)

SECRET AVENGERS (The Heroic Age)
Marvel Comics: Jul, 2010 - No. 37, Mar, 2013 ($3.99)

1-Bendis-s/Deodato-a/Djurdjevic-c; Steve Rogers assembles covert squad 4.00
1-Variant-c by Yardin 6.00
2-12: 2-Two covers. 2-4-Deodato-a. 5-Nick Fury app.; Aja-a 4.00
12.1 ($2.99) Spencer-s/Eaton-a/Deodato-c 3.00
13-21: 13-15-Fear Itself tie-in; Granov-c. 15-Aftermath of Bucky's demise. 16-21-Ellis-s 4.00
21.2-($2.99) Remender-s/Zircher-a; intro. new Masters of Evil 3.00
22-37: 22-25-Remender-s/Hardman-a/Art Adams-c. 23-Venom joins. 26-28-A vs. X 4.00

SECRET AVENGERS (Marvel NOW!)
Marvel Comics: Apr, 2013 - No. 16, Apr, 2014 ($3.99)

1-16: 1-5-Spencer-s/Luke Ross-a/Coker-c; Agent Coulson app. 5,7-Hulk app. 7,9-Guice-a 9,16-Winter Soldier app. 4.00

SECRET AVENGERS (All-New Marvel NOW!)
Marvel Comics: May, 2014 - No. 15, Jun, 2015 ($3.99)

1-15: 1-Ales Kot-s/Michael Walsh-a; M.O.D.O.K. app. 7-Deadpool app. 4.00

SECRET CITY SAGA (See Jack Kirby's Secret City Saga)

SECRET DEFENDERS (Also see The Defenders & Fantastic Four #374)
Marvel Comics: Mar, 1993 - No. 25, Mar, 1995 ($1.75/$1.95)

1-($2.50)-Red foil stamped-c; Dr. Strange, Nomad, Wolverine, Spider Woman & Darkhawk begin 4.00
2-11,13-24: 9-New team w/Silver Surfer, Thunderstrike, Dr. Strange & War Machine. 13-Thanos replaces Dr. Strange as leader; leads into Cosmic Powers limited series; 14-Dr. Druid. 15-Bound in card sheet. 15-17-Deadpool app. 18-Giant Man & Iron Fist app. 3.00
12,25: 12-($2.50)-Prismatic foil-c. 25 ($2.50, 52 pgs.) 4.00

SECRET DIARY OF EERIE ADVENTURES
Avon Periodicals: 1953 (25¢ giant, 100 pgs., one-shot)

	GD	VG	FN	VF	VF/NM	NM-
nn-(Rare)-Kubert-a; Hollingsworth-c; Sid Check back-c	343	686	1029	2400	4200	6000

Secret Empire #8 © MAR

Secret Hearts #127 © DC

Secret Invasion #8 © MAR

	GD 2.0	VG 4.0	FN 6.0	VF 8.0	VF/NM 9.0	NM- 9.2

SECRET EMPIRE (Also see Free Comic Book Day 2017 Secret Empire)
Marvel Comics: No. 0, Jun, 2017 - No. 10, Oct, 2017 ($4.99/$3.99, limited series)

0-2-($4.99): 0-Spencer-s/Acuña-a; Steve Rogers and Hydra take over. 1-McNiven-a 5.00
3-5,7-($3.99) 3,5-Sorrentino-a. 4-Yu-a. 5-Bruce Banner returns 4.00
6,8-10-($4.99): 6,9-Yu-a. 7-Black Widow killed. 8-Acuña-a. 10-McNiven-a 5.00
... Omega 1 (11/17, $4.99) Epilogue to series; Sorrentino & Bennett-a 5.00
...: Underground 1 (8/17, $4.99) Whitley-s/Koda-a; takes place after #4; Sauron app. 5.00
...: United 1 (8/17, $4.99) X-Men & Deadpool app.; Anindito-a 5.00
...: Uprising 1 (7/17, $4.99) The Champions & Black Widow app.; Landy-s/Cassara-a 5.00

SECRET EMPIRE: BRAVE NEW WORLD
Marvel Comics: Aug, 2017 - No. 5, Oct, 2017 ($3.99, limited series)

1-5: Namor/Invaders and back-up short stories of various heroes under Hydra rule 5.00

SECRET FILES & ORIGINS GUIDE TO THE DC UNIVERSE
DC Comics: Mar, 2000; Feb, 2002 ($6.95/$4.95)

2000 (3/00, $6.95)-Overview of DC characters; profile pages by various 7.00
2001-2002 (2/02, $4.95) Olivetti-c 5.00

SECRET FILES PRESIDENT LUTHOR
DC Comics: Mar, 2001 ($4.95, one-shot)

1-Short stories & profile pages by various; Harris-c 5.00

SECRET HEARTS
National Periodical Publications (Beverly)(Arleigh No. 50-113):
9-10/49 - No. 6, 7-8/50; No. 7, 12-1/51-52 - No. 153, 7/71

	GD	VG	FN	VF	VF/NM	NM-
1-Kinstler-a; photo-c begin, end #6	65	130	195	416	708	1000
2-Toth-a (1 pg.); Kinstler-a	36	72	108	211	343	475
3,6 (1950)	31	62	96	186	303	420
4,5-Toth-a	32	64	96	190	310	430
7(12-1/51-52) (Rare)	43	86	129	271	461	650
8-10 (1952)	24	48	72	140	230	320
11-20	18	36	54	107	169	230
21-26: 26-Last precode (2-3/55)	16	32	48	92	144	195
27-40	8	16	24	51	96	140
41-50	6	12	18	40	73	105
51-60	5	10	15	35	63	90
61-75,100: 75-Last 10¢ issue	5	10	15	31	53	75
76-99,101-109: 83,88-Each has panel which inspired a famous Roy Lichtenstein painting	4	8	12	23	37	50
110- "Reach for Happiness" serial begins, ends #138	4	8	12	25	40	55
111-119,121-126: 114-Colan-a/c	3	6	9	17	26	35
120,134-Neal Adams-c	4	8	12	25	40	55
127 (4/68)-Beatles cameo	4	8	12	27	44	60
128-133,135-142: 141,142- "20 Miles to Heartbreak", Chapter 2 & 3 (see Young Love for Chapters 1 & 4); Toth, Colletta-a	3	6	9	16	24	32
143-148,150-152: 144-Morrow-a	3	6	9	14	20	26
149,153: 149-Toth-a. 153-Kirby-i	3	6	9	15	22	28

SECRET HISTORY OF THE AUTHORITY: HAWKSMOOR
DC Comics (WildStorm): May, 2008 - No. 6, Oct, 2008 ($2.99, limited series)

1-6-Costa-s/Staples-a/Hamner-c 3.00
TPB (2009, $19.99) r/#1-6 20.00

SECRET IDENTITIES
Image Comics: Feb, 2015 - No. 7, Sept, 2015 ($3.50/$3.99)

1-6-Faerber & Joines-s/Kyriazis-a 3.50
7-($3.99) 4.00

SECRET INVASION (Also see Mighty Avengers, New Avengers, and Skrulls!)
Marvel Comics: June, 2008 - No. 8, Jan, 2009 ($3.99, limited series)

1-Skrull invasion; Bendis-s/Yu-a/Dell'Otto-c 4.00
1-Variant cover with blank area for sketches 4.00
1-McNiven variant-c 12.00
1-Yu variant-c 30.00
1-2nd printing with old Avengers variant-c by Yu 4.00
1 Director's Cut (2008, $4.99) r/#1 with script; concept and promo art; cover gallery 5.00
2-8-Dell'Otto-c. 8-Wasp killed 4.00
2-4-McNiven variant-c. 2-Avengers. 3-Nick Fury. 4-Tony Stark, Spider-Woman, Black Widow 6.00
2-8-Yu variant-c. 2-Hawkeye & Mockingbird. 3-Spider-Woman. 4-Nick Fury 10.00
5-Rubi variant-c 5.00
6-Cho Spider-Woman variant-c 8.00
...:Aftermath: Beta Ray Bill - The Green of Eden (6/09, $3.99) Brereton-a 4.00
...: Chronicles 1,2 (4/09,6/09, $5.99) reprints from New Avengers & Illuminati issues 6.00
... Dark Reign (2/09, $3.99) villain meeting after #8; previews new series; Maleev-a/c 4.00
... Dark Reign (2/09, $3.99) Variant Green Goblin cover by Bryan Hitch 8.00
... Requiem (2009, $3.99) Hank Pym becomes The Wasp; r/TTA #44 & Avengers #215 4.00
... Saga (2008, giveaway) history of the Skrulls told through reprint panels and text 3.00
...: The Infiltration TPB (2008, $19.99) r/FF #2; New Avengers #31,32,38,39; New Avengers: Illuminati #1,5; Mighty Avengers #7; and Avengers: The Initiative Annual #1 20.00
...: War of Kings (2/09, $3.99) Black Bolt and the Inhumans; Pelletier & Dazo-a 4.00
...: Who Do You Trust? (8/08, $3.99) short tie-in stories by various; Jimenez-c 4.00

SECRET INVASION: AMAZING SPIDER-MAN
Marvel Comics: Oct, 2008 - No. 3, Dec, 2008 ($2.99, limited series)

1-3-Jackpot battles a Super-Skrull; Santucci-a. 2-Menace app. 3.00

SECRET INVASION: FANTASTIC FOUR
Marvel Comics: July, 2008 - No. 3, Sept, 2008 ($2.99, limited series)

1-3-Skrulls and Lyja invade; Kitson-a/Davis-c 3.00
1-Variant Skrull cover by McKone 5.00

SECRET INVASION: FRONT LINE
Marvel Comics: Sept, 2008 - No. 5, Jan, 2009 ($2.99, limited series)

1-5-Ben Urich covering the Skrull invasion; Reed-s/Castiello-a 3.00

SECRET INVASION: INHUMANS
Marvel Comics: Oct, 2008 - No. 4, Jan, 2009 ($2.99, limited series)

1-4-Raney-a/Sejic-c/Pokasky-s; search for Black Bolt 3.00

SECRET INVASION: RUNAWAYS/YOUNG AVENGERS (Follows Runaways #30)
Marvel Comics: Aug, 2008 - No. 3, Nov, 2008 ($2.99, limited series)

1-3-Miyazawa-a/Ryan-c 3.00

SECRET INVASION: THOR
Marvel Comics: Oct, 2008 - No. 3, Dec, 2008 ($2.99, limited series)

1-3-Fraction-s/Braithwaite-a; Skrulls invade Asgard; Beta Ray Bill app. 3.00
1-2nd printing with Beta Ray Bill cover 3.00

SECRET INVASION: X-MEN
Marvel Comics: Oct, 2008 - No. 4, Jan, 2009 ($2.99, limited series)

1-4-Carey-s/Nord-a/Dodson-c; Skrulls invade San Francisco 3.00
1-2nd printing with variant Nord-c 3.00

SECRET ISLAND OF OZ, THE (See First Comics Graphic Novel)

SECRET LOVE (See Fox Giants & Sinister House of...)

SECRET LOVE
Ajax-Farrell/Four Star Comic Corp. No. 2 on: 12/55 - No. 3, 8/56; 4/57 - No. 5, 2/58; No. 6, 6/58

	GD	VG	FN	VF	VF/NM	NM-
1(12/55-Ajax, 1st series)	14	28	42	78	112	145
2,3	10	20	30	56	76	95
1(4/57-Ajax, 2nd series)	11	22	33	64	90	115
2-6: 5-Bakerish-a	9	18	27	50	65	80

SECRET LOVES
Comic Magazines/Quality Comics Group: Nov, 1949 - No. 6, Sept, 1950

	GD	VG	FN	VF	VF/NM	NM-
1-Ward-c	32	64	96	188	307	425
2-Ward-c	25	50	75	150	245	340
3-Crandall-a	17	34	51	98	154	210
4,6	15	30	45	84	127	170
5-Suggestive art "Boom Town Babe"; photo-c	20	40	60	117	189	260

SECRET LOVE STORIES (See Fox Giants)

SECRET MISSIONS (Admiral Zacharia's...)
St. John Publishing Co.: February, 1950

	GD	VG	FN	VF	VF/NM	NM-
1-Joe Kubert-c; stories of U.S. foreign agents	22	44	66	128	209	290

SECRET MYSTERIES (Formerly Crime Mysteries & Crime Smashers)
Ribage/Merit Publications No. 17 on: No. 16, Nov, 1954 - No. 19, July, 1955

	GD	VG	FN	VF	VF/NM	NM-
16-Horror, Palais-a; Myron Fass-c	39	78	117	231	378	525
17-19-Horror. 17-Fass-c; mis-dated 3/54?	30	60	90	177	289	400

SECRET ORIGINS (1st Series) (See 80 Page Giant #8)
National Periodical Publications: Aug-Oct, 1961 (Annual) (Reprints)

	GD	VG	FN	VF	VF/NM	NM-
1-Origin Adam Strange (Showcase #17), Green Lantern (Green Lantern #1), Challengers (partial-r/Showcase #6, 6 pgs. Kirby-a), J'onn J'onzz (Det. #225), The Flash (Showcase #4), Green Arrow (1 pg. text), Superman-Batman team (World's Finest #94), Wonder Woman (Wonder Woman #105)	44	88	132	326	738	1150

Replica Edition (1998, $4.95) r/entire book and house ads 5.00
Even More Secret Origins (2003, $6.95) reprints origins of Hawkman, Eclipso, Kid Flash, Blackhawks, Green Lantern's oath, and Jimmy Olsen-Robin team in 80 pg. Giant style 7.00

SECRET ORIGINS (2nd Series)

Secret Origins (2nd series) #5 © DC

Secret Service #6 © Millar & Gibbons

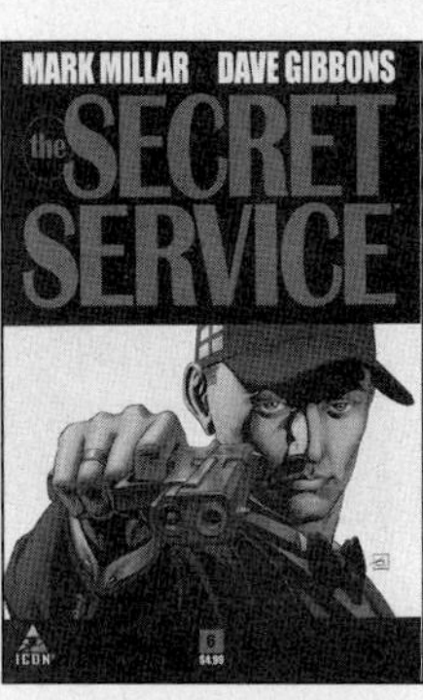

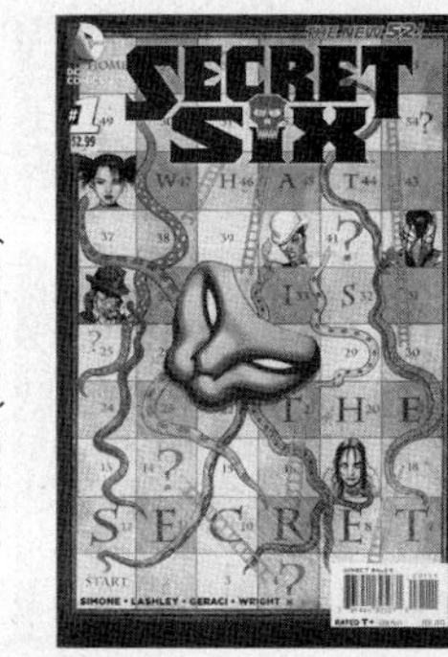

Secret Six (2015 series) #1 © DC

	GD 2.0	VG 4.0	FN 6.0	VF 8.0	VF/NM 9.0	NM- 9.2

National Periodical Publications: Feb-Mar, 1973 - No. 6, Jan-Feb, 1974; No. 7, Oct-Nov, 1974 (All 20¢ issues) (All origin reprints)

1-Superman(r/1 pg. origin/Action #1, 1st time since G.A.), Batman(Detective #33), Ghost(Flash #88), The Flash(Showcase #4) 5 10 15 34 60 85
2-7: 2-Green Lantern & The Atom(Showcase #22 & 34), Supergirl(Action #252). 3-Wonder Woman (W.W. #1), Wildcat (Sensation #1). 4-Vigilante (Action #42) by Meskin, Kid Eternity(Hit #25). 5-The Spectre by Baily (More Fun #52,53). 6-Blackhawk(Military #1) & Legion of Super-Heroes(Superboy #147). 7-Robin (Detective #38), Aquaman (More Fun #73) 3 6 9 19 30 40

NOTE: ***Infantino** a-1. **Kane** a-2. **Kubert** a-1.*

SECRET ORIGINS (3rd Series)
DC Comics: Apr, 1986 - No. 50, Aug, 1990 (All origins)(52 pgs. #6 on)(#27 on: $1.50)

1-Origin Superman 1 2 3 5 6 8
2-6: 2-Blue Beetle. 3-Shazam. 4-Firestorm. 5-Crimson Avenger. 6-Halo/G.A. Batman 4.00
7-9,11,12,15-20,22-26: 7-Green Lantern (Guy Gardner)/G.A. Sandman. 8-Shadow Lass/Doll Man. 9-G.A. Flash/Skyman.11-G.A. Hawkman/Power Girl. 12-Challengers of Unknown/ G.A. Fury (2nd modern app.). 15-Spectre/Deadman. 16-G.A. Hourman/Warlord. 17-Adam Strange story by Carmine Infantino; Dr. Occult. 18-G.A. Gr. Lantern/The Creeper. 19-Uncle Sam/The Guardian. 20-Batgirl/G.A. Dr. Mid-Nite. 22-Manhunters. 23-Floronic Man/Guardians of the Universe. 24-Blue Devil/Dr. Fate. 25-LSH/Atom. 26-Black Lightning/Miss America 4.00
10-Phantom Stranger w/Alan Moore scripts; Legends spin-off 4.00
13-Origin Nightwing; Johnny Thunder app. 4.00
14-Suicide Squad; Legends spin-off 1 2 3 5 6 8
21-Jonah Hex/Black Condor 4.00
27-30,36-38,40-49: 27-Zatara/Zatanna. 28-Midnight/Nightshade. 29-Power of the Atom/Mr. America; new 3 pg. Red Tornado story by Mayer (last app. of Scribbly, 8/88). 30-Plastic Man/Elongated Man. 36-Poison Ivy by Neil Gaiman & Mark Buckingham/Green Lantern. 37-Legion Of Substitute Heroes/Doctor Light. 38-Green Arrow/Speedy; Grell scripts. 40-All Ape issue. 41-Rogues Gallery of Flash. 42-Phantom Girl/GrimGhost. 43-Original Hawk & Dove/Cave Carson/Chris KL-99. 44-Batman app.; story based on Det. #40. 45-Blackhawk/ El Diablo. 46-JLA/LSH/New Titans. 47-LSH. 48-Ambush Bug/Stanley & His Monster/Rex the Wonder Dog/Trigger Twins. 49-Newsboy Legion/Silent Knight/Bouncing Boy 3.00
31-35,39: 31-JSA. 32-JLA. 33-35-JLI. 39-Animal Man-c/story continued in Animal Man #10; Grant Morrison scripts; Batman app. 3.00
50-($3.95, 100 pgs.)-Batman & Robin in text, Flash of Two Worlds, Johnny Thunder, Dolphin, Black Canary & Space Museum 5.00
Annual 1 (8/87)-Capt. Comet/Doom Patrol 4.00
Annual 2 ('88, $2.00)-Origin Flash II & Flash III 4.00
Annual 3 ('89, $2.95, 84 pgs.)-Teen Titans; 1st app. new Flamebird who replaces original Bat-Girl 4.00
Special 1 (10/89, $2.00)-Batman villains: Penguin, Riddler, & Two-Face; Bolland-c; Sam Kieth-a; Neil Gaiman scripts(2) 5.00

NOTE: ***Art Adams** a-33i(part). **M. Anderson** 8, 19, 21, 25i; c-19(part). **Aparo** c/a-10. **Bissette** c-23. **Bolland** c-7. **Byrne** c/a-Annual 1. **Colan** c/a-5p. **Forte** a-37. **Giffen** a-18p, 44p, 48. **Infantino** a-17, 50p. **Kaluta** c-39. **Gil Kane** a-2, 28; c-2p. **Kirby** c-19(part). **Erik Larsen** a-13. **Mayer** a-29. **Morrow** a-21. **Orlando** a-10. **Perez** a-50i, Annual 3i; c- Annual 3. **Rogers** a-6p. **Russell** a-27i. **Simonson** c-22. **Staton** a-36, 50p. **Steacy** a-35. **Tuska** a-4p, 9p.*

SECRET ORIGINS (4th Series)(DC New 52)
DC Comics: Jun, 2014 - No. 11, May, 2015 ($4.99)

1-3,5-9,11: 1-Origin Superman, Robin. 2-Batman. 6-Wonder Woman 5.00
4-Harley Quinn 2 4 6 8 10 12
10-Batgirl; Stewart & Fletcher-s/Koh-a; Firestorm & Poison Ivy 6.00

SECRET ORIGINS 80 PAGE GIANT (Young Justice)
DC Comics: Dec, 1998 ($4.95, one-shot)

1-Origin-s of Young Justice members; Ramos-a (Impulse) 5.00

SECRET ORIGINS FEATURING THE JLA
DC Comics: 1999 ($14.95, TPB)

1-Reprints recent origin-s of JLA members; Cassaday-c 15.00

SECRET ORIGINS OF SUPER-HEROES (See DC Special Series #10, 19)

SECRET ORIGINS OF SUPER-VILLAINS 80 PAGE GIANT
DC Comics: Dec, 1999 ($4.95, one-shot)

1-Origin-s of Sinestro, Amazo and others; Gibbons-c 5.00

SECRET ORIGINS OF THE WORLD'S GREATEST SUPER-HEROES
DC Comics: 1989 ($4.95, 148 pgs.)

nn-Reprints Superman, JLA origins; new Batman origin-s; Bolland-c 1 2 3 4 5 7

SECRET ROMANCE
Charlton Comics: Oct, 1968 - No. 41, Nov, 1976; No. 42, Mar, 1979 - No. 48, Feb, 1980

1-Begin 12¢ issues, ends #? 3 6 9 17 26 35
2-10: 9-Reese-a 2 4 6 11 16 20
11-16,18,19,21-30 2 4 6 9 13 16
17,20: 17-Susan Dey poster. 20-David Cassidy pin-up 2 4 6 11 16 20
31-48 2 4 6 8 10 12

NOTE: *Beyond the Stars app.-No. 9, 11, 12, 14.*

SECRET ROMANCES (Exciting Love Stories)
Superior Publications Ltd.: Apr, 1951 - No. 27, July, 1955

1 21 42 63 124 202 280
2 15 30 45 84 127 170
3-10 14 28 42 76 108 140
11-13,15-18,20-27 12 24 36 67 94 120
14,19-Lingerie panels 12 24 36 69 97 125

SECRET SERVICE (See Kent Blake of the...)

SECRET SERVICE (Inspired the 2015 movie Kingsmen: The Secret Service)(Also see Kingsmen: The Red Diamond)
Marvel Comics (Icon): Jun, 2012 - No. 6, Jun, 2013 ($2.99/$4.99, limited series)

1-5-Mark Millar-s/Dave Gibbons-a/c 3.00
6-($4.99) 5.00

SECRET SIX (See Action Comics Weekly)
National Periodical Publications: Apr-May, 1968 - No. 7, Apr-May, 1969 (12¢)

1-Origin/1st app. 6 12 18 37 66 95
2-7 4 8 12 23 37 50

SECRET SIX (See Tangent Comics/ Secret Six)

SECRET SIX (See Villains United)
DC Comics: Jul, 2006 - No. 6, Jan, 2007 ($2.99, limited series)

1-6-Gail Simone-s/Brad Walker-a. 4-Doom Patrol app. 3.00
...: Six Degrees of Devastation TPB (2007, $14.99) r/#1-6 15.00

SECRET SIX
DC Comics: Nov, 2008 - No. 36, Oct, 2011 ($2.99)

1-36: 1-Gail Simone-s/Nicola Scott-a. 2-Batman app. 8-Rodriguez-a. 11-13-Wonder Woman & Artemis app. 16-Black Alice app. 17,18-Blackest Night 3.00
...: Cats in the Cradle TPB (2011, $14.99) r/#19-24 15.00
...: Danse Macabre TPB (2010, $14.99) r/#15-18 & Suicide Squad #67 (Blackest Night) 15.00
...: Depths TPB (2010, $14.99) r/#8-14 15.00
...: The Reptile Brain TPB (2011, $14.99) r/#25-29 15.00
...: Unhinged TPB (2009, $14.99) r/#1-7; intro. by Paul Cornell 15.00

SECRET SIX
DC Comics: Feb, 2015 - No. 14, Jul, 2016 ($2.99)

1-14: 1,2-Simone-s/Lashley-a; Catman & Black Alice app. 10-Superman app. 12-14-Shiva app.; Elongated Man returns 3.00

SECRET SOCIETY OF SUPER-VILLAINS
National Per. Publ./DC Comics: May-June, 1976 - No. 15, June-July, 1978

1-Origin; JLA cameo & Capt. Cold app. 3 6 9 14 19 24
2-5,15: 2-Re-intro/origin Capt. Comet; Green Lantern x-over. 5-Green Lantern, Hawkman x-over; Darkseid app. 15-G.A. Atom, Dr. Midnite, & JSA app. 2 4 6 8 11 14
6-14: 9,10-Creeper x-over. 11-Capt. Comet; Orlando-i 2 3 4 6 8 10

SECRET SOCIETY OF SUPER-VILLAINS SPECIAL (See DC Special Series #6)

SECRETS OF HAUNTED HOUSE
National Periodical Publications/DC Comics: 4-5/75 - #5, 12-1/75-76; #6, 6-7/77 - #14, 10-11/78; #15, 8/79 - #46, 3/82

1 5 10 15 34 60 85
2-4 3 6 9 19 30 40
5-Wrightson-c 4 8 12 23 37 50
6-14 2 4 6 11 16 20
15-30 2 4 6 8 11 14
31,44: 31-(12/80) Mr. E series begins (1st app.), ends #41. 44-Wrightson-c 2 4 6 9 13 16
32-(1/81) Origin of Mr. E 2 4 6 8 11 14
33-43,45,46: 34,35-Frankenstein Monster app. 1 3 4 6 8 10

NOTE: ***Aparo** c-7. **Aragones** a-1. **B. Bailey** a-8. **Bissette** a-46. **Buckler** c-32-40p. **Ditko** a-9, 12, 41, 45. **Golden** a-10. **Howard** a-13i. **Kaluta** c-8, 10, 11, 14, 16, 29. **Kubert** c-41, 42. **Sheldon Mayer** a-43p. **McWilliams** a-35. **Nasser** a-24. **Newton** a-30p. **Nino** a-1, 13, 19. **Orlando** c-13, 30, 43, 45i. **N. Redondo** a-4, 5, 29. **Rogers** c-26. **Spiegle** a-31-41. **Wrightson** c-5, 44.*

SECRETS OF HAUNTED HOUSE SPECIAL (See DC Special Series #12)

SECRETS OF LIFE (Movie)
Dell Publishing Co.: 1956 (Disney)

Four Color 749-Photo-c 5 10 15 31 53 75

SECRETS OF LOVE (See Popular Teen-Agers...)

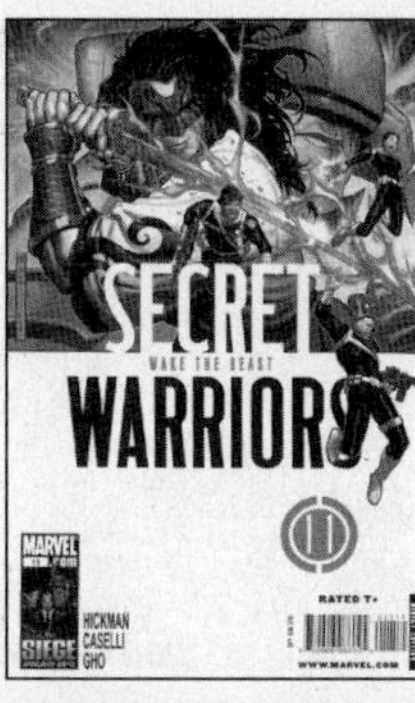

Secret Warriors #11 © MAR

Secret Wars (2015 series) #9 © MAR

Secret Weapons #4 © VAL

	GD 2.0	VG 4.0	FN 6.0	VF 8.0	VF/NM 9.0	NM- 9.2

SECRETS OF LOVE AND MARRIAGE
Charlton Comics: V2#1, Aug, 1956 - V2#25, June, 1961

	GD	VG	FN	VF	VF/NM	NM-
V2#1-Matt Baker-c?	6	12	18	42	79	115
V2#2-6	4	8	12	23	37	50
V2#7-9-(All 68 pgs.)	5	10	15	35	63	90
10-25	3	6	9	19	30	40

SECRETS OF MAGIC (See Wisco)

SECRETS OF SINISTER HOUSE (Sinister House of Secret Love #1-4)
National Periodical Publ.: No. 5, June-July, 1972 - No. 18, June-July, 1974

	GD	VG	FN	VF	VF/NM	NM-
5-(52 pgs.).	6	12	18	38	69	100
6-9: 7-Redondo-a	4	8	12	23	37	50
10-Neal Adams-a(i)	4	8	12	25	40	55
11-18: 15-Redondo-a. 17-Barry-a; early Chaykin 1 pg. strip	3	6	9	16	23	30

NOTE: ***Alcala** a-6, 13, 14. **Glanzman** a-7. **Kaluta** c-6, 7. **Nino** a-8, 11-13. Ambrose Bierce adapt.-#14.*

SECRETS OF THE LEGION OF SUPER-HEROES
DC Comics: Jan, 1981 - No. 3, Mar, 1981 (Limited series)

1-3: 1-Origin of the Legion. 2-Retells origins of Brainiac 5, Shrinking Violet, Sun-Boy, Bouncing Boy, Ultra-Boy, Matter-Eater Lad, Mon-El, Karate Kid & Dream Girl 5.00

SECRETS OF TRUE LOVE
St. John Publishing Co.: Feb, 1958

	GD	VG	FN	VF	VF/NM	NM-
1-Matt Baker-c	26	52	78	154	252	350

SECRETS OF YOUNG BRIDES
Charlton Comics: No. 5, Sept, 1957 - No. 44, Oct, 1964; July, 1975 - No. 9, Nov, 1976

	GD	VG	FN	VF	VF/NM	NM-
5	5	10	15	33	57	80
6-10: 8-Negligee panel	4	8	12	23	37	50
11-20	3	6	9	21	33	45
21-30: Last 10¢ issue?	3	6	9	19	30	40
31-44(10/64)	3	6	9	15	22	28
1-(2nd series) (7/75)	3	6	9	16	23	30
2-9	2	4	6	9	12	15

SECRET SQUIRREL (TV)(See Kite Fun Book)
Gold Key: Oct, 1966 (12¢) (Hanna-Barbera)

	GD	VG	FN	VF	VF/NM	NM-
1-1st Secret Squirrel and Morocco Mole, Squiddly Diddly, Winsome Witch	9	18	27	61	123	185

SECRET STORY ROMANCES (Becomes True Tales of Love)
Atlas Comics (TCI): Nov, 1953 - No. 21, Mar, 1956

	GD	VG	FN	VF	VF/NM	NM-
1-Everett-a; Jay Scott Pike-c	23	46	69	138	227	315
2	14	28	42	82	121	160
3-11: 11-Last pre-code (2/55)	14	28	42	76	108	140
12-21	11	22	33	64	90	115

NOTE: ***Colletta** a-10, 14, 15, 17, 21; c-10, 14, 17.*

SECRET VOICE, THE (See Great American Comics Presents...)

SECRET WAR
Marvel Comics: Apr, 2004 - No. 5, Dec, 2005 ($3.99, limited series)

1-Bendis-s/Dell'Otto painted-a/c; 5.00
1-2nd printing with gold logo on white cover and full-color Spider-Man 4.00
1-3rd printing with white cover and B&W sketched Spider-Man 4.00
2-Wolverine-c; intro. Daisy Johnson (Quake) 12.00
2-2nd printing with white cover and B&W sketched Wolverine 12.00
3-5: 3-Capt. America-c. 4-Black Widow-c. 5-Daredevil-c 4.00
... : From the Files of Nick Fury (2005, $3.99) Fury's journal entries; profiles of characters 4.00
HC (2005, $29.99, dust jacket) r/#1-5 & ...From the Files of Nick Fury; additional art 30.00
SC (2006, $24.99) r/#1-5 & ...From the Files of Nick Fury; additional art 25.00

SECRET WARRIORS (Also see 2009 Dark Reign titles)
Marvel Comics: Apr, 2009 - No. 28, Sept, 2011 ($3.99/$2.99)

1-Bendis & Hickman-s/Caselli-a/Cheung-c; Nick Fury app.; Hydra dossier; sketch pages 4.00
2-24,26-28-($2.99) 8-Dark Avengers app. 17-19-Howling Commandos return 3.00
25-($3.99) Baron Strucker app.; Vitti-a 4.00

SECRET WARRIORS (Tie-in to Secret Empire)
Marvel Comics: Jul, 2017 - No. 12, Mar, 2018 ($3.99)

1-12: 1-Rosenberg-s/Garrón-a; Ms. Marvel, Moon Girl, Karnak app. 7-Deadpool app. 4.00

SECRET WARS
Marvel Comics: 2014 (Giveaway)

... No. 1 Halloween Comic Fest 2014 - Reprints Marvel Super Heroes Secret Wars #1 3.00

SECRET WARS (See Free Comic Book Day 2015 for prelude)
Marvel Comics: Jul, 2015 - No. 9, Mar, 2016 ($4.99/$3.99, limited series, originally planned as 8 issues)

1,2-($4.99) Hickman-s/Ribic-a; end of the Marvel 616 and Ultimate universes 5.00
3-8-($3.99): 3-Miles Morales app. 4.00
9-($4.99) End of Battleworld, beginning of the Prime Earth 5.00
...: Agents of Atlas (12/15, $4.99) Taylor-s/Pugh-a/Kirk-c; Baron Zemo app. 5.00
...: Official Guide to the Marvel Multiverse 1 (12/15, $4.99) Handbook-style info on characters, events and realities tied-in with the Secret Wars series 5.00
...: Secret Love 1 (10/15, $4.99) Romance stories by various; Ms. Marvel, Squirrel Girl, Daredevil, Ghost Rider, Iron Fist & Misty Knight app.; 2 covers 5.00
..., Too 1 (1/16, $4.99) Humor short stories by various incl. Powell, Guillory, Leth 5.00

SECRET WARS: BATTLEWORLD
Marvel Comics: Jul, 2015 - No. 4, Oct, 2015 ($3.99, limited series)

1-4-Short stories by various. 2-Howard the Duck app. 4-Silver Surfer app.; Francavilla-c 4.00

SECRET WARS: JOURNAL
Marvel Comics: Jul, 2015 - No. 5, Nov, 2015 ($3.99, limited series)

1-5-Short stories by various. 1-Leads into Siege #1. 3-Isanove-a. 4-Lashley-a 4.00

SECRET WARS 2099
Marvel Comics: Jul, 2015 - No. 5, Nov, 2015 ($3.99, limited series)

1-5-Peter David-s/Will Sliney-a; Avengers vs. Defenders; Baron Mordo app. 4.00

SECRET WARS II (Also see Marvel Super Heroes...)
Marvel Comics Group: July, 1985 - No. 9, Mar, 1986 (Maxi-series)

1,9: 9-(52 pgs.) X-Men app., Spider-Man app. 6.00
2-8: 2,8-X-Men app. 5-1st app. Boom Boom. 5,8-Spider-Man app. 4.00

SECRET WEAPONS
Valiant: Sept, 1993 - No. 21, May, 1995 ($2.25)

1-10,12-21: 3-Reese-a(i). 5-Ninjak app. 9-Bound-in trading card. 12-Bloodshot app. 3.00
11-(Sept. on envelope, Aug on-c, $2.50)-Enclosed in manilla envelope; Bloodshot app; intro new team. 5.00

SECRET WEAPONS
Valiant Entertainment: Jun, 2017 - No. 4, Sept, 2017 ($3.99)

1-4-Heisserer-s/Allén-a 4.00
#0-(1/18, $3.99) Heisserer-s/Pollina-a; origin of Nikki Finch 4.00

SECTAURS
Marvel Comics: June, 1985 - No. 8, Sept, 1986 (75¢) (Based on Coleco Toys)

1-8, 1-Giveaway; same-c with "Coleco 1985 Toy Fair Collectors' Edition" 4.00

SECTION ZERO
Image Comics (Gorilla): June, 2000 - No. 3, Sept, 2000 ($2.50)

1-3-Kesel-s/Grummett-a 3.00

SEDUCTION OF THE INNOCENT (Also see New York State Joint Legislative Committee to Study...)
Rinehart & Co., Inc., N. Y.: 1953, 1954 (400 pgs.) (Hardback, $4.00)(Written by Fredric Wertham, M.D.)(Also printed in Canada by Clarke, Irwin & Co. Ltd.)

	GD	VG	FN	VF	VF/NM	NM-
(1st Version)-with bibliographical note intact (pages 399 & 400)(several copies got out before the comic publishers forced the removal of this page)	233	466	699	1002	1201	1400
Dust jacket only	45	90	135	284	467	675
(1st Version)-without bibliographical note	113	226	339	486	581	675
Dust jacket only	26	52	78	151	251	350
(2nd Version)-Published in England by Rinehart, 1954, 399 pgs. has bibliographical page; "Second print" listed on inside flap of the dust jacket; publication page has no "R" colophon; unlike 1st version	19	38	57	111	176	240
1972 r-/of 2nd version; 400 pgs. w/bibliography page; Kennikat Press	7	14	21	44	82	120
2004 r/with new intro. by Wertham scholar James E. Reibman, 424 pgs; 6" x 9"; limited to 220 copies	7	14	21	44	82	120

NOTE: *Material from this book appeared in the November, 1953 (Vol.70, pp50-53,214) issue of the **Ladies' Home Journal** under the title "What Parents Don't Know About Comic Books". With the release of this book, Dr. Wertham reveals seven years of research attempting to link juvenile delinquency to comic books. Many illustrations showing excessive violence, sex, sadism, and torture are shown. This book was used at the Kefauver Senate hearings which led to the Comics Code Authority. Because of the influence this book had on the comic industry and the collector's interest in it, we feel this listing is justified. Modern printings exist in limited editions. Also see **Parade of Pleasure.***

SEDUCTION OF THE INNOCENT! (Also see Halloween Horror)
Eclipse Comics: Nov, 1985 - 3-D#2, Apr, 1986 ($1.75)

1-6: Double listed under cover title from #7 on 5.00

	GD	VG	FN	VF	VF/NM	NM-
3-D 1 (10/85, $2.25, 36 pgs.)-contains unpublished Advs. Into Darkness #15 (pre-code); Dave Stevens-c	2	4	6	9	12	15
2-D 1 (100 copy limited signed & #ed edition)(B&W)	4	8	12	23	37	50
3-D 2 (4/86)-Baker, Toth, Wrightson-c	1	2	3	5	6	8

Seeker 3000 #1 © MAR

Sensational Spider-Man #25 © MAR

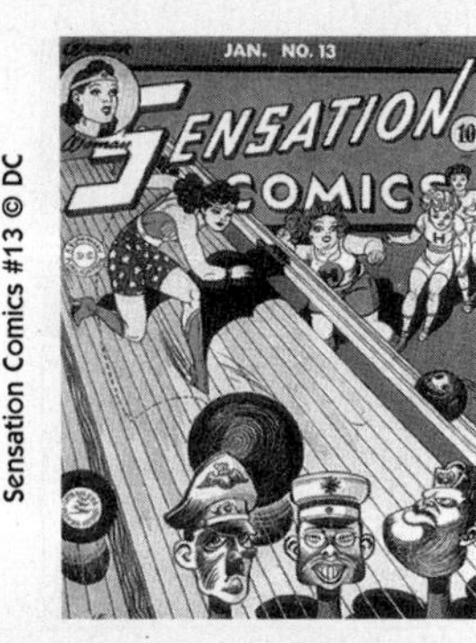

Sensation Comics #13 © DC

GD 2.0 | VG 4.0 | FN 6.0 | VF 8.0 | VF/NM 9.0 | NM- 9.2

GD 2.0 | VG 4.0 | FN 6.0 | VF 8.0 | VF/NM 9.0 | NM- 9.2

2-D 2 (100 copy limited signed & #ed edition)(B&W) 3 6 9 16 23 30
NOTE: ***Anderson** r-2, 3. **Crandall** c/a(r)-1. **Meskin** c/a(r)-3, 3-D 1. **Moreira** r-2. **Toth** a-1-6r; c-4r. **Tuska** r-6.*

SEDUCTION OF THE INNOCENT
Dynamite Entertainment: 2015 - No. 4, 2016 ($3.99, limited series)
1-4-Ande Parks-s/Esteve Polls-a/Francesco Francavilla-c 4.00

SEEKERS INTO THE MYSTERY
DC Comics (Vertigo): Jan, 1996 - No. 15, Apr, 1997 ($2.50)
1-14: J.M. DeMatteis scripts in all. 1-4-Glenn Barr-a. 5,10-Muth-c/a. 6-9-Zulli-c/a. 11-14-Bolton-c; Jill Thompson-a 3.00
15-($2.95)-Muth-c/a 3.00

SEEKER 3000 (See Marvel Premiere #41)
Marvel Comics: Jun, 1998 - No. 4, Sept, 1998 ($2.99/$2.50, limited series)
1-($2.99)-Set 25 years after 1st app.; wraparound-c 4.00
2-4-($2.50) 3.00
...Premiere 1 (6/98, $1.50) Reprints 1st app. from Marvel Premiere #41; wraparound-c 3.00

SELECT DETECTIVE (Exciting New Mystery Cases)
D. S. Publishing Co.: Aug-Sept, 1948 - No. 3, Dec-Jan, 1948-49
1-Matt Baker-a 37 74 111 218 354 490
2-Baker, McWilliams-a 23 46 69 138 227 315
3 18 36 54 107 169 230

SEMPER FI (Tales of the Marine Corp)
Marvel Comics: Dec, 1988- No.9, Aug, 1989 (75¢)
1-9: Severin-c/a 4.00

SENSATIONAL POLICE CASES (Becomes Captain Steve Savage, 2nd Series)
Avon Periodicals: 1952; No. 2, 1954 - No. 4, July-Aug, 1954
nn-(1952, 25¢, 100 pgs.)-Kubert-a?; Check, Larsen, Lawrence & McCann-a; Kinstler-c 52 104 156 328 552 775
2-4: 2-Kirbyish-a (3-4/54). 4-Reprint/Saint #5 20 40 60 117 189 260
I.W. Reprint #5-(1963?, nd)-Reprints Prison Break #5(1952-Realistic); Infantino-a 3 6 9 16 23 30

SENSATIONAL SHE-HULK, THE (She-Hulk #21-23) (See Savage She-Hulk)
Marvel Comics: V2#1, 5/89 - No. 60, Feb, 1994 ($1.50/$1.75, deluxe format)
V2#1-Byrne-c/a(p)/scripts begin, end #8 2 4 6 11 16 20
2,3,5-8: 3-Spider-Man app. 4.00
4,14-17,21-23: 4-Reintro G.A. Blonde Phantom. 14-17-Howard the Duck app. 21-23-Return of the Blonde Phantom. 22-All Winners Squad app. 4.00
9-13,18-20,24-49,51-60: 25-Thor app. 26-Excalibur app.; Guice-c. 29-Wolverine app. (3 pgs.). 30-Hobgoblin-c & cameo. 31-Byrne-c/a/scripts begin again. 35-Last $1.50-c. 37-Wolverine/Punisher/Spidey-c, but no app. 39-Thing app. 56-War Zone app.; Hulk cameo. 57-Vs. Hulk-c/story. 58-Electro-c/story. 59-Jack O'Lantern app. 3.00
50-($2.95, 52 pgs.)-Embossed green foil-c; Byrne app.; last Byrne-c/a; Austin, Chaykin, Simonson-a; Miller-a(2 pgs.) 5.00
NOTE: ***Dale Keown** a(p)-13, 15-22.*

SENSATIONAL SHE-HULK IN CEREMONY, THE
Marvel Comics: 1989 - No. 2, 1989 ($3.95, squarebound, 52 pgs.)
nn-Part 1, nn-Part 2 6.00

SENSATIONAL SPIDER-MAN
Marvel Comics: Apr, 1989 ($5.95, squarebound, 80 pgs.)
1-r/Amazing Spider-Man Annual #14,15 by Miller & Annual #8 by Kirby & Ditko 6.00

SENSATIONAL SPIDER-MAN, THE
Marvel Comics: Jan, 1996 - No. 33, Nov, 1998 ($1.95/$1.99)
0 ($4.95)-Lenticular-c; Jurgens-a/scripts 1 2 3 5 6 8
1 5.00
1-($2.95) variant-c; polybagged w/cassette 3 6 9 21 33 45
2-5: 2-Kaine & Rhino app. 3-Giant-Man app. 4.00
6-18: 9-Onslaught tie-in; revealed that Peter & Mary Jane's unborn baby is a girl. 11-Revelations. 13-15-Ka-Zar app. 14,15-Hulk app. 3.00
19-24: Living Pharoah app. 22,23-Dr. Strange app. 3.00
25-($2.99) Spiderhunt pt. 1; Normie Osborne kidnapped 4.00
25-Variant-c 1 2 3 5 6 8
26-33: 26-Nauck-a. 27-Double-c with "The Sensational Hornet #1"; Vulture app. 28-Hornet vs. Vulture. 29,30-Black Cat-c/app. 33-Last issue; Gathering of Five concludes 3.00
33.1, 33.2 (10/12, $2.99) DeFalco-s/Barberi-a/Bianchi-c 3.00
#(-1) Flashback(7/97) Dezago-s/Wieringo-a 3.00
'96 Annual ($2.95) 4.00

SENSATIONAL SPIDER-MAN, THE (Previously Marvel Knights Spider-Man #1-22)
Marvel Comics: No. 23, Apr, 2006 - No. 41, Dec, 2007 ($2.99)
23-40: 23-25-Aguirre-Sacasa-s/Medina-a. 23-Wraparound-c. 24,34,37-Black Cat app. 26-New costume. 28-Unmasked; Dr. Octopus app.; Crain-a. 35-Black costume resumes 3.00
41-($3.99) One More Day pt. 3; Straczynski-s/Quesada-a/c 4.00
... Annual 1 (2007, $3.99) Flashbacks of Peter & MJ's relationship; Larroca-a/Fraction-s 4.00
... Feral HC (2006, $19.99, dustjacket) r/#23-27; sketch pages 20.00
Civil War: Peter Parker, Spider-Man TPB (2007, $17.99) r/#28-34; Crain cover concepts 18.00

SENSATION COMICS (Sensation Mystery #110 on)
National Per. Publ./All-American: Jan, 1942 - No. 109, May-June, 1952
1-Origin Mr. Terrific (1st app.), Wildcat (1st app.), The Gay Ghost, & Little Boy Blue; Wonder Woman (cont'd from All Star #8), The Black Pirate begin; intro. Justice & Fair Play Club 7500 15,000 22,500 50,000 87,500 125,000
1-Reprint, Oversize 13-1/2x10". WARNING: This comic is an exact duplicate reprint of the original except for its size. DC published it in 1974 with a second cover titling it as a Famous First Edition. There have been many reported cases of the outer cover being removed and the interior sold as the original edition. The reprint with the new outer cover removed is practically worthless. See Famous First Edition for value.
2-Etta Candy begins 649 1298 1947 4738 8369 12,500
3-W. Woman gets secretary's job 400 800 1200 2800 4900 7000
4-1st app. Stretch Skinner in Wildcat 300 600 900 1950 3375 4800
5-Intro. Justin, Black Pirate's son 258 516 774 1651 2826 4000
6-Origin/1st app. Wonder Woman's magic lasso 400 800 1200 2800 4900 7000
7-10 206 412 618 1318 2259 3200
11,12,14-20 142 284 426 909 1555 2200
13-Hitler, Tojo, Mussolini-c (as bowling pins) 343 686 1029 2400 4200 6000
21-30: 22-Cheetah app. 110 220 330 704 1202 1700
31-33 90 180 270 576 988 1400
34-Sargon, the Sorcerer begins (10/44), ends #36; begins again #52 94 188 282 597 1024 1450
35-40: 36-2nd app. Giganta/1st cover; Cheetah app. 38-Christmas-c 87 174 261 553 952 1350
41-50: 43-The Whip app. 77 154 231 493 847 1200
51-60: 51-Last Black Pirate. 56,57-Sargon by Kubert 74 148 222 470 810 1150
61-67,70-80: 63-Last Mr. Terrific. 66-Wildcat by Kubert 68 136 204 435 743 1050
68-Origin & 1st app. Huntress (8/47) 129 258 387 826 1413 2000
69-2nd app. Huntress 77 154 231 493 847 1200
81-Used in **SOTI**, pg. 33,34; Krigstein-a 81 162 243 518 884 1250
82-93: 83-Last Sargon. 86-The Atom app. 90-Last Wildcat. 91-Streak begins by Alex Toth. 92-Toth-a (2 pgs.) 74 148 222 470 810 1150
94-1st all girl issue 123 246 369 787 1344 1900
95-99,101-106: 95-Unmasking of Wonder Woman-c/story. 99-1st app. Astra, Girl of the Future, ends #106. 103-Robot-c. 105-Last 52 pgs. 106-Wonder Woman ends 103 206 309 659 1130 1600
100-(11-12/50) 126 252 378 806 1378 1950
107-(Scarce, 1-2/52)-1st mystery issue; Johnny Peril by Toth(p), 8 pgs. & begins; continues from Danger Trail #5 (3-4/51)(see Comic Cavalcade #15 for 1st app.) 103 206 309 659 1130 1600
108-(Scarce)-Johnny Peril by Toth(p) 94 188 282 597 1024 1450
109-(Scarce)-Johnny Peril by Toth(p) 100 200 300 635 1093 1550
NOTE: ***Krigstein** a-(Wildcat)-81, 83, 84. **Moldoff** Black Pirate-1-25; Black Pirate not in 34-36, 43-48. **Oskner** c(i)-89-91, 94-106. Wonder Woman by **H. G. Peter**, all issues except #8, 17-19, 21; c-4-7, 9-18, 20-88, 92, 93. **Toth** a-91, 98; c-107. Wonder Woman c-1-106.*

SENSATION COMICS (Also see All Star Comics 1999 crossover titles)
DC Comics: May, 1999 ($1.99, one-shot)
1-Golden Age Wonder Woman and Hawkgirl; Robinson-s 3.00

SENSATION COMICS FEATURING WONDER WOMAN
DC Comics: Oct, 2014 - No. 17, Feb, 2016 ($3.99, printing of digital-first comics)
1-17-Short story anthology. 1-Simone-s/Van Sciver-a. 2-Gene Ha-c. 5-Darkseid app. 8-Noelle Stevenson-a; Jae Lee-c. 10-Francavilla-c. 12-Poison Ivy app. 13-Superwoman app. 15-Garcia-López-a; Cheetah app.; McNeil-s/a. 16-Scott Hampton-a; Harley Quinn app. 4.00

SENSATION MYSTERY (Formerly Sensation Comics #1-109)
National Periodical Publ.: No. 110, July-Aug, 1952 - No. 116, July-Aug, 1953
110-Johnny Peril continues 60 120 180 381 653 925
111-116-Johnny Peril in all. 116-M. Anderson-a 60 120 180 381 653 925
NOTE: ***M. Anderson** c-110. **Colan** a-114p. **Giunta** a-112. **G. Kane** c(p)-108, 109, 111-115.*

SENSE & SENSABILITY
Marvel Comics: July, 2010 - No. 5, Nov, 2010 ($3.99, limited series)
1-5-Adaptation of the Jane Austen novel; Nancy Butler-s/Sonny Liew-a/c 4.00

SENSUOUS STREAKER
Marvel Publ.: 1974 (B&W magazine, 68pgs.)
1 4 8 12 27 44 60

Sentinel #3 © MAR

Serenity Better Days #1 © Universal

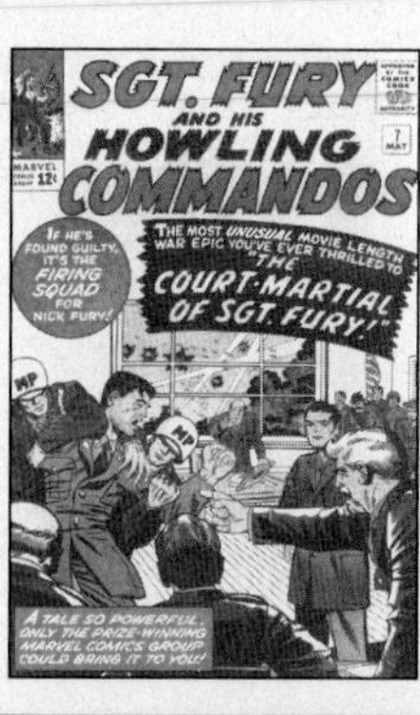

Sgt. Fury #7 © MAR

GD 2.0 · VG 4.0 · FN 6.0 · VF 8.0 · VF/NM 9.0 · NM- 9.2

GD 2.0 · VG 4.0 · FN 6.0 · VF 8.0 · VF/NM 9.0 · NM- 9.2

SENTENCES: THE LIFE OF M.F. GRIMM
DC Comics (Vertigo): 2007 ($19.99, B&W graphic novel)

HC-Autobiography of Percy Carey (M.F. Grimm); Ronald Wimberly-a 20.00
SC (2008, $14.99) 15.00

SENTINEL
Marvel Comics: June, 2003 - No. 12, April, 2004 ($2.99/$2.50)

1-Sean McKeever-s/Udon Studios-a 3.00
2-12 3.00
Marvel Age Sentinel Vol. 1: Salvage (2004, $7.99, digest size) r/#1-6 8.00
Vol. 2: No Hero (2004, $7.99, digest size) r/#7-12; sketch pages 8.00

SENTINEL (2nd series)
Marvel Comics: Jan, 2006 - No. 5, May, 2006 ($2.99, limited series)

1-5-Sean McKeever-s/Joe Vriens-a 3.00
Vol. 3: Past Imperfect (2006, $7.99, digest size) r/#1-5 8.00

SENTINELS OF JUSTICE, THE (See Americomics & Captain Paragon &...)

SENTINEL SQUAD O*N*E
Marvel Comics: Mar, 2006 - No. 5, July, 2006 ($2.99, limited series)

1-5-Lopresti-a/Layman-s 3.00
Decimation: Sentinel Squad O*N*E (2006, $13.99, TPB) r/series; sketch pg. by Caliafore 14.00

SENTRY (Also see New Avengers and Siege)
Marvel Comics: Sept, 2000 - No. 5, Jan, 2001 ($2.99, limited series)

1-5-Paul Jenkins-s/Jae Lee-a. 3-Spider-Man-c/app. 4-X-Men, FF app. 3.00
.../Fantastic Four (2/01, $2.99) Continues story from #5; Winslade-a 3.00
.../Hulk (2/01, $2.99) Sienkiewicz-c/a 3.00
.../Spider-Man (2/01, $2.99) back story of the Sentry; Leonardi-a 3.00
.../The Void (2/01, $2.99) Conclusion of story; Jae Lee-a 3.00
.../X-Men (2/01, $2.99) Sentry and Archangel; Texeira-a 3.00
TPB (10/01, $24.95) r/#1-5 & all one-shots; Stan Lee interview 25.00
TPB (2nd edition, 2005, $24.99) 25.00

SENTRY (Follows return in New Avengers #10)
Marvel Comics: Nov, 2005 - No. 8, Jun, 2006 ($2.99, limited series)

1-8-Paul Jenkins-s/John Romita Jr.-a. 1-New Avengers app. 3-Hulk app. 3.00
1-(Rough Cut) (12/05, $3.99) Romita sketch art and Jenkins script; cover sketches 4.00
...: Fallen Sun (7/10, $3.99) Siege epilogue; Jenkins-s/Raney-a/Yu-c 4.00
...: Reborn TPB (2006, $21.99) r/#1-8 22.00

SEPTEMBER MOURNING
Image Comics (Top Cow): Feb, 2017 ($4.99)

1-Marc Silvestri-c; Lazar & McCourt-s 5.00

SERENITY (Based on 2005 movie Serenity and 2003 TV series Firefly)
Dark Horse Comics: July, 2005 - No. 3, Sept, 2005 ($2.99, limited series)

1-3: Whedon & Matthews-s/Conrad-a. Three covers for each issue by various 4.00
...: Float Out (6/10, $3.50) Story of Wash; Patton Oswalt-s; covers by Jo Chen & Stockton 3.50
...: One For One (9/10, $1.00) reprints #1, Cassaday-c with red cover frame 3.00
...: Those Left Behind HC (11/07, $19.95, dustjacket) r/series; intro. by Nathan Fillion; pre-production art for the movie; Hughes-c 20.00
...: Those Left Behind TPB (1/06, $9.95) r/series; intro. by Nathan Fillion; Hughes-c 10.00

SERENITY BETTER DAYS (Firefly)
Dark Horse Comics: Mar, 2008 - No. 3, May, 2008 ($2.99, limited series)

1-3: Whedon & Matthews-s/Conrad-a; Adam Hughes-c 3.00

SERENITY: FIREFLY CLASS 03-K64 - LEAVES ON THE WIND (Follows movie)
Dark Horse Comics: Jan, 2014 - No. 6, Jun, 2014 ($3.50, limited series)

1-6: Zack Whedon-s/Georges Jeanty-a; covers by Dos Santos & Jeanty 3.50

SERENITY: FIREFLY CLASS 03-K64 - NO POWER IN THE 'VERSE (Follows movie)
Dark Horse Comics: Oct, 2016 - No. 6, Mar, 2017 ($3.99, limited series)

1-6: Chris Roberson-s/Georges Jeanty-a; covers by Dos Santos & Jeanty 4.00

SERGEANT BARNEY BARKER (Becomes G. I. Tales #4 on)
Atlas Comics (MCI): Aug, 1956 - No. 3, Dec, 1956

	GD	VG	FN	VF	VF/NM	NM-
1-Severin-c/a(4)	23	46	69	138	227	315
2,3: 2-Severin-c/a(4). 3-Severin-c/a(5)	15	30	45	88	137	185

SERGEANT BILKO (Phil Silvers Starring as...) (TV)
National Periodical Publications: May-June, 1957 - No. 18, Mar-Apr, 1960

	GD	VG	FN	VF	VF/NM	NM-
1-All have Bob Oskner-c	60	120	180	381	653	925
2	32	64	96	188	307	425
3-5	26	52	78	154	252	350
6-18: 11,12,15,17-Photo-c	21	42	63	124	202	280

SGT. BILKO'S PVT. DOBERMAN (TV)
National Periodical Publications: June-July, 1958 - No. 11, Feb-Mar, 1960

	GD	VG	FN	VF	VF/NM	NM-
1-Bob Oskner c-1-4,7,11	23	46	69	161	356	550
2	12	24	36	79	170	260
3-5: 5-Photo-c	19	18	27	60	120	180
6-11: 6,9-Photo-c	7	14	21	44	82	120

SGT. DICK CARTER OF THE U.S. BORDER PATROL (See Holyoke One-Shot)

SGT. FURY (& His Howling Commandos)(See Fury & Special Marvel Edition)
Marvel Comics Group (BPC earlier issues): May, 1963 - No. 167, Dec, 1981

	GD	VG	FN	VF	VF/NM	NM-
1-1st app. Sgt. Nick Fury (becomes agent of Shield in Strange Tales #135); Kirby/Ayers-c/a; 1st Dum-Dum Dugan & the Howlers	433	866	1299	3680	8340	13,000
2-Kirby-a	59	118	177	472	1061	1650
3-5: 3-Reed Richards x-over. 4-Death of Junior Juniper. 5-1st Baron Strucker app.; Kirby-a	31	62	93	223	499	775
6-10: 8-Baron Zemo, 1st Percival Pinkerton app. 9-Hitler-c & app. 10-1st app. Capt. Savage (the Skipper)(9/64)	16	32	48	112	249	385
11,12,14-20: 14-1st Blitz Squad. 18-Death of Pamela Hawley	9	18	27	61	123	185
13-Captain America & Bucky app.(12/64); 2nd solo Capt. America x-over outside The Avengers; Kirby-a	42	84	126	311	706	1100
13-2nd printing (1994)	2	4	6	9	12	15
21-24,26,28-30	6	12	18	40	73	105
25,27: 25-Red Skull app. 27-1st app. Eric Koenig; origin Fury's eye patch	6	12	18	41	76	110
31-33,35-50: 35-Eric Koenig joins Howlers. 43-Bob Hope, Glen Miller app. 44-Flashback on Howlers' 1st mission	4	8	12	27	44	60
34-Origin Howling Commandos	4	8	12	28	47	65
51-60	4	8	12	23	37	50
61-67: 64-Capt. Savage & Raiders x-over; peace symbol-c. 67-Last 12¢ issue; flag-c	3	6	9	19	30	40
68-80: 76-Fury's Father app. in WWI story	3	6	9	16	24	32
81-91: 91-Last 15¢ issue	3	6	9	14	20	26
92-(52 pgs.)	3	6	9	16	24	32
93-99: 98-Deadly Dozen x-over	3	6	9	14	19	24
100-Capt. America, Fantastic 4 cameos; Stan Lee, Martin Goodman & others app.	3	6	9	16	24	32
101-120: 101-Origin retold	2	4	6	10	14	18
121-130: 121-123-r/#19-21	2	4	6	8	11	14
131-167: 167-Reprints (from 1963)	2	4	6	8	10	12
133,134-(30¢-c variants, limited dist.)(5,7/76)	8	16	24	54	102	150
141,142-(35¢-c variants, limited dist.)(7,9/77)	17	34	51	117	259	400
Annual 1(1965, 25¢, 72 pgs.)-r/#4,5 & new-a	13	26	39	89	195	300
Special 2(1966)	6	12	18	42	79	115
Special 3(1967) All new material	5	10	15	30	50	70
Special 4(1968)	3	6	9	21	33	45
Special 5-7(1969-11/71)	3	6	9	17	26	35

NOTE: *Ayers a-8, Annual 1.* ***Ditko*** *a-15i.* ***Gil Kane*** *c-37, 96.* ***Kirby*** *a-1-7, 13p, 167p(r). Special 5; c-1-8, 10-20, 25, 167p.* ***Severin*** *a-44-46, 48, 162, 164; inks-49-79, Special 4, 6; c-4i, 5, 6, 44, 46, 110, 149i, 155i, 162-166.* ***Sutton*** *a-57p. Reprints in #80, 82, 85, 87, 89, 91, 93, 95, 99, 101, 103, 105, 107, 109, 111, 121-123, 145-155, 167.*

SGT. FURY AND HIS HOWLING COMMANDOS
Marvel Comics: July, 2009 ($3.99, one-shot)

1-John Paul Leon-a/c; WWII tale set in 1942; Baron Strucker app. 4.00

SGT. FURY AND HIS HOWLING DEFENDERS (See The Defenders #147)

SERGEANT PRESTON OF THE YUKON (TV)
Dell Publishing Co.: No. 344, Aug, 1951 - No. 29, Nov-Jan, 1958-59

	GD	VG	FN	VF	VF/NM	NM-
Four Color 344(#1)-Sergeant Preston & his dog Yukon King begin; painted-c begin, end #18	12	24	36	81	176	270
Four Color 373,397,419('52)	8	16	24	54	102	150
5(11-1/52-53)-10(2-4/54): 6-Bondage-c.	5	10	15	35	63	90
11,12,14-17	5	10	15	33	57	80
13-Origin Sgt. Preston	5	10	15	35	63	90
18-Origin Yukon King; last painted-c	5	10	15	35	63	90
19-29: All photo-c	6	12	18	41	76	110

SGT. ROCK (Formerly Our Army at War; see Brave & the Bold #52 & Showcase #45)
National Periodical Publications/DC Comics: No. 302, Mar, 1977 - No. 422, July, 1988

	GD	VG	FN	VF	VF/NM	NM-
302	4	8	12	28	47	65
303-310	3	6	9	16	23	30
311-320: 318-Reprints	2	4	6	10	16	20
321-350	2	4	6	8	11	14
329-Whitman variant	3	6	9	14	19	24
351-399,401-421: 412-Mlle Marie & Haunted Tank	1	2	3	5	7	9

Sgt. Rock: The Prophecy #1 © DC

Sergio Aragonés Funnies #1 © Sergio Aragonés

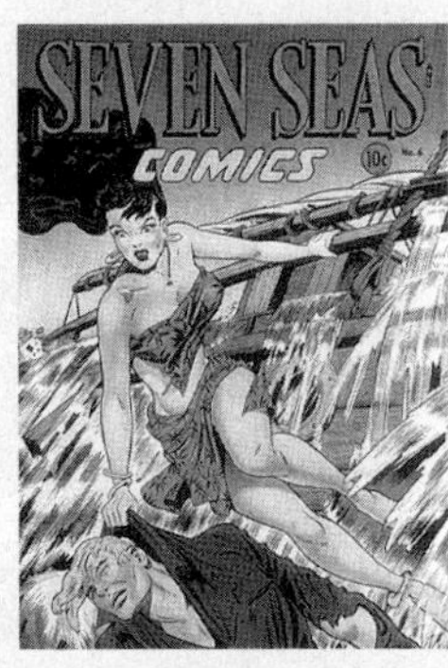

Seven Seas Comics #6 © UPF

GD 2.0 VG 4.0 FN 6.0 VF 8.0 VF/NM 9.0 NM- 9.2

400-(6/85) Anniversary issue 2 4 6 8 11 14
422-1st Joe, Adam, Andy Kubert-a team; last issue 2 4 6 10 14 18
Annual 2-4: 2(1982)-Formerly Sgt. Rock's Prize Battle Tales #1. 3(1983). 4(1984)
2 4 6 8 10 12
NOTE: ***Estrada*** *a-322, 327, 331, 336, 337, 341, 342i.* ***Glanzman*** *a-384, 421.* ***Kubert*** *a-302, 303, 305r, 306, 328, 351, 356, 368, 373, 422; c-317, 318r, 319-323, 325-333-on, Annual 2, 3.* ***Severin*** *a-347.* ***Spiegle*** *a-382, Annual 2, 3.* ***Thorne*** *a-384.* ***Toth*** *a-385r.* ***Wildey*** *a-307, 311, 313, 314.*

SGT. ROCK: BETWEEN HELL AND A HARD PLACE
DC Comics (Vertigo): 2003 ($24.95, hardcover one-shot)
HC-Joe Kubert-a/c; Brian Azzarello-s 25.00
SC (2004, $17.95) 18.00

SGT. ROCK'S COMBAT TALES
DC Comics: 2005 ($9.99, digest)
Vol. 1-Reprints early app. in Our Army at War, G.I. Combat, Star Spangled War Stories 10.00

SGT. ROCK SPECIAL (Sgt. Rock #14 on; see DC Special Series #3)
DC Comics: Oct, 1988 - No. 21, Feb, 1992; No. 1, 1992; No. 2, 1994 ($2.00, quarterly/monthly, 52 pgs)
1-Reprint begin 2 4 6 8 11 14
2-21: All-r; 5-r/early Sgt. Rock/Our Army at War #81. 7-Tomahawk-r by Thorne. 9-Enemy Ace-r by Kubert. 10-All Rock issue. 11-r/1st Haunted Tank story. 12-All Kubert issue; begins monthly. 13-Dinosaur story by Heath(r). 14-Enemy Ace-r (22 pgs.) by Adams/Kubert. 15-Enemy Ace (22 pgs.) by Kubert. 16-Iron Major-c/story. 16,17-Enemy Ace-r. 19-r/Batman/Sgt. Rock team-up/B&B #108 by Aparo
1 2 3 5 6 8
1 (1992, $2.95, 68 pgs.)-Simonson-c; unpubbed Kubert-a; Glanzman, Russell, Pratt, & Wagner-a 6.00
2 (1994, $2.95) Brereton painted-c 4.00
NOTE: ***Neal Adams*** *r-1, 8, 14p.* ***Chaykin*** *a-2; r-3, 9(2pgs.); c-3.* ***Drucker*** *r-6.* ***Glanzman*** *r-20.* ***Golden*** *a-1.* ***Heath*** *a-2; r-5, 9-13, 16, 19, 21.* ***Krigstein*** *r-4, 8.* ***Kubert*** *r-1-17, 20, 21; c-1p, 2, 8, 14-21.* ***Miller*** *r-6p.* ***Severin*** *r-3, 6, 10.* ***Simonson*** *r-2, 4; c-4.* ***Thorne*** *r-7.* ***Toth*** *r-2, 8, 11.* ***Wood*** *r-4.*

SGT. ROCK SPECTACULAR (See DC Special Series #13)

SGT. ROCK'S PRIZE BATTLE TALES (Becomes Sgt. Rock Annual #2 on; see DC Special Series #18 & 80 Page Giant #7)
National Periodical Publications: Winter, 1964 (Giant - 80 pgs., one-shot)
1-Kubert, Heath-r; new Kubert-c 33 66 99 238 532 825
... Replica Edition (2000, $5.95) Reprints entire issue 6.00

SGT. ROCK: THE LOST BATTALION
DC Comics: Jan, 2009 - No. 6, Jun, 2009 ($2.99, limited series)
1-6-Billy Tucci-s/a. 1-Tucci & Sparacio-c 3.00
HC (2009, $24.99, d.j.) r/#1-6; production art; cover art gallery 25.00
SC (2010, $17.99) r/#1-6; production art; cover art gallery 18.00

SGT. ROCK: THE PROPHECY
DC Comics: Mar, 2006 - No. 6, Aug, 2006 ($2.99, limited series)
1-6-Joe Kubert-s/a/c. 1-Variant covers by Andy and Adam Kubert 3.00
TPB (2007, $17.99) r/#1-6 18.00

SGT. STRYKER'S DEATH SQUAD (See Savage Combat Tales)

SERGIO ARAGONÉS' ACTIONS SPEAK
Dark Horse Comics: Jan, 2001 - No. 6, Jun, 2001 ($2.99, B&W, limited series)
1-6-Aragonés-c/a; wordless one-page cartoons 3.00

SERGIO ARAGONÉS' BLAIR WHICH?
Dark Horse Comics: Dec, 1999 ($2.95, B&W, one-shot)
nn-Aragonés-c/a; Evanier-s. Parody of "Blair Witch Project" movie 3.00

SERGIO ARAGONÉS' BOOGEYMAN
Dark Horse Comics: June, 1998 - No. 4, Sept, 1998 ($2.95, B&W, lim. series)
1-4-Aragonés-c/a 3.00

SERGIO ARAGONÉS DESTROYS DC
DC Comics: June, 1996 ($3.50, one-shot)
1-DC Superhero parody book; Aragonés-c/a; Evanier scripts 4.00

SERGIO ARAGONÉS' DIA DE LOS MUERTOS
Dark Horse Comics: Oct, 1998 ($2.95, one-shot)
1-Aragonés-c/a; Evanier scripts 3.00

SERGIO ARAGONÉS FUNNIES
Bongo Comics: 2011 - Present ($3.50)
1-12-Color and B&W humor strips by Aragonés 3.50

SERGIO ARAGONÉS' GROO & RUFFERTO
Dark Horse Comics: Dec, 1998 - No. 4, Mar, 1999 ($2.95, lim. series)
1-3-Aragonés-c/a 3.00

SERGIO ARAGONÉS' GROO: DEATH AND TAXES
Dark Horse Comics: Dec, 2001 - No. 4, Apr, 2002 ($2.99, lim. series)
1-4-Aragonés-c/a; Evanier-s 3.00

SERGIO ARAGONÉS' GROO: HELL ON EARTH
Dark Horse Comics: Nov, 2007 - No. 4, Apr, 2008 ($2.99, lim. series)
1-4-Aragonés-c/a; Evanier-s 3.00

SERGIO ARAGONÉS' GROO: MIGHTIER THAN THE SWORD
Dark Horse Comics: Jan, 2000 - No. 4, Apr, 2000 ($2.95, lim. series)
1-4-Aragonés-c/a; Evanier-s 3.00

SERGIO ARAGONÉS' GROO: THE HOGS OF HORDER
Dark Horse Comics: Oct, 2009 - No. 4, Mar, 2010 ($3.99, lim. series)
1-4-Aragonés-c/a; Evanier-s 4.00

SERGIO ARAGONÉS' GROO THE WANDERER (See Groo...)

SERGIO ARAGONÉS' GROO: 25TH ANNIVERSARY SPECIAL
Dark Horse Comics: Aug, 2007 ($5.99, one-shot)
nn-Aragonés-c/a; Evanier scripts; wraparound cover 6.00

SERGIO ARAGONÉS' LOUDER THAN WORDS
Dark Horse Comics: July, 1997 - No. 6, Dec, 1997 ($2.95, B&W, limited series)
1-6-Aragonés-c/a 3.00

SERGIO ARAGONÉS MASSACRES MARVEL
Marvel Comics: June, 1996 ($3.50, one-shot)
1-Marvel Superhero parody book; Aragonés-c/a; Evanier scripts 4.00

SERGIO ARAGONÉS STOMPS STAR WARS
Marvel Comics: Jan, 2000 ($2.95, one-shot)
1-Star Wars parody; Aragonés-c/a; Evanier scripts 3.00

SESAME STREET
Ape Entertainment: 2013 ($3.99)
1-Short stories by various; multiple covers 4.00
Free Comic Book Day edition (2013) Flip book with Strawberry Shortcake 3.00

SEVEN
Intrinsic Comics: July, 2007 ($3.00)
1-Jim Shooter-s/Paul Creddick-a 3.00

SEVEN BLOCK
Marvel Comics (Epic Comics): 1990 ($4.50, one-shot, 52 pgs.)
1-Dixon-s/Zaffino-a 6.00
nn-(IDW Publ., 2004, $5.99) reprints #1 6.00

SEVEN BROTHERS (John Woo's...)
Virgin Comics: Oct, 2006 - No. 5, Feb, 2007 ($2.99)
1-5-Garth Ennis-s/Jeevan Kang-a. 1-Two covers by Amano & Horn. 2-Kang var-c 3.00
TPB (6/07, $14.99) r/#1-5; cover gallery, deleted scenes and concept art 15.00
Volume 2 (9/07 - No. 5, 2/08) 1-Edison George-a. 4,5-David Mack-c 3.00

SEVEN DEAD MEN (See Complete Mystery #1)

SEVEN DWARFS (Also see Snow White)
Dell Publishing Co.: No. 227, 1949 (Disney-Movie)
Four Color 227 10 20 30 64 132 200

SEVEN MILES A SECOND
DC Comics (Vertigo Verité): 1996 ($7.95, one-shot)
nn-Wojnarowicz-s/Romberg-a 8.00

SEVEN-PER-CENT SOLUTION
IDW Publishing: Aug, 2015 - No. 5 ($3.99)
1-4-Sherlock Holmes/Sigmund Freud team-up; David & Scott Tipton-s/Joseph-a/Jones-c 4.00

SEVEN SAMUROID, THE (See Image Graphic Novel)

SEVEN SEAS COMICS
Universal Phoenix Features/Leader No. 6: Apr, 1946 - No. 6, 1947(no month)
1-South Sea Girl by Matt Baker, Capt. Cutlass begin; Tugboat Tessie by Baker app.
94 188 282 602 1026 1450
2-Swashbuckler-c 71 142 213 454 777 1100
3,5: 3-Six pg. Feldstein-a 135 270 405 864 1482 2100
4-Classic Baker-c 486 972 1458 3550 6775 9000
6-Baker Good Girl-c 206 412 618 1318 2259 3200
NOTE: ***Baker*** *a-1-6; c-3-6.*

SEVEN SOLDIERS OF VICTORY (Book-ends for seven related mini-series)

Seven to Eternity #5 © Remender & Opena

Sex Criminals #20 © Milkfed & Zdarsco

Shade the Changing Girl #5 © DC

	GD 2.0	VG 4.0	FN 6.0	VF 8.0	VF/NM 9.0	NM- 9.2

DC Comics: No. 0, Apr, 2005; No. 1; Dec, 2006 ($2.95/$3.99)

0-Grant Morrison-s/J.H. Williams-a 3.00
1-($3.99) Series conclusion; Grant Morrison-s/J.H. Williams-a 4.00
... Volume One (2006, $14.99) r/#0, Shining Knight #1,2; Zatanna #1,2; Guardian #1,2; and Klarion the Witch Boy #1; intro. by Morrison; character design sketches 15.00
... Volume Two (2006, $14.99) r/Shining Knight #3,4; Zatanna #3; Guardian #3,4; and Klarion the Witch Boy #2,3 15.00
... Volume Three ('06, $14.99) r/Zatanna #4; Mister Miracle #1,2; Bulleteer #1,2; Frankenstein #1 and Klarion the Witch Boy #4; 15.00
... Volume Four ('07, $14.99) r/Mister Miracle #3,4; Bulleteer #3,4; Frankenstein #2-4 and Seven Soldiers of Victory #1; script pages 15.00

SEVEN SOLDIERS: BULLETEER
DC Comics: Jan, 2006 - No. 4, May, 2006 ($2.99, limited series)

1-4-Grant Morrison-s/Yanick Paquette-a/c 3.00

SEVEN SOLDIERS: FRANKENSTEIN
DC Comics: Jan, 2006 - No. 4, May, 2006 ($2.99, limited series)

1-4-Grant Morrison-s/Doug Mahnke-a/c 3.00

SEVEN SOLDIERS: GUARDIAN
DC Comics: May, 2005 - No. 4, Nov, 2005 ($2.99, limited series)

1-4-Grant Morrison-s/Cameron Stewart-a; Newsboy Army app. 3.00

SEVEN SOLDIERS: KLARION THE WITCH BOY
DC Comics: June, 2005 - No. 4, Dec, 2005 ($2.99, limited series)

1-4-Grant Morrison-s/Frazer Irving-a 3.00

SEVEN SOLDIERS: MISTER MIRACLE
DC Comics: Nov, 2005 - No. 4, May, 2006 ($2.99, limited series)

1-4: 1-Grant Morrison-s/Pasqual Ferry-a/c. 3,4-Freddie Williams II-a/c 3.00

SEVEN SOLDIERS: SHINING KNIGHT
DC Comics: May, 2005 - No. 4, Oct, 2005 ($2.99, limited series)

1-4-Grant Morrison-s/Simone Bianchi-a 3.00

SEVEN SOLDIERS: ZATANNA
DC Comics: June, 2005 - No. 4, Dec, 2005 ($2.99, limited series)

1-4-Grant Morrison-s/Ryan Sook-a 3.00

1776 (See Charlton Classic Library)

7TH SWORD, THE
IDW Publishing (Darby Pop): Apr, 2014 - Present ($3.99)

1-6: 1-John Raffo-s/Nelson Blake II-a. 3-6-Nur Iman-a 4.00

7TH VOYAGE OF SINBAD, THE (Movie)
Dell Publishing Co.: Sept, 1958 (photo-c)

Four Color 944-Buscema-a 11 22 33 73 157 240

SEVEN TO ETERNITY
Image Comics: Sept, 2016 -Present ($3.99)

1-Rick Remender-s/Jerome Opeña-a 40.00
2 10.00
3-9: 7,8-James Harren-a 4.00

77 SUNSET STRIP (TV)
Dell Publ. Co./Gold Key: No. 1066, Jan-Mar, 1960 - No. 2, Feb, 1963 (All photo-c)

Four Color 1066-Toth-a 9 18 27 61 123 185
Four Color 1106,1159-Toth-a 7 14 21 49 92 135
Four Color 1211,1263,1291, 01-742-209(7-9/62)-Manning-a in all 7 14 21 46 86 125
1,2: Manning-a. 1(11/62-G.K.) 7 14 21 46 86 125

77TH BENGAL LANCERS, THE (TV)
Dell Publishing Co.: May, 1957

Four Color 791-Photo-c 6 12 18 41 76 110

SEVERED
Image Comics: Aug, 2011 - No. 7, Feb, 2012 ($2.99)

1-7-Scott Snyder & Scott Tuft-s/Attila Futaki-a/c 3.00

SEX
Image Comics: Mar, 2013 - Present ($2.99/$3.99)

1-26-Joe Casey-s/Piotr Kowalski-a/c 3.00
27-34-($3.99) 4.00

SEX CRIMINALS
Image Comics: Sept, 2013 - Present ($3.50/$3.99)

1-Matt Fraction-s/Chip Zdarsky-a/c 3 6 9 14 20 25
1-Variant-c by Shimizu 2 4 6 12 17 20
2 1 3 4 6 8 10
3-10 5.00
11-22 4.00
11-22-($4.69) Variant cover in pink polybag 5.00

SEYMOUR, MY SON (See More Seymour)
Archie Publications (Radio Comics): Sept, 1963

1-DeCarlo-c/a 4 8 12 28 47 65

SHADE, THE (See Starman)
DC Comics: Apr, 1997 - No. 4, July, 1997 ($2.25, limited series)

1-4-Robinson-s/Harris-c: 1-Gene Ha-a. 2-Williams/Gray-a 3-Blevins-a. 4-Zulli-a 3.00

SHADE, THE (From Starman)
DC Comics: Dec, 2011 - No. 12, Nov, 2012 ($2.99, limited series)

1-12: 1-Robinson-s/Hamner-a/Harris-c; Deathstroke app. 4-Cooke-a. 8-Thompson-a 12-Origin of the Shade; Gene Ha-a 3.00
1-12-Variant covers. 1-3-Hamner. 4-Darwyn Cooke. 5-7-Pulido. 11-Irving 4.00

SHADE, THE CHANGING GIRL (Continues as Shade, The Changing Woman)
DC Comics (Young Animal): Dec, 2016 - No. 12, Nov, 2017 ($3.99)

1-12: 1-Castellucci-s/Zarcone-a; intro. Megan Boyer/Loma Shade. 4-Element Girl back-up. 7-Sauvage-a 4.00
.../ Wonder Woman Special 1 (4/18, $4.99) Part 3 of Milk Wars crossover; Quitely-c 5.00

SHADE, THE CHANGING MAN (See Cancelled Comic Cavalcade)
National Per. Publ./DC Comics: June-July, 1977 - No. 8, Aug-Sept, 1978

1-1st app. Shade; Ditko-c/a in all 3 6 9 14 19 24
2-8 2 3 4 6 8 10

SHADE, THE CHANGING MAN (2nd series) (Also see Suicide Squad #16)
DC Comics (Vertigo imprint #33 on): July, 1990 - No. 70, Apr, 1996 ($1.50-$2.25, mature)

1-($2.50, 52 pgs.)-Peter Milligan scripts in all 4.00
2-41,45-49,51-59: 6-Preview of World Without End. 17-Begin $1.75-c. 33-Metallic ink on-c. 41-Begin $1.95-c 3.00
42-44-John Constantine app. 3.50
50-($2.95, 52 pgs.) 4.00
60-70: 60-begin $2.25-c 3.00
...: Edge of Vision TPB (2009, $19.99) r/#7-13 20.00
...: Scream Time TPB (2010, $19.99) r/#14-19 20.00
...: The American Scream TPB (2003, 2009, $17.95/$17.99) r/#1-6 18.00
NOTE: *Bachalo a-1-9, 11-13, 15-21, 23-26, 33-39, 42-45, 47, 49, 50; c-30, 33-41.*

SHADE, THE CHANGING WOMAN (Continues from Shade, The Changing Girl)
DC Comics (Young Animal): May, 2018 - Present ($3.99)

1-Castellucci-s/Zarcone-a 4.00

SHADO: SONG OF THE DRAGON (See Green Arrow #63-66)
DC Comics: 1992 - No. 4, 1992 ($4.95, limited series, 52 pgs.)

Book One - Four: Grell scripts; Morrow-a(i) 6.00

SHADOW, THE (See Batman #253, 259 & Marvel Graphic Novel #35)

SHADOW, THE (Pulp, radio)
Archie Comics (Radio Comics): Aug, 1964 - No. 8, Sept, 1965 (All 12¢)

1-Jerry Siegel scripts in all; Shadow-c. 8 16 24 55 105 155
2-8: 2-App. in super-hero costume on-c only; Reinman-a(backup). 3-Superhero begins; Reinman-a (book-length novel). 3,4,6,7-The Fly 1 pg. strips. 4-8-Reinman-a. 5-8-Siegel scripts. 7-Shield app. 5 10 15 33 57 80

SHADOW, THE
National Periodical Publications: Oct-Nov, 1973 - No. 12, Aug-Sept, 1975

1-Kaluta-a begins 6 12 18 38 69 100
2 3 6 9 21 33 45
3-Kaluta/Wrightson-a 4 8 12 23 37 50
4,6-Kaluta-a ends. 4-Chaykin, Wrightson part-i 3 6 9 18 28 38
5,7-12: 11-The Avenger (pulp character) x-over 2 4 6 13 18 22
NOTE: ***Craig** a-10. **Cruz** a-10-12. **Kaluta** a-1, 2, 3p, 4, 6; c-1-4, 6, 10-12. **Kubert** c-9. **Robbins** a-5, 7-9; c-5, 7, 8.*

SHADOW, THE
DC Comics: May, 1986 - No. 4, Aug, 1986 (limited series)

1-4: Howard Chaykin art in all 4.00
Blood & Judgement ($12.95)-r/1-4 13.00

SHADOW, THE
DC Comics: Aug, 1987 - No. 19, Jan, 1989 ($1.50)

1-19: Andrew Helfer scripts in all. 4.00

The Shadow (2013 series) #9 © AMP

Shadow Comics #2 © C-N

Shadowhawk #13 © Valentino

	GD	VG	FN	VF	VF/NM	NM-
	2.0	4.0	6.0	8.0	9.0	9.2

Annual 1,2 (12/87, '88,)-2-The Shadow dies; origin retold (story inspired by the movie "Citizen Kane"). 5.00

NOTE: ***Kyle Baker** a-7i, 8-19, Annual 2. **Chaykin** c-Annual 1. **Helfer** scripts in all. **Orlando** a-Annual 1. **Rogers** c/a-7. **Sienkiewicz** c/a-1-6.*

SHADOW, THE (Movie)
Dark Horse Comics: June, 1994 - No. 2, July, 1994 ($2.50, limited series)

1,2-Adaptation from Universal Pictures film 4.00

NOTE: ***Kaluta** c/a-1, 2.*

SHADOW, THE
Dynamite Entertainment: 2012 - No. 25, 2014 ($3.99)

1-25: 1-Ennis-s/Campbell-a; multiple covers on all. 7-10-Gischler-s 4.00
#0-(2014, $3.99) Cullen Bunn-s/Colton Worley-a/Gabriel Hardman-c 4.00
#100-(2014, $7.99, squarebound) Short stories by various incl. Francavilla, Chaykin, Wagner, Uslan; 2 covers by Wagner & Hack 8.00
Annual 1 (2012, $4.99) Sniegoski-s/Calero-a/Alex Ross-c 5.00
Annual 2013 ($4.99) Parks-s/Evely-a/Worley-c 5.00
One Shot 2014: Agents of the Shadow ($7.99, squarebound) Robert Hack-c 8.00
... Over Innsmouth (2014, $4.99) Ron Marz-s/Ivan Rodriguez-a 5.00
Special 1 (2012, $4.99) Beatty-s/Cliquet-a/Alex Ross-c 5.00
Special 2014: Death Factory ($7.99, squarebound) Phil Hester-s/c; Ivan Rodriguez-a 8.00

SHADOW, THE (Volume 2)
Dynamite Entertainment: 2014 - No. 5, 2015 ($1.00/$3.99, limited series)

1-($1.00) Bunn-s/Timpano-a/Guice-c 3.00
2-5-($3.99) Bunn-s/Timpano-a/Guice-c 4.00

SHADOW, THE (Volume 3)
Dynamite Entertainment: 2017 - No. 6, 2018 ($3.99, limited series)

1-6: 1-Spurrier & Watters-s/Daniel HDR-a; multiple covers on all. 4-Jaime-a 4.00

SHADOW AND DOC SAVAGE, THE
Dark Horse Comics: July, 1995 - No. 2, Aug, 1995 ($2.95, limited series)

1,2 4.00

SHADOW AND THE MYSTERIOUS 3, THE
Dark Horse Comics: Sept, 1994 ($2.95, one-shot)

1-Kaluta co-scripts. 4.00

NOTE: ***Stevens** c-1.*

SHADOW, THE / BATMAN
Dynamite Entertainment: 2017 - No. 6, 2018 ($3.99, limited series)

1-6-Orlando-s/Timpano-a; multiple covers on each; Ra's al Ghul & Shiwan Khan app. 4.00

SHADOW CABINET (See Heroes)
DC Comics (Milestone): No. 0, Jan, 1994 - No. 17, Oct, 1995 ($1.75/$2.50)

0-(1/94, $2.50, 52 pgs.)-Silver ink-c; Simonson-c 4.00
1-17: 1-(6/94) Byrne-c 3.00

SHADOW COMICS (Pulp, radio)
Street & Smith Publications: Mar, 1940 - V9#5, Aug-Sept, 1949

NOTE: *The Shadow first appeared on radio in 1929 and was featured in pulps beginning in April, 1931, written by Walter Gibson. The early covers of this series were reprinted from the pulp covers.*

	GD 2.0	VG 4.0	FN 6.0	VF 8.0	VF/NM 9.0	NM- 9.2
V1#1-Shadow, Doc Savage, Bill Barnes, Nick Carter (radio), Frank Merriwell, Iron Munro, the Astonishing Man begin	595	1190	1785	4350	7675	11,000
2-The Avenger begins, ends #6; Capt. Fury only app.	232	464	696	1485	2543	3600
3(nn-5/40)-Norgil the Magician app.; cover is exact swipe of Shadow pulp from 1/33	168	336	504	1075	1838	2600
4-The Three Musketeers begins, ends #8; classic painted decapitation-c	161	322	483	1030	1765	2500
5-Doc Savage ends	119	238	357	762	1306	1850
6,8,9: 9-Norgil the Magician app.	97	194	291	621	1061	1500
7-Origin/1st app. The Hooded Wasp & Wasplet (11/40); series ends V3#8; Hooded Wasp/Wasplet app. on-c thru #9	102	204	306	648	1112	1575
10-Origin The Iron Ghost, ends #11; The Dead End Kids begins, ends #14	95	190	285	603	1039	1475
11-Origin Hooded Wasp & Wasplet retold	95	190	285	603	1039	1475
12-Dead End Kids app.	89	178	267	565	970	1375
V2#1(11/41, Vol. II#2 in indicia) Dead End Kids -s	87	174	261	553	952	1350
2-(Rare, 1/42, Vol. II#3 in indicia) Giant ant-c	194	388	582	1242	2121	3000
3-Origin & 1st app. Supersnipe (3/42); series begins; Little Nemo story (Vol.II#4 in indicia)	139	278	417	883	1517	2150
4,5: 4,8-Little Nemo story	81	162	243	518	884	1250
6-9: 6-Blackstone the Magician story	77	154	231	493	847	1200
10,12: 10-Supersnipe app.' Skull-c	74	148	222	470	810	1150
11-Classic Devil Kyoti World War 2 sunburst-c	95	190	285	603	1039	1475
V3#1,2,5,7-12: 10-Doc Savage begins, not in V5#5, V6#10-12, V8#4	71	142	213	454	777	1100
3-1st Monstrodamus-c/sty	100	200	300	635	1093	1550
4-2nd Monstrodamus; classic-c of giant salamander getting shot in the head	107	214	321	680	1165	1650
6-Classic underwater-c	110	220	330	704	1202	1700
V4#1,3-12	50	100	150	315	533	750
2-Classic severed head-c	148	296	444	947	1624	2300
V5#1-12: 1-(4/45). 12-(3/46)	47	94	141	296	498	700
V6#1-11: 9-Intro. Shadow, Jr. (12/46)	43	86	129	271	461	650
12-Powell-c/a; atom bomb panels	47	94	141	246	498	700
V7#1,2,5,7-9,12: 2,5-Shadow, Jr. app.; Powell-a	41	82	123	256	428	600
3,6,11-Powell-c/a	47	94	141	296	498	700
4-Powell-c/a; Atom bomb panels	48	96	144	302	514	725
10(1/48)-Flying Saucer-c/story (2nd of this theme; see The Spirit 9/28/47); Powell-c/a	71	142	213	454	777	1100
V8#1,2,4-12-Powell-a.	47	94	141	296	498	700
3-Powell Spider-c/a	48	96	144	302	514	725
V9#1,5-Powell-a	45	90	135	284	480	675
2-4-Powell-c/a	47	94	141	296	498	700

NOTE: ***Binder** c-V3#1. **Powell** art in most issues beginning V6#12. Painted c-1-6.*

SHADOWDRAGON
DC Comics: 1995 ($3.50, annual)

Annual 1-Year One story 4.00

SHADOW EMPIRES: FAITH CONQUERS
Dark Horse Comics: Aug, 1994 - No. 4, Nov, 1994 ($2.95, limited series)

1-4 3.00

SHADOW GLASS, THE
Dark Horse Comics: Mar, 2016 - Present ($3.99)

1-3-Aly Fell-s/a 4.00

SHADOW/GREEN HORNET: DARK NIGHTS (Pulp characters)
Dynamite Entertainment: 2013 - No. 5, 2013 ($3.99)

1-5-Lamont Cranston & Britt Reid team-up in 1939; Uslan-s; multiple covers on each 4.00

SHADOWHAWK (See Images of Shadowhawk, New Shadowhawk, Shadowhawk II, Shadowhawk III & Youngblood #2)
Image Comics (Shadowline Ink): Aug, 1992 - No. 4, Mar, 1993; No. 12, Aug, 1994 - No. 18, May, 1995 ($1.95/$2.50)

1-($2.50)-Embossed silver foil stamped-c; Valentino/Liefeld-c; Valentino-c/a/scripts in all; has coupon for Image #0; 1st Shadowline Ink title 5.00
1-With coupon missing 2.00
1-($1.95)-Newsstand version w/o foil stamp 3.00
2-13,0,1418: 2-Shadowhawk poster w/McFarlane-i; brief Spawn app.; wraparound-c w/silver ink highlights. 3-($2.50)-Glow-in-the-dark-c. 4-Savage Dragon-c/story; Valentino/Larsen-c. 5-11-(See Shadowhawk II and III). 12-Cont'd from Shadowhawk III; pull-out poster by Texeira.13-w/ShadowBone poster; WildC.A.T.s app. 0 (10/94)-Liefeld c/a/story; ShadowBart poster. 14-(10/94, $2.50)-The Others app. 16-Supreme app. 17-Spawn app.; story cont'd from Badrock & Co. #6. 18-Shadowhawk dies; Savage Dragon & Brigade app. 3.00
Special 1(12/94, $3.50, 52 pgs.)-Silver Age Shadowhawk flip book 4.00
Gallery (4/94, $1.95) 3.00
Out of the Shadows ($19.95)-r/Youngblood #2, Shadowhawk #1-4, Image Zero #0, Operation: Urban Storm (Never published) 20.00
.../Vampirella (2/95, $4.95)-Pt.2 of x-over (See Vampirella/Shadowhawk for Pt. 1) 5.00

NOTE: *Shadowhawk was originally a four issue limited series. The story continued in Shadowhawk II, Shadowhawk III & then became Shadowhawk again with issue #12.*

SHADOWHAWK II (Follows Shadowhawk #4)
Image Comics (Shadowline Ink): V2#1, May, 1993 - V2#3, Aug, 1993 ($3.50/$1.95/$2.95, limited series)

V2#1 ($3.50)-Cont'd from Shadowhawk #4; die-cut mirricard-c 4.00
2 ($1.95)-Foil embossed logo; reveals identity; gold-c variant exists 4.00
3 ($2.95)-Pop-up-c w/Pact ashcan insert 4.00

SHADOWHAWK III (Follows Shadowhawk II #3)
Image Comics (Shadowline Ink): V3#1, Nov, 1993 - V3#4, Mar, 1994 ($1.95, limited series);

V3#1-4: 1-Cont'd from Shadowhawk II; intro Valentine; gold foil & red foil stamped-c variations. 2-(52 pgs.)-Shadowhawk contracts HIV virus; U.S. Male by M. Anderson (p) in free 16 pg.insert. 4-Continues in Shadowhawk #12 4.00

SHADOWHAWK (Volume 2) (Also see New Man #4)
Image Comics: May, 2005 - No. 15, Sept, 2006 ($2.99/$3.50)

1-4-Eddie Collins as Shadowhawk; Rodríguez-a; Valentino-co-plotter 3.50
5-15-($3.50) 5-Cover swipe of Superman Vs. Spider-Man treasury edition 3.50
...One Shot #1 (7/06, $1.99) r/Return of Shadowhawk 3.00

Shadowland: Elektra #1 © MAR

Shadow Man V3 #1 © ACC

Shadowman End Times #1 © VAL

GD VG FN VF VF/NM NM-
2.0 4.0 6.0 8.0 9.0 9.2

Return of Shadowhawk (12/04, $2.99) Valentino-s/a/c; Eddie Collins origin retold 3.00

SHADOWHAWK (Volume 3)
Image Comics: May, 2010 - No. 5, Dec, 2010 ($3.50)
1-5-Rodríguez-a. 1-Back-up with Valentino-a/Niles-s 3.50

SHADOWHAWKS OF LEGEND
Image Comics (Shadowline Ink): Nov, 1995 ($4.95, one-shot)
nn-Stories of past Shadowhawks by Kurt Busiek, Beau Smith & Alan Moore 5.00

SHADOW, THE: HELL'S HEAT WAVE (Movie, pulp, radio)
Dark Horse Comics: Apr, 1995 - No. 3, June, 1995 ($2.95, limited series)
1-3: Kaluta story 4.00

SHADOW HUNTER (Jenna Jameson's...)
Virgin Comics: No. 0, Dec, 2007 - No. 3 ($2.99)
0-Preview issue; creator interviews; gallery of covers for upcoming issues; Greg Horn-c 3.00
1-3: 1-Two covers by Horn & Land; Jameson & Christina Z-s/Singh-a. 2-Three covers 3.00

SHADOWHUNT SPECIAL
Image Comics (Extreme Studios): Apr, 1996 ($2.50)
1-Retells origin of past Shadowhawks; Valentino script; Chapel app. 3.00

SHADOW, THE: IN THE COILS OF THE LEVIATHAN (Movie, pulp, radio)
Dark Horse Comics: Oct, 1993 - No. 4, Apr, 1994 ($2.95, limited series)
1-4-Kaluta-c & co-scripter 4.00
Trade paperback (10/94, $13.95)-r/1-4 14.00

SHADOWLAND (Also see Daredevil #508-512 & Black Panther: The Man Without Fear #513)
Marvel Comics: Sept, 2010 - No. 5, Jan, 2011 ($3.99, limited series)
1-5: 1-Diggle-s/Tan-a; Bullseye killed; Cassaday-c. 2-Ghost Rider app. 4.00
1-Variant-c by Tan 6.00
...: After the Fall 1 (2/11, $3.99) Finch-c; Black Panther app. 4.00
...: Bullseye 1 (10/10, $3.99) Chen-a; Bullseye's funeral 4.00
...: Elektra 1 (11/10, $3.99) Wells-s/Rios-a/Takeda-c 4.00
...: Ghost Rider 1 (11/10, $3.99) Williams-s/Crain-a/c 4.00
...: Spider-Man 1 (12/10, $3.99) Shang-Chi & Mr. Negative app.; Siqueira-a 4.00

SHADOWLAND: BLOOD IN THE STREETS (Leads into Heroes For Hire)
Marvel Comics: Oct, 2010 - No. 4, Jan, 2011 ($3.99, limited series)
1-4-Johnston-s/Alves-a; Misty Knight, Silver Sable, Paladin, Shroud app. 4.00

SHADOWLAND: DAUGHTERS OF THE SHADOW
Marvel Comics: Oct, 2010 - No. 3, Dec, 2010 ($3.99, limited series)
1-3-Henderson-s/Rodriguez-a; Colleen Wing app. 3-Preview of Black Panther #513 4.00

SHADOWLAND: MOON KNIGHT
Marvel Comics: Oct, 2010 - No. 3, Dec, 2010 ($3.99, limited series)
1-3-Hurwitz-s/Dazo-a 4.00

SHADOWLAND: POWER MAN
Marvel Comics: Oct, 2010 - No. 4, Jan, 2011 ($3.99, limited series)
1-4-Van Lente-s/Asrar-a. 1-New Power Man debut; Iron Fist app. 4.00

SHADOWLINE SAGA: CRITICAL MASS, A
Marvel Comics (Epic): Jan, 1990 - No. 7, July, 1990 ($4.95, lim. series, 68 pgs)
1-6: Dr. Zero, Powerline, St. George 5.00
7 ($5.95, 84 pgs.)-Morrow-a, Williamson-c(i) 6.00

SHADOWMAN (See X-O Manowar #4)
Valiant/Acclaim Comics (Valiant): May, 1992 - No. 43, Dec, 1995 ($2.50)
1-Partial origin 3 6 9 14 20 25
2-5: 3-1st app. Sousa the Soul Eater 5.00
6,7,9-42: 15-Minor Turok app. 16-1st app. Dr. Mirage (8/93). 17,18-Archer & Armstrong x-over. 19-Aerosmith-c/story. 23-Dr. Mirage x-over. 24-(4/94). 25-Bound-in trading card. 29-Chaos Effect. 4.00
8-1st app. Master Darque 2 4 6 8 10 12
43-Shadowman jumps to his death 1 2 3 5 6 8
0-($2.50, 4/94)-Regular edition 6.00
0-($3.50)-Wraparound chromium-c edition 1 2 3 5 6 8
0-Gold 20.00
Yearbook 1 (12/94, $3.95) 5.00

SHADOWMAN (Volume 2)
Acclaim Comics (Valiant Heroes): Mar, 1997 - No. 20, Jun, 1998 ($2.50, mature)
1-1st app. Zero; Garth Ennis scripts begin, end #4 1 2 3 5 6 8
2-20: 2-Zero becomes new Shadowman. 4-Origin; Jack Boniface (original Shadowman) rises from the grave. 5-Jamie Delano scripts begin. 9-Copycat-c 3.00
1-Variant painted cover 1 2 3 5 6 8

GD VG FN VF VF/NM NM-
2.0 4.0 6.0 8.0 9.0 9.2

#0 Gold 5.00

SHADOWMAN (Volume 3)
Acclaim Comics: July, 1999 - No. 5, Nov, 1999 ($3.95/$2.50)
1-($3.95)-Abnett & Lanning-s/Broome & Benjamin-a 1 2 3 5 6 8
2-5-($2.50): 3,4-Flip book with Unity 2000 3.00

SHADOWMAN
Valiant Entertainment: Nov, 2012 - No. 16, Mar, 2014 ($3.99)
1-Jordan-s/Zircher-a; two covers by Zircher (regular & pullbox) 5.00
1-Variant-c by Dave Johnson 8.00
1-Variant-c by Bill Sienkiewicz 20.00
2-16: 2-6-Jordan-s/Zircher-a 4.00
2-4-Pullbox variants 6.00
5-16-Pullbox variants 4.00
11-Variant-c with detachable Halloween mask 4.00
13X-(10/13, bagged with Bleeding Cool Magazine #7) prelude to #13; Milligan-s 3.00
#0-(5/13, $3.99) Origin of Master Darque 4.00

SHADOWMAN END TIMES
Valiant Entertainment: Apr, 2014 - No. 3, Jun, 2014 ($3.99, limited series)
1-3-Milligan-s/De Landro-a 4.00

SHADOWMAN / RAE SREMMURD
Valiant Entertainment: Oct, 2017 ($3.99, one-shot)
1-Rahal-s/Guedes-a; bonus preview of Ninja•K #1 4.00

SHADOWMASTERS
Marvel Comics: Oct, 1989 - No.4, Jan, 1990 ($3.95, squarebound, 52 pgs.)
1-4: Heath-a(i). 1-Jim Lee-c; story cont'd from Punisher 4.00

SHADOW, THE: MIDNIGHT IN MOSCOW (Pulp character)
Dynamite Entertainment: 2014 - No. 6, 2014 ($3.99, limited series)
1-6:-Howard Chaykin-s/a/c 4.00

SHADOW NOW, THE (Pulp character)
Dynamite Entertainment: 2013 - No. 6, 2014 ($3.99, limited series)
1-6: 1-David Liss-s/ColtonWorley-a; The Shadow in present day New York 4.00

SHADOW OF THE BATMAN
DC Comics: Dec, 1985 - No. 5, Apr, 1986 ($1.75, limited series)
1-Detective-r (all have wraparound-c) 1 2 3 5 6 8
2,3,5: 3-Penguin-c & cameo. 5-Clayface app. 6.00
4-Joker-c/story 1 2 3 4 5 7
NOTE: ***Austin** a(new)-2i, 3i; r-2-4i. **Rogers** a(new)-1, 2p, 3p, 4, 5; r-1-5p; c-1-5. **Simonson** a-1r.*

SHADOW ON THE TRAIL (See Zane Grey & Four Color #604)

SHADOWPACT (See Day of Vengeance)
DC Comics: Jul, 2006 - No. 25, Jul, 2008 ($2.99)
1-25: 1-Bill Willingham-s; Detective Chimp, Ragman, Blue Devil, Nightshade, Enchantress and Nightmaster app. 1-Superman app. 13-Zauriel app.; S. Hampton-a 3.00
...: Cursed TPB (2007, $14.99) r/#4,9-13 15.00
...: Darkness and Light TPB (2008, $14.99) r/#14-19 15.00
...: The Burning Age TPB (2008, $17.99) r/#20-25 18.00
...: The Pentacle Plot TPB (2007, $14.99) r/#1-3,5-8 15.00

SHADOW PLAY (Tales of the Supernatural)
Whitman Publications: June, 1982
1-Painted-c 1 2 3 5 6 8

SHADOWPLAY
IDW Publ.: Sept, 2005 - No. 4, Dec, 2005 ($3.99)
1-4-Benson-s/Templesmith-a; Christina Z-s/Wood-a; 2 covers by Templesmith & Wood 4.00
TPB (3/06, $17.99) r/series; flip book format 18.00

SHADOW REAVERS
Black Bull Ent.: Oct, 2001 - No. 5, Mar, 2002 ($2.99)
1-5-Nelson-a; two covers for each issue 3.00
Limited Preview Edition (5/01, no cover price) 3.00

SHADOW RIDERS
Marvel Comics UK, Ltd.: June, 1993 - No. 4, Sept, 1993 ($1.75, limited series)
1-($2.50)-Embossed-c; Cable-c/story 4.00
2-4-Cable app. 2-Ghost Rider app. 3.00

SHADOWS
Image Comics: Feb, 2003 - No. 4, Nov, 2003 ($2.95)
1-4-Jade Dodge-s/Matt Camp-a/c 3.00

SHADOWS & LIGHT

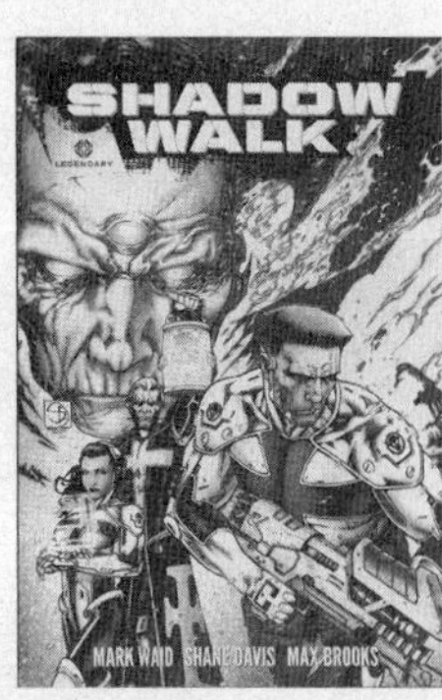

Shadow Walk © Legendary

Shahrazed #1 © Tom Hutchinson

Shaolin Cowboy #2 © G. Darrow

	GD	VG	FN	VF	VF/NM	NM-
	2.0	4.0	6.0	8.0	9.0	9.2

GD VG FN VF VF/NM NM- 2.0 4.0 6.0 8.0 9.0 9.2

Marvel Comics: Feb, 1998 - No. 3, July, 1998 ($2.99, B&W, quarterly)

1-3: 1-B&W anthology of Marvel characters; Black Widow art by Gene Ha, Hulk by Wrightson, Iron Man by Ditko & Daredevil by Stelfreeze; Stelfreeze painted-c. 2-Weeks, Sharp, Starlin, Thompson-a. 3-Buscema, Grindberg, Giffen, Layton-a 3.00

SHADOW'S FALL
DC Comics (Vertigo): Nov, 1994 - No. 6, Apr, 1995 ($2.95, limited series)

1-6: Van Fleet-c/a in all. 3.00

SHADOWS FROM BEYOND (Formerly Unusual Tales)
Charlton Comics: V2#50, October, 1966

V2#50-Ditko-c 4 8 12 28 47 65

SHADOWS ON THE GRAVE
Dark Horse Comics: Dec, 2016 - No. 8, Sept, 2017 ($3.99, B&W, limited series)

1-8-Horror story anthology; Richard Corben-s/a/c 4.00

SHADOW STATE
Broadway Comics: Dec, 1995 - No. 5, Apr, 1996 ($2.50)

1-5: 1,2-Fatale back-up story; Cockrum-a(p) 3.00
Preview Edition 1,2 (10-11/95, $2.50, B&W) 3.00

SHADOW STRIKES!, THE (Pulp, radio)
DC Comics: Sept, 1989 - No.31, May, 1992 ($1.75)

1-4,7-31: 31-Mignola-c 4.00
5,6-Doc Savage x-over 5.00
Annual 1 (1989, $3.50, 68 pgs.)-Spiegle a; Kaluta-c 5.00

SHADOW, THE : THE DEATH OF MARGO LANE (Pulp characters)
Dynamite Entertainment: 2016 - Present ($3.99)

1-4-Matt Wagner-s/a/c. 4-The Red Empress app. 4.00

SHADOW WALK
Legendary Comics: Nov, 2013 ($24.99, graphic novel)

HC - Mark Waid-s/Shane Davis-a 25.00

SHADOW WAR OF HAWKMAN
DC Comics: May, 1985 - No. 4, Aug, 1985 (limited series)

1-4 4.00

SHADOW, THE: YEAR ONE
Dynamite Entertainment: 2012 - No. 10, 2014 ($3.99)

1-9: 1-Matt Wagner-s/Wilfredo Torres-a; multiple covers 4.00
10-($4.99) 5.00

SHAFT (Based on the movie character)
Dynamite Entertainment: 2014 - No. 6, 2015 ($3.99, limited series)

1-6-David F. Walker-s/Bilquis Evely-a; multiple covers on each 4.00

SHAFT: IMITATION OF LIFE (Based on the movie character)
Dynamite Entertainment: 2016 - No. 4, 2016 ($3.99, limited series)

1-4-David F. Walker-s/Dietrich Smith-a/Matthew Clark-c 4.00

SHAGGY DOG & THE ABSENT-MINDED PROFESSOR (See Movie Comics & Walt Disney Showcase #46)(Disney-Movie)
Dell Publ. Co.: No. 985, Apr-Jun, 1959; No. 1199, Apr, 1961; Aug, 1967

Four Color 985 7 14 21 46 86 125
Four Color 1199 (4/61) Movie, photo-c; variant "Double Feature" edition; has a "Fabulous Formula" strip on back-c 7 14 21 46 86 125
Four Color 1199-(8/67) Movie, photo-c 7 14 21 46 86 125

SHAHRAZAD
Big Dog Ink: No. 0, Apr, 2013 - No. 5, Apr, 2014 ($1.99/$3.99)

0-($1.99) Hutchison-s/Krome-a; multiple covers 3.00
1-3 ($3.99) Hutchison & Castor-s/Krome-a; multiple covers on each 4.00

SHAHRAZAD
Aspen MLT: Apr, 2015 - No. 5, Aug, 2015 ($2.99/$3.99)

1,2-($2.99) Remastered reprints of 2013 series; multiple covers on each 3.00
3-5-($3.99) Hutchison & Castor-s/Krome-a; multiple covers on each 4.00

SHALOMAN (Jewish-themed stories and history)
Al Wiesner/ Mark 1 Comics: 1988 - 2012 (B&W)

V1#1-Al Wiesner-s/a in all 5.00
2-9 3.00
V2 #1(The New Adventures)-4,6-10, V3 (The Legend of...) #1-12 3.00
V2 #5 (Color)-Shows Vol 2, No. 4 in indicia 3.00
V4 (The Saga of ...) #1(2004), 2-8: 8-Chanukah & The Holocaust 3.00
...: The Sequel (2010) "11-9" , ...: The Sequel 2 (2011) Genesis #2 Jews in Space 3.00
...: The Sequel 3 (2012) Purim and the X-Suit 3.00
The Saga of Shaloman (20th Anniversary Edition) TPB (10/08, $15.99) r/V4 #1-8 16.00

SHAMAN'S TEARS (Also see Maggie the Cat)
Image Comics (Creative Fire Studio): 5/93 - No. 2, 8/93; No. 3, 11/94 - No. 0, 1/96 ($2.50/$1.95)

0-2: 0-(DEC-c, 1/96)-Last Issue. 1-(5/93)-Embossed red foil-c; Grell-c/a & scripts in all. 2-Cover unfolds into poster (8/93-c, 7/93 inside) 4.00
3-12: 3-Begin $1.95-c. 5-Re-intro Jon Sable. 12-Re-intro Maggie the Cat (1 pg.) 3.00

SHAME ITSELF
Marvel Comics: Jan, 2012 ($3.99, one-shot)

1-Spoof of "Fear Itself" x-over event; short stories by various incl. Cenac & Kupperman 4.00

SHANG-CHI: MASTER OF KUNG-FU ("Master of Kung Fu" on cover for #1&2)
Marvel Comics: Nov, 2002 - No. 6, Apr, 2003 ($2.99, limited series)

1-6-Moench-s/Gulacy-c/a 3.00
...One-Shot 1 (11/09, $3.99, B&W) Deadpool app. 4.00
... Vol. 1: The Hellfire Apocalypse TPB (2003, $14.99) r/#1-6 15.00

SHANNA, THE SHE-DEVIL (See Savage Tales #8)
Marvel Comics Group: Dec, 1972 - No. 5, Aug, 1973 (All are 20¢ issues)

1-1st app. Shanna; Steranko-c; Tuska-a(p) 5 10 15 35 63 90
2-Steranko-c; heroin drug story 3 6 9 21 33 45
3-5 3 6 9 14 20 25

SHANNA, THE SHE-DEVIL
Marvel Comics: Apr, 2005 - No. 7, Oct, 2005 ($3.50, limited series)

1-7-Reintro of Shanna; Frank Cho-s/a/c in all 3.50
HC (2005, $24.99, dust jacket) r/#1-7 25.00
SC (2006, $16.99) r/#1-7 17.00

SHANNA, THE SHE-DEVIL: SURVIVAL OF THE FITTEST
Marvel Comics: Oct, 2007 - No. 4, Jan, 2008 ($2.99, limited series)

1-4-Khari Evans-a/c; Gray & Palmiotti-s 3.00
SC (2008, $10.99) r/#1-4 11.00

SHAOLIN COWBOY
Burlyman Entertainment: Dec, 2004 - No. 7, May, 2007 ($3.50)

1-7-Geof Darrow-s/a. 3-Moebius-c 3.50

SHAOLIN COWBOY
Dark Horse Comics: Oct, 2013 - No. 4, Feb, 2014 ($3.99)

1-4-Geof Darrow-s/a. 1-Variant-c by Simonson 4.00

SHAOLIN COWBOY: WHO'LL STOP THE REIGN?
Dark Horse Comics: Apr, 2017 - No. 4, Jul, 2017 ($3.99)

1-4-Geof Darrow-s/a. 1-Variant-c by Frank Miller 4.00

SHAPER
Dark Horse Comics: Mar, 2015 - No. 5, Jul, 2015 ($3.99)

1-5: 1-Heisserer-s/Massafera-a. 2-5-Continuado-a 4.00

SHARK FIGHTERS, THE (Movie)
Dell Publishing Co.: Jan, 1957

Four Color 762-Buscema-a; photo-c 7 14 21 48 89 130

SHARK-MAN
Thrill House/Image Comics: Jul, 2006; Jul, 2007; Jan, 2008 - No. 3, Jun, 2008 ($3.99/$3.50)

1,2: 1-(Thrill House, 7/06, $3.99)-Steve Pugh-s/a. 2-(Image Comics, 7/07) 4.00
1-3: 1-(Image, 1/08, $3.50) reprints Thrill House #1 3.50

SHARKY
Image Comics: Feb, 1998 - No. 4, 1998 ($2.50, bi-monthly)

1-4: 1-Mask app.; Elliot-s/a. Horley painted-c. 3-Three covers by Horley, Bisley, & Horley/Elliot. 4-Two covers (swipe of Avengers #4 and wraparound) 3.00
1-($2.95) "$1,000,000" variant 3.00
2-($2.50) Savage Dragon variant-c 3.00

SHARP COMICS (Slightly large size)
H. C. Blackerby: Winter, 1945-46 - V1#2, Spring, 1946 (52 pgs.)

V1#1-Origin Dick Royce Planetarian 52 104 156 328 552 775
2-Origin The Pioneer; Michael Morgan, Dick Royce, Sir Gallagher, Planetarian, Steve Hagen, Weeny and Pop app. 52 104 156 328 552 775

SHARPY FOX (See Comic Capers & Funny Frolics)
I. W. Enterprises/Super Comics: 1958; 1963

1,2-I.W. Reprint (1958): 2-r/Kiddie Kapers #1 2 4 6 8 11 14
14-Super Reprint (1963) 2 4 6 8 10 12

Shazam!: The Monster Society of Evil #3 © DC

Sheena, Queen of the Jungle #15 © FH

She-Hulks #1 © MAR

GD 2.0 VG 4.0 FN 6.0 VF 8.0 VF/NM 9.0 NM- 9.2

SHATTER (See Jon Sable #25-30)
First Comics: June, 1985; Dec, 1985 - No. 14, Apr, 1988. ($1.75, Baxter paper/deluxe paper)

1 (6/85)-1st computer generated-a in a comic book (1st printing) 4.00
1-(2nd print.); 1(12/85)-14: computer generated-a & lettering in all 3.00
Special 1 (1988) 3.00

SHATTERED IMAGE
Image Comics (WildStorm Productions): Aug, 1996 - No. 4, Dec, 1996 ($2.50, lim. series)

1-4: 1st Image company-wide x-over; Kurt Busiek scripts in all. 1-Tony Daniel-c/a(p). 2-Alex Ross-c/swipe (Kingdom Come) by Ryan Benjamin & Travis Charest 3.00

SHAUN OF THE DEAD (Movie)
IDW Publishing: June, 2005 - No. 4, Sept, 2005 ($3.99, limited series)

1-4-Adaptation of 2004 movie; Zach Howard-a 4.00
TPB (12/05, $17.99) r/series; sketch pages and cover gallery 18.00

SHAZAM (See Billy Batson and the Magic of Shazam!, Giant Comics to Color, Limited Collectors' Edition, Power Of Shazam! and Trials of Shazam!)

SHAZAM! (TV)(See World's Finest #253 for story from unpublished #36)
National Periodical Publ./DC Comics: Feb, 1973 - No. 35, May-June, 1978

1-1st revival of original Captain Marvel since G.A. (origin retold), by C.C. Beck; Mary Marvel & Captain Marvel Jr. app.; Superman-c 7 14 21 48 89 130
2-5: 2-Infinity photo-c.; re-intro Mr. Mind & Tawny. 3-Capt. Marvel-r. (10/46). 4-Origin retold; Capt. Marvel-r. (1949). 5-Capt. Marvel Jr. origin retold; Capt. Marvel-r. (1948, 7 pgs.) 3 6 9 18 28 38
6,7,9-11: 6-photo-c; Capt. Marvel-r (1950, 6 pgs.). 9-Mr. Mind app. 10-Last C.C. Beck issue. 11-Schaffenberger-a begins. 3 6 9 15 22 28
8-(100 pgs.) 8-r/1st Black Adam app. from Marvel Family #1; r/Capt. Marvel Jr. by Raboy; origin/C.M. #80; origin Mary Marvel/C.M.A. #18; origin Mr. Tawny/C.M.A. #79 6 12 18 41 76 110
12-17-(All 100 pgs.). 15-vs. Lex Luthor & Mr. Mind 5 10 15 30 50 70
18-24,26,27,29,30: 21-24-All reprints. 26-Sivana app. (10/76). 27-Kid Eternity teams up w/Capt. Marvel. 30-1st DC app. 3 Lt. Marvels 3 6 9 14 20 25
25-1st app. Isis 6 12 18 42 79 115
28-(3-4/77) 1st Bronze Age app. of Black Adam 15 30 45 103 227 350
31-35: 31-1st DC app. Minuteman. 34-Origin Capt. Nazi & Capt. Marvel Jr. retold 3 6 9 16 23 30
...: The Greatest Stories Ever Told TPB (2008, $24.99) reprints; Alex Ross-c 25.00

NOTE: *Reprints in #1-8, 10, 12-17, 21-24.* **Beck** *a-1-10, 12-17r, 21-24r; c-1, 3-9.* **Nasser** *c-35p.* **Newton** *a-35p.* **Raboy** *a-5r, 8r, 17r.* **Schaffenberger** *a-11, 14-20, 25, 26, 27p, 28, 29-31p, 33i, 35i; c-20, 22, 23, 25, 26i, 27i, 28-33.*

SHAZAM!
DC Comics: March, 2011 ($2.99, one-shot)

1-Richards-a/Chiang-c; Blaze app.; story continues in Titans #32 3.00

SHAZAM! AND THE SHAZAM FAMILY! ANNUAL
DC Comics: 2002 ($5.95, squarebound, one-shot)

1-Reprints Golden Age stories including 1st Mary Marvel and 1st Black Adam 1 3 4 6 8 10

SHAZAM!: POWER OF HOPE
DC Comics: Nov, 2000 ($9.95, treasury size, one-shot)

nn-Painted art by Alex Ross; story by Alex Ross and Paul Dini 10.00

SHAZAM!: THE MONSTER SOCIETY OF EVIL
DC Comics: 2007 - No. 4, 2007 ($5.99, square-bound, limited series)

1-4: Jeff Smith-s/a/c in all. 1-Retelling of origin. 2-Mary Marvel & Dr. Sivana app. 6.00
HC (2007, $29.99, over-sized with dust jacket that unfolds to a poster) r/#1-4; Alex Ross intro.; Smith afterword; sketch pages, script pages and production notes 30.00
SC (2009, $19.99) r/#1-4; Alex Ross intro. 20.00

SHAZAM: THE NEW BEGINNING
DC Comics: Apr, 1987 - No. 4, July, 1987 (Legends spin-off) (Limited series)

1-4: 1-New origin & 1st modern app. Captain Marvel; Marvel Family cameo. 2-4-Sivana & Black Adam app. 4.00

SHEA THEATRE COMICS
Shea Theatre: No date (1940's) (32 pgs.)

nn-Contains Rocket Comics; MLJ cover in one color 15 30 45 88 137 185

SHE-BAT (See Murcielaga, She-Bat & Valeria the She-Bat)

SHE-DRAGON (See Savage Dragon #117)
Image Comics: July, 2006 ($5.99, one-shot)

nn- She-Dragon in Dimension-X; origin retold; Franchesco-a/Larsen-s; sketch pages 6.00

SHEENA (Movie)
Marvel Comics: Dec, 1984 - No. 2, Feb, 1985 (limited series)

1,2-r/Marvel Comics Super Special #34; Tanya Roberts movie 4.00

SHEENA, QUEEN OF THE JUNGLE (See Jerry Iger's Classic..., Jumbo Comics, & 3-D Sheena)
Fiction House Magazines: Spr, 1942; No. 2, Wint, 1942-43; No. 3, Spr, 1943; No. 4, Fall, 1948; No. 5, Sum, 1949; No. 6, Spr, 1950; No. 7-10, 1950(nd); No. 11, Spr, 1951 - No. 18, Wint, 1952-53 (#1-3: 68 pgs.; #4-7: 52 pgs.)

1-Sheena begins 300 600 900 1980 3440 4900
2 (Winter, 1942-43) 168 336 504 1075 1838 2600
3 (Spring, 1943) Classic Giant Ape-c 168 336 504 1075 1838 2600
4,5 (Fall, 1948, Sum, 1949): 4-New logo; cover swipe from Jumbo #20 61 122 183 390 670 950
6,7 (Spring, 1950, 1950) 50 100 150 315 533 750
8-10(1950 - Win/50, 36 pgs.) 43 86 129 271 461 650
11-17: 15-Cover swipe from Jumbo #43 40 80 120 246 411 575
18-Used in **POP**, pg. 98 42 84 126 265 445 625
I.W. Reprint #9-r/#18; c-r/White Princess #3 4 8 12 28 44 60

NOTE: **Baker** *c-5-10?* **Whitman** *c-11-18(most).* **Zolnerowich** *c-1-3.*

SHEENA, QUEEN OF THE JUNGLE
Devil's Due Publishing: Mar, 2007; Jun, 2007 - No. 5, Jan, 2008 (99¢/$3.50)

1-5: 1-Rodi-s/Merhoff-a; 5 covers 3.50
... 99¢ Special (3/07) Revival of the character; Rodi-s/Cummings-a; sketch pages; history 3.00
...: Dark Rising (10/08 - No. 3, 12/08) 1-3 3.50
... Trail of the Mapinguari (4/08, $5.50) Two covers 5.50

SHEENA, QUEEN OF THE JUNGLE
Dynamite Entertainment: No. 0 - Present (25¢/$3.99)

0-(25¢) Marguerite Bennett & Christina Trujillo-s/Moritat-a; multiple covers 3.00
1-6-($3.99) 1-Bennett & Trujillo-s/Moritat-a. 4-6-Sanapo-a 4.00

SHEENA 3-D SPECIAL (Also see Blackthorne 3-D Series #1)
Eclipse Comics: Jan, 1985 ($2.00)

1-Dave Stevens-c 2 4 6 9 12 15

SHE-HULK (Also see The Savage She-Hulk & The Sensational She-Hulk)
Marvel Comics: May, 2004 - No. 12, Apr, 2005 ($2.99)

1-Bobillo-a/Slott-s/Granov-c; Avengers app. 5.00
2-4-Bobillo-a/Slott-s/Granov-c. 4-Spider-Man-c/app. 3.00
5-12: Mayhew-c. 9-12-Pelletier-a. 10-Origin of Titania 3.00
Vol. 1: Single Green Female TPB (2004, $14.99) r/#1-6 15.00
Vol. 2: Superhuman Law TPB (2005, $14.99) r/#7-12 15.00

SHE-HULK (2nd series)
Marvel Comics: Dec, 2005 - No. 38, Apr, 2009 ($2.99)

1-Bobillo-a/Slott-s/Horn-c; New Avengers app. 5.00
2,4-7,9-24: 2-Hawkeye-c/app. 9-Jen marries John Jameson. 12-Thanos app. 16-Wolverine app. 3.00
3-($3.99) 100th She-Hulk issue; new story w/art by various incl. Bobillo, Conner, Mayhew & Powell; r/Savage She-Hulk #1 and r/Sensational She-Hulk #1 4.00
8-Civil War 15.00
8-2nd printing with variant Bobillo-c 3.00
25-($3.99) Intro. the Behemoth; Juggernaut cameo; Handbook bio pages of She-Hulk 4.00
26-37: 27-Iron Man app. 30-Hercules app. 31-X-Factor app. 32,33-Secret Invasion 3.00
38-($3.99) Thundra, Valkyrie and Invisible Woman app. 4.00
...: Cosmic Collision 1 (2/09, $3.99) Lady Liberators app.; David-s/Asrar-a/Sejic-c 4.00
... Sensational 1 (5/10, $4.99) 30th Anniversary celebration; Stan Lee app.; Frank-c 5.00
Vol. 3: Time Trials (2006, $14.99) r/#1-5; Bobillo sketch page 15.00
Vol. 4: Laws of Attraction (2007, $19.99) r/#6-12; Paul Smith sketch page 20.00
Vol. 5: Planet Without a Hulk (2007, $19.99) r/#14-21; Slott's original series pitch 20.00
...: Jaded HC (2008, $19.99) r/#22-27; cover gallery 20.00

SHE-HULK (3rd series)
Marvel Comics: Apr, 2014 - No. 12, Apr, 2015 ($2.99)

1-12: 1-4-Soule-s/Pulido-a/Wada-c. 1-Tony Stark app. 2-Hellcat app. 3.00

SHE-HULK (Marvel Legacy)
Marvel Comics: No. 159, Jan, 2018 - No. 163, May, 2018 ($3.99)

159-163: 159-Tamaki-s/Lindsay-a. 159-161-The Leader app. 4.00

SHE-HULKS
Marvel Comics: Jan, 2011 - No. 4, Apr, 2011 ($3.99/$2.99, limited series)

1-($3.99) She-Hulk & Lyra team-up; Stegman-a/McGuinness-c; character profile pages 4.00
2-4-($2.99) McGuinness-c 3.00

SHELTERED
Image Comics: Jul, 2013 - No. 15, Mar, 2015 ($2.99)

1-15-Brisson-s/Christmas-a 3.00

SHERIFF BOB DIXON'S CHUCK WAGON (TV) (See Wild Bill Hickok #22)

Sherlock Holmes #1 © DYN

Shi: Black, White & Red #2 © Billy Tucci

S.H.I.E.L.D. (2015 series) #7 © MAR

	GD 2.0	VG 4.0	FN 6.0	VF 8.0	VF/NM 9.0	NM- 9.2

Avon Periodicals: Nov, 1950

1-Kinstler-c/a(3)	15	30	45	88	137	185

SHERIFF OF BABYLON, THE
DC Comics (Vertigo): Feb, 2016 - No. 12, Jan, 2017 ($3.99)

1-12-Tom King-s/Mitch Gerads-a/John Paul Leon-c 4.00

SHERIFF OF TOMBSTONE
Charlton Comics: Nov, 1958 - No. 17, Sept, 1961

V1#1-Giordano-c; Severin-a	6	12	18	41	66	90
2	4	8	12	22	34	45
3-10	3	6	9	17	25	32
11-17	3	6	9	14	20	25

SHERLOCK: A STUDY IN PINK (Adaptation of episode from the BBC TV series)
Titan Comics: Jul, 2016 - No. 6, Dec, 2016 ($4.99/$3.99, B&W, reads back to front, right to left)

1-English version of original Japanese manga; art by Jay.; multiple covers 5.00
2-6-($3.99) 4.00

SHERLOCK FRANKENSTEIN AND THE LEGION OF EVIL (Also see Black Hammer)
Dark Horse Comics: Oct, 2017 - No. 4, Jan, 2018 ($3.99, limited series)

1-4-Lemire-s/Rubín-a 4.00

SHERLOCK HOLMES (See Classic Comics #33, Marvel Preview, New Adventures of..., & Spectacular Stories)

SHERLOCK HOLMES (All New Baffling Adventures of...)(Young Eagle #3 on?)
Charlton Comics: Oct, 1955 - No. 2, Mar, 1956

1-Dr. Neff, Ghost Breaker app.	41	82	123	250	418	585
2	36	72	108	214	347	480

SHERLOCK HOLMES (Also see The Joker)
National Periodical Publications: Sept-Oct, 1975

1-Cruz-a; Simonson-c	3	6	9	16	23	30

SHERLOCK HOLMES
Dynamite Entertainment: 2009 - No. 5, 2009 ($3.50, limited series)

1-5-Cassaday-c/Moore & Reppion-s/Aaron Campbell-a 3.50

SHERLOCK HOLMES: MORIARTY LIVES
Dynamite Entertainment: 2014 - No. 5, 2014 ($3.99, limited series)

1-5-Liss-s/Indro-a/Francavilla-c 4.00

SHERLOCK HOLMES: THE LIVERPOOL DEMON
Dynamite Entertainment: 2012 - No. 5, 2013 ($3.99, limited series)

1-5-Moore & Reppion-s/Triano-a/Francavilla-c 4.00

SHERLOCK HOLMES VS. HARRY HOUDINI
Dynamite Entertainment: 2014 - No. 5, 2015 ($3.99, limited series)

1-5-Del Col & McCreery-s/Furuzono-a; multiple covers on each 4.00

SHERLOCK HOLMES: YEAR ONE
Dynamite Entertainment: 2011 - No. 6, 2011 ($3.99, limited series)

1-6-Beatty-s; multiple covers on each 4.00

SHERLOCK: THE BLIND BANKER (Adaptation of episode from the BBC TV series)
Titan Comics: Feb, 2017 - No. 6, Jul, 2017 ($4.99/$3.99, B&W, reads back to front, right to left)

1-6-English version of original Japanese manga; art by Jay.; multiple covers 5.00

SHERLOCK: THE GREAT GAME (Adaptation of episode from the BBC TV series)
Titan Comics: Sept, 2017 - No. 6, Feb, 2018 ($4.99, B&W, reads back to front, right to left)

1-6-English version of original Japanese manga; art by Jay.; multiple covers 5.00

SHERRY THE SHOWGIRL (Showgirls #4)
Atlas Comics: July, 1956 - No. 3, Dec, 1956; No. 5, Apr, 1957 - No. 7, Aug, 1957

1-Dan DeCarlo-c/a in all	161	322	483	1030	1765	2500
2	37	74	111	222	361	500
3,5-7	30	60	90	177	289	400

SHE'S JOSIE (See Josie)

SHEVA'S WAR
DC Comics (Helix): Oct, 1998 - No. 5, Feb, 1999 ($2.95, mini-series)

1-5-Christopher Moeller-s/painted-a/c 3.00

SHI (one-shots and TPBs)
Crusade Comics

...: Akai (2001, $2.99)-Intro. Victoria Cross; Tucci-a/c; J.C. Vaughn-s 3.00
...: Akai Victoria Cross Ed. ($5.95, edition of 2000) variant Tucci-c 6.00
...: C.G.I. (2001, $4.99) preview of unpublished series 5.00
.../ Cyblade: The Battle for the Independents (9/95, $2.95) Tucci-c; Hellboy, Bone app. 3.00
.../ Cyblade: The Battle for the Independents (9/95, $2.95) Silvestri variant-c 3.00
.../ Daredevil: Honor Thy Mother (1/97, $2.95) Flip book 3.00
...: Judgment Night (200, $3.99) Wolverine app.; Battlebook card and pages; Tucci-a 4.00
...: Kaidan (10/96, $2.95) Two covers; Tucci-c; Jae Lee wraparound-c 3.00
...: Masquerade (3/98, $3.50) Painted art by Lago, Texeira, and others 3.50
...: Nightstalkers (9/97, $3.50) Painted art by Val Mayerik 3.50
...: Rekishi (1/97, $2.95) Character bios and story summaries of Shi: The Way of the Warrior told in Detective Joe Labianca's point of view; Christopher Golden script; Tucci-c; J.G. Jones-a; flip book w/Shi: East Wind Rain preview 3.00
...: The Art of War Tourbook (1998, $4.95) Blank cover for sketches; early Tucci-a inside 5.00
.../ Vampirella (10/97, $2.95) Ellis-s/Lau-a 3.00
... Vs. Tomoe (8/96, $3.95) Tucci-a/scripts; wraparound foil-c 4.00
... Vs. Tomoe (6/96, $5.00. B&W)-Preview Ed.; sold at San Diego Comic Con 5.00
The Definitive Shi Vol. 1 (2006-2007, $24.99, TPB) B&W r/Way of the Warrior, Tomoe, Rekishi, and Senryaku series; cover gallery with sketches; Tucci & Sparacio-c 25.00

SHI: BLACK, WHITE AND RED
Crusade Comics: Mar, 1998 - No. 2, May, 1998 ($2.95, B&W&Red, mini-series)

1,2-J.G. Jones-painted art 3.00
...- Year of the Dragon Collected Edition (2000, $5.95) r/#1&2 6.00

SHIDIMA
Image Comics: Jan, 2001 - No. 7, Nov, 2002 ($2.95, limited series)

1-7-Prequel to Warlands 3.00
#0-(10/01, $2.25) Short story and sketch pages 3.00

SHI: EAST WIND RAIN
Crusade Comics: Nov, 1997 - No. 2, Feb, 1998 ($3.50, limited series)

1,2-Shi at WW2 Pearl Harbor 3.50

S.H.I.E.L.D. (Nick Fury & His Agents of...) (Also see Nick Fury)
Marvel Comics Group: Feb, 1973 - No. 5, Oct, 1973 (All 20¢ issues)

1-All contain reprint stories from Strange Tales #146-155; new Steranko-c	3	6	9	19	30	40
2-New Steranko flag-c	3	6	9	14	20	25
3-5: 3-Kirby/Steranko-c(r). 4-Steranko-c(r)	2	4	6	9	12	15

NOTE: *Buscema a-3p(r). Kirby layouts 1-5; c-3 (w/Steranko). Steranko a-3r, 4r(2).*

S.H.I.E.L.D.
Marvel Comics: Jun, 2010 - No. 6, Apr, 2011; Aug, 2011 - No. 4, Feb, 2012 ($3.99/$2.99)

1-($3.99) Leonardo DaVinci app.; Weaver-a/Hickman-s/Parel-c; 4 printings 4.00
1-Variant-c by Weaver 6.00
1-Director's Cut (9/10, $4.99) r/#1 with character sketch-a and bios; design-a 5.00
2-6-($2.99) 2-Three printings. 3-Galactus app. 3.00
Infinity (6/11, $4.99) DaVinci, Nostradamus, Newton & Tesla app.; Parel-c 5.00
1 (2nd series) (8/11, $3.99) Weaver-a/Hickman-s/Parel-c; profile pgs of main characters 4.00
2-4-($2.99) 3.00
... Origins (1/14, $7.99) r/Battle Scars #6, Secret Avengers #1, Strange Tales #135 8.00

S.H.I.E.L.D. (Based on the TV series)
Marvel Comics: Feb, 2015 - No. 12, Jan, 2016 ($4.99/$3.99)

1-($4.99) Waid-s/Pacheco-a/Tedesco-c; Avengers app. 5.00
2-8-($3.99) 2-Ms. Marvel (Kamala Khan) app.; Ramos-a. 3-Spider-Man app.; Davis-a 4.00
9-($5.99) 50th Anniversary issue; Howling Commandos app.; r/Strange Tales #135 6.00
10-12: 10-Howard the Duck app. 11-Dominic Fortune app.; Chaykin-a 4.00

SHIELD, THE (Becomes Shield-Steel Sterling #3; #1 titled Lancelot Strong; also see Advs. of the Fly, Double Life of Private Strong, Fly Man, Mighty Comics, The Mighty Crusaders, The Original... & Pep Comics #1)
Archie Enterprises, Inc.: June, 1983 - No. 2, Aug, 1983

1,2: Steel Sterling app. 1-Weiss-c/a. 2-Kanigher-s/Buckler-c/Nebres-a 5.00
America's 1st Patriotic Comic Book Hero, The Shield (2002, $12.95, TPB) r/Pep Comics #1-5, Shield-Wizard Comics #1; foreward by Robert M. Overstreet 13.00

SHIELD, THE (Archie Ent. character) (Continued from The Red Circle)
DC Comics: Nov, 2009 - No. 10, Aug, 2010 ($3.99)

1-10: 1-Magog app.; Inferno back-up feature thru #6; Green Arrow app. 2,3-Grodd app. 4,5-The Great Ten app. 7-10-The Fox back-up feature; Oeming-a 4.00
...: Kicking Down the Door TPB ('10, $19.99) r/#1-6, Red Circle: The Web & RC: The Shield 20.00

SHIELD, THE
Archie Comic Publications: Dec, 2015 - No. 4, Jan, 2017 ($3.99)

1-4-Christopher & Wendig-s/Drew Johnson-a; a new Shield recruited; multiple covers 4.00

SHIELD, THE: SPOTLIGHT (TV)
IDW Publishing: Jan, 2004 - No. 5, May, 2004 ($3.99)

1-5-Jeff Marriote-s/Jean Diaz-a/Tommy Lee Edwards-c 4.00
TPB (7/04, $19.99) r/#1-5; Michael Chiklis photo-c 20.00

Shield Wizard Comics #5 © MLJ

Shi: Ju-Nen #2 © Billy Tucci

Shirtless Bear Fighter #1 © Fuzzy Wipes

GD VG FN VF VF/NM NM-
2.0 4.0 6.0 8.0 9.0 9.2

GD VG FN VF VF/NM NM-
2.0 4.0 6.0 8.0 9.0 9.2

SHIELD-STEEL STERLING (Formerly The Shield)
Archie Enterprises, Inc.: No. 3, Dec, 1983 (Becomes Steel Sterling No. 4)

3-Nino-a; Steel Sterling by Kanigher & Barreto 5.00

SHIELD WIZARD COMICS (Also see Pep Comics & Top-Notch Comics)
MLJ Magazines: Summer, 1940 - No. 13, Spring, 1944

1-(V1#5 on inside)-Origin The Shield by Irving Novick & The Wizard by Ed Ashe, Jr; Flag-c
450 900 1350 3300 6650 10,000
2-(Winter/40)-Origin The Shield retold; Wizard's sidekick, Roy the Super Boy begins
(see Top-Notch #8 for 1st app.) 290 580 870 1856 3178 4500
3,4 194 388 582 1242 2121 3000
5-Dusty, the Boy Detective begins; Nazi bondage-c 168 336 504 1075 1838 2600
6,7: 6-Roy the Super Boy app. 7-Shield dons new costume (Summer, 1942); S & K-c?
161 322 483 1030 1765 2500
8-Nazi bondage-c; Hitler photo on-c 258 516 774 1651 2826 4000
9-Japanese WWII bondage-c 161 322 483 1030 1765 2500
10-Nazi swastica-c 168 336 504 1075 1838 2600
11,12 123 246 369 787 1344 1900
13-Japanese WWII bondage/torture-c (scarce) 194 388 582 1242 2121 3000

NOTE: ***Bob Montana** c-13. **Novick** c-1,3-6,8-11. **Harry Sahle** c-12.*

SHI: FAN EDITIONS
Crusade Comics: 1997

1-3-Two covers polybagged in FAN #19-21 3.00
1-3-Gold editions 4.00

SHI: HEAVEN AND EARTH
Crusade Comics: June, 1997 - No. 4, Apr, 1998 ($2.95)

1-4 3.00
4-($4.95) Pencil-c variant 5.00
Rising Sun Edition-signed by Tucci in FanClub Starter Pack 4.00
"Tora No Shi" variant-c 3.00

SHI: JU-NEN
Dark Horse Comics: July, 2004 - No. 4, May, 2005 ($2.99, mini-series)

1-4-Tucci-a/Tucci & Vaughn-s; origin retold 3.00
TPB (2/06, $12.95) r/#1-4; Tucci and Sparacio-c 13.00

SHINING KNIGHT (See Adventure Comics #66)

SHINKU
Image Comics: Jun, 2011 - No. 5, Oct, 2012 ($2.99)

1-5-Marz-s/Moder-a 3.00

SHINOBI (Based on Sega video game)
Dark Horse Comics: Aug, 2002 ($2.99, one-shot)

1-Medina-a/c 3.00

SHIP AHOY
Spotlight Publishers: Nov, 1944 (52 pgs.)

1-L. B. Cole-c 22 44 66 132 216 300

SHIP OF FOOLS
Image Comics: Aug, 1997 - No. 3 ($2.95, B&W)

0-3-Glass-s/Oeming-a 3.00

SHI: POISONED PARADISE
Avatar Press: July, 2002 - No. 2, Aug, 2002 ($3.50, limited series)

1,2-Vaughn and Tucci-s/Waller-a; 1-Four covers 3.50

SHIPWRECK
AfterShock Comics: Oct, 2016 - Present ($3.99)

1-5-Warren Ellis-s/Phil Hester-a 3.00

SHIPWRECKED! (Disney-Movie)
Disney Comics: 1990 ($5.95, graphic novel, 68 pgs.)

nn-adaptation; Spiegle-a 6.00

SHIRTLESS BEAR FIGHTER
Image Comics: Jun, 2017 - No. 5, Oct, 2017 ($3.99, limited series)

1-5-Leheup & Girner-s/Vendrell-a; multiple covers on each 4.00

SHI: SEMPO
Avatar Press: Aug, 2003 - No. 2, ($3.50, B&W, limited series)

1,2-Vaughn and Tucci-s/Alves-a; 1-Four covers 3.50

SHI: SENRYAKU
Crusade Comics: Aug, 1995 - No. 3, Nov, 1995 ($2.95, limited series)

1-3: 1-Tucci-c; Quesada, Darrow, Sim, Lee, Smith-a. 2-Tucci-c; Silvestri, Balent, Perez, Mack-a. 3-Jusko-c; Hughes, Ramos, Bell, Moore-a 3.00
1-variant-c (no logo) 4.00
Hardcover ($24.95)-r/#1-3; Frazetta-c. 25.00
Trade Paperback ($13.95)-r/#1-3; Frazetta-c. 14.00

SHI: THE ILLUSTRATED WARRIOR
Crusade Comics: 2002 - No. 7, 2003 ($2.99, B&W)

1-7-Story text with Tucci full page art 3.00

SHI: THE SERIES
Crusade Comics: Aug, 1997 - No. 13 ($2.95, color #1-10, B&W #11)

1-10 3.00
11-13: 11-B&W. 12-Color; Lau-a 3.00
#0 Convention Edition 5.00

SHI: THE WAY OF THE WARRIOR
Crusade Comics: Mar, 1994 - No. 12, Apr, 1997 ($2.50/$2.95)

1/2 4.00
1 2 4 6 8 10 12
1-Commemorative ed., B&W, new-c; given out at 1994 San Diego Comic Con
2 4 6 10 14 18
1-Fan appreciation edition -r/#1 3.00
1-Fan appreciation edition (variant) 6.00
1- 10th Anniversary Edition (2004, $2.99) 3.00
2 5.00
2-Commemorative edition (3,000) 2 4 6 9 13 16
2-Fan appreciation edition -r/#2 3.00
3 4.00
4-7: 4-Silvestri poster. 7-Tomoe app. 3.00
5,6: 5-Silvestri variant-c. 6-Tomoe #1 variant-c 3.50
5-Gold edition 12.00
6,8-12: 6-Fan appreciation edition 3.00
8-Combo Gold edition 6.00
8-Signed Edition-(5000) 4.00
Trade paperback (1995, $12.95)-r/#1-4 15.00
Trade paperback (1995, $14.95)-r/#1-4 revised; Julie Bell-c 15.00

SHI: YEAR OF THE DRAGON
Crusade Comics: 2000 - No. 3, 2000 ($2.99, limited series)

1-3: 1-Two covers; Tucci-a/c; flashback to teen-aged Ana 3.00

SHMOO (See Al Capp's... & Washable Jones &...)

SHOCK (Magazine)
Stanley Publ.: May, 1969 - V3#4, Sept, 1971 (B&W reprints from horror comics, including some pre-code) (No V2#1,3)

V1#1-Cover-r/Weird Tales of the Future #7 by Bernard Baily; r/Weird Chills #1
7 14 21 48 89 130
2-Wolverton-r/Weird Mysteries 5; r-Weird Mysteries #7 used in **SOTI**; cover reprints cover to Weird Chills #1 5 10 15 35 63 90
3,5,6 4 8 12 28 47 65
4-Harrison/Williamson-r/Forbid. Worlds #6 5 10 15 30 50 70
V2#2(5/70), V1#8(7/70), V2#4(9/70)-6(1/71), V3#1-4: V2#4-Cover swipe from Weird Mysteries #6 4 8 12 27 44 60

NOTE: ***Disbrow** r-V2#4; Bondage c-V1#4, V2#6, V3#1.*

SHOCK DETECTIVE CASES (Formerly Crime Fighting Detective)
(Becomes Spook Detective Cases No. 22)
Star Publications: No. 20, Sept, 1952 - No. 21, Nov, 1952

20,21-L.B. Cole-c; based on true crime cases 30 60 90 177 289 400

NOTE: ***Palais** a-20. No. 21-Fox-r.*

SHOCK ILLUSTRATED (...Adult Crime Stories; Magazine format)
E. C. Comics: Sept-Oct, 1955 - No. 3, Spring, 1956 (Adult Entertainment on-c #1,2)(All 25¢)

1-All by Kamen; drugs, prostitution, wife swapping 23 46 69 138 227 315
2-Williamson-a redrawn from Crime SuspenStories #13 plus Ingels, Crandall, Evans & part Torres-i; painted-c 21 42 63 126 206 285
3-Only 100 known copies bound & given away at E.C. office; Crandall, Evans-a; painted-c; shows May, 1956 on-c 155 310 465 992 1696 2400

SHOCKING MYSTERY CASES (Formerly Thrilling Crime Cases)
Star Publications: No. 50, Sept, 1952 - No. 60, Oct, 1954 (All crime reprints?)

50-Disbrow "Frankenstein" story 55 110 165 352 601 850
51-Disbrow-a 39 78 117 231 378 525
52-60: 56-Drug use story 37 74 111 222 361 500

NOTE: ***L. B. Cole** covers on all; a-60(2 pgs.). **Hollingsworth** a-52. **Morisi** a-55.*

SHOCKING TALES DIGEST MAGAZINE
Harvey Publications: Oct, 1981 (95¢)

1-1957-58-r; Powell, Kirby, Nostrand-a 2 4 6 9 13 16

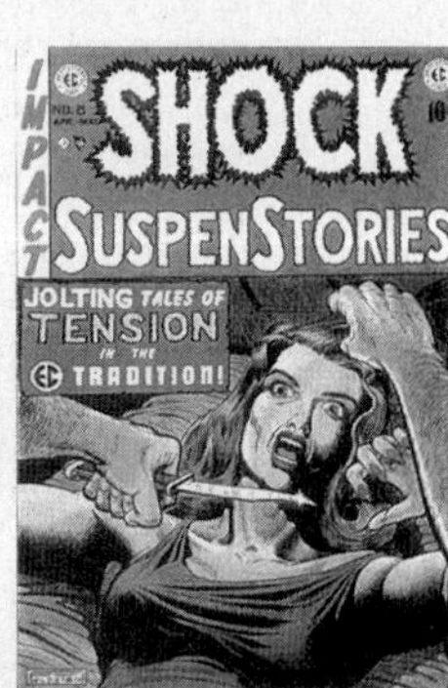

Shock SuspenStories #8 © WMG

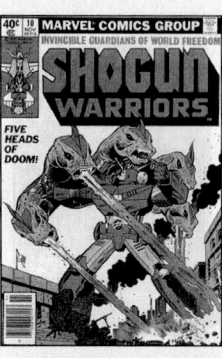

Shogun Warriors #10 © MAR

Showcase #13 © DC

GD 2.0 | VG 4.0 | FN 6.0 | VF 8.0 | VF/NM 9.0 | NM- 9.2

SHOCK ROCKETS
Image Comics (Gorilla): Apr, 2000 - No. 6, Oct, 2000 ($2.50)
1-6-Busiek-s/Immonen & Grawbadger-a. 6-Flip book w/Superstar preview 3.00
...: We Have Ignition TPB (Dark Horse, 8/04, $14.95, 6" x 9") r/#1-6 15.00

SHOCK SUSPENSTORIES (Also see EC Archives • Shock SuspenStories)
E. C. Comics: Feb-Mar, 1952 - No. 18, Dec-Jan, 1954-55
1-Classic Feldstein electrocution-c 126 252 378 1008 1604 2200
2 54 108 162 432 691 950
3,4: 3-Classic decapitation splash. 4-Used in **SOTI**, pg. 387,388
46 92 138 368 584 800
5-Hanging-c 56 112 168 448 712 975
6-Classic hooded vigilante bondage-c 120 240 360 960 1530 2100
7-Classic face melting-c 71 142 213 568 909 1250
8-Williamson-a 44 88 132 352 564 775
9-11: 9-Injury to eye panel. 10-Junkie story 36 72 108 288 457 625
12- "The Monkey" classic junkie cover/story; anti-drug propaganda issue
63 126 189 504 802 1100
13-Frazetta's only solo story for E.C., 7 pgs, draws himself as main male character
53 106 159 424 675 925
14-Used in Senate Investigation hearings 34 68 102 272 436 600
15-Used in 1954 Reader's Digest article, "For the Kiddies to Read"
31 62 93 248 399 550
16-18: 16- "Red Dupe" editorial; rape story 30 60 90 240 383 525
NOTE: ***Ray Bradbury** adaptations-1, 7, 9. **Craig** a-11; c-11. **Crandall** a-9-13, 15-18. **Davis** a-1-5. **Evans** a-7, 8, 14-18; c-16-18. **Feldstein** c-1, 7-9, 12. **Ingels** a-1, 2, 6. **Kamen** a-in all; c-10, 13, 15. **Krigstein** a-14, 18. **Orlando** a-1, 3-7, 9, 10, 12, 16, 17. **Wood** a-2-15; c-2-6, 14.*

SHOCK SUSPENSTORIES (Also see EC Archives • Shock SuspenStories)
Russ Cochran/Gemstone Publishing: Sept, 1992 - No. 18, Dec, 1996 ($1.50/$2.00/$2.50, quarterly)
1-18: 1-3: Reprints with original-c. 17-r/HOF #17 4.00

SHOGUN WARRIORS
Marvel Comics Group: Feb, 1979 - No. 20, Sept, 1980 (Based on Mattel toys of the classic Japanese animation characters) (1-3: 35¢; 4-19: 40¢; 20: 50¢)
1-Raydeen, Combatra, & Dangard Ace begin; Trimpe-a
2 4 6 11 16 20
2-20: 2-Lord Maurkon & Elementals of Evil app.; Rok-Korr app. 6-Shogun vs. Shogun. 7,8-Cerberus. 9-Starchild. 11-Austin-c. 12-Simonson-c. 14-16-Doctor Demonicus. 17-Juggernaut. 19,20-FF x-over 2 3 4 6 8 10

SHOOK UP (Magazine) (Satire)
Dodsworth Publ. Co.: Nov, 1958
V1#1 4 8 12 28 44 60

SHORT RIBS
Dell Publishing Co.: No. 1333, Apr - June, 1962
Four Color 1333 5 10 15 35 63 90

SHORTSTOP SQUAD (Baseball)
Ultimate Sports Ent. Inc.: 1999 ($3.95, one-shot)
1-Ripken Jr., Larkin, Jeter, Rodriguez app.; Edwards-c/a 4.00

SHORT STORY COMICS (See Hello Pal,...)

SHORTY SHINER (The Five-Foot Fighter in the Ten Gallon Hat)
Dandy Magazine (Charles Biro): June, 1956 - No. 3, Oct, 1956
1 8 16 24 42 54 65
2,3 6 12 18 31 38 45

SHOTGUN SLADE (TV)
Dell Publishing Co.: No. 1111, July-Sept, 1960
Four Color 1111-Photo-c 6 12 18 37 66 95

SHOWCASE (See Cancelled Comic Cavalcade & New Talent...)
National Per. Publ./DC Comics: 3-4/56 - No. 93, 9/70; No. 94, 8-9/77 - No. 104, 9/78
1-Fire Fighters; w/Fireman Farrell 315 630 945 2600 5900 9200
2-Kings of the Wild; Kubert-a (animal stories) 125 250 375 1000 2250 3500
3-The Frogmen by Russ Heath; Heath greytone-c (early DC example, 7-8/56)
111 222 333 888 1994 3100
4-Origin/1st app. The Flash (1st DC Silver Age hero, Sept-Oct, 1956); Kanigher-s; Infantino & Kubert-c/a; 1st app. Iris West and The Turtle; r/in Secret Origins #1 ('61 & '73); Flash shown reading G.A. Flash Comics #13; back-up story w/Broome-s/Infantino & Kubert-a
6500 13,000 26,000 58,000 104,000 150,000
5-Manhunters; Meskin-a 96 192 288 768 1734 2700
6-Origin/1st app. Challengers of the Unknown by Kirby, partly r/in Secret Origins #1 & Challengers #64,65 (1st S.A. hero team & 1st original concept S.A. series)(1-2/57)
350 700 1050 2975 6738 10,500
7-Challengers of the Unknown by Kirby (2nd app.) reprinted in Challengers of the Unknown #75 152 304 456 1254 2827 4400
8-The Flash (5-6/57, 2nd app.); origin & 1st app. Captain Cold
880 1760 2640 7900 14,950 22,000
9-Lois Lane (Pre-#1, 7-8/57) (1st Showcase character to win own series)
Superman app. on-c 660 1320 1980 5280 9640 14,000
10-Lois Lane; Jor-El cameo; Superman app. on-c 220 440 660 1815 4108 6400
11-Challengers of the Unknown by Kirby (3rd) 141 284 423 1142 2571 4000
12-Challengers of the Unknown by Kirby (4th) 141 284 423 1142 2571 4000
13-The Flash (3rd app.); origin Mr. Element 350 700 1050 2975 6738 10,500
14-The Flash (4th app.); origin Dr. Alchemy, former Mr. Element (rare in NM)
367 734 1101 3120 7060 11,000
15-Space Ranger (7-8/58, 1st app., also see My Greatest Aventure #22)
166 332 498 1370 3085 4800
16-Space Ranger (9-10/58, 2nd app.) 89 178 267 712 1606 2500
17-(11-12/58)-Adventures on Other Worlds; origin/1st app. Adam Strange by Gardner Fox & Mike Sekowsky 333 666 999 2831 6416 10,000
18-Adventures on Other Worlds (2nd A. Strange) 96 192 288 768 1734 2700
19-Adam Strange; 1st Adam Strange logo 102 204 306 816 1833 2850
20-Rip Hunter; origin & 1st app. (5-6/59); Moreira-a 139 278 417 1112 2506 3900
21-Rip Hunter (7-8/59, 2nd app.); Sekowsky-c/a 56 112 168 448 999 1550
22-Origin & 1st app. Silver Age Green Lantern by Gil Kane and John Broome (9-10/59); reprinted in Secret Origins #2 1100 2200 4400 13,500 29,250 45,000
23-Green Lantern (11-12/59, 2nd app.); nuclear explosion-c
200 400 600 1650 3725 5800
24-Green Lantern (1-2/60, 3rd app.) 166 332 498 1370 3085 4800
25,26-Rip Hunter by Kubert. 25-Grey tone-c 46 92 138 340 770 1200
27-Sea Devils (7-8/60, 1st app.); Heath-c/a; Grey tone-c
79 158 237 632 1416 2200
28-Sea Devils (9-10/60, 2nd app.); Heath-c/a; Grey tone-c
39 78 117 289 657 1025
29-Sea Devils; Heath-c/a; grey tone c-27-29 42 84 126 311 706 1100
30-Origin Silver Age Aquaman (1-2/61) (see Adventure #260 for 1st S.A. origin)
241 482 723 1988 4494 7000
31-Aquaman 54 108 162 432 966 1500
32,33-Aquaman 41 82 123 303 689 1075
34-Origin & 1st app. Silver Age Atom by Gil Kane & Murphy Anderson (9-10/61); reprinted in Secret Origins #2 159 318 477 1312 2956 4600
35-The Atom by Gil Kane (2nd); last 10¢ issue 50 100 150 400 900 1400
36-The Atom by Gil Kane (1-2/62, 3rd app.) 40 80 120 296 673 1050
37-Metal Men (3-4/62, 1st app.) 100 200 300 800 1800 2800
38-Metal Men (5-6/62, 2nd app.) 30 60 90 219 490 760
39-Metal Men (7-8/62, 3rd app.) 23 46 69 164 362 560
40-Metal Men (9-10/62, 4th app.) 21 42 63 147 324 500
41,42-Tommy Tomorrow (parts 1 & 2). 42-Origin 13 26 39 91 201 310
43-Dr. No (James Bond); Nodel-a; originally published as British Classics Illustrated #158A & as #6 in a European Detective series, all with diff. painted-c. This Showcase #43 version is actually censored, deleting all racial skin color and dialogue thought to be racially demeaning (1st DC S.A. movie adaptation)(based on Ian Fleming novel & movie)
56 112 168 448 999 1550
44-Tommy Tomorrow 10 20 30 66 138 210
45-Sgt. Rock (7-8/63); pre-dates B&B #52; origin retold; Heath-c
33 66 99 238 532 825
46,47-Tommy Tomorrow 9 18 27 61 123 185
48,49-Cave Carson (3rd tryout series; see B&B) 8 16 24 54 102 150
50,51-I Spy (Danger Trail-r by Infantino), King Farady story (#50 has new 4 pg. story)
7 14 21 48 89 130
52-Cave Carson 7 14 21 49 92 135
53,54-G.I. Joe (11-12/64, 1-2/65); Heath-a 11 22 33 73 157 240
55-Dr. Fate & Hourman (3-4/65); origin of each in text; 1st solo app. G.A. Green Lantern in Silver Age (pre-dates Gr. Lantern #40); 1st S.A. app. Solomon Grundy
28 56 84 202 451 700
56-Dr. Fate & Hourman 12 24 36 84 185 285
57-Enemy Ace by Kubert (7-8/65, 4th app. after Our Army at War #155)
19 38 57 131 291 450
58-Enemy Ace by Kubert (5th app.) 16 32 48 107 236 365
59-Teen Titans (11-12/65, 3rd app.) 17 34 51 117 259 400
60-1st S. A. app. The Spectre; Anderson-a (1-2/66); origin in text
24 48 72 168 372 575
61-The Spectre by Anderson (2nd app.) 12 24 36 82 179 275
62-Origin & 1st app. Inferior Five (5-6/66) 8 16 24 56 108 160
63,65-Inferior Five. 63-Hulk parody. 65-X-Men parody (11-12/66)
6 12 18 37 66 95

Showcase #97 © DC

Showcase '95 #2 © DC

Showcase Presents Dial H for Hero © DC

	GD 2.0	VG 4.0	FN 6.0	VF 8.0	VF/NM 9.0	NM- 9.2
64-The Spectre by Anderson (5th app.)	12	24	36	80	173	265
66,67-B'wana Beast	5	10	15	35	63	90
68-Maniaks (1st app., spoof of The Monkees)	5	10	15	35	63	90
69,71-Maniaks. 71-Woody Allen-c/app.	5	10	15	34	60	85
70-Binky (9-10/67)-Tryout issue; 1950's Leave It To Binky reprints with art changes	6	12	18	37	66	95
72-Top Gun (Johnny Thunder-r)-Toth-a	5	10	15	31	53	75
73-Origin/1st app. Creeper; Ditko-c/a (3-4/68)	10	20	30	69	147	225
74-Intro/1st app. Anthro; Post-c/a (5/68)	7	14	21	49	92	135
75-Origin/1st app. Hawk & the Dove; Ditko-c/a	10	20	30	67	141	215
76-1st app. Bat Lash (8/68)	8	16	24	51	96	140
77-1st app. Angel & The Ape (9/68)	6	12	18	41	76	110
78-1st app. Jonny Double (11/68)	5	10	15	30	50	70
79-1st app. Dolphin (12/68); Aqualad origin-r	8	16	24	51	96	140
80-1st S.A. app. Phantom Stranger (1/69); Neal Adams-c	12	24	36	79	170	260
81-Windy & Willy; r/Many Loves of Dobie Gillis #26 with art changes	5	10	15	34	60	85
82-1st app. Nightmaster (5/69) by Grandenetti & Giordano; Kubert-c	6	12	18	41	76	110
83,84-Nightmaster by Wrightson w/Jones/Kaluta ink assist in each; Kubert-c. 83-Last 12¢ issue 84-Origin retold; begin 15¢	6	12	18	41	76	110
85-87-Firehair; Kubert-a	3	6	9	16	23	30
88-90-Jason's Quest: 90-Manhunter 2070 app.	3	6	9	14	20	25
91-93-Manhunter 2070: 92-Origin. 93-(9/70) Last 15¢ issue	3	6	9	14	20	25
94-Intro/origin new Doom Patrol & Robotman(8-9/77)	3	6	9	14	20	25
95,96-The Doom Patrol. 95-Origin Celsius	2	3	4	6	8	10
97-Power Girl; origin; JSA cameos	3	6	9	21	33	45
98,99-Power Girl; origin in #98; JSA cameos	2	4	6	11	16	20
100-(52 pgs.)-Most Showcase characters featured	2	4	6	11	16	20
101-103-Hawkman; Adam Strange x-over	2	3	4	6	8	10
104-(52 pgs.)-O.S.S. Spies at War	2	3	4	6	8	10

NOTE: ***Anderson** a-22-24i, 34-36i, 55, 56, 60, 61, 64, 101-103i; c-50i, 51i, 55, 56, 60, 61, 64. **Aparo** c-94-96. **Boring** c-10. **Estrada** a-104. **Fraden** c(p)-30, 31, 33. **Heath** c-3, 27-29. **Infantino** c/a(p)-4, 8, 13, 14; c-50p, 51p. **Gil Kane** a-22-24p, 34-36p; c-17-19, 22-24p(w/**Giella**), 31. **Kane/Anderson** c-34-36. **Kirby** c-11, 12. **Kirby/Stein** c-6, 7. **Kubert** a-2, 4i, 25, 26, 45, 53, 54, 72; c-25, 26, 53, 54, 57, 58, 82-87, 101-104; c-2, 4i. **Moreira** c-5. **Orlando** a-62p, 63p, 97i; c-62, 63, 97i. **Sekowsky** a-65p. **Sparling** a-78. **Staton** a-94, 95-99p, 100; c-97-100p.*

SHOWCASE '93

DC Comics: Jan, 1993 - No. 12, Dec, 1993 ($1.95, limited series, 52 pgs.)

1-12: 1-Begin 4 part Catwoman story & 6 part Blue Devil story; begin Cyborg story; Art Adams/Austin-c. 3-Flash by Charest (p). 6-Azrael in Bat-costume (2 pgs.). 7,8-Knightfall parts 13 & 14. 6-10-Deathstroke app. (6,10-cameo). 9,10-Austin-i. 10-Azrael as Batman in new costume app.; Gulacy-c. 11-Perez-c. 12-Creeper app.; Alan Grant scripts 4.00

NOTE: ***Chaykin** c-9. **Fabry** c-8. **Giffen** a-12. **Golden** c-3. **Zeck** c-6.*

SHOWCASE '94

DC Comics: Jan, 1994 - No. 12, Dec, 1994 ($1.95, limited series, 52 pgs.)

1-12: 1,2-Joker & Gunfire stories. 1-New Gods. 4-Riddler story. 5-Huntress-c/story w/app. new Batman. 6-Huntress-c/story w/app. Robin; Atom story. 7-Penguin story by Peter David, P. Craig Russell, & Michael T. Gilbert; Penguin-c by Jae Lee. 8,9-Scarface origin story by Alan Grant, John Wagner,& Teddy Kristiansen; Prelude to Zero Hour. 10-Zero Hour tie-in story. 11-Man-Bat. 4.00

NOTE: ***Alan Grant** scripts-3, 4. **Kelley Jones** c-12. **Mignola** c-3. **Nebres** a(i)-2. **Quesada** c-10. **Russell** a-7p. **Simonson** c-5.*

SHOWCASE '95

DC Comics: Jan, 1995 - No. 12, Dec, 1995 ($2.50/$2.95, limited series)

1-4-Supergirl story. 3-Eradicator-c.; The Question story. 4-Thorn c/story 4.00

5-12: 5-Thorn-c/story; begin $2.95-c. 8-Spectre story. 12-The Shade story by James Robinson & Wade Von Grawbadger; Maitresse story by Claremont & Alan Davis 4.00

SHOWCASE '96

DC Comics: Jan, 1996 - No. 12, Dec, 1996 ($2.95, limited series)

1-12: 1-Steve Geppi cameo. 3-Black Canary & Lois Lane-c/story; Deadman story by Jamie Delano & Wade Von Grawbadger, Gary Frank-c. 4-Firebrand & Guardian-c/story; The Shade & Dr. Fate "Times Past" story by James Robinson & Matt Smith begins, ends #5. 6-Superboy-c/app.; Atom app.; Capt. Marvel (Mary Marvel)-c/app. 8-Supergirl by David & Dodson. 11-Scare Tactics app. 11,12-Legion of Super-Heroes vs. Brainiac. 12-Jesse Quick app. 4.00

SHOWCASE PRESENTS... (B&W archive reprints of DC Silver Age stories)

DC Comics: 2005 - 2011 ($9.99/$16.99/$17.99/$19.99, B&W, over 500 pgs., squarebound)

Adam Strange Vol. 1 (2007, $16.99) r/Showcase #17-19 & Mystery in Space #53-84 17.00
Ambush Bug (2009, $16.99) r/first app. in DC Comics Presents #52 other early app. 17.00
Aquaman Vol. 1 (2007, $16.99) r/Aquaman #1-6 & other early app. 17.00
Aquaman Vol. 2 (2008, $16.99) r/Aquaman #7-23 & other early app. 17.00
Aquaman Vol. 3 (2009, $16.99) r/Aquaman #24-39 & other early app. 17.00
The Atom Vol. 1 (2007, $16.99) r/Showcase #34-36 & The Atom #1-17 17.00
The Atom Vol. 2 (2008, $16.99) r/The Atom #18-38 17.00
Batgirl Vol. 1 (2007, $16.99) r/early apps. from Detective #359 (1967) thru 1975 17.00
Bat Lash Vol. 1 (2009, $9.99) r/#1-7, Showcase #76, DC Special Series #16, and Jonah Hex #49,51,52 10.00
Batman Vol. 1 (2006, $16.99) r/"new look" from Detective #327-342, Batman #164-174 17.00
Batman Vol. 2 (2007, $16.99) r/"new look" from Detective #343-358, Batman #175-188 17.00
Batman Vol. 3 (2008, $16.99) r/"new look" from Detective #359-375, Batman #189, 190-192,194-197,199-202 17.00
Batman and the Outsiders Vol. 1 (2007, $16.99) r/#1-19, Annual #1; Brave and the Bold #200; and New Teen Titans #37 17.00
Blackhawk Vol. 1 (2008, $16.99) r/#108-127 17.00
Booster Gold Vol. 1 (2008, $16.99) r/#1-25 & Action Comics #594 17.00
The Brave and the Bold Batman Team-ups Vol. 1 (2007, $16.99) r/#59,64,67-71,74-87 17.00
The Brave and the Bold Batman Team-ups Vol. 2 (2007, $16.99) r/#88-108 17.00
The Brave and the Bold Batman Team-ups Vol. 3 (2008, $16.99) r/#109-134 17.00
Challengers of the Unknown Vol. 1 (2006, $16.99) r/#1-17 & Showcase #6,7,11,12 17.00
Challengers of the Unknown Vol. 2 (2008, $16.99) r/#18-37 17.00
DC Comics Presents: The Superman Team-ups Vol. 1 (2009, $17.99) r/#1-26 18.00
Dial H For Hero ('10, $9.99) r/early apps. in House of Mystery #156-173 10.00
Doc Savage ('11, $19.99) r/Doc Savage #1-8 (1975-77 Marvel B&W magazine) 20.00
The Doom Patrol Vol. 1 (2009, $16.99) r/#86-101 and My Greatest Adventure #80-85 17.00
The Doom Patrol Vol. 2 (2010, $19.99) r/#102-121 20.00
The Elongated Man Vol. 1 ('06, $16.99) r/early apps. in Flash & Detective ('60-'68) 17.00
Eclipso Vol. 1 (2009, $9.99) r/stories from House of Secrets #61-80 10.00
Enemy Ace Vol. 1 (2008, $16.99) r/Our Army at War #151 & other early app. 17.00
The Flash Vol. 1 (2007, $16.99) r/Flash Comics #104 (last G.A. issue), Showcase #4,8,13,14 & The Flash #105-119 17.00
The Flash Vol. 2 (2008, $16.99) r/The Flash #120-140 17.00
The Flash Vol. 3 (2009, $16.99) r/The Flash #141-161 17.00
The Flash, The Trial of ... (2011, $19.99) r/The Flash #323-327,329-336,340-350 20.00
The Great Disaster Featuring The Atomic Knights and Hercules Vol. 1 (2007, $16.99) 17.00
Green Arrow Vol. 1 (2006, $16.99) r/Adventure #250-269, Brave and the Bold #50,71,85; Justice League of America #4; World's Finest #95-134,136,138,140 17.00
Green Lantern Vol. 1 (2005, $9.99) r/Showcase #22-24 & Green Lantern #1-17 20.00
Green Lantern Vol. 1 (2010, $19.99) r/Showcase #22-24 & Green Lantern #1-17 20.00
Green Lantern Vol. 2 (2007, $16.99) r/Green Lantern #18-38 17.00
Green Lantern Vol. 3 (2008, $16.99) r/Green Lantern #39-59 17.00
Green Lantern Vol. 4 (2009, $16.99) r/Green Lantern #60-75 17.00
Green Lantern Vol. 5 (2011, $19.99) r/Green Lantern #76-87,89 and back up stories from Flash #217-246 20.00
Haunted Tank Vol. 1 ('06, $16.99) r/G.I. Combat #87-119, Brave & The Bold #52 and Our Army at War #155; Russ Heath-c 17.00
Haunted Tank Vol. 2 ('08, $16.99) r/G.I. Combat #120-156 17.00
Hawkman Vol. 1 ('07, $16.99) r/Brave & The Bold #34-36,42-44, Mystery in Space #87-90, Hawkman #1-11, and The Atom #7 17.00
Hawkman Vol. 2 ('08, $16.99) r/Brave & The Bold #70, Hawkman #12-27, The Atom #31, & The Atom and Hawkman #39-45 17.00
The House of Mystery Vol. 1 ('06, $16.99) r/House of Mystery #174-194 ('68-'71) 17.00
The House of Mystery Vol. 2 ('07, $16.99) r/House of Mystery #195-211 ('71-'73) 17.00
The House of Mystery Vol. 3 ('09, $16.99) r/House of Mystery #212-226 ('73-'74) 17.00
The House of Secrets Vol. 1 ('08, $16.99) r/House of Secrets #81-98 ('69-'72) 17.00
The House of Secrets Vol. 2 ('09, $17.99) r/House of Secrets #99-119 ('72-'74) 18.00
Jonah Hex Vol. 1 (2005, $16.99) r/All Star Western #10-12, Weird Western Tales #13,14, 16-33; plus the complete adventures of Outlaw from All Star Western #2-8 17.00
Justice League of America Vol. 1 ('05, $16.99) r/Brave & the Bold #28-30, J.L. of A. #1-16 and Mystery in Space #75 17.00
Justice League of America Vol. 2 ('07, $16.99) r/Justice League of America #17-36 17.00
Justice League of America Vol. 3 ('07, $16.99) r/Justice League of America #37-60 17.00
Justice League of America Vol. 4 ('09, $16.99) r/Justice League of America #61-83 17.00
Justice League of America Vol. 5 ('11, $19.99) r/Justice League of America #84-106 20.00
Legion of Super-Heroes Vol. 1 ('07, $16.99) r/Adventure #247 & early app. thru 1964 17.00
Legion of Super-Heroes Vol. 2 ('08, $16.99) r/app. in Adventure & Superboy 1964-66 17.00
Legion of Super-Heroes Vol. 3 ('09, $16.99) r/Adventure #349-368 & S.P. Jimmy Olsen #106 17.00
Legion of Super-Heroes Vol. 4 ('10, $19.99) r/app. in Adv., Action & Superboy 1968-72 20.00
Martian Manhunter Vol. 1 (2007, $16.99) r/Detective #225-304 & Batman #78 (prototype) 17.00
Martian Manhunter Vol. 2 ('09, $16.99) r/Detective #305-326 & House of Myst. #143-173 17.00
Metal Men Vol. 1 (2007, $16.99) r/#1-16; Brave & Bold #55, Showcase #37-40 17.00
Metamorpho Vol. 1 ('05, $16.99) r/Brave&Bold #57,58,66,68; Metamorpho #1-17;JLA #42 17.00
Our Army at War Vol. 1 ('10, $19.99) r/#1-20 20.00
Phantom Stranger Vol. 1 (2006, $16.99) r/#1-21 (2nd series) & Showcase #80 17.00
Phantom Stranger Vol. 2 (2008, $16.99) r/#22-41 and various 1970-1978 appearances 17.00

Shrek #2 © Dreamworks

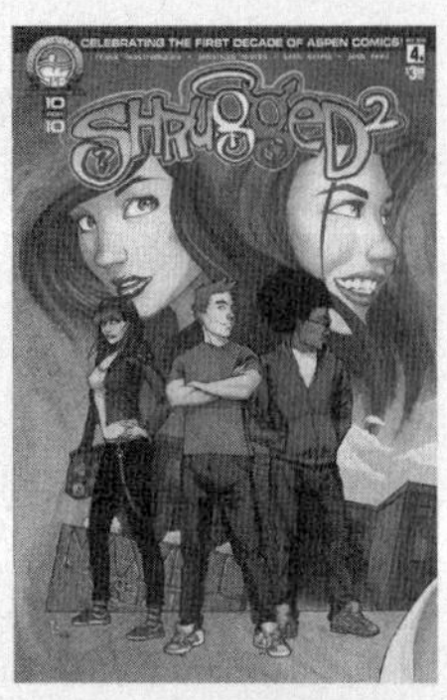

Shrugged V2 #4 © Aspen MLT

Sick #35 © Feature Pub.

	GD 2.0	VG 4.0	FN 6.0	VF 8.0	VF/NM 9.0	NM- 9.2

Robin The Boy Wonder Vol. 1 (2007, $16.99) r/back-ups from Batman, Detective, WF 17.00
Secrets of Sinister House ('10, $17.99) r/#5-18 and Sinister House of Secret Love #1-4 18.00
Sgt. Rock Vol. 1 ('07, $16.99) r/G.I. Combat #68, Our Army at War #81-117 17.00
Sgt. Rock Vol. 2 ('08, $16.99) r/Our Army at War #118-148 17.00
Sgt. Rock Vol. 3 ('10, $19.99) r/Our Army at War #149-163,165-172,174-176,178-180 20.00
Shazam! Vol. 1 ('06, $16.99) r/#1-33 17.00
Strange Adventures Vol. 1 ('08, $16.99) r/#54-73 17.00
Supergirl Vol. 1 ('07, $16.99) r/prototype from Superman #123 (8/58); 1st app. Action #252 (5/59) and early appearances thru Nov. 1961 17.00
Supergirl Vol. 2 ('08, $16.99) r/appearances in Action Comics #283-321 (1961-1965) 17.00
Superman Vol. 1 ('05, $9.99) r/Action #241-257 & Superman #122-134 (1958-59) 20.00
Superman Vol. 1 ('10, $19.99) r/Action #241-257 & Superman #122-134 (1958-59) 20.00
Superman Vol. 2 ('06, $16.99) r/Action #258-275 & Superman #134-145 (1959-61) 17.00
Superman Vol. 3 ('07, $16.99) r/Action #279-292 & Superman #146-156 & Annual #3,4 17.00
Superman Vol. 4 ('08, $16.99) r/Action #293-309 & Superman #157-166 (1962-64) 17.00
Superman Family Vol. 1 ('06, $16.99) Superman's Pal, Jimmy Olsen #1-22; Showcase #9 and Superman #22 17.00
Superman Family Vol. 2 ('08, $16.99) Superman's Pal, Jimmy Olsen #23-34; Showcase #10 and Superman's Girl Friend, Lois Lane #1-7 17.00
Superman Family Vol. 3 ('09, $16.99) Superman's Pal, Jimmy Olsen #35-44 and Superman's Girl Friend, Lois Lane #8-16 17.00
Teen Titans Vol. 1 ('06, $16.99) r/#1-18; Brave & the Bold #54,60; Showcase #59 17.00
Teen Titans Vol. 2 ('07, $16.99) r/#19-37, World's Finest #205 and Brave & Bold #83,94 17.00
The Unknown Soldier Vol. 1 ('06, $16.99) r/Star Spangled War Stories #158-188 17.00
The War That Time Forgot Vol. 1 ('07, $16.99) r/S.S.W.S. #90,92,94-125,127,128 17.00
Warlord Vol. 1 ('09, $16.99) r/#1-28 and debut in 1st Issue Special #1 17.00
The Witching Hour Vol. 1 ('11, $19.99) r/#1-19 20.00
Wonder Woman Vol. 1 ('07, $16.99) r/#98-117 17.00
Wonder Woman Vol. 2 ('08, $16.99) r/#118-137 17.00
World's Finest Vol. 1 ('07, $16.99) r/#71-111 & Superman #76 17.00
World's Finest Vol. 2 ('08, $16.99) r/#112-145 17.00
World's Finest Vol. 3 ('10, $17.99) r/#146-160,162-169,171-173 ('64-'68) 18.00

SHOWGIRLS (Formerly Sherry the Showgirl #3)
Atlas Comics (MPC No. 2): No. 4, 2/57; June, 1957 - No. 2, Aug, 1957

4-(2/57) Dan DeCarlo-c/a begins 37 74 111 222 361 500
1-(6/57) Millie, Sherry, Chili, Pearl & Hazel begin 53 106 159 334 567 800
2 30 60 90 177 289 400

SHREK (Movie)
Dark Horse Comics: Sept, 2003 - No. 3, Dec, 2003 ($2.99, limited series)

1-3-Takes place after 1st movie; Evanier-s/Bachs-a; CGI cover 4.00

SHREK (Movie)
Ape Entertainment: 2010 - No. 4, 2011 ($3.95, limited series)

1-3-Short stories by various 4.00

SHROUD, THE (See Super-Villain Team-Up #5)
Marvel Comics: Mar, 1994 - No. 4, June, 1994 ($1.75, mini-series)

1-4: 1,2,4-Spider-Man & Scorpion app. 3.00

SHROUD OF MYSTERY
Whitman Publications: June, 1982

1 1 2 3 4 5 7

SHRUGGED
Aspen MLT, Inc.: No. 0, June, 2006 - No. 8, Feb, 2009 ($2.50/$2.99)

0-($2.50) Turner & Mastromauro-s/Gunnell-a; intro. story and character profiles 3.00
1-8-($2.99) 1-Six covers. 2-Three covers 3.00
... : Beginnings (5/06, $1.99) Prequel intro. to Ange and Dev; Gunnell-a; development art 3.00
Volume 2 (3/13, $1.00) 1-Marks & Gunnell-a; multiple covers 3.00
V2 #2-6-($3.99) Mastromauro-s/Marks-a. 6-(2/18) 4.00
Volume 3 (2/18, $3.99) 1-Mastromauro-s/André Risso-a; multiple covers 4.00

SHUTTER
Image Comics: Apr, 2014 - No. 30, Jul, 2017 ($3.50/$3.99)

1-11-Keatinge-s/Del Duca-a 3.50
12-30-($3.99) 4.00

SHUT UP AND DIE
Image Comics/Halloween: 1998 - No. 3, 1998 ($2.95,B&W, bi-monthly)

1-3: Hudnall-s 3.00

SICK (Sick Special #131) (Magazine) (Satire)
Feature Publ./Headline Publ./Crestwood Publ. Co./Hewfred Publ./ Pyramid Comm./Charlton Publ. No. 109 (4/76) on: Aug, 1960 - No. 134, Fall, 1980

V1#1-Jack Paar photo on-c; Torres-a; Untouchables-s; Ben Hur movie photo-s 14 28 42 96 211 325
2-Torres-a; Elvis app.; Lenny Bruce app. 9 18 27 61 123 185
3-5-Torres-a in all. 3-Khruschev-c; Hitler-s. 4-Newhart-s; Castro-s; John Wayne. 5-JFK/Castro-c; Elvis pin-up; Hitler. 8 16 24 55 105 155
6-Photo-s of Ricky Nelson & Marilyn Monroe; JFK 9 18 27 57 111 165
V2#1,2,4-8 (#7,8,10-14): 1-(#7) Hitler-s; Brando photo-s. 2-(#8) Dick Clark-s. 4-(#10) Untouchables-c; Candid Camera-s. 5-(#11) Nixon-c; Lone Ranger-s; JFK-s. 6-(#12) Beatnik-c/s. 8-(#14) Liz Taylor pin-up, JFK-s; Dobie Gillis-s; Sinatra & Dean Martin photo-s 8 16 24 51 96 140
3-(#9) Marilyn Monroe/JFK-c; Kingston Trio-s 8 16 24 55 105 155
V3#1-7(#15-21): 1-(#15) JFK app.; Liz Tayor/Richard Burton-s. 2-(#16) Ben Casey/ Frankenstein-c/s; Hitler photo-s. 5-(#19) Nixon back-c/s; Sinatra photo-s. 6-(#20) 1st Huckleberry Fink-c 5 10 15 33 57 80
8-(#22) Cassius Clay vs. Liston-s; 1st Civil War Blackouts-/Pvt. Bo Reargard w/ Jack Davis-a 5 10 15 35 63 90
V4#1-5 (#23-27): Civil War Blackouts-/Pvt. Bo Reargard w/ Jack Davis-a in all. 1-(#23) Smokey Bear-c; Tarzan-s. 2-(#24) Goldwater & Paar-s; Castro-s. 3-(#25) Frankenstein-c; Cleopatra/Liz Taylor-s; Steve Reeves photo-s. 4-(#26) James Bond-s; Hitler-s. 5-(#27) Taylor/Burton pin-up; Sinatra, Martin, Andress, Ekberg photo-s 4 8 12 27 44 60
28,31,36,39: 31-Pink Panther movie photo-s; Burke's Law-s. 39-Westerns; Elizabeth Montgomery photo-s; Beat mag-s 4 8 12 23 37 50
29,34,37,38: 29-Beatles-c by Jack Davis. 34-Two pg. Beatles-s & photo pin-up. 37-Playboy parody issue. 38-Addams Family-s 4 8 12 27 44 60
30,32,35,40: 30-Beatles photo pin-up; James Bond photo-s. 32-Ian Fleming-s; LBJ-s; Tarzan-s. 35-Beatles cameo; Three Stooges parody. 40-Tarzan-s; Crosby/Hope-s; Beatles parody 4 8 12 28 47 65
33-Ringo Starr photo-c & spoof on "A Hard Day's Night"; inside-c has Beatles photos 5 10 15 35 63 90
41,50,51,53,54,60: 41-Sports Illustrated parody-c/s. 50-Mod issue; flip-c w/1967 calendar w/Bob Taylor-a. 51-Get Smart-s. 53-Beatles cameo; nudity panels. 54-Monkees-c. 60-TV Daniel Boone-s 3 6 9 19 30 40
42-Fighting American-c revised from Simon/Kirby-c; "Good girl" art by Sparling; profile on Bob Powell; superhero parodies 5 10 15 33 57 80
43-49,52,55-59: 43-Sneaker set begins by Sparling. 45-Has #44 on-c & #45 on inside; TV Westerns-s; Beatles cameo. 46-Hell's Angels-s; NY Mets-s. 47-UFO/Space-c. 49-Men's Adventure mag. parody issue; nudity. 52-LBJ-s. 55-Underground culture special. 56-Alfred E. Neuman-c; inventors issue. 58-Hippie issue-c/s. 59-Hippie-s 3 6 9 16 24 32
61-64,66-69,71,73,75-80: 63-Tiny Tim-c & poster; Monkees-s. 64-Flip-c. 66-Flip-c; Mod Squad-s. 69-Beatles cameo; Peter Sellers photo-s. 71-Flip-c; Clint Eastwood-s. 76-Nixon-s; Marcus Welby-s. 78-Ma Barker-s; Courtship of Eddie's Father-s; Abbie Hoffman-s 3 6 9 15 22 28
65,70,74: 65-Cassius Clay/Brando/J. Wayne-c; Johnny Carson-s. 70-(9/69) John & Yoko-c, 1/2 pg. story. 74-Clay, Agnew, Namath & others as superheroes-c/s; Easy Rider-s; Ghost and Mrs. Muir-s 3 6 9 16 24 32
72-(84 pgs.) Xmas issue w/2 pg. slick color poster; Tarzan-s; 2 pg. Superman & superheroes-s 3 6 9 21 33 45
81-85,87-95,98,99: 81-(2/71) Woody Allen photo-s. 85 Monster Mag. parody-s; Nixon-s w/Ringo & John cameo. 88-Klute photo-s; Nixon paper dolls page. 92-Lily Tomlin; Archie Bunker pin-up. 93-Woody Allen 2 4 6 13 18 22
86,96,97,100: 86-John & Yoko, Tiny Tim-c; Love Story movie photo-s. 96-Kung Fu-c; Mummy-s, Dracula & Frankenstein app. 97-Superman-s; 1974 Calendar; Charlie Brown & Snoopy pin-up. 100-Serpico-s; Cosell-s; Jacques Cousteau-s 3 6 9 14 19 24
101-103,105-114,116,119,120: 101-Three Musketeers-s; Dick Tracy-s. 102-Young Frankenstein-s. 103-Kojak-s; Evel Knievel-s. 105-Towering Inferno-s; Peanuts/Snoopy-s. 106-Cher-c/s. 10 7-Jaws-c/s. 108-Pink Panther-c/s; Archie-s. 109-Adam & Eve-s(nudity). 110-Welcome Back Kotter-s. 111-Sonny & Cher-s. 112-King Kong-c/s. 120-Star Trek-s 2 4 6 9 13 16
104,115,117,118: 104-Muhammad Ali-c/s. 115-Charlie's Angels-s. 117-Bionic Woman & Six Million $ Man-c/s; Cher D'Flower begins by Sparling (nudity). 118-Star Wars-s; Popeye-s 2 4 6 11 16 20
121-125,128-130: 122-Darth Vader-s. 123-Jaws II-s. 128-Superman-c/movie parody. 130-Alien movie-s 2 4 6 10 14 18
126,127: 126-(68 pgs.) Battlestar Galactica-c/s; Star Wars-s; Wonder Woman-s. 127-Mork & Mindy-s; Lord of the Rings-s 2 4 6 13 18 22
131-(1980 Special) Star Wars/Star Trek/Flash Gordon wraparound-c/s; Superman parody; Battlestar Galactica-s 3 6 9 14 19 24
132,133: 132-1980 Election-c/s; Apocalypse Now-s. 133-Star Trek-s; Chips-s; Superheroes page 2 4 6 13 18 22
134 (scarce)(68 pg. Giant)-Star Wars-c; Alien-s; WKRP-s; Mork & Mindy-s; Taxi-s; MASH-s 4 8 12 19 30 40

Sideways #1 © DC

Sif #1 © MAR

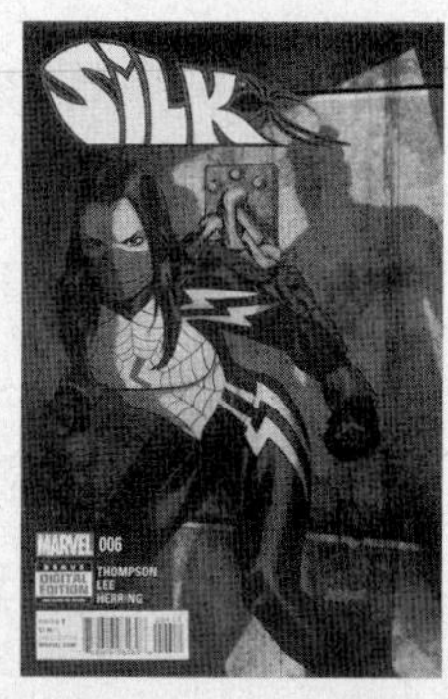

Silk #6 © MAR

GD VG FN VF VF/NM NM-
2.0 4.0 6.0 8.0 9.0 9.2

Annual 1- Birthday Annual (1966)-3 pg. Huckleberry Fink fold out
4 8 12 23 37 50
Annual 2- 7th Annual Yearbook (1967)-Davis-c, 2 pg. glossy poster insert
4 8 12 23 37 50
Annual 3 (1968) "Big Sick Laff-in" on-c (84 pgs.)-w/psychedelic posters; Frankenstein poster
3 6 9 17 26 35
Annual 1969 "Great Big Fat Annual Sick", 1969 "9th Year Annual Sick", 1970, 1971
3 6 9 16 24 32
Annual 12,13-(1972,1973, 84 pgs.) 13-Monster-c 3 6 9 16 24 32
Annual 14,15-(1974,1975, 84 pgs.) 14-Hitler photo-s 3 6 9 16 24 32
Annual 2-4 (1980) 2 4 6 9 13 16
Special 1 (1980) Buck Rogers-c/s; MASH-s 3 6 9 14 19 24
Special 2 (1980) Wraparound Star Wars:Empire Strikes Back-c; Charlie's Angels/Farrah-s;
Rocky-s; plus reprints 3 6 9 14 19 24
Yearbook 15(1975, 84 pgs.) Paul Revere-c 3 6 9 16 23 30

*NOTE: **Davis** a-42, 87; c-22, 23, 25, 29, 31, 32. **Powell** a-7, 31, 57. **Simon** a-1-3, 10, 41, 42, 87, 99; c-1, 47, 57, 59, 69, 91, 95-97, 99, 100, 102, 107, 112. **Torres** a-1-3, 29, 31, 47, 49. **Tuska** a-14, 41-43. Civil War Blackouts-23, 24. #42 has biography of Bob Powell.*

SIDEKICK (Paul Jenkins'...)
Image Comics (Desperado): June, 2006 - No. 5, May, 2007 ($3.50, limited series)
1-5-Paul Jenkins-s/Chris Moreno-a 3.50
... Super Summer Sidekick Spectacular 1 (7/07, $2.99) 3.50
... Super Summer Sidekick Spectacular 2 (9/07, $3.50) 3.50

SIDEKICK
Image Comics (Joe's Comics): Aug, 2013 - No. 12, Dec, 2015 ($2.99)
1-7,9-12: 1-Straczynski-a/Mandrake-a; intro. The Cowl and Flyboy; 6 covers. 4-6-Two covers 3.00
8-($3.99) Chrome-c 4.00

SIDEKICKS
Fanboy Ent., Inc.: Jun, 2000 - No. 3, Apr, 2001 ($2.75, B&W, lim. series)
1-3-J.Torres-s/Takesi Miyazawa-a. 3-Variant-c by Wieringo 3.00
...: Super Fun Summer Special (Oni Press, 7/03, $2.99) art by various incl. Wieringo 3.00
...: The Substitute (Oni Press, 7/02, $2.95) 3.00
...: The Transfer Student TPB (Oni Press, 6/02, $8.95, 9" x 6") r/#1-3 9.00
...: The Transfer Student TPB 2nd Ed. (10/03, $11.95, 9" x 6") r/#1-3; The Substitute 12.00

SIDESHOW
Avon Periodicals: 1949 (one-shot)
1-(Rare)-Similar to Bachelor's Diary 123 246 369 767 1344 1900

SIDEWAYS
DC Comics: Apr, 2018 - Present ($2.99)
1-Didio-s/Rocafort-a; intro Derek James 4.00

SIEGE
Marvel Comics: Mar, 2010 - No. 4, Jun, 2010 ($3.99, limited series)
1-4-Asgard is invaded; Bendis-s/Coipel-a. 4-End of The Sentry 4.00
1-4-Variant covers by Dell'Otto 8.00
...: Captain America (6/10, $2.99) Gage-s/Dallocchio-a/Djurdjevic-c; both Caps app. 4.00
...: Loki (6/10, $2.99) Gillen-s/McKelvie-a/Djurdjevic-c; Hela & Mephisto app. 4.00
...: Secret Warriors (6/10, $2.99) Hickman-s/Vitti-a/Djurdjevic-c; Phobos attacks 4.00
...: Spider-Man (6/10, $2.99) Reed-s/Santucci-a/Djurdjevic-c; Venom & Ms. Marvel app. 4.00
...: Storming Asgard - Heroes & Villains (3/10, $3.99) Dossiers on participants; Land-c 4.00
...: The Cabal (2/10, $3.99) series prelude; Bendis-s/Lark-a; covers by Finch & Davis 4.00
...: Young Avengers (6/10, $2.99) McKeever-s/Asrar-a/Djurdjevic-c; Wrecking Crew app. 4.00

SIEGE (Secret Wars tie-in) (Continued from Secret Wars: Journal #1)
Marvel Comics: Sept, 2015 - No. 4, Dec, 2015 ($3.99, limited series)
1-4-Gillen-s/Andrade-a; Abigail Brand, Kate Bishop & Ms. America app. 4.00

SIEGE: EMBEDDED
Marvel Comics: Mar, 2010 - No. 4, Jul, 2010 ($3.99, limited series)
1-4-Reed-s/Samnee-a/Granov-c; Ben Urich & Volstagg cover the invasion 4.00

SIEGEL AND SHUSTER: DATELINE 1930s
Eclipse Comics: Nov, 1984 - No. 2, Sept, 1985 ($1.50/$1.75, Baxter paper #1)
1,2: 1-Unpublished samples of strips from the '30s; includes 'Interplanetary Police'; Shuster-c. 2 ($1.75, B&W)-unpublished strips; Shuster-c 4.00

SIF (See Thor titles)
Marvel Comics: Jun, 2010 ($3.99, one shot)
1-Deconnick-s/Stegman-a/Foreman-c; Beta Ray Bill app. 4.00

SIGIL (Also see CrossGen Chronicles)
CrossGeneration Comics: Jul, 2000 - No. 43, Jan, 2004 ($2.95)
1-43: 1-Barbara Kesel-s/Ben & Ray Lai-a. 12-Waid-s begin. 21-Chuck Dixon-s begin 3.00

GD VG FN VF VF/NM NM-
2.0 4.0 6.0 8.0 9.0 9.2

SIGIL
Marvel Comics: May, 2011 - No. 4, Aug, 2011 ($2.99)
1-4-Carey-s/Kirk-a 3.00
1-Variant-c by McGuinness 5.00

SIGMA
Image Comics (WildStorm): March, 1996 - No. 3, June, 1996 ($2.50, limited series)
1-3: 1-"Fire From Heaven" prelude #2; Coker-a. 2-"Fire From Heaven" pt. 6. 3-"Fire From Heaven" pt. 14. 3.00

SILENCER, THE
DC Comics: Mar, 2018 - Present ($2.99)
1,2: 1-Abnett-s/Romita Jr.-a; intro Honor Guest; Talia al Ghul app. 4.00

SILENT DRAGON
DC Comics (WildStorm): Sept, 2005 - No. 6, Feb, 2006 ($2.99, limited series)
1-6-Tokyo 2066 A.D.; Leinil Yu-a/c; Andy Diggle-s 3.00
TPB (2006, $19.99) r/series; sketch page 20.00

SILENT HILL: DEAD/ALIVE
IDW Publishing: Dec, 2005 - No. 5, Apr, 2006 ($3.99, limited series)
1-5-Stakal-a/Ciencin-s. 1-Four covers. 2-5-Two covers 4.00

SILENT HILL DOWNPOUR: ANNE'S STORY
IDW Publishing: Aug, 2014 - No. 4, Nov, 2014 ($3.99, limited series)
1-4-Tom Waltz-s/Tristan Jones-a; two covers on each 4.00

SILENT HILL: DYING INSIDE
IDW Publishing: Feb, 2004 - No. 5, June, 2004 ($3.99, limited series)
1-5-Based on the Konami computer game. 1-Templesmith-a; Ashley Wood-c 4.00
...: Paint It Black (2/05, $7.49) Ciencin-s/Thomas-a 7.50
...: The Grinning Man 5/05, $7.49) Ciencin-s/Stakal-a 7.50
TPB (8/04, $19.99) r/#1-5; Ashley Wood-c 20.00

SILENT HILL: PAST LIFE
IDW Publishing: Oct, 2010 - No. 4, Jan, 2011 ($3.99, limited series)
1-4-Waltz-s; two covers on each 4.00

SILENT HILL: SINNER'S REWARD
IDW Publishing: Feb, 2008 - No. 4, Apr, 2008 ($3.99, limited series)
1-4-Waltz-s/Stamb-a 4.00

SILENT INVASION, THE
Rengade Press: Apr, 1986 - No.12, Mar, 1988 ($1.70/$2.00, B&W)
1-12-UFO sightings of the '50's 3.00
Book 1- reprints ($7.95) 8.00

SILENT MOBIUS
Viz Select Comics: 1991 - No. 5, 1992 ($4.95, color, squarebound, 44 pgs.)
1-5: Japanese stories translated to English 5.00

SILENT SCREAMERS (Based on the Aztech Toys figures)
Image Comics: Oct, 2000 ($4.95)
Nosferatu Issue - Alex Ross front & back-c 5.00

SILENT WAR
Marvel Comics: Mar, 2007 - No. 6, Aug, 2007 ($2.99, limited series)
1-6-Inhumans, Black Bolt and Fantastic Four app.; Hine-s/Irving-a/Watson-c 3.00
TPB (2007, $14.99) r/series 15.00

SILK (See Amazing Spider-Man 2014 series #1 & #4 for debut)
Marvel Comics: Apr, 2015 - No. 7, Nov, 2015 ($3.99)
1-Robbie Thompson-s/Stacey Lee-a/Dave Johnson-c; Spider-Man app.
1 2 3 5 6 8
2-7: 3-6-Black Cat app. 4-Fantastic Four app. 7-Secret Wars tie-in 4.00

SILK (Spider-Man)
Marvel Comics: Jan, 2016 - No. 19, Jun, 2017 ($3.99)
1-19: 1-Robbie Thompson-s/Stacey Lee-a; Black Cat & Mockingbird app. 4,5-Fish-a. 7,8-"Spider-Women" tie-in; Spider-Woman & Spider-Gwen app. 14-17-Clone Conspiracy 4.00

SILKE
Dark Horse Comics: Jan, 2001 - No. 4, Sept, 2001 ($2.95)
1-4-Tony Daniel-s/a 3.00

SILKEN GHOST
CrossGen Comics: June, 2003 - No. 5, Oct, 2003 ($2.95, limited series)
1-5-Dixon-s/Rosado-a 3.00
Traveler Vol. 1 (2003, $9.95) digest-sized reprint #1-5 10.00

Silly Tunes #1 © MAR

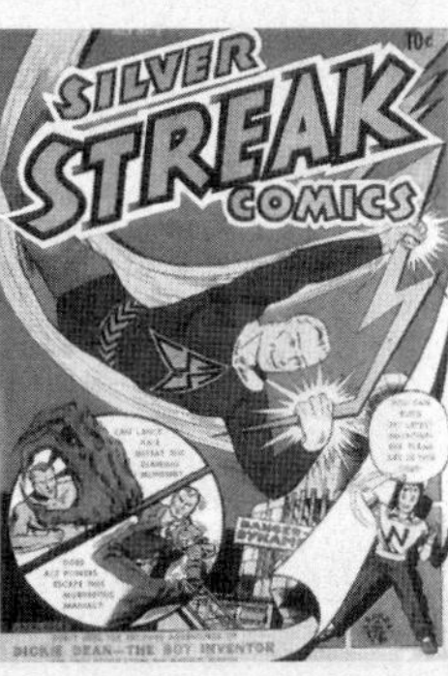

Silver Streak Comics #5 © LEV

Silver Surfer #11 © MAR

	GD 2.0	VG 4.0	FN 6.0	VF 8.0	VF/NM 9.0	NM- 9.2

SILLY PILLY (See Frank Luther's...)

SILLY SYMPHONIES (See Dell Giants)

SILLY TUNES
Timely Comics: Fall, 1945 - No. 7, June, 1947

1-Silly Seal, Ziggy Pig begin 31 62 93 186 303 420
2-(2/46) 18 36 54 103 162 220
3-7: 6-New logo 15 30 45 88 137 185

SILVER (See Lone Ranger's Famous Horse...)

SILVER AGE
DC Comics: July, 2000 ($3.95, limited series)

1-Waid-s/Dodson-a; "Silver Age" style x-over; JLA & villains switch bodies 4.00
...: Challengers of the Unknown ($2.50) Joe Kubert-c; vs. Chronos 3.00
...: Dial H For Hero ($2.50) Jim Mooney-c; Waid-s/Kitson-a; vs. Martian Manhunter 3.00
...: Doom Patrol ($2.50) Ramona Fradon-c/Peyer-s 3.00
...: Flash ($2.50) Carmine Infantino-c; Kid Flash and Elongated Man app. 3.00
...: Green Lantern ($2.50) Gil Kane-c/Busiek-s/Anderson-a; vs. Sinestro 3.00
...: Justice League of America ($2.50) Ty Templeton-c; Millar-s/Kolins-a 3.00
...: Showcase ($2.50) Dick Giordano-c/a; Johns-s; Batgirl, Adam Strange app. 3.00
... Secret Files ($4.95) Intro. Agamemno; short stories & profile pages 5.00
...: Teen Titans ($2.50) Nick Cardy-c; vs. Penguin, Mr. Element, Black Manta 3.00
...: The Brave and the Bold ($2.50) Jim Aparo-c; Batman & Metal Men 3.00
... 80-Page Giant ($5.95) Conclusion of x-over; "lost" Silver Age stories 6.00

SILVERBACK
Comico: 1989 - No. 3, 1990 ($2.50, color, limited series, mature readers)

1-3: Character from Grendel: Matt Wagner-a 3.00

SILVERBLADE
DC Comics: Sept, 1987 - No. 12, Sept, 1988

1-12: Colan-c/a in all 4.00

SILVERHAWKS
Star Comics/Marvel Comics #6: Aug, 1987 - No. 6, June, 1988 ($1.00)

1-6 4.00

SILVERHEELS
Pacific Comics: Dec, 1983 - No. 3, May, 1984 ($1.50)

1-3-Bruce Jones-s, Scott Hampton-c/a; Steacy-a in back-up stories 4.00

SILVER KID WESTERN
Key/Stanmor Publications: Oct, 1954 - No. 5, July, 1955

1 10 20 30 54 72 90
2 6 12 18 31 38 45
3-5 6 12 18 28 34 40
I.W. Reprint #1,2-Severin-c: 1-r/#? 2-r/#1 2 4 6 8 11 14

SILVER SABLE AND THE WILD PACK (See Amazing Spider-Man #265 and Sable & Fortune)
Marvel Comics: June, 1992 - No. 35, Apr, 1995; No. 36, Jan, 2018 ($1.25/$1.50)

1-($2.00)-Embossed & foil stamped-c; Spider-Man app. 4.00
2-24,26-35: 4,5-Dr. Doom-c/story. 6,7-Deathlok-c/story. 9-Origin Silver Sable. 10-Punisher-c/s. 15-Capt. America-c/s. 16,17-Intruders app. 18,19-Venom-c/s. 19-Siege of Darkness x-over. 23-Daredevil (in new costume) & Deadpool app. 24-Bound-in card sheet. Li'l Sylvie backup story 3.00
25-($2.00, 52 pgs.)-Li'l Sylvie backup story 4.00
36-(1/18, $3.99) Marvel Legacy one-shot; Faust-s/Siqueira-a 4.00

SILVER STAR (Also see Jack Kirby's...)
Pacific Comics: Feb, 1983 - No. 6, Jan, 1984 ($1.00)

1-6: 1-1st app. Last of the Viking Heroes. 1-5-Kirby-c/a. 2-Ditko-a 5.00
...: Graphite Edition TPB (TwoMorrows Publ., 3/06, $19.95) r/series in B&W including Kirby's original pencils; sketch pages; original screenplay 20.00
Jack Kirby's Silver Star, Volume 1 HC (Image Comics, 2007, $34.99) r/series in color; sketch pages; original screenplay 35.00

SILVER STREAK COMICS (Crime Does Not Pay #22 on)
Your Guide Publs. No. 1-7/New Friday Publs. No. 8-17/Comic House Publ./Newsbook Publ.: Dec, 1939 - No. 21, May, 1942; No. 23, 1946; nn, Feb, 1946 (Silver logo-#1-5)

1-(Scarce)-Intro the Claw by Cole (r-in Daredevil #21), Red Reeves Boy Magician (ends #2), Captain Fearless (ends #2), The Wasp (ends #2), Mister Midnight (ends #2) begin; Spirit Man only app. Calling The Duke begins (ends #2). Barry Lane only app. Silver Metallic-c begin, end #5; Claw-c 1,2,6-8 1025 2050 3075 7800 14,900 22,000
2-The Claw ends (by Cole); makes pact w/Hitler; Simon-c/a (The Claw); ad for Marvel Mystery Comics #2 (12/39). Lance Hale begins (receives super powers). Solar Patrol app. 438 876 1314 3197 5649 8100

	GD 2.0	VG 4.0	FN 6.0	VF 8.0	VF/NM 9.0	NM- 9.2

3-1st app. & origin Silver Streak (2nd with Lightning speed); Dickie Dean the Boy Inventor, Lance Hale, Ace Powers (ends #6), Bill Wayne The Texas Terror (ends #6) & The Planet Patrol (ends #6) begin. Detective Snoop, Sergeant Drake only app. 406 812 1218 2842 4971 7100
4-Sky Wolf begins (ends #6); Silver Streak by Jack Cole (new costume); 1st app. Jackie, Lance Hale's sidekick. Lance Hale gains immortality 184 368 552 1168 2009 2850
5-Cole c/a(2); back-c ad for Claw app. in #6 216 432 648 1372 2361 3350
6-(Scarce, 9/40)-Origin & 1st app. Daredevil (blue & yellow costume) by Jack Binder; The Claw returns as the Green Claw; classic Cole Claw-c 2100 4200 6300 14,700 26,350 38,000
7-Claw vs. Daredevil serial begins c/sty, ends #11. Daredevil new costume-blue & red by Jack Cole & 3 other Cole stories (38 pgs.). Origin Whiz, S. S.'s Falcon 2nd app. Daredevil & 1st Daredevil-c (by Cole). Cloud Curtis, Presto Martin begins. Dynamo Hill & Zongar The Miracleman only app. 854 1708 2562 6234 11,017 15,800
8-Classic Claw vs. Daredevil by Cole c/sty; last Cole Silver streak. Dan Dearborn begins (ends #12). Secret Agent X-101 begins, (ends #9) 703 1406 2109 5132 9066 13,000
9-Claw vs. Daredevil by Cole. Silver Streak-c by Bob Wood 255 510 765 1619 2785 3950
10-Origin & 1st app. Captain Battle (5/41) by Binder; Claw vs. Daredevil by Cole; Silver Streak/robot-c by Bob Wood 213 426 639 1363 2332 3300
11-Intro./origin Mercury by Bob Wood, Silver Streak's sidekick; conclusion Claw vs. Daredevil by Rico; in 'Presto Martin,' 2nd pg., newspaper says 'Roussos does it again' 171 342 513 1086 1868 2650
12-Daredevil-c by Rico; Lance Hale finds lost valley w/cave men, battles dinosaurs, sabre-toothed cats; his last app. 148 296 444 947 1624 2300
13-Origin Thun-Dohr; Scarlet Skull (a Red Skull swipe) vs. Daredevil; Bingham Boys app. 142 284 426 909 1555 2200
14-Classic Nazi skull men-c/sty 232 464 696 1485 2543 3600
15-Classic Mummy horror-c 213 426 639 1363 2332 3300
16-(11/41) Hitler-c; Silver Streak battles Hitler sty w/classic splash page. Capt. Battle fights walking corpses 284 568 852 1818 3109 4400
17-Last Daredevil issue. 142 284 426 909 1555 2200
18-The Saint begins (2/42, 1st app.) by Leslie Charteris (see Movie Comics #2 by DC); The Saint-c 135 270 405 864 1482 2100
19,20 (1942)-Ned of the Navy app. 19-Silver Streak ends. 20-Japanese WWII-c/sty; last Captain Battle, Dickie Dean, Cloud Curtis; Red Reed, Alonzo Appleseed only app.; Wolverton's Scoop Scuttle app. 65 130 195 416 708 1000
21-(5/42)-Hitler app. in strip on cover; Wolverton's Scoop Scuttle app. 90 180 270 576 988 1400
nn(#22, 2/46, 60 pgs.)(Newsbook Publ.)-R-/S.S. story from #4-7 by Jack Cole plus 2 Captain Fearless stories-r from #1&2, all in color; bondage/torture-c by Dirk Briefer w/torture meter 258 516 774 1651 2826 4000
23 (nd, 11/1946?, 52 pgs.)(An Atomic Comic) bondage-c, Silver Streak c/sty 97 194 291 621 1061 1500

NOTE: **Jack Binder** *a-8-12, 15; c-3, 4, 13-15, 17.* **Dick Briefer** *a-9-20; c-nn(#22).* **Jack Cole** *a-(Claw)-#2, 3, 6-10, nn(#22). (Daredevil)-#6-10, (Dickie Dean)-#3-10, (Pirate Prince)-#7, (Silver Streak)-#4-8, nn; c-5 (Silver Streak), 6 (Claw), 7, 8 (Daredevil).* **Bill Everett** *Red Reed begins #20.* **Fred Guardineer** *a-#8-12.* **Don Rico** *a-11-17 (Daredevil), 15, 19 (Silver Streak); c-11, 12, 16.* **Joe Simon** *a-2 (Solar Patrol), 3 (Silver Streak); c-2.* **Basil Wolverton** *a-20, 21.* **Bob Wood** *a-8-15 (Presto Martin), 9 (Silver Streak); c-9, 10. Captain Battle c-11, 13-15, 17. Claw c-#1, 2, 6-8. Daredevil c-7, 8, 12. Dickie Dean c-19. Ned of the Navy c-20 (war). The Saint c-18. Silver Streak c-5, 10, 16, nn(#22), 23.*

SILVER STREAK COMICS (Homage with Golden Age size and Golden Age art styles)
Image Comics: No. 24, Dec, 2009 ($3.99, one-shot)

24-New Daredevil, Claw, Silver Streak & Captain Battle stories; Larsen, Grist, Gilbert-a 5.00

SILVER SURFER (See Fantastic Four, Fantasy Masterpieces V2#1, Fireside Book Series, Marvel Graphic Novel, Marvel Presents #8, Marvel's Greatest Comics & Tales To Astonish #92)

SILVER SURFER, THE (Also see Essential Silver Surfer)
Marvel Comics Group: Aug, 1968 - No. 18, Sept, 1970; June, 1982

1-More detailed origin by John Buscema (p); The Watcher back-up stories begin (origin), end #7; (No. 1-7: 25¢, 68 pgs.) 63 126 189 504 1127 1750
2-1st app. Badoon 19 38 57 131 291 450
3-1st app. Mephisto 22 44 66 154 340 525
4-Lower distribution; Thor & Loki app. 45 90 135 333 754 1175
5-7-Last giant size. 5-The Stranger app.; Fantastic Four app. 6-Brunner inks. 7-(8/69)-Early cameo Frankenstein's monster (see X-Men #40) 12 24 36 84 185 285
8-10: 8-18-(15¢ issues) 10 20 30 68 144 220
11-13,15-18: 15-Silver Surfer vs. Human Torch; Fantastic Four app. 17-Nick Fury app. 18-Vs. The Inhumans; Kirby-a; Trimpe-c 10 20 30 64 132 200
14-Spider-Man x-over 15 30 45 105 233 360
... Omnibus Vol. 1 Hardcover (2007, $74.99, dustjacket) r/#1-18 re-colored with original letter pages, Fantastic Four Annual #5 & Not Brand Echh #13; Lee and Buscema bios 75.00
V2#1 (6/82, 52 pgs.)-Byrne-c/a 2 4 6 9 12 15

Silver Surfer V2 #6 © MAR

Silver Surfer V2 #86 © MAR

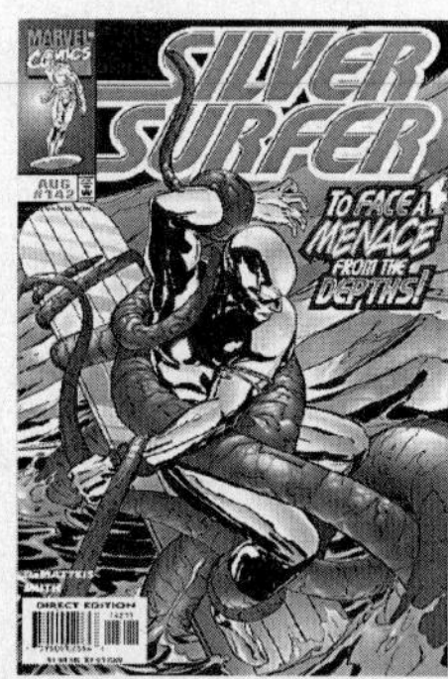

Silver Surfer V2 #142 © MAR

	GD	VG	FN	VF	VF/NM	NM-
	2.0	4.0	6.0	8.0	9.0	9.2

NOTE: ***Adkins*** *a-8-15i.* ***Brunner*** *a-6i.* ***J. Buscema*** *a-1-17p.* ***Colan*** *a-1-3p.* ***Reinman*** *a-1-4i. #1-14 were reprinted in Fantasy Masterpieces V2#1-14.*

SILVER SURFER (Volume 3) (See Marvel Graphic Novel #38)
Marvel Comics Group: V3#1, July, 1987 - No. 146, Nov, 1998

1-Double-size ($1.25)-Englehart & Rogers-s/a begins; vs. the Champion; Fantastic Four app. w/She-Hulk; Nova (Frankie Raye) & Galactus app; Surfers exile on Earth ends 2 4 6 8 10 12

2-9: 2-Surfer returns to Zenn-La; Shalla-Bal app. as Empress of Zenn-La; Skrulls app.; Surfer story next in West Coat Avengers Annual #2 and Avengers Annual #16. 3-Collector & Champion app.; Surfer vs. the Runner; re-intro Mantis (not seen since 1975). 4-Elders of the Universe app.; Collector, Champion, Runner, Gardener, Contemplator, Grandmaster & Possessor; 1st app. of Astronomer, Obliterator & Trader; Ego revealed as an Elder; origin Mantis. 5-vs. the Obliterator. 6-Origin of the Obliterator. 7-Supreme Intelligence & the Elders app. 8-Supreme Intelligence app.; Surfer gains the Soul Gem. 9-Elders vs. Galactus; six Soul Gems app. 6.00

10-Galactus absorbs the Elders; Eternity app. 1 3 4 6 8 9

11-14: 11-1st app. Reptyl, Clumsy Foulup & the fake Surfer; Nova (Frankie Raye) app. 12-Death of fake Contemplator; Reptyl & Nova (Frankie Raye) app. 13-Ronan the Accuser vs. Surfer and Nova (Frankie Raye); fake Surfer app.; last Rogers-a. 14-Origin & death of the fake Surfer; Ronan app.; Nova (Frankie Raye) app.; story continues in Surfer Ann. #1 5.00

15,16: 15-Ron Lim-c/a begin (9/88); Soul Gems app.; Reed, Sue and Franklin of the Fantastic Four app.; Galactus & Nova (Frankie Raye), Elders of the Universe app.: Astronomer, Possessor & Trader. 16-Astromoner, Trader & In-Betweener app.; brief x-over w/Fantastic Four #319 6.00

17,18: 17-Elders of the Universe, In-Betweener, Death & Galactus app. 18-Galactus vs. the In-Betweener; Elders of the Universe, the Soul Gems & Lord Order & Master Chaos app. 1 2 3 5 6 7

19,20-Firelord & Starfox app. 5.00

21-24,26-30,32,33,39-43: 21-vs. the Obliterator. 22-Ego the Living Planet app. 26-Super-Skrull app. 27-Stranger & Super-Skrull app. 28-Death of Super-Skrull; Reptyl app. 29-Midnight Sun app; death of Reptyl. 30-Midnight Sun & the Stranger app. 32,33-Jim Valentino-s; 33-Impossible Man app. 39-Alan Grant scripts. 40-43-Surfer in Dynamo City 4.00

25,31-($1.50, 52 pgs.) 25-New Kree/Skrull war; Badoon app; Skrulls regain their shape-shifting ability. 31-Conclusion of Kree/Skrull war; Stranger & the Living Tribunal app. 5.00

34-Thanos returns (cameo); Starlin scripts begin; Death app. 3 6 9 16 23 30

35-38: 35-1st full Thanos in Silver Surfer (3/90); reintro Drax the Destroyer on last pg. (cameo). 36-Recaps history of Thanos, Captain Marvel & Warlock app. in recap. 37-Full reintro Drax the Destroyer; Drax-c. 38-Silver Surfer battles Thanos; Nebula app; Thanos story continues in Thanos Quest #1-2 1 3 4 6 8 10

44-Classic Thanos-c; 1st app. of the Infinity Gauntlet; Thanos defeats the Surfer & Drax; Mephisto cameo 5 10 15 31 53 75

45-Thanos-c; Mephisto app.; origin of the Infinity Gems 3 6 9 14 20 25

46-Return of Adam Warlock (2/91); reintro Gamora & Pip the Troll (within Soul World) 2 4 6 11 16 20

47-49: 47-Warlock vs. Drax. 48-Galactus app; last Starlin scripts (also #50). 49-Thanos & Mephisto app.; Ron Marz scripts begin 1 3 4 6 8 10

50-($1.50, 52 pgs.)-Embossed & silver foil-c; Silver Surfer has brief battle w/Thanos; story cont'd in Infinity Gauntlet #1; extended origin flashback to the Silver Surfer's life on Zenn-La 2 4 6 10 14 18

50-2nd & 3rd printings 5.00

51-59-Infinity Gauntlet x-overs; 51-Galactus and Nova (Frankie Raye) app. 52-Firelord vs. Drax; continued in Infinity Gauntlet #2. 53-Death of Clumsy Foulup. 54-vs the Rhino; Hulk cameo. 55,56-Thanos kills everyone (Surfer dream sequence); Warlock app; continued in Infinity Gauntlet #4. 57-x-over w/Infinity Gauntlet #4. 58-Defenders app. (dream sequence); Warlock app. 59-Warlock, Dr. Strange, Dr. Doom, Thor, Firelord, Drax & Thanos app; concluded in Infinity Gauntlet #6 5.00

60-69,71-73: 60-vs. Midnight Sun; Warlock & Dr. Strange cameo; Black Bolt, Gorgon & Karnak of the Inhumans app. 61-Collector app. 63-Captain Marvel app. 64-Collector app. 65-Reptyl returns. 66-Mistress Love & Master Hate app. 67-69-Infinity War x-overs. 67-Continued from Infinity War #1; x-over w/Dr. Strange #42; Nebula, Galactus, Nova (Frankie Raye) & Dr. Strange app; Magus cameo; continued in Infinity War #2. 68,69-Galactus, Nova & Dr. Strange app. 69-Magus cameo; continues in Infinity War #3. 71-Herald Ordeal Pt. 2; Nebula, Firelord & Galactus app; Surfer vs. Morg. 72-Herald Ordeal Pt. 3; 1st app. Cyborg Nebula (as seen in the GOTG movie); Firelord, Nova, Galactus & Morg app. 73-Herald Ordeal Pt. 4; reintro Gabriel the Airwalker; Firelord, Galactus, Nova, Morg app; Terrax cameo 3.00

70,74: Herald Ordeal Pts.1,5. 70-1st app. Morg (becomes the new Herald of Galactus), Nova released of her duties; Nebula app. 74-Terrax, Firelord, Airwalker, Nova, Nebula app. 4.00

75-($2.50, 52 pgs.)-Embossed foil-c; Lim-c/a; Herald Ordeal Pt. 6; Surfer, Firelord, Airwalker, Terrax & Nova vs. Morg; death of Nova; Morg stripped of the power cosmic; Firelord & Airwalker resume Herald duties 4.00

76-81,83-87,90-97: 76-Origin Jack of Hearts retold; Galactus, Airwalker, Firelord & Nebula app.; Morg cameo. 77-Jack of Hearts & Nebula app; return of Morg. 78-New Jack of Hearts costume; Nebula, Morg & Galactus app. 79-Captain Atlas & Dr. Minerva app.; Morg vs. Terrax; Gladiator & Beta Ray Bill cameo. 80-1st app. Ganymede (named in issue #81); Morg vs. Terrax. 81-1st cameo app. Tyrant; Morg, Terrax, Gladiator, Beta Ray Bill cameos. 83-85-Infinity Crusade x-overs. 83-Surfer vs. Firelord; x-over w/Infinity Crusade #3; Thanos cameo; cont'd in Infinity Crusade #4. 84-Thanos app. 85-Wonder Man & Storm vs. Surfer; concluded in Infinity Crusade #6. 86-Blood & Thunder Pt. 2; cont'd from Thor #468; Surfer & Beta Ray Bill vs. insane Thor; Pip the Troll & Warlock cameo; cont'd in Warlock Chronicles #6. 87-Blood & Thunder Pt. 6; cont'd from Thor #469; Dr. Strange, Warlock & the Infinity Watch app; cont'd in Warlock Chronicles #7. 89-Colleen Doran-a(p). 90-Legacy (son of Capt. Marvel) app. 92-Marvel Masterprints card insert; last Lim-a. 93-Fantastic Four app; Thing, Human Torch & Ant-Man (Scott Lang); Spider-Man cameo. 94-Fantastic Four & Warlock and the Infinity Watch app. 95-Fantastic Four app.; Hulk cameo. 97-Terrax app; Champion cameo 3.00

82-($1.75. 52 pgs.)-Surfer, Morg, Terrax, Gladiator, Beta Ray Bill, Jack of Hearts & Ganymede vs. Tyrant; Galactus app. 4.00

88,99: 88-Blood & Thunder Pt. 10-cont'd from Thor #470; Thanos vs. insane Thor; Dr. Strange, Warlock & the Infinity Watch app; cont'd in Warlock Chronicles #8; 'Kay-bee Toys' coupon insert for Ghost Rider 'Hot Pursuit' comic; 7-pg. Punisher 'Suicide Run' advertisement; 7-pg. 'Juice' magazine insert featuring interviews with the New Warriors. 99-Mephisto cameo 4.00

98-vs. Champion; Drax & Thanos app. 5.00

100-($2.25, 52 pgs.)-Wraparound-c; vs. Mephisto 6.00

100-($3.95, 52 pgs.)-Enhanced-silver holofoil-c 4.00

101-108,110: 101-Tyrant cameo; Surfer returns to Zenn-La; Shalla-Bal app. 102-Galactus & Morg app; Tyrant cameo; last Marz script. 104-Morg app. Galactus, Morg & Legacy app; Surfer vs. Super-Skrull; 4-pg Rune/Silver Surfer preview. 106-Galactus, Morg & Tyrant app. 108-Tyrant vs. Galactus; Morg & Legacy app. 110-Legacy & Nebula app; John Buscema-a. 4.00

109-Tyrant vs. Galactus; Legacy app.; Morg no longer Herald. 5.00

111-121: 111-New direction; Pérez scripts begin. 112-1st app. Uni-Lord. 114-Watcher app. 120-vs. Uni-Lord. 121-End of the Uni-Lord saga; Beta Ray Bill & Quasar cameo 4.00

122-Legacy & Beta Ray Bill app. 5.00

123-124,126-127,129-130: 123-1st Dematteis script; Surfer returns to Earth; Alicia Masters app. 124-Kymaera (Namorita) app. 126-Dr. Strange app. 127-Alicia Masters & the Puppet Master app. 130-Surfer learns that Zenn-La has been destroyed; Galactus app. 4.00

125 ($2.95)-Wraparound-c; vs. Hulk-c/app. 5.00

128-Spider-Man & Daredevil-c/app. 1 3 4 6 8 10

131-134: 131-Galactus app. 133-Puppet Master app. 134-Scrier & The Other app. 4.00

135-140: 135-Agatha Harkness, Scrier & the Thing app. 136,137-Scrier & Mephisto app. 138-Thing app. 140-Jon J. Muth-a begins 6.00

141-144: 143,144-Psycho-Man app. 1 2 3 4 6 7

145-Alicia Masters; Surfer returns to Earth 1 2 3 4 6 8

146-Firelord app; last issue. 2 4 6 9 12 15

#(-1) Flashback (7/97)-Stan Lee app; 1st app. The Other; Galactus app. 3.00

Annual 1 (1988, $1.75)-Evolutionary War Pt. 3; continued from Punisher Annual #1; 1st Ron Lim-a on Silver Surfer (20 pg. back-up story & pin-ups); Eternals app. Surfer & Super-Skrull team-up; Mantis app.; story continues in West Coast Avengers #37; Evolutionary War continues in New Mutants Annual #4 5.00

Annual 2 (1989, $2.00)-Atlantis Attacks Pt. 1; Ghaur the Deviant app; Dr. Strange cameo; story continues in Iron Man Annual #10 4.00

Annual 3-6: 3-(1990, $2.00)-Lifeform Pt. 4; continued from Punisher Annual #3. 4-(1991, $2.00)-The Korvac Quest Pt. 3; continued from Thor Annual #16; 3-pg. origin story; Silver Surfer battles the Guardians of the Galaxy (30th Century version); continued in Guardians of the Galaxy Annual #1. 5-(1992, $2.25)- Return of the Defenders Pt. 3; continued from Namor the Sub-Mariner Annual #2; Hulk & Dr. Strange app.; continued in Dr. Strange Annual #2; Nebula app. in Firelord & Starfox back-up story. 6-(1993, $2.95)-Polybagged w/trading card; 1st app. Legacy; card is by Lim/Austin; Surfer & Legacy vs. Ronan the Accuser; Terrax, Jack of Hearts & Ganymede back up features 3.00

Annual 7-(1994, $2.95)-Morg resumes being Herald to Galactus; Firelord leaves; Legacy app. in back-up 4.00

Annual '97-($2.99)-Scrier app. Annual '98-($2.99)..& Thor; vs. Millennius; Avengers app. 4.00

...Dangerous Artifacts-(1996, 48 pgs.)-Marz scripts w/Claudio Castellini-a; Galactus & Thanos app; 1st app. White Raven 1 2 3 5 6 8

Graphic Novel (1988, HC, $14.95)-Judgment Day; Lee-s/Buscema-a; Galactus vs. Mephisto 30.00

Graphic Novel (1988, SC, $10.95)-Judgment Day; Jusko-c 20.00

Graphic Novel (1990, HC, $16.95)-The Enslavers; Stan Lee-s & Pollard-a; non-canon Marvel universe story 25.00

Graphic Novel (1991, SC, $12.95)-Homecoming; Starlin-a; death of Shalla-Bal 15.00

Inner Demons TPB (4/98, $3.50)r/#123,125,126 5.00

...: Rebirth of Thanos TPB (2006, $24.99) r/#34-38, Thanos Quest #1,2; Logan's Run #6 25.00

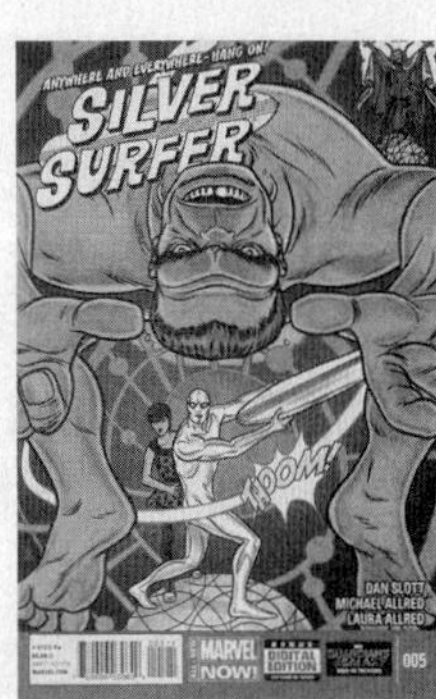

Silver Surfer (2014 series) #5 © MAR

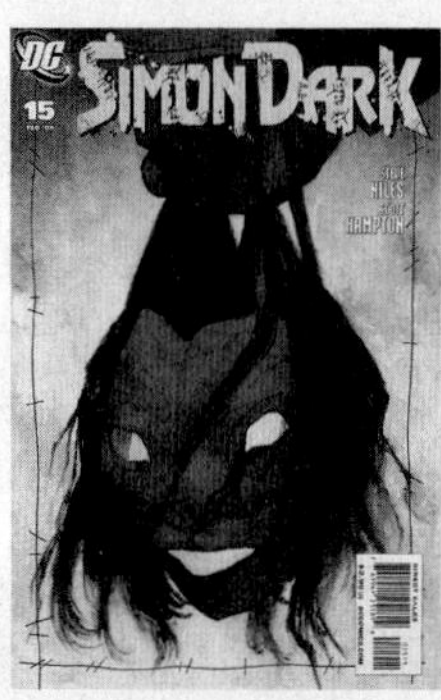

Simon Dark #15 © Niles, Hampton, & DC

Simpsons Comics #177 © Bongo

GD VG FN VF VF/NM NM-
2.0 4.0 6.0 8.0 9.0 9.2

GD VG FN VF VF/NM NM-
2.0 4.0 6.0 8.0 9.0 9.2

...: The First Coming of Galactus nn (11/92, $5.95, 68 pgs.)-Reprints Fantastic Four #48-50 with new Lim-c 6.00
Wizard 1/2 2 4 6 9 12 15

NOTE: *Austin c(i)-7, 8, 71, 73, 74, 76, 79.* ***Cowan*** *a-143,146.* ***Cully Hamner*** *a-83p.* ***Ron Lim*** *a(p)-15-31, 33-38, 40-55, (56, 57-part-p), 60-65, 73-82, Annual 2, 4; c(p)-15-31, 32-38, 40-84, 86-92, Annual 2, 4-6.* ***Muth*** *c/a-140-142,144,145.* ***M. Rogers*** *a-1-10, 12, 19, 21; c-1-9, 11, 12, 21.*

SILVER SURFER (Volume 4)
Marvel Comics: Sept, 2003 - No. 14, Dec, 2004 ($2.25/$2.99)

1-6: 1-Milx-a; Jusko-c. 2-Jae Lee-c 3.00
7-14-($2.99) 3.00
...Vol. 1: Communion (2004, $14.99) r/#1-6 15.00

SILVER SURFER (Volume 5)
Marvel Comics: Apr, 2011 - No. 5, Aug, 2011 ($2.99, limited series)

1-5-Pagulayan-c. 1-Segovia-a. 4,5-Fantastic Four app. 3.00

SILVER SURFER (6th series)
Marvel Comics: May, 2014 - No. 15, Jan, 2016 ($3.99)

1-10: 1-Dan Slott-s/Michael Allred-a/c. 3-Guardians of the Galaxy app. 8-10-Galactus app. 4.00
11-($4.99) Story runs upside down on top or bottom halves of the pages 5.00
12-15: 13-15-Secret Wars tie-in 4.00

SILVER SURFER (7th series)
Marvel Comics: Mar, 2016 - No. 14, Dec, 2017 ($3.99)

1-5,7-14-Slott-s/Allred-a. 1-4-The Thing app. 3-50th Anniversary issue; Shalla Bal app. 4.00
6-(10/16, $4.99) 200th issue; Spider-Man app.; cover gallery 5.00

SILVER SURFER, THE
Marvel Comics (Epic): Dec, 1988 - No. 2, Jan, 1989 ($1.00, lim. series)

1-By Stan Lee scripts & Moebius-c/a 1 3 4 6 8 10
2 5.00
HC (1988, $19.95, dust jacket) r/#1,2; "Making Of" text section and sketch pages 30.00
... By Stan Lee & Moebius (3/13, $7.99) r/#1&2; bonus production diary from Moebius 8.00
...: Parable ('98, $5.99) r/#1&2 6.00

SILVER SURFER: IN THY NAME
Marvel Comics: Jan, 2008 - No. 4, Apr, 2008 ($2.99, limited series)

1-4-Spurrier-s/Huat-a. 1-Turner-c. 2-Dell'Otto-c. 3-Paul Pope-c. 4-Galactus app. 3.00

SILVER SURFER: LOFTIER THAN MORTALS
Marvel Comics: Oct, 1999 - No. 2, Oct, 1999 ($2.50, limited series)

1,2-Remix of Fantastic Four #57-60; Velluto-a 3.00

SILVER SURFER: REQUIEM
Marvel Comics: July, 2007 - No. 4, Oct, 2007 ($3.99, limited series)

1-4-Straczynski-s/Ribic-a. 1-Origin retold; Fantastic Four app. 4.00
HC (2007, $19.99) r/#1-4, Ribic cover sketches 20.00

SILVER SURFER/SUPERMAN
Marvel Comics: 1996 ($5.95,one-shot)

1-Perez-s/Lim-c/a(p) 6.00

SILVER SURFER VS. DRACULA
Marvel Comics: Feb, 1994 ($1.75, one-shot)

1-r/Tomb of Dracula #50; Everett Vampire-r/Venus #19; Howard the Duck back-up by Brunner; Lim-c(p) 4.00

SILVER SURFER/WARLOCK: RESURRECTION
Marvel Comics: Mar, 1993 - No. 4, June, 1993 ($2.50, limited series)

1-4-Starlin-c/a & scripts. 1-Surfer joins Warlock & the Infinity Watch to rescue Shalla-Bal; story continued from the 'Homecoming' GN. 2-Death app.; Mephisto cameo. 3-Surfer vs. Mephisto. 4-Warlock vs. Mephisto; Shalla-Bal revived. 4.00

SILVER SURFER/WEAPON ZERO
Marvel Comics: Apr, 1997 ($2.95, one-shot)

1-"Devil's Reign" pt. 8 3.00

SILVERTIP (Max Brand)
Dell Publishing Co.: No. 491, Aug, 1953 - No. 898, May, 1958

Four Color 491 (#1); all painted-c 8 16 24 52 99 145
Four Color 572,608,637,667,731,789,898-Kinstler-a 5 10 15 34 60 85
Four Color 835 5 10 15 34 60 85

SIMON DARK
DC Comics: Dec, 2007 - No. 18, May, 2009 ($2.99)

1-Intro. Simon Dark; Steve Niles-s/Scott Hampton-a/c 4.00
1-Second printing with full face variant cover 3.00
2-18 3.00
...: Ashes TPB (2009, $17.99) r/#7-12 18.00
...: The Game of Life TPB (2009, $17.99) r/#13-18 18.00
...: What Simon Does TPB (2008, $14.99) r/#1-6 18.00

SIMPSONS COMICS (See Bartman, Futurama, Itchy & Scratchy & Radioactive Man)
Bongo Comics Group: 1993 - Present ($1.95/$2.50/$2.99)

1-($2.25)-FF#1-c swipe; pull-out poster; flip book 3 6 9 14 20 25
2-5: 2-Patty & Selma flip-c/sty. 3-Krusty, Agent of K.L.O.W.N. flip-c/story. 4-Infinity-c; flip-c of Busman #1; w/trading card. 5-Wraparound-c w/trading card 1 2 3 5 6 8
6-40: All Flip books. 6-w/Chief Wiggum's "Crime Comics". 7-w/"McBain Comics". 8-w/"Edna, Queen of the Congo". 9-w/"Barney Gumble". 10-w/"Apu". 11-w/"Homer". 12-w/"White Knuckled War Stories". 13-w/"Jimbo Jones' Wedgie Comics". 14-w/"Grampa". 15-w/"Itchy & Scratchy". 16-w/"Bongo Grab Bag". 17-w/"Headlight Comics". 18-w/"Milhouse". 19,20-w/"Roswell." 21,22-w/"Roswell". 23-w/"Hellfire Comics". 24-w/"Lil' Homey". 36-39-Flip book w/Radioactive Man 5.00
41-49,51-99: 43-Flip book w/Poochie. 52-Dini-s. 77-Dixon-s. 85-Begin $2.99-c 4.00
50-($5.95) Wraparound-c; 80 pgs.; square-bound 1 2 3 5 6 8
100-($6.99) 100 pgs.; square-bound; clip issue of past highlights 1 2 3 5 6 8
101-182,184-199,201-224: 102-Barks Ducks homage. 117-Hank Scorpio app. 122-Archie spoof. 132-Movie poster enclosed. 132-133-Two-parter. 144-Flying Hellfish flashback. 150-w/Poster. 163-Aragonés-s/a. 218-Guardians of the Galaxy spoof 3.00
183-Archie Comics #1 cover swipe; Archie homage with Stan Goldberg-a 3.00
200-(2013, $4.99) Wraparound-c; short stories incl. Dorkin-s/a; Matt Groening cameo 5.00
225-242-($3.99) 225-Bonus back-up 1970s Eddie & Lou story. 237-Bartman app. 4.00
... A Go-Go (1999, $11.95)-r/#32-35; ...Big Bonanza (1998, $11.95)-r/#28-31, ...Extravaganza (1994, $10.00)-r/#1-4; infinity-c, ...On Parade (1998, $11.95)-r/#24-27, ...Simpsorama (1996, $10.95)-r/#11-14 12.00
Simpsons Classics 1-30 (2004-Present, $3.99, magazine-size, quarterly) reprints 4.00
Simpsons Comics Barn Burner ('04, $14.95) r/#57-61,63 15.00
Simpsons Comics Beach Blanket Bongo ('07, $14.95) r/#71-75,77 15.00
Simpsons Comics Belly Buster ('04, $14.95) r/#49,51,53-56 15.00
Simpsons Comics Hit the Road! ('08, $15.95) r/#85,86,88,89,90 16.00
Simpsons Comics Jam-Packed Jamboree ('06, $14.95) r/#64-69 15.00
Simpsons Comics Madness ('03, $14.95) r/#43-48 15.00
Simpsons Comics Royale ('01, $14.95) r/various Bongo issues 15.00
Simpsons Comics Treasure Trove 1-4 ('08-'09, $3.99, 6" x 8") r/various Bongo issues 4.00
Simpsons Summer Shindig ('07-'15, $4.99) 1-9-Anthology. 1-Batman/Ripken insert 5.00
Simpsons Winter Wing Ding ('06-'14, $4.99) 1-10-Holiday anthology. 1-Dini-s 5.00

SIMPSONS COMICS AND STORIES
Welsh Publishing Group: 1993 ($2.95, one-shot)

1-(Direct Sale)-Polybagged w/Bartman poster 3 6 9 14 20 25
1-(Newsstand Edition)-Without poster 6.00

SIMPSONS COMICS PRESENTS BART SIMPSON
Bongo Comics Group: 2000 - No. 100, 2016 ($2.50/$2.99)

1-99: 7-9-Dan DeCarlo-layouts. 13-Begin $2.99-c. 17,37-Bartman app. 50-Aragonés-s/a 3.00
100-($4.99) 100-year old Bart, Mrs. Krabappel, Fruit Bat Man app. 5.00
The Big Book of Bart Simpson TPB (2002, $12.95) r/#1-4 15.00
The Big Bad Book of Bart Simpson TPB (2003, $12.95) r/#5-8 15.00
The Big Bratty Book of Bart Simpson TPB (2004, $12.95) r/#9-12 15.00
The Big Beefy Book of Bart Simpson TPB (2005, $13.95) r/#13-16 15.00
The Big Bouncy Book of Bart Simpson TPB (2006, $13.95) r/#17-20 15.00
The Big Beastly Book of Bart Simpson TPB (2007, $14.95) r/#21-24 15.00
The Big Brilliant Book of Bart Simpson TPB (2008, $14.95) r/#25-28 15.00

SIMPSONS FUTURAMA CROSSOVER CRISIS II (TV) (Also see Futurama/Simpsons Infinitely Secret Crossover Crisis)
Bongo Comics: 2005 - No. 2, 2005 ($3.00, limited series)

1,2-The Professor brings the Simpsons' Springfield crew to the 31st century 3.00

SIMPSONS ILLUSTRATED (TV)
Bongo Comics: 2012 - Present ($3.99, quarterly)

1-20-Reprints 4.00
21-27-($4.99) 25-All-monster issue 5.00

SIMPSONS ONE-SHOT WONDERS (TV)
Bongo Comics: 2012 - 2018 ($2.99/$3.99)

...: Bart Simpson's Pal Milhouse 1 - Short stories; centerfold with decal 3.00
...: Duffman 1 ($3.99) - Green Lantern spoof; centerfold with die-cut Duffman mask 4.00
...: Grampa 1 ($3.99) - "Choose Your Adventure" format; wraparound-c 4.00
...: Jimbo 1 ($3.99) - Short stories; centerfold with die-cut skull sticker 4.00
...: Kang & Kodos 1 ($3.99) - Short stories; centerfold with bumper stickers 4.00
...: Krusty 1 ($3.99) - Krusty's backstory; back-c swipe of Uncanny X-Men #141 4.00

Sin City: Hell and Back #1 © Frank Miller

Sinergy #1 © Soming Inc.

Sinestro #23 © DC

...: Li'l Homer 1 - Short stories of Homer's childhood; centerfold with cut-outs 3.00
...: Lisa 1 ($3.99) - Short stories by Matsumoto and others; sticker page centerfold 4.00
...: Maggie 1 - Short stories by Aragonés and others; paperdoll centerfold; Aragonés-c 3.00
...: McBain 1 ($3.99) - Entire issue unfolds for a poster on the back 4.00
...: Mr. Burns 1 ($3.99) - Short stories incl. Richie Rich spoof; Fruit Bat Man mask 4.00
...: Professor Frink 1 ($3.99) - Short stories; 3-D glasses insert; 3-D story and back-c 4.00
...: Ralph Wiggums Comics 1 - Short stories by Aragonés and others 3.00

SIMPSONS SUPER SPECTACULAR (TV)
Bongo Comics: 2006 - Present ($2.99)

1-16: 2-Bartman, Stretch Dude and The Cupcake Kid team up; back-up story Brereton-a. 5-Fradon-a on Metamorpho spoof. 8-Spirit spoof. 9,10,14-16-Radioactive Man app. 3.00

SINBAD, JR (TV Cartoon)
Dell Publishing Co.: Sept-Nov, 1965 - No. 3, May, 1966

	GD	VG	FN	VF	VF/NM	NM-
1	4	8	12	23	37	50
2,3	3	6	9	17	26	35

SIN BOLDLY
Image Comics: Dec, 2013 ($3.50, B&W, one-shot)

1-J.M. Linsner-s/a/c; short stories with Sinful Suzi and Obsidian Stone 3.50

SIN CITY (See Dark Horse Presents, A Decade of Dark Horse, & San Diego Comic Con Comics #2,4)
Dark Horse Comics (Legend)
TPB ($15.00) Reprints early DHP stories 15.00
Booze, Broads & Bullets TPB ($15.00) 15.00
Frank Miller's Sin City: One For One (8/10, $1.00) reprints debut story from DHP #51 3.00

SIN CITY (FRANK MILLER'S...) (Reissued TPBs to coincide with the April 2005 movie)
Dark Horse Books: Feb, 2005 ($17.00/$19.00, 6" x 9" format with new Miller covers)

Volume 1: The Hard Goodbye ($17.00) reprints stories from Dark Horse Presents #51-62 and DHP Fifth Anniv. Special; covers and publicity pieces 17.00
Volume 2: A Dame to Kill For ($17.00) r/Sin City: A Dame to Kill For #1-6 17.00
Volume 3: The Big Fat Kill ($17.00) r/Sin City: The Big Fat Kill #1-5; pin-up gallery 17.00
Volume 4: That Yellow Bastard ($19.00) r/Sin City: That Yellow Bastard #1-6; pin-up gallery by Mike Allred, Kyle Baker, Jeff Smith and Bruce Timm; cover gallery 19.00
Volume 5: Family Values ($12.00) r/Sin City: Family Values GN 12.00
Volume 6: Booze, Broads & Bullets ($15.00) r/Sin City: The Babe Wore Red and Other Stories; Silent Night; story from A Decade of Dark Horse; Lost Lonely & Lethal; Sex & Violence; and Just Another Saturday Night 15.00
Volume 7: Hell and Back ($28.00) r/Sin City: Hell and Back #1-9; pin-up gallery 28.00

SIN CITY: A DAME TO KILL FOR
Dark Horse Comics (Legend): Nov, 1993 - No. 6, May, 1994 ($2.95, B&W, limited series)

1-6: Frank Miller-c/a & story in all. 1-1st app. Dwight. 6.00
Limited Edition Hardcover 85.00
Hardcover 25.00
TPB ($15.00) 15.00

SIN CITY: FAMILY VALUES
Dark Horse Comics (Legend): Oct, 1997 ($10.00, B&W, squarebound, one-shot)

nn-Miller-c/a & story 10.00
Limited Edition Hardcover 75.00

SIN CITY: HELL AND BACK
Dark Horse (Maverick): Jul, 1999 - No. 9 ($2.95/$4.95, B&W, limited series)

1-8-Miller-c/a & story. 7-Color 4.00
9-($4.95) 6.00

SIN CITY: JUST ANOTHER SATURDAY NIGHT
Dark Horse Comics (Legend): Aug, 1997 (Wizard 1/2 offer, B&W, one-shot)

	GD	VG	FN	VF	VF/NM	NM-
1/2-Miller-c/a & story	1	2	3	5	6	8
nn (10/98, $2.50) r/#1/2						4.00

SIN CITY: LOST, LONELY & LETHAL
Dark Horse Comics (Legend): Dec, 1996 ($2.95, B&W and blue, one-shot)

nn-Miller-c/s/a; w/pin-ups 5.00

SIN CITY: SEX AND VIOLENCE
Dark Horse Comics (Legend): Mar, 1997 ($2.95, B&W and blue, one-shot)

nn-Miller-c/a & story 5.00

SIN CITY: SILENT NIGHT
Dark Horse Comics (Legend): Dec, 1995 ($2.95, B&W, one-shot)

1-Miller-c/a & story; Marv app. 6.00

SIN CITY: THAT YELLOW BASTARD (Second Ed. TPB listed under Sin City (Frank Miller's...)
Dark Horse Comics (Legend): Feb, 1996 - No. 6, July, 1996 ($2.95/$3.50, B&W and yellow, limited series)

1-5: Miller-c/a & story in all. 1-1st app. Hartigan. 6.00
6-($3.50) Error & corrected 6.00
Limited Edition Hardcover 25.00
TPB ($15.00) 15.00

SIN CITY: THE BABE WORE RED AND OTHER STORIES
Dark Horse Comics (Legend): Nov, 1994 ($2.95, B&W and red, one-shot)

1-r/serial run in Previews as well as other stories; Miller-c/a & scripts; Dwight app. 6.00

SIN CITY: THE BIG FAT KILL (Second Edition TPB listed under Sin City (Frank Miller's...)
Dark Horse Comics (Legend): Nov, 1994 - No. 5, Mar, 1995 ($2.95, B&W, limited series)

1-5-Miller story & art in all; Dwight app. 6.00
Hardcover 25.00
TPB ($15.00) 15.00

SIN CITY: THE FRANK MILLER LIBRARY
Dark Horse Books: Set 1, Nov, 2005; Set 2, Mar, 2006 ($150, slipcased hardcover, 8" x 12")

Set 1 - Individual hardcovers for Volume 1: The Hard Goodbye, Volume 2: A Dame to Kill For, Volume 3: The Big Fat Kill, Volume 4: That Yellow Bastard; new red foil stamped covers; slipcase box is black with red foil graphics 150.00
Set 2 - Individual hardcovers for Volume 5: Family Values, Volume 6: Booze, Broads & Bullets, Volume 7: Hell and Back, new red foil stamped covers; The Art of Sin City red hardcover; slipcase box is black with red foil graphics 150.00

SINDBAD (See Capt. Sindbad under Movie Comics, and Fantastic Voyages of Sindbad)

SINERGY
Image Comics (Shadowline): Nov, 2014 - No. 5, Mar, 2015 ($3.50)

1-5: 1-Oeming & Soma-s/Oeming-a/c 3.50

SINESTRO
DC Comics: Jun, 2014 - No. 23, Jul, 2016 ($2.99)

1-23: 1-Bunn-s/Eaglesham-a; Lyssa Drak & Arkillo app. 6-8-Godhead x-over; New Gods app. 7-Van Sciver-a. 9-11-Mongul app. 15-Lobo app. 16-20-Black Adam app. 17-20-Wonder Woman app. 19,20-Harley Quinn & Superman app. 3.00
Annual 1 (6/15, $4.99) Bunn-s/Eaglesham-c; art by various 5.00
...: Futures End 1 (11/14, $2.99, regular-c) Five years later; Bunn-s/Lima-a/Nowlan-c 3.00
...: Futures End 1 (11/14, $3.99, 3-D cover) 4.00

SINGING GUNS (See Fawcett Movie Comics)

SINGLE SERIES (Comics on Parade #30 on)(Also see John Hix...)
United Features Syndicate: 1938 - No. 28, 1942 (All 68 pgs.)

Note: See Individual Alphabetical Listings for prices

1-Captain and the Kids (#1)
2-Broncho Bill (1939) (#1)
3-Ella Cinders (1939)
4-Li'l Abner (1939) (#1)
5-Fritzi Ritz (#1)
6-Jim Hardy by Dick Moores (#1)
7-Frankie Doodle
8-Peter Pat (On sale 7/14/39)
9-Strange As It Seems
10-Little Mary Mixup
11-Mr. and Mrs. Beans
12-Joe Jinks
13-Looy Dot Dope
14-Billy Make Believe
15-How It Began (1939)
16-Illustrated Gags (1940)-Has ad for Captain and the Kids #1 reprint listed below
17-Danny Dingle
18-Li'l Abner (#2 on-c)
19-Broncho Bill (#2 on-c)
20-Tarzan by Hal Foster
21-Ella Cinders (#2 on-c; on sale 3/19/40)
22-Iron Vic
23-Tailspin Tommy by Hal Forrest (#1)
24-Alice in Wonderland (#1)
25-Abbie and Slats
26-Little Mary Mixup (#2 on-c, 1940)
27-Jim Hardy by Dick Moores (1942)
28-Ella Cinders & Abbie and Slats (1942)
1-Captain and the Kids (1939 reprint)-2nd Edition
1-Fritzi Ritz (1939 reprint)-2nd ed.

NOTE: *Some issues given away at the 1939-40 New York World's Fair (#6).*

SINISTER DEXTER
IDW Publishing: Dec, 2013 - No. 7, Jun, 2014 ($3.99)

1-7: 1-Dan Abnett-s/Andy Clarke-a; two covers by Clarke and Fuso 4.00

SINISTER HOUSE OF SECRET LOVE, THE (Becomes Secrets of Sinister House No. 5 on)
National Periodical Publ.: Oct-Nov, 1971 - No. 4, Apr-May, 1972

	GD	VG	FN	VF	VF/NM	NM-
1 (All 52 pgs.) -Grey-tone-c	13	26	39	91	201	310
2,4	7	14	21	48	89	130
3-Toth-a; Grey-tone-c	8	16	24	51	96	140

SINS OF YOUTH... (Also see Young Justice: Sins of Youth)
DC Comics: May 2000 ($4.95/$2.50, limited crossover series)

Secret Files 1 ($4.95) Short stories and profile pages; Nauck-c 5.00
...Aquaboy/Lagoon Man; Batboy and Robin; JLA Jr.; Kid Flash/Impulse; Starwoman and the

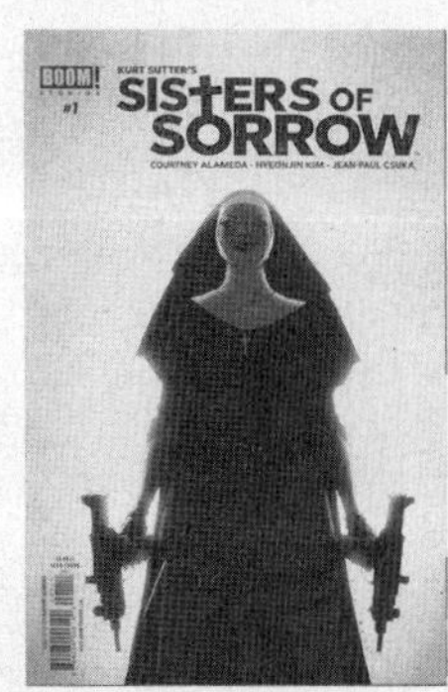

Sisters of Sorrow #1 © SutterInk

Six-Gun Heroes #20 © FAW

Skaar, King of the Savage Land #1 © MAR

GD 2.0 | VG 4.0 | FN 6.0 | VF 8.0 | VF/NM 9.0 | NM- 9.2

JSA, Superman, Jr./Superboy, Sr.; The Secret/ Deadboy, Wonder Girls ($2.50-c)
Old and young heroes switch ages 3.00

SIP KIDS (Strangers in Paradise)
Abstract Studio: 2014 - No. 4, 2015 ($4.99, color)
1-4-Strangers in Paradise characters as young kids; Terry Moore-s/a/c 5.00

SIR CHARLES BARKLEY AND THE REFEREE MURDERS
Hamilton Comics: 1993 ($9.95, 8-1/2" x 11", 52 pgs.)
nn-Photo-c; Sports fantasy comic book fiction (uses real names of NBA superstars). Script by Alan Dean Foster, art by Joe Staton. Comes with bound-in sheet of 35 gummed "Moods of Charles Barkley" stamps. Photo/story on Barkley 2 4 6 9 12 15
Special Edition of 100 copies for charity signed on an affixed book plate by Barkley, Foster & Staton 175.00
Ashcan edition given away to dealers, distributors & promoters (low distribution).
Four pages in color, balance of story in b&w 2 4 6 9 12 15

SIR EDWARD GREY, WITCHFINDER: IN THE SERVICE OF ANGELS (From Hellboy)
Dark Horse Comics: July, 2009 - No. 5, Nov, 2009 ($2.99, limited series)
1-5-Mignola-s/c; Stenbeck-a 3.00

SIR EDWARD GREY, WITCHFINDER: THE MYSTERIES OF UNLAND (From Hellboy)
Dark Horse Comics: Jun, 2014 - No. 5, Oct, 2014 ($3.50, limited series)
1-5-Newman & McHugh-s/Crook-a/Tedesco-c 3.50

SIREN (Also see Eliminator & Ultraforce)
Malibu Comics (Ultraverse): Sept, 1995 - No. 3, Dec, 1995 ($1.50)
Infinity, 1-3: Infinity-Black-c & painted-c exists. 1-Regular-c & painted-c; War Machine app. 2-Flip book w/Phoenix Resurrection Pt. 3 3.00
Special 1-(2/96, $1.95, 28 pgs.)-Origin Siren; Marvel Comic's Juggernaut-c/app. 3.00

SIRENS (See George Pérez's Sirens)

SIR LANCELOT (TV)
Dell Publishing Co.: No. 606, Dec, 1954 - No. 775, Mar, 1957
Four Color 606 (not TV) 6 12 18 42 79 115
Four Color 775(...and Brian)-Buscema-a; photo-c 9 18 27 59 117 175

SIR WALTER RALEIGH (Movie)
Dell Publishing Co.: May, 1955 (Based on movie "The Virgin Queen")
Four Color 644-Photo-c 6 12 18 42 79 115

SISTERHOOD OF STEEL (See Eclipse Graphic Adventure Novel #13)
Marvel Comics (Epic Comics): Dec, 1984 - No. 8, Feb, 1986 ($1.50, Baxter paper, mature)
1-8 4.00

SISTERS OF SORROW
BOOM! Studios: Jul, 2017 - No. 4, Oct, 2017 ($3.99, limited series)
1-4-Kurt Sutter & Courtney Alameda-s/Hyeonjin Kim-a. 1-Jae Lee-c 4.00

SITUATION, THE (TV's Jersey Shore)
Wizard World: July, 2012 (no cover price)
1-Jenkins-s/Caldwell-a; two covers by Horn & Caldwell 3.00

6 BLACK HORSES (See Movie Classics)

SIX FROM SIRIUS
Marvel Comics (Epic Comics): July, 1984 - No. 4, Oct, 1984 ($1.50, limited series, mature)
1-4: Moench scripts; Gulacy-c/a in all 4.00

SIX FROM SIRIUS II
Marvel Comics (Epic Comics): Feb, 1986 - No. 4, May, 1986 ($1.50, limited series, mature)
1-4: Moench scripts; Gulacy-c/a in all 4.00

SIX-GUN GORILLA
BOOM! Studios: Jun, 2013 - No. 6, Nov, 2013 ($3.99, limited series)
1-6: 1-Spurrier-s/Stokely-a 4.00

SIX-GUN HEROES
Fawcett Publications: March, 1950 - No. 23, Nov, 1953 (Photo-c #1-23)
1-Rocky Lane, Hopalong Cassidy, Smiley Burnette begin (same date as Smiley Burnette #1)
31 62 93 186 303 420
2 16 32 48 94 147 200
3-5: 5-Lash LaRue begins 14 28 42 76 108 140
6-15 11 22 33 62 86 110
16-22: 17-Last Smiley Burnette. 18-Monte Hale begins
10 20 30 54 72 90
23-Last Fawcett issue 10 20 30 58 79 100
NOTE: *Hopalong Cassidy photo c-1-3. Monte Hale photo c-18. Rocky Lane photo c-4, 5, 7, 9, 11, 13, 15, 17, 20, 21, 23. Lash LaRue photo c-6, 8, 10, 12, 14, 16, 19, 22.*

SIX-GUN HEROES (Cont'd from Fawcett; Gunmasters #84 on) (See Blue Bird)
Charlton Comics: No. 24, Jan, 1954 - No. 83, Mar-Apr, 1965 (All Vol. 4)
24-Lash LaRue, Hopalong Cassidy, Rocky Lane & Tex Ritter begin; photo-c
14 28 42 80 115 150
25 10 20 30 54 72 90
26-30: 26-Rod Cameron story. 28-Tom Mix begins? 9 18 27 47 61 75
31-40: 38-40-Jingles & Wild Bill Hickok (TV) 8 16 24 42 54 65
41-46,48,50: 41-43-Wild Bill Hickok (TV) 8 16 24 40 50 60
47-Williamson-a, 2 pgs; Torres-a 8 16 24 42 54 65
49-Williamson-a (5 pgs.) 9 18 27 50 65 80
51-56,58-60: 58-Gunmaster app. 3 6 9 19 30 40
57-Origin & 1st app. Gunmaster 4 8 12 25 40 55
61,63-70 3 6 9 16 23 30
62-Origin Gunmaster 3 6 9 19 30 40
71-75,77,78,80-83 2 4 6 13 18 22
76,79: 76-Gunmaster begins. 79-1st app. & origin of Bullet, the Gun-Boy
3 6 9 14 19 24

SIXGUN RANCH (See Luke Short & Four Color #580)

SIX GUNS
Marvel Comics: Jan, 2012 - No. 5, Apr, 2012 ($2.99, limited series)
1-5-Diggle-s/Gianfelice-a; Tarantula and Tex Dawson app. 3.00

SIX-GUN WESTERN
Atlas Comics (CDS): Jan, 1957 - No. 4, July, 1957
1-Crandall-a; two Williamson text illos 22 44 66 132 216 300
2,3-Williamson-a in both 16 32 48 92 144 195
4-Woodbridge-a 14 28 42 78 112 145
NOTE: ***Ayers** a-2, 3. **Maneely** a-1; c-2, 3. **Orlando** a-2. **Pakula** a-2. **Powell** a-3. **Romita** a-1, 4. **Severin** c-1, 4. **Shores** a-2.*

SIX MILLION DOLLAR MAN, THE (TV) (Also see The Bionic Man)
Charlton Comics: 6/76 - No. 4, 12/76; No. 5, 10/77; No. 6, 2/78 - No. 9, 6/78
1-Staton-c/a; Lee Majors photo on-c 3 6 9 19 30 40
2-Neal Adams-c; Staton-a 3 6 9 14 20 25
3-9 2 4 6 13 18 22

SIX MILLION DOLLAR MAN, THE (TV)(Magazine)
Charlton Comics: July, 1976 - No. 7, Nov, 1977 (B&W)
1-Neal Adams-c/a 3 6 9 21 33 45
2-Neal Adams-c 3 6 9 16 23 30
3-N. Adams part inks; Chaykin-a 3 6 9 14 19 24
4-7 2 4 6 11 16 20

SIX MILLION DOLLAR MAN, THE: FALL OF MAN (TV)
Dynamite Entertainment: 2016 - No. 5, 2016 ($3.99)
1-5: 1-Van Jensen-s/Ron Salas-a; three covers 4.00

SIX MILLION DOLLAR MAN, THE: SEASON 6 (TV)
Dynamite Entertainment: 2014 - No. 6, 2014 ($3.99)
1-Jim Kuhoric-s/Juan Antonio Ramirez-a; covers by Alex Ross & Ken Haeser & photo-c 4.00
2-6-Two covers by Ross & Haeser on each. 2-Maskatron returns 4.00

SIXPACK AND DOGWELDER: HARD TRAVELIN' HEROZ (See All-Star Section Eight)
DC Comics: Oct, 2016 - No. 6, Mar, 2017 ($3.99, limited series)
1-6-Ennis-s/Braun-a/Dillon-c. 1-Power Girl, Catwoman, & Starfire app. 2-6-Constantine app. 2-The Spectre app. 4.00

SIX STRING SAMURAI
Awesome-Hyperwerks: Sept, 1998 ($2.95)
1-Stinsman & Fraga-a 3.00

1602 WITCH HUNTER ANGELA (Secret Wars tie-in)
Marvel Comics: Aug, 2015 - No. 4, Dec, 2015 ($3.99, limited series)
1-4-Marguerite Bennett-s; Hans & Sauvage-a; The Enchantress app. 4.00

67 SECONDS
Marvel Comics (Epic Comics): 1992 ($15.95, 54 pgs., graphic novel)
nn-James Robinson scripts; Steve Yeowell-c/a 2 4 6 11 14 18

SKAAR: KING OF THE SAVAGE LAND
Marvel Comics: Jun, 2011 - No. 5 ($2.99, limited series)
1-5-Shanna & Ka-Zar app.; Ching-a. 1-Komarck-c. 2-McGuinness-c 3.00

SKAAR: SON OF HULK (Title continues in Son of Hulk #13)(Also see World War Hulk x-over)
Marvel Comics: Aug, 2008 - No. 12, Aug, 2009 ($2.99)
1-Garney-a/Pak-s; 2 covers by Pagulayan and Julie Bell; origin 4.00
1-Second printing - 2 covers by Garney and Hulk movie image 3.00
1-Third printing - Garney sketch variant-c 3.00

Skeleton Hand #1 © ACG

Skullkickers #100 © Jim Zub

Skybourne #2 © Frank Cho

GD 2.0 | VG 4.0 | FN 6.0 | VF 8.0 | VF/NM 9.0 | NM- 9.2

2-12: 2-6-Back-up story with Guice-a. 7-12-Silver Surfer app. 3.00
Planet Skaar Prologue 1 (7/09, $3.99) Panosian-a; Fantastic Four & She-Hulk app. 4.00
... Presents - Savage World of Sakaar (11/08, $3.99) Pak-s/art by various; Garney-c 4.00

SKATEMAN
Pacific Comics: Nov, 1983 (Baxter paper, one-shot)

1-Adams-c/a 4.00

SKELETON HAND (...In Secrets of the Supernatural)
American Comics Gr. (B&M Dist. Co.): Sept-Oct, 1952 - No. 6, Jul-Aug, 1953

	GD	VG	FN	VF	VF/NM	NM-
1	65	130	195	416	708	1000
2	40	80	120	246	411	575
3-6	36	72	108	211	343	475

SKELETON KEY
Amaze Ink: July, 1995 - No. 30, Jan, 1998 ($1.25/$1.50/$1.75, B&W)

1-30 3.00
Special #1 (2/98, $4.95) Unpublished short stories 5.00
Sugar Kat Special (10/98, $2.95) Halloween stories 3.00
Beyond The Threshold TPB (6/96. $11.95)-r/#1-6 12.00
Cats and Dogs TPB ($12.95)-r/#25-30 13.00
The Celestial Calendar TPB ($19.95)-r/#7-18 20.00
Telling Tales TPB ($12.95)-r/#19-24 13.00

SKELETON KEY (Volume 2)
Amaze Ink: 1999 - No. 4, 1999 ($2.95, B&W)

1-4-Andrew Watson-s/a 3.00

SKELETON WARRIORS
Marvel Comics: Apr, 1995 - No. 4, July, 1995 ($1.50)

1-4: Based on animated series. 3.00

SKIN GRAFT: THE ADVENTURES OF A TATTOOED MAN
DC Comics (Vertigo): July, 1993 - No. 4, Oct, 1993 ($2.50, lim. series, mature)

1-4 3.00

SKINWALKER
Oni Press: May, 2002 - No. 4, Sept, 2002 ($2.95, limited series)

1-4-Hurtt & Dela Cruz-a; Talon-c 3.00
1-(5/05) Free Comic Book Day Edition 3.00

SKI PARTY (See Movie Classics)

SKREEMER
DC Comics: May, 1989 - No. 6, Oct, 1989 ($2.00, limited series, mature)

1-6: Contains graphic violence; Milligan-s 3.00
TPB (2002, $19.95) r/#1-6 20.00

SKRULL KILL KREW
Marvel Comics: Sept, 1995 - No. 5, Dec, 1995 ($2.95, limited series)

1-5: Grant Morrison & Mark Millar scripts; Steve Yeowell-a. 2,3-Cap America app. 5.00
TPB (2006, $16.99) r/#1-5 17.00

SKRULL KILL KREW
Marvel Comics: Jun, 2009 - No. 5, Dec, 2009 ($3.99, limited series)

1-5-Felber-s/Robinson-a 4.00

SKRULLS! (Tie-in to Secret Invasion crossover)
Marvel Comics: 2008 ($4.99, one-shot)

1-Skrull history, profiles of Skrulls, their allies & foes; checklist of appearances; Horn-c 5.00

SKRULLS VS. POWER PACK (Tie-in to Secret Invasion crossover)
Marvel Comics: Sept, 2008 - No. 4 ($2.99, limited series)

1-4-Van Lente-s/Hamscher-a; Franklin Richards app. 3.00

SKUL, THE
Virtual Comics (Byron Preiss Multimedia): Oct, 1996 - No. 3, Dec, 1996 ($2.50, lim. series)

1-3: Ron Lim & Jimmy Palmiotti-a 3.00

SKULL & BONES
DC Comics: 1992 - No. 3, 1992 ($4.95, limited series, 52 pgs.)

Book 1-3: 1-1st app. 5.00

SKULLKICKERS
Image Comics: Sept, 2010 - No. 33, Jul, 2015; No. 100, Aug, 2015 ($2.99/$3.50)

1-Jim Zubkavich-s/Edwin Huang-a; two covers 4.00
1-(2nd & 3rd printings), 2-18 3.00
24-29,31-33: 24-($3.50) "Before Watchmen" cover swipe (no issues #34-99) 3.50
30-($3.99) Multi-dimensional variant Skullkickers 4.00
#100 ($3.99, 8/15) Last issue; conclusion of Infinite Icons of the Endless Epic 4.00
All-New Secret Skullkickers 1 (6/13, $3.50) issue #22; cover swipe of X-Men #125 ('79) 3.50
Dark Skullkickers Dark 1 (7/13, $3.50) issue #23; cover swipe of Green Lantern #85 ('71) 3.50
Savage Skullkickers 1 (3/13, $3.50) issue #20; cover swipe of Savage Wolverine #1 3.50
The Mighty Skullkickers 1 (4/13, $3.50) issue #21; cover swipe of Thor #337 3.50
Uncanny Skullkickers 1 (2/13, $3.50) issue #19 3.50

SKULL, THE SLAYER
Marvel Comics Group: Aug, 1975 - No. 8, Nov, 1976 (20¢/25¢)

	GD	VG	FN	VF	VF/NM	NM-
1-Origin & 1st app.; Gil Kane-c	3	6	9	14	20	25
2-8: 2-Gil Kane-c. 5,6-(Regular 25¢-c). 8-Kirby-c	2	4	6	8	10	12
5,6-(30¢-c variants, limited distribution)(5,7/76)	3	6	9	21	33	45

SKY BLAZERS (CBS Radio)
Hawley Publications: Sept, 1940 - No. 2, Nov, 1940

	GD	VG	FN	VF	VF/NM	NM-
1-Sky Pirates, Ace Archer, Flying Aces begin	77	154	231	493	847	1200
2-WWII air battle grey-tone-c	41	82	123	250	418	585

SKYBOURNE
BOOM! Studios: Sept, 2016 - No. 5, Feb, 2018 ($3.99)

1-5-Frank Cho-s/a 4.00

SKY DOLL
Marvel Comics (Soleil): 2008 - No. 3, 2008 ($5.99, mature)

1-3-Barbucci & Canepa-s/a; English version of French comic; preview of other titles 6.00
...: Doll's Factory 1,2 (2009 - No. 2, 2009, $5.99) Barbucci & Canepa-s/a 6.00
...: Lacrima Christi 1,2 (9/10 - No. 2, 10/10, $5.99) Barbucci & Canepa and others-s/a 6.00
...: Space Ship 1,2 (7/10 - No. 2, 8/10, $5.99) Barbucci & Canepa and others-s/a 6.00

SKY DOLL: SUDRA
Titan Comics: Apr, 2017 - No. 2, May, 2017 ($3.99, mature)

1,2-Barbucci & Canepa-s/a; English version of French comic 4.00

SKYE RUNNER
DC Comics (WildStorm): June, 2006 - No. 6, Mar, 2007 ($2.99)

1-6: 1-Three covers; Warner-s/Garza-a. 2-Three covers, incl. Campbell 3.00

SKYLANDERS (Based on the Activision video game)
IDW Publishing: No. 0, Jul, 2014 - No. 12, Aug, 2015 ($3.99)

0-(no cover price) Lord Kaos app.; Bowden-a; character bios 3.00
1-12: 1-Marz & Rodriguez-s/Baldeón-a 4.00
... Quarterly - Spyro & Friends: Biting Back (3/18, $4.99) Marz & Rodriguez-s 5.00
... Quarterly - Spyro & Friends: Full Blast (7/17, $4.99) Marz & Rodriguez-s 5.00
... Quarterly - Spyro & Friends: Goldslinger (11/17, $4.99) Marz & Rodriguez-s 5.00
... Superchargers 1-6 (10/15 - No. 6, 3/16, $3.99) Marz & Rodriguez-s 4.00

SKYMAN (See Big Shot Comics & Sparky Watts)
Columbia Comics Gr.: Fall?, 1941 - No. 2, Fall?, 1942; No. 3, 1948 - No. 4, 1948

	GD	VG	FN	VF	VF/NM	NM-
1-Origin Skyman, The Face, Sparky Watts app.; Whitney-c/a; 3rd story-r from Big Shot #1; Whitney c-1-4	129	258	387	826	1413	2000
2 (1942)-Yankee Doodle	69	138	207	442	759	1075
3,4 (1948)	41	82	123	256	428	600

SKYMAN (Also see Captain Midnight 2013 series #4)
Dark Horse Comics: Jan, 2014 - No. 4, Apr, 2014 ($2.99)

1-4: 1-Fialkov-s/Garcia-a; origin of a new Skyman. 3,4-Captain Midnight app. 3.00
... One-Shot (11/14, $2.99) Garcia-a 3.00

SKYPILOT
Ziff-Davis Publ. Co.: No. 10, 1950(nd) - No. 11, Apr-May, 1951

	GD	VG	FN	VF	VF/NM	NM-
10,11-Frank Borth-a; Saunders painted-c	17	34	51	98	154	210

SKY RANGER (See Johnny Law...)

SKYROCKET
Harry 'A' Chesler: 1944

	GD	VG	FN	VF	VF/NM	NM-
nn-Alias the Dragon, Dr. Vampire, Skyrocket & The Desperado app.; WWII Japan zero-c	53	106	159	334	567	800

SKY SHERIFF (Breeze Lawson...) (Also see Exposed & Outlaws)
D. S. Publishing Co.: Summer, 1948

	GD	VG	FN	VF	VF/NM	NM-
1-Edmond Good-c/a	16	32	48	94	147	200

SKY WOLF (Also see Airboy)
Eclipse Comics: Mar, 1988 - No. 3, Oct, 1988 ($1.25/$1.50/$1.95, lim. series)

1-3 3.00

SLAINE, THE BERSERKER (Slaine the King #21 on)
Quality: July, 1987 - No. 28, 1989 ($1.25/$1.50)

1-28 3.00

Slam! #1 © Ribon & Fish

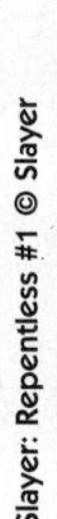
Slayer: Repentless #1 © Slayer

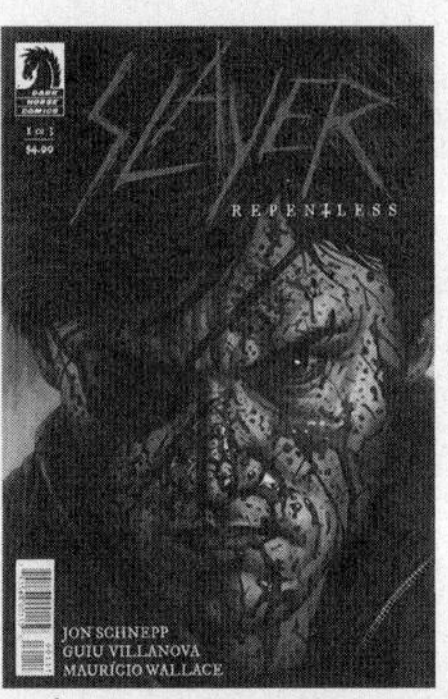

Sleepless #1 © Vaughn & Del Duca

	GD 2.0	VG 4.0	FN 6.0	VF 8.0	VF/NM 9.0	NM- 9.2

SLAINE, THE HORNED GOD
Fleetway: 1998 - No. 3 ($6.99)

1-3-Reprints series from 2000 A.D.; Bisley-a 7.00

SLAM!
BOOM! Studios (Boom! Box): Nov, 2016 - No. 4, Feb, 2017 ($3.99)

1-4-Roller derby; Pamela Ribon-s/Veronica Fish-a 4.00

SLAM BANG COMICS (Western Desperado #8)
Fawcett Publications: Mar, 1940 - No. 7, Sept, 1940 (Combined with Master Comics #7)

	GD	VG	FN	VF	VF/NM	NM-
1-Diamond Jack, Mark Swift & The Time Retarder, Lee Granger, Jungle King begin & continue in Master	265	530	795	1694	2897	4100
2	116	232	348	742	1271	1800
3-Classic monster-c (scarce)	300	600	900	2070	3635	5200
4,6,7: 6-Intro Zoro, the Mystery Man (also in #7)	94	188	282	597	1024	1450
5-Classic Dragon-c	103	206	309	659	1130	1600

Ashcan (1940) Not distributed to newsstands, only for in house use. A copy sold in 2006 for $4,500.

SLAM! THE NEXT JAM
BOOM! Studios (Boom! Box): Sept, 2017 - No. 4, Dec, 2017 ($3.99)

1-4-Roller derby; Pamela Ribon-s/Marina Julia-a 4.00

SLAPSTICK
Marvel Comics: Nov, 1992 - No. 4, Feb, 1993 ($1.25, limited series)

1-4: Fry/Austin-c/a. 4-Ghost Rider, D.D., F.F. app. 3.00

SLAPSTICK
Marvel Comics: Feb, 2017 - No. 6, Jul, 2017 ($3.99, limited series)

1-6-Brown & Van Lente-s/Olortegui-a 4.00

SLAPSTICK COMICS
Comic Magazines Distributors: nd (1946?) (36 pgs.)

	GD	VG	FN	VF	VF/NM	NM-
nn-Firetop feature; Post-a(2); Munson Paddock-c	36	72	108	211	343	475

SLASH & BURN
DC Comics (Vertigo): Jan, 2016 - No. 6, Jun, 2016 ($3.99/$4.99)

1-5-Si Spencer-s/Max Dunbar-a 4.00
6-($4.99) 5.00

SLASH-D DOUBLECROSS
St. John Publishing Co.: 1950 (Pocket-size, 132 pgs.)

	GD	VG	FN	VF	VF/NM	NM-
nn-Western comics	23	46	69	136	223	310

SLASH MARAUD
DC Comics: Nov, 1987 - No. 6, Apr, 1988 ($1.75, limited series)

1-6-Moench-s/Gulacy-a/c 3.00

SLAUGHTERMAN
Comico: Feb, 1983 - No. 2, 1983 ($1.50, B&W)

1,2 4.00

SLAVE GIRL COMICS (See Malu… & White Princess of the Jungle #2)
Avon Periodicals/Eternity Comics (1989): Feb, 1949 - No. 2, 1949 (52 pgs.); Mar, 1989 (B&W, 44 pgs)

	GD	VG	FN	VF	VF/NM	NM-
1-Larsen-c/a	142	284	426	909	1555	2200
2-Larsen-a (no month listed)	123	246	369	787	1344	1900

1-(3/89, $2.25, B&W, 44 pgs.)-r/#1 5.00

SLAVE LABOR STORIES
SLG Publishing: May, 2003 (Giveaway, B&W)

1-Free Comic Book Day Edition; short stories by various; Dorkin Milk & Cheese-c 3.00

SLAYER: REPENTLESS (Based on the band Slayer)
Dark Horse Comics: Jan, 2017 - No. 3, Jun, 2017 ($4.99, limited series)

1-3-Jon Schnepp-s/Guiu Villanova-a/Glenn Fabry-c; Slayer app. 5.00

SLEDGE HAMMER (TV)
Marvel Comics: Feb, 1988 - No. 2, Mar,1988 ($1.00, limited series)

1,2 3.00

SLEDGEHAMMER 44
Dark Horse Comics: Mar, 2013 - No. 2, Apr, 2013 ($3.50, limited series)

1,2-Mignola & Arcudi-s/Latour-a; Mignola-c 3.50

SLEDGEHAMMER 44: THE LIGHTNING WAR
Dark Horse Comics: Nov, 2013 - No. 3, Jan, 2014 ($3.50, limited series)

1-3-Mignola & Arcudi-s/Laurence Campbell-a. 1-Mignola-c. 2,3-Campbell-c 3.50

SLEEPER
DC Comics (WildStorm): Mar, 2003 - No. 12, Mar, 2004 ($2.95)

	GD 2.0	VG 4.0	FN 6.0	VF 8.0	VF/NM 9.0	NM- 9.2

1-12-Brubaker-s/Phillips-c/a. 3-Back-up preview of The Authority: High Stakes pt. 2 3.00
...: All False Moves TPB (2004, $17.95) r/#7-12 18.00
...: Out in the Cold TPB (2004, $17.95) r/#1-6 18.00

SLEEPER: SEASON TWO
DC Comics (WildStorm): Aug, 2004 - No. 12, July, 2005 ($2.95/$2.99)

1-12-Brubaker-s/Phillips-c/a. 3.00
TPB (2009, $24.99) r/#1-12 25.00
...: A Crooked Line TPB (2005, $17.99) r/#1-6 18.00
...: The Long Way Home TPB (2005, $14.99) r/#7-12 15.00

SLEEPING BEAUTY (See Dell Giants & Movie Comics)
Dell Publishing Co.: No. 973, May, 1959 - No. 984, June, 1959 (Disney)

	GD	VG	FN	VF	VF/NM	NM-
Four Color 973 (...and the Prince)	10	20	30	69	147	225
Four Color 984 (...Fairy Godmother's)	9	18	27	58	114	170

SLEEPLESS
Image Comics: Dec, 2017 - Present ($3.99)

1-3-Sarah Vaughn-s/Leila Del Duca-a 4.00

SLEEPWALKER
Marvel Comics: June, 1991 - No. 33, Feb, 1994 ($1.00/$1.25)

1-1st app. Sleepwalker 4.00
2-33: 4-Williamson-i. 5-Spider-Man-c/story. 7-Infinity Gauntlet x-over. 8-Vs. Deathlok-c/story. 11-Ghost Rider-c/story. 12-Quesada-c/a(p) 14-Intro Spectra. 15-F.F.-c/story. 17-Darkhawk & Spider-Man x-over. 18-Infinity War x-over; Quesada/Williamson-c. 21,22-Hobgoblin app. 19-($2.00)-Die-cut Sleepwalker mask-c 3.00
25-($2.95, 52 pgs.)-Holo-grafx foil-c; origin 4.00
Holiday Special 1 (1/93, $2.00, 52 pgs.)-Quesada-c(p) 4.00

SLEEPWALKING
Hall of Heroes: Jan, 1996 ($2.50, B&W)

1-Kelley Jones-c 3.00

SLEEPY HOLLOW (Movie Adaption)
DC Comics (Vertigo): 2000 ($7.95, one-shot)

1-Kelley Jones-a/Seagle-s 8.00

SLEEPY HOLLOW (Based on the Fox TV show)
BOOM! Studios: Oct, 2014 - No. 4, Jan, 2015 ($3.99, limited series)

1-4-Marguerite Bennett-s/Jorge Coelho-a/Phil Noto-c 4.00
...: Origins 1 (4/15, $4.99) Mike Johnson-s/Matias Bergara-a; Quinones-c 5.00
...: Providence 1-4 (8/15 - No. 4 11/15, $3.99) Carrasco-s/Santos-a 4.00

SLEEZE BROTHERS, THE
Marvel Comics (Epic Comics): Aug, 1989 - No. 6, Jan, 1990 ($1.75, mature)

1-6: 4-6 (9/89 - 11/89 indicia dates) 3.00
nn-(1991, $3.95, 52 pgs.) 4.00

SLICK CHICK COMICS
Leader Enterprises: 1947(nd) - No. 3, 1947(nd)

	GD	VG	FN	VF	VF/NM	NM-
1-Teenage humor	21	42	63	126	206	285
2,3	15	30	45	88	137	185

SLIDERS (TV)
Acclaim Comics (Armada): June, 1996 - No. 2, July, 1996 ($2.50, lim. series)

1,2: D.G. Chichester scripts; Dick Giordano-a. 3.00

SLIDERS: DARKEST HOUR (TV)
Acclaim Comics (Armada): Oct, 1996 - No. 3, Dec, 1996 ($2.50, limited series)

1-3 3.00

SLIDERS SPECIAL
Acclaim Comics (Armada): Nov, 1996 - No 3, Mar, 1997 ($3.95, limited series)

1-3: 1-Narcotica-Jerry O'Connell-s. 2-Blood and Splendor. 3-Deadly Secrets 4.00

SLIDERS: ULTIMATUM (TV)
Acclaim Comics (Armada): Sept, 1996 - No. 2, Sept, 1996 ($2.50, lim. series)

1,2 3.00

SLIMER! (TV cartoon) (Also see the Real Ghostbusters)
Now Comics: 1989 - No. 19, Nov, 1990 ($1.75)

1-19: Based on animated cartoon 4.00

SLIM MORGAN (See Wisco)

SLINGERS (See Spider-Man: Identity Crisis issues)
Marvel Comics: Dec, 1998 - No. 12, Nov, 1999 ($2.99/$1.99)

0-(Wizard #88 supplement) Prelude story 3.00
1-($2.99) Four editions w/different covers for each hero, 16 pages common to all,

Slots #1 © Skybound

Smallville: Lantern #2 © DC

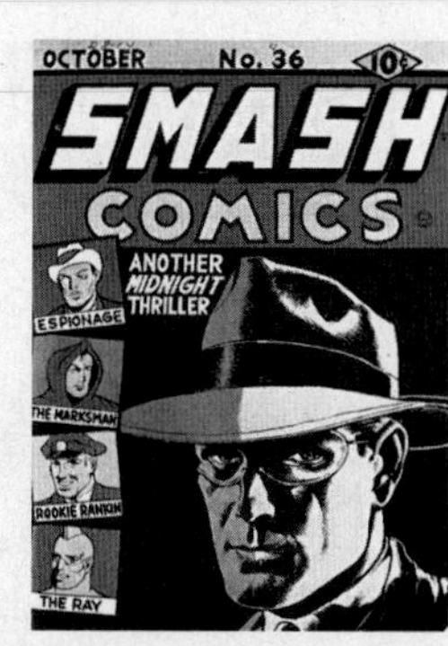

Smash Comics #36 © QUA

	GD 2.0	VG 4.0	FN 6.0	VF 8.0	VF/NM 9.0	NM- 9.2

the other pages from each hero's perspective 4.00
2-12: 2-Two-c. 12-Saltares-a 3.00

SLITHISS ATTACKS! (Also see Very Weird Tales)
Oceanspray Comics Group: Dec, 2001 – No. 4, Aug, 2004 ($3.00/$4.00)

1-($3.00) Origin and 1st app. of the monster Slithiss; 1st app. Overconfident Man 15.00
2-($4.00) 2nd app. Overconfident Man; "Chris Lamo" Newport, OR murder parody 12.00
3-($3.00) Rutland Vermont Halloween x-over; 3rd app. Overconfident Man 12.00
4-($3.00) 4th app. Overconfident Man 10.00
Special Edition 1($20.00) reprints #1-2 without letter column 20.00
Special Edition 1($20.00) second printing 20.00
NOTE: *Created in prevention classes taught by Jon McClure at the Oceanspray Family Center in Newport, OR and paid for by the Housing Authority of Lincoln County, all books are b&w with color covers. Bob Overstreet and other comics' professionals wrote letters of encouragement that were published in issues #2-4. Issues #1-2 penciled and inked by various artists; #3-4 penciled by James Gilmer. All comics feature characters created by students, signed and numbered by Jon McClure. Issue #1 had a 200 issue print run, while issues #2-4 have print runs of 100 each. Special Edition #1 had a print run of 26 issues, while the second printing had a 10 issue print run. Ties in with live action movie Face Eater released in 2007 and card game FaceEater released in 2010.*

SLOTS
Image Comics: Oct, 2017 - No. 6, Mar, 2018 ($3.99)

1-6-Dan Panosian-s/a/c 4.00

SLUDGE
Malibu Comics (Ultraverse): Oct, 1993 - No. 12, Dec, 1994 ($2.50/$1.95)

1-($2.50, 48 pgs.)-Intro/1st app. Sludge; Rune flip-c/story Pt. 1 (1st app., 3 pgs.) by Barry Smith; The Night Man app. (3 pg. preview); The Mighty Magnor 1 pg strip begins by Aragonés (cont. in other titles) 4.00
1-Ultra 5000 Limited silver foil 8.00
2-11: 3-Break-Thru x-over. 4-2 pg. Mantra origin. 8-Bloodstorm app. 3.00
12 ($3.50)-Ultraverse Premiere #8 flip book; Alex Ross poster 4.00
...:Red Xmas (12/94, $2.50, 44 pgs.) 4.00

SLUGGER (Little Wise Guys Starring...)(Also see Daredevil Comics)
Lev Gleason Publications: April, 1956

	GD	VG	FN	VF	VF/NM	NM-
1-Biro-c	8	16	24	44	57	70

SMALLVILLE (Based on TV series)
DC Comics: May, 2003 - No. 11, Jan, 2005 ($3.50/$3.95, bi-monthly)

1-6-Photo-c. 1-Plunkett-a; interviews with cast; season 1 episode guide begins 4.00
7-11-($3.95) 7-Chloe Chronicles begin; season 2 episode guide begins 4.00
Vol. 1 TPB (2004, $9.95) r/#1-4 & Smallville: The Comic; photo-c 10.00

SMALLVILLE: ALIEN (Based on TV series)
DC Comics: Feb, 2014 - No. 4, May, 2014 ($3.99, printings of previously released digital comics)

1-4: 1-The Monitor lands on Earth; Staggs-a. 2-4-Batman app. 4.00

SMALLVILLE: CHAOS (Based on TV series)(Season 11)
DC Comics: Oct, 2014 - No. 4, Jan, 2015 ($3.99, printings of previously released digital comics)

1-4: 1-Eclipso app.; Padilla-a. 3-Darkseid app. 3,4-Supergirl & Superboy app. 4.00

SMALLVILLE: LANTERN (Based on TV series)
DC Comics: Jun, 2014 - No. 4, Sept, 2014 ($3.99, printings of previously released digital comics)

1-4: 1-Kal-El joins the Green Lantern Corps; Takara-a. 2-4-Parallax app. 4.00

SMALLVILLE SEASON 11 (Based on TV series)
DC Comics: Jul, 2012 - No. 19, Jan, 2014 ($3.99, printings of previously released digital comics)

1-19: 1-Two covers by Gary Frank & Cat Staggs; Pere Perez-a. 5-8-Batman app. 13-15-Legion app. 15-Doomsday app. 16-19-Diana of Themyscira app. 4.00
... Special 1 (7/13, $4.99) Batman, Nightwing and Martian Manhunter app. 5.00
... Special 2 (9/13, $4.99) Lana Lang and John Corben app. 5.00
... Special 3 (12/13, $4.99) Spotlight on Luthor and Tess; Lobel-a 5.00
... Special 4 (3/14, $4.99) Superboy, Jay Garrick, Blue Beetle, Wonder Twins app. 5.00
... Special 5 (9/14, $4.99) Zatanna and John Constantine app. 5.00

SMALLVILLE SEASON 11: CONTINUITY (Based on TV series)
DC Comics: Feb, 2015 - No. 4, May, 2015 ($3.99, printings of previously released digital comics)

1-4-The Crisis vs. the Monitors; Legion of Super-Heroes app.; Guara-a 4.00

SMALLVILLE: THE COMIC (Based on TV series)
DC Comics: Nov, 2002 ($3.95, 64 pages, one-shot)

1-Photo-c; art by Martinez and Leon; interviews with cast; season 2 preview 5.00

SMASH COMICS (Becomes Lady Luck #86 on)
Quality Comics Group: Aug, 1939 - No. 85, Oct, 1949

	GD	VG	FN	VF	VF/NM	NM-
1-Origin Hugh Hazard & His Iron Man, Bozo the Robot, Espionage, Starring Black X by Eisner, & Hooded Justice (Invisible Justice #2 on); Chic Carter & Wings Wendall begin; 1st Robot on the cover of a comic book (Bozo)	337	674	1011	2359	4130	5900
2-The Lone Star Rider app; Invisible Hood gains power of invisibility; bondage/torture-c	148	296	444	947	1624	2300
3-Captain Cook & Eisner's John Law begin	89	178	267	565	970	1375
4,5: 4-Flash Fulton begins	84	168	252	538	919	1300
6-12: 12-One pg. Fine-a	81	162	243	518	884	1250
13-Magno begins (8/40); last Eisner issue; The Ray app. in full page ad; The Purple Trio begins	81	162	243	518	884	1250
14-Intro. The Ray (9/40) by Lou Fine & others	303	606	909	2121	3711	5300
15-1st Ray-c, 2nd app.	158	316	474	1003	1727	2450
16-The Scarlet Seal begins	129	258	387	826	1413	2000
17-Wun Cloo becomes plastic super-hero by Jack Cole (9-months before Plastic Man); Ray-c	139	278	417	883	1517	2150
18-Midnight by Jack Cole begins (origin & 1st app., 1/41)	174	348	522	1114	1907	2700
19-22: Last Ray by Fine; The Jester begins-#22. 19,21-Ray-c	92	184	276	584	1005	1425
23,24: 23-Ray-c. 24-The Sword app.; last Chic Carter; Wings Wendall dons new costume #24,25	77	154	231	493	847	1200
25-Origin/1st app. Wildfire; Rookie Rankin begins; Ray-c	79	158	237	502	864	1225
26-30: 28-Midnight-c begin, end #85	65	130	195	416	708	1000
31,32,34: The Ray by Rudy Palais; also #33	60	120	180	381	653	925
33-Origin The Marksman	63	126	189	403	689	975
35-37	50	100	150	315	533	750
38-The Yankee Eagle begins; last Midnight by Jack Cole; classic-c by Cole	102	204	306	653	1114	1575
39,40-Last Ray issue	50	100	150	315	533	750
41,44-50	41	82	123	256	428	600
42-Lady Luck begins by Klaus Nordling	135	270	405	864	1482	2100
43-Lady Luck-c (1st & only in Smash)	90	180	270	576	988	1400
51-60	32	64	96	188	307	425
61-70	24	48	72	142	234	325
71-85: 79-Midnight battles the Men from Mars-c/s	21	42	63	122	199	275

NOTE: ***Al Bryant** c-54, 63-68. **Cole** a-17-38, 68, 69, 72, 73, 78, 80, 83, 85; c-38, 60-62, 69-84. **Crandall** a-(Ray)-23-29, 35-38; c-36, 39, 40, 42-44, 46. **Fine** a(Ray)-14, 15, 16(w/**Tuska**), 17-22. **Fox** c-24-35. **Fuje** Ray-30. **Gil Fox** a-6-7, 9, 11-13. **Guardineer** a-(The Marksman)-39-?, 49, 52. **Gustavson** a-4-7, 9, 11-13 (The Jester)-22-46; (Magno)-13-21; (Midnight)-39(Cole inks), 49, 52, 63-65. **Kotzky** a-(Espionage)-33-38; c-45, 47-53. **Nordling** a-49, 52, 63-65. **Powell** a-11, 12, (Abdul the Arab)-13-24.Black X c-2, 6, 9, 11, 13, 16. Bozo the Robot c-1, 3, 5, 8, 10, 12, 14, 18, 20, 22, 24, 26. Midnight c-28-85. The Ray c-15, 17, 19, 21, 23, 25, 27. Wings Wendall c-4, 7.*

SMASH COMICS (Also see All Star Comics 1999 crossover titles)
DC Comics: May, 1999 ($1.99, one-shot)

1-Golden Age Doctor Mid-nite and Hourman 3.00

SMASH HIT SPORTS COMICS
Essankay Publications: V2#1, Jan, 1949

	GD	VG	FN	VF	VF/NM	NM-
V2#1-L.B. Cole-c/a	29	58	87	170	278	385

SMAX (Also see Top Ten)
America's Best Comics: Oct, 2003 - No. 5, May, 2004 ($2.95, limited series)

1-5-Alan Moore-s/Zander Cannon-a 3.00
... Collected Edition (2004, $19.95, HC with dustjacket) r/#1-5 20.00
... Collected Edition SC (2005, $12.99) r/#1-5 13.00

SMILE COMICS (Also see Gay Comics, Tickle, & Whee)
Modern Store Publ.: 1955 (52 pgs.; 5x7-1/4") (7¢)

	GD	VG	FN	VF	VF/NM	NM-
1	8	16	24	44	57	70

SMILEY BURNETTE WESTERN (Also see Patches #8 & Six-Gun Heroes)
Fawcett Publ.: March, 1950 - No. 4, Oct, 1950 (All photo front & back-c)

	GD	VG	FN	VF	VF/NM	NM-
1-Red Eagle begins	25	50	75	150	245	340
2-4	16	32	48	94	147	200

SMILEY (THE PSYCHOTIC BUTTON) (See Evil Ernie)
Chaos! Comics: July, 1998 - May, 1999 ($2.95, one-shots)

1-Ivan Reis-a 3.00
... Holiday Special (1/99), ...'s Spring Break (4/99), ...Wrestling Special (5/99) 3.00

SMILIN' JACK (See Famous Feature Stories and Popular Comics) (Also see Super Book of Comics #1&2 and Super-Book of Comics #7&19 in the Promotional Comics section)
Dell Publishing Co.: No. 5, 1940 - No. 8, Oct-Dec, 1949

	GD	VG	FN	VF	VF/NM	NM-
Four Color 5	87	174	261	553	952	1350
Four Color 10 (1940)	71	142	213	454	777	1100
Large Feature Comic 12,14,25 (1941)	66	132	198	419	722	1025
Four Color 4 (1942)	38	76	114	285	641	1000
Four Color 14 (1943)	30	60	90	216	483	750
Four Color 36,58 (1943-44)	21	42	63	147	324	500
Four Color 80 (1945)	13	26	39	89	195	300
Four Color 149 (1947)	9	18	27	62	126	190
1 (1-3/48)	11	22	33	72	154	235

Smokey Bear #6 © GK

Smosh #6 © DYN

Snotgirl #1 © O'Malley & Hung

GD 2.0 | VG 4.0 | FN 6.0 | VF 8.0 | VF/NM 9.0 | NM- 9.2

2 6 12 18 38 69 100
3-8 (10-12/49) 5 10 15 33 57 80

SMILING SPOOK SPUNKY (See Spunky)

SMITTY (See Popular Comics, Super Book #2, 4 & Super Comics)
Dell Publishing Co.: No. 11, 1940 - No. 7, Aug-Oct, 1949; No. 909, Apr, 1958

Four Color 11 (1940) 54 108 162 343 574 825
Large Feature Comic 26 (1941) 41 82 123 256 428 600
Four Color 6 (1942) 23 46 69 161 356 550
Four Color 32 (1943) 15 30 45 103 227 350
Four Color 65 (1945) 12 24 36 84 185 285
Four Color 99 (1946) 10 20 30 66 138 210
Four Color 138 (1947) 9 18 27 59 117 175
1 (2-4/48) 9 18 27 57 111 165
2-(5-7/48) 5 10 15 31 53 75
3,4: 3-(8-10/48), 4-(11-1/48-49) 4 8 12 27 44 60
5-7, Four Color 909 (4/58) 4 8 12 23 37 50

SMOKEY BEAR (TV) (See March Of Comics #234, 362, 372, 383, 407)
Gold Key: Feb, 1970 - No. 13, Mar, 1973

1 3 6 9 18 28 38
2-5 2 4 6 10 14 18
6-13 2 4 6 8 10 12

SMOKEY STOVER (See Popular Comics, Super Book #5,17,29 & Super Comics)
Dell Publishing Co.: No. 7, 1942 - No. 827, Aug, 1957

Four Color 7 (1942)-Reprints 25 50 75 175 388 600
Four Color 35 (1943) 15 30 45 103 227 350
Four Color 64 (1944) 12 24 36 82 179 275
Four Color 229 (1949) 6 12 18 42 79 115
Four Color 730,827 5 10 15 34 60 85

SMOKEY THE BEAR (See Forest Fire for 1st app.)
Dell Publ. Co.: No. 653, 10/55 - No. 1214, 8/61 (See March of Comics #234)

Four Color 653 (#1) 10 20 30 66 138 210
Four Color 708,754,818,932 6 12 18 40 73 105
Four Color 1016,1119,1214 5 10 15 31 53 75

SMOKY (See Movie Classics)

SMOSH
Dynamite Entertainment: 2016 - No. 6, 2016 ($3.99)

1-6: 1-3-McDermott-s/Viglino-a; back-up with Yale Stewart-s/a. 4-Boxman origin 4.00

SMURFS (TV)
Marvel Comics: 1982 (Dec) - No. 3, 1983

1-3 2 4 6 13 18 22
...Treasury Edition 1 (64 pgs.)-r/#1-3 3 6 9 17 26 35

SNAFU (Magazine)
Atlas Comics (RCM): Nov, 1955 - V2#2, Mar, 1956 (B&W)

V1#1-Heath/Severin-a; Everett, Maneely-a 16 32 48 94 147 200
V2#1,2-Severin-a 14 28 42 76 108 140

SNAGGLEPUSS (TV)(See Hanna-Barbera Band Wagon, Quick Draw McGraw #5 & Spotlight #4)
Gold Key: Oct, 1962 - No. 4, Sept, 1963 (Hanna-Barbera)

1 8 16 24 51 96 140
2-4 6 12 18 37 66 95

SNAGGLEPUSS CHRONICLES (See Exit Stage Left: The Snagglepuss Chronicles)

SNAKE EYES (G.I. Joe)
Devil's Due Publ.: Aug, 2005 - No. 6, Jan, 2006 ($2.95)

1-6-Santalucia-a 3.00
...: Declassified TPB (4/06, $18.95) r/series; source guide 19.00

SNAKE EYES (... and Storm Shadow #13-on)(Cont. from G.I. Joe: Snake Eyes, Volume 2 #7)
IDW Publishing: No. 8, Dec, 2011 - Present ($3.99)

8-21: 13-Title change to Snake Eyes and Storm Shadow 4.00

SNAKE PLISSKEN CHRONICLES, (John Carpenter's...)
Hurricane Entertainment: June, 2003 - No. 4 ($2.99)

Preview Issue (8/02, no cover price) B&W preview; John Carpenter interview 3.00
1-4: 1-Three covers; Rodriguez-a 3.00

SNAKES AND LADDERS
Eddie Campbell Comics: 2001 ($5.95, B&W, one-shot)

nn-Alan Moore-s/Eddie Campbell-a 6.00

GD 2.0 | VG 4.0 | FN 6.0 | VF 8.0 | VF/NM 9.0 | NM- 9.2

SNAKES ON A PLANE (Adaptation of the 2006 movie)
Virgin Comics: Oct, 2006 - No. 2, Nov, 2006 ($2.99, limited series)

1,2: 1-Dixon-s/Purcell-a. JG Jones and photo-c. 2-Klebs, Jr.-a; Moore & photo-c 3.00

SNAKE WOMAN (Shekhar Kapur's...)
Virgin Comics: July, 2006 - No. 10, Apr, 2007 ($2.99)

1-10: 1-6-Michael Gaydos-a/Zeb Wells-s. 1-Two covers by Gaydos & Singh 3.00
#0 (5/07, 99¢) origin of the Snake Goddess; background info; Gaydos-a/c 3.00
... Curse of the 68 (3/08 - No. 4, 5/08, $2.99) 1-4: 1-Ingale-a. 2-Manu-a 3.00
... Tale of the Snake Charmer 1-6 (6/07-12/07, $2.99) Vivek Shinde-a 3.00
... Vol. 1 TPB (6/07, $14.99) r/#1-5; Gaydos sketch pages; creator commentary 15.00
... Vol. 2 TPB (9/07, $14.99) r/#6-10; Cebulski intro. 15.00

SNAP (Formerly Scoop #8; becomes Jest #10,11 & Komik Pages #10)
Harry 'A' Chesler: No. 9, 1944

9-Manhunter, The Voice; WWII gag-c 32 64 96 188 307 425

SNAPPY COMICS
Cima Publ. Co. (Prize Publ.): 1945

1-Airmale app.; 9 pg. Sorcerer's Apprentice adapt; Kiefer-a
37 74 111 222 361 500

SNAPSHOT
Image Comics: Feb, 2013 - No. 4, May, 2013 ($2.99, B&W, limited series)

1-4-Andy Diggle-s/Jock-a/c 3.00

SNARKED
Boom Entertainment (Kaboom!): No. 0, Aug, 2011 - No. 12, Sept, 2012 ($1.00/$3.99)

0-($1.00) Roger Langridge-s/a; sketch gallery, bonus content and games 3.00
1-12: 1-($3.99) Covers by Langridge & Samnee 4.00

SNARKY PARKER (See Life With...)

SNIFFY THE PUP
Standard Publ. (Animated Cartoons): No. 5, Nov, 1949 - No. 18, Sept, 1953

5-Two Frazetta text illos 14 28 42 80 115 150
6-10 9 18 27 47 61 75
11-18 8 16 24 40 50 60

SNOOPER AND BLABBER DETECTIVES (TV) (See Whitman Comic Books)
Gold Key: Nov, 1962 - No. 3, May, 1963 (Hanna-Barbera)

1 6 12 18 42 79 115
2,3 5 10 15 33 57 80

SNOTGIRL
Image Comics: Jul, 2016 - Present ($2.99)

1-9-Bryan O'Malley-s/Leslie Hung-a; two covers by O'Malley & Hung on each 3.00

SNOW BLIND
BOOM! Studios: Dec, 2015 - No. 4, Mar, 2016 ($3.99)

1-4-Ollie Masters-s/Tyler Jenkins-a 4.00

SNOWFALL
Image Comics: Feb, 2016 - No. 9, Jun, 2017 ($3.99)

1-9-Joe Harris-s/Martín Morazzo-a 4.00

SNOW WHITE (See Christmas With... (in Promotional Comics section), Mickey Mouse Magazine, Movie Comics & Seven Dwarfs)
Dell Publishing Co.: No. 49, July, 1944 - No. 382, Mar, 1952 (Disney-Movie)

Four Color 49 (...& the Seven Dwarfs) 46 92 138 368 834 1300
Four Color 382 (1952)-origin; partial reprint of Four Color 49
10 20 30 69 147 225

SNOW WHITE
Marvel Comics: Jan, 1995 ($1.95, one-shot)

1-r/1937 Sunday newspaper pages 3.00

SNOW WHITE AND THE SEVEN DWARFS
Whitman Publications: April, 1982 (60¢)

nn-r/Four Color 49 1 3 4 6 8 10

SNOW WHITE AND THE SEVEN DWARFS GOLDEN ANNIVERSARY
Gladstone: Fall, 1987 ($2.95, magazine size, 52 pgs.)

1-Contains poster 2 4 6 9 13 16

SOAP OPERA LOVE
Charlton Comics: Feb, 1983 - No. 3, June, 1983

1-3-Low print run 3 6 9 19 30 40

SOAP OPERA ROMANCES
Charlton Comics: July, 1982 - No. 5, March, 1983

Sojourn #11 © CRO

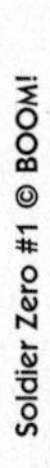
Soldier Zero #1 © BOOM!

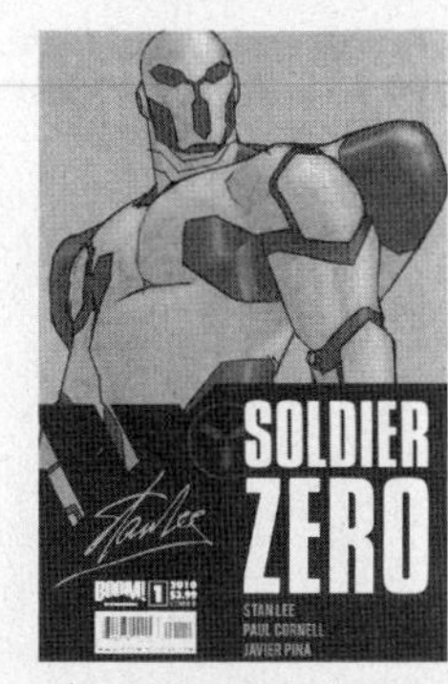

Solo (2016 series) #1 © MAR

GD VG FN VF VF/NM NM-
2.0 4.0 6.0 8.0 9.0 9.2

1-5-Nurse Betsy Crane-r; low print run 3 6 9 19 30 40

SOCK MONKEY
Dark Horse Comics: Sept, 1998 - No. 2, Oct, 1998 ($2.95/$2.99, B&W)
1,2-Tony Millionaire-s/a 4.00
Vol. 2 -(Tony Millionaire's Sock Monkey) July, 1999 - No. 2, Aug, 1999
1,2 3.00
Vol. 3 -(Tony Millionaire's Sock Monkey) Nov, 2000 - No. 2, Dec, 2000
1,2 3.00
Vol. 4 -(Tony Millionaire's Sock Monkey) May, 2003 - No. 2, Aug, 2003
1,2 3.00
...The Inches Incident (Sept, 2006 - No. 4, Apr, 2007) 1-4-Tony Millionaire-s/a 3.00

SOJOURN
White Cliffs Publ. Co.: Sept, 1977 - No. 2, 1978 ($1.50, B&W & color, tabloid size)
1,2: 1-Tor by Kubert, Eagle by Severin, E. V. Race, Private Investigator by Doug Wildey, T. C. Mars by Aragonés begin plus other strips 2 4 6 8 10 12
NOTE: Most copies came folded. Unfolded copies are worth 50% more.

SOJOURN
CrossGeneration Comics: July, 2001 - No. 34, May, 2004 ($2.95)
Prequel -Ron Marz-s/Greg Land-c/a; preview pages 3.00
1-Ron Marz-s/Greg Land-c/a in most 6.00
2,3 5.00
4-24: 7-Immonen-a. 12-Brigman-a. 17-Lopresti-a. 21-Luke Ross-a 3.00
25-34: 25-$1.00-c. 34-Cariello-a 3.00
...: From the Ashes TPB (2001, $19.95) r/#1-6; Land painted-c 20.00
...: The Dragon's Tale TPB (2002, $15.95) r/#7-12; Jusko painted-c 16.00
...: The Warrior's Tale TPB (2003, $15.95) r/#13-18 16.00
Vol. 4: The Thief's Tale (2003, $15.95) r/#19-24 16.00
Vol. 5: The Sorcerer's Tale (Checker Book Publ.,2007, $17.95) r/#25-30 18.00
Vol. 6: The Berzerker's Tale (Checker Book Publ.,2007, $17.95) r/#31-34, Prequel 18.00
Traveler Vol.1,2 ($9.95) digest-sized reprints of TPBs 10.00

SOLAR (...Man of the Atom) (Also see Doctor Solar)
Valiant/Acclaim Comics (Valiant): Sept, 1991 - No. 60, Apr, 1996 ($1.75-$2.50, 44 pgs.)
1-Layton-a(i) on Solar; Barry Windsor-Smith-c/a 2 4 6 10 14 18
2,4-9: 2-Layton-a(i) on Solar, B. Smith-a. 7-vs. X-O Armor 1 2 3 5 6 8
3-1st app. Harada (11/91); intro. Harbinger 3 6 9 19 30 40
10-(6/92, $3.95)-1st app. Eternal Warrior (6 pgs.); black embossed-c; origin & 1st app. Geoff McHenry (Geomancer) 3 6 9 21 33 45
10-($3.95)-2nd printing 6.00
11-15: 11-1st full app. Eternal Warrior. 12,13-Unity x-overs. 14-1st app. Fred Bender (becomes Dr. Eclipse). 15-2nd Dr. Eclipse 5.00
16-60: 17-X-O Manowar app. 23-Solar splits. 29-1st Valiant Vision book. 33-Valiant Vision; bound-in trading card. 38-Chaos Effect Epsilon Pt.1. 46-52-Dan Jurgens-a(p)/scripts w/Giordano-i. 53,54-Jurgens scripts only. 60-Giffen scripts; Jeff Johnson-a(p) 4.00
0-($9.95, trade paperback)-r/Alpha and Omega origin story; polybagged w/poster 12.00
...: Second Death (1994, $9.95)-r/issues #1-4. 10.00
NOTE: *#1-10 all have free 8 pg. insert "Alpha and Omega" which is a 10 chapter Solar origin story. All 10 centerfolds can pieced together to show climax of story.* ***Ditko*** *a-11p, 14p.* ***Giordano*** *a-46, 47, 48, 49, 50, 51, 52i.* ***Johnson*** *a-60p.* ***Jurgens*** *a-46, 47, 48, 49, 50 , 51, 52p.* ***Layton*** *a-1-3i; c-2i, 11i, 17i, 25i.* ***Miller*** *c-12.* ***Quesada*** *c-17p, 20-23p, 29p.* ***Simonson*** *c-13.* ***B. Smith*** *a-1-10; c-1, 3, 5, 7, 19i.* ***Thibert*** *c-22i, 23i.*

SOLARMAN (See Pendulum Ill. Originals)
Marvel Comics: Jan, 1989 - No. 2, May, 1990 ($1.00, limited series)
1,2 3.00

SOLAR, MAN OF THE ATOM (Man of the Atom on cover)
Acclaim Comics (Valiant Heroes): Vol. 2, May, 1997 ($3.95, one-shot, 46 pgs) (1st Valiant Heroes Special Event)
Vol. 2-Reintro Solar; Ninjak cameo; Warren Ellis scripts; Darick Robertson-a 4.00

SOLAR: MAN OF THE ATOM
Dynamite Entertainment: 2014 - No. 12, 2015 ($3.99)
1-12: 1-Barbiere-s/Bennett-a; 5 covers. 3-Female Solar in costume. 5-White costume 4.00

SOLAR, MAN OF THE ATOM: HELL ON EARTH
Acclaim Comics (Valiant Heroes): Jan, 1998 - No. 4 ($2.50, limited series)
1-4-Priest-s/ Zircher-a(p) 3.00

SOLAR, MAN OF THE ATOM: REVELATIONS
Acclaim Comics (Valiant Heroes): Nov, 1997 ($3.95, one-shot, 46 pgs.)
1-Krueger-s/ Zircher-a(p) 4.00

SOLDIER & MARINE COMICS (Fightin' Army #16 on)
Charlton Comics (Toby Press of Conn. V1#11): No. 11, Dec, 1954 - No. 15, Aug, 1955; V2#9, Dec, 1956

GD VG FN VF VF/NM NM-
2.0 4.0 6.0 8.0 9.0 9.2

V1#11 (12/54)-Bob Powell-a 11 22 33 62 86 110
V1#12(2/55)-15: 12-Photo-c. 14-Photo-c; Colan-a 8 16 24 44 57 70
V2#9(Formerly Never Again; Jerry Drummer V2#10 on) 8 16 24 40 50 60

SOLDIER COMICS
Fawcett Publications: Jan, 1952 - No. 11, Sept, 1953
1 14 28 42 82 121 160
2 9 18 27 50 65 80
3-5: 4-What Happened in Taewah 9 18 27 47 61 75
6-11: 8-Illo. in **POP** 8 16 24 42 54 65

SOLDIERS OF FORTUNE
American Comics Group (Creston Publ. Corp.): Mar-Apr, 1951 - No. 13, Feb-Mar, 1953
1-Capt. Crossbones by Shelly, Ace Carter, Lance Larson begin 26 52 78 154 252 350
2-(52 pgs.) 15 30 45 84 127 170
3-10: 6-Bondage-c 13 26 39 74 105 135
11-13 (War format) 9 18 27 52 69 85
NOTE: ***Shelly*** *a-1-3, 5.* ***Whitney*** *a-6, 8-11, 13; c-1-3, 5, 6.*

SOLDIERS OF FREEDOM
Americomics: 1987 - No. 2, 1987 ($1.75)
1,2 3.00

SOLDIER X (Continued from Cable)
Marvel Comics: Sept, 2002 - No. 12, Aug, 2003 ($2.99/$2.25)
1,10,11,12-($2.99) 1-Kordey-a/Macan-s. 10-Bollers-s/Ranson-a 3.00
2-9-($2.25) 3.00

SOLDIER ZERO (From Stan Lee)
BOOM! Studios: Oct, 2010 - No. 12, Sept, 2011 ($3.99)
1-12: 1-4-Cornell-s/Pina-a 4.00

SOLITAIRE (Also See Prime V2#6-8)
Malibu Comics (Ultraverse): Nov, 1993 - No. 12, Dec, 1994 ($1.95)
1-($2.50)-Collector's edition bagged w/playing card 4.00
1-12: 1-Regular edition w/o playing card. 2,4-Break-Thru x-over. 3-2 pg. origin The Night Man. 4-Gatefold-c. 5-Two pg. origin the Strangers 3.00

SOLO
Marvel Comics: Sept, 1994 - No. 4, Dec, 1994 ($1.75, limited series)
1-4: Spider-Man app. 3.00

SOLO (Movie)
Dark Horse Comics: July, 1996 - No. 2, Aug, 1996 ($2.50, limited series)
1,2: Adaptation of film; photo-c 3.00

SOLO (Anthology showcasing individual artists)
DC Comics: Dec, 2004 - No. 12, Oct, 2006 ($4.95/$4.99)
1-11: 1-Tim Sale-a; stories by Sale and various. 2-Richard Corben-a; stories by Corben and Arcudi. 3-Paul Pope. 4-Howard Chaykin. 5-Darwyn Cooke. 6-Jordi Bernet. 7-Michael Allred; Teen Titans & Doom Patrol app. 8-Teddy Kristiansen. 9-Scott Hampton. 10-Damion Scott. 11-Sergio Aragonés. 12-Brendan McCarthy 5.00

SOLO
Marvel Comics: Dec, 2016 - Present ($3.99)
1-5: 1-Thorne & Duggan-s/Diaz-a; Dum Dum Dugan app. 4.00

SOLO AVENGERS (Becomes Avenger Spotlight #21 on)
Marvel Comics: Dec, 1987 - No. 20, July, 1989 (75¢/$1.00)
1-Jim Lee-a on back-up story 1 2 3 5 6 8
2-20: 11-Intro Bobcat 4.00

SOLOMON AND SHEBA (Movie)
Dell Publishing Co.: No. 1070, Jan-Mar, 1960
Four Color 1070-Sekowsky-a; photo-c 9 18 27 57 111 165

SOLOMON GRUNDY
DC Comics: May, 2009 - No. 7, Nov, 2009 ($2.99)
1-7-Scott Kolins-s/a. 2-Bizarro app. 7-Blackest Night prelude 3.00
TPB (2010, $19.99) r/#1-7 20.00

SOLOMON KANE (Based on the Robert E. Howard character. Also see Blackthorne 3-D Series #60 & Marvel Premiere)
Marvel Comics: Sept, 1985 - No. 6, July, 1986 (Limited series)
1-Double size 5.00
2-6: 3-6-Williamson-a(i) 4.00

SOLOMON KANE

The Solution #10 © MAL

Sonic the Hedgehog #250 © Sega

Son of M #1 © MAR

GD VG FN VF VF/NM NM-
2.0 4.0 6.0 8.0 9.0 9.2

GD VG FN VF VF/NM NM
2.0 4.0 6.0 8.0 9.0 9.2

Dark Horse Comics: Sept, 2008 - No. 5, Feb, 2009 ($2.99)

1-5: 1-Two covers by Cassaday and Joe Kubert; Guevara-a 3.00
...: Death's Black Riders 1-4 (1/10 - No. 4, 6/10, $3.50) Robertson-c 3.50
...: Red Shadows 1-4 (4/11 - No. 4, 7/11, $3.50) Bruce Jones-s/Rahsan Ekedal-a; two covers by Davis & Manchess on each 3.50

SOLUS
CG Entertainment, Inc.: Apr, 2003 - No. 8, Jan, 2004 ($2.95)

1-8: 1-4,6,7-George Pérez-a/c; Barbara Kesel-s. 5-Ryan-a. 8-Kirk-a 3.00
Vol. 1: Genesis (1/04, $15.95) r/#1-6 16.00

SOLUTION, THE
Malibu Comics (Ultraverse): Sept, 1993 - No. 17, Feb, 1995 ($1.95)

1,3-15: 1-Intro Meathook, Deathdance, Black Tiger, Tech. 4-Break-Thru x-over; gatefold-c. 5-2 pg. origin The Strangers. 11-Brereton-c 3.00
1-($2.50)-Newsstand ed. polybagged w/trading card 4.00
1-Ultra 5000 Limited silver foil 8.00
0-Obtained w/Rune #0 by sending coupons from 11 comics 5.00
2-($2.50, 48 pgs.)-Rune flip-c/story by B. Smith; The Mighty Magnor 1 pg. strip by Aragonés 4.00
16 ($3.50)-Flip-c Ultraverse Premiere #10 4.00
17 ($2.50) 3.00

SOMERSET HOLMES (See Eclipse Graphic Novel Series)
Pacific Comics/ Eclipse Comics No. 5, 6: Sept, 1983 - No. 6, Dec, 1984 ($1.50, Baxter paper)

1-6: 1-Brent Anderson-c/a. Cliff Hanger by Williamson in all 4.00

SONG OF THE SOUTH (See Brer Rabbit)

SONIC & KNUCKLES
Archie Comics: Aug, 1995 ($2.00)

1 2 4 6 8 10 12

SONIC BOOM
Archie Comic Publications: Dec, 2014 - No. 11, Oct, 2015 ($3.99)

1-11: 1-Regular-c and 4 interlocking variant covers. 2-7,11-Two covers on each. 8-10-"Worlds Unite" Sonic/Mega Man x-over; 3 covers 4.00

SONIC COMIC ORIGINS AND MEGA MAN X
Archie Comic Publications: Jun/Jul 2014 (giveaway)

... Free Comic Book Day Edition - Flipbook; Freedom Fighters app. 3.00

SONIC DISRUPTORS
DC Comics: Dec, 1987 - No. 7, July, 1988 ($1.75, unfinished limited series)

1-7 3.00

SONIC MEGA DRIVE
Archie Comic Publications: Aug, 2016 ($3.99, limited series)

1-25th Anniversary celebration; Flynn-s/Hesse-a 4.00
... - The Next Level (12/16, $4.99) Flynn-s/Hesse-a; Metal Sonic app. 5.00

SONIC'S FRIENDLY NEMESIS KNUCKLES
Archie Publications: July, 1996 - No. 3, Sept, 1996 ($1.50, limited series)

1-3 6.00

SONIC SUPER DIGEST
Archie Publications: Dec, 2012 - Present ($3.99/$4.99)

1-7-($3.99) 4.00
8-17-($4.99) 5.00

SONIC SUPER SPECIAL
Archie Publications: 1997 - No. 15, Feb, 2001 ($2.00/$2.25/$2.29, 48 pgs)

1-3 5.00
4-6,8-15: 10-Sabrina-c/app. 15-Sin City spoof 4.00
7-(w/Image) Spawn, Maxx, Savage Dragon-c/app.; Valentino-a 4.00

SONIC THE HEDGEHOG (TV, video game)
Archie Comics: No. 0, Feb, 1993 - No. 3, May, 1993 ($1.25, mini-series)

0(2/93),1: Shaw-a(p) & covers on all 4 8 12 25 40 55
2,3 3 6 9 16 23 30
Beginnings TPB (2003, $10.95) r/#0-3 11.00
...: The Beginning TPB (2006, $10.95) r/#0-3 11.00

SONIC THE HEDGEHOG (TV, video game)
Archie Comics: July, 1993 - Present ($1.25-$2.99)

1 5 10 15 31 53 75
2 3 6 9 19 30 40
3 3 6 9 16 23 30
4-10: 8-Neon ink-c. 2 4 6 11 16 20
11-20 2 4 6 9 13 16
21-30 ($1.50): 25-Silver ink-c 2 4 6 8 10 12
31-50 1 2 3 5 6 8
51-93 4.00
94-212: 117-Begin $2.19-c. 152-Begin $2.25-c. 157-Shadow app. 198-Begin $2.50 3.00
213-249,251-263: 213-Begin $2.99-c. 248-263-Two covers 3.00
250-($3.99) Wraparound-c; part 9 of Worlds Collide x-over with Mega Man 4.00
264-274,276-290-($3.99) Two covers on most. 273,274-"Worlds Unite" Sonic/Mega Man x-over; 3 covers on each. 288-291-Genesis of a Hero 4.00
275-($4.99) "Worlds Unite" Sonic/Mega Man x-over; six covers 5.00
Free Comic Book Day Edition 1 (2007)- Leads into Sonic the Hedgehog #175 3.00
Free Comic Book Day Edition 2009 - Reprints Sonic the Hedgehog #1 from July 1993 3.00
Free Comic Book Day Edition 2010 - 2012: 2010-New story 3.00
Sonic and Mega Man: World's Collide Prelude, FCBD Edition (6-7/13) 3.00
Sonic and Mega Man: Worlds Unite FCBD Edition (6-7/15) Prelude to crossover 3.00
Sonic Sampler: Free Comic Book Day Edition (5/16) Sonic & Sonic Universe stories 3.00
Sonic: Worlds Unite Battles (9/15, $3.99) Sonic/Mega Man x-over; 3 wraparound covers 4.00
Triple Trouble Special (10/95, $2.00, 48 pgs.) 1 3 4 6 8 10

SONIC UNIVERSE (Sonic the Hedgehog)
Archie Publications: Apr, 2009 - Present ($2.50/$2.99/$3.99)

1-15 3.00
16-66: 16-Begin $2.99-c. 51-66-Two covers. 51-54-Worlds Collide 3.00
67-94-($3.99) Two covers on most. 75-"Worlds Unite" Sonic/Mega Man x-over prelude with nine covers. 76-78-"Worlds Unite" x-over; 3 covers on each. 87-90-Shattered 4.00

SONIC VS. KNUCKLES "BATTLE ROYAL" SPECIAL
Archie Publications: 1997 ($2.00, one-shot)

1 1 2 3 5 6 8

SONIC X (Sonic the Hedgehog)
Archie Publications: Nov, 2005 - No. 40, Feb, 2009 ($2.25)

1-Sam Speed app. 4.00
2-40 3.00

SON OF AMBUSH BUG (See Ambush Bug)
DC Comics: July, 1986 - No. 6, Dec, 1986 (75¢)

1-6: Giffen-c/a in all. 5-Bissette-a. 4.00

SON OF BLACK BEAUTY (Also see Black Beauty)
Dell Publishing Co.: No. 510, Oct, 1953 - No. 566, June, 1954

Four Color 510,566 5 10 15 31 53 75

SON OF FLUBBER (See Movie Comics)

SON OF HULK (Continues from Skaar: Son of Hulk #12) (See Realm of Kings)
Marvel Comics: No. 13, Sept, 2009 - No. 17, Jan, 2010 ($2.99)

13-17: 13,15-17-Galactus app. 3.00

SON OF M (Also see House of M series)
Marvel Comics: Feb, 2006 - No. 6, July, 2006 ($2.99, limited series)

1-6: 1-Powerless Quicksilver; Martinez-a. 2-Quicksilver regains powers; Inhumans app. 3.00
Decimation: Son of M (2006, $13.99, TPB) r/series; Martinez sketch pages 14.00

SON OF MERLIN
Image Comics (Top Cow): Feb, 2013 - No. 5, Jun, 2013 ($1.00/$2.99, limited series)

1-5: 1-($1.00-c); Napton-s/Zid-a; covers by Zid & Sejic. 2-($2.99) 3.00

SON OF MUTANT WORLD
Fantagor Press: 1990 - No. 5, 1990? ($2.00, bi-monthly)

1-5: 1-3: Corben-c/a. 4,5 ($1.75, B&W) 3.00

SON OF ORIGINS OF MARVEL COMICS (See Fireside Book Series)

SON OF SATAN (Also see Ghost Rider #1 & Marvel Spotlight #12)
Marvel Comics Group: Dec, 1975 - No. 8, Feb, 1977 (25¢)

1-Mooney-a; Kane-c(p), Starlin splash(p) 4 8 12 25 40 55
2,6-8: 2-Origin The Possessor. 8-Heath-a 2 4 6 11 16 20
3-5-(Regular 25¢ editions)(4-8/76): 5-Russell-p 2 4 6 11 16 20
3-5-(30¢-c variants, limited distribution) 4 8 12 23 37 50

SON OF SINBAD (Also see Abbott & Costello & Daring Adventures)
St. John Publishing Co.: Feb, 1950

1-Kubert-c/a 53 106 159 334 567 800

SON OF SUPERMAN (Elseworlds)
DC Comics: 1999 ($14.95, prestige format, one-shot)

nn-Chaykin & Tischman-s/Williams III & Gray-a 15.00

SON OF TOMAHAWK (See Tomahawk)

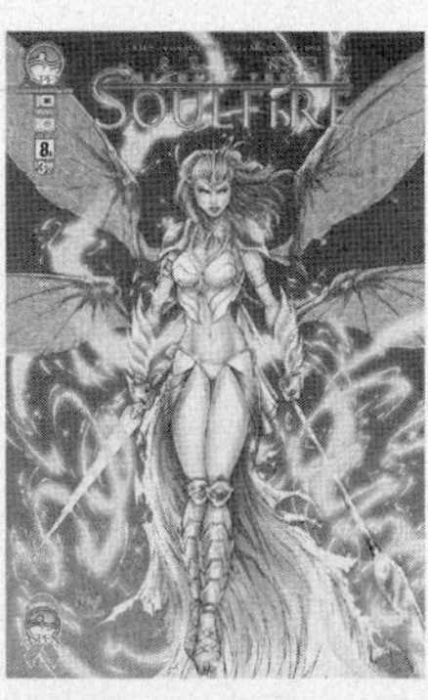

Soulfire V5 #8 © Aspen MLT

Southern Cross #1 © Cloonan & Belanger

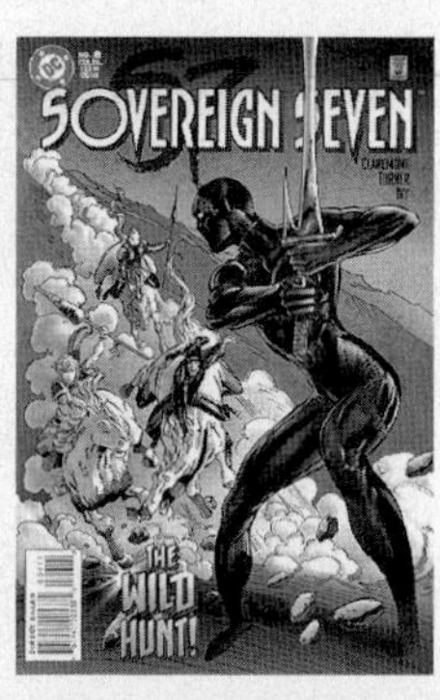

Sovereign Seven #8 © C. Claremont

GD 2.0 | VG 4.0 | FN 6.0 | VF 8.0 | VF/NM 9.0 | NM- 9.2

SON OF VULCAN (Formerly Mysteries of Unexplored Worlds #1-48; Thunderbolt V3#51 on)
Charlton Comics: V2#49, Nov, 1965 - V2#50, Jan, 1966
V2#49,50: 50-Roy Thomas scripts (1st pro work) 3 6 9 17 26 35

SONS OF ANARCHY (Based on the TV series)
BOOM! Studios: Sept, 2013 - No. 25, Sept, 2015 ($3.99, originally a 6-issue limited series)
1-24: 1-6-Christopher Golden-s/Damian Couceiro-a; multiple covers on each 4.00
25-($4.99) Last issue; Ferrier-s/Bergara-a; three covers 5.00

SONS OF ANARCHY REDWOOD ORIGINAL (TV series)
BOOM! Studios: Aug, 2016 - No. 12, Jul, 2017 ($3.99)
1-12: 1-Prequel with 18-year-old Jax Teller. 1-4-Masters-s/Pizzari-a; multiple covers 4.00

SONS OF KATIE ELDER (See Movie Classics)

SONS OF THE DEVIL
Image Comics: May, 2015 - No. 14, Jul, 2017 ($2.99/$3.99)
1-5: 1-Brian Buccellato-s/Toni Infante-a 3.00
6-14-($3.99) 4.00

SORCERY (See Chilling Adventures in... & Red Circle...)

SORORITY SECRETS
Toby Press: July, 1954
1 17 34 51 98 154 210

SOULFIRE (MICHAEL TURNER PRESENTS:...) (Also see Eternal Soulfire)
Aspen MLT, Inc.: No. 0, 2004 - No. 10, Jul, 2009 ($2.50/$2.99)
0-($2.50) Turner-a/c; Loeb-s; intro. to characters & development sketches 3.00
1-($2.99) Two covers 3.00
1-Diamond Previews Exclusive 5.00
2-9: 2,3-Two covers. 4-Four covers 3.00
10-($3.99) Benitez-a 4.00
... Sourcebook 1 (3/15, $4.99) Character profiles; two covers by Turner 5.00
...: The Collected Edition Vol. 1 (5/05, $6.99) r/#1,2; cover gallery 7.00
Hardcover Volume 1 (12/05, $24.99) r/#0-5 & preview from Wizard Mag.; Johns intro. 25.00

SOULFIRE (MICHAEL TURNER PRESENTS:...) (Volume 2)
Aspen MLT, Inc.: No. 0, Oct, 2009 - No. 9, Jan, 2011 ($2.50/$2.99)
0-($2.50) Marcus To-a 3.00
1-9-($2.99) 1-Five covers. 9-Covers by To and Linsner 3.00

SOULFIRE (MICHAEL TURNER'S...) (Volume 3)
Aspen MLT, Inc.: No. 0, Apr, 2011 - No. 8, May, 2012 ($1.99/$2.99)
0-($1.99) Krul-s/Fabok-a; 4 covers 3.00
1-8-($2.99) 1-Four covers 3.00
... Despair (7/12, $3.99) Schwartz-s/Marks-a; 3 covers 4.00
... Faith (7/12, $3.99) McMurray-s/Oum-a; 3 covers 4.00
... Hope (7/12, $3.99) Krul-s/Varese-a; 3 covers 4.00
... Power (7/12, $3.99) Wohl-s/Randolph-a; 3 covers 4.00
... Primer (6/12, $1.00) Reprints and story summaries 3.00

SOULFIRE (MICHAEL TURNER'S...) (Volume 4)
Aspen MLT, Inc.: Aug, 2012 - No. 8, Oct, 2013 ($3.99)
1-8-Krul-s/DeBalfo-a; multiple covers on each 4.00

SOULFIRE (MICHAEL TURNER'S...) (Volume 5)
Aspen MLT, Inc.: Nov, 2013 - No. 8, Oct, 2014 ($1.00/$3.99)
1-($1.00) Krul-s/Marion-a; multiple covers 3.00
2-8-($3.99) Multiple covers on each 4.00
Annual 1 2014 (7/14, $5.99) Art by Garbowska, Hanson, Turner, Cafaro 6.00

SOULFIRE (ALL NEW MICHAEL TURNER'S...) (Volume 6)
Aspen MLT, Inc.: Mar, 2017 - No. 8, Oct, 2017 ($3.99)
1-8-($3.99) Multiple covers on each. 1-Krul-s/Cafaro-a 4.00

SOULFIRE: CHAOS REIGN
Aspen MLT, Inc.: No. 0, June, 2006 - No. 3, Jan, 2007 ($2.50/$2.99)
0-($2.50) Three covers; Marcus To-a; J.T. Krul-s 3.00
1-3-($2.99) 1-Three covers 3.00
...: Beginnings (7/06, $1.99) Marcus To-a; J.T. Krul-s 3.00
...: Beginnings 1 (7/07, $1.99) Francisco Herrera-a; J.T. Krul-s 3.00

SOULFIRE: DYING OF THE LIGHT
Aspen MLT, Inc.: No. 0, 2004 - No. 5, Feb, 2006 ($2.50/$2.99)
0-($2.50) Three covers; Gunnell-a; Krul-s; back-story to the Soulfire universe 3.00
1-5-($2.99) 1-Five covers 3.00
... Vol. 1 TPB (2007, $14.99) r/#0-5; Gunnell sketch pages, cover gallery 15.00

SOULFIRE: NEW WORLD ORDER
Aspen MLT, Inc.: No. 0, Jul, 2007; May, 2009 - No. 5, Dec, 2009 ($2.50/$2.99)
0 (7/07, $2.50) Two covers; Herrera-a/Krul-s 3.00
1-5-($2.99) 1-Four covers 3.00

SOULFIRE: SHADOW MAGIC
Aspen MLT, Inc.: No. 0, Nov, 2008 - No. 5, May, 2009 ($2.50/$2.99)
0-($2.50) Two covers; Sana Takeda-a 3.00
1-5-($2.99) 1-Two covers 3.00

SOUL SAGA
Image Comics (Top Cow): Feb, 2000 - No. 5, Apr, 2001 ($2.50)
1-5: 1-Madureira-c; Platt & Batt-a 3.00

SOULSEARCHERS AND COMPANY
Claypool Comics: June, 1995 - No. 82, Jan, 2007 ($2.50, B&W)
1-10: Peter David scripts 5.00
11-82 3.00

SOULWIND
Image Comics: Mar, 1997 - No. 8 ($2.95, B&W, limited series)
1-8: 5-"The Day I Tried To Live" pt. 1 3.00
Book Five; The August Ones (Oni Press, 3/01, $8.50) 8.50
...The Kid From Planet Earth (1997, $9.95, TPB) 10.00
...The Kid From Planet Earth (Oni Press, 1/00, $8.50, TPB) 8.50
...The Day I Tried to Live (Oni Press, 4/00, $8.50, TPB) 8.50
The Complete Soulwind TPB ($29.95, 11/03, 8" x 5 1/2") r/Oni Books #1-5 30.00

SOUPY SALES COMIC BOOK (TV)(The Official...)
Archie Publications: 1965
1-(Teen-age) 8 16 24 56 108 160

SOUTHERN BASTARDS
Image Comics: Apr, 2014 - Present ($3.50/$3.99)
1-Jason Aaron-s/Jason Latour-a 8.00
2-19: 18-Chris Brunner-a 4.00

SOUTHERN CROSS
Image Comics: Mar, 2014 - No. 13, Oct, 2017 ($2.99/$3.99)
1-6-Becky Cloonan-s/c; Andy Belanger-a 3.00
7-13-($3.99) Cloonan-s/c; Belanger-a 4.00

SOUTHERN KNIGHTS, THE (See Crusaders #1)
Guild Publ/Fictioneer Books: No. 2, 1983 - No. 41, 1993 (B&W)
2-Magazine size 1 2 3 5 6 8
3-35, 37-41 3.00
36-($3.50-c) 4.00
Dread Halloween Special 1, Primer Special 1 (Spring, 1989, $2.25) 3.00
Graphic Novels #1-4 4.00

SOVEREIGNS
Dynamite Entertainment: No. 0, 2017 - No. 5, 2017 ($1.00/$3.99)
0-($1.00) Short stories of Magnus, Turok, Solar and Doctor Spektor 3.00
1-5-($3.99) Fawkes-s/Desjardins-a; back-up stories on each 4.00

SOVEREIGN SEVEN (Also see Showcase '95 #12)
DC Comics: July, 1995 - No. 36, July, 1998 ($1.95) (1st creator-owned mainstream DC comic)
1-1st app. Sovereign Seven (Reflex, Indigo, Cascade, Finale, Cruiser, Network & Rampart); 1st app. Maitresse; Darkseid app.; Chris Claremont-s & Dwayne Turner-c/a begins 4.00
1-Gold 8.00
1-Platinum 40.00
2-36: 2-Wolverine cameo. 4-Neil Gaiman cameo. 5,8-Batman app. 7-Ramirez cameo (from the movie Highlander). 9-Humphrey Bogart cameo from Casablanca. 10-Impulse app; Manoli Wetherell & Neal Conan cameo from Uncanny X-Men #226. 11-Robin app. 16-Final Night. 24-Superman app. 25-Power Girl app. 28-Impulse-c/app. 3.00
Annual 1 (1995, $3.95)-Year One story; Big Barda & Lobo app.; Jeff Johnson-c/a 4.00
Annual 2 (1996, $2.95)-Legends of the Dead Earth; Leonardi-c/a 4.00
...Plus 1(2/97, $2.95)-Legion-c/app. 4.00
TPB-($12.95) r/#1-5, Annual #1 & Showcase '95 #12 13.00

SPACE: ABOVE AND BEYOND (TV)
Topps Comics: Jan, 1996 - No. 3, Mar, 1996 ($2.95, limited series)
1-3: Adaptation of pilot episode; Steacy-c. 3.00

SPACE: ABOVE AND BEYOND--THE GAUNTLET (TV)
Topps Comics: May, 1996 -No. 2, June, 1996 ($2.95, limited series)
1,2 3.00

SPACE ACE (Also see Manhunt!)

Space Action #3 © ACE

Space Ghost #4 © H-B

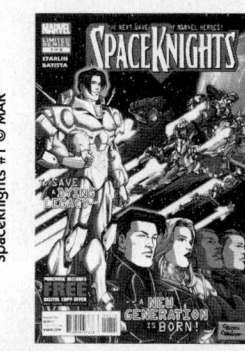

Spaceknights #1 © MAR

	GD 2.0	VG 4.0	FN 6.0	VF 8.0	VF/NM 9.0	NM- 9.2

Magazine Enterprises: No. 5, 1952

5(A-1 #61)-Guardineer-a 68 136 204 435 743 1050

SPACE ACE: DEFENDER OF THE UNIVERSE (Based on the Don Bluth video game)
CrossGen Comics: Oct, 2003 - No. 6 ($2.95, limited series)

1,2-Kirkman-s/Borges-a 3.00

SPACE ACTION
Ace Magazines (Junior Books): June, 1952 - No. 3, Oct, 1952

1-Cameron-a in all (1 story) 90 180 270 576 988 1400
2,3 60 120 180 381 803 925

SPACE ADVENTURES (War At Sea #22 on)
Capitol Stories/Charlton Comics: 7/52 - No. 21, 8/56; No. 23, 5/58 - No. 59, 11/64; V3#60, 10/67; V1#2, 7/68 - V1#8, 7/69; No. 9, 5/78 - No. 13, 3/79

1-Fago/Morales world on fire-c 68 136 204 435 743 1050
2 32 64 96 190 310 430
3-5: 4,6-Flying saucer-c/stories 27 54 81 158 259 360
6,8,9: 8-Robot-c. 9-A-Bomb panel 24 48 72 140 230 320
7-Sex change story "Transformation" 34 68 102 199 325 450
10,11-Ditko-c/a. 10-Robot-c. 11-Two Ditko stories 63 126 189 403 689 975
12-Ditko-c (classic) 155 310 465 992 1696 2400
13-(Fox-r, 10-11/54); Blue Beetle-c/story 16 32 48 94 147 200
14,15,17,18: 14-Blue Beetle-c/story; Fox-r (12-1/54-55, last pre-code).
15,17,18-Rocky Jones-c/s.(TV); 15-Part photo-c 20 40 60 118 192 265
16-Krigstein-a; Rocky Jones-c/story (TV) 22 44 66 128 209 290
19 15 30 45 88 137 185
20-Reprints Fawcett's "Destination Moon" 22 44 66 132 216 300
21-(8/56) (no #22)(Becomes War At Sea) 15 30 45 88 137 185
23-(5/58; formerly Nyoka, The Jungle Girl)-Reprints Fawcett's "Destination Moon"
20 40 60 118 192 265
24,25,31,32-Ditko-a. 24-Severin-a(signed "LePoer") 20 40 60 118 192 265
26,27-Ditko-a(4) each. 26,28-Flying saucer-c 21 42 63 126 206 285
28-30 11 22 33 64 90 115
33-Origin/1st app. Capt. Atom by Ditko (3/60) 142 284 426 909 1555 2200
34-40,42-All Captain Atom by Ditko 26 52 78 154 252 350
41,43,45-59: 43-Alan Shephard strory, 2nd man in space. 45-Mercury Man app.
5 10 15 30 50 70
44-1st app. Mercury Man 5 10 15 35 63 90
V3#60(#1, 10/67)-Presents UFO origin & 1st app. Paul Mann & The Saucers From the Future
5 10 15 30 50 70
2,5,6,8 (1968-69)-Ditko-a: 2-Aparo-c/a 3 6 9 19 30 40
3,4,7: 4-Aparo-c/a 3 6 9 16 23 30
9-13(1978-79)-Capt. Atom-r/Space Adventures by Ditko; 9-Reprints origin/1st app. Capt. Atom from #33 6.00

NOTE: ***Aparo** a-V3#60. c-V3#8. **Ditko** c-12, 31-42. **Giordano** c-3, 4, 7-9, 18p. **Krigstein** c-15. **Shuster** a-11. Issues 13 & 14 have Blue Beetle logos; #15-18 have Rocky Jones logos.*

SPACE BUSTERS
Ziff-Davis Publ. Co.: Spring, 1952 - No. 2, Fall, 1952

1-Krigstein-a(3); Painted-c by Norman Saunders 88 176 264 559 960 1360
2-Kinstler-a(2 pgs.); Saunders painted-c 71 142 213 454 777 1100

NOTE: ***Anderson** a-2. Bondage c-2.*

SPACE CADET (See Tom Corbett,...)

SPACE CIRCUS
Dark Horse Comics: July, 2000 - No. 4, Oct, 2000 ($2.95, limited series)

1-4-Aragonés-a/Evanier-s 3.00

SPACE COMICS (Formerly Funny Tunes)
Avon Periodicals: No. 4, Mar-Apr, 1954 - No. 5, May-June, 1954

4,5-Space Mouse, Peter Rabbit, Super Pup (formerly Spotty the Pup), & Merry Mouse continue from Funny Tunes 9 18 27 50 65 80
I.W. Reprint #8 (nd)-Space Mouse-r 2 4 6 8 11 14

SPACED
Anthony Smith Publ. #1,2/Unbridled Ambition/Eclipse Comics #10 on: 1982 - No. 13, 1988 ($1.25/$1.50, B&W, quarterly)

1-($1.25-c) 4.00
2-13, Special Edition (1983, Mimeo) 3.00

SPACE DETECTIVE
Avon Periodicals: July, 1951 - No. 4, July, 1952

1-Rod Hathway, Space Detective begins, ends #4; Wood-c/a(3)-23 pgs.; "Opium Smugglers of Venus" drug story; Lucky Dale-r/Saint #4 155 310 465 992 1696 2400
2-Tales from the Shadow Squad story; Wood/Orlando-c; Wood inside layouts; "Slave Ship of Saturn" story 113 226 339 718 1234 1750

	GD 2.0	VG 4.0	FN 6.0	VF 8.0	VF/NM 9.0	NM 9.2

3,4: 3-Kinstler-c. 4-Kinstlerish-a by McCann 54 108 162 343 574 825
I.W. Reprint #1(Reprints #2), 8(Reprints cover #1 & part Famous Funnies #191)
4 8 12 23 37 50

SPACE EXPLORER (See March of Comics #202)

SPACE FAMILY ROBINSON (TV)(...Lost in Space #15-37, ...Lost in Space On Space Station One #38 on)(See Gold Key Champion)
Gold Key: Dec, 1962 - No. 36, Oct, 1969; No. 37, 10/73 - No. 54, 11/78; No. 55, 3/81 - No. 59, 5/82 (All painted covers)

1-(Low distribution); Spiegle-a in all 31 62 93 223 499 775
2(3/63)-Family becomes lost in space 11 22 33 76 163 250
3-5 7 14 21 46 86 125
6-10: 6-Captain Venture back-up stories begin 6 12 18 37 66 95
11-20: 14-(10/65). 15-Title change (1/66) 4 8 12 28 47 65
21-36: 28-Last 12¢ issue. 36-Captain Venture ends 3 6 9 21 33 45
37-48: 37-Origin retold 2 4 6 10 14 18
49-59: Reprints #49,50,55-59 2 4 6 8 10 12

NOTE: *The TV show first aired on 9/15/65. Title changed after TV show debuted.*

SPACE FAMILY ROBINSON (See March of Comics #320, 328, 352, 404, 414)

SPACE GHOST (TV) (Also see Golden Comics Digest #2 & Hanna-Barbera Super TV Heroes #3-7)
Gold Key: March, 1967 (Hanna-Barbera) (TV debut was 9/10/66)

1 (10199-703)-Spiegle-a 29 58 87 209 467 725

SPACE GHOST (TV cartoon)
Comico: Mar, 1987 ($3.50, deluxe format, one-shot) (Hanna-Barbera)

1-Steve Rude-c/a; Evanier-s; Steacy painted-a 2 4 6 10 14 18

SPACE GHOST (TV cartoon)
DC Comics: Jan, 2005 - No. 6, June, 2005 ($2.95/$2.99, limited series)

1-6-Alex Ross-c/Ariel Olivetti-a/Joe Kelly-s; origin of Space Ghost 3.00
TPB (2005, $14.99) r/series; cover gallery 15.00

SPACE GIANTS, THE (TV cartoon)
FBN Publications: 1979 ($1.00, B&W, one-shots)

1-Based on Japanese TV series 3 6 9 14 20 25

SPACEHAWK
Dark Horse Comics: 1989 - No. 3, 1990 ($2.00, B&W)

1-3-Wolverton-c/a(r) plus new stories by others. 4.00

SPACE JAM
DC Comics: 1996 ($5.95, one-shot, movie adaption)

1-Wraparound photo cover of Michael Jordan 2 4 6 8 10 12

SPACE KAT-ETS (...in 3-D)
Power Publishing Co.: Dec, 1953 (25¢, came w/glasses)

1 31 62 93 182 296 410

SPACEKNIGHTS
Marvel Comics: Oct, 2000 - No. 5, Feb, 2001 ($2.99, limited series)

1-5-Starlin-s/Batista-a 3.00

SPACEKNIGHTS
Marvel Comics: Dec, 2012 - No. 3, Feb, 2013 ($3.99, limited series)

1-3-Reprints the 2000-2001 series & Annihilation: Conquest Prologue 4.00

SPACEMAN (Speed Carter...)
Atlas Comics (CnPC): Sept, 1953 - No. 6, July, 1954

1-Grey tone-c 103 206 309 659 1130 1600
2 54 108 162 343 574 825
3-6: 4-A-Bomb explosion-c 50 100 150 315 533 750

NOTE: ***Everett** c-1, 3. **Heath** a-1. **Maneely** a-1(3), 2(4), 3(3), 4-6; c-5, 6. **Romita** a-1. **Sekowsky** c-4. **Sekowsky/Abel** a-4(3). **Tuska** a-5(3).*

SPACE MAN
Dell Publ. Co.: No. 1253, 1-3/62 - No. 8, 3-5/64; No. 9, 7/72 - No. 10, 10/72

Four Color 1253 (#1)(1-3/62)(15¢-c) 7 14 21 48 89 130
2,3: 2-(15¢-c). 3-(12¢-c) 4 8 12 27 44 60
4-8-(12¢-c) 3 6 9 21 33 45
9,10-(15¢-c): 9-Reprints #1253. 10-Reprints #2 2 4 6 9 12 15

SPACEMAN (From the Atomics)
Oni Press: July, 2002 ($2.95, one-shot)

1-Mike Allred-s/a; Lawrence Marvit additional art 3.00

SPACEMAN
DC Comics (Vertigo): Dec, 2011 - No. 9, Oct, 2012 ($1.00/$2.99, limited series)

Spaceman #7 © Azzarello & Risso

Space War #16 © CC

Sparkle Comics #2 © UFS

GD VG FN VF VF/NM NM-
2.0 4.0 6.0 8.0 9.0 9.2

1-($1.00) Azzarello-s/Risso-a/Johnson-c 4.00
2-9-($2.99) 3.00

SPACE MOUSE (Also see Funny Tunes & Space Comics)
Avon Periodicals: April, 1953 - No. 5, Apr-May, 1954
1 14 28 42 78 112 145
2 9 18 27 47 61 75
3-5 8 16 24 40 50 60

SPACE MOUSE (Walter Lantz...#1; see Comic Album #17)
Dell Publishing Co./Gold Key: No. 1132, Aug-Oct, 1960 - No. 5, Nov, 1963 (Walter Lantz)
Four Color 1132,1244, 1(11/62)(G.K.) 5 10 15 33 57 80
2-5 4 8 12 23 37 50

SPACE MYSTERIES
I.W. Enterprises: 1964 (Reprints)
1-r/Journey Into Unknown Worlds #4 w/new-c 3 6 9 15 22 28
8,9: 9-r/Planet Comics #73 3 6 9 15 22 28

SPACE: 1999 (TV) (Also see Power Record Comics)
Charlton Comics: Nov, 1975 - No. 7, Nov, 1976
1-Origin Moonbase Alpha; Staton-c/a 3 6 9 19 30 40
2,7: 2-Staton-a 2 4 6 13 18 22
3-6: All Byrne-a; c-3,5,6 3 6 9 16 23 30
nn (Charlton Press, digest, 100 pgs., B&W, no cover price) new stories & art
4 8 12 27 44 60

SPACE: 1999 (TV)(Magazine)
Charlton Comics: Nov, 1975 - No. 8, Nov, 1976 (B&W) (#7 shows #6 inside)
1-Origin Moonbase Alpha; Morrow-c/a 3 6 9 16 24 32
2-8: 2,3-Morrow-c/a. 4-6-Morrow-c. 5,8-Morrow-a 2 4 6 11 16 20

SPACE PATROL (TV)
Ziff-Davis Publishing Co. (Approved Comics): Summer, 1952 - No. 2, Oct-Nov, 1952 (Painted-c by Norman Saunders)
1-Krigstein-a 95 190 285 603 1039 1475
2-Krigstein-a(3) 67 134 201 426 731 1035

SPACE PIRATES (See Archie Giant Series #533)

SPACE: PUNISHER
Marvel Comics: Sept, 2012 - No. 4, Dec, 2012 ($3.99, limited series)
1-4-Outer space sci-fi pulp version of the Punisher; Tieri-s/Texeira-a/c 4.00

SPACE RANGER (See Mystery in Space #92, Showcase #15 & Tales of the Unexpected)

SPACE SQUADRON (In the Days of the Rockets)(Becomes Space Worlds #6)
Marvel/Atlas Comics (ACI): June, 1951 - No. 5, Feb, 1952
1-Space team; Brodsky c-1,5 94 188 282 597 1024 1450
2: Tuska c-2-4 68 136 204 435 743 1050
3-5: 3-Capt. Jet Dixon by Tuska(3); Maneely-a. 4-Weird advs. begin
60 120 180 381 653 925

SPACE THRILLERS
Avon Periodicals: 1954 (25¢ Giant)
nn-(Scarce)-Robotmen of the Lost Planet; contains 3 rebound comics of The Saint & Strange Worlds. Contents could vary 155 310 465 992 1696 2400

SPACE TRIP TO THE MOON (See Space Adventures #23)

SPACE USAGI
Mirage Studios: June, 1992 - No. 3, 1992 ($2.00, B&W, mini-series)
V2#1, Nov, 1993 - V2#3, Jan, 1994 ($2.75)
1-3: Stan Sakai-c/a/scripts, V2#1-3 3.00

SPACE USAGI
Dark Horse Comics: Jan, 1996 - No. 3, Mar, 1996 ($2.95, B&W, limited series)
1-3: Stan Sakai-c/a/scripts 3.00

SPACE WAR (Fightin' Five #28 on)
Charlton Comics: Oct, 1959 - No. 27, Mar, 1964; No. 28, Mar, 1978 - No. 34, 3/79
V1#1-Giordano-c begin, end #3 12 24 36 83 182 280
2,3 8 16 24 51 96 140
4-6,8,10-Ditko-c/a 12 24 36 81 176 270
7,9,11-15 (3/62): Last 10¢ issue 6 12 18 38 69 100
16 (6/62)-27 (3/64): 18,19-Robot-c 5 10 15 31 53 75
28 (3/78),29-31,33,34-Ditko-c/a(r): 30-Staton, Sutton/Wood-a. 31-Ditko-c/a(3); same-c as Strange Suspense Stories #2 (1968); atom blast-c
1 3 4 6 8 10
32-r/Charlton Premiere V2#2; Sutton-a 6.00

SPACE WARPED
Boom Entertainment (Kaboom!): Jun, 2011 - No. 6, Dec, 2011 ($3.99, limited series)
1-6-Star Wars spoof; Bourhis-s/Spiessert-a 4.00

SPACE WESTERN (Formerly Cowboy Western Comics; becomes Cowboy Western Comics #46 on)
Charlton Comics (Capitol Stories): No. 40, Oct, 1952 - No. 45, Aug, 1953
40-Intro Spurs Jackson & His Space Vigilantes; flying saucer story
65 130 195 416 708 1000
41,43: 41-Flying saucer-c 47 94 141 296 498 700
42-Atom bomb explosion-c 52 104 156 328 552 775
44-Cowboys battle Nazis on Mars 90 180 270 576 988 1400
45-"The Valley That Time Forgot", a pre-Turok story with dinosaurs & a bow-hunting Indian; Hitler app. 54 108 162 343 574 825

SPACE WORLDS (Formerly Space Squadron #1-5)
Atlas Comics (Male): No. 6, April, 1952
6-Sol Brodsky-c 53 106 159 334 567 800

SPANKY & ALFALFA & THE LITTLE RASCALS (See The Little Rascals)

SPARKIE, RADIO PIXIE (Radio)(Becomes Big Jon & Sparkie #4)
Ziff-Davis Publ. Co.: Winter, 1951 - No. 3, July-Aug, 1952 (Painted-c)(Sparkie #2,3; #1?)
1-Based on children's radio program 27 54 81 158 259 360
2,3: 3-Big Jon and Sparkie on-c only 18 36 54 105 165 225

SPARKLE COMICS
United Features Synd.: Oct-Nov, 1948 - No. 33, Dec-Jan, 1953-54
1-Li'l Abner, Nancy, Captain & the Kids, Ella Cinders (#1-3: 52 pgs.)
15 30 45 90 140 190
2 10 20 30 54 72 90
3-10 8 16 24 42 54 65
11-20 7 14 21 37 46 55
21-32 6 12 18 31 38 45
33-(2-3/54) 2 pgs. early Peanuts by Schulz 13 26 39 72 101 130

SPARKLE PLENTY (See Harvey Comics Library #2 & Dick Tracy)
Dell Publishing Co.: 1949
Four Color 215 - Dick Tracy reprint by Gould 10 20 30 69 147 225

SPARKLER COMICS (1st series)
United Feature Comic Group: July, 1940 - No. 2, 1940
1-Jim Hardy 40 80 120 246 411 575
2-Frankie Doodle 32 64 96 188 307 425

SPARKLER COMICS (2nd series)(Nancy & Sluggo #121 on)(Cover title becomes Nancy and Sluggo #101? on)
United Features Syndicate: July, 1941 - No. 120, Jan, 1955
1-Origin 1st app. Sparkman; Tarzan (by Hogarth in all issues), Captain & the Kids, Ella Cinders, Danny Dingle, Dynamite Dunn, Nancy, Abbie & Slats, Broncho Bill, Frankie Doodle, begin; Spark Man c-1-9,11,12; Hap Hopper c-10,13
187 374 561 1197 2049 2900
2 61 122 183 390 670 950
3,4 47 94 141 296 498 700
5-9: 9-Spark Man's new costume 40 80 120 246 411 575
10-Spark Man's secret ID revealed 41 82 123 256 428 600
11,12-Spark Man war-c. 12-Spark Man's new costume (color change)
39 78 117 231 378 525
13-Hap Hopper war-c 31 62 93 186 303 420
14-Tarzan-c by Hogarth 63 126 189 403 689 975
15,17: 15-Capt & Kids-c. 17-Nancy & Sluggo-c 24 48 72 140 230 320
16,18-Spark Man-c. 16-Japanese WWII-c. 18-Nazi WWII-c
39 78 117 240 395 550
19-1st Race Riley and the Commandos-c/s 37 74 111 222 361 500
20-Nancy war-c 28 56 84 168 274 380
21,25,28,31,34,37-Tarzan-c by Hogarth 47 94 141 296 498 700
22-24,26,27,29,30: 22-Race Riley & the Commandos strips begin, ends #44
22 44 66 132 216 300
32,33,35,36,38,40 14 28 42 80 115 150
39-Classic Tarzan shooting an arrow into a dinosaur's eye on cover by Hogarth
77 154 231 493 847 1200
41,43,45,46,48,49 11 22 33 60 83 105
42,44,47,50-Tarzan-c (42,47,50 by Hogarth) 25 50 75 150 245 340
51,52,54-68,70: 57-Li'l Abner begins (not in #58); Fearless Fosdick app. in #58
10 20 30 58 79 100
53-Tarzan-c by Hogarth 24 48 72 144 237 330
69-Wolverton-*esque* Horror-c 12 24 36 67 94 120

Spartacus V1 #1 © Starz

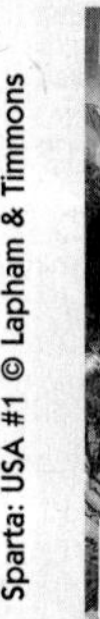
Sparta: USA #1 © Lapham & Timmons

Spawn #221 © TMP

	GD 2.0	VG 4.0	FN 6.0	VF 8.0	VF/NM 9.0	NM- 9.2
71-80	9	18	27	47	61	75
81,82,84-86: 86 Last Tarzan; lingerie panels	8	16	24	40	50	60
83-Tarzan-c; Li'l Abner ends	12	24	36	69	97	125
87-96,98-99	7	14	21	37	46	55
97-Origin Casey Ruggles by Warren Tufts	8	16	24	42	54	65
100	8	16	24	42	54	65
101-107,109-112,114-119	6	12	18	31	38	45
108,113-Toth-a	7	14	21	37	46	55
120-(10-11/54) 2 pgs. early Peanuts by Schulz	11	22	33	62	86	110

SPARKLING LOVE
Avon Periodicals/Realistic (1953): June, 1950; 1953

1(Avon)-Kubert-a; photo-c	36	72	108	211	343	475
nn(1953)-Reprint; Kubert-a	14	28	42	82	121	160

SPARKLING STARS
Holyoke Publishing Co.: June, 1944 - No. 33, March, 1948

1-Hell's Angels, FBI, Boxie Weaver, Petey & Pop, & Ali Baba begin	22	44	66	132	216	300
2-Speed Spaulding story	14	28	42	80	115	150
3-Actual FBI case photos & war photos	11	22	33	60	83	105
4-10: 7-X-Mas-c	10	20	30	54	72	90
11-19: 13-Origin/1st app. Jungo the Man-Beast-c/s	9	18	27	50	65	80
20-Intro Fangs the Wolf Boy	10	20	30	54	72	90
21-33: 29-Bondage-c. 31-Sid Greene-a	9	18	27	47	61	75

SPARK MAN (See Sparkler Comics)
Frances M. McQueeny: 1945 (36 pgs., one-shot)

1-Origin Spark Man r/Sparkler #1-3; female torture story; cover redrawn from Sparkler #1	36	72	108	211	343	475

SPARKY WATTS (Also see Big Shot Comics & Columbia Comics)
Columbia Comic Corp.: Nov?, 1942 - No. 10, 1949

1(1942)-Skyman & The Face app; Hitler/Goering story/c	116	232	348	742	1271	1800
2(1943)	37	74	111	222	361	500
3(1944) "6000 Lbs. Block Buster to Bust Adolf"-c	24	48	72	142	234	325
4(1944)-Origin	20	40	60	114	182	250
5(1947)-Skyman app.; Boody Rogers-c/a	16	32	48	94	147	200
6,7,9,10: 6(1947). 9-Haunted House-c. 10(1949)	12	24	36	67	94	120
8(1948)-Surrealistic-c	14	28	42	80	115	150

NOTE: *Boody Rogers c-1-8.*

SPARTACUS (Movie)
Dell Publishing Co.: No. 1139, Nov, 1960 (Kirk Douglas photo-c)

Four Color 1139-Buscema-a	10	20	30	69	147	225

SPARTACUS (Television series)
Devil's Due Publishing: Oct, 2009 - No. 2 ($3.99)

1,2: 1-DeKnight-s. 2-Palmiotti-s						4.00

SPARTAN: WARRIOR SPIRIT (Also see WildC.A.T.S: Covert Action Teams)
Image Comics (WildStorm Productions): July, 1995 - No. 4, Nov, 1995 ($2.50, lim. series)

1-4: Kurt Busiek scripts; Mike McKone-c/a						3.00

SPARTA: USA
DC Comics (WildStorm): May, 2010 - No. 6, Oct, 2010 ($2.99, limited series)

1-6: 1-Lapham-s/Timmons-a; covers by Timmons and Lapham						3.00

SPAWN (Also see Curse of the Spawn and Sam & Twitch)
Image Comics (Todd McFarlane Prods.): May, 1992 - Present ($1.95/$2.50/$2.99)

1-1st app. Spawn; McFarlane-c/a begins; McFarlane/Steacy-c; 1st Todd McFarlane Productions title.	3	6	9	18	27	36
1-Black & white edition	10	20	30	69	147	225
2,3: 2-1st app. Violator; McFarlane/Steacy-c	2	4	6	10	14	18
4-Contains coupon for Image Comics #0	2	4	6	8	10	12
4-With coupon missing						3.00
4-Newsstand edition w/o poster or coupon						3.00
5-Cerebus cameo (1 pg.) as stuffed animal; Spawn mobile poster #1	2	4	6	8	10	12
6-8,10: 7-Spawn Mobile poster #2. 8-Alan Moore scripts; Miller poster. 10-Cerebus app.; Dave Sim scripts; 1 pg. cameo app. by Superman						6.00
9-Neil Gaiman scripts; Jim Lee poster; 1st Angela.	3	6	9	15	22	28
11-17,19,20,22-30: 11-Miller script; Darrow poster. 12-Bloodwulf poster by Liefeld. 14,15-Violator app. 16,17-Grant Morrison scripts; Capullo-c/a(p). 23,24-McFarlane-a/stories. 25-(10/94). 19-(10/94). 20-(11/94)						5.00
18-Grant Morrison script, Capullo-c/a(p); low distr.	1	3	4	6	8	10
21-low distribution	1	3	4	6	8	10
31-49: 31-1st app. The Redeemer; new costume (brief). 32-1st full app. new costume. 38-40,42,44,46,48-Tony Daniel-c/a(p). 38-1st app. Cy-Gor. 40,41-Cy-Gor & Curse app.						4.00
50-($3.95, 48 pgs.)						6.00
51-96: 52-Savage Dragon app. 56-w/ Darkchylde preview. 57-Cy-Gor-c/app. 64-Polybagged w/McFarlane Toys catalog. 65-Photo-c of movie Spawn and McFarlane. 81-Billy Kincaid returns						4.00
97-Angela-c/app.	2	4	6	8	10	12
98,99-Angela app.						6.00
100-($4.95) Angela dies; 6 total covers; the 3 variants by McFarlane, Miller, and Mignola	2	4	6	8	10	12
100-($4.95) 3 variant covers by Ross, Capullo, and Wood	1	2	3	5	6	8
101-149,151-199,201-219: 101-149-($2.50). 151-($2.95) Wraparound-c by Tan. 167-Clown app. 179-Mayhew-a. 185-McFarlane & Holguin-s/Portacio-a begins. 193-Sam & Twitch app. 210-215-Michael Golden-c						3.00
150-($4.95) 4 covers by McFarlane, Capullo, Tan, Jim Lee						5.00
200-(1/11, $3.99) 7 covers by McFarlane, Capullo, Finch, Jim Lee, Liefeld, Silvestri, Wood						4.00
220-(6/12, $3.99) 20th Anniversary issue; McFarlane-s/Kudranski-a; bonus interview, timeline and cover gallery						4.00
220: 20th Anniversary Collector's Special-(6/12, $4.99) B&W version of #220 w/bonuses						5.00
221-249,251-283: 221-231-Cover swipes of classic covers. 221-Amazing Fantasy #15. 225-Election special with 2 covers (Obama & Romney). 228-Action #1 c-swipe. 231-Spider-Man #1 ('90) c-swipe. 234-Haunt app. 251-Follows Spawn Resurrection #1. 258-Erik Larsen & McFarlane-a begin. 265-Ant app. 266-Savage Dragon app. 267-275-Kudranski-a. 276-282-Darragh Savage-s/Alexander-a						3.00
250-($5.99) McFarlane-s/Kudranski-a; Al Simmons returns; multiple covers						6.00
Annual 1-Blood & Shadows ('99, $4.95) Ashley Wood-c/a; Jenkins-s						5.00
... #1 Director's Cut (5/17, $4.99) 25th Anniversary edition; r/#1 B&W inked art with McFarlane commentary; bonus promotional art; 3 covers (McFarlane, Crain, Ashley Wood)						5.00
...: Architects of Fear (2/11, $6.99, squarebound GN) Briclot-a						7.00
...: Armegeddon Complete Collection TPB ('07, $29.95) r/#150-163						30.00
...: Armegeddon, Part 1 TPB (10/06, $14.99) r/#150-155						15.00
...: Armegeddon, Part 2 TPB (2/07, $15.95) r/#156-164						16.00
...Bible-(8/96, $1.95)-Character bios						4.00
Book 1 TPB($9.95) r/#1-5; Book 2-r/#6-9,11; Book 3 -r/#12-15, Book 4- r/#16-20; Book 5-r/#21-25; Book 6- r/#26-30; Book 7-r/#31-34; Book 8-r/#35-38; Book 9-r/#39-42; Book 10-r/#43-47						11.00
Book 11 TPB ($10.95) r/#48-50; Book 12-r/#51-54						11.00
... Collection Vol. 1 (10/05, $19.95) r/#1-8,11,12; intro. by Frank Miller						20.00
... Collection Vol. 2 HC (7/07, $49.95) r/#13-33						50.00
... Collection Vol. 2 SC (9/06, $29.95) r/#13-33						30.00
... Collection Vol. 3 (3/07, $29.95) r/#34-54						30.00
... Collection Vol. 4 (9/07, $29.95) r/#55-75						30.00
... Collection Vol. 5 ('08, $29.95) r/#76-95						30.00
... Collection Vol. 6 (8/08, $29.95) r/#96-116; cover gallery						30.00
Image Firsts: Spawn #1 (4/10, $1.00) reprints #1						3.00
... Godslayer Vol. 1 (9/06, $6.99) Anacleto-c/a; Holguin-s; sketch pages						7.00
... Kills Everyone! 1 (8/16, $2.99) McFarlane-s/JJ Kirby-a; mini Spawn vs. cosplayers						3.00
...: Neonoir TPB (11/08, $14.95) r/#170-175						15.00
...: New Flesh TPB ('07, $14.95) r/#166-169						15.00
... Resurrection 1 (3/15, $2.99) Follows issue #250; Jenkins-s/Jonboy-a						3.00
...Simony (5/04, $7.95) English translation of French Spawn story; Briclot-a						8.00

NOTE: ***Capullo** a-16p-18p; c-16p-18p. **Daniel** a-38-40, 42, 44, 46. **McFarlane** a-1-15; c-1-15p. **Thibert** a-16i(part). Posters come with issues 1, 4, 7-9, 11, 12. #25 was released before #19 & 20.*

SPAWN-BATMAN (Also see Batman/Spawn: War Devil under Batman: One-Shots)
Image Comics (Todd McFarlane Productions): 1994 ($3.95, one-shot)

1-Miller scripts; McFarlane-c/a	2	4	6	11	16	20

SPAWN: BLOOD FEUD
Image Comics (Todd McFarlane Prods.): June, 1995 - No. 4, Sept, 1995 ($2.25, lim. series)

1-4-Alan Moore scripts, Tony Daniel-a						4.00

SPAWN FAN EDITION
Image Comics (Todd McFarlane Productions): Aug, 1996 - No. 3, Oct, 1996 (Giveaway, 12 pgs.) (Polybagged w/Overstreet's FAN)

1-3: Beau Smith scripts; Brad Gorby-a(p). 1-1st app. Nordik, the Norse Hellspawn. 2-1st app. McFallon. 3-1st app. Mercy	1	2	3	5	6	8
1-3-(Gold): All retailer incentives						16.00
1-3-Variant-c	1	2	3	5	6	8
2-(Platinum)-Retailer incentive						25.00

SPAWN GODSLAYER
Image Comics (Todd McFarlane Prods.): May, 2007 - No. 8, Apr, 2008 ($2.99)

1-8: 1-Holguin-s/Tan-a/Anacleto-c						3.00

Spawn: The Undead #1 © TMP

Species #4 © MGM

Spectacular Spider-Man #8 © MAR

GD VG FN VF VF/NM NM-
2.0 4.0 6.0 8.0 9.0 9.2

GD VG FN VF VF/NM NM-
2.0 4.0 6.0 8.0 9.0 9.2

SPAWN: THE DARK AGES
Image Comics (Todd McFarlane Productions): Mar, 1999 - No. 28, Oct, 2001 ($2.50)
1-Fabry-c; Holguin-s/Sharp-a; variant-c by McFarlane 3.00
2-28 3.00

SPAWN THE IMPALER
Image Comics (Todd McFarlane Prods.): Oct, 1996 - No. 3, Dec, 1996 ($2.95, limited series)
1-3-Mike Grell scripts, painted-a 4.00

SPAWN: THE UNDEAD
Image Comics (Todd McFarlane Prod.): Jun, 1999 - No. 9, Feb, 2000 ($1.95/$2.25)
1-9-Dwayne Turner-c/a; Jenkins-s. 7-9-($2.25-c) 3.00
TPB (6/08, $24.99) r/#1-9 25.00

SPAWN/WILDC.A.T.S
Image Comics (WildStorm): Jan, 1996 - No. 4, Apr, 1996 ($2.50, lim. series)
1-4: Alan Moore scripts in all. 4.00

SPEAKER FOR THE DEAD (ORSON SCOTT CARD'S...) (Ender's Game)
Marvel Comics: Mar, 2011 - No. 5, Jul, 2011 ($3.99, limited series)
1-3-Johnston-s/Mhan-a/Camuncoli-c 4.00

SPECIAL AGENT (Steve Saunders...)(Also see True Comics #68)
Parents' Magazine Institute (Commended Comics No. 2): Dec, 1947 - No. 8, Sept, 1949 (Based on true FBI cases)
1-J. Edgar Hoover photo on-c 15 30 45 84 127 170
2 9 18 27 52 69 85
3-8 8 16 24 44 57 70

SPECIAL COLLECTORS' EDITION (See Savage Fists of Kung-Fu)

SPECIAL COMICS (Becomes Hangman #2 on)
MLJ Magazines: Winter, 1941-42
1-Origin The Boy Buddies (Shield & Wizard x-over); death of The Comet retold (see Pep #17); origin The Hangman retold; Hangman-c 406 812 1218 2842 4971 7100

SPECIAL EDITION (See Gorgo and Reptisaurus)

SPECIAL EDITION COMICS (See Promotional Section)

SPECIAL EDITION COMICS
Fawcett Publications: 1940 (August) (68 pgs., one-shot)
1-1st book devoted entirely to Captain Marvel; C.C. Beck-c/a; only app. of Captain Marvel with belt buckle; Capt. Marvel appears with button-down flap; 1st story (came out before Captain Marvel #1) 838 1676 2514 6117 10,809 15,500
NOTE: *Prices vary widely on this book. Since this book is all Captain Marvel stories, it is actually a pre-Captain Marvel #1. There is speculation that this book almost became **Captain Marvel** #1. After **Special Edition** was published, there was an editor change at Fawcett. The new editor commissioned Kirby to do a nn **Captain Marvel** book early in 1941. This book was followed by a 2nd book several months later. This 2nd book was advertised as a #3 (making Special Edition the #1, & the nn issue the #2). However, the 2nd book did come out as a #2.*

SPECIAL EDITION: SPIDER-MAN VS. THE HULK (See listing under The Amazing Spider-Man)

SPECIAL EDITION X-MEN
Marvel Comics Group: Feb, 1983 ($2.00, one-shot, Baxter paper)
1-r/Giant-Size X-Men #1 plus one new story 2 4 6 11 16 20

SPECIAL FORCES
Image Comics: Oct, 2007 - No. 4, Mar, 2009 ($2.99)
1-4-Iraq war combat; Kyle Baker-s/a/c 3.00

SPECIAL MARVEL EDITION (Master of Kung Fu #17 on)
Marvel Comics Group: Jan, 1971 - No. 16, Feb, 1974 (#1-3: 25¢, 68 pgs.; #4: 52 pgs.; #5-16: 20¢, regular ed.)
1-Thor-r by Kirby; 68 pgs. 4 8 12 27 44 60
2-4: Thor-r by Kirby; 2,3-68 pg. Giant. 4-(52 pgs.) 3 6 9 16 23 30
5-14: Sgt. Fury-r; 11-r/Sgt. Fury #13 (Capt. America) 2 4 6 9 12 15
15-Master of Kung Fu (Shang-Chi) begins (1st app., 12/73); Starlin-a; origin/1st app. Nayland Smith & Dr. Petrie 13 26 39 89 195 300
16-1st app. Midnight; Starlin-a (2nd Shang-Chi) 6 12 18 41 76 110
NOTE: *Kirby c-10-14.*

SPECIAL MISSIONS (See G.I. Joe...)

SPECIAL WAR SERIES (Attack V4#3 on?)
Charlton Comics: Aug, 1965 - No. 4, Nov, 1965
V4#1-D-Day (also see D-Day listing) 4 8 12 28 47 65
2-Attack! 3 6 9 16 23 30
3-War & Attack (also see War & Attack) 3 6 9 14 20 25
4-Judomaster (intro/1st app.; see Sarge Steel) 9 18 27 58 114 170

SPECIES (Movie)
Dark Horse Comics: June, 1995 - No. 4, Sept, 1995 ($2.50, limited series)
1-4: Adaptation of film 3.00

SPECIES: HUMAN RACE (Movie)
Dark Horse Comics: Nov, 1996 - No. 4, Feb, 1997 ($2.95, limited series)
1-4 3.00

SPECTACULAR ADVENTURES (See Adventures)

SPECTACULAR FEATURE MAGAZINE, A (Formerly My Confession) (Spectacular Features Magazine #12)
Fox Feature Syndicate: No. 11, April, 1950
11 (#1)-Samson and Delilah 27 54 81 160 263 365

SPECTACULAR FEATURES MAGAZINE (Formerly A Spectacular Feature Magazine)
Fox Feature Syndicate: No. 12, June, 1950 - No. 3, Aug, 1950
12 (#2)-Iwo Jima; photo flag-c 27 54 81 158 259 360
3-True Crime Cases From Police Files 22 44 66 128 209 290

SPECTACULAR SCARLET SPIDER
Marvel Comics: Nov, 1995 - No. 2, Dec, 1995 ($1.95, limited series)
1,2: Replaces Spectacular Spider-Man 3.00

SPECTACULAR SPIDER-GIRL
Marvel Comics: Jul, 2010 - No. 4, Oct, 2010 ($3.99, limited series)
1-4-Frenz-a; Frank Castle and the Hobgoblin app. 4.00

SPECTACULAR SPIDER-MAN, THE (See Marvel Special Edition and Marvel Treasury Edition)

SPECTACULAR SPIDER-MAN, THE (Magazine)
Marvel Comics Group: July, 1968 - No. 2, Nov, 1968 (35¢)
1-(B&W)-Romita/Mooney 52 pg. story plus updated origin story with Everett-a(i) 10 20 30 69 147 225
1-Variation w/single c-price of 40¢ 10 20 30 69 147 225
2-(Color)-Green Goblin-c & 58 pg. story; Romita painted-c (story reprinted in King Size Spider-Man #9); Romita/Mooney-a 9 18 27 61 123 185

SPECTACULAR SPIDER-MAN, THE (Peter Parker...#54-132, 134)
Marvel Comics Group: Dec, 1976 - No. 263, Nov, 1998
1-Origin recap in text; return of Tarantula 5 10 15 35 63 90
2-Kraven the Hunter app. 3 6 9 17 26 35
3-5: 3-Intro Lightmaster. 4-Vulture app. 3 6 9 14 20 25
6-8-Morbius app.; 6-r/Marvel Team-Up #3 w/Morbius 3 6 9 15 22 28
7,8-(35¢-c variants, limited distribution)(6,7/77) 8 16 24 51 96 140
9-20: 9,10-White Tiger app. 11-Last 30¢-c. 17,18-Angel & Iceman app. (from Champions); Ghost Rider cameo. 18-Gil Kane-c 2 4 6 8 11 14
9-11-(35¢-c variants, limited distribution)(8-10/77) 7 14 21 48 89 130
21,24-26: 21-Scorpion app. 26-Daredevil app. 2 3 4 6 8 10
22,23-Moon Knight app. 2 4 6 8 10 12
27-Miller's 1st art on Daredevil (2/79); also see Captain America #235 5 10 15 34 60 85
28-Miller Daredevil (p) 4 8 12 25 40 55
29-55,57,59: 33-Origin Iguana. 38-Morbius app. 1 2 3 4 5 7
56-2nd app. Jack O'Lantern (Macendale) & 1st Spidey/Jack O'Lantern battle (7/81) 1 2 3 5 6 8
58-Byrne-a(p) 1 2 3 5 6 8
60-Double size; origin retold with new facts revealed 1 2 3 5 6 8
61-63,65-68,71-74: 65-Kraven the Hunter app. 6.00
64-1st app. Cloak & Dagger (3/82) 6 12 18 41 76 110
69,70-Cloak & Dagger app. (origin retold in #69). 70-1st app. of Silvermane in cyborg form 2 4 6 8 10 12
75-Double size 1 2 3 5 6 8
76-80: 78,79-Punisher cameo 6.00
81,82-Punisher, Cloak & Dagger app. 1 3 4 6 8 10
83-Origin Punisher retold (10/83) 2 4 6 9 12 15
84,86-89,91-99: 94-96-Cloak & Dagger app. 98-Intro The Spot 6.00
85-Hobgoblin (Ned Leeds) app. (12/83); gains powers of original Green Goblin (see Amazing Spider-Man #238) 2 4 6 8 10 12
90-Spider-Man's new black costume, last panel (ties w/Amazing Spider-Man #252 & Marvel Team-Up #141 for 1st app.) 3 6 9 19 30 40
100-(3/85)-Double size 1 2 3 4 5 7
101-115,117,118,120-129: 107-110-Death of Jean DeWolff. 111-Secret Wars II tie-in. 128-Black Cat new costume 5.00
116,119-Sabretooth-c/story 2 4 6 9 12 15
130-132: 130-Hobgoblin app. 131-Six part Kraven tie-in. 132-Kraven tie-in 2 3 4 6 8 10
133-137,139,140: 140-Punisher cameo 5.00
138-1st full app. Tombstone (origin #139) 1 3 4 6 8 10

Spectacular Spider-Man V2 #23 © MAR

The Spectre (4th series) #27 © DC

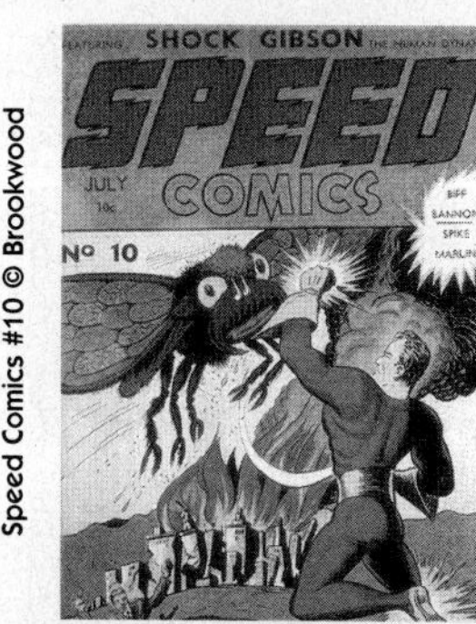

Speed Comics #10 © Brookwood

	GD 2.0	VG 4.0	FN 6.0	VF 8.0	VF/NM 9.0	NM- 9.2

141-143-Punisher app. 1 2 3 4 5 7
144-146,148-157: 151-Tombstone returns 4.00
147-1st brief app. new Hobgoblin (Macendale), 1 page; continued in Web of Spider-Man #48 2 4 6 8 11 14
158-Spider-Man gets new powers (1st Cosmic Spidey, cont'd in Web of Spider-Man #59) 1 2 3 5 6 8
159-Cosmic Spider-Man app. 1 2 3 4 5 7
160-188,190-199: 161-163-Hobgoblin app. 168-170-Avengers x-over. 169-1st app. The Outlaws. 180-184-Green Goblin app. 197-199-Original X-Men-c/story 3.00
189-($2.95, 52 pgs.)-Silver hologram on-c; battles Green Goblin; origin Spidey retold; Vess poster w/Spidey & Hobgoblin 6.00
189-(2nd printing)-Gold hologram on-c 4.00
195-(Deluxe ed.)-Polybagged w/"Dirt" magazine #2 & Beastie Boys/Smithereens music cassette 1 3 4 6 8 10
200-($2.95)-Holo-grafx foil-c; Green Goblin-c/story 5.00
201-219,221,222,224,226-228,230-247: 212-w/card sheet. 203-Maximum Carnage x-over. 204-Begin 4 part death of Tombstone story. 207,208-The Shroud-c/story. 208-Siege of Darkness x-over (#207 is a tie-in). 209-Black Cat back-up. 215,216-Scorpion app. 217-Power & Responsibility Pt. 4. 231-Return of Kaine; Spider-Man corpse discovered. 232-New Doc Octopus app. 233-Carnage-c/app. 235-Dragon Man cameo. 236-Dragon Man-c/app; Lizard app.; Peter Parker regains powers. 238,239-Lizard app. 239-w/card insert. 240-Revelations storyline begins. 241-Flashback 3.00
213-Collectors ed. polybagged w/16 pg. preview & animation cel; foil-c; 1st meeting Spidey & Typhoid Mary 4.00
213-Version polybagged w/Gamepro #7; no-c date, price 3.00
217,219 ($2.95)-Deluxe edition foil-c: flip book 4.00
220 ($2.25, 52 pgs.)-Flip book, Mary Jane reveals pregnancy 4.00
223,229: ($2.50) 229-Spidey quits 4.00
223,225: ($2.95)-223-Die Cut-c. 225-Newsstand ed. 4.00
225,229: ($3.95) 225-Direct Market Holodisk-c (Green Goblin). 229-Acetate-c, Spidey quits 5.00
240-Variant-c 4.00
248,249,251-254,256: 249-Return of Norman Osborn 256-1st app. Prodigy 3.00
250-($3.25) Double gatefold-c 4.00
255-($2.99) Spiderhunt pt. 4 4.00
257-262: 257-Double cover with "Spectacular Prodigy #1"; battles Jack O'Lantern. 258-Spidey is cleared. 259,260-Green Goblin & Hobgoblin app. 262-Byrne-s 3.00
263-Final issue; Byrne-c; Aunt May returns 5.00
#(-1) Flashback (7/97) 3.00
1000 (6/11, $4.99) Punisher app.; Nauck & Ryan-a/Rivera-c; r/ASM #129 5.00
Annual 1 (1979)-Doc Octopus-c & 46 pg. story 2 4 6 8 11 14
Annual 2 (1980)-Origin/1st app. Rapier 1 2 3 5 6 8
Annual 3-5: ('81-'83) 3-Last Man-Wolf 5.00
Annual 6-14: 8 ('88,$ 1.75)-Evolutionary War x-over; Daydreamer returns Gwen Stacy "clone" back to real self (not Gwen Stacy). 9 ('89, $2.00, 68 pgs.)-Atlantis Attacks. 10 ('90, $2.00, 68 pgs.)-McFarlane-a. 11 ('91, $2.00, 68 pgs.)-Iron Man app. 12 ('92, $2.25, 68 pgs.)-Venom solo story cont'd from Amazing Spider-Man Annual #26. 13 ('93, $2.95, 68 pgs.)-Polybagged w/trading card; John Romita, Sr. back-up-a 4.00
Special 1 (1995, $3.95)-Flip book 4.00
NOTE: ***Austin** c-21i, Annual 11i. **Buckler** a-103, 107-111, 116, 117, 119, 122, Annual 1, Annual 10; c-103, 107-111, 113, 116-119, 122, Annual 1. **Buscema** a-121. **Byrne** c(p)-17, 43, 58, 101, 102. **Giffen** a-120p. **Hembeck** c/a-86p. **Larsen** c-Annual 11p. **Miller** c-46p, 48p, 50, 51p, 52p, 54p, 55, 56p, 57, 60. **Mooney** a-7i, 11i, 21p, 23p, 25p, 26p, 29-34p, 36p, 37p, 39i, 41, 42i, 49p, 50i, 51i, 53p, 54-57i, 59-66i, 68i, 71i, 73-79i, 81-83i, 85i, 87-99i, 102i, 125p, Annual 1i, 2p. **Nasser** c-37p. **Perez** c-10. **Simonson** c-54i. **Zeck** a-22, 118, 131, 132; c-131, 132.*

SPECTACULAR SPIDER-MAN (2nd series)
Marvel Comics: Sept, 2003 - No. 27, June, 2005 ($2.25/$2.99)

1-Jenkins-s/Ramos-a/c; Venom-c/app. 4.00
2-26: 2-5-Venom app. 6-9-Dr. Octopus app. 11-13-The Lizard app. 14-Rivera painted-a. 15,16-Capt. America app. 17,18-Ramos-a. 20-Spider-Man gets organic webshooters 21,22-Caldwell-a. 23-26-Sarah & Gabriel app.; Land-c 3.00
27-($2.99) Last issue; Uncle Ben app. in flashback; Buckingham-a 4.00
... Vol. 1: The Hunger TPB (2003, $11.99) r/#1-5 12.00
... Vol. 2: Countdown TPB (2004, $11.99) r/#6-10 12.00
... Vol. 3: Here There Be Monsters TPB (2004, $9.99) r/#11-14 10.00
... Vol. 4: Disassembled TPB (2004, $14.99) r/#15-20 15.00
... Vol. 5: Sins Remembered (2005, $9.99) r/#23-26 10.00
... Vol. 6: The Final Curtain (2005, $14.99) r/#21,22,27 & Peter Parker: Spider-Man #39-41 15.00

SPECTACULAR STORIES MAGAZINE (Formerly A Star Presentation)
Fox Feature Syndicate (Hero Books): No. 4, July, 1950; No. 3, Sept, 1950

4-Sherlock Holmes (true crime stories) 36 72 108 216 351 485
3-The St. Valentine's Day Massacre (true crime) 24 48 72 142 234 325

SPECTRE, THE (1st Series) (See Adventure Comics #431-440, More Fun & Showcase)
National Periodical Publ.: Nov-Dec, 1967 - No. 10, May-June, 1969 (All 12¢)

1-(11-12/67)-Anderson-c/a 13 26 39 89 195 300
2-5-Neal Adams-c/a; 3-Wildcat x-over 9 18 27 57 111 165
6-8,10: 6-8-Anderson inks. 7-Hourman app. 6 12 18 41 76 110
9-Wrightson-a 7 14 21 44 82 120

SPECTRE, THE (2nd Series) (See Saga of the Swamp Thing #58, Showcase '95 #8 & Wrath of the...)
DC Comics: Apr, 1987 - No. 31, Oct, 1989 ($1.00, new format)

1-Colan-a begins 5.00
2-32: 9-Nudity panels. 10-Batman cameo. 10,11-Millennium tie-ins 3.00
Annual 1 (1988, $2.00)-Deadman app. 4.00
NOTE: ***Art Adams** c-Annual 1. **Colan** a-1-6. **Kaluta** c-1-3. **Mignola** c-7-9. **Morrow** a-9-15. **Sears** c/a-22. **Vess** c-13-15.*

SPECTRE, THE (3rd Series) (Also see Brave and the Bold #72, 75, 116, 180, 199 & Showcase '95 #8)
DC Comics: Dec, 1992 - No. 62, Feb, 1998 ($1.75/$1.95/$2.25/$2.50)

1-($1.95)-Glow-in-the-dark-c; Mandrake-a begins 5.00
2,3 4.00
4-7,9-12,14-20: 10-Kaluta-c. 11-Hildebrandt painted-c. 16-Aparo/K. Jones-a. 19-Snyder III-c. 20-Sienkiewicz-c 3.00
8,13-($2.50)-Glow-in-the-dark-c 4.00
21-62: 22-(9/94)-Superman-c & app. 23-(11/94). 43-Kent Williams-c. 44-Kaluta-c. 47-Final Night x-over. 49-Begin Bolton-c. 51-Batman-c/app. 52-Gianni-c. 54-1st app. Michael Holt (Mr. Terrific); Corben-c. 60-Harris-c 3.00
#0 (10/94) Released between #22 & #23 3.00
Annual 1 (1995, $3.95)-Year One story 4.00
NOTE: ***Bisley** c-27. **Fabry** c-2. **Kelley Jones** c-31. **Vess** c-5.*

SPECTRE, THE (4th Series) (Hal Jordan; also see Day of Judgment #5 and Legends of the DC Universe #33-36)
DC Comics: Mar, 2001 - No. 27, May, 2003 ($2.50/$2.75)

1-DeMatteis-s/Ryan Sook-c/a 4.00
2-27: 3,4-Superman & Batman-c/app. 5-Two-Face-c/app. 20-Begin $2.75-c. 21-Sinestro returns. 24-JLA app. 3.00

SPECTRE, THE (See Crisis Aftermath: The Spectre)

SPEEDBALL (See Amazing Spider-Man Annual #12, Marvel Super-Heroes & The New Warriors)
Marvel Comics: Sept, 1988(10/88-inside) - No. 10, Jun, 1989 (75¢)

1-Ditko/Guice-a/c 1 3 4 6 8 10
2-10: Ditko/Guice-a-2-4; Ditko a-2-10; c-2-10p 4.00

SPEED BUGGY (TV)(Also see Fun-In #12, 15)
Charlton Comics: July, 1975 - No. 9, Nov, 1976 (Hanna-Barbera)

1 3 6 9 15 22 28
2-9 2 4 6 10 14 18

SPEED CARTER SPACEMAN (See Spaceman)

SPEED COMICS (New Speed)(Also see Double Up)
Brookwood Publ./Speed Publ./Harvey Publications No. 14 on:
10/39 - #11, 8/40; #12, 3/41 - #44, 1-2/47 (#14-16: pocket size, 100 pgs.)

1-Origin & 1st app. Shock Gibson; Ted Parrish, the Man with 1000 Faces begins; Powell-a; becomes Champion #2 on?; has earliest? full page panel in comics; classic war-c 423 846 1269 3088 5444 7800
2-Powell-a 194 388 582 1242 2121 3000
3-War-c 142 284 426 909 1555 2200
4,5: 4-Powell-a. 5-Dinosaur-c 129 258 387 826 1413 2000
6-9,11: 7-Mars Mason begins, ends #11. 9,11-War-c 123 246 369 787 1344 1900
10-Classsic Giant Moth Monster-c 155 310 465 992 1696 2400
12 (3/41; shows #11 in indicia)-The Wasp begins; Major Colt app. (Capt. Colt #12) 129 258 387 826 1413 2000
13-Intro. Captain Freedom & Young Defenders; Girl Commandos, Pat Parker (costumed heroine), War Nurse begins; Major Colt app. 142 284 426 909 1555 2200
14,15-(100 pg. pocket size, 1941): 14-2nd Harvey comic (See Pocket); Shock Gibson dons new costume; Nazi war-c. 15-Pat Parker dons costume, last in costume #23; no Girl Commandos; Nazi monsters war-c. 300 600 900 1920 3310 4700
16-(100 pg. pocket size, 1941) Cover with Hitler leading an army of Nazi ghouls to the White House 300 600 900 2070 3635 5200
17-Classic Simon & Kirby WWII Nazi bondage/torture-c; Black Cat begins (4/42, early app.; see Pocket #1); origin Black Cat-r/Pocket #1; not in #40,41 300 600 900 1920 3310 4700
18-20-S&K-c. 18-Bondage/torture-c. 19,20-Japanese war-c 232 464 696 1485 2543 3600
21-Hitler, Tojo-c; Kirby-c 300 600 900 2010 3505 5000

Speed Racer #6 © Speed Racer Ent.

Spellbound #3 © MAR

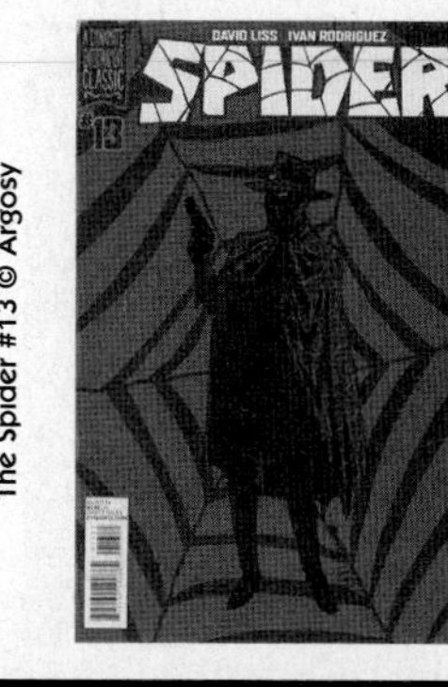

The Spider #13 © Argosy

GD 2.0 VG 4.0 FN 6.0 VF 8.0 VF/NM 9.0 NM- 9.2

22-Nazi WWII-c by Kirby 194 388 582 1242 2121 3000
23-Origin Girl Commandos; war-c by Kirby 194 388 582 1242 2121 3000
24-Pat Parker team-up with Girl Commandos; Hitler, Tojo, & Mussolini-c
265 530 795 1694 2897 4100
25,27,29: 25-War-c. 27 Nazi WWII-c. 29-Nazi WWII bondage-c
174 348 522 1114 1907 2700
26-Flag-c 226 452 678 1446 2473 3500
28-Classic Nazi monster WWII-c 331 662 993 2317 4059 5800
30-Nazi WWII Death Chamber bondage-c 206 412 618 1318 2259 3200
31-Classic Schomburg Hitler & Tojo-c 331 662 993 2317 4059 5800
32-35-Schomburg-c. 32,34-Nazi war-c. 33,35-Japanese war-c
174 348 522 1114 1907 2700
36-Schomburg Japanese war-c 110 220 330 704 1202 1700
37,39-42,44: 37-Japanese war-c. 41-War-c 43 86 129 271 461 650
38-Iwo-Jima Flag-c 52 104 156 328 552 775
43-Robot-c 53 106 159 334 567 800

NOTE: ***Al Avison*** *c-14-16, 30, 43.* ***Briefer*** *a-6, 7.* ***Jon Henri*** *(Kirbyesque) c-17-20.* ***Kubert*** *a-37, 38, 42-44.* ***Kirby/Caseneuve*** *c-21-23.* ***Cecelia Munson*** *a-7-11(Mars Mason).* ***Palais*** *c-37, 39-42.* ***Powell*** *a-1, 2, 4-7, 28, 31, 44.* ***Schomburg*** *c-31-36.* ***Tuska*** *a-3, 6, 7. Bondage c-18, 35. Captain Freedom c-16-24, 25(part), 26-44(w/Black Cat #27, 29, 31, 32-40). Shock Gibson c-1-15.*

SPEED DEMON (Also see Marvel Versus DC #3 & DC Versus Marvel #4)
Marvel Comics (Amalgam): Apr, 1996 ($1.95, one-shot)
1 3.00

SPEED DEMONS (Formerly Frank Merriwell at Yale #1-4?; Submarine Attack #11 on)
Charlton Comics: No. 5, Feb, 1957 - No. 10, 1958
5-10 7 14 21 35 43 50

SPEED FORCE (See The Flash 2nd Series #143-Cobalt Blue)
DC Comics: Nov, 1997 ($3.95, one-shot)
1-Flash & Kid Flash vs. Cobalt Blue; Waid-s/Aparo & Sienkiewicz-a; Flash family stories and pin-ups by various 4.00

SPEED RACER (Also see The New Adventures of...)
Now Comics: July, 1987 - No. 38, Nov, 1990 ($1.75)
1 4.00
2-38, 1-2nd printing 3.00
Special 1 (1988, $2.00) 4.00
Special 2 (1988, $3.50) 4.00

SPEED RACER (Also see Racer X)
DC Comics (WildStorm): Oct, 1999 - No. 3, Dec, 1999 ($2.50, limited series)
1-3-Tommy Yune-s/a; origin of Racer X; debut of the Mach 5 3.00
...: Born To Race (2000, $9.95, TPB) r/series & conceptual art 10.00
...: The Original Manga Vol. 1 ('00, $9.95, TPB) r/1950s B&W manga 10.00

SPEED RACER: CHRONICLES OF THE RACER
IDW Publishing: 2007 - No. 4, Apr, 2008 ($3.99)
1-4-Multiple covers for each 4.00

SPEED RACER FEATURING NINJA HIGH SCHOOL
Now Comics: Aug, 1993 - No. 2, 1993 ($2.50, mini-series)
1,2: 1-Polybagged w/card. 2-Exists? 3.00

SPEED RACER: RETURN OF THE GRX
Now Comics: Mar, 1994 - No. 2, Apr, 1994 ($1.95, limited series)
1,2 3.00

SPEED SMITH-THE HOT ROD KING (Also see Hot Rod King)
Ziff-Davis Publishing Co.: Spring, 1952
1-Saunders painted-c 25 50 75 147 241 335

SPEEDY GONZALES
Dell Publishing Co.: No. 1084, Mar, 1960
Four Color 1084 6 12 18 41 76 110

SPEEDY RABBIT (See Television Puppet Show)
Realistic/I. W. Enterprises/Super Comics: nd (1953); 1963
nn (1953)-Realistic Reprint? 2 4 6 11 16 20
I.W. Reprint #1 (2 versions w/diff. c/stories exist)-Peter Cottontail #?
Super Reprint #14(1963) 2 4 6 8 11 14

SPELLBINDERS
Quality: Dec, 1986 - No. 12, Jan, 1988 ($1.25)
1-12: Nemesis the Warlock, Amadeus Wolf 3.00

SPELLBINDERS
Marvel Comics: May, 2005 - No. 6, Oct, 2005 ($2.99, limited series)
1-6-Carey-s/Perkins-a 3.00
...: Signs and Wonders TPB (2006, $7.99, digest) r/#1-6 8.00

SPELLBOUND (See The Crusaders)

SPELLBOUND (Tales to Hold You... #1, Stories to Hold You...)
Atlas Comics (ACI 1-15/Male 16-23/BPC 24-34): Mar, 1952 - #23, June, 1954; #24, Oct, 1955 - #34, June, 1957
1-Horror/weird stories in all 123 246 369 787 1344 1900
2-Edgar A. Poe app. 65 130 195 416 708 1000
3-Whitney-a; cannibalism story; classic Heath-c 97 194 291 621 1061 1500
4,5 57 114 171 362 619 875
6-Krigstein-a 58 116 174 371 636 900
7-10: 7,8-Ayers-a 50 100 150 315 533 750
11-13,15,16,18-20 45 90 135 284 480 675
14-Ed Win-a; classic Everett-c 129 258 387 826 1413 2000
17-Krigstein-a; classic Everett skeleton-c 103 206 309 659 1130 1600
21-23: 23-Last precode (6/54) 39 78 117 240 395 550
24-28,30,31,34: 25-Orlando-a 32 64 96 188 307 425
29-Ditko-a (4 pgs.) 34 68 102 199 325 450
32,33-Torres-a 32 64 96 188 307 425

NOTE: ***Brodsky*** *a-5; c-1, 5-7, 10, 11, 13, 15, 25-27, 32.* ***Colan*** *a-17.* ***Everett*** *a-2, 5, 7, 10, 16, 28, 31; c-2, 8, 9, 14, 17-19, 28, 30.* ***Forgione/Abel*** *a-29.* ***Forte/Fox*** *a-16.* ***Al Hartley*** *a-2.* ***Heath*** *a-2, 4, 8, 9, 12, 14, 16; c-3, 4, 12, 16, 20, 21.* ***Infantino*** *a-15.* ***Keller*** *a-5.* ***Kida*** *a-2, 14.* ***Maneely*** *a-7, 14, 27; c-24, 29, 31.* ***Mooney*** *a-5, 13, 18.* ***Mac Pakula*** *a-22, 32.* ***Post*** *a-8.* ***Powell*** *a-19, 20, 32.* ***Robinson*** *a-1.* ***Romita*** *a-24, 26, 27.* ***R.Q. Sale*** *a-29.* ***Sekowsky*** *a-5.* ***Severin*** *c-29.* ***Sinnott*** *a-8, 16, 17.*

SPELLBOUND
Marvel Comics: Jan, 1988 - Apr, 1988 ($1.50, bi-weekly, Baxter paper)
1-5 3.00
6 ($2.25, 52 pgs.) 4.00

SPELLJAMMER (Also see TSR Worlds Comics Annual)
DC Comics: Sept, 1990 - No. 15, Nov, 1991 ($1.75)
1-15: Based on TSR game. 11-Heck-a. 3.00

SPELL ON WHEELS
Dark Horse Comics: Oct, 2016 - Present ($3.99)
1-5-Kate Leth-s/Megan Levens-a. 1-Ming Doyle-c 4.00

SPENCER SPOOK (Formerly Giggle Comics)
American Comics Group: No. 100, Mar-Apr, 1955 - No. 101, May-June, 1955
100,101 8 16 24 40 50 60

SPIDER, THE
Eclipse Books: 1991 - Book 3, 1991 ($4.95, 52 pgs., limited series)
Book 1-3-Truman-c/a 5.00

SPIDER, THE
Dynamite Entertainment: 2012 - No. 18, 2014 ($3.99)
1-18: 1-Revival of the pulp character; Liss-s/Worley-a; 4 covers. 2-18-Multiple covers 4.00
Annual 1 (2013, $4.99) Denton-s/Vitorino-a/c 5.00

SPIDER-BOY (Also see Marvel Versus DC #3)
Marvel Comics (Amalgam): Apr, 1996 ($1.95)
1-Mike Wieringo-c/a; Karl Kesel story; 1st app. of Bizarnage, Insect Queen, Challengers of the Fantastic, Sue Storm: Agent of S.H.I.E.L. D., & King Lizard 3.00

SPIDER-BOY TEAM-UP
Marvel Comics (Amalgam): June, 1997 ($1.95, one-shot)
1-Karl Kesel & Roger Stern-s/Jo Ladronn-a(p) 3.00

SPIDER-GIRL (See What If... #105)
Marvel Comics: Oct, 1998 - No. 100, Sept, 2006 ($1.99/$2.25/$2.99)
0-($2.99)-r/1st app. Peter Parker's daughter from What If #105; previews regular series, Avengers-Next and J2 1 2 3 4 5 7
1-DeFalco-s/Olliffe & Williamson-s 1 2 3 5 6 8
2-Two covers 4.00
3-16,18-20: 3-Fantastic Five-c/app. 10,11-Spider-Girl time-travels to meet teenaged Spider-Man 3.00
17-($2.99) Peter Parker suits up 4.00
21-24,26-49,51-59: 21-Begin $2.25-c. 31-Avengers app. 3.00
25-($2.99) Spider-Girl vs. the Savage Six 4.00
50-($3.50) 4.00
59-99-($2.99) 59-Avengers app.; Ben Parker born. 75-May in Black costume. 82-84-Venom bonds with Normie Osborn. 93-Venom-c. 95-Tony Stark app. 3.00
100-($3.99) Last issue; story plus Rogues Gallery, profile pages; r/#27,53 4.00
1999 Annual ($3.99) 4.00
...: The End! (10/10, $3.99) Frenz & Buscema-a; Mayhem app. 4.00

Spider-Gwen #26 © MAR

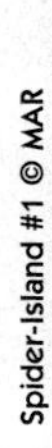
Spider-Island #1 © MAR

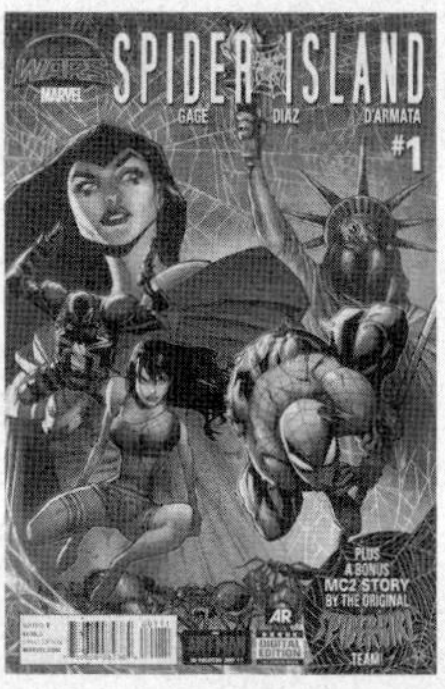

Spider-Man #93 © MAR

	GD	VG	FN	VF	VF/NM	NM-
	2.0	4.0	6.0	8.0	9.0	9.2

Wizard #1/2 (1999) 3.00
... A Fresh Start (1/99,$5.99, TPB) r/#1&2 6.00
... Presents The Buzz and Darkdevil (2007, $7.99, digest) r/mini-series 8.00

SPIDER-GIRL (Araña Corazon from Arana Heart of the Spider)
Marvel Comics: Jan, 2011 - No. 8, Sept, 2011 ($3.99/$2.99)

1-($3.99) Tobin-s/Henry-a/Kitson-c; back-up w/Haspiel-a; Fantastic Four app. 4.00
1-Variant-c by Del Mundo 5.00
2-8-($2.99) 2,3-Red Hulk app. 4,5-Ana Kravenoff app. 6-Hobgoblin app. 8-Powers return 3.00

SPIDER-GWEN (See debut in Edge of Spider-Verse #2)
Marvel Comics: Apr, 2015 - No. 5, Aug, 2015 ($3.99)

1-Latour-s/Robbi Rodriguez-a/c; The Vulture app. 6.00
2-5: 2-Spider-Ham app. 3-The Vulture & The Punisher app. 4.00

SPIDER-GWEN
Marvel Comics: Dec, 2015 - Present ($3.99)

1-29: 1-Latour-s/Robbi Rodriguez-a; The Lizard & female Capt. America app. 7,8-"Spider-Women" tie-in; Silk & Spider-Woman app. 10-Kraven app. 16-18-Miles app.; x-over with Spider-Man #12-14. 24-29-Gwenom app. 4.00
#0 (1/16, $4.99) Reprints #1 (4/15) plus script of Edge of Spider-Verse #2 5.00
Annual 1 (8/16, $4.99) Short stories; Latour-s; art by various 5.00

SPIDER-HAM 25TH ANNIVERSARY SPECIAL
Marvel Comics: Aug, 2010 ($3.99, one-shot)

1-Jusko-c/DeFalco-s/Chabot-a; Peter Porker vs. the Swinester Six 4.00

SPIDER ISLAND... (one-shots) (See Amazing Spider-Man #666-673)
Marvel Comics

...: Deadly Foes 1 (10/11, $4.99) Hobgoblin & Jackal stories; Caselli-c 5.00
...: Emergence of Evil - Jackal & Hobgoblin 1 (10/11, $4.99) Hobgoblin & Jackal reprints 5.00
...: Heroes For Hire 1 (12/11, $2.99) Misty Knight & Paladin; Hotz-a/Yardin-c 3.00
...: I Love New York City 1 (11/11, $3.99) Short stories by various; Punisher app. 4.00
...: Spider-Woman 1 (11/11, $2.99) Van Lente-s/Camuncoli-a; Alicia Masters app. 3.00
... Spotlight 1 ('11, $3.99) Creator interviews and story previews 4.00
...: The Avengers 1 (11/11, $2.99) McKone-a/Yu-c; Frog-Man app. 3.00

SPIDER-ISLAND (Secret Wars tie-in)(Back-up MC2 Spider-Girl story in each issue)
Marvel Comics: Sept, 2015 - No. 5, Dec, 2015 ($4.99/$3.99, limited series)

1-($4.99) Gage-s/Diaz-a/Ramos-c; Venom and Werewolf By Night app. 5.00
2-5-($3.99) Tony Stark as the Green Goblin. 3-5-Peter Parker returns 4.00

SPIDER ISLAND: CLOAK & DAGGER (See Amazing Spider-Man #666-673)
Marvel Comics: Oct, 2011 - No. 3, Dec, 2011 ($2.99, limited series)

1-3-Spencer-s/Rios-a/Choi-c; Mr. Negative app. 3.00

SPIDER ISLAND: DEADLY HANDS OF KUNG FU (See Amazing Spider-Man #666-673)
Marvel Comics: Oct, 2011 - No. 3, Dec, 2011 ($2.99, limited series)

1-3-Johnston-s/Fiumara-a; Madame Web & Iron Fist app. 3.00

SPIDER ISLAND: THE AMAZING SPIDER-GIRL (Continued from Spider-Girl #8)
Marvel Comics: Oct, 2011 - No. 3, Dec, 2011 ($2.99, limited series)

1-3-Hobgoblin & Kingpin app.; Tobin-s/Larraz-a 3.00

SPIDER-MAN (See Amazing..., Friendly Neighborhood..., Giant-Size..., Marvel Age..., Marvel Knights..., Marvel Tales, Marvel Team-Up, Spectacular..., Spidey Super Stories, Ultimate Marvel Team-Up, Ultimate..., Venom, & Web Of...)

SPIDER-MAN (Peter Parker Spider-Man on cover but not indicia #75-on)
Marvel Comics: Aug, 1990 - No. 98, Nov, 1998 ($1.75/$1.95/ $1.99)

1-Silver edition, direct sale only (unbagged) 1 3 4 6 8 10
1-Silver bagged edition; direct sale, no price on comic, but $2.00 on plastic bag (125,000 print run) 3 6 9 16 23 30
1-Regular edition w/Spidey face in UPC area (unbagged); green-c 1 2 3 5 6 8
1-Regular bagged edition w/Spidey face in UPC area; green cover (125,000) 12.00
1-Newsstand bagged w/UPC code 8.00
1-Gold edition, 2nd printing (unbagged) with Spider-Man in box (400,000-450,000) 3 6 9 16 23 30
1-Gold 2nd printing w/UPC code; (less than 10,000 print run) intended for Wal-Mart; much scarcer than originally believed 10 20 30 66 138 210
1-Platinum ed. mailed to retailers only (10,000 print run); has new McFarlane-a & editorial material instead of ads; stiff-c, no cover price 9 18 27 63 129 195
2-10: 2-McFarlane-c/a/scripts continue. 6,7-Ghost Rider & Hobgoblin app. 8-Wolverine cameo; Wolverine storyline begins 6.00
11-25: 12-Wolverine storyline ends. 13-Spidey's black costume returns; Morbius app. 14-Morbius app. 15-Erik Larsen-c/a; Beast c/s. 16-X-Force-c/story w/Liefeld assists; continues in X-Force #4; reads sideways; last McFarlane issue. 17-Thanos-c/story; Leonardi/Williamson-c/a. 18-Ghost Rider-c/story. 18-23-Sinister Six storyline w/Erik Larsen-c/a/scripts. 19-Hulk & Hobgoblin-c & app. 20-22-Deathlok app. 22,23-Ghost Rider, Hulk, Hobgoblin app. 23-Wrap-around gatefold-c. 24-Infinity War x-over w/Demogoblin & Hobgoblin-c/story. 24-Demogoblin dons new costume & battles Hobgoblin-c/story 4.00
26-($3.50, 52 pgs.)-Silver hologram on-c w/gatefold poster by Ron Lim; origin retold 6.00
26-2nd printing; gold hologram on-c 4.00
27-45: 32-34-Punisher-c/story. 37-Maximum Carnage x-over. 39,40-Electro-c/s (cameo #38). 41-43-Iron Fist-c/stories w/Jae Lee-c/a. 42-Intro Platoon. 44-Hobgoblin app. 3.50
46-49,51-53, 55, 56,58-74,76-81: 46-Begin $1.95-c; bound-in card sheet. 51-Power & Responsibility Pt. 3. 52,53-Venom app. 60-Kaine revealed. 61-Origin Kaine. 65-Mysterio app. 66-Kaine-c/app.; Peter Parker app. 67-Carnage-c/app. 68,69-Hobgoblin-c/app. 72-Onslaught x-over; Spidey vs. Sentinels. 74-Daredevil-c/app. 77-80-Morbius-c/app. 3.00
46-($2.95)-Polybagged; silver ink-c w/16 pg. preview of cartoon series & animation style print; bound-in trading card sheet 4.00
50-($2.50)-Newsstand edition 4.00
50-($3.95)-Collectors edition w/holographic-c 5.00
51-($2.95)-Deluxe edition foil-c; flip book 4.00
54-($2.75, 52 pgs.)-Flip book 4.00
57-($2.50) 4.00
57-($2.95)-Die cut-c 5.00
65-($2.95)-Variant-c; polybagged w/cassette 4.00
75-($2.95)-Wraparound-c; Green Goblin returns; death of Ben Reilly (who was the clone) 4.00
82-97: 84-Juggernaut app. 91-Double cover with "Dusk #1"; battles the Shocker. 93-Ghost Rider app. 3.00
98-Double cover; final issue 4.00
#(-1) Flashback (7/97) 3.00
Annual '97 ($2.99), '98 ($2.99)-Devil Dinosaur-c/app. 4.00
NOTE: ***Erik Larsen*** *c/a-15, 18-23.* ***M. Rogers/Keith Williams*** *c/a-27, 28.*

SPIDER-MAN (Miles Morales in regular Marvel Universe)
Marvel Comics: Apr, 2016 - No. 21, Dec, 2017; No. 234, Jan, 2018 - Present ($3.99)

1-21: 1,2-Bendis-s/Pichelli-a; Avengers & Peter Parker app. 3-Ms. Marvel app. 6-10-Civil War II tie-ins. 12,13-Crossover with Spider-Gwen #16-18. 16,18-Black Cat app. 20,21-Nico Leon-a 4.00

[Title switches to legacy numbering after #21 (12/17)]

234-238-Hobgoblin, Sandman, Electro, The Spot, Bombshell, Iron Spider app. 4.00

SPIDER-MAN (one-shots, hardcovers and TPBs)

...& Arana Special: The Hunter Revealed (5/06, $3.99) Del Rio-s; art by Del Rio & various 4.00
...and Batman ('95, $5.95) DeMatteis-s; Joker, Carnage app. 8.00
...and Daredevil ('84, $2.00) 1-r/Spectacular Spider-Man #26-28 by Miller 6.00
...and The Human Torch in...Bahia de Los Muertos! 1 (5/09, $3.99) Beland-s/Juan Doe-a; Diablo app.; printed in two versions (English and Spanish language) 4.00
...: Back in Black HC (2007, $34.99, dustjacket) oversized r/Amaz. S-M #539-543, Friendly Neighborhood S-M #17-23 & Annual #1; cover pencils and sketch pages 35.00
...: Back in Black SC (2008, $24.99) same contents as HC 25.00
...: Back in Black Handbook (2007, $3.99) Official Handbook format; Lopresti-c 10.00
...: Back in Quack (11/10, $3.99) Howard the Duck, Beverly and Man-Thing app. 4.00
...: Birth of Venom TPB (2007, $29.99) r/Secret Wars #8, AS-M #252-259,298-300,315-317, AS-M Annual #25, Fantastic Four #274 and Web of Spider-Man #1 30.00
...: Brand New Day HC (2008, $24.99, dustjacket) r/Amaz. S-M #546-551, Spider-Man: Swing Shift and story from Venom Super-Special 25.00
...: Carnage nn (6/93, $6.95, TPB)-r/Amazing S-M #344,345,359-363; spot varnish-c 10.00
.../Daredevil (10/02, $2.99) Vatche Mavlian-c/a; Brett Matthews-s 3.00
...: Dead Man's Hand 1 (4/97, $2.99) 3.00
...: Death of the Stacys HC (2007, $19.99, dustjacket) r/Amazing Spider-Man #88-92 and #121,122; intro. by Gerry Conway; afterword by Romita; cover gallery incl. reprints 20.00
.../Dr. Strange: "The Way to Dusty Death" nn (1992, $6.95, 68 pgs.) 8.00
...: Election Day HC (2009, $29.99) r/#584-588; includes Barack Obama app from #583 30.00
.../Elektra '98-($2.99) vs. The Silencer 3.00
... Family (2005, $4.99, 100 pgs.) new story and reprints; Spider-Ham app. 5.00
... Fear Itself (3/09, $3.99) Spider-Man and Man-Thing; Stuart Moore-s/Joe Suitor-a 4.00
... Fear Itself Graphic Novel (2/92, $12.95) 18.00
Free Comic Book Day 2012 (Spider-Man: Season One) #1 (Giveaway) Previews the GN 3.00
Giant-Sized Spider-Man (12/98, $3.99) r/team-ups 4.00
...: Grim Hunt - The Kraven Saga (5/10, free) prelude to Grim Hunt arc; Kraven history 3.00
Holiday Special 1995 ($2.95) 4.00
...: Hot Shots nn (1/96, $2.95) fold out posters by various, inc. Vess and Ross 4.00
Identity Crisis (9/98, $19.95, TPB) 20.00
...: Kraven's Last Hunt HC (2006, $19.99) r/Amaz. S-M #293,294; Web of S-M #31,32 and Spect. S-M #131-132; intro. by DeMatteis; Zeck-a; cover pencils and interior pencils 20.00
...: Legacy of Evil 1 (6/96, $3.95) Kurt Busiek script & Mark Texeira-c/a 4.00
...Legends Vol. 1: Todd McFarlane ('03, $19.95, TPB)-r/Amaz. S-M #298-305 20.00
...Legends Vol. 2: Todd McFarlane ('03, $19.99, TPB)-r/Amaz. S-M #306-314, & Spec. Spider-Man Annual #10 20.00
...Legends Vol. 3: Todd McFarlane ('04, $24.99, TPB)-r/Amaz. S-M #315-323,325,328 25.00
...Legends Vol. 4: Spider-Man & Wolverine ('03, $13.95, TPB) r/Spider-Man & Wolverine #1-4

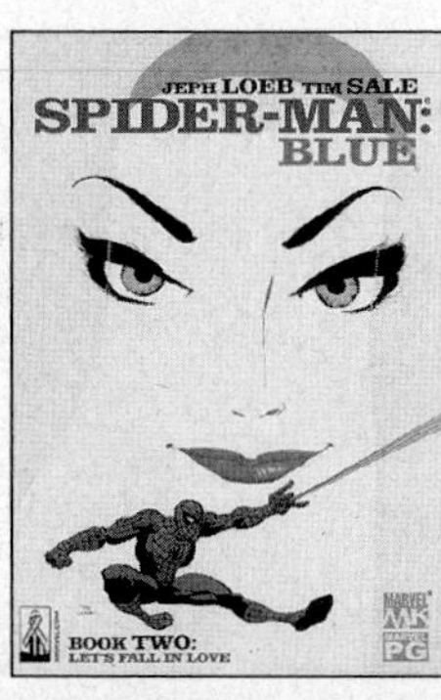

Spider-Man: Blue #2 © MAR

Spider-Man: Classics #5 © MAR

Spider-Man / Deadpool #8 © MAR

GD 2.0	VG 4.0	FN 6.0	VF 8.0	VF/NM 9.0	NM- 9.2

and Spider-Man/Daredevil #1 14.00
.../Marrow (2/01, $2.99) Garza-a 3.00
.../Mary Jane: ... You Just Hit the Jackpot TPB (2009, $24.99) early apps. & key stories 25.00
...: Master Plan 1 (9/17, $3.99) Thompson-s/Stockman-a; bonus r/ASM #2 4.00
100th Anniversary Special: Spider-Man 1 (9/14, $3.99) In-Hyk Lee-a/c; Venom app. 4.00
...: One More Day HC (2008. $24.99, dustjacket) r/Amaz. S-M #544-545, Friendly N.S-M #24, Sensational S-M #41 and Marvel Spotlight: Spider-Man-One More Day 25.00
...: Origin of the Hunter (6/10, $3.99) r/Kraven apps. in ASM #15 & 34; new Mayhew-a 4.00
..., Peter Parker: Back in Black HC (2007, $34.99) oversized r/Sensational Spider-Man #35-40 & Annual #1, Spider-Man Family #1,2; Marvel Spotlight: Spider-Man and Spider-Man Back in Black Handbook; cover sketches 35.00
..., Punisher, Sabretooth: Designer Genes (1993, $8.95) 10.00
...Return of the Goblin TPB (See Peter Parker: Spider-Man)
...Revelations ('97, $14.99, TPB) r/end of Clone Saga plus 14 new pages by Romita Jr. 15.00
...: Saga of the Sandman TPB (2007, $19.99) r/1st app. Amazing S-M #4 and other app. 20.00
...: Season One HC (2012, $24.99) Origin and early days; Bunn-s/Neil Edwards-a 25.00
...: Son of the Goblin (2004, $15.99, TPB) r/AS-M#136-137,312 & Spec. S-M #189,200 16.00
... Special: Black and Blue and Read All Over 1 (11/06, $3.99) new story and r/ASM #12 4.00
Special Edition 1 (12/92-c, 11/92 inside)-The Trial of Venom; ordered thru mail with $5.00 donation or more to UNICEF; embossed metallic ink; came bagged w/bound-in poster; Daredevil app. 2 4 6 10 14 18
... Spectacular 1 (8/14, $4.99) Reprints all-ages tales; Green Goblin, Kraven app. 5.00
Super Special (7/95, $3.95)-Planet of the Symbiotes 4.00
The Best of Spider-Man Vol. 2 (2003, $29.99, HC with dust jacket) r/AS-M V2 #37-45, Peter Parker: S-M #44-47, and S-M's Tangled Web #10,11; Pearson-c 30.00
The Best of Spider-Man Vol. 3 (2004, $29.99, HC with d.j.) r/AS-M V2 #46-58, 500 30.00
The Best of Spider-Man Vol. 4 (2005, $29.99, HC with d.j.) r/#501-514; sketch pages 30.00
The Best of Spider-Man Vol. 5 (2006, $29.99, HC with d.j.) r/#515-524; sketch pages 30.00
The Complete Frank Miller Spider-Man (2002, $29.95, HC) r/Miller-s/a 30.00
The Death of Captain Stacy ($3.50) r/AS-M#88-90 5.00
The Death of Gwen Stacy ($14.95) r/AS-M#96-98,121,122 15.00
...: The Movie ($12.95) adaptation by Stan Lee-s/Alan Davis-a; plus r/Ultimate Spider-Man #8, Peter Parker #35, Tangled Web #10; photo-c 13.00
...: The Official Movie Adaptation ($5.95) Stan Lee-s/Alan Davis-a 6.00
...: The Other HC (2006, $29.99, dust jacket) r/Amazing S-M #525-528, Friendly Neighborhood S-M #1-4 and Marvel Knights S-M #19-22; gallery of variant covers 30.00
...: The Other SC (2006, $24.99) r/crossover; gallery of variant covers 25.00
...: The Other Sketchbook (2005, $2.99) sketch page preview of 2005-6 x-over 3.00
Torment TPB (5/01$15.95) r/#1-5, Spec. S-M #10 16.00
... Vs. Doctor Octopus ($17.95) reprints early battles; Sean Chen-c 18.00
... Vs. Punisher (7/00, $2.99) Michael Lopez-c/a 3.00
...Vs. Silver Sable (2006, $15.99, TPB)-r/Amazing Spider-Man #265,279-281 & Peter Parker, The Spectacular Spider-Man #128,129 16.00
...Vs. The Black Cat (2005, $14.99, TPB)-r/Amaz. S-M #194,195,204,205,226,227 15.00
...Vs. Vampires (12/10, $3.99) Blade app.; Castro-a/Grevioux-s 4.00
...Vs. Venom (1990, $8.95, TPB)-r/Amaz. S-M #300,315-317 w/new McFarlane-c 12.00
...Visionaries (10/01, $19.95, TPB)-r/Amaz. S-M #298-305; McFarlane-a 20.00
...Visionaries: John Romita (8/01, $19.95, TPB)-r/Amaz. S-M #39-42, 50,68,69,108,109; new Romita-c 20.00
...Visionaries: Kurt Busiek (2006, $19.99, TPB)-r/Untold Tales of Spider-Man #1-8 20.00
...Visionaries: Roger Stern (2007, $24.99, TPB)-r/Amazing Spider-Man #206 & Spectacular Spider-Man #43-52,54; Stern interview 25.00
Wizard 1/2 ($10.00) Leonardi-a; Green Goblin app. 10.00

SPIDER-MAN ADVENTURES
Marvel Comics: Dec, 1994 - No. 15, Mar, 1996 ($1.50)
1-15 ($1.50)-Based on animated series 3.00
1-($2.95)-Foil embossed-c 4.00

SPIDER-MAN AND HIS AMAZING FRIENDS (See Marvel Action Universe)
Marvel Comics Group: Dec, 1981 (one-shot)
1-Adapted from NBC TV cartoon show; Green Goblin-c/story; 1st Spidey, Firestar, Iceman team-up; Spiegle-p 4 8 12 25 40 55

SPIDER-MAN AND POWER PACK
Marvel Comics: Jan, 2007 - No. 4, Apr, 2007 ($2.99, limited series)
1-4-Sumerak-s/Gurihiru-a; Sandman app. 3,4-Venom app. 3.00
...: Big City Heroes (2007, $6.99, digest) r/#1-4 7.00

SPIDER-MAN AND THE FANTASTIC FOUR
Marvel Comics: Jun, 2007 - No. 4, Sept, 2007 ($2.99, limited series)
1-4-Mike Wieringo-a/c; Jeff Parker-s. 1,4-Impossible Man app. 3.00
...: Silver Rage TPB (2007, $10.99) r/#1-4; series outline and cover sketches 11.00

SPIDER-MAN AND THE SECRET WARS
Marvel Comics: Feb, 2010 - No. 4, May, 2010 ($2.99, limited series)
1-4-Tobin-s/Scherberger-a. 3-Black costume app. 3.00

SPIDER-MAN AND THE INCREDIBLE HULK (See listing under Amazing...)

SPIDER-MAN AND THE UNCANNY X-MEN
Marvel Comics: Mar, 1996 ($16.95, trade paperback)
nn-r/Uncanny X-Men #27, Uncanny X-men #35, Amazing Spider-Man #92, Marvel Team-Up Annual #1, Marvel Team-Up #150, & Spectacular Spider-Man #197-199 17.00

SPIDER-MAN & THE X-MEN
Marvel Comics: Feb, 2015 - No. 6, Jub, 2015 ($3.99)
1-3: Spider-Man teaching at the Jean Grey School; Kalan-s/Failla-a. 2,3-Mojo app. 4.00

SPIDER-MAN & WOLVERINE (See Spider-Man Legends Vol. 4 for TPB reprint)
Marvel Comics: Aug, 2003 - No. 4, Nov, 2003 ($2.99, limited series)
1-4-Matthews-s/Mavlian-a 3.00

SPIDER-MAN AND X-FACTOR
Marvel Comics: May, 1994 - No. 3, July, 1994 ($1.95, limited series)
1-3 3.00

SPIDER-MAN /BADROCK
Maximum Press: Mar, 1997 ($2.99, mini-series)
1A, 1B(#2)-Jurgens-s 3.00

SPIDER-MAN/BLACK CAT: THE EVIL THAT MEN DO (Also see Marvel Must Haves)
Marvel Comics: Aug, 2002 - No. 6, Mar, 2006 ($2.99, limited series)
1-6-Kevin Smith-s/Terry Dodson-c/a 3.00
HC (2006, $19.99, dust jacket) r/#1-6; script to #6 with sketches 20.00

SPIDER-MAN: BLUE
Marvel Comics: July, 2002 - No. 6, Apr, 2003 ($3.50, limited series)
1-6: Jeph Loeb-s/Tim Sale-a/c; flashback to early MJ and Gwen Stacy 3.50
HC (2003, $21.99, with dust jacket) over-sized r/#1-6; intro. by John Romita 22.00
SC (2004, $14.99) r/#1-6; cover gallery 15.00

SPIDER-MAN: BRAND NEW DAY (See Amazing Spider-Man Vol. 2)

SPIDER-MAN: BREAKOUT (See New Avengers #1)
Marvel Comics: June, 2005 - No. 5, Oct, 2005 ($2.99, limited series)
1-5-Bedard-s/Garcia-a. 1-U-Foes app. 5-New Avengers app. 3.00
TPB (2006, $13.99) r/#1-5 14.00

SPIDER-MAN: CHAPTER ONE
Marvel Comics: Dec, 1998 - No. 12, Oct, 1999 ($2.50, limited series)
1-Retelling/updating of origin; John Byrne-s/c/a 3.00
1-($6.95) DF Edition w/variant-c by Jae Lee 7.00
2-11: 2-Two covers (one is swipe of ASM #1); Fantastic Four app. 9-Daredevil. 11-Giant-Man-c/app. 3.00
12-($3.50) Battles the Sandman 4.00
0-(5/99) Origins of Vulture, Lizard and Sandman 3.00

SPIDER-MAN CLASSICS
Marvel Comics: Apr, 1993 - No. 16, July, 1994 ($1.25)
1-14,16: 1-r/Amaz. Fantasy #15 & Strange Tales #115. 2-16-r/Amaz. Spider-Man #1-15. 6-Austin-c(i) 3.00
15-($2.95)-Polybagged w/16 pg. insert & animation style print; r/Amazing Spider-Man #14 (1st Green Goblin) 4.00

SPIDER-MAN COLLECTOR'S PREVIEW
Marvel Comics: Dec, 1994 ($1.50, 100 pgs., one-shot)
1-wraparound-c; no comics 4.00

SPIDER-MAN COMICS MAGAZINE
Marvel Comics Group: Jan, 1987 - No. 13, 1988 ($1.50, digest-size)
1-13-Reprints 6.00

SPIDER-MAN/DEADPOOL
Marvel Comics: Mar, 2016 - Present ($3.99)
1-28: 1-Joe Kelly-s/Ed McGuinness-a; back-up reprint of Vision #1. 6-Aukerman-s. 7-Art in 1968 Ditko-style by Koblish. 8-New black Spidey suit. 11-Penn Jillette-s. 16-Dracula app. 17,18-McGuinness-a. 19,20-Slapstick app. 23-25,27,28-Bachalo-a 4.00
#1.MU (3/17, $4.99) Corin-s/Walker-a/Dave Johnson-c 5.00

SPIDER-MAN: DEATH AND DESTINY
Marvel Comics: Aug, 2000 - No. 3, Oct, 2000 ($2.99, limited series)
1-3-Aftermath of the death of Capt. Stacy 3.00

SPIDER-MAN/ DOCTOR OCTOPUS: OUT OF REACH
Marvel Comics: Jan, 2004 - No. 5, May, 2004 ($2.99, limited series)
1-5: 1-Keron Grant-a/Colin Mitchell-s 3.00

Spider-Man Fairy Tales #4 © MAR

Spider-Man Loves Mary Jane #13 © MAR

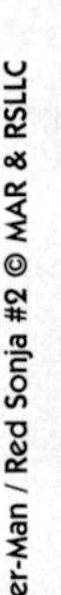
Spider-Man / Red Sonja #2 © MAR & RSLLC

GD 2.0 | VG 4.0 | FN 6.0 | VF 8.0 | VF/NM 9.0 | NM- 9.2

Marvel Age... TPB (2004, $5.99, digest size) r/#1-5 6.00

SPIDER-MAN/ DOCTOR OCTOPUS: YEAR ONE
Marvel Comics: Aug, 2004 - No. 5, Dec, 2004 ($2.99, limited series)
1-5-Kaare Andrews-a/Zeb Wells-s 3.00

SPIDER-MAN FAIRY TALES
Marvel Comics: July, 2007 - No. 4, Oct, 2007 ($2.99, limited series)
1-4: 1-Cebulski-s/Tercio-a. 2-Henrichon-a. 3-Kobayashi-a. 4-Dragotta-p/Allred-i 3.00
TPB (2007, $10.99) r/#1-4 11.00

SPIDER-MAN FAMILY (Also see Amazing Spider-Man Family)
Marvel Comics: Apr, 2007 - No. 9, Aug, 2008 ($4.99, anthology)
1-9-New tales and reprints. 1-Black costume, Sandman, Black Cat app. 4-Agents of Atlas app., Kirk-a; Puppet Master by Eliopoulos. 8-Iron Man app. 9-Hulk app. 5.00
... Featuring Spider-Clan 1 (1/07, $4.99) new Spider-Clan story; reprints w/Spider-Man 2099 and Amazing Spider-Man #252 (black costume) 5.00
... Featuring Spider-Man's Amazing Friends 1 (10/06, $4.99) new story with Iceman and Firestar; Mini Marvels w/Giarrusso-a; reprints w/Spider-Man 2099 5.00
...: Back In Black (2007, $7.99, digest) r/new content from #1-3 8.00
...: Untold Team-Ups (2008, $9.99, digest) r/new content from #4-6 10.00

SPIDER-MAN/FANTASTIC FOUR (Spider-Man and the Fantastic Four on cover)
Marvel Comics: Sept, 2010 - No. 4, Dec, 2010 ($3.99, limited series)
1-4-Gage-s/Alberti-a; Dr. Doom app. 4.00

SPIDER-MAN: FEVER
Marvel Comics: Jun, 2010 - No. 3, Aug, 2010 ($3.99, limited series)
1-3-Brendan McCarthy-s/a; Dr. Strange app. 4.00

SPIDER-MAN: FRIENDS AND ENEMIES
Marvel Comics: Jan, 1995 - No. 4, Apr, 1995 ($1.95, limited series)
1-4-Darkhawk, Nova & Speedball app. 3.00

SPIDER-MAN: FUNERAL FOR AN OCTOPUS
Marvel Comics: Mar, 1995 - No. 3, May, 1995 ($1.50, limited series)
1-3 3.00

SPIDER-MAN/ GEN 13
Marvel Comics: Nov, 1996 ($4.95, one-shot)
nn-Peter David-s/Stuart Immonen-a 5.00

SPIDER-MAN: GET KRAVEN
Marvel Comics: Aug, 2002 - No. 6, Jan, 2003 ($2.99/$2.25, limited series)
1-($2.99) McCrea-a/Quesada-c; back-up story w/Rio-a 4.00
2-6-($2.25) 2-Sub-Mariner app. 3.00

SPIDER-MAN: HOBGOBLIN LIVES
Marvel Comics: Jan, 1997 - No. 3, Mar, 1997 ($2.50, limited series)
1-3-Wraparound-c 3.00
TPB (1/98, $14.99) r/#1-3 plus timeline 15.00

SPIDER-MAN: HOUSE OF M (Also see House of M and related x-overs)
Marvel Comics: Aug, 2005 - No. 5, Dec, 2005 ($2.99, limited series)
1-5-Waid & Peyer-s/Larroca-a; rich and famous Peter Parker in mutant-ruled world 3.00
House of M: Spider-Man TPB (2006, $13.99) r/series 14.00

SPIDER-MAN/ HUMAN TORCH
Marvel Comics: Mar, 2005 - No. 5, July, 2005 ($2.99, limited series)
1-5-Ty Templeton-a/Dan Slott-s; team-ups from early days to the present 3.00
...: I'm With Stupid (2006, $7.99, digest) r/#1-5 8.00

SPIDER-MAN: INDIA
Marvel Comics: Jan, 2005 - No. 4, Apr, 2005 ($2.99, limited series)
1-4-Pavitr Prabhakar gains spider powers; Kang-a/Seetharaman-s 3.00

SPIDER-MAN: LEGEND OF THE SPIDER-CLAN (See Marvel Mangaverse for TPB)
Marvel Comics: Dec, 2002 - No. 5, Apr, 2003 ($2.25, limited series)
1-5-Marvel Mangaverse Spider-Man; Kaare Andrews-s/Skottie Young-c/a 3.00

SPIDER-MAN: LIFELINE
Marvel Comics: Apr, 2001 - No. 3, June, 2001 ($2.99, limited series)
1-3-Nicieza-s/Rude-c/a; The Lizard app. 3.00

SPIDER-MAN LOVES MARY JANE (Also see Mary Jane limited series)
Marvel Comics: Feb, 2006 - No. 20, Sept, 2007 ($2.99)
1-20-Mary Jane & Peter in high school; McKeever-s/Miyazawa-a/c. 5-Gwen Stacy app. 16-18,20-Firestar app. 17-Felecia Hardy app. 3.00
... Vol. 1: Super Crush (2006, $7.99, digest) r/#1-5; cover concepts page 8.00
... Vol. 2: The New Girl (2006, $7.99, digest) r/#6-10; sketch pages 8.00
... Vol. 3: My Secret Life (2007, $7.99, digest) r/#11-15; sketch pages 8.00
... Vol. 4: Still Friends (2007, $7.99, digest) r/#16-20 8.00
Hardcover Vol. 1 (2007, $24.99) oversized reprints of #1-5, Mary Jane #1-4 and Mary Jane: Homecoming #1-4; series proposals, sketch pages and covers; coloring process 25.00
Hardcover Vol. 2 (2008, $39.99) oversized reprints of #6-20, sketch & layout pages 40.00

SPIDER-MAN LOVES MARY JANE SEASON 2
Marvel Comics: Oct, 2008 - No. 5, Feb, 2009 ($2.99, limited series)
1-5-Terry Moore-s/c; Craig Rousseau-a 3.00
1-Variant-c by Alphona 8.00

SPIDER-MAN: MADE MEN
Marvel Comics: Aug, 1998 ($5.99, one-shot)
1-Spider-Man & Daredevil vs. Kingpin 6.00

SPIDER-MAN MAGAZINE
Marvel Comics: 1994 - No. 3, 1994 ($1.95, magazine)
1-3: 1-Contains 4 S-M promo cards & 4 X-Men Ultra Fleer cards; Spider-Man story by Romita, Sr.; X-Men story; puzzles & games. 2-Doc Octopus & X-Men stories 4.00

SPIDER-MAN: MAXIMUM CLONAGE
Marvel Comics: 1995 ($4.95)
Alpha #1-Acetate-c, Omega #1-Chromium-c. 6.00

SPIDER-MAN MEGAZINE
Marvel Comics: Oct, 1994 - No. 6, Mar, 1995 ($2.95, 100 pgs.)
1-6: 1-r/ASM #16,224,225, Marvel Team-Up #1 5.00

SPIDER-MAN NOIR
Marvel Comics: Dec, 2008 - No. 4, May, 2009 ($3.99, limited series)
1-4-Pulp-style Spider-Man in 1933; DiGiandomenico-a; covers by Zircher & Calero 4.00
...: Eyes Without a Face 1-4 (2/10 - No. 4, 5/10) DiGiandomenico-a; Zircher & Calero-c 4.00

SPIDER-MAN: POWER OF TERROR
Marvel Comics: Jan, 1995 - No. 4, Apr, 1995 ($1.95, limited series)
1-4-Silvermane & Deathlok app. 3.00

SPIDER-MAN/PUNISHER: FAMILY PLOT
Marvel Comics: Feb, 1996 - No. 2, Mar, 1996 ($2.95, limited series)
1,2 3.00

SPIDER-MAN: QUALITY OF LIFE
Marvel Comics: Jul, 2002 - No. 4, Oct, 2002 ($2.99, limited series)
1-4-All CGI art by Scott Sava; Rucka-s; Lizard app. 3.00
TPB (2002, $12.99) r/#1-4; a "Making of..." section detailing the CGI process 13.00

SPIDER-MAN: REDEMPTION
Marvel Comics: Sept, 1996 - No. 4, Dec, 1996 ($1.50, limited series)
1-4: DeMatteis scripts; Zeck-a 3.00

SPIDER-MAN/ RED SONJA
Marvel Comics: Oct, 2007 - No. 5, Feb, 2008 ($2.99, limited series)
1-5-Rubi-a/Oeming-s/Turner-c; Venom & Kulan Gath app. 3.00
HC (2008, $19.99, dustjacket) r/#1-5 and Marvel Team-Up #79; sketch pages 20.00

SPIDER-MAN: REIGN
Marvel Comics: Feb, 2007 - No. 4, May, 2007 ($3.99, limited series)
1-Kaare Andrews-s/a; red costume on cover 4.00
1-Variant cover with black costume 10.00
2-4 4.00
HC (2007, $19.99, dustjacket) r/#1-4; sketch pages and cover variant gallery 20.00
HC 2nd printing (2007, $19.99, dustjacket) with variant black cover 20.00
SC (2008, $14.99) r/#1-4; sketch pages and cover variant gallery 15.00

SPIDER-MAN: REVENGE OF THE GREEN GOBLIN
Marvel Comics: Oct, 2000 - No. 3, Dec, 2000 ($2.99, limited series)
1-3-Frenz & Olliffe-a; continues in AS-M #25 & PP:S-M #25 3.00

SPIDER-MAN SAGA
Marvel Comics: Nov, 1991 - No. 4, Feb, 1992 ($2.95, limited series)
1-4: Gives history of Spider-Man: text & illustrations 3.00

SPIDER-MAN 1602
Marvel Comics: Dec, 2009 - No. 5, Apr, 2010 ($3.99, limited series)
1-5- Peter Parquagh from Marvel 1602; Parker-s/Rosanas-a 4.00

SPIDER-MAN: SWEET CHARITY
Marvel Comics: Aug, 2002 ($4.95, one-shot)
1-The Scorpion-c/app.; Campbell-c/Zimmerman-s/Robertson-a 5.00

SPIDER-MAN'S TANGLED WEB (Titled **"Tangled Web"** in indicia for #1-4)

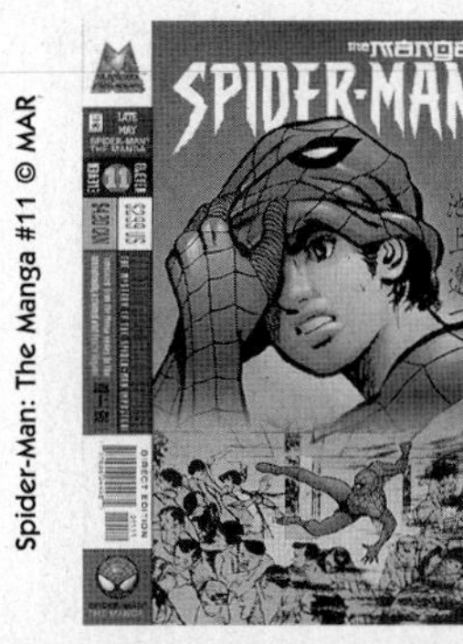

Spider-Man: The Manga #11 © MAR

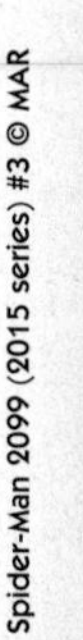

Spider-Man 2099 (2015 series) #3 © MAR

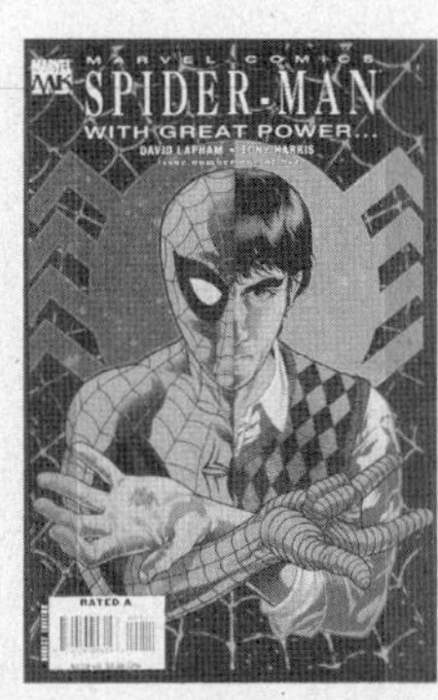

Spider-Man: With Great Power... #1 © MAR

GD 2.0	VG 4.0	FN 6.0	VF 8.0	VF/NM 9.0	NM- 9.2

Marvel Comics: Jun, 2001 - No. 22, Mar, 2003 ($2.99)

1-3: "The Thousand" on-c; Ennis-s/McCrea-a/Fabry-c 4.00
4-"Severance Package" on-c; Rucka-s/Risso-a; Kingpin-c/app. 5.00
5,6-Flowers for Rhino; Milligan-s/Fegredo-a 3.00
7-10,12,15-20,22: 7-9-Gentlemen's Agreement; Bruce Jones-s/Lee Weeks-a. 10-Andrews-s/a. 12-Fegredo-a. 15-Paul Pope-s/a. 18-Ted McKeever-s/a. 19-Mahfood-a. 20-Haspiel-a 3.00
11,13,21-($3.50) 11-Darwyn Cooke-s/a. 13-Phillips-a. 21-Christmas-s by Cooke & Bone 4.00
14-Azzarello & Scott Levy (WWE's Raven)-s about Crusher Hogan 4.00
TPB (10/01, $15.95) r/#1-6 16.00
Volume 2 TPB (4/02, $14.95) r/#7-11 15.00
Volume 3 TPB (2002, $15.99) r/#12-17; Jason Pearson-c 16.00
Volume 4 TPB (2003, $15.99) r/#18-22; Frank Cho-c 16.00

SPIDER-MAN TEAM-UP
Marvel Comics: Dec, 1995 - No. 7, June, 1996 ($2.95)

1-7: 1-w/ X-Men. 2-w/Silver Surfer. 3-w/Fantastic Four. 4-w/Avengers. 5-Gambit & Howard the Duck-c/app. 7-Thunderbolts-c/app. 4.00
... Special 1 (5/05, $2.99) Fantastic Four app.; Todd Dezago-s/Shane Davis-a 4.00

SPIDER-MAN: THE ARACHNIS PROJECT
Marvel Comics: Aug, 1994 - No. 6, Jan, 1995 ($1.75, limited series)

1-6-Venom, Styx, Stone & Jury app. 3.00

SPIDER-MAN: THE CLONE JOURNAL
Marvel Comics: Mar, 1995 ($2.95, one-shot)

1 4.00

SPIDER-MAN: THE CLONE SAGA
Marvel Comics: Nov, 2009 - No. 6, Apr, 2010 ($3.99, limited series)

1-6-Retelling of the saga with different ending; DeFalco & Mackie-s/Nauck-a 4.00

SPIDER-MAN: THE FINAL ADVENTURE
Marvel Comics: Nov, 1995 - No. 4, Feb, 1996 ($2.95, limited series)

1-4: 1-Nicieza scripts; foil-c 3.00

SPIDER-MAN: THE JACKAL FILES
Marvel Comics: Aug, 1995 ($1.95, one-shot)

1 3.00

SPIDER-MAN: THE LOST YEARS
Marvel Comics: Aug, 1995-No. 3, Oct, 1995; No. 0, 1996 ($2.95/$3.95,lim. series)

0-(1/96, $3.95)-Reprints. 4.00
1-3-DeMatteis scripts, Romita, Jr.-c/a 3.00
NOTE: ***Romita** c-0i. **Romita, Jr.** a-0r, 1-3p. c-0-3p. **Sharp** a-0r.*

SPIDER-MAN: THE MANGA
Marvel Comics: Dec, 1997 - No. 31, June, 1999 ($3.99/$2.99, B&W, bi-weekly)

1-($3.99)-English translation of Japanese Spider-Man 4.00
2-31-($2.99) 3.00

SPIDER-MAN: THE MUTANT AGENDA
Marvel Comics: No. 0, Feb, 1994; No. 1, Mar, 1994 - No. 3, May, 1994 ($1.75, limited series)

0-(2/94, $1.25, 52 pgs.)-Crosses over w/newspaper strip; has empty pages to paste in newspaper strips; gives origin of Spidey 4.00
1-3: Beast & Hobgoblin app. 1-X-Men app. 3.00

SPIDER-MAN: THE MYSTERIO MANIFESTO (Listed as "Spider-Man and Mysterio" in indicia)
Marvel Comics: Jan, 2001 - No. 3, Mar, 2001 ($2.99, limited series)

1-3-Daredevil-c/app.; Weeks & McLeod-a 3.00

SPIDER-MAN: THE PARKER YEARS
Marvel Comics: Nov, 1995 ($2.50, one-shot)

1 3.00

SPIDER-MAN 2: THE MOVIE
Marvel Comics: Aug, 2004 ($3.50/$12.99, one-shot)

1-($3.50) Movie adaptation; Johnson, Lim & Olliffe-a 4.00
TPB-($12.99) Movie adaptation; r/Amazing Spider-Man #50, Ultimate Spider-Man #14,15 13.00

SPIDER-MAN 2099 (See Amazing Spider-Man #365)
Marvel Comics: Nov, 1992 - No. 46, Aug, 1996 ($1.25/$1.50/$1.95)

1-(stiff-c)-Red foil stamped-c; begins origin of Miguel O'Hara (Spider-Man 2099); Leonardi/Williamson-c/a begins 1 2 3 5 6 8
1-2nd printing, 2-12,14-24,26-34,39,40: 2-Origin continued, ends #3. 4-Doom 2099 app. 19-Bound-in trading cards. 3.00
13-Extra 16 pg. insert on Midnight Sons 4.00
25-($2.25, 52 pgs.)-Newsstand edition 4.00
25-($2.95, 52 pgs.)-Deluxe edition w/embossed foil-c 5.00
35-38-Venom app. 35-Variant-c. 36-Two-c; Jae Lee-a. 37,38-Two-c 5.00
41-46: 46-The Vulture app; Mike McKone-a(p) 3.00
Annual 1 (1994, $2.95, 68 pgs.) 4.00
Special 1 (1995, $3.95) 4.00
NOTE: ***Chaykin** c-37. **Ron Lim** a(p)-18; c(p)-13, 16, 18. **Kelley Jones** c/a-9. **Leonardi/Williamson** a-1-8, 10-13, 15-17, 19, 20, 22-25; c-1-13, 15, 17-19, 20, 22-25, 35.*

SPIDER-MAN 2099
Marvel Comics: Sept, 2014 - No. 12, Jul, 2015 ($3.99)

1-12: 1-Miguel O'Hara in 2014; Peter David-s/Will Sliney-a. 5-8-Spider-Verse tie-in 4.00

SPIDER-MAN 2099
Marvel Comics: Dec, 2015 - No. 25, Sept, 2017 ($3.99)

1-24: 1-Miguel O'Hara still in the present; David-s/Sliney-a. 2-New costume. 13-16-Civil War II tie-ins. 14-16-Power Pack app. 17-19-Elektra app. 4.00
25-($4.99) David-s/Sliney-a 5.00

SPIDER-MAN 2099 MEETS SPIDER-MAN
Marvel Comics: 1995 ($5.95, one-shot)

nn-Peter David script; Leonardi/Williamson-c/a. 6.00

SPIDER-MAN UNIVERSE
Marvel Comics: Mar, 2000 - No. 7, Oct, 2000 ($4.95/$3.99, reprints)

1-5-Reprints recent issues from the various Spider-Man titles 5.00
6,7-($3.99) 4.00

SPIDER-MAN UNLIMITED
Marvel Comics: May, 1993 - No. 22, Nov, 1998 ($3.95, #1-12 were quarterly, 68 pgs.)

1-Begin Maximum Carnage storyline, ends; Carnage-c/story 5.00
2-12: 2-Venom & Carnage-c/story; Lim-c/a(p) in #2-6. 10-Vulture app. 4.00
13-22: 13-Begin $2.99-c; Scorpion-c/app. 15-Daniel-c; Puma-c/app. 19-Lizard-c/app. 20-Hannibal King and Lilith app. 21,22-Deodato-a 3.00

SPIDER-MAN UNLIMITED (Based on the TV animated series)
Marvel Comics: Dec, 1999 - No. 5, Apr, 2000 ($2.99/$1.99)

1-($2.99) Venom and Carnage app. 4.00
2-5: 2-($1.99) Green Goblin app. 3.00

SPIDER-MAN UNLIMITED (3rd series)
Marvel Comics: Mar, 2004 - No. 15, July, 2006 ($2.99)

1-16: 1-Short stories by various incl. Miyazawa & Chen-a. 2-Mays-a. 6-Allred-c. 14-Finch-c/a; Black Cat app. 3.00

SPIDER-MAN UNMASKED
Marvel Comics: Nov, 1996 ($5.95, one-shot)

nn-Art w/text 6.00

SPIDER-MAN: VENOM AGENDA
Marvel Comics: Jan, 1998 ($2.99, one-shot)

1-Hama-s/Lyle-c/a 3.00

SPIDER-MAN VS. DRACULA
Marvel Comics: Jan, 1994 ($1.75, 52 pgs., one-shot)

1-r/Giant-Size Spider-Man #1 plus new Matt Fox-a 4.00

SPIDER-MAN VS. WOLVERINE
Marvel Comics Group: Feb, 1987; V2#1, 1990 (68 pgs.)

1-Williamson-c/a(i); intro Charlemagne; death of Ned Leeds (old Hobgoblin) 3 6 9 19 30 40
V2#1 (1990, $4.95)-Reprints #1 (2/87) 6.00

SPIDER-MAN: WEB OF DOOM
Marvel Comics: Aug, 1994 - No. 3, Oct, 1994 ($1.75, limited series)

1-3 3.00

SPIDER-MAN: WITH GREAT POWER...
Marvel Comics: Mar, 2008 - No. 5, Sept, 2008 ($3.99, limited series)

1-5-Origin and early days re-told; Lapham-s/Harris-a/c 4.00

SPIDER-MAN: WITH GREAT POWER COMES GREAT RESPONSIBILITY
Marvel Comics: Jun, 2011 - No. 7, Dec, 2011 ($3.99, limited series)

1-7: Reprints of noteworthy Spider-Man stories. 1-R/Ultimate Spider-Man #33,97, and Ultimate Comics Spider-Man #1. 4-R/ Amazing Spider-Man #1,11,20 4.00

SPIDER-MAN: YEAR IN REVIEW
Marvel Comics: Feb, 2000 ($2.99)

1-Text recaps of 1999 issues 3.00

SPIDER-MEN
Marvel Comics: Aug, 2012 - No. 5, Nov, 2012 ($3.99, limited series)

Spider-Men II #1 © MAR

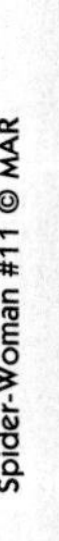
Spider-Woman #11 © MAR

Spidey #6 © MAR

1-5-Peter Parker goes to Ultimate Universe; teams with Miles Morales; Pichelli-a 4.00

SPIDER-MEN II
Marvel Comics: Sept, 2017 - No. 5, Feb, 2018 ($3.99, limited series)

1-5-Peter Parker teams with Miles Morales; Bendis-s/Pichelli-a 4.00

SPIDER REIGN OF THE VAMPIRE KING, THE (Also see The Spider)
Eclipse Books: 1992 - No. 3, 1992 ($4.95, limited series, coated stock, 52 pgs.)

Book One - Three: Truman scripts & painted-c 5.00

SPIDER'S WEB, THE (See G-8 and His Battle Aces)

SPIDER-VERSE (See Amazing Spider-Man 2014 series #7-14)
Marvel Comics: Jan, 2015 - No. 2, Mar, 2015 ($4.99, limited series)

1,2-Short stories of alternate Spider-Men; s/a by various. 2-Anarchic Spider-Man 5.00

SPIDER-VERSE (Secret Wars tie-in)
Marvel Comics: Jul, 2015 - No. 5, Nov, 2015 ($4.99/$3.99, limited series)

1-($4.99) Costa-s/Araujo-a; Spider-Gwen, Spider-Ham & Norman Osborn app. 5.00
2-5-($3.99) Alternate Spider-Men vs. Sinister Six 4.00

SPIDER-VERSE TEAM-UP (See Amazing Spider-Man 2014 series #7-14)
Marvel Comics: Jan, 2015 - No. 3, Mar, 2015 ($3.99, limited series)

1-3-Short stories of alternate Spider-Men team-ups; s/a by various. 2-Spider-Gwen, Miles Morales and '67 animated Spider-Man app. 4.00

SPIDER-WOMAN (Also see The Avengers #240, Marvel Spotlight #32, Marvel Super Heroes Secret Wars #7, Marvel Two-In-One #29 and New Avengers)
Marvel Comics Group: April, 1978 - No. 50, June, 1983 (New logo #47 on)

1-New complete origin & mask added 4 8 12 23 37 50
2-5,7-18: 2-Excalibur app. 3,11,12-Brother Grimm app. 13,15-The Shroud-c/s. 16-Sienkiewicz-c 1 2 3 4 5 7
6,19,20,28,29,32: 6-Morgan LeFay app. 6,19,32-Werewolf by Night-c/s. 20,28,29-Spider-Man app. 32-Universal Monsters photo/Miller-c 1 2 3 5 6 8
21-27,30,31,33-36 6.00
37-1st app. Siryn of X-Force; X-Men x-over; origin retold 3 6 9 14 20 25
38-X-Men x-over 2 4 6 8 10 12
39-49: 46-Kingpin app. 49-Tigra-c/story 5.00
50-(52 pgs.)-Death of Spider-Woman; photo-c 2 4 6 9 13 16
NOTE: ***Austin** a-37i. **Byrne** c-26p. **Infantino** a-1-19. **Layton** c-19. **Miller** c-32p.*

SPIDER-WOMAN
Marvel Comics: Nov, 1993 - No. 4, Feb, 1994 ($1.75, mini-series)

V2#1-4: 1,2-Origin; U.S. Agent app. 3.00

SPIDER-WOMAN
Marvel Comics: July, 1999 - No. 18, Dec, 2000 ($2.99/$1.99/$2.25)

1-($2.99) Byrne-s/Sears-a 4.00
2-18: 2-11-($1.99). 2-Two covers. 12-Begin $2.25-c. 15-Capt. America-c/app. 3.00

SPIDER-WOMAN (Printed version of the motion comic for computers)
Marvel Comics: Nov, 2009 - No. 7, May, 2010 ($3.99/$2.99)

1-($3.99) Bendis-s/Maleev-a; covers by Maleev & Alex Ross; Jessica joins S.W.O.R.D. 4.00
2-6-($2.99) 2-4-Madame Hydra app. 6-Thunderbolts app. 3.00
7-($3.99) New Avengers app. 4.00

SPIDER-WOMAN (Also see Spider-Verse event in Amazing Spider-Man 2014 series #7-14)
Marvel Comics: Jan, 2015 - No. 10, Oct, 2015 ($3.99)

1-4-Spider-Verse tie-ins; Silk app.; Hopeless-s/Land-a/c. 4-Avengers app. 4.00
5-10: 5-New costume; Javier Rodriguez-a/c. 10-Black Widow app. 4.00

SPIDER-WOMAN
Marvel Comics: Jan, 2016 - No. 17, May, 2017 ($3.99)

1-17: 1-5-Hopeless-s/Javier Rodriguez-a. 4-Jessica's baby is born. 6,7-"Spider-Women x-over; Spider-Gwen & Silk app.; Joelle Jones-a. 9-11-Civil War II tie-in. 13-16-Hobgoblin app. 4.00

SPIDER-WOMAN: ORIGIN (Also see New Avengers)
Marvel Comics: Feb, 2006 - No. 5, June, 2006 ($2.99, limited series)

1-5-Bendis & Reed-s/Jonathan & Joshua Luna-a/c 3.00
1-Variant cover by Olivier Coipel 3.00
HC (2006, $19.99) r/series 20.00
SC (2007, $13.99) r/series 14.00

SPIDER-WOMEN (Crossover with Silk, Spider-Gwen and Spider-Woman)
Marvel Comics: Alpha, Jun, 2016 - Omega, Aug, 2016 ($4.99, limited series)

... Alpha 1 - Thompson-s/Del Rey-a/Putri-c; part 1 of x-over; intro. Earth-65 Cindy Moon 5.00
... Omega 1 - Hopeless-s/Leon-a/Putri-c; part 8 conclusion of x-over 5.00

SPIDEY (Spider-Man)
Marvel Comics: Feb, 2016 - No. 12, Jan, 2017 ($3.99)

1-12-High school-era Spider-Man. 1-3-Bradshaw-a. 1-Doc Ock app. 7-Black Panther app. 4.00
... No. 1 Halloween Comic Fest 2016 (12/16, giveaway) r/#1 3.00

SPIDEY SUPER STORIES (Spider-Man) (Also see Fireside Books)
Marvel/Children's TV Workshop: Oct, 1974 - No. 57, Mar, 1982 (35¢, no ads)

1-Origin (stories simplified for younger readers) 5 10 15 34 60 85
2-Kraven 3 6 9 17 26 35
3-10,15: 6-Iceman. 15-Storm-c/sty 3 6 9 14 20 26
11-14,16-20: 19,20-Kirby-c 3 6 9 14 19 24
21-30: 22-Early Ms. Marvel app. 2 4 6 13 18 22
31-53: 31-Moondragon-c/app.; Dr. Doom app. 33-Hulk. 34-Sub-Mariner. 38-F.F. 39-Thanos-c/story. 44-Vision. 45-Silver Surfer & Dr. Doom app. 2 4 6 11 16 20
54-57: 56-Battles Jack O'Lantern-c/sty (exactly one year after 1st app. in Machine Man #19) 3 6 9 14 20 26

SPIKE AND TYKE (See M.G.M.'s...)

SPIKE... (Also see Buffy the Vampire Slayer and related titles)
IDW Publ.: Aug, 2005; Jan, 2006; Apr, 2006 ($7.49, squarebound, one-shots)

...: Lost & Found (4/06, $7.49) Scott Tipton-s/Fernando Goni-a 8.00
...: Old Times (8/05, $7.49) Peter David-s/Fernando Goni-a; Cecily/Halfrek app. 8.00
...: Old Wounds (1/06, $7.49) Tipton-s/Goni-a; flashback to Black Dahlia murder case 8.00
TPB (7/06, $19.99) r/one-shots 20.00

SPIKE (Buffy the Vampire Slayer)
IDW Publ.: Oct, 2010 - No. 8, May, 2011 ($3.99, limited series)

1-8-Lynch-s; multiple covers on each. 1,2-Urru-a. 5-7-Willow app. 4.00
... 100 Page Spectacular (6/11, $7.99) reprints of four IDW Spike stories; Frison-c 8.00

SPIKE (A Dark Place) (From Buffy the Vampire Slayer)
Dark Horse Comics: Aug, 2012 - No. 5, Dec, 2012 ($2.99, limited series)

1-5-Paul Lee-a; 2 covers by Frison & Morris on each 3.00

SPIKE: AFTER THE FALL (Also see Angel: After the Fall) (Follows the last Angel TV episode)
IDW Publ.: July, 2008 - No. 4, Oct, 2008 ($3.99, limited series)

1-4-Lynch-s/Urru-a; multiple covers on each 4.00

SPIKE: ASYLUM (Buffy the Vampire Slayer)
IDW Publ.: Sept, 2006 - No. 5, Jan, 2007 ($3.99, limited series)

1-5-Lynch-s/Urru-a; multiple covers on each 4.00

SPIKE: SHADOW PUPPETS (Buffy the Vampire Slayer)
IDW Publ.: June, 2007 - No. 4, Sept, 2007 ($3.99, limited series)

1-4-Lynch-s/Urru-a; multiple covers on each 4.00

SPIKE: THE DEVIL YOU KNOW (Buffy the Vampire Slayer)
IDW Publ.: Jun, 2010 - No. 4, Sept, 2010 ($3.99, limited series)

1-4-Bill Williams-s/Chris Cross-a/Urru-c 4.00

SPIKE VS. DRACULA (Buffy the Vampire Slayer)
IDW Publ.: Feb, 2006 - No. 5, Mar, 2006 ($3.99, limited series)

1-5: 1-Peter David-s/Joe Corroney-a; Dru and Bela Lugosi app. 4.00

SPIN & MARTY (TV) (Walt Disney's)(See Walt Disney Showcase #32)
Dell Publishing Co. (Mickey Mouse Club): No. 714, June, 1956 - No. 1082, Mar-May, 1960 (All photo-c)

Four Color 714 (#1) 11 22 33 72 154 235
Four Color 767,808 (#2,3) 8 16 24 56 108 160
Four Color 826 (#4)-Annette Funicello photo-c 18 36 54 124 275 425
5(3-5/58) - 9(6-8/59) 7 14 21 44 82 120
Four Color 1026,1082 7 14 21 44 82 120

SPIN ANGELS
Marvel Comics (Soleil): 2009 - No. 4, 2009 ($5.99)

1-4-English version of French comics; Jean-Luc Sala-s/Pierre-Mony Chan-a 6.00

SPINE-TINGLING TALES (Doctor Spektor Presents...)
Gold Key: May, 1975 - No. 4, Jan, 1976 (All 25¢ issues)

1-1st Tragg-r/Mystery Comics Digest #3 2 4 6 9 13 16
2-4: 2-Origin Ra-Ka-Tep-r/Mystery Comics Digest #1; Dr. Spektor #12. 3-All Durak-r issue; 4-Baron Tibor's 1st app.-r/Mystery Comics Digest #4; painted-c 1 2 3 5 7 9

SPINWORLD
Amaze Ink (Slave Labor Graphics): July, 1997 - No. 4, Jan, 1998 ($2.95/$3.95, B&W, mini-series)

1-3-Brent Anderson-a(p) 3.00
4-($3.95) 4.00

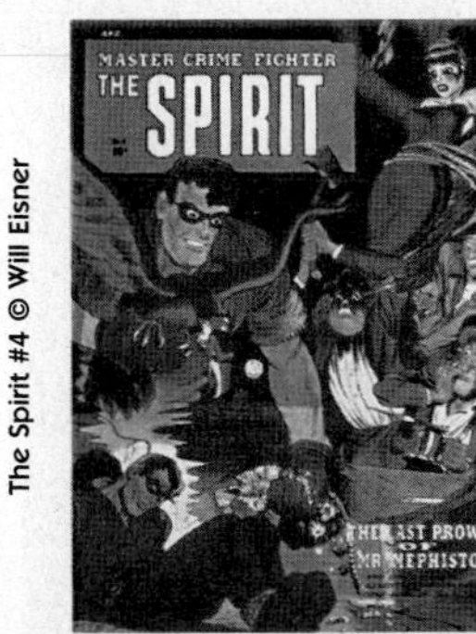

The Spirit #4 © Will Eisner

The Spirit (2010 series) #16 © Will Eisner Studios

Spirits of Vengeance #1 © MAR

SPIRAL ZONE
DC Comics: Feb, 1988 - No. 4, May, 1988 ($1.00, mini-series)

	GD 2.0	VG 4.0	FN 6.0	VF 8.0	VF/NM 9.0	NM- 9.2
1-4-Based on Tonka toys						3.00

SPIRIT, THE (Newspaper comics - see Promotional Comics section)

SPIRIT, THE (1st Series)(Also see Police Comics #11 and The Best of the Spirit TPB)
Quality Comics Group (Vital): 1944 - No. 22, Aug, 1950

	GD 2.0	VG 4.0	FN 6.0	VF 8.0	VF/NM 9.0	NM- 9.2
nn(#1)- "Wanted Dead or Alive"	142	284	426	909	1555	2200
nn(#2)- "Crime Doesn't Pay"	53	106	159	334	567	800
nn(#3)- "Murder Runs Wild"	47	94	141	296	498	700
4,5: 4-Flatfoot Burns begins, ends #22. 5-Wertham app.	40	80	120	246	411	575
6-10	36	72	108	211	343	475
11-Crandall-c	34	68	102	199	325	450
12-17-Eisner-c. 19-Honeybun app.	45	90	135	284	480	675
18,19-Strip-r by Eisner; Eisner-c	63	126	189	403	689	975
20,21-Eisner good girl covers; strip-r by Eisner	84	168	252	538	919	1300
22-Used by N.Y. Legis. Comm; classic Eisner-c	459	918	1377	3350	5925	8500
Super Reprint #11-r/Quality Spirit #19 by Eisner	3	6	9	18	27	35
Super Reprint #12-r/Spirit #17 by Fine; Sol Brodsky-c	3	6	9	18	27	35

SPIRIT, THE (2nd Series)
Fiction House Magazines: Spring, 1952 - No. 5, 1954

	GD 2.0	VG 4.0	FN 6.0	VF 8.0	VF/NM 9.0	NM- 9.2
1-Not Eisner	54	108	162	343	574	825
2-Eisner-c/a(2)	52	104	156	328	552	775
3-Eisner/Grandenetti-c	47	94	141	296	498	700
4-Eisner/Grandenetti-c; Eisner-a	48	96	144	302	514	725
5-Eisner-c/a(4)	52	104	156	328	552	775

SPIRIT, THE
Harvey Publications: Oct, 1966 - No. 2, Mar, 1967 (Giant Size, 25¢, 68 pgs.)

	GD 2.0	VG 4.0	FN 6.0	VF 8.0	VF/NM 9.0	NM- 9.2
1-Eisner-r plus 9 new pgs.(origin Denny Colt, Take 3, plus 2 filler pgs.) (#3 was advertised, but never published)	8	16	24	54	102	150
2-Eisner-r plus 9 new pgs.(origin of the Octopus)	7	14	21	44	82	120

SPIRIT, THE (Underground)
Kitchen Sink Enterprises (Krupp Comics): Jan, 1973 - No. 2, Sept, 1973 (Black & White)

	GD 2.0	VG 4.0	FN 6.0	VF 8.0	VF/NM 9.0	NM- 9.2
1-New Eisner-c & 4 pgs. new Eisner-a plus-r (titled Crime Convention)	4	8	12	23	37	50
2-New Eisner-c & 4 pgs. new Eisner-a plus-r (titled Meets P'Gell)	4	8	12	25	40	55

SPIRIT, THE (Magazine)
Warren Publ. Co./Krupp Comic Works No. 17 on: 4/74 - No. 16, 10/76; No. 17, Winter, 1977 - No. 41, 6/83 (B&W w/color) (#6-14,16 are squarebound)

	GD 2.0	VG 4.0	FN 6.0	VF 8.0	VF/NM 9.0	NM- 9.2
1-Eisner-r begin; 8 pg. color insert	6	12	18	41	76	110
2-5: 2-Powder Pouf-s; UFO-s. 4-Silk Satin-s	4	8	12	27	44	60
6-9,11-15: 7-All Ebony issue. 8-Female Foes issue. 8,12-Sand Seref-s. 9-P'Gell & Octopus-s. 12-X-Mas issue	4	8	12	25	40	55
10-Giant Summer Special ($1.50)-Origin	4	8	12	27	44	60
16-Giant Summer Special ($1.50)-Olga Bustle-c/s	4	8	12	25	40	55
17,18(8/78): 17-Lady Luck-r	3	6	9	17	26	35
19-21-New Eisner-a. 20,21-Wood-r (#21-r/A DP on the Moon by Wood). 20-Outer Space-r	3	6	9	17	26	35
22-41: 22,23-Wood-r (#22-r/Mission the Moon by Wood). 28-r/last story (10/5/52). 30-(7/81)-Special Spirit Jam issue w/Caniff, Corben, Bolland, Byrne, Miller, Kurtzman, Rogers, Sienkiewicz-a & 40 others. 36-Begin Spirit Section-r; r/1st story (6/2/40) in color; new Eisner-c/a(18 pgs.)($2.95). 37-r/2nd story in color plus 18 pgs. new Eisner-a. 38-41: r/3rd - 6th stories in color. 41-Lady Luck Mr. Mystic in color	3	6	9	15	22	28
Special 1(1975)-All Eisner-a (mail only, 1500 printed, full color)	13	26	39	89	195	300

NOTE: *Covers pencilled/inked by* **Eisner** *only #1-9,12-16; painted by Eisner & Ken Kelly #10 & 11; painted by Eisner #17-up; one color story reprinted in #1-10.* **Austin** *a-30i.* **Byrne** *a-30p.* **Miller** *a-30p.*

SPIRIT, THE
Kitchen Sink Enterprises: Oct, 1983 - No. 87, Jan, 1992 ($2.00, Baxter paper)

	GD 2.0	VG 4.0	FN 6.0	VF 8.0	VF/NM 9.0	NM- 9.2
1-60: 1-Origin-r/12/23/45 Spirit Section. 2-r/ 1/20/46-2/10/46. 3-r/2/17/46-3/10/46. 4-r/3/17/46-4/7/46. 11-Last color issue. 54-r/section 2/19/50						4.00
61-87: 85-87-Reprint the Outer Space Spirit stories by Wood. 86-r/A DP on the Moon by Wood from 1952						4.00

SPIRIT, THE (Also see Batman/The Spirit in Batman one-shots)
DC Comics: Feb, 2007 - No. 32, Oct, 2009 ($2.99)

	GD 2.0	VG 4.0	FN 6.0	VF 8.0	VF/NM 9.0	NM- 9.2
1-32: 1-6,8-12-Darwyn Cooke-s/a/c. 2-P'Gell app. 3-Origin re-told. 7-Short stories by Baker, Bernet, Palmiotti, Simonson & Sprouse; Cooke-c. 13-Short stories by various						3.00
... Femme Fatales TPB (2008, $19.99) r/1940s stories focusing on the Spirit's female adversaries like Silk Satin, P'gell, Powder Pouf and Silken Floss; Michael Uslan intro.						20.00
... Special 1 (2008, $2.99) r/stories from '47, '49, '50 newspaper strips; the Octopus app.						3.00

SPIRIT, THE (First Wave)
DC Comics: Jun, 2010 - No. 17, Oct, 2011 ($3.99/$2.99)(B&W back-up stories by various)

	GD 2.0	VG 4.0	FN 6.0	VF 8.0	VF/NM 9.0	NM- 9.2
1-10: 1-Schultz-s/Moritat-a; covers by Ladronn and Schultz; back-up by O'Neil & Sienkiewicz. 2-Back-up by Ellison & Baker. 7-Corben-a back-up. 8-Ploog-a back-up						4.00
11-17-($2.99) 11-16-Hine-s/Moritat-a; no back-up story. 17-B&W; Bolland, Russell-a						3.00
...: Angel Smerti TPB (2011, $17.99) r/#1-7						18.00

SPIRIT, (WILL EISNER'S THE...)
Dynamite Entertainment: 2015 - No. 12, 2016 ($3.99)

	GD 2.0	VG 4.0	FN 6.0	VF 8.0	VF/NM 9.0	NM- 9.2
1-12: 1-Wagner-s/Schkade-a; multiple covers. 2-12-Powell-c						4.00

SPIRIT, (WILL EISNER'S THE...): CORPSE MAKERS (Volume 2)
Dynamite Entertainment: 2017 - No. 5, 2018 ($3.99)

	GD 2.0	VG 4.0	FN 6.0	VF 8.0	VF/NM 9.0	NM- 9.2
1-5-Francesco Francavilla-s/a/c						4.00

SPIRIT JAM
Kitchen Sink Press: Aug, 1998 ($5.95, B&W, oversized, square-bound)

	GD 2.0	VG 4.0	FN 6.0	VF 8.0	VF/NM 9.0	NM- 9.2
nn-Reprints Spirit (Magazine) #30 by Eisner & 50 others; and "Cerebus Vs. The Spirit" from Cerebus Jam #1						6.00

SPIRIT, THE: THE NEW ADVENTURES
Kitchen Sink Press: 1997 - No. 8, Nov, 1998 ($3.50, anthology)

	GD 2.0	VG 4.0	FN 6.0	VF 8.0	VF/NM 9.0	NM- 9.2
1-Moore-s/Gibbons-c/a						4.00
2-8: 2-Gaiman-s/Eisner-c. 3-Moore-s/Bolland-c/Moebius back-c. 4-Allred-s/a; Busiek-s/Anderson-a. 5-Chadwick-s/c/a(p); Nyberg-i. 6-S.Hampton & Mandrake-a						3.50
Will Eisner's The Spirit Archives Volume 27 (Dark Horse, 2009, $49.95) r/#1-8						50.00

SPIRIT: THE ORIGIN YEARS
Kitchen Sink Press: May, 1992 - No. 10, Dec, 1993 ($2.95, B&W)

	GD 2.0	VG 4.0	FN 6.0	VF 8.0	VF/NM 9.0	NM- 9.2
1-10: 1-r/sections 6/2/40(origin)-6/23/40 (all 1940s)						3.00

SPIRITMAN (Also see Three Comics)
No publisher listed: No date (1944) (10¢)(Triangle Sales Co. ad on back cover)

	GD 2.0	VG 4.0	FN 6.0	VF 8.0	VF/NM 9.0	NM- 9.2
1-Three 16pg. Spirit sections bound together, (1944, 10¢, 52 pgs.)	30	60	90	177	289	400
2-Two Spirit sections (3/26/44, 4/2/44) bound together; by Lou Fine	26	52	78	154	252	350

SPIRIT OF THE BORDER (See Zane Grey & Four Color #197)

SPIRIT OF THE TAO
Image Comics (Top Cow): Jun, 1998 - No. 15, May, 2000 ($2.50)

	GD 2.0	VG 4.0	FN 6.0	VF 8.0	VF/NM 9.0	NM- 9.2
Preview						5.00
1-14: 1-D-Tron-s/Tan & D-Tron-a						3.00
15-($4.95)						5.00

SPIRITS OF VENGEANCE (Marvel Legacy)
Marvel Comics: Dec, 2017 - No. 5, Apr, 2018 ($3.99)

	GD 2.0	VG 4.0	FN 6.0	VF 8.0	VF/NM 9.0	NM- 9.2
1-5-Gischler-s/Baldeón-a; Blade, Ghost Rider, Daimon Hellstrom, Satana app.						4.00

SPIRIT WORLD (Magazine)
Hampshire Distributors Ltd.: Fall, 1971 (B&W)

	GD 2.0	VG 4.0	FN 6.0	VF 8.0	VF/NM 9.0	NM- 9.2
1-New Kirby-a; Neal Adams-c; poster inside	6	12	18	40	73	105

(1/2 price without poster)

SPITFIRE (Female undercover agent)
Malverne Herald (Elliot)(J. R. Mahon): No. 132, 1944 (Aug) - No. 133, 1945
Both have Classics Gift Box ads on back-c with checklist to #20

	GD 2.0	VG 4.0	FN 6.0	VF 8.0	VF/NM 9.0	NM- 9.2
132-British spitfire WWII-c.	37	74	111	222	361	500
133-Female agent/Nazi WWII-c	110	220	330	704	1202	1700

SPITFIRE (WW2 speedster from MI:13)
Marvel Comics: Oct, 2010 ($3.99, one-shot)

	GD 2.0	VG 4.0	FN 6.0	VF 8.0	VF/NM 9.0	NM- 9.2
1-Cornell-s/Casagrande-a; Blade app.						4.00

SPITFIRE AND THE TROUBLESHOOTERS
Marvel Comics: Oct, 1986 - No. 9, June, 1987 (Codename: Spitfire #10 on)

	GD 2.0	VG 4.0	FN 6.0	VF 8.0	VF/NM 9.0	NM- 9.2
1-3,5-9						3.00
4-McFarlane-a						4.00

SPITFIRE COMICS (Also see Double Up) (Tied with Pocket Comics #1 for earliest Harvey)
Harvey Publications: Aug, 1941 - No. 2, Oct, 1941 (Pocket size; 100 pgs.)

	GD 2.0	VG 4.0	FN 6.0	VF 8.0	VF/NM 9.0	NM- 9.2
1-Origin The Clown, The Fly-Man, The Spitfire & The Magician From Bagdad; British spitfire, Nazi bomber WWII-c	97	194	291	621	1061	1500
2-(Rare) Fly-Man-c	90	180	270	576	988	1400

Spongebob Comics #63 © UPP

Spook House #3 © Eric Powell

Spotlight Comics #3 © CHES

GD 2.0 | VG 4.0 | FN 6.0 | VF 8.0 | VF/NM 9.0 | NM- 9.2

SPLITTING IMAGE
Image Comics: Mar, 1993 - No. 2, 1993 ($1.95)

1,2-Simpson-c/a; parody comic 3.00
...80-Page Giant 1 (4/17, $7.99) r/#1,2 plus Normalman - Megaton Man Special 8.00

SPONGEBOB COMICS (TV's Spongebob Squarepants)
United Plankton Pictures: 2011 - Present ($2.99)

1-51-Short stories by various. 1-Kochalka back-c. 3-Aquaman homage w/Fradon-a. 32-36-Showdown at the Shady Shoals; Mermaid Man app; Ordway-a 3.00
52-77-($3.99) 53,59,60,68-Chuck Dixon-s. 63,64-Mermaid Girl spotlight. 66-70-Ordway-a 4.00
Annual-Size Super-Giant Swimtacular 1 (2013, $4.99) art by Fradon, Ordway, Kochalka 5.00
Annual-Size Super-Giant Swimtacular 2 (2014, $4.99) Mermaid Man app. 5.00
Annual-Size Super-Giant Swimtacular 3 (2015, $4.99) art by Barta, Kochalka, Chabot 5.00
Annual-Size Super-Giant Swimtacular 4 (2016, $4.99) Neal Adams & others-a; Ordway-c 5.00
Annual-Size Super-Giant Swimtacular 2017 (2017, $4.99) Mayerik & others-a; Chabot-c 5.00
SpongeBob Freestyle Funnies 1 (2013, Free Comic Book Day giveaway) Short stories 3.00
SpongeBob Freestyle Funnies 2014 (Free Comic Book Day giveaway) Short stories 3.00
SpongeBob Freestyle Funnies 2015 (Free Comic Book Day giveaway) Short stories 3.00
SpongeBob Freestyle Funnies 2016 (FCBD giveaway) Short stories; Fradon-a 3.00

SPOOF
Marvel Comics Group: Oct, 1970; No. 2, Nov, 1972 - No. 5, May, 1973

1-Infinity-c; Dark Shadows-c & parody 4 8 12 25 40 55
2-5: 2-All in the Family. 3-Beatles, Osmond's, Jackson 5, David Cassidy, Nixon & Agnew-c. 5-Rod Serling, Woody Allen, Ted Kennedy-c 3 6 9 16 24 32

SPOOK (Formerly Shock Detective Cases)
Star Publications: No. 22, Jan, 1953 - No. 30, Oct, 1954

22-Sgt. Spook-r; acid in face story; hanging-c 50 100 150 315 533 750
23,25,27: 25-Jungle Lil-r. 27-Two Sgt. Spook-r 39 78 117 229 375 520
24-Used in **SOTI**, pgs. 182,183-r/Inside Crime #2; Transvestism story 39 78 117 240 395 550
26,28-30: 26-Disbrow-a. 28,29-Rulah app. 29-Jo-Jo app. 30-Disbrow-c/a(2); only Star-c 39 78 117 229 375 520
NOTE: ***L. B. Cole*** *covers-all issues except #30; a-28(1 pg.).* ***Disbrow*** *a-26(2), 28, 29(2), 30(2); No. 30 r/Blue Bolt Weird Tales #114.*

SPOOK COMICS
Baily Publications/Star: 1946

1-Mr. Lucifer story 39 78 117 240 395 550

SPOOK HOUSE
Albatross Funnybooks: 2016 - No. 5, 2017 ($3.99)

1-5-Horror anthology by Eric Powell and others; Powell-c 4.00

SPOOKY (The Tuff Little Ghost; see Casper The Friendly Ghost)
Harvey Publications: 11/55 - 139, 11/73; No. 140, 7/74 - No. 155, 3/77; No. 156, 12/77 - No. 158, 4/78; No. 159, 9/78; No. 160, 10/79; No. 161, 9/80

1-Nightmare begins (see Casper #19) 64 128 192 512 1156 1800
2 20 40 60 141 313 485
3-10(1956-57) 11 22 33 76 163 250
11-20(1957-58) 7 14 21 44 82 120
21-40(1958-59) 5 10 15 33 57 80
41-60 4 8 12 27 44 60
61-80,100 3 6 9 19 30 40
81-99 3 6 9 16 24 32
101-120 2 4 6 11 16 20
121-126,133-140 2 4 6 8 11 14
127-132: All 52 pg. Giants 2 4 6 11 16 20
141-161 1 2 3 5 7 9

SPOOKY
Harvey Comics: Nov, 1991 - No. 4, Sept, 1992 ($1.00/$1.25)

1 4.00
2-4: 3-Begin $1.25-c 3.00
...Digest 1-3 (10/92, 6/93, 10/93, $1.75, 100 pgs.)-Casper, Wendy, etc. 4.00

SPOOKY HAUNTED HOUSE
Harvey Publications: Oct, 1972 - No. 15, Feb, 1975

1 3 6 9 17 26 35
2-5 2 4 6 10 14 18
6-10 2 4 6 8 10 12
11-15 1 2 3 5 7 9

SPOOKY MYSTERIES
Your Guide Publ. Co.: No date (1946) (10¢)

1-Mr. Spooky, Super Snooper, Pinky, Girl Detective app. 26 52 78 154 252 350

SPOOKY SPOOKTOWN
Harvey Publ.: 9/61; No. 2, 9/62 - No. 52, 12/73; No. 53, 10/74 - No. 66, 12/76

1-Casper, Spooky; 68 pgs. begin 14 28 42 94 207 320
2 8 16 24 54 102 150
3-5 6 12 18 38 69 100
6-10 5 10 15 31 53 75
11-20 4 8 12 23 37 50
21-39: 39-Last 68 pg. issue 3 6 9 19 30 40
40-45: All 52 pgs. 2 4 6 11 16 20
46-66: 61-Hot Stuff/Spooky team-up story 1 2 3 5 7 9

SPORT COMICS (Becomes True Sport Picture Stories #5 on)
Street & Smith Publications: Oct, 1940 (No mo.) - No. 4, Nov, 1941

1-Life story of Lou Gehrig 57 114 171 362 619 875
2 31 62 93 186 303 420
3,4: 4-Story of Notre Dame coach Frank Leahy 27 54 81 158 259 360

SPORT LIBRARY (See Charlton Sport Library)

SPORTS ACTION (Formerly Sport Stars)
Marvel/Atlas Comics (ACI No. 2,3/SAI No. 4-14): No. 2, Feb, 1950 - No. 14, Sept, 1952

2-Powell-a; George Gipp life story 43 86 129 269 455 640
1-(nd,no price, no publ., 52pgs, #1 on-c; has same-c as #2; blank inside-c (giveaway?) 22 44 66 132 216 300
3-Everett-a 24 48 72 142 234 325
4-11,14: Weiss-a 22 44 66 128 209 290
12,13: 12-Everett-c. 13-Krigstein-a 23 46 69 136 223 310
NOTE: *Title may have changed after No. 3, to Crime Must Lose No. 4 on, due to publisher change.* ***Sol Brodsky*** *c-4-7, 13, 14.* ***Maneely*** *c-3, 8-11.*

SPORT STARS
Parents' Magazine Institute (Sport Stars): Feb-Mar, 1946 - No. 4, Aug-Sept, 1946 (Half comic, half photo magazine)

1- "How Tarzan Got That Way" story of Johnny Weissmuller 40 80 120 243 402 560
2-Baseball greats 26 52 78 154 252 350
3,4 23 46 69 136 223 310

SPORT STARS (Becomes Sports Action #2 on)
Marvel Comics (ACI): Nov, 1949 (52 pgs.)

1-Knute Rockne; painted-c 45 90 135 284 480 675

SPORT THRILLS (Formerly Dick Cole; becomes Jungle Thrills #16)
Star Publications: No. 11, Nov, 1950 - No. 15, Nov, 1951

11-Dick Cole begins; Ted Williams & Ty Cobb life stories 28 56 84 165 270 375
12-Joe DiMaggio, Phil Rizzuto stories & photos on-c; L.B. Cole-c/a 22 44 66 132 216 300
13-15-All L. B. Cole-c. 13-Jackie Robinson, Pee Wee Reese stories & photo on-c. 14-Johnny Weissmuler life story 22 44 66 132 216 300
Accepted Reprint #11 (#15 on-c, nd); L.B. Cole-c 10 20 30 54 72 90
Accepted Reprint #12 (nd); L.B. Cole-c; Joe DiMaggio & Phil Rizzuto life stories-r/#12 10 20 30 54 72 90

SPOTLIGHT (TV) (newsstand sales only)
Marvel Comics Group: Sept, 1978 - No. 4, Mar, 1979 (Hanna-Barbera)

1-Huckleberry Hound, Yogi Bear; Shaw-a 3 6 9 19 30 40
2,4: 2-Quick Draw McGraw, Augie Doggie, Snooper & Blabber. 4-Magilla Gorilla, Snagglepuss 3 6 9 16 23 30
3-The Jetsons; Yakky Doodle 3 6 9 19 30 40

SPOTLIGHT COMICS
Country Press Inc.: Sept, 1940

nn-Ashcan, not distributed to newsstands, only for in house use. A NM copy sold in 2009 for $1015.

SPOTLIGHT COMICS (Becomes Red Seal Comics #14 on?)
Harry 'A' Chesler (Our Army, Inc.): Nov, 1944, No. 2, Jan, 1945 - No. 3, 1945

1-The Black Dwarf (cont'd in Red Seal?), The Veiled Avenger, & Barry Kuda begin; Tuska-c 135 270 405 864 1482 2100
2 71 142 213 454 777 1100
3-Injury to eye story (reprinted from Scoop #3) 74 148 222 470 810 1150

SPOTTY THE PUP (Becomes Super Pup #4, see Television Puppet Show)
Avon Periodicals/Realistic Comics: No. 2, Oct-Nov, 1953 - No. 3, Dec-Jan, 1953-54 (Also see Funny Tunes)

2,3 8 16 24 44 57 70
nn (1953, Realistic-r) 5 10 15 24 30 35

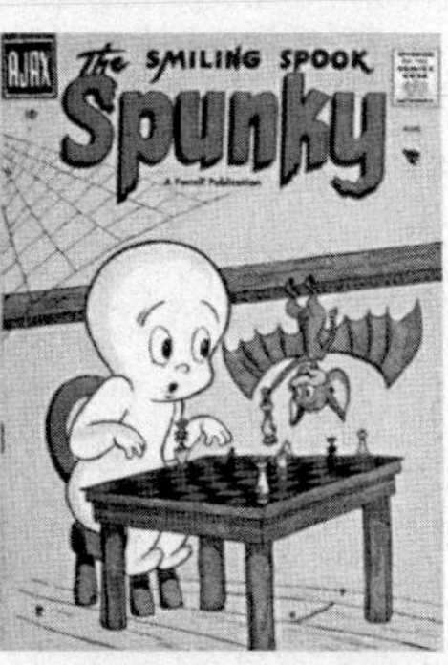

Spunky the Smiling Spook #1 © AJAX

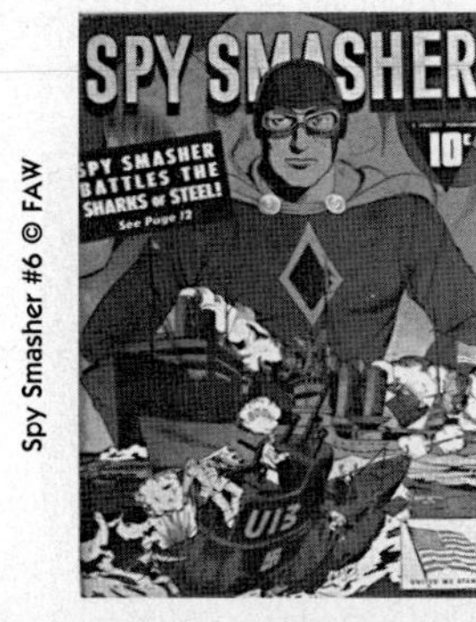

Spy Smasher #6 © FAW

Squadron Sinister #4 © MAR

GD 2.0 | VG 4.0 | FN 6.0 | VF 8.0 | VF/NM 9.0 | NM- 9.2

SPUNKY (...Junior Cowboy)(...Comics #2 on)
Standard Comics: April, 1949 - No. 7, Nov, 1951

1-Text illos by Frazetta 15 30 45 86 133 180
2-Text illos by Frazetta 11 22 33 62 86 110
3-7 9 18 27 47 61 75

SPUNKY THE SMILING SPOOK
Ajax/Farrell (World Famous Comics/Four Star Comic Corp.): Aug, 1957 - No. 4, May, 1958

1-Reprints from Frisky Fables 11 22 33 64 90 115
2-4 7 14 21 37 46 55

SPY AND COUNTERSPY (Becomes Spy Hunters #3 on)
American Comics Group: Aug-Sept, 1949 - No. 2, Oct-Nov, 1949 (52 pgs.)

1-Origin, 1st app. Jonathan Kent, Counterspy 31 62 93 184 300 415
2 18 36 54 107 169 230

SPYBOY
Dark Horse Comics: Oct, 1999 - No. 17, May, 2001 ($2.50/$2.95/$2.99)

1-17: 1-6-Peter David-s/Pop Mhan-a. 7,8-Meglia-a. 9-17-Mhan-a 3.00
13.1-13.3 (4/03-8/03, $2.99), 13.2,13.3-Mhan-a 3.00
... Special (5/02, $4.99) David-s/Mhan-a 5.00

SPYBOY: FINAL EXAM
Dark Horse Comics: May, 2004 - No. 4, Aug, 2004 ($2.99, limited series)

1-4-Peter David-s/Pop Mhan-a/c 3.00
TPB (2005, $12.95) r/series 13.00

SPYBOY/ YOUNG JUSTICE
Dark Horse Comics: Feb, 2002 - No. 3, Apr, 2002 ($2.99, limited series)

1-3: 1-Peter David-s/Todd Nauck-a/Pop Mhan-c. 2-Mhan-a 3.00

SPY CASES (Formerly The Kellys)
Marvel/Atlas Comics (Hercules Publ.): No. 26, Sept, 1950 - No. 19, Oct, 1953

26 (#1) 32 64 96 190 310 430
27(#2),28(#3, 2/51): 27-Everett-a; bondage-c 18 36 54 103 162 220
4(4/51) - 7,9,10: 4-Heath-a 16 32 48 92 144 195
8-A-Bomb-c/story 17 34 51 100 158 215
11-19: 10-14-War format 15 30 45 84 127 170

NOTE: ***Sol Brodsky*** *c-1-5, 8, 9, 11-14, 17, 18.* ***Maneely*** *a-8; c-7, 10.* ***Tuska*** *a-7.*

SPY FIGHTERS
Marvel/Atlas Comics (CSI): March, 1951 - No. 15, July, 1953
(Cases from official records)

1-Clark Mason begins; Tuska-a; Brodsky-c 32 64 96 190 310 430
2-Tuska-a 18 36 54 103 162 220
3-13: 3-5-Brodsky-c. 7-Heath-c 16 32 48 92 144 195
14,15-Pakula-a(3), Ed Win-a. 15-Brodsky-c 16 32 48 94 147 200

SPY-HUNTERS (Formerly Spy & Counterspy)
American Comics Group: No. 3, Dec-Jan, 1949-50 - No. 24, June-July, 1953 (#3-14: 52 pgs.)

3-Jonathan Kent continues, ends #10 23 46 69 136 223 310
4-10: 4,8,10-Starr-a 14 28 42 80 115 150
11-15,17-22,24: 18-War-c begin. 21-War-c/stories begin
10 20 30 56 76 95
16-Williamson-a (9 pgs.) 15 30 45 88 137 185
23-Graphic torture, injury to eye panel 20 40 60 114 182 250

NOTE: ***Drucker*** *a-12.* ***Whitney*** *a-many issues; c-7, 8, 10-12, 15, 16.*

SPYMAN (Top Secret Adventures on cover)
Harvey Publications (Illustrated Humor): Sept, 1966 - No. 3, Feb, 1967 (12¢)

1-Origin and 1st app. of Spyman. Steranko-a(p)-1st pro work; 1 pg. Neal Adams ad;
Tuska-c/a, Crandall-a(i) 8 16 24 54 102 150
2-Simon-c; Steranko-a(p) 5 10 15 30 50 70
3-Simon-c 4 8 12 25 40 55

SPY SMASHER (See Mighty Midget, Whiz & Xmas Comics) (Also see Crime Smasher)
Fawcett Publications: Fall, 1941 - No. 11, Feb, 1943

1-Spy Smasher begins; silver metallic-c 337 674 1011 2359 4130 5900
2-Raboy-c 155 310 465 992 1696 2400
3,4: 3-Bondage-c. 4-Irvin Steinberg-c 103 206 309 659 1130 1600
5-7: Raboy-a; 6-Raboy-c/a. 7-Part photo-c (movie) Japanese dragon-c
90 180 270 576 988 1400
8,11: War-c 76 152 228 486 831 1175
9-Hitler, Tojo, Mussolini-c. 142 284 426 909 1555 2200
10-Hitler-c 129 258 387 826 1413 2000

SPY THRILLERS (Police Badge No. 479 #5)
Atlas Comics (PrPl): Nov, 1954 - No. 4, May, 1955

1-Brodsky c-1,2 27 54 81 158 259 360
2-Last precode (1/55) 16 32 48 92 144 195
3,4 14 28 42 81 118 155

SQUADRON SINISTER (Secret Wars tie-in)
Marvel Comics: Aug, 2015 - No. 4, Jan, 2016 ($3.99, limited series)

1-4-Guggenheim-s/Pacheco-a/c. 1-Squadron Supreme app. 2-Frightful Four app. 4.00

SQUADRON SUPREME (Also see Marvel Graphic Novel - ...: Death of a Universe)
Marvel Comics Group: Aug, 1985 - No. 12, Aug, 1986 (Maxi-series)

1-Double size 5.00
2-12 4.00
TPB ($24.99) r/#1-12; Alex Ross painted-c; printing inks contain some of the cremated remains of late writer Mark Gruenwald 50.00
TPB-2nd printing ($24.99): Inks contain no ashes 25.00
...Death of a Universe TPB (2006, $24.99) r/Marvel Graphic Novel, Thor #280, Avengers #5,6; Avengers/Squadron Supreme Annual and Squadron Supreme: New World Order 25.00

SQUADRON SUPREME (Also see Supreme Power)
Marvel Comics: May, 2006 - No. 7, Nov, 2006 ($2.99)

1-7-Straczynski-s/Frank-a/c 3.00
Saga of Squadron Supreme (2006, $3.99) summary of Supreme Power #1-18; plus Hyperion and Nighthawk limited series; wraparound-c; preview of Squadron Supreme #1 4.00
... Vol. 1: The Pre-War Years (2006, $20.99, dustjacket) r/#1-5 & Saga of S.S. 21.00

SQUADRON SUPREME
Marvel Comics: Sept, 2008 - No. 12, Aug, 2009 ($2.99)

1-12: 1-Set 5 years after Ultimate Power; Nick Fury app.; Chaykin-s/Turini-a/Land-c 3.00

SQUADRON SUPREME
Marvel Comics: Feb, 2016 - No. 15, Mar, 2017 ($3.99)

1-15-Robinson-s; main covers by Alex Ross thru #4. 1-Kirk-a; Namor killed. 3-Avengers app. 9-12-Civil War II tie-in. 10-Thundra & Blue Marvel app. 11,12-Spider-Man app. 4.00

SQUADRON SUPREME: HYPERION VS. NIGHTHAWK
Marvel Comics: Mar, 2007 - No. 4, June, 2007 ($2.99, limited series)

1-4-Hyperion and Nighthawk in Darfur; Gulacy-a/c; Guggenheim-s 3.00
TPB (2007, $10.99) r/#1-4 11.00

SQUADRON SUPREME: NEW WORLD ORDER
Marvel Comics: Sept, 1998 ($5.99, one-shot)

1-Wraparound-c; Kaminski-s 6.00

SQUALOR
First Comics: Dec, 1989 - Aug, 1990 ($2.75, limited series)

1-4: Sutton-a 3.00

SQUARRIORS
Devil's Due: Dec, 2014 - No. 4, Sept, 2015 ($3.99, limited series)

1-4: Maczko-s/Witter-a 4.00
Vol. 2 (5/16 - No. 4) 1-Maczko-s/Witter-a 4.00

SQUEE (Also see Johnny The Homicidal Maniac)
Slave Labor Graphics: Apr, 1997 - No. 4, May, 1998 ($2.95, B&W)

1-4: Jhonen Vasquez-s/a in all 3.00

SQUEEKS (Also see Boy Comics)
Lev Gleason Publications: Oct, 1953 - No. 5, June, 1954

1-Funny animal; Biro-c; Crimebuster's pet monkey "Squeeks" begins
10 20 30 58 79 100
2-Biro-c 7 14 21 37 46 55
3-5: 3-Biro-c 6 12 18 31 38 45

S.R. BISSETTE'S SPIDERBABY COMIX
SpiderBaby Grafix: Aug, 1996 - No. 2 ($3.95, B&W, magazine size)

Preview-(8/96, $3.95)-Graphic violence & nudity; Laurel & Hardy app. 4.00
1,2 4.00

S.R. BISSETTE'S TYRANT
SpiderBaby Grafix: Sept, 1994 - No. 4 ($2.95, B&W)

1-4 4.00

STALKER (Also see All Star Comics 1999 and crossover issues)
National Periodical Publications: June-July, 1975 - No. 4, Dec-Jan, 1975-76

1-Origin & 1st app; Ditko/Wood-c/a 2 4 6 10 14 18
2-4-Ditko/Wood-c/a 2 3 4 6 8 10

STALKERS

Stanley and His Monster (1993 series) #3 © DC

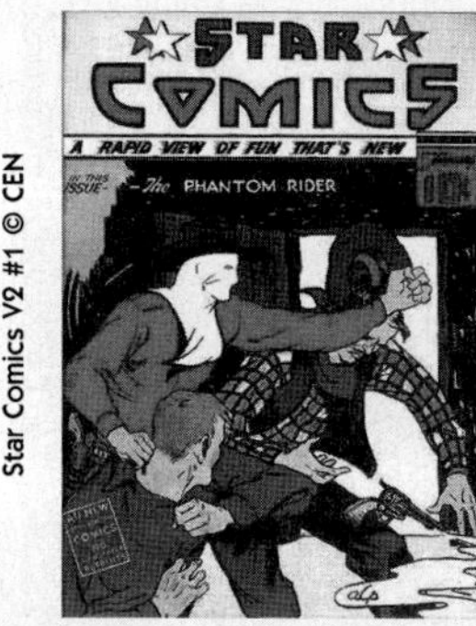

Star Comics V2 #1 © CEN

Starfire (2015 series) #1 © DC

GD 2.0 | VG 4.0 | FN 6.0 | VF 8.0 | VF/NM 9.0 | NM- 9.2

Marvel Comics (Epic Comics): Apr, 1990 - No. 12, Mar, 1991 ($1.50)
1-12: 1-Chadwick-c 3.00

STAMP COMICS (Stamps... on-c; Thrilling Adventures In...#8)
Youthful Magazines/Stamp Comics, Inc.: Oct, 1951 - No. 7, Oct, 1952
1-(15¢) ('Stamps' on indicia No. 1-3,5,7) 26 52 78 152 249 345
2 15 30 45 86 133 180
3-6: 3,4-Kiefer, Wildey-a 14 28 42 81 118 155
7-Roy Krenkel (4 pgs.) 17 34 51 98 154 210
NOTE: *Promotes stamp collecting; gives stories behind various commemorative stamps. No. 2, 10¢ printed over 15¢ c-price.* ***Kiefer*** *a-1-7.* ***Kirkel*** *a-1-6.* ***Napoli*** *a-2-7.* ***Palais*** *a-2-4, 7.*

STAND, THE ... (Based on the Stephen King novel)
Marvel Comics: 2008 - 2012 ($3.99, limited series)
...: American Nightmares 1-5 (5/09 - No. 5, 10/09, $3.99) Aguirre-Sacasa-s/Perkins-a 4.00
...: Captain Trips 1-5 (12/08 - No. 5, 3/09, $3.99) Aguirre-Sacasa-s/Perkins-a 4.00
...: Hardcases 1-5 (8/10 - No. 5, 1/11, $3.99) Aguirre-Sacasa-s/Perkins-a 4.00
...: No Man's Land 1-5 (4/11 - No. 5, 8/11, $3.99) Aguirre-Sacasa-s/Perkins-a 4.00
...: Soul Survivors 1-5 (12/09 - No. 5, 5/10, $3.99) Aguirre-Sacasa-s/Perkins-a 4.00
...: The Night Has Come 1-6 (10/11 - No. 6, 3/12, $3.99) Aguirre-Sacasa-s/Perkins-a 4.00

STAN LEE MEETS...
Marvel Comics: Nov, 2006 - Jan, 2007 ($3.99, series of one-shots)
Doctor Doom 1 (12/06) Lee-s/Larroca-a/c; Loeb-s/McGuinness-a; r/Fantastic Four #87 4.00
Doctor Strange 1 (11/06) Lee-s/Davis-a/c; Bendis-s/Bagley-a; r/Marvel Premiere #3 4.00
Silver Surfer 1 (1/07) Lee-s/Wieringo-a/c; Jenkins-s/Buckingham-a; r/S.S. #14 4.00
Spider-Man 1 (11/06) Lee-s/Coipel-a/c; Whedon-s/Gaydos-a; Hembeck-s/a; r/AS-M #87 4.00
The Thing 1 (12/06) Lee-s/Weeks-a/c; Thomas-s/Kolins-a; r/FF #79; FF #51 cover swipe 4.00
HC (2007, $24.99, dustjacket) r/one-shots; interviews and features 25.00

STAN LEE'S MIGHTY 7
Archie Comics (Stan Lee Comics): May, 2012 - No. 3, Sept, 2012 ($2.99, limited series)
1-3-Co-written by Stan Lee; Alex Saviuk-a; multiple covers on each 3.00

STANLEY & HIS MONSTER (Formerly The Fox & the Crow)
National Periodical Publ.: No. 109, Apr-May, 1968 - No. 112, Oct-Nov, 1968
109-112 3 6 9 21 33 45

STANLEY & HIS MONSTER
DC Comics: Feb, 1993 - No. 4, May, 1993 ($1.50, limited series)
1-4 3.00

STAN SHAW'S BEAUTY & THE BEAST
Dark Horse Comics: Nov, 1993 ($4.95, one-shot)
1 5.00

STAR
Image Comics (Highbrow Entertainment): June, 1995 - No. 4, Oct, 1995 ($2.50, lim. series)
1-4 3.00

STARBLAST
Marvel Comics: Jan, 1994 - No. 4, Apr, 1994 ($1.75, limited series)
1-($2.00, 52 pgs.)-Nova, Quasar, Black Bolt; painted-c 4.00
2-4 3.00

STAR BLAZERS
Comico: Apr, 1987 - No. 4, July, 1987 ($1.75, limited series)
1-4 3.00

STAR BLAZERS
Comico: 1989 ($1.95/$2.50, limited series)
1-5- Steacy wraparound painted-c on all 3.00

STAR BLAZERS (The Magazine of Space Battleship Yamato)
Argo Press: No. 0, Aug, 1995 - No. 3, Dec, 1995 ($2.95)
0-3 3.00

STARBORN (From Stan Lee)
BOOM! Studios: Dec, 2010 - No. 12, Nov, 2011 ($3.99)
1-12: 1-9,11-Roberson-s/Randolph-a. 1-7-Three covers on each. 10-Scalera-a 4.00

STAR BRAND
Marvel Comics (New Universe): Oct, 1986 - No. 19, May, 1989 (75¢/$1.25)
1-15: 14-begin $1.25-c 3.00
16-19-Byrne story & art; low print run 5.00
Annual 1 (10/87) 4.00
... Classic Vol. 1 TPB (2006, $19.99) r/#1-7 20.00

STARBRAND & NIGHTMASK
Marvel Comics: Feb, 2016 - No. 6, Jul, 2016 ($3.99)
1-6: 1-Weisman-s/Stanton-a; Kevin and Adam go to college; Nitro & Graviton app. 4.00

STARCHILD
Tailspin Press: 1992 - No. 12 ($2.25/$2.50, B&W)
1,2-('92),0(4/93),3-12: 0-Illos by Chadwick, Eisner, Sim, M. Wagner. 3-(7/93). 4-(11/93). 6-(2/94) 3.00

STARCHILD: MYTHOPOLIS
Image Comics: No. 0, July, 1997 - No. 4, Apr, 1998 ($2.95, B&W, limited series)
0-4-James Owen-s/a 3.00

STAR COMICS
Ultem Publ. (Harry `A' Chesler)/Centaur Publications: Feb, 1937 - V2#7 (No. 23), Aug, 1939 (#1-6: large size)
V1#1-Dan Hastings (s/f) begins 423 846 1269 3000 5250 7500
2 232 464 696 1485 2543 3600
3-Classic Black Americana cover (rare) 423 846 1269 3067 5384 7700
4,5-Classic Winsor McCay Little Nemo-c/stories (rare)
271 542 813 1734 2967 4200
6-(9/37) 219 438 657 1402 2401 3400
7-9: 8-Severed head centerspread; Impy & Little Nemo by Winsor McCay Jr, Popeye app. by Bob Wood; Mickey Mouse & Popeye app. as toys in Santa's bag on-c; X-Mas-c 155 310 465 992 1696 2400
10 (1st Centaur; 3/38)-Impy by Winsor McCay Jr; Don Marlow by Guardineer begins
181 362 543 1158 1979 2800
11-1st Jack Cole comic-a, 1 pg. (4/38) 226 452 678 1446 2473 3500
12-15: 12-Riders of the Golden West begins; Little Nemo app. 15-Speed Silvers by Gustavson & The Last Pirate by Burgos begins
110 220 330 704 1202 1700
16 (12/38)-The Phantom Rider & his horse Thunder begins, ends V2#6
126 252 378 806 1378 1950
V2#1(#17, 2/39)-Phantom Rider-c (only non-funny-c)
148 296 444 947 1624 2300
2-7(#18-23): 2-Diana Deane by Tarpe Mills app. 3-Drama of Hollywood by Mills begins. 7-Jungle Queen app. 90 180 270 576 988 1400
NOTE: ***Biro*** *c-6, 9, 10.* ***Burgos*** *a-15, 16, V2#1-7.* ***Ken Ernst*** *a-10, 12, 14.* ***Filchock*** *c-15, 18, 22.* ***Gill Fox*** *c-14, 19.* ***Guardineer*** *a-6, 8-14.* ***Gustavson*** *a-13-16, V2#1-7.* ***Winsor McCay*** *c-4, 5.* ***Tarpe Mills*** *a-15, V2#1-7.* ***Schwab*** *c-20, 23.* ***Bob Wood*** *a-10, 12, 13; c-7, 8.*

STAR COMICS MAGAZINE
Marvel Comics (Star Comics): Dec, 1986 - No. 13, 1988 ($1.50, digest-size)
1,9-Spider-Man-c/s 2 4 6 8 11 14
2-8-Heathcliff, Ewoks, Top Dog, Madballs-r in #1-13 1 2 3 5 7 9
10-13 2 4 6 8 10 12

S.T.A.R. CORPS
DC Comics: Nov, 1993 - No. 6, Apr, 1994 ($1.50, limited series)
1-6: 1,2-Austin-c(i). 1-Superman app. 3.00

STARCRAFT (Based on the video game)
DC Comics (WildStorm): July, 2009 - No. 7, Jan, 2010 ($2.99)
1-7-Furman-s; two covers on each 3.00
HC (2010, $19.99, dustjacket) r/#1-7 20.00
SC (2011, $14.99) r/#1-7 15.00

STAR CROSSED
DC Comics (Helix): June, 1997 - No. 3, Aug, 1997 ($2.50, limited series)
1-3-Matt Howarth-s/a 3.00

STARDUST (See Neil Gaiman and Charles Vess' Stardust)

STARDUST KID, THE
Image Comics/Boom! Studios #4-on: May, 2005 - No. 4 ($3.50)
1-4-J.M. DeMatteis-s/Mike Ploog-a 3.50

STAR FEATURE COMICS
I. W. Enterprises: 1963
Reprint #9-Stunt-Man Stetson-r/Feat. Comics #141 2 4 6 10 13 16

STARFIRE (Not the Teen Titans character)
National Periodical Publ./DC Comics: Aug-Sept, 1976 - No. 8, Oct-Nov, 1977
1-Origin (CCA stamp fell off cover art; so it was approved by code)
2 4 6 10 14 18
2-8 1 2 3 5 6 8

STARFIRE (Teen Titans character)(Also see Red Hood and the Outlaws)
DC Comics: Aug, 2015 - No. 12, Jul, 2016 ($2.99)
1-12: 1-Conner & Palmiotti-s/Lupacchino-a; Conner-c. 3-Intro. Atlee. 7,8-Grayson app. 9-Charretier-a begins; intro. Syl'khee 3.00

Stargate Atlantis #1 © MGM

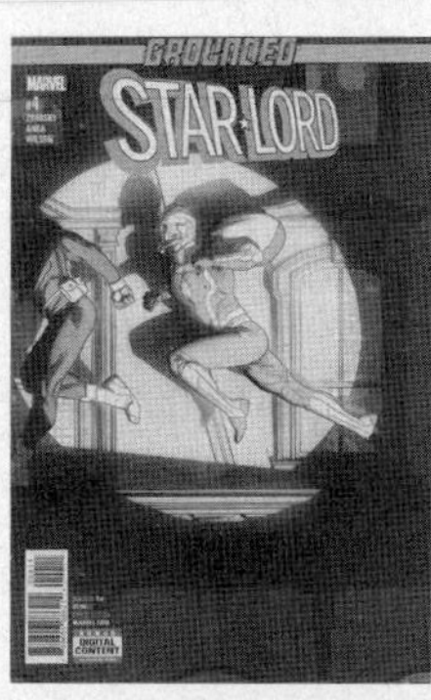

Star-Lord (2017 series) #4 © MAR

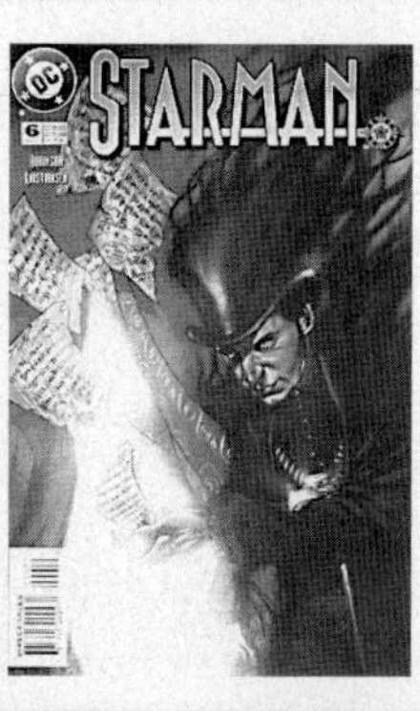

Starman (2nd series) #6 © DC

	GD 2.0	VG 4.0	FN 6.0	VF 8.0	VF/NM 9.0	NM- 9.2

STARGATE
Dynamite Entertainment
...: Daniel Jackson 1-4 (2010 - No. 4, 2010, $3.99) Watson-a/Murray-s 4.00
...: Vala Mal Doran 1-5 (2010 - No. 5, 2010, $3.99) Razek-a/Jerwa-s 4.00

STARGATE ATLANTIS (Based on the TV series)
American Mythology Prods.: 2016 - Present ($3.99)
1-6: 1-Haynes & Vaughn-s/LaRocque-a; covers by Wheatley & LaRocque. 4-6-Gateways #1-3 on cover; Watson-a 4.00

STARGATE ATLANTIS HEARTS & MINDS
American Mythology Prods.: 2017 - No. 3, 2017 ($3.99)
1-3-Haynes & Vaughn-s/LaRocque-a 4.00

STARGATE ATLANTIS / STARGATE UNIVERSE ANTHOLOGY
American Mythology Prods.: 2018 - Present ($3.99)
1-Haynes & Vaughn-s/LaRocque & Purcell-a; 3 covers 4.00

STARGATE UNIVERSE (Based on the TV series)
American Mythology Prods.: 2017 - Present ($3.99)
1-3: 1-Haynes & Vaughn-s/Caracuzzo-a. 2,3-Gouveia-a 4.00

STAR HUNTERS (See DC Super Stars #16)
National Periodical Publ./DC Comics: Oct-Nov, 1977 - No. 7, Oct-Nov, 1978

	GD	VG	FN	VF	VF/NM	NM-
1,7: 1-Newton-a(p). 7-44 pgs.	2	4	6	8	10	12
2-6	1	2	3	4	5	7

NOTE: *Buckler a-4-7p; c-1-7p.* ***Layton*** *a-1-5i; c-1-6i.* ***Nasser*** *a-3p.* ***Sutton*** *a-6i.*

STARJAMMERS (See X-Men Spotlight on Starjammers)

STARJAMMERS (Also see Uncanny X-Men)
Marvel Comics: Oct, 1995 - No. 4, Jan, 1996 ($2.95, limited series)
1-4: Foil-c; Ellis scripts 4.00

STARJAMMERS
Marvel Comics: Sept, 2004 - No. 6, Jan, 2005 ($2.99, limited series)
1-6-Kevin J. Anderson-s. 1-Garza-a. 2-6-Lucas-a 3.00

STARK TERROR
Stanley Publications: Dec, 1970 - No. 5, Aug, 1971 (B&W, magazine, 52 pgs.)
(1950s Horror reprints, including pre-code)

	GD	VG	FN	VF	VF/NM	NM-
1-Bondage, torture-c	7	14	21	44	82	120
2-4 (Gillmor/Aragon-r)	4	8	12	27	44	65
5 (ACG-r)	4	8	12	25	38	55

STARLET O'HARA IN HOLLYWOOD (Teen-age) (Also see Cookie)
Standard Comics: Dec, 1948 - No. 4, Sept, 1949

	GD	VG	FN	VF	VF/NM	NM-
1-Owen Fitzgerald-a in all	41	82	123	256	428	600
2	30	60	90	177	289	400
3,4	22	44	66	132	216	300

STARLIGHT
Image Comics: Mar, 2014 - No. 6, Oct, 2014 ($2.99)
1-5-Mark Millar-s/Goran Parlov-a. 1-Covers by Cassaday & Parlov. 2-Sienkiewicz var-c 3.00
6-($4.99) Two covers by Cassaday and Chiang 5.00

STARLORD
Marvel Comics: Dec, 1996 - No. 3, Feb, 1997 ($2.50, limited series)
1-3-Timothy Zahn-s 3.00

STAR-LORD (Guardians of the Galaxy)
Marvel Comics: Aug, 2013; 2014 ($7.99, series of reprints)
...: Annihilation - Conquest 1 (2014) r/Annihilation: Conquest - Starlord #1-4; design art 8.00
...: Tears For Heaven 1 (2014) r/Marvel Preview #18, Marvel Spotlight #6,7, and Marvel Premiere #61; bonus art; new cover by Pichelli 8.00
...: The Hollow Crown 1 (8/13) r/Marvel Preview #4,11 and Star-Lord Special Edition 8.00

STAR-LORD
Marvel Comics: Jan, 2016 - No. 8, Aug, 2016 ($3.99)
1-8: 1-Humphries-s/Garron-a; 18-year-old Peter Quill's 1st meeting with Yondu 4.00

STAR-LORD
Marvel Comics: Feb, 2017 - No. 6, Jun, 2017 ($3.99)
1-6-Zdarsky-s/Anka-a. 1,5,6-Old Man Logan app. 3-5-Daredevil app. 4.00
Annual 1 (7/17, $4.99) Zdarsky-s/Morissette-a/Anka-c 5.00

STAR-LORD & KITTY PRYDE (Secret Wars tie-in)
Marvel Comics: Sept, 2015 - No. 3, Nov, 2015 ($3.99, limited series)
1-3-Humphries-s/Firmansyah-a; Gambit app. 4.00

	GD 2.0	VG 4.0	FN 6.0	VF 8.0	VF/NM 9.0	NM- 9.2

STARLORD MEGAZINE
Marvel Comics: Nov, 1996 ($2.95, one-shot)
1-Reprints w/preview of new series 3.00

STAR-LORD THE SPECIAL EDITION (Also see Marvel Comics Super Special #10, Marvel Premiere & Preview & Marvel Spotlight V2#6,7)
Marvel Comics Group: Feb, 1982 (one-shot, direct sales) (1st Baxter paper comic)

	GD	VG	FN	VF	VF/NM	NM-
1-Byrne/Austin-a; Austin-c; 8 pgs. of new-a by Golden (p); Dr. Who story by Dave Gibbons; 1st deluxe format comic	2	4	6	11	16	20

STAR MAGE
IDW Publishing: Apr, 2014 - No. 6, Sept, 2014 ($3.99, limited series)
1-6: 1-JC De La Torre-s/Ray Dillon-a. 2-6-Franco Cespedes-a 4.00

STARMAN (1st Series) (Also see Justice League & War of the Gods)
DC Comics: Oct, 1988 - No. 45, Apr, 1992 ($1.00)
1-Origin 5.00
2-25,29-45: 4-Intro The Power Elite. 9,10,34-Batman app. 14-Superman app. 17-Power Girl app. 38-War of the Gods x-over. 42-45-Eclipso-c/stories 3.00
26-1st app. David Knight (G.A.Starman's son). 5.00
27,28: 27-Starman (David Knight) app. 28-Starman disguised as Superman; leads into Superman #50 4.00

STARMAN (2nd Series) (Also see The Golden Age, Showcase 95 #12, Showcase 96 #4,5)
DC Comics: No. 0, Oct, 1994 - No. 80, Aug, 2001; No. 81, Mar, 2010 ($1.95/$2.25/$2.50)

	GD	VG	FN	VF	VF/NM	NM-
0,1: 0-James Robinson scripts, Tony Harris-c/a(p) & Wade Von Grawbadger-a(i) begins; Sins of the Father storyline begins, ends #3; 1st app. new Starman (Jack Knight); reintro of the G.A. Mist & G.A. Shade; 1st app. Nash; David Knight dies	1	3	4	6	8	10

2-7: 2-Reintro Charity from Forbidden Tales of Dark Mansion. 3-Reintro/2nd app. "Blue" Starman (1st app. in 1st Issue Special #12); Will Payton app. (both cameos). 5-David Knight app. 6-The Shade "Times Past" story; Kristiansen-a. 7-The Black Pirate cameo 5.00
8-17: 8-Begin $2.25-c. 10-1st app. new Mist (Nash). 11-JSA "Times Past" story; Matt Smith-a. 12-16-Sins of the Child. 17-The Black Pirate app. 4.00
18-37: 18-G.A. Starman "Times Past" story; Watkiss-a. 19-David Knight app. 20-23-G.A. Sandman app. 24-26-Demon Quest; all 3 covers make-up triptych. 33-36-Batman-c/app. 37-David Knight and deceased JSA members app. 3.00
38-49,51-56: 38-Nash vs. Justice League Europe. 39,40-Crossover w/ Power of Shazam! #35,36; Bulletman app. 42-Demon-c/app. 43-JLA-c/app. 44-Phantom Lady-c/app. 46-Gene Ha-a. 51-Jor-El app. 52,53-Adam Strange-c/app. 3.00
50-($3.95) Gold foil logo on-c; Star Boy (LSH) app. 4.00
57-79: 57-62-Painted covers by Harris and Alex Ross. 72-Death of Ted Knight 3.00
80-($3.95) Final issue; cover by Harris & Robinson 4.00
81-(3/10, $2.99) Blackest Night one-shot; The Shade vs. David Knight; Harris-c 3.00
#1,000,000 (11/98) 853rd Century x-over; Snejbjerg-a 3.00
Annual 1 (1996, $3.50)-Legends of the Dead Earth story; Prince Gavyn & G.A. Starman stories; J.H. Williams III, Bret Blevins, Craig Hamilton-c/a(p) 4.00
Annual 2 (1997, $3.95)-Pulp Heroes story; 4.00
...80 Page Giant (1/99, $4.95) Harris-c 5.00
...Secret Files 1 (4/98, $4.95)-Origin stories and profile pages 5.00
...The Mist (6/98, $1.95) Girlfrenzy; Mary Marvel app. 3.00
A Starry Knight-($17.95, TPB) r/#47-53 18.00
Grand Guignol-(2004, $19.95, TPB)-r/#61-73 20.00
Infernal Devices-($17.95, TPB) r/#29-35,37,38 18.00
Night and Day-($14.95, TPB)-r/#7-10,12-16 15.00
Sins of the Father-($12.95, TPB)-r/#0-5 13.00
Sons of the Father-($14.99, TPB)-r/#75-80 15.00
Stars My Destination-(2003, $14.95, TPB)-r/#55-60 15.00
Times Past-($17.95, TPB)-r/stories of other Starmen 18.00
The Starman Omnibus Vol. One (2008, $49.99, HC with dj) r/#0,1-16; James Robinson intro. 50.00
The Starman Omnibus Vol. Two (2009, $49.99, HC with dj) r/#17-29, Annual #1, Showcase '95 #12, Showcase '96 #4,5; Harris intro.; merchandise gallery 50.00
The Starman Omnibus Vol. Three (2009, $49.99, HC with dj) r/#30-38, Annual #2, Starman Secret Files #1 and The Shade #1-4 50.00
The Starman Omnibus Vol. Four (2010, $49.99, HC with dj) r/#39-46, 80 Page Giant #1, Power of Shazam! #35,36; Starman: The Mist #1 and Batman/Hellboy/Starman #1,2 50.00
The Starman Omnibus Vol. Five (2010, $49.99, HC with dj) r/#47-60, #1,000,000; Stars and S.T.R.I.P.E. #0; All Star Comics 80 Page Giant #1; JSA: All Stars #4 50.00
The Starman Omnibus Vol. Six (2011, $49.99, HC with dj) r/#61-81, Johns intro. 50.00

STARMAN/CONGORILLA (See Justice League: Cry For Justice)
DC Comics: Mar, 2011 ($2.99, one-shot)
1-Animal Man and Rex the Wonder Dog app.; Robinson-s/Booth-a/Ha-c 3.00

STARMASTERS

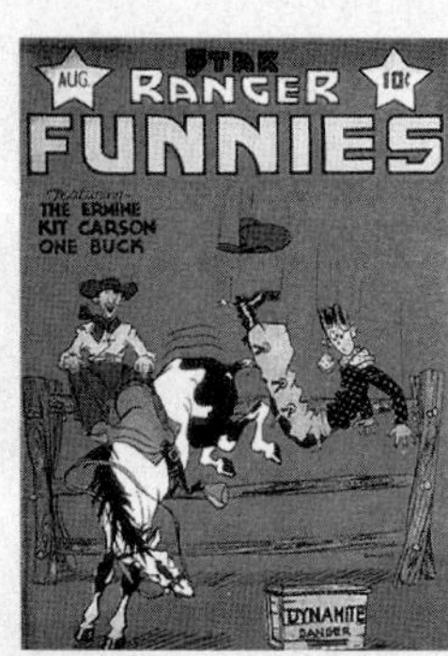

Star Ranger Funnies V2 #4 © CEN

Stars and S.T.R.I.P.E. #1 © DC

Star Spangled Comics #7 © DC

GD 2.0 | VG 4.0 | FN 6.0 | VF 8.0 | VF/NM 9.0 | NM- 9.2

GD 2.0 | VG 4.0 | FN 6.0 | VF 8.0 | VF/NM 9.0 | NM- 9.2

Marvel Comics: Dec, 1995 - No. 3, Feb, 1996 ($1.95, limited series)

1-3-Continues in Cosmic Powers Unlimited #4 3.00

STAR PRESENTATION, A (Formerly My Secret Romance #1,2; Spectacular Stories #4 on) (Also see This Is Suspense)
Fox Feature Syndicate (Hero Books): No. 3, May, 1950

3-Dr. Jekyll & Mr. Hyde by Wood & Harrison (reprinted in Startling Terror Tales #10); "The Repulsing Dwarf" by Wood; Wood-c 69 138 207 442 759 1075

STAR QUEST COMIX (Warren Presents... on cover)
Warren Publications: Oct, 1978 ($1.50, B&W magazine, 84 pgs., square-bound)

1-Corben, Maroto, Neary-a; Ken Kelly-c; Star Wars 2 4 6 9 12 15

STAR RAIDERS (See DC Graphic Novel #1)

STAR RANGER (Cowboy Comics #13 on)
Chesler Publ./Centaur Publ.: Feb, 1937 - No. 12, May, 1938 (Large size: No. 1-6)

1-(1st Western comic)-Ace & Deuce, Air Plunder; Creig Flessel-a
300 600 900 2010 3505 5000
2 155 310 465 992 1696 2400
3-6 142 284 426 909 1555 2200
7-9: 8(12/37)-Christmas-c; Air Patrol, Gold coast app.; Guardineer centerfold
116 232 348 742 1271 1800
V2#10 (1st Centaur; 3/38) 129 258 387 826 1413 2000
11,12 110 220 330 704 1202 1700

NOTE: ***J. Cole*** *a-10, 12; c-12.* ***Ken Ernst*** *a-11.* ***Gill Fox*** *a-8(illo), 9, 10.* ***Guardineer*** *a-1-3, 5-7, 8(illos), 9, 10, 12.* ***Gustavson*** *a-8-10, 12.* ***Fred Schwab*** *c-2-11.* ***Bob Wood*** *a-8-10.*

STAR RANGER FUNNIES (Formerly Cowboy Comics)
Centaur Publications: V1#15, Oct, 1938 - V2#5, Oct, 1939

V1#15-Lyin Lou, Ermine, Wild West Junior, The Law of Caribou County by Eisner, Cowboy Jake, The Plugged Dummy, Spurs by Gustavson, Red Coat, Two Buckaroos & Trouble Hunters begin 123 246 369 787 1344 1900
V2#1 (1/39) 100 200 300 635 1093 1550
2-5: 2-Night Hawk by Gustavson. 4-Kit Carson app.
84 168 252 538 919 1300

NOTE: ***Jack Cole*** *a-V2#1, 3; c-V2#1.* ***Filchock*** *c-V2#2, 3.* ***Guardineer*** *a-V2#3.* ***Gustavson*** *a-V2#2.* ***Pinajian*** *c/a-V2#5.*

STAR REACH (Mature content)
Star Reach Publ.: Apr, 1974 - No. 18, Oct, 1979 (B&W, #12-15 w/color)

1-(75¢, 52 pgs.) Art by Starlin, Simonson. Chaykin-c/a; origin Death. Cody Starbuck-sty
3 6 9 17 26 35
1-2nd, 3th, and 4th printings ($1.00-$1.50-c) 6.00
2-11: 2-Adams, Giordano-a; 1st Stephanie Starr-c/s. 3-1st Linda Lovecraft. 4-1st Sherlock Duck. 5-1st Gideon Faust by Chaykin. 6-Elric-c. 7-BWS-c. 9-14-Sacred & Profane-c/s by Steacy. 11-Samurai 2 4 6 8 11 14
2-2nd printing 4.00
12-15 (44 pgs.): 12-Zelazny-s. Nasser-a, Brunner-c 2 4 6 9 13 16
16-18-Magazine size: 17-Poe's Raven-c/s 2 4 6 9 13 16

NOTE: ***Adams*** *c-2.* ***Bonivert*** *a-17.* ***Brunner*** *a-3,5; c-3,10,12.* ***Chaykin*** *a-1,4,5; c-1(1st ed),4,5; back-c-1(2nd,3rd,4th ed).* ***Gene Day*** *a-6,8,9,11,15.* ***Friedrich*** *s-2,3,8,10.* ***Gasbarri*** *a-7.* ***Gilbert*** *a-9,12.* ***Giordano*** *a-2.* ***Gould*** *a-6.* ***Hirota/Mukaide*** *s/a-7.* ***Jones*** *c-6.* ***Konz*** *a-17.* ***Leialoha*** *a-3,4,6-i, 13,15; c-13,15.* ***Lyda*** *a-6,12-15.* ***Marrs*** *a-2-5,7,10,14,15,16,18; c-18; back-c-2.* ***Mukaide*** *a-18.* ***Nasser*** *a-12.* ***Nino*** *a-6;* ***Russell*** *a-8,10; c-8.* ***Dave Sim*** *s-7; lettering-9.* ***Simonson*** *a-1.* ***Skeates*** *a-1,2.* ***Starlin*** *a-1(x2), 2(x2); back-c-1(1st ed); c-1(2nd,3rd,4th ed).* ***Barry Smith*** *c-7.* ***Staton*** *a-5,6,7.* ***Steacy*** *a-8-14; c-9,11,14,16.* ***Vosburg*** *a-2-5,7,10.* ***Workman*** *a-2-5,8.* *Nudity panels in most. Wraparound-c: 3-5,7-11,13-16,18.*

STAR REACH CLASSICS
Eclipse Comics: Mar, 1984 - No. 6, Aug, 1984 ($1.50, Baxter paper)

1-6: 1-Neal Adams-r/Star Reach #1; Sim & Starlin-a 3.00

STARR FLAGG, UNDERCOVER GIRL (See Undercover...)

STARRIORS
Marvel Comics: Aug, 1984 - Feb, 1985 (Limited series) (Based on Tomy toys)

1-4 4.00

STARR THE SLAYER
Marvel Comics (MAX): Nov, 2009 - No. 4, Feb, 2010 ($3.99, limited series)

1-4- Richard Corben-c/a; Daniel Way-s 4.00

STARS AND S.T.R.I.P.E. (Also see JSA)
DC Comics: July, 1999 - No. 14, Sept, 2000 ($2.95/$2.50)

0-($2.95) 1st app. Courtney Whitmore; Moder and Weston-a; Starman app. 3.00
1-Johns and Robinson-s/Moder-a; origin new Star Spangled Kid 3.00
2-14: 4-Marvel Family app. 9-Seven Soldiers of Victory-c/app. 3.00
JSA Presents: Stars and S.T.R.I.P.E. Vol. 1 TPB (2007, $17.99) r/#1-8; Johns intro. 18.00
JSA Presents: Stars and S.T.R.I.P.E. Vol. 2 TPB (2008, $17.99) r/#0,9-14 18.00

STARS AND STRIPES COMICS
Centaur Publications: No. 2, May, 1941 - No. 6, Dec, 1941

2(#1)-The Shark, The Iron Skull, A-Man, The Amazing Man, Mighty Man, Minimidget begin; The Voice & Dash Dartwell, the Human Meteor, Reef Kinkaid app.; Gustavson Flag-c
245 490 735 1568 2684 3800
3-Origin Dr. Synthe; The Black Panther app. 161 322 483 1030 1765 2500
4-Origin/1st app. The Stars and Stripes; injury to eye-c
135 270 405 864 1482 2100
5(#5 on cover & inside) 103 206 309 659 1130 1600
5(#6)-(#5 on cover, #6 on inside) 103 206 309 659 1130 1600

NOTE: ***Gustavson*** *c/a-3.* ***Myron Strauss*** *c-4, 5(#5), 5(#6).*

STAR SEED (Formerly Powers That Be)
Broadway Comics: No. 7, 1996 - No. 9 ($2.95)

7-9 3.00

STARSHIP TROOPERS
Dark Horse Comics: 1997 - No. 2, 1997 ($2.95, limited series)

1,2-Movie adaptation 3.00

STARSHIP TROOPERS: BRUTE CREATIONS
Dark Horse Comics: 1997 ($2.95, one-shot)

1 3.00

STARSHIP TROOPERS: DOMINANT SPECIES
Dark Horse Comics: Aug, 1998 - No. 4, Nov, 1998 ($2.95, limited series)

1-4-Strnad-s/Bolton-c 3.00

STARSHIP TROOPERS: INSECT TOUCH
Dark Horse Comics: 1997 - No. 3, 1997 ($2.95, limited series)

1-3 3.00

STAR SLAMMERS (See Marvel Graphic Novel #6)
Malibu Comics (Bravura): May, 1994 - No. 4, Aug, 1994 ($2.50, unfinished limited series)

1-4: W. Simonson-a/stories; contain Bravura stamps 3.00

STAR SLAMMERS
IDW Publishing: Mar, 2014 - No. 8, Oct, 2014 ($3.99)

1-8-Recolored reprint of 1994 series; Walt Simonson-s/a. 1-4-Two covers by Simonson 4.00

STAR SLAMMERS SPECIAL
Dark Horse Comics (Legend): June, 1996 ($2.95, one-shot)

nn-Simonson-c/a/scripts; concludes Bravura limited series. 3.00

STARSLAYER
Pacific Comics/First Comics No. 7 on: Feb, 1982 - No. 6, Apr, 1983; No. 7, Aug, 1983 - No. 34, Nov, 1985

1-Origin & 1st app.; 1 pg. Rocketeer brief app. which continues in #2
2 4 6 9 12 15
2-Origin/1st full app. the Rocketeer (4/82) by Dave Stevens (Chapter 1 of Rocketeer saga; see Pacific Presents #1,2) 3 6 9 17 26 35
3-Chapter 2 of Rocketeer saga by Stevens 2 4 6 10 14 18
4,6,7: 7-Grell-a ends 4.00
5-2nd app. Groo the Wanderer by Aragonés 2 4 6 8 10 12
8,9,11-34: 18-Starslayer meets Grimjack. 20-The Black Flame begins (9/84, 1st app.), ends #33. 27-Book length Black Flame story 3.00
10-1st app. Grimjack (11/83, ends #17) 5.00

NOTE: ***Grell*** *a-1-7; c-1-8.* ***Stevens*** *back c-2, 3.* ***Sutton*** *a-17p, 20-22p, 24-27p, 29-33p.*

STARSLAYER (The Director's Cut)
Acclaim Comics (Windjammer): June, 1994 - No. 8, Dec, 1995 ($2.50)

1-8: Mike Grell-c/a/scripts 3.00

STAR SPANGLED COMICS (Star Spangled War Stories #131 on)
National Periodical Publications: Oct, 1941 - No. 130, July, 1952

1-Origin/1st app. Tarantula; Captain X of the R.A.F., Star Spangled Kid (see Action #40), Armstrong of the Army begin; Robot-c 524 1048 1572 3825 6763 9700
2 194 388 582 1242 2121 3000
3-5 116 232 348 742 1271 1800
6-Last Armstrong/Army; Penniless Palmer begins 71 142 213 454 777 1100
7-(4/42)-Origin/1st app. The Guardian by S&K, & Robotman (by Paul Cassidy & created by Siegel);The Newsboy Legion (1st app.), Robotman & TNT begin; last Captain X
811 1622 2433 5920 10,460 15,000
8-Origin TNT & Dan the Dyna-Mite 252 504 756 1613 2757 3900
9,10 168 336 504 1075 1838 2600
11-17 123 246 369 787 1344 1900
18-Origin Star Spangled Kid 155 310 465 992 1696 2400
19-Last Tarantula 123 246 369 787 1344 1900
20-Liberty Belle begins (5/43) 155 310 465 992 1696 2400

Star Spangled Comics #125 © DC

Star Spangled War Stories #4 © DC

Star Spangled War Stories #174 © DC

GD VG FN VF VF/NM NM-
2.0 4.0 6.0 8.0 9.0 9.2

21-29-Last S&K issue; 23-Last TNT. 25-Robotman by Jimmy Thompson begins.
29-Intro Robbie the Robotdog 103 206 309 659 1130 1600
30-40: 31-S&K-c 63 126 189 403 689 975
41-51: 41,49-Kirby-c. 51-Robot-c by Kirby 57 114 171 362 619 875
52-64: 53 by S&K. 64-Last Newsboy Legion & The Guardian
52 104 156 328 552 775
65-Robin begins with c/app. (2/47); Batman cameo in 1 panel; Robin-c begins, end #95
219 438 657 1402 2401 3400
66-Batman cameo in Robin story 94 188 282 597 1024 1450
67,68,70-80: 68-Last Liberty Belle? 72-Burnley Robin-c
74 148 222 470 810 1150
69-Origin/1st app. Tomahawk by F. Ray; atom bomb story & splash (6/47);
black-c (rare in high grade) 239 278 717 1530 2615 3700
81-Origin Merry, Girl of 1000 Gimmicks in Star Spangled Kid story
61 122 183 390 670 950
82,85: 82-Last Robotman? 85-Last Star Spangled Kid?
55 110 165 352 601 850
83-Tomahawk enters the lost valley, a land of dinosaurs; Capt. Compass begins, ends #130
58 116 174 371 636 900
84,87 (Rare): 87-Batman cameo in Robin 87 174 261 553 952 1350
86-Batman cameo in Robin story 62 124 186 395 678 960
88(1/49)-94: Batman-c/stories in all. 91-Federal Men begin, end #93. 94-Manhunters Around
the World begin, end #121 69 138 207 442 759 1075
95-Batman story; last Robin-c 58 116 174 371 636 900
96,98-Batman cameo in Robin stories. 96-1st Tomahawk-c (also #97-121)
41 82 123 256 428 600
97,99 37 74 111 222 361 500
100 (1/50)-Pre-Bat-Hound tryout in Robin story (pre-dates Batman #92).
43 86 129 271 461 650
101-109,118,119,121: 121-Last Tomahawk-c 34 68 102 199 325 450
110,111,120-Batman cameo in Robin stories. 120-Last 52 pg. issue
34 68 102 206 336 465
112-Batman & Robin story 37 74 111 222 361 500
113-Frazetta-a (10 pgs.) 41 82 123 260 435 610
114-Retells Robin's origin (3/51); Batman & Robin story
44 88 132 277 469 660
115,117-Batman app. in Robin stories 37 74 111 218 354 490
116-Flag-c 37 74 111 218 354 490
122-(11/51)-Ghost Breaker-c/stories begin (origin/1st app.), ends #130 (Ghost Breaker
covers #122-130) 55 110 165 352 601 850
123-126,128,129 37 74 111 222 361 500
127-Batman app. 39 78 117 231 378 525
130-Batman cameo in Robin story 40 80 120 246 411 575

NOTE: *Most all issues after #29 signed by Simon & Kirby are not by them.* **Bill Ely** *c-122-130.* **Mortimer** *c-65-74(most), 76-95(most).* **Fred Ray** *c-96-106, 109, 110, 112, 113, 115-120.* **S&K** *c-7-31, 33, 34, 36, 37, 39, 40, 48, 49, 50-54, 56-58.* **Hal Sherman** *c-1-6.* **Dick Sprang** *c-75.*

STAR SPANGLED COMICS (Also see All Star Comics 1999 crossover titles)
DC Comics: May, 1999 ($1.99, one-shot)

1-Golden Age Sandman and the Star Spangled Kid 3.00

STAR SPANGLED KID (See Action #40, Leading Comics & Star Spangled Comics)

STAR SPANGLED WAR STORIES
DC Comics: Aug/Sept 1952

nn - Ashcan comic, not distributed to newsstands, only for in-house use. Cover art is Western Comics #28 with interior being Western Comics #13 (a VG- copy sold for $2151 in 2012)

STAR SPANGLED WAR STORIES (Formerly Star Spangled Comics #1-130; Becomes The Unknown Soldier #205 on) (See Showcase)
National Periodical Publ.: No. 131, 8/52 - No. 133, 10/52; No. 3, 11/52 - No. 204, 2-3/77

131(#1) 200 400 600 1280 2190 3100
132 113 226 339 718 1234 1750
133-Used in **POP**, pg. 94 97 194 291 621 1061 1500
3-6: 4-Devil Dog Dugan app. 6-Evans-a 65 130 195 416 708 1000
7-10 32 64 96 230 515 800
11-20 27 54 81 194 435 675
21-30: 30-Last precode (2/55) 24 48 72 168 372 575
31-33,35-40 20 40 60 138 307 475
34-Krigstein-a 20 40 60 140 310 480
41-44,46-50: 50-1st S.A. issue 18 36 54 125 276 430
45-1st DC grey tone war-c (5/56) 46 92 138 359 805 1250
51,52,54-63,65,66, 68-83 16 32 48 108 239 370
53-"Rock Sergeant," 3rd Sgt. Rock prototype; inspired "P.I. & The Sand Fleas"
in G.I. Combat #56 (1/57) 27 54 81 185 415 645
64-Pre-Sgt. Rock Easy Co. story (12/57) 20 40 60 136 303 470
67-Two Easy Co. stories without Sgt. Rock 20 40 60 140 310 480

GD VG FN VF VF/NM NM-
2.0 4.0 6.0 8.0 9.0 9.2

84-Origin Mlle. Marie 61 122 183 488 1094 1700
85-89-Mlle. Marie in all 29 58 87 209 467 725
90-1st app. "War That Time Forgot" series; dinosaur issue-c/story (4-5/60)
(also see Weird War Tales #94 & #99) 93 186 279 744 1672 2600
91,93-No dinosaur stories 17 34 51 119 265 410
92-2nd dinosaur-c/s 28 56 84 202 451 700
94 (12/60)- "Ghost Ace" story; Baron Von Richter as The Enemy Ace (predates
Our Army at War #151) 32 64 96 230 515 800
95-99: Dinosaur-c/s 20 40 60 141 313 485
100-Dinosaur-c/story. 22 44 66 151 336 520
101-115: All dinosaur issues. 102-Panel inspired a famous Roy Lichtenstein painting
15 30 45 105 233 360
116-125,127-133,135-137: 120-1st app. Caveboy and Dino. 137-Last dinosaur story;
Heath Birdman-#129,131 13 26 39 89 195 300
126-No dinosaur story 11 22 33 73 157 240
134-Dinosaur story; Neal Adams-a 15 30 45 103 227 350
138-New Enemy Ace-c/stories begin by Joe Kubert (4-5/68), end #150 (also see Our Army
at War #151 and Showcase #57) 16 32 48 112 249 385
139-Origin Enemy Ace (7/68) 10 20 30 69 147 225
140-143,145: 145-Last 12¢ issue (6-7/69) 8 16 24 54 102 150
144-Neal Adams/Kubert-a 9 18 27 58 114 170
146-Enemy Ace-c/app. 6 12 18 41 76 110
147,148-New Enemy Ace stories 7 14 21 48 89 130
149,150-Last new Enemy Ace by Kubert. Viking Prince by Kubert
7 14 21 44 82 120
151-1st solo app. Unknown Soldier (6-7/70); Enemy Ace-r begin (from Our Army at War,
Showcase & SSWS); end #161 18 36 54 122 271 420
152-Reprints 2nd Enemy Ace app. 6 12 18 38 69 100
153,155-Enemy Ace reprints; early Unknown Soldier stories
5 10 15 34 60 85
154-Origin Unknown Soldier 12 24 36 84 185 285
156-1st Battle Album; Unknown Soldier story; Kubert-c/a
5 10 15 31 53 75
157-Sgt. Rock x-over in Unknown Soldier story. 4 8 12 28 47 65
158-163-(52 pgs.): New Unknown Soldier stories; Kubert-c/a. 161-Last Enemy Ace-r
4 8 12 25 40 55
164-183,200: 181-183-Enemy Ace vs. Balloon Buster serial app; Frank Thorne-a.
200-Enemy Ace back-up 3 6 9 15 22 28
184-199,201-204 2 4 6 13 18 22

NOTE: **Anderson** *a-28.* **Chaykin** *a-167.* **Drucker** *a-59, 61, 64, 66, 67, 73-84.* **Estrada** *a-149.* **John Giunta** *a-72.* **Glanzman** *a-167, 171, 172, 174.* **Heath** *a-42,122, 132, 133; c-67, 122, 132-134.* **Kaluta** *a-197i; c-167.* **G. Kane** *a-169.* **Kubert** *a-6-163(most later issues), 200.* **Maurer** *a-160, 165.* **Severin** *a-65, 162.* **S&K** *c-7-31, 33, 34, 37, 40.* **Simonson** *a-170, 172, 174, 180.* **Sutton** *a-168.* **Thorne** *a-183.* **Toth** *a-164.* **Wildey** *a-161. Suicide Squad in 110, 116-118, 120, 121, 127.*

STAR SPANGLED WAR STORIES (Featuring Mademoiselle Marie)
DC Comics: Nov, 2010 ($3.99, one-shot)

1-Mademoiselle Marie in 1944 France; Tucci-s/Justiniano-a/Bolland-c 4.00

STAR SPANGLED WAR STORIES (Featuring G.I. Zombie)
DC Comics: Sept, 2014 - No. 8, May, 2015 ($2.99)

1-8-Palmiotti & Gray-s/Scott Hampton-a. 1-6-Darwyn Cooke-c. 7-Dave Johnson-c 3.00
...: Futures End 1 (11/14, $2.99, regular-c) Five years later; Dave Johnson-c 3.00
...: Futures End 1 (11/14, $3.99, 3-D cover) 4.00

STARSTREAM (Adventures in Science Fiction)(See Questar illustrated)
Whitman/Western Publishing Co.: 1976 (79¢, 68 pgs, cardboard-c)

1-4: 1-Bolle-a. 2-4-McWilliams & Bolle-a 2 4 6 10 14 18

STARSTRUCK
Marvel Comics (Epic Comics): Feb, 1985 - No. 6, Feb, 1986 ($1.50, mature)

1-6: Kaluta-a 6.00

STARSTRUCK
Dark Horse Comics: Aug, 1990 - No. 4, Nov?, 1990 ($2.95, B&W, 52pgs.)

1-3: Kaluta-r/Epic series plus new-c/a in all 4.00
4 (68 pgs.)-contains 2 trading cards 5.00
Reprint 1-13 (IDW, 8/09 - No. 13, Sept, 2010, $3.99) newly colored; Galactic Girl Guides 4.00

STARSTRUCK: OLD PROLDIERS NEVER DIE
IDW Publishing: Feb, 2017 - No. 6, Jul, 2017 ($4.99)

1-Expanded version of old stories with new art; Elaine Lee-s/Michael Kaluta-a 5.00

STAR STUDDED
Cambridge House/Superior Publishers: 1945 (25¢, 132 pgs.); 1945 (196 pgs.)

nn-Captain Combat by Giunta, Ghost Woman, Commandette, & Red Rogue app.; Infantino-a
42 84 126 265 445 625
nn-The Cadet, Edison Bell, Hoot Gibson, Jungle Lil (196 pgs.); copies vary; Blue Beetle

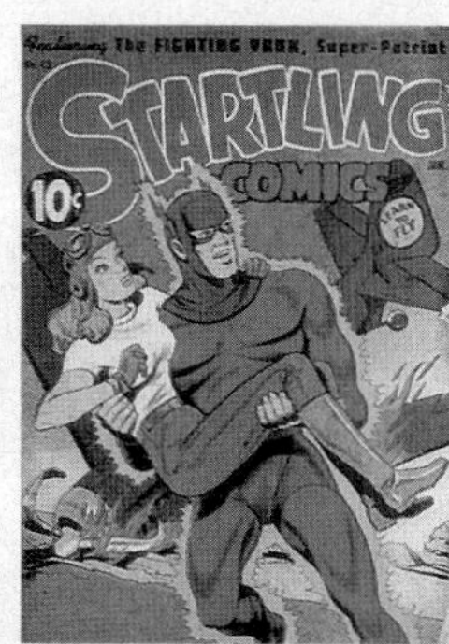

Startling Comics #43 © Nedor

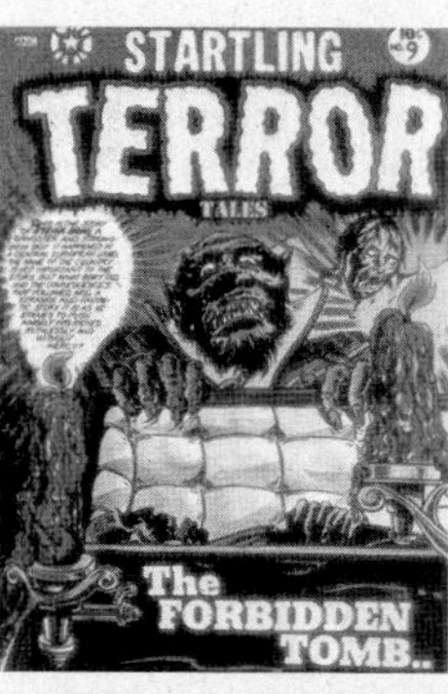

Startling Terror Tales #9 © STAR

Star Trek (1989 series) #58 © Paramount

GD 2.0 | VG 4.0 | FN 6.0 | VF 8.0 | VF/NM 9.0 | NM- 9.2

in some 45 90 135 284 480 675

STARTLING COMICS
Better Publications (Nedor): June, 1940 - No. 53, Sept, 1948

1-Origin Captain Future-Man Of Tomorrow, Mystico (By Sansone), The Wonder Man; The Masked Rider & his horse Pinto begins; Masked Rider formerly in pulps; drug use story 349 698 1047 2443 4272 6100
2 -Don Davis, Espionage Ace begins 174 348 522 1114 1907 2700
3 142 284 426 909 1555 2200
4 116 232 348 742 1271 1800
5,6,9 97 194 291 621 1061 1500
7,8-Nazi WWII-c 116 232 348 742 1271 1800
10-The Fighting Yank begins (9/41, origin/1st app.); Nazi WWII-c 784 1568 2352 5723 10,112 14,500
11-2nd app. Fighting Yank; Nazi WWII-c 245 490 735 1568 2684 3800
12-Hitler, Tojo, Mussolini-c 300 600 900 1920 3310 4700
13-15 116 232 348 742 1271 1800
16-Origin The Four Comrades; not in #32,35 135 270 405 864 1482 2100
17-Last Masked Rider & Mystico 116 232 348 742 1271 1800
18-Pyroman begins (12/42, origin)(also see America's Best Comics #3 for 1st app., 11/42) 174 348 522 1114 1907 2700
19-Nazi WWII-c 194 388 582 1242 2121 3000
20-Classic hooded Nazi giant snake bondage/torture-c (scarce); The Oracle begins (3/43); not in issues 26,28,33,34 300 600 900 2010 3505 5000
21-Origin The Ape, Oracle's enemy; Schomburg hypo-c 168 336 504 1075 1838 2600
22-34: All have Schomburg WWII-c. 34-Origin The Scarab & only app. 142 284 426 909 1555 2200
35-Hypodermic syringe attacks Fighting Yank in drug story; Schomburg WWII-c 142 284 426 909 1555 2200
36-43: 36-Last Four Comrades. 38-Bondage/torture-c. 40-Last Capt. Future & Oracle. 41-Front Page Peggy begins; A-Bomb-c. 43-Last Pyroman 63 126 189 403 689 975
44,45: 44-Lance Lewis, Space Detective begins; Ingels-c; sci/fi-c begin. 45-Tygra begins (intro/origin, 5/47); Ingels-c/a (splash pg. & inside f/c B&W ad) 106 212 318 673 1162 1650
46-Classic Ingels-c; Ingels-a 161 322 483 1030 1765 2500
47,48,50-53: 50,51-Sea-Eagle app. 123 246 369 787 1344 1900
49-Classic Schomburg Robot-c; last Fighting Yank 975 1950 2919 7100 12,550 18,000

NOTE: ***Ingels** a-44, 45; c-44, 45, 46(wash). **Schomburg (Xela)** c-21-43; 47-53 (airbrush). **Tuska** c-45? Bondage c-16, 21, 37, 46-49. Captain Future c-1-9, 13, 14. Fighting Yank c-10-12, 15-17, 21, 22, 24, 26, 28, 30, 32, 34, 36, 38, 40, 42. Pyroman c-18-20, 23, 25, 27, 29, 31, 33, 35, 37, 39, 41, 43.*

STARTLING STORIES: BANNER
Marvel Comics: July, 2001 - No. 4, Oct, 2001 ($2.99, limited series)

1-4-Hulk story by Azzarello; Corben-c/a 3.00
TPB (11/01, $12.95) r/1-4 13.00

STARTLING STORIES: FANTASTIC FOUR - UNSTABLE MOLECULES (See Fantastic Four - ...)

STARTLING STORIES: THE MEGALOMANIACAL SPIDER-MAN
Marvel Comics: Jun, 2002 ($2.99, one-shot)

1-Spider-Man spoof; Peter Bagge-s/a 3.00

STARTLING STORIES: THE THING
Marvel Comics: 2003 ($3.50, one-shot)

1-Zimmerman-s/Kramer-a; Inhumans and the Hulk app. 3.50

STARTLING STORIES: THE THING - NIGHT FALLS ON YANCY STREET
Marvel Comics: Jun, 2003 - No. 4, Sept, 2003 ($3.50, limited series)

1-4-Dorkin-s/Haspiel-a. 2,3-Frightful Four app. 3.50

STARTLING TERROR TALES
Star Publications: No. 10, May, 1952 - No. 14, Feb, 1953; No. 4, Apr, 1953 - No. 11, 1954

10-(1st Series)-Wood/Harrison-a (r/A Star Presentation #3) Disbrow/Cole-c; becomes 4 different titles after #10; becomes Confessions of Love #11 on, The Horrors #11 on, Terrifying Tales #11 on, Terrors of the Jungle #11 on & continues w/Startling Terror #11 103 206 309 659 1130 1600
11-(8/52)-L. B. Cole Spider-c; r-Fox's "A Feature Presentation" #5 (blue-c) 300 600 900 2070 3635 5200
11-Black-c (variant; believed to be a pressrun change) (Unique) 309 618 927 2163 3782 5400
12,14 41 82 123 256 428 600
13-Jo-Jo-r; Disbrow-a 42 84 126 265 445 625
4-9,11(1953-54) (2nd Series): 11-New logo 39 78 117 240 395 550
10-Disbrow-a 42 84 126 265 445 625

NOTE: ***L. B. Cole** covers-all issues. **Palais** a-V2#8r, V2#11r.*

STAR TREK (TV) (See Dan Curtis Giveaways, Dynabrite Comics & Power Record Comics)
Gold Key: 7/67; No. 2, 6/68; No. 3, 12/68; No. 4, 6/69 - No. 61, 3/79

1-Photo-c begin, end #9; photo back-c is on all copies, no variant exists with an ad on the back-c 75 150 225 600 1350 2100
2-Regular version has an ad on back-c 24 48 72 168 372 575
2 (rare variation w/photo back-c) 40 80 120 296 673 1050
3-5-All have back-c ads 16 32 48 112 249 385
3 (rare variation w/photo back-c) 29 58 87 209 467 725
6-9 11 22 33 73 157 240
10-20 6 12 18 37 66 95
21-30 5 10 15 31 53 80
31-40 4 8 12 27 44 60
41-61: 52-Drug propaganda story 3 6 9 21 33 45
... Gold Key 100-Page Spectacular (IDW, 2/17, $7.99) r/#1,8,14; cover & pin-up gallery 8.00
...the Enterprise Logs nn (8/76)-Golden Press, ($1.95, 224 pgs.)-r/#1-8 plus 7 pgs. by McWilliams (#11185)-Photo-c 5 10 15 34 60 85
...the Enterprise Logs Vol. 2 ('76)-r/#9-17 (#11187)-Photo-c 5 10 15 31 53 75
...the Enterprise Logs Vol. 3 ('77)-r/#18-26 (#11188); McWilliams-a (4 pgs.)-Photo-c 5 10 15 31 53 75
Star Trek Vol. 4 (Winter '77)-Reprints #27,28,30-34,36,38 (#11189) plus 3 pgs. new art 5 10 15 31 53 75
... : The Key Collection (Checker Book Publ. Group, 2004, $22.95) r/#1-8 23.00
... : The Key Collection Volume 2 (Checker, 2004, $22.95) r/#9-16 23.00
... : The Key Collection Volume 3 (Checker, 2005, $22.95) r/#17-24 23.00
... : The Key Collection Volume 4 (Checker, 2005, $22.95) r/#25-33 23.00
... : The Key Collection Volume 5 (Checker, 2006, $22.95) r/#34,36,38,39,40-43 23.00

NOTE: ***McWilliams** a-38, 40-44, 46-61. #29 reprints #1; #35 reprints #4; #37 reprints #5; #45 reprints #7. The tabloids all have photo covers and blank inside covers. Painted covers #10-44, 46-59.*

STAR TREK
Marvel Comics Group: April, 1980 - No. 18, Feb, 1982

1: 1-3-r/Marvel Super Special; movie adapt. 2 4 6 11 16 20
2-16: 5-Miller-c 1 3 4 6 8 10
17-Low print run 2 4 6 8 11 14
18-Last issue; low print run 2 4 6 11 16 20

NOTE: ***Austin** c-18i. **Buscema** a-13. **Gil Kane** a-15. **Nasser** c/a-7. **Simonson** c-17.*

STAR TREK (Also see Who's Who In Star Trek)
DC Comics: Feb, 1984 - No. 56, Nov, 1988 (75¢, Mando paper)

1-Sutton-a(p) begins 2 4 6 8 10 12
2-5 6.00
6-10: 7-Origin Saavik 5.00
11-32,34-49,51-56: 19-Walter Koenig story. 37-Painted-c 4.00
33-($1.25, 52 pgs.)-20th anniversary issue 5.00
50-($1.50, 52 pgs.) 5.00
Annual 1-3: 1(1985). 2(1986). 3(1988, $1.50) 5.00
...: To Boldly Go TPB (Titan Books, 7/05, $19.95) r/#1-6; Koenig foreward; cast interviews 20.00
...: The Trial of James T. Kirk TPB (Titan Books, 6/06, $19.95) r/#7-12; cast interviews 20.00
...: The Return of the Worthy TPB (Titan Books, 12/06, $19.95) r/#13-18; cast interviews 20.00

NOTE: ***Morrow** a-28, 35, 36, 56. **Orlando** c-8i. **Perez** c-1-3. **Spiegle** a-19. **Starlin** c-24, 25. **Sutton** a-1-6p, 8-18p, 20-27p, 29p, 31-34p, 39-52p, 55p; c-4-6p, 8-22p, 46p.*

STAR TREK
DC Comics: Oct, 1989 - No. 80, Jan, 1996 ($1.50/$1.75/$1.95/$2.50)

1-Capt. Kirk and crew 6.00
2,3 4.00
4-23,25-30: 10-12-The Trial of James T. Kirk. 21-Begin $1.75-c 3.00
24-($2.95, 68 pgs.)-40 pg. epic w/pin-ups 4.00
31-49,51-74,76-80 3.00
50-($3.50, 68 pgs.)-Painted-c 4.00
75 ($3.95) 4.00
Annual 1-6('90-'95, 68 pgs.): 1-Morrow-a. 3-Painted-c 4.00
Special 1-3 ('9-'95, 68 pgs.)-1-Sutton-a. 4.00
...: The Ashes of Eden (1995, $14.95, 100 pgs.)-Shatner story 18.00
...Generations (1994, $3.95, 68 pgs.)-Movie adaptation 4.00
...Generations (1994, $5.95, 68 pgs.)-Squarebound 6.00

STAR TREK...(TV)
DC Comics (WildStorm): one-shots

All of Me (4/00, $5.95, prestige format) Lopresti-a 6.00
Enemy Unseen TPB (2001, $17.95) r/Perchance to Dream, Embrace the Wolf, The Killing Shadows; Struzan-c 18.00
Enter the Wolves (2001, $5.95) Crispin & Weinstein-s; Mota-a/c 6.00
New Frontier - Double Time (11/00, $5.95)-Captain Calhoun's USS Excalibur; Peter David-s; Stelfreeze-c 6.00

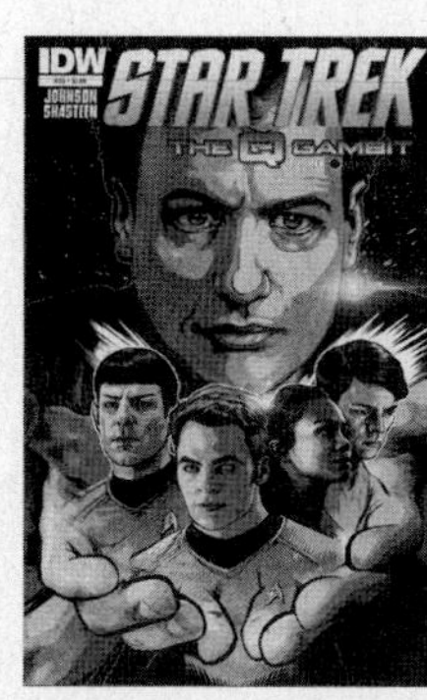

Star Trek (2011 series) #35 © CBS Studios

Star Trek: Deep Space Nine #4 © Paramount

Star Trek / Green Lantern #6 © CBS Studios & DC

	GD 2.0	VG 4.0	FN 6.0	VF 8.0	VF/NM 9.0	NM- 9.2

Other Realities TPB (2001, $14.95) r/All of Me, New Frontier - Double Time, and DS9-N-Vector; Van Fleet-c 15.00
Special (2001, $6.95) Stories from all 4 series by various; Van Fleet-c 7.00

STAR TREK (Further adventures of the crew from the 2009 movie)
IDW Publishing: Sept, 2011 - No. 60, Aug, 2016 ($3.99)

1-49: 1,2-Gary Mitchell app.; Molnar-a. 11,12-Tribbles. 15,16-Mirror Universe. 21-Follows the 2013 movie; Klingons & Section 31 app. 35-40-The Q Gambit; DS9 crew app. 4.00
50-($4.99) Mirror Universe; Khan app.; bonus history of Star Trek comics, aliens 5.00
51-60: 51,52-Mirror Universe. 52-Variant Archie Comics cover. 55-58-Legacy of Spock 4.00
Annual (12/13, $7.99) "Strange New Worlds" on cover; photonovel by John Byrne 8.00
... #1: Greatest Hits (3/16, $1.00) reprints #1 3.00
... #1: Hundred Penny Press (8/13, $1.00) reprints #1 3.00
...: Deviations 1 (3/17, $4.99) Timeline where Romulans, not Vulcans made 1st Contact 5.00
...: Flesh and Stone (7/14, $3.99) Doctors Bashir, Crusher, Pulaski, McCoy app. 4.00
...: 50th Anniversary Cover Celebration (8/16, $7.99) Gallery of IDW Star Trek covers 8.00
... Space Spanning Treasury Edition (4/13, $9.99, 13" x 8.5") Reprints #9,10,13 10.00

STAR TREK: ALIEN SPOTLIGHT
IDW Publishing: Sept, 2007 - Feb, 2008 ($3.99, series of one-shots)

... Andorians (11/07) Storrie-s/O'Grady-a; Counselor Troi app.; two art & one photo-c 4.00
... Borg (1/08) Harris-s/Murphy-a; Janeway & Next Gen crew app.; two art & one photo-c 4.00
... Cardassians (12/09) Padilla-a; Garak & Kira app. 4.00
... The Gorn (9/07) Messina-a; Chekov app.; two art & one photo-c 4.00
... Orions (12/07) Casagrande-a; Capt. Pike app.; two art & one photo-c 4.00
... Q (8/09) Casagrande-a; takes place after Star Trek 8 movie; two art & one photo-c 4.00
... Romulans (2/08) John Byrne-s/a; Kirk era; two art & one photo-c 4.00
... Romulans (5/09) Wagner Reis-a; David Williams-c 4.00
... Tribbles (3/09) Hawthorne-a; first encounter with Klingons; one art & one photo-c 4.00
... Vulcans (10/07) Spock's early Enterprise days with Capt. Pike; two art & one photo-c 4.00

STAR TREK: ASSIGNMENT EARTH
IDW Publishing: May, 2008 - No. 5, Sept, 2008 ($3.99, limited series)

1-5-Further adventures of Gary Seven and Roberta; John Byrne-s/a/c. 5-Nixon app. 4.00

STAR TREK: BOLDLY GO (Takes place after the 2016 movie Star Trek Beyond)
IDW Publishing: Oct, 2016 - Present ($3.99)

1-17-The 2009 movie crew; Mike Johnson-s/Shasteen-a; The Borg app.; multiple covers 4.00

STAR TREK: BURDEN OF KNOWLEDGE
IDW Publishing: Jun, 2010 - No. 4, Sept, 2010 ($3.99, limited series)

1-4-Original series Kirk and crew; Manfredi-a 4.00

STAR TREK: CAPTAIN'S LOG
IDW Publishing: one-shots

...: Harriman (4/10, $3.99) Captain of the Enterprise-B following Kirk's "demise"; Currie-a 4.00
...: Jellico (10/10, $3.99) Woodward-a 4.00
...: Pike (9/10, $3.99) Events that put Pike in the chair; Woodward-a 4.00
...: Sulu (1/10, $3.99) Manfredi-a 4.00

STAR TREK: COUNTDOWN (Prequel to the 2009 movie)
IDW Publishing: Jan, 2009 - No. 4, Apr, 2009 ($3.99, limited series)

1-4: 1-Ambassador Spock on Romulus; intro. Nero; Messina-a 4.00
Hundred Penny Press: Star Trek: Countdown #1 (4/11, $1.00) r/#1 w/new cover frame 3.00

STAR TREK: COUNTDOWN TO DARKNESS (Prequel to the 2013 movie)
IDW Publishing: Jan, 2013 - No. 4, Apr, 2013 ($3.99, limited series)

1-4-Captain April app.; Messina-a; regular & photo covers on each 4.00

STAR TREK: CREW
IDW Publishing: Mar, 2009 - No. 5, Jul, 2009 ($3.99, limited series)

1-5: John Byrne-s/a; Captain Pike era 4.00

STAR TREK: DEBT OF HONOR
DC Comics: 1992 ($24.95/$14.95, graphic novel)

Hardcover ($24.95) Claremont-s/Hughes-a(p) 25.00
Softcover ($14.95) 15.00

STAR TREK: DEEP SPACE NINE (TV)
Malibu Comics: Aug, 1993 - No. 32, Jan, 1996 ($2.50)

1-Direct Sale Edition w/line drawn-c 5.00
1-Newsstand Edition with photo-c 4.00
0-(1/95, $2.95)-Terok Nor 4.00
2-30: 2-Polybagged w/trading card. 9-4 pg. prelude to Hearts & Minds 4.00
31-($3.95) 5.00
32-($3.50) 5.00
Annual 1 (1/95, $3.95, 68 pgs.) 5.00
Special 1 (1995, $3.50) 5.00
Ultimate Annual 1 (12/95, $5.95) 6.00
...:Lightstorm (12/94, $3.50) 5.00

STAR TREK: DEEP SPACE NINE (TV)
Marvel Comics (Paramount Comics): Nov, 1996 - No. 15, Mar, 1998 ($1.95/$1.99)

1-15: 12,13-"Telepathy War" pt. 2,3 4.00

STAR TREK: DEEP SPACE NINE: FOOL'S GOLD
IDW Publishing: Dec, 2009 - No. 4, Mar, 2010 ($3.99)

1-4-Mantovani-a 4.00

STAR TREK: DEEP SPACE NINE -- N-VECTOR (TV)
DC Comics (WildStorm): Aug, 2000 - No. 4, Nov, 2000 ($2.50, limited series)

1-4-Cypress-a 3.00

STAR TREK DEEP SPACE NINE-THE CELEBRITY SERIES
Malibu Comics: May, 1995 ($2.95)

1-Blood and Honor; Mark Lenard script 4.00
1-Rules of Diplomacy; Aron Eisenberg script 4.00

STAR TREK: DEEP SPACE NINE HEARTS AND MINDS
Malibu Comics: June, 1994 - No. 4, Sept, 1994 ($2.50, limited series)

1-4 4.00
1-Holographic-c 5.00

STAR TREK: DEEP SPACE NINE, THE MAQUIS
Malibu Comics: Feb, 1995 - No. 3, Apr, 1995 ($2.50, limited series)

1-3-Newsstand-c, 1-Photo-c 4.00

STAR TREK: DEEP SPACE NINE/THE NEXT GENERATION
Malibu Comics: Oct, 1994 - No. 2, Nov, 1994 ($2.50, limited series)

1,2: Parts 2 & 4 of x-over with Star Trek: TNG/DS9 from DC Comics 4.00

STAR TREK: DEEP SPACE NINE WORF SPECIAL
Malibu Comics: Dec, 1995 ($3.95, one-shot)

1-Includes pinups 5.00

STAR TREK: DISCOVERY: THE LIGHT OF KAHLESS (Based on the 2017 TV series)
IDW Publishing: Oct, 2017 - Present ($3.99)

1,2-Beyer & Johnson-s/Shasteen-a 4.00

STAR TREK: DIVIDED WE FALL
DC Comics (WildStorm): July, 2001 - No. 4, Oct, 2001 ($2.95, limited series)

1-4: Ordover & Mack-s; Lenara Kahn, Verad and Odan app. 3.00

STAR TREK EARLY VOYAGES (TV)
Marvel Comics (Paramount Comics): Feb, 1997 - No. 17, Jun, 1998 ($2.95/$1.95/$1.99)

1-($2.95) 5.00
2-17 4.00

STAR TREK: ENTERPRISE EXPERIMENT
IDW Publishing: Apr, 2008 - No. 5, Aug, 2008 ($3.99, limited series)

1-5-Year Four story; D.C. Fontana & Derek Chester-s; Purcell-a 4.00

STAR TREK: FIRST CONTACT (Movie)
Marvel Comics (Paramount Comics): Nov, 1996 ($5.95, one-shot)

nn-Movie adaption 6.00

STAR TREK/ GREEN LANTERN (The Spectrum War)
IDW Publishing: Jul, 2015 - No. 6, Dec, 2015 ($3.99, limited series)

1-6-Crew from 2009 movie and Hal Jordan; Sinestro & Nekron app.; multiple covers 4.00

STAR TREK/ GREEN LANTERN (Stranger Worlds)
IDW Publishing: Dec, 2016 - No. 6, May, 2017 ($3.99, limited series)

1-6-Sinestro & The Manhunters app.; multiple covers. 2-6-Khan app. 4.00

STAR TREK: HARLAN ELLISON'S ORIGINAL CITY ON THE EDGE OF FOREVER TELEPLAY
IDW Publishing: Jun, 2014 - No. 5, Oct, 2014 ($3.99, limited series)

1-5-Adaptation of Ellison's teleplay; J.K. Woodward-a; two covers on each 4.00

STAR TREK: INFESTATION (Crossover with G.I. Joe, Transformers & Ghostbusters)
IDW Publishing: Feb, 2011 - No. 2, Feb, 2011 ($3.99, limited series)

1,2-Zombies in the Kirk era; Maloney & Erskine-a; two covers on each 4.00

STAR TREK: KHAN
IDW Publishing: Oct, 2013 - No. 5, Feb, 2014 ($3.99, limited series)

1-5-Follows the 2013 movie; Khan's origin; Messina & Balboni-a 4.00

STAR TREK: KHAN RULING IN HELL
IDW Publishing: Oct, 2010 - No. 4, Jan, 2011 ($3.99, limited series)

1-4-Khan and the Botany Bay crew after banishment on Ceti Alpha V; Mantovani-a 4.00

Star Trek: Mirror Broken #1 © CBS Studios

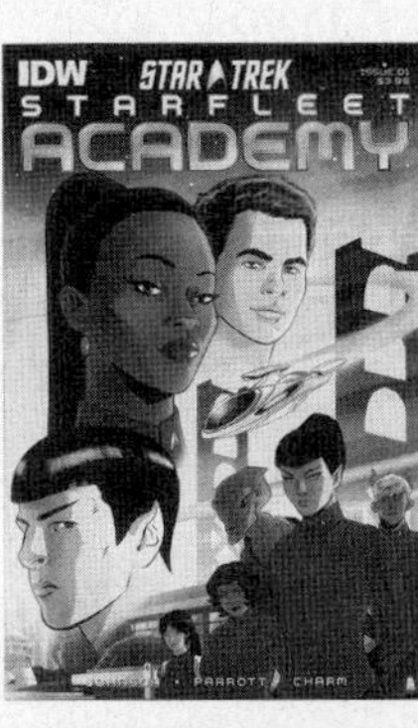
Star Trek: Starfleet Academy #1 © CBS Studios

Star Trek: The Next Generation #5 © Paramount

GD 2.0 | VG 4.0 | FN 6.0 | VF 8.0 | VF/NM 9.0 | NM- 9.2

STAR TREK: KLINGONS: BLOOD WILL TELL
IDW Publishing: Apr, 2007 - No. 5 ($3.99, limited series)

1-5-Star Trek TOS episodes from the Klingon viewpoint; Messina-a. 2-Tribbles 4.00
1-($4.99) Klingon Language Variant; comic with Kliingon text; English script 5.00

STAR TREK/ LEGION OF SUPER-HEROES
IDW Publishing: Oct, 2011 - No. 6, Mar, 2012 ($3.99, limited series)

1-6-Jeff Moy-a/Jimenez-c 1-Giffen var-c. 2-Lightle var-c. 3-Grell var-c. 5-Allred var-c 4.00

STAR TREK: LEONARD McCOY, FRONTIER DOCTOR
IDW Publishing: Apr, 2010 - No. 4, Jul, 2010 ($3.99, limited series)

1-4-Dr. McCoy right before Star Trek: TMP; John Byrne-s/a 4.00

STAR TREK: MANIFEST DESTINY
IDW Publishing: Apr, 2016 - No. 4, May, 2016 ($4.99/$3.99, limited series)

1-The 2009 movie crew vs. Klingons; Angel Hernandez-a 5.00
2-4-($3.99) 4.00

STAR TREK: MIRROR BROKEN (Series previewed in Star Trek: The Next Generation: Mirror Broken #0 FCBD giveaway)
IDW Publishing: May, 2017 - No. 5, Oct, 2017 ($3.99, limited series)

1-5-The Mirror Universe Next Generation crew; David & Scott Tipton-s/Woodward-a 4.00

STAR TREK: MIRROR IMAGES
IDW Publishing: June, 2008 - No. 5, Nov, 2008 ($3.99, limited series)

1-5-Further adventures in the Mirror Universe. 3-Mirror-Picard app. 4.00

STAR TREK: MIRROR MIRROR
Marvel Comics (Paramount Comics): Feb, 1997 ($3.95, one-shot)

1-DeFalco-s 4.00

STAR TREK: MISSION'S END
IDW Publishing: Mar, 2009 - No. 5, July, 2009 ($3.99, limited series)

1-5-Kirk, Spock, Bones crew, their last mission on the pre-movie Enterprise 4.00

STAR TREK MOVIE ADAPTATION
IDW Publishing: Feb, 2010 - No. 6, Aug, 2010 ($3.99, limited series)

1-6-Adaptation of 2009 movie; Messina-a; regular & photo-c on each 4.00

STAR TREK MOVIE SPECIAL
DC Comics: 1984 (June) - No. 2, 1987 ($1.50); No. 1, 1989 ($2.00, 52 pgs)

nn-(#1)-Adapts Star Trek III; Sutton-p (68 pgs.) 5.00
2-Adapts Star Trek IV; Sutton-a; Chaykin-c. (68 pgs.) 5.00
1 (1989)-Adapts Star Trek V; painted-c 5.00

STAR TREK: NERO
IDW Publishing: Aug, 2009 - No. 4, Nov, 2009 ($3.99, limited series)

1-4-Nero's ship after the attack on the Kelvin to the arrival of Spock 4.00

STAR TREK: NEW FRONTIER
IDW Publishing: Mar, 2008 - No. 5, July, 2008 ($3.99, limited series)

1-5-Capt. Calhoun & Adm. Shelby app.; Peter David-s 4.00

STAR TREK: NEW VISIONS
IDW Publishing: May, 2014 - Present ($7.99, squarebound)

1-20-Photonovels of original crew by John Byrne. 1-Mirror Universe 8.00
... Special: More Of The Serpent Than The Dove (9/16, Humble Bundle) Gorn app. 20.00
... Special: The Cage (7/16, $7.99) 8.00

STAR TREK 100 PAGE...
IDW Publishing: Nov, 2011 - 2012 ($7.99)

...Spectacular #1 (11/11) Reprints stories of the original crew; s/a by Byrne and others 8.00
...Spectacular 2012 (2/12) Reprints; Khan, Q, Capt. Pike, the Gorn app. 8.00
...Spectacular Summer 2012 (8/12) Reprints of TNG and Voyager stories 8.00
...Spectacular Winter 2012 - Reprints; Capt. Harriman, Mirror Universe 8.00

STAR TREK: OPERATION ASSIMILATION
Marvel Comics (Paramount Comics): Dec, 1996 ($2.95, one-shot)

1 4.00

STAR TREK/PLANET OF THE APES: THE PRIMATE DIRECTIVE
IDW Publishing: Dec, 2014 - No. 5, Apr, 2015 ($3.99, limited series)

1-5-Classic crew on the Planet of the Apes; Klingons app. 2-Kirk meets Taylor 8.00

STAR TREK: ROMULANS SCHISMS
IDW Publishing: Sept, 2009 - No. 3, Nov, 2009 ($3.99, limited series)

1-3-John Byrne-s/a/c 4.00

STAR TREK: ROMULANS THE HOLLOW CROWN
IDW Publishing: Sept, 2008 - No. 2, Oct, 2008 ($3.99, limited series)

1,2-John Byrne-s/a/c 4.00

STAR TREK VI: THE UNDISCOVERED COUNTRY (Movie)
DC Comics: 1992

1-($2.95, regular edition, 68 pgs.)-Adaptation of film 5.00
nn-($5.95, prestige edition)-Has photos of movie not included in regular edition; painted-c by Palmer; photo back-c 1 2 3 5 6 8

STAR TREK: SPOCK: REFLECTIONS
IDW Publishing: July, 2009 - No. 4, Oct, 2009 ($3.99, limited series)

1-4-Flashbacks of Spock's childhood and career; Messina & Manfredi-a 4.00

STAR TREK: STARFLEET ACADEMY
Marvel Comics (Paramount Comics): Dec, 1996 - No. 19, Jun, 1998 ($1.95/$1.99)

1-19: Begin new series. 12-"Telepathy War" pt. 1. 18-English & Klingon editions 4.00

STAR TREK: STARFLEET ACADEMY
IDW Publishing: Dec, 2015 - No. 5, Apr, 2016 ($3.99, limited series)

1-5-Crew of the 2009 movie at the academy; Charm-a 4.00

STAR TREK: TELEPATHY WAR
Marvel Comics (Paramount Comics): Nov, 1997 ($2.99, 48 pgs., one-shot)

1-"Telepathy War" x-over pt. 6 4.00

STAR TREK - THE MODALA IMPERATIVE
DC Comics: Late July, 1991 - No. 4, Late Sept, 1991 ($1.75, limited series)

1-4 4.00
TPB ($19.95) r/series and ST:TNG - The Modala Imperative 20.00

STAR TREK: THE NEXT GENERATION (TV)
DC Comics: Feb, 1988 - No. 6, July, 1988 (limited series)

1 ($1.50, 52 pgs.)-Sienkiewicz painted-c 1 2 3 5 7 9
2-6 ($1.00) 5.00

STAR TREK: THE NEXT GENERATION (TV)
DC Comics: Oct, 1989 -No. 80, 1995 ($1.50/$1.75/$1.95)

1-Capt. Picard and crew from TV show 2 4 6 8 10 12
2,3 6.00
4-10 5.00
11-23,25-49,51-60 4.00
24,50: 24-($2.50, 52 pgs.). 50-($3.50, 68 pgs.)-Painted-c 6.00
61-74,76-80 4.00
75-($3.95, 50 pgs.) 5.00
Annual 1-6 ('90-'95, 68 pgs.) 5.00
Special 1 -3('93-'95, 68 pgs.)-1-Contains 3 stories 5.00
...-The Series Finale (1994, $3.95, 68 pgs.) 5.00

STAR TREK: THE NEXT GENERATION (TV)
DC Comics (WildStorm): one-shots

Embrace the Wolf (6/00, $5.95, prestige format) Golden & Sniegoski-s 6.00
Forgiveness (2001, $24.95, HC) David Brin-s/Scott Hampton painted-a; dust jacket-c 30.00
Forgiveness (2002, $17.95, SC) 18.00
The Gorn Crisis (1/01, $29.95, HC) Kordey painted-a/dust jacket-c 30.00
The Gorn Crisis (1/01, $17.95, SC) Kordey painted-a 18.00

STAR TREK: THE NEXT GENERATION/DEEP SPACE NINE (TV)
DC Comics: Dec, 1994 - No. 2, Jan, 1995 ($2.50, limited series)

1,2-Parts 1 & 3 of x-over with Star Trek: DS9/TNG from Malibu Comics 4.00

STAR TREK: THE NEXT GENERATION / DOCTOR WHO: ASSIMILATION^2
IDW Publishing: May, 2012 - No. 8, Dec, 2012 ($3.99, limited series)

1-8-The Borg and Cybermen team-up; Tipton-s/Woodward-a; multiple covers on each 4.00

STAR TREK: THE NEXT GENERATION: GHOSTS
IDW Publishing: Nov, 2009 - No. 5, Mar, 2010 ($3.99)

1-5-Cannon-s/Aranda-a 4.00

STAR TREK: THE NEXT GENERATION - ILL WIND
DC Comics: Nov, 1995 - No. 4, Feb, 1996 ($2.50, limited series)

1-4: Hugh Fleming painted-c on all 4.00

STAR TREK: THE NEXT GENERATION: INTELLIGENCE GATHERING
IDW Publishing: Jan, 2008 - No. 5, May, 2008 ($3.99)

1-5-Messina-a/Scott & David Tipton-s; two covers on each 4.00

STAR TREK: THE NEXT GENERATION: MIRROR BROKEN (See Star Trek: Mirror Broken)
IDW Publishing: May, 2017 (free giveaway)

0-(5/17, FCBD giveaway) Mirror Universe crew, prelude to series; J.K. Woodward-a/c; bonus design art 3.00

Star Trek: The Next Generation: The Space Between #5 © Paramount

Star Trek: Voyager - False Colors © Paramount

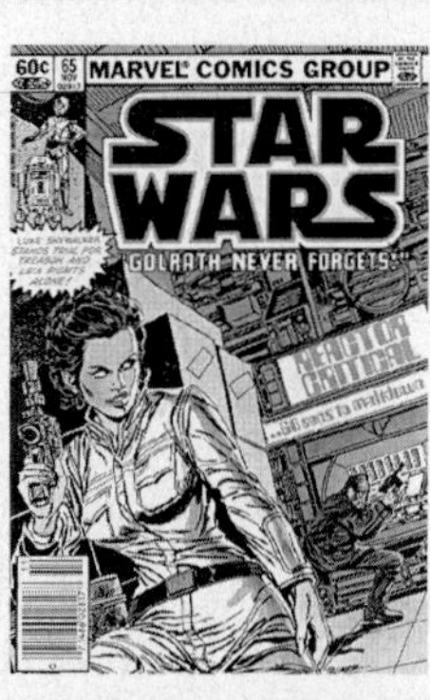

Star Wars #65 © Lucasfilm

GD VG FN VF VF/NM NM-
2.0 4.0 6.0 8.0 9.0 9.2

STAR TREK: THE NEXT GENERATION - PERCHANCE TO DREAM
DC Comics/WildStorm: Feb, 2000 - No. 4, May, 2000 ($2.50, limited series)
1-4-Bradstreet-c 3.00

STAR TREK: THE NEXT GENERATION - RIKER
Marvel Comics (Paramount Comics): July, 1998 ($3.50, one-shot)
1-Riker joins the Maquis 4.00

STAR TREK: THE NEXT GENERATION - SHADOWHEART
DC Comics: Dec, 1994 - No. 4, Mar, 1995 ($1.95, limited series)
1-4 4.00

STAR TREK: THE NEXT GENERATION - THE KILLING SHADOWS
DC Comics/WildStorm: Nov, 2000 - No. 4, Feb, 2001 ($2.50, limited series)
1-4-Scott Ciencin-s; Sela app. 3.00

STAR TREK: THE NEXT GENERATION: THE LAST GENERATION
IDW Publishing: Nov, 2008 - No. 5, Mar, 2009 ($3.99, limited series)
1-5-Purcell-a; alternate timeline with Klingon war; Sulu app. 4.00

STAR TREK: THE NEXT GENERATION - THE MODALA IMPERATIVE
DC Comics: Early Sept, 1991 - No. 4, Late Oct, 1991 ($1.75, limited series)
1-4 4.00

STAR TREK: THE NEXT GENERATION: THE SPACE BETWEEN
IDW Publishing: Jan, 2007 - No. 6, June, 2007 ($3.99)
1-6-Single issue stories from various seasons; photo & art covers 4.00

STAR TREK: THE WRATH OF KHAN
IDW Publishing: Jun, 2009 - No. 3, Jul, 2009 ($3.99, limited series)
1-3-Movie adaptation; Chee Yang Ong-a 4.00

STAR TREK: TNG: HIVE
IDW Publishing: Sept, 2012 - No. 4, Feb, 2013 ($3.99, limited series)
1-4-Brannon Braga-s/Joe Corroney-a; Next Generation crew vs. the Borg 4.00

STAR TREK UNLIMITED
Marvel Comics (Paramount Comics): Nov, 1996 - No. 10, July, 1998 ($2.95/$2.99)
1,2-Stories from original series and Next Generation 5.00
3-10: 3-Begin $2.99-c. 6-"Telepathy War" pt. 4. 7-Q & Trelane swap Kirk & Picard 4.00

STAR TREK UNTOLD VOYAGES
Marvel Comics (Paramount Comics): May, 1998 - No. 5, July, 1998 ($2.50)
1-5-Kirk's crew after the 1st movie 4.00

STAR TREK: VOYAGER
Marvel Comics (Paramount Comics): Nov, 1996 - No. 15, Mar, 1998 ($1.95/$1.99)
1-15: 13-"Telepathy War" pt. 5. 14-Seven of Nine joins crew 4.00

STAR TREK: VOYAGER
DC Comics/WildStorm: one-shots and trade paperbacks
- Elite Force (7/00, $5.95) The Borg app.; Abnett & Lanning-s 6.00
... Encounters With the Unknown TPB (2001, $19.95) reprints 20.00
- False Colors (1/00, $5.95) Photo-c and Jim Lee-c; Jeff Moy-a 6.00

STAR TREK: VOYAGER-- THE PLANET KILLER
DC Comics/WildStorm: Mar, 2001 - No. 3, May, 2001 ($2.95, limited series)
1-3-Voyager vs. the Planet Killer from the ST:TOS episode; Teranishi-a 3.00

STAR TREK: VOYAGER SPLASHDOWN
Marvel Comics (Paramount Comics): Apr, 1998 - No. 4, July, 1998 ($2.50, limited series)
1-4-Voyager crashes on a water planet 4.00

STAR TREK: WAYPOINT
IDW Publishing: Sept, 2016 - No. 6, Jul, 2017 ($4.99/$3.99)
1-($4.99) Short story anthology; future Next Gen Data & Geordi; multiple covers 5.00
2-6-($3.99) 2-Gold Key style story. 3-Voyager & DS9 crews 4.00

STAR TREK/ X-MEN
Marvel Comics (Paramount Comics): Dec, 1996 ($4.99, one-shot)
1-Kirk's crew & X-Men; art by Silvestri, Tan, Winn & Finch; Lobdell-s 6.00

STAR TREK/ X-MEN: 2ND CONTACT
Marvel Comics (Paramount Comics): May, 1998 ($4.99, 64 pgs., one-shot)
1-Next Gen. crew & X-Men battle Kang, Sentinels & Borg following First Contact movie 6.00
1-Painted wraparound variant cover 6.00

STAR TREK: YEAR FOUR (Also see Star Trek: Enterprise Experiment)
IDW Publishing: July, 2007 - No. 5, Nov, 2007 ($3.99, limited series)
1-5: 1-Original series crew; Tischman-s/Conley-a; three covers on each 4.00

GD VG FN VF VF/NM NM-
2.0 4.0 6.0 8.0 9.0 9.2

STARVE
Image Comics: Jun, 2015 - No. 10, Jun, 2016 ($3.99)
1-10-Brian Wood-s/Danijel Zezelj-a 4.00

STAR WARS (Movie) (See Classic..., Contemporary Motivators, Dark Horse Comics, The Droids, The Ewoks, Marvel Movie Showcase, Marvel Special Ed.)
Marvel Comics Group: July, 1977 - No. 107, Sept, 1986
1-(Regular 30¢ edition)-Price in square w/UPC code; #1-6 adapt first movie; first issue on sale before movie debuted 10 20 30 67 141 215
1-(35¢-c; limited distribution - 1500 copies?)- Price in square w/UPC code (Prices vary widely on this book. In 2005 a CGC certified 9.4 sold for $6,500, a CGC certified 9.2 sold for $3,403, and a CGC certified 6.0 sold for $610) 367 734 1101 3120 7060 11,000

NOTE: *The rare 35¢ edition has the cover price in a square box, and the UPC box in the lower left hand corner has the UPC code lines running through it.*

1-Reprint; has "reprint" in upper lefthand corner of cover or on inside or price and number inside a diamond with no date or UPC on cover; 30¢ and 35¢ issues published 5 10 15 30 50 70
2-9: Reprints; has "reprint" in upper lefthand corner of cover or on inside or price and number inside a diamond with no date or UPC on cover; 30¢ and 35¢ issues published 1 3 4 6 8 10
2-4-(30¢ issues). 4-Battle with Darth Vader 5 10 15 30 50 70
2-4-(35¢ with UPC code; not reprints) 57 114 171 456 1028 1600
5,6: 5-Begin 35¢-c on all editions. 6-Stevens-a(i) 3 6 9 21 33 45
7-20 2 4 6 11 16 20
21-38,45-67,69,70: 50-Giant 2 4 6 8 10 12
39-41,43,44-The Empire Strikes Back-r by Al Williamson in all 2 4 6 9 12 15
42-1st Boba Fett 6 12 18 41 76 110
68-Reintro Boba Fett 5 10 15 30 50 70
71-80 2 4 6 8 11 14
81-Boba Fett app. 4 8 12 23 37 50
82-90 2 4 6 9 13 16
91,93-99: 98-Williamson-a 2 4 6 11 16 20
92,100-106: 92,100-($1.00, 52 pgs.) 3 6 9 14 20 26
107 (low dist.); Portacio-a(i) 5 10 15 35 63 90
Annual 1 (12/79, 52 pgs.)-Simonson-c 2 4 6 11 16 20
Annual 2 (11/82, 52 pgs.), 3(12/83, 52 pgs.) 2 4 6 9 12 15
... A Long Time Ago...Vol. 1 TPB (Dark Horse Comics, 6/02, $29.95) r/#1-14 30.00
... A Long Time Ago...Vol. 2 TPB (Dark Horse Comics, 7/02, $29.95) r/#15-28 30.00
... A Long Time Ago...Vol. 3 TPB (Dark Horse Comics, 11/02, $29.95) r/#39-53 30.00
... A Long Time Ago...Vol. 4 TPB (Dark Horse Comics, 1/03, $29.95) r/#54-67 & Ann. 2 30.00
... A Long Time Ago...Vol. 5 TPB (Dark Horse Comics, 3/03, $29.95) r/#68-81 & Ann. 3 30.00
... A Long Time Ago...Vol. 6 TPB (Dark Horse Comics, 5/03, $29.95) r/#82-93 30.00
... A Long Time Ago...Vol. 7 TPB (Dark Horse Comics, 6/03, $29.95) r/#96-107 30.00

***Austin** a-11-15i, 21i, 38; c-12-15i, 21i. **Byrne** c-13p. **Chaykin** a-1-10p; c-1. **Golden** c/a-38. **Miller** c-47p; pin-up-43. **Nebres** c/a-Annual 2i. **Portacio** a-107i. **Sienkiewicz** c-92i, 98. **Simonson** a-16p, 49p, 51-63p, 65p, 66p; c-16, 49-51, 52p, 53-62, Annual 1. **Steacy** painted a-105i, 106i; c-105. **Williamson** a-39-44p, 50p, 98; c-39, 40, 41-44p. Painted c-81, 87, 92, 95, 98, 100, 105.*

STAR WARS (Monthly series) (Becomes Star Wars Republic #46-on)
Dark Horse Comics: Dec, 1998 - No. 45, Aug, 2005 ($2.50/$2.95/$2.99)
1-Prelude To Rebellion; Strnad-s 1 2 3 5 6 8
2-45: 2-6-Prelude To Rebellion; Strnad-s. 4-Brereton-c. 7-12-Outlander. 13,17-18-($2.95). 13-18-Emissaries to Malastare; Truman-s. 14-16-($2.50) Schultz-c. 19-22-Twilight; Duursema-a. 23-26-Infinity's End. 42-45-Rite of Passage 3.00
5,6 (Holochrome-c variants) 6.00
#0 Another Universe.com Ed.($10.00) r/serialized pages from Pizzazz Magazine; new Dorman painted-c 12.00
... A Valentine Story (2/03, $3.50) Leia & Han Solo on Hoth; Winick-s/Chadwick-a/c 3.50
...: Rite of Passage (2004, $12.95) r/#42-45 13.00
...: The Stark Hyperspace War (903, $12.95) r/#36-39 13.00

STAR WARS (Monthly series)
Dark Horse Comics: Jan, 2013 - No. 20, Aug, 2014 ($2.99)
1-Takes place after Episode IV; Brian Wood-s/Carlos D'Anda-a/Alex Ross-c 8.00
2-Ross-c 5.00
3-20: 3,4-Ross-c. 5-7-Migliari-c 3.00

STAR WARS
Dark Horse Comics (Free Comic Book Day giveaways)
...: and Captain Midnight (5/13) flip book with new Captain Midnight story & Avatar 3.00
...: Clone Wars #0 (5/09) flip book with short stories of Usagi Yojimbo, Emily the Strange 3.00
...: Clone Wars Adventures (7/04) based on Cartoon Network series; Fillbach Bros. -a 3.00
...: FCBD 2005 Special (5/05) Anakin & Obi-Wan during Clone Wars 3.00
...: FCBD 2006 Special (5/06) Clone Wars story; flip book with Conan FCBD Special 3.00

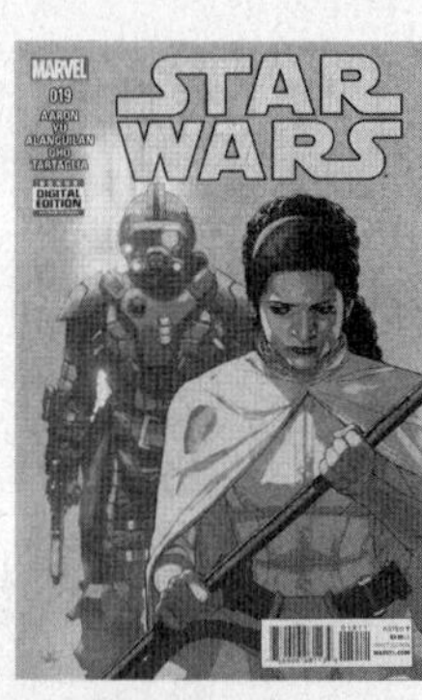

Star Wars (2015 series) #19 © Lucasfilm

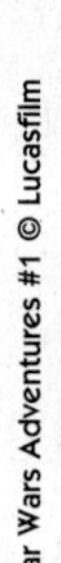

Star Wars Adventures #1 © Lucasfilm

Star Wars: Dark Empire #1 © Lucasfilm

GD 2.0 | VG 4.0 | FN 6.0 | VF 8.0 | VF/NM 9.0 | NM- 9.2

...: Tales - A Jedi's Weapon (5/02, 16 pgs.) Anakin Skywalker Episode 2 photo-c 3.00
Free Comic Book Day and Star Wars: The Clone Wars (5/11) flip book with Avatar: The Last Airbender 3.00

STAR WARS (Also see Darth Vader and Star Wars: Vader Down)
Marvel Comics: Mar, 2015 - Present ($4.99/$3.99)

1-($4.99) Takes place after Episode IV; Aaron-s/Cassaday-a; multiple covers 5.00
2-6-($3.99) Darth Vader app.; Cassaday-a. 4-6-Boba Fett app. 6-Intro Sana Solo 4.00
7-24,26-36: 7-Bianchi-a; Obi-Wan flashback. 8-12-Immonen-a. 13,14-Vader Down pts. 3,5; Deodato-a. 15,20-Obi-Wan flashback; Mayhew-a. 16-19-Yu-a. 26-30-Yoda app. 31,32-Doctor Aphra app. 4.00
25-($4.99) Darth Vader app.; Molina-a; back-up Droids story by Eliopoulos 5.00
37-($4.99) SCAR Squadron app.; back-up Tusken Raiders story; Sorrentino-a 5.00
38-44-Larroca-a 4.00
Annual 1 (2/16, $4.99) Gillen-s/Unzueta-a/Cassaday-c; Emperor Palpatine app. 5.00
Annual 2 (1/17, $4.99) Kelly Thompson-s/Emilio Laiso-a; intro. Pash Davane 5.00
Annual 3 (11/17, $4.99) Latour-s/Walsh-a 5.00
... Special: C-3PO 1 (6/16, $4.99) Robinson-s/Harris-a/c; story of C-3PO's red arm 5.00

STAR WARS, THE
Dark Horse Comics: Sept, 2013 - No. 8, May, 2014 ($3.99)

1-8-Adaptation of George Lucas' original rough-draft screenplay; Mayhew-a/Runge-c 4.00
#0-(1/14, $3.99) Design work of characters, settings, vehicles 4.00

STAR WARS ADVENTURES (Anthology of All-ages stories)
IDW Publishing: Sept, 2017 - Present ($3.99)

1-7: 2-Charretier-a. 3-Tudyk-s. 5-Porgs app. 6-Rose app. 4.00

STAR WARS: AGENT OF THE EMPIRE - HARD TARGETS
Dark Horse Comics: Oct, 2012 - No. 5, Feb, 2013 ($2.99, limited series)

1-5: 1-Ostrander-s/Fabbri-a; Boba Fett app. 3.00

STAR WARS: AGENT OF THE EMPIRE - IRON ECLIPSE
Dark Horse Comics: Dec, 2011 - No. 5, Apr, 2012 ($3.50, limited series)

1-5: 1-Ostrander-s/Roux-a; Han Solo & Chewbacca app. 3.50

STAR WARS: A NEW HOPE - THE SPECIAL EDITION
Dark Horse Comics: Jan, 1997 - No. 4, Apr, 1997 ($2.95, limited series)

1-4-Dorman-c 4.00

STAR WARS: BLOOD TIES - BOBA FETT IS DEAD
Dark Horse Comics: Apr, 2012 - No. 4, Jul, 2012 ($3.50, limited series)

1-4-Scalf painted-a/c 3.50

STAR WARS: BLOOD TIES: JANGO AND BOBA FETT
Dark Horse Comics: Aug, 2010 - No. 4, Nov, 2010 ($3.50, limited series)

1-4-Scalf painted-a/c 3.50

STAR WARS: BOBA FETT
Dark Horse Comics: Dec, 1995 - No. 3, Aug, 1997 ($3.95) (Originally intended as a one-shot)

1-Kennedy-c/a 1 2 3 5 6 8
2,3 5.00
Death, Lies, & Treachery TPB (1/98, $12.95) r/#1-3 13.00
... - Agent of Doom (11/00, $2.99) Ostrander-s/Cam Kennedy-a 3.00
... - Overkill (3/06, $2.99) Hughes-c/Andrews-s/Velasco-a 3.00
Twin Engines of Destruction (1/97, $2.95) 4.00

STAR WARS: BOBA FETT: ENEMY OF THE EMPIRE
Dark Horse Comics: Jan, 1999 - No. 4, Apr, 1999 ($2.95, limited series)

1-4-Recalls 1st meeting of Fett and Vader 4.00

STAR WARS: CHEWBACCA
Dark Horse Comics: Jan, 2000 - No. 4, Apr, 2000 ($2.95, limited series)

1-4-Macan-s/art by various incl. Anderson, Kordey, Gibbons; Phillips-c 3.00

STAR WARS: CLONE WARS ADVENTURES
Dark Horse Comics: 2004 - No. 10, 2007 ($6.95, digest-sized)

1-10-Short stories inspired by Clone Wars animated series 7.00

STAR WARS: CRIMSON EMPIRE
Dark Horse Comics: Dec, 1997 - No. 6, May, 1998 ($2.95, limited series)

1-Richardson-s/Gulacy-a 1 2 3 4 5 7
2-6 5.00

STAR WARS: CRIMSON EMPIRE II: COUNCIL OF BLOOD
Dark Horse Comics: Nov, 1998 - No. 6, Apr, 1999 ($2.95, limited series)

1-6-Richardson & Stradley-s/Gulacy-a 4.00

STAR WARS: CRIMSON EMPIRE III: EMPIRE LOST
Dark Horse Comics: Oct, 2011 - No. 6, Apr, 2012 ($3.50, limited series)

1-6: 1-Richardson-s/Gulacy-a/Dorman-c 3.50

STAR WARS: DARK EMPIRE
Dark Horse Comics: Dec, 1991 - No. 6, Oct, 1992 ($2.95, limited series)

Preview-(99¢) 4.00
1-All have Dorman painted-c 1 3 4 6 8 10
1-3-2nd printing 4.00
2-Low print run 2 4 6 8 10 12
3 6.00
4-6 4.00
Gold Embossed Set (#1-6)-With gold embossed foil logo (price is for set) 60.00
Platinum Embossed Set (#1-6) 90.00
Trade paperback (4/93, 16.95) 17.00
Dark Empire 1 - TPB 3rd printing (2003, $16.95) 17.00
Ltd. Ed. Hardcover ($99.95) Signed & numbered 100.00

STAR WARS: DARK EMPIRE II
Dark Horse Comics: Dec, 1994 - No. 6, May, 1995 ($2.95, limited series)

1-Dave Dorman painted-c 5.00
2-6: Dorman-c in all. 4.00
Platinum Embossed Set (#1-6) 35.00
Trade paperback ($17.95) 18.00
TPB Second Edition (9/06, $19.95) r/#1-6 and Star Wars: Empire's End #1,2 20.00

STAR WARS: DARK FORCE RISING
Dark Horse Comics: May, 1997 - No. 6, Oct, 1997 ($2.95, limited series)

1-6 4.00
TPB (2/98, $17.95) r/#1-6 18.00

STAR WARS: DARK TIMES (Continued from Star Wars Republic #83)(Storyline continues in Star Wars: Rebellion #15)
Dark Horse Comics: Oct, 2006 - No. 17, Jun, 2010 ($2.99)

1-17-Nineteen years before Episode IV; Doug Wheatley-a. 11-Celeste Morne awakens 13-17-Blue Harvest 3.00
#0-(7/09, $2.99) Prologue to Blue Harvest 3.00

STAR WARS: DARK TIMES - A SPARK REMAINS
Dark Horse Comics: Jul, 2013 - No. 5, Dec, 2013 ($3.50, limited series)

1-5-Stradley-s/Wheatley-a; Darth Vader app. 3.50

STAR WARS: DARK TIMES - FIRE CARRIER
Dark Horse Comics: Feb, 2013 - No. 5, Jun, 2013 ($2.99, limited series)

1-5-Stradley-s/Guzman-a; Darth Vader app. 3.00

STAR WARS: DARK TIMES - OUT OF THE WILDERNESS
Dark Horse Comics: Aug, 2011 - No. 5, Apr, 2012 ($2.99, limited series)

1-5-Doug Wheatley-a 3.00

STAR WARS: DARTH MAUL
Dark Horse Comics: Sept, 2000 - No. 4, Dec, 2000 ($2.95, limited series)

1-4-Photo-c and Struzan painted-c; takes place 6 months before Ep. 1 3.00

STAR WARS: DARTH MAUL (Issue #1 titled Darth Maul)
Marvel Comics: Apr, 2015 - No. 5, Sept, 2017 ($4.99, limited series)

1-($4.99) Cullen Bunn-s/Luke Ross-a; back-up by Eliopoulos-s/a 5.00
2-5-($3.99) Aurra Sing & Cad Bane app. 4.00
... Halloween Comic Fest 2017 1 (12/17, giveaway) r/#1 without Eliopoulos back-up 3.00

STAR WARS: DARTH MAUL - DEATH SENTENCE
Dark Horse Comics: Jul, 2012 - No. 4, Oct, 2012 ($2.99, limited series)

1-4-Tom Taylor-s/Bruno Redondo-a/Dave Dorman-c 3.00

STAR WARS: DARTH MAUL - SON OF DATHOMIR
Dark Horse Comics: May, 2014 - No. 4, Aug, 2014 ($3.50, limited series)

1-4-Barlow-s/Frigeri-a/Scalf-c 3.50

STAR WARS: DARTH VADER AND THE CRY OF SHADOWS
Dark Horse Comics: Dec, 2013 - No. 5, Apr, 2014 ($3.50, limited series)

1-5-Siedell-s/Guzman-a/Massaferra-c 3.50

STAR WARS: DARTH VADER AND THE GHOST PRISON
Dark Horse Comics: May, 2012 - No. 5, Sept, 2012 ($3.50, limited series)

1-5-Blackman-s/Alessio-a/Wilkins-c. 1-Variant-c by Sanda 3.50

STAR WARS: DARTH VADER AND THE LOST COMMAND
Dark Horse Comics: Jan, 2011 - No. 5, May, 2011 ($3.50, limited series)

1-5-Blackman-s/Leonardi-a/Sanda-c. 1-Variant-c by Wheatley 3.50

STAR WARS: DARTH VADER AND THE NINTH ASSASSIN
Dark Horse Comics: Apr, 2013 - No. 5, Aug, 2013 ($3.50, limited series)

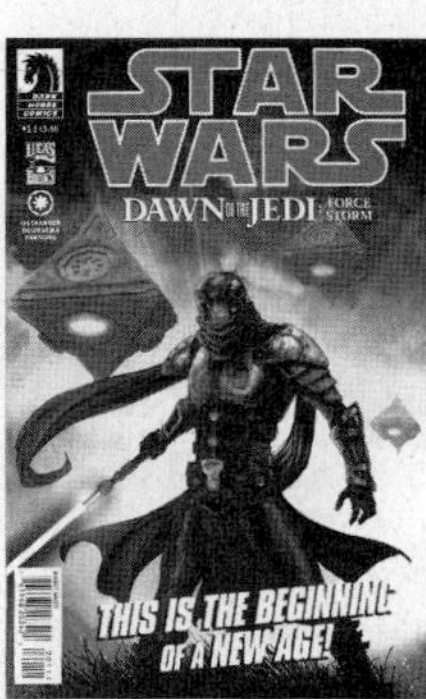

Star Wars: Dawn of the Jedi #1 © Lucasfilm

Star Wars: Episode II #4 © Lucasfilm

Star Wars: Knight Errant #1 © Lucasfilm

	GD 2.0	VG 4.0	FN 6.0	VF 8.0	VF/NM 9.0	NM- 9.2

1-5-Siedell-s. 1,2,4-Thompson-a. 3,5-Fernandez-a 3.50

STAR WARS: DAWN OF THE JEDI
Dark Horse Comics: No. 0, Feb, 2012 - Present ($3.50)

0-Guide to the worlds, characters, sites, vehicles; Migliari-c 3.50
... - Force Storm (2/12 - No. 5, 6/12, $3.50) 1-5-Ostrander-s/Duursema-a/c 3.50
... - Force War (11/13 - No. 5, 3/14, $3.50) 1-5-Ostrander-s/Duursema-a/c 3.50
... - Prisoner of Bogan (11/12 - No. 5, 5/13, $2.99) 1-5-Ostrander-s/Duursema-a/c 3.00

STAR WARS: DOCTOR APHRA (See Doctor Aphra for #1-6)(See Darth Vader #3 for debut)
Marvel Comics: No. 7, Jul, 2017 - Present ($3.99)

7-17: 7,8-Luke, Han, Leia & Sana app. 12,13-Darth Vader app. 4.00
Annual 1 (10/17, $4.99) Gillen-s/Laming & Sliney-a 5.00

STAR WARS: DROIDS (See Dark Horse Comics #17-19)
Dark Horse Comics: Apr, 1994 - #6, Sept, 1994; V2#1, Apr, 1995 - V2#8, Dec, 1995 ($2.50, limited series)

1-($2.95)-Embossed-c 5.00
2-6 , Special 1 (1/95, $2.50), V2#1-8 4.00
Star Wars Omnibus: Droids One TPB (6/08, $24.95) r/#1-6, Special 1, V2#1-8, Star Wars: The Protocol Offensive and "Artoo's Day Out" story from Star Wars Galaxy Magazine #1 25.00

STAR WARS: DROIDS UNPLUGGED
Marvel Comics: Aug, 2017 ($4.99, one-shot)

1-Chris Eliopoulos-s/a; short stories with R2-D2, BB-8 and a probe droid 5.00

STAR WARS: EMPIRE
Dark Horse Comics: Sept, 2002 - No. 40, Feb, 2006 ($2.99)

1-40: 1-Benjamin-a; takes place weeks before SW: A New Hope. 7,28-Boba Fett-c. 14-Vader after the destruction of the Death Star. 15-Death of Biggs; Wheatley-a 3.00
... Volume 1 (2003, $12.95, TPB) r/#1-4 13.00
... Volume 2 (2004, $17.95, TPB) r/#8-12,15 18.00
... Volume 3: The Imperial Perspective (2004, $17.95, TPB) r/#13,14,16-19 18.00
... Volume 4: The Heart of the Rebellion (2005, $17.95, TPB) r/#5,6,20-22 & Star Wars: A Valentine Story 18.00
... Volume 5 (2006, $14.95, TPB) r/#23-27 15.00
... Volume 6: In the Shadows of Their Fathers (10/06, $17.95, TPB) r/#29-34 18.00
... Volume 7: The Wrong Side of the War (1/07, $17.95, TPB) r/#34-40 18.00

STAR WARS: EMPIRE'S END
Dark Horse Comics: Oct, 1995 - No. 2, Nov, 1995 ($2.95, limited series)

1,2-Dorman-c 4.00

STAR WARS: EPISODE 1 THE PHANTOM MENACE
Dark Horse Comics: May, 1999 - No. 4 ($2.95, movie adaptation)

1-4-Regular and photo-c; Damaggio & Williamson-a 4.00
TPB ($12.95) r/#1-4 13.00
...Anakin Skywalker-Photo-c & Bradstreet-c, ...Obi-Wan Kenobi-Photo-c & Egeland-c, ...Queen Amidala-Photo-c & Bradstreet-c, ...Qui-Gon Jinn-Photo-c & Bradstreet-c 4.00
Gold foil covers; Wizard 1/2 10.00

STAR WARS: EPISODE II - ATTACK OF THE CLONES
Dark Horse Comics: Apr, 2002 - No. 4, May, 2002 ($3.99, movie adaptation)

1-4-Regular and photo-c; Duursema-a 4.00
TPB ($17.95) r/#1-4; Struzan-c 18.00

STAR WARS: EPISODE III - REVENGE OF THE SITH
Dark Horse Comics: May, 2005 - No. 4, May, 2005 ($2.99, movie adaptation)

1-4-Wheatley-a/Dorman-c 3.00
TPB ($12.95) r/#1-4; Dorman-c 13.00

STAR WARS FORCES OF DESTINY (All-ages anthology spotlighting female characters)
IDW Publishing: Jan, 2018 ($3.99, series of one-shots)

... – Ahsoka & Padme - Revis-s/Pinto-a 4.00
... – Hera - Grayson-s/Widermann-a 4.00
... – Leia - Charretier-a; Leia on planet Hoth before thte events of Empire 4.00
... – Rey - Houser-s/Florean-a; Rey meets BB-8 on Jakku 4.00
... – Rose & Paige - Dawson-s/Baldari-a; the sisters before the events of The Last Jedi 4.00

STAR WARS: GENERAL GRIEVOUS
Dark Horse Comics: Mar, 2005 - No. 4, June, 2005 ($2.99, limited series)

1-4-Leonardi-a/Dixon-s 3.00
TPB (2005, $12.95) r/#1-4 13.00

STAR WARS HANDBOOK
Dark Horse Comics: July, 1998 - Mar, 2000 ($2.95, one-shots)

...X-Wing Rogue Squadron (7/98)-Guidebook to characters and spacecraft 4.00
...Crimson Empire (7/99) Dorman-c 4.00
...Dark Empire (3/00) Dorman-c 4.00

STAR WARS: HEIR TO THE EMPIRE
Dark Horse Comics: Oct, 1995 - No.6, Apr, 1996 ($2.95, limited series)

1-6: Adaptation of Zahn novel 4.00

STAR WARS: INFINITIES - A NEW HOPE
Dark Horse Comics: May, 2001 - No. 4, Oct, 2001 ($2.99, limited series)

1-4: "What If..." the Death Star wasn't destroyed in Episode 4 3.00
TPB (2002, $12.95) r/ #1-4 13.00

STAR WARS: INFINITIES - THE EMPIRE STRIKES BACK
Dark Horse Comics: July, 2002 - No. 4, Oct, 2002 ($2.99, limited series)

1-4: "What If..." Luke died on the ice planet Hoth; Bachalo-c 3.00
TPB (2/03, $12.95) r/ #1-4 13.00

STAR WARS: INFINITIES - RETURN OF THE JEDI
Dark Horse Comics: Nov, 2003 - No. 4, Mar, 2004 ($2.99, limited series)

1-4:"What If..." ; Benjamin-a 3.00

STAR WARS: INVASION
Dark Horse Comics: July, 2009 - No. 5, Nov, 2009 ($2.99)

1-5-Jo Chen-c 3.00
#0-(10/09, $3.50) Dorman-c; Han Solo and Chewbacca app. 3.50
... - Rescues 1-6 (5/10 - No. 6, 12/10) Chen-c 3.00
... - Revelations 1-5 (7/11 - No. 5, 11/11, $3.50) Luke Skywalker app.; Scalf-c 3.50

STAR WARS: JABBA THE HUTT
Dark Horse Comics: Apr, 1995 ($2.50, one-shots)

nn, ...The Betrayal, ...The Dynasty Trap, ...The Hunger of Princess Nampi 4.00

STAR WARS: JANGO FETT - OPEN SEASONS
Dark Horse Comics: Apr, 2002 - No. 4, July, 2002 ($2.99, limited series)

1-4: 1-Bachs & Fernandez-a 3.00

STAR WARS: JEDI
Dark Horse Comics: Feb, 2003 - Jun, 2004 ($4.99, one-shots)

... - Aayla Secura (8/03) Ostrander-s/Duursema-a 5.00
... - Count Dooku (11/03) Duursema-a 5.00
... - Mace Windu (2/03) Duursema-a 5.00
... - Shaak Ti (5/03) Ostrander-s/Duursema-a 5.00
... - Yoda (6/04) Barlow-s/Hoon-a 5.00

STAR WARS: JEDI ACADEMY - LEVIATHAN
Dark Horse Comics: Oct, 1998 - No. 4, Jan, 1999 ($2.95, limited series)

1-4: 1-Lago-c. 2-4-Chadwick-c 4.00

STAR WARS: JEDI COUNCIL: ACTS OF WAR
Dark Horse Comics: Jun, 2000 - No. 4, Sept, 2000 ($2.95, limited series)

1-4-Stradley-s; set one year before Episode 1 3.00

STAR WARS: JEDI QUEST
Dark Horse Comics: Sept, 2001 - No. 4, Dec, 2001 ($2.99, limited series)

1-4-Anakin's Jedi training; Windham-s/Mhan-a 3.00

STAR WARS: JEDI - THE DARK SIDE
Dark Horse Comics: May, 2011 - No. 5, Sept, 2011 ($2.99, limited series)

1-5: 1-Qui-Gon Jinn 21 years befor Episode 1; Asrar-a 3.00

STAR WARS: JEDI VS. SITH
Dark Horse Comics: Apr, 2001 - No. 6, Sept, 2001 ($2.99, limited series)

1-6: Macan-s/Bachs-a/Robinson-c 3.00

STAR WARS: KNIGHT ERRANT
Dark Horse Comics: Oct, 2010 - No. 5, Feb, 2011 ($2.99)

1-5: 1-John Jackson Miller-s/Federico Dallocchio-a 3.00
... - Deluge 1-5 (8/11 - No. 5 12/11, $3.50) 1-Miller-s/Rodriguez-a/Quinones-c 3.50
... - Escape 1-5 (6/12 - No. 5 10/12, $3.50) 1-Miller-s/Castiello-a/Carré-c 3.50

STAR WARS: KNIGHTS OF THE OLD REPUBLIC
Dark Horse Comics: Jan, 2006 - No. 50, Feb, 2010 ($2.99)

1-50-Takes place 3,964 years before Episode IV. 1-6-Brian Ching-a/Travis Charest-c 3.00
... Handbook (11/07, $2.99) profiles of characters, ships, locales 3.00
.../Rebellion #0 (3/06, 25¢) flip book preview of both series 3.00
... - War 1-5 (1/12 - No. 5, 5/12, $3.50) J.J. Miller-s/Mutti-a 3.50
... Vol. 1 Commencement TPB (11/06, $18.95) r/#0-6 19.00
... Vol. 2 Flashpoint TPB (5/07, $18.95) r/#17-12 19.00
... Vol. 3 Days of Fear, Nights of Anger TPB (1/08, $18.95) r/#13-18 19.00

STAR WARS: LEGACY

Star Wars: Mara Jade #4 © Lucasfilm

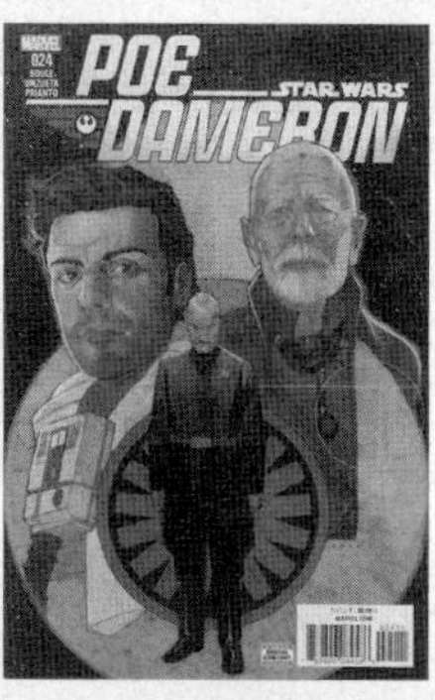

Star Wars: Poe Dameron #24 © Lucasfilm

Star Wars: Rogue One Adaptation #6 © Lucasfilm

GD VG FN VF VF/NM NM-
2.0 4.0 6.0 8.0 9.0 9.2

GD VG FN VF VF/NM NM-
2.0 4.0 6.0 8.0 9.0 9.2

Dark Horse Comics: No. 0, June, 2006 - No. 50, Aug, 2010 ($2.99)
Volume 2, Mar, 2013 - No. 18, Aug, 2014 ($2.99)

0-(25¢) Dossier of characters, settings, ships and weapons; Duursema-c 3.00
0 1/2-(1/08, $2.99) Updated dossier of characters, settings, ships, and history 3.00
1-50: 1-Takes place 130 years after Episode IV; Hughes-c/Duursema-a. 4-Duursema-c 7,39-Luke Skywalker on-c. 16-Obi-Wan Kenobi app. 50-Wraparound-c 3.00
...: Broken Vol. 1 TPB (4/07, $17.95) r/#1-3,5,6 18.00
...: One for One (9/10, $1.00) reprints #1 with red cover frame 3.00
... Volume Two 1 (3/13 - No. 18, 8/14, $2.99) 1-18: 1-Bechko-s/Hardman-a/Wilkins-c 3.00
... War 1-6 (12/10 - No. 6, 5/11, $3.50) 1-Ostrander-s/Duursema-a; Darth Krayt app. 3.50

STAR WARS: LOST TRIBE OF THE SITH - SPIRAL
Dark Horse Comics: Aug, 2012 - No. 5, Dec, 2012 ($2.99, limited series)

1-5-J.J. Miller-s/Mutti-a/Renaud-c 3.00

STAR WARS: MACE WINDU
Marvel Comics: Oct, 2017 - No. 5, Feb, 2018 ($3.99, limited series)

1-5-Matt Owens-s/Denys Cowan-a; follows after the Battle of Geonosis 4.00

STAR WARS: MARA JADE
Dark Horse Comics: Aug, 1998 - No. 6, Jan, 1999 ($2.95, limited series)

1-6-Ezquerra-a 4.00

STAR WARS: OBSESSION (Clone Wars)
Dark Horse Comics: Nov, 2004 - No. 5, Apr, 2005 ($2.99, limited series)

1-5-Blackman-s/Ching-a/c; Anakin & Obi-Wan 5 months before Episode III 3.00
...: Clone Wars Vol. 7 (2005, $17.95) r/#1-5 and 2005 Free Comic Book Day edition 18.00

STAR WARS: POE DAMERON (Titled Poe Dameron for #1-12)
Marvel Comics: No. 13, Jun, 2017 - Present ($3.99)

13-24: 13-Soule-s/Noto-a. 14-22-Unzueta-a. 20-24-Lor San Tekka app. 4.00
Annual 1 (8/17, $4.99) Thompson-s/Virella-a; General Organa app. 5.00

STAR WARS: PURGE
Dark Horse Comics: Dec, 2005 ($2.99, one-shot)

nn-Vader vs. remaining Jedi one month after Episode III; Hughes-c/Wheatley-a 5.00
... - Seconds To Die (11/09, $3.50) Vader app.; Charest-c/Ostrander-s 3.50
... - The Hidden Blade (4/10, $3.50) Vader app.; Scalf-c/a; Blackman-s 3.50
... - The Tyrant's Fist 1,2 (12/12 - No, 2, 1/13, $3.50) Vader app.; Freed-s/Dan Scott-c 3.50

STAR WARS: QUI-GON & OBI-WAN - LAST STAND ON ORD MANTELL
Dark Horse Comics: Dec, 2000 - No. 3, Mar, 2001 ($2.99, limited series)

1-3: 1-Three covers (photo, Tony Daniel, Bachs) Windham-s 3.00

STAR WARS: QUI-GON & OBI-WAN - THE AURORIENT EXPRESS
Dark Horse Comics: Feb, 2002 - No. 2, Mar, 2002 ($2.99, limited series)

1,2-Six years prior to Phantom Menace; Marangon-a 3.00

STAR WARS: REBEL HEIST
Dark Horse Comics: Apr, 2014 - No. 4, Jul, 2014 ($3.50)

1-4-Kindt-s/Castiello-a; two covers by Kindt and Adam Hughes on each 3.50

STAR WARS: REBELLION (Also see Star Wars: Knights of the Old Republic flip book)
Dark Horse Comics: Apr, 2006 - No. 16, Aug, 2008 ($2.99)

1-16-Takes place 9 months after Episode IV; Luke Skywalker app. 1-Badeaux-a/c 3.00
Vol. 1 TPB (2/07, $14.95) r/#0 (flip book) & #1-5 15.00

STAR WARS: REPUBLIC (Formerly Star Wars monthly series)
Dark Horse Comics: No. 46, Sept, 2002 - No. 83, Feb, 2006 ($2.99)

46-83-Events of the Clone Wars 3.00
...: Clone Wars Vol. 1 (2003, $14.95) r/#46-50 15.00
...: Clone Wars Vol. 2 (2003, $14.95) r/#51-53 & Star Wars: Jedi - Shaak Ti 15.00
...: Clone Wars Vol. 3 (2004, $14.95) r/#55-59 15.00
...: Clone Wars Vol. 4 (2004, $16.95) r/#54, 63 & Star Wars: Jedi - Aayla Secura & Dooku 17.00
...: Clone Wars Vol. 5 (2004, $17.95) r/#60-62, 64 & Star Wars: Jedi - Yoda 18.00
...: Clone Wars Vol. 6 (2005, $17.95) r/#65-71 18.00
(Clone Wars Vol. 7 - see Star Wars: Obsession)
...: Clone Wars Vol. 8 (2006, $17.95) r/#72-78 18.00
...: Clone Wars Vol. 9 (2006, $17.95) r/#79-83 & Star Wars: Purge 18.00
...: Honor and Duty TPB (5/06, $12.95) r/#46-48,78 13.00

STAR WARS: RETURN OF THE JEDI (Movie)
Marvel Comics Group: Oct, 1983 - No. 4, Jan, 1984 (limited series)

1-Williamson-p in all; r/Marvel Super Special #27 2 4 6 11 16 20
2-4-Continues r/Marvel Super Special #27 2 4 6 9 12 15
Oversized issue (1983, $2.95, 10-3/4x8-1/4", 68 pgs., cardboard-c)-r/#1-4 2 4 6 10 13 16

STAR WARS: RIVER OF CHAOS
Dark Horse Comics: June, 1995 - No. 4, Sept, 1995 ($2.95, limited series)

1-4: Louise Simonson scripts 4.00

STAR WARS: ROGUE ONE ADAPTATION
Marvel Comics: Jun, 2017 - No. 6, Nov, 2017 ($4.99/$3.99, limited series)

1-($4.99) Houser-s/Laiso & Bazaldua-a; Noto-c; afterword by director Gareth Edwards 5.00
2-6-($3.99) 3-Villanelli-a. 4-6-Laiso-a 4.00
Star Wars: Rogue One - Cassian & K2-SO Special 1 (10/17, $4.99) Swierczynski-s 5.00

STAR WARS: SHADOWS OF THE EMPIRE
Dark Horse Comics: May, 1996 - No. 6, Oct, 1996 ($2.95, limited series)

1-6: Story details events between The Empire Strikes Back & Return of the Jedi; Russell-a(i). 4.00

STAR WARS: SHADOWS OF THE EMPIRE - EVOLUTION
Dark Horse Comics: Feb, 1998 - No. 5, June, 1998 ($2.95, limited series)

1-5: Perry-s/Fegredo-c. 4.00

STAR WARS: SHADOW STALKER
Dark Horse Comics: Sept, 1997 ($2.95, one-shot)

nn-Windham-a. 4.00

STAR WARS: SPLINTER OF THE MIND'S EYE
Dark Horse Comics: Dec, 1995 - No. 4, June, 1996 ($2.50, limited series)

1-4: Adaption of Alan Dean Foster novel 4.00

STAR WARS: STARFIGHTER
Dark Horse Comics: Jan, 2002 - No. 3, March, 2002 ($2.99, limited series)

1-3-Williams & Gray-c 3.00

STAR WARS: TAG & BINK ARE DEAD
Dark Horse Comics: Oct, 2001 - No. 2, Nov, 2001($2.99, limited series)

1,2-Rubio-s 3.00
Star Wars: Tag & Bink Were Here TPB (11/06, $14.95) r/both SW: Tag & Bink series 15.00

STAR WARS: TAG & BINK II
Dark Horse Comics: Mar, 2006 - No. 2, Apr, 2006($2.99, limited series)

1-Tag & Bink invade Return of the Jedi; Rubio-s. 2-Tag & Bink as Jedi younglings during Ep II 3.00

STAR WARS TALES
Dark Horse Comics: Sept, 1999 - No. 24, Jun, 2005 ($4.95/$5.95/$5.99, anthology)

1-4-Short stories by various 6.00
5-24 ($5.95/$5.99-c) Art and photo-c on each 6.00
Volume 1-6 ($19.95) 1-(1/02) r/#1-4. 2-('02) r/#5-8. 3-(1/03) r/#9-12. 4-(1/04) r/#13-16 5-(1/05) r/#17-20; introduction pages from #1-20. 6-(1/06) r/#21-24 20.00

STAR WARS: TALES FROM MOS EISLEY
Dark Horse Comics: Mar, 1996 ($2.95, one-shot)

nn-Bret Blevins-a. 4.00

STAR WARS: TALES OF THE JEDI (See Dark Horse Comics #7)
Dark Horse Comics: Oct, 1993 - No. 5, Feb, 1994 ($2.50, limited series)

1-5: All have Dave Dorman painted-c. 3-r/Dark Horse Comics #7-9 w/new coloring & some panels redrawn 5.00
1-5-Gold foil embossed logo; limited # printed-7500 (set) 50.00
Star Wars Omnibus: Tales of the Jedi Volume One TPB (11/07, $24.95) r/#1-5, ... - The Golden Age of the Sith #0-5 and ... - The Fall of the Sith Empire #1-5 25.00

STAR WARS: TALES OF THE JEDI-DARK LORDS OF THE SITH
Dark Horse Comics: Oct, 1994 - No. 6, Mar, 1995 ($2.50, limited series)

1-6: 1-Polybagged w/trading card 4.00

STAR WARS: TALES OF THE JEDI-REDEMPTION
Dark Horse Comics: July, 1998 - No. 5, Nov, 1998 ($2.95, limited series)

1-5: 1-Kevin J. Anderson-s/Kordey-c 4.00

STAR WARS: TALES OF THE JEDI-THE FALL OF THE SITH EMPIRE
Dark Horse Comics: June, 1997 - No. 5, Oct, 1997 ($2.95, limited series)

1-5 4.00

STAR WARS: TALES OF THE JEDI-THE FREEDON NADD UPRISING
Dark Horse Comics: Aug, 1994 - No. 2, Nov, 1994 ($2.50, limited series)

1,2 4.00

STAR WARS: TALES OF THE JEDI-THE GOLDEN AGE OF THE SITH
Dark Horse Comics: July, 1996 - No. 5, Feb, 1997 (99¢/$2.95, limited series)

0-(99¢)-Anderson-s 3.00
1-5-Anderson-s 4.00

Star Wars: Thrawn #1 © Lucasfilm

Static Shock #1 © DC

Steel #7 © DC

GD 2.0 | VG 4.0 | FN 6.0 | VF 8.0 | VF/NM 9.0 | NM- 9.2

STAR WARS: TALES OF THE JEDI-THE SITH WAR
Dark Horse Comics: Aug, 1995 - No. 6, Jan, 1996 ($2.50, limited series)
1-6: Anderson scripts 4.00

STAR WARS: THE BOUNTY HUNTERS
Dark Horse Comics: July, 1999 - Oct, 1999 ($2.95, one-shots)
...Aurra Sing (7/99), ...Kenix Kil (10/99), ...Scoundrel's Wages (8/99) Lando Calrissian app. 4.00

STAR WARS: THE CLONE WARS (Based on the Cartoon Network series)
Dark Horse Comics: Sept, 2008 - No. 12, Jan, 2010 ($2.99)
1-12: 1-6-Gilroy-s/Hepburn-a/Filoni-c 3.00

STAR WARS: THE FORCE AWAKENS ADAPTATION (Episode VII movie)
Marvel Comics: Aug, 2016 - No. 6, Jan, 2017 ($4.99, limited series)
1-6: 1-Chuck Wendig-s/Luke Ross-a/Esad Ribic-c. 3-Marc Laming-a 5.00

STAR WARS: THE FORCE UNLEASHED (Based on the LucasArts video game)
Dark Horse Comics: Aug, 2008 ($15.95, one-shot graphic novel)
GN-Intro. Starkiller, Vader's apprentice; takes place 2 years before Battle of Yavin 16.00

STAR WARS: THE JABBA TAPE
Dark Horse Comics: Dec, 1998 ($2.95, one-shot)
nn-Wagner-s/Plunkett-a 4.00

STAR WARS: THE LAST COMMAND
Dark Horse Comics: Nov, 1997 - No. 6, July, 1998 ($2.95, limited series)
1-6: Based on the Timothy Zaun novel 4.00

STAR WARS: THE LAST JEDI - DJ - MOST WANTED
Marvel Comics: Mar, 2018 ($4.99, one-shot)
1-Acker & Blacker-s/Walker-a 5.00

STAR WARS: THE OLD REPUBLIC (Based on the video game)
Dark Horse Comics: July, 2010 - No. 6, Dec, 2010 ($2.99, limited series)
1-3 (Threat of Peace)-Chestny-s/Sanchez-a. 1-Two covers 3.00
4-6 (Blood of the Empire)-Freed-s/Dave Ross-a 3.00

STAR WARS: THE OLD REPUBLIC - THE LOST SUNS (Based on the video game)
Dark Horse Comics: Jun, 2011 - No. 5, Oct, 2011 ($3.50, limited series)
1-5-Freed-s/Carré-c/Freeman-a 3.50

STAR WARS: THE PROTOCOL OFFENSIVE
Dark Horse Comics: Sept, 1997 ($4.95, one-shot)
nn-Anthony Daniels & Ryder Windham-s 5.00

STAR WARS: THRAWN
Marvel Comics: Apr, 2018 - Present ($3.99)
1-Houser-s/Luke Ross-a; Thrawn's intro to the Empire; Palpatine app. 4.00

STAR WARS: UNDERWORLD - THE YAVIN VASSILIKA
Dark Horse Comics: Dec, 2000 - No. 5, June, 2001 ($2.99, limited series)
1-5-(Photo and Robinson covers) 3.00

STAR WARS: UNION
Dark Horse Comics: Nov, 1999 - No. 4, Feb, 2000 ($2.95, limited series)
1-4-Wedding of Luke and Mara Jade; Teranishi-a/Stackpole-s 4.00

STAR WARS: VADER DOWN
Marvel Comics: Jan, 2016 ($4.99, one-shot)
1-Part 1 of x-over with Star Wars (2015) #13,14 and Darth Vader #13-15; Deodato-a 5.00

STAR WARS: VADER'S QUEST
Dark Horse Comics: Feb, 1999 - No. 4, May, 1999 ($2.95, limited series)
1-4-Follows destruction of 1st Death Star; Gibbons-a 4.00

STAR WARS: VISIONARIES
Dark Horse Comics: Apr, 2005 ($17.95, TPB)
nn-Short stories from the concept artists for Revenge of the Sith movie 18.00

STAR WARS: X-WING ROGUE SQUADRON (Star Wars: X-Wing Rogue Squadron-The Phantom Affair #5-8 appears on cover only)
Dark Horse Comics: July, 1995 - No. 35, Nov, 1998 ($2.95)
1/2 8.00
1-24,26-35: 1-4-Baron scripts. 5-20-Stackpole scripts 4.00
25-($3.95) 5.00
The Phantom Affair TPB ($12.95) r/#5-8 13.00

STAR WARS: X-WING ROGUE SQUADRON: ROGUE LEADER
Dark Horse Comics: Sept, 2005 - No. 3, Nov, 2005 ($2.99)
1-3-Takes place one week after the Batttle of Endor 3.00

GD 2.0 | VG 4.0 | FN 6.0 | VF 8.0 | VF/NM 9.0 | NM- 9.2

STATIC (See Charlton Action: Featuring "Static")

STATIC (See Heroes)
DC Comics (Milestone): June, 1993 - No. 45, Mar, 1997 ($1.50/$1.75/$2.50)
1-($2.95)-Collector's Edition; polybagged w/poster & trading card & backing board (direct sales only) 4.00
1-Platinum Edition with red background cover 6.00
1-13,15-24,26-45: 2-Origin. 8-Shadow War; Simonson silver ink-c. 27-Kent Williams-c 3.00
14-($2.50, 52 pgs.)-Worlds Collide Pt. 14 4.00
25 ($3.95) 4.00
...: Trial by Fire (2000, $9.95) r/#1-4; Leon-c 10.00

STATIC SHOCK (DC New 52)
DC Comics: Nov, 2011 - No. 8, Jun, 2012 ($2.99)
1-8: 1-McDaniel & Rozum-s/McDaniel-a/c. 6-Hardware & Technique app. 8-Origin retold 3.00

STATIC SHOCK!: REBIRTH OF THE COOL (TV)
DC Comics: Jan, 2001 - No. 4, Sept, 2001 ($2.50, limited series)
1-4: McDuffie-s/Leon-c/a 3.00

STATIC SHOCK SPECIAL
DC Comics: Aug, 2011 ($2.99, one-shot)
1-Cowan-a/Williams III-c; pin-ups by various; tribute to Dwayne McDuffie 3.00

STATIC-X
Chaos! Comics: Aug, 2002 ($5.99)
1-Polybagged with music CD; metal band as super-heroes; Pulido-s 6.00

STEALTH (Pilot Season: ...)
Image Comics (Top Cow): May, 2010 ($2.99)
1-Kirkman-s/Mitchell-a/Silvestri-c 3.00

STEAM MAN, THE
Dark Horse Comics: Oct, 2015 - No. 5, Feb, 2016 ($3.99)
1-5-Kowalski-a; Steam robot and crew in 1899 4.00

STEAMPUNK
DC/WildStorm (Cliffhanger): Apr, 2000 - No. 12, Aug, 2002 ($2.50/$3.50)
Catechism (1/00) Prologue -Kelly-s/Bachalo-a 3.00
1-4,6-11: 4-Four covers by Bachalo, Madureira, Ramos, Campbell 3.00
5,12-($3.50) 4.00
...: Drama Obscura ('03, $14.95) r/#6-12 15.00
...: Manimatron ('01, $14.95) r/#1-5, Catechism, Idiosincratica 15.00

STEAMPUNK BATTLESTAR GALACTICA 1880 (See Battlestar Galactica 1880)

STEED AND MRS. PEEL (TV)(Also see The Avengers)
Eclipse Books/ ACME Press: 1990 - No. 3, 1991 ($4.95, limited series)
Books One - Three: Grant Morrison scripts/Ian Gibson-a 5.00
1-6: 1-(BOOM! Studios, 1/12 - No. 6, 6/12, $3.99) r/Books One - Three 4.00

STEED AND MRS. PEEL (TV)(The Avengers)
BOOM! Studios: No. 0, Aug, 2012 - No. 11, Jul, 2013 ($3.99)
0-11: 0-Mark Waid-s/Steve Bryant-a; eight covers. 1-3-Sliney-a; five covers 4.00

STEED AND MRS. PEEL: WE'RE NEEDED (TV)(The Avengers)
BOOM! Studios: Jul, 2014 - No. 3, Sept, 2014 ($3.99)(Issue #1 says "1 of 6")
1-3-Edginton-s/Cosentino-a. 1-Two covers 4.00

STEEL (Also see JLA)
DC Comics: Feb, 1994 - No. 52, July, 1998 ($1.50/$1.95/$2.50)
1-8,0,9-52: 1-From Reign of the Supermen storyline. 6,7-Worlds Collide Pt. 5 &12. 8-(9/94). 0-(10/94). 9-(11/94). 46-Superboy-c/app. 50-Millennium Giants x-over 3.00
1-(3/11, $2.99, one-shot) Benes-a/Garner-c; Reign of Doomsday x-over 4.00
Annual 1 (1994, $2.95)-Elseworlds story 4.00
Annual 2 (1995, $3.95)-Year One story 4.00
...Forging of a Hero TPB (1997, $19.95) reprints early app. 20.00

STEEL: THE OFFICIAL COMIC ADAPTION OF THE WARNER BROS. MOTION PICTURE
DC Comics: 1997 ($4.95, Prestige format, one-shot)
nn-Movie adaption; Bogdanove & Giordano-a 5.00

STEELGRIP STARKEY
Marvel Comics (Epic): June, 1986 - No. 6, July, 1987 ($1.50, lim. series, Baxter paper)
1-6 3.00

STEEL STERLING (Formerly Shield-Steel Sterling; see Blue Ribbon, Jackpot, Mighty Comics, Mighty Crusaders, Roly Poly & Zip Comics)
Archie Enterprises, Inc.: No. 4, Jan, 1984 - No. 7, July, 1984

Steel, The Indestructible Man #4 © DC

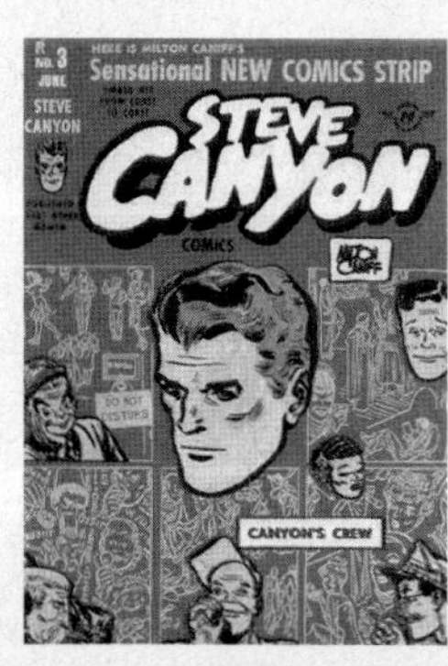

Steve Canyon Comics #3 © HARV

Steven Universe #7 © CN

	GD 2.0	VG 4.0	FN 6.0	VF 8.0	VF/NM 9.0	NM- 9.2

4-7: 4-6-Kanigher-s; Barreto-a. 5,6-Infantino-a. 6-McWilliams-a 5.00

STEEL, THE INDESTRUCTIBLE MAN (See All-Star Squadron #8 and J.L. of A. Annual #2)
DC Comics: Mar, 1978 - No. 5, Oct-Nov, 1978

1 2 4 6 11 16 20
2-5: 5-44 pgs. 1 2 3 4 6 8

STEELTOWN ROCKERS
Marvel Comics: Apr, 1990 - No. 6, Sept, 1990 ($1.00, limited series)

1-6: Small town teens form rock band 3.00

STEPHEN COLBERT'S TEK JANSEN (From the animated shorts on The Colbert Report)
Oni Press: July, 2007 - No. 5, Jan, 2009 ($3.99, limited series)

1-Chantier-a/Layman & Peyer-s; back-up story by Massey-s/Rodriguez-a; Chantier-c 4.00
1-Variant-c by John Cassaday 6.00
1-Second printing with flip book of Cassaday & Chantier covers 4.00
2-5: 2-(6/08) Flip book with covers by Rodriguez & Wagner. 3-Flip-c by Darwyn Cooke 4.00

STEPHEN KING'S N. THE COMIC SERIES
Marvel Comics: May, 2010 - No. 4, Aug, 2010 ($3.99, limited series)

1-4-Guggenheim-s/Maleev-a/c 4.00

STEVE AUSTIN (See Stone Cold Steve Austin)

STEVE CANYON (See Harvey Comics Hits #52)
Dell Publishing Co.: No. 519, 11/53 - No. No. 1033, 9/59 (All Milton Caniff-a except #519, 939, 1033)

Four Color 519 (1, '53) 8 16 24 54 102 150
Four Color 578 (8/54), 641 (7/55), 737 (10/56), 804 (5/57), 939 (10/58),
1033 (9/59) (photo-c) 5 10 15 35 63 90

STEVE CANYON
Grosset & Dunlap: 1959 (6-3/4x9", 96 pgs., B&W, no text, hardcover)

100100-Reprints 2 stories from strip (1953, 1957) 6 12 18 31 38 45
100100 (softcover edition) 5 10 15 24 30 35

STEVE CANYON COMICS
Harvey Publ.: Feb, 1948 - No. 6, Dec, 1948 (Strip reprints, No. 4,5: 52pgs.)

1-Origin; has biography of Milton Caniff; Powell-a, 2 pgs.; Caniff-a
20 40 60 120 195 270
2-Caniff, Powell-a in #2-6 14 28 42 80 115 150
3-6: 6-Intro Madame Lynx-c/story 14 28 42 76 108 140

STEVE CANYON IN 3-D
Kitchen Sink Press: June, 1986 ($2.25, one-shot)

1-Contains unpublished story from 1954 5.00

STEVE DITKO'S STRANGE AVENGING TALES
Fantagraphics Books: Feb, 1997 ($2.95, B&W)

1-Ditko-c/s/a 5.00

STEVE DONOVAN, WESTERN MARSHAL (TV)
Dell Publishing Co.: No. 675, Feb, 1956 - No. 880, Feb, 1958 (All photo-c)

Four Color 675-Kinstler-a 7 14 21 48 89 130
Four Color 768-Kinstler-a 6 12 18 38 69 100
Four Color 880 5 10 15 31 53 75

STEVEN UNIVERSE (TV)
BOOM! Studios (kaBOOM): Aug, 2014 - No. 8, Mar, 2015 ($3.99)

1-8: 1-Four covers; Uncle Grandpa preview. 2-8-Three covers 4.00
...: Anti-Gravity OGN (11/17, $14.99, 9" x 6") Perper-s/Chan & Ayoub-a 15.00
...: Greg Universe Special 1 (4/15, $4.99) Short stories by various; two covers 5.00
...: 2016 Special 1 (12/16, $7.99) Short donut-themed stories by various; two covers 8.00

STEVEN UNIVERSE (Ongoing)(TV)
BOOM! Studios (kaBOOM): Feb, 2017 - No. 12, Jan, 2018 ($3.99)

1-13: 1-Four covers; Lapis & Peridot app. 4.00

STEVEN UNIVERSE AND THE CRYSTAL GEMS (TV)
BOOM! Studios (kaBOOM): Mar, 2016 - No. 4, Jun, 2016 ($3.99)

1-4-Fenton-s/Garland-a; multiple covers on each. 1-Preview of Over the Garden Wall 4.00

STEVE ROGERS: SUPER-SOLDIER (Captain America - The Heroic Age)
Marvel Comics: Sept, 2010 - No. 4, Dec, 2010 ($3.99, limited series)

1-4-Brubaker-s/Eaglesham-a/Pacheco-c. 1-Back-up rep. of origin from CA #1 ('41) 4.00
Annual 1 (6/11, $3.99) Continued from Uncanny X-Men Annual #3; Roberson-a 4.00

STEVE ROPER
Famous Funnies: Apr, 1948 - No. 5, Dec, 1948

1-Contains 1944 daily newspaper-r 13 26 39 72 101 130
2 9 18 27 47 61 75
3-5 8 16 24 40 50 60

STEVE SAUNDERS SPECIAL AGENT (See Special Agent)

STEVE SAVAGE (See Captain...)

STEVE ZODIAC & THE FIRE BALL XL-5 (TV)
Gold Key: Jan, 1964

10108-401 (#1) 7 14 21 48 89 130

STEVIE (Mazie's boy friend)(Also see Flat-Top, Mazie & Mortie)
Mazie (Magazine Publ.): Nov, 1952 - No. 6, Apr, 1954

1-Teenage humor; Stevie, Mortie & Mazie begin 11 22 33 64 90 115
2-6 7 14 21 37 46 55

STEVIE MAZIE'S BOY FRIEND (See Harvey Hits #5)

STEWART THE RAT (See Eclipse Graphic Album Series)

ST. GEORGE (See listing under Saint...)

STIG'S INFERNO
Vortex/Eclipse: 1985 - No. 7, Mar, 1987 ($1.95, B&W)

1-7 ($1.95) 3.00
Graphic Album (1988, $6.95, B&W, 100 pgs.) 7.00

STING OF THE GREEN HORNET (See The Green Hornet)
Now Comics: June, 1992 - No. 4, 1992 ($2.50, limited series)

1-4: Butler-c/a 3.00
1-4 ($2.75)-Collectors Ed.; polybagged w/poster 4.00

STOKER'S DRACULA (Reprints unfinished Dracula story from 1974-75 with new ending)
Marvel Comics: 2004 - No. 4, May, 2005 ($3.99, B&W)

1-4: 1-Reprints from Dracula Lives! #5-8; Roy Thomas-s/Dick Giordano-a. 2-R/#10,11 & Legion of Monsters #1. 3,4-New story/artwork to finish story. 4-Giordano afterword 4.00
HC (2005, $24.99) r/#1-4; foreward by Thomas; Giordano afterword; bonus art & covers 25.00

STONE
Avalon Studios: Aug, 1998 - No. 4, Apr, 1999 ($2.50, limited series)

1-4-Portacio-a/Haberlin-s 3.00
1-Alternate-c 5.00
2-($14.95) DF Stonechrome Edition 15.00

STONE (Volume 2)
Avalon Studios: Aug, 1999 - No. 4, May, 2000 ($2.50)

1-4-Portacio-a/Haberlin-s 3.00
1-Chrome-c 5.00

STONE COLD STEVE AUSTIN (WWF Wrestling)
Chaos! Comics: Oct, 1999 - No. 4, Feb, 2000 ($2.95)

1-4-Reg. & photo-c; Steven Grant-s 3.00
1-Premium Ed. ($10.00) 10.00
Preview ($5.00) 5.00

STONE PROTECTORS
Harvey Pubications: May, 1994 - No. 3, Sept, 1994

nn (1993, giveaway)(limited distribution, scarce) 6.00
1-3-Ace Novelty action figures 4.00

STONEY BURKE (TV Western)
Dell Publishing Co.: June-Aug, 1963 - No. 2, Sept-Nov, 1963

1,2-Jack Lord photo-c on both 3 6 9 16 24 32

STONY CRAIG
Pentagon Publishing Co.: 1946 (No #)

nn-Reprints Bell Syndicate's "Sgt. Stony Craig" newspaper strips; story of the Japanese soldier who wouldn't surrender 10 20 30 58 79 100

STORIES BY FAMOUS AUTHORS ILLUSTRATED (Fast Fiction #1-5)
Seaboard Publ./Famous Authors Ill.: No. 6, Aug, 1950 - No. 13, Mar, 1951

1-Scarlet Pimpernel-Baroness Orczy 27 54 81 160 263 365
2-Capt. Blood-Raphael Sabatini 26 52 78 154 252 350
3-She, by Haggard 30 60 90 177 289 400
4-The 39 Steps-John Buchan 18 36 54 107 169 230
5-Beau Geste-P. C. Wren 18 36 54 107 169 230

NOTE: *The above five issues are exact reprints of Fast Fiction #1-5 except for the title change and new Kiefer covers on #1 and 2. Kiefer c(r)-3-5. The above 5 issues were released before Famous Authors #6.*

6-Macbeth, by Shakespeare; Kiefer art (8/50); used in **SOTI**, pg. 22,143; Kiefer-c; 36 pgs. 24 48 72 142 234 325
7-The Window; Kiefer-c/a; 52 pgs. 18 36 54 107 169 230
8-Hamlet, by Shakespeare; Kiefer-c/a; 36 pgs. 21 42 63 126 206 285

Stories of Romance #5 © MAR

StormWatch (2011 series) #28 © DC

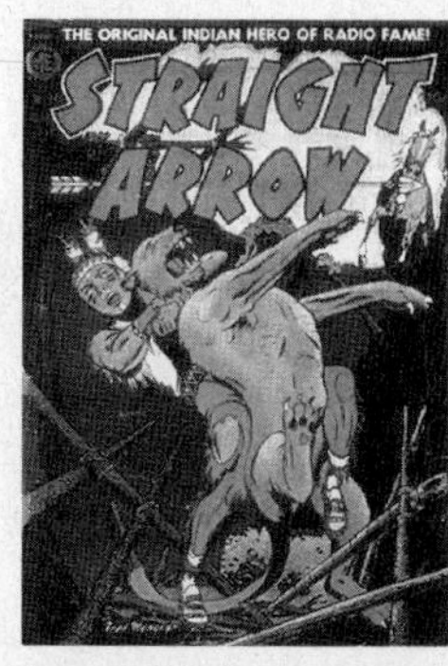

Straight Arrow #16 © ME

	GD 2.0	VG 4.0	FN 6.0	VF 8.0	VF/NM 9.0	NM- 9.2

9,10: 9-Nicholas Nickleby, by Dickens; G. Schrotter-a; 52 pgs. 10-Romeo & Juliet, by Shakespeare; Kiefer-c/a; 36 pgs. 18 36 54 107 169 230
11-13: 11-Ben-Hur; Schrotter-a; 52 pgs. 12-La Svengali; Schrotter-a; 36 pgs.
13-Scaramouche; Kiefer-c/a; 36 pgs. 18 36 54 103 162 220

NOTE: *Artwork was prepared/advertised for #14, The Red Badge Of Courage. Gilberton bought out Famous Authors, Ltd. and used that story as C.I. #98. Famous Authors, Ltd. then published the Classics Junior series. The Famous Authors titles were published as part of the regular Classics Ill. Series in Brazil starting in 1952.*

STORIES FROM THE TWILIGHT ZONE
Skylark Pub: Mar, 1979, 68 pgs. (B&W comic digest, 5-1/4x7-5/8")

15405-2: Pfevfer-a, 56 pgs, new comics 3 6 9 17 26 35

STORIES OF ROMANCE (Formerly Meet Miss Bliss)
Atlas Comics (LMC): No. 5, Mar, 1956 - No. 13, Aug, 1957

5-Baker-a? 18 36 54 105 165 225
6-10,12,13 13 26 39 72 101 130
11-Baker, Romita-a; Colletta-c/a 18 36 54 105 165 225

NOTE: *Ann Brewster a-13.* ***Colletta*** *a-9(2), 11; c-5, 11.*

STORM (X-Men)
Marvel Comics: Feb, 1996 - No. 4, May, 1996 ($2.95, limited series)

1-4-Foil-c; Dodson-a(p); Ellis-s: 2-4-Callisto app. 4.00

STORM (X-Men)
Marvel Comics: Apr, 2006 - No. 6, Sept, 2006 ($2.99, limited series)

1-6: Ororo and T'Challa meet as teens; Eric Jerome Dickey-s 3.00
HC (2007, $19.99, dustjacket) r/#1-6 20.00
SC (2008, $14.99) r/#1-6 15.00

STORM (X-Men)
Marvel Comics: Sept, 2014 - No. 11, Jul, 2015 ($3.99)

1-11: 1-Greg Pak-s/Victor Ibañez-a. 9-Gambit app. 4.00

STORMBREAKER: THE SAGA OF BETA RAY BILL (Also see Thor)
Marvel Comics: Mar, 2005 - No. 6, Aug, 2005 ($2.99, limited series)

1-6-Oeming & Berman-s/DiVito-a; Galactus app. 6-Spider-Man app. 3.00
TPB (2006, $16.99) r/#1-6 17.00

STORMING PARADISE
DC Comics (WildStorm): Sept, 2008 - No. 6, Aug, 2009 ($2.99, limited series)

1-6-WWII invasion of Japan; Dixon-s/Guice-a/c 3.00
TPB (2009, $19.99) r/#1-6 20.00

STORM SHADOW (G.I. Joe character)
Devil's Due Publishing: May, 2007 - No. 7, Nov, 2007 ($3.50)

1-7-Larry Hama-s 3.50

STORMWATCH (Also see The Authority)
Image Comics (WildStorm Prod.): May, 1993 - No. 50, Jul, 1997 ($1.95/$2.50)

1-8,0,9-36: 1-Intro StormWatch (Battalion, Diva, Winter, Fuji, & Hellstrike); 1st app. Weatherman; Jim Lee-c & part scripts; Lee plots in all. 1-Gold edition.1-3-Includes coupon for limited edition StormWatch trading card #00 by Lee. 3-1st brief app. Backlash. 0-($2.50)-Polybagged w/card; 1st full app. Backlash. 9-(4/94, $2.50)-Intro Defile. 10-(6/94),11,12-Both (8/94). 13,14-(9/94). 15-(10/94). 21-Reads #1 on-c. 22-Direct Market; Wildstorm Rising Pt. 9, bound-in card. 23-Spartan joins team. 25-(6/94, June 1995 on-c, $2.50). 35-Fire From Heaven Pt. 5. 36-Fire From Heaven Pt. 12 3.00
10-Alternate Portacio-c, see Deathblow #5 3.00
22-($1.95)-Newsstand, Wildstorm Rising Pt. 9 3.00
37-(7/96, $3.50, 38 pgs.)-Weatherman forms new team; 1st app. Jenny Sparks, Jack Hawksmoor & Rose Tattoo; Warren Ellis scripts begin; Justice League #1-c/swipe 4.00
38-49: 44-Three covers. 3.00
50-($4.50) 4.50
Special 1 ,2(1/94, 5/95, $3.50, 52 pgs.) 4.00
Sourcebook 1 (1/94, $2.50) 3.00

STORMWATCH (Also see The Authority)
Image Comics (WildStorm): Oct, 1997 - No. 11, Sept, 1998 ($2.50)

1-Ellis-s/Jimenez-a(p); two covers by Bennett 3.00
1-($3.50)-Voyager Pack bagged w/Gen 13 preview 4.00
2-11: 4-1st app. Midnighter and Apollo. 7,8-Freefall app. 9-Gen13 & DV8 app. 3.00
A Finer World ('99, $14.95, TPB) r/V2 #4-9 15.00
Change or Die ('99, $14.95, TPB) r/V1 #48-50 & V2 #1-3 15.00
Final Orbit ('01, $9.95, TPB) r/V2 #10,11 & WildC.A.T.S./Aliens; Hitch-c 10.00

STORMWATCH (DC New 52)
DC Comics: Nov, 2011 - No. 30, Jun, 2014 ($2.99)

1-Cornell-s/Sepulveda-a; Martian Manhunter app.; blue bkgrd cover 4.00
1-(2nd printing, cover has red bkgrd), 2-8: 7,8-Jenkins-s. 12-Martian Manhunter leaves 3.00
13-30: 13,14-Etrigan returns. 18-Team re-booted; Starlin-s/c. 20-Lobo origin 3.00
#0-(11/12, $2.99) Flashback to Demon Knights; Milligan-s/Conrad-a 3.00

STORMWATCH: P.H.D. (Post Human Division)
DC Comics (WildStorm): Jan, 2007 - No. 24, Jan, 2010 ($2.99)

1-24: 1-Two covers by Mahnke & Hairsine; Gage-s/Mahnke-a. 2-Var-c by Dell'Otto 3.00
...: Armageddon 1 (2/08, $2.99) Gage-s/Fernández-a/McKone-c 3.00
TPB (2007, $17.99) r/#1-4,6,7 & story from Worldstorm #1 18.00
... Book Two TPB (2008, $17.99) r/#5,8-12; sketch pages and concept art 18.00
... Book Three TPB (2009, $17.99) r/#13-19 18.00

STORMWATCH: TEAM ACHILLES
DC Comics (WildStorm): Sept, 2002 - No. 23, Aug, 2004 ($2.95)

1-8: 1-Two covers by Portacio; Portacio-a/Wright-s. 5,6-The Authority app. 3.00
9-23: 9-Back-up preview of The Authority: High Stakes pt. 1 3.00
TPB (2003, $14.95) r/Wizard Preview and #1-6; Portacio art pages 15.00
Book 2 (2004, $14.95) r/#7-11 & short story from Eye of the Storm Annual 15.00

STORMY (Disney) (Movie)
Dell Publishing Co.: No. 537, Feb, 1954

Four Color 537 (...the Thoroughbred)-on top 2/3 of each page; Pluto story on bottom 1/3 5 10 15 33 57 80

STORY OF JESUS (See Classics Illustrated Special Issue)

STORY OF MANKIND, THE (Movie)
Dell Publishing Co.: No. 851, Jan, 1958

Four Color 851-Vincent Price/Hedy Lamarr photo-c 7 14 21 44 82 120

STORY OF MARTHA WAYNE, THE
Argo Publ.: April, 1956

1-Newspaper strip-r 6 12 18 31 38 45

STORY OF RUTH, THE
Dell Publishing Co.: No. 1144, Nov-Jan, 1961 (Movie)

Four Color 1144-Photo-c 8 16 24 54 102 150

STORY OF THE COMMANDOS, THE (Combined Operations)
Long Island Independent: 1943 (15¢, B&W, 68 pgs.) (Distr. by Gilberton)

nn-All text (no comics); photos & illustrations; ad for Classic Comics on back cover (Rare) 42 84 126 265 445 625

STORY OF THE GLOOMY BUNNY, THE (See March of Comics #9)

STORYTELLER, THE: FAIRIES (Jim Henson's)
BOOM! Studios (Archaia): Dec, 2017 - No. 4 ($3.99, limited series)

1-3: 1-Matt Smith-s/a. 2-Benjamin Schipper-s/a. 3-Tyler Jenkins-s/a 4.00

STORYTELLER, THE: GIANTS (Also see Jim Henson's The Storyteller)
BOOM! Studios (Archaia): Dec, 2016 - No. 4, Mar, 2017 ($3.99, limited series)

1-4: 1-Conor Nolan-s/a. 2-Brandon Dayton-s/a. 3-Jared Cullum-s/a. 4-Feifei Ruan-s/a 4.00

STRAIGHT ARROW (Radio)(See Best of the West & Great Western)
Magazine Enterprises: Feb-Mar, 1950 - No. 55, Mar, 1956 (All 36 pgs.)

1-Straight Arrow (alias Steve Adams) & his palomino Fury begin; 1st mention of Sundown Valley & the Secret Cave 47 94 141 296 498 700
2-Red Hawk begins (1st app?) by Powell (origin), ends #55 23 46 69 136 223 310
3-Frazetta-c 34 68 102 199 325 450
4,5: 4-Secret Cave-c 21 42 63 122 199 275
6-10 17 34 51 100 158 215
11-Classic story "The Valley of Time", with an ancient civilization made of gold 22 44 66 128 209 290
12-19 14 28 42 82 121 160
20-Origin Straight Arrow's Shield 16 32 48 92 144 195
21-Origin Fury 19 38 57 109 172 235
22-Frazetta-c 28 56 84 165 270 375
23,25-30: 25-Secret Cave-c. 28-Red Hawk meets The Vikings 11 22 33 62 86 110
24-Classic story "The Dragons of Doom!" with prehistoric pteradactyls 14 28 42 82 121 160
31-38: 36-Red Hawk drug story by Powell 10 20 30 54 72 90
39-Classic story "The Canyon Beast", with a dinosaur egg hatching a Tyranosaurus Rex 14 28 42 76 108 140
40-Classic story "Secret of The Spanish Specters", with Conquistadors' lost treasure 11 22 33 64 90 115
41,42,44-54: 45-Secret Cave-c 9 18 27 50 65 80
43-Intro & 1st app. Blaze, S. Arrow's Warrior dog 10 20 30 58 79 100
55-Last issue 11 22 33 62 86 110

NOTE: ***Fred Meagher*** *a 1-55; c-1, 2, 4-21, 23-55.* ***Powell*** *a 2-55.* ***Whitney*** *a-1. Many issues advertise the radio premiums associated with Straight Arrow.*

Strange (2004 series) #1 © MAR

Strange Adventures #19 © DC

Strange Adventures #231 © DC

GD VG FN VF VF/NM NM-
2.0 4.0 6.0 8.0 9.0 9.2

STRAIGHT ARROW'S FURY (Also see A-1 Comics)
Magazine Enterprises: No. 119, 1954 (one-shot)

A-1 119-Origin; Fred Meagher-c/a 15 30 45 88 137 185

STRAIN, THE (Adaptation of novels by Guillermo del Toro and Chuck Hogan)
Dark Horse Comics: Dec, 2011 - No. 11, Feb, 2013 ($1.00/$3.50)

1-($1.00) Lapham, Hogan & del Toro-s/Huddleston-a/c; variant-c by Morris 3.50
2-11-($3.50) Lapham-s/Huddleston-a/c 3.50

STRAIN, THE: MISTER QUINLAN - VAMPIRE HUNTER
Dark Horse Comics: Sept, 2016 - Present ($3.99)

1-5: 1-Lapham, Hogan & del Toro-s/Salazar-a; origin of Mister Quinlan in ancient Rome 4.00

STRAIN, THE: THE FALL (Guillermo del Toro and Chuck Hogan)
Dark Horse Comics: Jul, 2013 - No. 9, Mar, 2014 ($3.99)

1-9-Lapham, Hogan & del Toro-s/Huddleston-a/Gist-c 4.00

STRAIN, THE: THE NIGHT ETERNAL (Guillermo del Toro and Chuck Hogan)
Dark Horse Comics: Aug, 2014 - No. 12, Aug, 2015 ($3.99)

1-12-Lapham, Hogan & del Toro-s/Huddleston-a/Gist-c 4.00

STRANGE (Tales You'll Never Forget)
Ajax-Farrell Publ. (Four Star Comic Corp.): March, 1957 - No. 6, May, 1958

1 27 54 81 162 266 370
2-Censored r/Haunted Thrills 15 30 45 88 137 185
3-6 14 28 42 78 112 145

STRANGE (Dr. Strange)
Marvel Comics (Marvel Knghts): Nov, 2004 - No. 6, July, 2005 ($3.50)

1-6-Straczynski & Barnes-s/Peterson-a; Dr. Strange's origin retold 3.50
...: Beginnings and Endings TPB (2006, $17.99) r/#1-6 18.00

STRANGE (Dr. Strange)
Marvel Comics: Jan, 2010 - No. 4, Apr, 2010 ($3.99, limited series)

1-4-Waid-s/Rios-a/Coker-c 4.00

STRANGE ADVENTURE MAGAZINE
CJH Publications: Dec, 1936 (10¢)

1-Flash Gordon, The Master of Mars, text stories w/some full pg. panels of art by Fred Meagher (a FN+ copy sold for $1075 in 2012)

STRANGE ADVENTURES
DC Comics: July/Aug 1950

nn - Ashcan comic, not distributed to newsstands, only for in-house use. Cover art is All Star Comics #47 with interior being Detective Comics #140. A second example has the interior of Detective Comics #146. A third example has an unidentified issue of Detective Comics as the interior. This is the only ashcan with multiple interiors. A FN+ copy sold for $1,000 in 2007.

STRANGE ADVENTURES
National Periodical Publ.: Aug-Sept, 1950 - No. 244, Oct-Nov, 1973 (No. 1-12: 52 pgs.)

1-Adaptation of "Destination Moon"; preview of movie w/photo-c from movie (also see Fawcett Movie Comic #2); adapt. of Edmond Hamilton's "Chris KL-99" in #1-3; Darwin Jones begins 179 358 537 1477 3339 5200
2 79 158 237 632 1416 2200
3,4 56 112 168 439 995 1550
5-8,10: 7-Origin Kris KL-99 46 92 138 359 805 1250
9-(6/51)-Origin/1st app. Captain Comet (c/story) 102 204 306 816 2241 2850
11-20: 12,13,17,18-Toth-a. 14-Robot-c 31 62 93 223 504 785
21-30: 28-Atomic explosion panel. 30-Robot-c 29 58 87 209 467 725
31,34-38 27 54 81 194 435 675
32,33-Krigstein-a 29 58 87 196 441 685
39-Ill. in SOTI "Treating police contemptuously" (top right) 32 64 96 230 515 800
40-49-Last Capt. Comet; not in 45,47,48 27 54 81 191 426 660
50-53-Last precode issue (2/55) 23 46 69 161 356 550
54-70 19 38 57 131 291 450
71-79,81-99 15 30 45 103 227 350
80-Grey-tone-c 23 46 69 161 356 550
100 16 32 48 112 249 385
101-110: 104-Space Museum begins by Sekowsky 12 24 36 81 176 270
111-116,118,119: 114-Star Hawkins begins, ends #185; Heath-a in Wood E.C. style 12 24 36 79 170 260
117-(6/60)-Origin/1st app. Atomic Knights. 46 92 138 350 788 1225
120-2nd app. Atomic Knights 21 42 63 147 324 500
121,122,125,127,128,130,131,133,134: 134-Last 10¢ issue 10 20 30 69 147 225
123,126-3rd & 4th app. Atomic Knights 13 26 39 89 195 300
124-Intro/origin Faceless Creature 14 28 42 96 211 325
129,132,135,138,141,147-Atomic Knights app. 11 22 33 76 163 250
136,137,139,140,143,145,146,148,149,151,152,154,155,157-159: 136-Robot cover. 159-Star Rovers app.; Gil Kane/Anderson-a. 9 18 27 59 117 175
142-2nd app. Faceless Creature 10 20 30 64 132 200
144-Only Atomic Knights-c (by M. Anderson) 12 24 36 82 179 275
150,153,156,160: Atomic Knights in each. 150-Greytone-c. 153-(6/63)-3rd app. Faceless Creature; atomic explosion-c. 160-Last Atomic Knights 9 18 27 62 126 190
161-179: 161-Last Space Museum. 163-Star Rovers app. 170-Infinity-c. 177-Intro/origin Immortal Man 7 14 21 46 86 125
180-Origin/1st app. Animal Man 42 84 126 311 706 1100
181-183,185,186,188,189 6 12 18 37 66 95
184-2nd app. Animal Man by Gil Kane 10 20 30 69 147 225
187-Intro/origin The Enchantress 32 64 96 230 515 800
190-1st app. Animal Man in costume 13 26 39 87 191 295
191-194,196-200,202-204 5 10 15 34 60 85
195-1st full app. Animal Man 8 16 24 54 102 150
201-Last Animal Man; 2nd full app. 6 12 18 41 76 110
205-(10/67)-Intro/origin Deadman by Infantino & begin series, ends #216 50 100 150 384 867 1350
206-Neal Adams-a begins 12 24 36 84 185 285
207-210 10 20 30 64 132 200
211-216: 211-Space Museum-r. 216-(1-2/69)-Deadman story finally concludes in Brave & the Bold #86 (10-11/69); secret message panel by Neal Adams (pg. 13); tribute to Steranko 9 18 27 57 111 165
217-r/origin & 1st app. Adam Strange from Showcase #17, begin-r; Atomic Knights-r begin 3 6 9 17 25 34
218-221,223-225: 218-Last 12¢ issue. 225-Last 15¢ issue 3 6 9 14 20 26
222-New Adam Strange story; Kane/Anderson-a 3 6 9 20 31 42
226,227,230-236-(68-52 pgs.): 226, 227-New Adam Strange text story w/illos by Anderson (8,6 pgs.) 231-Last Atomic Knights-r. 235-JLA-c/s 3 6 9 14 20 26
228,229 (68 pgs.) 3 6 9 16 24 32
237-243 2 4 6 10 14 18
244-Last issue 2 4 6 11 16 20

NOTE: ***Neal Adams*** *a-206-216; c-207-218, 228, 235.* ***Anderson*** *a-8-52, 94, 96, 99, 115, 117, 119-163, 217r, 218r, 222, 223-225r, 226, 229r, 242i(r); c-18, 19, 21, 23, 24, 27, 30, 32-44(most); c/r-157i, 190i, 217-224, 228-231, 233, 235-239, 241-243.* ***Ditko*** *a-188, 189.* ***Drucker*** *a-42, 43, 45.* ***Elias*** *a-212.* ***Finlay*** *a-2, 3, 6, 7, 210r, 229r.* ***Giunta*** *a-237r.* ***Heath*** *a-116.* ***Infantino*** *a-10-101, 106-151, 154, 157-163, 180, 190, 218-221r, 223-244p(r); c-50; c(r)-190p, 197, 199-211, 218-221, 223-244.* ***Kaluta*** *c-238, 240.* ***Gil Kane*** *a-8-116, 124, 125, 130, 138, 146-157, 173-186, 204r, 222r, 227-231r; c(p)-11-17, 25, 154, 157.* ***Kubert*** *a-55(2 pgs.), 226; c-219, 220, 225-227, 232, 234.* ***Moreira*** *c-26, 28, 29, 71.* ***Morrow*** *c-230.* ***Mortimer*** *c-8.* ***Powell*** *a-4.* ***Sekowsky*** *a-71p, 97-162p, 217p(r), 218p(r); c-206, 217-219r.* ***Simon & Kirby*** *a-2r (2 pgs)* ***Sparling*** *a-201.* ***Toth*** *a-8, 12, 13, 17-19.* ***Wood*** *a-154i. Atomic Knights in #117, 120, 123, 126, 129, 132, 135, 138, 141, 144, 147, 150, 153, 156, 160. Atomic Knights reprints by* ***Anderson*** *in 217-221, 223-231. Chris KL99 in 1-3, 5, 7, 9, 11, 15. Capt. Comet covers-9-14, 17-19, 24, 26, 27, 32-44.*

STRANGE ADVENTURES
DC Comics (Vertigo): Nov, 1999 - No. 4, Feb, 2000 ($2.50, limited series)

1-4: 1-Bolland-c; art by Bolland, Gibbons, Quitely 3.00

STRANGE ADVENTURES
DC Comics: May, 2009 - No. 8, Dec, 2009 ($3.99, limited series)

1-8: 1-Starlin-s in all; Adam Strange, Capt. Comet, Bizarro & Prince Gavyn app. 4.00
TPB (2010, $19.99) r/#1-8; cover gallery 20.00

STRANGE ADVENTURES
DC Comics (Vertigo): Jul, 2011 ($7.99, one-shot)

1-Short story anthology; s/a by Azzarello, Risso, Milligan and others; Paul Pope-c 8.00

STRANGE AS IT SEEMS (See Famous Funnies-A Carnival of Comics, Feature Funnies #1, The John Hix Scrap Book & Peanuts)

STRANGE AS IT SEEMS
United Features Syndicate: 1939

Single Series 9, 1, 2 36 72 108 211 343 475

STRANGE ATTRACTORS
RetroGraphix: 1993 - No. 15, Feb, 1997 ($2.50, B&W)

1-15: 1-(5/93), 2-(8/93), 3-(11/93), 4-(2/94) 3.00
Volume One-($14.95, trade paperback)-r/#1-7 15.00

STRANGE ATTRACTORS: MOON FEVER
Caliber Comics: Feb, 1997 - No. 3, June, 1997 ($2.95, B&W, mini-series)

1-3 3.00

STRANGE CEREBUS (Reprints from Cerebus in Hell)
Aardvark-Vanaheim: Oct, 2017 ($4.00, B&W)

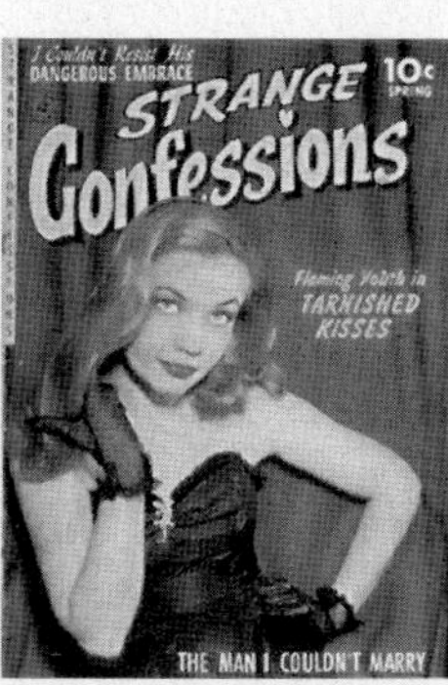

Strange Confessions #1 © Z-D

Strange Fantasy #5 © AJAX

Strangers #8 © MAL

GD VG FN VF VF/NM NM-
2.0 4.0 6.0 8.0 9.0 9.2

GD VG FN VF VF/NM NM-
2.0 4.0 6.0 8.0 9.0 9.2

1-Cerebus figures placed over original Doré artwork of Hell; Dr. Strange #180-c swipe 4.00

STRANGE COMBAT TALES
Marvel Comics (Epic Comics): Oct, 1993 - No. 4, Jan, 1994 ($2.50, limited series)
1-4 3.00

STRANGE CONFESSIONS
Ziff-Davis Publ. Co.: Jan-Mar (Spring on-c), 1952 - No. 4, Fall, 1952 (All have photo-c)
1(Scarce)-Kinstler-a 77 154 231 493 847 1200
2(Scarce, 7-8/52) 50 100 150 315 533 750
3(Scarce, 9-10/52)-#3 on-c, #2 on inside; Reformatory girl story; photo-c
48 96 144 302 514 725
4(Scarce) 47 94 141 296 498 700

STRANGE DAYS
Eclipse Comics: Oct, 1984 - No. 3, Apr, 1985 ($1.75, Baxter paper)
1-3: Freakwave, Johnny Nemo, & Paradax from Vanguard Illustrated; nudity, violence & strong language 4.00

STRANGE DAYS (Movie)
Marvel Comics: Dec, 1995 ($5.95, squarebound, one-shot)
1-Adaptation of film 6.00

STRANGE FANTASY (Eerie Tales of Suspense!)(Formerly Rocketman #1)
Ajax-Farrell: Aug, 1952 - No. 14, Oct-Nov, 1954
2(#1, 8/52)-Jungle Princess story; Kamenish-a; reprinted from Ellery Queen #1
71 142 213 454 777 1100
2(10/52)-No Black Cat or Rulah; Bakerish, Kamenish-a; hypo/meathook-c
61 122 183 390 670 950
3-Rulah story, called Pulah 50 100 150 315 533 750
4-Rocket Man app. (2/53) 45 90 135 284 480 675
5,6,8,10,12,14 40 80 120 246 411 575
7-Madam Satan/Slave story 48 96 144 302 514 725
9(w/Black Cat), 9(w/Boy's Ranch; S&K-a), 9(w/War)(A rebinding of Harvey interiors; not publ. by Ajax) 42 84 126 265 445 625
9-Regular issue; Steve Ditko's 3rd published work (tied with Captain 3D)
77 154 231 493 847 1200
11-Jungle story 45 90 135 284 480 675
13-Bondage-c; Rulah (Kolah) story 45 90 135 284 480 675

STRANGE FRUIT
BOOM! Studios: Jul, 2015 - No. 4 ($3.99, limited series)
1-3-J.G. Jones-a; Jones & Mark Waid-s 4.00

STRANGE GALAXY
Eerie Publications: V1#8, Feb, 1971 - No. 11, Aug, 1971 (B&W, magazine)
V1#8-Reprints-c/Fantastic V19#3 (2/70) (a pulp) 3 6 9 21 33 45
9-11 3 6 9 17 26 35

STRANGE GIRL
Image Comics: June, 2005 - No. 18, Sept, 2007 ($2.95/$2.99/$3.50)
1-12: 1-Rick Remender-s/Eric Nguyen-a 3.50
13-18-($3.50) 3.50
... Vol. 1: Girl Afraid TPB (2005, $12.99) r/#1-4; sketch pages and pin-ups 13.00

STRANGE JOURNEY
America's Best (Steinway Publ.) (Ajax/Farrell): Sept, 1957 - No. 4, Jun, 1958 (Farrell reprints)
1-The Phantom Express 21 42 63 126 206 285
2-4: 2-Flying saucer-c. 3-Titanic-c 15 30 45 90 140 190

STRANGE LOVE (See Fox Giants)

STRANGE MYSTERIES
Superior/Dynamic Publications: Sept, 1951 - No. 21, Jan, 1955
1-Kamenish-a & horror stories begin 81 162 243 518 884 1250
2 47 94 141 296 498 700
3-5 43 86 129 271 461 650
6-8 40 80 120 246 411 575
9-Bondage 3-D effect-c 50 100 150 315 533 750
10-Used in **SOTI**, pg. 181 43 86 129 271 461 650
11-18: 13-Eyeball-c 34 68 102 204 332 460
19-r/Journey Into Fear #1; cover is a splash from one story; Baker-r(2)
36 72 108 211 343 475
20,21-Reprints; 20-r/#1 with new-c (The Devil) 27 54 81 162 266 370

STRANGE MYSTERIES
I. W. Enterprises/Super Comics: 1963 - 1964
I.W. Reprint #9; Rulah-r/Spook #28; Disbrow-a 3 6 9 19 30 40
Super Reprint #10-12,15-17(1963-64): 10,11-r/Strange #2,1. 12-r/Tales of Horror #5 (3/53) less-c. 15-r/Dark Mysteries #23. 16-r/The Dead Who Walk. 17-r/Dark Mysteries #22
3 6 9 19 30 40
Super Reprint #18-r/Witchcraft #1; Kubert-a 3 6 9 19 30 40

STRANGE PLANETS
I. W. Enterprises/Super Comics: 1958; 1963-64
I.W. Reprint #1(nd)-Reprints E. C. Incredible S/F #30 plus-c/Strange Worlds #3
5 10 15 34 60 85
I.W. Reprint #9-Orlando/Wood-r/Strange Worlds #4; cover-r from Flying Saucers #1
6 12 18 41 76 110
Super Reprint #10-Wood-r (22 pg.) from Space Detective #1; cover-r/Attack on Planet Mars
6 12 18 41 76 110
Super Reprint #11-Wood-r (25 pg.) from An Earthman on Venus
7 14 21 46 86 125
Super Reprint #12-Orlando-r/Rocket to the Moon 7 14 21 48 89 130
Super Reprint #15-Reprints Journey Into Unknown Worlds #8; Heath, Colan-r
4 8 12 27 44 60
Super Reprint #16-Reprints Avon's Strange Worlds #6; Kinstler, Check-a
4 8 12 28 47 65
Super Reprint #18-r/Great Exploits #1 (Daring Adventures #6); Space Busters, Explorer Joe, The Son of Robin Hood; Krigstein-a 4 8 12 23 37 50

STRANGERS
Image Comics: Mar, 2003 - No. 6, Sept, 2003 ($2.95)
1-6-Randy & Jean-Marc Lofficier-s; two covers. 2-Nexus back-up story 3.00

STRANGERS, THE
Malibu Comics (Ultraverse): June, 1993 - No. 24, May, 1995 ($1.95/$2.50)
1-4,6-12,14-20: 1-1st app. The Strangers; has coupon for Ultraverse Premiere #0; 1st app. the Night Man (not in costume). 2-Polybagged w/trading card. 7-Break-Thru x-over. 8-2 pg. origin Solution. 12-Silver foil logo; wraparound-c. 17-Rafferty app. 3.00
1-With coupon missing 2.00
1-Full cover holographic edition, 1st of kind w/Hardcase #1 & Prime #1
1 2 3 5 6 8
1-Ultra 5000 limited silver foil 6.00
4-($2.50)-Variant Newsstand edition bagged w/card 4.00
5-($2.50, 52 pgs.)-Rune flip-c/story by B. Smith (3 pgs.); The Mighty Magnor 1 pg. strip by Aragones; 3-pg. Night Man preview 4.00
13-($3.50, 68 pgs.)-Mantra app.; flip book w/Ultraverse Premiere #4 4.00
21-24 ($2.50) 3.00
...:The Pilgrim Conundrum Saga (1/95, $3.95, 68pgs.) 4.00

STRANGERS IN PARADISE (Also see SIP Kids)
Antarctic Press: Nov, 1993 - No. 3, Feb, 1994 ($2.75, B&W, limited series)
1 9 18 27 58 114 170
1-2nd/3rd prints 1 3 4 6 8 10
2 (2300 printed) 4 8 12 28 47 65
3 3 6 9 17 26 35
Trade paperback (Antarctic Press, $6.95)-Red -c (5000 print run) 10.00
Trade paperback (Abstract Studios, $6.95)-Red-c (2000 print run) 15.00
Trade paperback (Abstract Studios, $6.95, 1st-4th printing)-Blue- 7.00
Hardcover ('98, $29.95) includes first draft pages 30.00
Gold Reprint Series ($2.75) 1-3-r/#1-3 3.00

STRANGERS IN PARADISE
Abstract Studios: Sept, 1994 - No. 14, July, 1996 ($2.75, B&W)
1 2 4 6 9 13 16
1,3- 2nd printings 4.00
2,3: 2-Color dream sequence 1 2 3 5 6 8
4-10 4.00
4-6-2nd printings 3.00
11-14: 14-The Letters of Molly & Poo 4.00
Gold Reprint Series ($2.75) 1-13-r/#1-13 3.00
I Dream Of You ($16.95, TPB) r/#1-9 17.00
It's a Good Life ($8.95, TPB) r/#10-13 9.00

STRANGERS IN PARADISE (Volume Three)
Homage Comics #1-8/Abstract Studios #9-on: Oct, 1996 - No. 90, May, 2007 ($2.75-$2.99, color #1-5, B&W #6-on)
1-Terry Moore-c/s/a in all; dream seq. by Jim Lee-a 5.00
1-Jim Lee variant-c 1 2 3 6 7 8
2-5 4.00
6-16: 6-Return to B&W. 13-15-High school flashback. 16-Xena Warrior Princess parody; two covers 3.00
17-89: 33-Color issue. 46-Molly Lane. 49-Molly & Poo. 86-David dies 3.00
90-Last issue; 3 covers of Katchoo, Francine and David forming a triptych 3.00

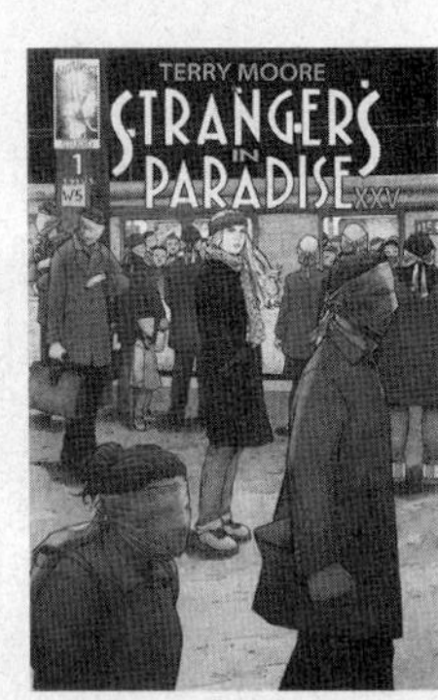

Strangers in Paradise XXV #1 © Terry Moore

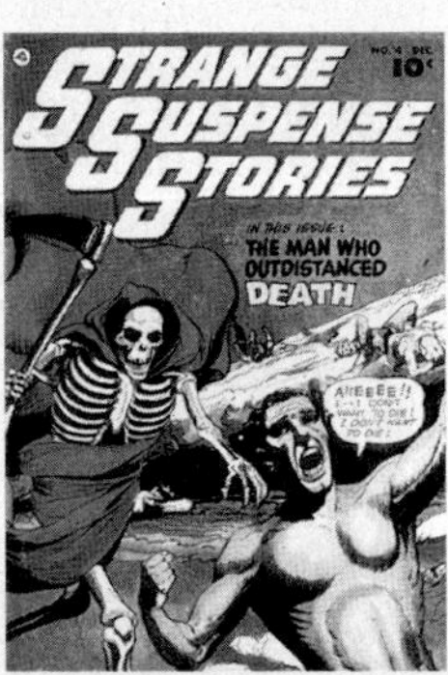

Strange Suspense Stories #4 © FAW

Strange Tales #7 © MAR

GD VG FN VF VF/NM NM-
2.0 4.0 6.0 8.0 9.0 9.2

...Lyrics and Poems (2/99) 3.00
...Source Book (2003, $2.95) Background on characters & story arcs, checklists 3.00
Brave New World ('02, $8.95, TPB) r/#44,45,47,48 9.00
Child of Rage ($15.95, TPB) r/#31-38 16.00
David's Story (6/04, $8.95, TPB) r/#61-63 9.00
Ever After ('07, $15.95, TPB) r/#83-90 16.00
Flower to Flame ('03, $15.95, TPB) r/#55-60 16.00
Heart in Hand ('03, $12.95, TPB) r/#50-54 13.00
High School ('98, $8.95, TPB) r/#13-16 9.00
Immortal Enemies ('98, $14.95, TPB) r/#6-12 15.00
Love & Lies (2006, $14.95, TPB)r/#77-82 15.00
Love Me Tender ($12.95, TPB) r/#1-5 in B&W w/ color Lee seq. 13.00
Molly & Poo (2005, $8.95, TPB)r/#46,49,73 9.00
My Other Life ($14.95, TPB) r/#25-30 15.00
Pocket Book 1-5 ($17.95, 5 1/2" x 8", TPB) 1-r/Vol.1 & 2. 2-r/#1-17 in B&W. 3-r/#18-24,26-32,34-38. 4-r/#41-45,47,48,50-60. 5-r/#46,49,61-76 18.00
Sanctuary ($15.95, TPB) r/#17-24 16.00
Tattoo ($14.95, TPB) r/#70-76; sketch pages and fan tattoo photos 15.00
Tomorrow Now (11/04, $14.95, TPB) r/#64-69 15.00
Tropic of Desire ($12.95, TPB) r/#39-43 13.00
The Complete... : Volume 3 Part 1 HC ($49.95) r/#1-12 50.00
The Complete... : Volume 3 Part 2 HC ($49.95) r/#13-15,17-25 50.00
The Complete... : Volume 3 Part 3 HC ('01, $49.95) r/#26-38 50.00
The Complete... : Volume 3 Part 4 HC ('02, $39.95) r/#39-46,49 40.00
The Complete... : Volume 3 Part 5 HC ('03, $49.95) r/#47,48,50-57 50.00
The Complete... : Volume 3 Part 6 HC ('04, $49.95) r/#58-69 50.00
The Complete... : Volume 3 Part 7 HC ('06, $49.95) r/#70-80 50.00

STRANGERS IN PARADISE XXV
Abstract Studio: 2018 - Present ($3.99, B&W)

1,2-Terry Moore-c/s/a 4.00

STRANGE SPORTS STORIES (See Brave & the Bold #45-49, DC Special, and DC Super Stars #10)
National Periodical Publications: Sept-Oct, 1973 - No. 6, July-Aug, 1974

1-Devil-c 3 6 9 16 23 30
2-6: 2-Swan/Anderson-a 2 4 6 9 13 16

STRANGE SPORTS STORIES
DC Comics (Vertigo): May, 2015 - No. 4, Aug, 2015 ($4.99, limited series)

1-4-Anthology of short stories by various. 1-Paul Pope-c. 4-Pope-s/a 5.00

STRANGE STORIES FROM ANOTHER WORLD (Unknown World #1)
Fawcett Publications: No. 2, Aug, 1952 - No. 5, Feb, 1953

2-Saunders painted-c 50 100 150 315 533 750
3-5-Saunders painted-c 41 82 123 250 418 585

STRANGE STORIES OF SUSPENSE (Rugged Action #1-4)
Atlas Comics (CSI): No. 5, Oct, 1955 - No. 16, Aug, 1957

5(#1) 52 104 156 328 552 775
6,7,9 36 72 108 211 343 475
8-Morrow/Williamson-a; Pakula-a 37 74 111 222 361 500
10-Crandall, Torres, Meskin-a 35 70 105 208 339 470
11-13: 12-Torres, Pakula-a. 13-E.C. art swipes 31 62 93 184 300 415
14-16: 14-Williamson/Mayo-a. 15-Krigstein-a. 16-Fox, Powell-a
32 64 96 192 314 435

NOTE: ***Everett*** *a-6, 7, 13; c-8, 9, 11-14.* ***Forte*** *a-12, 16.* ***Heath*** *a-5.* ***Maneely*** *c-5.* ***Morisi*** *a-11.* ***Morrow*** *a-13.* ***Powell*** *a-8.* ***Sale*** *a-11.* ***Severin*** *c-7.* ***Wildey*** *a-14.*

STRANGE STORY (Also see Front Page)
Harvey Publications: June-July, 1946 (52 pgs.)

1-The Man in Black Called Fate by Powell 40 80 120 246 411 575

STRANGE SUSPENSE STORIES (Lawbreakers Suspense Stories #10-15; This Is Suspense #23-26; Captain Atom V1#78 on)
Fawcett Publications/Charlton Comics No. 16 on: 6/52 - No. 5, 2/53; No. 16, 1/54 - No. 22, 11/54; No. 27, 10/55 - No. 77, 10/65; V3#1, 10/67 - V1#9, 9/69

1-(Fawcett)-Powell, Sekowsky-a 90 180 270 576 988 1400
2-George Evans horror story 50 100 150 315 533 750
3-5 (2/53)-George Evans horror stories 41 82 123 256 428 600
16(1-2/54)-Formerly Lawbreakers S.S. 34 68 102 199 325 450
17 27 54 81 158 259 360
18-E.C. swipe/HOF 7; Ditko-c/a(2) 50 100 150 315 533 750
19-Ditko electric chair-c; Ditko-a 81 162 243 518 884 1250
20-Ditko-c/a(2) 42 84 126 265 445 625
21-Shuster-a; a woman dangling over an alligator pit while a madman smashes her fingers with a hammer 41 82 123 256 428 600

GD VG FN VF VF/NM NM-
2.0 4.0 6.0 8.0 9.0 9.2

22(11/54)-Ditko-c, Shuster-a; last pre-code issue; becomes This Is Suspense
39 78 117 240 395 550
27(10/55)-(Formerly This Is Suspense #26) 16 32 48 92 144 195
28-30,38 13 26 39 72 101 130
31-33,35,37,40-Ditko-c/a(2-3 each) 21 42 63 126 206 285
34-Story of ruthless business man, Wm. B. Gaines; Ditko-c/a
47 94 141 296 498 700
36-(15¢, 68 pgs.); Ditko-a(4) 26 52 78 154 252 350
39,41,52,53-Ditko-a 19 38 57 111 176 240
42-44,46,49,54-60 5 10 15 34 60 85
45,47,48,50,51-Ditko-c/a 12 24 36 80 173 265
61-74: 72-Has panel which inspired a famous Roy Lichtenstein painting
4 8 12 28 47 65
75(6/65)-Reprints origin/1st app. Captain Atom by Ditko from Space Advs. #33; r/Severin-a/Space Advs. #24 (75-77: 12¢ issues) 10 20 30 66 138 210
76,77-Captain Atom-r by Ditko/Space Advs. 6 12 18 37 66 95
V3#1(10/67): 12¢ issues begin 3 6 9 19 30 40
V1#2-Ditko-c/a; atom bomb-c 3 6 9 19 30 40
V1#3-9: 3-8-All 12¢ issues. 9-15¢ issue 2 4 6 13 18 22

NOTE: ***Alascia*** *a-19.* ***Aparo*** *a-60, V3#1, 2, 4; c-V1#4, 8, 9.* ***Baily*** *a-1-3; c-2, 5.* ***Evans*** *c-3, 4.* ***Giordano*** *c-16, 17p, 24p, 25p.* ***Montes/Bache*** *c-66.* ***Powell*** *a-4.* ***Shuster*** *a-19, 21.* ***Marcus Swayze*** *a-27.*

STRANGE TALENT OF LUTHER STRODE, THE (Also see The Legend of Luther Strode)
Image Comics: Oct, 2011 - No. 6, Mar, 2012 ($2.99, limited series)

1-6: Justin Jordan-s/Tradd Moore-a 3.00

STRANGE TALES (...Featuring Warlock #178-181; Doctor Strange #169 on)
Atlas (CCPC #1-67/ZPC #68-79/VPI #80-85)/Marvel #86(7/61) on:
June, 1951 - No. 168, May, 1968; No. 169, Sept, 1973 - No. 188, Nov, 1976

1-Horror/weird stories begin 649 1298 1947 4738 8369 12,000
2 200 400 600 1280 2190 3100
3,5: 3-Atom bomb panels 152 304 456 965 1658 2350
4-Cosmic eyeball story "The Evil Eye" 158 316 474 1003 1727 2450
6-9: 6-Heath-c/a. 7-Colan-a 126 252 378 806 1378 1950
10-Krigstein-a 127 254 381 807 1391 1975
11-14,16-20 100 200 300 635 1093 1550
15-Krigstein-a; detached head-c 103 206 309 659 1130 1600
21,23-27,29-34: 27-Atom bomb panels. 33-Davis-a. 34-Last pre-code issue (2/55)
86 172 258 546 936 1325
22-Krigstein, Forte/Fox-a 90 180 270 576 988 1400
28-Jack Katz story used in Senate Investigation report, pgs. 7 & 169; classic skull-c
300 600 900 2010 3505 5000
35-41,43,44: 37-Vampire story by Colan 46 92 138 340 770 1200
42,45,59,61-Krigstein-a; #61 (2/58) 46 92 138 350 788 1225
46-57,60: 51-(10/56) 1st S.A. issue. 53,56-Crandall-a. 60-(8/57)
41 82 123 303 689 1075
58,64-Williamson-a in each, with Mayo-#58 42 84 126 311 706 1100
62,63,65,66: 62-Torres-a. 66-Crandall-a 41 82 123 303 689 1075
67-Prototype ish. (Quicksilver) 46 92 138 359 805 1250
68,71,72,74,77,80: Ditko/Kirby-a in #67-80 41 82 123 303 689 1075
69,70,73,75,76,78,79: 69-Prototype ish. (Prof. X). 70-Prototype ish. (Giant Man). 73-Prototype ish. (Ant-Man). 75-Prototype ish. (Iron Man). 76-Prototype ish. (Human Torch). 78-Prototype ish. (Ant-Man). 79-Prototype ish. (Dr. Strange) (12/60)
46 92 138 350 788 1225
81-83,85-88,90,91-Ditko/Kirby-a in all: 86-Robot-c. 90-(11/61)-Atom bomb blast panel
38 76 114 285 641 1000
84-Prototype ish. (Magneto)(5/61); has powers like Magneto of X-Men, but two years earlier; Ditko/Kirby-a 46 92 138 368 834 1300
89-1st app. Fin Fang Foom (10/61) by Kirby 276 552 828 2277 5139 8000
92-Prototype ish. (Ancient One & Ant-Man); last 10¢ issue
40 80 120 296 673 1050
93,95,96,98-100: Kirby-a 34 68 102 245 548 850
94-Creature similar to The Thing; Kirby-a 40 80 120 296 673 1050
97-1st app. of an Aunt May & Uncle Ben by Ditko (6/62), before Amazing Fantasy #15; (see Tales Of Suspense #7); Kirby-a 118 236 354 944 2122 3300
101-Human Torch begins by Kirby (10/62); origin recap Fantastic Four & Human Torch; Human Torch-c begin 166 332 498 1370 3085 4800
102-1st app. Wizard; robot-c 45 90 135 333 754 1175
103-105: 104-1st app. Trapster. 105-2nd Wizard 39 78 117 289 657 1025
106,108,109: 106-Fantastic Four guests (3/63) 32 64 96 230 515 800
107-(4/63)-Human Torch/Sub-Mariner battle; 4th S.A. Sub-Mariner app. & 1st x-over outside of Fantastic Four 53 106 159 416 933 1450
110-(7/63)-Intro Doctor Strange, Ancient One & Wong by Ditko
600 1200 2400 5600 12,300 19,000
111-2nd Dr. Strange; intro. Baron Mordo 61 122 183 488 1094 1700

Strange Tales #146 © MAR

Strange Tales II #2 © MAR

Strange Tales: Dark Corners #1 © MAR

	GD 2.0	VG 4.0	FN 6.0	VF 8.0	VF/NM 9.0	NM- 9.2

112-1st Eel 27 54 81 189 420 650
113-Origin/1st app. Plantman 26 52 78 182 404 625
114-Acrobat disguised as Captain America, 1st app. since the G.A.; intro. & 1st app. Victoria Bentley; 3rd Dr. Strange app. & begin series (11/63) 46 92 138 368 834 1300
115-Origin Dr. Strange; Human Torch vs. Sandman (Spidey villain; 2nd app. & brief origin); early Spider-Man x-over, 12/63 86 172 258 688 1544 2400
116-(1/64)-Human Torch battles The Thing; 1st Thing x-over 22 44 66 154 340 525
117,118,120: 118-1st cover app. of Dr. Strange. 120-1st Iceman x-over (from X-Men) 15 30 45 105 233 360
119-Spider-Man x-over (2 panel cameo) 17 34 51 119 265 410
121,122,124,127-134: Thing/Torch team-up in 121-134. 128-Quicksilver & Scarlet Witch app. (1/65). 130-The Beatles cameo. 134-Last Human Torch; The Watcher-c/story; Wood-a(i) 12 24 36 82 179 275
123-1st app. The Beetle (see Amazing Spider-Man #21 for next app.); 1st Thor x-over (8/64); Loki app. 15 30 45 100 220 340
125-Torch & Thing battle Sub-Mariner (10/64) 16 32 48 107 236 365
126-Intro Clea and Dormammu (cont'd in #127) 43 86 129 318 722 1125
135-Col. (formerly Sgt.) Nick Fury becomes Nick Fury Agent of Shield (origin/1st app.) by Kirby (8/65); series begins 38 76 114 281 628 975
136-140: 138-Intro Eternity 8 16 24 51 96 140
141-147,149: 145-Begins alternating-c features w/Nick Fury (odd #'s) & Dr. Strange (even #'s). 146-Last Ditko Dr. Strange who is in consecutive stories since #113; only full Ditko Dr. Strange-c this title. 147-Dr. Strange (by Everett #147-152) continues thru #168, then Dr. Strange #169 6 12 18 40 73 105
148-Origin Ancient One 8 16 24 51 96 140
150(11/66)-John Buscema's 1st work at Marvel 7 14 21 44 82 120
151-Kirby/Steranko-c/a; 1st Marvel work by Steranko 9 18 27 59 117 175
152,153-Kirby/Steranko-a 7 14 21 44 82 120
154-158-Steranko-a/script 7 14 21 44 82 120
159-Origin Nick Fury retold; Intro Val; Captain America-c/story; Steranko-a 9 18 27 60 120 180
160-162-Steranko-a/scripts; Capt. America app. 7 14 21 44 82 120
163-166,168-Steranko-a(p). 168-Last Nick Fury (gets own book next month) & last Dr. Strange who also gets own book 6 12 18 42 79 115
167-Steranko pen/script; classic flag-c 9 18 27 59 117 175
169-1st app. Brother Voodoo(origin in #169,170) & begin series, ends #173 13 26 39 91 201 310
170-174: 174-Origin Golem 3 6 9 16 23 30
175-177: 177-Brunner-c 3 6 9 14 20 25
178-(2/75)-Warlock by Starlin begins; origin Warlock & Him retold; 1st app. Magus; Starlin-c/a/scripts in #178-181 (all before Warlock #9) 8 16 24 55 105 155
179-Intro/1st app. Pip the Troll; Warlock app. 5 10 15 34 60 85
180-(6/75) Intro. Gamora (Guardians of the Galaxy) (5 panels); Warlock by Starlin 9 18 27 63 129 195
181-(8/75)-Warlock story continued in Warlock #9; 1st full app. of Gamora 4 8 12 28 47 65
182-188: 185,186-(Regular 25¢ editions) 2 4 6 8 10 12
185,186-(30¢-c variants, limited distribution)(5,7/76) 4 8 12 25 40 55
Annual 1(1962)-Reprints from Strange Tales #73,76,78, Tales of Suspense #7,9, Tales to Astonish #1,6,7, & Journey Into Mystery #53,55,59; (1st Marvel annual) 66 132 198 528 1189 1850
Annual 2(7/63)-Reprints from Strange Tales #67, Strange Worlds (Atlas) #1-3, World of Fantasy #16; new Human Torch vs. Spider-Man story by Kirby/Ditko (1st Spidey x-over; 4th app.); Kirby-c 100 200 300 800 1800 2800

NOTE: **Briefer** *a-17.* **Burgos** *a-123p.* **J. Buscema** *a-174p.* **Colan** *a-7, 11, 20, 37, 53, 169-173p, 188p.* **Davis** *c-71.* **Ditko** *a-46, 50, 67-122, 123-125p, 126-146, 175r, 182-188r; c-51, 93, 115, 121, 146.* **Everett** *a-4, 21, 40-42, 73, 147-152, 164i; c-8, 10, 11, 13, 15, 24, 45, 49-54, 56, 58, 60, 61, 63, 148, 150, 152, 158i.* **Forte** *a-27, 43, 50, 53, 54, 60.* **Heath** *a-2, 6; c-6, 18-20.* **Kamen** *a-45.* **G. Kane** *c-170-173, 182p.* **Kirby** *Human Torch-101-105, 108, 109, 114, 120; Nick Fury-135p, 141-143p; (Layouts)-135-153; other* **Kirby** *a-67-100p; c-68-70, 72-74, 76-92, 94, 95, 101-114, 116-123, 125-130, 132-135, 136p, 138-145, 147, 149, 151p.* **Kirby/Ayers** *c-101-106, 108-110.* **Kirby/Ditko** *a-80, 88, 121; c-75, 93, 97, 100, 139.* **Lawrence** *a-29.* **Leiber/ Fox** *a-110-113.* **Maneely** *a-3, 7, 37, 42; c-33, 40.* **Moldoff** *a-20.* **Mooney** *a-174i.* **Morisi** *a-53, 56.* **Morrow** *a-54.* **Orlando** *a-41, 44, 46, 49, 52.* **Powell** *a-42, 44, 49, 54, 130-134p; c-131p.* **Reinman** *a-11, 50, 74, 88, 91, 95, 104, 106, 112i, 124-127i.* **Robinson** *a-17.* **Romita** *c-169.* **Roussos** *c-201i.* **R.Q. Sale** *a-56; c-16.* **Sekowski** *a-3, 11.* **Severin** *a(i)-136-138; c-137.* **Starlin** *a-178, 179, 180p, 181p; c-178-180, 181p.* **Steranko** *a-151-161, 162-168p; c-151i, 153, 155, 157, 159, 161, 163, 165, 167.* **Torres** *a-53, 62.* **Tuska** *a-14, 166p.* **Whitney** *a-149.* **Wildey** *a-42, 56.* **Woodbridge** *a-59. Fantastic Four cameos #101-134. Jack Katz app.-26.*

STRANGE TALES
Marvel Comics Group: Apr, 1987 - No. 19, Oct, 1988

V2#1-19 4.00

STRANGE TALES
Marvel Comics: Nov, 1994 ($6.95, one-shot)

	GD 2.0	VG 4.0	FN 6.0	VF 8.0	VF/NM 9.0	NM- 9.2

V3#1-acetate-c 1 2 3 5 6 8

STRANGE TALES (Anthology; continues stories from Man-Thing #8 and Werewolf By Night #6)
Marvel Comics: Sept, 1998 - No. 2, Oct, 1998 ($4.99)

1,2: 1-Silver Surfer app. 2-Two covers 5.00

STRANGE TALES (Humor anthology)
Marvel Comics: Nov, 2009 - No. 3, Jan, 2010 ($4.99, limited series)

1-3: 1-Paul Pope, Kochalka, Bagge and others-s/a. 2-Bagge-c/a. 3-Sakai-c/a 5.00

STRANGE TALES II (Humor anthology)
Marvel Comics: Dec, 2010 - No. 3, Feb, 2011 ($4.99, limited series)

1-3: 2-Jaime Hernandez-c. 3-Terry Moore-s/a; Pekar-s/Templeton-a 5.00

STRANGE TALES: DARK CORNERS
Marvel Comics: May, 1998 ($3.99, one-shot)

1-Anthology; stories by Baron & Maleev, McGregor & Dringenberg, DeMatteis & Badger; Estes painted-c 4.00

STRANGE TALES OF THE UNUSUAL
Atlas Comics (ACI No. 1-4/WPI No. 5-11): Dec, 1955 - No. 11, Aug, 1957

1-Powell-a 55 110 165 352 601 850
2 36 72 108 211 343 475
3-Williamson-a (4 pgs.) 37 74 111 222 361 500
4,6,8,11: 4-UFO-c 28 56 84 165 270 375
5-Crandall, Ditko-a 33 66 99 194 317 440
7,9: 7-Kirby, Orlando-a. 9-Krigstein-a 31 62 93 182 296 410
10-Torres, Morrow-a 28 56 84 165 270 375

NOTE: **Baily** *a-6.* **Brodsky** *c-2-4.* **Everett** *a-2, 6; c-6, 9, 11.* **Heck** *a-1.* **Maneely** *c-1.* **Orlando** *a-7.* **Pakula** *a-10.* **Romita** *a-1.* **R.Q. Sale** *a-3.* **Wildey** *a-3.*

STRANGE TERRORS
St. John Publishing Co.: June, 1952 - No. 7, Mar, 1953

1-Bondage-c; Zombies spelled Zoombies on-c; Fine-*esque* -a 81 162 243 518 884 1250
2 40 80 120 246 411 575
3-Kubert-a; painted-c 48 96 144 302 514 725
4-Kubert-a (reprinted in Mystery Tales #18); Ekgren painted-c; Fine-*esque* -a; Jerry Iger caricature 81 162 243 518 884 1250
5-Kubert-a; painted-c 48 96 144 302 514 725
6-Giant (25¢, 100 pgs.)(1/53); Tyler classic bondage/skull-c 71 142 213 454 777 1100
7-Giant (25¢, 100 pgs.); Kubert-c/a 65 130 195 416 708 1000

NOTE: **Cameron** *a-6, 7.* **Morisi** *a-6.*

STRANGE WORLD OF YOUR DREAMS
Prize Publications: Aug, 1952 - No. 4, Jan-Feb, 1953

1-Simon & Kirby-a 71 142 213 454 777 1100
2,3-Simon & Kirby-c/a. 2-Meskin-a 53 106 159 334 567 800
4-S&K-c; Meskin-a 43 86 129 271 461 650

STRANGE WORLDS (#18 continued from Avon's Eerie #1-17)
Avon Periodicals: 11/50 - No. 9, 11/52; No. 18, 10-11/54 - No. 22, 9-10/55 (No #11-17)

1-Kenton of the Star Patrol by Kubert (r/Eerie #1 from 1947); Crom the Barbarian by John Giunta 165 330 495 1048 1799 2550
2-Wood-a; Crom the Barbarian by Giunta; Dara of the Vikings app.; used in **SOTI**, pg. 112; injury to eye panel 148 296 444 947 1624 2300
3-Wood/Orlando-a (Kenton), Wood/Williamson/Frazetta/Krenkel/Orlando-a (7 pgs.); Malu Slave Girl Princess app.; Kinstler-c 258 516 774 1651 2826 4000
4-Wood-c/a (Kenton); Orlando-a; origin The Enchanted Daggar; Sultan-a; classic cover 206 412 618 1318 2259 3200
5-Orlando/Wood-a (Kenton); Wood-c 116 232 348 742 1271 1800
6-Kinstler-a(2); Orlando/Wood-c; Check-a 63 126 189 403 689 975
7-Fawcette & Becker/Alascia-a 58 116 174 371 636 900
8-Kubert, Kinstler, Hollingsworth & Lazarus-a; Lazarus Robot-c 55 110 165 352 601 850
9-Kinstler, Fawcette, Alascia, Kubert-a 52 104 156 328 552 775
18-(Formerly Eerie #17)-Reprints "Attack on Planet Mars" by Kubert 39 78 117 231 378 525
19-r/Avon's "Robotmen of the Lost Planet"; last pre-code issue; Robot-c 39 78 117 231 378 525
20-War-c/story; Wood-c(r)/U.S. Paratroops #1 13 26 39 72 101 130
21,22-War-c/stories. 22-New logo 11 22 33 62 86 110
I.W. Reprint #5-Kinstler-a(r)/Avon's #9 4 8 12 24 37 50

STRANGE WORLDS
Marvel Comics (MPI No. 1,2/Male No. 3,5): Dec, 1958 - No. 5, Aug, 1959

Strange Worlds #1 © MAR

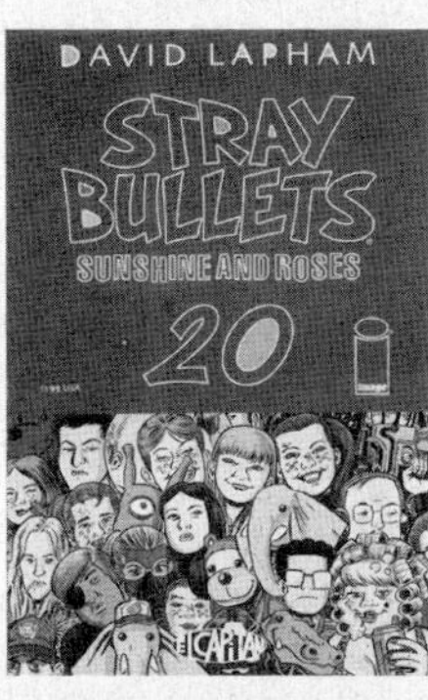

Stray Bullets: Sunshine and Roses #20 © David Lapham

Strayer #1 © Justin Jordan

	GD 2.0	VG 4.0	FN 6.0	VF 8.0	VF/NM 9.0	NM- 9.2
1-Kirby & Ditko-a; flying saucer issue	118	236	354	749	1287	1825
2-Ditko-c/a	63	126	189	403	689	975
3-Kirby-a(2)	57	114	171	362	619	875
4-Williamson-a	52	104	156	328	552	775
5-Ditko-a	48	96	144	302	514	725

NOTE: ***Buscema** a-3, 4. **Ditko** a-1-5; c-2.. **Heck** a-2. **Kirby** a-1, 3. **Kirby/Brodsky** c-1, 3-5.*

STRAWBERRY SHORTCAKE
Marvel Comics (Star Comics): Jun, 1985 - No. 6, Feb, 1986 (Children's comic)
1-6: Howie Post-a 2 4 6 8 10 12

STRAWBERRY SHORTCAKE
Ape Entertainment: 2011 - No. 4, 2011 ($3.95, limited series)
1-4: 1-Scratch 'n' sniff cover 4.00
Volume 2 (2012, $3.99) 1,2 4.00

STRAWBERRY SHORTCAKE
IDW Publishing: Apr, 2016 - No. 8, Nov, 2016 ($3.99)
1-8: Multiple covers on each. 1-Georgia Ball-s/Amy Mebberson-a 4.00
... Funko Universe One-Shot (5/17, $4.99) Ball-s; art in Funko Pop! style 5.00

STRAY
DC Comics (Homage Comics): 2001 ($5.95, prestige format, one-shot)
1-Pollina-c/a; Lobdell & Palmiotti-s 6.00

STRAY
Dark Horse Comics: 2004 (8 1/2"x 5 1/2", Diamond Comic Dist. Halloween giveaway)
nn-Reprint from The Dark Horse Book of Hauntings; Evan Dorkin-s/Jill Thompson-a 3.00

STRAY BULLETS
El Capitan Books/Image Comics: 1995 - No. 41, Mar, 2014 ($2.95/$3.50, B&W, mature)
1-David Lapham-c/a/scripts 2 4 6 10 14 18
2,3 6.00
4-8 4.00
9-21,31,32-($2.95) 3.50
22-30,33-41-($3.50) 22-Includes preview to Murder Me Dead. 40-(10/05). 41-(3/14) 3.50
Free Comic Book Day giveaway (5/02) Reprints #2 with "Free Comic Book Day" banner on-c; flip book with The Matrix (printing of internet comic) 3.00
Innocence of Nihilism Volume 1 HC ($29.95, hardcover) r/#1-7 30.00
Somewhere Out West Volume 2 HC ($34.95, hardcover) r/#8-14 35.00
Other People Volume 3 HC ($34.95, hardcover) r/#15-22 35.00
Volume 1-3 TPB ($11.95, softcover) 1-r/#1-4. 2-r/#5-8. 3-r/ #9-12 12.00
Volume 4-7 TPB ($14.95) 4- r/#13-16. 5- r/#17-20. 6- r/#21-24. 7-r/#25-28 15.00
NOTE: *Multiple printings of most issues exist & are worth cover price.*

STRAY BULLETS: KILLERS
Image Comics (El Capitan Books): Mar, 2014 - No. 8, Oct, 2014 ($3.50, B&W)
1-8-David Lapham-c/a/scripts; set in 1978 3.50

STRAY BULLETS: SUNSHINE AND ROSES
Image Comics (El Capitan Books): Feb, 2015 - Present ($3.50/$3.99, B&W)
1-10-David Lapham-c/a/scripts; set in 1979 Baltimore 3.50
11-32-($3.99) 20-Amy Racecar app. 4.00

STRAYER
AfterShock Comics: Jan, 2016 - Present ($3.99)
1-5-Justin Jordan-s/Juan Gedeon-a 4.00

STRAY TOASTERS
Marvel Comics (Epic Comics): Jan, 1988 - No. 4, April, 1989 ($3.50, squarebound, limited series)
1-4: Sienkiewicz-c/a/scripts 4.00

STREET COMIX
Street Enterprises/King Features: 1973 (50¢, B&W, 36 pgs.)(20,000 print run)
1-Rip Kirby 2 4 6 8 11 14
2-Flash Gordon 2 4 6 10 14 18

STREETFIGHTER
Ocean Comics: Aug, 1986 - No. 4, Spr, 1987 ($1.75, limited series)
1-4: 2-Origin begins 3.00

STREET FIGHTER
Malibu Comics: Sept, 1993 - No. 3, Nov, 1993 ($2.95)
1-3: 3-Includes poster; Ferret x-over 3.00

STREET FIGHTER
Image Comics: Sept, 2003 - No. 14, Feb, 2005 ($2.95)
1-Back-up story w/Madureira-a; covers by Madureira and Tsang 3.00
2-6,8-14: 2-Two covers by Campbell and Warren; back-up story w/Warren-a 3.00
7-($4.50) Larocca-c 4.50
... Vol. 1 (3/04, $9.99, digest-size) r/main stories from #1-6 10.00

STREET FIGHTER: THE BATTLE FOR SHADALOO
DC Comics/CAP Co. Ltd.: 1995 ($3.95, one-shot)
1-Polybagged w/trading card & Tattoo 4.00

STREET FIGHTER II
Tokuma Comics (Viz): Apr, 1994 - No. 8, Nov, 1994 ($2.95, limited series)
1-8 3.00

STREET FIGHTER II
UDON Comics: No. 0, Oct, 2005 - No. 6, Nov, 2006 ($1.99/$3.95/$2.95)
0-(10/05, $1.99) prelude to series; Alvin Lee-a 3.00
1-($3.95) Two covers by Alvin Lee & Ed McGuinness 4.00
2-6-($2.95) 3.00
... Legends 1 (8/06, $3.95) Spotlight on Sakura; two covers 4.00

STREET FIGHTER X G.I. JOE
IDW Publishing: Feb, 2016 - No. 6, Jul, 2016 ($4.99)
1-Sitterson-s/Laiso-a; multiple covers; Destro, Snake Eyes, Baroness, Ryu app. 5.00
2-6-($3.99) Multiple covers on each 4.00

STREET SHARKS
Archie Publications: Jan, 1996 - No. 3, Mar, 1996 ($1.50, limited series)
1-3 3.00

STREET SHARKS
Archie Publications: May, 1996 - No. 6 ($1.50)
1-6 3.00

STRETCH ARMSTRONG AND THE FLEX FIGHTERS (Based on the Netfix animated series)
IDW Publishing: Jan, 2018 - Present ($3.99)
1,2-Burke & Wyatt-s/Koutsis-a; 3 covers 4.00

STRICTLY PRIVATE (You're in the Army Now)
Eastern Color Printing Co.: July, 1942 (#1 on sale 6/15/42)
1,2: Private Peter Plink. 2-Says 128 pgs. on-c 34 68 102 199 325 450

STRIKE!
Eclipse Comics: Aug, 1987 - No. 6, Jan, 1988 ($1.75)
1-6, ...Vs. Sgt. Strike Special 1 (5/88, $1.95) 3.00

STRIKEBACK! (The Hunt For Nikita)
Malibu Comics (Bravura): Oct, 1994 - No. 3, Jan, 1995 ($2.95, unfinished limited series)
1-3: Jonathon Peterson script, Kevin Maguire-c/a 3.00
1-Gold foil embossed-c 5.00

STRIKEBACK!
Image Comics (WildStorm Productions): Jan, 1996 - No. 5, May, 1996 ($2.50, lim. series)
1-5: Reprints original Bravura series w/additional story & art by Kevin Maguire & Jonathon Peterson; new Maguire-c in all. 4,5-New story & art 3.00

STRIKEFORCE: AMERICA
Comico: Dec, 1995 ($2.95)
V2#1-Polybagged w/gaming card; S. Clark-a(p) 3.00

STRIKEFORCE: MORITURI
Marvel Comics Group: Dec, 1986 - No. 31, July, 1989
1,13: 13-Double size 4.00
2-12,14-31: 14-Williamson-i. 25-Heath-c 3.00
... – We Who Are About To Die 1 (3/12, $0.99) r/#1 with profile pages and cover gallery 3.00

STRIKEFORCE MORITURI: ELECTRIC UNDERTOW
Marvel Comics: Dec, 1989 - No. 5, Mar, 1990 ($3.95, 52 pgs., limited series)
1-5 Squarebound 4.00

STRONG GUY REBORN (See X-Factor)
Marvel Comics: Sept, 1997 ($2.99, one-shot)
1-Dezago-s/Andy Smith, Art Thibert-a 3.00

STRONG MAN (Also see Complimentary Comics & Power of...)
Magazine Enterprises: Mar-Apr, 1955 - No. 4, Sept-Oct, 1955
1(A-1 #130)-Powell-c/a 23 46 69 136 223 310
2-4: (A-1 #132,134,139)-Powell-a. 2-Powell-c 18 36 54 105 165 225

STRONTIUM DOG
Eagle Comics: Dec, 1985 - No. 4, Mar, 1986 ($1.25, limited series)
1-4, Special 1: 4-Moore script. Special 1 (1986)-Moore script 4.00

Stupid Comics #2 © Jim Mahfood

Sub-Mariner #6 © MAR

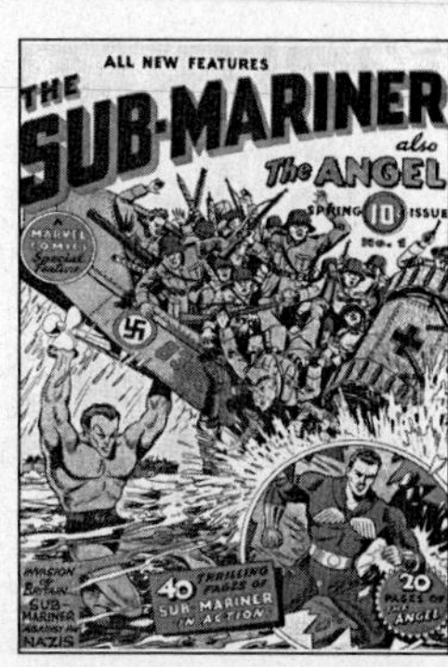

Sub-Mariner Comics #1 © MAR

	GD	VG	FN	VF	VF/NM	NM-
	2.0	4.0	6.0	8.0	9.0	9.2

STRYFE'S STRIKE FILE
Marvel Comics: Jan, 1993 ($1.75, one-shot, no ads)

1-Stroman, Capullo, Andy Kubert, Brandon Peterson-a; silver metallic ink-c; X-Men tie-in to X-Cutioner's Song 4.00
1-Gold metallic ink 2nd printing 3.00

STRYKEFORCE
Image Comics (Top Cow): May, 2004 - No. 5, Oct, 2004 ($2.99)

1-5-Faerber-s/Kirkham-a. 4,5-Preview of HumanKind 3.00
Vol. 1 TPB (2005, $16.99) r/#1-5 & Codename: Strykeforce #0-3; sketch pages 17.00

STUMBO THE GIANT (See Harvey Hits #49,54,57,60,63,66,69,72,78,88 & Hot Stuff #2)

STUMBO TINYTOWN
Harvey Publications: Oct, 1963 - No. 13, Nov, 1966 (All 25¢ giants)

1-Stumbo, Hot Stuff & others begin 13 26 39 89 195 300
2 8 16 24 52 99 145
3-5 6 12 18 38 69 100
6-13 5 10 15 33 57 80

STUNT DAWGS
Harvey Comics: Mar, 1993 ($1.25, one-shot)

1 3.00

STUNTMAN COMICS (Also see Thrills Of Tomorrow)
Harvey Publ.: Apr-May, 1946 - No. 2, June-July, 1946; No. 3, Oct-Nov, 1946

1-Origin Stuntman by S&K reprinted in Black Cat #9; S&K-c
123 246 369 787 1344 1900
2-S&K-c/a; The Duke of Broadway story 68 136 204 435 743 1050
3-Small size (5-1/2x8-1/2"; B&W; 32 pgs.); distributed to mail subscribers only; S&K-a; Kid Adonis by S&K reprinted in Green Hornet #37
123 246 369 787 1344 1900
(Also see All-New #15, Boy Explorers #2, Flash Gordon #5 & Thrills of Tomorrow)

STUPID COMICS (Also see 40 oz. Collected)
Oni Press/Image Comics: July, 2000; Sept, 2002 - Present ($2.95, B&W)

1-(Oni Press, 7/00) Jim Mahfood 1 page satire strips reprinted from JAVA magazine 3.00
1-3-(Image Comics, 9/02; 10/03) Jim Mahfood 1 page and 2 page satire strips 3.00
TPB (4/06, $12.99) r/#1(Oni) and #1-3(Image); Phoenix New Times strips 13.00

STUPID HEROES
Mirage Studios: Sept, 1993 - No. 3, Dec, 1994 ($2.75, unfinished limited series)

1-3-Laird-c/a & scripts; 2 trading cards bound in 3.00

STUPID, STUPID RAT TAILS (See Bone)
Cartoon Books: Dec, 1999 - No. 3, Feb, 2000 ($2.95, limited series)

1-3-Jeff Smith-a/Tom Sniegoski-s 3.00

SUBMARINE ATTACK (Formerly Speed Demons)
Charlton Comics: No. 11, May, 1958 - No. 54, Feb-Mar, 1966

11 4 8 12 27 44 60
12-20: 16-Atomic bomb panels 3 6 9 19 30 40
21-30 3 6 9 17 26 35
31-54: 43-Cuban missile crisis story. 47-Atomic bomb panels
3 6 9 15 22 28

NOTE: *Glanzman c/a-25. Montes/Bache a-38, 40, 41.*

SUB-MARINER (See All-Select, All-Winners, Blonde Phantom, Daring, The Defenders, Fantastic Four #4, Human Torch, The Invaders, Iron Man &..., Marvel Mystery, Marvel Spotlight #27, Men's Adventures, Motion Picture Funnies Weekly, Namora, Namor, The..., Prince Namor, The Sub-Mariner, Saga Of The..., Tales to Astonish #70 & 2nd series, USA & Young Men)

SUB-MARINER, THE (2nd Series)(Sub-Mariner #31 on)
Marvel Comics Group: May, 1968 - No. 72, Sept, 1974 (No. 43: 52 pgs.)

1-Origin Sub-Mariner; story continued from Iron Man & Sub-Mariner #1
23 46 69 164 362 560
2-Triton app. 10 20 30 64 132 200
3,4 7 14 21 46 86 125
5-1st Tiger Shark (9/68) 10 20 30 64 132 200
6,7,9,10: 6-Tiger Shark-c & 2nd app., cont'd from #5. 7-Photo-c. (1968). 9-1st app. Serpent Crown (origin in #10 & 12) 5 10 15 33 57 80
8-Sub-Mariner vs. Thing 10 20 30 64 132 200
8-2nd printing (1994) 2 4 6 9 12 15
11-13,15: 15-Last 12¢ issue 4 8 12 28 47 65
14-Sub-Mariner vs. G.A. Toro, who assumes identity of G. A. Human Torch; death of Toro (1st modern app. & only app. Toro, 6/69) 6 12 18 38 69 100
16-20: 19-1st Sting Ray (11/69); Stan Lee, Romita, Heck, Thomas, Everett & Kirby cameos. 20-Dr. Doom app. 3 6 9 21 33 45
21,23-33,37-42: 25-Origin Atlantis. 30-Capt. Marvel x-over. 37-Death of Lady Dorma. 38-Origin retold. 40-Spider-Man x-over. 42-Last 15¢ issue
3 6 9 16 24 32
22-Dr. Strange x-over 5 10 15 30 50 70
34-Prelude (w/#35) to 1st Defenders story; Hulk & Silver Surfer x-over
10 20 30 66 138 210
35-Namor/Hulk/Silver Surfer team-up to battle The Avengers-c/story (3/71); hints at teaming up again 6 12 18 42 79 115
36-Wrightson-a(i) 3 6 9 19 30 40
43-King Size Special (52 pgs.) 3 6 9 20 31 42
44,45-Sub-Mariner vs. Human Torch 3 6 9 18 28 38
46-49,56,62,64-72: 47,48-Dr. Doom app. 49-Cosmic Cube story. 62-1st Tales of Atlantis, Chaykin-s/a; ends #66. 64-Hitler cameo. 67-New costume; F.F. x-over. 69-Spider-Man x-over (6 panels) 2 4 6 9 13 16
50-1st app. Nita, Namor's niece (later Namorita in New Warriors)
4 8 12 23 37 50
51-55,57,58,60,61,63-Everett issues: 57-Venus app. (1st since 4/52); anti-Vietnam War panels. 61-Last artwork by Everett; 1st 4 pgs. completed by Mortimer; pgs. 5-20 by Mooney
2 4 6 10 14 18
59-1st battle with Thor; Everett-a 4 8 12 25 40 55
Special 1 (1/71)-r/Tales to Astonish #70-73 3 6 9 21 33 45
Special 2 (1/72)-(52 pgs.)-r/T.T.A. #74-76; Everett-a 3 6 9 16 24 32

NOTE: ***Bolle** a-67i. **Buscema** a(p)-1-8, 20, 24. **Colan** a(p)-10, 11, 40, 43, 46-49, Special 1, 2; c(p)-10, 11, 40. **Craig** a-17i, 19-23i. **Everett** a-45r, 50-55, 57, 58, 59-61(plot), 63(plot); c-47, 48i, 55, 57, 58-59i, 61, Spec. 2. **G. Kane** c(p)-42-52, 58, 66, 70, 71. **Mooney** a-24i, 25i, 32-35i, 39i, 42i, 44i, 45i, 60i, 61i, 65p, 66p, 68i. **John Severin** c/a-38i. **Marie Severin** c-a 14p. **Starlin** c-59p. **Tuska** a-41p, 42p, 69-71p. **Wrightson** a-36i. #53, 54-r/stories Sub-Mariner Comics #41 & 39.*

SUB-MARINER (The Initiative, follows Civil War series)
Marvel Comics: Aug, 2007 - No. 6, Jan, 2008 ($2.99, limited series)

1-6: 1-Turner-c/Briones-a/Cherniss & Johnson-s; Iron Man app. 3-Yu-c; Venom app. 3.00
...: Revolution TPB (2008, $14.99) r/#1-6 15.00

SUB-MARINER COMICS (1st Series) (The Sub-Mariner #1, 2, 33-42)(Official True Crime Cases #24 on; Amazing Mysteries #32 on; Best Love #33 on)
Timely/Marvel Comics (TCI 1-7/SePI 8/MPI 9-32/Atlas Comics (CCC 33-42)):
Spring, 1941 - No. 23, Sum, 1947; No. 24, Wint, 1947 - No. 31, 4/49; No. 32, 7/49; No. 33, 4/54 - No. 42, 10/55

1-The Sub-Mariner by Everett & The Angel begin: Nazi WWII-c
2900 5800 8700 21,750 52,875 84,000
2-Everett-a; Nazi WWII-c 730 1460 2190 5329 9415 13,500
3-Churchill assassination-c; 40 pg. S-M story 649 1298 1947 4738 8369 12,000
4-Everett-a, 40 pgs.; 1 pg. Wolverton-a; Nazi WWII-c
459 918 1377 3350 5925 8500
5-Gabrielle/Klein-c; Japanese WWII-c 400 800 1200 2800 4900 7000
6-8,10-Japanese WWII-c 383 766 1149 2681 4691 6700
9-Classic Japanese WWII flag-c (Spr. 1943); Wolverton-a, 3 pgs.
400 800 1200 2800 4900 7000
11-Classic Schomburg-c 470 940 1410 3431 6066 8700
12,14-Nazi WWII-c 314 628 942 2198 3849 5500
13-Classic Schomburg hooded Japanese WWII bondage-c
383 766 1149 2681 4691 6700
15-Schomburg Japanese WWII-c 309 618 927 2163 3782 5400
16,17-Japanese WWII-c 300 600 900 1920 3310 4700
18-20 245 490 735 1568 2684 3800
21-Last Angel; Everett-a 155 310 465 992 1696 2400
22-Young Allies app. 155 310 465 992 1696 2400
23-The Human Torch, Namora x-over (Sum/47); 2nd app. Namora after Marvel Mystery #82 190 380 570 1207 2079 2950
24-Namora x-over (3rd app.) 190 380 570 1207 2079 2950
25-The Blonde Phantom begins (Spr/48), ends No. 31; Kurtzman-a; Namora x-over; last quarterly issue 181 362 543 1158 1979 2800
26,27: 26-Namora c/app. 168 336 504 1075 1838 2600
28-Namora cover; Everett-a 200 400 600 1280 2190 3100
29-31 (4/49): 29-The Human Torch app. 31-Capt. America app.
184 368 552 1168 2009 2850
32 (7/49, Scarce)-Origin Sub-Mariner 411 822 1233 2877 5039 7200
33 (4/54)-Origin Sub-Mariner; The Human Torch app.; Namora x-over in Sub-Mariner #33-42
142 284 426 909 1555 2200
34,35-Human Torch in ea. 34-Namora bondage-c 110 220 330 704 1202 1700
36,37,39-41: 36,39-41-Namora app. 108 216 324 686 1181 1675
38-Origin Sub-Mariner's wings; Namora app.; last pre-code (2/55)
113 226 339 718 1234 1750
42-Last issue 119 238 357 762 1306 1850

NOTE: *Angel by **Gustavson**-#1, 8. **Brodsky** c-34-36, 42. **Everett** a-1-4, 22-24, 26-42; c-32, 33, 40. **Maneely** a-38; c-37, 39-41. **Rico** c-27-31. **Schomburg** c-1-4, 6, 8-18, 20. **Sekowsky** c-24. 25, 26(w/**Rico**). **Shores** c-21-23, 38. Bondage c-13, 22, 24, 25, 34.*

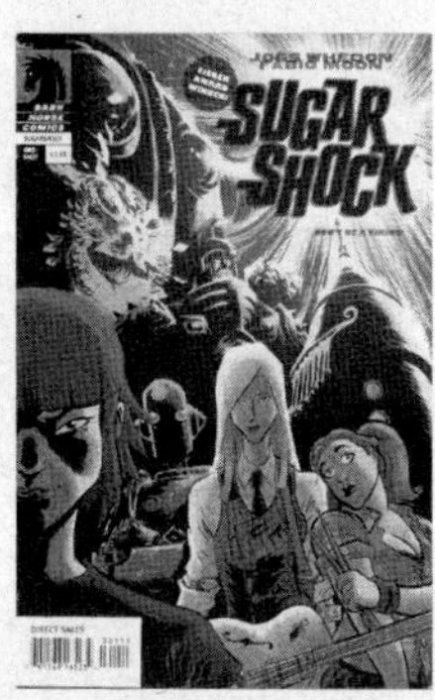

Sugar Shock © Joss Whedon

Suicide Risk #8 © BOOM! & Mike Carey

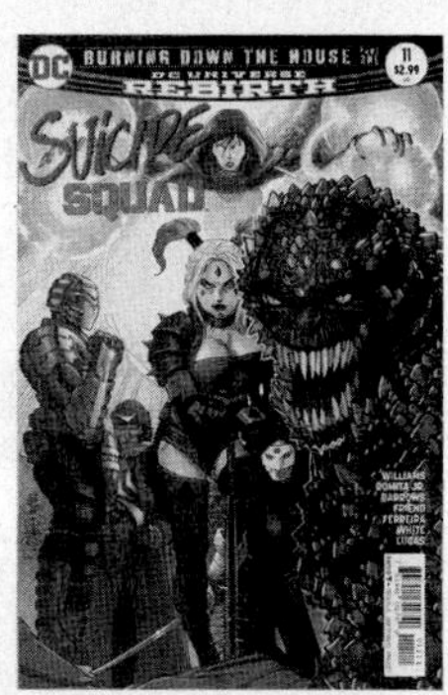

Suicide Squad (2016 series) #11 © DC

GD VG FN VF VF/NM NM-
2.0 4.0 6.0 8.0 9.0 9.2

SUB-MARINER COMICS 70th ANNIVERARY SPECIAL
Marvel Comics: June, 2009 ($3.99, one-shot)
1-New WWII story, Breitweiser-a; Williamson-a; r/debut app. from Marvel Comics #1 5.00

SUB-MARINER: THE DEPTHS
Marvel Comics: Nov, 2008 - No. 5, May, 2009 ($3.99, limited series)
1-5-Peter Milligan-s/Esad Ribic-a/c 4.00

SUBSPECIES
Eternity Comics: May, 1991 - No. 4, Aug, 1991 ($2.50, limited series)
1-4: New stories based on horror movie 3.00

SUBTLE VIOLENTS
CFD Productions: 1991 ($2.50, B&W, mature)
1-Linsner-c & story 1 3 4 8 10 12
San Diego Limited Edition 4 8 12 23 37 50

SUE & SALLY SMITH (Formerly My Secret Life)
Charlton Comics: V2#48, Nov, 1962 - No. 54, Nov, 1963 (Flying Nurses)
V2#48-2nd app. 3 6 9 16 24 32
49-54 2 4 6 13 18 22

SUGAR & SPIKE (Also see The Best of DC, DC Silver Age Classics and Legends of Tomorrow)
National Periodical Publications: Apr-May, 1956 - No. 98, Oct-Nov, 1971
1 (Scarce) 459 918 1377 3350 5925 8500
2 152 304 456 965 1658 2350
3-5: 3-Letter column begins 84 168 252 538 919 1300
6-10 50 100 150 315 533 750
11-20 39 78 117 231 378 525
21-29: 26-Christmas-c 26 52 78 154 252 350
30-Scribbly & Scribbly, Jr. x-over 27 54 81 158 259 360
31-40 20 40 60 117 189 260
41-60 8 16 24 54 102 150
61-80: 69-1st app. Tornado-Tot-c/story. 72-Origin & 1st app. Bernie the Brain
6 12 18 42 79 115
81-84,86-93,95: 84-Bernie the Brain apps. as Superman in 1 panel (9/69)
5 10 15 34 60 85
85 (68 pgs.)-r/#72 6 12 18 37 66 95
94-1st app. Raymond, African-American child 6 12 18 37 66 95
96 (68 pgs.) 6 12 18 40 73 105
97,98 (52 pgs.) 6 12 18 37 66 95
No. 1 Replica Edition (2002, $2.95) reprint of #1 4.00
NOTE: *All written and drawn by* ***Sheldon Mayer.*** *Issues with Paper Doll pages cut or missing are common.*

SUGAR BOWL COMICS (Teen-age)
Famous Funnies: May, 1948 - No. 5, Jan, 1949
1-Toth-c/a 15 30 45 88 137 185
2,4,5 9 18 27 52 69 85
3-Toth-a 10 20 30 58 79 100

SUGARFOOT (TV)
Dell Publishing Co.: No. 907, May, 1958 - No. 1209, Oct-Dec, 1961
Four Color 907 (#1)-Toth-a, photo-c 10 20 30 67 141 215
Four Color 992 (5-7/59), Toth-a, photo-c 9 18 27 63 129 195
Four Color 1059 (11-1/60), 1098 (5-7/60), 1147 (11-1/61), 1209-all photo-c. 1059,1098,1147-all have variant edition, back-c comic strip 7 14 21 49 92 135

SUGARSHOCK (Also see MySpace Dark Horse Presents)
Dark Horse Comics: Oct, 2009 ($3.50, one-shot)
1-Joss Whedon-s/Fabio Moon-a/c; story from online comic; Moon sketch pgs. 3.50

SUICIDE RISK
BOOM! Studios: May, 2013 - No. 25, May, 2015 ($3.99)
1-25: 1-Carey-s/Casagrande-a. 5-Joëlle Jones-a. 10-Coelho-a 4.00

SUICIDERS
DC Comics (Vertigo): Apr, 2015 - No. 6, Nov, 2015 ($3.99)
1-6-Lee Bermejo-s/a/c 4.00

SUICIDERS: KINGS OF HELL.A.
DC Comics (Vertigo): May, 2016 - No. 6 ($3.99)
1-6-Lee Bermejo-s/c. 1-5-Alessandro Vitti-a. 6-Gerardo Zaffino-a; Bermejo-a (2 pgs.) 4.00

SUICIDE SQUAD (See Brave & the Bold, Doom Patrol & Suicide Squad Spec., Legends #3 & note under Star Spangled War stories)
DC Comics: May, 1987 - No. 66, June, 1992; No. 67, Mar, 2010 (Direct sales only #32 on)
1-Chaykin-c 5 10 15 31 53 75
2-10: 9-Millennium x-over. 10-Batman-c/story 6.00
11-22,24-47,50-66: 13-JLI app. (Batman). 16-Re-intro Shade The Changing Man. 27-34,36,37-Snyder-a. 38-Origin Bronze Tiger. 40-43-"The Phoenix Gambit" Batman storyline. 40-Free Batman/Suicide Squad poster 4.00
23-1st Oracle 3 6 9 19 30 40
48-Joker/Batgirl-c/s 3 6 9 19 30 40
49-Joker/Batgirl-c/s 2 4 6 10 14 18
67-(3/10, $2.99) Blackest Night one-shot; Fiddler rises as a Black Lantern; Califiore-a 4.00
Annual 1 (1988, $1.50)-Manhunter x-over 5.00
...: Trial By Fire TPB (2011, $19.99) r/#1-8 & Secret Origins #14 20.00

SUICIDE SQUAD (2nd series)
DC Comics: Nov, 2001 - No. 12, Oct, 2002 ($2.50)
1-Giffen-s/Medina-a; Sgt. Rock app. 5.00
2-9: 4-Heath-a 4.00
10-12-Suicide Squad vs. Antiphon: 10-J. Severin-a. 12-JSA app.
1 3 4 6 8 10

SUICIDE SQUAD (3rd series)
DC Comics: Nov, 2007 - No. 8, Jun, 2008 ($2.99, limited series)
1-8-Ostrander-s/Pina-a/Snyder III-c 4.00
...: From the Ashes TPB (2008, $19.99) r/#1-8 20.00

SUICIDE SQUAD (DC New 52)(Also see New Suicide Squad)
DC Comics: Nov, 2011 - No. 30, Jul, 2014 ($2.99)
1-Harley Quinn, Deadshot, King Shark, El Diablo, Voltaic, Black Spider team up
5 10 15 30 50 70
1-(2nd printing) 2 4 6 13 28 22
1 Special Edition (5/16, FCBD giveaway) 3.00
2-5 1 2 3 5 6 8
6-Origin Harley Quinn part 1 3 6 9 17 26 35
6,7-(2nd printing) 1 2 3 5 6 8
7-Origin Harley Quinn part 2 3 6 9 14 20 25
8-13,16-20,22-30: 19-Unknown Soldier joins. 24-29-Forever Evil tie-in. 24-Omac returns 4.00
14,15-Death of the Family tie-in; Joker app. 5.00
14-Variant die-cut Joker mask-c; Death of the Family tie-in 6.00
21-Harley Quinn-c/s 1 3 4 6 8 10
30-($3.99) Forever Evil tie-in; Coelho-a/Mahnke-c 4.00
#0 (11/12, $2.99) Amanda Waller pre-Suicide Squad; Dagnino-a 5.00
...: Amanda Waller (5/14, $4.99) Jim Zub-s/Coelho-a 5.00

SUICIDE SQUAD (DC Rebirth)
DC Comics: Oct, 2016 - Present ($2.99)
1-Harley Quinn, Deadshot, Killer Croc, Katana, Boomerang team up; Jim Lee-a; back-up origin of Deadshot retold; Fabok-a 3.00
1-Director's Cut (5/17, $5.99) r/#1,2 with pencil-a; bonus original script for #1 6.00
2-7: 2,3-Zod app. 2-Back-up Boomerang origin w/Reis-a. 3-Back-up Katana origin 3.00
8-24: 8-Killer Frost joins; Justice League vs. Suicide Squad prelude; Lee-a. 9,10-JL vs. SS tie-ins. 11-15-Romita Jr.-a. 16-18-Daniel-a. 20-Sejic-a. 23,24-Batman app. 3.00
25-($3.99) Batman app.; Cafaro-a; cameo app. Rick Flag & Karin Grace 4.00
26-36: 26-Dark Nights: Metal tie-in. 27-32-Secret History of Task Force X 3.00
.../Banana Splits Special 1 (5/17, $4.99) Caldwell-a; Snagglepuss back-up; Porter-a 5.00
...: Rebirth (10/16, $2.99) Rick Flag joins; Harley Quinn, Deadshot, Boomerang app. 3.00
... Special: War Crimes 1 (10/16, $4.99) Ostrander-s/Gus Vazquez-a; Shado app. 5.00

SUICIDE SQUAD MOST WANTED: DEADSHOT & KATANA
DC Comics: Mar, 2016 - No. 6, Aug, 2016 ($4.99, limited series)
1-6-Deadshot by Buccellato-s/Bogdanovic-a; Katana by Barr-s/Neves-a; Nord-c 5.00

SUICIDE SQUAD MOST WANTED: EL DIABLO & BOOMERANG (Title changes to Suicide Squad Most Wanted: El Diablo & Amanda Waller for #5,6)
DC Comics: Oct, 2016 - No. 6, Mar, 2017 ($4.99, limited series)
1-4-El Diablo by Nitz-s/Richards-a; Boomerang by Moreci-s/Bazaldua-a; Huddleston-c 5.00
5,6-Amanda Waller by Ayala-s/Merhoff-a; El Diablo by Nitz-s/Richards-a 5.00

SUMMER FUN (See Dell Giants)

SUMMER FUN (Formerly Li'l Genius; Holiday Surprise #55)
Charlton Comics: No. 54, Oct, 1966 (Giant)
54 3 6 9 21 33 45

SUMMER FUN (Walt Disney's...)
Disney Comics: Summer, 1991 ($2.95, annual, 68 pgs.)
1-D. Duck, M. Mouse, Brer Rabbit, Chip 'n' Dale & Pluto, Li'l Bad Wolf, Super Goof, Scamp stories 4.00

SUMMER LOVE (Formerly Brides in Love?)
Charlton Comics: V2#46, Oct, 1965; V2#47, Oct, 1966; V2#48, Nov, 1968

Sun Girl #1 © MAR

Super Bad James Dynomite #1 © 5-D

Superboy #107 © DC

	GD 2.0	VG 4.0	FN 6.0	VF 8.0	VF/NM 9.0	NM- 9.2

V2#46-Beatles-c & 8 pg. story 11 22 33 76 163 250
47-(68 pgs.) Beatles-c & 12 pg. story 9 18 27 61 123 185
48 3 6 9 15 22 28

SUMMER MAGIC (See Movie Comics)

SUNDANCE (See Hotel Deparee...)

SUNDANCE KID (Also see Blazing Six-Guns)
Skywald Publications: June, 1971 - No. 3, Sept, 1971 (52 pgs.)(Pre-code reprints & new-s)

1-Durango Kid; Two Kirby Bullseye-r 3 6 9 16 23 30
2,3: 2-Swift Arrow, Durango Kid, Bullseye by S&K; Meskin plus 1 pg. origin.
3-Durango Kid, Billy the Kid, Red Hawk-r 2 4 6 11 16 20

SUNDAY PIX (Christian religious)
David C. Cook Pub/USA Weekly Newsprint Color Comics: V1#1, Mar,1949 - V16#26, July 19, 1964 (7x10", 12 pgs., mail subscription only)

V1#1 8 16 24 42 54 65
V1#2-up 6 12 18 27 33 38
V2#1-52 (1950) 5 10 15 23 28 32
V3-V6 (1951-1953) 4 9 13 18 22 26
V7-V11#1-7,23-52 (1954-1959) 2 4 6 13 18 22
V11#8-22 (2/22-5/31/59) H.G. Wells First Men in the Moon serial
3 6 9 14 19 24
V12#1-19,21-52; V13-V15#1,2,9-52; V16#1-26(7/19/64)
2 4 6 10 14 18
V12#20 (5/15/60) 2 page interview with Peanuts' Charles Schulz
4 8 12 23 37 50
V15#3-8 (2/24/63) John Glenn, Christian astronaut 3 6 9 16 23 30

SUN DEVILS
DC Comics: July, 1984 - No. 12, June, 1985 ($1.25, maxi series)

1-12: 6-Death of Sun Devil 4.00

SUNDIATA: A LEGEND OF AFRICA
NBM Publishing Inc.: 2002 ($15.95, hardcover with dustjacket)

nn-Will Eisner-s/a; adaptation of an African folk tale 16.00

SUNDOWNERS
Dark Horse Comics: Aug, 2014 - No. 6, Jan, 2015 ($3.50)

1-6: 1-Tim Seeley-s/Jim Terry-a 3.50

SUN FUN KOMIKS
Sun Publications: 1939 (15¢, B&W & red)

1-Satire on comics (rare); 1st Hitler app. in comics?
622 1244 1866 4541 8021 11,500

NOTE: *Hitler, Stalin and Mussolini featured gag in 1-page story written in Hebrew and English. Nazi swastika and Nazi flag app. in a different 1-page "Gussie the Gob" story.*

SUNFIRE & BIG HERO SIX (See Alpha Flight)
Marvel Comics: Sept, 1998 - No. 3, Nov, 1998 ($2.50, limited series)

1-Lobdell-s 4 8 12 27 44 60
2,3 2 4 6 11 16 20

SUN GIRL (See The Human Torch & Marvel Mystery Comics #88)
Marvel Comics (CCC): Aug, 1948 - No. 3, Dec, 1948

1-1st app. Sun Girl; Miss America app. 271 542 813 1734 2967 4200
2,3: 2-The Blonde Phantom begins 181 362 543 1158 1979 2800

SUNNY, AMERICA'S SWEETHEART (Formerly Cosmo Cat #1-10)
Fox Feature Syndicate: No. 11, Dec, 1947 - No. 14, June, 1948

11-Feldstein-c/a 152 304 456 965 1658 2350
12-14: 12,13-Feldstein-a; 13,14-Lingerie panels. 13-L.B. Cole-a
100 200 300 635 1093 1550
I.W. Reprint #8-Feldstein-a; r/Fox issue 10 20 30 73 129 185

SUN-RUNNERS (Also see Tales of the...)
Pacific Comics/Eclipse Comics/Amazing Comics: 2/84 - No. 3, 5/84; No. 4, 11/84 - No. 7, 1986 (Baxter paper)

1-7: P. Smith-a in #2-4 4.00
Christmas Special 1 (1987, $1.95)-By Amazing 4.00

SUNSET CARSON (Also see Cowboy Western)
Charlton Comics: Feb, 1951 - No. 4, 1951 (No month) (Photo-c on each)

1-Photo/retouched-c (Scarce, all issues) 58 116 174 371 636 900
2-Kit Carson story; adapts "Kansas Raiders" w/Brian Donlevy, Audie Murphy & Margaret Chapman 41 82 123 256 428 600
3,4 34 68 102 199 325 450

SUNSET PASS (See Zane Grey & 4-Color #230)

SUPER ANGRY BIRDS (Based on Rovio videogame Angry Birds)
IDW Publishing: Sept, 2015 - No. 4, Dec, 2015 ($3.99, limited series)

1-4: 1-The Eagle's Eye - Jeff Parker-s/Ron Randall-a; two covers 4.00

SUPER ANIMALS PRESENTS PIDGY & THE MAGIC GLASSES
Star Publications: Dec, 1953 (25¢, came w/glasses)

1-(3-D Comics)-L. B. Cole-c 40 80 120 246 411 575

SUPER BAD JAMES DYNOMITE
5-D Comics: Dec, 2005 - No. 5, Feb, 2007 ($3.99)

1-5-Created by the Wayans brothers 4.00

SUPERBOY
DC Comics: Jan, 1942

nn-Ashcan comic, not distributed to newsstands, only for in house use. Covers were produced, but not the rest of the book. A CGC certified 9.2 copy sold in 2003 for $6,600.

SUPERBOY (See Adventure, Aurora, DC Comics Presents, DC 100 Page Super Spectacular #15, DC Super Stars, 80 Page Giant #10, More Fun Comics, The New Advs. of... & Superman Family #191, Young Justice)

SUPERBOY (1st Series)(...& the Legion of Super-Heroes with #231)
(Becomes The Legion of Super-Heroes No. 259 on)
National Periodical Publ./DC Comics: Mar-Apr, 1949 - No. 258, Dec, 1979 (#1-16: 52 pgs.)

1-Superman cover; intro in More Fun #101 (1-2/45)
1000 2000 3000 7500 13,500 19,500
2-Used in **SOTI**, pg. 35-36,226 271 542 813 1734 2967 4200
3 194 388 582 1242 2121 3000
4,5: 5-1st pre-Supergirl tryout (c/story, 11-12/49) 142 284 426 909 1555 2200
6-9: 8-1st Superbaby 123 246 369 787 1344 1900
10-1st app. Lana Lang 148 296 444 947 1624 2300
11-15: 11-2nd Lana Lang app.; 1st Lana cover 90 180 270 576 988 1400
16-20: 20-2nd Jor-El cover 63 126 189 403 689 975
21-26,28-30: 21-Lana Lang app. 54 108 162 343 574 825
27-Low distribution 58 116 174 371 636 900
31-38: 38-Last pre-code issue (1/55) 47 94 141 296 498 700
39-48,50 (7/56) 42 84 126 265 445 625
49 (6/56)-1st app. Metallo (this one's Jor-El's robot) 77 154 231 493 847 1200
51-60: 51-Krypto app. 52-1st S.A. issue. 56-Krypto-c 34 68 102 199 325 450
61-67 28 56 84 165 270 375
68-Origin/1st app. original Bizarro (10-11/58) 290 580 870 1856 3178 4500
69-77,79: 76-1st Supermonkey 24 48 72 142 234 325
78-Origin Mr. Mxyzptlk & Superboy's costume 34 68 102 204 332 460
80-1st meeting Superboy/Supergirl (4/60) 37 74 111 222 361 500
81,83-85,87,88: 83-Origin/1st app. Kryptonite Kid 13 26 39 86 188 290
82-1st Bizarro Krypto 16 32 48 110 243 375
86-(1/61)-4th Legion app; Intro Pete Ross 25 50 75 175 388 600
89-(6/61)-1st app. Mon -El; 2nd Phantom Zone 35 70 105 252 564 875
90-92: 90-Pete Ross learns Superboy's I.D. 92-Last 10¢ issue
11 22 33 76 163 250
93-10th Legion app.(12/61); Chameleon Boy app. 12 24 36 82 179 275
94-97,99: 94-1st app. Superboy Revenge Squad 10 20 30 68 144 220
98-(7/62) Legion app; origin & 1st app. Ultra Boy; Pete Ross joins Legion
15 30 45 100 220 340
100-(10/62)-Ultra Boy app; 1st app. Phantom Zone villains, Dr. Xadu & Erndine. 2 pg. map of Krypton; origin Superboy retold; r-cover of Superman #1
17 34 51 117 259 400
101-120: 104-Origin Phantom Zone. 115-Atomic bomb-c. 117-Legion app.
9 18 27 57 111 165
121-128: 124-(10/65)-1st app. Insect Queen (Lana Lang). 125-Legion cameo. 126-Origin Krypto the Super Dog retold with new facts 7 14 21 49 92 135
129-(80-pg. Giant G-22)-Reprints origin Mon-El 9 18 27 57 111 165
130-137,139,140: 131-Legion statues cameo in Dog Legionnaires story. 132-1st app. Supremo. 133-Superboy meets Robin 6 12 18 41 76 110
138 (80-pg. Giant G-35) 7 14 21 46 86 125
141-146,148-155,157: 145-Superboy's parents regain their youth. 148-Legion app. 157-Last 12¢ issue 5 10 15 35 63 90
147(6/68)-Giant G-47; 1st origin of L.S.H. (Saturn Girl, Lightning Lad, Cosmic Boy); origin Legion of Super-Pets-r/Adv. #293 7 14 21 44 82 120
147 Replica Edition (2003, $6.95) reprints entire issue; cover recreation by Ordway 7.00
156-(Giant G-59) 6 12 18 38 69 100
158-164,166-171,175: 171-1st app. Aquaboy 3 6 9 18 28 38
165,174 (Giant G-71,G-83): 165-r/1st app. Krypto the Superdog from Adventure Comics #210
5 10 15 34 60 85
172,173,176-Legion app.: 172-1st app. & origin Yango (The Super Ape). 176-Partial photo-c; last 15¢ issue 3 6 9 19 30 40
177-184,186,187 (All 52 pgs.): 182-All new origin of the classic World's Finest team

Superboy #223 © DC

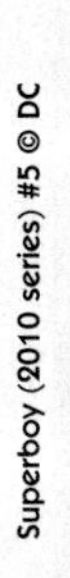

Superboy (2010 series) #5 © DC

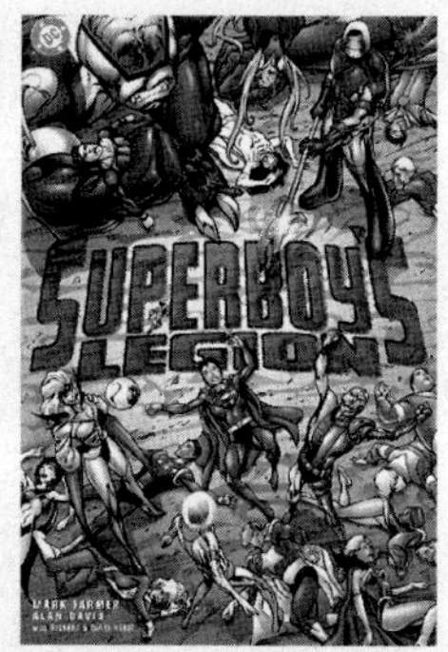

Superboy's Legion #2 © DC

GD 2.0 | VG 4.0 | FN 6.0 | VF 8.0 | VF/NM 9.0 | NM- 9.2

(Superman & Batman) as teenagers (2/72, 22pgs). 184-Origin Dial H for Hero-r 3 6 9 20 31 42
185-Also listed as DC 100 Pg. Super Spectacular #12; Legion-c/story; Teen Titans, Kid Eternity(r/Hit #46), Star Spangled Kid-r(S.S. #55) 7 14 21 48 89 130
188-190,192,194,196: 188-Origin Karkan. 196-Last Superboy solo story 3 6 9 14 19 24
191,193,195: 191-Origin Sunboy retold; Legion app. 193-Chameleon Boy & Shrinking Violet get new costumes. 195-1st app. Erg-1/Wildfire; Phantom Girl gets new costume 3 6 9 14 20 26
197-Legion series begins; Lightning Lad's new costume 4 8 12 23 37 50
198,199: 198-Element Lad & Princess Projectra get new costumes 3 6 9 14 20 26
200-Bouncing Boy & Duo Damsel marry; J'onn J'onzz cameo 3 6 9 16 23 30
201,204,206,207,209: 201-Re-intro Erg-1 as Wildfire. 204-Supergirl resigns from Legion. 206-Ferro Lad & Invisible Kid app. 209-Karate Kid gets new costume 2 4 6 11 16 20
202,205-(100 pgs.): 202-Light Lass gets new costume; Mike Grell's 1st comic work-i (5-6/74) 4 8 12 28 47 65
203-Invisible Kid killed by Validus 3 6 9 15 22 28
208,210: 208-(68 pgs.). 208-Legion of Super-Villains app. 210-Origin Karate Kid 3 6 9 14 20 26
211-220: 212-Matter-Eater Lad resigns. 216-1st app. Tyroc, who joins the Legion in #218 2 4 6 9 13 16
221-230,246-249: 226-Intro. Dawnstar. 228-Death of Chemical King 2 4 6 8 10 12
231-245: (Giants). 240-Origin Dawnstar; Chaykin-a. 242-(52 pgs.). 243-Legion of Substitute Heroes app. 243-245-(44 pgs.). 2 4 6 9 13 16
244,245-(Whitman variants; low print run, no issue# shown on cover) 3 6 9 14 20 26
246-248-(Whitman variants; low ...) 2 4 6 11 16 20
250-258: 253-Intro Blok. 257-Return of Bouncing Boy & Duo Damsel by Ditko 2 3 4 6 8 10
251-258-(Whitman variants; low print run) 2 4 6 10 14 18
Annual 1 (Sum/64, 84 pgs.)-Origin Krypto-r 15 30 45 103 227 350
Spectacular 1 (1980, Giant)-1st comic distributed only through comic stores; mostly-r 2 4 6 8 10 12
...: The Greatest Team-Up Stories Ever Told TPB (2010, $19.99) r/team-ups with Robin, Supergirl, young versions of Aquaman, Green Arrow, Bruce Wayne; Davis-c 20.00

NOTE: **Neal Adams** *c-143, 145, 146, 148-155, 157-161, 163, 164, 166-168, 172, 173, 175, 176, 178.* **M. Anderson** *a-178,179, 245i.* **Ditko** *a-257p.* **Grell** *a-202i, 203-219, 220-224p, 235p; c-207-232, 235, 236p, 237, 239p, 240p, 243p, 246, 258.* **Nasser** *a(p)-222, 225, 226, 230, 231, 233, 236.* **Simonson** *a-237p.* **Starlin** *a(p)-239, 250, 251; c-238.* **Staton** *a-227p, 243-249p, 252-258p; c-247-251p.* **Swan/Moldoff** *c-109.* **Tuska** *a-172, 173, 176, 183, 235p.* **Wood** *inks-153-155, 157-161. Legion app.-172, 173, 176, 177, 183, 184, 188, 190, 191, 193, 195, 197-258.*

SUPERBOY (TV)(2nd Series)(The Adventures of...#19 on)
DC Comics: Feb, 1990 - No. 22, Dec, 1991 ($1.00/$1.25)

1-Photo-c from TV show; Mooney-a(p) 4.00
2-22: Mooney-a in 2-8,18-20; 8-Bizarro-c/story; Arthur Adams-a(i). 9-12,14-17-Swan-a 3.00
...Special 1 (1992, $1.75) Swan-a 4.00

SUPERBOY (3rd Series)
DC Comics: Feb, 1994 - No. 100, Jul, 2002 ($1.50/$1.95/$1.99/$2.25)

1-Metropolis Kid from Reign of the Supermen 4.00
2-8,0,9-24,26-76: 6,7-Worlds Collide Pts. 3 & 8. 8-(9/94)-Zero Hour x-over. 0-(10/94). 9-(11/94)-King Shark app. 21-Legion app. 28-Supergirl-c/app. 33-Final Night. 38-41-"Meltdown". 45-Legion-c/app. 47-Green Lantern-c/app. 50-Last Boy on Earth begins. 60-Crosses Hypertime. 68-Demon-c/app. 3.00
25-($2.95)-New Gods & Female Furies app.; w/pin-ups 4.00
77-99: 77-Begin $2.25-c. 79-Superboy's powers return. 80,81-Titans app. 83-New costume. 85-Batgirl app. 90,91-Our Worlds at War x-over 3.00
100-($3.50) Sienkiewicz-c; Grummett & McCrea-a; Superman cameo 4.00
#1,000,000 (11/98) 853rd Century x-over 3.00
Annual 1 (1994, $2.95, 68 pgs.)-Elseworlds story, Pt. 2 of The Super Seven (see Adventures Of Superman Annual #6) 4.00
Annual 2 (1995, $3.95)-Year One story 4.00
Annual 3 (1996, $2.95)-Legends of the Dead Earth 4.00
Annual 4 (1997, $3.95)-Pulp Heroes story 4.00
...Plus 1 (Jan, 1997, $2.95) w/Capt. Marvel Jr. 4.00
...Plus 2 (Fall, 1997, $2.95) w/Slither (Scare Tactics) 4.00
.../Risk Double-Shot 1 (Feb, 1998, $1.95) w/Risk (Teen Titans) 3.00

SUPERBOY (4th Series)
DC Comics: Jan, 2011 - No. 11, Early Oct, 2011 ($2.99)

1-11: 1-Lemire-s/Gallo-a/Albuquerque-c; Parasite & Poison Ivy app. 2,3-Noto-c 3.00
1-5: 1-Variant-c by Cassaday. 2-March-var-c. 3-Nguyen var-c. 4-Lau var-c. 5-Manapul 4.00

SUPERBOY (DC New 52)
DC Comics: Nov, 2011 - No. 34, Oct, 2014 ($2.99)

1-34: 1-New origin; Lobdell-s/Silva-a/Canete-c; Caitlin Fairchild app. 6-Supergirl app. 8-Grunge, Beast Boy & Terra app. 9-"The Culling" x-over cont. from Teen Titans Annual #1; Teen Titans and the Legion app. 14-17-H'El on Earth tie-in; Batman app. 3.00
#0-(11/12, $2.99) Origin of Kryptonian clones; Silva-a 3.00
Annual 1 (3/13, $4.99) H'El on Earth tie-in between Superboy #16 & Superman #16 5.00
...: Futures End 1 (11/14, $2.99, regular-c) Five years later, Freefall app.; Caldwell-a 3.00
...: Futures End 1 (11/14, $3.99, 3-D cover) 4.00

SUPERBOY AND THE LEGION OF SUPER-HEROES
DC Comics: 2011 ($14.99, TPB)

SC-Reprints stories from Adventure Comics #515-520 15.00

SUPERBOY & THE RAVERS
DC Comics: Sept, 1996 - No. 19, March, 1998 ($1.95)

1-19: 4-Adam Strange app. 7-Impulse-c/app. 9-Superman-c/app. 3.00

SUPERBOY COMICS
DC Comics: Jan. 1942

nn - Ashcan comic, not distributed to newsstands, only for in-house use. Cover art is Detective Comics #57 with interior being Action Comics #38. A CGC certified 9.2 copy sold for $6,600 in 2003 and for $15,750 in 2008.

SUPERBOY/ROBIN: WORLD'S FINEST THREE
DC Comics: 1996 - No. 2, 1996 ($4.95, squarebound, limited series)

1,2: Superboy & Robin vs. Metallo & Poison Ivy; Karl Kesel & Chuck Dixon scripts; Tom Grummett-c(p)/a(p) 5.00

SUPERBOY'S LEGION (Elseworlds)
DC Comics: 2001 - No. 2, 2001 ($5.95, squarebound, limited series)

1,2-31st century Superboy forms Legion; Farmer-s/i; Davis-a(p)/c 6.00

SUPERBOY: THE BOY OF STEEL
DC Comics: 2010 ($19.99, hardcover with dustjacket)

HC-Reprints stories from Adventure Comics #0-3,5,6 & Superman Secret Files 2009 20.00
SC-(2011, $14,99) Same contents as HC 15.00

SUPER BRAT (Li'l Genius #6 on)
Toby Press: Jan, 1954 - No. 4, July, 1954

1 10 20 30 58 79 100
2-4: 4-Li'l Teevy by Mel Lazarus 7 14 21 35 43 50
I.W. Reprint #1,2,3,7,8('58): 1-r/#1 2 4 6 8 11 14
I.W. (Super) Reprint #10('63) 2 4 6 8 10 12

SUPERCAR (TV)
Gold Key: Nov, 1962 - No. 4, Aug, 1963 (All painted-c)

1 10 20 30 69 147 225
2,3 6 12 18 41 76 110
4-Last issue 7 14 21 46 86 125

SUPER CAT (Formerly Frisky Animals; also see Animal Crackers)
Star Publications #56-58/Ajax/Farrell Publ. (Four Star Comic Corp.):
No. 56, Nov, 1953 - No. 58, May, 1954; Aug, 1957 - No. 4, May, 1958

56-58-L.B. Cole-c on all 20 40 60 114 182 250
1(1957-Ajax)- "The Adventures of..." c-only 10 20 30 54 72 90
2-4 7 14 21 35 43 50

SUPER CIRCUS (TV)
Cross Publishing Co.: Jan, 1951 - No. 5, Sept, 1951 (Mary Hartline)

1-(52 pgs.)-Cast photos on-c 18 36 54 107 169 230
2-Cast photos on-c 11 22 33 64 90 115
3-5 10 20 30 56 76 95

SUPER CIRCUS (TV)
Dell Publ. Co.: No. 542, Mar, 1954 - No. 694, Mar, 1956 (Mary Hartline)

Four Color 542: Mary Hartline photo-c 7 14 21 46 86 125
Four Color 592,694: Mary Hartline photo-c 6 12 18 37 66 95

SUPER COMICS
Dell Publishing Co.: May, 1938 - No. 121, Feb-Mar, 1949

1-Terry & The Pirates, The Gumps, Dick Tracy, Little Orphan Annie, Little Joe, Gasoline Alley, Smilin' Jack, Smokey Stover, Smitty, Tiny Tim, Moon Mullins, Harold Teen, Winnie Winkle begin 239 478 717 1530 2615 3700
2 87 174 261 553 952 1350
3 77 154 231 493 847 1200

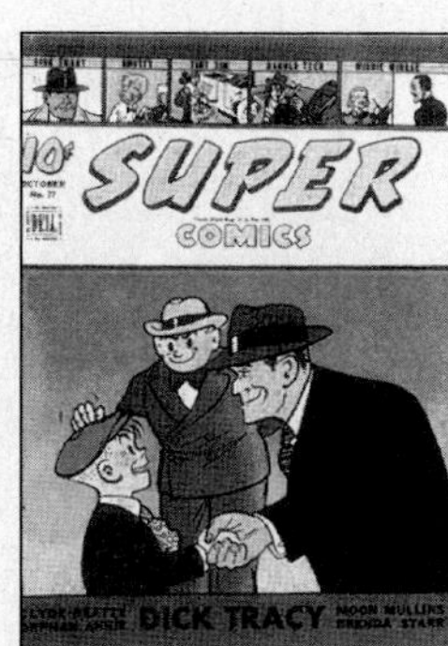

Super Comics #77 © DELL

Super Friends #26 © DC

Supergirl #1 © DC

	GD 2.0	VG 4.0	FN 6.0	VF 8.0	VF/NM 9.0	NM- 9.2
4,5: 4-Dick Tracy-c; also #8-10,17,26(part),31	58	116	174	371	636	900
6-10	47	94	141	296	498	700
11-20: 20-Smilin' Jack-c (also #29,32)	39	78	117	240	395	550
21-29: 21-Magic Morro begins (origin & 1st app., 2/40). 22,27-Ken Ernst-c (also #25?); Magic Morro c-22,25,27,34	34	68	102	199	325	450
30- "Sea Hawk" movie adaptation-c/story with Errol Flynn	35	70	105	208	339	470
31-40: 34-Ken Ernst-c	28	56	84	165	270	375
41-50: 41-Intro Lightning Jim. 43-Terry & The Pirates ends	23	46	69	138	227	315
51-60	19	38	57	109	172	235
61-70: 62-Flag-c. 65-Brenda Starr-r begin? 67-X-Mas-c	17	34	51	98	154	210
71-80	14	28	42	80	115	150
81-99	13	26	39	74	105	135
100	14	28	42	78	112	145
101-115-Last Dick Tracy (moves to own title)	10	20	30	56	76	95
116-121: 116,118-All Smokey Stover. 117-All Gasoline Alley. 119-121-Terry & The Pirates app. in all	9	18	27	50	65	80

SUPER COPS, THE
Red Circle Productions (Archie): July, 1974 (one-shot)

	GD	VG	FN	VF	VF/NM	NM-
1-Morrow-c/a; art by Pino, Hack, Thorne	2	4	6	8	11	14

SUPER COPS
Now Comics: Sept, 1990 - No. 4, Dec?, 1990 ($1.75)

	GD	VG	FN	VF	VF/NM	NM-
1-($2.75, 52 pgs.)-Dave Dorman painted-c (both printings)						4.00
2-4						3.00

SUPER CRACKED (See Cracked)

SUPERCROOKS
Marvel Comics (Icon): May, 2012 - No. 4, Aug, 2012 ($2.99/$4.99)

	GD	VG	FN	VF	VF/NM	NM-
1-3-($2.99) Millar-s/Yu-a. 1-Covers by Yu & Gibbons. 2-Covers by Yu & Hitch						3.00
4-($4.99) Bonus preview of Jupiter's Children (later re-titled Jupiter's Legacy)						5.00

SUPER DC GIANT (25-50¢, all 68-52 pg. Giants)
National Per. Publ.: No. 13, 9-10/70 - No. 26, 7-8/71; V3#27, Summer, 1976 (No #1-12)

	GD	VG	FN	VF	VF/NM	NM-
S-13-Binky	10	20	30	64	132	200
S-14-Top Guns of the West; Kubert-c; Trigger Twins, Johnny Thunder, Wyoming Kid-r; Moreira-r (9-10/70)	5	10	15	33	57	80
S-15-Western Comics; Kubert-c; Pow Wow Smith, Vigilante, Buffalo Bill-r; new Gil Kane-a (9-10/70)	5	10	15	33	57	80
S-16-Best of the Brave & the Bold; Batman-r & Metamorpho origin-r from Brave & the Bold; Spectre pin-up.	4	8	12	27	44	60
S-17-Love 1970 (scarce)	23	46	69	161	356	550
S-18-Three Mouseketeers; Dizzy Dog, Doodles Duck, Bo Bunny-r; Sheldon Mayer-a	9	18	27	57	111	165
S-19-Jerry Lewis; Neal Adams pin-up	9	18	27	59	117	175
S-20-House of Mystery; N. Adams-c; Kirby-r(3)	7	14	21	44	82	120
S-21-Love 1971 (scarce)	27	54	81	194	435	675
S-22-Top Guns of the West; Kubert-c	4	8	12	25	40	55
S-23-The Unexpected	4	8	12	28	47	65
S-24-Supergirl	4	8	12	25	40	55
S-25-Challengers of the Unknown; all Kirby/Wood-r	4	8	12	22	35	48
S-26-Aquaman (1971)-r/S.A. Aquaman origin story from Showcase #30	4	8	12	27	44	60
27-Strange Flying Saucers Adventures (Sum, 1976)	3	6	9	18	28	38

NOTE: *Sid Greene r-27p(2), Heath r-27. G. Kane a-14r(2), 15, 27r(p). Kubert r-16.*

SUPER DINOSAUR
Image Comics: Apr, 2011 - Present ($2.99)

	GD	VG	FN	VF	VF/NM	NM-
1-23: 1-Robert Kirkman-s/Jason Howard-a; origin story and character profiles						3.00
... Origin Special #1 FCBD Edition (5/11, giveaway) r/#1						3.00

SUPER-DOOPER COMICS
Able Mfg. Co./Harvey: 1946 - No. 7, May, 1946; No. 8, 1946 (10¢, 32 pgs., paper-c)

	GD	VG	FN	VF	VF/NM	NM-
1-The Clock, Gangbuster app. (scarce)	94	188	282	597	1024	1450
2	20	40	60	114	182	250
3-6	18	36	54	105	165	225
7,8-Shock Gibson. 7-Where's Theres A Will by Ed Wheelan, Steve Case Crime Rover, Penny & Ullysses Jr. 8-Sam Hill app.	22	44	66	132	216	300

SUPER DUCK COMICS (The Cockeyed Wonder) (See Jolly Jingles)
MLJ Mag. No. 1-4(9/45)/Close-Up No. 5 on (Archie): Fall, 1944 - No. 94, Dec, 1960 (Also see Laugh #24)(#1-5 are quarterly)

	GD	VG	FN	VF	VF/NM	NM-
1-Origin; Hitler & Hirohito-c	161	322	483	1030	1765	2500
2-Bill Vigoda-c	36	72	108	211	343	475
3-5: 4-20-Al Fagaly-c (most)	22	44	66	128	209	290
6-10	15	30	45	86	133	180
11-20(6/48)	12	24	36	67	94	120
21,23-40 (10/51)	10	20	30	58	79	100
22-Used in **SOTI**, pg. 35,307,308	12	24	36	69	97	125
41-60 (2/55)	9	18	27	50	65	80
61-94	8	16	24	40	50	60

SUPER DUPER (Formerly Pocket Comics #1-4?)
Harvey Publications: No. 5, 1941 - No. 11, 1941

	GD	VG	FN	VF	VF/NM	NM-
5-Captain Freedom & Shock Gibson app.	69	138	207	442	759	1075
8,11	48	96	144	302	514	725

SUPER DUPER COMICS (Formerly Latest Comics?)
F. E. Howard Publ.: No. 3, May-June, 1947

	GD	VG	FN	VF	VF/NM	NM-
3-1st app. Mr. Monster	65	130	195	416	708	1000

SUPER FRIENDS (TV) (Also see Best of DC & Limited Collectors' Edition)
National Periodical Publications/DC Comics: Nov, 1976 - No. 47, Aug, 1981 (#14 is 44 pgs.)

	GD	VG	FN	VF	VF/NM	NM-
1-Superman, Batman, Robin, Wonder Woman, Aquaman, Atom, Wendy, Marvin & Wonder Dog begin (1st Super Friends)	6	12	18	37	66	95
2-Penquin-c/sty	3	6	9	16	23	30
3-5	3	6	9	14	20	26
6,8-10,14: 8-1st app. Jack O'Lantern. 9-1st app. Icemaiden. 14-Origin Wonder Twins	2	4	6	13	18	22
7-1st app. Wonder Twins & The Seraph	7	14	21	46	86	125
11-13,15-30: 13-1st app. Dr. Mist. 25-1st app. Fire as Green Fury. 28-Bizarro app.	2	4	6	9	13	16
13-16,20-23,25,32-(Whitman variants; low print run, no issue# on cover)	2	4	6	11	16	20
31,47: 31-Black Orchid app. 47-Origin Fire & Green Fury	2	4	6	10	14	18
32-46: 36,43-Plastic Man app.	2	4	6	8	11	14
TBP (2001, $14.95) r/#1,6-9,14,21,27 & Limited Collectors' Edition C-41; Alex Ross-c						15.00
...: Truth, Justice and Peace TPB (2003, $14.95) r/#10,12,13,25,28,29,31,36,37						15.00

NOTE: *Estrada a-1p, 2p. Orlando a-1p. Staton a-43, 45.*

SUPER FRIENDS (All ages stories with puzzles and games)(Based on Mattel toy line)
DC Comics: May, 2008 - No. 29, Sept, 2010 ($2.25/$2.99)

	GD	VG	FN	VF	VF/NM	NM-
1-29-Superman, Batman, Wonder Woman, Aquaman, Flash & Green Lantern. 29-Begin $2.99-c; Bat-Mite & Mr. Mxyzptlk app.						3.00
...: Calling All Super Friends TPB (2009, $12.99) r/#8-14; puzzles and games						13.00
...: For Justice TPB (2009, $12.99) r/#1-7; puzzles and games						13.00
...: Head of the Class TPB (2010, $12.99) r/#15-21; puzzles and games						13.00
...: Mystery in Space TPB (2011, $12.99) r/#22-28; puzzles and games						13.00

SUPER FUN
Gillmor Magazines: Jan, 1956 (By A.W. Nugent)

	GD	VG	FN	VF	VF/NM	NM-
1-Comics, puzzles, cut-outs by A.W. Nugent	9	18	27	50	65	80

SUPER FUNNIES (...Western Funnies #3,4)
Superior Comics Publishers Ltd. (Canada): Dec, 1953 - No. 4, Sept, 1954

	GD	VG	FN	VF	VF/NM	NM-
1-(3-D, 10¢)-...Presents Dopey Duck; make your own 3-D glasses cut-out inside front-c; did not come w/glasses	39	78	117	231	378	525
2-Horror & crime satire	15	30	45	86	133	180
3-Phantom Ranger-c/s; Geronimo, Billy the Kid app.	10	20	30	56	76	95
4-Phantom Ranger-c/story	10	20	30	56	76	95

SUPERGIRL
DC Comics: Feb. 1944

nn - Ashcan comic, not distributed to newsstands, only for in-house use. Cover art is Boy Commandos #1 with interior being Action Comics #80. A copy sold for $15,750 in 2008.

SUPERGIRL (See Action, Adventure #281, Brave & the Bold, Crisis on Infinite Earths #7, Daring New Advs. of..., Super DC Giant, Superman Family, & Super-Team Family)

SUPERGIRL
National Periodical Publ.: Nov, 1972 - No. 9, Dec-Jan, 1973-74; No. 10, Sept-Oct, 1974 (1st solo title)(20¢)

	GD	VG	FN	VF	VF/NM	NM-
1-Zatanna back-up stories begin, end #5	12	24	36	81	176	270
2-4,6,7,9	4	8	12	25	40	55
5,8,10: 5-Zatanna origin-r. 8-JLA x-over; Batman cameo. 10-Prez	4	8	12	27	44	60

NOTE: *Zatanna in #1-5, 7(Guest); Prez app. in #10. #1-10 are 20¢ issues.*

SUPERGIRL (Formerly Daring New Adventures of...)
DC Comics: No. 14, Dec, 1983 - No. 23, Sept, 1984

	GD	VG	FN	VF	VF/NM	NM-
14-23: 16-Ambush Bug app. 20-JLA & New Teen Titans app.						4.00
...Movie Special (1985)-Adapts movie; Morrow-a; photo back-c						4.00

Supergirl #79 © DC

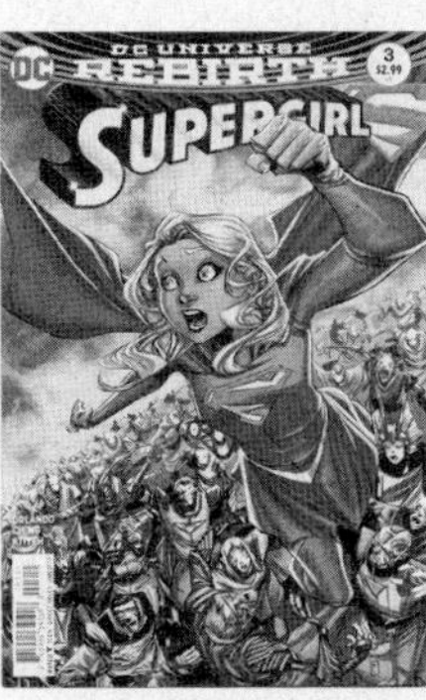

Supergirl (2016 series) #3 © DC

Super Goof #45 © DIS

	GD 2.0	VG 4.0	FN 6.0	VF 8.0	VF/NM 9.0	NM- 9.2

SUPERGIRL
DC Comics: Feb, 1994 - No. 4, May, 1994 ($1.50, limited series)
1-4: Guice-a(i) 4.00

SUPERGIRL (See Showcase '96 #8)
DC Comics: Sept, 1996 - No. 80, May, 2003 ($1.95/$1.99/$2.25/$2.50)

	GD	VG	FN	VF	VF/NM	NM-
1-Peter David scripts & Gary Frank-c/a	2	4	6	9	12	15

1-2nd printing 3.00
2,4-9: 4-Gorilla Grodd-c/app. 6-Superman-c/app. 9-Last Frank-a 4.00
3-Final Night, Gorilla Grodd app. 5.00
10-19: 14-Genesis x-over. 16-Power Girl app. 3.50
20-35: 20-Millennium Giants x-over; Superman app. 23-Steel-c/app. 24-Resurrection Man x-over. 25-Comet ID revealed; begin $1.99-c 3.00
36-46: 36,37-Young Justice x-over 3.00
47-49,51-74: 47-Begin $2.25-c. 51-Adopts costume from animated series. 54-Green Lantern app. 59-61-Our Worlds at War x-over. 62-Two-Face-c/app. 66,67-Demon-c/app. 68-74-Mary Marvel app. 70-Nauck-a. 73-Begin $2.50-c 3.00
50-($3.95) Supergirl's final battle with the Carnivore 4.00
75-80: 75-Re-intro. Kara Zor-El; cover swipe of Action Comics #252 by Haynes; Benes-a. 78-Spectre app. 80-Last issue; Romita-c 3.00
#1,000,000 (11/98) 853rd Century x-over 3.00
Annual 1 (1996, $2.95)-Legends of the Dead Earth 4.00
Annual 2 (1997, $3.95)-Pulp Heroes; LSH app.; Chiodo-c 4.00
...: Many Happy Returns TPB (2003, $14.95) r/#75-80; intro. by Peter David 15.00
...Plus (2/97, $2.95) Capt.(Mary) Marvel-c/app.; David-s/Frank-a 4.00
.../Prysm Double-Shot 1 (Feb, 1998, $1.95) w/Prysm (Teen Titans) 3.00
...: Wings (2001, $5.95) Elseworlds; DeMatteis-s/Tolagson-a 6.00
TPB-('98, $14.95) r/Showcase '96 #8 & Supergirl #1-9 15.00

SUPERGIRL (See Superman/Batman #8 & #19)
DC Comics: No. 0, Oct, 2005 - No. 67, Oct, 2011 ($2.99)
0-Reprints Superman/Batman #19 with white variant of that cover 3.00
1-Loeb-s/Churchill-a; two covers by Churchill & Turner; Power Girl app. 5.00
1-2nd printing with B&W sketch variant of Turner-c 3.00
1-3rd printing with variant-c homage to Action Comics #252 by Churchill 3.00
2-4: 2-Teen Titans app. 3-Outsiders app.; covers by Turner & Churchill 3.00
5-($3.99) Supergirl vs. Supergirl; Churchill & Turner-c 4.00
6-49: 6-9-One Year Later; Power Girl app. 11-Intro. Powerboy. 12-Terra debut; Conner-a 20-Amazons Attack x-over. 21,22-Karate Kid app. 28-31-Resurrection Man app. 35,36-New Krypton x-over; Argo City story re-told; Superwoman app. 35-Ross-c. 36-Zor-El dies 3.00
50-($4.99) Lana Lang Insect Queen app.; Superwoman returns; back-up story co-written by Helen Slater with Chiang-a; Turner-c 5.00
50-Variant cover by Middleton 6.00
51-67: 51-52-New Krypton. 52-Brainiac 5 app. 53-57-Bizarro-Girl app. 55-63-Reeder-c 3.00
58-DC 75th Anniversary variant cover by Conner 6.00
Annual 1 (11/09, $3.99) Origin of Superwoman 4.00
Annual 2 (12/10, $4.99) Silver Age Legion of Super-Heroes app.; Reeder-c 5.00
...: Beyond Good and Evil TPB (2008, $17.99) r/#23-27 and Action Comics #850 18.00
...: Bizarrogirl TPB (2011, $19.99) r/#53-59 & Annual #2 20.00
...: Candor TPB (2007, $14.99) r/#6-9; and pages from JSA Classified #2, Superman #223, Superman/Batman #27 and JLA #122,123 15.00
...: Death & The Family TPB (2010, $17.99) r/#48-50 & Annual #1 18.00
...: Friends & Fugitives TPB (2010, $17.99) r/#43,45-47; Action Comics #881,882 18.00
...: Identity TPB (2007, $19.99) r/#10-16 and story from DCU Infinite Holiday Special 20.00
...: Power TPB (2006, $14.99) r/#1-5 and Superman/Batman #19; variant-c gallery 15.00
...: Way of the World TPB (2009, $17.99) r/#28-33 18.00
...: Who is Superwoman TPB (2009, $17.99) r/#34,37-42 18.00

SUPERGIRL (DC New 52)
DC Comics: Nov, 2011 - No. 40, May, 2015 ($2.99)
1-New origin; Green & Johnson-s/Asrar-a/c; Superman app. 4.00
2-40: 2,3-Superman app. 8-Pérez-a. 14-17-H'El on Earth tie-in. 17-Wonder Woman app. 19,20-Power Girl app. 19-Power Girl gets classic costume. 23,24-Cyborg Superman app. 26-28-Lobo app. 28-33-Kara joins Red Lanterns. 33-Gen13 app. 36-40-Maxima app. 3.00
#0-(11/12, $2.99) Kara's escape from Krypton 3.00
...: Futures End 1 (11/14, $2.99, regular-c) Five years later; Cyborg Superman app. 3.00
...: Futures End 1 (11/14, $3.99, 3-D cover) 4.00
... Special Edition 1 (12/15, $1.00) reprints #1 with Supergirl TV banner at top of cover 3.00

SUPERGIRL (DC Rebirth)
DC Comics: Nov, 2016 - No. 20, Jun, 2018 ($2.99)
1-7: 1-Orlando-s/Ching-a; Cyborg Superman app. 3.00
8-18-($3.99) 8-Superman & Emerald Empress app. 9-11-Batgirl app. 12-Fatal Five. 12-18-Variant covers by Stanley "Artgerm" Lau 4.00
Annual 1 (10/17, $4.99) The new Fatal Five app.; takes place between #11,12 5.00
...: Rebirth 1 (10/16, $2.99) Orlando-s/Lupacchino-a; gets the Kara Danvers identity 3.00

SUPERGIRL AND THE LEGION OF SUPER-HEROES (Continues from Legion of Super-Heroes #15, Apr, 2006)(Continues as Legion of Super-Heroes #37)
DC Comics: No. 16, May, 2006 - No. 36, Jan, 2008 ($2.99)
16-Supergirl appears in the 31st century 4.00
16-2nd printing 3.00
17-36: 23-Mon-El cameo. 24,25-Mon-El returns 3.00
...: Adult Education TPB (2007, $14.99) r/#20-25 & LSH #6,9,13-15 15.00
...: Dominator War TPB (2007, $14.99) r/#26-30 15.00
...: Strange Visitor From Another Century TPB (2006, $14.99) r/#16-19 & LSH #11,12,15 15.00
...: The Quest For Cosmic Boy TPB (2008, $14.99) r/#31-36 15.00

SUPERGIRL: BEING SUPER
DC Comics: Feb, 2017 - No. 4, Aug, 2017 ($5.99, limited series)
1-4-Mariko Tamaki-s/Joëlle Jones-a 6.00

SUPERGIRL: COSMIC ADVENTURES IN THE 8TH GRADE (Cartoony all-ages title)
DC Comics: Feb, 2008 - No. 6, Jul, 2009 ($2.50, limited series)
1-6: 1-Supergirl lands on Earth; Eric Jones-a. 5,6-Comet & Streaky app. 3.00
TPB (2009, $12.99) r/#1-6; sketch art 13.00

SUPERGIRL/LEX LUTHOR SPECIAL (Supergirl and Team Luthor on-c)
DC Comics: 1993 ($2.50, 68 pgs., one-shot)
1-Pin-ups by Byrne & Thibert 4.00

SUPERGOD (Warren Ellis'...)
Avatar Press: Oct, 2009 - No. 5, Nov, 2010 ($3.99, limited series)
1-5-Warren Ellis-s/Garrie Gastony-a; multiple covers on each 4.00

SUPER GOOF (Walt Disney) (See Dynabrite & The Phantom Blot)
Gold Key No. 1-57/Whitman No. 58 on: Oct, 1965 - No. 74, July, 1984

	GD	VG	FN	VF	VF/NM	NM-
1	4	8	12	28	47	65
2-5	3	6	9	16	23	30
6-10	3	6	9	14	19	24
11-20	2	4	6	8	11	14
21-30	1	3	4	6	8	10
31-50	1	2	3	4	5	7
51-57						6.00
58,59 (Whitman)	1	2	3	5	6	8
60(8/80), 62(11/80) 3-pack only (scarce)	6	12	18	37	66	95
61(9-10/80) 3-pack only (rare)	8	16	24	56	108	160
63-66('81)	1	2	3	5	6	8
63 (1/81, 40¢-c) Cover price error variant (scarce)	2	4	6	11	16	20
67-69: 67(2/82), 68(2-3/82), 69(3/82)						6.00
70-74 (#90180 on-c; pre-pack, nd, nd code): 70(5/83), 71(8/83), 72(5/84), 73(6/84), 74(7/84)	3	6	9	15	22	28

NOTE: *Reprints in #16, 24, 28, 29, 37, 38, 43, 45, 46, 54(1/2), 56-58, 65(1/2), 72(r-#2).*

SUPER GREEN BERET (Tod Holton...)
Lightning Comics (Milson Publ. Co.): Apr, 1967 - No. 2, Jun, 1967

	GD	VG	FN	VF	VF/NM	NM-
1-(25¢, 68 pgs)	5	10	15	30	50	70
2-(25¢, 68 pgs)	3	6	9	21	33	45

SUPER HEROES (See Giant-Size... & Marvel...)

SUPER HEROES
Dell Publishing Co.: Jan, 1967 - No. 4, June, 1967

	GD	VG	FN	VF	VF/NM	NM-
1-Origin & 1st app. Fab 4	4	8	12	28	47	65
2-4	3	6	9	16	24	32

SUPER-HEROES BATTLE SUPER-GORILLAS (See DC Special #16)
National Periodical Publications: Winter, 1976 (52 pgs., all reprints, one-shot)

	GD	VG	FN	VF	VF/NM	NM-
1-Superman, Batman, Flash stories; Infantino-a(p)	2	4	6	11	16	20

SUPER HEROES VERSUS SUPER VILLAINS
Archie Publications (Radio Comics): July, 1966 (no month given)(68 pgs.)

	GD	VG	FN	VF	VF/NM	NM-
1-Flyman, Black Hood, Web, Shield-r; Reinman-a	6	12	18	37	66	95

SUPER HERO SQUAD (See Marvel Super Hero Squad)

SUPERHERO WOMEN, THE - FEATURING THE FABULOUS FEMALES OF MARVEL COMICS (See Fireside Book Series)

SUPERICHIE (Formerly Super Richie)
Harvey Publications: No. 5, Oct, 1976 - No. 18, Jan, 1979 (52 pgs. giants)

	GD	VG	FN	VF	VF/NM	NM-
5-Origin/1st app. new costumes for Rippy & Crashman	2	4	6	9	13	16
6-18	2	4	6	8	10	12

SUPERIOR
Marvel Comics (ICON): Dec, 2010 - No. 7, Mar, 2012 ($2.99/$4.99)

Superior Iron Man #5 © MAR

Super-Magician Comics #8 © C-N

Superman #41 © DC

GD VG FN VF VF/NM NM-
2.0 4.0 6.0 8.0 9.0 9.2

1-6-Mark Millar-s/Leinil Yu-a. 1-1st & 2nd printings 3.00
7-($4.99) Bonus preview of Supercrooks #1 5.00
... World Record Special 1 (12/11, $2.99, B&W) Comic created in less than 12 hours 3.00

SUPERIOR CARNAGE
Marvel Comics: Sept, 2013 - No. 5, Jan, 2014 ($3.99)

1-5: 1-Shinick-s/Segovia-a; covers by Crain & Checchetto. 2-5-Superior Spider-Man app. 4.00
Annual 1 (4/14, $4.99) Bunn-s/Jacinto & Henderson-a; follows #5; Kasady in prison 5.00

SUPERIOR FOES OF SPIDER-MAN (Superior Spider-Man)
Marvel Comics: Sept, 2013 - No. 17, Jan, 2015 ($3.99)

1-17: 1-Boomerang, Shocker, Overdrive, Speed Demon & Beetle team; Spencer-s 4.00

SUPERIOR IRON MAN (Follows events of the Avengers & X-Men: Axis series)
Marvel Comics: Jan, 2015 - No. 9, Aug, 2015 ($3.99)

1-9: 1-Tom Taylor-s/Yildiray Cinar-a. 1-4-Daredevil app. 4.00

SUPERIOR SPIDER-MAN (Follows Amazing Spider-Man #700)
Marvel Comics: Mar, 2013 - No. 31, Jun, 2014; No. 32, Oct, 2014 - No. 33, Nov, 2014 ($3.99)

1-Doc Ock as Spider-Man; new Sinister Six app.; Slott-s/Stegman-a 8.00
1-Variant baby-c by Skottie Young 10.00
2-6: 4,5-Camuncoli-a. 4-Green Goblin cameo. 6-Ramos-a 5.00
6AU (5/13, $3.99) Alternate timeline Age of Ultron tie-in; Gage-s/Soy-a 4.00
7-24: 7,8-Ramos-a; Avengers app. 9-Peter's memories removed. 14-New costume. 17-19-Spider-Man 2099 app. 20-Black Cat app. 22-24-Venom app. 4.00
25-($4.99) Superior Venom vs. the Avengers; Ramos-a 5.00
26-30: 27-Goblin Nation begins. 29-Spider-Man 2099 app. 4.00
31-($5.99) Goblin Nation finale; covers by Camuncoli & Campbell; Silver Surfer bonus 6.00
32,33-($4.99) Edge of Spider-Verse tie-ins; takes place during issue #19 5.00
Annual 1 (1/14, $4.99) Blackout app.; Gage-s/Rodriguez-a 5.00
Annual 2 (5/14, $4.99) Leads into Superior Spider-Man #30; Gage-s/Rodriguez-a 5.00

SUPERIOR SPIDER-MAN TEAM UP
Marvel Comics: Sept, 2013 - No. 12, Jun, 2014 ($3.99)

1-10: 1-Avengers app. 8-Namor app. 9,10-Daredevil & The Punisher app. 4.00
... Special 1 (12/13, $4.99) Hulk & the original X-Men app.; Dialynas-a/Lozano-c 5.00

SUPERIOR STORIES
Nesbit Publishers, Inc.: May-June, 1955 - No. 4, Nov-Dec, 1955

1-The Invisible Man by H.G. Wells 24 48 72 140 230 320
2-4: 2-The Pirate of the Gulf by J.H. Ingrahams. 3-Wreck of the Grosvenor by William Clark Russell. 4-The Texas Rangers by O'Henry 11 22 33 64 90 115
NOTE: *Morisi c/a in all. Kiwanis stories in #3 & 4. #4 has photo of Gene Autry on-c.*

SUPER MAGIC (Super Magician Comics #2 on)
Street & Smith Publications: May, 1941

V1#1-Blackstone the Magician-c/story; origin/1st app. Rex King (Black Fury); Charles Sultan-c; Blackstone-c begin 200 400 600 1280 2190 3100

SUPER MAGICIAN COMICS (Super Magic #1)
Street & Smith Publications: No. 2, Sept, 1941 - V5#8, Feb-Mar, 1947

V1#2-Blackstone the Magician continues; Rex King, Man of Adventure app. 81 162 243 518 884 1250
3-Tao-Anwar, Boy Magician begins 50 100 150 315 533 750
4-7,9-12: 4-Origin Transo. 11-Supersnipe app. 45 90 135 284 480 675
8-Abbott & Costello story (1st app?, 11/42) 48 96 144 302 514 725
V2#1-The Shadow app. 45 90 135 284 480 675
2-12: 5-Origin Tigerman. 8-Red Dragon begins 28 56 84 165 270 375
V3#1-12: 5-Origin Mr. Twilight 26 52 78 154 252 350
V4#1-4,6-12: 11-Nigel Elliman Ace of Magic begins (3/46) 21 42 63 126 206 285
5-KKK-c/sty 39 78 117 240 395 550
V5#1-6 21 42 63 122 199 275
7,8-Red Dragon by Edd Cartier-c/a 40 80 120 246 411 575
NOTE: *Jack Binder c-1-14(most). Red Dragon c-V5#7, 8.*

SUPERMAN (See Action Comics, Advs. of..., All-New Coll. Ed., All-Star Comics, Best of DC, Brave & the Bold, Cosmic Odyssey, DC Comics Presents, Heroes Against Hunger, JLA, The Kents, Krypton Chronicles, Limited Coll. Ed., Man of Steel, Phantom Zone, Power Record Comics, Special Edition, Steel, Super Friends, Superman: The Man of Steel, Superman: The Man of Tomorrow, Taylor's Christmas Tabloid, Three-Dimension Advs., World Of Krypton, World Of Metropolis, World Of Smallville & World's Finest)

SUPERMAN (Becomes Adventures of...#424 on)
National Periodical Publ./DC Comics: Summer, 1939 - No. 423, Sept, 1986
(#1-5 are quarterly)

1(nn)-1st four Action stories reprinted; origin Superman by Siegel & Shuster; has a new 2 pg. origin plus 4 pgs. omitted in Action story; see The Comics Magazine #1 & More Fun #14-17 for Superman prototype app.; cover r/splash page from Action #10; 1st pin-up Superman on back-c - 1st pin-up in comics 86,000 172,000 344,000 645,000 972,500 1,300,000
1-Reprint, Oversize 13-1/2x10". **WARNING**: This comic is an exact duplicate reprint of the original except for its size. DC published it in 1978 with a second cover titling it as a Famous First Edition. There have been many reported cases of the outer cover being removed and the interior sold as the original edition. The reprint with the new outer cover removed is practically worthless. See Famous First Edition for value.
2-All daily strip-r; full pg. ad for N.Y. World's Fair 2900 5800 8700 21,750 45,875 70,000
3-2nd story-r from Action #5; 3rd story-r from Action #6 1600 3200 4800 11,700 24,000 38,000
4-2nd mention of Daily Planet (Spr/40); also see Action #23; 2nd & 3rd app. Luthor (red-headed; also see Action #23); first issue of title to feature original stories 919 1838 2757 6709 11,855 17,000
5-4th Luthor app. (grey hair) 730 1460 2190 5329 9415 13,500
6,7: 6-1st splash pg. in a Superman comic. 7-1st Perry White? (11-12/40) 492 984 1476 3592 6346 9100
8-10: 10-5th app. Luthor (1st bald Luthor, 5-6/41) 438 876 1314 3197 5649 8100
11-13,15: 13-Jimmy Olsen & Luthor app. 349 698 1047 2443 4272 6100
14-Patriotic Shield-c classic by Fred Ray 1000 2000 3000 7400 13,200 19,000
16,19,20: 16-1st Lois Lane-c this title (5-6/42); 2nd Lois-c after Action #29 300 600 900 2040 3570 5100
17-Hitler, Hirohito-c 975 1950 2919 7100 12,550 18,000
18-Classic WWII-c 320 640 960 2240 3920 5600
21,22,25: 25-Clark Kent's only military service; Fred Ray's only super-hero story 213 426 639 1363 2332 3300
23-Classic periscope-c 314 628 942 2198 3849 5500
24-Classic Jack Burnley flag-c 423 846 1269 3067 5384 7700
26-Classic war-c 337 674 1011 2359 4130 5900
27-29: 27,29-Lois Lane-c. 28-Lois Lane Girl Reporter series begins, ends #40,42 181 362 543 1158 1979 2800
28-Overseas edition for Armed Forces; same as reg. #28 81 362 543 1158 1979 2800
30-Origin & 1st app. Mr. Mxyztplk (9-10/44)(pronounced "Mix-it-plk") in comic books; name later became Mxyzptlk ("Mix-yez-pit-l-ick"); the character was inspired by a combination of the name of Al Capp's Joe Blyfstyk (the little man with the black cloud over his head) & the devilish antics of Bugs Bunny; he first app. in newspapers 3/7/44; Superman flies for the first time 300 600 900 2070 3635 5200
31-40: 33-(3-4/45)-3rd app. Mxyztplk. 35,36-Lois Lane-c. 38-Atomic bomb story (1-2/46); delayed because of gov't censorship; Superman shown reading Batman #32 on cover. 40-Mxyztplk-c 142 284 426 909 1555 2200
41-50: 42-Lois Lane-c. 45-Lois Lane as Superwoman (see Action #60 for 1st app.). 46-(5-6/47)-1st app. Superboy this title? 48-1st time Superman travels thru time 119 238 357 762 1306 1850
51,52: 51-Lois Lane-c 113 226 339 718 1234 1750
53-Third telling of Superman origin; 10th anniversary issue ('48); classic origin-c by Boring 366 732 1098 2562 4481 6400
54,56-60: 57-Lois Lane as Superwoman-c. 58-Intro Tiny Trix. 59-Early use of heat vision (possibly first time) 113 226 339 718 1234 1750
55-Used in **SOTI**, pg. 33 115 230 345 730 1253 1775
61-Origin Superman retold; origin Green Kryptonite (1st Kryptonite story); Superman returns to Krypton for 1st time & sees his parents for 1st time since infancy, discovers he's not an Earth man 190 380 570 1207 2079 2950
62-70: 62-Orson Welles-c/story. 65-1st Krypton Foes: Mala, Kizo, & U-Ban. 66-2nd Superbaby story. 67-Perry Como-c/story. 68-1st Luthor-c this title (see Action Comics) 111 222 333 705 1215 1725
71-75: 74-2nd Luthor-c this title. 75-Some have #74 on-c 108 216 324 686 1181 1675
76-Batman x-over; Superman & Batman learn each other's I.D. for the 1st time (5-6/52) (also see World's Finest #71) 354 708 1062 2478 4339 6200
77-81: 78-Last 52 pg. issue; 1st meeting of Lois Lane & Lana Lang. 81-Used in **POP**, pg. 88. 81-"Superwoman From Space" story 95 190 285 603 1039 1475
82-87,89,90: 89-1st Curt Swan-c in title 87 174 261 553 952 1350
88-Prankster, Toyman & Luthor team-up 90 180 270 576 988 1400
91-95: 95-Last precode issue (2/55) 79 158 237 502 864 1225
96-99: 96-Mr. Mxyztplk-c/story 73 146 219 467 796 1125
100 (9-10/55)-Shows cover to #1 on-c 258 516 774 1651 2826 4000
101-105,107-110: 109-1st S.A. issue 52 104 156 328 702 1075
106 (7/56)-Retells origin 53 106 159 334 730 1125
111-120 47 94 141 296 636 975
121,122,124-127,129: 127-Origin/1st app. Titano. 129-Intro/origin Lori Lemaris, The Mermaid 41 82 123 256 553 850
123-Pre-Supergirl tryout-c/story (8/58). 165 330 660 1540 3520 5500
128-(4/59)-Red Kryptonite used. Bruce Wayne x-over who protects Superman's i.d. (3rd story) 42 84 126 265 570 875
130-(7/59)-2nd app, Krypto, the Superdog with Superman (see Sup.'s Pal Jimmy Olsen #29) (all other previous app. w/Superboy) 43 86 129 271 586 900
131-139: 135-2nd Lori Lemaris app. 139-Lori Lemaris app.; 34 68 102 199 425 650

Superman #165 © DC

Superman #416 © DC

Superman (2nd series) #50 © DC

GD VG FN VF VF/NM NM-
2.0 4.0 6.0 8.0 9.0 9.2

140-1st Blue Kryptonite & Bizarro Supergirl; origin Bizarro Jr. #1
34 68 102 206 423 640
141-145,148: 142-2nd Batman x-over 29 58 87 170 365 560
146-(7/61)-Superman's life story; back-up hints at Earth II. Classic-c
39 78 117 235 543 850
147(8/61)-7th Legion app; 1st app. Legion of Super-Villains; 1st app. Adult Legion; swipes-c to Adv. #247 36 72 108 216 458 700
149(11/61)-8th Legion app. (cameo); "The Death of Superman" imaginary story; last 10¢ issue 36 72 108 216 446 675
150,151,153,154,157,159,160: 157-Gold Kryptonite used (see Adv. #299); Mon -El app.; Lightning Lad cameo (11/62) 13 26 39 89 195 300
152,155,156,158,162: 152(4/62)-15th Legion app. 155-(8/62)-Legion app; Lightning Man & Cosmic Man, & Adult Legion app. 156,162-Legion app. 158-1st app. Superman as Nightwing & Jimmy Olsen as Flamebird & Nor-Kann of Kandor (12/62)
13 26 39 91 201 310
161-1st told death of Ma and Pa Kent 14 28 42 94 207 320
161-2nd printing (1987, $1.25)-New DC logo; sold thru So Much Fun Toy Stores (cover title: Superman Classic) 4.00
163-166,168-180: 166-XMas-c. 168-All Luthor issue; JFK tribute/memorial. 169-Bizarro Invasion of Earth-c/story; last Sally Selwyn. 170-Pres. Kennedy story is finally published after delay from #168 due to assassination. 172,173-Legion cameos. 174-Super-Mxyzptlk; Bizarro app. 176-Legion of Super-Pets 10 20 30 69 147 225
167-New origin Brainiac, text reference of Brainiac 5 descending from adopted human son Brainiac II; intro Tharla (later Luthor's wife) 13 26 39 89 195 300
181,182,184-186,188-192,194-196,198,200: 181-1st 2465 story/series. 182-1st S.A. app. of The Toyman (1/66). 189-Origin/destruction of Krypton II.
8 16 24 56 108 160
183 (Giant G-18) 11 22 33 73 157 240
187,193,197 (Giants G-23,G-31,G-36) 9 18 27 59 117 175
199-1st Superman/Flash race (8/67): also see Flash #175 & World's Finest #198,199 (r-in Limited Coll. Ed. C-48) 36 72 108 266 596 925
201,203-206,208-211,213-216: 213-Brainiac-5 app. 216-Last 12¢ issue
6 12 18 37 66 95
202 (80-pg. Giant G-42)-All Bizarro issue 6 12 18 41 76 110
207,212,217 (Giants G-48,G-54,G-60): 207-30th anniversary Superman (6/68)
6 12 18 41 76 110
218-221,223-226,228-231 5 10 15 33 57 80
222,239(Giants, G-66,G-84) 6 12 18 38 69 100
227,232(Giants, G-72,G-78): 232-All Krypton issue 6 12 18 38 69 100
233-2nd app. Morgan Edge; Clark Kent switches from newspaper reporter to TV newscaster; all Kryptonite on Earth destroyed; classic Neal Adams-c; 1st Fabulous World of Krypton story; Superman pin-up by Swan 14 28 42 93 204 315
234-238 5 10 15 31 53 75
240-Kaluta-a; last 15¢ issue 4 8 12 27 44 60
241-244 (All 52 pgs.): 241-New Wonder Woman app. 243-G.A.-r/#38
4 8 12 28 47 65
245-Also listed as DC 100 Pg. Super Spectacular #7; Air Wave, Kid Eternity, Hawkman-r; Atom-r/Atom #3 9 18 27 60 120 180
246-248,250,251,253 (All 52 pgs.): 246-G.A.-r/#40. 248-World of Krypton story. 251-G.A.-r/#45. 253-Finlay-a, 2 pgs., G.A.-r/#1 4 8 12 28 47 65
249,254-Neal Adams-a. 249-(52 pgs.); 1st app. Terra-Man (Swan-a) & origin-s by Dick Dillin (p) & Neal Adams (inks) 5 10 15 35 63 90
252-Also listed as DC 100 Pg. Super Spectacular #13; Ray(r/Smash #17), Black Condor, (r/Crack #18), Hawkman(r/Flash #24); Starman-r/Adv. #67; Dr. Fate & Spectre-r/More Fun #57; N. Adams-c 10 20 30 66 138 210
255-271,273-277,279-283: 263-Photo-c. 264-1st app. Steve Lombard. 276-Intro Capt. Thunder. 279-Batman, Batgirl app. 282-Luthor battlesuit 3 6 9 14 19 24
272,278,284-All 100 pgs. G.A.-r in all. 272-r/2nd app. Mr. Mxyztplk from Action #80
5 10 15 30 50 70
285-299: 289-Partial photo-c. 292-Origin Lex Luthor retold
2 4 6 9 13 16
300-(6/76) Superman in the year 2001 3 6 9 21 33 45
301-316,318-350: 301,320-Solomon Grundy app. 323-Intro. Atomic Skull. 327-329-(44 pgs.). 327-Kobra app. 330-More facts revealed about I.D. 331,332-1st/2nd app. Master Jailer. 335-Mxyzptlk marries Ms. Bgbznz. 336-Rose & Thorn app. 338-(8/79) 40th Anniv. issue; the bottled city of Kandor enlarged. 344-Frankenstein & Dracula app.
1 3 4 6 8 10
317-Classic Neal Adams kryptonite cover 3 6 9 17 26 35
321-323,325-327,329-332,335-345,348,350 (Whitman variants; low print run; no issue # on cover) 2 4 6 9 13 16
351-399: 353-Brief origin. 354,355,357-Superman 2020 stories (354-Debut of Superman III). 356-World of Krypton story (also #360,367,375). 366-Fan letter by Todd McFarlane. 369-Christmas-c. 372-Superman 2021 story. 376-Free 6 pg. preview Daring New Advs. of Supergirl. 377-Terra-Man-c/app.; free 16 pg. preview Masters of the Universe

GD VG FN VF VF/NM NM-
2.0 4.0 6.0 8.0 9.0 9.2

379-Bizarro World app. 1 2 3 4 5 7
400 (10/84, $1.50, 68 pgs.)-Many top artists featured; Chaykin painted cover, Miller back-c; Steranko-s/a (10 pages) 2 4 6 8 10 12
401-422: 405-Super-Batman story. 408-Nuclear Holocaust-c/story. 411-Special Julius Schwartz tribute issue. 414,415-Crisis x-over. 422-Horror-c by Bolland 6.00
409-(7/85) Variant-c with Superman/Superhombre logo (no reported sales)
423-Alan Moore scripts; Curt Swan-a/George Pérez-a(i); "Whatever Happened to the Man of Tomorrow?" story, cont'd in Action #583 2 4 6 8 12 15
Annual 1 (10/60, 84 pgs.)-Reprints 1st Supergirl story/Action #252; r/Lois Lane #1; Krypto-r (1st Silver Age DC annual) 84 168 252 672 1511 2350
Annual 2 (Win, 1960-61)-Super-villain issue; Brainiac, Titano, Metallo, Bizarro origin-r
35 70 105 252 564 875
Annual 3 (Sum, 1961)-Strange Lives of Superman 24 48 72 168 372 575
Annual 4(Win, 1961-62)-11th Legion app; 1st Legion origins (text & pictures); advs. in time, space & on alien worlds 20 40 60 135 300 465
Annual 5 (Sum, 1962)-All Krypton issue 16 32 48 112 249 385
Annual 6 (Win, 1962-63)-Legion-r/Adv. #247; Superman Family portrait on back-c
14 28 42 97 214 330
Annual 7 (Sum, 1963)-Silver Anniversary Issue; origin-r/Superman-Batman team/Adv. #275; cover gallery of famous issues 11 22 33 76 163 250
Annual 8 (Win, 1963-64)-All origins issue 11 22 33 73 157 240
Annual 9 (8/64)-Was advertised but came out as 80 Page Giant #1 instead
Annual 9 (1983)-Toth/Austin-a 1 2 3 4 5 7
Annuals 10,12: 10(1984, $1.25)-M. Anderson-i. 12(1986)-Bolland-c 6.00
Annual 11 (1985) "For the Man Who Has Everything" story; Alan Moore-s/Dave Gibbons-a; Mongul and the Black Mercy app.; Wonder Woman, Batman & Robin app. (adapted for a Justice League Unlimited animated episode 4 8 12 23 37 50
Special 1-3 ('83-'85): 1-G. Kane-c/a; contains German-r 6.00
The Amazing World of Superman "Official Metropolis Edition" (1973, $2.00, treasury-size)-Origin retold; Wood-r(i) from Superboy #153,161; poster incl. (half price if poster missing)
4 8 12 27 44 60
11195 (2/79, $1.95, 224 pgs.)-Golden Press 4 8 12 23 37 50

NOTE: **N. Adams** a-249i, 254p; c-204-206, 210, 212-215, 219, 231i, 233-237, 240-243, 249-252, 254, 263, 307, 308, 313, 314, 317. **Adkins** a-323i. **Austin** c-368i. **Wayne Boring** art-late 1940's to early 1960's. **Buckler** a(p)-352, 363, 364, 369; c(p)-324-327, 356, 363, 368, 369, 373, 376, 378. **Burnley** a-252r; c-19-25, 30, 33, 34, 35p, 38p, 39p, 45p. **Fine** a-252r. **Kaluta** a-400. **Gil Kane** a-272r, 367, 372, 375, Special 2; c-374p, 375p, 377, 381, 382, 384-390, 392, Annual 9, Special 2. **Joe Kubert** c-216. **Morrow** a-238. **Mortimer** a-250r. **Perez** c-364p. **Fred Ray** a-25; c-6, 8-18. **Starlin** c-355. **Staton** a-354i, 355i. **Swan/Moldoff** c-149. **Williamson** a(i)-408-410, 412-416; c-408i, 409i. **Wrightson** a-400, 416.

SUPERMAN (2nd Series) (Title continues numbering from Adventures of Superman #649)
DC Comics: Jan, 1987 - No. 226, Apr, 2006; No. 650, May, 2006 - No. 714, Oct, 2011

0-(10/94) Zero Hour; released between #93 & #94 3.00
1-Byrne-c/a begins; intro new Metallo 2 4 6 8 10 12
2-8,10: 3-Legends x-over; Darkseid-c & app. 7-Origin/1st app. Rampage. 8-Legion app. 4.00
9-Joker-c 5.00
11-15,17-20,22-49,51,52,54-56,58-67: 11-1st new Mr. Mxyzptlk. 12-Lori Lemaris revived. 13-1st app. new Toyman. 13,14-Millennium x-over. 20-Doom Patrol app.; Supergirl cameo. 31-Mr. Mxyzptlk app. 37-Newsboy Legion app. 41-Lobo app. 44-Batman storyline, part 1. 45-Free extra 8 pgs. 54-Newsboy Legion story. 63-Aquaman x-over. 67-Last $1.00-c 3.00
16,21: 16-1st app. new Supergirl (4/88). 21-Supergirl-c/story; 1st app. Matrix who becomes new Supergirl 4.00
50-($1.50, 52 pgs.)-Clark Kent proposes to Lois 5.00
50-2nd printing 4.00
53-Clark reveals i.d. to Lois (Cont'd from Action #662) 4.00
53-2nd printing 3.00
57-($1.75, 52 pgs.) 4.00
68-72: 65,66,68-Deathstroke-c/stories. 70-Superman & Robin team-up 3.00
73-Doomsday cameo 6.00
74-Doomsday Pt. 2 (Cont'd from Justice League #69); Superman battles Doomsday
1 2 3 5 6 8
73,74-2nd printings 3.00
75-(1/93, $2.50)-Collector's Ed.; Doomsday Pt. 6; Superman dies; polybagged w/poster of funeral, obituary from Daily Planet, postage stamp & armband premiums (direct sales only)
3 6 9 16 23 30
75-Direct sales copy (no upc code, 1st print) 1 3 4 6 8 10
75-Direct sales copy (no upc code, 2nd-4th prints) 4.00
75-Newsstand copy w/upc code 1 3 4 6 8 10
75-Platinum Edition; given away to retailers 6 12 18 38 69 100
76,77-Funeral For a Friend parts 4 & 8 4.00
78-($1.95)-Collector's Edition with die-cut outer-c & mini poster; Doomsday cameo 4.00
78-($1.50)-Newsstand Edition w/poster and different-c; Doomsday-c & cameo 3.00
79-81,83-89: 83-Funeral for a Friend epilogue; new Batman (Azrael) cameo. 87,88-Bizarro-c/story 3.00
82-($3.50)-Collector's Edition w/all chromium-c; real Superman revealed; Green Lantern x-over from G.L. #46; no ads 6.00

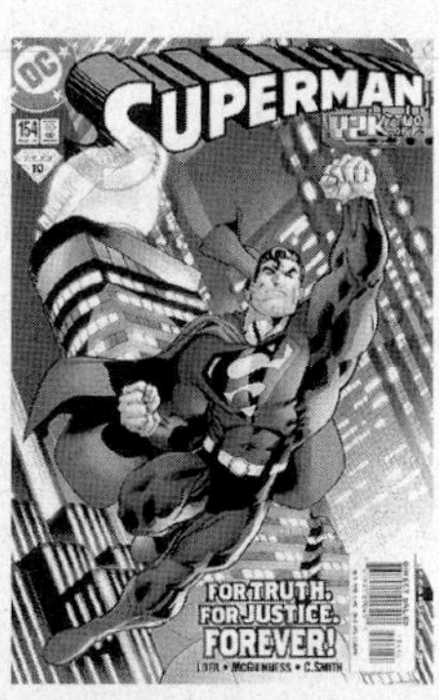

Superman (2nd series) #154 © DC

Superman (2011 series) #52 © DC

Superman (2016 series) #20 © DC

	GD 2.0	VG 4.0	FN 6.0	VF 8.0	VF/NM 9.0	NM- 9.2

82-($2.00, 44 pgs.)-Regular Edition w/different-c 4.00
90-99: 93-(9/94)-Zero Hour. 94-(11/94). 95-Atom app. 96-Brainiac returns 3.00
100-Death of Clark Kent foil-c 4.00
100-Newsstand 3.00
101-122: 101-Begin $1.95-c; Black Adam app. 105-Green Lantern app. 110-Plastic Man-c/app. 114-Brainiac app; Dwyer-c. 115-Lois leaves Metropolis. 116-(10/96)-1st app. Teen Titans by Jurgens & Perez in 8 pg. preview. 117-Final Night. 118-Wonder Woman app. 119-Legion app. 122-New powers 3.00
123-Collector's Edition w/glow in the dark-c, new costume 6.00
123-Standard ed., new costume 4.00
124-149: 128-Cyborg-c/app. 131-Birth of Lena Luthor. 132-Superman Red/Superman Blue. 134-Millennium Giants. 136,137-Superman 2999. 139-Starlin-a. 140-Grindberg-a 3.00
150-($2.95) Standard Ed.; Brainiac 2.0 app.; Jurgens-s 4.00
150-($3.95) Collector's Ed. w/holo-foil enhanced variant-c 5.00
151-158: 151-Loeb-s begins; Daily Planet reopens 3.00
159-174: 159-$2.25-c begin. 161-Joker-c/app. 162-Aquaman-c/app. 163-Young Justice app. 165-JLA app.; Ramos; Madureira, Liefeld, A. Adams, Wieringo, Churchill-a. 166-Collector's and reg. editions. 167-Return to Krypton. 168-Batman-c/app.(cont'd in Detective #756). 171-173-Our Worlds at War. 173-Sienkiewicz-a (2 pgs.). 174-Adopts black & red "S" logo 3.00
175-($3.50) Joker: Last Laugh x-over; Doomsday-c/app. 4.00
176-189,191-199: 176,180-Churchill-a. 180-Dracula app. 181-Bizarro-c/app. 184-Return to Krypton II. 189-Van Fleet-c. 192,193,195,197-199-New Supergirl app. 3.00
190-($2.25) Regular edition 3.00
190-($3.95) Double-Feature Issue; included reprint of Superman: The 10¢ Adventure 4.00
200-($3.50) Gene Ha-c/art by various; preview art by Yu & Bermejo 4.00
201-Mr Majestic-c/app.; cover swipe of Action #1 3.00
202,203-Godfall parts 3,6; Turner-c; Caldwell-a(p). 203-Jim Lee sketch pages 3.00
204-Jim Lee-c/a begins; Azzarello-s 3.00
204-Diamond Retailer Summit edition with sketch-c 5 10 15 31 53 75
205-214: 205-Two covers by Jim Lee and Michael Turner. 208-JLA app. 211-Battles Wonder Woman 3.00
215-($2.99) Conclusion to Azzarello/Lee arc 4.00
216-218,220-226: 216-Captain Marvel app. 221-Bizarro & Zoom app. 226-Earth-2 Superman story; Chaykin,Sale, Benes, Ordway-a 3.00
219-Omac/Sacrifice pt. 1; JLA app. 4.00
219-2nd printing with red background variant-c 3.00
(Title continues numbering from Adventures of Superman #649)
650-(5/06) One Year Later; Clark powerless after Infinite Crisis 4.00
651-665,667-669,671-674.676-680: 652-Begin $2.99-c. 654-658,662-664,667-Pacheco-a. 665-Origin of Jimmy Olsen. 671-673-Insect Queen. 676-680-Ross-c 3.00
666, 670,675-($3.99) 666-Simonson-a. 670-The Third Kryptonian. 675-Ross-c 4.00
681-699: 681-683-New Krypton x-over; Ross-c. 685-Mon-El freed from Phantom Zone. 694-Mon-El new costume. 698,699-Last Stand of New Krypton x-over 3.00
700-(8/10, $4.99) Cover by Gary Frank; Robinson-s; Straczynski-s begin 5.00
700-Variant-c by Risso 8.00
701-714: 701-"Grounded" begins; Straczynski-s/Cassaday-c. 704,706-Wilson-s 3.00
701-DC 75th Variant-c by Cassaday (Superman #1 swipe) 8.00
#1,000,000 (11/98) 853rd Century x-over; Gene Ha-c 3.00
Annual 1,2: 1 (1987)-No Byrne-a. 2 (1988)-Byrne-a; Newsboy Legion; Guardian returns 4.00
Annual 3-6 ('91-'94 68 pgs.): 1-Armageddon 2001 x-over; Batman app.; Austin-c(i) & part inks. 4-Eclipso app. 6-Elseworlds sty 4.00
Annual 3-2nd & 3rd printings; 3rd has silver ink 4.00
Annual 7 (1995, $3.95, 69 pgs.)-Year One story 4.00
Annual 8 (1996, $2.95)-Legends of the Dead Earth story 4.00
Annual 9 (1997, $3.95)-Pulp Heroes story 4.00
Annual 10 (1998, $2.95)-Ghosts; Wrightson-c 4.00
Annual 11 (1999, $2.95)-JLApe; Art Adams-c 4.00
Annual 12 (2000, $3.50)-Planet DC 4.00
Annual 13 (1/08, $3.99) Finale of Camelot Falls 4.00
Annual 14 (10/09, $3.99) Origin of Mon-El re-told; Pina-a/Guedes-c 4.00
...: 80 Page Giant (2/99, $4.95) Jurgens-c 6.00
...: 80 Page Giant 1 (5/10, $5.99) Lopresti-c; short stories by various 6.00
...: 80 Page Giant 2 (6/99, $4.95) Harris-c 6.00
...: 80 Page Giant 3 (11/00, $5.95) Nowlan-c; art by various 6.00
...: 80 Page Giant 2011 (4/11, $5.99) Nguyen-c; art by various; Bizarros app. 6.00
Special 1 (1992, $3.50, 68 pgs.)-Simonson-c/a 6.00

SUPERMAN (DC New 52)
DC Comics: Nov, 2011 - No. 52, Jul, 2016 ($2.99/$3.99)

1-Pérez-s/c; Merino-a 2 4 6 10 14 18
1-Variant-c by Jim Lee 18.00
2-23: 3-6-Nicola Scott-a. 6-Supergirl app. 13-Clark quits job. 14-17-H'El on Earth x-over with Superboy & Supergirl. 17-H'El on Earth conclusion. 19,20-Orion app. 3.00
23.1, 23.2, 23.3, 23.4 (11/13, $2.99, regular covers) 3.00
23.1 (11/13, $3.99, 3-D cover) "Bizarro #1" on cover; Fisch-s/Kuder-c/Jeff Johnson-a 5.00
23.2 (11/13, $3.99, 3-D cover) "Brainiac #1" on cover; origin; Bedard-s/Alixe-a 5.00
23.3 (11/13, $3.99, 3-D cover) "H'El #1" on cover; Jor-El app.; Lobdell-s/Jurgens-a 5.00
23.4 (11/13, $3.99, 3-D cover) "Parasite #1" on cover; origin; Kuder-s/a 5.00
24-31: 25-Krypton Returns pt. 4. 26,27-Parasite app. 28,29-Starfire app. 3.00
32-($3.99) Romita Jr.-a/Johns-s begin; intro. Ulysses; wraparound-c by Romita Jr. 4.00
33-49: 33-39-Romita Jr.-a/Johns-s. 41-Yang-s begin. 45-48-Porter-a. 49-Vandal Savage 4.00
50-($4.99) Conclusion vs. Vandal Savage; Romita Jr. -c 5.00
51,52-Final Days of Superman x-over. 52-Superman dies; pre-Flashpoint Superman app. 4.00
#0-(11/12, $2.99) Jor-El & Lara flashback on Krypton; Rocafort-a/c 3.00
Annual 1 (10/12, $4.99) Alixe-a/Rocafort-c; Helspont app. 5.00
Annual 2 (9/13, $4.99) Jurgens-a/Andy Kubert-c; Brainiac app. 5.00
Annual 3 (2/16, $4.99) Origin/history of Vandal Savage; art by Sienkiewicz & others 5.00
... By Geoff Johns and John Romita Jr. Director's Cut 1 (11/14, $4.99) r/#32 B&W pencil art and full script 5.00
...: Futures End 1 (11/14, $2.99, regular-c) Five years later; Jurgens-s/Weeks-a 3.00
...: Futures End 1 (11/14, $3.99, 3-D cover) 4.00

SUPERMAN (DC Rebirth)
DC Comics: Aug, 2016 - Present ($2.99)

1-24-Tomasi & Gleason-s. 2-The Eradicator returns. 8,9-Dinosaur Island. 10,11-Batman & Robin (Damian) app. 14-16-Multiplicity; alternate Earth Supermans & Capt. Carrot app. 18,19-Superman Reborn. 23,24-Manchester Black app. 3.00
25-($3.99) Manchester Black & Batman app.; Mahnke & Gleason-a 4.00
26-42: 29,30-Parallax & Sinestro app. 31,32-Deathstroke app. 38-Teen Titans app. 3.00
Annual 1 (1/17, $4.99) Swamp Thing app.; Tomasi & Gleason-s/Jimenez-a 5.00
...: Rebirth (8/16, $2.99) Pre-52 Superman and Lana Lang app.; Tomasi-s/Mahnke-a 3.00

SUPERMAN (Hardcovers and Trade Paperbacks)
... and the Legion of Super-Heroes HC (2008, $24.99) r/Action Comics #858-863, covers and variants; intro. by Giffen; Gary Frank design sketch pages 25.00
... and the Legion of Super-Heroes SC (2009, $14.99) same contents as HC 15.00
...: Back in Action TPB (2007, $14.99) r/Action Comics #841-843 and DC Comics Presents #4,17,24; commentary by Busiek 15.00
.../Batman: Saga of the Super Sons TPB (2007, $19.99) r/Super Sons stories from '70s World's Finest #215,216,221,222,224,228,230,231,233,242,263 & Elseworlds 80-Page Giant 20.00
...: Brainiac HC (2009, $19.99, dustjacket) r/Action Comics #866-870 & Superman: New Krypton Special #1 20.00
...: Brainiac SC (2010, $12.99) r/Action #866-870 & Superman: New Krypton Spec. #1 13.00
...: Camelot Falls HC (2007, $19.99, dustjacket) r/Superman #654-658 20.00
...: Camelot Falls SC (2008, $12.99) r/Superman #654-658 13.00
...: Camelot Falls Vol. 2 HC (2008, $19.99, dj) r/Superman #662-664,667 & Ann. #13 20.00
...: Camelot Falls Vol. 2 The Weight of the World SC (2008, $12.99) r/Superman #662-664,667 & Ann. #13 13.00
...: Chronicles Vol. 1 ('06, $14.99, TPB) r/early Superman app. in Action Comics #1-13, New York World's Fair 1939 and Superman #1 15.00
...: Chronicles Vol. 2 ('07, $14.99, TPB) r/early Superman app. in Action Comics #14-20 and Superman #2,3 15.00
...: Chronicles Vol. 3 ('07, $14.99, TPB) r/early Superman app. in Action Comics #21-25, Superman #3,4 and New York World's Fair 1940 15.00
...: Chronicles Vol. 4 ('08, $14.99, TPB) r/early Superman app. in Action Comics #26-31, Superman #6,7 15.00
...: Chronicles Vol. 5 ('08, $14.99, TPB) r/early Superman app. in Action Comics #32-36, Superman #8,9 and World's Best Comics #1 15.00
...: Chronicles Vol. 6 ('09, $14.99, TPB) r/early Superman app. in Action Comics #37-40, Superman #10,11 and World's Finest Comics #2,3 15.00
...: Chronicles Vol. 7 ('09, $14.99, TPB) r/early Superman app. in Action Comics #41-43, Superman #12,13 and World's Finest Comics #4 15.00
...: Chronicles Vol. 8 ('10, $14.99, TPB) r/early Superman app. in Action Comics #44-47, and Superman #14,15 15.00
...: Chronicles Vol. 9 ('11, $17.99, TPB) r/early Superman app. in Action Comics #48-52, and Superman #16,17 and World's Finest Comics #6 18.00
...: Codename: Patriot HC ('10, $24.99, d.j.) r/partial New Krypton storyline 25.00
...: Codename: Patriot SC ('11, $14.99) r/partial New Krypton storyline 15.00
...: Critical Condition ('03, $14.95, TPB) r/2000 Kryptonite poisoning storyline 15.00
.../ Doomsday: The Collection Edition (2006, $19.99) r/Superman/Doomsday: Hunter/Prey #1-3, Doomsday Ann. #1, Superman: The Doomsday Wars #1-3, Advs. of Superman #594 and Superman #175; intro. by Dan Jurgens 20.00
...: Daily Planet (2006, $19.99, TPB)-Reprints stories of Daily Planet staff 20.00
... Earth One HC (2010, $19.99)-Updated re-imagining of Superman's debut in Metropolis; Straczynski-s/Shane Davis-a; sketch pages by Davis 20.00
... Earth One Volume Two HC (2012, $22.99)-Straczynski-s/Davis-a; sketch pages 23.00
... Earth One Volume Three HC (2014, $22.99)-Straczynski-s/Syaf-a; sketch pages 23.00
...: Emperor Joker TPB (2007, $14.99) reprints 2000 x-over from Superman titles 15.00
...: Endgame (2000, $14.95, TPB)-Reprints Y2K and Brainiac story line 15.00

Superman: Mon-El - Man of Valor HC © DC

Superman: The Black Ring HC © DC

Superman: Infinite City HC © DC

	GD 2.0	VG 4.0	FN 6.0	VF 8.0	VF/NM 9.0	NM- 9.2

...: Ending Battle (2009, $14.99, TPB) r/crossover of Superman titles from 2002 15.00
...: Eradication! The Origin of the Eradicator (1996, $12.95, TPB) 13.00
...: Escape From Bizarro World HC (2008, $24.99, dustjacket) r/Action #855-857; early apps. in Superman #140, DC Comics Presents #71 and Man of Steel #5; Vaughan intro. 25.00
...: Escape From Bizarro World SC (2009, $14.99) same contents as hardcover 15.00
...: Exile (1998, $14.95, TPB)-Reprints space exile following execution of Kryptonian criminals; 1st Eradicator 15.00
...: For Tomorrow Volume 1 HC (2005, $24.99, dustjacket) r/#204-209; intro by Azzarello; new cover and sketch section by Lee 25.00
...: For Tomorrow Volume 1 SC (2005, $14.99) r/#204-209; foil-stamped S emblem-c 15.00
...: For Tomorrow Volume 2 HC (2005, $24.99, dustjacket) r/#210-215; afterword and sketch section by Lee; new Lee-c with foil-stamped S emblem 25.00
...: For Tomorrow Volume 2 SC (2005, $14.99) r/#210-215; foil-stamped S emblem-c 15.00
...: Godfall HC (2004, $19.95, dustjacket) r/Action #812-813, Advs. of Superman #625-626, Superman #202-203; Caldwell sketch pages; Turner cover gallery; new Turner-c 20.00
...: Godfall SC (2004, $9.99) r/Action #812-813, Advs. of Superman #625-626, Superman #202-203; Caldwell sketch pages; Turner cover gallery; new Turner-c 10.00
...: Infinite Crisis TPB (2006, $12.99) r/Infinite Crisis #5, I.C. Secret Files and Origins 2006, Action Comics #836, Superman #226 and Advs. of Superman #649 13.00
... In the Forties ('05, $19.99, TPB) Intro. by Bob Hughes 20.00
... In the Fifties ('02, $19.95, TPB) Intro. by Mark Waid 20.00
... In the Sixties ('01, $19.95, TPB) Intro. by Mark Waid 20.00
... In the Seventies ('00, $19.95, TPB) Intro. by Christopher Reeve 20.00
... In the Eighties ('06, $19.99, TPB) Intro. by Jerry Ordway 20.00
... In the Name of Gog ('05, $17.99, TPB) r/Action Comics #820-825 18.00
... Kryptonite HC ('08, $24.99) r/Superman Confidential #1-5,11; Darwyn Cooke intro. 25.00
...: Last Son HC (2008, $19.99) r/Action Comics #844-846,851 and Annual #11; sketch pages and variant covers; Marc McClure intro. 20.00
... Mon-El HC ('10, $24.99) r/Superman #684-690, Action #874 & Annual #1, Superman: Secret Files 2009 #1 25.00
... Mon-El SC ('11, $17.99) r/Superman #684-690, Action #874 & Annual #1, Superman: Secret Files 2009 #1 18.00
... Mon-El - Man of Valor HC ('10, $24.99) r/Superman #692-697 & Annual #14, Adventure #11, Superman: Secret Files 2009 #1 25.00
... : New Krypton Vol. 1 HC ('09, $24.99, d.j.) r/Superman #681, Action #871 & one-shots 25.00
... : New Krypton Vol. 1 SC ('10, $17.99) r/Superman #681, Action #871 & one-shots 18.00
... : New Krypton Vol. 2 HC ('09, $24.99, d.j.) r/Superman #682,683, Action #872,873 & Supergirl #35,36; gallery of covers and variants 25.00
... : New Krypton Vol. 2 SC ('10, $17.99) same contents as HC 18.00
... : New Krypton Vol. 3 HC ('10, $24.99, d.j.) r/Superman: World of New Krypton #1-5 & Action Comics Annual #10; gallery of covers and variants 25.00
... : New Krypton Vol. 3 SC ('11, $17.99) same contents as HC 18.00
... : New Krypton Vol. 4 HC ('10, $24.99, d.j.) r/Superman: World of New Krypton #6-12; gallery of covers and variants; sketch and design art 25.00
... : New Krypton Vol. 4 SC ('11, $17.99) same contents as HC 18.00
... : Nightwing and Flamebird HC ('10, $24.99, d.j.) r/Action #875-879 & Annual #12 25.00
... : Nightwing and Flamebird SC ('10, $17.99) r/Action #875-879 & Annual #12 18.00
... : Nightwing and Flamebird Vol. 2 HC ('10, $24.99, d.j.) r/Action #883-889, Superman #696 & Adventure Comics #8-10 25.00
... No Limits ('00, $14.95, TPB) Reprints early 2000 stories 15.00
...: Our Worlds at War Book 1 ('02, $19.95, TPB) r/1st half of x-over 20.00
...: Our Worlds at War Book 2 ('02, $19.95, TPB) r/2nd half of x-over 20.00
...: Our Worlds at War - The Complete Collection ('06, $24.99, TPB) r/entire x-over 25.00
...: Past and Future (2008, $19.99, TPB) r/time travel stories 1947-1983 20.00
...: President Lex TPB (2003, $17.95) r/Luthor's run for the White House; Harris-c 18.00
...: Redemption TPB (2007, $12.99) r/Superman #659,666 & Action Comics #848,849 13.00
...: Return to Krypton (2004, $17.95, TPB) r/2001-2002 x-over 18.00
...: Sacrifice (2005, $14.99, TPB) prelude x-over to Infinite Crisis; r/Superman #218-220, Advs. of Superman #642,643; Action #829, Wonder Woman #219,220 15.00
...: Shadows Linger (2008, $14.99, TPB) r/Superman #671-675 15.00
... : Strange Attractors (2006, $14.99, TPB) r/Action Comics #827,828,830-835 15.00
... : Tales From the Phantom Zone ('09, $19.99, TPB) r/Phantom Zone stories 1961-68 20.00
...: That Healing Touch TPB (2005, $14.99) r/Advs. of Superman #633-638 & Superman Secret Files 2004 15.00
...: The Adventures of Nightwing and Flamebird TPB (2009, $19.99)-reprints appearances in Superman Family #173,183-194 20.00
...: The Black Ring Volume One HC (2011, $19.99, d.j.) r/Action Comics #890-895 20.00
The Bottle City of Kandor TPB (2007, $14.99)-Reprints 1st app. in Action #242 and other stories; Nightwing and Flamebird app. 15.00
The Coming of Atlas HC (2009, $19.99, dustjacket)-r/Superman #677-680 & Atlas' debut from First Issue Special #1 (1975); intro by James Robinson 20.00
The Coming of Atlas SC (2010, $14.99) same contents as HC 15.00
The Death of Clark Kent (1997, $19.95, TPB)-Reprints Man of Steel #43 (1 page), Superman #99 (1 page),#100-102, Action #709 (1 page), #710,711, Advs. of Superman #523-525, Superman:The Man of Tomorrow #1 20.00
The Death of Superman (1993, $4.95, TPB)-Reprints Man of Steel #17-19, Superman #73-75, Advs. of Superman #496,497, Action #683,684, & Justice League #69 2 4 6 9 12 15
The Death of Superman, 2nd & 3rd printings 1 3 4 6 8 10
The Death of Superman Platinum Edition 25.00
...: The Greatest Stories Ever Told ('04, $19.95, TPB) Ross-c, Uslan intro. 20.00
...: The Greatest Stories Ever Told Vol. 2 ('06, $19.99, TPB) Ross-c, Greenberger intro. 20.00
...: The Journey ('06, $14.99, TPB) r/Action Comics #831 & Superman #217,221-225 15.00
...: The Man of Steel Vol. 2 ('03, $19.95, TPB) r/Superman #1-3, Action #584-586, Advs. of Superman #424-426 & Who's Who Update '87 20.00
...: The Man of Steel Vol. 3 ('04, $19.95, TPB) r/Superman #4-6, Action #587-589, Advs. of Superman #427-429; intro. by Ordway; new Ordway-c 20.00
...: The Man of Steel Vol. 4 ('05, $19.99, TPB) r/Superman #7,8; Action #590,591; Advs. of Superman #430,431; Legion of Super-Heroes #37,38; new Ordway-c 20.00
...: The Man of Steel Vol. 5 ('06, $19.99, TPB) r/Superman #9-11, Action #592-593, Advs. of Superman #432-435; intro. by Mike Carlin; new Ordway-c 20.00
...: The Man of Steel Vol. 6 ('08, $19.99, TPB) r/Superman #12 & Ann. #1, Action #594-595 & Ann. #1, Advs. of Superman Ann.#1; Booster Gold #23; new Ordway-c 20.00
The Third Kryptonian ('08, $14.99, TPB) r/Action #847, Superman #668-670 & Ann. #13 15.00
The Trial of Superman ('97, $14.95, TPB) reprints story arc 15.00
The World of Krypton ('08, $14.99, TPB) r/World of Krypton Vol. 2 #1-4 and various tales of Krypton and its history; Kupperberg intro. 15.00
The Wrath of Gog ('05, $14.99, TPB) reprints Action Comics #812-819 15.00
...: They Saved Luthor's Brain ('00, $14.95) r/ "death" and return of Luthor 15.00
...: 3-2-1 Action! ('08, $14.99) Jimmy Olsen super-powered stories; Steve Rude-c 15.00
...: 'Til Death Do Us Part ('01, $17.95) reprints; Mahnke-c 18.00
...: Time and Time Again (1994, $7.50, TPB)-Reprints 10.00
...: Transformed ('98, $12.95, TPB) r/post Final Night powerless Superman to Electric Superman 13.00
...: Unconventional Warfare (2005, $14.95, TPB) r/Adventures of Superman #625-632 and pages from Superman Secret Files 2004 15.00
...: Up, Up and Away! (2006, $14.99, TPB) r/Superman #650-653 and Action #837-840 15.00
... Vs. Brainiac (2008, $19.99, TPB) reprints 1st meeting in Action #242 and other duels 20.00
... Vs. Lex Luthor (2006, $19.99, TPB) reprints 1st meeting in Action #23 and 11 other classic duels 1940-2001 20.00
... Vs. The Flash (2005, $19.99, TPB) reprints their races from Superman #199, Flash #175, World's Finest #198, DC Comics Presents #1&2, Advs. of Superman #463 & DC First: Flash/Superman; new Alex Ross-c 20.00
... Vs. The Revenge Squad (1999, $12.95, TPB) 13.00
...: Whatever Happened to the Man of Tomorrow? TPB (1/97, $5.99) r/Superman #423 & Action Comics #583, intro. by Paul Kupperberg 8.00
...: Whatever Happened to the Man of Tomorrow? Deluxe Edition HC (2009, $24.99, d.j.) r/Superman #423, Action #583, DC Comics Presents #85, Superman Ann #11 25.00
...: Whatever Happened to the Man of Tomorrow? SC (2010, $14.99) r/same as HC 15.00

NOTE: ***Austin*** *a(i)-1-3.* ***Byrne*** *a-1-16p, 17, 19-21p, 22; c-1-17, 20-22; scripts-1-22.* ***Guice*** *c/a-64.* ***Kirby*** *c-37p.* ***Joe Quesada*** *c-Annual 4.* ***Russell*** *c/a-23i.* ***Simonson*** *c-69i. #19-21 2nd printings sold in multi-packs.*

SUPERMAN (one-shots)

Daily News Magazine Presents DC Comics' Superman nn-(1987, 8 pgs.)-Supplement to New York Daily News; Perez-c/a 5.00
...: A Nation Divided (1999, $4.95)-Elseworlds Civil War story 5.00
... & Savage Dragon: Chicago (2002, $5.95) Larsen-a; Ross-c 6.00
... & Savage Dragon: Metropolis (11/99, $4.95) Bogdanove-a 5.00
...: At Earth's End (1995, $4.95)-Elseworlds story 5.00
...Beyond #0 (10/11, $3.99) The Batman Beyond future; Frenz-a/Nguyen-c 4.00
...: Blood of My Ancestors (2003, $6.95)-Gil Kane & John Buscema-a 7.00
...: Distant Fires (1998, $5.95)-Elseworlds; Chaykin-s 6.00
...: Emperor Joker (10/00, $3.50)-Follows Action #769 4.00
...: End of the Century (2/00, $24.95, HC)-Immonen-s/a 25.00
...: End of the Century (2003, $17.95, SC)-Immonen-s/a 18.00
... For Earth (1991, $4.95, 52 pgs, printed on recycled paper)-Ordway wraparound-c 6.00
...IV Movie Special (1987, $2.00)-Movie adaptation; Heck-a 4.00
...Gallery, The 1 (1993, $2.95)-Poster-a 3.00
..., Inc. (1999, $6.95)-Elseworlds Clark as a sports hero; Garcia-Lopez-a 7.00
...: Infinite City HC (2005, $24.99, dustjacket) Mike Kennedy-s/Carlos Meglia-a 25.00
...: Infinite City SC (2006, $17.99) Mike Kennedy-s/Carlos Meglia-a 18.00
...: Kal (1995, $5.95)-Elseworlds story 6.00
...: Lex 2000 (1/01, $3.50) Election night for the Luthor Presidency 4.00
...: Lois Lane 1 (4/14, $4.99) Marguerite Bennett-s; Rocafort-c 5.00
...: Monster (1999, $5.95)-Elseworlds story; Anthony Williams-a 6.00
... Movie Special-(9/83)-Adaptation of Superman III; other versions exist with store logos on bottom 1/3 of-c 4.00
...: New Krypton Special 1-(12/08, $3.99) Funeral of Pa Kent; newly enlarged Kandor 4.00
...: Our Worlds at War Secret Files 1-(8/01, $5.95)-Stories & profile pages 6.00

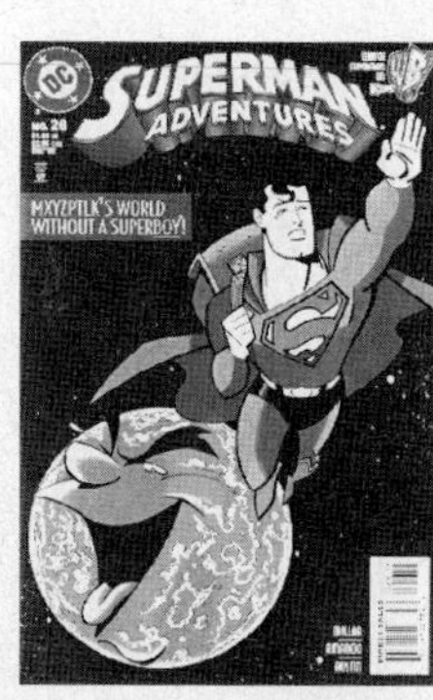

Superman Adventures #26 © DC

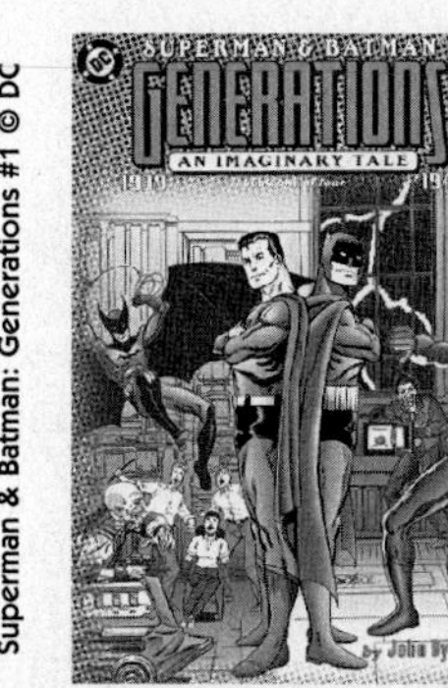

Superman & Batman: Generations #1 © DC

Superman / Batman Annual #4 © DC

	GD	VG	FN	VF	VF/NM	NM-
	2.0	4.0	6.0	8.0	9.0	9.2

... Plus 1(2/97, $2.95)-Legion of Super-Heroes-c/app. 4.00
...'s Metropolis-(1996, $5.95, prestige format)-Elseworlds; McKeever-c/a 6.00
...: Speeding Bullets-(1993, $4.95, 52 pgs.)-Elseworlds 6.00
.../Spider-Man-(1995, $3.95)-r/DC and Marvel Presents... 4.00
... 10-Cent Adventure 1 (3/02, 10¢) McDaniel-a; intro. Cir-El Supergirl 3.00
...: The Earth Stealers 1-(1988, $2.95, 52 pgs, prestige format) Byrne script; painted-c 6.00
...: The Earth Stealers 1-2nd printing 4.00
...: The Legacy of Superman #1 (3/93, $2.50, 68 pgs.)-Art Adams-c; Simonson-a 6.00
...: The Last God of Krypton ('99,$4.95) Hildebrandt Bros.-a/Simonson-s 5.00
...: The Last Son of Krypton FCBD Special Edition (7/13) r/Action #844; Jim Lee-c 3.00
...: The Odyssey ('99, $4.95) Clark Kent's post-Smallville journey 5.00
...: 3-D (12/98, $3.95)-with glasses 4.00
.../Thundercats (1/04, $5.95) Winick-s/Garza-a; two covers by Garza & McGuinness 6.00
.../Through the Ages (2006, $3.99) r/Action #1, Superman ('87) #7; origins and pin-ups 4.00
.../Toyman-(1996, $1.95) 3.00
...: True Brit (2004, $24.95, HC w/dust jacket) Elseworlds; Kal-El's rocket lands in England; co-written by John Cleese and Kim Howard Johnson; John Byrne-a 25.00
...: True Brit (2005, $17.99, TPB) Elseworlds; Kal-El's rocket lands in England 18.00
...: Under A Yellow Sun (1994, $5.95, 68 pgs.)-A Novel by Clark Kent; embossed-c 6.00
... Vs. Darkseid: Apokolips Now! 1 (3/03, $2.95) McKone-a; Kara (Supergirl #75) app. 4.00
...: War of the Worlds (1999, $5.95)-Battles Martians 6.00
...: Where is thy Sting? (2001, $6.95)-McCormack-Sharp-c/a 7.00
...: Y2K (2/00, $4.95)-1st Brainiac 13 app.; Guice-c/a 5.00

SUPERMAN ADVENTURES, THE (Based on animated series)
DC Comics: Oct, 1996 - No. 66, Apr, 2002 ($1.75/$1.95/$1.99)

1-Rick Burchett-c/a begins; Paul Dini script; Lex Luthor app.; 1st app. Mercy Graves in comics; silver ink, wraparound-c 4.00
2-20,22: 2-McCloud scripts begin; Metallo-c/app. 3-Brainiac-c/app. 5-1st app. Livewire in comics. 6-Mxyzptlk-c/app. 3.00
21-($3.95) 1st animated Supergirl 5.00
23-66: 23-Begin $1.99-c; Livewire app. 25-Batgirl-c/app. 28-Manley-a. 54-Retells Superman #233 "Kryptonite Nevermore" 58-Ross-c 3.00
Annual 1 (1997, $3.95)-Zatanna and Bruce Wayne app. 4.00
Special 1 (2/98, $2.95) Superman vs. Lobo 4.00
TPB (1998, $7.95) r/#1-6 8.00
... Vol 1: Up, Up and Away (2004, $6.95, digest) r/#16,19,22-24; Amancio-a 7.00
... Vol 2: The Never-Ending Battle (2004, $6.95) r/#25-29 7.00
... Vol 3: Last Son of Krypton (2006, $6.99) r/#30-34 7.00
... Vol 4: The Man of Steel (2006, $6.99) r/#35-39 7.00

SUPERMAN ALIENS 2: GOD WAR (Also see Superman Vs. Aliens)
DC Comics/Dark Horse Comics: May, 2002 - No. 4, Nov, 2002 ($2.99, limited series)

1-4-Bogdanove & Nowlan-a; Darkseid & New Gods app. 3.00
TPB (6/03, $12.95) r/#1-4 13.00

SUPERMAN: AMERICAN ALIEN
DC Comics: Jan, 2016 - No. 7, Jul, 2016 ($3.99, limited series)

1-7-Flashbacks to Clark Kent's upbringing; Max Landis-s in all. 1-Dragotta-a. 4-Jae Lee-a; Batman app. 7-Lobo app.; Jock-a 4.00

SUPERMAN & BATMAN: GENERATIONS (Elseworlds)
DC Comics: 1999 - No. 4, 1999 ($4.95, limited series)

1-4-Superman & Batman team-up from 1939 to the future; Byrne-c/s/a 5.00
TPB (2000, $14.95) r/series 15.00

SUPERMAN & BATMAN: GENERATIONS II (Elseworlds)
DC Comics: 2001 - No. 4, 2001 ($5.95, limited series)

1-4-Superman, Batman & others team-up from 1942-future; Byrne-c/s/a 6.00
TPB (2003, $19.95) r/series 20.00

SUPERMAN & BATMAN: GENERATIONS III (Elseworlds)
DC Comics: Mar, 2003 - No. 12, Feb, 2004 ($2.95, limited series)

1-12-Superman & Batman through the centuries; Byrne-c/s/a 3.00

SUPERMAN & BATMAN VS. ALIENS AND PREDATOR
DC Comics: 2007 - No. 2, 2007 ($5.99, squarebound, limited series)

1,2-Schultz-s/Olivetti-a 6.00
TPB (2007, $12.99) r/#1,2; pencil breakdown pages 13.00

SUPERMAN AND BATMAN VS. VAMPIRES AND WEREWOLVES
DC Comics: Early Dec, 2008 - No. 6, Late Feb, 2009 ($2.99, limited series)

1-6-Van Hook-s/Mandrake-a/c. 1-Wonder Woman app. 5-Demon-c/app. 3.00
TPB (2009, $14.99) r/#1-6; intro. by John Landis 15.00

SUPERMAN & BATMAN: WORLD'S FUNNEST (Elseworlds)
DC Comics: 2000 ($6.95, square-bound, one-shot)

nn-Mr. Mxyzptlk and Bat-Mite destroy each DC Universe; Dorkin-s; art by various incl. Ross, Timm, Miller, Allred, Moldoff, Gibbons, Cho, Jimenez 7.00

SUPERMAN & BUGS BUNNY
DC Comics: Jul, 2000 - No. 4, Oct, 2000 ($2.50, limited series)

1-4-JLA & Looney Tunes characters meet 3.00

SUPERMAN/BATMAN
DC Comics: Oct, 2003 - No. 87, Oct, 2011 ($2.95/$2.99)

	GD 2.0	VG 4.0	FN 6.0	VF 8.0	VF/NM 9.0	NM- 9.2
1-Two covers (Superman or Batman in foreground) Loeb-s/McGuinness-a; Metallo app.	1	2	3	5	6	8
1-2nd printing (Batman cover)						3.00
1-3rd printing; new McGuinness cover						3.00
1-Diamond/Alliance Retailer Summit Edition-variant	7	14	21	46	86	125

1-(6/06, Free Comic Book Day giveaway) reprints #1 3.00
2-6: 2,5-Future Superman app. 6-Luthor in battlesuit 3.00
7-Pat Lee-c/a; Superboy & Robin app. 3.00
8-Michael Turner-c/a; intro. new Kara Zor-El 5.00
8-Second printing with sketch cover 3.00
8-Third printing with new Turner cover 3.00
9-13-Michael Turner-c/a; Wonder Woman app. 10,13-Variant-c by Jim Lee 3.00
14-25: 14-18-Pacheco-a; Lightning Lord, Saturn Queen & Cosmic King app. 19-Supergirl app.; leads into Supergirl #1. 21-25-Bizarro app. 25-Superman & Batman covers; 2nd printing with white bkgrd cover 3.00
26-($3.99) Sam Loeb tribute issue; 2 covers by Turner; story & art by 26 various; back-up by Loeb & Sale 5.00
27-49: 27-Flashback to Earth-2 Power Girl & Huntress; Maguire-a. 34-36-Metal Men app. 3.00
50-($3.99) Thomas Wayne meets Jor-El; Justice League app. 4.00
51-74: 51,52-Mr. Mxyzptlk app. 66,67-Blackest Night; Man-Bat and Bizarro app. 3.00
75-($4.99) Quitely-c; Legion of Super-Heroes app.; Ordway-a; 2-pg. features by various 5.00
76-87: 76-Aftermath of Batman's "death". 77-Supergirl/Damian team-up 3.00
Annual #1 (12/06, $3.99) Re-imaging of 1st meeting from World's Finest #71 4.00
Annual #2 (5/08, $3.99) Kolins-a; re-imaging of Superman as Supernova story 4.00
Annual #3 (3/09, $3.99) Composite Superman-c by Wrightson; Batista-a 4.00
Annual #4 (8/10, $4.99) Batman Beyond; Levitz-s/Guedes-a/Lau-c 8.00
Annual #5 (6/11, $4.99) Reign of Doomsday x-over, Cyborg Superman app.; Sepulveda-a 5.00
...Absolute Power HC (2005, $19.99) r/#14-18 20.00
...Absolute Power SC (2006, $12.99) r/#14-18 13.00
..."Batman V Superman: Dawn of Justice Day" Special Edition 1 (4/16, free) r/#1 3.00
...Big Noise SC (2010, $14.99) r/#64,68-71 15.00
...Enemies Among Us SC (2009, $12.99) r/#28-33 13.00
...Finest Worlds SC (2010, $14.99) r/#50-56 15.00
...Night and Day HC (2010, $19.99) r/#60-63,65-67 20.00
...Public Enemies HC (2004, $19.95) r/#1-6 & Secret Files 2003; sketch art pages 20.00
...Public Enemies SC (2005, $12.99) r/#1-6 & Secret Files 2003; sketch art pages 15.00
...Public Enemies SC (2009, $14.99) r/#1-6 & Secret Files 2003; sketch art pages 15.00
...Secret Files 2003 (11/03, $4.95) Reis-a; pin-ups by various; Loeb/Sale short-s 5.00
... : Supergirl HC (2004, $19.95) r/#8-13; intro by Loeb, cover gallery, sketch pages 20.00
... : Supergirl SC (2005, $12.99) r/#8-13; intro by Loeb, cover gallery, sketch pages 13.00
... : The Search For Kryptonite HC (2008, $19.99) r/#44-49; Davis sketch pages 20.00
... : The Search For Kryptonite SC (2009, $12.99) r/#44-49; Davis sketch pages 13.00
... : Torment HC (2008, $19.99) r/#37-42; cover gallery, Nguyen sketch pages 20.00
... : Vengeance HC (2006, $19.99) r/#20-25; sketch pages 20.00
... : Vengeance SC (2008, $12.99) r/#20-25; sketch pages 13.00
... : Worship SC (2011, $17.99) r/#72-75 & Annual #4 18.00

SUPERMAN/BATMAN: ALTERNATE HISTORIES
DC Comics: 1996 ($14.95, trade paperback)

nn-Reprints Detective Comics Annual #7, Action Comics Annual #6, Steel Annual #1, Legends of the Dark Knight Annual #4 15.00

SUPERMAN: BIRTHRIGHT
DC Comics: Sept, 2003 - No. 12, Sept, 2004 ($2.95, limited series)

1-12-Waid-s/Leinil Yu-a; retelling of origin and early Superman years 3.00
HC (2004, $29.95, dustjacket) r/series; cover gallery; Waid proposal with Yu concept art 30.00
SC (2005, $19.99) r/series; cover gallery; Waid proposal with Yu concept art 20.00

SUPERMAN COMICS
DC Comics: 1939

nn - Ashcan comic, not distributed to newsstands, only for in-house use. Cover art is Action Comics #7 with interior being Action Comics #8. A CGC certified 9.0 copy sold for $37,375 in 2005 and for $90,000 in 2007.

SUPERMAN CONFIDENTIAL (See Superman Hardcovers and TPBs listings for reprint)
DC Comics: Jan, 2007 - No. 14, Jun, 2008 ($2.99)

1-14: 1-5,9-Darwyn Cooke-s/Tim Sale-a/c; origin of Kryptonite re-told. 8-10-New Gods and

Superman Family #171 © DC

Superman For All Seasons #2 © DC

Superman: Lois and Clark #7 © DC

	GD 2.0	VG 4.0	FN 6.0	VF 8.0	VF/NM 9.0	NM- 9.2

Darkside app. 3.00
...: Kryptonite TPB (2009, $14.99) r/#1-5,11; intro. by Darwyn Cooke; Tim Sale sketch-a 15.00

SUPERMAN: DAY OF DOOM
DC Comics: Jan, 2003 - No. 4, Feb, 2003 ($2.95, weekly limited series)

1-4-Jurgens-s/Jurgens & Sienkiewicz-a 3.00
TPB (2003, $9.95) r/#1-4 10.00

SUPERMAN DOOMED (DC New 52) (See Action Comics #31-34 and Superman/Wonder Woman)
DC Comics: Jul, 2014 - No. 2, Nov, 2014 ($4.99, bookends for crossover)

1,2: 1-Lashley-a; Wonder Woman & Steel app. 2-Superman vs. Brainiac 6.00

SUPERMAN/DOOMSDAY: HUNTER/PREY
DC Comics: 1994 - No. 3, 1994 ($4.95, limited series, 52 pgs.)

1-3 6.00

SUPERMAN FAMILY, THE (Formerly Superman's Pal Jimmy Olsen)
National Per. Publ./DC Comics: No. 164, Apr-May, 1974 - No. 222, Sept, 1982

	GD	VG	FN	VF	VF/NM	NM-
164-(100 pgs.) Jimmy Olsen, Supergirl, Lois Lane begin	4	8	12	28	47	65
165-169 (100 pgs.)	3	6	9	18	28	38
170-176 (68 pgs.)	3	6	9	14	19	24
177-190 (52 pgs.): 177-181-52 pgs. 182-Marshall Rogers-a; $1.00 issues begin; Krypto begins, ends #192. 183-Nightwing-Flamebird begins, ends #194. 189-Brainiac 5, Mon -El app.	2	4	6	9	13	16
191-193,195-199: 191-Superboy begins, ends #198	2	3	4	6	8	10
194,200: 194-Rogers-a. 200-Book length sty	2	4	6	8	10	12
201-210,212-222	1	2	3	5	6	8
211-Earth II Batman & Catwoman marry	2	4	6	8	11	14

NOTE: ***N. Adams** c-182-185. **Anderson** a-186i. **Buckler** c(p)-190, 191, 209, 210, 215, 217, 220. **Jones** a-191-193. **Gil Kane** c(p)-221, 222. **Mortimer** a(p)-191-193, 199, 201-222. **Orlando** a(i)-186, 187. **Rogers** a-182, 194. **Staton** a-191-194, 196p. **Tuska** a(p)-203, 207-209.*

SUPERMAN FAMILY ADVENTURES
DC Comics: Jul, 2012 - No. 12, Jun, 2013 ($2.99)

1-12-Young-reader stories, games and DC Nation character profiles; Baltazar-a 3.00

SUPERMAN/FANTASTIC FOUR
DC Comics/Marvel Comics: 1999 ($9.95, tabloid size, one-shot)

1-Battle Galactus and the Cyborg; wraparound-c by Alex Ross and Dan Jurgens; Jurgens-s/a; Thibert-a 10.00

SUPERMAN FOR ALL SEASONS
DC Comics: 1998 - No, 4, 1998 ($4.95, limited series, prestige format)

1-Loeb-s/Sale-a/c; Superman's first year in Metropolis 6.00
2-4 5.00
Hardcover (1999, $24.95) r/#1-4 25.00

SUPERMAN FOR EARTH (See Superman one-shots)

SUPERMAN FOREVER
DC Comics: Jun, 1998 ($5.95, one-shot)

1-($5.95)-Collector's Edition with a 7-image lenticular-c by Alex Ross; Superman returns to normal; s/a by various 7.00
1-($4.95) Standard Edition with single image Ross-c 5.00

SUPERMAN/GEN13
DC Comics (WildStorm): Jun, 2000 - No. 3, Aug, 2000 ($2.50, limited series)

1-3-Hughes-s/ Bermejo-a; Campbell variant-c for each 3.00
TPB (2001, $9.95) new Bermejo-c; cover gallery 10.00

SUPERMAN: KING OF THE WORLD
DC Comics: June, 1999 ($3.95/$4.95, one-shot)

1-($3.95) Regular Ed. 4.00
1-($4.95) Collectors' Ed. with gold foil enhanced-c 5.00

SUPERMAN: LAST SON OF EARTH
DC Comics: 2000 - No. 2, 2000 ($5.95, limited series, prestige format)

1,2-Elseworlds; baby Clark rockets to Krypton; Gerber-s/Wheatley-a 6.00

SUPERMAN: LAST STAND OF NEW KRYPTON
DC Comics: May, 2010 - No. 3, Late June, 2010 ($3.99, limited series)

1-3-Robinson & Gates-s/Woods-a. 2-Pérez-c. 3-Sook-c 4.00
HC (2010, $24.99, DJ) r/#1,2, Adventure Comics #8,9, Supergirl #51 & Superman #698 25.00
Vol. 2 HC (2010, $19.99, DJ) r/#3, Adventure #10,11, Supergirl #52 & Superman #699 20.00

SUPERMAN: LAST STAND ON KRYPTON
DC Comics: 2003 ($6.95, one-shot, prestige format)

1-Sequel to Superman: Last Son of Earth; Gerber-s/Wheatley-a 7.00

SUPERMAN: LOIS & CLARK (See Convergence Superman #1 & 2)
DC Comics: Dec, 2015 - No. 8, Jul, 2016 ($3.99)

1-8: 1-Pre-Flashpoint Superman & Lois on New 52 Earth; Jurgens-s/Weeks-a 4.00

SUPERMAN: LOIS LANE (Girlfrenzy)
DC Comics: Jun, 1998 ($1.95, one shot)

1-Connor & Palmiotti-a 3.00

SUPERMAN/MADMAN HULLABALOO!
Dark Horse Comics: June, 1997 - No. 3, Aug, 1997 ($2.95, limited series)

1-3-Mike Allred-c/s/a 3.00
TPB (1997, $8.95) 9.00

SUPERMAN: METROPOLIS
DC Comics: Apr, 2003 - No. 12, Mar, 2004 ($2.95, limited series)

1-12-Focus on Jimmy Olsen; Austen-s. 1-6-Zezelj-a. 7-12-Kristiansen-a. 8,9-Creeper app. 3.00

SUPERMAN METROPOLIS SECRET FILES
DC Comics: Jun, 2000 ($4.95, one shot)

1-Short stories, pin-ups and profile pages; Hitch and Neary-c 5.00

SUPERMAN: PEACE ON EARTH
DC Comics: Jan, 1999 ($9.95, Treasury-sized, one-shot)

1-Alex Ross painted-c/a; Paul Dini-s 12.00

SUPERMAN: RED SON
DC Comics: 2003 - No. 3, 2003 ($5.95, limited series, prestige format)

1-Elseworlds; Superman's rocket lands in Russia; Mark Millar-s/Dave Johnson-c/a 10.00
2,3 6.00
TPB (2004, $17.95) r/#1-3; intro. by Tom DeSanto; sketch pages 18.00
... - The Deluxe Edition HC (2009, $24.99, d.j.) r/#1-3; sketch art by various 25.00

SUPERMAN RED/ SUPERMAN BLUE
DC Comics: Feb, 1998 ($4.95, one shot)

1-Polybagged w/3-D glasses and reprint of Superman 3-D (1955); Jurgens-plot/3-D cover; script and art by various 5.00
1-($3.95)-Standard Ed.; comic only, non 3-D cover 4.00

SUPERMAN RETURNS... (2006 movie)
DC Comics: Aug, 2006 ($3.99, movie tie-in stories by Singer, Dougherty and Harris)

Prequel 1 - Krypton to Earth; Olivetti-a/Hughes-c; retells Jor-El's story 6.00
Prequel 2 - Ma Kent; Kerschl-a/Hughes-c; Ma Kent during Clark childhood and absence 4.00
Prequel 3 - Lex Luthor; Leonardi-a/Hughes-c; Luthor's 5 years in prison 4.00
Prequel 4 - Lois Lane; Dias-a/Hughes-c; Lois during Superman's absence 4.00
The Movie and Other Tales of the Man of Steel (2006, $12.99, TPB) adaptation; origin from Amazing World of Superman; Action #810, Superman #185; Advs. of Superman #575 13.00
The Official Movie Adaptation (2006, $6.99) Pasko-s/Haley-a; photo-c 7.00
...: The Prequels TPB (2006, $12.99) r/the 4 prequels 13.00

SUPERMAN: SAVE THE PLANET
DC Comics: Oct, 1998 ($2.95, one-shot)

1-($2.95) Regular Ed.; Luthor buys the Daily Planet 3.00
1-($3.95) Collector's Ed. with acetate cover 4.00

SUPERMAN SCRAPBOOK (Has blank pages; contains no comics)

SUPERMAN: SECRET FILES
DC Comics: Jan, 1998; May 1999 ($4.95)

1,2: 1-Retold origin story, "lost" pages & pin-ups 5.00
... & Origins 2004 (8/04) pin-ups by Lee, Turner and others 5.00
... & Origins 2005 (1/06) short stories and pin-ups by various 5.00
... 2009 (10/09, $4.99) short stories and pin-ups about New Krypton x-over 5.00

SUPERMAN: SECRET IDENTITY
DC Comics: 2004 - No. 4, 2004 ($5.95, squarebound, limited series)

1-4-Busiek-s/Immonen-a/c 6.00

SUPERMAN: SECRET ORIGIN
DC Comics: Nov, 2009 - No. 6, Oct, 2010 ($3.99, limited series)

1-6-Geoff Johns-s/Gary Frank-a/c; origin mythos re-told. 2-Legion app. 5-Metallo app. 4.00
1-6-Variant covers by Frank 6.00
HC (2011, $29.99) r/#1-6; intro. by David Goyer; variant covers 30.00

SUPERMAN'S GIRLFRIEND LOIS LANE (See Action Comics #1, 80 Page Giant #3, 14, Lois Lane, Showcase #9, 10, Superman #28 & Superman Family)

SUPERMAN'S GIRLFRIEND LOIS LANE (See Showcase #9,10)
National Periodical Publ.: Mar-Apr, 1958 - No. 136, Jan-Feb, 1974; No. 137, Sept-Oct, 1974

	GD	VG	FN	VF	VF/NM	NM-
1-(3-4/58)	325	650	1300	3600	8300	13,000
2	104	208	312	832	1866	2900
3	68	136	204	544	1222	1900

Superman's Girlfriend Lois Lane #9 © DC

Superman's Pal Jimmy Olsen #142 © DC

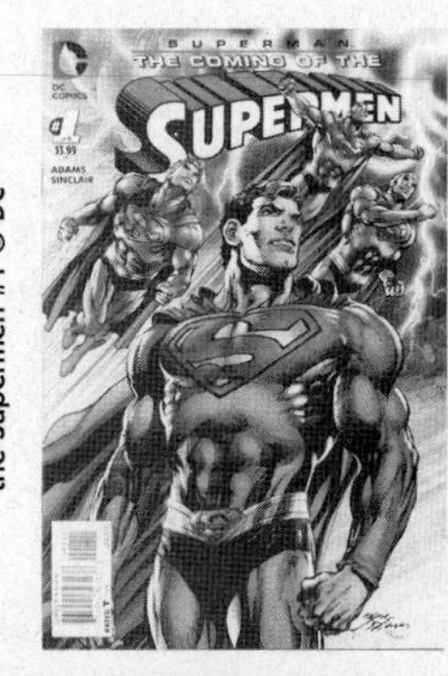

Superman: The Coming of the Supermen #1 © DC

	GD 2.0	VG 4.0	FN 6.0	VF 8.0	VF/NM 9.0	NM- 9.2
4,5	47	94	141	364	820	1275
6,7	37	74	111	274	612	950
8-10: 9-Pat Boone-c/story	32	64	96	230	515	800
11-13,15-19: 12-(10/59)-Aquaman app. 17-(5/60) 2nd app. Brainiac.	19	38	57	131	291	450
14-Supergirl x-over; Batman app. on-c only	20	40	60	141	313	485
20-Supergirl-c/sty	20	40	60	138	307	475
21-28: 23-1st app. Lena Thorul, Lex Luthor's sister; 1st Lois as Elastic Lass. 27-Bizarro-c/story	14	28	42	96	211	325
29-Aquaman, Batman, Green Arrow cover app. and cameo; last 10¢ issue	16	32	48	110	243	375
30-32,34-46,48,49	9	18	27	59	117	175
33(5/62)-Mon -El app.	9	18	27	61	123	185
47-Legion app.	9	18	27	61	123	185
50(7/64)-Triplicate Girl, Phantom Girl & Shrinking Violet app.	9	18	27	61	123	185
51-55,57-67,69: 59-Jor -El app.; Batman back-up sty	7	14	21	44	82	120
56-Saturn Girl app.	7	14	21	46	86	125
68-(Giant G-26)	8	16	24	54	102	150
70-Penguin & Catwoman app. (1st S.A. Catwoman, 11/66; also see Detective #369 for 3rd app.); Batman & Robin cameo	27	54	81	189	420	650
71-Batman & Robin cameo (3 panels); Catwoman story cont'd from #70 (2nd app.); see Detective #369 for 3rd app	10	20	30	69	147	225
72,73,75,76,78	5	10	15	34	60	85
74-1st Bizarro Flash (5/67); JLA cameo	6	12	18	37	66	95
77-(Giant G-39)	6	12	18	42	79	115
79-Neal Adams-c or c(i) begin, end #95,108	6	12	18	37	66	95
80-85,87,88,90-92: 92-Last 12¢ issue	4	8	12	28	47	65
86,95 (Giants G-51,G-63)-Both have Neal Adams-c	6	12	18	37	66	95
89,93: 89-Batman x-over; all N. Adams-c. 93-Wonder Woman-c/story	5	10	15	30	50	70
94,96-99,101-103,107-110	4	8	12	23	37	50
100	4	8	12	25	40	55
104-(Giant G-75)	5	10	15	34	60	85
105-Origin/1st app. The Rose & the Thorn.	5	10	15	34	60	85
106-"I Am Curious (Black)" story; Lois changes her skin color to black (11/70)	10	20	30	64	132	200
111-Justice League-c/s; Morrow-a; last 15¢ issue	4	8	12	27	44	60
112,114-123 (52 pgs.): 122-G.A. Lois Lane-r/Superman #30. 123-G.A. Batman-r/Batman #35 (w/Catwoman)	4	8	12	23	37	50
113-(Giant G-87) Kubert-a (previously unpublished G.A. story)(scarce in NM)	6	12	18	37	66	95
124-135: 130-Last Rose & the Thorn. 132-New Zatanna story	3	6	9	16	23	30
136,137: 136-Wonder Woman x-over	3	6	9	17	26	35
Annual 1(Sum, 1962)-r/L. Lane #12; Aquaman app.	18	36	54	128	284	440
Annual 2(Sum, 1963)	13	26	39	89	195	300

NOTE: ***Buckler** a-117-121p. **Curt Swan or Kurt Schaffenberger** a-1-81(most); c(p)-1-15.*

SUPERMAN/SHAZAM: FIRST THUNDER
DC Comics: Nov, 2005 - No. 4, Feb, 2006 ($3.50, limited series)

1-4-Retells first meeting; Winick-s/Middleton-a. Dr. Sivana app. 3.50

SUPERMAN: SILVER BANSHEE
DC Comics: Dec, 1998 - No. 2, Jan, 1999 ($2.25, mini-series)

1,2-Brereton-s/c; Chin-a 3.00

SUPERMAN'S NEMESIS: LEX LUTHOR
DC Comics: Mar, 1999 - No. 4, Jun, 1999 ($2.50, mini-series)

1-4-Semeiks-a 3.00

SUPERMAN'S PAL JIMMY OLSEN (Superman Family #164 on)
(See Action Comics #6 for 1st app. & 80 Page Giant)
National Periodical Publ.: Sept-Oct, 1954 - No. 163, Feb-Mar, 1974 (Fourth World #133-148)

	GD 2.0	VG 4.0	FN 6.0	VF 8.0	VF/NM 9.0	NM- 9.2
1	500	1000	1750	5000	11,250	17,500
2	169	338	507	1394	3147	4900
3-Last pre-code issue	104	208	312	832	1866	2900
4,5	66	132	198	528	1189	1850
6-10	45	90	135	333	754	1175
11-20: 15-1st S.A. issue	32	64	96	230	515	800
21-28,30	21	42	63	147	324	500
29-(6/58) 1st app. Krypto with Superman	23	46	69	161	356	550
31-Origin & 1st app. Elastic Lad (Jimmy Olsen)	20	40	60	141	313	485
32-40: 33-One pg. biography of Jack Larson (TV Jimmy Olsen). 36-Intro Lucy Lane. 37-2nd app. Elastic Lad & 1st cover app.	13	26	39	89	195	300
41-50: 41-1st J.O. Robot. 48-Intro/origin Superman Emergency Squad	10	20	30	66	138	210
51-56: 56-Last 10¢ issue	8	16	24	54	102	150
57-62,64-70: 57-Olsen marries Supergirl. 62-Mon-El & Elastic Lad app. but not as Legionnaires. 70-Element Boy (Lad) app.	6	12	18	40	73	105
63 (9/62)-Legion of Super-Villains app.	6	12	18	42	79	115
71,74,75,78,80-84,86,89,90: 86-Jimmy Olsen Robot becomes Congorilla	5	10	15	33	57	80
72,73,76,77,79,85,87,88: 72(10/63)-Legion app; Elastic Lad (Olsen) joins. 73-Ultra Boy app. 76,85-Legion app. 76-Legion app. 77-Olsen with Colossal Boy's powers & costume; origin Titano retold. 79-(9/64)-Titled The Red-headed Beatle of 1000 B.C. 85-Legion app. 87-Legion of Super-Villains app. 88-Star Boy app.	5	10	15	34	60	85
91-94,96-98	4	8	12	28	47	65
95 (Giant G-25)	6	12	18	42	79	115
99-Olsen w/powers & costumes of Lightning Lad, Sun Boy & Element Lad	5	10	15	30	50	70
100-Legion cameo	5	10	15	31	53	75
101-103,105-112,114-120: 106-Legion app. 110-Infinity-c. 117-Batman & Legion cameo. 120-Last 12¢ issue	4	8	12	23	37	50
104 (Giant G-38)	5	10	15	34	60	85
113,122,131,140 (Giants G-50,G-62,G-74,G-86)	5	10	15	31	53	75
121,123-130,132	3	6	9	21	33	45
133-(10/70)-Jack Kirby story & art begins; re-intro Newsboy Legion; 1st app. Morgan Edge	6	12	18	41	76	110
134-1st app. Darkseid (1 panel, 12/70)	50	100	150	350	575	800
135-2nd app. Darkseid (1 pg. cameo; see New Gods & Forever People); G.A. Guardian app.	8	16	24	56	108	160
136-139: 136-Origin new Guardian. 138-Partial photo-c. 139-Last 15¢ issue	4	8	12	23	37	50
141-150: (25¢,52 pgs.). 141-Photo-c with Don Rickles; Newsboy Legion-r by S&K begin; full pg. self-portrait of Jack Kirby; Don Rickles cameo. 149,150-G.A. Plastic Man-r in both; 150-Newsboy Legion app.	3	6	9	21	33	45
151-163	3	6	9	16	23	30

... Special 1 (12/08, $4.99) New Krypton tie-in; The Guardian and Dubbilex app. 5.00
... Special 2 (10/09, $4.99) New Krypton tie-in; Mon-El app.; Chang-a 5.00
Superman: The Amazing Transformations of Jimmy Olsen TPB (2007, $14.99) reprints Olsen's transformations into Wolf-Man, Elastic Lad, Turtle Boy and others; new Bolland-c 15.00

NOTE: *Issues #141-148 contain **Simon & Kirby** Newsboy Legion reprints from Star Spangled #7, 8, 9, 10, 11, 12, 13, 14 in that order. **N. Adams** c-109-112, 115, 117, 118, 120, 121, 132, 134-136, 147, 148. **Kirby** a-133-139p, 141-148p; c-133, 137, 139, 142, 145p. **Kirby/N. Adams** c-137, 138, 141-144, 146. **Curt Swan** c-1-14(most)., 140.*

SUPERMAN SPECTACULAR (Also see DC Special Series #5)
DC Comics: 1982 (Magazine size, 52 pgs., square binding)

	GD 2.0	VG 4.0	FN 6.0	VF 8.0	VF/NM 9.0	NM- 9.2
1-Saga of Superman Red/ Superman Blue; Luthor and Terra-Man app.; Gonzales & Colletta-a	1	3	4	6	8	10

SUPERMAN: STRENGTH
DC Comics: 2005 - No. 3, 2005 ($5.95, limited series)

1-3: Alex Ross-c/Scott McCloud-s/Aluir Amancio-a 6.00

SUPERMAN / SUPERGIRL: MAELSTROM
DC Comics: Early Jan, 2009 - No. 5, Mar, 2009 ($2.99, limited series)

1-5: Palmiotti & Gray-s/Noto-c/a; Darkseid app. 3.00
TPB (2009, $12.99) r/#1-5 13.00

SUPERMAN / SUPERHOMBRE
DC Comics: Apr, 1945

nn - Ashcan comic, not distributed to newsstands, only for in-house use (no known sales)

SUPERMAN / TARZAN: SONS OF THE JUNGLE
Dark Horse Comics: Oct, 2001 - No. 3, May, 2002 ($2.99, limited series)

1-3-Elseworlds; Kal-El lands in the jungle; Dixon-s/Meglia-a/Ramos-c 3.00

SUPERMAN: THE COMING OF THE SUPERMEN
DC Comics: Apr, 2016 - No. 6, Sept, 2016 ($3.99, limited series)

1-6: 1-Neal Adams-s/a/c in all; Kalibak app. 3,4-Orion app. 3-6-Darkseid app. 4.00

SUPERMAN: THE DARK SIDE
DC Comics: 1998 - No. 3, 1998 ($4.95, squarebound, mini-series)

1-3: Elseworlds; Kal-El lands on Apokolips 5.00

SUPERMAN: THE DOOMSDAY WARS
DC Comics: 1998 - No. 3, 1999 ($4.95, squarebound, mini-series)

1-3: Superman & JLA vs. Doomsday; Jurgens-s/a(p) 5.00

SUPERMAN: THE KANSAS SIGHTING
DC Comics: 2003 - No. 2, 2003 ($6.95, squarebound, mini-series)

1,2-DeMatteis-s/Tolagson-a 7.00

Superman: The Man of Steel #19 © DC

Superman: The Man of Tomorrow #15 © DC

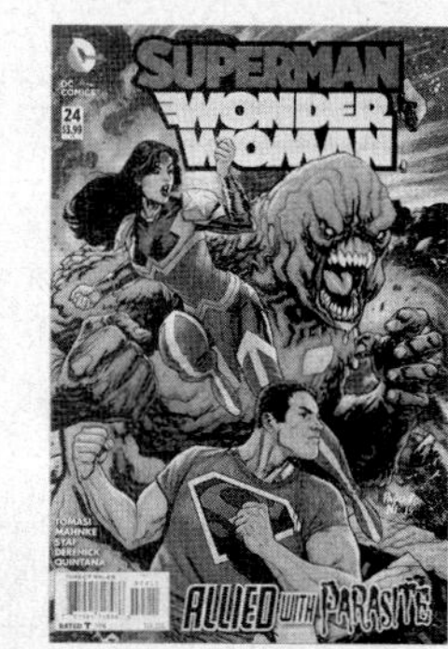
Superman / Wonder Woman #24 © DC

GD 2.0 | VG 4.0 | FN 6.0 | VF 8.0 | VF/NM 9.0 | NM- 9.2

SUPERMAN: THE LAST FAMILY OF KRYPTON
DC Comics: Oct, 2010 - No. 3, Dec, 2010 ($4.99, limited series)

1-3-Elseworlds; the El family lands on Earth; Bates-s/Arlem-a/Massafera-c 5.00

SUPERMAN: THE MAN OF STEEL (Also see Man of Steel, The)
DC Comics: July, 1991 - No. 134, Mar, 2003 ($1.00/$1.25/$1.50/$1.95/$2.25)

0-(10/94) Zero Hour; released between #37 & #38 3.00
1-($1.75, 52 pgs.)-Painted-c 5.00
2-16: 3-War of the Gods x-over. 5-Reads sideways. 10-Last $1.00-c. 14-Superman & Robin team-up 3.00
17-1st brief app. Doomsday 4 8 12 25 40 55
17-(2nd printing) 3 6 9 17 26 35
18-1st full app. Doomsday 3 6 9 17 26 35
18-(2nd-4th printings) 2 4 6 11 16 20
18-(5th printing) 4 8 12 23 37 50
19-Doomsday battle issue (c/story) 2 4 6 8 10 12
19-(2nd & 3rd printings) 3 6 9 16 23 30
20-22: 20,21-Funeral for a Friend. 22-($1.95)-Collector's Edition w/die-cut outer-c & bound-in poster; Steel-c/story 5.00
22-($1.50)-Newsstand Ed. w/poster & different-c 4.00
23-49,51-99: 30-Regular edition. 32-Bizarro-c/story. 35,36-Worlds Collide Pt. 1 & 10. 37-(9/94)-Zero Hour x-over. 38-(11/94). 48-Aquaman app. 54-Spectre-c/app; Lex Luthor app. 56-Mxyzptlk-c/app. 57-G.A. Flash app. 58-Supergirl app. 59-Parasite-c/app.; Steel app. 60-Reintro Bottled City of Kandor. 62-Final Night. 64-New Gods app. 67-New powers. 75-"Death" of Mxyzptlk. 78,79-Millennium Giants. 80-Golden Age style. 92-JLA app. 98-Metal Men app. 3.00
30-($2.50)-Collector's Edition; polybagged with Superman & Lobo vinyl clings that stick to wraparound-c; Lobo-c/story 4.00
50 ($2.95)-The Trial of Superman 4.00
100-($2.99) New Fortress of Solitude revealed 3.00
100-($3.99) Special edition with fold out cardboard-c 4.00
101,102-101-Batman app. 3.00
103-133: 103-Begin $2.25. 105-Batman-c/app. 111-Return to Krypton. 115-117-Our Worlds at War. 117-Maxima killed. 121-Royal Flush Gang app. 128-Return to Krypton II. 3.00
134-($2.75) Last issue; Steel app.; Bogdanove-c 3.00
#1,000,000 (11/98) 853rd Century x-over; Gene Ha-c 3.00
Annual 1-5 ('92-'96,68 pgs.): 1-Eclipso app.; Joe Quesada-c(p). 2-Intro Edge. 3 -Elseworlds; Mignola-c; Batman app. 4-Year One story. 5-Legends of the Dead Earth story 4.00
Annual 6 (1997, $3.95)-Pulp Heroes story 4.00
...Gallery (1995, $3.50) Pin-ups by various 4.00

SUPERMAN: THE MAN OF TOMORROW
DC Comics: 1995 - No. 15, Fall, 1999 ($1.95-$2.95, quarterly)

1-15: 1-Lex Luthor app. 3-Lex Luthor-c/app; Joker app. 4-Shazam! app. 5-Wedding of Lex Luthor. 10-Maxima-c/app. 13-JLA-c/app. 3.00
#1,000,000 (11/98) 853rd Century x-over; Gene Ha-c 3.00

SUPERMAN: THE SECRET YEARS
DC Comics: Feb, 1985 - No. 4, May, 1985 (limited series)

1-4-Miller-c on all 4.00

SUPERMAN: THE WEDDING ALBUM
DC Comics: Dec, 1996 ($4.95, 96 pgs, one-shot)

1-Standard Edition-Story & art by past and present Superman creators; gatefold back-c. Byrne-c 5.00
1-Collector's Edition-Embossed cardstock variant-c w/ metallic silver ink and matte and gloss varnishes 8.00
Retailer Rep. Program Edition (#'d to 250, signed by Bob Rozakis on back-c) 55.00
TPB ('97, $14.95) r/Wedding and honeymoon stories 15.00

SUPERMAN 3-D (See Three-Dimension Adventures)

SUPERMAN-TIM (See Promotional Comics section)

SUPERMAN UNCHAINED (DC New 52)
DC Comics: Aug, 2013 - No. 9, Jan, 2015 ($4.99/$3.99)

1-($4.99) Snyder-s/Jim Lee-a/c; back-up with Nguyen-a; bonus creator interviews 5.00
1-Director's Cut (9/13, $5.99) Lee's pencil art and Scott Snyder's scripts; cover gallery 6.00
2-8-($3.99) 2,6,7-Batman app. 4.00
9-($4.99) Wraparound-c by Jim Lee 5.00

SUPERMAN VILLAINS SECRET FILES
DC Comics: Jun, 1998 ($4.95, one shot)

1-Origin stories, "lost" pages & pin-ups 5.00

SUPERMAN VS. ALIENS (Also see Superman Aliens 2: God War)
DC Comics/Dark Horse Comics: July, 1995 - No. 3, Sept, 1995 ($4.95, limited series)

1-3: Jurgens/Nowlan-a 5.00

GD 2.0 | VG 4.0 | FN 6.0 | VF 8.0 | VF/NM 9.0 | NM 9.

SUPERMAN VS. MUHAMMAD ALI (See All-New Collectors' Edition C-56 for original 1978 printing)
DC Comics: 2010

... Deluxe Edition (2010, $19.99, HC w/dustjacket) recolored reprint in comic size; new intro. by Neal Adams; afterword by Jenette Kahn; sketch pages, key to cover celebs 20.0
... Facsimile Edition (2010, $39.99, HC no dustjacket) recolored reprint in original Treasury size; new intro. by Neal Adams; key to cover celebs 40.0

SUPERMAN VS. PREDATOR
DC Comics/Dark Horse Comics: 2000 - No. 3, 2000 ($4.95, limited series)

1-3-Micheline-s/Maleev-a 5.0
TPB (2001, $14.95) r/series 15.0

SUPERMAN VS. THE AMAZING SPIDER-MAN (Also see Marvel Treasury Edition No. 28)
National Periodical Publications/Marvel Comics Group: 1976
($2.00, Treasury sized, 100 pgs.)

1-Superman and Spider-Man battle Lex Luthor and Dr. Octopus; Andru/Giordano-a; 1st Marvel/DC x-over. 9 18 27 59 117 17
1-2nd printing; 2000 numbered copies signed by Stan Lee on front cover & sold through mai 16 32 48 110 243 37
nn-(1995, $5.95)-r/#1 2 4 6 11 16 2

SUPERMAN VS. THE TERMINATOR: DEATH TO THE FUTURE
Dark Horse/DC Comics: Dec, 1999 - No. 4, Mar, 2000 ($2.95, limited series)

1-4-Grant-s/Pugh-a/c: Steel and Supergirl app. 3.0

SUPERMAN: WAR OF THE SUPERMEN
DC Comics: No. 0, Jun, 2010 - No. 4, Jul, 2010 ($2.99, limited series)

0-Free Comic Book Day issue; Barrows-c 3.0
1-4: 1-New Krypton destroyed 3.0
HC (2011, $19.99) r/#0-4 & Superman #700 20.0

SUPERMAN/WONDER WOMAN (DC New 52)
DC Comics: Dec, 2013 - No. 29, Jul, 2016 ($3.99)

1-Soule-s/Daniel-a; wraparound gatefold-c; Doomsday app. 4.0
2-29: 2-6-Zod app. 4-6-Faora app. 7-Doomsday app. 8-12-Doomed x-over. 14-17-Magog app. 18,19-Suicide Squad app. 26,27-Vandal Savage app. 28,29-Supergirl app. 4.0
Annual 1 (9/14, $4.99) Doomsday Superman vs. Cyborg Superman 5.0
Annual 2 (2/16, $4.99) Short stories by various; Paquette-c 5.0
...: Futures End 1 (11/14, $2.99, regular-c) Cont'd from Wonder Woman: FE #1 3.0
...: Futures End 1 (11/14, $3.99, 3-D cover) 4.0

SUPERMAN/WONDER WOMAN: WHOM GODS DESTROY
DC Comics: 1997 ($4.95, prestige format, limited series)

1-4-Elseworlds; Claremont-s 5.0

SUPERMAN WORKBOOK
National Periodical Publ./Juvenile Group Foundation: 1945 (B&W, reprints, 68 pgs)

nn-Cover-r/Superman #14 245 490 735 1568 2684 380

SUPERMAN: WORLD OF NEW KRYPTON
DC Comics: May, 2009 - No. 12,Apr, 2010 ($2.99, limited series)

1-12: Robinson & Rucka-s/Woods-a; Frank-c and variant for each. 4-Green Lantern app. 3.0

SUPER MARIO BROS. (Also see Adventures of the..., Blip, Gameboy, and Nintendo Comics System)
Valiant Comics: 1990 - No. 6, 1991 ($1.95, slick-c) V2#1, 1991 - No. 5, 1991

1-Wildman-a 3 6 9 14 20 2
2-6, V2#1-5-($1.50) 1 3 4 6 8 1
Special Edition 1 (1990, $1.95)-Wildman-a; 1st Valiant comic 1 3 4 6 8 1

SUPER MARKET COMICS
Fawcett Publications: No date (1950s)

nn - Ashcan comic, not distributed to newsstands, only for in-house use (no known sales)

SUPER MARKET VARIETIES
Fawcett Publications: No date (1950s)

nn - Ashcan comic, not distributed to newsstands, only for in-house use (no known sales)

SUPERMEN OF AMERICA
DC Comics: Mar, 1999 ($3.95/$4.95, one-shot)

1-($3.95) Regular Ed.; Immonen-s/art by various 4.0
1-($4.95) Collectors' Ed. with membership kit 5.0

SUPERMEN OF AMERICA (Mini-series)
DC Comics: Mar, 2000 - No. 6, Aug, 2000 ($2.50)

1-6-Nicieza-s/Braithwaite-a 3.0

SUPERMOUSE (...the Big Cheese; see Coo Coo Comics)

Super-Mystery Comics V4 #3 © ACE

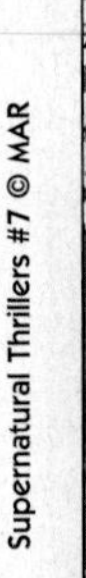
Supernatural Thrillers #7 © MAR

Super Powers (2017 series) #2 © DC

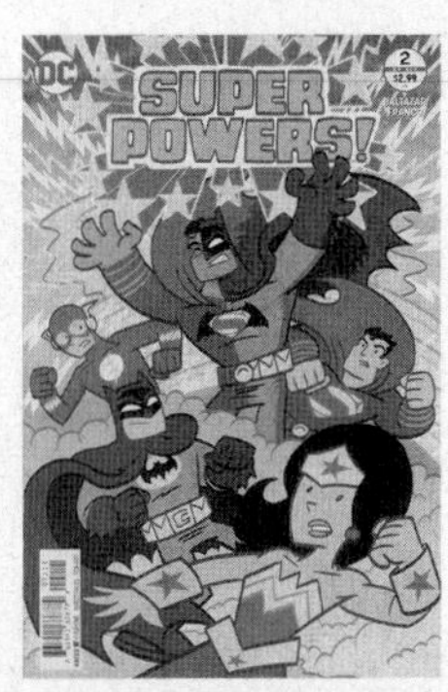

GD VG FN VF VF/NM NM-
2.0 4.0 6.0 8.0 9.0 9.2

Standard Comics/Pines No. 35 on (Literary Ent.): Dec, 1948 - No. 34, Sept, 1955; No. 35, Apr, 1956 - No. 45, Fall, 1958

1-Frazetta text illos (3) 39 78 117 236 388 540
2-Frazetta text illos 17 34 51 100 158 215
3,5,6-Text illos by Frazetta in all 15 30 45 83 124 165
4-Two pg. text illos by Frazetta 15 30 45 85 130 175
7-10 10 20 30 54 72 90
11-20: 13-Racist humor (Indians) 8 16 24 44 57 70
21-45 7 14 21 37 46 55
1-Summer Holiday issue (Summer, 1957, 25¢, 100 pgs.)-Pines
14 28 42 82 121 160
2-Giant Summer issue (Summer, 1958, 25¢, 100 pgs.)-Pines; has games, puzzles & stories 11 22 33 60 83 105

SUPER-MYSTERY COMICS
Ace Magazines (Periodical House): July, 1940 - V8#6, July, 1949

V1#1-Magno, the Magnetic Man & Vulcan begins (1st app.); Q-13, Corp. Flint, & Sky Smith begin 400 800 1200 2800 4900 7000
2 206 412 618 1318 2259 3200
3-The Black Spider begins (1st app.) 168 336 504 1075 1838 2600
4-Origin Davy 116 232 348 742 1271 1800
5-Intro. The Clown & begin series (12/40) 123 246 369 787 1344 1900
6(2/41) 100 200 300 635 1093 1550
V2#1(4/41)-Origin Buckskin 97 194 291 621 1061 1500
2-6(2/42): 3-Hitler & Mussolini app. 4-WWII Nazi-c. 6-Vulcan begins again; bondage/torture-c 90 180 270 576 988 1400
V3#1(4/42),2: 1-Black Ace begins 97 194 291 621 1061 1500
3-Classic Kurtzman Japanese WWII giant robot bondage-c; intro. The Lancer; Dr. Nemesis & The Sword begin; Kurtzman-a(2)(Mr. Risk & Paul Revere Jr.)
142 284 426 909 1555 2200
4-Kurtzman-c/a; classic-c 194 388 582 1242 2121 3000
5-Kurtzman-a(2); L.B. Cole-a; Mr. Risk app. 110 220 330 704 1202 1700
6(10/43)-Mr. Risk app.; Kurtzman's Paul Revere Jr.; L.B. Cole-a
90 180 270 576 988 1400
V4#1(1/44)-L.B. Cole-a; Hitler app. 65 130 195 416 708 1000
2-6(4/45): 2,5,6-Mr. Risk app. 55 110 165 352 601 850
V5#1(7/45)-6 53 106 159 334 567 800
V6#1,2,4,5,6: 4-Last Magno. Mr. Risk app. in #2,4-6. 6-New logo
50 100 150 315 533 750
3-Classic torture c/story 174 348 522 1114 1907 2700
V7#1-6, V8#1-4,6 47 94 141 296 498 700
V8#5-Meskin, Tuska, Sid Greene-a 48 96 144 302 514 725

NOTE: ***Sid Greene** a-V7#4. **Mooney** c-V1#5, 6, V2#1-6. **Palais** a-V5#3, 4; c-V4#6-V5#4, V6#2, V8#4. Bondage c-V2#5, 6, V3#2, 5. Magno c-V1#1-V3#6, V4#2-V5#5, V6#2. The Sword c-V4#1, 6(w/Magno).*

SUPERNATURAL (Volume 4) (Based on the CW television series)
DC Comics: Dec, 2011 - No. 6, May, 2012 ($2.99, limited series)

1-6: 1-Sam in Scotland; Brian Wood-s/Grant Bond-a 3.00

SUPERNATURAL: BEGINNING'S END (Based on the CW television series)
DC Comics (WildStorm): Mar, 2010 - No. 6, Aug, 2010 ($2.99, limited series)

1-6-Prequel to the series; Dabb & Loflin-s/Olmos-a. 1-Olmos and photo-c 3.00
TPB (2010, $14.99) r/#1-6; character sketch pages 15.00

SUPERNATURAL FREAK MACHINE: A CAL MCDONALD MYSTERY
IDW Publishing: Mar, 2005 - No. 3 ($3.99)

1-3-Steve Niles-s/Kelley Jones-a 4.00

SUPERNATURAL LAW (Formerly Wolff & Byrd, Counselors of the Macabre)
Exhibit A Press: No. 24, Oct, 1999 - Present ($2.50/$2.95/$3.50, B&W)

24-35-Batton Lash-s/a. 29-Marie Severin-c. 33-Cerebus spoof 3.00
36-40-($2.95). 37-Frank Cho pin-up and story panels 3.00
(#41) ...First Amendment Issue (2005, $3.50) anti-censorship story; CBLDF info 3.50
(#42) With a Silver Bullet (2006, $3.50) new stories and pin-ups 3.50
(#43) At the Box Office (2006, $3.50) new stories and pin-ups 3.50
(#44) Wolff & Byrd: The Movie (2007, $3.50) new stories and pin-ups 3.50
45-($3.50) Toxic Avenger and Lloyd Kaufman app. 3.50
#1 (2005, $2.95) r/Wolff & Byrd with redrawn and re-toned art; relettered 3.00

SUPERNATURAL LAW SECRETARY MAVIS
Exhibit A Press: 2001 - No. 5 ($2.95/$3.50, B&W)

1-3: 3-DeCarlo-c 3.00
4,5-($3.50) Jaime Hernandez-c 3.50

SUPERNATURAL: ORIGINS (Based on the CW television series)
DC Comics (WildStorm): July, 2007 - No. 6, Dec, 2007 ($2.99, limited series)

1-6: 1-Bradstreet-c; Johnson-s/Smith-a; back-up w/Johns-s/Hester-a 3.00
TPB (2008, $14.99) r/#1-6; sketch pages 15.00

SUPERNATURAL: RISING SON (Based on the CW television series)
DC Comics (WildStorm): Jun, 2008 - No. 6, Nov, 2008 ($2.99, limited series)

1-6-Johnson & Dessertine-s/Olmos-a. 1-Oliver-c 3.00
1-Variant-c by Nguyen 6.00
TPB (2009, $14.99) r/#1-6 15.00

SUPERNATURALS
Marvel Comics: Dec, 1998 - No. 4, Dec, 1998 ($3.99, weekly limited series)

1-4-Pulido-s/Balent-c; bound-in Halloween masks 4.00
1-4-With bound-in Ghost Rider mask (1 in 10) 4.00
... Preview Tour Book (10/98, $2.99) Reis-c 4.00

SUPERNATURAL THRILLERS
Marvel Comics Group: Dec, 1972 - No. 6, Nov, 1973; No. 7, Jun, 1974 - No. 15, Oct, 1975

1-It!; Sturgeon adap. (see Astonishing Tales #21) 4 8 12 23 37 50
2-4,6: 2-The Invisible Man; H.G. Wells adapt. 3-The Valley of the Worm; R.E. Howard adapt. 4-Dr. Jekyll & Mr. Hyde; R.L. Stevenson adapt.. 6-The Headless Horseman; last 20¢ issue
3 6 9 14 20 25
5-1st app. The Living Mummy 6 12 18 40 73 105
7-15: 7-The Living Mummy begins 3 6 9 17 26 35

NOTE: ***Brunner** c-11. **Buckler** a-5p. **Ditko** a-8r, 9r. **G. Kane** a-3p; c-3, 9p, 15p. **Mayerik** a-2p, 7, 8, 9p, 10p, 11. **McWilliams** a-14i. **Mortimer** a-4. **Steranko** c-1, 2. **Sutton** a-15. **Tuska** a-6p.*

SUPERPATRIOT (Also see Freak Force & Savage Dragon #2)
Image Comics (Highbrow Entertainment): July, 1993 - No. 4, Dec, 1993 ($1.95, lim. series)

1-4: Dave Johnson-c/a; Larsen scripts; Giffen plots 3.00

SUPERPATRIOT: AMERICA'S FIGHTING FORCE
Image Comics: July, 2002 - No. 4, Oct, 2002 ($2.95, limited series)

1-4-Cory Walker-a/c; Savage Dragon app. 3.00

SUPERPATRIOT: LIBERTY & JUSTICE
Image Comics (Highbrow Entertainment): July, 1995 - No. 4, Oct, 1995 ($2.50, lim. series)

1-4: Dave Johnson-c/a. 1-1st app. Liberty & Justice 3.00
TPB (2002, $12.95) r/#1-4; new cover by Dave Johnson; sketch pages 13.00

SUPERPATRIOT: WAR ON TERROR
Image Comics: July, 2004 - No. 4, May, 2007 ($2.95/$2.99, limited series)

1-4-Kirkman-s/Su-a 3.00

SUPER POWERS (1st Series)
DC Comics: July, 1984 - No. 5, Nov, 1984

1-5: 1-Joker/Penguin-c/story; Batman app.; all Kirby-c. 5-Kirby c/a 6.00

SUPER POWERS (2nd Series)
DC Comics: Sept, 1985 - No. 6, Feb, 1986

1-6: Kirby-c/a; Capt. Marvel & Firestorm join; Batman cameo; Darkseid storyline in all. 4-Batman cameo. 5,6-Batman app. 5.00

SUPER POWERS (3rd Series)
DC Comics: Sept, 1986 - No. 4, Dec, 1986

1-4: 1-Cyborg joins; 1st app. Samurai from Super Friends TV show. 1-4-Batman cameos; Darkseid storyline in #1-4 4.00

SUPER POWERS (All ages series)
DC Comics: Jan, 2017 - No. 6, Jun, 2017 ($2.99, limited series)

1-6-Franco & Baltazar-s/Baltazar-a/c; Superman, Batman & Wonder Woman vs. Brainiac 3.00

SUPER PUP (Formerly Spotty The Pup) (See Space Comics)
Avon Periodicals: No. 4, Mar-Apr, 1954 - No. 5, 1954

4,5: 4-Atom bomb-c. 5-Robot-c 9 18 27 50 65 80

SUPER RABBIT (See All Surprise, Animated Movie Tunes, Comedy Comics, Comic Capers, Ideal Comics, It's A Duck's Life, Movie Tunes & Wisco)
Timely Comics (CmPl): Fall, 1944 - No. 14, Nov, 1948

1-Hitler & Hirohito-c; war effort paper recycling PSA by S&K; Ziggy Pig & Silly Seal begin
258 516 774 1651 2826 4000
2 50 100 150 315 533 750
3-5 34 68 102 196 321 445
6-Origin 34 68 102 204 332 460
7-10: 9-Infinity-c 22 44 66 128 209 290
11-Kurtzman's "Hey Look" 23 46 69 136 223 310
12-14 22 44 66 128 209 290
I.W. Reprint #1,2('58),7,10('63): 1-r/#13. 2-r/#10. 3 6 9 14 20 25

SUPER RICHIE (Superichie #5 on) (See Richie Rich Millions #68)
Harvey Publications: Sept, 1975 - No. 4, Mar, 1976 (All 52 pg. Giants)

Super Sons #2 © DC

Superwoman #1 © DC

Supreme #7 © Rob Liefeld

GD VG FN VF VF/NM NM-
2.0 4.0 6.0 8.0 9.0 9.2

1 3 6 9 16 23 30
2-4 2 4 6 11 16 20

SUPER SECRET CRISIS WAR! (Crossover of Cartoon Network characters)
IDW Publishing: Jun, 2014 - No. 6, Nov, 2014 ($3.99, limited series)

1-6-Powerpuff Girls, Samurai Jack, Dexter, Ben 10 vs. Aku, Mojo Jojo, Mandark 4.00
... Codename: Kids Next Door One-Shot (11/14 $3.99) 3 covers; Jampole-a 4.00
... Cow and Chicken One-Shot (10/14 $3.99) 3 covers; Jim Zub-s 4.00
... Foster's Home For Imaginary Friends One-Shot (9/14 $3.99) 3 covers; Ganucheau-a 4.00
... Johnny Bravo One-Shot (7/14 $3.99) 3 covers; Erica Henderson-a 4.00
... The Grimm Adventures of Billy and Mandy One-Shot (7/14 $3.99) 3 covers; Leth-s 4.00

SUPER SLUGGERS (Baseball)
Ultimate Sports Ent. Inc.: 1999 ($3.95, one-shot)

1-Bonds, Piazza, Caminiti, Griffey Jr. app.; Martinbrough-c/a 4.00

SUPERSNIPE COMICS (Formerly Army & Navy #1-5)
Street & Smith Publications: V1#6, Oct, 1942 - V5#1, Aug-Sept, 1949
(See Shadow Comics V2#3)

V1#6-Rex King - Man of Adventure (costumed hero, see Super Magic/Magician) by Jack Binder begins; Supersnipe by George Marcoux continues from Army & Navy #5; Bill Ward-a 81 162 243 518 884 1250
7,10-12: 10,11-Little Nemo app. 50 100 150 315 533 750
8-Hitler, Tojo, Mussolini in Hell with Devil-c 239 478 717 1530 2615 3700
9-Doc Savage x-over in Supersnipe; Hitler-c 226 452 678 1446 2473 3500
V2 #1: Both V2#1(2/44) & V2#2(4/44) have V2#1 on outside-c; Huck Finn by Clare Dwiggins begins, ends V3#5 (rare) 57 114 171 362 619 875
V2#2 (4/44) has V2#1 on outside-c; classic shark-c 43 86 129 271 461 650
3-12: 12-Statue of Liberty-c 23 46 69 136 223 310
V3#1-12: 8-Bobby Crusoe by Dwiggins begins, ends V3#12. 9-X-Mas-c
20 40 60 117 189 260
V4#1-12, V5#1: V4#10-X-Mas-c 17 34 51 98 154 210
NOTE: ***George Marcoux*** *c-V1#6-V3#4. Doc Savage app. in some issues.*

SUPER SOLDIER (See Marvel Versus DC #3)
DC Comics (Amalgam): Apr, 1996 ($1.95, one-shot)

1-Mark Waid script & Dave Gibbons-c/a. 3.00

SUPER SOLDIER: MAN OF WAR
DC Comics (Amalgam): June, 1997 ($1.95, one-shot)

1-Waid & Gibbons-s/Gibbons & Palmiotti-c/a. 3.00

SUPER SOLDIERS
Marvel Comics UK: Apr, 1993 - No. 8, Nov, 1993 ($1.75)

1-($2.50)-Embossed silver foil logo 4.00
2-8: 5-Capt. America app. 6-Origin; Nick Fury app.; neon ink-c 3.00

SUPER SONS
DC Comics: Apr, 2017 - No. 16 ($2.99)

1,2: 1-Damian Wayne (Robin) & Jon Kent (Superboy) team-up; Tomasi-s/Jimenez-a 3.00
3-13-($3.99) 3,4-Battle Kid Amazo. 6,7-Teen Titans app. 11,12-Future adult Superboy (Conner), Wonder Girl (Cassie) and Kid Flash (Bart) app. 13-Talia app. 4.00
Annual 1 (1/18, $4.99) Tomasi-s/Pelletier-a; Krypto, Titus & the Super-Pets app. 5.00

SUPERSPOOK (Formerly Frisky Animals on Parade)
Ajax/Farrell Publications: No. 4, June, 1958

4 8 16 24 44 57 70

SUPER SPY (See Wham Comics)
Centaur Publications: Oct, 1940 - No. 2, Nov, 1940 (Reprints)

1-Origin The Sparkler 94 188 282 597 1024 1450
2-The Inner Circle, Dean Denton, Tim Blain, The Drew Ghost, The Night Hawk by Gustavson, & S.S. Swanson by Glanz app. 58 116 174 371 636 900

SUPERSTAR: AS SEEN ON TV
Image Comics (Gorilla): 2001 ($5.95)

1-Busiek-s/Immonen-a 6.00

SUPER STAR HOLIDAY SPECIAL (See DC Special Series #21)

SUPER-TEAM FAMILY
National Periodical Publ./DC Comics: Oct-Nov, 1975 - No. 15, Mar-Apr, 1978

1-Reprints by Neal Adams & Kane/Wood; 68 pgs. begin, ends #4. New Gods app.
3 6 9 16 23 30
2,3: New stories 3 6 9 14 20 25
4-7: Reprints. 4-G.A. JSA-r & Superman/Batman/Robin-r from World's Finest. 5-52 pgs. begin 2 4 6 10 14 18
8-14: 8-10-New Challengers of the Unknown stories. 9-Kirby-a. 11-14: New stories
3 6 9 14 19 24
15-New Gods app. New stories 3 6 9 14 20 26
NOTE: ***Neal Adams*** *r-1-3.* ***Brunner*** *c-3.* ***Buckler*** *c-8p.* ***Tuska*** *a-7r.* ***Wood*** *a-1i(r), 3.*

SUPER TV HEROES (See Hanna-Barbera...)

SUPER-VILLAIN CLASSICS
Marvel Comics Group: May, 1983

1-Galactus -The Origin; Kirby-a 2 4 6 8 10 12

SUPER-VILLAIN TEAM-UP (See Fantastic Four #6 & Giant-Size...)
Marvel Comics Group: 8/75 - No. 14, 10/77; No. 15, 11/78; No. 16, 5/79; No. 17, 6/80

1-Continued from Giant-Size Super-Villain Team-Up #2; Sub-Mariner & Dr. Doom begin, end #10 4 8 12 28 47 65
2-5: 5-1st app. The Shroud 3 6 9 14 19 24
5-(30¢-c variant, limited distribution)(4/76) 4 8 12 27 44 60
6,7-(25¢ editions) 6-(6/76)-F.F., Shroud app. 7-Origin Shroud
2 4 6 8 11 14
6,7-(30¢-c, limited distribution)(6,8/76) 4 8 12 27 44 60
8,9,11-17: 9-Avengers app. 11-15-Dr. Doom & Red Skull app.
2 4 6 8 11 14
10-Classic Dr. Doom, Red Skull, Captain America battle-c
2 4 6 10 14 18
12-14-(35¢-c variants, limited distribution)(6,8,10/77)
10 20 30 67 141 215
NOTE: ***Buckler*** *c-4p, 5p, 7p.* ***Buscema*** *c-1.* ***Byrne/Austin*** *c-14.* ***Evans*** *a-1p, 3p.* ***Everett*** *a-1p.* ***Giffen*** *a-8p, 13p, c-13p.* ***Kane*** *c-2p, 9p.* ***Mooney*** *a-4i.* ***Starlin*** *c-6.* ***Tuska*** *r-1p, 15p.* ***Wood*** *r-15p.*

SUPER-VILLAIN TEAM-UP/ MODOK'S 11
Marvel Comics: Sept, 2007 - No. 5, Jan, 2008 ($2.99, limited series)

1-5: 1-MODOK's origin re-told; Portela-a/Powell-c; Purple Man & Mentallo app. 3.00
... TPB (2008, $13.99) r/#1-5 14.00

SUPER WESTERN COMICS (Also see Buffalo Bill)
Youthful Magazines: Aug, 1950 (One shot)

1-Buffalo Bill begins; Wyatt Earp, Calamity Jane & Sam Slade app; Powell-c/a
16 32 48 94 147 200

SUPER WESTERN FUNNIES (See Super Funnies)

SUPERWOMAN
DC Comics: Jan 1942

nn - Ashcan comic, not distributed to newsstands, only for in-house use. Cover art is More Fun Comics #73 with interior being Action Comics #38 (no known sales)

SUPERWOMAN (DC Rebirth)
DC Comics: Oct, 2016 - No. 18, Mar, 2018 ($2.99/$3.99)

1-8: 1-Phil Jimenez-s/a; Lois and Lana with powers. 2-8-Lena Luthor app. 3.00
9-18-($3.99): 9,10-Segovia-a. 13-15-Supergirl app. 14-18-Maxima app. 4.00

SUPERWORLD COMICS
Hugo Gernsback (Komos Publ.): Apr, 1940 - No. 3, Aug, 1940 (68 pgs.)

1-Origin & 1st app. Hip Knox, Super Hypnotist; Mitey Powers & Buzz Allen, the Invisible Avenger, Little Nemo begin; cover by Frank R. Paul (all have sci/fi-c) (Scarce) 865 1730 2595 6315 13,408 20,500
2-Marvo 1-2 Go+, the Super Boy of the Year 2680 (1st app.); Paul-c (Scarce)
595 1190 1785 4350 7675 11,000
3 (Scarce) 470 940 1410 3431 6066 8700

SUPERZERO
AfterShock Comics: Dec, 2015 - No. 6, Jun, 2016 ($3.99)

1-6-Conner & Palmiotti-s/De Latorre-a. 1-Covers by Conner, Cooke & Hester 4.00

SUPER ZOMBIES
Dynamite Entertainment: 2009 - No. 5, 2009 ($3.50)

1-5-Mel Rubi-a; Guggenheim & Gonzales-s; two covers for each by Rubi & Neves 3.50

SUPREME (Becomes ...The New Adventures #43-48)(See Youngblood #3)
(Also see Bloodwulf Special, Legend of Supreme, & Trencher #3)
Image Comics (Extreme Studios)/ Awesome Entertainment #49 on:
V2#1, Nov, 1992 - V2#42, Sept, 1996; V3#49 - No. 56, Feb, 1998

V2#1-Liefeld-a(i) & scripts; embossed foil logo 4.00
1-Gold Edition 1 2 3 5 6 8
2-(3/93)-Liefeld co-plots & inks; 1st app. Grizlock 3.00
3-42: 3-Intro Bloodstrike; 1st app. Khrome. 5-1st app. Thor. 6-1st brief app. The Starguard. 7-1st full app. The Starguard. 10-Black and White Pt 1 (1st app.) by Art Thibert (2 pgs. ea. installment). 25-(5/94)-Platt-c. 11-Coupon #4 for Extreme Prejudice #0; Black and White Pt. 7 by Thibert. 12-(4/94)-Platt-c. 13,14-(6/94). 15 (7/94). 16 (7/94)-Stormwatch app. 18-Kid Supreme Sneak Preview; Pitt app.19,20-Polybagged w/trading card. 20-1st app. Woden & Loki (as a dog); Overkill app. 21-1st app. Loki (in true form). 21-23-Poly-bagged trading card. 32-Lady Supreme cameo. 33-Origin & 1st full app. of

Supurbia #1 © BOOM! & Grace Randolph

Sure-Fire Comics #1 © ACE

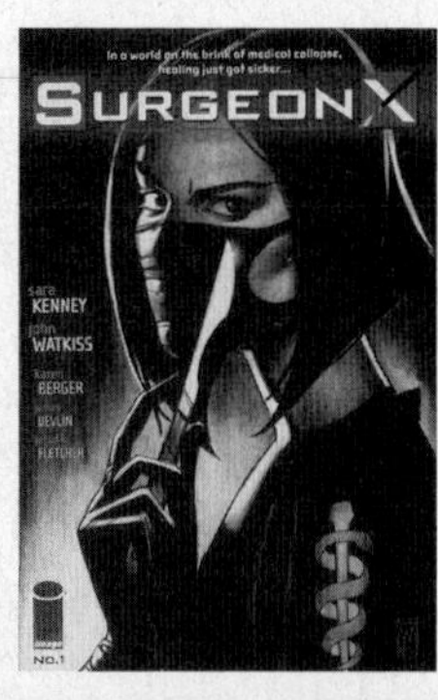

Surgeon X #1 © Wowbagger Prods.

	GD 2.0	VG 4.0	FN 6.0	VF 8.0	VF/NM 9.0	NM- 9.2

Lady Supreme (Probe from the Starguard); Babewatch! tie-in. 37-Intro Loki; Fraga-c. 40-Retells Supreme's past advs. 41-Alan Moore scripts begin; Supreme revised; intro The Supremacy; Jerry Ordway-c (Joe Bennett variant-c exists). 42-New origin w/Rick Veitch-a; intro Radar, The Hound Supreme & The League of Infinity 3.00
28-Variant-c by Quesada & Palmiotti 3.00
(#43-48-**See Supreme: The New Adventures**)
V3#49,51: 49-Begin $2.99-c 3.00
50-($3.95)-Double sized, 2 covers, pin-up gallery 4.00
52a,52b-($3.50) 4.00
53-56: 53-Sprouse-a begins. 56-McGuinness-c 3.00
Annual 1-(1995, $2.95) 4.00
...: Supreme Sacrifice (3/06, $3.99) Flip book with Suprema; Kirkman-s/Malin-a 4.00
...: The Return TPB (Checker Book Publ., 2003, $24.95) r/#53-56 & Supreme; The Return #1-6; Ross-c; additional sketch pages by Ross 25.00
...: The Story of the Year TPB (Checker Book Publ., 2002, $26.95) r/#41-52; R[illegible]-c 27.00
NOTE: ***Rob Liefeld** a(i)-1, 2; co-plots-2-4; scripts-1, 5, 6.* ***Ordway** c-41.* ***Platt** c-12, 25.* ***Thiber**[illegible] (i)-7-9.*

SUPREME
Image Comics: No. 63, Apr, 2012 - Present ($2.99)
63-66: 63-Moore-s; two covers by Larsen & Hamscher 3.00
67,68-($3.99) 67-Omni-Man app. 4.00

SUPREME BLUE ROSE
Image Comics: Jul, 2014 - No. 7, Mar, 2015 ($2.99)
1-7-Warren Ellis-s/Tula Lotay-a 00

SUPREME: GLORY DAYS
Image Comics (Extreme Studios): Oct, 1994 - No. 2, Dec, 1994 ($2.95/$2.50, limited series)
1,2: 2-Diehard, Roman, Superpatriot, & Glory app. 3.00

SUPREME POWER (Also see Squadron Supreme 2006 series)
Marvel Comics (MAX): Oct, 2003 - No. 18, Oct, 2005 ($2.99)
1-($2.99) Straczynski-s/Frank-a; Frank-c 3.00
1-($4.99) Special Edition with variant Quesada-c; includes r/early Squadron Supreme apps. 5.00
2-18: 4-Intro. Nighthawk. 6-The Blur debuts. 10-Princess Zarda returns. 17-Hyperion revealed as alien. 18-Continues in mini-series 3.00
... MGC #1 (7/11, $1.00) r/#1 with "Marvel's Greatest Comics" banner on cover 3.00
Vol. 1: Contact TPB (2004, $14.99) r/#1-6 15.00
Vol. 2: Powers & Principalities TPB (2004, $14.99) r/#7-12 15.00
Vol. 3: High Command TPB (2005, $14.99) r/#13-18 15.00
Vol. 1 HC (2005, $29.99, 7 1/2" x 11" with dustjacket) r/#1-12; Avengers #85 & 86, Straczynski intro., Frank cover sketches and character design pages 30.00
Vol. 2 HC (2006, $29.99, 7 1/2" x 11" with dustjacket) r/#13-18; ...: Hyperion #1-5; character design pages 30.00

SUPREME POWER
Marvel Comics (MAX): Aug, 2011 - No. 4, Nov, 2011 ($3.99, limited series)
1-4-Higgins-s/Garcia-a/Fiumara-c; Doctor Spectrum app. 4.00

SUPREME POWER: HYPERION
Marvel Comics (MAX): Nov, 2005 - No. 5, Mar, 2006 ($2.99, limited series)
1-5: 1-Straczynski-s/Jurgens-a/Dodson-c 3.00
TPB (2006, $14.99) r/#1-5 15.00

SUPREME POWER: NIGHTHAWK
Marvel Comics (MAX): Nov, 2005 - No. 6, Apr, 2006 ($2.99, limited series)
1-6-Daniel Way-s/Steve Dillon-a; origin of Whiteface 3.00
TPB (2006, $16.99) r/#1-6; cover concept art 17.00

SUPREME: THE NEW ADVENTURES (Formerly Supreme)
Maximum Press: V3#43, Oct, 1996 - V3#48, May, 1997 ($2.50)
V3#43-48: 43-Alan Moore scripts begin; Joe Bennett-a; Rick Veitch-a (8 pgs.); Dan Jurgens-a (1 pg.); intro Citadel Supreme & Suprematons; 1st Allied Supermen of America 3.00

SUPREME: THE RETURN
Awesome Entertainment: May, 1999 - No. 6, June, 2000 ($2.99)
1-6: Alan Moore-s. 1,2-Sprouse & Gordon-a/c. 2,4-Liefeld-c. 6-Kirby app. 3.00

SUPURBIA (GRACE RANDOLPH'S...)
BOOM! Studios: Mar, 2012 - No. 4, Jun, 2012 ($3.99, limited series)
1-4-Grace Randolph-s/Dauterman-a. 1-Garza-c 4.00

SUPURBIA (GRACE RANDOLPH'S...)(Volume 2)
BOOM! Studios: Nov, 2012 - No. 12, Oct, 2013 ($3.99, limited series)
1-12-Grace Randolph-s/Dauterman-a; multiple covers on #1-5 4.00

SURE-FIRE COMICS (Lightning Comics #4 on)
Ace Magazines: June, 1940 - No. 4, Oct, 1940 (Two No. 3's)
V1#1-Origin Flash Lightning & begins; X-The Phantom Fed, Ace McCoy, Buck Steele, Marvo the Magician, The Raven, Whiz Wilson (Time Traveler) begin (all 1st app.); Flash Lightning c-1-4 258 516 774 1651 2826 4000
2 142 284 426 909 1555 2200
3(9/40), 3(#4)(10/40)-nn on-c, #3 on inside 110 220 330 704 1202 1700

SURFACE TENSION
Titan Comics: Jun, 2015 - No. 5, Oct, 2015 ($3.99, limited series)
1-5-Jay Gunn-s/a. 1,2-Two covers 4.00

SURF 'N' WHEELS
Charlton Comics: Nov, 1969 - No. 6, Sept, 1970
1 3 6 9 19 30 40
2-6 3 6 9 14 19 24

SURGE
Eclipse Comics: July, 1984 - No. 4, Jan, 1985 ($1.50, lim. series, Baxter paper)
1-4-Ties into DNAgents series 3.00

SURGEON X
Image Comics: Sept, 2016 - No. 6, Feb, 2017 ($3.99)
1-6: 1-Sara Kenney-s/John Watkiss-a/c. 6-Watkiss & Pleece-a 4.00

SURPRISE ADVENTURES (Formerly Tormented)
Sterling Comic Group: No. 3, Mar, 1955 - No. 5, July, 1955
3-5: 3,5-Sekowsky-a 11 22 33 60 83 105

SURVIVE (Follows Cataclysm: The Ultimates Last Stand)
Marvel Comics: May, 2014 ($3.99, one-shot)
1-Bendis-s/Quinones-a; the new Ultimates team is formed 4.00

SURVIVORS' CLUB
DC Comics (Vertigo): Dec, 2015 - No. 9, Aug, 2016 ($3.99)
1-9-Beukes & Halvorsen-s/Ryan Kelly-a/Sienkiewicz-c 4.00

SUSIE Q. SMITH
Dell Publishing Co.: No. 323, Mar, 1951 - No. 553, Apr, 1954
Four Color 323 (#1) 6 12 18 37 66 95
Four Color 377, 453 (2/53), 553 5 10 15 30 50 70

SUSPENSE (Radio/TV issues #1-11; Real Life Tales of... #1-4) (Amazing Detective Cases #3 on?)
Marvel/Atlas Comics (CnPC No. 1-10/BFP No. 11-29): Dec, 1949 - No. 29, Apr, 1953 (#1-8, 17-23: 52 pgs.)
1-Powell-a; Peter Lorre, Sidney Greenstreet photo-c from Hammett's "The Verdict" 100 200 300 635 1093 1550
2-Crime stories; Dennis O'Keefe & Gale Storm photo-c from Universal movie "Abandoned" 43 86 129 271 461 650
3-Change to horror 54 108 162 343 574 825
4,7-10: 7-Dracula-sty 43 86 129 271 461 650
5-Krigstein, Tuska, Everett-a 45 90 135 284 480 675
6-Tuska, Everett, Morisi-a 43 86 129 269 457 645
11-13,15-17,19,20 39 78 117 240 395 550
14-Classic Heath Hypo-c; A-Bomb panels 52 104 156 328 552 775
18,22-Krigstein-a 40 80 120 244 402 560
21,23,24,26-29: 24-Tuska-a 37 74 111 218 354 490
25-Electric chair-c/story 43 86 129 271 461 650
NOTE: ***Ayers** a-20.* ***Briefer** a-5, 7, 27.* ***Brodsky** c-4, 6-9, 11, 16, 17, 25.* ***Colan** a-8(2), 9.* ***Everett** a-5, 6(2), 19, 23, 28; c-21-23, 26.* ***Fuje** a-29.* ***Heath** a-5, 6, 8, 10, 12, 14; c-14, 19, 24.* ***Maneely** a-11, 12, 23, 24, 28, 29; c-5, 6p, 10, 13, 15, 18.* ***Mooney** a-24, 28.* ***Morisi** a-6, 12.* ***Palais** a-10.* ***Rico** a-7-9.* ***Robinson** a-29.* ***Romita** a-20(2), 25.* ***Sekowsky** a-11, 13, 14.* ***Sinnott** a-23, 25.* ***Tuska** a-5, 6(2), 12; c-12.* ***Whitney** a-15, 16, 22.* ***Ed Win** a-27.*

SUSPENSE COMICS
Continental Magazines: Dec, 1943 - No. 12, Sept, 1946
1-The Grey Mask begins; bondage/torture-c; L. B. Cole-a (7 pgs.) 595 1190 1785 4350 7675 11,000
2-Intro. The Mask; Rico, Giunta, L. B. Cole-a (7 pgs.) 300 600 900 1950 3375 4800
3-L.B. Cole-a; classic Schomburg-c (Scarce) 7800 15,600 23,400 46,800 80,900 115,000
4-L. B. Cole-c begin 297 594 891 1901 3251 4600
5,6 245 490 735 1568 2684 3800
7,9,10,12: 9-L.B. Cole eyeball-c 187 374 561 1197 2049 2900
8-Classic L. B. Cole spider-c 465 930 1395 3395 5998 8600
11-Classic Devil-c 383 766 1149 2681 4691 6700
NOTE: ***L. B. Cole** c-4-12.* ***Fuje** a-8.* ***Larsen** a-11.* ***Palais** a-10, 11. Bondage c-1, 3, 4.*

SUSPENSE DETECTIVE
Fawcett Publications: June, 1952 - No. 5, Mar, 1953
1-Evans-a (11 pgs); Baily-c/a 47 94 141 296 498 700
2-Evans-a (10 pgs.) 28 56 84 165 270 375
3-5 24 48 72 140 230 320

Suzie Comics #76 © MLJ

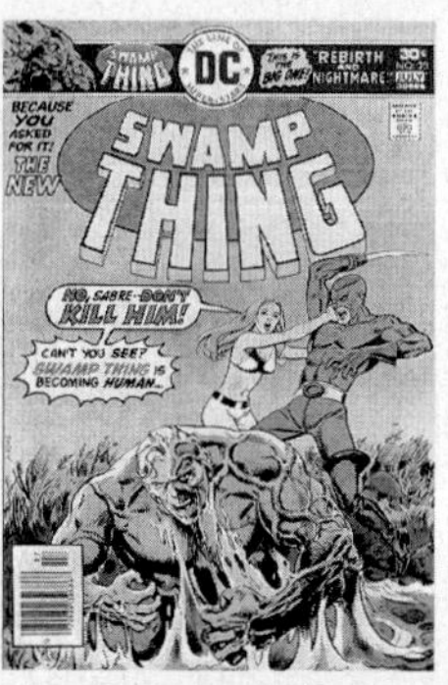

Swamp Thing #23 © DC

Swamp Thing (2011 series) #34 © DC

GD VG FN VF VF/NM NM-
2.0 4.0 6.0 8.0 9.0 9.2

NOTE: ***Baily** a-4, 5; c-1-3. **Sekowsky** a-2, 4, 5; c-5.*

SUSPENSE STORIES (See Strange Suspense Stories)

SUSSEX VAMPIRE, THE (Sherlock Holmes)
Caliber Comics: 1996 ($2.95, 32 pgs., B&W, one-shot)
nn-Adapts Sir Arthur Conan Doyle's story; Warren Ellis scripts 3.00

SUZIE COMICS (Formerly Laugh Comix; see Laugh Comics, Liberty Comics #10, Pep Comics & Top-Notch Comics #28)
Close-Up No. 49,50/MLJ Mag./Archie No. 51 on: No. 49, Spring, 1945 - No. 100, Aug, 1954
49-Ginger begins 53 106 159 334 567 800
50-55: 54-Transvestism story. 55-Woggon-a 37 74 111 222 361 500
56-Katy Keene begins by Woggon 47 94 141 296 498 700
57-65 21 42 63 122 199 275
66-80 17 34 51 98 154 210
81-87,89-99 15 30 45 88 137 185
88,100: 88-Used in **POP**, pgs. 76,77; Bill Woggon draws himself in story.
100-Last Katy Keene 17 34 51 98 154 210
NOTE: ***Al Fagaly** c-49-67. Katy Keene app. in 53-82, 85-100.*

SWAMP FOX, THE (TV, Disney)(See Walt Disney Presents #2)
Dell Publishing Co.: No. 1179, Dec, 1960
Four Color 1179-Leslie Nielsen photo-c 8 16 24 54 102 150

SWAMP THING (See Brave & the Bold, Challengers of the Unknown #82, DC Comics Presents #8 & 85, DC Special Series #2, 14, 17, 20, House of Secrets #92, Limited Collectors' Edition C-59, & Roots of the...)

SWAMP THING
National Per. Publ./DC Comics: Oct-Nov, 1972 - No. 24, Aug-Sept, 1976
1-Wrightson-c/a begins; origin 17 34 51 115 255 395
2-1st brief app. Patchwork Man (1 panel) 8 16 24 54 102 150
3-1st full app. Patchwork Man (see House of Secrets #140)
6 12 18 40 73 105
4-6, 5 10 15 34 60 85
7-Batman-c/story 6 12 18 37 66 95
8-10: 10-Last Wrightson issue 5 10 15 31 53 75
11-20: 11-19-Redondo-a. 13-Origin retold (1 pg.) 3 6 9 18 28 38
21-24: 23,24-Swamp Thing reverts back to Dr. Holland. 23-New logo
3 6 9 18 28 38
Secret of the Swamp Thing (2005, $9.99, digest) r/#1-10 10.00
NOTE: ***J. Jones** a-9i(assist). **Kaluta** a-9i. **Redondo** c-12-19, 21. **Wrightson** issues (#1-10) reprinted in DC Special Series #2, 14, 17, 20 & Roots of the Swamp Thing.*

SWAMP THING (Saga Of The... #1-38,42-45) (See Essential Vertigo:...)
DC Comics (Vertigo imprint #129 on): May, 1982 - No. 171, Oct, 1996
(Direct sales #65 on)
1-Origin retold; Phantom Stranger series begins; ends #13; Yeates-c/a begins
2 4 6 8 11 14
2-15: 2-Photo-c from movie. 13-Last Yeates-a 4.00
16-19: Bissette-a. 5.00
20-1st Alan Moore issue 3 6 9 21 33 45
21-New origin 3 6 9 17 25 34
21 Special Editon (5/09, $1.00) reprint with "After Watchmen" cover frame 3.00
22,23 2 4 6 9 12 15
24-JLA x-over; last Yeates-c. 2 4 6 9 13 16
25-John Constantine 1-panel cameo 4 8 12 23 37 50
26-30 1 2 3 5 6 8
31-33,35,36: 33-r/1st app. from House of Secrets #92 6.00
34-Classic-c 2 4 6 8 10 12
37-1st app. John Constantine (Hellblazer) (6/85) 8 16 24 52 99 145
38-40: John Constantine app. 2 4 6 8 11 14
41-52,54-64: 44-Batman cameo. 44-51-John Constantine app. 46-Crisis x-over; Batman cameo. 49-Spectre app. 50-($1.25, 52 pgs.)-Deadman, Dr. Fate, Demon. 52-Arkham Asylum-c/story; Joker-c/cameo. 58-Spectre preview. 64-Last Moore issue 4.00
53-($1.25, 52 pgs.)-Arkham Asylum; Batman-c/story 5.00
65-83,85-99,101-124,126-149,151-153: 65-Direct sales only begins. 66-Batman & Arkham Asylum story. 70,76-John Constantine x-over; 76-X-over w/Hellblazer #9. 79-Superman-c/story. 85-Jonah Hex app. 102-Preview of World Without End. 116-Photo-c. 129-Metallic ink on-c. 140-Millar scripts begin, end #171 3.00
84-Sandman (Morpheus) cameo. 4.00
100,125,150: 100 ($2.50, 52 pgs.). 125-($2.95, 52 pgs.)-20th anniversary issue. 150 (52 pgs.)-Anniversary issue 4.00
154-171: 154-$2.25-c begins. 165-Curt Swan-a(p). 166,169,171-John Constantine & Phantom Stranger app. 168-Arcane returns 3.00
Annual 1,3-6('82-91): 1-Movie Adaptation; painted-c. 3-New format; Bolland-c. 4-Batman-c/story. 5-Batman cameo; re-intro Brother Power (Geek),1st app. since 1968 4.00
Annual 2 (1985)-Moore scripts; Bissette-a(p); Deadman, Spectre app. 7.00
Annual 7(1993, $3.95)-Children's Crusade 4.00
...A Murder of Crows (2001, $19.95)-r/#43-50; Moore-s 20.00
...: Earth To Earth (2002, $17.95)-r/#51-56; Batman app. 18.00
...: Infernal Triangles (2006, $19.99, TPB) r/#77-81 & Annual #3; cover gallery 20.00
...Love and Death (1990, $17.95)-r/#28-34 & Annual #2; Totleben painted-c 18.00
...: Regenesis (2004, $17.95, TPB) r/#65-70; Veitch-s 18.00
...: Reunion (2003, $19.95, TPB) r/#57-64; Moore-s 20.00
...: Roots (1998, $7.95) Jon J Muth-s/painted-a/c 8.00
Saga of the Swamp Thing ('87, '89)-r/#21-27 (1st & 2nd print) 15.00
Saga of the Swamp Thing Book One HC (2009, $24.99, d.j.) r/#20-27; Wein intro. 25.00
Saga of the Swamp Thing Book Two HC (2009, $24.99, d.j.) r/#28-34 & Annual #2 25.00
Saga of the Swamp Thing Book Three HC (2010, $24.99, d.j.) r/#35-42; Bissette intro. 25.00
Saga of the Swamp Thing Book Four HC (2010, $24.99, d.j.) r/#43-50; Gaiman foreword 25.00
Saga of the Swamp Thing Book Five HC (2011, $24.99, d.j.) r/#51-56; Bissette intro. 25.00
...: Spontaneous Generation (2005, $19.99) r/#71-76 20.00
...: The Curse (2000, $19.95, TPB) r/#35-42; Bisley-c 20.00
NOTE: ***Bissette** a(p)-16-19, 21-27, 29, 30, 34-36, 39-42, 44, 46, 50, 64; c-17i, 24-32p, 35-37p, 40p, 44p, 46-50p, 51-58, 61, 62, 63p. **Kaluta** c/a-74. **Spiegle** a-1-3, 6. **Sutton** a-98p. **Totleben** a(i)-10, 16-27, 29, 31, 34-40, 42, 44, 46, 48, 50, 53, 55i; c-25-32i, 33, 35-40i, 42i, 44i, 46-50i, 53, 55i, 59p, 64, 65, 68, 73, 76, 80, 82, 84, 89, 91-100, Annual 4, 5. **Vess** painted c-121, 129-139, Annual 7. **Williamson** 86i. **Wrightson** a-18i(r), 33r. John Constantine appears in #37-40, 44-51, 65-67, 70-77, 80-90, 99, 114, 115, 130, 134-138.*

SWAMP THING
DC Comics (Vertigo): May, 2000 - No. 20, Dec, 2001 ($2.50)
1-3-Tefé Holland's return; Vaughan-s/Petersen-a; Hale painted-c. 4.00
4-20: 7-9-Bisley-c. 10-John Constantine-c/app. 10-12-Fabry-c. 13-15-Mack-c 18-Swamp Thing app. 3.00
Preview-16 pg. flip book w/Lucifer Preview 3.00

SWAMP THING
DC Comics (Vertigo): May, 2004 - No. 29, Sept, 2006 ($2.95/$2.99)
1-29: 1-Diggle-s/Breccia-a; Constantine app. 2-6-Sargon app. 7,8,20-Corben-c/a. 21-29-Eric Powell-c 3.00
...: Bad Seed (2004, $9.95) r/#1-6 10.00
...: Healing the Breach (2006, $17.99) r/#15-20 18.00
...: Love in Vain (2005, $14.99) r/#9-14 15.00

SWAMP THING (DC New 52)
DC Comics: Nov, 2011 - No. 40, May, 2015 ($2.99)
1-Snyder-s/Paquette-a; Superman app. 8.00
1-(2nd & 3rd printing) 3.00
2-18: 2-Abigail Arcane returns. 7-Holland transforms. 10-Francavilla-a; Anton Arcane returns. 12-X-over with Animal Man #12. 13-Poison Ivy & Deadman app.; leads into Annual #1 3.00
19-23: 19-Soule-s/Kano-a begin. 19,20-Superman app. 22,23-Constantine app. 3.00
23.1 (11/13, $2.99, regular cover) 3.00
23.1 (11/13, $3.99, 3-D cover) "Arcane #1" on cover; Soule-s/Saiz-a/c; origin of Arcane 5.00
24-39: 24-Leads into Annual #2. 26-Woodrue's origin; Animal Man app. 32-Aquaman app. 39-Constantine app. 3.00
40-($3.99) 4.00
#0-(11/12, $2.99) Kano-a; Arcane app.; Swamp Thing origin re-told 3.00
Annual #1 (12/12, $4.99) Flashback to 1st meeting of Alec & Abby; Cloonan-a 5.00
Annual #2 (12/13, $4.99) Soule-s/Pina-a 5.00
Annual #3 (12/14, $4.99) Soule-s/Pina-a: Etrigan app. 5.00
...: Futures End 1 (11/14, $2.99, regular-c) Five years later; Soule-s/Saiz-a; Arcane app. 3.00
...: Futures End 1 (11/14, $3.99, 3-D cover) 4.00

SWAMP THING
DC Comics: Mar, 2016 - No. 6, Aug, 2016 ($2.99)
1-6-Len Wein-s/Kelley Jones-a. 1,2-Phantom Stranger app. 2-Matt Cable returns. 3,4,6-Zatanna app. 3.00
... Winter Special 1 (3/18, $7.99) Wein-s/Jones-a; King-s/Fabok-a; Wein script & tribute 8.00

SWAT MALONE (America's Home Run King)
Swat Malone Enterprises: Sept, 1955
V1#1-Hy Fleishman-a 11 22 33 62 86 110

SWEATSHOP
DC Comics: Jun, 2003 - No. 6, Nov, 2003 ($2.95)
1-6-Peter Bagge-s/a; Destefano-a 3.00

SWEENEY (Formerly Buz Sawyer)
Standard Comics: No. 4, June, 1949 - No. 5, Sept, 1949
4,5: 5-Crane-a 9 18 27 50 65 80

SWEE'PEA (Also see Popeye #46)
Dell Publishing Co.: No. 219, Mar, 1949
Four Color 219 9 18 27 57 111 165

SWEET CHILDE

Sweet Love #1 © HARV

Swift Arrow #1 © AJAX

Switch #1 © TCOW

	GD 2.0	VG 4.0	FN 6.0	VF 8.0	VF/NM 9.0	NM- 9.2

Advantage Graphics Press: 1995 - No. 2, 1995 ($2.95, B&W, mature)

1,2 3.00

SWEETHEART DIARY (Cynthia Doyle #66-on)
Fawcett Publications/Charlton Comics No. 32 on: Wint, 1949; #2, Spr, 1950; #3, 6/50 - #5, 10/50; #6, 1951(nd); #7, 9/51 - #14, 1/53; #32, 10/55; #33, 4/56 - #65, 8/62 (#1-14: photo-c)

	GD	VG	FN	VF	VF/NM	NM-
1	21	42	63	126	206	285
2	14	28	42	78	112	145
3,4-Wood-a	16	32	48	94	147	200
5-10: 8-Bailey-a	10	20	30	56	76	95
11-14: 13-Swayze-a. 14-Last Fawcett issue	9	18	27	47	61	75
32 (10/55; 1st Charlton issue)(Formerly Cowboy Love #31)	9	18	27	52	69	85
33-40: 34-Swayze-a	7	14	21	35	43	50
41-(68 pgs.)	8	16	24	40	50	60
42-60	3	6	9	19	30	40
61-65	3	6	9	17	26	35

SWEETHEARTS (Formerly Captain Midnight)
Fawcett Publications/Charlton No. 122 on: #68, 10/48 - #121, 5/53; #122, 3/54; V2#23, 5/54 - #137, 12/73

	GD	VG	FN	VF	VF/NM	NM-
68-Photo-c begin	19	38	57	111	176	240
69,70	11	22	33	62	86	110
71-80	9	18	27	52	69	85
81-84,86-93,95-99,105	9	18	27	47	61	75
85,94,103,110,117-George Evans-a	10	20	30	54	72	90
100	9	18	27	52	69	85
101,107-Powell-a	9	18	27	50	65	80
102,104,106,108,109,112-116,118	8	16	24	44	57	70
111-1 pg. Ronald Reagan biography	10	20	30	56	76	95
119-Marilyn Monroe & Richard Widmark photo-c (1/54?); also appears in story; part Wood-a	97	194	291	621	1061	1500
120-Atom Bomb story	12	24	36	67	94	120
121-Liz Taylor/Fernanado Lamas photo-c	37	74	111	218	354	490
122-(1st Charlton? 3/54)-Marijuana story	13	26	39	72	101	130
V2#23 (5/54)-28: 28-Last precode issue (2/55)	8	16	24	42	54	65
29-39,41,43,45,47-50	4	8	12	25	40	55
40-Photo-c; Tommy Sands story	4	8	12	27	44	60
42-Ricky Nelson photo-c/story	7	14	21	49	92	135
44-Pat Boone photo-c/story	4	8	12	27	44	60
46-Jimmy Rodgers photo-c/story	4	8	12	27	44	60
51-60	3	6	9	21	33	45
61-80,100	3	6	9	18	28	38
81-99	3	6	9	16	24	32
101-110	2	4	6	13	18	22
111-120,122-124,126-137	2	4	6	10	14	18
121,125-David Cassidy pin-ups	2	4	6	13	18	22

NOTE: *Photo c-68-121(Fawcett), 40, 42, 46(Charlton).* ***Swayze*** *a(Fawcett)-70-118(most).*

SWEETHEART SCANDALS (See Fox Giants)

SWEETIE PIE
Dell Publishing Co.: No. 1185, May-July, 1961 - No. 1241, Nov-Jan, 1961/62

	GD	VG	FN	VF	VF/NM	NM-
Four Color 1185 (#1)	5	10	15	34	60	85
Four Color 1241	4	8	12	28	47	65

SWEETIE PIE
Ajax-Farrell/Pines (Literary Ent.): Dec, 1955 - No. 15, Fall, 1957

	GD	VG	FN	VF	VF/NM	NM-
1-By Nadine Seltzer	10	20	30	56	76	95
2 (5/56; last Ajax?)	7	14	21	35	43	50
3-15	6	12	18	28	34	40

SWEET LOVE
Home Comics (Harvey): Sept, 1949 - No. 5, May, 1950 (All photo-c)

	GD	VG	FN	VF	VF/NM	NM-
1	11	22	33	60	83	105
2	7	14	21	37	46	55
3,4: 3-Powell-a	6	12	18	31	38	45
5-Kamen, Powell-a	9	18	27	47	61	75

SWEET ROMANCE
Charlton Comics: Oct, 1968

	GD	VG	FN	VF	VF/NM	NM-
1	3	6	9	14	20	25

SWEET SIXTEEN (...Comics and Stories for Girls)
Parents' Magazine Institute: Aug-Sept, 1946 - No. 13, Jan, 1948 (All have movie stars photos on covers)

	GD	VG	FN	VF	VF/NM	NM-
1-Van Johnson's life story; Dorothy Dare, Queen of Hollywood Stunt Artists begins (in all issues); part photo-c	29	58	87	170	278	385
2-Jane Powell, Roddy McDowall "Holiday in Mexico" photo on-c; Alan Ladd story	19	38	57	109	172	235
3,5,6,8-11: 5-Ann Francis photo on-c; Gregory Peck story. 6-Dick Haymes story. 8-Shirley Jones photo on-c. 10-Jean Simmons photo on-c; James Stewart story	15	30	45	85	130	175
4-Elizabeth Taylor photo on-c	34	68	102	204	332	460
7-Ronald Reagan's life story	27	54	81	162	266	370
12-Bob Cummings, Vic Damone story	15	30	45	86	133	180
13-Robert Mitchum's life story	15	30	45	88	137	185

SWEET XVI
Marvel Comics: May, 1991 - No. 5, Sept, 1991 ($1.00)

1-5: Barbara Slate story & art 4.00

SWEET TOOTH
DC Comics (Vertigo): Nov, 2009 - No. 40, Feb, 2013 ($1.00/$2.99)

1-($1.00) Jeff Lemire-s/a 3.00
2-39-($2.99) 18,33-Printed sideways. 26-28-Kindt-a 3.00
40-($4.99) Final issue; two covers by Lemire and Truman 5.00
...: Animal Armies TPB (2011, $14.99) r/#12-17 15.00
...: In Captivity TPB (2010, $12.99) r/#6-11 13.00
...: Out of the Deep Woods TPB (2010, $9.99) r/#1-5 10.00

SWIFT ARROW (Also see Lone Rider & The Rider)
Ajax/Farrell Publications: Feb-Mar, 1954 - No. 5, Oct-Nov, 1954; Apr, 1957 - No. 3, Sept, 1957

	GD	VG	FN	VF	VF/NM	NM-
1(1954) (1st Series)	16	32	48	92	144	195
2	10	20	30	56	76	95
3-5: 5-Lone Rider story	9	18	27	50	65	80
1 (2nd Series) (Swift Arrow's Gunfighters #4)	9	18	27	50	65	80
2,3: 2-Lone Rider begins	8	16	24	40	50	60

SWIFT ARROW'S GUNFIGHTERS (Formerly Swift Arrow)
Ajax/Farrell Publ. (Four Star Comic Corp.): No. 4, Nov, 1957

	GD	VG	FN	VF	VF/NM	NM-
4	8	16	24	40	50	60

SWING WITH SCOOTER
National Periodical Publ.: June-July, 1966 - No. 35, Aug-Sept, 1971; No. 36, Oct-Nov, 1972

	GD	VG	FN	VF	VF/NM	NM-
1	9	18	27	58	114	170
2,6-10: 9-Alfred E. Newman swipe in last panel	5	10	15	33	57	80
3-5: 3-Batman cameo on-c. 4-Batman cameo inside. 5-JLA cameo	5	10	15	34	60	85
11-13,15-19: 18-Wildcat of JSA 1pg. text. 19-Last 12¢-c	3	6	9	20	31	42
14-Alfred E. Neuman cameo	3	6	9	21	33	45
20 (68 pgs.)	5	10	15	30	50	70
21-23,25-31	3	6	9	17	26	35
24-Frankenstein-c.	3	6	9	21	33	45
32-34 (68 pgs.). 32-Batman cameo. 33-Interview with David Cassidy. 34-Interview with Rick Ely (The Rebels)	4	8	12	28	47	65
35-(52 pgs.). 1 pg. app. Clark Kent and 4 full pgs. of Superman	6	12	18	42	79	115
36-Bat-signal refererence to Batman	3	6	9	21	33	45

NOTE: ***Aragonés*** *a-13 (1pg.), 18(1pg.), 30(2pgs.)* ***Orlando*** *a-1-11; c-1-11, 13. #20, 33, 34: 68 pgs.; #35: 52 pgs.*

SWISS FAMILY ROBINSON (Walt Disney's..; see King Classics & Movie Comics)
Dell Publishing Co.: No. 1156, Dec, 1960

	GD	VG	FN	VF	VF/NM	NM-
Four Color 1156-Movie-photo-c	7	14	21	48	89	130

SWITCH (Also see Witchblade titles)
Image Comics: Oct, 2015 - No. 4, Jul, 2016 ($3.99)

1-4-Stjepan Sejic-s/a; 3 covers on each 4.00

S.W.O.R.D. (Sentient World Observation and Response Department)
Marvel Comics: Jan, 2010 - No. 5, May, 2010 ($3.99/$2.99)

1-($3.99) Cassaday-c/Gillen-s/Sanders-a; Commander Brand & Henry Gyrich app. 4.00
2-5-($2.99): 2,3-Cassaday-c. 4,5-Del Mundo-c 3.00

SWORD, THE
Image Comics: Oct, 2007 - No. 24, May, 2010 ($2.99/$4.99)

1-Luna Brothers-s/a 4.00
1-(2nd printing) 3.00
2-23: 12-Zakros killed 3.00
24-($4.99) Final issue 5.00

SWORD & THE DRAGON, THE
Dell Publishing Co.: No. 1118, June, 1960

Sword of Ages #1 © Rodriguez & IDW

Swordquest (2017 series) #3 © Atari

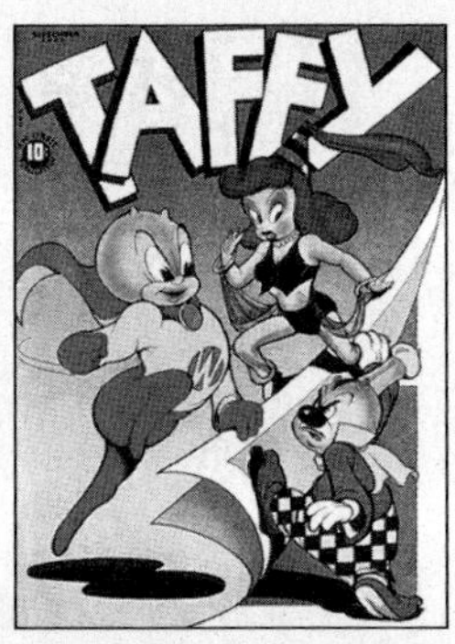

Taffy Comics #4 © Orbit

GD 2.0 | VG 4.0 | FN 6.0 | VF 8.0 | VF/NM 9.0 | NM- 9.2

GD 2.0 | VG 4.0 | FN 6.0 | VF 8.0 | VF/NM 9.0 | NM- 9.2

Four Color 1118-Movie, photo-c 7 14 21 48 89 130

SWORD & THE ROSE, THE (Disney)
Dell Publishing Co.: No. 505, Oct, 1953 - No. 682, Feb, 1956

Four Color 505-Movie, photo-c 8 16 24 52 99 145
Four Color 682-When Knighthood Was in Flower-Movie, reprint of #505; Renamed the Sword & the Rose for the novel; photo-c 6 12 18 40 73 105

SWORD IN THE STONE, THE (See March of Comics #258 & Movie Comics & Wart and the Wizard)

SWORD OF AGES
IDW Publishing: Nov, 2017 - Present ($3.99)

1,2-Gabriel Rodríguez-s/a 4.00

SWORD OF DAMOCLES
Image Comics (WildStorm Productions): Mar, 1996 - No. 2, Apr, 1996 ($2.50, limited series)

1,2: Warren Ellis scripts. 1-Prelude to "Fire From Heaven" x-over; 1st app. Sword 3.00

SWORD OF DRACULA
Image Comics: Oct, 2003 - No. 6, Sept, 2004 ($2.95, B&W, limited series)

1-6-Tony Harris-c. 1,2-Greg Scott-a 3.00
TPB (IDW, 2/05, $14.99) r/series 15.00

SWORD OF RED SONJA: DOOM OF THE GODS
Dynamite Entertainment: 2007 - No. 4, 2007 ($3.50, limited series)

1-4-Lui Antonio-a; multiple covers on each 3.50

SWORD OF SORCERY
National Periodical Publications: Feb-Mar, 1973 - No. 5, Nov-Dec, 1973 (20¢)

1-Leiber Fafhrd & The Grey Mouser; Chaykin/Neal Adams (Crusty Bunkers) art; Kaluta-c 3 6 9 16 23 30
2,3: 2-Wrightson-c(i); Adams-a(i). 3-Wrightson-i(5 pgs.) 2 4 6 9 13 16
4,5: 5-Starlin-a(p); Conan cameo 2 4 6 8 10 12
NOTE: *Chaykin a-1-4p; c-2p, 3-5. Kaluta a-3i. Simonson a-3i, 4i, 5p; c-5.*

SWORD OF SORCERY (DC New 52)
DC Comics: No. 0, Nov, 2012 - No. 8, Jun, 2013 ($3.99)

0-8: 0-Origin of Amethyst retold; Lopresti-a; Beowulf back-up; Saiz-a. 4-Stalker back-up 4.00

SWORD OF THE ATOM
DC Comics: Sept, 1983 - No. 4, Dec, 1983 (Limited series)

1-4: Gil Kane-c/a in all 4.00
Special 1-3('84, '85, '88): 1,2-Kane-c/a each 4.00
TPB (2007, $19.99) r/#1-4 and Special #1-3 20.00

SWORDQUEST (Based on the Atari game)
Dynamite Entertainment: No. 0, 2017 - No. 5, 2017 (25¢/$3.99)

0-(25¢) Bowers & Sims-s/Ghostwriter X-a; bonus game history and character art 3.00
1-5-($3.99) Multiple covers on each; George Peréz & others 4.00

SWORDS OF SORROW
Dynamite Entertainment: 2015 - No. 6, 2015 ($3.99, limited series with tie-in series)

1-6-Simone-s/Davila-a; crossover of Vampirella, Red Sonja, Dejah Thoris, Lady Zorro and other female Dynamite characters; multiple covers on each 4.00
...: Black Sparrow & Lady Zorro Special 1 ($3.99, one-shot) Schultz-s/Zamora-a 4.00
...: Chaos! Prequel 1 ($3.99, one-shot) Mairghread Scott-s/Mirka Andolfo-a 4.00
...: Dejah Thoris & Irene Adler 1-3 ($3.99, lim. series) Leah Moore-s/Francesco Manna-a 4.00
...: Masquerade & Kato 1 ($3.99, one-shot) G. Willow Wilson & Erica Schultz-s 4.00
...: Miss Fury & Lady Rawhide 1 ($3.99, one-shot) Mikki Kendall-s/Ronilson Freire-a 4.00
...: Pantha & Jane Porter ($3.99, one-shot) Emma Beeby-s/Rod Rodolfo-a 4.00
...: Red Sonja & Jungle Girl 1-3 ($3.99, lim. series) Bennett-s/Andolfo-a/Anacleto-c 4.00
...: Vampirella & Jennifer Blood 1-4 ($3.99, lim. series) Nancy Collins-s/Dave Acosta-a 4.00

SWORDS OF TEXAS (See Scout #15)
Eclipse Comics: Oct, 1987 - No. 4, Jan, 1988 ($1.75, color, Baxter paper)

1-4: Scout app. 3.00

SWORDS OF THE SWASHBUCKLERS (See Marvel Graphic Novel)
Marvel Comics (Epic Comics): May, 1985 - No. 12, Jun, 1987 ($1.50; mature)

1-12-Butch Guice-c/a (cont'd from Marvel G.N.) 3.00

SWORN TO PROTECT
Marvel Comics: Sept, 1995 ($1.95) (Based on card game)

nn-Overpower Game Guide; Jubilee story 3.00

SYMMETRY
Image Comics (Top Cow): Dec, 2015 - No. 8, Oct, 2016 ($3.99)

1-8-Hawkins-s/Ienco-a 4.00

SYN
Dark Horse Comics: Aug, 2003 - No. 5, Feb, 2004 ($2.99, limited series)

1-5-Giffen-s/Titus-a 3.00

SYPHONS
Now Comics: V2#1, May, 1994 - V2#3, 1994 ($2.50, limited series)

V2#1-3: 1-Stardancer, Knightfire, Raze & Brigade begin 3.00
TPB (9/04, $15.95) B&W reprints #1-3; intro. by Tony Caputo 16.00

SYSTEM, THE
DC Comics (Vertigo Verite): May, 1996 - No. 3, July, 1996 ($2.95, lim. series)

1-3: Kuper-c/a 3.00
TPB (1997, $12.95) r/#1-3 13.00

TAFFY COMICS (Also see Dotty Dripple)
Rural Home/Orbit Publ.: Mar-Apr, 1945 - No. 12, 1948

1-L.B. Cole-c; origin & 1st app. of Wiggles The Wonderworm plus 7 chapter WWII funny animal adventures 65 130 195 416 708 1000
2-L.B. Cole-c with funny animal Hitler; Wiggles-c/stories in #1-4 47 94 141 296 498 700
3,4,6-12: 6-Perry Como-c/story. 7-Duke Ellington, 2 pgs. 8-Glenn Ford-c/story. 9-Lon McCallister part photo-c & story. 10-Mort Leav-c. 11-Mickey Rooney-c/story 16 32 48 92 144 195
5-L.B. Cole-c; Van Johnson-c/story 22 44 66 132 216 300

TAILGUNNER JO
DC Comics: Sept, 1988 - No. 6, Jan, 1989 ($1.25)

1-6 3.00

TAILS
Archie Publications: Dec, 1995 - No. 3, Feb, 1996 ($1.50, limited series)

1-3: Based on Sonic, the Hedgehog video game 6.00

TAILS OF THE PET AVENGERS (Also see Lockjaw and the Pet Avengers)
Marvel Comics: Apr, 2010 ($3.99, one-shot)

1-Lockjaw, Frog Thor, Zabu, Lockheed and Redwing in short solo stories by various 4.00
...: The Dogs of Summer (9/10, $3.99) Eliopolous-s; see Avengers vs. the Pet Avengers 4.00

TAILSPIN
Spotlight Publishers: November, 1944

nn-Firebird app.; L.B. Cole-c 36 72 108 211 343 475

TAILSPIN TOMMY (Also see Popular Comics)
United Features Syndicate/Service Publ. Co.: 1940; 1946

Single Series 23(1940) 42 84 126 265 445 625
1-Best Seller (nd, 1946)-Service Publ. Co. 20 40 60 114 182 250

TAKIO
Marvel Comics (Icon): 2011; May, 2012 - No. 4 ($3.95/$9.95)

HC (2011, $9.95) Bendis-s/Oeming-a/c; Oeming sketch pages 10.00
1-4: 1-(5/12, $3.95) Bendis-s/Oeming-a/c 4.00

TAKION
DC Comics: June, 1996 - No. 7, Dec, 1996 ($1.75)

1-7: Lopresti-c/a(p). 1-Origin; Green Lantern app. 6-Final Night x-over 3.00

TALENT SHOWCASE (See New Talent Showcase)

TALE OF ONE BAD RAT, THE
Dark Horse Comics: Oct, 1994 - No. 4, Jan, 1995 ($2.95, limited series)

1-4: Bryan Talbot-c/a/scripts 3.00
HC ($69.95, signed and numbered) R/#1-4 70.00

TALES CALCULATED TO DRIVE YOU BATS
Archie Publications: Nov, 1961 - No. 7, Nov, 1962; 1966 (Satire)

1-Only 10¢ issue; has cut-out Werewolf mask (price includes mask) 15 30 45 103 227 350
2-Begin 12¢ issues 9 18 27 58 114 170
3-6: 3-UFO cover 7 14 21 49 92 135
7-Storyline change 7 14 21 46 86 125
1(1966, 25¢, 44 pg. Giant)-r/#1; UFO cover 7 14 21 44 82 120

TALES CALCULATED TO DRIVE YOU MAD
E.C. Publications: Summer, 1997 - No. 8, Winter, 1999 ($3.99/$4.99, satire)

1-6-Full color reprints of Mad: 1-(#1-3), 2-(#4-6), 3-(#7-9), 4-(#10-12) 5-(#13-15), 6-(#16-18) 6.00
7,8-($4.99-c): 7-(#19-21), 8-(#22,23) 6.00

TALES FROM RIVERDALE DIGEST
Archie Publ.: June, 2005 - No. 39, Oct, 2010 ($2.39/$2.49/$2.69, digest-size)

1-39: 1-Sabrina and Josie & the Pussycats app. 11-Begin $2.49-c. 34-Begin $2.69 3.00

Tales From the Clerks TPB © View Askew

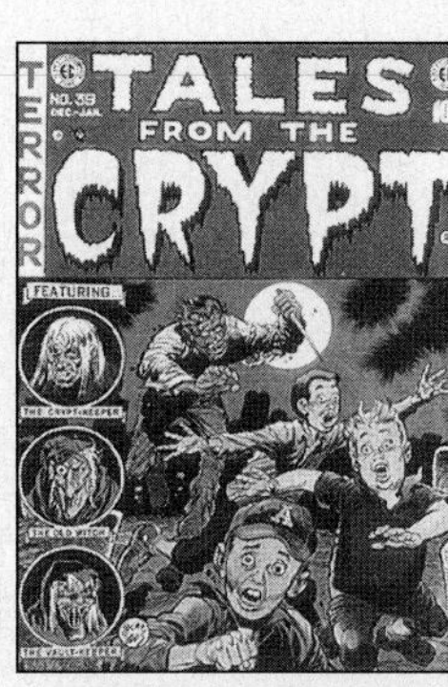

Tales From the Crypt #39 © WMG

Tales of Horror #11 © Minoan

GD 2.0 | VG 4.0 | FN 6.0 | VF 8.0 | VF/NM 9.0 | NM- 9.2

GD 2.0 | VG 4.0 | FN 6.0 | VF 8.0 | VF/NM 9.0 | NM- 9.2

TALES FROM THE AGE OF APOCALYPSE
Marvel Comics: 1996 ($5.95, prestige format, one-shots)
1, ...: Sinister Bloodlines (1997, $5.95) 6.00

TALES FROM THE BOG
Aberration Press: Nov, 1995 - No. 7, Nov, 1997 ($2.95/$3.95, B&W)
1-7 4.00
Alternate #1 (Director's Cut) (1998, $2.95) 3.00

TALES FROM THE BULLY PULPIT
Image Comics: Aug, 2004 ($6.95, square-bound)
1-Teddy Roosevelt and Edison's ghost with a time machine; Cereno-s/MacDonald-a 7.00

TALES FROM THE CLERKS (See Jay and Silent Bob, Clerks and Oni Double Feature)
Graphitti Designs, Inc.: 2006 ($29.95, TPB)
nn-Reprints all the Kevin Smith Clerks and Jay and Silent Bob stories; new Clerks II story with Mahfood-a; cover gallery, sketch pages, Mallrats credits covers; Smith intro. 30.00

TALES FROM THE CON
Image Comics: May, 2014 ($3.50, one-shot)
...: Year 1 - Brad Guigar-s/Chris Giarrusso-a/c; comic convention humor strips 3.50

TALES FROM THE CRYPT (Formerly The Crypt Of Terror; see Three Dimensional...) (Also see EC Archives • Tales From the Crypt)
E.C. Comics: No. 20, Oct-Nov, 1950 - No. 46, Feb-Mar, 1955
20-See Crime Patrol #15 for 1st Crypt Keeper 149 298 447 1192 1896 2600
21-Kurtzman-r/Haunt of Fear #15(#1) 114 228 342 912 1456 2000
22-Moon Girl costume at costume party, one panel 91 182 273 728 1164 1600
23-25: 23-"Reflection of Death" adapted for 1972 TFTC film. 24-E. A. Poe adaptation 76 152 228 608 967 1325
26-30: 26-Wood's 2nd EC-c 63 126 189 504 802 1100
31-Williamson-a(1st at E.C.); B&W and color illos. in **POP**; Kamen draws himself, Gaines & Feldstein; Ingels, Craig & Davis draw themselves in his story 61 122 183 488 782 1075
32,35-39: 38-Censored-c 56 112 168 448 712 975
33-Origin The Crypt Keeper 74 148 222 592 946 1300
34-Used in **POP**, pg. 83; classic Frankenstein Monster, Jack the Ripper-c by Davis; lingerie panels 56 112 168 448 712 975
40-Used in Senate hearings & in Hartford Courant anti-comics editorials-1954 54 108 162 432 691 950
41-45: 45-2 pgs. showing E.C. staff; anti-censorship editorial of upcoming Senate hearings 53 106 159 424 675 925
46-Low distribution; pre-advertised cover for unpublished 4th horror title "Crypt of Terror" used on this book; "Blind Alleys" adapted for 1972 TFTC film; classic werewolf-c by Davis 63 126 189 504 802 1100
NOTE: ***Ray Bradbury** adaptations-34, 36. **Craig** a-20, 22-24; c-20. **Crandall** a-38, 44. **Davis** a-24-46; c-29-46. **Elder** a-37, 38. **Evans** a-32-34, 36, 40, 41, 43, 46. **Feldstein** a-20-23; c-21-25, 28. Ingels a-in all. **Kamen** a-20, 22, 25, 27-31, 33-36, 39, 41-45. **Krigstein** a-40, 42, 45. **Kurtzman** a-21. **Orlando** a-27-30, 35, 37, 39, 41-45. **Wood** a-21, 24, 25; c-26, 27. Canadian reprints known; see Table of Contents.*

TALES FROM THE CRYPT (Magazine)
Eerie Publications: No. 10, July, 1968 (35¢, B&W)
10-Contains Farrell reprints from 1950s 5 10 15 35 63 90

TALES FROM THE CRYPT
Gladstone Publishing: July, 1990 - No. 6, May, 1991 ($1.95/$2.00, 68 pgs.)
1-r/TFTC #33 & Crime S.S. #17; Davis-c(r) 5.00
2-6: 2,3,5,6-Davis-c(r). 4-Begin $2.00-c; Craig-c(r) 5.00

TALES FROM THE CRYPT
Extra-Large Comics (Russ Cochran)/Gemstone Publishing: Jul, 1991 - No. 6 ($3.95, 10 1/4 x13 1/4", 68 pgs.)
1-6: 1-Davis-c(r); Craig back-c(r); E.C. reprints. 2-6 ($2.00, comic sized) 5.00

TALES FROM THE CRYPT
Russ Cochran: Sept, 1991 - No. 7, July, 1992 ($2.00, 64 pgs.)
1-7 5.00

TALES FROM THE CRYPT (Also see EC Archives • Tales From the Crypt)
Russ Cochran/Gemstone: Sept, 1992 - No. 30, Dec, 1999 ($1.50, quarterly)
1-4-r/Crypt of Terror #17-19, TFTC #20 w/original-c 4.00
5-30: 5-15 ($2.00)-r/TFTC #21-23 w/original-c. 16-30 ($2.50) 4.00
Annual 1-6('93-'99) 1-r/#1-5. 2- r/#6-10. 3- r/#11-15. 4- r/#16-20. 5-r/#21-25. 6- r/#26-30 14.00

TALES FROM THE DARKSIDE
IDW Publishing: Jun, 2016 - No. 4, Sept, 2016 ($3.99, limited series)
1-4-Joe Hill-s/Gabriel Rodriguez-a. 1-Five covers. 2-4-Two covers 4.00

TALES FROM THE GREAT BOOK
Famous Funnies: Feb, 1955 - No. 4, Jan, 1956 (Religious themes)
1-Story of Samson; John Lehti-a in all 10 20 30 56 76 95
2-4: 2-Joshua. 3-Joash the Boy King. 4-David 8 16 24 40 50 60

TALES FROM THE HEART OF AFRICA (The Temporary Natives)
Marvel Comics (Epic Comics): Aug, 1990 ($3.95, 52 pgs.)
1 4.00

TALES FROM THE TOMB (Also see Dell Giants)
Dell Publishing Co.: Oct, 1962 (25¢ giant)
1(02-810-210)-All stories written by John Stanley 14 28 42 96 211 325

TALES FROM THE TOMB (Magazine)
Eerie Publications: V1#6, July, 1969 - V7#3, 1975 (52 pgs.)
V1#6 8 16 24 54 102 150
V1#7,8 6 12 18 38 69 100
V2#1-6: 4-LSD story-r/Weird V3#5. 6-Rulah-r 5 10 15 34 60 85
V3#1-Rulah-r 6 12 18 37 66 95
2-6('71),V4#1-5('72),V5#1-6('73),V6#1-6('74),V7#1-3('75) 5 10 15 31 53 75

TALES OF ASGARD
Marvel Comics Group: Oct, 1968 (25¢, 68 pgs.); Feb, 1984 ($1.25, 52 pgs.)
1-Reprints Tales of Asgard (Thor) back-up stories from Journey into Mystery #97-106; new Kirby-c; Kirby-a 6 12 18 41 76 110
V2#1 (2/84)-Thor-r; Simonson-c 5.00

TALES OF ARMY OF DARKNESS
Dynamite Entertainment: 2006 ($5.95, one-shot)
1-Short stories by Kuhoric, Kirkman, Bradshaw, Sablik, Ottley, Acs, O'Hare and others 6.00

TALES OF EVIL
Atlas/Seaboard Publ.: Feb, 1975 - No. 3, July, 1975 (All 25¢ issues)
1-3: 1-Werewolf w/Sekowsky-a. 2-Intro. The Bog Beast; Sparling-a. 3-Origin The Man-Monster; Buckler-a(p) 2 4 6 11 16 20
NOTE: ***Grandenetti** a-1, 2. **Lieber** c-1. **Sekowsky** a-1. **Sutton** a-2. **Thorne** c-2.*

TALES OF GHOST CASTLE
National Periodical Publications: May-June, 1975 - No. 3, Sept-Oct, 1975 (All 25¢ issues)
1-Redondo-a; 1st app. Lucien the Librarian from Sandman (1989 series) 3 6 9 17 26 35
2,3: 2-Nino-a. 3-Redondo-a. 2 4 6 10 14 18

TALES OF G.I. JOE
Marvel Comics: Jan, 1988 - No. 15, Mar, 1989
1 ($2.25, 52 pgs.) 4.00
2-15 ($1.50): 1-15-r/G.I. Joe #1-15 3.00

TALES OF HONOR (Based on the David Weber novels)
Image Comics (Top Cow): Mar, 2014 - No. 5, Oct, 2015 ($2.99)
1-5: 1-Matt Hawkins-s/Jung-Geun Yoon-a. 2-5-Sang-il Jeong-a 3.00

TALES OF HONOR VOLUME 2 (Bred to Kill on cover)
Image Comics (Top Cow): No. 0, May, 2015 - No. 4, Dec, 2015 ($3.99)
0-Free Comic Book Day giveaway; Hawkins-s/Linda Sejic-a 3.00
1-4-Hawkins-s/Linda Sejic-a 4.00

TALES OF HORROR
Toby Press/Minoan Publ. Corp.: June, 1952 - No. 13, Oct, 1954
1-"This is Terror-Man" 50 100 150 315 533 750
2-Torture scenes 39 78 117 240 395 550
3-11,13: 9-11-Reprints Purple Claw #1-3 29 58 87 170 278 385
12-Myron Fass-c/a; torture scenes 31 62 93 184 300 415
NOTE: ***Andru** a-5. **Baily** a-5. **Myron Fass** a-2, 3, 12; c-1-3, 12. **Hollingsworth** a-2. **Sparling** a-6, 9; c-9.*

TALES OF JUSTICE
Atlas Comics(MjMC No. 53-66/Male No. 67): No. 53, May, 1955 - No. 67, Aug, 1957
53 19 38 57 109 172 235
54-57: 54-Powell-a 14 28 42 78 112 145
58,59-Krigstein-a 14 28 42 82 121 160
60-63,65: 60-Powell-a 13 26 39 72 101 130
64,66,67: 64,67-Crandall-a. 66-Torres, Orlando-a 13 26 39 74 105 135
NOTE: ***Everett** a-53, 60. **Orlando** a-65, 66. **Severin** a-64; c-58, 60, 65. **Wildey** a-64, 67.*

TALES OF LEONARDO BLIND SIGHT (See Tales of the TMNT Vol. 2 #5)
Mirage Publishing: June, 2006 - No. 4, Sept, 2006 ($3.25, B&W, limited series)
1-4-Jim Lawson-s/a 3.25

TALES OF SUSPENSE (Becomes Captain America #100 on)
Atlas (WPI No. 1,2/Male No. 3-12/VPI No. 13-18)/Marvel No. 19 on:

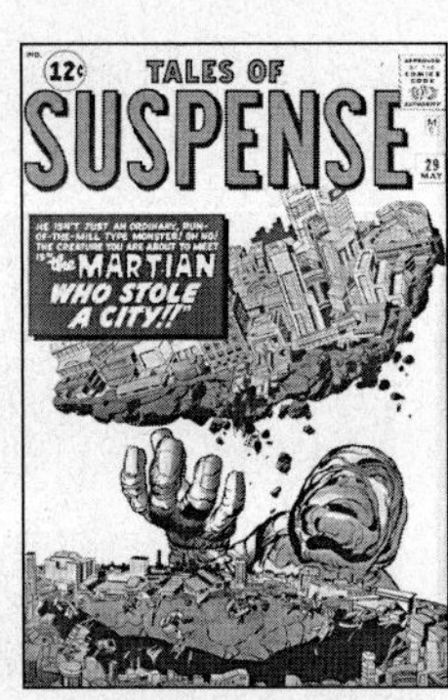

Tales of Suspense #29 © MAR

Tales of Suspense #74 © MAR

Tales of Terror Annual (1951) © WMG

Jan, 1959 - No. 99, Mar, 1968

	GD 2.0	VG 4.0	FN 6.0	VF 8.0	VF/NM 9.0	NM- 9.2
1-Williamson-a (5 pgs.); Heck-c; #1-4 have sci/fi-c	400	800	1200	3400	7700	12,000
2-Ditko robot-c	118	236	354	944	2122	3300
3-Flying saucer-c/story	104	208	312	832	1866	2900
4-Williamson-a (4 pgs.); Kirby/Everett-c/a	96	192	288	768	1734	2700
5-Kirby monster-c begin	79	158	237	632	1416	2200
6,8,10	61	122	183	488	1094	1700
7-Prototype ish. (Lava Man); 1 panel app. Aunt May (see Str. Tales #97)	63	126	189	504	1127	1750
9-Prototype ish. (Iron Man)	59	118	177	472	1061	1650
11,12,15,17-19: 12-Crandall-a.	46	92	138	368	834	1300
13-Elektro-c/story	50	100	150	390	870	1350
14-Intro/1st app. Colossus-c/sty	57	114	171	456	1028	1600
16-1st Metallo-c/story (4/61, Iron Man prototype)	50	100	150	400	900	1400
20-Colossus-c/story (2nd app.)	51	102	153	398	887	1375
21-25: 25-Last 10¢ issue	40	80	120	296	673	1050
26,27,29,30,31,33,34,36-38: 33-(9/62)-Hulk 1st x-over cameo (picture on wall)	36	72	108	266	596	925
28-Prototype ish. (Stone Men)	38	76	114	285	641	1000
31-Prototype ish. (Doctor Doom)	40	80	120	296	673	1050
32-Prototype ish. (Dr. Strange)(8/62)-Sazzik The Sorcerer app.; "The Man and the Beehive" story, 1 month before TTA #35 (2nd Antman), came out after "The Man in the Ant Hill" in TTA #27 (1/62) (1st Antman)-Characters from both stories were tested to see which got best fan response	57	114	171	456	1028	1600
35-Prototype issue (The Watcher)	38	76	114	281	628	975
39 (3/63)-Origin/1st app. Iron Man & begin series; 1st Iron Man story has Kirby layouts	1750	3500	6125	12,200	31,100	50,000
40-2nd app. Iron Man (in new armor)	200	400	600	1650	3725	5800
41-3rd app. Iron Man; Dr. Strange (villain) app.	129	258	387	1032	2316	3600
42-45: 45-Intro. & 1st app. Happy & Pepper	88	176	264	704	1577	2450
46,47: 46-1st app. Crimson Dynamo	61	122	183	488	1094	1700
48-New Iron Man red & gold armor by Ditko	66	132	198	528	1189	1850
49-1st X-Men x-over (same date as X-Men #3, 1/64); also 1st Avengers x-over (w/o Captain America); 1st Tales of the Watcher back-up story & begins (2nd app. Watcher; see F.F. #13)	84	168	252	672	1511	2350
50-1st app. Mandarin	57	114	171	456	1028	1600
51-1st Scarecrow	32	64	96	230	515	800
52-1st app. The Black Widow (4/64)	145	290	435	1196	2698	4200
53-Origin The Watcher; 2nd Black Widow app.	36	72	108	259	580	900
54,55-2nd & 3rd Mandarin app.	26	52	78	182	404	625
56-1st app. Unicorn	27	54	81	189	420	650
57-Origin/1st app. Hawkeye (9/64)	100	200	300	800	1800	2800
58-Captain America battles Iron Man (10/64)-Classic-c; 2nd Kraven app. (Cap's 1st app. in this title)	54	108	162	432	966	1500
59-Iron Man plus Captain America double feature begins (11/64); 1st S.A. Captain America solo story; intro Jarvis, Avenger's butler; classic-c	42	84	126	311	706	1100
60-2nd app. Hawkeye (#64 is 3rd app.)	27	54	81	189	420	650
61,62,64: 62-Origin Mandarin (2/65)	15	30	45	105	233	360
63-1st Silver Age origin Captain America (3/65)	29	58	87	209	467	725
65-G.A. Red Skull in WWII stories(also in #66);-1st Silver-Age Red Skull (5/65).	27	54	81	189	420	650
66-Origin Red Skull	17	34	51	117	259	400
67,68,70: 70-Begin alternating-c features w/Capt. America (even #'s) & Iron Man (odd #'s)	9	18	27	61	123	185
69-1st app. Titanium Man	10	20	30	68	144	220
71-74,78: 78-Col. Nick Fury app.	7	14	21	46	86	125
75-1st app. Agent 13 later named Sharon Carter; intro Batroc	15	30	45	100	220	340
76-2nd app. Batroc & 1st cover app.	8	16	24	52	99	145
77-1st app. Peggy Carter (unnamed) in WW2 flashback (see Captain America #161 & 162)	7	14	21	49	92	135
79-Begin 3 part Iron Man Sub-Mariner battle story; Sub-Mariner-c & cameo; 1st app. Cosmic Cube; 1st modern Red Skull	9	18	27	57	111	165
80-Iron Man battles Sub-Mariner story cont'd in Tales to Astonish #82; classic Red Skull-c	9	18	27	58	114	170
81-93,95,96: 82-Intro the Adaptoid by Kirby (also in #83,84). 88-Mole Man app. in Iron Man story. 92-1st Nick Fury x-over (cameo, as Agent of S.H.I.E.L.D., 8/67). 95-Capt. America's i.d. revealed	6	12	18	40	73	105
94-Intro Modok	10	20	30	66	138	210
97-1st Whiplash	9	18	27	57	111	165
98-Black Panther-c/s; 1st brief app. new Zemo (son?); #99 is 1st full app.	9	18	27	61	123	185
99-Captain America story cont'd in Captain America #100; Iron Man story cont'd in Iron Man & Sub-Mariner #1	8	16	24	51	96	140

Onmibus (See Iron Man Omnibus for reprints of #39-83)

NOTE: ***Abel*** *a-73-81i(as Gary Michaels),* ***J. Buscema*** *a-1; c-3.* ***Colan*** *a-39, 73-99p; c(p)-73, 75, 77, 79, 81, 83, 85-87, 89, 91, 93, 95, 97, 99.* ***Crandall*** *a-12.* ***Davis*** *a-38.* ***Ditko*** *a-1-15, 17-44, 46, 47-49p; c-2, 10i, 13i, 23i.* ***Kirby/Ditko*** *a-7; c-10, 13, 22, 28, 34.* ***Everett*** *a-8.* ***Forte*** *a-5, 9.* ***Giacoia*** *a-82.* ***Heath*** *a-2, 10.* ***Gil Kane*** *a-88p, 89-91; c-88, 89-91p.* ***Kirby*** *a(p)-2-4, 6-35, 40, 41, 43, 59-75, 77-86, 92-99; layouts-69-75, 77; c(p)4-28(most), 29-56, 58-72, 74, 76, 78, 80, 82, 84, 86, 92, 94, 96, 98.* ***Leiber/Fox*** *a-42, 43, 45, 51.* ***Reinman*** *a-13, 26, 44i, 49i, 52i, 53i.* ***Tuska*** *a-58, 70-74.* ***Wood*** *c/a-71i.*

TALES OF SUSPENSE
Marvel Comics: V2#1, Jan, 1995 ($6.95, one-shot)

	GD 2.0	VG 4.0	FN 6.0	VF 8.0	VF/NM 9.0	NM- 9.2
V2#1-James Robinson script; acetate-c.	1	2	3	5	6	8

TALES OF SUSPENSE (Marvel Legacy)
Marvel Comics: No. 100, Feb, 2018 - Present ($3.99)

100-102-Hawkeye & Winter Soldier team-up; Foreman-a 4.00

TALES OF SUSPENSE: CAPTAIN AMERICA & IRON MAN #1 COMMEMORATIVE EDITION
Marvel Comics: 2004 ($3.99, one-shot)

nn-Reprints Captain America (2004) #1 and Iron Man (2004) #1 5.00

TALES OF SWORD & SORCERY (See Dagar)

TALES OF TELLOS (See Tellos)
Image Comics: Oct, 2004 - No. 3, ($3.50, anthology)

1-3: 1-Dezago-s; art by Yates & Rousseau; Wieringo-c. 3-Porter-a 3.50

TALES OF TERROR
Toby Press Publications: 1952 (no month)

	GD 2.0	VG 4.0	FN 6.0	VF 8.0	VF/NM 9.0	NM- 9.2
1-Fawcette-c; Ravielli-a	39	78	117	231	378	525

NOTE: *This title was cancelled due to similarity to the E.C. title.*

TALES OF TERROR (See Movie Classics)

TALES OF TERROR (Magazine)
Eerie Publications: Summer, 1964

	GD 2.0	VG 4.0	FN 6.0	VF 8.0	VF/NM 9.0	NM- 9.2
1	6	12	18	41	76	110

TALES OF TERROR
Eclipse Comics: July, 1985 - No. 13, July, 1987 ($2.00, Baxter paper, mature)

1-13: 5-1st Lee Weeks-a. 7-Sam Kieth-a. 10-Snyder-a. 12-Vampire story 4.00

TALES OF TERROR (IDW's...)
IDW Publishing: Sept, 2004 ($16.99, hardcover)

1-Anthology of short graphic stories and text stories; incl. 30 Days of Night 17.00

TALES OF TERROR ANNUAL
E.C. Comics: 1951 - No. 3, 1953 (25¢, 132 pgs., 16 stories each)

	GD 2.0	VG 4.0	FN 6.0	VF 8.0	VF/NM 9.0	NM- 9.2
nn(1951)(Scarce)-Feldstein infinity-c	1350	2700	4050	10,800	-	-
2(1952)-Feldstein-c	300	600	900	1950	3375	4800
3(1953)-Feldstein bondage/torture-c	252	504	756	1613	2757	3900

NOTE: *No. 1 contains three horror and one science fiction comic which came out in 1950. No. 2 contains a horror, crime, and science fiction book which generally had cover dates in 1951, and No. 3 had horror, crime, and shock books that generally appeared in 1952. All E.C. annuals contain four complete books that did not sell on the stands which were rebound in the annual format, minus the covers, and sold from the E.C. office and on the stands in key cities. The contents of each annual may vary in the same year. Crypt Keeper, Vault Keeper, Old Witch app. on all-c.*

TALES OF TERROR ILLUSTRATED (See Terror Illustrated)

TALES OF TEXAS JOHN SLAUGHTER (See Walt Disney Presents, 4-Color #997)

TALES OF THE BEANWORLD
Beanworld Press/Eclipse Comics: Feb, 1985 - No. 19, 1991; No. 20, 1993 - No. 21, 1993 ($1.50/$2.00, B&W)

1-21 3.00

TALES OF THE BIZARRO WORLD
DC Comics: 2000 ($14.95, TPB)

nn-Reprints early Bizarro stories; new Jaime Hernandez-c 15.00

TALES OF THE DARKNESS
Image Comics (Top Cow): Apr, 1998 - No. 4, Dec, 1998 ($2.95)

1-4: 1,2-Portacio-c/a(p). 3,4-Lansing & Nocon-a(p) 3.00
1-American Entertainment Ed. 3.00
#1/2 (1/01, $2.95) 3.00

TALES OF THE DRAGON GUARD (English version of French comic title)
Marvel Comics (Soleil): Apr, 2010 - No. 3, Jun, 2010 ($5.99, limited series)

1-3: 1-Ange-s/Varanda-a. 2-Briones-a. 3-Guinebaud-a 6.00
...: Into the Veil 1-3 (11/10 - No. 3, 1/11) 1-Briones-a. 2-Paty-a. 3-Sieurac-a 6.00

TALES OF THE GREEN BERET
Dell Publishing Co.: Jan, 1967 - No. 5, Oct, 1969

	GD 2.0	VG 4.0	FN 6.0	VF 8.0	VF/NM 9.0	NM- 9.2
1-Glanzman-a in 1-4 & 5r	3	6	9	19	30	40
2-5: 5-Reprints #1	3	6	9	16	23	30

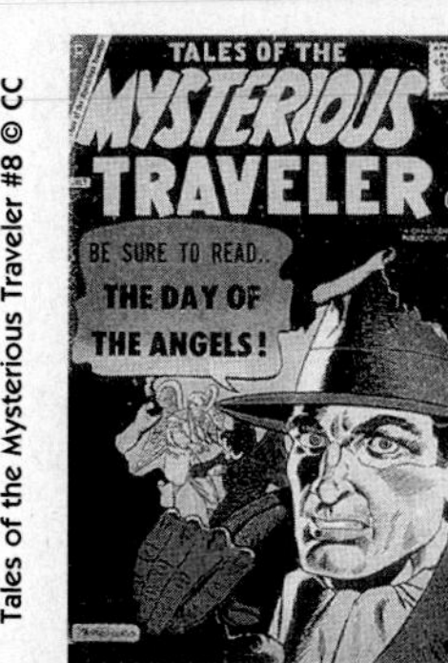

Tales of the Mysterious Traveler #8 © CC

Tales of the Teen Titans #52 © DC

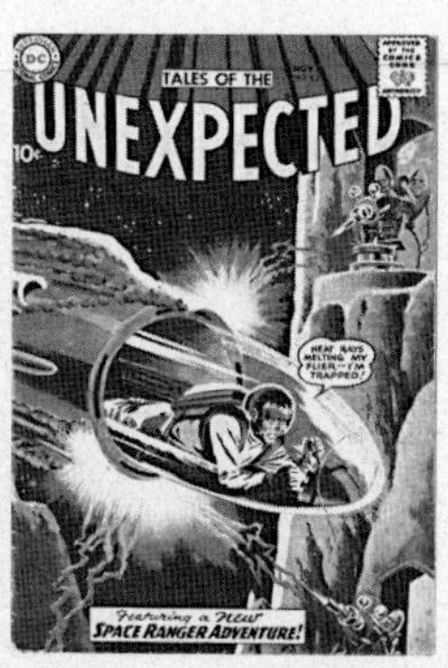

Tales of the Unexpected #43 © DC

GD VG FN VF VF/NM NM-
2.0 4.0 6.0 8.0 9.0 9.2

TALES OF THE GREEN HORNET
Now Comics: Sept, 1990 - No. 2, 1990; V2#1, Jan, 1992 - No.4, Apr, 1992; V3#1, Sept, 1992 - No. 3, Nov, 1992

1,2 3.00
V2#1-4 ($1.95) 3.00
V3#1 ($2.75)-Polybagged w/hologram trading card 4.00
V3#2,3 ($2.50) 3.00

TALES OF THE GREEN LANTERN CORPS (See Green Lantern #107)
DC Comics: May, 1981 - No. 3, July, 1981 (Limited series)

1-Origin of G.L. & the Guardians 2 4 6 10 14 18
2 2 4 6 8 10 12
3 1 3 4 6 8 10
Annual 1 (1/85)-Gil Kane-c/a 1 2 3 5 6 8
TPB (2009, $19.99) r/#1-3 & stories from G.L. #148-151-154,161,162,164-167 ('82-'83) 20.00
Volume 2 TPB (2010, $19.99) r/Annual #1 and stories from G.L. ('83-'85) 20.00
Volume 3 TPB (2010, $19.99) r/Green Lantern #201-206 ('86) 20.00

TALES OF THE INVISIBLE SCARLET O'NEIL (See Harvey Comics Hits #59)

TALES OF THE KILLERS (Magazine)
World Famous Periodicals: V1#10, Dec, 1970 - V1#11, Feb, 1971 (B&W, 52 pg)

V1#10-One pg. Frazetta; r/Crime Does Not Pay 5 10 15 30 50 70
11-similar-c to Crime Does Not Pay #47; contains r/Crime Does Not Pay 4 8 12 27 44 60

TALES OF THE LEGION (Formerly Legion of Super-Heroes)
DC Comics: No. 314, Aug, 1984 - No. 354, Dec, 1987

314-354: 326-r-begin 4.00
Annual 4,5 (1986, 1987)-Formerly LSH Annual 5.00

TALES OF THE MARINES (Formerly Devil-Dog Dugan #1-3)
Atlas Comics (OPI): No. 4, Feb, 1957 (Marines At War #5 on)

4-Powell-a; Severin-c 15 30 45 85 130 175

TALES OF THE MARVELS
Marvel Comics: 1995/1996 (all acetate, painted-c)

...Blockbuster 1 (1995, $5.95, one-shot), ...Inner Demons 1 (1996, $5.95, one shot), ...Wonder Years 1,2 (1995, $4.95, limited series) 6.00

TALES OF THE MARVEL UNIVERSE
Marvel Comics: Feb, 1997 ($2.95, one-shot)

1-Anthology; wraparound-c; Thunderbolts, Ka-Zar app. 4.00

TALES OF THE MYSTERIOUS TRAVELER (See Mysterious...)
Charlton Comics: Aug, 1956 - No. 13, June, 1959; V2#14, Oct, 1985 - No. 15, Dec, 1985

1-No Ditko-a; Giordano/Alascia-c 50 100 150 315 533 750
2-Ditko-a(1) 41 82 123 256 428 600
3-Ditko-c/a(1) 42 84 126 265 445 625
4-7-Ditko-c/a(3-4 stories each) 48 96 144 302 514 725
8,9-Ditko-a(1-3 each). 8-Rocke-c 41 82 123 250 418 585
10,11-Ditko-c/a(3-4 each) 44 88 132 277 469 660
12 18 36 54 105 165 225
13-Baker-a (r?) 19 38 57 111 176 240
V2#14,15 (1985)-Ditko-c/a-low print run 2 3 4 6 8 10

TALES OF THE NEW GODS
DC Comics: 2008 ($19.99, TPB)

SC-Reprints from Jack Kirby's Fourth World, Orion and Mister Miracle Special; includes previously unpublished story by Millar-s/Ditko-a 20.00

TALES OF THE NEW TEEN TITANS
DC Comics: June, 1982 - No. 4, Sept, 1982 (Limited series)

1 2 4 6 11 16 20
2-4 1 3 4 6 8 10

TALES OF THE PONY EXPRESS (TV)
Dell Publishing Co.: No. 829, Aug, 1957 - No. 942, Oct, 1958

Four Color 829 (#1) -Painted-c 5 10 15 35 63 90
Four Color 942-Title -Pony Express 5 10 15 31 53 75

TALES OF THE REALM
CrossGen Comics/MVCreations #4-on: Oct, 2003 - No. 5, May, 2004 ($2.95, limited series)

1-5-Robert Kirkman-s/Matt Tyree-a 3.00
Volume 1 HC (8/04, $39.95, dust jacket) r/#1-5; sketch pages and concept art 40.00

TALES OF THE SINESTRO CORPS (See Green Lantern and Green Lantern Corps x-over)
DC Comics: Nov, 2007 - Jan, 2008 ($2.99/$3.99, one-shots)

...: Cyborg-Superman (12/07, $2.99) Burnett-s/Blaine-a/VanSciver-c; JLA app. 3.00
...: Ion (1/08, $2.99) Marz-s/Lacombe-a/Benes-c; Sodam Yat app. 3.00
...: Parallax (11/07, $2.99) Marz-s/Melo-a; Kyle Rayner vs. Parallax 3.00
...: Superman-Prime (12/07, $3.99) Johns-s/VanSciver-c; origin re-told w/Ordway-a 4.00

TALES OF THE TEENAGE MUTANT NINJA TURTLES (See Teenage Mutant...)
Mirage Studios: May, 1987 - No. 7, Aug (Apr-c), 1989 (B&W, $1.50)

1 2 4 6 10 14 18
2-Title merges w/Teenage Mutant Ninja... 1 2 3 5 6 8

TALES OF THE TEEN TITANS (Formerly The New Teen Titans)
DC Comics: No. 41, Apr, 1984 - No. 91, July, 1988 (75¢)

41,45-49: 46-Aqualad & Aquagirl join 4.00
42,43: The Judas Contract parts 1&2 with Deathstroke the Terminator; concludes with part 4 in Annual #3. 6.00
44-Dick Grayson becomes Nightwing (3rd to be Nightwing) & joins Titans; Judas Contract part 3; Jericho (Deathstroke's son) joins; origin Deathstroke 5 10 15 34 60 85
50-Double size; app. Betty Kane (Bat-Girl) out of costume 6.00
51,52,56-91: 52-1st brief app. Azrael (not same as newer character). 56-Intro Jinx. 57-Neutron app. 59-r/DC Comics Presents #26. 60-91-r/New Teen Titans Baxter series. 68-B. Smith-c. 70-Origin Kole 3.00
53-55: 53-1st full app. Azrael; Deathstroke cameo. 54,55-Deathstroke-c/stories 4.00
Annual 3(1984, $1.25)-Part 4 of The Judas Contract; Deathstroke-c/story; Death of Terra; indicia says Teen Titans Annual; previous annuals listed as New Teen Titans Annual #1,2 1 3 4 6 8 10
Annual 4-(1986, $1.25) 4.00

TALES OF THE TEXAS RANGERS (See Jace Pearson...)

TALES OF THE THING (Fantastic Four)
Marvel Comics: May, 2005 - No. 3, July, 2005 ($2.50, limited series)

1-3-Dr. Strange app; Randy Green-c 3.00

TALES OF THE TMNT (Also see Teenage Mutant Ninja Turtles)
Mirage Studios: Jan, 2004 - Present ($2.95/$3.25, B&W)

1-7: 1-Brizuela-a 5.00
8-70: 8-Begin $3.25-c. 47-Origin of the Super Turtles 4.00

TALES OF THE UNEXPECTED (Becomes The Unexpected #105 on)(See Adventure #75, Super DC Giant)
National Periodical Publications: Feb-Mar, 1956 - No. 104, Dec-Jan, 1967-68

1 132 264 396 1056 2378 3700
2 46 92 138 368 834 1300
3-5 36 72 108 259 580 900
6-10: 6-1st Silver Age issue 28 56 84 202 451 700
11,14,19,20 21 42 63 147 324 500
12,13,16,18,21-24: All have Kirby-a. 16-Characters named 'Thor' (with a magic hammer) and Loki by Kirby (8/57, characters do not look like Marvel's Thor & Loki) 24 48 72 168 372 575
15,17-Grey tone-c; Kirby-a 27 54 81 189 420 650
25-30 17 34 51 119 265 410
31-39 15 30 45 105 233 360
40-Space Ranger begins (8/59, 3rd ap.), ends #82 121 242 363 968 2184 3400
41,42-Space Ranger stories 41 82 123 303 689 1075
43-1st Space Ranger-c this title; grey tone-c 71 142 213 568 1284 2000
44-46 30 60 90 216 483 750
47-50 25 50 75 175 388 600
51-60: 54-Dinosaur-c/story 21 42 63 147 324 500
61-67: 67-Last 10¢ issue 17 34 51 117 259 400
68-82: 82-Last Space Ranger 10 20 30 66 138 210
83-90,92-99 6 12 18 40 73 105
91,100: 91-1st Automan (also in #94,97) 6 12 18 41 76 110
101-104 6 12 18 37 66 95

NOTE: ***Neal Adams*** *c-104.* ***Anderson*** *a-50.* ***Brown*** *a-50-82(Space Ranger); c-19, 40, & many Space Ranger-c.* ***Cameron*** *a-24, 27, 29; c-24.* ***Heath*** *a-49.* ***Bob Kane*** *a-24, 48.* ***Kirby*** *a-12, 13, 15-18, 21-24; c-13, 18, 22.* ***Meskin*** *a-15, 18, 26, 27, 35, 66.* ***Moreira*** *a-16, 20, 29, 38, 44, 62, 71; c-38.* ***Roussos*** *c-10.* ***Wildey*** *a-31.*

TALES OF THE UNEXPECTED (See Crisis Aftermath: The Spectre)
DC Comics: Dec, 2006 - No. 8, Jul, 2007 ($3.99, limited series)

1-8-The Spectre, Lapham-s/Battle-a; Dr. 13, Azzarello-s/Chiang-a. 4-Wrightson-c 4.00
1-Variant Spectre cover by Neal Adams 5.00
The Spectre: Tales of the Unexpected TPB (2007, $14.99) r/#4-8 15.00

TALES OF THE VAMPIRES (Also see Buffy the Vampire Slayer and related titles)
Dark Horse Comics: 2003 - No. 5, Apr, 2004 ($2.99, limited series)

1-Short stories by Joss Whedon and others. 1-Totleben-c. 3-Powell-c. 4-Edlund-c 3.00
TPB (11/04, $15.95) r/#1-5; afterword by Marv Wolfman 16.00

TALES OF THE WEST (See 3-D...)

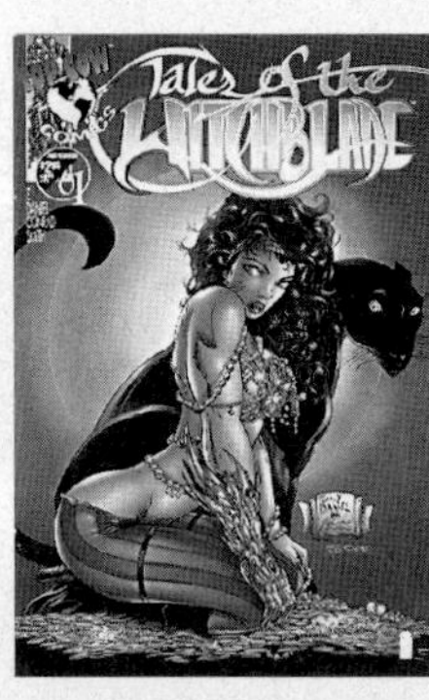

Tales of the Witchblade #1 © TCOW

Tales to Astonish #7 © MAR

Tales to Astonish #93 © MAR

TALES OF THE WITCHBLADE
Image Comics (Top Cow Productions): Nov, 1996 - No. 9 ($2.95)

	GD 2.0	VG 4.0	FN 6.0	VF 8.0	VF/NM 9.0	NM- 9.2
1/2	1	2	3	5	7	9
1/2 Gold	2	4	6	9	12	15
1-Daniel-c/a(p)	1	3	4	6	8	10
1-Variant-c by Turner	2	4	6	9	12	15
1-Platinum Edition	3	6	9	16	23	30
2,3						6.00
4-6: 6-Green-c						5.00
7-9: 9-Lara Croft-c						4.00
7-Variant-c by Turner	1	2	3	5	6	8
Witchblade: Distinctions (4/01, $14.95, TPB) r/#1-6; Green-c						15.00

TALES OF THE WITCHBLADE COLLECTED EDITION
Image Comics (Top Cow): May, 1998 - No. 2 ($4.95/$5.95, square-bound)

	GD 2.0	VG 4.0	FN 6.0	VF 8.0	VF/NM 9.0	NM- 9.2
1,2: 1-r/#1,2. 2-($5.95) r/#3,4						6.00

TALES OF THE WIZARD OF OZ (See Wizard of OZ, 4-Color #1308)

TALES OF THE ZOMBIE (Magazine)
Marvel Comics Group: Aug, 1973 - No. 10, Mar, 1975 (75¢, B&W)

	GD 2.0	VG 4.0	FN 6.0	VF 8.0	VF/NM 9.0	NM- 9.2
V1#1-Reprint/Menace #5; origin Simon Garth	6	12	18	37	66	95
2,3: 2-2nd app. of Brother Voodoo; Everett biog. & memorial	4	8	12	25	40	55
V2#1(#4)-Photos & text of James Bond movie "Live & Let Die"	3	6	9	20	31	42
5-10: 8-Kaluta-a	3	6	9	18	28	38
Annual 1(Summer,'75)(#11)-B&W; Everett, Buscema-a	3	6	9	20	31	42

NOTE: *Brother Voodoo app. 2, 5, 6, 10.* ***Alcala*** *a-7-9.* ***Boris*** *c-1-4.* ***Colan*** *a-2r, 6.* ***Heath*** *a-5r.* ***Reese*** *a-2.* ***Tuska*** *a-2r.*

TALES OF VOODOO
Eerie Publications: V1#11, Nov, 1968 - V7#6, Nov, 1974 (Magazine)

	GD 2.0	VG 4.0	FN 6.0	VF 8.0	VF/NM 9.0	NM- 9.2
V1#11	7	14	21	48	89	130
V2#1(3/69)-V2#4(9/69)	5	10	15	33	57	80
V3#1-6('70): 4- "Claws of the Cat" redrawn from Climax #1	4	8	12	28	47	65
V4#1-6('71), V5#1-7('72), V6#1-6('73), V7#1-6('74)	4	8	12	28	47	65
Annual 1	5	10	15	30	50	70

NOTE: *Bondage-c-V1#10, V2#4, V3#4.*

TALES OF WELLS FARGO (TV)(See Western Roundup under Dell Giants)
Dell Publishing Co.: No. 876, Feb, 1958 - No. 1215, Oct-Dec, 1961

	GD 2.0	VG 4.0	FN 6.0	VF 8.0	VF/NM 9.0	NM- 9.2
Four Color 876 (#1)-Photo-c	8	16	24	52	99	145
Four Color 968 (2/59), 1023, 1075 (3/60), 1113 (7-9/60)-All photo-c. 1075,1113-Both have variant edition, back-c comic strip	7	14	21	48	89	130
Four Color 1167 (3-5/61), 1215-Photo-c	7	14	21	44	82	120

TALESPIN (Also see Cartoon Tales & Disney's Talespin Limited Series)
Disney Comics: June, 1991 - No. 7, Dec, 1991 ($1.50)

	GD 2.0	VG 4.0	FN 6.0	VF 8.0	VF/NM 9.0	NM- 9.2
1-7						3.00

TALES TO ASTONISH (Becomes The Incredible Hulk #102 on)
Atlas (MAP No. 1/ZPC No. 2-14/VPI No. 15-21/Marvel No. 22 on: Jan, 1959 - No. 101, Mar, 1968

	GD 2.0	VG 4.0	FN 6.0	VF 8.0	VF/NM 9.0	NM- 9.2
1-Jack Davis-a; monster-c.	417	834	1251	3545	8023	12,500
2-Ditko flying saucer-c (Martians); #2-4 have sci/fi-c.	114	228	342	912	2056	3200
3,4	96	192	288	768	1734	2700
5-Prototype issue (Stone Men); Williamson-a (4 pgs.); Kirby monster-c begin	82	164	246	656	1478	2300
6-Prototype issue (Stone Men)	63	126	189	504	1127	1750
7-Prototype issue (Toad Men)	63	126	189	504	1127	1750
8-10	59	118	177	472	1061	1650
11,12,14,17-20	46	92	138	368	834	1300
13-(11/60) 1st app. Groot (Guardians of the Galaxy) by Kirby-cvr/sty; swipes story from Menace #8	550	1100	1650	4000	7000	10,000
15-Prototype issue (Electro)	50	100	150	400	900	1400
16-Prototype issue (Stone Men) named "Thorr"	50	100	150	384	867	1350
21-(7/61)-Hulk prototype	53	106	159	416	933	1450
22-26,28-31,33,34	37	74	111	274	610	950
27-1st Ant-Man app. (1/62); last 10¢ issue (see Strange Tales #73,78 & Tales of Suspense #32)	950	1900	3800	11,550	29,775	48,000
32-Sandman prototype	38	76	114	285	641	1000
35-(9/62)-2nd app. Ant-Man, 1st in costume; begin series & Ant-Man-c	325	650	975	2800	7150	11,500
36-3rd app. Ant-Man	93	186	279	744	1672	2600
37,39,40	50	100	150	400	900	1400
38-1st app. Egghead	53	106	159	413	932	1450
41-43	45	90	135	333	757	1180
44-Origin & 1st app. The Wasp (6/63)	258	516	774	1651	2826	4000
45-47	29	58	87	209	467	725
48-Origin & 1st app. The Porcupine	30	60	90	216	483	750
49-Ant-Man becomes Giant Man (11/63)	53	106	159	416	933	1450
50,51,53-56,58: 50-Origin/1st app. Human Top (alias Whirlwind). 58-Origin Colossus	19	38	57	131	291	450
52-Origin/1st app. Black Knight (2/64)	23	46	69	161	356	550
57-Early Spider-Man app. (7/64)	37	74	111	274	612	950
59-Giant Man vs. Hulk feature story (9/64); Hulk's 1st app. this title; 1st mention that anger triggers his transformation	36	72	108	266	596	925
60-Giant Man & Hulk double feature begins	27	54	81	189	420	650
61,64-69: 61-All Ditko issue; 1st app. of Glenn Talbot; 1st mailbag. 65-New Giant Man costume. 68-New Human Top costume. 69-Last Giant Man	13	26	39	89	195	300
62-1st app./origin The Leader; new Wasp costume; Hulk pin-up page missing from many copies	20	40	60	141	313	485
63-Origin Leader continues	15	30	45	100	220	340
70-Sub-Mariner & Incredible Hulk begins (8/65)	14	28	42	96	211	325
71-81: 72-Begin alternating-c features w/Sub-Mariner (even #'s) & Hulk (odd #'s). 79-Hulk vs. Hercules-c/story. 81-1st app. Boomerang	7	14	21	44	82	120
82-Iron Man battles Sub-Mariner (1st Iron Man x-over outside The Avengers & TOS); story cont'd from Tales of Suspense #80	8	16	24	54	102	150
83-89,94-99: 97-X-Men cameo (brief)	6	12	18	37	66	95
90-1st app. The Abomination	10	20	30	65	135	200
91-The Abomination debut continues & 1st cover	9	18	27	57	111	165
92-1st Silver Surfer x-over (outside of Fantastic Four, 6/67); 1 panel cameo only	7	14	21	48	89	130
93-Hulk battles Silver Surfer-c/story (1st full x-over)	20	40	60	141	313	485
100-Hulk battles Sub-Mariner full-length story	7	14	21	48	89	130
101-Hulk story cont'd in Incredible Hulk #102; Sub-Mariner story continued in Iron Man & Sub-Mariner #1	8	16	24	54	102	150

NOTE: ***Ayers*** *c(i)-9-12, 16, 18, 19.* ***Berg*** *a-1.* ***Burgos*** *a-62-64p.* ***Buscema*** *a-85-87p.* ***Colan*** *a(p)-70-76, 78-82, 84, 85, 101; c(p)-71-76, 78, 80, 82, 84, 86, 88, 90.* ***Ditko*** *a-1, 3-48, 50i, 60-67p; c-2, 7i, 8i, 14i, 17i.* ***Everett*** *a-78, 79i, 80-84, 85-90i, 94i, 95, 96; c(i)-79-81, 83, 86, 88.* ***Forte*** *a-6.* ***Kane*** *a-76, 88-91; c-89, 91.* ***Kirby*** *a(p)-1, 5-34-40, 44, 49-51, 68-70, 82, 83; layouts-71-84; c(p)-1, 3-48, 50-70, 72, 73, 75, 77, 78, 79, 81, 85, 90.* ***Kirby/Ditko*** *a-7, 8, 12, 13, 50; c-7, 8, 10, 13.* ***Leiber/Fox*** *a-47, 48, 50, 51.* ***Powell*** *a-65-69p, 73, 74.* ***Reinman*** *a-6, 36, 45, 46, 54i, 56-60i.*

TALES TO ASTONISH (2nd Series)
Marvel Comics Group: Dec, 1979 - No. 14, Jan, 1981

	GD 2.0	VG 4.0	FN 6.0	VF 8.0	VF/NM 9.0	NM- 9.2
V1#1-Reprints Sub-Mariner #1 by Buscema	2	4	6	10	14	18
2-14: Reprints Sub-Mariner #2-14	1	3	4	6	8	10

TALES TO ASTONISH
Marvel Comics: V3#1, Oct, 1994 ($6.95, one-shot)

	GD 2.0	VG 4.0	FN 6.0	VF 8.0	VF/NM 9.0	NM- 9.2
V3#1-Peter David scripts; acetate, painted-c						7.00

TALES TO HOLD YOU SPELLBOUND (See Spellbound)

TALES TO OFFEND
Dark Horse Comics: July, 1997 ($2.95, one-shot)

	GD 2.0	VG 4.0	FN 6.0	VF 8.0	VF/NM 9.0	NM- 9.2
1-Frank Miller-s/a, EC-style cover						4.00

TALES TOO TERRIBLE TO TELL (Becomes Terrology #10, 11)
New England Comics: Wint, 1989-90 - No. 11, Nov-Dec.1993 ($2.95/$3.50, B&W with card-stock covers)

	GD 2.0	VG 4.0	FN 6.0	VF 8.0	VF/NM 9.0	NM- 9.2
1-($2.95) Reprints of non-EC pre-code horror; EC-style cover by Bissette						5.00
1-($3.50, 5-6/93) Second printing with alternate cover not by Bissette						4.00
2-8-($3.50) Story reprints, history of the pre-code titles and creators; cover galleries (B&W) inside & on back-c (color)						4.00
9-11-($2.95) 10,11-"Terrology" on cover						4.00

TALKING KOMICS
Belda Record & Publ. Co.: 1947 (20 pgs, slick-c)

	GD 2.0	VG 4.0	FN 6.0	VF 8.0	VF/NM 9.0	NM- 9.2
Each comic contained a record that followed the story - much like the Golden Record sets. Known titles: Chirpy Cricket, Lonesome Octopus, Sleepy Santa, Grumpy Shark, Flying Turtle, Happy Grasshopper with records...	3	6	9	19	30	40

TALLY-HO COMICS
Swappers Quarterly (Baily Publ. Co.): Dec, 1944

	GD 2.0	VG 4.0	FN 6.0	VF 8.0	VF/NM 9.0	NM- 9.2
nn-Frazetta's 1st work as Giunta's assistant; Man in Black horror story; violence; Giunta-c	58	116	174	371	636	900

TALULLAH (See Comic Books Series I)

Tangent Comics / The Batman #1 © DC

Tank Girl 2 #4 © Deadline

Target Comics V2 #1 © NOVP

	GD 2.0	VG 4.0	FN 6.0	VF 8.0	VF/NM 9.0	NM- 9.2

TALON (From Batman Court of Owls crossover)
DC Comics: No. 0, Nov, 2012 - No. 17, May, 2014 ($2.99)

0-17: 0-Origin of Calvin Rose; March-a. 7-11-Bane app. 3.00

TAMMY, TELL ME TRUE
Dell Publishing Co.: No. 1233, 1961

Four Color 1233-Movie 6 12 18 38 69 100

TANGENT COMICS
.../ THE ATOM, DC Comics: Dec, 1997 ($2.95, one-shot)
1-Dan Jurgens-s/Jurgens & Paul Ryan-a 3.00
.../ THE BATMAN, DC Comics: Sept, 1998 ($1.95, one-shot)
1-Dan Jurgens-s/Klaus Janson-a 3.00
.../ DOOM PATROL, DC Comics: Dec, 1997 ($2.95, one-shot)
1- Dan Jurgens-s/Sean Chen & Kevin Conrad-a 3.00
.../ THE FLASH, DC Comics: Dec, 1997 ($2.95, one-shot)
1-Todd Dezago-s/Gary Frank & Cam Smith-a 3.00
.../ GREEN LANTERN, DC Comics: Dec, '97 ($2.95, one-shot)
1-James Robinson-s/J.H. Williams III & Mick Gray-a 3.00
.../ JLA, DC Comics: Sept, 1998 ($1.95, one-shot)
1-Dan Jurgens-s/Banks & Rapmund-a 3.00
.../ THE JOKER, DC Comics: Dec, 1997 ($2.95, one-shot)
1-Karl Kesel-s/Matt Haley & Tom Simmons-a 3.00
.../ THE JOKER'S WILD, DC Comics: Sept, 1998 ($1.95, one-shot)
1-Kesel & Simmons-s/Phillips & Rodriguez-a 3.00
.../ METAL MEN, DC Comics: Dec, 1997 ($2.95, one-shot)
1-Ron Marz-s/Mike McKone & Mark McKenna-a 3.00
.../ NIGHTWING, DC Comics: Dec, 1997 ($2.95, one-shot)
1-John Ostrander-s/Jan Duursema-a 3.00
.../ NIGHTWING: NIGHTFORCE, DC Comics: Sept, 1998 ($1.95, one-shot)
1-John Ostrander-s/Jan Duursema-a 3.00
.../ POWERGIRL, DC Comics: Sept, 1998 ($1.95, one-shot)
1-Marz-s/Abell & Vines-a 3.00
.../ SEA DEVILS, DC Comics: Dec, 1997 ($2.95, one-shot)
1-Kurt Busiek-s/Vince Giarrano & Tom Palmer-a 3.00
.../ SECRET SIX, DC Comics: Dec, 1997 ($2.95, one-shot)
1-Chuck Dixon-s/Tom Grummett & Lary Stucker-a 3.00
.../ THE SUPERMAN, DC Comics: Sept, 1998 ($1.95, one-shot)
1-Millar-s/Guice-a 3.00
.../ TALES OF THE GREEN LANTERN, DC Comics: Sept, 1998 ($1.95, one-shot)
1-Story & art by various 3.00
.../ THE TRIALS OF THE FLASH, DC Comics: Sept, 1998 ($1.95, one-shot)
1-Dezago-s/Pelletier & Lanning-a 3.00
.../ WONDER WOMAN DC Comics: Sept, 1998 ($1.95, one-shot),
1-Peter David-s/Unzueta & Mendoza-a 3.00
... Volume One TPB (2007, $19.99) r/The Atom, Metal Men, Green Lantern, The Flash, Sea Devils one-shots; intro and new cover by Jurgens 20.00
... Volume Two TPB (2008, $19.99) r/Batman, Doom Patrol, Joker, Nightwing and Secret Six one-shots; new cover by Jurgens 20.00
... Volume Three TPB (2008, $19.99) r/The Superman, Wonder Woman, Nightwing: Nightforce, The Joker's Wild, The Trials of the Flash, Tales of the Green Lantern, Powergirl, and JLA one-shots; new cover by Jurgens 20.00

TANGENT: SUPERMAN'S REIGN
DC Comics: May, 2008 - No. 12, Apr, 2009 ($2.99, limited series)

1-12-Jurgens-s; Flash & Green Lantern app.; back-up histories of Tangent heroes 3.00
Volume 1 TPB (2009, $19.99) r/#1-6 & Justice League of America #16 20.00
Volume 2 TPB (2009, $19.99) r/#7-12 20.00

TANGLED (Disney movie)
IDW Publishing: Jan, 2018 - Present ($3.99)

1-Three covers 4.00

TANGLED WEB (See Spider-Man's Tangled Web)

TANK GIRL
Dark Horse Comics: May, 1991 - No. 4, Aug, 1991 ($2.25, B&W, mini-series)

1-Contains Dark Horse trading cards 6.00
2-4 4.00
...: Dark Nuggets (Image Comics, 12/09, $3.99) Martin-s/Dayglo-a 4.00
...: Dirty Helmets (Image Comics, 4/10, $3.99) Martin-s/Dayglo-a 4.00
...: Hairy Heroes (Image Comics, 8/10, $3.99) Martin-s/Dayglo-a 4.00

TANK GIRL: APOCALYPSE
DC Comics: Nov, 1995 - No. 4, Feb, 1996 ($2.25, limited series)

1-4 4.00

TANK GIRL: MOVIE ADAPTATION
DC Comics: 1995 ($5.95, 68 pgs., one-shot)

nn-Peter Milligan scripts 6.00

TANK GIRL: TANK GIRL GOLD
Titan Comics: Sept, 2016 - No. 4, Mar, 2017 ($3.99, limited series)

1-4: Alan Martin-s/Brett Parson-a. 2-MAD spoof 4.00

TANK GIRL: THE GIFTING
IDW Publishing: May, 2007 - No. 4, Aug, 2007 ($3.99, limited series)

1-4: 1-Ashley Wood-a/c; Alan Martin-s; 3 covers 4.00

TANK GIRL: THE ODYSSEY
DC Comics: May, 1995 - No.4, Oct, 1995 ($2.25, limited series)

1-4: Peter Milligan scripts; Hewlett-a 4.00

TANK GIRL: THE ROYAL ESCAPE
IDW Publishing: Mar, 2010 - No. 4, Jun, 2010 ($3.99, limited series)

1-4: Alan Martin-s/Rufus Dayglo-a/c 4.00

TANK GIRL: 21ST CENTURY TANK GIRL
Titan Comics: Jul, 2015 - No. 3, Sept, 2015 ($3.99, limited series)

1-3: Alan Martin-s; art by Hewlett, Bond, Mahfood, Parson & others 4.00

TANK GIRL 2
Dark Horse Comics: June, 1993 - No. 4, Sept, 1993 ($2.50, lim. series, mature)

1-4: Jamie Hewlett & Alan Martin-s/a 4.00
TPB (2/95, $17.95) r/#1-4 18.00

TANK GIRL: TWO GIRLS, ONE TANK
Titan Comics: Jun, 2016 - No. 4, Sept, 2016 ($3.99, limited series)

1-4: Alan Martin-s/Brett Parson-a 4.00

TAPPAN'S BURRO (See Zane Grey & 4-Color #449)

TAPPING THE VEIN (Clive Barker's...)
Eclipse Comics: 1989 - No. 5, 1992 ($6.95, squarebound, mature, 68 pgs.)

Book 1-5: 1-Russell-a, Bolton-c. 2-Bolton-a. 4-Die-cut-c 7.00
TPB (2002, $24.95, Checker Book Publ. Group) r/#1-5 25.00

TARANTULA (See Weird Suspense)

TARGET: AIRBOY
Eclipse Comics: Mar, 1988 ($1.95)

1 3.00

TARGET COMICS (...Western Romances #106 on)
Funnies, Inc./Novelty Publications/Star Publ.: Feb, 1940 - V10#3 (#105), Aug-Sept, 1949

V1#1-Origin & 1st app. Manowar, The White Streak by Burgos, & Bulls-Eye Bill by Everett; City Editor (ends #5), High Grass Twins by Jack Cole (ends #4), T-Men by Joe Simon (ends #9), Rip Rory (ends #4), Fantastic Feature Films by Tarpe Mills (ends #39), & Calling 2-R (ends #14) begin; marijuana use story
459 918 1377 3350 5925 8500
2-Everett-c/a 252 504 756 1613 2757 3900
3,4-Everett, Jack Cole-a 168 336 504 1075 1838 2600
5-Origin The White Streak in text; Space Hawk by Wolverton begins (6/40) (see Blue Bolt & Circus) 459 918 1377 3350 5925 8500
6-The Chameleon by Everett begins (7/40, 1st app.); White Streak origin cont'd. in text; early mention of comic collecting in letter column; 1st letter column in comics? (7/40)
252 504 756 1613 2757 3900
7-Wolverton Spacehawk-c/story (scarce) 1250 2500 3750 9200 17,600 26,000
8-Classic sci-fi cover (scarce) 354 708 1062 2478 4339 6200
9-White Streak-c 181 362 543 1158 1979 2800
10-Intro/1st app. The Target (11/40); Simon-c; Spacehawk-s; text piece by Wolverton
300 600 900 1950 3375 4800
11-Origin The Target & The Targeteers 187 374 561 1197 2049 2900
12-(1/41) Target & The Targeteers-c 142 284 426 909 1555 2200
V2#1-Target by Bob Wood; Uncle Sam flag-c 100 200 300 635 1093 1550
2-Ten part Treasure Island serial begins; Harold Delay-a; reprinted in Catholic Comics V3#1-10 (see Key Comics #5) 68 136 204 435 743 1050
3-5: 4-Kit Carter, The Cadet begins 65 130 195 416 708 1000
6-9: Red Seal with White Streak in #6-10 61 122 183 390 670 950
10-Classic-c 116 232 348 742 1271 1800
11,12: 12-10-part Last of the Mohicans serial begins; Delay-a

Targitt #2 © Seaboard

Tarot: Witch of the Black Rose #4 © Jim Balent

Tarzan #239 © ERB

	GD 2.0	VG 4.0	FN 6.0	VF 8.0	VF/NM 9.0	NM- 9.2
	58	116	174	371	636	900
V3#1-3,5-7,9,10: 10-Last Wolverton issue	47	94	141	296	498	700
4-V for Victory-c	73	146	219	467	796	1125
8-Hitler, Tojo, Flag-c; 6-part Gulliver Travels serial begins; Delay-a.	103	206	309	659	1130	1600
11,12	21	42	63	122	199	275
V4#1-4,7-12: 8-X-Mas-c	15	30	45	86	133	180
5-Classic Statue of Liberty-c	26	52	78	154	252	350
6-Targetoons by Wolverton	19	38	57	111	176	240
V5#1-8	14	28	42	80	115	150
V6#1-4,6-10	14	28	42	76	108	140
5-Classic Tojo hanging/Buy War Bonds WWII-c	81	162	243	518	884	1250
V7#1-12	12	24	36	67	94	120
V8#1,3-5,8,9,11,12	11	22	33	60	83	105
2,6,7-Krigstein-a	12	24	36	67	94	120
10-L.B. Cole-c	25	50	75	150	245	340
V9#1,4,6,8,10-L.B. Cole-c	25	50	75	150	245	340
2,3,5,7,9,11, V10#1	11	22	33	60	83	105
12-Classic L.B. Cole-c	40	80	120	246	411	575
V10#2,3-L.B. Cole-c	25	50	75	150	245	340

NOTE: ***Certa*** *c-V8#9, 11, 12, V9#5, 9, 11, V10#1.* ***Jack Cole*** *a-1-8.* ***Everett*** *a-1-9; c(signed Blake)-1, 2.* ***Al Fago*** *c-V6#8.* ***Sid Greene*** *c-V2#9, 12, V3#3.* ***Walter Johnson*** *c-V5#6, V6#4.* ***Tarpe Mills*** *a-1-4, 6, 8, 11, V3#1.* ***Rico*** *a-V7#4, 10, V8#5, 6, V9#3; c-V7#6, 8, 10, V8#2, 4, 6, 7.* ***Simon*** *a-1, 2.* ***Bob Wood*** *c-V2#2, 3, 5, 6.*

TARGET: THE CORRUPTORS (TV)
Dell Publishing Co.: No. 1306, Mar-May, 1962 - No. 3, Oct-Dec, 1962
(All have photo-c)

	GD 2.0	VG 4.0	FN 6.0	VF 8.0	VF/NM 9.0	NM- 9.2
Four Color 1306(#1), #2,3	5	10	15	33	57	80

TARGET WESTERN ROMANCES (Formerly Target Comics; becomes Flaming Western Romances #3)
Star Publications: No. 106, Oct-Nov, 1949 - No. 107, Dec-Jan, 1949-50

	GD 2.0	VG 4.0	FN 6.0	VF 8.0	VF/NM 9.0	NM- 9.2
106(#1)-Silhouette nudity panel; L.B. Cole-c	25	50	75	150	245	340
107(#2)-L.B. Cole-c; lingerie panels	22	44	66	132	216	300

TARGITT
Atlas/Seaboard Publ.: March, 1975 - No. 3, July, 1975

	GD 2.0	VG 4.0	FN 6.0	VF 8.0	VF/NM 9.0	NM- 9.2
1-3: 1-Origin; Nostrand-a in all. 2-1st in costume. 3-Becomes Man-Stalker	2	4	6	10	14	18

TAROT: WITCH OF THE BLACK ROSE
Broadsword Comics: Mar, 2000 - Present ($2.95, mature)

	GD 2.0	VG 4.0	FN 6.0	VF 8.0	VF/NM 9.0	NM- 9.2
1-Jim Balent-s/c/a; at least two covers on all issues	4	8	12	25	40	55
1-Second printing (10/00)						6.00
2	2	4	6	13	18	22
3-20	1	2	3	5	6	8
21-40						5.00
41-108: 84-The Krampus app. 90-Crossover with School Bites characters						3.00

TARZAN (See Aurora, Comics on Parade, Crackajack, DC 100-Page Super Spec., Edgar Rice Burroughs'..., Famous Feature Stories #1, Golden Comics Digest #4, 9, Jeep Comics, Jungle Tales of..., Limited Collectors' Edition, Popular, Sparkler, Sport Stars #1, Tip Top & Top Comics)

TARZAN
Dell Publishing Co./United Features Synd.: No. 5, 1939 - No. 161, Aug, 1947

	GD 2.0	VG 4.0	FN 6.0	VF 8.0	VF/NM 9.0	NM- 9.2
Large Feature Comic 5('39)-(Scarce)-By Hal Foster; reprints 1st dailies from 1929	245	490	735	1568	2684	3800
Single Series 20('40)-By Hal Foster	181	362	543	1158	1979	2800
Four Color 134(2/47)-Marsh-c/a	56	112	168	448	999	1550
Four Color 161(8/47)-Marsh-c/a	46	92	138	340	770	1200

TARZAN (...of the Apes #138 on)
Dell Publishing Co./Gold Key No. 132 on: 1-2/48 - No. 131, 7-8/62; No. 132, 11/62 - No. 206, 2/72

	GD 2.0	VG 4.0	FN 6.0	VF 8.0	VF/NM 9.0	NM- 9.2
1-Jesse Marsh-a begins	100	200	300	800	1800	2800
2	43	86	129	318	722	1125
3-5	31	62	93	223	499	775
6-10: 6-1st Tantor the Elephant. 7-1st Valley of the Monsters	26	52	78	182	404	625
11-15: 11-Two Against the Jungle begins, ends #24. 13-Lex Barker photo-c begin	19	38	57	131	291	450
16-20	15	30	45	105	233	360
21-24,26-30	13	26	39	86	188	290
25-1st "Brothers of the Spear" episode; series ends #156,160,161,196-206	14	28	42	96	211	325
31-40	10	20	30	66	138	210
41-54: Last Barker photo-c	8	16	24	56	108	160
55-60: 56-Eight pg. Boy story	7	14	21	49	92	135
61,62,64-70	6	12	18	41	76	110
63-Two Tarzan stories, 1 by Manning	6	12	18	42	79	115
71-79	6	12	18	37	66	95
80-99: 80-Gordon Scott photo-c begin	5	10	15	34	60	85
100	6	12	18	37	66	95
101-109	5	10	15	33	57	80
110 (Scarce)-Last photo-c	6	12	18	37	66	95
111-120	5	10	15	31	53	75
121-131: Last Dell issue	5	10	15	30	50	70
132-1st Gold Key issue	5	10	15	31	53	75
133-138,140-154	4	8	12	25	40	55
139-(12/63)-1st app. Korak (Boy); leaves Tarzan & gets own book (1/64)	6	12	18	40	73	105
155-Origin Tarzan; text article on Tarzana, CA	5	10	15	30	50	70
156-161: 157-Banlu, Dog of the Arande begins, ends #159, 195. 169-Leopard Girl app.	3	6	9	21	33	45
162,165,168,171 (TV)-Ron Ely photo covers	4	8	12	22	35	48
163,164,166,167,169,170: 169-Leopard Girl app.	3	6	9	20	31	42
172-199,201-206: 178-Tarzan origin-r/#155; Leopard Girl app., also in #179, 190-193	3	6	9	18	28	38
200	3	6	9	21	33	45
Story Digest 1-(6/70, G.K., 148pp.)(scarce)	6	12	18	41	76	110

NOTE: *#162, 165, 168, 171 are TV issues. #1-153 all have* ***Marsh*** *art on Tarzan. #154-161, 163, 164, 166, 167, 172-177 all have* ***Manning*** *art on Tarzan. #178, 202 have* ***Manning*** *Tarzan reprints. No "Brothers of the Spear" in #1-24, 157-159, 162-195. #39-126, 128-156 all have* ***Russ Manning*** *art on "Brothers of the Spear". #196-201, 203-205 all have* ***Manning*** *B.O.T.S. reprints; #25-38, 127 all have Jesse* ***Marsh*** *art on B.O.T.S. #206 has a Marsh B.O.T.S. reprint.* ***Gollub*** *c-8-12.* ***Marsh*** *c-1-7.* ***Doug Wildey*** *a-162, 179-187. Many issues have front and back photo covers.*

TARZAN (Continuation of Gold Key series)
National Periodical Publications: No. 207, Apr, 1972 - No. 258, Feb, 1977

	GD 2.0	VG 4.0	FN 6.0	VF 8.0	VF/NM 9.0	NM- 9.2
207-Origin Tarzan by Joe Kubert, part 1; John Carter begins (origin); 52 pg. issues thru #209	5	10	15	35	63	90
208,209-(52 pgs.): 208-210-Parts 2-4 of origin. 209-Last John Carter	3	6	9	21	33	45
210-220: 210-Kubert-a. 211-Hogarth, Kubert-a. 212-214: Adaptations from "Jungle Tales of Tarzan". 213-Beyond the Farthest Star begins, ends #218. 215-218,224,225-All by Kubert. 215-part Foster-r. 219-223: Adapts "The Return of Tarzan" by Kubert	3	6	9	14	20	25
221-229: 221-223-Continues adaptation of "The Return of Tarzan". 226-Manning-a	2	4	6	10	14	18
230-DC 100 Page Super Spectacular; Kubert, Kaluta-a(p); Korak begins, ends #234; Carson of Venus app.	4	8	12	25	40	55
231-235-New Kubert-a.: 231-234-(All 100 pgs.)-Adapts "Tarzan and the Lion Man"; Rex, the Wonder Dog r-#232, 233. 235-(100 pgs.)-Last Kubert issue.	4	8	12	23	37	50
236,237,239-258: 240-243 adapts "Tarzan & the Castaways". 250-256 adapts "Tarzan the Untamed." 252,253-r/#213	2	4	6	8	10	12
238-(68 pgs.)	2	4	6	13	18	22
Digest 1-(Fall, 1972, 50¢, 164 pgs.)(DC)-Digest size; Kubert-c; Manning-a	4	8	12	25	40	55
Edgar Rice Burroughs' Tarzan The Joe Kubert Years - Volume One HC (Dark Horse Books, 10/05, $49.95, dust jacket) recolored r/#207-214; intro. by Joe Kubert						50.00
Edgar Rice Burroughs' Tarzan The Joe Kubert Years - Volume Two HC (Dark Horse Books, 2/06, $49.95, dust jacket) recolored r/#215-224; intro. by Joe Kubert						50.00
Edgar Rice Burroughs' Tarzan The Joe Kubert Years - Volume Three HC (Dark Horse Books, 6/06, $49.95, dust jacket) recolored r/#225,227-235; Kubert intro. and sketch pages						50.00

NOTE: ***Anderson*** *a-207, 209, 217, 218.* ***Chaykin*** *a-216.* ***Finlay*** *a(r)-212.* ***Foster*** *strip-r #207-209, 211, 212, 221.* ***Heath*** *a-230i.* ***G. Kane*** *a(r)-232p, 233p.* ***Kubert*** *a-207-225, 227-235, 257r, 258r; c-207-249, 253.* ***Lopez*** *a-250-255p; c-250p, 251, 252, 254.* ***Manning*** *strip-r 230-235, 238.* ***Morrow*** *a-208.* ***Nino*** *a-231-234.* ***Sparling*** *a-230, 231.* ***Starr*** *a-233r.*

TARZAN (Lord of the Jungle)
Marvel Comics Group: June, 1977 - No. 29, Oct, 1979

	GD 2.0	VG 4.0	FN 6.0	VF 8.0	VF/NM 9.0	NM- 9.2
1-New adaptions of Burroughs stories; Buscema-a	2	4	6	11	16	20
1-(35¢-c variant, limited distribution)(6/77)	5	10	15	35	63	90
2-29: 2-Origin by John Buscema. 9-Young Tarzan. 12-14-Jungle Tales of Tarzan. 25-29-New stories	1	2	3	5	6	8
2-5-(35¢-c variants, limited distribution)(7-10/77)	4	8	12	27	44	60
Annual 1-3: 1-(1977). 2-(1978). 3-(1979)	1	3	4	6	8	10

NOTE: ***N. Adams*** *c-11i, 12i.* ***Alcala*** *a-9i, 10i; c-8i, 9i.* ***Buckler*** *c-25-27p, Annual 3p.* ***John Buscema*** *a-1-3, 4-18p, Annual 1; c-1-7, 8p, 9p, 10, 11p, 12p, 13, 14-19p, 21p, 22, 23p, 24p, 28p, Annual 1.* ***Mooney*** *a-22i.* ***Nebres*** *a-22i.* ***Russell*** *a-29i.*

TARZAN
Dark Horse Comics: July, 1996 - No. 20, Mar, 1998 ($2.95)

	GD 2.0	VG 4.0	FN 6.0	VF 8.0	VF/NM 9.0	NM- 9.2
1-20: 1-6-Suydam-c						3.00

Tarzan on the Planet of the Apes #1 © ERB & 20th Century Fox

Taskmaster #1 © MAR

Team Titans #11 © DC

	GD	VG	FN	VF	VF/NM	NM-
	2.0	4.0	6.0	8.0	9.0	9.2

TARZAN / CARSON OF VENUS
Dark Horse Comics: May, 1998 - No. 4, Aug, 1998 ($2.95, limited series)
1-4-Darko Macan-s/Igor Korday-a 3.00

TARZAN FAMILY, THE (Formerly Korak, Son of Tarzan)
National Periodical Publications: No. 60, Nov-Dec, 1975 - No. 66, Nov-Dec, 1976
60-62-(68 pgs.): 60-Korak begins; Kaluta-r 2 4 6 11 16 20
63-66 (52 pgs.) 2 4 6 9 12 15
NOTE: *Carson of Venus-r 60-65. New John Carter-62-64, 65r, 66r. New Korak-60-66. Pellucidar feature-66. Foster strip r-60(9/4/32-10/16/32), 62(6/29/32-7/31/32), 63(10/11/31-12/13/31).* ***Kaluta*** *Carson of Venus-60-65.* ***Kubert*** *a-61, 64; c-60-64.* ***Manning*** *strip-r 60-62, 64.* ***Morrow*** *a-66r.*

TARZAN/JOHN CARTER: WARLORDS OF MARS
Dark Horse Comics: Jan, 1996 - No. 4, June, 1996 ($2.50, limited series)
1-4: Bruce Jones scripts in all. 1,2,4-Bret Blevins-c/a. 2-(4/96)-Indicia reads #3 3.00

TARZAN KING OF THE JUNGLE (See Dell Giant #37, 51)

TARZAN, LORD OF THE JUNGLE
Gold Key: Sept, 1965 (Giant) (25¢, soft paper-c)
1-Marsh-r 7 14 21 48 89 130

TARZAN: LOVE, LIES AND THE LOST CITY (See Tarzan the Warrior)
Malibu Comics: Aug. 10, 1992 - No. 3, Sept, 1992 ($2.50, limited series)
1-($3.95, 68 pgs.)-Flip book format; Simonson & Wagner scripts 4.00
2,3-No Simonson or Wagner scripts 3.00

TARZAN MARCH OF COMICS (See March of Comics #82, 98, 114, 125, 144, 155, 172, 185, 204, 223, 240, 252, 262, 272, 286, 300, 332, 342, 354, 366)

TARZAN OF THE APES
Metropolitan Newspaper Service: 1934? (Hardcover, 4x12", 68 pgs.)
1-Strip reprints 25 50 75 150 245 340

TARZAN OF THE APES
Marvel Comics Group: July, 1984 - No. 2, Aug, 1984 (Movie adaptation)
1,2: Origin-r/Marvel Super Spec. 4.00

TARZAN ON THE PLANET OF THE APES
Dark Horse Comics: Sept, 2016 - No. 5, Jan, 2017 ($3.99, limited series)
1-5-Seeley & Walker-s/Dagnino-a. 1-Cornelius & Zira adopt young Tarzan on Earth 4.00

TARZAN'S JUNGLE ANNUAL (See Dell Giants)

TARZAN'S JUNGLE WORLD (See Dell Giant #25)

TARZAN: THE BECKONING
Malibu Comics: 1992 - No. 7, 1993 ($2.50, limited series)
1-7 3.00

TARZAN: THE LOST ADVENTURE (See Edgar Rice Burroughs' ...)

TARZAN-THE RIVERS OF BLOOD
Dark Horse Comics: Nov, 1999 - No. 8 ($2.95, limited series)
1-4: Korday-c/a 3.00

TARZAN THE SAVAGE HEART
Dark Horse Comics: Apr, 1999 - No. 4, July, 1999 ($2.95, limited series)
1-4: Grell-c/a 3.00

TARZAN THE WARRIOR (Also see Tarzan: Love, Lies and the Lost City)
Malibu Comics: Mar, 19, 1992 - No. 5, 1992 ($2.50, limited series)
1-5: 1-Bisley painted pack-c (flip book format-c) 3.00
1-2nd printing w/o flip-c by Bisley 3.00

TARZAN VS. PREDATOR AT THE EARTH'S CORE
Dark Horse Comics: Jan, 1996 - No. 4, June, 1996 ($2.50, limited series)
1-4: Lee Weeks-c/a; Walt Simonson scripts 3.00

TASKMASTER
Marvel Comics: Apr, 2002 - No. 4, July, 2002 ($2.99, limited series)
1-4-Udon Studio-s/a. 1-Iron Man app. 3.00

TASKMASTER
Marvel Comics: Nov, 2010 - No. 4, ($3.99, limited series)
1-4-Van Lente-s/Palo-a; Hydra & A.I.M. app. 4.00

TASMANIAN DEVIL & HIS TASTY FRIENDS
Gold Key: Nov, 1962 (12¢)
1-Bugs Bunny, Elmer Fudd, Sylvester, Yosemite Sam, Road Runner & Wile E. Coyote x-over
15 30 45 105 233 360

TATTERED BANNERS
DC Comics (Vertigo): Nov, 1998 - No. 4, Feb, 1999 ($2.95, limited series)
1-4-Grant & Giffen-s/McMahon-a 3.00

TATTERED MAN
Image Comics: May 2011 ($4.99, one-shot)
1-Justin Gray & Jimmy Palmiotti-s/Norberto Fernandez-a; covers by Fernandez & Conner 5.00

TEAM AMERICA (See Captain America #269)
Marvel Comics Group: June, 1982 - No. 12, May, 1983
1,12: 1-Origin; Ideal Toy motorcycle characters. 12-Double size 5.00
2-11: 9-Iron Man app. 11-Ghost Rider app. 4.00
NOTE: *There are 16 pg. variants known for most issues, possibly all. The only ad is on the inside front cover.*

TEAM HELIX
Marvel Comics: Jan, 1993 - No. 4, Apr, 1993 ($1.75, limited series)
1-4: Teen Super Group. 1,2-Wolverine app. 3.00

TEAM ONE: STORMWATCH (Also see StormWatch)
Image Comics (WildStorm Productions): June, 1995 - No. 2, Aug, 1995 ($2.50, lim. series)
1,2: Steven T. Seagle scripts 3.00

TEAM ONE: WILDC.A.T.S (Also see WildC.A.T.S)
Image Comics (WildStorm Productions): July, 1995 - No. 2, Aug, 1995 ($2.50, lim. series)
1,2: James Robinson scripts 3.00

TEAM 7
Image Comics (WildStorm): Oct, 1994 - No.4, Feb, 1995 ($2.50, limited series)
1-4: Dixon scripts in all, 1-Portacio variant-c 3.00

TEAM 7 (DC New 52)
DC Comics: No. 0, Nov, 2012 - No. 8, Jul, 2013 ($2.99)
0-8: 0-Merino-a/Lashley-c; Slade Wilson, John Lynch, Grifter and others assemble team. 3,4-Eclipso returns. 7-Pandora & Majestic app. 3.00

TEAM 7-DEAD RECKONING
Image Comics (WildStorm): Jan, 1996 - No. 4, Apr, 1996 ($2.50, limited series)
1-4: Dixon scripts in all 3.00

TEAM 7-OBJECTIVE HELL
Image Comics (WildStorm): May, 1995 - No. 3, July, 1995 ($1.95/$2.50, limited series)
1-($1.95)-Newstand; Dixon scripts in all; Barry Smith-c 3.00
1-3: 1-($2.50)-Direct Market; Barry Smith-c, bound-in card 3.00

TEAM SUPERMAN
DC Comics: July, 1999 ($2.95, one-shot)
1-Jeanty-a/Stelfreeze-c 3.00
...Secret Files 1 (5/98, $4.95)Origin-s and pin-ups of Superboy, Supergirl and Steel 5.00

TEAM TITANS (See Deathstroke & New Titans Annual #7)
DC Comics: Sept, 1992 - No. 24, Sept, 1994 ($1.75/$1.95)
1-Five different #1s exist w/origins in 1st half & the same 2nd story in each: Kilowat, Mirage, Nightrider w/Netzer/Pérez-a, Redwing, & Terra w/part Pérez-p; Total Chaos Pt. 3 4.00
2-24: 2-Total Chaos Pt 6. 11-Metallik app. 24-Zero Hour x-over 3.00
Annual 1,2 ('93, '94, $3.50, 68 pgs.): 2-Elseworlds tory 4.00

TEAM X/TEAM 7
Marvel Comics: Nov, 1996 ($4.95, one-shot)
1 5.00

TEAM X 2000
Marvel Comics: Feb, 1999 ($3.50, one-shot)
1-Kevin Lau-a; Bishop vs. Shi'ar Empire 4.00

TEAM YANKEE
First Comics: Jan, 1989 - No. 6, Feb, 1989 ($1.95, weekly limited series)
1-6 3.00

TEAM YOUNGBLOOD (Also see Youngblood)
Image Comics (Extreme Studios): Sept, 1993 - No. 22, Sept, 1995 ($1.95/$2.50)
1-22: 1-9-Liefeld scripts in all: 1,2,4-6,8-Thibert-c(i). 1-1st app. Dutch & Masada. 3-Spawn cameo. 5-1st app. Lynx. 7,8-Coupons 1 & 4 for Extreme Prejudice #0; Black and White Pt. 4 & 8 by Thibert. 8-Coupon #4 for E. P. #0. 9-Liefeld wraparound-c &(p)/a(p) on Pt. I. 16,17-Bagged w/trading card. 21-Angela & Glory-app. 3.00

TEAM ZERO
DC Comics (WildStorm Productions): Feb, 2006 - No. 6, Jul, 2006 ($2.99, limited series)
1-6-Dixon-s/Mahnke-a 3.00
TPB (2008, $17.99) r/#1-6 18.00

TECH JACKET
Image Comics: Nov, 2002 - No. 6, Apr, 2003 ($2.95)

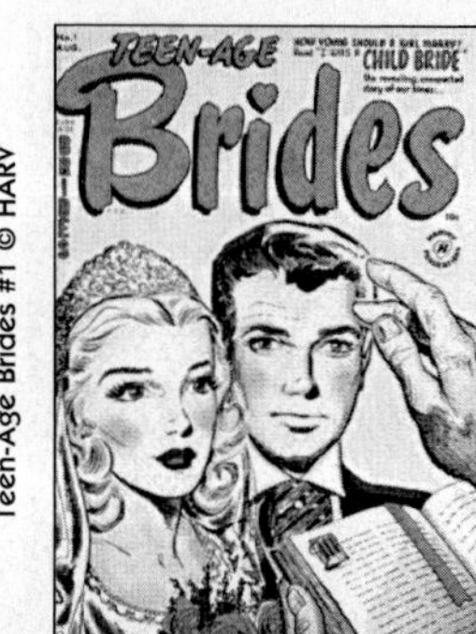

Teen-Age Brides #1 © HARV

Teen-Age Diary Secrets #12 © STJ

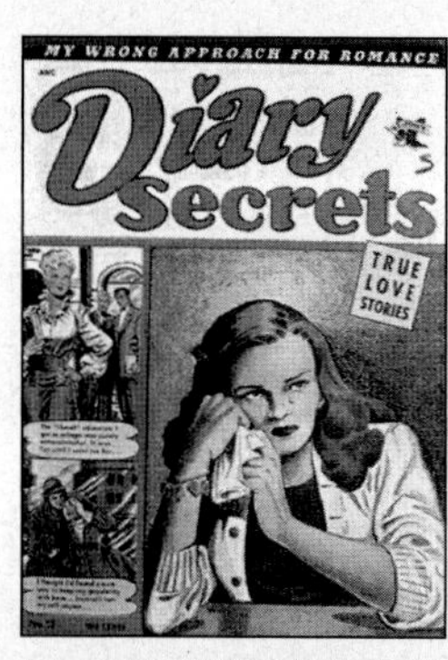

Teenage Mutant Ninja Turtles #22 © Mirage

GD VG FN VF VF/NM NM-
2.0 4.0 6.0 8.0 9.0 9.2

1-6-Kirkman-s/Su-a 3.00
Vol. 1: Lost and Found TPB (7/03, $12.95, 7-3/4" x 5-1/4") B&W r/#1-6; Valentino intro. 13.00

TECH JACKET (2nd series)
Image Comics: Jul, 2014 - No. 12, Dec, 2015 ($2.99)

1-12-Keatinge-s/Randolph-a 3.00

TEDDY ROOSEVELT & HIS ROUGH RIDERS (See Real Heroes #1)
Avon Periodicals: 1950

1-Kinstler-c; Palais-a; Flag-c 20 40 60 117 189 260

TEDDY ROOSEVELT ROUGH RIDER (See Battlefield #22 & Classics Illustrated Special Issue)

TED MCKEEVER'S METROPOL (See Transit)
Marvel Comics (Epic Comics): Mar, 1991 - No. 12, Mar, 1992 ($2.95, limited series)

V1#1-12: Ted McKeever-c/a/scripts 4.00

TED MCKEEVER'S METROPOL A.D.
Marvel Comics (Epic Comics): Oct, 1992 - No. 3, Dec, 1992 ($3.50, limited series)

V2#1-3: Ted McKeever-c/a/scripts 4.00

TEENA
Magazine Enterprises/Standard Comics No. 20 on: No. 11, 1948 - No. 15, 1948; No. 20, Aug, 1949 - No. 22, Oct, 1950

A-1 #11-Teen-age; Ogden Whitney-c 14 28 42 82 121 160
A-1 #12, 15 12 24 36 69 97 125
20-22 (Standard) 10 20 30 56 76 95

TEEN-AGE BRIDES (True Bride's Experiences #8 on)
Harvey/Home Comics: Aug, 1953 - No. 7, Aug, 1954

1-Powell-a 11 22 33 62 86 110
2-Powell-a 8 16 24 44 57 70
3-7: 3,6-Powell-a 8 16 24 40 50 60

TEEN-AGE CONFESSIONS (See Teen Confessions)

TEEN-AGE CONFIDENTIAL CONFESSIONS
Charlton Comics: July, 1960 - No. 22, 1964

1 4 8 12 23 37 50
2-10 3 6 9 16 23 30
11-22 2 4 6 13 18 22

TEEN-AGE DIARY SECRETS (Formerly Blue Ribbon Comics; becomes Diary Secrets #10 on)
St. John Publishing Co.: No. 4, 9/49; nn (#5), 9/49 - No. 7, 11/49; No. 8, 2/50; No. 9, 8/50

4(9/49)-Oversized; part mag., part comic 54 108 162 343 574 825
nn(#5)(no indicia)-Oversized, all comics; contains sty "I Gave Boys the Green Light."
54 108 162 343 574 825
6-(Reg. size) pre-fame Marilyn Monroe photo-c; Baker-a(2-3)
61 122 183 390 670 950
7-Digest size (Pocket Comics); Baker-a(5); same contents as #9; diff.-c
81 162 243 518 884 1250
8-(Reg. size) Photo-c; Baker-a(2-3) 58 116 174 371 636 900
9-Digest size (Pocket Comics); Baker-a(5); same contents as #7; diff.-c by Baker
135 270 405 864 1482 2100

TEEN-AGE DOPE SLAVES (See Harvey Comics Library #1)

TEENAGE HOTRODDERS (Top Eliminator #25 on; see Blue Bird)
Charlton Comics: Apr, 1963 - No. 24, July, 1967

1 5 10 15 34 60 85
2-10 3 6 9 19 30 40
11-24 3 6 9 16 24 32

TEEN-AGE LOVE (See Fox Giants)

TEEN-AGE LOVE (Formerly Intimate)
Charlton Comics: V2#4, July, 1958 - No. 96, Dec, 1973

V2#4 4 8 12 27 44 60
5-9 3 6 9 19 30 40
10(9/59)-20 3 6 9 16 24 32
21-35 3 6 9 15 22 28
36-70 2 4 6 13 18 22
71-79,81,82,85-87,90-96: 61&62-Jonnie Love begins (origin)
2 4 6 10 14 18
80,84,88-David Cassidy pin-ups 3 6 9 14 19 24
83,89: 83-Bobby Sherman pin-up. 89-Danny Bonaduce pin-up
2 4 6 13 18 22

TEENAGE MUTANT NINJA TURTLES (Also see Anything Goes, Donatello, First Comics Graphic Novel, Gobbledygook, Grimjack #26, Leonardo, Michaelangelo, Raphael & Tales Of The...)
Mirage Studios: 1984 - No. 62, Aug, 1993 ($1.50/$1.75, B&W; all 44-52 pgs.)

1-1st printing (3000 copies)-Origin and 1st app. of the Turtles and Splinter. Only printing to have ad for Gobbledygook #1 & 2; Shredder app. (#1-4: 7-1/2x11")
575 1150 1725 2875 4038 5200
1-2nd printing (6/84)(6,000 copies) 24 48 72 168 372 575
1-3rd printing (2/85)(36,000 copies) 12 24 36 79 170 260
1-4th printing, new-c (50,000 copies) 3 6 9 19 30 40
1-5th printing, new-c (8/88-c, 11/88 inside) 3 6 9 17 26 35
1-Counterfeit. **Note**: Most counterfeit copies have a half inch wide white streak or scratch marks across the center of back cover. Black part of cover is a bluish black instead of a deep black. Inside paper is very white & inside cover is bright white (no value)
2-1st printing (1984; 15,000 copies) 12 24 36 79 170 260
2-2nd printing 3 6 9 21 33 45
2-3rd printing; new Corben-c/a (2/85) 2 4 6 9 12 15
2-Counterfeit with glossy cover stock (no value).
3-1st printing (1985, 44 pgs.) 9 18 27 57 111 165
3-Variant, 500 copies, cover printed at different plant, has 'Laird's Photo' in white rather than light blue 33 64 96 230 515 800
3-2nd printing; contains new back-up story 2 4 6 9 12 15
4-1st printing (1985, 44 pgs.) 6 12 18 40 73 105
4-2nd printing (5/87) all have manufacturing error 9 18 27 60 120 180
5-Fugitoid begins, ends #7; 1st full color-c (1985) 4 8 12 28 47 65
5-2nd printing (11/87) 2 4 6 9 12 15
6-1st printing (1986) 3 6 9 17 26 35
6-2nd printing (4/88-c, 5/88 inside) 6.00
7-4 pg. Eastman/Corben color insert; 1st color TMNT (1986, $1.75-c); Bade Biker back-up story 2 4 6 13 18 22
7-2nd printing (1/89) w/o color insert 6.00
8-Cerebus-c/story with Dave Sim-a (1986) 2 4 6 11 16 20
9,10: 9-(9/86)-Rip In Time by Corben 2 4 6 8 10 12
11-15 1 3 4 6 8 10
16-18: 18-Mark Bode'-a 1 2 3 5 6 8
18-2nd printing ($2.25, color, 44 pgs.)-New-c 5.00
19-34: 19-Begin $1.75-c. 24-26-Veitch-c/a. 6.00
32-2nd printing ($2.75, 52 pgs., full color) 5.00
35-49,51: 35-Begin $2.00-c. 5.00
50-Features pin-ups by Larsen, McFarlane, Simonson, etc.
1 2 3 5 6 8
52-62: 52-Begin $2.25-c 5.00
nn (1990, $5.95, B&W)-Movie adaptation 6.00
Book 1,2($1.50, B&W): 2-Corben-c 6.00
...Christmas Special 1 (12/90, $1.75, B&W, 52 pgs.)-Cover title: Michaelangelo Christmas Special; r/Michaelangelo one-shot plus new Raphael story
1 3 4 6 8 10
... Color Special (11/09, $3.25) full color reprint of #1
1 3 4 6 8 10
...Special: The Haunted Pizza nn (10/92, $2.25, B&W, 32 pgs.) Howarth-s/a 6.00
...Special (The Maltese Turtle) nn (1/93, $2.95, color, 44 pgs.) 6.00
...Special: "Times" Pipeline nn (9/92, $2.95, color, 44 pgs.)-Mark Bode-c/a 6.00
Hardcover ($100)-r/#1-10 plus one-shots w/dust jackets - limited to 1000 w/letter of authenticity 150.00
Softcover ($40)-r/#1-10 45.00

TEENAGE MUTANT NINJA TURTLES
Mirage Studios: V2#1, Oct, 1993 - V2#13, Oct, 1995 ($2.75)

V2#1-Wraparound-c 2 4 6 8 10 12
2-13 4.00

TEENAGE MUTANT NINJA TURTLES
Image Comics (Highbrow Ent.): June, 1996 - No. 23, Oct, 1999 ($1.95-$2.95)

1-Erik Larsen-c(i) 2 4 6 8 10 12
2-23: 2-8-Erik Larsen-c(i) on all. 10-Savage Dragon-c/app. 4.00

TEENAGE MUTANT NINJA TURTLES
Mirage Publishing: V4#1, Dec, 2001 - No. 28 ($2.95, B&W)

V4#1-9,11-28-Laird-s/a(i)/Lawson-a(p). 3.00
10-($3.95) Splinter dies 4.00

TEENAGE MUTANT NINJA TURTLES
Dreamwave Productions: June 2003 - No. 7 ($2.95, color)

1-7-Animated style; Peter David-s/Lesean-a 3.00

TEENAGE MUTANT NINJA TURTLES
IDW Publishing: Aug, 2011 - Present ($3.99)

1-Kevin Eastman-s & layouts; four covers by Duncan (each turtle); origin flashback
2 4 6 11 16 20

Teenage Mutant Ninja Turtles (2011 series) #60 © Viacom

Teenage Mutant Ninja Turtles Universe #1 © Viacom

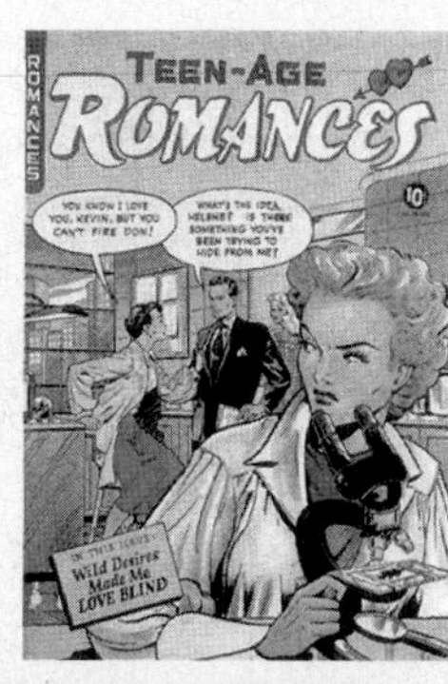

Teen-Age Romances #12 © STJ

	GD 2.0	VG 4.0	FN 6.0	VF 8.0	VF/NM 9.0	NM- 9.2
1-Variant-c by Eastman	3	6	9	17	26	35
1-Halloween Edition (10/12, no cover price) Reprints #1						4.00
2-43,45-49,51-74,76-79-Multiple variant covers on each						4.00
44-Donatello killed						10.00
50-(9/15, $7.99) Multiple variant covers; Turtles & Splinter vs. Shredder; Santolouco-a						8.00
75-(10/17, $7.99) Multiple variant covers; Trial of Krang pt. 3; Santolouco-a						8.00
Annual 2012 (10/12, $8.99) Eastman-s/a; wraparound-c						9.00
Annual 2014 (8/14, $7.99) Eastman-s/a; Renet app.						8.00
...: Deviations (3/16, $4.99) What If... the Turtles joined Shredder; Waltz-s/Howard-a						5.00
... FCBD (3/15, giveaway) Santolouco-a						3.00
... Funko Universe One Shot (5/17, $4.99) Character rendered in Funko Pop figure style						5.00
Greatest Hits - Teenage Mutant Ninja Turtles #1 (2/16, $1.00) r/#1						3.00
... Kevin Eastman Cover Gallery (12/13, $3.99) Collection of recent Eastman covers						4.00
... Microseries 1-8 (11/11 - No. 8, 9/12) 1-Raphael. 2-Michelangelo. 3-Donatello. 4-Leonardo. 5-Splinter. 6-Casey Jones. 7-April. 8-Fugitoid						4.00
...100 Page Spectacular (4/12, $7.99) r/TMNT Adventures (1988) mini-series #1-3						8.00
... Samurai Special (7/17, no price, B&W) Stan Sakai-s/a; reprints Usagi Yojimbo x-overs						3.00
... 30th Anniversary Special (5/14, $7.99) History and reprints from all eras; pin-ups by various; multiple covers						8.00
.../ Usagi Yojimbo (7/17, $7.99) Stan Sakai-s/a; multiple covers						8.00
... Villains Microseries 1-8 (4/13 - No. 8, 11/13, $3.99) 1-Krang. 2-Baxter. 8-Shredder						4.00

TEENAGE MUTANT NINJA TURTLES (Adventures)
Archie Publications: Jan, 1996 - No. 3, Mar, 1996 ($1.50, limited series)

	GD	VG	FN	VF	VF/NM	NM-
1	2	4	6	11	16	20
2,3						5.00

TEENAGE MUTANT NINJA TURTLES ADVENTURES (TV)
Archie Comics: Oct, 1988 - No. 3, Dec, 1988; Mar, 1989 - No. 72, Oct, 1995 ($1.00-$1.75)

	GD	VG	FN	VF	VF/NM	NM-
1-Adapts TV cartoon; not by Eastman/Laird	3	6	9	15	22	28
2,3 (Mini-series)	1	2	3	5	6	8
1 (2nd on-going series)	2	4	6	8	10	12
1-2nd printing						5.00
2-18,20-30: 5-Begins original stories not based on TV. 14-Simpson-a(p). 22-Colan-c/a						5.00
2-11: 2nd printings						4.00
19,20,51-54: 19-1st Mighty Mutanimals (also in #20, 51-54	2	4	6	9	12	15
31-49						5.00
50-Poster by Eastman/Laird	1	2	3	5	7	9
55-60	1	2	3	4	5	7
61-70: 62-w/poster	2	3	4	6	8	10
71	2	4	6	8	10	12
72- Last issue	2	4	6	9	13	16
nn (1990, $2.50)-Movie adaptation						5.00
nn (Spring, 1991, $2.50, 68 pgs.)-(Meet Archie)						5.00
nn (Sum, 1991, $2.50, 68 pgs.)-(Movie II)-Adapts movie sequel						5.00
...Meet the Conservation Corps 1 (1992, $2.50, 68 pgs.)						4.00
...III The Movie: The Turtles are Back...In Time (1993, $2.50, 68 pgs.)						5.00
Special 1,4,5 (Sum/92, Spr/93, Sum/93, 68 pgs.)-1-Bill Wray-c						4.00
Giant Size Special 6 (Fall/93, $1.95, 52 pgs.)						4.00
Special 7-10 (Win/93-Fall//94, 52 pgs.): 9-Jeff Smith-c						4.00

NOTE: *There are 2nd printings of #1-11 w/B&W inside covers. Originals are color.*

TEENAGE MUTANT NINJA TURTLES AMAZING ADVENTURES
IDW Publishing: Aug, 2015 - No. 14, Sept, 2016 ($3.99)

1-14-All-ages animated-style stories; two covers						4.00
... Carmelo Anthony Special One-Shot (5/16, $5.99) Turtles meet the NBA player						6.00

TEENAGE MUTANT NINJA TURTLES AMAZING ADVENTURES: ROBOTANIMALS
IDW Publishing: Jun, 2017 - No. 3, Sept, 2017 ($3.99, limited series)

1-3-All-ages animated-style stories; three covers on each; Goellner-s/Thomas-a 4.00

TEENAGE MUTANT NINJA TURTLES BEBOP & ROCKSTEADY DESTROY EVERYTHING
IDW Publishing: Jun, 2016 - No. 5, Jun, 2016 ($3.99, weekly limited series)

1-5-Dustin Weaver-s; art by various; interlocking covers 4.00

TEENAGE MUTANT NINJA TURTLES: CASEY AND APRIL
IDW Publishing: Jun, 2015 - No. 4, Sept, 2015 ($3.99, limited series)

1-4-Mariko Tamaki-s/Irene Koh-a; two covers on each 4.00

TEENAGE MUTANT NINJA TURTLES CLASSICS DIGEST (TV)
Archie Comics: Aug, 1993 - No. 8, Mar, 1995? ($1.75)

1-8: Reprints TMNT Advs. 4.00

TEENAGE MUTANT NINJA TURTLES COLOR CLASSICS
IDW Publishing: May, 2012 - Present ($3.99)

1-11-Colored reprints of the original 1984 B&W series 4.00

	GD 2.0	VG 4.0	FN 6.0	VF 8.0	VF/NM 9.0	NM- 9.2
...: Donatello Micro-Series One-Shot (3/13, $3.99) r/Donatello, TMNT #1 (1986)						4.00
...: Leonardo Micro-Series One-Shot (4/13, $3.99) r/Leonardo, TMNT #1						4.00
...: Michaelangelo Micro-Series One-Shot (12/12, $3.99) r/Michaelangelo, TMNT #1						4.00
...: Raphael Micro-Series One-Shot (8/12, $3.99) r/Raphael #1 (1985)						4.00
... Volume 2 (11/13 - No. 7, 5/14, $3.99) 1-7: 1-Reprints TMNT #12 (1987)						4.00
... Volume 3 (1/15 - Present, $3.99) 1-14: 1-Reprints TMNT #48 (1992)						4.00

TEENAGE MUTANT NINJA TURTLES: DIMENSION X
IDW Publishing: Aug, 2017 - No. 5, Aug, 2017 ($3.99, weekly limited series)

1-5-Takes place during the Trial of Krang (between TMNT #73 & 74); multiple-c on each 4.00

TEENAGE MUTANT NINJA TURTLES/FLAMING CARROT CROSSOVER
Mirage Publishing: Nov, 1993 - No. 4, Feb, 1994 ($2.75, limited series)

1-4: Bob Burden story 4.00

TEENAGE MUTANT NINJA TURTLES / GHOSTBUSTERS
IDW Publishing: Oct, 2014 - No. 4, Jan, 2015 ($3.99, limited series)

1-4-Burnham & Waltz-s/Schoening-a; multiple covers on each						4.00
... #1 Director's Cut (5/15, $5.99) r/#1 with creator commentary; bonus script pages						6.00

TEENAGE MUTANT NINJA TURTLES / GHOSTBUSTERS 2
IDW Publishing: Nov, 2017 - No. 5, Nov, 2017 ($3.99, limited series)

1-5-Burnham & Waltz-s/Schoening-a; multiple covers on each 4.00

TEENAGE MUTANT NINJA TURTLES: MUTANIMALS
IDW Publishing: Feb, 2015 - No. 4, May, 2015 ($3.99, limited series)

1-4-Paul Allor-s/Andy Kuhn-a; two covers 4.00

TEENAGE MUTANT NINJA TURTLES NEW ANIMATED ADVENTURES
IDW Publishing: Jul, 2013 - No. 24, Jun, 2015 ($3.99)

1-24-Multiple covers on each						4.00
... Free Comic Book Day (5/13) Burnham-s/Brizuela-a						3.00

TEENAGE MUTANT NINJA TURTLES PRESENTS: APRIL O'NEIL
Archie Comics: Mar, 1993 - No. 3, June, 1993 ($1.25, limited series)

1-3 4.00

TEENAGE MUTANT NINJA TURTLES PRESENTS: DONATELLO AND LEATHERHEAD
Archie Comics: July, 1993 - No. 3, Sept, 1993 ($1.25, limited series)

1-3 4.00

TEENAGE MUTANT NINJA TURTLES PRESENTS: MERDUDE
Archie Comics: Oct, 1993 - No. 3, Dec, 1993 ($1.25, limited series)

1-3-See Mighty Mutanimals #7 for 1st app. Merdude 4.00

TEENAGE MUTANT NINJA TURTLES/SAVAGE DRAGON CROSSOVER
Mirage Studios: Aug, 1995 ($2.75, one-shot)

1 4.00

TEENAGE MUTANT NINJA TURTLES: THE SECRET HISTORY OF THE FOOT CLAN
IDW Publishing: Dec, 2012 - No. 4, Mar, 2013 ($3.99, limited series)

1-4-Santolouco-a/Santolouco & Burnham-s 4.00

TEENAGE MUTANT NINJA TURTLES: TURTLES IN TIME
IDW Publishing: Jun, 2014 - No. 4, Sept, 2014 ($3.99, limited series)

1-4: 1-Paul Allor-s/Ross Campbell-a; Renet app.; three covers. 2-4-Two covers each 4.00

TEENAGE MUTANT NINJA TURTLES UNIVERSE
IDW Publishing: Aug, 2016 - Present ($4.99)

1-19: 1-Allor-s/Couceiro-a; Eastman & Sienkiewicz-a; multiple covers on each 4.00

TEENAGE MUTANT NINJA TURTLES UTROM EMPIRE
IDW Publishing: Jan, 2014 - No. 3, Mar, 2014 ($3.99, limited series)

1-3-Paul Allor-s/Andy Kuhn-a; two covers on each 4.00

TEEN-AGE ROMANCE (Formerly My Own Romance)
Marvel Comics (ZPC): No. 77, Sept, 1960 - No. 86, Mar, 1962

	GD	VG	FN	VF	VF/NM	NM-
77-83	6	12	18	40	73	105
84-86-Kirby-c. 84-Kirby-a(2 pgs.). 85,86-(3 pgs.)	7	14	21	44	82	120

TEEN-AGE ROMANCES
St. John Publ. Co. (Approved Comics): Jan, 1949 - No. 45, Dec, 1955 (#3,7,10-18,21 are 1/2 inch taller than other issues)

	GD	VG	FN	VF	VF/NM	NM-
1-Baker-c/a(1)	110	220	330	704	1202	1700
2,3: 2-Baker-c/a. 3-Baker-c/a(3)	68	136	204	435	743	1050
4,5,7,8-Photo-c; Baker-a(2-3) each	41	82	123	256	428	600
6-Photo-c; part magazine; Baker-a (10/49)	43	86	129	271	461	650
9-Baker-c/a; Kubert-a	84	168	252	538	919	1300
10-12,20-Baker-c/a(2-3) each	74	148	222	470	810	1150
13-19,21,22-Complete issues by Baker	81	162	243	518	884	1250

Teen-Age Temptations #9 © STJ

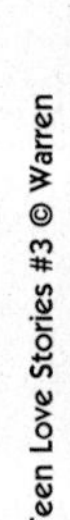
Teen Love Stories #3 © Warren

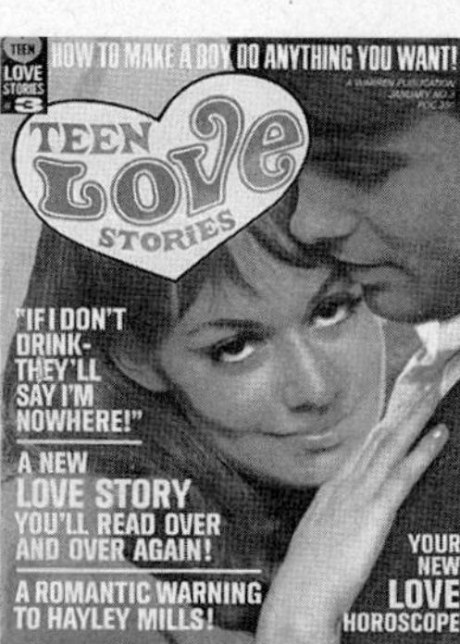

Teen Titans #9 © DC

	GD 2.0	VG 4.0	FN 6.0	VF 8.0	VF/NM 9.0	NM- 9.2
23-25-Baker-c/a(2-3) each	68	136	204	435	743	1050
26,27,33,34,36,37,39,40,42: Baker-c/a. 33,40-Signed story by Estrada. 42-r/Cinderella Love #9; last pre-code (3/55)	60	120	180	381	653	925
28-30-No Baker-a	18	36	54	103	162	220
31,32-Baker-c. 31-Estrada-s	54	108	162	343	574	825
35-Baker-c/a (16 pgs.)	60	120	180	381	653	925
38-Baker-c/a; suggestive-c	103	206	309	659	1130	1600
41-Baker-c; Infantino-a(r); all stories are Ziff-Davis-r	54	108	162	343	574	825
43-45-Baker-c/a	57	114	171	362	619	875

TEEN-AGE TALK
I.W. Enterprises: 1964

Reprint #1	2	4	6	10	14	18
Reprint #5,8,9: 5-r/Hector #? 9-Punch Comics #?; L.B. Cole-c reprint from School Day Romances #1	2	4	6	9	13	16

TEEN-AGE TEMPTATIONS (Going Steady #10 on)(See True Love Pictorial)
St. John Publishing Co.: Oct, 1952 - No. 9, Aug, 1954

1-Baker-c/a; has story "Reform School Girl" by Estrada	142	284	426	909	1555	2200
2,4-Baker-c	84	168	252	538	919	1300
3,5-7,9-Baker-c/a	90	180	270	576	988	1400
8-Teenagers smoke reefer; Baker-c/a	103	206	309	659	1130	1600

NOTE: *Estrada a-1, 3-5.*

TEEN BEAM (Formerly Teen Beat #1)
National Periodical Publications: No. 2, Jan-Feb, 1968

2-Superman cameo; Herman's Hermits, Yardbirds, Simon & Garfunkel, Lovin Spoonful, Young Rascals app.; Orlando, Drucker-a(r); Monkees photo-c;	15	30	45	105	233	360

TEEN BEAT (Becomes Teen Beam #2)
National Periodical Publications: Nov-Dec, 1967

1-Photos & text only; Monkees photo-c; Beatles, Herman's Hermits, Animals, Supremes, Byrds app.	17	34	51	117	259	400

TEEN COMICS (Formerly All Teen; Journey Into Unknown Worlds #36 on)
Marvel Comics (WFP): No. 21, Apr, 1947 - No. 35, May, 1950

21-Kurtzman's "Hey Look"; Patsy Walker, Cindy (1st app.?), Georgie, Margie app.; Syd Shores-a begins, end #23	31	62	93	182	296	410
22,23,25,27,29,31-35: 22-(6/47)-Becomes Hedy Devine #22 (8/47) on?	21	42	63	126	206	285
24,26,28,30-Kurtzman's "Hey Look". 30-Has anti-Wertham editorial	22	44	66	130	213	295

TEEN CONFESSIONS
Charlton Comics: Aug, 1959 - No. 97, Nov, 1976

1	7	14	21	48	89	130
2	4	8	12	27	44	60
3-10	3	6	9	21	33	45
11-30	3	6	9	17	26	35
31-Beatles-c	10	20	30	68	144	220
32-36,38-55	3	6	9	15	21	26
37 (1/66)-Beatles Fan Club story; Beatles-c	10	20	30	66	138	210
56-58,60-76,78-97: 89,90-Newton-c	2	4	6	10	14	18
59-Kaluta's 1st pro work? (12/69)	3	6	9	19	30	40
77-Partridge Family poster	3	6	9	14	20	24

TEEN DOG
BOOM! Entertainment (BOOM! Box): Sept, 2014 - No. 8, Apr, 2015 ($3.99)

1-8-Jake Lawrence-s/a/c; multiple covers on #1-4 — 4.00

TEENIE WEENIES, THE (America's Favorite Kiddie Comic)
Ziff-Davis Publishing Co.: No. 10, 1950 - No. 11, Apr-May, 1951 (Newspaper reprints)

10,11-Painted-c	20	40	60	114	182	250

TEEN-IN (Tippy Teen)
Tower Comics: Summer, 1968 - No. 4, Fall, 1969

nn(#1, Summer, 1968)(25¢) Has 3 full pg. B&W photos of Sonny & Cher, Donovan and Herman's Hermits; interviews and photos of Eric Clapton, Jim Morrison and others	9	18	27	62	126	190
nn(#2, Spring, 1969),3,4	6	12	18	37	66	95

TEEN LIFE (Formerly Young Life)
New Age/Quality Comics Group: No. 3, Winter, 1945 - No. 5, Fall, 1945 (Teenage magazine)

3-June Allyson photo on-c & story	14	28	42	80	115	150
4-Duke Ellington photo on-c & story	12	24	36	69	97	125
5-Van Johnson, Woody Herman & Jackie Robinson articles; Van Johnson & Woody Herman photos on-c	14	28	42	80	115	150

TEEN LOVE STORIES (Magazine)
Warren Publ. Co.: Sept, 1969 - No. 3, Jan, 1970 (68 pgs., photo covers, B&W)

1-Photos & articles plus 36-42 pgs. new comic stories in all; Frazetta-a	8	16	24	51	96	140
2,3: 2-Anti-marijuana story	5	10	15	34	60	85

TEEN ROMANCES
Super Comics: 1964

10,11,15-17-Reprints	2	4	6	8	11	14

TEEN SECRET DIARY (Nurse Betsy Crane #12 on)
Charlton Comics: Oct, 1959 - No. 11, June, 1961

1	5	10	15	30	50	70
2	3	6	9	20	31	42
3-11	3	6	9	17	26	35

TEEN TALK (See Teen)

TEEN TITANS (See Brave & the Bold #54,60, DC Super-Stars #1, Marvel & DC Present, New Teen Titans, New Titans, Official…Index and Showcase #59)
National Periodical Publ./DC Comics: 1-2/66 - No. 43, 1-2/73; No. 44, 11/76 - No. 53, 2/78

1-(1-2/66)-Titans join Peace Corps; Batman, Flash, Aquaman, Wonder Woman cameos	38	76	114	281	628	975
2	14	28	42	96	211	325
3-5: 4-Speedy app.	9	18	27	62	126	190
6-10: 6-Doom Patrol app.; Beast Boy x-over; readers polled on him joining Titans	7	14	21	49	92	135
11-18: 11-Speedy app. 13-X-Mas-c	6	12	18	40	73	105
19-Wood-i; Speedy begins as regular	6	12	18	41	76	110
20-22: All Neal Adams-a. 21-Hawk & Dove app.; last 12¢ issue. 22-Origin Wonder Girl	8	16	24	56	108	160
23-Wonder Girl dons new costume	5	10	15	34	60	85
24-31: 25-Flash, Aquaman, Batman, Green Arrow, Green Lantern, Superman, & Hawk & Dove guests; 1st app. Lilith who joins T.T. West in #50. 29-Hawk & Dove & Ocean Master app. 30-Aquagirl app. 31-Hawk & Dove app.	5	10	15	30	50	70
32-34,40-43: 34-Last 15¢ issue	3	6	9	19	30	40
35-39-(52 pgs.): 36,37-Superboy-r. 38-Green Arrow/Speedy-r; Aquaman/Aqualad story. 39-Hawk & Dove-r.	4	8	12	22	35	48
44-(11/76) Dr. Light app.; Mal becomes the Guardian	3	6	9	14	20	26
45,47,49,51,52	3	6	9	14	19	24
46,48: 46-Joker's daughter begins (see Batman Family). 48-Intro Bumblebee; Joker's daughter becomes Harlequin	3	6	9	21	33	45
50-1st revival original Bat-Girl; intro. Teen Titans West (Bat-Girl, Golden Eagle, Hawk & Dove, Lilith and Beast Boy)	3	6	9	21	33	45
53-Origin retold	3	6	9	15	22	28

... Lost Annual 1 (3/08, $4.99) Sixties-era story by Bob Haney; Jay Stephens & Mike Allred-a; President Kennedy app.; Nick Cardy-c and sketch pages — 5.00

NOTE: *Aparo a-36.* ***Buckler*** *c-46-53.* ***Cardy*** *a(p)-1-5, 7, 13, 14, 16, 17, 25, 26, 28-30, 32, c-1-43.* ***Kane*** *a(p)-19, 22-24, 39r.* ***Tuska*** *a(p)-31, 36, 38, 39. DC Super-Stars #1 (3/76) was released before #44.*

TEEN TITANS (Also see Titans Beat in the Promotional Comics section)
DC Comics: Oct, 1996 - No. 24, Sept, 1998 ($1.95)

1-Dan Jurgens-c/a(p)/scripts & George Pérez-c/a(i) begin; Atom forms new team (Risk, Argent, Prysm, & Joto); 1st app. Loren Jupiter & Omen; no indicia. 1-3-Origin. — 4.00
2-24: 4,5-Robin, Nightwing, Supergirl, Capt. Marvel Jr. app. 12-"Then and Now" begins w/original Teen Titans-c/app. 15-Death of Joto. 17-Capt. Marvel Jr. and Fringe join. 19-Millennium Giants x-over. 23,24-Superman app. — 3.00
Annual 1 (1997, $3.95)-Pulp Heroes story — 4.00

TEEN TITANS (Also see Titans/Young Justice: Graduation Day)
DC Comics: Sept, 2003 - No. 100, Late Oct, 2011 ($2.50/$2.99/$3.99)

1-McKone-c/a;Johns-s — 5.00
1-Variant-c by Michael Turner — 6.00
1-2nd and 3rd printings — 3.00
2-Deathstroke app. — 5.00
2-2nd printing — 3.00
3-15: 4-Impulse becomes Kid Flash. 5-Raven returns. 6-JLA app. — 4.00
16-33: 16-Titans go to 31st Century; Legion and Fatal Five app. 17-19-Future Titans app. 21-23-Dr. Light. 24,25-Outsiders #24,25 x-over. 27,28-Liefeld-a. 32,33-Infinite Crisis — 3.00
34-49,51-71: 34-One Year Later begins; two covers by Daniel and Benes. 36-Begin $2.99-c. 40-Jericho returns. 42-Kid Devil origin; Snejbjerg-a. 43-Titans East. 48,49-Amazons Attack x-over; Supergirl app. 51-54-Future Titans app. — 3.00
50-($3.99) Art by Pérez (4 pgs.), McKone (6 pgs.), Nauck and Green; future Titans app. — 4.00
72-88: 72-Begin $3.99-c; Ravager back-up features. 77,78-Blackest Night. 83-87-Coven of Three back-up; Naifeh-a. 88-Nicola Scott-a begins — 4.00

Teen Titans (2011 series) #16 © DC

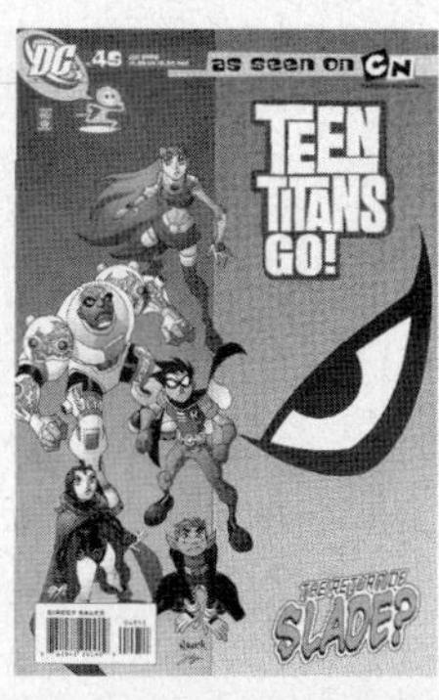

Teen Titans Go! #49 © DC

Tell It to the Marines #6 © TOBY

	GD 2.0	VG 4.0	FN 6.0	VF 8.0	VF/NM 9.0	NM- 9.2

89-99-($2.99) 89-Robin (Damian) joins. 93-Solstice app. 98 Superboy-Prime returns 3.00
100-($4.99) Nicola Scott-a; pin-ups by various 5.00
Annual 1 (4/06, $4.99) Infinite Crisis x-over; Benes-c 5.00
Annual 2009 (6/09, $4.99) Deathtrap x-over prelude; McKeever-s 5.00
... And Outsiders Secret Files and Origins 2005 (10/05, $4.99) Daniel-c 5.00
...: Cold Case (2/11, $4.99) Captain Cold and the Rogues app.; Sean Murphy-a 6.00
.../Legion Special (11/04, $3.50) (cont'd from #16) Reis-a; leads into 2005 Legion of Super-Heroes series; LSH preview by Waid & Kitson 4.00
#1/2 (Wizard mail offer) origin of Ravager; Reis-a 8.00
.../Outsiders Secret Files 2003 (12/03, $5.95) Reis & Jimenez-a; pin-ups by various 6.00
...: A Kid's Game TPB (2004, $9.95) r/#1-7; Turner-c from #1; McKone sketch pages 10.00
...: Beast Boys and Girls TPB (2005, $9.99) r/#13-15 and Beast Boy #1-4 10.00
...: Changing of the Guard TPB (2009, $14.99) r/#62-69 15.00
...: Child's Play TPB (2010, $14.99) r/#71-78 15.00
...: Deathtrap TPB (2009, $14.99) r/#70, Annual #1, Titans #12,13, Vigilante #4-6 15.00
...: Family Lost TPB (2004, $9.95) r/#8-12 & #1/2 10.00
...: Life and Death TPB (2006, $14.99) r/#29-33 and pages from Infinite Crisis x-over 15.00
...: On the Clock TPB (2008, $14.99) r/#55-61 15.00
.../ Outsiders: The Death and Return of Donna Troy (2006, $14.99) r/Titans/Young Justice: Graduation Day #1-3, Teen Titans/Outsiders Secret Files 2003 and DC Special: The Return of Donna Troy #1-4; cover gallery 15.00
.../ Outsiders: The Insiders (2006, $14.99) r/Teen Titans/ #24-26 & Outsiders #24,25,28 15.00
...: Ravager - Fresh Hell TPB (2010, $14.99) r/#71-76,79-82 & Faces of Evil: Deathstroke 15.00
... Spotlight: Cyborg TPB (2009, $19.99) r/DC Special: Cyborg #1-6 20.00
... Spotlight: Raven TPB (2008, $14.99) r/DC Special: Raven #1-5 15.00
...: The Future is Now (2005, $9.99) r/#15-23 & Teen Titans/Legion Special 10.00
...: The Hunt For Raven (2011, $17.99) r/#79-87 18.00
...: Titans Around the World TPB (2007, $14.99) r/#34-41 15.00
...: Titans of Tomorrow TPB (2008, $14.99) r/#50-54 15.00

TEEN TITANS (DC New 52)
DC Comics: Nov, 2011 - No. 30, Jun, 2014 ($2.99)

1-14,17-23: 1-Lobdell-s/Booth-a/c; Red Robin assembles a team; Kid Flash, Wonder Girl app. 5-Superboy app. 9-The Culling conclusion. 13,14-Wonder Girl origin; Garza-a 3.00
15,16-"Death of the Family" tie-in. 15-Die-cut Joker mask cover. 16-Red Hood app. 5.00
23.1, 23.2 (11/13, $2.99, regular covers) 3.00
23.1 (11/13, $3.99, 3-D cover) "Trigon #1" on cover; origin; Wolfman-s/Cafu-a 5.00
23.2 (11/13, $3.99, 3-D cover) "Deathstroke #1" on cover; flashback; Deathblow app. 1 2 3 5 6 8
24-29: 24-Leads into Annual #2. 25,26-Origin of Kid Flash 3.00
30-($3.99) Last issue; origin of Skitter; Kirkham-a 4.00
#0 (11/12, $2.99) Origin of Red Robin; Kirkham-a 3.00
Annual 1 (7/12, $4.99) The Culling x-over part 1; Legion Lost members app. 5.00
Annual 2 (12/13, $4.99) Future Teen Titans; Lobdell-s/Kitson-a 5.00
Annual 3 (7/14, $4.99) Follows #30; Harvest app. 5.00
... Earth One Volume One HC (2014, $22.99) Lemire-s/Dodson-a/c; new origin story 23.00

TEEN TITANS (DC New 52)
DC Comics: Sept, 2014 - No. 24, Nov, 2016 ($2.99)

1-24: 1-Pfeifer-s/Rocafort-a/c; Manchester Black app. 5-Hepburn-a; new Power Girl app. 15-Robin War tie-in; Professor Pyg app. 18,19-Wonder Woman app. 3.00
Annual 1 (6/15, $4.99) Superboy returns; Borges & St. Claire-a; March-c 5.00
Annual 2 (8/16, $4.99) Lobdell-s/Cory Smith-a/Jonboy Meyers-c; Sister Blood app. 5.00
...: Futures End 1 (11/14, $2.99, regular-c) Five years later; Andy Smith-a 3.00
...: Futures End 1 (11/14, $3.99, 3-D cover) 4.00

TEEN TITANS (DC Rebirth)
DC Comics: Nov, 2016 - Present ($2.99/$3.99)

1-6: 1-Percy-s/Meyers-a; Ra's al Ghul app. 3-6-Pham-a. 6-Intro. Aqualad (Jackson Hyde) 3.00
7-11,13-17-($3.99) 7-Aqualad joins; Black Manta cameo. 8-Lazarus Contact x-over; Titans & Deathstroke app. 9-11-Black Manta app. 15-Future adult Superboy (Conner), Wonder Girl (Cassie) and Kid Flash (Bart) app. 4.00
12-Dark Nights: Metal tie-in; 1st full app. The Batman Who Laughs, Harley Quinn app. 24.00
Annual 1 (7/17, $4.99) Conclusion of Lazarus Contact x-over; Titans & Deathstroke app. 5.00
...: Rebirth 1 (11/16, $2.99) Meyers-a; Robin, Raven, Starfire, Beast Boy, Kid Flash app. 3.00

TEEN TITANS GO! (Based on Cartoon Network series)
DC Comics: Jan, 2004 - No. 55, Jul, 2008 ($2.25)

1-12,14-55: 1,2-Nauck-a/Bullock-c/J. Torres-s. 8-Mad Mod app. 14-Speedy-c. 28-Doom Patrol app. 31-Nightwing app. 36-Wonder Girl. 38-Mad Mod app.; Clugston-a 3.00
1-(9/04, Free Comic Book Day giveaway) r/#1; 2 bound-in Wacky Packages stickers 4.00
13-($2.95) Bonus pages with Shazam! reprint 4.00
Jam Packed Action (2005, $7.99, digest) adaptations of two TV episodes 8.00
... Vol 1: Truth, Justice, Pizza! (2004, $6.95, digest-size) r/#1-5 7.00
... Vol 2: Heroes on Patrol (2005, $6.99, digest-size) r/#6-10 7.00
... Vol 3: Bring It On! (2005, $6.99, digest-size) r/#11-15 7.00
... Vol 4: Ready For Action! (2006, $6.99, digest-size) r/#16-20 7.00
... Vol 5: On The Move! (2006, $6.99, digest-size) r/#21-25 7.00
... Titans Together TPB (2007, $12.99) r/#26-32 13.00

TEEN TITANS GO! (Based on the 2013 Cartoon Network series)
DC Comics: Feb, 2014 - Present ($2.99)

1-26: 1-Fisch-s. 2-Brotherhood of Evil app. 4-HIVE Five app. 13-Aqualad app. 3.00
... FCBD Special Edition 1 (6/14, giveaway) r/#1 3.00
... FCBD Special Edition 1 (6/15, giveaway) flipbook with Scooby-Doo! Team Up 3.00

TEEN TITANS SPOTLIGHT
DC Comics: Aug, 1986 - No. 21, Apr, 1988

1-21: 7-Guice's 1st work at DC. 14-Nightwing; Batman app. 15-Austin-c(i). 18,19-Millennium x-over. 21-($1.00-c)-Original Teen Titans; Spiegle-a 4.00
*Note: **Guice** a-7p, 8p; c-7,8. **Orlando** c/a-11p. **Perez** c-1, 17i, 19. **Sienkiewicz** c-10*

TEEN TITANS YEAR ONE
DC Comics: Mar, 2008 - No. 6, Aug, 2008 ($2.99, limited series)

1-6-The original five form a team; Wolfram-s/Kerschl-a 3.00
TPB (2008, $14.99) r/#1-6; bonus pin-up 15.00

TEEN WOLF: BITE ME (Based on the MTV series)
Image Comics (Top Cow): Sept, 2011 - No. 3, Nov, 2011 ($3.99, limited series)

1-3: 1-Tischman-s/Mooney-a/c 4.00

TEEPEE TIM (...Heap Funny Indian Boy)(Formerly Ha Ha Comics)(Also see "Cookie")
American Comics Group: No. 100, Feb-Mar, 1955 - No. 102, June-July, 1955

	GD	VG	FN	VF	VF/NM	NM-
100-102	7	14	21	35	43	50

TEGRA JUNGLE EMPRESS (Zegra Jungle Empress #2 on)
Fox Feature Syndicate: August, 1948

	GD	VG	FN	VF	VF/NM	NM-
1-Blue Beetle, Rocket Kelly app.; used in **SOTI**, pg. 31	81	162	243	518	884	1250

TEK JANSEN (See Stephen Colbert's...)

TEKKEN: BLOOD FEUD (Based on the Bandai Namco video game)
Titan Comics: Jun, 2017 - No. 4, Sept, 2017 ($3.99, limited series)

1-4-Cavan Scott-s/Andie Tong-a; multiple covers on each 4.00

TEKNO COMIX HANDBOOK
Tekno Comix: May, 1996 ($3.95, one-shot)

1-Guide to the Tekno Universe 4.00

TEKNOPHAGE (See Neil Gaiman's...)

TEKNOPHAGE VERSUS ZEERUS
BIG Entertainment: July, 1996 ($3.25, one-shot)

1-Paul Jenkins script 3.25

TEKWORLD (William Shatner's... on-c only)
Epic Comics (Marvel): Sept, 1992 - Aug, 1994 ($1.75)

1-Based on Shatner's novel, TekWar, set in L.A. in the year 2120 4.00
2-24 3.00

TELARA CHRONICLES (Based on the videogame Rift: Planes of Telara)
DC Comics (WildStorm): Jan, 2010; Nov, 2010 - No. 4, Feb, 2011 ($3.99, limited series)

0-(1/10, free) Preview of series 3.00
1-4-Pop Mhan-a/Drew Johnson-c 4.00
TPB (2011, $17.99) r/#0-4; background info on Telara 18.00

TELEVISION (See TV)

TELEVISION COMICS (Early TV comic)
Standard Comics (Animated Cartoons): No. 5, Feb, 1950 - No. 8, Nov, 1950

	GD	VG	FN	VF	VF/NM	NM-
5-1st app. Willy Nilly	11	22	33	62	86	110
6-8: #6 on inside has #2 on cover	9	18	27	47	61	75

TELEVISION PUPPET SHOW (Early TV comic) (See Spotty the Pup)
Avon Periodicals: 1950 - No. 2, Nov, 1950

	GD	VG	FN	VF	VF/NM	NM-
1-1st app. Speedy Rabbit, Spotty The Pup	23	46	69	136	223	310
2	16	32	48	92	144	195

TELEVISION TEENS MOPSY (See TV Teens)

TELL IT TO THE MARINES
Toby Press Publications: Mar, 1952 - No. 15, July, 1955

	GD	VG	FN	VF	VF/NM	NM-
1-Lover O'Leary and His Liberty Belles (with pin-ups), ends #6; Spike & Bat begin, end #6	34	68	102	204	332	460
2-Madame Cobra-c/story	23	46	69	136	223	310
3-5	18	36	54	107	169	230
6-12,14,15: 7-9,14,15-Photo-c	15	30	45	84	127	170

Tellos #9 © Dezago & Wieringo

Ten Grand #7 © Studio JMS

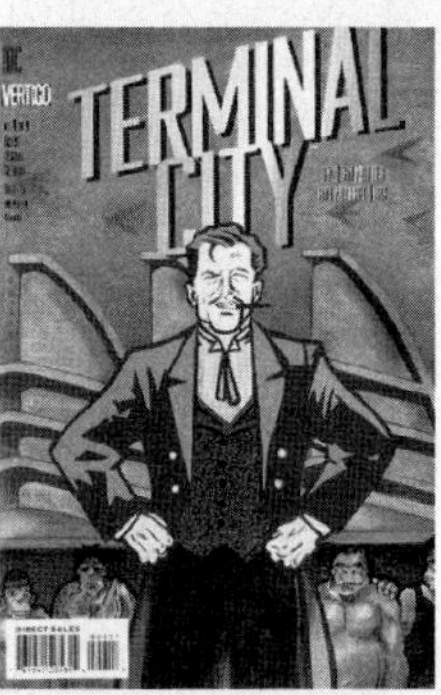

Terminal City #4 © Dean Motter

	GD 2.0	VG 4.0	FN 6.0	VF 8.0	VF/NM 9.0	NM- 9.2
13-John Wayne photo-c	21	42	63	124	202	280
I.W. Reprint #9-r/#1 above	2	4	6	11	16	20
Super Reprint #16(1964)-r/#4 above	2	4	6	8	11	14

TELLOS
Image Comics: May, 1999 - No. 10, Nov, 2000 ($2.50)

1-Dezago-s/Wieringo-a 3.00
1-Variant-c ($7.95) 8.00
2-10: 4-Four covers 3.00
...: Maiden Voyage (3/01, $5.95) Didier Crispeels-a/c 6.00
...: Sons & Moons (2002, $5.95) Nick Cardy-c 6.00
...: The Last Heist (2001, $5.95) Rousseau-a/c 6.00
Prelude ($5.00, AnotherUniverse.com) 5.00
Prologue ($3.95, Dynamic Forces) 4.00
...Collected Edition 1 (12/99, $8.95) r/#1-3 9.00
... Colossal, Vol. 1 TPB (2008, $17.99) r/#1-10, Prelude, Prologue, Scatterjack-s from Section Zero #1, cover gallery, Wieringo sketch pages; Dezago afterword 18.00
...: Kindred Spirits (2/01, $17.95) r/#6-10, Section Zero #1 (Scatterjack-s) 18.00
...: Reluctant Heroes (2/01, $17.95) r/#1-5, Prelude, Prologue; sketchbook 18.00

TELOS (See Convergence)
DC Comics: Dec, 2015 - No. 6, May, 2016 ($2.99)

1-6: 1,2-King-s/Pagulayan-a. 1-Brainiac app. 2-Arak, Son of Thunder and Validus app. 3-6-Hal Jordan Parallax app. 3.00

TEMPEST (See Aquaman, 3rd Series)
DC Comics: Nov, 1996 - No. 4, Feb, 1997 ($1.75, limited series)

1-4: Formerly Aqualad; Phil Jimenez-c/a/scripts in all 3.00

TEMPLARS (Assassin's Creed)
Titan Comics: Apr, 2016 - No. 9, Feb, 2017 ($3.99)

1-9-Black Cross; set in 1927; Van Lente-s/Calero-a 4.00

TEMPUS FUGITIVE
DC Comics: 1990 - No. 4, 1991 ($4.95, squarebound, 52 pgs.)

Book 1,2: Ken Steacy painted-c/a & scripts 6.00
Book 3,4-($5.95-c) 6.00
TPB (Dark Horse Comics, 1/97, $17.95) 18.00

TEN COMMANDMENTS (See Moses & the... and Classics Illustrated Special)

TENDER LOVE STORIES
Skywald Publ. Corp.: Feb, 1971 - No. 4, July, 1971 (Pre-code reprints and new stories)

	GD 2.0	VG 4.0	FN 6.0	VF 8.0	VF/NM 9.0	NM- 9.2
1 (All 25¢, 52 pgs.)	7	14	21	44	82	120
2-4	5	10	15	33	57	80

TENDER ROMANCE (Ideal Romance #3 on)
Key Publications (Gilmour Magazines): Dec, 1953 - No. 2, Feb, 1954

	GD 2.0	VG 4.0	FN 6.0	VF 8.0	VF/NM 9.0	NM- 9.2
1-Headlight & lingerie panels; B. Baily-c	28	56	84	165	270	375
2-Bernard Baily-c	15	30	45	88	137	185

TEN GRAND
Image Comics (Joe's Comics): May, 2013 - Present ($2.99)

1-12: 1-4-Straczynski-s/Templesmith-a. 1-Multiple variant covers. 2-Two covers 3.00

TENSE SUSPENSE
Fago Publications: Dec, 1958 - No. 2, Feb, 1959

	GD 2.0	VG 4.0	FN 6.0	VF 8.0	VF/NM 9.0	NM- 9.2
1	13	26	39	74	105	135
2	9	18	27	52	69	85

TEN STORY LOVE (Formerly a pulp magazine with same title)
Ace Periodicals: V29#3, June-July, 1951 - V36#5(#209), Sept, 1956 (#3-6: 52 pgs.)

	GD 2.0	VG 4.0	FN 6.0	VF 8.0	VF/NM 9.0	NM- 9.2
V29#3(#177)-Part comic, part text; painted-c	19	38	57	111	176	240
4-6(1/52)	12	24	36	69	97	125
V30#1(3/52)-6(1/53)	12	24	36	67	94	120
V31#1(2/53),V32#2(4/53)-6(12/53)	11	22	33	64	90	115
V33#1(1/54)-3(5#54, #195), V34#4(7/54, #196)-6(10/54, #198)	11	22	33	62	86	110
V35#1(12/54, #199)-3(4/55, #201)-Last precode	11	22	33	60	83	105
V35#4-6(9/55, #201-204), V36#1(11/55, #205)-3, 5(9/56, #209)	10	20	30	58	79	100
V36#4-L.B. Cole-a	12	24	36	67	94	120

TENTH, THE
Image Comics: Jan, 1997 - No. 4, June, 1997 ($2.50, limited series)

1-4-Tony Daniel-c/a, Beau Smith-s 5.00
Abuse of Humanity TPB ($10.95) r/#1-4 12.00
Abuse of Humanity TPB (10/98, $11.95) r/#1-4 & 0(8/97) 12.00

TENTH, THE
Image Comics: Sept, 1997 - No. 14, Jan, 1999 ($2.50)

0-(8/97, $5.00) American Ent. Ed. 6.00
1-Tony Daniel-c/a, Beau Smith-s 6.00
2-9: 3,7-Variant-c 4.00
10-14 3.00
...Configuration (8/98) Re-cap and pin-ups 3.00
...Collected Edition 1 ('98, $4.95, square-bound) r/#1,2 5.00
...Special (4/00, $2.95) r/#0 and Wizard #1/2 3.00
Wizard #1/2-Daniel-s/Steve Scott-a 10.00

TENTH, THE (Volume 3) (The Black Embrace)
Image Comics: Mar, 1999 - No. 4, June, 1999 ($2.95)

1-4-Daniel-c/a 3.00
TPB (1/00, $12.95) r/#1-4 13.00

TENTH, THE (Volume 4) (Evil's Child)
Image Comics: Sept, 1999 - No. 4, Mar, 2000 ($2.95, limited series)

1-4-Daniel-c/a 3.00

TENTH, THE (Darkk Dawn)
Image Comics: July, 2005 ($4.99, one-shot)

1-Kirkham-a/Bonny-s 5.00

TENTH, THE : RESURRECTED
Dark Horse Comics: July, 2001 - No. 4, Feb, 2002 ($2.99, limited series)

1-4: 1-Two covers; Daniel-s/c; Romano-a 3.00

10th MUSE
Image Comics (TidalWave Studios): Nov, 2000 - No. 9, Jan, 2002 ($2.95)

1-Character based on wrestling's Rena Mero; regular & photo covers 3.00
2-9: 2-Photo and 2 Lashley covers; flip book Dollz preview. 5-Savage Dragon app.; 2 covers by Lashley and Larsen. 6-Tellos x-over 3.00

TEN WHO DARED (Disney)
Dell Publishing Co.: No. 1178, Dec, 1960

	GD 2.0	VG 4.0	FN 6.0	VF 8.0	VF/NM 9.0	NM- 9.2
Four Color 1178-Movie, painted-c; cast member photo on back-c	7	14	21	46	86	125

TERMINAL CITY
DC Comics (Vertigo): July, 1996 - No. 9, Mar, 1997 ($2.50, limited series)

1-9: Dean Motter scripts, 7,8-Matt Wagner-c 3.00
TPB ('97, $19.95) r/series 20.00

TERMINAL CITY: AERIAL GRAFFITI
DC Comics (Vertigo): Nov, 1997 - No. 5, Mar, 1998 ($2.50, limited series)

1-5: Dean Motter-s/Lark-a/Chiarello-c 3.00

TERMINAL HERO
Dynamite Entertainment: 2014 - No. 6, 2015 ($2.99, limited series)

1-6-Milligan-s/Kowalski-a/Jae Lee-c 3.00

TERMINATOR, THE (See Robocop vs. ... & Rust #12 for 1st app.)
Now Comics: Sept, 1988 - No. 17, 1989 ($1.75, Baxter paper)

	GD 2.0	VG 4.0	FN 6.0	VF 8.0	VF/NM 9.0	NM- 9.2
1-Based on movie	1	3	4	6	8	10

2-5 6.00
6-11,13-17 4.00
12-($2.95, 52 pgs.)-Intro. John Connor 5.00
Trade paperback (1989, $9.95) 15.00

TERMINATOR, THE
Dark Horse Comics: Aug, 1990 - No. 4, Nov, 1990 ($2.50, limited series)

1-Set 39 years later than the movie 5.00
2-4 4.00

TERMINATOR, THE
Dark Horse Comics: 1998 - No. 4, Dec, 1998 ($2.95, limited series)

1-4-Alan Grant-s/Steve Pugh-a/c 4.00
...Special (1998, $2.95) Darrow-c/Grant-s 4.00

TERMINATOR, THE: ALL MY FUTURES PAST
Now Comics: V3#1, Aug, 1990 - V3#2, Sept, 1990 ($1.75, limited series)

V3#1,2 4.00

TERMINATOR, THE: ENDGAME
Dark Horse Comics: Sept, 1992 - No. 3, Nov, 1992 ($2.50, limited series)

1-3: Guice-a(p); painted-c 4.00

TERMINATOR, THE: ENEMY OF MY ENEMY

Terminator: Revolution #1 © Studio Canal

The Terrifics #1 © DC

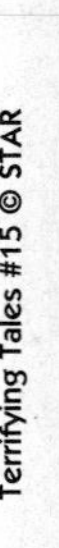
Terrifying Tales #15 © STAR

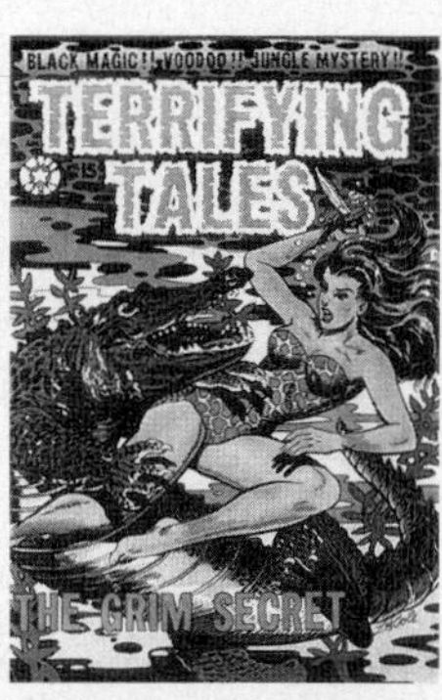

GD 2.0 VG 4.0 FN 6.0 VF 8.0 VF/NM 9.0 NM- 9.2

GD 2.0 VG 4.0 FN 6.0 VF 8.0 VF/NM 9.0 NM- 9.2

Dark Horse Comics: Feb, 2014 - No. 6, Oct, 2014 ($3.99, limited series)
1-6-Jolley-s/Igle-a; set in 1985 4.00

TERMINATOR, THE: HUNTERS AND KILLERS
Dark Horse Comics: Mar, 1992 - No. 3, May, 1992 ($2.50, limited series)
1-3 4.00

TERMINATOR, THE: 1984
Dark Horse Comics: Sept, 2010 - No. 3, Nov, 2010 ($3.50, limited series)
1-3: Takes place during and after the 1st movie; Zack Whedon-s/Andy MacDonald-a 3.50

TERMINATOR, THE: ONE SHOT
Dark Horse Comics: July, 1991 ($5.95, 56 pgs.)
nn-Matt Wagner-a; contains stiff pop-up inside 6.00

TERMINATOR: REVOLUTION (Follows Terminator 2: Infinity series)
Dynamite Entertainment: 2008 - No. 5, 2009 ($3.50, limited series)
1-5-Furman-s/Antonio-a. 1-3-Two covers 3.50

TERMINATOR / ROBOCOP: KILL HUMAN
Dynamite Entertainment: 2011 - No. 4, 2011 ($3.99, limited series)
1-4: 1-Covers by Simonson, Lau & Feister. 2-4-Three covers on each 4.00

TERMINATOR: SALVATION MOVIE PREQUEL
IDW Publishing: Jan, 2009 - No. 4, Apr, 2009 ($3.99, limited series)
1-4: Alan Robinson-a/Dara Naraghi-s 4.00
0-Salvation Movie Preview (4/09) Mariotte-s/Figueroa-a 4.00

TERMINATOR SALVATION: THE FINAL BATTLE
Dark Horse Comics: Dec, 2013 - No. 12, Dec, 2014 ($3.99, limited series)
1-12-Straczynski-s/Woods-a 4.00

TERMINATOR, THE: SECONDARY OBJECTIVES
Dark Horse Comics: July, 1991 - No. 4, Oct, 1991 ($2.50, limited series)
1-4: Gulacy-c/a(p) in all 4.00

TERMINATOR, THE: THE BURNING EARTH
Now Comics: V2#1, Mar, 1990 - V2#5, July, 1990 ($1.75, limited series)

	GD 2.0	VG 4.0	FN 6.0	VF 8.0	VF/NM 9.0	NM- 9.2
V2#1: Alex Ross painted art (1st published work)	2	4	6	9	12	15
2-5: Ross-c/a in all	1	3	4	6	8	10

Trade paperback (1990, $9.95)-Reprints V2#1-5 18.00
Trade paperback (ibooks, 2003, $17.95)-Digitally remastered reprint 18.00

TERMINATOR, THE: THE DARK YEARS
Dark Horse Comics: Aug, 1999 - No. 4, Dec, 1999 ($2.95, limited series)
1-4-Alan Grant-s/Mel Rubi-a; Jae Lee-c 4.00

TERMINATOR, THE: THE ENEMY FROM WITHIN
Dark Horse Comics: Nov, 1991 - No. 4, Feb, 1992 ($2.50, limited series)
1-4: All have Simon Bisley painted-c 4.00

TERMINATOR, THE: 2029
Dark Horse Comics: Mar, 2010 - No. 3, May, 2010 ($3.50, limited series)
1-3: Kyle Reese before his time-jump to 1984; Zack Whedon-s/Andy MacDonald-a 3.50

TERMINATOR 2: CYBERNETIC DAWN
Malibu: Nov, 1995 - No.4, Feb, 1996; No. 0. Apr, 1996 ($2.50, lim. series)
0 (4/96, $2.95)-Erskine-c/a; flip book w/Terminator 2: Nuclear Twilight 4.00
1-4: Continuation of film. 4.00

TERMINATOR 2: INFINITY
Dynamite Entertainment: 2007 - No. 7 ($3.50)
1-7: 1-Furman-s/Raynor-a; 3 covers. 6,7-Painkiller Jane x-over 3.50

TERMINATOR 2: JUDGEMENT DAY
Marvel Comics: Early Sept, 1991 - No. 3, Early Oct, 1991 ($1.00, lim. series)
1-3: Based on movie sequel; 1-3-Same as nn issues 4.00
nn (1991, $4.95, squarebound, 68 pgs.)-Photo-c 6.00
nn (1991, $2.25, B&W, magazine, 68 pgs.) 4.00

TERMINATOR 2: NUCLEAR TWILIGHT
Malibu: Nov, 1995 - No.4, Feb, 1996; No. 0, Apr, 1996 ($2.50, lim. series)
0 (4/96, $2.95)-Erskine-c/a; flip book w/Terminator 2: Cybernetic Dawn 4.00
1-4:Continuation of film. 4.00

TERMINATOR 3: RISE OF THE MACHINES (... BEFORE THE RISE on cover)
Beckett Comics: July, 2003 - No. 6, Jan, 2004 ($5.95, limited series)
1-6: 1,2-Leads into movie; 2 covers on each. 3-6-Movie adaptation 6.00

TERM LIFE
Image Comics (Shadowline): Jan, 2011 ($16.99, graphic novel)
SC-Lieberman-s/Thornborrow-a/DeStefano-l 17.00

TERRA (See Supergirl {2005 series} #12)
DC Comics: Jan, 2009 - No. 4, Feb, 2009 ($2.99, limited series)
1-4-Conner-a/c. 1,2,4-Power Girl app. 2-4-Geo-Force app. 4.00
TPB (2009, $14.99) r/#1-4 & Supergirl #12 15.00

TERRAFORMERS
Wonder Color Comics: April, 1987 - No. 2, 1987 ($1.95, limited series)
1,2-Kelley Jones-a 3.00

TERRA OBSCURA (See Tom Strong)
America's Best Comics: Aug, 2003 - No. 6, Feb, 2004 ($2.95)
1-6-Alan Moore & Peter Hogan-s/Paquette-a 3.00
TPB (2004, $14.95) r/#1-6 15.00

TERRA OBSCURA VOLUME 2 (See Tom Strong)
America's Best Comics: Oct, 2004 - No. 6, May, 2005 ($2.95)
1-6-Alan Moore & Peter Hogan-s/Paquette-a; Tom Strange app. 3.00
TPB (2005, $14.99) r/#1-6 15.00

TERRARISTS
Marvel Comics (Epic): Nov, 1993 - No. 4, Feb, 1994 ($2.50, limited series)
1-4-Bound-in trading cards in all 3.00

TERRIFIC COMICS (Also see Suspense Comics)
Continental Magazines: Jan, 1944 - No. 6, Nov, 1944

	GD 2.0	VG 4.0	FN 6.0	VF 8.0	VF/NM 9.0	NM- 9.2
1-Kid Terrific; opium story	326	652	978	2282	3991	6000
2-1st app. The Boomerang by L.B. Cole & Ed Wheelan's "Comics" McCormick, called the world's #1 comic book fan begins	290	580	870	1856	3178	4500
3-Diana becomes Boomerang's costumed aide; L.B. Cole-c	232	464	696	1485	2643	3800
4-Classic war-c (Scarce)	476	952	1428	3475	6138	8800
5-The Reckoner begins; Boomerang & Diana by L.B. Cole; Classic Schomburg bondage & hooded vigilante-c (Scarce)	1700	3400	5100	10,200	20,200	35,000
6-L.B. Cole-c/a	210	420	630	1334	2567	3800

NOTE: ***L.B. Cole** a-1, 2(2), 3-6. **Fuje** a-5, 6. **Rico** a-2; c-1. **Schomburg** c-2, 5.*

TERRIFIC COMICS (Formerly Horrific; Wonder Boy #17 on)
Mystery Publ.(Comic Media)/(Ajax/Farrell): No. 14, Dec, 1954; No. 16, Mar, 1955 (No #15)

	GD 2.0	VG 4.0	FN 6.0	VF 8.0	VF/NM 9.0	NM- 9.2
14-Art swipe/Advs. into the Unknown #37; injury-to-eye-c; pg. 2, panel 5 swiped from Phantom Stranger #4; surrealistic Palais-a; Human Cross story; classic-c	94	188	282	597	1024	1450
16-Wonder Boy-c/story (last pre-code)	30	60	90	177	289	400

TERRIFICS, THE
DC Comics: Apr, 2018 - Present ($2.99)
1-Mr. Terrific, Metamorpho, Phantom Girl & Plastic Man team; Lemire-s/Reis-a 3.00

TERRIFYING TALES (Formerly Startling Terror Tales #10)
Star Publications: No. 11, Jan, 1953 - No. 15, Apr, 1954

	GD 2.0	VG 4.0	FN 6.0	VF 8.0	VF/NM 9.0	NM- 9.2
11-Used in **POP**, pgs. 99,100; all Jo-Jo-r	63	126	189	403	689	975
12-Reprints Jo-Jo #19 entirely; L.B. Cole splash	55	110	165	352	601	850
13-All Rulah-r; classic devil-c	71	142	213	454	777	1100
14-All Rulah reprints	53	106	159	334	567	800
15-Rulah, Zago-r; used in **SOTI**-r/Rulah #22	52	104	156	328	552	775

NOTE: *All issues have **L.B. Cole** covers; bondage covers-No. 12-14.*

TERROR ILLUSTRATED (Adult Tales of...)
E.C. Comics: Nov-Dec, 1955 - No. 2, Spring (April on-c), 1956 (Magazine, 25¢)

	GD 2.0	VG 4.0	FN 6.0	VF 8.0	VF/NM 9.0	NM- 9.2
1-Adult Entertainment on-c	25	50	75	150	245	340
2-Charles Sultan-a	18	36	54	103	162	220

NOTE: ***Craig, Evans, Ingels, Orlando** art in each. **Crandall** c-1, 2.*

TERROR INC. (See A Shadowline Saga #3)
Marvel Comics: July, 1992 - No. 13, July, 1993 ($1.75)
1-8,11-13: 6,7-Punisher-c/story. 13-Ghost Rider app. 3.00
9,10-Wolverine-c/story 4.00

TERROR INC.
Marvel Comics (MAX): Oct, 2007 - No. 5, Apr, 2008 ($3.99, limited series)
1-5: 1-Lapham-s/Zircher-a; origin of Mr. Terror retold 4.00

TERROR INC. - APOCALYPSE SOON
Marvel Comics (MAX): July, 2009 - No. 4, Sept, 2009 ($3.99, limited series)
1-4: 1-Lapham-s/Turnbull-a 4.00

TERRORS OF DRACULA (Magazine)
Modern Day Periodical/Eerie Publ.: Vol. 1 #3, May, 1979 - Vol. 3 #2, Sept, 1981 (B&W)

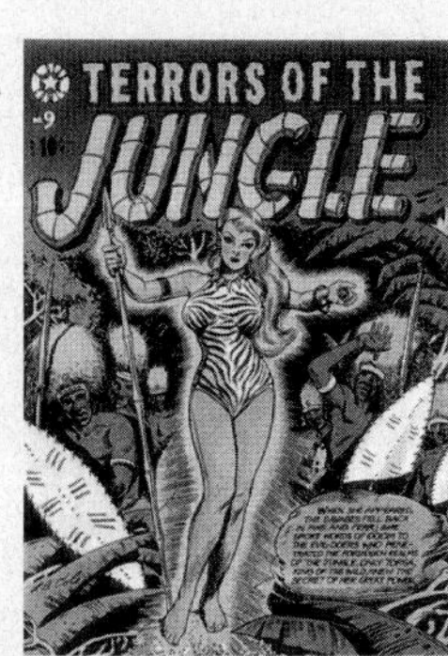

Terrors of the Jungle #9 © STAR

Terry-Toons Comics #9 © MAR

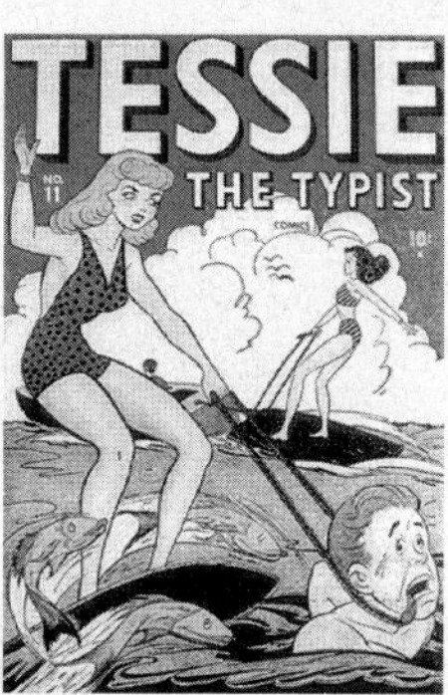

Tessie the Typist #11 © MAR

	GD 2.0	VG 4.0	FN 6.0	VF 8.0	VF/NM 9.0	NM- 9.2
Vol. 1 #3 (5/79, 1st issue)	4	8	12	25	40	55
#4(8/79), #5(11/79)	3	6	9	19	30	40
Vol. 2 #1-3: 1-(2/80). 2-(5/80). 3-(8/80)	3	6	9	16	24	32
Vol. 3 #1 (5/81), #2 (9/81)	3	6	9	18	28	38

TERRORS OF THE JUNGLE (Formerly Jungle Thrills)
Star Publications: No. 17, 5/52 - No. 21, 2/53; No. 4, 4/53 - No. 10, 9/54

	GD	VG	FN	VF	VF/NM	NM-
17-Reprints Rulah #21, used in **SOTI**; L.B. Cole bondage-c	61	122	183	390	670	950
18-Jo-Jo-r	48	96	144	302	514	725
19,20(1952)-Jo-Jo-r; Disbrow-a	45	90	135	284	480	675
21-Jungle Jo, Tangi-r; used in **POP**, pg. 100 & color illos.	48	96	144	302	514	725
4-10: All Disbrow-a. 5-Jo-Jo-r. 8-Rulah, Jo-Jo-r. 9-Jo-Jo-r; Disbrow-a; Tangi by Orlando10-Rulah-r	48	96	144	302	514	725

NOTE: ***L.B. Cole** c-all; bondage c-17, 19, 21, 5, 7.*

TERROR TALES (See Beware Terror Tales)

TERROR TALES (Magazine)
Eerie Publications: V1#7, 1969 - V6#6, Dec, 1974; V7#1, Apr, 1976 - V10, 1979? (V1-V6: 52 pgs.; V7 on: 68 pgs.)

	GD	VG	FN	VF	VF/NM	NM-
V1#7	8	16	24	52	99	145
V1#8-11('69): 9-Bondage-c	5	10	15	35	63	90
V2#1-6('70), V3#1-6('71), V4#1-7('72), V5#1-6('73), V6#1-6('74), V7#1,4('76) (no V7#2), V8#1-3('77)	5	10	15	33	57	80
V7#3-(7/76) LSD story-r/Weird V3#5	5	10	15	33	57	80
V9#2-4, V10#1(1/79)	5	10	15	34	60	85

TERROR TITANS
DC Comics: Dec, 2008 - No. 6, May, 2009 ($2.99, limited series)

	NM-
1-6: 1-Ravager and Clock King at the Dark Side Club; Bennett-a. 3-Static app.	3.00
TPB (2009, $17.99) r/#1-6	18.00

TERRY AND THE PIRATES (See Famous Feature Stories, Merry Christmas From Sears Toyland, Popular Comics, Super Book #3,5,9,16,28, & Super Comics)

TERRY AND THE PIRATES
Dell Publishing Co.: 1939 - 1953 (By Milton Caniff)

	GD	VG	FN	VF	VF/NM	NM-
Large Feature Comic 2(1939)	110	220	330	704	1202	1700
Large Feature Comic 6(1938)-r/1936 dailies	84	168	252	538	919	1300
Four Color 9(1940)	77	154	231	493	847	1200
Large Feature Comic 27('41), 6('42)	68	136	204	435	743	1050
Four Color 44('43)	31	62	93	223	499	775
Four Color 101('45)	20	40	60	135	300	465
Family Album(1942)	20	40	60	118	192	265

TERRY AND THE PIRATES (Formerly Boy Explorers; Long John Silver & the Pirates #30 on) (Daily strip-r) (Two #26's)
Harvey Publications/Charlton No. 26-28: No. 3, 4/47 - No. 26, 4/51; No. 26, 6/55 - No. 28, 10/55

	GD	VG	FN	VF	VF/NM	NM-
3(#1)-Boy Explorers by S&K; Terry & the Pirates begin by Caniff; 1st app. The Dragon Lady	40	80	120	246	411	575
4-S&K Boy Explorers	22	44	66	132	216	300
5-11: 11-Man in Black app. by Powell	13	26	39	72	101	130
12-20: 16-Girl threatened with red hot poker	10	20	30	56	76	95
21-26(4/51)-Last Caniff issue & last pre-code issue	10	20	30	54	72	90
26-28('55)(Formerly This Is Suspense)-No Caniff-a	9	18	27	47	61	75

NOTE: ***Powell** a (Tommy Tween)-5-10, 12, 14; 15-17(1/2 to 2 pgs. each).*

TERRY BEARS COMICS (TerryToons, The... #4)
St. John Publishing Co.: June, 1952 - No. 3, Mar, 1953

	GD	VG	FN	VF	VF/NM	NM-
1-By Paul Terry	13	26	39	72	101	130
2,3	8	16	24	44	57	70

TERRY-TOONS ALBUM (See Giant Comics Edition)

TERRY-TOONS COMICS (1st Series) (Becomes Paul Terry's Comics #85 on; later issues titled "Paul Terry's...")
Timely/Marvel No. 1-59 (8/47)(Becomes Best Western No. 58 on?, Marvel)/ St. John No. 60 (9/47) on: Oct, 1942 - No. 86, May, 1951

	GD	VG	FN	VF	VF/NM	NM-
1 (Scarce)-Features characters that 1st app. on movie screen; Gandy Goose & Sourpuss begin; war-c; Gandy Goose c-1-37	265	530	795	1694	2897	4100
2	94	188	282	597	1024	1450
3-5	61	122	183	390	670	950
6,8-10: 9,10-World War II gag-c	47	94	141	296	498	700
7-Hitler, Hirohito, Mussolini-c	232	464	696	1485	2543	3600
11-20	34	68	102	196	321	445
21-37	24	48	72	140	230	320
38-Mighty Mouse begins (1st app., 11/45); Mighty Mouse-c begin, end #86; Gandy, Sourpuss welcome Mighty Mouse on-c	226	452	678	1446	2473	3500
39-2nd app. Mighty Mouse	65	130	195	416	708	1000
40-49: 43-Infinity-c	37	74	111	222	361	500
50-1st app. Heckle & Jeckle (11/46)	65	130	195	416	708	1000
51-60: 55-Infinity-c. 60-(9/47)-Atomic explosion panel; 1st St. John issue	20	40	60	114	182	250
61-86: 85,86-Same book as Paul Terry's Comics #85,86 with only a title change; published at same time?	15	30	45	88	137	185

TERRY-TOONS COMICS (2nd Series)
St. John Publishing Co./Pines: June, 1952 - No. 9, Nov, 1953; 1957; 1958

	GD	VG	FN	VF	VF/NM	NM-
1-Gandy Goose & Sourpuss begin by Paul Terry	18	36	54	105	165	225
2	10	20	30	56	76	95
3-9	9	18	27	52	69	85
Giant Summer Fun Book 101,102-(Sum, 1957, Sum, 1958, 25¢, Pines)(TV) CBS Television Presents...; Tom Terrific, Mighty Mouse, Heckle & Jeckle Gandy Goose app.	14	28	42	80	115	150

TERRYTOONS, THE TERRY BEARS (Formerly Terry Bears Comics)
Pines Comics: No. 4, Summer, 1958 (CBS Television Presents...)

	GD	VG	FN	VF	VF/NM	NM-
4	8	16	24	42	54	65

TESSIE THE TYPIST (Tiny Tessie #24; see Comedy Comics, Gay Comics & Joker Comics)
Timely/Marvel Comics (20CC): Summer, 1944 - No. 23, Aug, 1949

	GD	VG	FN	VF	VF/NM	NM-
1-Doc Rockblock & others by Wolverton	181	362	543	1158	1979	2800
2-Wolverton's Powerhouse Pepper	65	130	195	416	708	1000
3-(3/45)-No Wolverton	39	78	117	240	395	550
4,5,7,8-Wolverton-a. 4-(Fall/45)	43	86	129	271	461	650
6-Kurtzman's "Hey Look", 2 pgs. Wolverton-a	45	90	135	284	480	675
9-Wolverton's Powerhouse Pepper (8 pgs.) & 1 pg. Kurtzman's "Hey Look"	43	86	129	271	461	650
10-Wolverton's Powerhouse Pepper (4 pgs.)	43	86	129	271	461	650
11-Wolverton's Powerhouse Pepper (8 pgs.)	45	90	135	284	480	675
12-Wolverton's Powerhouse Pepper (4 pgs.) & 1 pg. Kurtzman's "Hey Look"	43	86	129	271	461	650
13-Wolverton's Powerhouse Pepper (4 pgs.)	43	86	129	271	461	650
14,15: 14-Wolverton's Dr. Whackyhack (1 pg.); 1-1/2 pgs. Kurtzman's "Hey Look". 15-Kurtzman's "Hey Look" (3 pgs.) & 3 pgs. Giggles 'n' Grins	34	68	102	204	332	460
16-18-Kurtzman's "Hey Look" (?, 2 & 1 pg.)	27	54	81	162	266	370
19-Annie Oakley story (8 pgs.)	21	42	63	126	206	285
20-23: 20-Anti-Wertham editorial (2/49)	20	40	60	120	195	270

NOTE: *Lana app.-21. Millie The Model app.-13, 15, 17, 21. Rusty app.-10, 11, 13, 15, 17.*

TESTAMENT
DC Comics (Vertigo): Feb, 2006 - No. 22, Mar, 2008 ($2.99)

	NM-
1-22: 1-5-Rushkoff-s/Sharp-a. 6,7-Gross & Erskine-a	3.00

TEXAN, THE (Fightin' Marines #15 on; Fightin' Texan #16 on)
St. John Publishing Co.: Aug, 1948 - No. 15, Oct, 1951

	GD	VG	FN	VF	VF/NM	NM-
1-Buckskin Belle	19	38	57	111	176	240
2	12	24	36	67	94	120
3,10: 10-Oversized issue	13	26	39	72	101	130
4,5,7,15-Baker-c/a	32	64	96	188	307	425
6,9-Baker-c	26	52	78	154	252	350
8,11,13,14-Baker-c/a(2-3) each	36	72	108	211	343	475
12-All Matt Baker-c/a; Peyote story	39	78	117	240	395	550

NOTE: ***Matt Baker** c-4-9, 11-15. **Larsen** a-4-6, 8-10, 15. **Tuska** a-1, 2, 7-9.*

TEXAN, THE (TV)
Dell Publishing Co.: No. 1027, Sept-Nov, 1959 - No. 1096, May-July, 1960

	GD	VG	FN	VF	VF/NM	NM-
Four Color 1027 (#1)-Photo-c	8	16	24	52	99	145
Four Color 1096-Rory Calhoun photo-c	7	14	21	46	86	125

TEXAS CHAINSAW MASSACRE
DC Comics (WildStorm): Jan, 2007 - No. 6, Jun, 2007 ($2.99, limited series)

	NM-
1-6: 1-Two covers by Bermejo & Bradstreet; Abnett & Lanning-s	3.00
...: About a Boy #1 (9/07, $2.99) Abnett & Lanning-s/Gomez-a/Robertson-c	3.00
...: Book Two TPB (2009, $14.99) r/one shots & New Line Cinema's Tales of Horror story	15.00
...: By Himself #1 (10/07, $2.99) Abnett & Lanning-s/Craig-a/Robertson-c	3.00
...: Cut! #1 (8/07, $2.99) Pfeiffer-s/Raffaele-a/Robertson-c	3.00
...: Raising Cain 1-3 (7/08 - No. 3, 9/08, $3.50) Bruce Jones-s/Chris Gugliotti-a	3.50

TEXAS JOHN SLAUGHTER (See Walt Disney Presents, 4-Color #997, 1181 & #2)

TEXAS KID (See Two-Gun Western, Wild Western)
Marvel/Atlas Comics (LMC): Jan, 1951 - No. 10, July, 1952

Tex Morgan #2 © MAR

Tex Taylor #1 © MAR

Thanos (2017 series) #10 © MAR

GD VG FN VF VF/NM NM-
2.0 4.0 6.0 8.0 9.0 9.2

1-Origin; Texas Kid (alias Lance Temple) & his horse Thunder begin;
Tuska-a 28 56 84 168 274 380
2 15 30 45 84 127 170
3-10 12 24 36 69 97 125
NOTE: ***Maneely** a-1-4; c-1, 3, 5-10.*

TEXAS RANGERS, THE (See Jace Pearson of... and Superior Stories #4)

TEXAS RANGERS IN ACTION (Formerly Captain Gallant or Scotland Yard?)
Charlton Comics: No. 5, Jul, 1956 - No. 79, Aug, 1970 (See Blue Bird Comics)

5 8 16 24 44 57 70
6,7,9,10 6 12 18 28 34 40
8-Ditko-a (signed) 10 20 30 54 72 90
11-(68 pg. Giant) Williamson-a (5&8 pgs.); Torres/Williamson-a (5 pgs.)
10 20 30 54 72 90
12-(68 pg. Giant, 6/58) 6 12 18 28 34 40
13-Williamson-a (5 pgs); Torres, Morisi-a 8 16 24 42 54 65
14-20 5 10 15 23 28 32
21-30 3 6 9 15 22 28
31-59: 32-Both 10¢-c & 15¢-c exist 2 4 6 13 18 22
60-Riley's Rangers begin 3 6 9 14 19 24
61-65,68-70 2 4 6 8 11 14
66,67: 66-1st app. The Man Called Loco. 67-Origin 2 4 6 9 13 16
71-79: 77-(4/70) Ditko-c & a (8 pgs.) 1 3 4 6 8 10
76 (Modern Comics-r, 1977) 6.00

TEXAS SLIM (See A-1 Comics)

TEX DAWSON, GUN-SLINGER (Gunslinger #2 on)
Marvel Comics Group: Jan, 1973 (20¢)(Also see Western Kid, 1st series)

1-Steranko-c; Williamson-r (4 pgs.); Tex Dawson-r by Romita(3) from 1955;
Tuska-r 3 6 9 19 30 40

TEX FARNUM (See Wisco)

TEX FARRELL (...Pride of the Wild West)
D. S. Publishing Co.: Mar-Apr, 1948

1-Tex Farrell & his horse Lightning; Shelly-c 15 30 45 88 137 185

TEX GRANGER (Formerly Calling All Boys; see True Comics)
Parents' Magazine Inst./Commended: No. 18, Jun, 1948 - No. 24, Sept, 1949

18-Tex Granger & his horse Bullet begin 13 26 39 74 105 135
19 10 20 30 56 76 95
20-24: 22-Wild Bill Hickok story. 23-Vs. Billy the Kid; Tim Holt app.
9 18 27 47 61 75

TEX MORGAN (See Blaze Carson and Wild Western)
Marvel Comics (CCC): Aug, 1948 - No. 9, Feb, 1950

1-Tex Morgan, his horse Lightning & sidekick Lobo begin
29 58 87 170 278 385
2 19 38 57 109 172 235
3-6: 3,4-Arizona Annie app. 5-Blaze Carson app. 14 28 42 76 108 140
7-9: All photo-c. 7-Captain Tootsie by Beck. 8-18 pg. story "The Terror of Rimrock Valley";
Diablo app. 18 36 54 105 165 225
NOTE: *Tex Taylor app. 2-6, 7, 9. **Brodsky** c-6. **Syd Shores** c-2, 5.*

TEX RITTER WESTERN (Movie star; singing cowboy; see Six-Gun Heroes and Western Hero)
Fawcett No. 1-20 (1/54)/Charlton No. 21 on: Oct, 1950 - No. 46, May, 1959 (Photo-c: 1-21)

1-Tex Ritter, his stallion White Flash & dog Fury begin; photo front/back-c begin
43 86 129 271 461 650
2 21 42 63 124 202 280
3-5: 5-Last photo back-c 16 32 48 94 147 200
6-10 14 28 42 80 115 150
11-19 10 20 30 58 79 100
20-Last Fawcett issue (1/54) 11 22 33 62 86 110
21-1st Charlton issue; photo-c (3/54) 14 28 42 80 115 150
22-B&W photo back-c begin, end #32 9 18 27 52 69 85
23-30: 23-25-Young Falcon app. 9 18 27 47 61 75
31-38,40-45 8 16 24 42 54 65
39-Williamson-a; Whitman-c (1/58) 9 18 27 47 61 75
46-Last issue 8 16 24 44 57 70

TEX TAYLOR (...The Fighting Cowboy on-c #1, 2)(See Blaze Carson, Kid Colt, Tex Morgan, Wild Western, & Wisco)
Marvel Comics (HPC): Sept, 1948 - No. 9, March, 1950

1-Tex Taylor & his horse Fury begin; Blaze Carson app.
30 60 90 177 289 400
2-Blaze Carson app. 15 30 45 90 140 190
3-Arizona Annie app. 15 30 45 83 124 165

GD VG FN VF VF/NM NM-
2.0 4.0 6.0 8.0 9.0 9.2

4-6: All photo-c; Blaze Carson app. 4-Anti-Wertham editorial
16 32 48 94 147 200
7-9: 7-Photo-c;18 pg. Movie-Length Thriller "Trapped in Time's Lost Land!" with sabretoothed tigers, dinosaurs; Diablo app. 8-Photo-c; 18 pg. Movie-Length Thriller "The Mystery of Devil-Tree Plateau!" with dwarf horses, dwarf people & a lost miniature Inca type village; Diablo app. 9-Photo-c; 18 pg. Movie-Length Thriller "Guns Along the Border!" Captain Tootsie by Schreiber; Nimo the Mountain Lion app.; Heth-a
19 38 57 111 176 240
NOTE: ***Syd Shores** c-1-3.*

THANE OF BAGARTH (Also see Hercules, 1967 series)
Charlton Comics: No. 24, Oct, 1985 - No. 25, Dec, 1985

24,25-Low print run 6.00

THANOS
Marvel Comics: Dec, 2003 - No. 12, Sept, 2004 ($2.99)

1-12: 1-6-Starlin-s/a(p)/Milgrom-i; Galactus app. 7-12-Giffen-s/Lim-a 5.00
Annual 1 (7/14, $4.99) Starlin-s/Lim-a/Keown-c 5.00
...: The Final Threat (11/12, $4.99) r/Avengers Ann. #7 & Marvel Two-In-One Ann. #2 5.00
Vol. 4: Epiphany TPB (2004, $14.99) r/#1-6 15.00
Vol. 5: Samaritan TPB (2004, $14.99) r/#7-12 15.00

THANOS
Marvel Comics: Jan, 2017 - Present ($3.99)

1-12: 1-6-Lemire-s/Deodato-a. 1-Starfox & Thane app. 2-Nebula app. 3-Imperial Guard app.
7-12-Peralta-a 4.00
13-1st app. Cosmic Ghost Rider 30.00
14-Cosmic Ghost Rider app. 10.00
15-Cosmic Ghost Rider revealed as Frank Castle 30.00
16-Origin Cosmic Ghost Rider 5.00

THANOS: A GOD UP THERE LISTENING
Marvel Comics: Dec, 2014 - No. 4, Dec, 2014 ($3.99, weekly limited series)

1-4-Thane and Ego The Living Planet app. 4.00

THANOS IMPERATIVE, THE
Marvel Comics: Aug, 2010 - No. 6, Jan, 2011 ($3.99, limited series)

1-6-Abnett & Lanning-s/Sepulveda-a; Vision and Silver Surfer app. 4.00
...: Devastation (3/11, $3.99) Sepulveda-a; leads into The Annihilators #1 4.00
...: Ignition (7/10, $3.99) Walker-a; prequel to series 4.00
Thanos Sourcebook (8/10, $3.99) profiles/history of Thanos and Nova Corps members 4.00

THANOS QUEST, THE (See Capt. Marvel #25, Infinity Gauntlet, Iron Man #55, Logan's Run, Marvel Feature #12, Marvel Universe: The End, Silver Surfer #34 & Warlock #9)
Marvel Comics: 1990 - No. 2, 1990 ($4.95, squarebound, 52 pgs.)

1,2-Both have Starlin scripts & covers (both printings) 3 6 9 16 24 32
1-(3/2000, $3.99) r/material from #1&2 5.00
1-(11/12, $7,99) r/#1&2, new cover by Andy Park 8.00

THANOS: THE INFINITY FINALE (Conclusion to The Infinity Entity series)
Marvel Comics: 2016 ($24.99, HC original graphic novel)

HC - Jim Starlin-s/Ron Lim-a; Adam Warlock & Annihilus app. 25.00

THANOS: THE INFINITY REVELATION (Prelude to The Infinity Entity series)
Marvel Comics: 2014 ($24.99, HC original graphic novel)

HC - Jim Starlin-s/a; Adam Warlock & Silver Surfer app. 25.00

THANOS: A GOD UP THERE LISTENING
Marvel Comics: Dec, 2014 - No. 4, Dec, 2014 ($3.99, weekly limited series)

1-4-Thane and Ego The Living Planet app. 4.00

THANOS VS. HULK
Marvel Comics: Feb, 2015 - No. 4, May, 2015 ($3.99, limited series)

1-4-Jim Starlin-s/a/c; Annihilus, Pip the Troll and Iron Man app. 4.00

THAT DARN CAT (See Movie Comics & Walt Disney Showcase #19)

THAT'S MY POP! GOES NUTS FOR FAIR
Bystander Press: 1939 (76 pgs., B&W)

nn-by Milt Gross 36 72 108 216 351 485

THAT WILKIN BOY (Meet Bingo...)
Archie Publications: Jan, 1969 - No. 52, Oct, 1982

1-1st app. Bingo's Band, Samantha & Tough Teddy 4 8 12 28 47 65
2-5 3 6 9 16 23 30
6-11 2 4 6 13 18 22
12-26-Giants. 12-No # on-c 3 6 9 14 20 26
27-40(1/77) 2 4 6 8 10 12
41-49 1 2 3 4 5 7

Thief of Thieves #1 © R.Kirkman

Thimk #1 © Counterpoint

The Thing #1 © MAR

	GD 2.0	VG 4.0	FN 6.0	VF 8.0	VF/NM 9.0	NM- 9.2
50-52 (low print)	2	4	6	8	10	12

THB
Horse Press: Oct, 1994 - 2002 ($5.50/$2.50/$2.95, B&W)

	GD 2.0	VG 4.0	FN 6.0	VF 8.0	VF/NM 9.0	NM- 9.2
1 ($5.50) Paul Pope-s/a in all	3	6	9	18	28	38
1 (2nd Printing)-r/#1 w/new material						5.00
2 ($2.50)	2	4	6	10	14	18
3-5	1	2	3	5	6	8
69 (1995, no price, low distribution, 12 pgs.)-story reprinted in #1 (2nd Printing)						3.00
Giant THB-($4.95)						5.00
Giant THB 1 V2-(2003, $6.95)						7.00
...M3/THB: Mars' Mightiest Mek #1 (2000, $3.95)						4.00
...6A: Mek-Power #1, 6B: Mek-Power #2, 6C: Mek-Power #3 (2000, $3.95)						4.00
... 6D: Mek-Power #4 (2002, $4.95)						5.00

T.H.E. CAT (TV)
Dell Publishing Co.: Mar, 1967 - No. 4, Oct, 1967 (All have photo-c)

	GD 2.0	VG 4.0	FN 6.0	VF 8.0	VF/NM 9.0	NM- 9.2
1	3	6	9	21	33	45
2-4	3	6	9	16	24	32

THERE'S A NEW WORLD COMING
Spire Christian Comics/Fleming H. Revell Co.: 1973 (35/49¢)

	GD 2.0	VG 4.0	FN 6.0	VF 8.0	VF/NM 9.0	NM- 9.2
nn	2	4	6	10	14	18

THEY ALL KISSED THE BRIDE (See Cinema Comics Herald)

THEY'RE NOT LIKE US
Image Comics: Dec, 2014 - Present ($2.99)

	GD 2.0	VG 4.0	FN 6.0	VF 8.0	VF/NM 9.0	NM- 9.2
1-16-Stephenson-s/Gane-a/c						3.00

THIEF OF BAGHDAD
Dell Publishing Co.: No. 1229, Oct-Dec, 1961 (one-shot)

	GD 2.0	VG 4.0	FN 6.0	VF 8.0	VF/NM 9.0	NM- 9.2
Four Color 1229-Movie, Crandall/Evans-a, photo-c	6	12	18	41	76	110

THIEF OF THIEVES
Image Comics: Feb, 2012 - Present ($2.99)

	GD 2.0	VG 4.0	FN 6.0	VF 8.0	VF/NM 9.0	NM- 9.2
1-Kirkman & Spencer-s/Martinbrough-a/c						60.00
1-Second printing						8.00
2						25.00
3,4						15.00
5-37: 8-13-Asmus-s						3.00

THIMK (Magazine) (Satire)
Counterpoint: May, 1958 - No. 6, May, 1959

	GD 2.0	VG 4.0	FN 6.0	VF 8.0	VF/NM 9.0	NM- 9.2
1	10	20	30	58	79	100
2-6	8	16	24	40	50	60

THING!, THE (Blue Beetle #18 on)
Song Hits No. 1,2/Capitol Stories/Charlton: Feb, 1952 - No. 17, Nov, 1954

	GD 2.0	VG 4.0	FN 6.0	VF 8.0	VF/NM 9.0	NM- 9.2
1-Weird/horror stories in all; shrunken head-c	119	238	357	762	1306	1850
2,3	74	148	222	470	810	1150
4,6,8,10: 6-Classic decapitation story	68	136	204	435	743	1050
5-Severed head-c; headlights	74	148	222	470	810	1150
7-Injury to eye-c & inside panel	87	174	261	553	952	1350
9-Used in **SOTI**, pg. 388 & illo "Stomping on the face is a form of brutality which modern children learn early"	106	212	318	673	1162	1650
11-Necronomicon story; Hansel & Gretel parody; Injury-to-eye panel; Check-a	81	162	243	518	884	1250
12-1st published Ditko-c; "Cinderella" parody; lingerie panels. Ditko-a	148	296	444	947	1624	2300
13,15-Ditko-c/a(3 & 5)	132	264	396	838	1444	2050
14-Extreme violence/torture; Rumpelstiltskin story; Ditko-c/a(4)	129	258	387	826	1413	2000
16-Injury to eye panel	37	74	111	222	361	500
17-Ditko-c; classic parody "Through the Looking Glass"; Powell-r/Beware Terror Tales #1 & recolored	94	188	282	597	1024	1450

NOTE: *Excessive violence, severed heads, injury to eye are common No. 5 on.* ***Al Fago*** *c-4.* ***Forgione*** *c-1i, 2, 6, 8, 9. All* ***Ditko*** *issues #14, 15.* ***Giordano*** *a-6.*

THING, THE (See Fantastic Four, Marvel Fanfare, Marvel Feature #11,12, Marvel Two-In-One and Startling Stories:...- Night Falls on Yancy Street)
Marvel Comics Group: July, 1983 - No. 36, June, 1986

	GD 2.0	VG 4.0	FN 6.0	VF 8.0	VF/NM 9.0	NM- 9.2
1-Life story of Ben Grimm; Byrne scripts begin	3	6	9	16	24	32
2-5: 5-Spider-Man, She-Hulk and Wonder-Man app.						6.00
6-10: 7-1st app. Goody Two-Shoes. 8-She-Hulk app. 10-Secret Wars tie-in						5.00
11-36						4.00

NOTE: ***Byrne*** *a-2i, 7; c-1, 7, 36i; scripts-1-13, 19-22.* ***Sienkiewicz*** *c-13i.*

THING, THE (Fantastic Four)
Marvel Comics: Jan, 2006 - No. 8, Aug, 2006 ($2.99)

	GD 2.0	VG 4.0	FN 6.0	VF 8.0	VF/NM 9.0	NM- 9.2
1-8: 1-DiVito-a/Slott-s. 4-Lockjaw app. 6-Spider-Man app. 8-Super-Hero poker game						3.00
...: Idol of Millions TPB (2006, $20.99) r/#1-8; Divito sketch page						21.00

THING & SHE-HULK: THE LONG NIGHT (Fantastic Four)
Marvel Comics: May, 2002 ($2.99, one-shot)

	GD 2.0	VG 4.0	FN 6.0	VF 8.0	VF/NM 9.0	NM- 9.2
1-Hitch-c/a(pg. 1-25); Reis-a(pg. 26-39); Dezago-s						3.00

THING, THE (From Another World)
Dark Horse Comics: 1991 - No. 2, 1992 ($2.95, mini-series, stiff-c)

	GD 2.0	VG 4.0	FN 6.0	VF 8.0	VF/NM 9.0	NM- 9.2
1,2-Based on Universal movie; painted-c/a						5.00

THING, THE: FREAKSHOW (Fantastic Four)
Marvel Comics: Aug, 2002 - No. 4, Nov, 2002 ($2.99, limited series)

	GD 2.0	VG 4.0	FN 6.0	VF 8.0	VF/NM 9.0	NM- 9.2
1-4-Geoff Johns-s/Scott Kolins-a						3.00
TPB (2005, $17.99) r/#1-4 & Thing & She-Hulk: The Long Night one-shot						18.00

THING FROM ANOTHER WORLD: CLIMATE OF FEAR, THE
Dark Horse Comics: July, 1992 - No. 4, Dec, 1992 ($2.50, mini-series)

	GD 2.0	VG 4.0	FN 6.0	VF 8.0	VF/NM 9.0	NM- 9.2
1-4: Painted-c						4.00

THING FROM ANOTHER WORLD: ETERNAL VOWS
Dark Horse Comics: Dec, 1993 - No. 4, 1994 ($2.50, mini-series)

	GD 2.0	VG 4.0	FN 6.0	VF 8.0	VF/NM 9.0	NM- 9.2
1-4-Gulacy-c/a						4.00

THINK TANK (Also see Eden's Fall)
Image Comics (Top Cow): Aug, 2012 - No. 12, Feb, 2014 ($3.99)

	GD 2.0	VG 4.0	FN 6.0	VF 8.0	VF/NM 9.0	NM- 9.2
1-12-Hawkins-s/Ekedal-a						4.00

THINK TANK: ANIMAL
Image Comics (Top Cow): Mar, 2017 - No. 3 ($3.99)

	GD 2.0	VG 4.0	FN 6.0	VF 8.0	VF/NM 9.0	NM- 9.2
1-3-Hawkins-s/Ekedal-a						4.00

THINK TANK: CREATIVE DESTRUCTION
Image Comics (Top Cow): Apr, 2016 - No. 4, Jul, 2016 ($3.99, limited series)

	GD 2.0	VG 4.0	FN 6.0	VF 8.0	VF/NM 9.0	NM- 9.2
1-4-Hawkins-s/Ekedal-a						4.00

THIRTEEN (...Going on 18)
Dell Publishing Co.: 11-1/61-62 - No. 25, 12/67; No. 26, 7/69 - No. 29, 1/71

	GD 2.0	VG 4.0	FN 6.0	VF 8.0	VF/NM 9.0	NM- 9.2
1	5	10	15	35	63	90
2-10	4	8	12	28	47	65
11-25	4	8	12	23	37	50
26-29-r	3	6	9	17	26	35

NOTE: ***John Stanley*** *script-No. 3-29; art?*

13: ASSASSIN
TSR, Inc.: 1990 - No. 8, 1991 ($2.95, 44 pgs.)

	GD 2.0	VG 4.0	FN 6.0	VF 8.0	VF/NM 9.0	NM- 9.2
1-8: Agent 13; Alcala-a(i); Springer back-up-a						4.00

13th ARTIFACT, THE
Image Comics (Top Cow): Mar, 2016 ($3.99, one-shot)

	GD 2.0	VG 4.0	FN 6.0	VF 8.0	VF/NM 9.0	NM- 9.2
1-Amit Chauhan-s/Eli Powell-a						4.00

13th SON, THE
Dark Horse Comics: Nov, 2005 - No. 4, Feb, 2006 ($2.99, limited series)

	GD 2.0	VG 4.0	FN 6.0	VF 8.0	VF/NM 9.0	NM- 9.2
1-4-Kelley Jones-s/a/c						3.00

30 DAYS OF NIGHT
Idea + Design Works: June, 2002 - No. 3, Oct, 2002 ($3.99, limited series)

	GD 2.0	VG 4.0	FN 6.0	VF 8.0	VF/NM 9.0	NM- 9.2
1-Vampires in Alaska; Steve Niles-s/Ben Templesmith-a/Ashley Wood-c						65.00
1-2nd printing						10.00
2						26.00
3						12.00
Annual 2004 (1/04, $4.99) Niles-s/art by Templesmith and others						5.00
Annual 2005 (12/05, $7.49) Niles-s/art by Nat Jones						7.50
... 5th Anniversary (10/07 - No. 3, $2.99) reprints original series						3.00
... Sourcebook (10/07, $7.49) Illustrated guide to the 30 Days world						7.50
... Three Tales TPB (7/06, $19.99) r/Annual 2005, ...: Dead Space #1-3, and short story from Tales of Terror (IDW's...)						20.00
Hundred Penny Press: 30 Days of Night #1 (5/11, $1.00) r/#1						3.00
TPB (2003, $17.99) r/#1-3, foreward by Clive Barker; script for #1						18.00
The Complete 30 Days of Night (2004, $75.00, oversized hardcover with slipcase) r/#1-3; prequel; script pages for #1-3; original cover and promotional materials						75.00

30 DAYS OF NIGHT
IDW Publishing: July, 2004 (Free Comic Book Day edition)

	GD 2.0	VG 4.0	FN 6.0	VF 8.0	VF/NM 9.0	NM- 9.2
Previews CSI: Bad Rap; The Shield: Spotlight; 24: One Shot; and 30 Days of Night						3.00

30 DAYS OF NIGHT (Ongoing series)
IDW Publishing: Oct, 2011 - No. 12, Nov, 2012 ($3.99)

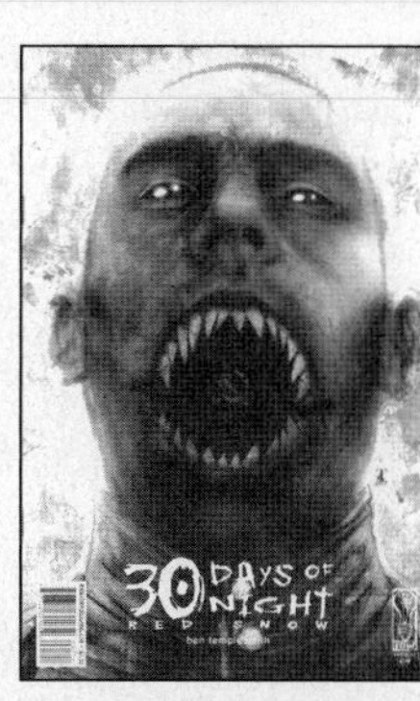

30 Days of Night: Red Snow #3 © Niles & Templesmith

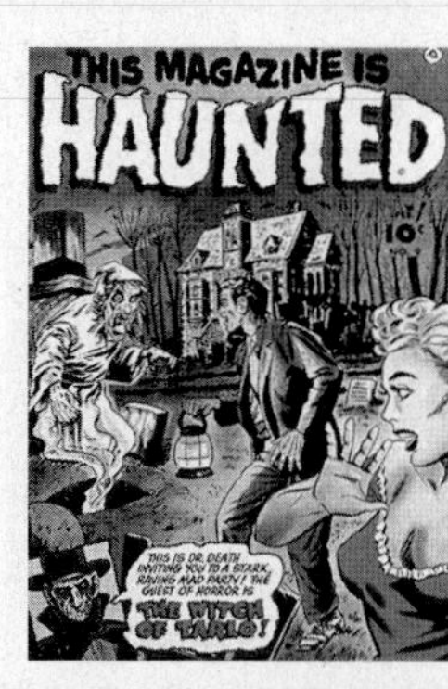

This Magazine is Haunted #9 © FAW

Thor #160 © MAR

GD VG FN VF VF/NM NM-
2.0 4.0 6.0 8.0 9.0 9.2

1-12: 1-4-Niles-s/Kieth-a; covers by Kieth and Furno. 5-12-Niles-s 4.00

30 DAYS OF NIGHT (2017 reimagining of original series)
IDW Publishing: Dec, 2017 - Present ($3.99)
1-3-Niles-s/Kowalski-a; covers by Kowalski, Wood and Templesmith 4.00

30 DAYS OF NIGHT: BEYOND BARROW
IDW Publishing: Sept, 2007 - No. 3, Dec, 2007 ($3.99, limited series)
1-3-Niles-s/Sienkiewicz-a/c 4.00

30 DAYS OF NIGHT: BLOODSUCKER TALES
IDW Publishing: Oct, 2004 - No. 8, May, 2005 ($3.99, limited series)
1-8-Niles-s/Chamberlain-a; Fraction-s/Templesmith-a/c 4.00
HC (8/05, $49.99) r/#1-8; cover gallery 50.00
SC (8/05, $24.99) r/#1-8; cover gallery 25.00

30 DAYS OF NIGHT: DEAD SPACE
IDW Publishing: Jan, 2006 - No. 3, Mar, 2006 ($3.99, limited series)
1-3-Niles and Wickline-s/Milx-a/c 4.00

30 DAYS OF NIGHT: EBEN & STELLA
IDW Publishing: May, 2007 - No. 3, July, 2007 ($3.99, limited series)
1-3-Niles and DeConnick-s/Randall-a/c 4.00

30 DAYS OF NIGHT: NIGHT, AGAIN
IDW Publishing: May, 2011 - No. 4, Aug, 2011 ($3.99, limited series)
1-4-Lansdale-s/Kieth-a/c 4.00

30 DAYS OF NIGHT: RED SNOW
IDW Publishing: Aug, 2007 - No. 3, Oct, 2007 ($3.99, limited series)
1-3-Ben Templesmith-s/a/c 4.00

30 DAYS OF NIGHT: RETURN TO BARROW
IDW Publishing: Mar, 2004 - No. 6, Aug, 2004 ($3.99, limited series)
1-6-Steve Niles-s/Ben Templesmith-a/c 4.00
TPB (2004, $19.99) r/#1-6; cover gallery 20.00

30 DAYS OF NIGHT: SPREADING THE DISEASE
IDW Publishing: Dec, 2006 - No. 5, Apr, 2007 ($3.99, limited series)
1-5: 1-Wickline-s/Sanchez-a. 3-5-Sandoval-a 4.00

30 DAYS OF NIGHT: 30 DAYS 'TIL DEATH
IDW Publishing: Dec, 2008 - No. 4, Mar, 2009 ($3.99, limited series)
1-4-David Lapham-s/a; covers by Lapham and Templesmith 4.00

THIRTY SECONDS OVER TOKYO (See American Library)

THIS DAMNED BAND
Dark Horse Comics: Aug, 2016 - No. 6, Jan, 2016 ($3.99, limited series)
1-6-Paul Cornell-s/Tony Parker-a 4.00

THIS IS SUSPENSE! (Formerly Strange Suspense Stories; Strange Suspense Stories #27 on)
Charlton Comics: No. 23, Feb, 1955 - No. 26, Aug, 1955
23-Wood-a(r)/A Star Presentation #3 "Dr. Jekyll & Mr. Hyde"; last pre-code issue
24 48 72 144 237 330
24-Censored Fawcett-r; Evans-a (r/Suspense Detective #1)
14 28 42 82 121 160
25,26: 26-Marcus Swayze-a 10 20 30 58 79 100

THIS IS THE PAYOFF (See Pay-Off)

THIS IS WAR
Standard Comics: No. 5, July, 1952 - No. 9, May, 1953
5-Toth-a 18 36 54 105 165 225
6,9-Toth-a 14 28 42 80 115 150
7,8: 8-Ross Andru-c 11 22 33 62 86 110

THIS IS YOUR LIFE, DONALD DUCK (See Donald Duck..., Four Color #1109)

THIS MAGAZINE IS CRAZY (Crazy #? on)
Charlton Publ. (Humor Magazines): V3#2, July, 1957 - V4#8, Feb, 1959 (25¢, magazine, 68 pgs.)
V3#2-V4#7: V4#5-Russian Sputnik-c parody 11 22 33 60 83 105
V4#8-Davis-a (8 pgs.) 11 22 33 64 90 115

THIS MAGAZINE IS HAUNTED (Danger and Adventure #22 on)
Fawcett Publications/Charlton No. 15(2/54) on: Oct, 1951 - No. 14, 12/53; No. 15, 2/54 - V3#21, Nov, 1954
1-Evans-a; Dr. Death as host begins 81 162 243 518 884 1250
2,5-Evans-a 50 100 150 315 533 750
3,4: 3-Vampire-c/story 41 82 123 256 428 600

GD VG FN VF VF/NM NM-
2.0 4.0 6.0 8.0 9.0 9.2

6-9,12 37 74 111 222 361 500
10-Severed head-c 77 154 231 493 847 1200
11-Classic skeleton-c 40 80 120 246 411 575
13-Severed head-c/story 68 136 204 435 743 1050
14-Classic burning skull-c 52 104 156 328 552 775
15,20: 15-Dick Giordano-c. 20-Cover is swiped from panel in The Thing #16
28 56 84 165 270 375
16,19-Ditko-c. 19-Injury-to-eye panel; story-r/#1 50 100 150 315 533 750
17-Ditko-c/a(4); blood drainage story 61 122 183 390 670 950
18-Ditko-c/a(1 story); E.C. swipe/Haunt of Fear #5; injury-to-eye panel; reprints "Caretaker of the Dead" from Beware Terror Tales & recolored
53 106 159 334 567 800
21-Ditko-c, Evans-r/This Magazine Is Haunted #1 43 86 129 271 461 650
NOTE: *Baily a-1, 3, 4, 21r/#1. Moldoff c/a-1-13. Powell a-3-5, 11, 12, 17. Shuster a-18-20. Issues 19-21 have reprints which have been recolored from This Magazine is Haunted #1.*

THIS MAGAZINE IS HAUNTED (2nd Series) (Formerly Zaza the Mystic; Outer Space #17 on)
Charlton Comics: V2#12, July, 1957 - V2#16, May, 1958
V2#12-14-Ditko-c/a in all 48 96 144 302 514 725
15-No Ditko-c/a 19 38 57 109 172 235
16-Ditko-a(4). 36 72 108 216 351 485

THIS MAGAZINE IS WILD (See Wild)

THIS WAS YOUR LIFE (Religious)
Jack T. Chick Publ.: 1964 (3 1/2 x 5 1/2", 40 pgs., B&W and red)
nn, Another version (5x2 3/4", 26 pgs.) 2 4 6 10 14 18

THOR (See Avengers #1, Giant-Size..., Marvel Collectors Item Classics, Marvel Graphic Novel #33, Marvel Preview, Marvel Spectacular, Marvel Treasury Edition, Special Marvel Edition & Tales of Asgard)

THOR (Journey Into Mystery #1-125, 503-on)(The Mighty Thor #413-490)
Marvel Comics Group: No. 126, Mar, 1966 - No. 502, Sept, 1996
126-Thor continues (#125-130 Thor vs. Hercules); Tales of Asgard back-up stories continue through issue #145 36 72 108 259 580 900
127-130: 127-1st app. Pluto. 129-1st Ares Olympian God of War & Tana Nile of the Rigillian Colonizers 10 20 30 67 141 215
131,135,137-140: 135-Origin of the High Evolutionary. 137-1st Ulik the Troll. 138-139-Thor vs. Ulik. 140-Kang app; 1st Growing Man 9 18 27 57 111 165
132-1st app. Ego the Living Planet 10 20 30 64 132 200
133-Thor vs. Ego 12 24 36 79 170 260
134-Intro High Evolutionary and Man-Beast 10 20 30 66 138 210
136-(1/67) Re-intro. Sif 9 18 27 60 120 180
141-145: 142-Thor vs. Super-Skrull. 143,144-Thor vs. the Enchanters
7 14 21 49 92 135
146,147: 146-Inhumans origin; begin (early app.) in back-up stories, end #152 (see Fantastic Four #45 for 1st app.). 147-Origin continues 8 16 24 54 102 150
148,149-Origin Black Bolt in each. 148-1st app. Wrecker. 149-Origin Medusa, Crystal, Maximus, Gorgon, Karnak 9 18 27 59 117 175
150-152: Inhumans app. 150-Hela app. 151,152-Destroyer and Ulik app.
8 16 24 52 99 145
153-157,159: 154-1st Mangog. 155-157-Thor vs Mangog. 159-Origin Dr. Blake (Thor) concl.
6 12 18 42 79 115
158-Origin-r/#83; origin Dr. Blake 9 18 27 57 111 165
160-162-Galactus app. 7 14 21 46 86 125
163,164-2nd & 3th brief app. Warlock (Him) 5 10 15 35 63 90
165-1st full app. Warlock (Him) (6/69, see Fantastic Four #67); last 12¢ issue; Kirby-a
40 80 120 296 673 1050
166-2nd full app. Warlock (Him); battles Thor; see Marvel Premiere #1
10 20 30 69 147 225
167,170-179: 170-1st Thermal Man. 171-Thor vs. the Wrecker. 173-Circus of Crime app. 174-1st Crypto-Man. 176-177-Surtur app. 178-1st Buscema-a on Thor; vs the Abomination. 179-Last Kirby issue 5 10 15 34 60 85
168,169-Origin Galactus; Kirby-a 8 16 24 56 108 160
180,181-Neal Adams-a; Mephisto & Loki app. 6 12 18 37 66 95
182,183-Thor vs. Doctor Doom. 182-Buscema-a begins (11/70)
5 10 15 34 60 85
184-192: 184-1st Infinity & the Silent One. 187-Thor vs Odin. 188-Origin of Infinity. 189,190-Thor vs. Hela. 191-1st Durok the Demolisher. 192-Last 15¢ issue; Thor vs. Durok
4 8 12 27 44 60
193-(25¢, 52 pgs.); Silver Surfer x-over; Thor vs. Durok; last Stan Lee story as regular writer
11 22 33 72 154 235
194-199: 194-Gerry Conway stories begin (ends #238). 195-Mangog returns. 196-198-Thor vs. Mangog. 199-1st Ego-Prime; Pluto app. 4 8 12 23 37 50
200-Special Ragnarok issue by Stan Lee 4 8 12 28 47 65
201-206,208-220,222-224; 201-Pluto & Hela app; origin of Ego-Prime. 202-vs Ego-Prime. 203-1st Young Gods. 204-Thor exiled on Earth; Mephisto app. 205-vs Mephisto; Hitler app.

Thor #342 © MAR

Thor #492 © MAR

Thor V2 #3 © MAR

GD VG FN VF VF/NM NM-
2.0 4.0 6.0 8.0 9.0 9.2

206-vs. the Absorbing Man. 208-1st Mercurio the 4th Dimensional Man. 210-211-vs. Ulik. 214-Mercurio the 4-D Man app; 1st Xorr the God-Jewel. 215-Origin of Xorr; Mecurio the 4-D Man app. 216-Xorr & Mecurio app. 217-Thor vs Odin-c. 218-220-Saga of the Black Stars. 222,223-vs Pluto. 224-The Destroyer app. 3 6 9 14 20 25

207-Rutland, Vermont Halloween x-over; leads into Avengers/Defenders war 3 6 9 19 30 40

221-Thor vs. Hercules; Hercules guest stars through issue #232,234-239 3 6 9 16 23 30

225-Intro. Firelord 6 12 18 41 76 110

226-Galactus and Firelord app. 3 6 9 14 20 25

227-231: 227-228-Thor, Firelord & Galactus vs Ego the Living Planet 2 4 6 10 14 18

232,233: 232-Firelord app. 233-Numerous guest stars; Asgard invades Earth 3 6 9 14 20 25

234-245: 234-Iron Man & Firelord app. 235-1st Kamo Tharnn, Elder of the Universe. 236-Thor vs. Absorbing Man. 237-239-Thor vs. Ulik. 240-1st Egyptian Gods; Osiris & Horus; 1st Seth-Egyptian God of Death. 241-Thor vs. Seth. 242-Len Wein scripts begin; ends #271. 242-245-Thor vs. Time-Twisters; Zarko the Tomorrow Man app. 2 4 6 10 14 18

246-250-(Regular 25¢ editions)(4-8/76): 246-247-Firelord app. 249-250-Thor vs. Mangog 2 4 6 10 14 18

246-250-(30¢-c variants, limited distribution) 4 8 12 27 44 60

251-280: 251-Thor vs. Hela. 252,253-Thor vs. Ulik. 255-Re-intro Stone Men of Saturn. 257-259-Thor vs. Grey Gargoyle. 260-Thor vs. Enchantress & Executioner. 261-272-Simonson-a. 264-266-Thor vs. Loki. 265,266-The Destroyer app. 269-Thor vs. Stilt-Man. 270-Thor vs. Blastaar. 271-Iron Man x-over. 272-Roy Thomas scripts begin. 274-Death of Balder the Brave. 276-Thor vs. Red Norvell Thor. 280-Thor vs. Hyperion 1 3 4 6 8 10

260-264-(35¢-c variants, limited distribution)(6-10/77) 8 16 24 51 96 140

281-299: 281-Space Phantom app. 282-Immortus app. 283,284-Celestials app. 284-286-Eternals app. 287-288-Thor vs. the Forgotten one. 291,292-Asgard vs Olympus. 292-1st Eye of Odin (as sentient being). 294-Origin Asgard & Odin 1 2 3 5 6 8

300-(12/80)-End of Asgard; origin of Odin & The Destroyer; double-size 2 4 6 8 10 12

301-Numerous pantheons (skyfathers) app. 1 2 3 5 6 8

302-304 5.00

305-306: 305-Airwalker app. 306-Firelord 1 2 3 5 6 8

307-331,334-336: 310-Thor vs. Mephisto. 314-Moondragon and Drax app. 315,316-Bi-Beast & Man-Beast app. 316-Iron Man x-over. 325-Mephisto app. 331-1st Crusader 5.00

332,333-Dracula app. 1 2 3 5 6 8

337-Simonson-c/a begins, ends #382; 1st app. of Beta Ray Bill who becomes the new Thor; intro Lorelei 4 8 12 23 37 50

338-Beta Ray Bill vs. Thor 2 4 6 9 12 18

339,340: 339-Beta Ray Bill gains Thor's powers. 340-Donald Blake returns as Thor 6.00

341-343,345-373,375-381,383,386: 341-Clark Kent & Lois Lane cameo. 345-349-Malekith the Accursed app. 350-352-Avengers app. 353-'Death' of Odin. 356-Hercules app. 363-Secret Wars II crossover. 364-366-Thor as a frog. 367-Malekith app. 373-X-Factor tie-in. 383-Secret Wars flashback 4.00

344-(6/84) 1st app. of Malekith the Accursed (Ruler of the Dark Elves)(villain in the 2013 movie Thor: The Dark World); Simonson-c/a 2 4 6 9 12 15

374-Mutant Massacre; X-Factor app. 5.00

382-($1.25)-Anniversary issue; last Simonson-a 6.00

384-Intro. Thor of the 26th century (Dargo Ktor) 6.00

385-Thor vs. Hulk by Stan Lee and Erik Larsen 6.00

387,388,390-399: Thor vs. the Celestials. 390-Avengers app.; Captain America lifts Mjolnir. 391-Spider-Man x-over; 1st Eric Masterson. 393-395-Daredevil app. 395-Intro. Earth Force. 396-399-Black Knight app. 4.00

389- 'Alone against the Celestials' climax 5.00

400-($1.75, 68 pgs.)-Origin Loki 6.00

401-410: 404,405-Annihilus app. 409-410-Dr. Doom app. 4.00

411-Intro New Warriors (appear in costume in last panel); Juggernaut-c/story 3 6 9 14 19 24

412-1st full app. New Warriors (Marvel Boy, Kid Nova, Namorita, Night Thrasher, Firestar & Speedball) 3 6 9 15 22 28

413-426: 413-Dr. Strange app. 419-425-Black Galaxy saga; origin Celestials 4.00

427-428-Excalibur app. 428-Ghost Rider app. 5.00

429-431: 429-Thor vs Juggernaut; Ghost Rider app. 430-Ghost Rider app. 3.00

432-(52 pgs.) Thor's 350th issue (vs. Loki) reprints origin and 1st app. from Journey into Mystery #83 4.00

433-449,451-467: 433-Intro. Eric Masterson as Thor. 434,435-Annihilus app. 437-Quasar app.; Tales of Asgard back-up stories begin. 438-441-Thor War; Beta Ray Bill app. 443-Dr. Strange & Silver Surfer x-over; last $1.00-c. 445,446-Operation Galactic Storm. 445-Thor vs. Gladiator. 448-Spider-Man app. 451,452-Bloodaxe app. 457-Original Thor returns. 458-Thor vs. Thor. 459-Intro Thunderstrike. 460-Starlin scripts begin. 461-Thor vs. Beta Ray Bill. 463-467-Infinity Crusade x-over. 466-Drax app. 3.00

GD VG FN VF VF/NM NM-
2.0 4.0 6.0 8.0 9.0 9.2

450-($2.50, 68 pgs.)-Flip-book format; r/story JIM #85 (1st Loki) plus-c plus a gallery of past-c; gatefold-c 4.00

468,469-Blood and Thunder x-over. 468-Thor vs. Silver Surfer. 469-Infinity Watch app. 5.00

470,471-Blood and Thunder x-over. 470-Thanos and the Infinity Watch app. 471-Blood and Thunder story conclusion; Infinity Watch and Silver Surfer app. 6.00

472-474: 472-Intro the Godlings. 474-Begin $1.50-c; bound-in trading cards 3.00

475 ($2.00, 52 pgs.)-Regular edition; High Evolutionary and Man-Beast app. 4.00

475 ($2.50, 52 pgs.)-Collectors edition w/foil embossed-c 5.00

476-481: 476-Destroyer app. 477-Thunderstrike app. 478-Return of Red Norvell Thor. 479-Detailed Origin of Thor 3.00

482 ($2.95, 84 pgs.)-400th Thor issue 5.00

483,486,487,488: 486-Kurse app. 4.00

484,485,490: 484-War Machine app. 485-Thing app. 490-Absorbing Man app.; Buscema-a 5.00

489-Hulk app. 6.00

491-Warren Ellis scripts begins, ends #494; Worldengine pt.1; Deodato-c/a begins 6.00

492-494: Worldengine pt. 2-4. 492-Reintro The Enchantress; Beta Ray Bill dies 5.00

495-499: 495-Messner-Loebs scripts begin; Isherwood-c/a. 496-Captain America app. 3.00

500 ($2.50)-Double-size; wraparound-c; Deodato-c/a; Dr. Strange app. 5.00

501-Reintro Red Norvell 4.00

502-(9/96) Onslaught tie-in; Red Norvell, Jane Foster & Hela app. 5.00

NOTE: *Numbering continues with Journey Into Mystery #503 (11/96)*

600-up (See Thor 2007 series)

Special 2(9/66)-(See Journey Into Mystery for 1st annual) Destroyer app. 9 18 27 63 129 195

Special 2 (2nd printing, 1994) 2 4 6 8 10 12

King Size Special 3 (1/71) 4 8 12 23 37 50

Special 4 (12/71)-r/Thor #131,132 & JIM #113 3 6 9 19 30 40

Annual 5 (11/76)-Asgard vs Olympus; Hercules app. 2 4 6 11 16 20

Annual 6 (10/77)-Guardians of the Galaxy app. 4 8 12 25 40 55

Annual 7,8: 7 (1978)-Eternals app. 8 (1979)-Thor vs. Zeus-c/story 2 4 6 8 11 14

Annual 9-13: 9 ('81)-Dormammu app. 10 ('82)-1st Demogorge-the God Eater. 11 ('83)-Origin of Thor expanded. 12 ('84)-Intro Vidar (Thor's brother). 13 ('85)-Mephisto app. 6.00

Annual 14-19 ('86-'94, 68 pgs.): 14-Atlantis Attacks. 15 ('90)-Terminus factor Pt. 3. 16-3 pg. origin; Guardians of the Galaxy x-over. 17 ('92)-Citizen Kang Pt. 2. 18-Polybagged w/card; intro the Flame. 19 ('94) vs. Pluto 4.00

...Alone Against the Celestials nn (6/92, $5.95)-r/Thor #387-389 6.00

...Legends Vol. 2: Walter Simonson Book 2 TPB (2003, $24.99) r/#349-355,357-359 25.00

...Legends Vol. 3: Walter Simonson Book 3 TPB (2004, $24.99) r/#360-369 25.00

...: The Eternals Saga TPB (2006, $24.99) r/#283-291 & Annual #7; profile pages 25.00

...: The Eternals Saga Vol. 2 TPB ('07, $24.99) r/#292-301; Thomas & Gruenwald essays 25.00

... Visionaries: Mike Deodato Jr. TPB (2004, $19.99) r/#491-494,498-500 20.00

... Visionaries: Walter Simonson (Vol. 1) TPB (5/01, $24.95) r/#337-348 25.00

... Visionaries: Walter Simonson Vol. 4 TPB (2007, $24.99) r/#371-373 & Balder the Brave #1-4 25.00

... Visionaries: Walter Simonson Vol. 5 TPB (2008, $24.95) r/#375-382 25.00

...: Worldengine (8/96, $9.95)-r/#491-494; Deodato-c/a; story & new intermission by Warren Ellis 10.00

NOTE: ***Neal Adams** a-180,181; c-179-181. **Austin** a-342i, 346i; c-312i. **Buscema** a(p)-178, 182-213, 215-226, 231-238, 241-253, 254r, 256-259, 272-278, 283-285, 370, Annual 6, 8, 11i; c(p)-175, 178, 182-196, 198-200, 202-204, 206, 211, 212, 215, 219, 221, 226, 256, 259, 261, 262, 272-278, 283, 289, 370, Annual 6. **Everett** a(i)-143, 170-175; c(i)-171, 172, 174, 176, 241. **Gil Kane** a-318p; c(p)-201, 205, 207-210, 216, 220, 222, 223, 231, 233-240, 242, 243, 318. **Kirby** a(p)-126-177, 179, 194r, 254r; c(p)-126-169, 171-174, 176, 177, 249-253, 255, 257, 258, Annual 5, Special 2-4. **Mooney** a(i)-201, 204, 214-216, 218, 322i, 324i, 325i, 327i. **Sienkiewicz** c-332, 333, 335. **Simonson** a-260-271p, 337-354, 357-367, 380, Annual 7p; c-260, 263-271, 337-355, 357-369, 371, 373-382, Annual 7. **Starlin** c-213.*

THOR (Volume 2)

Marvel Comics: July, 1998 - No. 85, Dec, 2004 ($2.99/$1.99/$2.25)

1-($2.99)-Follows Heroes Return; Jurgens-s/Romita Jr. & Janson-a; wraparound-c; battles the Destroyer 6.00

1-Variant-c 1 2 3 5 6 8

1-Rough Cut-($2.99) Features original script and pencil pages 3.00

1-Sketch cover 28.00

2-($1.99) Two covers; Avengers app. 4.00

3-11,13-23: 3-Assumes Jake Olson ID. 4-Namor-c/app. 8-Spider-Man-c/app. 14-Iron Man c/app. 17-Juggernaut-c 3.00

12-($2.99) Wraparound-c; Hercules appears 4.00

12-($10.00) Variant-c by Jusko 10.00

24,26-31,33,34: 24-Begin $2.25-c. 26-Mignola-c/Larsen-a. 29-Andy Kubert-a. 30-Maximum Security x-over; Beta Ray Bill-c/app. 33-Intro. Thor Girl 3.00

25-($2.99) Regular edition 4.00

25-($3.99) Gold foil enhanced cover 5.00

32-($3.50, 100 pgs.) new story plus reprints w/Kirby-a; Simonson-a 5.00

Thor (2007 series) #11 © MAR

Thor (2014 series) #8 © MAR

Thor: Son of Asgard #1 © MAR

GD 2.0 VG 4.0 FN 6.0 VF 8.0 VF/NM 9.0 NM- 9.2

35-($2.99) Thor battles The Gladiator; Andy Kubert-a 4.00
36-49,51-61: 37-Starlin-a. 38,39-BWS-c. 38-42-Immonen-a. 40-Odin killed. 41-Orbik-c. 44-'Nuff Said silent issue. 51-Spider-Man app. 57-Art by various. 58-Davis-a; x-over with Iron Man #64. 60-Brereton-c 3.00
50-($4.95) Raney-c/a; back-ups w/Nuckols-a & Armenta-s/Bennett-a 5.00
62-84: 62-Begin $2.99-c. 64-Loki-c/app. 80-Oeming-s begins; Avengers app. 3.00
85-Last issue; Thor dies; Oeming-s/DiVito-a/Epting-c 4.00
...1999 Annual ($3.50) Jurgens-s/a(p) 4.00
...2000 Annual ($3.50) Jurgens-s/Ordway-a(p); back-up stories 4.00
...2001 Annual ($3.50) Jurgens-s/Grummett-a(p); Lightle-c 4.00
...Across All Worlds (9/01, $19.95, TPB) r/#28-35 20.00
Avengers Disassembled: Thor TPB (2004, $16.99) r/#80-85; afterword by Oeming 17.00
...Resurrection ($5.99, TPB) r/#1,2 6.00
...: The Dark Gods (7/00, $15.95, TPB) r/#9-13 16.00
...Vol. 1: The Death of Odin (7/02, $12.99, TPB) r/#39-44 13.00
...Vol. 2: Lord of Asgard (9/02, $15.99, TPB) r/#45-50 16.00
...Vol. 3: Gods on Earth (2003, $21.99, TPB) r/#51-58, Avengers #63, Iron Man #64, Marvel Double-Shot #1; Beck-c 22.00
...Vol. 4: Spiral (2003, $19.99, TPB) r/#59-67; Brereton-c 20.00
...Vol. 5: The Reigning (2004, $17.99, TPB) r/#68-74 18.00
...Vol. 6: Gods and Men (2004, $13.99, TPB) r/#75-79 14.00

THOR (Also see Fantastic Four #538)(Resumes original numbering with #600)
Marvel Comics: Sept, 2007 - No. 12, Mar, 2009; No. 600, Apr, 2009 - No. 621, May, 2011 ($2.99/$3.99) (Continues numbering as Journey Into Mystery #622) (Also see Mighty Thor #1)

1-Straczynski-s/Coipel-a/c 4.00
1-Variant-c by Michael Turner 5.00
1-Zombie variant-c by Suydam 5.00
1-Non-zombie variant-c by Suydam 5.00
1-"Marvel's Greatest Comics" edition (5/10, $1.00) r/#1 3.00
2-12: 2-Two covers by Dell'Otto and Coipel. 3-Iron Man app.; McGuinness var-c. 4-Bermejo var-c. 5-Campbell var-c. 6-Art Adams var-c. 7,8-Djurdjevic-a/c; Coipel var-c 3.00
2-Second printing with wraparound-c 3.00
7-"Marvel's Greatest Comics" edition (6/11, $1.00) r/#7 3.00

(After #12 [Mar, 2009] numbering reverted back to original Journey Into Mystery/Thor numbering with #600, Apr, 2009)

600 (4/09, $4.99) Two wraparound-c by Coipel & Djurdjevic; Coipel, Djurdjevic & Aja-a; r/Tales of Asgard from Journey Into Mystery #106,107,112,113,115; Kirby-a 5.00
601-603,611-621-($3.99) 601-603-Djurdjevic-a. 602-Sif returns. 617-Loki returns 4.00
604-610-($2.99) Tan-a. 607-609-Siege x-over. 610-Braithwaite-a; Ragnarok app. 3.00
620.1 (5/11, $2.99) Brooks-a; Grey Gargoyle app. 3.00
Annual 1 (11/09, $3.99) Suayan, Grindberg, Gaudiano-a; Djurdjevic-c 4.00
...: Ages of Thunder (6/08, $3.99) Fraction-s/Zircher-a/Djurdjevic-c 4.00
... & Hercules: Encyclopædia Mythologica (2009, $4.99) profile pages of the Pantheons 5.00
... Asgard's Avenger 1 (6/11, $4.99) profile pages of Thor characters 5.00
... By Simonson Halloween Comic Fest 2017 1 (12/17, giveaway) r/#354 & JIM #102 3.00
... Crown of Fools 1 (12/13, $3.99) Di Vito & Simonson-a 4.00
... Giant-Size Finale 1 (1/01, $3.99) Dr. Doom app.; r/origin from JIM #83 4.00
... God-Size Special (2/09, $3.99) story of Skurge the Executioner re-told; art by Brereton, Braithwaite, Allred and Sepulveda; plus reprint of Thor #362 (1985) 4.00
... Goes Hollywood 1 ('11, $3.99) Collection of movie-themed variant Thor covers 4.00
...: Man of War (1/09, $3.99) Fraction-s/Mann & Zircher-a/Djurdjevic-c 4.00
...: Reign of Blood (8/08, $3.99) Fraction-s/Evans & Zircher-a/Djurdjevic-c 4.00
...: Spotlight (5/11, $3.99) movie photo-c; movie preview; creator interviews 4.00
...: The Rage of Thor (10/10, $3.99) Milligan-s/Suayan-c/a 4.00
...: The Trial of Thor (8/09, $3.99) Milligan-s/Nord-c/a 4.00
...: Truth of History (12/08, $3.99) Thor and crew in ancient Egypt; Alan Davis-s/a/c 4.00
...: Where Walk the Frost Giants 1 (12/17, $3.99) Macchio-s/Nauck-a; plus r/JIM #112 4.00
...: Whosoever Wields This Hammer 1 (6/11, $4.99) recolored r/J.I.M. #83,84,88 5.00
...: Wolves of the North (2/11, $3.99) Carey-s/Perkins-a 4.00
... By J. Michael Straczynski Vol. 1 HC (2008, $19.99) r/#1-6; variant cover gallery 20.00

THOR (Female Thor)
Marvel Comics: Dec, 2014 - No. 8, Jul, 2015 ($3.99)

1-Aaron-s/Dauterman-a/c; Thor, Odin and Malekith app. 10.00
2-8 2-4-Malekith app. 4-Thor vs. Thor. 5-Molina-a. 8-Identity revealed 4.00
Annual 1 (4/15, $4.99) Female Thor, King Thor stories; Young Thor by CM Punk-s 5.00

THOR ADAPTATION (MARVEL'S...)
Marvel Comics: Mar, 2012 - No. 2, Apr, 2012 ($2.99, limited series)

1,2-Adaptation of 2012 movie; Gage-s/Medina-a; photo-c 3.00

THOR AND THE WARRIORS FOUR
Marvel Comics: Jun, 2010 - No. 4, Sept, 2010 ($2.99, limited series)

1-4-Thor and Power Pack team-up; Gurihiru-a; back-up with Coover-s/a 3.00

GD 2.0 VG 4.0 FN 6.0 VF 8.0 VF/NM 9.0 NM- 9.2

THOR: BLOOD OATH
Marvel Comics: Nov, 2005 - No. 6, Feb, 2006 ($2.99, limited series)

1-6-Oeming-s/Kolins-a/c 3.00
HC (2006, $19.99, dust jacket) r/series; afterword by Oeming 20.00
SC (2006, $14.99) r/series; afterword by Oeming 15.00

THOR CORPS
Marvel Comics: Sept, 1993 - No. 4, Jan, 1994 ($1.75, limited series)

1-4: 1-Invaders cameo. 2-Invaders app. 3-Spider-Man 2099, Rawhide Kid, Two-Gun Kid & Kid Colt app. 4-Painted-c 3.00

THOR: FIRST THUNDER
Marvel Comics: Nov, 2010 - No. 5, Mar, 2011 ($3.99, limited series)

1-5: 1-Huat-a; new retelling of origin; reprint of debut in JIM #83 4.00

THOR: FOR ASGARD
Marvel Comics: Nov, 2010 - No. 6, Apr, 2011 ($3.99, limited series)

1-6-Bianchi-a/c. 1-Frost Giants app. 4.00

THOR: GOD OF THUNDER (Marvel NOW!)
Marvel Comics: Jan, 2013 - No. 25, Nov, 2014 ($3.99)

1-24: 1-5-Aaron-s/Ribic-a. 6-Guice-a. 13-17-Malekith app. 19-23-Galactus app. 21-1st app. S.H.I.E.L.D. Agent Roz Solomon 4.00
25-($4.99) Art by Guera, Bisley, and Ribic; Malekith app.; new female Thor cameo 5.00

THOR: GODSTORM
Marvel Comics: Nov, 2001 - No. 3, Jan, 2002 ($3.50, limited series)

1-3-Steve Rude-c/a; Busiek-s. 1-Avengers app. 4.00

THOR: HEAVEN & EARTH
Marvel Comics: Sept, 2011 - No. 4, Nov, 2011 ($2.99, limited series)

1-4: 1-Jenkins-s/Olivetti-a/c; Loki app. 2-Texeira-a/c. 3-Alixe-a. 4-Medina-a 3.00

THORION OF THE NEW ASGODS
Marvel Comics (Amalgam): June, 1997 ($1.95, one-shot)

1-Keith Giffen-s/John Romita Jr.-c/a 3.00

THORS (Secret Wars Battleworld tie-in)
Marvel Comics: Aug, 2015 - No. 4, Jan, 2016 ($3.99, limited series)

1-4: Police squad of Thors on Doomworld; Aaron-s/Sprouse-a. 2,3-Sudzuka-a 4.00

THOR: SON OF ASGARD
Marvel Comics: May, 2004 - No. 12, Mar, 2005 ($2.99, limited series)

1-12: Teenaged Thor, Sif, and Balder; Tocchini-a. 1-6-Granov-c. 7-12-Jo Chen-c 3.00
... Vol. 1: The Warriors Teen (2004, $7.99, digest) r/#1-6 8.00
... Vol. 2: Worthy (2005, $7.99, digest) r/#7-12 8.00

THOR: TALES OF ASGARD BY STAN LEE & JACK KIRBY
Marvel Comics: 2009 - No. 6, 2009 ($3.99, limited series)

1-6-Reprints back-up stories from Journey Into Mystery #97-120; new covers by Coipel 4.00

THOR: THE DEVIANTS SAGA
Marvel Comics: Jan, 2012 - No. 5, May, 2012 ($3.99, limited series)

1-5-Rodi-s/Segovia-a; Ereshkigal app. 4.00

THOR: THE DARK WORLD PRELUDE (MARVEL'S...)
Marvel Comics: Aug, 2013 - No. 2, Aug, 2013 ($2.99, limited series)

1,2-Prelude to 2013 movie; Eaton-a; photo-c 3.00

THOR: THE LEGEND
Marvel Comics: Sept, 1996 ($3.95, one-shot)

nn-Tribute issue 4.00

THOR THE MIGHTY AVENGER
Marvel Comics: Sept, 2010 - No. 8, Mar, 2011 ($2.99, limited series)

1-8-Re-imagining of Thor's origin; Langridge-s/Samnee-a. 1-Mr. Hyde app. 3.00
Free Comic Book Day 2011 (giveaway) Captain America app. 3.00

THOR: VIKINGS
Marvel Comics (MAX): Sept, 2003 - No. 5, Jan, 2004 ($3.50, limited series)

1-5-Garth Ennis-s/Glenn Fabry-a/c 3.50
TPB (2004, $13.99) r/series 14.00

THOSE MAGNIFICENT MEN IN THEIR FLYING MACHINES (See Movie Comics)

THRAX
Event Comics: Nov, 1996 ($2.95, one-shot)

1 3.00

THREE
Image Comics: Oct, 2013 - No. 5, Feb, 2014 ($2.99)

3-D Batman 1953 © DC

3-D-ell #3 © DELL

3-D Zone #18 © RP

GD 2.0 | VG 4.0 | FN 6.0 | VF 8.0 | VF/NM 9.0 | NM- 9.2

1-5-Spartans 100 years after the Battle of Thermopylae; Ryan Kelly-a/Kieron Gillen-s 3.00

THREE CABALLEROS (Walt Disney's...)
Dell Publishing Co.: No. 71, 1945
Four Color 71-by Walt Kelly, c/a 60 120 180 480 1078 1675

THREE CHIPMUNKS, THE (TV) (Also see Alvin)
Dell Publishing Co.: No. 1042, Oct-Dec, 1959
Four Color 1042 (#1)-(Alvin, Simon & Theodore) 9 18 27 60 120 180

THREE COMICS (Also see Spiritman)
The Penny King Co.: 1944 (10¢, 52 pgs.) (2 different covers exist)
1,3,4-Lady Luck, Mr. Mystic, The Spirit app. (3 Spirit sections bound together); Lou Fine-a
32 64 96 188 307 425
NOTE: *No. 1 contains Spirit Sections 4/9/44 - 4/23/44, and No. 4 is also from 4/44.*

3-D (NOTE: The prices of all the 3-D comics listed include glasses. Deduct 40-50 percent if glasses are missing, and reduce slightly if glasses are loose.)

3-D ACTION
Atlas Comics (ACI): Jan, 1954 (Oversized, 15¢)(2 pairs of glasses included)
1-Battle Brady; Sol Brodsky-c 50 100 150 315 533 750

3-D ALIEN TERROR
Eclipse Comics: June, 1986 ($2.50)
1-Old Witch, Crypt-Keeper, Vault Keeper cameo; Morrow, John Pound-a, Yeates-c 6.00
...in 2-D: 100 copies signed, numbered(B&W) 3 6 9 14 20 25

3-D ANIMAL FUN (See Animal Fun)

THREE DAYS IN EUROPE
Oni Press: Nov, 2002 - No. 5, Apr, 2003 ($2.95, B&W, limited series)
1-5-Johnston-s/Hawthorne-a 3.00
TPB (11/03, $14.95, digest-sized) r/#1-5 15.00

3-D BATMAN (Also see Batman 3-D)
National Periodical Publications: 1953 (Reprinted in 1966)
1953-(25¢)-Reprints Batman #42 & 48 (Penguin-c/story); Tommy Tomorrow story;
came with pair of 3-D Bat glasses 106 212 318 673 1162 1650
1966-Reprints 1953 issue; new cover by Infantino/Anderson; has inside-c photos of
Batman & Robin from TV show (50¢) 19 38 57 131 291 450

3-D CIRCUS
Fiction House Magazines (Real Adventures Publ.): 1953 (25¢, w/glasses)
1 28 56 84 165 270 375

3-D COMICS (See Mighty Mouse, Tor and Western Fighters)

3-D DOLLY
Harvey Publications: December, 1953 (25¢, came with 2 pairs of glasses)
1-Richie Rich story redrawn from his 1st app. in Little Dot #1; shows cover in 3-D on inside
47 94 141 296 498 700

3-D-ELL
Dell Publishing Co.: No. 1, 1953; No. 3, 1953 (3-D comics) (25¢, came w/glasses)
1-Rootie Kazootie (#2 does not exist) 30 60 90 177 289 400
3-Flukey Luke 28 56 84 165 270 375

3 DEVILS
IDW Publishing: Mar, 2016 - No. 4, Jun, 2016 ($3.99, limited series)
1-4-Bo Hampton-s/a/c 4.00

3-D EXOTIC BEAUTIES
The 3-D Zone: Nov, 1990 ($2.95, 28 pgs.)
1-L.B. Cole-c 1 2 3 5 7 9

3-D FEATURES PRESENTS JET PUP
Dimensions Publications: Oct-Dec (Winter on-c), 1953 (25¢, came w/glasses)
1-Irving Spector-a(2) 30 60 90 177 289 400

3-D FUNNY MOVIES
Comic Media: 1953 (25¢, came w/glasses)
1-Bugsey Bear & Paddy Pelican 34 68 102 199 325 450

THREE-DIMENSION ADVENTURES (Superman)
National Periodical Publications: 1953 (25¢, large size, came w/glasses)
nn-Origin Superman (new art) 106 212 318 673 1162 1650

THREE DIMENSIONAL ALIEN WORLDS (See Alien Worlds)
Pacific Comics: July, 1984 (1st Ray Zone 3-D book)(one-shot)
1-Bolton-a(p); Stevens-a(i); Art Adams 1st published-a(p) 6.00

THREE DIMENSIONAL DNAGENTS (See New DNAgents)

THREE DIMENSIONAL E. C. CLASSICS (Three Dimensional Tales From the Crypt No. 2)
E. C. Comics: Spring, 1954 (Prices include glasses; came with 2 pair)
1-Stories by Wood (Mad #3), Krigstein (W.S. #7), Evans (F.C. #13), & Ingels (CSS #5);
Kurtzman-c (rare in high grade due to unstable paper)
106 212 318 673 1162 1650
NOTE: *Stories redrawn to 3-D format. Original stories not necessarily by artists listed. CSS: Crime SuspenStories; F.C.: Frontline Combat; W.S.: Weird Science.*

THREE DIMENSIONAL TALES FROM THE CRYPT (Formerly Three Dimensional E. C. Classics)(Cover title: ...From the Crypt of Terror)
E. C. Comics: No. 2, Spring, 1954 (Prices include glasses; came with 2 pair)
2-Davis (TFTC #25), Elder (VOH #14), Craig (TFTC #24), & Orlando (TFTC #22) stories;
Feldstein-c (rare in high grade) 105 210 315 667 1146 1625
NOTE: *Stories redrawn to 3-D format. Original stories not necessarily by artists listed. TFTC: Tales From the Crypt; VOH: Vault of Horror.*

3-D LOVE
Steriographic Publ. (Mikeross Publ.): Dec, 1953 (25¢, came w/glasses)
1 36 72 108 211 343 475

3-D NOODNICK (See Noodnick)

3-D ROMANCE
Steriographic Publ. (Mikeross Publ.): Jan, 1954 (25¢, came w/glasses)
1 34 68 102 199 325 450

3-D SHEENA, JUNGLE QUEEN (Also see Sheena 3-D)
Fiction House Magazines: 1953 (25¢, came w/glasses)
1-Maurice Whitman-c 71 142 213 454 777 1100

3-D SUBSTANCE
The 3-D Zone: July, 1990 ($2.95, 28 pgs.)
1-Ditko-c/a(r) 5.00

3-D TALES OF THE WEST
Atlas Comics (CPS): Jan, 1954 (Oversized) (15¢, came with 2 pair of glasses)
1 (3-D)-Sol Brodsky-c 47 94 141 296 498 700

3-D THREE STOOGES (Also see Three Stooges)
Eclipse Comics: Sept, 1986 - No. 2, Nov, 1986; No. 3, Oct, 1987; No. 4, 1989 ($2.50)
1-4: 3-Maurer-r. 4-r-/"Three Missing Links" 5.00
1-3 (2-D) 5.00

3-D WHACK (See Whack)

3-D ZONE, THE
The 3-D Zone (Renegade Press)/Ray Zone: Feb, 1987 - No. 20, 1989 ($2.50)
1,3,4,7-9,11,12,14,15,17,19,20: 1-r/A Star Presentation. 3-Picture Scope Jungle Advs.
4-Electric Fear. 7-Hollywood 3-D Jayne Mansfield photo-c. 8-High Seas 3-D, 9-Redmask-r.
11-Danse Macabre; Matt Fox c/a(r). 12-3-D Presidents. 14-Tyranostar. 15-3-Dementia
Comics; Kurtzman-c, Kubert, Maurer-a. 17-Thrilling Love. 19-Cracked Classics.
20-Commander Battle and His Atomic Submarine 1 2 3 5 6 8
2,5,6,10,13,18: 2-Wolverton-r. 5-Krazy Kat-r. 6-Ratfink. 10-Jet 3-D; Powell & Williamson-r.
13-Flash Gordon. 18-Spacehawk; Wolverton-r 1 3 4 6 8 10
16-Space Vixens; Dave Stevens-c/a 3 6 9 21 33 45
NOTE: ***Davis** r-19. **Ditko** r-19. **Elder** r-19. **Everett** r-19. **Feldstein** r-17. **Frazetta** r-17. **Heath** r-19. **Kamen** r-17. **Severin** r-19. **Ward** r-17,19. **Wolverton** r-2,18,19. **Wood** r-1,17. Photo c-12*

3 GEEKS, THE (Also see Geeksville)
3 Finger Prints: 1996 - No. 11, Jun, 1999 (B&W)
1,2 -Rich Koslowski-s/a in all 1 2 3 5 6 8
1-(2nd printing) 3.00
3-7, 9-11 3.00
8-(48 pgs.) 4.00
10-Variant-c 3.50
...48 Page Super-Sized Summer Spectacular (7/04, $4.95) 5.00
...Full Circle (7/03, $4.95) Origin story of the 3 Geeks; "Buck Rodinski" app. 5.00
How to Pick Up Girls If You're a Comic Book Geek (color)(7/97) 4.00
When the Hammer Falls TPB (2001, $14.95) r/#8-11 15.00

3 GEEKS: SLAB MADNESS!
3 Finger Prints: Sept, 2008 - No. 3, Mar, 2009 ($2.99, B&W, limited series)
1-3-Rich Koslowski-s/a; intro. The Cee-Gee-Cee 3.00

3 GUNS
BOOM! Studios: Aug, 2013 - No. 6, Jan, 2014 ($3.99)
1-6-Steven Grant-s/Emilio Laiso-a 4.00

300 (Adapted for 2007 movie)
Dark Horse Comics: May, 1998 - No. 5, Sept, 1998 ($2.95/$3.95, limited series)

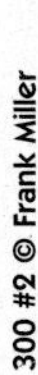
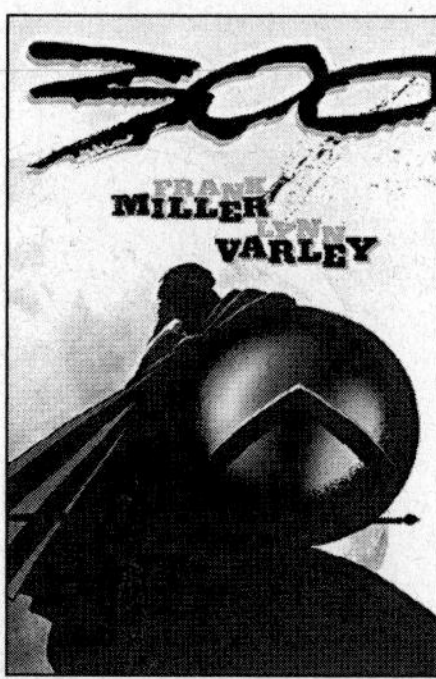

300 #2 © Frank Miller

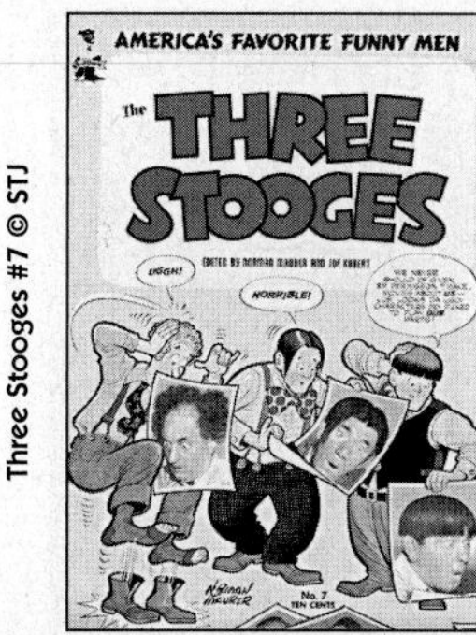

Three Stooges #7 © STJ

Thrilling Comics #7 © BP

	GD 2.0	VG 4.0	FN 6.0	VF 8.0	VF/NM 9.0	NM- 9.2
1-Frank Miller-s/c/a; Spartans vs. Persians war	3	6	9	15	22	28
1-Second printing						5.00
2-4	2	4	6	8	10	12
5-($3.95-c)	2	4	6	8	10	12
HC ($30.00) -oversized reprint of series						30.00

3 LITTLE KITTENS
BroadSword Comics: Aug, 2002 - No. 3, Dec, 2002 ($2.95, limited series)

	GD	VG	FN	VF	VF/NM	NM-
1-3-Jim Balent-s/a; two covers						3.00

3 LITTLE PIGS (Disney)(...and the Wonderful Magic Lamp)
Dell Publishing Co.: No. 218, Mar, 1949

	GD	VG	FN	VF	VF/NM	NM-
Four Color 218 (#1)	10	20	30	66	138	210

3 LITTLE PIGS, THE (See Walt Disney Showcase #15 & 21)
Gold Key: May, 1964; No. 2, Sept, 1968 (Walt Disney)

	GD	VG	FN	VF	VF/NM	NM-
1-Reprints Four Color #218	3	6	9	19	30	40
2	3	6	9	15	21	26

THREE MOUSEKETEERS, THE (1st Series)(See Funny Stuff #1)
National Per. Publ.: 3-4/56 - No. 24, 9-10/59; No. 25, 8-9/60 - No. 26, 10-12/60

	GD	VG	FN	VF	VF/NM	NM-
1	23	46	69	164	362	560
2	11	22	33	73	157	240
3-5,7,9,10	8	16	24	56	108	160
6,8-Grey tone-c	10	20	30	66	138	210
11-26: 24-Cover says 11/59, inside says 9-10/59	7	14	21	49	92	135

NOTE: *Rube Grossman a-1-26. Sheldon Mayer a-1-8; c-1-7.*

THREE MOUSEKETEERS, THE (2nd Series) (See Super DC Giant)
National Periodical Publications: May-June, 1970 - No. 7, May-June, 1971 (#5-7: 68 pgs.)

	GD	VG	FN	VF	VF/NM	NM-
1-Mayer-r in all	6	12	18	40	73	105
2-4: 4-Doodles Duck begins (1st app.)	4	8	12	25	40	55
5-7:(68 pgs.). 5-Dodo & the Frog, Bo Bunny begin	5	10	15	31	53	75

THREE MUSKETEERS, THE (Also see Disney's The Three Musketeers)
Gemstone Publishing: 2004 ($3.95, squarebound, one-shot)

	GD	VG	FN	VF	VF/NM	NM-
nn-Adaptation of the 2004 DVD movie; Petrossi-c/a						4.00

THREE NURSES (Confidential Diary #12-17; Career Girl Romances #24 on)
Charlton Comics: V3#18, May, 1963 - V3#23, Mar, 1964

	GD	VG	FN	VF	VF/NM	NM-
V3#18-23	3	6	9	21	33	45

THREE RASCALS
I. W. Enterprises: 1958; 1963

	GD	VG	FN	VF	VF/NM	NM-
I.W. Reprint #1,2,10: 1-(Says Super Comics on inside)-(M.E.'s Clubhouse Rascals) DeCarlo-a. #2-(1958). 10-(1963)-r/#1	2	4	6	8	11	14

THREE RING COMICS
Spotlight Publishers: March, 1945

	GD	VG	FN	VF	VF/NM	NM-
1-Funny animal	20	40	60	117	189	260

THREE RING COMICS (Also see Captain Wizard & Meteor Comics)
Century Publications: April, 1946

	GD	VG	FN	VF	VF/NM	NM-
1-Prankster-c; Captain Wizard, Impossible Man, Race Wilkins, King O'Leary, & Dr. Mercy app.	40	80	120	246	411	575

THREE ROCKETEERS (See Blast-Off)

THREE STOOGES (See Comic Album #18, Top Comics, The Little Stooges, March of Comics #232, 248, 268, 280, 292, 304, 316, 336, 373, Movie Classics & Comics & 3-D Three Stooges)

THREE STOOGES
Jubilee No. 1/St. John No. 1 (9/53) on: Feb, 1949 - No. 2, May, 1949; Sept, 1953 - No. 7, Oct, 1954

	GD	VG	FN	VF	VF/NM	NM-
1-(Scarce, 1949)-Kubert-a; infinity-c	168	336	504	1075	1838	2600
2-(Scarce)-Kubert, Maurer-a	100	200	300	635	1093	1550
1(9/53)-Hollywood Stunt Girl by Kubert (7 pgs.)	84	168	252	538	919	1300
2(3-D, 10/53, 25¢)-Came w/glasses; Stunt Girl story by Kubert	42	84	126	265	445	625
3(3-D, 10/53, 25¢)-Came w/glasses; has 3-D-c	40	80	120	246	411	575
4(3/54)-7(10/54): 4-1st app. Li'l Stooge?	40	80	120	246	411	575

NOTE: *All issues have **Kubert-Maurer** art & **Maurer** covers. 6, 7-Partial photo-c.*

THREE STOOGES
Dell Publishing Co./Gold Key No. 10 (10/62) on: No. 1043, Oct-Dec, 1959 - No. 55, June, 1972

	GD	VG	FN	VF	VF/NM	NM-
Four Color 1043 (#1)	22	44	66	155	345	535
Four Color 1078,1127,1170,1187	11	22	33	73	157	240
6(9-11/61) - 10: 6-Professor Putter begins; ends #16	9	18	27	58	114	170
11-14,16,18-20	7	14	21	48	89	130
15-Go Around the World in a Daze (movie scenes)	8	16	24	51	96	140
17-The Little Monsters begin (5/64)(1st app.?)	8	16	24	51	96	140
21,23-30	6	12	18	38	69	100
22-Movie scenes from "The Outlaws Is Coming"	6	12	18	41	76	110
31-55	5	10	15	31	53	75

NOTE: *All Four Colors, 6-50, 52-55 have photo-c.*

THREE STOOGES IN 3-D, THE
Eternity Comics: 1991 ($3.95, high quality paper, w/glasses)

	GD	VG	FN	VF	VF/NM	NM-
1-Reprints Three Stooges by Gold Key; photo-c						5.00

THREE STOOGES
American Mythology Prods.: 2016 - Present (series of one-shots)

	GD	VG	FN	VF	VF/NM	NM-
...: April Fools' Day Special (2017, $3.99) Check-s/Fraim brothers-a; 5 covers						4.00
...: Curse of the Frankenstooge (2016, $4.99) New stories and reprint from #24; 5 covers						5.00
...: Halloween Hullabaloo (2016, giveaway) New stories by various; Ropp-c						3.00
...: Halloween Stoogetacular (2017, $3.99) Check-s/Fraim brothers-a; 4 covers						4.00
...: Merry Stoogemas (2016, $3.99) New stories and reprint from #7; 5 covers						4.00
...: Red, White, & Stooge (2016, $3.99) New story and reprint from #44; 4 covers						4.00
...: Shemptastic Shemptacular (2018, $3.99) New story and reprint from #1; 4 covers						4.00
...: Stooge-A-Palooza 1 (2016, $4.99) New stories and reprint from FC #1170; 3 covers						5.00
...: The Boys are Back (2016, $3.99) New stories and reprint from FC #1170; 4 covers						4.00
...: TV Time Special (2017, $3.99) Check-s/Fraim brothers-a; 4 covers						4.00

3 WORLDS OF GULLIVER
Dell Publishing Co.: No. 1158, July, 1961 (2 issues exist with diff. covers)

	GD	VG	FN	VF	VF/NM	NM-
Four Color 1158-Movie, photo-c	6	12	18	42	79	115

THRESHOLD
DC Comics: Mar, 2013 - No. 8 ($3.99)

	GD	VG	FN	VF	VF/NM	NM-
1-8-Anthology. 1-5-Back-up Larfleeze stories. 5,6-Brainiac app.						4.00

THRILL COMICS (See Flash Comics, Fawcett)

THRILLER
DC Comics: Nov, 1983 - No. 12, Nov, 1984 ($1.25, Baxter paper)

	GD	VG	FN	VF	VF/NM	NM-
1-12: 1-Intro Seven Seconds; Von Eeden-c/a begins. 2-Origin. 5,6-Elvis satire						4.00

THRILLING ADVENTURE HOUR PRESENTS:...
Image Comics: ($3.50)

	GD	VG	FN	VF	VF/NM	NM-
... Beyond Belief 1-3 (4/15 - No. 3, 3/16) Acker & Blacker-s/Hester-a						3.50
... Sparks Nevada: Marshal on Mars 1-4 (2/15 - No. 4, 7/15) Acker & Blacker-s/Bone-a						3.50

THRILLING ADVENTURES IN STAMPS COMICS (Formerly Stamp Comics)
Stamp Comics, Inc. (Very Rare): V1#8, Jan, 1953 (25¢, 100 pgs.)

	GD	VG	FN	VF	VF/NM	NM-
V1#8-Harrison, Wildey, Kiefer, Napoli-a	76	152	228	486	831	1175

THRILLING ADVENTURE STORIES (See Tigerman)
Atlas/Seaboard Publ.: Feb, 1975 - No. 2, Aug, 1975 (B&W, 68 pgs.)

	GD	VG	FN	VF	VF/NM	NM-
1-Tigerman, Kromag the Killer begin; Heath, Thorne-a; Doc Savage movie photos of Ron Ely	3	6	9	17	26	35
2-Heath, Toth, Severin, Simonson-a; Adams-c	4	8	12	23	37	50

THRILLING COMICS
Better Publ./Nedor/Standard Comics: Feb, 1940 - No. 80, April, 1951

	GD	VG	FN	VF	VF/NM	NM-
1-Origin & 1st app. Dr. Strange (37 pgs.), ends #?; Nickie Norton of the Secret Service begins	400	800	1200	2800	4900	7000
2-The Rio Kid, The Woman in Red, Pinocchio begins	213	426	639	1363	2332	3300
3-The Ghost & Lone Eagle begin	174	348	522	1114	1907	2700
4-6,8,9: 5-Dr. Strange changed to Doc Strange	161	322	483	1030	1765	2500
7-Classic-c	232	464	696	1485	2543	3600
10-1st WWII-c (Nazi)(11/40)	168	336	504	1075	1838	2600
11-18,20: 17-WWII-Nazi-c	155	310	465	992	1696	2400
19-Origin & 1st app. The American Crusader (8/41), ends #39,41; Schomburg Nazi WWII-c	206	412	618	1318	2259	3200
21-26,28-30: 24-Intro. Mike, Doc Strange's sidekick (1/42). 29-Last Rio Kid	116	232	348	742	1271	1800
27-Robot-c	148	296	444	947	1624	2300
31-35,37,39,40: 39-Nazi WWII-c. 40-Japan WWII-c	97	194	291	621	1061	1500
36-Commando Cubs begin (7/43, 1st app.)	106	212	318	673	1162	1650
38-Classic Nazi bondage-c	219	438	657	1402	2401	3400
41-Classic Hitler & Mussolini WWII-c	420	840	1260	2940	5170	7400
42-Classic Schomburg Japanese WWII-c	142	284	426	909	1555	2200
43,46-51: 51(12/45)-Last WWII-c (Japanese)	84	168	252	538	919	1300
44-Hitler WWII-c by Schomburg	331	662	993	2317	4059	5800
45-Hitler pict. on-c	113	226	339	718	1234	1750

Thrilling Crime Comics #42 © STAR

Thrillkiller #3 © DC

Thulsa Doom #1 © TD Corp.

GD 2.0 | VG 4.0 | FN 6.0 | VF 8.0 | VF/NM 9.0 | NM- 9.2

52-Classic Schomburg hooded bondage-c; the Ghost ends
94 188 282 597 1024 1450
53,54: 53-The Phantom Detective begins. The Cavalier app. in both; no Commando Cubs in either 58 116 174 371 636 900
55-The Lone Eagle ends 47 94 141 296 498 700
56 (10/46)-Princess Pantha begins (not on-c), 1st app.
63 126 189 403 689 975
57-Doc Strange-c; 2nd Princess Pantha 54 108 162 343 574 825
58-66: All Princess Pantha jungle-c, w/Doc Strange #59, his last-c. 61-Ingels-a; The Lone Eagle app. 65-Last Phantom Detective & Commando Cubs. 66-Frazetta text illo
53 106 159 334 567 800
67,70,71-Last jungle-c; Frazetta-a(5-7 pgs.) in each 57 114 171 362 619 875
68,69-Frazetta-a(2), 8 & 6 pgs.; 9 & 7 pgs. 60 120 180 381 653 925
72,73: 72-Buck Ranger, Cowboy Detective c/stys begin (western theme), end #80; Frazetta-a(5-7 ps.) in each 41 82 123 256 428 600
74-Last Princess Pantha; Tara app. 31 62 93 184 300 415
75-78: 75-All western format begins 17 34 51 98 154 210
79-Krigstein-a 18 36 54 103 162 220
80-Severin & Elder, Celardo, Moreira-a 18 36 54 103 162 220

NOTE: *Bondage c-5, 9, 13, 20, 22, 27-30, 38, 41, 52, 54, 70.* ***Kinstler*** *a-45.* ***Leo Morey*** *a-7.* ***Schomburg*** *(sometimes signed as* ***Xela****) c-7, 9-19, 36-80 (airbrush 62-71).* ***Tuska*** *a-62, 63. Woman in Red not in #19, 23, 31-33, 39-45. No. 45 exists as a Canadian reprint but numbered #48. No. 72 exists as a Canadian reprint with no* ***Frazetta*** *story. American Crusader c-20-24. Buck Ranger c-72-80. Commando Cubs c-37, 39, 41, 43, 45, 47, 49, 51. Doc Strange c-1-19, 25-36, 38, 40, 42, 44, 46, 48, 50, 52-57, 59. Princess Pantha c-58, 60-71.*

THRILLING COMICS (Also see All Star Comics 1999 crossover titles)
DC Comics: May, 1999 ($1.99, one-shot)
1-Golden Age Hawkman and Wildcat; Russ Heath-a 3.00

THRILLING CRIME CASES (Formerly 4Most; becomes Shocking Mystery Cases #50 on)
Star Publications: No. 41, June-July, 1950 - No. 49, July, 1952
41 37 74 111 222 361 500
42-45: 42-L. B. Cole-c/a (1); Chameleon story (Fox-r)
33 66 99 194 317 440
46-48: 47-Used in **POP**, pg. 84 31 62 93 186 303 420
49-(7/52)-Classic L. B. Cole-c 129 258 387 826 1413 2000
NOTE: ***L. B. Cole*** *c-all; a-43p, 45p, 46p, 49(2 pgs.).* ***Disbrow*** *a-48.* ***Hollingsworth*** *a-48.*

THRILLING ROMANCES
Standard Comics: No. 5, Dec, 1949 - No. 26, June, 1954
5 21 42 63 126 206 285
6,8 14 28 42 80 115 150
7-Severin/Elder-a (7 pgs.) 15 30 45 85 130 175
9,10-Severin/Elder-a; photo-c 15 30 45 83 124 165
11,14-21,26: 14-Gene Tierney & Danny Kaye photo-c from movie "On the Riviera". 15-Tony Martin/Janet Leigh photo-c 14 28 42 76 108 140
12-Wood-a (2 pgs.); Tyrone Power/ Susan Hayward photo-c
15 30 45 86 133 180
13-Severin-a 14 28 42 80 115 150
22-25-Toth-a 15 30 45 83 124 165
NOTE: *All photo-c.* ***Celardo*** *a-9, 16.* ***Colletta*** *a-23, 24(2).* ***Toth*** *text illos-19.* ***Tuska*** *a-9.*

THRILLING SCIENCE TALES
AC Comics: 1989 - No. 2 ($3.50, 2/3 color, 52 pgs.)
1,2: 1-r/Bob Colt #6(saucer); Frazetta, Guardineer (Space Ace), Wood, Krenkel, Orlando, WIlliamson-r; Kaluta-c. 2-Capt. Video-r by Evans, Capt. Science-r by Wood, Star Pirate-r by Whitman & Mysta of the Moon-r by Moreira 4.00

THRILLING TRUE STORY OF THE BASEBALL...
Fawcett Publications: 1952 (Photo-c, each)
...Giants-photo-c; has Willie Mays rookie photo-biography; Willie Mays, Eddie Stanky & others photos on-c 68 136 204 432 746 1060
...Yankees-photo-c; Yogi Berra, Joe DiMaggio, Mickey Mantle & others photos on-c
66 132 198 419 722 1025

THRILLING WONDER TALES
AC Comics : 1991 ($2.95, B&W)
1-Includes a Bob Powell Thun'da story 3.00

THRILLKILLER
DC Comics : Jan, 1997 - No. 3, Mar, 1997($2.50, limited series)
1-3-Elseworlds Robin & Batgirl; Chaykin-s/Brereton-c/a 3.00
...'62 ('98, $4.95, one-shot) Sequel; Chaykin-s/Brereton-c/a 5.00
TPB-(See Batman: Thrillkiller)

THRILLOGY
Pacific Comics: Jan, 1984 (One-shot, color)
1-Conrad-c/a 4.00

THRILL-O-RAMA
Harvey Publications (Fun Films): Oct, 1965 - No. 3, Dec, 1966
1-Fate (Man in Black) by Powell app.; Doug Wildey-a(2); Simon-c
5 10 15 31 53 75
2-Pirana begins (see Phantom #46); Williamson 2 pgs.; Fate (Man in Black) app.; Tuska/Simon-c 3 6 9 21 33 45
3-Fate (Man in Black) app.; Sparling-c 3 6 9 18 28 38

THRILLS OF TOMORROW (Formerly Tomb of Terror)
Harvey Publications: No. 17, Oct, 1954 - No. 20, April, 1955
17-Powell-a (horror); r/Witches Tales #7 15 30 45 88 137 185
18-Powell-a (horror); r/Tomb of Terror #1 14 28 42 82 121 160
19,20-Stuntman-c/stories by S&K (r/from Stuntman #1 & 2); 19 has origin & is last pre-code (2/55) 31 62 93 182 296 410
NOTE: ***Kirby*** *c-19, 20.* ***Palais*** *a-17.* ***Simon*** *c-18?*

THROBBING LOVE (See Fox Giants)

THROUGH GATES OF SPLENDOR
Spire Christian Comics (Flemming H. Revell Co.): 1973, 1974 (36 pages) (39-49 cents)
nn-1973 Edition 3 6 9 14 19 24
nn-1974 Edition 2 4 6 9 13 16

THULSA DOOM (Robert E. Howard character)
Dynamite Entertainment: 2009 - No. 4, 2009 ($3.50, limited series)
1-4-Alex Ross-c/Lui Antonio-a 3.50

THUMPER (Disney)
Dell Publishing Co.: No, 19, 1942 - No. 243, Sept, 1949
Four Color 19-Walt Disney's...Meets the Seven Dwarfs; reprinted in Silly Symphonies
44 88 132 326 738 1150
Four Color 243-...Follows His Nose 11 22 33 72 154 235

THUN'DA (...King of the Congo)
Magazine Enterprises: 1952 - No. 6, 1953
1(A-1 #47)-Origin; Frazetta c/a; only comic done entirely by Frazetta; all Thun'da stories, no Cave Girl 226 452 678 1446 2473 3500
2(A-1 #56)-Powell-c/a begins, ends #6; Intro/1st app. Cave Girl in filler strip (also app. in 3-6)
32 64 96 188 307 425
3(A-1 #73), 4(A-1 #78) 22 44 66 128 209 290
5(A-1 #83), 6(A-1 #86) 21 42 63 124 202 280

THUN'DA
Dynamite Entertainment: 2012 - No. 5, 2012 ($3.99, limited series)
1-5-Napton-s/Richards-a/Jae Lee-c. 1-4-Bonus reprints of Thun'da #1 (1952) Frazetta-a 4.00

THUN'DA TALES (See Frank Frazetta's...)

THUNDER AGENTS (See Dynamo, Noman & Tales Of Thunder)
Tower Comics: 11/65 - No. 17, 12/67; No. 18, 9/68, No. 19, 11/68, No. 20, 11/69 (No. 1-16: 68 pgs.; No. 17 on: 52 pgs.)(All are 25¢)
1-Origin & 1st app. Dynamo, Noman, Menthor, & The Thunder Squad; 1st app. The Iron Maiden 17 34 51 119 265 410
2-Death of Egghead; A-bomb blast panel 9 18 27 61 123 185
3-5: 4-Guy Gilbert becomes Lightning who joins Thunder Squad; Iron Maiden app.
7 14 21 49 92 135
6-10: 7-Death of Menthor. 8-Origin & 1st app. The Raven
6 12 18 38 69 100
11-15: 13-Undersea Agent app.; no Raven story 5 10 15 35 63 90
16-19 5 10 15 34 60 85
20-Special Collectors Edition; all reprints 4 8 12 27 44 60
...Archives Vol. 1 (DC Comics, 2003, $49.95, HC) r/#1-4, restored and recolored 50.00
...Archives Vol. 2 (DC Comics, 2003, $49.95, HC) r/#5-7, Dynamo #1 50.00
...Archives Vol. 3 (DC Comics, 2003, $49.95, HC) r/#8-10, Dynamo #2 50.00
...Archives Vol. 4 (DC Comics, 2004, $49.95, HC) r/#11, Noman #1,2 & Dynamo #3 50.00
NOTE: ***Crandall*** *a-1, 4p, 5p, 18, 20r; c-18.* ***Ditko*** *a-6, 7p, 12p, 13?, 14p, 16, 18.* ***Giunta*** *a-6.* ***Kane*** *a-1, 5p, 6p?, 14, 16p; c-14, 15.* ***Reinman*** *a-13.* ***Sekowsky*** *a-6.* ***Tuska*** *a-1p, 7, 8, 10, 13-17, 19.* ***Whitney*** *a-9p, 10, 13, 15, 17, 18; c-17.* ***Wood*** *a-1-11, 15(w/****Ditko****-12, 18), (inks-#9, 13, 14, 16, 17), 19i, 20r; c-1-8, 9i, 10-13(#10 w/****Williamson****(p)), 16.*

T.H.U.N.D.E.R. AGENTS (See Blue Ribbon Comics, Hall of Fame Featuring the..., JCP Features & Wally Wood's...)
JC Comics (Archie Publications): May, 1983 - No. 2, Jan, 1984
1,2: 1-New Manna/Blyberg-c/a. 2-Blyberg-c 6.00

T.H.U.N.D.E.R. AGENTS
DC Comics: Jan, 2011 - No. 10, Oct, 2011 ($3.99/$2.99)
1-3-($3.99): 1-Spencer-s/Cafu-a/Quitely-c. 3-Chaykin-a (5 pgs.) 4.00
4-10-($2.99): 4-Pérez-a (5 pgs.). 7-10-Grell & Dragotta-a 3.00

Thunderbolts #12 © MAR

Thunderbolts (2016 series) #11 © MAR

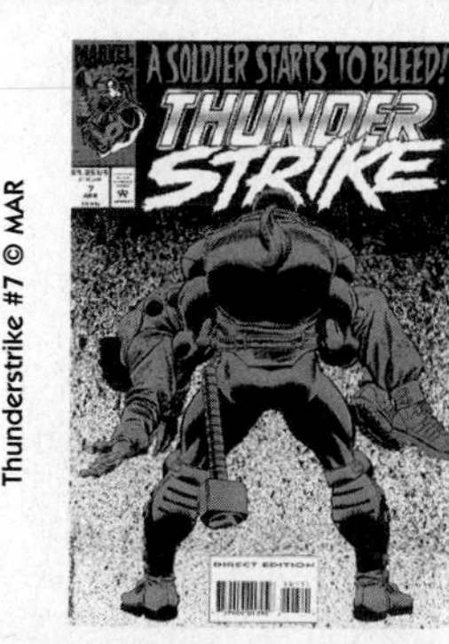

Thunderstrike #7 © MAR

GD 2.0 | VG 4.0 | FN 6.0 | VF 8.0 | VF/NM 9.0 | NM- 9.2

1-Variant-c by Darwyn Cooke 8.00

T.H.U.N.D.E.R. AGENTS
DC Comics: Jan, 2012 - No. 6, Jun, 2012 ($2.99, limited series)
1-6-Spencer-s/Craig-a. 1-Andy Kubert-c. 3-Craig & Simonson-a 3.00

T.H.U.N.D.E.R. AGENTS
IDW Publishing: Aug, 2013 - No. 8, Apr, 2014 ($3.99)
1-8: 1-4-Hester-s/Di Vito-a. 1-Four interlocking covers by Di Vito. 5-8-Roger Robinson-a 4.00

THUNDER BIRDS (See Cinema Comics Herald)

THUNDERBOLT (See The Atomic...)

THUNDERBOLT (Peter Cannon...; see Crisis on Infinite Earths, Peter Cannon, Captain Atom and Judomaster)
Charlton Comics: Jan, 1966; No. 51, Mar-Apr, 1966 - No. 60, Nov, 1967

	GD	VG	FN	VF	VF/NM	NM-
1-Origin & 1st app. Thunderbolt	5	10	15	30	50	70
51-(Formerly Son of Vulcan #50)	3	6	9	19	30	40
52-Judomaster story	3	6	9	16	23	30
53-Captain Atom story, 2 pgs.	3	6	9	16	23	30
54-59: 54-Sentinels begin. 59-Last Thunderbolt & Sentinels (back-up story)	3	6	9	14	19	24
60-Prankster only app.	3	6	9	15	21	26
57,58 ('77)-Modern Comics-r	1	3	4	6	8	10

NOTE: ***Aparo** a-60. **Morisi** a-1, 51-56, 58; c-1, 51-56, 58, 59.*

THUNDERBOLT JAXON (Revival of 1940s British comics character)
DC Comics (WildStorm): Apr, 2006 - No. 5, Sept, 2006 ($2.99, limited series)
1-5-Dave Gibbons-s/John Higgins-a 3.00
TPB (2007, $19.99) r/#1-5; intro. by Gibbons; cover gallery 20.00

THUNDERBOLTS (Title re-named Dark Avengers with #175)(Also see New Thunderbolts and Incredible Hulk #449)
Marvel Comics: Apr, 1997 - No. 81, Sept, 2003; No. 100, May, 2006 - No. 174, Jul, 2012 ($1.95-$2.99)

	GD	VG	FN	VF	VF/NM	NM-
1-($2.99)-Busiek-s/Bagley-c/a	2	4	6	8	10	12

1-2nd printing; new cover colors 3.00
2-4: 2-Two covers. 4-Intro. Jolt 6.00
5-11: 9-Avengers app. 3.50
12-($2.99)-Avengers and Fantastic Four-c/app. 4.00
13-24: 14-Thunderbolts return to Earth. 21-Hawkeye app. 3.00
25-($2.99) Wraparound-c 4.00
26-38: 26-Manco-a 3.00
39-($2.99) 100 Page Monster; Iron Man reprints 4.00
40-49: 40-Begin $2.25-c; Sandman-c/app. 44-Avengers app. 47-Captain Marvel app. 49-Zircher-a 3.00
50-($2.99) Last Bagley-a; Captain America becomes leader 4.00
51-74,76,77,80,81: 51,52-Zircher-a; Dr. Doom app. 80,81-Spider-Man app. 3.00
75-($3.50) Hawkeye leaves the team; Garcia-a 4.00
78,79-($2.99-c) Velasco-a begins 3.00
(See New Thunderbolts for #82-99)
100 (5/06, $3.99) resumes from New Thunderbolts #18; back-up origin stories 4.00
101-109: 103-105-Civil War x-over 3.00
110-New team begins including Bullseye, Venom and Norman Osborn; Ellis-s/Deodato-a 5.00
111-136,138-149: 111-121-Ellis-s/Deodato-a. 112-Stan Lee cameo. 123-125-Secret Invasion x-over. 128-Dark Reign begins. 130,131-X-over with Deadpool #8,9. 141-143-Siege 3.00
137-(12/09, $3.99) Iron Fist and Luke Cage app. 4.00
150-(1/11, $4.99) Thunderbolts vs. Avengers; r/#1; storyline synopses of #1-150 5.00
151-158,160-163, 163.1, 164-174-($2.99) 151-153-Land-c. 155-Satana joins. 158-162-Fear Itself tie-in. 163-165-Thunderbolts in WWII; Invaders app. 3.00
159-($4.99) Fear Itelf tie-in; Juggernaut app.; short stories of escape from The Raft 5.00
Annual '97 ($2.99)-Wraparound-c 4.00
Annual 2000 ($3.50) Breyfogle-a 4.00
...: Breaking Point (1/08, $2.99, one-shot) Gage-s/Denham-a/Djurdjevic-c 3.00
... By Warren Ellis Vol. 1 HC (2007, $24.99, dustjacket) r/#150-154, ...: Desperate Measures and stories from Civil War: Choosing Sides and The Initiative 25.00
... By Warren Ellis Vol. 1: Faith in Monsters SC (2008, $19.99) same contents as HC 20.00
Civil War: Thunderbolts TPB (2007, $13.99) r/#101-105 14.00
...: Desperate Measures (9/07, $2.99, one-shot) Jenkins-s/Steve Lieber-a 3.00
...: Distant Rumblings (#-1) (7/97, $1.95) Busiek-s 5.00
First Strikes (1997, $4.99,TPB) r/#1,2 5.00
...: From the Marvel Vault (6/11, $3.99) Jack Monroe app.; Nicieza-s/Aucoin-a 4.00
...: Guardian Protocols (2007, $10.99) r/#106-109 11.00
...: International Incident (4/08, $2.99, one-shot) Gage-s/Oliver-a/Djurdjevic-c 3.00
...: Life Sentences (7/01, $3.50) Adlard-a 4.00
...: Marvel's Most Wanted TPB ('98, $16.99) r/origin stories of original Masters of Evil 17.00
...: Reason in Madness (7/08, $2.99, one-shot) Gage-s/Oliver-a/Djurdjevic-c 3.00
Wizard #0 (bagged with Wizard #89) 3.00

THUNDERBOLTS (Marvel NOW!)
Marvel Comics: Feb, 2013 - No. 32, Dec, 2014 ($2.99)
1-32: 1-Punisher, Red Hulk, Elektra, Venom & Deadpool team; Dillon-a. 7-11-Noto-a. 14-18-Infinity tie-ins; Soule-s/Palo-a. 20-Ghost Rider joins 3.00
Annual 1 (2/14, $4.99) Dr. Strange & Elsa Bloodstone app.; Lolli-a 5.00

THUNDERBOLTS
Marvel Comics: Jul, 2016 - No. 12, Jun, 2017 ($3.99)
1-9,11,12: 1-Bucky Barnes leads the team of Kobik, Atlas, Fixer, Moonstone, & Mach-X. 4-Squadron Supreme app. 5-Spider-Man (Miles) app. 11,12-Secret Empire tie-ins 4.00
10-($4.99) 20th Anniversary Special; prologue by Busiek-s/Bagley-a; Jolt returns 5.00

THUNDERBOLTS PRESENTS: ZEMO - BORN BETTER
Marvel Comics: Apr, 2007 - No. 4, July, 2007 ($2.99, limited series)
1-4-History of Baron Zemo; Nicieza-s/Grummett-a/c 3.00
TPB (2007, $10.99) r/#1-4 11.00

THUNDERBUNNY (See Blue Ribbon Comics #13, Charlton Bullseye & Pep Comics #393)
Red Circle Comics: Jan, 1984 (Direct sale only)
WaRP Graphics: Second series No. 1, 1985 - No. 6, 1985
Apple Comics: No. 7, 1986 - No. 12, 1987
1-Humor/parody; origin Thunderbunny; 2 page pin-up by Anderson 5.00
(2nd series) 1,2-Magazine size 4.00
3-12-Comic size 4.00

THUNDERCATS (TV)
Marvel Comics (Star Comics)/Marvel #22 on: Dec, 1985 - No. 24, June, 1988 (75¢)

	GD	VG	FN	VF	VF/NM	NM-
1-Mooney-c/a begins	3	6	9	17	26	35
2-20: 2-(65¢ & 75¢ cover exists). 12-Begin $1.00-c. 18-20-Williamson-i	1	2	3	5	7	9
21-24: 23-Williamson-c(i)	1	3	4	6	8	10

THUNDERCATS (TV)
DC Comics (WildStorm): No. 0, Oct, 2002 - No. 5, Feb, 2003 ($2.50/$2.95, limited series)
0-($2.50) J. Scott Campbell-c/a 3.00
1-5-($2.95) 1-McGuinness-a/c; variant cover by Art Adams; rebirth of Mumm-Ra 3.00
.../ Battle of the Planets (7/03, $4.95) Kaare Andrews-s/a; 2 covers by Campbell & Ross 5.00
...: Origins-Heroes & Villains (2/04, $3.50) short stories by various 3.50
...Reclaiming Thundera TPB (2003, $12.95) r/#0-5 13.00
... Sourcebook (1/03, $2.95) pin-ups and info on characters; art by various; A. Adams-c 3.00

THUNDERCATS: DOGS OF WAR
DC Comics (WildStorm): Aug, 2003 - No. 5, Dec, 2003 ($2.95, limited series)
1-5: 1-Two covers by Booth & Pearson; Booth-a/Layman-s. 2-4-Two covers 3.00
TPB (2004, $14.95) r/#1-5 15.00

THUNDERCATS: ENEMY'S PRIDE
DC Comics (WildStorm): Aug, 2004 - No. 5 ($2.95, limited series)
1-5-Vriens-a/Layman-s 3.00
TPB (2005, $14.99) r/#1-5 15.00

THUNDERCATS: HAMMERHAND'S REVENGE
DC Comics (WildStorm): Dec, 2003 - No. 5, Apr, 2004 ($2.95, limited series)
1-5-Avery-s/D'Anda-a. 2-Variant-c by Warren 3.00
TPB (2004, $14.95) r/#1-5 15.00

THUNDERCATS: THE RETURN
DC Comics (WildStorm): Apr, 2003 - No. 5, Aug, 2003 ($2.95, limited series)
1-5: 1-Two covers by Benes & Cassaday; Gilmore-s 3.00
TPB (2004, $12.95) r/series 13.00

THUNDER MOUNTAIN (See Zane Grey, Four Color #246)

THUNDERSTRIKE (See Thor #459)
Marvel Comics: June, 1993 - No. 24, July, 1995 ($1.25)
1-($2.95, 52 pgs.)-Holo-grafx lightning patterned foil-c; Bloodaxe returns 4.00
2-24: 2-Juggernaut-c/s. 4-Capt. America app. 4-6-Spider-Man app. 8-bound-in trading card sheet. 18-Bloodaxe app. 24-Death of Thunderstrike 3.00
Marvel Double Feature...Thunderstrike/Code Blue #13 ($2.50)-Same as Thunderstrike #13 w/Code Blue flip book 4.00

THUNDERSTRIKE
Marvel Comics: Jan, 2011 - No. 5, Jun, 2011 ($3.99, limited series)
1-5-DeFalco-s/Frenz-a. 1-Back-up origin retold; Nauck-a 4.00

TICK, THE (Also see The Chroma-Tick)
New England Comics Press: Jun, 1988 - No. 12, May, 1993

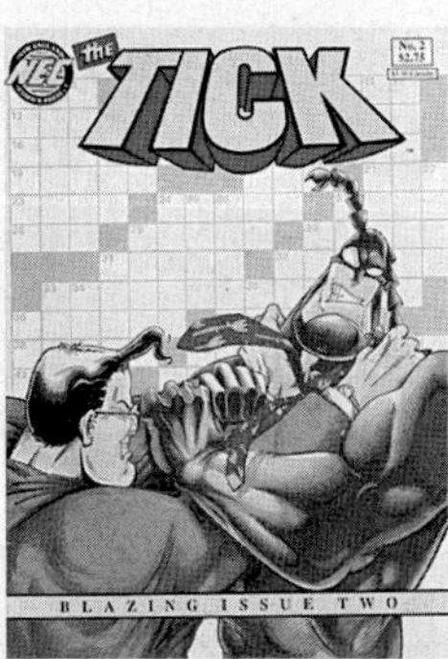

The Tick #2 © Ben Edlund

The Tick Karma Tornado #2 © Ben Edlund

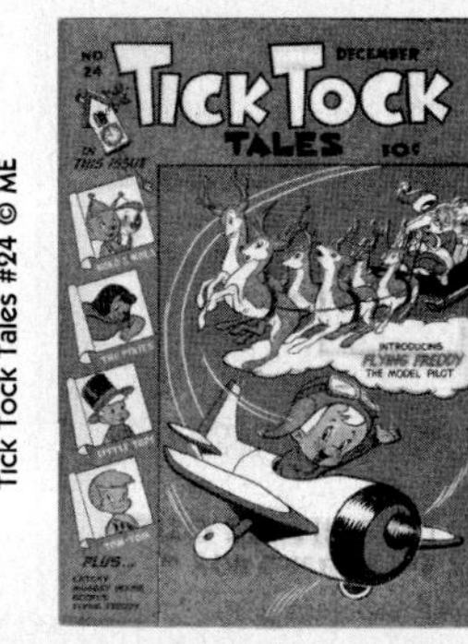

Tick Tock Tales #24 © ME

	GD 2.0	VG 4.0	FN 6.0	VF 8.0	VF/NM 9.0	NM- 9.2

($1.75/$1.95/$2.25; B&W, over-sized)
Special Edition 1-1st comic book app. serially numbered & limited to 5,000 copies
8 16 24 54 102 150
Special Edition 1-(5/96, $5.95)-Double-c; foil-c; serially numbered (5,001 thru 14,000) & limited to 9,000 copies 3 6 9 14 20 25
Special Edition 2-Serially numbered and limited to 3000 copies
5 10 15 31 53 75
Special Edition 2-(8/96, $5.95)-Double-c; foil-c; serially numbered (5,001 thru 14,000) & limited to 9,000 copies 1 2 3 5 6 8
1-Regular Edition 1st printing; reprints Special Ed. 1 w/minor changes
5 10 15 30 50 70
1-2nd printing 6.00
1-3rd-5th printing 4.00
2-Reprints Special Ed. 2 w/minor changes 2 4 6 13 18 22
2-8-All reprints 4.00
3-5: 4-1st app. Paul the Samurai 1 3 4 6 8 10
6,8 ($2.25) 6.00
7-1st app. Man-Eating Cow 1 2 3 5 6 8
8-Variant with no logo, price, issue number or company logos.
3 6 9 14 20 25
9-12 ($2.75) 5.00
12-Special Edition; card-stock, virgin foil-c; numbered edition
2 4 6 13 18 22
100: The Tick Meets Invincible (6/12, $6.99) Invincible travels to Tick's universe 7.00
101: The Tick Meets Madman (11/12, $6.99) Bonus publishing history of the Tick 7.00
Pseudo-Tick #13 (11/00, $3.50) Continues story from #12 (1993) 5.00
Promo Sampler-(1990)-Tick-c/story 1 2 3 5 6 8

TICK, THE (One shots)
... Big Back to School Special 1-(10/98, $3.50, B&W) Tick & Arthur undercover in H.S. 4.00
... Big Cruise Ship Vacation Special 1-(9/00, $3.50, B&W) 4.00
... Big Father's Day Special 1-(6/00, $3.50, B&W) 4.00
... Big Halloween Special 1-(10/99, $3.50, B&W) 4.00
... Big Halloween Special 2000 (10/00, $3.50) 4.00
... Big Halloween Special 2001 (9/01, $3.95) 4.00
... Big Mother's Day Special 1-(4/00, $3.50, B&W) 4.00
... Big Red-N-Green Christmas Spectacle 1-(12/01, $3.95) 4.00
... Big Romantic Adventure 1-(2/98, $2.95, B&W) Candy box-c with candy map on back 4.00
... Big Summer Annual 1-(7/99, $3.50, B&W) Chainsaw Vigilante vs. Barry 4.00
... Big Summer Fun Special 1-(8/98, $3.50, B&W) Tick and Arthur at summer camp 4.00
... Big Tax Time Terror 1-(4/00, $3.50, B&W) 4.00
... Big Year 2000 Spectacle 1-(3/00, $3.50, B&W) 4.00
FCBD Special Edition (5/10) - reprints debut from 1988; Ben Edlund-s/a 3.00
Free Comic Book Day 2013 (6/13) - New stories; McClelland-s/Redhead-a 3.00
Free Comic Book Day 2014 (6/14) - New stories; McClelland-s/Redhead-a 3.00
Free Comic Book Day 2015 (6/15) - New stories; McClelland-s/Redhead-a 3.00
Free Comic Book Day 2016 (6/16) - New stories; McClelland-s/Redhead-a; Nichols-a 3.00
...: Halloween Comicfest 2017 (11/17, giveaway) r/#1 (1988) in color 3.00
... Incredible Internet Comic 1-(7/01, $3.95, color) r/New England Comics website story 4.00
Introducing the Tick 1-(4/02, $3.95, color) summary of Tick's life and adventures 4.00
The Tick's Back #0 -(8/97, $2.95, B&W) 4.00
The Tick's Comic Con Extravaganza -(6/07, $3.95, color) Wang-c 4.00
The Tick's 20th Anniversary Special Edition #1 (5/07, $5.95) short stories by various; history of the character; creator profiles; 2 covers by Suydam & Bisley 6.00

--MASSIVE SUMMER DOUBLE SPECTACLE
1,2-(7,8/00, $3.50, B&W) 4.00

TICK & ARTIE
1-(6/02, $3.50, color) prints strips from Internet comic 4.00
2-(10/02, $3.95) 4.00

TICK AND ARTHUR, THE
New England Comics: Feb, 1999 - No. 6 ($3.50, B&W)
1-6-Sean Wang-s/a 4.00

TICK BIG BLUE DESTINY, THE
New England Comics: Oct, 1997 - No. 9 ($2.95)
1-4: 1-"Keen" Ed. 2-Two covers 4.00
1-($4.95) "Wicked Keen" Ed. w/die cut-c 5.00
5-($3.50) 4.00
6-Luny Bin Trilogy Preview #0 (7/98, $1.50) 4.00
7-9: 7-Luny Bin Trilogy begins 4.00

TICK BIG BLUE YULE LOG SPECIAL, THE
New England Comics: Dec, 1997; 1999 ($2.95, B&W)
1-"Jolly" and "Traditional" covers; flip book w/"Arthur Teaches the Tick About Hanukkah" 4.00
...1999 ($3.50) 4.00
Tick Big Yule Log Special 2001-(12/00, $3.50, B&W) 4.00

TICK, THE : CIRCUS MAXIMUS
New England Comics: Mar, 2000 - No. 4, Jun, 2000 ($3.50, B&W)
1-4-Encyclopedia of characters from Tick comics 4.00
Giant No. 1 (8/03, $14.95) r/#1-4, Redux 15.00
Redux No. 1 (4/01, $3.50) 4.00

TICK, THE - COLOR
New England Comics: Jan, 2001 - No. 6 ($3.95)
1-6: 1-Marc Sandroni-a 4.00

TICK, THE : DAYS OF DRAMA
New England Comics: July, 2005 - No. 6, June, 2006 ($4.95/$3.95, limited series)
1-($4.95) Dave Garcia-a; has a mini-comic attached to cover 5.00
2-6-($3.95) 4.00

TICK, THE - HEROES OF THE CITY
New England Comics: Feb, 1999 - No. 6 ($3.50, B&W)
1-6-Short stories by various 4.00

TICK KARMA TORNADO (The...)
New England Comics Press: Oct, 1993 - No. 9, Mar, 1995 ($2.75, B&W)
1-($3.25) 5.00
2-9: 2-$2.75-c begins 4.00

TICK NEW SERIES (The...)
New England Comics: Dec, 2009 - No. 8 ($4.95)
1-8 5.00

TICK'S BIG XMAS TRILOGY, THE
New England Comics: Dec, 2002 - No. 3, Dec, 2002 ($3.95, limited series)
1-3 4.00

TICK'S GOLDEN AGE COMIC, THE
New England Comics: May, 2002 - No. 3, Feb, 2003 ($4.95, Golden Age size)
1-3-Facsimile 1940s-style Tick issue; 2 covers 5.00
Giant Edition TPB (9/03, $12.95) r/#1-3 13.00

TICK'S GIANT CIRCUS OF THE MIGHTY, THE
New England Comics: Summer, 1992 - No. 3, Fall, 1993 ($2.75, B&W, magazine size)
1-(A-O). 2-(P-Z). 3-1993 Update 5.00

TICK 2017, THE
New England Comics: Sept, 2017 - Present ($3.99)
1-3: 1-Bunn & JimmyZ-s/Paszkiewicz-a 4.00

TICKLE COMICS (Also see Gay, Smile, & Whee Comics)
Modern Store Publ.: 1955 (7¢, 5x7-1/4", 52 pgs)
1 8 16 24 42 54 65

TICK TOCK TALES
Magazine Enterprises: Jan, 1946 - V3#33, Jan-Feb, 1951
1-Koko & Kola begin 22 44 66 128 209 290
2 14 28 42 78 112 145
3-10 13 26 39 72 101 130
11-33: 19-Flag-c. 23-Muggsy Mouse, The Pixies & Tom-Tom the Jungle Boy app. 24-X-mas-c. 25-The Pixies & Tom-Tom app. 11 22 33 64 90 115

TIGER (Also see Comics Reading Libraries in the Promotional Comics section)
Charlton Press (King Features): Mar, 1970 - No. 6, Jan, 1971 (15¢)
1 3 6 9 14 19 24
2-6: 3-Ad for life-size inflatable doll 2 4 6 8 11 14

TIGER BOY (See Unearthly Spectaculars)

TIGER GIRL
Gold Key: Sept, 1968 (15¢)
1(10227-809)-Sparling-c/a; Jerry Siegel scripts; advertising on back-c
4 8 12 27 44 60
1-Variant edition with pin-up on back cover 5 10 15 33 57 80

TIGERMAN (Also see Thrilling Adventure Stories)
Seaboard Periodicals (Atlas): Apr, 1975 - No. 3, Sept, 1975 (All 25¢ issues)
1-3: 1-Origin; Colan-c. 2,3-Ditko-p in each 2 4 6 11 16 20

TIGER WALKS, A (See Movie Comics)

TIGRA (The Avengers)
Marvel Comics: May, 2002 - No. 4, Aug, 2002 ($2.99, limited series)

Timecop #2 © Mark Verhaiden

Timely Presents: All Winners #1 © MAR

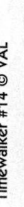

Timewalker #14 © VAL

	GD 2.0	VG 4.0	FN 6.0	VF 8.0	VF/NM 9.0	NM- 9.2
1-4-Christina Z-s/Deodato-c/a						3.00

TIGRESS, THE
Hero Graphics: Aug, 1992 - No. 6?, June, 1993 ($3.95/$2.95, B&W)

	GD 2.0	VG 4.0	FN 6.0	VF 8.0	VF/NM 9.0	NM- 9.2
1,6: 1-Tigress vs. Flare. 6-44 pgs.						4.00
2-5: 2-$2.95-c begins						3.00

TILLIE THE TOILER (See Comic Monthly)
Dell Publishing Co.: No. 15, 1941 - No. 237, July, 1949

	GD 2.0	VG 4.0	FN 6.0	VF 8.0	VF/NM 9.0	NM- 9.2
Four Color 15(1941)	57	114	171	362	619	875
Large Feature Comic 30(1941)	39	78	117	236	388	540
Four Color 8(1942)	24	48	72	170	378	585
Four Color 22(1943)	17	34	51	119	265	410
Four Color 55(1944), 89(1945)	13	26	39	86	188	290
Four Color 106('45),132('46): 132-New stories begin	10	20	30	64	132	200
Four Color 150,176,184	9	18	27	60	120	180
Four Color 195,213,237	8	16	24	51	96	140

TIMBER WOLF (See Action Comics #372, & Legion of Super-Heroes)
DC Comics: Nov, 1992 - No. 5, Mar, 1993 ($1.25, limited series)

	GD 2.0	VG 4.0	FN 6.0	VF 8.0	VF/NM 9.0	NM- 9.2
1-5						3.00

TIME AND WINE
IDW Publishing: Jul, 2017 - No. 4, Oct, 2017 ($4.99, limited series)

	GD 2.0	VG 4.0	FN 6.0	VF 8.0	VF/NM 9.0	NM- 9.2
1-4-Thomas Zahler-s/a						5.00

TIME BANDITS
Marvel Comics Group: Feb, 1982 (one-shot, Giant)

	GD 2.0	VG 4.0	FN 6.0	VF 8.0	VF/NM 9.0	NM- 9.2
1-Movie adaptation						4.00

TIME BEAVERS (See First Comics Graphic Novel #2)

TIME BOMB
Radical Comics: Jul, 2010 - No. 3, Dec, 2010 ($4.99, limited series)

	GD 2.0	VG 4.0	FN 6.0	VF 8.0	VF/NM 9.0	NM- 9.2
1-3-Palmiotti & Gray-s/Gulacy-a/c						5.00

TIMECOP (Movie)
Dark Horse Comics: Sept, 1994 - No. 2, Nov, 1994 ($2.50, limited series)

	GD 2.0	VG 4.0	FN 6.0	VF 8.0	VF/NM 9.0	NM- 9.2
1,2-Adaptation of film						3.00

TIME FOR LOVE (Formerly Romantic Secrets)
Charlton Comics: V2#53, Oct, 1966; Oct, 1967 - No. 47, May, 1976

	GD 2.0	VG 4.0	FN 6.0	VF 8.0	VF/NM 9.0	NM- 9.2
V2#53(10/66) Herman-s Hermits app.	3	6	9	19	30	40
1-(10/67)	3	6	9	21	33	45
2-(12/67) -10	3	6	9	15	21	26
11,12,14-20	2	4	6	11	16	20
13-(11/69) Ditko-a (7 pgs.)	3	6	9	16	23	30
21-27	2	4	6	9	13	16
28,29,31: 28-Shirley Jones poster. 29-Bobby Sherman pin-up. 31-Bobby Sherman pin-up	2	4	6	11	16	20
30-(10/72)-David Cassidy full page poster	3	6	9	16	24	32
32-47	2	4	6	8	11	14

TIMELESS TOPIX (See Topix)

TIMELY COMICS... (Reprints of recent Marvel issues)
Marvel Comics: Aug, 2016 ($3.00)

	GD 2.0	VG 4.0	FN 6.0	VF 8.0	VF/NM 9.0	NM- 9.2
...: All-New, All-Different Avengers (8/16) r/#1-3; Alex Ross-c						3.00
...: All-New Inhumans (8/16) r/#1-3; Caselli-c						3.00
...: Carnage (8/16) r/#1-3; Del Mundo-c						3.00
...: Daredevil (8/16) r/#1-3; Garney-c						3.00
...: Doctor Strange (8/16) r/#1-3; Bachalo-c						3.00
...: Drax (8/16) r/#1-3; Hepburn-c						3.00
...: Invincible Iron Man (8/16) r/#1-3; Marquez-c						3.00
...: Moon Girl and Devil Dinosaur (8/16) r/#1-3; Reeder-c						3.00
...: New Avengers (8/16) r/#1-3; Sandoval-c						3.00
...: Scarlet Witch (8/16) r/#1-3; Aja-c						3.00
...: Squadron Supreme (8/16) r/#1-3; Alex Ross-c						3.00
...: The Totally Awesome Hulk (8/16) r/#1-3; Cho-c						3.00
...: Ultimates (8/16) r/#1-3; Rocafort-c						3.00
...: Uncanny Inhumans (8/16) r/#1-3; McNiven-c						3.00
...: Venom: Space Knight (8/16) r/#1-3; Olivetti-c						3.00
...: Web Warriors (8/16) r/#1-3; Tedesco-c						3.00

TIMELY PRESENTS: ALL WINNERS
Marvel Comics: Dec, 1999 ($3.99)

	GD 2.0	VG 4.0	FN 6.0	VF 8.0	VF/NM 9.0	NM- 9.2
1-Reprints All Winners Comics #19 (Fall 1946); new Lago-c						5.00

TIMELY PRESENTS: HUMAN TORCH
Marvel Comics: Feb, 1999 ($3.99)

	GD 2.0	VG 4.0	FN 6.0	VF 8.0	VF/NM 9.0	NM- 9.2
1-Reprints Human Torch Comics #5 (Fall 1941); new Lago-c						5.00

TIME MACHINE, THE
Dell Publishing Co.: No. 1085, Mar, 1960 (H.G. Wells)

	GD 2.0	VG 4.0	FN 6.0	VF 8.0	VF/NM 9.0	NM- 9.2
Four Color 1085-Movie, Alex Toth-a; Rod Taylor photo-c	12	24	36	84	185	285

TIME MASTERS
DC Comics: Feb, 1990 - No. 8, Sept, 1990 ($1.75, mini-series)

	GD 2.0	VG 4.0	FN 6.0	VF 8.0	VF/NM 9.0	NM- 9.2
1-8: New Rip Hunter series. 5-Cave Carson, Viking Prince app. 6-Dr. Fate app.						3.00
TPB (2008, $19.99) r/#1-8 and Secret Origins #43; intro. by Geoff Johns						20.00

TIME MASTERS: VANISHING POINT (Tie-in to Batman: The Return of Bruce Wayne)
DC Comics: Sept, 2010 - No. 6, Feb, 2011 ($3.99, limited series)

	GD 2.0	VG 4.0	FN 6.0	VF 8.0	VF/NM 9.0	NM- 9.2
1-6-Jurgens-s/a/c; Rip Hunter, Superman, Green Lantern & Booster Gold app.						4.00
TPB (2011, $14.99) r/#1-6						15.00

TIMESLIP COLLECTION
Marvel Comics: Nov, 1998 ($2.99, one-shot)

	GD 2.0	VG 4.0	FN 6.0	VF 8.0	VF/NM 9.0	NM- 9.2
1-Pin-ups reprinted from Marvel Vision magazine						3.00

TIMESLIP SPECIAL (The Coming of the Avengers)
Marvel Comics: Oct, 1998 ($5.99, one-shot)

	GD 2.0	VG 4.0	FN 6.0	VF 8.0	VF/NM 9.0	NM- 9.2
1-Alternate world Avengers vs. Odin						6.00

TIMESTORM 2009/2099
Marvel Comics: June, 2009 - No. 4, Oct, 2009 ($3.99, limited series)

	GD 2.0	VG 4.0	FN 6.0	VF 8.0	VF/NM 9.0	NM- 9.2
1-4-Punisher 2099 transports Spider-Man to 2099; Wolverine app.; Battle-a						4.00
...: Spider-Man One Shot (8/09, $3.99) Reed-s/Craig-a/Renaud-c						4.00
...: X-Men One Shot (8/09, $3.99) Reed-s/Irving-a/Renaud-c						4.00

TIME TO RUN (Based on 1973 Billy Graham movie)
Spire Christian Comics (Fleming H. Revell Co.): 1975 (39¢)

	GD 2.0	VG 4.0	FN 6.0	VF 8.0	VF/NM 9.0	NM- 9.2
nn-By Al Hartley	2	4	6	13	18	22

TIME TUNNEL, THE (TV)
Gold Key: Feb, 1967 - No. 2, July, 1967 (12¢)

	GD 2.0	VG 4.0	FN 6.0	VF 8.0	VF/NM 9.0	NM- 9.2
1-Photo back-c on both issues	6	12	18	41	76	110
2	5	10	15	31	53	75

TIME TWISTERS
Quality Comics: Sept, 1987 - No. 21, 1989 ($1.25/$1.50)

	GD 2.0	VG 4.0	FN 6.0	VF 8.0	VF/NM 9.0	NM- 9.2
1-21: Alan Moore scripts in 1-4, 6-9, 14 (2 pg.). 14-Bolland-a (2 pg.). 15,16-Guice-c						4.00

TIME 2: THE EPIPHANY (See First Comics Graphic Novel #9)

TIMEWALKER (Also see Archer & Armstrong)
Valiant: Jan, 1994 - No. 15, Oct, 1995 ($2.50)

	GD 2.0	VG 4.0	FN 6.0	VF 8.0	VF/NM 9.0	NM- 9.2
1-15,0(3/96): 2-"JAN" on-c, February, 1995 in indicia.						3.00
Yearbook 1 (5/95, $2.95)						3.00

TIME WARP (See The Unexpected #210)
DC Comics, Inc.: Oct-Nov, 1979 - No. 5, June-July, 1980 ($1.00, 68 pgs.)

	GD 2.0	VG 4.0	FN 6.0	VF 8.0	VF/NM 9.0	NM- 9.2
1	2	4	6	13	18	22
2-5	2	4	6	8	11	14

NOTE: *Aparo a-1. Buckler a-1p. Chaykin a-2. Ditko a-1-4. Kaluta c-1-5. G. Kane a-2. Nasser a-4. Newton a-1-5p. Orlando a-2. Sutton a-1-3.*

TIME WARP
DC Comics (Vertigo): May, 2013 ($7.99, one-shot)

	GD 2.0	VG 4.0	FN 6.0	VF 8.0	VF/NM 9.0	NM- 9.2
1-Short story anthology by various incl. Lindelof, Simone; covers by Risso & Jae Lee						8.00

TIME WARRIORS: THE BEGINNING
Fantasy General Comics: 1986 (Aug) - No. 2, 1986? ($1.50)

	GD 2.0	VG 4.0	FN 6.0	VF 8.0	VF/NM 9.0	NM- 9.2
1,2-Alpha Track/Skellon Empire						3.00

TIM HOLT (Movie star) (Becomes Red Mask #42 on; also see Crack Western #72, & Great Western)
Magazine Enterprises: 1948 - No. 41, April-May, 1954 (All 36 pgs.)

	GD 2.0	VG 4.0	FN 6.0	VF 8.0	VF/NM 9.0	NM- 9.2
1-(A-1 #14)-Line drawn-c w/Tim Holt photo on-c; Tim Holt, His horse Lightning & sidekick Chito begin	54	108	162	343	574	825
2-(A-1 #17)(9-10/48)-Photo-c begin, end #18	27	54	81	158	259	360
3-(A-1 #19)-Photo back-c	20	40	60	117	189	260
4(1-2/49),5: 5-Photo front/back-c	15	30	45	85	130	175
6-(5/49)-1st app. The Calico Kid (alias Rex Fury), his horse Ebony & Sidekick Sing-Song (begin series); photo back-c	23	46	69	136	223	310
7-10: 7-Calico Kid by Ayers. 8-Calico Kid by Guardineer (r-in/Great Western #10). 9-Map of Tim's Home Range	15	30	45	83	124	165
11-The Calico Kid becomes The Ghost Rider (origin & 1st app.) by Dick Ayers (r-in/Great Western I.W. #8); his horse Spectre & sidekick Sing-Song begin series						

Tim Holt #36 © ME

Tiny Titans #4 © DC

Tip Top Comics #25 © UFS

	GD 2.0	VG 4.0	FN 6.0	VF 8.0	VF/NM 9.0	NM- 9.2
	71	142	213	454	777	1100
12-16,18-Last photo-c	13	26	39	74	105	135
17-Frazetta Ghost Rider-c	47	94	141	296	498	700
19,22,24: 19-Last Tim Holt-c; Bolle line-drawn-c begin; Tim Holt photo on covers #19-28, 30-41. 22-interior photo-c	11	22	33	62	86	110
20-Tim Holt becomes Redmask (origin); begin series; Redmask-c #20-on	15	30	45	90	140	190
21-Frazetta Ghost Rider/Redmask-c	39	78	117	231	378	525
23-Frazetta Redmask-c	30	60	90	177	289	400
25-1st app. Black Phantom	19	38	57	112	179	245
26-30: 28-Wild Bill Hickok, Bat Masterson team up with Redmask. 29-B&W photo-c	10	20	30	58	79	100
31-33-Ghost Rider ends	10	20	30	54	72	90
34-Tales of the Ghost Rider begins (horror)-Classic "The Flower Women" & "Hard Boiled Harry!"	14	28	42	82	121	160
35-Last Tales of the Ghost Rider	11	22	33	62	86	110
36-The Ghost Rider returns, ends #41; liquid hallucinogenic drug story	14	28	42	76	108	140
37-Ghost Rider classic "To Touch Is to Die!", about Inca treasure	14	28	42	76	108	140
38-The Black Phantom begins (not in #39); classic Ghost Rider "The Phantom Guns of Feather Gap!"	14	28	42	76	108	140
39-41: All 3-D effect c/stories	14	28	42	81	118	155

NOTE: ***Dick Ayers** a-7, 9-41. **Bolle** a-1-41; c-19, 20, 22, 24-28, 30-41.*

TIM McCOY (Formerly Zoo Funnies; Pictorial Love Stories #22 on)
Charlton Comics: No. 16, Oct, 1948 - No. 21, Aug, 1949 (Western Movie Stories)

	GD 2.0	VG 4.0	FN 6.0	VF 8.0	VF/NM 9.0	NM- 9.2
16-John Wayne, Montgomery Clift app. in "Red River"; photo back-c	34	68	102	204	332	460
17-21: 17-Allan "Rocky" Lane guest stars. 18-Rod Cameron guest stars. 19-Whip Wilson, Andy Clyde guest star; Jesse James story. 20-Jimmy Wakely guest stars. 21-Johnny Mack Brown guest stars	25	50	75	147	241	335

TIMMY
Dell Publishing Co.: No. 715, Aug, 1956 - No. 1022, Aug-Oct, 1959

	GD 2.0	VG 4.0	FN 6.0	VF 8.0	VF/NM 9.0	NM- 9.2
Four Color 715 (#1)	5	10	15	35	63	90
Four Color 823 (8/57), 923 (8/58), 1022	5	10	15	31	53	75

TIMMY THE TIMID GHOST (Formerly Win-A-Prize?; see Blue Bird)
Charlton Comics: No. 3, 2/56 - No. 44, 10/64; No. 45, 9/66; 10/67 - No. 23, 7/71; V4#24, 9/85 - No. 26, 1/86

	GD 2.0	VG 4.0	FN 6.0	VF 8.0	VF/NM 9.0	NM- 9.2
3(1956) (1st Series)	14	28	42	76	108	140
4,5	8	16	24	44	57	70
6-10	3	6	9	19	30	40
11,12(4/58,10/58)-(100 pgs.)	6	12	18	37	66	95
13-20	3	6	9	17	26	35
21-45(1966): 27-Nazi story	3	6	9	14	19	24
1(10/67, 2nd series)	3	6	9	15	22	28
2-10	2	4	6	10	14	18
11-23: 23 (7/71)	1	3	4	8	10	12
24-26 (1985-86): Fago-r (low print run)						6.00

TIM TYLER (See Harvey Comics Hits #54)

TIM TYLER (Also see Comics Reading Libraries in the Promotional Comics section)
Better Publications: 1942

	GD 2.0	VG 4.0	FN 6.0	VF 8.0	VF/NM 9.0	NM- 9.2
1	15	30	45	88	137	185

TIM TYLER COWBOY
Standard Comics (King Features Synd.): No. 11, Nov, 1948 - No. 18, Aug, 1950

	GD 2.0	VG 4.0	FN 6.0	VF 8.0	VF/NM 9.0	NM- 9.2
11-By Lyman Young	9	18	27	52	69	85
12-18: 13-15-Full length western adventures	7	14	21	37	46	55

TINKER BELL (Disney, TV)(See Walt Disney Showcase #37)
Dell Publishing Co.: No. 896, Mar, 1958 - No. 982, Apr-June, 1959

	GD 2.0	VG 4.0	FN 6.0	VF 8.0	VF/NM 9.0	NM- 9.2
Four Color 896 (#1)-The Adventures of...	9	18	27	59	117	175
Four Color 982-The New Advs. of...	8	16	24	54	102	150

TINY FOLKS FUNNIES
Dell Publishing Co.: No. 60, 1944

	GD 2.0	VG 4.0	FN 6.0	VF 8.0	VF/NM 9.0	NM- 9.2
Four Color 60	14	28	42	97	214	330

TINY TESSIE (Tessie #1-23; Real Experiences #25)
Marvel Comics (20CC): No. 24, Oct, 1949 (52 pgs.)

	GD 2.0	VG 4.0	FN 6.0	VF 8.0	VF/NM 9.0	NM- 9.2
24	18	36	54	105	165	225

TINY TIM (Also see Super Comics)
Dell Publishing Co.: No. 4, 1941 - No. 235, July, 1949

	GD 2.0	VG 4.0	FN 6.0	VF 8.0	VF/NM 9.0	NM- 9.2
Large Feature Comic 4('41)	45	90	135	284	480	675
Four Color 20(1941)	41	82	123	250	418	585
Four Color 42(1943)	16	32	48	110	243	375
Four Color 235	6	12	18	41	76	110

TINY TITANS (Teen Titans)
DC Comics: Apr, 2008 - No. 50, May, 2012 ($2.25/$2.50/$2.99)

	GD 2.0	VG 4.0	FN 6.0	VF 8.0	VF/NM 9.0	NM- 9.2
1-29-All ages stories of Teen Titans in Elementary school; Baltazar & Franco-s/a						3.00
1-(6/08, Free Comic Book Day giveaway) r/#1; Baltazar & Franco-s/a						3.00
30-50: 30-Begin $2.99-c. 37-Marvel Family app. 44-Doom Patrol app.						3.00

TINY TITANS / LITTLE ARCHIE (Teen Titans) (Digest-size reprint in World of Archie Double Digest Magazine #5)
DC Comics: Dec, 2010 - No. 3, Feb, 2011 ($2.99, limited series)

	GD 2.0	VG 4.0	FN 6.0	VF 8.0	VF/NM 9.0	NM- 9.2
1-3-Character crossover; Baltazar & Franco-s/a. 2-Josie and the Pussycats app.						3.00

TINY TITANS: RETURN TO THE TREEHOUSE
DC Comics: Aug, 2014 - No. 6, Jan, 2015 ($2.99, limited series)

	GD 2.0	VG 4.0	FN 6.0	VF 8.0	VF/NM 9.0	NM- 9.2
1-6-Baltazar & Franco-s/a. 1-Brainiac app. 3-Marvel Family app.						3.00

TINY TOT COMICS
E. C. Comics: Mar, 1946 - No. 10, Nov-Dec, 1947 (For younger readers)

	GD 2.0	VG 4.0	FN 6.0	VF 8.0	VF/NM 9.0	NM- 9.2
1(nn)-52 pg. issues begin, end #4	47	94	141	296	498	700
2 (5/46)	29	58	87	170	278	385
3-10: 10-Christmas-c	25	50	75	150	245	340

TINY TOT FUNNIES (Formerly Family Funnies; becomes Junior Funnies)
Harvey Publ. (King Features Synd.): No. 9, June, 1951

	GD 2.0	VG 4.0	FN 6.0	VF 8.0	VF/NM 9.0	NM- 9.2
9-Flash Gordon, Mandrake, Dagwood, Daisy, etc.	8	16	24	42	54	65

TINY TOTS COMICS
Dell Publishing Co.: 1943 (Not reprints)

	GD 2.0	VG 4.0	FN 6.0	VF 8.0	VF/NM 9.0	NM- 9.2
1-Kelly-a(2); fairy tales	39	78	117	240	395	550

TIPPY & CAP STUBBS (See Popular Comics)
Dell Publishing Co.: No. 210, Jan, 1949 - No. 242, Aug, 1949

	GD 2.0	VG 4.0	FN 6.0	VF 8.0	VF/NM 9.0	NM- 9.2
Four Color 210 (#1)	7	14	21	44	82	120
Four Color 242	5	10	15	31	53	75

TIPPY'S FRIENDS GO-GO & ANIMAL
Tower Comics: July, 1966 - No. 15, Oct, 1969 (25¢)

	GD 2.0	VG 4.0	FN 6.0	VF 8.0	VF/NM 9.0	NM- 9.2
1	9	18	27	61	123	185
2-5,7,9-15: 12-15 titled "Tippy's Friend Go-Go"	5	10	15	35	63	90
6-The Monkees photo-c	8	16	24	54	102	150
8-Beatles app. on front/back-c	10	20	30	66	138	210

TIPPY TEEN (See Vicki)
Tower Comics: Nov, 1965 - No. 25, Oct, 1969 (25¢)

	GD 2.0	VG 4.0	FN 6.0	VF 8.0	VF/NM 9.0	NM- 9.2
1	10	20	30	68	144	220
2-4,6-10	6	12	18	40	73	105
5-1 pg. Beatles pin-up	7	14	21	44	82	120
11-20: 16-Twiggy photo-c	6	12	18	37	66	95
21-25	5	10	15	34	60	85
Special Collectors' Editions nn-(1969, 25¢)	6	12	18	37	66	95

TIPPY TERRY
Super/I. W. Enterprises: 1963

	GD 2.0	VG 4.0	FN 6.0	VF 8.0	VF/NM 9.0	NM- 9.2
Super Reprint #14('63)-r/Little Groucho #1	2	4	6	8	10	12
I.W. Reprint #1 (nd)-r/Little Groucho #1	2	4	6	8	10	12

TIP TOP COMICS
United Features #1-188/St. John #189-210/Dell Publishing Co. #211 on:
4/36 - No. 210, 1957; No. 211, 11-1/57-58 - No. 225, 5-7/61

	GD 2.0	VG 4.0	FN 6.0	VF 8.0	VF/NM 9.0	NM- 9.2
1-Tarzan by Hal Foster, Li'l Abner, Broncho Bill, Fritzi Ritz, Ella Cinders, Capt. & The Kids begin; strip-r (1st comic book app. of each)	900	1800	2700	5500	9750	14,000
2-Tarzan-c (6/36)	200	400	600	1280	2190	3100
3-Tarzan-c (7/36)	181	362	543	1158	1979	2800
4-(8/36)	100	200	300	635	1093	1550
5-8,10: 7-Photo & biography of Edgar Rice Burroughs. 8-Christmas-c	71	142	213	454	777	1100
9-Tarzan-c (1/37)	94	188	282	597	1024	1450
11,13,16,18-Tarzan-c: 11-Has Tarzan pin-up	71	142	213	454	777	1100
12,14,15,17,19,20: 20-Christmas-c	52	104	156	328	552	775
21,24,27,30-(10/38)-Tarzan-c	57	114	171	362	619	875
22,23,25,26,28,29	39	78	117	234	385	535
31,35,38,40	36	72	108	216	351	485
32,36-Tarzan-c: 32-1st published Jack Davis-a (cartoon). 36-Kurtzman panel (1st published comic work)	57	114	171	362	619	875

Tip Topper Comics #1 © UFS

Titans (2016 series) #8 © DC

T-Man #21 © QUA

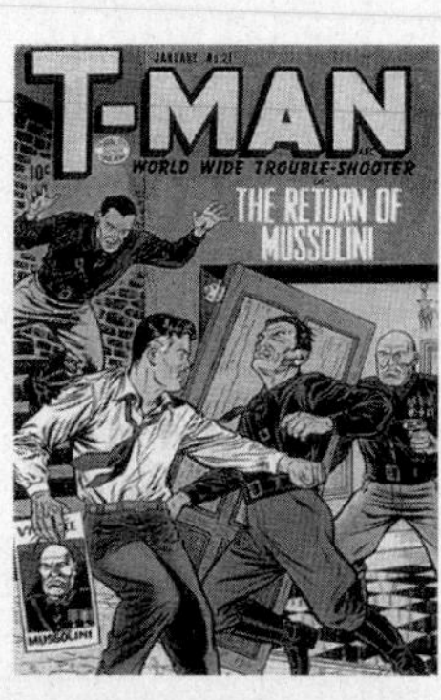

	GD 2.0	VG 4.0	FN 6.0	VF 8.0	VF/NM 9.0	NM- 9.2
33,34,37,39-Tarzan-c	53	106	159	334	567	800
41-Reprints 1st Tarzan Sunday; Tarzan-c	57	114	171	362	619	875
42,44,46,48,49	31	62	93	182	296	410
43,45,47,50,52-Tarzan-c. 43-Mort Walker panel	40	80	120	246	411	575
51,53	29	58	87	170	278	385
54-Origin Mirror Man & Triple Terror, also featured on cover	37	74	111	218	354	490
55,56,58: Last Tarzan by Foster	24	48	72	142	234	325
57,59-62-Tarzan by Hogarth	31	62	93	182	296	410
63-80: 65,67-70,72-74,77,78-No Tarzan	15	30	45	88	137	185
81-90	14	28	42	80	115	150
91-99	13	26	39	72	101	130
100	14	28	42	76	108	140
101-140: 110-Gordo story. 111-Li'l Abner app. 118, 132-No Tarzan. 137-Sadie Hawkins Day story	10	20	30	54	72	90
141-170: 145,151-Gordo stories. 153-Fritzi Ritz lingerie panels. 157-Last Li'l Abner; lingerie panels	8	16	24	44	57	70
171,172,174-183: 171-Tarzan reprints by B. Lubbers begin; end #188	9	18	27	47	61	75
173-(3/52) Ties with United Comics #21 for first app. of Peanuts in comics; reprints Peanuts dailies 2/06/51 & 3/05/51 (also see Tip Topper Comics)	129	258	387	826	1413	2000
184-Peanuts app.	19	38	57	112	179	245
185-188-Peanuts stories with Charlie Brown & Snoopy on the covers	200	400	600	1200	1450	1700
189,191-225-Peanuts apps.(4 pg. to 8 pg stories) in most						
Issues with Peanuts	13	26	39	72	101	130
Issues without Peanuts	8	16	24	40	50	60
190-Peanuts with Charlie Brown & Snoopy partial-c (comic strip at bottom of cover)	28	56	84	165	270	375
Bound Volumes (Very Rare) sold at 1939 World's Fair; bound by publisher in pictorial comic boards (also see Comics on Parade)						
Bound issues 1-12 (Rare)	377	754	1131	2639	4620	6600
Bound issues 13-24	181	362	543	1158	1979	2800
Bound issues 25-36	155	310	465	992	1696	2400

NOTE: *Tarzan by* ***Foster****-#1-40, 44-50; by* ***Rex Maxon****-#41-43; by* ***Burne Hogarth****-#57, 59, 62.*

TIP TOPPER COMICS
United Features Syndicate: Oct-Nov, 1949 - No. 28, 1954

	GD 2.0	VG 4.0	FN 6.0	VF 8.0	VF/NM 9.0	NM- 9.2
1-Li'l Abner, Abbie & Slats	15	30	45	83	124	165
2	10	20	30	54	72	90
3-5: 5-Fearless Fosdick app.	9	18	27	50	65	80
6-10: 6-Fearless Fosdick app.	8	16	24	44	57	70
11-15	8	16	24	40	50	60
16(4-5/52)-2nd app. of Peanuts (2 pgs.) by Schulz in comics (See United Comics #21 for 1st app. & #22 for 5-6/52 app.)(Also see Tip Top Comics #173)	47	94	141	296	498	700
17(6-7/52)-4th app. of Peanuts by Schulz, 2 pgs.	30	60	90	177	289	400
18-28: 18-24,26-28-Early Peanuts (2 pgs.). 25-Early Peanuts (3 pgs.) 26-28-Twin Earths	15	30	45	84	127	170

NOTE: *Many lingerie panels in Fritzi Ritz stories.*

TITAN A.E.
Dark Horse Comics: May, 2000 - No. 3, July, 2000 ($2.95, limited series)

1-3-Movie prequel; Al Rio-a 3.00

TITANS (Also see Teen Titans, New Teen Titans and New Titans)
DC Comics: Mar, 1999 - No. 50, Apr, 2003 ($2.50/$2.75)

1-Titans re-form; Grayson-s; 2 covers 4.00
2-11,13-24,26-50: 2-Superman-c/app. 9,10,21,22-Deathstroke app. 24-Titans from "Kingdom Come" app. 32-36-Asamiya-c. 44-Begin $2.75-c 3.00
12-($3.50, 48 pages) 4.00
25-($3.95) Titans from "Kingdom Come" app.; Wolfman & Faerber-s; art by Pérez, Cardy, Grumment, Jimenez, Dodson, Pelletier 4.00
Annual 1 ('00, $3.50) Planet DC; intro Bushido 4.00
... East Special 1 (1/08, $3.99) Winick-s/Churchill-a; continues in Titans #1 (2008) 4.00
...Secret Files 1,2 (3/99, 10/00; $4.95) Profile pages & short stories 5.00

TITANS (Also see Teen Titans)
DC Comics: Jun, 2008 - No. 38, Oct, 2011 ($3.50/$2.99)

1-($3.50) Titans re-form again; Winick-s/Churchill-a; covers by Churchill & Van Sciver 4.00
2-38: 2-4-Trigon returns. 6-10-Jericho app. 24-Deathstroke & Luthor app. 3.00
Annual 1 (9/11, $4.99) Justice League app.; Jericho returns; Richards-a 5.00
...: Villains For Hire Special 1 (7/10, $4.99) Deathstroke's team; Atom (Ryan Choi) killed 5.00
...: Fractured TPB (2010, $17.99) r/#14,16-22 18.00
...: Lockdown TPB (2009, $14.99) r/#7-11 15.00
...: Old Friends HC (2008, $24.99) r/#1-6 & Titans East Special 25.00
...: Villains For Hire TPB (2011, $14.99) r/#24-27 & Villains For Hire Special 1 15.00

TITANS (DC Rebirth)(Follows Titans Hunt series)
DC Comics: Aug, 2016 - Present ($2.99/$3.99)

1-9: 1-Abnett-s/Booth-a; Abra Kadabra returns. 7-Superman app. 3.00
10-20-($3.99) 10-Fearsome Five app. 11-Lazarus Contract x-over; Teen Titans & Deathstroke app. 12-Rocafort-a 4.00
Annual 1 (5/17, $4.99) Justice League and The Key app.; Abnett-s/Jung-a 5.00
...: Rebirth 1 (8/16, $2.99) Abnett-s/Booth-a; Wally West reunites with the Titans 3.00

TITANS HUNT (Also see DC Universe: Rebirth)
DC Comics: Dec, 2015 - No. 8, Jun, 2016 ($3.99, limited series)

1-7: 1-Abnett-s/Siqueira-a; 1970s-era Titans app. incl. Lilith & Gnarrk. 2,4-Segovia-a 4.00
8-Titans vs. Mr. Twister 4.00

TITANS/ LEGION OF SUPER-HEROES: UNIVERSE ABLAZE
DC Comics: 2000 - No. 4, 2000 ($4.95, prestige format, limited series)

1-4-Jurgens-s/a; P. Jimenez-a; teams battle Universo 5.00

TITAN SPECIAL
Dark Horse Comics: June, 1994 ($3.95, one-shot)

1-($3.95, 52 pgs.) 4.00

TITANS: SCISSORS, PAPER, STONE
DC Comics: 1997 ($4.95, one-shot)

1-Manga style Elseworlds; Adam Warren-s/a(p) 5.00

TITANS SELL-OUT SPECIAL
DC Comics: Nov, 1992 ($3.50, 52 pgs., one-shot)

1-Fold-out Nightwing poster; 1st Teeny Titans 4.00

TITANS/ YOUNG JUSTICE: GRADUATION DAY
DC Comics: Early July, 2003 - No. 3, Aug, 2003 ($2.50, limited series)

1,2-Winick-s/Garza-a; leads into Teen Titans and The Outsiders series. 2-Lilith dies 3.00
3-Death of Donna Troy (Wonder Girl) 3.00
TPB (2003, $6.95) r/#1-3; plus previews of Teen Titans and The Outsiders series 7.00

TITHE, THE (Also see Eden's Fall)
Image Comics (Top Cow): Apr, 2015 - No. 8 ($3.99, limited series)

1-7-Hawkins-s/Ekedal-a; multiple covers on each. 5-7-Sevy-a 4.00

T-MAN (Also see Police Comics #103)
Quality Comics Group: Sept, 1951 - No. 38, Dec, 1956

	GD 2.0	VG 4.0	FN 6.0	VF 8.0	VF/NM 9.0	NM- 9.2
1-Pete Trask, T-Man begins; Jack Cole-a	52	104	156	328	552	775
2-Crandall-c	29	58	87	170	278	385
3,7,8: All Crandall-c	26	52	78	154	252	350
4,5-Crandall-c/a each	27	54	81	162	266	370
6-"The Man Who Could Be Hitler" c/story; Crandall-c.	39	78	117	236	388	540
9,10-Crandall-c	23	46	69	136	223	310
11-Used in **POP**, pg. 95 & color illo.	20	40	60	117	189	260
12,13,15-19,22-26: 23-H-Bomb panel. 24-Last pre-code issue (4/55). 25-Not Crandall-a	16	32	48	94	147	200
14-Hitler-c	31	62	93	182	296	410
20-H-Bomb explosion-c/story	20	40	60	117	189	260
21- "The Return of Mussolini" c/story	20	40	60	117	189	260
27-33,35-38	15	30	45	86	133	180
34-Hitler-c	28	56	84	165	270	375

NOTE: *Anti-communist stories common.* ***Crandall*** *c-2-10p.* ***Cuidera*** *c(i)-1-38. Bondage c-15.*

TMNT... (Also see Teenage Mutant Ninja Turtles and related titles)
Mirage Publishing: March 2007 ($3.25/$4.95, B&W, one-shots)

...: Raphael Movie Prequel 1; ...: Michelangelo Movie Prequel 2; ...: Donatello Movie Prequel 3; ...: April Movie Prequel 4; ...: Leonardo Movie Prequel 5; back-story for movie 3.25
...: The Official Movie Adaptation ($4.95) adapts 2007 movie; Munroe-c 5.00

TMNT MUTANT UNIVERSE SOURCEBOOK
Archie Comics: 1992 - No. 3, 1992? ($1.95, 52 pgs.)(Lists characters from A-Z)

1-3: 3-New characters; fold-out poster 5.00

TNT COMICS
Charles Publishing Co.: Feb, 1946 (36 pgs.)

	GD 2.0	VG 4.0	FN 6.0	VF 8.0	VF/NM 9.0	NM- 9.2
1-Yellowjacket app.	39	78	117	231	378	525

TOBY TYLER (Disney, see Movie Comics)
Dell Publishing Co.: No. 1092, Apr-June, 1960

	GD 2.0	VG 4.0	FN 6.0	VF 8.0	VF/NM 9.0	NM- 9.2
Four Color 1092-Movie, photo-c	6	12	18	38	69	100

TODAY'S BRIDES

Toil and Trouble #1 © Marguerite Scott

Tomahawk #9 © DC

Tomb of Dracula #11 © MAR

	GD 2.0	VG 4.0	FN 6.0	VF 8.0	VF/NM 9.0	NM- 9.2

Ajax/Farrell Publishing Co.: Nov, 1955; No. 2, Feb, 1956; No. 3, Sept, 1956; No. 4, Nov, 1956

1	12	24	36	67	94	120
2-4	9	18	27	50	65	80

TODAY'S ROMANCE
Standard Comics: No. 5, March, 1952 - No. 8, Sept, 1952 (All photo-c?)

5-Photo-c	14	28	42	81	118	155
6-Photo-c; Toth-a	14	28	42	82	121	160
7,8	12	24	36	67	94	120

TODD, THE UGLIEST KID ON EARTH
Image Comics: Jan, 2013 - No. 8, Jan, 2014 ($2.99)

1-8-Perker-a/Kristensen-s 3.00

TOE TAGS FEATURING GEORGE A. ROMERO
DC Comics: Dec, 2004 - No. 6, May, 2005 ($2.95/$2.99)

1-6-Zombie story by George Romero; Wrightson-c/Castillo-a 3.00

TOIL AND TROUBLE
BOOM! Studios (Archaia): Sept, 2015 - No. 6 ($3.99)

1-6-Mairghread Scott-s/Kelly & Nicole Matthews-a 4.00

TOKA (Jungle King)
Dell Publishing Co.: Aug-Oct, 1964 - No. 10, Jan, 1967 (Painted-c #1,2)

1	4	8	12	28	47	65
2	3	6	9	17	26	35
3-10	3	6	9	15	22	28

TOKYO GHOST
Image Comics: Sept, 2015 - No. 10, Aug, 2016 ($3.99)

1-10-Rick Remender-s/Sean Murphy-a 4.00

TOKYO STORM WARNING (See Red/Tokyo Storm Warning for TPB)
DC Comics (Cliffhanger): Aug, 2003 - No. 3, Dec, 2003 ($2.95, limited series)

1-3-Warren Ellis-s/James Raiz-a 3.00

TOMAHAWK (Son of... on-c of #131-140; see Star Spangled Comics #69 & World's Finest Comics #65)
National Periodical Publications: Sept-Oct, 1950 - No. 140, May-June, 1972

1-Tomahawk & boy sidekick Dan Hunter begin by Fred Ray	187	374	561	1197	2049	2900
2-Frazetta/Williamson-a (4 pgs.)	68	136	204	435	743	1050
3-5	41	82	123	256	428	600
6-10: 7-Last 52 pg. issue	36	72	108	211	343	475
11-20	24	48	72	142	234	325
21-27,30: 30-Last precode (2/55)	21	42	63	126	206	285
28-1st app. Lord Shilling (arch-foe)	22	44	66	132	216	300
29-Frazetta-r/Jimmy Wakely #3 (3 pgs.)	26	52	78	154	252	350
31-40	18	36	54	107	169	230
41-50	10	20	30	64	132	200
51-56,58-60	9	18	27	58	114	170
57-Frazetta-r/Jimmy Wakely #6 (3 pgs.)	10	20	30	64	132	200
61-77: 77-Last 10¢ issue	8	16	24	54	102	150
78-85: 81-1st app. Miss Liberty. 83-Origin Tomahawk's Rangers	7	14	21	46	86	125
86-99: 96-Origin/1st app. The Hood, alias Lady Shilling	5	10	15	35	63	90
100	6	12	18	37	66	95
101-110: 107-Origin/1st app. Thunder-Man	5	10	15	30	50	70
111-115,120,122: 122-Last 12¢ issue	4	8	12	28	47	65
116-1st Neal Adams cover	22	44	66	154	340	525
117-119,121,123-130-Neal Adams-c. 118-Origin of the Rangers	6	12	18	38	69	100
131-Frazetta-r/Jimmy Wakely #7 (3 pgs.); origin Firehair retold	3	6	9	21	33	45
132-135: 135-Last 15¢ issue	3	6	9	16	24	32
136-138,140 (52 pg. Giants)	3	6	9	19	30	40
139-Frazetta-r/Star Spangled #113	3	6	9	21	33	45

NOTE: ***Fred Ray** c-1, 2, 8, 11, 30, 34, 35, 40-43, 45, 46, 82. Firehair by **Kubert**-131-134, 136. **Maurer** a-138. **Severin** a-135. **Starr** a-5. **Thorne** a-137, 140.*

TOM AND JERRY (See Comic Album #4, 8, 12, Dell Giant #21, Dell Giants, Golden Comics Digest #1, 5, 8, 13, 15, 18, 22, 25, 28, 35, Kite fun Book & March of Comics #21, 46, 61, 70, 88, 103, 119, 128, 145, 154, 173, 190, 207, 224, 281, 295, 305, 321,333, 345, 361, 365, 388, 400, 444, 451, 463, 480)

TOM AND JERRY (...Comics, early issues) (M.G.M.)
(Formerly Our Gang No. 1-59) (See Dell Giants for annuals)
Dell Publishing Co./Gold Key No. 213-327/Whitman No. 328 on: No. 193, 6/48; No. 60, 7/49 - No. 212, 7-9/62; No. 213, 11/62 - No. 291, 2/75; No. 292, 3/77 - No. 342, 5/82 - No. 344, 6/84

Four Color 193 (#1)-Titled "M.G.M. Presents..."	24	48	72	168	372	575
60-Barney Bear, Benny Burro cont. from Our Gang; Droopy begins	12	24	36	79	170	260
61	9	18	27	60	120	180
62-70: 66-X-Mas-c	7	14	21	49	92	135
71-80: 77,90-X-Mas-c. 79-Spike & Tyke begin	6	12	18	40	73	105
81-99	5	10	15	35	63	90
100	6	12	18	37	66	95
101-120	5	10	15	31	53	75
121-140: 126-X-Mas-c	4	8	12	28	47	65
141-160	4	8	12	25	40	55
161-200	4	8	12	23	37	50
201-212(7-9/62)(Last Dell issue)	3	6	9	21	33	45
213,214-(84 pgs.)-Titled "...Funhouse"	5	10	15	35	63	90
215-240: 215-Titled "...Funhouse"	3	6	9	16	24	32
241-270	2	4	6	11	16	20
271-300: 286- "Tom & Jerry"	2	4	6	8	11	14
301-327 (Gold Key)	1	3	4	6	8	10
328,329 (Whitman)	2	4	6	8	11	14
330(8/80),331(10/80), 332-(3-pack only)	4	8	12	27	44	60
333-341: 339(2/82), 340(2-3/82), 341(4/82)	2	4	6	8	10	12
342-344 (All #90058, no date, date code, 3-pack): 342(6/83), 343(8/83), 344(6/84)	3	6	9	16	24	32
Mouse From T.R.A.P. 1(7/66)-Giant, G. K.	4	8	12	28	47	65
Summer Fun 1(7/67, 68 pgs.)(Gold Key)-Reprints Barks' Droopy from Summer Fun #1	4	8	12	28	47	65

NOTE: *#60-87, 98-121, 268, 277, 289, 302 are 52 pgs.. Reprints-#225, 241, 245, 247, 252, 254, 266, 268, 270, 292-327, 329-342, 344.*

TOM & JERRY
Harvey Comics: Sept, 1991 - No. 18, Aug, 1994 ($1.25)

1-18: 1-Tom & Jerry, Barney Bear-r by Carl Barks 3.00
50th Anniversary Special 1 (10/91, $2.50, 68 pgs.)-Benny the Lonesome Burro-r by Barks (story/a)/Our Gang #9 4.00

TOMB OF DARKNESS (Formerly Beware)
Marvel Comics Group: No. 9, July, 1974 - No. 23, Nov, 1976

9	4	8	12	23	37	50
10-23: 11,16,18-21-Kirby-a. 15,19-Ditko-r. 17-Woodbridge-r/Astonishing #62; Powell-r. 20-Everett Venus-r/Venus #19. 23-Everett-r	3	6	9	16	23	30
20,21-(30¢-c variants, limited distribution)(5,7/76)	8	16	24	54	102	150

TOMB OF DRACULA (See Giant-Size Dracula, Dracula Lives, Nightstalkers, Power Record Comics & Requiem for Dracula)
Marvel Comics Group: Apr, 1972 - No. 70, Aug, 1979

1-1st app. Dracula & Frank Drake; Colan-p in all; Neal Adams-c	15	30	45	105	233	360
2	8	16	24	51	96	140
3-6: 3-Intro. Dr. Rachel Van Helsing & Inspector Chelm. 6-Neal Adams-c	6	12	18	40	73	105
7-9	5	10	15	35	63	90
10-1st app. Blade the Vampire Slayer (who app. in 1998, 2002 and 2004 movies)	28	56	84	202	451	700
11,14-16,20:	5	10	15	30	50	70
12-2nd app. Blade; Brunner-c(p)	8	16	24	54	102	150
13-Origin Blade	9	18	27	61	123	185
17,19: 17-Blade bitten by Dracula. 19-Blade discovers he is immune to vampire's bite. 1st mention of Blade having vampire blood in him	6	12	18	38	69	100
18-Two-part x-over cont'd in Werewolf by Night #15	5	10	15	35	63	90
21,24-Blade app.	5	10	15	30	50	70
22,23,26,27,29	3	6	9	19	30	40
25-1st app. & origin Hannibal King	4	8	12	27	44	60
25-2nd printing (1994)	2	4	6	8	10	12
28-Blade app. on-c & inside as an illusion	4	8	12	27	44	60
30,41,42,44,45-Blade app. 45-Intro. Deacon Frost, the vampire who bit Blade's mother	4	8	12	25	40	55
31-40	3	6	9	17	26	35
43-Blade-c by Wrightson	4	8	12	28	47	65
43-45-(30¢-c variants, limited distribution)	7	14	21	44	82	120
46,47-(Regular 25¢ editions)(4-8/76)	3	6	9	14	20	25
46,47-(30¢-c variants, limited distribution)	6	12	18	37	66	95
48,49,51-57,59,60: 57,59,60-(30¢-c)	3	6	9	14	20	25
50-Silver Surfer app.	4	8	12	23	37	50
57,59,60-(35¢-c variants)(6-9/77)	10	20	30	66	138	210

Tomb of Terror #9 © HARV

Tomb Raider (2014 series) #1 © Square Enix

Tom Mix Western #8 © FAW

	GD 2.0	VG 4.0	FN 6.0	VF 8.0	VF/NM 9.0	NM- 9.2
58-All Blade issue (Regular 30¢ edition)	4	8	12	28	47	65
58-(35¢-c variant)(7/77)	11	22	33	76	163	250
61-69	3	6	9	14	20	25
70-Double size	4	8	12	23	37	50

NOTE: ***N. Adams** c-1, 6. **Colan** a-1-70p; c(p)-8, 38-42, 44-56, 58-70. **Wrightson** c-43.*

TOMB OF DRACULA, THE (Magazine)
Marvel Comics Group: Oct, 1979 - No. 6, Aug, 1980 (B&W)

	GD	VG	FN	VF	VF/NM	NM-
1,3: 1-Colan-a; features on movies "Dracula" and "Love at First Bite" w/photos. 3-Good girl cover-a; Miller-a (2 pg. sketch)	2	4	6	11	16	20
2,6: 2-Ditko-a (36 pgs.); Nosferatu movie feature. 6-Lilith story w/Sienkiewicz-a	2	4	6	8	11	14
4,5: Stephen King interview	2	4	6	13	18	22

NOTE: ***Buscema** a-4p, 5p. **Chaykin** c-5, 6. **Colan** a(p)-1, 3-6. **Miller** a-3. **Romita** a-2p.*

TOMB OF DRACULA
Marvel Comics (Epic Comics): 1991 - No. 4, 1992 ($4.95, 52 pgs., squarebound, mini-series)

Book 1-4: Colan/Williamson-a; Colan painted-c 5.00

TOMB OF DRACULA
Marvel Comics: Dec, 2004 - No. 4, Mar, 2005 ($2.99, limited series)

1-4-Blade app.; Tolagson-a/Sienkiewicz-c 3.00

TOMB OF DRACULA PRESENTS: THRONE OF BLOOD
Marvel Comics: Jun, 2011 ($3.99, one-shot)

1-Story of Raizo Kodo in 1585 Japan; Parlov-a; Hitch-c 4.00

TOMB OF LEGEIA (See Movie Classics)

TOMB OF TERROR (Thrills of Tomorrow #17 on)
Harvey Publications: June, 1952 - No. 16, July, 1954

	GD	VG	FN	VF	VF/NM	NM-
1	55	110	165	352	601	850
2	40	80	120	244	402	560
3-Bondage-c; atomic disaster story	39	78	117	240	395	550
4-12: 4-Heart ripped out. 8-12-Nostrand-a	39	78	117	231	378	525
13-Special S/F issue (1/54) White letter shadow-c	53	106	159	334	567	800
13-Logo variant-c (striped letter shadow)	58	116	174	371	636	900
14-Classic S/F-c; Check-a	71	142	213	454	777	1100
15-S/F issue; c-shows face exploding	252	504	756	1613	2757	3900
16-Special S/F issue; horror-c; Nostrand-a	50	100	150	315	533	750

NOTE: ***Edd Cartier** a-13? **Elias** c-2, 5-16. **Kremer** a-1, 7; c-1. **Nostrand** a-8-12, 15r 16. **Palais** a-2, 3, 5-7. **Powell** a-1, 3, 5, 9-16. **Sparling** a-12, 13, 15.*

TOMB OF TERROR
Marvel Comics: Dec, 2010 ($3.99, B&W, one-shot)

1-Short stories of Man-Thing, Son of Satan, Werewolf By Night & The Living Mummy 4.00

TOMB RAIDER (Also see Lara Croft And The Frozen Omen)
Dark Horse Comics: Feb, 2014 - No. 18, Jul, 2015 ($3.50/$3.99)

1-18: 1-6-Gail Simone-s/Nicolás Daniel Selma-a. 13-Begin $3.99-c 4.00

TOMB RAIDER
Dark Horse Comics: Feb, 2016 - No. 12, Jan, 2017 ($3.99)

1-12-Mariko Tamaki-s/Phillip Sevy-a 4.00

TOMB RAIDER (one-shots)
Image Comics (Top Cow Prod.)

...: Arabian Nights (8/04, $5.99) Avery-s/Tan-a/c 6.00
... Cover Gallery 2006 (4/06, $2.99) artist galleries and series gallery; pin-ups 3.00
.../The Darkness Special 1 (2001, TopCowStore.com)-Wohl-s/Tan-a 3.00
Epiphany 1 (8/03, $4.99)-Jurgens-s/Banks-a/Haley-c; preview of Witchblade Animated 5.00
Takeover 1 (1/04, $2.99)-Benefiel-a/Daniel-c 3.00
... Vs. The Wolf-Men: Monster War 2005 (7/05, $2.99) 2nd part of Monster War x-over 3.00
.../Witchblade/Magdalena/Vampirella #1 (8/05, $2.99, B&W) three covers; Chin-a 3.00

TOMB RAIDER: JOURNEYS
Image Comics (Top Cow Prod.): Jan, 2002 - No. 12, May, 2003 ($2.50/$2.99)

1-12: 1-Avery-s/Drew Johnson-a. 1-Two covers by Johnson & Hughes 3.00

TOMB RAIDER: SURVIVOR'S CRUSADE
Dark Horse Comics: Nov, 2017 - Present ($3.99)

1-3-Lanzing & Kelly-s/Woods-a 4.00

TOMB RAIDER: THE GREATEST TREASURE OF ALL
Image Comics (Top Cow Prod.): 2002; Oct, 2005 ($6.99)

Prelude (2002, 16 pgs., no cover price) Jusko-c/a 3.00
1-(10/05, $6.99) Jusko-a/Jurgens-s; sketch pages, reference photos, art in progress 7.00

TOMB RAIDER: THE SERIES (Also see Witchblade/Tomb Raider)
Image Comics (Top Cow Prod.): Dec, 1999 - No. 50, Mar, 2005 ($2.50/$2.99)

1-Jurgens-s/Park-a; 3 covers by Park, Finch, Turner 5.00
2-24,26-29,31-50: 21-Black-c w/foil. 31-Mhan-a. 37-Flip book preview of Stryke Force 3.00
25-Michael Turner-c/a; Witchblade app.; Endgame x-over with Witchblade #60 & Evo #1 4.00
30-($4.99) Tony Daniel-a 5.00
#0 (6/01, $2.50) Avery-s/Ching-a/c 3.00
#1/2 (10/01, $2.95) Early days of Lara Croft; Jurgens-s/Lopez-a 3.00
...: Chasing Shangri-La (2002, $12.95, TPB) r/#11-15 13.00
Free Comic Book Day giveaway - (5/02) r/#1 with "Free Comic Book Day" banner on-c 3.00
... Gallery (12/00, $2.95) Pin-ups & previous covers by various 3.00
... Magazine (6/01, $4.95) Hughes-c; r/#1,2; Jurgens interview 5.00
...: Mystic Artifacts (2001, $14.95, TPB) r/#5-10 15.00
...: Saga of the Medusa Mask (9/00, $9.95, TPB) r/#1-4; new Park-c 10.00
... Vol. 1 Compendium (11/06, $59.99) r/#1-50; variant covers and pin-up art 60.00

TOMB RAIDER/WITCHBLADE SPECIAL (Also see Witchblade/Tomb Raider)
Top Cow Prod.: Dec, 1997 (mail-in offer, one-shot)

	GD	VG	FN	VF	VF/NM	NM-
1-Turner-s/a(p); green background cover	1	3	4	6	8	10
1-Variant-c with orange sun background	1	3	4	6	8	10
1-Variant-c with black sides	1	3	4	6	8	10
1-Revisited (12/98, $2.95) reprints #1, Turner-c						3.00
...: Trouble Seekers TPB (2002, $7.95) rep. T.R./W & W/T.R. & W/T.R. 1/2; new Turner-c						8.00

TOMBSTONE TERRITORY
Dell Publishing Co.: No. 1123, Aug, 1960

	GD	VG	FN	VF	VF/NM	NM-
Four Color 1123	7	14	21	49	92	135

TOM CAT (Formerly Bo; Atom The Cat #9 on)
Charlton Comics: No. 4, Apr, 1956 - No. 8, July, 1957

	GD	VG	FN	VF	VF/NM	NM-
4-Al Fago-c/a	8	16	24	44	57	70
5-8	6	12	18	31	38	45

TOM CLANCY'S SPLINTER CELL: ECHOES
Dynamite Entertainment: 2014 - No. 4, 2014 ($3.99)

1-4-Nathan Edmonson-s/Marc Laming-a 4.00

TOM CORBETT, SPACE CADET (TV)
Dell Publishing Co.: No. 378, Jan-Feb, 1952 - No. 11, Sept-Nov, 1954 (All painted covers)

	GD	VG	FN	VF	VF/NM	NM-
Four Color 378 (#1)-McWilliams-a	16	32	48	112	249	385
Four Color 400,421-McWilliams-a	10	20	30	64	132	200
4(11-1/53) - 11	7	14	21	46	86	125

TOM CORBETT SPACE CADET (See March of Comics #102)

TOM CORBETT SPACE CADET (TV)
Prize Publications: V2#1, May-June, 1955 - V2#3, Sept-Oct, 1955

	GD	VG	FN	VF	VF/NM	NM-
V2#1-Robot-c	35	70	105	208	339	470
2,3-Meskin-c	26	52	78	154	252	350

TOM, DICK & HARRIET (See Gold Key Spotlight)

TOM LANDRY AND THE DALLAS COWBOYS
Spire Christian Comics/Fleming H. Revell Co.: 1973 (35/49¢)

	GD	VG	FN	VF	VF/NM	NM-
nn-35¢ edition	3	6	9	16	23	30
nn-49¢ edition	2	4	6	10	16	20

TOM MIX WESTERN (Movie, radio star) (Also see The Comics, Crackajack Funnies, Master Comics, 100 Pages Of Comics, Popular Comics, Real Western Hero, Six Gun Heroes, Western Hero & XMas Comics)
Fawcett Publications: Jan, 1948 - No. 61, May, 1953 (1-17: 52 pgs.)

	GD	VG	FN	VF	VF/NM	NM-
1 (Photo-c, 52 pgs.)-Tom Mix & his horse Tony begin; Tumbleweed Jr. begins, ends #52,54,55	53	106	159	334	567	800
2 (Photo-c)	25	50	75	150	245	340
3-5 (Painted/photo-c): 5-Billy the Kid & Oscar app.	19	38	57	111	176	240
6-8: 6,7 (Painted/photo-c). 8-Kinstler tempera-c	16	32	48	94	147	200
9,10 (Paint/photo-c) 9-Used in **SOTI**, pgs. 323-325	15	30	45	90	140	190
11-Kinstler oil-c	14	28	42	82	121	160
12 (Painted/photo-c)	14	28	42	78	112	145
13-17 (Painted-c, 52 pgs.)	14	28	42	78	112	145
18,22 (Painted-c, 36 pgs.)	12	24	36	69	97	125
19 (Photo-c, 52 pgs.)	13	26	39	74	105	135
20,21,23 (Painted-c, 52 pgs.)	12	24	36	69	97	125
24,25,27-29 (52 pgs.): 24-Photo-c begin, end #61. 29-Slim Pickens app.	11	22	33	60	83	105
26,30 (36 pgs.)	10	20	30	56	76	95
31-33,35-37,39,40,42 (52 pgs.): 39-Red Eagle app.	10	20	30	56	76	95
34,38 (36 pgs. begin)	9	18	27	52	69	85
41,43-60: 57-(9/52)-Dope smuggling story	8	16	24	40	50	60
61-Last issue	9	18	27	47	61	75

NOTE: *Photo-c from 1930s Tom Mix movies (he died in 1940). Many issues contain ads for Tom Mix, Rocky*

Tomorrow Stories #9 © ABC

Tom Strong #12 © ABC

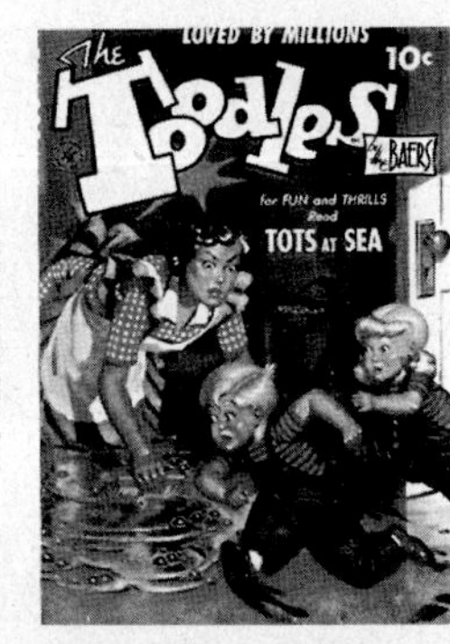

The Toodles #10 © Z-D

GD 2.0 | VG 4.0 | FN 6.0 | VF 8.0 | VF/NM 9.0 | NM- 9.2

GD 2.0 | VG 4.0 | FN 6.0 | VF 8.0 | VF/NM 9.0 | NM- 9.2

Lane, Space Patrol and other premiums. Captain Tootsie by ***C.C. Beck*** *in #6-11, 20.*

TOM MIX WESTERN
AC Comics: 1988 - No. 2, 1989? ($2.95, B&W w/16 pgs. color, 44 pgs.)

1-Tom Mix-r/Master #124,128,131,102 plus Billy the Kid-r by Severin; photo front/back/inside-c 4.00
2-($2.50, B&W)-Gabby Hayes-r; photo covers 4.00
...Holiday Album 1 (1990, $3.50, B&W, one-shot, 44 pgs.)-Contains photos & 1950s Tom Mix-r; photo inside-c 4.00

TOMMY OF THE BIG TOP (Thrilling Circus Adventures)
King Features Synd./Standard Comics: No. 10, Sep, 1948 - No. 12, Mar, 1949

10-By John Lehti 13 26 39 72 101 130
11,12 9 18 27 52 69 85

TOMMY TOMORROW (See Action Comics #127, Real Fact #6, Showcase #41,42,44,46,47 & World's Finest #102)

TOMOE (Also see Shi: The Way Of the Warrior #6)
Crusade Comics: July, 1995 - No. 3, June, 1996($2.95)

0-3: 2-B&W Dogs o' War preview. 3-B&W Demon Gun preview 3.00
0 (3/96, $2.95)-variant-c. 3.00
0-Commemorative edition (5,000) 2 4 6 8 10 12
1-Commemorative edition (5,000) 2 4 6 9 12 15
1-($2.95)-FAN Appreciation edition 3.00
TPB (1997, $14.95) r/#0-3 15.00

TOMOE: UNFORGETTABLE FIRE
Crusade Comics: June, 1997 ($2.95, one-shot)

1-Prequel to Shi: The Series 3.00

TOMOE-WITCHBLADE/FIRE SERMON
Crusade Comics: Sept, 1996 ($3.95, one-shot)

1-Tucci-c 5.00
1-($9.95)-Avalon Ed. w/gold foil-c 10.00

TOMOE-WITCHBLADE/MANGA SHI PREVIEW EDITION
Crusade Comics: July, 1996 ($5.00, B&W)

nn-San Diego Preview Edition 5.00

TOMORROW KNIGHTS
Marvel Comics (Epic Comics): June, 1990 - No. 6, Mar, 1991 ($1.50)

1-($1.95, 52 pgs.) 4.00
2-6 3.00

TOMORROW STORIES
America's Best Comics: Oct, 1999 - No. 12, Aug, 2002 ($3.50/$2.95)

1-Two covers by Ross and Nowlan; Moore-s 4.00
2-12-($2.95) 6-1st app. Splash Brannigan 3.00
... Special (1/06, $6.99) Nowlan-c; Moore-s; Greyshirt tribute to Will Eisner 7.00
... Special 2 (5/06, $6.99) Gene Ha-c; Moore-s; Promethea app. 7.00
Book 1 Hardcover (2002, $24.95) r/#1-6 25.00
Book 1 TPB (2003, $17.95) r/#1-6 18.00
Book 2 Hardcover (2004, $24.95) r/#7-12 25.00
Book 2 TPB (2005, $17.99) r/#7-12 18.00

TOM SAWYER (See Adventures of... & Famous Stories)

TOM SKINNER-UP FROM HARLEM (See Up From Harlem)

TOM STRONG (Also see Many Worlds of Tesla Strong)
America's Best Comics: June, 1999 - No. 36, May, 2006 ($3.50/$2.95/$2.99)

1-Two covers by Ross and Sprouse; Moore-s/Sprouse-a 4.00
1-Special Edition (9/09, $1.00) reprint with "After Watchmen" cover frame 3.00
2-36: 4-Art Adams-a (8 pgs.) 13-Fawcett homage w/art by Sprouse, Baker, Heath 20-Origin of Tom Stone. 22-Ordway-a. 31,32-Moorcock-s 3.00
...: Book One HC ('00, $24.95) r/#1-7, cover gallery and sketchbook 25.00
...: Book One TPB ('01, $14.95) r/#1-7, cover gallery and sketchbook 15.00
...: Book Two HC ('02, $24.95) r/#8-14, sketchbook 25.00
...: Book Two TPB ('03, $14.95) r/#8-14, sketchbook 15.00
...: Book Three HC ('04, $24.95) r/#15-19, sketchbook 25.00
...: Book Three TPB ('04, $17.95) r/#15-19, sketchbook 18.00
...: Book Four HC ('04, $24.95) r/#20-25, sketch pages 25.00
...: Book Four TPB ('05, $17.99) r/#20-25, sketch pages 18.00
...: Book Five HC ('05, $24.99) r/#26-30, sketch pages 25.00
...: Book Five TPB ('06, $17.99) r/#26-30, sketch pages 18.00
...: Book Six HC ('06, $24.99) r/#31-36 25.00
...: Book Six TPB ('08, $17.99) r/#31-36 18.00
...: The Deluxe Edition Book One (2009, $39.99, d.j.) r/#1-12; Moore intro.; sketch-a 40.00
...: The Deluxe Edition Book Two (2010, $39.99, d.j.) r/#13-24; sketch-a 40.00

TOM STRONG AND THE PLANET OF PERIL
DC Comics (Vertigo): Sept, 2013 - No. 6, Feb, 2014 ($2.99, limited series)

1-6-Hogan-s/Sprouse-a/c. 2-Travel to Terra Obscura 3.00

TOM STRONG AND THE ROBOTS OF DOOM
DC Comics (WildStorm): Aug, 2010 - No. 6, Jan, 2011 ($3.99, limited series)

1-6-Hogan-s/Sprouse-a. 1-Covers by Sprouse & Williams 4.00
TPB (2011, $17.99) r/#1-6 18.00

TOM STRONG'S TERRIFIC TALES
America's Best Comics: Jan, 2002 - No. 12 ($3.50/$2.95)

1-Short stories; Moore-s; art by Art Adams, Rivoche, Hernandez, Weiss 3.50
2-12-($2.95) 2-Adams, Ordway, Weiss-a; Adams-c. 4-Rivoche-a. 5-Pearson, Aragonés-a 11-Timm-a 3.00
...: Book One HC ('04, $24.95) r/#1-6, cover gallery and sketch pages 25.00
...: Book One SC ('05, $17.99) r/#1-6, cover gallery and sketch pages 18.00
...: Book Two HC ('05, $24.95) r/#7-12, covers 25.00

TOM TERRIFIC! (TV)(See Mighty Mouse Fun Club Magazine #1)
Pines Comics (Paul Terry): Summer, 1957 - No. 6, Fall, 1958
(See Terry Toons Giant Summer Fun Book)

1-1st app.?; CBS Television Presents... 21 42 63 126 206 285
2-6-(scarce) 16 32 48 94 147 200

TOM THUMB
Dell Publishing Co.: No. 972, Jan, 1959

Four Color 972-Movie, George Pal 8 16 24 52 99 145

TOM-TOM, THE JUNGLE BOY (See A-1 Comics & Tick Tock Tales)
Magazine Enterprises: 1947 - No. 3, 1947; Nov, 1957 - No. 3, Mar, 1958

1-Funny animal 14 28 42 80 115 150
2,3(1947): 3-Christmas issue 10 20 30 56 76 95
Tom-Tom & Itchi the Monk 1(11/57) - 3(3/58) 6 12 18 28 34 40
I.W. Reprint No. 1,2,8,10: 1,2,8-r/Koko & Kola #? 2 4 6 8 10 12

TONGUE LASH
Dark Horse Comics: Aug, 1996 - No. 2, Sept, 1996 ($2.95, lim. series, mature)

1,2: Taylor-c/a 3.00

TONGUE LASH II
Dark Horse Comics: Feb, 1999 - No. 2, Mar, 1999 ($2.95, lim. series, mature)

1,2: Taylor-c/a 3.00

TONKA (Disney)
Dell Publishing Co.: No. 966, Jan, 1959

Four Color 966-Movie (Starring Sal Mineo)-photo-c 8 16 24 54 102 150

TONTO (See The Lone Ranger's Companion...)

TONY TRENT (The Face #1,2)
Big Shot/Columbia Comics Group: No. 3, 1948 - No. 4, 1949

3,4: 3-The Face app. by Mart Bailey 19 38 57 111 176 240

TOODLES, THE (The Toodle Twins with #1)
Ziff-Davis (Approved Comics)/Argo: No. 10, July-Aug, 1951; Mar, 1956 (Newspaper-r)

10-Painted-c, some newspaper-r by The Baers 14 28 42 82 121 160
...Twins 1(Argo, 3/56)-Reprints by The Baers 8 16 24 42 54 65

TOO MUCH COFFEE MAN
Adhesive Comics: July, 1993 - No. 10, Dec, 2000 ($2.50, B&W)

1-Shannon Wheeler story & art 2 4 6 9 12 15
2,3 1 2 3 5 7 9
4,5 6.00
6-10 4.00
Full Color Special-nn($2.95),2-(7/97, $3.95) 4.00

TOO MUCH COFFEE MAN SPECIAL
Dark Horse Comics: July, 1997 ($2.95, B&W)

nn-Reprints Dark Horse Presents #92-95 4.00

TOO MUCH HOPELESS SAVAGES
Oni Press: June, 2003 - No. 4, Apr, 2004 ($2.99, B&W, limited series)

1-4-Van Meter-s/Norrie-a 3.00
TPB (8/04, $11.95, digest-size) r/series 12.00

TOOTH & CLAW (See Autumnlands: Tooth & Claw)

TOOTS AND CASPER
Dell Publishing Co.: No. 5, 1942

Large Feature Comic 5 23 46 69 136 223 310

Top Cat #17 © H-B

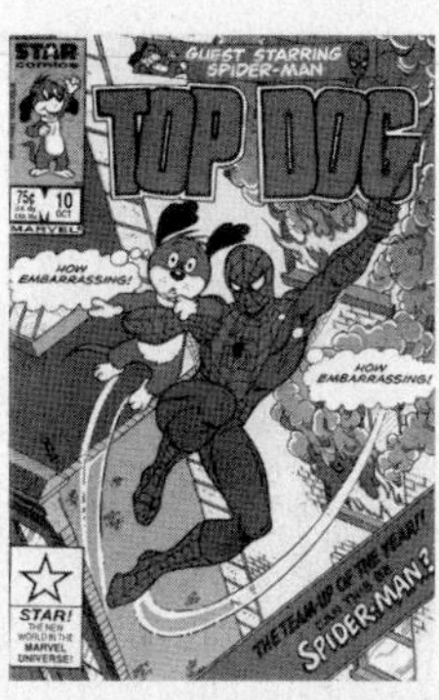

Top Dog #10 © MAR

Top-Notch Comics #5 © ACP

	GD 2.0	VG 4.0	FN 6.0	VF 8.0	VF/NM 9.0	NM- 9.2

TOP ADVENTURE COMICS
I. W. Enterprises: 1964 (Reprints)

1-r/High Adv. (Explorer Joe #2); Krigstein-r	2	4	6	11	16	20
2-Black Dwarf-r/Red Seal #22; Kinstler-c	2	4	6	13	18	22

TOP CAT (TV) (Hanna-Barbera)(See Kite Fun Book)
Dell Publ.Co./Gold Key No. 4 on: 12-2/61-62 - No. 3, 6-8/62; No. 4, 10/62 - No. 31, 9/70

1 (TV show debuted 9/27/61)	13	26	39	89	195	300
2-Augie Doggie back-ups in #1-4	7	14	21	48	89	130
3-5: 3-Last 15¢ issue. 4-Begin 12¢ issues; Yakky Doodle app. in 1 pg. strip. 5-Touché Turtle app.	6	12	18	37	66	95
6-10	5	10	15	30	50	70
11-20	4	8	12	23	37	50
21-31-Reprints	3	6	9	18	28	38

TOP CAT (TV) (Hanna-Barbera)(See TV Stars #4)
Charlton Comics: Nov, 1970 - No. 20, Nov, 1973

1	6	12	18	38	69	100
2-10	3	6	9	19	30	40
11-20	3	6	9	16	24	32

NOTE: *#8 (1/72) went on sale late in 1972 between #14 and #15 with the 1/73 issues.*

TOP COMICS
K. K. Publications/Gold Key: July, 1967 (All reprints)

nn-The Gnome-Mobile (Disney-movie)	2	4	6	13	18	22
1-Beagle Boys (#7), Beep Beep the Road Runner (#5), Bugs Bunny, Chip 'n' Dale, Daffy Duck (#50), Flipper, Huey, Dewey & Louie, Junior Woodchucks, Lassie, The Little Monsters (#71), Moby Duck, Porky Pig (has Gold Key label - says Top Comics on inside), Scamp, Super Goof, Tom & Jerry, Top Cat (#21), Tweety & Sylvester (#7), Walt Disney C&S (#322), Woody Woodpecker known issues; each character given own book	2	4	6	9	13	16
1-Donald Duck (not Barks), Mickey Mouse	2	4	6	13	18	22
1-Flintstones	3	6	9	21	33	45
1-Huckleberry Hound, Yogi Bear (#30)	3	6	9	14	19	24
1-The Jetsons	4	8	12	28	47	65
1-Tarzan of the Apes (#169)	3	6	9	15	22	28
1-Three Stooges (#35)	3	6	9	17	26	35
1-Uncle Scrooge (#70)	3	6	9	16	23	30
1-Zorro (r/G.K. Zorro #7 w/Toth-a; says 2nd printing)	3	6	9	14	19	24
2-Bugs Bunny, Daffy Duck, Mickey Mouse (#114), Porky Pig, Super Goof, Tom & Jerry, Tweety & Sylvester, Walt Disney's C&S (r/#325), Woody Woodpecker	2	4	6	9	12	15
2-Donald Duck (not Barks), Three Stooges, Uncle Scrooge (#71)-Barks-c, Yogi Bear (#30), Zorro (r/#8; Toth-a)	2	4	6	11	16	20
2-Snow White & 7 Dwarfs(6/67)(1944-r)	2	4	6	10	14	18
3-Donald Duck	2	4	6	11	16	20
3-Uncle Scrooge (#72)	2	4	6	13	18	22
3,4-The Flintstones	3	6	9	21	33	45
3,4: 3-Mickey Mouse (r/#115), Tom & Jerry, Woody Woodpecker, Yogi Bear. 4-Mickey Mouse, Woody Woodpecker	2	4	6	9	12	15

NOTE: *Each book in this series is identical to its counterpart except for cover, and came out at same time. The number in parentheses is the original issue it contains.*

TOP COW (Company one-shots)
Image Comics (Top Cow Productions)

... Book of Revelations (7/03, $3.99)-Pin-ups and info; art by various; Gossett-c	4.00
... Convention Sketchbook 2004 (4/04, $3.00, B&W) art by various	3.00
... Holiday Special Vol. 1 (12/10, $12.99) Flip book with Jingle Belle	13.00
... Preview Book 2005 (3/05, 99¢) Preview pages of Tomb Raider, Darkness, Rising Stars	3.00
... Productions, Inc./Ballistic Studios Swimsuit Special (5/95, $2.95)	3.00
...'s Best of: Dave Finch Vol. 1 TPB (8/06, $19.99) r/issues of Cyberforce, Aphrodite IX, Ascension and The Darkness; art & cover gallery	20.00
...'s Best of: Michael Turner Vol. 1 TPB (12/05, $24.99) r/Witchblade #1,10,12,18,19,25 & Witchblade/Tomb Raider chapters 1&3; Tomb Raider #25; art & cover gallery	25.00
... Secrets: Special Winter Lingerie Edition 1 (1/96, $2.95) Pin-ups	3.00
... 2001 Preview (no cover price) Preview pages of Tomb Raider; Jusko-a; flip cover & pages of Inferno	3.00

TOP COW CLASSICS IN BLACK AND WHITE
Image Comics (Top Cow): Feb, 2000 - Present ($2.95, B&W reprints)

...: Aphrodite IX #1(9/00) B&W reprint	3.00
...: Ascension #1(4/00) B&W reprint plus time-line of series	3.00
...: Battle of the Planets #1(1/03) B&W reprint plus script and cover gallery	3.00
...: Darkness #1(3/00) B&W reprint plus time-line of series	3.00
...: Fathom #1(5/00) B&W reprint	3.00
...: Magdalena #1(10/02) B&W reprint plus time-line of series	3.00
...: Midnight Nation #1(9/00) B&W preview	3.00
...: Rising Stars #1(7/00) B&W reprint plus cover gallery	3.00
...: Tomb Raider #1(12/00) B&W reprint plus back-story	3.00
...: Witchblade #1(2/00) B&W reprint plus back-story	3.00
...: Witchblade #25(5/01) B&W reprint plus interview with Wohl & Haberlin	3.00

TOP DETECTIVE COMICS
I. W. Enterprises: 1964 (Reprints)

9-r/Young King Cole #14; Dr. Drew (not Grandenetti)	2	4	6	10	14	18

TOP DOG (See Star Comics Magazine, 75¢)
Star Comics (Marvel): Apr, 1985 - No. 14, June, 1987 (Children's book)

1-14: 10-Peter Parker & J. Jonah Jameson cameo	5.00

TOP ELIMINATOR (Teenage Hotrodders #1-24; Drag 'n' Wheels #30 on)
Charlton Comics: No. 25, Sept, 1967 - No. 29, July, 1968

25-29	3	6	9	16	23	30

TOP FLIGHT COMICS: Four Star Publ.: 1947 (Advertised, not published)

TOP FLIGHT COMICS
St. John Publishing Co.: July, 1949

1(7/49, St. John)-Hector the Inspector; funny animal	11	22	33	60	83	105

TOP GUN (See Luke Short, 4-Color #927 & Showcase #72)

TOP GUNS OF THE WEST (See Super DC Giant)

TOPIX (...Comics) (Timeless Topix-early issues) (Also see Men of Battle, Men of Courage & Treasure Chest)(V1-V5#1,V7 on-paper-c)
Catechetical Guild Educational Society: 11/42 - V10#15, 1/28/52 (Weekly - later issues)

V1#1(8 pgs.,8x11")	24	48	72	140	230	320
2,3(8 pgs.,8x11")	14	28	42	80	115	150
4-8(16 pgs.,8x11")	11	22	33	64	90	115
V2#1-10(16 pgs.,8x11"): V2#8-Pope Pius XII	10	20	30	56	76	95
V3#1-10(16 pgs.,8x11"): V3#1-(9/44)	10	20	30	54	72	90
V4#1-10: V4#1-(9/45)	9	18	27	47	61	75
V5#1(10/46,52 pgs.,2(11/46),no #3),4(1/47)-9(6/47),10(7/47), no #13,4(10/47), 14(11/47),15(12/47)	8	16	24	40	50	60
11(8/47),12(9/47)-Life of Christ editions	10	20	30	54	72	90
V6#4(1/48),5(2/48),7(3/48),8(4/48),9(5/48),10(6/48),11(7/48)-14 (no #1-3,6)	7	14	21	35	43	50
V7#1(9/1/48)-20(6/15/49), 36 pgs.	6	12	18	29	36	42
V8#1(9/19/49)-3,5-11,13-30(5/15/50) 30-Hitler app.	6	12	18	28	34	40
4-Dagwood Splits the Atom(10/10/49)-Magazine format	8	16	24	42	54	65
12-Ingels-a	10	20	30	54	72	90
V9#1(9/25/50)-11,13-30(5/14/51)	6	12	18	27	33	38
12-Special 36 pg. Xmas issue, text illos format	6	12	18	28	34	40
V10#1(10/1/51)-15: 14-Hollingsworth-a	6	12	18	27	33	38

TOP JUNGLE COMICS
I. W. Enterprises: 1964 (Reprint)

1(nd)-Reprints White Princess of the Jungle #3, minus cover; Kintsler-a	3	6	9	16	23	30

TOP LOVE STORIES (Formerly Gasoline Alley #2)
Star Publications: No. 3, 5/51 - No. 19, 3/54

3(#1)	26	52	78	154	252	350
4,5,7-9: 8-Wood story	21	42	63	124	202	280
6-Wood-a	27	54	81	158	259	360
10-16,18,19-Disbrow-a	21	42	63	124	202	280
17-Wood art (Fox-r)	22	44	66	128	209	290

NOTE: *All have* **L. B. Cole** *covers.*

TOP-NOTCH COMICS (...Laugh #28-45; Laugh Comix #46 on)
MLJ Magazines: Dec, 1939 - No. 45, June, 1944

1-Origin/1st app. The Wizard; Kardak the Mystic Magician, Swift of the Secret Service (ends #3), Air Patrol, The Westpointer, Manhunters (by J. Cole), Mystic (ends #2) & Scott Rand (ends #3) begin; Wizard covers begin, end #8	530	1060	1590	3869	6835	9800
2-(1/40)-Dick Storm (ends #8), Stacy Knight M.D. (ends #4) begin; Jack Cole-a; 1st app. Nazis swastika on-c	277	554	831	1759	3030	4300
3-Bob Phantom, Scott Rand on Mars begin; J. Cole-a	187	374	561	1197	2049	2900
4-Origin/1st app. Streak Chandler on Mars; Moore of the Mounted only app.; J. Cole-a	168	336	504	1075	1838	2600

5-Flag-c; origin/1st app. Galahad; Shanghai Sheridan begins (ends #8); Shield cameo;

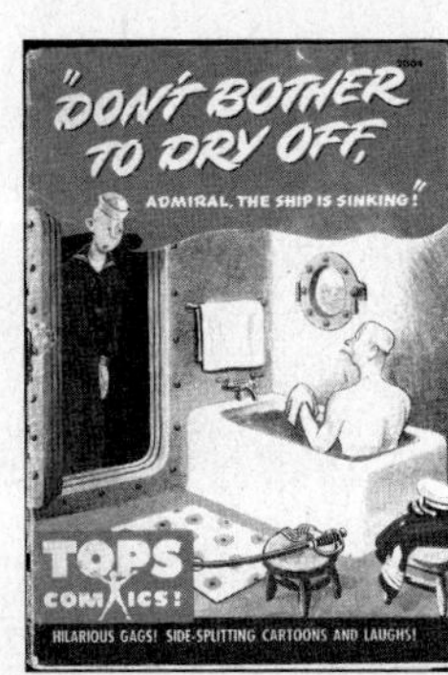

Tops Comics 2004 © LEV

Tor #2 © DC

The Torch #2 © MAR

	GD 2.0	VG 4.0	FN 6.0	VF 8.0	VF/NM 9.0	NM- 9.2

Novick-a; classic-c 200 400 600 1280 2190 3100
6-Meskin-a 129 258 387 826 1413 2000
7-The Shield x-over in Wizard; The Wizard dons new costume
155 310 465 992 1696 2400
8-Origin/1st app. The Firefly & Roy, the Super Boy (9/40, 2nd costumed boy hero after Robin?; also see Toro in Human Torch #1 (Fall/40)
161 322 483 1030 1765 2500
9-Origin & 1st app. The Black Hood; 1st Black Hood-c & logo (10/40); Fran Frazier begins (Scarce) 649 1298 1947 4738 8369 12,000
10-2nd app. Black Hood 232 464 696 1485 2543 3600
11-3rd Black Hood 158 316 474 1003 1727 2450
12-15 129 258 387 826 1413 2000
16-18,20 119 238 357 762 1306 1850
19-Classic bondage-c 132 264 396 838 1444 2050
21-30: 23-26-Roy app. 24-No Wizard. 25-Last Bob Phantom. 27-Last Firefly; Nazi war-c. 28-Suzie, Pokey Oakey begin. 29-Last Kardak 90 180 270 576 988 1400
31-44: 33-Dotty & Ditto by Woggon begins (2/43, 1st app.). 44-Black Hood series ends
47 94 141 296 498 700
45-Last issue 53 106 159 334 567 800

NOTE: ***J. Binder** a-1-3. **Meskin** a-2, 3, 6, 15. **Bob Montana** a-30; c-28-31. **Harry Sahle** c-42-45. **Woggon** a-33-40, 42. Bondage c-17, 19. Black Hood also appeared on radio in 1944.Black Hood app. on c-9-34, 41-44. Roy the Super Boy app. on c-8, 9, 11-27. The Wizard app. on c-1-8, 11-13, 15-22, 24, 25, 27. Pokey Oakey app. on c-28-43. Suzie app. on c-44-on.*

TOPPER & NEIL (TV)
Dell Publishing Co.: No. 859, Nov, 1957

Four Color 859 5 10 15 35 63 90

TOPPS COMICS: Four Star Publications: 1947 (Advertised, not published)

TOPS
July, 1949 - No. 2, Sept, 1949 (25¢, 10-1/4x13-1/4", 68 pgs.)
Tops Magazine, Inc. (Lev Gleason): (Large size-magazine format; for the adult reader)

1 (Rare)-Story by Dashiell Hammett; Crandall/Lubbers, Tuska, Dan Barry, Fuje-a; Biro painted-c 297 594 891 1901 3251 4600
2 (Rare)-Crandall/Lubbers, Biro, Kida, Fuje, Guardineer-a
252 504 756 1613 2757 3900

TOPS COMICS
Consolidated Book Publishers: 1944 (10¢, 132 pgs.)

2000-(Color-c, inside in red shade & some in full color)-Ace Kelly by Rick Yager, Black Orchid, Don on the Farm, Dinky Dinkerton (Rare) 47 94 141 296 498 700

NOTE: *This book is printed in such a way that when the staple is removed, the strips on the left side of the book correspond with the same strips on the right side. Therefore, if strips are removed from the book, each strip can be folded into a complete comic section of its own.*

TOPS COMICS (See Tops in Humor)
Consolidated Book (Lev Gleason): 1944 (7-1/4x5", 32 pgs.)

2001-The Jack of Spades (costumed hero) 28 56 84 165 270 375
2002-Rip Raider 19 38 57 111 176 240
2003-Red Birch (gag cartoons) 10 20 30 58 79 100
2004-Gag cartoons 19 38 57 111 176 240

TOP SECRET
Hillman Publ.: Jan, 1952

1 24 48 72 144 237 330

TOP SECRET ADVENTURES (See Spyman)

TOP SECRETS (...of the F.B.I.)
Street & Smith Publications: Nov, 1947 - No. 10, July-Aug, 1949

1-Powell-c/a 36 72 108 211 343 475
2-Powell-c/a 25 50 75 147 241 335
3-6,8,10-Powell-a 22 44 66 132 216 300
9-Powell-c/a 23 46 69 136 223 310
7-Used in **SOTI**, pg. 90 & illo. "How to hurt people"; used by N.Y. Legis. Comm.; Powell-c/a 34 68 102 206 336 465

NOTE: ***Powell** c-1-3, 5-10.*

TOPS IN ADVENTURE
Ziff-Davis Publishing Co.: Fall, 1952 (25¢, 132 pgs.)

1-Crusader from Mars, The Hawk, Football Thrills, He-Man; Powell-a; painted-c
50 100 150 315 533 750

TOPS IN HUMOR (See Tops Comics?)
Consolidated Book Publ. (Lev Gleason)/Wise Publs.: 1944 (7-1/4x5", #2 digest size)

2001(#1)-Origin The Jack of Spades, Ace Kelly by Rick Yager, Black Orchid (female crime fighter) app. 26 52 78 154 252 350
2-Wise Publs.; WWII serviceman humor 15 30 45 90 140 190

TOP SPOT COMICS
Top Spot Publ. Co.: 1945

1-The Menace, Duke of Darkness app. 43 86 129 271 461 650

TOPSY-TURVY (Teenage)
R. B. Leffingwell Publ.: Apr, 1945

1-1st app. Cookie 26 52 78 154 252 350

TOP TEN
America's Best Comics: Sept, 1999 - No. 12, Oct, 2001 ($3.50/$2.95)

1-Two covers by Ross and Ha/Cannon; Alan Moore-s/Gene Ha-a 3.50
2-11-($2.95) 3.00
12-($3.50) 3.50
Hardcover ('00, $24.95) Dust jacket with Gene Ha-a; r/#1-7 25.00
Softcover ('00, $14.95) new Gene Ha-c; r/#1-7 15.00
Book 2 HC ('02, $24.95) Dust jacket with Gene Ha-a; r/#8-12 25.00
Book 2 SC ('03, $14.95) new Gene Ha-c; r/#8-12 15.00
...: The Forty-Niners HC (2005, $24.99, dust jacket) prequel set in 1949; Moore-s/Ha-a 25.00

TOP TEN: BEYOND THE FARTHEST PRECINCT
America's Best Comics: Oct, 2005 - No. 5, Feb, 2006 ($2.99, limited series)

1-5-Jerry Ordway-a/Paul DiFilippo-s 3.00
TPB (2006, $14.99) r/series; cover sketch pages 15.00

TOP TEN SEASON TWO
America's Best Comics: Dec, 2008 - No. 4, Mar, 2009 ($2.99, limited series)

1-4-Cannon-s/Ha-a 3.00
... Special (5/09, $2.99) Cannon-s/Daxiong-a/Ha-c 3.00

TOR (Prehistoric Life on Earth) (Formerly One Million Years Ago)
St. John Publ. Co.: No. 2, Oct, 1953; No. 3, May, 1954 - No. 5, Oct, 1954

3-D 2(10/53)-Kubert-c/a 15 30 45 84 127 170
3-D 2(10/53)-Oversized, otherwise same contents 14 28 42 78 112 145
3-D 2(11/53)-Kubert-c/a; has 3-D cover 14 28 42 78 112 145
3-5-Kubert-c/a: 3-Danny Dreams by Toth; Kubert 1 pg. story (w/self portrait)
15 30 45 90 140 190

NOTE: *The two October 3-D's have same contents and **Powell** art; the October & November issues are titled 3-D Comics. All 3-D issues are 25¢ and came with 3-D glasses.*

TOR (See Sojourn)
National Periodical Publications: May-June, 1975 - No. 6, Mar-Apr, 1976

1-New origin by Kubert 2 4 6 11 16 20
2-6: 2-Origin-r/St. John #1 1 2 3 5 6 8

NOTE: ***Kubert** a-1, 2-6r; c-1-6. **Toth** a(p)-3r.*

TOR (3-D)
Eclipse Comics: July, 1986 - No. 2, Aug, 1987 ($2.50)

1,2: 1-r/One Million Years Ago. 2-r/Tor 3-D #2 5.00
...2-D: 1,2-Limited signed & numbered editions 2 4 6 11 16 20

TOR
Marvel Comics (Epic Comics/Heavy Hitters): June, 1993 - No. 4, 1993 ($5.95, lim. series)

1-4: Joe Kubert-c/a/scripts 6.00

TOR (Joe Kubert's...)
DC Comics: Jul, 2008 - No. 6, Dec, 2008 ($2.99, limited series)

1-6-New story; Joe Kubert-c/a/scripts 3.00
...: A Prehistoric Odyssey HC (2009, $24.99, DJ) r/#1-6; Roy Thomas intro.; sketch-a 25.00
...: A Prehistoric Odyssey SC (2010, $14.99) r/#1-6; Roy Thomas intro.; sketch-a 15.00

TOR BY JOE KUBERT
DC Comics: 2001 - 2003 ($49.95, hardcovers with dust jacket)

Volume 1 (2001) r/One Million Years Ago #1 & 3-D Comics #1&2 in flat color; script pages, sketch pages, proposals for TV and newspapers strips; intro. by Roy Thomas 50.00
Volume 2 (2002) r/Tor (St. John) #3-5; Danny Dreams; portfolio section 50.00
Volume 3 (2003) r/Tor (DC '75) #1; (Marvel '93) #1-4; portfolio section 50.00

TORCH, THE
Marvel Comics (with Dynamite Ent.): Nov, 2009 - No. 8, Jul, 2010 ($3.99, limited series)

1-8-Thinker resurrects the Golden Age Human Torch; Toro app; Alex Ross-c on all; Berkenkotter-a. 3-5-Namor app. 4.00

TORCH OF LIBERTY SPECIAL
Dark Horse Comics (Legend): Jan, 1995 ($2.50, one-shot)

1-Byrne scripts 3.00

TORCHWOOD (Based on the BBC TV series)
Titan Comics: Sept, 2010 - No. 6, Jan, 2011 ($3.99)

1-6: 1-Barrowman-s/Edwards-a; Churchill & photo-c. 2-Art by Yeowell & Grist 4.00

Torchwood (2016 series) #1 © BBC

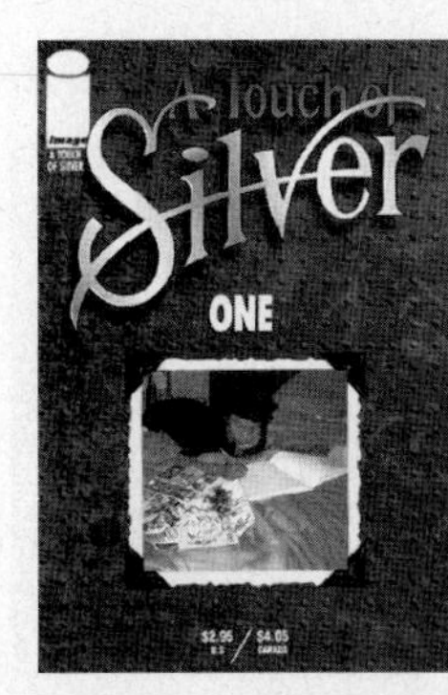

A Touch of Silver #1 © Jim Valentino

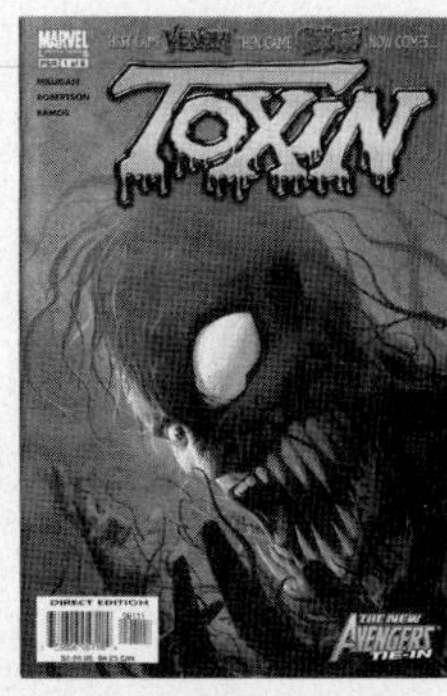

Toxin #1 © MAR

GD 2.0 | VG 4.0 | FN 6.0 | VF 8.0 | VF/NM 9.0 | NM- 9.2

TORCHWOOD (Based on the BBC TV series)
Titan Comics: Aug, 2016 - No. 4, Jan, 2017; Vol. 2: Mar, 2017 - No. 4, Jun, 2017; Vol. 3: Nov, 2017 - No. 4, Mar, 2018 ($3.99)

1-4-John & Carole Barrowman-s/Fuso & Qualano-a; multiple covers 4.00
Vol. 2 1-4-John & Carole Barrowman-s/Edwards-a; multiple covers 4.00
Vol. 3 1-4-John & Carole Barrowman-s/Edwards-a; multiple covers; Capt. John Hart app. 4.00

TORCHY (...Blonde Bombshell) (See Dollman, Military, & Modern)
Quality Comics Group: Nov, 1949 - No. 6, Sept, 1950

	GD	VG	FN	VF	VF/NM	NM-
1-Bill Ward-c, Gil Fox-a	213	426	639	1363	2332	3300
2,3-Fox-c/a	84	168	252	538	919	1300
4-Fox-c/a(3), Ward-a (9 pgs.)	110	220	330	704	1202	1700
5,6-Ward-c/a, 9 pgs; Fox-a(3) each	116	232	348	742	1271	1800
Super Reprint #16(1964)-r/#4 with new-c	7	14	21	49	92	135

TO RIVERDALE AND BACK AGAIN (Archie Comics Presents...)
Archie Comics: 1990 ($2.50, 68 pgs.)

nn-Byrne-c, Colan-a(p); adapts NBC TV movie 5.00

TORMENTED, THE (Becomes Surprise Adventures #3 on)
Sterling Comics: July, 1954 - No. 2, Sept, 1954

	GD	VG	FN	VF	VF/NM	NM-
1,2: Weird/Horror stories	39	78	117	231	378	525

TORNADO TOM (See Mighty Midget Comics)

TORSO (See Jinx: Torso)

TOTAL ECLIPSE
Eclipse Comics: May, 1988 - No. 5, Apr, 1989 ($3.95, 52 pgs., deluxe size)

Book 1-5: 3-Intro/1st app. new Black Terror. 4-Many copies have upside down pages and are mis-cut 5.00

TOTAL ECLIPSE
Image Comics: July, 1998 (one-shot)

1-McFarlane-c; Eclipse Comics character pin-ups by Image artists 3.00

TOTAL ECLIPSE: THE SERAPHIM OBJECTIVE
Eclipse Comics: Nov, 1988 ($1.95, one-shot, Baxter paper)

1-Airboy, Valkyrie, The Heap app. 3.00

TOTAL JUSTICE
DC Comics: Oct, 1996 - No. 3, Nov, 1996 ($2.25, bi-weekly limited series) (Based on toyline)

1-3 3.00

TOTALLY AWESOME HULK, THE (Amadeus Cho as The Hulk)(Continues in Inc. Hulk #709)
Marvel Comics: Feb, 2016 - No. 23, Nov, 2017 ($4.99/$3.99)

1-($4.99) Frank Cho-a/Greg Pak-s; She-Hulk and Spider-Man (Miles) app. 5.00
2-23-($3.99) 2,3-Fin Fang Foom and Lady Hellbender app. 5,6-Mike Choi-a. 7,8-Alan Davis-a. 9-11-Civil War II tie-in. 9-Del Mundo-a. 10-12-Black Panther app. 13-15-Jeremy Lin app. 19-22-Crossover with Weapon X #5,6 and Weapons of Mutant Destruction: Alpha #1; Old Man Logan & Sabretooth app. 23-Frank Cho-c 4.00
#1.MU (5/17, $4.99) Monsters Unleashed tie-in; art by Templeton, Ortiz, Lindsay 5.00

TOTAL RECALL (Movie)
DC Comics: 1990 ($2.95, 68 pgs., movie adaptation, one-shot)

1-Arnold Schwarzenegger photo-c 4.00

TOTAL RECALL (Continuation of movie)
Dynamite Entertainment: 2011 - No. 4, 2011 ($3.99, limited series)

1-4-Quaid and Melina on Mars following the movie; Razek-a/Robertson-c 4.00

TOTAL WAR (M.A.R.S. Patrol #3 on)
Gold Key: July, 1965 - No. 2, Oct, 1965 (Painted-c)

	GD	VG	FN	VF	VF/NM	NM-
1-Wood-a in both issues	6	12	18	38	69	100
2	5	10	15	31	53	75

TOTEMS (Vertigo V2K)
DC Comics (Vertigo): Feb, 2000 ($5.95, one-shot)

1-Swamp Thing, Animal Man, Zatanna, Shade app.; Fegredo-c 6.00

TO THE HEART OF THE STORM
Kitchen Sink Press: 1991 (B&W, graphic novel)

Softcover-Will Eisner-s/a/c 20.00
Hardcover ($24.95) 30.00
TPB-(DC Comics, 9/00, $14.95) reprints 1991 edition 15.00

TO THE LAST MAN (See Zane Grey Four Color #616)

TOUCH OF SILVER, A
Image Comics: Jan, 1997 - No. 6, Nov, 1997 ($2.95, B&W, bi-monthly)

1-6-Valentino-s/a; photo-c: 5-color pgs. w/Round Table 3.00
TPB ($12.95) r/#1-6 13.00

TOUGH KID SQUAD COMICS
Timely Comics (TCI): Mar, 1942

	GD	VG	FN	VF	VF/NM	NM-
1-(Scarce)-Origin & 1st app.The Human Top & The Tough Kid Squad; The Flying Flame app.	920	1840	2760	6700	12,600	18,500

TOWER OF SHADOWS (Creatures on the Loose #10 on)
Marvel Comics Group: Sept, 1969 - No. 9, Jan, 1971

	GD	VG	FN	VF	VF/NM	NM-
1-Romita-c, classic Steranko-a; Craig-a(p)	8	16	24	51	96	140
2,3: 2-Neal Adams-a. 3-Barry Smith, Tuska-a	5	10	15	30	50	70
4,6: 4-Marie Severin-c. 6-Wood-a	4	8	12	27	44	60
5-B. Smith-a(p), Wood-a; Wood draws himself (1st pg., 1st panel)	4	8	12	28	47	65
7-9: 7-B. Smith-a(p), Wood-a. 8-Wood-a; Wrightson-c. 9-Wrightson-c; Roy Thomas app.	5	10	15	30	50	70
Special 1(12/71, 52 pgs.)-Neal Adams-a; Romita-c	4	8	12	27	44	60

NOTE: *J. Buscema a-1p, 2p, Special 1r. Colan a-3p, 6p, Special 1. J. Craig a(r)-1p. Ditko a-6, 8, 9r, Special 1. Everett a-9(i)r; c-5i. Kirby a-9(p)r. Severin c-5p, 6. Steranko a-1p. Tuska a-3. Wood a-5-8. Issues 1-9 contain new stories with some pre-Marvel age reprints in 6-9. H. P. Lovecraft adaptation-9.*

TOXIC AVENGER (Movie)
Marvel Comics: Apr, 1991 - No. 11, Feb, 1992 ($1.50)

1-11: Based on movie character. 3,10-Photo-c 3.00

TOXIC CRUSADERS (TV)
Marvel Comics: May, 1992 - No. 8, Dec, 1992 ($1.25)

1-8: 1-3,8-Sam Kieth-c; based on USA Network cartoon 3.00

TOXIN (Son of Carnage)
Marvel Comics: June, 2005 - No. 6, Nov, 2005 ($2.99, limited series)

1-6-Milligan-s/Robertson-a; Spider-Man app. 3.00
...: The Devil You Know TPB (2006, $17.99) r/#1-6 18.00

TOYBOY
Continuity Comics: Oct, 1986 - No. 7, Mar, 1989 ($2.00, Baxter paper)

1-7 3.00

NOTE: *N. Adams a-1; c-1, 2,5. Golden a-7p; c-6,7. Nebres a(i)-1,2.*

TOYLAND COMICS
Fiction House Magazines: Jan, 1947 - No. 2, Mar, 1947; No. 3, July, 1947

	GD	VG	FN	VF	VF/NM	NM-
1-Wizard of the Moon begins	30	60	90	177	289	400
2,3-Bob Lubbers-c. 3-Tuska-a	17	34	51	100	158	215

NOTE: *All above contain strips by Al Walker.*

TOY STORY (Disney/Pixar movies)
BOOM! Entertainment (BOOM! KIDS): No. 0, Nov, 2009 - No. 7, Sept, 2010 ($2.99)

0-7: 0,1-Three covers. 2-7-Two covers 3.00
Free Comic Book Day Edition (5/10, giveaway) r/#0 The Return of Buzz Lightyear 3.00
...: The Return of Buzz Lightyear (10/10, Halloween giveaway, 8-1/2" x 5-1/4") 3.00

TOY STORY (Disney/Pixar movies)
Marvel Comics: May, 2012 - No. 4, 2012 ($2.99, limited series)

1-4: 1-Master Woody. 2-A Scary Night. 3-To The Attic. 4-Water Rescue 3.00

TOY STORY: MYSTERIOUS STRANGER (Disney/Pixar movies)
BOOM! Entertainment (BOOM! KIDS): May, 2009 - No. 4, July, 2009 ($2.99)

1-4-Jolley-s/Moreno-a. 1-Three covers. 2-4-Two covers 3.00

TOY STORY: TALES FROM THE TOY CHEST (Disney/Pixar movies)
BOOM! Entertainment (BOOM! KIDS): July, 2010 - No. 4, Oct, 2010 ($2.99)

1-4-Snider-s/Luthi-a. 1-Two covers. 2-4-One cover 3.00

TOY TOWN COMICS
Toytown/Orbit Publ./B. Antin/Swapper Quarterly: 1945 - No. 7, May, 1947

	GD	VG	FN	VF	VF/NM	NM-
1-Mertie Mouse; L. B. Cole-c/a; funny animal	40	80	120	246	411	575
2-L. B. Cole-a	22	44	66	132	216	300
3-7-L. B. Cole-a. 5-Wiggles the Wonderworm-c	20	40	60	114	182	250

TRACKER
Image Comics (Top Cow): Nov, 2009 - No. 5, Sept, 2010 ($2.99/$3.99)

1,2-Lincoln-s/Tsai-a. 1-Two covers 3.00
3-5-($3.99) 4.00

TRAGG AND THE SKY GODS (See Gold Key Spotlight, Mystery Comics Digest #3,9 & Spine Tingling Tales)
Gold Key/Whitman No. 9: June, 1975 - No. 8, Feb, 1977; No. 9, May, 1982 (Painted-c #3-8)

	GD	VG	FN	VF	VF/NM	NM-
1-Origin	3	6	9	14	19	24
2-8: 4-Sabre-Fang app. 8-Ostellon app.	2	4	6	8	11	14
9-(Whitman, 5/82) r/#1	1	2	3	5	7	9

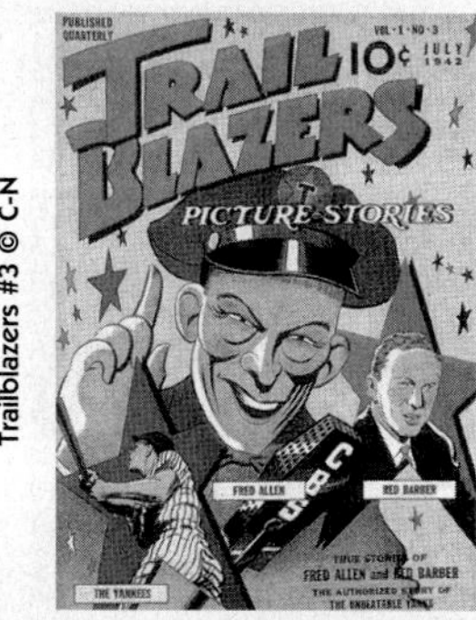

Trailblazers #3 © C-N

Transformers #8 © Hasbro

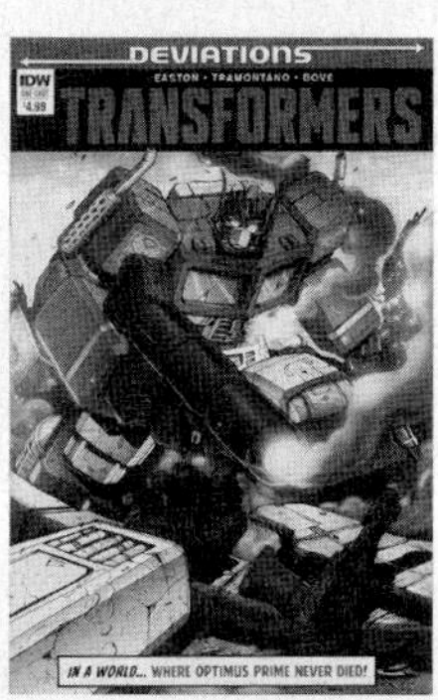

Transformers: Deviations © Hasbro

GD VG FN VF VF/NM NM-
2.0 4.0 6.0 8.0 9.0 9.2

NOTE: *Santos a-1, 2, 9r; c-3-7. Spiegel a-3-8.*

TRAILBLAZER
Image Comics: June 2011 ($5.99, one shot, graphic novel)
nn-Gray & Palmiotti-s/Daly-a; covers by Johnson and Conner 6.00

TRAIL BLAZERS (Red Dragon #5 on)
Street & Smith Publications: 1941; No. 2, Apr, 1942 - No. 4, Oct, 1942
(True stories of American heroes)
1-Life story of Jack Dempsey & Wright Brothers 39 78 117 240 395 550
2-Brooklyn Dodgers-c/story; Ben Franklin story 23 46 69 136 223 310
3,4: 3-Fred Allen, Red Barber, Yankees stories 20 40 60 120 195 270

TRAIL COLT (Also see Extra Comics, Manhunt! & Undercover Girl)
Magazine Enterprises: 1949 - No. 2, 1949
nn(A-1 #24)-7 pg. Frazetta-a r-in Manhunt #13; Undercover Girl app.; The Red Fox by L. B. Cole; Ingels-c; Whitney-a (Scarce) 39 78 117 240 395 550
2(A-1 #26)-Undercover Girl; Ingels-c; L. B. Cole-a (6 pgs.) 31 62 93 182 296 410

TRAIN CALLED LOVE, A
Dynamite Entertainment: 2015 - No. 10, 2016 ($3.99)
1-9-Garth Ennis-s/Mark Dos Santos-a 4.00
10-($5.99) Last issue 6.00

TRANSFORMERS, THE (TV)(See G.I. Joe and...)
(Continues in Transformers: Regeneration)
Marvel Comics Group: Sept, 1984 - No. 80, July, 1991 (75¢/$1.00)
1-Based on Hasbro Toys 7 14 21 46 86 125
1-2nd & 3rd printing 2 4 6 11 16 20
2-5: 2-Golden-c. 3-(1/85) Spider-Man (black costume)-c/app. 4-Texeira-c; brief app. of Dinobots 3 6 9 14 20 25
2-10: 2nd & 3rd prints 4.00
6,7,9: 6-1st Josie Beller. 9-Circuit Breaker 1st full app. 2 4 6 8 11 14
8-Dinobots 1st full app. 3 6 9 16 24 32
10-Intro. Constructicons 2 4 6 11 16 20
11,14: 11-1st app. Jetfire. 14-Jetfire becomes an Autobot; 1st app. of Grapple, Hoist, Smokescreen, Skids, and Tracks 2 4 6 8 10 12
12,13,15,17,18,20-24,26-49: 17-1st app. of Blaster, Powerglide, Cosmos, Seaspray, Warpath, Beachcomber, Preceptor, Straxus, Kickback, Bombshell, Shrapnel, Dirge, and Ramjet. 21-1st app. of Aerialbots; 1st Slingshot; Circuit Breaker app. 22-Retells origin of Circuit Breaker, 1st Stunticons. 23-Battle at Statue of Liberty. 24-1st app. Protectobots, Combaticons; Optimus Prime killed. 26-Intro The Mechanic, Prime's Funeral. 27-Grimlock named new Autobot leader. 28-The Mechanic app. 29-Intro Scraplets, 1st app. of Triple Changers 1 2 3 5 6 8
16-Plight of the Bumblebee 2 4 6 9 12 15
19-1st Omega Supreme 1 3 4 6 8 10
25-1st Predacons 2 4 6 8 10 12
50-60: 53-Jim Lee-c. 54-Intro Micromasters. 60-Brief 1st app. of Primus 2 4 6 8 10 12
61-70: 61-Origin of Cybertron and the Transformers, Unicron app.; app. of Primus, creator of the Transformers. 62-66 Matrix Quest 5-part series. 67-Jim Lee-c 2 4 6 10 14 18
71-77: 75-($1.50, 52 pgs.) (Low print run) 3 6 9 17 26 35
78,79 (Low print run) 4 8 12 23 37 50
80-Last issue 5 10 15 31 53 75
NOTE: Second and third printings of most early issues (1-9?) exist and are worth less than originals. Was originally planned as a four issue mini-series. ***Wrightson*** *a-64i(4 pgs.).*

TRANSFORMERS
IDW Publishing: No. 0, Oct, 2005 (99¢, one-shot)
0-Prelude to Transformers: Infiltration series; Furman-s/Su-a; 4 covers 3.00

TRANSFORMERS
IDW Publishing: Nov, 2009 - No. 31, Dec, 2011 ($3.99)
1-31: Multple covers on each, 21-Chaos arc begins 4.00
...: Continuum (11/09, $3.99) Plot synopses of recent Transformers storylines 4.00
...: Death of Optimus Prime (12/11, $3.99) Roche-a 4.00
Hundred Penny Press: Transformers Classics #1 (6/11, $1.00) r/#1 (1984 Marvel series) 3.00
Hundred Penny Press (3/14, $1.00) r/#1 (1984 Marvel series) 3.00

TRANSFORMERS (See Transformers: Robots in Disguise for #1-34)
IDW Publishing: No. 34, Nov, 2014 - No. 57, Sept, 2016 ($3.99)
35-49: 39-42-Combiner Wars x-over 4.00
50-($7.99, squarebound) Barber-s/Griffith-a 8.00
51-57: 51-55-All Hail Optimus. 56-Revolution tie-in 4.00
Annual 2017 (2/17, $7.99) Barber-s/Tramontano-a; bonus character profile pages 8.00
...: Deviations (3/16, $4.99) What If... Optimus Prime never died; Easton-s; 2 covers 5.00
... First Strike 1 (10/17, $3.99) Part of Hasbro character crossover 4.00
... Holiday Special (12/15, $5.99) Covers by Coller & Garbowska 6.00
...: Revolution 1 (10/16, $3.99) Revolution tie-in; Barber-s/Griffith-a; multiple covers 4.00
...: Salvation One Shot (6/17, $7.99) Barber-s/Ramondelli-a; 2 covers 8.00
...: Titans Return (7/16, $4.99) Road to Revolution; Ramondelli-a 5.00

TRANSFORMERS (Free Comic Book Day Editions)
Dreamwave Productions/IDW Publishing
... Animated (IDW, 5/08) Free Comic Book Day Edition; from the Cartoon Network series 3.00
... Armada (Dreamwave Prods., 5/03) Free Comic Book Day Edition 3.00
.../Beast Wars Special (IDW, 2006) Free Comic Book Day Edition; flip book 3.00
.../G.I. Joe (IDW, 2009) Free Comic Book Day Edition; flip book 3.00
... Movie Prequel (IDW, 5/07) Free Comic Book Day Edition; Figueroa-c 3.00

TRANSFORMERS: ALL HAIL MEGATRON
IDW Publishing: Jul, 2008 - No. 16, Oct, 2009 ($3.99, limited series)
1-16: 1-8,10-12-McCarthy-s/Guidi-a; 2 covers 4.00

TRANSFORMERS: ALLIANCE (Prequel to 2009 Transformers 2 movie)
IDW Publishing: Dec, 2008 - No. 4, Mar, 2009 ($3.99, limited series)
1-4-Milne-a; 2 covers 4.00

TRANSFORMERS ANIMATED: THE ARRIVAL
IDW Publishing: Sept, 2008 - No. 5, Dec, 2008 ($3.99, limited series)
1-5-Brizuela-a; 2 covers 4.00

TRANSFORMERS ARMADA (Continues as Transformers Energon with #19)
Dreamwave Productions: July, 2002 - No. 18, Dec, 2003 ($2.95)
1-Sarracini-s/Raiz-a; wraparound gatefold-c 5.00
2-18 4.00
Vol. 1 TPB (2003, $13.95) r/#1-5 14.00
Vol. 2 TPB (2003, $15.95) r/#6-11 16.00

TRANSFORMERS ARMADA: MORE THAN MEETS THE EYE
Dreamwave Productions: Mar, 2004 - No. 3, May, 2004 ($4.95, limited series)
1-3-Pin-ups with tech info; art by Pat Lee & various 5.00

TRANSFORMERS, BEAST WARS: THE ASCENDING
IDW Publishing: Aug, 2007 - No. 4, Nov, 2007 ($3.99, limited series)
1-4-Furman-s/Figueroa-a; multiple covers on all 4.00

TRANSFORMERS, BEAST WARS: THE GATHERING
IDW Publishing: Feb, 2006 - No. 4, May, 2006 ($2.99, limited series)
1-4-Furman-s/Figueroa-a; multiple covers on all 4.00
TPB (8/06, $17.99) r/series; sketch pages & gallery of covers and variants 18.00

TRANSFORMERS: BUMBLEBEE
IDW Publishing: Dec, 2009 - No. 4, Mar, 2010 ($3.99, limited series)
1-4: Zander Cannon-s; multiple covers on all 4.00

TRANSFORMERS COMICS MAGAZINE (Digest)
Marvel Comics: Jan, 1987 - No. 10, July, 1988
1,2-Spider-Man-c/s 2 4 6 10 14 18
3-10 2 4 6 8 10 12

TRANSFORMERS: DARK CYBERTRON
IDW Publishing: Nov, 2013 ($3.99)
1-Part 1 of a 12-part crossover with Transformers: More Than Meets the Eye #23-27 and Transformers: Robots in Disguise #23-27; multiple covers 4.00
1-Deluxe Edition ($7.99, squarebound) r/#1 with bonus script and B&W art pages 8.00
... Finale (3/14, $3.99) Three covers 4.00

TRANSFORMERS: DARK OF THE MOON MOVIE ADAPTATION (2011 movie)
IDW Publishing: Jun, 2011 - No. 4, Jun, 2011 ($3.99, weekly limited series)
1-4-Barber-s/Jimenez-a 4.00

TRANSFORMERS: DEFIANCE (Prequel to 2009 Transformers 2 movie)
IDW Publishing: Jan, 2009 - No. 4, Apr, 2009 ($3.99, limited series)
1-4-Mowry-s; 2 covers 4.00

TRANSFORMERS: DEVASTATION
IDW Publishing: Sept, 2007 - No. 6, Feb, 2008 ($3.99, limited series)
1-6-Furman-s/Su-a; multiple covers on all 4.00

TRANSFORMERS: DRIFT
IDW Publishing: Sept, 2010 - No. 4, Oct, 2010 ($3.99, limited series)
1-4-McCarthy-s/Milne-a; multiple covers on all 4.00

TRANSFORMERS: DRIFT – EMPIRE OF STONE

Transformers: Foundation #1 © Hasbro

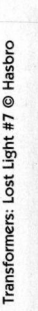

Transformers: Lost Light #7 © Hasbro

Transformers: Nefarious #5 © Hasbro

GD 2.0 | VG 4.0 | FN 6.0 | VF 8.0 | VF/NM 9.0 | NM- 9.2

IDW Publishing: Nov, 2014 - No. 4, Feb, 2015 ($3.99, limited series)
1-4-McCarthy-s/Guidi & Ferreira-a; multiple covers on all 4.00

TRANSFORMERS ENERGON (Continued from Transformers Armada #18)
Dreamwave Productions: No. 19, Jan, 2004 - No. 30, Dec, 2004 ($2.95)
19-30-Furman-s 4.00

TRANSFORMERS: ESCALATION
IDW Publishing: Nov, 2006 - No. 6, Apr, 2007 ($3.99, limited series)
1-6-Furman-s/Su-a; multiple covers 4.00

TRANSFORMERS: EVOLUTIONS - HEARTS OF STEEL
IDW Publishing: June, 2006 - No. 4, Sept, 2006 ($2.99, limited series)
1-4-Bumblebee meets John Henry in 1880s railroad times 4.00

TRANSFORMERS: FOUNDATION (Prequel to 2011 Transformers: Dark of the Moon movie)
IDW Publishing: Feb, 2011 - No. 4, May, 2011 ($3.99, limited series)
1-4-Barber-s/Griffith-a; 2 covers 4.00

TRANSFORMERS: GENERATION 1
Dreamwave Productions: Apr, 2002 - No. 6, Oct, 2002 ($2.95)
Preview- 6 pg. story; robot sketch pages; Pat Lee-a 3.00
1-Pat Lee-a; 2 wraparound covers by Lee 5.00
2-6: 2-Optimus Prime reactivated; 2 covers by Pat Lee 4.00
...Vol. 1 HC (2003, $49.95) r/#1-6; black hardcover with red foil lettering and art 50.00
...Vol. 1 TPB (2002, $17.95) r/#1-6 plus six page preview; 8 pg. preview of future issues 18.00

TRANSFORMERS: GENERATION 1 (Volume 2)
Dreamwave Productions: Apr, 2003 - No. 6, Sept, 2003 ($2.95)
1-6: 1-Pat Lee-a; 2 wraparound gatefold covers by Lee 4.00
1-($5.95) Chrome wraparound variant-c 6.00
...Vol. 2 TPB (IDW Publ., 3/06, $19.99) r/#1-6 plus cover gallery 20.00

TRANSFORMERS: GENERATION 1 (Volume 3)
Dreamwave Productions: No. 0, Dec, 2003 - Present ($2.95)
0-10: 0-Pat Lee-a. 1-Figueroa-a; wrapaound-c 4.00

TRANSFORMERS: GENERATION 2
Marvel Comics: Nov, 1993 - No. 12, Oct, 1994 ($1.75)
1-($2.95, 68 pgs.)-Collector's ed. w/bi-fold metallic-c 2 4 6 8 10 12
1-11: 1-Newsstand edition (68 pgs.). 2-G.I. Joe app., Snake-Eyes, Scarlett, Cobra Commander app. 5-Red Alert killed, Optimus Prime gives Grimlock leadership of Autobots. 6-G.I. Joe app. 1 2 3 4 5 7
12-($2.25, 52 pgs.) 1 3 4 6 8 10

TRANSFORMERS: GENERATIONS
IDW Publishing: Mar, 2006 - No. 12, Mar, 2007 ($1.99/$2.49/$3.99)
1,2: 1-R/Transformers #7 (1985); preview of Transformers, Beast Wars. 2-R/#13 4.00
3-10-($2.49) 3-R/Transformers #14 (1986). 4-6-Reprint #16-18. 7-R/#24 4.00
11,12-($3.99) 4.00
Volume 1 (12/06, $19.99) r/#1-6; cover gallery 20.00

TRANSFORMERS/G.I. JOE
Dreamwave Productions: Aug, 2003 - No. 6, Mar, 2004 ($2.95/$5.25)
1-Art & gatefold wraparound-c by Jae Lee; Ney Rieber-s; variant-c by Pat Lee 4.00
1-($5.95) Holofoil wraparound-c by Norton 6.00
2-6-Jae Lee-a/c 4.00
TPB (8/04, $17.95) r/#1-6; cover gallery and sketch pages 18.00

TRANSFORMERS/G.I. JOE: DIVIDED FRONT
Dreamwave Productions: Oct, 2004 ($2.95)
1-Art & gatefold wraparound-c by Pat Lee 4.00

TRANSFORMERS: HEADMASTERS
Marvel Comics Group: July, 1987 - No. 4, Jan, 1988 ($1.00, limited series)
1-Springer, Akin, Garvey-a 1 2 3 5 6 8
2-4-Springer-c on all 6.00

TRANSFORMERS: HEART OF DARKNESS
IDW Publishing: Mar, 2011 - No. 4, Jun, 2011 ($3.99, limited series)
1-4-Abnett & Lanning-s/Farinas-a 4.00

TRANSFORMERS: INFESTATION (Crossover with Star Trek, Ghostbusters & G.I. Joe)
IDW Publishing: Feb, 2011 - No. 2, Feb, 2011 ($3.99, limited series)
1,2-Abnett & Lanning-s/Roche-a; covers by Roche & Snyder III 4.00

TRANSFORMERS: INFILTRATION
IDW Publishing: Jan, 2006 - No. 6, June, 2006 ($2.99, limited series)
1-6-Furman-s/Su-a; multiple covers on all 4.00

GD 2.0 | VG 4.0 | FN 6.0 | VF 8.0 | VF/NM 9.0 | NM- 9.2

... Cover Gallery (8/06, $5.99) 6.00

TRANSFORMERS: IRONHIDE
IDW Publishing: May, 2010 - No. 4, Aug, 2010 ($3.99, limited series)
1-4: Mike Costa-s; multiple covers on all 4.00

TRANSFORMERS: LAST STAND OF THE WRECKERS
IDW Publishing: Jan, 2010 - No. 5, May, 2010 ($3.99, limited series)
1-5-Nick Roche-s/a; two covers 4.00

TRANSFORMERS: LOST LIGHT
IDW Publishing: Dec, 2016 - Present ($3.99)
1-15: 1-7-James Roberts-s/Jack Lawrence-a; multiple covers on each. 8,9-Tramontano-a 4.00

TRANSFORMERS: MAXIMUM DINOBOTS
IDW Publishing: Dec, 2008 - No. 5, Apr, 2009 ($3.99, limited series)
1-5-Furman-s/Roche-a; 2 covers for each 4.00

TRANSFORMERS: MEGATRON ORIGIN
IDW Publishing: May, 2007 - No. 4, Sept, 2008 ($3.99, limited series)
1-4-Alex Milne-a; 2 covers 4.00

TRANSFORMERS: MICROMASTERS
Dreamwave Productions: June, 2004 - No. 4 ($2.95, limited series)
1-4-Ruffolo-a; Pat Lee-c 4.00

TRANSFORMERS: MONSTROSITY
IDW Publishing: Jun, 2013 - No. 4, Sept, 2013 ($3.99)
1-4: 1-Three covers; Ramondelli-a 4.00

TRANSFORMERS: MORE THAN MEETS THE EYE
Dreamwave Productions: Apr, 2003 - No. 8, Nov, 2003 ($5.25)
1-8-Pin-ups with tech info on Autobots and Decepticons; art by Pat Lee & various 5.25
Vol. 1,2 (2004, $24.95, TPB) 1-r/#1-4. 2-r/#5-8 25.00

TRANSFORMERS: MORE THAN MEETS THE EYE
IDW Publishing: Jan, 2012 - No. 57, Sept, 2016 ($3.99)
1-49: 1-Five covers; Roche-a. 2-Three covers; Milne-a. 23-27-Dark Cybertron x-over. 26-1st app. of Windblade 4.00
50-(2/16, $7.99) "The Dying of the Light" begins; five covers 8.00
51-57: 51-55-The Dying of the Light. 56,57-Titans Return 4.00
Annual 2012 (8/12, $7.99) Salgado & Cabaltierra-a; three covers 8.00
...: Revolution 1 (11/16, $3.99) Revolution tie-in; Roche-s/Roberts-a; multiple covers 4.00

TRANSFORMERS: MOVIE ADAPTATION (For the 2007 live action movie)
IDW Publishing: June, 2007 - No. 4, June, 2007 ($3.99, weekly limited series)
1-4: Wraparound covers on each; Milne-a 4.00

TRANSFORMERS: MOVIE PREQUEL (For the 2007 live action movie)
IDW Publishing: Feb, 2007 - No. 4, May, 2007 ($3.99, limited series)
1-4: 1-Origin of the Transformers on Cybertron; multiple covers on each 4.00
Special (6/08, $3.99) 2 covers 4.00
TPB (6/07, $19.99) r/series; gallery of covers and variants 20.00

TRANSFORMERS: NEFARIOUS (Sequel to Transformers: Revenge of the Fallen movie)
IDW Publishing: Mar, 2010 - No. 6, Aug, 2010 ($3.99, limited series)
1-6: Furman-s; multiple covers on all 4.00

TRANSFORMERS: PRIMACY
IDW Publishing: Aug, 2014 - No. 4, Nov, 2014 ($3.99, limited series)
1-4-Metzen & Dille-s/Ramondelli-a; Omega Supreme app.; multiple covers on each 4.00

TRANSFORMERS: PRIME
IDW Publishing: Jan, 2011 - No. 4, Jan, 2011 ($3.99, weekly limited series)
1-4: 1-Mike Johnson-s/E.J. Su-a 4.00

TRANSFORMERS PRIME: BEAST HUNTERS
IDW Publishing: May, 2013 - No. 8, Dec, 2013($3.99, limited series)
1-8-Agustin Padilla-a 4.00

TRANSFORMERS PRIME: RAGE OF THE DINOBOTS
IDW Publishing: Nov, 2012 - No. 4, Feb, 2013 ($3.99, limited series)
1-4: 1-Mike Johnson-s/Agustin Padilla-a 4.00

TRANSFORMERS: PUNISHMENT
IDW Publishing: Jan, 2015 ($5.99, squarebound, one-shot)
1-Windblade app.; Barber-s/Ramondelli-a 6.00

TRANSFORMERS: REDEMPTION
IDW Publishing: Oct, 2015 ($7.99, squarebound, one-shot)

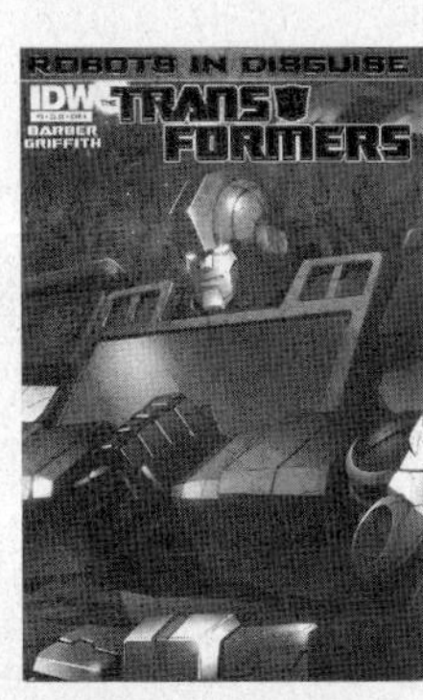

Transformers: Robots in Disguise #1 © Hasbro

Transformers: Sector 7 #1 © Hasbro

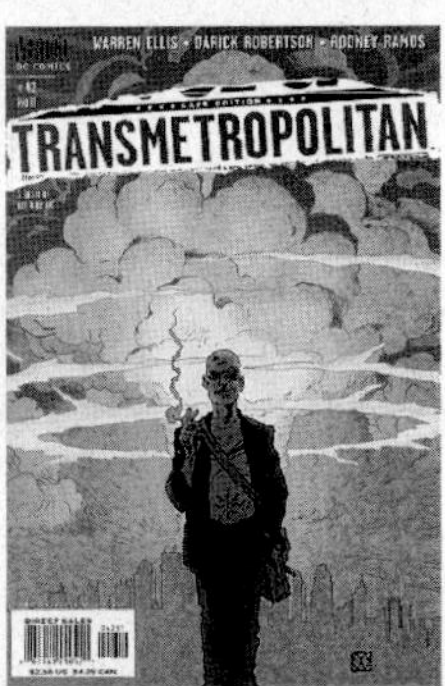

Transmetropolitan #42 © Ellis & Robertson

GD 2.0 | VG 4.0 | FN 6.0 | VF 8.0 | VF/NM 9.0 | NM- 9.2

1-Dinobots app.; John Barber-s/Livio Ramondelli-a 8.00

TRANSFORMERS: REGENERATION ONE (Continues story from Transformers #80 (1991))
IDW Publishing: No. 80.5, May, 2012 - No. 100, Mar, 2014 ($3.99)

80.5 (5/12, Free Comic Book Day giveaway) Furman-s/Wildman-a 3.00
81-99 ($3.99) 81-92-Furman-s/Wildman-a; multiple covers on all 4.00
100-($5.99) Six covers; Furman-s/Wildman, Senior & Guidi-a; bonus cover gallery 6.00
#0 (9/13, $3.99) Hot Rod in the timestream; various artists; 4 covers 4.00
... 100-Page Spectacular (7/12, $7.99) Reprints Transformers #76-80 (1991) 8.00

TRANSFORMERS: REVENGE OF THE FALLEN OFFICIAL MOVIE ADAPTATION
(For the 2009 live action movie sequel)
IDW Publishing: May, 2009 - No. 4, June, 2009 ($3.99, weekly limited series)

1-4: Furman-s; 2 covers on each 4.00

TRANSFORMERS: RISING STORM (Prequel to 2011 Transformers: Dark of the Moon movie)
IDW Publishing: Feb, 2011 - No. 4, May, 2011 ($3.99, limited series)

1-3-Barber-s/Magno-a; 2 covers 4.00

TRANSFORMERS: ROBOTS IN DISGUISE (Re-titled Transformers #35-on)
IDW Publishing: Jan, 2012 - No. 34, Oct, 2014 ($3.99)

1-34: 1-Five covers; Griffith-a. 2-27-Three covers. 23-27-Dark Cybertron x-over 4.00

TRANSFORMERS: ROBOTS IN DISGUISE (Based on the animated series)
IDW Publishing: No. 0, May, 2015 - No. 5, Dec, 2015 ($3.99)

0-Free Comic Book Day Edition; Barber-s/Tramontano-a; Bumblebee & Strongarm app. 3.00
1-5: 1-Georgia Ball-s/Priscilla Tramontano-a 4.00

TRANSFORMERS: SAGA OF THE ALLSPARK (From the 2007 live action movie)
IDW Publishing: Jul, 2008 - No. 4, Oct, 2008 ($3.99, limited series)

1-4-Launch of the Allspark into outer space; Furman-s/Roche-c 4.00

TRANSFORMERS: SECTOR 7 (From the 2007 live action movie)
IDW Publishing: Sept, 2010 - No. 5, Jan, 2011 ($3.99, limited series)

1-5-Barber-s 4.00

TRANSFORMERS: SINS OF THE WRECKERS
IDW Publishing: Nov, 2015 - No. 5, May, 2016 ($3.99, limited series)

1-5-Roche-s/Burcham-a 4.00

TRANSFORMERS: SPOTLIGHT
IDW Publishing: Sept, 2006 - Present ($3.99, multiple covers on each)

... Arcee (2/08); ... Blaster (1/08); ... Blurr (11/08); ... Bumblebee (3/13); ... Cliffjumper (6/09); ... Cyclonus (6/08); ...Doubledealer (8/08); ...Drift (4/09); ...Galvatron (7/07);...Grimlock (3/08); ...Hardhead (7/08); ... Hoist (5/13); ... Hot Rod (11/06); ... Jazz (3/09); ... Kup (4/07); ... Megatron (2/13); ... Metroplex (7/09); ... Mirage (3/08); ... Nightbeat (10/06); ... Orion Pax (12/12); ... Prowl (4/10);... Ramjet (11/07); ... Shockwave (9/06); ... Sideswipe (9/08); ... Sixshot (12/06); ... Soundwave (3/07); Thundercracker (1/13); ... Trailcutter (4/13); ... Ultra Magnus (1/07) 4.00
... Optimus Prime: 3-D (11/08, $5.99, with glasses) Furman-s/Figueroa-a 6.00

TRANSFORMERS: STORMBRINGER
IDW Publishing: Jul, 2006 - No. 4, Oct, 2006 ($2.99, limited series)

1-4-Furman-s/Figueroa-a; multiple covers on all 4.00
TPB (2/07, $17.99) r/series; cover gallery and sketch pages 18.00

TRANSFORMERS SUMMER SPECIAL
Dreamwave Productions: May, 2004 ($4.95)

1-Pat Lee-a; Figueroa-a 5.00

TRANSFORMERS: TALES OF THE FALLEN
IDW Publishing: Aug, 2009 - No. 6 ($3.99, limited series)

1-6: 2,4-Furman-s mulitple covers on all 4.00

TRANSFORMERS: TARGET 2006
IDW Publishing: Apr, 2007 - No. 5, Aug, 2007 ($3.99, limited series)

1-5-Reprints from 1980s series; multiple covers on all 4.00

TRANSFORMERS: THE ANIMATED MOVIE
IDW Publishing: Oct, 2006 - No. 4, Jan, 2007 ($3.99, limited series)

1-4-Adapts animated movie; Don Figueroa-a 4.00

TRANSFORMERS, THE MOVIE
Marvel Comics Group: Dec, 1986 - No. 3, Feb, 1987 (75¢, limited series)

1-3-Adapts animated movie 2 4 6 8 10 12

TRANSFORMERS: THE REIGN OF STARSCREAM
IDW Publishing: Apr, 2008 - No. 5, Aug, 2008 ($3.99, limited series)

1-5-Continuation of the 2007 movie; Milne-a; multiple covers 4.00

GD 2.0 | VG 4.0 | FN 6.0 | VF 8.0 | VF/NM 9.0 | NM- 9.2

TRANSFORMERS: THE WAR WITHIN
Dreamwave Productions: Oct, 2002 - No. 6, Mar, 2003 ($2.95)

1-6-Furman-s/Figueroa-a. 1-Wraparound gatefold-c 4.00
TPB (2003, $15.95) r/#1-6; plus cover gallery 16.00

TRANSFORMERS: TILL ALL ARE ONE
IDW Publishing: Jun, 2016 - No. 12, Jul, 2017 ($3.99)

1-12-Road to Revolution; Mairghread Scott-s; multiple covers on all 4.00
Annual 2017 (12/17, $7.99) Mairghread Scott-s/Pitre-Durocher-a
...: Revolution 1 (10/16, $3.99) Revolution tie-in; Windblade app.; multiple covers 4.00

TRANSFORMERS UNIVERSE
Marvel Comics Group: Dec, 1986 - No. 4, Mar, 1987 ($1.25, limited series)

1-4-A guide to all characters 1 3 4 6 8 10
TPB-r/#1-4 15.00

TRANSFORMERS VS. G.I. JOE
IDW Publishing: No. 0, May, 2014 - No. 13, Jun, 2016 ($3.99)

Free Comic Book Day #0 (5/14, giveaway) Tom Scioli-a; Scioli & John Barber-s 3.00
1-12-Tom Scioli-a; Scioli & John Barber-s; multiple covers on each; creator commentary 4.00
13-($7.99, squarebound) Last issue; bonus commentary; 3 covers 8.00
...: The Movie Adaptation (3/17, $4.99) Tom Scioli-s/a; 4 covers; bonus sketch-a 5.00

TRANSFORMERS VS. VISIONARIES
IDW Publishing: Dec, 2017 - Present ($3.99, limited series)

1-3-Vissagio-s/Ossio-a 4.00

TRANSFORMERS WAR WITHIN: THE AGE OF WRATH
Dreamwave Productions: Sept, 2004 - No. 6 ($2.95, limited series)

1-3-Furman-s/Ng-a 4.00

TRANSFORMERS WAR WITHIN: THE DARK AGES
Dreamwave Productions: Oct, 2003 - No. 6 ($2.95)

1-6: 1-Furman-s/Wildman-a; two covers by Pat Lee & Figueroa 4.00
TPB (2004, $17.95) r/#1-6; plus cover gallery and design sketches 18.00

TRANSFORMERS: WINDBLADE (See Transformers More Than Meets the Eye #26)
IDW Publishing: Apr, 2014 - No. 4, Jul, 2014 ($3.99, limited series)

1-4-Mairghread Scott-s/Sarah Stone-a; three covers on each 4.00
Vol. 2 (3/15 - No. 7, 9/15, $3.99) 1-7-Scott-s; multiple covers on each. 1-Stone-a 4.00

TRANSFUSION
IDW Publishing: Oct, 2012 - No. 3, Feb, 2013 ($3.99, limited series)

1-3-Vampires vs. Robots; Niles-s/Menton3-a 4.00

TRANSIT
Vortex Publ.: March, 1987 - No. 5, Nov, 1987 (B&W)

1-5-Ted McKeever-s/a 1 2 3 5 6 8

TRANSLUCID
BOOM! Studios: Apr, 2014 - No. 6, Sept, 2014 ($3.99)

1-6-Sanchez & Echert-s/Bayliss-a; multiple covers on each 4.00

TRANSMETROPOLITAN
DC Comics (Helix/Vertigo): Sept, 1997 - No. 60, Nov, 2002 ($2.50)

1-Warren Ellis-s/Darick Robertson-a(p) 4 8 12 27 44 60
1-Special Edition (5/09, $1.00) r/#1 with "After Watchmen" cover frame 3.00
2,3 1 3 4 6 8 10
4-8 5.00
9-60: 15-Jae Lee-c. 25-27-Jim Lee-c. 37-39-Bradstreet-c 3.00
Back on the Street ('97, $7.95) r/#1-3 10.00
Back on the Street ('09, $14.99) r/#1-6; intro. by Garth Ennis 15.00
Dirge ('03/'10, $14.95/$14.95) r/#43-48 15.00
Filth of the City ('01, $5.95) Spider's columns with pin-up art by various 6.00
Gouge Away ('02/'09, $14.95/$14.99) r/#31-36 15.00
I Hate It Here ('00, $5.95) Spider's columns with pin-up art by various 6.00
Lonely City ('01/'09, $14.95/$14.99) r/#25-30; intro. by Patrick Stewart 15.00
Lust For Life ('98, $14.95) r/#4-12 20.00
Lust For Life ('09, $14.99) r/#7-12 15.00
One More Time ('04, $14.95) r/#55-60 15.00
One More Time ('11, $19.99) r/#55-60 & Filth of the City & I Hate It Here one-shots 20.00
Spider's Thrash ('02/'10, $14.95/$14.99) r/#37-42; intro. by Darren Aronofsky 15.00
Tales of Human Waste ('04, $9.95) r/Filth of the City, I Hate It Here & story from Vertigo Winter's Edge 2 10.00
The Cure ('03/'11, $14.95/$14.99) r/#49-54 15.00
The New Scum ('00, $12.95) r/#19-24 & Vertigo: Winter's Edge #3 15.00
The New Scum ('09, $14.99) r/#19-24 & Vertigo: Winter's Edge #3 15.00
Year of the Bastard ('99, $12.95)('09, $12.99) r/#13-18 13.00

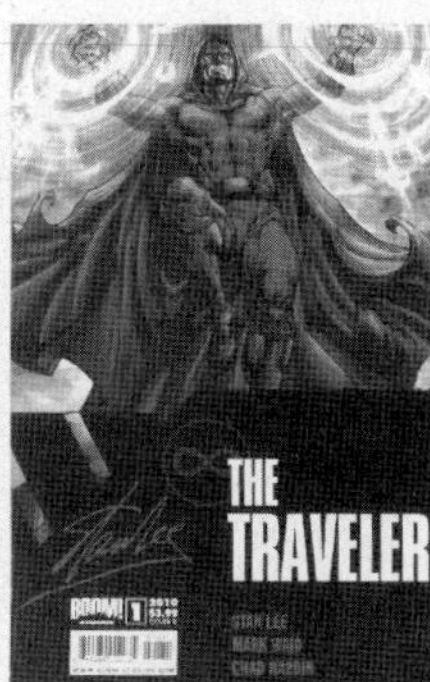

The Traveler #1 © BOOM! & POW

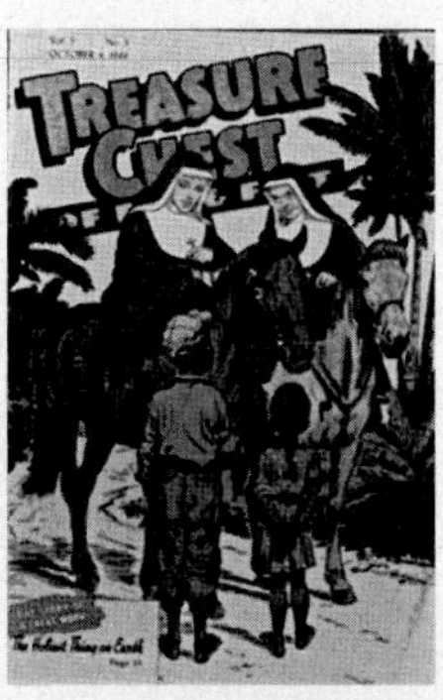

Treasure Chest V5 #3 © G. Pflaum

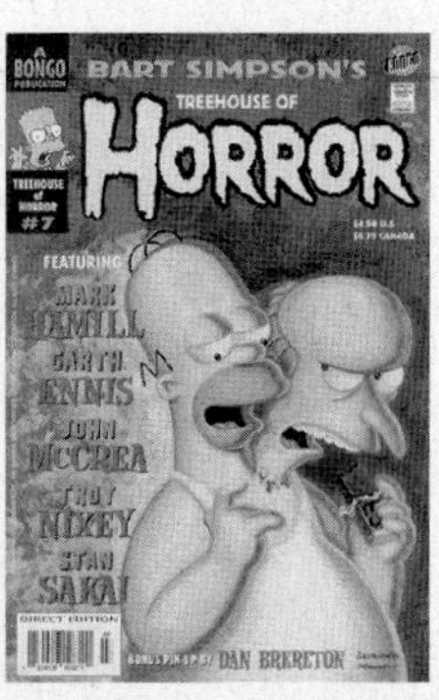

Treehouse of Horror #7 © Bongo

GD VG FN VF VF/NM NM-
2.0 4.0 6.0 8.0 9.0 9.2

GD VG FN VF VF/NM NM-
2.0 4.0 6.0 8.0 9.0 9.2

TRANSMUTATION OF IKE GARUDA, THE
Marvel Comics (Epic Comics): July, 1991 - No. 2, 1991 ($3.95, 52 pgs.)
1,2 4.00

TRAPPED!
Periodical House Magazines (Ace): Oct, 1954 - No. 4, April, 1955
1 (All reprints) 10 20 30 54 72 90
2-4: 4-r/Men Against Crime #4 in its entirety 7 14 21 35 43 50
NOTE: ***Colan** a-1, 4. **Sekowsky** a-1.*

TRASH
Trash Publ. Co.: Mar, 1978 - No. 4, Oct, 1978 (B&W, magazine, 52 pgs.)
1,2: 1-Star Wars parody. 2-UFO-c 2 4 6 10 14 18
3-Parodies of KISS, the Beatles, and monsters 3 6 9 14 19 24
4-(84 pgs.)-Parodies of Happy Days, Rocky movies 3 6 9 14 20 26

TRAVELER, THE (Developed by Stan Lee)
BOOM! Studios: Nov, 2010 - No. 12, Oct, 2011 ($3.99)
1-12-Waid-s/Hardin-a; three covers on each 4.00

TRAVELS OF JAIMIE McPHEETERS, THE (TV)
Gold Key: Dec, 1963
1-Kurt Russell photo on-c plus photo back-c 4 8 12 25 40 55

TREASURE CHEST (Catholic Guild; also see Topix)
George A. Pflaum: 3/12/46 - V27#8, July, 1972 (Educational comics)
(Not published during Summer)
V1#1 30 60 90 177 289 400
2-6 (5/21/46): 5-Dr. Styx app. by Baily 14 28 42 80 115 150
V2#1-20 (9/3/46-5/27/47) 11 22 33 60 83 105
V3#1-5,7-20 (1st slick cover) 10 20 30 54 72 90
V3#6-Jules Verne's "Voyage to the Moon" 12 24 36 67 94 120
V4#1-20 (9/9/48-5/31/49) 9 18 27 47 61 75
V5#1-20 (9/6/49-5/31/50) 8 16 24 44 57 70
V6#1-20 (9/14/50-5/31/51) 8 16 24 42 54 65
V7#1-20 (9/13/51-6/5/52) 8 16 24 40 50 60
V8#1-20 (9/11/52-6/4/53) 7 14 21 37 46 55
V9#1-20 ('53-'54), V10#1-20 ('54-'55) 7 14 21 35 43 50
V11('55-'56), V12('56-'57) 6 12 18 29 36 42
V13#1,3-5,7,9-20-V17#1 ('57-'63) 6 12 18 27 33 38
V13#2,6,8-Ingels-a 5 10 15 35 63 90
V17#2- "This Godless Communism" series begins(not in odd #'d issues); cover shows hammer & sickle over Statue of Liberty; 8 pg. Crandall-a of family life under communism (9/28/61) 16 32 48 112 249 385
V17#3,5,7,9,11,13,15,17,19 3 6 9 16 24 32
V17#4,6,14- "This Godless Communism" stories 12 24 36 84 185 285
V17#8-Shows red octopus encompassing Earth, firing squad; 8 pgs. Crandall-a (12/21/61) 15 30 45 105 233 360
V17#10- "This Godless Communism" - how Stalin came to power, part I; Crandall-a 13 26 39 91 201 310
V17#12-Stalin in WWII, forced labor, death by exhaustion; Crandall-a 13 26 39 91 201 310
V17#16-Kruschev takes over; de-Stalinization 13 26 39 91 201 310
V17#18-Kruschev's control; murder of revolters, brainwash, space race by Crandall 13 26 39 91 201 310
V17#20-End of series; Kruschev-people are puppets, firing squads hammer & sickle over Statue of Liberty, snake around communist manifesto by Crandall 16 32 48 112 249 385
V18#1,3,4,6-10,12-20, V19#11-20, V20#1-20(1964-65): V20#6-JFK photo-c & story. V20#16-Babe Ruth-c & story by Sinnott 3 6 9 16 23 30
V18#2-Kruschev on-c (9/27/62) 3 6 9 19 30 40
V18#5- "What About Red China?" - describes how communists took over China 9 18 27 58 99 140
V18#11-Crandall draws himself & 13 other artists on cover (1/31/63) 3 6 9 20 30 40
V19#1-10- "Red Victim" anti-communist series in all 8 16 24 51 96 140
V21, V22 #1-16,18-20,V23-V25(1965-70)-(two V24#5's 11/7/68 & 11/21/68) (no V24#6): 3 6 9 14 19 24
V22#17-Flying saucer wraparound-c 3 6 9 16 24 32
V26, V27#1-8 (V26,27-68 pgs.) 3 6 9 15 22 28
Summer Edition V1#1-6('66), V2#1-6('67) 3 6 9 16 23 30
NOTE: ***Anderson** a-V18#13. **Borth** a-V7#10-19 (serial), V8#8-17 (serial), V9#1-10 (serial), V13#2, 6, 11, V14-V25 (except V22#1-3, 11-13), Summer Ed. V1#3-6. **Crandall** a-V16#7, 9, 12, 14, 16-18, 20; V17#1, 2, 4-6, 10, 12, 14, 16-18, 20; V18#1, 2, 3(2 pg.), 7, 9-20; V19#4, 11, 13, 16, 19, 20; V20#1, 2, 4, 6, 8-10, 12, 14-16, 18, 20; V21#1-5, 8-11, 13, 16-18; V22#3, 7, 9-11, 14; V23#3, 6, 9, 16, 18; V24#7, 8, 10, 13, 16; V25#8, 16; V27#1-7r, 8r(2 pg.), Summer Ed. V1#3-5, V2#3; c-V16#7, V18#2(part), 7, 11, V19#4, 19, 20, V20#15, V21#5, 9, V22#3, 7, 9, 11, V23#9, 16, V24#13, 16, V25#8, Summer Ed. V1#2 (back c-V1#2-5). **Powell** a-V10#11. V19#11, 15, V10#13, V13#6, 8 all have wraparound covers.*

TREASURE CHEST OF THE WORLD'S BEST COMICS
Superior, Toronto, Canada: 1945 (500 pgs., hard-c)
Contains Blue Beetle, Captain Combat, John Wayne, Dynamic Man, Nemo, Li'l Abner; contents can vary - represents random binding of extra books; Captain America on-c 142 284 426 909 1555 2200

TREASURE COMICS
Prize Publications? (no publisher listed): No date (1943) (50¢, 324 pgs., cardboard-c)
1-(Rare)-Contains rebound Prize Comics #7-11 from 1942 (blank inside-c) 377 754 1131 2639 4620 6600

TREASURE COMICS
Prize Publ. (American Boys' Comics): June-July, 1945 - No. 12, Fall, 1947
1-Paul Bunyan & Marco Polo begin; Highwayman & Carrot Topp only app.; Kiefer-a 54 108 162 343 574 825
2-Arabian Knight, Gorilla King, Dr. Styx begin 32 64 96 190 310 430
3,4,9,12: 9-Kiefer-a 25 50 75 150 245 340
5-Marco Polo-c; Krigstein-a 32 64 96 190 310 430
6,11-Krigstein-a; 11-Krigstein-c 31 62 93 186 303 420
7,8-Frazetta-a (5 pgs. each). 7-Capt. Kidd Jr. app. 41 82 123 260 435 610
10-Simon & Kirby-c/a 38 76 114 228 369 510
NOTE: ***Barry** a-9-11; c-12. **Kiefer** a-3, 5, 7; c-2, 6, 7. **Roussos** a-11.*

TREASURE ISLAND (See Classics Illustrated #64, Doc Savage Comics #1, King Classics, Movie Classics & Movie Comics)
Dell Publishing Co.: No. 624, Apr, 1955 (Disney)
Four Color 624-Movie, photo-c 7 14 21 48 89 130

TREASURY OF COMICS
St. John Publishing Co.: 1947; No. 2, July, 1947 - No. 4, Sept, 1947; No. 5, Jan, 1948
nn(#1)-Abbie an' Slats (nn on-c, #1 on inside) 14 28 42 82 121 160
2-Jim Hardy Comics; featuring Windy & Paddles 11 22 33 64 90 115
3-Bill Bumlin 10 20 30 56 76 95
4-Abbie an' Slats 11 22 33 64 90 115
5-Jim Hardy Comics #1 11 22 33 64 90 115

TREASURY OF COMICS
St. John Publishing Co.: Mar, 1948 - No. 5, 1948 (Reg. size); 1948-1950
(Over 500 pgs., $1.00)
1 20 40 60 114 182 250
2(#2 on-c, #1 on inside) 12 24 36 69 97 125
3-5 10 20 30 58 79 100
1-(1948, 500 pgs., hard-c)-Abbie & Slats, Abbott & Costello, Casper, Little Annie Rooney, Little Audrey, Jim Hardy, Ella Cinders (16 books bound together) (Rare) 206 412 618 1318 2259 3200
1(1949, 500 pgs.)-Same format as above 161 322 483 1030 1765 2500
1(1950, 500 pgs.)-Same format as above; different-c; (also see Little Audrey Yearbook) (Rare) 161 322 483 1030 1765 2500

TREASURY OF DOGS, A (See Dell Giants)

TREASURY OF HORSES, A (See Dell Giants)

TREEHOUSE OF HORROR (Bart Simpson's...)
Bongo Comics: 1995 - Present ($2.95/$2.50/$3.50/$4.50/$4.99, annual)
1-(1995, $2.95)-Groening-c; Allred, Robinson & Smith stories 2 4 6 11 16 20
2-(1996, $2.50)-Stories by Dini & Bagge; infinity-c by Groening 5.00
3-(1997, $2.50)-Dorkin-s/Groening-c 5.00
4-(1998, $2.50)-Lash & Dixon-s/Groening-c 5.00
5-(1999, $3.50)-Thompson-s; Shaw & Aragonés-s/a; TenNapel-s/a 5.00
6-(2000, $4.50)-Mahfood-s/a; DeCarlo-a; Morse-s/a; Kuper-s/a 5.00
7-(2001, $4.50)-Hamill-s/Morrison-a; Ennis-s/McCrea-a; Sakai-s/a; Nixey-s/a; Brereton back-c 5.00
8-(2002, $3.50)-Templeton, Shaw, Barta, Simone, Thompson-s/a 5.00
9-(2003, $4.99)-Lord of the Rings-Brereton-a; Dini, Naifeh, Millidge, Boothby, Noto-s/a 5.00
10-(2004, $4.99)-Monsters of Rock w/Alice Cooper, Gene Simmons, Rob Zombie and Pat Boone; art by Rodriguez, Morrison, Morse, Templeton 5.00
11-(2005, $4.99)-EC style w/art by John Severin, Angelo Torres & Al Williamson and flip book with Dracula by Wolfman/Colan and Squish Thing by Wein/Wrightson 5.00
12-(2006, $4.99)-Terry Moore, Kyle Baker, Eric Powell-s/a 5.00
13-(2007, $4.99)-Oswalt, Posehn, Lennon-s; Guerra, Austin, Barta, Rodriguez-a 5.00
14-(2008, $4.99)-s/a by Niles & Fabry; Boothby & Matsumoto; Gilbert Hernandez 5.00
15-(2009, $4.99)-s/a by Jeffrey Brown, Tim Hensley, Ben Jones and others 5.00
16-(2010, $4.99)-s/a by Kelley Jones, Evan Dorkin and others; Mars Attacks homage 5.00
17-(2011, $4.99)-s/a by Gene Ha, Jane Wiedlin and others; Nosferatu homage 5.00

The Trenchcoat Brigade #1 © DC

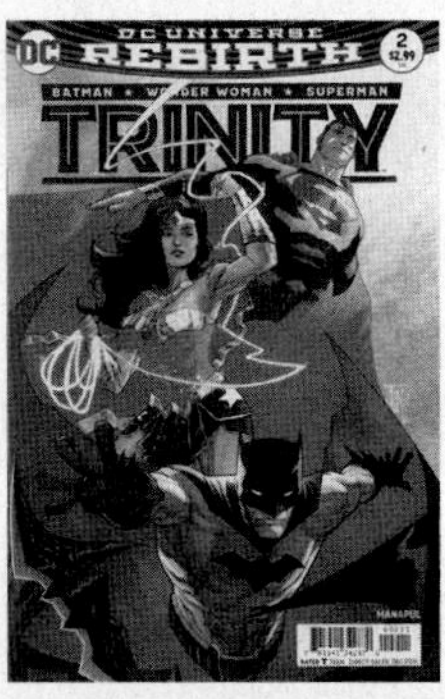

Trinity (2016 series) #2 © DC

Triumph #2 © DC

	GD	VG	FN	VF	VF/NM	NM-
	2.0	4.0	6.0	8.0	9.0	9.2

GD VG FN VF VF/NM NM-
2.0 4.0 6.0 8.0 9.0 9.2

18-(2012, $4.99)-s/a by Jim Valentino, Phil Noto and others; Rosemary's Baby spoof 5.00
19-(2013, $4.99)-s/a by Len Wein, Dan Brereton and others; Cthulhu spoof 5.00
20-(2014, $4.99)-All Zombie issue, including The Walking Ned 5.00
21-(2015, $4.99)-Gremlins & Metropolis spoofs 5.00
22-(2016, $4.99)-Ghostbusters & Gossamer spoofs 5.00
23-(2017, $4.99)-Spoofs of Stephen King stories: It, Dreamcatcher and Thinner 5.00

TREES
Image Comics: May, 2014 - Present ($2.99)
1-14-Warren Ellis-s/Jason Howard-a 3.00

TREKKER (See Dark Horse Presents #6)
Dark Horse Comics: May, 1987 - No. 6, Mar, 1988 ($1.50, B&W)
1-6: Sci/Fi stories 3.00
Color Special 1 (1989, $2.95, 52 pgs.) 4.00
Collection ($5.95, B&W) 6.00
Special 1 (6/99, $2.95, color) 3.00

TRENCHCOAT BRIGADE, THE
DC Comics (Vertigo): Mar, 1999 - No. 4, Jun, 1999 ($2.50, limited series)
1-4: Hellblazer, Phantom Stranger, Mister E, Dr. Occult app. 3.00

TRENCHER (See Blackball Comics)
Image Comics: May, 1993 - No. 4, Oct, 1993 ($1.95, unfinished limited series)
1-4: Keith Giffen-c/a/scripts. 3-Supreme-c/story 3.00

TRIALS OF SHAZAM!
DC Comics: Oct, 2006 - No. 12, May, 2008 ($2.99)
1-12: 1-8-Winick-s/Porter-a. 9-11-Cascioli-a. 10-Shadowpact app. 12-JLA app. 3.00
... Volume 1 TPB (2007, $14.99) r/#1-6 and story from DCU Brave New World #1 15.00
... Volume 2 TPB (2008, $14.99) r/#7-12 15.00

TRIB COMIC BOOK, THE
Winnipeg Tribune: Sept. 24, 1977 - Vol. 4, #36, 1980 (8-1/2"x11", 24 pgs., weekly) (155 total issues)
V1# 1-Color pages (Sunday strips)-Spiderman, Asterix, Disney's Scamp, Wizard of Id, Doonesbury, Inside Woody Allen, Mary Worth, & others (similar to Spirit sections) 2 4 6 10 14 18
V1#2-15, V2#1-52, V3#1-52, V4#1-33 1 3 4 6 8 10
V4#34-36 (not distributed) 2 4 6 11 16 20
NOTE: *All issues have Spider-Man. Later issues contain Star Trek and Star Wars. 20 strips in ea. The first newspaper to put Sunday pages into a comic book format.*

TRIBE (See WildC.A.T.S #4)
Image Comics/Axis Comics No. 2 on: Apr, 1993; No. 2, Sept, 1993 - No. 3, 1994 ($2.50/$1.95)
1-By Johnson & Stroman; gold foil & embossed on black-c 4.00
1-($2.50)-Ivory Edition; gold foil & embossed on white-c; available only through the creators 4.00
2,3: 2-1st Axis Comics issue. 3-Savage Dragon app. 3.00

TRIBUTE TO STEVEN HUGHES, A
Chaos! Comics: Sept, 2000 ($6.95)
1-Lady Death & Evil Ernie pin-ups by various artists; testimonials 7.00

TRICK 'R TREAT
DC Comics (WildStorm): 2009 ($19.95,SC)
nn-Short Halloween-themed story anthology; Andreyko-s; art by Huddleston & others 20.00

TRIGGER (See Roy Rogers'...)

TRIGGER
DC Comics (Vertigo): Feb, 2005 - No. 8, Sept, 2005 ($2.95/$2.99)
1-8-Jason Hall-s/John Watkiss-a/c 3.00

TRIGGER TWINS
National Periodical Publications: Mar-Apr, 1973 (20¢, one-shot)
1-Trigger Twins & Pow Wow Smith-r/All-Star Western #94,103 & Western Comics #81; Infantino-r(p) 2 4 6 13 18 22

TRILLIUM
DC Comics (Vertigo): Oct, 2013 - No. 8, Jun, 2014 ($2.99)
1-8-Jeff Lemire-s/a. 1-Flip-book 3.00

TRINITY (See DC Universe: Trinity)

TRINITY
DC Comics: Aug, 2008 - No. 52, July, 2009 ($2.99, weekly series)
1-52-Superman, Batman & Wonder Woman star; Busiek-s/Bagley-a. 52-Wraparound-c 3.00
Vol. 1 TPB (2009, $29.99) r/#1-17 30.00
Vol. 2 TPB (2009, $29.99) r/#18-35 30.00
Vol. 3 TPB (2009, $29.99) r/#36-52 30.00

TRINITY (DC Rebirth)
DC Comics: Nov, 2016 - Present ($2.99/$3.99)
1-7: 1-Superman, Batman & Wonder Woman; Manapul-s/a. 3-Mann-a. 4-6-Mongul app. 3.00
8-18-($3.99): 9-11-Manapul-s/a; Justice League app. 12-15-Zatanna, Constantine & Deadman app.; Marion-a. 16-Deadshot app. 17,18-Warlord of Skartaris app. 4.00
Annual 1 (7/17, $4.99) Ra's al Ghul, Circe and Etrigan app.; Guillem March-a/c 5.00

TRINITY ANGELS
Acclaim Comics (Valiant Heroes): July, 1997 - No. 12, June, 1998 ($2.50)
1-12-Maguire-s/a(p). 4-Copycat-c 3.00

TRINITY: BLOOD ON THE SANDS
Image Comics (Top Cow): July, 2009 ($2.99, one-shot)
1-Witchblade, The Darkness and Angelus in the 14th century Arabian desert 3.00

TRINITY OF SIN (DC New 52)
DC Comics: Dec, 2014 - No. 6, May, 2015 ($2.99)
1-6-Pandora, The Question and Phantom Stranger; Guichet-a 3.00

TRINITY OF SIN: PANDORA (DC New 52)
DC Comics: Aug, 2013 - No. 14, Oct, 2014 ($2.99)
1-14: 1-Fawkes-s; origin re-told. 1-3-Trinity War tie-ins. 4-9-Forever Evil tie-ins 3.00
...: Futures End 1 (11/14, $2.99, regular-c) Five years later; Pandora vs. 7 Deadly Sins 3.00
...: Futures End 1 (11/14, $3.99, 3-D cover) 4.00

TRINITY OF SIN: THE PHANTOM STRANGER (See Phantom Stranger 2012 series)

TRIO (Continues in Triple Helix #1)
IDW Publishing: May, 2012 - No. 4, Aug, 2012 ($3.99, limited series)
1-4-John Byrne-s/a/c 4.00

TRIPLE GIANT COMICS (See Archie All-Star Specials under Archie Comics)

TRIPLE HELIX (Also see Trio)
IDW Publishing: Oct, 2013 - No. 4, Jan, 2014 ($3.99, limited series)
1-4-John Byrne-s/a/c; The Trio app. 4.00

TRIPLE THREAT
Special Action/Holyoke/Gerona Publ.: Winter, 1945
1-Duke of Darkness, King O'Leary 37 74 111 222 361 500

TRISH OUT OF WATER
Aspen MLT: Oct, 2013 - No. 5, Mar, 2014 ($1.00/$3.99)
1-($1.00) Vince Hernandez-s/Giuseppe Cafaro-a; multiple covers 3.00
2-5-($3.99) Multiple covers on each 4.00

TRIUMPH (Also see JLA #28-30, Justice League Task Force & Zero Hour)
DC Comics: June, 1995 - No. 4, Sept, 1995 ($1.75, limited series)
1-4: 3-Hourman, JLA app. 3.00

TRIUMPHANT UNLEASHED
Triumphant Comics: No. 0, Nov, 1993 - No. 1, Nov, 1993 ($2.50, lim. series)
0-Serially numbered, 0-Red logo, 0-White logo (no cover price; giveaway), 1-Cover is negative & reverse of #0-c 3.00

TROJAN WAR (Adaptation of Trojan war histories from ancient Greek and Roman sources)
Marvel Comics: July, 2009 - No. 5, Nov, 2009 ($3.99, limited series)
1-5-Roy Thomas-s/Miguel Sepulveda-a/Dennis Calero-c 4.00

TROLL (Also see Brigade)
Image Comics (Extreme Studios): Dec, 1993 ($2.50, one-shot, 44 pgs.)
1-1st app. Troll; Liefeld scripts; Matsuda-c/a(p) 4.00
Halloween Special (1994, $2.95)-Maxx app. 4.00
...Once A Hero (8/94, $2.50) 4.00

TROLLORDS
Tru Studios/Comico V2#1 on: 2/86 - No. 15, 1988; V2#1, 11/88 - V2#4, 1989 (1-15: $1.50, B&W)
1-First printing 5.00
1-Second printing, 2-15: 6-Christmas issue; silver logo 3.00
V2#1-4 ($1.75, color, Comico) 3.00
Special 1 ($1.75, 2/87, color)-Jerry's Big Fun Bk. 3.00

TROLLORDS
Apple Comics: July, 1989 - No. 6, 1990 ($2.25, B&W, limited series)
1-6: 1-"The Big Batman Movie Parody" 3.00

TROLL PATROL

Trouble #5 © MAR

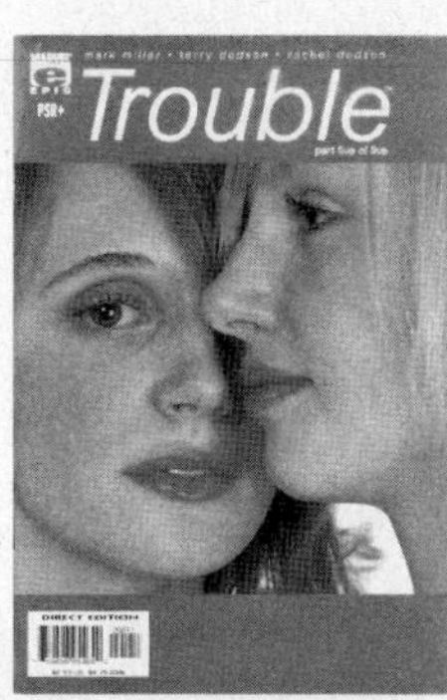

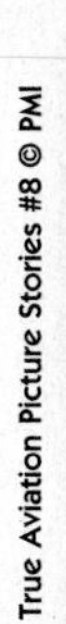
True Aviation Picture Stories #8 © PMI

True Believers: Droids #1 © Lucasfilm

GD 2.0 | VG 4.0 | FN 6.0 | VF 8.0 | VF/NM 9.0 | NM- 9.2

Harvey Comics: Jan, 1993 ($1.95, 52 pgs.)

1 4.00

TROLL II (Also see Brigade)
Image Comics (Extreme Studios): July, 1994 ($3.95, one-shot)

1 4.00

TRON (Based on the video game and film)
Slave Labor Graphics: Apr, 2006 - No. 6 ($3.50/$3.95)

1-4: 1-DeMartinis-a/Walker & Jones-s 4.00
5,6-($3.95) 4.00

TRON: BETRAYAL
Marvel Comics: Nov, 2010 - No. 2, Dec, 2010 ($3.99, limited series)

1,2-Prequel to Tron Legacy movie; Larroca-c 4.00

TRON: ORIGINAL MOVIE ADAPTATION
Marvel Comics: Jan, 2011 - No. 2, Feb, 2011 ($3.99, limited series)

1,2-Peter David-s/Mirco Pierfederici-a/Greg Land-c 4.00

TROUBLE
Marvel Comics (Epic): Sept, 2003 - No. 5, Jan, 2004 ($2.99, limited series)

1-5-Photo-c; Richard and Ben meet Mary and May; Millar-s/Dodson-a 3.00
1-2nd printing with variant Frank Cho-c 5.00

TROUBLED SOULS
Fleetway: 1990 ($9.95, trade paperback)

nn-Garth Ennis scripts & John McCrea painted-c/a. 10.00

TROUBLEMAKERS
Acclaim Comics (Valiant Heroes): Apr, 1997 - No. 19, June, 1998 ($2.50)

1-19: Fabian Nicieza scripts in all. 1-1st app. XL, Rebound & Blur; 2 covers. 8-Copycat-c. 12-Shooting of Parker 3.00

TROUBLE SHOOTERS, THE (TV)
Dell Publishing Co.: No. 1108, Jun-Aug, 1960

Four Color 1108-Keenan Wynn photo-c 6 12 18 37 66 95

TROUBLE WITH GIRLS, THE
Malibu Comics (Eternity Comics) #7-14/Comico V2#1-4/Eternity V2#5 on:
8/87 - #14, 1988; V2#1, 2/89 - V2#23, 1991? ($1.95, B&W/color)

1-14 ($1.95, B&W, Eternity)-Gerard Jones scripts & Tim Hamilton-c/a in all 3.00
V2#1-23-Jones scripts, Hamilton-c/a. 3.00
Annual 1 (1988, $2.95) 4.00
Christmas Special 1 (12/91, $2.95, B&W, Eternity)-Jones scripts, Hamilton-c/a 4.00
Graphic Novel 1,2 (7/88, B&W)-r/#1-3 & #4-6 8.00

TROUBLE WITH GIRLS, THE: NIGHT OF THE LIZARD
Marvel Comics (Epic Comics/Heavy Hitters): 1993 - No. 4, 1993 ($2.50/$1.95, lim. series)

1-Embossed-c; Gerard Jones scripts & Bret Blevins-c/a in all 4.00
2-4: 2-Begin $1.95-c. 3.00

TRUE ADVENTURES (Formerly True Western)(Men's Adventures #4 on)
Marvel Comics (CCC): No. 3, May, 1950 (52 pgs.)

3-Powell, Sekowsky, Maneely-a; Brodsky-c 23 46 69 136 223 310

TRUE ANIMAL PICTURE STORIES
True Comics Press: Winter, 1947 - No. 2, Spring-Summer, 1947

1 13 26 39 72 101 130
2 11 22 33 62 86 110

TRUE AVIATION PICTURE STORIES (Becomes Aviation Adventures & Model Building #16 on)
Parents' Mag. Institute: 1942; No. 2, Jan-Feb, 1943 - No. 15, Sept-Oct, 1946

1-(#1 & 2 titled ...Aviation Comics Digest)(not digest size)
17 34 51 100 158 215
2 11 22 33 62 86 110
3-14: 3-10-Plane photos on-c. 11,13-Photo-c 10 20 30 54 72 90
15-(Titled "True Aviation Adventures & Model Building")
9 18 27 50 65 80

TRUE BELIEVERS
Marvel Comics: Sept, 2008 - No. 5, Jan, 2009 ($2.99, limited series)

1-5-Cary Bates-s/Paul Gulacy-a. 1,2-Reed Richards app. 3-Luke Cage app. 3.00

TRUE BELIEVERS...
Marvel Comics: Jun, 2015 - Present ($1.00, series of one-shot reprints)

...: Age of Apocalypse 1 - Reprints X-Men: Alpha #1; Cruz & Epting-a; wraparound-c 3.00
...: Age of Ultron 1 - Reprints Age of Ultron #1; Bendis-s/Hitch-a 3.00
...: All-New, All-Different Avengers - Cyclone 1 - Reprints issue #4; Waid-s/Asrar-a 3.00
...: All-New Wolverine 1 - Reprints issue #1; Taylor-s/Lopez-a 3.00
...: Amazing Spider-Man - The Dark Kingdom 1 - Reprints Amazing Spider-Man #6 3.00
...: Armor Wars 1 - Reprints Iron Man #225; Michelinie-s/Bright & Layton-a 3.00
...: Astonishing X-Men 1 - Reprints Astonishing X-Men #1 (2004); Whedon-s/Cassaday-a 3.00
...: Black Widow 1 - Reprints Black Widow #1 (2014); Edmondson-s/Noto-a 3.00
...: Cable & The New Mutants 1 - Reprints New Mutants #87; L. Simonson-s/Liefeld-a 3.00
...: Captain Marvel 1 - Reprints Captain Marvel #1 (2014); DeConnick-s/Lopez-a 3.00
...: Chewbacca 1 - Reprints Chewbacca #1; Duggan-s/Noto-a 3.00
...: Civil War 1 - Reprints Civil War #1; Millar-s/McNiven-a 3.00
...: Daredevil - Practice to Deceive 1 - Reprints Daredevil #6 (2016); Soule-s/Buffagni-a 3.00
...: Darth Vader 1 - Reprints Darth Vader #1; Gillen-s/Larroca-a 3.00
...: Deadpool 1 - Reprints 1st app. from New Mutants #98 (1991); Liefeld-a 3.00
...: Deadpool - Deadpool vs. Sabretooth 1 - Reprints Deadpool #8 (2016) 3.00
...: Deadpool Origins 1 - Reprints Wolverine Origins #25; Dillon-a 3.00
...: Deadpool The Musical 1 - Reprints Deadpool #49.1; McCrea-a 3.00
...: Deadpool Variants 1 - Gallery of variant covers 3.00
...: Death of Phoenix 1 - Reprints New X-Men #150 3.00
...: Detective Deadpool 1 - Reprints Cable & Deadpool #13; Nicieza-s/Zircher-a 3.00
...: Doctor Strange - The Last Days of Magic 1 - Reprints Doctor Strange #6 (2015) 3.00
...: Droids 1 - Reprints Droids #1; Star Wars C-3PO & R2-D2 app.; John Romita-a 3.00
...: Enter – The Phoenix 1 - Reprints X-Men #100-101 (1976) Cockrum-a 3.00
...: Evil Deadpool 1 - Reprints Deadpool #45; Espin-a 3.00
...: Extraordinary X-Men - The Burning Man 1 - Reprints issue #6; Ibañez-a 3.00
...: Generation X 1 - Reprints Generation X #1; Lobdell-s/Bachalo-a 3.00
...: Giant-Size X-Men 1 - Reprints Giant-Size X-Men #1; Wein-s/Cockrum-a 3.00
...: Guardians of the Galaxy - Galaxy's Most Wanted 1 - Reprints GOTG #6 (2015) 3.00
...: House of M 1 - Reprints House of M #1; Bendis-s/Coipel-a 3.00
...: Infinity Gauntlet 1 - Reprints Infinity Gauntlet #1; Starlin-s/Pérez-a 3.00
...: Invincible Iron Man - The War Machines 1 - Reprints Invincible Iron Man #6 3.00
...: Kanan 1 - Reprints Kanan #1; Star Wars; Weisman-s/Larraz-a 3.00
...: Lando 1 - Reprints Lando #1; Star Wars; Soule-s/Maleev-a 3.00
...: Marvel Zombies 1 - Reprints Marvel Zombies #1; Bendis-s/Phillips-a 3.00
...: Mighty Thor - The Strongest Viking There Is 1 - Reprints Mighty Thor #6 3.00
...: Miles Morales 1 - Reprints Ultimate Comics Spider-Man #1; Bendis-s/Pichelli-a 3.00
...: Ms. Marvel 1 - Reprints Ms. Marvel #1 (2014); Wilson-s/Alphona-a 3.00
...: New Mutants 1 - Reprints New Mutants #1; Claremont-s/McLeod-a 3.00
...: Old Man Logan 1 - Reprints Wolverine #66 (2008); Millar-s/McNiven-a; wraparound-c 3.00
...: Phoenix – Bizarre Adventures 1 - Reprints Bizarre Adventures #27; Buscema-a 3.00
...: Phoenix Classic 1 - Reprints Classic X-Men #13 & 18; Bolton-a 3.00
...: Phoenix Origins 1 - Reprints X-Men Origins: Jean Grey; Mayhew-a 3.00
...: Phoenix Presents Cyclops & Marvel Girl 1 - Reprints X-Men #48 & 57 (1968,1969) 3.00
...: Phoenix Presents Jean Grey vs. Sabretooth 1 - Reprints X-Men #28 (1994) 3.00
...: Phoenix Presents The Wedding of Scott Summers & Jean Grey 1 - Reprints X-Men #30 3.00
...: Phoenix Returns 1 - Reprints Fantastic Four #286; Byrne-s/a 3.00
...: Phoenix – What If? 1 - Reprints What If? #27 (Phoenix Had Not Died?) 3.00
...: Planet Hulk 1 - Reprints Incredible Hulk #92 (2006); Pak-s/Pagulayan-a 3.00
...: Princess Leia 1 - Reprints Princess Leia #1; Waid-s/Dodson-a 3.00
...: Shattered Empire 1 - Reprints Journey to Star Wars: The Force Awakens – Shattered Empire #1; Rucka-s/Checchetto-a 3.00
...: She-Hulk 1 - Reprints She-Hulk #1 (2014); Soule-s/Pulido-a 3.00
...: Silk 1 - Reprints Silk #1 (2015); Thompson-a/Stacey Lee-a; Spider-Man app. 3.00
...: Spider-Gwen 1 - Reprints Spider-Gwen #1 (2015); Latour-s/Robbi Rodriguez-a 3.00
...: Spider-Woman 1 - Reprints Spider-Woman #5 (2015); Hopeless-s/Javier Rodriguez-a 3.00
...: Star Wars 1 - Reprints Star Wars #1 (2015); Aaron-s/Cassaday-a 3.00
...: Star Wars Classic 1 - Reprints Star Wars #1 (1977); Roy Thomas-s/Howard Chaykin-a 3.00
...: Star Wars Covers 1 - Gallery of variant covers for Star Wars #1 (2015) 3.00
...: Vader Down 1 - Reprints Star Wars: Vader Down #1; Aaron-s/Deodato-a 3.00
...: The Groovy Deadpool 1 - Reprints Deadpool #13 (2013) 1970s art style 3.00
...: The Meaty Deadpool 1 - Reprints Deadpool #11 (2008) Bullseye (as Hawkeye) app. 3.00
...: The Unbeatable Squirrel Girl 1 - Reprints The Unbeatable Squirrel Girl #1 (2015) 3.00
...: The Wedding of Deadpool 1 - Reprints Deadpool #27 (2013) wraparound-c 3.00
...: Thor 1 - Reprints Thor #1 (2014); debut of female Thor; Aaron-s/Dauterman-a 3.00
...: Uncanny Avengers - The Bagalia Job 1 - Reprints Uncanny Avengers #5 3.00
...: Uncanny Deadpool 1 - Reprints Cable & Deadpool #38; Nicieza-s/Brown-a 3.00
...: Venom - Agent Venom 1 - Reprints Venom #1 (2011) Remender-s/Moore-a 3.00
...: Venom - Carnage 1 - Reprints Amazing Spider-Man #363 (1992) Bagley-a 3.00
...: Venom - Dark Origin 1 - Reprints Venom: Dark Origin #3 (2008) Wells-s/Medina-a 3.00
...: Venom - Flashpoint 1 - Reprints Amazing Spider-Man #654.1 (2011) Ramos-a 3.00
...: Venom - Homecoming 1 - Reprints Venom #6 (2017) Costa-s/Sandoval-a 3.00
...: Venom - Lethal Protector 1 - Reprints Venom: Lethal Protector #1; Bagley-a 3.00
...: Venom - Shiver 1 - Reprints Venom #1 (2003) Way-s/Herrera-a 3.00
...: Venom - Symbiosis 1 - Reprints Web of Spider-Man #1 (1985) Larocque-a 3.00
...: Venom - Toxin 1 - Reprints Venom #17 (2011) Remender & Bunn-s/Walker-a 3.00
...: Venom vs. Spider-Man 1 - Reprints Amazing Spider-Man #300 (1988) McFarlane-a 3.00

True Blood #1 © HBO

True Comics #71 © PMI

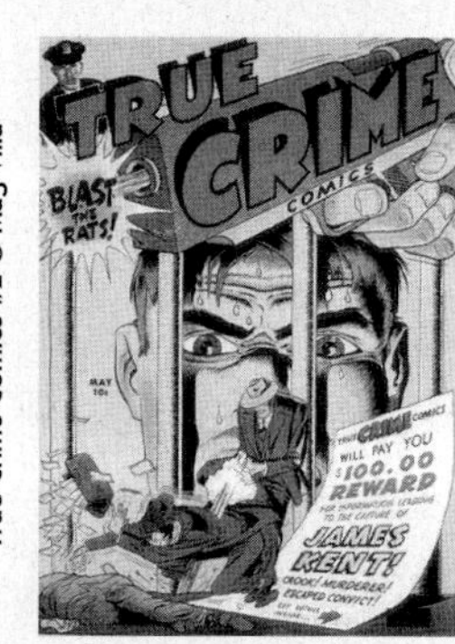

True Crime Comics #2 © Mag Villa

GD 2.0 | VG 4.0 | FN 6.0 | VF 8.0 | VF/NM 9.0 | NM- 9.2

...: Wolverine 1 - Reprints #1 (1982) Claremont-s/Miller-a 3.00
...: Wolverine and the X-Men 1 - Reprints #1; Aaron-s/Bachalo-a 3.00
...: Wolverine - Enemy of the State 1 - Reprints Wolverine #20 (2003); Millar-s/Romita Jr.-a 3.00
...: Wolverine - Old Man Logan 1 - Reprints Old Man Logan #1; Bendis-s/Sorrentino-a 3.00
...: Wolverine - Origin 1 - Reprints Wolverine: The Origin #1; Andy Kubert-a 3.00
...: Wolverine - Save the Tiger 1 - Reprints Marvel Comics Presents #1-3; Buscema-a 3.00
...: Wolverine vs. Hulk 1 - Reprints Incredible Hulk #181; Wein-s/Trimpe-a 3.00
...: Wolverine - Weapon X 1 - Reprints Marvel Comics Presents #72-74 3.00
...: Wolverine - X-23 1 - Reprints X-23 #1; Craig Kyle-s/Billy Tan-a 3.00
...: X-Factor - Mutant Genesis 1 - Reprints X-Factor #71; David-s/Stroman-a 3.00
...: X-Force 1 - Reprints X-Force #1; Liefeld-s/a; Nicieza-s 3.00
...: X-Men 1 - Reprints X-Men #1 (1963); Stan Lee-s/Jack Kirby-a 3.00
...: X-Men Blue 1 - Reprints X-Men #1 (1991); Chris Claremont-s/Jim Lee-a 3.00
...: X-Men Gold 1 - Reprints Uncanny X-Men #281; Byrne-s/Portacio-a 3.00

TRUE BELIEVERS: KIRBY 100TH
Marvel Comics: Oct, 2017 ($1.00, one-shot reprints celebrating Jack Kirby's 100th birthday)

... – Ant-Man and The Wasp #1 - Reprints Tales to Astonish #27 & #44 3.00
... – Avengers: Captain America Lives Again! #1 - Reprints Avengers #4; bonus pin-ups 3.00
... – Black Panther #1 - Reprints Black Panther #1 3.00
... – Captain America #1 - Reprints Captain America Comics #1 & Tales of Suspense #63 3.00
... – Devil Dinosaur #1 - Reprints Devil Dinosaur #1; cover gallery & letter columns 3.00
... – Eternals #1 - Reprints Eternals #1; pin-ups & letter columns 3.00
... – Groot #1 - Reprints Tales to Astonish #13 & Journey Into Mystery #62 (Hulk/Xemnu) 3.00
... – Inhumans #1 - Reprints Amazing Adventures #1,2; bonus pin-ups 3.00
... – Introducing... The Mighty Thor #1 - Reprints Journey Into Mystery #83,85 3.00
... – Iron Man #1 - Reprints Tales of Suspense #40,41 3.00
... – Nick Fury #1 - Reprints Strange Tales #135,141 3.00
... – Thor vs. Hulk #1 - Reprints Journey Into Mystery #112 3.00

TRUE BLOOD (Based on the HBO vampire series)
IDW Publishing: Aug, 2010 - No. 6, Dec, 2010 ($3.99)

1-Messina-a; 4 covers by Messina, Campbell, Currie and Corroney 5.00
2-6-Multiple covers on each 4.00
...: Legacy Edition (1/11, $4.99) r/#1, cover gallery; full script 5.00

TRUE BLOOD (2nd series)(Based on the HBO vampire series)
IDW Publishing: May, 2012 - No. 14, Jun, 2013 ($3.99)

1-14-Gaydos-a in most; 2 covers (photo & Bradstreet-c) on each. 5-Manfredi-a 4.00

TRUE BLOOD: TAINTED LOVE (Based on the HBO vampire series)
IDW Publishing: Feb, 2011 - No. 6, Jul, 2011 ($3.99, limited series)

1-4: 1,2,4,5-Corroney-a; multiple covers. 3-Molnar-a 4.00
... Legacy Edition 1 (7/11, $4.99) r/#1 with full script and cover gallery 5.00

TRUE BLOOD: THE FRENCH QUARTER (Based on the HBO vampire series)
IDW Publishing: Aug, 2011 - No. 6, Jan, 2012 ($3.99, limited series)

1-6-Huehner & Tischman-s; multiple covers. 3-Molnar-a 4.00

TRUE BLOOD: THE GREAT REVELATION (Prequel to the 2008 HBO vampire series)
HBO/Top Cow: July, 2008 (no cover price, one shot continued on HBO website)

1-David Wohl-s/Jason Badower-a/c 4.00

TRUE BRIDE'S EXPERIENCES (Formerly Teen-Age Brides)
(True Bride-To-Be Romances No. 17 on)
True Love (Harvey Publications): No. 8, Oct, 1954 - No. 16, Feb, 1956

8-"I Married a Farmer" 10 20 30 54 72 90
9,10: 10-Last pre-code (2/55) 7 14 21 37 46 55
11-15 6 12 18 31 38 45
16-Last issue 7 14 21 37 46 55
NOTE: *Powell a-8-10, 12, 13.*

TRUE BRIDE-TO-BE ROMANCES (Formerly True Bride's Experiences)
Home Comics/True Love (Harvey): No. 17, Apr, 1956 - No. 30, Nov, 1958

17-S&K-c, Powell-a 10 20 30 56 76 95
18-20,22,25-28,30 6 12 18 31 38 45
21,23,24,29-Powell-a. 29-Baker-a (1 pg.) 7 14 21 35 43 50

TRUE COMICS (Also see Outstanding American War Heroes)
True Comics/Parents' Magazine Press: April, 1941 - No. 84, Aug, 1950

1-Marathon run story; life story Winston Churchill 36 72 108 211 343 475
2-Red Cross story; Everett-a 17 34 51 98 154 210
3-Baseball Hall of Fame story; Chiang Kai-Shek-c/s 18 36 54 105 165 225
4,5: 4-Story of American flag "Old Glory". 5-Life story of Joe Louis
14 28 42 82 121 160
6-Baseball World Series story 16 32 48 94 147 200
7-10: 7-Buffalo Bill story. 10,11-Teddy Roosevelt 12 24 36 67 94 120
11-14,16,18-20: 11-Thomas Edison, Douglas MacArthur stories. 13-Harry Houdini story.
14-Charlie McCarthy story. 18-Story of America begins, ends #26. 19-Eisenhower-c/s
10 20 30 58 79 100
15-Flag-c; Bob Feller story 11 22 33 62 86 110
17-Brooklyn Dodgers story 12 24 36 69 97 125
21-30: 24-Marco Polo story. 28-Origin of Uncle Sam. 29-Beethoven story.
30-Cooper Brothers baseball story 9 18 27 50 65 80
31-Red Grange "Galloping Ghost" story 8 16 24 42 54 65
32-46: 33-Origin/1st app. Steve Saunders, Special Agent of the FBI, series begins.
35-Mark Twain story. 38-General Bradley-c/s. 39-FDR story. 44-Truman story.
46-George Gershwin story 8 16 24 40 50 60
47-Atomic bomb issue (c/story, 3/46) 10 20 30 58 79 100
48-(4/46) "Hero Without a Gun" Desmond Doss story; inspired 2016 movie Hacksaw Ridge
9 18 27 47 61 75
49-54,56-65: 49-1st app. Secret Warriors. 53-Bobby Riggs story. 58-Jim Jeffries (boxer) story; Harry Houdini story. 59-Bob Hope story; pirates-c/s. 60-Speedway Speed Demon-c/story.
7 14 21 37 46 55
55-(12/46)-1st app. Sad Sack by Baker (1/2 pg.) 30 60 90 177 289 400
66-Will Rogers-c/story 8 16 24 40 50 60
67-1st oversized issue (12/47); Steve Saunders, Special Agent begins
9 18 27 47 61 75
68-70,74-77,79: 68-70,74-77-Features Steve Sanders True FBI advs.
68-Oversized; Admiral Byrd-c/s. 69-Jack Benny story. 74-Amos 'n' Andy story
7 14 21 37 46 55
71-Joe DiMaggio-c/story. 9 18 27 52 69 85
72-Jackie Robinson story; True FBI advs. 8 16 24 44 57 70
73-Walt Disney's life story 9 18 27 52 69 85
78-Stan Musial-c/story; True FBI advs. 8 16 24 44 57 70
80-84 (Scarce)-All distr. to subscribers through mail only; paper-c. 80-Rocket trip to the moon story. 81-Red Grange story. 84-Wyatt Earp app. (1st app. in comics?); Rube Marquard story
18 36 54 107 169 230
(Prices vary widely on issues 80-84)
NOTE: ***Bob Kane** a-7. **Palais** a-80. **Powell** c/a-80. #80-84 have soft covers and combined with Tex Granger, Jack Armstrong, and Calling All Kids. #68-78 featured true FBI adventures.*

TRUE COMICS AND ADVENTURE STORIES
Parents' Magazine Institute: 1965 (Giant) (25¢)

1,2: 1-Fighting Hero of Viet Nam; LBJ on-c 3 6 9 17 26 35

TRUE COMPLETE MYSTERY (Formerly Complete Mystery)
Marvel Comics (PrPl): No. 5, Apr, 1949 - No. 8, Oct, 1949

5-Criminal career of Rico Mancini 30 60 90 177 289 400
6-8: 6-8-Photo-c 21 42 63 126 206 285

TRUE CONFIDENCES
Fawcett Publications: 1949 (Fall) - No. 4, June, 1950 (All photo-c)

1-Has ad for Fawcett Love Adventures #1, but publ. as Love Memoirs #1 as Marvel published the title first; Swayze-a 18 36 54 105 165 225
2-4: 3-Swayze-a. 4-Powell-a 12 24 36 67 94 120

TRUE CRIME CASES (...From Official Police Files)
St. John Publishing Co.: 1951 (25¢, 100 pg. Giant)

nn-Matt Baker-c 77 154 231 493 847 1200

TRUE CRIME COMICS (Also see Complete Book of...)
Magazine Village: No. 2, May, 1947; No. 3, July-Aug, 1948 - No. 6, June-July, 1949; V2#1, Aug-Sept, 1949 (52 pgs.)

2-Jack Cole-c/a; used in **SOTI**, pgs. 81,82 plus illo. "A sample of the injury-to-eye motif" & illo. "Dragging living people to death"; used in **POP**, pg. 105; "Murder, Morphine and Me" classic drug propaganda story used by N.Y. Legis. Comm.
239 478 717 1530 2615 3700
3-Classic Cole-c/a; drug story with hypo, opium den & with drawing addict
168 336 504 1075 1838 2600
4-Jack Cole-c/a; c-taken from a story panel in #3 (r-(2) **SOTI** & **POP** stories/#2?) 116 232 348 742 1271 1800
5-Jack Cole-c, Marijuana racket story (Canadian ed. w/cover similar to #3 exists w/out drug story) 81 162 243 518 884 1250
6-Not a reprint, original story (Canadian ed. reprints #4 w/different coloring on-c)
68 136 204 435 743 1050
V2#1-Used in **SOTI**, pgs. 81,82 & illo. "Dragging living people to death"; Toth, Wood (3 pgs.), Roussos-a; Cole-r from #2 113 226 339 718 1234 1750
NOTE: *V2#1 was reprinted in Canada as V2#9 (12/49); same-c & contents minus Wood-a.*

TRUE FAITH
Fleetway: 1990 ($9.95, graphic novel)

nn-Garth Ennis scripts 2 4 6 12 16 20
Reprinted by DC/Vertigo ('97, $12.95) 13.00

TRUE GHOST STORIES (See Ripley's...)

True Love Pictorial #11 © STJ

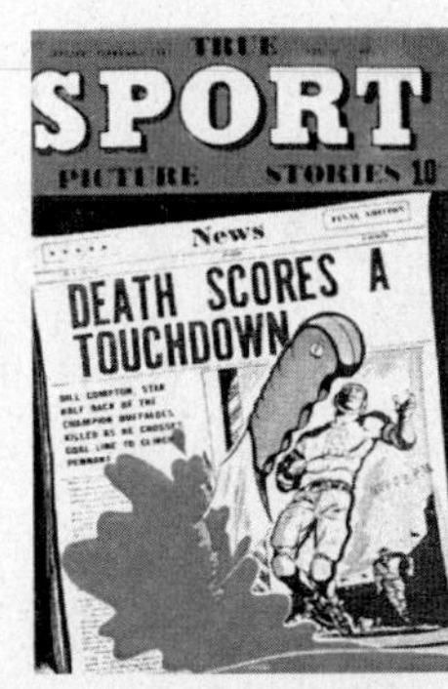

True Sport Picture Stories V3 #11 © S&S

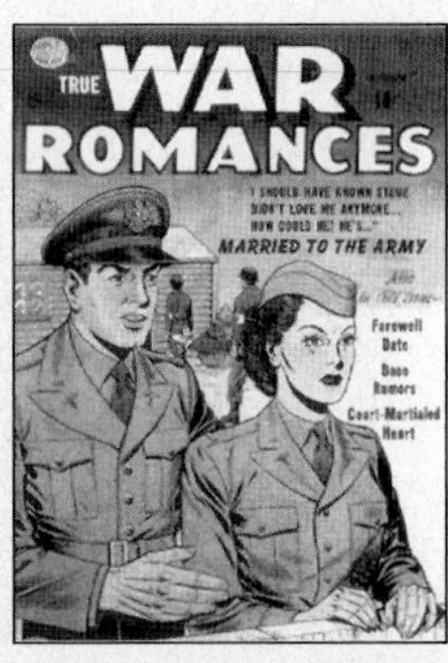

True War Romances #2 © QUA

	GD 2.0	VG 4.0	FN 6.0	VF 8.0	VF/NM 9.0	NM- 9.2

TRUE LIFE ROMANCES (...Romance on cover)
Ajax/Farrell Publications: Dec, 1955 - No. 3, Aug, 1956

1	14	28	42	82	121	160
2	10	20	30	56	76	95
3-Disbrow-a	11	22	33	60	83	105

TRUE LIFE SECRETS
Romantic Love Stories/Charlton: Mar-April, 1951 - No. 28, Sept, 1955; No. 29, Jan, 1956

1-Photo-c begin, end #3?	20	40	60	117	189	260
2	13	26	39	72	101	130
3-11,13-19:	11	22	33	62	86	110
12-"I Was An Escort Girl" story	14	28	42	82	121	160
20-22,24-29: 25-Last precode (3/55)	10	20	30	56	76	95
23-Classic-c	26	52	78	154	252	350

TRUE LIFE TALES (Formerly Mitzi's Romances #8?)
Marvel Comics (CCC): No. 8, Oct, 1949 - No. 2, Jan, 1950 (52 pgs.)

8(#1, 10/49), 2-Both have photo-c	15	30	45	84	127	170

TRUE LIVES OF THE FABULOUS KILLJOYS
Dark Horse Comics: Jun, 2013 - No. 6, Jan, 2014 ($3.99)

1-6-Gerald Way & Shaun Simon-s/Becky Cloonan-a; covers by Cloonan & Bá						4.00

TRUE LOVE
Eclipse Comics: Jan, 1986 - No. 2, Jan, 1986 ($2.00, Baxter paper)

1-Love stories reprinted from pre-code Standard Comics; Toth-a(p); Dave Stevens-c	1	3	4	6	8	10
2-Toth-a; Mayo-a						4.00

TRUE LOVE CONFESSIONS
Premier Magazines: May, 1954 - No. 11, Jan, 1956

1-Marijuana story	20	40	60	117	189	260
2	13	26	39	74	105	135
3-11	12	24	36	67	94	120

TRUE LOVE PICTORIAL
St. John Publishing Co.: Dec, 1952 - No. 11, Aug, 1954

1-Only photo-c	34	68	102	204	332	460
2-Baker-c/a	84	168	252	538	919	1300
3-5(All 25¢, 100 pgs.): 4-Signed story by Estrada. 5-(4/53)-Formerly Teen-Age Temptations; Kubert-a in #3; Baker-c/a in #3-5	119	238	357	762	1306	1850
6,7: Baker-c/a; signed stories by Estrada	71	142	213	454	777	1100
8,10,11-Baker-c/a	71	142	213	454	777	1100
9-Baker-c	63	126	189	403	689	975

TRUE LOVE PROBLEMS AND ADVICE ILLUSTRATED (Becomes Romance Stories of True Love No. 45 on)
McCombs/Harvey Publ./Home Comics: June, 1949 - No. 6, Apr, 1950; No. 7, Jan, 1951 - No. 44, Mar, 1957

V1#1	15	30	45	90	140	190
2-Elias-c	10	20	30	54	72	90
3-10: 3,4,7-9-Elias-c	8	16	24	42	54	65
11-13,15-23,25-31: 31-Last pre-code (1/55)	7	14	21	35	43	50
14,24-Rape scene	8	16	24	40	50	60
32-37,39-44	6	12	18	29	36	42
38-S&K-c	9	18	27	52	69	85

NOTE: ***Powell** a-1, 2, 7-14, 17-25, 28, 29, 33, 40, 41. #3 has True Love... on inside.*

TRUE MOVIE AND TELEVISION (Part teenage magazine)
Toby Press: Aug, 1950 - No. 3, Nov, 1950; No. 4, Mar, 1951 (52 pgs.)(1-3: 10¢)

1-Elizabeth Taylor photo-c; Gene Autry, Shirley Temple app.	71	142	213	454	777	1100
2-(9/50)-Janet Leigh/Liz Taylor/Ava Gardner & others photo-c; Frazetta John Wayne illo from J.Wayne Adv. Comics #2 (4/50)	52	104	156	328	552	775
3-June Allyson photo-c; Montgomery Cliff, Esther Williams, Andrews Sisters app; Li'l Abner featured; Sadie Hawkins' Day	34	68	102	204	332	460
4-Jane Powell photo-c (15¢)	22	44	66	130	213	295

NOTE: *16 pgs. in color, rest movie material in black & white.*

TRUE SECRETS (Formerly Our Love?)
Marvel (IPS)/Atlas Comics (MPI) #4 on: No. 3, Mar, 1950; No. 4, Feb, 1951 - No. 40, Sept, 1956

3 (52 pgs.)(IPS one-shot)`	21	42	63	122	199	275
4,5,7-10	14	28	42	82	121	160
6,22-Everett-a	15	30	45	88	137	185
11-20	14	28	42	76	108	140
21,23-28: 24-Colletta-c. 28-Last pre-code (2/55)	13	26	39	72	101	130
29-40: 34,36-Colletta-a	12	24	36	67	94	120

TRUE SPORT PICTURE STORIES (Formerly Sport Comics)
Street & Smith Publications: V1#5, Feb, 1942 - V5#2, July-Aug, 1949

V1#5-Joe DiMaggio-c/story	37	74	111	218	354	490
6-12 (1942-43): 12-Jack Dempsey story	21	42	63	122	199	275
V2#1-12 (1943-45): 7-Stan Musial-c/story; photo story of the New York Yankees	20	40	60	115	185	255
V3#1-12 (1946-47): 7-Joe DiMaggio, Stan Musial, Bob Feller & others back from the armed service story. 8-Billy Conn vs. Joe Louis-c/story	19	38	57	111	176	240
V4#1-12 (1947-49), V5#1,2: v4#8-Joe Louis on-c	18	36	54	105	165	225

NOTE: ***Powell** a-V3#10, V4#1-4, 6-8, 10-12; V5#1, 2; c-V3#10-12, V4#2-7, 9-12. **Ravielli** c-V5#2.*

TRUE STORIES OF ROMANCE
Fawcett Publications: Jan, 1950 - No. 3, May, 1950 (All photo-c)

1	15	30	45	84	127	170
2,3: 3-Marcus Swayze-a	11	22	33	62	86	110

TRUE STORY OF JESSE JAMES, THE (See Jesse James, Four Color 757)

TRUE SWEETHEART SECRETS
Fawcett Publs.: 5/50; No. 2, 7/50; No. 3, 1951(nd); No. 4, 9/51 - No. 11, 1/53 (All photo-c)

1-Photo-c; Debbie Reynolds?	17	34	51	98	154	210
2-Wood-a (11 pgs.)	20	40	60	114	182	250
3-11: 4,5-Powell-a. 8-Marcus Swayze-a. 11-Evans-a	13	26	39	72	101	130

TRUE TALES OF LOVE (Formerly Secret Story Romances)
Atlas Comics (TCI): No. 22, April, 1956 - No. 31, Sept, 1957

22	14	28	42	80	115	150
23-24,26-31-Colletta-a in most:	10	20	30	58	79	100
25-Everett-a; Colletta-a	11	22	33	62	86	110

TRUE TALES OF ROMANCE
Fawcett Publications: No. 4, June, 1950

4-Photo-c	11	22	33	62	86	110

TRUE 3-D
Harvey Publications: Dec, 1953 - No. 2, Feb, 1954 (25¢)(Both came with 2 pair of glasses)

1-Nostrand, Powell-a	5	10	15	35	55	75
2-Powell-a	6	12	18	37	59	80

NOTE: *Many copies of #1 surfaced in 1984.*

TRUE-TO-LIFE ROMANCES (Formerly Guns Against Gangsters)
Star Publ.: #8, 11-12/49; #9, 1-2/50; #3, 4/50 - #5, 9/50; #6, 1/51 - #23, 10/54

8(#1, 1949)	32	64	96	192	314	435
9(#2),4-10	23	46	69	136	223	310
3-Janet Leigh/Glenn Ford photo on-c plus true life story of each	24	48	72	144	237	330
11,22,23	21	42	63	124	202	280
12-14,17-21-Disbrow-a	22	44	66	132	216	300
15,16-Wood & Disbrow-a in each	24	48	72	144	237	330

NOTE: ***Kamen** a-13. **Kamen/Feldstein** a-14. All have **L.B. Cole** covers.*

TRUE WAR EXPERIENCES
Harvey Publications: Aug, 1952 - No. 4, Dec, 1952

1-Korean War	8	16	24	51	96	140
2-4	5	10	15	32	51	70

TRUE WAR ROMANCES (Becomes Exotic Romances #22 on)
Quality Comics Group: Sept, 1952 - No. 21, June, 1955

1-Photo-c	18	36	54	103	162	220
2-(10/52)	11	22	33	62	86	110
3-10: 3-(12/52). 8,9-Whitney-a	10	20	30	56	76	95
11-21: 20-Last precode (4/55). 14-Whitney-a	9	18	27	52	69	85

TRUE WAR STORIES (See Ripley's...)

TRUE WESTERN (True Adventures #3)
Marvel Comics (MMC): Dec, 1949 - No. 2, March, 1950

1-Photo-c; Billy The Kid story	18	36	54	103	162	220
2-Alan Ladd photo-c	20	40	60	117	189	260

TRUMP
HMH Publishing Co.: Jan, 1957 - No. 2, Mar, 1957 (50¢, magazine)

1-Harvey Kurtzman satire	27	54	81	158	259	360
2-Harvey Kurtzman satire	21	42	63	122	199	275

NOTE: ***Davis, Elder, Heath, Jaffee** art-#1,2; **Wood** a-1. Article by Mel Brooks in #2.*

TRUMPETS WEST (See Luke Short, Four Color #875)

TRUTH ABOUT CRIME (See Fox Giants)

Tuff Ghosts Starring Spooky #23 © HARV

Tuffy #8 © STD

Turok (2017 series) #1 © RH

TRUTH ABOUT MOTHER GOOSE (See Mother Goose, Four Color #862)

TRUTH BEHIND THE TRIAL OF CARDINAL MINDSZENTY, THE (See Cardinal Mindszenty in the Promotional Comics section))

TRUTHFUL LOVE (Formerly Youthful Love)
Youthful Magazines: No. 2, July, 1950

	GD 2.0	VG 4.0	FN 6.0	VF 8.0	VF/NM 9.0	NM- 9.2
2-Ingrid Bergman's true life story	15	30	45	84	127	170

TRUTH RED, WHITE & BLACK
Marvel Comics: Jan, 2003 - No. 6 ($3.50, limited series)

	GD 2.0	VG 4.0	FN 6.0	VF 8.0	VF/NM 9.0	NM- 9.2
1-Kyle Baker-a/Robert Morales-s; the testing of Captain America's super-soldier serum						3.50
2-7: 3-Isaiah Bradley 1st dons the Captain America costume						3.50
TPB (2004, $17.99) r/series						18.00

TRY-OUT WINNER BOOK
Marvel Comics: Mar, 1988

	GD 2.0	VG 4.0	FN 6.0	VF 8.0	VF/NM 9.0	NM- 9.2
1-Spider-Man vs. Doc Octopus						5.00

TSR WORLD (...Annual on cover only)
DC Comics: 1990 ($3.95, 84 pgs.)

	GD 2.0	VG 4.0	FN 6.0	VF 8.0	VF/NM 9.0	NM- 9.2
1-Advanced D&D, ForgottenRealms, Dragonlance & 1st app. Spelljammer						4.00

TSUNAMI GIRL
Image Comics: 1999 - No. 3, 1999 ($2.95)

	GD 2.0	VG 4.0	FN 6.0	VF 8.0	VF/NM 9.0	NM- 9.2
1-3-Sorayama-c/Paniccia-s/a						3.00

TUBBY (See Marge's...)

TUFF GHOSTS STARRING SPOOKY
Harvey Publications: July, 1962 - No. 39, Nov, 1970; No. 40, Sept, 1971 - No. 43, Oct, 1972

	GD 2.0	VG 4.0	FN 6.0	VF 8.0	VF/NM 9.0	NM- 9.2
1-12¢ issues begin	11	22	33	76	163	250
2-5	6	12	18	41	76	110
6-10	5	10	15	30	50	70
11-20	4	8	12	23	37	50
21-30: 29-Hot Stuff/Spooky team-up story	3	6	9	16	23	30
31-39,43	2	4	6	13	18	22
40-42: 52 pg. Giants	3	6	9	14	20	25

TUFFY
Standard Comics: No. 5, July, 1949 - No. 9, Oct, 1950

	GD 2.0	VG 4.0	FN 6.0	VF 8.0	VF/NM 9.0	NM- 9.2
5-All by Sid Hoff	9	18	27	50	65	80
6-9	7	14	21	35	43	50

TUFFY TURTLE
I. W. Enterprises: No date

	GD 2.0	VG 4.0	FN 6.0	VF 8.0	VF/NM 9.0	NM- 9.2
1-Reprint	2	4	6	8	11	14

TUG & BUSTER
Art & Soul Comics: Nov, 1995 - No. 7, Feb, 1998 ($2.95, B&W, bi-monthly)

	GD 2.0	VG 4.0	FN 6.0	VF 8.0	VF/NM 9.0	NM- 9.2
1-7: Marc Hempel-c/a/scripts						3.00
1-(Image Comics, 8/98, $2.95, B&W)						3.00

TUKI
Cartoon Books: Jul, 2014 - Present ($3.99)

	GD 2.0	VG 4.0	FN 6.0	VF 8.0	VF/NM 9.0	NM- 9.2
1-4-Jeff Smith-s/a/c; story reads sideways						4.00

TURF
Image Comics: Apr, 2010 - No. 2 ($2.99, limited series)

	GD 2.0	VG 4.0	FN 6.0	VF 8.0	VF/NM 9.0	NM- 9.2
1,2-Jonathan Ross-s/Tommy Lee Edwards-a						3.00

TUROK
Acclaim Comics: Mar, 1998 - No. 4, Jun, 1998 ($2.50)

	GD 2.0	VG 4.0	FN 6.0	VF 8.0	VF/NM 9.0	NM- 9.2
1-4-Nicieza-s/Kayanan-a						3.00
..., Child of Blood 1 (1/98, $3.95) Nicieza-s/Kayanan-a						4.00
... Evolution 1 (8/02, $2.50) Nicieza-s/Kayanan-a						3.00
..., Redpath 1 (10/97, $3.95) Nicieza-s/Kayanan-a						4.00
... / Shadowman 1 (2/99, $3.95) Priest-s/Broome & Jimenez-a						4.00
...: Spring Break in the Lost Land 1 (7/97, $3.95) Nicieza-s/Kayanan-a						4.00
...: Tales of the Lost Land 1 (4/98, $3.95)						4.00
...: The Empty Souls 1 (4/97, $3.95) Nicieza-s/Kayanan-a; variant-c						4.00

TUROK (Volume1) (Also see Sovereigns and Magnus)
Dynamite Entertainment: 2017 - No. 5, 2017 ($3.99)

	GD 2.0	VG 4.0	FN 6.0	VF 8.0	VF/NM 9.0	NM- 9.2
1-5: 1-Wendig-s/Sarraseca-a; Doctor Spektor back-up serial with other Sovereigns titles						4.00

TUROK, DINOSAUR HUNTER (See Magnus Robot Fighter #12 & Archer & Armstrong #2)
Valiant/Acclaim Comics: June, 1993 - No. 47, Aug, 1996 ($2.50)

	GD 2.0	VG 4.0	FN 6.0	VF 8.0	VF/NM 9.0	NM- 9.2
1-($3.50)-Chromium & foil-c						4.00
1-Gold foil-c variant						15.00
0, 2-47: 4-Andar app. 5-Death of Andar. 7-9-Truman/Glanzman-a. 11-Bound-in trading card. 16-Chaos Effect						3.00
Yearbook 1 (1994, $3.95, 52 pgs.)						4.00

TUROK: DINOSAUR HUNTER
Dynamite Entertainment: 2014 - No. 12, 2015 ($3.99)

	GD 2.0	VG 4.0	FN 6.0	VF 8.0	VF/NM 9.0	NM- 9.2
1-12: 1-5-New version; Greg Pak-s/Mirko Colak-a; Sears-c. 6-8-Miyazawa-a						4.00
1-12-Variant-c by Jae Lee						4.00

TUROK, SON OF STONE (See Dan Curtis, Golden Comics Digest #31, Space Western #45 & March of Comics #378, 399, 408)
Dell Publ. Co. #1-29(9/62)/Gold Key #30(12/62)-85(7/73)/Gold Key or Whitman #86(9/73)-125(1/80)/Whitman #126(3/81) on: No. 596, 12/54 - No. 29, 9/62; No. 30, 12/62 - No. 91, 7/74; No. 92, 9/74 - No. 125, 1/80; No. 126, 3/81 - No. 130, 4/82

	GD 2.0	VG 4.0	FN 6.0	VF 8.0	VF/NM 9.0	NM- 9.2
Four Color 596 (12/54)(#1)-1st app./origin Turok & Andar; dinosaur-c. Created by Matthew H. Murphy; written by Alberto Giolitti	82	164	246	656	1478	2300
Four Color 656 (10/55)(#2)-1st mention of Lanok	35	70	105	252	564	875
3(3-5/56)-5: 3-Cave men	21	42	63	147	324	500
6-10: 8-Dinosaur of the deep; Turok enters Lost Valley; series begins. 9-Paul S. Newman-s (most issues thru end)	15	30	45	103	227	350
11-20: 17-Prehistoric Pygmies	11	22	33	76	163	250
21-29	9	18	27	58	114	170
30-1st Gold Key. 30-33-Painted back-c.	9	18	27	59	117	175
31-Drug use story	9	18	27	58	114	170
32-40	7	14	21	46	86	125
41-50	6	12	18	37	66	95
51-57,59,60	5	10	15	34	60	85
58-Flying Saucer c/story	5	10	15	35	63	90
61-70: 62-12¢ & 15¢ covers. 63,68-Line drawn-c	5	10	15	30	50	70
71-84: 84-Origin & 1st app. Hutec	4	8	12	27	44	60
85-99: 93-r-c/#19 w/changes. 94-r-c/#28 w/changes. 97-r-c/#31 w/changes. 98-r/#58 w/o spaceship & spacemen on-c. 99-r-c/#52 w/changes.	4	8	12	23	37	50
100	4	8	12	28	47	65
101-129: 114,115-(52 pgs.). 129(2/82)	4	8	12	23	37	50
130(4/82)-Last issue	5	10	15	35	63	90
Giant 1(30031-611) (11/66)-Slick-c; r/#10-12 & 16 plus cover to #11	9	18	27	63	126	190
Giant 1-Same as above but with paper-c	10	20	30	67	141	210

NOTE: *Most painted-c; line-drawn #63 & 130.* ***Alberto Gioletti*** *a-24-27, 30-119, 123; painted-c No. 30-129.* ***Sparling*** *a-117, 120-130. Reprints-#36, 54, 57, 75, 112, 114(1/3), 115(1/3), 118, 121, 125, 127(1/3), 128, 129(1/3), 130(1/3), Giant 1. Cover r-93, 94, 97-99, 126(all different from original covers.*

TUROK, SON OF STONE
Dark Horse Comics: Oct, 2010 - No. 4, Oct, 2011 ($3.50)

	GD 2.0	VG 4.0	FN 6.0	VF 8.0	VF/NM 9.0	NM- 9.2
1-4: 1-Shooter-s/Francisco-a/Swanland-c; back-up reprint of debut in Four Color 596						3.50
1-Variant-c by Francisco						3.50

TUROK THE HUNTED
Valiant/Acclaim Comics: Mar, 1995 - No. 2, Apr, 1995 ($2.50, limited series)

	GD 2.0	VG 4.0	FN 6.0	VF 8.0	VF/NM 9.0	NM- 9.2
1,2-Mike Deodato-a(p); price omitted on #1						3.00

TUROK THE HUNTED
Acclaim Comics (Valiant): Feb, 1996 - No. 2, Mar, 1996 ($2.50, limited series)

	GD 2.0	VG 4.0	FN 6.0	VF 8.0	VF/NM 9.0	NM- 9.2
1,2-Mike Grell story						3.00

TUROK, TIMEWALKER
Acclaim Comics (Valiant): Aug, 1997 - No. 2, Sept, 1997 ($2.50, limited series)

	GD 2.0	VG 4.0	FN 6.0	VF 8.0	VF/NM 9.0	NM- 9.2
1,2-Nicieza story						3.00

TUROK 2 (Magazine)
Acclaim Comics: Oct, 1998 ($4.99, magazine size)

	GD 2.0	VG 4.0	FN 6.0	VF 8.0	VF/NM 9.0	NM- 9.2
...Seeds of Evil-Nicieza-s/Broome & Benjamin-a; origin back-up story						5.00
#2 Adon's Curse -Mack painted-c/Broome & Benjamin-a; origin pt. 2						5.00

TUROK 3: SHADOW OF OBLIVION
Acclaim Comics: Sept, 2000 ($4.95, one-shot)

	GD 2.0	VG 4.0	FN 6.0	VF 8.0	VF/NM 9.0	NM- 9.2
1-Includes pin-up gallery						5.00

TURTLE SOUP
Mirage Studios: Sept, 1987 ($2.00, 76 pgs., B&W, one-shot)

	GD 2.0	VG 4.0	FN 6.0	VF 8.0	VF/NM 9.0	NM- 9.2
1-Featuring Teenage Mutant Ninja Turtles	1	2	3	5	6	8

TURTLE SOUP
Mirage Studios: Nov, 1991 - No. 4, 1992 ($2.50, limited series, coated paper)

	GD 2.0	VG 4.0	FN 6.0	VF 8.0	VF/NM 9.0	NM- 9.2
1-4: Features the Teenage Mutant Ninja Turtles						4.00

TV CASPER & COMPANY
Harvey Publications: Aug, 1963 - No. 46, April, 1974 (25¢ Giants)

TV Stars #3 © H-B

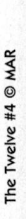

The Twelve #4 © MAR

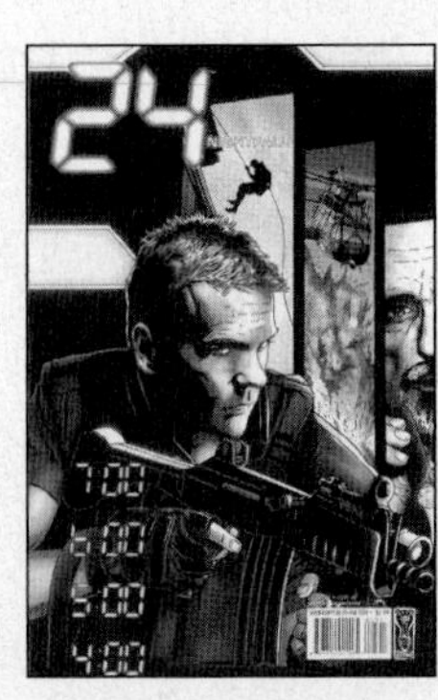

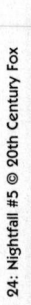

24: Nightfall #5 © 20th Century Fox

	GD 2.0	VG 4.0	FN 6.0	VF 8.0	VF/NM 9.0	NM- 9.2
1- 68 pg. Giants begin; Casper, Little Audrey, Baby Huey, Herman & Catnip, Buzzy the Crow begin	10	20	30	66	138	210
2-5	6	12	18	37	66	95
6-10	4	8	12	28	47	65
11-20	4	8	12	23	37	50
21-31: 31-Last 68 pg. issue	3	6	9	17	26	35
32-46: All 52 pgs.	3	6	9	16	23	30

NOTE: *Many issues contain reprints.*

TV FUNDAY FUNNIES (See Famous TV...)

TV FUNNIES (See New Funnies)

TV FUNTIME (See Little Audrey)

TV LAUGHOUT (See Archie's...)

TV SCREEN CARTOONS (Formerly Real Screen)
National Periodical Publ.: No. 129, July-Aug, 1959 - No. 138, Jan-Feb, 1961

	GD 2.0	VG 4.0	FN 6.0	VF 8.0	VF/NM 9.0	NM- 9.2
129-138 (Scarce) Fox and the Crow	6	12	18	37	66	95

TV STARS (TV) (Newsstand sales only)
Marvel Comics Group: Aug, 1978 - No. 4, Feb, 1979 (Hanna-Barbera)

	GD 2.0	VG 4.0	FN 6.0	VF 8.0	VF/NM 9.0	NM- 9.2
1-Great Grape Ape app.	3	6	9	17	26	35
2,4: 4-Top Cat app.	3	6	9	15	22	28
3-Toth-c/a; Dave Stevens inks	3	6	9	16	24	32

TV TEENS (Formerly Ozzie & Babs; Rock and Rollo #14 on)
Charlton Comics: V1#14, Feb, 1954 - V2#13, July, 1956

	GD 2.0	VG 4.0	FN 6.0	VF 8.0	VF/NM 9.0	NM- 9.2
V1#14 (#1)-Ozzie & Babs	12	24	36	67	94	120
15 (#2)	8	16	24	42	54	65
V2#3(6/54) - 6-Don Winslow	8	16	24	40	50	60
7-13-Mopsy. 8(7/55). 9-Paper dolls	7	14	21	37	46	55

TWEETY AND SYLVESTER (1st Series) (TV) (Also see Looney Tunes and Merrie Melodies)
Dell Publishing Co.: No. 406, June, 1952 - No. 37, June-Aug, 1962

	GD 2.0	VG 4.0	FN 6.0	VF 8.0	VF/NM 9.0	NM- 9.2
Four Color 406 (#1)	12	24	36	83	182	280
Four Color 489,524	8	16	24	51	96	140
4 (3-5/54) - 20	5	10	15	35	63	90
21-37	5	10	15	31	53	75

(See March of Comics #421, 433, 445, 457, 469, 481)

TWEETY AND SYLVESTER (2nd Series)(See Kite Fun Book)
Gold Key No. 1-102/Whitman No. 103 on: Nov, 1963; No. 2, Nov, 1965 - No. 121, Jun, 1984

	GD 2.0	VG 4.0	FN 6.0	VF 8.0	VF/NM 9.0	NM- 9.2
1	6	12	18	38	69	100
2-10	3	6	9	19	30	40
11-30	3	6	9	14	20	25
31-50	2	4	6	9	12	15
51-70	1	3	4	6	8	10
71-102	1	2	3	5	6	8
103,104 (Whitman)	1	3	4	6	8	10
105(9/80),106(10/80),107(12/80) 3-pack only	4	8	12	28	47	65
108-116: 113(2/82),114(2-3/82),115(3/82),116(4/82)	2	4	6	8	10	12
117-121 (All # 90094 on-c; nd, nd code): 117(6/83). 118(7/83). 119(2/84)-r(1/3). 120(5/84). 121(6/84)	3	6	9	17	26	35
Digest nn (Charlton/Xerox Pub., 1974) (low print run)	3	6	9	16	23	30
Mini Comic No. 1(1976, 3-1/4x6-1/2")	1	3	4	6	8	10

TWELVE, THE (Golden Age Timely heroes)
Marvel Comics: No. 0; 2008; No. 1, Mar, 2008 - No. 12, Jun, 2012 ($2.99, limited series)

0-Rockman, Laughing Mask & Phantom Reporter intro. stories (1940s); series preview 4.00
1/2 (2008, $3.99) r/early app. of Fiery Mask, Mister E and Rockman; Weston-c 5.00
1-12-Straczynski-s/Weston-a; Timely heroes re-surface in the present 4.00
... Must Have 1 (4/12, $3.99) r/#7,8 4.00
...: Spearhead 1 (5/10, $3.99) Weston-s/a; Phantom Reporter in WW2; Invaders app. 5.00

12 O'CLOCK HIGH (TV)
Dell Publishing Co.: Jan-Mar, 1965 - No. 2, Apr-June, 1965 (Photo-c)

	GD 2.0	VG 4.0	FN 6.0	VF 8.0	VF/NM 9.0	NM- 9.2
1- Sinnott-a	5	10	15	34	60	85
2	4	8	12	28	47	65

TWELVE REASONS TO DIE
Black Mask Studios: 2013 - No. 6, 2014 ($3.50)

1-6: 1-Five covers; created by Ghostface Killah 3.50

2099 A.D.
Marvel Comics: May, 1995 ($3.95, one-shot)

1-Acetate-c by Quesada & Palmiotti 4.00

2099 APOCALYPSE
Marvel Comics: Dec, 1995 ($4.95, one-shot)

1-Chromium wraparound-c; Ellis script 5.00

2099 GENESIS
Marvel Comics: Jan, 1996 ($4.95, one-shot)

1-Chromium wraparound-c; Ellis script 5.00

2099 MANIFEST DESTINY
Marvel Comics: Mar, 1998 ($5.99, one-shot)

1-Origin of Fantastic Four 2099; intro Moon Knight 2099 6.00

2099 UNLIMITED
Marvel Comics: Sept, 1993 - No. 10, 1996 ($3.95, 68 pgs.)

1-10: 1-1st app. Hulk 2099 & begins. 1-3-Spider-Man 2099 app. 9-Joe Kubert-c; Len Wein & Nancy Collins scripts 4.00

2099 WORLD OF DOOM SPECIAL
Marvel Comics: May, 1995 ($2.25, one-shot)

1-Doom's "Contract w/America" 3.00

2099 WORLD OF TOMORROW
Marvel Comics: Sept, 1996 - No. 8, Apr, 1997 ($2.50) (Replaces 2099 titles)

1-8: 1-Wraparound-c. 2-w/bound-in card. 4,5-Phalanx 3.00

21
Image Comics (Top Cow Productions): Feb, 1996 - No. 3, Apr, 1996 ($2.50)

1-3: Len Wein scripts 3.00
1-Variant-c 3.00

21 DOWN
DC Comics (WildStorm): Nov, 2002 - No. 12, Nov, 2003 ($2.95)

1-12: 1-Palmiotti & Gray-s/Saiz-a/Jusko-c 3.00
...: The Conduit (2003, $19.95, TPB) r/#1-7; intro. by Garth Ennis 20.00

24 (Based on TV series)
IDW Publishing: Apr, 2014 - No. 5, Aug, 2014 ($3.99, limited series)

1-5-Brisson-s/Gaydos-a; multiple covers on each 4.00

24 (Based on TV series)
IDW Publishing: July, 2004 - July, 2005 ($6.99/$7.49, square-bound, one-shots)

...: Midnight Sun (7/05, $7.49) J.C. Vaughn & Mark Haynes-s; Renato Guedes-a 7.50
...: One Shot (7/04, $6.99)-Jack Bauer's first day on the job at CTU; Vaughn & Haynes-s; Guedes-a 7.50
...: Stories (1/05, $7.49) Manny Clark-a; Vaughn & Haynes-s 7.50

24: LEGACY – RULES OF ENGAGEMENT (Based on TV series)
IDW Publishing: Apr, 2017 - No. 5, Aug, 2017 ($3.99, limited series)

1-5-Early days of Eric Carter in DC & Iraq; Farnsworth-s/Fuso-a; art and photo-c 4.00

24: NIGHTFALL (Based on TV series)
IDW Publishing: Nov, 2006 - No. 5, Mar, 2007 ($3.99, limited series)

1-5-Two years before Season One; Vaughn & Haynes-s; Diaz-a; two covers 4.00

28 DAYS LATER (Based on the 2002 movie)
Boom! Studios: July, 2009 - No. 24, Jun, 2011 ($3.99)

1-24: 1-Covers by Bradstreet and Phillips 4.00

2020 VISIONS
DC Comics (Vertigo): May, 1997 - No. 12, Apr, 1998 ($2.25, limited series)

1-12-Delano-s: 1-3-Quitely-a. 4-"la tormenta"-Pleece-a 3.00

20,000 LEAGUES UNDER THE SEA (Movie)(See King Classics, Movie Comics & Power Record Comics)
Dell Publishing Co.: No. 614, Feb, 1955 (Disney)

	GD 2.0	VG 4.0	FN 6.0	VF 8.0	VF/NM 9.0	NM- 9.2
Four Color 614-Movie, painted-c	8	16	24	56	108	160

TWICE TOLD TALES (See Movie Classics)

TWILIGHT
DC Comics: 1990 - No. 3, 1991 ($4.95, 52 pgs, lim. series, squarebound, mature)

1-3: Tommy Tomorrow app; Chaykin scripts, Garcia-Lopez-c/a 5.00

TWILIGHT CHILDREN, THE
DC Comics (Vertigo): Dec, 2015 - No. 4, Mar, 2016 ($4.99, limited series)

1-4-Gilbert Hernandez-s/Darwyn Cooke-a/c 5.00

TWILIGHT EXPERIMENT
DC Comics (WildStorm): Apr, 2004 - No. 6, Sept, 2005 ($2.95, limited series)

1-6-Gray & Palmiotti-s/Santacruz-a 3.00
TPB (2011, $17.99) r/#1-6 18.00

TWILIGHT GUARDIAN (Also see Pilot Season: Twilight Guardian)

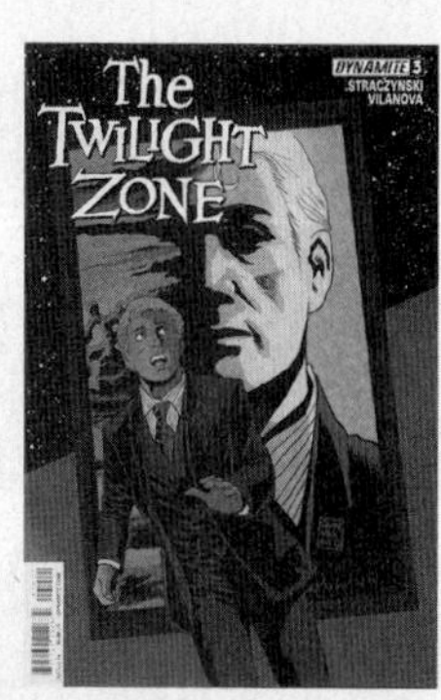

The Twilight Zone (2014 series) #3 © CBS

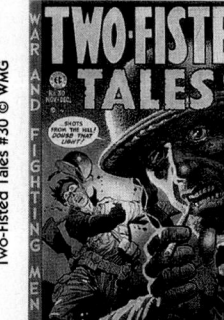

Two-Fisted Tales #30 © WMG

Two-Gun Kid #19 © MAR

	GD 2.0	VG 4.0	FN 6.0	VF 8.0	VF/NM 9.0	NM- 9.2

Image Comics (Top Cow): Jan, 2011 - No. 4, Apr, 2011 ($3.99, limited series)
1-4-Hickman-s/Kotean-a 4.00

TWILIGHT MAN
First Publishing: June, 1989 - No. 4, Sept, 1989 ($2.75, limited series)
1-4 3.00

TWILIGHT ZONE, THE (TV) (See Dan Curtis & Stories From...)
Dell Publishing Co./Gold Key/Whitman No. 92: No. 1173, 3-5/61 - No. 91, 4/79; No. 92, 5/82

	GD	VG	FN	VF	VF/NM	NM-
Four Color 1173 (#1)-Crandall-c/a	18	36	54	128	284	440
Four Color 1288-Crandall/Evans-c/a	10	20	30	69	147	225
01-860-207 (5-7/62-Dell, 15¢)	9	18	27	57	111	165
12-860-210 on-c; 01-860-210 on inside(8-10/62-Dell)-Evans-c/a (3 stories); art by Frazetta & Crandall	8	16	24	54	102	150
1(11/62-Gold Key)-Crandall/Frazetta-a (10 & 11 pgs.); Evans-a	14	28	42	96	211	325
2	7	14	21	49	92	135
3-11: 3(11 pgs.),4(10 pgs.),9-Toth-a	6	12	18	37	66	95
12-15: 12-Williamson-a. 13,15-Crandall-a. 14-Orlando/Crandall/Torres-a	5	10	15	31	53	75
16-20	4	8	12	25	40	55
21-25: 21-Crandall-a(r). 25-Evans/Crandall-a(r); Toth-r/#4; last 12¢ issue	3	6	9	19	30	40
26,27: 26-Flying Saucer-c/story; Crandall, Evans-a(r). 27-Evans-r(2)	3	6	9	18	28	38
28-32: 32-Evans-a(r)	3	6	9	16	24	32
33-51: 43-Celardo-a. 51-Williamson-a	2	4	6	13	18	22
52-70	2	4	6	10	14	18
71-82,86-91: 71-Reprint	2	4	6	8	11	14
83-(52 pgs.)	3	6	9	14	20	25
84-(52 pgs.) Frank Miller's 1st comic book work	10	20	30	64	132	200
85-Frank Miller-a (2nd)	5	10	15	34	60	85
92-(Whitman, 5/82) Last issue; r/#1.	2	4	6	9	13	16
Mini Comic #1(1976, 3-1/4x6-1/2")	2	4	6	8	10	12

NOTE: ***Bolle** a-13(w/**McWilliams**), 50, 55, 57, 59, 77, 78, 80, 83, 84. **McWilliams** a-59, 78, 80, 82, 84. **Miller** a-84, 85. **Orlando** a-15, 19, 20, 22, 23. **Sekowsky** a-3. **Simonson** a-50, 54, 55, 83r. **Weiss** a-39, 79r(#39). (See Mystery Comics Digest 3, 6, 9, 12, 15, 18, 21, 24). Reprints-26(1/3), 71, 73, 79, 83, 84, 86, 92. Painted c-1-91.*

TWILIGHT ZONE, THE (TV)
Now Comics: Nov, 1990 ($2.95); Oct, 1991; V2#1, Nov, 1991 - No. 11, Oct, 1992 ($1.95); V3#1, 1993 - No. 4, 1993 ($2.50)
1-(11/90, $2.95, 52 pgs.)-Direct sale edition; Neal Adams-a, Sienkiewicz-c; Harlan Ellison scripts 5.00
1-(11/90, $1.75)-Newsstand ed. w/N. Adams-c 4.00
1-Prestige Format (10/91, $4.95)-Reprints above with extra Harlan Ellison short story 5.00
1-Collector's Edition (10/91, $2.50)-Non-code approved and polybagged; reprints 11/90 issue; gold logo, 1-Reprint ($2.50)-r/direct sale 11/90 version, 1-Reprint ($2.50)-r/newsstand 11/90 version each... 4.00
V2#1-Direct sale & newsstand ed. w/different-c 3.00
V2#2-8,10-11 3.00
V2#9-($2.95)-3-D Special; polybagged w/glasses & hologram on-c 4.00
V2#9-($4.95)-Prestige Edition; contains 2 extra stories & a different hologram on-c; polybagged w/glasses 5.00
V3#1-4, Anniversary Special 1 (1992, $2.50) 3.00
Annual 1 (4/93, $2.50)-No ads 4.00
...Science Fiction Special (3/93, $3.50) 4.00

TWILIGHT ZONE, THE (TV)
Dynamite Entertainment: 2014 - No. 12, 2015 ($3.99)
1-12-Straczynski-s/Vilanova-a/Francavilla-c 4.00
#1959 (2016, $5.99) Short stories set in 1959; Valiente & Worley-a; Lau-c 6.00
Annual 2014 ($7.99) Three short stories; Rahner-s/Valiente, Malaga, Menna-a 8.00

TWILIGHT ZONE THE SHADOW (TV)
Dynamite Entertainment: 2016 - No. 4, 2016 ($3.99, limited series)
1-4-Avallone-s/Acosta-a/Francavilla-c; Shiwwan Khan app. 4.00

TWILIGHT ZONE, THE: SHADOW & SUBSTANCE (TV)
Dynamite Entertainment: 2015 - No. 4, 2015 ($3.99)
1-4-Rahner-s/Menna-a; multiple covers on each 4.00

TWINKLE COMICS
Spotlight Publishers: May, 1945

	GD	VG	FN	VF	VF/NM	NM-
1	27	54	81	158	259	360

TWIST, THE
Dell Publishing Co.: July-Sept, 1962

	GD	VG	FN	VF	VF/NM	NM-
01-864-209-Painted-c	4	8	12	25	40	55

TWISTED TALES (See Eclipse Graphic Album Series #15)
Pacific Comics/Independent Comics Group (Eclipse) #9,10: 11/82 - No. 8, 5/84; No. 9, 11/84; No. 10, 12/84 (Baxter paper)

	GD	VG	FN	VF	VF/NM	NM-
1-9: 1-B. Jones/Corben-c; Alcala-a; nudity/violence in al. 2-Wrightson-c; Ploog-a						5.00
10-Wrightson painted art; Morrow-a	1	2	3	4	5	7

NOTE: ***Bolton** painted c-4, 6, 7; a-7. **Conrad** a-1, 3, 5; c-1i, 3, 5. **Guice** a-8. **Wildey** a-3.*

TWO BIT THE WACKY WOODPECKER (See Wacky...)
Toby Press: 1951 - No. 3, May, 1953

	GD	VG	FN	VF	VF/NM	NM-
1	12	24	36	69	97	125
2,3	8	16	24	40	50	60

TWO FACE: YEAR ONE
DC Comics: 2008 - No. 2, 2008 ($5.99, squarebound, limited series)
1,2-Origin re-told; Sable-s/Saiz & Haun-a 6.00

TWO-FISTED TALES (Formerly Haunt of Fear #15-17)
(Also see EC Archives • Two-Fisted Tales)
E. C. Comics: No. 18, Nov-Dec, 1950 - No. 41, Feb-Mar, 1955

	GD	VG	FN	VF	VF/NM	NM-
18(#1)-Kurtzman-c	114	228	342	912	1456	2000
19-Kurtzman-c	74	148	222	592	946	1300
20-Kurtzman-c	51	102	153	408	654	900
21,22-Kurtzman-c	41	82	123	328	527	725
23-25-Kurtzman-c	31	62	93	248	399	550
26-29,31-Kurtzman-c. 31-Civil War issue	24	48	72	192	309	425
30-Classic Davis-c	30	60	90	240	383	525
32-34: 33- "Atom Bomb" by Wood	24	48	72	192	309	425
35-Classic Davis Civil War-c/s	31	62	93	248	399	550
36-41	19	38	57	152	246	340
Two-Fisted Annual (1952, 25¢, 132 pgs.)	123	146	369	787	1344	1900
Two-Fisted Annual (1953, 25¢, 132 pgs.)	87	174	261	553	952	1350

NOTE: ***Berg** a-29. **Colan** a-30,39p. **Craig** a-18, 19, 32. **Crandall** a-35, 36. **Davis** a-20-36, 40; c-30, 34, 35, 41, Annual 2. **Estrada** a-30. **Evans** a-34, 40, 41; c-40. **Feldstein** a-18. **Krigstein** a-41. **Kubert** a-32, 33. **Kurtzman** a-18-25; c-18-29, 31, Annual 1. **Severin** a-26, 28, 29, 31, 34-41 (No. 37-39 are all-**Severin** issues); c-36-39. **Severin/Elder** a-19-29, 31, 33, 36. **Wood** a-18-28, 30-35, 41; c-32, 33. Special issues: #26 (ChanJin Reservoir), 31 (Civil War), 35 (Civil War). Canadian reprints known; see Table of Contents. #25-Davis biog. #27-Wood biog. #28-Kurtzman biog.*

TWO-FISTED TALES
Russ Cochran/Gemstone Publishing: Oct, 1992 - No. 24, May, 1998 ($1.50/$2.00/$2.50)
1-24: 1-4r/Two-Fisted Tales #18-21 w/original-c 4.00

TWO-GUN KID (Also see All Western Winners, Best Western, Black Rider, Blaze Carson, Kid Colt, Western Winners, Wild West, & Wild Western)
Marvel/Atlas (MCI No. 1-10/HPC No. 11-59/Marvel No. 60 on): 3/48(No mo.) - No. 10, 11/49; No. 11, 12/53 - No. 59, 4/61; No. 60, 11/62 - No. 92, 3/68; No. 93, 7/70 - No. 136, 4/77

	GD	VG	FN	VF	VF/NM	NM-
1-Two-Gun Kid & his horse Cyclone begin; The Sheriff begins	152	304	456	965	1658	2350
2	57	114	171	362	619	875
3,4: 3-Annie Oakley app.	42	84	126	265	445	625
5-Pre-Black Rider app. (Wint. 48/49); Anti-Wertham editorial (1st?)	43	86	129	271	461	650
6-10(11/49): 8-Blaze Carson app. 9-Black Rider app.	37	74	111	222	361	500
11(12/53)-Black Rider app.; 1st to have Atlas globe on-c; explains how Kid Colt became an outlaw	32	64	96	188	307	425
12-Black Rider app.	27	54	81	158	259	360
13-20: 14-Opium story	23	46	69	136	223	310
21-24,26-29	21	42	63	126	206	285
25,30: 25-Williamson-a (5 pgs.). 30-Williamson/Torres-a (4 pgs.)	22	44	66	132	216	300
31-33,35,37-40	12	24	36	79	170	260
34-Crandall-a	12	24	36	80	173	265
36,41,42,48-Origin in all	12	24	36	82	179	275
43,44,47	11	22	33	73	157	240
45,46-Davis-a	11	22	33	76	163	250
49,50,52,53-Severin-a(2/3) in each	10	20	30	70	150	230
51-Williamson-a (5 pgs.)	11	22	33	76	163	250
54,55,57,59-Severin-a(3) in each. 59-Kirby-a; last 10¢ issue (4/61)	10	20	30	70	150	230
56	11	22	33	73	157	240
58-New origin; Kirby/Ayers-c/a "The Monster of Hidden Valley" cover/story (Kirby monster-c)	28	56	84	202	451	700
60-New origin	57	114	171	456	1028	1600
60-Edition w/handwritten issue number on cover	61	122	183	488	1094	1700

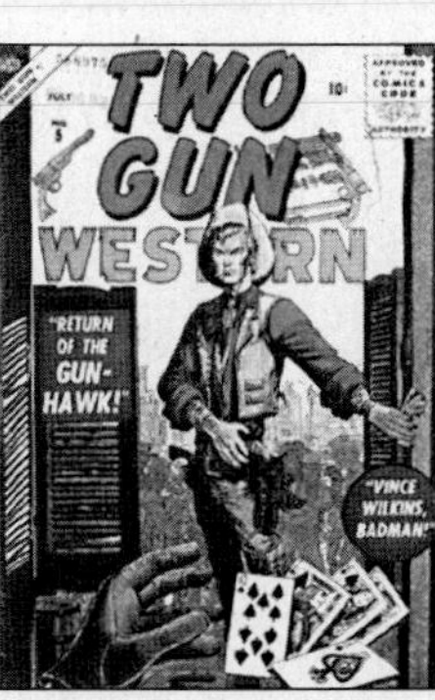

Two-Gun Western #5 © MAR

2001: A Space Odyssey #7 © MAR

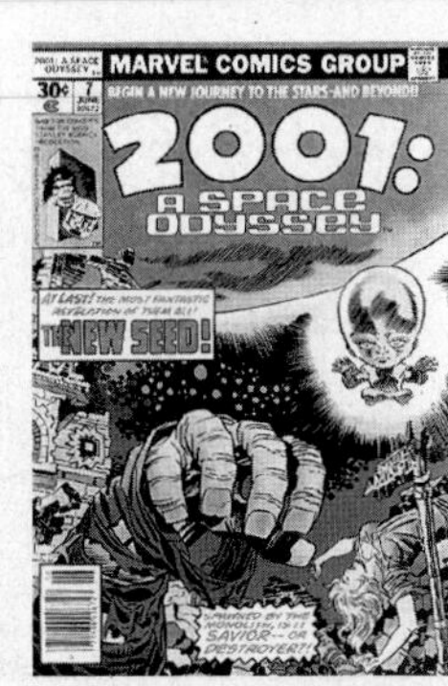

UFO & Outer Space #18 © GK

	GD 2.0	VG 4.0	FN 6.0	VF 8.0	VF/NM 9.0	NM- 9.2
61,62-Kirby-a	13	26	39	89	195	300
63-74: 64-Intro. Boom-Boom	8	16	24	54	102	150
75,76-Kirby-a (reprint)	8	16	24	56	108	160
77-Kirby-a (reprint); Black Panther-esque villain	10	20	30	64	132	200
78-89	5	10	15	31	53	75
90,95-Kirby-a	5	10	15	31	53	75
91,92: 92-Last new story; last 12¢ issue	4	8	12	28	47	65
93,94,96-99	3	6	9	16	23	30
100-Last 15¢-c	3	6	9	16	24	32
101-Origin retold/#58; Kirby-a	3	6	9	16	24	32
102-120-reprints	2	4	6	11	16	20
121-136-reprints. 129-131-(Regular 25¢ editions)	2	4	6	11	16	20
129-131-(30¢-c variants, limited distribution)(4-8/76)	7	14	21	46	86	125

NOTE: ***Ayers** a-13, 24, 26, 27, 63, 66. **Davis** c-45-47. **Drucker** a-23. **Everett** a-82, 91. **Fuje** a-13. **Heath** a-3(2), 4(3), 5(2), 7; c-13, 21, 23, 53. **Keller** a-16, 19, 28, 42. **Kirby** a-54, 55, 57-62, 75-77, 90, 95, 101, 119, 120, 129; c-10, 52, 54-65, 67-72, 74-76, 116. **Maneely** a-20; c-11, 12, 16, 19, 20, 24-28, 30, 35, 41, 42, 49. **Powell** a-38, 102, 104. **Severin** a-9, 29, 51, 55, 57, 99r(3); c-9, 39, 51. **Shores** c-1-8, 11. **Trimpe** c-99. **Tuska** a-11, 12. **Whitney** a-87, 89-92, 98-113, 124, 129; c-87, 89, 91, 113. **Wildey** a-21. **Williamson** a-110r. Kid Colt in #13, 14, 16-21.*

TWO GUN KID: SUNSET RIDERS
Marvel Comics: Nov, 1995 - No. 2, Dec, 1995 ($6.95, squarebound, lim. series)

1,2: Fabian Nicieza scripts in all. 1-Painted-c. 7.00

TWO GUN WESTERN (1st Series) (Formerly Casey Crime Photographer #1-4? or My Love #1-4?)
Marvel/Atlas Comics (MPC): No. 5, Nov, 1950 - No. 14, June, 1952

	GD	VG	FN	VF	VF/NM	NM-
5-The Apache Kid (Intro & origin) & his horse Nightwind begin by Buscema	32	64	96	192	314	435
6-10: 8-Kid Colt, The Texas Kid & his horse Thunder begin?	22	44	66	128	209	290
11-14: 13-Black Rider app.	16	32	48	94	147	200

NOTE: ***Maneely** a-6, 7, 9; c-6, 11-13. **Morrow** a-9. **Romita** a-8. **Wildey** a-8.*

2-GUN WESTERN (2nd Series) (Formerly Billy Buckskin #1-3; Two-Gun Western #5 on)
Atlas Comics (MgPC): No. 4, May, 1956

	GD	VG	FN	VF	VF/NM	NM-
4-Colan, Ditko, Severin, Sinnott-a; Maneely-c	19	38	57	111	176	240

TWO-GUN WESTERN (Formerly 2-Gun Western)
Atlas Comics (MgPC): No. 5, July, 1956 - No. 12, Sept, 1957

	GD	VG	FN	VF	VF/NM	NM-
5-Return of the Gun-Hawk-c/story; Black Rider app.	19	38	57	109	172	235
6,7	15	30	45	85	130	175
8,10,12-Crandall-a	15	30	45	88	137	185
9,11-Williamson-a in both (5 pgs. each)	16	32	48	92	144	195

NOTE: ***Ayers** a-9. **Colan** a-5. **Everett** c-12. **Forgione** a-5, 6. **Kirby** a-12. **Maneely** a-6, 8, 12; c-5, 6, 8, 11. **Morrow** a-9, 10. **Powell** a-7, 11. **Severin** c-10. **Sinnott** a-5. **Wildey** a-9.*

TWO MINUTE WARNING
Ultimate Sports Ent.: 2000 - No. 2 ($3.95, cardstock covers)

1,2-NFL players & Teddy Roosevelt battle evil 4.00

TWO MOUSEKETEERS, THE (See 4-Color #475, 603, 642 under M.G.M.'s...;

TWO ON A GUILLOTINE (See Movie Classics)

TWO-STEP
DC Comics (Cliffhanger): Dec, 2003 - No. 3, Jul, 2004 ($2.95, limited series)

1-3-Warren Ellis-s/Amanda Conner-a 3.00
TPB (2010, $19.99) r/#1-3; sketch pages; script for #1 with B&W art 20.00

2000 A.D. MONTHLY/PRESENTS (Showcase #25 on)
Eagle Comics/Quality Comics No. 5 on: 4/85 - #6, 9/85; 4/86 - #54, 1991 ($1.25-$1.50, Mando paper)

1-6,1-25:1-4 r/British series featuring Judge Dredd; Alan Moore scripts begin.
1-25 ($1.25)-Reprints from British 2000 AD 4.00
26,27/28, 29/30, 31-54: 27/28, 29/30,31-Guice-c 3.00

2001, A SPACE ODYSSEY (Movie) (See adaptation in Treasury edition)
Marvel Comics Group: Dec, 1976 - No. 10, Sept, 1977 (30¢)

	GD	VG	FN	VF	VF/NM	NM-
1-Kirby-c/a in all	3	6	9	19	30	40
2-7,9,10	2	4	6	9	12	15
7,9,10-(35¢-c variants, limited distribution)(6-9/77)	8	16	24	54	102	150
8-Origin/1st app. Machine Man (called Mr. Machine)	5	10	15	33	57	80
8-(35¢-c variant, limited distribution)(6,8/77)	17	34	51	119	265	410
...Treasury 1 ('76, 84 pgs.)-All new Kirby-a	3	6	9	16	23	30

2001 NIGHTS
Viz Premiere Comics: 1990 - No. 10, 1991 ($3.75, B&W, lim. series, mature readers, 84 pgs.)

1-10: Japanese sci-fi. 1-Wraparound-c 5.00

2010 (Movie)
Marvel Comics Group: Apr, 1985 - No. 2, May, 1985

1,2-r/Marvel Super Special movie adaptation. 4.00

TYPHOID (Also see Daredevil)
Marvel Comics: Nov, 1995 - No. 4, Feb, 1996 ($3.95, squarebound, lim. series)

1-4: Van Fleet-c/a 4.00

ÜBER
Avatar Press: No. 0, Mar, 2013 - No. 27, Jul, 2015 ($3.99)

0-27: 0-11-Kieron Gillen-s/Caanan White-a. 12-14-Andrade-a 4.00
... FCBD 2014 (2/14, Free Comic Book Day giveaway) Text synopsis of early storyline 3.00
... Special 1 (3/14, $5.99) Andrade-a 6.00

UFO & ALIEN COMIX
Warren Publishing Co.: Jan, 1978 (B&W magazine, 84 pgs., one-shot)

	GD	VG	FN	VF	VF/NM	NM-
nn-Toth-a, J. Severin-a(r); Pie-s	2	4	6	10	14	18

UFO & OUTER SPACE (Formerly UFO Flying Saucers)
Gold Key: No. 14, June, 1978 - No. 25, Feb, 1980 (All painted covers)

	GD	VG	FN	VF	VF/NM	NM-
14-Reprints UFO Flying Saucers #3	1	3	4	6	8	10
15,16-Reprints	1	3	4	6	8	10
17-25: 17-20-New material. 23-McWilliams-a. 24-(3 pg.-r). 25-Reprints UFO Flying Saucers #2 w/cover	1	3	4	6	8	10

UFO ENCOUNTERS
Western Publishing Co.: May, 1978 ($1.95, 228 pgs.)

	GD	VG	FN	VF	VF/NM	NM-
11192-Reprints UFO Flying Saucers	4	8	12	27	44	60
11404-Vol.1 (128 pgs.)-See UFO Mysteries for Vol. 2	4	8	12	23	37	50

UFO FLYING SAUCERS (UFO & Outer Space #14 on)
Gold Key: Oct, 1968 - No. 13, Jan, 1977 (No. 2 on, 36 pgs.)

	GD	VG	FN	VF	VF/NM	NM-
1(30035-810) (68 pgs.)	5	10	15	33	57	80
2(11/70), 3(11/72), 4(11/74)	3	6	9	17	26	35
5(2/75)-13: Bolle-a #4 on	2	4	6	13	18	22

UFOLOGY
BOOM! Studios: Apr, 2015 - No. 6, Nov, 2015 ($3.99, limited series)

1-6-James Tynion IV & Noah J. Yuenkel-s/Matthew Fox-a 4.00

UFO MYSTERIES
Western Publishing Co.: 1978 ($1.00, reprints, 96 pgs.)

	GD	VG	FN	VF	VF/NM	NM-
11400-(Vol.2)-Cont'd from UFO Encounters, pgs. 129-224	4	8	12	23	37	50

ULTIMAN GIANT ANNUAL (See Big Bang Comics)
Image Comics: Nov, 2001 ($4.95, B&W, one-shot)

1-Homage to DC 1960's annuals 5.00

ULTIMATE... (Collects 4-issue alternate titles from X-Men Age of Apocalypse crossovers)
Marvel Comics: May, 1995 ($8.95, trade paperbacks, gold foil covers)

Amazing X-Men, Astonishing X-Men, Factor-X, Gambit & the X-Ternals, Generation Next, X-Calibre, X-Man 9.00
Weapon X 10.00

ULTIMATE ADVENTURES
Marvel Comics: Nov, 2002 - No. 6, Dec, 2003 ($2.25)

1-6: 1-Intro. Hawk-Owl; Zimmerman-s/Fegredo-a. 3-Ultimates app. 3.00
One Tin Soldier TPB (2005, $12.99) r/#1-6 13.00

ULTIMATE ANNUALS
Marvel Comics: 2006; 2007 ($13.99, SC)

Vol. 1 (2006, $13.99) r/Ult. FF Ann. #1, Ult. X-Men Ann. #1, Ult S-M #1, Ultimates Ann #1 14.00
Vol. 2 (2007, $13.99) r/Ult. FF Ann. #2, Ult. X-Men Ann. #2, Ult S-M #2, Ultimates Ann #2 14.00

ULTIMATE ARMOR WARS (Follows Ultimatum x-over)
Marvel Comics: Nov, 2009 - No. 4, Apr, 2010 ($3.99, limited series)

1-4-Warren Ellis-s/Steve Kurth-a/Brandon Peterson-c. 1-Variant-c by Kurth 4.00

ULTIMATE AVENGERS (Follows Ultimatum x-over)
Marvel Comics: Oct, 2009 - No. 18 ($3.99)

1-6-Mark Millar-s/Carlos Pacheco-a/c; Red Skull app. 4.00
1-Variant Red Skull-c by Leinil Yu 8.00
7-12-(Ultimate Avengers 2 #1-6 on cover) Yu-a; Punisher joins. 10-Origin Ghost Rider 4.00
7-Variant Ghost Rider-c by Silvestri 8.00
13-18-(Ultimate Avengers 3 #1-6 on cover) Dillon-a; Blade and a new Daredevil app. 4.00

ULTIMATE AVENGERS VS. NEW ULTIMATES (Death of Spider-Man tie-in)
Marvel Comics: Apr, 2011 - No. 6, Sept, 2011 ($3.99, limited series)

1-6: 1-Millar-s/Yu-a/c; variant covers by Cho & Hitch. 3-6-Punisher app. 4.00

ULTIMATE CAPTAIN AMERICA

Ultimate Daredevil and Elektra #2 © MAR

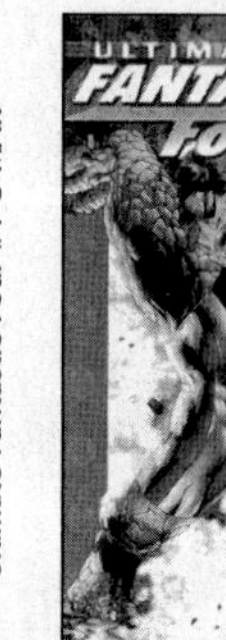

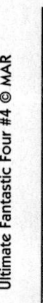

Ultimate Fantastic Four #4 © MAR

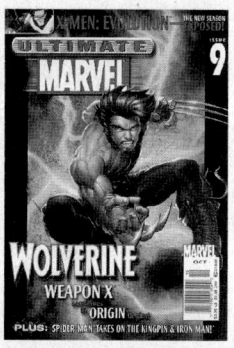

Ultimate Marvel #9 © MAR

GD 2.0 | VG 4.0 | FN 6.0 | VF 8.0 | VF/NM 9.0 | NM- 9.2

Marvel Comics: Mar, 2011 - No. 4, Jun, 2011 ($3.99)
1-4: 1-Aaron-s/Garney-a; 2 covers by Garney & McGuinness 4.00
Annual 1 (12/08, $3.99, one-shot) Origin of the Black Panther; Djurdjevic-a 4.00

ULTIMATE CIVIL WAR: SPIDER-HAM (See Civil War and related titles)
Marvel Comics: March, 2007 ($2.99, one-shot)
1-Spoof of Civil War series featuring Spider-Ham; art by various incl. Olivetti, Severin 3.00

ULTIMATE COMICS IRON MAN
Marvel Comics: Dec, 2012 - No. 4, Mar, 2013 ($3.99, limited series)
1-4-Edmonson-s/Buffagni-a/Stockton-c 4.00

ULTIMATE COMICS SPIDER-MAN (See Ultimate Spider-Man 2011 series)

ULTIMATE COMICS ULTIMATES (See Ultimates 2011 series)

ULTIMATE COMICS WOLVERINE
Marvel Comics: May, 2013 - No. 4, Jul, 2013 ($3.99, limited series)
1-4: 1-Bunn-s/Messina-a/Art Adams-c; Wolverine app. in flashback 4.00

ULTIMATE COMICS X-MEN (See Ultimate X-Men 2011 series)

ULTIMATE DAREDEVIL AND ELEKTRA
Marvel Comics: Jan, 2003 - No. 4, Mar, 2003 ($2.25, limited series)
1-4-Rucka-s/Larroca-c/a; 1st meeting of Elektra and Matt Murdock 3.00
... Vol.1 TPB (2003, $11.99) r/#1-4, Daredevil Vol. 2 #9; Larroca sketch pages 12.00

ULTIMATE DOOM (Follows Ultimate Mystery mini-series)
Marvel Comics: Feb, 2011 - No. 4, May, 2011 ($3.99, limited series)
1-4-Bendis-s/Sandoval-a; Fantastic Four, Spider-Man, Jessica Drew & Nick Fury app. 4.00

ULTIMATE ELEKTRA
Marvel Comics: Oct, 2004 - No. 5, Feb, 2005 ($2.25, limited series)
1-5-Carey-s/Larroca-c/a. 2-Bullseye app. 3.00
... : Devil's Due TPB (2005, $11.99) r/#1-5 12.00

ULTIMATE END (Secret Wars Battleworld tie-in)
Marvel Comics: Jul, 2015 - No. 5, Feb, 2016 ($3.99, limited series)
1-5-Bendis-s/Bagley-a; Spider-Man & Earth-616 Avengers & Ultimate Universe app. 4.00

ULTIMATE ENEMY (Follows Ultimatum x-over)(Leads into Ultimate Mystery)
Marvel Comics: Mar, 2010 - No. 4, July, 2010 ($3.99, limited series)
1-4-Bendis-s/Sandoval-a 1-Covers by McGuinness and Pearson 4.00

ULTIMATE EXTINCTION (See Ultimate Nightmare and Ultimate Secret limited series)
Marvel Comics: Mar, 2006 - No. 5, July, 2006 ($2.99, limited series)
1-5-The coming of Gah Lak Tus; Ellis-s/Peterson-a 3.00
TPB (2006, $12.99) r/#1-5 13.00

ULTIMATE FALLOUT (Follows Death of Spider-Man in Ultimate Spider-Man #160)
Marvel Comics: Sept, 2011 - No. 6, Oct, 2011 ($3.99, weekly limited series)
1-3,5,6: 1-Bendis-s/Bagley-a/c. 2,6-Hitch-c. 3,5-Andy Kubert-c 4.00
4-Debut of Miles Morales as the new Spider-Man; polybagged
3 6 9 16 23 30

ULTIMATE FANTASTIC FOUR (Continues in Ultimatum mini-series)
Marvel Comics: Feb, 2004 - No. 60, Apr, 2009 ($2.25/$2.50/$2.99)
1-Bendis & Millar-s/Adam Kubert-a/Hitch-c 5.00
2-20: 2-Adam Kubert-a/c; intro. Moleman 7-Ellis-s/Immonen-a begin; Dr. Doom app.
13-18-Kubert-a. 19,20-Jae Lee-a. 20-Begin $2.50-c 3.50
21-Marvel Zombies; begin Greg Land-c/a; Mark Millar-s; variant-c by Land 5.00
22-29,33-59: 24-26-Namor app. 28-President Thor. 33-38-Ferry-a. 42-46-Silver Surfer 3.00
30-32-Marvel Zombies; Millar-s/Land-a; Dr. Doom app. 5.00
30-32-Zombie variant-c by Suydam 6.00
50-White variant-c by Kirkham 5.00
60-($3.99) Ultimatum crossover; Kirkham-a 4.00
Annual 1 (10/05, $3.99) The Inhumans app.; Jae Lee-a/Mark Millar-s/Greg Land-c 4.00
Annual 2 (10/06, $3.99) Mole Man app.; Immonen & Irving-a/Carey-s 4.00
... MGC #1 (6/11, $1.00) r/#1 with "Marvel's Greatest Comics" logo on cover 3.00
.../Ult. X-Men Annual 1 (11/08, $3.99) Continued from Ult. X-Men/Ult. F.F. Annual #1 4.00
.../X-Men 1 (3/06, $2.99) Carey-s/Ferry-a; continued from Ult. X-Men/Fantastic Four #1 3.00
... Vol. 1: The Fantastic (2004, $12.99, TPB) r/#1-6; cover gallery 13.00
... Vol. 2: Doom (2004, $12.99, TPB) r/#7-12 13.00
... Vol. 3: N-Zone (2005, $12.99, TPB) r/#13-18 13.00
... Vol. 4: Inhuman (2005, $12.99, TPB) r/#19,20 & Annual #1 13.00
... Vol. 5: Crossover (2006, $12.99, TPB) r/#21-26 13.00
... Vol. 6: Frightful (2006, $14.99, TPB) r/#27-32; gallery of cover sketches & variants 15.00
... Vol. 7: God War (2007, $16.99, TPB) r/#33-38 17.00
... Vol. 8: Devils (2007, $12.99, TPB) r/#39-41 & Annual #2 13.00
... Vol. 9: Silver Surfer (2007, $13.99, TPB) r/#42-46 14.00
Volume 1 HC (2005, $29.99, 7x11", dust jacket) r/#1-12; introduction, proposals and scripts by Millar and Bendis; character design pages by Hitch 30.00
Volume 2 HC (2006, $29.99, 7x11", dust jacket) r/#13-20; Jae Lee sketch page 30.00
Volume 3 HC (2007, $29.99, 7x11", dust jacket) r/#21-32; Greg Land sketch pages 30.00
Volume 4 HC (2007, $29.99, 7x11", dust jacket) r/#33-41, Annual #2, Ultimate FF/X-Men and Ultimate X-Men/FF; character design pages 30.00
Volume 5 HC (2008, $34.99, 7x11", dust jacket) r/#42-53 35.00

ULTIMATE FF
Marvel Comics: Jun, 2014 - No. 6, Oct, 2014 ($3.99)
1-6: 1-Team of Sue Storm, Iron Man, Falcon, Machine Man. 4,5-Spider-Ham app. 4.00

ULTIMATE GALACTUS TRILOGY
Marvel Comics: 2007 ($34.99, hardcover, dustjacket)
HC-Oversized reprint of Ultimate Nightmare #1-5, Ultimate Secret #1-4, Ultimate Vision #0, and Ultimate Extinction #1-5; sketch pages and cover galery 35.00

ULTIMATE HAWKEYE (Ultimate Comics)
Marvel Comics: Oct, 2011 - No. 4, Jan, 2012 ($3.99, limited series)
1-4: 1-Hickman-s/Sandoval-a/Andrews-c; polybagged. 2-4-Hulk app. 4.00
1-Variant-c by Neal Adams 6.00
1-Variant-c by Adam Kubert 8.00

ULTIMATE HULK
Marvel Comics: Dec, 2008 ($3.99, one-shot)
Annual 1 (12/08, $3.99) Zarda battles Hulk; McGuinness & Djurdjevic-a/Loeb-s 4.00

ULTIMATE HUMAN
Marvel Comics: Mar, 2008 - No. 4, Jun, 2008 ($2.99, limited series)
1-4-Iron Man vs. The Hulk; The Leader app.; Ellis-s/Nord-a 3.00
HC (2008, $19.99) r/#1-4 20.00

ULTIMATE IRON MAN
Marvel Comics: May, 2005 - No. 5, Feb, 2006 ($2.99, limited series)
1-Origin of Iron Man; Orson Scott Card-s/Andy Kubert-a; two covers 4.00
1-2nd & 3rd printings; each with B&W variant-c 3.00
2-5-Kubert-c 3.00
Volume 1 HC (2006, $19.99, dust jacket) r/#1-5; rough cut of script for #1, cover sketches 20.00
Volume 1 SC (2006, $14.99) r/#1-5; rough cut of script for #1, cover sketches 15.00

ULTIMATE IRON MAN II
Marvel Comics: Feb, 2008 - No. 5, July, 2008 ($2.99, limited series)
1-5-Early days of the Iron Man prototype; Orson Scott Card-s/Pasqual Ferry-a/c 3.00

ULTIMATE MARVEL FLIP MAGAZINE
Marvel Comics: July, 2005 - No. 26, Aug, 2007 ($3.99/$4.99)
1-11-Reprints Ultimate Fantastic Four and Ultimate X-Men in flip format 4.00
12-26-($4.99) 5.00

ULTIMATE MARVEL MAGAZINE
Marvel Comics: Feb, 2001 - No. 11, 2002 ($3.99, magazine size)
1-11: Reprints of recent stories from the Ultimate titles plus Marvel news and features. 1-Reprints Ultimate Spider-Man #1&2. 11-Lord of the Rings-c 4.00

ULTIMATE MARVEL SAMPLER
Marvel Comics: 2007 (no cover price, limited series)
1-Previews of 2008 Ultimate Marvel story arcs; Finch-c 3.00

ULTIMATE MARVEL TEAM-UP (Spider-Man Team-up)
Marvel Comics: Apr, 2001 - No. 16, July, 2002 ($2.99/$2.25)
1-Spider-Man & Wolverine; Bendis-s in all; Matt Wagner-a/c 5.00
2,3-Hulk; Hester-a 3.50
4,5,9-16: 4,5-Iron Man; Allred-a. 9-Fantastic Four; Mahfood-a. 10-Man-Thing; Totleben-a. 11-X-Men; Clugston-Major-a. 12,13-Dr. Strange; McKeever-a.14-Black Widow; Terry Moore-a. 15,16-Shang-Chi; Mays-a 3.00
6-8-Punisher; Sienkiewicz-a. 7,8-Daredevil app. 4.00
TPB (11/01, $14.95) r/#1-5 15.00
... Ultimate Collection TPB ('06, $29.99) r/#1-16 & Ult. Spider-Man Spec.; sketch pages 30.00
HC (8/02, $39.99) r/#1-16 & Ult. Spider-Man Special; Bendis afterword 40.00
...: Vol. 2 TPB (2003, $11.99) r/#9-13; Mahfood-c 12.00
...: Vol. 3 TPB (2003, $12.99) r/#14-16 & Ultimate Spider-Man Super Special; Moore-c 13.00

ULTIMATE MYSTERY (Follows Ultimate Enemy)(Leads into Ultimate Doom)
Marvel Comics: Sept, 2010 - No. 4, Dec, 2010 ($3.99, limited series)
1-4-Bendis-s/Sandoval-a; Rick Jones returns; Captain Marvel app. 1-3-Campbell-c 4.00

ULTIMATE NEW ULTIMATES (Follows Ultimatum x-over)
Marvel Comics: May, 2010 - No. 5, Mar, 2011 ($3.99)
1-5: 1-Jeph Loeb-s/Frank Cho-a; 6-page wraparound-c by Cho; Defenders app. 4.00

Ultimate Power #1 © MAR

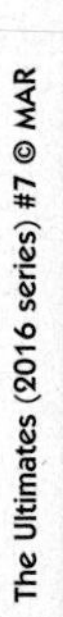

The Ultimates (2016 series) #7 © MAR

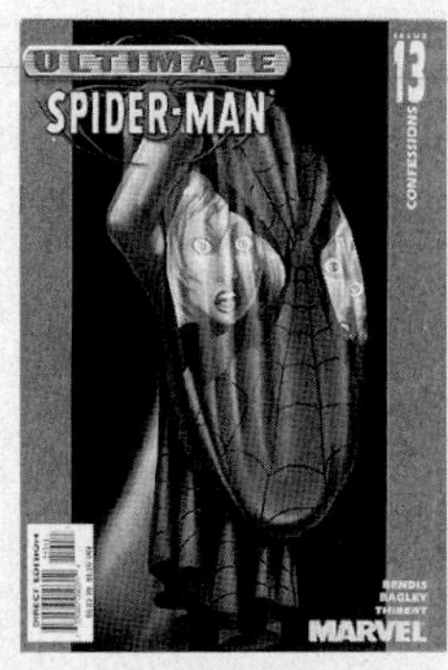
Ultimate Spider-Man #13 © MAR

	GD 2.0	VG 4.0	FN 6.0	VF 8.0	VF/NM 9.0	NM- 9.2

1-Villains variant-c by Yu 8.00

ULTIMATE NIGHTMARE (Leads into Ultimate Secret limited series)
Marvel Comics: Oct, 2004 - No. 5, Feb, 2005 ($2.25, limited series)

1-5: Ellis-s; Ultimates, X-Men, Nick Fury app. 1,2,4,5-Hairsine-a/c. 3-Epting-a 3.00
Ultimate Galactus Book 1: Nightmare TPB (2005, $12.99) r/Ultimate Nightmare #1-5 13.00

ULTIMATE ORIGINS
Marvel Comics: Aug, 2008 - No. 5, Dec, 2008 ($2.99, limited series)

1-5-Bendis-s/Guice-a. 1-Nick Fury origin in the 1940s. 2-Capt. America origin 3.00

ULTIMATE POWER
Marvel Comics: Dec, 2006 - No. 9, Feb, 2008 ($2.99, limited series)

1-9: 1-Ultimate FF meets the Squadron Supreme; Bendis-s; Land-a/c. 2-Spider-Man, X-Men and the Ultimates app. 6-Doom app. 3.00
1-Variant sketch-c 5.00
1-Director's Cut (2007, $3.99) r/#1 and B&W pencil and ink pages; covers to #2,3 4.00
HC (2008, $34.99) oversized r/series; profile pages; B&W sketch art 35.00

ULTIMATES, THE (Avengers of the Ultimate line)
Marvel Comics: Mar, 2002 - No. 13, Apr, 2004 ($2.25)

1-Intro. Capt. America; Millar-s/Hitch-a & wraparound-c 6.00
2-Intro. Giant-Man and the Wasp 4.00
3-12: 3-1st Capt. America in new costume. 4-Intro. Thor. 5-Ultimates vs. The Hulk. 8-Intro. Hawkeye 3.00
13-($3.50) 4.00
... MGC #1 (5/11, $1.00) r/#1 with "Marvel's Greatest Comics" logo on cover 3.00
... Saga (2007, $3.99) Re-caps 1st 2 Ultimates series; new framing art by Charest; prelude to Ultimates 3 series; Brooks-c 4.00
... Volume 1 HC (2004, $29.99) oversized r/series; commentary pages with Millar & Hitch; cover gallery and character design pages; intro. by Joss Whedon 30.00
... Volume 1: Super-Human TPB (8/02, $12.99) r/#1-6 13.00
... Volume 2: Homeland Security TPB (2004, $17.99) r/#7-13 18.00

ULTIMATES (Ultimate Comics) (Continues in Hunger)
Marvel Comics: Oct, 2011 - No. 30, Nov, 2013 ($3.99)

1-30: 1-Hickman-s/Ribic-a/Andrews-c; polybagged. 4-Reed Richards returns 4.00
1-Variant-c by Esad Ribic 6.00
#18.1 (2/13, $2.99) Eaglesham-a; Stark gets the Iron Patriot armor 3.00
Ultimate Comics Ultimates Must Have 1 (2/12, $4.99) r/#1-3 5.00

ULTIMATES (Follows Secret War event)
Marvel Comics: Jan, 2016 - No. 12, Dec, 2016 ($3.99)

1-12: 1-Ewing-s/Rocafort-a; team of Capt. Marvel, Blue Marvel, Black Panther, Spectrum, and Ms. America; Galactus app. 5,7-11-Thanos app. 6,12-Christian Ward-a. 8-12-Civil War II tie-ins 4.00

ULTIMATES 2
Marvel Comics: Feb, 2005 - No. 13, Feb, 2007 ($2.99/$3.99)

1-Millar-s/Hitch-a; Giant-Man becomes Ant-Man 4.00
2-11: 6-Intro. The Defenders. 7-Hawkeye shot. 8-Intro The Liberators 3.00
12,13-($3.99) Wraparound-c; X-Men, Fantastic Four, Spider-Man app. 4.00
13-Variant white cover featuring The Wasp 15.00
Annual 1 (10/05, $3.99) Millar-s/Dillon-a/Hitch-c; Defenders app. 4.00
Annual 2 (10/06, $3.99) Deodato-a; flashback to WWII with Sook-a; Falcon app. 4.00
HC (2007, $34.99) oversized r/series; commentary pages with Millar & Hitch; cover gallery, sketch and script pages; intro. by Jonathan Ross 35.00
... Volume 1: Gods & Monsters TPB (2005, $15.99) r/#1-6 16.00
... Volume 2: Grand Theft America TPB (2007, $19.99) r/#7-13; cover gallery w/sketches 20.00

ULTIMATES 2
Marvel Comics: Jan, 2017 - No. 9, Sept, 2017; No. 100, Oct, 2017 ($3.99)

1-9: 1-Ewing-s/Foreman-a; team of Capt. Marvel, Blue Marvel, Black Panther, Spectrum, and Ms. America. 7,8-Secret Empire tie-ins; Koch-a. 8,9-Ego the Living Planet app. 4.00
100-(10/17, $4.99) The original Ultimates app. 5.00

ULTIMATES 3
Marvel Comics: Feb, 2008 - No. 5, Nov, 2008 ($2.99)

1-Loeb-s/Madureira-a; two gatefold wraparound covers by Madureira; Scarlet Witch shot 4.00
1,2-Second printings: 1-Wraparound cover by Madureira. 2-Madureira-c 3.00
2-5: 2-Spider-Man app. 3-Wolverine app. 5-Two gatefold wraparound-c (Heroes & Ultron) 3.00
2-Variant Thor cover by Turner 8.00
3-Variant Scarlet Witch cover by Cho 8.00
4-Variant Valkyrie cover by Finch 4.00

ULTIMATE SECRET (See Ultimate Nightmare limited series)
Marvel Comics: May, 2005 - No. 4, Dec, 2005 ($2.99, limited series)

1-4-Ellis-s; Captain Marvel app. 1,2-McNiven-a. 2,3-Ultimates & FF app. 3.00

Ultimate Galactus Book 2: Secret TPB (2006, $12.99) r/#1-4 13.00

ULTIMATE SECRETS
Marvel Comics: 2008 ($3.99, one-shot)

1-Handbook-styled profiles of secondary teams and characters from Ultimate universe 4.00

ULTIMATE SIX (Reprinted in Ultimate Spider-Man Vol. 5 hardcover)
Marvel Comics: Nov, 2003 - No. 7, June, 2004 ($2.25) (See Ultimate Spider-Man for TPB)

1-The Ultimates & Spider-Man team-up; Bendis-s/Quesada & Hairsine-a; Cassaday-c 5.00
2-7-Hairsine-a; Cassaday-c 3.00

ULTIMATE SPIDER-MAN
Marvel Comics: Oct, 2000 - No. 133, June, 2009 ($2.99/$2.25/$2.99/$3.99)

	GD 2.0	VG 4.0	FN 6.0	VF 8.0	VF/NM 9.0	NM- 9.2
1-Bendis-s/Bagley & Thibert-a; cardstock-c; introduces revised origin and cast separate from regular Spider-continuity	6	12	18	41	76	110
1-Variant white-c (Retailer incentive)	9	18	27	62	126	190
1-Dynamic Forces Edition	5	10	15	35	63	90
1-Kay Bee Toys variant edition	2	4	6	9	12	15
2-Cover with Spider-Man on car	3	6	9	18	27	35
2-Cover with Spider-Man swinging past building	3	6	9	18	27	35
3,4: 4-Uncle Ben killed	2	4	6	10	14	18
5-7: 6,7-Green Goblin app.	2	4	6	9	12	15
8-13: 13-Reveals secret to MJ	1	3	4	6	8	10

14-21: 14-Intro. Gwen Stacy & Dr. Octopus 5.00
22-($3.50) Green Goblin returns 6.00
23-32 4.00
33-1st Ultimate Venom-c; intro. Eddie Brock 5.00
34-38-Ultimate Venom 4.00
39-49,51-59: 39-Nick Fury app. 43,44-X-Men app. 46-Prelude to Ultimate Six; Sandman app. 51-53-Elektra app. 54-59-Doctor Octopus app. 3.00
50-($2.99) Intro. Black Cat 4.00
60-Intro. Ultimate Carnage on cover 4.00
61-Intro Ben Reilly; Punisher app. 3.00
62-Gwen Stacy killed by Carnage 4.00
63-92: 63,64-Carnage app. 66,67-Wolverine app. 68,69-Johnny Storm app. 78-Begin $2.50-c. 79-Debut Moon Knight. 81-85-Black Cat app. 90-Vulture app. 91-94-Deadpool 3.00
93-99: 93-Begin $2.99-c. 95-Morbius & Blade app. 97-99-Clone Saga 3.00
100-($3.99) Wraparound-c; Clone Saga; re-cap of previous issues 4.00
101-103-Clone Saga continues; Fantastic Four app. 102-Spider-Woman origin 3.00
104-($3.99) Clone Saga concludes; Fantastic Four and Dr. Octopus app. 4.00
105-132: 106-110-Daredevil app. 111-Last Bagley art; Immonen-a (6 pgs.) 112-Immonen-a; Norman Osborn app. 118-Liz Allen ignites. 123,128-Venom app. 129-132-Ultimatum 3.00
133-($3.99) Ultimatum crossover; Spider-Woman app. 4.00
(Issues #150-up, see second series)
Annual 1 (10/05, $3.99) Kitty Pryde app.; Bendis-s/Brooks-a/Bagley-c 4.00
Annual 2 (10/06, $3.99) Punisher, Moon Knight and Daredevil app.; Bendis-s/Brooks-a 4.00
Annual 3 (12/08, $3.99) Mysterio app.; Bendis-s/Lafuente-a 4.00
Collected Edition (1/01, $3.99) r/#1-3 4.00
Free Comic Book Day giveaway (5/02) - r/#1 with "Free Comic Book Day" banner on-c 3.00
... MGC #1 (5/11, $1.00) r/#1 with "Marvel's Greatest Comics" logo on cover 3.00
...Special (7/02, $3.50) art by Bagley and various incl. Romita, Sr., Brereton, Cho, Mack, Sienkiewicz, Phillips, Pearson, Oeming, Mahfood, Russell 4.00
Ultimate Spider-Man 100 Project (2007, $10.00, SC, charity book for the HERO Initiative) collection of 100 variant covers by Romita Sr. & Jr., Cho, Bagley, Quesada and more 10.00
...: Venom HC (2007, $19.99) r/#33-39 20.00
...(Vol. 1): Power and Responsibility TPB (4/01, $14.95) r/#1-7 15.00
...(Vol. 2): Learning Curve TPB (12/01, $14.95) r/#8-13 15.00
...(Vol. 3): Double Trouble TPB (6/02, $17.95) r/#14-21 18.00
Vol. 4: Legacy TPB (2002, $14.99) r/#22-27 15.00
Vol. 5: Public Scrutiny TPB (2003, $11.99) r/#28-32 12.00
Vol. 6: Venom TPB (2003, $15.99) r/#33-39 16.00
Vol. 7: Irresponsible TPB (2003, $12.99) r/#40-45 13.00
Vol. 8: Cats & Kings TPB (2004, $17.99) r/#47-53 18.00
Vol. 9: Ultimate Six TPB (2004, $17.99) r/#46 & Ultimate Six #1-7 18.00
Vol. 10: Hollywood TPB (2004, $12.99) r/#54-59 13.00
Vol. 11: Carnage TPB (2004, $12.99) r/#60-65 13.00
Vol. 12: Superstars TPB (2005, $12.99) r/#66-71 13.00
Vol. 13: Hobgoblin TPB (2005, $15.99) r/#72-78 16.00
Vol. 14: Warriors TPB (2005, $17.99) r/#79-85 18.00
Vol. 15: Silver Sable TPB (2006, $15.99) r/#86-90 & Annual #1 16.00
Vol. 16: Deadpool TPB (2006, $19.99) r/#91-96 & Annual #2 20.00
Vol. 17: Clone Saga TPB (2007, $24.99) r/#97-105 25.00
Vol. 18: Ultimate Knights TPB (2007, $13.99) r/#106-111 14.00
Vol. 19: Death of a Goblin TPB (2008, $14.99) r/#112-117 15.00
Hardcover (3/02, $34.95, 7x11", dust jacket) r/#1-13 & Amazing Fantasy #15;

Ultimate Spider-Man V3 #1 © MAR

Ultimate X-Men #1 © MAR

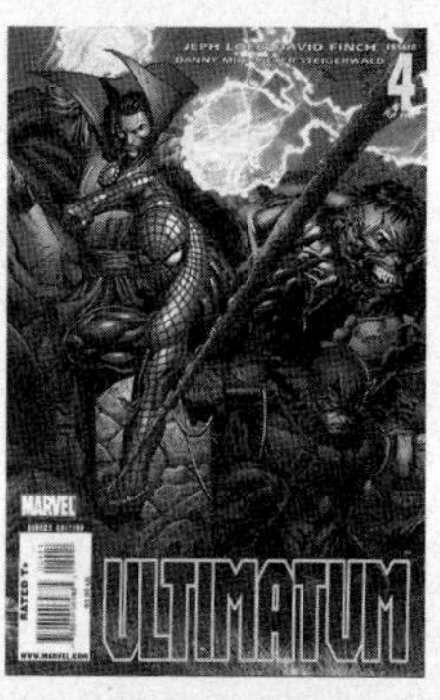

Ultimatum #4 © MAR

GD 2.0 | VG 4.0 | FN 6.0 | VF 8.0 | VF/NM 9.0 | NM- 9.2

sketch pages and Bill Jemas' initial plot and character outlines 35.00
Volume 2 HC (2003, $29.99, 7x11", dust jacket) r/#14-27; pin-ups & sketch pages 30.00
Volume 3 HC (2003, $29.99, 7x11", dust jacket) r/#28-39 & #1/2; script pages 30.00
Volume 4 HC (2004, $29.99, 7x11", dust jacket) r/#40-45, 47-53; sketch pages 30.00
Volume 5 HC (2004, $29.99, 7x11", dust jacket) r/#46,54-59, Ultimate Six #1-7 30.00
Volume 6 HC (2005, $29.99, 7x11", dust jacket) r/#60-71; sketch page 30.00
Volume 7 HC (2006, $29.99, 7x11", dust jacket) r/#72-85; sketch & profile pages 30.00
Volume 8 HC (2007, $29.99, 7x11", dust jacket) r/#86-96 & Annual #1&2; sketch page 30.00
Volume 9 HC (2008, $39.99, 7x11", dust jacket) r/#97-111; sketch pages 40.00
Volume 10 HC (2009, $39.99, 7x11", dust jacket) r/#112-122; sketch pages 40.00
Wizard #1/2 1 3 4 6 8 10

ULTIMATE SPIDER-MAN (2nd series)(Follows Ultimatum x-over)
Marvel Comics: Oct, 2009 - No. 15, Dec, 2010; No. 150, Jan, 2011 - No. 160, Aug, 2011 ($3.99)

1-15: 1-Bendis-s/Lafuente-a/c; new Mysterio. 1-Variant-c by Djurdjevic. 7,8-Miyazawa-a. 9-Spider-Woman app. 4.00
150-(1/11, $5.99) Resumes original numbering; wraparound-c by Lafuente; Bendis-s with art by Lafuente, Pichelli, Joëlle Jones, McKelvie & Young; r/Ult. S-M Special #1 6.00
150-Variant wraparound-c by Bagley 10.00
151-159: 151-154-Black Cat & Mysterio app. 157-Spider-Man shot by Punisher 4.00
153-159-Variant covers. 153-155-Pichelli. 157-McGuinness. 158-McNiven. 159-Cho 8.00
160-Black Polybagged; Bagley cover inside; Death of Spider-Man part 5 4.00
160-Red Polybagged variant; Kaluta cover inside; Death of Spider-Man part 5 20.00

ULTIMATE SPIDER-MAN (3rd series, with Miles Morales)(See Ultimate Fallout #4 for debut)
Marvel Comics: Nov, 2011 - No. 28, Dec, 2013 ($3.99)

1-Polybagged, with Kaare Andrews-c; Bendis-s/Pichelli-a; origin 1 3 4 6 8 10
1-Variant Pichelli-c with unmasked Spider-Man 4 8 12 28 47 65
1-Variant Pichelli-c with Spider-Man & city bkgrd 6 12 18 37 66 95
2-28: 4,5-Spider-Woman app. 5-Nick Fury & Ultimates app. 6-Samnee-a. 19-22-Venom War; Pichelli-a. 23-Cloak and Dagger app. 28-Leads into Cataclysm 4.00
#16.1 (12/12, $2.99) Marquez-a; Venom returns 3.00
200-(6/14, $4.99) Art by Marquez and others; 2 interlocking covers by Bagley & Marquez 5.00
Ultimate Comics Spider-Man Must Have 1 (2/12, $4.99) r/#1-3 5.00

ULTIMATE SPIDER-MAN (Based on the animated series)(See Marvel Universe...)

ULTIMATE TALES FLIP MAGAZINE
Marvel Comics: July, 2005 - No. 26, Aug, 2007 ($3.99/$4.99)

1-11-Each reprints 2 issues of Ultimate Spider-Man in flip format 4.00
12-26-($4.99) 5.00

ULTIMATE THOR
Marvel Comics: Dec, 2010 - No. 4, Apr, 2011 ($3.99, limited series)

1-4: 1-Hickman-s/Pacheco-a; two covers by Pacheco & Choi; origin story 4.00

ULTIMATE VISION
Marvel Comics: No. 0, Jan, 2007 - No. 5, Jan, 2008 ($2.99, limited series)

0-Reprints back-up serial from Ultimate Extinction and related series; pin-ups 3.00
1-5: 1-(2/07) Carey-s/Peterson-a/c 3.00
TPB (2007, $14.99) r/#0-5; design pages and cover gallery 15.00

ULTIMATE WAR
Marvel Comics: Feb, 2003 - No. 4, Apr, 2003 ($2.25, limited series)

1-4-Millar-s/Bachalo-c/a; The Ultimates vs. Ultimate X-Men 3.00
Ultimate X-Men Vol. 5: Ultimate War TPB (2003, $10.99) r/#1-4 11.00

ULTIMATE WOLVERINE VS. HULK
Marvel Comics: Feb, 2006 - No. 6, July, 2009 ($2.99, limited series)

1,2-Leinil Yu-a/c; Damon Lindelof-s. 2-(4/06) 4.00
1,2-(2009) New printings 3.00
3-6: 3-(5/09) Intro. She-Hulk. 4-Origin She-Hulk 3.00

ULTIMATE X (Follows Ultimatum x-over)
Marvel Comics: Apr, 2010 - No. 5, Aug, 2011 ($3.99)

1-5: 1-Jeph Loeb-s/Art Adams-a; two covers by Adams. 5-Hulk app. 4.00

ULTIMATE X-MEN
Marvel Comics: Feb, 2001 - No. 100, Apr, 2009 ($2.99/$2.25/$2.50)

1-Millar-s/Adam Kubert & Thibert-a; cardstock-c; introduces revised origin and cast separate from regular X-Men continuity 2 4 6 9 12 15
1-DF Edition 2 4 6 11 16 20
1-DF Sketch Cover Edition 3 6 9 14 20 25
1-Free Comic Book Day Edition (7/03) r/#1 with "Free Comic Book Day" banner on-c 3.00
2 2 4 6 9 12 15
3-6 1 3 4 6 8 10
7-10 6.00
11-24,26-33: 13-Intro. Gambit. 18,19-Bachalo-a. 23,24-Andrews-a 4.00
25-($3.50) leads into the Ultimate War mini-series; Kubert-a 5.00
34-Spider-Man-c/app.; Bendis-s begin; Finch-a 5.00
35-74: 35-Spider-Man app. 36,37-Daredevil-c/app. 40-Intro. Angel. 42-Intro. Dazzler. 44-Beast dies. 46-Intro. Mr. Sinister. 50-53-Kubert-a; Gambit app. 54-57,59-63-Immonen-a. 60-Begin $2.50-c. 61-Variant Coipel-c. 66-Kirkman-s begin. 69-Begin $2.99-c 3.00
61-Retailer Edition with variant Coipel B&W sketch-c 10.00
75-($3.99) Turner-c; intro. Cable; back-up story with Emma Frost's students 4.00
76-99: 76-Intro. Bishop. 91-Fantastic Four app. 92-96-Phoenix app. 96-Spider-Man app. 99-Ultimatum x-over 3.00
100-($3.99) Ultimatum x-over; Brooks-a 4.00
Annual 1 (10/05, $3.99) Vaughan-s/Raney-a; Gambit & Rogue in Vegas 4.00
Annual 2 (10/06, $3.99) Kirkman-s/Larroca-a; Nightcrawler & Dazzler 4.00
.../Fantastic Four 1 (2/06, $2.99) Carey-s/Ferry-a; concluded in Ult. Fantastic Four/X-Men 3.00
... MGC #1 (6/11, $1.00) r/#1 with "Marvel's Greatest Comics" logo on cover 3.00
.../Ult. Fantastic Four Ann. 1 (11/08, $3.99) Continues in Ult. F.F./Ult. X-Men Annual #1 4.00
.../Fantastic Four TPB (2006, $12.99) reprints Ult X-Men/Ult. FF x-over and Official Handbook of the Ultimate Marvel Universe #1-2 13.00
... Ultimate Collection Vol. 1 (2006, $24.99) r/#1-12 & #1/2; unused Bendis script for #1 25.00
... Ultimate Collection Vol. 2 (2007, $24.99) r/#13-25; Kubert cover sketch pages 25.00
...: (Vol. 1) The Tomorrow People TPB (7/01, $14.95) r/#1-6 15.00
...: (Vol. 2) Return to Weapon X TPB (4/02, $14.95) r/#7-12 15.00
Vol. 3: World Tour TPB (2002, $17.99) r/#13-20 18.00
Vol. 4: Hellfire and Brimstone TPB (2003, $12.99) r/#21-25 13.00
Vol. 5 (See Ultimate War)
Vol. 6: Return of the King TPB (2003, $16.99) r/#26-33 17.00
Vol. 7: Blockbuster TPB (2004, $12.99) r/#34-39 13.00
Vol. 8: New Mutants TPB (2004, $12.99) r/#40-45 13.00
Vol. 9: The Tempest TPB (2004, $10.99) r/#46-49 11.00
Vol. 10: Cry Wolf TPB (2005, $8.99) r/#50-53 9.00
Vol. 11: The Most Dangerous Game TPB (2005, $9.99) r/#54-57 10.00
Vol. 12: Hard Lessons TPB (2005, $12.99) r/#58-60 & Annual #1 13.00
Vol. 13: Magnetic North TPB (2006, $12.99) r/#61-65 13.00
Vol. 14: Phoenix? TPB (2006, $14.99) r/#66-71 15.00
Vol. 15: Magical TPB (2007, $11.99) r/#72-74 & Annual #2 12.00
Vol. 16: Cable TPB (2007, $14.99) r/#75-80; sketch pages 15.00
Vol. 17: Sentinels TPB (2008, $17.99) r/#81-88 18.00
Volume 1 HC (8/02, $34.99, 7x11", dust jacket) r/#1-12 & Giant-Size X-Men #1; sketch pages and Millar and Bendis' initial plot and character outlines 35.00
Volume 2 HC (2003, $29.99, 7x11", dust jacket) r/#13-25; script for #20 30.00
Volume 3 HC (2003, $29.99, 7x11", dust jacket) r/#26-33 & Ultimate War #1-4 30.00
Volume 4 HC (2005, $29.99, 7x11", dust jacket) r/#34-45 30.00
Volume 5 HC (2006, $29.99, 7x11", dust jacket) r/#46-57; Vaughan intro.; sketch pages 30.00
Volume 6 HC (2006, $29.99, 7x11", dust jacket) r/#58-65, Annual #1 & Wizard #1/2 30.00
Volume 7 HC (2007, $29.99, 7x11", dust jacket) r/#66-74, Annual #2 30.00
Wizard #1/2 2 4 6 9 12 15

ULTIMATE X-MEN (Ultimate Comics X-Men) (See Cataclysm)
Marvel Comics: Nov, 2011 - No. 33, Dec, 2013 ($3.99)

1-Spencer-s/Medina-a/Andrews-c; polybagged 4.00
1-Variant-c by Mark Bagley 6.00
2-33: 2-Rogue returns. 6-Prof. X returns. 21-Iron Patriot app. 4.00
#18.1 (1/13, $2.99) Andrade-a/Pichelli-c 3.00
Ultimate Comics X-Men Must Have 1 (2/12, $4.99) r/#1-3 5.00

ULTIMATUM
Marvel Comics: Jan, 2009 - No. 5, July, 2009 ($3.99, limited series)

1-5-Loeb-s/Finch-a; cover by Finch & ; Ultimate heroes vs. Magneto 4.00
1-5-Variant covers by McGuinness 8.00
5-Double gatefold variant-c by Finch 4.00
March on Ultimatum Saga ('08, giveaway) text and art panel history of Ultimate universe 3.00
...: Fantastic Four Requiem 1 (9/09,$3.99) Pokaski-s/Atkins-a; Dr. Strange app. 4.00
...: Spider-Man Requiem 1,2 (8/09, 9/09,$3.99) Bendis-s/Bagley & Immonen-a 4.00
...: X-Men Requiem 1 (9/09,$3.99) Coleite-s/Oliver-a/Brooks-c 4.00
NOTE: *Numerous variant covers and 2nd & 3rd printings exist.*

ULTRA
Image Comics: Aug, 2004 - No. 8, Mar, 2005 ($2.95, limited series)

1-8: 1-Intro. Ultra/Pearl Penalosa; Luna Brothers-s/a 3.00
Vol. 1: Seven Days TPB (4/05, $17.95) r/#1-8; sketch pages 18.00

ULTRAFORCE (1st Series) (Also see Avengers/Ultraforce #1)
Malibu Comics (Ultraverse): Aug, 1994 - No. 10, Aug, 1995 ($1.95/$2.50)

0 (9/94, $2.50)-Perez-c/a. 4.00
1-($2.50, 44 pgs.)-Bound-in trading card; team consisting of Prime, Prototype, Hardcase, Pixx, Ghoul, Contrary & Topaz; Gerard Jones scripts begin, ends #6; Pérez-c/a begins 4.00

Ultraforce #7 © MAL

Unbeatable Squirrel Girl #4 © MAR

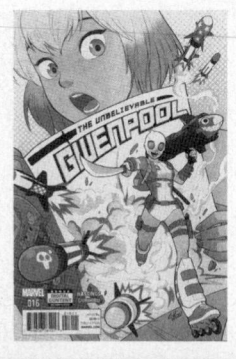

Unbelievable Gwenpool #16 © MAR

	GD 2.0	VG 4.0	FN 6.0	VF 8.0	VF/NM 9.0	NM- 9.2
1-Ultra 5000 Limited Silver Foil Edition	1	2	3	5	6	8
1-Holographic-c, no price	1	2	3	6	8	10

2-5: Perez-c/a in all. 2 (10/94, $1.95)-Prime quits, Strangers cameo. 3-Origin of Topaz; Prime rejoins. 5-Pixx dies. 3.00
2 ($2.50)-Florescent logo; limited edition stamp on-c 4.00
6-10: 6-Begin $2.50-c, Perez-c/a. 7-Ghoul story, Steve Erwin-a. 8-Marvel's Black Knight enters the Ultraverse (last seen in Avengers #375); Perez-c/a. 9,10-Black Knight app.; Perez-c. 10-Leads into Ultraforce/Avengers Prelude 3.00
Malibu "Ashcan": Ultraforce #0A (6/94) 3.00
.../Avengers Prelude 1 (8/95, $2.50)-Perez-c. 3.00
.../Avengers 1 (8/95, $3.95)-Warren Ellis script; Perez-c/a; foil-c 4.00

ULTRAFORCE (2nd Series)(Also see Black September)
Malibu Comics (Ultraverse): Infinity, Sept, 1995 - V2#15, Dec, 1996 ($1.50)

Infinity, V2#1-15: Infinity-Team consists of Marvel's Black Knight, Ghoul, Topaz, Prime & redesigned Prototype; Warren Ellis scripts begin, ends #3; variant-c exists. 1-1st app.Cromwell, Lament & Wreckage. 2-Contains free encore presentation of Ultraforce #1; flip book "Phoenix Resurrection" Pt. 7. 7-Darick Robertson, Jeff Johnson & others-a. 8,9-Intro. Future Ultraforce (Prime, Hellblade, Angel of Destruction, Painkiller & Whipslash); Gary Erskine-c/a. 9-Foxfire app. 10-Len Wein scripts & Deodato Studios-c/a begin. 10-Lament back-up story. 11-Ghoul back-up story by Pander Bros. 12-Ultraforce vs. Maxis (cont'd in Ultraverse Unlimited #2); Exiles & Iron Clad app. 13-Prime leaves; Hardcase returns 3.00
Infinity (2000 signed) 4.00
.../Spider-Man ($3.95)-Marv Wolfman script; Green Goblin app; 2 covers exist. 4.00

ULTRAGIRL
Marvel Comics: Nov, 1996 - No. 3 Mar, 1997($1.50, limited series)

1-3: 1-1st app. 3.00

ULTRA KLUTZ
Onward Comics: 1981; 6/86 - #27, 1/89, #28, 4/90 - #31, 1990? ($1.50/$1.75/$2.00, B&W)

1 (1981)-Re-released after 2nd #1 3.00
1-30: 1-(6/86). 27-Photo back-c 3.00
31-($2.95, 52 pgs.) 4.00

ULTRAMAN
Nemesis Comics: Mar, 1994 - No. 4, Sept, 1994 ($1.75/$1.95)

1-($2.25)-Collector's edition; foil-c; special 3/4 wraparound-c 4.00
1-($1.75)-Newsstand edition 3.00
2-4: 3-$1.95-c begins 3.00
#(-1) (3/93) 3.00

ULTRAMAN TIGA
Dark Horse Comics: Aug, 2003 - No. 10, June, 2004 ($3.99)

1-10-Khoo Fuk Lung-a/Tony Wong-s 4.00

ULTRAVERSE DOUBLE FEATURE
Malibu Comics (Ultraverse): Jan, 1995 ($3.95, one-shot, 68 pgs.)

1-Flip-c featuring Prime & Solitaire. 4.00

ULTRAVERSE ORIGINS
Malibu Comics (Ultraverse): Jan, 1994 (99¢, one-shot)

1-Gatefold-c; 2 pg. origins all characters 3.00
1-Newsstand edition; different-c, no gatefold 3.00

ULTRAVERSE PREMIERE
Malibu Comics (Ultraverse): 1994 (one-shot)

0-Ordered thru mail w/coupons 5.00

ULTRAVERSE UNLIMITED
Malibu Comics (Ultraverse): June, 1996; No. 2, Sept, 1996 ($2.50)

1,2: 1-Adam Warlock returns to the Marvel Universe; Rune-c/app. 2-Black Knight, Reaper & Sierra Blaze return to the Marvel Universe 3.00

ULTRAVERSE YEAR ONE
Malibu Comics (Ultraverse): 1994 ($4.95, one-shot)

nn-In-depth synopsis of the first year's titles & stories. 5.00

ULTRAVERSE YEAR TWO
Malibu Comics (Ultraverse): Aug, 1995 ($4.95, one-shot)

nn-In-depth synopsis of second year's titles & stories 5.00

ULTRAVERSE YEAR ZERO: THE DEATH OF THE SQUAD
Malibu Comics (Ultraverse): Apr, 1995 - No. 4, July, 1995 ($2.95, lim. series)

1-4: 3-Codename: Firearm back-up story. 3.00

ULTRON (See Age of Ultron series)
Marvel Comics: Jun, 2013 ($3.99, one-shot)

1AU-Victor Mancha from the Runaways (son of Ultron); K. Immonen-s/Pinna-a 4.00

UMBRAL
Image Comics: Nov, 2013 - Present ($2.99)

1-12-Johnston-s/Mitten-a 3.00

UMBRELLA ACADEMY (Zero Killer & Pantheon City on back-c)
Dark Horse Comics: Apr, 2007

1-Free Comic Book Day Edition - previews of the upcoming series; James Jean-c 5.00

UMBRELLA ACADEMY: APOCALYPSE SUITE
Dark Horse Comics: Sept, 2007 - No. 6, Feb, 2008 ($2.99, limited series)

1-Origin of the Umbrella Academy; Gerald Way-s/Gabriel Bá-a/James Jean-c 5.00
1-White variant-c by Bá 25.00
1-Variant-c by Gerald Way 20.00
1-2nd printing with variant-c by Bá 3.00
2-6 3.00
...: One for One (9/10, $1.00) r/#1 with red cover frame 3.00
Vol.1: Apocalypse Suite TPB (7/08, $17.95) r/#1-6, FCBD story and web shorts; design art; Grant Morrison intro.; cover gallery 18.00

UMBRELLA ACADEMY: DALLAS
Dark Horse Comics: Nov, 2008 - No. 6, May, 2009 ($2.99, limited series)

1-6-Gerald Way-s/Gabriel Bá-a/c 3.00
1-Wraparound variant-c by Jim Lee 5.00

UNBEATABLE SQUIRREL GIRL, THE
Marvel Comics: Mar, 2015 - No. 8, Oct, 2015 ($3.99)

1-8: 1-Doreen Green and Tippy-Toe at college; North-s/Henderson-a. 1-Kraven app. 3,4-Galactus app. 7-Avengers cameo. 8-Lady Thor, Odinson & Loki app. 4.00

UNBEATABLE SQUIRREL GIRL, THE
Marvel Comics: Dec, 2015 - Present ($3.99)

1-25,27-29: 1-North-s/Henderson-a. 2-Doreen goes to the 1960s; Doctor Doom app. 6-Crossover with Howard the Duck #6. 10-Mole Man app. 13,14-Scott Lang app. 16-25th Anniversary issue; origin re-told; Hulk app. 23-25-Dinosaur Ultron app. 4.00
26-"Zine" issue; includes Silver Surfer/Galactus by Garfield's Jim Davis (2 pgs.) 4.00
... Beats Up The Marvel Universe (2016, $24.99, HC) original graphic novel; North-s; Henderson-a; Spider-Man & Avengers app.; bonus game pages and design art 25.00
...: You Choose the Story No. 1 Halloween Comic Fest 2016 (giveaway, 12/16) r/#7 3.00

UNBELIEVABLE GWENPOOL, THE (Also see Gwenpool Special)
Marvel Comics: Jun, 2016 - No. 25, Apr, 2018 ($3.99)

1-($4.99) Hastings-s/Gurihiru-a; MODOK app. 5.00
2-25-($3.99) 2-Thor (Jane) app. 3-Doctor Strange app. 5,6,19,20-Spider-Man (Miles) app. 13-Deadpool app. 14,15-Hawkeye & Ghost Rider app. 22,23-Doctor Doom app. 4.00
#0-(7/16, $4.99) Reprints apps. in Howard the Duck #1-3 & Gwenpool Special #1 5.00

UNBIRTHDAY PARTY WITH ALICE IN WONDERLAND (See Alice In Wonderland, Four Color #341)

UNCANNY
Dynamite Entertainment: 2013 - No. 6, 2014 ($3.99)

1-6-Andy Diggle-s/Aaron Campbell-a 4.00

UNCANNY, (SEASON TWO)
Dynamite Entertainment: 2015 - No. 6, 2015 ($3.99)

1-6-Andy Diggle-s/Aaron Campbell-a 4.00

UNCANNY AVENGERS (Marvel NOW!)
Marvel Comics: Dec, 2012 - No. 25, Dec, 2014 ($3.99)

1-25: 1-Capt. America, Thor, Scarlet Witch, Wolverine, Havok & Rogue team; Remender-s/Cassaday-a; Red Skull app. 5-Coipel-a. 14-Rogue & Scarlet Witch die. 24,25-Axis 4.00
8AU-(7/13, $3.99) Age of Ultron tie-in; Adam Kubert-a 4.00
Annual 1 (6/14, $4.99) Remender-s/Renaud-a/Art Adams-c; Mojo app. 5.00

UNCANNY AVENGERS
Marvel Comics: Mar, 2015 - No. 5, Aug, 2015 ($3.99)

1-5: 1-Capt. America (Sam Wilson), Vision, Scarlet Witch, Quicksilver, Sabretooth, Rogue & Doctor Voodoo team; Remender-s/Acuna-a 4.00

UNCANNY AVENGERS
Marvel Comics: Dec, 2015 - No. 30, Feb, 2018 ($3.99)

1-($4.99) Steve Rogers, Spider-Man, Deadpool, Human Torch, Quicksilver, Rogue, Synapse & Doctor Voodoo team; Duggan-s/Stegman-a 5.00
2-20,26-30-($3.99) 2-5-Cable app. 5,6-Pacheco-a. 7,8-Pleasant Hill Standoff tie-ins. 13,14-Civil War II tie-in. 16,17-Hulk returns. 24-Secret Empire tie-in. 26-Scarlet Witch joins. 29-Juggernaut app. 4.00
25-($4.99) Secret Empire tie-in; Shocker & Scorpina app.; Zub-s/Jacinto-a 5.00
Annual 1 (1/16, $4.99) Robinson-s/Laming & Giles-a/Deodato-c; Emerald Warlock app. 5.00

Uncanny Inhumans #9 © MAR

Uncanny Tales #17 © MAR

Uncanny X-Men (2016 series) #1 © MAR

GD VG FN VF VF/NM NM-
2.0 4.0 6.0 8.0 9.0 9.2

UNCANNY AVENGERS: ULTRON FOREVER
Marvel Comics: Jul, 2015 ($4.99)(Continued from New Avengers: Ultron Forever)
1-Part 3 of 3-part crossover with Avengers and New Avengers; Ewing-s/Alan Davis-a; team-up of past, present and future Avengers vs. Ultron 5.00

UNCANNY INHUMANS
Marvel Comics: No. 0, Jun, 2015; No. 1, Dec, 2015 - No. 20, May, 2017 ($4.99/$3.99)
0-Soule-s/McNiven-a/c; Black Bolt, Medusa & Kang the Conqueror app. 5.00
1-($4.99) Johnny Storm, Beast & Kang the Conqueror app. 5.00
2-19-($3.99) 2-4-Kang app. 5-Mad Thinker and The Leader app. 11-14-Civil War II tie-in 4.00
20-($4.99) Leads into Inhumans Prime #1 5.00
#1.MU (4/17, $4.99) Monsters Unleashed tie-in; Allor-s/Level-a 5.00
Annual 1 (10/16, $4.99) Soule-s/Kev Walker-a 5.00

UNCANNY ORIGINS
Marvel Comics: Sept, 1996 - No. 14, Oct, 1997 (99¢)
1-14: 1-Cyclops. 2-Quicksilver. 3-Archangel. 4-Firelord. 5-Hulk. 6-Beast. 7-Venom. 8-Nightcrawler. 9-Storm. 10-Black Cat. 11-Black Knight. 12-Dr. Strange. 13-Daredevil. 14-Iron Fist 3.00

UNCANNY SKULLKICKERS (See Skullkickers #19)

UNCANNY TALES
Atlas Comics (PrPI/PPI): June, 1952 - No. 56, Sept, 1957
1-Heath-a; horror/weird stories begin 142 284 426 909 1555 2200
2 68 136 204 435 743 1050
3-5 61 122 183 390 670 950
6-Wolvertonish-a by Matt Fox 63 126 189 403 689 975
7-10: 8-Atom bomb story; Tothish-a (by Sekowsky?). 9-Crandall-a 54 108 162 343 574 825
11-20: 17-Atom bomb panels; anti-communist story; Hitler story. 19-Krenkel-a. 20-Robert Q. Sale-c 45 90 135 284 480 675
21-25,27: 25-Nostrand-a? 40 80 120 246 411 575
26-Spider-Man prototype c/story 68 136 204 435 745 1050
28-Last precode issue (1/55); Kubert-a; #1-28 contain 2-3 sci/fi stories each 40 80 120 244 405 565
29-41,43-49,51: 29-Variant-c exists with Feb. blanked out and Mar. printed on. Regular version just has Mar. 30 60 90 177 289 400
42,54,56-Krigstein-a 31 62 93 182 296 410
50,53,55-Torres-a 30 60 90 177 289 400
52-Oldest Iron Man prototype (2/57) 37 74 111 222 361 500
NOTE: ***Andru** a-15, 27. **Ayers** a-14, 22, 28, 37. **Bailey** a-51. **Briefer** a-19, 20. **Brodsky** c-1, 3, 4, 6, 8, 12-16, 19. **Brodsky/Everett** c-9. **Cameron** a-47. **Colan** a-11, 16, 17, 49, 52. **Drucker** a-37, 42, 45. **Everett** a-2, 9, 12, 32, 36, 39, 48; c-7, 11, 17, 39, 41, 50, 52, 53. **Fass** a-9, 10, 15, 24. **Forte** a-18, 27, 33-35, 52, 53. **Heath** a-13, 14; c-5, 10, 18. **Keller** a-3. **Lawrence** a-14, 17, 19, 23, 27, 28, 35. **Maneely** a-4, 8, 10, 16, 29, 35; c-2, 22, 26, 33, 38. **Moldoff** a-23. **Morisi** a-48, 52. **Morrow** a-46, 51. **Orlando** a-49, 50, 53. **Powell** a-12, 18, 34, 36, 38, 43, 50, 56. **Robinson** a-3, 13. **Reinman** a-12, 36. **Romita** a-10. **Roussos** a-8. **Sale** a-34, 47, 53; c-20. **Sekowsky** a-25. **Sinnott** a-14, 15, 38, 52. **Torres** a-53. **Tothish**-a by **Andru**-27. **Wildey** a-22, 48.*

UNCANNY TALES
Marvel Comics Group: Dec, 1973 - No. 12, Oct, 1975
1-Crandall-r/Uncanny Tales #9('50s) 4 8 12 25 40 55
2-12: 7,12-Kirby-a 3 6 9 17 26 35
NOTE: ***Ditko** reprints-#4, 6-8, 10-12.*

UNCANNY X-FORCE
Marvel Comics: Dec, 2010 - No. 35, Feb, 2013 ($3.99)
1-17: 1-Wolverine, Psylocke, Archangel, Fantomex & Deadpool team; Opeña-a; Ribic-c 4.00
1-Variant-c by Clayton Crain 10.00
5.1 (5/11, $2.99) Albuquerque-a/Bianchi-c; Lady Deathstrike app. 3.00
18-Polybagged; Dark Angel Saga conclusion 4.00
19-35: 19-Grampa-c. 20-Yu-c 4.00
19.1 (3/12, $2.99) Remender-s/Tan-a; other-dimension X-Men vs. Apocalypse 3.00
...: The Apocalypse Solution 1 (5/11, $4.99) r/#1-3 5.00

UNCANNY X-FORCE (Marvel NOW!)
Marvel Comics: Mar, 2013 - No. 17, Mar, 2014 ($3.99)
1-17: 1-Storm, Psylocke, Spiral, Fantomex & Puck team; Bishop app.; Garney-a 4.00

UNCANNY X-MEN, THE (See **X-Men, The**, 1st series, #142-on)

UNCANNY X-MEN (2nd series) (X-Men Regenesis)
Marvel Comics: Dec, 2010 - No. 20, Dec, 2012 ($3.99)
1-10: 1-3-Gillen-s/Pacheco-a/c; Mr. Sinister app. 4-Peterson-a. 5-8-Land-a 4.00
1-Variant-c by Keown 6.00
11-20: 11-19-Avengers vs. X-Men x-over 4.00

UNCANNY X-MEN (3rd series) (Marvel NOW!)
Marvel Comics: Apr, 2013 - No. 35, Sept, 2015 ($3.99)

GD VG FN VF VF/NM NM-
2.0 4.0 6.0 8.0 9.0 9.2

1-24,26-35: 1-Cyclops, Emma Frost, Magneto, Magik team; Bendis-s/Bachalo-a. 2,3-Avengers app. 5-7,10,11-Irving-a. 8,9,12,13,16,17,19,20-22,25,27-32-Bachalo-a. 12,13-Battle of the Atom. 23,24-Original Sin tie-in 4.00
25-($4.99) Original Sin tie-in 5.00
#600-(1/16, $5.99) Stories by various incl. Bendis, Pichelli, Immonen; Bachalo-c 6.00
Annual 1 (2/15, $4.99) Story of Eva Bell; Bendis-s/Sorrentino-a 5.00
Special 1 (8/14, $4.99) Death's Head & Iron Man app.; Ackins-a 5.00

UNCANNY X-MEN (4th series) (After Secret Wars)
Marvel Comics: Mar, 2016 - No. 19, May, 2017 ($3.99)
1-5: 1-Bunn-s/Land-a; Magneto, Psylocke, Sabretooth, M, and Archangel team 4.00
6-($4.99) Apocalypse Wars x-over; Lashley-a 5.00
7-19: 7-10-Apocalypse Wars x-over; Lashley-a. 11-14-Land-a; Hellfire Club app. 4.00
Annual 1 (1/17, $4.99) Bunn-s/Lashley-a; Elixir returns 5.00

UNCANNY X-MEN AND THE NEW TEEN TITANS (See Marvel and DC Present...)

UNCANNY X-MEN: FIRST CLASS
Marvel Comics: Sept, 2009 - No. 8, Apr, 2010 ($2.99)
1-8: 1-The X-Men #94 (1975) team; Cruz-a; Inhumans app. 3.00
... Giant-Size Special (8/09, $3.99) short stories by various; Scottie Young-c 4.00

UNCENSORED MOUSE, THE
Eternity Comics: Apr, 1989 - No. 2, Apr, 1989 ($1.95, B&W)(Came sealed in plastic bag) (Both contain racial stereotyping & violence)
1,2-Early Gottfredson strip-r in each 2 4 6 11 16 20
NOTE: *Both issues contain unauthorized reprints. Series was cancelled. **Win Smith** r-1, 2.*

UNCHARTED (Based on the video game)
DC Comics: Jan, 2012 - No. 6, Jun, 2012 ($2.99, limited series)
1-6-Williamson-s/Sandoval-a. 1-3-Harris-c 3.00

UNCLE CHARLIE'S FABLES (Also see Adventures in Wonderland)
Lev Gleason Publ.: Jan, 1952 - No. 5, Sept, 1952 (All have Biro painted-c)
1-Peter Pester by Hy Mankin begins, ends #5. Michael the Misfit by Kida, Janice & the Lazy Giant by Maurer, Lawrence the Fortune Teller app.; has photo of Biro 17 34 51 98 154 210
2-Fuje-a; Biro photo 11 22 33 60 83 105
3-5: 5-Two Who Built a Dream, The Blacksmith & The Gypsies by Maurer, The Sleepy King by Hubbel; has photo of Biro 9 18 27 52 69 85
NOTE: ***Kida** a-1. Hubbell a- 5. **Hy Mankin** a-1-5. **Norman Maurer** a-1, 5. **Dick Rockwell** a-5.*

UNCLE DONALD & HIS NEPHEWS DUDE RANCH (See Dell Giant #52)

UNCLE DONALD & HIS NEPHEWS FAMILY FUN (See Dell Giant #38)

UNCLE GRANDPA (Based on the Cartoon Network series)
BOOM! Studios (kaboom!): Oct, 2014 - No. 4, Jan, 2015 ($3.99)
1-4-Short stories and gag pages; multiple covers on each 4.00
...: Good Morning Special 1 (4/16, $4.99) Short stories and gag pages; back-c mask 5.00
...: Pizza Steve Special 1 (6/15, $4.99) Short stories and gag pages 5.00

UNCLE JOE'S FUNNIES
Centaur Publications: 1938 (B&W)
1-Games, puzzles & magic tricks, some interior art; Bill Everett-c 123 246 369 787 1344 1900

UNCLE MILTY (TV)
Victoria Publications/True Cross: Dec, 1950 - No. 4, July, 1951 (52 pgs.)(Early TV comic)
1-Milton Berle photo on-c of #1,2 54 108 162 343 574 825
2 35 70 105 208 339 470
3,4 29 58 87 172 281 390

UNCLE REMUS & HIS TALES OF BRER RABBIT (See Brer Rabbit, 4-Color #129, 208, 693)

UNCLE SAM
DC Comics (Vertigo): 1997 - No. 2, 1997 ($4.95, limited series)
1,2-Alex Ross painted c/a. Story by Ross and Steve Darnell 5.00
Hardcover (1998, $17.95) 18.00
Softcover (2000, $9.95) 10.00

UNCLE SAM AND THE FREEDOM FIGHTERS
DC Comics: Sept, 2006 - No. 8, Apr, 2007 ($2.99, limited series)
1-8-Acuña-a/c; Gray & Palmiotti-s. 3-Intro. Black Condor 3.00
TPB (2007, $14.99) r/#1-8 and story from DCU Brave New World #1 15.00

UNCLE SAM AND THE FREEDOM FIGHTERS
DC Comics: Nov, 2007 - No. 8, Jun, 2008 ($2.99, limited series)
1-8-Gray & Palmiotti-s/Arlem-a/Johnson-c 3.00
...: Brave New World TPB (2008, $14.99) r/#1-8 15.00

Uncle Scrooge #14 © DIS

Uncle Scrooge (2015 series) #19 © DIS

Underdog #23 © Leonardo TV

GD 2.0 VG 4.0 FN 6.0 VF 8.0 VF/NM 9.0 NM- 9.2

UNCLE SAM QUARTERLY (Blackhawk #9 on)(See Freedom Fighters)
Quality Comics Group: Autumn, 1941 - No. 8, Autumn, 1943 (see National Comics)

1-Origin Uncle Sam; Fine/Eisner-c, chapter headings, 2 pgs. by Eisner; (2 versions: dark cover, no price; light cover with price sticker); Jack Cole-a 377 754 1131 2639 4620 6600
2-Cameos by The Ray, Black Condor, Quicksilver, The Red Bee, Alias the Spider, Hercules & Neon the Unknown; Eisner, Fine-c/a 152 304 456 965 1658 2350
3-Tuska-c/a; Eisner-a(2) 116 232 348 742 1271 1800
4-Hitler app. 113 226 339 718 1234 1750
5,7-Hitler, Mussolini & Tojo-c 152 304 456 965 1658 2350
6,8 74 148 222 470 810 1150
NOTE: *Kotzky (or Tuska) a-3-8.*

UNCLE SCROOGE (Disney) (Becomes Walt Disney's... #210 on) (See Cartoon Tales, Dell Giants #33, 55, Disney Comic Album, Donald and Scrooge, Dynabrite, Four Color #178, Gladstone Comic Album, Walt Disney's Comics & Stories #98, Walt Disney's ...)
Dell #1-39/Gold Key #40-173/Whitman #174-209: No. 386, 3/52 - No. 39, 8-10/62; No. 40, 12/62 - No. 209, 7/84

Four Color 386(#1)-in "Only a Poor Old Man" by Carl Barks; r-in Uncle Scrooge & Donald Duck #1('65) & The Best of Walt Disney Comics ('74). The 2nd cover app. of Uncle Scrooge (see Dell Giant Vacation Parade #2 (7/51) for 1st-c) 179 358 537 1477 3839 6200
1-(1986)-Reprints F.C. #386; given away with lithograph "Dam Disaster at Money Lake" & as a subscription offer giveaway to Gladstone subscribers 3 6 9 15 20 24
Four Color 456(#2)-in "Back to the Klondike" by Carl Barks; r-in Best of U.S. & D.D. #1('66) & Gladstone C.A. #4 88 176 264 704 1802 2900
Four Color 495(#3)-r-in #105 59 118 177 472 1186 1900
4(12-2/53-54)-r-in Gladstone Comic Album #11 44 88 132 326 738 1150
5-r-in Gladstone Special #2 & Walt Disney Digest #1 36 72 108 266 596 925
6-r-in U.S. #106,165,233 & Best of U.S. & D.D. #1('66) 32 64 96 230 515 800
7-The Seven Cities of Cibola by Barks; r-in #217 & Best of D.D. & U.S. #2 ('67) 28 56 84 202 451 700
8-10: 8-r-in #111,222. 9-r-in #104,214. 10-r-in #67 25 50 75 175 388 600
11-20: 11-r-in #237. 17-r-in #215. 19-r-in Gladstone C.A. #1. 20-r-in #213 20 40 60 141 313 485
21-30: 24-X-Mas-c. 26-r-in #211 16 32 48 112 249 385
31-35,37-40: 34-r-in #228. 40-X-Mas-c 13 26 39 89 195 300
36-1st app. Magica De Spell; Number one dime 1st identified by name 15 30 45 100 220 340
41-60: 48-Magica De Spell-c/story (3/64). 49-Sci/fi-c. 51-Beagle Boys-c/story (8/64) 11 22 33 73 157 240
61-63,65,66,68-71:71-Last Barks issue w/original story (#71-he only storyboarded the script) 10 20 30 66 138 210
64-(7/66) Barks Vietnam War story "Treasure of Marco Polo" banned for reprints by Disney from 1977-1989 because of its Third World revolutionary war theme. It later appeared in the hardcover Carl Barks Library set (4/89) and Walt Disney's Uncle Scrooge Adventures #42 (1/97) 15 30 45 100 220 340
67,72,73: 67,72,73-Barks-r 9 18 27 60 120 180
74-84: 74-Barks-r(1pg.). 75-81,83-Not by Barks. 82,84-Barks-r begin 7 14 21 44 82 120
85-100 6 12 18 38 69 100
101-110 5 10 15 33 57 80
111-120 4 8 12 27 44 60
121-141,143-152,154-157 3 6 9 21 33 45
142-Reprints Four Color #456 with-c 4 8 12 22 35 48
153,158,162-164,166,168-170,178,180: No Barks 3 6 9 15 22 28
155-Whitman edition 3 6 9 17 26 35
159-160,165,167 3 6 9 16 23 30
161(r/#14), 171(r/#11), 177(r/#16),183(r/#6)-Barks-r 3 6 9 16 23 30
172(1/80),173(2/80)-Gold Key. Barks-a 3 6 9 17 26 35
174(3/80),175(4/80),176(5/80)-Whitman. Barks-a 4 8 12 22 35 48
177(6/80),178(7/80) 4 8 12 23 37 50
179(9/80)(r/#9)-(Very low distribution) 57 114 171 456 1028 1600
180(11/80),181(12/80, r/4-Color #495), pre-pack? 8 16 24 51 96 140
182-195: 182-(50¢-c). 184,185,187,188-Barks-a. 182,186,191-194-No Barks. 189(r/#5), 190(r/#4), 195(r/4-Color #386) 3 6 9 16 23 30
182(1/81, 40¢-c) Cover price error variant 4 8 12 22 35 48
196(4/82),197(5/82): 196(r/#13) 3 6 9 17 26 35
198-209 (All #90038 on-c; pre-pack; no date or date code): 198(4/83), 199(5/83), 200(6/83), 201(6/83), 202(7/83), 203(7/83), 204(8/83), 205(8/83), 206(4/84), 207(5/83), 208(6/84), 209(7/84). 198-202,204-206: No Barks. 203(r/#12), 207(r/#93,92), 208(r/U.S. #18), 209(r/U.S. #21)-Barks-r 4 8 12 25 40 55
Uncle Scrooge & Money(G.K.)-Barks-r/from WDC&S #130 (3/67) 5 10 15 31 53 75
Mini Comic #1(1976)(3-1/4x6-1/2")-r/U.S. #115; Barks-c 2 4 6 8 10 12
NOTE: *Barks c-Four Color 386, 456, 495, #4-37, 39, 40, 43-71.*

UNCLE SCROOGE (See Walt Disney's Uncle Scrooge for previous issues)
Boom Entertainment (BOOM! Kids): No. 384, Oct, 2009 - No. 404, Jun, 2011 ($2.99/$3.99)

384-399: 384-Magica de Spell app.; 2 covers. 392-399-Duck Tales 3.00
400-(2/11, $3.99) "Carl Barks" apps. as Scrooge story-teller; Rosa wraparound-c 4.00
400-$6.99) Deluxe Edition with Barks painted cover of Four Color #386 cover image 7.00
401-404: 401-($3.99)-Rosa-s/a 4.00
...: The Mysterious Stone Ray and Cash Flow (5/11, $6.99) reprints; Barks-s/a; Rosa-s/a 7.00

UNCLE SCROOGE
IDW Publishing: Apr, 2015 - Present ($3.99)

1-Legacy numbered #405; art by Scarpa and others; multiple covers 4.00
2-33-English translations of Dutch, Norwegian & Italian stories; multiple covers on each 4.00

UNCLE SCROOGE AND DONALD DUCK
Gold Key: June, 1965 (25¢, paper cover)

1-Reprint of Four Color #386(#1) & lead story from Four Color #29 7 14 21 46 86 125

UNCLE SCROOGE COMICS DIGEST
Gladstone Publishing: Dec, 1986 - No. 5, Aug, 1987 ($1.25, Digest-size)

1,3 1 2 3 5 6 8
2,4 6.00
5 (low print run) 1 2 3 5 7 9

UNCLE SCROOGE GOES TO DISNEYLAND (See Dell Giants)
Gladstone Publishing Ltd.: Aug, 1985 ($2.50)

1-Reprints Dell Giant w/new-c by Mel Crawford, based on old cover 2 4 6 8 10 12
...Comics Digest 1 ($1.50, digest size) 2 4 6 8 11 14

UNCLE SCROOGE IN COLOR
Gladstone Publishing: 1987 ($29.95, Hardcover, 9-1/4"X12-1/4", 96 pgs.)

nn-Reprints "Christmas on Bear Mountain" from Four Color 178 by Barks; Uncle Scrooge's Christmas Carol (published as Donald Duck & the Christmas Carol, A Little Golden Book), reproduced from the original art as adapted by Norman McGary from pencils by Barks; and Uncle Scrooge the Lemonade King, reproduced from the original art, plus Barks' original pencils 4 8 12 25 40 55
nn-Slipcase edition of 750, signed by Barks, issued at $79.95 300.00

UNCLE SCROOGE THE LEMONADE KING
Whitman Publishing Co.: 1960 (A Top Top Tales Book, 6-3/8"x7-5/8", 32 pgs.)

2465-Storybook pencilled by Carl Barks, finished art adapted by Norman McGary 33 66 99 238 532 825

UNCLE WIGGILY (See March of Comics #19) (Also see Animal Comics)
Dell Publishing Co.: No. 179, Dec, 1947 - No. 543, Mar, 1954

Four Color 179 (#1)-Walt Kelly-c 14 28 42 94 207 320
Four Color 221 (3/49)-Part Kelly-c 9 18 27 58 114 170
Four Color 276 (5/50), 320 (#1, 3/51) 7 14 21 49 92 135
Four Color 349 (9-10/51), 391 (4-5/52) 6 12 18 41 76 110
Four Color 428 (10/52), 503 (10/53), 543 5 10 15 34 63 90

UNDEAD, THE
Chaos! Comics (Black Label): Feb, 2002 ($4.99, B&W)

1-Pulido-s/Denham-a 5.00

UNDERCOVER GIRL (Starr Flagg) (See Extra Comics, Manhunt! & Trail Colt)
Magazine Enterprises: No. 5, 1952 - No. 7, 1954

5(#1)(A-1 #62)-Fallon of the F.B.I. in all 29 58 87 170 278 385
6(A-1 #98), 7(A-1 #118)-All have Starr Flagg 27 54 81 158 259 360
NOTE: *Powell c-6, 7. Whitney a-5-7.*

UNDERDOG (TV)(See Kite Fun Book, March of Comics #426, 438, 467, 479)
Charlton Comics/Gold Key: July, 1970 - No. 10, Jan, 1972; Mar, 1975 - No. 23, Feb, 1979

1 (1st series, Charlton)-1st app. Underdog 10 20 30 64 132 200
2-10 6 12 18 37 66 95
1 (2nd series, Gold Key) 6 12 18 41 76 110
2-10 4 8 12 23 37 50
11-20: 13-1st app. Shack of Solitude 3 6 9 18 28 38
21-23 3 6 9 19 30 40

UNDERDOG
Spotlight Comics: 1987 - No. 3?, 1987 ($1.50)

1-3 4.00

Undersea Agent #4 © Tower

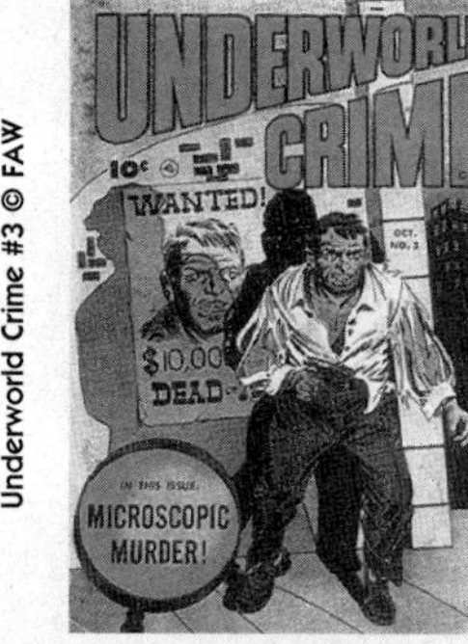

Underworld Crime #3 © FAW

The Unexpected #191 © DC

GD VG FN VF VF/NM NM-
2.0 4.0 6.0 8.0 9.0 9.2

UNDERDOG (Volume 2)
Harvey Comics: Nov, 1993 - No. 5, July, 1994 ($2.25)

1-5 4.00
Summer Special (10/93, $2.25, 68 pgs.) 4.00

UNDERDOG
American Mythology Productions: Apr, 2017 ($3.99)

1,2: 1-New stories and reprint #1 (1970); multiple covers incl. Action #1 swipe 4.00
... 1975 #1 (2017, $3.99) Reprints stories from #23 (1979) and unpublished #24 4.00

UNDERSEA AGENT
Tower Comics: Jan, 1966 - No. 6, Mar, 1967 (25¢, 68 pgs.)

1-Davy Jones, Undersea Agent begins 8 16 24 51 96 140
2-6: 2-Jones gains magnetic powers. 5-Origin & 1st app. of Merman.
6-Kane/Wood-c(r) 5 10 15 34 60 85
NOTE: ***Gil Kane** a-3-6; c-4, 5. **Moldoff** a-2i.*

UNDERSEA FIGHTING COMMANDOS (See Fighting Undersea...)
I.W. Enterprises: 1964

I.W. Reprint #1,2('64): 1-r/#? 2-r/#1; Severin-c 2 4 6 9 13 16

UNDERTAKER (World Wrestling Federation)(Also see WWE Undertaker)
Chaos! Comics: Feb, 1999 - No. 10, Jan, 2000 ($2.50/$2.95)

Preview (2/99) 3.00
1-10: Reg. and photo covers for each. 1-(4/99) 3.00
1-($6.95) DF Ed.; Brereton painted-c 7.00
...Halloween Special (10/99, $2.95) Reg. & photo-c 3.00
Wizard #0 3.00

UNDERWATER CITY, THE
Dell Publishing Co.: No. 1328, 1961

Four Color 1328-Movie, Evans-a 6 12 18 42 79 115

UNDERWINTER
Image Comics: Mar, 2017 - No. 6, Aug, 2017 ($3.99)

1-6-Ray Fawkes-s/a/c. 1-Lemire var-c. 2-Nguyen var-c. 3-Zdarsky var-c 4.00

UNDERWINTER: A FIELD OF FEATHERS
Image Comics: Oct, 2017 - No. 5, Feb, 2018 ($3.99)

1-4-Ray Fawkes-s/a/c. 1-Fawkes var-c 4.00

UNDERWORLD (...True Crime Stories)
D. S. Publishing Co.: Feb-Mar, 1948 - No. 9, June-July, 1949 (52 pgs.)

1-Moldoff (Shelly)-c; excessive violence 50 100 150 315 533 750
2-Moldoff (Shelly)-c; Ma Barker story used in **SOTI**, pg. 95; female electrocution panel;
lingerie art 44 88 132 277 469 660
3-McWilliams-c/a; extreme violence, mutilation 41 82 123 250 418 585
4-Used in Love and Death by Legman; Ingels-a 41 82 123 256 428 600
5-Ingels-a 24 48 72 142 234 325
6-9: 8-Ravielli-a. 9-R.Q. Sale-a 20 40 60 114 182 250

UNDERWORLD
DC Comics: Dec, 1987 - No. 4, Mar, 1988 ($1.00, limited series, mature)

1-4 3.00

UNDERWORLD (Movie)
IDW Publishing: Sept, 2003; Dec, 2005 ($6.99)

1-Movie adaptation; photo-c 7.00
... Evolution (12/05, $7.49) adaptation of movie sequel; Vazquez-a 7.50
TPB (7/04, $19.99) r/#1 and Underworld:Red in Tooth and Claw #1-3 20.00

UNDERWORLD
Marvel Comics: Apr, 2006 - No. 5, Aug, 2006 ($2.99, limited series)

1-5: Staz Johnson-a. 2-Spider-Man app. 3,4-Punisher app. 3.00

UNDERWORLD CRIME
Fawcett Publications: June, 1952 - No. 7, Sept, 1953

1 34 68 102 206 336 465
2 21 42 63 126 206 285
3-6 20 40 60 114 182 250
7-(9/53)-Red hot poker/bondage/torture-c 271 542 813 1734 2967 4200

UNDERWORLD: RED IN TOOTH AND CLAW (Movie)
IDW Publishing: Feb, 2004 - No. 3, Apr, 2004 ($3.99, limited series)

1-3-The early days of the Vampire and Lycan war; Postic & Marinkovich-a 4.00

UNDERWORLD: RISE OF THE LYCANS (Movie)
IDW Publishing: Nov, 2008 - No. 2, Nov, 2008 ($3.99, limited series)

1,2-Grevioux-s/Huerta-a 4.00

GD VG FN VF VF/NM NM-
2.0 4.0 6.0 8.0 9.0 9.2

UNDERWORLD STORY, THE (Movie)
Avon Periodicals: 1950

nn-(Scarce)-Ravielli-c 34 68 102 204 332 460

UNDERWORLD UNLEASHED
DC Comics: Nov, 1995 - No. 3, Jan, 1996 ($2.95, limited series)

1-3: Mark Waid scripts & Howard Porter-c/a(p) 3.50
...: Abyss: Hell's Sentinel 1-($2.95)-Alan Scott, Phantom Stranger, Zatanna app. 3.00
...: Apokolips-Dark Uprising 1 ($1.95) 3.00
...: Batman-Devil's Asylum 1-($2.95)-Batman app. 3.00
...: Patterns of Fear-($2.95) 3.00
TPB (1998, $17.95) r/#1-3 & Abyss-Hell's Sentinel 18.00

UNEARTHLY SPECTACULARS
Harvey Publications: Oct, 1965 - No. 3, Mar, 1967

1-(12¢)-Tiger Boy; Simon-c 4 8 12 25 40 55
2-(25¢ giants)-Jack Q. Frost, Tiger Boy & Three Rocketeers app.; Williamson, Wood, Kane-a;
r-1 story/Thrill-O-Rama #2 4 8 12 28 47 65
3-(25¢ giants)-Jack Q. Frost app.; Williamson/Crandall-a; r-from Alarming Advs. #1,1962
4 8 12 28 47 65
NOTE: ***Crandall** a-3r. **G. Kane** a-2. **Orlando** a-3. **Simon, Sparling, Wood** c-2. **Simon/Kirby** a-3r. **Torres** a-1?. **Wildey** a-1(3). **Williamson** a-2, 3r. **Wood** a-2(2).*

UNEXPECTED, THE (Formerly Tales of the...)
National Per. Publ./DC Comics: No. 105, Feb-Mar, 1968 - No. 222, May, 1982

105-Begin 12¢ cover price 6 12 18 40 73 105
106-113: 113-Last 12¢ issue (6-7/69) 5 10 15 30 50 70
114,115,117,118,120-125 4 8 12 22 35 48
116 (36 pgs.)-Wrightson-a 4 8 12 23 37 50
119-Wrightson-a, 8pgs.(36 pgs.) 5 10 15 31 53 75
126,127,129-136-(52 pgs.) 4 8 12 22 35 48
128(52 pgs.)-Wrightson-a 5 10 15 31 53 75
137-156 3 6 9 15 22 28
157-162-(100 pgs.) 4 8 12 28 47 65
163-188: 187,188-(44 pgs.) 2 4 6 11 16 20
189,190,192-195 ($1.00, 68 pgs.): 189 on are combined with House of Secrets
& The Witching Hour 2 4 6 13 18 22
191-Rogers-a(p) ($1.00, 68 pgs.) 3 6 9 14 19 24
196-222: 200-Return of Johhny Peril by Tuska. 205-213-Johnny Peril app.
210-Time Warp story. 222-Giffen-a 2 4 6 8 10 12
NOTE: ***Neal Adams** c-110, 112-115, 118, 121, 124. **J. Craig** a-195. **Ditko** a-189, 221p, 222p; c-222. **Drucker** a-107r, 132r. **Giffen** a-219, 222. **Kaluta** c-203, 212. **Kirby** a-127r, 162. **Kubert** c-204, 214-216, 219-221. **Mayer** a-217p, 220, 221p. **Moldoff** a-136r. **Moreira** a-133. **Mortimer** a-212p. **Newton** a-204p. **Orlando** a-202; c-191. **Perez** a-217p. **Redondo** a-155, 166, 195. **Reese** a-145. **Sparling** a-107, 205-209p, 212p. **Spiegle** a-217. **Starlin** c-198. **Toth** a-126r, 127r. **Tuska** a-127, 132, 134, 136, 139, 152, 180, 200p. **Wildey** a-128r, 193. **Wood** a-122i, 133i, 137i, 138i. **Wrightson** a-161r(2 pgs.). Johnny Peril in #106-114, 116, 117, 200, 205-213.*

UNEXPECTED, THE
DC Comics: Dec, 2011 ($7.99, one-shot)

1-Short horror stories by various incl. Gibbons, Thompson, Lapham, Fialkov; 2 covers 8.00

UNEXPECTED ANNUAL, THE (See DC Special Series #4)

UNFOLLOW
DC Comics (Vertigo): Jan, 2016 - No 18, Jun, 2017 ($3.99)

1-18: 1-Rob Williams-s/Mike Dowling-a. 6-R.M. Guéra-a. 7-Marguerite Sauvage-a 4.00
... Special Edition 1 (3/16, $4.99) r/#1&2 5.00

UNHOLY GRAIL
AfterShock Comics: July, 2017 - No. 5, Dec, 2017 ($3.99)

1-5-Cullen Bunn-s/Mirko Colak-a. 1-Multiple covers. 2-Covers by Colak & Francavillla 4.00

UNHOLY UNION
Image Comics (Top Cow): July, 2007 ($3.99, one-shot)

1-Witchblade & The Darkness meet Hulk, Ghost Rider & Doctor Strange; Silvestri-c 4.00

UNIDENTIFIED FLYING ODDBALL (See Walt Disney Showcase #52)

UNION
Image Comics (WildStorm Productions): June, 1993 - No. 0, July, 1994 ($1.95, lim. series)

0-(7/94, $2.50) 3.00
0-Alternate Portacio-c (See Deathblow #5) 5.00
1-($2.50)-Embossed foil-c; Texeira-c/a in all 4.00
1-($1.95)-Newsstand edition w/o foil-c 3.00
2-4: 4-(7/94) 3.00

UNION
Image Comics (WildStorm Prod.): Feb, 1995 - No. 9, Dec, 1995 ($2.50)

1-3,5-9: 3-Savage Dragon app. 6-Fairchild from Gen 13 app. 3.00
4-($1.95, Newsstand)-WildStorm Rising Pt. 3 3.00

United Comics #25 © UFS

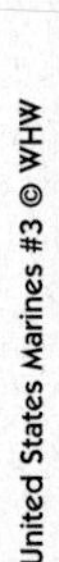
United States Marines #3 © WHW

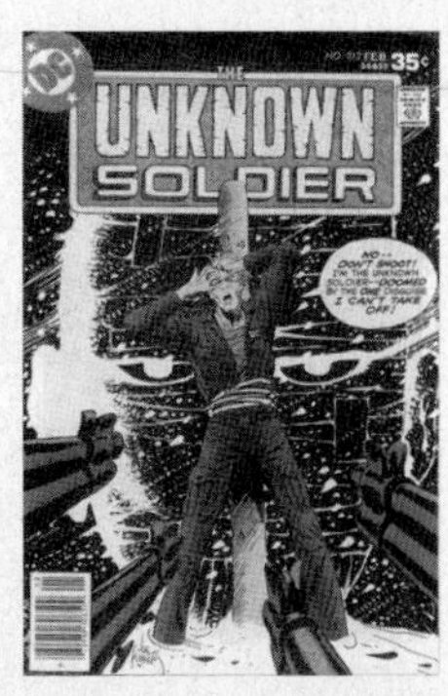

Unknown Soldier #212 © DC

GD 2.0 | VG 4.0 | FN 6.0 | VF 8.0 | VF/NM 9.0 | NM- 9.2

4-($2.50, Direct Market)-WildStorm Rising Pt. 3, bound-in card 3.00

UNION: FINAL VENGEANCE
Image Comics (WildStorm Productions): Oct, 1997 ($2.50)
1-Golden-c/Heisler-s 3.00

UNION JACK
Marvel Comics: Dec, 1998 - No. 3, Feb, 1999 ($2.99, limited series)
1-3-Raab-s/Cassaday-s/a 3.00

UNION JACK
Marvel Comics: Nov, 2006 - No. 4, Feb, 2007 ($2.99, limited series)
1-4-Gage-s/Perkins-c/a 3.00
...: London Falling TPB (2007, $10.99) r/#1-4; Perkins sketch page 11.00

UNITED COMICS (Formerly Fritzi Ritz #7; has Fritzi Ritz logo)
United Features Syndicate: Aug, 1940; No. 8, 1950 - No. 26, Jan-Feb, 1953
1(68 pgs.)-Fritzi Ritz & Phil Fumble 29 58 87 170 278 385
8-Fritzi Ritz, Abbie & Slats 11 22 33 62 86 110
9-20: 20-Strange As It Seems; Russell Patterson Cheesecake-a
10 20 30 56 76 95
21-(3-4/52) 2 pg. early Peanuts by Schulz; ties with Tip Top Comics #173 for 1st app. of Peanuts in comics. (Also see Tip Topper Comics) 129 258 387 826 1413 2000
22-(5-6/52) 2 pgs. early Peanuts by Schulz (3rd app.)
47 94 141 296 498 700
23-26: 23-(7-8/52). 24-(9-10/52). 25-(11-12/52). 26-(1-2/53). All have 2 pgs. early Peanuts by Schulz 25 50 75 150 245 340
NOTE: *Abbie & Slats reprinted from Tip Top.*

UNITED NATIONS, THE (See Classics Illustrated Special Issue)

UNITED STATES AIR FORCE PRESENTS: THE HIDDEN CREW
U.S. Air Force: 1964 (36 pgs.)
nn-Schaffenberger-a 2 4 6 11 16 20

UNITED STATES FIGHTING AIR FORCE (Also see U.S. Fighting Air Force)
Superior Comics Ltd.: Sept, 1952 - No. 29, Oct, 1956
1 17 34 51 100 158 215
2 11 22 33 62 86 110
3-10 10 20 30 54 72 90
11-29 9 18 27 50 65 80

UNITED STATES MARINES
William H. Wise/Life's Romances Publ. Co./Magazine Ent. #5-8/Toby Press #7-11: 1943 - No. 4, 1944; No. 5, 1952 - No. 8, 1952; No. 7 - No. 11, 1953
nn-Mart Bailey-c/a; Marines in the Pacific theater 34 68 102 204 332 460
2-Bailey-a; Tojo classic-c 119 238 357 762 1306 1850
3-Classic WWII Tojo-c 106 212 318 673 1162 1650
4-WWII photos; Tony DiPreta-a; grey-tone-c 18 36 54 107 169 230
5(A-1 #55)-Bailey-a, 6(A-1 #60), 8(A-1 #72) 14 28 42 76 108 140
7(A-1 #68) Flamethrower with burning bodies-c 20 40 60 117 189 260
7-11 (Toby) 12 24 36 69 97 125
NOTE: ***Powell** a-5-7.*

UNITED STATES OF MURDER INC., THE
Marvel Comics (Icon): May, 2014 - No. 6, Feb, 2015 ($3.99)
1-6-Bendis-s/Oeming-a 4.00

UNITY
Valiant: No. 0, Aug, 1992 - No. 1, 1992 (Free comics w/limited dist., 20 pgs.)
0 (Blue)-Prequel to Unity x-overs in all Valiant titles; B. Smith-c/a. (Free to everyone that bought all 8 titles that month.) 5.00
0 (Red)-Same as above, but w/red logo (5,000) 4 8 12 25 40 55
1-Epilogue to Unity x-overs; B. Smith-c/a. (1 copy available for every 8 Valiant books ordered by dealers.) 5.00
1 (Gold), 1-(Platinum)-Promotional copy. 2 4 6 8 10 12
... : The Lost Chapter 1 (Yearbook) (2/95, $3.95)-"1994" in indicia 4.00

UNITY
Valiant Entertainment: Nov, 2013 - Present ($3.99)
1-24: Multiple covers on each. 1-Kindt-s/Braithwaite-a. 5,6-Cafu-a 4.00
25-($4.99) Short stories by various incl. Kindt, Asmus, Kano, Jordan, Schkade 5.00
#0 (10/14, $3.99) Kindt-s/Nord-a; the story of Unit Y in WW One 4.00

UNITY 2000 (See preludes in Shadowman #3,4 flipbooks)
Acclaim Comics: Nov, 1999 - No. 3, Jan, 2000 ($2.50, unfinished limited series planned for 6 issues)
Preview -B&W plot preview and cover art; paper cover 3.00
1-3-Starlin-a/Shooter-s 3.00

UNIVERSAL MONSTERS
Dark Horse Comics: 1993 ($4.95/$5.95, 52 pgs.)(All adapt original movies)
Creature From the Black Lagoon nn-($4.95)-Art Adams/Austin-c/a, Dracula nn-($4.95), Frankenstein nn-($3.95)-Painted-c/a, The Mummy nn-($4.95)-Painted-c
1 2 3 4 5 7
...: Cavalcade of Horror TPB (1/06, $19.95) r/one-shots; Eric Powell intro. & cover 20.00

UNIVERSAL PICTURES PRESENTS DRACULA-THE MUMMY& OTHER STORIES
Dell Publishing Co.: Sept-Nov, 1963 (one-shot, 84 pgs.) (Also see Dell Giants)
02-530-311-r/Dracula 12-231-212, The Mummy 12-437-211 & part of Ghost Stories No. 1
15 30 45 100 220 340

UNIVERSAL SOLDIER (Movie)
Now Comics: Sept, 1992 - No. 3, Nov, 1992 (Limited series, polybagged, mature)
1-3 ($2.50, Direct Sales) 1-Movie adapatation; hologram on-c (all direct sales editions have painted-c) 4.00
1-3 ($1.95, Newsstand)-Rewritten & redrawn code approved version; all newsstand editions have photo-c 3.00

UNIVERSAL WAR ONE
Marvel Comics (Soleil): 2008 - No. 3, 2008 ($5.99, limited series)
1-3-Denis Bajram-s/a; English version of French comic. 1-Bajram interview 6.00
...: Revelations 1-3 (2009 - No. 3, 2009, $5.99) Bajram-s/a 6.00

UNIVERSE
Image Comics (Top Cow): Sept, 2001 - No. 8, July, 2002 ($2.50)
1-7-Jenkins-s 3.00
8-($4.95) extra short-s by Jenkins; pin-up pages 5.00

UNIVERSE X (See Earth X)
Marvel Comics: Sept, 2000 - No. 12, Sept, 2001 ($3.99/$3.50, limited series)
0-Ross-c/Braithwaite-a/Ross & Krueger-s 4.00
1-12: 5-Funeral of Captain America 4.00
... Beasts (6/00, $3.99) Yeates-a/Ross-c 4.00
... Cap (Capt. America) (2/01, $3.99) Yeates & Totleben-a/Ross-c; Cap dies 4.00
... 4 (Fantastic 4) (10/00, $3.99) Brent Anderson-a/Ross-c 4.00
... Iron Men (9/01, $3.99) Anderson-a/Ross-c; leads into #12 4.00
... Omnibus (6/01, $3.99) Ross B&W sketchbook and character bios 4.00
Sketchbook- Wizard supplement; B&W character sketches and bios 3.00
...Spidey (1/01, $3.99) Romita Sr. flashback-a/Guice-a/Ross-c 4.00
...X (11/01, $3.99) Series conclusion; Braithwaith-a/Ross wraparound-c 4.00
Volume 1 TPB (1/02, $24.95) r/#0-7 & Spidey, 4, & Cap; new Ross-c 25.00
Volume 2 TPB (6/02, $24.95) r/#8-12 &X, Beasts, Iron Men and Omnibus 25.00

UNKNOWN, THE
BOOM! Studios: May, 2009 - No. 4, Aug, 2009 ($3.99)
1-4-Mark Waid-s/Minck Oosterveer-a; two covers on each 4.00
...: The Devil Made Flesh 1-4 (9/09 - No. 4, 12/09, $3.99) Waid-s/Oosterveer-a 4.00

UNKNOWN MAN, THE (Movie)
Avon Periodicals: 1951
nn-Kinstler-c 34 68 102 204 332 460

UNKNOWN SOLDIER (Formerly Star-Spangled War Stories)
National Periodical Publications/DC Comics: No. 205, Apr-May, 1977 - No. 268, Oct, 1982 (See Our Army at War #168 for 1st app.)
205 3 6 9 17 26 35
206-210,220,221,251: 220,221 (44pgs.). 251-Enemy Ace begins
3 6 9 14 19 24
211-218,222-247,250,252-264 2 4 6 11 16 20
219-Miller-a (44 pgs.) 3 6 9 16 23 30
248,249,265-267: 248,249-Origin. 265-267-Enemy Ace vs. Balloon Buster.
2 4 6 11 16 20
268-Death of Unknown Soldier 3 6 9 19 30 40
NOTE: ***Chaykin** a-234. **Evans** a-265-267; c-235. **Kubert** c-Most. **Miller** a-219p. **Severin** a-251-253, 260, 261, 265-267. **Simonson** a-254-256. **Spiegle** a-258, 259, 262-264.*

UNKNOWN SOLDIER, THE (Also see Brave &the Bold #146)
DC Comics: Winter, 1988-'89 - No. 12, Dec, 1989 ($1.50, maxi-series, mature)
1-12: 8-Begin $1.75-c 5.00

UNKNOWN SOLDIER
DC Comics (Vertigo): Apr, 1997 - No 4, July, 1997 ($2.50, mini-series)
1-Ennis-s/Plunkett-a/Bradstreet-c in all 6.00
2-4 4.00
TPB (1998, $12.95) r/#1-4 13.00

UNKNOWN SOLDIER

Unlimited Access #2 © DC & MAR

The Unstoppable Wasp #3 © MAR

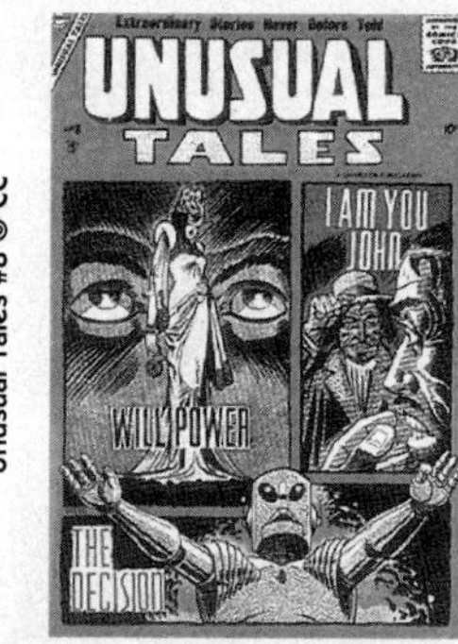

Unusual Tales #8 © CC

	GD 2.0	VG 4.0	FN 6.0	VF 8.0	VF/NM 9.0	NM- 9.2

DC Comics (Vertigo): Dec, 2008 - No. 25, Dec, 2010 ($2.99)

1-25: 1-Dysart-s/Ponticelli-a; intro. Lwanga Moses; two covers by Kordey and Corben. 2-20,22-25-Ponticelli-a. 21-Veitch-a 3.00
...: Beautiful World TPB (2011, $14.99) r/#21-25; Dysart afterword; sketch/design art 15.00
...: Dry Season TPB (2010, $14.99) r/#15-20; war history 15.00
...: Easy Kill TPB (2010, $17.99) r/#7-14; war history 18.00
...: Haunted House TPB (2009, $9.99) r/#1-6; glossary 10.00

UNKNOWN WORLD (Strange Stories From Another World #2 on)
Fawcett Publications: June, 1952

	GD	VG	FN	VF	VF/NM	NM-
1-Norman Saunders painted-c	57	114	171	362	619	875

UNKNOWN WORLDS (See Journey Into...)

UNKNOWN WORLDS
American Comics Group/Best Synd. Features: Aug, 1960 - No. 57, Aug, 1967

	GD	VG	FN	VF	VF/NM	NM-
1-Schaffenberger-c	21	42	63	147	324	500
2-Dinosaur-c/story	10	20	30	64	132	200
3-5	8	16	24	56	108	160
6-11: 9-Dinosaur-c/story. 11-Last 10¢ issue	7	14	21	46	86	125
12-19: 12-Begin 12¢ issues?; ends #57	6	12	18	37	66	95
20-Herbie cameo (12-1/62-63)	6	12	18	38	69	100
21-35: 27-Devil on-c. 31-Herbie one pagers thru #39	5	10	15	30	50	70
36- "The People vs. Hendricks" by Craig; most popular ACG story ever	5	10	15	31	53	75
37-46	4	8	12	27	44	60
47-Williamson-a r-from Adventures Into the Unknown #96, 3 pgs.; Craig-a	4	8	12	28	47	65
48-57: 53-Frankenstein app.	4	8	12	25	40	55

NOTE: ***Ditko** a-49, 50p, 54. **Forte** a-3, 6, 11. **Landau** a-56(2). **Reinman** a-3, 9, 13, 20, 22, 23, 36, 38, 54. **Whitney** c/a-most issues. John Force, Magic Agent app.-35, 36, 48, 50, 52, 54, 56.*

UNKNOWN WORLDS OF FRANK BRUNNER
Eclipse Comics: Aug, 1985 - No. 2, Aug, 1985 ($1.75)

1,2-B&W-r in color 4.00

UNKNOWN WORLDS OF SCIENCE FICTION
Marvel Comics: Jan, 1975 - No. 6, Nov, 1975; 1976 ($1.00, B&W Magazine)

	GD	VG	FN	VF	VF/NM	NM-
1-Williamson/Krenkel/Torres/Frazetta-r/Witzend #1, Neal Adams-r/Phase 1; Brunner & Kaluta-r; Freas/Romita-c	3	6	9	16	23	30
2-6: 5-Kaluta text illos	3	6	9	14	19	24
Special 1(1976,100 pgs.)-Newton painted-c	3	6	9	15	22	28

NOTE: ***Brunner** a-2; c-4, 6. **Buscema** a-Special 1p. **Chaykin** a-5. **Colan** a(p)-1, 3, 5, 6. **Corben** a-4. **Kaluta** a-2, Special 1(ext illos); c-2. **Morrow** a-3, 5. **Nino** a-3, 6, Special 1. **Perez** a-2, 3. Ray Bradbury interview in #1.*

UNLIMITED ACCESS (Also see Marvel Vs. DC))
Marvel Comics: Dec, 1997 - No. 4, Mar, 1998 ($2.99/$1.99, limited series)

1-Spider-Man, Wonder Woman, Green Lantern & Hulk app. 4.00
2,3-($1.99): 2-X-Men, Legion of Super-Heroes app. 3-Original Avengers vs. original Justice League 3.00
4-($2.99) Amalgam Legion vs. Darkseid & Magneto 4.00

UN-MEN, THE
DC Comics (Vertigo): Oct, 2007 - No. 13, Oct, 2008 ($2.99)

1-13-Whalen-s/Hawthorne-a/Hanuka-c 3.00
...: Children of Paradox TPB (2008, $19.99) r/#6-13 20.00
...: Get Your Freak On! TPB (2008, $9.99) r/#1-5; cover gallery 10.00

UNSANE (Formerly Mighty Bear #13, 14? or The Outlaws #10-14?)(Satire)
Star Publications: No. 15, June, 1954

	GD	VG	FN	VF	VF/NM	NM-
15-Disbrow-a(2); L. B. Cole-c	36	72	108	211	343	475

UNSEEN, THE
Visual Editions/Standard Comics: No. 5, 1952 - No. 15, July, 1954

	GD	VG	FN	VF	VF/NM	NM-
5-Horror stories in all; Toth-a	52	104	156	328	552	775
6,7,9,10-Jack Katz-a	41	82	123	250	418	585
8,11,13,14	37	74	111	222	361	500
12,15-Toth-a. 12-Tuska-a	41	82	123	250	418	585

NOTE: ***Nick Cardy** c-12. **Fawcette** a-13, 14. **Sekowsky** a-7, 8(2), 10, 13, 15.*

UNSTOPPABLE WASP, THE
Marvel Comics: Mar, 2017 - No. 8, Oct, 2017 ($3.99)

1-8: 1-6-Whitley-s/Charretier-a. 1-Ms. Marvel & Mockingbird app. 2,3-Moon Girl app. 4.00

UNTAMED
Marvel Comics (Epic Comics/Heavy Hitters): June, 1993 - No. 3, Aug, 1993 ($1.95, lim. series)

1-($2.50)-Embossed-c 4.00
2,3 3.00

UNTAMED LOVE (Also see Frank Frazetta's Untamed Love)
Quality Comics Group (Comic Magazines): Jan, 1950 - No. 5, Sept, 1950

	GD	VG	FN	VF	VF/NM	NM-
1-Ward-c, Gustavson-a	41	82	123	250	418	485
2,4: 2-5-Photo-c	21	42	63	126	206	285
3,5-Gustavson-a	22	44	66	132	216	300

UNTOLD LEGEND OF CAPTAIN MARVEL, THE
Marvel Comics: Apr, 1997 - No. 3, June, 1997 ($2.50, limited series)

1-3 5.00

UNTOLD LEGEND OF THE BATMAN, THE (Also see Promotional section)
DC Comics: July, 1980 - No. 3, Sept, 1980 (Limited series)

	GD	VG	FN	VF	VF/NM	NM-
1-Origin; Joker-c; Byrne's 1st work at DC	1	3	4	6	8	10
2,3						6.00

NOTE: ***Aparo** a-1i, 2, 3. **Byrne** a-1p.*

UNTOLD ORIGIN OF THE FEMFORCE, THE (Also see Femforce)
AC Comics: 1989 ($4.95, 68 pgs.)

1-Origin Femforce; Bill Black-a(i) & scripts 6.00

UNTOLD TALES OF BLACKEST NIGHT (Also see Blackest Night crossover titles)
DC Comics: Dec, 2010 ($4.99, one-shot)

1-Short stories by various incl. Johns, Benes, Booth; 2 covers by Kirkham & Van Sciver 5.00

UNTOLD TALES OF CHASTITY
Chaos! Comics: Nov, 2000 ($2.95, one-shot)

1-Origin; Steven Grant-s/Peter Vale-c/a 3.00
1-Premium Edition with glow in the dark cover 10.00

UNTOLD TALES OF LADY DEATH
Chaos! Comics: Nov, 2000 ($2.95, one-shot)

1-Origin of Lady Death; Cremator app.; Kaminski-s 3.00
1-Premium Edition with glow in the dark cover by Steven Hughes 10.00

UNTOLD TALES OF PUNISHER MAX
Marvel Comics: Aug, 2012 - No. 5, Dec, 2012 ($4.99/$3.99, limited series)

1-($4.99) Anthology; Starr-s/Boschi-a/c 5.00
2-5-($3.99) 2-Andrews-c. 3-Ribic-c. 5-Skottie Young-s/Del Mundo-c 4.00

UNTOLD TALES OF PURGATORI
Chaos! Comics: Nov, 2000 ($2.95, one-shot)

1-Purgatori in 57 B.C.; Rio-a/Grant-s 3.00
1-Premium Edition with glow in the dark cover 10.00

UNTOLD TALES OF SPIDER-MAN (Also see Amazing Fantasy #16-18)
Marvel Comics: Sept, 1995 - No. 25, Sept, 1997 (99¢)

1-Kurt Busiek scripts begin; Pat Olliffe-c/a in all (except #9). 4.00
2-22, -1(7/97), 23-25: 2-1st app. Batwing. 4-1st app. The Spacemen (Gantry, Orbit, Satellite & Vacuum). 8-1st app. The Headsman; The Enforcers (The Big Man, Montana, The Ox & Fancy Dan) app. 9-Ron Frenz-a. 10-1st app. Commanda. 16-Reintro Mary Jane Watson. 21-X-Men-c/app. 25-Green Goblin 3.00
...'96-(1996, $1.95, 46 pgs.)-Kurt Busiek scripts; Mike Allred-c/a; Kurt Busiek & Pat Olliffe app. in back-up story; contains pin-ups 4.00
...'97-(1997, $1.95)-Wraparound-c 4.00
...: Strange Encounters ('98, $5.99) Dr. Strange app. 6.00

UNTOLD TALES OF THE NEW UNIVERSE (Based on Marvel's 1986 New Universe titles)
Marvel Comics: May, 2006 ($2.99, series of one-shots)

...: D. P. 7 - Takes place between issues #4 & 5 of D. P. 7 series; Bright-a/Cebulski-s 3.00
...: Justice - Peter David-s/Carmine Di Giandomenico-a 3.00
...: Nightmask - Takes place between issues #4 & 5 of Nightmask series; The Gnome app. 3.00
...: Psi-Force - Tony Bedard-s/Russ Braun-a 3.00
...: Star Brand - Romita & Romita Jr.-c/Pulido-a 3.00
TPB (2006, $15.99) r/one-shots & stories from Amaz. Fantasy #18,19 & New Avengers #16 16.00

UNTOUCHABLES, THE (TV)
Dell Publishing Co.: No. 1237, 10-12/61 - No. 4, 8-10/62 (All have Robert Stack photo-c)

	GD	VG	FN	VF	VF/NM	NM-
Four Color 1237(#1)	17	34	51	114	252	390
Four Color 1286	12	24	36	80	173	265
01-879-207, 12-879-210(01879-210 on inside)	8	16	24	54	102	150

UNTOUCHABLES
Caliber Comics: Aug, 1997 - No. 4 ($2.95, B&W)

1-4: 1-Pruett-s; variant covers by Kaluta & Showman 3.00

UNUSUAL TALES (Blue Beetle & Shadows From Beyond #50 on)
Charlton Comics: Nov, 1955 - No. 49, Mar-Apr, 1965

	GD	VG	FN	VF	VF/NM	NM-
1	32	64	96	192	314	435
2	17	34	51	98	154	210
3-5	14	28	42	82	121	160

The Unworthy Thor #5 © MAR

USA Comics #4 © MAR

Usagi Yojimbo #57 © Stan Sakai

GD VG FN VF VF/NM NM-
2.0 4.0 6.0 8.0 9.0 9.2

6-Ditko-c only 20 40 60 114 182 250
7,8-Ditko-c/a. 8-Robot-c 30 60 90 177 289 400
9-Ditko-c/a (20 pgs.) 32 64 96 192 314 435
10-Ditko-c/a(4) 34 68 102 199 325 450
11-(3/58, 68 pgs.)-Ditko-a(4) 32 64 96 192 314 435
12,14-Ditko-a 20 40 60 114 182 250
13,16-20 6 12 18 41 76 110
15-Ditko-c/a 25 50 75 150 245 340
21,24,28 5 10 15 35 63 90
22,23,25-27,29-Ditko-a 9 18 27 59 117 175
30-49 5 10 15 30 50 70
NOTE: ***Colan*** *a-11.* ***Ditko*** *c-22, 23, 25-27, 31(part).*

UNWORTHY THOR, THE (See Original Sin)
Marvel Comics: Jan, 2017 - No. 5, May, 2017 ($3.99)
1-5-Aaron-s/Coipel-a; multiple covers; Beta Ray Bill app. 2-Thanos app. 4.00

UNWRITTEN, THE
DC Comics (Vertigo): July, 2009 - Present ($1.00/$2.99)
1-($1.00) Intro. Tommy Taylor; Mike Carey-s/Peter Gross-a; two covers (white & black) 3.00
2-16,18-31,(31.5), 32, (32.5), 33, (33.5), 34, (34.5), (35.5), 36-49-($2.99): 31.5-Art by Gross, Kaluta, Geary & Talbot. 37-Series re-cap 3.00
17-($3.99) Story printed sideways; Pick-a-Story format 4.00
35-($4.99) 5.00
50-(8/13, $4.99) Fables characters app.; Carey & Willingham-s; Gross & Buckingham-a 5.00
51-54-Fables characters app. 3.00
...: Dead Man's Knock TPB (2011, $14.99) r/#13-18; intro. by novelist Steven Hall 15.00
...: Inside Man TPB (2010, $12.99) r/#6-12; intro. by Paul Cornell 13.00
...: Tommy Taylor and the Bogus Identity TPB (2010, $9.99) r/#1-5; sketch art; prose 10.00

UNWRITTEN, THE: APOCALYPSE
DC Comics (Vertigo): Mar, 2014 - No. 12, Mar, 2015 ($3.99)
1-11-Mike Carey-s/Peter Gross-a 4.00
12-($4.99) Mike Carey-s/Peter Gross-a 5.00

UP FROM HARLEM (Tom Skinner...)
Spire Christian Comics (Fleming H. Revell Co.): 1973 (35/49¢)
nn-(35¢ cover) 3 6 9 14 19 24
nn-(49¢ cover) 2 4 6 9 13 16

UP-TO-DATE COMICS
King Features Syndicate: No date (1938) (36 pgs.; B&W cover) (10¢)
nn-Popeye & Henry cover; The Phantom, Jungle Jim & Flash Gordon by Raymond, The Katzenjammer Kids, Curley Harper & others. Note: Variations in content exist. 32 64 96 188 307 425

UP YOUR NOSE AND OUT YOUR EAR (Satire)
Klevart Enterprises: Apr, 1972 - No. 2, June, 1972 (52 pgs., magazine)
V1#1,2 2 4 6 11 16 20

URTH 4 (Also see Earth 4)
Continuity Comics: May, 1989 - No. 4, Dec, 1990 ($2.00, deluxe format)
1-4: Ms. Mystic characters. 2-Neal Adams-c(i) 3.00

URZA-MISHRA WAR ON THE WORLD OF MAGIC THE GATHERING
Acclaim Comics (Armada): 1996 - No. 2, 1996 ($5.95, limited series)
1,2 6.00

U.S. (See Uncle Sam)

USA COMICS
Timely Comics (USA): Aug, 1941 - No. 17, Fall, 1945
1-Origin Major Liberty (called Mr. Liberty #1), Rockman by Wolverton; 1st app. The Whizzer by Avison; The Defender with sidekick Rusty & Jack Frost begin; The Young Avenger only app.; S&K-c plus 1 pg. art 1000 2000 3000 7000 12,500 20,000
2-Origin Captain Terror & The Vagabond; last Wolverton Rockman; Hitler-c 481 962 1443 3511 6206 8900
3-No Whizzer 371 742 1113 2600 4550 6500
4-Last Rockman, Major Liberty, Defender, Jack Frost, & Capt. Terror; Corporal Dix app.; "Remember Pearl Harbor" small cover logo 349 698 1047 2443 4272 6100
5-Origin American Avenger & Roko the Amazing; The Blue Blade, The Black Widow & Victory Boys, Gypo the Gypsy Giant & Hills of Horror only app.; Sergeant Dix begins; no Whizzer; Hitler, Mussolini & Tojo-c 497 994 1491 3628 6414 9200
6-Captain America (ends #17), The Destroyer, Jap Buster Johnson, Jeep Jones begin; Terror Squad only app. 919 1838 2757 6709 11,855 17,000
7-Captain Daring, Disk-Eyes the Detective by Wolverton app.; origin & only app. Marvel Boy (3/43); Secret Stamp begins; no Whizzer, Sergeant Dix; classic Schomburg-c 1200 2400 3600 9120 16,560 24,000

GD VG FN VF VF/NM NM-
2.0 4.0 6.0 8.0 9.0 9.2

8-Classic Japanese WWII bondage/torture-c 865 1730 2595 6315 11,158 16,000
9-Last Secret Stamp; Hitler-c; classic-c 919 1838 2757 6709 11,855 17,000
10-The Thunderbird only app.; Schomburg Japanese WWII-c 757 1514 2271 5526 9763 14,000
11-13: 11-No Jeep Jones. 13-No Whizzer; Jeep Jones ends; Schomburg Japanese WWII-c 459 918 1377 3350 5925 8500
14-17: 15-No Destroyer; Jap Buster Johnson ends 219 438 657 1402 2401 3400
NOTE: ***Brodsky*** *c-14.* ***Gabrielle*** *c-4.* ***Schomburg*** *c-6, 7, 10, 12, 13, 15-17.* ***Shores*** *a-1, 4; c-9, 11.* ***Ed Win*** *a-4. Cover features: 1-The Defender; 2, 3-Captain Terror; 4-Major Liberty; 5-Victory Boys; 6-17-Captain America & Bucky.*

USA COMICS 70TH ANNIVERSARY SPECIAL
Marvel Comics: Sept, 2009 ($3.99, one-shot)
1-New story of The Destroyer; Arcudi-s/Ellis-a; r/All Winners #3; two covers 5.00

U.S. AGENT (See Jeff Jordan...)

U.S. AGENT (See Captain America #354)
Marvel Comics: June, 1993 - No. 4, Sept, 1993 ($1.75, limited series)
1-4 3.00

U.S. AGENT
Marvel Comics: Aug, 2001 - No. 3, Oct, 2001 ($2.99, limited series)
1-3: Ordway-s/a(p)/c. 2,3-Captain America app. 3.00

USAGI YOJIMBO (See Albedo, Doomsday Squad #3 & Space Usagi)
Fantagraphics Books: July, 1987 - No. 38 ($2.00/$2.25, B&W)
1 4 8 12 25 40 55
1,8,10-2nd printings 3.00
2-9 6.00
10,11: 10-Leonardo app. (TMNT). 11-Aragonés-a 1 2 3 5 6 8
12-29 4.00
30-38: 30-Begin $2.25-c 5.00
Color Special 1 (11/89, $2.95, 68 pgs.)-new & r 4.00
Color Special 2 (10/91, $3.50) 4.00
Color Special #3 (10/92, $3.50)-Jeff Smith's Bone promo on inside-c 4.00
Summer Special 1 (1986, B&W, $2.75)-r/early Albedo issues 4.00

USAGI YOJIMBO
Mirage Studios: V2#1, Mar, 1993 - No. 16, 1994 ($2.75)
V2#1-16: 1-Teenage Mutant Ninja Turtles app. 3.00

USAGI YOJIMBO
Dark Horse Comics: V3#1, Apr, 1996 - Present ($2.95/$2.99/$3.50, B&W)
V3#1-99,101-116: Stan Sakai-c/a 3.50
100-(1/07, $3.50) Stan Sakai roast by various incl. Aragonés, Wagner, Miller, Geary 1 2 3 5 6 8
117-150-($3.50) 136-Variant-c. 141-"200th issue" 3.50
151-165-($3.99) 152-The River Rising 4.00
...: One For One (8/10, $1.00) Reprints #1 3.00
Color Special #4 (7/97, $2.95) "Green Persimmon" 3.00
Color Special #5: The Artist (7/14, $3.99) Bonus preview of Usagi Yojimbo: Senso 4.00
Daisho TPB ('98, $14.95) r/Mirage series #7-14 15.00
Demon Mask TPB ('01, $15.95) 16.00
Glimpses of Death TPB (7/06, $15.95) r/#76-82 16.00
Grasscutter TPB ('99, $16.95) r/#13-22 17.00
Gray Shadows TPB ('00, $14.95) r/#23-30 15.00
Seasons TPB ('99, $14.95) r/#7-12 15.00
Shades of Death TPB ('97, $14.95) r/Mirage series #1-6 15.00
The Brink of Life and Death TPB ('98, $14.95) r/Mirage series #13,15,16 & Dark Horse series #1-6 15.00
The Shrouded Moon TPB (1/03, $15.95) r/#46-52 16.00

USAGI YOJIMBO: SENSO
Dark Horse Comics: Aug, 2014 - No. 6, Jan, 2015 ($3.99, B&W)
1-6-Stan Sakai-s/c/a; Martian invasion set 20 years later; wraparound-c on each 4.00

U.S. AIR FORCE COMICS (Army Attack #38 on)
Charlton Comics: Oct, 1958 - No. 37, Mar-Apr, 1965
1 6 12 18 41 76 110
2 4 8 12 25 40 55
3-10 3 6 9 21 33 45
11-20 3 6 9 19 30 40
21-37 3 6 9 16 23 30
NOTE: ***Glanzman*** *c/a-9, 10, 12.* ***Montes/Bache*** *a-33.*

USA IS READY
Dell Publishing Co.: 1941 (68 pgs., one-shot)
1-War propaganda 50 100 150 315 533 750

U.S.Avengers #3 © MAR

U.S. War Machine #8 © MAR

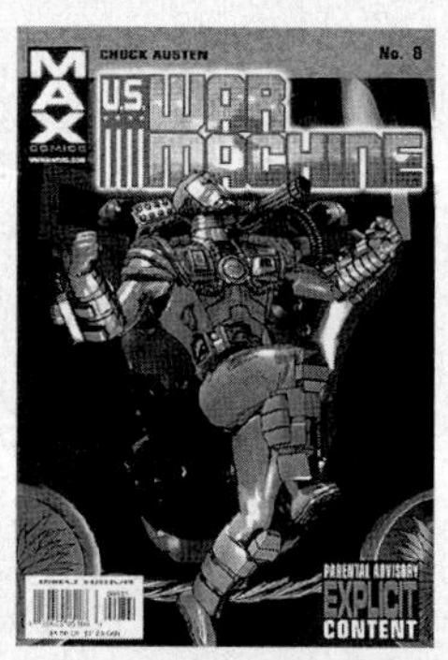

Valor #1 © WMG

GD VG FN VF VF/NM NM-
2.0 4.0 6.0 8.0 9.0 9.2

U.S.AVENGERS (Also see Avengers #675 -678)
Marvel Comics: Mar, 2017 - No. 12, Jan, 2017 ($3.99)

1-3-Ewing-s/Medina-a; team of Squirrel Girl, Cannonball, Iron Patriot, Enigma, Red Hulk. 5-9-Secret Empire tie-ins. 11,12-Archie Riverdale spoof; Skrulls app. 4.00

U.S. BORDER PATROL COMICS (Sgt. Dick Carter of the...) (See Holyoke One Shot)

USER
DC Comics (Vertigo): 2001 - No. 3, 2001 ($5.95, limited series)

1-3-Devin Grayson-s; Sean Phillips & John Bolton-a 6.00

U.S. FIGHTING AIR FORCE (Also see United States Fighting Air Force)
I. W. Enterprises: No date (1960s?)

1,9(nd): 1-r/United States Fighting...#?. 9-r/#1 2 4 6 8 11 14

U.S. FIGHTING MEN
Super Comics: 1963 - 1964 (Reprints)

10-r/With the U.S. Paratroops #4(Avon) 2 4 6 9 13 16
11,12,15-18: 11-r/Monty Hall #10. 12,16,17,18-r/U.S. Fighting Air Force #10,3,?&? 15-r/Man Comics #11 2 4 6 9 13 16

U.S. JONES (Also see Wonderworld Comics #28)
Fox Feature Syndicate: Nov, 1941 - No. 2, Jan, 1942

1-U.S. Jones & The Topper begin; Nazi-c 226 452 678 1446 2473 3500
2-Nazi-c 206 412 618 1318 2259 3200

U.S. MARINES
Charlton Comics: Fall, 1964 (12¢, one-shot)

1-1st app. Capt. Dude; Glanzman-a 5 10 15 30 50 70

U.S. MARINES IN ACTION
Avon Periodicals: Aug, 1952 - No. 3, Dec, 1952

1-Louis Ravielli-c/a 14 28 42 82 121 160
2,3: 3-Kinstler-c 10 20 30 58 79 100

U.S. 1
Marvel Comics Group: May, 1983 - No. 12, Oct, 1984 (7,8: painted-c)

1-12: 2-Sienkiewicz-c. 3-12-Michael Golden-c 4.00

U.S. PARATROOPS (See With the...)

U.S. PARATROOPS
I. W. Enterprises: 1964?

1,8: 1-r/With the U.S. Paratroops #1; Wood-c. 8-r/With the U.S. Paratroops #6; Kinstler-c 2 4 6 9 13 16

U.S. TANK COMMANDOS
Avon Periodicals: June, 1952 - No. 4, Mar, 1953

1-Kinstler-c 14 28 42 82 121 160
2-4: Kinstler-c 11 22 33 62 86 110
I.W. Reprint #1,8: 1-r/#1. 8-r/#3 2 4 6 9 13 16

NOTE: ***Kinstler*** *a-I.W. #1; c-1-4, I.W. #1, 8.*

U.S. WAR MACHINE (Also see Iron Man and War Machine)
Marvel Comics (MAX): Nov, 2001 - No. 12, Jan, 2002 ($1.50, B&W, weekly limited series)

1-12-Chuck Austen-s/a/c 3.00
TPB (12/01, $14.95) r/#1-12 15.00

U.S. WAR MACHINE 2.0
Marvel Comics (MAX): Sept, 2003 - No. 3, Sept, 2003 ($2.99, weekly, limited series)

1-3-Austen-s/Christian Moore-CGI art 3.00

"V" (TV)
DC Comics: Feb, 1985 - No. 18, July, 1986

1-Based on TV movie & series (Sci/Fi) 5.00
2-18: 17,18-Denys Cowan-c/a 4.00

VACATION COMICS (Also see A-1 Comics)
Magazine Enterprises: No. 16, 1948 (one-shot)

A-1 16-The Pixies, Tom Tom, Flying Fredd & Koko & Kola 9 18 27 50 65 80

VACATION DIGEST
Harvey Comics: Sept, 1987 ($1.25, digest size)

1 1 2 3 5 6 8

VACATION IN DISNEYLAND (Also see Dell Giants)
Dell Publishing Co./Gold Key (1965): Aug-Oct, 1959; May, 1965 (Walt Disney)

Four Color 1025-Barks-a 14 28 42 93 204 315
1(30024-508)(G.K., 5/65, 25¢)-r/Dell Giant #30 & cover to #1 ('58); celebrates Disneyland's 10th anniversary 5 10 15 31 53 75

VACATION PARADE (See Dell Giants)

VALEN THE OUTCAST
BOOM! Studios: Dec, 2011 - No. 8, Jul, 2012 ($1.00/$3.99)

1-($1.00) Nelson-s/Scalera-a; eight covers 3.00
2-8-($3.99) 2-4-Six covers on each. 5-8-Five covers on each 4.00

VALERIA THE SHE BAT
Continuity Comics: May, 1993 - No. 5, Nov, 1993

1-Premium; acetate-c; N. Adams-a/scripts; given as gift to retailers 1 2 3 5 6 8
5 (11/93)-Embossed-c; N. Adams-a/scripts 3.00

NOTE: *Due to lack of continuity, #2-4 do not exist.*

VALERIA THE SHE BAT
Acclaim Comics (Windjammer): Sept, 1995 - No.2, Oct, 1995 ($2.50, limited series)

1,2 3.00

VALHALLA MAD
Image Comics: May, 2015 - No. 4, Aug, 2015 ($3.50, limited series)

1-4-Joe Casey-s/Paul Maybury-a 3.50

VALIANT, THE (Leads into Bloodshot Reborn series)
Valiant Entertainment: Dec, 2014 - No. 4, Mar, 2015 ($3.99, limited series)

1-4-Lemire & Kindt-s/Rivera-a; Eternal Warrior & Bloodshot app. 4.00

VALIANT...
Valiant Entertainment: May, 2012 - Present (giveaways)

... Comics FCBD 2012 Special 1 (5/12) Previews X-O Manowar, Harbinger and other Valiant 2012 titles; creator interviews 3.00
... FCBD 2013 Special #1 (5/13) Previews Harbinger Wars, X-O Manowar and others 3.00
... FCBD 2014 Armor Hunters Special #1 (5/14) Previews Armor Hunters and others 3.00
... FCBD 2014 Valiant Universe Handbook #1 (5/14) Character profiles 3.00
... FCBD 2015 Valiant 25th Anniversary Special (5/15) Previews Bloodshot and Ninjak 3.00
... : 4001 A.D. FCBD Special (5/16) Prelude to the 4001 A.D. series; Crain-c 3.00
... Masters: 2013 Showcase Edition #1 (5/13) Samples of hardcover volume offerings 3.00
... Universe Handbook 2015 Edition #1 (5/15, $2.99) Character profiles 3.00
... Universe Handbook 2016 Edition #1 (8/16, $2.99) Character profiles 3.00
... : X-O Manowar 2017 FCBD Special (5/17) Short stories of X-O Manowar, Secret Weapons, Bloodshot Salvation 3.00

VALKYRIE (See Airboy)
Eclipse Comics: May, 1987 - No. 3, July, 1987 ($1.75, limited series)

1-3: 2-Holly becomes new Black Angel 3.00

VALKYRIE
Marvel Comics: Jan, 1997; Nov, 2010 ($2.95/$3.99, one-shots)

1-(1/97, $2.95) w/pin-ups 4.00
1-(11/10, $3.99) Origin re-told; Winslade-a/Glass-s; Anacleto-c 4.00

VALKYRIE!
Eclipse Comics: July, 1988 - No. 3, Sept, 1988 ($1.95, limited series)

1-3 3.00

VALLEY OF THE DINOSAURS (TV)
Charlton Comics: Apr, 1975 - No. 11, Dec, 1976 (Hanna-Barbera)

1-W. Howard-i 3 6 9 15 20 26
2,4-11: 2-W. Howard-i 2 4 6 8 11 14
3-Byrne text illos (early work, 7/75) 2 4 6 10 14 18

VALLEY OF THE DINOSAURS (Volume 2)
Harvey Comics: Oct, 1993 ($1.50, giant-sized)

1-Reprints 5.00

VALLEY OF GWANGI (See Movie Classics)

VALOR
E. C. Comics: Mar-Apr, 1955 - No. 5, Nov-Dec, 1955

1-Williamson/Torres-a; Wood-c/a 31 62 93 248 392 535
2-Williamson-c/a; Wood-a 25 50 75 200 318 435
3,4: 3-Williamson, Crandall-a. 4-Wood-c 19 38 57 152 244 335
5-Wood-c/a; Williamson/Evans-a 18 36 54 144 227 310

NOTE: ***Crandall*** *a-3, 4.* ***Ingels*** *a-1, 2, 4, 5.* ***Krigstein*** *a-1-5.* ***Orlando*** *a-3, 4; c-3.* ***Wood*** *a-1, 2, 5; c-1, 4, 5.*

VALOR
Gemstone Publishing: Oct, 1998 - No. 5, Feb, 1999 ($2.50)

1-5-Reprints 4.00

VALOR (Also see Legion of Super-Heroes & Legionnaires)
DC Comics: Nov, 1992 - No. 23, Sept, 1994 ($1.25/$1.50)

Valor #21 © DC

Vampirella #38 © WP

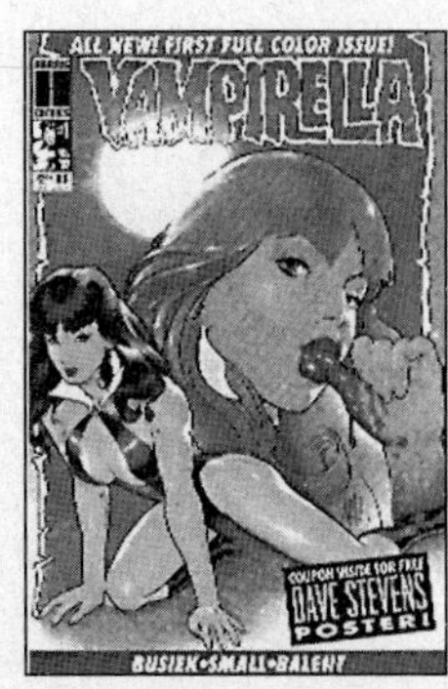

Vampirella (1992 series) #1 © Harris

1-22: 1-Eclipso The Darkness Within aftermath. 2-Vs. Supergirl. 4-Vs. Lobo. 12-Lobo cameo. 14-Legionnaires, JLA app. 17-Austin-c(i); death of Valor. 18-22-Build-up to Zero Hour 3.00
23-Zero Hour tie-in 3.00

VALOR THUNDERSTAR AND HIS FIREFLIES
Now Comics: Dec, 1986 ($1.50)
1-Ordway-c(p) 3.00

VAMPI (Vampirella's...)
Harris Publications (Anarchy Studios): Aug, 2000 - No. 25, Feb, 2003 ($2.95/$2.99)
Limited Edition Preview Book (5/00) Preview pages & sketchbook 3.00
1-(8/00, $2.95) Lau-a(p)/Conway-s 5.00
1-Platinum Edition 20.00
2-25: 17-Barberi-a 4.00
2-25-Deluxe Edition variants ($9.95): 4-Finch-c. 5-Wieringo-c. 6-Cha-c 10.00
...Digital 1 (11/01, $2.95) CGI art; Haberlin-s 4.00
...Digital Preview (Anarchy Studios, 7/01, $2.95) preview of CGI art 4.00
Switchblade Kiss HC (2001, $24.95) r/#1-6 25.00
Vicious Preview Ed. (Apr, 2003, $1.99) Flip book w/ Xin: Journey of the Monkey King Preview Ed. 4.00
Wizard #1/2 (mail order, $9.95) includes sketch pages 10.00

VAMPIRE BITES
Brainstorm Comics: May, 1995 - No. 2, Sept, 1996 ($2.95, B&W)
1,2:1-Color pin-up 3.00

VAMPIRE DIARIES, THE (Based on the CW television series)
DC Comics: Mar, 2014 - Present ($3.99, printings of online comics)
1-6: 1,3-Doran-s/Shasteen-a. 5-Calero-a. 6-Doran-s/a 4.00

VAMPIRE LESTAT, THE
Innovation Publishing: Jan, 1990 - No. 12, 1991 ($2.50, painted limited series)
1-Adapts novel; Bolton painted-c on all 2 4 6 10 14 18
1-2nd printing (has UPC code, 1st prints don't) 3.00
1-3rd & 4th printings 3.00
2-1st printing 1 2 3 5 6 8
2-2nd & 3rd printings 3.00
3-5 5.00
3-6,9-2nd printings 3.00
6-12 4.00

VAMPIRELLA (Magazine)(See Warren Presents)(Also see Heidi Saha)
Warren Publishing Co./Harris Publications #113: Sept, 1969 - No. 112, Feb, 1983; No. 113, Jan, 1988? (B&W)
1-Intro. Vampirella in original costume & wings; Frazetta-c/intro. page; Adams-a; Crandall-a 46 92 138 368 834 1300
2-1st app. Vampirella's cousin Evily-c/s; 1st/only app. Draculina, Vampirella's blonde twin sister 12 24 36 79 170 260
3 (Low distribution) 25 50 75 175 388 600
4,6 8 16 24 54 102 150
5,7,9: 5,7-Frazetta-c. 9-Barry Smith-a; Boris/Wood-c 9 18 27 57 111 165
8-Vampirella begins by Tom Sutton as serious strip (early issues-gag line) 9 18 27 59 117 175
10-No Vampi story; Brunner, Adams, Wood-a 6 12 18 40 73 105
11-Origin & 1st app. Pendragon; Frazetta-c 7 14 21 46 86 125
12-Vampi by Gonzales begins 7 14 21 46 86 125
13-15: 14-1st Maroto-a; Ploog-a 6 12 18 42 79 115
16,22,25: 16-1st full Dracula-c/app. 22-Color insert preview of Maroto's Dracula. 25-Vampi on cocaine-s 6 12 18 41 76 110
17,18,20,21,23,24: 17-Tomb of the Gods begins by Maroto, ends #22. 18-22-Dracula-s 6 12 18 38 69 100
19 (1973 Annual) Creation of Vampi text bio 7 14 21 44 82 120
26,28,34,35,39,40: All have 8 pg. color inserts. 28-Board game inside covers. 34,35-1st Fleur the Witch Woman. 39,40-Color Dracula-s. 40-Wrightson bio 5 10 15 33 57 80
27 (1974 Annual) New color Vampi-s; mostly-r 6 12 18 37 66 95
29,38,45: 38-2nd Vampi as Cleopatra/Blood Red Queen of Hearts; 1st Mayo-a. 5 10 15 31 53 75
30-32: 30-Intro. Pantha; Corben-a(color). 31-Origin Luana, the Beast Girl. 32-Jones-a 5 10 15 33 57 80
33-Wrightson-a; Pantha ends 5 10 15 33 57 80
36,37: 36-1st Vampi as Cleopatra/Blood Red Queen of Hearts; issue has 8 pg. color insert. 37-(1975 Annual) 5 10 15 34 60 85
41-44,47,48: 41-Dracula-s 4 8 12 28 47 65
46-(10/75) Origin-r from Annual 1 5 10 15 30 50 70
49-1st Blind Priestess; The Blood Red Queen of Hearts storyline begins; Poe-s 4 8 12 28 47 65
50-Spirit cameo by Eisner; 40 pg. Vampi-s; Pantha & Fleur app.; Jones-a 4 8 12 28 47 65
51-53,56,57,59-62,65,66,68,75,79,80,82-86,88,89: 60-62,65,66-The Blood Red Queen of Hearts app. 60-1st Blind Priestess-c 4 8 12 23 37 50
54,55,63,81,87: 54-Vampi-s (42 pgs.); 8 pg. color Corben-a. 55-All Gonzales-a(r). 63-10 pgs. Wrightson-a 4 8 12 23 37 50
58,70,72: 58-(92 pgs.) 70-Rook app. 4 8 12 27 44 60
64,73: 64-(100 pg. Giant) All Mayo-a; 70 pg. Vampi-s. 73-69 pg. Vampi-s; Mayo-a 4 8 12 28 47 65
67,69,71,74,76-78-All Barbara Leigh photo-c 4 8 12 27 44 60
90-99: 90-Toth-a. 91-All-r; Gonzales-a. 93-Cassandra St. Knight begins, ends #103; new Pantha series begins, ends #108 4 8 12 23 37 50
100 (96 pg. r-special)-Origin reprinted from Ann. 1; mostly reprints; Vampirella appears topless in new 21 pg. story 6 12 18 41 76 110
101-104,106,107: All lower print run. 101,102-The Blood Red Queen of Hearts app. 107-All Maroto reprint-a issue 5 10 15 34 60 85
105,108-110: 108-Torpedo series by Toth begins; Vampi nudity splash page. 110-(100 pg. Summer Spectacular) 5 10 15 34 60 85
111,112: Low print run. 111-Giant Collector's Edition ($2.50) 112-(84 pgs.) last Warren issue 7 14 21 46 86 125
113 (1988)-1st Harris Issue; very low print run 23 46 69 161 356 550
Annual 1(1972)-New definitive origin of Vampirella by Gonzales; reprints by Neal Adams (from #1), Wood (from #9) 19 38 57 131 291 450
Special 1 (1977) Softcover (color, large-square bound)-Only available thru mail order 14 28 42 94 207 320
Special 1 (1977) Hardcover (color, large-square bound)-Only available through mail order (scarce)(500 produced, signed & #'d) 30 60 90 212 476 740
#1 1969 Commemorative Edition (2001, $4.95) reprints entire #1 5.00
...Crimson Chronicles Vol. 1 (2004, $19.95, TPB) reprints stories from #1-10 20.00
...Crimson Chronicles Vol. 2 (2005, $19.95, TPB) reprints stories from #11-18 20.00
...Crimson Chronicles Vol. 3 (2005, $19.95, TPB) reprints stories from #19-28 20.00
...Crimson Chronicles Vol. 4 (2006, $19.95, TPB) reprints stories from #29-41 20.00
NOTE: ***Ackerman*** *s-1-3.* ***Neal Adams*** *a-1, 10p, 19p(r/#10), 44(1 pg.), Annual 1.* ***Alcala*** *a-78, 90, 93i.* ***Bodé/Todd*** *c-3.* ***Bodé/Jones*** *c-4.* ***Boris/Wood*** *c-9.* ***Brunner*** *a-10, 12(1 pg.).* ***Corben*** *a-30, 31, 33, 36, 54; c-30, 31, 33, 54.* ***Crandall*** *a-1, 19(r/#1).* ***Frazetta*** *c-1, 5, 7, 11, 31.* ***Heath*** *a-58, 61, 67, 76-78, 83.* ***Infantino*** *a-57-62.* ***Jones*** *a-5, 9, 12, 27, 32 (color), 33(2 pg.), 34, 50i, 83r.* ***Ken Kelly*** *c-6, 38, 39, 40(back-c), 46, 70, 95.* ***Nebres*** *a-84, 88-90, 92-96.* ***Nino*** *a-59i, 61i, 67, 76, 85, 90.* ***Ploog*** *a-14.* ***Barry Smith*** *a-9.* ***Starlin*** *a-78.* ***Sutton*** *a-1-5, 7-11, Annual 1.* ***Toth*** *a-90i, 108, 110.* ***Wood*** *a-9, 10, 12, 19(r/#12), 27r, Annual 1; c-9(partial).* ***Wrightson*** *a-33(w/****Jones****), 40(Bio cameo) 63r. All reprint issues-19, 74, 83, 91, 105, 107, 109, 111. Annuals from 1973 on are included in regular numbering. Later annuals are same format as regular issues. Color inserts (8 pgs.) in 22, 25-28, 30-35, 39, 40, 45, 46, 49, 54, 55, 67, 72. 16 pg color insert in #36.*

VAMPIRELLA (Also see Cain/... & Vengeance of...)
Harris Publications: Nov, 1992 - No. 5, Nov, 1993 ($2.95)
0-Bagged 6.00
0-Gold 3 6 9 16 24 32
1-Jim Balent inks in #1-3; Adam Hughes c-1-3 2 4 6 13 18 22
1-2nd printing 5.00
1-(11/97) Commemorative Edition 4.00
2 2 4 6 9 13 16
3-5: 4-Snyder III-c. 5-Brereton painted-c 1 2 3 5 6 8
Trade paperback nn (10/93, $5.95)-r/#1-4; Jusko-c 1 3 4 6 8 10
NOTE: *Issues 1-5 contain certificates for free* ***Dave Stevens*** *Vampirella poster.*

VAMPIRELLA (THE NEW MONTHLY)
Harris Publications: Nov, 1997 - No. 26, Apr, 2000 ($2.95)
1-3-"Ascending Evil" -Morrison & Millar-s/Conner & Palmiotti-a. 1-Three covers by Quesada/Palmiotti, Conner, and Conner/Palmiotti 5.00
1-3-($9.95) Jae Lee variant covers 10.00
1-($24.95) Platinum Ed.w/Quesada-c 25.00
4-6-"Holy War"-Small & Stull-a, 4-Linsner variant-c 4.00
7-9-"Queen's Gambit"-Shi app. 7-Two covers. 8-Pantha-c/app. 4.00
7-($9.95) Conner variant-c 10.00
10-12-"Hell on Earth"; Small-a/Coney-s. 12-New costume 4.00
10-Jae Lee variant-c 1 3 4 6 8 10
13-15-"World's End" Zircher-p; Pantha back-up, Texeira-a 4.00
16,17: 16-Pantha-c;Texeira-a; Vampi back-up story. 17-(Pantha #2) 4.00
18-20-"Rebirth": Jae Lee-c on all. 18-Loeb-s/Sale-a. 19-Alan Davis-a. 20-Bruce Timm-a 4.00
18-20-($9.95) Variant covers: 18-Sale. 19-Davis. 20-Timm 12.00
21-26: 21,22-Dangerous Games; Small-a. 23-Lady Death-c/app.; Cleavenger-a. 24,25-Lau-a. 26-Lady Death & Pantha-c/app.; Cleavenger-a. 4.00
0-(1/99) also variant-c with Pantha #0; same contents 4.00
TPB ($7.50) r/#1-3 "Ascending Evil" 8.00
Ascending Evil Ashcan (8/97, $1.00) 3.00
...: Grant Morrison/Mark Millar Collection TPB (2006, $24.95) r/#1-6; interviews 25.00
Hell on Earth Ashcan (7/98, $1.00) 3.00

Vampirella (2010 series) #38 © DYN

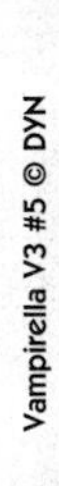
Vampirella V3 #5 © DYN

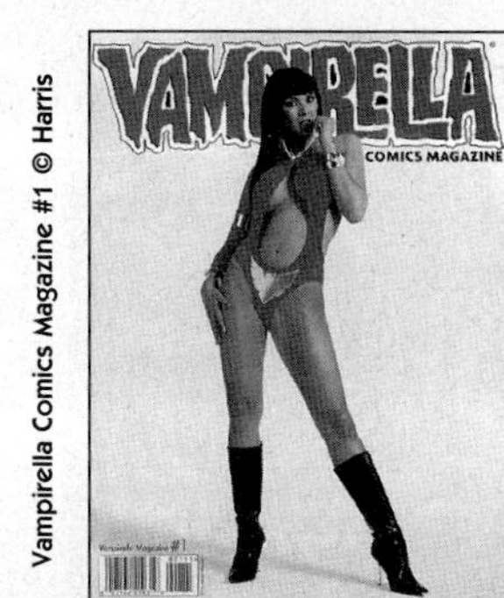

Vampirella Comics Magazine #1 © Harris

GD 2.0 | VG 4.0 | FN 6.0 | VF 8.0 | VF/NM 9.0 | NM- 9.2

... Presents: Tales of Pantha TPB (2006, $19.95) r/stories from #13-17 & one-shots 20.00
The End Ashcan (3/00, $6.00) 6.00
...30th Anniversary Celebration Preview (7/99) B&W preview of #18-20 10.00

VAMPIRELLA
Harris Publications: June, 2001 - No. 22, Aug, 2003 ($2.95/$2.99)

1-Four covers (Mayhew w/foil logo, Campbell, Anacleto, Jae Lee) Mayhew-a; Mark Millar-s 5.00
2-22: 2-Two covers (Mayhew & Chiodo). 3-Timm var-c. 4-Horn var-c. 7-10-Dawn Brown-a; Pantha back-up w/Texeira-a. 15-22-Conner-c 4.00
Giant-Size Ashcan (5/01, $5.95) B&W preview art and Mayhew interview 6.00
...: Halloween Trick & Treat (10/04, $4.95) stories & art by various; three covers 5.00
... : Nowheresville Preview Edition (3/01, $2.95)- previews Mayhew art and photo models 4.00
...Nowheresville TPB (1/02, $12.95) r/#1-3 with cover gallery 13.00
... Summer Special #1 (2005, $5.95) Batman Begins photo-c and 2 variant-c 6.00
...: 2006 Halloween Special (2006, $2.95) Conner-c; Hester-s/Segovia-a; 4 covers 4.00

VAMPIRELLA
Dynamite Entertainment: 2010 - No. 38, 2014 ($3.99)

1-Four covers (Campbell, Madureira, J. Djurdjevic, Alex Ross swipe of Frazetta's #1) 4.00
1-Variant-c of blood-soaked Vampirella by Alex Ross 8.00
2-37: 2-6-Trautmann-s/Wagner Reis-a; four covers. 7-Geovani-a 4.00
38-($4.99, 40 pgs.) Pantha and Dracula app. 5.00
Annual 1 (2011, $4.99) Jerwa-s/Casalos-a; reprint with Alan Davis-a 5.00
Annual 2 (2012, $4.99) Rahner-s/Kyriazis-a; reprint with Pantha app.; Linsner-c 5.00
Annual 2013 ($4.99) Rahner-s/Valiente-a/Bolson-c 5.00
...: NuBlood (2013, $4.99) Spoof of True Blood; Rahner-s/Razek-a/c; back-up w/Timm-a 5.00
... Vs. Fluffy (2012, $4.99) Spoof of Buffy the Vampire Slayer; Bradshaw-c 5.00

VAMPIRELLA (Volume 2)
Dynamite Entertainment: 2014 - No. 13, 2015 ($3.99)

1-12: Multiple covers on each. 1-Nancy Collins-s/Berkenkotter-a 4.00
13-($4.99) Lord Drago app.; Collins-s/Berkenkotter-a; 3 covers 5.00
#100 (2015, $7.99) Short stories by various incl. Tim Seeley; multiple covers 8.00
#1969 (2015, $7.99) Short stories by various incl. Hester & Worley; 2 covers 8.00
Annual 2015 ($5.99) Collins-s/Aneke-a/Anacleto-c 6.00
...: Prelude to Shadows (2014, $7.99) Collins-s/Zamora-a; r/Vampirella #13 w/new color 8.00

VAMPIRELLA (Volume 3)
Dynamite Entertainment: 2016 - No. 6, 2016 ($3.99)

1-6: Multiple covers on each. 1-Kate Leth-s/Eman Casallos-a; new costume 4.00

VAMPIRELLA (Volume 4)
Dynamite Entertainment: 2017 - Present ($3.99)

#0-(25¢) Multiple covers; Cornell-s/Broxton-a 3.00
1-10-($3.99) Vampirella in the far future. 1-5-Cornell-s/Broxton-a. 6-10-Belanger-a 4.00

VAMPIRELLA / ALIENS
Dynamite Entertainment: 2015 - No. 6, 2016 ($3.99, limited series)

1-6-Corinna Bechko-s/Javier Garcia-Miranda-a; multiple covers on each 4.00

VAMPIRELLA & PANTHA SHOWCASE
Harris Publications: Jan, 1997 ($1.50, one-shot)

1-Millar-s/Texeira-c/a; flip book w/"Blood Lust"; Robinson-s/Jusko-c/a 4.00

VAMPIRELLA & THE BLOOD RED QUEEN OF HEARTS
Harris Publications: Sept, 1996 ($9.95, 96 pgs., B&W, squarebound, one-shot)

nn-r/Vampirella #49,60-62,65,66,101,102; John Bolton-c; Michael Bair back-c 1 3 4 6 8 10

VAMPIRELLA AND THE SCARLET LEGION
Dynamite Entertainment: 2011 - No. 5 ($3.99)

1-5: 1-Three covers (Campbell, Chen and Tucci); Malaga-a 4.00

VAMPIRELLA / ARMY OF DARKNESS
Dynamite Entertainment: 2015 - No. 4, 2015 ($3.99, limited series)

1-4-Ash meets Vampirella in 1300 AD; Mark Rahner-s/Jeff Morales-a 4.00

VAMPIRELLA: BLOODLUST
Harris Publications: July, 1997 - No. 2, Aug, 1997 ($4.95, limited series)

1,2-Robinson-s/Jusko-painted c/a 5.00

VAMPIRELLA CLASSIC
Harris Publications: Feb, 1995 - No. 5, Nov, 1995 ($2.95, limited series)

1-5: Reprints Archie Goodwin stories. 4.00

VAMPIRELLA COMICS MAGAZINE
Harris Publications: Oct, 2003 - No. 9 ($3.95/$9.95, magazine-sized)

1-9-($3.95) 1-Texiera-c; b&w and color stories, Alan Moore interview; reviews. 2-KISS interview. 4-Chiodo-c. 6-Brereton-c 4.00
1-9-($9.95) 1-Three covers (Model Photo cover, Palmiotti-c, Wheatley Frankenstein-c) 10.00

VAMPIRELLA: CROSSOVER GALLERY
Harris Publications: Sept, 1997 ($2.95, one-shot)

1-Wraparound-c by Campbell, pinups by Jae Lee, Mack, Allred, Art Adams, Quesada & Palmiotti and others 4.00

VAMPIRELLA: DEATH & DESTRUCTION
Harris Publications: July, 1996 - No. 3, Sept, 1996 ($2.95, limited series)

1-3: Amanda Conner-a(p) in all. 1-Tucci-c. 2-Hughes-c. 3-Jusko-c 4.00
1-($9.95)-Limited Edition; Beachum-c 10.00

VAMPIRELLA/DRACULA & PANTHA SHOWCASE
Harris Publications: Aug, 1997 ($1.50, one-shot)

1-Ellis, Robinson, and Moore-s; flip book w/"Pantha" 4.00

VAMPIRELLA/DRACULA: THE CENTENNIAL
Harris Publications: Oct, 1997 ($5.95, one-shot)

1-Ellis, Robinson, and Moore-s; Beachum, Frank/Smith, and Mack/Mays-a Bolton-painted-c 6.00

VAMPIRELLA: FEARY TALES
Dynamite Entertainment: 2014 - No. 5, 2015 ($3.99, limited series)

1-5: Anthology of short stories by various; multiple covers on each 4.00

VAMPIRELLA: INTIMATE VISIONS
Harris Publications: 2006 ($3.95, one-shots)

..., Amanda Conner 1 - r/Vampirella Monthly #1 with commentary; interview; 2 covers 4.00
..., Joe Jusko 1 - r/Vampirella; Blood Lust #1 with commentary; interview; 2 covers 4.00

VAMPIRELLA: JULIE STRAIN SPECIAL
Harris Publications: Sept, 2000 ($3.95, one-shot)

1-Photo-c w/yellow background; interview and photo gallery 4.00
1-Limited Edition ($9.95); cover photo w/black background 10.00

VAMPIRELLA/LADY DEATH (Also see Lady Death/Vampirella)
Harris Publications: Feb, 1999 ($3.50, one-shot)

1-Small-a/Nelson painted-c 4.00
1-Valentine Edition ($9.95); pencil-c by Small 10.00

VAMPIRELLA: LEGENDARY TALES
Harris Publications: May, 2000 - No. 2, June, 2000 ($2.95, B&W)

1,2-Reprints from magazine; Cleavenger painted-c 4.00
1,2-($9.95) Variant painted-c by Mike Mayhew 10.00

VAMPIRELLA LIVES
Harris Publications: Dec, 1996 - No. 3, Feb, 1997 ($3.50/$2.95, limited series)

1-Die cut-c; Quesada & Palmiotti-c, Ellis-s/Conner-a 5.00
1-Deluxe Ed.-photo-c 5.00
2,3-($2.95)-Two editions (1 photo-c): 3-J. Scott Campbell-c 4.00

VAMPIRELLA: MORNING IN AMERICA
Harris Publications/Dark Horse Comics: 1991 - No. 4, 1992 ($3.95, B&W, lim. series, 52 pgs.)

1,2-All have Kaluta painted-c 1 2 3 5 6 8
3,4 1 3 4 6 8 10

VAMPIRELLA OF DRAKULON
Harris Publications: Jan, 1996 - No. 5, Sept, 1996 ($2.95)

0-5: All reprints. 0-Jim Silke-c. 3-Polybagged w/card. 4-Texeira-c 4.00

VAMPIRELLA/PAINKILLER JANE
Harris Publications: May, 1998 ($3.50, one-shot)

1-Waid & Augustyn-s/Leonardi & Palmiotti-a 4.00
1-($9.95) Variant-c 10.00

VAMPIRELLA PIN-UP SPECIAL
Harris Publications: Oct, 1995 ($2.95, one-shot)

1-Hughes-c, pin-ups by various 5.00
1-Variant-c 5.00

VAMPIRELLA QUARTERLY
Harris Publications: Spring, 2007 - Summer, 2008 ($4.95/$4.99, quarterly)

Spring, 2007 - Summer, 2008-New stories and re-colored reprints; five or six covers 5.00

VAMPIRELLA: RETRO
Harris Publications: Mar, 1998 - No. 3, May, 1998 ($2.50, B&W, limited series)

1-3: Reprints; Silke painted covers 4.00

VAMPIRELLA: REVELATIONS

Vampire, PA #2 © Vaughn & Solof

Vampire Tales #6 © MAR

Vanguard #6 © Image

GD VG FN VF VF/NM NM-
2.0 4.0 6.0 8.0 9.0 9.2

Harris Publications: No. 0, Oct, 2005 - No. 3, Feb, 2006 ($2.99, limited series)

0-3-Vampirella's origin retold, Lilith app.; Carey-s/Lilly-a; two covers on each 4.00
... Book 1 TPB (2006, $12.95) r/series; Carey interview, script for #1, Lilly sketch pages 13.00

VAMPIRELLA: SAD WINGS OF DESTINY
Harris Publications: Sept, 1996 ($3.95, one-shot)

1-Jusko-c 5.00

VAMPIRELLA: SECOND COMING
Harris Publications: 2009 - No. 4 ($1.99, limited series)

1-4: 1-Hester-s/Sampere-a; multiple covers on each. 3,4-Rio-a 4.00

VAMPIRELLA/SHADOWHAWK: CREATURES OF THE NIGHT (Also see Shadowhawk)
Harris Publications: 1995 ($4.95, one-shot)

1 5.00

VAMPIRELLA/SHI (See Shi/Vampirella)
Harris Publications: Oct, 1997 ($2.95, one-shot)

1-Ellis-s 4.00
1-Chromium-c 6.00

VAMPIRELLA: SILVER ANNIVERSARY COLLECTION
Harris Publications: Jan, 1997 - No. 4 Apr, 1997 ($2.50, limited series)

1-4: Two editions: Bad Girl by Beachum, Good Girl by Silke 4.00

VAMPIRELLA: SOUTHERN GOTHIC
Dynamite Entertainment: 2013 - No. 5, 2014 ($3.99)

1-5-Nate Cosby-s/José Luis-a; regular & photo-c on each 4.00

VAMPIRELLA'S SUMMER NIGHTS
Harris Publications: 1992 (one-shot)

1-Art Adams infinity cover; centerfold by Stelfreeze 2 4 6 10 14 18

VAMPIRELLA STRIKES
Harris Publications: Sept, 1995 - No. 8, Dec, 1996 ($2.95, limited series)

1-8: 1-Photo-c. 2-Deodato-c; polybagged w/card. 5-Eudaemon-c/app; wraparound-c; alternate-c exists. 6-(6/96)-Mark Millar script; Texeira-c; alternate-c exists. 7-Flip book 4.00
1-Newsstand Edition; diff. photo-c., 1-Limited Ed.; diff. photo-c 4.00
Annual 1-(12/96, $2.95) Delano-s; two covers 4.00

VAMPIRELLA STRIKES
Dynamite Entertainment: 2013 - No. 6, 2013 ($3.99)

1-6: 1-Five covers (Turner, Finch, Manara, Desjardins & photo); Desjardins-a 4.00

VAMPIRELLA THE RED ROOM
Dynamite Entertainment: 2012 - No. 4, 2012 ($3.99)

1-4-Three covers on each; Brereton-s/Diaz-a 4.00

VAMPIRELLA: 25TH ANNIVERSARY SPECIAL
Harris Publications: Oct, 1996 ($5.95, squarebound, one-shot)

nn-Reintro The Blood Red Queen of Hearts; James Robinson, Grant Morrison & Warren Ellis scripts; Mark Texeira, Michael Bair & Amanda Conner-a(p); Frank Frazetta-c 7.00
nn-($6.95)-Silver Edition 8.00

VAMPIRELLA VS. DRACULA
Dynamite Entertainment: 2012 - No. 6, 2012 ($3.99, limited series)

1-6-Harris-s/Rodriguez-a/Linsner-c 4.00

VAMPIRELLA VS. HEMORRHAGE
Harris Publications: Apr, 1997 ($3.50)

1 4.00

VAMPIRELLA VS. PANTHA
Harris Publications: Mar, 1997 ($3.50)

1-Two covers; Millar-s/Texeira-c/a 4.00

VAMPIRELLA/WETWORKS (See Wetworks/Vampirella)
Harris Publications: June, 1997 ($2.95, one-shot)

1 4.00
1-($9.95) Alternate Edition; cardstock-c 10.00

VAMPIRELLA/WITCHBLADE
Harris Publications: 2003; Oct, 2004; Oct, 2005 ($2.99, one-shots)

1-Brian Wood-s/Steve Pugh-a; 3 covers by Texeira, Conner and Pugh 4.00
...: The Feast (10/05, $2.99) Joyce Chin-a; covers by Chin, Conner, Rodriguez 4.00
...: Union of the Damned (10/04, $2.99, one-shot) Sharp-a; three covers 4.00
Trilogy TPB (2006, $12.95) r/one-shots; art gallery and gallery of multiple covers 13.00

VAMPIRE, PA
Moonstone: 2010 - No. 3, Oct, 2010 ($3.99)

1-3: 1-Intro. Vampire Hunter Dean; J.C. Vaughn-s/Brendon & Brian Fraim-a; three covers. 3-Zombie Proof back-up; Spencer-a 4.00

VAMPIRE'S CHRISTMAS, THE (Also see Dark Ivory)
Image Comics: Oct, 2003 ($5.95, over-sized graphic novel)

nn-Linsner-s/a; Dubisch-painted-a 6.00

VAMPIRES: THE MARVEL UNDEAD
Marvel Comics: Dec, 2011 ($3.99, one-shot)

1-Handbook-style profiles of vampire characters in the Marvel Universe; Seeley-c 4.00

VAMPIRE TALES
Marvel Comics Group: Aug, 1973 - No. 11, June, 1975 (75¢, B&W, magazine)

	GD 2.0	VG 4.0	FN 6.0	VF 8.0	VF/NM 9.0	NM- 9.2
1-Morbius, the Living Vampire begins by Pablo Marcos (1st solo Morbius series & 5th Morbius app.)	7	14	21	48	89	130
2-Intro. Satana; Steranko-r	9	18	27	59	117	175
3,5,6: 3-Satana app. 5-Origin Morbius. 6-1st full Lilith app. in this title (continued from Giant-Size Chillers #1)	5	10	15	30	50	70
4,7: 4-1st Lilith cameo app. on inside back-c	4	8	12	27	44	60
8-1st solo Blade story (see Tomb of Dracula)	6	12	18	40	73	105
9-Blade app.	5	10	15	30	50	70
10,11	4	8	12	23	37	50
Annual 1(10/75)-Heath-r/#9	4	8	12	25	40	55

NOTE: ***Alcala** a-6, 8, 9i. **Boris** c-4, 6. **Chaykin** a-7. **Everett** a-1r. **Gulacy** a-7p. **Heath** a-9. **Infantino** a-3r. **Gil Kane** a-4, 5r.*

VAMPIRE VERSES, THE
CFD Productions: Aug, 1995 - No. 4, 1995 ($2.95, B&W, mature)

1-4 3.00

VAMPI VICIOUS
Harris Publications (Anarchy Studios): Aug, 2003 - No. 3, Nov, 2003 ($2.99)

1-3: 1-McKeever-s/Dogan-a; 3 covers by Dogan, Lau & Noto. 3-Kau-a 4.00

VAMPI VICIOUS CIRCLE
Harris Publications (Anarchy Studios): Jun, 2004 - No. 3, Sept, 2004 ($2.99/$9.95)

1-3: B. Clay Moore-s 4.00
1-3-($9.95) Limited Edition w/variant-c. 1-Noto-c. 2-Norton-c. 3-Lucas-c 10.00

VAMPI VICIOUS RAMPAGE
Harris Publications (Anarchy Studios): Feb, 2005 - No. 2, Apr, 2005 ($2.99)

1,2: Raab-s/Lau-a; two covers on each 4.00

VAMPI VS. XIN
Harris Publications (Anarchy Studios): Oct, 2004 - No. 2, Jan, 2005 ($2.99)

1,2-Faerber-s/Lau-a; two covers 4.00

VAMPS
DC Comics (Vertigo): Aug, 1994 - No. 6, Jan, 1995 ($1.95, lim. series, mature)

1-6-Bolland-c 3.00
Trade paperback ($9.95)-r/#1-6 10.00

VAMPS: HOLLYWOOD & VEIN
DC Comics (Vertigo): Feb, 1996 - No. 6, July, 1996 ($2.25, lim. series, mature)

1-6: Winslade-c 3.00

VAMPS: PUMPKIN TIME
DC Comics (Vertigo): Dec, 1998 - No. 3, Feb, 1999 ($2.50, lim. series, mature)

1-3: Quitely-c 3.00

VANDROID
Dark Horse Comics: Feb, 2014 - No. 5, Jun, 2014 ($3.99, limited series)

1-5-Tommy Lee Edwards & Noah Smith-s/Dan McDaid-a/Edwards-c 4.00

VANGUARD (...Outpost: Earth) (See Megaton)
Megaton Comics: 1987 ($1.50)

1-Erik Larsen-c(p) 4.00

VANGUARD (See Savage Dragon #2)
Image Comics (Highbrow Entertainment): Oct, 1993 - No. 6, 1994 ($1.95)

1-6: 1-Wraparound gatefold-c; Erik Larsen back-up-a; Supreme x-over. 3-(12/93)-Indicia says December 1994. 4-Berzerker back-up. 5-Angel Medina-a(p) 3.00

VANGUARD (See Savage Dragon #2)
Image Comics: Aug, 1996 - No. 4, Feb, 1997 ($2.95, B&W, limited series)

1-4 3.00

VANGUARD: ETHEREAL WARRIORS
Image Comics: Aug, 2000 ($5.95, B&W)

1-Fosco & Larsen-a 6.00

Vault of Horror #15 © WMG

Velocity V2 #1 © TCOW

Venom (2003 series) #2 © MAR

VANGUARD ILLUSTRATED
Pacific Comics: Nov, 1983 - No. 11, Oct, 1984 (Baxter paper)(Direct sales only)

	GD 2.0	VG 4.0	FN 6.0	VF 8.0	VF/NM 9.0	NM- 9.2
1,3-6,8-11: 1-Nudity scenes						3.00
2-1st app. Stargrazers (see Legends of the Stargrazers; Dave Stevens-c	1	3	4	6	8	10
7-1st app. Mr. Monster (r-in Mr. Monster #1); nudity scenes						5.00

NOTE: ***Evans** a-7. **Kaluta** c-5, 7p. **Perez** a-6; c-6. **Rude** a-1-4; c-4. **Williamson** c-3.*

VANGUARD: STRANGE VISITORS
Image Comics: Oct, 1996 - No.4, Feb, 1997 ($2.95, B&W, limited series)

	GD 2.0	VG 4.0	FN 6.0	VF 8.0	VF/NM 9.0	NM- 9.2
1-4: 3-Supreme-c/app.						3.00

VAN HELSING: FROM BENEATH THE RUE MORGUE (Based on the 2004 movie)
Dark Horse Comics: Apr, 2004 ($2.99, one-shot)

	GD 2.0	VG 4.0	FN 6.0	VF 8.0	VF/NM 9.0	NM- 9.2
1-Hugh Jackman photo-c; Dysart-s/Alexander-a						3.00

VANITY (See Pacific Presents #3)
Pacific Comics: Jun, 1984 - No. 2, Aug, 1984 ($1.50, direct sales)

	GD 2.0	VG 4.0	FN 6.0	VF 8.0	VF/NM 9.0	NM- 9.2
1,2: Origin						3.00

VARIETY COMICS (The Spice of Comics)
Rural Home Publ./Croyden Publ. Co.: 1944 - No. 2, 1945; No. 3, 1946

	GD 2.0	VG 4.0	FN 6.0	VF 8.0	VF/NM 9.0	NM- 9.2
1-Origin Captain Valiant	26	52	78	154	252	350
2-Captain Valiant	16	32	48	94	147	200
3(1946-Croyden)-Captain Valiant	15	30	45	84	127	170

VARIETY COMICS (See Fox Giants)

VARSITY
Parents' Magazine Institute: 1945

	GD 2.0	VG 4.0	FN 6.0	VF 8.0	VF/NM 9.0	NM- 9.2
1	11	22	33	62	86	110

VAULT OF EVIL
Marvel Comics Group: Feb, 1973 - No. 23, Nov, 1975

	GD 2.0	VG 4.0	FN 6.0	VF 8.0	VF/NM 9.0	NM- 9.2
1 (1950s reprints begin)	4	8	12	27	44	60
2-23: 3,4-Brunner-c. 11-Kirby-a	3	6	9	17	26	35

NOTE: ***Ditko** a-14r, 15r, 20-22r. **Drucker** a-10r(Mystic #52), 13r(Uncanny Tales #42). **Everett** a-11r(Menace #2), 13r(Menace #4); c-10. **Heath** a-5r. **Gil Kane** c-1, 6. **Kirby** a-11. **Krigstein** a-20r(Uncanny Tales #54). **Reinman** r-1. **Tuska** a-6r.*

VAULT OF HORROR (Formerly War Against Crime #1-11) (Also see EC Archives)
E. C. Comics: No. 12, Apr-May, 1950 - No. 40, Dec-Jan, 1954-55

	GD 2.0	VG 4.0	FN 6.0	VF 8.0	VF/NM 9.0	NM- 9.2
12 (Scarce)-ties w/Crypt Of Terror as 1st horror comic	600	1200	1800	4800	7650	10,500
13-Morphine story	120	240	360	960	1530	2100
14	97	194	291	776	1238	1700
15- "Terror in the Swamp" is same story w/minor changes as "The Thing in the Swamp" from Haunt of Fear #15	89	178	267	712	1131	1550
16	71	142	213	568	909	1250
17-Classic werewolf-c	80	160	240	640	1020	1400
18,19	57	114	171	456	728	1000
20-25: 22-Frankenstein-c & adaptation. 23-Used in **POP**, pg. 84; Davis-a(2); Ingels bio. 24-Craig bio.	53	106	159	424	675	925
26-B&W & color illos in **POP**	53	106	159	424	675	925
27-29,31,33,34,36: 31-Ray Bradbury bio. 36- "Pipe Dream" classic opium addict story by Krigstein; "Twin Bill" cited in articles by T.E. Murphy, Wertham	49	98	147	392	621	850
30-Classic severed arm-c	77	154	231	616	983	1350
32-Censored-c	66	132	198	528	839	1150
35-X-Mas-c; "And All Through the House" adapted for 1972 Tales From The Crypt film	83	166	249	664	1057	1450
37-1st app. Drusilla, a Vampirella look alike; Williamson-a	60	120	180	480	765	1050
38	49	98	147	392	621	850
39-Classic Craig woman in bondage/torture-c	71	142	213	568	909	1250
40-Low distribution	53	106	159	424	675	925

NOTE: ***Craig** art in all but No. 13 & 33; c-12-40. **Crandall** a-33, 34, 39. **Davis** a-17-38. **Evans** a-27, 28, 30, 32, 33. **Feldstein** a-12-16. **Ingels** a-13-20, 22-40. **Kamen** a-15-22, 25, 29, 35. **Krigstein** a-36, 38-40. **Kurtzman** a-12, 13. **Orlando** a-24, 31, 40. **Wood** a-12-14. #22, 29 & 31 have Ray Bradbury adaptations. #16 & 17 have H. P. Lovecraft adaptations.*

VAULT OF HORROR, THE
Gladstone Publ.: Aug, 1990 - No. 6, June, 1991 ($1.95, 68 pgs.)(#4 on: $2.00)

	GD 2.0	VG 4.0	FN 6.0	VF 8.0	VF/NM 9.0	NM- 9.2
1-Craig-c(r); all contain EC reprints						5.00
2-6: 2,4-6-Craig-c(r). 3-Ingels-c(r)						5.00

VAULT OF HORROR
Russ Cochran/Gemstone Publishing: Sept, 1991 - No. 5, May, 1992 ($2.00); Oct, 1992 - No. 29, Oct, 1999 ($1.50/$2.00/$2.50)

	GD 2.0	VG 4.0	FN 6.0	VF 8.0	VF/NM 9.0	NM- 9.2
1-29: E.C reprints. 1-4r/VOH #12-15 w/original-c						4.00

V...-COMICS (Morse code for "V" - 3 dots, 1 dash)
Fox Feature Syndicate: Jan, 1942 - No. 2, Mar-Apr, 1942

	GD 2.0	VG 4.0	FN 6.0	VF 8.0	VF/NM 9.0	NM- 9.2
1-Origin V-Man & the Boys; The Banshee & The Black Fury, The Queen of Evil, & V-Agents begin; Nazi-c	258	516	774	1651	2826	4000
2-Nazi bondage/torture-c	245	490	735	1568	2684	3800

VECTOR
Now Comics: 1986 - No. 4, 1986? ($1.50, 1st color comic by Now Comics)

	GD 2.0	VG 4.0	FN 6.0	VF 8.0	VF/NM 9.0	NM- 9.2
1-4: Computer-generated art						3.00

VEIL
Dark Horse Comics: Mar, 2014 - No. 5, Oct, 2014 ($3.50)

	GD 2.0	VG 4.0	FN 6.0	VF 8.0	VF/NM 9.0	NM- 9.2
1-5-Greg Rucka-s/Toni Fejzula-a/c						3.50

VEILS
DC Comics (Vertigo): 1999 ($24.95, one-shot)

	GD 2.0	VG 4.0	FN 6.0	VF 8.0	VF/NM 9.0	NM- 9.2
Hardcover-($24.95) Painted art and photography; McGreal-s						25.00
Softcover ($14.95)						15.00

VELOCITY (Also see Cyberforce)
Image Comics (Top Cow Productions): Nov, 1995 - No. 3, Jan, 1996 ($2.50, limited series)

	GD 2.0	VG 4.0	FN 6.0	VF 8.0	VF/NM 9.0	NM- 9.2
1-3: Kurt Busiek scripts in all. 2-Savage Dragon-c/app.						4.00
...: Pilot Season 1 (10/07, $2.99) Casey-s/Maguire-a						4.00
Vol. 2 #1-4 (6/10 - No. 4, 4/11, $3.99) Rocafort-a/Marz-s; multiple covers						4.00

VELVET
Image Comics: Oct, 2013 - No. 15, Jul, 2016 ($3.50/$3.99)

	GD 2.0	VG 4.0	FN 6.0	VF 8.0	VF/NM 9.0	NM- 9.2
1-14-Brubaker-s/Epting-a/c. 5-$2.99-c						3.50
15-($3.99)						4.00

VENGEANCE
Marvel Comics: Sept, 2011 - No. 6, Feb, 2012 ($3.99, limited series)

	GD 2.0	VG 4.0	FN 6.0	VF 8.0	VF/NM 9.0	NM- 9.2
1-6-Casey-s/Dragotta-a. 1-Magneto and Red Skull app. 4-Loki cover						4.00

VENGEANCE OF THE MOON KNIGHT
Marvel Comics: Nov, 2009 - No. 10, Sept, 2010 ($3.99/$2.99)

	GD 2.0	VG 4.0	FN 6.0	VF 8.0	VF/NM 9.0	NM- 9.2
1,9: 1-($3.99) Hurwitz-s/Opeña-a; covers by Yu, Ross & Finch; back-up r/Moon Knight #1 ('80) 9-Spider-Man & Sandman app.; Campbell-c						4.00
2-8,10: 2-Sentry app. 5-Spider-Man app. 7,8-Deadpool app. 10-Secret Avengers app.						3.00

VENGEANCE OF VAMPIRELLA (Becomes Vampirella: Death & Destruction)
Harris Comics: Apr, 1994 - No. 25, Apr, 1996 ($2.95)

	GD 2.0	VG 4.0	FN 6.0	VF 8.0	VF/NM 9.0	NM- 9.2
1-($3.50)-Quesada/Palmiotti "bloodfoil" wraparound-c	1	2	3	5	6	8
1-2nd printing; blue foil-c						4.00
1-Gold						20.00
2-8: 8-Polybagged w/trading card						5.00
9-25: 10-w/coupon for Hyde -25 poster. 11,19-Polybagged w/ trading card. 25-Quesada & Palmiotti red foil-c						4.00
...: Bloodshed (1995, $6.95)						7.00

VENGEANCE OF VAMPIRELLA: THE MYSTERY WALK
Harris Comics: Nov, 1995 ($2.95, one-shot)

	GD 2.0	VG 4.0	FN 6.0	VF 8.0	VF/NM 9.0	NM- 9.2
0						4.00

VENGEANCE SQUAD
Charlton Comics: July, 1975 - No. 6, May, 1976 (#1-3 are 25¢ issues)

	GD 2.0	VG 4.0	FN 6.0	VF 8.0	VF/NM 9.0	NM- 9.2
1-Mike Mauser, Private Eye begins by Staton	2	4	6	9	13	16
2-6: Morisi-a in all	1	2	3	5	7	9
5,6 (Modern Comics-r, 1977)						6.00

VENOM
Marvel Comics: June, 2003 - No. 18, Nov, 2004 ($2.25/$2.99)

	GD 2.0	VG 4.0	FN 6.0	VF 8.0	VF/NM 9.0	NM- 9.2
1-15: 1-7-Herrera-a/Way-s. 6,7-Wolverine app. 8-10-Wolverine-c/app.; Kieth-c. 11-Fantastic Four app.						4.00
16-18						6.00
... Vol. 1: Shiver (2004, $13.99, TPB) r/#1-5						14.00
... Vol. 2: Run (2004, $19.99, TPB) r/#6-13						20.00
... Vol. 3: Twist (2004, $13.99, TPB) r/#14-18						14.00

VENOM (See Amazing Spider-Man #654 & 654.1)(Also see Secret Avengers)
Marvel Comics: May, 2011 - No. 42, Dec, 2013 ($3.99/$2.99)

	GD 2.0	VG 4.0	FN 6.0	VF 8.0	VF/NM 9.0	NM- 9.2
1-Flash Thompson with the symbiote; Remender-s/Tony Moore-a/Quesada-c	2	4	6	11	16	20
2-Cover swipe of ASM #300; Kraven app.	3	6	9	14	20	25
3-12-($2.99) 3-Deodato-c. 6-8-Spider Island						4.00
13-($3.99) Circle of Four; Red Hulk, X-23, and Ghost Rider app.						4.00
13.1, 13.2, 13.3, 13.4, 14-($2.99) Circle of Four parts 2-6						3.00

Venom (2017 series) #1 © MAR

Venus #6 © MAR

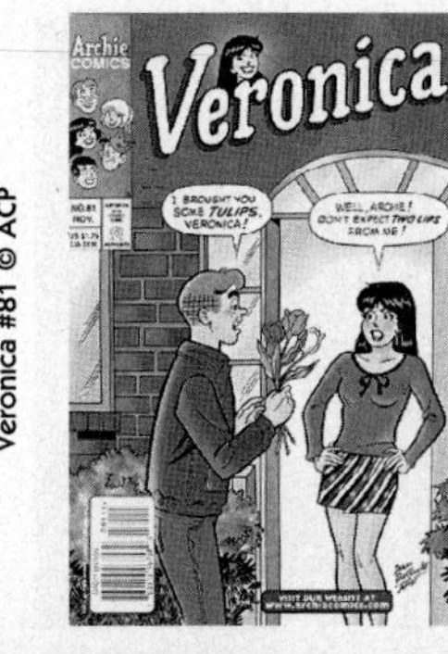

Veronica #81 © ACP

GD VG FN VF VF/NM NM-
2.0 4.0 6.0 8.0 9.0 9.2

15-27, 27.1, 28-42: 15-Secret Avengers app. 16,17-Toxin app. 26,27-Minimum Carnage. 38-1st app. Mania. 42-Mephisto app. 4.00
...: Flashpoint 1 (2011, $4.99) r/Amazing Spider-Man #654, 654.1 and Venom #1 2 4 6 9 12 15

VENOM (Also see Amazing Spider-Man: Venom Inc.)
Marvel Comics: Jan, 2017 - No. 6, Jun, 2017; No. 150, Jul, 2017 - Present ($3.99)

1-6: 1-Mike Costa-s/Gerardo Sandoval-a; intro. Lee Price; Mac Gargan app. 4.00
[Title switches to legacy numbering after #6 (6/17)]
150-($5.99) Eddie Brock as Venom; Spider-Man app.; Tradd Moore-a; cover gallery 6.00
151-163: 152,153-Moon Girl and Devil Dinosaur app. 155-158-Kraven app.; Bagley-a. 159-Venom Inc. part 3; Sandoval-a. 160-Venom Inc. part 5 4.00

VENOM: LETHAL PROTECTOR
Marvel Comics: Feb, 1993 - No. 6, July, 1993 ($2.95, limited series)

1-Red holo-grafx foil-c; Bagley-c/a in all 2 4 6 10 14 18
1-Gold variant sold to retailers 6 12 18 38 69 100
1-Black-c (at least 146 copies have been authenticated by CGC since 2000) 21 42 63 147 324 500
NOTE: Counterfeit copies of the black-c exist and are valueless
2-6: Spider-Man app. in all 6.00

VENOM: SPACE KNIGHT
Marvel Comics: Jan, 2016 - No. 13, Dec, 2016 ($3.99)

1-13: 1-Robbie Thompson-s/Ariel Olivetti-a. 8-10-Jacinto-a. 11,12-Civil War II tie-in 4.00

VENOM: Marvel Comics (Also see Amazing Spider-Man #298-300)
... ALONG CAME A SPIDER, 1/96 - No. 4, 4/96 ($2.95)-Spider-Man & Carnage app. 6.00
... CARNAGE UNLEASHED, 4/95 - No. 4, 7/95 ($2.95) 4.00
... DARK ORIGIN, 10/08 - No. 5, 2/09 ($2.99) 1-5-Medina-a 4.00
... /DEADPOOL: WHAT IF?, 4/11 ($2.99) Remender-s/Moll-a/Young-c; Galactus app. 8 16 24 56 108 160
... DEATHTRAP: THE VAULT, 3/93 ($6.95) r/Avengers: Deathtrap: The Vault 7.00
... FUNERAL PYRE, 8/93- No. 3, 10/93 ($2.95)-#1-Holo-grafx foil-c; Punisher app. in all 4.00
... LICENSE TO KILL,6/97 - No. 3, 8/97 ($1.95) 5.00
... NIGHTS OF VENGEANCE, 8/94 - No. 4, 11/94 ($2.95), #1-Red foil-c 4.00
... ON TRIAL, 3/97 - No. 3, 5/97 ($1.95) 4.00
... SEED OF DARKNESS, 7/97 ($1.95) #(-1) Flashback 4.00
... SEPARATION ANXIETY,12/94- No. 4, 3/95 ($2.95) #1-Embossed-c 4.00
... SIGN OF THE BOSS,3/97 - No. 2, 10/97 ($1.99) 4.00
... SINNER TAKES ALL, 8/95 - No. 5, 10/95 ($2.95) 4.00
... SUPER SPECIAL, 8/95($3.95) #1-Flip book 5.00
... THE ENEMY WITHIN, 2/94 - No. 3, 4/94 ($2.95)-Demogoblin & Morbius app.
1-Glow-in-the-dark-c 6.00
... THE FINALE, 11/97 - No. 3, 1/98 ($1.99) 4.00
... THE HUNGER, 8/96- No. 4, 11/96 ($1.95) 4.00
... THE HUNTED, 5/96-No. 3, 7/96 ($2.95) 4.00
... THE MACE, 5/94 - No. 3, 7/94 ($2.95)-#1-Embossed-c 4.00
... THE MADNESS, 11/93- No. 3, 1/94 ($2.95)-Kelley Jones-c/a(p).
1-Embossed-c; Juggernaut app. 4.00
... TOOTH AND CLAW, 12/96 - No. 3, 2/97 ($1.95)-Wolverine-c/app. 4.00
... VS. CARNAGE, 9/04 - No. 4, 12/04 ($2.99)-Milligan-s/Crain-a; Spider-Man app. 10.00
TPB (2004, $9.99) r/#1-4 10.00

VENOMVERSE
Marvel Comics: Nov, 2017 - No. 5, Dec, 2017 ($4.99/$3.99, weekly limited series)

1-($4.99) Bunn-s/Coello-a; Venoms vs. The Poisons 5.00
2-5-($3.99) Bunn-s/Coello-a 4.00
...: War Stories 1 (11/17, $4.99) Multiverse of Venoms; short stories by various 5.00

VENTURE
AC Comics (Americomics): Aug, 1986 - No. 3, 1986? ($1.75)

1-3: 1-3-Bolt. 1-Astron. 2-Femforce. 3-Fazers 3.00

VENTURE
Image Comics: Jan, 2003 - No. 4, Sept, 2003 ($2.95)

1-4-Faerber-s/Igle-a 3.00

VENUS (See Agents of Atlas, Marvel Spotlight #2 & Weird Wonder Tales)
Marvel/Atlas Comics (CMC 1-9/LCC 10-19): Aug, 1948 - No. 19, Apr, 1952 (Also see Marvel Mystery #91)

1-Venus & Hedy Devine begin; 1st app. Venus; Kurtzman's "Hey Look" 239 478 717 1530 2615 3700
2 129 258 387 826 1413 2000
3,5 87 174 261 553 952 1350
4-Kurtzman's "Hey Look" 90 180 270 576 988 1400
6-9: 6-Loki app. 7,8-Painted-c. 9-Begin 52 pgs.; book-length feature "Whom the Gods Destroy!" 77 154 231 493 847 1200
10-S/F-horror issues begin (7/50) 106 212 318 673 1162 1650
11-S/F end of the world (11/50) 119 238 357 762 1306 1850
12-Colan-a 74 148 222 470 810 1150
13-16-Venus by Everett, 2-3 stories each; covers-#13,15,16; 14-Everett part cover (Venus). 135 270 405 864 1482 2100
17-Classic Everett horror & skeleton/bondage-c (scarce) 432 864 1296 3154 5577 8000
18-Classic Everett horror-c 320 640 960 2240 3920 5600
19-Classic Everett skeleton Good Girl-c 443 886 1329 3234 5717 8200
NOTE: ***Berg*** *s/f story-13.* ***Everett*** *c-13, 14(part; Venus only), 15-19.* ***Heath*** *s/f story-11.* ***Maneely*** *s/f story 10(3pg.), 16.* ***Morisi*** *a-19.* ***Syd Shores*** *c-6.*

VENUS
BOOM! Studios: Dec, 2015 - No. 4, Mar, 2016 ($3.99)

1-4-Loverd-s/Danlan-a 4.00

VERI BEST SURE FIRE COMICS
Holyoke Publishing Co.: No date (circa 1945) (Reprints Holyoke one-shots)

1-Captain Aero, Alias X, Miss Victory, Commandos of the Devil Dogs, Red Cross, Hammerhead Hawley, Capt. Aero's Sky Scouts, Flagman app.; same-c as Veri Best Sure Shot #1 47 94 141 296 498 700

VERI BEST SURE SHOT COMICS
Holyoke Publishing Co.: No date (circa 1945) (Reprints Holyoke one-shots)

1-Capt. Aero, Miss Victory by Quinlan, Alias X, The Red Cross, Flagman, Commandos of the Devil Dogs, Hammerhead Hawley, Capt. Aero's Sky Scouts; same-c as Veri Best Sure Fire #1 47 94 141 296 498 700

VERMILLION
DC Comics (Helix): Oct, 1996 - No. 12, Sept, 1997 ($2.25/$2.50)

1-12: 1-4: Lucius Shepard scripts. 4,12-Kaluta-c 3.00

VERONICA (Also see Archie's Girls, Betty &...)
Archie Comics: Apr, 1989 - No. 210, Feb, 2012

1-(75¢-c) 2 4 6 9 12 15
2-10: 2-(75¢-c) 5.00
11-38 4.00
39-Love Showdown pt. 4, Cheryl Blossom 6.00
40-70: 34-Neon ink-c 3.00
71-201,203-206: 134-Begin $2.19-c. 152,155-Cheryl Blossom app. 163-Begin $2.25-c 3.00
202-Intro. Kevin Keller, 1st openly gay Archie character; cover has blue background 2 4 6 9 12 15
202-Second printing; cover has black background 1 3 4 6 8 10
207-210-Kevin Keller mini-series 3.00

VERONICA'S PASSPORT DIGEST MAGAZINE (Becomes Veronica's Digest Magazine #3 on)
Archie Comics: Nov, 1992 - No. 6 ($1.50/$1.79, digest size)

1 5.00
2-6 3.00

VERONICA'S SUMMER SPECIAL (See Archie Giant Series Magazine #615, 625)

VERTICAL
DC Comics (Vertigo): 2003 ($4.95, 3-1/4" wide pages, one-shot)

1-Seagle-s/Allred & Bond-a; odd format 1/2 width pages with some 20" long spreads 5.00

VERTIGO DOUBLE SHOT
DC Comics (Vertigo): 2008 ($2.99)

1-Reprints House of Mystery (2008) #1 and Young Liars #1 in flip-book format 3.00

VERTIGO ESSENTIALS
DC Comics (Vertigo): Dec, 2013 - Feb, 2014 ($1.00, Flip book reprints with DC & Vertigo Essential Graphics novels catalog)

...: American Vampire 1 (2/14) Reprints #1; flip-c by Ryan Sook 3.00
...: Fables 1 (1/14) Reprints #1; flip-c by Ryan Sook 3.00
...: 100 Bullets 1 (2/14) Reprints #1; flip-c by Ryan Sook 3.00
...: The Sandman #1 (12/13, $1.00) Reprints Sandman #1 (1989) with flipbook 3.00
...: V For Vendetta 1 (12/13) Reprints first chapter; flip-c by Ryan Sook 3.00
...: Y: The Last Man 1 (1/14) Reprints #1; flip-c by Ryan Sook 3.00

VERTIGO: FIRST BLOOD
DC Comics (Vertigo): Feb, 2012 ($7.99, squarebound)

Vertigo Pop! London #4 © Milligan & Bond

Vext #1 © DC

Vice #1 © TCOW

GD	VG	FN	VF	VF/NM	NM-
2.0	4.0	6.0	8.0	9.0	9.2

TPB-Reprints first issues of American Vampire, I Zombie, The Unwritten & Sweet Tooth 8.00

VERTIGO: FIRST CUT
DC Comics (Vertigo): 2008 ($4.99, TPB)

TPB-Reprints first issues of DMZ, Army@Love, Jack of Fables, Exterminators, Scalped, Crossing Midnight, and Loveless; preview of Air 5.00

VERTIGO: FIRST OFFENSES
DC Comics (Vertigo): 2005 ($4.99, TPB)

TPB-Reprints first issues of The Invisibles, Preacher, Fables, Sandman Mystery Theater, and Lucifer 5.00

VERTIGO: FIRST TASTE
DC Comics (Vertigo): 2005 ($4.99, TPB)

TPB-Reprints first issues of Y: The Last Man, 100 Bullets, Transmetropolitan, Books of Magick: Life During Wartime, Death: The High Cost of Living, and Saga of the Swamp Thing #21 (Alan Moore's first story on that title) 5.00

VERTIGO GALLERY, THE: DREAMS AND NIGHTMARES
DC Comics (Vertigo): 1995 ($3.50, one-shot)

1-Pin-ups of Vertigo characters by Sienkiewicz, Toth, Van Fleet & others; McKean-c 4.00

VERTIGO JAM
DC Comics (Vertigo): Aug, 1993 ($3.95, one-shot, 68 pgs.)(Painted-c by Fabry)

1-Sandman by Neil Gaiman, Hellblazer, Animal Man, Doom Patrol, Swamp Thing, Kid Eternity & Shade the Changing Man 5.00

VERTIGO POP! BANGKOK
DC Comics (Vertigo): July, 2003 - No. 4, Oct, 2003 ($2.95, limited series)

1-4-Camuncoli-c/a; Jonathan Vankin-s 3.00

VERTIGO POP! LONDON
DC Comics (Vertigo): Jan, 2003 - No. 4, Apr, 2003 ($2.95, limited series)

1-4-Philip Bond-c/a; Peter Milligan-s 3.00

VERTIGO POP! TOKYO
DC Comics (Vertigo): Sept, 2002 - No. 4, Dec, 2002 ($2.95, limited series)

1-4-Seth Fisher-c/a; Jonathan Vankin-s 3.00
Tokyo Days, Bangkok Nights TPB (2009, $19.99) r/#1-4 & Vertogo Pop! Bangkok #1-4 20.00

VERTIGO PREVIEW
DC Comics (Vertigo): 1992 (75¢, one-shot, 36 pgs.)

1-Vertigo previews; Sandman story by Neil Gaiman 3.00

VERTIGO QUARTERLY CMYK
DC Comics (Vertigo): Jun, 2014 - No. 4, Mar, 2015 ($7.99, limited series)

1-4-Color themed short story anthology. 1-Cyan. 2-Magenta. 3-Yellow. 4-Black 8.00

VERTIGO QUARTERLY SFX
DC Comics (Vertigo): Jun, 2015 - No. 4, Mar, 2016 ($7.99, limited series)

1-4-Sound effect-themed short story anthology. 1-"Pop!". 2-"Slam!". 3-"Krak!". 4-"Bang" 8.00

VERTIGO RAVE
DC Comics (Vertigo): Fall, 1994 (99¢, one-shot)

1-Vertigo previews 3.00

VERTIGO RESURRECTED: ...
DC Comics (Vertigo): Dec, 2010 - Present ($7.99, squarebound, reprints)

The Extremist 1 (1/11, 12/13) r/The Extremist #1-4 8.00
Finals 1 (5/11) r/Finals #1-4; Jill Thompson-a 8.00
Hellblazer 1 (2/11) r/Hellblazer #57,58,245,246 8.00
Hellblazer - Bad Blood 1 (6/11) r/Hellblazer Special: Bad Blood #1-4 8.00
Jonny Double 1 (10/11) r/Jonny Double #1-4; Azzarello-s/Risso-a 8.00
My Faith in Frankie 1 (1/12) r/My Faith in Frankie #1-4; Carey-s 8.00
Sandman Presents - Petrefax 1 (8/11) r/Sandman Presents: Petrefax #1-4 8.00
Sgt. Rock: Between Hell and a Hard Place 1,2 (1/12, 2/12) r/the 2003 HC 8.00
Shoot 1 (12/10) r/short stories by various incl. Quitely, Sale, Bolland, Risso, Jim Lee 8.00
The Eaters 1 (12/11) r/Vertigo Visions - The Eaters and other short stories 8.00
Winter's Edge 1 (2/11) r/Vertigo's Winter Edge #1-3; Bermejo-c 8.00

VERTIGO SECRET FILES
DC Comics (Vertigo): Aug, 2000 ($4.95)

...: Hellblazer 1 (8/00, $4.95) Background info and story summaries 5.00
...: Swamp Thing 1 (11/00, $4.95) Backstories and origins; Hale-c 5.00

VERTIGO VERITE: THE UNSEEN HAND
DC Comics (Vertigo): Sept, 1996 - No. 4, Dec, 1996 ($2.50, limited series)

1-4: Terry LaBan scripts in all 3.00

VERTIGO VISIONS
DC Comics (Vertigo): June, 1993 - Present (one-shots)

Dr. Occult 1 (7/94, $3.95) 4.00
Dr. Thirteen 1 (9/98, $5.95) Howarth-s 6.00
Prez 1 (7/95, $3.95) 4.00
The Geek 1 (6/93, $3.95) 4.00
The Eaters ($4.95, 1995)-Milligan story. 5.00
The Phantom Stranger 1 (10/93, $3.50) 4.00
Tomahawk 1 (7/98, $4.95) Pollack-s 5.00

VERTIGO WINTER'S EDGE
DC Comics (Vertigo): 1998, 1999 ($7.95/$6.95, square-bound, annual)

1-Winter stories by Vertigo creators; Desire story by Gaiman/Bolton; Bolland wraparound-c 8.00
2,3-($6.95)-Winter stories: 2-Allred-c. 3-Bond-c; Desire by Gaiman/Zulli 7.00

VERTIGO X ANNIVERSARY PREVIEW
DC Comics (Vertigo): 2003 (99¢, one-shot, 48 pgs.)

1-Previews of upcoming titles and interviews; Endless Nights, Shade, The Originals 4.00

VERY BEST OF DENNIS THE MENACE, THE
Fawcett Publ.: July, 1979 - No. 2, Apr, 1980 (95¢/$1.00, digest-size, 132 pgs.)

1,2-Reprints 2 4 6 8 10 12

VERY BEST OF DENNIS THE MENACE, THE
Marvel Comics Group: Apr, 1982 - No. 3, Aug, 1982 ($1.25, digest-size)

1-3: Reprints 2 3 4 6 8 10
1,2-Mistakenly printed with DC logo on cover 2 4 6 9 12 15

NOTE: ***Hank Ketcham*** *c-all. A few thousand of #1 & 2 were printed with DC emblem.*

VERY VICKY
Meet Danny Ocean: 1993? - No. 8, 1995 ($2.50, B&W)

1-8, ...: Calling All Hillbillies (1995, $2.50) 3.00

VERY WEIRD TALES (Also see Slithiss Attacks!)
Oceanspray Comics Group: Aug, 2002 - No. 2, Oct, 2002 ($4.00)

1-Mutant revenge, methamphetamine, corporate greed horror stories 3 6 9 16 23 30
2-Weird fantasy and horror stories 2 4 6 9 12 15

NOTE: *Created in prevention classes taught by Jon McClure at the Oceanspray Family Center in Newport, Oregon, and paid for by the Housing Authority of Lincoln County. All books are b&w with color covers. Issues #1-2 penciled and inked by various artists. All comics feature characters created by students and are signed and numbered by Jon McClure. Issues #1-2 have print runs of 100 each.*

VEXT
DC Comics: Mar, 1999 - No. 6, Aug, 1999 ($2.50, limited series)

1-6-Giffen-s. 1-Superman app. 3.00

V FOR VENDETTA
DC Comics: Sept, 1988 - No. 10, May, 1989 ($2.00, maxi-series)

1-Alan Moore scripts in all; David Lloyd-a 3 6 9 21 33 45
2-10 1 3 4 6 8 10
HC (1990) Limited edition 60.00
HC (2005, $29.99, dustjacket) r/series; foreward by Lloyd; promo art and sketches 30.00
Trade paperback (1990, $14.95) 20.00

VIBE (See Justice League of America's Vibe)

VIC BRIDGES FAZERS SKETCHBOOK AND FACT FILE
AC Comics: Nov, 1986 ($1.75)

1 3.00

VICE
Image Comics (Top Cow): Nov, 2005 - No. 5 ($2.99)

1-5-Coleite-s/Kirkham-a. 1-Three covers 3.00
1-Code Red Edition; variant Benitez-c 3.00

VIC FLINT(Crime Buster...)(See Authentic Police Cases #10-14 & Fugitives From Justice #2)
St. John Publ. Co.: Aug, 1948 - No. 5, Apr, 1949 (Newspaper reprints; NEA Service)

1 18 36 54 103 162 220
2 14 28 42 76 108 140
3-5 12 24 36 67 94 120

VIC FLINT (Crime Buster...)
Argo Publ.: Feb, 1956 - No. 2, May, 1956 (Newspaper reprints)

1,2 9 18 27 50 65 80

VIC JORDAN (Also see Big Shot Comics #32)
Civil Service Publ.: April, 1945

1-1944 daily newspaper-r 15 30 45 90 140 190

VICKI (Humor)

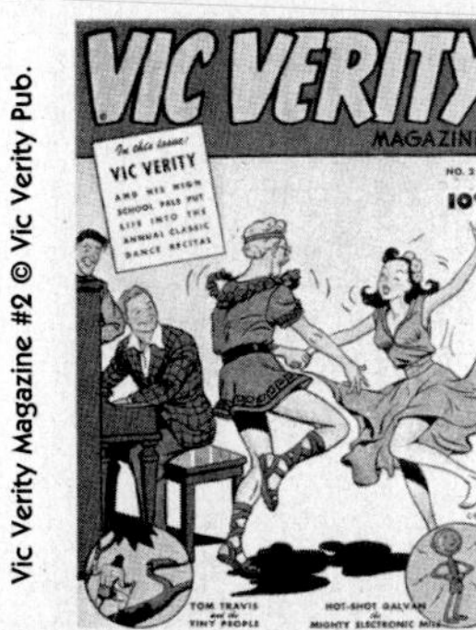

Vic Verity Magazine #2 © Vic Verity Pub.

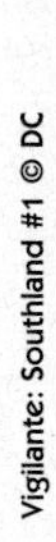
Vigilante: Southland #1 © DC

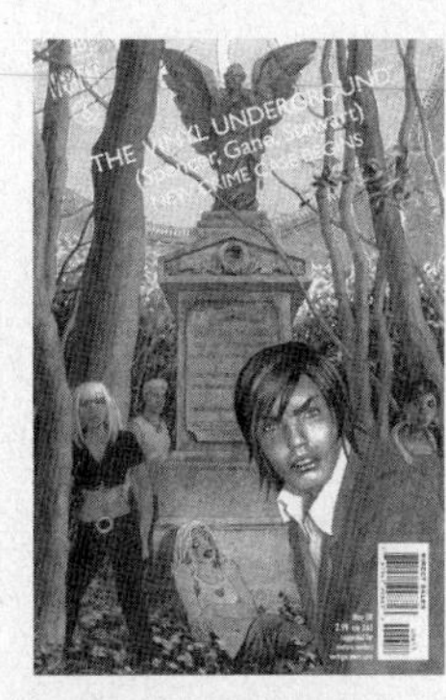
Vinyl Underground #6 © Spencer & Gane

GD 2.0 | VG 4.0 | FN 6.0 | VF 8.0 | VF/NM 9.0 | NM- 9.2

Atlas/Seaboard Publ.: Feb, 1975 - No. 4, Aug, 1975 (No. 1,2: 68 pgs.)

1,2-(68 pgs.)-Reprints Tippy Teen; Good Girl art 5 10 15 30 50 70
3,4 (Low print) 5 10 15 31 53 75

VICKI VALENTINE (...Summer Special #1)
Renegade Press: July, 1985 - No. 4, July, 1986 ($1.70, B&W)

1-4: Woggon, Rausch-a; all have paper dolls. 2-Christmas issue 3.00

VICKY
Ace Magazine: Oct, 1948 - No. 5, June, 1949

nn(10/48)-Teenage humor 13 26 39 72 101 130
4(12/48), nn(2/49), 4(4/49), 5(6/49): 5-Dotty app. 10 20 30 56 76 95

VICTORIAN UNDEAD
DC Comics (WildStorm): Jan, 2010 - No. 6, Jun, 2010 ($2.99)

1-6-Sherlock Holmes vs. Zombies; Edginton-s/Fabbri-a. 1-Two covers (Moore, Coleby) 3.00
...: Sherlock Holmes vs. Jekyll and Hyde (12/10, $4.99) Domingues-a/Van Sciver-c 5.00
...: Sherlock Holmes vs. Zombies TPB (2010, $17.99) r/#1-6; character design sketch art 18.00
... Volume 2 (1/11 - No. 5, 5/11) 1-3-($3.99) "Sherlock Holmes vs. Dracula" on-c; Fabbri-a 4.00
... Volume 2 - 4,5-($2.99) "Sherlock Holmes vs. Dracula" on-c; Fabbri-a 3.00

VICTORIES, THE
Dark Horse Comics: Aug, 2012 - No. 5, Dec, 2012 ($3.99 limited series)

1-5-Michael Avon Oeming-s/a/c 4.00
...Volume 2: Transhuman 1-15 (6/13 - No. 15, 9/14) Oeming-s/a/c. 11-15 Metahuman 4.00

VIC TORRY & HIS FLYING SAUCER (Also see Mr. Monster's...#5)
Fawcett Publications: 1950 (one-shot)

nn-Book-length saucer story by Powell; photo/painted-c 69 138 207 442 759 1075

VICTORY
Topps Comics: June, 1994 ($2.50, unfinished limited series)

1-Kurt Busiek script; Giffen-c/a; Rob Liefeld variant-c exists 3.00

VICTORY
Image Comics: May, 2003 - No. 4, Feb, 2004 ($2.95, limited series)

1-4: 1-Two covers; Francisco-a. 4-Two covers 3.00

VICTORY (Volume 2)
Image Comics: Aug, 2004 - No. 4, Jan, 2005 ($2.95, limited series)

1-4: 1-Three covers; Francisco-a 3.00

VICTORY COMICS
Hillman Periodicals: Aug, 1941 - No. 4, Dec, 1941 (#1 by Funnies, Inc.)

1-The Conqueror by Bill Everett, The Crusader, & Bomber Burns begin; Conqueror's origin in text; Everett-c 349 698 1047 2443 4272 6100
2-Everett-c/a 174 348 522 1114 1907 2700
3,4: 4-WWII Japanese-c 142 284 426 909 1555 2200

VIC VERITY MAGAZINE
Vic Verity Publ: 1945; No. 2, Jan?, 1946 - No. 7, Sept, 1946 (A comic book)

1-C. C. Beck-c/a 41 82 123 256 428 600
2-Beck-c 28 56 84 165 270 375
3-7: 6-Beck-a. 7-Beck-c 26 52 78 154 252 350

VIDEO JACK
Marvel Comics (Epic Comics): Nov, 1987 - No. 6, Nov, 1988 ($1.25)

1-5 3.00
6-Neal Adams, Keith Giffen, Wrightson, others-a 5.00

VIETNAM JOURNAL
Apple Comics: Nov, 1987 - No. 16, Apr, 1991 ($1.75/$1.95, B&W)

1-16: Don Lomax-c/a/scripts in all, 1-2nd print 4.00
...: Indian Country Vol. 1 (1990, $12.95)-r/#1-4 plus one new story 13.00

VIETNAM JOURNAL: VALLEY OF DEATH
Apple Comics: June, 1994 - No. 2, Aug, 1994 ($2.75, B&W, limited series)

1,2: By Don Lomax 4.00

VIGILANTE, THE (Also see New Teen Titans #23 & Annual V2#2)
DC Comics: Oct, 1983 - No. 50, Feb, 1988 ($1.25, Baxter paper)

1-Origin 1 2 3 5 6 8
2-16,19-49: 3-Cyborg app. 4-1st app. The Exterminator; Newton-a(p). 6,7-Origin. 20,21-Nightwing app. 35-Origin Mad Bomber. 47-Batman-c/s 4.00
17,18-Alan Moore scripts 5.00
50-Ken Steacy painted-c 5.00
Annual nn, 2 ('85, '86) 5.00

VIGILANTE
DC Comics: Nov, 2005 - No. 6, Apr, 2006 ($2.99, limited series)

1-6-Bruce Jones-s. 1,2,4-6-Ben Oliver-a 3.00

VIGILANTE
DC Comics: Feb, 2009 - No. 12, Jan, 2010 ($2.99)

1-12: 1-Wolfman-s/Leonardi-a. 3-Nightwing app. 5-X-over with Titans and Teen Titans 3.00

VIGILANTE: CITY LIGHTS, PRAIRIE JUSTICE (Also see Action Comics #42, Justice League of America #78, Leading Comics & World's Finest #244)
DC Comics: Nov, 1995 - No. 4, Feb, 1996 ($2.50, limited series)

1-4: James Robinson scripts/Tony Salmons-a/Mark Chiarello-c 3.00
TPB (2009, $19.99) r/#1-4 20.00

VIGILANTE 8: SECOND OFFENSE
Chaos! Comics: Dec, 1999 ($2.95, one-shot)

1-Based on video game 3.00

VIGILANTES, THE
Dell Publishing Co.: No. 839, Sept, 1957

Four Color 839-Movie 7 14 21 46 86 125

VIGILANTE: SOUTHLAND
DC Comics: Dec, 2016 - No. 3, Feb, 2017 ($3.99, unfinished series originally set for 6 issues)

1-3-Phillips-s/Casagrande-a; intro. Donny Fairchild 4.00

VIKING PRINCE, THE
DC Comics: 2010 ($39.99, hardcover with dustjacket)

HC-Recolored reprints of apps. in Brave and the Bold #1-5, 7-24 & team-up with Sgt. Rock in Our Army at War #162,163; new intro. by Joe Kubert 40.00

VIKINGS, THE (Movie)
Dell Publishing Co.: No. 910, May, 1958

Four Color 910-Buscema-a, Kirk Douglas photo-c 8 16 24 54 102 150

VIKINGS: GODHEAD (Based on the History Channel series)
Titan Comics: May, 2016 - No. 4, Sept, 2016 ($3.99)

1-4: 1-Cavan Scott-s/Staz Johnson-a; 3 covers 4.00

VIKINGS: UPRISING (Based on the History Channel series)
Titan Comics: Oct, 2016 - No. 4, Jan, 2017 ($3.99)

1-4: 1-Cavan Scott-s/Daniel Indro-a. 1-Five covers. 2-4-Three covers 4.00

VILLAINS AND VIGILANTES
Eclipse Comics: Dec, 1986 - No. 4, May, 1987 ($1.50/$1.75, limited series, Baxter paper)

1-4: Based on role-playing game. 2-4 ($1.75-c) 3.00

VILLAINS FOR HIRE
Marvel Comics: No. 0.1, Jan, 2012; No. 1, Feb, 2012 - No. 4, May, 2012 ($2.99)

0.1-Misty Knight, Silver Sable, Black Panther app.; Arlem-a 3.00
1-4-Abnett & Lanning-s/Arlem-a; Misty Knight app. 3.00

VILLAINS UNITED (Leads into Infinite Crisis)
DC Comics: July, 2005 - No. 6, Dec, 2005 ($2.95/$2.50, limited series)

1-6-Simone-s/JG Jones-c. 1-The Secret Six and the "Society" form 3.00
...: Infinite Crisis Special 1 (6/06, $4.99) Simone-s/Eaglesham-a 5.00

VILLAINY OF DOCTOR DOOM, THE
Marvel Comics: 1999 ($17.95, TPB)

nn-Reprints early battle with the Fantastic Four 18.00

VIMANARAMA
DC Comics (Vertigo): Apr, 2005 - No. 3, June, 2005 ($2.95, limited series)

1-3-Grant Morrison-s/Philip Bond-a 3.00
TPB (2005, $12.99) r/#1-3 13.00

VINTAGE MAGNUS (...Robot Fighter)
Valiant: Jan, 1992 - No. 4, Apr, 1992 ($2.25, limited series)

1-4: 1-Layton-c; r/origin from Magnus R.F. #22 3.00

VINYL UNDERGROUND
DC Comics (Vertigo): Dec, 2007 - No. 12, Nov, 2008 ($2.99)

1-12: 1-Spencer-s/Gane & Stewart-a/Phillips-c 3.00
...: Pretty Dead Things TPB ('08, $17.99) r/#6-12 18.00
...: Watching the Detectives TPB ('08, $9.99) r/#1-5; David Laphan intro. 10.00

VIOLATOR (Also see Spawn #2)
Image Comics (Todd McFarlane Prods.): May, 1994 - No. 3, Aug, 1994 ($1.95, lim. series)

1-Alan Moore scripts in all 5.00
2,3: Bart Sears-c(p)/a(p) 4.00

Violent Love #4 © Barberie & Santos

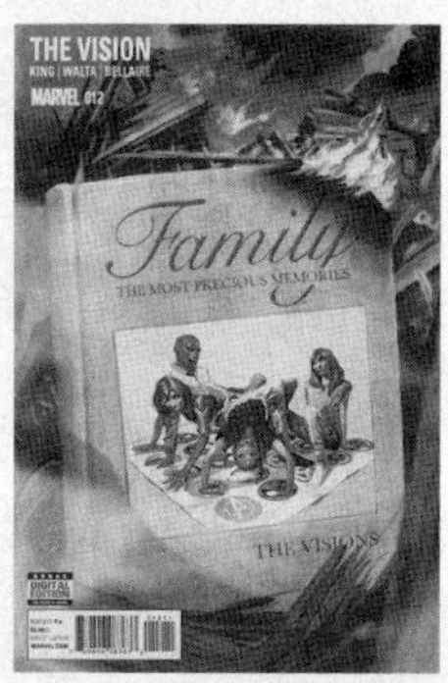

The Vision (2016 series) #12 © MAR

Voltron (2012 series) #1 © WEP

	GD 2.0	VG 4.0	FN 6.0	VF 8.0	VF/NM 9.0	NM- 9.2

VIOLATOR VS. BADROCK
Image Comics (Extreme Studios): May, 1995 - No. 4, Aug, 1995 ($2.50, limited series)
1-4: Alan Moore scripts in all. 1-1st app Celestine; variant-c (3?) 3.00

VIOLENT, THE
Image Comics: Dec, 2015 - No. 5, Jul, 2016 ($2.99)
1-5-Brisson-s/Gorham-a 3.00

VIOLENT LOVE
Image Comics: Nov, 2016 - No. 10, Dec, 2017 ($3.99)
1-10-Frank Barbiere-s/Victor Santos-a/c 4.00

VIOLENT MESSIAHS (...: Lamenting Pain on cover for #9-12, numbered as #1-4)
Image Comics: June, 2000 - No. 12 ($2.95)
1-Two covers by Travis Smith and Medina 4.00
1-Tower Records variant edition 5.00
2-8: 5-Flip book sketchbook 3.00
9-12-Lamenting Pain; 2 covers on each 3.00
...: Genesis (12/01, $5.95) r/'97 B&W issue, Wizard 1/2 prologue 6.00
...: The Book of Job TPB (7/02, $24.95) r/#1-8; Foreward by Gossett 25.00

VIP (TV)
TV Comics: 2000 ($2.95, unfinished series)
1-Based on the Pamela Lee (Anderson) TV show; photo-c 3.00

VIPER (TV)
DC Comics: Aug, 1994 - No. 4, Nov, 1994 ($1.95, limited series)
1-4-Adaptation of television show 3.00

VIRGINIAN, THE (TV)
Gold Key: June, 1963
1(10060-306)-Part photo-c of James Drury plus photo back-c 4 8 12 27 44 60

VIRTUA FIGHTER (Video Game)
Marvel Comics: Aug, 1995 (2.95, one-shot)
1-Sega Saturn game 3.00

VIRUS
Dark Horse Comics: 1993 - No. 4, 1993 ($2.50, limited series)
1-4: Ploog-c 3.00

VISION, THE
Marvel Comics: Nov, 1994 - No. 4, Feb, 1995 ($1.75, limited series)
1-4 4.00

VISION, THE (AVENGERS ICONS: ...)
Marvel Comics: Oct, 2002 - No. 4, Jan, 2003 ($2.99, limited series)
1-4-Geoff Johns-s/Ivan Reis-a 4.00
...: Yesterday and Tomorrow TPB (2005, $14.99) r/#1-4 & Avengers #57 (1st app.) 15.00

VISION (From the Avengers)
Marvel Comics: Jan, 2016 - No. 12, Dec, 2016 ($3.99)
1-12: 1-Tom King-s/Gabriel Walta-a; the Vison and his new synthezoid family 4.00
... Director's Cut 1-6 (8/17 - No. 6, 1/18, $6.99) r/2 issues each with script and bonus art 7.00

VISION AND THE SCARLET WITCH, THE (See Marvel Fanfare)
Marvel Comics Group: Nov, 1982 - No. 4, Feb, 1983 (Limited series)
1-4: 2-Nuklo & Future Man app. 5.00

VISION AND THE SCARLET WITCH, THE
Marvel Comics Group: Oct, 1985 - No. 12, Sept, 1986 (Maxi-series)
V2#1-12: 1-Origin; 1st app. in Avengers #57. 2-West Coast Avengers x-over 5.00

VISIONS
Vision Publications: 1979 - No. 5, 1983 (B&W, fanzine)
1-Flaming Carrot begins (1st app?); N. Adams-c 6 12 18 38 69 100
2-N. Adams, Rogers-a; Gulacy back-c; signed & numbered to 2000 5 10 15 31 53 75
3-Williamson-c(p); Steranko back-c 4 8 12 23 37 50
4-Flaming Carrot-c & info. 4 8 12 25 40 55
5-1 pg. Flaming Carrot 3 6 9 19 30 40

NOTE: **Eisner** a-4. **Miller** a-4. **Starlin** a-3. **Williamson** a-5. *After #4, Visions became an annual publication of The Atlanta Fantasy Fair.*

VISITOR, THE
Valiant/Acclaim Comics (Valiant): Apr, 1995 - No. 13, Nov, 1995 ($2.50)
1-13: 8-Harbinger revealed. 13-Visitor revealed to be Sting from Harbinger 3.00

VISITOR: HOW AND WHY HE STAYED, THE (Character from Hellboy)
Dark Horse Comics: Feb, 2017 - No. 5, Jul, 2017 ($3.99, limited series)
1-5-Mignola & Roberson-s/Grist-a/c; Hellboy app. 4.00

VISITOR VS. THE VALIANT UNIVERSE, THE
Valiant: Feb, 1995 - No. 2, Mar, 1995 ($2.95, limited series)
1,2 3.00

VIXEN: RETURN OF THE LION (From Justice League of America)
DC Comics: Dec, 2008 - No. 5, Apr, 2009 ($2.99, limited series)
1-5-G. Willow Wilson-s/Cafu-a; Justice League app. 3.00
TPB (2009, $17.99) r/#1-5 18.00

VOGUE (Also see Youngblood)
Image Comics (Extreme Studios): Oct, 1995 - No.3, Jan, 1996 ($2.50, limited series)
1-3: 1-Liefeld-c, 1-Variant-c 3.00

VOID INDIGO (Also see Marvel Graphic Novel)
Marvel Comics (Epic Comics): 11/84 - No. 2, 3/85 ($1.50, direct sales, unfinished series, mature)
1,2: Cont'd from Marvel G.N.; graphic sex & violence 3.00

VOLCANIC REVOLVER
Oni Press: Dec, 1998 - No. 3, Mar, 1999 ($2.95, B&W, limited series)
1-3: Scott Morse-s/a 3.00
TPB (12/99, $9.95, digest size) r/#1-3 and Oni Double Feature #7 prologue 10.00

VOLTRON (TV)
Modern Publishing: 1985 - No. 3, 1985 (75¢, limited series)
1-Ayers-a in all 3 6 9 14 20 25
2,3 2 4 6 8 10 12

VOLTRON (Volume 1)
Dynamite Entertainment: 2011 - No. 12, 2013 ($3.99)
1-12: 1-Padilla-a; covers by Alex Ross, Sean Chen & Wagner Reis. 2-5-Two covers 4.00

VOLTRON: A LEGEND FORGED (TV)
Devils Due Publishing: Jul, 2008 - No. 5, Apr, 2009 ($3.50)
1-5-Blaylock-s/Bear-a; 4 covers 3.50

VOLTRON: DEFENDER OF THE UNIVERSE (TV)
Image Comics: No. 0, May, 2003 - No. 5, Sept, 2003 ($2.50)
0-Jolley-s/Brooks-a; character pin-ups with background info 3.00
1-5-($2.95) 1-Three covers by Norton, Brooks and Andrews; Norton-a 3.00
...: Revelations TPB (2004, $11.95, digest-sized) r/#1-5; cover gallery 12.00

VOLTRON: DEFENDER OF THE UNIVERSE (TV)
Image Comics: Jan, 2004 - No. 11, Dec, 2004 ($2.95)
1-11: 1-Jolley-s; wraparound-c 3.00

VOLTRON: FROM THE ASHES
Dynamite Entertainment: 2015 - No. 6, 2016 ($3.99)
1-6: 1-Cullen Bunn-s/Blacky Shepherd-a 4.00

VOLTRON: YEAR ONE
Dynamite Entertainment: 2012 - No. 6, 2012 ($3.99, limited series)
1-6: 1-Two covers; Brandon Thomas-s/Craig Cermak-a 4.00

VOODA (Jungle Princess) (Formerly Voodoo) (See Crown Comics)
Ajax-Farrell (Four Star Publications): No. 20, April, 1955 - No. 22, Aug, 1955
20-Baker-c/a (r/Seven Seas #6) 55 110 165 352 601 850
21,22-Baker-a plus Kamen/Baker story, Kimbo Boy of Jungle, & Baker-c(p) in all. 22-Censored Jo-Jo-r (name Powaa) 50 100 150 315 533 750

NOTE: *#20-22 each contain one heavily censored-r of South Sea Girl by* **Baker** *from Seven Seas Comics with name changed to Vooda. #20-r/Seven Seas #6; #21-r/#4; #22-r/#3.*

VOODOO (Weird Fantastic Tales) (Vooda #20 on)
Ajax-Farrell (Four Star Publ.): May, 1952 - No. 19, Jan-Feb, 1955
1-South Sea Girl-r by Baker 87 174 261 553 952 1350
2-Rulah story-r plus South Sea Girl from Seven Seas #2 by Baker (name changed from Alani to El'nee) 74 148 222 470 810 1150
3-Bakerish-a; man stabbed in face 60 120 180 381 653 925
4,8-Baker-r. 8-Severed head panels 60 120 180 381 653 925
5-Nazi death camp story (flaying alive) 61 122 183 390 670 950
6,7,9,10: 6-Severed head panels 53 106 159 334 567 800
11-18: 14-Zombies take over America. 15-Opium drug story-r/Ellery Queen #3. 16-Post nuclear world story.17-Electric chair panels 50 100 150 315 533 750
19-Bondage-c; Baker-r(2)/Seven Seas #5 w/minor changes & #1, heavily modified; last pre-code; contents & covers change to jungle theme

Voodoo #3 © Aegis

Vote Loki #1 © MAR

Wacky Duck #6 © MAR

	GD 2.0	VG 4.0	FN 6.0	VF 8.0	VF/NM 9.0	NM- 9.2
	55	110	165	352	601	850
Annual 1(1952, 25¢, 100 pgs.)-Baker-a (scarce)	194	388	582	1242	2121	3000

VOODOO
Image Comics (WildStorm): Nov, 1997 - No. 4, Mar, 1998 ($2.50, lim. series)

1-4: Alan Moore-s in all; Hughes-c. 2-4-Rio-a 3.00
1-Platinum Ed 10.00
Dancing on the Dark TPB ('99, $9.95) r/#1-4 10.00
...-Zealot: Skin Trade (8/95, $4.95) 5.00

VOODOO (DC New 52) (Also see Grifter)
DC Comics: Nov, 2011 - No. 12, Oct, 2012; No. 0, Nov, 2012 ($2.99)

1-12: 1-Marz-s/Basri-a/c. 3-Green Lantern (Kyle) app. 3.00
#0 (11/12, $2.99) Origin of Voodoo; Basri-a/c 3.00

VOODOO (See Tales of...)

VOODOO CHILD (Weston Cage & Nicolas Cage's...)
Virgin Comics: July, 2007 - No. 6, Dec, 2007 ($2.99)

1-6: 1-Mike Carey-s/Dean Hyrapiet-a; covers by Hyrapiet & Templesmith 3.00
Vol. 1 TPB (1/08, $14.99) r/#1-6; variant covers; intro by Weston Cage & Nicolas Cage 15.00

VOODOOM
Oni Press: June, 2000 ($4.95, B&W)

1-Scott Morse-s/Jim Mahfood-a 5.00

VORTEX
Vortex Publs.: Nov, 1982 - No. 15, 1988 (No month) ($1.50/$1.75, B&W)

	GD	VG	FN	VF	VF/NM	NM-
1 ($1.95)-Peter Hsu-a; Ken Steacy-c; nudity	1	2	3	5	7	9

2,12: 2-1st app. Mister X (on-c only). 12-Sam Kieth-a 6.00
3-11,13-15 3.00

VORTEX
Comico: 1991 - No. 2? ($2.50, limited series)

1,2: Heroes from The Elementals 3.00

VOTE LOKI
Marvel Comics: Aug, 2016 - No. 4, Nov, 2016 ($3.99, limited series)

1-4: 1-Loki runs for President; Hastings-s/Foss-a. 2-McCaffrey-a 4.00

VOYAGE TO THE BOTTOM OF THE SEA (Movie, TV)
Dell Publishing Co./Gold Key: No. 1230, Sept-Nov, 1961; Dec, 1964 - #16, Apr, 1970 (Painted-c)

	GD	VG	FN	VF	VF/NM	NM-
Four Color 1230 (1961)	10	20	30	64	132	200
10133-412(#1, 12/64)(Gold Key)	7	14	21	48	89	130
2(7/65) - 5: Photo back-c, 1-5	5	10	15	31	53	75
6-14	4	8	12	27	44	60
15,16-Reprints	3	6	9	17	26	35

VOYAGE TO THE DEEP
Dell Publishing Co.: Sept-Nov, 1962 - No. 4, Nov-Jan, 1964 (Painted-c)

	GD	VG	FN	VF	VF/NM	NM-
1	5	10	15	31	53	75
2-4	4	8	12	23	37	50

VS
Image Comics: Feb, 2018 - Present ($3.99)

1-Ivan Brandon-s/Esad Ribic-a 4.00

V-WARS
IDW Publishing: Apr, 2014 - No. 11, Mar, 2015 ($3.99)

1-11: 1-Vampire epidemic; Jonathan Maberry-s/Alan Robinson-a 4.00

WACKO
Ideal Publ. Corp.: Sept, 1980 - No. 3, Oct, 1981 (84 pgs., B&W, magazine)

	GD	VG	FN	VF	VF/NM	NM-
1-3	2	4	6	8	11	14

WACKY ADVENTURES OF CRACKY (Also see Gold Key Spotlight)
Gold Key: Dec, 1972 - No. 12, Sept, 1975

	GD	VG	FN	VF	VF/NM	NM-
1	3	6	9	14	20	26
2	2	4	6	10	14	18
3-12	2	4	6	8	10	12

(See March of Comics #405, 424, 436, 448)

WACKY DUCK (...Comics #3-6; formerly Dopey Duck; Justice Comics #7 on) (See Film Funnies)
Marvel Comics (NPP): No. 3, Fall, 1946 - No. 6, Summer, 1947; Aug, 1948 - No. 2, Oct, 1948

	GD	VG	FN	VF	VF/NM	NM-
3	33	66	99	194	317	440
4-Infinity-c	25	50	75	147	241	335
5,6(1947)-Becomes Justice comics	21	42	63	126	206	285
1(1948)	23	46	69	136	223	310
2(1948)	17	34	51	98	154	210
I.W. Reprint #1,2,7('58): 1-r/Wacky Duck #6	2	4	6	10	14	18
Super Reprint #10(I.W. on-c, Super-inside)	2	4	6	9	13	16

WACKY QUACKY (See Wisco)

WACKY RACELAND (Update of Hanna-Barbera's Wacky Races)
DC Comics: Aug, 2016 - No. 6, Jan, 2017 ($3.99)

1-6: 1-Pontac-s/Manco-a; multiple covers; Penelope Pitstop & Dick Dastardly app. 4.00

WACKY RACES (TV)
Gold Key: Aug, 1969 - No. 7, Apr, 1972 (Hanna-Barbera)

	GD	VG	FN	VF	VF/NM	NM-
1	5	10	15	31	53	75
2-7	3	6	9	21	33	45

WACKY SQUIRREL (Also see Dark Horse Presents)
Dark Horse Comics: Oct, 1987 - No. 4, 1988 ($1.75, B&W)

1-4: 4-Superman parody 3.00
Halloween Adventure Special 1 (1987, $2.00) 3.00
Summer Fun Special 1 (1988, $2.00) 3.00

WACKY WITCH (Also see Gold Key Spotlight)
Gold Key: March, 1971 - No. 21, Dec, 1975

	GD	VG	FN	VF	VF/NM	NM-
1	4	8	12	23	37	50
2	3	6	9	14	20	26
3-10	2	4	6	10	14	18
11-21	2	4	6	8	10	12

(See March of Comics #374, 398, 410, 422, 434, 446, 458, 470, 482)

WACKY WOODPECKER (See Two Bit the...)
I. W. Enterprises/Super Comics: 1958; 1963

	GD	VG	FN	VF	VF/NM	NM-
I.W. Reprint #1,2,7 (nd-reprints Two Bit...): 7-r/Two-Bit, the Wacky Woodpecker #1.	2	4	6	9	13	16
Super Reprint #10('63): 10-r/Two-Bit, The Wacky Woodpecker #?	2	4	6	8	11	14

WAGON TRAIN (1st Series) (TV) (See Western Roundup under Dell Giants)
Dell Publishing Co.: No. 895, Mar, 1958 - No. 13, Apr-June, 1962 (All photo-c)

	GD	VG	FN	VF	VF/NM	NM-
Four Color 895 (#1)	9	18	27	62	126	190
Four Color 971(#2),1019(#3)	6	12	18	41	76	110
4(1-3/60),6-13	5	10	15	34	60	85
5-Toth-a	6	12	18	37	66	95

WAGON TRAIN (2nd Series)(TV)
Gold Key: Jan, 1964 - No. 4, Oct, 1964 (All front & back photo-c)

	GD	VG	FN	VF	VF/NM	NM-
1-Tufts-a in all	5	10	15	30	50	70
2-4	4	8	12	23	37	50

WAITING PLACE, THE
Slave Labor Graphics: Apr, 1997 - No. 6, Sept, 1997 ($2.95)

1-6-Sean McKeever-s 3.00
Vol. 2 - 1(11/99), 2-11 3.00
12-($4.95) 5.00

WAITING ROOM WILLIE (See Sad Case of...)

WAKE, THE
DC Comics (Vertigo): Jul, 2013 - No. 10, Sept, 2014 ($2.99)

1-Scott Snyder-s/Sean Murphy-a/c 5.00
1-Variant-c by Andy Kubert 8.00
1-Director's Cut (10/13, $4.99) B&W version, behind-the-scenes production content 5.00
2-10: 6-Story jumps 200 years ahead; Leeward app. 3.00
... Part One TPB (2/14, $9.99) r/#1-5 10.00

WAKE THE DEAD
IDW Publishing: Sept, 2003 - No. 5, Mar, 2004 ($3.99, limited series)

1-5-Steve Niles-s/Chee-a 4.00
TPB (6/04, $19.99) r/series; intro. by Michael Dougherty; embossed die cut cover 20.00

WALK IN (Dave Stewart's ...)
Virgin Comics: Dec, 2006 - No. 6, May, 2007 ($2.99)

1-6: 1-5-Parker-s/Padlekar-a. 6-Parker-a 3.00

WALKING DEAD, THE (Inspired the 2010 AMC television series)
Image Comics: Oct, 2003 - Present ($2.95/$2.99, B&W)

	GD	VG	FN	VF	VF/NM	NM-
1-Robert Kirkman-s in all/Tony Moore-a; 1st app. Rick Grimes, Shane, Morgan & Duane	46	92	138	340	770	1200
1 Special Edition (5/08, $3.99) r/#1; Kirkman afterword; original script and proposal	3	6	9	16	23	30
2-Tony Moore-a through #6	15	30	45	105	233	360

The Walking Dead #31 © R. Kirkman

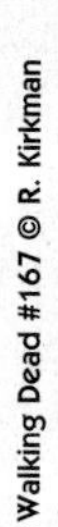

The Walking Dead #167 © R. Kirkman

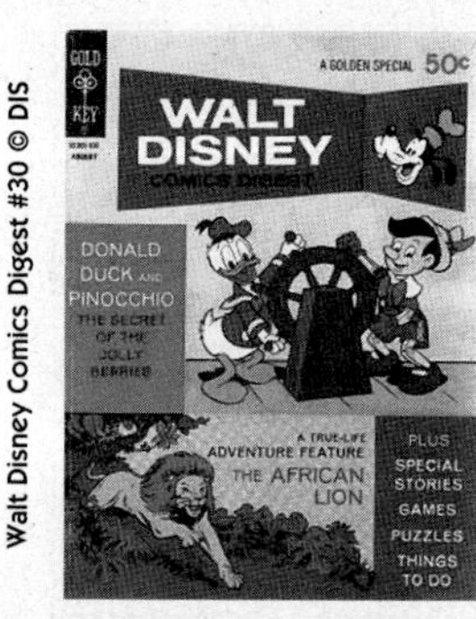

Walt Disney Comics Digest #30 © DIS

	GD 2.0	VG 4.0	FN 6.0	VF 8.0	VF/NM 9.0	NM- 9.2
3	9	18	27	61	123	185
4	8	16	24	52	99	145
5,6: 6-Shane killed	6	12	18	41	76	110
7-Charlie Adlard-a begins; 1st app. Tyreese	6	12	18	37	66	95
8-10	4	8	12	25	40	55
11-18,20: 13-Prison arc begins	3	6	9	16	23	30
19-1st app. Michonne	11	22	33	76	163	250
21-26,28-47,49,50: 25-Adlard covers begin. 28-Rick loses his hand. 46-Tyreese killed.	2	4	6	9	12	15
27-1st app of The Governor	8	16	24	54	102	150
48-Lori, Herschel, others killed	4	8	12	25	40	55
50-Variant wraparound superhero-style cover by Erik Larsen	5	10	15	34	60	85
51,52,54-60: 58-Morgan returns	2	4	6	8	10	12
53-1st app. Abraham & Rosita	5	10	15	33	57	80
61-Preview of Chew; 1st app. Gabriel	4	8	12	25	40	55
62,64-74: 66-Dale dies. 70-1st Douglas Monroe	1	3	4	6	8	10
63-Flip book with B&W reprint of Chew #1	3	6	9	16	24	32
75-(7/10, $3.99) Orange background-c; back-up alien/sci-fi "fantasy" in color; TV series preview with cast photos	2	4	6	9	12	15
75-Variant-c homage to issue #1	3	6	9	17	26	35
76-91: 85-Flip book w/Witch Doctor #0. 86-Flip book w/Elephantmen	1	2	3	5	6	8
92-Intro. Paul Monroe (Jesus)	5	10	15	33	57	80
93-96						6.00
97-99,101-114: 97-"Something to Fear" pt. 1. 98-Abraham killed. 107-Intro Ezekiel						4.00
100-(7/12, $3.99) 1st app. Negan; Glen killed; multiple covers by Adlard, Silvestri, Quitely, McFarlane, Phillips, Hitch, & Ottley	1	3	4	6	8	10
100-Wraparound-c by Adlard						6.00
106-Variant wraparound-c by Adlard for his 100th issue	2	4	6	11	16	20
115-"All Out War" begins; 10 connecting covers by Adlard	1	2	3	5	6	8
116-126-"All Out War"						4.00
127-(5/14) Intro. Magna; bonus preview of Outcast	2	4	6	8	10	12
128-174: 132-1st Whisperers attack. 135-Intro. Lydia. 138-Intro. Alpha. 139-Michonne returns 144-Death of Ezekiel and Rosita and others. 150-Six covers. 156-Death of Alpha. 157-162-Whisperer War; 2 covers (Adlard & Art Adams). 163-(25¢-c). 167-Death of Andrea. 171-Intro Princess						4.00
175-177-($3.99) 175-1st app. The Commonwealth						4.00
... FCBD 2013 Special (5/13, giveaway) reprints bonus stories from Michonne Special and The Governor Special; new Tyreese background story						3.00
Image Firsts: The Walking Dead #1 (3/10, $1.00) reprints #1	2	4	6	10	14	18
...: Michonne Special (10/12, $2.99) Reprints debut from #19 and story from Playboy						6.00
...: Michonne Special - 2nd printing (3/13, $2.99)						3.00
... #1 Tenth Anniversary Special (10/13, $5.99) reprints #1 with color; Kirkman's original series proposal; Kirkman interview	1	3	4	6	8	10
...: The Governor Special (2/13, $2.99) Reprints debut from #27 and story from CBLDF Liberty Annual 2012						4.00
...: Tyreese Special (10/13, $2.99) Reprints debut from #7 and story from FCBD 2013						4.00
... Book 1 HC (2006, $29.99) r/#1-12; sketch pages, cover gallery; Kirkman afterword						45.00
... Book 2 HC (2006, $29.99) r/#13-24; sketch pages, cover gallery						40.00
... Book 3 HC (2007, $29.99) r/#25-36; sketch pages, cover gallery						35.00
... Book 4 HC (2008, $29.99) r/#37-48; sketch pages, cover gallery						35.00
... Book 5 HC (2010, $29.99) r/#49-60; sketch pages, cover gallery						35.00
... Book 6 HC (2010, $34.99) r/#61-72; sketch pages, cover gallery						35.00
... Book 7 HC (2011, $34.99) r/#73-84; sketch pages, cover gallery						35.00
... Book 8 HC (2012, $34.99) r/#85-96; sketch pages, cover gallery						35.00
... Book 9 HC (2013, $34.99) r/#97-108; sketch pages, cover gallery						35.00
... Book 10 HC (2014, $34.99) r/#109-120; sketch pages, cover gallery						35.00
... Book 11 HC (2015, $34.99) r/#121-132; sketch pages, cover gallery						35.00
...Vol. 1: Days Gone Bye (5/04, $9.95, TPB) r/#1-4						20.00
...Vol. 2: Miles Behind Us (10/04, $12.95, TPB) r/#7-12						18.00
...Vol. 3: Safety Behind Bars (2005, $12.95, TPB) r/#13-18						18.00
...Vol. 4: The Heart's Desire (2005, $12.99, TPB) r/#19-24						18.00
...Vol. 5: The Best Defense (2006, $12.99, TPB) r/#25-30						18.00
...Vol. 6: This Sorrowful Life (2007, $12.99, TPB) r/#31-36						15.00
...Vol. 7: The Calm Before (2007, $12.99, TPB) r/#37-42						15.00
...Vol. 8: Made to Suffer (2008, $14.99, TPB) r/#43-48						15.00
...Vol. 9: Here We Remain (2009, $14.99, TPB) r/#49-54						15.00
...Vol. 10: The Road Ahead (2009, $14.99, TPB) r/#55-60						15.00
...Vol. 11: Fear the Hunters (2010, $14.99, TPB) r/#61-66						15.00
...Vol. 12: Life Among Them (2010, $14.99, TPB) r/#67-72						15.00
...Vol. 13: Too Far Gone (2010, $14.99, TPB) r/#73-78						15.00
...Vol. 14: No Way Out (2011, $14.99, TPB) r/#79-84						15.00
...Vol. 15: We Find Ourselves (2011, $14.99, TPB) r/#85-90						15.00
...Vol. 16: A Larger World (2012, $14.99, TPB) r/#91-96						15.00
...Vol. 17: Something to Fear (2012, $14.99, TPB) r/#97-102						15.00
...Vol. 18: What Comes After (2013, $14.99, TPB) r/#103-108						15.00
...Vol. 19: March To War (2013, $14.99, TPB) r/#109-114						15.00
...Vol. 20: All Out War Part 1 (2014, $14.99, TPB) r/#115-120						15.00
...Vol. 21: All Out War Part 2 (2014, $14.99, TPB) r/#121-126						15.00
...Vol. 22: A New Beginning (2014, $14.99, TPB) r/#127-132						15.00
...Vol. 23: Whispers Into Screams (2015, $14.99, TPB) r/#133-138						15.00
...Vol. 24: Life and Death (2015, $14.99, TPB) r/#139-144						15.00
...Vol. 25: No Turning Back (2016, $14.99, TPB) r/#145-150						15.00
...Vol. 26: Call to Arms (2016, $14.99, TPB) r/#151-156						15.00
...Vol. 27: The Whisperer War (2017, $14.99, TPB) r/#157-162						15.00
...Vol. 28: A Certain Doom (2017, $16.99, TPB) r/#163-168						17.00
...Vol. 29: Lines We Cross (2018, $16.99, TPB) r/#169-174						17.00

WALKING DEAD SURVIVORS' GUIDE, THE
Image Comics: Apr, 2011 - No. 4 ($2.99, B&W)

	GD 2.0	VG 4.0	FN 6.0	VF 8.0	VF/NM 9.0	NM- 9.2
1,2-Alphabetical listings of character profiles, first (and last) apps. and current status	2	4	6	10	14	18
3,4	1	2	3	5	6	8

WALKING DEAD WEEKLY, THE (Reprints)
Image Comics: Jan, 2011 - No. 52, Dec, 2011 ($2.99, B&W, weekly)

	GD 2.0	VG 4.0	FN 6.0	VF 8.0	VF/NM 9.0	NM- 9.2
1-Reprints issues with original letter columns; new Kirkman afterword	3	6	9	21	33	45
1-Arizona Comic Con variant-c	3	6	9	16	23	30
2-4,7	2	4	6	9	12	15
5-Death of Amy	4	8	12	27	44	60
6-Death of Shane	3	6	9	19	30	40
8-18,20-26,28-52	1	2	3	5	6	8
19-r/1st Michonne	6	12	18	38	69	100
27-r/1st app. The Governor	3	6	9	16	23	30

WALL·E (Based on the Disney/Pixar movie)
BOOM! Studios: No. 0, Nov, 2009 - No. 7, Jun, 2010 ($2.99)

	GD 2.0	VG 4.0	FN 6.0	VF 8.0	VF/NM 9.0	NM- 9.2
0-7: 0-Prequel; J. Torres-s						3.00

WALLY (Teen-age)
Gold Key: Dec, 1962 - No. 4, Sept, 1963

	GD 2.0	VG 4.0	FN 6.0	VF 8.0	VF/NM 9.0	NM- 9.2
1	3	6	9	20	31	42
2-4	3	6	9	16	24	32

WALLY THE WIZARD
Marvel Comics (Star Comics): Apr, 1985 - No. 12, Mar, 1986 (Children's comic)

	GD 2.0	VG 4.0	FN 6.0	VF 8.0	VF/NM 9.0	NM- 9.2
1-12: Bob Bolling a-1,3; c-1,9,11,12						5.00
1-Variant with "Star Chase" game on last page and inside back-c	2	4	6	9	12	15

WALLY WOOD'S T.H.U.N.D.E.R. AGENTS (See Thunder Agents)
Deluxe Comics: Nov, 1984 - No. 5, Oct, 1986 ($2.00, 52 pgs.)

	GD 2.0	VG 4.0	FN 6.0	VF 8.0	VF/NM 9.0	NM- 9.2
1-5: 5-Jerry Ordway-c/a in Wood style						6.00

NOTE: ***Anderson*** *a-2i, 3i.* ***Buckler*** *a-4.* ***Ditko*** *a-3, 4.* ***Giffen*** *a-1p-4p.* ***Perez*** *a-1p, 2, 4; c-1-4.*

WALT DISNEY CHRISTMAS PARADE (Also see Christmas Parade)
Whitman Publ. Co. (Golden Press): Wint, 1977 ($1.95, cardboard-c, 224 pgs.)

	GD 2.0	VG 4.0	FN 6.0	VF 8.0	VF/NM 9.0	NM- 9.2
11191-Barks-r/Christmas in Disneyland #1, Dell Christmas Parade #9 & Dell Giant #53	4	8	12	25	40	55

WALT DISNEY COMICS DIGEST
Gold Key: June, 1968 - No. 57, Feb, 1976 (50¢, digest size)

	GD 2.0	VG 4.0	FN 6.0	VF 8.0	VF/NM 9.0	NM- 9.2
1-Reprints Uncle Scrooge #5; 192 pgs.	6	12	18	42	79	115
2-4-Barks-r	5	10	15	31	53	75
5-Daisy Duck by Barks (8 pgs.); last published story by Barks (art only) plus 21 pg. Scrooge-r by Barks	7	14	21	44	82	120
6-13-All Barks-r	3	6	9	21	33	45
14,15	3	6	9	16	23	30
16-Reprints Donald Duck #26 by Barks	3	6	9	20	31	42
17-20-Barks-r	3	6	9	17	26	35
21-31,33,35-37-Barks-r; 24-Toth Zorro	3	6	9	16	23	30
32,41,45,47-49	2	4	6	11	16	20
34,38,39: 34-Reprints 4-Color #318. 38-Reprints Christmas in Disneyland #1. 39-Two Barks-r/WDC&S #272, 4-Color #1073 plus Toth Zorro-r	3	6	9	16	23	30
40-Mickey Mouse-r by Gottfredson	2	4	6	13	18	22

Walt Disney's Christmas Parade #5 © DIS

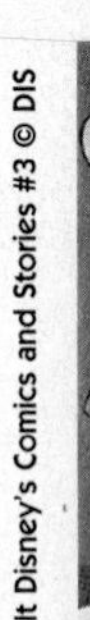

Walt Disney's Comics and Stories #3 © DIS

Walt Disney's Comics and Stories #142 © DIS

	GD 2.0	VG 4.0	FN 6.0	VF 8.0	VF/NM 9.0	NM- 9.2
42,43-Barks-r	2	4	6	13	18	22
44-(Has Gold Key emblem, 50¢)-Reprints 1st story of 4-Color #29,256,275,282	5	10	15	30	50	70
44-Republished in 1976 by Whitman; not identical to original; a bit smaller, blank back-c, 69¢	3	6	9	16	23	30
46,50,52-Barks-r. 52-Barks-r/WDC&S #161,132	2	4	6	11	16	20
51-Reprints 4-Color #71	3	6	9	16	23	30
53-55: 53-Reprints Dell Giant #30. 54-Reprints Donald Duck Beach Party #2. 55-Reprints Dell Giant #49	2	4	6	10	14	18
56-r/Uncle Scrooge #32 (Barks)	2	4	6	13	18	22
57-r/Mickey Mouse Almanac('57) & two Barks stories	2	4	6	11	16	20

NOTE: *Toth a-52r. #1-10, 196 pgs.; #11-41, 164 pgs.; #42 on, 132 pgs. Old issues were being reprinted & distributed by Whitman in 1976.*

WALT DISNEY GIANT (Disney)
Bruce Hamilton Co. (Gladstone): Sept, 1995 - No. 7, Sept, 1996 ($2.25, bi-monthly, 48 pgs.)

1-7: 1-Scrooge McDuck in "Hearts of the Yukon"; Rosa-c/a/scripts plus r/F.C. #218; Scrooge & Glittering Goldie-c. 2-Uncle Scrooge-r by Barks plus 17 pg. text story. 3-Donald the Mighty Duck; Rosa-c; Barks & Rosa-r. 4-Mickey and Goofy; new-a (story actually stars Goofy. Mickey Mouse by Caesar Ferioli; Donald Duck by Giorgio Cavazzano (1st in U.S.). 6-Uncle Scrooge & the Jr. Woodchucks; new-a and Barks-r. 7-Uncle Scrooge-r by Barks plus new-a 4.00

NOTE: *Series was initially solicited as Uncle Walt's Collectory. Issue #8 was advertised, but later cancelled.*

WALT DISNEY PAINT BOOK SERIES
Whitman Publ. Co.: No dates; circa 1975 (Beware! Has 1930s copyright dates) (79¢-c, 52 pgs. B&W, treasury-sized) (Coloring books, text stories & comics-r)

	GD 2.0	VG 4.0	FN 6.0	VF 8.0	VF/NM 9.0	NM- 9.2
#2052 (Whitman #886-r) Mickey Mouse & Donald Duck Gag Book	3	6	9	20	31	42
#2053 (Whitman #677-r)	3	6	9	20	31	42
#2054 (Whitman #670-r) Donald-c	4	8	12	22	35	48
#2055 (Whitman #627-r) Mickey-c	3	6	9	20	31	42
#2056 (Whitman #660-r) Buckey Bug-c	3	6	9	18	28	38
#2057 (Whitman #887-r) Mickey & Donald-c	3	6	9	20	31	42

WALT DISNEY PRESENTS (TV)(Disney)
Dell Publishing Co.: No. 997, 6-8/59 - No. 6, 12-2/1960-61; No. 1181, 4-5/61 (All photo-c)

	GD 2.0	VG 4.0	FN 6.0	VF 8.0	VF/NM 9.0	NM- 9.2
Four Color 997 (#1)	6	12	18	42	79	115
2(12-2/60)-The Swamp Fox(origin), Elfego Baca, Texas John Slaughter (Disney TV show) begin	5	10	15	30	50	70
3-6: 5-Swamp Fox by Warren Tufts	4	8	12	28	47	65
Four Color 1181-Texas John Slaughter	5	10	15	35	63	90

WALT DISNEY'S CHRISTMAS PARADE (Also see Christmas Parade)
Gladstone: Winter, 1988; No. 2, Winter, 1989 ($2.95, 100 pgs.)

	GD 2.0	VG 4.0	FN 6.0	VF 8.0	VF/NM 9.0	NM- 9.2
1-Barks-r/painted-c	2	4	6	8	10	12
2-Barks-r	1	2	3	5	7	9

WALT DISNEY'S CHRISTMAS PARADE
Gemstone Publishing: Dec, 2003; 2004, 2005, 2006,2008 ($8.95/$9.50, prestige format)

1-4: 1-Reprints and 3 new European holiday stories. 2-All reprints. 3-Reprints and 2 new stories, 4-Reprints and 5 new stories 9.00
5-($9.50) R/Uncle Scrooge #47 and European stories 9.50

WALT DISNEY'S COMICS AND STORIES (Cont. of Mickey Mouse Magazine)
(#1-30 contain Donald Duck newspaper reprints) (Titled "Comics And Stories" #264 to #?; titled "Walt Disney's Comics And Stories" #511 on)
Dell Publishing Co./Gold Key #264-473/Whitman #474-510/Gladstone #511-547/ Disney Comics #548-585/Gladstone #586-633/Gemstone Publishing #634-698/ Boom! Kids #699-720/IDW Publishing #721-on: 10/40 - #263, 8/62; #264, 10/62 - #510, 7/84; #511, 10/86 - #633, 2/99; #634, 7/03 - #698, 11/08; #699, 10/09 - #720, 6/11; #721, 7/15 - Present

NOTE: The whole number can always be found at the bottom of the title page in the lower left-hand or right hand panel.

	GD 2.0	VG 4.0	FN 6.0	VF 8.0	VF/NM 9.0	NM- 9.2
1(V1#1-c; V2#1-indicia)-Donald Duck strip-r by Al Taliaferro & Gottfredson's Mickey Mouse begin	2261	4522	6780	15,820	33,910	52,000
2	826	1652	2478	5782	12,391	19,000
3	378	756	1134	2646	5673	8700
4-X-Mas-c; 1st Huey, Dewey & Louie-c this title (See Mickey Mouse Magazine V4#2 for 1st-c ever)	313	626	939	2191	4696	7200
4-Special promotional, complimentary issue; cover same except one corner was blanked out & boxed in to identify the giveaway (not a paste-over). This special pressing was probably sent out to former subscribers to Mickey Mouse Mag. whose subscriptions had expired. (Very rare-5 known copies)	442	884	1326	3094	7297	11,500
5-Goofy-c	251	502	753	1606	3253	4900
6-10: 8-Only Clarabelle Cow-c. 9-Taliaferro-c (1st)	210	420	630	1344	2722	4100
11-14: 11-Huey, Dewey & Louie-c/app.	159	318	477	1018	2059	3100
15-17: 15-The 3 Little Kittens (17 pgs.). 16-The 3 Little Pigs (29 pgs.); X-Mas-c. 17-The Ugly Duckling (4 pgs.)	133	266	399	851	1726	2600
18-21	123	246	369	787	1594	2400
22-30: 22-Flag-c. 24-The Flying Gauchito (1st original comic book story done for WDC&S). 27-Jose Carioca by Carl Buettner (2nd original story in WDC&S)	103	206	309	659	1330	2000
31-New Donald Duck stories by Carl Barks begin (See F.C. #9 for 1st Barks Donald Duck)	400	800	1200	2560	5180	7800
32-Barks-a	232	464	696	1485	2543	3600
33-Barks-a; Gremlins app. (Vivie Risto-s; Infinity-c	163	326	489	1043	1822	2600
34-Gremlins by Walt Kelly begin, end #41; Barks-a	138	276	414	883	1542	2200
35,36-Barks-a	138	276	414	883	1542	2200
37-Donald Duck by Jack Hannah	81	162	243	518	909	1300
38-40-Barks-a. 39-X-Mas-c. 40,41-Gremlins by Kelly	88	176	264	563	982	1400
41-50-Barks-a. 43-Seven Dwarfs-c app. (4/44). 45-50-Nazis in Gottfredson's Mickey Mouse Stories. 46-War Bonds-c	78	156	234	499	875	1250
51-60-Barks-a. 51-X-Mas-c. 52-Li'l Bad Wolf begins, ends #203 (not in #55). 58-Kelly flag-c	32	64	96	230	515	800
61-70: Barks-a. 61-Dumbo story. 63,64-Pinocchio stories. 63-Cover swipe from New Funnies #94. 64-X-Mas-c. 65-Pluto story. 66-Infinity-c. 67,68-Mickey Mouse Sunday-r by Bill Wright	28	56	84	202	451	700
71-80: Barks-a. 75-77-Brer Rabbit stories, no Mickey Mouse. 76-X-Mas-c	25	50	75	175	388	600
81-87,89,90: Barks-a. 82-Goofy-c. 82-84-Bongo stories. 86-90-Goofy & Agnes app. 89-Chip 'n' Dale story	20	40	60	138	307	475
88-1st app. Gladstone Gander by Barks (1/48)	24	48	72	168	372	575
91-97,99: Barks-a. 95-1st WDC&S Barks-c. 96-No Mickey Mouse; Little Toot begins, ends #97. 99-X-Mas-c	18	36	54	126	281	435
98-1st Uncle Scrooge app. in WDC&S (11/48)	30	60	90	216	483	750
100-(1/49)-Barks-a	21	42	63	147	324	500
101-110-Barks-a. 107-Taliaferro-c; Donald acquires super powers	16	32	48	107	236	365
111,114,117-All Barks-a	13	26	39	89	195	300
112-Drug (ether) issue (Donald Duck)	17	34	51	117	259	400
113,115,116,118-123: No Barks. 116-Dumbo x-over. 121-Grandma Duck begins, ends #168; not in #135,142,146,155	10	20	30	64	132	200
124,126-130-All Barks-a. 124-X-Mas-c	10	20	30	70	150	230
125-1st app. Junior Woodchucks (2/51); Barks-a	17	34	51	117	259	400
131,133,135-137,139-All Barks-a	10	20	30	67	141	215
132-Barks-a(2) (D. Duck & Grandma Duck)	10	20	30	69	147	225
134-Intro. & 1st app. The Beagle Boys (11/51)	20	40	60	138	307	475
138-Classic Scrooge money story	14	28	42	96	211	325
140-(5/52)-1st app. Gyro Gearloose by Barks; 2nd Barks Uncle Scrooge-c; 3rd Uncle Scrooge cover app.	20	40	60	138	307	475
141-150-All Barks-a. 143-Little Hiawatha begins, ends #151,159	9	18	27	58	114	170
151-170-All Barks-a	8	16	24	51	96	140
171-199-All Barks-a	7	14	21	46	86	125
200	7	14	21	49	92	135
201-240: All Barks-a. 204-Chip 'n' Dale & Scamp begin	6	12	18	40	73	105
241-283: Barks-a. 241-Dumbo x-over. 247-Gyro Gearloose begins, ends #274. 256-Ludwig Von Drake begins, ends #274	5	10	15	35	63	90
284,285,287,290,295,296,309-311-Not by Barks	3	6	9	19	30	40
286,288,291-294,297,298,308-All Barks stories; 293-Grandma Duck's Farm Friends. 297-Gyro Gearloose. 298-Daisy Duck's Diary-r	4	8	12	23	37	50
289-Annette-c & back-c & story; Barks-s	4	8	12	27	44	60
299-307-All contain early Barks-r (#43-117). 305-Gyro Gearloose	4	8	12	25	40	55
312-Last Barks issue with original story	4	8	12	25	40	55
313-315,317-327,329-334,336-341	3	6	9	15	22	28
316-Last issue published during life of Walt Disney	3	6	9	15	22	28
328,335,342-350-Barks-r	3	6	9	15	22	28
351-360-With posters inside; Barks reprints (2 versions of each with & without posters)	4	8	12	25	40	55
351-360-Without posters...	3	6	9	14	19	24
361-400-Barks-r	3	6	9	14	20	26
401-429-Barks-r	3	6	9	14	19	24
430,433,437,438,441,444,445,466-No Barks	2	4	6	8	11	14
431,432,434-436,439,440,442,443-Barks-r	2	4	6	10	14	18
440-Whitman edition	3	6	9	14	19	24
446-465,467-473-Barks-r	2	4	6	9	13	16

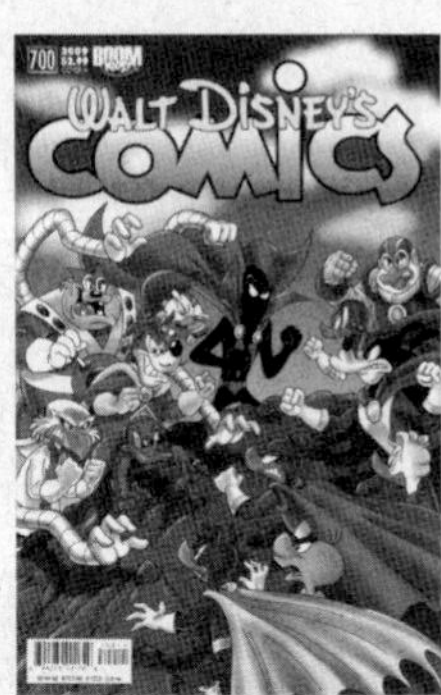
Walt Disney's Comics and Stories #700 © DIS

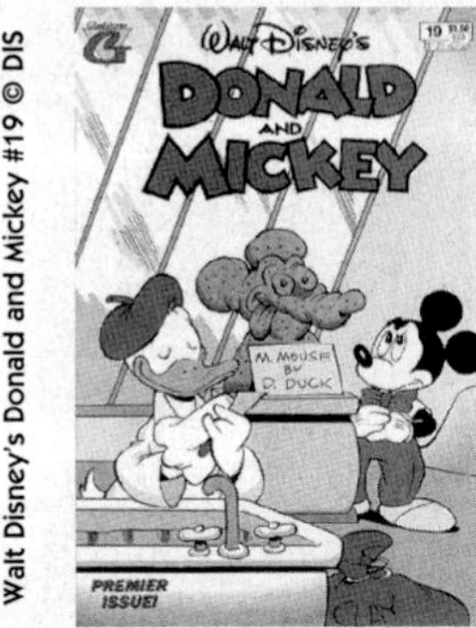

Walt Disney's Donald and Mickey #19 © DIS

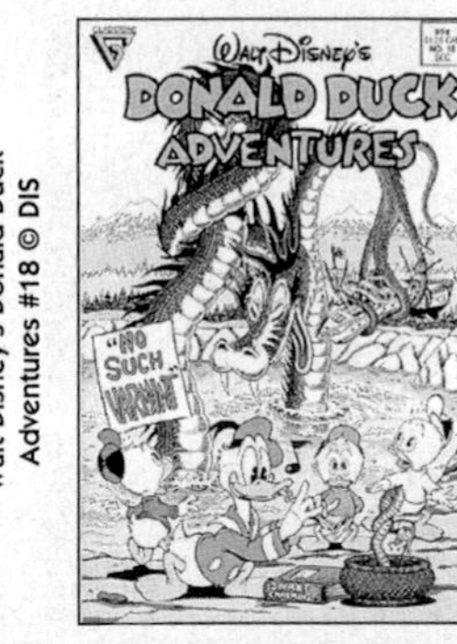

Walt Disney's Donald Duck Adventures #18 © DIS

	GD 2.0	VG 4.0	FN 6.0	VF 8.0	VF/NM 9.0	NM- 9.2
474(3/80),475-478 (Whitman)	3	6	9	14	19	24
479(8/80),481(10/80)-484(1/81) pre-pack only	5	10	15	30	50	70
480 (8-12/80)-(Very low distribution)	12	24	36	79	170	260
484 (1/81, 40¢-c) Cover price error variant (scarce)	6	12	18	38	69	100
484 (1/81) Regular 50¢ cover price; not pre-pack	3	6	9	19	30	40
485-499: 494-r/WDC&S #98	2	4	6	11	16	20
500-510 (All #90011 on-c; pre-packs): 500(4/83), 501(5/83), 502&503(7/83), 504-506(all 8/83), 507(4/84), 508(5/84), 509(6/84), 510(7/84). 506-No Barks	2	4	6	13	18	22
511-Donald Duck by Daan Jippes (1st in U.S.; in all through #518); Gyro Gearloose Barks-r begins (in most through #547); Wuzzles by Disney Studio (1st by Gladstone)	3	6	9	16	24	32
512,513	2	4	6	10	14	18
514-516,520	2	4	6	8	10	12

517-519,521,522,525,527,529,530,532-546: 518-Infinity-c. 522-r/1st app. Huey, Dewey & Louie from D. Duck Sunday. 535-546-Barks-r. 537-1st Donald Duck by William Van Horn in WDC&S. 541-545-52 pgs. 546,547-68 pgs. 546-Kelly-r. 547-Rosa-a 6.00

	GD 2.0	VG 4.0	FN 6.0	VF 8.0	VF/NM 9.0	NM- 9.2
523,524,526,528,531,547: Rosa-s/a in all. 523-1st Rosa 10 pager	2	4	6	9	12	15
548-($1.50, 6/90)-1st Disney issue; new-a; no M. Mouse	1	2	3	4	5	7

549,551-570,572,573,577-579,581,584 ($1.50): 549-Barks-r begin, ends #585, not in #555, 556, & 564. 551-r/1 story from F.C. #29. 556,578-r/Mickey Mouse Cheerios Premium by Dick Moores. 562,563,568-570, 572, 581-Gottfredson strip-r. 570-Valentine issue; has Mickey/Minnie centerfold. 584-Taliaferro strip-r 4.00
550 ($2.25, 52 pgs.)-Donald Duck by Barks; previously printed only in The Netherlands (1st time in U.S.); r/Chip 'n Dale & Scamp from #204 5.00
571-($2.95, 68 pgs)-r/Donald Duck's Atom Bomb by Barks from 1947 Cheerios premium 6.00
574-576,580,582,583 ($2.95, 68 pgs.): 574-r/1st Pinocchio Sunday strip (1939-40). 575-Gottfredson-r, Pinocchio-r/WDC&S #64. 580-r/Donald Duck's 1st app. from Silly Symphony strip 12/16/34 by Taliaferro; Gottfredson strip-r begin; not in #584 & 600. 582,583-r/Mickey Mouse on Sky Island from WDC&S #1,2 5.00
585 ($2.50, 52 pgs.)-r/#140; Barks-r/WDC&S #140 5.00
586,587: 586-Gladstone issues begin again; begin $1.50-c; Gottfredson-r begins (not in #600). 587-Donald Duck by William Van Horn begins 4.00
588-597: 588,591-599-Donald Duck by William Van Horn 3.00
598,599 ($1.95, 36 pgs.): 598-r/1st drawings of Mickey Mouse by Ub Iwerks 3.00
600 ($2.95, 48 pgs.)-L.B. Cole-c(r)/WDC&S #1; Barks-r/WDC&S #32 plus Rosa, Jippes, Van Horn-r and new Rosa centerspread 4.00
601-611 ($5.95, 64 pgs., squarebound, bi-monthly): 601-Barks-c, r/Mickey Mouse V1#1, Rosa-a/scripts. 602-Rosa-c. 604-Taliaferro strip-r/1st Silly Symphony Sundays from 1932. 604,605-Jippes-a. 605-Walt Kelly-c; Gottfredson "Mickey Mouse Outwits the Phantom Blot" r/F.C. #16 6.00
612-633 ($6.95): 633-(2/99) Last Gladstone issue 7.00
634-675: 634-(7/03) First Gemstone issue; William Van Horn-c. 666-Mickey's Inferno 7.00
676-681: 676-Begin $7.50-c. 677-Bucky Bug's 75th Anniversary 7.50
682-698-($7.99) 8.00
699-714: 699-(9/09, $2.99) First BOOM! Kids issue. 700-Back-up story w/Van Horn-a 3.00
715-720: 715-(1/11, $3.99) 70th Anniverary issue; cover swipe of #1 by Van Horn; Jippes, Rosa-a. 716-Barks reprints 4.00
721-738: 721-(7/15, $3.99) First IDW issue; Italian, Dutch & classic reprints 4.00
739-741-($5.99): 741-Eurasia Toft app. 6.00
... 75th Anniversary Special (10/15, $5.99) Classic short story reprints by various 6.00

NOTE: *(#1-38, 68 pgs.; #39-42, 60 pgs.; #43-57, 61-134, 143-168, 446, 447, 52 pgs.; #58-60, 135-142, 169-540, 36 pgs.)*

NOTE: ***Barks*** *art in all issues #31 on, except where noted; c-95, 96, 104, 108, 109, 130-172, 174-178, 183, 198-200, 204, 206-209, 212-216, 218, 220, 226, 228-233, 235-238, 240-243, 247, 250, 253, 256, 260, 261, 276-283, 288-292, 295-298, 301, 303, 304, 306, 307, 309, 310, 313-316, 319, 321, 322, 324, 326, 328, 329, 331, 332, 334, 341, 342, 350, 351, 527r, 530r, 540(never before published), 546r, 557-586r(most), 596p, 601p.* ***Kelly*** *a-24p, 34-41, 43; r-522-524, 546, 547, 582, 583; covers(most)-34-118, 531r, 537r, 541r-543r, 562r, 571r, 605r. Walt Disney's Comics & Stories featured Mickey Mouse serials which were in practically every issue from #1 through #394 and #511 to date. The titles of the serials, along with the issues they are in, are listed in previous editions of this price guide.* ***Floyd Gottfredson*** *Mickey Mouse serials in issues #1-14, 18-66, 69-74, 78-100, 128, 562, 563, 568-572, 582, 583, 586-599 , 601-603 , 605-present , plus "Service with a Smile" in #13; "Mickey Mouse in a Warplant" (3 pgs.), and "Pluto Catches a Nazi Spy" (4 pgs.) in #62; "Mystery Next Door", #93; "Sunken Treasure", #94; "Aunt Marissa", #95 (r in #575); "Gangland", #98 (r in #562); "Thanksgiving Dinner", #99 (r in #567); and "The Talking Dog", #100 (r in #563); "Morty's Escapade," #128. "The Brave Little Tailor", #580; "Introducing Mickey Mouse Movies ", #581; Circus Roustabout, #585; "Rumplewatt the Giant", #604. Mickey Mouse by* ***Paul Murry*** *#152-547 except 155-57 (****Dick Moore****), 327-29 (****Tony Strobl****), 348-50 (****Jack Manning****), 533 (****Bill Wright****).* ***Don Rosa*** *story/a-523, 524, 526, 528, 531, 547, 601-present.* ***Al Taliaferro*** *Silly Symphonies in #5-"Three Little Pigs"; #13-"Birds of a Feather"; #14-"The Boarding School Mystery"; #15-"Cookieland" and "Three Little Kittens"; #16-"The Practical Pig"; #17-"The Ugly Duckling"; "The Wise Little Hen" in #580; and "Ambrose the Robber Kitten"; #19-"Penguin Isle"; and "Bucky Bug" in #20-23, 25, 26, 28 (one continuous story from 1932-34; first 2 pgs. not Taliaferro).* ***Gottfredson*** *strip r-562, 563, 568-572, 581, 585, 586, 590.* ***Taliaferro*** *strip r-584, 580.* ***Van Horn*** *a-537, 545, 561, 574, 587, 588, 591-on.*

WALT DISNEY'S COMICS DIGEST
Gladstone: Dec, 1986 - No. 7, Sept, 1987

	GD 2.0	VG 4.0	FN 6.0	VF 8.0	VF/NM 9.0	NM- 9.2
1	1	2	3	5	6	8
2-7						6.00

WALT DISNEY'S COMICS PENNY PINCHER
Gladstone: May, 1997 - No. 4, Aug, 1997 (99¢, limited series)

1-4 3.00

WALT DISNEY'S DONALD AND MICKEY (Formerly Walt Disney's Mickey and Donald)
Gladstone (Bruce Hamilton Co.): No. 19, Sept, 1993 - No. 30, 1995 ($1.50, 36 & 68 pgs.)

19,21-24,26-30: New & reprints. 19,21,23,24-Barks-r. 19,26-Murry-r. 22-Barks "Omelet" story r/WDC&S #146. 27-Mickey Mouse story by Caesar Ferioli (1st U.S work). 29-Rosa-c; Mickey Mouse story actually starring Goofy (does not include Mickey except on title page.) 4.00
20,25-($2.95, 68 pgs.): 20-Barks, Gottfredson-r 5.00
NOTE: *Donald Duck stories were all reprints.*

WALT DISNEY'S DONALD DUCK
Gemstone Publishing: 2006, 2008

... Free Comic Book Day (5/06) r/WDC&S #531; Rosa-s/a; P&S. Block-s/a; Van Horn-s/a 3.00
nn-(8-1/2"x 5-1/2", Halloween giveaway) r/"A Prank Above" -Barks-s/a; Rosa-s/a 2.50
nn-(2008, 8-1/2"x 5-1/2", Halloween giveaway) "The Halloween Huckster"; Rota-s/a 2.50

WALT DISNEY'S DONALD DUCK ADVENTURES (D.D. Adv. #1-3)
Gladstone: 11/87-No. 20, 4/90 (1st Series); No. 21,8/93-No. 48, 2/98(3rd Series)

	GD 2.0	VG 4.0	FN 6.0	VF 8.0	VF/NM 9.0	NM- 9.2
1	1	2	3	5	6	8

2-r/F.C. #308 4.00
3,4,6,7,9-11,13,15-18: 3-r/F.C. #223. 4-r/F.C. #62. 9-r/F.C. #159, "Ghost of the Grotto". 11-r/F.C. #159, "Adventure Down Under." 16-r/F.C. #291; Rosa-c. 18-r/FC #318; Rosa-c 4.00
5,8: 5-Don Rosa-c/a. 8-Rosa-a 5.00
12($1.50, 52pgs)-Rosa-c/s/a; "Return to Plain Awful" story; sequel to Four Color #223 (square egg story); Barks centerfold poster 6.00
14-r/F.C. #29, "Mummy's Ring" 4.00
19($1.95, 68 pgs.)-Barks-r/F.C. #199 (1 pg.) 4.00
20($1.95, 68 pgs.)-Barks-r/F.C. #189 & cover-r; William Van Horn-a 4.00
21,22: 21-r/D.D. #46. 22-r/F.C. #282 3.00
23-25,27,29,31,32-($1.50, 36 pgs.): 21,23,29-Rosa-c. 23-Intro/1st app. Andold Wild Duck by Marco Rota. 24-Van Horn-a. 27-1st Pat Block-a, "Mystery of Widow's Gap." 31,32-Block-c 3.00
26,28($2.95, 68 pgs.): 26-Barks-r/F.C. #108, "Terror of the River". 28-Barks-r/F.C. #199, "Sheriff of Bullet Valley" 4.00
30($2.95, 68 pgs.)-r/F.C. #367, Barks' "Christmas for Shacktown" 4.00
33($1.95, 68 pgs.)-r/F.C. #408, Barks' "The Golden Helmet;"Van Horn-c 4.00
34-43: 34-Resume $1.50-c. 34,35,37-Block-a/scripts. 38-Van Horn-c/a 3.00
44-48-($1.95-c) 3.00
NOTE: ***Barks*** *a-1-22r, 26r, 28r, 33r, 36r; c-3r, 8r, 10r, 14r, 20r.* ***Block*** *a-27, 30, 34, 35, 37; c-27, 30-32, 34, 35, 37; c-27, 30, 31, 32, 34, 35, 37.* ***Rosa*** *a-5, 8, 12, 43; c-13, 16, 18, 21, 23, 43.*

WALT DISNEY'S DONALD DUCK ADVENTURES (2nd Series)
Disney Comics: June, 1990 - No. 38, July, 1993 ($1.50)

1-Rosa-a & scripts 5.00
2-21,23,25,27-33,35,36,38: 2-Barks-r/WDC&S #35; William Van Horn-a begins, ends #20. 9-Barks-r/F.C. #178. 9,11,14,17-No Van Horn-a. 11-Mad #1 cover parody. 14-Barks-r. 17-Barks-r. 21-r/FC #203 by Barks. 29-r/MOC #20 by Barks 3.00
22,24,26,34,37: 22-Rosa-a (10 pgs.) & scripts. 24-Rosa-a & scripts. 26-r/March of Comics #41 by Barks. 34-Rosa-c/a. 37-Rosa-a; Barks-r 4.00
NOTE: ***Barks*** *r-2, 4, 9(F.C. #178), 14(D.D. #45), 17, 21, 26, 27, 29 , 35, 36(D.D #60)-38.* ***Taliaferro*** *a-34r, 36r.*

WALT DISNEY'S DONALD DUCK ADVENTURES
Gemstone Publishing: May, 2003 (giveaway promoting 2003 return of Disney Comics)

...Free Comic Book Day Edition - cover logo on red background; reprints "Maharajah Donald" & "The Peaceful Hills" from March of Comics #4; Barks-s/a; Kelly original-c on back-c 3.00
...San Diego Comic-Con 2003 Edition - cover logo on gold background 3.00
...ANA World's Fair of Money Baltimore Edition - cover logo on green background 3.00
...WizardWorld Chicago 2003 Edition - cover logo on blue background 3.00

WALT DISNEY'S DONALD DUCK ADVENTURES (Take-Along Comic)
Gemstone Publishing: July, 2003 - No. 21, Nov, 2006 ($7.95, 5" x 7-1/2")

1-21-Mickey Mouse & Uncle Scrooge app. 9-Christmas-c 8.00
... , The Barks/Rosa Collection Vol. 2 (3/08, $8.99) reprints Donald Duck's Atom Bomb, Super Snooper & The Trouble With Dimes by Barks; The Duck Who Fell to Earth, Super Snooper Strikes Again & The Money Pit by Rosa 9.00
... , The Barks/Rosa Collection Vol. 3 (9/08, $8.99) r/FC #408 "The Golden Helmet" by Barks & DDA #43 "The Lost Charts of Columbus" by Rosa; cover gallery and bonus art 9.00

WALT DISNEY'S DONALD DUCK AND FRIENDS (Continues as Donald Duck and Friends)
Gemstone Publishing: No. 308, Oct, 2003 - No. 346, Dec, 2006 ($2.95)

308-346: 308-Numbering resumes from Gladstone Donald Duck series; Halloween-c. 332-Halloween-c; r/#26 by Carl Barks 3.00

Walt Disney Showcase #41 © DIS

Walt Disney's Mickey and Donald #6 © DIS

Walt Disney's Spring Fever #1 © DIS

WALT DISNEY'S DONALD DUCK AND MICKEY MOUSE (Formerly Walt Disney's Donald and Mickey)
Gladstone (Bruce Hamilton Company): Sept, 1995 - No. 7, Sept, 1996 ($1.50, 32 pgs.)

	GD 2.0	VG 4.0	FN 6.0	VF 8.0	VF/NM 9.0	NM- 9.2
1-7: 1-Barks-r and new Mickey Mouse stories in all. 5,6-Mickey Mouse stories by Caesar Ferioli. 7-New Donald Duck and Mickey Mouse x-over story; Barks-r/WDC&S #51						3.00

NOTE: *Issue #8 was advertised, but cancelled.*

WALT DISNEY'S DONALD DUCK AND UNCLE SCROOGE
Gemstone Publishing: Nov, 2005 ($6.95, square-bound one-shot)

nn-New story by John Lustig and Pat Block and r/Uncle Scrooge #59 — 7.00

WALT DISNEY'S DONALD DUCK FAMILY
Gemstone Publishing: Jun, 2008 ($8.99, square-bound)

... The Daan Jippes Collection Vol. 1 - R/Barks-s re-drawn by Jippes for Dutch comics — 9.00

WALT DISNEY'S DONALD DUCK IN THE CASE OF THE MISSING MUMMY
Gemstone Publishing: Oct, 2007 ($8.99, square-bound one-shot)

nn-New story by Shelley and Pat Block and r/Donald Duck FC #29 — 9.00

WALT DISNEY'S GYRO GEARLOOSE
Gemstone Publishing: May, 2008

... Free Comic Book Day (5/08) short stories by Barks, Rosa, Van Horn, Gerstein — 3.00

WALT DISNEY SHOWCASE
Gold Key: Oct, 1970 - No. 54, Jan, 1980 (No. 44-48: 68pgs., 49-54: 52pgs.)

	GD 2.0	VG 4.0	FN 6.0	VF 8.0	VF/NM 9.0	NM- 9.2
1-Boatniks (Movie)-Photo-c	3	6	9	17	26	35
2-Moby Duck	3	6	9	14	19	24
3,4,7: 3-Bongo & Lumpjaw-r. 4,7-Pluto-r	2	4	6	10	14	18
5-$1,000,000 Duck (Movie)-Photo-c	3	6	9	15	22	28
6-Bedknobs & Broomsticks (Movie)	3	6	9	15	22	28
8-Daisy & Donald	2	4	6	11	16	20
9- 101 Dalmatians (cartoon feat.); r/F.C. #1183	3	6	9	16	24	32
10-Napoleon & Samantha (Movie)-Photo-c	3	6	9	15	22	28
11-Moby Duck-r	2	4	6	10	14	18
12-Dumbo-r/Four Color #668	2	4	6	11	16	20
13-Pluto-r	2	4	6	10	14	18
14-World's Greatest Athlete (Movie)-Photo-c	3	6	9	15	22	28
15- 3 Little Pigs-r	2	4	6	11	16	20
16-Aristocats (cartoon feature); r/Aristocats #1	3	6	9	15	22	28
17-Mary Poppins; r/M.P. #10136-501-Photo-c	3	6	9	15	22	28
18-Gyro Gearloose; Barks-r/F.C. #1047,1184	3	6	9	17	26	35
19-That Darn Cat; r/That Darn Cat #10171-602-Hayley Mills photo-c	3	6	9	15	22	28
20,23-Pluto-r	2	4	6	11	16	20
21-Li'l Bad Wolf & The Three Little Pigs	2	4	6	10	14	18
22-Unbirthday Party with Alice in Wonderland; r/Four Color #341	3	6	9	14	19	24
24-26: 24-Herbie Rides Again (Movie); sequel to "The Love Bug"; photo-c. 25-Old Yeller (Movie); r/F.C. #869; Photo-c. 26-Lt. Robin Crusoe USN (Movie); r/Lt. Robin Crusoe USN #10191-601; photo-c	2	4	6	11	16	20
27-Island at the Top of the World (Movie)-Photo-c	3	6	9	14	19	24
28-Brer Rabbit, Bucky Bug-r/WDC&S #58	2	4	6	11	16	20
29-Escape to Witch Mountain (Movie)-Photo-c	3	6	9	14	19	24
30-Magica De Spell; Barks-r/Uncle Scrooge #36 & WDC&S #258	3	6	9	20	31	42
31-Bambi (cartoon feature); r/Four Color #186	2	4	6	13	18	22
32-Spin & Marty-r/F.C. #1026; Mickey Mouse Club (TV)-Photo-c	3	6	9	14	19	24
33-40: 33-Pluto-r/F.C. #1143. 34-Paul Revere's Ride with Johnny Tremain (TV); r/F.C. #822. 35-Goofy-r/F.C. #952. 36-Peter Pan-r/F.C. #442. 37-Tinker Bell & Jiminy Cricket-r/F.C. #982,989. 38,39-Mickey & the Sleuth, Parts 1 & 2. 40-The Rescuers (cartoon feature)	2	4	6	9	13	16
41-Herbie Goes to Monte Carlo (Movie); sequel to "Herbie Rides Again"; photo-c	2	4	6	10	14	18
42-Mickey & the Sleuth	2	4	6	9	13	16
43-Pete's Dragon (Movie)-Photo-c	2	4	6	13	18	22
44-Return From Witch Mountain (new) & In Search of the Castaways-r (Movies)-Photo-c; 68 pg. giants begin	3	6	9	14	19	24
45-The Jungle Book (Movie); r/#30033-803	3	6	9	16	24	32
46-48: 46-The Cat From Outer Space (Movie)(new), & The Shaggy Dog (Movie)-r/F.C. #985; photo-c. 47-Mickey Mouse Surprise Party-r. 48-The Wonderful Advs. of Pinocchio-r/F.C. #1203; last 68 pg. issue	2	4	6	10	14	18
49-54: 49-North Avenue Irregulars (Movie); Zorro-r/Zorro #11; 52 pgs. begin; photo-c. 50-Bedknobs & Broomsticks-r/#6; Mooncussers-r/World of Adv. #1; photo-c. 51-101 Dalmatians-r. 52-Unidentified Flying Oddball (Movie); r/Picnic Party #8; photo-c. 53-The Scarecrow-r (TV). 54-The Black Hole (Movie)-Photo-c (predates Black Hole #1)	2	4	6	9	13	16

WALT DISNEY SHOWCASE
IDW Publishing: Jan, 2018 - Present ($3.99)

1-English versions of Italian Donald Duck stories; 3 covers — 4.00

WALT DISNEY'S MAGAZINE (TV)(Formerly Walt Disney's Mickey Mouse Club Magazine) (50¢, bi-monthly)
Western Publishing Co.: V2#4, June, 1957 - V4#6, Oct, 1959

	GD 2.0	VG 4.0	FN 6.0	VF 8.0	VF/NM 9.0	NM- 9.2
V2#4-Stories & articles on the Mouseketeers, Zorro, & Goofy and other Disney characters & people	6	12	18	38	69	100
V2#5, V2#6(10/57)	5	10	15	35	63	90
V3#1(12/57), V3#3-5	5	10	15	33	57	80
V3#2-Annette Funicello photo-c	9	18	27	63	129	195
V3#6(10/58)-TV Zorro photo-c	7	14	21	44	82	120
V4#1(12/58) - V4#2-4,6(10/59)	5	10	15	33	57	80
V4#5-Annette Funicello photo-c, w/ 2-photo articles	9	18	27	63	129	195

NOTE: *V2#4-V3#6 were 11-1/2x8-1/2", 48 pgs.; V4#1 on were 10x8", 52 pgs. (Peak circulation of 400,000).*

WALT DISNEY'S MERRY CHRISTMAS (See Dell Giant #39)

WALT DISNEY'S MICKEY AND DONALD (M & D #1,2)(Becomes Walt Disney's Donald & Mickey #19 on)
Gladstone: Mar, 1988 - No. 18, May, 1990 (95¢)

	NM- 9.2
1-Don Rosa-a; r/1949 Firestone giveaway	6.00
2-8: 3-Infinity-c. 4-8-Barks-r	4.00
9-15: 9-r/1948 Firestone giveaway; X-Mas-c	3.00
16($1.50, 52 pgs.)-r/FC #157	5.00
17-(68 pgs.) Barks M.M.-r/FC #79 plus Barks D.D.-r; Rosa-a; x-mas-c	6.00
18($1.95, 68 pgs.)-Gottfredson-r/WDC&S #13,72-74; Kelly-c(r); Barks-r	5.00

NOTE: ***Barks** reprints in 1-15, 17, 18. **Kelly** c-13r, 14 (r/Walt Disney's C&S #58), 18r.*

WALT DISNEY'S MICKEY MOUSE
Gemstone Publishing: May, 2007

... Free Comic Book Day (5/07) Floyd Gottfredson-s/a — 3.00

WALT DISNEY'S MICKEY MOUSE ADVENTURES (Take-Along Comic)
Gemstone Publishing: Aug, 2004 - No. 12 ($7.95, 5" x 7-1/2")

1-12-Goofy, Donald Duck & Uncle Scrooge app. — 8.00

WALT DISNEY'S MICKEY MOUSE AND BLOTMAN IN BLOTMAN RETURNS
Gemstone Publishing: Dec, 2006 ($5.99, squarebound, one-shot)

nn-Wraparound-c by Noel Van Horn; Super Goof back-up story — 6.00

WALT DISNEY'S MICKEY MOUSE AND FRIENDS (See Mickey Mouse and Friends for #296)
Gemstone Publishing: No. 257, Oct, 2003 - No. 295, Dec, 2006 ($2.95)

257-295: 257-Numbering resumes from Gladstone Mickey Mouse series; Halloween-c. 285-Return of the Phantom Blot — 3.00

WALT DISNEY'S MICKEY MOUSE AND UNCLE SCROOGE
Gemstone Publishing: June, 2004 (Free Comic Book Day giveaway)

nn-Flip book with r/Uncle Scrooge #15 and r/Mickey Mouse Four Color #79 (only Barks drawn Mickey Mouse story) — 3.00

WALT DISNEY'S MICKEY MOUSE CLUB MAGAZINE (TV)(Becomes Walt Disney's Magazine)
Western Publishing Co.: Winter, 1956 - V2#3, Apr, 1957 (11-1/2x8-1/2", quarterly, 48 pgs.)

	GD 2.0	VG 4.0	FN 6.0	VF 8.0	VF/NM 9.0	NM- 9.2
V1#1	12	24	36	83	182	280
2-4	8	16	24	51	96	140
V2#1,2	6	12	18	41	76	110
3-Annette photo-c	11	22	33	76	163	250
Annual(1956)-Two different issues; ($1.50-Whitman); 120 pgs., cardboard covers, 11-3/4x8-3/4"; reprints	12	24	36	83	182	280
Annual(1957)-Same as above	10	20	30	69	147	225

WALT DISNEY'S MICKEY MOUSE MEETS BLOTMAN
Gemstone Publishing: Aug, 2005 ($5.99, squarebound, one-shot)

nn-Wraparound-c by Noel Van Horn; Super Goof back-up story — 6.00

WALT DISNEY'S PINOCCHIO SPECIAL
Gladstone: Spring, 1990 ($1.00)

1-50th anniversary edition; Kelly-r/F.C. #92 — 3.00

WALT DISNEY'S SEBASTIAN
Disney Comics, Inc.: 1992

1-(36 pgs.) — 3.00

WALT DISNEY'S SPRING FEVER
Gemstone Publishing: Apr, 2007; Apr, 2008 ($9.50, squarebound)

1,2: 1-New stories and reprints incl. "Mystery of the Swamp" by Carl Barks — 9.50

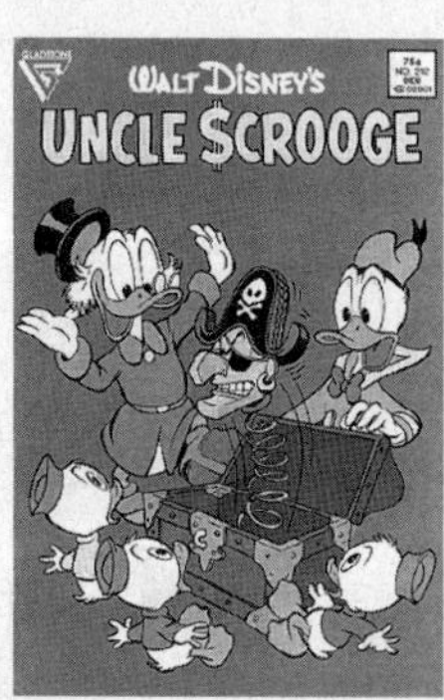

Walt Disney's Uncle Scrooge #212 © DIS

Walt Disney's Uncle Scrooge Adventures #12 © DIS

Wanderers #10 © DC

	GD 2.0	VG 4.0	FN 6.0	VF 8.0	VF/NM 9.0	NM- 9.2

WALT DISNEY'S THE ADVENTUROUS UNCLE SCROOGE MCDUCK
Gladstone: Jan, 1998 - No. 2, Mar, 1998 ($1.95)

1,2: 1-Barks-a(r). 2-Rosa-a(r) 3.00

WALT DISNEY'S THE JUNGLE BOOK
W.D. Publications (Disney Comics): 1990 ($5.95, graphic novel, 68 pgs.)

nn-Movie adaptation; movie rereleased in 1990 6.00
nn-($2.95, 68 pgs.)-Comic edition; wraparound-c 4.00

WALT DISNEY'S UNCLE SCROOGE (Formerly Uncle Scrooge #1-209)
Gladstone #210-242/Disney Comics #243-280/Gladstone #281-318/Gemstone #319 on: No. 210, 10/86 - No. 242, 4/90; No. 243, 6/90 - No. 318, 2/99; No. 319, 7/03 - No. 383, 11/08

210-1st Gladstone issue; r/WDC&S #134 (1st Beagle Boys) 2 4 6 9 13 16
211-218: 216-New story ("Go Slowly Sands of Time") plotted and partly scripted by Barks. 217-r/U.S. #7, "Seven Cities of Cibola" 2 4 6 9 12 15
219-"Son Of The Sun" by Rosa (his 1st pro work) 3 6 9 14 20 25
220-Don Rosa-a/scripts 1 2 3 5 6 8
221-223,225,228-234,236-240 4.00
224,226,227,235: 224-Rosa-c/a. 226,227-Rosa-a. 235-Rosa-a/scripts 5.00
241-($1.95, 68 pgs.)-Rosa finishes over Barks-r 6.00
242-($1.95, 68 pgs.)-Barks-r; Rosa-a(1 pg.) 6.00
243-249,251-260,264-275,277-280,282-284-($1.50): 243-1st by Disney Comics. 274-All Barks issue. 275-Contains centerspread by Rosa. 279-All Barks issue; Rosa-c. 283-r/WDC&S #98 3.00
250-($2.25, 52 pgs.)-Barks-r; wraparound-c 4.00
261-263,276-Don Rosa-c/a 5.00
281-Gladstone issues start again; Rosa-c 6.00
285-The Life and Times of Scrooge McDuck Pt. 1; Rosa-c/a/scripts 1 3 4 6 8 10
286-293: The Life and Times of Scrooge McDuck Pt. 2-9; Rosa-c/a/scripts. 292-Scrooge & Glittering Goldie & Goose Egg Nugget on-c 6.00
294-299, 301-308-($1.50, 32 pgs.): 294-296-The Life and Times of Scrooge McDuck Pt. 10-12. 295-Titanic on-c. 296-Beagle Boys & Christmas-c. 297-The Life and Times of Uncle Scrooge Pt. 0; Rosa-c/a/scripts 3.00
300-($2.25, 48 pgs.)-Rosa-c; Barks-r/WDC&S #104 and U.S. #216; r/U.S. #220; includes new centerfold. 4.00
309-($6.95) Low print run 3 6 9 14 20 25
310-($6.95) Low print run 4 8 12 27 44 60
311-320-($6.95) 318-(2/99) Last Gladstone issue. 319-(7/03) First Gemstone issue; The Dutchman's Secret by Don Rosa 2 4 6 8 10 12
321-360 7.00
361-366: 361-Begin $7.50-c 7.50
367-383-($7.99) 8.00
... Adventures, The Barks/Rosa Collection Vol. 1 (Gemstone, 7/07, $8.50) reprints Pygmy Indians appearances in U.S. #18 by Barks and WDC&S #633 by Rosa 8.50
Walt Disney's The Life and Times of Scrooge McDuck by Don Rosa TPB (Gemstone, 2005, $16.99) Reprints #285-296, with foreword, commentaries & sketch pages by Rosa 17.00
Walt Disney's The Life and Times of Scrooge McDuck Companion by Don Rosa TPB (Gemstone, 2006, $16.99) additional chapters, with foreword & commentaries 17.00

NOTE: ***Barks*** *r-210-218, 220-223, 224(2pg.), 225-234, 236-242, 245, 246, 250-253, 255, 256, 258, 261(2 pg.), 265, 267, 268, 270(2), 272-284, 299-present; c(r)-210, 212, 221, 228, 229, 232, 233, 284. scripts-287, 293.* ***Rosa*** *a-219, 220, 224, 226, 227, 235, 261-263, 268, 275-277, 285-297; c-219, 224, 231, 261-263, 276, 278-281, 285-296; scripts-219, 220, 224, 235, 261-263, 268, 276, 285-296.*

WALT DISNEY'S UNCLE SCROOGE
Gemstone Publishing

nn-(5/05, FCBD) Reprints Uncle Scrooge's debut in Four Color Comics #386; Barks-s/a 3.00
nn-(2007, 8-1/2"x 5-1/2", Halloween giveaway) Hound of the Whiskevilles; Barks-s/a 3.00

WALT DISNEY'S UNCLE SCROOGE ADVENTURES (U. Scrooge Advs. #1-3)
Gladstone Publishing: Nov, 1987 - No. 21, May, 1990; No. 22, Sept, 1993 - No. 54, Feb, 1998

1-Barks-r begin, ends #26 2 4 6 8 10 12
2-4 4.00
5,9,14: 5-Rosa-c/a; no Barks-r. 9,14-Rosa-a 5.00
6-8,10-13,15-19: 10-r/U.S. #18(all Barks) 3.00
20,21 ($1.95, 68 pgs.) 20-Rosa-c/a. 21-Rosa-a 5.00
22 ($1.50)-Rosa-c; r/U.S. #26 5.00
23-($2.95, 68 pgs.)-Vs. The Phantom Blot-r/P.B. #3; Barks-r 4.00
24-26,29,31,32,34-36: 24,25,29,31,32-Rosa-c. 25-r/U.S. #21 3.00
27-Guardians of the Lost Library - Rosa-c/a/story; origin of Junior Woodchuck Guidebook 4.00
28-($2.95, 68 pgs.)-r/U.S. #13 w/restored missing panels 4.00
30-($2.95, 68 pgs.)-r/U.S. #12; Rosa-c 4.00
33-($2.95, 64 pgs.)-New Barks story 4.00
37-54 3.00

NOTE: ***Barks*** *r-1-4, 6-8, 10-13, 15-21, 23, 22, 24; c(r)-15, 16, 17, 21.* ***Rosa*** *a-5, 9, 14, 20, 21, 27, 51; c-5, 13, 14, 17(finishes), 20, 22, 24, 25, 27, 28, 51; scripts-5, 9, 14, 27.*

WALT DISNEY'S UNCLE SCROOGE AND DONALD DUCK
Gladstone: Jan, 1998 - No. 2, Mar, 1998 ($1.95)

1,2: 1-Rosa-a(r) 3.00

WALT DISNEY'S UNCLE SCROOGE ADVENTURES IN COLOR
Gladstone Publ.: Dec, 1995 - Present ($8.95/$9.95, squarebound, 56 issue limited series) (Polybagged w/card) (Series chronologically reprints all the stories written & drawn by Carl Barks)

1-56: 1-(12/95)-r/FC #386. 15-(12/96)-r/US #15. 16-(12/96)-r/US #16. 18-(1/97)-r/US #18 10.00

WALT DISNEY'S VACATION PARADE
Gemstone Publishing: 2004 - No. 5, July, 2008 ($8.95/$9.95, squarebound, annual)

1-3: 1-Reprints stories from Dell Giant Comics Vacation Parade 1 (July 1950) 10.00
4,5-($9.95): 4-(5/07). 5-(7/08) 10.00

WALT DISNEY'S WHEATIES PREMIUMS (See Wheaties in the Promotional section)

WALT DISNEY'S WORLD OF THE DRAGONLORDS
Gemstone Publishing: 2005 ($12.99, squarebound, graphic novel)

SC-Uncle Scrooge, Donald & nephews app.; Byron Erickson-s/Giorgio Cavazzano-a 13.00

WALT DISNEY TREASURES - DISNEY COMICS: 75 YEARS OF INNOVATION
Gemstone Publishing: 2006 ($12.99, TPB)

SC-Reprints from 1930-2004, including debut of Mickey Mouse newspaper strip 13.00

WALT DISNEY TREASURES - UNCLE SCROOGE: A LITTLE SOMETHING SPECIAL
Gemstone Publishing: 2008 ($16.99, TPB)

SC-Uncle Scrooge classics from 1954-2006, including "The Seven Cities of Cibola" 17.00

WALT DISNEY UNCLE SCROOGE AND DONALD DUCK
Fantagraphic Books: 2014 (giveaway)

Free Comic Book Day - A Matter of Some Gravity; Don Rosa-s/a 3.00

WALTER LANTZ ANDY PANDA (Also see Andy Panda)
Gold Key: Aug, 1973 - No. 23, Jan, 1978 (Walter Lantz)

1-Reprints 3 6 9 14 19 24
2-10-All reprints 2 4 6 9 12 15
11-23: 15,17-19,22-Reprints 1 2 3 5 7 9

WALT KELLY'S...
Eclipse Comics: Dec, 1987; Apr, 1988 ($1.75/$2.50, Baxter paper)

...Christmas Classics 1 (12/87)-Kelly-r/Peter Wheat & Santa Claus Funnies, ...Springtime Tales 1 (4/88, $2.50)-Kelly-r 4.00

WALTONS, THE (See Kite Fun Book)

WALT SCOTT (See Little People)

WALT SCOTT'S CHRISTMAS STORIES (See Little People, 4-Color #959, 1062)

WAMBI, JUNGLE BOY (See Jungle Comics)
Fiction House Magazines: Spr, 1942; No. 2, Win, 1942-43; No. 3, Spr, 1943; No. 4, Fall, 1948; No. 5, Sum, 1949; No. 6, Spr, 1950; No. 7-10, 1950(nd); No. 11, Spr, 1951 - No. 18, Win, 1952-53 (#1-3: 68 pgs.)

1-Wambi, the Jungle Boy begins 106 212 318 673 1162 1650
2 (1942)-Kiefer-c 45 90 135 284 480 675
3 (1943)-Kiefer-c/a 40 80 120 246 411 575
4 (1948)-Origin in text 32 64 96 188 307 425
5 (Fall, 1949, 36 pgs.)-Kiefer-c/a 21 42 63 126 206 285
6-10: 7-(52 pgs.)-New logo 17 34 51 100 158 215
11-18 15 30 45 83 124 165
I.W. Reprint #8('64)-r/#12 with new-c 3 6 9 14 20 25

NOTE: ***Alex Blum*** *c-8.* ***Kiefer*** *c-1-5.* ***Whitman*** *c-11-18.*

WANDERERS (See Adventure Comics #375, 376)
DC Comics: June, 1988 - No. 13, Apr, 1989 ($1.25) (Legion of Super-Heroes spin off)

1-13: 1,2-Steacy-c. 3-Legion app. 3.00

WANDERING STAR
Pen & Ink Comics/Sirius Entertainment No. 12 on: 1993 - No. 21, Mar, 1997 ($2.50/$2.75, B&W)

1-1st printing; Teri Sue Wood c/a/scripts in all 1 2 3 5 6 8
1-2nd and 3rd printings 3.00
2-1st printing. 4.00
2-21: 2-2nd printing. 12-(1/96)-1st Sirius issue 3.00
Trade paperback ($11.95)-r/1-7; 1st printing of 1000, signed and #'d 18.00
Trade paperback-2nd printing, 2000 signed 15.00

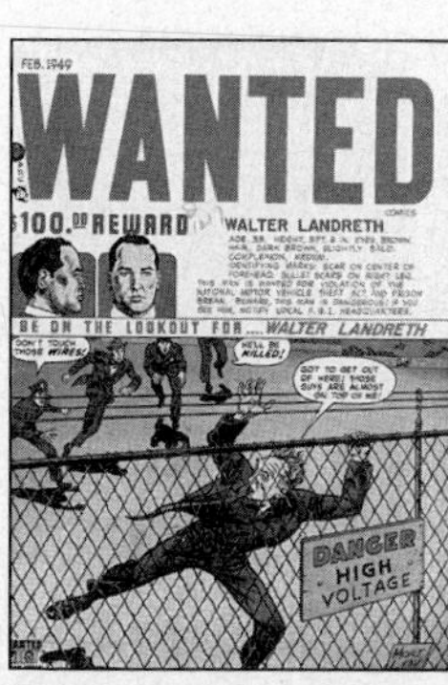

Wanted Comics #18 © Toytown

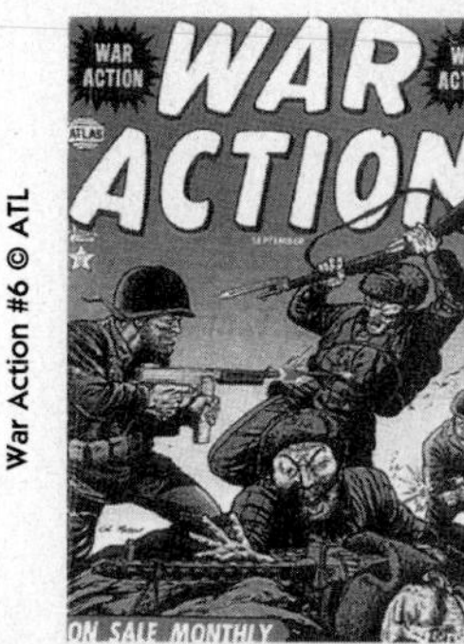

War Action #6 © ATL

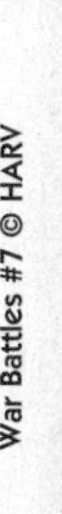
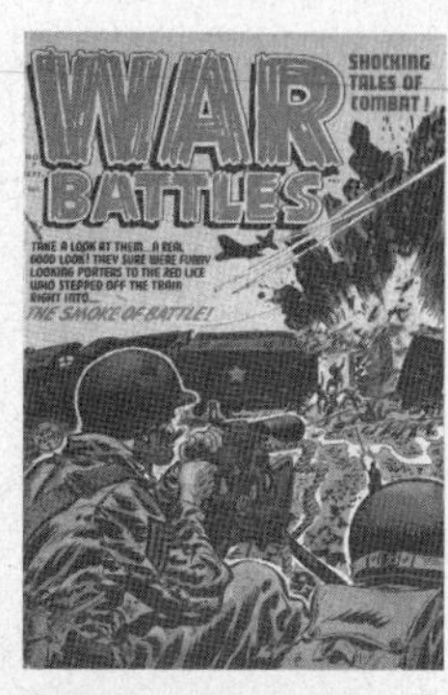

War Battles #7 © HARV

	GD 2.0	VG 4.0	FN 6.0	VF 8.0	VF/NM 9.0	NM- 9.2
TPB Volume 2,3 (11/98, 12/98, $14.95) 2-r/#8-14, 3-r/#15-21						15.00

WANTED
Image Comics (Top Cow): Dec, 2003 - No. 6, Feb, 2004 ($2.99)

	GD 2.0	VG 4.0	FN 6.0	VF 8.0	VF/NM 9.0	NM- 9.2
1-Three covers; Mark Millar-s/J.G. Jones-a; intro Wesley Gibson						4.00
1-4-Death Row Edition; r/#1-4 with extra sketch pages and deleted panels						3.00
2-6: 2-Cameos of DC villains. 6-Giordano-a in flashback scenes						3.00
...Dossier (5/04, $2.99) Pin-ups and character info; art by Jones, Romita Jr. & others						3.00
Image Firsts: Wanted #1 (9/10, $1.00) reprints #1						3.00
... Movie Edition Vol. 1 TPB (2008, $19.99) r/#1-6 & Dossier; movie photo-c; sketch pages & cover gallery; interviews with movie cast and director						20.00
HC (2005, $29.99) r/#1-6 & Dossier; intro by Vaughan, sketch pages & cover gallery						30.00

WANTED COMICS
Toytown Publications/Patches/Orbit Publ.: No. 9, Sept-Oct, 1947 - No. 53, April, 1953 (#9-33: 52 pgs.)

	GD 2.0	VG 4.0	FN 6.0	VF 8.0	VF/NM 9.0	NM- 9.2
9-True crime cases; radio's Mr. D. A. app.	39	78	117	231	378	525
10,11: 10-Giunta-a; radio's Mr. D. A. app.	24	48	72	140	230	320
12-Used in **SOTI**, pg. 277	25	50	75	150	245	340
13-Heroin drug propaganda story	24	48	72	142	234	325
14-Marijuana drug mention story (2 pgs.)	22	44	66	128	209	290
15-17,19,20	19	38	57	111	176	240
18-Marijuana story, "Satan's Cigarettes"; r-in #45 & retitled	41	82	123	250	418	585
21,22: 21-Krigstein-a. 22-Extreme violence	19	38	57	111	176	240
23,25-32,34,36-38,40-44,46-48,53	16	32	48	94	147	200
24-Krigstein-a; "The Dope King", marijuana mention story	22	44	66	128	209	290
33-Spider web-c	23	46	69	136	223	310
35-Used in **SOTI**, pg. 160	22	44	66	128	209	290
39-Drug propaganda story "The Horror Weed"	30	60	90	177	289	400
45-Marijuana story from #18	20	40	60	115	185	255
49-Has unstable pink-c that fades easily; rare in mint condition	27	54	81	158	259	360
50-Has unstable pink-c like #49; surrealist-c by Buscema; horror stories	34	68	102	199	325	450
51- "Holiday of Horror" junkie story; drug-c	32	64	96	188	307	425
52-Classic "Cult of Killers" opium use story	47	94	141	296	498	700

NOTE: ***Buscema*** *c-50, 51.* ***Lawrence*** *and* ***Leav*** *c/a most issues.* ***Syd Shores*** *c/a-48; c-37. Issues 9-46 have wanted criminals with their descriptions & drawn picture on cover.*

WANTED: DEAD OR ALIVE (TV)
Dell Publishing Co.: No. 1102, May-July, 1960 - No. 1164, Mar-May, 1961

	GD 2.0	VG 4.0	FN 6.0	VF 8.0	VF/NM 9.0	NM- 9.2
Four Color 1102 (#1)-Steve McQueen photo-c	11	22	33	73	157	240
Four Color 1164-Steve McQueen photo-c	8	16	24	56	108	160

WANTED, THE WORLD'S MOST DANGEROUS VILLAINS (See DC Special)
National Periodical Publ.: July-Aug, 1972 - No. 9, Aug-Sept, 1973 (All reprints & 20¢ issues)

	GD 2.0	VG 4.0	FN 6.0	VF 8.0	VF/NM 9.0	NM- 9.2
1-Batman, Green Lantern (story r-from G.L. #1), & Green Arrow	3	6	9	21	33	45
2-Batman/Joker/Penguin-c/story r-from Batman #25; plus Flash story (r-from Flash #121)	3	6	9	16	24	32
3-9: 3-Dr. Fate(r/More Fun #65), Hawkman(r/Flash #100), & Vigilante(r/Action #69). 4-Green Lantern(r/All-American #61) & Kid Eternity(r/Kid Eternity #15). 5-Dollman/Green Lantern. 6-Burnley Starman; Wildcat/Sargon. 7-Johnny Quick(r/More Fun #76), Hawkman(r/Flash #90), Hourman by Baily(r/Adv. #72). 8-Dr. Fate/Flash(r/Flash #114). 9-S&K Sandman/Superman	3	6	9	14	20	26

NOTE: ***B. Bailey*** *a-7r.* ***Infantino*** *a-2r.* ***Kane*** *r-1, 5.* ***Kubert*** *r-3i, 6, 7.* ***Meskin*** *r-3, 7.* ***Reinman*** *r-4, 6.*

WAR (See Fightin' Marines #122)
Charlton Comics: Jul, 1975 - No. 9, Nov, 1976; No. 10, Sept, 1978 - No. 47, 1984

	GD 2.0	VG 4.0	FN 6.0	VF 8.0	VF/NM 9.0	NM- 9.2
1-Boyette painted-c	3	6	9	14	19	24
2-10: 3-Sutton painted-c	2	4	6	8	10	12
11-20	1	2	3	5	6	8
21-40	1	2	3	4	5	7
41,42,44-47 (lower print run): 47-Reprints	1	2	3	5	6	8
43 (2/84) (lower print run) Ditko-a (7 pgs.)	2	4	6	8	10	12
7,9 (Modern Comics-r, 1977)						6.00

WAR, THE (See The Draft & The Pitt)
Marvel Comics: 1989 - No. 4, 1990 ($3.50, squarebound, 52 pgs.)

	GD 2.0	VG 4.0	FN 6.0	VF 8.0	VF/NM 9.0	NM- 9.2
1-4: Characters from New Universe						4.00

WAR ACTION (Korean War)
Atlas Comics (CPS): April, 1952 - No. 14, June, 1953

	GD 2.0	VG 4.0	FN 6.0	VF 8.0	VF/NM 9.0	NM- 9.2
1	36	72	108	211	343	475
2-Hartley-a	19	38	57	111	176	240
3-10,14: 7-Pakula-a. 14-Colan-a	16	32	48	94	147	200
11-13-Krigstein-a. 11-Romita-a	17	34	51	98	154	210

NOTE: ***Berg*** *c-11.* ***Brodsky*** *a-2; c-1-4.* ***Heath*** *a-1; c-7, 14.* ***Keller*** *a-6.* ***Maneely*** *a-1; c-12.* ***Sale*** *a-7.* ***Tuska*** *a-2, 8.*

WAR ADVENTURES (Korean War)
Atlas Comics (HPC): Jan, 1952 - No. 13, Feb, 1953

	GD 2.0	VG 4.0	FN 6.0	VF 8.0	VF/NM 9.0	NM- 9.2
1-Tuska-a	34	68	102	204	332	460
2	19	38	57	109	172	235
3-7,9-11,13: 3-Pakula-a. 7-Maneely-c. 9-Romita-a	16	32	48	94	147	200
8-Krigstein-a	17	34	51	98	154	210
12-Grey tone-c	20	40	60	114	182	250

NOTE: ***Brodsky*** *c-1-3, 6, 8, 11, 12.* ***Heath*** *a-2, 5, 7, 10; c-4, 5, 9, 13.* ***Reinman*** *a-13.* ***Robinson*** *a-3; c-10.*

WAR ADVENTURES ON THE BATTLEFIELD (See Battlefield)

WAR AGAINST CRIME! (Becomes Vault of Horror #12 on)
E. C. Comics: Spring, 1948 - No. 11, Feb-Mar, 1950

	GD 2.0	VG 4.0	FN 6.0	VF 8.0	VF/NM 9.0	NM- 9.2
1-Real Stories From Police Records on-c #1-9	116	232	348	742	1271	1800
2,3	61	122	183	390	670	950
4-9	53	106	159	334	567	800
10-1st Vault Keeper app. & 1st Vault of Horror	213	426	639	1363	2332	3300
11-2nd Vault Keeper app.; 1st EC horror-c	200	400	600	1280	2190	3100

NOTE: *All have* ***Johnny Craig*** *covers.* ***Feldstein*** *a-4, 7-9.* ***Harrison/Wood*** *a-11.* ***Ingels*** *a-1, 2, 8.* ***Palais*** *a-8. Changes to horror with #10.*

WAR AGAINST CRIME
Gemstone Publishing: Apr, 2000 - No. 11, Feb, 2001 ($2.50)

	GD 2.0	VG 4.0	FN 6.0	VF 8.0	VF/NM 9.0	NM- 9.2
1-11: E.C. reprints						4.00

WAR AND ATTACK (Also see Special War Series #3)
Charlton Comics: Fall, 1964; V2#54, June, 1966 - V2#63, Dec, 1967

	GD 2.0	VG 4.0	FN 6.0	VF 8.0	VF/NM 9.0	NM- 9.2
1-Wood-a (25 pgs.)	5	10	15	35	63	90
V2#54(6/66)-#63 (Formerly Fightin' Air Force)	3	6	9	15	22	28

NOTE: ***Montes/Bache*** *a-55, 56, 60, 63.*

WAR AT SEA (Formerly Space Adventures)
Charlton Comics: No. 22, Nov, 1957 - No. 42, June, 1961

	GD 2.0	VG 4.0	FN 6.0	VF 8.0	VF/NM 9.0	NM- 9.2
22	8	16	24	42	54	65
23-30: 26-Pearl Harbor, FDR app.	6	12	18	29	36	42
31-42: 42-Cuba's Fidel Castro story	3	6	9	18	28	38

WAR BATTLES
Harvey Publications: Feb, 1952 - No. 9, Dec, 1953

	GD 2.0	VG 4.0	FN 6.0	VF 8.0	VF/NM 9.0	NM- 9.2
1-Powell-a; Elias-c	9	18	27	59	117	175
2-Powell-a	5	10	15	34	55	75
3,4,7-9: 3,7-Powell-a	5	10	15	32	51	70
5-Flamethrower cover	9	18	27	58	114	170
6-Nostrand-a	6	12	18	39	62	85

WAR BIRDS
Fiction House Magazines: 1952(nd) - No. 3, Winter, 1952-53

	GD 2.0	VG 4.0	FN 6.0	VF 8.0	VF/NM 9.0	NM- 9.2
1	21	42	63	124	202	280
2,3	14	28	42	78	112	145

WARBLADE: ENDANGERED SPECIES (Also see WildC.A.T.S: Covert Action Teams)
Image Comics (WildStorm Productions): Jan, 1995 - No. 4, Apr, 1995 ($2.50, limited series)

	GD 2.0	VG 4.0	FN 6.0	VF 8.0	VF/NM 9.0	NM- 9.2
1-4: 1-Gatefold wraparound-c						3.00

WAR COMBAT (Becomes Combat Casey #6 on)
Atlas Comics (LBI No. 1/SAI No. 2-5): March, 1952 - No. 5, Nov, 1952

	GD 2.0	VG 4.0	FN 6.0	VF 8.0	VF/NM 9.0	NM- 9.2
1	33	66	99	194	317	440
2	18	36	54	103	162	220
3-5	16	32	48	94	147	200

NOTE: ***Berg*** *a-2, 4, 5.* ***Brodsky*** *c-1, 2, 4.* ***Henkel*** *a-5.* ***Maneely*** *a-1, 4; c-3.* ***Reinman*** *a-2.* ***Sale*** *a-5; c-5.*

WAR COMICS (War Stories #5 on)(See Key Ring Comics)
Dell Publishing Co.: May, 1940 (No month given) - No. 4, Sept, 1941

	GD 2.0	VG 4.0	FN 6.0	VF 8.0	VF/NM 9.0	NM- 9.2
1-Sikandur the Robot Master, Sky Hawk, Scoop Mason, War Correspondent begin; McWilliams-c; 1st war comic	113	226	339	718	1234	1750
2-Origin Greg Gilday (5/41)	42	84	126	265	445	625
3-Joan becomes Greg Gilday's aide	34	68	102	204	332	460
4-Origin Night Devils	36	72	108	211	343	475

WAR COMICS
Marvel/Atlas (USA No. 1-41/JPI No. 42-49): Dec, 1950 - No. 49, Sept, 1957

	GD 2.0	VG 4.0	FN 6.0	VF 8.0	VF/NM 9.0	NM- 9.2
1-1st Atlas War comic	47	94	141	296	498	700
2	25	50	75	147	241	335
3-10	21	42	63	126	206	285
11-Flame thrower w/burning bodies on-c	61	122	183	390	670	950
12-20: 16-Romita-a	20	40	60	114	182	250

Warfront #8 © HARV

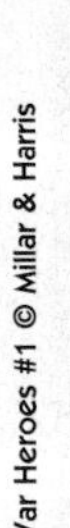

War Heroes #1 © Millar & Harris

Warlands #1 © Dreamwave

	GD 2.0	VG 4.0	FN 6.0	VF 8.0	VF/NM 9.0	NM- 9.2
21,23-32: 26-Valley Forge story. 32-Last pre-code issue (2/55)	18	36	54	107	169	230
22-Krigstein-a	19	38	57	111	176	240
33-37,39-42,44,45,47,48: 40-Romita-a	18	36	54	103	162	220
38-Kubert/Moskowitz-a	18	36	54	107	169	230
43,49-Torres-a. 43-Severin/Elder E.C. swipe from Two-Fisted Tales #31	18	36	54	107	169	230
46-Crandall-a	18	36	54	107	169	230

NOTE: ***Ayers** a-17, 32. **Berg** a-13. **Colan** a-4, 28, 34, 36, 48, 49; c-17. **Drucker** a-37, 43, 48. **Everett** a-17. **Heath** a-6-9, 16, 19, 25, 36; c-11, 16, 19, 23, 25, 26, 29-32, 36. **G. Kane** a-19. **Katz** a-34. **Lawrence** a-36. **Maneely** a-7, 9, 13, 14, 20, 23, 28; c-6, 27, 37. **Orlando** a-42, 48. **Pakula** a-26, 40. **Ravielli** a-27. **Reinman** a-11, 16, 26. **Robinson** a-15; c-13. **Sale** c-28. **Severin** a-26, 27; c-48. **Shores** a-13. **Sinnott** a-37.*

WAR DANCER (Also see Charlemagne, Doctor Chaos #2 & Warriors of Plasm)
Defiant: Feb, 1994 - No. 6, July, 1994 ($2.50)

1-3,5,6: 1-Intro War Dancer; Weiss-c/a begins. 1-3-Weiss-a(p). 6-Pre-Schism issue 3.00
4-($3.25, 52 pgs.)-Charlemagne app.; Billy Ballistic gains quantum powers 4.00

WAR DOGS OF THE U.S. ARMY
Avon Periodicals: 1952

1-Kinstler-c/a 17 34 51 100 158 215

WAREHOUSE 13 (Based on the Syfy TV series)
Dynamite Entertainment: 2011 - No. 5, 2012 ($3.99)

1-5: 1-Raab & Hughes-s/Morse-a 4.00

WAR FOR THE PLANET OF THE APES (Prequel to the 2017 movie)
BOOM! Studios: Jul, 2017 - No. 4, Oct, 2017 ($3.99, limited series)

1-4-David F. Walker-s/Jonas Scharf-a 4.00

WARFRAME: GHOULS (Based on the video game)
Image Comics (Top Cow): Oct, 2017 - Present ($3.99)

1-3-Matt Hawkins & Ryan Cady-s/Studio Hive-a 4.00

WARFRONT
Harvey Publications: 9/51 - #35, 11/58; #36, 10/65; #39, 2/67

	GD 2.0	VG 4.0	FN 6.0	VF 8.0	VF/NM 9.0	NM- 9.2
1-Korean War	9	18	27	61	123	185
2	5	10	15	34	60	85
3-10	5	10	15	30	50	70
11,12,14,16-20	4	8	12	27	44	60
13,15,22-Nostrand-a	5	10	15	34	60	85
21,23-27,31-33,35	4	8	12	27	44	60
28-30,34-Kirby-c	5	10	15	35	63	90
36-(12/66)-Dynamite Joe begins, ends #39; Williamson-a	5	10	15	30	50	70
37-Wood-a (17 pgs.)	5	10	15	30	50	70
38,39-Wood-a, 2-3 pgs.; Lone Tiger app.	4	8	12	27	44	60

NOTE: ***Powell** a-1-6, 9-11, 14, 17, 20, 23, 25-28, 30, 31, 34, 36. **Powell/Nostrand** a-12, 13, 15. **Simon** c-36?, 38.*

WAR FURY
Comic Media/Harwell (Allen Hardy Assoc.): Sept, 1952 - No. 4, Mar, 1953

	GD 2.0	VG 4.0	FN 6.0	VF 8.0	VF/NM 9.0	NM- 9.2
1-Heck-c/a in all; Palais-a; bullet hole in forehead-c; all issues are very violent; soldier using flame thrower on enemy	135	270	405	864	1482	2100
2-4: 4-Morisi-a	39	78	117	231	378	525

WAR GODS OF THE DEEP (See Movie Classics)

WARHAWKS
TSR, Inc.: 1990 - No. 10, 1991 ($2.95, 44 pgs.)

1-10-Based on TSR game, Spiegle a-1-6 4.00

WARHEADS
Marvel Comics UK: June, 1992 - No. 14, Aug, 1993 ($1.75)

1-Wolverine-c/story; indicia says #2 by mistake 4.00
2-14: 2-Nick Fury app. 3-Iron Man-c/story. 4,5-X-Force. 5-Liger vs. Cable. 6,7-Death's Head II app. (#6 is cameo) 3.00

WAR HEROES (See Marine War Heroes)

WAR HEROES
Dell Publishing Co.: 7-9/42 (no month); No. 2, 10-12/42 - No. 10, 10-12/44 (Quarterly)

	GD 2.0	VG 4.0	FN 6.0	VF 8.0	VF/NM 9.0	NM- 9.2
1-General Douglas MacArthur-c	31	62	93	182	296	410
2-James Doolittle and other officers-c	17	34	51	98	154	210
3,5: 3-Pro-Russian back-c; grey-tone-c. 5-General Patton-c	15	30	45	84	127	170
4-Disney's Gremlins app.; grey-tone-c	20	40	60	117	189	260
6-10: 6-Tothish-a by Discount. 6,9-Grey-tone-c	12	24	36	67	94	120

NOTE: *No. 1 was to be released in July, but was delayed. Painted c-4, 6-9.*

WAR HEROES
Ace Magazines: May, 1952 - No. 8, Apr, 1953

	GD 2.0	VG 4.0	FN 6.0	VF 8.0	VF/NM 9.0	NM- 9.2
1	15	30	45	86	133	180
2-Lou Cameron-a	11	22	33	62	86	110
3-8: 6,7-Cameron-a	10	20	30	56	76	95

WAR HEROES (Also see Blue Bird Comics)
Charlton Comics: Feb, 1963 - No. 27, Nov, 1967

	GD 2.0	VG 4.0	FN 6.0	VF 8.0	VF/NM 9.0	NM- 9.2
1,2: 2-John F. Kennedy story	4	8	12	25	40	55
3-10	3	6	9	17	26	35
11-26: 22-True story about plot to kill Hitler	3	6	9	14	20	26
27-1st Devils Brigade by Glanzman	3	6	9	17	26	35

NOTE: ***Montes/Bache** a-3-7, 21, 25, 27; c-3-7.*

WAR HEROES
Image Comics: July, 2008 - No. 6 ($2.99, limited series)

1-3-Soldiers given super powers; Mark Millar-s/Tony Harris-a/c; four covers 3.00

WAR IS HELL
Marvel Comics Group: Jan, 1973 - No. 15, Oct, 1975

	GD 2.0	VG 4.0	FN 6.0	VF 8.0	VF/NM 9.0	NM- 9.2
1-Williamson-a(r), 5 pgs.; Ayers-a	3	6	9	19	30	40
2-8-Reprints. 6-(11/73). 7-(6/74). 7,8-Kirby-a	2	4	6	10	14	18
9-Intro Death	6	12	18	41	76	110
10-15-Death app.	3	6	9	17	26	35

NOTE: ***Bolle** a-3r. **Powell** a-1. **Woodbridge** a-1. Sgt. Fury reprints-7, 8.*

WAR IS HELL: THE FIRST FLIGHT OF THE PHANTOM EAGLE
Marvel Comics (MAX): May, 2008 - No. 5, Sept, 2008 ($3.99, limited series)

1-5-World War I fighter pilots; Ennis-s/Chaykin-a/Cassaday-c 4.00

WARLANDS
Image Comics: Aug, 1999 - No. 12, Feb, 2001 ($2.50)

1-9,11,12-Pat Lee-a(p)/Adrian Tsang-s 3.00
10-($2.95) Flip book w/Shidima preview 4.00
... Chronicles 1,2 (2/00, 7/00; $7.95) 1-r/#1-3. 2-r/#4-6 8.00
...Darklyte TPB (8/01, $14.95) r/#0,1/2,1-6 w/cover gallery; new Lee-c 15.00
...Epilogue: Three Stories (3/01, $5.95) includes r/Wizard #1/2 & AE #0 6.00
Another Universe #0 3.00
Wizard #1/2 5.00

WARLANDS: THE AGE OF ICE (Volume 2)
Image Comics: July, 2001 - No. 9, Nov, 2002 ($2.95)

#0-(2/02, $2.25) 3.00
#1/2 (4/02, $2.25) 3.00
1-9: 2-Flip book preview of Banished Knights 3.00
TPB (2003, $15.95) r/#1-9 16.00

WARLANDS: DARK TIDE RISING (Volume 3)
Image Comics: Dec, 2002 - No. 6, May, 2003 ($2.95)

1-6: 1-Wraparound gatefold-c 3.00

WARLOCK (The Power of...)(Also see Avengers Annual #7, Fantastic Four #66, 67, Incredible Hulk #178, Infinity Crusade, Infinity Gauntlet, Infinity War, Marvel Premiere #1, Marvel Two-In-One Annual #2, Silver Surfer V3#46, Strange Tales #178-181 & Thor #165)
Marvel Comics Group: Aug, 1972 - No. 8, Oct, 1973; No. 9, Oct, 1975 - No. 15, Nov, 1976

	GD 2.0	VG 4.0	FN 6.0	VF 8.0	VF/NM 9.0	NM- 9.2
1-Origin by Kane	9	18	27	60	120	180
2,3	4	8	12	28	47	65
4-8: 4-Death of Eddie Roberts	3	6	9	17	26	35
9-Starlin's 2nd Thanos saga begins, ends #15; new costume Warlock; Thanos cameo only; story cont'd from Strange Tales #178-181; Starlin-c/a in #9-15	5	10	15	30	50	70
10-Origin Thanos & Gamora; recaps events from Capt. Marvel #25-34. Thanos vs.The Magus-c/story	5	10	15	30	50	70
11-Thanos app.; Warlock dies	3	6	9	20	31	42
12-14: (Regular 25¢ edition) 14-Origin Star Thief; last 25¢ issue	3	6	9	17	26	35
12-14-(30¢-c, limited distribution)	5	10	15	30	50	70
15-Thanos-c/story	3	6	9	19	30	40

NOTE: ***Buscema** a-2p; c-8p. **G. Kane** a-1p, 3-5p; c-1p, 2, 3, 4p, 5p, 7p. **Starlin** a-9-14p, 15; c-9, 10, 11p, 12p, 13-15. **Sutton** a-1-8i.*

WARLOCK (...Special Edition on-c)
Marvel Comics Group: Dec, 1982 - No. 6, May, 1983 ($2.00, slick paper, 52 pgs.)

1-Warlock-r/Strange Tales #178-180. 6.00
2-6: 2-r/Str. Tales #180,181 & Warlock #9. 3-r/Warlock #10-12(Thanos origin recap). 4-r/Warlock #12-15. 5-r/Warlock #15, Marvel Team-Up #55 & Avengers Ann. #7. 6-r/2nd half Avengers Annual #7 & Marvel Two-in-One Annual #2 5.00
Special Edition #1(12/83) 5.00

NOTE: ***Byrne** a-5r. **Starlin** a-1-6r; c-1-6(new). Direct sale only.*

WARLOCK

Warlock and the Infinity Watch #32 © MAR

Warlord #58 © DC

War Machine #6 © MAR

GD VG FN VF VF/NM NM-
2.0 4.0 6.0 8.0 9.0 9.2

Marvel Comics: V2#1, May, 1992 - No. 6, Oct, 1992 ($2.50, limited series)

V2#1-6: 1-Reprints 1982 reprint series w/Thanos 4.00

WARLOCK
Marvel Comics: Nov, 1998 - No. 4, Feb, 1999 ($2.99, limited series)

1-4-Warlock vs. Drax 3.00

WARLOCK (M-Tech)
Marvel Comics: Oct, 1999 - No. 9, June, 2000 ($1.99/$2.50)

1-5: 1-Quesada-c. 2-Two covers 3.00
6-9: 6-Begin $2.50-c. 8-Avengers app. 3.00

WARLOCK
Marvel Comics: Nov, 2004 - No. 4, Feb, 2005 ($2.99, limited series)

1-4-Adlard-a/Williams-c 3.00

WARLOCK AND THE INFINITY WATCH (Also see Infinity Gauntlet)
Marvel Comics: Feb, 1992 - No. 42, July, 1995 ($1.75) (Sequel to Infinity Gauntlet)

1-Starlin-s begin; continued from Infinity Gauntlet #6; brief origin recap; Living Tribunal app. 1 3 4 6 8 10
2-7: 2-1st app. Infinity Watch: Infinity Gauntlet broken up; Warlock (Soul gem), Gamora (Time gem), Drax (Power gem), Moondragon (Mind gem) & Pip (Space gem). 3,4-High Evolutionary app. 5,6-Man-Beast app. 7-Re-intro Magus (dream sequence); brief Thanos app; leads into Infinity War #1. Tom Raney-a begins 4.00
8-10: 8-Thanos teams up w/Infinity Watch; Magus app; X-Men, Avengers, Alpha Flight & Fantastic Four cameo; leads into Infinity War #4. 9-Origin Gamora; Galactus, Eternity, Thanos & Infinity app; leads into Infinity War #5. 10-Thanos vs. his doppelganger; Magus app.; continues in Infinity War #6 4.00
11-22: 11-Eternity & Living Tribunal app.; origins of the Watch. 12-1st app Maxam (brief cameo); Hulk cameo. 13-Drax vs Hulk; last Raney-a. 14-1st app. Count Abyss. 15-Eternity app. 16-1st full app. Maxam; Count Abyss app. 17-Maxam joins the Watch. 18-22-Infinity Crusade tie-ins; 18-Goddess & Reed Richards app; continued in Infinity Crusade #2. 19-X-Men, Avengers, Fantastic Four, Thanos app.; continued in Infinity Crusade #3. 20-Pip becomes master of reality; Goddess app; continued in Infinity Crusade #4. 21-Drax vs. Thor; continued in Infinity Crusade #5. 22-Goddess app; continued in Infinity Crusade #6 4.00
23,24-Blood and Thunder Pts. 4 & 8; continued from Warlock Chronicles #6; Silver Surfer & Warlock vs. Thor; continued in Thor #469. 24-Continued from Warlock Chronicles #7; Silver Surfer app.; continued in Thor #470 5.00
25-($2.95, 52 pgs.)-Die-cut & embossed double-c; Blood & Thunder Pt.12; continued from Warlock Chronicles #8; Thor, Dr. Strange, Beta Ray Bill & Silver Surfer app.; Thanos vs. Odin 2 4 6 9 12 15
26-32: 26-Avengers & Count Abyss app. 27-vs. the Avengers. 28-Avengers, Man-Beast & Count Abyss app. 29,30-Count Abyss app. 31-Origin Count Abyss; last Starlin-s. 32-Count Abyss defeats the Watch 4.00
33-35: 33-vs. Count Abyss. 34-Mole Man app.; Tyrannus cameo. 35-Mole Man & Tyrannus app. 4.00
36-Dr. Strange app; as 'Strange' 7.00
37-39: 37-1st app. Zakaius; Firelord app. 38-1st app. Domitan; Zakaius app. 39-Zakaius, Domitan & Firelord app. 6.00
40,41: 40-Thanos app.; Gamora leaves the Watch; Maxam receives the Time gem. 41-Origin Maxam; Gamora joins Thanos 1 2 3 5 6 8
42-Last issue; the Watch breaks up; the Infinity Gems disappear (see Rune/Silver Surfer #1); Thanos app. 2 4 6 9 12 15

NOTE: ***Austin*** *c/a-1-4i, 7i.* ***Leonardi*** *a(p)-3, 4.* ***Medina*** *c/a(p)-1, 2, 5; 6, 9, 10, 14, 15, 20.* ***Williams*** *a(i)-8, 12, 13, 16-19.*

WARLOCK CHRONICLES
Marvel Comics: June, 1993 - No. 8, Feb, 1994 ($2.00, limited series)

1-($2.95)-Holo-grafx foil & embossed-c; Starlin/Raney-s/a; Infinity Crusade tie-in; 1st app. Darklore; origin of Warlock & the Infinity Gems; cont'd in Warlock & the Infinity Watch #18 5.00
2-5-Infinity Crusade x-overs; 2-Cont'd from Infinity Crusade #2; Lord Order, Master Chaos, Eternity & Thanos app.; cont'd in Warlock & the Infinity Watch #19. 3-Cont'd from Infinity Crusade #3; Mephisto teams up w/Warlock & Thanos; cont'd in Warlock & the Infinity Watch #20. 4-Magus app.; cont'd in Warlock & the Infinity Watch #21. 5-Cont'd from Infinity Crusade #5; Goddess & Magus app.; cont'd in Warlock & the Infinity Watch #22 4.00
6-Blood & Thunder Pt. 3; cont'd from Silver Surfer #86; insane Thor cameo; brief Silver Surfer app.; cont'd in Warlock & the Infinity Watch #23 5.00
7-Blood & Thunder Pt. 7; cont'd from Silver Surfer #87; Dr. Strange, Beta Ray Bill & Silver Surfer app.; cont'd in Warlock & the Infinity Watch #24 6.00
8-Blood & Thunder Pt. 11; cont'd from Silver Surfer #88; Thanos, Silver Surfer, Dr. Strange app.; cont'd in Warlock & the Infinity Watch #25 1 2 3 5 6 8

WARLOCK 5
Aircel Pub.: 11/86 - No. 22, 5/89; V2#1, June, 1989 - V2#5, 1989 ($1.70, B&W)

1-5,7-11-Gordon Derry-s/Denis Beauvais-a thru #11. 5-Green Cyborg on-c. 5-Misnumbered as #6 (no #6); Blue Girl on-c. 3.00
12-22-Barry Blair-s/a. 18-$1.95-c begins 4.00
V2#1-5 ($2.00, B&W)-All issues by Barry Blair 3.00
Compilation 1,2: 1-r/#1-5 (1988, $5.95); 2-r/#6-9 6.00

WARLORD (See 1st Issue Special #8) (B&W reprints in Showcase Presents: Warlord)
National Periodical Publications/DC Comics #123 on: 1-2/76; No.2, 3-4/76; No.3, 10-11/76 - No. 133, Win, 1988-89

1-Story cont'd. from 1st Issue Special #8 4 8 12 23 37 50
2-Intro. Machiste 3 6 9 14 20 25
3-5 2 4 6 9 12 15
6-10: 6-Intro Mariah. 7-Origin Machiste. 9-Dons new costume 1 3 4 6 8 10
11-20: 11-Origin-r. 12-Intro Aton. 15-Tara returns; Warlord has son 6.00
21-36,40,41: 27-New facts about origin. 28-1st app. Wizard World. 32-Intro Shakira. 40-Warlord gets new costume 5.00
22-Whitman variant edition 2 4 6 13 18 22
37-39: 37,38-Origin Omac by Starlin; cont'd from Kamandi #59. 38-Intro Jennifer Morgan, Warlord's daughter. 39-Omac ends. 6.00
42-48: 42-47-Omac back-up series. 48-(52 pgs.)-1st app. Arak; contains free 14 pg. Arak Son of Thunder; Claw The Unconquered app. 5.00
49-62,64-99,101-132: 49-Claw The Unconquered app. 50-Death of Aton. 51-Reprints #1. 55-Arion Lord of Atlantis begins, ends #62. 91-Origin w/new facts. 114,115-Legends x-over. 125-Death of Tara. 131-1st DC work by Rob Liefeld (9/88) 4.00
63-The Barren Earth begins; free 16pg. Masters of the Universe preview 5.00
100-($1.25, 52 pgs.) 5.00
133-($1.50, 52 pgs.) 5.00
Annual 1-6 ('82-'87): 1-Grell-c,/a(p). 6-New Gods app. 5.00
The Savage Empire TPB (1991, $19.95) r/#1-10,12 & First Issue Special #8; Grell intro. 25.00

NOTE: ***Grell*** *a-1-15, 16-50p, 51r, 52p, 59p, Annual 1p; c-1-70, 100-104, 112, 116, 117, Annual 1, 5.* ***Wayne Howard*** *a-64i.* ***Starlin*** *a-37-39p.*

WARLORD
DC Comics: Jan, 1992 - No. 6, June, 1992 ($1.75, limited series)

1-6: Grell-c & scripts in all 3.00

WARLORD
DC Comics: Apr, 2006 - No. 10, Jan, 2007 ($2.99)

1-10: 1-Bruce Jones-s/Bart Sears-a. 10-Winslade-a 3.00

WARLORD
DC Comics: Jun, 2009 - No. 16, Sept, 2010 ($2.99)

1-16: 1-Grell-s/Prado-a/Grell-c. 7-9,11,12,15,16-Grell-s/a/c. 10-Hardin-a 3.00
...: The Saga SC (2010, $17.99) r/#1-6; cover gallery 18.00

WARLORD OF MARS
Dynamite Entertainment: 2010 - No. 35, 2014 ($1.00/$3.99)

1-($1.00) John Carter on Earth; Sadowski-a; covers by Ross, Campbell, Jusko. Parrillo 3.00
2-35-($3.99) Multiple covers on each. 3-Carter arrives on Mars. 4-Dejah Thoris intro. 4.00
100-($7.99, squarebound) Short stories; art by Antonio, Malaga, Luis; multiple covers 8.00
#0 (2014, $3.99) Brady-s/Jadson-a; John Carter back on Earth 4.00
... Annual 1 (2012, $4.99) Sadowski-a/Parrillo-c 5.00

WARLORD OF MARS: DEJAH THORIS
Dynamite Entertainment: 2011 - No. 37, 2014 ($3.99/$4.99)

1-36: 1-Five covers; Nelson-s/Rafael-a. 2-5-Four covers. 6-31-Multiple covers on all 4.00
37-($4.99) Napton-s/Carita-a; Neves & Anacleto-c 5.00

WARLORD OF MARS: FALL OF BARSOOM
Dynamite Entertainment: 2011 - No. 5, 2012 ($3.99, limited series)

1-5-Napton-s/Castro-a/Jusko-c 4.00

WARLORDS (See DC Graphic Novel #2)

WARLORDS OF APPALACHIA
BOOM! Studios: Oct, 2016 - No. 4 ($3.99)

1,2-Phillip Kennedy Johnson-s/Jonas Scharf-a 4.00

WAR MACHINE (Also see Iron Man #281,282 & Marvel Comics Presents #152)
Marvel Comics: Apr, 1994 - No. 25, Apr, 1996 ($1.50)

"Ashcan" edition (nd, 75¢, B&W, 16 pgs.) 3.00
1-($2.00, 52 pgs.)-Newsstand edition; Cable app. 5.00
1-($2.95, 52 pgs.)-Collectors ed.; embossed foil-c 6.00
2-14, 16-25: 2-Bound-in trading card sheet; Cable app. 2,3-Deathlok app. 8-red logo 3.00
8-($2.95)-Polybagged w/16 pg. Marvel Action Hour preview & acetate print; yellow logo 4.00
15 ($2.50)-Flip book 4.00

WAR MACHINE (Also see Dark Reign and Secret Invasion crossovers)

War of Kings #1 © MAR

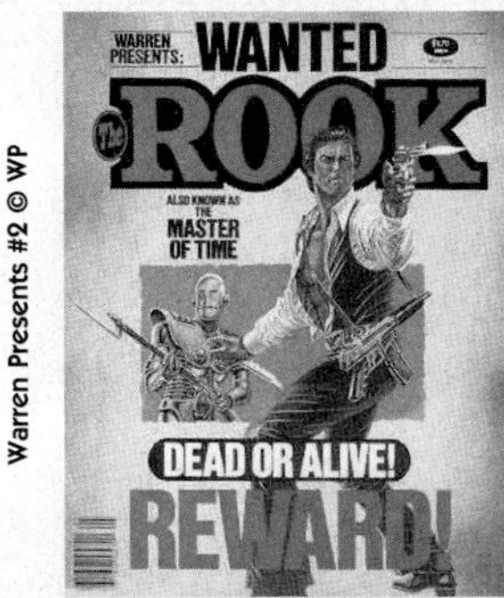

Warren Presents #2 © WP

Warriors of Mars #1 © Savage Tales

	GD 2.0	VG 4.0	FN 6.0	VF 8.0	VF/NM 9.0	NM- 9.2

Marvel Comics: Feb, 2009 - No. 12, Feb, 2010 ($2.99)
1-12: 1-5-Pak-s/Manco-a/c; cyborg Jim Rhodes. 10-12-Dark Reign 3.00
1-Variant Titanium Man cover by Deodato 6.00

WAR MAN
Marvel Comics (Epic Comics): Nov, 1993 - No. 2, Dec, 1993 ($2.50, limited series)
1,2-Chuck Dixon-s 3.00

WAR MOTHER
Valiant Entertainment: Aug, 2017 - No. 4, Nov, 2017 ($3.99, limited series)
1-4-Van Lente-s/Segovia-a; multiple covers; Ana in 4001 AD 4.00

WAR OF KINGS
Marvel Comics: May, 2009 - No. 6, Oct, 2009 ($3.99, limited series)
1-6-Pelletier-a/Abnett & Lanning-s; Inhumans vs. the Shi'Ar 4.00
... Saga (2009, giveaway) synopsies of stories involving Kree, Shi'Ar, Inhumans, etc. 3.00
...: Savage World of Skaar 1 (8/09, $3.99) Gorgon & Starbolt land on Sakaar 4.00
...: Who Will Rule? 1 (11/09, $3.99) Pelletier-a; profile pages 4.00

WAR OF KINGS: ASCENSION
Marvel Comics: June, 2009 - No. 4, Sept, 2009 ($3.99, limited series)
1-4-Alves-a/Abnett & Lanning-s; Darkhawk app. 4.00

WAR OF KINGS: DARKHAWK (Leads into War Of Kings: Ascension limited series)
Marvel Comics: Apr, 2009 - No. 2, May, 2009 ($3.99, limited series)
1,2-Cebulski-s/Tolibao & Dazo-a/Peterson-c; r/Darkhawk #1,2 (1991) origin 4.00

WAR OF KINGS: WARRIORS
Marvel Comics: Sept, 2009 - No. 2, Oct, 2009 ($3.99, limited series)
1,2-Prequel to x-over; Gage-s/Asrar & Magno-a 4.00

WAR OF THE GODS
DC Comics: Sept, 1991 - No. 4, Dec, 1991 ($1.75, limited series)
1-4: Perez layouts, scripts & covers. 1-Contains free mini posters (Robin, Deathstroke). 2-4-Direct sale versions include 4 pin-ups printed on cover stock plus different-c 4.00

WAR OF THE GREEN LANTERNS: AFTERMATH
DC Comics: Sept, 2011 - No. 2, Oct, 2011 ($3.99, limited series)
1,2: 1-Bedard-s/Sepulveda & Kirkham-a. 2-Getty & Smith-a 4.00

WAR OF THE UNDEAD
IDW Publishing: Jan, 2007 - No. 3, Apr, 2007 ($3.99, limited series)
1-3-Bryan Johnson-s/Walter Flanagan-a 4.00

WAR OF THE WORLDS, THE
Caliber: 1996 - No. 5 ($2.95, B&W, 32 pgs.)(Based on H. G. Wells novel)
1-5: 1-Randy Zimmerman scripts begin 3.00

WARP
First Comics: Mar, 1983 - No. 19, Feb, 1985 ($1.00/$1.25, Mando paper)
1-Sargon-Mistress of War app.; Brunner-c/a thru #9 4.00
2-19: 2-Faceless Ones begin. 10-New Warp advs., & Outrider begin 3.00
Special 1-3: 1(7/83, 36 pgs.)-Origin Chaos-Prince of Madness; origin of Warp Universe begins, ends #3. 2(1/84)-Lord Cumulus vs. Sargon Mistress of War ($1.00). 3(6/84)-Chaos-Prince of Madness 3.00

WARPATH (Indians on the...)
Key Publications/Stanmor: Nov, 1954 - No. 3, Apr, 1955

	GD	VG	FN	VF	VF/NM	NM-
1	11	22	33	62	86	110
2,3	8	16	24	40	50	60

WARPED
Empire Entertainment (Solson): Jun, 1990 - No. 2, Oct-Nov, 1990 (B&W mag)
1,2 3.00

WARP GRAPHICS ANNUAL
WaRP Graphics: Dec, 1985; 1988 ($2.50)
1-Elfquest, Blood of the Innocent, Thunderbunny & Myth Adventures 5.00
1 (1988) 4.00

WARREN PRESENTS
Warren Publications: Jan, 1979 - No. 14, Nov, 1981(B&W magazine)

	GD	VG	FN	VF	VF/NM	NM-
1-Eerie, Creepy, & Vampirella-r; Ring of the Warlords; Merlin-s; Dax-s; Sanjulian-c	3	6	9	15	21	26
2-6(10/79): 2-The Rook. 3-Alien Invasions Comix. 4-Movie Aliens. 5-Dracula '79. 6-Strange Stories of Vampires Comix	2	4	6	9	13	16
8(10/80)-r/1st app. Pantha from Vamp. #30	2	4	6	11	16	20
9(11/80) Empire Encounters Comix	2	4	6	10	14	18
13(10/81),14(11/81):13-Sword and Sorcery Comix	3	6	9	14	19	24
(#7,10,11,12 may not exist, or may be a Special below)						
Special-Alien Collectors Edition (1979)	3	6	9	14	19	24
Special-Close Encounters of the Third Kind (1978)	2	4	6	9	13	16
Special-Lord of the Rings (6/79)	3	6	9	18	28	38
Special-Meteor (1/80)	2	4	6	9	13	16
Special-Moonraker/James Bond (10/79)	2	4	6	9	13	16
Special-Star Wars (1977)	3	6	9	18	28	38

WAR REPORT
Ajax/Farrell Publications (Excellent Publ.): Sept, 1952 - No. 5, May, 1953

	GD	VG	FN	VF	VF/NM	NM-
1	18	36	54	103	162	220
2-Flame thrower w/burning bodies on-c	26	52	78	154	252	350
3,5	11	22	33	62	86	110
4-Used in **POP**, pg. 94	12	24	36	67	94	120

WARRIOR (Wrestling star)
Ultimate Creations: May, 1996 - No. 4, 1997 ($2.95)
1-4: Warrior scripts; Callahan-c/a. 3-Wraparound-c. 4-Warrior #3 in indicia; pin-ups 3.00
1-Variant-c. 5.00
X-Mas (11/96, $3.50) listed as "No. 3" in indicia; pin-ups by various; Quesada-c 4.00

WARRIOR COMICS
H.C. Blackerby: 1945 (1930s DC reprints)

	GD	VG	FN	VF	VF/NM	NM-
1-Wing Brady, The Iron Man, Mark Markon	22	44	66	132	216	300

WARRIOR OF WAVERLY STREET, THE
Dark Horse Comics: Nov, 1996 - No. 2, Dec, 1996 ($2.95, mini-series)
1,2-Darrow-c 3.00

WARRIORS
CFD Productions: 1993 (B&W, one-shot)

	GD	VG	FN	VF	VF/NM	NM-
1-Linsner, Dark One-a	2	4	6	11	16	20

WARRIORS, THE: OFFICIAL MOVIE ADAPTATION (Based on the 1979 movie)
Dabel Brothers Publishing/Dynamite Ent.: Feb, 2009 - No. 5, 2010 ($3.99, limited series)
1-5: 1-Three covers plus wraparound photo-c; Dibari-a. 3-Eric Powell-c 4.00
...: Jailbreak 1 (7/09, $3.99) Apon & Herman-a 4.00

WARRIORS OF MARS (Also see Warlord of Mars titles)
Dynamite Entertainment: 2012 - No. 5, 2012 ($3.99, limited series)
1-5-Gullivar Jones visits Barsoom; Jusko-c 4.00

WARRIORS OF PLASM (Also see Plasm and Dogs of War #5)
Defiant: Aug, 1993 - No. 13, Aug, 1995 ($2.95/$2.50)
1-4: Shooter-scripts; Lapham-c/a: 1-1st app. Glory. 4-Bound-in fold-out poster 4.00
5-7,10-13: 5-Begin $2.50-c. 13-Schism issue; last Defiant comic published 3.00
8,9-($2.75, 44 pgs.) 4.00
...Graphic Novel #1 (Home for the Holidays)(11/93, $5.95) Len Wein story; Cockrum-a; Christmas issue; story takes place between Warriors of Plasm #4 and #5 6.00
The Collected Edition (2/94, $9.95)-r/Plasm #0, WOP #1-4 & Splatterball 10.00

WARRIORS THREE (Fandral, Volstagg, and Hogun from Thor)
Marvel Comics: Jan, 2011 - No. 4, Apr, 2011 ($3.99, limited series)
1-4-Bill Willingham-s/Neil Edwards-a. 2,4-Conner-c 4.00

WAR ROMANCES (See True...)

WAR SHIPS
Dell Publishing Co.: 1942 (36 pgs.)(Similar to Large Feature Comics)

	GD	VG	FN	VF	VF/NM	NM-
nn-Cover by McWilliams; contains photos & drawings of U.S. war ships	20	40	60	117	189	260

WAR STORIES (Formerly War Comics)
Dell Publ. Co.: No. 5, 1942(nd); No. 6, Aug-Oct, 1942 - No. 8, Feb-Apr, 1943

	GD	VG	FN	VF	VF/NM	NM-
5-Origin The Whistler	34	68	102	199	325	450
6-8: 6-8-Night Devils app. 8-Painted-c	26	52	78	154	252	350

WAR STORIES (Korea)
Ajax/Farrell Publications (Excellent Publ.): Sept, 1952 - No. 5, May, 1953

	GD	VG	FN	VF	VF/NM	NM-
1	18	36	54	103	162	220
2	11	22	33	62	86	110
3-5	10	20	30	56	76	95

WAR STORIES
Avatar Press: Sept, 2014 - Present ($3.99)
1-23: Garth Ennis-s in all; multiple covers on all. 1-Matt Martin-a 4.00

WAR STORIES (See Star Spangled...)

WAR STORY
DC Comics (Vertigo): Nov, 2001 - Apr, 2003 ($4.95, series of World War II one-shots)

Warstrike #4 © MAL

Watchmen #2 © DC

Weapon X (2017 series) #1 © MAR

GD 2.0 | VG 4.0 | FN 6.0 | VF 8.0 | VF/NM 9.0 | NM- 9.2

...: Archangel (4/03) Ennis-s/Erskine-a 5.00
...: Condors (3/03) Ennis-s/Ezquerra-a 5.00
...: D-Day Dodgers (12/01) Ennis-s/Higgins-a 5.00
...: J For Jenny (2/03) Ennis-s/Lloyd-a 5.00
...: Johann's Tiger (11/01) Ennis-s/Weston-a 5.00
...: Nightingale (2/02) Ennis-s/Lloyd-a 5.00
...: Screaming Eagles (1/02) Ennis-s/Gibbons-a 5.00
...: The Reivers (1/03) Ennis-s/Kennedy-a 5.00
Vol. 1 (2004, $19.95) r/Johann's Tiger, D-Day Dodgers, Screaming Eagles, Nightingale 20.00
Vol. 2 (2006, $19.99) r/J For Jenny, The Reivers, Condors, Archangel; Ennis afterword 20.00

WARSTRIKE
Malibu Comics (Ultraverse): May, 1994 - No. 7, Nov, 1995 ($1.95)

1-7: 1-Simonson-c 3.00
1-Ultra 5000 Limited silver foil 6.00
Giant Size 1 (12/94, $2.50, 44pgs.)-Prelude to Godwheel 4.00

WART AND THE WIZARD (See The Sword & the Stone under Movie Comics)
Gold Key: Feb, 1964 (Walt Disney)(Characters from Sword in the Stone movie)

1 (10102-402) 4 8 12 27 44 60

WAR THAT TIME FORGOT, THE
DC Comics: Jul, 2008 - No. 12, Jun, 2009 ($2.99, limited series)

1-12: 1-Bruce Jones-s/Al Barrionuevo-a/Neal Adams-c; Enemy Ace app. 3.00

WARTIME ROMANCES
St. John Publishing Co.: July, 1951 - No. 18, Nov, 1953

1-All Baker-c/a 116 232 348 742 1271 1800
2-All Baker-c/a 68 136 204 435 743 1050
3,4-All Baker-c/a 65 130 195 416 708 1000
5-8-Baker-c/a(2-3) each 60 120 180 381 653 925
9,11,12,16,18: Baker-c/a each. 9-Two signed stories by Estrada
55 110 165 352 601 850
10,13-15,17-Baker-c only 52 104 156 328 552 775

WAR VICTORY ADVENTURES (#1 titled War Victory Comics)
U.S. Treasury Dept./War Victory/Harvey Publ.: Sum, 1942 - No. 3, Wint, 1943-44 (5¢/10¢)

1-(5¢)(Promotion of Savings Bonds)-Featuring America's greatest comic art by top syndicated cartoonists; Blondie, Joe Palooka, Green Hornet, Dick Tracy, Superman, Gumps, etc.; (36 pgs.); all profits were contributed to U.S.O. & Army/Navy relief funds
60 120 180 381 653 925
2-(10¢) Battle of Stalingrad story; Powell-a (8/43); flag & WWII Japanese-c
94 188 282 597 1024 1450
3-(10¢) Capt. Red Cross-c & text only; WWII Nazi-c; Powell-a
81 162 243 518 884 1250

WAR WAGON, THE (See Movie Classics)

WAR WINGS
Charlton Comics: Oct, 1968

1 3 6 9 14 20 26

WARWORLD!
Dark Horse Comics: Feb, 1989 ($1.75, B&W, one-shot)

1-Gary Davis sci/fi art in Moebius style 3.00

WASHABLE JONES AND THE SHMOO (Also see Al Capp's Shmoo)
Toby Press: June, 1953

1- "Super-Shmoo" 20 40 60 114 182 250

WASH TUBBS (See The Comics, Crackajack Funnies)
Dell Publishing Co.: No. 11, 1942 - No. 53, 1944

Four Color 11 (#1) 26 52 78 182 404 625
Four Color 28 (1943) 17 34 51 117 259 400
Four Color 53 13 26 39 89 195 300

WASP (See Unstoppable Wasp)

WASTELAND
DC Comics: Dec, 1987 - No. 18, May, 1989 ($1.75-$2.00 #13 on, mature)

1-5(4/88), 5(5/88), 6(5/88)-18: 13,15-Orlando-a 3.00
NOTE: ***Orlando** a-12, 13, 15. **Truman** a-10; c-13.*

WATCHMEN (Also see 2012-2013 Before Watchmen prequel titles)
DC Comics: Sept, 1986 - No. 12, Oct, 1987 (maxi-series)

1-Alan Moore scripts & Dave Gibbons-c/a in all 5 10 15 30 50 70
1-(2009, $1.50) Second printing 3.00
2-12 2 4 6 10 14 18
Hardcover Collection-Slip-cased-r/#1-12 w/new material; produced by Graphitti Designs 100.00
HC (2008, $39.99) recolored r/#1-12; design & promotional art; Moore & Gibbons intros 40.00
Trade paperback (1987, $14.95)-r/#1-12 25.00

WATCHVARK COMICS (Reprints from Cerebus in Hell)(Also see Aardvark Comics)
Aardvark-Vanaheim: Jan, 2018 ($4.00, B&W)

1-Cerebus figures placed over original Doré artwork of Hell; Watchmen #6-c swipe 4.00

WATER BIRDS AND THE OLYMPIC ELK (Disney)
Dell Publishing Co.: No. 700, Apr, 1956

Four Color 700-Movie 5 10 15 33 57 80

WATERWORLD: CHILDREN OF LEVIATHAN
Acclaim Comics: Aug, 1997 - No. 4, Nov, 1997 ($2.50, mini-series)

1-4 3.00

WAY OF THE RAT
CrossGeneration Comics: Jun, 2002 - No. 24, June, 2004 ($2.95)

1-24: 1-Dixon-s/ Jeff Johnson-a. 5-Whigham-a. 9,14-Luke Ross-a 3.00
Free Comic Book Day Special (6/03) reprints #1 w/features, interviews, CrossGen info 3.00
...: The Walls of Zhumar Vol. 1 (1/03, $15.95) r/#1-6 16.00
Vol. 2: The Dragon's Wake (2003, $15.95) r/#7-12 16.00

WAYWARD
Image Comics: Aug, 2014 - Present ($3.50/$3.99)

1-25: 1-Jim Zub-s/Cummings-a; multiple covers. 16-Begin $3.99-c 4.00

WEAPONS OF MUTANT DESTRUCTION: ALPHA
Marvel Comics: Aug, 2017 ($4.99, one-shot)

1-Crossover with Weapon X #4-6 and Totally Awesome Hulk #19-22; Stryker app. 4.00

WEAPON X
Marvel Comics: Apr, 1994 ($12.95, one-shot)

nn-r/Marvel Comics Presents #72-84 13.00

WEAPON X
Marvel Comics: Mar, 1995 - No. 4, June, 1995 ($1.95)

1-Age of Apocalypse 4.00
2-4 3.00

WEAPON X
Marvel Comics: Nov, 2002 - No. 28, Nov, 2004 ($2.25/$2.99)

1-7: 1-Sabretooth-c/app.; Tieri-s/Jeanty-a 3.00
8-28: 8-Begin $2.99-c. 14-Invaders app. 15-Chamber joins. 16-18,21-25-Wolverine app. 3.00
Vol. 1: The Draft TPB (2003, $21.99) r/#1-5, #1/2 & The Draft one-shots 22.00
Vol. 2: The Underground TPB (2003, $19.99) r/#6-13 20.00
Wizard #1/2 (2002) 5.00

WEAPON X
Marvel Comics: Jun, 2017 - Present ($3.99)

1-14: 1-Pak-s/Land-a; Old Man Logan & Sabretooth. 4-6-Crossover with Totally Awesome Hulk #19-22. 6-Intro. Weapon H 4.00

WEAPON X: DAYS OF FUTURE NOW
Marvel Comics: Sept, 2005 - No. 5, Jan, 2006 ($2.99, limited series)

1-5-Tieri-s/Sears-a; Chamber, Sauron & Fantomex app. 3.00
TPB (2006, $13.99) r/#1-5 14.00

WEAPON X: FIRST CLASS
Marvel Comics: Jan, 2009 - No. 3, Mar, 2009 ($3.99, limited series)

1-3:1-Sabretooth-c/app. 2-Deadpool-c/app. 4.00

WEAPON X NOIR
Marvel Comics: May, 2010 ($3.99, one-shot)

1-Dennis Calero-s/a; C.P. Smith-c 4.00

WEAPON X: THE DRAFT (Leads into 2002 Weapon X series)
Marvel Comics: Oct, 2002 ($2.25, one-shots)

...Kane 1- JH Williams-c/Raimondi-a 3.00
...Marrow 1- JH Williams-c/Badeaux-a 3.00
...Sauron 1- JH Williams-c/Kerschl-a; Emma Frost app. 3.00
...Wild Child 1- JH Williams-c/Van Sciver-a; Aurora (Alpha Flight) app. 3.00
...Zero 1- JH Williams-c/Plunkett-a; Wolverine app. 3.00

WEAPON ZERO
Image Comics (Top Cow Productions): No. T-4(#1), June, 1995 - No. T-0(#5), Dec, 1995 ($2.50, limited series)

T-4(#1): Walt Simonson scripts in all. 5.00
T-3(#2) - T-1(#4) 4.00
T-0(#5) 3.00

WEAPON ZERO

We Are Robin #12 © DC

Web of Horror #3 © Major Mag.

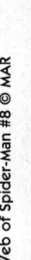

Web of Spider-Man #8 © MAR

GD 2.0 | VG 4.0 | FN 6.0 | VF 8.0 | VF/NM 9.0 | NM- 9.2

GD 2.0 | VG 4.0 | FN 6.0 | VF 8.0 | VF/NM 9.0 | NM- 9.2

Image Comics (Top Cow Productions): V2#1, Mar, 1996 - No. 15, Dec, 1997 ($2.50)
V2#1-Walt Simonson scripts. 4.00
2-14: 8-Begin Top Cow. 10-Devil's Reign 3.00
15-($3.50) Benitez-a 4.00

WEAPON ZERO/SILVER SURFER
Image Comics/Marvel Comics: Jan, 1997 ($2.95, one-shot)
1-Devil's Reign Pt. 1 3.00

WE ARE ROBIN (Also see Batman: Rebirth #1)
DC Comics: Aug, 2015 - No. 12, Jul, 2016 ($3.99)
1-12: 1-Bermejo-s/c; Corona-a. 3-Batman (Gordon) app. 4-Batgirl app.; Harvey-a 4.00

WEASELGUY: ROAD TRIP
Image Comics: Sept, 1999 - No. 2 ($3.50, limited series)
1,2-Steve Buccellato-s/a 3.50
1-Variant-c by Bachalo 5.00

WEASELGUY/WITCHBLADE
Hyperwerks: July, 1998 ($2.95, one-shot)
1-Steve Buccellato-s/a; covers by Matsuda and Altstaetter 3.00

WEASEL PATROL SPECIAL, THE (Also see Fusion #17)
Eclipse Comics: Apr, 1989 ($2.00, B&W, one-shot)
1-Funny animal 3.00

WEAVEWORLD
Marvel Comics (Epic): Dec, 1991 - No. 3, 1992 ($4.95, lim. series, 68 pgs.)
1-3: Clive Barker adaptation 5.00

WEB, THE (Also see Mighty Comics & Mighty Crusaders)
DC Comics (Impact Comics): Sept, 1991 - No. 14, Oct, 1992 ($1.00)
1-14: 5-The Fly x-over 9-Trading card inside 5.00
Annual 1 (1992, $2.50, 68 pgs.)-With Trading card 5.00
NOTE: ***Gil Kane*** *c-5, 9, 10, 12-14.* ***Bill Wray*** *a(i)-1-9, 10(part).*

WEB, THE (Continued from The Red Circle)
DC Comics: Nov, 2009 - No. 10, Aug, 2010 ($3.99)
1-10: 1-Roger Robinson-a; The Hangman back-up feature. 3-Batgirl app. 5-Caldwell-a 4.00

WEB OF EVIL
Comic Magazines/Quality Comics Group: Nov, 1952 - No. 21, Dec, 1954
1-Used in **SOTI**, pg. 388. Jack Cole-a; morphine use story
81 162 243 518 884 1250
2-4,6,7: 2,3-Jack Cole-a. 4,6,7-Jack Cole-c/a 47 94 141 296 498 700
5-Electrocution-c/story; Jack Cole-c/a 74 148 222 470 810 1150
8-11-Jack Cole-a 42 84 126 265 445 625
12,13,15,16,19-21 33 66 99 194 317 440
14-Part Crandall-c; Old Witch swipe 37 74 111 222 361 500
17-Opium drug propaganda story 36 72 108 211 343 475
18-Acid-in-face story 37 74 111 222 361 500
NOTE: ***Jack Cole*** *a(2 each)-2, 6, 8, 9.* ***Cuidera*** *c-1-21i.* ***Ravielli*** *a-13.*

WEB OF HORROR
Major Magazines: Dec, 1969 - No. 3, Apr, 1970 (Magazine)
1-Jeff Jones painted-c; Wrightson-a, Kaluta-a 8 16 24 54 102 150
2-Jones painted-c; Wrightson-a(2), Kaluta-a 7 14 21 48 89 130
3-Wrightson-c/a (1st published-c); Brunner, Kaluta, Bruce Jones-a
9 18 27 58 114 170

WEB OF MYSTERY
Ace Magazines (A. A. Wyn): Feb, 1951 - No. 29, Sept, 1955
1 71 142 213 454 777 1100
2-Bakerish-a 40 80 120 246 411 575
3-10: 4-Colan-a 39 78 117 231 378 525
11-18,20-26: 12-John Chilly's 1st cover art. 13-Surrealistic-c. 20-r/The Beyond #1
36 72 108 211 343 475
19-Reprints Challenge of the Unknown #6 used in N.Y. Legislative Committee
36 72 108 211 343 475
27-Bakerish-a(r/The Beyond #2); last pre-code ish 32 64 96 188 307 425
28,29: 28-All-r 24 48 72 142 234 325
NOTE: *This series was to appear as "Creepy Stories", but title was changed before publication.* ***Cameron*** *a-6, 8, 11-13, 17-20, 22, 24, 25, 27; c-8, 13, 17.* ***Palais*** *a-28r.* ***Sekowsky*** *a-1-3, 7, 8, 11, 14, 21, 29.* ***Tothish*** *a-by* ***Bill Discount*** *#16. 29-all-r, 19-28-partial-r.*

WEB OF SCARLET SPIDER
Marvel Comics: Oct, 1995 - No. 4, Jan, 1996 ($1.95, limited series)
1-4: Replaces "Web of Spider-Man" 3.00

WEB OF SPIDER-MAN (Replaces Marvel Team-Up)
Marvel Comics Group: Apr, 1985 - No. 129, Sept, 1995
1-Painted-c (5th app. black costume?) 3 6 9 15 22 28
2,3 6.00
4-8: 7-Hulk x-over; Wolverine splash 5.00
9-13: 10-Dominic Fortune guest stars; painted-c 4.00
14-17,19-28: 19-Intro Humbug & Solo 4.00
18-1st app. Venom (behind the scenes, 9/86) 2 4 6 11 16 20
29-Wolverine, new Hobgoblin (Macendale) app. 1 3 4 6 8 10
30-Origin recap The Rose & Hobgoblin I (entire book is flashback story);
Punisher & Wolverine cameo 5.00
31,32-Six part Kraven storyline begins 2 4 6 9 12 15
33-35,37,39-47,49 3.00
36-1st app. Tombstone 3 6 9 16 23 30
38-Hobgoblin app.; begin $1.00-c 4.00
48-Origin Hobgoblin II(Demogoblin) cont'd from Spectacular Spider-Man #147;
Kingpin app. 1 3 4 6 8 10
50-($1.50, 52 pgs.) 4.00
51-58 3.00
59-Cosmic Spidey cont'd from Spect. Spider-Man 4.00
60-89,91-99,101-106: 66,67-Green Goblin (Norman Osborn) app. as a super-hero. 69,70-Hulk x-over. 74-76-Austin-c(i). 76-Fantastic Four x-over. 78-Cloak & Dagger app. 81-Origin/1st app. Bloodshed. 84-Begin 6 part Rose & Hobgoblin II storyline; last $1.00-c. 86-Demon leaves Hobgoblin; 1st Demogoblin. 93-Gives brief history of Hobgoblin. 93,94-Hobgoblin (Macendale) Reborn-c/story, parts 1,2; MoonKnight app. 94-Venom cameo. 95-Begin 4 part x-over w/Spirits of Venom w/Ghost Rider/Blaze/Spidey vs. Venom & Demogoblin (cont'd in Ghost Rider/Blaze #5,6). 96-Spirits of Venom part 3; painted-c. 101,103-Maximum Carnage x-over. 103-Venom & Carnage app. 104-Infinity Crusade tie-in. 104-106-Nightwatch back-up stories 3.00
90-($2.95, 52 pgs.)-Polybagged w/silver hologram-c, gatefold poster showing
Spider-Man & Spider-Man 2099 (Williamson-i) 2 4 6 8 10 12
90-2nd printing; gold hologram-c 4.00
100-($2.95, 52 pgs.)-Holo-grafx foil-c; intro new Spider-Armor 4.00
107-111: 107-Intro Sandstorm; Sand & Quicksand app. 3.00
112-116,121-124, 126-128: 112-Begin $1.50-c; bound-in trading card sheet.
113-Regular Ed.; Gambit & Black Cat app. 3.00
113-($2.95)-Collector's ed. polybagged w/foil-c; 16 pg. preview of Spider-Man cartoon & animation cel 4.00
117-($1.50)-Flip book; Power & Responsibility Pt.1 3.00
117-($2.95)-Collector's edition; foil-c; flip book 4.00
118-1st solo Scarlet Spider story; Venom app. 2 4 6 13 18 22
119-Regular edition 6.00
119-($6.45)-Direct market edition; polybagged w/ Marvel Milestone Amazing Spider-Man #150 & coupon for Amazing Spider-Man #396, Spider-Man #53, & Spectacular Spider-Man #219.
1 3 4 6 8 10
120 ($2.25)-Flip book w/ preview of the Ultimate Spider-Man 4.00
125 ($3.95)-Holodisk-c; Gwen Stacy clone 5.00
125,129: 125 ($2.95)-Newsstand. 129-Last issue 4.00
#129.1, #129.2 (both 10/12, $2.99) Brooklyn Avengers app.; Damion Scott-a 3.00
Annual 1 (1985) 5.00
Annual 2 (1986)-New Mutants; Art Adams-a 1 2 3 5 6 8
Annual 3-10 ('87-'94, 68 pgs.): 4-Evolutionary War x-over. 5-Atlantis Attacks; Captain Universe by Ditko (p) & Silver Sable stories; F.F. app. 6-Punisher back-up plus Capt. Universe by Ditko; G. Kane-a. 7-Origins of Hobgoblin I, Hobgoblin II, Green Goblin I & II & Venom; Larsen/Austin-c. 9-Bagged w/card 4.00
Super Special 1 (1995, $3.95)-flip book 4.00
NOTE: ***Art Adams*** *a-Annual 2.* ***Byrne*** *c-3-6.* ***Chaykin*** *c-10.* ***Mignola*** *a-Annual 2.* ***Vess*** *c-1, 8, Annual 1, 2.* ***Zeck*** *a-6i, 31, 32; c-31, 32.*

WEB OF SPIDER-MAN (Anthology)
Marvel Comics: Dec, 2009 - No. 12, Nov, 2010 ($3.99)
1-12: 1-Spider-Girl app. thru #7; Ben Reilly app. 2-6-Origins of villains retold. 7-Kraven origin; Paper Doll app.; Mahfood-a. 9-11-Jackpot back-up; Takeda-a. 11,12-Black Cat app. 4.00

WEBSPINNERS: TALES OF SPIDER-MAN
Marvel Comics: Jan, 1999 - No. 18, Jun, 2000 ($2.99/$2.50)
1-DeMatteis-s/Zulli-a; back-up story w/Romita Sr. art 4.00
1-($6.95) DF Edition 7.00
2,3: 2-Two covers 3.00
4-11,13-18: 4,5-Giffen-a; Silver Surfer-c/app. 7-9-Kelly-s/Sears and Smith-a.
10,11-Jenkins-s/Sean Phillips-a 3.00
12-($3.50) J.G. Jones-c/a; Jenkins-s 4.00

WEB WARRIORS
Marvel Comics: Jan, 2016 - No. 11, Nov, 2016 ($4.99/$3.99)

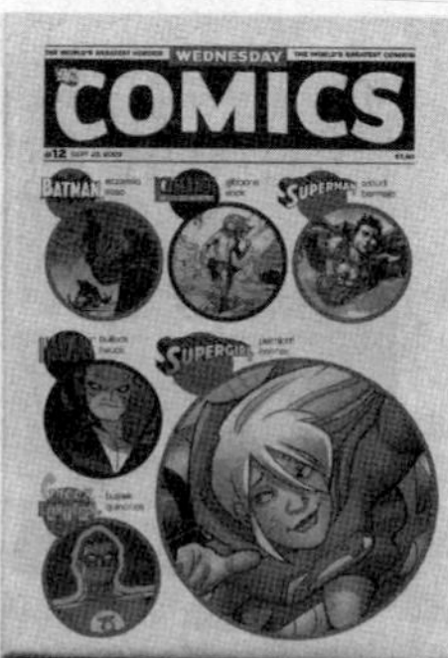

Wednesday Comics #12 © DC

Weird Comics #5 © FOX

Weird Fantasy #16 © WMG

	GD 2.0	VG 4.0	FN 6.0	VF 8.0	VF/NM 9.0	NM- 9.2

1-($4.99) Spider-verse characters team-up; Costa-s/Baldeon-a; alternate Black Cat app. 5.00
2-11-($3.99) 2-5-Multiple Spider-Mans vs. multiple Electros 4.00

WEDDING BELLS
Quality Comics Group: Feb, 1954 - No. 19, Nov, 1956

	GD	VG	FN	VF	VF/NM	NM-
1-Whitney-a	20	40	60	117	189	260
2	14	28	42	76	108	140
3-9: 8-Last precode (4/55)	11	22	33	62	86	110
10-Ward-a (9 pgs.)	16	32	48	94	147	200
11-14,17	10	20	30	58	79	100
15-Baker-c	17	34	51	100	158	215
16-Baker-c/a	20	40	60	117	189	260
18,19-Baker-a each	14	28	42	82	121	160

WEDDING OF DRACULA
Marvel Comics: Jan, 1993 ($2.00, 52 pgs.)

1-Reprints Tomb of Dracula #30,45,46 4.00

WEDNESDAY COMICS (Newspaper-style, twice folded pages on 20" x 14" newsprint)
DC Comics: Sept, 2009 - No. 12, Nov, 2009 ($3.99, weekly limited series)

1-12-Superman, Batman, Kamandi, Hawkman, Deadman, Green Lantern, Flash, Teen Titans, Metamorpho, Adam Strange, Supergirl, Metal Men, Wonder Woman, The Demon with Catwoman, Sgt. Rock; s-a/ by various incl. Ryan Sook, Joe Kubert, Gaiman, Allred, Risso, Kyle Baker, Paul Pope, Conner, Simonson, Garcia-Lopez, Stelfreeze, Bermejo 4.00
HC (2010, $49.99, 17-3/4"x11-1/4") r/#1-12 plus new 1 pg. stories of Plastic Man by Dorkin-s/DeStefano-a and Beware the Creeper by Giffen-s/Canete-a; bonus sketch art 50.00

WEEKENDER, THE (Illustrated...)
Rucker Pub. Co.: V1#1, Sept, 1945? - V1#4, Nov, 1945; V2#1, Jan, 1946 - V2#3, Aug, 1946 (52 pgs.)

	GD	VG	FN	VF	VF/NM	NM-
V1#1-4: 1-Same-c as Zip Comics #45, inside-c and back-c blank; Steel Sterling, Senor Banana, Red Rube and Ginger. 2-Capt. Victory on-c. 3-Super hero-c; Mr. E, Dan Hastings, Sky Chief and the Echo. 4-Same-c as Punch Comics #10 (9/44); r/Hale the Magician (7 pgs.) & r/Mr. E (8 pgs.-Lou Fine? or Gustavson?) plus 3 humor strips & many B&W photos & r/newspaper articles plus cheesecake photos of Hollywood stars	41	82	123	256	428	600
V2#1-Same-c as Dynamic Comics #11; 36 pgs. comics, 16 in newspaper format with photos; partial Dynamic Comics reprints; 4 pgs. of cels from the Disney film Pinocchio; Little Nemo story by Winsor McCay, Jr.; Jack Cole-a	58	116	174	371	636	900
V2#2,3: 2-Same-c as Dynamic Comics #9 by Raboy; Dan Hastings (Tuska), Rocket Boy, The Echo, Lucky Coyne. 3-Humor-c by Boddington?; Dynamic Man, Ima Slooth, Master Key, Dynamic Boy, Captain Glory	37	74	111	222	361	500

WEIRD
Eerie Publications: V1#10, 1/66 - V8#6, 12/74; V9#1, 1/75 - V14#3, Nov, 1981 (Magazine) (V1-V8: 52 pgs.; V9 on: 68 pgs.)

	GD	VG	FN	VF	VF/NM	NM-
V1#10(#1)-Intro. Morris the Caretaker of Weird (ends V2#10); Burgos-a	8	16	24	54	102	150
11,12	5	10	15	35	63	90
V2#1-4(10/67), V3#1(1/68), V2#6(4/68)-V2#7,9,10(12/68)	5	10	15	35	63	90
V2#8-r/Ditko's 1st story/Fantastic Fears #5	6	12	18	40	73	105
V3#1(2/69)-V3#4	5	10	15	33	57	80
V3#5(12/69)-Rulah reprint; "Rulah" changed to "Pulah", LSD story reprinted in Horror Tales V4#4, Tales From the Tomb V2#4, & 20	5	10	15	33	57	80
V4#1-6('70), V5#1-6('71), V6#1-7('72), V7#1-7('73), V8#1-3, V8#4(8/74), V8#4(10/74), (V8#5 does not exist), V8#6('74), V9#1-4(1/75-'76), V10#1-3('77), V11#1-4('78), V12#1(2/79)-V14#3(11/81)	5	10	15	31	53	75

NOTE: *There are two V8#4 issues (8/74 & 10/74). V9#4 (12/76) has a cover swipe from Horror Tales V5#1 (2/73). There are two V13#3 issues (6/80 & 9/80).*

WEIRD
DC Comics (Paradox Press): Sum, 1997 - No. 4 ($2.99, B&W, magazine)

1-4: 4-Mike Tyson-c 3.00

WEIRD, THE
DC Comics: Apr, 1988 - No. 4, July, 1988 ($1.50, limited series)

1-4: Wrightson-c/a in all 5.00

WEIRD ADVENTURES
P. L. Publishing Co. (Canada): May-June, 1951 - No. 3, Sept-Oct, 1951

	GD	VG	FN	VF	VF/NM	NM-
1- "The She-Wolf Killer" by Matt Baker (6 pgs.)	66	132	198	419	722	1025
2-Bondage/hypodermic panel	52	104	156	328	552	775
3-Male bondage/torture-c; severed head story	45	90	135	284	480	675

WEIRD ADVENTURES
Ziff-Davis Publishing Co.: No. 10, July-Aug, 1951

	GD	VG	FN	VF	VF/NM	NM-
10-Painted-c	43	86	129	271	461	650

WEIRD CHILLS
Key Publications: July, 1954 - No. 3, Nov, 1954

	GD	VG	FN	VF	VF/NM	NM-
1-Wolverton-r/Weird Mysteries No. 4; blood transfusion-c by Baily	168	336	504	1075	1838	2600
2-Extremely violent injury to eye-c by Baily; Hitler story	174	348	522	1114	1907	2700
3-Bondage E.C. swipe-c by Baily	129	258	387	826	1413	2000

WEIRD COMICS
Fox Feature Syndicate: Apr, 1940 - No. 20, Jan, 1942

	GD	VG	FN	VF	VF/NM	NM-
1-The Birdman, Thor, God of Thunder (ends #5), The Sorceress of Zoom, Blast Bennett, Typhon, Voodoo Man, & Dr. Mortal begin; George Tuska bondage-c	865	1730	2595	6315	11,158	16,000
2-Lou Fine-c	432	864	1296	3154	5577	8000
3,4: 3-Simon-c. 4-Torture-c	284	568	852	1818	3109	4400
5-Intro. Dart & sidekick Ace (8/40) (ends #20); bondage/hypo-c	284	568	852	1818	3109	4400
6-Dynamite Thor app.; super hero covers begin	161	322	483	1030	1765	2500
7-Dynamite Thor app.	226	452	678	1446	2473	3500
8-Dynamo, the Eagle (11/40, early app.; see Science #1) & sidekick Buddy & Marga, the Panther Woman begin	174	348	522	1114	1907	2700
9,10: 10-Navy Jones app.	142	284	426	909	1555	2200
11-19: 16-The Eagle vs. Nazi battle-c/flag-c. 17-Origin The Black Rider; WWII Nazi-c	129	258	387	826	1413	2000
20-Origin The Rapier; Swoop Curtis app; Churchill & Hitler-c	811	1622	2433	5920	10,460	15,000

NOTE *Cover features: Sorceress of Zoom-4; Dr. Mortal-5; Dart & Ace-6-13, 15; Eagle-14, 16-20.*

WEIRD DETECTIVE
Dark Horse Comics: Jun, 2016 - No. 5, Oct, 2016 ($3.99)

1-5-Van Lente-s/Vilanova-a 4.00

WEIRD FANTASY (Formerly A Moon, A Girl, Romance; becomes Weird Science-Fantasy #23 on)
E. C. Comics: No. 13, May-June, 1950 - No. 22, Nov-Dec, 1953

	GD	VG	FN	VF	VF/NM	NM-
13(#1) (1950)	229	458	687	1832	2916	4000
14-Necronomicon story; Cosmic Ray Bomb explosion-c/story by Feldstein; Feldstein & Gaines star	114	228	342	912	1456	2000
15,16: 16-Used in **SOTI**, pg. 144	89	178	267	712	1131	1550
17 (1951)	66	132	198	528	839	1150
6-Robot-c	60	120	180	480	765	1050
7-10	56	112	168	448	712	975
11-13 (1952): 11-Feldstein bio. 12-E.C. artists cameo; Orlando bio. 13-Anti-Wertham "Cosmic Correspondence"	46	92	138	368	584	800
14-Frazetta/Williamson(1st team-up at E.C.)/Krenkel-a (7 pgs.); Orlando draws E.C. staff	57	114	171	456	728	1000
15-Williamson/Evans-a(3), 4,3,&7 pgs.	47	94	141	376	601	825
16-19-Williamson/Krenkel-a in all. 17-Feldstein dinosaur-c; classic sci-fi story "The Aliens". 18-Williamson/Feldstein-c; classic anti-prejudice story "Judgment Day". 19-Williamson bio.	44	88	132	352	564	775
20-Frazetta/Williamson-a (7 pgs.); contains house ad for original, uncensored cover to Vault of Horror #32 (meat cleaver in forehead)	49	98	147	392	621	850
21-Frazetta/Williamson-c & Williamson/Krenkel-a	77	154	231	616	983	1350
22-Bradbury adaptation	37	74	111	296	473	650

NOTE: ***Crandall** a-22. **Elder** a-17. **Feldstein** a-13(#1)-8; c-13(#1)-18 (#18 w/**Williamson**), 20. **Harrison/Wood** a-13. **Kamen** a-13(#1)-16, 18-22. **Krigstein** a-22. **Kurtzman** a-13(#1)-17(#5), 6. **Orlando** a-9-22 (2 stories in #16); c-19, 22. **Severin/Elder** a-18-21. **Wood** a-13(#1)-14, 17(2 stories ea. in #10-13). Ray Bradbury adaptations in #13,17-22. Canadian reprints exist; see Table of Contents.*

WEIRD FANTASY
Russ Cochran/Gemstone Publ.: Oct, 1992 - No. 22, Jan, 1998 ($1.50/$2.00/$2.50)

1-22: 1,2: 1,2-r/Weird Fantasy #13,14; Feldstein-c. 3-5-r/Weird Fantasy #15-17 4.00

WEIRD HORRORS (Nightmare #10 on)
St. John Publishing Co.: June, 1952 - No. 9, Oct, 1953

	GD	VG	FN	VF	VF/NM	NM-
1-Tuska-a	77	154	231	493	847	1200
2,3: 3-Hashish story	42	84	126	265	445	625
4,5	39	78	117	240	395	550
6-Ekgren-c; atomic bomb story	87	174	261	553	952	1350
7-Ekgren-c; Kubert, Cameron-a	90	180	270	576	988	1400
8,9-Kubert-c/a	50	100	150	315	533	750

NOTE: ***Cameron** a-7, 9. **Finesque** a-1-5. **Forgione** a-6. **Morisi** a-3. Bondage c-8.*

WEIRD MYSTERIES
Gillmor Publications: Oct, 1952 - No. 12, Sept, 1954

	GD	VG	FN	VF	VF/NM	NM-
1-Partial Wolverton-c swiped from splash page "Flight to the Future" in Weird Tales of the Future #2; "Eternity" has an Ingels swipe	152	304	456	965	1658	2350

2- "Robot Woman" by Wolverton; Bernard Baily-c reprinted in Mister Mystery #18;

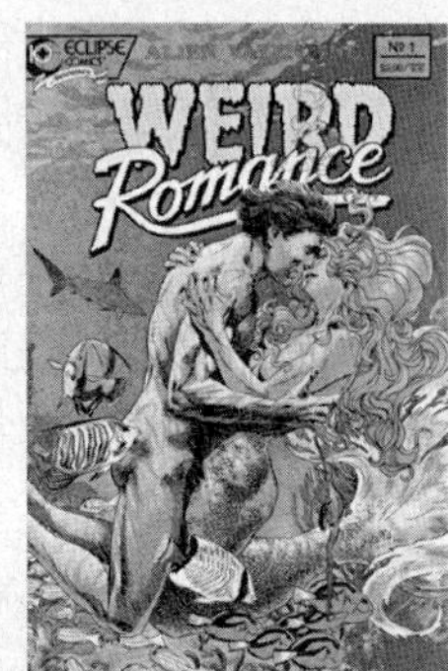

Weird Romance #1 © ECL

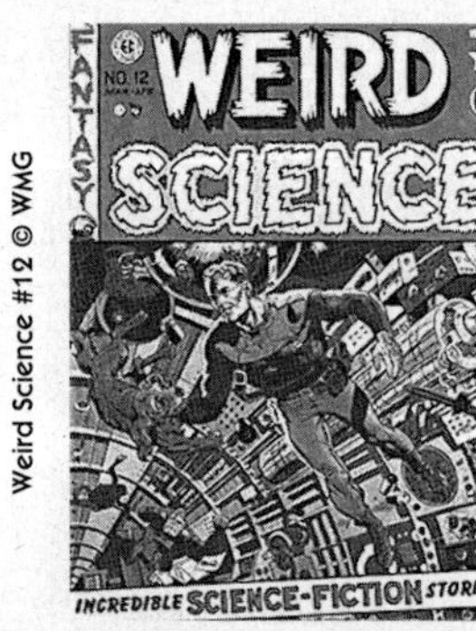

Weird Science #12 © WMG

Weird Tales of the Future #7 © Aragon

	GD 2.0	VG 4.0	FN 6.0	VF 8.0	VF/NM 9.0	NM- 9.2
acid in face panel	213	426	639	1363	2332	3300
3,6: Both have decapitation-c	110	220	330	704	1202	1700
4- "The Man Who Never Smiled" (3 pgs.) by Wolverton; Classic B. Baily skull-c	486	972	1458	3550	6275	9000
5-Wolverton story "Swamp Monster" (6 pgs.). Classic exposed brain-c	865	1730	2595	6315	11,158	16,000
7-Used in **SOTI**, illo "Indeed", illo "Sex and blood"	142	284	426	909	1555	2200
8-Wolverton-c panel-r/#5; used in a '54 Readers Digest anti-comics article by T. E. Murphy entitled "For the Kiddies to Read"	84	168	252	538	919	1300
9-Excessive violence, gore & torture	77	154	231	493	847	1200
10-Silhouetted nudity panel	71	142	213	454	777	1100
11,12: 12-r/Mr. Mystery #8(2), Weird Mysteries #3 & Weird Tales of the Future #6	71	142	213	454	777	1100

NOTE: ***Baily** c-2-12. Anti-Wertham column in #5. #1-12 all have 'The Ghoul Teacher' (host).*

WEIRD MYSTERIES (Magazine)
Pastime Publications: Mar-Apr, 1959 (35¢, B&W, 68 pgs.)

1-Torres-a; E. C. swipe from Tales From the Crypt #46 by Tuska "The Ragman"	14	28	42	82	121	160

WEIRD MYSTERY TALES (See DC 100 Page Super Spectacular)

WEIRD MYSTERY TALES (See Cancelled Comic Cavalcade)
National Periodical Publications: July-Aug, 1972 - No. 24, Nov, 1975

1-Kirby-a; Wrightson splash pg.	5	10	15	33	57	80
2-Titanic-c/s	3	6	9	20	31	42
3,21: 21-Wrightson-c	3	6	9	17	26	35
4-10	3	6	9	14	19	24
11-20,22-24	2	4	6	11	16	20

NOTE: ***Alcala** a-5, 10, 13, 14. **Aparo** c-4. **Bailey** a-8. **Bolle** a-8?. **Howard** a-4. **Kaluta** a-4, 24; c-1. **G. Kane** a-10. **Kirby** a-1, 2p, 3p. **Nino** a-5, 6, 9, 13, 16, 21. **Redondo** a-9, 17. **Sparling** c-6. **Starlin** a-3?, 4. **Wood** a-23.*

WEIRD ROMANCE (Seduction of the Innocent #9)
Eclipse Comics: Feb, 1988 ($2.00, B&W)

1-Pre-code horror-r; Lou Cameron-r(2) 4.00

WEIRD SCIENCE (Formerly Saddle Romances) (Becomes Weird Science-Fantasy #23 on)
(Also see EC Archives • Weird Science)
E. C. Comics: No. 12, May-June, 1950 - No. 22, Nov-Dec, 1953

12(#1) (1950)-"Lost in the Microcosm" classic-c/story by Kurtzman; "Dream of Doom" stars Gaines & E.C. artists	286	572	858	2288	3644	5000
13-Flying saucers over Washington-c/story, 2 years before supposed UFO sighting	120	240	360	960	1530	2100
14-Robot, End of the World-c/story by Feldstein	103	206	309	824	1312	1800
15-War of Worlds-c/story (1950)	91	182	273	728	1164	1600
5-Atomic explosion-c	69	138	207	552	876	1200
6-8,10	60	120	180	480	765	1050
9-Wood's 1st EC-c	74	148	222	592	946	1300
11-14 (1952) 11-Kamen bio. 12-Wood bio	46	92	138	368	584	800
15-18-Williamson/Krenkel-a in each; 15-Williamson-a. 17-Used in **POP**, pgs. 81,82. 18-Bill Gaines doll app. in story	47	94	141	376	601	825
19,20-Williamson/Frazetta-a (7 pgs. each). 19-Used in **SOTI**, illo "A young girl on her wedding night stabs her sleeping husband to death with a hatpin..." 19-Bradbury bio.	60	120	180	480	765	1050
21-Williamson/Frazetta-a (6 pgs.); Wood draws E.C. staff; Gaines & Feldstein app. in story	60	120	180	480	765	1050
22-Williamson/Frazetta/Krenkel-a (8 pgs.); Wood draws himself in his story (last pg. & panel)	63	126	189	504	802	1100

NOTE: ***Elder** a-14, 19. **Evans** a-22. **Feldstein** a-12(#1)-8; c-12(#1)-8, 11. **Ingels** a-15. **Kamen** a-12(#1)-13, 15-18, 20, 21. **Kurtzman** a-12(#1)-7. **Orlando** a-10-22. **Wood** a-12(#1), 13(#2), 5-22 (#9, 10, 12, 13 all have 2 **Wood** stories); c-9, 10, 12-22. Canadian reprints exist; see Table of Contents. Ray Bradbury adaptations in #17-22.*

WEIRD SCIENCE
Gladstone Publishing: Sept, 1990 - No. 4, Mar, 1991 ($1.95/$2.00, 68 pgs.)

1-4: Wood-c(r); all reprints in each 5.00

WEIRD SCIENCE (Also see EC Archives • Weird Science)
Russ Cochran/Gemstone Publishing: Sept, 1992 - No. 22, Dec, 1997 ($1.50/$2.00/$2.50)

1-22: 1,2: r/Weird Science #12,13 w/original-c. ,4-r/#14,15. 5-7-w/original-c 4.00

WEIRD SCIENCE-FANTASY (Formerly Weird Science & Weird Fantasy)
(Becomes Incredible Science Fiction #30)
E. C. Comics: No. 23 Mar, 1954 - No. 29, May-June, 1955 (#23,24: 15¢)

23-Williamson, Wood-a; Bradbury adaptation	43	86	129	344	547	750
24-Williamson & Wood-a; Harlan Ellison's 1st professional story, "Upheaval!", later adapted into a short story as "Mealtime", and then into a TV episode of Voyage to the Bottom of the Sea as "The Price of Doom"	43	86	129	344	547	750
25-Williamson dinosaur-c; Williamson/Torres/Krenkel-a plus Wood-a; Bradbury adaptation and fan letter; cover price back to 10¢	49	98	147	392	621	850
26-Flying Saucer Report; Wood, Crandall-a; A-bomb panels	44	88	132	352	564	775
27-Adam Link/I Robot series begins	43	86	129	344	547	750
28-Williamson/Krenkel/Torres-a; Wood-a	43	86	129	344	552	760
29-Classic Frazetta-c; Williamson/Krenkel & Wood-a; Adam Link/I Robot series concludes; last pre-code issue; new logo	171	342	513	1368	2184	3000

NOTE: ***Crandall** a-26, 27, 29. **Evans** a-26. **Feldstein** c-24, 26, 28. **Kamen** a-27, 28. **Krigstein** a-23-25. **Orlando** a-in all. **Wood** a-in all; c-23, 27. The cover to #29 was originally intended for Famous Funnies #217 (Buck Rogers), but was rejected for being "too violent."*

WEIRD SCIENCE-FANTASY
Russ Cochran/Gemstone Publishing: Nov, 1992 - No. 7, May , 1994 ($1.50/$2.00/$2.50)

1-7: 1,2: r/Weird Science-Fantasy #23,24. 3-7 r/#25-29 4.00

WEIRD SCIENCE-FANTASY ANNUAL
E. C. Comics: 1952, 1953 (Sold thru the E. C. office & on the stands in some major cities) (25¢, 132 pgs.)

1952-Feldstein-c	310	620	930	2325	3563	4800
1953-Feldstein-c	174	348	522	1305	2003	2700

NOTE: *The 1952 annual contains books cover-dated in 1951 & 1952, and the 1953 annual from 1952 & 1953. Contents of each annual may vary in same year.*

WEIRD SECRET ORIGINS
DC Comics: Oct, 2004 ($5.95, square-bound, one-shot)

nn-Reprints origins of Dr. Fate, Spectre, Congorilla, Metamorpho, Animal Man & others 6.00

WEIRD SUSPENSE
Atlas/Seaboard Publ.: Feb, 1975 - No. 3, July, 1975

1-3: 1-Tarantula begins. 3-Freidrich-s	2	4	6	10	14	18

NOTE: ***Boyette** a-1-3. **Buckler** c-1, 3.*

WEIRD SUSPENSTORIES
Superior Comics (Canada): Oct, 1951 - No. 3, Dec, 1951; No. 3, no date (EC reprints)

1-3,3(no date)-(Rare): Reprints Crime SuspenStories #1-3, covers & contents w/Canadian ads replacing U.S. ads	967	1934	2900	-	-	-

NOTE: *Canada passed a law against importing crime comic books between 1949-1953, thus Crime Suspenstories became Weird Suspenstories in Canada creating a new EC title. The word "crime" was not allowed on comic books in Canada during this time.*

WEIRD TALES ILLUSTRATED
Millennium Publications: 1992 - No. 2, 1992 ($2.95, high quality paper)

1,2-Bolton painted-c. 1-Adapts E.A. Poe & Harlan Ellison stories. 2-E.A. Poe & H.P. Lovecraft adaptations 4.00
1-($4.95, 52 pgs.)-Deluxe edition w/Tim Vigil-a not in regular #1; stiff-c; Bolton painted-c 6.00

WEIRD TALES OF THE FUTURE
S.P.M. Publ. No. 1-4/Aragon Publ. No. 5-8: Mar, 1952 - No. 8, July-Aug, 1953

1-Andru-a(2); Wolverton partial-c	142	284	426	909	1555	2200
2,3-Wolverton-c/a(3) each. 2- "Jumpin Jupiter" satire by Wolverton begins, ends #5	297	594	891	1886	3243	4600
4-Wolverton-c put together from 3 panels of "Nightmare World" from #3 that were cut out & pasted up to form the cover with additional art added. "Jumping Jupiter" satire by Wolverton	165	330	495	1048	1799	2550
5-Wolverton-c/a(2); "Jumpin Jupiter" satire	343	686	1029	2400	4200	6000
6-Bernard Baily-c	84	168	252	538	919	1300
7- "The Mind Movers" from the art to Wolverton's "Brain Bats of Venus" from Mr. Mystery #7 which was cut apart, pasted up, partially redrawn, and rewritten by Harry Kantor, the editor; Baily-c	181	362	543	1158	1979	2800
8-Reprints Weird Mysteries #1(10/52) minus cover; gory cover showing heart ripped out, by B. Baily	194	388	582	1242	2121	3000

WEIRD TALES OF THE MACABRE (Magazine)
Atlas/Seaboard Publ.: Jan, 1975 - No. 2, Mar, 1975 (75¢, B&W)

1-Jeff Jones painted-c; Boyette-a	4	8	12	28	47	65
2-Boris Vallejo painted-c; Severin-a	5	10	15	32	53	75

WEIRD TERROR (Also see Horrific)
Allen Hardy Associates (Comic Media): Sept, 1952 - No. 13, Sept, 1954

1- "Portrait of Death", adapted from Lovecraft's "Pickman's Model"; lingerie panels, Hitler story	74	148	222	470	810	1150
2,3: 2-Text on Marquis DeSade, Torture, Demonology, & St. Elmo's Fire. 3-Extreme violence, whipping, torture; article on sin eating, dowsing	58	116	174	371	636	900
4-Dismemberment, decapitation, article on human flesh for sale, Devil, whipping	60	120	180	381	653	925
5-Article on body snatching, mutilation; cannibalism story	54	108	162	343	574	825
6-Dismemberment, decapitation, man hit by lightning						

Weird War Tales #14 © DC

Weird Western Tales #12 © DC

Weirdworld (2016 series) #4 © MAR

GD 2.0 | VG 4.0 | FN 6.0 | VF 8.0 | VF/NM 9.0 | NM- 9.2

55 110 165 352 601 850
7-Body burning in fireplace-c 60 120 180 381 653 925
8,11: 8-Decapitation story; Ambrose Bierce adapt. 11-End of the world story w/atomic blast panels; Tothish-a by Bill Discount 53 106 159 334 567 800
9,10,13: 13-Severed head panels 45 90 135 284 480 675
12-Discount-a 45 90 135 284 480 675
NOTE: *Don Heck a-most issues; c-1-13.* ***Landau*** *a-6.* ***Morisi*** *a-2-5, 7, 9, 12.* ***Palais*** *a-1, 5, 6, 8(2), 10, 12.* ***Powell*** *a-10.* ***Ravielli*** *a-11.*

WEIRD THRILLERS
Ziff-Davis Publ. Co. (Approved Comics): Sept-Oct, 1951 - No. 5, Oct-Nov, 1952 (#2-5: painted-c)

1-Rondo Hatton photo-c 110 220 330 704 1202 1700
2-Toth, Anderson, Colan-a 74 148 222 470 810 1150
3-Two Powell, Tuska-a; classic-c; Everett-a 103 206 309 659 1130 1600
4-Kubert, Tuska-a 68 136 204 435 743 1050
5-Powell-a 63 126 189 403 689 975
NOTE: ***M. Anderson*** *a-2, 3.* ***Roussos*** *a-4. #2, 3 reprinted in Nightmare #10 & 13; #4, 5 reprinted in Amazing Ghost Stories #16 & #15.*

WEIRD VAMPIRE TALES (Comic magazine)
Modern Day Periodical Pub.: V3 #1, Apr, 1979 - V5 #3, Mar, 1982 (B&W)

V3 #1 (4/79) First issue, no V1 or V2 4 8 12 25 40 55
V3 #2-4 3 6 9 19 30 40
V4 #2 (4/80), V4 #3 (7/80) (no V4 #1) 3 6 9 17 26 35
V5 #1 (1/81), V5 #2 (two issues, 4/81 & 8/81) 3 6 9 17 26 35
V5 #3 (3/82) Last issue; low print 3 6 9 21 33 45

WEIRD WAR TALES
National Periodical Publ./DC Comics: Sept-Oct, 1971 - No. 124, June, 1983 (#1-5: 52 pgs.)

1-Kubert-a in #1-4,7; c-1-7 21 42 63 147 324 500
2,3-Drucker-a: 2-Crandall-a. 3-Heath-a 10 20 30 64 132 200
4,5: 5-Toth-a; Heath-a 8 16 24 54 102 150
6,7,9,10: 6,10-Toth-a. 7-Heath-a 6 12 18 37 66 95
8-Neal Adams-c/a(i) 6 12 18 41 76 110
11-20 4 8 12 22 35 48
21-35 3 6 9 16 24 32
36-(68 pgs.)-Crandall & Kubert-r/#2; Heath-r/#3; Kubert-c 3 6 9 18 28 38
37-50: 38,39-Kubert-c 2 4 6 10 14 18
51-63: 58-Hitler-c/app. 60-Hindenburg-c/s 2 4 6 9 13 16
64-Frank Miller-a (1st DC work) 5 10 15 33 57 80
65-67,69-89,91,92: 89-Nazi Apes-c/s. 2 4 6 8 10 12
68-Frank Miller-a (2nd DC work) 3 6 9 21 33 45
90-Hitler app. 2 4 6 8 11 14
93-Intro/origin Creature Commandos 2 4 6 8 11 14
94-Return of War that Time Forgot; dinosaur-c/s 2 4 6 10 14 18
95,96,98,102-123: 98-Sphinx-c. 102-Creature Commandos battle Hitler. 110-Origin/1st app. Medusa. 123-1st app. Captain Spaceman 2 4 6 8 10 12
97,99,100,101,124: 99-War that Time Forgot. 100-Creature Commandos in War that Time Forgot. 101-Intro/origin G.I. Robot 2 4 6 8 11 14
NOTE: ***Chaykin*** *a-76, 82.* ***Ditko*** *a-95, 99, 104-106.* ***Evans*** *c-73, 74, 83, 85.* ***Kane*** *c-116, 118.* ***Kubert*** *c-55, 58, 60, 62, 72, 75-81, 87, 88, 90-96, 100, 103, 104, 106, 107.* ***Newton*** *a-122.* ***Starlin*** *c-89.* ***Sutton*** *a-91, 92, 103.* ***Creature Commandos*** *-93, 97, 100, 102, 105, 108-112, 114, 116-119, 121, 124.* ***G.I. Robot*** *- 101, 108, 111, 113, 116-118, 120, 122.* ***War That Time Forgot*** *- 94, 99, 100, 103, 106, 109, 120.*

WEIRD WAR TALES
DC Comics (Vertigo): June, 1997 - No. 4, Sept, 1997 ($2.50)

1-4-Anthology by various 3.00

WEIRD WAR TALES
DC Comics (Vertigo): April, 2000 ($4.95, one-shot)

1-Anthology by various; last Biukovic-a 5.00

WEIRD WAR TALES
DC Comics: Nov, 2010 ($3.99, one-shot)

1-Anthology by various incl. Cooke, Strnad, Pugh; Cooke-c 4.00

WEIRD WESTERN TALES (Formerly All-Star Western)
National Per. Publ./DC Comics: No. 12, June-July, 1972 - No. 70, Aug, 1980

12-(52 pgs.)-3rd app. Jonah Hex; Bat Lash, Pow Wow Smith reprints; El Diablo by Neal Adams/Wrightson 12 24 36 82 179 275
13-Jonah Hex-c & 4th app.; Neal Adams-a 8 16 24 56 108 160
14-Toth-a 6 12 18 41 76 110
15-Adams-c/a; no Jonah Hex 4 8 12 28 47 65
16,17,19,20 4 8 12 28 47 65
18,29: 18-1st all Jonah Hex issue (7-8/73) & begins. 29-Origin Jonah Hex; 1st full app. of Quentin Turnbull 6 12 18 37 66 95
21-28,30: Jonah Hex in all 4 8 12 23 37 50
31-38: Jonah Hex in all. 38-Last Jonah Hex 3 6 9 18 28 38
39-Origin/1st app. Scalphunter & begins 2 4 6 13 18 22
40-47,50-69: 64-Bat Lash-c/story 2 4 6 8 10 12
48,49: (44 pgs.)-1st & 2nd app. Cinnamon 2 4 6 8 11 14
70-Last issue 2 4 6 9 13 16
NOTE: ***Alcala*** *a-16, 17.* ***Evans*** *inks-39-48; c-39i, 40, 47.* ***G. Kane*** *a-15, 20.* ***Kubert*** *c-12, 33.* ***Starlin*** *c-44, 45.* ***Wildey*** *a-26. 48 & 49 are 44 pgs..*

WEIRD WESTERN TALES (Blackest Night crossover)
DC Comics: No. 71, March, 2010 ($2.99, one-shot)

71-Jonah Hex, Scalphunter, Super-Chief, Firehair and Bat Lash rise as Black Lanterns 3.00

WEIRD WESTERN TALES
DC Comics (Vertigo): Apr, 2001 - No. 4, Jul, 2001 ($2.50, limited series)

1-4-Anthology by various 3.00

WEIRD WONDER TALES
Marvel Comics Group: Dec, 1973 - No. 22, May, 1977

1-Wolverton-r/Mystic #6 (Eye of Doom) 4 8 12 24 38 55
2-10 3 6 9 17 26 35
11-22: 16-18-Venus-r by Everett from Venus #19,18 & 17. 19-22-r/Dr. Droom (re-named Dr. Druid) by Kirby. 22-New art by Byrne 3 6 9 16 23 30
15-17-(30¢-c variants, limited distribution)(4-8/76) 5 10 15 30 50 70
NOTE: *All 1950s & early 1960s reprints.* ***Check*** *r-1.* ***Colan*** *r-17.* ***Ditko*** *r-4, 5, 10-13, 19-21.* ***Drucker*** *r-12, 20.* ***Everett*** *r-3(Spellbound #16), 6(Astonishing #10), 9(Adv. Into Mystery #5).* ***Heath*** *a-13r.* ***Heck*** *a-1or, 14r.* ***Gil Kane*** *c-1, 2, 10.* ***Kirby*** *r-4, 6, 10, 11, 13, 15-22; c-17, 19, 20.* ***Krigstein*** *r-19.* ***Kubert*** *r-22.* ***Maneely*** *r-8.* ***Mooney*** *r-7p.* ***Powell*** *r-3, 7.* ***Torres*** *r-7.* ***Wildey*** *r-2, 7.*

WEIRDWORLD (Secret Wars tie-in)
Marvel Comics: Aug, 2015 - No. 5, Dec, 2015 ($3.99, limited series)

1-5-Aaron-s/Del Mundo-a; Arkon, Morgan Le Fay, and Skull the Slayer app. 4.00

WEIRDWORLD (After Secret Wars)
Marvel Comics: Feb, 2016 - No. 6, Jul, 2016 ($3.99)

1-6-Humphries-s/Del Mundo-a; Goleta the Wizardslayer & Morgan Le Fay app. 4.00

WEIRD WORLD OF JACK STAFF (See Jack Staff)
Image Comics: Feb, 2010 - No. 6, Apr, 2011 ($3.50)

1-6-Paul Grist-s/a. 2-Ian Churchill-c 3.50

WEIRD WORLDS (See Adventures Into...)

WEIRD WORLDS (Magazine)
Eerie Publications: V1#10(12/70), V2#1(2/71) - No. 4, Aug, 1971 (52 pgs.)

V1#10-Sci-fi/horror 5 10 15 33 57 80
V2#1-4 5 10 15 30 50 70

WEIRD WORLDS (Also see Ironwolf: Fires of the Revolution)
National Periodical Publications: Aug-Sept, 1972 - No. 9, Jan-Feb, 1974; No. 10, Oct-Nov, 1974 (All 20¢ issues)

1-Edgar Rice Burrough's John Carter Warlord of Mars & David Innes begin (1st DC app.); Kubert-c 3 6 9 17 26 35
2-4: 2-Infantino/Orlando-c. 3-Murphy Anderson-c. 4-Kaluta-a 2 4 6 10 14 18
5-7: .5-Kaluta-c. 7-Last John Carter. 2 4 6 8 11 14
8-10: 8-Iron Wolf begins by Chaykin (1st app.) 2 4 6 8 11 14
NOTE: ***Neal Adams*** *a-2i, 3i. John Carter by* ***Andersonin*** *#1-3.* ***Chaykin*** *c-7, 8.* ***Kaluta*** *a-4; c-4-6, 10.* ***Orlando*** *a-4i; c-2, 3, 4i.* ***Wrightson*** *a-2i, 4i.*

WEIRD WORLDS
DC Comics: Mar, 2011 - No. 6, Aug, 2011 ($3.99, limited series)

1-6-Short stories of Lobo, Garbage Man and Tanga; Ordway-a; Maguire-s/a; Lopresti-s/a 4.00

WELCOME BACK, KOTTER (TV) (See Limited Collectors' Edition #57 for unpublished #11)
National Periodical Publ./DC Comics: Nov, 1976 - No. 10, Mar-Apr, 1978

1-Sparling-a(p) 3 6 9 16 23 30
2-10: 3-Estrada-a 2 4 6 10 14 18

WELCOME SANTA (See March of Comics #63,183)

WELCOME TO HOLSOM
Gospel Publishing House: 2005 - Present (no cover price)

1-12-Craig Schutt-s/Steven Butler-a 3.00

WELCOME TO THE LITTLE SHOP OF HORRORS
Roger Corman's Cosmic Comics: May, 1995 -No. 3, July, 1995 ($2.50, limited series)

1-3 4.00

WELCOME TO TRANQUILITY
DC Comics (WildStorm): Feb, 2007 - No. 12, Jan, 2008 ($2.99)

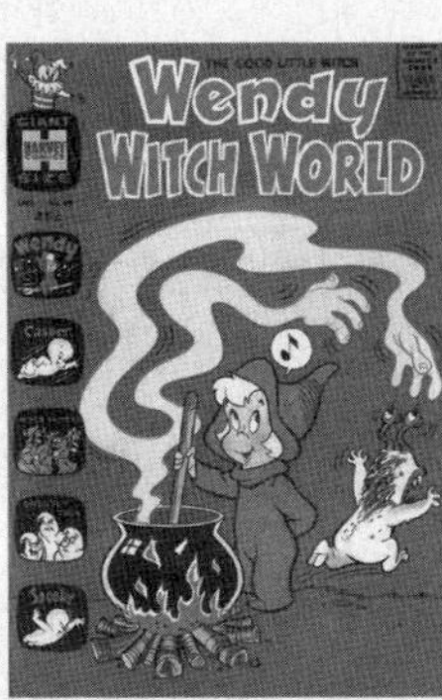

Wendy Witch World #39 © HARV

Werewolf By Night V2 #2 © MAR

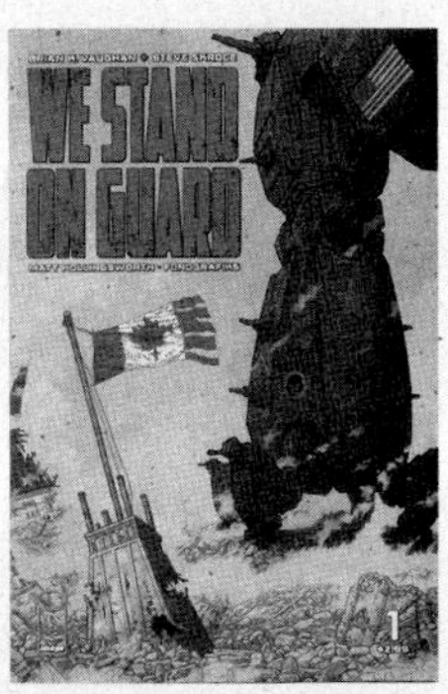

We Stand on Guard #1 © Vaughan & Skroce

	GD 2.0	VG 4.0	FN 6.0	VF 8.0	VF/NM 9.0	NM- 9.2
1-12: 1-Simone-s/Googe-a; two covers by Googe and Campbell. 8-Pearson-a						3.00
...: Armageddon 1 (1/08, $2.99) Gage-s/Googe-a						3.00
...: One Foot in the Grave 1-6 (7/10 - No. 6, 2/11, $3.99) Simone-s/Domingues-a						4.00
...: One Foot in the Grave TPB (2011, $17.99) r/mini-series #1-6						18.00
... Book One TPB (2008, $19.99) r/#1-6 and variant cover gallery						20.00
... Book Two TPB (2008, $19.99) r/#7-12; sketch pages						20.00

WELLS FARGO (See Tales of...)

WENDY AND THE NEW KIDS ON THE BLOCK
Harvey Comics: Mar, 1991 - No. 3, July, 1991 ($1.25)

	GD 2.0	VG 4.0	FN 6.0	VF 8.0	VF/NM 9.0	NM- 9.2
1-3						5.00

WENDY DIGEST
Harvey Comics: Oct, 1990 - No. 5, Mar, 1992 ($1.75, digest size)

	GD 2.0	VG 4.0	FN 6.0	VF 8.0	VF/NM 9.0	NM- 9.2
1-5						4.00

WENDY PARKER COMICS
Atlas Comics (OMC): July, 1953 - No. 8, July, 1954

	GD 2.0	VG 4.0	FN 6.0	VF 8.0	VF/NM 9.0	NM- 9.2
1	30	60	90	177	289	400
2	22	44	66	132	216	300
3-8	20	40	60	114	182	250

WENDY, THE GOOD LITTLE WITCH (TV)
Harvey Publ.: 8/60 - #82, 11/73; #83, 8/74 - #93, 4/76; #94, 9/90 - #97, 12/90

	GD 2.0	VG 4.0	FN 6.0	VF 8.0	VF/NM 9.0	NM- 9.2
1-Wendy & Casper the Friendly Ghost begin	36	72	108	259	580	900
2	12	24	36	84	185	285
3-5	9	18	27	62	126	190
6-10	7	14	21	44	82	120
11-20	5	10	15	34	60	85
21-30	4	8	12	27	44	60
31-50	3	6	9	17	26	35
51-64,66-69	2	4	6	13	18	22
65 (2/71)-Wendy origin.	3	6	9	16	24	32
70-74: All 52 pg. Giants	3	6	9	16	23	30
75-93	2	4	6	9	13	16
94-97 (1990, $1.00-c): 94-Has #194 on-c						5.00

(See Casper the Friendly Ghost #20 & Harvey Hits #7, 16, 21, 23, 27, 30, 33)

WENDY THE GOOD LITTLE WITCH (2nd Series)
Harvey Comics: Apr, 1991 - No. 15, Aug, 1994 ($1.00/$1.25 #7-11/$1.50 #12-15)

	GD 2.0	VG 4.0	FN 6.0	VF 8.0	VF/NM 9.0	NM- 9.2
1-15-Reprints Wendy & Casper stories. 12-Bunny app.						3.00

WENDY WITCH WORLD
Harvey Publications: 10/61; No. 2, 9/62 - No. 52, 12/73; No. 53, 9/74

	GD 2.0	VG 4.0	FN 6.0	VF 8.0	VF/NM 9.0	NM- 9.2
1-(25¢, 68 pg. Giants begin)	12	24	36	84	185	285
2-5	7	14	21	44	82	120
6-10	5	10	15	33	57	80
11-20	4	8	12	27	44	60
21-30	3	6	9	21	33	45
31-39: 39-Last 68 pg. issue	3	6	9	16	24	32
40-45: 52 pg. issues	2	4	6	13	18	22
46-53	2	4	6	9	13	16

WEREWOLF (Super Hero) (Also see Dracula & Frankenstein)
Dell Publishing Co.: Dec, 1966 - No. 3, April, 1967

	GD 2.0	VG 4.0	FN 6.0	VF 8.0	VF/NM 9.0	NM- 9.2
1-1st app.	4	8	12	23	37	50
2,3	3	6	9	16	23	30

WEREWOLF BY NIGHT (See Giant-Size..., Marvel Spotlight #2-4 & Power Record Comics)
Marvel Comics Group: Sept, 1972 - No. 43, Mar, 1977

	GD 2.0	VG 4.0	FN 6.0	VF 8.0	VF/NM 9.0	NM- 9.2
1-Ploog-a cont'd. from Marvel Spotlight #4	12	24	36	82	179	275
2	6	12	18	40	73	105
3-5	5	10	15	31	53	75
6-10	4	8	12	25	40	55
11-14,16-20	3	6	9	18	28	38
15-New origin Werewolf; Dracula-c/story cont'd from Tomb of Dracula #18; classic Ploog-c	4	8	12	28	47	65
21-31	3	6	9	14	20	26
32-Origin & 1st app. Moon Knight (8/75)	100	200	300	600	975	1350
33-2nd app. Moon Knight	9	18	27	61	123	185
34,36,38-43	3	6	9	14	19	24
35-Starlin/Wrightson-c	3	6	9	16	24	32
37-Moon Knight app; part Wrightson-c	5	10	15	30	50	70
38,39-(30¢-c variants, limited distribution)(5,7/76)	4	8	12	28	47	65

NOTE: ***Bolle** a-6i. **G. Kane** a-11p, 12p; c-21, 22, 24-30, 34p. **Mooney** a-7i. **Ploog** 1-4p, 5, 6p, 7p, 13-16p; c-5-8, 13-16. **Reinman** a-8i. **Sutton** a(i)-9, 11, 16, 35.*

WEREWOLF BY NIGHT (Vol. 2, continues in Strange Tales #1 (9/98))
Marvel Comics Group: Feb, 1998 - No. 6, July, 1998 ($2.99)

	GD 2.0	VG 4.0	FN 6.0	VF 8.0	VF/NM 9.0	NM- 9.2
1-6-Manco-a: 2-Two covers. 6-Ghost Rider-c/app.						3.00

WEREWOLVES & VAMPIRES (Magazine)
Charlton Comics: 1962 (One Shot)

	GD 2.0	VG 4.0	FN 6.0	VF 8.0	VF/NM 9.0	NM- 9.2
1	9	18	27	58	114	170

WEREWOLVES ON THE MOON: VERSUS VAMPIRES
Dark Horse Comics: June, 2009 - No. 3 ($3.50, limited series)

	GD 2.0	VG 4.0	FN 6.0	VF 8.0	VF/NM 9.0	NM- 9.2
1,2-Dave Land-s & Fillbach Brothers-s/a						3.50

WE STAND ON GUARD
Image Comics: Jul, 2015 - No. 6, Dec, 2015 ($2.99, limited series)

	GD 2.0	VG 4.0	FN 6.0	VF 8.0	VF/NM 9.0	NM- 9.2
1-U.S. invasion of Canada; Vaughan-s/Skroce-a						5.00
2-6						3.00

WEST COAST AVENGERS
Marvel Comics Group: Sept, 1984 - No. 4, Dec, 1984 (lim. series, Mando paper)

	GD 2.0	VG 4.0	FN 6.0	VF 8.0	VF/NM 9.0	NM- 9.2
1-Origin & 1st app. W.C. Avengers (Hawkeye, Iron Man, Mockingbird & Tigra)	1	3	4	6	8	10
2-4						5.00

WEST COAST AVENGERS (Becomes Avengers West Coast #48 on)
Marvel Comics Group: Oct, 1985 - No. 47, Aug, 1989

	GD 2.0	VG 4.0	FN 6.0	VF 8.0	VF/NM 9.0	NM- 9.2
V2#1	1	2	3	5	6	8
2-41						4.00
42-47: 42-Byrne-a(p)/scripts begin. 46-Byrne-c; 1st app. Great Lakes Avengers						4.00
Annual 1-3 (1986-1988): 3-Evolutionary War app.						5.00
Annual 4 (1989, $2.00)-Atlantis Attacks; Byrne/Austin-a						5.00

WESTERN ACTION
I. W. Enterprises: No. 7, 1964

	GD 2.0	VG 4.0	FN 6.0	VF 8.0	VF/NM 9.0	NM- 9.2
7-Reprints Cow Puncher #? by Avon	2	4	6	8	11	14

WESTERN ACTION
Atlas/Seaboard Publ.: Feb, 1975

	GD 2.0	VG 4.0	FN 6.0	VF 8.0	VF/NM 9.0	NM- 9.2
1-Kid Cody by Wildey & The Comanche Kid stories; intro. The Renegade	2	4	6	11	16	20

WESTERN ACTION THRILLERS
Dell Publishers: Apr, 1937 (10¢, square binding; 100 pgs.)

	GD 2.0	VG 4.0	FN 6.0	VF 8.0	VF/NM 9.0	NM- 9.2
1-Buffalo Bill, The Texas Kid, Laramie Joe, Two-Gun Thompson, & Wild West Bill app.	129	258	387	826	1413	2000

WESTERN ADVENTURES COMICS (Western Love Trails #7 on)
Ace Magazines: Oct, 1948 - No. 6, Aug, 1949

	GD 2.0	VG 4.0	FN 6.0	VF 8.0	VF/NM 9.0	NM- 9.2
nn(#1)-Sheriff Sal, The Cross-Draw Kid, Sam Bass begin	22	44	66	130	213	295
nn(#2)(12/48)	14	28	42	78	112	145
nn(#3)(2/49)-Used in **SOTI**, pgs. 30,31	14	28	42	80	115	150
4-6	12	24	36	67	94	120

WESTERN BANDITS
Avon Periodicals: 1952 (Painted-c)

	GD 2.0	VG 4.0	FN 6.0	VF 8.0	VF/NM 9.0	NM- 9.2
1-Butch Cassidy, The Daltons by Larsen; Kinstler-a; c-part-r/paperback Avon Western Novel #1	20	40	60	114	182	250

WESTERN BANDIT TRAILS (See Approved Comics)
St. John Publishing Co.: Jan, 1949 - No. 3, July, 1949

	GD 2.0	VG 4.0	FN 6.0	VF 8.0	VF/NM 9.0	NM- 9.2
1-Tuska-a; Baker-c; Blue Monk, Ventrilo app.	36	72	108	211	343	475
2-Baker-c	30	60	90	177	289	400
3-Baker-c/a; Tuska-a	34	68	102	199	325	450

WESTERN COMICS (See Super DC Giant #15)
National Per. Publ: Jan-Feb, 1948 - No. 85, Jan-Feb, 1961 (1-27: 52pgs.)

	GD 2.0	VG 4.0	FN 6.0	VF 8.0	VF/NM 9.0	NM- 9.2
1-Wyoming Kid & his horse Racer, The Vigilante in "Jesse James Rides Again" (Meskin-a), Cowboy Marshal, Rodeo Rick begin	77	154	231	493	847	1200
2	36	72	108	211	343	475
3,4-Last Vigilante	32	64	96	188	307	425
5-Nighthawk & his horse Nightwind begin (not in #6); Captain Tootsie by Beck	28	56	84	165	270	375
6,7,9,10	21	42	63	122	199	275
8-Origin Wyoming Kid; 2 pg. pin-ups of rodeo queens	34	68	102	199	325	450
11-20	18	36	54	103	162	220
21-40: 24-Starr-a. 27-Last 52 pgs. 28-Flag-c	14	28	42	82	121	160
41,42,44-49: 49-Last precode issue (2/55)	14	28	42	80	115	150
43-Pow Wow Smith begins, ends #85	14	28	42	81	118	155

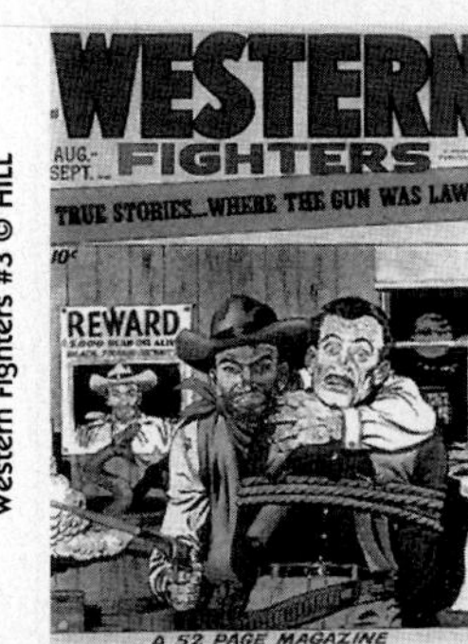

Western Fighters #3 © HILL

Western Hearts #2 © STD

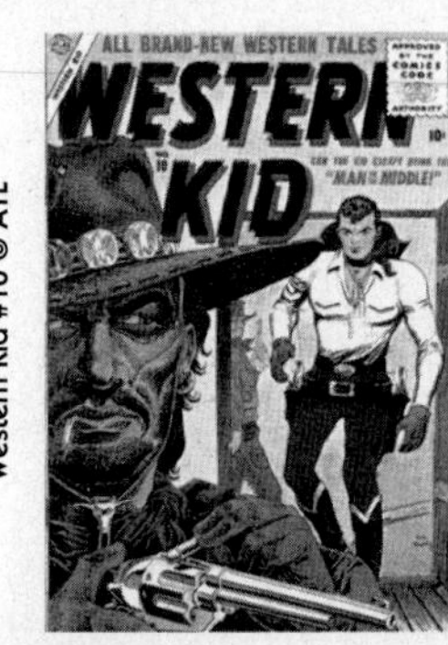

ALL BRAND-NEW WESTERN TALES
WESTERN
KID
10¢

Western Kid #10 © ATL

	GD 2.0	VG 4.0	FN 6.0	VF 8.0	VF/NM 9.0	NM- 9.2
50-60	12	24	36	67	94	120
61-85-Last Wyoming Kid. 77-Origin Matt Savage Trail Boss. 82-1st app. Fleetfoot, Pow Wow's girlfriend	10	20	30	56	76	95

NOTE: ***G. Kane, Infantino*** *art in most.* ***Meskin*** *a-1-4.* ***Moreira*** *a-28-39.* ***Post*** *a-3-5.*

WESTERN CRIME BUSTERS
Trojan Magazines: Sept, 1950 - No. 10, Mar-Apr, 1952

	GD 2.0	VG 4.0	FN 6.0	VF 8.0	VF/NM 9.0	NM- 9.2
1-Six-Gun Smith, Wilma West, K-Bar-Kate, & Fighting Bob Dale begin; headlight-a	36	72	108	216	351	485
2	19	38	57	111	176	240
3-5: 3-Myron Fass-c	18	36	54	105	165	225
6-Wood-a	32	64	96	188	307	425
7-Six-Gun Smith by Wood	32	64	96	188	307	425
8	18	36	54	105	165	225
9-Tex Gordon & Wilma West by Wood; Lariat Lucy app.	32	64	96	188	307	425
10-Wood-a	29	58	87	172	281	390

WESTERN CRIME CASES (Formerly Indian Warriors #7,8; becomes The Outlaws #10 on)
Star Publications: No. 9, Dec, 1951

	GD 2.0	VG 4.0	FN 6.0	VF 8.0	VF/NM 9.0	NM- 9.2
9-White Rider & Super Horse; L. B. Cole-c	22	44	66	132	216	300

WESTERNER, THE (Wild Bill Pecos)
"Wanted" Comic Group/Toytown/Patches: No. 14, June, 1948 - No. 41, Dec, 1951 (#14-31: 52 pgs.)

	GD 2.0	VG 4.0	FN 6.0	VF 8.0	VF/NM 9.0	NM- 9.2
14	15	30	45	85	130	175
15-17,19-21: 19-Meskin-a	9	18	27	52	69	85
18,22-25-Krigstein-a	11	22	33	60	83	105
26(4/50)-Origin & 1st app. Calamity Kate, series ends #32; Krigstein-a	14	28	42	78	112	145
27-Krigstein-a(2)	13	26	39	74	105	135
28-41: 33-Quest app. 37-Lobo, the Wolf Boy begins	8	16	24	40	50	60

NOTE: ***Mort Lawrence*** *a-20-27, 29, 37, 39; c-19, 22-24, 26, 27.* ***Leav*** *c-14-18, 20, 31.* ***Syd Shores*** *a-39; c-34, 35, 37-41.*

WESTERNER, THE
Super Comics: 1964

	GD 2.0	VG 4.0	FN 6.0	VF 8.0	VF/NM 9.0	NM- 9.2
Super Reprint 15-17: 15-r/Oklahoma Kid #? 16-r/Crack West. #65; Severin-c; Crandall-r. 17-r/Blazing Western #2; Severin-c	2	4	6	8	11	14

WESTERN FIGHTERS
Hillman Periodicals/Star Publ.: Apr-May, 1948 - V4#7, Mar-Apr, 1953 (#1-V3#2: 52 pgs.)

	GD 2.0	VG 4.0	FN 6.0	VF 8.0	VF/NM 9.0	NM- 9.2
V1#1-Simon & Kirby-c	37	74	111	222	361	500
2-Not Kirby-a	14	28	42	82	121	160
3-Fuje-c	13	26	39	72	101	130
4-Krigstein, Ingels, Fuje-a	14	28	42	78	112	145
5,6,8,9,12	10	20	30	58	79	100
7,10-Krigstein-a	12	24	36	67	94	120
11-Williamson/Frazetta-a	31	62	93	182	296	410
V2#1-Krigstein-a	12	24	36	67	94	120
2-12: 4-Berg-a	9	18	27	47	61	75
V3#1-11,V4#1,4-7	8	16	24	44	57	70
12,V4#2,3-Krigstein-a	12	24	36	67	94	120
3-D 1(12/53, 25¢, Star Publ.)-Came w/glasses; L. B. Cole-c	36	72	108	216	351	485

NOTE: ***Kinstlerish*** *a-V2#6, 8, 9, 12; V3#2, 5-7, 11, 12; V4#1(plus cover).* ***McWilliams*** *a-11.* ***Powell*** *a-V2#2.* ***Reinman*** *a-1-12, V4#3.* ***Rowich*** *c-5, 6i.* ***Starr*** *a-5.*

WESTERN FRONTIER
P. L. Publishers: Apr-May, 1951 - No. 7, 1952

	GD 2.0	VG 4.0	FN 6.0	VF 8.0	VF/NM 9.0	NM- 9.2
1	15	30	45	86	133	180
2	10	20	30	54	72	90
3-7	9	18	27	47	61	75

WESTERN GUNFIGHTERS (1st Series) (Apache Kid #11-19)
Atlas Comics (CPS): No. 20, June, 1956 - No. 27, Aug, 1957

	GD 2.0	VG 4.0	FN 6.0	VF 8.0	VF/NM 9.0	NM- 9.2
20	16	32	48	94	147	200
21-Crandall-a	16	32	48	94	147	200
22-Wood & Powell-a	21	42	63	126	206	285
23,24: 23-Williamson-a. 24-Toth-a	16	32	48	94	147	200
25-27	14	28	42	78	112	145

NOTE: ***Berg*** *a-20.* ***Colan*** *a-20, 26, 27.* ***Crandall*** *a-21.* ***Heath*** *a-25.* ***Maneely*** *a-24, 25; c-22, 23, 25.* ***Morisi*** *a-24.* ***Morrow*** *a-26.* ***Pakula*** *a-23.* ***Severin*** *c-20, 27.* ***Torres*** *a-26.* ***Woodbridge*** *a-27.*

WESTERN GUNFIGHTERS (2nd Series)
Marvel Comics Group: Aug, 1970 - No. 33, Nov, 1975 (#1-6: 25¢, 68 pgs.)

	GD 2.0	VG 4.0	FN 6.0	VF 8.0	VF/NM 9.0	NM- 9.2
1-Ghost Rider begins; Fort Rango, Renegades & Gunhawk app.	6	12	18	38	69	100
2,3,5,6: 2-Origin Nightwind (Apache Kid's horse)	3	6	9	21	33	45
4-Barry Smith-a	4	8	12	23	37	50
7-(52 pgs) Origin Ghost Rider retold	3	6	9	19	30	40
8-13: 10-Origin Black Rider. 12-Origin Matt Slade	3	6	9	14	20	25
14-Steranko-c	3	6	9	16	24	32
15-20	2	4	6	10	14	18
21-33	2	4	6	9	13	16

NOTE: ***Baker*** *r-2, 3.* ***Colan*** *r-2.* ***Drucker*** *r-3.* ***Everett*** *a-6i.* ***G. Kane*** *c-29, 31.* ***Kirby*** *a-1p(r), 5, 10-12; c-19, 21.* ***Kubert*** *r-2.* ***Maneely*** *r-2, 10.* ***Morrow*** *r-29.* ***Severin*** *c-10.* ***Shores*** *a-3, 4.* ***Barry Smith*** *a-4.* ***Steranko*** *c-14.* ***Sutton*** *a-1, 2i, 5, 4.* ***Torres*** *r-26('57).* ***Wildey*** *r-8, 9.* ***Williamson*** *r-2, 18.* ***Woodbridge*** *r-27('57). Renegades in #4, 5; Ghost Rider in #1-7.*

WESTERN HEARTS
Standard Comics: Dec, 1949 - No. 10, Mar, 1952 (All photo-c)

	GD 2.0	VG 4.0	FN 6.0	VF 8.0	VF/NM 9.0	NM- 9.2
1-Severin-a; Whip Wilson & Reno Browne photo-c	23	46	69	136	223	310
2-Beverly Tyler & Jerome Courtland photo-c from movie "Palomino"; Williamson/Frazetta-a (2 pgs.)	23	46	69	136	223	310
3-Rex Allen photo-c	14	28	42	80	115	150
4-7,10: 4-Severin & Elder, Al Carreno-a. 5-Ray Milland & Hedy Lamarr photo-c from movie "Copper Canyon". 6-Fred MacMurray & Irene Dunn photo-c from movie "Never a Dull Moment". 7-Jock Mahoney photo-c. 10-Bill Williams & Jane Nigh photo-c	14	28	42	78	112	145
8-Randolph Scott & Janis Carter photo-c from "Santa Fe"; Severin & Elder-a	14	28	42	80	115	150
9-Whip Wilson & Reno Browne photo-c; Severin & Elder-a	15	30	45	83	124	165

WESTERN HERO (Wow Comics #1-69; Real Western Hero #70-75)
Fawcett Publications: No. 76, Mar, 1949 - No. 112, Mar, 1952

	GD 2.0	VG 4.0	FN 6.0	VF 8.0	VF/NM 9.0	NM- 9.2
76(#1, 52 pgs.)-Tom Mix, Hopalong Cassidy, Monte Hale, Gabby Hayes, Young Falcon (ends #78,80), & Big Bow and Little Arrow (ends #102,105) begin; painted-c begin	16	32	48	94	147	200
77 (52 pgs.)	11	22	33	64	90	115
78,80-82 (52 pgs.): 81-Capt. Tootsie by Beck	11	22	33	60	83	105
79,83 (36 pgs.): 83-Last painted-c	10	20	30	54	72	90
84-86,88-90 (52 pgs.): 84-Photo-c begin, end #112. 86-Last Hopalong Cassidy	10	20	30	53	76	95
87,91,95,99 (36 pgs.): 87-Bill Boyd begins, ends #95	9	18	27	50	65	80
92-94,96-98,101 (52 pgs.): 96-Tex Ritter begins. 101-Red Eagle app.	9	18	27	52	69	85
100 (52 pgs.)	10	20	30	56	76	95
102-111: 102-Begin 36 pg. issues	9	18	27	50	65	80
112-Last issue	9	18	27	52	69	85

NOTE: *1/2 to 1 pg. Rocky Lane (Carnation) in 80-83, 86, 88, 97. Photo covers feature Hopalong Cassidy #84, 86, 89; Tom Mix #85, 87, 90, 92, 94, 97; Monte Hale #88, 91, 93, 95, 98, 100, 104, 107, 110; Tex Ritter #96, 99, 101, 105, 108, 111; Gabby Hayes #103.*

WESTERN KID (1st Series)
Atlas Comics (CPC): Dec, 1954 - No. 17, Aug, 1957

	GD 2.0	VG 4.0	FN 6.0	VF 8.0	VF/NM 9.0	NM- 9.2
1-Origin; The Western Kid (Tex Dawson), his stallion Whirlwind & dog Lightning begin	23	46	69	136	223	310
2 (2/55)-Last pre-code	14	28	42	82	121	160
3-8	13	26	39	72	101	130
9,10-Williamson-a in both (4 pgs. each)	13	26	39	74	105	135
11-17	11	22	33	62	86	110

NOTE: ***Ayers*** *a-6, 7.* ***Heck*** *a-3.* ***Maneely*** *c-2-7, 10, 13-15.* ***Romita*** *a-1-17; c-1, 12.* ***Severin*** *c-11, 16, 17.*

WESTERN KID, THE (2nd Series)
Marvel Comics Group: Dec, 1971 - No. 5, Aug, 1972 (All 20¢ issues)

	GD 2.0	VG 4.0	FN 6.0	VF 8.0	VF/NM 9.0	NM- 9.2
1-Reprints; Romita-c/a(3)	3	6	9	17	26	35
2,4,5: 2-Romita-a; Severin-c. 4-Everett-r	2	4	6	13	18	22
3-Williamson-a	3	6	9	14	20	26

WESTERN KILLERS
Fox Feature Syndicate: nn, July?, 1948; No. 60, Sept, 1948 - No. 64, May, 1949; No. 6, July, 1949

	GD 2.0	VG 4.0	FN 6.0	VF 8.0	VF/NM 9.0	NM- 9.2
nn(#59?)(nd, F&J Trading Co.)-Range Busters; formerly Blue Beetle #57?	26	52	78	152	249	345
60 (#1, 9/48)-Extreme violence; lingerie panel	27	54	81	162	266	370
61-Jack Cole, Starr-a	22	44	66	130	213	295
62-64, 6 (#6-exist?)	20	40	60	117	189	260

WESTERN LIFE ROMANCES (My Friend Irma #3 on?)
Marvel Comics (IPP): Dec, 1949 - No. 2, Mar, 1950 (52 pgs.)

	GD 2.0	VG 4.0	FN 6.0	VF 8.0	VF/NM 9.0	NM- 9.2
1-Whip Wilson & Reno Browne photo-c	21	42	63	124	202	280
2-Audie Murphy & Gale Storm photo-c	17	34	51	100	158	215

Western Picture Stories #3 © CM

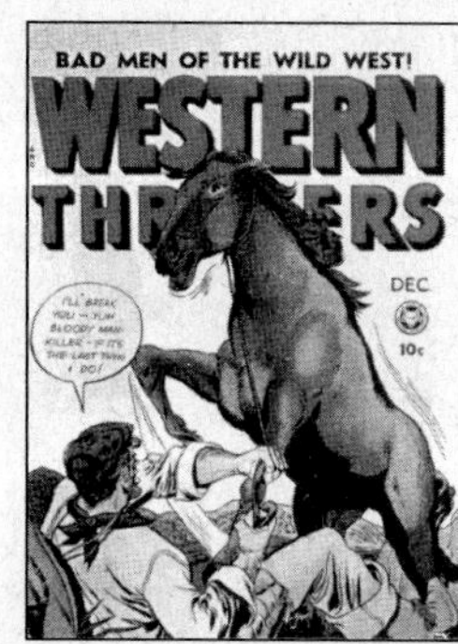

Western Thrillers #3 © FOX

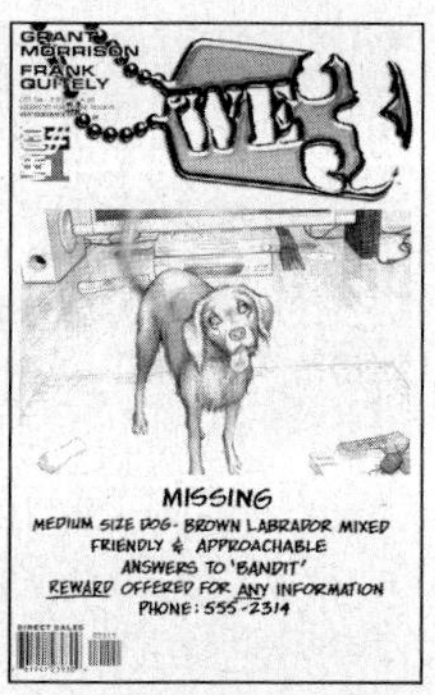

We3 #1 © Morrison & Quitely

GD VG FN VF VF/NM NM-
2.0 4.0 6.0 8.0 9.0 9.2

GD VG FN VF VF/NM NM-
2.0 4.0 6.0 8.0 9.0 9.2

WESTERN LOVE
Prize Publ.: July-Aug, 1949 - No. 5, Mar-Apr, 1950 (All photo-c & 52 pgs.)
1-S&K-a; Randolph Scott photo-c from movie "Canadian Pacific" (see Prize Comics #76)
32 64 96 188 307 425
2,5-S&K-a: 2-Whip Wilson & Reno Browne photo-c. 5-Dale Robertson photo-c 24 48 72 142 234 325
3,4: 3-Pat Williams photo-c 15 30 45 88 137 185
NOTE: ***Meskin & Severin/Elder** a-2-5.*

WESTERN LOVE TRAILS (Formerly Western Adventures)
Ace Magazines (A. A. Wyn): No. 7, Nov, 1949 - No. 9, Mar, 1950
7 12 24 36 67 94 120
8,9 10 20 30 54 72 90

WESTERN MARSHAL (See Steve Donovan...)
Dell Publishing Co.: No. 534, 2-4/54 - No. 640, 7/55 (Based on Ernest Haycox's "Trailtown")
Four Color 534 (#1)-Kinstler-a 6 12 18 38 69 100
Four Color 591 (10/54), 613 (2/55), 640-All Kinstler-a 5 10 15 34 60 85

WESTERN OUTLAWS (Junior Comics #9-16; My Secret Life #22 on)
Fox Feature Syndicate: No. 17, Sept, 1948 - No. 21, May, 1949
17-Kamen-a; Iger shop-a in all; 1 pg. "Death and the Devil Pills" r-in Ghostly Weird #122
34 68 102 199 325 450
18-21 20 40 60 114 182 250

WESTERN OUTLAWS
Atlas Comics (ACI No. 1-14/WPI No. 15-21): Feb, 1954 - No. 21, Aug, 1957
1-Heath, Powell-a; Maneely hanging-c 28 56 84 168 274 380
2 15 30 45 85 130 175
3-10: 7-Violent-a by R.Q. Sale 13 26 39 74 105 135
11,14-Williamson-a in both (6 pgs. each) 14 28 42 80 115 150
12,18,20,21: Severin covers 12 24 36 69 97 125
13,15: 13-Baker-a. 15-Torres-a 13 26 39 74 105 135
16-Williamson text illo 12 24 36 69 97 125
17,19-Crandall-a. 17-Williamson text illo 14 28 42 76 108 140
NOTE: ***Ayers** a-7, 10, 18, 20. **Bolle** a-21. **Colan** a-5, 10, 11, 17. **Drucker** a-11. **Everett** a-9, 10. **Heath** a-1; c-3, 4, 8, 16. **Kubert** a-9p. **Maneely** a-13, 16, 17, 19; c-1, 5, 7, 9, 10, 12, 13. **Morisi** a-18. **Powell** a-3, 16. **Romita** a-7, 13. **Severin** a-8, 16, 19; c-17, 18, 20, 21. **Tuska** a-6, 15.*

WESTERN OUTLAWS & SHERIFFS (Formerly Best Western)
Marvel/Atlas Comics (IPC): No. 60, Dec, 1949 - No. 73, June, 1952
60 (52 pgs.) Photo-c; first Maneely Atlas work 24 48 72 144 237 330
61-65: 61-Photo-c 19 38 57 111 176 240
66-Story contains 5 hangings 20 40 60 114 182 250
67-Cannibalism story 20 40 60 114 182 250
68-72 15 30 45 85 130 175
73-Black Rider story; Everett-c 17 34 51 98 154 210
NOTE: ***Maneely** a-60-62, 67; c-62, 69-73. **Robinson** a-68. **Sinnott** a-70. **Tuska** a-69-71.*

WESTERN PICTURE STORIES (1st Western comic)
Comics Magazine Company: Feb, 1937 - No. 4, June, 1937
1-Will Eisner-a 245 490 735 1568 2684 3800
2-Will Eisner-a 129 258 387 826 1413 2000
3,4: 3-Eisner-a. 4-Caveman Cowboy story 110 220 330 704 1202 1700

WESTERN PICTURE STORIES (See Giant Comics Edition #6, 11)

WESTERN ROMANCES (See Target...)

WESTERN ROUGH RIDERS
Gillmor Magazines No. 1,4 (Stanmor Publ.): Nov, 1954 - No. 4, May, 1955
1 10 20 30 56 76 95
2-4 8 16 24 40 50 60

WESTERN ROUNDUP (See Dell Giants & Fox Giants)

WESTERN SERENADE
DC Comics: May/June, 1949
nn - Ashcan comic, not distributed to newsstands, only for in-house use (no known sales)

WESTERN TALES (Formerly Witches...)
Harvey Publications: No. 31, Oct, 1955 - No. 33, July-Sept, 1956
31,32-All S&K-a; Davy Crockett app. in each 15 30 45 86 133 180
33-S&K-a; Jim Bowie app. 15 30 45 84 127 170
NOTE: *#32 & 33 contain Boy's Ranch reprints. **Kirby** c-31.*

WESTERN TALES OF BLACK RIDER (Formerly Black Rider; Gunsmoke Western #32 on)
Atlas Comics (CPS): No. 28, May, 1955 - No. 31, Nov, 1955
28 (#1): The Spider (a villain) dies 23 46 69 136 223 310
29-31 17 34 51 98 154 210
NOTE: ***Lawrence** a-30. **Maneely** c-28-30. **Severin** a-28. **Shores** c-31.*

WESTERN TEAM-UP
Marvel Comics Group: Nov, 1973 (20¢)
1-Origin & 1st app. The Dakota Kid; Rawhide Kid-r; Gunsmoke Kid-r by Jack Davis
3 6 9 21 33 45

WESTERN THRILLERS (My Past Confessions #7 on)
Fox Feature Syndicate/M.S. Distr. No. 52: Aug, 1948 - No. 6, June, 1949; No. 52, 1954?
1- "Velvet Rose" (Kamenish-a); "Two-Gun Sal", "Striker Sisters" (all women outlaws issue); Brodsky-c 60 120 180 381 653 925
2 28 56 84 165 270 375
3-6: 4,5-Bakerish-a; 5-Butch Cassidy app. 21 42 63 124 202 280
52-(Reprint, M.S. Dist.)-1954? No date given (becomes My Love Secret #53)
10 20 30 54 72 90

WESTERN THRILLERS (Cowboy Action #5 on)
Atlas Comics (ACI): Nov, 1954 - No. 4, Feb, 1955 (All-r/Western Outlaws & Sheriffs)
1 20 40 60 114 182 250
2-4 12 24 36 69 97 125
NOTE: ***Heath** c-3. **Maneely** a-1; c-2. **Powell** a-4. **Robinson** a-4. **Romita** c-4. **Tuska** a-2.*

WESTERN TRAILS (Ringo Kid Starring in...)
Atlas Comics (SAI): May, 1957 - No. 2, July, 1957
1-Ringo Kid app.; Severin-c 16 32 48 92 144 195
2-Severin-c 11 22 33 62 86 110
NOTE: ***Bolle** a-1, 2. **Maneely** a-1, 2. **Severin** c-1, 2.*

WESTERN TRUE CRIME (Becomes My Confessions)
Fox Feature Syndicate: No. 15, Aug, 1948 - No. 6, June, 1949
15(#1)-Kamen-a; formerly Zoot #14 (5/48)? 32 64 96 192 314 435
16(#2)-Kamenish-a; headlight panels, violence 23 46 69 138 227 315
3-Kamen-a 25 50 75 147 241 335
4-6: 4-Johnny Craig-a 15 30 45 90 140 190

WESTERN WINNERS (Formerly All-Western Winners; becomes Black Rider #8 on & Romance Tales #7 on?)
Marvel Comics (CDS): No. 5, June, 1949 - No. 7, Dec, 1949
5-Two-Gun Kid, Kid Colt, Black Rider; Shores-c 32 64 96 192 314 435
6-Two-Gun Kid, Black Rider, Heath Kid Colt story; Captain Tootsie by C.C. Beck
27 54 81 158 259 360
7-Randolph Scott Photo-c w/true stories about the West
27 54 81 158 259 360

WEST OF THE PECOS (See Zane Grey, 4-Color #222)

WESTWARD HO, THE WAGONS (Disney)(Also see Classic Comics #14)
Dell Publishing Co.: No. 738, Sept, 1956 (Movie)
Four Color 738-Fess Parker photo-c 8 16 24 54 102 150

WE3
DC Comics (Vertigo): Oct, 2004 - No. 3, May, 2005 ($2.95, limited series)
1-3-Domestic animal cyborgs: Grant Morrison-s/Frank Quitely-a 3.00
TPB (2005, $12.99) r/series 13.00

WETWORKS (See WildC.A.T.S: Covert Action Teams #2)
Image Comics (WildStorm): June, 1994 - No. 43, Aug, 1998 ($1.95/$2.50)
1-"July" on-c; gatefold wraparound-c; Portacio/Williams-c/a 4.00
1-Chicago Comicon edition 6.00
1-(2/98, $4.95) "3-D Edition" w/glasses 5.00
2-4 3.00
2-Alternate Portacio-c, see Deathblow #5 6.00
5-7,9-24: 5-($2.50). 13-Portacio-c. 16,17-Fire From Heaven Pts. 4 & 11 3.00
8 ($1.95)-Newstand, Wildstorm Rising Pt. 7 3.00
8 ($2.50)-Direct Market, Wildstorm Rising Pt. 7 3.00
25-($3.95) 4.00
26-43: 32-Variant-c by Pat Lee & Charest. 39,40-Stormwatch app. 42-Gen 13 app. 3.00
Sourcebook 1 (10/94, $2.50)-Text & illustrations (no comics) 3.00
Voyager Pack (8/97, $3.50)- #32 w/Phantom Guard preview 4.00

WETWORKS
DC Comics (WildStorm): Nov, 2006 - No. 15, Jan, 2008 ($2.99)
1-15: 1-Carey-s/Portacio-a; two covers by Portacio and Van Sciver. 2-Golden var-c 3-Pearson var-c. 4-Powell var-c 3.00
...: Armageddon 1 (1/08, $2.99) Gage-s/Badeaux-a 3.00
... Book One (2007, $14.99) r/#1-5 and stories from Eye of the storm Annual and Coup D'Etat Afterword 15.00
... Book Two (2008, $14.99) r/#6-9,13-15 15.00
...: Mutations 1 (11/10, $3.99) Grevioux & Long-s/Gopez-a 4.00

WETWORKS/VAMPIRELLA (See Vampirella/Wetworks)

What If? #3 © MAR

What If? #42 © MAR

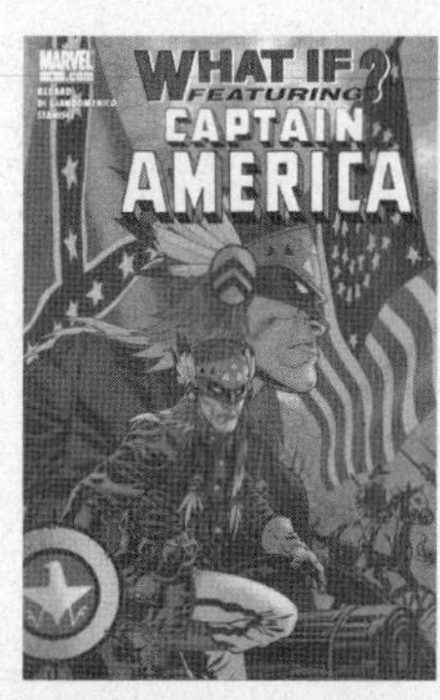

What If? (2006) Captain America #1 © MAR

GD 2.0 VG 4.0 FN 6.0 VF 8.0 VF/NM 9.0 NM- 9.2

Image Comics (WildStorm Productions): July, 1997 ($2.95, one-shot)

1-Gil Kane-c 4.00

WHACK (Satire)
St. John Publishing Co. (Jubilee Publ.): Oct, 1953 - No. 3, May, 1954

1-(3-D, 25¢)-Kubert-a; Maurer-c; came w/glasses 25 50 75 147 241 335
2,3-Kubert-a in each. 2-Bing Crosby on-c; Mighty Mouse & Steve Canyon parodies. 3-Li'l Orphan Annie parody; Maurer-c 15 30 45 85 130 175

WHACKY (See Wacky)

WHA...HUH?
Marvel Comics: 2005 ($3.99, one-shot)

1-Humor spoofs of Marvel characters; Mahfood-a/c; Bendis, Stan Lee and others-s 4.00

WHAM COMICS (See Super Spy)
Centaur Publications: Nov, 1940 - No. 2, Dec, 1940

1-The Sparkler, The Phantom Rider, Craig Carter and his Magic Ring, Detecto, Copper Slug, Speed Silvers by Gustavson, Speed Centaur & Jon Linton (s/f) begin 194 388 582 1242 2121 3000
2-Origin Blue Fire & Solarman; The Buzzard app. 155 310 465 992 1696 2400

WHAM-O GIANT COMICS
Wham-O Mfg. Co. : April, 1967 (98¢, newspaper size, one-shot)(Six issue subscription was advertised)

1-Radian & Goody Bumpkin by Wood; 1 pg. Stanley-a; Fine, Tufts-a; flying saucer reports; wraparound-c 9 18 27 62 126 190

WHATEVER HAPPENED TO BARON VON SHOCK?
Image Comics: May, 2010 - No. 4, Nov, 2010 ($3.99, unfinished limited series)

1-4-Rob Zombie-s/Donny Hadiwidjaja-a 4.00

WHAT IF? (1st Series) (What If? Featuring... #13 & #?-33) (Also see Hero Initiative)
Marvel Comics Group: Feb, 1977 - No. 47, Oct, 1984; June, 1988 (All 52 pgs.)

1-Brief origin Spider-Man, Fantastic Four 4 8 12 25 40 55
2-Origin The Hulk retold 2 4 6 10 14 18
3-5: 3-Avengers. 4-Invaders. 5-Capt. America 2 4 6 8 11 14
6-9,13,17: 7-Betty Brant as Spider-Girl. 8-Daredevil; Spidey parody. 9-Origins Venus, Marvel Boy, Human Robot, 3-D Man. 13-Conan app.; John Buscema-c/a(p). 17-Ghost Rider & Son of Satan app. 2 3 4 6 8 10
10-(8/78) What if Jane Foster was Thor 4 8 12 28 47 65
11,12,14-16: 11-Marvel Bullpen as F.F. 1 2 3 5 6 8
18-26,29: 18-Dr. Strange. 19-Spider-Man. 22-Origin Dr. Doom retold 1 2 3 4 5 7
27-X-Men app.; Miller-c 3 6 9 14 20 26
28-Daredevil by Miller; Ghost Rider app. 2 4 6 10 16 20
30-"What If...Spider-Man's Clone Had Lived?" 2 4 6 8 10 12
31-Begin $1.00-c; featuring Wolverine & the Hulk; X-Men app.; death of Hulk, Wolverine & Magneto 3 6 9 17 26 35
32-34,36-47: 32,36-Byrne-a. 34-Marvel crew each draw themselves. 37-Old X-Men & Silver Surfer app. 39-Thor battles Conan 5.00
35-What if Elektra had lived?; Miller/Austin-a. 2 4 6 8 10 12
Special 1 ($1.50, 6/88)-Iron Man, F.F., Thor app. 5.00
... Classic Vol. 1 TPB (2004, $24.99) r/#1-6; checklist 25.00
... Classic Vol. 2 TPB (2005, $24.99) r/#7-12 25.00
... Classic Vol. 3 TPB (2006, $24.99) r/#14,15,17-20 25.00
... Classic Vol. 4 TPB (2007, $24.99) r/#21-26; checklist of all What If? series/issues 25.00

NOTE: ***Austin*** *a-27p, 32i, 34, 35i; c-35i, 36i.* ***J. Buscema*** *a-13p, 15p; c-10, 13p, 23p.* ***Byrne*** *a-32i, 36; c-36p.* ***Colan*** *a-21p; c-17p, 18p, 21p.* ***Ditko*** *a-35, Special 1.* ***Golden*** *c-29, 40-42.* ***Guice*** *a-40p.* ***Gil Kane*** *a-3p, 24p; c(p)-2-4, 7, 8.* ***Kirby*** *a-11p; c-9p, 11p.* ***Layton*** *a-32i, 33i; c-30, 32p, 33i, 34.* ***Mignola*** *c-39i.* ***Miller*** *a-28p, 32i, 34(1), 35p; c-27, 28p.* ***Mooney*** *a-8i, 30i.* ***Perez*** *a-15p.* ***Robbins*** *a-4p.* ***Sienkiewicz*** *c-43-46.* ***Simonson*** *a-15p, 32i.* ***Starlin*** *a-32i.* ***Stevens*** *a-8, 16i(part).* ***Sutton*** *a-2i, 18p, 28.* ***Tuska*** *a-5p.* ***Weiss*** *a-37p.*

WHAT IF...? (2nd Series)
Marvel Comics: V2#1, July, 1989 - No. 114, Nov, 1998 ($1.25/$1.50)

V2#1-...The Avengers Had Lost the Evolutionary War 5.00
2-5: 2-Daredevil, Punisher app. 4.00
6-X-Men app. 5.00
7-Wolverine app.; Liefeld-c/a(1st on Wolvie?) 6.00
8,10,11,13-15,17-30: 10-Punisher app. 11-Fantastic Four app.; McFarlane-c(i).13-Prof. X; Jim Lee-c. 14-Capt. Marvel; Lim/Austin-c.15-F.F.; Capullo-c/a(p). 17-Spider-Man/Kraven. 18-F.F. 19-Vision. 20,21-Spider-Man. 22-Silver Surfer by Lim/Austin-c/a 23-X-Men. 24-Wolverine; Punisher app. 25-(52 pgs.)-Wolverine app. 26-Punisher app. 27-Namor/F.F. 28,29-Capt. America. 29-Swipes cover to Avengers #4. 30-(52 pgs.)-F.F. 4.00
9,12-X-Men 5.00
16-Wolverine battles Conan; Red Sonja app.; X-Men cameo 5.00
31-40,42-48: 31-Cosmic Spider-Man & Venom app.; Hobgoblin cameo. 32,33-Phoenix; X-Men app. 35-Fantastic Five (w/Spidey). 36-Avengers vs. Guardians of the Galaxy. 37-Wolverine; Thibert-c(i). 38-Thor; Rogers-p(part). 40-Storm; X-Men app. 42-Spider-Man. 43-Wolverine. 44-Venom/Punisher. 45-Ghost Rider. 46-Cable. 47-Magneto 3.00
41,50: 41-(52 pgs.)-Avengers vs. Galactus. 50-(52 pgs.)-Foil embossed-c; "What If Hulk Had Killed Wolverine" 1 2 3 5 6 8
49-Infinity Gauntlet w/Silver Surfer & Thanos 3 6 9 16 23 30
51-(7/93) "What If the Punisher Became Captain America" (see it happen in 2007's Punisher War Journal #6-10) 6.00
52-99,101-103: 52-Dr. Doom. 54-Death's Head. 57-Punisher as Shield. 58-"What if Punisher Had Killed Spider-Man" w/cover similar to Amazing S-M #129. 59-...Wolverine led Alpha Flight. 60-X-Men Wedding Album. 61-Bound-in card sheet. 61,86,88-Spider-Man. 74,77,81,84,85-X-Men. 76-Last app. Watcher in title. 78-Bisley-c. 80-Hulk. 87-Sabretooth. 89-Fantastic Four. 90-Cyclops & Havok. 91-The Hulk. 93-Wolverine. 94-Juggernaut. 95-Ghost Rider 3.00
100-($2.99, double-sized) Gambit and Rogue, Fantastic Four 1 2 3 5 6 8
104-Silver Surfer, Thanos vs. Impossible Man 1 2 3 5 6 8
105-Spider-Girl (Peter Parker's daughter) debut; Sienkiewicz-a; (Betty Brant also app. as a Spider-Girl in What If? (1st series) #7) 4 8 12 23 37 50
106,107,109-114: 106-Gambit. 111-Wolverine. 114-Secret Wars 3.00
108-Avengers vs. Carnage 2 4 6 9 12 15
#(-1) Flashback (7/97) 3.00

WHAT IF...? (one-shots)
Marvel Comics: Feb, 2005 ($2.99)

... Aunt May Had Died Instead of Uncle Ben? - Brubaker-s/DiVito-a/Brase-c 3.00
... Dr. Doom Had Become The Thing? - Karl Kesel-s/Paul Smith-a/c 3.00
... General Ross Had Become The Hulk? - Peter David-s/Pat Olliffe-a/Gary Frank-c 3.00
... Jessica Jones Had Joined The Avengers? - Bendis-s/Gaydos-a/McNiven-c 3.00
... Karen Page Had Lived? - Bendis-s/Lark-a/c 3.00
... Magneto and Professor X Had Formed The X-Men Together? - Claremont-s/Raney-a 3.00
What If...: Why Not? TPB (2005, $16.99) r/one-shots 17.00

WHAT IF... (one-shots)
Marvel Comics: Feb, 2006 ($2.99)

... : Captain America - Fought in the Civil War?; Bedard-s/Di Giandomenico-a 3.00
... : Daredevil - The Devil Who Dares; Daredevil in feudal Japan; Veitch-s/Edwards-a 3.00
... : Fantastic Four - Were Cosmonauts?; Marshall Rogers-a/c; Mike Carey-s 3.00
... : Submariner - Grew Up on Land?; Pak-s/Lopez-a 3.00
... : Thor - Was the Herald of Galactus?; Kirkman-s/Oeming-a/c 3.00
... : Wolverine - In the Prohibition Era; Way-s/Proctor-a/Harris-c 3.00
What If: Mirror Mirror TPB (2006, $16.99) r/one-shots; design pages and Rogers sketches 17.00

WHAT IF ?... (one-shots altering recent Marvel "event" series)
Marvel Comics: Jan, 2007 - Feb, 2007 ($3.99)

... Avengers Disassembled; Parker-s/Lopresti-a/c 4.00
... Spider-Man The Other; Peter David-s/Khoi Pham-a; Venom app. 4.00
... Wolverine Enemy of the State; Robinson-s/DiGiandomenico-a/Alexander-c 4.00
... X-Men Age of Apocalypse; Remeder-s/Wilkins-a/Djurdjevic-c 4.00
... X-Men Deadly Genesis; Hine-s/Yardin-a/c 4.00
What If?: Event Horizon TPB (2007, $16.99) r/one-shots; design pages and cover sketches 17.00

WHAT IF ?... (one-shots altering recent Marvel "event" series)
Marvel Comics: Dec, 2007 - Feb, 2008 ($3.99)

... Annihilation; Nova, Iron Man, Captain America app. 2 4 6 9 12 15
... Civil War; 2 covers by Silvestri & Djurdjevic 1 2 3 5 6 8
... Planet Hulk; Pagulayan-c; Kirk, Sandoval & Hembeck-a 10.00
... Spider-Man vs. Wolverine; Romita Jr.-c; Henry-a; Nick Fury app. 6.00
... X-Men - Rise and Fall of the Shi'ar Empire; Coipel-c 4.00
What If?: Civil War TPB (2008, $16.99) r/one-shots; design pages and cover sketches 17.00

WHAT IF ?... (one-shots altering recent Marvel "event" series)
Marvel Comics: Feb, 2009 ($3.99) (Serialized back-up Runaways story in each issue)

... Fallen Son; if Iron Man had died instead of Capt. America; McGuinness-c 4.00
... House of M; if the Scarlet Witch had said "No more powers" instead; Cheung-c 4.00
... Newer Fantastic Four; team of Spider-Man, Hulk, Iron Man and Wolverine 4.00
... Secret Wars; if Doctor Doom had kept the Beyonder's power; origin re-told 4.00
... Spider-Man Back in Black; if Mary Jane had been shot instead of Aunt May 4.00

WHAT IF ?... (one-shots)
Marvel Comics: Feb, 2010 ($3.99)

... Astonishing X-Men; if Ord resurrected Jean Grey; Campbell-c 4.00
... Daredevil vs. Elektra; Kayanan-a; Klaus Janson-c swipe of Daredevil #168 4.00
... Secret Invasion; if the Skrulls succeeded; Yu-c 4.00
... Spider-Man: House of M; if Gwen Stacy survived the House of M; Dodson-c 4.00
... World War Hulk; if the heroes lost the war; Romita Jr.-c 4.00

WHAT IF ?... (one-shots) (4 part Deadpool back-up story in all but #200)

What If? #200 © MAR

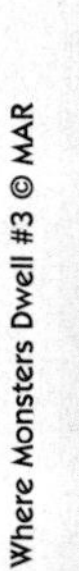

Where Monsters Dwell #3 © MAR

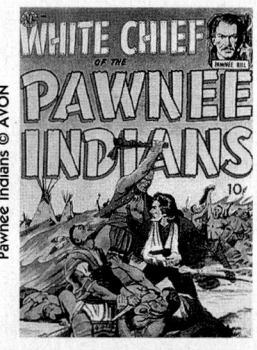

White Chief of the Pawnee Indians © AVON

	GD 2.0	VG 4.0	FN 6.0	VF 8.0	VF/NM 9.0	NM- 9.2

(Also see Venom/Deadpool: What If?)
Marvel Comics: Feb, 2011 ($3.99)

... #200 ($4.99) Siege on cover; if Osborn won the Siege of Asgard; Stan Lee back-up 5.00
... Dark Reign; if Norman Osborn was killed; Tanaka-a/Deodato-c 4.00
... Iron Man: Demon in an Armor; if Tony Stark became Dr. Doom; Nolan-a 4.00
... Spider-Man; if Spider-Man killed Kraven; Jimenez-c 4.00
... Wolverine: Father; if Wolverine raised Daken; Tocchini-a; Yu-a 4.00

WHAT IF ? AGE OF ULTRON
Marvel Comics: Jun, 2014 - No. 5, Jun, 2014 ($3.99, weekly limited series)

1-5: 1-Hank Pym's story. 2-Wolverine, Hulk, Spider-Man, Ghost Rider app. 4.00

WHAT IF ? AVX (Avengers vs. X-Men)
Marvel Comics: Sept, 2013 - No. 4, Sept, 2013 ($3.99, weekly limited series)

1-4-Palmiotti-s/Molina-a; Hope merges with the Phoenix force 4.00

WHAT IF ? INFINITY - ... (one-shots)
Marvel Comics: Dec, 2015 ($3.99)

... Dark Reign; if The Green Goblin stole the Infinity Gauntlet; Williamson-s/Sudzuka-a 4.00
... Guardians of the Galaxy; if The Guardians tried to free Thanos; Copland-a 4.00
... Inhumans; if Black Bolt betrayed Earth; Rossmo-a 4.00
... Thanos; if Thanos joined the Avengers; Henderson-a 4.00
... X-Men; if the X-Men were the sole survivors of Infinity; Norton-a 4.00

'WHAT'S NEW? - THE COLLECTED ADVENTURES OF PHIL & DIXIE'
Palliard Press: Oct, 1991 - No. 2, 1991 ($5.95, mostly color, sq.-bound, 52 pgs.)

1,2-By Phil Foglio 6.00

WHAT THE- -?!
Marvel Comics: Aug, 1988 - No. 26, 1993 ($1.25/$1.50/$2.50, semi-annual #5 on)

1-All contain parodies 4.00
2-24: 3-X-Men parody; Todd McFarlane-a. 5-Punisher/Wolverine parody; Jim Lee-a. 6-Punisher, Wolverine, Alpha Flight. 9-Wolverine. 16-EC back-c parody. 17-Wolverine/Punisher parody. 18-Star Trek parody w/Wolverine. 19-Punisher, Wolverine, Ghost Rider. 21-Weapon X parody. 22-Punisher/Wolverine parody 3.00
25-Summer Special 1 (1993, $2.50)-X-Men parody 4.00
26-Fall Special ($2.50, 68 pgs.)-Spider-Ham 2099-c/story; origin Silver Surfer; Hulk & Doomsday parody; indica reads "Winter Special." 4.00
NOTE: *Austin a-6i.* ***Byrne*** *a-2, 6, 10; c-2, 6-8, 10, 12, 13.* ***Golden*** *a-22.* ***Dale Keown*** *a-8p(8 pgs.).* ***McFarlane*** *a-3.* ***Rogers*** *c-15i, 16p.* ***Severin*** *a-2.* ***Staton*** *a-21p.* ***Williamson*** *a-2i.*

WHEDON THREE WAY, THE
Dark Horse Comics: Sept, 2014 ($1.00, one-shot)

1-Reprints Buffy Season 10 #1, Angel & Faith Season 10 #1, Serenity: Leaves #1 3.00

WHEE COMICS (Also see Gay, Smile & Tickle Comics)
Modern Store Publications: 1955 (7¢, 5x7-1/4", 52 pgs.)

	GD	VG	FN	VF	VF/NM	NM-
1-Funny animal	8	16	24	42	54	65

WHEEDIES (See Panic #11 -EC Comics)

WHEELIE AND THE CHOPPER BUNCH (TV)
Charlton Comics: July, 1975 - No. 7, July, 1976 (Hanna-Barbera)

	GD	VG	FN	VF	VF/NM	NM-
1-3: 1-Byrne text illo (see Nightmare for 1st art); Staton-a. 2-Byrne-a. 2,3-Mike Zeck text illos. 3-Staton-a; Byrne-c/a	3	6	9	17	26	35
4-7-Staton-a	2	4	6	12	16	20

WHEN KNIGHTHOOD WAS IN FLOWER (See The Sword & the Rose, 4-Color #505, 682)

WHEN SCHOOL IS OUT (See Wisco in Promotional Comics section)

WHERE CREATURES ROAM
Marvel Comics Group: July, 1970 - No. 8, Sept, 1971

	GD	VG	FN	VF	VF/NM	NM-
1-Kirby/Ayers-c/a(r)	5	10	15	33	57	80
2-8: 2-5,7,8-Kirby-c/a(r). 6-Kirby-a(r)	4	8	12	22	35	48

NOTE: ***Ditko*** *r-1-6, 7.* ***Heck*** *r-2, 5. All contain pre super-hero reprints.*

WHERE IN THE WORLD IS CARMEN SANDIEGO (TV)
DC Comics: June, 1996 - No. 4, Dec, 1996 ($1.75)

1-4: Adaptation of TV show 3.00

WHERE MONSTERS DWELL
Marvel Comics Group: Jan, 1970 - No. 38, Oct, 1975

	GD	VG	FN	VF	VF/NM	NM-
1-Kirby/Ditko-r; all contain pre super-hero-r	5	10	15	35	63	90
2-5,7-10: 4-Crandall-a(r)	4	8	12	23	37	50
6-(11/70) Reprints Groot's 1st app. in Tales to Astonish #13	5	10	15	33	57	80
11,13-20: 11-Last 15¢ issue. 18,20-Starlin-c	3	6	9	19	30	40
12-Giant issue (52 pgs.)	4	8	12	25	40	55
21-Reprints 1st Fin Fang Foom app.	3	6	9	21	33	45
22-37	3	6	9	16	24	32
38-Williamson-r/World of Suspense #3	3	6	9	17	26	35

NOTE: ***Colan*** *r-12.* ***Ditko*** *a(r)-4, 6, 8, 10, 12, 17-19, 23-25, 37.* ***Kirby*** *r-1-3, 5-16, 18-27, 30-32, 34-36, 38; c-12?* ***Reinman*** *a-3r, 4r, 12r.* ***Severin*** *c-15.*

WHERE MONSTERS DWELL (Secret Wars tie-in)
Marvel Comics: Jul, 2015 - No. 5, Dec, 2015 ($3.99, limited series)

1-5-Garth Ennis-s/Russ Braun-a/Frank Cho-c; The Phantom Eagle app. 4.00

WHERE'S HUDDLES? (TV) (See Fun-In #9)
Gold Key: Jan, 1971 - No. 3, Dec, 1971 (Hanna-Barbera)

	GD	VG	FN	VF	VF/NM	NM-
1	3	6	9	18	28	38
2,3: 3-r/most #1	2	4	6	11	16	20

WHIP WILSON (Movie star) (Formerly Rex Hart; Gunhawk #12 on; see Western Hearts, Western Life Romances, Western Love)
Marvel Comics: No. 9, April, 1950 - No. 11, Sept, 1950 (#9,10: 52 pgs.)

	GD	VG	FN	VF	VF/NM	NM-
9-Photo-c; Whip Wilson & his horse Bullet begin; origin Bullet; issue #23 listed on splash page; cover changed to #9; Maneely-a	49	98	147	309	522	735
10,11: Both have photo-c. 11-36 pgs.; Maneely-a	28	56	84	168	274	380
I.W. Reprint #1(1964)-Kinstler-c; r-Marvel #11	3	6	9	15	22	28

WHIRLWIND COMICS (Also see Cyclone Comics)
Nita Publication: June, 1940 - No. 3, Sept, 1940

	GD	VG	FN	VF	VF/NM	NM-
1-Origin & 1st app. Cyclone; Cyclone-c	300	600	900	2070	3635	5200
2,3: Cyclone-c	174	348	522	1114	1907	2700

WHIRLYBIRDS (TV)
Dell Publishing Co.: No. 1124, Aug, 1960 - No. 1216, Oct-Dec, 1961

	GD	VG	FN	VF	VF/NM	NM-
Four Color 1124 (#1)-Photo-c	7	14	21	49	92	135
Four Color 1216-Photo-c	7	14	21	46	86	125

WHISKEY DICKEL, INTERNATIONAL COWGIRL
Image Comics: Aug, 2003 ($12.95, softcover, B&W)

nn-Mark Ricketts-s/Mike Hawthorne-a; pin-up by various incl. Oeming, Thompson, Mack 13.00

WHISPER (Female Ninja)
Capital Comics: Dec, 1983 - No. 2, 1984 ($1.75, Baxter paper)

1,2: 1-Origin; Golden-c, Special (11/85, $2.50) 4.00

WHISPER (Vol. 2)
First Comics: Jun, 1986 - No. 37, June, 1990 ($1.25/$1.75/$1.95)

1-37 3.00

WHISPER
Boom! Studios: Nov, 2006 ($3.99)

1-Grant-s/Dzialowski-a 4.00

WHISPERS
Image Comics: Jan, 2012 - No. 6, Oct, 2013 ($2.99)

1-6-Joshua Luna-s/a 3.00

WHITE CHIEF OF THE PAWNEE INDIANS
Avon Periodicals: 1951

	GD	VG	FN	VF	VF/NM	NM-
nn-Kit West app.; Kinstler-c	19	38	57	111	176	240

WHITE EAGLE INDIAN CHIEF (See Indian Chief)

WHITE FANG
Disney Comics: 1990 ($5.95, 68 pgs.)

nn-Graphic novel adapting new Disney movie 6.00

WHITE INDIAN
Magazine Enterprises: No. 11, July, 1953 - No. 15, 1954

	GD	VG	FN	VF	VF/NM	NM-
11(A-1 94), 12(A-1 101), 13(A-1 104)-Frazetta-r(Dan Brand) in all from Durango Kid. 11-Powell-c	20	40	60	117	189	260
14(A-1 117), 15(A-1 135)-Check-a; Torres-a-#15	14	28	42	78	112	145

NOTE: *#11 contains reprints from Durango Kid #1-4; #12 from #5, 9, 10, 11; #13 from #7, 12, 13, 16. #14 & 15 contain all new stories.*

WHITEOUT (Also see Queen & Country)
Oni Press: July, 1998 - No. 4, Nov, 1998 ($2.95, B&W, limited series)

1-4: 1-Matt Wagner-c. 2-Mignola-c. 3-Gibbons-c 3.00
TPB (5/99, $10.95) r/#1-4; Miller-c 11.00

WHITEOUT: MELT
Oni Press: Sept, 1999 - No. 4, Feb, 2000 ($2.95, B&W, limited series)

1-4-Greg Rucka-s/Steve Lieber-a 3.00
Whiteout: Melt, The Definitive Edition TPB (9/07, $13.95) r/#1-4; Rucka afterword 14.00

WHITE PRINCESS OF THE JUNGLE (Also see Jungle Adventures & Top Jungle Comics)

White Princess of the Jungle #5 © AVON

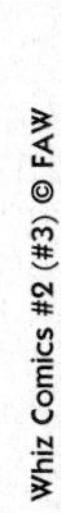
Whiz Comics #2 (#3) © FAW

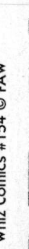

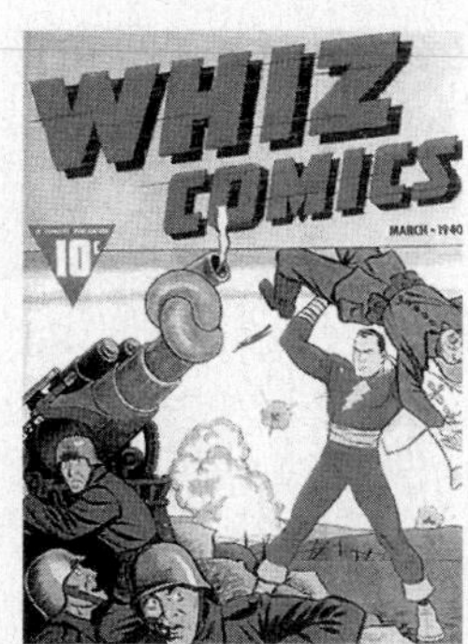

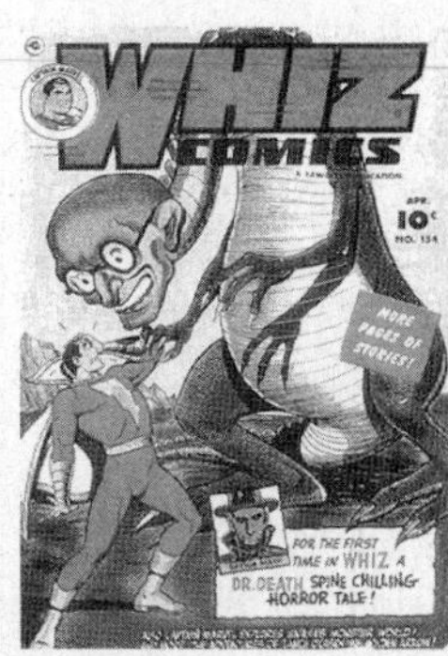

Whiz Comics #154 © FAW

GD VG FN VF VF/NM NM-
2.0 4.0 6.0 8.0 9.0 9.2

Avon Periodicals: July, 1951 - No. 5, Nov, 1952
1-Origin of White Princess (Taanda) & Capt'n Courage (r); Kinstler-c 69 138 207 442 759 1075
2-Reprints origin of Malu, Slave Girl Princess from Avon's Slave Girl Comics #1 w/Malu changed to Zora; Kinstler-c/a(2) 47 94 141 296 498 700
3-Origin Blue Gorilla; Kinstler-c/a 42 84 126 265 445 625
4-Jack Barnum, White Hunter app.; r/Sheena #9 39 78 117 238 392 545
5-Blue Gorilla by McCann?; Kinstler inside-c; Fawcette/Alascia-a(3) 40 80 120 246 411 575

WHITE RIDER AND SUPER HORSE (Formerly Humdinger V2#2; Indian Warriors #7 on; also see Blue Bolt #1, 4Most & Western Crime Cases)
Novelty-Star Publications/Accepted Publ.: No. 4, 9/50 - No. 6, 3/51
4-6-Adapts "The Last of the Mohicans". 4(#1)-(9/50)-Says #11 on inside 16 32 48 94 147 200
Accepted Reprint #5(r/#5),6 (nd); L.B. Cole-c 9 18 27 50 65 80
NOTE: *All have* **L. B. Cole** *covers.*

WHITE SUITS, THE
Dark Horse Comics: Feb, 2014 - No. 4, Jul, 2014 ($3.99, limited series)
1-4-Barbiere-s/Cypress-a 4.00

WHITE TIGER
Marvel Comics: Jan, 2007 - No. 6, Nov, 2007 ($2.99, limited series)
1-6: 1-David Mack-c; Pierce & Liebe-s/Briones-a; Spider-Man & Black Widow app. 3.00
...: A Hero's Compulsion SC (2007,$14.99) r/#1-6; re-cap art and profile page 15.00

WHITE WILDERNESS (Disney)
Dell Publishing Co.: No. 943, Oct, 1958
Four Color 943-Movie 6 12 18 37 66 95

WHITMAN COMIC BOOK, A
Whitman Publishing Co.: Sept., 1962 (136 pgs.; 7-3/4x5-3/4; hardcover) (B&W)
1-3,5,7: 1-Yogi Bear. 2-Huckleberry Hound. 3-Mr. Jinks and Pixie & Dixie. 5-Augie Doggie & Loopy de Loop. 7-Bugs Bunny-r from #47,51,53,54 & 55 6 12 18 38 69 100
4,6: 4-The Flintstones. 6-Snooper & Blabber Fearless Detectives/Quick Draw McGraw of the Wild West 6 12 18 41 76 110
8-Donald Duck-reprints most of WDC&S #209-213. Includes 5 Barks stories, 1 complete Mickey Mouse serial by Paul Murry & 1 Mickey Mouse serial missing the 1st episode 7 14 21 46 86 125
NOTE: *Hanna-Barbera #1-6(TV), reprints of British tabloid comics. Dell reprints-#7,8.*

WHIZ COMICS (Formerly Flash & Thrill Comics #1)(See 5 Cent Comics)
Fawcett Publications: No. 2, Feb, 1940 - No. 155, June, 1953
1-(nn on cover, #2 inside)-Origin & 1st newsstand app. Captain Marvel (formerly Captain Thunder) by C. C. Beck (created by Bill Parker), Spy Smasher, Golden Arrow, Ibis the Invincible, Dan Dare, Scoop Smith, Sivana, & Lance O'Casey begin 22,500 45,000 67,500 135,000 202,500 270,000
(The only Mint copy sold in 1995 for $176,000 cash)
1-Reprint, oversize 13-1/2x10". **WARNING:** This comic is an exact duplicate reprint (except for dropping "Gangway for Captain Marvel" from-c) of the original except for its size. DC published it in 1974 with a second cover titling it as a Famous First Edition. There have been many reported cases of the outer cover being removed and the interior sold as the original edition. The reprint with the new outer cover removed is practically worthless. See Famous First Edition for value.
2-(3/40, nn on cover, #3 inside); cover to Flash #1 redrawn, pg. 12, panel 4; Spy Smasher reveals I.D. to Eve 811 1622 2433 5920 10,460 15,000
3-(4/40, #3 on-c, #4 inside)-1st app. Beautia 470 940 1410 3431 6066 8700
4-(5/40, #4 on cover, #5 inside)-Brief origin Capt. Marvel retold 389 778 1167 2723 4762 6800
5-Captain Marvel wears button-down flap on splash page only 331 662 993 2317 4059 5800
6-10: 7-Dr. Voodoo begins (by Raboy-#9-22) 265 530 795 1694 2897 4100
11-14: 12-Capt. Marvel does not wear cape 187 374 561 1197 2049 2900
15-Origin Sivana; Dr. Voodoo by Raboy 194 388 582 1242 2121 3000
16-18-Spy Smasher battles Captain Marvel 213 426 639 1363 2332 3300
19-Classic shark-c 200 400 600 1280 2190 3100
20 116 232 348 742 1271 1800
21-(9/41)-Origin & 1st cover app. Lt. Marvels, the 1st team in Fawcett comics. In this issue, Capt. Death similar to Ditko's later Dr. Strange 119 238 357 762 1306 1850
22-24: 23-Only Dr. Voodoo by Tuska 94 188 282 597 1024 1450
25-(12/41)-Captain Nazi jumps from Master Comics #21 to take on Capt. Marvel solo after being beaten by Capt. Marvel/Bulletman team, causing the creation of Capt. Marvel Jr.; 1st app./origin of Capt. Marvel Jr. (part II of trilogy origin by CC. Beck & Mac Raboy); Captain Marvel sends Jr. back to Master #22 to aid Bulletman against Capt. Nazi; origin Old Shazam in text 595 1190 1785 4350 7675 11,000
26-30 65 130 195 416 708 1000
31,32: 32-1st app. The Trolls; Hitler/Mussolini satire by Beck 57 114 171 362 619 875
33-Spy Smasher, Captain Marvel x-over on cover and inside 74 148 222 470 810 1150
34,36-40: 37-The Trolls app. by Swayze 43 86 129 271 461 650
35-Captain Marvel & Spy Smasher-c 65 130 195 416 708 1000
41-50: 42-Classic time travel-c. 43-Spy Smasher, Ibis, Golden Arrow x-over in Capt. Marvel. 44-Flag-c. 47-Origin recap (1 pg.) 39 78 117 240 395 550
51-60: 52-Capt. Marvel x-over in Ibis. 57-Spy Smasher, Golden Arrow, Ibis cameo 32 64 96 188 307 425
61-70 30 60 90 177 289 400
71,77-80 28 56 84 165 270 375
72-76-Two Captain Marvel stories in each; 76-Spy Smasher becomes Crime Smasher 28 56 84 168 274 380
81-85,87-99: 91-Infinity-c 28 56 84 165 270 375
86-Captain Marvel battles Sivana Family; robot-c 33 66 99 194 317 440
100-(8/48)-Anniversary issue 39 78 117 231 378 525
101-106: 102-Commando Yank app. 106-Bulletman app. 30 60 90 177 289 400
107-149: 107-Capitol Building photo-c. 108-Brooklyn Bridge photo-c. 112-Photo-c. 139-Infinity-c. 140-Flag-c. 142-Used in **POP**, pg. 89 31 62 93 182 296 410
150-152-(Low dist.) 39 78 117 235 385 535
153-155-(Scarce):154,155-1st/2nd Dr. Death stories 52 104 156 328 552 775
NOTE: **C.C. Beck** *Captain Marvel-No. 25(part).* **Krigstein** *Golden Arrow-No. 75, 78, 91, 95, 96, 98-100.* **Mac Raboy** *Dr. Voodoo-No. 9-22. Captain Marvel-No. 25(part).* **M.Swayze** *a-37, 38, 59; c-38.* **Schaffenberger** *c-138-155(most).* **Wolverton** *1/2 pg. "Culture Corner"-No. 65-67, 68(2 1/2 pgs), 70-85, 87-96, 98-100, 102-109, 112-121, 123, 125, 126, 128-131, 133, 134, 136, 142, 143, 146.*

WHIZ KIDS (Also see Big Bang Comics)
Image Comics: Apr, 2003 ($4.95, B&W, one-shot)
1-Galahad, Cyclone, Thunder Girl and Moray app.; Jeff Austin-a 5.00

WHOA, NELLIE (Also see Love & Rockets)
Fantagraphics Books: July, 1996 - No. 3, Sept, 1996 ($2.95, B&W, lim. series)
1-3: Jamie Hernandez-c/a/scripts 3.00

WHODUNIT
D.S. Publishing Co.: Aug-Sept, 1948 - No. 3, Dec-Jan, 1948-49 (#1,2: 52 pgs.)
1-Baker-a (7 pgs.) 32 64 96 188 307 425
2,3-Detective mysteries 15 30 45 85 130 175

WHODUNNIT?
Eclipse Comics: June, 1986 - No. 3, Apr, 1987 ($2.00, limited series)
1-3: Spiegle-a. 2-Gulacy-c 3.00

WHO FRAMED ROGER RABBIT (See Marvel Graphic Novel)

WHO IS NEXT?
Standard Comics: No. 5, Jan, 1953
5-Toth, Sekowsky, Andru-a; crime stories; Strangler on the Loose-c 58 116 174 371 636 900

WHO IS THE CROOKED MAN?
Crusade: Sept, 1996 ($3.50, B&W, 40 pgs.)
1-Intro The Martyr, Scarlet 7 & Garrison 4.00

WHO'S MINDING THE MINT? (See Movie Classics)

WHO'S WHO IN STAR TREK
DC Comics: Mar, 1987 - #2, Apr, 1987 ($1.50, limited series)
1,2 6.00
NOTE: **Byrne** *a-1, 2.* **Chaykin** *c-1, 2.* **Morrow** *a-1, 2.* **McFarlane** *a-2.* **Perez** *a-1, 2.* **Sutton** *a-1, 2.*

WHO'S WHO IN THE LEGION OF SUPER-HEROES
DC Comics: Apr, 1987 - No. 7, Nov, 1988 ($1.25, limited series)
1-7 4.00

WHO'S WHO: THE DEFINITIVE DIRECTORY OF THE DC UNIVERSE
DC Comics: Mar, 1985 - No. 26, Apr, 1987 (Maxi-series, no ads)
1-DC heroes from A-Z 4.00
2-26: All have 1-2 pgs-a by most DC artists 4.00
NOTE: **Art Adams** *a-4, 11, 18, 20.* **Anderson** *a-1-5, 7-12, 14, 15, 19, 21, 23-25.* **Aparo** *a-2, 3, 9, 10, 12, 13, 14, 15, 17, 18, 21, 23.* **Byrne** *a-4, 7, 14, 16, 18i, 19, 22i, 24; c-22.* **Cowan** *a-3-5, 8, 10-13, 16-18, 22-25.* **Ditko** *a-19-22.* **Evans** *a-20.* **Giffen** *a-1, 3,-6, 8, 13, 15, 17, 18, 23.* **Grell** *a-6, 9, 14, 20, 23, 25, 26.* **Infantino** *a-1-10, 12, 15, 17-22, 24, 25.* **Kaluta** *a-14, 21.* **Gil Kane** *a-1-11, 13, 14, 16, 19, 21-23, 25.* **Kirby** *a-2-6, 8-18, 20, 22, 25.* **Kubert** *a-2, 3, 7-11, 19, 20, 25.* **Erik Larsen** *a-24.* **McFarlane** *a-10-12, 17, 19, 25, 26.* **Morrow** *a-4, 7, 25, 26.* **Orlando** *a-1, 4, 10, 11, 21i.* **Perez** *a-1-5, 8-19, 22-26; c-1-4, 13-18.* **Rogers** *a-1, 2, 5-7, 11, 12, 15, 24.* **Starlin** *a-13, 14, 16.* **Stevens** *a-4, 7, 18.*

The Wicked + The Divine #26 © Gillen

Wilbur Comics #8 © ACP

Wild Boy of the Congo #12 © Z-D

WHO'S WHO UPDATE '87
DC Comics: Aug, 1987 - No. 5, Dec, 1987 ($1.25, limited series)

	GD 2.0	VG 4.0	FN 6.0	VF 8.0	VF/NM 9.0	NM- 9.2
1-5: Contains art by most DC artists						4.00

NOTE: ***Giffen** a-1. **McFarlane** a-1-4; c-4. **Perez** a-1-4.*

WHO'S WHO UPDATE '88
DC Comics: Aug, 1988 - No. 4, Nov, 1988 ($1.25, limited series)

	GD 2.0	VG 4.0	FN 6.0	VF 8.0	VF/NM 9.0	NM- 9.2
1-4: Contains art by most DC artists						4.00

NOTE: ***Giffen** a-1. **Erik Larsen** a-1.*

WICKED, THE
Avalon Studios: Dec, 1999 - No. 7, Aug, 2000 ($2.95)

	GD 2.0	VG 4.0	FN 6.0	VF 8.0	VF/NM 9.0	NM- 9.2
Preview-(7/99, $5.00, B&W)						5.00
1-7-Anacleto-c/Martinez-a						3.00
...: Medusa's Tale (11/00, $3.95, one shot) story plus pin-up gallery						4.00
...: Vol. 1: Omnibus (2003, $19.95) r/#0-8; Drew-c						20.00

WICKED + THE DIVINE, THE
Image Comics: Jun, 2014 - Present ($3.50/$3.99)

	GD 2.0	VG 4.0	FN 6.0	VF 8.0	VF/NM 9.0	NM- 9.2
1-25: 1-Gillen-s/McKelvie-a. 12-Kate Brown-a. 13-Lotay-a. 15-Hans-a. 23-Wada-a						3.50
26-34-($3.99)						4.00
... Christmas Annual (12/17, $3.99) Art by Anka, Clugston, McNeil						4.00
455 One-Shot (5/17, $3.99) Set in 455 AD Rome; André Araújo-a						4.00
1831 One-Shot (9/16, $3.99) Set in 1831; Stephanie Hans-a						4.00
1923 One-Shot (9/16, $4.99) Set in 1923; Aud Koch-a						5.00

WIDOWMAKER
Marvel Comics: Feb, 2011 - No. 4, Apr, 2011 ($3.99, limited series)

	GD 2.0	VG 4.0	FN 6.0	VF 8.0	VF/NM 9.0	NM- 9.2
1-4-Black Widow, Hawkeye & Mockingbird app. 1,2-Jae Lee-c. 3,4-Noto-c						4.00

WIDOW WARRIORS
Dynamite Entertainment: 2010 - No. 4, 2010 ($3.99, limited series)

	GD 2.0	VG 4.0	FN 6.0	VF 8.0	VF/NM 9.0	NM- 9.2
1-4-Pat Lee-a/c						4.00

WILBUR COMICS (Teen-age) (Also see Laugh Comics, Laugh Comix, Liberty Comics #10 & Zip Comics)
MLJ Magazines/Archie Publ. No. 8, Spring, 1946 on: Sum', 1944 - No. 87, 11/59; No. 88, 9/63; No. 89, 10/64; No. 90, 10/65 (No. 1-46: 52 pgs.) (#1-11 are quarterly)

	GD 2.0	VG 4.0	FN 6.0	VF 8.0	VF/NM 9.0	NM- 9.2
1	71	142	213	454	777	1100
2(Fall, 1944)	39	78	117	231	378	525
3,4(Wint, '44-45; Spr, '45)	27	54	81	158	259	360
5-1st app. Katy Keene (Sum, '45) & begin series; Wilbur story same as Archie story in Archie #1 except Wilbur replaces Archie	161	322	483	1030	1765	2500
6-10: 10-(Fall, 1946)	31	62	93	184	300	415
11-20	17	34	51	98	154	210
21-30: 30-(4/50)	12	24	36	69	97	125
31-50	10	20	30	54	72	90
51-70	9	18	27	47	61	75
71-90: 88-Last 10¢ issue (9/63)	4	8	12	27	44	60

NOTE: *Katy Keene in No. 5-56, 58-61, 63-69. **Al Fagaly** c-6-9, 12-24 at least. **Vigoda** c-2.*

WILD
Atlas Comics (IPC): Feb, 1954 - No. 5, Aug, 1954

	GD 2.0	VG 4.0	FN 6.0	VF 8.0	VF/NM 9.0	NM- 9.2
1	37	74	111	222	361	500
2	21	42	63	122	199	275
3-5	19	38	57	112	179	245

NOTE: ***Berg** a-5; c-4. **Burgos** c-3. **Colan** a-4. **Everett** a-1-3. **Heath** a-2, 3, 5. **Maneely** a-1-3, 5; c-1, 5. **Post** a-2, 5. **Ed Win** a-1, 3.*

WILD! (This Magazine Is...) (Satire)
Dell Publishing Co.: Jan, 1968 - No. 3, 1968 (35¢, magazine, 52 pgs.)

	GD 2.0	VG 4.0	FN 6.0	VF 8.0	VF/NM 9.0	NM- 9.2
1-3: Hogan's Heroes, The Rat Patrol & Mission Impossible TV spoofs	3	6	9	16	23	30

WILD ANIMALS
Pacific Comics: Dec, 1982 ($1.00, one-shot, direct sales)

	GD 2.0	VG 4.0	FN 6.0	VF 8.0	VF/NM 9.0	NM- 9.2
1-Funny animal; Sergio Aragonés-a; Shaw-c/a						4.00

WILD BILL ELLIOTT (Also see Western Roundup under Dell Giants)
Dell Publishing Co.: No. 278, 5/50 - No. 643, 7/55 (No #11,12) (All photo-c)

	GD 2.0	VG 4.0	FN 6.0	VF 8.0	VF/NM 9.0	NM- 9.2
Four Color 278 (#1, 52pgs.)-Titled "Bill Elliott"; Bill & his horse Stormy begin; photo front/back-c begin	12	24	36	79	170	260
2 (11/50), 3 (52 pgs.)	7	14	21	44	82	120
4-10 (10-12/52)	5	10	15	35	63	90
Four Color 472 (6/53), 520(12/53)-Last photo back-c	5	10	15	35	63	90
13 (4-6/54) - 17 (4-6/55)	5	10	15	30	50	70
Four Color 643 (7/55)	5	10	15	33	57	80

WILD BILL HICKOK (Also see Blazing Sixguns)
Avon Periodicals: Sept-Oct, 1949 - No. 28, May-June, 1956

	GD 2.0	VG 4.0	FN 6.0	VF 8.0	VF/NM 9.0	NM- 9.2
1-Ingels-c	29	58	87	170	278	385
2-Painted-c; Kit West app.	15	30	45	86	133	180
3-5-Painted-c (4-Cover by Howard Winfield)	13	26	39	72	101	130
6-10,12: 8-10-Painted-c. 12-Kinsler-c?	12	24	36	69	97	125
11,13,14-Kinstler-c/a (#11-c & inside-f/c art only)	13	26	39	74	105	135
15,17,18,20: 18-Kit West story. 20-Kit West by Larsen	11	22	33	62	86	110
16-Kamen-a; r-3 stories/King of the Badmen of Deadwood	11	22	33	64	90	115
19-Meskin-a	11	22	33	62	86	110
21-Reprints 2 stories/Chief Crazy Horse	11	22	33	60	83	105
22-McCann-a?; r/Sheriff Bob Dixon's...	11	22	33	60	83	105
23-27: 23-Kinstler-c. 24-27-Kinstler-c/a(r) (24,25-r?)	11	22	33	60	83	105
28-Kinstler-c/a (new); r-/Last of the Comanches	11	22	33	62	86	110
I.W. Reprint #1-r/#2; Kinstler-c	2	4	6	9	13	16
Super Reprint #10-12: 10-r/#18. 11-r/#?. 12-r/#8	2	4	6	9	13	16

NOTE: *#23, 25 contain numerous editing deletions in both art and script due to code. **Kinstler** c-6, 7, 11-14, 17, 18, 20-22, 24-28. **Howard Larsen** a-1, 2, 4, 5, 6(3), 7-9, 11, 12, 17, 18, 20-24, 26. **Meskin** a-7. **Reinman** a-6, 17.*

WILD BILL HICKOK AND JINGLES (TV)(Formerly Cowboy Western) (Also see Blue Bird)
Charlton Comics: No. 68, Aug, 1958 - No. 75, Dec, 1959

	GD 2.0	VG 4.0	FN 6.0	VF 8.0	VF/NM 9.0	NM- 9.2
68,69-Williamson-a (all are 10¢ issues)	11	22	33	60	83	105
70-Two pgs. Williamson-a	8	16	24	42	54	65
71-75 (#76, exist?)	6	12	18	28	34	40

WILD BILL PECOS WESTERN (Also see The Westerner)
AC Comics: 1989 ($3.50, 1/2 color, 1/2 B&W, 52 pgs.)

	GD 2.0	VG 4.0	FN 6.0	VF 8.0	VF/NM 9.0	NM- 9.2
1-Syd Shores-c/a(r)/Westerner; photo back-c						4.00

WILD BOY OF THE CONGO (Also see Approved Comics)
Ziff-Davis No. 10-12,4-8/St. John No. 9,11 on: No. 10, 2-3/51 - No. 12, 8-9/51; No. 4, 10-11/51 - No. 9, 10/53; No. 11-#15,6/55 (No #10, 1953)

	GD 2.0	VG 4.0	FN 6.0	VF 8.0	VF/NM 9.0	NM- 9.2
10(#1)(2-3/51)-Origin; bondage-c by Saunders (painted); used in **SOTI**, pg. 189; painted-c begin thru #9 (except #7)	32	64	96	192	314	435
11(4-5/51),12(8-9/51)-Norman Saunders painted-c	17	34	51	98	154	210
4(10-11/51)-Saunders painted bondage-c	16	32	48	94	147	200
5(Winter,'51)-Saunders painted-c	15	30	45	85	130	175
6,8,9(10/53): Painted-c. 6-Saunders-c	15	30	45	85	130	175
7(8-9/52)-Kinstler-a	16	32	48	94	147	200
11-13-Baker-c. 11-r/#7 w/new Baker-c; Kinstler-a (2 pgs.)	20	40	60	117	189	260
14(4/55)-Baker-c; r-#12('51)	20	40	60	117	189	260
15(6/55)	14	28	42	81	118	155

WILDCAT (See Sensation Comics #1)

WILDC.A.T.S ADVENTURES (TV cartoon)
Image Comics (WildStorm): Sept, 1994 - No. 10, June, 1995 ($1.95/$2.50)

	GD 2.0	VG 4.0	FN 6.0	VF 8.0	VF/NM 9.0	NM- 9.2
1-10						3.00
Sourcebook 1 (1/95, $2.95)						3.00

WILDC.A.T.S: COVERT ACTION TEAMS (Also see Alan Moore's... for TPB reprints)
Image Comics (WildStorm Productions): Aug, 1992 - No. 4, Mar, 1993; No. 5, Nov, 1993 - No. 50, June, 1998 ($1.95/$2.50)

	GD 2.0	VG 4.0	FN 6.0	VF 8.0	VF/NM 9.0	NM- 9.2
1-1st app; Jim Lee/Williams-c/a & Lee scripts begin; contains 2 trading cards (Two diff versions of cards inside); 1st WildStorm Productions title						5.00
1-All gold foil signed edition						20.00
1-All gold foil unsigned edition						10.00
1-Newsstand edition w/o cards						3.00
1-"3-D Special"(8/97, $4.95) w/3-D glasses; variant-c by Jim Lee.						5.00
2-($2.50)-Prism foil stamped-c; contains coupon for Image Comics #0 & 4 pg. preview to Portacio's Wetworks (back-up)						5.00
2-With coupon missing						2.00
2-Direct sale misprint w/o foil-c						5.00
2-Newsstand ed., no prism or coupon						3.00
3-Lee/Liefeld-c (1/93-c, 12/92 inside)						4.00
4-($2.50)-Polybagged w/Topps trading card; 1st app. Tribe by Johnson & Stroman; Youngblood cameo						4.00
4-Variant w/red card						6.00
5-7-Jim Lee/Williams-c/a; Lee script						3.00
8-X-Men's Jean Grey & Scott Summers cameo						4.00
9-12: 10-1st app. Huntsman & Soldier; Claremont scripts begin, ends #13. 11-1st app. Savant, Tapestry & Mr. Majestic.						3.00
11-Alternate Portacio-c, see Deathblow #5						5.00
13-19,21-24: 15-James Robinson scripts begin, ends #20. 15,16-Black Razor story.						

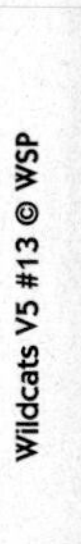
WildC.A.Ts #47 © Aegis

Wildcats V5 #13 © WSP

Wildsiderz #0 © Atomico

	GD 2.0	VG 4.0	FN 6.0	VF 8.0	VF/NM 9.0	NM- 9.2

21-Alan Moore scripts begin, end #34; intro Tao & Ladytron; new WildC.A.T.S team forms (Mr. Majestic, Savant, Condition Red (Max Cash), Tao & Ladytron). 22-Maguire-a 3.00
20-($2.50)-Direct Market, WildStorm Rising Pt. 2 w/bound-in card 4.00
20-($1.95)-Newsstand, WildStorm Rising Part 2 3.00
25-($4.95)-Alan Moore script; wraparound foil-c. 5.00
26-49: 29-(5/96)-Fire From Heaven Pt 7; reads Apr on-c. 30-(6/96)-Fire From Heaven Pt. 13; Spartan revealed to have transplanted personality of John Colt (from Team One: WildC.A.T.S). 31-(9/96)-Grifter rejoins team; Ladytron dies 3.00
40-($3.50)Voyager Pack bagged w/Divine Right preview 5.00
50-($3.50) Stories by Robinson/Lee, Choi & Peterson/Benes, and Moore/Charest; Charest sketchbook; Lee wraparound-c 4.00
50-Chromium cover 6.00
Annual 1 (2/98, $2.95) Robinson-s 4.00
Compendium (1993, $9.95)-r/#1-4; bagged w/#0 15.00
Sourcebook 1 (9/93, $2.50)-Foil embossed-c 3.00
Sourcebook 1-($1.95)-Newsstand ed. w/o foil embossed-c 3.00
Sourcebook 2 (11/94, $2.50)-wraparound-c 3.00
Special 1 (11/93, $3.50, 52 pgs.)-1st Travis Charest WildC.A.T.S-a 4.00
...A Gathering of Eagles (5/97, $9.95, TPB) r/#10-12 10.00
.../ Cyberforce: Killer Instinct TPB (2004, $14.95) r/#5-7 & Cyberforce V2 #1-3 15.00
...Gang War ('98, $16.95, TPB) r/#28-34 17.00
...Homecoming (8/98, $19.95, TPB) r/#21-27 20.00
James Robinson's Complete Wildc.a.t.s TPB (2009, $24.99) r/#15-20,50; Annual 1, WildStorm Rising #1, Team One Wildc.a.t.s #1,2; cover and pin-up gallery 25.00

WILDCATS (3rd series)
DC Comics (WildStorm): Mar, 1999 - No. 28, Dec, 2001 ($2.50)

1-Charest-a; six covers by Lee, Adams, Bisley, Campbell, Madureira and Ramos; Lobdell-s 4.00
1-($6.95) DF Edition; variant cover by Ramos 7.00
2-28: 2-Voodoo cover. 3-Bachalo variant-c. 5-Hitch-a/variant-c. 7-Meglia-a. 8-Phillips-a begins. 17-J.G. Jones-c. 18,19-Jim Lee-c. 20,21-Dillon-a 3.00
Annual 2000 (12/00, $3.50) Bermejo-a; Devil's Night x-over 4.00
...: Battery Park ('03, $17.95, TPB) r/#20-28; Phillips-c 18.00
... Ladytron (10/00, $5.95) Origin; Casey-s/Canete-a 6.00
... Mosaic (2/00, $3.95) Tuska-a (10 pg. back-up story) 4.00
...: Serial Boxes ('01, $14.95, TPB) r/#14-19; Phillips-c 15.00
...: Street Smart ('00, $24.95, HC) r/#1-6; Charest-c 25.00
...: Street Smart ('02, $14.95, SC) r/#1-6; Charest-c 15.00
...: Vicious Circles ('00, $14.95, TPB) r/#8-13; Phillips-c 15.00

WILDCATS (Volume 4)
DC Comics (WildStorm): Dec, 2006 ($2.99)

1-Grant Morrison-s/Jim Lee-a; Jim Lee-c 3.00
1-Variant-c by Todd McFarlane/Jim Lee 6.00
...: Armageddon 1 (2/08, $2.99) Gage-s/Caldwell-a 3.00

WILDCATS (Volume 5) (World's End on cover for #1,2)
DC Comics (WildStorm): Sept, 2008 - No. 30, Feb, 2011 ($2.99)

1-30: 1-Christos Gage-s/Neil Googe-a. 5-Woods-a 3.00
...: Family Secrets TPB (2010, $17.99) r/#8-12 18.00
...: World's End TPB (2009, $17.99) r/#1-7 18.00

WILDC.A.T.S/ ALIENS
Image Comics/Dark Horse: Aug, 1998 ($4.95, one-shot)

	GD	VG	FN	VF	VF/NM	NM-
1-Ellis-s/Sprouse-a/c; Aliens invade Skywatch; Stormwatch app.; death of Winter; destruction of Skywatch	1	2	3	5	6	8
1-Variant-c by Gil Kane	1	3	4	6	8	10

WILDCATS: NEMESIS
DC Comics (WildStorm): Nov, 2005 - No. 9, July, 2006 ($2.99, limited series)

1-9: 1-Robbie Morrison-s/Talent Caldwell & Horacio Domingues-a/Caldwell-c 3.00
TPB (2006, $19.99) r/#1-9; cover gallery 20.00

WILDC.A.T.S: SAVANT GARDE FAN EDITION
Image Comics/WildStorm Productions: Feb, 1997 - No. 3, Apr, 1997 (Giveaway, 8 pgs.) (Polybagged w/Overstreet's FAN)

1-3: Barbara Kesel-s/Christian Uche-a(p) 3.00
1-3-(Gold): All retailer incentives 10.00

WILDC.A.T.S TRILOGY
Image Comics (WildStorm Productions): June, 1993 - No. 3, Dec, 1993 ($1.95, lim. series)

1-($2.50)-1st app. Gen 13 (Fairchild, Burnout, Grunge, Freefall) Multi-color foil-c; Jae Lee-c/a in all 5.00
1-($1.95)-Newsstand ed. w/o foil-c 3.00
2,3-($1.95)-Jae Lee-c/a 3.00

WILDCATS VERSION 3.0
DC Comics (WildStorm): Oct, 2002 - No. 24, Oct, 2004 ($2.95)

1-24: 1-Casey-s/Nguyen-a; two covers by Nguyen and Rian Hughes and Nguyen. 8-Back-up preview of The Authority: High Stakes pt. 3 3.00
...: Brand Building TPB (2003, $14.95) r/#1-6 15.00
...: Full Disclosure TPB (2004, $14.95) r/#7-12 15.00
...: Year One TPB (2010, $24.99) r/#1-12 25.00
...: Year Two TPB (2011, $24.99) r/#13-24 25.00

WILDC.A.T.S/ X-MEN: THE GOLDEN AGE (See also X-Men/WildC.A.T.S.: The Dark Age)
Image Comics (WildStorm Productions): Feb, 1997 ($4.50, one-shot)

1-Lobdell-s/Charest-a; Two covers (Charest, Jim Lee) 5.00
1-"3-D" Edition ($6.50) w/glasses 7.00

WILDC.A.T.S/ X-MEN: THE MODERN AGE
Image Comics (WildStorm Productions): Aug, 1997 ($4.50, one-shot)

1-Robinson-s/Hughes-a; Two covers (Hughes, Paul Smith) 5.00
1-"3-D" Edition ($6.50) w/glasses 7.00

WILDC.A.T.S/ X-MEN: THE SILVER AGE
Image Comics (WildStorm Productions): June, 1997 ($4.50, one-shot)

1-Lobdell-s/Jim Lee-a; Two covers(Neal Adams, Jim Lee) 5.00
1-"3-D" Edition ($6.50) w/glasses 7.00

WILDCORE
Image Comics (WildStorm Prods.): Nov, 1997 - No. 10, Dec, 1998 ($2.50)

1-10: 1-Two covers (Booth/McWeeney, Charest) 3.00
1-($3.50)-Voyager Pack w/DV8 preview 4.00
1-Chromium-c 5.00

WILD DOG
DC Comics: Sept, 1987 - No. 4, Dec, 1987 (75¢, limited series)

1-4 3.00
Special 1 (1989, $2.50, 52 pgs.) 4.00

WILDERNESS TREK (See Zane Grey, Four Color 333)

WILDFIRE (See Zane Grey, FourColor 433)

WILDFIRE
Image Comics (Top Cow): Jun, 2014 - No. 4, Oct, 2014 ($3.99, limited series)

1-4-Matt Hawkins-s/Linda Sejic-a 4.00

WILD FRONTIER (Cheyenne Kid #8 on)
Charlton Comics: Oct, 1955 - No. 7, Apr, 1957

	GD	VG	FN	VF	VF/NM	NM-
1-Davy Crockett	10	20	30	54	72	90
2-6-Davy Crockett in all	7	14	21	37	46	55
7-Origin & 1st app. Cheyenne Kid	9	18	27	47	61	75

WILD GIRL
DC Comics (WildStorm): Jan, 2005 - No. 6, Jun, 2005 ($2.95/$2.99)

1-6-Leah Moore & John Reppion-s/Shawn McManus-a/c 3.00

WILDGUARD: CASTING CALL
Image Comics: Sept, 2003 - No. 6, Feb, 2004 ($2.95)

1-6: 1-Nauck-s/a; two covers by Nauck and McGuinness. 2-Wieringo var-c. 6-Noto var-c 3.00
... Vol. 1: Casting Call (1/05, $17.95, TPB) r/#1-6; cover gallery; Todd Nauck bio 18.00
Wildguard: Fire Power 1 (12/04, $3.50) Nauck-a; two covers 3.50
Wildguard: Fool's Gold (7/05 - No. 2, 7/05, $3.50) 1,2-Todd Nauck-s/a 3.50
Wildguard: Insider (5/08 - No. 3, 7/08, $3.50) 1-3-Todd Nauck-s/a 3.50

WILD'S END
BOOM! Studios: Sept, 2014 - No. 6, Feb, 2015 ($3.99, limited series)

1-6-Dan Abnett-s/I.N.J. Culbard-a/c 4.00

WILD'S END: THE ENEMY WITHIN
BOOM! Studios: Sept, 2015 - No. 6, Feb, 2016 ($3.99, limited series)

1-6-Dan Abnett-s/I.N.J. Culbard-a/c 4.00

WILDSIDERZ
DC Comics (WildStorm): No. 0, Aug, 2005 - No. 2, Jan, 2006 ($1.99/$3.50)

0-(8/05, $1.99) Series preview & character profiles; J. Scott Campbell-a 3.00
1,2: 1-(10/05, $3.50) J. Scott Campbell-s/a; Andy Hartnell-s 3.50

WILDSTAR (Also see The Dragon & The Savage Dragon)
Image Comics (Highbrow Entertainment): Sept, 1995 - No. 3, Jan, 1996 ($2.50, lim. series)

1-3: Al Gordon scripts; Jerry Ordway-c/a 3.00

WILDSTAR: SKY ZERO
Image Comics (Highbrow Entertainment): Mar, 1993 - No. 4, Nov, 1993 ($1.95, lim. series)

Wildstorm #4 © WSP

Wild Storm: Michael Cray #4 © DC

Wild Western #10 © MAR

	GD 2.0	VG 4.0	FN 6.0	VF 8.0	VF/NM 9.0	NM- 9.2

1-4: 1-($2.50)-Embossed-c w/silver ink; Ordway-c/a in all 3.00
1-($1.95)-Newsstand ed. w/silver ink-c, not embossed 3.00
1-Gold variant 6.00

WILD STARS
Collector's Edition/Little Rocket Productions: Summer, 1984 - Present (B&W)

Vol. 1 #1 (Summer 1984, $1.50) 5.00
Vol. 2 #1 (Winter 1988, $1.95) Foil-c; die-cut front & back-c 5.00
Vol. 3: #1-6-Brunner-c; Tierney-s. 1,2-Brewer-a. 3-6-Simons-a 3.00
7-($5.95) Simons-a 6.00
TPB (2004, $17.95) r/Vol. 1-3 18.00

WILDSTORM
Image Comics/DC Comics (WildStorm Publishing): 1994 - Present (one-shots, TPBs)

... After the Fall TPB (2009, $19.99) r/back-up stories from Wildcats V5 #1-11, The Authority V5 #1-11; Gen 13 V4 #21-28, and Stormwatch: PHD #13-20 20.00
...Annual 2000 (12/00, $3.50) Devil's Night x-over; Moy-a 4.00
...: Armageddon TPB (2008, $17.99) r/Armageddon one-shots in Midnighter, Welcome To Tranquility, Wetworks, Gen13, Stormwatch PHD, and Wildcats titles 18.00
...Chamber of Horrors (10/95, $3.50)-Bisley-c 4.00
...Fine Arts: Spotlight on Gen13 (2/08, $3.50) art and covers with commentary 3.50
...Fine Arts: Spotlight on Jim Lee (2/07, $3.50) art and covers by Lee with commentary 3.50
...Fine Arts: Spotlight on J. Scott Campbell (5/07, $3.50) art and covers with commentary 3.50
...Fine Arts: Spotlight on The Authority (1/08, $3.50) art and covers with commentary 3.50
...Fine Arts: Spotlight on WildCATs (3/08, $3.50) art and covers with commentary 3.50
...Fine Arts: The Gallery Collection (12/98, $19.95) Lee-c 20.00
...Halloween 1 (10/97, $2.50) Warner-c 3.00
...Rarities 1(12/94, $4.95, 52 pgs.)-r/Gen 13 1/2 & other stories 5.00
...Summer Special 1 (2001, $5.95) Short stories by various; Hughes-c 6.00
...Swimsuit Special 1 (12/94, $2.95), ...Swimsuit Special 2 (1995, $2.50) 3.00
...Swimsuit Special '97 #1 (7/97, $2.50) 3.00
...Thunderbook 1 (10/00, $6.95) Short stories by various incl. Hughes, Moy 7.00
...Ultimate Sports 1 (8/97, $2.50) 3.00
...Universe Sourcebook (5/95, $2.50) 3.00
...Universe 2008 Convention Exclusive ('08, no cover price) preview of World's End x-over 3.00

WILDSTORM!
Image Comics (WildStorm): Aug, 1995 - No. 4, Nov, 1995 ($2.50, B&W/color, anthology)

1-4: 1-Simonson-a 3.00

WILD STORM, THE
DC Comics (WildStorm): Apr, 2017 - Present ($3.99)

1-12-Warren Ellis-s/Jon Davis-Hunt-a; Zealot and the Engineer app. 4.00

WILD STORM: MICHAEL CRAY, THE
DC Comics (WildStorm): Dec, 2017 - Present ($3.99)

1-5-Bryan Hill-s/N. Steven Harris-a; Oliver Queen app. 4.00

WILDSTORM PRESENTS: ...
DC Comics (WildStorm): Jan, 2011 - Present ($7.99, squarebound, reprints)

1-(1/11) r/short stories by various incl. Pearson, Conner, Corben, Jeanty, Mahnke 8.00
Planetary: Lost Worlds (2/11) r/Planetary/Authority & Planetary/JLA: Terra Occulta 8.00

WILDSTORM REVELATIONS
DC Comics (WildStorm): Mar, 2008 - No. 6, May, 2008 ($2.99, limited series)

1-6-Beatty & Gage-s/Craig-a. 2-The Authority app. 3.00
TPB (2008, $17.99) r/#1-6; cover sketches 18.00

WILDSTORM RISING
Image Comics (WildStorm Publishing): May, 1995 - No.2, June, 1995 ($1.95/$2.50)

1-($2.50)-Direct Market, WildStorm Rising Pt. 1 w/bound-in card 3.00
1-($1.95)-Newstand, WildStorm Rising Pt. 1 3.00
2-($2.50)-Direct Market, WildStorm Rising Pt. 10 w/bound-in card; continues in WildC.A.T.S #21. 3.00
2-($1.95)-Newstand, WildStorm Rising Pt. 10 3.00
Trade paperback (1996, $19.95)-Collects x-over; B. Smith-c 20.00

WILDSTORM SPOTLIGHT
Image Comics (WildStorm Publishing): Feb, 1997 - No. 4 ($2.50)

1-4: 1-Alan Moore-s 3.00

WILDSTORM UNIVERSE '97
Image Comics (WildStorm Publishing): Dec, 1996 - No. 3 ($2.50, limited series)

1-3: 1-Wraparound-c. 3-Gary Frank-c 3.00

WILDTHING
Marvel Comics UK: Apr, 1993 - No. 7, Oct, 1993 ($1.75)

1-($2.50)-Embossed-c; Venom & Carnage cameo 4.00

	GD 2.0	VG 4.0	FN 6.0	VF 8.0	VF/NM 9.0	NM 9.2

2-7: 2-Spider-Man & Venom. 6-Mysterio app. 3.00

WILD THING (Wolverine's daughter in the M2 universe)
Marvel Comics: Oct, 1999 - No. 5, Feb, 2000 ($1.99)

1-5: 1-Lim-a in all. 2-Two covers 3.00
Wizard #0 supplement; battles the Hulk 3.00
Spider-Girl Presents Wild Thing. Crash Course (2007, $7.99, digest) r/#0-5 8.00

WILDTIMES
DC Comics (WildStorm Productions): Aug, 1999 ($2.50, one-shots)

...Deathblow #1 -set in 1899; Edwards-a; Jonah Hex app., ...DV8 #1 -set in 1944; Altieri-s/p; Sgt. Rock app., ...Gen13 #1 -set in 1969; Casey-s/Johnson-a; Teen Titans app., ...Grifter #1 -set in 1923; Paul Smith-a, ...Wetworks #1 -Waid-s/Lopresti-a; Superman app. 3.00
...WildC.A.T.s #0 -Wizard supplement; Charest-c 3.00

WILD WEST (Wild Western #3 on)
Marvel Comics (WFP): Spring, 1948 - No. 2, July, 1948

	GD 2.0	VG 4.0	FN 6.0	VF 8.0	VF/NM 9.0	NM 9.2
1-Two-Gun Kid, Arizona Annie, & Tex Taylor begin; Shores-c	39	78	117	231	378	525
2-Captain Tootsie by Beck; Shores-c	25	50	75	150	245	340

WILD WEST (Black Fury #1-57)
Charlton Comics: V2#58, Nov, 1966

	GD 2.0	VG 4.0	FN 6.0	VF 8.0	VF/NM 9.0	NM 9.2
V2#58	2	4	6	11	16	20

WILD WEST C.O.W.-BOYS OF MOO MESA (TV)
Archie Comics: Dec, 1992 - No. 3, Feb, 1993 (limited series)
V2#1, Mar, 1993 - No. 3, July, 1993 ($1.25)

1-3,V2#1-3 3.00

WILD WESTERN (Formerly Wild West #1,2)
Marvel/Atlas (WFP): No. 3, 9/48 - No. 57, 9/57 (3-11: 52 pgs, 12-on: 36 pgs)

	GD 2.0	VG 4.0	FN 6.0	VF 8.0	VF/NM 9.0	NM 9.2
3(#1)-Tex Morgan begins; Two-Gun Kid, Tex Taylor, & Arizona Annie continue from Wild West	30	60	90	177	289	400
4-Last Arizona Annie; Captain Tootsie by Beck; Kid Colt app.	21	42	63	126	206	285
5-2nd app. Black Rider (1/49); Blaze Carson, Captain Tootsie (by Beck) app.	26	52	78	154	252	350
6-8: 6-Blaze Carson app; anti-Wertham editorial	17	34	51	98	154	210
9-Photo-c; Black Rider app., also in #11-19	20	40	60	120	195	270
10-Charles Starrett photo-c	24	48	72	140	230	320
11-(Last 52 pg. issue) The Prairie Kid app.	18	36	54	103	162	220
12-14,16-19: All Black Rider-c/stories. 12-14-The Prairie Kid & his horse Fury app.	20	40	60	117	189	260
15-Red Larabee, Gunhawk (origin), his horse Blaze, & Apache Kid begin, end #22; Black Rider-c/story	20	40	60	120	195	270
20-30: 20-Kid Colt-c begin. 24-Has 2 Kid Colt stories. 26-1st app. The Ringo Kid? (2/53); 4 pg. story. 30-Katz-a	14	28	42	82	121	160
31-40	11	22	33	67	94	120
41-47,49-51,53,57	11	22	33	60	83	105
48-Williamson/Torres-a (4 pgs); Drucker-a	13	26	39	72	101	130
52-Crandall-a	13	26	39	72	101	130
54,55-Williamson-a in both (5 & 4 pgs.), #54 with Mayo plus 2 text illos	13	26	39	72	101	130
56-Baker-a?	11	22	33	60	83	105

NOTE: *Annie Oakley in #46, 47. Apache Kid in #15-22, 39. Arizona Kid in #21, 23. Arrowhead in #34-39. Black Rider in #5, 8-19, 33-44. Fighting Texan in #17. Kid Colt in #4-6, 8-11, 20-47, 51, 52, 54-56. Outlaw Kid in #43. Red Hawkins in #13, 14. Ringo Kid in #26, 39, 41, 43, 44, 46, 47, 50-56. Tex Morgan in #3, 4, 6, 9, 11. Tex Taylor in #3-6, 9, 11. Texas Kid in #23-25. Two-Gun Kid in #3-6, 8, 9, 11, 12, 33-39, 41. Wyatt Earp in #47.* **Ayers** *a-41, 42, 53, 54.* **Berg** *a-26; c-24.* **Colan** *a-49.* **Forte** *a-28, 30.* **Al Hartley** *a-16, 51.* **Heath** *a-4, 5, 8; c-34, 44.* **Keller** *a-24, 26(2), 29-40, 44-46, 48, 51, 52.* **Maneely** *a-10, 12, 15, 16, 28, 35, 38, 40-45; c-11, 18-22, 33, 35, 36, 38-42, 45, 51, 53, 54, 56, 57.* **Morisi** *a-23, 52.* **Pakula** *a-42, 52.* **Powell** *a-51.* **Romita** *a-24(2).* **Severin** *a-46, 47; c-48.* **Shores** *a-3, 5, 30, 31, 33, 35, 36, 38, 41; c-3-5.* **Sinnott** *a-34-39.* **Wildey** *a-43. Bondage c-19.*

WILD WESTERN ACTION (Also see The Bravados)
Skywald Publ. Corp.: Mar, 1971 - No. 3, June, 1971 (25¢, reprints, 52 pgs.)

	GD 2.0	VG 4.0	FN 6.0	VF 8.0	VF/NM 9.0	NM 9.2
1-Durango Kid, Straight Arrow-r; with all references to "Straight" in story relettered to "Swift"; Bravados begin; Shores-a (new)	3	6	9	16	24	32
2,3: 2-Billy Nevada, Durango Kid. 3-Red Mask, Durango Kid	2	4	6	13	18	22

WILD WESTERN ROUNDUP
Red Top/Decker Publications/I. W. Enterprises: Oct, 1957; 1960-'61

	GD 2.0	VG 4.0	FN 6.0	VF 8.0	VF/NM 9.0	NM 9.2
1(1957)-Kid Cowboy-r	5	10	15	22	26	30
I.W. Reprint #1('60-61)-r/#1 by Red Top	2	4	6	8	11	14

WILD WEST RODEO
Star Publications: 1953 (15¢)

Willie the Penguin #1 © STD

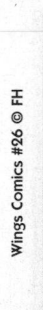

Win A Prize Comics #1 © CC

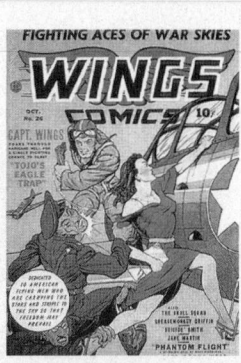

Wings Comics #26 © FH

GD 2.0 | VG 4.0 | FN 6.0 | VF 8.0 | VF/NM 9.0 | NM- 9.2

1-A comic book coloring book with regular full color cover & B&W inside
10 20 30 54 72 90

WILD WILD WEST, THE (TV)
Gold Key: June, 1966 - No. 7, Oct, 1969 (All have Robert Conrad photo-c)

1-McWilliams-a 10 20 30 69 147 225
1-Variant edition with photo back-c (scarce) 11 22 33 76 163 250
2-Robert Conrad photo-c; McWilliams-a 8 16 24 52 99 145
2-Variant edition with Conrad photo back-c (scarce) 9 18 27 59 117 175
3-7 6 12 18 42 79 115
3-Variant edition with photo back-c (scarce) 8 16 24 56 108 160

WILD, WILD WEST, THE (TV)
Millennium Publications: Oct, 1990 - No. 4, Jan?, 1991 ($2.95, limited series)

1-4-Based on TV show 3.00

WILKIN BOY (See That...)

WILL EISNER READER
Kitchen Sink Press: 1991 ($9.95, B&W, 8 1/2" x 11", TPB)

nn-Reprints stories from Will Eisner's Quarterly; Eisner-s/a/c 15.00
nn-(DC Comics, 10/00, $9.95) 10.00

WILL EISNER'S JOHN LAW: ANGELS AND ASHES, DEVILS AND DUST
IDW Publ.: Apr, 2006 - No. 4 ($3.99, B&W, limited series)

1-New stories with Will Eisner's characters; Gary Chaloner-s/a 4.00

WILLIE COMICS (Formerly Ideal #1-4; Crime Cases #24 on; Li'l Willie #20 & 21) (See Gay Comics, Laugh, Millie The Model & Wisco)
Marvel Comics (MgPC): #5, Fall, 1946 - #19, 4/49; #22, 1/50 - #23, 5/50 (No #20 & 21)

5(#1)-George, Margie, Nellie the Nurse & Willie begin
39 78 117 240 395 550
6,8,9 22 44 66 132 216 300
7(1),10,11-Kurtzman's "Hey Look" 23 46 69 136 223 310
12,14-18,22,23 21 42 63 124 202 280
13,19-Kurtzman's "Hey Look" (#19-last by Kurtzman?)
22 44 66 128 209 290

NOTE: *Cindy app. in #17. Jeanie app. in #17. Little Lizzie app. in #22.*

WILLIE MAYS (See The Amazing...)

WILLIE THE PENGUIN
Standard Comics: Apr, 1951 - No. 6, Apr, 1952

1-Funny animal 11 22 33 62 86 110
2-6 7 14 21 37 46 55

WILLIE THE WISE-GUY (Also see Cartoon Kids)
Atlas Comics (NPP): Sept, 1957

1-Kida, Maneely-a 16 32 48 94 147 200

WILLOW
Marvel Comics: Aug, 1988 - No. 3, Oct, 1988 ($1.00)

1-3-R/Marvel Graphic Novel #36 (movie adaptation) 4.00

WILLOW (From Buffy the Vampire Slayer)
Dark Horse Comics: Nov, 2012 - No. 5, Mar, 2013 ($2.99, limited series)

1-5-Jeff Parker-s/Brian Ching-a; covers by David Mack & Megan Lara; Aluwyn app. 3.00

WILL ROGERS WESTERN (Formerly My Great Love #1-4; see Blazing & True Comics #66)
Fox Feature Syndicate: No. 5, June, 1950 - No. 2, Aug, 1950

5(#1) Photo-c 31 62 93 186 303 420
2: Photo-c 26 52 78 154 252 350

WILL TO POWER (Also see Comic's Greatest World)
Dark Horse Comics: June, 1994 - No. 12, Aug, 1994 ($1.00, weekly limited series, 20 pgs.)

1-12: 12-Vortex kills Titan. 3.00

NOTE: ***Mignola** c-10-12. **Sears** c-1-3.*

WILL-YUM!
Dell Publishing Co.: No. 676, Feb, 1956 - No. 902, May, 1958

Four Color 676 (#1), 765 (1/57), 902 4 8 12 28 47 65

WIN A PRIZE COMICS (Timmy The Timid Ghost #3 on?)
Charlton Comics: Feb, 1955 - No. 2, Apr, 1955

V1#1-S&K-a; Poe adapt; E.C. War swipe 68 136 204 435 743 1050
2-S&K-a 50 100 150 315 533 750

WINDY & WILLY (Also see Showcase #81)
National Periodical Publications: May-June, 1969 - No. 4, Nov-Dec, 1969

1- r/Dobie Gillis with some art changes begin 5 10 15 31 53 75
2-4 3 6 9 21 33 45

GD 2.0 | VG 4.0 | FN 6.0 | VF 8.0 | VF/NM 9.0 | NM- 9.2

WINGS COMICS
Fiction House Mag.: 9/40 - No. 109, 9/49; No. 110, Wint, 1949-50; No. 111, Spring, 1950; No. 112, 1950(nd); No. 113 - No. 115, 1950(nd); No. 116, 1952(nd); No. 117, Fall, 1952 - No. 122, Wint, 1953-54; No. 123 - No. 124, 1954(nd)

1-Skull Squad, Clipper Kirk, Suicide Smith, Jane Martin, War Nurse, Phantom Falcons, Greasemonkey Griffin, Parachute Patrol & Powder Burns begin; grey-tone-c
300 600 900 1950 3375 4800
2 129 258 387 826 1413 2000
3-5 87 174 261 553 952 1350
6-10: 8-Indicia shows #7 (#8 on cover) 68 136 204 435 743 1050
11-15 63 126 189 403 689 975
16-Origin & 1st app. Captain Wings & begin series 68 136 204 435 743 1050
17-20: 20-(4/42) 1st Japanese WWII-c 54 108 162 343 574 825
21-25,27-30 49 98 147 309 522 735
26-1st Good Girl WWII-c for this title 77 154 231 493 847 1200
31-34,36-40 41 82 123 256 428 600
35-Classic Nazi WWII-c 50 100 150 315 533 750
41-50 36 72 108 211 343 475
51-60: 60-Last Skull Squad 32 64 96 192 314 435
61-67: 66-Ghost Patrol begins (becomes Ghost Squadron #71 on), ends #112?
30 60 90 177 289 400
68,69: 68-Clipper Kirk becomes The Phantom Falcon-origin, Part 1; part 2 in #69
30 60 90 177 289 400
70-72: 70-1st app. The Phantom Falcon in costume, origin-Part 3; Capt. Wings battles Col. Kamikaze in all 29 58 87 170 278 385
73-85,87,88,92,93,95-99: 80-Phantom Falcon by Larsen. 99-King of the Congo begins?
29 58 87 170 278 385
86-Graphic decapitation panel 30 60 90 177 289 400
89-91,94-Classic Good Girl covers 84 168 252 538 919 1300
100-(12/48) 30 60 90 177 289 400
101-124: 111-Last Jane Martin. 112-Flying Saucer-c (1950). 115-Used in **POP**, pg. 89.
121-Atomic Explosion-c. 122-Korean War 22 44 66 130 213 295

NOTE: *World War II covers (Nazi or Japanese) on #1-17, 19-67. Bondage covers are common. Captain Wings battles Sky Hag-#75, 76; ...Mr. Atlantis-#85-92; ...Mr. Pupin(Red Agent)-#98-103. Capt. Wings by **Elias**-#52-64, 68, 69; by **Lubbers**-#29-32, 70-111; by **Renee**-#33-46. **Evans** a-85-106, 108-111(Jane Martin); text illos-72-84. **Larsen** a-52, 59, 64, 73-77. Jane Martin by **Fran Hopper**-#68-84; Suicide Smith by **John Celardo**-#72, 74, 76, 80-104; by **Hollingsworth**-#68-70, 105-109, 111; Ghost Squadron by **Astarita**-#67-79; by **Maurice Whitman**-#80-111. King of the Congo by **Moreira**-#99, 100. Skull Squad by **M. Baker**-#52-60; Clipper Kirk by **Baker**-#60, 61; by **Colan**-#53; by **Ingels**-(some issues?). Phantom Falcon by **Larsen**-#73-84. **Elias** c-58-72. **Fawcette** c-3-12, 16, 17, 19, 22-33. **Lubbers** c-74-109. **Tuska** a-5. **Whitman** c-110-124. **Zolnerwich** c-15, 21.*

WINGS OF THE EAGLES, THE
Dell Publishing Co.: No. 790, Apr, 1957 (10¢ & 15¢ editions exist)

Four Color 790-Movie; John Wayne photo-c; Toth-a 12 24 36 83 182 280

WINKY DINK (Adventures of...)
Pines Comics: No. 75, Mar, 1957 (one-shot)

75-Marv Levy-c/a 7 14 21 35 43 50

WINKY DINK (TV)
Dell Publishing Co.: No. 663, Nov, 1955

Four Color 663 (#1) 8 16 24 51 96 140

WINNEBAGO GRAVEYARD
Image Comics: Jun, 2017 - No. 4, Sept, 2017 ($3.99)

1-4-Steve Niles-s/Alison Sampson- 4.00

WINNIE-THE-POOH (Also see Dynabrite Comics)
Gold Key No. 1-17/Whitman No. 18 on: January, 1977 - No. 33, July, 1984 (Walt Disney) (Winnie-The-Pooh began as Edward Bear in 1926 by Milne)

1-New art 4 8 12 25 40 55
2-5: 5-New material 2 4 6 13 18 22
6-17: 12-up-New material 2 4 6 9 13 16
18,19(Whitman) 2 4 6 13 18 22
20,21('80) pre-pack only 4 8 12 28 47 65
22('80) (scarcer) pre-pack only 7 14 21 46 86 125
23-28: 27(2/82), 28(4/82) 3 6 9 14 19 24
29-33 (#90299 on-c, no date or date code; pre-pack): 29(4/82), 30(5/83), 31(8/83), 32(4/84), 33(7/84) 3 6 9 20 31 42

WINNIE WINKLE (See Popular Comics & Super Comics)
Dell Publishing Co.: 1941 - No. 7, Sept-Nov, 1949

Large Feature Comic 2 (1941) 33 66 99 194 317 440
Four Color 94 (1945) 12 24 36 79 170 260
Four Color 174 8 16 24 54 102 150
1(3-5/48)-Contains daily & Sunday newspaper-r from 1939-1941
8 16 24 51 96 140

Winter Soldier #19 © MAR

Wise Son: The White Wolf #4 © Milestone

Witchblade #5 © TCOW

GD 2.0 | VG 4.0 | FN 6.0 | VF 8.0 | VF/NM 9.0 | NM- 9.2

2 (6-8/48) 5 10 15 33 57 80
3-7 4 8 12 27 44 60

WINTER MEN, THE
DC Comics (WildStorm): Oct, 2005 - No. 5, Nov, 2006 ($2.99, limited series)
1-5-Brett Lewis-s/John Paul Leon-a 3.00
... Winter Special (2/09, $3.99) Lewis-s/Leon-a 4.00
TPB (2010, $19.99) r/#1-5 & Winter Special; original proposal, development & sketch-a 20.00

WINTER SOLDIER (See Captain America 2005 series)
Marvel Comics: Apr, 2012 - No. 19, Aug, 2013 ($2.99)
1-19: 1-Black Widow app.; Brubaker-s/Guice-a/Bermejo-c. 3-5-Dr. Doom app. 3.00

WINTER SOLDIER: THE BITTER MARCH
Marvel Comics: Apr, 2014 - No. 5, Sept, 2014 ($3.99, limited series)
1-5: 1-Remender-s/Boschi-a/Robinson-c; set in 1966; Nick Fury app. 4.00

WINTER SOLDIER: WINTER KILLS
Marvel Comics: Feb, 2007 ($3.99, one-shot)
1-Flashback to Christmas Eve 1944; Toro & Sub-Mariner app.; Brubaker-s/Weeks-a 5.00

WINTERWORLD
Eclipse Comics: Sept, 1987 - No. 3, Mar, 1988 ($1.75, limited series)
1-3 3.00

WINTERWORLD
IDW Publishing: Jun, 2014 - No. 7, Jan, 2015 ($3.99)
1-7: 1-Chuck Dixon-s/Butch Guice-a; three covers. 5-7-Giorello-a 4.00
#0-(3/15, $3.99) Origin of Wynn; Dixon-s/Edwards-a; covers by Edwards & Guice 4.00

WINTERWORLD: FROZEN FLEET
IDW Publishing: May, 2015 - No. 3, Jul, 2015 ($3.99, limited series)
1-3: 1-Chuck Dixon-s/Esteve Polls-a; three covers. 2,3-Two covers 4.00

WISDOM
Marvel Comics (MAX): Jan, 2007 - No. 6, July, 2007 ($3.99, limited series)
1-6: 1-Hairsine-a/c; Cornell-s. 3-6-Manuel Garcia-a 4.00
...: Rudiments of Wisdom TPB (2007, $21.99) r/#1-6; series pitch and sketch page 22.00

WISE GUYS (See Harvey...)

WISE LITTLE HEN, THE
David McKay Publ./Whitman: 1934 ,1935(48 pgs.); 1937 (Story book)
nn-(1934 edition w/dust jacket)(48 pgs. with color, 8-3/4x9-3/4") -Debut of Donald Duck (see Advs. of Mickey Mouse); Donald app. on cover with Wise Little Hen & Practical Pig; painted cover; same artist as the B&W's from Silly Symphony Cartoon, The Wise Little Hen (1934) (McKay)
Book w/dust jacket 265 530 795 1694 2897 4100
Dust jacket only 63 126 189 403 689 975
nn-(1935 edition w/dust jacket), same as 1934 ed. 152 304 456 965 1658 2350
888 (1937)(9-1/2x13", 12 pgs.)(Whitman) Donald Duck app.
39 78 117 231 378 525

WISE SON: THE WHITE WOLF
DC Comics (Milestone): Nov, 1996 - No. 4, Feb, 1997 ($2.50, limited series)
1-4: Ho Che Anderson-c/a 3.00

WIT AND WISDOM OF WATERGATE (Humor magazine)
Marvel Comics: 1973, 76 pgs., squarebound
1-Low print run 5 10 15 31 53 75

WITCHBLADE (Also see Cyblade/Shi, Tales Of The..., & Top Cow Classics)
Image Comics (Top Cow Productions): Nov, 1995 - No. 185, Nov, 2015 ($2.50/$2.99)
0 1 2 3 5 6 8
1/2-Mike Turner/Marc Silvestri-c. 3 6 9 19 30 40
1/2 Gold Ed., 1/2 Chromium-c 3 6 9 19 30 40
1/2-(Vol. 2, 11/02, $2.99) Wohl-s/Ching-a/c 3.00
1-Mike Turner-a(p) 4 8 12 19 30 40
1,2-American Ent. Encore Ed. 1 2 3 4 5 7
2,3 2 4 6 11 16 20
4,5 2 4 6 8 10 12
6-9: 8-Wraparound-c. 9-Tony Daniel-a(p) 1 2 3 5 6 8
9-Sunset variant-c 2 4 6 8 10 12
9-DF variant-c 2 4 6 9 12 15
10-Flip book w/Darkness #0, 1st app. the Darkness 1 3 4 6 8 10
10-Variant-c 2 4 6 8 10 12
10-Gold logo 3 6 9 14 20 25
10-($3.95) Dynamic Forces alternate-c 1 2 3 5 6 8
11-15 5.00
16-19: 18,19-"Family Ties" Darkness x-over pt. 1,4 4.00
18-Face to face variant-c, 18-American Ent. Ed., 19-AE Gold Ed.
1 2 3 5 6 8
20-25: 24-Pearson, Green-a. 25-($2.95) Turner-a(p) 4.00
25 (Prism variant) 25.00
25 (Special) 10.00
26-39: 26-Green-a begins 3.00
27 (Variant) 6.00
40-49,51-53: 40-Begin Jenkins & Veitch-s/Keu Cha-a. 47-Zulli-c/a 3.00
40-Pittsburgh Convention Preview edition; B&W preview of #40 3.00
49-Gold logo 5.00
50-($4.95) Darkness app.; Ching-a; B&W preview of Universe 5.00
54-59: 54-Black outer-c with gold foil logo; Wohl-s/Manapul-a 3.00
60-74,76-91,93-99: 60-($2.99) Endgame x-over with Tomb Raider #25 & Evo #1. 64,65-Magdalena app. 71-Kirk-a. 77,81-85-Land-c. 80-Four covers. 87-Bachalo-a 3.00
75-($4.99) Manapul-a 5.00
92-($4.99) Origin of the Witchblade; art by various incl. Bachalo, Perez, Linsner, Cooke 5.00
100-($4.99) Five covers incl. Turner, Silvestri, Linsner; art by various; Jake dies 5.00
101-124,126-143: 103-Danielle Baptiste gets the Witchblade; Linsner variant-c. 116-124,140,141-Sejic-a. 126-128-War of the Witchblades. 134-136-Aphrodite IV app. 139-Gaydos-a. 143-Matt Dow Smith-a 3.00
125-($3.99) War of the Witchblades begins; 3 covers; Sejic-a 4.00
144-($4.99) Origin retold; wraparound-c; Sejic-a; back-up w/Sablik-s; pin-up gallery 5.00
145-149-($3.99) Sejic-a/c. 149-Angelus app. 4.00
150-($4.99) Four covers; last Marz-s; Sejic-a; cover gallery & series timeline 5.00
151-174-($2.99) Altered reality after Artifacts #13; Seeley-s; multiple covers 3.00
175-($5.99) Three covers; Marz-s; Laura Braga-a; Temple of Shadows back-up 6.00
176-184-($3.99) 180-Hine-s/Rearte-a 4.00
185-($5.99)-Last issue; Marz & Hawkins-s; art by various; bonus preview of Switch #1 6.00
... and Tomb Raider (4/05, $2.99) Jae Lee-c; art by Lee and Texiera 3.00
...: Animated (8/03, $2.99) Magdalena & Darkness app.; Dini-s/Bone, Bullock, Cooke-a/c 3.00
... Annual 2009 (4/09, $3.99) Basaldua-a 4.00
... Annual #1 (12/10, $4.99) the Witchblade in Stalingrad 1942, Shasteen-a; Haley-a 5.00
...: Art of the Witchblade (7/06, $2.99) pin-ups by various incl. Turner, Land, Linsner 3.00
...: Bearers of the Blade (7/06, $2.99) pin-up/profiles of bearers of the Witchblade 3.00
...: Blood Oath (8/04, $4.99) Sara teams with Phenix & Sibilla; Roux-a 5.00
...: Blood Relations TPB (2003, $12.99) r/#54-58 13.00
... Case Files 1 (10/14, $3.99) Character profiles and story summaries 4.00
... Compendium Vol. 1 (2006, $59.99) r/#1-50; gallery of variant covers and art 60.00
... Compendium Vol. 2 (2007, $59.99) r/#51-100; gallery of variant covers and art 60.00
... Cover Gallery Vol. 1 (12/05, $2.99) intro. by Stan Lee 3.00
.../Darkchylde (7/00, $2.50) Green-s/a(p) 3.00
.../Dark Minds (6/04, $9.99) new story plus r/Dark Minds/Witchblade #1 10.00
.../Darkness: Family Ties Collected Edition (10/98, $9.95) r/#18,19 and Darkness #9,10 10.00
.../Darkness Special (12/99, $3.95) Green-c/a 4.00
... Day of the Outlaws (4/13, $3.99) Fialkov-s/Blake-a; Witchblade in 1878 Colorado 4.00
...: Demon 1 (2003, $6.99) Mark Millar-s/Jae Lee-c/a 7.00
.../Devi (4/08, $3.99) Basaldua-a/Land-c; continues in Devi/Witchblade 4.00
...: Distinctions (See Tales of the Witchblade)
...: Due Process (8/10, $3.99) Alina Urusov-a/c; Phil Smith-s 4.00
.../Elektra (3/97, $2.95) Devil's Reign Pt. 6 4.00
... Gallery (11/00, $2.95) Profile pages and pin-ups by various; Turner-c 3.00
Image Firsts: Witchblade #1 (4/10, $1.00) reprints #1 3.00
Infinity (5/99, $3.50) Lobdell-s/Pollina-c/a 4.00
.../Lady Death (11/01, $4.95) Manapul-c/a 5.00
...: Prevailing TPB (2000, $14.95) r/#20-25; new Turner-c 15.00
...: Revelations TPB (2000, $24.95) r/#9-17; new Turner-c 25.00
.../The Punisher (6/07, $3.99) Marz-s/Melo-a/Linsner-c 4.00
.../Tomb Raider #1/2 (7/00, $2.95) Covers by Turner and Cha 4.00
... Unbalanced Pieces FCBD Edition (5/12, giveaway) Christopher-c 3.00
...: Vol. 1 TPB (1/08, $4.99) r/#80-85; Marz intro.; cover gallery 5.00
...: Vol. 2 TPB (2/08, $14.99) r/#86-92; cover gallery 15.00
...: Vol. 3 TPB (3/08, $14.99) r/#93-100; Edginton intro.; cover gallery 15.00
... vs. Frankenstein: Monster War 2005 (8/05, $2.99) pt. 3 of x-over 3.00
...: Witch Hunt Vol. 1 TPB (2/06, $14.99) r/#80-85; Marz intro.; Choi afterward; cover gallery 15.00
Wizard #500 10.00
.../Wolverine (6/04, $2.99) Basaldua-c/a; Claremont-s 3.00

WITCHBLADE
Image Comics (Top Cow): Dec, 2017 - Present ($3.99)
1-3: 1-Kittredge-s/Ingranata-a; intro. Alex Underwood 4.00

WITCHBLADE/ALIENS/THE DARKNESS/PREDATOR
Dark Horse Comics/Top Cow Productions: Nov, 2000 ($2.99)
1-3-Mel Rubi-a 4.00

Witchcraft: La Terreur #2 © DC

Witches #1 © MAR

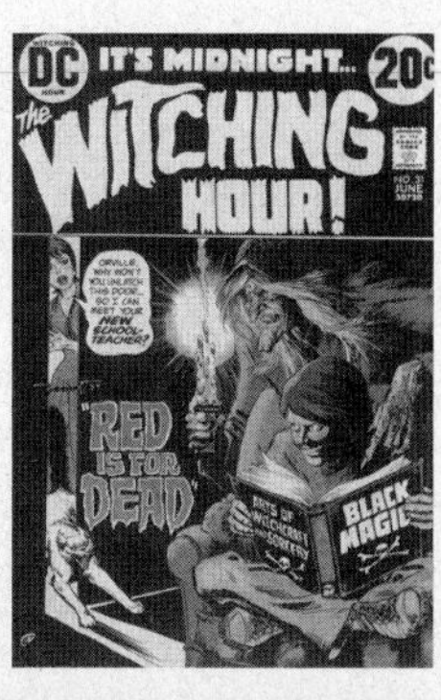

The Witching Hour #31 © DC

	GD 2.0	VG 4.0	FN 6.0	VF 8.0	VF/NM 9.0	NM- 9.2

WITCHBLADE COLLECTED EDITION
Image Comics (Top Cow Productions): July, 1996 - No. 8 ($4.95/$6.95, squarebound, limited series)

1-7-($4.95): Two issues reprinted in each 5.00
8-($6.95) r/#15-17 7.00
...Slipcase (10/96, $10.95)-Packaged w/ Coll. Ed. #1-4 11.00

WITCHBLADE: DEMON REBORN
Dynamite Entertainment: 2012 - No. 4, 2012 ($3.99, limited series)

1-4-Ande Parks-s/Jose Luis-a; covers by Calero & Jae Lee 4.00

WITCHBLADE: DESTINY'S CHILD
Image Comics (Top Cow): Jun, 2000 - No. 3, Sept, 2000 ($2.95, limited series)

1-3: 1-Boller-a/Keu Cha-c 3.00

WITCHBLADE: MANGA (Takeru Manga)
Image Comics (Top Cow): Feb, 2007 - No. 12, Mar, 2008 ($2.99/$3.99)

1-4-Colored reprints of Japanese Witchblade manga. 1-Three covers. 2-Two covers 3.00
5-12-($3.99) 4.00

WITCHBLADE: OBAKEMONO
Image Comics (Top Cow Productions): 2002 ($9.95, one-shot graphic novel)

1-Fiona Avery-s/Billy Tan-a; forward by Straczynski 10.00

WITCHBLADE/ RED SONJA
Dynamite Ent./Top Cow: 2012 - No. 5, 2012 ($3.99, limited series)

1-5-Doug Wagner-s/Cezar Razek-a/Alé Garza-c 4.00

WITCHBLADE: SHADES OF GRAY
Dynamite Ent./Top Cow: 2007 - No. 4, 2007 ($3.50, lim. series)

1,2: 1-Sara Pezzini meets Dorian Gray; Segovia-a; multiple covers 3.50

WITCHBLADE/ TOMB RAIDER SPECIAL (Also see Tomb Raider/...)
Image Comics (Top Cow Productions): Dec, 1998 ($2.95)

1-Based on video game character; Turner-a(p) 4.00
1-Silvestri variant-c 6.00
1-Turner bikini variant-c 10.00
1-Prism-c 12.00
Wizard 1/2 -Turner-s 10.00

WITCHCRAFT (See Strange Mysteries, Super Reprint #18)
Avon Periodicals: Mar-Apr, 1952 - No. 6, Mar, 1953

	GD	VG	FN	VF	VF/NM	NM-
1-Kubert-a; 1 pg. Check-a	94	188	282	597	1024	1450
2-Kubert & Check-a; classic skull-c	90	180	270	576	988	1400
3,6: 3-Lawrence-a; Kinstler inside-c	55	110	165	352	601	850
4-People cooked alive c/story	84	168	252	538	919	1300
5-Kelly Freas painted-c	90	180	270	576	988	1400

NOTE: ***Hollingsworth*** *a-4-6; c-4, 6.* ***McCann*** *a-3?*

WITCHCRAFT
DC Comics (Vertigo): June, 1994 - No. 3, Aug, 1994 ($2.95, limited series)

1-3: James Robinson scripts & Kaluta-c in all 4.00
1-Platinum Edition 15.00
Trade paperback-(1996, $14.95)-r/#1-3; Kaluta-c 15.00

WITCHCRAFT: LA TERREUR
DC Comics (Vertigo): Apr, 1998 - No. 3, Jun, 1998 ($2.50, limited series)

1-3: Robinson-s/Zulli & Locke-a; interlocking cover images 3.00

WITCH DOCTOR (See Walking Dead #85 flip book for preview)
Image Comics: Jun, 2011 - No. 4, Nov, 2011 ($2.99, limited series)

1-4-Seifert-s/Ketner-a/c 3.00
...: Mal Practice 1-6 (11/12 - No. 6, 4/13, $2.99) Seifert-s/Ketner-a/c 3.00
...: The Resuscitation (12/11, $2.99) Seifert-s/Ketner-a/c 3.00

WITCHER, THE
Dark Horse Comics: Mar, 2014 - No. 5, Jul, 2014 ($3.99, limited series)

1-5-Tobin-s/Querio-a 4.00

WITCHER, THE: FOX CHILDREN
Dark Horse Comics: Apr, 2015 - No. 5, Aug, 2015 ($3.99, limited series)

1-5-Tobin-s/Querio-a 4.00

WITCHES
Marvel Comics: Aug, 2004 - No. 4, Sept, 2004 ($2.99, limited series)

1-4: 1,2-Deodato, Jr-a; Dr. Strange app. 3,4-Conrad-a 3.00
... Vol. 1: The Gathering (2004, $9.99) r/series 10.00

WITCHES TALES (Witches Western Tales #29,30)
Witches Tales/Harvey Publications: Jan, 1951 - No. 28, Dec, 1954 (date misprinted as 4/55)

	GD	VG	FN	VF	VF/NM	NM-
1-Powell-a (1 pg.)	68	136	204	435	743	1050
2-Eye injury panel	40	80	120	246	411	575
3-7,9,10	36	72	108	211	343	475
8-Eye injury panels	38	76	114	228	369	510
11-13,15,16: 12-Acid in face story	32	64	96	190	310	430
14,17-Powell/Nostrand-a. 17-Atomic disaster story	34	68	102	199	325	450
18-Nostrand-a; E.C. swipe/Shock S.S.	34	68	102	199	325	450
19-Nostrand-a; E.C. swipe/ "Glutton"; Devil-c	40	80	120	246	411	575
20-24-Nostrand-a. 21-E.C. swipe; rape story. 23-Wood E.C. swipes/Two-Fisted Tales #34	34	68	102	199	325	450
25-Nostrand-a; E.C. swipe/Mad Barber; decapitation-c	123	246	369	787	1344	1900
26-28: 27-r/#6 with diff.-c. 28-r/#8 with diff.-c	21	42	63	126	206	285

NOTE: ***Check*** *a-24.* ***Elias*** *c-8, 10, 16-27.* ***Kremer*** *a-18; c-25.* ***Nostrand*** *a-17-25; 14, 17(w/****Powell****).* ***Palais*** *a-1, 2, 4(2), 5(2), 7-9, 12, 14, 15, 17.* ***Powell*** *a-3-7, 10, 11, 19-27. Bondage-c 1, 3, 5, 6, 8, 9.*

WITCHES TALES (Magazine)
Eerie Publications: V1#7, July, 1969 - V7#1, Feb, 1975 (B&W, 52 pgs.)

	GD	VG	FN	VF	VF/NM	NM-
V1#7(7/69)	7	14	21	46	86	125
V1#8(9/69), 9(11/69)	6	12	18	37	66	95
V2#1-6('70), V3#1-6('71)	5	10	15	31	53	75
V4#1-6('72), V5#1-6('73), V6#1-6('74), V7#1	4	8	12	28	47	65

NOTE: *Ajax/Farrell reprints in early issues.*

WITCHES' WESTERN TALES (Formerly Witches Tales)(Western Tales #31 on)
Harvey Publications: No. 29, Feb, 1955 - No. 30, Apr, 1955

	GD	VG	FN	VF	VF/NM	NM-
29,30-Featuring Clay Duncan & Boys' Ranch; S&K-r/from Boys' Ranch including-c. 29-Last pre-code	15	30	45	86	133	180

WITCHFINDER, THE
Image Comics (Liar): Sept, 1999 - No. 3, Jan, 2000 ($2.95)

1-3-Romano-a/Sharon & Matthew Scott-plot 3.00

WITCHFINDER: CITY OF THE DEAD
Dark Horse Comics: Aug, 2016 - No. 5, Dec, 2016 ($3.99, limited series)

1-5-Mignola & Roberson-s/Stenbeck-a/Tedesco-c 4.00

WITCHFINDER: LOST AND GONE FOREVER
Dark Horse Comics: Feb, 2011 - No. 5, Jun, 2011 ($3.50, limited series)

1-5-John Severin-a; Mignola & Arcudi-s. 1-Two covers by Mignola & Severin 3.50

WITCH HUNTER
Malibu Comics (Ultraverse): Apr, 1996 ($2.50, one-shot)

1 3.00

WITCHING, THE
DC Comics (Vertigo): Aug, 2004 - No. 10, May, 2005 ($2.95/$2.99)

1-10-Vankin-s/Gallagher-a/McPherson-c. 1,2-Lucifer app. 3.00

WITCHING HOUR ("The ..." in later issues)
National Periodical Publ./DC Comics: Feb-Mar, 1969 - No. 85, Oct, 1978

	GD	VG	FN	VF	VF/NM	NM-
1-Toth-a, plus Neal Adams-a (2 pgs.)	13	26	39	91	201	310
2,6: 6-Toth-a	6	12	18	42	79	115
3,5-Wrightson-a; Toth-p. 3-Last 12¢ issue	7	14	21	46	86	125
4,12-Toth-a	5	10	15	31	53	75
7-11-Adams-c; Toth-a in all. 8-Adams-a	6	12	18	41	76	110
13-Neal Adams-c/a, 2pgs.	6	12	18	42	79	115
14-Williamson/Garzon, Jones-a; N. Adams-c	7	14	21	44	82	120
15	3	6	9	19	30	40
16-21-(52 pg. Giants)	4	8	12	23	37	50
22-37,39,40	3	6	9	14	19	24
38-(100 pgs.)	5	10	15	31	53	75
41-60	2	4	6	10	14	18
61-83,85	2	4	6	8	11	14
84-(44 pgs.)	2	4	6	9	13	16

NOTE: *Combined with The Unexpected with #189.* ***Neal Adams*** *c-7-11, 13, 14.* ***Alcala*** *a-24, 27, 33, 41, 43.* ***Anderson*** *a-9, 38.* ***Cardy*** *c-4, 5.* ***Kaluta*** *a-7.* ***Kane*** *a-12p.* ***Morrow*** *a-10, 13, 15, 16.* ***Nino*** *a-31, 40, 45, 47.* ***Redondo*** *a-20, 23, 24, 34, 65; c-53.* ***Reese*** *a-23.* ***Sparling*** *a-1.* ***Toth*** *a-1, 3-12, 38r.* ***Tuska*** *a-11, 12.* ***Wood*** *a-15.*

WITCHING HOUR, THE
DC Comics (Vertigo): 1999 - No. 3, 2000 ($5.95, limited series)

1-3-Bachalo & Thibert-c/a; Loeb & Bachalo-s 6.00
Hardcover (2000, $29.95) r/#1-3; embossed cover 30.00
Softcover (2003, $19.95), (2009, $19.99) r/#1-3 20.00

WITCHING HOUR, THE
DC Comics (Vertigo): Dec, 2013 ($7.99, one-shot)

1-Short story anthology by various incl. DeConnick, Doyle, Buckingham; Frison-c 8.00

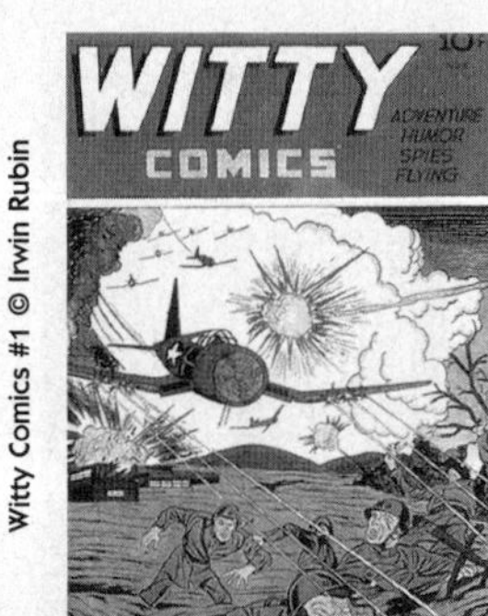

Witty Comics #1 © Irwin Rubin

Wolverine #25 © MAR

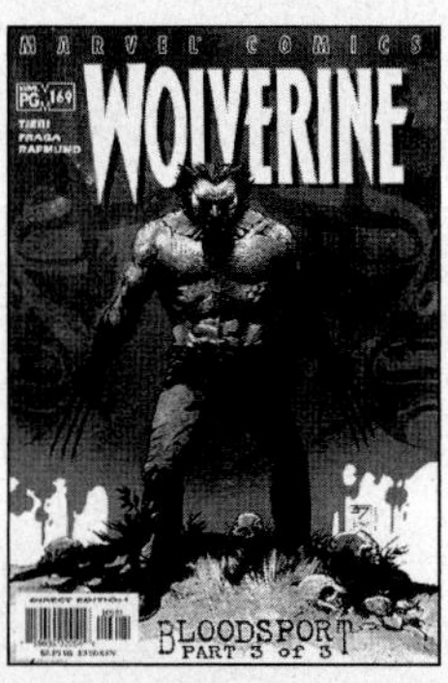

Wolverine #169 © MAR

	GD 2.0	VG 4.0	FN 6.0	VF 8.0	VF/NM 9.0	NM- 9.2
WITHIN OUR REACH						
Star Reach Productions: 1991 ($7.95, 84 pgs.)						
nn-Spider-Man, Concrete by Chadwick, Gift of the Magi by Russell; Christmas stories; Chadwick-c; Spidey back-c						8.00
WITH THE MARINES ON THE BATTLEFRONTS OF THE WORLD						
Toby Press: 1953 (no month) - No. 2, Mar, 1954 (Photo covers)						
1-John Wayne story	31	62	93	186	303	420
2-Monty Hall in #1,2	11	22	33	64	90	115
WITH THE U.S. PARATROOPS BEHIND ENEMY LINES (Also see U.S. Paratroops...; #2-6 titled U.S. Paratroops...)						
Avon Periodicals: 1951 - No. 6, Dec, 1952						
1-Wood-c & inside f/c	21	42	63	124	202	280
2-Kinstler-c & inside f/c only	14	28	42	78	112	145
3-6: 6-Kinstler-c & inside f/c only	12	24	36	69	97	125
NOTE: *Kinstler c-2, 4-6.*						
WITNESS, THE (Also see Amazing Mysteries, Captain America #71, Ideal #4, Marvel Mystery #92 & Mystic #7)						
Marvel Comics (MjMe): Sept, 1948						
1(Scarce)-Rico-c?	300	600	900	2040	3570	5100
WITTY COMICS						
Irwin H. Rubin Publ./Chicago Nite Life News No. 2: 1945 - No. 2, 1945						
1-The Pioneer, Junior Patrol; Japanese war-c	37	74	111	222	361	500
2-The Pioneer, Junior Patrol	17	34	51	98	154	210
WIZARD OF FOURTH STREET, THE						
Dark Horse Comics: Dec, 1987 - No. 2, 1988 ($1.75, B&W, limited series)						
1,2: Adapts novel by S/F author Simon Hawke						3.00
WIZARD OF OZ (See Classics Illustrated Jr. 535, Dell Jr. Treasury No. 5, First Comics Graphic Novel, Marvel Treasury of Oz, and MGM's Marvelous...)						
Dell Publishing Co.: No. 1308, Mar-May, 1962 (TV)						
Four Color 1308	11	22	33	76	163	250
WIZARDS OF MICKEY (Mickey Mouse)						
BOOM! Studios: Jan, 2010 - No. 8, Aug, 2010 ($2.99)						
1-8: 1,2-Ambrosio-s; 3 covers on each. 3-8-Two covers						3.00
WIZARD'S TALE, THE						
Image Comics (Homage Comics): 1997 ($19.95, squarebound, one-shot)						
nn-Kurt Busiek-s/David Wenzel-painted-a/c						20.00
WOLF & RED						
Dark Horse Comics: Apr, 1995 - No. 3, June, 1995 ($2.50, limited series)						
1-3: Characters created by Tex Avery						3.00
WOLF COP						
Dynamite Entertainment: 2016 - No. 3, 2016 ($3.99)						
1-3-Max Marks-s/Arcana Studios-a						4.00
WOLFF & BYRD, COUNSELORS OF THE MACABRE (Becomes Supernatural Law with issue #24)						
Exhibit A Press: May, 1994 - No. 23, Aug, 1999 ($2.50, B&W)						
1-23-Batton Lash-s/a						3.00
WOLF GAL (See Al Capp's...)						
WOLFMAN, THE (See Movie Classics)						
WOLF MOON						
DC Comics (Vertigo): Feb, 2015 - No. 6, Jul, 2015 ($3.99, limited series)						
1-6-Bunn-s/Haun-a. 1-Covers by Jae Lee and Jeremy Haun						4.00
WOLFPACK						
Marvel Comics: Feb, 1988 ($7.95); Aug, 1988 - No. 12, July, 1989 (Lim. series)						
1-(2/88) 1st app./origin (Marvel Graphic Novel #31)	2	4	6	8	10	12
1-12: 1-(8/88) Hama-s						4.00
WOLVERINE (See Alpha Flight, Daredevil #196, 249, Ghost Rider; Wolverine; Punisher, Havok &..., Incredible Hulk #180, Incredible Hulk &..., Kitty Pryde And..., Marvel Comics Presents, New Avengers, Power Pack, Punisher and..., Rampaging ..., Spider-Man vs... & X-Men #94)						
WOLVERINE (See Incredible Hulk #180 for 1st app.)						
Marvel Comics Group: Sept, 1982 - No. 4, Dec, 1982 (limited series)						
1-Frank Miller-c/a(p) in all; Claremont-s	6	12	18	37	66	95
2-4	4	8	12	27	44	60
... By Claremont & Miller HC (2006, $19.99) r/#1-4 & Uncanny X-Men #172-173						20.00
TPB 1(7/87, $4.95)-Reprints #1-4 with new Miller-c	2	4	6	11	16	20
TPB nn (2nd printing, $9.95)-r/#1-4	2	4	6	8	10	12
WOLVERINE						
Marvel Comics: Nov, 1988 - No. 189, June, 2003 ($1.50/$1.75/$1.95/$1.99/$2.25)						
1	4	8	12	27	44	60
2	3	6	9	14	20	25
3-5: 4-BWS back-c	2	4	6	9	13	16
6,7,9: 6-McFarlane back-c. 7-Hulk app.	1	3	4	6	8	10
8-Classic Grey Hulk-c; Hulk app.	3	6	9	16	23	30
10-1st battle with Sabretooth (before Wolverine had his claws)	3	6	9	19	30	40
11-16: 11-New costume	1	2	3	5	6	8
17-20: 17-Byrne-c/a(p) begins, ends #23	1	2	3	4	5	7
21-30: 24,25,27-Jim Lee-c. 26-Begin $1.75-c						5.00
31-40,44,47						4.00
41-Sabretooth claims to be Wolverine's father; Cable cameo	1	3	4	6	8	10
41-Gold 2nd printing ($1.75)	2	4	6	8	10	12
42-Sabretooth, Cable & Nick Fury app.; Sabretooth proven not to be Wolverine's father	1	3	4	6	8	10
42-Gold ink 2nd printing ($1.75)	1	3	4	6	8	10
43-Sabretooth cameo (2 panels); saga ends						5.00
45,46-Sabretooth-c/stories						5.00
48,49,51-Sabretooth app. 48-Begin 3 part Weapon X sequel. 51-Sabretooth-c & app.						5.00
50-(64 pgs.)-Die cut-c; Wolverine back to old yellow costume; Forge, Cyclops, Jubilee, Jean Grey & Nick Fury app.	1	2	3	5	6	8
52-74,76-80: 54-Shatterstar (from X-Force) app. 55-Gambit, Jubilee, Sunfire-c/story. 55-57,73-Gambit app. 57-Mariko Yashida dies (Late 7/92). 58,59-Terror, Inc. x-over. 60-64-Sabretooth storyline (60,62,64-c)						4.00
75-($3.95, 68 pgs.)-Wolverine hologram on-c						6.00
81-84,86: 81-bound-in card sheet						4.00
85-($2.50)-Newsstand edition						4.00
85-($3.50)-Collectors edition						5.00
87-90 ($1.95)-Deluxe edition						4.00
87-90 ($1.50)-Regular edition						3.00
91-99,101-114: 91-Return from "Age of Apocalypse," 93-Juggernaut app. 94-Gen X app. 101-104-Elektra app. 104-Origin of Onslaught. 105-Onslaught x-over. 110-Shaman-c/app. 114-Alternate-c						3.00
100 ($3.95)-Hologram-c; Wolverine loses humanity	2	4	6	8	10	12
100 ($2.95)-Regular-c.						5.00
102.5 (1996 Wizard mail-away)-Deadpool app.; Vallejo-c/Buckingham-a						100.00
115-124: 115- Operation Zero Tolerance						3.00
125-($2.99) Wraparound-c; Viper secret						4.00
125-($6.95) Jae Lee variant-c						8.00
126-144: 126,127-Sabretooth-c/app. 128-Sabretooth & Shadowcat app.; Platt-a. 129-Wendigo-c/app. 131-Initial printing contained lettering error. 133-Begin Larsen-s/ Matsuda-a. 138-Galactus-c/app. 139-Cable app.; Yu-a. 142,143-Alpha Flight app.						3.00
145-($2.99) 25th Anniversary issue; Hulk and Sabretooth app.						4.00
145-($3.99) Foil enhanced cover (also see Promotional section for Nabisco mail-in ed.)						5.00
146,147-Apocalypse: The Twelve; Angel-c/app.	1	2	3	5	6	8
148,149: 149-Nova-c/app.						3.00
150-($2.99) Steve Skroce-s/a						4.00
151-153,156-174,176-182,184-189: 151-Begin $2.25-c. 156-Churchill-a. 159-Chen-a begins. 160-Sabretooth app. 163-Texeira-a(p). 167-BWS-c. 172,173-Alpha Flight app. 176-Colossus app. 185,186-Punisher app.						3.00
154,155-Deadpool app.; Liefeld-s/a.	2	4	6	11	16	20
175,183-($3.50) 175-Sabretooth app.						4.00
#(-1) Flashback (7/97) Logan meets Col. Fury; Nord-a						3.00
Annual nn (1990, $4.50, squarebound, 52 pgs.)-The Jungle Adventure; Simonson scripts; Mignola-c/a						6.00
Annual 2 (12/90, $4.95, squarebound, 52 pgs.)-Bloodlust						6.00
Annual nn (#3, 8/91, $5.95, 68 pgs.)-Rahne of Terror; Cable & The New Mutants app.; Andy Kubert-c/a (2nd print exists)						6.00
Annual '95 (1995, $3.95)						4.00
Annual '96 (1996, $2.95)- Wraparound-c; Silver Samurai, Yukio, and Red Ronin app.						4.00
Annual '97 ($2.99) - Wraparound-c						4.00
Annual 1999, 2000 ($3.50) : 1999-Deadpool app.						4.00
Annual 2001 ($2.99) - Tieri-s; JH Williams-c						4.00
...Battles The Incredible Hulk nn (1989, $4.95, squarebound, 52 pg.) r/Incr. Hulk #180,181	2	4	6	8	10	12
Best of Wolverine Vol. 1 HC (2004, $29.99) oversized reprints of Hulk #181, mini-series #1-4, Capt. America Ann, #8, Uncanny X-Men #205 & Marvel Comics Presents #72-84						30.00
...Black Rio (11/98, $5.99)-Casey-s/Oscar Jimenez-a						6.00
...Blood Debt TPB (7/01, $12.95)-r/#150-153; Skroce-c						13.00
...Blood Hungry nn (1993, $6.95, 68 pgs.)-Kieth-r/Marvel Comics Presents #85-92						

Wolverine V3 #67 © MAR

Wolverine V4 #4 © MAR

Wolverine #304 © MAR

GD VG FN VF VF/NM NM-
2.0 4.0 6.0 8.0 9.0 9.2

w/ new Kieth-c 7.00
..: Bloody Choices nn (1993, $7.95, 68 pgs.)-r/Graphic Novel; Nick Fury app. 8.00
.. Cable Guts and Glory (10/99, $5.99) Platt-a 6.00
.. Classic Vol. 1 TPB (2005, $12.99) r/#1-5 15.00
.. Classic Vol. 2 TPB (2005, $12.99) r/#6-10 15.00
.. Classic Vol. 3 TPB (2006, $14.99) r/#11-16; The Gehenna Stone Affair 15.00
.. Classic Vol. 4 TPB (2006, $14.99) r/#17-23 15.00
.. Classic Vol. 5 TPB (2007, $14.99) r/#24-30 15.00
../Deadpool: Weapon X TPB (7/02, $21.99)-r/#162-166 & Deadpool #57-60 22.00
.. Doombringer (11/97, $5.99)-Silver Samurai-c/app. 6.00
.. Evilution (9/94, $5.95) 6.00
..: Global Jeopardy 1 (12/93, $2.95, one-shot)-Embossed-c; Sub-Mariner, Zabu, Ka-Zar, Shanna & Wolverine app.; produced in cooperation with World Wildlife Fund 5.00
...:Inner Fury nn (1992, $5.95, 52 pgs.)-Sienkiewicz-c/a 6.00
...: Judgment Night (2000, $3.99) Shi app.; Battlebook 4.00
...: Killing (9/93)-Kent Williams-a 6.00
...: Knight of Terra (1995, $6.95)-Ostrander script 7.00
... Legends Vol. 2: Meltdown (2003, $19.99) r/Havok & Wolverine: Meltdown #1-4 20.00
.. Legends Vol. 3 (2003, $12.99) r/#181-186 13.00
.. Legends Vol. 4,5: 4-(See Wolverine: Xisle). 5-(See Wolverine: Snikt!)
.. Legends Vol. 6: Marc Silvestri Book 1 (2004, $19.99) r/#31-34, 41-42, 48-50 20.00
../ Nick Fury: The Scorpio Connection Hardcover (1989, $16.95) 25.00
../ Nick Fury: The Scorpio Connection Softcover(1990, $12.95) 15.00
..: Not Dead Yet (12/98, $14.95, TPB)-r/#119-122 15.00
..: Save The Tiger 1 (7/92, $2.95, 84 pgs.)-Reprints Wolverine stories from Marvel Comics Presents #1-10 w/new Kieth-c 4.00
...Scorpio Rising ($5.95, prestige format, one-shot) 6.00
../Shi: Dark Night of Judgment (Crusade Comics, 2000, $2.99) Tucci-a 4.00
..Triumphs And Tragedies-(1995, $16.95, trade paperback)-r/Uncanny X-Men #109,172,173, Wolverine limited series #4, & Wolverine #41,42,75 17.00
...Typhoid's Kiss (6/94, $6.95)-r/Wolverine stories from Marvel Comics Presents #109-116 7.00
..Vs. Spider-Man 1 (3/95, $2.50) -r/Marvel Comics Presents #48-50 5.00
.../Witchblade 1 (3/97, $2.95) Devil's Reign Pt. 5 4.00
Wizard #1/2 (1997) Joe Phillips-a(p) 10.00

NOTE: ***Austin*** *c-3i.* ***Bolton*** *c(back)-5.* ***Buscema*** *a-1-16,25,27p; c-1-10.* ***Byrne*** *a-17-22p, 23; c-1(back), 17-22, 23p.* ***Colan*** *a-24.* ***Andy Kubert*** *c/a-51.* ***Jim Lee*** *c-24, 25, 27.* ***Silvestri*** *a(p)-31-43, 45, 46, 48-50, 52, 53, 55-57; c-31-42p, 43, 45p, 46p, 48, 49p, 50p, 52p, 53p, 55-57p.* ***Stroman*** *a-44p; c-60p.* ***Williamson*** *a-1i, 3-8i; c(i)-1, 3-6.*

WOLVERINE (Volume 3) (Titled Dark Wolverine from #75-90)(See Daken: Dark Wolverine)
Marvel Comics: July, 2003 - No. 90, Oct, 2010 ($2.25/$2.50/$2.99)

1-Rucka-s/Robertson-a 5.00
2-19: 6-Nightcrawler app. 13-16-Sabretooth app. 3.00
20-Millar-s/Romita, Jr.-a begin, Elektra app. 4.00
20-B&W variant-c 1 3 4 6 8 10
21-39: 21-Elektra-c/app. 23,24-Daredevil app. 26-28-Land-c. 29-Quesada-c; begin $2.50-c. 33-35-House of M. 36,37-Decimation. 36-Quesada-c. 39-Winter Soldier app. 3.00
40,43-48: 40-Begin $2.99-c; Winter Soldier app.; Texeira-a. 43-46-Civil War; Ramos-a. 45-Sub-Mariner app. 3.00
41,49-($3.99) 41-C.P. Smith-a/Stuart Moore-s 4.00
42-Civil War 5.00
50-($3.99) Sabretooth app.; Bianchi-a/c & Loeb-s begin; wraparound-c; McGuinness-a 4.00
50-($3.99) Variant Edition; uncolored art and cover; Bianchi pencil art page 4.00
51-55-(Regular and variant uncolored editions) Bianchi-a/Loeb-s; Sabretooth app. 3.00
55-EC-style variant-c by Greg Land 5.00
56-($3.99) Howard Chaykin-a/c 4.00
57-65: 57-61-Suydam Zombie-c; Chaykin-a. 62-65-Mystique app. 3.00
66-Old Man Logan begins; Millar-s/McNiven-a; McNiven wraparound-c
3 6 9 17 26 35
66-Variant-c by Michael Turner 5 10 15 33 57 80
66-Variant sketch-c by Michael Turner 100.00
66-2nd printing with McNiven variant-c of Logan and Hulk gang member
3 6 9 16 23 30
66-(5/10, $1.00) Reprint with "Marvel's Greatest Comics" on cover 3.00
67-72-Old Man Logan (concludes in Wolverine: Old Man Logan Giant-Sized Special). 67-Intro. Ashley, Spider-Man's granddaughter. 72-Red Skull app.
1 3 4 6 8 10
73,74-Andy Kubert-a 4.00
75-($3.99) Dark Reign, Daken as Wolverine on Osborn's team; Camuncoli-a 5.00
76-90: 76-86-Multiple covers for each. 76-Dark Reign; Yu-c. 82-84-Siege. 88,89-Franken-Castle x-over; Punisher app. 3.00
#900 (7/10, $4.99) Short stories by various incl. Finch, Rivera, Segovia, McGuinness 5.00
Annual 1 (12/07, $3.99) Hurwitz-s/Frusin-a 4.00
Annual 2 (11/08, $3.99) Swierczynski-s/Deodato-a/c 4.00
...: Blood & Sorrow TPB (2007, $13.99) r/#41,49, stories from Giant-Size Wolverine #1 and X-Men Unlimited #12 14.00
...: Chop Shop 1 (1/09, $2.99) Benson-s/Boschi-a/Hanuka-c 3.00
Civil War: Wolverine TPB (2007, $17.99) r/#42-48; gallery of B&W cover inks 18.00
... Dangerous Games 1 (8/08, $3.99) Spurrier-s/Oliver-a; Remender-s/Opena-a 4.00
...Enemy of the State HC Vol. 1 (2005, $19.99) r/#20-25; Ennis intro.; variant covers 20.00
...Enemy of the State HC Vol. 2 (2005, $19.99) r/#26-32 20.00
...Enemy of the State SC Vol. 1 (2005, $14.99) r/#20-25; Ennis intro.; variant covers 15.00
...Enemy of the State SC Vol. 2 (2006, $16.99) r/#26-32 17.00
...Enemy of the State - The Complete Edition (2006, $34.99) r/#20-32; Ennis intro.; sketch pages, variant covers and pin-up art 35.00
...: Evolution SC (2008, $14.99) r/#50-55 15.00
...: Flies to a Spider (2/09, $3.99) Bradstreet-c/Hurwitz-s/Opena-a 4.00
...: Killing Made Simple (10/08, $3.99) Yost-s/Turnbull-a 4.00
...: Enemy of the State MGC #20 (7/11, $1.00) r/#20 with "Marvel's Greatest Comics" logo 3.00
...: Japan's Most Wanted HC (2014, $34.99) printing of material that debuted online 35.00
...: Mr. X (5/10, $3.99) Tieri-s/Diaz-a/Mattina-c 4.00
...: Old Man Logan Giant-Sized Special (11/09, $4.99) Continued from #72; cover gallery 5.00
...Origins & Endings HC (2006, $19.99) r/#36-40 20.00
...Origins & Endings SC (2006, $13.99) r/#36-40 14.00
...: Origin of an X-Man Free Comic Book Day 2009 (5/09) Gurihiru-a/McGuinness-c 3.00
...: Revolver (8/09, $3.99) Gischler-s/Pastoras-a 4.00
... Saga (2009, giveaway) history of the character in text and comic panels 3.00
...: Saudade (2008, $4.99) English adaptation of Wolverine story from French comic 5.00
...: Savage (4/10, $3.99) J. Scott Campbell-c; The Lizard app. 4.00
...Special: Firebreak (2/08, $3.99) Carey-s/Kolins-a; Lolos-a 4.00
...: Switchback 1 (3/09, $3.99) short stories; art by Pastoras & Doe 4.00
...: The Amazing Immortal Man & Other Bloody Tales (7/08, $3.99) Lapham short stories 4.00
...: The Anniversary (6/09, $3.99) Mariko flashback short stories; art by various 4.00
...: The Death of Wolverine HC (2008, $19.99) r/#56-61 20.00
...: The Road to Hell (11/10, $3.99) Previews new Wolverine titles and Generation Hope 4.00
...: Under the Boardwalk (2/10, $3.99) Coker-a 4.00
...Vol. 1: The Brotherhood (2003, $12.99) r/#1-6 13.00
...Vol. 2: Coyote Crossing (2004, $11.99) r/#7-11 12.00
... Weapon X Files (2009, $4.99) Handbook-style pages of Wolverine characters 5.00
...: Wendigo! 1 (3/10, $3.99) Gulacy-a; back-up with Thor 4.00

WOLVERINE (Volume 4) (Also see Savage Wolverine)
Marvel Comics: Nov, 2010 - No. 20, Feb, 2012; No. 300, Mar, 2012 - No. 317, Feb, 2013 ($3.99/$4.99)

1-5-Jae Lee-c/Guedes-a; Wolverine Goes to Hell. 1-Back-up with Silver Samurai 4.00
5.1-(4/11, $2.99) Aaron-s/Palo-a/Rivera-c 3.00
6-20: 6-Jae Lee-c/Acuña-a; X-Men & Magneto app. 20-Kingpin & Sabretooth app. 4.00
300-(3/12, $4.99) Adam Kubert-c; Sabretooth & new Silver Samurai app. 5.00
301-308,310-317: 301-304-Aaron-s. 302-Art Adams-c. 310-313-Bianchi-a/c 4.00
309-($4.99) Elixir with X-Force; Albuquerque-a; Ribic-c 5.00
#1000 (4/11, $4.99) Short stories by various incl. Palmiotti, Green, Luke Ross; Segovia-c 5.00
Annual 1 (10/12, $4.99) Alan Davis-s/a/c; the Clan Destine app. (see Daredevil Ann. #1) 5.00
...: Debt of Death 1 (11/11, $3.99) Lapham-s/Aja-a/c; Nick Fury app. 4.00
.../Deadpool: The Decoy 1 (9/11, $3.99) prints online story from Marvel.com; Young-c 4.00

WOLVERINE (5th series)
Marvel Comics: May, 2013 - No. 13, Mar, 2014 ($3.99)

1-13: 1-4-Cornell-s/Alan Davis-a/c; Nick Fury II app. 5-7-Pierfederici-a. 8-13-Killable 4.00
... In the Flesh (9/13, $3.99) Cosentino-s/Talajic-a 4.00

WOLVERINE (6th series)
Marvel Comics: Apr, 2014 - No. 12, Oct, 2014 ($3.99)

1-11: 1-Cornell-s/Stegman-a. 2-Superior Spider-Man app. 8,9-Iron Fist app. 4.00
12-($5.99) "1 Month To Die"; Cornell-s/Woods-a; Thor & Sabretooth app. 6.00
Annual 1 (10/14, $4.99) Jubilee app; Nguyen-c/Kalan-s/Marks-a 5.00

WOLVERINE & BLACK CAT: CLAWS 2 (See Claws for 1st series)
Marvel Comics: Aug, 2011 - No. 3, Nov, 2011 ($3.99, limited series)

1-3-Linsner-a/c; Palmiotti & Gray-s; Killraven app. 4.00

WOLVERINE AND JUBILEE
Marvel Comics: Mar, 2011 - No. 4, Jun, 2011 ($2.99, limited series)

1-4: 1-Vampire Jubilee; Kathryn Immonen-s/Phil Noto-a; Coipel-c 3.00

WOLVERINE AND POWER PACK
Marvel Comics: Jan, 2009 - No. 4, Apr, 2009 ($2.99, limited series)

1-4-Sumerak-s. 1,2-GuriHiru-a. 1-Sauron app. 3-Meet Wolverine as a child; Koblish-a 3.00

WOLVERINE AND THE PUNISHER: DAMAGING EVIDENCE
Marvel Comics: Oct, 1993 - No. 3, Dec, 1993 ($2.00, limited series)

1-3: 2,3-Indicia says "The Punisher and Wolverine..." 4.00

WOLVERINE & THE X-MEN (Regenesis)(See X-Men: Schism)

Wolverine and the X-Men #11 © MAR

Wolverine: Origins #50 © MAR

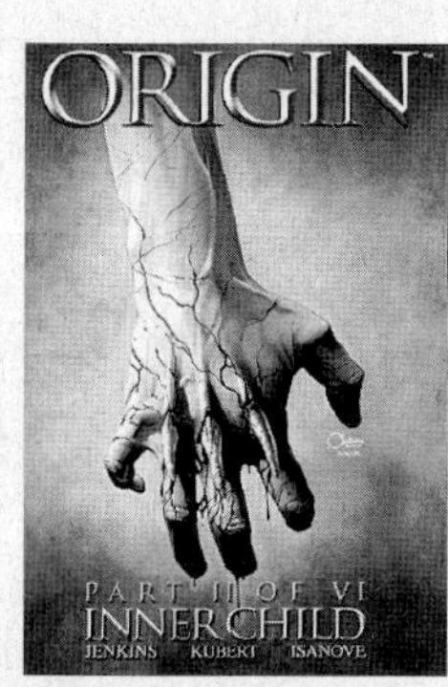

Wolverine: The Origin #2 © MAR

	GD 2.0	VG 4.0	FN 6.0	VF 8.0	VF/NM 9.0	NM- 9.2

Marvel Comics: Dec, 2011 - No. 42, Apr, 2014 ($3.99)
1-8: 1-3-Aaron-s/Bachalo-a/c. 3-Sabretooth app. 4-Bradshaw-a; Deathlok app. 4.00
9-27: 9-16,18-Avengers vs. X-Men tie-in. 17-Allred-a 4.00
27AU (6/13, $3.99) Age of Ultron tie-in; continues in Age of Ultron #6 4.00
28-41: 30-35-Hellfire Saga. 36,37-Battle of the Atom 4.00
42-($4.99) Cover swipe of X-Men #141 (1981) Graduation Day 5.00
Annual 1 (1/14, $4.99) Aaron-s/Bradshaw-a; Gladiator app. 5.00

WOLVERINE & THE X-MEN (2nd series)
Marvel Comics: May, 2014 - No. 12, Jan, 2015 ($3.99)
1-9,11,12: 1-Latour-s/Asrar-a; Fantomex app. 7-Daredevil app. 11-Spider-Man app. 4.00
10-($4.99) Follows Wolverine's death; art by various incl. Anka, Bertram, Rugg, Shalvey 5.00

WOLVERINE AND THE X-MEN: ALPHA & OMEGA
Marvel Comics: Dec, 2011 - No. 5, Jul, 2012 ($3.99, limited series)
1-5-Brooks-c/Boschi & Brooks-a; Quentin Quire vs. Wolverine 4.00

WOLVERINE/CAPTAIN AMERICA
Marvel Comics: Apr, 2004 - No. 4, Apr, 2004 ($2.99, limited series)
1-4-Derenick-a/c 3.00

WOLVERINE: DAYS OF FUTURE PAST
Marvel Comics: Dec, 1997 - No. 3, Feb, 1998 ($2.50, limited series)
1-3: J.F. Moore-s/Bennett-a 4.00

WOLVERINE/DOOP (Also see X-Force and X-Statix)(Reprinted in X-Statix Vol. 2)
Marvel Comics: July, 2003 - No. 2, July, 2003 ($2.99, limited series)
1,2-Peter Milligan-s/Darwyn Cooke & J. Bone-a 3.00

WOLVERINE: FIRST CLASS
Marvel Comics: May, 2008 - No. 21, Jan, 2010 ($2.99)
1-21: 1-Wolverine and Kitty Pryde's first mission; DiVito-a. 2,9-Sabretooth app. 3.00

WOLVERINE/GAMBIT: VICTIMS
Marvel Comics: Sept, 1995 - No. 4, Dec, 1995 ($2.95, limited series)
1-4: Jeph Loeb scripts & Tim Sale-a; foil-c 5.00

WOLVERINE/HERCULES: MYTHS, MONSTERS & MUTANTS
Marvel Comics: May, 2011 - No. 4, Aug, 2011 ($2.99, limited series)
1-4-Tieri-s/Santacruz-a/Jusko-c 3.00

WOLVERINE/HULK
Marvel Comics: Apr, 2002 - No. 4, July, 2002 ($3.50, limited series)
1-4-Sam Kieth-s/a/c 4.00
Wolverine Legends Vol. 1: Wolverine/Hulk (2003, $9.99, TPB) r/#1-4 10.00

WOLVERINE: MANIFEST DESTINY
Marvel Comics: Dec, 2008 - No. 4, Mar, 2009 ($2.99, limited series)
1-4-Aaron-s/Segovia-a 3.00

WOLVERINE MAX
Marvel Comics: Dec, 2012 - No. 15, Mar, 2014 ($3.99)
1-15: 1-5-Starr-s/Boschi-a/Jock-c; Victor Creed app. 4.00

WOLVERINE: NETSUKE
Marvel Comics: Nov, 2002 - No. 4, Feb, 2003 ($3.99, limited series)
1-4-George Pratt-s/painted-a 4.00

WOLVERINE: NOIR (1930s Pulp-style)
Marvel Comics: Apr, 2009 - No. 4, Sept, 2009 ($3.99, limited series)
1-4-C.P. Smith-a/Stuart Moore; covers by Smith & Calero; alternate Logan as detective 4.00

WOLVERINE: ORIGINS
Marvel Comics: June, 2006 - No. 50, Sept, 2010 ($2.99)
1-15: 1-Daniel Way-s/Steve Dillon-a/Quesada-c 3.00
1-10-Variant covers. 1-Turner. 2-Quesada & Hitch. 3-Bianchi. 4-Dell'Otto. 7-Deodato 4.00
16-($3.99) Captain America WW2 app.; preview of Wolverine #56; r/X-Men #268 4.00
16-Variant-c by McGuinness 4.00
17-24: 17-20-Capt. America & Bucky app. 21-24-Deadpool app.; Bianchi-c 3.00
25-($3.99) Deadpool app.; Bianchi-c; r/Deadpool's 1st app. in New Mutants #98 5.00
26-49: 26-Origin of Dakan; Way-s/Segovia-a/Land-c. 28-Hulk & Wendigo app. 3.00
50-($3.99) Last issue; Nick Fury app. 4.00
Annual 1 (9/07, $3.99) Way-s/Andrews-a; flashback to 1932 4.00
... Vol. 1 - Born in Blood HC (2006, $19.99, dustjacket) r/#1-5; variant covers 20.00
... Vol. 1 - Born in Blood SC (2007, $13.99) r/#1-5; variant covers 14.00
... Vol. 2 - Savior HC (2007, $19.99, dustjacket) r/#6-10; variant covers 20.00
... Vol. 2 - Savior SC (2007, $13.99) r/#6-10; variant covers 14.00
... Vol. 3 - Swift & Terrible HC (2007, $19.99, dustjacket) r/#11-15 20.00
... Vol. 3 - Swift & Terrible SC (2007, $13.99) r/#11-15 14.00
... Vol. 4 - Our War HC (2008, $19.99, dustjacket) r/#16-20 & Annual #1 20.00
... Vol. 4 - Our War SC (2008, $14.99) r/#16-20 & Annual #1 15.00

WOLVERINE/PUNISHER
Marvel Comics: May, 2004 - No. 5, Sept, 2004 ($2.99, limited series)
1-5: Milligan-s/Weeks-a 3.00
... Vol. 1 TPB (2004, $13.99) r/series 14.00

WOLVERINE, PUNISHER & GHOST RIDER: OFFICIAL INDEX TO THE MARVEL UNIVERSE
Marvel Comics: Oct, 2011 - No. 8, May, 2012 ($3.99)
1-8-Each issue has chronological synopsies, creator credits, character lists for 30-40 issues of their own titles and headlining mini-series 4.00

WOLVERINE/PUNISHER REVELATIONS (Marvel Knights)
Marvel Comics: Jun, 1999 - No. 4, Sept, 1999 ($2.95, limited series)
1-4: Pat Lee-a(p) 4.00
...: Revelation (4/00, $14.95, TPB) r/#1-4 15.00

WOLVERINES (Follows Death of Wolverine)
Marvel Comics: Mar, 2015 - No. 20, Aug, 2015 ($3.99, weekly series)
1-20: 1-Soule-s/Bradshaw-a; Sabretooth, Daken, Mystique, X-23 app. 13-Deadpool app. 4.00

WOLVERINE SAGA
Marvel Comics: Sept, 1989 - No. 4, Mid-Dec, 1989 ($3.95, lim. series, 52 pgs.)
1-Gives history; Liefeld/Austin-c (front & back) 6.00
2-4: 2-Romita, Jr./Austin-c. 4-Kaluta-c 6.00

WOLVERINE: SNIKT!
Marvel Comics: July, 2003 - No. 5, Nov, 2003 ($2.99, limited series)
1-5-Manga-style; Tsutomu Nihei-s/a 3.00
Wolverine Legends Vol. 5: Snikt! TPB (2003, $13.99) r/#1-5 14.00

WOLVERINE: SOULTAKER
Marvel Comics: May, 2005 - No. 5, Aug, 2005 ($2.99, limited series)
1-5-Yoshida-s/Nagasawa-a/Terada-c; Yukio app. 3.00
TPB (2005, $13.99) r/#1-5 14.00

WOLVERINE: THE BEST THERE IS
Marvel Comics: Feb, 2011 - No. 12, Jan, 2012 ($3.99)
1-12: 1,2-Huston-s/Ryp-a; covers by Hitch and Djurdjevic. 3-12-Hitch-c 4.00
... - Contagion 1 (6/11, $4.99) r/#1-3, cover gallery 5.00

WOLVERINE: THE END
Marvel Comics: Jan, 2004 - No. 6, Dec, 2004 ($2.99, limited series)
1-5-Jenkins-s/Castellini-a 3.00
1-Wizard World Texas variant-c 20.00
TPB (2005, $14.99) r/#1-5 15.00

WOLVERINE: THE ORIGIN
Marvel Comics: Nov, 2001 - No. 6, July, 2002 ($3.50, limited series)
1-Origin of Logan; Jenkins-s/Andy Kubert-a; Quesada-c 35.00
1-DF edition 25.00
2 10.00
3-6 6.00
HC (3/02, $34.95, 11" x 7-1/2") r/#1-6; dust jacket; sketch pages and treatments 35.00
HC (2006, $19.99) r/#1-6; dust jacket; sketch pages and treatments 20.00
SC (2002, $14.95) r/#1-6; afterwords by Jemas and Quesada 15.00

WOLVERINE WEAPON X
Marvel Comics: June, 2009 - No. 16, Oct, 2010 ($3.99)
1-16: 1-5,11-Aaron-s/Garney-a. 1-Four covers. 2,3-Two covers. 11-15-Deathlok app. 4.00

WOLVERINE: XISLE
Marvel Comics: June, 2003 - No. 5, June, 2003 ($2.50, weekly limited series)
1-5-Bruce Jones-s/Jorge Lucas-a 3.00
Wolverine Legends Vol. 4 TPB (2003, $13.99) r/ #1-5 14.00

WOMANTHOLOGY: SPACE
IDW Publishing: Sept, 2012 - No. 5, Feb, 2013 ($3.99)
1-5-Anthology of short stories by women creators 4.00

WOMEN IN LOVE (A Feature Presentation #5)
Fox Feature Synd./Hero Books: Aug, 1949 - No. 4, Feb, 1950

	GD 2.0	VG 4.0	FN 6.0	VF 8.0	VF/NM 9.0	NM- 9.2
1	43	86	129	271	461	650
2-Kamen/Feldstein-c	39	78	117	240	395	550
3	30	60	90	177	289	400
4-Wood-a	36	72	108	211	343	475

WOMEN IN LOVE (Thrilling Romances for Adults)
Ziff-Davis Publishing Co.: Winter, 1952 (25¢, 100 pgs.)

Women of Marvel #2 © MAR

Wonder Comics #14 © FOX

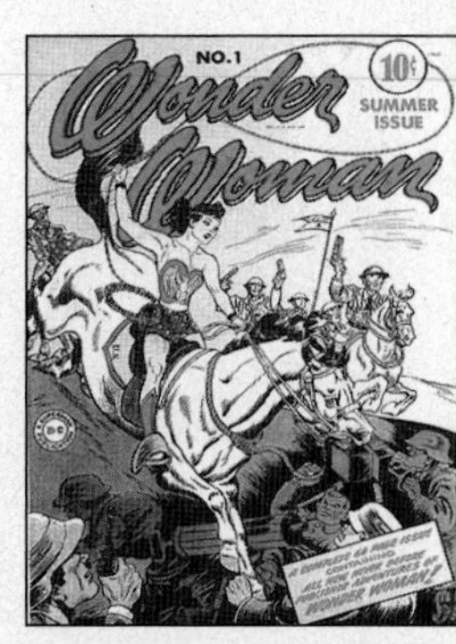

Wonder Woman #1 © DC

	GD 2.0	VG 4.0	FN 6.0	VF 8.0	VF/NM 9.0	NM- 9.2
nn-(Scarce)-Kinstler-a; painted-c	84	168	252	538	919	1300

WOMEN OF MARVEL
Marvel Comics: 2006, 2007 ($24.99, TPB)

SC-Reprints 1st apps. of Dazzler, Ms. Marvel, Shanna, The Cat plus notable stories of other female Marvel characters; Mayhew-c — 25.00
Vol. 2 (2007) More stories of female Marvel characters; Mayhew-c; cover process art — 25.00

WOMEN OF MARVEL
Marvel Comics: Jan, 2011 - No. 2, Feb, 2011 ($3.99, limited series)

1,2-Short stories of female Marvel characters. 1-Pichelli-c. 2-Land-c — 4.00

WOMEN OUTLAWS (My Love Memories #9 on)(Also see Red Circle)
Fox Feature Syndicate: July, 1948 - No. 8, Sept, 1949

	GD	VG	FN	VF	VF/NM	NM-
1-Used in **SOTI**, illo "Giving children an image of American womanhood"; negligee panels	94	188	282	597	1024	1450
2,3: 3-Kamenish-a	68	136	204	435	743	1050
4-8	59	108	162	343	574	825
nn(nd)-Contains Cody of the Pony Express; same cover as #7	28	56	84	165	270	375

WOMEN TO LOVE
Realistic: No date (1953)

	GD	VG	FN	VF	VF/NM	NM-
nn-(Scarce)-Reprints Complete Romance #1; c-/Avon paperback #165	43	86	129	271	461	650

WONDER BOY (Formerly Terrific Comics) (See Blue Bolt, Bomber Comics & Samson)
Ajax/Farrell Publ.: No. 17, May, 1955 - No. 18, July, 1955 (Code approved)

	GD	VG	FN	VF	VF/NM	NM-
17-Phantom Lady app. Bakerish-c/a	52	104	156	328	552	775
18-Phantom Lady app.	42	84	126	265	445	625

NOTE: *Phantom Lady not by Matt Baker.*

WONDER COMICS (Wonderworld #3 on)
Fox Feature Syndicate: May, 1939 - No. 2, June, 1939 (68 pgs.)

	GD	VG	FN	VF	VF/NM	NM-
1-(Scarce)-Wonder Man only app. by Will Eisner; Dr. Fung (by Powell), K-5 begins; Bob Kane-a; Eisner-c	2500	5000	7500	17,500	30,750	44,000
2-(Scarce)-Yarko the Great, Master Magician (see Samson) by Eisner begins; 'Spark' Stevens by Bob Kane, Patty O'Day, Tex Mason app. Lou Fine's 1st-c; Fine-a (2 pgs.); Yarko-c (Wonder Man-c #1)	838	1676	2514	6117	10,809	15,500

WONDER COMICS
Great/Nedor/Better Publications: May, 1944 - No. 20, Oct, 1948

	GD	VG	FN	VF	VF/NM	NM-
1-The Grim Reaper & Spectro, the Mind Reader begin; Hitler/Hirohito bondage-c	354	708	1062	2478	4339	6200
2-Origin The Grim Reaper; Super Sleuths begin, end #8,17; Schomburg Nazi WWII-c	194	388	582	1242	2121	3000
3-5: All Schomburg Nazi WWII-c. 3-Indicia reads "Vol. 1, #2"	181	362	543	1158	1979	2800
6-Japanese WWII Flag-c	123	246	369	787	1344	1900
7-10: 8-Last Spectro. 9-Wonderman begins	90	180	270	576	988	1400
11-13: 11-Dick Devens, King of Futuria begins, ends #14. 11,12-Ingels-c & splash pg. 12-Bondage/headlight-c by Ingels	110	220	330	704	1202	1700
14-Classic Schomburg sci-fi good girl bondage-c	135	270	405	864	1482	2100
15-Tara begins (origin), ends #20; classic Schomburg bondage/torture-c	232	464	696	1485	2543	3600
16,18: 16-Spectro app.; last Grim Reaper. 18-The Silver Knight begins	77	154	231	493	847	1200
17-Wonderman with Frazetta panels; Jill Trent with all Frazetta inks	87	174	261	553	952	1350
19-Frazetta panels	87	174	261	553	952	1350
20-Most of Silver Knight by Frazetta	103	206	309	659	1130	1600

NOTE: ***Ingels** c-11, 12. **Roussos** a-19. **Schomburg (Xela)** c-1-10; (airbrush)-13-20. Bondage c-12, 13, 15. Cover features: Grim Reaper #1-8; Wonder Man #9-15; Tara #16-20.*

WONDER DUCK (See Wisco)
Marvel Comics (CDS): Sept, 1949 - No. 3, Mar, 1950

	GD	VG	FN	VF	VF/NM	NM-
1-Funny animal	22	44	66	132	216	300
2,3	15	30	45	86	133	180

WONDERFUL ADVENTURES OF PINOCCHIO, THE (See Movie Comics & Walt Disney Showcase #48)
Whitman Publishing Co.: April, 1982 (Walt Disney)

nn-(#3 Continuation of Movie Comics?); r/FC #92 — 6.00

WONDERFUL WIZARD OF OZ (Adaptation of the original 1900 L. Frank Baum book) (Also see the sequels Marvelous Land of Oz, Ozma of Oz, and Dorothy & The Wizard in Oz)
Marvel Comics: Feb, 2009 - No. 8, Sept, 2009 ($3.99, limited series)

1-8-Eric Shanower-a/Skottie Young-a/c — 4.00
1-Variant Good Witch & Dorothy wraparound cover by J. Scott Campbell — 8.00
1-Variant Scarecrow & Dorothy cover by Eric Shanower — 10.00
1-(4/10, $1.00) Reprint with "Marvel's Greatest Comics" on cover — 3.00
... Sketchbook (2008, giveaway) Young character design sketches; Shanower intro. — 3.00
HC (2009, $29.99, dustjacket) r/#1-8; Shanower intro.; cover gallery; sketch art — 30.00

WONDERFUL WORLD FOR BOYS AND GIRLS
DC Comics: May, 1964

nn - Ashcan comic, not distributed to newsstands, only for in-house use — (no known sales)

WONDERFUL WORLD OF DISNEY, THE (Walt Disney)
Whitman Publishing Co.: 1978 (Digest, 116 pgs.)

	GD	VG	FN	VF	VF/NM	NM-
1-Barks-a (reprints)	3	6	9	16	23	30
2 (no date)	2	4	6	11	16	20

WONDERFUL WORLD OF TANK GIRL
Titan Comics: Nov, 2017 - Present ($3.99, limited series)

1,2: 1-Tank Girl Strikes Again; Martin-s/Parson-a; multiple covers — 4.00

WONDERFUL WORLD OF THE BROTHERS GRIMM (See Movie Comics)

WONDER GIRL (Cassandra Sandsmark from Teen Titans)
DC Comics: Nov, 2007 - No. 6, Apr, 2008 ($2.99, limited series)

1-6-Torres-s/Greene-a; Hercules app. 2-6-Female Furies app. 5,6-Wonder Woman app. — 3.00
Teen Titans Spotlight: Wonder Girl TPB (2008, $17.99) r/#1-6 — 18.00
1-(3/11, $2.99, one-shot) Nicola Scott-c; intro. Solstice — 3.00

WONDERLAND (See Grimm Fairy Tales Presents Wonderland)

WONDERLAND COMICS
Feature Publications/Prize: Summer, 1945 - No. 9, Feb-Mar, 1947

	GD	VG	FN	VF	VF/NM	NM-
1-Alex in Wonderland begins; Howard Post-c	34	68	102	204	332	460
2-Howard Post-c/a(2)	18	36	54	107	169	230
3-9: 3,4-Post-c	16	32	48	96	151	205

WONDER MAN (See The Avengers #9, 151)
Marvel Comics Group: Mar, 1986 ($1.25, one-shot, 52 pgs.)

1 — 5.00

WONDER MAN
Marvel Comics Group: Sept, 1991 - No. 29, Jan, 1994 ($1.00)

1-29: 1-Free fold out poster by Johnson/Austin. 1-3-Johnson/Austin-c/a. 2-Avengers West Coast x-over. 4 Austin-c(i) — 3.00
Annual 1 (1992, $2.25)-Immonen-a (10 pgs.) — 4.00
Annual 2 (1993, $2.95)-Bagged w/trading card — 4.00

WONDER MAN
Marvel Comics: Feb, 2007 - No. 5, June, 2007 ($2.99, limited series)

1-5: 1-Peter David-s/Andrew Currie-a; Beast app. 4-Nauck-a — 3.00
...: My Fair Super Hero TPB (2007, $13.99) r/#1-5; Currie sketch page — 14.00

WONDERS OF ALADDIN, THE
Dell Publishing Co.: No. 1255, Feb-Apr, 1962

	GD	VG	FN	VF	VF/NM	NM-
Four Color 1255-Movie	6	12	18	40	73	105

WONDER WOMAN (See Adventure Comics #459, All-Star Comics, Brave & the Bold, DC Comics Presents, JLA, Justice League of America, Legend of..., Power Record Comics, Sensation Comics, Super Friends and World's Finest Comics #244)

WONDER WOMAN
DC Comics: Jan 1942

1-Ashcan comic, not distributed to newsstands, only for in-house use. Cover art is Sensation Comics #1 with interior being Sensation Comics #2. A CGC certified 8.5 copy sold for $17,250 in 2002.

WONDER WOMAN
National Periodical Publications/All-American Publ./DC Comics: Summer, 1942 - No. 329, Feb, 1986

	GD	VG	FN	VF	VF/NM	NM-
1-Origin Wonder Woman retold (more detailed than All Star #8); H. G. Peter-c/a begins	9000	18,000	27,000	60,000	110,000	160,000

1-Reprint, Oversize 13-1/2x10". **WARNING:** This comic is an exact reprint of the original except for its size. DC published it in 1974 with a second cover titling it as a Famous First Edition. There have been many reported cases of the outer cover being removed and the interior sold as the original edition. The reprint with the new outer cover removed is practically worthless. See Famous First Edition for value.

	GD	VG	FN	VF	VF/NM	NM-
2-Origin/1st app. Mars; Duke of Deception app.	649	1298	1947	4738	8369	12,000
3	343	686	1029	2400	4200	6000
4,5: 5-1st Dr. Psycho app.	300	600	900	1950	3375	4800
6-1st Cheetah app.	649	1298	1947	4738	8369	12,000
7-Wonder Woman for President-c/sty	649	1298	1947	4738	8369	12,000
8,9: 9-1st app. Giganta (Sum/44)	226	452	678	1446	2473	3500
10-Invasion from Saturn classic sci-fi-c/s	232	464	696	1485	2543	3600

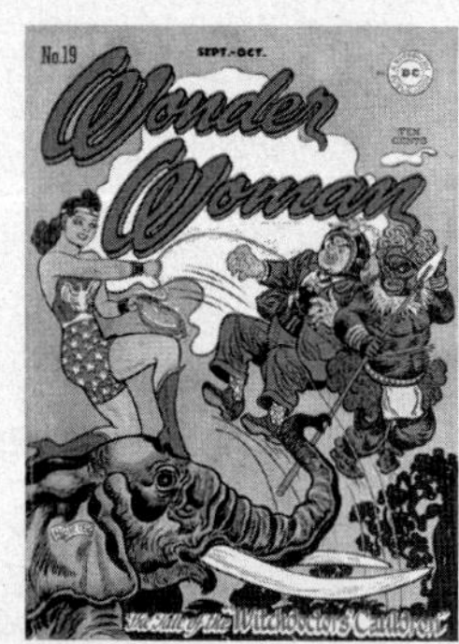

Wonder Woman #19 © DC

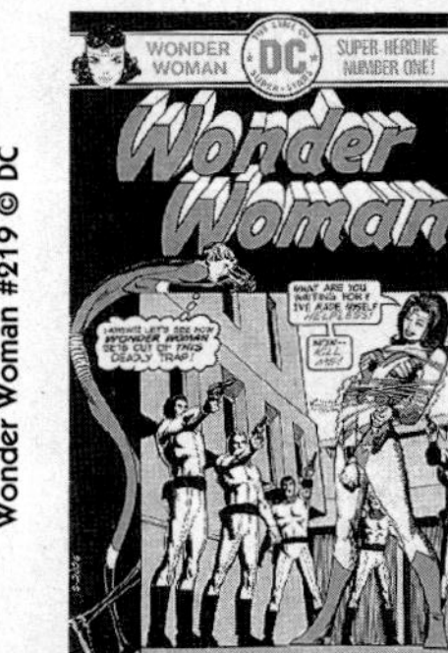

Wonder Woman #219 © DC

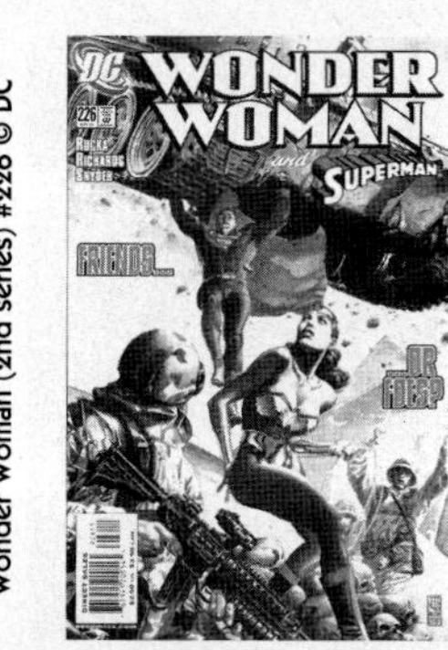

Wonder Woman (2nd series) #226 © DC

	GD 2.0	VG 4.0	FN 6.0	VF 8.0	VF/NM 9.0	NM- 9.2
11-20	135	270	405	864	1482	2100
21-30: 23-Story from Wonder Woman's childhood. 28-Cheetah and Giganta-c/app.	113	226	339	718	1234	1750
31-33,35-40: 38-Last H.G. Peter-c	103	206	309	659	1130	1600
34-Robot-c	106	212	318	673	1162	1650
41-44,46-48	100	200	300	635	1093	1550
45-Origin retold	206	412	618	1318	2259	3200
49-Used in **SOTI**, pgs. 234,236; last 52 pg. issue	103	206	309	659	1130	1600
50-(44 pgs.)-Used in **POP**, pg. 97	103	206	309	659	1130	1600
51-60: 60-New logo	94	188	282	597	1024	1450
61-72: 62-Origin of W.W. i.d. 64-Story about 3-D movies. 70-1st Angle Man app. 72-Last pre-code (2/55)	90	180	270	576	988	1400
73-90: 80-Origin The Invisible Plane. 89-Flying saucer-c/story	81	162	243	518	884	1250
91-94,96,97: 97-Last H. G. Peter-a	68	136	204	435	743	1050
95-A-Bomb-c	71	142	213	454	777	1100
98-(5/58) 1st Silver Age Wonder Woman; new origin & new art team (Andru & Esposito) begin; Kanigher-s; 1st meets Steve Trevor	371	742	1113	2600	4550	6500
99-New origin continues; origin Diana Prince i.d.	77	154	231	493	847	1200
100-(8/58)	71	142	213	454	777	1100
101-104,106,108-110	50	100	150	315	533	750
105-(Scarce, 4/59)-Wonder Woman's origin (part 3); she appears as a girl (no costume yet) (called Wonder Girl - see DC Super-Stars #1)	258	516	774	1651	2826	4000
107-1st advs. of Wonder Girl; 1st Merboy; tells how Wonder Woman won her costume	57	114	171	362	619	875
111-120	39	78	117	231	378	525
121-126: 121-1st app. Wonder Woman Family. 122-1st app. Wonder Tot. 124-Wonder Woman Family app. 126-Last 10¢ issue	32	64	96	188	307	425
127-130: 128-Origin The Invisible Plane retold. 129-3rd app. Wonder Woman Family (#133 is 4th app.)	14	28	42	96	211	325
131-150: 132-Flying saucer-c	12	24	36	79	170	260
151-155,157,158,161-170 (1967): 151-Wonder Girl solo issue.	9	18	27	59	117	175
156-(8/65)-Early mention of a comic book shop & comic collecting; mentions DCs selling for $100 a copy	9	18	27	62	126	190
159-Origin retold (1/66); 1st S.A. origin?	11	22	33	73	157	240
160-1st S.A. Cheetah app.	15	30	45	103	227	350
171-176	7	14	21	48	89	130
177-W. Woman/Supergirl battle	9	18	27	59	117	175
178-(10/68) 1st new Wonder Woman on-c only; appears in old costume w/powers inside	10	20	30	64	132	200
179-Classic-c; wears no costume to issue #203	9	18	27	62	126	190
180-195: 180-Death of Steve Trevor. 182-Last 12¢ issue. 195-Wood inks	5	10	15	35	63	90
196 (52 pgs.)-Origin-r/All Star #8 (6 out of 9 pgs.)	6	12	18	41	76	110
197,198 (52 pgs.)-Reprints	6	12	18	37	66	95
199-Jeff Jones painted-c; 52 pgs.	8	16	24	56	108	160
200 (5-6/72)-Jeff Jones-c; 52 pgs.	8	16	24	56	108	160
201,202-Catwoman app. 202-Fafhrd & The Grey Mouser debut.	4	8	12	28	47	65
203,205-210,212: 212-The Cavalier app.	3	6	9	18	28	38
204-(2/73) Return to old costume; death of I Ching; intro. Nubia	8	16	24	54	102	150
211,214-(100 pgs.)	7	14	21	44	82	120
213,215,216,218-220: 220-N. Adams assist	3	6	9	16	24	32
217: (68 pgs.)	3	6	9	21	33	45
221,222,224-227,229,230,233-236,238-240: 227-Judy Garland tribute	2	4	6	10	14	18
223,228,231,232,237,241,248: 223-Steve Trevor revived as Steve Howard & learns W.W.'s I.D. 228-Both Wonder Women team up & new World War II stories begin, end #243. 231,232: JSA app. 237-Origin retold. 240-G.A. Flash app. 241-Intro Bouncer; Spectre app. 248-Steve Trevor Howard dies (44 pgs.)	2	4	6	11	16	20
242-246,252-266,269,270: 243-Both W. Women team-up again. 269-Last Wood a(i) for DC? (7/80)	2	3	4	6	8	10
247,249,250,271: 247,249 (44 pgs.). 249-Hawkgirl app. 250-Origin/1st app. Orana, the new Wonder Woman. 271-Huntress & 3rd Life of Steve Trevor begin	2	4	6	8	10	12
250-252,255-262-264-(Whitman variants, low print run, no issue # on cover)	2	4	6	13	18	22
251-Orana dies	2	4	6	11	16	20
267,268-Re-intro Animal Man (5/80 & 6/80)	2	4	6	8	10	12
272-280,284-286,289,290,294-299,301-325						6.00
281-283: Joker-c/stories in Huntress back-ups	2	3	4	6	8	10
287,288,291-293: 287-New Teen Titans x-over. 288-New costume & logo.						
291-293-Three part epic with Super-Heroines	1	2	3	4	5	7
300-($1.50, 76 pgs.)-Anniv. issue; Giffen-a; New Teen Titans, Bronze Age Sandman, JLA & G.A. Wonder Woman app.; 1st app. Lyta Trevor who becomes Fury in All-Star Squadron #25; G.A. Wonder Woman & Steve Trevor revealed as married	1	2	3	5	7	9
326-328	1	2	3	4	5	7
329 (Double size)-S.A. W.W. & Steve Trevor wed	2	4	6	9	13	16
...: Chronicles Vol. 1 TPB (2010, $17.99) reprints debut in All Star Comics #8, apps. in Sensation Comics #1-9 and Wonder Woman #1						18.00
Diana Prince: Wonder Woman Vol. 1 TPB (2008, $19.99) r/#178-183						20.00
Diana Prince: Wonder Woman Vol. 2 TPB (2008, $19.99) r/#185-189, Brave and the Bold #87, and Superman's Girl Friend, Lois Lane #93						20.00
Diana Prince: Wonder Woman Vol. 3 TPB ('08, $19.99) r/#190-198, World's Finest #204						20.00
Diana Prince: Wonder Woman Vol. 4 TPB ('09, $19.99) r/#199-204, Brave & Bold #105						20.00
...: The Greatest Stories Ever Told TPB (2007, $19.99) intro. by Lynda Carter; Ross-c						20.00

NOTE: ***Andru/Esposito** c-66-160(most). **Buckler** a-300. **Colan** a-288-305p; c-288-290p. **Giffen** a-300p. **Grell** c-217. **Kaluta** c-297. **Gil Kane** c-294p, 303-305, 307, 312, 314. **Miller** c-298p. **Morrow** c-233. **Nasser** a-232p; c-231p, 232p. **Bob Oskner** c(i)-39-65(most). **Perez** c-283p, 284p. **Spiegle** a-312. **Staton** a(p)-241, 271-287, 289, 290, 294-299; c(p)-241, 245, 246. Huntress back-up stories 271-287, 289, 290, 294-299, 301-321.*

WONDER WOMAN

DC Comics: Feb, 1987 - No. 226, Apr, 2006 (75¢/$1.00/$1.25/$1.95/$1.99/$2.25/$2.50)

	GD 2.0	VG 4.0	FN 6.0	VF 8.0	VF/NM 9.0	NM- 9.2
0-(10/94) Zero Hour; released between #90 & #91						6.00
1-New origin; Perez-c/a begins	3	6	9	16	23	30
2-5						6.00
6-20: 9-Origin Cheetah. 12,13-Millennium x-over. 18,26-Free 16 pg. story						5.00
21-49: 24-Last Perez-a; scripts continue thru #62						4.00
50-($1.50, 52 pgs.)-New Titans, Justice League						5.00
51-62: Perez scripts. 60-Vs. Lobo; last Perez-c. 62-Last $1.00-c						4.00
63-New direction & Bolland-c begin; Deathstroke story continued from W. W. Special #1						5.00
64-84						4.00
85-1st Deodato-a; ends #100	3	5	7	10	12	14
86-88: 88-Superman-c & app.						6.00
89-97: 90-(9/94)-1st Artemis. 91-(11/94). 93-Hawkman app. 96-Joker-c						5.00
98,99						4.00
100 ($2.95, Newsstand)-Death of Artemis; Bolland-c ends.						4.00
100 ($3.95, Direct Market)-Death of Artemis; foil-c.						6.00
101-119, 121-125: 101-Begin $1.95-c; Byrne-c/a/scripts begin. 101-104-Darkseid app. 105-Phantom Stranger cameo. 106-108-Phantom Stranger & Demon app. 107,108-Arion app. 111-1st app. new Wonder Girl. 111,112-Vs. Doomsday. 112-Superman app. 113-Wonder Girl-c/app; Sugar & Spike app.						3.00
120 ($2.95)-Perez-c						4.00
126-149: 128-Hippolyta becomes new W.W. 130-133-Flash (Jay Garrick) & JSA app. 136-Diana returns to W.W. role; last Byrne issue. 137-Priest-s. 139-Luke-s/Paquette-a begin; Hughes-c thru #146						3.00
150-($2.95) Hughes-c/Clark-a; Zauriel app.						4.00
151-158-Hughes-c. 153-Superboy app.						3.00
159-163: 159-Begin $2.25-c. 160,161-Clayface app. 162,163-Aquaman app.						3.00
164-171: Phil Jimenez-s/a begin; Hughes-c; Batman app. 168,169-Pérez co-plot 169-Wraparound-c.170-Lois Lane-c/app.						3.00
172-Our Worlds at War; Hippolyta killed						4.00
173,174: 173-Our Worlds at War; Darkseid app. 174-Every DC heroine app.						3.00
175-($3.50) Joker: Last Laugh; JLA app.; Jim Lee-c						4.00
176-199: 177-Paradise Island returns. 179-Jimenez-c. 184,185-Hippolyta-c/app.; Hughes-c 186-Cheetah app. 189-Simonson-s/Ordway-a begin. 190-Diana's new look. 195-Rucka-s/Drew Johnson-a begin. 197-Flash-c/app. 198,199-Noto-c						3.00
200-($3.95) back-up stories in 1940s and 1960s styles; pin-ups by various						4.00
201-218,220-225: 203,204-Batman-c/app. 204-Matt Wagner-c. 212-JLA app. 214-Flash app. 215-Morales-a begins. 218-Begin $2.50-c. 220-Batman app.						3.00
219-Omac tie-in/Sacrifice pt. 4; Wonder Woman kills Max Lord; Superman app.						4.00
219-(2nd printing) Altered cover with red background						3.00
226-Last issue; flashbacks to meetings with Superman; Rucka-s/Richards-a						4.00
#1,000,000 (11/98) 853rd Century x-over; Deodato-c						3.00
Annual 1,2: 1 ('88, $1.50)-Art Adams-a. 2 ('89, $2.00, 68 pgs.)-All women artists issue; Perez-c(i)/a.						4.00
Annual 3 (1992, $2.50, 68 pgs.)-Quesada-c(p)						4.00
Annual 4 (1995, $3.50)-Year One						4.00
Annual 5 (1996, $2.95)-Legends of the Dead Earth story; Byrne scripts; Cockrum-a						4.00
Annual 6 (1997, $3.95)-Pulp Heroes						4.00
Annual 7,8 ('98,'99, $2.95)-7-Ghosts; Wrightson-c. 8-JLApe, A.Adams-c						4.00
...: Beauty and the Beasts TPB (2005, $19.95) r/#15-19 & Action Comics #600						20.00
...: Bitter Rivals TPB (2004, $13.95) r/#200-205; Jones-c						14.00
...: Challenge of the Gods TPB ('04, $19.95) r/#8-14; Pérez-s/a						20.00
...: Destiny Calling TPB (2006, $19.99) r/#20-24 & Annual #1; Pérez-c & pin-up gallery						20.00
...Donna Troy (6/98, $1.95) Girlfrenzy; Jimenez-a						3.00

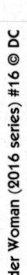

Wonder Woman (2006 series) #17 © DC

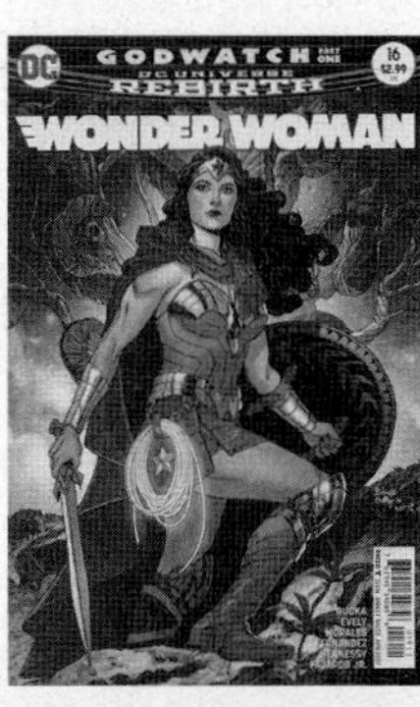

Wonder Woman (2016 series) #16 © DC

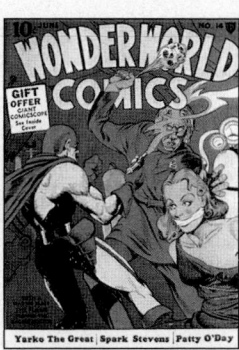

Wonderworld Comics #14 © FOX

	GD 2.0	VG 4.0	FN 6.0	VF 8.0	VF/NM 9.0	NM- 9.2

...: Down To Earth TPB (2004, $14.95) r/#195-200; Greg Land-c 15.00
... 80-Page Giant 1 (2002, $4.95) reprints in format of 1960s' 80-Page Giants 5.00
...: Eyes of the Gorgon TPB ('05, $19.99) r/#206-213 20.00
Gallery (1996, $3.50)-Bolland-c; pin-ups by various 4.00
...: Gods and Mortals TPB ('04, $19.95) r/#1-7; Pérez-a 20.00
...: Gods of Gotham TPB ('01, $5.95) r/#164-167; Jimenez-s/a 6.00
...: Land of the Dead TPB ('06, $12.99) r/#214-217 & Flash #219 13.00
Lifelines TPB ('98, $9.95) r/#106-112; Byrne-c/a 10.00
...: Mission's End TPB ('06, $19.99) r/#218-226; cover gallery 20.00
...: Our Worlds at War (10/01, $2.95) History of the Amazons; Jae Lee-c 3.00
...: Paradise Found TPB ('03, $14.95) r/#171-177, Secret Files #3; Jimenez-s/a 15.00
...: Paradise Lost TPB ('02, $14.95) r/#164-170; Jimenez-s/a 15.00
Plus 1 (1/97, $2.95)-Jesse Quick-c/app. 4.00
Second Genesis TPB (1997, $9.95)-r/#101-105 10.00
Secret Files 1-3 (3/98, 7/99, 5/02; $4.95) 5.00
Special 1 (1992, $1.75, 52 pgs.)-Deathstroke-c/story continued in Wonder Woman #63 5.00
...: The Blue Amazon (2003, $6.95) Elseworlds; McKeever-a 7.00
The Challenge Of Artemis TPB (1996, $9.95)-r/#94-100; Deodato-c/a 10.00
...: The Once and Future Story (1998, $4.95) Trina Robbins-s/Doran & Guice-a 5.00

NOTE: ***Art Adams*** *a-Annual 1.* ***Byrne*** *c/a 101-107.* ***Bolton*** *a-Annual 1.* ***Deodato*** *a-85-100.* ***Perez*** *a-Annual 1; c-Annual 1(i).* ***Quesada*** *c(p)-Annual 3.*

WONDER WOMAN (Also see Amazons Attack mini-series)
DC Comics: Aug, 2006 - No. 44, Jul, 2010; No. 600, Aug, 2010 - No. 614, Oct, 2011 ($2.99)

1-Donna Troy as Wonder Woman after Infinite Crisis; Heinberg-s/Dodson-a/c 3.00
1-Variant-c by Adam Kubert 6.00
2-44: 2-4-Giganta & Hercules app. 6-Jodi Picoult-s begins. 8-Hippolyta returns. 9-12-Amazons Attack tie-in; JLA app. 14-17-Simone-s/Dodson-a/c. 20-23-Stalker app. 26-33-Rise of the Olympian. 40,41-Power Girl app. 3.00
14-DC Nation Convention giveaway edition 6.00
(Title re-numbered after #44, July 2010 to cumilative numbering of #600)
600-(8/10, $4.99) Short stories and pin-ups by various incl. Pérez, Conner, Kramer, Jim Lee; intro. by Lynda Carter; debut of new costume; cover by Pérez 5.00
600-Variant cover by Adam Hughes 8.00
600-2nd printing with new costume cover by Don Kramer 5.00
601-614: 601-606-Kramer-a; two covers by Kramer and Garner. 608-Borges-a 3.00
... Annual 1 (11/07, $3.99) Story cont'd from #4; Heinberg-s/Dodson-a/c; back-up Frank-a 4.00
...: Contagion SC (2010, $14.99) r/#40-44 15.00
...: Ends of the Earth HC (2009, $24.99) r/#20-25 25.00
...: Ends of the Earth SC (2010, $14.99) r/#20-25 15.00
...: Love and Murder HC (2007, $19.99) r/#6-10 20.00
...: Odyssey Volume One HC (2011, $22.99) r/#600-606; afterwords by Jim Lee & JMS 23.00
...: Rise of the Olympian HC (2009, $24.99) r/#26-33 & pages from DC Universe #0 25.00
...: Rise of the Olympian SC (2009, $14.99) r/#26-33 & pages from DC Universe #0 15.00
...: The Circle HC (2008, $24.99) r/#14-19; Mercedes Lackey intro.; Dodson sketch pages 25.00
...: The Circle SC (2009, $14.99) r/#14-19; Mercedes Lackey intro.; Dodson sketch pages 15.00
...: Warkiller SC (2010, $14.99) r/#34-39 15.00
...: Who is Wonder Woman? HC (2007, $19.99) r/#1-4 & Annual #1; Vaughan intro. 20.00
...: Who is Wonder Woman? SC (2009, $14.99) r/#1-4 & Annual #1; Vaughan intro. 15.00

WONDER WOMAN (DC New 52)
DC Comics: Nov, 2011 - No. 52, Jul, 2016 ($2.99/$3.99)

1-Azzarello-s/Chiang-a/c 2 4 6 10 14 18
2-23: 2-4-Azzarello-s/Chiang-a/c. 5,6,9,10,13,14,17-Akins-a. 14-19,21-23-Orion app. 3.00
23.1, 23.2 (11/13, $2.99, regular covers) 3.00
23.1 (11/13, $3.99, 3-D cover) "Cheetah #1" on cover; origin; Ostrander-s/Ibanez-a 5.00
23.2 (11/13, $3.99, 3-D cover) "First Born #1" on cover; origin; Azzarello-s/Aco-a 5.00
24-35: 25-Orion app. 29-Diana becomes God of War. 35-Last Azzarello-s/Chiang-a/c 3.00
36-40: 36-Meredith Finch-s/David Finch-a begins. 37-Donna Troy returns 3.00
41-49,51,52: 41-New costume; begin $3.99-c. 43-Churchill-a 4.00
50-($4.99) Finch & Desjardins-a; Ares app.; back-up Donna Troy story 5.00
#0 (11/12, $2.99) 12 year-old Princess Diana's training; Azzarello-s/Chiang-a/c 3.00
Annual 1 (8/15, $4.99) Concludes "War Torn" arc from #36-40; David Finch-a 5.00
...: Futures End 1 (11/14, $2.99, regular-c) Five years later; Soule-s/Morales-a 3.00
...: Futures End 1 (11/14, $3.99, 3-D cover) 4.00

WONDER WOMAN (DC Rebirth)
DC Comics: Aug, 2016 - Present ($2.99)

1-24: 1,3,5,7-Rucka-s/Sharp-a; Cheetah app. 2,4,6,10,12,14-Year One; Nicola Scott-a 3.00
25-($3.99) Justice League and Shaggy Man app. 4.00
26-41: 26-Andolfo-a. 31,33-Grail & baby Darkseid app. 35-Intro. Jason. 37-Zeus vs. Darkseid. 38-40-Silver Swan app. 3.00
Annual 1 (7/17, $4.99) Retells 1st meeting with Superman & Batman; Scott-a 5.00
... #1 FCBD 2017 Special Edition (5/17, giveaway) r/#2; Year One; Nicola Scott-a 3.00
...: Rebirth 1 (8/16, $2.99) Rucka-s; multiples origins; new costume 3.00
... 75th Anniversary Special 1 (12/16, $7.99) short stories and pin-ups by various incl. Sharp, Moon, Bolland, DeLiz, Frison, Albuquerque, Larson, Jimenez, Sauvage; Jim Lee-c 8.00
...: Steve Trevor 1 (8/17, $3.99) Seeley-s/Duce-a 4.00
... / Tasmanian Devil Special 1 (8/17, $4.99) Bedard-s/Kitson-a; Circe app.; cartoon-style back-up with Caldwell-a; Daffy Duck & Wile E. Coyote app. 5.00

WONDER WOMAN: AMAZONIA
DC Comics: 1997 ($7.95, Graphic Album format, one shot)

1-Elseworlds; Messner-Loebs-s/Winslade-a 8.00

WONDER WOMAN / CONAN
DC Comics: Nov, 2017 - No. 6, Apr, 2018 ($3.99, limited series)

1-6-Simone-s/Lopresti-a; meet-up in Conan's time; the Corvidae app. 4.00

WONDER WOMAN: EARTH ONE
DC Comics: 2016 ($22.99, HC Graphic Novel)

Volume 1 - Grant Morrison-s/Yanick Paquette-a; alternate retelling of origin; bonus art 23.00

WONDER WOMAN '77
DC Comics: Jun, 2015 - Present ($7.99, square-bound, printing of digital-first stories)

1-4-Stories based on the Lynda Carter series. 1-Covers by Nicola Scott & Phil Jimenez; Dr. Psycho app.; bonus sketch design art; afterword by Mangels. 2-(11/15) Scott-c; The Cheetah, Celsia & Solomon Grundy app. 3-Clayface app. 8.00

WONDER WOMAN '77 MEETS THE BIONIC WOMAN (TV)
Dynamite Entertainment: 2016 - No. 6, 2017 ($3.99, limited series)

1-6-Andy Mangels-s/Judit Tondora-a; multiple covers 4.00

WONDER WOMAN SPECTACULAR (See DC Special Series #9)

WONDER WOMAN: SPIRIT OF TRUTH
DC Comics: Nov, 2001 ($9.95, treasury size, one-shot)

nn-Painted art by Alex Ross; story by Alex Ross and Paul Dini 10.00

WONDER WOMAN: THE HIKETEIA
DC Comics: 2002 ($24.95, hardcover, one-shot)

nn-Wonder Woman battles Batman; Greg Rucka-s/J.G. Jones-a 25.00
Softcover (2003, $17.95) 18.00

WONDER WOMAN: THE TRUE AMAZON
DC Comics: 2016 ($22.99, HC Graphic Novel)

HC-Retelling of childhood & origin; Jill Thompson-s/painted-a; bonus design pages 23.00

WONDERWORLD COMICS (Formerly Wonder Comics)
Fox Feature Syndicate: No. 3, July, 1939 - No. 33, Jan, 1942

	GD 2.0	VG 4.0	FN 6.0	VF 8.0	VF/NM 9.0	NM- 9.2
3-Intro The Flame by Fine; Dr. Fung (Powell-a), K-51 (Powell-a?), & Yarko the Great, Master Magician (Eisner-a) continues; Eisner/Fine-c	1000	2000	3000	7600	13,800	20,000
4-Lou Fine-c	411	822	1233	2877	5039	7200
5,6,9,10: Lou Fine-c	300	600	900	1920	3310	4700
7-Classic Lou Fine-c	811	1622	2433	5920	10,460	15,000
8-Classic Lou Fine-c	486	972	1458	3550	6275	9000
11-Origin The Flame	245	490	735	1568	2684	3800
12-15:13-Dr. Fung ends; last Fine-c(p)	200	400	600	1280	2190	3100
16-20	142	284	426	909	1555	2200
21-Origin The Black Lion & Cub	142	284	426	909	1555	2200
22-27: 22,25-Dr. Fung app.	116	232	348	742	1271	1800
28-Origin & 1st app. U.S. Jones (8/41); Lu-Nar, the Moon Man begins	181	362	543	1158	1979	2800
29,31: 29-Torture-c	103	206	309	659	1130	1600
30-Intro & Origin Flame Girl	142	284	426	909	1555	2200
32-Hitler-c	300	600	900	2010	3505	5000
33-Last issue	258	516	774	1651	2826	4000

NOTE: *Spies at War by* ***Eisner*** *in #13, 17. Yarko by* ***Eisner*** *in #3-11.* ***Eisner*** *text illos-3.* ***Lou Fine*** *a-3-11; c-3-13, 15(i); text illos-4.* ***Nordling*** *a-4-14.* ***Powell*** *a-3-12.* ***Tuska*** *a-5-9. Bondage-c 14, 15, 28, 31, 32. Cover features: The Flame-#3, 5-31; U.S. Jones-#32, 33.*

WONDERWORLDS
Innovation Publishing: 1992 ($3.50, squarebound, 100 pgs.)

1-Rebound super-hero comics, contents may vary; Hero Alliance, Terraformers, etc. 5.00

WOODS, THE
BOOM! Studios: May, 2014 - No. 36, Oct, 2017 ($3.99)

1-36: 1-Tynion-s/Dialynas-a; multiple covers 4.00

WOODSY OWL (See March of Comics #395)
Gold Key: Nov, 1973 - No. 10, Feb, 1976 (Some Whitman printings exist)

	GD 2.0	VG 4.0	FN 6.0	VF 8.0	VF/NM 9.0	NM- 9.2
1	2	4	6	13	18	22
1-Whitman variant	3	6	9	14	20	25
2-10	2	4	6	8	10	12

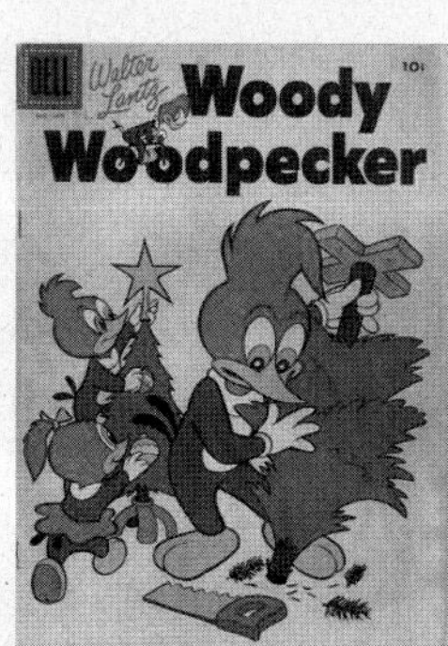

Woody Woodpecker #34 © W. Lantz

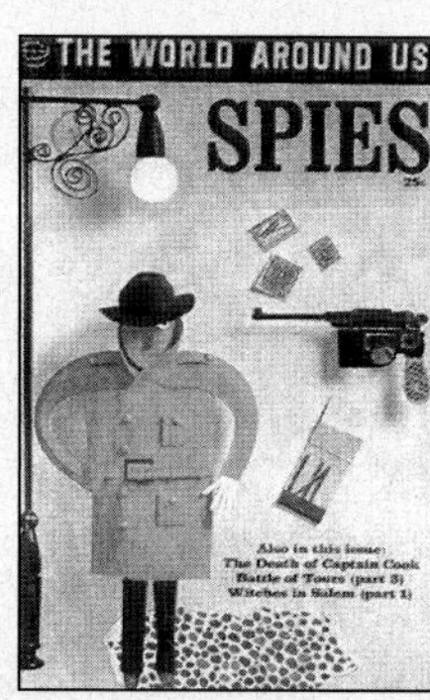

The World Around Us #35 © GIL

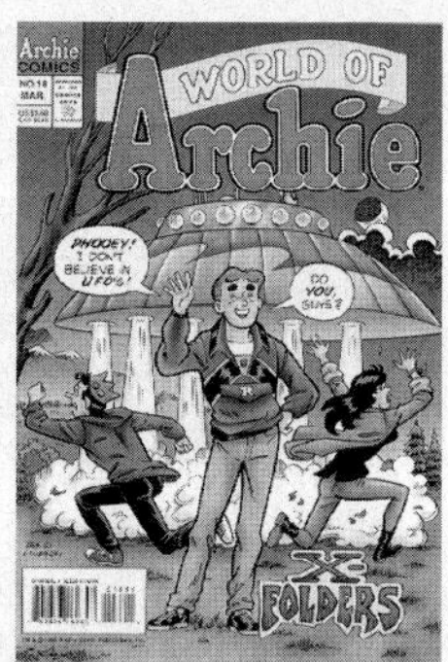

World of Archie #18 © ACP

GD 2.0 | VG 4.0 | FN 6.0 | VF 8.0 | VF/NM 9.0 | NM- 9.2

WOODY WOODPECKER (Walter Lantz... #73 on?)(See Dell Giants for annuals)
(Also see The Funnies, Jolly Jingles, Kite Fun Book, New Funnies)
Dell Publishing Co./Gold Key No. 73-187/Whitman No. 188 on:
No. 169, 10/47 - No. 72, 5-7/62; No. 73, 10/62 - No. 201, 3/84 (nn 192)

Four Color 169(#1)-Drug turns Woody into a Mr. Hyde
18 36 54 128 284 440
Four Color 188 11 22 33 73 157 240
Four Color 202,232,249,264,288 8 16 24 56 108 160
Four Color 305,336,350 6 12 18 41 76 110
Four Color 364,374,390,405,416,431('52) 6 12 18 37 66 95
16 (12-1/52-53) - 30('55) 4 8 12 27 44 60
31-50 3 6 9 21 33 45
51-72 (Last Dell) 3 6 9 17 26 35
73-75 (Giants, 84 pgs., Gold Key) 5 10 15 30 50 70
76-80 3 6 9 15 22 28
81-103: 103-Last 12¢ issue 3 6 9 14 19 24
104-120 2 4 6 11 16 20
121-140 2 4 6 9 12 15
141-160: 141-UFO-c 1 3 4 6 8 10
161-187 1 2 3 5 7 9
188,189 (Whitman) 2 4 6 9 13 16
190(9/80),191(11/80)-pre-pack only 6 12 18 38 69 100
(No #192)
193-197: 196(2/82), 197(4/82) 2 4 6 11 16 20
198-201 (All #90062 on-c, no date or date code, pre-pack): 198(6/83), 199(7/83), 200(8/83), 201(3/84) 3 6 9 16 24 32
Christmas Parade 1(11/68-Giant)(G.K.) 4 8 12 25 40 55
Summer Fun 1(6/66-G.K.)(84 pgs.) 4 8 12 28 47 65
nn (1971, 60¢, 100 pgs. digest) B&W one page gags 3 6 9 16 24 32
NOTE: *15¢ Canadian editions of the 12¢ issues exist. Reprints-No. 92, 102, 103, 105, 106, 124, 125, 152, 153, 157, 162, 165, 194(1/3)-200(1/3).*

WOODY WOODPECKER (See Comic Album #5,9,13, Dell Giant #24, 40, 54, Dell Giants, The Funnies, Golden Comics Digest #1, 3, 5, 8, 15, 16, 20, 24, 32, 37, 44, March of Comics #16, 34, 85, 93, 109, 124, 139, 158, 177, 184, 203, 222, 239, 249, 261, 420, 454, 466, 478, New Funnies & Super Book #12, 24)

WOODY WOODPECKER
Harvey Comics: Sept, 1991 - No. 15, Aug, 1994 ($1.25)
1-15: 1-r/W.W. #53 4.00
50th Anniversary Special 1 (10/91, $2.50, 68 pgs.) 5.00

WOODY WOODPECKER AND FRIENDS
Harvey Comics: Dec, 1991 - No. 4, 1992 ($1.25)
1-4 4.00

WOOL (Hugh Howey's...)
Cryptozoic Entertainment: Jul, 2014 - No. 6, Nov, 2014 ($3.99)
1-6-Palmiotti & Gray-s/Broxton-a/Darwyn Cooke-c 4.00

WORD WARRIORS (Also see Quest for Dreams Lost)
Literacy Volunteers of Chicago: 1987 ($1.50, B&W)(Proceeds donated to help literacy)
1-Jon Sable by Grell, Ms. Tree, Streetwolf; Chaykin-c 3.00

WORLD AROUND US, THE (Illustrated Story of...)
Gilberton Publishers (Classics Illustrated): Sep, 1958 -No. 36, Oct, 1961 (25¢)
1-Dogs; Evans-a 9 18 27 52 69 85
2-4: 2-Indians; Check-a. 3-Horses; L. B. Cole-c. 4-Railroads; L. B. Cole-a (5 pgs.)
9 18 27 47 61 75
5-Space; Ingels-a 10 20 30 56 76 95
6-The F.B.I.; Disbrow, Evans, Ingels-a 10 20 30 56 76 95
7-Pirates; Disbrow, Ingels, Kinstler-a 9 18 27 52 69 85
8-Flight; Evans, Ingels, Crandall-a 9 18 27 52 69 85
9-Army; Disbrow, Ingels, Orlando-a 9 18 27 47 61 75
10-13: 10-Navy; Disbrow, Kinstler-a. 11-Marine Corps. 12-Coast Guard; Ingels-a (9 pgs.). 13-Air Force; L.B. Cole-c 9 18 27 47 61 75
14-French Revolution; Crandall, Evans, Kinstler-a 10 20 30 56 76 95
15-Prehistoric Animals; Al Williamson-a, 6 & 10 pgs. plus Morrow-a
10 20 30 58 79 100
16-18: 16-Crusades; Kinstler-a. 17-Festivals; Evans, Crandall-a. 18-Great Scientists; Crandall, Evans, Torres, Williamson, Morrow-a 9 18 27 52 69 85
19-Jungle; Crandall, Williamson, Morrow-a 10 20 30 58 79 100
20-Communications; Crandall, Evans, Torres-a 10 20 30 56 76 95
21-American Presidents; Crandall/Evans, Morrow-a 10 20 30 56 76 95
22-Boating; Morrow-a 8 16 24 44 57 70
23-Great Explorers; Crandall, Evans-a 9 18 27 52 69 85
24-Ghosts; Morrow, Evans-a 10 20 30 56 76 95
25-Magic; Evans, Morrow-a 10 20 30 56 76 95
26-The Civil War 11 22 33 62 86 110
27-Mountains (High Advs.); Crandall/Evans, Morrow, Torres-a
9 18 27 52 69 85
28-Whaling; Crandall, Evans, Morrow, Torres, Wildey-a; L.B. Cole-c
9 18 27 52 69 85
29-Vikings; Crandall, Evans, Torres, Morrow-a 10 20 30 58 79 100
30-Undersea Adventure; Crandall/Evans, Kirby, Morrow, Torres-a
10 20 30 56 76 95
31-Hunting; Crandall/Evans, Ingels, Kinstler, Kirby-a 9 18 27 52 69 85
32,33: 32-For Gold & Glory; Morrow, Kirby, Crandall, Evans-a. 33-Famous Teens; Torres, Crandall, Evans-a 9 18 27 52 69 85
34-36: 34-Fishing; Crandall/Evans-a. 35-Spies; Kirby, Morrow?, Evans-a. 36-Fight for Life (Medicine); Kirby-a 9 18 27 52 69 85
NOTE: See Classics Illustrated Special Edition. Another *World Around Us* issue entitled *The Sea* had been prepared in 1962 but was never published in the U.S. It was published in the British/European *World Around Us* series. Those series then continued with seven additional WAU titles not in the U.S. series.

WORLD BELOW, THE
Dark Horse Comics: Mar, 1999 - No. 4, Jun, 1999 ($2.50, limited series)
1-4-Paul Chadwick-s/c/a 3.00
TPB (1/07, $12.95) r/#1-4; intro. by Chadwick; gallery of sketches and covers 13.00

WORLD BELOW, THE: DEEPER AND STRANGER
Dark Horse Comics: Dec, 1999 - No. 4, Mar, 2000 ($2.95, B&W)
1-4-Paul Chadwick-s/c/a 3.00

WORLD FAMOUS HEROES MAGAZINE
Comic Corp. of America (Centaur): Oct, 1941 - No. 4, Apr, 1942 (comic book)
1-Gustavson-c; Lubbers, Glanzman-a; Davy Crockett, Paul Revere, Lewis & Clark, John Paul Jones stories; Flag-c 119 238 357 762 1306 1850
2-Lou Gehrig life story; Lubbers-a 58 116 174 371 636 900
3,4-Lubbers-a. 4-Wild Bill Hickok story; 2 pg. Marlene Dietrich story
55 110 165 352 601 850

WORLD FAMOUS STORIES
Croyden Publishers: 1945
1-Ali Baba, Hansel & Gretel, Rip Van Winkle, Mid-Summer Night's Dream
14 28 42 76 108 140

WORLD IS HIS PARISH, THE
George A. Pflaum: 1953 (15¢)
nn-The story of Pope Pius XII 6 12 18 31 38 45

WORLD OF ADVENTURE (Walt Disney's...)(TV)
Gold Key: Apr, 1963 - No. 3, Oct, 1963 (12¢)
1-Disney TV characters; Savage Sam, Johnny Shiloh, Capt. Nemo, The Mooncussers
3 6 9 20 31 42
2,3 3 6 9 15 21 26

WORLD OF ANIMOSITY (See Animosity)
AfterShock Comics: Sept, 2017 ($3.99, one-shot)
nn-Character profiles and series summary 4.00

WORLD OF ARCHIE, THE (See Archie Giant Series Mag. #148, 151, 156, 160, 165, 171, 177, 182, 188, 193, 200, 208, 213, 225, 232, 237, 244, 249, 456, 461, 468, 473, 480, 485, 492, 497, 504, 509, 516, 521, 532, 543, 554, 565, 574, 587, 599, 612, 627)

WORLD OF ARCHIE
Archie Comics: Aug, 1992 - No. 22 ($1.25/$1.50)
1 4.00
2-15: 9-Neon ink-c 3.00
16-22 3.00

WORLD OF ARCHIE DOUBLE DIGEST MAGAZINE (World of Archie Comics Digest #41-on)
Archie Comics: Dec, 2010 - Present ($3.99/$4.99/$5.99/$6.99)
1-29,31-37,39,40: 5-r/Tiny Titans/Little Archie #1-3 with sketch-a. 17-Archie babies 4.00
30-($5.99) Double Double Digest 6.00
38-$4.99-c 5.00
41,46,51,55,60,63,67,71,73,75-77-($6.99) 41-World of Archie Double Double Digest 7.00
42-45,47-50,52,54,57,58,61,64,65,68-($4.99) Titled World of Archie Comics Digest 5.00
53,56,59,62,66,70,72,74-($5.99): 56-Winter Annual. 59,70-Summer Annual 6.00
World of Archie Digest, Free Comic Book Day Edition (6-7/13, giveaway) Reprints 3.00

WORLD OF FANTASY
Atlas Comics (CPC No. 1-15/ZPC No. 16-19): May, 1956 - No. 19, Aug, 1959
1 77 154 231 493 847 1200
2-Williamson-a (4 pgs.) 42 84 126 265 445 625
3-Sid Check, Roussos-a 40 80 120 246 411 575
4-7 36 72 108 214 347 480

World of Krypton #3 © DC

World of Mystery #5 © ATL

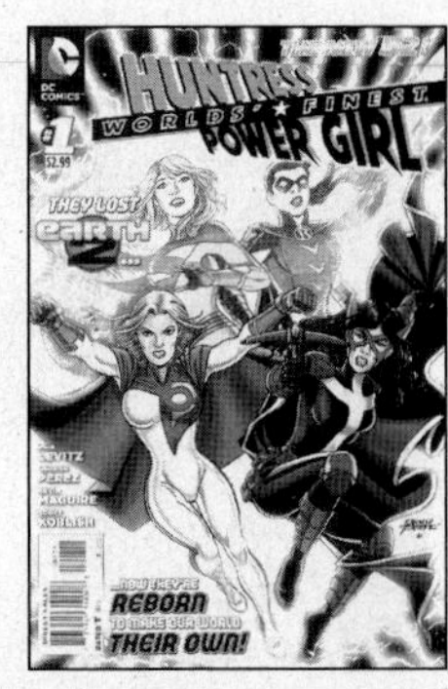

Worlds' Finest #1 © DC

GD VG FN VF VF/NM NM-
2.0 4.0 6.0 8.0 9.0 9.2

8-Matt Fox, Orlando, Berg-a 39 78 117 231 378 525
9-Krigstein-a 36 72 108 214 347 480
10-15: 10-Colan-a. 11-Torres-a 32 64 96 190 310 430
16-Williamson-a (4 pgs.); Ditko, Kirby-a 47 94 141 296 498 700
17-19-Ditko, Kirby-a 47 94 141 296 498 700

NOTE: ***Ayers** a-3. **B. Baily** a-4. **Berg** a-5, 6, 8. **Brodsky** c-3. **Check** a-3. **Ditko** a-17, 19. **Everett** a-2; c-4-7, 9, 12, 13. **Forte** a-4, 8. **Infantino** a-14. **Kirby** c-15, 17-19. **Krigstein** a-9. **Maneely** c-2, 14. **Mooney** a-14. **Morrow** a-7. **Orlando** a-8, 13, 14. **Pakula** a-9. **Powell** a-4, 6. **Reinman** a-8, 10. **R.Q. Sale** a-3, 7, 9, 10. **Severin** c-1.*

WORLD OF GIANT COMICS, THE (See Archie All-Star Specials under Archie Comics)

WORLD OF GINGER FOX, THE (Also see Ginger Fox)
Comico: Nov, 1986 ($6.95, 8 1/2 x 11", 68 pgs., mature)

Graphic Novel ($6.95) 10.00
Hardcover ($27.95) 30.00

WORLD OF JUGHEAD, THE (See Archie Giant Series Mag. #9, 14, 19, 24, 30, 136, 143, 149, 152, 157, 161, 166, 172, 178, 183, 189, 194, 202, 209, 215, 227, 233, 239, 245, 251, 457, 463, 469, 475, 481, 487, 493, 499, 505, 511, 517, 523, 531, 542, 553, 564, 577, 590, 602)

WORLD OF KRYPTON, THE (World of...#3) (See Superman #248)
DC Comics, Inc.: 7/79 - No. 3, 9/79; 12/87 - No. 4, 3/88 (Both are lim. series)

1-3 (1979, 40¢; 1st comic book mini-series): 1-Jor-El marries Lara. 3-Baby Superman sent to Earth; Krypton explodes; Mon-el app. 1 2 3 5 6 8
1-4 (75¢)-Byrne scripts; Byrne/Simonson-c 4.00

WORLD OF METROPOLIS, THE
DC Comics: Aug, 1988 - No. 4, July, 1988 ($1.00, limited series)

1-4: Byrne scripts 4.00

WORLD OF MYSTERY
Atlas Comics (GPI): June, 1956 - No. 7, July, 1957

1-Torres, Orlando-a; Powell-a? 57 114 171 362 619 875
2-Woodish-a 26 52 78 154 252 350
3-Torres, Davis, Ditko-a 30 60 90 177 289 400
4-Pakula, Powell-a 30 60 90 177 289 400
5,7: 5-Orlando-a 25 50 75 147 241 335
6-Williamson/Mayo-a (4 pgs.); Ditko-a; Colan-a; Crandall text illo 30 60 90 177 289 400

NOTE: ***Ayers** a-4. **Brodsky** c-2, 5, 6. **Colan** a-6, 7. **Everett** c-1, 3. **Pakula** a-4, 6. **Romita** a-2. **Severin** c-7.*

WORLD OF SMALLVILLE
DC Comics: Apr, 1988 - No. 4, July, 1988 (75¢, limited series)

1-4: Byrne scripts 4.00

WORLD OF SUSPENSE
Atlas News Co.: Apr, 1956 - No. 8, July, 1957

1 53 106 159 334 567 800
2-Ditko-a (4 pgs.) 30 60 90 177 289 400
3,7-Williamson-a in both (4 pgs.); #7-with Mayo 29 58 87 170 278 385
4-6,8 24 48 72 144 237 330

NOTE: ***Berg** a-6. **Cameron** a-2. **Ditko** a-2. **Drucker** a-1. **Everett** a-1, 5; c-6. **Heck** a-5. **Maneely** a-1; c-1-3. **Orlando** a-5. **Powell** a-6. **Reinman** a-4. **Roussos** a-6. **Sale** a-4. **Shores** a-1.*

WORLD OF TANKS
Dark Horse Comics: Aug, 2016 - No. 5, Feb, 2017 ($3.99)

1-5-Ennis-s/Ezquerra-a; set in 1944 Normandy 4.00

WORLD OF WARCRAFT (Based on the Blizzard Entertainment video game)
DC Comics (WildStorm): Jan, 2008 - No. 25, Jan, 2010 ($2.99)

1-Walt Simonson-s/Lullabi-a; cover by Samwise Didier 8.00
1-Variant cover by Jim Lee 12.00
1,2-Second printing with Jim Lee sketch cover 5.00
2-Two covers by Jim Lee and Samwise Didier 5.00
3-24: 3-14-Two covers on each 3.00
25-($3.99) Walt & Louise Simonson-s 4.00
... Special 1 (2/10, $3.99) Costa-s/Mhan-a/c 4.00
... Book One HC (2008, $19.99, dustjacket) r/#1-7; intro. by Chris Metzen of Blizzard 20.00
... Book One SC (2009, $14.99) r/#1-7; intro. by Chris Metzen of Blizzard 15.00
... Book Two HC (2009, $19.99, dustjacket) r/#8-14 20.00
... Book Two SC (2010, $14.99) r/#8-14 15.00
... Book Three HC (2010, $19.99, dustjacket) r/#15-21 20.00
... Book Three SC (2011, $17.99) r/#15-21 18.00

WORLD OF WARCRAFT: ASHBRINGER
DC Comics (WildStorm): Nov, 2008 - No. 4, Feb, 2009 ($3.99)

1-4-Neilson-s/Lullabi & Washington-a; 2 covers by Robinson & Lullabi 4.00
TPB (2010, $14.99) r/#1-4 15.00

WORLD OF WARCRAFT: CURSE OF THE WORGEN
DC Comics (WildStorm #1,2): Jan, 2011 - No. 5, May, 2011 ($3.99/$2.99)

GD VG FN VF VF/NM NM-
2.0 4.0 6.0 8.0 9.0 9.2

1,2-($3.99) Neilson & Waugh-s/Lullabi & Washington-a; Polidora-c 4.00
3-5-($2.99) 3.00

WORLD OF WHEELS (Formerly Dragstrip Hotrodders)
Charlton Comics: No. 17, Oct, 1967 - No. 32, June, 1970

17-20-Features Ken King 3 6 9 17 26 35
21-32-Features Ken King 3 6 9 15 22 28
Modern Comics Reprint 23(1978) 6.00

WORLD OF WOOD
Eclipse Comics: 1986 - No. 4, 1987; No. 5, 2/89 ($1.75, limited series)

1,2: 1-Dave Stevens-c. 2-Wood/Stevens-c 2 4 6 8 10 12
3-5: 5-($2.00, B&W)-r/Avon's Flying Saucers 5.00

WORLD READER
AfterShock Comics: Apr, 2017 - No. 6, Sept, 2017 ($3.99, limited series)

1-6-Jeff Loveness-s/Juan Doe-a 4.00

WORLD'S BEST COMICS
DC Comics: Feb 1940

nn - Ashcan comic, not distributed to newsstands, only for in-house use. Cover art is Action Comics #29 with interior being Action Comics #24. One copy sold for $21,000 in 2000.

WORLD'S BEST COMICS (World's Finest Comics #2 on)
National Per. Publications (100 pgs.): Spring, 1941 (Cardboard-c)(DC's 6th annual format comic)

1-The Batman, Superman, Crimson Avenger, Johnny Thunder, The King, Young Dr. Davis, Zatara, Lando, Man of Magic, & Red, White & Blue begin; Superman, Batman & Robin covers begin (inside-c is blank); Fred Ray-c; 15¢ cover price 1550 3100 4650 12,000 20,500 29,000

WORLD'S BEST COMICS: GOLDEN AGE SAMPLER
DC Comics: 2003 (99¢, one-shot, samples from DC Archive editions)

1-Golden Age reprints from Superman #6, Batman #5, Sensation #11, Police #11 3.00

WORLD'S BEST COMICS: SILVER AGE SAMPLER
DC Comics: 2004 (99¢, one-shot, samples from DC Archive editions)

1-Silver Age reprints from Justice League #4, Adventure #247, Our Army at War #81 3.00

WORLDS BEYOND (Stories of Weird Adventure)(Worlds of Fear #2 on)
Fawcett Publications: Nov, 1951

1-Powell, Bailey-a; Moldoff-c 60 120 180 381 653 925

WORLDS COLLIDE
DC Comics: July, 1994 ($2.50, one-shot)

1-($2.50, 52 pgs.)-Milestone & Superman titles x-over 4.00
1-($3.95, 52 pgs.)-Polybagged w/vinyl clings 5.00

WORLD'S FAIR COMICS (See New York...)

WORLD'S FINEST (Also see Legends of The World's Finest)
DC Comics: 1990 - No. 3, 1990 ($3.95, squarebound, limited series, 52 pgs.)

1-3: Batman & Superman team-up against The Joker and Lex Luthor; Dave Gibbons scripts & Steve Rude-c/a. 2,3-Joker/Luthor painted-c by Steve Rude 5.00
TPB-(1992, $19.95) r/#1-3; Gibbons intro. 20.00
...: The Deluxe Edition HC (2008, $29.99) r/#1-3; Gibbons intro. from 1992; Gibbons story outline and sketches; Rude sketch pages and notes 30.00

WORLD'S FINEST
DC Comics: Dec, 2009 - No. 4, Mar, 2010 ($2.99, limited series)

1-4: Gates-s/two covers by Noto on each. 3-Supergirl/Batgirl team up. 4-Noto-a 3.00
TPB (2010, $14.99) r/#1-4, Action Comics #865 & DC Comics Presents #31 15.00

WORLDS' FINEST (Also see Earth 2 series)
DC Comics: Jul, 2012 - No. 32, May, 2015 ($2.99)

1-32: 1-Huntress and Power Girl; Levitz-s/art by Pérez & Maguire. 6,7-Damian app. 19-Huntress meets Batman. 20,21-X-over with Batman/Superman #8,9. 25-Return to Earth-2. 27-29-Secret History of Earth 2. 32-Death of Lois 3.00
1-Variant-c by Maguire 5.00
#0-(11/12, $2.99) Flashback to Robin's and Supergirl's training 3.00
Annual 1 (3/14, $4.99) Earth 2 flashback; Wonder Woman & Fury app. 5.00
...: Futures End 1 (11/14, $2.99, regular-c) Five years later; Cinar-a; Deathstroke app. 3.00
...: Futures End 1 (11/14, $3.99, 3-D cover) 4.00

WORLD'S FINEST COMICS (Formerly World's Best Comics #1)
National Periodical Publ./DC Comics: No. 2, Sum, 1941 - No. 323, Jan, 1986 (#1-17 have cardboard covers) (#2-9 have 100 pgs.)

2 (100 pgs.)-Superman, Batman & Robin covers continue from World's Best; (cover price 15¢ #2-70) 423 846 1269 3067 5384 7700

World's Finest Comics #37 © DC

World's Finest Comics #41 © DC

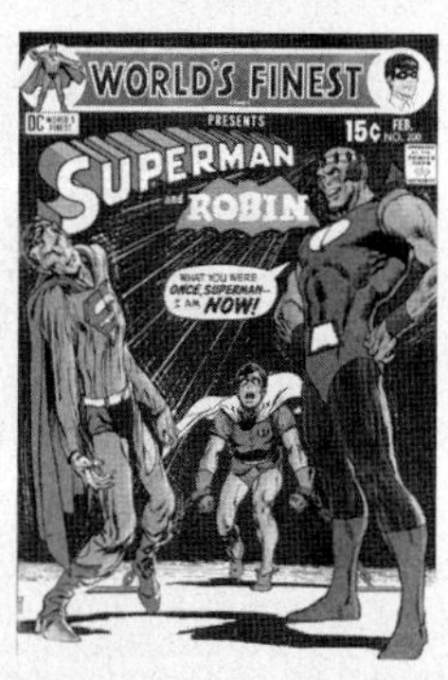

World's Finest Comics #200 © DC

GD 2.0 | VG 4.0 | FN 6.0 | VF 8.0 | VF/NM 9.0 | NM- 9.2

3-The Sandman begins; last Johnny Thunder; origin & 1st app. The Scarecrow 400 800 1200 2800 4900 7000

4-Hop Harrigan app.; last Young Dr. Davis 265 530 795 1694 2897 4100

5-Intro. TNT & Dan the Dyna-Mite; last King & Crimson Avenger 265 530 795 1694 2897 4100

6-Star Spangled Kid begins (Sum/42); Aquaman app.; S&K Sandman with Sandy in new costume begins, ends #7 194 388 582 1242 2121 3000

7-Green Arrow begins (Fall/42); last Lando & Red, White & Blue; S&K art 213 426 639 1363 2332 3300

8-Boy Commandos begin (by Simon(p) #12); last The King; includes "Minute Man Answers the Call" promo 187 374 561 1197 2049 2900

9-Batman cameo in Star Spangled Kid; S&K-a; last 100 pg. issue; Hitler, Mussolini, Tojo-c 258 516 774 1651 2826 4000

10-S&K-a; 76 pg. issues begin 168 336 504 1075 1838 2600

11-17: 17-Last cardboard cover issue 161 322 483 1030 1765 2500

18-20: 18-Paper covers begin; last Star Spangled Kid. 19-Joker story. 20-Last quarterly issue 155 310 465 992 1696 2400

21-30: 21-Begin bi-monthly. 30-Johnny Everyman app. 107 214 321 680 1165 1650

31-40: 33-35-Tomahawk app. 35-Penguin app. 103 206 309 659 1130 1600

41-43,45-50: 41-Boy Commandos end. 42-The Wyoming Kid begins (9-10/49), ends #63. 43-Full Steam Foley begins, ends #48. 48-Last square binding. 49-Tom Sparks, Boy Inventor begins; robot-c 100 200 300 635 1093 1550

44-Used in SOTI, ref. to Batman & Robin being gay, and a cop being shot in the face 116 232 348 742 1271 1800

51-60: 51-Zatara ends. 54-Last 76 pg. issue. 59-Manhunters Around the World begins (7-8/52), ends #62 97 194 291 621 1061 1500

61-64: 61-Joker story. 63-Capt. Compass app. 94 188 282 597 1024 1450

65-Origin Superman; Tomahawk begins (7-8/53), ends #101 135 270 405 864 1482 2100

66-70-(15¢ issues, scarce)-Last 15¢, 68pg. issue 100 200 300 635 1093 1550

71-(10¢ issue, scarce)-Superman & Batman begin as team (7-8/54); were in separate stories until now; Superman & Batman exchange identities; 10¢ issues begin 300 600 900 2010 3505 5000

72,73-(10¢ issue, scarce) 129 258 387 826 1413 2000

74-Last pre-code issue 97 194 291 621 1061 1500

75-(1st code approved, 3-4/55) 94 188 282 597 1024 1450

76-80: 77-Superman loses powers & Batman obtains them 68 136 204 435 743 1050

81-87,89: 84-1st S.A. issue. 89-2nd Batmen of All Nations (aka Club of Heroes) 32 64 96 230 515 800

88-1st Joker/Luthor team-up 60 120 180 381 653 925

90-Batwoman's 1st app. in World's Finest (10/57, 3rd app. anywhere) plus-c app. 71 142 213 454 777 1100

91-93,95-99: 96-99-Kirby Green Arrow. 99-Robot-c 25 50 75 175 388 600

94-Origin Superman/Batman team retold 61 122 183 488 1094 1700

100 (3/59) 36 72 108 259 580 900

101-110: 102-Tommy Tomorrow begins, ends #124 15 30 45 105 233 360

111-121: 111-1st app. The Clock King. 113-Intro. Miss Arrowette in Green Arrow; 1st Bat-Mite/Mr. Mxyzptlk team-up (11/60). 117-Batwoman-c. 121-Last 10¢ issue 12 24 36 79 170 260

122-128: 123-2nd Bat-Mite/Mr. Mxyzptlk team-up (2/62). 125-Aquaman begins (5/62), ends #139 (Aquaman #1 is dated 1-2/62) 10 20 30 64 132 200

129-Joker/Luthor team-up-c/story 12 24 36 82 179 275

130-142: 135-Last Dick Sprang story. 140-Last Green Arrow. 142-Origin The Composite Superman (villain); Legion app. 8 16 24 51 96 140

143-150: 143-1st Mailbag. 144-Clayface/Brainiac team-up. 148-Clayface/Luthor team-up; last Clayface until Action #443 6 12 18 42 79 115

151-153,155,157-160: 157-2nd Super Sons story; last app. Kathy Kane (Bat-Woman) until Batman Family #10; 1st Bat-Mite Jr. 5 10 15 35 63 90

154-1st Super Sons story; last Bat-Woman in costume until Batman Family #10. 6 12 18 41 76 110

156-1st Bizarro Batman; Joker-c/story 12 24 36 82 179 275

161,170 (80-Pg. Giants G-28,G-40) 6 12 18 40 73 105

162-165,167,168,171,172: 168,172-Adult Legion app. 5 10 15 31 53 75

166-Joker-c/story 6 12 18 38 69 100

169-3rd app. new Batgirl(9/67)(cover and 1 panel cameo); 3rd Bat-Mite/Mr. Mxyzptlk team-up 8 16 24 56 108 160

173-('68)-1st S.A. app. Two-Face as Batman becomes Two-Face in story 8 16 24 56 108 160

174-Adams-c 5 10 15 33 57 80

175,176-Neal Adams-c/a; both reprint J'onn J'onzz origin/Detective #225,226 6 12 18 38 69 100

GD 2.0 | VG 4.0 | FN 6.0 | VF 8.0 | VF/NM 9.0 | NM- 9.2

177-Joker/Luthor team-up-c/story 6 12 18 37 66 95

178-(9/68) Intro. of Super Nova (revived in "52" weekly series); Adams-c 6 12 18 37 66 95

179-(80 Page Giant G-52) -Adams-c; r/#94 6 12 18 37 66 95

180,182,183,185,186: Adams-c on all. 182-Silent Knight-r/Brave & Bold #6. 185-Last 12¢ issue. 186-Johnny Quick-r 4 8 12 27 44 60

181,184,187: 187-Green Arrow origin-r by Kirby (Adv. #256) 4 8 12 23 37 50

188,197:(Giants G-64,G-76; 64 pages) 5 10 15 34 60 85

189-196: 190-193-Robin-r 3 6 9 20 31 42

198,199-3rd Superman/Flash race (see Flash #175 & Superman #199). 199-Adams-c 10 20 30 66 138 210

200-Adams-c 4 8 12 25 40 55

201-203: 203-Last 15¢ issue. 3 6 9 18 38 38

204,205-(52 pgs.) Adams-c: 204-Wonder Woman app. 205-Shining Knight-r (6 pgs.) by Frazetta/Adv. #153; Teen Titans x-over 3 6 9 21 33 45

206 (Giant G-88, 64 pgs.) 5 10 15 31 53 75

207,212-(52 pgs.) 3 6 9 20 31 42

208-211(25¢-c) Adams-c: 208-(52 pgs.) Origin Robotman-r/Det. #138. 209-211-(52 pgs.) 3 6 9 21 33 45

213,214,216-222,229: 217-Metamorpho begins, ends #220; Batman/Superman team-ups resume. 229-r/origin Superman-Batman team 2 4 6 13 18 22

215-(12/72-1/73) Intro. Batman Jr. & Superman Jr. (see Superman/Batman: Saga of the Super Sons TPB for all the Super Sons stories) 3 6 9 18 28 38

223-228-(100 pgs.). 223-N. Adams-r. 223-Deadman origin. 226-N. Adams, S&K, Toth-r; Manhunter part origin-r/Det. #225,226. 227-Deadman app. 5 10 15 30 50 70

230-(68 pgs.) 3 6 9 17 26 35

231-243: 231, 233, 238, 242-Super Sons 2 4 6 9 13 16

244-246-Adams-c: 244-$1.00, 84 pg. issues begin; Green Arrow, Black Canary, Wonder Woman, Vigilante begin; 246-Death of Stuff in Vigilante; origin Vigilante retold 3 6 9 14 20 26

247-252 (84 pgs.): 248-Last Vigilante. 249-The Creeper begins by Ditko, 84 pgs. 250-The Creeper origin retold by Ditko. 251-1st app. Count Vertigo. 252-Last 84 pg. issue 2 4 6 13 18 22

253-257,259-265: 253-Capt. Marvel begins; 68 pgs. begin, end #265. 255-Last Creeper. 256-Hawkman begins. 257-Black Lightning begins. 263-Super Sons. 264-Clay Face app. 2 4 6 8 11 14

258-Adams-c 2 4 6 11 1 20

266-270,272-282-(52 pgs.). 267-Challengers of the Unknown app.; 3 Lt. Marvels return. 268-Capt. Marvel Jr. origin retold. 274-Zatanna begins. 279, 280-Capt. Marvel Jr. & Kid Eternity learn they are brothers 1 3 4 6 8 10

271-(52pgs.) Origin Superman/Batman team retold 2 4 6 8 10 12

283-299: 284-Legion app. 1 2 3 4 5 7

300-($1.25, 52pgs.)-Justice League of America, New Teen Titans & The Outsiders app.; Perez-a (4 pgs.) 1 2 3 5 7 9

301-322: 304-Origin Null and Void. 309,319-Free 16 pg. story in each (309-Flash Force 2000, 319-Mask preview) 5.00

323-Last issue 6.00

NOTE: ***Neal Adams** a-230ir; c-174-176, 178-180, 182, 183, 185, 186, 199-205, 208-211, 244-246, 258. **Austin** a-244-246i. **Burnley** a-8, 10; c-7-9, 11-14, 15p?, 16-18p, 20-31p. **Colan** a-274p, 297, 299. **Ditko** a-249-255. **Giffen** a-322; c-284p, 322. **G. Kane** a-38, 174r, 282, 283; c-281, 282, 289. **Kirby** a-187. **Kubert** Zatara-40-44. **Miller** c-285p. **Mooney** c-134. **Morrow** a-245-248. **Mortimer** c-16-21, 26-71. **Nasser** a(p)-244-246, 259, 260. **Newton** a-253-281p. **Orlando** a-224r. **Perez** a-300i; c-271, 276, 277p, 278p. **Fred Ray** c-1-5. **Fred Ray/Robinson** c-13-16. **Robinson** a-5, 6, 9-11, 13?, 14-16; c-6. **Rogers** a-259p. **Roussos** a-212r. **Simonson** c-291. **Spiegle** a-275-278, 284. **Staton** a-262p, 273p. **Swan/Moldoff** c-126. **Swan/Mortimer** c-79-82. **Toth** a-228r. **Tuska** a-230r, 250p, 252p, 254p, 257p, 283p, 284p, 308p. Boy Commandos by **Infantino** #39-41.*

WORLD'S FINEST COMICS DIGEST (See DC Special Series #23)

WORLD'S FINEST: OUR WORLDS AT WAR

DC Comics: Oct, 2001 ($2.95, one-shot)

1-Concludes the Our Worlds at War x-over; Jae Lee-c; art by various 3.00

WORLD'S GREATEST ATHLETE (See Walt Disney Showcase #14)

WORLD'S GREATEST SONGS

Atlas Comics (Male): Sept, 1954

1-(Scarce)-Heath & Harry Anderson-a; Eddie Fisher life story plus-c; gives lyrics to Frank Sinatra song "Young at Heart" 47 94 141 296 498 700

WORLD'S GREATEST STORIES

Jubilee Publications: Jan, 1949 - No. 2, May, 1949

1-Alice in Wonderland; Lewis Carroll adapt. 34 68 102 199 325 450

2-Pinocchio 32 64 96 188 307 425

WORLDS OF ASPEN

Aspen MLT, Inc.: 2006 - Present (Free Comic Book Day giveaways)

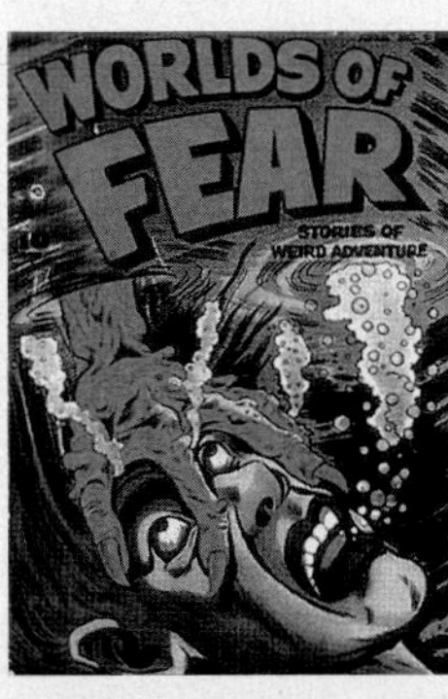

Worlds of Fear #9 © FAW

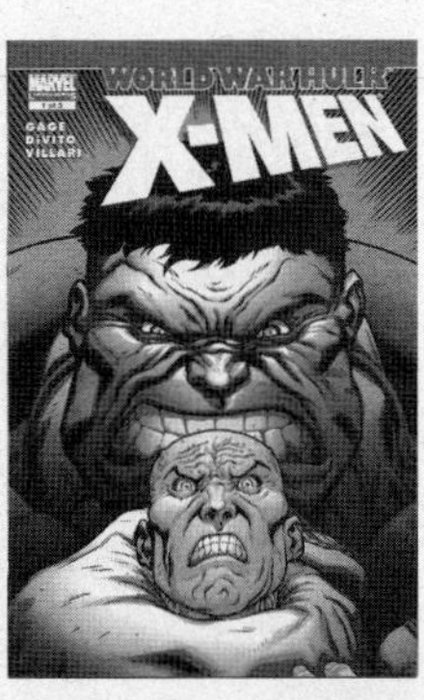

World War Hulk: X-Men #1 © MAR

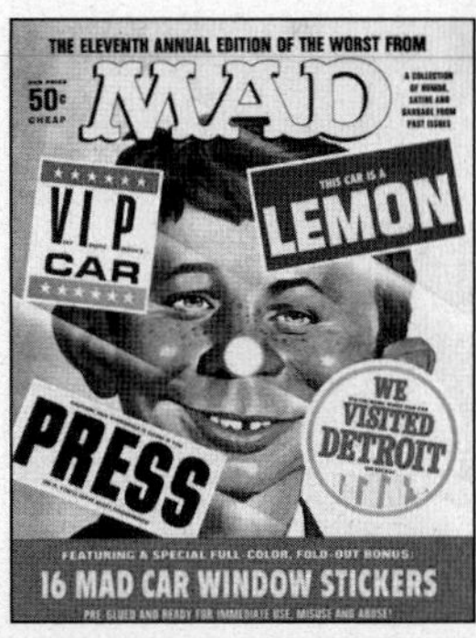

Worst From Mad #11 © EC Publ.

GD	VG	FN	VF	VF/NM	NM-
2.0	4.0	6.0	8.0	9.0	9.2

...: FCBD 2006, 2007, #3, #4 Editions; Fathom, Soulfire, Shrugged short stories; Turner-c 3.00
... 2010 (5/10) Previews Fathom, Mindfield, Soulfire, Executive Assistant: Iris and Dellec 3.00
... 2011 (5/11) Previews Fathom, Soulfire, Charismagic, Lady Mechanika & others 3.00
... 2012 (5/12) Previews Fathom, Homecoming, Idolized, Shrugged & others 3.00
... 2013 (5/13) Flip book; previews Fathom, Zoohunters & others 3.00
... 2014 (5/14) Flip book; previews Damsels in Excess & Zoohunters; pin-ups 3.00
... 2015 (5/15) Flip book; previews Eternal Soulfire & Fathom Blue; pin-ups 3.00
... 2016 (5/16) Prelude to Aspen Universe: Revelations; character profile pages 3.00

WORLDS OF FEAR (Stories of Weird Adventure)(Formerly Worlds Beyond #1)
Fawcett Publications: V1#2, Jan, 1952 - V2#10, June, 1953

V1#2 55 110 165 352 601 850
3-Evans-a 47 94 141 296 498 700
4-6(9/52) 41 82 123 256 428 600
V2#7,8 40 80 120 246 411 575
9-Classic drowning-c (4/53) 42 84 126 265 445 625
10-Saunders painted-c; man with no eyes surrounded by eyeballs-c plus eyes ripped out story 187 374 561 1197 2049 2900

NOTE: ***Moldoff** c-2-8. **Powell** a-2, 4, 5. **Sekowsky** a-4, 5.*

WORLDSTORM
DC Comics (WildStorm): Nov, 2006 (Dec on cover) - No. 2, May, 2007 ($2.99)

1,2-Previews and pin-ups for re-launched WildStorm titles.1-Art Adams-c 3.00

WORLDS UNKNOWN
Marvel Comics Group: May, 1973 - No. 8, Aug, 1974

1-r/from Astonishing #54; Torres, Reese-a 3 6 9 17 26 35
2-8 2 4 6 13 18 22

NOTE: ***Adkins/Mooney** a-5. **Buscema** c/a-4p. **W. Howard** c/a-3i. **Kane** a(p)-1,2; c(p)-5, 6, 8. **Sutton** a-2. **Tuska** a(p)-7, 8; c-7p. No. 7, 8 has Golden Voyage of Sinbad movie adaptation.*

WORLD WAR HULK (See Incredible Hulk #106)
Marvel Comics: Aug, 2007 - No. 5, Jan, 2008 ($3.99, limited series)

1-Hulk returns to Earth; Iron Man and Avengers app.; Romita Jr.-a/Pak-s/Finch-c 4.00
1-Variant cover by Romita Jr. 6.00
2-5: 2-Hulk battles The Avengers and FF; Finch-c. 3,4-Dr. Strange app. 5-Sentry app. 4.00
2-5-Variant cover by Romita Jr. 6.00
...: Aftersmash 1 (1/08, $3.99) Sandoval-a/Land-c; Hercules, Iron Man app. 4.00
...: Gamma Files (2007, $3.99) profile pages of Hulk characters 4.00
...Prologue: World Breaker 1 (7/07, one-shot) Rio, Weeks, Phillips, Miyazawa-a 4.00
TPB (2008, $19.99) r/#1-5 20.00

WORLD WAR HULK AFTERSMASH: DAMAGE CONTROL
Marvel Comics: Mar, 2008 - No. 3, May, 2008 ($2.99, limited series)

1-3-The clean-up; McDuffie-s. 2-Romita- Jr.-c. 3-Romita Sr.-c 3.00

WORLD WAR HULK AFTERSMASH: WARBOUND
Marvel Comics: Feb, 2008 - No. 5, Jun, 2008 ($2.99, limited series)

1-5-Kirk & Sandoval-a/Cheung-c 3.00

WORLD WAR HULK: FRONT LINE (See Incredible Hulk #106)
Marvel Comics: Aug, 2007 - No. 6, Dec, 2007 ($2.99, limited series)

1-6-Ben Urich & Sally Floyd report World War Hulk; Jenkins-s/Bachs-a 3.00
TPB (2008, $16.99) r/#1-5 & WWH Prologue: World Breaker 17.00

WORLD WAR HULK: GAMMA CORPS
Marvel Comics: Sept, 2007 - No. 4, Jan, 2008 ($2.99, limited series)

1-4-Tieri-s/Ferreira-a/Roux-c 3.00
TPB (2008, $10.99) r/#1-4 11.00

WORLD WAR HULKS
Marvel Comics: Jun, 2010; Sept, 2010 ($3.99, one-shot & limited series)

1-Short stories by various; Deadpool app.; Romita Jr.-c 4.00
...: Spider-Man vs. Thor 1,2 (9/10 - No. 2, 9/10) Gillen-s/Molina-a 4.00
...: Wolverine vs. Captain America 1,2 (9/10 - No. 2, 9/10) "Capt America vs Wolv." on-c 4.00

WORLD WAR HULK: X-MEN (See New Avengers: Illuminati and Incredible Hulk #92)
Marvel Comics: Aug, 2007 - No. 3, Oct, 2007 ($2.99, limited series)

1-3-Gage-s/DiVito-a/McGuinness-c; Hulk invades the Xavier Institute 3.00
TPB (2008, $24.99) r/#1-3, Avengers: The Initiative #4-5, Irredeemable Ant-Man #10, Iron Man #19-20, and Ghost Rider #12-13 25.00

WORLD WAR STORIES
Dell Publishing Co.: Apr-June, 1965 - No. 3, Dec, 1965

1-Glanzman-a in all 4 8 12 25 40 55
2,3 3 6 9 16 24 32

WORLD WAR TANK GIRL
Titan Comics: May, 2017 - No. 4, Sept, 2017 ($3.99, limited series)

1-4-Tank Girl and crew in 1944 Germany; Alan Martin-s/Brett Parson-a; multiple covers 4.00

WORLD WAR II (See Classics Illustrated Special Issue)

WORLD WAR III
Ace Periodicals: Mar, 1953 - No. 2, May, 1953

1-(Scarce)-Atomic bomb blast-c; Cameron-a 174 348 522 1114 1907 2700
2-Used in **POP**, pg. 78 & B&W & color illos; Cameron-a 84 168 252 538 919 1300

WORLD WAR X
Titan Comics: Jan, 2017 - No. 6, Jun, 2017 ($3.99, English version of French comic series)

1-6-Jerry Frissen-s/Peter Snejbjerg-a; multiple covers on each 4.00

WORLD WITHOUT END
DC Comics: 1990 - No. 6, 1991 ($2.50, limited series, mature, stiff-c)

1-6: Horror/fantasy; all painted-c/a 3.00

WORLD WRESTLING FEDERATION BATTLEMANIA
Valiant: 1991 - No. 5?, 1991 ($2.50, magazine size, 68 pgs.)

1-5: 5-Includes 2 free pull-out posters 4.00

WORST FROM MAD, THE (Annual)
E. C. Comics: 1958 - No. 12, 1969 (Each annual cover is reprinted from the cover of the Mad issues being reprinted)(Value is 1/2 if bonus is missing)

nn(1958)-Bonus; record labels & travel stickers; 1st Mad annual; r/Mad #29-34 43 86 129 271 461 650
2(1959)-Bonus is small 33 1/3 rpm record entitled "Meet the Staff of Mad"; r/Mad #35-40 42 84 126 265 445 625
3(1960)-Has 20x30" campaign poster "Alfred E. Neuman for President"; r/Mad #41-46 15 30 45 103 227 350
4(1961)-Sunday comics section; r/Mad #47-54 14 28 42 97 214 330
5(1962)-Has 33-1/3 record; r/Mad #55-62 20 40 60 138 307 475
6(1963)-Has 33-1/3 record; r/Mad #63-70 20 40 60 138 307 475
7(1964)-Mad protest signs; r/Mad #71-76 9 18 27 61 123 185
8(1965)-Build a Mad Zeppelin 10 20 30 66 138 210
9(1966)-33-1/3 rpm record; Beatles on-c 14 28 42 94 207 320
10(1967)-Mad bumper sticker 6 12 18 40 73 105
11(1968)-Mad cover window stickers 6 12 18 37 66 95
12(1969)-Mad picture postcards; Orlando-a 6 12 18 37 66 95

NOTE: *Covers: **Bob Clarke**-#8. **Mingo**-#7, 9-12.*

WOTALIFE COMICS (Formerly Nutty Life #2; Phantom Lady #13 on)
Fox Feature Syndicate/Norlen Mag.: No. 3, Aug-Sept, 1946 - No. 12, July, 1947; 1959

3-Cosmo Cat, Li'l Pan, others begin 14 28 42 82 121 160
4-12-Cosmo Cat, Li'l Pan in all 10 20 30 58 79 100
1(1959-Norlen)-Atomic Rabbit, Atomic Mouse; reprints cover to #6; reprints entire book? 8 16 24 40 50 60

WOTALIFE COMICS
Green Publications: 1959 - No. 5, 1959

1-Funny animal; Li'l Pan & Tamale app. 7 14 21 35 43 50
2-5 5 10 15 22 26 30

WOW COMICS ("Wow, What A Magazine!" on cover of first issue)
Henle Publishing Co.: July, 1936 - No. 4, Nov, 1936 (52 pgs., magazine size)

1-Buck Jones in "The Phantom Rider" (1st app. in comics), Fu Manchu; Capt. Scott Dalton begins; Will Eisner-a (1st in comics); Baily-a(1); Briefer-c 420 840 1260 2940 5170 7400
2-Ken Maynard, Fu Manchu, Popeye by Segar plus article on Popeye; Eisner-a 300 600 900 1920 3310 4700
3-Eisner-c/a(3); Popeye by Segar, Fu Manchu, Hiram Hick by Bob Kane, Space Limited app.; Jimmy Dempsey talks about Popeye's punch; Bob Ripley Believe it or Not begins; Briefer-a 290 580 870 1856 3178 4500
4-Flash Gordon by Raymond, Mandrake, Popeye by Segar, Tillie The Toiler, Fu Manchu, Hiram Hick by Bob Kane; Eisner-a(3); Briefer-c/a 309 618 927 2163 3782 5400

WOW COMICS (Real Western Hero #70 on)(See XMas Comics)
Fawcett Publ.: Winter, 1940-41; No. 2, Summer, 1941 - No. 69, Fall, 1948

nn(#1)-Origin Mr. Scarlet by S&K; Atom Blake, Boy Wizard, Jim Dolan, & Rick O'Shay begin; Diamond Jack, The White Rajah, & Shipwreck Roberts, only app.; 1st mention of Gotham City in comics; the cover was printed on unstable paper stock and is rarely found in fine or mint condition; blank inside-c; bondage-c by Beck 1350 2700 4050 10,400 18,700 27,000
2 (Scarce)-The Hunchback begins 177 354 531 1124 1937 2750
3 (Fall, 1941) 107 214 321 680 1165 1650
4-Origin & 1st app. Pinky 108 216 324 686 1181 1675

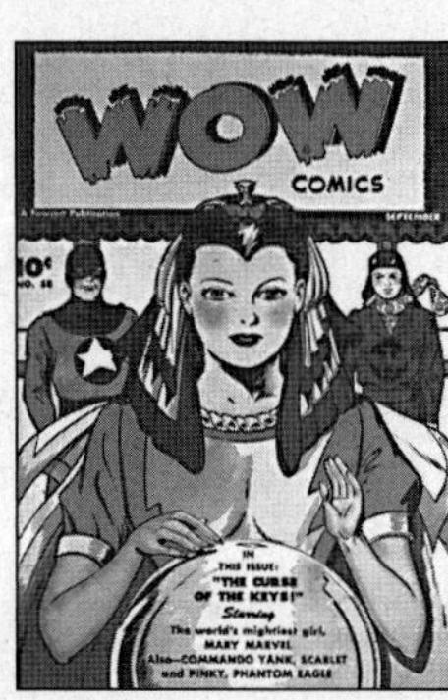

Wow Comics #58 © FAW

WWE #9 © WWE

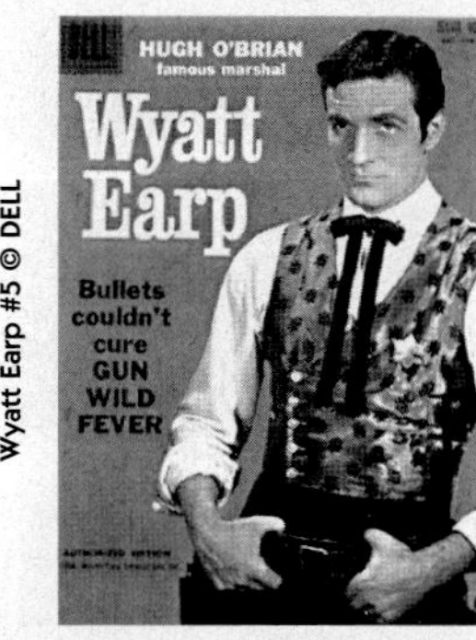

Wyatt Earp #5 © DELL

	GD 2.0	VG 4.0	FN 6.0	VF 8.0	VF/NM 9.0	NM- 9.2
5	66	132	198	419	722	1025
6-Origin & 1st app. The Phantom Eagle (7/15/42); Commando Yank begins	69	138	207	442	759	1075
7,8	58	116	174	371	636	900
9-(1/6/43)-Capt. Marvel, Capt. Marvel Jr., Shazam app.; Scarlet & Pinky x-over; Mary Marvel-c/stories begin	297	594	891	1900	3250	4600
10-Swayze-c/a on Mary Marvel	77	154	231	493	847	1200
11-17,19,20: 15-Flag-c	55	110	165	352	601	850
18-1st app. Uncle Marvel (10/43); infinity-c	61	122	183	390	670	950
21-30: 23-Robot-c. 28-Pinky x-over in Mary Marvel	39	78	117	235	385	535
31-40: 32-68-Phantom Eagle by Swayze	28	56	84	165	270	375
41-50	25	50	75	150	245	340
51-58: Last Mary Marvel	22	44	66	132	216	300
59-69: 59-Ozzie (teenage) begins. 62-Flying Saucer gag-c (1/48). 65-69-Tom Mix stories (cont'd in Real Western Hero)	20	40	60	114	182	250

NOTE: *Cover features: Mr. Scarlet-#1-5; Commando Yank-#6, 7, (w/Mr. Scarlet #8); Mary Marvel-#9-56, (w/Commando Yank-#46-50), (w/Mr. Scarlet & Commando Yank-#51), (w/Mr. Scarlet & Pinky #53), (w/Phantom Eagle #54, 56), (w/Commando Yank & Phantom Eagle #58); Ozzie-#59-69.*

WRAITH (Prequel to the novel NOS4A2)
IDW Publishing: Nov, 2013 (incorrect Nov, 2012 in indicia) - No. 7, May, 2014 ($3.99)

	GD 2.0	VG 4.0	FN 6.0	VF 8.0	VF/NM 9.0	NM- 9.2
1-7: Joe Hill-s/C.P. Wilson III-a. 5-(incorrect #4 in indicia)						4.00
1-Director's Cut (7/14, $4.99) Includes full script						5.00

WRAITHBORN
DC Comics (WildStorm): Nov, 2005 - No. 6, July, 2006 ($2.99, limited series)

	GD 2.0	VG 4.0	FN 6.0	VF 8.0	VF/NM 9.0	NM- 9.2
1-6-Marcia Chen & Joe Benitez-s/a						3.00
TPB (2007, $19.99) r/series; sketch pages and unused cover sketches						20.00

WRAITHBORN REDUX
Benitez Productions: Feb, 2016 - No. 6, Aug, 2016 ($3.99)

	GD 2.0	VG 4.0	FN 6.0	VF 8.0	VF/NM 9.0	NM- 9.2
1-6-Remastered printing of the 2005 series; Chen & Benitez-s/a; multiple covers						4.00
... HCF 2016 #1 (10/16, Halloween giveaway) r/#1						3.00

WRATH (Also see Prototype #4)
Malibu Comics: Jan, 1994 - No. 9, Nov, 1995 ($1.95)

	GD 2.0	VG 4.0	FN 6.0	VF 8.0	VF/NM 9.0	NM- 9.2
1-9: 2-Mantra x-over. 3-Intro/1st app. Slayer. 4,5-Freex app. 8-Mantra & Warstrike app. 9-Prime app.						3.00
1-Ultra 5000 Limited silver foil						6.00
Giant Size 1 (2.50, 44 pgs.)						4.00

WRATH OF THE ETERNAL WARRIOR
Valiant Entertainment: Nov, 2015 - No. 14, Dec, 2016 ($3.99)

	GD 2.0	VG 4.0	FN 6.0	VF 8.0	VF/NM 9.0	NM- 9.2
1-14: 1-Venditti-s/Allén-a						4.00

WRATH OF THE SPECTRE, THE
DC Comics: May, 1988 - No. 4, Aug, 1988 ($2.50, limited series)

	GD 2.0	VG 4.0	FN 6.0	VF 8.0	VF/NM 9.0	NM- 9.2
1-3: Aparo-r/Adventure #431-440						5.00
4-Three scripts intended for Adventure #441-on, but not drawn by Aparo until 1988	1	2	3	5	6	8
TPB (2005, $19.99) r/series; Peter Sanderson intro.						20.00

WRECK OF GROSVENOR (See Superior Stories #3)

WRETCH, THE
Caliber: 1996 ($2.95, B&W)

	GD 2.0	VG 4.0	FN 6.0	VF 8.0	VF/NM 9.0	NM- 9.2
1-Phillip Hester-a/scripts						3.00

WRETCH, THE
Amaze Ink: 1997 - No. 4, 1998 ($2.95, B&W)

	GD 2.0	VG 4.0	FN 6.0	VF 8.0	VF/NM 9.0	NM- 9.2
1-4-Phillip Hester-a/scripts						3.00
... Vol. 1: Everyday Doomsday (4/03, $13.95)						14.00

WRINGLE WRANGLE (Disney)
Dell Publishing Co.: No. 821, July, 1957

	GD 2.0	VG 4.0	FN 6.0	VF 8.0	VF/NM 9.0	NM- 9.2
Four Color 821-Based on movie "Westward Ho, the Wagons"; Marsh-a; Fess Parker photo-c	7	14	21	46	86	125

WULF
Ardden Entertainment: Mar, 2011 - No. 6, Sept, 2012 ($2.99)

	GD 2.0	VG 4.0	FN 6.0	VF 8.0	VF/NM 9.0	NM- 9.2
1-6-Steve Niles-s/Nat Jones-a/c; Lomax app. 3-6-Iron Jaw app.						3.00

WULF THE BARBARIAN
Atlas/Seaboard Publ.: Feb, 1975 - No. 4, Sept, 1975

	GD 2.0	VG 4.0	FN 6.0	VF 8.0	VF/NM 9.0	NM- 9.2
1,2: 1-Origin; Janson-a. 2-Intro. Berithe the Swordswoman; Janson-a w/Neal Adams, Wood, Reese-a assists	2	4	6	13	18	22
3,4: 3-Skeates-s. 4-Friedrich-s	2	4	6	9	13	16

WWE (WWE Wrestling)
BOOM! Studios: Jan, 2017 - Present ($3.99)

	GD 2.0	VG 4.0	FN 6.0	VF 8.0	VF/NM 9.0	NM- 9.2
1-14: 1-4-Seth Rollins & Triple H app.; Serg Acuña-a; multiple covers. 1-Back-up w/Guillory-a. 13-Raw 25 Years. 14-Spotlight on the Four Horsewomen						4.00
... Royal Rumble 2018 Special 1 (1/18, $7.99) Ric Flair and Randy Savage app.						8.00
...: Summerslam 2017 Special 1 (8/17, $7.99) Art by Guillory and others						8.00
... Survivor Series 2017 Special 1 (11/17, $7.99) Shawn Michaels & Kurt Angle app.						8.00
...Then. Now. Forever. 1 (11/16, $3.99) Short stories by various; multiple covers						4.00
...: Wrestlemania 2017 Special 1 (8/17, $7.99) Art by Guillory, Corona, Mora and others						8.00

WWE HEROES (WWE Wrestling) (#7 titled WWE Undertaker)
Titan Comics: Apr, 2010 - No. 8 ($3.99)

	GD 2.0	VG 4.0	FN 6.0	VF 8.0	VF/NM 9.0	NM- 9.2
1-6: 1-Two covers by Andy Smith and Liam Sharp. 5-Covers by Smith and Mayhew						4.00
7,8-"Undertaker" on cover; Rey Mysterio app.						4.00

WWE SUPERSTARS (WWE Wrestling)
Papercutz (Super Genius): Dec, 2013 - No. 12, Feb, 2015 ($2.99/$3.99)

	GD 2.0	VG 4.0	FN 6.0	VF 8.0	VF/NM 9.0	NM- 9.2
1-($2.99)-Mick Foley-s; John Cena, Randy Orton & CM Punk app.						3.00
2-12: 2-($3.99) Mick Foley-s. 9-Hulk Hogan cover by Jusko						4.00

WYATT EARP
Atlas Comics/Marvel No. 23 on (IPC): Nov, 1955 - #29, Jun, 1960; #30, Oct, 1972 - #34, Jun, 1973

	GD 2.0	VG 4.0	FN 6.0	VF 8.0	VF/NM 9.0	NM- 9.2
1	25	50	75	150	245	340
2-Williamson-a (4 pgs.)	15	30	45	84	127	170
3-6,8-11: 3-Black Bart app. 8-Wild Bill Hickok app.	12	24	36	69	97	125
7,12-Williamson-a, 4 pgs. ea.; #12 with Mayo	13	26	39	74	105	135
13-20: 17-1st app. Wyatt's deputy, Grizzly Grant	11	22	33	62	86	110
21-Davis-c	10	20	30	58	79	100
22-24,26-29: 22-Ringo Kid app. 23-Kid From Texas app. 29-Last 10¢ issue	9	18	27	52	69	85
25-Davis-a	10	20	30	54	72	90
30-Williamson-r (1972)	2	4	6	13	18	22
31-34-Reprints. 32-Torres-a(r)	2	4	6	9	13	16

NOTE: ***Ayers** a-8, 10(2), 16(4), 17, 20(4), 26(5), 27(3), 29(3). **Berg** a-9. **Everett** c-6. **Kirby** c-22, 24-26, 29. **Maneely** a-1; c-1-4, 8, 12, 17, 20. **Maurer** a-2(2), 3(4), 4(4), 8(4). **Severin** a-4, 9(4), 10; c-2, 9, 10, 14. **Wildey** a-5, 17, 24, 27, 28.*

WYATT EARP (TV) (Hugh O'Brian Famous Marshal)
Dell Publishing Co.: No. 860, Nov, 1957 - No. 13, Dec-Feb, 1960-61 (Hugh O'Brian photo-c)

	GD 2.0	VG 4.0	FN 6.0	VF 8.0	VF/NM 9.0	NM- 9.2
Four Color 860 (#1)-Manning-a	9	18	27	61	123	185
Four Color 890,921(6/58)-All Manning-a	7	14	21	44	82	120
4 (9-11/58) - 12-Manning-a. 4-Variant edition exists with back-c comic strip; Russ Manning-a. 5-Photo back-c	5	10	15	33	57	80
13-Toth-a	5	10	15	34	60	85

WYATT EARP FRONTIER MARSHAL (Formerly Range Busters) (Also see Blue Bird)
Charlton Comics: No. 12, Jan, 1956 - No. 72, Dec, 1967

	GD 2.0	VG 4.0	FN 6.0	VF 8.0	VF/NM 9.0	NM- 9.2
12	9	18	27	47	61	75
13-19	6	12	18	31	38	45
20-(68 pgs.)-Williamson-a(4), 8,5,5,& 7 pgs.	10	20	30	54	72	90
21-(100 pgs.) Mastroserio, Maneely, Severin-a (signed LePoer)	5	10	15	30	50	70
22-30	3	6	9	16	23	30
31-50	2	4	6	12	16	20
51-72 (1967)	2	4	6	9	11	14

WYNONNA EARP
Image Comics (WildStorm Productions): Dec, 1996 - No. 5, Apr, 1997 ($2.50)

	GD 2.0	VG 4.0	FN 6.0	VF 8.0	VF/NM 9.0	NM- 9.2
1-5-Beau Smith-s/Chin-a						3.00

WYNONNA EARP
IDW Publishing: Feb, 2016 - No. 8, Sept, 2016 ($3.99)

	GD 2.0	VG 4.0	FN 6.0	VF 8.0	VF/NM 9.0	NM- 9.2
1-8: 1-Beau Smith-s/Lora Innes-a; multiple covers; bonus look at the SyFy TV series						4.00

WYNONNA EARP: HOME ON THE STRANGE
IDW Publishing: Dec, 2003 - No. 3, Feb, 2004 ($3.99)

	GD 2.0	VG 4.0	FN 6.0	VF 8.0	VF/NM 9.0	NM- 9.2
1-3-Beau Smith-s/Ferreira-a						4.00

WYNONNA EARP LEGENDS: DOC HOLLIDAY
IDW Publishing: Nov, 2016 - No. 2, Dec, 2016 ($3.99)

	GD 2.0	VG 4.0	FN 6.0	VF 8.0	VF/NM 9.0	NM- 9.2
1,2: 1-Beau Smith & Tim Rozon-s/Chris Evenhuis-a; multiple covers;						4.00

WYNONNA EARP LEGENDS: THE EARP SISTERS
IDW Publishing: No. 3, Jan, 2017 - No. 4, Feb, 2017 ($3.99)

	GD 2.0	VG 4.0	FN 6.0	VF 8.0	VF/NM 9.0	NM- 9.2
3,4: 1-Beau Smith & Melanie Scrofano-s/Chris Evenhuis-a; multiple covers;						4.00

WYNONNA EARP SEASON ZERO
IDW Publishing: Jun, 2017 - No. 5, Oct, 2017 ($3.99)

	GD 2.0	VG 4.0	FN 6.0	VF 8.0	VF/NM 9.0	NM- 9.2
1-5-Beau Smith & Tim Rozon-s/Angel Hernandez-a; multiple covers;						4.00

WYNONNA EARP: THE YETI WARS

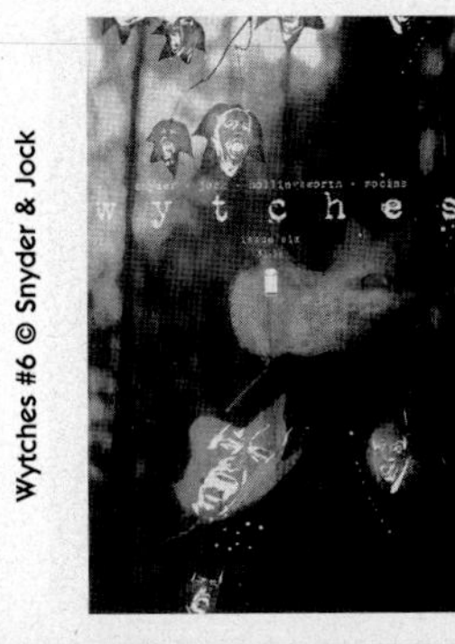

Wytches #6 © Snyder & Jock

Xena (2006 series) #1 © Universal

X-Factor #62 © MAR

GD VG FN VF VF/NM NM-
2.0 4.0 6.0 8.0 9.0 9.2

IDW Publishing: May, 2011 - No. 4, Aug, 2011 ($3.99)

1-4-Beau Smith-s/Enrique Villagran-a 4.00

WYRMS
Marvel Comics (Dabel Brothers): Feb, 2007 - No. 6, Jan, 2008 ($2.99)

1-6-Orson Scott Card & Jake Black-s. 1-3-Batista-a 3.00
TPB (2008, $14.99) r/#1-6 15.00

WYTCHES
Image Comics: Oct, 2014 - No. 6, May, 2015 ($2.99/$3.99)

1-Scott Snyder-s/Jock-a 5.00
2-5 3.00
6-($3.99) Bonus production art and Snyder afterword 4.00
Image Firsts: Wytches (12/14, $1.00) r/#1 3.00

X (Comics' Greatest World: X #1 only) (Also see Comics' Greatest World & Dark Horse Comics #8)
Dark Horse Comics: Feb, 1994 - No. 25, Apr, 1996 ($2.00/$2.50)

1-25: 3-Pit Bulls x-over. 8-Ghost-c & app. 18-Miller-c.; Predator app. 19-22-Miller-c. 3.00
Hero Illustrated Special #1,2 (1994, $1.00, 20 pgs.) 3.00
One Shot to the Head (1994, $2.50, 36 pgs.)-Miller-c. 3.00
NOTE: *Miller* c-18-22. *Quesada* c-6. *Russell* a-6.

X (Comics' Greatest World)
Dark Horse Comics: No. 0, Apr, 2013 - No. 24, Apr, 2015 ($2.99)

0-24: 0-Swierczynski-s/Eric Nguyen-a. 13,14-Atkins-a 3.00
One For One (1/14, $1.00) r/#1 3.00

XANADU COLOR SPECIAL
Eclipse Comics: Dec, 1988 ($2.00, one-shot)

1-Continued from Thoughts & Images 3.00

XAVIER INSTITUTE ALUMNI YEARBOOK (See X-Men titles)
Marvel Comics: Dec, 1996 ($5.95, square-bound, one-shot)

1-Text w/art by various 6.00

X-BABIES
Marvel Comics: Dec, 2009 - No. 4, Mar, 2010 ($3.99, limited series)

1-4-Schigiel-s/Chabot-a; Skottie Young-c 4.00
...: Murderama (8/98, $2.95) J.J. Kirby-a 4.00
...: Reborn (1/00, $3.50) J.J. Kirby-a 4.00

X-CALIBRE
Marvel Comics: Mar, 1995 - No. 4, July, 1995 ($1.95, limited series)

1-4-Age of Apocalypse 3.00

X-CAMPUS
Marvel Comics: July, 2010 - No. 4, Nov, 2010 ($4.99, limited series)

1-4-Alternate version of X-Men; stories by European creators; Nauck-c 5.00

X-CLUB
Marvel Comics: Feb, 2012 - No. 5, Jun, 2012 ($2.99, limited series)

1-5-X-Men scientist team; Dr. Nemesis & Danger app. 1-Bradshaw-c. 2-5-Esquejo-c 3.00

XENA (TV)
Dynamite Entertainment: 2006 - 2007 ($3.50)

1-4-Three covers on each; Neves-a/Layman-s 3.50
Vol. 2 #1-4-(Dark Xena) Four covers; Salonga-a/Layman-s 3.50
Annual 1 (2007, $4.95) Three covers; Salonga-a/Champagne-s 5.00
... Vol. 2: Dark Xena TPB (2007, $14.99) r/Vol. 2 #1-4; variant cover gallery 15.00

XENA / ARMY OF DARKNESS: WHAT...AGAIN?!
Dynamite Entertainment: 2008 - No. 4, 2009 ($3.50, limited series)

1-4-Xena, Gabrielle, & Autolycus team up with Ash; Montenegro-a; two covers on each 3.50

XENA: WARRIOR PRINCESS (TV)
Topps Comics: Aug, 1997 - No. 0, Oct, 1997 ($2.95)

1-Two stories by various; J. Scott Campbell-c 1 3 4 6 8 10
1,2-Photo-c 1 3 4 6 8 10
2-Stevens-c 1 3 4 6 8 10
0-(10/97)-Lopresti-c, 0-(10/97)-Photo-c 1 2 3 5 6 8
...First Appearance Collection ('97, $9.95) r/Hercules the Legendary Journeys #3-5 and 5-page story from TV Guide 10.00

XENA: WARRIOR PRINCESS (TV)
Dark Horse Comics: Sept, 1999 - No. 14, Oct, 2000 ($2.95/$2.99)

1-14: 1-Mignola-c and photo-c. 2,3-Bradstreet-c & photo-c 3.50

XENA: WARRIOR PRINCESS (Volume 2) (TV)
Dynamite Entertainment: 2016 - No. 6, 2016 ($3.99)

GD VG FN VF VF/NM NM-
2.0 4.0 6.0 8.0 9.0 9.2

1-6: 1-Valentine-s/Medel-a; main covers by Land & Frison 4.00

XENA: WARRIOR PRINCESS (Volume 4) (TV)
Dynamite Entertainment: 2018 - Present ($3.99)

1-Meredith Finch-s/Vicente Cifuentes-a; main covers by Cifuentes and David Finch 4.00

XENA: WARRIOR PRINCESS AND THE ORIGINAL OLYMPICS (TV)
Topps Comics: Jun, 1998 - No. 3, Aug, 1998 ($2.95, limited series)

1-3-Regular and Photo-c; Lim-a/T&M Bierbaum-s 3.50

XENA: WARRIOR PRINCESS-BLOODLINES (TV)
Topps Comics: May, 1998 - No. 2, June, 1998 ($2.95, limited series)

1,2-Lopresti-s/c/a. 2-Reg. and photo-c 3.50
1-Bath photo-c, 1-American Ent. Ed. 4.50

XENA: WARRIOR PRINCESS / JOXER: WARRIOR PRINCE (TV)
Topps Comics: Nov, 1997 - No. 3, Jan, 1998 ($2.95, limited series)

1-3-Regular and Photo-c; Lim-a/T&M Bierbaum-s 3.50

XENA: WARRIOR PRINCESS-THE DRAGON'S TEETH (TV)
Topps Comics: Dec, 1997 - No. 3, Feb, 1998 ($2.95, limited series)

1-3-Regular and Photo-c; Teranishi-a/Thomas-s 3.50

XENA: WARRIOR PRINCESS-THE ORPHEUS TRILOGY (TV)
Topps Comics: Mar, 1998 - No. 3, May, 1998 ($2.95, limited series)

1-3-Regular and Photo-c; Teranishi-a/T&M Bierbaum-s 3.50

XENA: WARRIOR PRINCESS VS. CALLISTO (TV)
Topps Comics: Feb, 1998 - No. 3, Apr, 1998 ($2.95, limited series)

1-3-Regular and Photo-c; Morgan-a/Thomas-s 3.50

XENOBROOD
DC Comics: No. 0, Oct, 1994 - No. 6, Apr, 1995 ($1.50, limited series)

0-6: 0-Indicia says "Xenobroods" 3.00

XENON
Eclipse Comics: Dec, 1987 - No. 23, Nov. 1, 1988 ($1.50, B&W, bi-weekly)

1-23 3.00

XENOZOIC TALES (Also see Cadillacs & Dinosaurs, Death Rattle #8)
Kitchen Sink Press: Feb, 1986 - No. 14, Oct, 1996

1-Mark Schultz-s/a in all 2 4 6 9 12 15
1(2nd printing)(1/89) 4.00
2-14 6.00
Volume 1 ($14.95) r/#1-6 & Death Rattle #8 15.00
Volume 2 (5/03, $14.95, TPB) B&W r/#7-14; intro by Frank Cho 15.00

XENYA
Sanctuary Press: Apr, 1994 - No. 3 ($2.95)

1-3: 1-Hildebrandt-c; intro Xenya 3.00

XERO
DC Comics: May, 1997 - No. 12, Apr, 1998 ($1.75)

1-7 3.00
8-12 3.00

X-FACTOR (Also see The Avengers #263, Fantastic Four #286 and Mutant X)
Marvel Comics Group: Feb, 1986 - No. 149, Sept, 1998

1-($1.25, 52 pgs)-Story recaps 1st app. from Avengers #263; story cont'd from F.F. #286; return of original X-Men (now X-Factor); Guice/Layton-a; Baby Nathan app. (2nd after X-Men #201) 3 6 9 14 19 24
2-4 6.00
5-1st brief app. Apocalypse (1 page) 3 6 9 16 24 32
6-1st full app. Apocalypse 6 12 18 37 66 95
7-10: 10-Sabretooth app. (11/86, 3 pgs.) cont'd in X-Men #212; 1st app. in an X-Men comic book 5.00
11-18,20-22: 13-Baby Nathan app. in flashback. 14-Cyclops vs. The Master Mold. 15-Intro wingless Angel 4.00
19-Apocalypse-c/app. 2 4 6 9 12 15
23-1st brief app. Archangel (2 pages) 2 4 6 8 10 12
24-1st full app. Archangel (now in Uncanny X-Men); Fall Of The Mutants begins; origin Apocalypse 4 8 12 23 37 50
25,26: Fall Of The Mutants; 26-New outfits 6.00
27-37,39,41-49,51-59,63-70,72-83,87-91,93-99,101: 35-Origin Cyclops. 51-53-Sabretooth app. 52-Liefeld-c(p). 54-Intro Crimson; Silvestri-c/a(p). 63-Portacio/Thibert-c/a(p) begins, ends #69. 65-68-Lee co-plots. 65-The Apocalypse Files begins, ends #68. 66,67-Baby Nathan app. 67-Inhumans app. 68-Baby Nathan is sent into future to save his life. 69,70-X-Men(w/Wolverine) x-over. 77-Cannonball (of X-Force) app. 87-Quesada-c/a(p) in monthly comic begins,ends #92. 88-1st app. Random 3.00

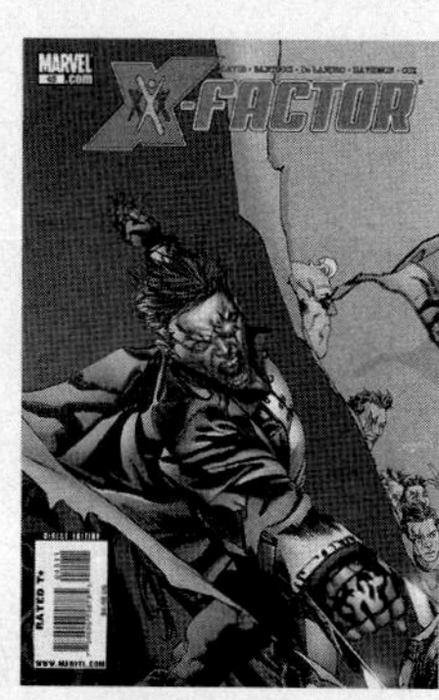

X-Factor (2006 series) #45 © MAR

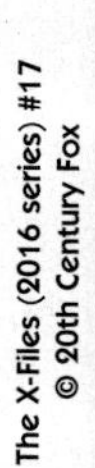

The X-Files (2016 series) #17 © 20th Century Fox

The X-Files: Ground Zero #3 © 20th Century Fox

GD VG FN VF VF/NM NM-
2.0 4.0 6.0 8.0 9.0 9.2

38,50,60-62,71,75: 38,50-(52 pgs.): 50-Liefeld/McFarlane-c. 60-X-Tinction Agenda x-over; New Mutants (w/Cable) x-over in #60-62; Wolverine in #62. 61,62-X-Tinction Agenda. 62-Jim Lee-c. 71-New team begins (Havok, Polaris, Strong Guy, Wolfsbane & Madrox); Stroman-c/a begins. 75-(52 pgs.) 4.00
40-Rob Liefield-c/a (4/89, 1st at Marvel?) 5.00
60,71-2nd printings. 60-Gold ink 2nd printing. 71-2nd printing ($1.25) 3.00
84-86 -Jae Lee a(p); 85,86-Jae Lee-c. Polybagged with trading card in each; X-Cutioner's Song x-overs. 4.00
92-($3.50, 68 pgs.)-Wraparound-c by Quesada w/Havok hologram on-c; begin X-Men 30th anniversary issues; Quesada-a. 6.00
92-2nd printing 4.00
100-($2.95, 52 pgs.)-Embossed foil-c; Multiple Man dies. 6.00
100-($1.75, 52 pgs.)-Regular edition 4.00
102-105,107: 102-bound-in card sheet 3.00
106-($2.00)-Newsstand edition 3.00
106-($2.95)-Collectors edition 4.00
108-124,126-148: 112-Return from Age of Apocalypse. 115-card insert. 119-123-Sabretooth app. 123-Hound app. 124-w/Onslaught Update. 126-Onslaught x-over; Beast vs. Dark Beast. 128-w/card insert; return of Multiple Man. 130-Assassination of Grayson Creed. 146,148-Moder-a 3.00
125-($2.95)-"Onslaught"; Post app.; return of Havok 4.00
149-Last issue 5.00
#(-1) Flashback (7/97) Matsuda-a 3.00
Annual 1-9: 1-(10/86-'94, 68 pgs.) 3-Evolutionary War x-over. 4-Atlantis Attacks; Byrne/Simonson-a;Byrne-c. 5-Fantastic Four, New Mutants x-over; Keown 2 pg. pin-up. 6-New Warriors app.; 5th app. X-Force cont'd from X-Men Annual #15. 7-1st Quesada-a(p) on X-Factor plus-c(p). 8-Bagged w/trading card. 9-Austin-a(i) 4.00
...Prisoner of Love (1990, $4.95, 52 pgs.)-Starlin scripts; Guice-a 5.00
... Visionaries: Peter David Vol. 1 TPB (2005, $15.99) r/#71-75 16.00
... Visionaries: Peter David Vol. 2 TPB (2007, $15.99) r/#76-78 & Incr. Hulk #390-392 16.00
... Visionaries: Peter David Vol. 3 TPB (2007, $15.99) r/#79-83 & Annual #7 16.00
NOTE: ***Art Adams** a-41p, 42p. **Buckler** a-50p. **Liefeld** a-40; c-40, 50i, 52p. **McFarlane** c-50i. **Mignola** c-70. **Brandon Peterson** a-78p(part). **Whilce Portacio** c/a(p)-63-69. **Quesada** a(p)-87-92, Annual 7. c(p)-78, 79, 82, Annual 7. **Simonson** c/a-10, 11, 13-15, 17-19, 21, 23-31, 33, 34, 36-39; c-12, 16. **Paul Smith** a-44-48; c-43. **Stroman** a(p)-71-75, 77, 78(part), 80, 81; c(p)-71-77, 80, 81, 84. **Zeck** c-2.*

X-FACTOR (Volume 2)
Marvel Comics: June, 2002 - No. 4, Oct, 2002 ($2.50)
1-4: Jensen-s/Ranson-a. 1-Phillips-c. 2,3-Edwards-c 3.00

X-FACTOR (Volume 3) (Also see All-New X-Factor)
Marvel Comics: Jan, 2006 - No. 262, Nov, 2013 ($2.99)
1-24: 1-Peter David-s/Ryan Sook-a. 8,9-Civil War. 21-24-Endangered Species back-up 3.00
25-49: 25-27-Messiah Complex x-over; Finch-c. 26-2nd printing with new Eaton-c 3.00
50-(12/09, $3.99) Madrox in the future; DeLandro-a/Yardin-c 4.00
200-(2/10, $4.99) Resumes original series numbering; 3 covers; Fantastic Four app. 5.00
201-224,224.1, 225-262 ($2.99) 201,202-Dr. Doom & Fant. Four app. 211,212-Thor app. 230-Wolverine app.; Havok & Polaris return 3.00
... Special: Layla Miller (10/08, $3.99) David-s/DeLandro-a 4.00
...: The Quick and the Dead (7/08, $2.99) Raimondi-a; Quicksilver regains powers 3.00
...: The Longest Night HC (2006, $19.99, dust jacket) r/#1-6; sketch pages by Sook 20.00
...: The Longest Night SC (2007, $14.99) r/#1-6; sketch pages by Sook 15.00
...: Life and Death Matters HC (2007, $19.99, dust jacket) r/#7-12 20.00
...: Life and Death Matters SC (2007, $14.99) r/#7-12 15.00
...: The Many Lives of Madrox SC (2007, $14.99) r/#13-17 15.00
...: Heart of Ice HC (2007, $19.99, dust jacket) r/#18-24 20.00
...: Heart of Ice SC (2008, $17.99, dust jacket) r/#18-24 18.00

X-FACTOR FOREVER
Marvel Comics: May, 2010 - No. 5, Sept, 2010 ($3.99, limited series)
1-5-Louise Simonson-s/Dan Panosian-a; back-up origin of Apocalypse 4.00

X-51 (Machine Man)
Marvel Comics: Sept, 1999 - No. 12, Jul, 2000 ($1.99/$2.50)
1-7: 1-Joe Bennett-a. 2-Two covers 3.00
8-12: 8-Begin $2.50-c 3.00
Wizard #0 3.00

X-FILES, THE (TV)
Topps Comics: Jan, 1995 - No. 41, July, 1998 ($2.50)
-2(9/96)-Black-c; r/X-Files Magazine #1&2 5.00
-1(9/96)-Silver-c; r/Hero Illustrated Giveaway 5.00
0-($3.95)-Adapts pilot episode 4.00
0-"Mulder" variant-c 1 2 3 5 6 8
0-"Scully" variant-c 1 2 3 5 6 8
1/2-W/certificate 1 2 3 5 6 8
1-New stories based on the TV show; direct market & newsstand editions; Miran Kim-c on all 3 6 9 14 20 25
2 1 2 3 6 8 10
3,4 6.00
5-10: 6-Begin $2.95-c 5.00
11-41: 21-W/bound-in card. 40,41-Reg. & photo-c 4.00
Annual 1,2 ($3.95) 4.00
Afterflight TPB ($5.95) Art by Thompson, Saviuk, Kim 6.00
Classics #1: Hundred Penny Press Edition (12/13 $1.00) r/#1 3.00
Collection 1 TPB ($19.95)-r/#1-6. 20.00
Collection 2 TPB ($19.95)-r/#7-12, Annual #1. 20.00
...Fight the Future ('98, $5.95) Movie adaptation 6.00
Hero Illustrated Giveaway (3/95) 1 2 3 5 6 8
Special Edition 1-5 ($3.95/$4.95)-r/#1-3, 4-6, 7-9, 10-12, 13, Annual 1 5.00
Star Wars Galaxy Magazine Giveaway (B&W) 1 3 4 6 8 10
Trade paperback ($19.95) 20.00
Volume 1 TPB (Checker Books, 2005, $19.95) r/#13-17, #0, Season One: Squeeze 20.00
Volume 2 TPB (Checker Books, 2005, $19.95) r/#18-24, #1/2, Comics Digest #1 20.00
Volume 3 TPB (Checker Books, 2006, $19.95) r/#23-26, Fire, Ice, Hero Ill. Giveaway 20.00

X-FILES, THE (TV)
DC Comics (WildStorm): No. 0, Sept, 2008 - No. 6, Jun, 2009 ($3.99/$3.50)
0-($3.99) Spotnitz-s/Denham-a; photo-c 4.00
1-6-($3.50) 1-Spotnitz-s/Denham-a; 2 covers. 4-Wolfman-s 3.50
TPB (2009, $19.99) r/#0-6 20.00

X-FILES, THE (TV)
IDW Publishing: Apr, 2016 - Present ($3.99)
1-17: 1-Joe Harris-s/Matthew Dow Smith-a. 12,13-Flashback to Skinner in Viet Nam 4.00
... Annual 2014 (4/14, $7.99) Back-up story with Dave Sim-s/Currie-a; 2 covers 8.00
... Annual 2016 (7/16, $7.99) Greg Scott-a; Valenzuela & photo-c 8.00
...: Art Gallery (5/14, $3.99) Gallery of sketch card art by various incl. Kim & Staggs 4.00
...: Deviations (3/16, $4.99) What If... young Fox Mulder was abducted by aliens 5.00
...: Deviations 2017 (3/17, $4.99) Samantha Mulder and Scully team; Califano-a 5.00
... Funko Universe One Shot (5/17, $4.99) Short stories with Funko Pop-styled characters 5.00
... X-Mas Special (12/14, $7.99) Joe Harris-s/Matt Smith-a; Kesel-s/Southworth-a 8.00
... X-Mas Special 2016 (12/16, $7.99) Joe Harris-s/Wayne Nichols-a 8.00

X-FILES COMICS DIGEST, THE
Topps Comics: Dec, 1995 - No. 3 ($3.50, quarterly, digest-size)
1-3: 1,2: New X-Files stories w/Ray Bradbury Comics-r. 1-Reg. & photo-c 4.00
NOTE: ***Adlard** a-1, 2. **Jack Davis** a-2r. **Russell** a-1r.*

X-FILES, THE: CONSPIRACY
IDW Publishing: Jan, 2014 - No. 2, Mar, 2014 ($3.99, limited series)
1,2-Bookends for 6-part Lone Gunmen series; Crilley-s/Stanisci-a; Kim & Corroney-c 4.00
X-Files/Ghostbusters: Conspiracy (1/14, $3.99) Part 2; Navarro-a 4.00
X-Files/Teenage Mutant Ninja Turtles: Conspiracy (2/14, $3.99) Part 3; Walsh-a 4.00
X-Files/Transformers: Conspiracy (2/14, $3.99) Part 4; Verma-a 4.00
X-Files/The Crow: Conspiracy (3/14, $3.99) Part 5; Malhotra-a 4.00

X-FILES, THE: GROUND ZERO (TV)
Topps Comics: Nov, 1997 - No. 4, March, 1998 ($2.95, limited series)
1-4-Adaptation of the Kevin J. Anderson novel 4.00

X-FILES, THE: JFK DISCLOSURE (TV)
IDW Publishing: Oct, 2017 - No. 2, Nov, 2017 ($4.99)
1,2-Tipton-s/Menton3-a 5.00

X-FILES, THE: ORIGINS (TV)
IDW Publishing: Aug, 2016 - No. 4, Nov, 2016 ($4.99)
1-4-Flipbooks with teenage Mulder and Scully 5.00

X-FILES, THE: ORIGINS – DOG DAYS OF SUMMER (TV)
IDW Publishing: Jun, 2017 - No. 4, Sept, 2017 ($3.99)
1-4-Flipbooks with teenage Mulder in 1974 and Scully in 1977 4.00

X-FILES, THE: SEASON ONE (TV)
Topps Comics: July, 1997 - July, 1998 ($4.95, adaptations of TV episodes)
1-(Pilot Episode, r/X-Files #0), 2-(Deep Throat), Squeeze, Conduit, Ice, Space, Fire, Beyond the Sea, Shadows 5.00

X-FILES, THE: SEASON 10 (TV)
IDW Publishing: Jun, 2013 - No. 25, Jun, 2015 ($3.99)
1-25: 1-5-Co-written by Chris Carter; multiple covers on each. 6,7-Flukeman returns. 17-Frank Black app. 18-Doggett & Reyes app. 4.00
... #1: IDW's Greatest Hits (4/16, $1.00) r/#1 3.00

X-FILES, THE: SEASON 11 (TV)
IDW Publishing: Aug, 2015 - No. 8, Mar, 2016 ($3.99)

X-Force #75 © MAR

X-Force (2008 series) #1 © MAR

X-Man #38 © MAR

GD VG FN VF VF/NM NM-
2.0 4.0 6.0 8.0 9.0 9.2

1-8: 1-Joe Harris-s/Matthew Smith-a 4.00

X-FILES, THE / 30 DAYS OF NIGHT
DC Comics (WildStorm)/IDW: Sept, 2010 - No. 6, Feb, 2011 ($3.99, limited series)

1-6-Steve Niles & Adam Jones-s/Tom Mandrake-a. 1-Three covers 4.00
TPB (2011, $17.99) r/#1-6; cover gallery 18.00

X-FILES, THE: YEAR ZERO (TV)
IDW Publishing: Jul, 2014 - No. 5, Nov, 2014 ($3.99)

1-5: 1-Karl Kesel-s; Greg Scott & Vic Malhotra-a; flashback to 1946 4.00

X-FORCE (Becomes X-Statix) (Also see The New Mutants #100)
Marvel Comics: Aug, 1991 - No. 129, Aug, 2002 ($1.00-$2.25)

1-($1.50, 52 pgs.)-Polybagged with 1 of 5 diff. Marvel Universe trading cards inside (1 each); 6th app. of X-Force; Liefeld-c/a begins 6.00
1-1st printing with Cable trading card inside 2 4 6 8 10 12
1-1st printing with Deadpool trading card inside 2 4 6 9 12 15
1-2nd printing; metallic ink-c (no bag or card) 4.00
2-Deadpool-c/story (2nd app.) 2 4 6 10 14 18
3,4: 3-New Brotherhood of Evil Mutants app. 4-Spider-Man x-over; cont'd from Spider-Man #16; reads sideways 4.00
5-10: 6-Last $1.00-c. 7,9-Weapon X back-ups. 8-Intro The Wild Pack (Cable, Kane, Domino, Hammer, G.W. Bridge, & Grizzly); Liefeld-c/a (4); Mignola-a. 10-Weapon X full-length story (part 3). 4.00
11-1st Weapon Prime; Deadpool-c/story (3rd app.) 2 4 6 11 16 20
12-14,20-22,24,26-33 3.00
15-Cable leaves X-Force; Deadpool-c/app. 2 4 6 10 14 18
16-18-Polybagged w/trading card in each; X-Cutioner's Song x-overs 4.00
19-1st Copycat 2 4 6 9 12 15
23-Deadpool-c/app. 6.00
25-($3.50, 52 pgs.)-Wraparound-c w/Cable hologram on-c; Cable returns 5.00
34-37,39-45: 34-bound-in card sheet 3.00
38,40-43: 38-($2.00)-Newsstand edition. 40-43 ($1.95)-Deluxe edition 3.00
38-($2.95)-Collectors edition (prismatic) 5.00
44-49,51-67: 44-Return from Age of Apocalypse. 45-Sabretooth app. 49-Sebastian Shaw app. 52-Blob app., Onslaught cameo. 55-Vs. S.H.I.E.L.D. 56-Deadpool app. 57-Mr. Sinister & X-Man-c/app. 57,58-Onslaught x-over. 59-W/card insert; return of Longshot. 60-Dr. Strange 3.00
50 ($3.95)-Gatefold wrap-around foil-c 4.00
50 ($3.95)-Liefeld variant-c 5.00
68-74: 68-Operation Zero Tolerance 3.00
75,100-($2.99): 75-Cannonball-c/app. 4.00
76-99,101,102: 81-Pollina poster. 95-Magneto-c. 102-Ellis-s/Portacio-a 3.00
103-115: 103-Begin $2.25-c; Portacio-a thru #106. 115-Death of old team 3.00
116-New team debuts; Allred-c/a; Milligan-s; no Comics Code stamp on-c 4.00
117-129: 117-Intro. Mr. Sensitive. 120-Wolverine-c/app. 123-'Nuff Said issue. 124-Darwyn Cooke-a/c. 128-Death of U-Go Girl. 129-Fegredo-a 3.00
#(-1) Flashback (7/97) story of John Proudstar; Pollina-a 3.00
Annual 1-3 ('92-'94, 68 pgs.) 1-1st Greg Capullo-a(p) on X-Force. 2-Polybagged w/trading card; intro X-Treme & Neurtap 4.00
...And Cable '95 (12/95, $3.95)-Impossible Man app. 4.00
...And Cable '96, ...'97 ('96, 7/97) -'96-Wraparound-c 4.00
...And Spider-Man: Sabotage nn (11/92, $6.95)-Reprints X-Force #3,4 & Spider-Man #16 7.00
.../ Champions '98 ($3.50) 4.00
Annual 99 ($3.50) 4.00
...: Famous, Mutant & Mortal HC (2003, $29.99) oversized r/#116-129; foreward by Milligan; gallery of covers and pin-ups; script for #123 30.00
...New Beginnings TPB (10/01, $14.95) r/#116-120 15.00
...Rough Cut ($2.99) Pencil pages and script for #102 3.00
...Youngblood (8/96, $4.95)-Platt-c 5.00
NOTE: ***Capullo*** *a(p)-15-25, Annual 1; c(p)-14-27.* ***Rob Liefeld*** *a-1-7, 9p; c-1-9, 11p; plots-1-12.* ***Mignola*** *a-8p.*

X-FORCE
Marvel Comics: Oct, 2004 - No. 6, Mar, 2005 ($2.99, limited series)

1-6-Liefeld-c/a; Nicieza-s. 5,6-Wolverine & The Thing app. 3.00
X-Force & Cable Vol. 1: The Legend Returns (2005, $14.99) r/#1-6 15.00

X-FORCE (Also see Uncanny X-Force)
Marvel Comics: Apr, 2008 - No. 28, Sept, 2010 ($2.99)

1-Crain-a; Wolverine & X-23 app.; two covers (regular and bloody) by Crain on #1-5 4.00
2-21,23-28: 2,3-Bastion app. 4-6-Archangel app. 7-10-Choi-a. 9-11-Ghost Rider app. 26-28-Second Coming x-over; Granov-c. 26-Nightcrawler killed 3.00
22-($3.99) Necrosha x-over; Crain-a 4.00
...: Angels and Demons MGC #1 (5/11, $1.00) r/#1 with "Marvel's Greatest Comics" on-c 3.00
... Annual 1 (2/10, $3.99) Kirkman-s/Pearson-a/c; Deadpool back-up w/Barberi-a 4.00
... /Cable: Messiah War 1 (5/09, $3.99) Choi-a; covers by Andrews and Choi 4.00
... Special: Ain't No Dog (8/08, $3.99) Huston-s/Palo-a; Dell'Edera-a; Hitch-c 4.00

X-FORCE
Marvel Comics: Apr, 2014 - No. 15, Apr, 2015 ($3.99)

1-15: 1-Team of Cable, Fantomex, Psylocke & Marrow; Rock-He Kim-a. 4-6-Molina-a 4.00

X-FORCE MEGAZINE
Marvel Comics: Nov, 1996 ($3.95, one-shot)

1-Reprints 4.00

X-FORCE: SEX AND VIOLENCE
Marvel Comics: Sept, 2010 - No. 3, Nov, 2010 ($3.99, limited series)

1-3-Dell'Otto-a/Kyle & Yost-s; Domino & Wolverine vs. The Hand & The Assassins Guild 4.00

X-FORCE: SHATTERSTAR
Marvel Comics: Apr, 2005 - No. 4, July, 2005 ($2.99, limited series)

1-4-Liefeld-c/s; Michaels-a 3.00
TPB (2005, $15.99) r/#1-4 & New Mutants #99,100 16.00

X-INFERNUS
Marvel Comics: Feb, 2009 - No. 4, May, 2009 ($3.99, limited series)

1-4-Illyana Rasputin in Limbo; Cebulski-s/Camuncoli-a/Finch-c 4.00

XIN: JOURNEY OF THE MONKEY KING
Anarchy Studios: May, 2003 - No. 3, July, 2003 ($2.99)

Preview Edition (Apr, 2003, $1.99) Flip book w/ Vampi Vicious Preview Edition 3.00
1-3-Kevin Lau-a. 1-Three covers by Lau, Park and Nauck. 2-Three covers 3.00

XIN: LEGEND OF THE MONKEY KING
Anarchy Studios: Nov, 2002 - No. 3, Jan, 2003 ($2.99)

Preview Edition (Summer 2002, Diamond Dateline supplement) 3.00
1-3-Kevin Lau-a. 1-Two covers by Lau & Madureira. 2-Two covers by Lau & Oeming 3.00
TPB (10/03, $12.95) r/#1-3; cover gallery and sketch pages 13.00

X-MAN (Also see X-Men Omega & X-Men Prime)
Marvel Comics: Mar, 1995 - No. 75, May, 2001 ($1.95/$1.99/$2.25)

1-Age of Apocalypse 5.00
1-2nd print 3.00
2-4,25: 25-($2.99)-Wraparound-c 4.00
5-24, 26-28: 5-Post Age of Apocalypse stories begin. 5-7-Madelyne Pryor app. 10-Professor X app. 12-vs. Excalibur. 13-Marauders, Cable app. 14-Vs. Cable; Onslaught app. 15-17-Vs. Holocaust. 17-w/Onslaught Update. 18-Onslaught x-over; X-Force-c/app; Marauders app. 19-Onslaught x-over. 20-Abomination-c/app.; w/card insert. 23-Bishop app. 24-Spider-Man, Morbius-c/app. 27-Re-appearance of Aurora(Alpha Flight) 3.00
29-49,51-62: 29-Operation Zero Tolerance. 37,38-Spider-Man-c/app. 56-Spider-Man app. 3.00
50-($2.99) Crossover with Generation X #50 4.00
63-74: 63-Ellis & Grant-s/Olivetti-a begins. 64-Begin $2.25-c 3.00
75 ($2.99) Final issue; Alcatena-a 4.00
#(-1) Flashback (7/97) 3.00
...'96, ...'97-($2.95)-Wraparound-c; '96-Age of Apocalypse 4.00
...: All Saints' Day ('97, $5.99) Dodson-a 6.00
.../Hulk '98 ($2.99) Wraparound-c; Thanos app. 4.00

XMAS COMICS
Fawcett Publications: 12?/1941 - No. 2, 12?/1942; (50¢, 324 pgs.)
No. 7, 12?/1947 (25¢, 132 pgs.)(#3-6 do not exist for this series, see 1949-1952 series)

1-Contains Whiz #21, Capt. Marvel #3, Bulletman #2, Wow #3, & Master #18; front & back-c by Raboy. Not rebound, remaindered comics; printed at same time as originals 476 952 1428 3475 6138 8800
2-Capt. Marvel, Bulletman, Spy Smasher 213 426 639 1363 2332 3300
7-Funny animals (Hoppy, Billy the Kid & Oscar) 84 168 252 538 919 1300

XMAS COMICS
Fawcett Publications: No. 4, Dec, 1949 - No. 7, Dec, 1952 (50¢, 196 pgs.)

4-Contains Whiz, Master, Tom Mix, Captain Marvel, Nyoka, Capt. Video, Bob Colt, Monte Hale, Hot Rod Comics, & Battle Stories. Not rebound, remaindered comics; printed at the same time as originals. Title logo and Santa's suit on cover are topped by red felt 113 226 339 718 1234 1750
5-7: 5-Green felt tree on-c. 6-Cover has red felt like #4. 7-Bill Boyd app.; stocking on cover is made of green felt (novelty cover) 90 180 270 576 988 1400

X-MEN, THE (See Adventures of Cyclops and Phoenix, Amazing Adventures, Archangel, Brotherhood, Capt. America #172, Classic X-Men, Exiles, Further Adventures of Cyclops & Phoenix, Gambit, Giant-Size..., Heroes For Hope..., Kitty Pryde & Wolverine, Marvel & DC Present, Marvel Collector's Edition:..., Marvel Fanfare, Marvel Graphic Novel, Marvel Super Heroes, Marvel Team-Up, Marvel Triple Action, The Marvel X-Men Collection, New Mutants, Nightcrawler, Official Marvel Index To..., Rogue, Special Edition..., Ultimate..., Uncanny..., Wolverine, X-Factor, X-Force, X-Terminators)

X-MEN, THE (1st series)(Becomes Uncanny X-Men at #142)(The X-Men #1-93; X-Men #94-141) (The Uncanny X-Men on-c only #114-141)

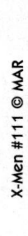

X-Men #34 © MAR

X-Men #111 © MAR

Uncanny X-Men #226 © MAR

GD VG FN VF VF/NM NM-
2.0 4.0 6.0 8.0 9.0 9.2

Marvel Comics Group: Sept, 1963 - No. 66, Mar, 1970; No. 67, Dec, 1970 - No. 141, Jan, 1981; Uncanny X-Men No. 142, Feb, 1981 - No. 544, Dec, 2011

1-Origin/1st app. X-Men (Angel, Beast, Cyclops, Iceman & Marvel Girl); 1st app. Magneto & Professor X 1300 2600 5200 12,000 31,000 50,000
2-1st app. The Vanisher 162 324 486 1337 3019 4700
3-1st app. The Blob (1/64) 104 208 312 832 1866 2900
4-1st Quicksilver & Scarlet Witch & Brotherhood of the Evil Mutants (3/64); 1st app. Toad; 2nd app. Magneto 207 414 621 1708 3854 6000
5-Magneto & Evil Mutants-c/story 71 142 213 568 1284 2000
6-Sub-Mariner app. 57 114 171 456 1028 1600
7-Magneto app. 53 106 159 424 937 1450
8,9,11: 8-1st Unus the Untouchable. 9-Early Avengers app. (1/65); 1st Lucifer. 11-1st app. The Stranger. 46 92 138 340 770 1200
10-1st S.A. app. Ka-Zar & Zabu the sabertooth (3/65) 46 92 138 340 770 1200
12-Origin Prof. X; Origin/1st app. Juggernaut 59 118 177 472 1061 1650
13-Juggernaut and Human Torch app. 32 64 96 230 515 800
14,15: 14-1st app. Sentinels. 15-Origin Beast 32 64 96 230 515 800
16-20: 19-1st app. The Mimic (4/66) 19 38 57 131 291 450
21-27,29,30: 27-Re-enter The Mimic (r-in #75); Spider-Man cameo 13 26 39 89 195 300
28-1st app. The Banshee (1/67)(r-in #76) 22 44 66 154 340 525
28-2nd printing (1994) 2 4 6 9 12 15
31-34,36,37,39: 34-Adkins-c/a. 39-New costumes 10 20 30 69 147 225
35-Spider-Man x-over (8/67)(r-in #83); 1st app. Changeling 24 48 72 168 372 575
38,40: 38-Origins of the X-Men series begins, ends #57. 40-(1/68) 1st app. Frankenstein's monster at Marvel 11 22 33 73 157 240
41-48: 42-Death of Prof. X (Changeling disguised as). 44-1st S.A. app. G.A. Red Raven. 10 20 30 64 132 200
49-Steranko-c; 1st Polaris 14 28 42 96 211 325
50,51-Steranko-c/a 10 20 30 68 144 220
52 9 18 27 61 123 185
53-Barry Smith-c/a (his 1st comic book work) 10 20 30 66 138 210
54,55-B. Smith-c. 54-1st app. Alex Summers who later becomes Havok. 55-Summers discovers he has mutant powers 10 20 30 67 141 215
56,57,59-63,65-Neal Adams-a(p). 56-Intro Havok w/o costume. 60-1st Sauron. 65-Return of Professor X. 11 22 33 73 157 240
58-1st app. Havok in costume; N. Adams-a(p) 14 28 42 94 207 320
62,63-2nd printings (1994) 2 4 6 8 10 12
64-1st app. Sunfire 11 22 33 72 154 235
66-Last new story w/original X-Men; battles Hulk 11 22 33 76 163 250
67-70: 67-Reprints begin, end #93. 67-70: (52 pgs.) 9 18 27 59 117 175
71-93: 71-Last 15¢ issue. 72: (52 pgs.). 73-86-r/#25-38 w/new-c. 83-Spider-Man-c/story. 87-93-r/#39-45 with covers 8 16 24 51 96 140
94 (8/75)-New X-Men begin (see Giant-Size X-Men for 1st app.); Colossus, Nightcrawler, Thunderbird, Storm, Wolverine, & Banshee join; Angel, Marvel Girl & Iceman resign 70 140 210 500 950 1400
95-Death of Thunderbird 15 30 45 105 233 360
96,97 10 20 30 64 132 200
98,99-(Regular 25¢ edition)(4,6/76) 9 18 27 63 129 195
98,99-(30¢-c variants, limited distribution) 24 48 72 168 372 575
100-Old vs. New X-Men; part origin Phoenix; last 25¢ issue (8/76) 10 20 30 70 150 230
100-(30¢-c variant, limited distribution) 27 54 81 194 435 675
101-Phoenix origin concludes 16 34 48 110 243 375
102-104: 102-Origin Storm. 104-1st brief app. Starjammers; Magneto-c/story 7 14 21 49 92 135
105-107-(Regular 30¢ editions). 106-(8/77)Old vs. New X-Men. 107-1st full app. Starjammers; last 30¢ issue 7 14 21 46 86 125
105-107-(35¢-c variants, limited distribution) 32 64 96 230 515 800
108-Byrne-a begins (see Marvel Team-Up #53) 7 14 21 49 92 135
109-1st app. Weapon Alpha (becomes Vindicator) 7 14 21 46 86 125
110,111: 110-Phoenix joins 6 12 18 38 69 100
112-116 6 12 18 38 69 100
117-119: 117-Origin Professor X 5 10 15 34 60 85
120-1st app. Alpha Flight, story line begins (4/79); 1st app. Vindicator (formerly Weapon Alpha); last 35¢ issue 7 14 21 46 86 125
121-1st full Alpha Flight story 6 12 18 42 79 115
122-128: 123-Spider-Man x-over. 124-Colossus becomes Proletarian 5 10 15 31 53 75
129-Intro Kitty Pryde (1/80); last Banshee; Dark Phoenix saga begins; intro. Emma Frost (White Queen) 8 16 24 56 108 160
130-1st app. The Dazzler by Byrne (2/80) 6 12 18 38 69 100
131-135: 131-Dazzler app.; 1st White Queen-c. 133-1st Wolverine solo-c. 134-Phoenix becomes Dark Phoenix 5 10 15 31 53 75
136,138: 138-History of the X-Men recounted; Dazzler app.; Cyclops leaves 4 8 12 28 47 65
137-Giant; death of Phoenix 6 12 18 38 69 100
139-Alpha Flight app.; Kitty Pryde joins; new costume for Wolverine 5 10 15 31 53 75
140-Alpha Flight app. 5 10 15 31 53 75
141-"Days of Future Past" part 1; intro Future X-Men & The New Brotherhood of Evil Mutants; 1st app. Rachel (Phoenix II); Death of alt. future Franklin Richards 7 14 21 46 86 125

X-MEN: Titled THE UNCANNY X-MEN No. 142, Feb, 1981 - No. 544, Dec, 2011

142-"Days of Future Past" part 2; Rachel app.; deaths of alt. future Wolverine, Storm & Colossus 6 12 18 37 66 95
143-Last Byrne issue 4 8 12 23 37 50
144-150: 144-Man-Thing app. 145-Old X-Men app. 148-1st app. Caliban; Spider-Woman, Dazzler app. 150-Double size 2 4 6 9 13 16
151-157,159-161,163,164: 161-Origin Magneto. 163-Origin Binary. 164-1st app. Binary as Carol Danvers 2 4 6 8 10 12
158-1st app. Rogue in X-Men (6/82, see Avengers Annual #10) 3 6 9 16 24 32
162-Wolverine solo story 2 4 6 11 16 20
165-Paul Smith-c/a begins, ends #175 2 4 6 9 13 16
166-170: 166-Double size; Paul Smith-a. 167-New Mutants app. (3/83); same date as New Mutants #1; 1st meeting w/X-Men; ties into N.M. #3,4; Starjammers app.; contains skin "Tattooz" decals. 168-1st brief app. Madelyne Pryor (last page) in X-Men (see Avengers Annual #10) 2 3 4 6 8 10
171-Rogue joins X-Men; Simonson-c/a 2 4 6 13 18 22
172-174: 172,173-Two part Wolverine solo story. 173-Two cover variations, blue & black. 174-Phoenix cameo 1 3 4 6 8 10
175-(52 pgs.)-Anniversary issue; Phoenix returns 2 4 6 8 10 12
176-185,187-192,194-199: 181-Sunfire app. 182-Rogue solo story. 184-1st app. Forge (8/84). 190,191-Spider-Man & Avengers x-over. 195-Power Pack x-over 1 2 3 5 7 9
186,193: 186-Double-size; Barry Smith/Austin-a. 193-Double size; 100th app. New X-Men; 1st app. Warpath in costume (see New Mutants #16) 1 3 4 6 8 10
200-(12/85, $1.25, 52 pgs.) 2 4 6 9 12 15
201-(1/86)-1st app. Cable? (as baby Nathan; see X-Factor #1); 1st Whilce Portacio-c/a(i) on X-Men (guest artist) 3 6 9 19 30 40
202-204,206-209: 204-Nightcrawler solo story; 2nd Portacio-a(i) on X-Men. 207-Wolverine/Phoenix story 1 2 3 5 7 9
205-Wolverine solo story by Barry Smith 2 4 6 10 14 18
210,211-Mutant Massacre begins 3 6 9 14 19 24
212,213-Wolverine vs. Sabretooth (Mutant Mass.) 3 6 9 15 22 28
214-220,223,224: 219-Havok joins (7/87); brief app. Sabretooth. 1 2 3 5 6 8
221-1st app. Mr. Sinister 3 6 9 19 30 40
222-Wolverine battles Sabretooth-c/story 3 6 9 14 20 26
225-242: 225-227: Fall Of The Mutants. 226-Double size. 240-Sabretooth app. 242-Double size, X-Factor app., Inferno tie-in 1 2 3 5 6 8
243,245-247: 245-Rob Liefeld-a(p) 1 2 3 5 6 8
244-1st app. Jubilee 3 6 9 21 33 45
248-1st Jim Lee art on X-Men (1989) 3 6 9 14 20 25
248-2nd printing (1992, $1.25) 1 3 4 6 8 10
249-252: 252-Lee-c 1 2 3 4 5 7
253-255: 253-All new X-Men begin. 254-Lee-c 1 2 3 4 5 7
256-Betsy Braddock (Psylocke) 1st app. as purple-haired Asian in ninja costume; Jim Lee-c/a 2 4 6 11 16 20
257-Jim Lee-c/a; Psylocke as Lady Mandarin 1 3 4 6 8 10
258-Wolverine solo story; Lee-c/a 1 3 4 6 8 10
259-Silvestri-c/a; no Lee-a 1 2 3 4 5 7
260-265-No Lee-a. 260,261,264-Lee-c 1 2 3 4 5 7
266-(8/90) 1st full app. Gambit (see Annual #14)-No Lee-a 7 14 21 46 86 125
267-Jim Lee-c/a resumes; 2nd full Gambit app. 2 4 6 10 14 18
268-Capt. America, Black Widow & Wolverine team-up; Lee-c/a 2 4 6 11 16 20
268,270: 268-2nd printing. 270-Gold 2nd printing 1 3 4 6 8 10
269,273,274: 269-Lee-a. 273-New Mutants (Cable) & X-Factor x-over; Golden, Byrne & Lee part pencils 1 2 3 4 5 7
270-X-Tinction Agenda begins 1 2 3 5 6 8
271,272-X-Tinction Agenda 1 2 3 5 6 8
275-(52 pgs.)-Tri-fold-c by Jim Lee (p); Prof. X 1 2 3 5 6 8
275-Gold 2nd printing 5.00

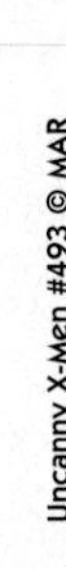
Uncanny X-Men #366 © MAR

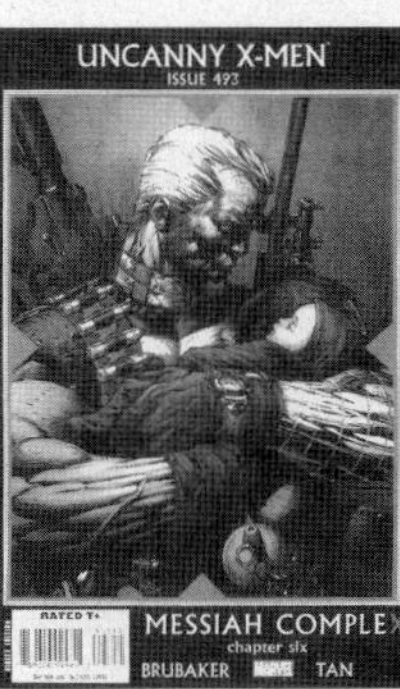

Uncanny X-Men #493 © MAR

Uncanny X-Men #538 © MAR

	GD 2.0	VG 4.0	FN 6.0	VF 8.0	VF/NM 9.0	NM- 9.2
276-280: 277-Last Lee-c/a. 280-X-Factor x-over						6.00
281-(10/91)-New team begins (Storm, Archangel, Colossus, Iceman & Marvel Girl); Whilce Portacio-c/a begins; Byrne scripts begin; wraparound-c (white logo)	1	2	3	5	6	8
281-2nd printing with red metallic ink logo w/o UPC box ($1.00-c); does not say 2nd printing inside						5.00
282-1st brief app. Bishop (cover & 1 page)	2	4	6	13	18	22
282-Gold ink 2nd printing ($1.00-c)	1	2	3	5	6	8
283-1st full app. Bishop (12/91)	2	4	6	8	10	12
284-299: 284-Last $1.00-c. 286,287-Lee plots. 287-Bishop joins team. 288-Lee/Portacio plots. 290-Last Portacio-c/a. 294-Peterson-a(p) begins (#292 is 1st Peterson-c). 294-296 ($1.50)-Bagged w/trading card in each; X-Cutioner's Song x-overs; Peterson/Austin-c/a on all						4.00
297-Gold Edition	12	24	36	79	170	260
300-($3.95, 68 pgs.)-Holo-grafx foil-c; Magneto app.						6.00
301-303,305-309,311						3.00
303,307-Gold Edition	4	8	12	27	44	60
304-($3.95, 68 pgs.)-Wraparound-c with Magneto hologram on-c; 30th anniversary issue; Jae Lee-a (4 pgs.)	1	3	4	6	8	10
310-($1.95)-Bound-in trading card sheet						3.00
312-$1.50-c begins; bound-in card sheet; 1st Madureira						4.00
313-321: 318-1st app. Generation X						3.00
316,317-($2.95)-Foil enhanced editions						4.00
318-321-($1.95)-Deluxe editions						4.00
322-Onslaught						5.00
323,324,326-346: 323-Return from Age of Apocalypse. 328-Sabretooth-c. 329,330-Dr. Strange app. 331-White Queen-c/app. 334-Juggernaut app.; w/Onslaught Update. 335-Onslaught, Avengers, Apocalypse, & X-Man app. 336-Onslaught. 338-Archangel's wings return to normal. 339-Havok vs. Cyclops; Spider-Man app. 341-Gladiator-c/app. 342-Deathbird cameo; two covers. 343,344-Phalanx						3.00
325-($3.95)-Anniversary issue; gatefold-c						5.00
342-Variant-c	2	4	6	8	11	14
347-349:347-Begin $1.99-c. 349-"Operation Zero Tolerance"						3.00
350-Newsstand version	2	4	6	9	12	15
350-($3.99, 48 pgs.) Prismatic etched foil gatefold wraparound-c; Trial of Gambit; Seagle-s begin	2	4	6	10	14	18
351-359: 353-Bachalo-a begins. 354-Regular-c. 355-Alpha Flight-c/app. 356-Original X-Men-c						3.00
354-Dark Phoenix variant-c	1	3	4	6	8	10
360-($2.99) 35th Anniv. issue; Pacheco-c						4.00
360-($3.99) Etched Holo-foil enhanced-c						5.00
360-($6.95) DF Edition with Jae Lee variant-c	1	3	4	6	8	10
361-374,378,379: 361-Gambit returns; Skroce-a. 362-Hunt for Xavier pt. 1; Bachelo-a. 364-Yu-a. 366-Magneto-c. 369-Juggernaut-c						3.00
375-($2.99) Autopsy of Wolverine						5.00
376,377-Apocalypse: The Twelve	1	2	3	5	6	8
380-($2.99) Polybagged with X-Men Revolution Genesis Edition preview						4.00
381,382,384-389,391-393: 381-Begin $2.25-c; Claremont-s. 387-Maximum Security						3.00
383-($2.99)						4.00
390-Colossus dies to cure the Legacy Virus	2	4	6	8	10	12
394-New look X-Men begins; Casey-s/Churchill-c/a						4.00
395-399-Poptopia. 398-Phillips & Wood-a						3.00
400-($3.50) Art by Ashley Wood, Eddie Campbell, Hamner, Phillips, Pulido and Matt Smith; wraparound-c by Wood						5.00
401-415: 401-'Nuff Said issue; Garney-a. 404,405,407-409,413-415-Phillips-a						3.00
416-421: 416-Asamiya-a begins. 421-Garney-a						3.00
422-($3.50) Alpha Flight app.; Garney-a						4.00
423-(25¢-c) Holy War pt. 1; Garney-a/Philip Tan-c						3.00
424-449,452-454: 425,426,429,430-Tan-a. 428-Birth of Nightcrawler. 437-Larroca-a begins. 444-New team, new costumes; Claremont-s/Davis-a begins. 448,449-Coipel-a						3.00
450-X-23 app.; Davis-a	1	3	4	6	8	10
451-X-23 app.; Davis-a	2	4	6	9	12	15
455-459-X-23 app.; Davis-a						5.00
460-471: 460-Begin $2.50-c; Raney-a. 462-465-House of M. 464-468-Bachalo-a						3.00
472-499: 472-Begin $2.99-c; Bachalo-a. 475-Wraparound-c. 492-494-Messiah Complex						3.00
500-($3.99) X-Men new HQ in San Francisco; Magneto app.; Land & Dodson-a; wraparound covers by Alex Ross and Greg Land						6.00
500-Classic X-Men Dynamic Forces variant-c by Ross						8.00
500-X-Men variant-c by Michael Turner	4	8	12	22	32	40
500-X-Men sketch variant-c by Michael Turner	11	22	33	76	163	250
500-X-Women variant-c by Dodson	3	6	9	14	20	25
500-X-Women sketch variant-c by Dodson	10	20	30	66	138	210
501-511,515-521,523-525: 501-Brubaker & Fraction-s/Land-a. 523-525-Second Coming						3.00
512-514,522-($3.99). 513,514-Utopia x-over. 522-Kitty Pryde returns to Earth; Portacio-a						4.00
526-543-($3.99) 526-The Heroic Age; aftermath of Second Coming. 530-534-Land-a						
540-543-Fear Itself tie-in, Juggernaut attacks; Land-a. 542-Colossus becomes the Juggernaut						4.00
534.1 (6/11, $2.99) Pacheco-a/c						3.00
544-(12/11, $3.99) Final issue; Land-a/c; Mr. Sinister app.	1	3	4	6	8	10
#(-1) Flashback (7/97) Ladronn-c/Hitch & Neary-a						3.00
Special 1(12/70)-Kirby-c/a; origin The Stranger	10	20	30	66	138	210
Special 2(11/71, 52 pgs.)	8	16	24	51	96	140
Annual 3(1979, 52 pgs.)-New story; Miller/Austin-c; Wolverine still in old yellow costume	5	10	15	30	48	65
Annual 4(1980, 52 pgs.)-Dr. Strange guest stars	3	6	9	14	20	25
Annual 5(1981, 52 pgs.)	2	4	6	8	10	12
Annual 6-8('82-'84 52 pgs.)-6-Dracula app.	1	2	3	5	6	8
Annual 9,10('85, '86)-9-New Mutants x-over cont'd from New Mutants Special Ed. #1; Art Adams-a. 10-Art Adams-a	2	4	6	8	10	12
Annual 11-13:('87-'89, 68 pgs.): 12-Evolutionary War; A.Adams-a(p). 13-Atlantis Attacks						5.00
Annual 14(1990, $2.00, 68 pgs.)-1st app. Gambit (minor app., 5 pgs.); Fantastic Four, New Mutants (Cable) & X-Factor x-over; Art Adams-c/a(p)	3	6	9	19	30	40
Annual 15 (1991, $2.00, 68 pgs.)-4 pg. origin; New Mutants x-over; 4 pg. Wolverine solo back-up story; 4th app. X-Force cont'd from New Warriors Annual #1						5.00
Annual 16-18 ('92-'94, 68 pgs.)-16-Jae Lee-c/a(p). 17-Bagged w/card						4.00
Annual '95-(11/95, $3.95)-Wraparound-c						4.00
Annual '96,'97-Wraparound-c						4.00
.../Fantastic Four Annual '98 ($2.99) Casey-s						4.00
Annual '99 ($3.50) Jubilee app.						4.00
Annual 2000 ($3.50) Cable app.; Ribic-a						4.00
Annual 2001 ($3.50, printed wide-ways) Ashley Wood-c/a; Casey-s						4.00
Annual (Vol. 2) #1 (8/06, $3.99) Storm & Black Panther wedding prelude						4.00
Annual (Vol. 2) #2 (3/09, $3.99) Dark Reign; flashback to Sub-Mariner/Emma Frost						4.00
Annual (Vol. 2) #3 (5/11, $3.99) Escape From the Negative Zone; Bradshaw-a						4.00
....At The State Fair of Texas (1983, 36 pgs., one-shot); Supplement to the Dallas Times Herald	2	4	6	9	12	15
...: The Dark Phoenix Saga TPB 1st printing (1984, $12.95)						40.00
...: The Dark Phoenix Saga TPB 2nd-5th printings						25.00
...: The Dark Phoenix Saga TPB 6th-10th printings						20.00
... Days of Future Past TPB (2004, $19.99) r/#138-143 & Annual #4						20.00
... Eve of Destruction TPB (2005, $14.99) r/#391-393 & X-Men #111-113; Churchill-c						15.00
...:Dream's End (2004, $17.99)-r/Death of Colossus story arc from Uncanny X-Men #388-390, Cable #87, Bishop #16 and X-Men #108,110; debut pages from Giant-Size X-Men #1						18.00
... From The Ashes TPB (1990, $14.95) r/#168-176						15.00
... Future History - The Messiah War Sourcebook (2009, $3.99) Cable's files on X-Men						4.00
...: God Loves, Man Kills ($6.95)-r/Marvel Graphic Novel #5						7.00
...: God Loves, Man Kills - Special Edition (2003, $4.99)-reprint with new Hughes-c						5.00
...: God Loves, Man Kills HC (2007, $19.99) reprint with Claremont & Anderson interviews; original artist Neal Adams' six sketch pages and interview						20.00
...: Hope (5/10, $2.99) Collects Cable and Hope back-ups; Dillon-a						3.00
House of M: Uncanny X-Men TPB (2006, $13.99) r/#462-465 and selections from Secrets Of The House of M one-shot						14.00
...In The Days of Future Past TPB (1989, $3.95, 52 pgs.)						10.00
...: No More Humans HC (2014, $24.99) Carey-s/Larroca-a						25.00
...Old Soldiers TPB (2004, $19.99) r/#213,215 & Ann. #11; New Mutants Ann. #2&3						20.00
...Poptopia TPB (10/01, $15.95) r/#394-399						16.00
...: Rise & Fall of the Shi'Ar Empire HC (2007, $34.99, dustjacket) r/#475-486; bonus art						35.00
...: Rise & Fall of the Shi'Ar Empire SC (2008, $29.99) r/#475-486; bonus art						30.00
...: Season One HC (2012, $24.99) Origin re-told; Hopeless-s/McKelvie-a						25.00
...: Sword of the Braddocks (5/09, $3.99) Psylocke vs. Slaymaster; Claremont-s						4.00
...: The Complete Onslaught Epic Book 1 TPB (2007, $29.99) r/X-Men #53-54, Uncanny X-Men #334-335, Fantastic Four #414-415, Avengers #400-401, Onslaught: X-Men, Cable #34 and Incredible Hulk #444						30.00
...: The Complete Onslaught Epic Book 2 TPB ('08, $29.99) r/Excalibur #100, Wolverine #104, X-Factor #125-126, Amazing Spider-Man #415, Green Goblin #12, Spider-Man #72, Punisher #11, X-Man #18 & X-Force #57						30.00
...: The Extremists TPB (2007, $13.99) r/#487-491						14.00
...: The Heroic Age (9/10, $3.99) Beast, Steve Rogers and Princess Powerful app.						4.00
Uncanny X-Men Omnibus Vol. 1 HC (2006, $99.99, dust jacket) r/Giant-Size X-Men #1, (Uncanny) X-Men #94-131 & Annual #3; cover gallery, promo and sketch art						140.00
Vignettes TPB (9/01, $17.95) r/Claremont & Bolton Classic X-Men #1-13						18.00
Vignettes Vol. 2 TPB (2005, $17.99) r/Claremont & Bolton Classic X-Men #14-25						18.00
... Vol. 1: Hope TPB (2003, $12.99) r/#410-415; Harris-c						13.00
... Vol. 2: Dominant Species TPB (2003, $11.99) r/#416-420; Asamiya-c						12.00
... Vol. 3: Holy War TPB (2003, $17.99) r/#421-427						18.00
... Vol. 4: The Draco TPB (2004, $15.99) r/#428-434						16.00
... Vol. 5: She Lies with Angels TPB (2004, $11.99) r/#437-441						12.00

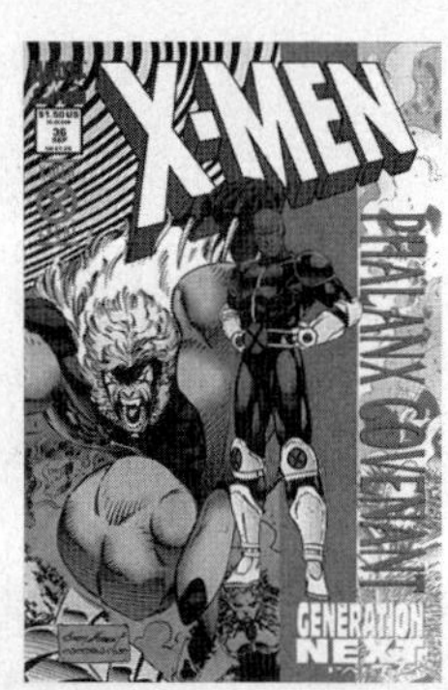
X-Men (2nd series) #36 © MAR

X-Men (2nd series) #103 © MAR

X-Men (2nd series) #200 © MAR

	GD 2.0	VG 4.0	FN 6.0	VF 8.0	VF/NM 9.0	NM- 9.2

... Vol. 6: Bright New Mourning TPB (2004, $14.99) r/#435,436,442,443 & (New) X-Men #155,156; Larroca sketch covers 15.00
...Vs. Apocalypse Vol. 1: The Twelve TPB (2008, $29.99) r/#376-377, Cable #73-76, X-Men #96,97 and Wolverine #145-147 30.00
... - The New Age Vol. 1: The End of History (2004, $12.99) r/#444-449 13.00
... - The New Age Vol. 2: The Cruelest Cut (2005, $11.99) r/#450-454 12.00
... - The New Age Vol. 3: On Ice (2006, $15.99) r/#455-461 16.00
... - The New Age Vol. 4: End of Greys (2006, $14.99) r/#466-471 15.00
... - The New Age Vol. 5: First Foursaken (2006, $11.99) r/#472-474 & Annual #1 12.00

NOTE: **Art Adams** *a-Annual 9, 10p, 12p, 14p; c-218p.* **Neal Adams** *a-56-63p, 65p; c-56-63.* **Adkins** *a-34, 35p; c-31, 34, 35.* **Austin** *a-108i, 109i, 111-117i, 119-143i, 186i, 204i, 228i, 294-297i, Annual 3i, 7i, 9i, 13; c-109-111i, 114-122i, 123, 124-141i, 142, 143, 196i, 204i, 228i, 294-297i, Annual 3i.* **J. Buscema** *c-42, 43, 45.* **Buscema/Tuska** *a-45.* **Byrne** *a(p)-108, 109, 111-143, 273; c(p)-113-116, 127, 129, 131-141.* **Capullo** *c-14.* **Ditko** *r-86, 89-91, 93.* **Everett** *c-73.* **Golden** *a-273, Annual 7p.* **Guice** *a-216p, 217p.* **G. Kane** *c(p)-33, 74-76, 79, 80, 94, 95.* **Kirby** *a(p)-1-17 (#12-17, 67r-layouts); c(p)-1-17, 25, 30 (18, 26-parts).* **Layton** *a-105i; c-112i, 113i.* **Jim Lee** *a(p)-248, 256-258, 267-277; c(p)-252, 254, 256-261, 264, 267, 268 ,270, 275-277, 286.* **Perez** *a-Annual 3p; c(p)-112, 128, Annual 3.* **Peterson** *a(p)-294-300, 304(part); c(p)-294-299.* **Whilce Portacio** *a(p)-281-286, 289, 290; a(i)-267; c-281-285p, 289p, 290; c(i)-267.* **Romita, Jr.** *a-300; c-300.* **Roussos** *a-84i.* **Simonson** *a-171p; c-171, 217.* **B. Smith** *a-53, 186p, 198p, 205, 214; c-53-55, 186p, 198, 205, 212, 214, 216.* **Paul Smith** *a(p)-165-170, 172-175, 278; c-165-170, 172-175, 278.* **Sparling** *a-78p.* **Steranko** *a-50p, 51p; c-49-51.* **Sutton** *a-106i.* **Art Thibert** *a(i)-281-286; c(i)-281, 282, 284, 285.* **Toth** *a-12p, 67p(r).* **Tuska** *a-40-42i, 43-46p, 88i(r); c-39-41, 77p, 78p.* **Williamson** *a-202i, 203i, 211i; c-202i, 203i, 206i.* **Wood** *c-14i.*

UNCANNY X-MEN AND THE NEW TEEN TITANS (See Marvel and DC Present...)

X-MEN (2nd Series)(Titled New X-Men with #114) (Titled X-Men Legacy with #210)
Marvel Comics: Oct, 1991 - No. 275, Dec, 2012 ($1.00-$2.99)

1 a-d (four different covers, $1.50, 52 pgs.)-Jim Lee-c/a begins, ends #11; new team begins (Cyclops, Beast, Wolverine, Gambit, Psylocke & Rogue); new Uncanny X-Men & Magneto app.; 1 2 3 5 6 8
1 e ($3.95)-Double gate-fold-c consisting of all four covers from 1a-d by Jim Lee; contains all pin-ups from #1a-d plus inside-c foldout poster; no ads; printed on coated stock 1 3 4 6 8 10
1-20th Anniversary Edition-(12/11, $3.99) r/#1 with double gatefold-c; Jim Lee pin-ups 5.00
2-7: 4-Wolverine back to old yellow costume (same date as Wolverine #50); last $1.00-c. 5-Byrne scripts. 6-Sabretooth-c/story 5.00
8-10: 8-Gambit vs. Bishop-c/story; last Lee-a; Ghost Rider cameo cont'd in Ghost Rider #26. 9-Wolverine vs. Ghost Rider; cont'd/G.R. #26. 10-Return of Longshot 5.00
11-13,17-24,26-29,31: 12,13-Art Thibert-c/a. 28,29-Sabretooth app. 4.00
11-Silver ink 2nd printing; came with X-Men board game 2 4 6 10 14 18
14-16-($1.50)-Polybagged with trading card in each; X-Cutioner's Song x-overs; 14-Andy Kubert-c/a begins 5.00
25-($3.50, 52 pgs.)-Wraparound-c with Gambit hologram on-c; Professor X erases Magneto's mind 2 4 6 10 14 18
25-30th anniversary issue w/B&W-c with Magneto in color & Magneto hologram & no price on-c 4 8 12 23 37 50
25-Gold 50.00
30-($1.95)-Wedding issue w/bound-in trading card sheet 5.00
32-37: 32-Begin $1.50-c; bound-in card sheet. 33-Gambit & Sabretooth-c/story 4.00
36,37-($2.95)-Collectors editions (foil-c) 5.00
38-44,46-49,51-65: 42,43- Paul Smith-a. 46,49,53-56-Onslaught app. 51-Waid scripts begin, end #56. 54-(Reg. edition)-Onslaught revealed as Professor X. 55,56-Onslaught x-over; Avengers, FF & Sentinels app. 56-Dr. Doom app. 57-Xavier taken into custody; Byrne-c/swipe (X-Men,1st Series #138). 59-Hercules-c/app. 61-Juggernaut-c/app. 62-Re-intro. Shang Chi; two covers. 63-Kingpin cameo. 64- Kingpin app. 4.00
45-($3.95)-Annual issue; gatefold-c 6.00
50-($2.95)-Vs. Onslaught, wraparound-c. 6.00
50-($3.95)-Vs. Onslaught, wraparound foil-c. 6.00
50-($2.95)-Variant gold-c. 4 8 12 23 37 50
50-($2.95)-Variant silver-c. 2 4 6 9 12 15
54-(Limited edition)-Embossed variant-c; Onslaught revealed as Professor X 3 6 9 19 30 40
66-69,71-74,76-79: 66-Operation Zero Tolerance. 76-Origin of Maggott 3.00
70-($2.99, 48 pgs.)-Joe Kelly-s begin, new members join 4.00
75-($2.99, 48 pgs.) vs. N'Garai; wraparound-c 4.00
80-($3.99) 35th Anniv. issue; holo-foil-c 5.00
80-($2.99) Regular-c 4.00
80-($6.95) Dynamic Forces Ed.; Quesada-c 7.00
81-93,95,98,99: 82-Hunt for Xavier pt. 2. 85-Davis-a. 86-Origin of Joseph. 87-Magneto War ends. 88-Juggernaut app. 3.00
94-($2.99) Contains preview of X-Men: Hidden Years 4.00
96,97-Apocalypse: The Twelve 1 2 3 5 6 8
100-($2.99) Art Adams-c; begin Claremont-s/Yu-a 4.00
100-DF alternate-c 1 3 4 6 8 10
101-105,107,108,110-114: 101-Begin $2.25-c. 107-Maximum Security x-over; Bishop-c/app. 108-Moira MacTaggart dies; Senator Kelly shot. 111-Magneto-c. 112,113-Eve of Destruction 3.00
106-($2.99) X-Men battle Domina 4.00
109-($3.50, 100 pgs.) new and reprinted Christmas-themed stories 5.00
114-(7/01) Title change to "New X-Men," Morrison-s/Quitely-c/a begins 4.00
114-(8/10, $1.00) "Marvel's Greatest Comics" reprint 3.00
115-Two covers (Quitely & BWS) 4.00
116-125,127,129-149: 116-Emma Frost joins. 117,118-Van Sciver-a. 121,122,135-Quitely-a. 127-Leon & Sienkiewicz-a. 132,139-141-Jimenez-a. 136-138-Quitely-a. 142-Sabretooth app.; Bachalo-c/a thru #145. 146-Magneto returns; Jimenez-a 3.00
126-($3.25) Quitely-a; defeat of Cassanova 4.00
128-1st app. Fantomex; Kordey-a 3 6 9 17 26 35
150-($3.50) Jean Grey dies again; last Jimenez-a 4.00
151-156: 151-154-Silvestri-c/a 3.00
157-169: 157-X-Men Reload begins 3.00
170-184: 171- Begin $2.50-c. 175,176-Crossover with Black Panther #8,9. 181-184-Apocalypse returns 3.00
185-199,201-229,231-249,251-261: 185-Begin $2.99-c. 188-190,192-194,197-199-Bachalo-a. 195,196,201-203-Ramos-a. 201-204-Endangered Species back-up. 205-207-Messiah Complex x-over. 208-Romita Jr.-a. 210-Starts X-Men: Legacy. 228,229-Acuña-a. 235-237-Second Coming x-over. 238-The Heroic Age. 245-Age of X begins 3.00
200-($3.99) Two wraparound covers by Bachalo & Finch; Bachalo & Ramos-a 4.00
230-($3.99) Acuña-a; Rogue vs. Emplate 4.00
250-($4.99) Suayan-c/Pham-a; back-up r/New Mutants #27 5.00
261.1-(3/12, $2.99) The N'Garai app.; Brooks-c 3.00
262-275-Brooks-c. 266-270-Avengers vs. X-Men tie-in 3.00
#(-1) Flashback (7/97); origin of Magneto 3.00
Annual 1-3 ('92-'94, $2.25-$2.95, 68 pgs.) 1-Lee-c & layouts; #2-Bagged w/card 4.00
Special '95 ($3.95) 4.00
... '96,...'97-Wraparound-c 4.00
.../ Dr. Doom '98 Annual ($2.99) Lopresti-a 4.00
... Annual '99 ($3.50) Adam Kubert-c 4.00
Annual 2000 ($3.50) Art Adams-c/Claremont-s/Eaton-a 4.00
...2001 Annual ($3.50) Morrison-s/Yu-a; issue printed sideways 4.00
...2007 Annual #1 (3/07, $3.99) Casey-s/Brooks-a; Cable and Mystique app. 4.00
...Legacy Annual 1 (11/09, $3.99) Acuña-a; Emplate returns 4.00
Animation Special Graphic Novel (12/90, $10.95) adapts animated series 12.00
Ashcan #1 (1994, 75¢) Introduces new team members 3.00
... Archives Sketchbook (12/00, $2.99) Early B&W character design sketches by various incl. Lee, Davis, Yu, Pacheco, BWS, Art Adams, Liefeld 3.00
...: Bizarre Love Triangle TPB (2005, $9.99)-r/X-Men #171-174 10.00
.../ Black Panther TPB (2006, $11.99)-r/X-Men #175,176 & Black Panther (2005) #8,9 12.00
...: Blinded By the Light (2007, $14.99)-r/X-Men #200-204 15.00
...: Blind Science (7/10, $3.99) Second Coming x-over; Parel-c 4.00
...: Blood of Apocalypse (2006, $17.99)-r/X-Men #182-187 18.00
...: Day of the Atom (2005, $19.99)-r/X-Men #157-165 20.00
Decimation: X-Men - The Day After TPB (2006, $15.99) r/#177-181 & Decimation: House of M - The Day After 16.00
...: Declassified (10/00, $3.50) Profile pin-ups by various; Jae Lee-c 4.00
...: Earth's Mutant Heroes (7/11, $4.99) Handbook-style profiles of mutants 5.00
...: Endangered Species (8/07, $3.99) prologue to 17-part back-up series in X-Men titles 4.00
...: Endangered Species HC (2008, $24.99, d.j.) over-sized r/prologue and 17-part series 25.00
...: Evolutions 1 (12/11, $3.99) Collection of variant covers from May 2011 Marvel titles 4.00
...: Fatal Attractions ('94, $17.95)-r/x-Factor #92, X-Force #25, Uncanny X-Men #304, X-Men #25, Wolverine #75, & Excalibur #71 18.00
...: Golgotha (2005, $12.99)-r/X-Men #166-170 13.00
... Millennial Visions (8/00, $3.99) Various artists interpret future X-Men 4.00
... Millennial Visions 2 (1/02, $3.50) Various artists interpret future X-Men 4.00
...: Mutant Genesis (2006, $19.99)-r/X-Men #1-7; sketch pages and extra art 20.00
New X-Men: E is for Extinction TPB (11/01, $12.95) r/#114-117 13.00
New X-Men: Imperial TPB (7/02, $19.99) r/#118-126; Quitely-c 20.00
New X-Men: New Worlds TPB (2002, $14.99) r/#127-133; Quitely-c 15.00
New X-Men: Riot at Xavier's TPB (2003, $11.99) r/#134-138; Quitely-c 12.00
New X-Men: Vol. 5: Assault on Weapon Plus TPB (2003, $14.99) r/#139-145 15.00
New X-Men: Vol. 6: Planet X TPB (2004, $12.99) r/#146-150 13.00
New X-Men: Vol. 7: Here Comes Tomorrow TPB (2004, $10.99) r/#151-154 11.00
New X-Men: Volume 1 HC (2002, $29.99) oversized r/#114-126 & 2001 Annual 30.00
New X-Men: Volume 2 HC (2003, $29.99) oversized r/#127-141; sketch & script pages 30.00
New X-Men: Volume 3 HC (2004, $29.99) oversized r/#142-154; sketch & script pages 30.00
New X-Men Omnibus HC (2006, $99.99) oversized r/#114-154 & Annual 2001; Morrison's original pitch; sketch & script pages; variant covers & promo art; Carey intro. 140.00
...: Odd Men Out (2008, $3.99) Two unpublished stories with Dave Cockrum-a 4.00
... Original Sin 1 (12/08, $3.99) Wolverine and Daken; Deodato & Eaton-a 4.00
... Origin: Colossus (7/08, $3.99) Yost-s/Hairsine-a; Piotr Rasputin before joining X-Men 4.00
... Phoenix Force Handbook (9/10, $4.99) bios of those related to the Phoenix; Raney-c 5.00
...: Pixies and Demons Director's Cut (2008, $3.99) r/FCBD 2008 story with script 4.00

X-Men (2010 series) #13 © MAR

X-Men Adventures #8 © MAR

X-Men Classic #78 © MAR

GD 2.0 | VG 4.0 | FN 6.0 | VF 8.0 | VF/NM 9.0 | NM- 9.2

GD 2.0 | VG 4.0 | FN 6.0 | VF 8.0 | VF/NM 9.0 | NM- 9.2

... Pizza Hut Mini-comics-(See Marvel Collector's Edition: X-Men in Promotional Comics section)
... Premium Edition #1 (1993)-Cover says "Toys 'R' Us Limited Edition X-Men" 4.00
...: Rarities (1995, $5.95)-Reprints 6.00
...: Return of Magik Must Have (2008, $3.99) r/X-Men Unlimited #14, New X-Men #37 and X-Men: Divided We Stand #2; Coipel-c 4.00
...: Road Trippin' ('99, $24.95, TPB) r/X-Men road trips 25.00
...: Supernovas ('07, $34.99, oversized HC w/d.j.) r/X-Men 188-199 & Annual #1 35.00
...: Supernovas ('08, $29.99, SC) r/X-Men 188-199 & Annual #1 30.00
...: The Coming of Bishop ('95, $12.95)-r/Uncanny X-Men #282-285, 287,288 13.00
...: The Magneto War (3/99, $2.99) Davis-a 4.00
...: The Rise of Apocalypse ('98, $16.99)-r/Rise Of Apocalypse #1-4, X-Factor #5,6 17.00
... Visionaries: Chris Claremont ('98, $24.95)-r/Claremont-s; art by Byrne, BWS, Jim Lee 25.00
... Visionaries: Jim Lee ('02, $29.99)-r/Jim Lee-a from various issues between Uncanny X-Men #248 & 286; r/Classic X-Men #39 and X-Men Annual #1 30.00
... Visionaries: Joe Madureira (7/00, $17.95)-r/Uncanny X-Men #325,326,329,330,341-343; new Madureira-c 18.00
... Vs. Hulk (3/09, $3.99) Claremont-s/Raapack-a; r/X-Men #66 4.00
...: Zero Tolerance ('00, $24.95, TPB) r/crossover series 25.00
NOTE: *Jim Lee a-1-11p; c-1-6p, 7, 8, 9p, 10, 11p.* *Art Thibert a-6-9i, 12, 13; c-6i, 12, 13.*

X-MEN (3rd series)
Marvel Comics: Sept, 2010 - No. 41, Apr, 2013 ($3.99)
1-41: 1-6-"Curse of the Mutants" x-over; Medina-a. 7-10-Spider-Man app.; Bachalo-a. 12-Continued from X-Men Giant-Size #1. 16-19-FF & Skull the Slayer app. 20-23-War Machine app. 16-Deadpool app. 28-FF & Spider-Man app. 38,39-Domino & Daredevil team-up 4.00
15.1 ($2.99) Pearson-c/Conrad-a; Ghost Rider app. 3.00
...: Curse of the Mutants - Blade 1 (10/10, $3.99) Tim Green-a 4.00
...: Curse of the Mutants - Smoke and Blood 1 (11/10, $3.99) Crain-c 4.00
...: Curse of the Mutants Spotlight 1 (1/11, $3.99) creator profiles and interviews 4.00
...: Curse of the Mutants - Storm and Gambit 1 (11/10, $3.99) Bachalo-a; 2 covers 4.00
...: Curse of the Mutants - X-Men vs. Vampires 1,2 (11/10 - No. 2, 12/10, $3.99) Bradshaw-c 4.00
... Giant-Size 1 (7/11, $4.99) Medina & Talajic-a; cover swipe of Giant-Size X-Men #1 5.00
...: Regenesis 1 (12/11, $3.99) Splits X-Men into 2 teams; Tan-a/Bachalo-c 4.00
... Spotlight 1 (7/11, $3.99) Character profiles and creator interviews 4.00
...: With Great Power 1 (2011, $4.99) r/#7-9 5.00

X-MEN (4th series)
Marvel Comics: Jul, 2013 - No. 26, Jun, 2015 ($3.99)
1-26: 1-All-female team; Brian Wood-s/Olivier Coipel-a. 5,6-Battle of the Atom 4.00
100th Anniversary Special: X-Men (9/14, $3.99) Takes place in 2061; Furth-s/Masters-a 4.00

X-MEN (Free Comic Book Day giveaways)
Marvel Comics: 2006; May, 2008
FCBD 2008 Edition #1-(5/08) Features Pixie; Carey-s/Land-a/c 3.00
.../Runaways: FCBD 2006 Edition; new x-over story; Mighty Avengers preview; Chen-c 3.00

X-MEN ADVENTURES (TV)
Marvel Comics: Nov, 1992 - No. 15, Jan, 1994 ($1.25)(Based on animated series)
1,15: 1-Wolverine, Cyclops, Jubilee, Rogue, Gambit. 15-($1.75, 52 pgs.) 4.00
2-14: 3-Magneto-c/story. 6-Sabretooth-c/story. 7-Cable-c/story. 10-Archangel guest star. 11-Cable-c/story. 3.00

X-MEN ADVENTURES II (TV)
Marvel Comics: Feb, 1994 - No. 13, Feb, 1995 ($1.25/$1.50)(Based on 2nd TV season)
1-13: 4-Bound-in trading card sheet. 5-Alpha Flight app. 3.00
...Captive Hearts/Slave Island (TPB, $4.95)-r/X-Men Adventures #5-8 5.00
...The Irresistible Force, The Muir Island Saga (5.95, 10/94, TPB) r/X-Men Advs. #9-12 6.00

X-MEN ADVENTURES III (TV)(See Adventures of the X-Men)
Marvel Comics: Mar, 1995 - No. 13, Mar, 1996 ($1.50) (Based on 3rd TV season)
1-13 3.00

X-MEN: AGE OF APOCALYPSE
Marvel Comics: May, 2005 - No. 6, June, 2005 ($2.99, weekly limited series)
1-6-Bachalo-c/a; Yoshida-s; follows events in the "Age of Apocalypse" storyline 4.00
... One Shot (5/05, $3.99) prequel to series; Hitch wraparound-c; pin-ups by various 4.00
X-Men: The New Age of Apocalypse TPB (2005, $20.99) r/#1-6 & one-shot 21.00

X-MEN ALPHA
Marvel Comics: 1994 ($3.95, one-shot)
nn-Age of Apocalypse; wraparound chromium-c 1 3 4 6 8 10
nn ($49.95)-Gold logo 55.00

X-MEN/ALPHA FLIGHT
Marvel Comics Group: Dec, 1985 - No. 2, Dec, 1985 ($1.50, limited series)
1,2: 1-Intro The Berserkers; Paul Smith-a 5.00

X-MEN/ALPHA FLIGHT
Marvel Comics Group: May, 1998 - No. 2, June, 1998 ($2.99, limited series)
1,2-Flashback to early meeting; Raab-s/Cassaday-s/a 3.00

X-MEN AND POWER PACK
Marvel Comics: Dec, 2005 - No. 4, Mar, 2006 ($2.99, limited series)
1-4-Sumerak-s/Gurihiru-a. 1-Wolverine & Sabretooth app. 3.00
...: The Power of X (2006, $6.99, digest size) r/#1-4 7.00

X-MEN AND THE MICRONAUTS, THE
Marvel Comics Group: Jan, 1984 - No. 4, Apr, 1984 (Limited series)
1-4: Guice-c/a(p) in all 5.00

X-MEN: APOCALYPSE/DRACULA
Marvel Comics: Apr, 2006 - No. 4, July, 2006 ($2.99, limited series)
1-4-Tieri-s/Henry-a/Jae Lee-c 3.00
TPB (2006, $10.99) r/series; cover gallery 11.00

X-MEN ARCHIVES
Marvel Comics: Jan, 1995 - No. 4, Apr, 1995 ($2.25, limited series)
1-4: Reprints Legion stories from New Mutants. 4-Magneto app. 3.00

X-MEN ARCHIVES FEATURING CAPTAIN BRITAIN
Marvel Comics: July, 1995 - No. 7, 1996 ($2.95, limited series)
1-7: Reprints early Capt. Britain stories 3.00

X-MEN: BATTLE OF THE ATOM
Marvel Comics: Nov, 2013 - No. 2, Dec, 2013 ($3.99, bookends for X-Men title crossover)
1,2: 1-Bendis-s/Cho-a/Art Adams-c; bonus pin-ups of the various X-teams 4.00

X-MEN BLACK SUN (See Black Sun:...)

X-MEN: BLUE (Continued from All-New X-Men)
Marvel Comics: Jun, 2017 - Present ($4.99/$3.99)
1-($4.99) Bunn-s/Molina-a; Juggernaut & Black Tom Cassidy app. 5.00
2-22-($3.99): 4-Jimmy Hudson joins. 7-9-Secret Empire tie-ins. 13-15-"Mojo Worldwide" 18-Generation X app. 21,22-Venom app. 4.00
Annual 1 (3/18, $4.99) Poison-X part 1; Venom app.; Bunn-s/Salazar-a 5.00

X-MEN BOOKS OF ASKANI
Marvel Comics: 1995 ($2.95, one-shot)
1-Painted pin-ups w/text 3.00

X-MEN: CHILDREN OF THE ATOM
Marvel Comics: Nov, 1999 - No. 6 ($2.99, limited series)
1-6-Casey-s; X-Men before issue #1. 1-3-Rude-c/a. 4-Paul Smith-a/Rude-c. 5,6-Essad Ribic-c/a 3.00
TPB (11/01, $16.95) r/series; sketch pages; Casey intro. 17.00

X-MEN CHRONICLES
Marvel Comics: Mar, 1995 - No. 2, June, 1995 ($3.95, limited series)
1,2: Age of Apocalypse x-over. 1-wraparound-c 5.00

X-MEN: CLANDESTINE
Marvel Comics: Oct, 1996 - No. 2, Nov, 1996 ($2.95, limited series, 48 pgs.)
1,2: Alan Davis-c(p)/a(p)/scripts & Mark Farmer-c(i)/a(i) in all; wraparound-c 4.00

X-MEN CLASSIC (Formerly Classic X-Men)
Marvel Comics: No. 46, Apr, 1990 - No. 110, Aug, 1995 ($1.25/$1.50)
46-110: Reprints from X-Men. 54-(52 pgs.). 57,60-63,65-Russell-c(i); 62-r/X-Men #158 (Rogue). 66-r/#162 (Wolverine). 69-Begins-r of Paul Smith issues (#165 on). 70,79,90,97 (52 pgs.). 70-r/X-Men #166. 90-r/#186. 100-($1.50). 104-r/X-Men #200 3.00

X-MEN CLASSICS
Marvel Comics Group: Dec, 1983 - No. 3, Feb, 1984 ($2.00, Baxter paper)
1-3: X-Men-r by Neal Adams 6.00
NOTE: *Zeck c-1-3.*

X-MEN: COLOSSUS BLOODLIINE
Marvel Comics: Nov, 2005 - No. 5, Mar, 2006 ($2.99, limited series)
1-5-Colossus returns to Russia; David Hine-s/Jorge Lucas-a; Bachalo-c 3.00
TPB (2006, $13.99) r/#1-5 14.00

X-MEN: DEADLY GENESIS (See Uncanny X-Men #475)
Marvel Comics: Jan, 2006 - No. 6, July, 2006 ($3.99/$3.50, limited series)
1-($3.99) Silvestri-c swipe of Giant-Size X-Men #1; Hairsine-a/Brubaker-s 4.00
2-6-($3.50) 2-Silvestri-c; Banshee killed. 4-Intro Kid Vulcan 3.50
HC (2006, $24.99, dust jacket) r/#1-6 25.00
SC (2006, $19.99) r/#1-6 20.00

X-MEN: DIE BY THE SWORD

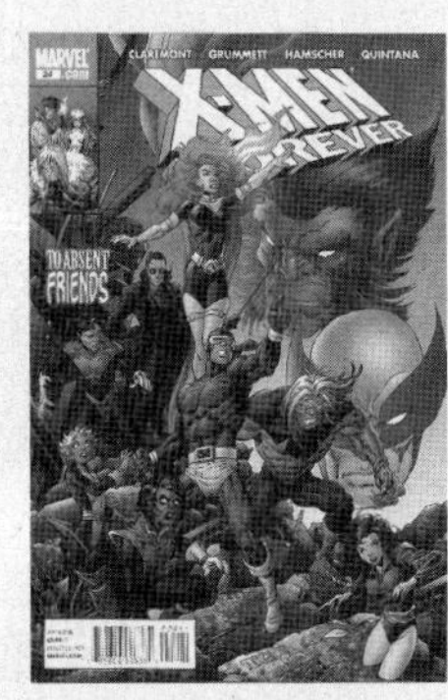

X-Men Forever #24 © MAR

X-Men: Hidden Years #3 © MAR

X-Men: Liberators #4 © MAR

	GD	VG	FN	VF	VF/NM	NM-
	2.0	4.0	6.0	8.0	9.0	9.2

Marvel Comics: Dec, 2007 - No. 5, Feb, 2008 ($2.99, limited series)
1-5-Excalibur and The Exiles app.; Claremont-s/Santacruz-a 3.00
TPB (2008, $13.99) r/#1-5; handbook pages of Merlyn, Roma and Saturne 14.00

X-MEN: DIVIDED WE STAND
Marvel Comics: June, 2008 - No. 2, July, 2008 ($3.99, limited series)
1,2-Short stories by various; Peterson-c 4.00

X-MEN: EARTHFALL
Marvel Comics: Sept, 1996 ($2.95, one-shot)
1-r/Uncanny X-Men #232-234; wraparound-c 4.00

X-MEN: EMPEROR VULCAN
Marvel Comics: Nov, 2007 - No. 5, Mar, 2008 ($2.99, limited series)
1-5: 1-Starjammers app.; Yost-s/Diaz-a/Tan-c 3.00
TPB (2008, $13.99) r/#1-5 14.00

X-MEN: EVOLUTION (Based on the animated series)
Marvel Comics: Feb, 2002 - No. 9, Sept, 2002 ($2.25)
1-9: 1-8-Grayson-s/Udon-a. 9-Farber-s/J.J.Kirby-a 3.00
TPB (7/02, $8.99) r/#1-4 9.00
Vol. 2 TPB (2003, $11.99) r/#5-9; Asamiya-c 12.00

X-MEN FAIRY TALES
Marvel Comics: July, 2006 - No. 4, Oct, 2006 ($2.99, limited series)
1-4-Re-imagining of classic stories; Cebulski-s. 2-Baker-a. 3-Sienkiewicz-a. 4-Kobayashi-a 3.00
TPB (2006, $10.99) r/#1-4 11.00

X-MEN/ FANTASTIC FOUR
Marvel Comics: Feb, 2005 - No. 5, June, 2005 ($3.50, limited series)
1-5-Pat Lee-a/c; Yoshida-s; the Brood app. 3.50
HC (2005, $19.99, 7 1/2" x 11", dustjacket) oversized r/#1-5; cover gallery 20.00

X-MEN FIRST CLASS
Marvel Comics: Nov, 2006 - No. 8, Jun, 2007 ($2.99, limited series)
1-8-Xavier's first class of X-Men; Cruz-a/Parker-s. 5-Thor app. 7-Scarlet Witch app. 3.00
... Special 1 (7/07, $3.99) Nowlan-c; Nowlan, Paul Smith, Coover, Dragotta & Allred-a 4.00
... - Tomorrow's Brightest HC (2007, $24.99, d.j) r/#1-8; cover & character design art 25.00
... - Tomorrow's Brightest SC (2007, $19.99) r/#1-8; cover & character design art 20.00

X-MEN FIRST CLASS (2nd series)
Marvel Comics: Aug, 2007 - No. 16, Nov, 2008 ($2.99)
1-16: 1-Cruz-a/Parker-s; Fantastic Four app. 8-Man-Thing app. 10-Romita Jr.-c 3.00
... Giant-Size Special 1 (12/08, $3.99) 5 new short stories; Haspiel-a; r/X-Men #40 4.00
... - Mutant Mayhem TPB (2008, $13.99) r/#1-5 & X-Men First Class Special 14.00

X-MEN FIRST CLASS FINALS
Marvel Comics: Apr, 2009 - No. 4, July, 2009 ($3.99, limited series)
1-4-Cruz-a/Parker-s. 1-3-Coover-a 4.00

X-MEN FIRSTS
Marvel Comics: Feb, 1996 ($4.95, one-shot)
1-r/Avengers Annual #10, Uncanny X-Men #266, #221; Incredible Hulk #181 5.00

X-MEN FOREVER
Marvel Comics: Jan, 2001 - No. 6, June, 2001 ($3.50, limited series)
1-6-Jean Grey, Iceman, Mystique, Toad, Juggernaut app.; Maguire-a 4.00

X-MEN FOREVER
Marvel Comics: Aug, 2009 - No. 24, July, 2010 ($3.99)
1-24: 1-Claremont-s/Grummett-a/c. 7-Nick Fury app. 4.00
... Alpha 1 (2009, $4.99) r/X-Men (1991) #1-3; 8 page preview of X-Men Forever #1 5.00
... Annual 1 (6/10, $4.99) Wolverine & Jean Grey romance; Sana Takeda-a/c 5.00
... Giant-Size 1 (7/10, $3.99) Grell-a/c; Lilandra & Gladiator app.; r/(Uncanny)X-Men #108 4.00

X-MEN FOREVER 2
Marvel Comics: Aug, 2010 - No. 16, Mar, 2011 ($3.99)
1-16: 1-Claremont-s/Grummett-a/c. 2,3-Spider-Man app. 9,10-Grell-a 4.00

X-MEN: GOLD
Marvel Comics: Jan, 2014 ($5.99, one-shot)
1-50th Anniversary anthology; short stories by various incl. Stan Lee, Simonson, Claremont, Thomas, Olliffe, Wein, Molina, McLeod, Larroca; Coipel-c 6.00

X-MEN: GOLD
Marvel Comics: Jun, 2017 - Present ($4.99/$3.99)
1-($4.99) Syaf-a; Storm, Nightcrawler, Old Man Logan, Colossus, Kitty Pryde team 5.00
2-23-($3.99): 4-6-Silva-a. 7,8-Secret Empire tie-ins; Lashley-a. 13-15-"Mojo Worldwide" 4.00
Annual 1 (3/18, $4.99) Excalibur reunion; Capt. Britain app.; Martinez-a 5.00

X-MEN: GRAND DESIGN
Marvel Comics: Feb, 2018 - No. 2, Mar, 2018 ($5.99, limited series)
1,2-Origins and early days of the X-Men re-told; Ed Piskor-s/a/c 6.00

X-MEN: HELLBOUND
Marvel Comics: July, 2010 - No. 3, Sept, 2010 ($3.99, limited series)
1-3-Second Coming x-over; Tolibao-a/Djurdjevic-c; Majik rescued from Limbo 4.00

X-MEN: HELLFIRE CLUB
Marvel Comics: Jan, 2000 - No. 4, Apr, 2000 ($2.50, limited series)
1-4-Origin of the Hellfire Club 3.00

X-MEN: HIDDEN YEARS
Marvel Comics: Dec, 1999 - No. 22, Sept. 2001 ($3.50/$2.50)
1-New adventures from pre-#94 era; Byrne-s/a(p) 4.00
2-4,6-11,13-22-($2.50): 2-Two covers. 3-Ka-Zar app. 8,9-FF-c/app. 3.00
5-($2.75) 3.00
12-($3.50) Magneto-c/app. 4.00

X-MEN: KING BREAKER
Marvel Comics: Feb, 2009 - No. 4, May, 2009 ($3.99, limited series)
1-4-Emperor Vulcan and a Shi'ar invasion; Havok, Rachel Grey and Polaris app. 4.00

X-MEN: KITTY PRYDE - SHADOW & FLAME
Marvel Comics: Aug, 2005 - No. 5, Dec, 2005 ($2.99, limited series)
1-5-Akira Yoshida-s/Paul Smith-a/c; Kitty & Lockheed go to Japan 3.00
TPB (2006, $14.99) r/#1-5 15.00

X-MEN LEGACY (See X-Men 2nd series)

X-MEN LEGACY (Marvel NOW!)
Marvel Comics: Jan, 2013 - No. 24, Apr, 2014; No. 300, May, 2014 ($2.99)
1-24: 1-Legion (Professor X's son); Spurrier-s/Huat-a. 2-X-Men app. 5,6-Molina-a 3.00
300-(5/14, $4.99) Spurrier, Carey & Gage-s/Huat, Kurth & Sandoval-a; Mann-c 5.00

X-MEN: LIBERATORS
Marvel Comics: Nov, 1998 - No. 4, Feb, 1999 ($2.99, limited series)
1-4-Wolverine, Nightcrawler & Colossus; P. Jimenez 4.00

X-MEN LOST TALES
Marvel Comics: 1997 ($2.99)
1,2-r/Classic X-Men back-up stories 4.00

X-MEN: MAGNETO TESTAMENT
Marvel Comics: Nov, 2008 - No. 5, Mar, 2009 ($3.99, limited series)
1-5-Max Eisenhardt in 1930s Nazi-occupied Poland; Pak-s/DiGiandomenico-a. 5-Back-up story of artist Dina Babbitt with Neal Adams-a 4.00

X-MEN: MANIFEST DESTINY
Marvel Comics: Nov, 2008 - No. 5, Mar, 2009 ($3.99, limited series)
1-5-Short stories of X-Men re-location to San Francisco; s/a by various 4.00
... Nightcrawler 1 (5/09, $3.99) Molina & Syaf-a; Mephisto app. 4.00

X-MEN: MESSIAH COMPLEX
Marvel Comics: Dec, 2007 ($3.99)
1-Part 1 of x-over with X-Men, Uncanny X-Men, X-Factor and New X-Men; 2 covers 4.00
... - Mutant Files (2007, $3.99) Handbook pages of x-over participants; Kolins-c 4.00
HC (2008, $39.99, oversized) r/#1, Uncanny X-Men #492-494, X-Men #205-207, New X-Men #44-46 and X-Factor #25-27 40.00

X-MEN '92 (Secret Wars tie-in)
Marvel Comics: Aug, 2015 - No. 4, Nov, 2015 ($4.99, limited series)
1-4-Koblish-a; Cassandra Nova app. 2-4-X-Force app. 4-Apocalypse cameo 5.00

X-MEN '92 (Follows Secret Wars)
Marvel Comics: May, 2016 - Present ($3.99)
1-10: 1-Firmansyah-a; Omega Red & Alpha Red app. 2-U-Go Girl joins. 3,4-Dracula app. 9,10-New Mutants app. 4.00

X-MEN NOIR
Marvel Comics: Nov, 2008 - No. 4, May, 2009 ($3.99, limited series)
1-4-Pulp-style story set in 1930s NY; Van Lente-s/Calero-a 4.00
...: Mark of Cain (2/10 - No. 4, 5/10, $3.99) Van Lente-s/Calero-a 4.00

X-MEN OMEGA
Marvel Comics: June, 1995 ($3.95, one-shot)
nn-Age of Apocalypse finale 1 3 4 6 8 10
nn-($49.95)-Gold edition 55.00

X-MEN: ORIGINS

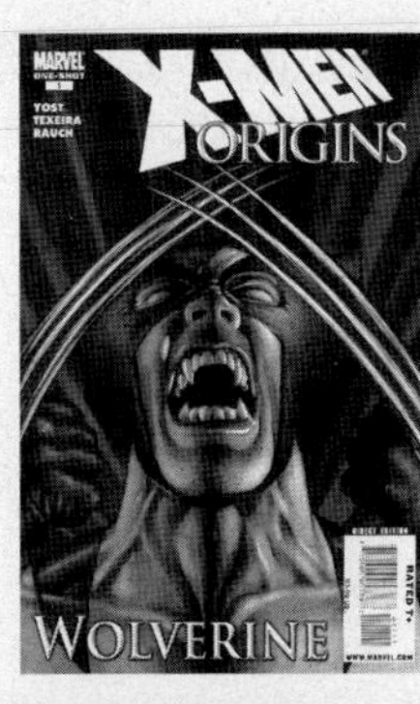

X-Men Origins: Wolverine #1 © MAR

X-Men: Red #1 © MAR

X-Men: The Manga #24 © MAR

GD 2.0 | VG 4.0 | FN 6.0 | VF 8.0 | VF/NM 9.0 | NM- 9.2

Marvel Comics: Oct, 2008 - Sept, 2010 ($3.99, series of one-shots)
...: Beast (11/08) High school years; Carey-s; painted-a/c by Woodward 5.00
...: Cyclops (3/10) Magneto app.; Delperdang-a/Granov-c 1 2 3 5 6 8
...: Deadpool (9/10) Fernandez-a/Swierczynski-s 4 8 12 23 37 50
...: Emma Frost (7/10) Moline-a; r/excerpt from 1st app. in Uncanny X-Men #129 5.00
...: Gambit (8/09) Mr. Sinister, Sabretooth and the Marauders app.; Yardin-a 2 4 6 11 16 20
...: Iceman (1/10) Noto-a 5.00
...: Jean Grey (10/08) Childhood & early X-days; McKeever-s; Mayhew painted-a/c 5.00
...: Nightcrawler (5/10) Cary Nord-a; r/excerpt from 1st app. in Giant-Size X-Men #1 5.00
...: Sabretooth (4/09) Childhood and early meetings with Wolverine; Panosian-a/c 1 2 3 5 6 8
...: Wolverine (6/09) Pre-X-Men days and first meeting with Xavier; Texeira-a/c 5.00

X-MEN: PHOENIX
Marvel Comics: Dec, 1999 - No. 3, Mar, 2000 ($2.50, limited series)
1-3: 1-Apocalypse app. 4.00

X-MEN: PHOENIX - ENDSONG
Marvel Comics: Mar, 2005 - No. 5, June, 2005 ($2.99, limited series)
1-5-The Phoenix Force returns to Earth; Greg Land-c/a; Greg Pak-s 3.00
HC (2005, $19.99, dust jacket) r/#1-5; Land sketch pages 20.00
SC (2006, $14.99) 15.00

X-MEN: PHOENIX - LEGACY OF FIRE
Marvel Comics: July, 2003 - No. 3, Sep, 2003 ($2.99, limited series)
1-3-Manga-style; Ryan Kinnard-s/a/c; intro page art by Adam Warren 3.00

X-MEN: PHOENIX - WARSONG
Marvel Comics: Nov, 2006 - No. 5, Mar, 2007 ($2.99, limited series)
1-5-Tyler Kirkham-a/Greg Pak-s/Marc Silvestri-c 3.00
HC (2007, $19.99, dustjacket) r/#1-5; variant cover gallery and Handbook pages 20.00
SC (2007, $14.99) r/#1-5; variant cover gallery and Handbook pages 15.00

X-MEN: PIXIE STRIKES BACK
Marvel Comics: Apr, 2010 - No. 4, July, 2010 ($3.99, limited series)
1-4-Kathryn Immonen-s/Sara Pichelli-a/Stuart Immonen-c 4.00

X-MEN: PRELUDE TO SCHISM
Marvel Comics: Jul, 2011 - No. 4, Aug, 2011 ($2.99, limited series)
1-4-Jenkins-s/Camuncoli-c. 1-De La Torre-a. 2-Magneto childhood. 3-Conrad-a 3.00

X-MEN PRIME
Marvel Comics: July, 1995 ($4.95, one-shot)
nn-Post Age of Apocalyse begins 1 3 4 6 8 10

X-MEN PRIME
Marvel Comics: May, 2017 ($4.99, one-shot)
1-Preludes to X-Men: Blue #1, X-Men: Gold #1 and Weapon X #1 5.00

X-MEN RARITIES
Marvel Comics: 1995 ($5.95, one-shot)
nn-Reprints hard-to-find stories 6.00

X-MEN: RED
Marvel Comics: Apr, 2018 - Present ($4.99/$3.99)
1-($4.99) Asrar-a; Jean Grey, Nightcrawler, Namor, Wolverine (X-23) team 5.00
2-($3.99) 4.00

X-MEN ROAD TO ONSLAUGHT
Marvel Comics: Oct, 1996 ($2.50, one-shot)
nn-Retells Onslaught Saga 3.00

X-MEN: RONIN
Marvel Comics: May, 2003 - No. 5, July, 2003 ($2.99, limited series)
1-5-Manga-style X-Men; Torres-s/Nakatsuka-a 3.00

X-MEN: SCHISM
Marvel Comics: Sept, 2011 - No. 5, Dec, 2011 ($4.99/$3.99, limited series)
1-($4.99) Aaron-s/Pacheco-a/c 5.00
2-5-($3.99) 2-Cho-a/c. 3-Acuña-a/c. 4-Alan Davis-a/c. 5-Adam Kubert-a 4.00

X-MEN: SEARCH FOR CYCLOPS
Marvel Comics: Oct, 2000 - No. 4, Mar, 2001 ($2.99, limited series)
1-4-Two covers (Raney, Pollina); Raney-a 4.00

X-MEN: SECOND COMING
Marvel Comics: May, 2010 - No. 2, Sept, 2010 ($3.99)
1-Cable & Hope return to the present; Bastion app.; Finch-a; covers by Granov & Finch 4.00
2-Conclusion to x-over; covers by Granov & Finch 4.00
...: Prepare (4/10, free) previews x-over; short story w/Immonen-a; cover sketch art 3.00

X-MEN / SPIDER-MAN ("X-Men and Spider-Man" on cover)
Marvel Comics: Jan, 2009 - No. 4, Apr, 2009 ($3.99, limited series)
1-4: 1-Team-up from pre-blue Beast days; Kraven app.; Gage-s/Alberti-a 4.00

X-MEN SPOTLIGHT ON... STARJAMMERS (Also see X-Men #104)
Marvel Comics: 1990 - No. 2, 1990 ($4.50, 52 pgs.)
1,2: Features Starjammers 5.00

X-MEN SURVIVAL GUIDE TO THE MANSION
Marvel Comics: Aug, 1993 ($6.95, spiralbound)
1 7.00

X-MEN: THE COMPLETE AGE OF APOCALYPSE EPIC
Marvel Comics: 2005 - Vol. 4, 2006 ($29.99, TPB)
Book 1-4: Chronological reprintings of the crossover 30.00

X-MEN: THE EARLY YEARS
Marvel Comics: May, 1994 - No. 17, Sept, 1995 ($1.50/$2.50)
1-16: r/X-Men #1-8 w/new-c 3.00
17-$2.50-c; r/X-Men #17,18 4.00

X-MEN: THE END
Marvel Comics: Oct, 2004 - No. 6, Feb, 2005 ($2.99, limited series)
1-6-Claremont-s/Chen-a/Land-c 3.00
... Book One: Dreamers and Demons TPB (2005, $14.99) r/#1-6 15.00

X-MEN: THE END - HEROES AND MARTYRS (Volume 2)
Marvel Comics: May, 2005 - No. 6, Oct, 2005 ($2.99, limited series)
1-6-Claremont-s/Chen-a/Land-c; continued from X-Men: The End 3.00
... Vol. 2 TPB (2006, $14.99) r/#1-6 15.00

X-MEN: THE END (MEN & X-MEN) (Volume 3)
Marvel Comics: Mar, 2006 - No. 6, Aug, 2006 ($2.99, limited series)
1-6-Claremont-s/Chen-a. 1-Land-c. 2-6-Gene Ha-c 3.00
... Vol. 3 TPB (2006, $14.99) r/#1-6 15.00

X-MEN: THE MANGA
Marvel Comics: Mar, 1998 - No. 26, June, 1999 ($2.99, B&W)
1-26-English version of Japanese X-Men comics: 23,24-Randy Green-c 4.00

X-MEN: THE MOVIE
Marvel Comics: Aug, 2000; Sept, 2000
Adaptation (9/00, $5.95) Macchio-s/Williams & Lanning-a 6.00
Adaptation TPB (9/00, $14.95) Movie adaptation and key reprints of main characters; four photo covers (movie X, Magneto, Rogue, Wolverine) 15.00
Prequel: Magneto (8/00, $5.95) Texeira & Palmiotti-a; art & photo covers 6.00
Prequel: Rogue (8/00, $5.95) Evans & Nikolakakis-a; art & photo covers 6.00
Prequel: Wolverine (8/00, $5.95) Waller & McKenna-a; art & photo covers 6.00
TPB X-Men: Beginnings (8/00, $14.95) reprints 3 prequels w/photo-c 15.00

X-MEN 2: THE MOVIE
Marvel Comics: 2003
Adaptation (6/03, $3.50) Movie adaptation; photo-c; Austen-s/Zircher-a 4.00
Adaptation TPB (2003, $12.99) Movie adaptation & r/Prequels Nightcrawler & Wolverine 13.00
Prequel: Nightcrawler (5/03, $3.50) Kerschl-a; photo cover 4.00
Prequel: Wolverine (5/03, $3.50) Mandrake-a; photo cover; Sabretooth app. 4.00

X-MEN: THE 198 (See House of M)
Marvel Comics: Mar, 2006 - No. 5, July, 2006 ($2.99, limited series)
1-5-Hine-s/Muniz-a 3.00
... Files (2006, $3.99) profiles of the 198 mutants who kept their powers after House of M 4.00
Decimation: The 198 (2006, $15.99, TPB) r/#1-5 & X-Men: The 198 Files 16.00

X-MEN: THE TIMES AND LIFE OF LUCAS BISHOP
Marvel Comics: Apr, 2009 - No. 3, June, 2009 ($3.99, limited series)
1-3-Swierczynski-s/Stroman-a. 1-Bishop's birth and childhood 4.00

X-MEN: THE ULTRA COLLECTION
Marvel Comics: Dec, 1994 - No. 5, Apr, 1995 ($2.95, limited series)
1-5: Pin-ups; no scripts 3.00

X-MEN: THE WEDDING ALBUM
Marvel Comics: 1994 ($2.95, magazine size, one-shot)
1-Wedding of Scott Summers & Jean Grey 4.00

X-MEN: TO SERVE AND PROTECT

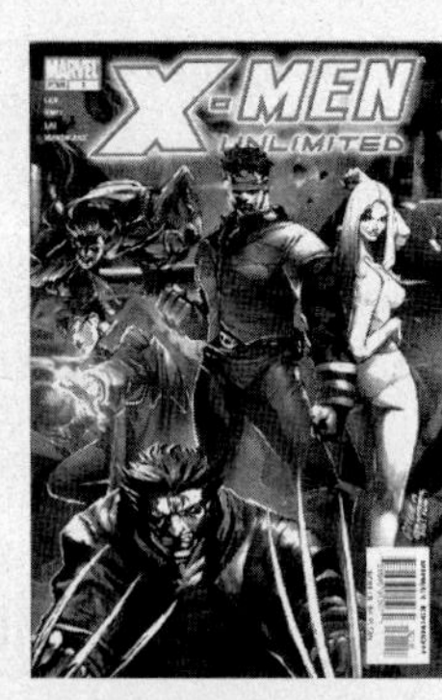

X-Men Unlimited (2004 series) #1 © MAR

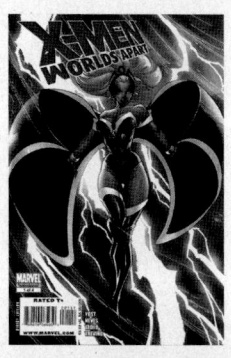

X-Men: Worlds Apart #1 © MAR

X-O Manowar (2012 series) #41 © VAL

GD VG FN VF VF/NM NM-
2.0 4.0 6.0 8.0 9.0 9.2

Marvel Comics: Jan, 2011 - No. 4, Apr, 2011 ($3.99, limited series)

1-4-Short story anthology by various.1-Bradshaw-c. 2-Camuncoli-c 4.00

X-MEN TRUE FRIENDS
Marvel Comics: Sept, 1999 - No. 3, Nov, 1999 ($2.99, limited series)

1-3-Claremont-s/Leonardi-a 4.00

X-MEN 2099 (Also see 2099: World of Tomorrow)
Marvel Comics: Oct, 1993 - No. 35, Aug, 1996 ($1.25/$1.50/$1.95)

1-($1.75)-Foil-c; Ron Lim/Adam Kubert-a begins 4.00
1-2nd printing ($1.75) 3.00
1-Gold edition (15,000 made); sold thru Diamond for $19.40 20.00
2-24,26-35: 3-Death of Tina; Lim-c/a(p) in #1-8. 8-Bound-in trading card sheet. 35-Nostromo (from X-Nation) app; storyline cont'd in 2099: World of Tomorrow 3.00
25-($2.50)-Double sized 4.00
Special 1 ($3.95) 4.00
...: Oasis ($5.95, one-shot) -Hildebrandt Bros.-c/a 6.00

X-MEN ULTRA III PREVIEW
Marvel Comics: 1995 ($2.95)

nn-Kubert-a 3.00

X-MEN UNIVERSE
Marvel Comics: Dec, 1999 - No. 15, Feb, 2001 ($4.99/$3.99)

1-8-Reprints stories from recent X-Men titles 5.00
9-15-($3.99) 4.00

X-MEN UNIVERSE: PAST, PRESENT AND FUTURE
Marvel Comics: Feb, 1999 ($2.99, one-shot)

1-Previews 1999 X-Men events; background info 3.00

X-MEN UNLIMITED
Marvel Comics: 1993 - No. 50, Sept, 2003 ($3.95/$2.99, 68 pgs.)

1-Chris Bachalo-c/a; Quesada-a. 6.00
2-11: 2-Origin of Magneto script. 3-Sabretooth-c/story. 10-Dark Beast vs. Beast; Mark Waid script. 11-Magneto & Rogue 5.00
12-33: 12-Begin $2.99-c; Onslaught x-over; Juggernaut-c/app. 19-Caliafore-a. 20-Generation X app. 27-Origin Thunderbird. 29-Maximum Security x-over; Bishop-c/app. 30-Mahfood-a. 31-Stelfreeze-c/a. 32-Dazzler; Thompson-c/a 33-Kaluta-c 4.00
34-37,39,40-42-($3.50) 34-Von Eeden-a. 35-Finch, Conner, Maguire-a. 36-Chiodo-c/a; Larroca, Totleben-a. 39-Bachalo-c; Pearson-a. 41-Bachalo-c; X-Statix app. 4.00
38-($2.25) Kitty Pryde; Robertson-a 3.00
43-50-($2.50) 43-Sienkiewicz-c/a; Paul Smith-a. 45-Noto-c. 46-Bisley-a. 47-Warren-s/Mays-a. 48-Wolverine story w/Isanove painted-a 3.00
X-Men Legends Vol. 4: Hated and Feared TPB (2003, $19.99) r/stories by various 20.00
NOTE: *Bachalo c/a-1. Quesada a-1. Waid scripts-10*

X-MEN UNLIMITED
Marvel Comics: Apr, 2004 - No. 14, Jun, 2006 ($2.99)

1-14: 1-6-Pat Lee-c; short stories by various. 2-District X preview; Granov-a 3.00

X-MEN VS. AGENTS OF ATLAS
Marvel Comics: Dec, 2009 - No. 2, Jan, 2010 ($3.99, limited series)

1,2-Pagulayan-a. 1-McGuinness-c. 2-Granov-c 4.00

X-MEN VS. DRACULA
Marvel Comics: Dec, 1993 ($1.75)

1-r/X-Men Annual #6; Austin-c(i) 4.00

X-MEN VS. THE AVENGERS, THE
Marvel Comics Group: Apr, 1987 - No. 4, July, 1987 ($1.50, limited series, Baxter paper)

1-Silvestri-a/c 1 2 3 5 6 8
2-4: 2,3-Silvestri-a/c. 4-Pollard-a/c 5.00

X-MEN VS. THE BROOD, THE
Marvel Comics Group: Sept, 1996 - No. 2, Oct, 1996 ($2.95, limited series)

1,2-Wraparound-c; Ostrander-s/Hitch-a(p) 4.00
TPB('97, $16.99) reprints X-Men/Brood: Day of Wrath #1,2 & Uncanny X-Men #232-234 17.00

X-MEN VISIONARIES
Marvel Comics: 1995,1996,2000 (trade paperbacks)

nn-($8.95) Reprints X-Men stories; Adam & Andy Kubert-a 9.00
...2: The Neal Adams Collection (1996) r/X-Men #56-63,65 30.00
...2: The Neal Adams Col. (2nd printing, 2000, $24.95) new Adams-c 25.00

X-MEN/WILDC.A.T.S.: THE DARK AGE (See also WildC.A.T.S./X-Men...)
Marvel Comics: 1998 ($4.50, one-shot)

1-Two covers (Broome & Golden); Ellis-s 5.00

X-MEN: WORLDS APART
Marvel Comics: Dec, 2008 - No. 4, Mar, 2009 ($3.99, limited series)

1-4-Storm and the Black Panther vs. the Shadow King. 1-Campbell-c 4.00

X-MEN: WORST X-MAN EVER
Marvel Comics: Apr, 2016 - No. 5, Aug, 2016 ($3.99, limited series)

1-5: 1-Intro. Bailey Hoskins; Max Bemis-s/Michael Walsh-a. 3,4-Magneto app. 4.00

X-NATION 2099
Marvel Comics: Mar, 1996 - No. 6, Aug, 1996 ($1.95)

1-($3.95)-Humberto Ramos-a(p); wraparound, foil-c 5.00
2-6: 2,3-Ramos-a. 4-Exodus-c/app. 6-Reed Richards app 3.00

X NECROSIA
Marvel Comics: Dec, 2009 ($3.99)

1-Beginning of X-Force/X-Men/New Mutants x-over; Crain-a; Selene returns 4.00
...: The Gathering (2/10, $3.99) Wither, Blink, Senyaka, Mortis & Eliphas short stories 4.00

X-O MANOWAR (1st Series)
Valiant/Acclaim Comics (Valiant) No. 43 on: Feb, 1992 - No. 68, Sept, 1996 ($1.95/$2.25/$2.50, high quality)

0-(8/93, $3.50)-Wraparound embossed chromium-c by Quesada; Solar app.; origin Aric (X-O Manowar) 6.00
0-Gold variant 2 4 6 13 18 22
1-Intro/1st app. & partial origin of Aric (X-O Manowar); Barry Smith/Layton-a; Shooter & Englehart-s 3 6 9 16 24 32
2,3: 2-B. Smith/Layton-c. 3-Layton-c(i) 1 3 4 6 8 10
4-1st app. Shadowman; Harbinger app. 3 6 9 20 31 42
5,6: 5-B. Smith-c. 6-Begin $2.25-c; Ditko-a(p) 1 2 3 5 6 8
7-15: 7,8-Unity x-overs. 7-Miller-c. 8-Simonson-c. 12-1st app. Randy Calder. 14,15-Turok-c/stories 4.00
15-Hot pink logo variant; came with Ultra Pro Rigid Comic Sleeves box; no price on-c 1 2 3 5 6 8
16-24,26-43: 20-Serial number contest insert. 27-29-Turok x-over. 28-Bound-in trading card. 30-1st app. new "good skin"; Solar app. 33-Chaos Effect Delta Pt. 3. 42-Shadowman app.; includes X-O Manowar Birthquake! Prequel 3.00
25-($3.50)-Has 16 pg. Armorines #0 bound-in w/origin 4.00
44-66: 44-Begin $2.50-c. 50-X, 50-O, 51, 52, 63-Bart Sears-c/a/scripts.
67 1 2 3 5 6 8
68-Revealed that Aric's past stories were premonitions of his future 2 4 6 11 16 20
...: Birth HC (2008, $24.95) recolored reprints #0-6; script and breakdowns for #0; cover gallery; new "The Rise of Lydia" story by Layton and Leeke 25.00
Trade paperback nn (1993, $9.95)-Polybagged with copy of X-O Database #1 inside 15.00
Yearbook 1 (4/95, $2.95) 4.00
NOTE: *Layton a-1i, 2i(part); c-1, 2i, 3i, 6i, 21i. Reese a-4i(part); c-26i.*

X-O MANOWAR (2nd Series)(Also see Iron Man/X-O Manowar: Heavy Metal)
Acclaim Comics (Valiant Heroes): V2#1, Oct, 1996 - No. 21, Jun, 1998 ($2.50)

V2#1-21: 1-Mark Waid & Brian Augustyn scripts begin; 1st app. Donavon Wylie; Rand Banion dies; painted variant-c exists. 2-Donavon Wylie becomes new X-O Manowar. 7-9-Augustyn-s. 10-Copycat-c 3.00

X-O MANOWAR (3rd series)
Valiant Entertainment: May, 2012 - No. 50, Sept, 2016 ($3.99)

1-Robert Venditti-s/Cary Nord-a/Esad Ribic-c; origin re-told 4.00
1-Pullbox variant-c by Nord 5.00
1-Variant-c by David Aja 10.00
1-QR Voice variant-c by Jelena Kevic-Djurdjevic 25.00
2-24: 2-Origin continues. 2,3-Kevic-Djurdjevic-c. 5-8-Ninjak app.; Garbett-a. 9,10-Hairsine-a. 11-14-Planet Death; Nord-a. 19-21-Unity tie-in 4.00
2-5,8-14-Pullbox variant covers. 2-Lozzi. 3-Suayan. 4-Kramer. 5-Tan. 14-Eight-bit art 5.00
25-($4.99) Hitch-a; Armor Hunters app., Owly & Wormy short story by Runton 5.00
26-37,39-49: 26-29-Armor Hunters tie-in. 30-32-Armorines app. 34-37-Dead Hand. 47-49-Polybagged with micro-print 4.00
38-(7/15, $4.99) Wedding of Aric and Saana; Doctor Mirage app.; flashbacks 5.00
50-(9/16, $4.99) Polybagged; wraparound-c by 50 artists; art by various 5.00
#0 (10/14, $3.99) Flashback to Aric before his kidnapping; Clay Mann-a 4.00
Annual 2016 #1 (5/16, $5.99) Art by JG Jones, Perez, McKone, Gorham, De La Torre 6.00
...: Commander Trill #0 (12/15, $3.99) Origin of Trill; Venditti-s/Portela-a 4.00
...: Valiant 25th Anniversary Special (6/15, $3.99) Origin of Shanhara; Venditti-s/Cafu-a 4.00

X-O MANOWAR (2017) (4th series)
Valiant Entertainment: Mar, 2017 - Present ($3.99)

1-12: 1-Kindt-s/Giorello-a; Aric on planet Gorin. 4-6 Braithwaite-a. 7-9-Crain-a 4.00

X-O MANOWAR FAN EDITION

Xombi (2011 series) #4 © Milestone

X-treme X-Men #25 © MAR

X-23 #20 © MAR

GD VG FN VF VF/NM NM-
2.0 4.0 6.0 8.0 9.0 9.2

Acclaim Comics (Valiant Heroes): Feb, 1997 (Overstreet's FAN giveaway)
1-Reintro the Armorines & the Hard Corps; 1st app. Citadel; Augustyn scripts; McKone-c/a 4.00

X-O MANOWAR/IRON MAN: IN HEAVY METAL (See Iron Man/X-O Manowar: Heavy Metal)
Acclaim Comics (Valiant Heroes): Sept, 1996 ($2.50, one-shot)
(1st Marvel/Valiant x-over)
1-Pt 1 of X-O Manowar/Iron Man x-over; Arnim Zola app.; Nicieza scripts; Andy Smith-a 5.00

XOMBI
DC Comics (Milestone): Jan, 1994 - No. 21, Feb, 1996 ($1.75/$2.50)
0-($1.95)-Shadow War x-over; Simonson silver ink varnish-c 3.00
1-21: 1-John Byrne-c 3.00
1-Platinum 8.00

XOMBI
DC Comics: May, 2011 - No. 6, Oct, 2011 ($2.99)
1-6-Rozum-s/Irving-a/c 3.00

X-PATROL
Marvel Comics (Amalgam): Apr, 1996 ($1.95, one-shot)
1-Cruz-a(p) 3.00

XSE
Marvel Comics: Nov, 1996 - No. 4, Feb, 1997 ($1.95, limited series)
1-4: 1-Bishop & Shard app. 3.00
1-Variant-c 4.00

X-STATIX
Marvel Comics: Sept, 2002 - No. 26, Oct, 2004 ($2.99/$2.25)
1-($2.99) Allred-a/c; intro. Venus Dee Milo; back-up w/Cooke-a 4.00
2-9-($2.25) 4-Quitely-c. 5-Pope-c/a 3.00
10-26: 10-Begin $2.99-c; Bond-a; U-Go Girl flashback. 13,14-Spider-Man app. 21-25-Avengers app. 26-Team dies 3.00
... Vol. 1: Good Omens TPB (2003, $11.99) r/#1-5 12.00
... Vol. 2: Good Guys & Bad Guys TPB (2003, $15.99) r/#6-10 & Wolverine/Doop #1&2 16.00
... Vol. 3: Back From the Dead TPB (2004, $19.99) r/#11-18 20.00
... Vol. 4: X-Statix Vs. the Avengers TPB (2004, $19.99) r/#19-26; pin-ups 20.00

X-STATIX PRESENTS: DEAD GIRL
Marvel Comics: Mar, 2006 - No. 5, July, 2006 ($2.99, limited series)
1-5-Dr. Strange, Dead Girl, Miss America, Tike app. Milligan-s/Dragotta & Allred-a 3.00
TPB (2006, $13.99) r/series 14.00

X-TERMINATION (Crossover with Astonishing X-Men and X-Treme X-Men)
Marvel Comics: May, 2013 - No. 2, Jun, 2013 ($3.99)
1,2-Lapham-s/David Lopez-a 4.00

X-TERMINATORS
Marvel Comics: Oct, 1988 - No. 4, Jan, 1989 ($1.00, limited series)
1-1st app.; X-Men/X-Factor tie-in; Williamson-i 5.00
2-4 4.00

X, THE MAN WITH THE X-RAY EYES (See Movie Comics)

X-TINCTION AGENDA (Secret Wars tie-in)
Marvel Comics: Aug, 2015 - No. 4, Nov, 2015 ($3.99, limited series)
1-4-Guggenheim-s/Di Giandomenico-a; Havok & Wolfsbane app. 4.00

X-TREME X-MEN (Also see Mekanix)
Marvel Comics: July, 2001 - No. 46, Jun, 2004 ($2.99/$3.50)
1-Claremont-s/Larroca-c/a 4.00
2-24: 2-Two covers (Larroca & Pacheco); Psylocke killed 3.00
25-35, 40-46: 25-30-God Loves, Man Kills II; Stryker app.; Kordey-a 3.00
36-39-($3.50) 3.50
Annual 2001 ($4.95) issue opens longways 5.00
... Vol. 1: Destiny TPB (2002, $19.95) r/#1-9 20.00
... Vol. 2: Invasion TPB (2003, $19.99) r/#10-18 20.00
... Vol. 3: Schism TPB (2003, $16.99) r/#19-23; X-Treme X-Posé #1&2 17.00
... Vol. 4: Mekanix TPB (2003, $16.99) r/Mekanix #1-6 17.00
... Vol. 5: God Loves Man Kills TPB (2003, $19.99) r/#25-30 20.00
... Vol. 6: Intifada TPB (2004, $16.99) r/#24,31-35 17.00
... Vol. 7: Storm the Arena TPB (2004, $16.99) r/#36-39 17.00
... Vol. 8: Prisoner of Fire TPB (2004, $19.99) r/#40-46 and Annual 2001 20.00

X-TREME X-MEN
Marvel Comics: Sept, 2012 - No. 13, Jun, 2013 ($2.99)
1-13: 1-Pak-s/Segovia-a; Dazzler with alternate reality Wolverine, Nightcrawler, Emma 3.00
7.1-(2/12) Cyclops & The Brood app. 3.00

GD VG FN VF VF/NM NM-
2.0 4.0 6.0 8.0 9.0 9.2

X-TREME X-MEN: SAVAGE LAND
Marvel Comics: Nov, 2001 - No. 4, Feb, 2002 ($2.99, limited series)
1-4-Claremont-s/Sharpe-c/a; Beast app. 3.00

X-TREME X-POSE
Marvel Comics: Jan, 2003 - No. 2, Feb, 2003 ($2.99, limited series)
1,2-Claremont-s/Ranson-a/Migliari-c 3.00

X-23 (See debut in NYX #3)(See NYX X-23 HC for reprint)
Marvel Comics: Mar, 2005 - No. 6, July, 2005 ($2.99, limited series)
1-Origin of the Wolverine clone girl; Tan-a 2 4 6 11 16 20
1-Variant Billy Tan-c with red background 3 6 9 14 20 25
2-6-Origin continues 1 2 3 5 6 8
2-Variant B&W sketch-c 2 4 6 9 12 15
One shot 1 (5/10, $3.99) Urasov-c/Liu-s; Wolverine & Jubilee app.
3 6 9 14 20 25
...: Innocence Lost MGC 1 (5/11, $1.00) r/#1 with "Marvel's Greatest Comics" cover logo 3.00
...: Innocence Lost TPB (2006, $15.99) r/#1-6 20.00

X-23
Marvel Comics: Nov, 2010 - No. 21, May, 2012 ($3.99/$2.99)
1-Marjorie Liu-s/Will Conrad-a; origin retold; Luo-c 3 6 9 14 20 25
1-Djurdjevic variant-c 3 6 9 14 20 25
1-Dell'Otto variant-c 22 44 66 154 340 525
2-Luo-c 1 3 4 6 8 10
2-Mayhew variant-c 6 12 18 42 79 115
3-21: 3,10-12,17-19-Takeda-a. 8,9-Daken app. 13-16-Spider-Man app.; Noto-a. 20-Jubilee app.; Noto-a. 21-Silent issue; Noto-a 4.00

X-23: TARGET X
Marvel Comics: Feb, 2007 - No. 6, July, 2007 ($2.99, limited series)
1-Kyle & Yost-s/Choi & Oback-a 2 4 6 10 14 18
2-6: 6-Gallery of variant covers and sketches 6.00
TPB (2007, $15.99) r/#1-6; gallery of variant covers and sketches 16.00

X-UNIVERSE
Marvel Comics: May, 1995 - No. 2, June, 1995 ($3.50, limited series)
1,2: Age of Apocalypse 5.00

X-VENTURE (Super Heroes)
Victory Magazines Corp.: July, 1947 - No. 2, Nov, 1947
1-Atom Wizard, Mystery Shadow, Lester Trumble begin
123 246 369 787 1344 1900
2 58 116 174 371 636 900

X-WOMEN
Marvel Comics: 2010 ($4.99, one-shot)
1-Milo Manara-a/Chris Claremont-s; a female X-Men adventure; Quesada afterword 5.00

XYR (See Eclipse Graphic Album Series #21)

YAK YAK
Dell Publishing Co.: No. 1186, May-July, 1961 - No. 1348, Apr-June, 1962
Four Color 1186 (#1)- Jack Davis-c/a; 2 versions, one minus 3 pgs.
8 16 24 54 102 150
Four Color 1348 (#2)-Davis c/a 7 14 21 46 86 125

YAKKY DOODLE & CHOPPER (TV) (See Dell Giant #44)
Gold Key: Dec, 1962 (Hanna-Barbera)
1 6 12 18 42 79 115

YANG (See House of Yang)
Charlton Comics: Nov, 1973 - No. 13, May, 1976; V14#15, Sept, 1985 - No. 17, Jan, 1986
(No V14#14, series resumes with #15)
1-Origin; Sattler-a begins; slavery-s 2 4 6 11 16 20
2-13(1976) 1 2 3 6 9 10
15-17(1986): 15-Reprints #1 (Low print run) 6.00
3,10,11(Modern Comics-r, 1977) 6.00

YANKEE COMICS
Harry 'A' Chesler: Sept, 1941 - No. 7, 1942?
1-Origin The Echo, The Enchanted Dagger, Yankee Doodle Jones, The Firebrand, & The Scarlet Sentry; Black Satan app.; Yankee Doodle Jones app. on all covers
232 464 696 1485 2543 3600
2-Origin Johnny Rebel; Major Victory app.; Barry Kuda begins
103 206 309 659 1130 1600
3,4: 4-(3/42) 84 168 252 538 919 1300
4 (nd, 1940s; 7-1/4x5", 68 pgs, distr. to the service)-Foxy Grandpa, Tom, Dick & Harry, Impy,

Yeah! #3 © Peter Bagge & DC

Yellowjacket Comics #1 © E. Levy

Yogi Bear Giant Size V2 #1 © H-B

	GD 2.0	VG 4.0	FN 6.0	VF 8.0	VF/NM 9.0	NM- 9.2
Ace & Deuce, Dot & Dash, Ima Slooth by Jack Cole (Remington Morse publ.)	19	38	57	111	176	240
5-7 (nd; 10¢, 7-1/4x5", 68 pgs.)(Remington Morse publ.)-urges readers to send their copies to servicemen.	15	30	45	90	140	190

YANKEE DOODLE THE SPIRIT OF LIBERTY
Spire Publications: 1984 (no price, 36 pgs)

	GD	VG	FN	VF	VF/NM	NM-
nn-Al Hartley-s/c/a	2	4	6	9	13	16

YANKS IN BATTLE
Quality Comics Group: Sept, 1956 - No. 4, Dec, 1956

	GD	VG	FN	VF	VF/NM	NM-
1-Cuidera-c(i)	14	28	42	80	115	150
2-4: Cuidera-c(i)	9	18	27	50	65	80

YARDBIRDS, THE (G. I. Joe's Sidekicks)
Ziff-Davis Publishing Co.: Summer, 1952

	GD	VG	FN	VF	VF/NM	NM-
1-By Bob Oskner	17	34	51	117	259	400

YARNS OF YELLOWSTONE
World Color Press: 1972 (50¢, 36 pgs.)

	GD	VG	FN	VF	VF/NM	NM-
nn-Illustrated by Bill Chapman	2	4	6	9	12	15

YEAH!
DC Comics (Homage): Oct, 1999 - No. 9, Jun, 2000 ($2.95)

	GD	VG	FN	VF	VF/NM	NM-
1-Bagge-s/Hernandez-a						3.00
2-9: 2-Editorial page contains adult language						3.00

YEAR OF MARVELS, A
Marvel Comics: ($4.99)

	GD	VG	FN	VF	VF/NM	NM-
...: The Amazing (6/16) Spider-Man vs. The Vulture; Ant-Man						5.00
...: The Incredible (8/16) Spider-Man & D-Man story; Wolverine (X-23) & She-Hulk story						5.00
...: The Unbeatable (12/16) Nick Fury story; Rocket Raccoon & Tippy-Toe story						5.00
...: The Uncanny (2/17) Hawkeye (Kate Bishop) story; Punisher story						5.00
...: The Unstoppable (10/16) Nova & Iron Man story; Winter Soldier story						5.00

YEARS OF FUTURE PAST (Secret Wars Battleworld tie-in)
Marvel Comics: Aug, 2015 - No. 5, Nov, 2015 ($4.99/$3.99, limited series)

	GD	VG	FN	VF	VF/NM	NM-
1-($4.99) Bennett-s/Norton-a; Art Adams-c; Kitty Pryde, Wolverine, Colossus app.						5.00
2-5-($3.99) Storm, Magneto, Mystique, Blob, Sentinels app.						4.00

YELLOW CLAW (Also see Giant Size Master of Kung Fu)
Atlas Comics (MjMC): Oct, 1956 - No. 4, Apr, 1957

	GD	VG	FN	VF	VF/NM	NM-
1-Origin by Joe Maneely	155	310	465	992	1696	2400
2-Kirby-a	123	246	369	787	1344	1900
3-Kirby-a	110	220	330	704	1202	1700
4-Kirby/Severin-a	116	232	348	742	1271	1800

NOTE: ***Everett** c-3. **Maneely** c-1. **Reinman** a-2i, 3. **Severin** c-2, 4.*

YELLOWJACKET COMICS (Jack in the Box #11 on)(See TNT Comics)
E. Levy/Frank Comunale/Charlton: Sept, 1944 - No. 5. Jan, 1945; No. 6, Dec, 1945 - No. 10, June, 1946

	GD	VG	FN	VF	VF/NM	NM-
1-Intro & origin Yellowjacket; Diana, the Huntress begins; "Famous Tales of Terror" begins with E.A. Poe's "The Black Cat" adaptation	71	142	213	454	777	1100
2-Yellowjacket-c begin, end #10; no "Famous Tales of Terror"	48	96	144	302	514	725
3,5: 3-"Famous Tales of Terror" with Poe's "The Pit and the Pendulum" adaptation. 5-No "Famous Tales of Terror"	47	94	141	296	498	700
4-"Famous Tales of Terror" with Poe's "Fall of the House Of Usher" adaptation; Palais-a	48	96	144	302	514	725
6-Last "Famous Tales of Terror", with Poe's "The Tell Tale Heart" adaptation	43	86	129	271	461	650
7-Classic Skull-c; "Tales of Terror" begins by Alan Mandel-narrated by the Ancient Witch, wearing a red cloak, stirring her bubbling cauldron at beginning and end of story just like E.C.'s Old Witch 5 years later; tells story "The Avenging Hand!" similar to "The Maestro's Hand!" in Crypt of Terror #18. (1st horror series?) Toth-a (1 pg. gag feature)	65	130	195	416	708	1000
8-"Tales of Terror" narrated by the Old Witch; classic splash & end panel with skull & bones; early "return from the grave story"	40	80	120	246	411	575
9,10-"Tales of Terror" in each, narrated by the Old Witch in a red cloak, w/classic splash and end panels	40	80	120	246	411	575

NOTE: *The Old Witch in #7-10 above may have inspired creation of E.C.'s Old Witch. Her costume, dialogue, use of bubbling cauldron, skull and bones and even the title "Tales of Terror" were possibly used.*

YELLOWSTONE KELLY (Movie)
Dell Publishing Co.: No. 1056, Nov-Jan, 1959/60

	GD	VG	FN	VF	VF/NM	NM-
Four Color 1056-Clint Walker photo-c	5	10	15	35	63	90

YELLOW SUBMARINE (See Movie Comics)

YEAR ONE: BATMAN/RA'S AL GHUL
DC Comics: 2005 - No. 2, 2005 ($5.99, squarebound, limited series)

	GD	VG	FN	VF	VF/NM	NM-
1-Devin Grayson-s/Paul Gulacy-a						6.00
TPB (2006, $9.99) r/#1,2						10.00

YEAR ONE: BATMAN SCARECROW
DC Comics: 2005 - No. 2, 2005 ($5.99, squarebound, limited series)

	GD	VG	FN	VF	VF/NM	NM-
1-Scarecrow's origin; Bruce Jones-s/Sean Murphy-a						6.00

YOGA HOSERS: A SUNDANCE SUPER SPECIAL
Dynamite Entertainment: 2016 ($10.00, one-shot)

	GD	VG	FN	VF	VF/NM	NM-
1-Prologue to the Kevin Smith movie; Smith-s/Jeff Quigley-a						10.00
1-Third printing (2017, $3.99)						4.00

YOGI BEAR (See Dell Giant #41, Golden Comics Digest, Kite Fun Book, March of Comics #253, 265, 279, 291, 309, 319, 337, 344, Movie Comics under "Hey There It's..." & Whitman Comic Books)

YOGI BEAR (TV) (Hanna-Barbera) (See Four Color #990)
Dell Publishing Co./Gold Key No. 10 on: No. 1067, 12-2/59-60 - No. 9, 7-9/62; No. 10, 10/62 - No. 42, 10/70

	GD	VG	FN	VF	VF/NM	NM-
Four Color 1067 (#1)-TV show debuted 1/30/61	12	24	36	82	179	275
Four Color 1104,1162 (5-7/61)	8	16	24	54	102	150
4(8-9/61) - 6(12-1/61-62)	5	10	15	33	57	80
Four Color 1271(11/61)	6	12	18	40	73	105
Four Color 1349(1/62)-Photo-c	8	16	24	54	102	150
7(2-3/62) - 9(7-9/62)-Last Dell	5	10	15	33	57	80
10(10/62-G.K.), 11(1/63)-titled "Yogi Bear Jellystone Jollies" (80 pgs.); 11-X-Mas-c	6	12	18	41	76	110
12(4/63), 14-20	4	8	12	28	47	65
13(7/63, 68 pgs.)-Surprise Party	6	12	18	40	73	105
21-30	3	6	9	19	30	40
31-42	3	6	9	16	24	32

YOGI BEAR (TV)
Charlton Comics: Nov, 1970 - No. 35, Jan, 1976 (Hanna-Barbera)

	GD	VG	FN	VF	VF/NM	NM-
1	5	10	15	31	53	75
2-6,8-10	3	6	9	16	24	32
7-Summer Fun (Giant, 52 pgs.)	4	8	12	27	44	60
11-20	3	6	9	15	22	28
21-35: 28-31-partial-r	2	4	6	11	16	20
Digest (nn, 1972, 75¢-c, B&W, 100 pgs.) (scarce)	3	6	9	18	28	38

YOGI BEAR (TV)(See The Flintstones, 3rd series & Spotlight #1)
Marvel Comics Group: Nov, 1977 - No. 9, Mar, 1979 (Hanna-Barbera)

	GD	VG	FN	VF	VF/NM	NM-
1,7-9: 1-Flintstones begin (Newsstand sales only)	3	6	9	16	23	30
2-6	2	4	6	11	16	20

YOGI BEAR (TV)
Harvey Comics: Sept, 1992 - No. 6, Mar, 1994 ($1.25/$1.50) (Hanna-Barbera)

	GD	VG	FN	VF	VF/NM	NM-
V2#1-6						3.00
...Big Book V2#1,2 ($1.95, 52 pgs): 1-(11/92). 2-(3/93)						4.00
...Giant Size V2#1,2 ($2.25, 68 pgs.): 1-(10/92). 2-(4/93)						4.00

YOGI BEAR (TV)
Archie Publ.: May, 1997

	GD	VG	FN	VF	VF/NM	NM-
1						3.00

YOGI BEAR'S EASTER PARADE (See The Funtastic World of Hanna-Barbera #2)

YOGI BERRA (Baseball hero)
Fawcett Publications: 1951 (Yankee catcher)

	GD	VG	FN	VF	VF/NM	NM-
nn-Photo-c (scarce)	77	154	231	493	847	1200

YOSEMITE SAM (...& Bugs Bunny) (TV)
Gold Key/Whitman: Dec, 1970 - No. 81, Feb, 1984

	GD	VG	FN	VF	VF/NM	NM-
1	5	10	15	31	53	75
2-10	3	6	9	16	23	30
11-20	2	4	6	11	16	20
21-30	2	4	6	9	13	16
31-50	2	4	6	8	10	12
51-65 (Gold Key)	1	2	3	5	7	9
66,67 (Whitman)	2	4	6	8	10	12
68(9/80), 69(10/80), 70(12/80) 3-pack only	5	10	15	30	50	70
71-78: 76(2/82), 77(3/82), 78(4/82)	2	4	6	9	13	16
79-81 (All #90263 on-c, no date or date code; 3-pack): 79(7/83). 80(8/83). 81(2/84)-(1/3-r)	3	6	9	16	24	32

(See March of Comics #363, 380, 392)

YOSSEL
DC Comics: 2003/2011 ($14.99, B&W graphic novel)

Young Allies Comics #13 © MAR

Young Avengers (2013 series) #13 © MAR

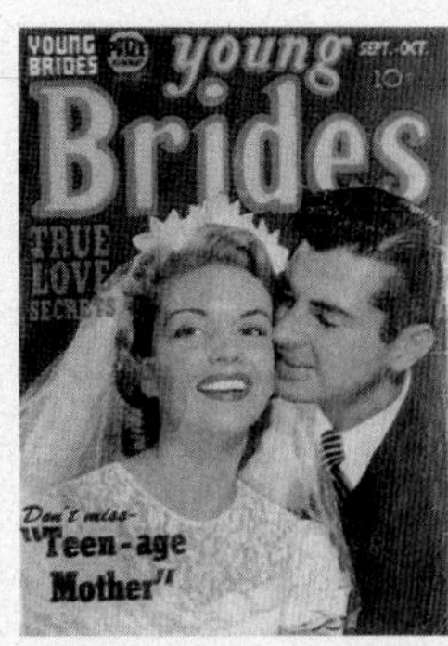

Young Brides #1 © Prize

GD VG FN VF VF/NM NM-
2.0 4.0 6.0 8.0 9.0 9.2

SC-Joe Kubert-s/a/c; Nazi-occupied Poland during World War II 15.00

YOUNG ALLIES
Marvel Comics: Aug, 2010 - No. 6, Jan, 2011 ($3.99/$2.99)

1-($3.99) Wraparound-c; Nomad, Araña, Firestar, Gravity, Toro team-up; origin pages 5.00
2-6-($2.99) 2-Lafuente-c/McKeever-s/Baldeon-a. 6-Miyazawa-c; Emma Frost app. 4.00

YOUNG ALLIES COMICS (All-Winners #21; see Kid Komics #2)
Timely Comics (USA 1-7/NPI 8,9/YAI 10-20): Sum, 1941 - No. 20, Oct, 1946

1-Origin/1st app. The Young Allies (Bucky, Toro, others); 1st meeting of Captain America & Human Torch; Red Skull-c & app.; S&K-c/splash; Hitler-c; Note: the cover was altered after its preview in Human Torch #5. Stalin was shown with Hitler but was removed due to Russia becoming an ally 1350 2700 4050 9450 16,875 27,000
2-(Winter, 1941)-Captain America & Human Torch app.; Simon & Kirby-c 432 864 1296 3154 5577 8000
3-Remember Pearl Harbor issue (Spring, 1942); Stan Lee scripts; Vs. Japanese-c/full-length story; Captain America & Human Torch app.; Father Time story by Alderman 400 800 1200 2800 4900 7000
4-The Vagabond & Red Skull, Capt. America, Human Torch app. Classic Red Skull-c 514 1028 1542 3750 6625 9500
5-Captain America & Human Torch app. 258 516 774 1651 2826 4000
6,7: 6-Japanese/Nazi war-c 194 388 582 1242 2121 3000
8-Classic Schomburg WWII Japanese bondage-c 213 426 639 1363 2332 3300
9-Hitler, Tojo, Mussolini-c. 300 600 900 2070 3635 5200
10-Classic Schomburg Hooded Villain bondage-c; origin Tommy Tyme & Clock of Ages; ends #19 181 362 543 1158 1979 2800
11-16: 12-Classic decapitation story; Japanese war-c. 16-Last Schomburg WWII-c 155 310 465 992 1696 2400
17-20 119 238 357 762 1306 1850

NOTE: ***Brodsky** c-15. **Ferstadt** a-3. **Gabriele** a-3; c-3, 4. **S&K** c-1, 2. **Schomburg** c-5-13, 16-19. **Shores** c-20.*

YOUNG ALLIES 70TH ANNIVERSARY SPECIAL
Marvel Comics: Aug, 2009 ($3.99, one-shot)

1-Bucky & Young Allies app.; Stern-s/Rivera-a; Terry Vance rep. from Marvel Myst. #14 5.00

YOUNG ALL-STARS
DC Comics: June, 1987 - No. 31, Nov, 1989 ($1.00, deluxe format)

1-31: 1-1st app. Iron Munro & The Flying Fox. 8,9-Millennium tie-ins 4.00
Annual 1 (1988, $2.00) 4.00

YOUNG AVENGERS
Marvel Comics: Apr, 2005 - No. 12, Aug, 2006 ($2.99)

1-Intro. Iron Lad, Patriot, Hulkling, Asgardian; Heinberg-s/Cheung-a 5.00
1-Director's Cut (2005, $3.99) r/#1 plus character sketches; original script 4.00
2-12: 3-6-Kang app. 7-DiVito-a. 9-Skrulls app. 3.00
... Special 1 (2/06, $3.99) origins of the heroes; art by various incl. Neal Adams, Jae Lee, Bill Sienkiewicz, Gene Ha, Michael Gaydos and Pasqual Ferry 4.00
... Vol. 1: Sidekicks HC (2005, $19.99, dustjacket) r/#1-6; character design sketches 20.00
... Vol. 1: Sidekicks TPB (2006, $14.99) r/#1-6; character design sketches 15.00
... Vol. 2: Family Matters HC (2006, $22.99, dustjacket) r/#7-12 & YA Special #1 23.00
... Vol. 2: Family Matters SC (2007, $17.99) r/#7-12 & YA Special #1 18.00
HC (2008, $29.99, d.j.) oversized reprint of #1-12 and Special #1; script & sketch pages 30.00

YOUNG AVENGERS (Marvel NOW!)
Marvel Comics: Mar, 2013 - No. 15, Mar, 2014 ($2.99)

1-15: 1-Loki assembles team; Marvel Boy, Miss America app.; Gillen-s/McKelvie-a/c. 11-Loki ages back to adult. 14,15-Multiple artists 3.00
1-Variant-c by Bryan Lee O'Malley 6.00
1-Variant-c by Skottie Young 6.00

YOUNG AVENGERS PRESENTS
Marvel Comics: Mar, 2008 - No. 6, Aug, 2008 ($2.99, limited series)

1-6: 1-Patriot; Bucky app. 2-Hulkling; Captain Marvel app. 3-Wiccan & Speed. 4-Vision. 5-Stature. 6-Hawkeye; Clint Barton app.; Alan Davis-a 3.00

YOUNGBLOOD (See Brigade #4, Megaton Explosion & Team Youngblood)
Image Comics (Extreme Studios): Apr, 1992 - No. 4, Feb, 1993 ($2.50, lim. series); No. 5-(Flip book w/Brigade #4); No. 6, June, 1994 - No. 10, Dec, 1994 ($1.95/$2.50)

1-Liefeld-c/a/scripts in all; flip book format with 2 trading cards; 1st Image/Extreme Studios title. 5.00
1,2-2nd printing 3.00
2-(JUN-c, July 1992 indicia)-1st app. Shadowhawk in solo back-up story; 2 trading cards inside; flip book format; 1st app. Prophet, Kirby, Berzerkers, Darkthorn 4.00
3,0,4,5: 3-(OCT-c, August 1992 indicia)-Contains 2 trading cards inside (flip book); 1st app. Supreme in back-up story; 1st app. Showdown. 0-(12/92, $1.95)-Contains 2 trading cards; 2 cover variations exist, green or beige logo; w/Image #0 coupon. 4-(2/93)-Glow-in-the-dark cover w/2 trading cards; 2nd app. Dale Keown's The Pitt; Bloodstrike app. 5-Flip book w/Brigade #4 3.00
6-($3.50, 52 pgs.)-Wraparound-c 4.00
7-10: 7, 8-Liefeld-c(p)/a(p)/story. 8,9-(9/94) 9-Valentino story & art 3.00
Battlezone 1 (May-c, 4/93 inside, $1.95)-Arsenal book; Liefeld-c(p) 3.00
Battlezone 2 (7/94, $2.95)-Wraparound-c 4.00
Image Firsts: Youngblood #1 (3/10, $1.00) reprints #1 3.00
...Super Special (Winter '97, $2.99) Sprouse -a 4.00
Yearbook 1 (7/93, $2.50)-Fold out panel; 1st app. Tyrax & Kanan 4.00
Vol. 1 HC (2008, $34.99) oversized r/#1-5, recolored and remastered; sketch art and cover gallery; Mark Millar intro. 35.00
TPB (1996, $16.95)-r/Team Youngblood #8-10 & Youngblood #6-8,10 17.00

YOUNGBLOOD
Image Comics (Extreme Studios)/Maximum Press No. 14: V2#1, Sept, 1995 - No. 14, Dec, 1996 ($2.50)

V2#1-10,14: Roger Cruz-a in all. 4-Extreme Destroyer Pt. 4 w/gaming card. 5-Variant-c exists. 6-Angela & Glory. 7-Shadowhunt Pt. 3; Shadowhawk app. 8,10-Thor (from Supreme) app. 10-(7/96). 14-(12/96)-1st Maximum Press issue 3.00

YOUNGBLOOD (Volume 3)
Awesome/ Awesome-Hyperwerks #2: Feb, 1998 - No. 2, Aug, 1998 ($2.50)

1-Alan Moore-s/Skroce & Stucker-a; 12 diff. covers 3.00
2-(8/98) Skroce & Liefeld covers 3.00
...Imperial 1 (Arcade Comics, 6/04, $2.99) Kirkman-sMychaels-a 3.00

YOUNGBLOOD (Volume 4)
Image Comics: Jan, 2008 - No. 9, Sept, 2009; No. 71, May, 2012 - No. 78, Jul, 2013 ($2.99/$3.99)

1-7-Casey-s/Donovan-a; two covers by Donovan & Liefeld on each 3.00
8-Obama flip cover by Liefeld; Obama app. in story 3.00
9-(9/09, $3.99) Obama flip cover by Liefeld; Free Agent rejoins; Obama app. in story 4.00
71-74: 71-(5/12, $2.99) Liefeld & Malin-a; three covers 3.00
75-(1/13, $4.99) Five covers; Malin-a 5.00
76-78-($3.99) Malin-a 4.00

YOUNGBLOOD (Volume 5)
Image Comics: May, 2017 - Present ($3.99)

1-9-Bowers-s/Towe-a; multiple covers on each. 1-Back-up story w/Liefeld-s/a. 4,5-Bloodstrike flip book; Liefeld-s/a 4.00

YOUNGBLOOD: STRIKEFILE
Image Comics (Extreme Studios): Apr, 1993 - No. 11, Feb, 1995 ($1.95/$2.50/$2.95)

1-10: 1-($1.95)-Flip book w/Jae Lee-c/a & Liefeld-c/a in #1-3; 1st app. The Allies,Giger, & Glory. 3-Thibert-i asisst. 4-Liefeld-c(p); no Lee-a. 5-Liefeld-c(p). 8-Platt-c 3.00

NOTE: *Youngblood: Strikefile began as a four issue limited series.*

YOUNGBLOOD/X-FORCE
Image Comics (Extreme Studios): July, 1996 ($4.95, one-shot)

1-Cruz-a(p); two covers exist 5.00

YOUNG BRIDES (True Love Secrets)
Feature/Prize Publ.: Sept-Oct, 1952 - No. 30, Nov-Dec, 1956 (Photo-c: V1 #1-6, V2 #1,2)

V1#1-Simon & Kirby-a 47 94 141 296 498 700
2-S&K-a 27 54 81 158 259 360
3-6-S&K-a 23 46 69 136 223 310
V2#1-7,10-12 (#7-18)-S&K-a 21 42 63 122 199 275
8,9-No S&K-a 12 24 36 69 97 125
V3#1-3(#19-21)-Last precode (3-4/55) 11 22 33 64 90 115
4,6(#22,24), V4#1,3(#25,27) 11 22 33 60 83 105
V3#5(#23)-Meskin-c 11 22 33 62 86 110
V4#2(#26)-All S&K issue 20 40 60 117 189 260
V4#4(#28)-S&K-a 17 34 51 98 154 210
V4#5,6(#29,30) 11 22 33 64 90 115

YOUNG DR. MASTERS (See The Adventures of Young Dr. Masters)

YOUNG DOCTORS, THE
Charlton Comics: Jan, 1963 - No. 6, Nov, 1963

V1#1 3 6 9 20 31 42
2-6 3 6 9 14 19 24

YOUNG EAGLE
Fawcett Publications/Charlton: 12/50 - No. 10, 6/52; No. 3, 7/56 - No. 5, 4/57 (Photo-c: 1-10)

1-Intro Young Eagle 18 36 54 103 162 220
2-Complete picture novelette "The Mystery of Thunder Canyon" 10 20 30 58 79 100
3-9 9 18 27 50 65 80
10-Origin Thunder, Young Eagle's Horse 8 16 24 44 57 70

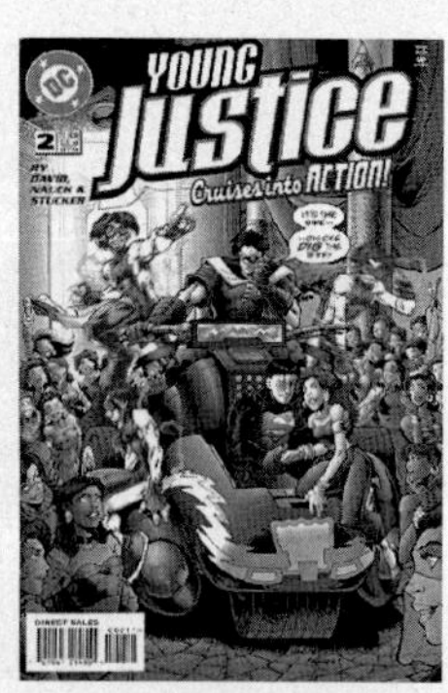

Young Justice #2 © DC

Young Liars #8 © David Lapham

Young Men #18 © MAR

	GD 2.0	VG 4.0	FN 6.0	VF 8.0	VF/NM 9.0	NM- 9.2
3-5(Charlton)-Formerly Sherlock Holmes?	7	14	21	35	43	50

YOUNG GUNS SKETCHBOOK
Marvel Comics: Feb, 2005 ($3.99, one-shot)

	GD 2.0	VG 4.0	FN 6.0	VF 8.0	VF/NM 9.0	NM- 9.2
1-Sketch pages from 2005 Marvel projects by Coipel, Granov, McNiven, Land & others						4.00

YOUNG HEARTS
Marvel Comics (SPC): Nov, 1949 - No. 2, Feb, 1950

	GD 2.0	VG 4.0	FN 6.0	VF 8.0	VF/NM 9.0	NM- 9.2
1-Photo-c	21	42	63	122	199	275
2-Colleen Townsend photo-c from movie	15	30	45	84	127	170

YOUNG HEARTS IN LOVE
Super Comics: 1964

	GD 2.0	VG 4.0	FN 6.0	VF 8.0	VF/NM 9.0	NM- 9.2
17,18: 17-r/Young Love V5#6 (4-5/62)	2	4	6	9	13	16

YOUNG HEROES (Formerly Forbidden Worlds #34)
American Comics Group (Titan): No. 35, Feb-Mar, 1955 - No. 37, Jun-Jul, 1955

	GD 2.0	VG 4.0	FN 6.0	VF 8.0	VF/NM 9.0	NM- 9.2
35-37-Frontier Scout	10	20	30	54	72	90

YOUNG HEROES IN LOVE
DC Comics: June, 1997 - No. 17; #1,000,000, Nov, 1998 ($1.75/$1.95/$2.50)

	GD 2.0	VG 4.0	FN 6.0	VF 8.0	VF/NM 9.0	NM- 9.2
1-1st app. Young Heroes; Madan-a						4.00
2-17: 3-Superman-c/app. 7-Begin $1.95-c						3.00
#1,000,000 (11/98, $2.50) 853 Century x-over						3.00

YOUNG INDIANA JONES CHRONICLES, THE
Dark Horse Comics: Feb, 1992 - No. 12, Feb, 1993 ($2.50)

	GD 2.0	VG 4.0	FN 6.0	VF 8.0	VF/NM 9.0	NM- 9.2
1-12: Dan Barry scripts in all						3.00

NOTE: ***Dan Barry*** *a(p)-1, 2, 5, 6, 10; c-1-10.* ***Morrow*** *a-3, 4, 5p, 6p.* ***Springer*** *a-1i, 2i.*

YOUNG INDIANA JONES CHRONICLES, THE
Hollywood Comics (Disney): 1992 ($3.95, squarebound, 68 pgs.)

	GD 2.0	VG 4.0	FN 6.0	VF 8.0	VF/NM 9.0	NM- 9.2
1-3: 1-r/YIJC #1,2 by D. Horse. 2-r/#3,4. 3-r/#5,6						4.00

YOUNG JUSTICE (Also see Teen Titans, Titans/Young Justice and DC Comics Presents: ...)
DC Comics: Sept, 1998 - No. 55, May, 2003 ($2.50/$2.75)

	GD 2.0	VG 4.0	FN 6.0	VF 8.0	VF/NM 9.0	NM- 9.2
1-Robin, Superboy & Impulse team-up; David-s/Nauck-a						4.00
2,3: 3-Mxyzptlk app.						3.00
4-20: 4-Wonder Girl, Arrowette and the Secret join. 6-JLA app. 13-Supergirl x-over. 20-Sins of Youth aftermath						3.00
21-49: 25-Empress ID revealed. 28,29-Forever People app. 32-Empress origin. 35,36-Our Worlds at War x-over. 38-Joker: Last Laugh. 41-The Ray joins. 42-Spectre-c/app. 44,45-World Without YJ x-over pt. 1,5; Ramos-c. 48-Begin $2.75-c						3.00
50-($3.95) Wonder Twins, CM3 and other various DC teen heroes app.						4.00
51-55: 53,54-Darkseid app. 55-Last issue; leads into Titans/Young Justice mini-series						3.00
#1,000,000 (11/98) 853 Century x-over						3.00
...: A League of Their Own (2000, $14.95, TPB) r/#1-7, Secret Files #1						15.00
...: 80-Page Giant (5/99, $4.95) Ramos-c; stories and art by various						5.00
...: In No Man's Land (7/99, $3.95) McDaniel-c						4.00
...: Our Worlds at War (8/01, $2.95) Jae Lee-c; Linear Men app.						3.00
...: Secret Files (1/99, $4.95) Origin-s & pin-ups						5.00
...: The Secret (6/98, $1.95) Girlfrenzy; Nauck-a						3.00

YOUNG JUSTICE (Based on the 2011 Cartoon Network series)
DC Comics: No. 0, Mar, 2011 - No. 25, Apr, 2013 ($2.99)

	GD 2.0	VG 4.0	FN 6.0	VF 8.0	VF/NM 9.0	NM- 9.2
0-19: 1-Miss Martian joins; Joker app. 2-Joker-c/app. 5-Kid Flash & Aqualad origins						3.00
20-25: 20-(11/12) Starts Invasion; 5 years later						3.00
FCBD 2011 Young Justice Batman BB Super Sampler (7/11) Flash app.						3.00

YOUNG JUSTICE: SINS OF YOUTH (Also see Sins of Youth x-over issues and Sins of Youth: Secret Files)
DC Comics: May, 2000 - No. 2, May, 2000 ($3.95, limited series)

	GD 2.0	VG 4.0	FN 6.0	VF 8.0	VF/NM 9.0	NM- 9.2
1,2-Young Justice, JLA & JSA swap ages; David-s/Nauck-a						4.00
TPB (2000, $19.95) r/#1,2 & all x-over issues)						20.00

YOUNG KING COLE (...Detective Tales)(Becomes Criminals on the Run)
Premium Group/Novelty Press: Fall, 1945 - V3#12, July, 1948

	GD 2.0	VG 4.0	FN 6.0	VF 8.0	VF/NM 9.0	NM- 9.2
V1#1-Toni Gayle begins	39	78	117	231	378	525
2	18	36	54	107	169	230
3-4	17	34	51	98	154	210
V2#1-7(8-9/46-7/47): 6,7-Certa-c	14	28	42	78	112	145
V3#1,3-6,8,9,12: 3-Certa-c. 5-McWilliams-c/a. 8,9-Harmon-c	14	28	42	76	108	140
2-L.B. Cole-a; Certa-c	18	36	54	107	169	230
7-L.B. Cole-c/a	23	46	69	136	223	310
10,11-L.B. Cole-c	27	54	81	158	259	360

YOUNG LAWYERS, THE (TV)
Dell Publishing Co.: Jan, 1971 - No. 2, Apr, 1971 (photo-c)

	GD 2.0	VG 4.0	FN 6.0	VF 8.0	VF/NM 9.0	NM- 9.2
1	3	6	9	16	23	30
2	2	4	6	11	16	20

YOUNG LIARS (David Lapham's...)(See Vertigo Double Shot for reprint of #1)
DC Comics (Vertigo): May, 2008 - No. 18, Oct, 2009 ($2.99)

	GD 2.0	VG 4.0	FN 6.0	VF 8.0	VF/NM 9.0	NM- 9.2
1-18: 1-Intro. Sadie Dawkins; David Lapham-s/a/c in all						3.00
...: Daydream Believer TPB (2008, $9.99) r/#1-6; Gerald Way intro.						10.00
...: Maestro TPB (2009, $14.99) r/#7-12; Peter Milligan intro.						15.00
...: Rock Life TPB (2010, $14.99) r/#13-18; Brian Azzarello intro.						15.00

YOUNG LIFE (Teen Life #3 on)
New Age Publ./Quality Comics Group: Summer, 1945 - No. 2, Fall, 1945

	GD 2.0	VG 4.0	FN 6.0	VF 8.0	VF/NM 9.0	NM- 9.2
1-Skip Homeier, Louis Prima stories	20	40	60	114	182	250
2-Frank Sinatra photo on-c plus story	21	42	63	126	206	285

YOUNG LOVE (Sister title to Young Romance)
Prize(Feature)Publ.(Crestwood): 2-3/49 - No. 73, 12-1/56-57; V3#5, 2-3/60 - V7#1, 6-7/63

	GD 2.0	VG 4.0	FN 6.0	VF 8.0	VF/NM 9.0	NM- 9.2
V1#1-S&K-c/a(2)	71	142	213	454	777	1100
2-Photo-c begin; S&K-a	37	74	111	222	361	500
3-S&K-a	24	48	72	140	230	320
4-6-Minor S&K-a	17	34	51	100	158	215
V2#1(#7)-S&K-a(2)	23	46	69	136	223	310
2-5(#8-11)-Minor S&K-a	15	30	45	85	130	175
6,8(#12,14)-S&K-c only. 14-S&K 1 pg. art	18	36	54	105	165	225
7,9-12(#13,15-18)-S&K-c/a	23	46	69	136	223	310
V3#1-4(#19-22)-S&K-c/a	21	42	63	122	199	275
5-7,9-12(#23-25,27-30)-Photo-c resume; S&K-a	17	34	51	100	158	215
8(#26)-No S&K-a	11	22	33	62	86	110
V4#1,6(#31,36)-S&K-a	15	30	45	90	140	190
2-5,7-12(#32-35,37-42)-Minor S&K-a	14	28	42	80	115	150
V5#1-12(#43-54), V6#3,7,9(#57,61,63)-Last precode	10	20	30	58	79	100
V6#1,2,4-6,8(#55,56,58-60,62) S&K-a	12	24	36	67	94	120
V6#10-12(#64-66)	5	10	15	34	60	85
V7#1-7(#67-73)	5	10	15	31	53	75
V3#5(2-3/60),6(4-5/60)(Formerly All For Love)	4	8	12	28	47	65
V4#1(6-7/60)-6(4-5/61)	4	8	12	27	44	60
V5#1(6-7/61)-6(4-5/62)	4	8	12	27	44	60
V6#1(6-7/62)-6(4-5/63), V7#1	4	8	12	25	40	55

NOTE: ***Meskin*** *a-14(2), 27, 42.* ***Powell*** *a-V4#6.* ***Severin/Elder*** *a-V1#3. S&K art not in #53, 57, 61, 63-65. Photo-c most V1 #1-6, V2 #3, V3#5-V5#11.*

YOUNG LOVE
National Periodical Publ.(Arleigh Publ. Corp #49-61)/DC Comics:
#39, 9-10/63 - #120, Wint./75-76; #121, 10/76 - #126, 7/77

	GD 2.0	VG 4.0	FN 6.0	VF 8.0	VF/NM 9.0	NM- 9.2
39	6	12	18	37	66	95
40-50	4	8	12	28	47	65
51-68,70	4	8	12	25	40	55
69-(68 pg. Giant)(8-9/68)	6	12	18	38	69	100
71,72,75-77,80	3	6	9	20	31	42
73,74,78,79-Toth-a	3	6	9	21	33	45
81-99: 88-96-(52 pg. Giants)	3	6	9	19	30	40
100	3	6	9	20	31	42
101-106,115-120	3	6	9	16	24	32
107 (100 pgs.)	7	14	21	49	92	135
108-114 (100 pgs.)	7	14	21	44	82	120
121-126 (52 pgs.)	4	8	12	26	41	55

NOTE: ***Bolle*** *a-117.* ***Colan*** *a-107r.* ***Nasser*** *a-123, 124.* ***Orlando*** *a-122.* ***Simonson*** *c-125.* ***Toth*** *a-73, 78, 79, 122-125r.* ***Wood*** *a-109r(4 pgs.).*

YOUNG LOVER ROMANCES (Formerly & becomes Great Lover...)
Toby Press: No. 4, June, 1952 - No. 5, Aug, 1952

	GD 2.0	VG 4.0	FN 6.0	VF 8.0	VF/NM 9.0	NM- 9.2
4,5-Photo-c	13	26	39	74	105	135

YOUNG LOVERS (My Secret Life #19 on)(Formerly Brenda Starr?)
Charlton Comics: No. 16, July, 1956 - No. 18, May, 1957

	GD 2.0	VG 4.0	FN 6.0	VF 8.0	VF/NM 9.0	NM- 9.2
16,17('56): 16-Marcus Swayze-a	14	28	42	76	108	140
18-Elvis Presley picture-c, text story (biography)(Scarce)	94	188	282	597	1024	1450

YOUNG MARRIAGE
Fawcett Publications: June, 1950

	GD 2.0	VG 4.0	FN 6.0	VF 8.0	VF/NM 9.0	NM- 9.2
1-Powell-a; photo-c	15	30	45	85	130	175

YOUNG MEN (Formerly Cowboy Romances)(...on the Battlefield #12-20(4/53); ...In Action #21)
Marvel/Atlas Comics (IPC): No. 4, 6/50 - No. 11, 10/51; No. 12, 12/51 - No. 28, 6/54

	GD 2.0	VG 4.0	FN 6.0	VF 8.0	VF/NM 9.0	NM- 9.2
4-(52 pgs.)	28	56	84	165	270	375
5-11	18	36	54	103	162	220
12-23: 12-20-War format. 21-23-Hot Rod issues starring Flash Foster						

Young Romance #7 © Prize

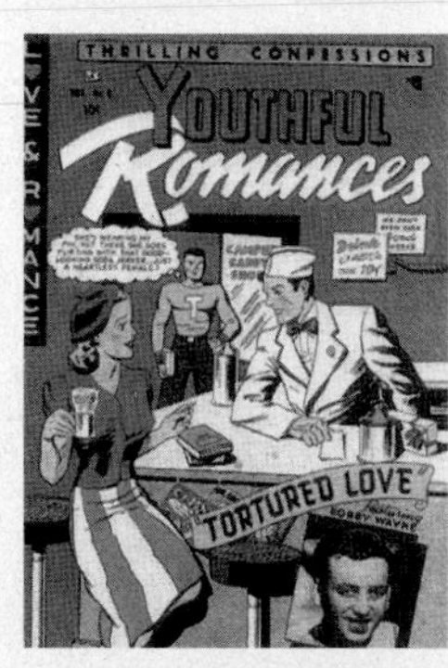

Youthful Romances #6 © Ribage

Y: The Last Man #57 © Vaughan & Guerra

	GD 2.0	VG 4.0	FN 6.0	VF 8.0	VF/NM 9.0	NM- 9.2
	19	38	57	109	172	235
24-(12/53)-Origin Captain America, Human Torch, & Sub-Mariner which are revived thru #28; Red Skull app.	383	766	1149	2681	4691	6700
25-28: 25-Romita-c/a (see Men's Advs.). 27-Death of Golden Age Red Skull	168	336	504	1075	1838	2600
25-2nd printing (1994)	2	4	6	8	10	12

NOTE: *Berg a-7, 14, 17, 18, 20; c-17? **Brodsky** c-4-9, 13, 14, 16, 17, 21-25. **Burgos** c-26-28. **Colan** a-14, 15, 20. **Everett** a-18-20. **Heath** a-13, 14. **Maneely** c-10-12, 15. **Pakula** a-14, 15. **Robinson** c-18. Captain America by **Romita**-#24?, 25, 26?, 27, 28. Human Torch by **Burgos**-#25, 27, 28. Sub-Mariner by **Everett**-#24-28.*

YOUNG MONSTERS IN LOVE
DC Comics: Apr, 2018 ($9.99, 80 pages, one-shot)

1-Horror short stories by various; Swamp Thing, Raven, Deadman app.; Kelley Jones-c 10.00

YOUNG REBELS, THE (TV)
Dell Publishing Co.: Jan, 1971

	GD	VG	FN	VF	VF/NM	NM-
1-Photo-c	3	6	9	14	19	24

YOUNG ROMANCE COMICS (The 1st romance comic)
Prize/Headline (Feature Publ.) (Crestwood): Sept-Oct, 1947 - V16#4, June-July, 1963 (#1-33: 52 pgs.)

	GD	VG	FN	VF	VF/NM	NM-
V1#1-S&K-c/a(2)	84	168	252	538	919	1300
2-S&K-c/a(2-3)	41	82	123	256	428	600
3-6-S&K-c/a(2-3) each	37	74	111	222	361	500
V2#1-6(#7-12)-S&K-c/a(2-3) each	32	64	96	192	314	435
V3#1-3(#13-15): V3#1-Photo-c begin; S&K-a	21	42	63	122	199	275
4-12(#16-24)-Photo-c; S&K-a	21	42	63	122	199	275
V4#1-11(#25-35)-S&K-a	20	40	60	117	189	260
12(#36)-S&K, Toth-a	21	42	63	122	199	275
V5#1-12(#37-48), V6#4-12(#52-60)-S&K-a	20	40	60	117	189	260
V6#1-3(#49-51)-No S&K-a	11	22	33	64	90	115
V7#1-11(#61-71)-S&K-a in most	15	30	45	90	140	190
V7#12(#72), V8#1-3(#73-75)-Last precode (12-1/54-55)-No S&K-a	10	20	30	58	79	100
V8#4(#76, 4-5/55), 5(#77)-No S&K-a	10	20	30	54	72	90
V8#6-8(#78-80, 12-1/55-56)-S&K-a	14	28	42	80	115	150
V9#3,5,6(#81, 2-3/56, 83,84)-S&K-a	14	28	42	80	115	150
4, V10#1(#82,85)-All S&K-a	15	30	45	83	124	165
V10#2-6(#86-90, 10-11/57)-S&K-a	8	16	24	54	102	150
V11#1,2,5,6(#91,92,95,96)-S&K-a	8	16	24	54	102	150
3,4(#93,94), V12#2,4,5(#98,100,101)-No S&K	5	10	15	31	57	80
V12#1,3,6(#97,99,102)-S&K-a	8	16	24	54	102	150
V13#1(#103)-Powell-a; S&K's last-a for Crestwood	8	16	24	54	102	150
2,4-6(#104-108)	5	10	15	30	50	70
V13#3(#105, 4-5/60)-Elvis Presley-c app. only	8	16	24	55	105	155
V14#1-6, V15#1-6, V16#1-4(#109-124)	4	8	12	28	47	65

NOTE: ***Meskin** a-16, 24(2), 33, 47, 50. **Robinson/Meskin** a-6. **Leonard Starr** a-11. Photo c-13-32, 34-65. Issues 1-3 say "Designed for the More **Adult** Readers of **Comics**" on cover.*

YOUNG ROMANCE COMICS (Continued from Prize series)
National Periodical Publ.(Arleigh Publ. Corp. No. 127): No. 125, Aug-Sept, 1963 - No. 208, Nov-Dec, 1975

	GD	VG	FN	VF	VF/NM	NM-
125	7	14	21	46	86	125
126-140	5	10	15	30	50	70
141-153,156-162,165-169	4	8	12	23	37	50
154-Neal Adams-c	5	10	15	31	53	75
155-1st publ. Aragonés-s (no art)	5	10	15	30	50	70
163,164-Toth-a	4	8	12	27	44	60
170-172 (68 pg. Giants): 170-Michell from Young Love ends; Lily Martin, the Swinger begins	5	10	15	30	50	70
173-183 (52 pgs.)	4	8	12	23	37	50
184-196	3	6	9	17	26	35
197-204-(100 pgs.)	7	14	21	44	82	120
205-208	3	6	9	16	24	32

YOUNG ROMANCE: THE NEW 52 VALENTINE'S DAY SPECIAL
DC Comics: Apr, 2013 ($7.99, one-shot)

1-Short stories by various; Superman/Wonder Woman-c by Rocafort; bonus valentines 8.00

YOUNG X-MEN
Marvel Comics: May, 2008 - No. 12, May, 2009 ($2.99)

1-12: 1-Cyclops forms new team; Guggenheim-s/Paquette-a/Dodson-c. 11,12-Acuña-a 3.00

YOUR DREAMS (See Strange World of...)

YOUR HIGHNESS
Dark Horse Comics: 2011 ($7.99, one-shot)

nn-Prequel to 2011 movie; Danny McBride & Jeff Fradley-s/Phillips-a/c 8.00

YOUR PAL ARCHIE
Archie Comic Publications: Sept, 2017 - Present ($3.99)

1-5-New stories with classic-style Archie gang, plus back-up reprints in #1-4 4.00

YOUR UNITED STATES
Lloyd Jacquet Studios: 1946

	GD	VG	FN	VF	VF/NM	NM-
nn-Used in **SOTI**, pg. 309,310; Sid Greene-a	27	54	81	158	259	360

YOUTHFUL HEARTS (Daring Confessions #4 on)
Youthful Magazines: May, 1952 - No. 3, Sept, 1952

	GD	VG	FN	VF	VF/NM	NM-
1- "Monkey on Her Back" swipes E.C. drug story/Shock SuspenStories #12; Frankie Laine photo on-c; Doug Wildey-a in al	40	80	120	246	411	575
2,3: 2-Vic Damone photo on-c. 3-Johnny Raye photo on-c	24	48	72	140	230	320

YOUTHFUL LOVE (Truthful Love #2)
Youthful Magazines: May, 1950

	GD	VG	FN	VF	VF/NM	NM-
1	27	54	81	158	259	360

YOUTHFUL ROMANCES
Pix-Parade #1-14/Ribage #15 on: 8-9/49 - No. 5, 4/50; No. 6, 2/51; No. 7, 5/51 - #14, 10/52; #15, 1/53 - #18, 7/53; No. 5, 9/53 - No. 9, 8/54

	GD	VG	FN	VF	VF/NM	NM-
1-(1st series)-Titled Youthful Love-Romances	36	72	108	211	343	475
2-Walter Johnson c-1-4	21	42	63	124	202	280
3-5	18	36	54	107	169	230
6,7,9-14(10/52, Pix-Parade; becomes Daring Love #15). 10(1/52)-Mel Torme photo-c/story. 12-Tony Bennett photo-c, 8pg. story & text bio.13-Richard Hayes (singer) photo-c/story; Bob & Ray photo/text story.	17	34	51	98	154	210
8-Frank Sinatra photo/text story; Wood-c/a	25	50	75	150	245	340
15-18 (Ribage)-All have photos on-c. 15-Spike Jones photo-c/story. 16-Tony Bavaar photo-c	16	32	48	94	147	200
5(9/53, Ribage)-Les Paul & Mary Ford photo-c/story; Charlton Heston photo/text story	15	30	45	90	140	190
6-9: 6-Bobby Wayne (singer) photo-c/story; Debbie Reynolds photo/text story. 7(2/54)-Tony Martin photo-c/story; Cyd Charise photo/text story. 8(5/54)-Gordon McCrae photo-c/story. (8/54)-Ralph Flanagan (band leader) photo-c/story; Audrey Hepburn photo/text story	15	30	45	86	133	180

YTHAQ: NO ESCAPE
Marvel Comics (Soleil): 2009 - No. 3, 2009 ($5.99, limited series)

1-3-English language version of French comic; Arleston-s/Floch-a 6.00

YTHAQ: THE FORSAKEN WORLD
Marvel Comics (Soleil): 2008 - No. 3, 2009 ($5.99, limited series)

1-3-English language version of French comic; Arleston-s/Floch-a 6.00

Y: THE LAST MAN
DC Comics (Vertigo): Sept, 2002 - No. 60, Mar, 2008 ($2.95/$2.99)

	GD	VG	FN	VF	VF/NM	NM-
1-Intro. Yorick Brown; Brian K. Vaughan-s/Pia Guerra-a/J.G. Jones-c	9	18	27	57	111	165
2	3	6	9	16	24	32
3-5	1	2	3	5	6	8
6-10						5.00
11-59: 16,17-Chadwick-a. 21,22-Parlov-a. 32,39-41,48,53,54-Sudzuka-a.						3.00
60-($4.99) Final issue; sixty years in the future						6.00
... Double Feature Edition (2002, $5.95) r/#1,2	1	2	3	5	6	8
... Special Edition (2009, $1.00) r/#1, "After Watchmen" trade dress on cover						3.00
... - Cycles TPB (2003, $12.95) r/#6-10; sketch pages by Guerra						13.00
... - Girl on Girl TPB (2005, $12.99) r/#32-36						13.00
... - Kimono Dragons TPB (2006, $14.99) r/#43-48						15.00
... - Motherland TPB (2007, $14.99) r/#49-54						15.00
... - One Small Step TPB (2004, $12.95) r/#11-17						13.00
... - Paper Dolls TPB (2006, $14.99) r/#37-42						15.00
... - Ring of Truth TPB (2005, $14.99) r/#24-31						15.00
... - Safeword TPB (2004, $12.95) r/#18-23						13.00
... - Unmanned TPB (2002, $12.95) r/#1-5						15.00
... - Whys and Wherefores TPB (2008, $14.99) r/#55-60						15.00
... - The Deluxe Edition Book One HC (2008, $29.99, dustjacket) oversized r/#1-10; Guerra sketch pages						30.00
... - The Deluxe Edition Book Two HC (2009, $29.99, dustjacket) oversized r/#11-23; full script to #18						30.00
... - The Deluxe Edition Book Three HC (2010, $29.99, dustjacket) oversized r/#24-36; full script to #36						30.00
... - The Deluxe Edition Book Four HC (2010, $29.99, dustjacket) oversized r/#37-48; full script to #42						30.00

... - The Deluxe Edition Book Five HC (2011, $29.99, dustjacket) oversized r/#49-60; full

Zatanna (2010 series) #15 © DC

Zegra #3 © FOX

Zero Hour #3 © DC

	GD 2.0	VG 4.0	FN 6.0	VF 8.0	VF/NM 9.0	NM- 9.2
script to #60						30.00

Y2K: THE COMIC
New England Comics Press: Oct, 1999 ($3.95, one-shot)

	GD 2.0	VG 4.0	FN 6.0	VF 8.0	VF/NM 9.0	NM- 9.2
1-Y2K scenarios and survival tips						4.00

YUPPIES FROM HELL (Also see Son of...)
Marvel Comics: 1989 ($2.95, B&W, one-shot, direct sales, 52 pgs.)

	GD 2.0	VG 4.0	FN 6.0	VF 8.0	VF/NM 9.0	NM- 9.2
1-Satire						4.00

ZAGO (..., Jungle Prince) (My Story #5 on)
Fox Feature Syndicate: Sept, 1948 - No. 4, Mar, 1949

	GD 2.0	VG 4.0	FN 6.0	VF 8.0	VF/NM 9.0	NM- 9.2
1-Blue Beetle app.; partial-r/Atomic #4 (Toni Luck)	76	152	228	486	831	1175
2,3-Kamen-a	60	120	180	381	653	925
4-Baker-c	53	106	159	334	567	800

ZANE GREY'S STORIES OF THE WEST
Dell Publishing Co./Gold Key 11/64: No. 197, 9/48 - No. 996, 5-7/59; 11/64 (All painted-c)

	GD 2.0	VG 4.0	FN 6.0	VF 8.0	VF/NM 9.0	NM- 9.2
Four Color 197(#1)(9/48)	11	22	33	73	157	240
Four Color 222,230,236('49)	7	14	21	46	86	125
Four Color 246,255,270,301,314,333,346	5	10	15	35	63	90
Four Color 357,372,395,412,433,449,467,484	5	10	15	33	57	80
Four Color 511-Kinstler-a; Kubert-a	5	10	15	35	63	90
Four Color 532,555,583,604,616,632(5/55)	5	10	15	33	57	80
27(9-11/55) - 39(9-11/58)	4	8	12	28	47	65
Four Color 996(5-7/59)	5	10	15	33	57	80
10131-411-(11/64-G.K.)-Nevada; r/4-Color #996	3	6	9	21	33	45

ZANY (Magazine)(Satire)(See Frantic & Ratfink)
Candor Publ. Co.: Sept, 1958 - No. 4, May, 1959

	GD 2.0	VG 4.0	FN 6.0	VF 8.0	VF/NM 9.0	NM- 9.2
1-Bill Everett-c	15	30	45	88	137	185
2-4: 4-Everett-c	11	22	33	62	86	110

ZATANNA (See Adv. Comics #413, JLA #161, Supergirl #1, World's Finest Comics #274)
DC Comics: July, 1993 - No. 4, Oct, 1993 ($1.95, limited series)

	GD 2.0	VG 4.0	FN 6.0	VF 8.0	VF/NM 9.0	NM- 9.2
1-4						6.00
...: Everyday Magic (2003, $5.95, one-shot) Dini-s/Mays-a/Bolland-c; Constantine app.	3	6	9	19	30	40
Special 1(1987, $2.00)-Gray Morrow-c/a	1	3	4	6	8	10

ZATANNA
DC Comics: Jul, 2010 - No. 16, Oct, 2011 ($2.99)

	GD 2.0	VG 4.0	FN 6.0	VF 8.0	VF/NM 9.0	NM- 9.2
1-Dini-s/Roux-a/c	1	3	4	6	8	10
1-Variant-c by Bolland	3	6	9	15	22	28
2-6-Variant-c by Bolland	2	4	6	10	14	18
2-10,12: 4,5,7-Hardin-a. 7-Beechen-s. 8-Chang-a						6.00
11,13,14-Hughes-c	2	4	6	10	14	18
15-Hughes-c	4	8	12	23	37	50
16-Hughes-c	4	8	12	25	40	55
...: The Mistress of Magic TPB (2011, $17.99) r/#1-6; variant cover gallery						18.00

ZAZA, THE MYSTIC (Formerly Charlie Chan; This Magazine Is Haunted V2#12 on)
Charlton Comics: No. 10, Apr, 1956 - No. 11, Sept, 1956

	GD 2.0	VG 4.0	FN 6.0	VF 8.0	VF/NM 9.0	NM- 9.2
10,11	14	28	42	80	115	150

ZEALOT (Also see WildC.A.T.S: Covert Action Teams)
Image Comics: Aug, 1995 - No. 3, Nov, 1995 ($2.50, limited series)

	GD 2.0	VG 4.0	FN 6.0	VF 8.0	VF/NM 9.0	NM- 9.2
1-3						3.00

ZEGRA (Jungle Empress) (Formerly Tegra)(My Love Life #6 on)
Fox Feature Syndicate: No. 2, Oct, 1948 - No. 5, April, 1949

	GD 2.0	VG 4.0	FN 6.0	VF 8.0	VF/NM 9.0	NM- 9.2
2	74	148	222	470	810	1150
3-5	54	108	162	346	591	835

ZEN INTERGALACTIC NINJA
No Publisher: 1987 -1993 ($1.75/$2.00, B&W)

	GD 2.0	VG 4.0	FN 6.0	VF 8.0	VF/NM 9.0	NM- 9.2
1	2	4	6	10	14	18
2-6: Copyright-Stern & Cote	1	3	4	6	8	10
V2#1-4-($2.00)						3.00
V3#1-5-($2.95)						3.00
... :Christmas Special 1 (1992, $2.95)						3.00
... :Earth Day Special 1 (1993, $2.95)						3.00

ZEN (Intergalactic Ninja)
Zen Comics Publishing: No. 0, Apr, 2003 - No. 4, Aug, 2003 ($2.95)

	GD 2.0	VG 4.0	FN 6.0	VF 8.0	VF/NM 9.0	NM- 9.2
0-4-Bill Maus-a/Steve Stern-s. 0-Wraparound-c						3.00

ZEN, INTERGALACTIC NINJA (mini-series)
Zen Comics/Archie Comics: Sept, 1992 - No. 3, 1992 ($1.25)(Formerly a B&W comic by Zen Comics)

	GD 2.0	VG 4.0	FN 6.0	VF 8.0	VF/NM 9.0	NM- 9.2
1-3: 1-Origin Zen; contains mini-poster						3.00

ZEN INTERGALACTIC NINJA
Entity Comics: No. 0, June-July, 1993 - No. 3, 1994 ($2.95, B&W, limited series)

	GD 2.0	VG 4.0	FN 6.0	VF 8.0	VF/NM 9.0	NM- 9.2
0-Gold foil stamped-c; photo-c of Zen model						3.00
1-3: Gold foil stamped-c; Bill Maus-c/a						3.00
0-(1993, $3.50, color)-Chromium-c by Jae Lee						4.00
...Sourcebook 1-(1993, $3.50)						4.00
...Sourcebook '94-(1994, $3.50)						4.00

ZEN INTERGALACTIC NINJA: APRIL FOOL'S SPECIAL
Parody Press: 1994 ($2.50, B&W)

	GD 2.0	VG 4.0	FN 6.0	VF 8.0	VF/NM 9.0	NM- 9.2
1-w/flip story of Renn Intergalactic Chihuahua						3.00

ZEN INTERGALACTIC NINJA COLOR
Entity Comics: 1994 - No. 7, 1995 ($2.25)

	GD 2.0	VG 4.0	FN 6.0	VF 8.0	VF/NM 9.0	NM- 9.2
1-($3.95)-Chromium die cut-c						4.00
1, 0-($2.25)-Newsstand; Jae Lee-c; r/...All New Color Special #0						3.00
2-($2.50)-Flip book						3.00
2-($3.50)-Flip book, polybagged w/chromium trading card						4.00
3-7						3.00
Summer Special (1994, $2.95)						3.00
Yearbook: Hazardous Duty 1 (1995)						3.00
Zen-isms 1 (1995, 2.95)						3.00
Ashcan-Tour of the Universe-(no price) w/flip cover						3.00

ZEN INTERGALACTIC NINJA COMMEMORATIVE EDITION
Zen Comics Publishing: 1997 ($5.95, color)

	GD 2.0	VG 4.0	FN 6.0	VF 8.0	VF/NM 9.0	NM- 9.2
1-Stern-s/Cote-a						6.00

ZEN INTERGALACTIC NINJA: HARD BOUNTY
1First Comics: 2015 - No. 6 ($3.99, limited series)

	GD 2.0	VG 4.0	FN 6.0	VF 8.0	VF/NM 9.0	NM- 9.2
1-Stern-s/Mychaels-a						4.00

ZEN INTERGALACTIC NINJA MILESTONE
Entity Comics: 1994 - No. 3, 1994 ($2.95, limited series)

	GD 2.0	VG 4.0	FN 6.0	VF 8.0	VF/NM 9.0	NM- 9.2
1-3: Gold foil logo; r/Defend the Earth						3.00

ZEN INTERGALATIC NINJA SPRING SPECTACULAR
Entity Comics: 1994 ($2.95, B&W, one-shot)

	GD 2.0	VG 4.0	FN 6.0	VF 8.0	VF/NM 9.0	NM- 9.2
1-Gold foil logo						3.00

ZEN INTERGALACTIC NINJA STARQUEST
Entity Comics: 1994 - No. 6, 1995 ($2.95, B&W)

	GD 2.0	VG 4.0	FN 6.0	VF 8.0	VF/NM 9.0	NM- 9.2
1-6: Gold foil logo						3.00

ZEN, INTERGALACTIC NINJA: THE HUNTED
Entity Comics: 1993 - No. 3, 1994 ($2.95, B&W, limited series)

	GD 2.0	VG 4.0	FN 6.0	VF 8.0	VF/NM 9.0	NM- 9.2
1-3: Newsstand Edition; foil logo						3.00
1-($3.50)-Polybagged w/chromium card by Kieth; foil logo						4.00

ZERO GIRL
DC Comics (Homage): Feb, 2001 - No. 5, Jun, 2001 ($2.95, limited series)

	GD 2.0	VG 4.0	FN 6.0	VF 8.0	VF/NM 9.0	NM- 9.2
1-5-Sam Kieth-s/a						3.00
TPB (2001, $14.95) r/#1-5; intro. by Alan Moore						15.00

ZERO GIRL: FULL CIRCLE
DC Comics (Homage): Jan, 2003 - No. 5, May, 2003 ($2.95, limited series)

	GD 2.0	VG 4.0	FN 6.0	VF 8.0	VF/NM 9.0	NM- 9.2
1-5-Sam Kieth-s/a						3.00
TPB (2003, $17.95) r/#1-5						18.00

ZERO HOUR: CRISIS IN TIME (Also see Showcase '94 #8-10)
DC Comics: No. 4(#1), Sept, 1994 - No. 0(#5), Oct, 1994 ($1.50, limited series)

	GD 2.0	VG 4.0	FN 6.0	VF 8.0	VF/NM 9.0	NM- 9.2
4(#1)-0(#5)						4.00
"Ashcan"-(1994, free, B&W, 8 pgs.) several versions exist						3.00
TPB ('94, $9.95)						10.00

ZERO KILLER
Dark Horse Comics: Jul, 2007 - No.6, Oct, 2009 ($2.99)

	GD 2.0	VG 4.0	FN 6.0	VF 8.0	VF/NM 9.0	NM- 9.2
1-6-Arvid Nelson-s/Matt Camp-a						3.00

ZERO PATROL, THE
Continuity Comics: Nov, 1984 - No. 2 ($1.50); 1987 - No. 5, May, 1989 ($2.00)

	GD 2.0	VG 4.0	FN 6.0	VF 8.0	VF/NM 9.0	NM- 9.2
1,2: Neal Adams-c/a; Megalith begins						4.00
1-5 (#1,2-reprints above, 1987)						3.00

ZERO TOLERANCE
First Comics: Oct, 1990 - No. 4, Jan, 1991 ($2.25, limited series)

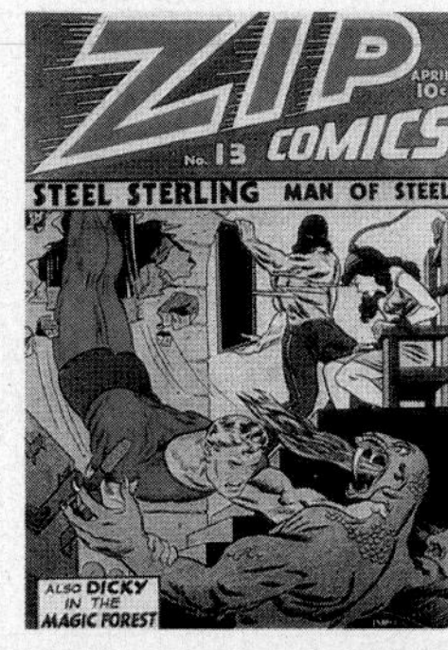

Zip Comics #13 © MLJ

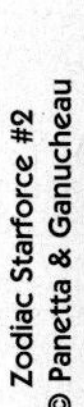
Zodiac Starforce #2 © Panetta & Ganucheau

Zombies Assemble #1 © MAR

GD 2.0 | VG 4.0 | FN 6.0 | VF 8.0 | VF/NM 9.0 | NM- 9.2

1-4: Tim Vigil-c/a(p) (his 1st color limited series) 3.00

'ERO ZERO
antagraphics: Mar, 1995 - No. 27 ($3.95/$4.95, B&W, anthology, mature)
1-7,9-15,17-25 5.00
8,16,26,27: 26-($4.95) Bagge-c 6.00

'IGGY PIG-SILLY SEAL COMICS (See Animal Fun, Animated Movie-Tunes, Comic Capers, .razy Komics, Silly Tunes & Super Rabbit)
'imely Comics (CmPL): Fall, 1944 - No. 4, Summer, 1945; No. 5, Summer, 1946; No. 6, ;ept, 1946
1-Vs. the Japanese 39 79 117 240 395 550
2-(Spring, 1945) 25 50 75 150 245 340
3-5 20 40 60 117 189 260
6-Infinity-c 21 42 63 126 206 285
.W. Reprint #1(1958)-r/Krazy Komics 2 4 6 10 14 18
.W. Reprint #2,7,8 2 4 6 10 14 18

'IP COMICS
/ILJ Magazines: Feb, 1940 - No. 47, Summer, 1944 (#1-7?: 68 pgs.)
1-Origin Kalathar the Giant Man, The Scarlet Avenger, & Steel Sterling; Mr. Satan (by Edd Ashe), Nevada Jones (masked hero) & Zambini, the Miracle Man, War Eagle, Captain Valor begins 459 918 1377 3350 5925 8500
2-Nevada Jones adds mask & horse Blaze 271 542 813 1734 2967 4200
3-Biro robot-c 297 594 891 1901 3251 4600
4,5-Biro WWII-c 194 388 582 1242 2121 3000
6-8-Biro-c 187 374 561 1197 2049 2900
9-Last Kalathar & Mr. Satan; classic-c 258 516 774 1651 2826 4000
10-Inferno, the Flame Breather begins, ends #13 206 412 618 1318 2259 3200
11-Inferno without costume 155 310 465 992 1696 2400
12-Biro bondage/torture-c with dwarf ghouls 187 374 561 1197 2049 2900
13-Electrocution-c 206 412 618 1318 2259 3200
14-Biro bondage/torture guillotine-c 174 348 522 1114 1907 2700
15-Classic spider-c 206 412 618 1318 2259 3200
16-Female hanging execution-c by Biro (Rare) 206 412 618 1318 2259 3200
17-Last Scarlet Avenger; women in bondage being cooked alive-c by Biro 226 452 678 1446 2473 3500
18-Wilbur begins (9/41, 1st app.); sci-fi-c 226 452 678 1446 2473 3500
19 168 336 504 1075 1838 2600
20-Origin & 1st app. Black Jack (11/41); Hitler-c 300 600 900 1920 3310 4700
21-Sinister Nazi using lethal chemical weapons on the General-c 181 362 543 1158 1979 2800
22-Classic Nazi Grim Reaper w/sickle, V for Victory-c 432 864 1296 3154 5577 8000
23-Nazi WWII-c 142 284 426 909 1555 2200
24,25: 25-Last Nevada Jones 129 258 387 826 1413 2000
26-Classic Nazi/Japanese "Remember Pearl Harbor!" WWII cover; Black Witch begins; last Captain Valor (scarce) 271 542 813 1734 2967 4200
27-Intro. Web (7/42) plus-c app.; Japanese WWII-c 284 568 852 1818 3109 4400
28-Origin Web; classic Baron Gastapo Nazi WWII-c 252 504 756 1613 2757 3900
29-The Hyena app. (scarce); Nazi WWII-c 206 412 618 1318 2259 3200
30-WWII-c 168 336 584 1075 1838 2600
31,35-WWII-c. 35-Last Zambini, Black Jack 142 284 426 909 1555 2200
32-Classic skeleton Nazi WWII-c 258 516 774 1651 2826 4000
33-Japanese war-c showing nurses bound, blindfolded, lined up at a firing squad 161 322 483 1030 1765 2500
34-Japanese WWII bondage & hanging-c; 1st Applejack app. 226 452 678 1446 2473 3500
36-38: 38-Last Web issue 65 130 195 416 708 1000
39-Red Rube begins (origin, 8/43) 66 132 198 419 722 1025
40-43 55 110 165 352 601 850
44-46: WWII covers. 45-Wilbur ends 65 130 195 416 708 1000
47-Last issue; scarce 68 136 204 435 743 1050
*IOTE: **Biro** a-5, 9, 17; c-3-17. **Meskin** a-1-3, 5-7, 9, 10, 12, 13, 15, 16 at least. **Montana** c-29, 30, 32-35. Iovick c-18-28, 31. **Sahle** c-37, 38, 40-46. Bondage c-8, 9, 33, 34. Cover features: Steel Sterling-1-43, 47; v/Blackjack-20-27 & Web-27-35), 28-39; (w/Red Rube-40-43); Red Rube-44-47.*

IP-JET (Hero)
it. John Publishing Co.: Feb, 1953 - No. 2, Apr-May, 1953
1-Rocketman-r from Punch Comics; #1-c from splash in Punch #10 103 206 309 659 1130 1600
2 57 114 171 362 619 875

IPPY THE CHIMP (CBS TV Presents...)
ines (Literary Ent.): No. 50, March, 1957; No. 51, Aug, 1957
50,51 8 16 24 40 50 60

Z NATION (Based on the 2014 TV series on Syfy)
Dynamite Entertainment: 2017 - No. 6, 2017 ($3.99)
1-6: 1-Engler & Van Lente-s/Menna-a; multiple covers 4.00

ZODIAC STARFORCE
Dark Horse Comics: Aug, 2015 - No. 4, Feb, 2016 ($3.99, limited series)
1-4-Kevin Panetta-s/Paulina Ganucheau-a. 2-Wada-c. 4-Babs Tarr-c 4.00

ZODIAC STARFORCE: CRIES OF THE FIRE PRINCE
Dark Horse Comics: Jul, 2017 - Present ($3.99, limited series)
1-3-Kevin Panetta-s/Paulina Ganucheau-a 4.00

ZODY, THE MOD ROB
Gold Key: July, 1970
1 3 6 9 16 23 30

ZOMBIE
Marvel Comics: Nov, 2006 - No. 4, Feb, 2007 ($3.99, limited series)
1-4-Kyle Hotz-a/c; Mike Raicht-s 4.00
TPB (2007, $13.99) r/#1-4 14.00
...: Simon Garth (1/08 - No. 4, 4/08) Hotz-s/a/c 4.00

ZOMBIE BOY
Timbuktu Graphics/Antarctic Press: Mar, 1988 - Nov, 1996 ($1.50/$2.50/$2.95, B&W)
1-Mark Stokes-s/a 3.00
...'s Hoodoo Tales (11/89, $1.50) 3.00
... Rises Again (1/94, $2.50) r/#1 and Hoodoo Tales 3.00
1-(Antarctic Press, 11/96, $2.95) new story 3.00

ZOMBIE KING
Image Comics: No. 0, June, 2005 ($2.95, B&W, one-shot)
0-Frank Cho-s/a 5.00

ZOMBIE PROOF
Moonstone: 2007 - Present ($3.50)
1-3: 1-J.C. Vaughn-s/Vincent Spencer-a; two covers by Spencer and Neil Vokes 4.00
1-Baltimore Comic-Con 2007 variant-c by Vokes (ltd. ed. of 500) 6.00
2-Big Apple 2008 Convention Edition; Tucci-c (ltd. ed. of 250) 6.00
3-Convention Edition; Beck-c (ltd. ed. of 100) 6.00
...: Zombie Zoo #1 Virginia Comicon Exclusive Edition (2012, ed. of 150) 10.00
...: Zombie Zoo - WVPOP Exclusive Edition (2012) 10.00

ZOMBIES ASSEMBLE
Marvel Comics: Jul, 2017 - No. 3, Aug, 2017 ($4.99, B&W, manga style back to front)
1-3-English translation of Avengers Japanese manga; Komiyama-s/a 5.00
#0-(9/17) Follows Tony Stark after Avengers: Age of Ultron; Komiyama-s/a 5.00

ZOMBIES ASSEMBLE 2
Marvel Comics: Oct, 2017 - No. 4, Jan, 2018 ($4.99, B&W, manga style back to front)
1-4-Continuation of story from Zombies Assemble #1-3; Komiyama-s/a 5.00

ZOMBIES CHRISTMAS CAROL (See Marvel Zombies Christmas Carol)

ZOMBIES!: ECLIPSE OF THE UNDEAD
IDW Publ.: Nov, 2006 - No. 4, Feb, 2007 ($3.99, limited series)
1-4-Torres-s/Herrera-a; two covers 4.00

ZOMBIES!: FEAST
IDW Publ.: May, 2006 - No. 5, Oct, 2006 ($3.99, limited series)
1-5: 1-Chris Bolton-a/Shane McCarthy-s. 3-Lorenzana-a 4.00

ZOMBIES!: HUNTERS
IDW Publ.: May, 2008 ($3.99)
1-Don Figueroa-a/c; Dara Naraghi-s 4.00

ZOMBIES VS. ROBOTS
IDW Publ.: Oct, 2006 - No. 2, Dec, 2006 ($3.99, limited series)
1-Chris Ryall-s/Ashley Wood-a; two covers by Wood 15.00
2 10.00

ZOMBIES VS. ROBOTS
IDW Publ.: Jan, 2015 - No. 10, Oct, 2015 ($3.99/$4.99)
1-8-Short stories by Chris Ryall-s/Ashley Wood-a and others 4.00
9,10-($4.99) Two covers on each 5.00

ZOMBIES VS. ROBOTS AVENTURE
IDW Publ.: Feb, 2010 - No. 4, May, 2010 ($3.99, limited series)
1-4-Short stories; Ryall-s; art by Matthews III, McCaffrey, & Hernandez; Wood-c 4.00

ZOMBIES VS. ROBOTS: UNDERCITY

Zoo Funnies #4 © CC

Zoot #13 © FOX

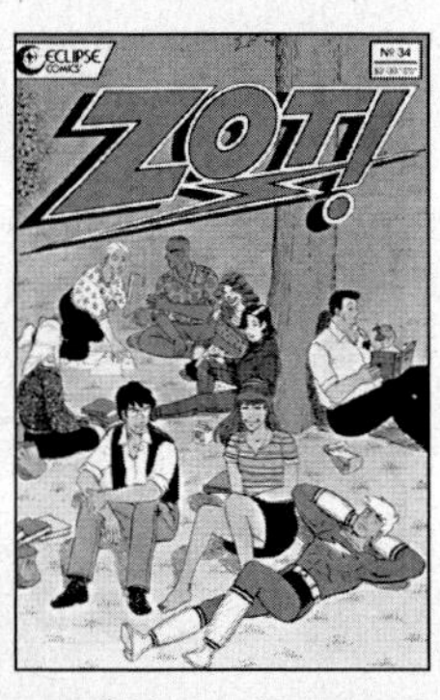

Zot #34 © Scott McCloud

GD 2.0 | VG 4.0 | FN 6.0 | VF 8.0 | VF/NM 9.0 | NM- 9.2

IDW Publ.: Apr, 2011 - No. 3, Jun, 2011 ($3.99, limited series)
1-3-Chris Ryall-s/Mark Torres; two covers on each by Torres and Garry Brown 4.00

ZOMBIES VS. ROBOTS VS. AMAZONS
IDW Publ.: Sept, 2007 - No. 3, Feb, 2008 ($3.99, limited series)
1-3-Chris Ryall-s/Ashley Wood-a; two covers by Wood on each 5.00

ZOMBIE TALES THE SERIES
BOOM! Studios: Apr, 2008 - No. 12, Mar, 2009 ($3.99)
1-Niles-s; Lansdale-s/Barreto-a; two covers on each 4.00

ZOMBIE WAR
IDW Publishing: Oct, 2013 - No. 2, Nov, 2013 ($3.99, limited series)
1,2-Kevin Eastman & Tom Skulan-s/Eastman & Eric Talbot-a; 2 covers on each 4.00

ZOMBIE WORLD (one-shots)
Dark Horse Comics
... :Eat Your Heart Out (4/98, $2.95) Kelley Jones-c/s/a 3.00
... :Home For The Holidays (12/97, $2.95) 3.00

ZOMBIE WORLD: CHAMPION OF THE WORMS
Dark Horse Comics: Sept, 1997 - No. 3, Nov, 1997 ($2.95, limited series)
1-3-Mignola & McEown-c/s/a 3.00

ZOMBIE WORLD: DEAD END
Dark Horse Comics: Jan, 1998 - No. 2, Feb, 1998 ($2.95, limited series)
1,2-Stephen Blue-c/s/a 3.00

ZOMBIE WORLD: TREE OF DEATH
Dark Horse Comics: Jun, 1999 - No. 4, Oct, 1999 ($2.95, limited series)
1-4-Mills-s/Deadstock-a 3.00

ZOMBIE WORLD: WINTER'S DREGS
Dark Horse Comics: May, 1998 - No. 4, Aug, 1998 ($2.95, limited series)
1-4-Fingerman-s/Edwards-a 3.00

ZOO ANIMALS
Star Publications: No. 8, 1954 (15¢, 36 pgs.)
8-(B&W for coloring) 8 16 24 44 57 70

ZOO FUNNIES (Tim McCoy #16 on)
Charlton Comics/Children Comics Publ.: Nov, 1945 - No. 15, 1947
101(#1)(11/45, 1st Charlton comic book)-Funny animal; Al Fago-c 22 44 66 132 216 300
2(12/45, 52 pgs.) Classic-c 15 30 45 84 127 170
3-5 11 22 33 64 90 115
6-15: 8-Diana the Huntress app. 10 20 30 54 72 90

ZOO FUNNIES (Becomes Nyoka, The Jungle Girl #14 on?)
Capitol Stories/Charlton Comics: July, 1953 - No. 13, Sept, 1955; Dec, 1984
1-1st app.? Timothy The Ghost; Fago-c/a 12 24 36 69 97 125
2 8 16 24 42 54 65
3-7 7 14 21 37 46 55
8-13-Nyoka app. 9 18 27 52 69 85
1(1984) (Low print run) 1 2 3 4 5 7

ZOOHUNTERS, THE
Aspen MLT: Nov, 2014 - Present ($3.99)
1-3-Peter Stiegerwald-s/a; five covers on each 4.00

ZOONIVERSE
Eclipse Comics: 8/86 - No. 6, 6/87 ($1.25/$1.75, limited series, Mando paper)
1-6 3.00

ZOO PARADE (TV)
Dell Publishing Co.: #662, 1955 (Marlin Perkins)
Four Color 662 5 10 15 33 57 80

ZOOM COMICS
Carlton Publishing Co.: Dec, 1945 (one-shot)
nn-Dr. Mercy, Satannas, from Red Band Comics; Capt. Milksop origin retold 43 86 129 271 461 650

ZOOT (Rulah Jungle Goddess #17 on)
Fox Feature Syndicate: nd (1946) - No. 16, July, 1948 (Two #13s & 14s)
nn-Funny animal only 28 56 84 165 270 375
2-The Jaguar app. 22 44 66 128 209 290
3(Fall, 1946) - 6-Funny animals & teen-age 15 30 45 85 130 175
7-(6/47)-Rulah, Jungle Goddess (origin/1st app.) 132 264 396 838 1444 2050
8-10 79 158 237 502 864 1225
11-Kamen bondage-c 95 190 285 603 1039 1475
12-Injury-to-eye panels, torture scene 66 132 198 419 722 1025
13(2/48) 61 122 183 390 670 950
14(3/48)-Used in **SOTI**, pg. 104, "One picture showing a girl nailed by her wrists to trees with blood flowing from the wounds, might be taken straight from an ill. ed. of the Marquis deSade" 87 174 261 553 952 1350
13(4/48),14(5/48)-Western True Crime #15 on? 60 120 180 381 653 925
15,16 60 120 180 381 653 925

ZORRO (Walt Disney with #882)(TV)(See Eclipse Graphic Album)
Dell Publishing Co.: May, 1949 - No. 15, Sept-Nov, 1961 (Photo-c 882 on)
(Zorro first appeared in a pulp story Aug 19, 1919)
Four Color 228 (#1) 20 40 60 138 307 475
Four Color 425,617,732 11 22 33 72 154 235
Four Color 497,538,574-Kinstler-a 11 22 33 76 163 250
Four Color 882-Photo-c begin;1st TV Disney; Toth-a 13 26 39 89 195 300
Four Color 920,933,960,976-Toth-a in all 10 20 30 66 138 210
Four Color 1003('59)-Toth-a 10 20 30 66 138 210
Four Color 1037-Annette Funicello photo-c 12 24 36 81 176 270
8(12-2/59-60) 7 14 21 48 89 130
9-Toth-a 8 16 24 51 96 140
10,11,13-15-Last photo-c 7 14 21 46 86 125
12-Toth-a; last 10¢ issue 8 16 24 51 96 140
NOTE: ***Warren Tufts*** *a-4-Color 1037, 8, 9, 10, 13.*

ZORRO (Walt Disney)(TV)
Gold Key: Jan, 1966 - No. 9, Mar, 1968 (All photo-c)
1-Toth-a 7 14 21 44 82 120
2,4,5,7-9-Toth-a. 5-r/F.C. #1003 by Toth 4 8 12 28 47 65
3,6-Tufts-a 4 8 12 27 44 60
NOTE: *#1-9 are reprinted from Dell issues.* ***Tufts*** *a-3, 4. #1-r/F.C. #882. #2-r/F.C. #960. #3-r/#12-c & #8 inside. #4-r/#9-c & insides. #6-r/#11(all); #7-r/#14-c. #8-r/F.C. #933 inside & back-c & #976-c. #9-r/F.C. #920.*

ZORRO (TV)
Marvel Comics: Dec, 1990 - No. 12, Nov, 1991 ($1.00)
1-12: Based on TV show. 12-Toth-c 3.00

ZORRO (Also see Mask of Zorro)
Topps Comics: Nov, 1993 - No. 11, Nov, 1994 ($2.50/$2.95)
0-(11/93, $1.00, 20 pgs.)-Painted-c; collector's ed. 3.00
1,4,6-9,11: 1-Miller-c. 4-Mike Grell-c. 6-Mignola-c. 7-Lady Rawhide-c by Gulacy. 8-Perez-c. 10-Julie Bell-c. 11-Lady Rawhide-c 3.00
2-Lady Rawhide-app. (not in costume) 5.00
3-1st app. Lady Rawhide in costume, 3-Lady Rawhide-c by Adam Hughes 1 3 4 6 8 10
5-Lady Rawhide app. 4.00
10-($2.95)-Lady Rawhide-c/app. 4.00
The Lady Wears Red (12/98, $12.95, TPB) r/#1-3 13.00
Zorro's Renegades (2/99, $14.95, TPB) r/#4-8 15.00

ZORRO
Dynamite Entertainment: 2008 - No. 20, 2010 ($3.50)
1-Origin retold; Wagner-s; three covers 3.50
2-20-Two covers on all 3.50

ZORRO MATANZAS
Dynamite Entertainment: 2010 - No. 4, 2010 ($3.99)
1-4-Mayhew-a/McGregor-s 4.00

ZORRO RIDES AGAIN
Dynamite Entertainment: 2011 - No. 12, 2012 ($3.99)
1-12: 1-6-Wagner-s/Polls-a. 7-12-Snyder III-a. 10-Lady Zorro on cover 4.00

ZOT!
Eclipse Comics: 4/84 - No. 10, 7/85; No. 11, 1/87 - No. 36 7/91 ($1.50, Baxter-p)
1 5.00
2,3 4.00
4-10: 4-Origin. 10-Last color issue 3.00
10 1/2 (6/86, 25¢, Not Available Comics) Ashcan; art by Feazell & Scott McCloud 4.00
11-14,15-35-($2.00-c) B&W issues 3.00
14 1/2 (Adventures of Zot! in Dimension 10 1/2)(7/87) Antisocialman app. 3.00
36-($2.95-c) B&W 5.00
... The Complete Black and White Collection TPB (2008, $24.95) r/#11-36 with commentary, interviews and bonus artwork 25.00

Z-2 COMICS (Secret Agent...)(See Holyoke One-Shot #7)

ZULU (See Movie Classics)

WANTED
COMIC BOOK ART
COMIC STRIP ART

BEFORE YOU SELL YOUR ART, CALL ME. I CAN AND WILL PAY YOU MORE.

STEPHEN FISHLER
36 W 37TH ST, 6TH FL, NEW YORK, NY 10018
TOLL-FREE 1.800.229.6387 OR CALL 212.260.4147 FAX 212.260.4304
STEPHENF@METROPOLISENT.COM

SERIOUS INFORMATION FOR SERIOUS COLLECTORS

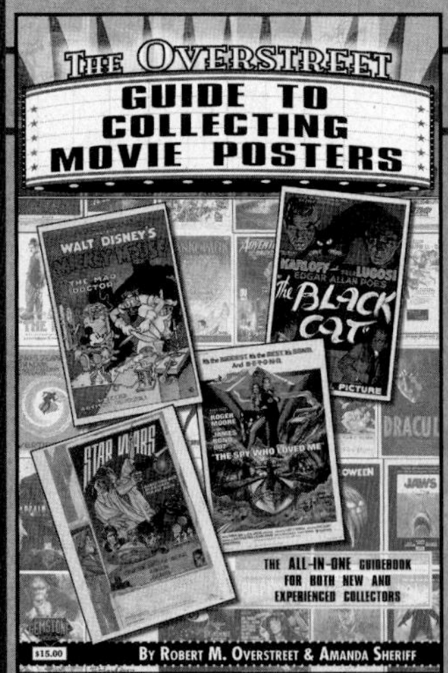

Soft cover $15.00

Soft cover $15.00

Soft cover $20.00

www.gemstonepub.com

COSMIC COMICS!
BUY
SELL
TRADE
Est. 1996
LAS VEGAS, NV
4,000 SQFT. OF COMIC GOODNESS
LOCATED MINUTES FROM THE STRIP!
JIM SAYS:
OVER 50.000 BACK ISSUES
FROM THE 1950'S TO THE PRESENT!
10,000+ GRAPHICS NOVELS!
PLUS T-SHIRTS, TOYS AND DO-DADS!
Mention this ad for 10% off Back Issues
3830 E Flamingo Las Vegas, NV 89121
702-451-6611 • info@cosmiccomicslv.com
WWW.COSMICCOMICSLV.COM
COSMIC COMICS!

DEALING in GOLDEN and SILVER AGE RARE COMIC BOOKS
RARE BOOKS & COMICS
JAMES PAYETTE
P.O. Box 750
Bethlehem, NH 03574
603-869-2097/Fax 603-869-3475
jamespayettecomics.com
jimpayette@msn.com
BIG LITTLE BOOKS ○ 1ST EDITION BOOKS ○ PULP MAGAZINES ○ SCI-FI FANTASY MATERIAL

To have your ads seen here in future editions, contact our Advertising Dept.
Gemstone Publishing, Inc.
10150 York Rd., Suite 300
Hunt Valley, MD 21030
or e-mail **feedback@gemstonepub.com.**

BEST COMICS INTERNATIONAL
(Est.1991)
TOMMY MALETTA
•COMIC BOOKS•BACK ISSUES
•GRAPHIC NOVELS•TOYS•STATUES
•SPORTS MEMORABILIA
1300 JERICHO TURNPIKE NEW HYDE PARK, NY 11040
Phone: 516-328-1900 WWW.BESTCOMICS.COM

Top Five Selection on the Web!

Strict, consistent grading.
NEW COLLECTIONS in the House!
EASY-TO-USE, secure WEBSITE!
FREE SHIPPING w/ $75 order!
info@houseofcomics.com Call us at (510) 847-3376
www.HouseofComics.com

Toy & Comic Heaven
COMICS • VIDEO GAMES • TOYS
James Gallo
Owner
21 Easton Road
Willow Grove Pa 19090
Phone: 215-643-7000
jgallony@aol.com
Mon/Wed/Fri 11-5
Tues/Thurs 11-8
Sat 11-5
www.toyandcomicheaven.com

BATMAN
WONDER WOMAN
COLLECTORS
E-mail: batt90@aol.com
wwali@aol.com
COLLECTORS
P.O. Box 604925
Flushing, NY 11360-4925

DIRECTORY LISTINGS

Items stocked by these shops are noted at the end of each listing and are coded as follows:

(a) Golden Age Comics
(b) Silver Age Comics
(c) Bronze Age Comics
(d) New Comics & Magazines
(e) Back Issue magazines
(f) Comic Supplies
(g) Collectible Card Games
(h) Role Playing Games
(i) Gaming Supplies
(j) Manga
(k) Anime
(l) Underground Comics
(m) Original Comic Art
(n) Pulps
(o) Big Little Books
(p) Books - Used
(q) Books - New
(r) Comic Related Posters
(s) Movie Posters
(t) Trading Cards
(u) Statues/Mini-busts, etc.
(v) Premiums (Rings, Decoders)
(w) Action Figures
(x) Other Toys
(y) Records/CDs
(z) DVDs/VHS
(1) Doctor Who Items
(2) Simpsons Items
(3) Star Trek Items
(4) Star Wars Items
(5) HeroClix

The Paper Escape
205 W First Street
Dixon, IL 61021
PH/FAX: (815) 284-7567
paperescape@paperescape.com
www.paperescape.com
(b-d,f-j,p-r,t,u,w,x,1-4)

INDIANA

Comics Ina Flash
P.O. Box 3611
Evansville, IN 47735-3611
PH/FAX: (812) 401-6127
comicflash@aol.com
www.comicsinaflash.com

IOWA

Oak Leaf Collectibles
221 North Federal
Mason City, IA 50401
PH: (641) 424-0333
MikeT@Dustcatchers.com
Dustcatchers.com
(a-j,r,t,u,w-z,1,3-5)

KENTUCKY

Dale Roberts Comics
P.O. Box 707
Calvert City, KY 42029
PH: (270) 556-2988
Dale@DaleRobertsComics.com
www.DaleRobertsComics.com

Comic Book World, Inc.
7130 Turfway Rd.
Florence, KY 41042
PH: (859) 371-9562
FAX: (859) 371-6925
mark@comicbookworld.com
www.comicbookworld.com
(a-j,l,m,o,p,r,t,u,w,x,1-5)

Comic Book World, Inc.
6905 Shepherdsville Rd.
Louisville, KY 40219
PH/FAX: (502) 964-5500
heather@comicbookworld.com
www.comicbookworld.com
(a-j,l,r,u,w,x,1-5)

Leroy Harper
P.O. Box 212
West Paducah, KY 42086
PH: (270) 748-9364
LHCOMICS@hotmail.com

MAINE

Top Shelf Comics
115 Main St.; 1st Floor
Bangor, ME 04401
PH: (207) 947-4939
topshelf@tcomics.com
www.tcomics.com
(a-f)

MARYLAND

E. Gerber
1720 Belmont Ave.; Suite C
Baltimore, MD 21244

Esquire Comics.com
Mark S. Zaid, ESQ.
P.O. Box 3422492
Bethesda, MD 20827
PH: (202) 498-0011
esquirecomics@aol.com
www.esquirecomics.com
(b-k,r,u,w,4,5)

Alternate Worlds
10854 York Road
Cockeysville, MD 21030
PH: (410) 666-3290
AltWorldStore@comcast.net
www.facebook.com/
AlternateWorldsComics
(b-j,q,r,u,w,x,1,3-5)

Reece's Rare Comics
11028 Graymarsh Pl.
Ijamsville, MD 21754
PH: (240) 575-8600
greg@gregreececomics.com
www.gregreececomics.com
(a,b,c,e,f)

Cards Comics and Collectibles
51 Main St.
Reisterstown, MD 21136
PH: (410) 526-7410
FAX: (410) 526-4006
cardscomicscollectibles
@yahoo.com
www.cardscomicscollectibles.
com
(a-d,f,g,j,t,w,5)

Diamond Comic Distributors
10150 York Road, Suite 300
Hunt Valley, MD 21030
PH: (443) 318-8001

Diamond International Galleries
1940 Greenspring Dr., Suite I-L
Timonium, MD 21093
Contact: pokevin@
DiamondGalleries.com
www.DiamondGalleries.com

MASSACHUSETTS

Gary Dolgoff Comics
116 Pleasant St.
Easthampton, MA 01027
PH: (413) 529-0326
FAX: (413) 529-9824
gary@gdcomics.com
www.gdcomics.com

That's Entertainment
56 John Fitch Highway
Fitchburg, MA 01420
PH: (978) 342-8607
fitch@thatse.com
www.ThatsE.com
(a-z,1-5)

SuperworldComics.com
456 Main St., Suite F
Holden, MA 01520
PH: (508) 829-2259
PH: (508) UB-WACKY
Ted@Superworldcomics.com
www.Superworldcomics.com
(a-c,m)

Bill Cole Enterprises Inc.
P.O. Box 60
Randolph, MA 02368-0060
PH: (781) 986-2653
FAX: (781) 986-2656
sales@bcemylar.com
www.bcemylar.com

That's Entertainment
244 Park Avenue
(At the corner of Lois Lane)
Worcester, MA 01609
PH: (508) 755-4207
Ken@thatse.com
www.ThatsE.com
(a-z,1-5)

MICHIGAN

Harley Yee Comics
P.O. Box 51758
Livonia, MI 48151-5758
PH: (800) 731-1029
FAX: (734) 421-7928
HarleyComx@aol.com
www.HarleyYeeComics.com

NEBRASKA

Robert Beerbohm Comic Art
P.O. Box 507
Fremont, NE 68026
PH: (402) 919-9393
BeerbohmRL@gmail.com
www.BLBcomics.com
(a,b,c,e,l-o,r)

NEVADA

Redbeard's Book Den
P.O. Box 217
Crystal Bay, NV 89402
PH: (775) 831-4848
FAX: (775) 831-4483
www.redbeardsbookden.com
(a,b,c,l,o,p)

Cosmic Comics!
3830 E. Flamingo Rd.
Suite F-2
Las Vegas, NV 89121
PH: (702) 451-6611
info@CosmicComicsLV.com
www.CosmicComicsLV.com
(a-g,i,j,l,n-r,u-x,1-3,5)

Torpedo Comics
7300 Arroyo Crossing Pkwy
Suite 105
Las Vegas, NV 89113
PH: (702) 444-4432
TorpedoComics@gmail.com

NEW HAMPSHIRE

Rare Books & Comics
James F. Payette
P.O. Box 750
Bethlehem, NH 03574
PH: (603) 869-2097
FAX: (603) 869-3475
JimPayette@msn.com
www.JamesPayetteComics.com
(a,b,c,e,n,o,p)

NEW JERSEY

Nationwide Comics
Buying All 10¢ & 12¢
original priced comics
Derek Woywood
Clementon, NJ 08021
PH: (856) 217-5737 or
Hotline: (800) 938-0325
FAX: (714) 288-8992
dwoywood@yahoo.com
www.philadelphiacomic-con.
com
(a,b,d-h,m,n,q)

Zapp Comics
700 Tennent Road
Manalapan, NJ 07726
PH: (732) 617-1333
Ben@zappcomics.com
www.zappcomics.com
(a-d,f,g,j,t,2-5)

Zapp Comics
574 Valley Road
Wayne, NJ 07470
PH: (973) 628-4500
ben@zappcomics.com
www.zappcomics.com
(a-g,i,j,l,t,u,w,x,1-5)

JHV Associates
(By Appointment Only)
P. O. Box 317
Woodbury Heights, NJ 08097
PH: (856) 845-4010
FAX: (856) 845-3977
JHVassoc@hotmail.com
(a,b,n,s)

NEW MEXICO

Age of Comics
3700 Osuna Rd. NE
Suite 513
Albuquerque, NM 87109
PH: (505) 884-1776
www.AgeOfComics.store

NEW YORK

Pinocchio Collectibles
1814 McDonald Ave.
(off Ave. P)
Brooklyn, NY 11223
PH: (718) 645-2573
a19gaba@aol.com
(b-d,f,i,w,x)

HighGradeComics.com
17 Bethany Drive
Commack, NY 11725
PH: (631) 543-1917
FAX: (631) 864-1921
BobStorms@
HighGradeComics.com
www.HighGradeComics.com
(a,b,c,e)

Amazing Comics
P.O. Box 403
Glenmont, NY 12158
PH: (631) 605-0143
info@AmazingCo.com
www.AmazingCo.com
(a-c,e,l,m,p,t,u,w,x,4)

Best Comics
1300 Jericho Turnpike
New Hyde Park, NY 11040
PH: (516) 328-1900
FAX: (516) 328-1909
TommyBest@aol.com
www.bestcomics.com
(a,b,d,f,m,t,u,w,3,4)

ComicConnect.com
36 West 37th St.; 6th Floor
New York, NY 10018
PH: (212) 895-3999
FAX: (212) 260-4304
support@comicconnect.com
www.comicconnect.com
(a,b,c,m,n,s,v)

Metropolis Collectibles
36 West 37th St.; 6th Floor
New York, NY 10018
PH: (800) 229-6387
FAX: (212) 260-4304
E-Mail: buying@
metropoliscomics.com
www.metropoliscomics.com

Dave and Adam's
55 Oriskany Dr.
Tonawanda, NY 14150
PH: (888) 440-9787
FAX: (716) 838-9896
service@dacardworld.com
www.dacardworld.com
(a-i,m,r,t,w,x,1-5)

Dave and Adam's
2217 Sheridan Dr.
Tonawanda, NY 14223
PH: (716) 837-4920
sheridan-store@dacardworld.com
www.dacwstore.com
(a-c,f-i,m,t,w,x,1-5)

Dan Gallo
White Plains, NY
PH: (954) 547-9063
DGallo1291@aol.com
eBay ID: DGallo1291
(a,b,c,m)

Dave and Adam's
8075 Sheridan Dr.
Williamsville, NY 14221
PH: (716) 626-0000
Transit-store@dacardworld.com
www.dacwstore.com
(a-d,f-i,m,r,t,w,x,1-5)

NORTH CAROLINA

Heroes Aren't Hard to Find
417 Pecan Avenue.
Charlotte, NC 28204
PH: (704) 375-7462
www.heroesonline.com

OHIO

Comics and Friends, LLC
7850 Mentor Ave.
Suite 1054
Mentor, OH 44096
PH: (440) 255-4242
comics.and.friends.store
@gmail.com
www.comicsandfriends.com
(a-g,i,j,l,m,n,r,t,u,w-z,1-5)

Parker's Records & Comics
1222 Suite C Rt. 28
Milford, OH 45150
PH/FAX: (513) 575-3665
dkparker39@fuse.net
www.parkersrc.com
(a-g,i,y)

New Dimension Comics
Ohio Valley Mall
67800 Mall Ring Rd Unit 875
Saint Clairsville, OH 43950
PH: (740) 695-1020
ohiovalley@ndcomics.com
www.ndcomics.com

All American Comics
161 West Market St.
Warren, OH 44481
PH: (330) 393-3137
iuz22000@yahoo.com
(a-k,m,r-u,w,x,z,1-5)

OKLAHOMA

Want List Comics
(Appointment Only)
P.O. Box 701932
Tulsa, OK 74170
PH: (918) 299-0440
E-Mail: wlc777@cox.net
(a,b,c,m,n,o,s,t,x,3)

OREGON

Future Dreams
1847 East Burnside St.
Suite 116
Portland, OR 97214-1587
PH: (503) 231-8311
fdb@hevanet.com
www.futuredreamsbooks.com
(a-g,i,j,l-n,p-u,w,x,3,4)

PENNSYLVANIA

New Dimension Comics
108 South Main Street
Butler, PA 16001
PH: (724) 282-5283
butler@ndcomics.com
www.ndcomics.com
(a-l,n,o,r,t,u,w,x,1-5)

New Dimension Comics
Piazza Plaza
20550 Route 19 (Perry Hwy.)
Cranberry Township, PA
16066
PH: (724) 776-0433
cranberry@ndcomics.com
www.ndcomics.com
(a-l,n,o,r,t,u,w,x,1-5)

New Dimension Comics
Megastore
516 Lawrence Ave.
Ellwood City, PA 16117
PH: (724) 758-2324
ec@ndcomics.com
www.ndcomics.com
(a-l,n,o,r,t,u,w,x,1-5)

Eide's Entertainment, LLC
1121 Penn Ave.
Pittsburgh, PA 15222
PH: (412) 261-0900
eBay store: eides_entertainment
skydive@eides.com
www.eides.com
(a-z,1-5)

New Dimension Comics
Pittsburgh Mills
590 Pittsburgh Mill Circle
Tarentum, PA 15084
PH: (724) 758-1560
mills@ndcomics.com
www.ndcomics.com
(a-l,n,o,r,t,u,w,x,1-5)

New Dimension Comics
Pittsburgh Century III Mall
3075 Clairton Rd. #940
West Mifflin, PA 15213
PH: (412) 655-8661
century3@ndcomics.com
www.ndcomics.com
(a-l,n,o,r,t,u,w,x,1-5)

Toy & Comic Heaven
21 Easton Rd.
Willow Grove, PA 19090
PH: (215) 643-7000
jgallony@aol.com
www.toyandcomicheaven.com
(a-c,e,f,w,x,2-4)

Hake's Americana & Collectibles
P.O. Box 12001
York, PA 17402
PH: (866) 404-9800
www.hakes.com

SOUTH DAKOTA

Top Notch Comics
P.O. Box 229
Yankton, SD 57078
PH: (605) 660-3135
topnotch@iw.net

TEXAS

Comic Heaven
P.O. Box 1400
Hawkins, TX 75765
PH: (214) 444-9503
www.ComicHeaven.net

Comic Book Certification Service (CBCS)
4635 McEwen Road
Dallas, TX 75244
PH: (727) 803-6822
PH: (844) 870-CBCS
www.CBCScomics.com

Heritage Auction Galleries
3500 Maple Avenue
17th Floor
Dallas, TX 75219-3941
PH: (800) 872-6467
www.HA.com

Worldwide Comics
29369 Raintree Ridge
Fair Oaks Ranch, TX 78015
PH: (830) 368-4103
stephen@wwcomics.com
wwcomics.com

William Hughes' Vintage Collectables
P.O. Box 270244
Flower Mound, TX 75027
PH: (972) 539-9190
PH: (973) 432-4070
Whughes199@yahoo.com
www.VintageCollectables.net

WASHINGTON

Pristine Comics
2008 South 314th Street
Federal Way, WA 98003
PH: (253) 941-1986
www.PristineComics.com

Fantasy Illustrated
P.O. Box 248
Silvana, WA 98287
PH: (425) 750-4513
rocketbat@msn.com
www.fantasyillustrated.net

Gabriel & Wayne Root
P.O. Box 9745
Spokane, WA 99209
comicbuyer1776@yahoo.com

WISCONSIN

Inner Child Collectibles and Comics
5921 Sixth Avenue "A"
Kenosha, WI 53140
PH: (262) 653-0400
StevenKahn@sbcglobal.net
innerchildcomics.com
(a-f,l-p,r,s,u-x,1-4)

Jef Hinds Comics
P.O. Box 44803
Madison, WI 53744-4803
PH: (608) 345-8750
jhcomics@jhcomics.com
www.jhcomics.com

The Turning Page
2452 North Murray Ave.
Milwaukee, WI 53211
PH: (414) 509-5611
TheTurningPageComics
@gmail.com

CANADA

MANITOBA

Doug Sulipa's Comic World
Box 21986
Steinbach, MB., R5G 1B5
PH: (204) 346-3674
FAX: (204) 346-1632
dsulipa@gmail.com
www.dougcomicworld.com
(a-e,h,l,n-t,y,z,3,4)

ONTARIO

Big B Comics
1045 Upper James St.
Hamilton, ON L9C 3A6
PH: (905) 318-9636
mailbox@bigbcomics.com
www.bigbcomics.com
(a-g,i,j,l,m,u-x,1-5)

The Goblin's Den
70 Port Street East, Suite 201
Mississauga, ON L5G 4V8
PH: (905) 990-2713
FAX: (416) 622-0574
GoblinsDen@rogers.com

Pendragon Comics & Books
3759 Lakeshore Boulevard West
Toronto, ON M8W 1R1
PH: (416) 253-6974
pendragoncomics@rogers.com
www.pendragoncomics.com
(a-g,l,n-p,u)

INTERNET

ComicLink Auctions & Exchange
PH: (617) 517-0062
buysell@ComicLink.com
www.ComicLink.com

Comix4Sale.com
Comix4Sale@aol.com
www.comix4sale.com
(a,d-f,h-s,u,v,x-z,1-5)

MyComicShop.com
PH: (817) 860-7827
buytrade@mycomicshop.com
www.mycomicshop.com

Sell My Comic Books
PH: (514) 803-0635
ash@SellMyComicBooks.com
www.SellMyComicBooks.com

Items stocked by these shops are noted at the end of each listing and are coded as follows:

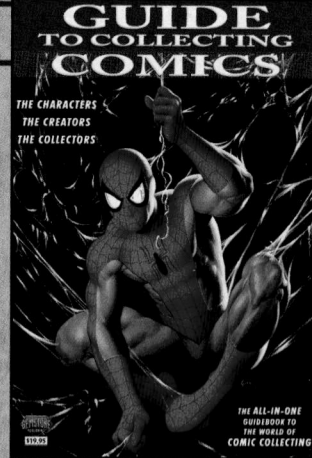

(a) Golden Age Comics
(b) Silver Age Comics
(c) Bronze Age Comics
(d) New Comics & Magazines
(e) Back Issue magazines
(f) Comic Supplies
(g) Collectible Card Games
(h) Role Playing Games
(i) Gaming Supplies
(j) Manga
(k) Anime
(l) Underground Comics
(m) Original Comic Art
(n) Pulps
(o) Big Little Books
(p) Books - Used
(q) Books - New
(r) Comic Related Posters
(s) Movie Posters
(t) Trading Cards
(u) Statues/Mini-busts, etc.
(v) Premiums (Rings, Decoders)
(w) Action Figures
(x) Other Toys
(y) Records/CDs
(z) DVDs/VHS
(1) Doctor Who Items
(2) Simpsons Items
(3) Star Trek Items
(4) Star Wars Items
(5) HeroClix

GLOSSARY

a - Story art; **a(i)** - Story art inks; **a(p)** - Story art pencils; **a(r)** - Story art reprint.

ADULT MATERIAL - Contains story and/or art for "mature" readers. Re: sex, violence, strong language.

ADZINE - A magazine primarily devoted to the advertising of comic books and collectibles as its first publishing priority as opposed to written articles.

ALLENTOWN COLLECTION - A collection discovered in 1987-88 just outside Allentown, Pennsylvania. The Allentown collection consisted of 135 Golden Age comics, characterized by high grade and superior paper quality.

ANNUAL - (1) A book that is published yearly; (2) Can also refer to some square bound comics.

ARRIVAL DATE - The date written (often in pencil) or stamped on the cover of comics by either the local wholesaler, newsstand owner, or distributor. The date precedes the cover date by approximately 15 to 75 days, and may vary considerably from one locale to another or from one year to another.

ASHCAN - A publisher's in-house facsimile of a proposed new title. Most ashcans have black and white covers stapled to an existing coverless comic on the inside; other ashcans are totally black and white. In modern parlance, it can also refer to promotional or sold comics, often smaller than standard comic size and usually in black and white, released by publishers to advertise the forthcoming arrival of a new title or story.

ATOM AGE - Comics published from 1946-1956.

B&W - Black and white art.

BACK-UP FEATURE - A story or character that usually appears after the main feature in a comic book; often not featured on the cover.

BAD GIRL ART - A term popularized in the early '90s to describe an attitude as well as a style of art that portrays women in a sexual and often action-oriented way.

BAXTER PAPER - A high quality, heavy, white paper used in the printing of some comics.

BC - Abbreviation for Back Cover.

BI-MONTHLY - Published every two months.

BI-WEEKLY - Published every two weeks.

BONDAGE COVER - Usually denotes a female in bondage.

BOUND COPY - A comic that has been bound into a book. The process requires that the spine be trimmed and sometimes sewn into a book-like binding.

BRITISH ISSUE - A comic printed for distribution in Great Britain; these copies sometimes have the price listed in pence or pounds instead of cents or dollars.

BRITTLENESS - A severe condition of paper deterioration where paper loses its flexibility and thus chips and/or flakes easily.

BRONZE AGE - Comics published from 1970 to 1984.

BROWNING - (1) The aging of paper characterized by the ever-increasing level of oxidation characterized by darkening; (2) The level of paper deterioration one step more severe than tanning and one step before brittleness.

c - Cover art; **c(i)** - Cover inks; **c(p)** - Cover pencils; **c(r)** - Cover reprint.

CAMEO - The brief appearance of one character in the strip of another.

CANADIAN ISSUE - A comic printed for distribution in Canada; these copies sometimes have no advertising.

CCA - Abbreviation for **Comics Code Authority**.

CCA SEAL - An emblem that was placed on the cover of all CCA approved comics beginning in April-May, 1955.

CENTER CREASE - See Subscription Copy.

CENTERFOLD or CENTER SPREAD - The two folded pages in the center of a comic book at the terminal end of the staples.

CERTIFIED GRADING - A process provided by a professional grading service that certifies a given grade for a comic and seals the book in a protective **Slab**.

CF - Abbreviation for Centerfold.

CFO - Abbreviation for Centerfold Out.

CGC - Abbreviation for the certified comic book grading company, Comics Guaranty, LLC.

CIRCULATION COPY - See Subscription Copy.

CIRCULATION FOLD - See Subscription Fold.

CLASSIC COVER - A cover considered by collectors to be highly desirable because of its subject matter, artwork, historical importance, etc.

CLEANING - A process in which dirt and dust is removed.

COLOR TOUCH - A restoration process by which colored ink is used to hide color flecks, color flakes, and larger areas of missing color. Short for Color Touch-Up.

COLORIST - An artist who paints the color guides for comics. Many modern colorists use computer technology.

COMIC BOOK DEALER - (1) A seller of comic books; (2) One who makes a living buying and selling comic books.
COMIC BOOK REPAIR - When a tear, loose staple or centerfold has been mended without changing or adding to the original finish of the book. Repair may involve tape, glue or nylon gossamer, and is easily detected; it is considered a defect.
COMICS CODE AUTHORITY - A voluntary organization comprised of comic book publishers formed in 1954 to review (and possibly censor) comic books before they were printed and distributed. The emblem of the CCA is a white stamp in the upper right hand corner of comics dated after February 1955. The term "post-Code" refers to the time after this practice started, or approximately 1955 to the present.
COMPLETE RUN - All issues of a given title.
CON - A convention or public gathering of fans.
CONDITION - The state of preservation of a comic book, often inaccurately used interchangeably with Grade.
CONSERVATION - The European Confederation of Conservator-Restorers' Organizations (ECCO) in its professional guidelines, defines conservation as follows: "Conservation consists mainly of direct action carried out on cultural heritage with the aim of stabilizing condition and retarding further deterioration."
COPPER AGE - Comics published from 1984 to 1992.
COSMIC AEROPLANE COLLECTION - A collection from Salt Lake City, Utah discovered by Cosmic Aeroplane Books, characterized by the moderate to high grade copies of 1930s-40s comics with pencil check marks in the margins of inside pages. It is thought that these comics were kept by a commercial illustration school and the check marks were placed beside panels that instructors wanted students to draw.
COSTUMED HERO - A costumed crime fighter with "developed" human powers instead of super powers.
COUPON CUT or COUPON MISSING - A coupon has been neatly removed with scissors or razor blade from the interior or exterior of the comic as opposed to having been ripped out.
COVER GLOSS - The reflective quality of the cover inks.
COVER TRIMMED - Cover has been reduced in size by neatly cutting away rough or damaged edges.
COVERLESS - A comic with no cover attached. There is a niche demand for coverless comics, particularly in the case of hard-to-find key books otherwise impossible to locate intact.
C/P - Abbreviation for **Cleaned and Pressed**. See **Cleaning**.
CREASE - A fold which causes ink removal, usually resulting in a white line. See **Reading Crease**.
CROSSOVER - A story where one character appears prominently in the story of another character. See **X-Over**.
CVR - Abbreviation for Cover.
DEALER - See **Comic Book Dealer**.
DEACIDIFICATION - Several different processes that reduce acidity in paper.
DEBUT - The first time that a character appears anywhere.
DEFECT - Any fault or flaw that detracts from perfection.
DENVER COLLECTION - A collection consisting primarily of early 1940s high grade number one issues bought at auction in Pennsylvania by a Denver, Colorado dealer.
DIE-CUT COVER - A comic book cover with areas or edges precut by a printer to a special shape or to create a desired effect.
DISTRIBUTOR STRIPES - Color brushed or sprayed on the edges of comic book stacks by the distributor/wholesaler to code them for expedient exchange at the sales racks. Typical colors are red, orange, yellow, green, blue, and purple. Distributor stripes are not a defect.
DOUBLE - A duplicate copy of the same comic book.
DOUBLE COVER - When two covers are stapled to the comic interior instead of the usual one; the exterior cover often protects the interior cover from wear and damage. This is considered a desirable situation by some collectors and may increase collector value; this is not considered a defect.
DRUG PROPAGANDA STORY - A comic that makes an editorial stand about drug use.
DRUG USE STORY - A comic that shows the actual use of drugs: needle use, tripping, harmful effects, etc.
DRY CLEANING - A process in which dirt and dust is removed.
DUOTONE - Printed with black and one other color of ink. This process was common in comics printed in the 1930s.
DUST SHADOW - Darker, usually linear area at the edge of some comics stored in stacks. Some portion of the cover was not covered by the comic immediately above it and it was exposed to settling dust particles. Also see **Oxidation Shadow** and **Sun Shadow**.
EDGAR CHURCH COLLECTION - See **Mile High Collection**.
EMBOSSED COVER - A comic book cover with a pattern, shape or image pressed into the cover from

the inside, creating a raised area.

ENCAPSULATION - Refers to the process of sealing certified comics in a protective plastic enclosure. Also see **Slabbing**.

EYE APPEAL - A term which refers to the overall look of a comic book when held at approximately arm's length. A comic may have nice eye appeal yet still possess defects which reduce grade.

FANZINE - An amateur fan publication.

FC - Abbreviation for Front Cover.

FILE COPY - A high grade comic originating from the publisher's file; contrary to what some might believe, not all file copies are in Gem Mint condition. An arrival date on the cover of a comic does not indicate that it is a file copy, though a copyright date may.

FIRST APPEARANCE - See **Debut**.

FLASHBACK - When a previous story is recalled.

FOIL COVER - A comic book cover that has had a thin metallic foil hot stamped on it. Many of these "gimmick" covers date from the early '90s, and might include chromium, prism and hologram covers as well.

FOUR COLOR - Series of comics produced by Dell, characterized by hundreds of different features; named after the four color process of printing. See **One Shot**.

FOUR COLOR PROCESS - The process of printing with the three primary colors (red, yellow, and blue) plus black.

FUMETTI - Illustration system in which individual frames of a film are colored and used for individual panels to make a comic book story. The most famous example is DC's *Movie Comics* #1-6 from 1939.

GATEFOLD COVER - A double-width fold-out cover.

GENRE - Categories of comic book subject matter; e.g. Science Fiction, Super-Hero, Romance, Funny Animal, Teenage Humor, Crime, War, Western, Mystery, Horror, etc.

GIVEAWAY - Type of comic book intended to be given away as a premium or promotional device instead of being sold.

GLASSES ATTACHED - In 3-D comics, the special blue and red cellophane and cardboard glasses are still attached to the comic.

GLASSES DETACHED - In 3-D comics, the special blue and red cellophane and cardboard glasses are not still attached to the comic; obviously less desirable than Glasses Attached.

GOLDEN AGE - Comics published from 1938 (*Action Comics* #1) to 1945.

GOOD GIRL ART - Refers to a style of art, usually from the 1930s-50s, that portrays women in a sexually implicit way.

GREY-TONE COVER - A cover art style in which pencil or charcoal underlies the normal line drawing, used to enhance the effects of light and shadow, thus producing a richer quality. These covers, prized by most collectors, are sometimes referred to as **Painted Covers** but are not actually painted.

HC - Abbreviation for Hardcover.

HEADLIGHTS - Forward illumation devices installed on all automobiles and many other vehicles... OK, OK, it's a euphemism for a comic book cover prominently featuring a woman's breasts in a provocative way. Also see **Bondage Cover** for another collecting euphemism that has long since outlived its appropriateness in these politically correct times.

HOT STAMPING - The process of pressing foil, prism paper and/or inks on cover stock.

HRN - Abbreviation for Highest Reorder Number. This refers to a method used by collectors of Gilberton's *Classic Comics* and *Classics Illustrated* series to distinguish first editions from later printings.

ILLO - Abbreviation for Illustration.

IMPAINT - Another term for **Color Touch**.

INDICIA - Publishing and title information usually located at the bottom of the first page or the bottom of the inside front cover. In some pre-1938 comics and many modern comics, it is located on internal pages.

INFINITY COVER - Shows a scene that repeats itself to infinity.

INKER - Artist that does the inking.

INTRO - Same as **Debut**.

INVESTMENT GRADE COPY - (1) Comic of sufficiently high grade and demand to be viewed by collectors as instantly liquid should the need arise to sell; (2) A comic in VF or better condition; (3) A comic purchased primarily to realize a profit.

ISSUE NUMBER - The actual edition number of a given title.

ISH - Short for Issue.

JLA - Abbreviation for Justice League of America.

JSA - Abbreviation for Justice Society of America.

KEY, KEY BOOK or KEY ISSUE - An issue that contains a first appearance, origin, or other historically or artistically important feature considered especially desirable by collectors.

LAMONT LARSON - Pedigreed collection of high grade 1940s comics with the initials or name of its original owner, Lamont Larson.

LENTICULAR COVERS or "FLICKER" COVERS - A comic book cover overlayed with a ridged plastic sheet such that the special artwork underneath appears to move when the cover is tilted at different angles perpendicular to the ridges.

LETTER COL or LETTER COLUMN - A feature in a comic book that prints and sometimes responds to letters written by its readers.

LINE DRAWN COVER - A cover published in the traditional way where pencil sketches are over-drawn with india ink and then colored. See also **Grey-Tone Cover**, **Photo Cover**, and **Painted Cover**.

LOGO - The title of a strip or comic book as it appears on the cover or title page.

LSH - Abbreviation for Legion of Super-Heroes.

MAGIC LIGHTNING COLLECTION - A collection of high grade 1950s comics from the San Francisco area.

MARVEL CHIPPING - A bindery (trimming/cutting) defect that results in a series of chips and tears at the top, bottom, and right edges of the cover, caused when the cutting blade of an industrial paper trimmer becomes dull. It was dubbed Marvel Chipping because it can be found quite often on Marvel comics from the late '50s and early '60s but can also occur with any company's comic books from the late 1940s through the middle 1960s.

MILE HIGH COLLECTION - High grade collection of over 22,000 comics discovered in Denver, Colorado in 1977, originally owned by Mr. Edgar Church. Comics from this collection are now famous for extremely white pages, fresh smell, and beautiful cover ink reflectivity.

MODERN AGE - A catch-all term applied to comics published since 1992.

MYLAR™ - An inert, very hard, space-age plastic used to make high quality protective bags and sleeves for comic book storage. "Mylar" is a trademark of the DuPont Co.

ND - Abbreviation for **No Date**.

NN - Abbreviation for **No Number**.

NO DATE - When there is no date given on the cover or indicia page.

NO NUMBER - No issue number is given on the cover or indicia page; these are usually first issues or one-shots.

N.Y. LEGIS. COMM. - New York Legislative Committee to Study the Publication of Comics (1951).

ONE-SHOT - When only one issue is published of a title, or when a series is published where each issue is a different title (e.g. Dell's *Four Color Comics*).

ORIGIN - When the story of a character's creation is given.

over guide - When a comic book is priced at a value over *Guide* list.

OXIDATION SHADOW - Darker, usually linear area at the edge of some comics stored in stacks. Some portion of the cover was not covered by the comic immediately above it, and it was exposed to the air. Also see **Dust Shadow** and **Sun Shadow**.

p - Art pencils.

PAINTED COVER - (1) Cover taken from an actual painting instead of a line drawing; (2) Inaccurate name for a grey-toned cover.

PANELOLOGIST - One who researches comic books and/or comic strips.

PANNAPICTAGRAPHIST - One possible term for someone who collects comic books; can you figure out why it hasn't exactly taken off in common parlance?

PAPER COVER - Comic book cover made from the same newsprint as the interior pages. These books are extremely rare in high grade.

PARADE OF PLEASURE - A book about the censorship of comics.

PB - Abbreviation for Paperback.

PEDIGREE - A book from a famous and usually high grade collection - e.g. Allentown, Lamont Larson, Edgar Church/Mile High, Denver, San Francisco, Cosmic Aeroplane, etc. Beware of non-pedigree collections being promoted as pedigree books; only outstanding high grade collections similar to those listed qualify.

PENCILER - Artist that does the pencils...you're figuring out some of these definitions without us by now, aren't you?

PERFECT BINDING - Pages are glued to the cover as opposed to being stapled to the cover, resulting in a flat binded side. Also known as **Square Back or Square Bound**.

PG - Abbreviation for Page.

PHOTO COVER - Comic book cover featuring a photographic image instead of a line drawing or painting.

PIECE REPLACEMENT - A process by which pieces are added to replace areas of missing paper.

PIONEER AGE - Comics published from the 1500s to 1828.

PLATINUM AGE - Comics published from 1883 to 1938.

POLYPROPYLENE - A type of plastic used in the manufacture of comic book bags; now considered harmful to paper and not recommended for long term storage of comics.

POP - Abbreviation for the anti-comic book volume, *Parade of Pleasure.*

POST-CODE - Describes comics published after February 1955 and usually displaying the CCA stamp in the upper right-hand corner.

POUGHKEEPSIE - Refers to a large collection of Dell Comics file copies believed to have originated from the warehouse of Western Publishing in Poughkeepsie, NY.

PP - Abbreviation for Pages.

PRE-CODE - Describes comics published before the **Comics Code Authority** seal began appearing on covers in 1955.

PRE-HERO DC - A term used to describe *More Fun* #1-51

(pre-Spectre), *Adventure* #1-39 (pre-Sandman), and *Detective* #1-26 (pre-Batman). The term is actually inaccurate because technically there were "heroes" in the above books.

PRE-HERO MARVEL - A term used to describe *Strange Tales* #1-100 (pre-Human Torch), *Journey Into Mystery* #1-82 (pre-Thor), *Tales To Astonish* #1-35 (pre-Ant-Man), and *Tales Of Suspense* #1-38 (pre-Iron Man).

PRESERVATION - Another term for **Conservation**.

PRESSING - A term used to describe a variety of processes or procedures, professional and amateur, under which an issue is pressed to eliminate wrinkles, bends, dimples and/or other perceived defects and thus improve its appearance. Some types of pressing involve disassembling the book and performing other work on it prior to its pressing and reassembly. Some methods are generally easily discerned by professionals and amateurs. Other types of pressing, however, can pose difficulty for even experienced professionals to detect. In all cases, readers are cautioned that unintended damage can occur in some instances. Related defects will diminish an issue's grade correspondingly rather than improve it.

PROVENANCE - When the owner of a book is known and is stated for the purpose of authenticating and documenting the history of the book. Example: A book from the Stan Lee or Forrest Ackerman collection would be an example of a value-adding provenance.

PULP - Cheaply produced magazine made from low grade newsprint. The term comes from the wood pulp that was used in the paper manufacturing process.

QUARTERLY - Published every three months (four times a year).

R - Abbreviation for Reprint.

RARE - 10-20 copies estimated to exist.

RAT CHEW - Damage caused by the gnawing of rats and mice.

RBCC - Abbreviation for Rockets Blast Comic Collector, one of the first and most prominent adzines instrumental in developing the early comic book market.

READING COPY - A comic that is in FAIR to GOOD condition and is often used for research; the condition has been sufficiently reduced to the point where general handling will not degrade it further.

READING CREASE - Book-length, vertical front cover crease at staples, caused by bending the cover over the staples. Square-bounds receive these creases just by opening the cover too far to the left.

REILLY, TOM - A large high grade collection of 1939-1945 comics with 5000+ books.

REINFORCEMENT - A process by which a weak or split page or cover is reinforced with adhesive and reinforcement paper.

REPRINT COMICS - In earlier decades, comic books that contained newspaper strip reprints; modern reprint comics usually contain stories originally featured in older comic books.

RESTORATION - Any attempt, whether professional or amateur, to enhance the appearance of an aging or damaged comic book using additive procedures. These procedures may include any or all of the following techniques: recoloring, adding missing paper, trimming, re-glossing, reinforcement, glue, etc. Amateur work can lower the value of a book, and even professional restoration has now gained a negative aura in the modern marketplace from some quarters. In all cases a restored book can never be worth the same as an unrestored book in the same condition. There is no consensus on the inclusion of pressing, non-aqueous cleaning, tape removal and in some cases staple replacement in this definition. Until such time as there is consensus, we encourage continued debate and interaction among all interested parties and reflection upon the standards in other hobbies and art forms.

REVIVAL - An issue that begins republishing a comic book character after a period of dormancy.

ROCKFORD - A high grade collection of 1940s comics with 2000+ books from Rockford, IL.

ROLLED SPINE - A condition where the left edge of a comic book curves toward the front or back; a defect caused by folding back each page as the comic was read.

ROUND BOUND - Standard saddle stitch binding typical of most comics.

RUN - A group of comics of one title where most or all of the issues are present. See **Complete Run**.

S&K - Abbreviation for the legendary creative team of Joe Simon and Jack Kirby, creators of Marvel Comics' Captain America.

SADDLE STITCH - The staple binding of magazines and comic books.

san francisco collection - (see **Reilly, Tom**)

SCARCE - 20-100 copies estimated to exist.

SEDUCTION OF THE INNOCENT - An inflammatory book written by Dr. Frederic Wertham and published in 1953; Wertham asserted that comics were responsible for rampant juvenile deliquency in American youth.

SET - (1) A complete run of a given title; (2) A grouping of comics for sale.

SEMI-MONTHLY - Published twice a month, but not necessarily **Bi-Weekly**.

SEWN SPINE - A comic with many spine perforations where binders' thread held it into a bound volume. This is considered a defect.

SF - Abbreviation for Science Fiction (the other commonly used term, "sci-fi," is often considered derogatory or indicative of more "low-brow" rather than "literary" science fiction, i.e. "sci-fi television."

SILVER AGE - Comics published from 1956 to 1970.

SILVER PROOF - A black and white actual size print on thick glossy paper hand-painted by an artist to indicate colors to the engraver.

SLAB - Colloquial term for the plastic enclosure used by grading certification companies to seal in certified comics.

SLABBING - Colloquial term for the process of encapsulating certified comics in a plastic enclosure.

SOTI - Abbreviation for **Seduction of the Innocent**.

SPINE - The left-hand edge of the comic that has been folded and stapled.

SPINE ROLL - A condition where the left edge of the comic book curves toward the front or back, caused by folding back each page as the comic was read.

SPINE SPLIT SEALED - A process by which a spine split is sealed using an adhesive.

SPLASH PAGE - A **Splash Panel** that takes up the entire page.

SPLASH PANEL - (1) The first panel of a comic book story, usually larger than other panels and usually containing the title and credits of the story; (2) An oversized interior panel.

SQUARE BACK or SQUARE BOUND - See **Perfect Binding**.

STORE STAMP - Store name (and sometimes address and telephone number) stamped in ink via rubber stamp and stamp pad.

SUBSCRIPTION COPY - A comic sent through the mail directly from the publisher or publisher's agent. Most are folded in half, causing a subscription crease or fold running down the center of the comic from top to bottom; this is considered a defect.

SUBSCRIPTION CREASE - See **Subscription Copy**.

SUBSCRIPTION FOLD - See **Subscription Copy**. Differs from a **Subscription Crease** in that no ink is missing as a result of the fold.

SUN SHADOW - Darker, usually linear area at the edge of some comics stored in stacks. Some portion of the cover was not covered by the comic immediately above it, and it suffered prolonged exposure to light. A serious defect, unlike a **Dust Shadow**, which can sometimes be removed. Also see **Oxidation Shadow**.

SUPER-HERO - A costumed crime fighter with powers beyond those of mortal man.

SUPER-VILLAIN - A costumed criminal with powers beyond those of mortal man; the antithesis of **Super-Hero**.

SWIPE - A panel, sequence, or story obviously borrowed from previously published material.

TEAR SEALS - A process by which a tear is sealed using an adhesive.

TEXT ILLO. - A drawing or small panel in a text story that almost never has a dialogue balloon.

TEXT PAGE - A page with no panels or drawings.

TEXT STORY - A story with few if any illustrations commonly used as filler material during the first three decades of comics.

3-D COMIC - Comic art that is drawn and printed in two color layers, producing a 3-D effect when viewed through special glasses.

3-D EFFECT COMIC - Comic art that is drawn to appear as if in 3-D but isn't.

TITLE - The name of the comic book.

TITLE PAGE - First page of a story showing the title of the story and possibly the creative credits and indicia.

TRIMMED - (1) A bindery process which separates top, right, and bottom of pages and cuts comic books to the proper size; (2) A repair process in which defects along the edges of a comic book are removed with the use of scissors, razor blades, and/or paper cutters. Comic books which have been repaired in this fashion are considered defectives.

TTA - Abbreviation for *Tales to Astonish*.

UK - Abbreviation for British edition (United Kingdom).

UNDER GUIDE - When a comic book is priced at a value less than Guide list.

UPGRADE - To obtain another copy of the same comic book in a higher grade.

VARIANT COVER - A different cover image used on the same issue.

VERY RARE - 1 to 10 copies estimated to exist.

VICTORIAN AGE - Comics published from 1828 to 1883.

WANT LIST - A listing of comics needed by a collector, or a list of comics that a collector is interested in purchasing.

WAREHOUSE COPY - Originating from a publisher's warehouse; similar to file copy.

WHITE MOUNTAIN COLLECTION - A collection of high grade 1950s and 1960s comics which originated in New England.

X-OVER - Short for **Crossover**.

ZINE - Short for **Fanzine**.

THE OVERSTREET HALL OF FAME

The Overstreet Hall of Fame was conceived to single out individuals who have made great contributions to the comic book arts.

This includes writers, artists, editors, publishers and others who have plied their craft in insightful and meaningful ways.

While such evaluations are inherently subjective, they also serve to aid in reflecting upon those who shaped the experience of reading comic books over the years.

This year's class of inductees begins on this next page.

THE PREVIOUS INDUCTEES

Class of 2006
Murphy Anderson
Jim Aparo
Jim Lee
Mac Raboy

Class of 2007
Dave Cockrum
Steve Ditko
Bruce Hamilton
Martin Nodell
George Pérez
Jim Shooter
Dave Stevens
Alex Toth
Michael Turner

Class of 2008
Carl Barks
Will Eisner
Al Feldstein
Harvey Kurtzman
Stan Lee
Marshall Rogers
John Romita, Sr.
John Romita, Jr.
Julius Schwartz
Mike Wieringo

Class of 2009
Neal Adams
Matt Baker
Chris Claremont
Palmer Cox
Bill Everett
Frank Frazetta
Neil Gaiman
William M. Gaines
Carmine Infantino
Jack Kirby
Joe Kubert
Paul Levitz
Russ Manning
Todd McFarlane
Don Rosa
John Severin
Joe Simon
Al Williamson

Class of 2010
Sergio Aragonés
M.C. Gaines
Archie Goodwin
Winsor McCay
Mike Mignola
Frank Miller
Robert M. Overstreet
Mike Richardson
Jerry Robinson
Joe Shuster
Jerry Siegel
Jim Steranko
Wally Wood

Class of 2011
Jack Davis
Martin Goodman
Dean Mullaney
Marie Severin
Walt Simonson
Major Malcolm Wheeler-Nicholson

Class of 2012
John Buscema
Dan DeCarlo
Jean Giraud (Moebius)
Larry Hama
Kurt Schaffenberger
Bill Sienkiewicz
Curt Swan
Roy Thomas

Class of 2013
Mark Chiarello
Mike Deodato, Jr.
Bill Finger
Jack Kamen
Bob Kane
Andy Kubert

Class of 2014
George Evans
Lou Fine
Gardner Fox
Terry Moore
Dave Sim
Jeff Smith

Class of 2015
Paul Gulacy
Don McGregor
Alex Schomburg
Mark Waid

Class of 2016
Darwyn Cooke
Russ Heath
Rob Liefeld
R.F. Outcault
Tim Truman

Class of 2017
Mike Grell
Osamu Tezuka
Jim Valentino
Mark Wheatley
Bernie Wrightson

Cartoonist and comic book artist Charles Clarence "C.C." Beck is celebrated for his work on Captain Marvel at Fawcett and DC. His style captured the youthful essence of comics with slightly exaggerated cartoony flair. He joined Fawcett Publications in 1933 as a staff artist, creating pulp magazines. Then he was tapped to draw Captain Marvel, Spy Smasher, and Ibis the Invincible in *Whiz Comics* and other titles. Beck defined the look of Captain Marvel, so his role expanded to overseeing the art of the character in various comics and he opened his own New York City comics studio in 1941. The studio provided art for the Marvel Family titles with Beck acting as chief artist, but when Fawcett folded their comics line, he left the industry. Beck returned to comics in the mid-1960s with a three-issue run of his creation, *Fatman the Human Flying Saucer*. In 1973, he was the initial artist on *Shazam!*, the Captain Marvel revival, but left after creative differences. In his later years he painted cover recreations of Golden Age comics and served as the editor for *Fawcett Collectors of America* in the early '80s.

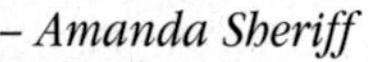
– Amanda Sheriff

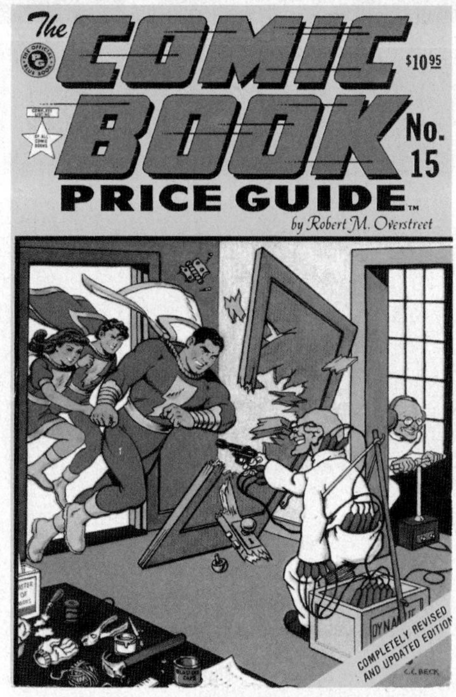

OVERSTREET COMIC BOOK PRICE GUIDE #15
1985. © Gemstone Publishing

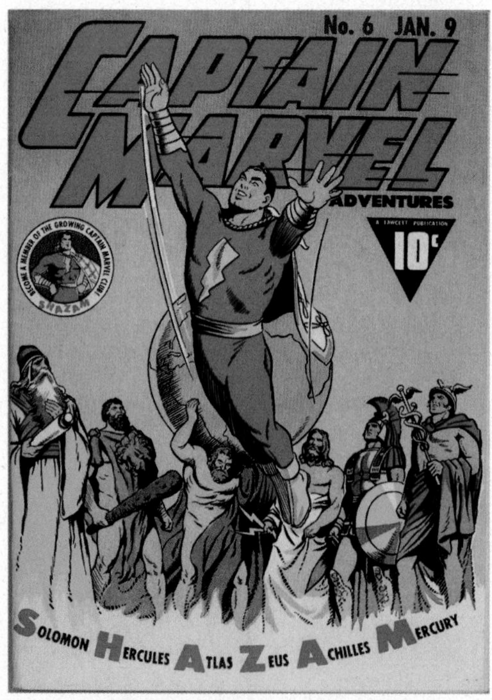

CAPTAIN MARVEL ADVENTURES #6
January 1942. © FAW

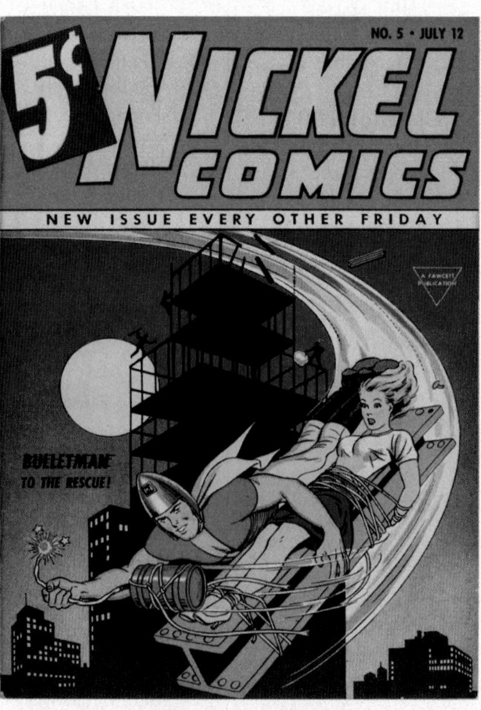

NICKEL COMICS #5
July 1940. © FAW

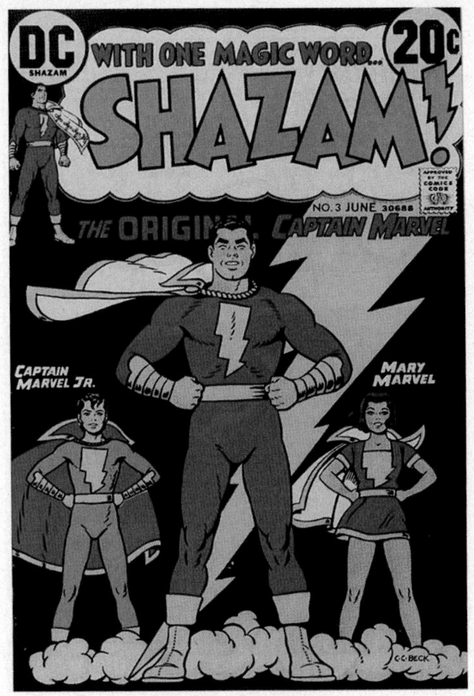

SHAZAM! #3
June 1973. © DC

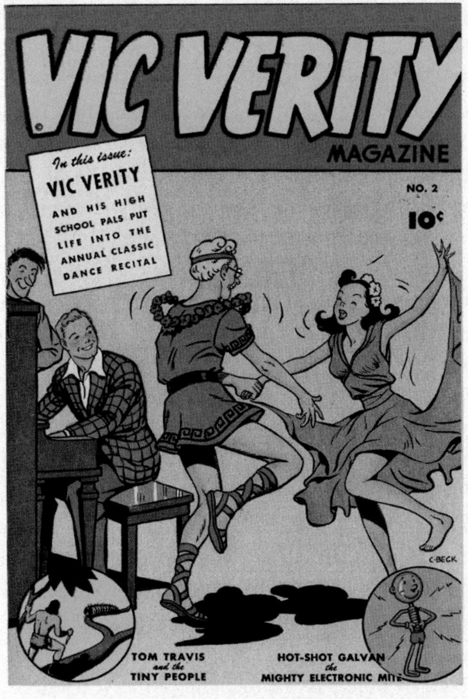

VIC VERITY MAGAZINE #2
1946. © Vic Verity Publ.

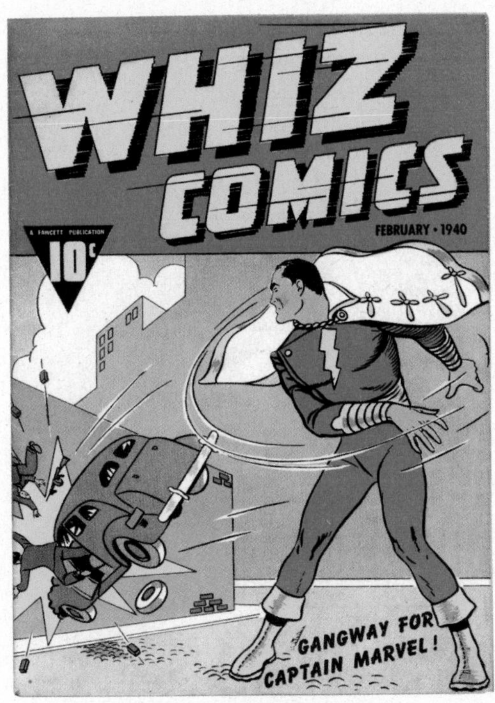

WHIZ COMICS #2 (#1)
February 1940. © FAW

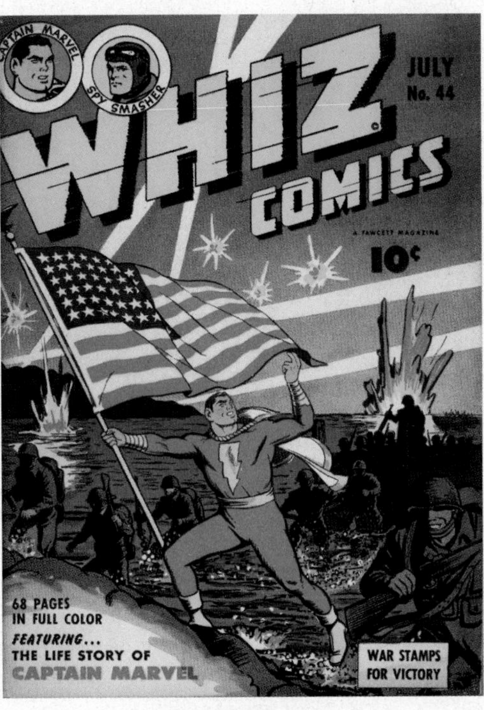

WHIZ COMICS #44
July 1943. © FAW

From his first published work in DC Comics' mystery, war and romance titles, Howard Chaykin hit the ground running and has never let up. Almost out of the gate he was creating his own characters, from Ironwolf to Dominic Fortune to Cody Starbuck. But he's also worked on a *Who's Who* of Marvel and DC characters: Batman, Wolverine, Punisher, Nick Fury, Challengers of the Unknown, Blade, Black Canary, Hawkgirl, Rawhide Kid and a revamp of The Shadow that set a high bar for modernizing a dusty pulp character. He's also worked for a variety of publishers, Atlas-Seaboard, Vortex, Bravura, Image, Vertigo, Wildstorm, BOOM! and others. He even spent some time in the Star Wars universe, adapting the original movie. He took side trips to places like *Heavy Metal*, original graphic novels like the acclaimed *Time²*, and television work on shows like *The Flash*, *Viper* and *Mutant X*, but he always returned to comics. Howard's influence is widely felt across modern comics, and techniques he pioneered in his own ground-breaking *American Flagg!* (many in conjunction with letterer Ken Bruzenak) and other titles have been copied and adapted by others in the medium in the years since.

– Tom Mason

AMERICAN FLAGG! #1
October 1983. © First Comics & Howard Chaykin

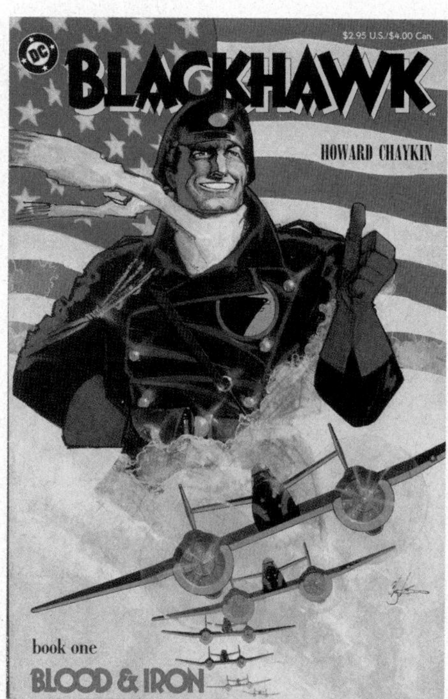

BLACKHAWK BOOK ONE: BLOOD AND IRON
1987. © DC

MARVEL SPOTLIGHT #31
December 1976. © MAR

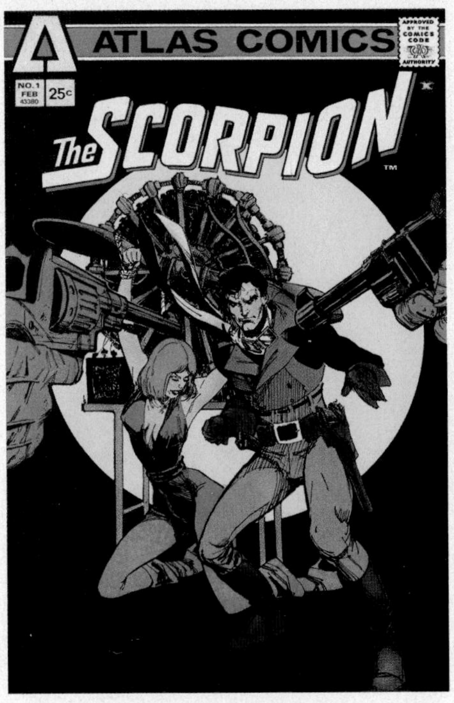

THE SCORPION #1
February 1975. © Atlas-Seaboard

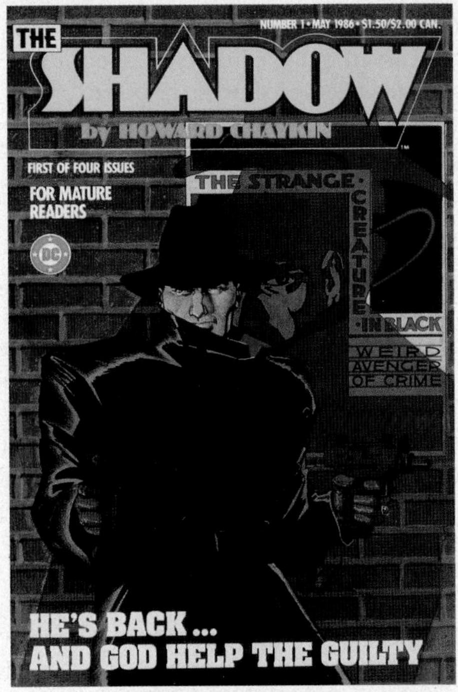

THE SHADOW #1
May 1986. © Conde Nast

STAR REACH #1
April 1974. © Star Reach Publ.

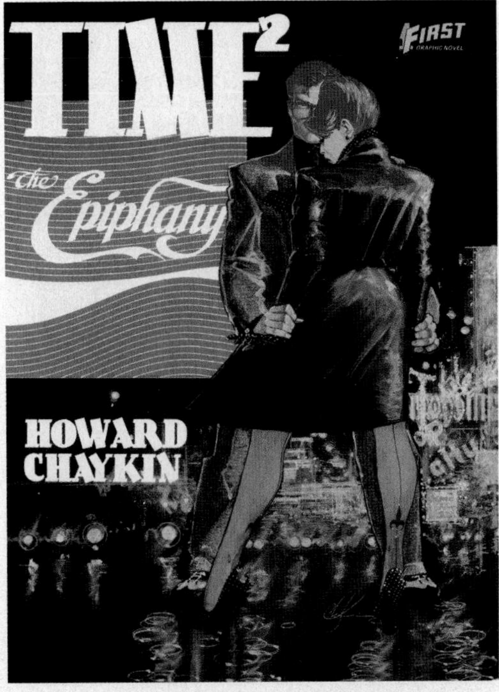

TIME²: THE EPIPHANY (FIRST COMICS GRAPHIC NOVEL #9)
November 1986. © First Comics & Howard Chaykin

Comic book writer-editor Dennis "Denny" O'Neil carved out for himself a special place as a distinctive voice who also had an eye for developing others' best work. As a writer, while he has worked on many different titles, O'Neil is best-known for his collaborations with Neal Adams on *Green Lantern*/Green Arrow and DC's *Batman* titles (where they created Ra's al Ghul, revitalized the Joker and brought back Two-Face), with Michael Kaluta on *The Shadow*, and with Denys Cowan on *The Question* (on which O'Neil had a 36-issue run). He is also credited with much of the storyline for *Transformers* and naming Optimus Prime. He wrote *Iron Man* for four years and kicked off DC's *Batman: Legends of the Dark Knight* with its first arc. His work as an editor for both Marvel and DC spans many different series. Among his top credits are supervising Frank Miller and Klaus Janson's *Daredevil* at Marvel and serving as group editor of the Batman family of comics at DC.

–J.C. Vaughn

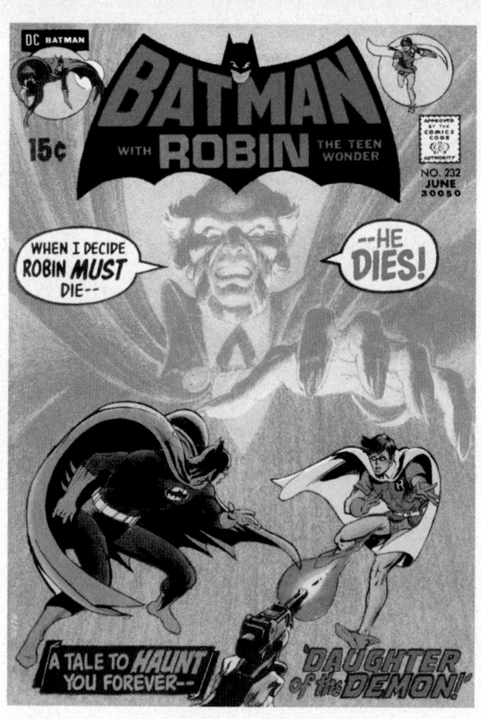

BATMAN #232
June 1971. © DC

BATMAN #234
August 1971. © DC

BATMAN: LEGENDS OF THE DARK KNIGHT #50
September 1993. © DC

DAREDEVIL #179
February 1982. © MAR

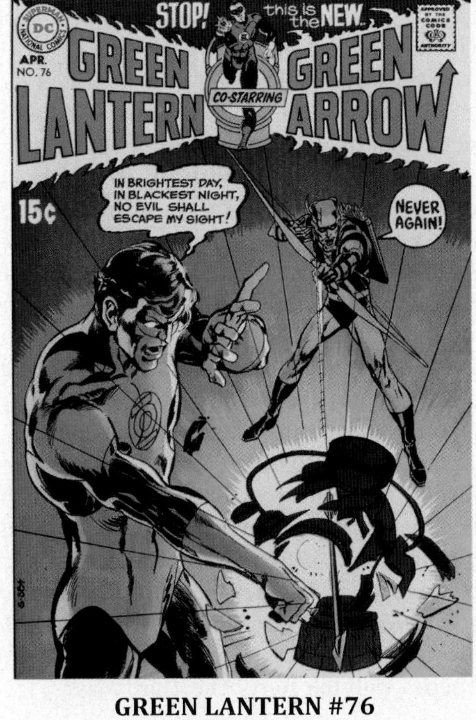

GREEN LANTERN #76
April 1970. © DC

THE QUESTION #1
February 1987. © DC

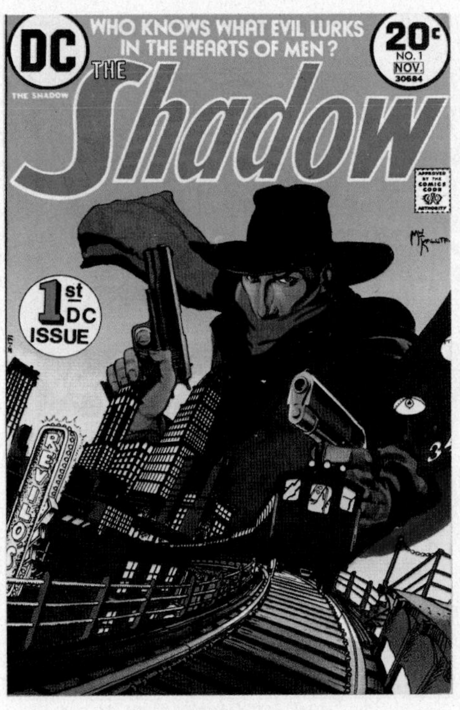

THE SHADOW #1
October - November 1973. © Condé Nast

A manga writer and artist in addition to being a screenwriter and director in film, Katsuhiro Otomo is easily best-known for his legendary work on *Akira*. In the world of manga, Otomo's career began by doing a number of short stories for *Action* magazine in the late 1970s, before he started on his first long-form work, *Fireball*. He followed up with *Domu* in 1980, and that in turn was followed up with *Akira*, which began serialization in 1983. It was around this time that he began working in anime, first as a character designer before moving on to directing. The 1988 animated feature film *Akira* was directed by Otomo, though the manga was actually still ongoing at the time; *Akira* is considered one of the most influential anime films of all time. While Otomo has continued to work in animation on films such as *Steamboy* and *Metropolis*, his comics work has also continued with series including *The Legend of Mother Sarah* and *Hipira: The Little Vampire*. He also contributed to the *Batman: Black & White* limited series with the story "The Third Mask.".

– Carrie Wood

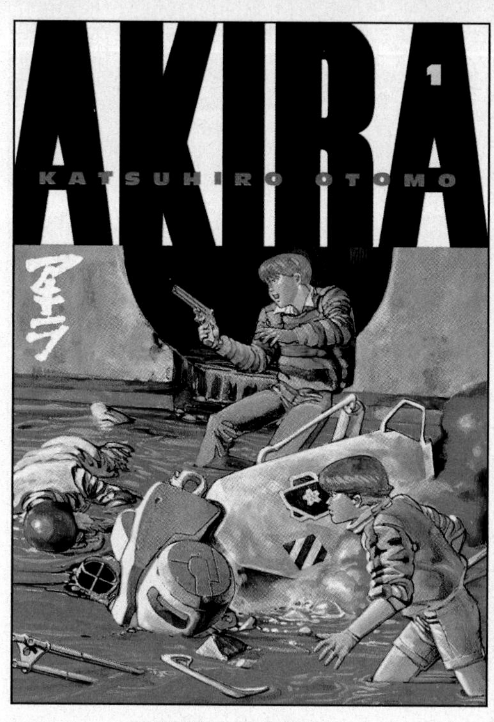

AKIRA - BOOK 1
English collection by Kodansha Comics. 2009.
© MASH • ROOM Co. Ltd.

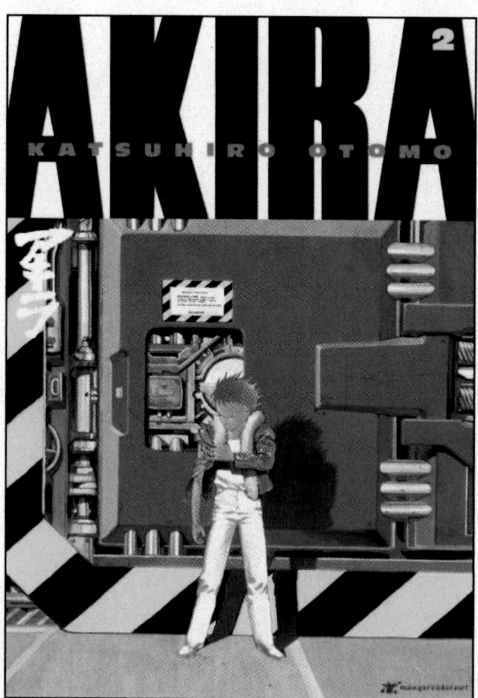

AKIRA - BOOK 2
English collection by Dark Horse Comics. 2001.
© MASH • ROOM Co. Ltd.

BATMAN: BLACK AND WHITE #4
Interior page - September 1996. © DC Comics

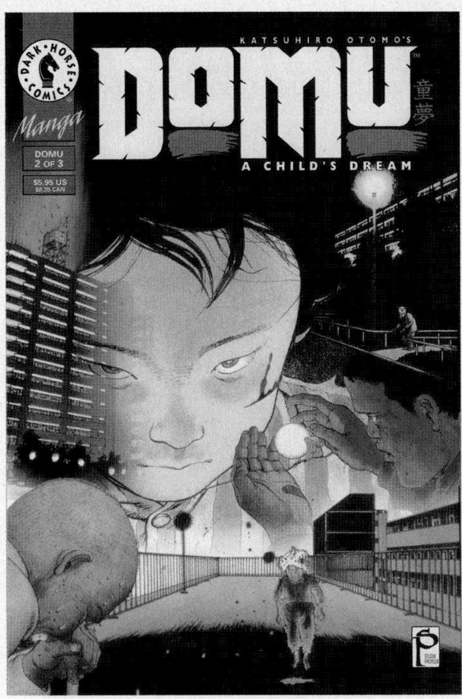

DOMU: A CHILD'S DREAM #2
1995. © Katsuhiro Otomo

HIGHWAY STAR
1979. © Katsuhiro Otomo

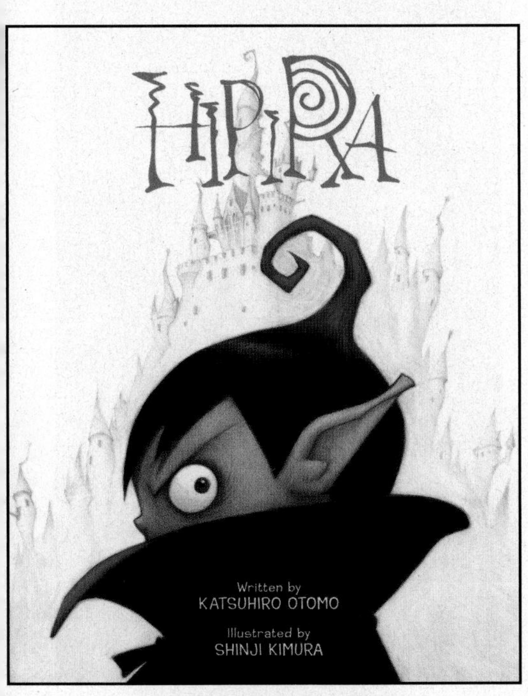

HIPIRA
Dark Horse cover - 2005. Art by Shinji Kimura.
© MASH ROOM & Shinji Kimura

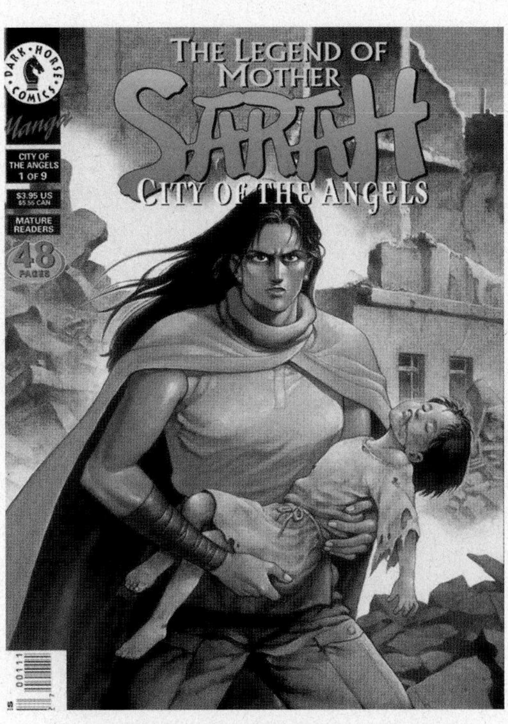

THE LEGEND OF MOTHER SARAH: CITY OF THE ANGELS #1
October 1996. English printing
by Dark Horse Comics. © Katsuhiro Otomo

Marc Silvestri has been a pioneer in the comics industry for dozens of years, having been part of the original artist collective to establish Image Comics in 1992. His career started in the '80s, working for both DC and First Comics before moving to Marvel, where he worked on *Uncanny X-Men* and *Wolverine*. After founding Image, Silvestri established the Top Cow imprint, where he's worked on a number of different titles, including *Cyberforce, Codename: Stryke Force, Witchblade, Hunter-Killer,* and *The Darkness*, among many others. *Witchblade* was actually adapted into an anime series in 2006, which Silvestri executive produced; *The Darkness* has seen two video game adaptations, in 2007 and 2012. Silvestri continues to run Top Cow as its CEO, though he has also contributed to various *X-Men* titles for Marvel within the last few years as well.

-Carrie Wood

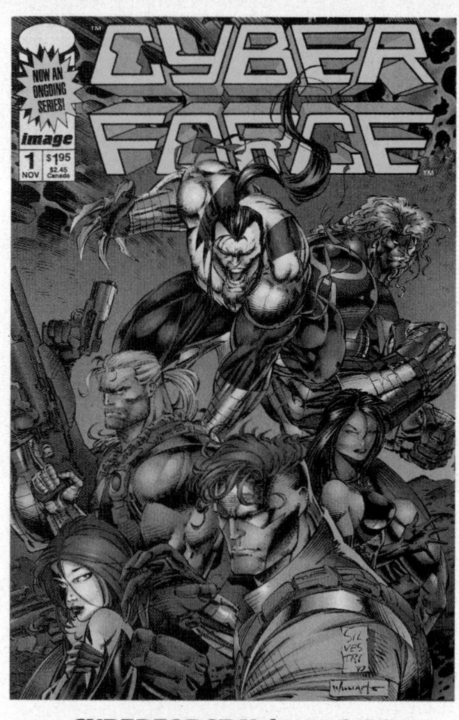

CYBERFORCE Volume 2 #1
November 1993. © TCOW

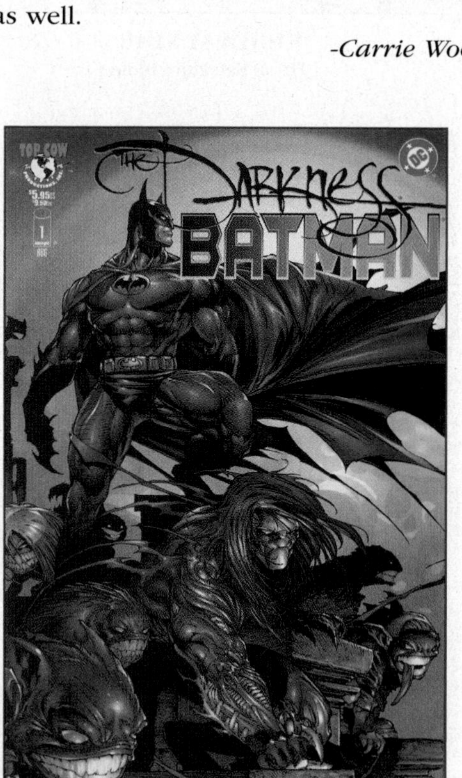

THE DARKNESS / BATMAN #1
August 1999. © TCOW & DC

HUNTER-KILLER #1
March 2005. © TCOW

INCREDIBLE HULK #1
December 2011. © MAR

UNCANNY X-MEN #221
September 1987. © MAR

WITCHBLADE #170
October 2013. © TCOW

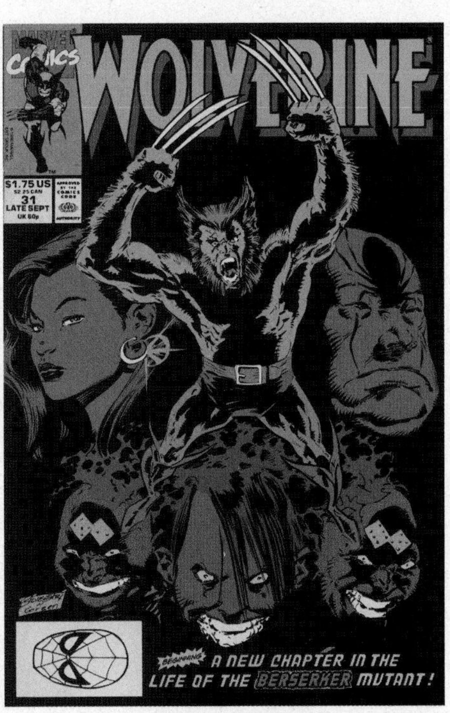

WOLVERINE #31
Late September 1990. © MAR

Throughout his career, writer-editor Len Wein made significant contributions to both DC and Marvel. Wein's career began with the *Teen Titans* #18 story "Eye of the Beholder" in 1968, followed by work on romance comics, horror magazines, and TV tie-ins. Wein and artist Bernie Wrightson co-created Swamp Thing in *House of Secrets* #92 in 1971 and worked on Swamp Thing's initial run, then in the mid-'80s Wein edited *Saga of the Swamp Thing*. In the early '70s he regularly wrote for Marvel titles like *Amazing Spider-Man* and *Thor*. Wein and artists John Romita Sr. and Herb Trimpe co-created Wolverine in *Incredible Hulk* #180 (cameo appearance) in '74, followed by the X-Men revival, reformatted as *Giant Size X-Men* with Dave Cockrum. Returning to DC, he wrote *Batman*, creating Lucius Fox, wrote the *Wonder Woman* reboot, and edited the acclaimed *Watchmen*. Later in his career, Wein wrote and story edited animated shows like *X-Men*, *Batman*, and *Spider-Man*, wrote for Cartoon Network shows, and in 2012 he penned the *Before Watchmen: Ozymandias* miniseries.

– *Amanda Sheriff*

AMAZING SPIDER-MAN #151
December 1975. © MAR

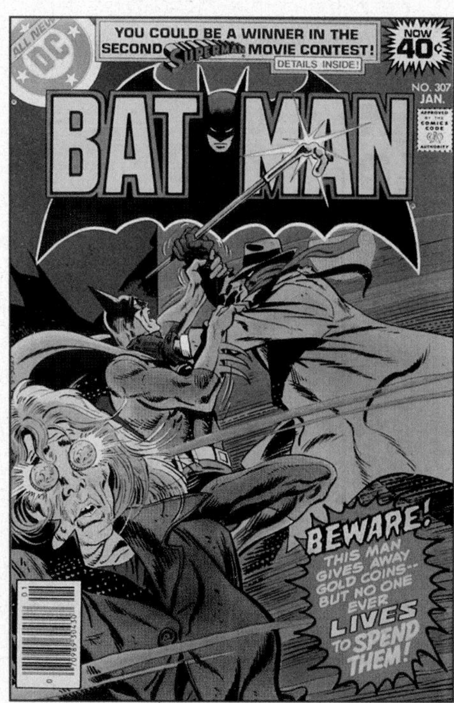

BATMAN #307
January 1979. © DC

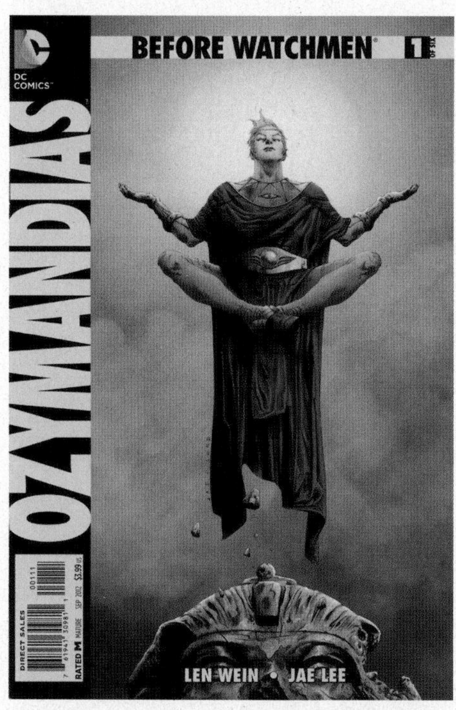

BEFORE WATCHMEN: OZYMANDIAS #1
September 2012. © DC

GIANT-SIZE X-MEN #1
Summer 1975. © MAR

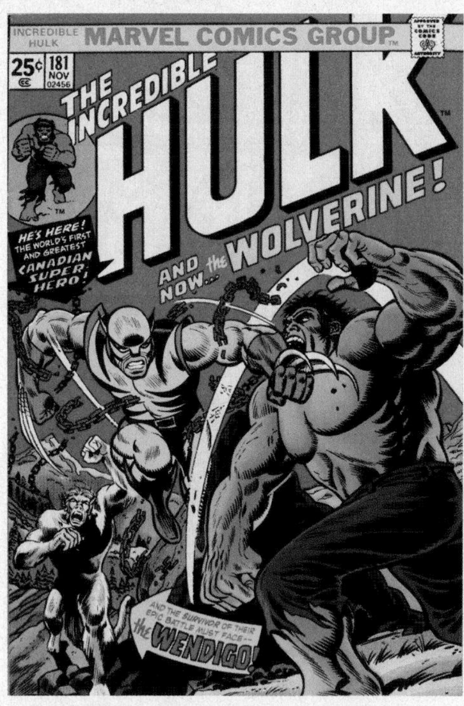

INCREDIBLE HULK #181
November 1974. © MAR

SWAMP THING #1
October-November 1972. © DC

WONDER WOMAN (2nd series) #7
August 1987. © DC

Action Comics #1 at 80

By Paul Levitz

There are several lenses through which we can measure importance. If you want to consider it on the basis of being first, in the world that the *The Overstreet Comic Book Price Guide* focuses on, *Funnies on Parade* or *Famous Funnies* would have a fair claim. The former is considered the first publication to adopt a version of the format we came to call to comic books as a way to reprint popular newspaper strips in 1933, and the latter is the first one that was actually sold to the public (*On Parade* being used as a premium giveaway). If being the first to open up creative possibilities, *New Fun Comics* in 1935 gets the nod, for being the first comic to continuously focus on original material.

But on almost any other basis, we have to acknowledge *Action Comics* #1 as the most important comic ever published.

In much of America, it arrived on April 19, 1938, some 80 years before this edition of the *Guide*. It was a country emerging from the Great Depression, and becoming deeply concerned by events in Europe that would lead to World War II. The newfangled comic books were a tiny corner of any newsstand, with just over a dozen issues published that month, most of them still dominated by newspaper strip reprints. Of the publishers that would long command the field, only Dell and the company that would ultimately be known as DC had begun publishing, and bluntly, virtually all the original material in any of these comics was derivative of the newspaper strips or formulaic genre stories like cowboys and Indians. The competition wasn't intense.

Most of what was in *Action Comics* #1 wasn't much better. A cowboy, a boxer, an adventurer, even a tale of Marco Polo were up to the (minimal) standards of the comics of the day, but no more. There was some potential in a stage magician named Zatara, who worked his magic by speaking backwards, but it was mostly the charming art by Fred Guardineer that lifted it above being a cheesy twist on the popular *Mandrake the Magician* newspaper strip. And if things had proceeded otherwise, *Action* might have been as forgettable as this list.

Here's where things get fuzzier. Not about the importance of the issue, but about its parentage. You've heard the saying that "Success has many fathers, failure is an orphan," right? Well, the story of *Action Comics* #1 could make for an interesting DNA test.

The undisputed parents of the ingredient that changed *Action Comics* from trivia to a cultural event of the first proportion were two young men from Cleveland, Ohio: Jerry Siegel and Joe Shuster. They had been working in the infant field of comic books pretty much from the beginning, while developing and polishing what they felt was their best shot as a newspaper comic strip—the format where the real money was, and where you could reach a massive audience instead of the small one comic books touched. The problem was, no matter how hard they pitched, no matter how persistent they were, no matter how much they polished their samples, no one wanted *Superman*.

It's a truism in entertainment marketing that the wisest thing to offer the public is something familiar, only done in a somewhat better or novel fashion. Truly daring and unprecedented projects crash and burn far more often than they fly – and Superman didn't even have the ability to fly in those first samples, only hurtling over skyscrapers - which didn't even look that tall (the Empire State Building having only opened seven years before, and young Clark picking smaller buildings than Cleveland's own Terminal Tower to demonstrate his ability in his first story, leaving the tallest building between Chicago and New York relegated to the background). *Superman* just

didn't seem like a good bet to any of the newspaper syndicates, the early comic book publishers, or even DC.

Also undisputed is that *Action Comics* was being prepared as the second title in a joint venture between Major Malcolm Wheeler-Nicholson's National Allied company, the venture which had launched *New Fun Comics*, and his distributor and occasional cover printer, Harry Donenfeld (ably assisted by Jack Liebowitz). Their *Detective Comics* was a little over a year along, and appeared to be running smoothly, at least to the public.

YOU NEEDN'T BE AFRAID OF ME. I WON'T HARM YOU

But it was not a happy partnership. Over Christmas, 1937, Donenfeld and Liebowitz pushed Nicholson's company into bankruptcy, and emerged almost instantaneously in complete control of their joint venture, and Nicholson's own two titles, *Adventure Comics* and *More Fun Comics*.

So this is where the collateral parentage gets fuzzy. Nicholson's advocates claim that he'd already seen *Superman* (almost certainly true, as Siegel and Shuster had been working for his titles and were offering *Superman* wherever there was an opportunity) and was thinking of it for *Action*. Vincent Sullivan, the cartoonist who served as Nicholson's editor and came with the company into Donenfeld's embrace never told his version of the story in detail, just saying he ultimately chose *Superman* to fill empty space in the new title as he was assembling it. And Shelly Mayer, the genius cartoonist and future editor, very vividly told his version of events, in which he basically pulled *Superman* from the reject stack of the McClure Syndicate where he worked, and convinced his boss, Max Gaines, to send it over to Donenfeld for consideration. Personally, this writer trusts Shelly... but until we get time viewers or time machines, we won't have proof.

Add to this Jack Liebowitz towards the end of his life telling me that he picked the illustration for the cover of *Action Comics* #1 – possibly the most meaningful cover choice in comics history. It's not implausible for a businessman acting as publisher to pick a cover, or approve it, but Liebowitz had long outlived anyone who could corroborate or dispute his view.

Even small details of Superman's leap in *Action Comics* #1 are disputed. The first story was prepared as samples for a newspaper strip, and needed some modest revision and art adjustments to fit the comic book format.

AND SO BEGINS THE STARTLING ADVENTURES OF THE MOST SENSATIONAL STRIP CHARACTER OF ALL TIME: SUPERMAN!
A PHYSICAL MARVEL, A MENTAL WONDER, SUPERMAN IS DESTINED TO RESHAPE THE DESTINY OF A WORLD!
Only in ACTION COMICS CAN YOU THRILL AT THE DARING DEEDS OF THIS SUPERB CREATION! DON'T MISS AN ISSUE!

Three different people told me directly over the years they did that work, all decent folk with plausible connections to the events: Sol Harrison (later DC's longtime head of production and ultimately President) was a color separator at the time, and the firm where he worked in 1938 colored *Action* and could have been asked to do the adjustments; Harry Lampert (the cartoonist who co-created the original Flash) knew Shelly Mayer from the Fleisher Brothers animation studio, and could have been suggested by him for the task; and, to me at least, the most likely, Frank Shuster, Joe's brother and sometime letterer.

What is objectively indisputable is the effect that *Action Comics* #1 had. *Funnies on Parade* had given birth to a format, *Famous Funnies* to a product, but *Action* truly birthed an industry, a genre, and a cultural movement that has lasted decades, become a powerful force in every modern media form, and touched everyone in the world. Siegel and Shuster's creation defined the superhero as something distinct from its ancestors in the pulp magazines (such as *Doc Savage*), newspaper strips (*The Phantom*), science fiction (Wylie's *The Gladiator*), literature (*The Scarlet Pimpernel*), and even the heroes of mythology. This was something new, something enduring and as powerful as the hero within the story.

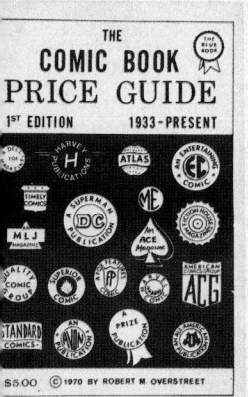

THE COMIC BOOK PRICE GUIDE
1ST EDITION 1933-PRESENT
$5.00 ©1970 BY ROBERT M. OVERSTREET

According to producer/comics historian Michael Uslan's memory of ancient DC records he saw in his youth, that first issue had a print run of 200,000 copies, two-thirds of which sold through on the newsstands, a very healthy percentage for the time. *Superman* didn't earn the spot as the permanent cover feature of *Action* for about a year – unsurprising, given the length of time it took to gather data from the newsstands in those pre-computerized days and the lead times for preparing new issues. But by the time he did, *Action* was selling over a half-million copies per issue, and DC took the then-unprecedented step of awarding him a comic of his own, whose first issue went through three printings to meet demand, and whose second issue became the first comic book to sell a million copies.

ACTION COMICS
June, 1938 - Present
National Periodical Publications

Issue #	Good	Fine	Mint
1-Origin Superman, Intro. Zatara.	200.00	250.00	300.00
2	50.00	60.00	70.00
3	40.00	50.00	65.00
4	35.00	45.00	55.00
5	30.00	35.00	45.00
6,8,9	25.00	30.00	35.00
7,10-Superman covers.	30.00	35.00	40.00

The *Superman* S-shield symbol, born in that first issue of *Action*, is one of the most recognized icons in the world.

Superman has starred in more major media than any other fictional character created in the 20th Century: comic books, newspaper strips, radio drama, children's books, movie serials, theatrical cartoons, television programs, television animation, motion pictures, television commercials, video games, novels, and the list goes on. But *Action Comics* #1 isn't simply his story, it's the beginning of the story of the whole superhero genre and concept and its extraordinary influence on American and world culture.

There are runners-up: a case can be made for the outsize importance of *Fantastic Four* #1 as the birth of the Marvel Comics cultural phenomenon, *MAD* #1 for the effect the magazine would ultimately have on American humor, or *Zap Comix* #1 for the counter cultural power of the underground comix. But it's fair to say that none of these three would have been likely to exist if *Action Comics* #1 hadn't established comic book publishing as a viable and highly profitable business that could withstand the attacks it would suffer in the decades to come.

I should have bought a copy for the $300 "mint condition" value estimated in the very first edition of *The Overstreet Comic Book Price Guide*. That amount invested at that time in the stock market could have yielded about $29,000... *Action Comics* #1 would have been a much wiser investment at a top sale price of $3.2 million.

Thanks, Jerry and Joe, and all the midwives who brought your magic to us.

Acclaimed comic book scribe and historian Paul Levitz is the former President and Publisher of DC Comics and a longtime Overstreet Advisor.

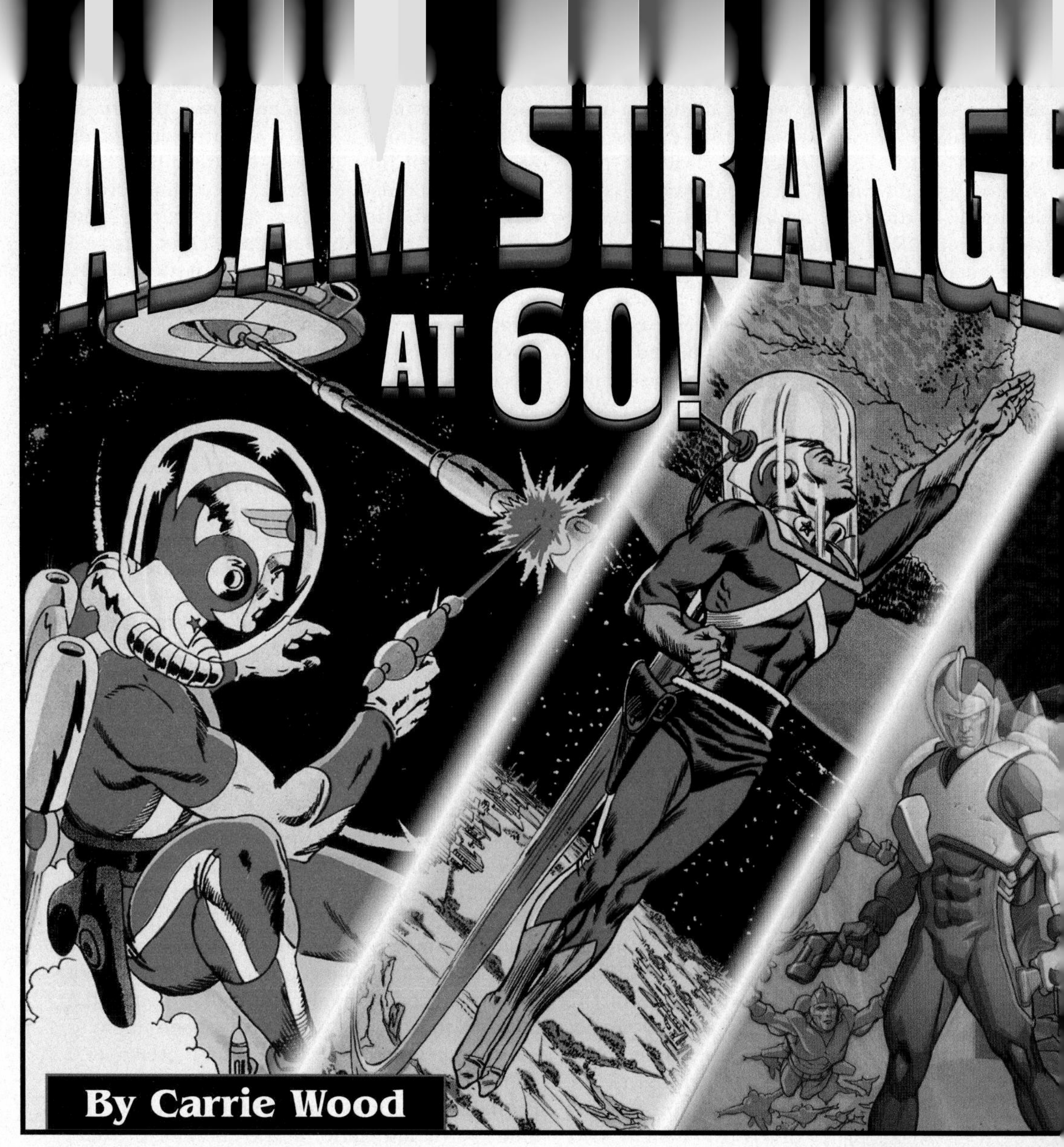

The 1950s proved to be a defining period for science fiction, as the world continued into the optimism of the Atomic Age and creators took inspiration from the blooming space race. Comics entered the Silver Age, and many already-established characters, such as Hawkman and Green Lantern, had their backstories retconned to match the sci-fi trend.

But of course, new heroes were on the horizon during this time as well. One of these was Adam Strange, who perfectly captured the feeling of what science fiction embodied at the time. Debuting in *Showcase* #17 in November 1958, Adam Strange was the creation of DC editor Julius Schwartz with a design courtesy of Murphy Anderson (who worked on designing Zatanna, the Silver Age Hawkman and many others). The character was the result of a challenge levied by DC's editorial director, Irwin Donenfeld, who wanted Schwartz and fellow editor Jack Schiff to each create a new sci-fi hero – one set in present time, and the other from the future. The future hero became Space Ranger, while Adam Strange debuted as the present-day hero.

Adam Strange is an archeologist studying in Peru when he's suddenly transported to the mysterious planet Rann by means of a "Zeta-Beam." He soon meets a woman named Alanna, who saves him from being attacked by one of the planet's native creatures. Alanna and her father, Sardath, explain to Adam that they used the Zeta-Beam in an attempt to make contact with Earth, hoping that intelligent life would trace the beam back to Rann.

Adam quickly befriends the native people of Rann and takes up a flight pack and a ray gun in order to assist and protect them from the dangers they face. However, the effects of the Zeta-Beam eventually wore off, and Adam was transported back to Earth; however, Sardath informed Adam of a schedule of Zeta-Beam firings at Earth, allowing him to intercept them and return to Rann. He also eventually marries Alanna.

The three-issue tryout run in *Showcase* (#17-19) proved to be successful enough sales-wise for the character to find a more permanent home in the *Mystery in Space* series, where he appeared in issues #53-100 and 102. Adam also later met the Justice League after helping them defeat Kanjar-Ro, and was even offered a spot on the team – but he declined, and instead continued to work to improve relations between Rann and Earth.

Adam later played a major role in the Rann-Thanagar conflict, which arose due to manipulation from Blackfire after Rann was transported into Thanagar's system. Adam teamed up with Green Lantern during this time in order to help save Rann and put an end to the war.

Recently, Adam played a major role as part of *Justice League United*, which ran from April 2014-December 2015. The team, which consisted of Adam, Animal Man, Green Arrow, Equinox, Martian Manhunter, Stargirl, Supergirl, as well as Adam's partner Alanna, formed following the "Forever Evil" event. This New 52 reboot series also retconned Adam's backstory a bit – he's now Canadian, though still an archeologist, and Alanna was not native to Rann but instead a former student of his.

Adam Strange is notable within the DC Universe for not really having any powers of his own, instead relying on his vast scientific knowledge and survival skills to get the job done. With his jetpack and ray gun, he epitomized many of the tropes of 1950s-era sci-fi, for better or for worse. Though very much a product of his time, Adam Strange remains a standout in the DC lineup, 60 years after his debut.

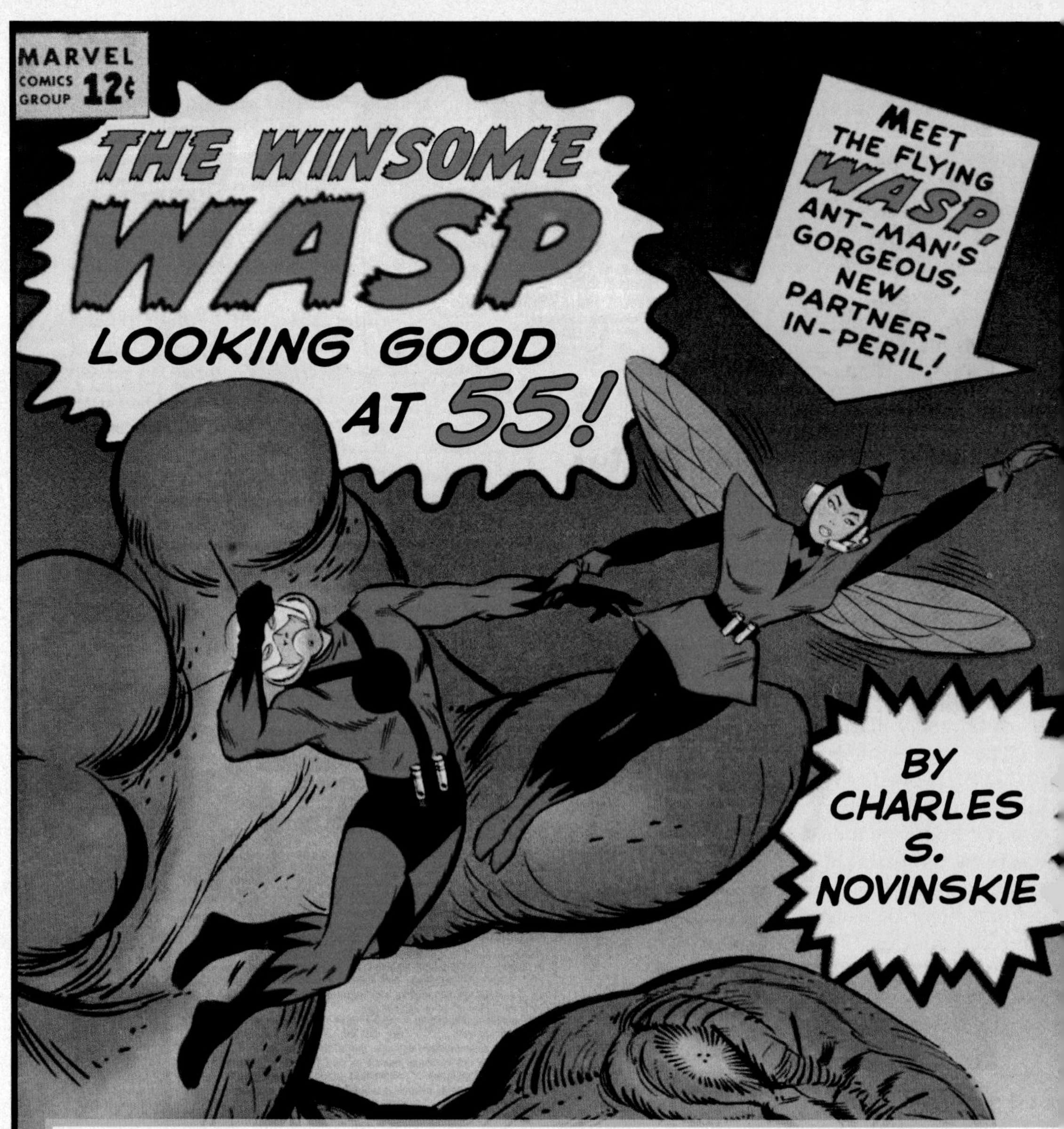

Janet van Dyne was a glamour girl in the '60s, the socialite daughter of Vernon van Dyne, noted scientist. Making her first appearance as the Wasp in *Tales To Astonish* #44 in June 1963, she was created by Stan Lee and Jack Kirby with the scripting, based on Stan's plotting, handled by H. E. Huntley.

Following the death of her father at the hands of an alien, Janet van Dyne turns to Hank Pym, her father's associate. Undergoing a process involving the shrink ray particles known as Pym Particles, Janet van Dyne takes on the persona of the superhero Wasp. Possessing the ability to shrink in size, fly using insectoid wings, and produce bioelectric blasts, she teams up with Ant-Man (Hank Pym) to avenge the death of her father. The Wasp falls in love with Pym and co-starred with him in the pages of *Tales To Astonish* #44-69. Classic Lee/Kirby villains included Egghead, Porcupine, and the Human Top (using the moniker of Whirlwind).

As a founding member of the Avengers, Janet appeared in *Avengers* #1 (September 1963) and was credited with giving the team its name. Over the course of time, Janet honed her skills as the Wasp, developing her wasp-sting and ability to control her shrinking powers without additional Pym Particles. She also appeared as a lead character in *Marvel Feature* #6-10 and eventually took over the role as the leader of the Avengers in issue #217. It was a role she played through issue #278 of *The Avengers* (except for a short stint of leadership by the Vision).

The Wasp and Yellowjacket wed in *The Avengers* #60 (January 1969). Hank Pym had assumed the secret identity of Yellowjacket after exposure to dangerous chemicals, which resulted in some memory loss. During their wedding (and an encounter with the Circus of Crime), Hank regained his memory and became the over-sized superhero, Goliath. Over time, due to the stress of being a superhero, Hank became abusive and the marriage between him and Janet ended in divorce.

In *The Avengers* #83 (December 1970), the Wasp became a member of the all-female team of Avengers knowns at the Lady Liberators, comprised of fellow superheroes Scarlet Witch, Black Widow, Valkyrie, and Medusa. Janet eventually returned to the Avengers as the team's Chairperson, a role she's elected to by the likes of Thor, Iron Man, and Captain America; under her guidance, the Avengers introduce a number of additional women to the team, such as She-Hulk and Monica Rambeau.

Once an Avenger, always an Avenger, the Wasp appeared in issue #32 of the *West Coast Avengers*, eventually becoming a full-time member with issue #42.

During the 2008 *Secret Invasion* storyline in which Skrulls attempt to infiltrate and take over the earth, the Wasp is injected with a serum by Hank Pym that enables her to both shrink and grow. But this Hank was a Skrull, and he had injected Janet with a deadly bio-bomb. In order to save everyone before exploding, Thor opens a spatial rift using his enchanted hammer Mjolnir, dispersing Janet into nothing, seemingly causing her death. Interestingly enough, after this event, it was Hank Pym himself who took on the moniker of the Wasp for a brief period of time.

In *Avengers* (Volume 4) #32-34, it is discovered that the Wasp did not die, but was sent to the Microverse, a result of the rift created by Thor. Giant-Man, Captain America, Thor, and Iron Man travel to the Microverse to rescue her and find that she is not only alive, but fighting against the evil Lord Gouzar, ruler of the Microverse. After the defeat of Lord Gouzar, Janet and the other Avengers return triumphantly to earth. Janet eventually returns to the Avengers, becoming a member of the Unity Squad team made up of both X-Men and Avengers.

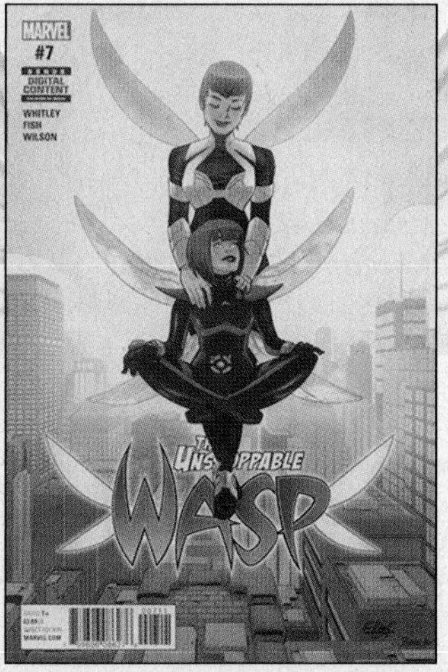

In 2017's *Unstoppable Wasp* series, it was revealed that Hank Pym had a daughter through his first marriage, named Nadia. Using a Pym Particle and her genius-level intellect, Nadia escapes her captivity in the Russian Red Room, constructs a costume, and assumes the identity of the Wasp. Nadia eventually meets and befriends Janet van Dyne and takes the surname van Dyne for herself, recognizing that Janet was the only person alive connected to her family who believed in her. Nadia forms the G.I.R.L. (Genius In Action Research Labs) program to form a team of like-minded ladies.

In other media, van Dyne has proved to be just as popular as she is in comics, appearing in numerous animated television series (*The Marvel Super Heroes, The Super Hero Squad Show, The Avengers: Earth's Mightiest Heroes*, and others), plus is a playable character in several video games. Janet Van Dyne will be appearing in 2018's Marvel Cinematic Universe entry, *Ant-Man and the Wasp*, portrayed by Michelle Pfeiffer; however, the titular Wasp will actually be Janet and Hank's daughter, Hope van Dyne, played by Evangeline Lilly, who received her mother's suit at the end of 2015's *Ant-Man* film. Between new series, new films and new comics, the legacy of Janet van Dyne clearly stretches far beyond five and a half decades.

PLANET OF THE APES AT 50

By Terry Hoknes

Based on the French novel Monkey Planet *by Pierre Boule*, Planet of the Apes *spawned the original five-film franchise that began in 1968, a TV series, a cartoon show, the 2001 reboot, and the more recent, successful movie trilogy. Centered around the 1974 "Go Ape" marathon re-release of the first five films, there was a bonanza of licensed products that went unmatched until George Lucas kept the licensing rights for* Star Wars.

Among the greatest POTA *material to come out were the comics.*

Planet of the Apes celebrated its 50th anniversary this year, having debuted in theaters on February 8, 1968. The classic sci-fi series has had nine movies released over the past five decades, and all nine movies have hit #1 at the box office. Only the *Star Wars* franchise has hit #1 more times in movie history.

POTA has achieved a lengthy and fascinating run in the comic book world worldwide in that time. The first American produced *POTA* comic book was a one-shot in 1970, tying into the release of the second film of the series, titled *Beneath the Planet of the Apes*. Gold Key Comics released a 44-page comic with a 25¢ cover price that included a poster. This comic is not only the first North American *POTA* comic but is the most valuable one. The comic is relatively hard to find in high grade and with the poster still intact. CGC now shows a total of 18 copies grade 9.0 or higher with only one copy graded at 9.6 on the census.

It was common for movie-themed magazines to publish articles about the *POTA* movies. Even some of the comic book magazines did articles about *POTA*, such as *Psycho* #4 (Skywald, Sept 1971) which had a four-page text article. *Beneath the Dignity of the Planet of the Apes* is a five-page parody comic strip drawn by Bernie Wrightson and written by Marv Wolfman, published in *Blast* #1 (G & D Publications, Feb 1971). *The Milking of the Planet that Went Ape* is an eight-page parody story with art by Mort Drucker published in *MAD* #157 (March 1973). Jack Kirby's *Kamandi*, published by DC Comics starting in 1972, was clearly derivative of *POTA*, but that didn't stop it from running 59 issues.

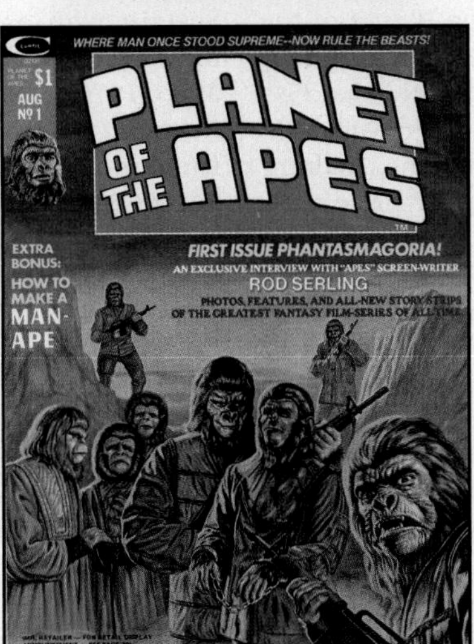

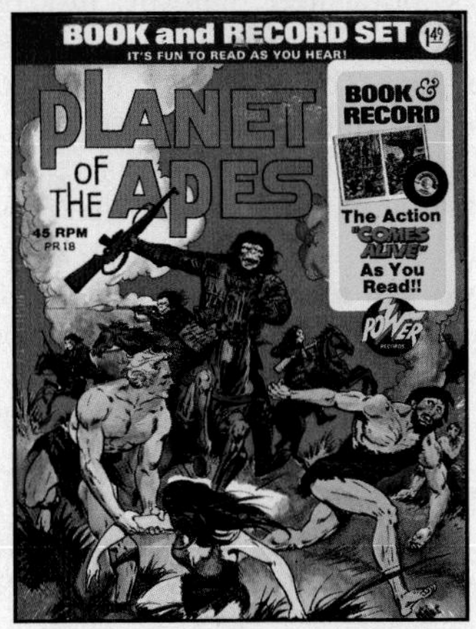

THE MARVEL ERA

As things were ramping up for the weekly TV series planned for prime time, Marvel Comics picked up the license for *Planet of the Apes*. At the time, Marvel published horror- and monster-themed magazines in addition to the others that comprised their black and white magazine line. The Apes seemed a natural fit.

Combining new original comic stories, adaptations of the movies, articles and interviews with cast and crew of the movies and new TV show, Marvel published this new series in for 29 issues from 1974 to 1977.

One of the company's prolific writers, Doug Moench, handled the scripts for the adaptations and created the new original stories as well. In doing so, he created the first original characters outside of the movie/TV universe.

Moench was teamed with a variety of artists for the project, most notably Mike Ploog and Tom Sutton on the serialized original "Terror on the Planet of the Apes." Herb Trimpe, George Tuska, Mike Esposito, Alfredo Alcala, and Rico Rival were also among those who illustrated the adventures.

While the adaptations followed the course of the first five films, the original stories were set at a variety of times between the fall of man and the rise of the apes. The two-part "Quest For The Planet of the Apes" bridged the time been the fourth film, *Conquest of the Planet of the Apes*, and the fifth, *Battle for The Planet of the Apes*.

The first 13 issues at a $1.00 cover price. With #14, the size was reduced and price lowered to 75¢ in 1975.

Issue #1 is by far the most common issue and had the highest print run. There are 60 copies of #1 CGC-certified 9.8. Exact print runs are not known. There is consistent high demand for

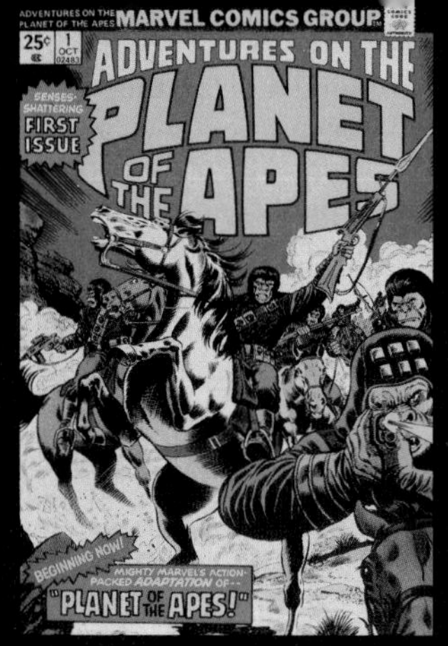

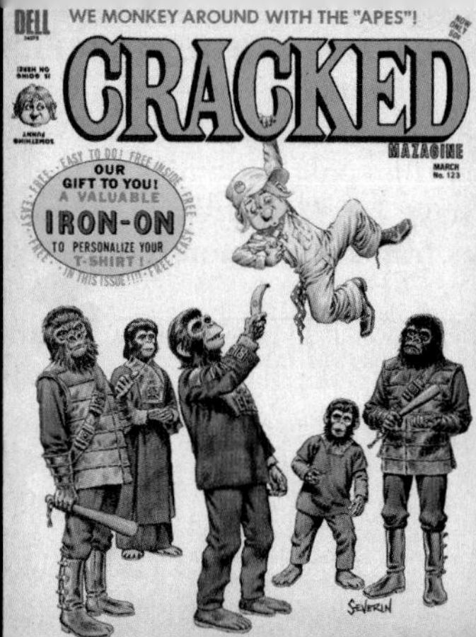

this magazine series.

Marvel reprinted their own comic book adaptations of the first two movies in a full color comic book sized series, *Adventures on the Planet of the Apes,* which ran for 11 issues. This series holds a spot among the Marvel 1976 price variants. *Adventures on the Planet of the Apes* #5-7 were produced with two different cover prices. The regular cover price was 25¢, while the test run issues with a 30¢ cover price were printed for only a few regions, making these extremely rare (like the other price variants, many collectors were not aware of their existence until decades later). These are now definitely the rarest *POTA* comic books ever published. It's estimated about 1,500 copies of each issue may have been printed. However only 14, 8 and 7 copies of these comics respectively appear on the CGC census in any condition, proving the true scarcity of these. It's estimated that less than 40 copies of each of these still exist.

Power Records adapted four of the five films into their popular line of book/record sets in 1974. A comic book was published with a pocket that would hold inside a 45 rpm record with audio narration of the story. These are highly collectible and fairly easy to find. A 32-part comic book strip in slide show form was produced by Chad Valley in 1975 and marketed with a projector.

The TV series, unfortunately, was not a big hit and was cancelled after one 13-episode season in the fall of 1974 (a fourteenth episode remained unaired until The Sci Fi Channel re-ran the series decades later).

In the fall of 1975 a new *POTA* cartoon series debuted on TV, also lasting just one season, called *Return to the Planet of the Apes*. This helped keep the demand for toys and items up for one more holiday season, but by 1976 sales were dropping, as there was no new product or merchandise beyond the magazine series.

Cracked Magazine #123 (Major Publications, March 1975) had a cover story drawn by John Severin with a five-page parody strip on the movie series. *Crazy Magazine* #17 (Marvel, May 1976) has a short parody of *POTA*. *National Lampoon Magazine* Vol 2 #9 (National Lampoon, April 1979) had a four-page parody. *MAD* #242 (EC, October 1983) had one panel showing an ape.

FOREIGN EDITIONS

Marvel had licensing in other countries, and so unique versions of the *POTA* magazine were printed in a dozen countries and in different languages. The most successful series was *POTA* published as a weekly comic magazine in the UK, which ran for 123 issues at 8 pence per week. These were slimmer issues than the US editions, and so they were able to stretch the material into many more issues (which were mostly just new packaging of the material). However, more than 100 of the UK issues have original cover art, making these fun to collect, and still very affordable as these can still be purchased for only a few dollars per issue. There are only a few key issues that collectors hunt out, such as #1 the debut issue. Issue #88 is the first team up issue of *POTA* and *Dracula Lives* into a combined series. These issues were not saved in decent condition and are very scarce in high grade. Only a single copy of #1 of the UK series is in the CGC census and grades at 8.5. *POTA* would eventually continue as a guest feature in *Mighty World of Marvel* #231-246 in 1977.

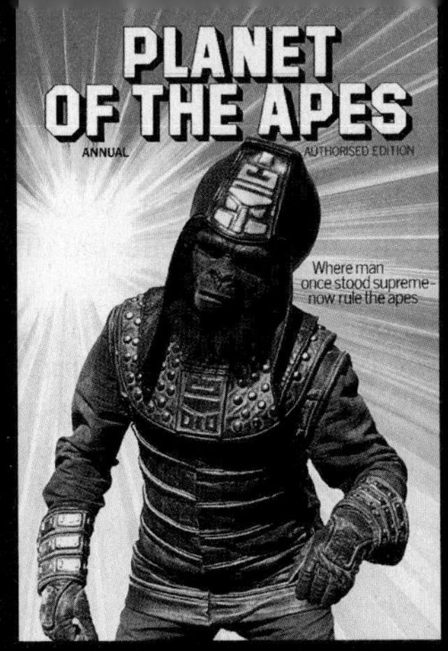

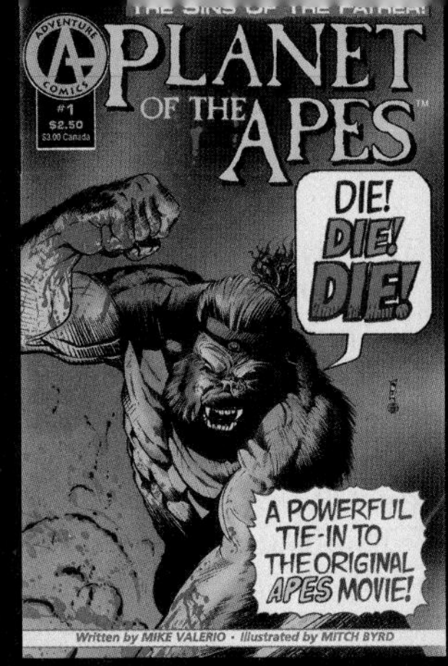

Brown Watson published a hardcover book annual for the UK market in the years 1975, 1976 and 1977. These contain original comic book strips, great artwork and fun games for young readers. These are highly popular, and the final one from 1977 is harder to find than the first two. Foreign language editions popped up worldwide with unique reprint adaptations of the Marvel magazines. including:

Planet Der Affen #1-13 (Germany, 1975)
Apeplaneten #1-10 (Norway, 1975)
Planet Of The Apes #1-19 (Australia, 1975)
El Planeta de los Simios (Mexico, 1975)
Planete Des Singes (France, 1975)
El Planeta De Los Monos (Spain, 1975)
Il Planeta Delle Scimmie (Italy, 1975)
Planeta Dos Macacos (Brazil, 1975)
Planeta Dos Macacos (Portugal, 1975)
Apen Planeet (Netherlands 1975)
Apornas Planet (Sweden, 1975)
Apinoiden Planeetta (Finland, 1975)
El Planeta de los Simios #1-7 (Argentina, 1977)
A Majmok Bolygõja #1 (English: The Monkey Planet) (Hungary, '81, one-shot)

THE MALIBU ERA

From 1990-1993 the *POTA* license was held by Malibu Comics, who published the largest amount of *POTA* related comics in the U.S. until BOOM! Studios' current run. Under their Adventure Comics imprint, the company planned to release only their first bi-monthly, four-issue mini-series. Sales were surprisingly high for the 1990 debut issue with cover artwork by *Incredible Hulk* artist Dale Keown. The series was extended and converted to a monthly ongoing series, and creating more and more new original characters and storylines. Charles Marshall was the head writer.

Malibu Comics also published a number of *POTA* mini-series all running four issues long including *Ape City* (1990), *Blood Of The Apes* (1991), *Urchak's Folly* (1991), *Ape Nation* (1991, a crossover with *Alien Nation*), *Terror On The POTA* (1992 which reprints Doug Moench original stories from the *Marvel Magazines* of 1974), *The Forbidden Zone* #1-4 (1992-1993), and *Monkey Planet (*reprinting first four issues of Malibu series). There was also 1992's *Sins Of The Father* one-shot, plus an *Annual* and three graphic novels in 1991, which reprint the complete movie adaptations of the first three movies from writer Doug Moench, originally published in the Marvel of 1974.

From 1993 to 2001 there was another lag in *POTA* comics product.

THE DARK HORSE ERA

The world was excited to receive a new *POTA* film in 2001 from director Tim Burton and it was a huge box office hit even though reviews were not great.

Dark Horse Comics who published a three-issue mini-series called *Planet of the Apes: The Human War* based on this new film. There are two covers for each issue (one photo and one art). J Scott Campbell did the artwork for issue #3 in 2001. Dynamic Forces released two limited variant covers of #1 with a print run of approximately 6,000 copies each. *The Human War* series was reprinted in a graphic novel.

The company then published a new six-issue mini-series continuing concepts from the new movie in 2001- 2002, and again featured two covers of each issue (one photo and one art). These issues were reprinted in two different graphic novels in 2002 called *Old Gods* and *Blood Lines*. Dark Horse also published a monthly, tabloid-sized, promotional newspaper which featured *POTA* in short strips in issues #34-38.

THE MR. COMICS ERA

In 2005 *POTA* licensing went to the Canadian indy publisher Mr. Comics, which released *Revolution on the Planet of the Apes*, a six-issue mini-series set during the immediate aftermath of Caesar's rebellion shown in *Conquest of the Planet of the Apes*.

The lead story was written by Joe O'Brien and Ty Templeton, with stand-alone back-up tales written by Templeton. Salgood Sam and colorist Bernie Mireault handled the art duties on the main story.

THE BOOM! STUDIOS ERA

BOOM! Studios has had the *POTA* license since 2011. A first look of their debut series appeared in a six-page preview in *The Traveler* #7 (May 2011) BOOM! put out a new ongoing original story series which ran for 16 issues from April 2011 to July 2012.

Written by novelist Daryl Gregory and illustrated by Carlos Magno, the story was set 1,300 years before Taylor's arrival. Humans still spoke – though some were being born mute – and their relationship between apes and humans was very tenuous. The Lawgiver and his writings, which set an imposing tone in the original films, play a critical role in the series.

After 16 monthly issues and an Annual, this incarnation of *Planet of the Apes* was concluded in three one-shots by Gregory and artist Diego Barreto, *POTA Special* (February 2013), *POTA: Spectacular* (July 2013) and *POTA Giant* (September 2013).

Of the monthly, all 16 issues were published with three different covers for each issue, ar a total of 48 covers. Issue #1 also had an extra fourth variant cover and a second printing cover as well. All were collected in trade paperbacks.

BOOM!'s original series was followed by *Betrayal of the Planet of the Apes*, a four-issue mini-series published in 2011-2012, which included two covers for each issue. It was followed by *Exile on the Planet of the Apes*, another four-issue mini-series (2012), which also had at least two covers per issue. After *Exile*, *Planet of the Apes: Cataclysm* was a 12-issue series published in 2012-2013 and featured at least two covers of each issue.

The two four-issue mini-series and the 12-issue series were set much closer to Taylor's arrival in the first film, starting just 20 years earlier. Written by Corinna Bechko and Gabriel Hardman, *Betrayal*, *Exile*, and *Cataclysm* show us a formative time for Zaius and other familiar characters. They also took on notable story points from the first and second films.

Betrayal was illustrated by co-author Hardman, *Exile* featured Marc Laming on art. Damian Couciero drew *Cataclysm*. Alex Ross was among the cover artists on *Cataclysm*. There are trade paperbacks collections of all of these issues as well.

The more recent film series – *Rise of the Planet of the Apes*, *Dawn of the Planet of the Apes*, *War for the Planet of the Apes* – also spawned comic book tie-ins from BOOM! *Dawn of the Planet of the Apes: Contagion* was a one-shot (July 2014) that bridged the time between *Rise* and *Dawn*.

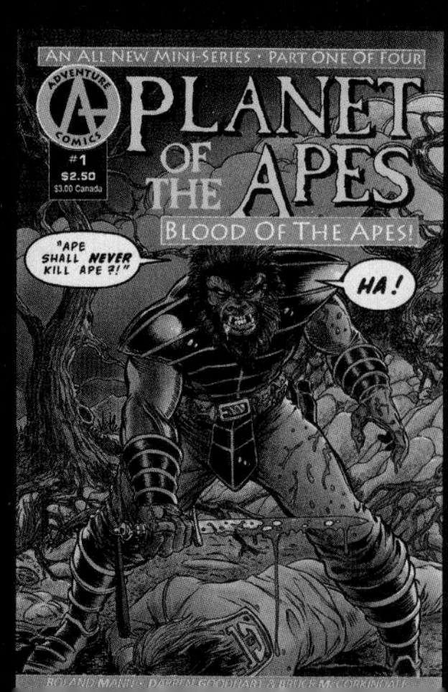

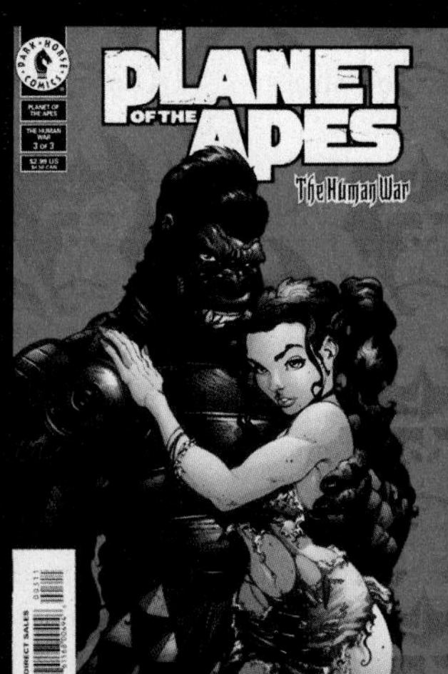

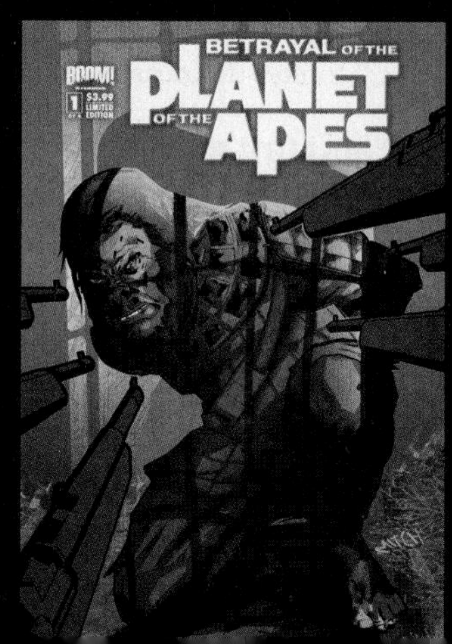

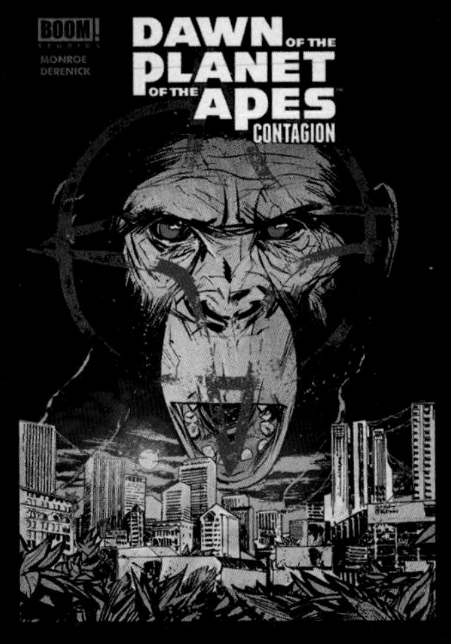

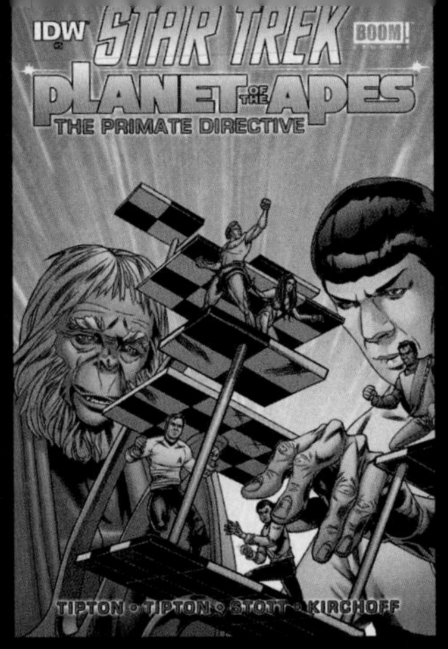

Dawn of the Planet of the Apes was a six-issue series that started in November 2014 and featured at least two covers of each issue. It also explored the 10-year gap between *Rise* and *Dawn*, just as BOOM!'s *War for the Planet of the Apes* staked out the territory between *Dawn* and *War*.

The company returned to the timeline of the original movies with Planet of the Apes: Ursus, a six-issue mini-series written by David Walker (who also wrote their *War for the Planet of the Apes*) and illustrated by Christopher Mooneyham. Ursus follows, no surprise to *POTA* fans, the story of General Ursus, first seen in the second film.

Since 2017, BOOM! Studios has issued three volumes thus far of *Planet of the Apes Archive*, a magazine-size hardcover series that collects restored versions Marvel's *POTA* black and white work.

In addition to their more continuity-friendly efforts, working with IDW Publishing, Dark Horse, and DC, respectively, BOOM! has propelled the apes into three high profile crossovers to date.

Star Trek/Planet of the Apes: The Primate Directive (beginning December 2014) was a five-issue mini-series that brought together the two franchises. Frequent IDW *Trek* writers Scott and David Tipton scripted the series, which was illustrated by Rachel Stott. There are at least three covers for each issue including photo covers using images from the 1960s. A five-page preview appeared in *Star Trek* #39 (IDW, November 2014).

Tarzan on the Planet of the Apes, a five-issue series that twists the premise of *Escape from the Planet of the Apes* with Zira, Cornelius and Dr. Milo landing further back in time, debuted in September 2016. It was written by David Walker and Tim Seely and illustrated by Fernando Dagnino.

The company teamed with DC for the six-issue *Planet of the Apes/Green Lantern* in 2017. Robbie Thompson supplied the story, Justin Jordan the script, and Barnaby Bagenda the art. There were as many as six covers per issue, including faux ape action figure variant covers. There is a 1:40 ratio cover for each of the six issues, potentially the scarcest printed *POTA* comic books ever in the U.S. Based on available information, the print run of these covers might be as low as 150 copies each.

Among other things, Terry Hoknes is a veteran Planet of the Apes collector who authored an earlier version of this article to Gemstone Publishing's Comic Book Marketplace *#68 (May 1999). Gemstone's J.C. Vaughn contributed to this piece.*

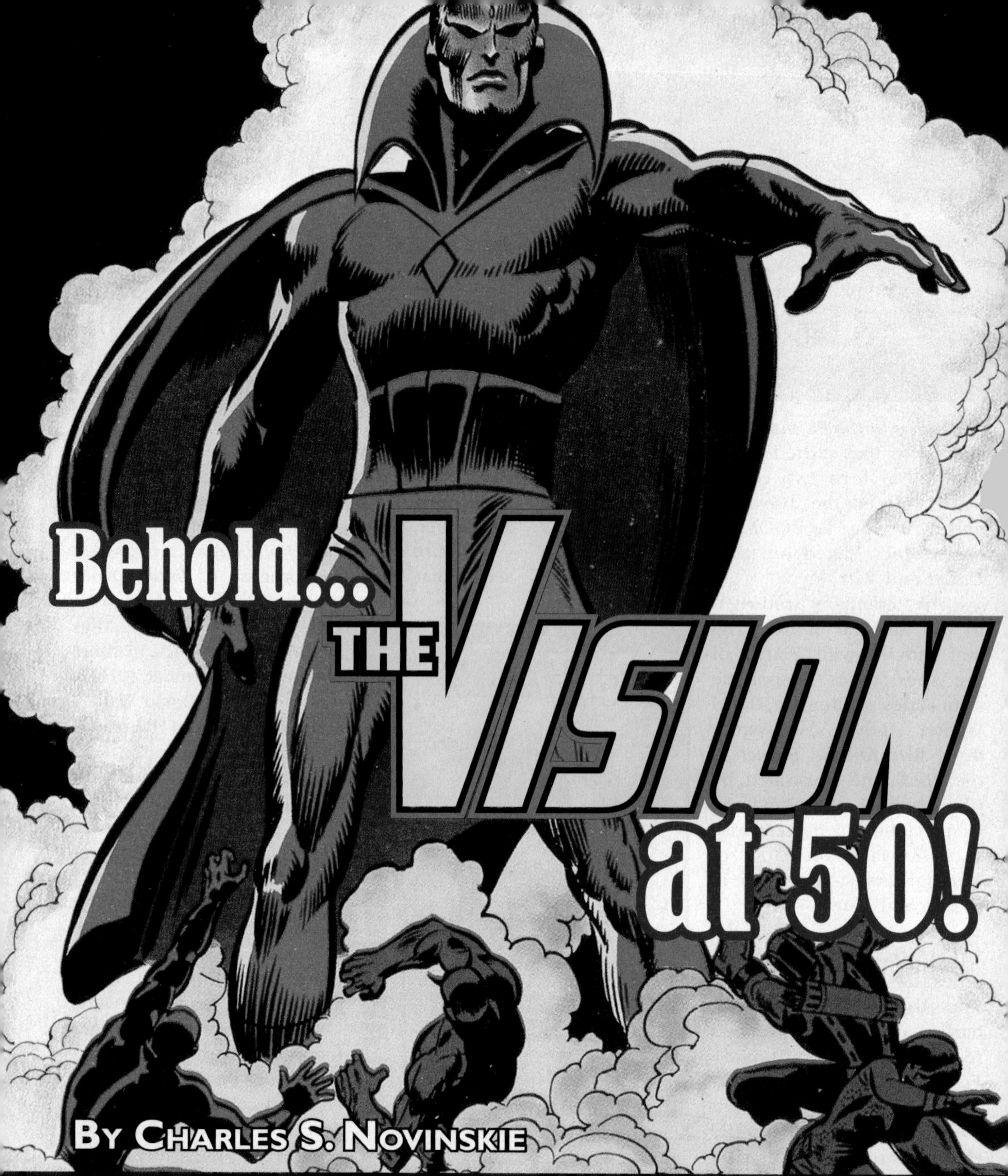

Behold... THE VISION at 50!

By Charles S. Novinskie

Cover-dated October 1968, *The Avengers* #57 introduced the modern-day version of the Vision, thanks to Roy Thomas, Stan Lee, and John Buscema. The android, cloaked in mystery, had the ability to control his density from diamond-hard to a near-zero density, making him intangible. While much of the Vision's abilities remained a mystery it was revealed that his power is derived from the solar jewel on his forehead, allowing him to absorb ambient solar energy, providing the power to function. The Vision's powers continued to be explored and expanded, although it would be several years before the Vision's origin would be truly developed.

In *The Avengers* #93, (Marvel's experimental 25 cent issue month), Roy Thomas, along with Neal Adams, hinted that the Vision may have been created from the body of the original Human Torch, himself an android, as created by Professor Phineas T. Horton back in *Marvel Comics* #1, October 1939. It wasn't until 1975 when issues 134-135 of *The Avengers* addressed the bombastic origin of the Vision. Scripted by Steve Englehart with the artistic talents of Sal Buscema (#134) and George Tuska (#135), the true beginnings of the Vision were revealed. After a period of inactivity, the Vision was reanimated, thanks to Ultron-5 and the kidnapped Professor Horton. Ultron wished to mold the synthetic humanoid into his image as a son.

As far as his quest for humanity, the Vision developed a love interest with Wanda, the Scarlet Witch, in issue #75 of *The Avengers,* back in April 1970. As the romance grew, wedding bells rang for the strange couple in *Giant-Size Avengers* #4 (June 1975). The Vision and Scarlet Witch went on to star in two mini-series - the first, a four-issue romp in 1982 by Bill Mantlo and penciler Rick Leonardi. The second volume of *The Vision and the Scarlet Witch* was a planned 12-issue series written by Steve Englehart with art by Richard Howell. The series gave birth to the couple conceiving twin boys through magical means.

Getting back to his android roots, writer/artist John Byrne took the reins *of West Coast Avengers*, crafting the *Vision Quest* storyline in issues 42-45 (March-June 1989). The story had the Vision break up with his wife, erased the birth of their children--explaining them away as imaginary constructs--and wiping out his human brain patterns. The mid-90s through early 2003 saw the Vision reduced to two, four-issue miniseries before a new form of the Vision made an appearance in the *Young Avengers*, a 12-issue series that ran in 2005/2006. That Vision consisted of the sy thezoid Vision's stored program files combined the mind of Iron Lad.

The last solo series for the Vision appear in 2016, providing him with a self-created fami The 12-issue series takes place in Fairfax, Virgi with the Vision living with his self-generat family: wife Virginia, son Vin, daughter Viv, a synthezoid dog, Sparky. Their attempt to live normal life in suburbia is explored by writer T King in a decidedly different look at the hum side of the Avenger. The series explores the life each family member as they try to cope and fit with humans. The storyline involves the death the Grim Reaper at the hands of Virginia and t Vision's attempt to protect his family.

The Vision continues to play a role of sign icance in the Marvel Universe and is currently member of the Avengers, Earth's Mightiest Hero

CAROL DANVERS AT 50

BY AMANDA SHERIFF

Ms. MARVEL MARVEL COMICS GROUP

30¢ 1 JAN 02198

FABULOUS FIRST ISSUE! Ms. MARVEL ALL-OUT ACTION!

THIS FEMALE FIGHTS BACK!

AT LAST! A BOLD NEW SUPER-HEROINE IN THE SENSES-STUNNING TRADITION OF SPIDER-MAN!

FEATURING THE MOST MYSTERIOUS WOMAN WARRIOR SINCE MADAME MEDUSA! AND, IF YOU THINK OUR LEADING LADY IS SOMETHING, WAIT'LL YOU SEE HER STAR-STUDDED SUPPORTING CAST!

From military officer to Marvel's most powerful superheroine, Carol Danvers has had a rich history. She was introduced in *Marvel Super-Heroes* #13 (March 1968) and later became the first incarnation of Ms. Marvel in *Ms. Marvel* #1 (January 1977). The popular character, co-created by writer Roy Thomas and artist Gene Colan, is celebrating her 50th anniversary.

Carol has been associated with the Avengers and the X-Men, saving the day as Ms. Marvel, Binary, Warbird, and Captain Marvel. Outside of comics, she has been in Marvel video games, animated TV shows, and will star in the *Captain Marvel* movie, set for 2019.

Before gaining superpowers, Major Carol Danvers was an Air Force officer and security chief on a military base. There she met Dr. Walter Lawson, who was secretly the alien Kree hero Mar-Vell, known as Captain Marvel. Caught in a Kree device explosion, her genes were fused with the alien, making her a superpowered human-Kree hybrid, in *Captain Marvel* #18 (November 1969).

Her powers include superhuman strength, flight, endurance, near indestructibility, resistance to most poisons, the ability to survive in space, and she can blast energy. As Binary, she could control heat, gravity, and the electromagnetic spectrum, as well as travel at light speed by using the energy of a white hole. Carol is also a talented spy, pilot, markswoman, and hand to hand fighter.

The *Ms. Marvel* series began in '77, written by Gerry Conway and later Chris Claremont. The late '70s comic was considered, progressive since it used the title "Ms." which was associated with the feminist movement. In a more overt sign of the times, Carol lobbied for equal pay for equal work.

In *The Avengers* #200 (October 1980) Ms. Marvel was kidnapped by Marcus, then brainwashed and impregnated. The storyline has since been criticized as an act of rape, rather than the previously labeled "seduction." Claremont, who considered it inappropriate, unmade the Marcus story in *Avengers Annual* #10 (1981), bringing Carol back to Earth where she confronts the Avengers for not realizing that Marcus had brainwashed her.

In *Uncanny X-Men* she deleted Pentagon files about herself, symbolically breaking away from being Ms. Marvel. While accompanying the X-Men in space, she temporarily became Binary because of experimentation by the alien race known as the Brood. Carol lost her connection to the white hole and reverted back to her Ms. Marvel powers in *Operation Galactic Storm*. This began her phase as Warbird, when she became an alcoholic while struggling to accept her loss of powers, in a story by Kurt Busiek.

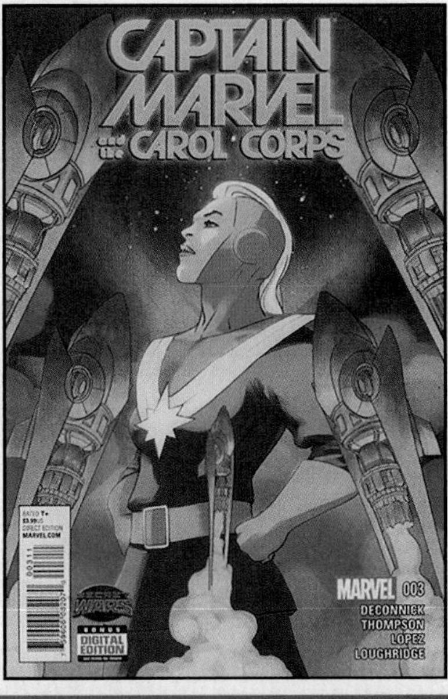

Carol returned to prominence as an advocate for the Superhuman Registration Act during the *Civil War* event in 2006-2007. Part of the story took place in *Ms. Marvel* when she fought anti-registration heroes led by Captain America.

During the *Secret Invasion* story (2008) she joined the New Avengers against the shapeshifting Skrulls. Norman Osborn, leading the Dark Avengers, orchestrated a battle that resulted in Carol's powers overloading. The second volume of *Ms. Marvel* ended after she fought Mystique, allied with Steve Rogers, and became friends with Spider-Man.

Carol became Captain Marvel in July 2012, in a series written by Kelly Sue DeConnick with art by Dexter Soy. Under her new name, she joined the Avengers and starred in the *Captain Marvel/Avengers Assemble* storyline.

The 2015 *Secret Wars* event tie-in series *Captain Marvel and the Carol Corps* joined her with an elite female fighter pilot team. She also appeared as a member of A-Force with She-Hulk, Medusa, and other ladies of Marvel.

During 2016's *Civil War II* she led a group of superheroes who wanted to use the precognitive abilities of the Inhuman Ulysses to prevent disasters before they happen. They were opposed by other Marvel heroes, led by Iron Man, in an event that crossed into several Marvel titles. In Carol's current series, *The Mighty Captain Marvel*, she has become a celebrity and served as commander of Alpha Flight.

In addition to being Marvel's biggest superheroine, Carol could also be the most powerful Avenger. With 50 years of experience under her belt, she continues to thrive as one of Earth's mightiest heroes.

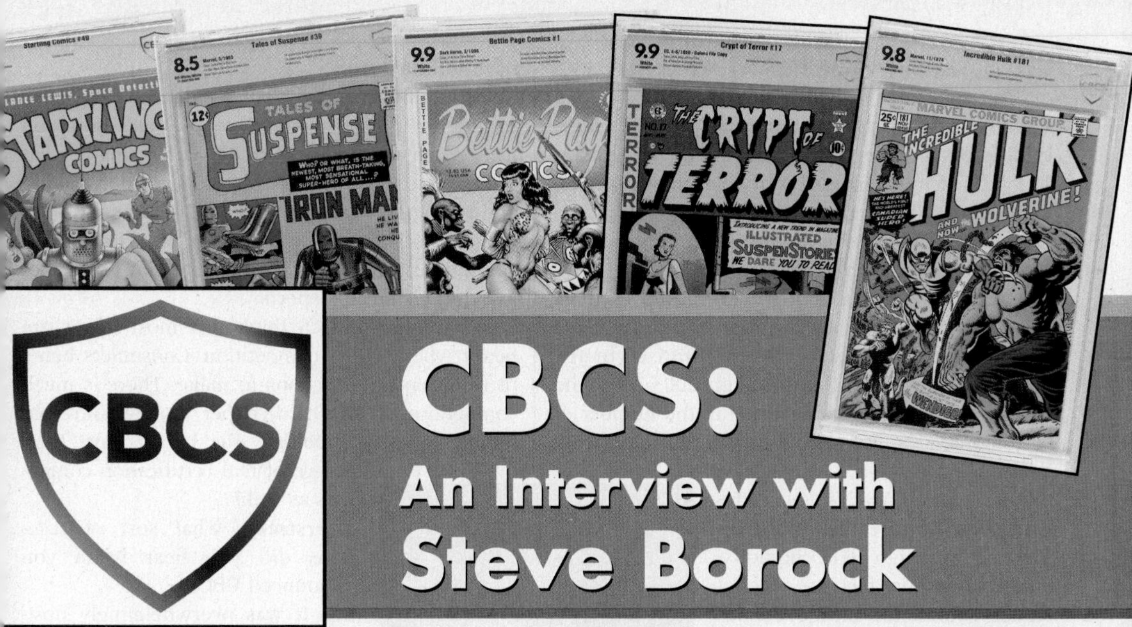

CBCS: An Interview with Steve Borock

By J.C. Vaughn & Carrie Wood

Steve Borock continues to put his passions to good use, not only as President and Primary Grader of Comic Book Certification Service (CBCS), but also as a board member of the Hero Initiative, the 501 (c)(3) charity that aids comic book creators in need, and as the auctioneer for the New York Comic Con and C2E2 fundraiser comic art auctions for St. Jude Children's Hospital.

The veteran comic book and original comic art collector has frequently shared his enthusiasm and his expertise with others. Prior to his tenure as the first President and Primary Grader for CGC or his stint as Senior Consignment Director for Heritage Auctions, he was profiled as a collector and was noted for his knowledge of stories, creators and the industry's history in addition to his attention to the physical details of comics.

Borock has also participated as an advisor for many years to The Overstreet Comic Book Price Guide, The Overstreet Guide to Grading Comics, *and* The Overstreet Guide to Collecting Comic and Animation Art.

Overstreet: How has CBCS fared from last year at this time?

Steve Borock (SB): Extremely well, I am very happy to say! We have basically doubled our incoming submissions and presence in the market place in the past year. That was way beyond our expectations.

Overstreet: A big change between last year and now is that CBCS is now part of a much bigger organization. What can you tell us about that?

SB: We became part of Beckett Media, a leading card grading service among other services, which is owned by Eli Global, a multinational group of about 100 entrepreneurial, independent businesses. They loved what they saw in CBCS and, from there, the rest in history.

Overstreet: What impact will the change in ownership have on the services you offer?

SB: Many things will stay status quo, like the grading, staying hobby friendly, listening to our customers, transparency, educating collectors, growing the comic market, as well as all the great programs CBCS already has in place. They are very cool and want the very high standards of CBCS's core values to stay the same. What's great is that we now have shared resources that will help us serve the collecting community even better! We have many new projects that we are talking about developing, even a new and better holder.

Overstreet: Independent third-party grading of comics is such a part of the industry and hobby now that it's difficult for many to remember how it was initially perceived when it was first introduced. What do you remember about the period in which it started?

SB: The fact is that the majority of people who expressed an opinion thought it wouldn't work, and they weren't shy about saying so. There were some early proponents, of course, but they were vastly outnumbered. That said, the need for independent grading had become very apparent to a core group. The market was largely stagnant. Key dealers with keen eyes for grading and sterling reputations, enjoyed the trust of their peers, but there was no mechanism for others to build up to that level of consumer or peer confidence.

Internet sales, largely through eBay, opened a whole new frontier, but they also came with a significant number of disputes about the grades. The lack of independent, verifiable grades was an impediment to a larger, healthier market.

Overstreet: What sort of turning points do you remember in its evolution?

SB: After slow going at first, certification saw its first real victory in an auction staged by Greg Manning Auctions. Watchers were surprised by the prices realized. After that, through 2003-2004, the industry saw a dramatic increase in the number of certified comics available at conventions and from dealers.

Since then, we've seen the evolution of the business, an increase in high end liquidity, and a substantial increase in consumer confidence in the comics they're buying in person, online or from catalogs. It's no longer only confined by having to know the dealer in question very well. Instead, the consumer can focus on the critical factors: "Is this the comic I'm looking for, is it in the grade I want and is this the price I am willing to pay?" Between 1999, when I helped start CGC and set their grading standards, and 2008, when I left, we saw the attitude of the marketplace entirely shift on the subject of certification.

Overstreet: What brought you back to grading?

SB: When I left grading to work as the Senior Consignment Director at Heritage, I really thought that was it. In the end, though, there's something very compelling about this challenge. Even with all our experience and transparency, we are still the "new kids on the block." We had to do something better just to get in the door. Again, I wouldn't be doing this if I didn't think we had something great to offer the hobby I love.

And speaking of experience, over the last few years people have come to know our staff and, I'm pleased to say, that West Stephan, Tim Bildhauser, Daniel Ertle, Joshua St. Amand, Steve Ricketts, Jim Noble, Mark Demuth and Paul Figura, among others, are on board. Between just me and these few hobbyists, we have about a combined 250 years of grading, pedigree knowledge, and restoration detection experience from buying and selling as well as "professional" grading. We have all been collecting and reading comic books for many more years than that, but I wanted to put a practical number of years for experience. Once again, it goes back to transparency.

CBCS believes that our graders should have experience in the marketplace, as that's how you truly learn to grade: learning and refining what hobbyists expect a grade should be when buying and selling. As many will tell you, grading is an art, not just a science. The overall look of an unrestored comic must really be factored into the grade, not just the "technical" aspects.

All of us at CBCS think that most things are better when there's competition. Consumers benefit from having selections to make. There is much competition in the card, paper money, and coin hobbies – why shouldn't our hobby have their choice of real certification companies as well?

Overstreet: What sort of reactions did you hear when you announced CBCS?

SB: It was overwhelmingly positive. Even people who said they would take a "wait and see" approach mentioned they would be very happy to submit once we were established and accepted by the collecting community. To me, it's clear that the collecting community has spoken by buying and selling CBCS-certified comic books. Even eBay has added a CBCS search since there are so many of our books on there.

Overstreet: What are some of the reactions you've received so far?

SB: Most have been very positive, I am very happy to say. I get emails, posts and PMs on Facebook and the CBCS forums that many collectors will only use CBCS. It is very humbling.

Overstreet: What, if anything, has worked out differently from how you thought it would in regards to the process of starting CBCS and getting it up and running?

SB: First of all, we never expected to be swamped with comic submissions from the start. That was a great thing - unexpected, but great! Because of that influx of books, even though we had the core team set in place, we needed to hire more people quickly. That is not an easy thing to do, especially for grading and restoration detection. That said, even filling other positions was easier, but not easy as we at CBCS want to hire collectors with a true passion for our hobby. As of this interview, we are now up to 34 employees and still looking to hire.

Another thing that we did not envision from the beginning was our Original Art tier. We at CBCS thought that it was silly that when you got your favorite artist to do a sketch on a "sketch" cover comic that people would say "Great piece! Too bad it's not a 9.8." That's crazy! Original art is original art. Now, hobbyists have a choice, they can choose to have a numerical grade on the CBCS label or just a label that states Original Art and who the artist is. Many collectors have taken to it and are loving it, so are many artists. As an original art collector myself, if I was allowed to submit to CBCS, this is the choice I would make. I do not care about the grade of the book, only the art on it.

Overstreet: What do you think the presence of CBCS in the marketplace has done for buyers and sellers?

SB: It's done a great thing by giving the buyers and sellers a choice. It has also forced our esteemed competitor to make some changes, and that is great for our hobby. Imagine, if you will, that Ford was still the only company making cars. We would be paying $70K for that car and getting eight miles a gallon. Competition is great for the hobby!

Overstreet: What are some of your high profile and/or record-setting sales?

SB: I don't pay attention to the market, as I need to stay impartial, but I know we have set record prices on some very high profile books. I was told we set huge records with CBCS-graded comics from the "Mr. Majik Woo" collection at Heritage Auctions as well as setting records on both the *Suspense Comics* #3 from the Edgar Church/ Mile High and the San Francisco pedigree collections, and ComicConnect has had record sales of CBCS graded comics, including an *Amazing Fantasy* #15 in 9.0 and a *Fantastic Four* #1 in 8.5. CBCS also graded a *Marvel Comics* #1. This was an unknown copy, and the owner thought CBCS would be the best company to have it certified. I have also been told by ComicLink, Heritage and Mycomicshop.com that we are setting new record prices every auction.

Overstreet: We've already mentioned it a few times, but over the years, transparency is a theme you've come back to repeatedly in our conversations. What are some of the ways you've implemented it at CBCS?

SB: We feel that transparency is the key to helping the collecting community buy and sell comics. This goes for all buyers and sellers, whether in high profile, public transactions or discreet, private deals. Full-time retailers, weekend show dealers, any seller of comic books benefits when consumer confidence is legitimately high. Likewise, any buyer who can make a purchase with confidence adds to the collective faith in the market. Toward that end, we published our free "grading guideline" on our website. We offer scheduled tours of our facility, so that our clients can see where their comics are graded and how they are safely stored, as well as seeing the flow and professionalism of the certification process. As I said when we started, it's our belief that once someone has paid CBCS to certify his or her comic, it is only fair that a submitter should know how our grading team factored in the defects that resulted in the given grade.

Overstreet: It took a while, but you've launched CBCS forums online. They will have been online only over a year when this book comes out. What are your hopes for them?

SB: As always, I hope to bring our great community together. I live for this hobby and want all to feel welcome. I love the fact the new collectors can learn from the veteran collectors and CBCS graders on our forum. I was blown away that the day we launched the forums we had 400 members! I have no clue how many we have now, but I am having a blast talking comics and other things on there. We also have our Facebook group, the CBCS Comic Collectors Club, which can be found at facebook.com/groups/cbcscomics.

Overstreet: When you launched CBCS, you said that based on experience you wanted to do some things differently. What were those things and have you succeeded thus far in doing them differently?

SB: Free grading notes have been a game changer for certification. We put each invoice and corresponding comic number on the front label, so that if you see a CBCS comic for sale online, you can look up the notes on our website to see why CBCS graded the comic the way we did. What's really cool is that we also put a QR code on the back of the CBCS label. If a collector or seller is at a convention or store, all they have to do is use their smart phone, with a free QR reader download, and the grading notes will pop up on their phone. We do not believe that a collector should ever have to pay to see how we came up with the grade for each book.

The CBCS Verified Signature Program (VSP) has been a huge success. There are so many un-witnessed signatures out there, and many collectors want them authenticated. We came up with a way to do this by first working with an independent company called CSA. We have now switched to the best signature verification company, BAS (Beckett Authentication Services). These guys are the real deal! Whether it's a comic book creator, sports, TV or movie celebrity, they can verify all of them as they have an unmatched library of exemplars. Once we get confirmation that the signature has passed BAS's very high standards, we put that it was signed by the professional on the CBCS label. It's great to see signatures by great creators from our hobby, particularly those who have passed away, in a CBCS holder and certified as genuine. Of course it's not only for creators who have passed. Additionally, with VSP, we're able to certify comics signed by celebrities since, as I mentioned, BAS can authenticate those as well.

Another thing we have done is made a crystal clear, safe holder that does not "dull" or "filmy" the look of a comic book. We also put the top label on the inside of the holder, so that it does not get dirty, can't be removed, and will not come off the holder from too much handling. I know that our esteemed competition has already followed us on this. That's great for everybody! The interior sleeve we use is made of virgin PETG and does not need to be changed out after many years because it is archival safe material that lets the comic "breathe." Another change that our competition has followed suit on.

Grade screening has become big, as there is no minimum submission and submitters may designate a different grade for each individual book sent in. The two-day Modern tier has also been huge. Many collectors and sellers have been using that for "hot" modern variants, so that they can get them to market quickly and affordably. The reactions to our online submission form have been solid, as expected. Most folks seem to love our no-fee, easy-to-use, online submission experience.

Overstreet: CBCS is part of the convention circuit. What services does the company offer onsite, and how has it been fine-tuned since you started up?

SB: It has only been "fine-tuned" by the fact that we are better at receiving the books quicker and have added more "witnesses" to go with a collector to have their book signed or sketched, so that we know for a fact that the signature or art is real. We make sure we have a super friendly, helpful and knowledgeable staff and it seems to be a big hit with both the buyers and sellers.

Overstreet: Are there other things you are doing – or not doing – to bolster consumer confidence?

SB: In addition to our interactions with our customers, we believe it's also very important how we conduct ourselves when it comes to potential conflicts of interest. Neither CBCS employees – full or part time – nor any of their family members are allowed to buy and sell CBCS-certified comics or submit comic books for CBCS grading.

Now, of course, just about everyone at CBCS loves comics. They wouldn't be here otherwise, but if our grades are going to be perceived in a light that is beneficial to everyone, the trust factor has to be there. This is one way we will work to cultivate it. A CBCS employee who collects comics should not have any need to have a comic certified, as they should be able to purchase a comic for their personal collection using their knowledge of comics or having one of our graders to look that book over for them. Full or part time, they are not allowed to sell a graded comic books through auction houses or any anonymous sources.

CBCS pre-graders, senior graders and management are not allowed to accept gifts of any kind, including food, drink or entertainment, from any CBCS submitter or potential submitter. These CBCS employees must pay their own way, at all times, during conventions for items not reimbursed to them by CBCS.

Overstreet: What are your current goals for future growth?

SB: We are looking into grading and restoration seminars and panels at conventions. We have done a couple of these and they seem to be a big hit with many convention attendees. Some would not only be CBCS graders, as I would also like to include other seasoned hobbyists to join the panels and share as well. This hobby is about all of us, not just CBCS. As always, there are some special projects coming in the near future, but I will save talking about them until next year's edition of *The Overstreet Comic Book Price Guide*.

CBCS OFFERS TWO SIGNATURE PROGRAMS FOR COLLECTORS

thentic Signature Program (ASP) for witnessed signatures.

rified Signature Program (VSP) for unwitnessed signatures.

CBCS PRESSING

Make the most out of your grading investment

Pressing/Dry Cleaning - A trusted service that removes many defects from comic books prior to grading.

(Optional) Screening Service - Determines if your comic is a good candidate for pressing.

FOREIGN COMICS GRADING SPECIALISTS

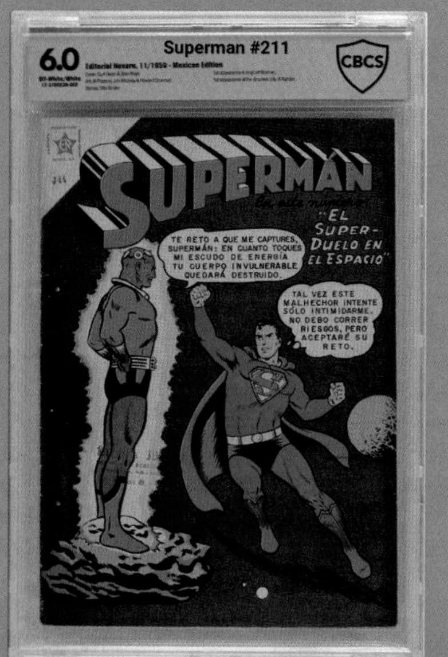

THE GRADERS YOU KNOW AND TRUST

STEVE BOROCK
President & Primary Grader

WEST STEPHAN
Restoration Detection Specialist & Senior Grader

For the past 40 years, Firestorm has heated things up at DC Comics. Created by Gerry Conway and Al Milgrom, the elemental-based hero debuted in *Firestorm, the Nuclear Man* #1 (March 1978). Utilizing energy abilities at the molecular level, Firestorm has been the mantle for several characters, typically with at least two individuals combining as body and mind.

The first incarnation combined high school student Ronnie Raymond and physicist Martin Stein, who were caught in an explosion at the Hudson nuclear facility which fused them as Firestorm. As the Nuclear Man, Ronnie commands the Firestorm physical form with Martin controlling the mental abilities.

With a name like Firestorm, there are bound to be a litany of impressive superhero abilities. He can transmute and manipulate matter and energy, fly at incredible speeds, pass through solid objects without being harmed, and shoot concussive blasts of nuclear fusion energy. He has incredible strength, genius intellect, and can regenerate damaged or lost tissue.

Initially, Martin was unaware of their dual identity during early encounters, leaving him concerned about his blackouts. But once he accepted the situation, Firestorm protected New York City against threats like Killer Frost and Black Bison and was even involved in the nuclear arms race. After Ronnie graduated high school, the pair relocated to Pittsburgh where Ronnie attended college and Martin became a professor.

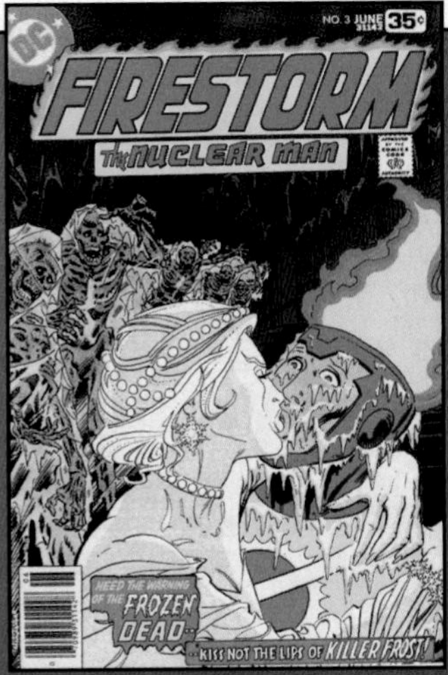

Firestorm became even more complicated in John Ostrander's 1987 *Fury of Firestorm* story that saw Russian hero Pozhar and Firestorm struck by a nuclear missile during a fight. As a result, Ronnie and Pozhar became the second Firestorm, controlled by Martin's amnesiac mind. In '89, the character learned that this version was meant to be Earth's fire elemental, taking part in an elemental war with Swamp Thing, Naiad, and Red Tornado.

Firestorm was then joined with another Russian, Svarozhich, with Martin no longer a part of the composite. But by the 100th issue, Martin discovered that *he* was meant to be the Fire Elemental and saved Earth, though he was consequently exiled to space.

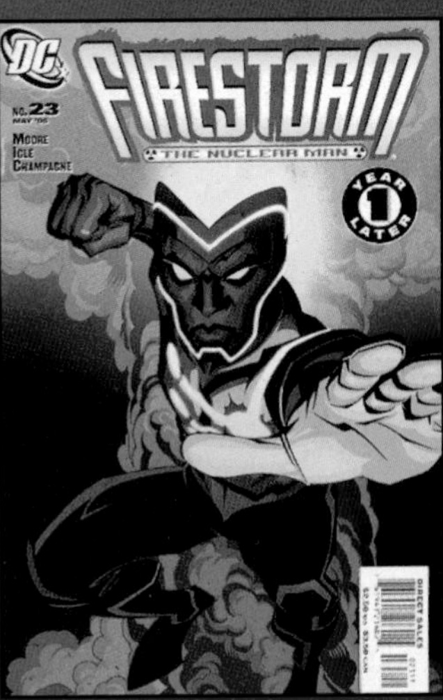

Ronnie learned that the Firestorm power had affected his genes, so he continued as a hero with Extreme Justice, then joined a replacement version of the Justice League. With Captain Atom's help, Ronnie returned to being the elemental Firestorm, but he died in a battle during *Identity Crisis*. Impaled by the Shining Knight's magical sword, his containment field was destroyed and Firestorm's body exploded with the essence passed to Jason Rusch.

Jason, the modern version of Firestorm, debuted in *Firestorm* #1 (July 2004), created by Dan Jolley and Chris Cross. Jason was a teenager from Detroit, living a hard life with an abusive father and working as a courier for a local thug. While learning to control his abilities, he was kidnapped by the Secret Society of Super Villains, who wanted to use him as a power source. In 2006, Jason fought in space during *Infinite Crisis* and was joined by Martin to be the other half of the Firestorm matrix.

During *Blackest Night*, Ronnie was summoned to the Black Lantern Corps, attacked Jason to absorb the Firestorm matrix, and killed Jason's girlfriend Gehenna. In the final fight, they were both restored to life and separated from Firestorm. Then when *Brightest Day* picked up, a fight between Ronnie and Jason merged them and they discovered something else was in Firestorm, which forced its way out as Deathstorm. Firestorm joined other DC heroes to stop Deathstorm and the Black Lanterns.

Following *Flashpoint*, The New 52 gave Firestorm a fresh origin, combining the three main characters. Ronnie and Jason were students at the same high school and both became Firestorm via the God Particle, created by Professor Stein. In this version, Ronnie was the body and Jason was the brains.

Outside of comics, the character has appeared in several DC animated features. The live-action Firestorm stars on The CW's *Legends of Tomorrow*. He was introduced on *The Flash* and has participated in crossover episodes within the Arrowverse.

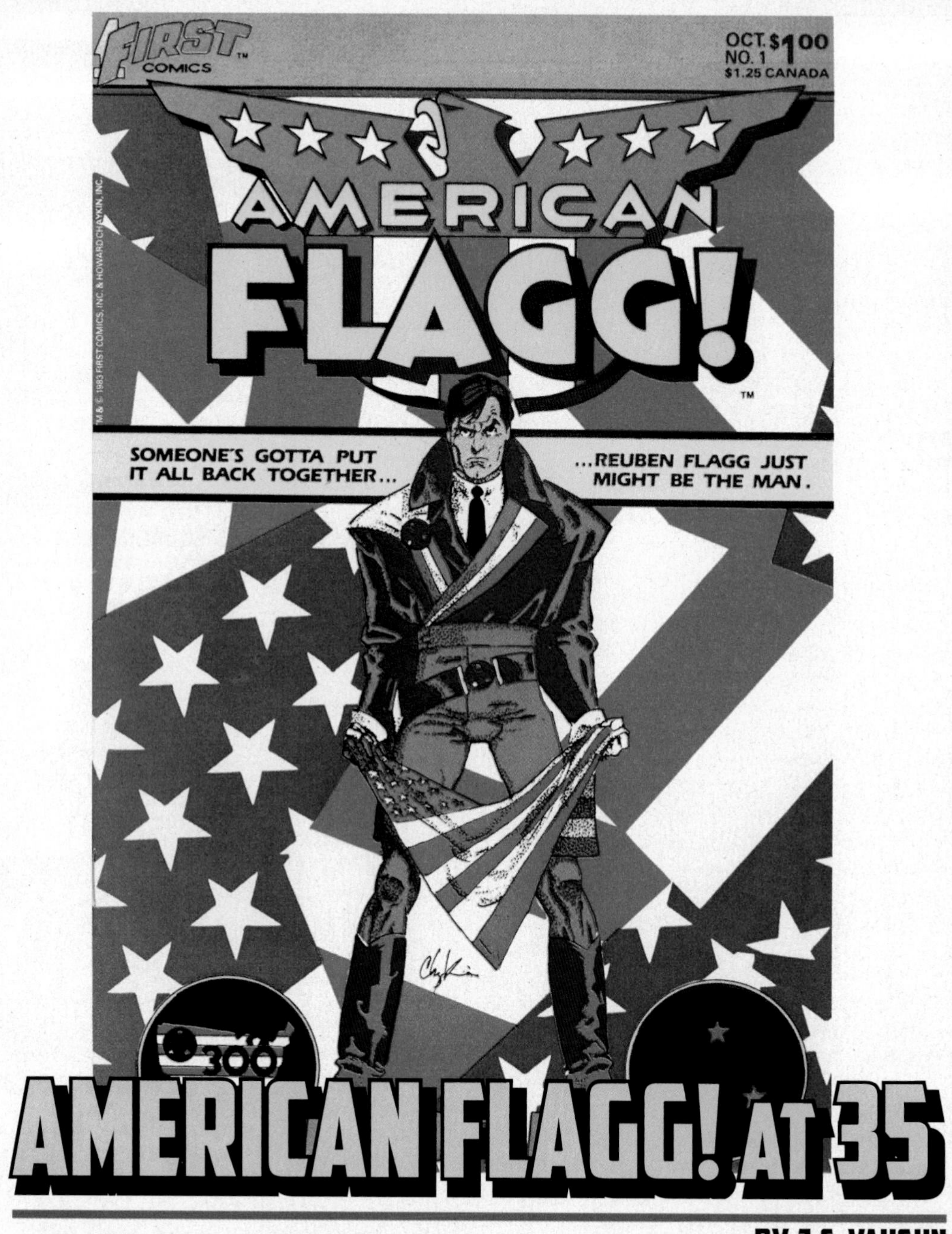

AMERICAN FLAGG! AT 35

BY J.C. VAUGHN

In 1983 and 1984, First Comics had captured lightning in a bottle. They had one of those rosters of comics that was small but spectacular – the kind of spectacular that somehow demanded readers pick up every title in their line. Among their offerings were the fantasy epic *Warp*!, the humorous superhero comic *E-Man*, the bounty-hunter-turned-children's-author *Jon Sable, Freelance*, and the science fiction adventure *Starslayer*.

It was a diverse group of titles from some top creators, but the cream of the crop was Howard Chaykin's *American Flagg!*.

Set in 2031 after long chain of catastrophic world events had led to the U.S. government to relocate to Mars and had by and large turned things over to a single mega-corporation, The Plex, the series is the story of Reuben Flagg.

Raised on Mars, Flagg was the former star of a popular television series. He had been replaced by a computer-generated version of himself, then was more or less exiled to Earth and drafted into the Plexus Rangers, which passed for law enforcement in Plex-run America. Upon his arrival at the Chicago Plexmall, he learned the situation on the ground was far from the America is parents remembered. What he discovered was a mess.

Heavily-armed, hyper-identity-driven political groups and regular gangs battled for turf and ratings on *Firefight All Night LIVE!* with weapons sold to them by the Plex (the show aired on one of the Plex's channels; they controlled all the media). Spurred on by subliminal messages the Plex planted in another popular show, *Bob Violence*, the gangs would raid and pillage the Plexmall.

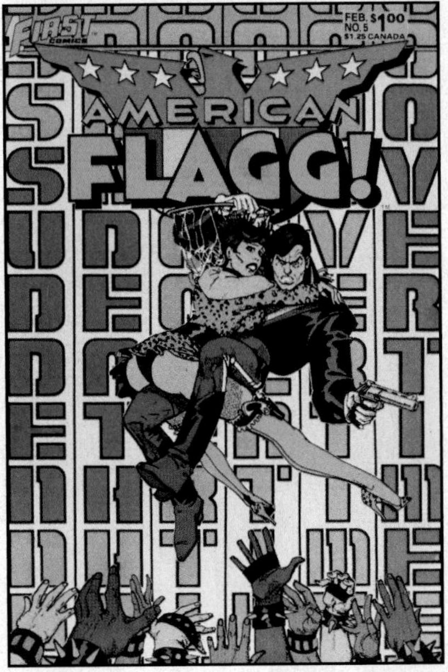

Flagg's predecessor had been killed and initially Reuben almost succumbed to the corrupt, what-are-you-gonna-do-for-me culture that existed. The sheer scope of the dysfunction suggested that no one person could change any of it.

Then Reuben Flagg decided to make a difference.

The tone and style of *American Flagg!* were ground-breaking. Before that point, no one had so successfully depicted (or predicted) the media-driven culture that was to come. By throwing the slightly idealistic Flagg into the proverbial deep end, writer-artist Howard Chaykin made his cast-off child of privilege an everyman who starts out tilting at windmills and ends up leading a revolution.

The dystopic world was filled with business, such as Jerry Rigg Custom Fire Arms, pharmaceuticals like Snowball, Somnambutol, Nachtmacher, Mananacillin, TV shows such as *Interspecies Romances* (all humorously tagged with the trademark TM), and gangs like the Genetic Warlords. And while the names indeed often brought a smile, the circumstances were always dangerous and often deadly.

In addition to Flagg himself, Chaykin populated *American Flagg!* with a distinctive and frequently humorously named supporting cast: Hilton "Hammerhead" Krieger, Mandy (Amanda) Krieger, Jules "Deathwish" Folquet, Mayor Charles Keenan Blitz, his daughter Medea Blitz, Cyril Farid-Khan, Sam Luis Obispo, and William Windsor-Jones. Flagg's most consistent backing came from Raul, an intelligent, talking orange tabby, and Luther Ironheart, his robot deputy Plexus Ranger.

After the first year of the series, Chaykin initially continued to write *American Flagg!*, then eventually stepped away all together to handle other projects. The results prior to his return for the last four issues of the original 50-issue run were not nearly as strong as when he was handling the book.

That said, the impact of his original tenure on the series is hard to overstate. Despite long ago passing his "domino" year when everything was supposed to go bad – 1996 – the hyper-partisan, shady world depicted in the series has never seemed very far off from our own.

American Flagg!'s impact on other creators is distinct. His use of the media as a narrative device – almost a character – has become ubiquitous in comics, and it remains difficult to find a creator who came of age during those days who doesn't owe Chaykin and Reuben Flagg a tip of the cap.

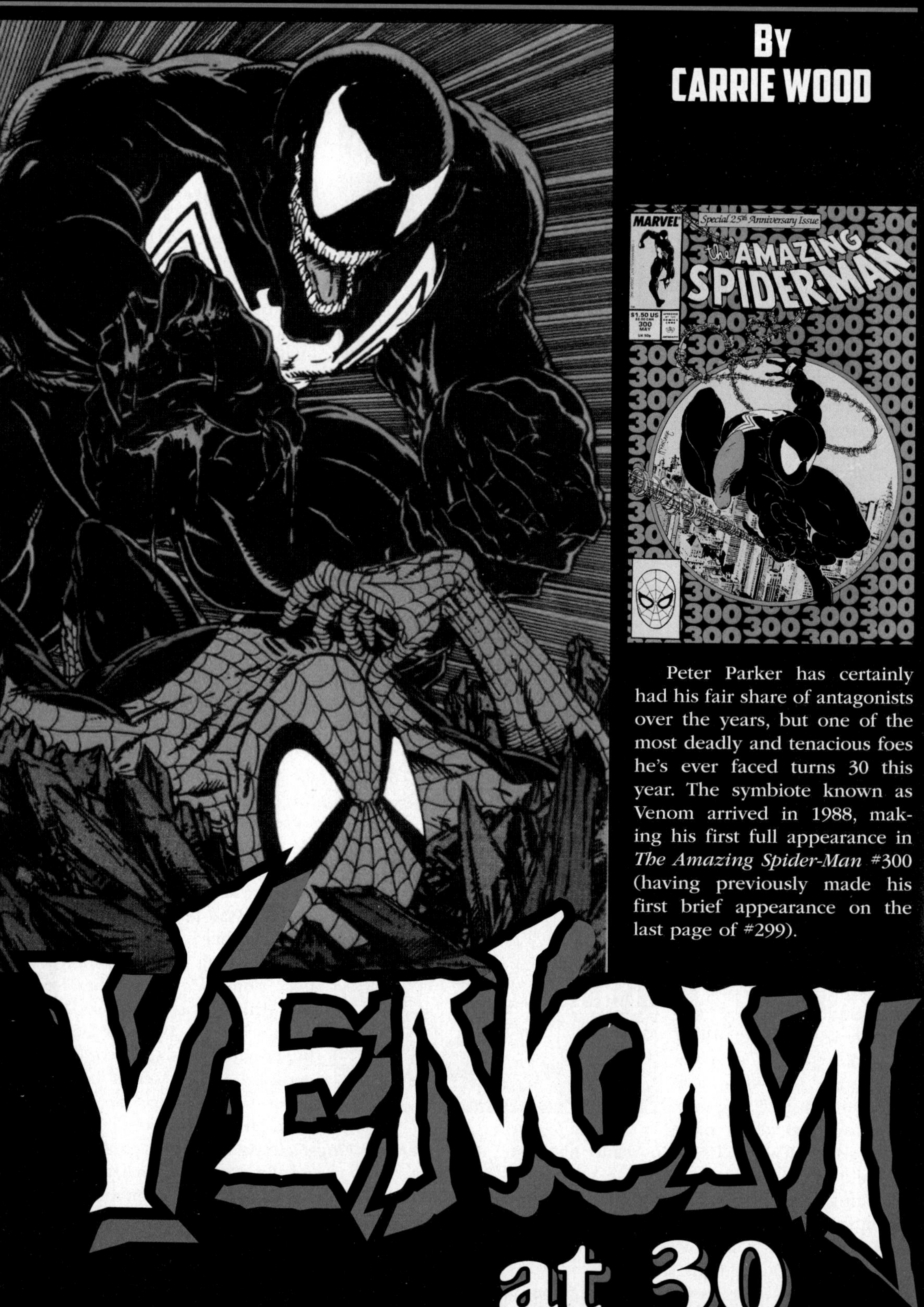

Venom at 30

By Carrie Wood

Peter Parker has certainly had his fair share of antagonists over the years, but one of the most deadly and tenacious foes he's ever faced turns 30 this year. The symbiote known as Venom arrived in 1988, making his first full appearance in *The Amazing Spider-Man* #300 (having previously made his first brief appearance on the last page of #299).

Venom was originally conceived of as simply a new costume for Spider-Man. Marvel actually purchased the idea of the suit off of an avid reader from Illinois, Randy Schueller, for $220, after Schueller submitted the idea to a company-run contest in the 1980s. The whole process for what the suit ended up looking like, plus deciding the fact that it was actually an alien species, was a collaborative effort between the likes of Mike Zeck, Rick Leonardi, Tom DeFalco and Ron Frenz.

The symbiote itself first appeared in *Marvel Super Heroes Secret Wars* #8, after Spider-Man comes into contact with it; it becomes a brand new, black-and-white outfit for the hero. Peter at first is enamored with it, as it provides stronger webbing and enhances his abilities. However, after he has it examined by Reed Richards, they discover its true alien nature – as well as the fact that it is trying to permanently bond with Peter – in *The Amazing Spider-Man* #258. Peter thusly rejects it, and the Fantastic Four attempt to contain it. However, it escapes, and Peter uses the sound waves from a church bell to exploit its weakness to sonic waves to defeat it.

But the creature didn't become known as Venom until it bonded with one of Peter's journalistic rivals, Eddie Brock. Brock blamed Spider-Man for his failures as a journalist during the "Sin Eater" storyline, and his hatred for the web-slinger drew the symbiote to him. He took on the name Venom, which is what he referred to the gossip tabloid writing he was forced into following his fall from the *Daily Globe*. Driven to kill Spider-Man, Venom fights him many times over the years, even going after his family.

On occasion, Venom acted as more of an anti-hero, protecting people from the likes of Carnage and even going so far as to enter a truce with Spidey in order to save Brock's ex-wife.

Other notable Venoms have included Mac Gargan – perhaps better known as the Scorpion – who bonded with the symbiote to join the Sinister Twelve. He was easily defeated by Spider-Man, however, and it's suggested that Gargan was a weaker Venom due to how he didn't hate Peter Parker as much as Eddie Brock did. Gargan also notably uses the symbiote to impersonate Spider-Man himself.

Later, more temporary hosts for the symbiote included Lee Price, Ann Weying, Patricia Robertson, Angelo Fortunato, and even Deadpool. Peter's high school bully Flash Thompson took on the symbiote himself to become Agent Venom in February 2011 (*The Amazing Spider-Man* #654), giving the character a far more heroic edge. Flash uses the symbiote to work for the U.S. military, and did so in order to regain the use of his legs. However, he can only stay bonded for two days, lest the symbiote completely take over his body. Agent Venom joined up with the Secret Avengers and even the Guardians of the Galaxy during his run.

A perfectly-1990s edgy appearance combined with some stellar sci-fi writing made Venom one of the most popular villains ever for Spider-Man. He's shown up in multiple iterations of the *Spider-Man* cartoon series and was one of the primary antagonists in the film *Spider-Man 3*. He's also appeared in dozens of Marvel-related video games. A solo film focused on the character is reportedly in development for a 2018 release by Sony Pictures, as well. It goes to show that after three decades, Venom is as cool as he's ever been.

Static, the clever teen superhero with some seriously shocking abilities, turns 25 this year. Introduced as one of the key characters for the Milestone Comics DC imprint, he was created by the team of Dwayne McDuffie, Denys Cowan, Derek Dingle, and Michael Davis. While many characters are introduced in established titles, Static met readers for the first time in his own *Static* #1 (June 1993).

The comic was initially written by McDuffie and Robert L. Washington III, with art provided by John Paul Leon. Static was inspired by fellow teen hero Spider-Man, and his civilian identity was named after Virgil Hawkins, a black man who'd been denied admission to the University of Florida law school in 1949.

When his story began, Virgil was a 15-year-old kid living in the city of Dakota. One night while seeking revenge against a bully, he ended up in the middle of a gang fight that was disrupted by the police. The cops used tear gas with a radioactive marker that *also* had an experimental mutagen. The event became known as Big Bang, which triggered metahuman birth in some people doused with the chemical, turning them into "Bang Babies."

Virgil was among the Bang Babies mutated by the chemical, gaining power over electricity. As Static, he can create and control electrical and magnetic energy, and can store electromagnetic energy in his body by controlling the current and voltage. Static can magnetize objects, electrocute people, levitate certain objects, adhere people or objects to surfaces using static cling, produce taser punches, and generate blinding flashes, electromagnetic pulses, lightning balls, and electromagnetic nets.

Imbued with powers, he decided to become a costumed crimefighter. Granted, he's still a teenager with friends and crushes, dealing with typical teen problems, along with the weight of being a superhero. Similar to his inspiration, Static drops humorous banter, as well as understanding of science and pop culture knowledge during fights. Much of this comes from his nerdy hobbies, which include tabletop games and even *Pokémon* card collecting (his favorite, of course, is the similarly-shocking Pikachu).

In *Static Shock: Rebirth of the Cool* Virgil had given up being a superhero, though he did miss it. After returning to being Static he fought alongside heroes like Blitzen and Hardware, then joined the unofficial group called Heroes to save the town of Iberia from a dam break.

Static joined the DCU in *Terror Titans* #4 (January 2009). Darkseid hired the Terror Titans to capture Static and other Bang Babies and forced them to compete in metahuman deathmatches. Fellow prisoner Rose Wilson was able to free Static to take revenge on their captors.

Once freed, Static and other Dark Side Club survivors sought asylum at Titans Tower. When Wonder Girl, the current Teen Titans leader, invited them to join the team, Static accepted the offer. Later, when Jericho took control of the Tower, Static defeated the former Titan by overloading the Tower with a high energy charge.

Deciding that it was time to go home, he went back to see his family in Dakota and learned that a deadly virus was infecting people. Tracing the location of where a vaccine was being manufactured, Static was confronted by Holocaust. The villain imprisoned Static, Aquagirl, and others, revealing his intentions to weaponize their powers. They were eventually saved by Cyborg, Kid Flash, and Superboy.

The New 52, saw Virgil and his family relocating to New York. He got a new costume and modified flying disk from Hardware that allowed them to stay in contact across different locations. Through his internship at S.T.A.R. Labs, he designed Red Robin's cape and wing apparatus and gave Kid Flash a new costume that could stabilize his powers.

Off the page, Static has starred in an animated series (voiced by Phil LaMarr), *Static Shock*, which ran for 52 episodes over four seasons between 2000 and 2004. *Static Shock* retooled much of the comic book material for a younger audience, as the show ran on the WB's kids-focused block; it went on to be nominated for numerous awards, including a Daytime Emmy. The series helped to popularize the character in a way not seen before, and his outfit from *Static Shock* remains one of his most popular. He has also appeared in DC team animated shows, including *Justice League Unlimited* and *Young Justice: Invasion*.

DEFIANT at 25

By J.C. Vaugh

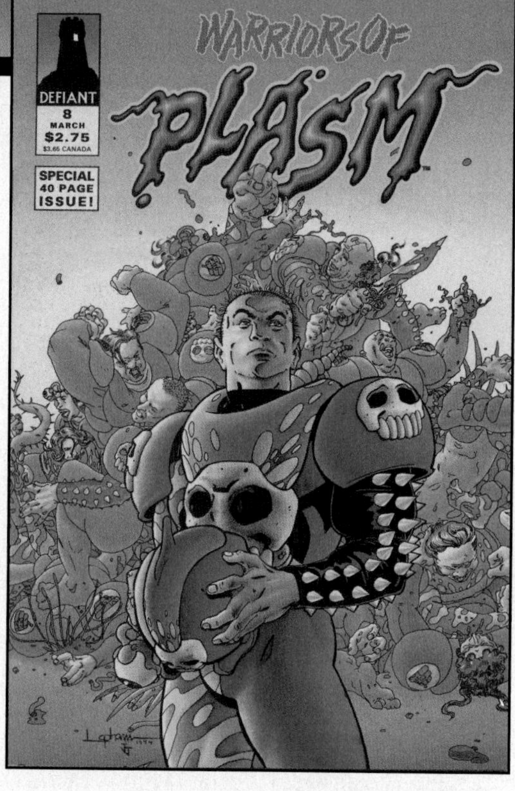

Following his ouster from Valiant, former Marvel Comic editor-in-chief Jim Shooter launched DEFIANT (stylized in all caps) as a new comic book company in 1993.

With the tagline "Beyond the imaginary limits…," Shooter teamed with Valiant alums Janet "JayJay" Jackson (who also worked at Marvel with him), artist David Lapham, publisher Winston Fowlkes, and general manager Debbie Fix, along with longtime friend and business associate J. Clark Smith, to launch the company. They were joined by comic book veterans such Len Wein, Steve Ditko, Chris Claremont, Dave Cockrum, Alan Weiss, and Steve Leialoha, as well as talented newcomers including artists Joe James, J.G. Jones, Adam Polina, and Charlie Adlard, and writer Art Holcomb, among others.

Warriors of Plasm, the company's first title, was primarily set on another world, one that was itself a living organism, The Org of Plasm. Written by Shooter and illustrated by Lapham, who had previously collaborated on *Harbinger*, among other titles, this new world featured concepts and values of life very different than our own. Life was cheap yet simultaneously perceived as continuing as long as a person's organic matter was recycled. And being recycled was a must, as The Org had a ravenous appetite.

Unlike science fantasy that so many enjoy, here was actual science fiction in comic book form. It featured challenging issues painted in bright colors that masked multiple shades of gray as the story played out on a vast stage.

Any sense of uniqueness or personhood is subordinate to the glory of The Org. Opposing views are treasonous, punishable by "mulching." Against their will, hundreds of thousands of humans from Earth were brought, though only a mere handful survived the process. They began manifesting powers, allied themselves with those who opposed the status quo, and the DEFIANT universe had its start. The series ran #0-13.

At about the same time, the company also launched *Dark Dominion*, which ran #0-10, and *The Good Guys*, which ran #1-9.

DEFIANT's second wave of titles included *Charlemagne* #0-5, *War Dancer* #1-6, *Dogs of War* #1-5, *Prudence & Caution* #1-2, and *The Great Grimmax* #0. Additionally, *DEFIANT Genesis* #1 and *Warriors of Plasm: Home for the Holidays* were issued as one-shots.

In part because one of their investors controlled a trading card company, but also because they tried innovative marketing, the company's efforts to go "Beyond the imaginary limits" extended to comic book formats.

Both *Warriors of Plasm* #0 and *Dark Dominion* #0 were issued as card sets with available binders. Additionally, a more standard comic book version of *Warriors of Plasm* #0 was bound into copies of *PREVIEWS* Volume III #6. *Birth of DEFIANT Universe* #1 was produced as a high-end, giveaway limited edition of 1,000 copies for retailers. *Prudence & Caution* #1-2 were issued in Spanish editions. *Charlemagne* #0 and *Great Grimmax* #0 were giveaways polybagged with *Hero Illustrated* magazine. *Glory* #0 was serialized in *Overstreet's Comic Book Monthly* #15-18, and *The Good Guys* #1.5 was serialized in *PREVIEWS* Volume III #7 – Volume IV #6.

A number of publishers succumbed to the boom-and-bust market in the mid-1990s, but former company insiders point elsewhere for DEFIANT's demise. When *Warriors of Plasm* was first announced as *Plasm*, Marvel Comics had filed suit, claiming similarity to its announced title, *Plasmer*. Despite the title change to *Warriors of Plasm*, Marvel's lawyers said consumers would confuse the two. Judge Michael Mukasey (later Attorney General of the United States) did not agree, and he issued a scathing ruling against Marvel. The damage had been done, though. The $300,000 in legal fees were too much for the company to sustain, and they would have had to go through an entire second trial for damages. The legal wrangling cost the company a lucrative licensing deal as well. DEFIANT ceased operations in 1995.

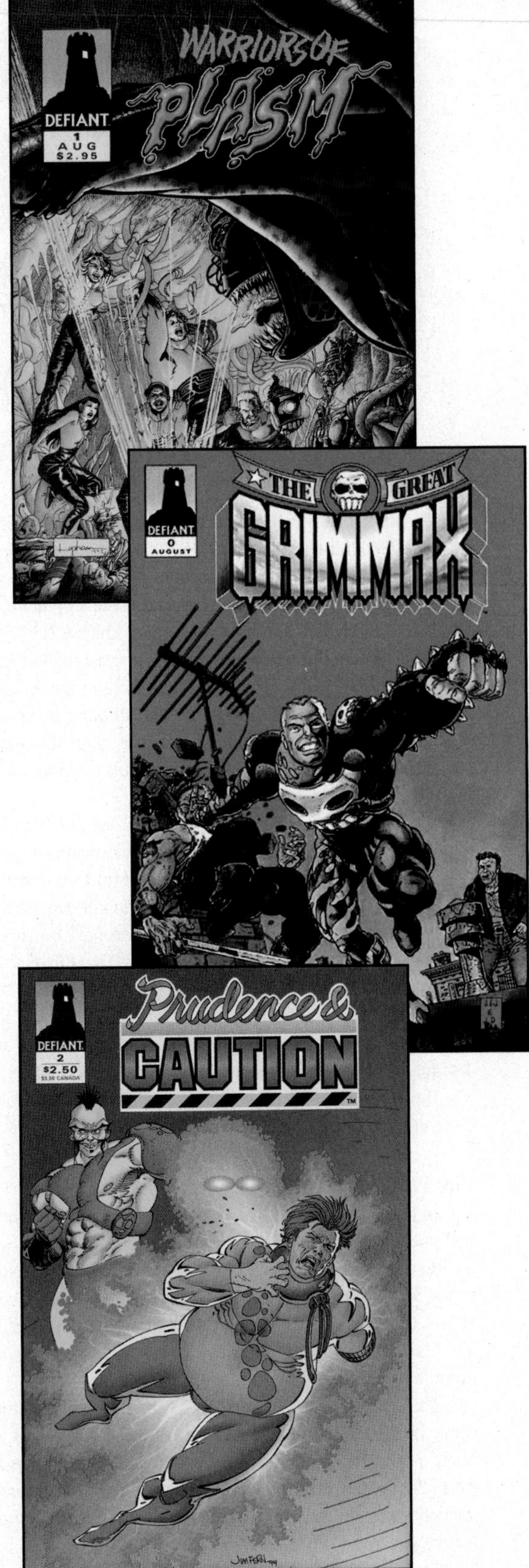

CGC

How the Company Has Grown and How It Works

By the CGC Grading Team

The world of comic book collecting has grown and matured considerably since the 2000 introduction of CGC (Certified Guaranty Company). Before the founding of CGC comic book transactions required sellers to grade their own comic books, a practice that often lacked consistency and impartiality. They also had to check their books for restoration, which was limited to each sellers' skills at detection. During the first decades of fandom most sales took place through mail order, as well as local comic shops or the occasional convention. The advent of the internet changed all that, allowing global buying and selling, regardless of a person's location or experience. While this greatly expanded the comic book market, it also greatly increased the potential for inaccurate grading and restoration detection.

CGC was created to help bring order and stability to comic book sales, and to put an end to the risk and the chaos that accompanied online sales. CGC is the first and largest independent, impartial, third-party comic book grading service. A proven and respected commitment to integrity, accuracy, consistency and impartiality has made CGC the leader in its field, becoming a tool to help people with their buying and selling decisions. The universally accepted grading scale ensures consistency and gives both dealers and collectors a sense of dependability when making purchasing decisions. With CGC certification, a collector knows what he or she is getting based on an accurate and comprehensive description that can be found on the CGC certification label.

If you've ever wondered about how it's done, here's a look at how CGC came together and how a book is certified.

The Formation of the Company

In January of 2000, CGC was launched under the umbrella of the Certified Collectibles Group, which includes Numismatic Guaranty Corporation (NGC), the largest third-party coin grading company in the world, Numismatic Conservation Services (NCS), the leading authority in numismatic conservation, Paper Money Guaranty (PMG), the world's leading currency certification company and Classic Collectible Services (CCS), the world's premier comic book restoration, restoration removal and pressing company.

The Collectibles Group sought out talented and ethical individuals to grade comic books. Experts needed a history of comics as well as necessary skills to verify a comic book's authenticity and to detect restoration that can affect its value. To identify these individuals, many of the most respected individuals in the hobby were consulted, and, based on their recommendations a core grading team was selected.

The members of the CGC grading team come from diverse backgrounds, and many were comic book dealers at some time in their careers. Experience in the commercial sector can be an essential ingredient in becoming familiar with market standards.

When it was time to develop a uniform grading standard, the hobby's leaders were once again called upon. Everyone agreed that the *Overstreet Guide* was the foundation of this standard, but there were a number of subjective interpretations of its published definitions. It was critical to understand how these guidelines were being applied to the everyday buying and selling of comics. To accomplish this, approximately 50 of the hobby's top experts took part in an extensive grading test. Their grades were averaged and an accurate grading standard reflecting the collective experience of the hobby's most prominent individuals was thus developed. CGC now had the best standard and the best team to apply it.

With the graders in place and the grading scale established, the next step was to develop a tamper-evident holder for the long-term storage and display of certified comics. This proved to be a technical challenge. Exhaustive material tests were conducted to determine that the holders were archival safe. To create a true first line of defense, it was determined that the comic book should be sealed in a soft inner well, then sealed again inside a tamper evident hard plastic case with interlocking ridges to enable compact storage. The CGC certified grade appears on a label sealed inside the holder for an additional level of security.

Submitting Books

Comic books may be submitted for certification in two ways - they can be submitted by authorized dealers or by Collectors Society members. The Collectors Society is an online community with direct access to certification service from CGC, and submissions can be prepared using online submission forms or paper forms. Both dealers and Collectors Society members typically send their comics to CGC's offices by registered mail or through an insured express company. Submissions are also accepted at many of the Comic Cons that occur around the country throughout the year. CGC will grade on-site at selected shows.

Receiving the Books

Every day, CGC's Receiving Department opens newly arrived packages and immediately verifies that the number of books in each package matches the number shown on the submitted invoice, and checks the submission for any damage sustained in shipping. Once this is done, a more detailed comparison is made to ensure that their invoice descriptions correspond to the actual comics. This information is entered into a computer, and from this time forth, the comics will be traceable at all stages of the grading process by their invoice number and their line number within that invoice. Each book is checked to see that it is properly prepared for grading in an appropriately sized comic bag with backing board and then is labeled with a numbered barcode containing the pertinent data of invoice number and line item information for quick reading by the computer. Before any grading is performed, the book is examined by a CGC Restoration Detection Specialist. If any form of restoration work is detected, this information is entered into the computer, making it available to the grading team.

The Grading Begins

After being examined by a Restoration Detection Specialist, the book is then passed on to the graders. At this stage the comics have been properly sleeved and barcoded for grading and have been separated from their original invoice. This step is taken to ensure that graders do not know whose books they are grading, as a further guarantee of impartiality. The grading process begins by having the book's pages counted and entering into the computer any peculiarities or flaws that may affect a book's grade. Some examples of this would be "Spine Stress Lines Break Color," "Right Top Front Cover Small Crease Breaks Color," "Top Back Cover Tear with Crease" and "Staple Rusted w/Rust Stained Interior." This information is entered into the "Graders Notes" field and a grade is assigned.

When other graders examine the comic, they do not see any previous assigned grades, so as to not influence their evaluation. Graders are able to view previous Graders Notes after determining their own grade. The Grader may then add to the existing commentary if he believes more remarks are in order. The Grading Finalizer is the last person to examine the book. He makes a final restoration check before determining his own grade, at which time he reviews the grades and notes entered by the previous graders. If all grades are in agreement or are very close, he will assign the book's final grade. The book is then forwarded to the Encapsulation Department for sealing. If there is disagreement among the graders, a discussion will ensue until a final determination is made and the book forwarded.

Each comic book receives a restoration check and the results appear on the label.

CGC RESTORED GRADE
X-Men #1
Marvel Comics, 9/63
Restoration includes: color touch, pieces added, tear seals, cover cleaned, interior lightened, reinforced.
OFF-WHITE Pages

Encapsulating the Comics

After each comic has been graded and the necessary numbers and text entered into their respective data fields, all the comics on a particular invoice are taken from the Grading Department into the Encapsulation Department. Here, appropriately color-coded labels are printed bearing the proper descriptive text, including each book's grade and identification number. This is critical, as it serves to make each certified comic unique and is also a significant deterrent to counterfeiting CGC's valued product. All of the above information is duplicated in a barcode, which also appears on the comic's label.

The newly-printed labels are stacked in the same sequence as the comics to be encapsulated with them, ensuring that each book and its label match one another. The comic is now ready to be fitted inside an archival-quality interior well, which is then sealed within a transparent capsule, along with the book's color-coded label. This is accomplished through a combination of compression and ultrasonic vibration.

The Comics are Shipped

After encapsulation, all comics are set briefly to the Quality Control for inspection. Here, they are examined to make certain that their labels are correct for both the grade and its accompanying descriptive information. Quality control also inspects each book for any flaws in its holder, such as scuffs or nicks. While these are quite rare, CGC is careful to make certain that the comics it certifies are not only accurately graded, but attractively presented as well. When all the comics have been inspected, they're delivered to our Shipping Department for packaging. The comics are counted and their labels checked against the original invoice to make certain that no mistakes have occurred. A Shipping Department employee then verifies the method of transport as selected by the submitter on the invoice and prepares the comics for delivery or they are held in CGC's vault for in-person pick-up by the submitter.

No matter whether the US Postal Service or some private carrier is used, the method of packaging is essentially the same. The encapsulated comics are placed vertically inside sturdy cardboard boxes. In 2005, CGC developed a custom shipping box to enable the highest level of stability during shipping. A copy of the submitter's invoice is included before the box is sealed and heavy tape is used to prevent accidental or unauthorized opening of the box while it's in transit.

The barcode of every comic book is scanned before it is placed into its shipping box. The status of the book is changed to "shipped" in our tracking system, and we retain a record of what books were shipped in which box. This is the final crucial step of our detailed internal tracking system.

The CGC Label

Comic books certified by CGC bear color-coded labels that have different meanings. Whenever purchasing a CGC-certified comic, be certain to note not only the book's grade but also its label category. A Universal label is denoted by the color blue and indicates that a book was not found to have any qualifying defects or signs of restoration. There is one exception to this policy: At CGC's discretion, comics having a very minor amount of color touch-up may still qualify for a Universal label provided such restoration is noted underneath the assigned grade.

As its name implies, the Restored label, identified by its purple color, is used for books found to have restoration work performed on them. The grade assigned is based on the book's appearance, with the restoration noted. The Restoration scale is as follows: **Quality (Aesthetic) Scale** – (Determined by materials used and visual quality of work)

A (Excellent)

- Material used: rice paper, wheat paste, acrylic or water color, leafcasting
- Color match near perfect, no bleed through
- Piece fill seamless and correct thickness
- No fading, excessive whiteness, ripples, cockling, or ink smudges from cover or interior cleaning
- Book feels natural
- Near perfect staple alignment, or replaced exactly as they were
- Filled edges cut to look natural and even
- Cleaned staples or staples replaced with vintage staples
- Married cover/pages match in size and page quality. Professionally attached

B (Fine)

- Material used: pencil, crayon, chalk, re-glossing agent, piece fill from cadavers
- Piece fill obvious upon close inspection, obvious to the touch
- Color touch obvious upon close inspection, or done with materials listed above
- Cover cleaning resulting in slight color fading or excessively white
- Interior cleaning resulting in slight puffiness, cockling, excessively white
- Enlarged staple holes, obviously crooked staples, or backwards staple insertion
- Replaced staples not vintage
- Married cover/pages do not match in size and/or page quality. Professionally attached

C (Poor)

- Material used: glue, pen, marker, white out, white paper to fill missing pieces
- Piece fill obvious at arm's length
- Bad color matching, use of pen or marker. Bleed through evident
- Cover cleaning resulting in washed out/speckled colors, moderate cockling and/or ripples
- New staple holes created upon reinsertion, or non-comic book staples used
- Trimming of any kind
- Married cover/pages poorly attached with non-professional materials

Quantity Scale – *(Determined primarily by extent of piece fill and color touch)*

1 (Slight)

All conservation work, re-glossing, interior lightening, piece fill no more than size of two bindery chips, light color touch in small areas like spine stress, corner crease or bindery chip fill. Married cover or interior pages/wraps (if other work is present)

2 (Slight/Moderate)

Piece fill up to the ½" x ½" and/or color touch covering up to 1" x 1". Interior piece fill up to 1" x 1"

3 (Moderate)

Piece fill up to the size of 1" x 1" and/or color touch covering up to 2" x 2". Interior piece fill up to 2" x 2"

4 (Moderate/Extensive)

Piece fill up to the size of 2" x 2" and/or color touch covering up to 4" x 4". Interior piece fill up to 4" x 4"

5 (Extensive)
Any piece fill over 2" x 2" and/or color touch over 4" x 4".
Recreated interior pages or cover

Conservation Repairs

- Tear seals
- Spine split seals
- Reinforcement
- Piece reattachment
- Some cover or interior cleaning (water or solvent)
- Staples cleaned or replaced
- Some leaf casting

Materials Used for Conservation Repairs:

- Rice paper
- Wheat glue
- Vintage staples
- Archival tape

Conserved Label (Similar to the blue Universal label, but differentiated by a silver bar across the top. Conservation is noted in a similar fashion on the label as on the purple CGC Restored Label.) This label is applied to any comic book with specific repairs done to improve the structural integrity and long-term preservation. These repairs include tear seals, support, staple replacement, piece reattachment and certain kinds of cleaning.

The Qualified label is green, and this indicates that one qualifying defect is present on a book. An example of such a qualifying feature would be a missing Marvel Value Stamp that does not affect the story. While such a book technically may grade 1.5, it may appear to grade 9.6. In such instances, assigning a grade of just 1.5 does not fully represent the value of the comic to a collector. Through use of the green Qualified label, a comic buyer is able to make an informed decision as to what he is purchasing in terms of its overall desirability. Because of the complexity involved, green labels are assigned quite seldom and then only when considered absolutely necessary. In addition, comic books that have an unwitnessed signature, and therefore are not eligible for the Signature Series label (see below), get the Qualified label. This is the most common use for the Qualified label. This shows what the grade of the book would have been if the signature was not present.

CGC's Signature Series label is yellow, and this is used when a comic book has been signed or been sketched on by a creator in the presence of a CGC representative, assuring the signature's or sketch's authenticity. Only books that meet CGC's strict criteria for authenticity are eligible for the Signature Series label. In addition to the certified grade, the yellow label includes who signed it and when it was signed. If appropriate, a Signature Series label may state where a book was signed. In 2007, CGC introduced a Signature Series Restored label. Similar to the CGC Signature Series label in color, it is differentiated by a purple bar across the top. Restoration is noted in the same fashion as on the purple CGC Restored label, and, as with the regular Signature Series label, restored books must be signed in the presence of CGC representatives in order to be eligible for signature authentication.

CGC encapsulation is not limited to standard size comics. Magazines and small promotional comics are included as well.

The Evolution of CGC and CCG

In October of 2003, CGC began to certify comic book related magazines. The certification process and label system for magazines is exactly the same as for comic books. Some examples of comic book related magazines CGC certifies are *MAD Magazine*, *Vampirella*, *Creepy*, *Eerie* and *Famous Monsters of Filmland*.

More recently CGC introduced grading and encapsulation for *Sports Illustrated* and *Playboy* magazines, Movie Lobby Cards, Photographs, and Concert Posters making us the first independent, impartial, expert third-party grading service for all types of collectibles. CGC has graded over 4.1 million collectibles to date.

In a move intended to strengthen CGC's commitment to promoting the comic collecting hobby and enhance the collecting experience, CGC's parent company Certified Collectibles Group acquired Classics Incorporated, the world's premier comic book restoration, restoration removal and pressing company, in 2012. Previously located in Dallas, TX, Classics Incorporated relocated to Sarasota, FL to become an independent member of the Certified Collectibles Group under the new name Classic Collectible Services (CCS). Customers who wish to send books in for pressing, restoration or restoration removal are be able to send them to CCS and have them transfer directly to CGC for grading — creating a synergistic relationship that saves customers time, shipping and insurance expenses.

For more information on comic book certification and CGC's many services, please visit our website at www.CGCcomics.com

OVERSTREET ADVISORS

DARREN ADAMS
Pristine Comics
Seattle, WA

WELDON ADAMS
Heritage Auctions
Fort Worth, TX

GRANT ADEY
Halo Certification
Brisbane, QLD, Australia

BILL ALEXANDER
Collector
Sacramento, CA

DAVID T. ALEXANDER
David Alexander Comics
Tampa, FL

TYLER ALEXANDER
David Alexander Comics
Tampa, FL

LON ALLEN
Heritage Auctions
Dallas, TX

DAVE ANDERSON
Want List Comics
Tulsa, OK

L.E. BECKER
Comic*Pop Collectibles
Wixom, MI

ROBERT BEERBOHM
Robert Beerbohm Comic Art
Fremont, NE

JON BERK
Collector
Hartford, CT

JIM BERRY
Collector
Portland, OR

JON BEVANS
Collector
Baltimore, MD

TIM BILDHAUSER
Foreign Comics Specialist
CBCS

PETER BILELIS, ESQ.
Collector
South Windsor, CT

DR. ARNOLD T. BLUMBERG
Collector
Baltimore, MD

MIKE BOLLINGER
Hake's Americana
York, PA

STEVE BOROCK
CBCS
Dallas, TX

SCOTT BRADEN
Comics Historian
Hanover, PA

RICHARD BROWN
Collector
Detroit, MI

SHAWN CAFFREY
Finalizer/Modern Age Specialist
CGC

MICHAEL CARBONARO
Dave & Adam's
New York

BRETT CARRERAS
VA Comicon
Richmond, VA

GARY CARTER
Collector
Coronado, CA

CHARLES CERRITO
Hotflips
Farmingdale, NY

JEFF CERRITO
Hotflips
Farmingdale, NY

JOHN CHRUSCINSKI
Tropic Comics
Lyndora, PA

PAUL CLAIRMONT
PNJ Comics
Winnipeg, MB
Canada

ART CLOOS
Collector/Historian
Flushing, NY

GARY COLABUONO
Dealer/Collector
Arlington Heights, IL

BILL COLE
Bill Cole Enterprises, Inc.
Randolph, MA

TIM COLLINS
RTS Unlimited, Inc.
Lakewood, CO

ANDREW COOKE
Writer/Director
New York City, NY

JON B. COOKE
Editor - Comic Book Artist Magazine
West Kingston, RI

JACK COPLEY
Coliseum of Comics
Florida

ASHLEY COTTER-CAIRNS
SellMyComicBooks.com
Montreal, Canada

JESSE JAMES CRISCIONE
Jesse James Comics
Glendale, AZ

FRANK CWIKLIK
Metropolis Comics
New York, NY

BROCK DICKINSON
Collector
St. Catharines, ONT
Canada

PETER DIXON
Paradise Comics
Toronto, ONT Canada

GARY DOLGOFF
Gary Dolgoff Comics
Easthampton, MA

JOHN DOLMAYAN
Torpedo Comics
Las Vegas, NV

SHELTON DRUM
Heroes Aren't Hard to Find
Charlotte, NC

WALTER DURAJLIJA
Big B Comics
Hamilton, ONT
Canada

KEN DYBER
Cloud 9 Comics
Portland, OR

TOMIS ERB
Comic Verification Authority
Brooklyn, NY

DANIEL ERTLE
Modern Age Specialist
CBCS

CONRAD ESCHENBERG
Collector/Dealer
Cold Spring, NY

MICHAEL EURY
Author
Concord, NC

RICHARD EVANS
Bedrock City Comics
Houston, TX

D'ARCY FARRELL
Pendragon Comics
Toronto, ONT Canada

BILL FIDYK
Collector
Annapolis, MD

PAUL FIGURA
Quality Control Specialist
CBCS

JOSEPH FIORE
ComicWiz.com
Toronto, ONT Canada

STEPHEN FISHLER
Metropolis Collectibles, Inc.
New York, NY

DAN FOGEL
Hippy Comix, Inc.
Cleveland, OH

BRAD FOSTER
SharpComics.com
Plainfield, IL

JOHN FOSTER
Collector
Philadelphia, PA

KEIF A. FROMM
Collector/Historian

DAN GALLO
Dealer/Comic Art Con
Westchester Co., NY

STEPHEN H. GENTNER
Golden Age Specialist
Portland, OR

JOSH GEPPI
Diamond Int. Galleries
ComicWow.com
Timonium, MD

STEVE GEPPI
Diamond Int. Galleries
Timonium, MD

DOUG GILLOCK
ComicLink
Portland, ME

MICHAEL GOLDMAN
Motor City Comics
Farmington Hills, MI

SEAN GOODRICH
SellMyComicBooks.com
Maine, USA

KEITH GOSS
Collector
Staten Island, NY

TOM GORDON III
Collector/Dealer
Westminster, MD

JAMIE GRAHAM
Graham Crackers
Chicago, IL

DANIEL GREENHALGH
Showcase
New England
Northford, CT

ANDY GREENHAM
Forest City Coins
London, ON Canada

ERIC J. GROVES
Dealer/Collector
Oklahoma City, OK

GARY GUZZO
Atomic Studios
Boothbay Harbor, ME

JOHN HAINES
Dealer/Collector
Kirtland, OH

JIM HALPERIN
Heritage Auctions
Dallas, TX

JAY HALSTEAD
International Comic
Exchange
Hamilton, ON Canada

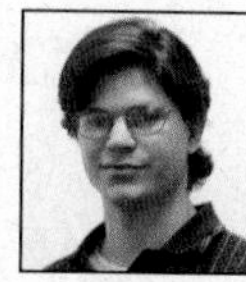

MARK HASPEL
Finalizer/
Pedigree Specialist
CGC

JEF HINDS
Jef Hinds Comics
Madison, WI

TERRY HOKNES
Hoknes Comics
Saskatoon, SK
Canada

GREG HOLLAND, Ph.D.
Collector
Alexander, AR

JOHN HONE
Collector
Silver Spring, MD

STEVEN HOUSTON
Torpedo Comics
Las Vegas, NV

BILL HUGHES
Dealer/Collector
Flower Mound, TX

ROB HUGHES
Arch Angels
Pacific Beach, CA

JEFF ITKIN
Elite Comic Source
Portland, OR

ED JASTER
Heritage Auctions
Dallas, TX

DR. STEVEN KAHN
Inner Child Comics
& Collectibles
Kenosha, WI

NICK KATRADIS
Collector
Tenafly, NJ

DENNIS KEUM
Fantasy Comics
Goldens Bridge, NY

IVAN KOCMAREK
Comics Historian
Hamilton, ON
Canada

ROBERT KRAUSE
Primo Comics
Venice, FL

MICHAEL KRONENBERG
Historian/Designer
Chapel Hill, NC

BENJAMIN LABONOG
Collector
Burlingame, CA

BEN LICHTENSTEIN
Zapp Comics
Wayne, NJ

STEPHEN LIPSON
Comics Historian
Mississauga, ON

PAUL LITCH
Primary Grader
CGC

DOUG MABRY
The Great Escape
Madison, TN

TOMMY MALETTA
Best Comics
International
New Hyde Park, NY

JOE MANNARINO
Heritage Auctions
Ridgewood, NJ

NADIA MANNARINO
Heritage Auctions
Ridgewood, NJ

BRIAN MARCUS
Cavalier Comics
Wise, VA

WILL MASON
Dave & Adam's
New York

HARRY MATETSKY
Collector
Middletown, NJ

JON McCLURE
Comics Historian,
Writer
Portland, OR

TODD McDEVITT
New Dimension Comics
Cranberry Township,
PA

MIKE McKENZIE
Alternate Worlds
Cockeysville, MD

ANDY McMAHON
Duncanville Bookstore
Duncanville, TX

PETER MEROLO
Collector
Sedona, AZ

JOHN JACKSON MILLER
Historian, Writer
Scandinavia, WI

STEVE MORTENSEN
Miracle Comics
Santa Clara, CA

MARC NATHAN
Cards, Comics &
Collectibles
Reisterstown, MD

JOSHUA NATHANSON
ComicLink
Portland, ME

MATT NELSON
President, CCS
Sarasota, FL

TOM NELSON
Top Notch Comics
Yankton, SD

JAMIE NEWBOLD
Southern California
Comics
San Diego, CA

CHARLIE NOVINSKIE
Silver Age Specialist
Lake Havasu City, AZ

VINCE OLIVA
Grader
CGC

RICHARD OLSON
Collector/Academician
Poplarville, MS

TERRY O'NEILL
Terry's Comics
Orange, CA

MICHAEL PAVLIC
Purple Gorilla Comics
Calgary, AB Canada

JIM PAYETTE
Golden Age Specialist
Bethlehem, NH

BILL PONSETI
Fantastic Worlds Comics
Scottsdale, AZ

RON PUSSELL
Redbeard's Book Den
Crystal Bay, NV

JEFF RADER
Offbeat Archives
Comics & Collectibles
Gilroy, CA

ALEX REECE
Reece's Rare Comics
Ijamsville, MD

GREG REECE
Reece's Rare Comics
Ijamsville, MD

ROB REYNOLDS
ComicConnect
New York, NY

STEVE RICKETTS
CBCS Pressing
Dallas, TX

STEPHEN RITTER
Worldwide Comics
Fair Oaks Ranch, TX

ROBERT ROGOVIN
Four Color Comics
Scarsdale, NY

CHUCK ROZANSKI
Mile High Comics
Denver, CO

SEAN RUTAN
Hake's Americana
York, PA

BEN SAMUELS
Golden Age/Foreign
Comics Specialist
Shanghai, China

BARRY SANDOVAL
Heritage Auctions
Dallas, TX

BUDDY SAUNDERS
MyComicShop.com
Arlington, TX

CONAN SAUNDERS
MyComicShop.com
Arlington, TX

MATT SCHIFFMAN
Bronze Age Specialist
Bend, OR

PHIL SCHLAEFER
CPRS/Champion Comics
Sunnyvale, CA

DOUG SCHMELL
Pedigree Comics, Inc.
Wellington, FL

BRIAN SCHUTZER
Sparkle City Comics
Neat Stuff Collectibles
North Bergen, NJ

DYLAN SCHWARTZ
DylanUniverseComics.com
Great Neck, NY

ALIKA SEKI
Maui Comics and
Collectibles
Waiehu, HI

TODD SHEFFER
Hake's Americana
York, PA

FRANK SIMMONS
Coast to Coast Comics
Rocklin, CA

DOUG SIMPSON
Paradise Comics
Toronto, ONT Canada

MARC SIMS
Big B Comics
Barrie, ONT

LAUREN SISSELMAN
Comics Journalist
Baltimore, MD

ANTHONY SNYDER
Anthony's
Comic Book Art
Leonia, NJ

MARK SQUIREK
Collector/Historian
Baltimore, MD

TONY STARKS
Silver Age Specialist
Evansville, IN

WEST STEPHAN
CBCS
Dallas, TX

MIKE STEVENS
Hake's Americana
York, PA

AL STOLTZ
Basement Comics
Havre de Grace, MD

DOUG SULIPA
"Everything 1960-1996"
Manitoba, Canada

CHRIS SWARTZ
Collector
San Diego, CA

MAGGIE THOMPSON
Collector/Historian
Iola, WI

MICHAEL TIERNEY
The Comic Book Store
Little Rock, AR

TED VAN LIEW
Superworld Comics
Worcester, MA

JOE VERENEAULT
JHV Associates
Woodbury Heights, NJ

JASON VERSAGGI
Collector
Brooklyn, NY

JOSEPH VETERI, ESQ.
Comic Art Con
Springfield, NJ

TODD WARREN
Collector
Fort Washington, PA

BOB WAYNE
Collector
Fairfield, CT

JEFF WEAVER
Victory Comics
Falls Church, VA

LON WEBB
Dark Adventure
Comics
Norcross, GA

RICK WHITELOCK
New Force Comics
Lynn Haven, FL

MIKE WILBUR
Diamond Int.
Galleries
Timonium, MD

ALEX WINTER
Hake's Americana
York, PA

HARLEY YEE
Dealer/Collector
Detroit, MI

MARK ZAID
EsquireComics.com
Bethesda, MD

VINCENT ZURZOLO, JR.
Metropolis
Collectibles, Inc.
New York, NY

OVERSTREET PRICE GUIDE BACK ISSUES

The Overstreet® Comic Book Price Guide has held the record for being the longest running annual comic book publication. We are now celebrating our 48th anniversary, and the demand for the Overstreet® price guides is very strong. Collectors have created a legitimate market for them, and they continue to bring record prices each year. Collectors also have a record of comic book prices going back further than any other source in comic fandom. The prices listed below are for NM condition only, with GD-25% and FN-50% of the NM value. Canadian editions exist for a couple of the early issues. Abbreviations: SC-softcover, HC-hardcover, L-leather bound.

1970

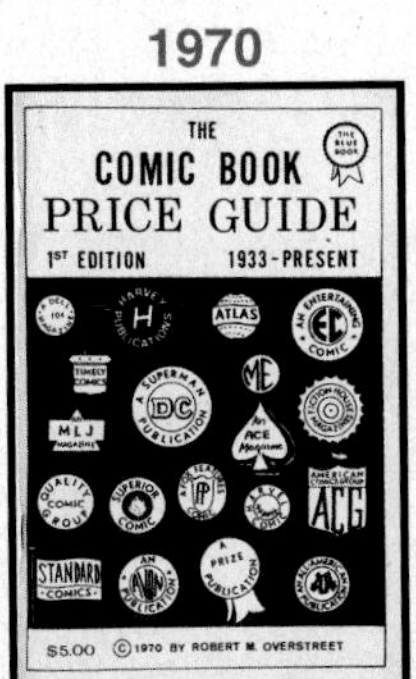

#1 White SC
$1825.00

1970

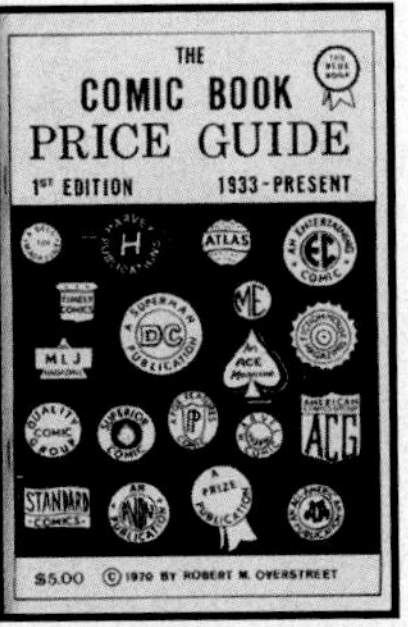

#1 Blue SC
(2nd Printing)
$1550.00

1972

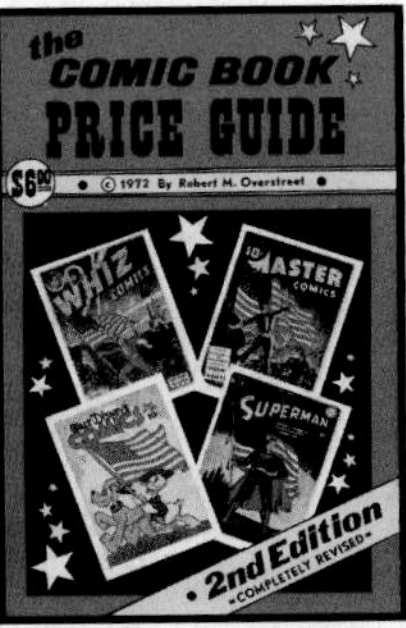

#2 SC $650.00
#2 HC $1100.00

1973

#3 SC $325.00
#3 HC $950.00

1974

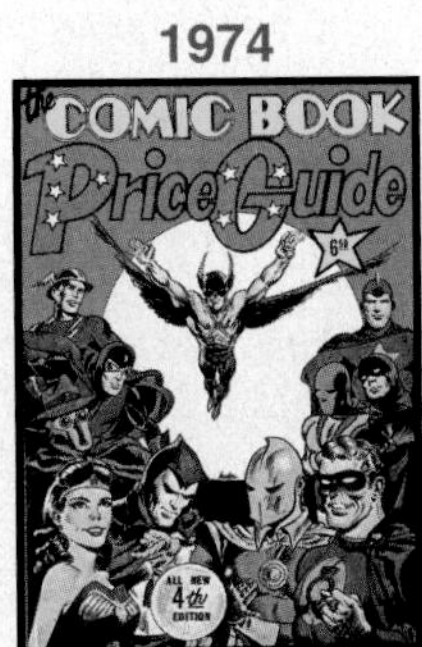

#4 SC $165.00
#4 HC $475.00

1975

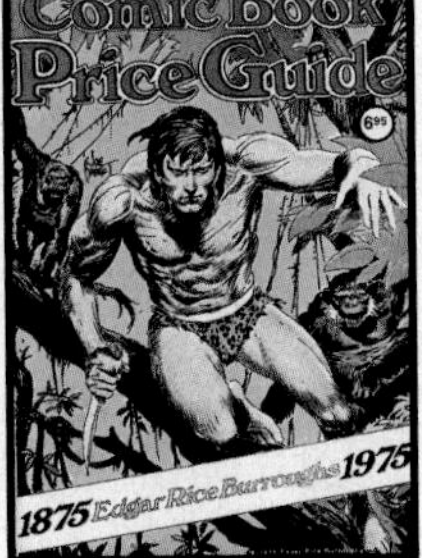

#5 SC $155.00
#5 HC $260.00

1976

#6 SC $105.00
#6 HC $155.00

1977

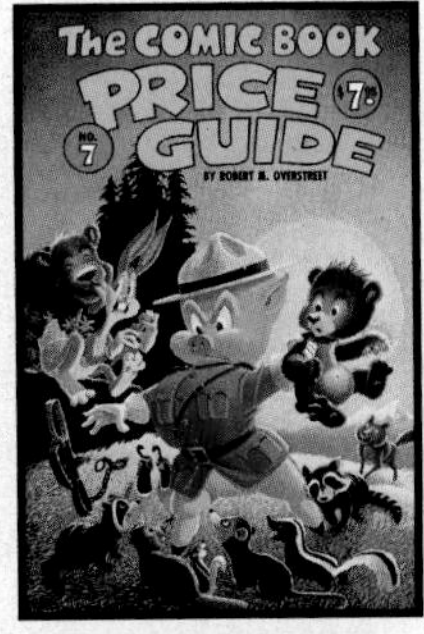

#7 SC $155.00
#7 HC $230.00

1978

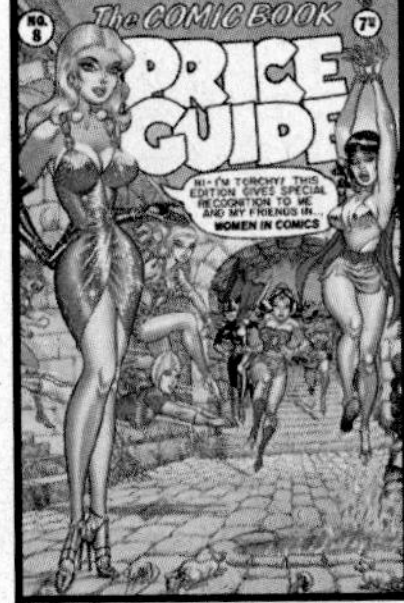

#8 SC $130.00
#8 HC $180.00

1979

#9 SC $130.00
#9 HC $180.00

1980

#10 SC $140.00
#10 HC $190.00

1981

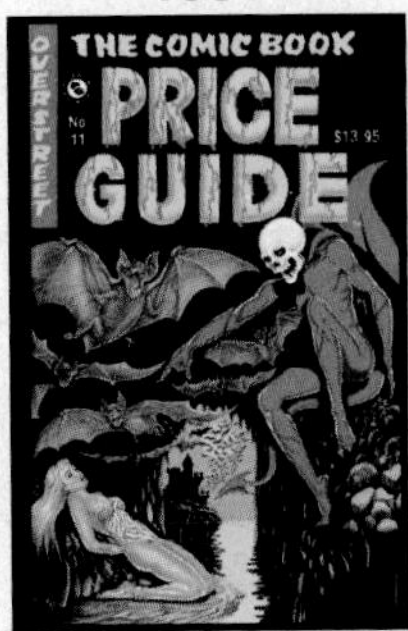

#11 SC $85.00
#11 HC $115.00

1982

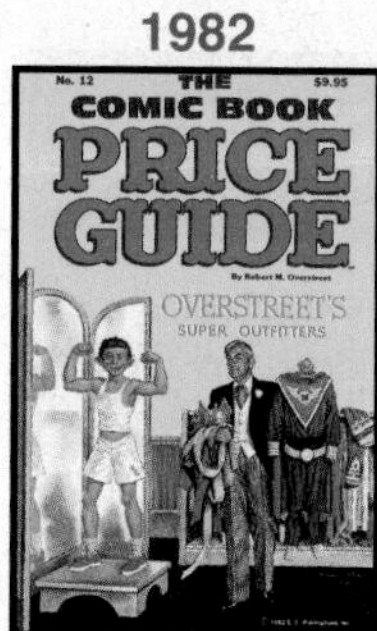

#12 SC $85.00
#12 HC $115.00

1983

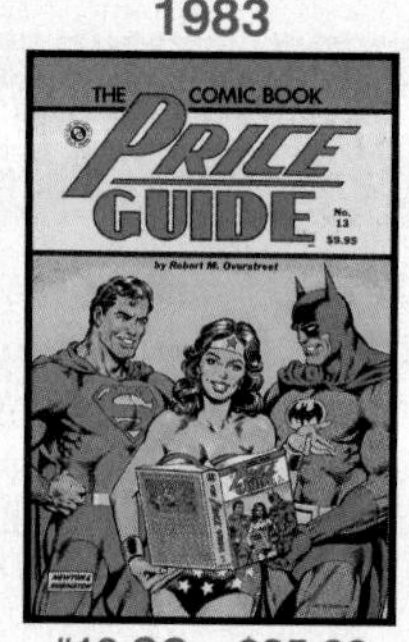

#13 SC $85.00
#13 HC $115.00

1984

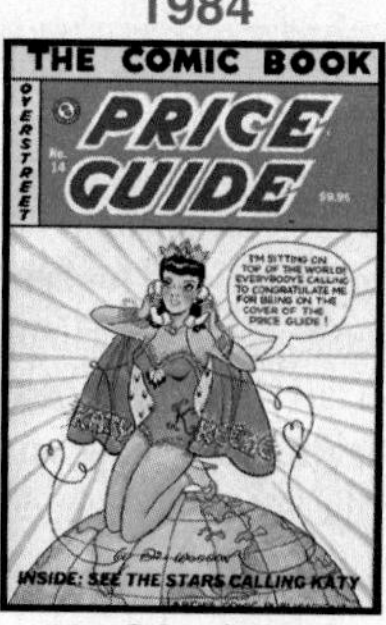

#14 SC $55.00
#14 HC $110.00
#14 L $170.00

1985

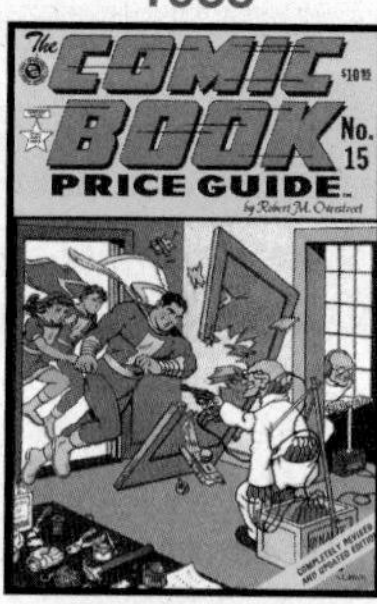

#15 SC $55.00
#15 HC $80.00
#15 L $160.00

1986

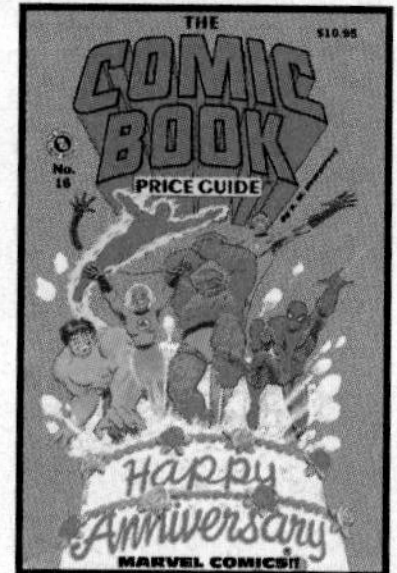

#16 SC $60.00
#16 HC $85.00
#16 L $170.00

1987

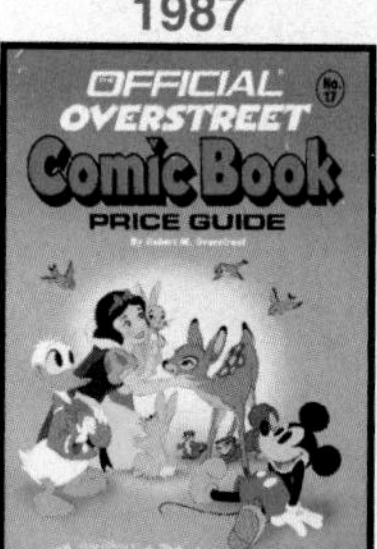

#17 SC $55.00
#17 HC $110.00
#17 L $160.00

1988

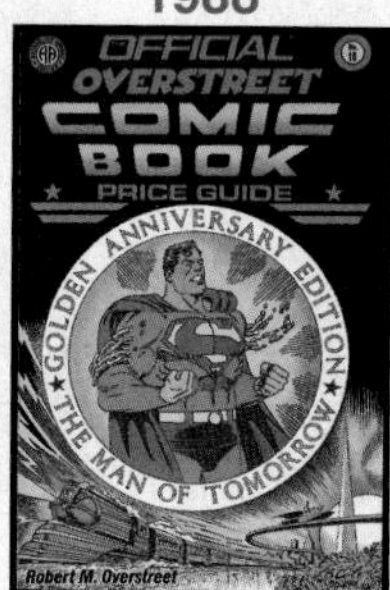

#18 SC $45.00
#18 HC $65.00
#18 L $160.00

1989

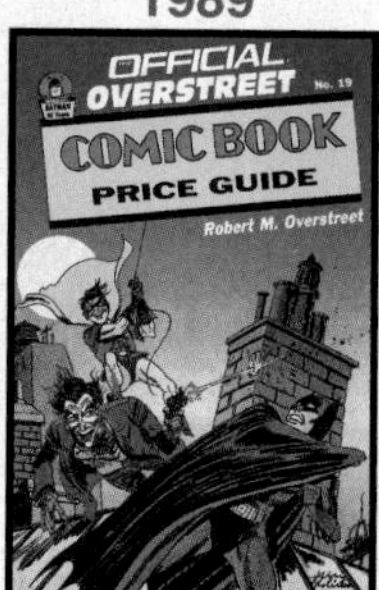

#19 SC $50.00
#19 HC $60.00
#19 L $170.00

1990

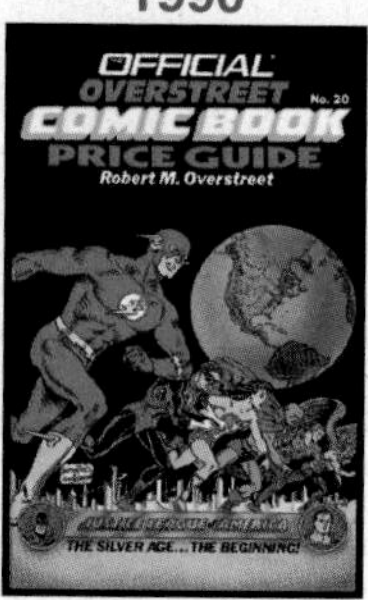

#20 SC $32.00
#20 HC $50.00
#20 L $135.00

1991

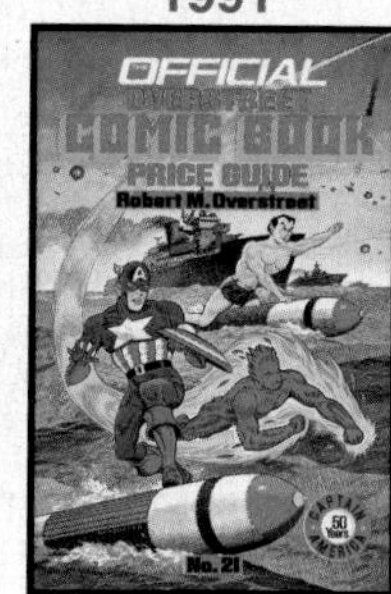

#21 SC $40.00
#21 HC $60.00
#21 L $145.00

1992

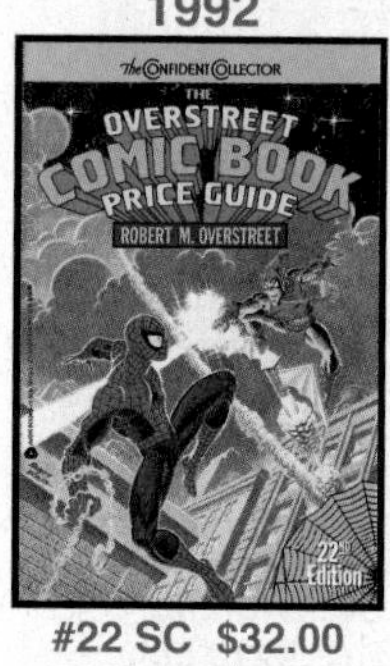

#22 SC $32.00
#22 HC $50.00

1993

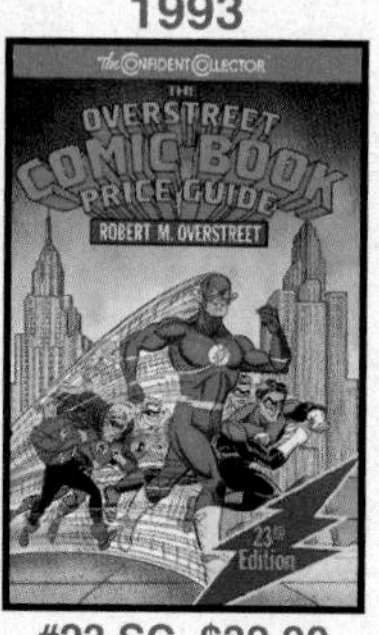

#23 SC $32.00
#23 HC $50.00

1994

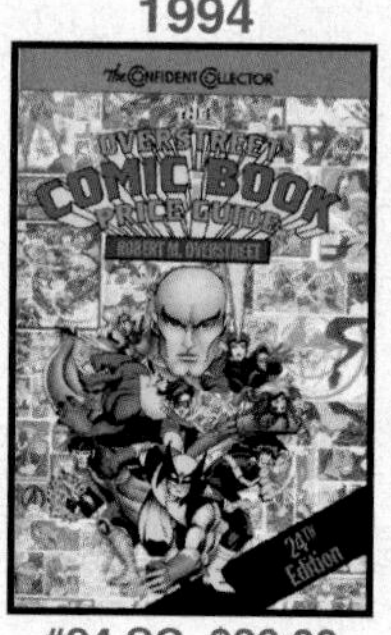

#24 SC $26.00
#24 HC $36.00

1995

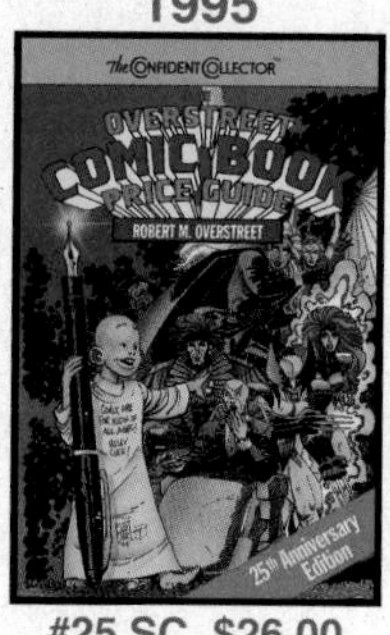

#25 SC $26.00
#25 HC $36.00
#25 L $110.00

1996

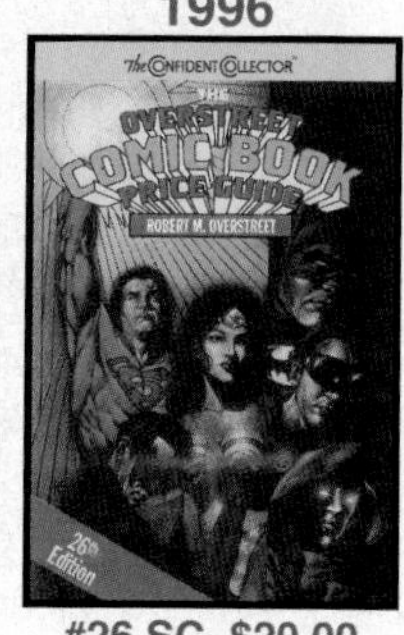

#26 SC $20.00
#26 HC $30.00
#26 L $100.00

1997

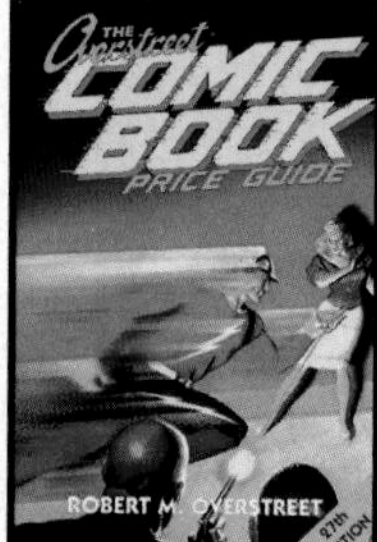

#27 SC $22.00
#27 HC $38.00
#27 L $125.00

1997

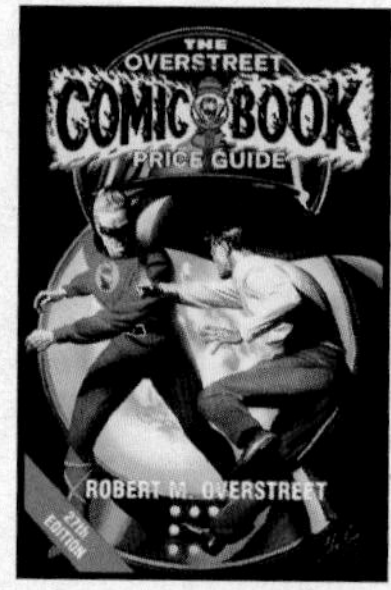

#27 SC $22.00
#27 HC $38.00
#27 L $125.00

1998

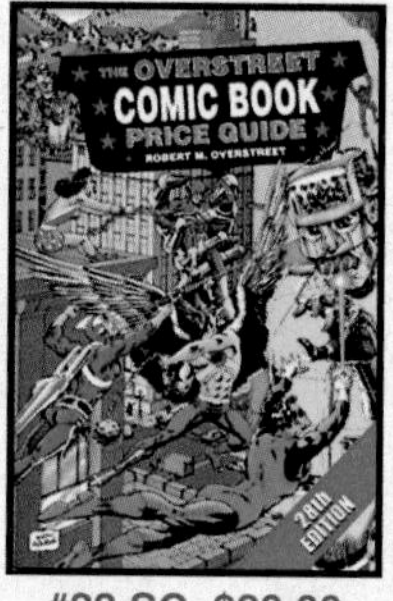

#28 SC $20.00
#28 HC $35.00

1998

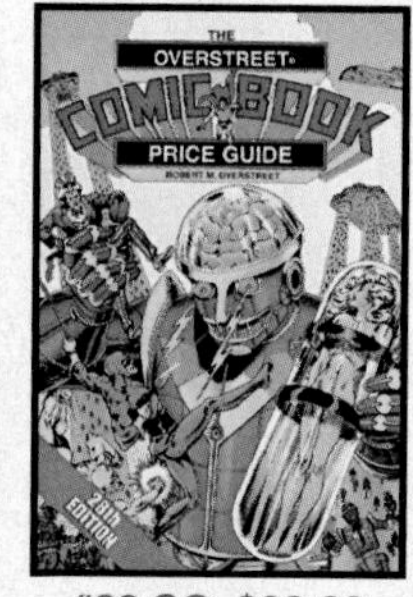

#28 SC $20.00
#28 HC $35.00

1999

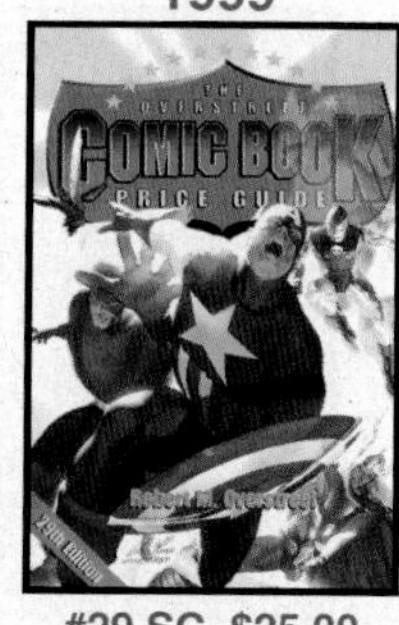

#29 SC $25.00
#29 HC $40.00

1999

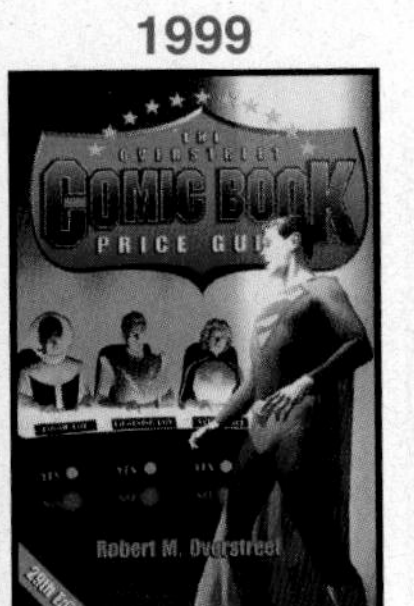

#29 SC $20.00
#29 HC $37.00

2000

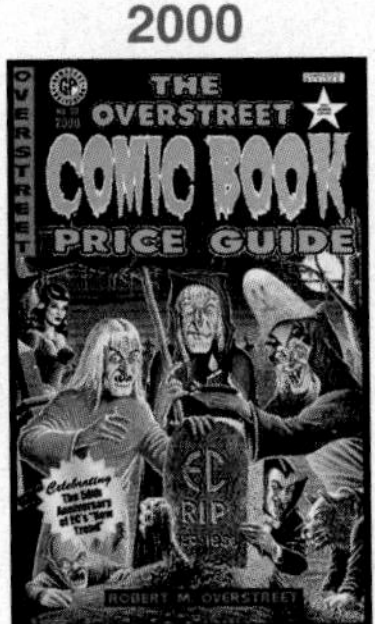

#30 SC $22.00
#30 HC $32.00

2000

#30 SC $22.00
#30 HC $32.00

2001

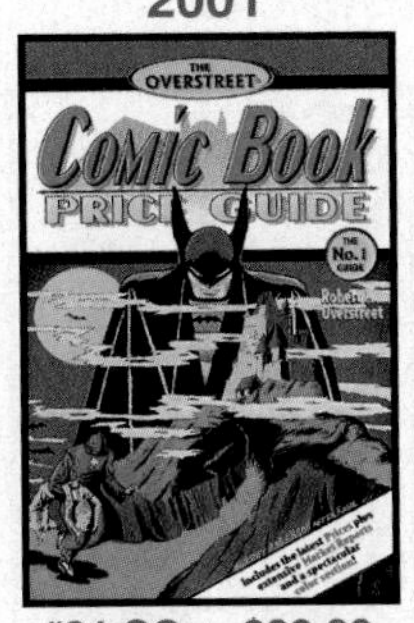

#31 SC $22.00
#31 HC $32.00

2001

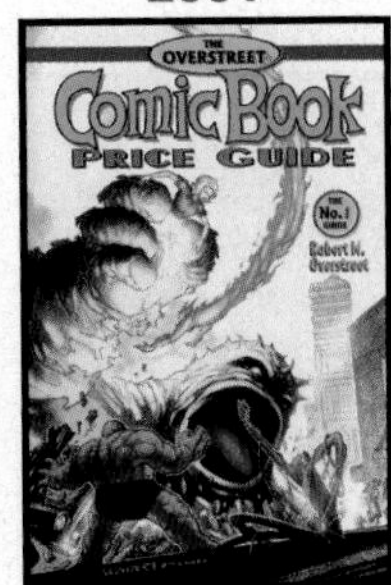

#31 SC $22.00
#31 HC $32.00

2001

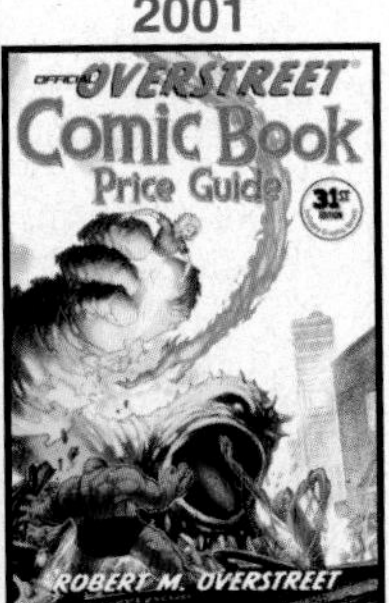

#31 Bookstore Ed.
SC only $22.00

2002

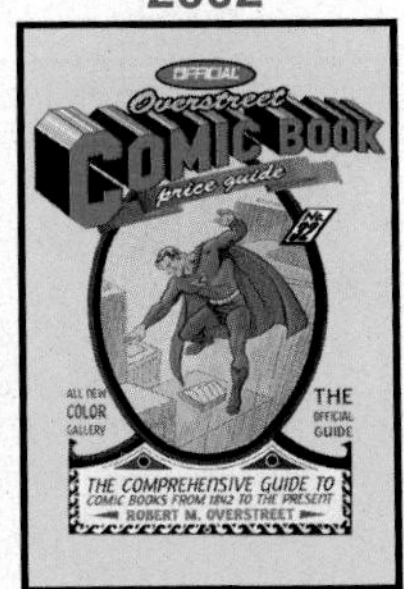

#32 SC $22.00
#32 HC $32.00

2002

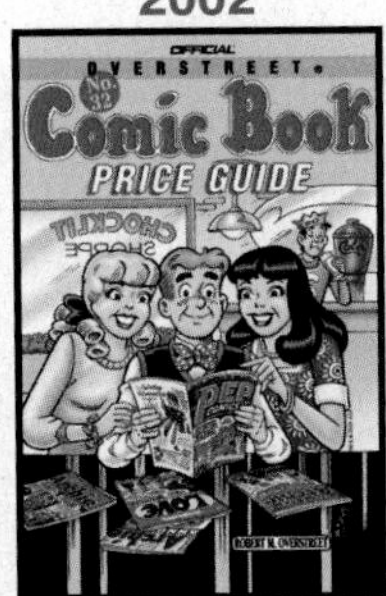

#32 SC $22.00
#32 HC $32.00

2002

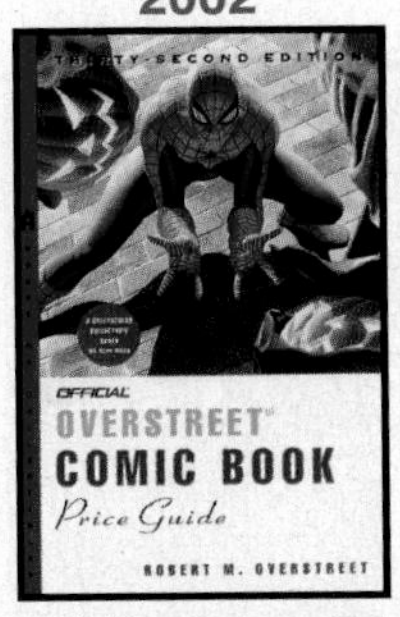

#32 Bookstore Ed.
SC only $22.00

2003

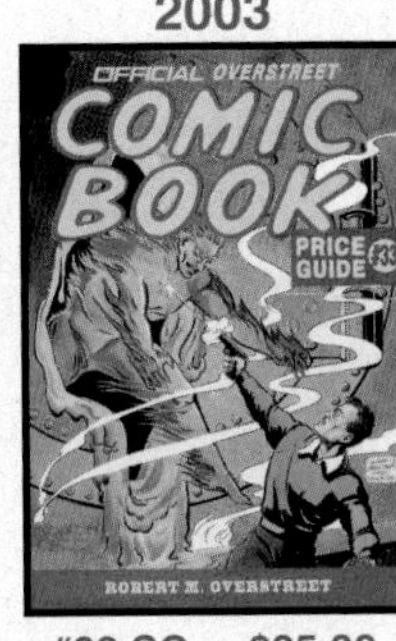

#33 SC $25.00
#33 HC $32.00

2003

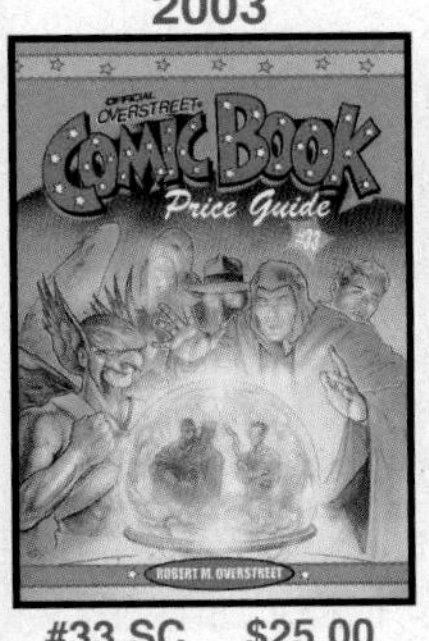

#33 SC $25.00
#33 HC $32.00

2003

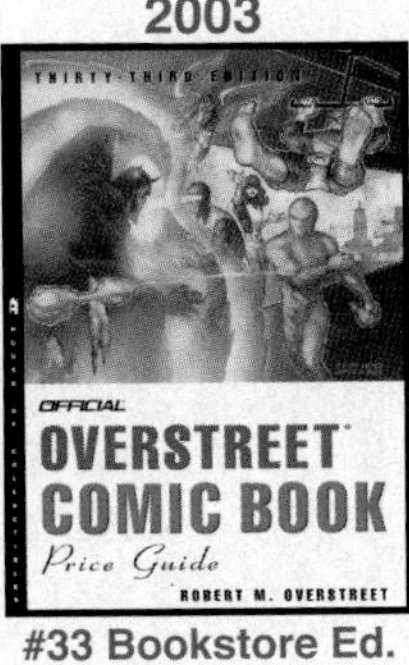

#33 Bookstore Ed.
SC only $25.00

2004

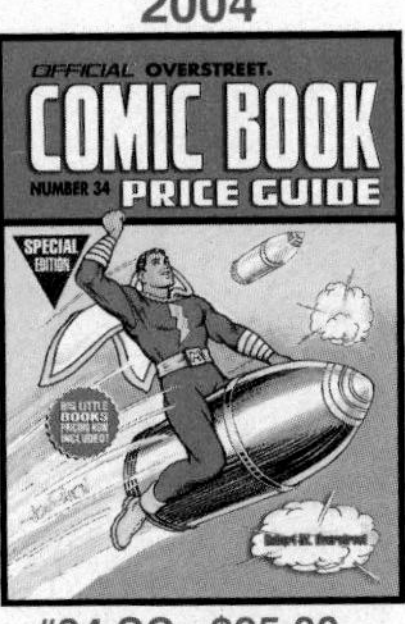

#34 SC $25.00
#34 HC $32.00

2004

#34 SC $25.00
#34 HC $32.00

2004

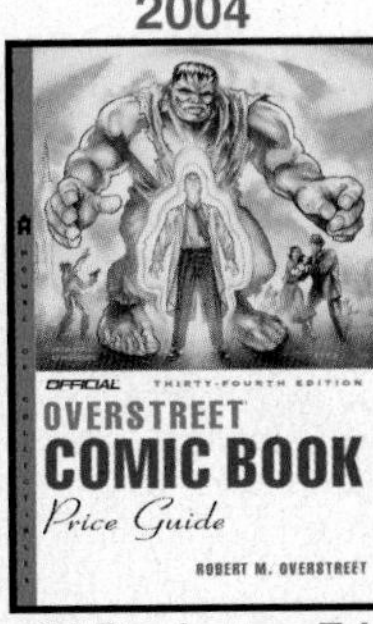

#34 Bookstore Ed.
SC only $25.00

2005

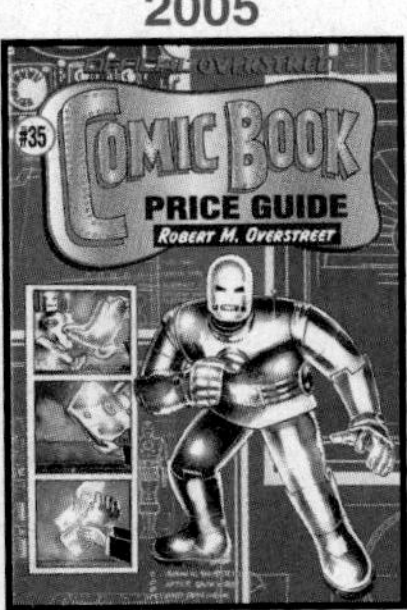

#35 SC $25.00
#35 HC $32.00

2005

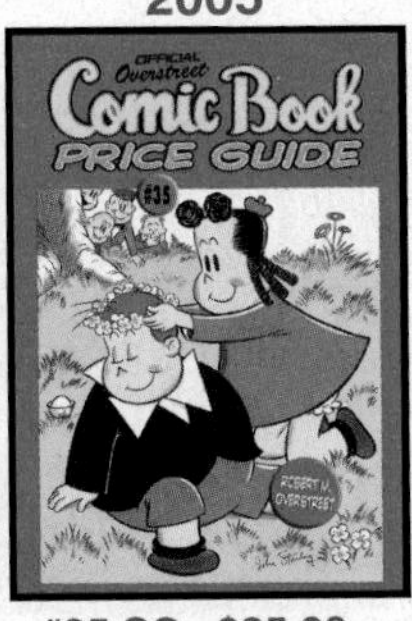

#35 SC $25.00
#35 HC $55.00

2005

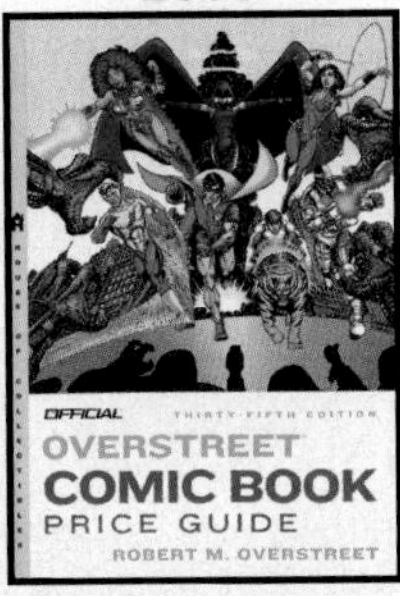

#35 Bookstore Ed.
SC only $25.00

2006

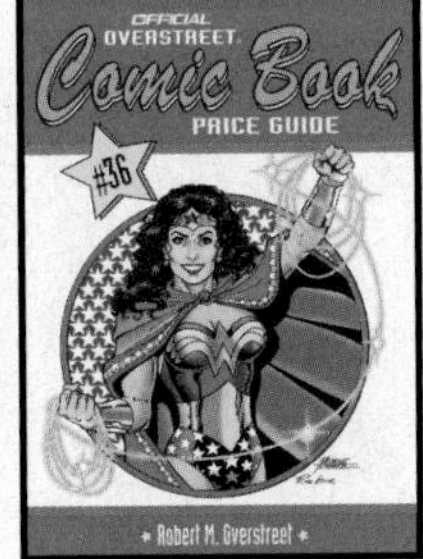

#36 SC $25.00
#36 HC $32.00

2006

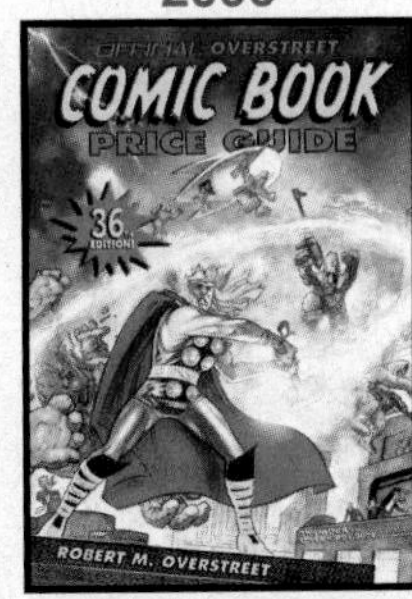

#36 SC $25.00
#36 HC $32.00

2006

#36 Bookstore Ed.
SC only $25.00

2007

#37 SC $30.00
#37 HC $35.00

2007

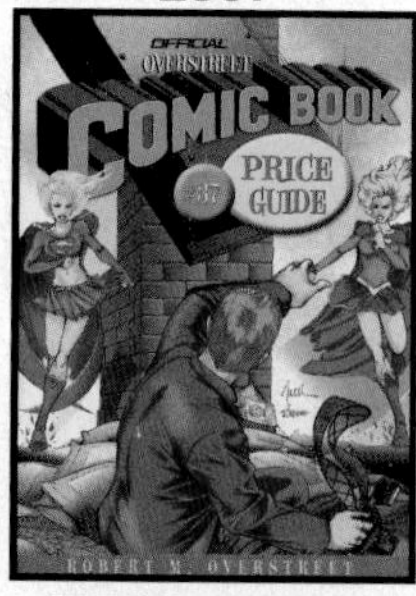

#37 SC $30.00
#37 HC $35.00

2007

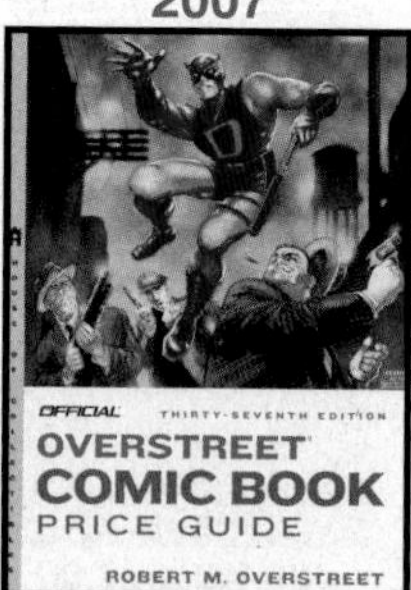

#37 Bookstore Ed.
SC only $30.00

2008

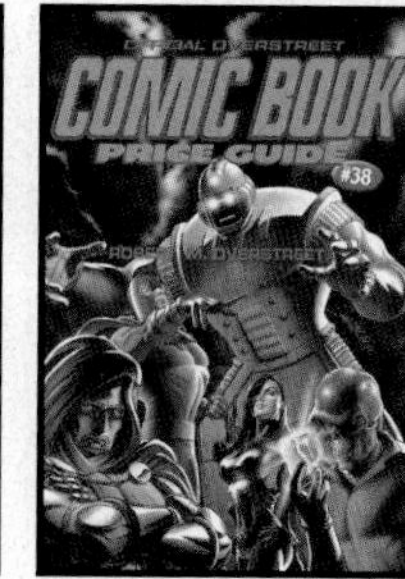

#38 SC $30.00
#38 HC $35.00

2008

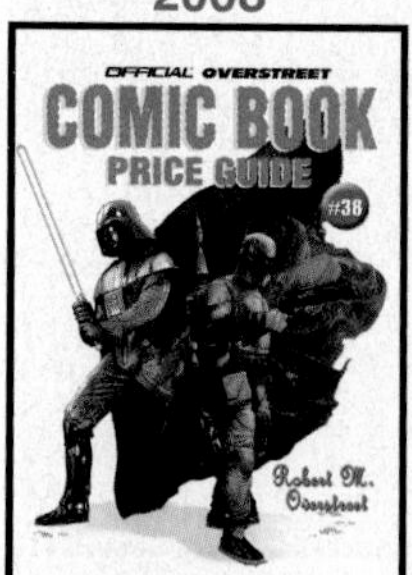

#38 SC $30.00
#38 HC $35.00

2008

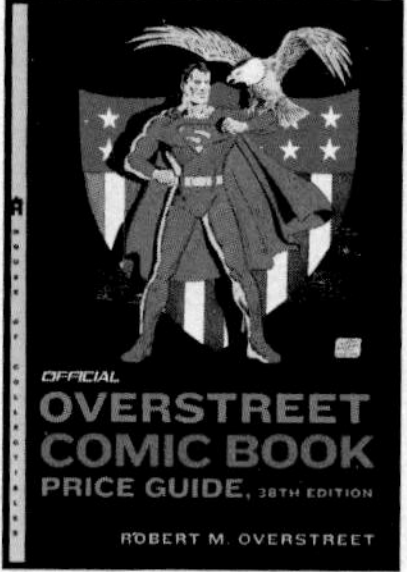

#38 Bookstore Ed.
SC only $30.00

2009

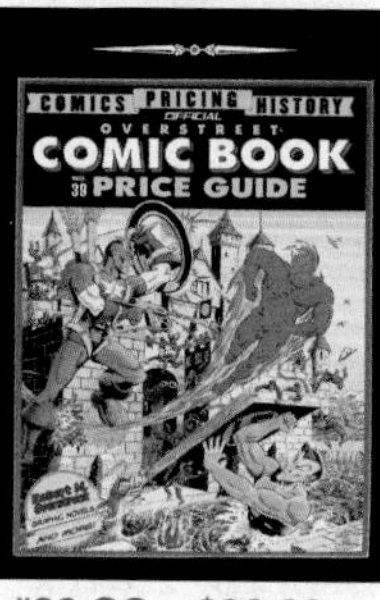

#39 SC $30.00
#39 HC $35.00

2009

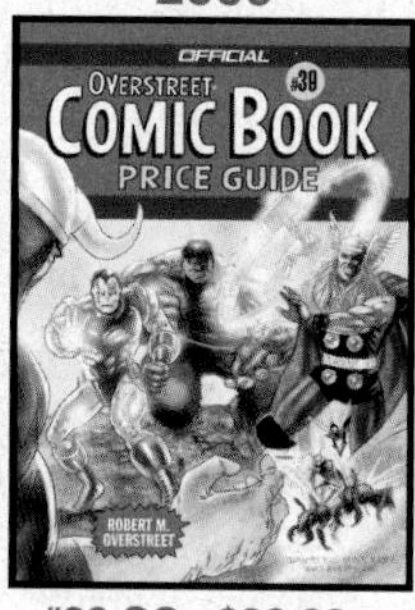

#39 SC $30.00
#39 HC $35.00

2009

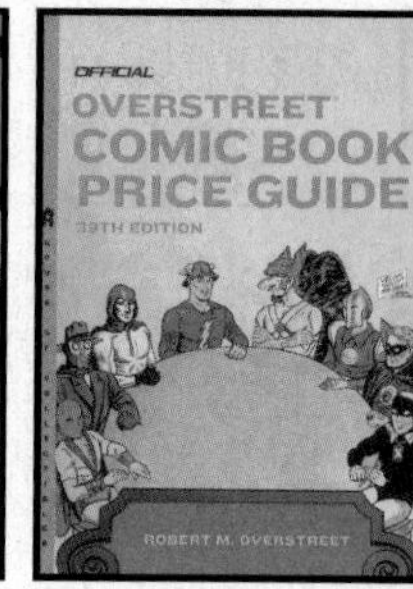

#39 Bookstore Ed.
SC only $30.00

2010

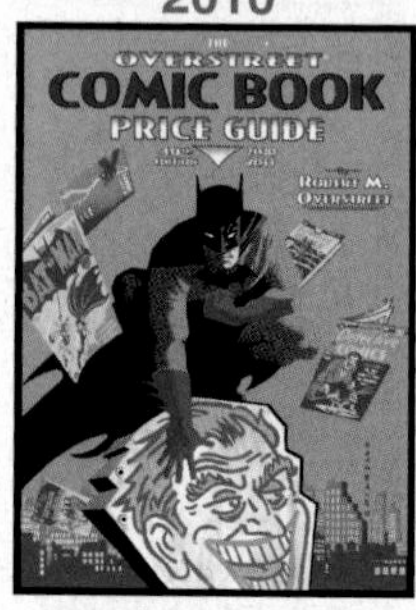

#40 SC $30.00
#40 HC $35.00

2010

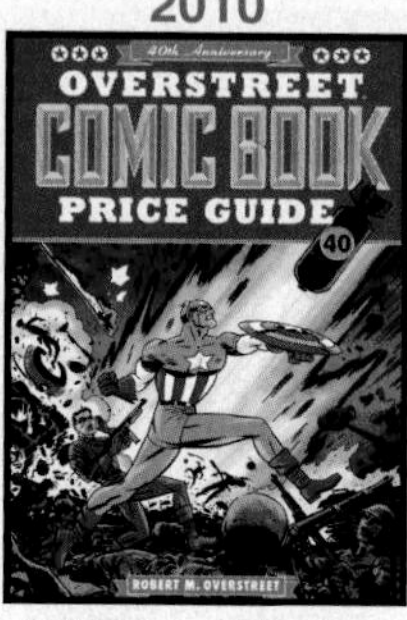

#40 SC $30.00
#40 HC $35.00

2010

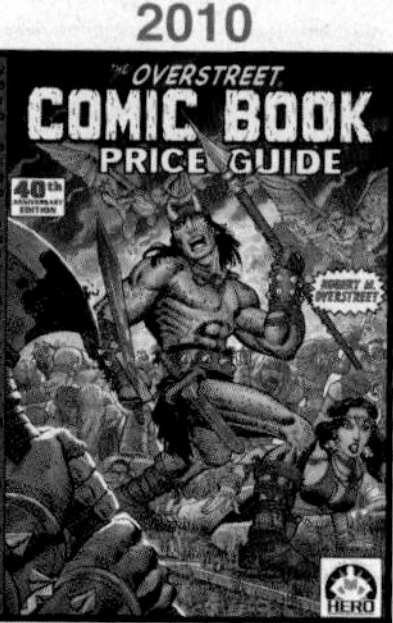

#40 HERO Initiative Ed.
HC only $35.00

2011

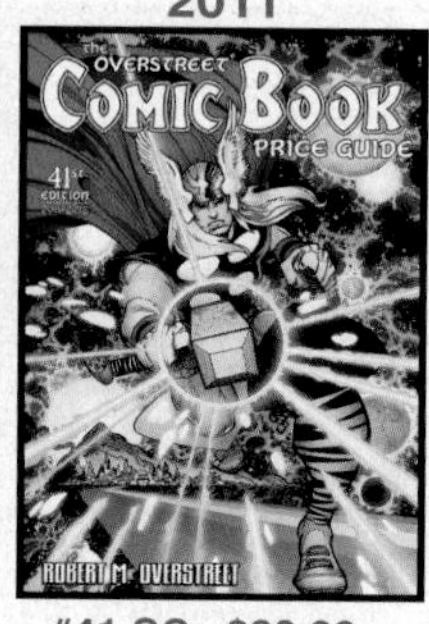

#41 SC $30.00
#41 HC $35.00

2011

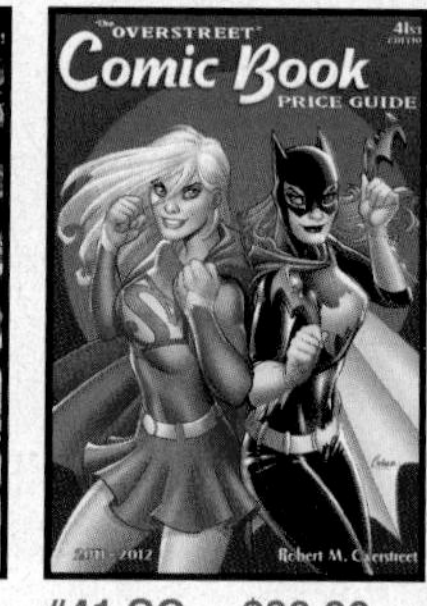

#41 SC $30.00
#41 HC $35.00

2011

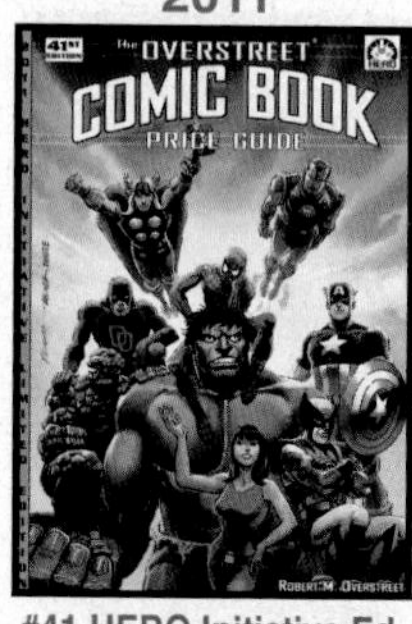

#41 HERO Initiative Ed.
HC only $35.00

2012

#42 SC $30.00
#42 HC $35.00

2012

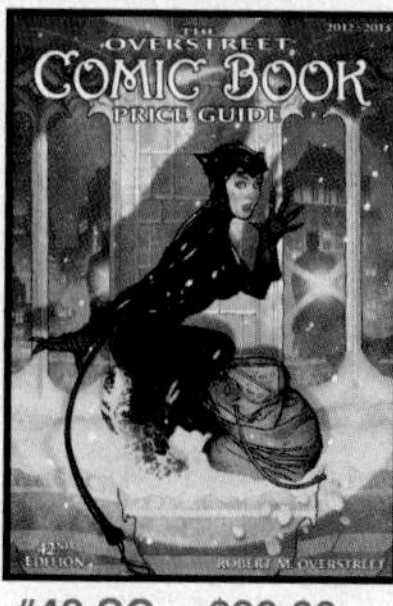

#42 SC $30.00
#42 HC $35.00

2012

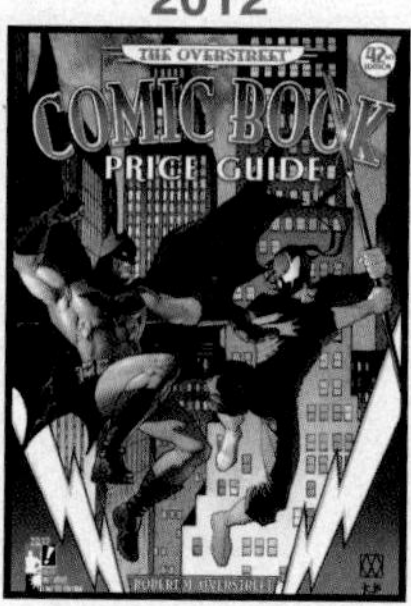

#42 HERO Initiative Ed.
HC only $35.00

2013

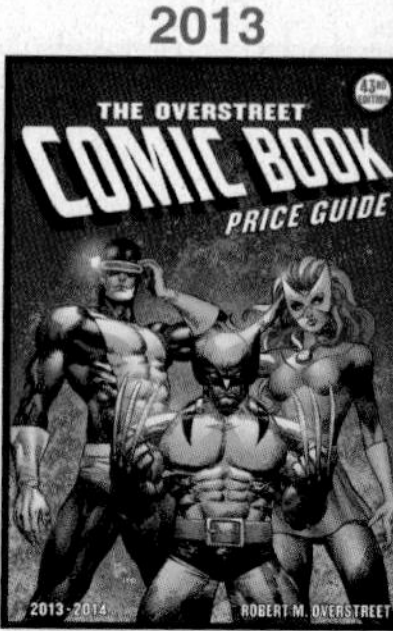

#43 SC $30.00
#43 HC $35.00

2013

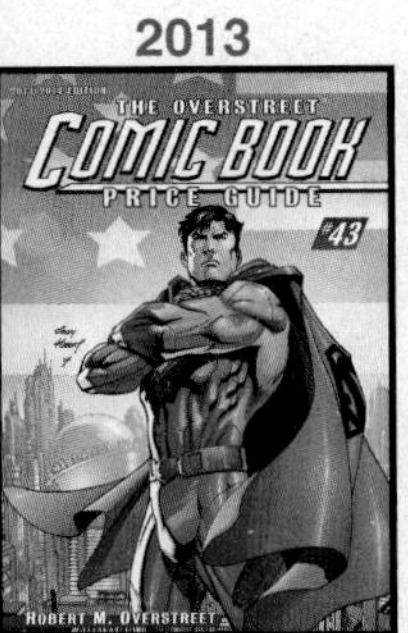

#43 SC $30.00
#43 HC $35.00

2013

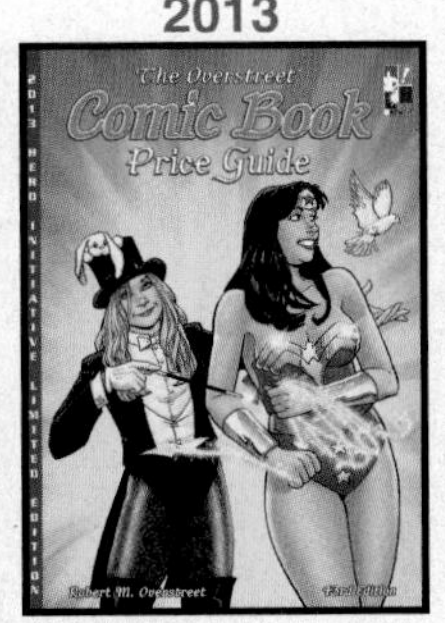

#43 HERO Initiative Ed.
HC only $35.00

2014

#44 SC $30.00
#44 HC $35.00

2014

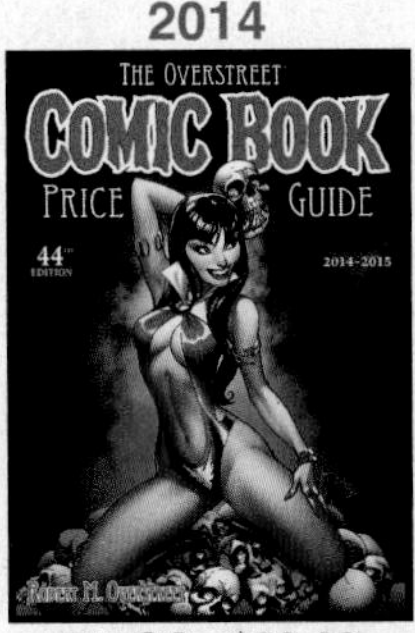

#44 SC $30.00
#44 HC $35.00

2014

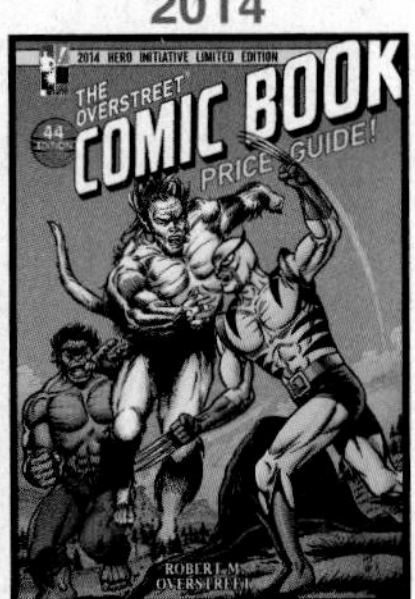

#44 HERO Initiative Ed.
HC only $35.00

2015

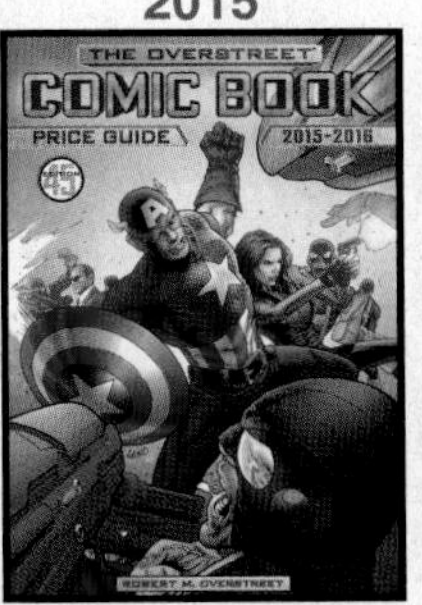

#45 SC $30.00
#45 HC $35.00

2015

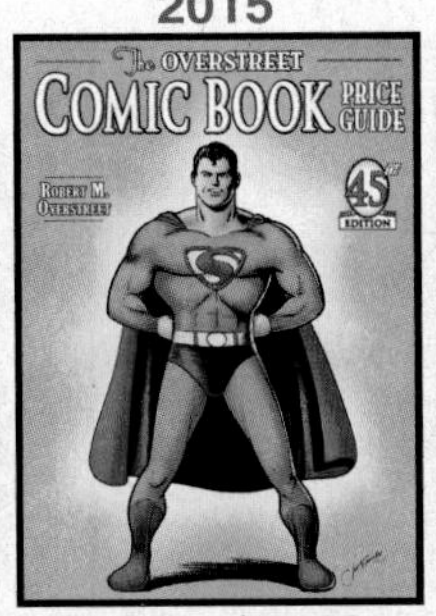

#45 SC $30.00
#45 HC $35.00

2015

#45 SC $30.00
#45 HC $35.00

2015

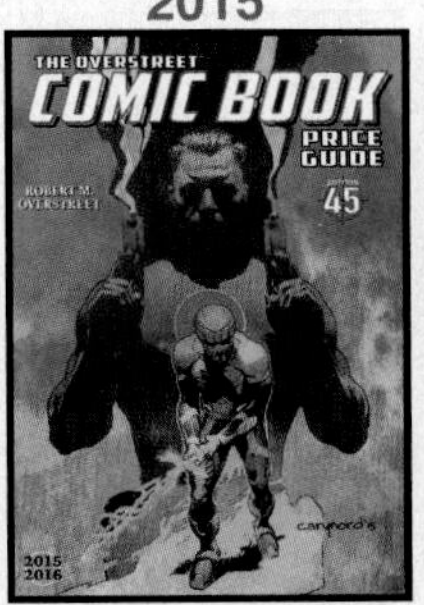

#45 SC $30.00
#45 HC $35.00

2015

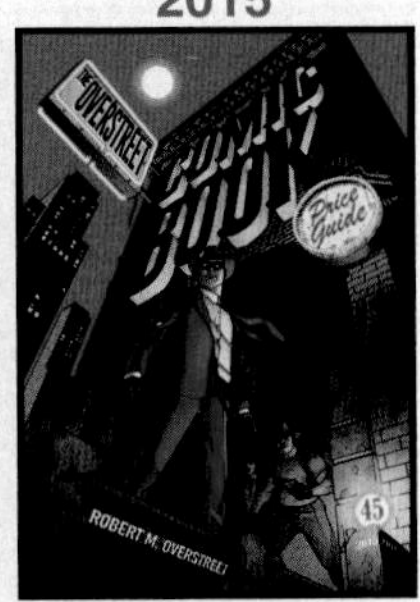

#45 HERO Initiative Ed.
HC only $35.00

2016

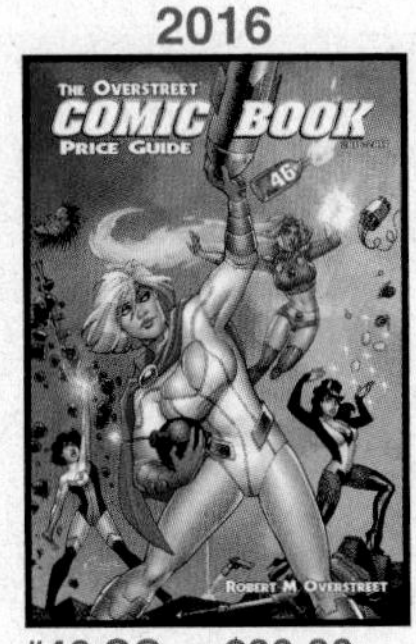

#46 SC $30.00
#46 HC $35.00

2016

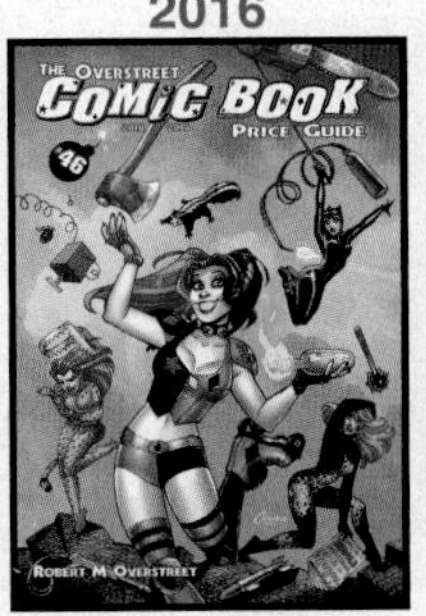

#46 SC $30.00
#46 HC $35.00

2016

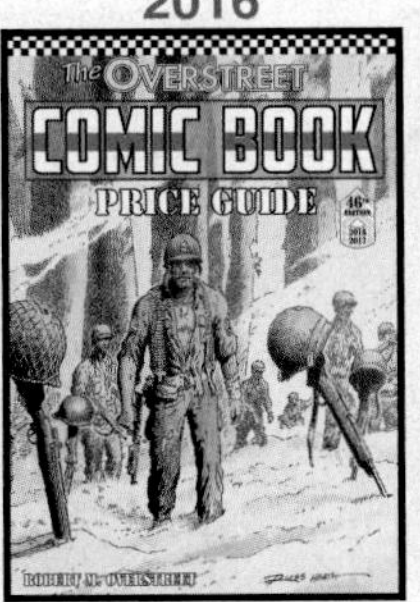

#46 SC $30.00
#46 HC $35.00

2016

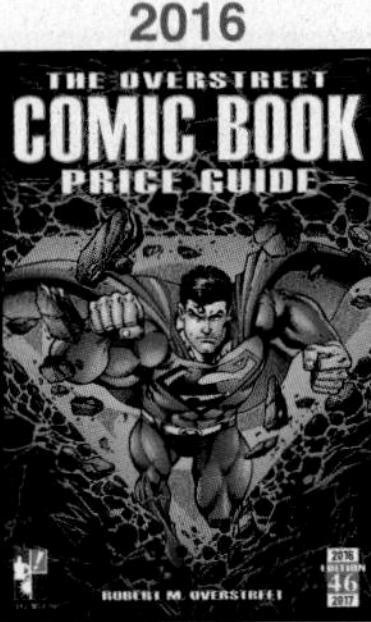

#46 HERO Initiative Ed.
HC only $35.00

2017

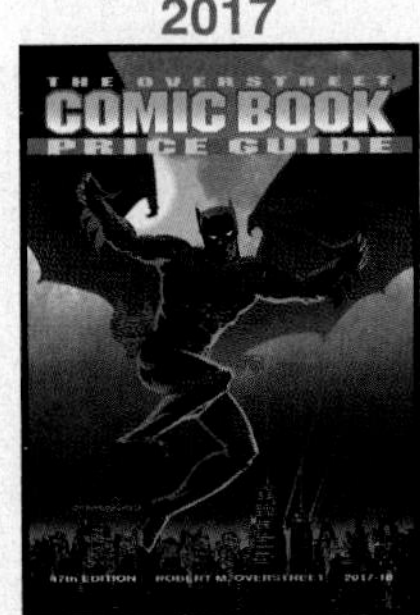

#47 SC $30.00
#47 HC $35.00

2017

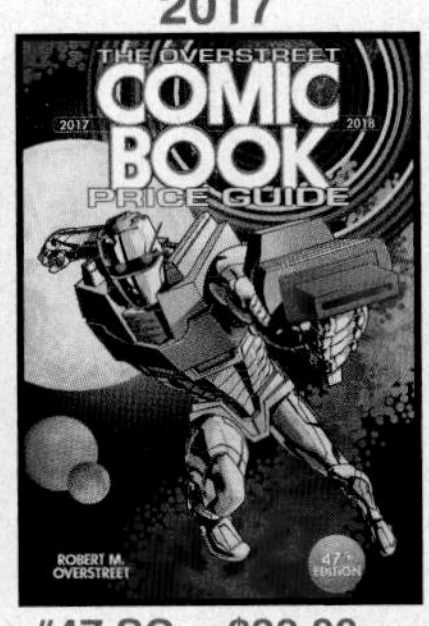

#47 SC $30.00
#47 HC $35.00

2017

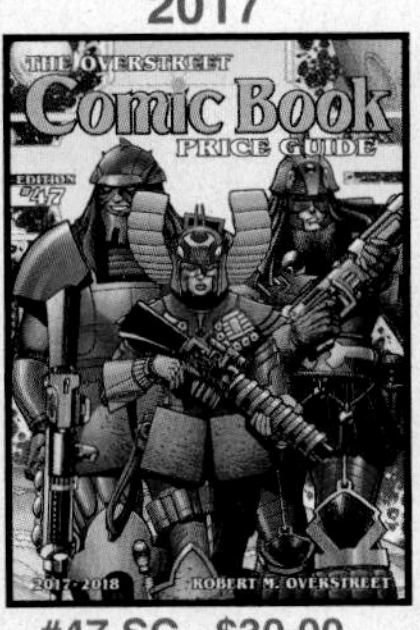

#47 SC $30.00
#47 HC $35.00

2017

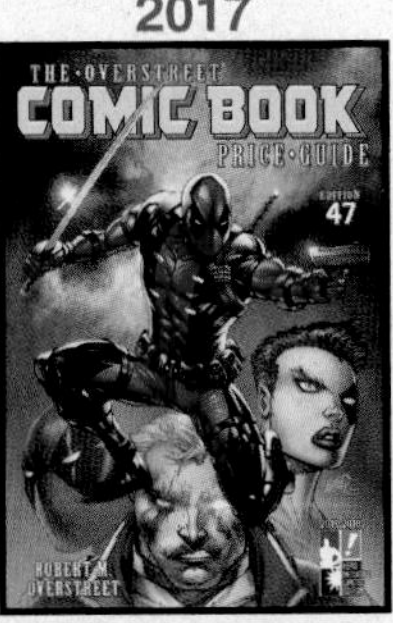

#47 HERO Initiative Ed.
HC only $35.00

2001

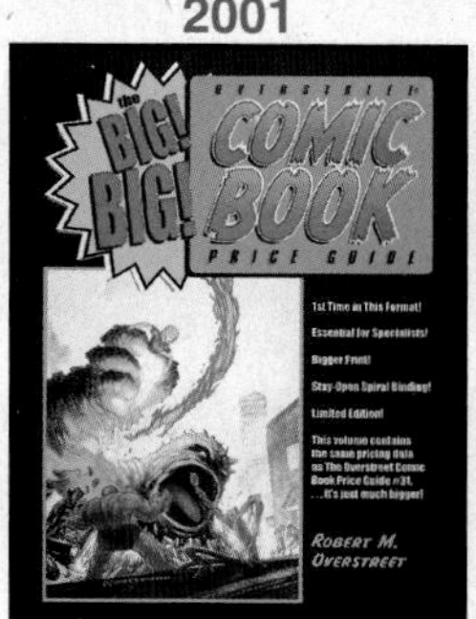

#31 Big Big CBPG
$35.00

2002

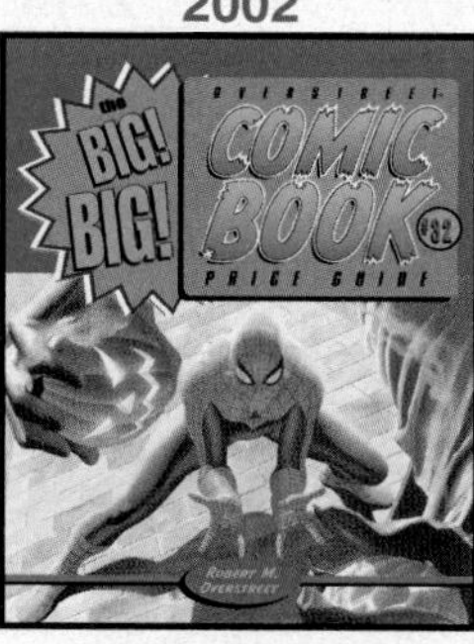

#32 Big Big CBPG
$35.00

2003

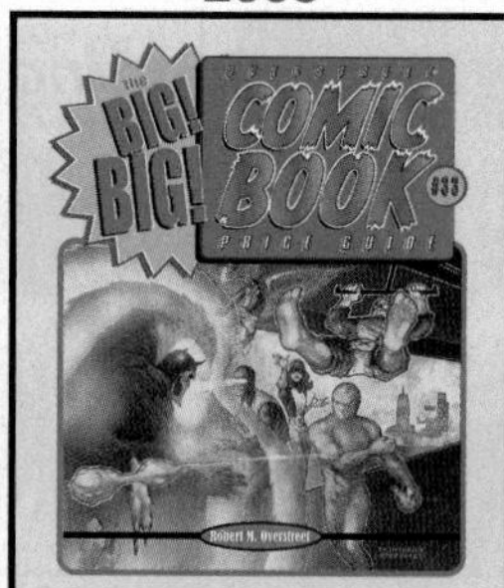

#33 Big Big CBPG
$37.00

2004

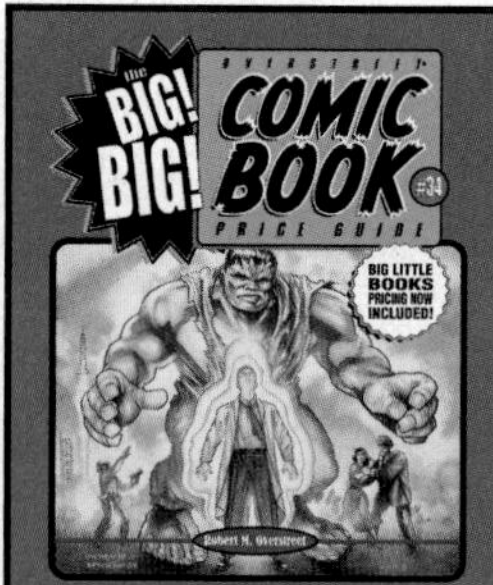

#34 Big Big CBPG
$37.00

2005

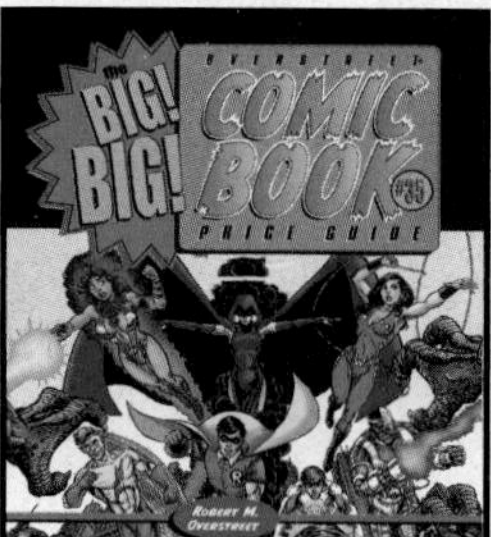

#35 Big Big CBPG
$37.00

2006

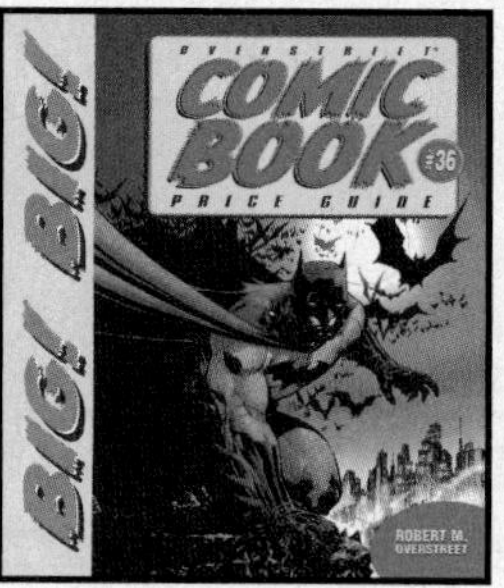

#36 Big Big CBPG
$37.00

2007

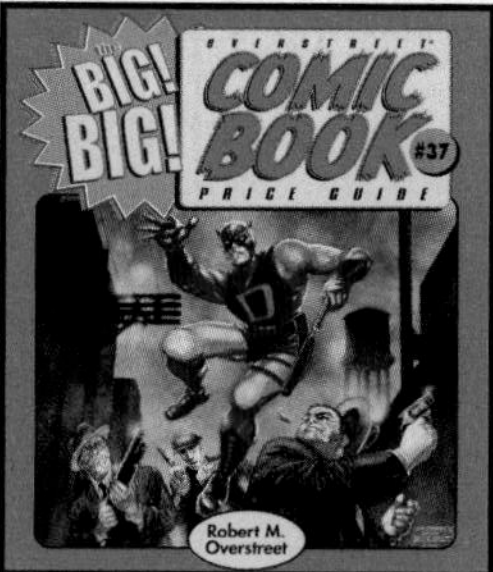

#37 Big Big CBPG
$37.00

2008

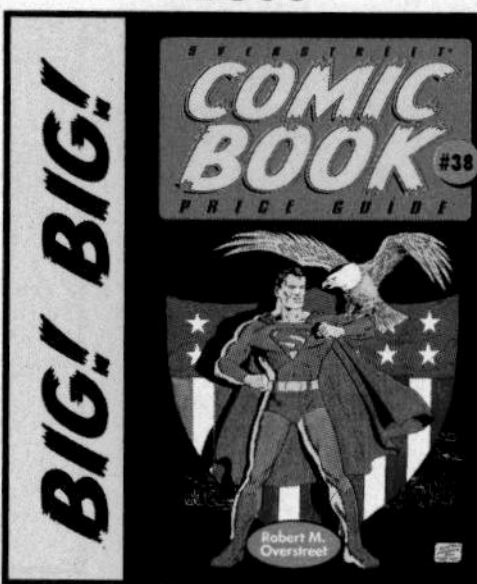

#38 Big Big CBPG
$37.00

2012

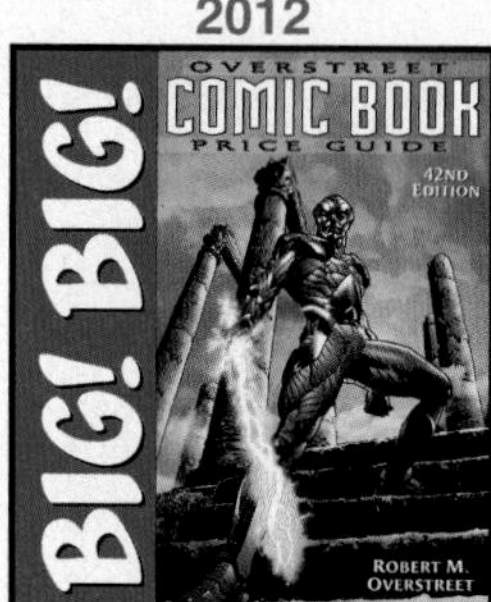

#42 Big Big CBPG
$45.00

2013

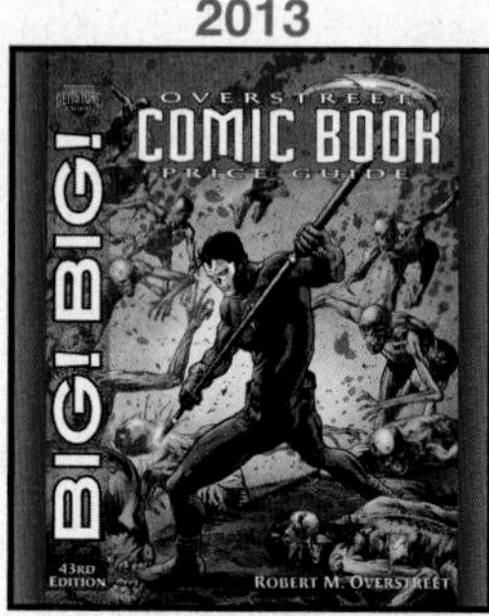

#43 Big Big CBPG
$45.00

2014

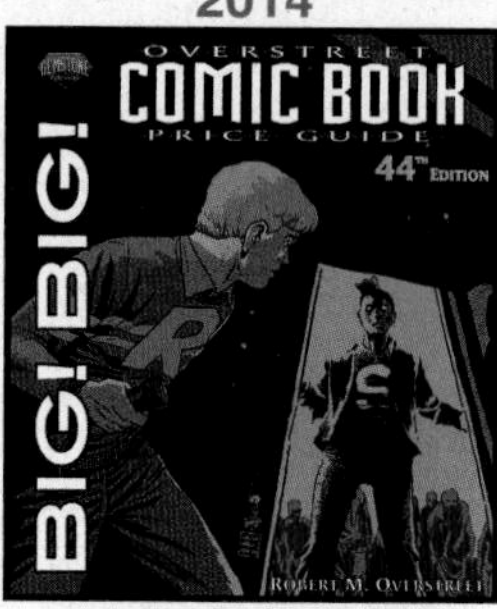

#44 Big Big CBPG
$45.00

2015

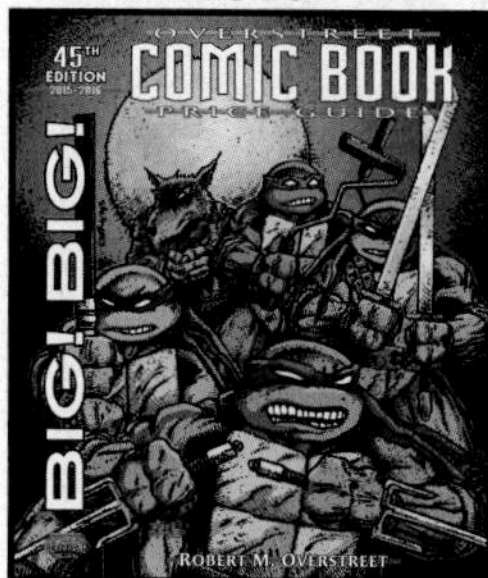

#45 Big Big CBPG
$47.50

2016

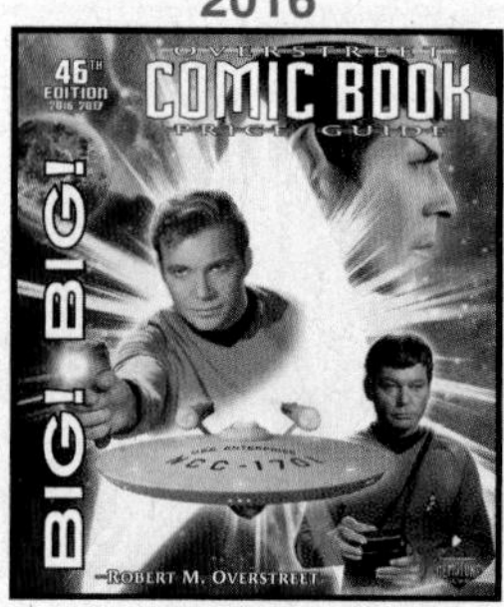

#46 Big Big CBPG
$47.50

2017

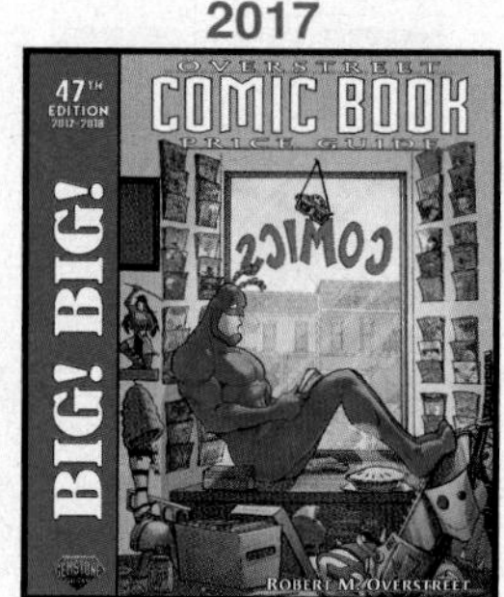

#47 Big Big CBPG
$47.50

ADVERTISERS' INDEX

A

B

C

D

E

F

G

H

Stephen A. Geppi

10150 York Road, Suite 300

Hunt Valley, MD 21030

443-318-8203

gsteve@diamondcomics.com

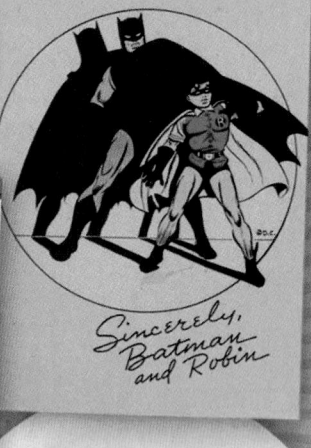